Stanley Gibbons
STAMP CATALOGUE

PART 1

British Commonwealth 1991

Ninety-third edition

Including post-independence issues of
Ireland, Fiji and South Africa

Stanley Gibbons Publications Ltd
London and Ringwood

By Appointment to Her Majesty The Queen
Stanley Gibbons Ltd, London
Philatelists

Published by **Stanley Gibbons Publications Ltd**
Editorial, Sales Offices and Distribution Centre:
5 Parkside, Christchurch Road, Ringwood,
Hants BH24 3SH.

ISBN: 0-85259-268-X

Item No. 0281 (91)

Text assembled by Black Bear Press Limited, Cambridge

Made and Printed in Great Britain by Mackays of Chatham, Kent

Preface to the 1991 Edition

HAPPY ANNIVERSARIES

It is 150 years since the Penny Black was issued. Originally envisaged as a secondary feature of Rowland Hill's inspired scheme for postal reform, stamps were enthusiastically adopted by the public as a very necessary prerequisite for a modern postal service. From 1840 the hobby of philately gradually evolved into today's world-wide hobby.

The celebrations this May were dominated by "Stamp World London 90", the international philatelic exhibition held at Alexandra Palace. On the last of its eleven days the organisers announced that over 95,000 had attended and, indeed, the halls were thronged each day. The success of the exhibition, supported by the efforts of the British Post Office, has placed the hobby on a firm footing for the years ahead.

The firm of Stanley Gibbons has also been celebrating its own anniversaries. Edward Stanley Gibbons, who founded the firm in 1856, was born in the same year as the Penny Black and 1990 also marks the 125th anniversary of the SG catalogue, of which this volume forms part, and the centenary of *Gibbons Stamp Monthly*.

There have been many changes in the hobby over the years and the catalogue has changed with it. Today's collectors require much more information than their predecessors and the listings have expanded to reflect this. A new feature added to this edition is a Select Bibliography of books which should be readily available to today's collector. Not so obvious to the reader is the use throughout the volume of the SG Publications Typecraft computer software system. Introduced for new issue listings in the 1990 publication its capacity was subsequently doubled to enable all corrections to be outputted also. No company can stand still, however, and Stanley Gibbons Publications Ltd are pleased to announce a special North American edition of the *Part 1 (British Commonwealth) 1991,* priced in U.S. dollars, for publication later this year.

PRICES

The end of the decade did not see a general surge in prices such has often in the past accompanied preparations for a London international philatelic exhibition. Today's market is essentially collector-based with resulting stability in many periods.

Stamps from the classic period continue to be in demand and there are important repricings in early **British Honduras**, **Cape of Good Hope** triangulars, **Ceylon**, **Fiji** *Times* stamps, **Labuan**, **Samoa** Express issues, **Trinidad**, **Uganda** type-written stamps and **Western Australia** Swans. In some cases rises extend to the later Queen Victoria period. Also in demand are scarcer overprints such as **British Post Office in Siam** and **Zanzibar.** Interest in stamps from the two World Wars is reflected in further increases for **New Guinea** "G.R.I." surcharges, **Japanese Occupation** issues for **Burma** and **Malaya**, and **Tanganyika Mafia Island** stamps. Other areas showing important price changes are **Australia** Kangaroos. **Malaysia Straits Settlements** and **Federated Malay States**, **New Zealand** postal fiscals from the 1882-1901 period, and **Queensland** where research provided by Mr. Neil Walker has enabled us to adjust a number of prices or provide them for the first time

Recent market movements strongly suggest that the often looked-for revival in King George VI issues is approaching. Recent auction realisations for major errors have been very high indeed and the trend is now reaching the scarcer values and varieties. Although such rises are not universal for the definitives of this period, significant alterations occur for **Ascension**, **Canada**, **Fiji**, **Mauritius** and a number of other territories.

Prices for stamps of the present reign remain generally depressed. There is a growing demand for certain commemorative sets from recent years but the only other major highlights are the prices paid for the major errors. A number of important **Great Britain** errors of the present reign have passed through the hands of Stanley Gibbons Ltd recently and the opportunity has been taken to reassess the catalogue prices of the scarcer items.

After eighteen years the effects of inflation have made it necessary to increase the minimum catalogue price from 5p. to 10p. Collectors should note that where a set includes a number of stamps at the minimum price the set price does *not* reflect this increase in the handling charge.

REVISIONS IN THIS EDITION

Shades occurring on early Queen Elizabeth II recess and photogravure printed stamps, previously listed in the *Elizabethan,* have been added throughout the volume. Such shades are often comparable to those already included for King George VI issues and a number are now difficult to obtain.

Barbados. Listings to 1952 have been improved with the assistance of Mr. Edmund Bayley. author of *The Stamps of Barbados*. The 1916 and 1925–35 issues have been revised.

Bermuda. The "Gash in Chin" flaw on the King George VI high value key types is now listed and illustrated.

Cook Islands and **Niue.** The opportunity provided by the sale of the "Fitzpatrick" collection has resulted in much additional information and some new listings, including the two settings of the 1893–1900 ½d. value.

Egypt. Improvements carried out in the 4th edition of *Part 19 (Middle East)* have been transferred. The two variations of watermark Type **8** are shown, the definitives from the 1881 to 1906 period relisted and illustrated notes on Egypt Post Offices Abroad added.

Falkland Islands. The revision of the King George V series has been completed with a relisting of the 1921–28 Script printings. We are grateful for the assistance of Mr. Malcolm Barton and other members of the Falkland Islands Study Group in this project.

Ghana. The 1988–89 provisional surcharges on definitive values are listed for the first time, together with a number of major errors, based on information supplied by Mr. A. Irani.

India—Cochin. The various perforation heads used between 1916 and 1930 are now identified.

Lesotho. Further errors and varieties have been added to the 1986–88 surcharges.

Madagascar. Much additional information is now given on both the British Consular Mail and the British Inland Mail. The listings of Type **2** have been rewritten.

Malaysia. The revisions of the pre-1939 period have been completed with further work on **Johore**, **Pahang** and **Trengganu**. Once again we are grateful for the advice of Mr. Andrew Norris and the Malaya Study Group. Following a suggestion from Mr. G. Bray the two dies of the **Kedah** Ploughman design are now listed and illustrated

New Zealand. Stamps from the 1891–93 period with advertisements on the reverse are now given separate listing.

Nigeria. Following research by Mr. Dudley Prestedge of the West Africa Study Circle a number of Biafra issues from 1968 have been deleted as there is no evidence that they were available for postal purposes.

Sierra Leone. Some additional notes and dates have been added with the help of Mr. Philip Beale, whose *The Postal Service of Sierra Leone* has been recently published. The 1897 provsionals have been relisted.

Tanzania. After considerable enquiries, and with assistance from local philatelists, we have been able to establish which issues since 1986 were available for postal purposes and these are now listed.

Tonga. Further watermark varieties for the 1897 and later sets have been added.

Transvaal. The revision, started in the 1989 edition, has been carried forward to 1900. Many additional notes have been included and the 1877–79 "V.R." overprints completely rewritten.

Turks and Caicos Islands. The notes on the early postal history of the islands have been revised, based on information from Mr. M.H. Ludington, and further bisects added.

Other revisions and new varieties appear throughout the listings. We are grateful to the many collectors, dealers and postal administrations who provide so much of the new material which appears in each fresh edition of the catalogue.

David J. Aggersberg

Stanley Gibbons Addresses

HEAD OFFICE, 399 STRAND, LONDON WC2R 0LX

Auction Room and Specialist Departments. Open Monday-Friday 9.30 a.m. to 5 p.m.

Shop. Open Monday–Friday 9.30 a.m. to 6 p.m. and Saturday 10 a.m. to 4 p.m.

Telephone 071 836 8444 and Telex 28883 for all departments.

RINGWOOD OFFICE

Stanley Gibbons Publications. 5 Parkside, Christchurch Road, Ringwood, Hants BH24 3SH. Telephone 0425 472363. Telex 41271.

OVERSEAS BRANCHES

Stanley Gibbons Australia Pty. Ltd. P.O. Box 863J, Melbourne 3001, Australia. Telephone (01 0613) 670 3332 and Telex AA 37223.

Stanley Gibbons (Singapore) Pte. Ltd. Marina Square, P.O. Box 0001, Singapore 9103, Republic of Singapore. Telephone 336 1998 and Telex RS 38398 SINGSG.

STANLEY GIBBONS PUBLICATIONS LIMITED OVERSEAS REPRESENTATION

Stanley Gibbons Publications Ltd are represented overseas by the following sole distributors (*) and main agents (**).

Australia*
Lighthouse Philatelic (Aust.) Pty Ltd
Box 62
Chippendale 2008
New South Wales
Australia

Belgium and Luxembourg**
Philac
Rue du Midi 48
Bruxelles
Belgium 1000

Canada*
Lighthouse Publications (Canada) Ltd
255 Duke Street
Montreal
Quebec
Canada H3C 2M2

Denmark**
Nordfrim
DK 5450
Otterup
Denmark

France*
Davo France SARL
30 Rue de Gren Elle
75007 Paris
France

West Germany (incl. West Berlin and Austria)*
Ka-Be Briefmarkenalben-Verlag
Volkhardt GMBH
Daimlerstrasse 15
Goppingen
West Germany

Hong Kong**
Po-on Stamp Service
GPO Box 2498
Hong Kong

Israel**
Capital Stamps
PO Box 3749
Jerusalem 91036
Israel

Italy*
Secrian Srl
Via Pantelleria 2
Milano
1-20156
Italy

Japan**
Japan Philatelic Co Ltd
PO Box 2
Suginami-Minami
Tokyo
Japan

Netherlands*
Davo Publications
PO Box 411
7400 AK Deventer
Netherlands

New Zealand*
Philatelic Distributors Ltd
PO Box 863
New Plymouth
New Zealand

Norway**
Wennergren Cappelen AS
Nedre Vollgate 4
PO Box 738
Sentrum N-0105
Oslo 1
Norway

South Africa**
Stanley Gibbons (Pty) Ltd
PO Box 930
Parklands
RSA 2121

Republic Coin and Stamp Accessories (Pty) Ltd
PO Box 260325
Excom 2023
Johannesburg
RSA

Sweden*
Chr Winther Soerensen AB
Box 43
S-310 Knaered
Sweden

Switzerland**
Phila Service
Burgstrasse 160
4125 Riehen/BS
Switzerland

USA*
Lighthouse Publications Inc.
274 Washington Avenue
Hackensack
New Jersey 07601
USA

West Indies/Caribbean**
Hugh Dunphy
PO Box 413
Kingston 10
Jamaica
West Indies

BUYING

Are you considering selling your collection, or some of those surplus stamps and covers that all collectors seem to accumulate?

Auctions have proliferated in the past few years, but many collectors fail to realise that the vast majority of bidders in auctions are members of the trade.

Many lots sell for well under dealers' "buying-in" prices, indeed some do not sell at all.

Very few auctions will receive, sell and pay you within three months.

When I make an offer I have valued EVERYTHING, not just the easily saleable items – because I have a market for almost everything philatelic.

AT THE MOMENT I PARTICULARLY NEED ...

Old-time multi-volume collections, Imperials, Ideals, Lincolns, etc., Cinderellas, G.B., British Commonwealth and Foreign (especially Far East), old correspondence and Postal History of all types, Picture Postcards, etc., etc. I can also provide probate and insurance valuations.

SAMPLE ACQUISITIONS RECENTLY

1.	G.B. FDCs	£2,100
2.	World Revenues	£6,000
3.	Part dealer's stock	£3,750
4.	Australian States	£1,000
5.	World Postal Stationery	£500
6.	Channel Islands	£500
7.	G.B. Collection	£850
8.	Japan Collection	£1,500

*INDIVIDUAL SENDINGS FROM ABROAD MUST BE OF LESS THAN £1,000 PER PACKAGE, AND MUST BEAR MY V.A.T. NUMBER (215 8575 500) ON THE OUTSIDE OF EACH PACKAGE.

Please write to, or send material* (minimum sending £10 please in view of postage costs) to:

JOHN AULD

THE BRITISH PHILATELIC FEDERATION

1 Hillview Villas
Hastingwood
Nr. Harlow
Essex CM17 9JK

Phone: 0279 33910
Mobile: 0860 500889

Index

INDEX

Stamps Added

Excluding new issues which have appeared in Gibbons *Stamp Monthly* Supplements, the following are the Catalogue numbers of stamps listed in this edition for the first time. Includes items previously only listed in the *Elizabethan* catalogue.

Great Britain. 346d, 440e/f, 441c, 449a, 508a, X903a, X905a, X954a, X958a, X959a, X978a, 888b, 1113ac, 1204a, 1207a, 1457ab/ad, 1463a, 1464a, 1479a, 1480a, **MS**1501a
Used Abroad. Army Field Offices. Z45*a*

Abu Dhabi. 17b
Aden. 53*a*/*b*, 55*a*, 57*a*, 64*a*, 66*a*, 68*a*, 72*a*, 82*a*, 83*a*
Qu'aiti State in Hadhramaut. 31*a*, 34*a*, 85a
Anguilla. 223a, 224a, 225a, 226c, 227a, 228a, 229a, 230a, 231a, 232a, 233a, 234a, 235a, 236a, 237a, 238a, 239a, 240a, 466a
Antigua. 124*a*, 126*a*, 132*a*, 154*a*, 158*a*, 170a, 193*a*
Australia. 1a, 224ab, 230da, 308*a*, 313*a*, 313*ba*, 317*a*, 335a, 401a/b, 407a, 425b, 525a, 614ba, 930a, 1208a, O6*a*, O21*a*, O41*a*/*c*, O49*a*, O64a, O75*b*, O81*a*, O118*a*/*b*
Bahamas. 204*a*, 206*a*, 209*a*, 210*a*, 211*a*, 212*a*, 214*a*
Bahrain. 78a
Bangladesh. 317a, O24/6
Barbados. 62, 86a, 153f, 184*a*, 185*a*, 201a, 202a/b, 205a, 211a, 264a/b, 264ca/cb, 292*a*, 296*a*/*b*, 299*a*, 350a, 352*a*, 524a, 626*a*, D7*a*, D9*a*
Basutoland. 12f, 46*a*, 51*a*, 72*a*, 79*a*
Bechuanaland. 146*a*, 159a, 160a
Bermuda. 116af, 116bf, 116cf, 117af, 117bf, 118bf, 118cf, 119bf, 119cf, 120af, 121af, 121bf, 135*a*, 136*a*, 145*a*, 149*a*, 152a, 153a, 164*d*, 233d, F1a
Botswana. 209*a*
British Guiana. 147, 334*ab*, 336*a*, 337a, 338*a*/*b*, 339*a*, 341*a*, 344a
British Honduras. 181*ba*, 183ab, 187*a*, 212*a*
British Indian Ocean Territory. 1a/b, 2a/b, 3a/b, 4a/b, 5a/b, 6a/b, 7a/c, 8a/b, 10a/b, 11a/b, 12a/b, 13a/b, 14a/b, 15a/c, 45*b*
British Virgin Islands. 104k, 149*a*, 150*a*, 185*a*, O4a, O7a
Brunei. 105*a*, 109*a*, 110*a*, 111*a*, 113*a*, 118*ab*, 121*a*/*b*, 122*ba*, 123*ab*, 124*ab*, 128*a*, 128*ba*, 207*a*, 247*a*, 250*a*
Canada. 702a, 703a, 705a, 706*a*, 760*a*, 869*ba*, 1160a
Cape of Good Hope. 37b
Cayman Islands. 148*a*, 155*a*/b, 165*a*
Ceylon. 201a, 387fa, 451*a*/*b*, 460*a*, 506a, 584c/d, O7a
Cook Islands. 11*a*/*ba*, 13*b*, 38a, 76a, 76ba, 77a, 78a, 79a, 80a, 85a, 87a, 179a, 180b, 181b, 182a, 183a, 184a
Cyprus. 175*a*, 179*a*, 190*a*, 192*b*, 194*a*, 284*a*, 361a, 410a
Turkish Cypriot Posts. 237a
Dominica. 142a, 147*a*, 150*a*, 366*a*, 1127a
Egypt. D75b/d, O86b

Falkland Islands. 75*b*, 193*a*, 194*a*, 195*a*, 204*a*
Falkland Islands Dependencies. G26*a*, G27*a*, G28*a*
Fiji. 257a, 285*a*, 288*a*, 292*a*, 319*a*, 320*a*
Gambia. 171*a*, 172*a*, 179*a*
Ghana. 170*a*, 177a, 1241/50
Gibraltar. 115c, 146*a*, 148*a*, 149*a*, 150*a*, 151*a*, 152a/ba, 153*a*/*b*, 154*a*, 155*a*, 163*a*, 398a
Gilbert and Ellice Islands. 66*a*, 69*a*
Gold Coast. 115d, 153*a*
Guyana. 420b/c, 421b/c, 422c, 423*a*, 433*a*, 433c, 2241a
Hong Kong. 179*a*, 180*a*, 182*a*, 183*a*, 184*a*, 188*a*, 189*a*, 190*a*, 191*a*, 197*a*, 199*a*, 201*a*, 203*a*, 230*a*, 313*a*/*b*, 315*a*, 320*a*, 321*a*, 322*a*, 324*a*, 324*ba*, D17*a*
India. 932ab, 935ba, 1073a, 1074a, O197*a*, O202*a*, O204*a*, O210*a*, O216*a*, O219*a*
Indian Expeditionary Force. E11a
Indian Convention States.
Nabha. O38a
Patiala. O8c
Indian Feudatory States.
Bhopal. O356c
Bundi. O33b
Bussahir. 25b, 31ba, 32a, 34a, 35a
Charkhari. 50b
Cochin. O55a, O92a, O93c, O94b, O95a, O96a, O97a, O98a, O99a
Hyderabad. O22*g*
Kishangarh. 90*b*/ba
Poonch. O7a
Ireland.124a, 124*ba*, 125*ab*, 287ab, 288ca, 291ba, 295ae, 358a, 363*a*
Jamaica. 116b, 170*a*, 189*a*, 224*b*, 257*a*
Kenya. 37*a*, 47*a*, 50*a*, 52*a*
Kenya, Uganda and Tanganyika. 173*a*, 177*a*, 180*a*
Kiribati. O21*a*
Kuwait. 90a, 91a
Leeward Islands. 114af
Lesotho. 147*a*, 149*a*, 150*a*, 409b, 715b/c, 721*d*, 722ab, 734a
Long Island. 5a, 6b, 12e
Malaysia.
British Military Administration. 13a
Malayan Federation. 1*a*/*b*, 4*ab*
Johore. 41*a*, 135*a*
Kedah. 30a, 32a, 33a, 34a, 35a, 36a, 79*ab*, 81*ab*
Kelantan. 62*b*, 65*a*, 81*a*, 100*a*
Malacca. 25*a*, 29*a*, 67*a*
Negri Sembilan. 46*a*, 47*a*, 87*a*
Pahang. 56*a*, 57*a*, 65*a*, 67*a*, 73*a*
Penang. 30*a*, 31*a*, 70*a*
Perak. 130*a*, 131*a*, 132*a*, 136*a*, 165a
Selangor. 94*a*
Trengganu. 74*a*
Japanese Occupation. J210c
Malta. 270*a*, 301*a*, 302*a*, 330b, D22*a*, D24*a*
Mauritius. 248h, 260*a*, 297*a*, 300*a*, 302*ab*, 303*a*, 305*a*, 314*a*, D12*a*, D13*a*
Montserrat. 142*ab*, 338a/b, 776a, O7b, O8a, O9b, O10c, O11a, O12c, O13a, O14a, O15a, O16a, O34a, O44a
Morocco Agencies. 10d

Nauru. 49*b*
Newfoundland. 95b, 106b, 109e
New Guinea. 70*b*
New Hebrides. 237b, 240a, F252b, F254a
New Republic. 41*a*
New Zealand. CC3*a*, 195ab/ag, 196ab/af, 197a, 198a/b, 199a, 200b, 201ab/ac, 203a/b, 205a, 206ab, 207ba, 216ba/bd, 216ia, 218f/l, 219d/i, 220c/e, 221d/f, 222c/d, 223a, 224bd/bf, 226c/f, 446ab, 792*b*, 815*a*/*b*, 1013a, 1105a, O59a/b, O60
Ross Dependency. 3*a*, 5*a*
Nigeria. 53a, 70a, 72*a*/*b*, 73a, 75*a*, 77*a*, 226a
Niue. 9e, 12b
Norfolk Island. 1a, 2a, 3a, 4a, 20a/ba, 204a, 205a
North Borneo. 159b, 374a, 382a, 384a
Northern Rhodesia. 18f, 20g
Nyasaland Protectorate. 57ad, 197*a*
Pakistan. 77a, 78a
Papua. 48a, 91*a*
Papua New Guinea. 7*a*
Pitcairn Islands. 18*a*, 19*a*/*b*, 28*a*, 75a
Rhodesia. 373a, **MS**392a
Rhodesia and Nyasaland. 2*ab*, 7*a*, 19ab, 35*a*, D4a
Sabah. 410*a*, 429*a*
St. Helena. 155*a*, 214*a*, 319c, 320c
St. Kitts-Nevis. 107*a*, 108*a*, 109*a*, 112*a*, 117*a*, 139*a*, 146a, 151a/b, 171*a*
St. Lucia. 176*a*, 177*a*, 179*a*, 180*a*, 199*a*
St. Vincent. 33c, 189*a*, 190*a*, 194*a*, 198*a*, 199*a*/*b*, 200*a*
Grenadines of St. Vincent. 26a
Samoa. 166*e*
Sarawak. 190*a*
Seychelles. 128e, 129e, 130e, 131c, 151a, 176*ab*
Sierra Leone. 182b, 183b, 273a, 274a, 278a, 279a, 280a, 281a, 282a, 283a, 284a
Singapore. 46*a*, 47*a*, D5a, D6a, D7a
Solomon Islands. 84*a*, 91*a*, 91*ba*, 93*a*, 106*a*, 142a, 298a, 300a, 460a
Somaliland Protectorate. 89j, 138*a*
South Africa. 114b, 130a, 198b, 213*a*, 217*a*/*b*, 233*a*, 238*c*/*d*, 240*a*/*b*, 241*a*, 242*a*, 243*a*, 244*a*, 246*a*, 249*a*, 285*a*, 286*a*, 296*a*, 320*a*, 350*ac*, 411a, 525*a*, D37*a*, D40*b*/ba, D41a, O14a
South West Africa. 140a, 203*a*, 206*a*, 221*a*
Southern Cameroons. 4*a*
Sudan. 127*a*, 129*a*, 130*a*, 136*a*, O74*b*, O76*a*, O80*a*
Swaziland. 21e, 93*a*, 95*a*, 97*a*, 146*a*, 148*a*/*b*
Tanganyika. M34a, M38a, M40a, 112b, 115*a*
Tanzania. 156*ab*, 162*a*, 170*a*
Tasmania. 251ba, 252a
Tonga. 41a, 42a, 44a, 45a, 51a, 52a, 54b, 68a, 70a, 163a, 195a, 605a, 976*a*/*b*
Transjordan. 5*a*, 34a, 78ab
Trinidad and Tobago.
Tobago. 24ca
Trinidàd and Tobago. 267*a*, 275*a*/*b*, 285*a*/*b*, 287*a*, 345*a*
Tristan da Cunha. 89a, 233a
Turks and Caicos Islands. 61a/b, 62a, 63a, 297a
Uganda. 100*a*/*b*, 141*b*, 642
Zambia. 280b
Zanzibar. 341*a*, 344*a*, 346*a*, 347*a*

Catalogue Numbers Altered

The table below is a cross-reference for those stamps, the Catalogue numbers of which have altered in this edition.

Old	New
Great Britain	
441c/d	441d/e
X905/10	X907/12
X911/14	X914/17
X958/63	X959/64
X964/9	X966/71
X970/2	X974/6
X973	X978
X974	X980
X975	X982
Northern Ireland	
NI40/6	NI41/7
NI47/50	NI49/52
NI51/4	NI54/7
Scotland	
S56/9	S57/60
S60/2	S62/4
S63/6	S66/9
Wales	
W41/7	W42/8
W48/51	W50/3
W52/5	W55/8
Anguilla	
802/5	807/10
806/10	802/6
Antigua	
Barbuda	
1051/64	1052/65
1071/88	1085/102
1089/102	1071/84
Australia	
300/a	294*a*/ab
313a	313b
O32	*Deleted*
O62	*Deleted*
Bahamas	
CC2	*Deleted*
Bangladesh	
295/305	296/306
313/14	315/16
O24/39	O27/43
Barbados	
86a/d	86b/d
182/3	181*a*/*b*
184/6	182/*b*
187/8	183/*b*
189/90	184/5
191/*a*	186/*a*
192/6	187/91
197a	*Deleted*
230II	230a
231II	231a
231*a*	231*b*
231*a*II	231ba
233*a*II	233ab
237II	237a
237*a*	237*b*
264*a*	264*c*
Bechuanaland	
146*a*	146*b*
Belize	
1049/53	1050/4
Bermuda	
110	*Deleted*
110*a*	110
512*a*	512*c*
517*a*	517*c*
Brunei	
122*b*	122*a*
122a	122b
Cape of Good Hope	
7	*Deleted*
7*a*	7
Ceylon	
194	*Deleted*
Cook Islands	
76a	76b
Penrhyn	
32b	*Deleted*
Egypt	
12a	*Deleted*
55/8	56/9
59/60	63/4
61/2*a*	60/1*a*
63	55
64/*a*	58b/ba
65	59ab
66	61ab
67	62
68/*a*	63c/ca
69/*a*	54c/ca
70/*a*	55a/ab
71	56b
72	64b
O79/b	O80/b
O79c	O79
Falkland Islands	
98/101	73/4*a*
102	*Deleted*
103/4	75*a*/*b*
105	76
106/7	77/*a*
108/10	76*a*/*c*
111/14	78/80
Ghana	
1241/69	1251/70
Hong Kong	
197b	197ab
199b	199ab
201b	201ab
203b	203ab
324*a*/*c*	324*b*/*d*
India	
China Expeditionary Force	
C6b	C1b
Iraq	
Mosul	
7b	7*d*
Ireland	
288d	288cb
290c	290ba
295b/d	295ab/ad
Kuwait	
90a	90b
Lesotho	
843/51	853/61
Madagascar	
8	8a
8a/b	8ab/ac
8c	8
21/5	28/32
26/9	39/42
30/6	21/7
37	24a
38	25a
39/44	33/8
45/9	43/7
Malawi	
763/808	767/812
Malaysia	
Federated Malay States	
10a	*Deleted*
Johore	
1a	*Deleted*
3	5
3a	*Deleted*
4	8
5/a	3/a
5b/ba	5/a
6/a	4/a
8/9a	9/10a
10	13
13/b	14/b
14/a	10*b*/ba
Pahang	
17	18
17a	18b
17b	17
17c	18a
18	18*c*
18a	17*a*
18b	18cb
21	22
22	21
Trengganu	
21	22
22	21
Malta	
1a	*Deleted*
86cc	*Deleted*
88c	*Deleted*
Mauritius	
260*a*	260*b*
Montserrat	
773/81	774/82
Newfoundland	
80b/c	*Deleted*
81a/b	*Deleted*
82a/c	*Deleted*
95b	95c
106b	106c
106c	*Deleted*
109d	*Deleted*
228aa/ab	228a/b
228*a*/b	228*c*/ca
New Guinea	
94a	*Deleted*
94ab	94a
New Zealand	
197*a*	197*b*
224c/d	224bb/bc
303db	*Deleted*
580a	580b
584a/b	584b/c
588a	588b
O60/b	O60*b*/bb
O60ca	O60a
O60d/e	O60ca/cb
O68	O72*a*
O71	O72
O72	O71
O100b	O100ab
O102b	O102ab
O105b	O105ab
Nigeria	
53*a*	53*b*
Biafra	
16c/dc	*Deleted*
22/34	*Deleted*
Nyasaland Protectorate	
57b/c	57ab/ac
Pakistan	
635	636
St. Kitts-Nevis	
112*a*	112*b*
117*a*	117*b*
St. Lucia	
994	995
995	997
St. Vincent	
1159/76	1160/77
Sierra Leone	
3	4
4	3
Solomon Islands	
91*a*	91*b*
South Africa	
114b	114ba
D78a	*Deleted*
O13c	*Deleted*
Southern Cameroons	
4*aa*/*a*	4*b*/*c*
Tasmania	
251*a*	251*b*
251*b*/*ba*	*Deleted*
251bb/bd	251c/e
251c/ca	*Deleted*
251d	251a
252a/b	252b/c
Tonga	
43a	43ab
43b	43a
50b	*Deleted*
Transjordan	
68d	*Deleted*
Transvaal	
116/44	*Rewritten*
189	192
190/2	189/91
Trinidad and Tobago	
46*b*	*Deleted*
Uganda	
642/75	643/76

Specialist Philatelic Societies

British Decimal Stamps Study Circle
Secretary—Mr. P. R. Daniels
70, Moor Park Close, Rainham, Gillingham, Kent ME8 8QT

Great Britain Philatelic Society
Membership Secretary—Mr. A. J. Walker
42, Jesmond Road, Newcastle upon Tyne, Tyne and Wear NE2 4PQ

Great Britain Decimal Stamp Book Study Circle
Membership Secretary—Mr. A. J. Wilkins
3, Buttermere Close, Brierley Hill, West Midlands DY5 3SD

Channel Islands Specialists Society
Membership Secretary—Mr. B. Cropp
17, Westlands Avenue, Huntercombe, Slough, Berkshire SL1 6AG

Ascension Study Circle
Secretary—Dr. R. C. F. Baker
Greys, Tower Road, Whitstable, Kent CT5 2ER

Bechuanalands and Botswana Society
Secretary—Mr. R. Setterfield
18, Goldsmid Road, Hove, East Sussex BN3 1QA

Bermuda Collectors Society
Secretary—Mr. T. J. McMahon
Nash Road, Purdy Station, N.Y. 10578, U.S.A.

Bermuda High (Keyplates)
Editor—Mr. R. W. Dickgiesser
P.O. Box 475, Derby, CT 06418, U.S.A.

British Caribbean Philatelic Study Group
Overseas Director—Mr. R. V. Swarbrick
The Four Winds, 919, Uppingham Road, Bushby, Leics LE7 9RR

British Society of Australian Philately
Secretary—Mr. T. R. Finlayson
86, Clarence Road, Fleet, Hants GU13 9RS

British West Indies Study Circle
Secretary—Mr. M. Wilson
Timbers, Chequers Lane, Tharston, Norwich, Norfolk NR15 2YA

Burma Philatelic Study Circle
Secretary—Mr. A. Meech
42, Fairway Drive, Edmonton, Alberta, Canada T6J 2C3

Canadian Philatelic Society of Great Britain
Secretary—Mr. B. T. Stalker
3, Rutherford Way, Tonbridge, Kent TN10 4RH

Ceylon Study Circle
Secretary—Mr. R. W. P. Frost
42, Lonsdale Road, Cannington, Bridgwater, Somerset TA5 2JS

Cyprus Study Circle
Secretary—Dr. R. I. Watson
Hill Cottage, Slinfold, West Sussex RH13 7SN

East Africa Study Circle
Secretary—Mr. R. Dunstan
Chantry Court, 1, The Close, Warminster, Wilts BA12 9AL

Falklands Islands Study Group
Membership Secretary—Mr. D. W. A. Jeffery
38, Bradstock Road, Stoneleigh, Epsom, Surrey KT17 2LH

Gibraltar Philatelic Society
Honorary Secretary—Mr. M. Ramagge
P.O. Box 270, Gibraltar

Gibraltar Study Circle
Membership Secretary—Mr. J. A. Paulson
36, Starkholmes Road, Matlock, Derbyshire DE4 3DD

Great Britain Overprints Society
Membership Secretary—Mr. A. H. Bishop
Bunkers, Titlarks Hill, Sunningdale, Berkshire SL5 0JD

The Hong Kong Study Circle
Membership Secretary—Mr. P. V. Ball
37, Hart Court, Newcastle-under-Lyme, Staffordshire ST5 2AL

Indian Ocean Study Circle (Western Islands)
Secretary—Mrs. D. J. Hopson
Field Acre, Hoe Benham, Newbury, Berkshire RG16 8PD

India Study Circle
Secretary—Mr. R. S. Nuttall
2, St. Georges Road, Great Yarmouth, Norfolk NR30 2JR

Irish Philatelic Circle
General Secretary—Mr. H. K. Jamieson
3, Cleves Way, Hampton, Middlesex TW12 2PL

King George V Silver Jubilee Study Circle
Secretary—Mr. N. Levinge
11, Broadway, Northampton NN1 4SF

King George VI Collectors Society
Secretary—Mr. F. R. Lockyer, OBE
24, Stourwood Road, Southbourne, Bournemouth, Dorset BH6 3QP

Malaya Study Group
Membership Secretary—Mr. D. Moon
Holly Cottage, Barrows Road, Cheddar, Somerset BS27 3BD

Malta Study Circle
Secretary—Mr. F. A. Gray
69, Stonecross Road, Hatfield, Herts AL10 0HP

New Zealand Society of Great Britain
General Secretary—Mrs. M. Frankcom
Queens House, 34a, Tarrant Street, Arundel, West Sussex BN18 9DJ

Orange Free State Study Circle
Secretary—Mr. J. R. Stroud
28, Oxford Street, Burnham-on-Sea, Somerset TA8 1LQ

Pacific Islands Study Circle of Great Britain
Honorary Secretary—Mr. J. D. Ray
24, Woodvale Avenue, London SE25 4AE

Papuan Philatelic Society
Secretary—Mr. G. Amedro
12, Main Street, Gorebridge, Midlothian EH23 4BX

Philatelic Errors and Varieties Society
The Secretary
6, Hornton Place, London W8 4LZ

Pitcairn Islands Study Group (U.K.)
Honorary Secretary—Mr. A. B. Meares
Ragnall Cottage, Ragnall Lane, Walkley Wood, Nailsworth, Stroud, Glos GL6 0RX

Pitcairn Islands Study Group (U.S.A.)
Publications Editor—Mr. E. L. Parker
PO Box 1306, Greenville, Maine 04441, U.S.A.

Rhodesian Study Circle
Membership Secretary—Mr. D. Lambert
25/27, Carr Road, Nelson, Lancs BB9 7JZ

St. Helena, Ascension, and Tristan da Cunha Philatelic Society
Secretary—Mrs. V. W. Finne
PO Box 366, Calpella, California 95418, U.S.A.

South African Collectors' Society
General Secretary—Mr. W. A. Page
138, Chastilian Road, Dartford, Kent DA1 3LG

Sudan Study Group
Secretary—Mr. J. W. Scott
Bemerton, Lingfield Road, East Grinstead, West Sussex RH19 2EJ

Tonga and Tin Can Mail Study Circle
Secretary—Mr. T. Jackson
121, Mullingar Ct. 1A, Schaumburg, IL 60193-3258, U.S.A.

Transvaal Study Circle
Honorary Secretary—Ms. J. Matthews
Bramley Cottage, 27b, Lancaster Gardens, Beltinge, Herne Bay, Kent CT6 6PU

Tuvalu and Kiribati Philatelic Society
Secretary—Mr. M. A. Butkiss
PO Box 1209, Temple Hills, Md 20748, U.S.A.

West Africa Study Circle
Secretary—Mr. J. Powell
6, Warren Bank, Simpson, Milton Keynes MK6 3AQ

General Philatelic Information

and Guidelines to the Scope of the Part 1 (British Commonwealth) Catalogue

The notes which follow seek to reflect current practice in compiling the Part 1 (British Commonwealth) Catalogue.

It scarcely needs emphasising that the *Stanley Gibbons Stamp Catalogue* has a very long history and that the vast quantity of information it contains has been carefully built up by successive generations through the work of countless individuals. Philately itself is never static and the Catalogue has evolved and developed during this long time-span. Thus, while these notes are important for today's criteria, they may be less precise the further back in the listings one travels. They are not intended to inaugurate some unwanted series of piecemeal alterations in a widely respected work, but it does seem to us useful that Catalogue users know as exactly as possible the policies currently in operation.

PRICES

The prices quoted in this catalogue are the estimated selling prices of Stanley Gibbons Ltd at the time of publication. They are, *unless it is specifically stated otherwise*, for examples in fine condition for the issue concerned. Superb examples are worth more; those of a lower quality considerably less.

All prices are subject to change without prior notice and Stanley Gibbons Ltd may from time to time offer stamps below catalogue price in consequence of special purchases or particular promotions.

No guarantee is given to supply all stamps priced, since it is not possible to keep every catalogued item in stock. Commemorative issues may, at times, only be available in complete sets and not as individual values.

Quotation of prices. The prices in the left-hand column are for unused stamps and those in the right-hand column are for used.

A dagger (†) denotes that the item listed does not exist in that condition and a blank, or dash, that it exists, or may exist, but no market price is known.

Prices are expressed in pounds and pence sterling. One pound comprises 100 pence (£1 = 100p).

The method of notation is as follows: pence in numerals (e.g. 10 denotes ten pence); pound and pence, up to £100, in numerals (e.g. 4·25 denotes four pounds and twenty-five pence); prices above £100 expressed in whole pounds with the "£"sign shown.

Unused stamps. Great Britain and Commonwealth: the prices for unused stamps of Queen Victoria to King George V are for lightly hinged examples. Unused prices for King Edward VIII to Queen Elizabeth II issues are for unmounted mint.

Some stamps from the King George VI period are often difficult to find in unmounted mint condition. In such instances we would expect that collectors would need to pay a high proportion of the price quoted to obtain mounted mint examples. Generally speaking lightly mounted mint stamps from this reign, issued before 1945, are in considerable demand.

Mounted mint stamps from the reign of Queen Elizabeth II are frequently available at lower prices than those quoted for the stamps unmounted.

Used stamps. The used prices are normally for stamps postally used but may be for stamps cancelled-to-order where this practice exists.

A pen-cancellation on early issues can sometimes correctly denote postal use. Instances are individually noted in the Catalogue in explanation of the used price given.

Prices quoted for bisects on cover or on large piece are for those dated during the period officially authorised.

Stamps not sold unused to the public (e.g. some official stamps) are priced used only.

The use of "unified" designs, that is stamps inscribed for both postal and fiscal purposes, results in a number of stamps of very high face value. In some instances these may not have been primarily intended for postal purposes, but if they are so inscribed we include them. We only price such items used, however, where there is evidence of normal postal usage.

Cover prices. To assist collectors, cover prices are quoted for issues up to 1945 at the beginning of each country.

The system gives a general guide in the form of a factor by which the corresponding used price of the loose stamp should be multiplied when found in fine average condition on cover.

Care is needed in applying the factors and they relate to a cover which bears a single of the denomination listed; strips and blocks would need individual valuation outside the scope. If more than one denomination is present the most highly priced attracts the multiplier and the remainder are priced at the simple figure for used singles in arriving at a total.

The cover should be of non-philatelic origin, bearing the correct postal rate for the period and distance involved and cancelled with the markings normal to the offices concerned. Purely philatelic items have a cover value only slightly greater than the catalogue value for the corresponding used stamps. This applies generally to those high-value stamps used philatelically rather than in the normal course of commerce. Low-value stamps, e.g. ¼d. and ½d., are desirable when used as a single rate on cover and merit an increase in "multiplier" value.

First-day covers in the period up to 1945 are not within the scope of the system and the multiplier should not be used. As a special category of philatelic usage, with wide variations in valuation according to scarcity, they require separate treatment.

Oversized covers, difficult to accommodate on an album page, should be reckoned as worth little more than the corresponding value of the used stamps. The condition of a cover affects its value. Except for "wreck covers", serious damage or soiling reduce the value where the postal markings and stamps are ordinary ones. Conversely, visual appeal adds to the value and this can include freshness of appearance, important addresses, old-fashioned but legible hand-writing, historic town-names, etc.

The multipliers are a base on which further value would be added to take account of the cover's postal historical importance in demonstrating such things as unusual, scarce or emergency cancels, interesting routes, significant postal markings, combination usage, the development of postal rates, and so on.

For *Great Britain*, rather than multiplication factors, the cover price is shown as a third column, following the prices for unused and used stamps. It will be extended beyond King Edward VII in subsequent editions.

Minimum price. The minimum price quoted is ten pence. This represents a handling charge rather than a basis for valuing common stamps, for which the 10p price should not be reckoned automatically, since it covers a variation in real scarcity.

Set prices. Set prices are generally for one of each value, excluding shades and varieties, but including major colour changes. Where there are alternative shades, etc., the cheapest is usually included. The number of stamps in the set is always stated for clarity. The mint prices for sets containing *se-tenant* pieces are based on the prices quoted for such combinations, and not on those for the individual stamps.

Specimen stamps. The pricing of these items is explained under that heading.

Repricing. Collectors will be aware that the market factors of supply and demand directly influence the prices quoted in this Catalogue. Whatever the scarcity of a particular stamp, if there is no one in the market who wishes to buy it it cannot be expected to achieve a high price. Conversely, the same item actively sought by numerous potential buyers may cause the price to rise.

All the prices in this Catalogue are examined during the preparation of each new edition by expert staff of Stanley Gibbons and repriced as necessary. They take many factors into account, including supply and demand, and are in close touch with the international stamp market and the auction world.

Commonwealth cover prices and advice on postal history material originally provided by Edward B. Proud.

GUARANTEE

All stamps are guaranteed genuine originals in the following terms:

If not as described, and returned by the purchaser, we undertake to refund the price paid to us in the original transaction. If any stamp is certified as genuine by the Expert Committee of the Royal Philatelic Society, London, or by B.P.A. Expertising Ltd, the purchaser shall not be entitled to make any claim against us for any error, omission or mistake in such certificate.

Consumers' statutory rights are not affected by the above guarantee.

The recognised Expert Committees in this country are those of the Royal Philatelic Society, 41 Devonshire Place, London W1N 1PE, and B.P.A. Expertising Ltd, P.O. Box 163, Carshalton Beeches, Surrey SM5 4QR. They do not undertake valuations under any circumstances and fees are payable for their services.

THE CATALOGUE IN GENERAL

Contents. The Catalogue is confined to adhesive postage stamps, including miniature sheets. For particular categories the rules are:

(*a*) Revenue (fiscal) stamps or telegraph stamps are listed only where they have been expressly authorised for postal duty.

(*b*) Stamps issued only precancelled are included, but normally issued stamps available additionally with precancel have no separate precancel listing unless the face value is changed.

(*c*) Stamps prepared for use but not issued, hitherto accorded full listing, are nowadays footnoted with a price (where possible).

(*d*) Bisects (trisects, etc.) are only listed where such usage was officially authorised.

(*e*) Stamps issued only on first day covers or in presentation packs and not available separately are not listed but may be priced in a footnote.

(*f*) New printings are only included in this catalogue where they show a major philatelic variety, such as a change in shade, watermark or paper. Further details of modern new printings, including changes in imprint dates, are given in the *Two Reigns Catalogue* series. (Details for the relevant areas are also given in the *Channel Islands Specialised Catalogue* and *Collect Channel Islands and Isle of Man Stamps*.)

(*g*) Official and unofficial reprints are dealt with by footnote.

(*h*) Stamps from imperforate printings of modern issues which also occur perforated are covered by footnotes, but are listed where widely available for postal use.

Exclusions. The following are excluded: (*a*) non-postal revenue or fiscal stamps; (*b*) postage stamps used fiscally; (*c*) local carriage labels and private local issues; (*d*) telegraph stamps; (*e*) bogus or phantom stamps; (*f*) railway or airline letter fee stamps, bus or road transport company labels; (*g*) cut-outs; (*h*) all types of non-postal labels and souvenirs; (*i*) documentary labels for the postal service, e.g. registration, recorded delivery, airmail etiquettes, etc.; (*j*) privately applied embellishments to official issues and privately commissioned items generally; (*k*) stamps for training postal officers.

Full listing. "Full listing" confers our recognition and implies allotting a catalogue number and (wherever possible) a price quotation.

In judging status for inclusion in the catalogue broad considerations are applied to stamps. They must be issued by a legitimate postal authority, recognised by the government concerned, and must be adhesives valid for proper postal use in the class of service for which they are inscribed. Stamps, with the exception of such categories as postage dues and officials, must be available to the general public, at face value, in reasonable quantities without any artificial restrictions being imposed on their distribution.

We record as abbreviated Appendix entries, without catalogue numbers or prices, stamps from countries which either persist in having far more issues than can be justified by postal need or have failed to maintain control over their distribution so that they have not been available to the public in reasonable quantities at face value. Miniature sheets and imperforate stamps are not mentioned in these entries.

The publishers of this catalogue have observed, with concern, the proliferation of "artificial" stamp-issuing territories. On several occasions this has resulted in separately inscribed issues for various component parts of otherwise united states or territories.

Stanley Gibbons Publications Ltd have decided that where such circumstances occur, they will not, in the future, list these items in the SG catalogue without first satisfying themselves that the stamps represent a genuine political, historical or postal division within the country concerned. Any such issues which do not fulfil this stipulation will be recorded in the Catalogue Appendix only.

For errors and varieties the criterion is legitimate (albeit inadvertent) sale through a postal administration in the normal course of business. Details of provenance are always important; printers' waste and fraudulently manufactured material is excluded.

Certificates. In assessing unlisted items due weight is given to Certificates from recognised Expert Committees and, where appropriate, we will usually ask to see them.

New issues. New issues are listed regularly in the Catalogue Supplement published in *Gibbons Stamp Monthly*, whence they are consolidated into the next available edition of the Catalogue.

Date of issue. Where local issue dates differ from dates of release by agencies, "date of issue" is the local date. Fortuitous stray usage before the officially intended date is disregarded in listing. For ease of reference, the Catalogue displays in the top corner the date of issue of the first set listed on each page.

Catalogue numbers. Stamps of each country are catalogued chronologically by date of issue. Subsidiary classes are placed at the end of the country, as separate lists, with a distinguishing letter prefix to the catalogue number, e.g. D for postage due, O for official and E for express delivery stamps.

The catalogue number appears in the extreme left column. The boldface Type numbers in the next column are merely cross-references to illustrations. Catalogue numbers in the *Gibbons Stamp Monthly* Supplement are provisional only and may need to be altered when the lists are consolidated. For the numbering of miniature sheets and sheetlets *see* section below.

Once published in the Catalogue, numbers are changed as little as possible; really serious renumbering is reserved for the occasions when a complete country or an entire issue is being rewritten. The edition first affected includes cross-reference tables of old and new numbers.

Our catalogue numbers are universally recognised in specifying stamps and as a hallmark of status.

Illustrations. Stamps are illustrated at three-quarters linear size. Stamps not illustrated are the same size and format as the value shown, unless otherwise indicated. Stamps issued only as miniature sheets have the stamp alone illustrated but sheet size is also quoted. Overprints, surcharges and watermarks are normally actual size. Illustrations of varieties are often enlarged to show the detail.

Designers. Designers' names are quoted where known, though space precludes naming every individual concerned in the production of a set. In particular, photographers supplying material are usually named only when they also make an active contribution in the design stage; posed photographs of reigning monarchs are, however, an exception to this rule.

CONTACTING THE CATALOGUE EDITOR

The editor is always interested in hearing from people who have new information which will improve or correct the Catalogue. As a general rule he must see and examine the actual stamps before they can be considered for listing; photographs or photocopies are insufficient evidence.

Submissions should be made in writing to the Catalogue Editor, Stanley Gibbons Publications Ltd. at the Ringwood office. The cost of return postage for items submitted is appreciated, and this should include the registration fee if required.

Where information is solicited purely for the benefit of the enquirer, the editor cannot undertake to reply if the answer is already contained in these published notes or if return postage is omitted. Written communications are greatly preferred to enquiries by telephone and the editor regrets that he or his staff cannot see personal callers without a prior appointment being made. Correspondence may be subject to delay during the production period of each new edition.

The editor welcomes close contact with study circles and is interested, too, in finding reliable local correspondents who will verify and supplement offical information in countries where this is deficient.

We regret we do not give opinions as to the genuineness of stamps, nor do we identify stamps or number them by our Catalogue.

TECHNICAL MATTERS

The meanings of the technical terms used in the Catalogue will be found in our *Philatelic Terms Illustrated* (3rd edition), (*price* £7.50 *plus* 80*p postage and packing*).

References below to "more specialised" listings are to be taken to indicate, as appropriate, the Stanley Gibbons *Great Britain Specialised Catalogue* in 5 volumes; the *Great Britain, Australia* or *New Zealand Concise Catalogues;* the *Channel Islands Specialised Catalogue* and (for Commonwealth stamps from 1937) the *Two Reigns Stamp Catalogue* series.

1. Printing

Printing errors. Errors in printing are of major interest to the Catalogue. Authenticated items meriting consideration would include: background, centre or frame inverted or omitted; centre or subject transposed; error of colour; error or omission of value; double prints and impressions; printed both sides; and so on. Designs *tête-bêche*, whether intentionally or by accident, are listable. *Se-tenant* arrangements of stamps are recognised in the listings or footnotes. Gutter pairs (a pair of stamps separated by blank margin) are not included in this volume. Colours only partially omitted are not listed. Stamps with embossing omitted and (for Commonwealth countries) stamps printed on the gummed side are reserved for our more specialised listings.

Printing varieties. Listing is accorded to major changes in the printing base which lead to completely new types. In recess-printing this could be a design re-engraved; in photogravure or photolithography a screen altered in whole or in part. It can also encompass flat-bed and rotary printing if the results are readily distinguishable.

To be considered at all, varieties must be constant.

Early stamps, produced by primitive methods, were prone to numerous imperfections: the lists reflect this, recognising re-entries, retouches, broken frames, misshapen letters, and so on. Printing technology has, however, radically improved over the years, during which time photogravure and lithography have become predominant. Varieties nowadays are more in the nature of flaws and these, being too specialised for this general catalogue, are almost always outside the scope. The development of our range of specialised catalogues allows us now to list those items which have philatelic significance in their appropriate volume.

In no catalogue, however, do we list such items as: dry prints, kiss prints, doctor-blade flaws, colour shifts or registration flaws (unless they lead to the complete omission of a colour from an individual stamp), lithographic ring flaws, and so on. Neither do we recognise fortuitous happenings like paper creases or confetti flaws.

Overprints (and surcharges). Overprints of different types qualify for separate listing. These include overprints in different colours; overprints from different printing processes such as litho and typo; overprints in totally different typefaces, etc.

Overprint errors and varieties. Major errors in machine-printed overprints are important and listable. They include: overprint inverted or omitted; overprint double (treble, etc.); overprint diagonal; overprint double, one inverted; pairs with one overprint omitted, e.g. from a radical shift to an adjoining stamp; error of colour; error of type fount; letters inverted or omitted, etc. If the overprint is handstamped, few of these would qualify and a distinction is drawn. We continue, however, to list pairs of stamps where one has a handstamped overprint and the other has not.

Varieties occurring in overprints will often take the form of broken letters, slight differences in spacing, rising spaces, etc. Only the most important would be considered for footnote mention.

Sheet positions. If space permits we quote sheet positions of listed varieties and authenticated data is solicited for this purpose.

De La Rue plates. The Catalogue classifies the general plates used by De La Rue for printing British Colonial stamps as follows:

VICTORIAN KEY TYPE

Die I

1. The ball of decoration on the second point of the crown appears as a dark mass of lines.
2. Dark vertical shading separates the front hair from the bun.
3. The vertical line of colour outlining the front of the throat stops at the sixth line of shading on the neck.

4. The white space in the coil of the hair above the curl is roughly the shape of a pin's head.

Die II

1. There are very few lines of colour in the ball and it appears almost white.
2. A white vertical strand of hair appears in place of the dark shading.
3. The line stops at the eighth line of shading.
4. The white space is oblong, with a line of colour partially dividing it at the left end.

Plates numbered 1 and 2 are both Die I. Plates 3 and 4 are Die II.

GEORGIAN KEY TYPE

Die I

A. The second (thick) line below the name of the country is cut slanting, conforming roughly to the shape of the crown on each side.
B. The labels of solid colour bearing the words "POSTAGE" and "& REVENUE" are square at the inner top corners.
C. There is a projecting "bud" on the outer spiral of the ornament in each of the lower corners.

Die II

A. The second line is cut vertically on each side of the crown.
B. The labels curve inwards at the top.
C. There is no "bud" in this position.

Unless otherwise stated in the lists, all stamps with watermark Multiple Crown CA (w **8**) are Die I while those with watermark Multiple Crown Script CA (w **9**) are Die II.

2. Paper

All stamps listed are deemed to be on "ordinary" paper of the wove type and white in colour; only departures from this are normally mentioned.

Types. Where classification so requires we distinguish such other types of paper as, for example, vertically and horizontally laid; wove and laid bâtonné; card(board); carton; cartridge; glazed; granite; native; pelure; porous; quadrillé; ribbed; rice; and silk thread.

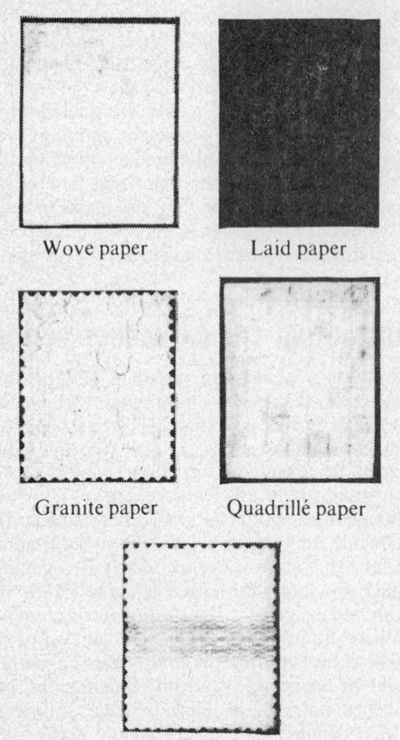

Wove paper — Laid paper

Granite paper — Quadrillé paper

Burelé band

The various makeshifts for normal paper are listed as appropriate. The varieties of double paper and joined paper are recognised. The security device of a printed burelé band on the back of a stamp, as in early Queensland, qualifies for listing.

Descriptive terms. The fact that a paper is handmade (and thus probably of uneven thickness) is mentioned where necessary. Such descriptive terms as "hard" and "soft"; "smooth" and "rough"; "thick", "medium" and "thin" are applied where there is philatelic merit in classifying papers. We do not, for example, even in more specialised listings, classify paper thicknesses in the Wilding and Machin definitives of Great Britain. Weight standards for the paper apply to complete reels only, so that differences on individual stamps are acceptable to the printer provided the reel conforms overall.

Coloured, very white and toned papers. A coloured paper is one that is coloured right through (front and back of the stamp). In the Catalogue the colour of the paper is given in *italics*, thus:

black/*rose* = black design on rose paper.

Papers have been made specially white in recent years by, for example, a very heavy coating of chalk. We do not classify shades of whiteness of paper as distinct varieties. There does exist, however, a type of paper from early days called toned. This is off-white, often brownish or buffish, but it cannot be assigned any definite colour. A toning effect brought on by climate, incorrect storage or gum staining is disregarded here, as this was not the state of the paper when issued.

Modern developments. Two modern developments also affect the listings: printing on self-adhesive paper and the use of metallic foils. For self-adhesive stamps *see* under "Gum", below. Care should be taken not to damage the embossing on stamps impressed on metallic foils, such as Sierra Leone 1965–67, by subjecting the album pages to undue pressure. The possibility of faked "missing gold heads" is noted at the appropriate places in the listing of modern Great Britain.

"Ordinary" and "Chalk-surfaced" papers. The availability of many postage stamps for revenue purposes made necessary some safeguard against the illegitimate re-use of stamps with removable cancellations. This was at first secured by using fugitive inks and later by printing on chalky (chalk-surfaced) paper, both of which made it difficult to remove any form of obliteration without also damaging the stamp design.

With some exceptions we do not list the varieties on chalky paper separately, but we have indicated the existence of the papers by the letters "**O**" (ordinary) and "**C**" (chalky) after the description of all stamps where the chalky paper may be found. Both letters shown together signify that the stamp exists on both papers; if a date is given it is that of the first-mentioned paper and the price quoted is that of the cheaper variety. Where no indication is given, the paper is "ordinary".

Our chalky paper is specifically one which shows a black mark when touched with a silver wire. The paper used during the Second World War for high values, as in Bermuda, the Leeward Islands, etc., was thinly coated with some kind of surfacing which does not react to silver and is therefore regarded (and listed) as "ordinary". Stamps on chalk-surfaced paper can easily lose this coating through immersion in water.

Another paper introduced during the War as a substitute for chalky is rather thick, very white and glossy, and shows little or no watermark, nor does it show a black line when touched with silver. In the Bahamas high values this paper might be mistaken for the chalky (which is thinner and poorer-looking) but for the silver test.

Glazed paper. In 1969 the Crown Agents introduced a new general-purpose paper for use in conjunction with all current printing processes. It generally has a marked glossy surface but the degree varies according to the process used, being more marked in recess-printing stamps. As it does not respond to the silver test this presents a further test where previous printings were on chalky paper. A change of paper to the glazed variety merits separate listing.

Green and yellow papers. Issues of the First World War and immediate postwar period occur on green and yellow papers and these are given separate Catalogue listing. The original coloured papers (coloured throughout) gave way to surface-coloured papers, the stamps having "white backs"; other stamps show one colour on the front and a different one at the back. Because of the numerous variations a grouping of colours is adopted as follows:

YELLOW PAPERS

(1) The original *yellow* paper (throughout), usually bright in colour. The gum is often sparse, of harsh consistency and dull-looking.

(2) The *white backs.*

(3) A bright *lemon* paper. The colour must have a pronounced greenish tinge, different from the "yellow" in (1). As a rule, the gum on stamps using this lemon paper is plentiful- smooth and shiny, and the watermark shows distinctly. Care is needed with stamps printed in green on yellow paper (1) as it may appear that the paper is this lemon.

(4) An *orange-buff* paper. The colour must have a distinct brownish tinge. It is not to be confused with a muddy yellow (1) nor the misleading appearance (on the surface) of stamps printed in red on yellow paper where an engraved plate has been insufficiently wiped.

(5) A *pale yellow* paper that has a creamy tone to the yellow.

GREEN PAPERS

(6) The original "green" paper, varying considerably through shades of *blue-green* and *yellow-green,* the front and back sometimes differing.

(7) The *white backs.*

(8) A paper blue-green on the surface with *pale olive* back. The back must be markedly paler than the front and this and the pronounced olive tinge to the back distinguish it from (6).

(9) Paper with a vivid green surface, commonly called *emerald-green*; it has the olive back of (8).

(10) Paper with *emerald-green* both back and front.

3. Perforation and Rouletting

Perforation gauge. The gauge of a perforation is the number of holes in a length of 2 cm. For correct classification the size of the holes (large or small) may need to be distinguished; in a few cases the actual number of holes on each edge of the stamp needs to be quoted.

Measurement. The Gibbons *Instanta* gauge is the standard for measuring perforations. The stamp is viewed against a dark background with the transparent gauge put on top of it. Though the gauge measures to decimal accuracy, perforations read from it are generally quoted in the Catalogue to the nearest half. For example:

Just over perf $12\frac{3}{4}$ to just under $13\frac{1}{4}$ = perf 13
Perf $13\frac{1}{4}$ exactly, rounded up = perf $13\frac{1}{2}$
Just over perf $13\frac{1}{4}$ to just under $13\frac{3}{4}$ = perf $13\frac{1}{2}$
Perf $13\frac{3}{4}$ exactly, rounded up = perf 14

However, where classification depends on it, actual quarter-perforations are quoted.

Notation. Where no perforation is quoted for an issue it is imperforate. Perforations are usually abbreviated (and spoken) as follows, though sometimes they may be spelled out for clarity. This notation for rectangular stamps (the majority) applies to diamond shapes if "top" is read as the edge to the top right.

P 14: perforated alike on all sides (read: "perf 14").

P 14 × 15: the first figure refers to top and bottom, the second to left and right sides (read: "perf 14 by 15"). This is a compound perforation. For an upright triangular stamp the first figure refers to the two sloping sides and the second to the base. In inverted triangulars the base is first and the second figure refers to the sloping sides.

P 14–15: perforation measuring anything between 14 and 15: the holes are irregularly spaced, thus the gauge may vary along a single line or even along a single edge of the stamp (read: "perf 14 to 15").

P 14 *irregular*: perforated 14 from a worn perforator, giving badly aligned holes irregularly spaced (read: "irregular perf 14").

P comp(ound) 14 × 15: two gauges in use but not necessarily on opposite sides of the stamp. It could be one side in one gauge and three in the other; or two adjacent sides with the same gauge. (Read: "perf compound of 14 and 15".) For three gauges or more, abbreviated as "*P* 14, $14\frac{1}{2}$, 15 *or compound*" for example.

P 14, $14\frac{1}{2}$: perforated approximately $14\frac{1}{4}$ (read: "perf 14 or $14\frac{1}{2}$"). It does *not* mean two stamps, one perf 14 and the other perf $14\frac{1}{2}$. This obsolescent notation is gradually being replaced in the Catalogue.

Imperf: imperforate (not perforated).

Imperf × *P* 14: imperforate at top and bottom and perf 14 at sides.

Perf × imperf

P 14 × *imperf*: perf 14 at top and bottom and imperforate at sides.

Such headings as "*P* 13 × 14 (*vert*) and *P* 14 × 13 (*horiz*)" indicate which perforations apply to which stamp format—vertical or horizontal.

Some stamps are additionally perforated so that a label or tab is detachable; others have been perforated suitably for use as two halves. Listings are normally for whole stamps, unless stated otherwise.

Other terms. Perforation almost always gives circular holes; where other shapes have been used they are specified, e.g. square holes; lozenge perf. Interrupted perfs are brought about by the omission of pins at regular intervals. Perforations merely simulated by being printed as part of the design are of course ignored. With few exceptions, privately applied perforations are not listed.

In the nineteenth century perforations are often described as clean cut (clean, sharply incised holes), intermediate or rough (rough holes, imperfectly cut, often the result of blunt pins).

Perforation errors and varieties. Authenticated errors, where a stamp normally perforated is accidentally issued imperforate, are listed provided no traces of perforation (blind holes or indentations) remain. They must be provided as pairs, both stamps wholly imperforate, and are only priced in that form.

In Great Britain, numerous of these part-perforated stamps have arisen from the introduction of the Jumelle Press. This has a rotary perforator with rows of pins on one drum engaging with holes on another. Engagement is only gradual when the perforating unit is started up or stopped, giving rise to perforations "fading out", a variety mentioned above as not listed.

Stamps from the Jumelle printings sometimes occur imperforate between stamp and sheet margin. Such errors are not listed in this catalogue, but are covered by the fourth or fifth volumes of the *Great Britain Specialised Catalogue*.

Pairs described as "imperforate between" have the line of perforations between the two stamps omitted.

Imperf between (*horiz pair*): a horizontal pair of stamps with perfs all around the edges but none between the stamps.

Imperf between (*vert pair*): a vertical pair of stamps with perfs all around the edges but none between the stamps.

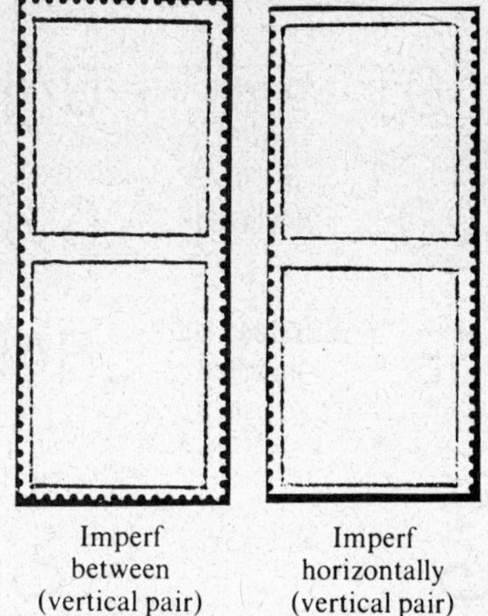

Imperf between (vertical pair) — Imperf horizontally (vertical pair)

Where several of the rows have escaped perforation the resulting varieties are listable. Thus:

Imperf vert (*horiz pair*): a horizontal pair of stamps perforated top and bottom; all three vertical directions are imperf—the two outer edges and between the stamps.

Imperf horiz (*vert pair*): a vertical pair perforated at left and right edges; all three horizontal directions are imperf—the top, bottom and between the stamps.

Straight edges. Large sheets cut up before issue to post offices can cause stamps with straight edges, i.e. imperf on one side or on two sides at right angles. They are not usually listable in this condition and are worth less than corresponding stamps properly perforated all round. This does not, however, apply to certain stamps, mainly from coils and booklets, where straight edges on various sides are the manufacturing norm affecting every stamp. The listings and notes make clear which sides are correctly imperf.

Malfunction. Varieties of double, misplaced or partial perforation caused by error or machine malfunction are not listable, neither are freaks, such as perforations placed diagonally from paper folds, nor missing holes caused by broken pins.

Centering. Well-centred stamps have designs surrounded by equal opposite margins. Where this condition affects the price the fact is stated.

Types of perforating. Where necessary for classification, perforation types are distinguished. These include:

Line perforation from one line of pins punching single rows of holes at a time.

Comb perforation from pins disposed across the sheet in comb formation, punching out holes at three sides of the stamp a row at a time.

Harrow perforation applied to a whole pane or sheet at one stroke.

Rotary perforation from toothed wheels operating across a sheet, then crosswise.

Sewing-machine perforation. The resultant condition, clean-cut or rough, is distinguished where required.

Pin-perforation is the commonly applied term for pin-roulette in which, instead of being punched out, round holes are pricked by sharp-pointed pins and no paper is removed.

Mixed perforation occurs when stamps with defective perforations are re-perforated in a different gauge.

Punctured stamps. Perforation holes can be punched into the face of the stamp. Patterns of small holes, often in the shape of initial letters, are privately applied devices against pilferage. These "perfins" are outside the scope except for Australia, Papua and Sudan where they were used as official stamps by the national administration. Identification devices, when officially inspired, are listed or noted; they can be shapes, or letters or words formed from holes, sometimes converting one class of stamp into another.

Rouletting. In rouletting the paper is cut, for ease of separation, but none is removed. The gauge is measured, when needed, as for perforations. Traditional French terms descriptive of the type of cut are often used and types include:

Arc roulette (*percé en arc*). Cuts are minute, spaced arcs, each roughly a semicircle.

Cross roulette (*percé en croix*). Cuts are tiny diagonal crosses.

Line roulette (*percé en ligne* or *en ligne droite*). Short straight cuts parallel to the frame of the stamp. The commonest basic roulette. Where not further described, "roulette" means this type.

Rouletted in colour or *coloured roulette* (*percé en lignes colorées* or *en lignes de couleur*). Cuts with coloured edges, arising from notched rule inked simultaneously with the printing plate.

Saw-tooth roulette (*percé en scie*). Cuts applied zigzag fashion to resemble the teeth of a saw.

Serpentine roulette (*percé en serpentin*). Cuts as sharply wavy lines.

Zigzag roulette (*percé en zigzags*). Short straight cuts at angles in alternate directions, producing sharp points on separation. U.S. usage favours "serrate(d) roulette" for this type.

Pin-roulette (originally *percé en points* and now *perforés trous d'epingle*) is commonly called pin-perforation in English.

4. Gum

All stamps listed are assumed to have gum of some kind; if they were issued without gum this is stated. Original gum (o.g.) means that which was present on the stamp as issued to the public. Deleterious climates and the presence of certain chemicals can cause gum to crack and, with early stamps, even make the paper deteriorate. Unscrupulous fakers are adept in removing it and regumming the stamp to meet the unreasoning demand often made for "full o.g." in cases where such a thing is virtually impossible.

The gum normally used on stamps has been gum arabic until the late 1960s when synthetic adhesives were introduced. Harrison and Sons Ltd for instance use *polyvinyl alcohol*, known to philatelists as PVA. This is almost invisible except for a slight yellowish tinge which was incorporated to make it possible to see that the stamps have been gummed. It has advantages in hot countries, as stamps do not curl and sheets are less likely to stick together. Gum arabic and PVA are not distinguished in the lists except that where a stamp exists with both forms this is indicated in footnotes. Our more specialised catalogues provide separate listing of gums for Great Britain.

Self-adhesive stamps are issued on backing paper, from which they are peeled before affixing to mail. Unused examples are priced as for backing paper intact, in which condition they are recommended to be kept. Used examples are best collected on cover or on piece.

5. Watermarks

Stamps are on unwatermarked paper except where the heading to the set says otherwise.

Detection. Watermarks are detected for Catalogue description by one of four methods: (1) holding stamps to the light; (2) laying stamps face down on a dark background; (3) adding a few drops of petroleum ether 40/60 to the stamp laid face down in a watermark tray; (4) by use of the Morley-Bright Detector, or other equipment, which work by revealing the thinning of the paper at the watermark (Note that petroleum ether is highly inflammable in use and can damage photogravure stamps.)

Listable types. Stamps occurring on both watermarked and unwatermarked papers are different types and both receive full listing.

Single watermarks (devices occurring once on every stamp) can be modified in size and shape as between different issues; the types are noted but not usually separately listed. Fortuitous absence of watermark from a single stamp or its gross displacement would not be listable.

To overcome registration difficulties the device may be repeated at close intervals (a *multiple watermark*), single stamps thus showing parts of several devices. Similarly, a large *sheet watermark* (or *all-over watermark*) covering numerous stamps can be used. We give informative notes and illustrations for them. The designs may be such that numbers of stamps in the sheet automatically lack watermark: this is not a listable variety. Multiple and all-over watermarks sometimes undergo modifications, but if the various types are difficult to distinguish from single stamps notes are given but not separate listings.

Papermakers' watermarks are noted where known but not listed separately, since most stamps in the sheet will lack them. Sheet watermarks which are nothing more than officially adopted papermakers' watermarks are, however, given normal listing.

Marginal watermarks, falling outside the pane of stamps, are ignored except where misplacement causes the adjoining row to be affected, in which case they are footnoted.

Watermark errors and varieties. Watermark errors are recognised as of major importance. They comprise stamps intended to be on unwatermarked paper but issued watermarked by mistake, or stamps printed on paper with the wrong watermark. Watermark varieties, on the other hand, such as broken or deformed bits on the dandy roll, are not listable.

Watermark positions. The diagram shows how watermark position is described in the Catalogue. Paper has a side intended for printing and watermarks are usually impressed so that they read normally when looked through from that printed side. However, since philatelists customarily detect watermarks by looking at the back of the stamp the watermark diagram also makes clear what is actually seen.

Illustrations in the Catalogue are of watermarks in normal positions (from the front of the stamps) and are actual size where possible.

Differences in watermark position are collectable as distinct varieties. In this Catalogue, however, only normal and sideways watermarks are listed (and "sideways inverted" is treated as "sideways"). Inverted and reversed watermarks have always been outside its scope: in the early days of flat-bed printing sheets of watermarked paper were fed indiscriminately through the press and the resulting watermark positions had no particular philatelic significance. Similarly, the special make-up of sheets for booklets can in some cases give equal quantities of normal and inverted watermarks.

Collectors are reminded that inverted and reversed watermarks are listed in the *Great Britain Specialised Catalogue, Great Britain, Australia* or *New Zealand Concise Catalogues* and (for Commonwealth stamps from 1937) in the *Two Reigns Catalogue* series.

Where a watermark comes indiscriminately in various positions our policy is to cover this by a general note: we do not give separate listings because the watermark position in these circumstances has no particular philatelic importance. There is a general note of this sort in modern Cyprus, for example. Issues printed since 1962 by Aspioti-Elka occur with the vertical stamps having the watermark normal or inverted, while horizontal stamps are likewise found with the watermark reading upwards or downwards.

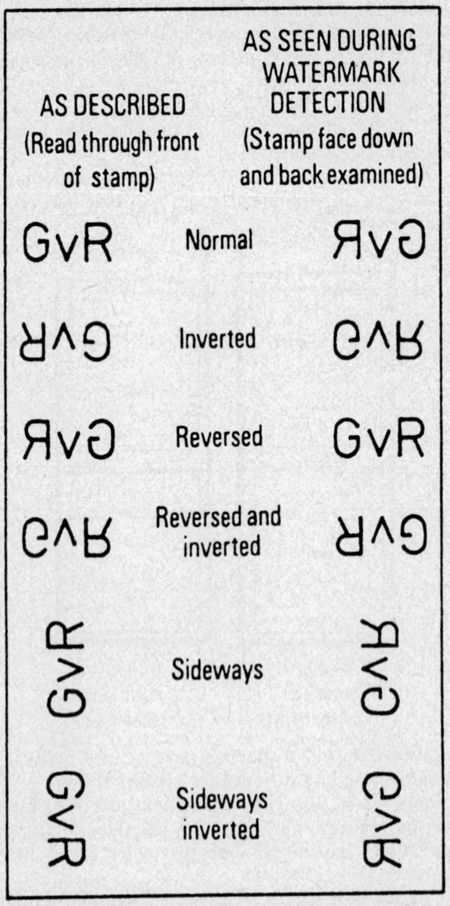
AS DESCRIBED
(Read through front of stamp)
AS SEEN DURING WATERMARK DETECTION
(Stamp face down and back examined)
Normal
Inverted
Reversed
Reversed and inverted
Sideways
Sideways inverted
GvR

Standard types of watermark. Some watermarks have been used generally for various British possessions rather than exclusively for a single colony. To avoid repetition the Catalogue classifies 15 general types, as under, with references in the headings throughout the listings being given either in words or in the form "*W* w **14**" (meaning "watermark type w **14**"). In those cases where watermark illustrations appear in the listings themselves, the respective reference reads, for example, *W* **153**, thus indicating that the watermark will be found in the normal sequence of illustrations as (type) **153**.

The general types are as follows, with an example of each quoted.

W	*Description*	*Example*
w **1**	Large Star	St. Helena No. 1
w **2**	Small Star	Turks Is. No. 4
w **3**	Broad (pointed) Star	Grenada No. 24
w **4**	Crown (over) CC, small stamp	Antigua No. 13
w **5**	Crown (over) CC, large stamp	Antigua No. 31
w **6**	Crown (over) CA, small stamp	Antigua No. 21
w **7**	Crown CA (CA over Crown), large stamp	Sierra Leone No. 54
w **8**	Multiple Crown CA	Antigua No. 41
w **9**	Multiple Crown Script CA	Seychelles No. 158
w **9*a***	do. Error	Seychelles No. 158a
w **9*b***	do. Error	Seychelles No. 158b
w **10**	V over Crown	N.S.W. No. 327
w **11**	Crown over A	N.S.W. No. 347
w **12**	Multiple St. Edward's Crown Block CA	Antigua No. 149
w **13**	Multiple PTM	Johore No. 166
w **14**	Multiple Crown CA Diagonal	Antigua No. 426
w **15**	Multiple POST OFFICE	Kiribati No. 141
w **16**	Multiple Crown Script CA Diagonal	Ascension No. 376
w **17**	Multiple CARTOR	Brunei No. 357

CC in these watermarks is an abbreviation for "Crown Colonies" and CA for "Crown Agents". Watermarks w **1**, w **2** and w **3** are on stamps printed by Perkins, Bacon; w **4** onwards on stamps from De La Rue and other printers.

w **1**
Large Star

w **2**
Small Star

w **3**
Broad (pointed) Star

Watermark w **1**, *Large Star*, measures 15 to 16 mm across the star from point to point and about 27 mm from centre to centre vertically between stars in the sheet. It was made for long stamps like Ceylon 1857 and St. Helena 1856.

Watermark w **2**, *Small Star*, is of similar design but measures 12 to 13½ mm from point to point and 24 mm from centre to centre vertically. It was for use with ordinary-size stamps such as Grenada 1863–71.

When the Large Star watermark was used with the smaller stamps it only occasionally comes in the centre of the paper. It is frequently so misplaced as to show portions of two stars above and below and this eccentricity will very often help in determining the watermark.

Watermark w **3**, *Broad (pointed) Star*, resembles w **1** but the points are broader.

w **4**
Crown (over) CC

w **5**
Crown (over) CC

Two *Crown (over) CC* watermarks were used: w **4** was for stamps of ordinary size and w **5** for those of larger size.

w **6**
Crown (over) CA

w **7**
CA over Crown

Two watermarks of *Crown CA* type were used, w **6** being for stamps of ordinary size. The other, w **7**, is properly described as *CA over Crown*. It was specially made for paper on which it was intended to print long fiscal stamps: that some were used postally accounts for the appearance of w **7** in the Catalogue. The watermark occupies twice the space of the ordinary Crown CA watermark, w **6**. Stamps of normal size printed on paper with w **7** watermark show it *sideways*; it takes a horizontal pair of stamps to show the entire watermark.

w **8**
Multiple Crown CA

w **9**
Multiple Crown Script CA

Multiple watermarks began in 1904 with w **8**, *Multiple Crown CA*, changed from 1921 to w **9**, *Multiple Crown Script CA*. On stamps of ordinary size portions of two or three watermarks appear and on the large-sized stamps a greater number can be observed. The change to letters in script character with w **9** was accompanied by a Crown of distinctly different shape.

w **9a**: Error, Crown missing

w **9b**: Error, St. Edward's Crown

The *Multiple Crown Script CA* watermark, w **9**, is known with two errors recurring among the 1950–52 printings of several territories. In the first a crown has fallen away from the dandy-roll that impresses the watermark into the paper pulp. It gives w **9a**, *Crown missing*, but this omission has been found in both "Crown only" (*illustrated*) and "Crown CA" rows. The resulting faulty paper was used for Seychelles, Johore and the postage due stamps of nine colonies.

When the omission was noticed a second mishap occurred, which was to insert a wrong crown in the space, giving w **9b**, *St. Edward's Crown*. This produced varieties in Bahamas, St. Kitts-Nevis and Singapore and the incorrect crown likewise occurs in "Crown only" and "Crown CA" rows.

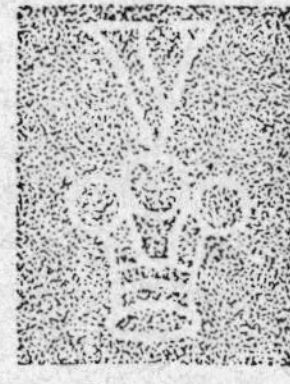

w **10**
V over Crown

w **11**
Crown over A

Resuming the general types, two watermarks found in issues of several Australian States are: w **10**, *V over Crown*, and w **11**, *Crown over A*.

w **12**
Multiple St. Edward's Crown Block CA

The *Multiple St. Edward's Crown Block CA* watermark, w **12**, was introduced in 1957 and besides the change in the Crown (from that used in *Multiple Crown Script CA*, w **9**) the letters reverted to block capitals. The new watermark began to appear sideways in 1966 and these stamps are generally listed as separate sets.

w **13**
Multiple PTM

The watermark w **13**, *Multiple PTM*, was introduced for new Malayan issues in November 1961.

w **14**
Multiple Crown CA Diagonal

By 1974 the two dandy-rolls (the "upright" and the "sideways") for w **12** were wearing out; the Crown Agents therefore discontinued using the sideways-watermark one and retained the other only as a stand-by. A new dandy-roll with the pattern of w **14**, *Multiple Crown CA Diagonal*, was introduced and first saw use with some Churchill Centenary issues.

The new watermark has the design arranged in gradually spiralling rows. It is improved in design to allow smooth passage over the paper (the gaps between letters and rows had caused jolts in previous dandy-rolls) and the sharp corners and angles, where fibres used to accumulate, have been eliminated by rounding.

This watermark has no "normal" sideways position amongst the different printers using it. To avoid confusion our more specialised listings do not rely on such terms as "sideways inverted" but describe the direction in which the watermark points.

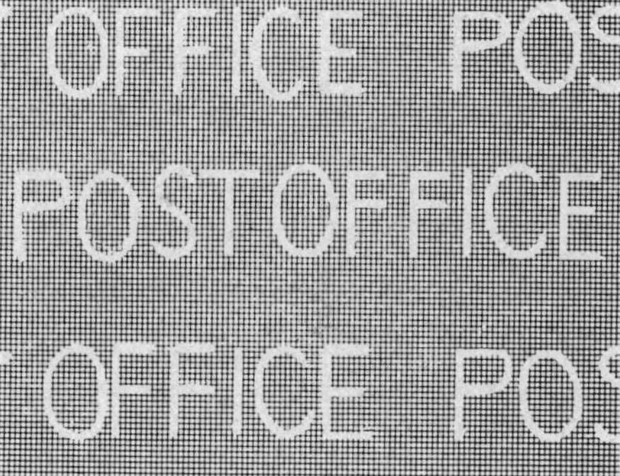

w **15**
Multiple POST OFFICE

During 1981 w **15**, *Multiple POST OFFICE*, was introduced for certain issues prepared by Philatelists Ltd, acting for various countries in the Indian Ocean, Pacific and West Indies.

w **16**
Multiple Crown Script CA Diagonal

A new Crown Agents watermark was introduced during 1985, w **16**, *Multiple Crown Script CA Diagonal*. This was very similar to the previous w **14**, but showed "CA" in script rather than block letters. It was first used on the omnibus series of stamps commemorating the Life and Times of Queen Elizabeth the Queen Mother.

w **17**
Multiple CARTOR

Watermark w **17**, *Multiple CARTOR*, was used from 1985 for issues printed by this French firm for countries which did not normally use the Crown Agents watermark.

In recent years the use of watermarks has, to a small extent, been superseded by fluorescent security markings. These are often more visible from the reverse of the stamp (Cook Islands from 1970 onwards), but have occurred printed over the design (Hong Kong Nos. 415/30). In 1982 the Crown Agents introduced a new stock paper, without watermark, known as "C-Kurity" on which a fluorescent pattern of blue rosettes is visible on the reverse, beneath the gum. This paper was used for issues from Gambia and Norfolk Island.

6. Colours

Stamps in two or three colours have these named in order of appearance, from the centre moving outwards. Four colours or more are usually listed as multicoloured.

In compound colour names the second is the predominant one, thus:

orange-red = a red tending towards orange;

red-orange = an orange containing more red than usual.

Standard colours used. The 100 colours most used for stamp identification are given in the Stanley Gibbons Colour Guide; these, plus a further 100 variations for more specialised use, are included in the Stanley Gibbons Stamp Colour Key. The Catalogue has used the Guide and Key as standards for describing new issues for some years. The names are also introduced as lists are rewritten, though exceptions are made for those early issues where traditional names have become universally established.

Determining colours. When comparing actual stamps with colour samples in the Guide or Key, view in a good north daylight (or its best substitute: fluorescent "colour-matching" light). Sunshine is not recommended. Choose a solid portion of the stamp design; if available, marginal markings such as solid bars of colour or colour check dots are helpful. Shading lines in the design can be misleading as they appear lighter than solid colour. Postmarked portions of a stamp appear darker than normal. If more than one colour is present, mask off the extraneous ones as the eye tends to mix them.

Errors of colour. Major colour errors in stamps or overprints which qualify for listing are: wrong colours; one colour inverted in relation to the rest; albinos (colourless impressions), where these have Expert Committee certificates; colours completely omitted, but only on unused stamps (if found on used stamps the information is footnoted) and with good credentials, missing colours being frequently faked.

Colours only partially omitted are not recognised. Colour shifts, however spectacular, are not listed.

Shades. Shades in philately refer to variations in the intensity of a colour or the presence of differing amounts of other colours. They are particularly significant when they can be linked to specific printings. In general, shades need to be quite marked to fall within the scope of this Catalogue; it does not favour nowadays listing the often numerous shades of a stamp, but chooses a single applicable colour name which will indicate particular groups of outstanding shades. Furthermore, the listings refer to colours as issued: they may deteriorate into something different through the passage of time.

Modern colour printing by lithography is prone to marked differences of shade, even within a single run, and variations can occur within the same sheet. Such shades are not listed.

Aniline colours. An aniline colour meant originally one derived from coal-tar; it now refers more widely to colour of a particular brightness suffused on the surface of a stamp and showing through clearly on the back.

Colours of overprints and surcharges. All overprints and surcharges are in black unless stated otherwise in the heading or after the description of the stamp.

7. Specimen Stamps

Originally, stamps overprinted SPECIMEN were circulated to postmasters or kept in official records, but after the establishment of the Universal Postal Union supplies were sent to Berne for distribution to the postal administrations of member countries.

During the period 1884 to 1928 most of the stamps of British Crown Colonies required for this purpose were overprinted SPECIMEN in various shapes and sizes by their printers from typeset formes. Some locally produced provisionals were handstamped locally, as were sets prepared for presentation. From 1928 stamps were punched with holes forming the word SPECIMEN, each firm of printers using a different machine or machines. From 1948 the stamps supplied for U.P.U. distribution were no longer punctured.

Stamps of some other Commonwealth territories were overprinted or handstamped locally, while stamps of Great Britain and those overprinted for use in overseas postal agencies (mostly of the higher denominations) bore SPECIMEN overprints and handstamps applied by the Inland Revenue or the Post Office.

Some of the commoner types of overprints or punctures are illustrated here. Collectors are warned that dangerous forgeries of the punctured type exist.

The *Part* 1 (*British Commonwealth*) *Catalogue* records those Specimen overprints or perforations intended for distribution by the U.P.U. to member countries. In addition the Specimen overprints of Australia and its dependent territories, which were sold to collectors by the Post Office, are also included.

All other Specimens are outside the scope of this volume. The *Two Reigns Catalogue* series contains details of modern Specimen overprints issued for publicity purposes.

Specimens are not quoted in Great Britain as they are fully listed in the Stanley Gibbons *Great Britain Specialised Catalogue*.

In specifying type of specimen for individual high-value stamps, "H/S" means handstamped, "Optd" is overprinted and "Perf" is punctured. Some sets occur mixed, e.g. "Optd/Perf". If unspecified, the type is apparent from the date or it is the same as for the lower values quoted as a set.

Prices. Prices for stamps up to £1 are quoted in sets; higher values are priced singly after the colours, thus "(S. £20)". Where specimens exist in more than one type the price quoted is for the cheapest. Specimen stamps have rarely survived even as pairs; these and strips of three, four or five are worth considerably more than singles.

8. Luminescence

Machines which sort mail electronically have been introduced in recent years. In consequence some countries have issued stamps on fluorescent or phosphorescent papers, while others have marked their stamps with phosphor bands.

The various papers can only be distinguished by ultraviolet lamps emitting particular wavelengths. They are separately listed only when the stamps have some other means of distinguishing them, visible without the use of these lamps. Where this is not so, the papers are recorded in footnotes or headings.

For this Catalogue we do not consider it appropriate that collectors be compelled to have use of an ultraviolet lamp before being able to identify stamps by our listings. Some experience will also be found necessary in interpreting the results given by ultraviolet. Collectors using the lamps, nevertheless, should exercise great care in their use as exposure to their light is extremely dangerous to the eyes.

Phosphor bands are listable, since they are visible to the naked eye (by holding stamps at an angle to the light and looking along them, the bands appear dark). Stamps existing with and without phosphor bands or with differing numbers of bands are given separate listings. Varieties such as double bands, bands omitted, misplaced or printed on the back are not listed.

Detailed descriptions appear at appropriate places in the listings in explanation of luminescent papers; *see*, for example, Australia above No. 308, Canada above Nos. 472 and 611, Cook Is. above No. 249, etc.

For Great Britain, where since 1959 phosphors have played a prominent and intricate part in stamp issues, the main notes above Nos. 599, 723 and below X1019 should be studied, as well as the footnotes to individual listings where appropriate. In general the classification is as follows and is particularly important in understanding the decimal "Machin" definitives (No. X841 onwards).

Stamps with *phosphor bands* are those where a separate cylinder applies the phosphor after the stamps are printed. Issues with "all-over" phosphor have the "band" covering the entire stamp. Parts of the stamp covered by phosphor bands, or the entire surface for "all-over" phosphor versions, appear matt. Stamps on *phosphorised paper* have the phosphor added to the paper coating before the stamps are printed. Issues on this paper have a completely shiny surface.

Further particularisation of phosphor—their methods of printing and the colours they exhibit under ultraviolet—is outside the scope. The more specialised listings should be consulted for this information.

9. Coil Stamps

Stamps issued only in coil form are given full listing. If stamps are issued in both sheets and coils the coil stamps are listed separately only where there is some feature (e.g. perforation or watermark sideways) by which singles can be distinguished. Coil strips containing different stamps *se-tenant* are also listed.

Coil join pairs are too random and too easily faked to permit of listing; similarly ignored are coil stamps which have accidentally suffered an extra row of perforations from the claw mechanism in a malfunctioning vending machine.

10. Booklet Stamps

Stamp booklets are outside the scope of this Catalogue.

Single stamps from booklets are listed if they are distinguishable in some way (such as watermark or perforation) from similar sheet stamps.

Booklet panes are listed where they contain stamps of different denominations *se-tenant*, where stamp-size labels are included, or where such panes are otherwise identifiable. Booklet panes are placed in the listing under the lowest denomination present.

Particular perforations (straight edges) are covered by appropriate notes.

11. Miniature Sheets and Sheetlets

We distinguish between "miniature sheets" and "sheetlets" and this affects the catalogue numbering. An item in sheet form that is postally valid, containing a single stamp, pair, block or set of stamps, with wide, inscribed and/or decorative margins, is a *miniature sheet* if it is sold at post offices as an indivisible entity. As such the Catalogue allots a single **MS** number and describes what stamps make it up. (*See* Great Britain 1978 Historic Buildings, No. **MS**1058, as an example.) The *sheetlet* or *small sheet* differs in that the individual stamps are intended to be purchased separately for postal purposes. For sheetlets, all the component postage stamps are numbered individually and the composition explained in a footnote. (The 1978 Christmas Island Christmas sheetlet, Nos. 99/107, is an example.) Note that the definitions refer to post office sale—not how items may be subsequently offered by stamp dealers.

Production as sheetlets is a modern marketing development chosen by postal administrations to interest collectors in purchasing the item complete; if he has done so he should, as with all *se-tenant* arrangements, keep the sheetlet intact in his collection.

The catalogue will in future no longer give full listing to designs, originally issued in normal sheets, which subsequently appear in sheetlets showing changes of colour, perforation, printing process or face value. Such stamps will be covered by footnotes.

12. Forgeries and Fakes

Forgeries. Where space permits, notes are considered if they can give a concise description that will permit unequivocal detection of a forgery. Generalised warnings, lacking detail, are not nowadays inserted, since their value to the collector is problematic.

Fakes. Unwitting fakes are numerous, particularly "new shades" which are colour changelings brought about by exposure to sunlight, soaking in water contaminated with dyes from adherent paper, contact with oil and dirt from a pocketbook, and so on. Fraudulent operators, in addition, can offer to arrange: removal of hinge marks; repairs of thins on white or coloured papers; replacement of missing margins or perforations; reperforating in true or false gauges; removal of fiscal cancellations; rejoining of severed pairs, strips and blocks; and (a major hazard) regumming. Collectors can only be urged to purchase from reputable sources and to insist upon Expert Committee certification where there is any kind of doubt.

The Catalogue can consider footnotes about fakes where these are specific enough to assist in detection.

Abbreviations

Printers

A.B.N. Co	American Bank Note Co, New York.
A. & M.	Alden & Mowbray Ltd, Oxford.
Ashton-Potter	Ashton-Potter Ltd, Toronto.
Aspioti-Elka (Aspiotis)	Aspioti-Elka, Greece.
B.A.B.N.	British American Bank Note Co, Ottawa.
B.D.T.	B.D.T. International Security Printing Ltd, Dublin, Ireland.
B.W.	Bradbury Wilkinson & Co, Ltd.
C.B.N.	Canadian Bank Note Co, Ottawa.
Continental B.N. Co	Continental Bank Note Co.
Courvoisier	Imprimerie Courvoisier S.A., La-Chaux-de-Fonds, Switzerland.
D.L.R.	De La Rue & Co, Ltd, London, and (from 1961) Bogota, Colombia.
Edila	Editions de l'Aubetin, S.A.
Enschedé	Joh. Enschedé en Zonen, Haarlem, Netherlands.
Format	Format International Security Printers, Ltd, London.
Harrison	Harrison & Sons, Ltd, London.
Heraclio Fournier	Heraclio Fournier S.A., Vitoria, Spain.
J.W.	John Waddington Security Print Ltd.
P.B.	Perkins Bacon Ltd, London.
Questa	Questa Colour Security Printers, Ltd.
Ueberreuter	Ueberreuter (incorporating Bruder Rosenbaum), Korneuburg, Austria
Walsall	Walsall Security Printers, Ltd.
Waterlow	Waterlow & Sons, Ltd, London.

General Abbreviations

Alph	Alphabet
Anniv	Anniversary
C, c	Chalky paper
Comp	Compound (perforation)
Des	Designer; designed
Diag	Diagonal; diagonally
Eng	Engraver; engraved
F.C.	Fiscal Cancellation
H/S	Handstamped
Horiz	Horizontal; horizontally
Imp, Imperf	Imperforate
Inscr	Inscribed
L	Left
Litho	Lithographed
mm	Millimetres
MS	Miniature sheet
N.Y.	New York
O, o	Ordinary paper
Opt(d)	Overprint(ed)
P or P-c	Pen-cancelled
P, Pf or Perf	Perforated
Photo	Photogravure
Pl	Plate
Pr	Pair
Ptd	Printed
Ptg	Printing
R	Right
R.	Row
Recess	Recess-printed
Roto	Rotogravure
Roul	Rouletted
S	Specimen (overprint)
Surch	Surcharge(d)
T.C.	Telegraph Cancellation
T	Type
Typo	Typographed
Un	Unused
Us	Used
Vert	Vertical; vertically
W or wmk	Watermark
Wmk s	Watermark sideways

(†) = Does not exist.

(—) (or blank price column) = Exists, or may exist, but no market price is known.

/ between colours means "on" and the colour following is that of the paper on which the stamp is printed.

Colours of Stamps

Bl (blue); blk (black); brn (brown); car, carm (carmine); choc (chocolate); clar (claret); emer (emerald); grn (green); ind (indigo); mag (magenta); mar (maroon); mult (multicoloured); mve (mauve); ol (olive); orge (orange); pk (pink); pur (purple); scar (scarlet); sep (sepia); turq (turquoise); ultram (ultramarine); verm (vermilion); vio (violet); yell (yellow).

Colours of Overprints and Surcharges

(B.) = blue, (Blk.) = black, (Br.) = brown, (C.) = carmine, (G.) = green, (Mag.) = magenta, (Mve.) = mauve, (Ol.) = olive, (O.) = orange, (P.) = purple, (Pk.) = pink, (R.) = red, (Sil.) = silver, (V.) = violet, (Vm.) or (Verm.) = vermilion, (W.) = white, (Y.) = yellow.

Arabic Numerals

As in the case of European figures, the details of the Arabic numerals vary in different stamp designs, but they should be readily recognised with the aid of this illustration.

٠	١	٢	٣	٤	٥	٦	٧	٨	٩
0	1	2	3	4	5	6	7	8	9

Stanley Gibbons Stamp Catalogue Complete List of Parts

1 British Commonwealth
(Annual in August)

2 Austria & Hungary (4th edition, 1988)
Austria, Bosnia & Herzegovina, U.N. (Vienna), Hungary

3 Balkans (3rd edition, 1987)
Albania, Bulgaria, Greece & Islands, Rumania, Yugoslavia

4 Benelux (3rd edition, 1988)
Belgium & Colonies, Netherlands & Colonies, Luxembourg

5 Czechoslovakia & Poland (3rd edition, 1985)
Czechoslovakia, Bohemia & Moravia, Slovakia, Poland

6 France (3rd edition, 1987)
France, Colonies, Post Offices, Andorra, Monaco

7 Germany (3rd edition, 1987)
Germany, States, Colonies, Post Offices

8 Italy & Switzerland (3rd edition 1987)
Italy & Colonies, Fiume, San Marino, Vatican City, Trieste, Liechtenstein, Switzerland, U.N. (Geneva)

9 Portugal & Spain (2nd edition, 1984)
Andorra, Portugal & Colonies, Spain & Colonies

10 Russia (3rd edition, 1986)
Russia, Baltic States, Mongolia, Tuva

11 Scandinavia (3rd edition, 1988)
Aland Island, Denmark, Faroe Islands, Finland, Greenland, Iceland, Norway, Sweden

12 Africa since Independence A-E (2nd edition, 1983)
Algeria, Angola, Benin, Bophuthatswana, Burundi, Cameroun, Cape Verde, Central African Republic, Chad, Comoro Islands, Congo, Djibouti, Equatorial Guinea, Ethiopia

13 Africa since Independence F-M (1st edition, 1981)
Gabon, Guinea, Guinea-Bissau, Ivory Coast, Liberia, Libya, Malagasy Republic, Mali, Mauritania, Morocco, Mozambique

14 Africa since Independence N-Z (1st edition, 1981)
Niger Republic, Rwanda, St. Thomas & Prince, Senegal, Somalia, Sudan, Togo, Transkei, Tunisia, Upper Volta, Venda, Zaire

15 Central America (2nd edition, 1984)
Costa Rica, Cuba, Dominican Republic, El Salvador, Guatemala, Haiti, Honduras, Mexico, Nicaragua, Panama

16 Central Asia (2nd edition, 1983)
Afghanistan, Iran, Turkey

17 China (4th edition, 1989)
China, Taiwan, Tibet, Foreign P.O.s

18 Japan & Korea (2nd edition 1984)
Japan, Ryukyus, Korean Empire, South Korea, North Korea

19 Middle East (4th edition, 1990)
Bahrain, Egypt, Iraq, Israel, Jordan, Kuwait, Lebanon, Oman, Qatar, Saudi Arabia, Syria, U.A.E., Yemen A.R., Yemen P.D.R.

20 South America (3rd edition, 1989)
Argentina, Bolivia, Brazil, Chile, Colombia, Ecuador, Paraguay, Peru, Surinam, Uruguay, Venezuela

21 South-East Asia (2nd edition, 1985)
Bhutan, Burma, Indonesia, Kampuchea, Laos, Nepal, Philippines, Thailand, Vietnam

22 United States (2nd edition, 1985)
U.S. & Possessions, Canal Zone, Marshall Islands, Micronesia, Palau, U.N. (New York, Geneva, Vienna)

THEMATIC CATALOGUES

Collect Birds on Stamps (2nd edition, 1988)
Collect Mammals on Stamps (1st edition, 1986)
Collect Railways on Stamps (2nd edition, 1990).
Collect Ships on Stamps (1st edition, 1989).
Collect Fungi on Stamps (forthcoming).
Collect Aircraft on Stamps (forthcoming).

Select Bibliography

The literature on British Commonwealth stamps is vast, but works are often difficult to obtain once they are out of print. The selection of books below has been made on the basis of authority together with availablility to the general reader, either as new or secondhand. Very specialised studies, and those covering aspects of postal history to which there are no references in the catalogue, have been excluded.

The following abbreviations are used to denote publishers:
CRL–Christie's Robson Lowe; HH–Harry Hayes; PB–Proud Bailey Co. Ltd.; PC–Philip Cockrill; RPSL–Royal Philatelic Society, London; SG–Stanley Gibbons Ltd.

Where no publisher is quoted, the book is published by its author.

GENERAL. *Encyclopaedia of British Empire Postage Stamps. Vols 1–5.* Edited Robson Lowe. (CRL, 1951–1973)

The Commemorative Stamps of the British Commonwealth. H.D.S. Haverbeck. (Faber, 1955)

Specimen Stamps of the Crown Colonies 1857–1948. Marcus Samuel. (RPSL, 1976 and 1984 Supplement)

U.P.U. Specimen Stamps. J. Bendon. (1988).

Silver Jubilee of King George V Stamps Handbook. A.J. Ainscough. (Ainwheel Developments, 1985)

The Printings of King George VI Colonial Stamps. W.J.W. Potter & Lt-Col R.C.M. Shelton. (1952)

King George VI Large Key Type Stamps of Bermuda, Leeward Islands, Nyasaland. R.W. Dickgiesser and E.P. Yendall. (Triad Publications, 1985)

GREAT BRITAIN. For extensive bibliographies see *Great Britain Specialised Catalogues. Vols 1–5.*

Channel Islands. *Stamps and Postal History of the Channel Islands.* W. Newport. (Heineman, 1972)

ADEN. *The Postal History of British Aden 1839–67.* Major R.W. Pratt (PB, 1985)

ASCENSION. *Ascension. The Stamps and Postal History.* J.H. Attwood. (CRL, 1981)

BAHAMAS. *The Postage Stamps and Postal History of the Bahamas.* H.G.D. Gisburn. (SG, 1950)

BARBADOS. *The Stamps of Barbados.* E.A. Bayley. (1989)

BASUTOLAND. *The Cancellations and Postal Markings of Basutoland/Lesotho Post Offices.* A.H. Scott. (Collectors Mail Auctions (Pty) Ltd, 1980)

BRITISH EAST AFRICA. *British East Africa. The Stamps and Postal Stationery.* J. Minns. (RPSL, 1982)

BRITISH GUIANA. *The Postage Stamps and Postal History of British Guiana.* W.A. Townsend and F.G. Howe. (RPSL, 1970)

BRITISH OCCUPATION OF GERMAN COLONIES. *G.R.I.* R.M. Gibbs. (CRL, 1989)

BRITISH POSTAL AGENCIES IN EASTERN ARABIA. *The Postal Agencies in Eastern Arabia and the Gulf.* N. Donaldson. (HH, 1975)

BRITISH WEST AFRICA. *The Postal History and Handstamps of British West Africa.* C. McCaig. (CRL, 1978)

BRUNEI. *Brunei. The Definitive Issues and Postal Cancellations to 1974.* E. Thorndike. (PC, 1983)

BURMA. *Burma Postal History.* G. Davis and D. Martin. (CRL, 1971 and 1987 Supplement)

CANADA. *Stamps of British North America.* F. Jarrett. (Quarterman Publications Inc, 1975)

The Postage Stamps and Postal History of Canada. W.S. Boggs. (Quarterman Publications Inc, 1974)

The First Decimal Issue of Canada 1859–68. G. Whitworth. (RPSL, 1966)

The Five Cents Beaver Stamp of Canada. G. Whitworth. (RPSL, 1985)

The Edward VII Issue of Canada. G.C. Marler. (National Postal Museum, Canada, 1975)

The Admiral Issue of Canada. G.C. Marler. (American Philatelic Society, 1982).

The Centennial Definitives of Canada. D. Gronbeck-Jones. (1972)

The Caricatures and Landscapes Definitives of Canada. D. Gronbeck-Jones. (1979)

CAPE OF GOOD HOPE. *Postmarks of the Cape of Good Hope.* R. Goldblatt. (Reijger Publishers (Pty) Ltd, 1984)

COOK ISLANDS. *The Early Cook Islands Post Office.* A.R. Burge. (Hawthorn Press, 1978)

CYPRUS. *Cyprus 1353–1986.* W. Castle. (CRL, 3rd edition, 1987)

FALKLAND ISLANDS. *The Postage Stamps of the Falkland Islands and Dependencies.* B.S.H. Grant. (SG, 1952)

The Falkland Islands Philatelic Digest. Nos. 1 & 2. M. Barton and R. Spafford. (HH, 1975 & 1979)

The De La Rue Definitives of the Falkland Islands 1901–29. J.P. Bunt. (1986)

The War Stamp Overprints of the Falkland Islands 1918–20. J.P. Bunt. (1981)

The Falkland Islands. Printings of the Pictorial Issue of 1938–49. C.E. Glass. (CRL, 1979)

The Falklands War. J.D. Davis. (1983)

GAMBIA. *The Stamps and Postal History of the Gambia.* Edited J.O. Andrew. (CRL, 1985)

GIBRALTAR. *Posted in Gibraltar.* W. Hine-Haycock. (CRL, 1978)

HONG KONG. *The Philatelic History of Hong Kong. Vol 1.* (Hong Kong Study Circle, 1984)

Cancellations of the Treaty Ports of Hong Kong. H. Schoenfeld. (1988)

The Crown Colony of Wei Hai Wei. M. Goldsmith and C.W. Goodwyn. (RPSL, 1985)

INDIA. *India Used Abroad.* V.S. Dastur. (Mysore Philatelics, 1982)

A Handbook on Gwalior Postal History and Stamps. V.K. Gupta. (1980)

MALAYSIA. *The Postal History of British Malaya. Vols 1–3.* E.B. Proud. (PB, 1982–84)

The Postage Stamps of Federated Malay States. W.A. Reeves. (Malaya Study Group, 1978)

MALTA. *Malta. The Postal History and Postage Stamps.* Edited R.E. Martin. (CRL, 1980 and 1985 Supplement)

MOROCCO AGENCIES. *British Post Offices and Agencies in Morocco 1857–1907 and Local Posts 1891–1914.* R.K. Clough. (Gibraltar Study Circle, 1984).

NEWFOUNDLAND. *The Postage Stamps and Postal History of Newfoundland.* W.S. Boggs. (Quarterman Publications, 1975)

NEW SOUTH WALES. *The Postal History of New South Wales 1788–1901.* Edited J.S. White. (Philatelic Association of New South Wales, 1988)

NEW ZEALAND. *The Postage Stamps of New Zealand. Vols I–VII.* (Royal Philatelic Society of New Zealand, 1939–88)

The Postal History and Postage Stamps of the Tokelau/Union Islands. A.H. Burgess. (Pacific Islands Study Circle, 1977)

NIGERIA. *The Stamps and Postal History of the Niger Territories and the Niger Coast Protectorate.* M.P. Nicholson. (PC, 1982)

The Local Bisects and Surcharges of the Oil Rivers and Niger Coast 1893–94. M.P. Nicholson. (PC, 1982)

NORTH BORNEO. *The Stamps and Postal History of North Borneo. Parts 1–3.* L.H. Shipman and P.K. Cassells. (Sarawak Specialists Society, 1976–88)

ORANGE FREE STATE. *Stamps of the Orange Free State. Parts 1–3.* G.D. Buckley & W.B. Marriott. (Orange Free State Study Circle, 1967–80)

PAPUA. *The Postal History of British New Guinea and Papua 1885–1942.* R. Lee. (CRL, 1983)

RHODESIA. *Rhodesia. A Postal History.* R.C. Smith. (1967 and 1970 Supplement)

ST. HELENA. *St. Helena. Postal History and Stamps.* E. Hibbert. (CRL, 1979)

SAMOA. *A Postal History of the Samoan Islands.* Edited R. Burge. (Royal Philatelic Society of New Zealand, 1987)

SARAWAK. *The Stamps and Postal History of Sarawak.* W.A. Forrester-Wood. (Sarawak Specialists Society, 1959 & 1970 Supplement)

SIERRA LEONE. *The Postal Service of Sierra Leone.* P.O. Beale. (RPSL, 1988)

SOLOMON ISLANDS. *British Solomon Islands Protectorate. Its Postage Stamps and Postal History.* H.G.D. Gisburn. (T. Sanders (Philatelist) Ltd., 1956)

SOUTH AUSTRALIA. *South Australia. The Long Stamps 1902–1912.* J.R.W. Purves. (Royal Philatelic Society of Victoria, 1978)

The Departmental Stamps of South Australia. A.R. Butler. (RPSL, 1978)

SOUTHERN NIGERIA. *The Stamps and Postal History of Southern Nigeria.* M.P. Nicholson. (PC, 1982)

SUDAN. *Sudan. The Stamps and Postal Stationery of 1867 to 1970.* E.C.W. Stagg. (HH, 1977)

TASMANIA. *Stamps and Postal History of Tasmania.* W.E. Tinsley. (RPSL, 1986)

TRANSVAAL. *Transvaal Philately.* Edited I.B. Mathews. (Reijger Publishers (Pty) Ltd, 1986)

TRISTAN DA CUNHA. *The History and Postal History of Tristan da Cunha.* G. Crabb. (1980)

TURKS AND CAICOS ISLANDS. *Turks Islands and Caicos Islands to 1950.* J.J. Challis. (Roses Caribbean Philatelic Society, 1983)

TUVALU. *Tuvalu. A Philatelic Handbook.* M. Forand. (Tuvalu Philatelic Society, 1982)

WESTERN AUSTRALIA. *Western Australia. The Stamps and Postal History.* Edited M. Hamilton and B. Pope. (Western Australia Study Group, 1979)

Postage Stamps and Postal History of Western Australia. Vols 1–3. M. Juhl. (1981–83)

STANLEY GIBBONS STAMP CATALOGUE

Part 1: BRITISH COMMONWEALTH

with Fiji, Ireland and South Africa

93rd EDITION—1991

Great Britain

STAMPS ON COVER. Prices are quoted, as a third price column, for those Victorian and Edwardian issues usually found used on cover. In general these prices refer to the cheapest version of each basic stamp with other shades, plates or varieties, together with unusual frankings and postmarks, being worth more.

QUEEN VICTORIA
20 June 1837—22 January 1901

MULREADY ENVELOPES AND LETTER SHEETS, so called from the name of the designer, William Mulready, were issued concurrently with the first British adhesive stamps.

1d. black

Envelopes: £120 *unused*; £160 *used*.
Letter Sheets: £100 *unused*; £135 *used*.

2d. blue

Envelopes: £175 *unused*; £550 *used*.
Letter Sheets: £150 *unused*; £525 *used*.

LINE-ENGRAVED ISSUES

GENERAL NOTES

Brief notes on some aspects of the line-engraved stamps follow, but for further information and a full specialist treatment of these issues collectors are recommended to consult Volume 1 of the Stanley Gibbons *Great Britain Specialised Catalogue*.

Alphabet I Alphabet II

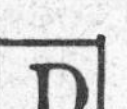

Alphabet III Alphabet IV

Typical Corner Letters of the four Alphabets

Alphabets. Four different letterings were used for the corner letters on stamps prior to the issue with letters in all four corners, these being known to collectors as:

Alphabet I. Used for all plates made from 1840 to the end of 1851. Letters small.

Alphabet II. Plates from 1852 to mid-1855. Letters larger, heavier and broader.

Alphabet III. Plates from mid-1855 to end of period. Letters tall and more slender.

Alphabet IV. 1861. 1d. Die II, Plates 50 and 51 only. Letters were hand-engraved instead of being punched on the plate. They are therefore inconsistent in shape and size but generally larger and outstanding.

While the general descriptions and the illustrations of typical letters given above may be of some assistance, only long experience and published aids can enable every stamp to be allocated to its particular Alphabet without hesitation, as certain letters in each are similar to those in one of the others.

Blued Paper. The blueing of the paper of the earlier issues is believed to be due to the presence of prussiate of potash in the printing ink, or in the paper, which, under certain conditions, tended to colour the paper when the sheets were damped for printing. An alternative term is bleuté paper.

Corner Letters. The corner letters on the early British stamps were intended as a safeguard against forgery, each stamp in the sheet having a different combination of letters. Taking the first 1d. stamp, printed in 20 horizontal rows of 12, as an example, the lettering is as follows:

Row 1. A A, A B, A C, etc. to A L.

Row 2. B A, B B, B C, etc. to B L.

and so on to

Row 20. T A, T B, T C, etc. to T L.

On the stamps with four corner letters, those in the upper corners are in the reverse positions to those in the lower corners. Thus in a sheet of 240 (12 × 20) the sequence is:

Row 1. AA/AA BA/AB CA/AC etc. to LA/AL

Row 2. AB/BA BB/BB CB/BC etc. to LB/BL

and so on to

Row 20. AT/TA BT/TB CT/TC etc. to LT/TL

Placing letters in all four corners was not only an added precaution against forgery but was meant to deter unmarked parts of used stamps being pieced together and passed off as an unused whole.

Dies. The first die of the 1d. was used for making the original die of the 2d., both the No Lines and White Lines issues. In 1855 the 1d. Die I was amended by retouching the head and deepening the lines on a transferred impression of the original. This later version, known to collectors as Die II, was used for making the dies for the 1d. and 2d. with letters in all four corners and also for the 1½d.

The two dies are illustrated above No. 17 in the catalogue.

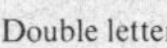

Double letter

Guide line in corner

Guide line through value

Double Corner Letters. These are due to the workman placing his letter-punch in the wrong position at the first attempt, when lettering the plate, and then correcting the mistake; or to a slight shifting of the punch when struck. If a wrong letter was struck in the first instance, traces of a wrong letter may appear in a corner in addition to the correct one. A typical example is illustrated.

Guide Lines and Dots. When laying down the impressions of the design on the early plates, fine vertical and horizontal guide lines were marked on the plates to assist the operative. These were usually removed from the gutter margins, but could not be removed from the stamp impressions without damage to the plate, so that in such cases they appear on the printed stamps, sometimes in the corners, sometimes through "POSTAGE" or the value. Typical examples are illustrated.

Guide dots or cuts were similarly made to indicate the spacing of the guide lines. These too sometimes appear on the stamps.

Ivory Head

"Ivory Head." The so-called "ivory head" variety is one in which the Queen's Head shows white on the back of the stamp. It arises from the comparative absence of ink in the head portion of the design, with consequent absence of blueing. (*See* "Blued Paper" note above.)

Line-engraving. In this context "line-engraved" is synonymous with recess-printing, in which the engraver cuts recesses in a plate and printing (the coloured areas) is from these recesses. "Line-engraved" is the traditional philatelic description for these stamps; other equivalent terms found are "engraving in *taille-douce*" (French) or "in *intaglio*" (Italian).

Plates. Until the introduction of the stamps with letters in all four corners, the number of the plate was not indicated in the design of the stamp, but was printed on the sheet margin. By long study of identifiable blocks and the minor variations in the design, coupled with the position of the corner letters, philatelists are now able to allot many of these stamps to their respective plates. Specialist collectors often endeavour to obtain examples of a given stamp printed from its different plates and our catalogue accordingly reflects this depth of detail.

Maltese Cross Type of Town postmark

Cheltenham
Penny Post

Type of Penny Post cancellation

Example of 1844 type postmark

Postmarks. The so-called "Maltese Cross" design was the first employed for obliterating British postage stamps and was in use from 1840 to 1844. Being hand-cut, the obliterating stamps varied greatly in detail and some distinctive types can be allotted to particular towns or offices. Local types, such as those used at Manchester, Norwich, Leeds, etc., are keenly sought. A red ink was first employed, but was superseded by black, after some earlier experiments, in February 1841. Maltese Cross obliterations in other colours are rare.

Obliterations of this type, numbered 1 to 12 in the centre, were used at the London Chief Office in 1843 and 1844.

Some straight-line cancellations were in use in 1840 at the Penny Post receiving offices, normally applied on the envelope, the adhesives then being obliterated at the Head Office. They are nevertheless known, with or without Maltese Cross, on the early postage stamps.

In 1842 some offices in S.W. England used dated postmarks in place of the Maltese Cross, usually on the back of the letter since they were not originally intended as obliterators. These town postmarks have likewise been found on adhesives.

In 1844 the Maltese Cross design was superseded by numbered obliterators of varied type, one of which is illustrated. They are naturally comparatively scarce on the first 1d. and 2d. stamps. Like the Maltese Cross they are found in various colours, some of which are rare.

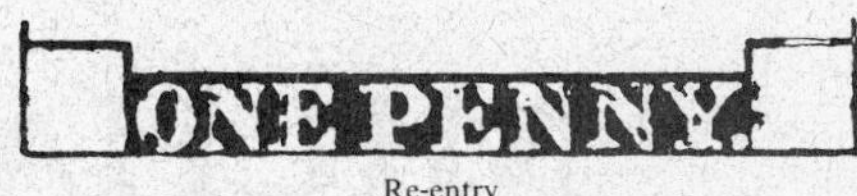

Re-entry

"Union Jack" re-entry

Re-entries. Re-entries on the plate show as a doubling of part of the design of the stamp generally at top or bottom. Many re-entries are very slight while others are most marked. A typical one is illustrated.

The *"Union Jack" re-entry*, so called owing to the effect of the re-entry on the appearance of the corner stars (*see illustration*) occurs on stamp L K of Plate 75 of the 1d. red, Die I.

Penny Plain or Tuppence Coloured

Available singly or by the dozen

MICHAEL CHIPPERFIELD

Specialist in the Stamps of Great Britain

Manfield House, 376-9 Strand
London WC2

Callers by appointment only please. Tel: 071-240 9179. Fax: 071-240 1626.

T A (T L) M A (M L)
Varieties of Large Crown Watermark

I Two states of Large Crown Watermark II

Watermarks. Two watermark varieties, as illustrated, consisting of crowns of entirely different shape, are found in sheets of the Large Crown paper and fall on stamps lettered M A and T A (or M L and T L when the paper is printed on the wrong side). Both varieties are found on the 1d. rose-red of 1857, while the M A (M L) variety comes also on some plates of the 1d. of 1864 (Nos. 43, 44) up to about Plate 96. On the 2d. the T A (T L) variety is known on plates 8 and 9, and the M A (M L) on later prints of plate 9. These varieties may exist inverted, or inverted reversed on stamps lettered A A and A L and H A and H L, and some are known.

In 1861 a minor alteration was made in the Large Crown watermark by the removal of the two vertical strokes, representing *fleurs-de-lis*, which projected upwards from the uppermost of the three horizontal curves at the base of the Crown. Hence two states are distinguishable, as illustrated.

CONDITION—IMPERFORATE LINE-ENGRAVED ISSUES

The prices quoted for the 1840 and 1841 imperforate Line-engraved issues are for "fine" examples. As condition is most important in assessing the value of a stamp, the following definitions will assist collectors in the evaluation of individual examples.

Four main factors are relevant when considering quality.

(a) **Impression.** This should be clean and the surface free of any rubbing or unnatural blurring which would detract from the appearance.

(b) **Margins.** This is perhaps the most difficult factor to evaluate. Stamps described as "fine", the standard adopted in this catalogue for pricing purposes, should have margins of the recognised width, defined as approximately one half of the distance between two adjoining unsevered stamps. Stamps described as "very fine" or "superb" should have margins which are proportionately larger than those of a "fine" stamp. Examples with close margins should not, generally, be classified as "fine".

(c) **Cancellation.** On a "fine" stamp this should be reasonably clear and not noticeably smudged. A stamp described as "superb" should have a neat cancellation, preferably centrally placed or to the right.

(d) **Appearance.** Stamps, at the prices quoted, should always be without any tears, creases, bends or thins and should not be toned on either the front or back. Stamps with such defects are worth only a proportion of the catalogue price.

Good

Fine

Very Fine

Superb

The above actual size illustrations of 1840 1d. blacks show the various grades of quality. When comparing these illustrations it should be assumed that they are all from the same plate and that they are free of any hidden defects.

PRINTERS. Nos. 1/53*a* were recess-printed by Perkins, Bacon & Petch, known from 1852 as Perkins, Bacon & Co.

1

1*a*

2 Small Crown

(Eng Charles and Frederick Heath)

1840 (6–8 May). *Letters in lower corners. Wmk Small Crown. W* **2.** *Imperf.*

No.	*Type*		*Un*	*Used*	*Used on cover*
1	**1**	1d. intense black	£3250	£190	
2		1d. black	£2750	£140	£225
3		1d. grey-black (worn plate) ..	£3000	£190	
4	**1***a*	2d. deep full blue (8.5.40) ..	£7000	£375	
5		2d. blue	£5500	£300	£650
6		2d. pale blue	£7000	£375	

The 1d. stamp in black was printed from Plates 1 to 11. Plate 1 exists in two states (known to collectors as 1*a* and 1*b*), the latter being the result of extensive repairs.

Repairs were also made to plates 2, 5, 6, 8, 9, 10 and 11, and certain impressions exist in two or more states.

The so-called "Royal reprint" of the 1d. black was made in 1864, from Plate 66, Die II, on paper with Large Crown watermark, inverted. A printing was also made in carmine, on paper with the same watermark, normal.

For 1d. black with "VR" in upper corners *see* No. V1 under Official Stamps.

The 2d. stamps were printed from Plates 1 and 2.

Plates of 1d. black

Plate	*Un*	*Used*
1*a*	£4500	£175
1*b*	£2750	£140
2	£2750	£140
3	£3500	£190
4	£3000	£160
5	£2750	£150
6	£2750	£140
7	£3250	£180
8	£3500	£200
9	£4000	£225
10	£4500	£300
11	£4500	£1600

Varieties of 1d. black

			Un	*Used*
a.	On *bleuté* paper (Plates 1 to 8) ..	*from*	—	£200
b.	Double letter in corner..	*from*	£3000	£175
bb.	Re-entry	*from*	£3250	£190
bc.	"PB" re-entry (Plate 5, 3rd state)		—	£3500
cc.	Large letters in each corner (E J, I L, J C and P A) (Plate 1*b*)	*from*	£3500	£300
c.	Guide line in corner		£3000	£175
d.	,, ,, through value		£3000	£175
e.	Watermark inverted		£3750	£350
g.	Obliterated by Maltese Cross			
	In red		—	£140
	In black		—	£140
	In blue		—	£1300
	In magenta		—	£550
	In yellow		—	£3250
h.	Obliterated by Maltese Cross with number in centre			
	No. 1		—	£1800
	No. 2		—	£1000
	No. 3		—	£1000
	No. 4		—	£1000
	No. 5		—	£1000
	No. 6		—	£1000
	No. 7		—	£1000
	No. 8		—	£1000
	No. 9		—	£1000
	No. 10		—	£1000
	No. 11		—	—
	No. 12		—	£1000
i.	Obliterated "Penny Post" in black ..	*from*	—	£950
j.	Obliterated by town postmark (without Maltese Cross)			
	In black	*from*	—	£900
	In yellow	*from*	—	£3750
	In red	*from*	—	£950
k.	Obliterated by 1844 type postmark in black	*from*	—	£400

Plates of 2d. blue

Plate		*Un*	*Used*
1	*Shades from*	£5500	£300
2	*Shades from*	£6500	£375

Varieties of 2d. blue

		Un	*Used*
a.	Double letter in corner	—	£425
aa.	Re-entry	—	£475
b.	Guide line in corner	—	£375
c.	,, ,, through value	—	£375
d.	Watermark inverted	£7000	£650
e.	Obliterated by Maltese Cross		
	In red	—	£300
	In black	—	£300
	In blue	—	£2250
	In magenta	—	£2000
f.	Obliterated by Maltese Cross with number in centre		
	No. 1	—	£2500
	No. 2	—	£2500
	No. 3	—	—
	No. 4	—	£2500
	No. 5	—	£2500
	No. 6	—	£2750
	No. 7	—	£2500
	No. 8	—	£2500
	No. 9	—	£3000
	No. 10	—	£2750
	No. 11	—	£2750
	No. 12	—	£2500
g.	Obliterated "Penny Post" in black .. *from*	—	£1400
h.	Obliterated by town postmark (without Maltese Cross) in black .. .. *from*	—	£1000
i.	Obliterated by 1844 type postmark		
	In black *from*	—	£650
	In blue *from*	—	£1500

1841 (10 Feb). *Printed from "black" plates. Wmk W* **2.** *Paper more or less blued. Imperf.*

No.	*Type*		*Un*	*Used*	*Used on cover*
7	**1**	1d. red-brown (*shades*)	£450	35·00	60·00
		a. "PB" re-entry (Plate 5, 3rd state)	—	£1000	

The first printings of the 1d. in red were made from Plates 1*b*, 2, 5 and 8 to 11 used for the 1d. black.

1d. red-brown from "black" plates

Plate	*Un*	*Used*
1*b*	£2750	£140
2	£1600	90·00
5	£600	45·00
8	£475	38·00
9	£450	35·00
10	£475	38·00
11	£500	35·00

1841 (late Feb). *Plate* 12 *onwards. Wmk W* **2.** *Paper more or less blued. Imperf.*

			Un	*Used*	*Used on cover*
8	**1**	1d. red-brown	£125	3·00	6·00
8*a*		1d. red-brown on very blue paper	£150	3·00	
9		1d. pale red-brown (worn plates)	£200	8·00	
10		1d. deep red-brown	£150	5·50	
11		1d. lake-red	£500	£180	
12		1d. orange-brown	£275	45·00	

Error. No letter "A" *in right lower corner* (*Stamp* B (A), *Plate* 77)

12*a*	**1**	1d. red-brown	—	£4000

The error "No letter A in right corner" was due to the omission to insert this letter on stamp B A of Plate 77. The error was discovered some months after the plate was registered and was then corrected.

There are innumerable variations in the colour and shade of the 1d. "red" and those given in the above list represent colour groups each covering a wide range.

Varieties of 1d. red-brown, etc.

			Un	*Used*
b.	Re-entry	*from*	—	20·00
c.	Double letter in corner	*from*	—	10·00
d.	Double Star (Plate 75) "Union Jack" re-entry		—	£400
e.	Guide line in corner		—	5·00
f.	,, ,, through value		—	10·00
g.	Thick outer frame to stamp		—	9·00
h.	Ivory head		£175	5·00
i.	Watermark inverted		£350	35·00
j.	Left corner letter "S" inverted (Plates 78, 105, 107)	*from*	—	35·00
k.	P converted to R (Plates 30, 33, 83, 86)	*from*	—	25·00
l.	Obliterated by Maltese Cross			
	In red		—	£800
	In black		—	7·50
	In blue		—	£100
m.	Obliterated by Maltese Cross with number in centre			
	No. 1		—	24·00
	No. 2		—	24·00
	No. 3		—	38·00
	No. 4		—	95·00
	No. 5		—	24·00
	No. 6		—	20·00
	No. 7		—	18·00
	No. 8		—	18·00
	No. 9		—	27·00
	No. 10		—	35·00
	No. 11		—	40·00
	No. 12		—	60·00
n.	Obliterated "Penny Post" in black		—	£150
o.	Obliterated by town postmark (without Maltese Cross)			
	In black	*from*	—	£100
	In blue	*from*	—	£200
	In green	*from*	—	£350
	In yellow	*from*	—	£3250
	In red	*from*	—	£1500
p.	Obliterated by 1844 type postmark			
	In blue	*from*	—	30·00
	In red	*from*	—	£800
	In green	*from*	—	85·00
	In violet	*from*	—	£500
	In black	*from*	—	3·00

Stamps with thick outer frame to the design are from plates on which the frame-lines have been strengthened or recut, particularly Plates 76 and 90.

For "Union Jack" re-entry *see* General Notes to Line-engraved Issues.

In "P converted to R" the corner letter "R" is formed from the "P", the distinctive long tail having been hand-cut.

POSTAGE DUE STAMPS

PERFORATIONS. All postage due stamps are perf 14 × 15.

D 1

D 2

(Typo by Somerset House (early trial printings of ½d., 1d., 2d. and 5d.; all printings of 1s.) and by Harrison (later printings of all values except 1s.). Not easily distinguishable except by the control)

1914 (20 Apr)–**23.** *W* **100** (*Simple Cypher*) *sideways.*

No.	Type	Description	Un	Used
D1	D 1	½d. emerald	40	40
D2		1d. carmine	50	40
		a. Pale carmine	75	40
D3		1½d. chestnut (1923)	40·00	15·00
D4		2d. agate	50	40
D5		3d. violet (1918)	2·00	1·00
		a. Bluish violet	2·50	3·00
D6		4d. dull grey-green (1921)	25·00	1·75
D7		5d. brownish cinnamon	2·50	1·50
D8		1s. bright blue (1915)	25·00	2·00
		a. Deep bright blue	25·00	2·00
D1/8		*Set of* 8	85·00	20·00

The 1d. is known bisected and used to make up a 1½d. rate on understamped letters from Ceylon (1921) and the 2d. bisected and used as 1d. at West Kensington and at Streatham both in the same year.

1924. *As* 1914–23, *but on thick chalk-surfaced paper.*

No.	Type	Description	Un	Used
D9	D 1	1d. carmine	2·25	3·00

(Typo Waterlow and (from 1934) Harrison)

1924–31. *W* **111** (*Block Cypher*) *sideways.*

No.	Type	Description	Un	Used
D10	D 1	½d. emerald (6.25)	30	30
D11		1d. carmine (4.25)	50	30
D12		1½d. chestnut (10.24)	35·00	15·00
D13		2d. agate (7.24)	1·60	40
D14		3d. dull violet (10.24)	2·00	40
		a. Printed on gummed side	£100	†
		b. Experimental paper W **111*a***	35·00	25·00
D15		4d. dull grey-green (10.24)	12·00	2·00
D16		5d. brownish cinnamon (1.31)	21·00	25·00
D17		1s. deep blue (9.24)	8·00	75
D18	D 2	2s. 6d. purple/*yellow* (10.24)	60·00	1·75
D10/18		*Set of* 9	£125	42·00

1936–37. *W* **125** (E 8 R) *sideways.*

No.	Type	Description	Un	Used
D19	D 1	½d. emerald (6.37)	5·50	5·00
D20		1d. carmine (5.37)	1·00	1·60
D21		2d. agate (5.37)	7·50	5·00
D22		3d. dull violet (3.37)	1·60	1·60
D23		4d. dull grey-green (12.36)	12·00	15·00
D24		5d. brownish cinnamon (11.36)	38·00	20·00
		a. Yellow-brown (1937)	12·00	15·00
D25		1s. deep blue (12.36)	7·50	4·50
D26	D 2	2s. 6d. purple/*yellow* (5.37)	£160	8·00
D19/26		*Set of* 8 (*cheapest*)	£180	55·00

The 1d. is known bisected (Solihull, 3 July 1937).

1937–38. *W* **127** (G VI R) *sideways.*

No.	Type	Description	Un	Used
D27	D 1	½d. emerald (1938)	7·00	3·25
D28		1d. carmine (1938)	1·75	40
D29		2d. agate (1938)	1·75	40
D30		3d. violet (1938)	8·00	40
D31		4d. dull grey-green (1937)	45·00	7·50
D32		5d. yellow-brown (1938)	7·00	1·50
D33		1s. deep blue (1937)	48·00	1·00
D34	D 2	2s. 6d. purple/*yellow* (1938)	55·00	3·00
D27/34		*Set of* 8	£150	15·00

The 2d. is known bisected in June 1951 (Harpenden and St. Albans) and on 30 October 1954 (Harpenden).

DATES OF ISSUE. The dates for Nos. D35/68 are those on which stamps were first issued by the Supplies Department to postmasters.

1951–52. *Colours changed and new value* (1½d.). *W* **127** (G VI R) *sideways.*

No.	Type	Description	Un	Used
D35	D 1	½d. orange (18.9.51)	1·75	2·00
D36		1d. violet-blue (6.6.51)	1·10	75
D37		1½d. green (11.2.52)	1·75	1·75
D38		4d. blue (14.8.51)	22·00	9·00
D39		1s. ochre (6.12.51)	28·00	4·00
D35/9		*Set of* 5	48·00	16·00

The 1d. is known bisected (Dorking, 1952, and Camberley, 6 April 1954).

1954–55. *W* **153** (*Mult Tudor Crown and* E 2 R) *sideways.*

No.	Type	Description	Un	Used
D40	D 1	½d. orange (8.6.55)	3·00	2·50
D41		2d. agate (28.7.55)	1·90	2·00
D42		3d. violet (4.5.55)	40·00	25·00
D43		4d. blue (14.7.55)	15·00	16·00
		a. Imperf (pair)	£175	
D44		5d. yellow-brown (19.5.55)	17·00	6·50
D45	D 2	2s. 6d. purple/*yellow* (11.54)	£120	3·00
D40/5		*Set of* 6	£175	50·00

1955–57. *W* **165** (*Mult St. Edward's Crown and* E 2 R) *sideways.*

No.	Type	Description	Un	Used
D46	D 1	½d. orange (16.7.56)	1·50	2·25
D47		1d. violet-blue (7.6.56)	4·00	1·25
D48		1½d. green (13.2.56)	3·75	3·75
D49		2d. agate (22.5.56)	35·00	3·00
D50		3d. violet (5.3.56)	4·50	1·25
D51		4d. blue (24.4.56)	18·00	3·00
D52		5d. brown-ochre (23.3.56)	27·00	2·00
D53		1s. ochre (22.11.55)	65·00	1·25
D54	D 2	2s. 6d. purple/*yellow* (28.6.57)	£160	7·50
D55		5s. scarlet/*yellow* (25.11.55)	90·00	19·00
D46/55		*Set of* 10	£375	40·00

The 2d. is known bisected (June 1956), and also the 4d. (Poplar, London, April 1959).

1959–63. *W* **179** (*Mult St Edward's Crown*) *sideways.*

No.	Type	Description	Un	Used
D56	D 1	½d. orange (18.10.61)	10	45
D57		1d. violet-blue (9.5.60)	10	15
D58		1½d. green (5.10.60)	90	1·50
D59		2d. agate (14.9.59)	1·25	30
D60		3d. violet (24.3.59)	40	15
D61		4d. blue (17.12.59)	40	20
D62		5d. yellow-brown (6.11.61)	45	45
D63		6d. purple (29.3.62)	60	30
D64		1s. ochre (11.4.60)	1·40	25
D65	D 2	2s. 6d. purple/*yellow* (11.5.61)	4·00	45
D66		5s. scarlet/*yellow* (8.5.61)	7·50	70
D67		10s. blue/*yellow* (2.9.63)	9·00	3·75
D68		£1 black/*yellow* (2.9.63)	45·00	7·00
D56/68		*Set of* 13	60·00	14·00

Whiter paper. The note after No. 586 also applies to Postage Due stamps.

The 1d. is known bisected (Newbury, Dec. 1962).

1968–69. *Typo. No wmk. Chalk-surfaced paper.*

No.	Type	Description	Un	Used
D69	D 1	2d. agate (11.4.68)	40	40
D70		3d. violet (9.9.68)	25	40
D71		4d. blue (6.5.68)	25	40
D72		5d. orange-brown (3.1.69)	4·50	5·25
D73		6d. purple (9.9.68)	80	60
D74		1s. ochre (19.11.68)	80	1·00
D69/74		*Set of* 6	6·50	7·00

The 2d. and 4d. exist with gum arabic and PVA gum; remainder with PVA gum only.

1968–69. *Photo. No wmk. Chalk-surfaced paper. PVA gum. P* 14 × 15.

No.	Type	Description	Un	Used
D75	D 1	4d. blue (12.6.69)	5·00	5·00
D76		8d. red (3.10.68)	1·25	75

Nos. D75/6 are smaller, 21½ × 17½ mm.

D 3

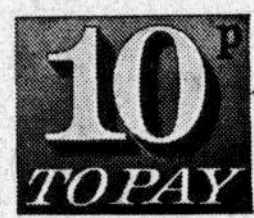

D 4

(Des J. Matthews. Photo Harrison)

1970 (17 June)–**75.** *Decimal Currency. Chalk-surfaced paper. P* 14 × 15.

No.	Type	Description	Un	Used
D77	D 3	½p. turquoise-blue (15.2.71)	10	20
D78		1p. deep reddish purple (15.2.71)	10	10
D79		2p. myrtle-green (15.2.71)	10	10
D80		3p. ultramarine (15.2.71)	10	10
D81		4p. yellow-brown (15.2.71)	15	15
D82		5p. violet (15.2.71)	20	20
D83		7p. red-brown (21.8.74)	35	45
D84	D 4	10p. carmine	30	20
D85		11p. slate-green (18.6.75)	50	60
D86		20p. olive-brown	60	50
D87		50p. ultramarine	1·50	40
D88		£1 black	2·75	60
D89		£5 orange-yellow and black (2.4.73)	16·00	2·00
D77/89		*Set of* 13	20·00	5·00

Later printings were on fluorescent white paper, some with dextrin added to the PVA gum (see notes after X1019 of Great Britain).

D 5

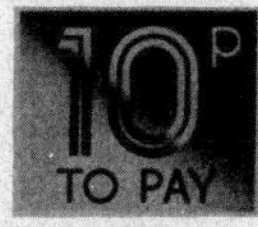

D 6

(Des Sedley Place Design Ltd. Photo Harrison)

1982 (9 June). *Chalk-surfaced paper. P* 14 × 15.

No.	Type	Description	Un	Used
D 90	D 5	1p. lake	10	10
D 91		2p. bright blue	10	10
D 92		3p. deep mauve	10	15
D 93		4p. deep blue	10	20
D 94		5p. sepia	10	20
D 95	D 6	10p. light brown	15	25
D 96		20p. olive-green	30	30
D 97		25p. deep greenish blue	40	70
D 98		50p. grey-black	75	1·00
D 99		£1 red	1·50	80
D100		£2 turquoise-blue	3·00	2·00
D101		£5 dull orange	7·50	1·50
D90/101		*Set of* 12	12·50	6·50

OFFICIAL STAMPS

In 1840 the 1d. black (Type **1**), with "V R" in the upper corners, was prepared for official use, but never issued for postal purposes. Obliterated specimens are those which were used for experimental trials of obliterating inks, or those that passed through the post by oversight.

V 1

1840. *Prepared for use but not issued; "V" "R" in upper corners. Imperf.*

No.	Type	Description	Un	Used	Used on cover
V1	V 1	1d. black	£6000	£4500	£15000

The following Official stamps would be more correctly termed Departmental stamps as they were exclusively for the use of certain government departments. Until 1882 official mail used ordinary postage stamps purchased at post offices, the cash being refunded once a quarter.

Later the government departments obtained Official stamps by requisition.

Official stamps were on sale to the public for a short time at Somerset House but they were not sold from post offices. The system of only supplying the Government departments was open to abuse so that all Official stamps were withdrawn on 14 May 1904.

OVERPRINTS, PERFORATIONS, WATERMARKS. All Official stamps were overprinted by Thomas De La Rue & Co. and are perf 14. They are on Crown watermarked paper unless otherwise stated.

INLAND REVENUE

These stamps were used by revenue officials in the provinces, mail to and from Head Office passing without a stamp. The London Office used these stamps only for foreign mail.

I.R.

OFFICIAL

(O 1)

I. R.

OFFICIAL

(O 2)

Optd with Types O **1** (*½d. to* 1s.) *or* O **2** (*others*)

1882–1901. *Stamps of Queen Victoria.* (*a*) *Issues of* 1880–81.

No.	Description	Un	Used	★ Used on cover
O 1	½d. green (1.11.82)	10·00	3·00	40·00
O 3	1d. lilac (Die II) (1.10.82)	1·00	65	15·00
	a. Optd in blue-black	60·00	30·00	
	b. "OFFICIAL" omitted	—	£2250	
O 4	6d. grey (Plate 18) (3.11.82)	75·00	20·00	

No. O3 with the lines of the overprint transposed is an essay.

(*b*) *Issues of* 1884–88

No.	Description	Un	Used	Used on cover
O 5	½d. slate-blue (8.5.85)	25·00	15·00	
O 6	2½d. lilac (12.3.85)	£110	35·00	
O 7	1s. green (12.3.85)	£2500	£450	
O 8	5s. rose (*blued paper*) (12.3.85)	£2750	£475	
O 9	5s. rose (3.90)	£1300	£400	
	a. Raised stop after "R"	£1600	£550	
	b. Optd in blue-black	£2000	£450	
O 9*c*	10s. cobalt (*blued paper*) (12.3.85)	£5000	£700	
O10	10s. ultramarine (3.90)	£2250	£475	
	a. Raised stop after "R"	£3000	£500	
	b. Optd in blue-black	£3500	£700	
O10*c*	10s. ultram (*blued paper*) (12.3.85)	£5000	£1400	
O11	£1 brown-lilac (wmk Crowns) (12.3.85)	£18000		
	a. Frame broken	£22000		
O12	£1 brown-lilac (wmk Orbs) (3.90)	£22000		
	a. Frame broken	£27000		

(*c*) *Issues of* 1887–92

No.	Description	Un	Used	Used on cover
O13	½d. vermilion (5.88)	1·10	40	12·00
	a. Without "I.R."	£1500		
	b. Imperf	£850		
	c. Opt double (imperf)	£1000		
O14	2½d. purple/*blue* (2.92)	50·00	4·00	
O15	1s. green (9.89)	£200	20·00	
O16	£1 green (6.92)	£3500	£450	
	a. No stop after "R"	—	£700	
	b. Frame broken	£5500	£900	

Nos. O3, O13, O15 and O16 may be found with two varieties of overprint, namely, 1887 printings, *thin* letters, and 1894 printings, *thicker* letters.

(*d*) *Issues of* 1887 *and* 1900

No.	Description	Un	Used	Used on cover
O17	½d. blue-green (4.01)	3·00	2·25	85·00
O18	6d. purple/*rose-red* (1.7.01)	£100	20·00	
O19	1s. green and carmine (12.01)	£600	£100	
★O1/19	**For well-centred, lightly used**		**+35%**	

1902–4. *Stamps of King Edward VII.*

No.	Description	Un	Used	Used on cover
O20	½d. blue-green, **O** (4.2.02)	15·00	1·50	80·00
O21	1d. scarlet, **O** (4.2.02)	10·00	70	40·00
O22	2½d. ultramarine, **O** (19.2.02)	£400	60·00	
O23	6d. dull purple, **O** (14.3.04)	£85000	£65000	
O24	1s. green and carmine, **O** (29.4.02)	£500	65·00	
O25	5s. carmine, **O** (29.4.02)	£4000	£1300	
	a. Raised stop after "R"	£4500	£1500	
O26	10s. ultramarine, **O** (29.4.02)	£15000	£9500	
	a. Raised stop after "R"	£17000	£11000	
O27	£1 dull blue-green, **O** (29.4.02)	£12000	£6000	

OFFICE OF WORKS

These were issued to Head and Branch (local) offices in London and to Branch (local) offices at Birmingham, Bristol, Edinburgh, Glasgow, Leeds, Liverpool, Manchester and Southampton. The overprints on stamps of value 2d. and upwards were created later in 1902, the 2d. for registration fees and the rest for overseas mail.

O. W.

OFFICIAL

(O 3)

Optd with Type O **3**

1896 (24 Mar)–**02.** *Stamps of Queen Victoria.*

No.	Description	Un	Used	Used on cover
O31	½d. vermilion	90·00	40·00	£180
O32	½d. blue-green (5.11.01)	£150	75·00	
O33	1d. lilac (Die II)	£150	40·00	£200
O34	5d. dull purple and blue (II) (29.4.02)	£750	£150	
O35	10d. dull purple and carmine (28.5.02)	£950	£225	

1902 (11 Feb)–**03**. *Stamps of King Edward VII.*

O36	½d.	blue-green, **O**	£350	80·00
O37	1d.	scarlet, **O**	£350	80·00
O38	2d.	green and carmine, **O** (29.4.02)	£600	75·00
O39	2½d.	ultramarine, **O** (29.4.02) ..	£700	£200
O40	10d.	purple and carmine, **O** (18.5.03)	£5000	£1500

★O31/40 **For well-centred, lightly used** .. +25%

ARMY

Letters to and from the War Office in London passed without postage. The overprinted stamps were distributed to District and Station Paymasters nationwide, including Cox and Co., the Army Agents, who were paymasters to the Household Division.

ARMY OFFICIAL (O 4) ARMY OFFICIAL (O 5) ARMY OFFICIAL (O 6)

1896 (1 Sept)–**01**. *Stamps of Queen Victoria optd with Type* O **4** (*½d., 1d.*) *or* O **5** (*2½d., 6d.*).

O41	½d. vermilion	1·10	50	20·00
	a. "OFFICIAI" (R. 13/7) ..	35·00	16·00	
	b. Lines of opt transposed ..	£1000		
O42	½d. blue-green (4.00)	1·75	3·00	
O43	1d. lilac (Die II)	1·00	50	30·00
	a. "OFFICIAI" (R. 13/7)	35·00	16·00	
O44	2½d. purple/*blue*	4·00	2·00	
O45	6d. purple/*rose-red* (8.01) ..	13·00	8·00	

Nos. O41a and O43a occur on sheets overprinted by Forme 1.

1902. *Stamps of King Edward VII optd with Type* O **4.**

O48	½d. blue-green, **O** (11.2.02)	1·75	65	50·00
O49	1d. scarlet, **O** (11.2.02)	1·25	55	50·00
	a. "ARMY" omitted			
O50	6d. dull purple, **O** (23.8.02) ..	60·00	30·00	

1903 (Dec). *Optd with Type* O **6**.

O52	6d. dull purple, **O**	£850	£275

GOVERNMENT PARCELS

These stamps were issued to all departments, including the Head Office, for use on parcels weighing over 3 lb. Below this weight government parcels were sent by letter post to avoid the 55% of the postage paid from accruing to the railway companies, as laid down by parcel-post regulations. Most government parcels stamps suffered heavy postmarks in use.

GOVT PARCELS

(O 7)

Optd as Type O **7**

1883 (1 July)–**86**. *Stamps of Queen Victoria.*

		Un	★ Used
O61	1½d. lilac (30.4.86)	£100	25·00
	a. No dot under "T"	£130	28·00
	b. Dot to left of "T"	£100	28·00
O62	6d. dull green (30.4.86)	£750	£275
O63	9d. dull green (1.8.83)	£625	£175
O64	1s. brown (wmk Crown, Pl 13)	£425	70·00
	a. No dot under "T"	£475	80·00
	b. Dot to left of "T"	£475	80·00
O64*c*	1s. brown (Pl 14)	£725	£110
	ca. No dot under "T"	£825	£100
	cb. Dot to left of "T"		

1887–90. *Stamps of Queen Victoria.*

O65	1½d. dull purple and pale green (29.10.87)	12·00	2·00
	a. No dot under "T"	18·00	6·00
	b. Dot to right of "T"	16·00	5·00
	c. Dot to left of "T"	16·00	5·00
O66	6d. purple/*rose-red* (19.12.87)	25·00	10·00
	a. No dot under "T"	30·00	12·00
	b. Dot to right of "T"	30·00	12·00
	c. Dot to left of "T"	30·00	11·00
O67	9d. dull purple and blue (21.8.88) ..	55·00	15·00
O68	1s. dull green (25.3.90)	£120	70·00
	a. No dot under "T"	£140	75·00
	b. Dot to right of "T"	£140	75·00
	c. Dot to left of "T"	£160	80·00
	d. Optd in blue-black		

1891–1900. *Stamps of Queen Victoria.*

O69	1d. lilac (Die II) (6.97)	25·00	8·00
	a. No dot under "T"	30·00	20·00
	b. Dot to left of "T"	30·00	20·00
	c. Opt inverted	£800	£450
	d. Ditto. Dot to left of "T"	£900	£500
O70	2d. grey-green and carmine (24.10.91) ..	45·00	7·00
	a. No dot under "T"	50·00	8·00
	b. Dot to left of "T"	50·00	9·00
O71	4½d. green and carmine (9.92) ..	£100	75·00
	b. Dot to right of "T"		
O72	1s. green and carmine (11.00) ..	£160	50·00
	a. Opt inverted	—	£3750

★O61/72 **For well-centred lightly used** .. .. +100%

1902. *Stamps of King Edward VII.*

O74	1d. scarlet, **O** (30.10.02)	15·00	5·00
O75	2d. green and carmine, **O** (29.4.02) ..	65·00	15·00
O76	6d. dull purple, **O** (19.2.02)	£100	15·00
O77	9d. purple and ultram (28.8.02) ..	£225	50·00
O78	1s. green and carmine, **O** (17.12.02)	£350	85·00

BOARD OF EDUCATION

BOARD OF EDUCATION

(O **8**)

Optd with Type O **8**

1902 (19 Feb). *Stamps of Queen Victoria.*

O81	5d. dull purple and blue (II)	£500	£100
O82	1s. green and carmine	£950	£375

1902–4. *Stamps of King Edward VII.*

O83	½d. blue-green, **O** (19.2.02)	16·00	7·00
O84	1d. scarlet, **O** (19.2.02)	16·00	6·00
O85	2½d. ultramarine, **O** (19.2.02) ..	£500	50·00
O86	5d. purple and blue, **O** (6.2.04) ..	£2000	£950
O87	1s. green and carmine, **O** (23.2.02) ..	£25000	£15000

ROYAL HOUSEHOLD

R.H. OFFICIAL

(O 9)

1902. *Stamps of King Edward VII optd with Type* O **9.**

		Un	Used	Used on cover
O91	½d. blue-green, **O** (29.4.02)	£150	95·00	£400
O92	1d. scarlet, **O** (19.2.02)	£130	85·00	£300

ADMIRALTY

ADMIRALTY OFFICIAL (O **10**) ADMIRALTY OFFICIAL (O **11**)

1903 (3 Mar). *Stamps of King Edward VII optd with Type* O **10.**

O101	½d. blue-green, **O**	9·00	3·00	£225
O102	1d. scarlet, **O**	5·00	2·50	50·00
O103	1½d. purple and green, **O**	60·00	40·00	
O104	2d. green and carmine, **O** ..	£100	50·00	
O105	2½d. ultramarine, **O**	£120	40·00	
O106	3d. purple/*yellow*, **O**	£100	35·00	

1903–4. *Stamps of King Edward VII optd with Type* O **11.**

O107	½d. blue-green, **O** (9.03)	7·00	4·00	£250
O108	1d. scarlet, **O** (11.03)	6·50	3·50	50·00
O109	1½d. purple and green, **O** (2.04) ..	£175	50·00	
O110	2d. green and carmine, **O** (3.04)	£400	£100	
O111	2½d. ultramarine, **O** (3.04) ..	£450	£225	
O112	3d. purple/*yellow*, **O** (2.04) ..	£350	85·00	

Stamps of various issues perforated with a Crown and initials ("H.M.O.W.", "O.W.", "B.T." or "S.O.") or with initials only ("H.M.S.O." or "D.S.I.R.") have also been used for official purposes, but these are outside the scope of the catalogue.

POSTAL FISCAL STAMPS

PRICES. Prices in the used column are for stamps with genuine postal cancellations dated from the time when they were authorised for use as postage stamps. Beware of stamps with fiscal cancellations removed and fraudulent postmarks applied.

VALIDITY. The 1d. Surface-printed stamps were authorised for postal use from 1 June 1881 and the 3d. and 6d. values, together with the Embossed issues, from 1 January 1883.

SURFACE-PRINTED ISSUES

(Typo Thomas De La Rue & Co)

F 1 Rectangular Buckle F 2

F 3 Octagonal Buckle F 4

F 5 Double-lined Anchor

F 6 Single-lined Anchor

1853–57. *P* 15½ × 15. (*a*) *Wmk* F **5** (*inverted*) (1853–55).

			Un	Used	Used on cover
F1	F **1**	1d. light blue (10.10.53) ..	12·00	16·00	75·00
F2	F **2**	1d. ochre (10.53)	50·00	35·00	£150
		a. *Tête-bêche* (in block of four)	£8000		
F3	F **3**	1d. pale turquoise-blue (1854)	15·00	15·00	£125
F4		1d. light blue/*blue* (1854) ..	30·00	22·00	£150
F5	F **4**	1d. reddish lilac/*blue glazed paper* (25.3.55)	45·00	11·00	£100

Only one example is known of No. F2a outside the National Postal Museum and the Royal Collection.

(*b*) *Wmk* F **6** (1856–57)

F6	F **4**	1d. reddish lilac (*shades*) ..	5·50	4·00	80·00
F7		1d. reddish lilac/*bluish* (*shades*) (1857)	5·50	4·00	80·00

INLAND REVENUE

(F 7)

1860 (3 Apr). *No.* F7 *optd with Type* F **7**, *in red.*

F8	F **4**	1d. dull reddish lilac/*blue* ..	£350	£300	£500

BLUE PAPER. In the following issues we no longer distinguish between bluish and white paper. There is a range of papers from white or greyish to bluish.

F 8

F 9

SIX PENCE INLAND REVENUE 6d 6d SIX PENCE

F 10

1860–67. *Bluish to white paper. P* 15½ × 15. (*a*) *Wmk* F **6** (1860).

F 9	F **8**	1d. reddish lilac (May) ..	6·00	6·00	80·00
F10	F **9**	3d. reddish lilac (June) ..	£225	80·00	£150
F11	F **10**	6d. reddish lilac (Oct) ..	85·00	60·00	£175

(*b*) *W* **40.** (*Anchor* 16 *mm high*) (1864)

F12	F **8**	1d. pale reddish lilac (Nov)	4·75	4·75	65·00
F13	F **9**	3d. pale reddish lilac ..	75·00	55·00	
F14	F **10**	6d. pale reddish lilac ..	75·00	55·00	£150

(*c*) *W* **40** (*Anchor* 18 *mm high*) (1867)

F15	F **8**	1d. reddish lilac	13·00	6·00	£130
F16	F **9**	3d. reddish lilac	60·00	60·00	£160
F17	F **10**	6d. reddish lilac	70·00	35·00	£150

For stamps perf 14, see Nos. F24/7.

F 11

F 12

Four Dies of Type F 12

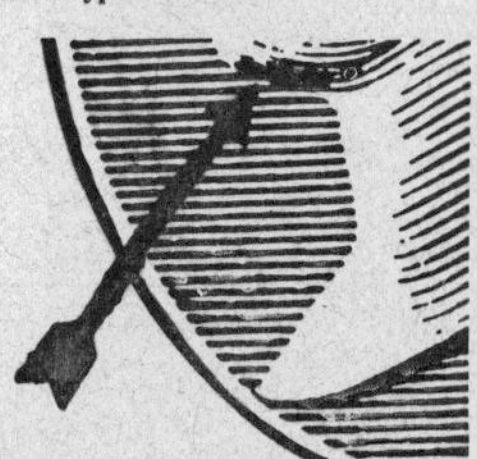

Die 1. Corner ornaments small and either joined or broken; heavy shading under chin

Plate	*Un*	*Used*	*Plate*	*Un*	*Used*
192	25·00	75	209	15·00	12·00
193	9·00	75	210	20·00	18·00
194	15·00	7·00	211	42·00	25·00
195	15·00	7·00	212	15·00	15·00
196	10·00	4·00	213	15·00	15·00
197	16·00	12·00	214	25·00	25·00
198	9·00	5·00	215	25·00	25·00
199	20·00	5·00	216	25·00	25·00
200	20·00	75	217	15·00	5·00
201	9·00	6·00	218	11·00	7·00
202	15·00	7·00	219	60·00	75·00
203	9·00	15·00	220	9·00	7·00
204	12·00	1·00	221	29·00	20·00
205	11·00	3·00	222	35·00	40·00
206	11·00	11·00	223	50·00	70·00
207	12·00	12·00	224	65·00	65·00
208	11·00	15·00	225	£1500	£400

Error. Imperf. Issued at Cardiff (Plate 116)

No.	Type	Description	*Un*	*Used*
44*b*	5	1d. rose-red (18.1.70)	£1500	£1000

The following plate numbers are also known imperf and used (No. 44a): 72, 79, 80, 81, 82, 83, 86, 87, 88, 90, 91, 92, 93, 96, 97, 100, 102, 103, 104, 105, 107, 108, 109, 112, 114, 117, 120, 121, 122, 136, 137, 142, 146, 148, 158, 162, 164, 166, 171, 174, 191 and 202.

The numbering of this series of 1d. red plates follows after that of the previous 1d. stamp, last printed from Plate 68.

Plates 69, 70, 75, 126 and 128 were prepared for this issue but rejected owing to defects, and stamps from these plates do not exist, so that specimens which appear to be from these plates (like many of those which optimistic collectors believe to be from Plate 77) bear other plate numbers. Owing to faulty engraving or printing it is not always easy to identify the plate number. Plate 77 was also rejected but some stamps printed from it were used. One specimen is in the Tapling Collection and six or seven others are known. Plates 226 to 228 were made but not used.

Specimens from most of the plates are known with inverted watermark. The variety of watermark described in the General Notes to this section occurs on stamp M A (or M L) on plates up to about 96 (*Prices from* £110 *used*).

Re-entries in this issue are few, the best being on stamps M K and T K of Plate 71 and on S L and T L, Plate 83.

No.	Type	Description	*Un*	*Used*	★ *Used on cover*
45	6	2d. blue (thick lines) (7.58)	£150	2·50	15·00
		a. Imperf (Plate 9)	—	£3000	
		Plate			
		7	£400	15·00	
		8	£450	11·00	
		9	£150	2·50	
		12	£700	40·00	
46		2d. blue (thin lines) (1.7.69)	£140	5·50	14·00
47		2d. deep blue (thin lines)	£140	5·50	
		a. Imperf (Plate 13)	£1750		
		Plate			
		13	£175	5·50	
		14	£200	7·50	
		15	£150	7·50	
★45/7		**For well-centred, lightly used**		+125%	

Plates 10 and 11 of the 2d. were prepared but rejected. Plates 13 to 15 were laid down from a new roller impression on which the white lines were thinner.

There are some marked re-entries and repairs, particularly on Plates 7, 8, 9 and 12.

Stamps with inverted watermark may be found and also the Γ A (T L) and M A (M L) watermark varieties (*see* General Notes to this section).

Though the paper is normally white, some printings showed blueing and stamps showing the "ivory head" may therefore be found.

7

Showing the plate number (9)

9

1870 (1 Oct). *Wmk W* 9, *extending over three stamps. P* 14.

No.	Type	Description	*Un*	*Used*	★ *Used on cover*
48	7	½d. rose-red	40·00	5·00	22·00
49		½d. rose	40·00	5·00	
		a. Imperf (Plates 1, 4, 5, 6, 8, 14) *from*	£950	£575	
		Plate			
		1	90·00	35·00	
		3	55·00	14·00	
		4	70·00	7·00	
		5	50·00	5·00	
		6	40·00	5·00	
		8	80·00	35·00	
		9	£2000	£300	
		10	70·00	5·00	
		11	40·00	5·00	
		12	40·00	5·00	
		13	40·00	5·00	
		14	40·00	5·00	
		15	55·00	9·00	
		19	85·00	18·00	
		20	90·00	30·00	
★48/9a		**For well-centred, lightly used**		+200%	

The ½d. was printed in sheets of 480 (24 × 20) so that the check letters run from A A X T to A A T X.

Plates 2, 7, 16, 17 and 18 were not completed while Plates 21 and 22, though made, were not used.

Owing to the method of perforating, the outer side of stamps in either the A or X row (ie the left or right side of the sheet) is imperf.

Stamps may be found with watermark inverted or reversed, or without watermark, the latter due to misplacement of the paper when printing.

8

Position of plate Number

1870 (1 Oct). *Wmk W* 4. *P* 14.

No.	Type	Description	*Un*	*Used*	★ *Used on cover*
51	8	1½d. rose-red	£150	16·00	£120
52		1½d. lake-red	£150	16·00	
		a. Imperf (Plates 1 and 3) *from*	£1850	†	
		Plate			
		(1)	£350	20·00	
		3	£150	16·00	
		Error of lettering. OP-PC *for* CP-PC (*Plate* 1)			
53	8	1½d. rose-red	£3500	£550	
★51/3		**For well-centred, lightly used**		+125%	

1860. *Prepared for use but not issued; blued paper. Wmk W* 4. *P* 14.

No.	Type	Description	*Un*	*Used*
53*a*	8	1½d. rosy mauve (Plate 1)	£1750	
		b. Error of lettering, OP-PC for CP-PC		

Owing to a proposed change in the postal rates, 1½d. stamps were first printed in 1860, in rosy mauve, No. 53*a*, but the change was not approved and the greater part of the stock was destroyed.

In 1870 a 1½d. stamp was required and was issued in rose-red.

Plate 1 did not have the plate number in the design of the stamps, but on stamps from Plate 3 the number will be found in the frame as shown above.

Plate 2 was defective and was not used.

The error of lettering OP-PC on Plate 1 was apparently not noticed by the printers, and therefore not corrected.

EMBOSSED ISSUES

Volume 1 of the Stanley Gibbons *Great Britain Specialised Catalogue* gives further detailed information on the embossed issues.

PRICES. The prices quoted are for cut-square stamps with average to fine embossing. Stamps with exceptionally clear embossing are worth more.

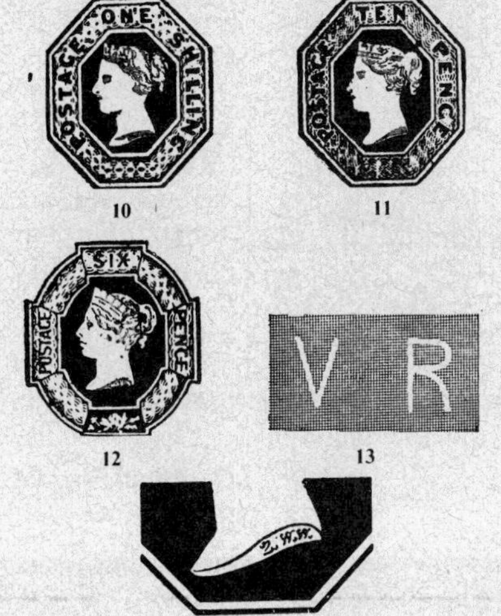

10 11

12 13

Position of die number

(Primary die engraved at the Royal Mint by William Wyon. Stamps printed at Somerset House)

1847–54. *Imperf.* (For paper and wmk see footnote.)

No.	Type	Description	*Un*	*Used*	*Used on cover*
54	10	1s. pale green (11.9.47)	£2750	£350	£450
55		1s. green	£2750	£400	
56		1s. deep green	£3250	£450	
		Die 1 (1847)	£2750	£350	
		Die 2 (1854)	£3250	£400	
57	11	10d. brown (6.11.48)	£2250	£550	£900
		Die 1 (1848)	£2500	£600	
		Die 2 (1850)	£2250	£550	
		Die 3 (1853)	£2250	£550	
		Die 4 (1854)	£2500	£600	
		Die 5	£16000		
58	12	6d. mauve (1.3.54)	£2500	£425	
59		6d. dull lilac	£2500	£375	£475
60		6d. purple	£2500	£375	
61		6d. violet	£3250	£600	

The 1s. and 10d. are on "Dickinson" paper with "silk" threads (actually a pale blue twisted cotton yarn). The 6d. is on paper watermarked V R in single-lined letters, W 13, which may be found in four ways—upright, inverted, upright reversed, and inverted reversed; upright reversed being the most common.

The die numbers are indicated on the base of the bust. Only Die 1 (1 WW) of the 6d. was used for the adhesive stamps. The 10d. is from Die 1 (W.W.1 on stamps), and Dies 2 to 5 (2 W.W., 3 W.W., 4 W.W. and 5 W.W.) but the number and letters on stamps from Die 1 are seldom clear and many specimens are known without any trace of them. Because of this the stamp we previously listed as "No die number" has been deleted. That they are from Die 1 is proved by the existence of blocks showing stamps with and without the die number. The 1s. is from Dies 1 and 2 (W.W.1, W.W.2).

The normal arrangement of the "silk" threads in the paper was in pairs running down each vertical row of the sheet, the space between the threads of each pair being approximately 5 mm and between pairs of threads 20 mm. Varieties due to misplacement of the paper in printing show a single thread on the first stamp from the sheet margin and two threads 20 mm apart on the other stamps of the row. Faulty manufacture is the cause of stamps with a single thread in the middle.

Through bad spacing of the impressions, which were handstruck, all values may be found with two impressions more or less overlapping. Owing to the small margin allowed for variation of spacing, specimens with good margins on all sides are not common.

Double impressions are known of all values.

Later printings of the 6d. had the gum tinted green to enable the printer to distinguish the gummed side of the paper.

SURFACE-PRINTED ISSUES

GENERAL NOTES

Volume 1 of the Stanley Gibbons *Great Britain Specialised Catalogue* gives further detailed information on the surface-printed issues.

"Abnormals". The majority of the great rarities in the surface-printed group of issues are the so-called "abnormals", whose existence is due to the practice of printing six sheets from every plate as soon as made, one of which was kept for record purposes at Somerset House, while the others were perforated and usually issued. If such plates were not used for general production or if, before they came into full use, a change of watermark or colour took place, the six sheets originally printed would differ from the main issue in plate, colour or watermark and, if issued, would be extremely rare.

The abnormal stamps of this class listed in this Catalogue and distinguished, where not priced, by an asterisk (*) are:

No.	
78	3d. Plate 3 (with white dots)
152	4d. vermilion, Plate 16
153	4d. sage-green, Plate 17
109	6d. mauve, Plate 10
123/*a*	6d. chestnut and 6d. pale chestnut, Plate 12
145	6d. pale buff, Plate 13
88	9d. Plate 3 (hair lines)
98	9d. Plate 5 (*see* footnote to No. 98)
113	10d. Plate 2
91	1s. Plate 3 ("Plate 2")
148/50	1s. green, Plate 14
120	2s. blue, Plate 3

Those which may have been issued, but of which no specimens are known, are 2½d. wmk. Anchor, Plates 4 and 5; 3d. wmk Emblems, Plate 5; 3d. wmk Spray, Plate 21; 6d. grey, wmk Spray, Plate 18; 8d. orange, Plate 2; 1s. wmk Emblems, Plate 5. 5s. wmk Maltese Cross, Plate 4.

The 10d. Plate 1, wmk Emblems (No. 99), is sometimes reckoned among the abnormals, but was an error, due to the use of the wrong paper.

Corner Letters. With the exception of the 4d., 6d. and 1s. of 1855–57, the ½d., 1½d., 2d. and 5d. of 1880, the 1d. lilac of 1881 and the £5 (which had letters in lower corners only, and in the reverse order to the normal), all the surface-printed stamps issued prior to 1887 had letters in all four corners, as in the later line-engraved stamps. The arrangement is the same, the letters running in sequence right across and down the sheets, whether these were divided into panes or not. The corner letters existing naturally depend on the number of stamps in the sheet and their arrangement.

Imprimaturs and Imperforate Stamps. The Post Office retained in their records (now in the National Postal Museum) one imperforate sheet from each plate, known as the Imprimatur (or officially approved) sheet. Some stamps were removed from time to time for presentation purposes and have come on to the market, but these imperforates are not listed as they were not issued. Full details can be found in Volume I of the *Great Britain Specialised Catalogue*.

However, other imperforate stamps are known to have been issued and these are listed where it has been possible to prove that they do not come from the Imprimatur sheets. It is therefore advisable to purchase these only when accompanied by an Expert Committee certificate of genuineness.

Plate Numbers. All stamps from No. 75 to No. 163 bear in their designs either the plate number or, in one or two earlier instances, some other indication by which one plate can be distinguished from another. With the aid of these and of the corner letters it is thus possible to "reconstruct" a sheet of stamps from any plate of any issue or denomination.

Surface-printing. In this context the traditional designation "surface-printing" is synonymous with typo(graphy)—a philatelic term—or letterpress—the printers' term—as meaning printing from (the surface of) raised type. It is also called relief-printing, as the image is in relief (in French, *en épargne*), unwanted parts of the design having been cut away. Duplicate impressions can be electrotyped or stereotyped from an original die, the resulting *clichés* being locked together to form the printing plate.

Wing Margins. As the vertical gutters (spaces) between the panes, into which sheets of stamps of most values were divided until the introduction of the Imperial Crown watermark, were perforated through the centre with a single row of holes, instead of each vertical row of stamps on the inner side of the panes having its own line of perforation as is now usual, a proportion of the stamps in each sheet have what is called a "wing margin" about 5 mm wide on one or other side.

The stamps with "wing margins" are the watermark Emblems and Spray of Rose series (3d. 6d. 9d. 10d. 1s. and 2s.) with letters D, E, H or I in S.E. corner, and the watermark Garter series (4d. and 8d.) with letters F or G in S.E. corner. Knowledge of this lettering will enable collectors to guard against stamps with wing margin cut down and re-perforated, but note that wing margin stamps of Nos. 62 to 73 are also to be found re-perforated.

PRINTERS. The issues of Queen Victoria, Nos. 62/214, were typo by Thomas De La Rue & Co.

PERFORATIONS. All the surface-printed issues of Queen Victoria are Perf 14, with the exception of Nos. 126/9.

ALTERED CATALOGUE NUMBERS

Any Catalogue numbers altered from the last edition are shown as a list in the introductory pages.

KEY TO SURFACE-PRINTED ISSUES 1855–83

S.G. Nos.	*Description*	*Watermark*	*Date of Issue*
	NO CORNER LETTERS		
62	4d. carmine	Small Garter	31.7.55
63/5	4d. carmine	Medium Garter	25.2.56
66/*a*	4d. carmine	Large Garter	Jan 1857
69/70	6d. lilac	Emblems	21.10.56
71/3	1s. green	Emblems	1.11.56
	SMALL WHITE CORNER LETTERS		
75/7	3d. carmine	Emblems	1.5.62
78	3d. carmine (dots)	Emblems	Aug 1862
79/82	4d. red	Large Garter	15.1.62
83/5	6d. lilac	Emblems	1.12.62
86/8	9d. bistre	Emblems	15.1.62
89/91	1s. green	Emblems	1.12.62
	LARGE WHITE CORNER LETTERS		
92	3d. rose	Emblems	1.3.65
102/3	3d. rose	Spray	July 1867
93/5	4d. vermilion	Large Garter	4.7.65
96/7	6d. lilac	Emblems	7.3.65
104/7	6d. lilac	Spray	21.6.67
108/9	6d. lilac	Spray	8.3.69
122/4	6d. chestnut	Spray	12.4.72
125	6d. grey	Spray	24.4.73
98	9d. straw	Emblems	30.10.65
110/11	9d. straw	Spray	3.10.67
99	10d. brown	Emblems	11.11.67
112/14	10d. brown	Spray	1.7.67
101	1s. green	Emblems	Feb 1865
115/17	1s. green	Spray	13.7.67
118/20*b*	2s. blue	Spray	1.7.67
121	2s. brown	Spray	27.2.80
126/7	5s. rose	Cross	1.7.67
128	10s. grey	Cross	26.9.78
129	£1 brown-lilac	Cross	26.9.78
130, 134	5s. rose	Anchor	25.11.82
131, 135	10s. grey-green	Anchor	Feb 1883
132, 136	£1 brown-lilac	Anchor	Dec 1882
133, 137	£5 orange	Anchor	21.3.82
	LARGE COLOURED CORNER LETTERS		
166	1d. Venetian red	Crown	1.1.80
138/9	2½d. rosy mauve	Anchor	1.7.75
141	2½d. rosy mauve	Orb	1.5.76
142	2½d. blue	Orb	5.2.80
157	2½d. blue	Crown	23.3.81
143/4	3d. rose	Spray	5.7.73
158	3d. rose	Crown	Jan 1881
159	3d. on 3d. purple	Crown	1.1.83
152	4d. vermilion	Large Garter	1.3.76
153	4d. sage-green	Large Garter	12.3.77
154	4d. brown	Large Garter	15.8.80
160	4d. brown	Crown	9.12.80
145	6d. buff	Spray	15.3.73
146/7	6d. grey	Spray	20.3.74
161	6d. grey	Crown	1.1.81
162	6d. on 6d. purple	Crown	1.1.83
156*a*	8d. purple-brown	Large Garter	July 1876
156	8d. orange	Large Garter	11.9.76
148/50	1s. green	Spray	1.9.73
151	1s. brown	Spray	14.10.80
163	1s. brown	Crown	29.5.81

Watermarks:	
Anchor	W **40, 47**
Cross	W **39**
Crown	W **49**
Emblems	W **20**
Large Garter	W **17**
Medium Garter	W **16**
Orb	W **48**
Small Garter	W **15**
Spray	W **33**

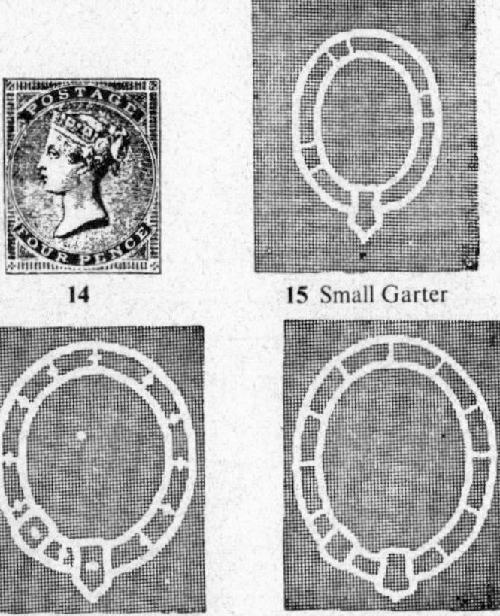

14 | 15 Small Garter | 16 Medium Garter | 17 Large Garter

1855–57. *No corner letters.*

(*a*) *Wmk Small Garter, W* **15**. *Highly glazed, deeply blued paper* (31 July 1855)

			Un	*Used*	★ *Used on cover*
62	**14**	4d. carmine (*shades*)	£2250	£150	£250
		a. Paper slightly blued	£2500	£140	
		b. White paper	£3000	£325	

(*b*) *Wmk Medium Garter, W* **16**

(i) *Thick, blued highly glazed paper* (25 February 1856)

63	**14**	4d. carmine (*shades*)	£2750	£140	£225
		a. White paper	£2500		

(ii) *Ordinary thin white paper* (September 1856)

64	**14**	4d. pale carmine	£1750	£130	£200
		a. Stamp printed double	†	—	

(iii) *Ordinary white paper, specially prepared ink* (1 November 1856)

65	**14**	4d. rose *or* deep rose	£1800	£140	£225

(*c*) *Wmk Large Garter, W* **17**. *Ordinary white paper* (January 1857)

66	**14**	4d. rose-carmine	£700	35·00	65·00
		a. Rose	£600	35·00	
		b. Thick glazed paper	£1700	80·00	

★62/6b For well-centred, lightly used +125%

18 | 19 | 20 Emblems wmk (normal)

20*a* Wmk error, three roses and shamrock | 20*b* Wmk error, three roses and thistle

(*d*) *Wmk Emblems, W* **20**

			Un	*Used*	★ *Used on cover*
69	**18**	6d. deep lilac (21.10.56)	£550	50·00	
70		6d. pale lilac	£500	35·00	65·00
		a. Azure paper	£2500	£350	
		b. Thick paper	£750	£110	
		c. Error. Wmk W **20***a*			
71	**19**	1s. deep green (1.11.56)	£1200	£125	
72		1s. green	£600	£100	£135
73		1s. pale green	£600	£110	
		a. Azure paper	—	£500	
		b. Thick paper	—	£140	

★69/73b For well-centred, lightly used +125%

21 | 22

23

24

25 Plate 2

A. White dots added

B. Hair lines

1862–64. *A small uncoloured letter in each corner, the 4d. wmk Large Garter. W* **17**, *the others Emblems, W* **20**.

			Un	*Used*	★ *Used on cover*
75	**21**	3d. deep carmine-rose (Plate 2) (1.5.62)	£1100	£125	
76		3d. bright carmine-rose	£700	£100	£225
77		3d. pale carmine-rose	£700	95·00	
		b. Thick paper	—	£150	
78		3d. rose (with white dots, Type A, Plate 3) (8.62)	*	£2500	
		a. Imperf (Plate 3)	£2000		
79	**22**	4d. bright red (Plate 3) (15.1.62)	£750	45·00	
80		4d. pale red	£500	30·00	80·00
81		4d. bright red (Hair lines, Type B, Plate 4) (16.10.63)	£650	35·00	
82		4d. pale red (Hair lines, Type B, Plate 4)	£550	26·00	70·00
		a. Imperf (Plate 4)	£1500		
83	**23**	6d. deep lilac (Plate 3) (1.12.62)	£750	50·00	
84		6d. lilac	£650	28·00	65·00
		a. Azure paper	—	£300	
		b. Thick paper	—	60·00	
		c. Error. Wmk W **20***b* (stamp TF)			
85		6d. lilac (Hair lines, Plate 4) (20.4.64)	£800	50·00	£120
		a. Imperf	£1100		
		c. Thick paper	£1200	75·00	
86	**24**	9d. bistre (Plate 2) (15.1.62)	£1100	£140	£250
87		9d. straw	£1100	£130	
		a. On azure paper			
		b. Thick paper	£1700	£160	
88		9d. bistre (Hair lines, Plate 3) (5.62)	£6000	£1800	
89	**25**	1s. deep green (Plate No. 1 = Plate 2) (1.12.62)	£800	£100	
90		1s. green (Plate No. 1 = Plate 2)	£700	60·00	£125
		a. "K" in lower left corner in white circle (stamp KD)	£4250	£500	
		aa. "K" normal (stamp KD)	—	£750	
		b. On azure paper			
		c. Thick paper	—	£150	
		ca. Thick paper, "K" in circle as No. 90a	—	£1000	
91		1s. deep green (Plate No. 2 = Plate 3)	£11000	*	
		a. Imperf	£1500		

★75/91 For well-centred, lightly used +125%

The 3d. as Type **21**, but with network background in the spandrels which is found overprinted SPECIMEN, was never issued.

The plates of this issue may be distinguished as follows:

3d. Plate 2. No white dots.
Plate 3. White dots as Illustration A.
4d. Plate 3. No hair lines. Roman I next to lower corner letters.
Plate 4. Hair lines in corners. (Illustration B.). Roman II.
6d. Plate 3. No hair lines.
Plate 4. Hair lines in corners.
9d. Plate 2. No hair lines.
Plate 3. Hair lines in corners. Beware of faked lines.
1s. Plate 2. Numbered 1 on stamps.
Plate 3. Numbered 2 on stamps and with hair lines.

The 9d. on azure paper (No. 87a) is very rare, only one confirmed example being known.

The variety "K" in circle, No. 90a, is believed to be due to a damaged letter having been cut out and replaced. It is probable that the punch was driven in too deeply, causing the flange to penetrate the surface, producing an indentation showing as an uncoloured circle.

The watermark variety "three roses and a shamrock" illustrated in W **20***a* was evidently due to the substitution of an extra rose for the thistle in a faulty watermark bit. It is found on stamp T A of Plates 2 and 4 of the 3d., Plates 1 (No. 70c), 3, 5 and 6 of the 6d., Plate 4 of the 9d. and Plate 4 of the 1s.

A similar variety, W **20***b*, but showing three roses and a thistle is found on stamp T F of the 6d. (No. 84) and 9d. (No. 98).

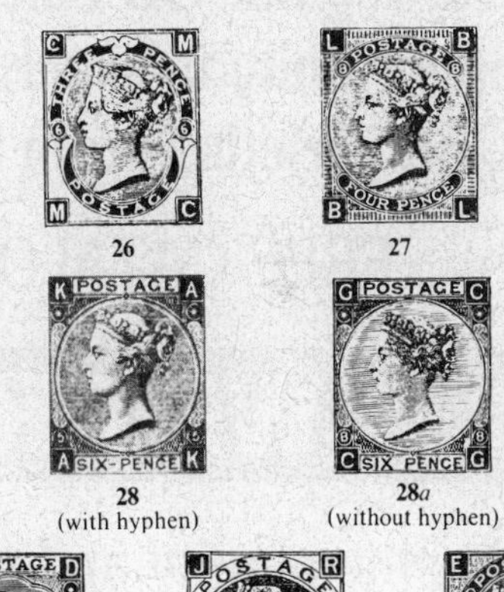

26 | 27

28 (with hyphen) | 28*a* (without hyphen)

29

30

31

1865–67. *Large uncoloured corner letters. Wmk Large Garter* (4d.); *others Emblems.*

			Un	*Used*	★ *Used on cover*
92	**26**	3d. rose (Plate 4) (1.3.65)	£375	35·00	90·00
		a. Error. Wmk W **20***a*	£900	£275	
		b. Thick paper	£500	45·00	
93	**27**	4d. dull vermilion (4.7.65)	£225	15·00	35·00
94		4d. vermilion	£225	15·00	
		a. Imperf (Plates 11, 12)	£500		
95		4d. deep vermilion	£225	20·00	
		Plate			
		7 (1865)	£300	19·00	
		8 (1866)	£250	19·00	
		9 (1867)	£250	15·00	
		10 (1868)	£300	26·00	
		11 (1869)	£250	15·00	
		12 (1870)	£225	15·00	
		13 (1872)	£250	17·00	
		14 (1873)	£300	30·00	
96	**28**	6d. deep lilac (with hyphen) (7.3.65)	£400	35·00	
97		6d. lilac (with hyphen)	£350	28·00	60·00
		a. Thick paper	£450	45·00	
		b. Stamp doubly printed (Plate 6)	—	£4000	
		c. Error. Wmk W **20***a* (Pl 5, 6) *from*	—	£300	
		Plate			
		5 (1865)	£350	28·00	
		6 (1867)	£1000	55·00	

			Un	Used	Used on cover
98	**29**	9d. straw (Plate 4) (30.10.65) ..	£700	£170	£275
		a. Thick paper	£950	£300	
		b. Error. Wmk W **20***a* ..	—	£350	
		c. Error. Wmk W **20***b* (stamp T F)			
99	**30**	10d. red-brown (Plate 1) (11.11.67)	†	£12000	
101	**31**	1s. green (Plate 4) (1.2.65) ..	£650	60·00	£100
		a. Error. Wmk W **20***a* ..	—	£350	
		b. Thick paper	£750	£100	
		c. Imperf between (vert pair)	—	£4000	
★92/101c		**For well-centred, lightly used** ..		+100%	

From mid-1866 to about the end of 1871 4d. stamps of this issue appeared generally with watermark inverted.

Unused examples of No. 98 from Plate 5 exist, but this was never put to press and all evidence points to the existing stamps being from a portion of the Imprimatur sheet which was perforated by De La Rue in 1887 for insertion in albums to be presented to members of the Stamp Committee (*Price* £10000 *un*).

The 10d. stamps, No. 99, were printed in *error* on paper watermarked "Emblems" instead of on "Spray of Rose".

32

33 Spray of Rose

34

1867–80. *Wmk Spray of Rose, W* **33**.

			Un	★ Used	Used on cover
102	**26**	3d. deep rose (12.7.67) ..	£225	18·00	
103		3d. rose	£200	12·00	38·00
		a. Imperf (Plates 5, 6, 8) *from*	£700		
		Plate			
		4 (1867)	£300	50·00	
		5 (1868)	£200	14·00	
		6 (1870)	£225	12·00	
		7 (1871)	£275	15·00	
		8 (1872)	£250	14·00	
		9 (1872)	£250	18·00	
		10 (1873)	£275	40·00	
104	**28**	6d. lilac (with hyphen) (Plate 6) (21.6.67)	£550	30·00	90·00
		a. Imperf			
105		6d. deep lilac (with hyphen) (Plate 6)	£550	28·00	
106		6d. purple (with hyphen) (Pl 6)	£550	40·00	
107		6d. bright violet (with hyphen) (Plate 6) (22.7.68) ..	£550	30·00	
108	**28***a*	6d. dull violet (without hyphen) (Plate 8) (18.3.69) ..	£325	25·00	
109		6d. mauve (without hyphen)	£275	25·00	55·00
		a. Imperf (Plate Nos. 8 and 9)	£750	£650	
		Plate			
		8 (1869, mauve) ..	£275	25·00	
		9 (1870, mauve) ..	£275	25·00	
		10 (1869, mauve) ..	*	£12000	
110	**29**	9d. straw (Plate No. 4) (3.10.67)	£600	90·00	£200
111		9d. pale straw (Plate No. 4) ..	£600	90·00	
		a. Imperf (Plate 4)	£1850		
112	**30**	10d. red-brown (1.7.67) ..	£1000	£120	£325
113		10d. pale red-brown	£1000	£130	
114		10d. deep red-brown	£1200	£150	
		a. Imperf (Plate 1)	£1800		
		Plate			
		1 (1867)	£1000	£120	
		2 (1867)	£12000	£2500	
115	**31**	1s. deep green (13.7.67) ..	£425	10·00	
117		1s. green	£350	10·00	20·00
		a. Imperf btwn (pair) (Pl 7) ..			
		b. Imperf (Plate 4)	£1000	£600	
		Plate			
		4 (1867)	£350	15·00	
		5 (1871)	£400	12·00	
		6 (1872)	£525	10·00	
		7 (1873)	£525	25·00	
118	**32**	2s. dull blue (1.7.67) ..	£950	55·00	£325
119		2s. deep blue	£950	55·00	
		a. Imperf (Plate 1)	£1800		
120		2s. pale blue	£1500	90·00	
		aa. Imperf (Plate 1)	£1800		
120*a*		2s. cobalt	£5000	£800	
120*b*		2s. milky blue	£3000	£350	
		Plate			
		1 (1867)	£950	55·00	
		3 (1868)	*	£3000	
121		2s. brown (Plate No. 1) (27.2.80)	£6000	£900	
		a. Imperf	£4000		
★102/21		**For well-centred, lightly used** ..		+75%	

1872–73. *Uncoloured letters in corners. Wmk Spray, W* **33**.

			Un	★ Used	Used on cover
122	**34**	6d. deep chestnut (12.4.72) ..	£425	18·00	50·00
123		6d. chestnut (22.5.72)	£350	18·00	
123*a*		6d. pale chestnut (1872)	*	£1200	
124		6d. pale buff (25.10.72)	£400	30·00	£130
		Plate			
		11 (1872, deep chestnut) ..	£425	18·00	
		11 (1872, chestnut)	£350	18·00	
		11 (1872, pale buff)	£400	30·00	
		12 (1872 pale chestnut) ..	*	£1300	
		12 (1872 chestnut)	*	£1300	
		12 (1872 pale buff)	£750	50·00	
125		6d. grey (Plate No. 12) (24.4.73)	£600	70·00	£125
		a. Imperf..	£1300		
★122/5		**For well-centred, lightly used** ..		+50%	

35

36

37

38

39 Maltese Cross

40 Large Anchor

1867–83. *Uncoloured letters in corners.*

(*a*) *Wmk Maltese Cross, W* **39**. *P* 15½ × 15

			Un	★ Used
126	**35**	5s. rose (1.7.67)	£2500	£250
127		5s. pale rose	£2750	£250
		a. Imperf (Plate 1)	£4000	
		Plate		
		1 (1867)	£2500	£250
		2 (1874)	£3500	£325
128	**36**	10s. greenish grey (Plate 1) (26.9.78) ..	£18000	£800
129	**37**	£1 brown-lilac (Plate 1) (26.9.78) ..	£22000	£1100
		(*b*) *Wmk Anchor, W* **40**. *P* 14. (i) *Blued paper*		
130	**35**	5s. rose (Plate 4) (25.11.82)	£4750	£800
131	**36**	10s. grey-green (Plate 1) (2.83)	£20000	£1000
132	**37**	£1 brown-lilac (Plate 1) (12.82) ..	£27000	£2000
133	**38**	£5 orange (Plate 1) (21.3.82)	£15000	£3000
		(ii) *White paper*		
134	**35**	5s. rose (Plate 4)	£4500	£800
135	**36**	10s. greenish grey (Plate 1)	£22000	£1000
136	**37**	£1 brown-lilac (Plate 1)	£32000	£1800
137	**38**	£5 orange (Plate 1)	£4000	£1200
★126/37		**For well-centred, lightly used**		+75%

41

42

43

44

45

46

47 Small Anchor

48 Orb

1873–80. *Large coloured letters in the corners.*

(*a*) *Wmk Anchor, W* **47**

			Un	★ Used	Used on cover
138	**41**	2½d. rosy mauve (*blued paper*) (1.7.75)	£375	35·00	
		a. Imperf			
139		2½d. rosy mauve (*white paper*) ..	£225	25·00	45·00
		Plate			
		1 (*blued paper*) (1875) ..	£375	35·00	
		1 (*white paper*) (1875) ..	£225	25·00	
		2 (*blued paper*) (1875) ..	£3000	£500	
		2 (*white paper*) (1875) ..	£225	25·00	
		3 (*white paper*) (1875) ..	£400	30·00	
		3 (*blued paper*) (1875) ..	—	£2250	
		Error of Lettering L H—F L for L H—H L (*Plate* 2)			
140	**41**	2½d. rosy mauve	£7000	£650	
		(*b*) *Wmk Orb, W* **48**			
141	**41**	2½d. rosy mauve (1.5.76) ..	£200	12·00	35·00
		Plate			
		3 (1876)	£500	30·00	
		4 (1876)	£200	12·00	
		5 (1876)	£200	16·00	
		6 (1876)	£200	12·00	
		7 (1877)	£200	12·00	
		8 (1877)	£200	16·00	
		9 (1877)	£200	12·00	
		10 (1878)	£225	17·00	
		11 (1878)	£200	12·00	
		12 (1878)	£200	16·00	
		13 (1878)	£200	16·00	
		14 (1879)	£200	12·00	
		15 (1879)	£200	12·00	
		16 (1879)	£200	12·00	
		17 (1880)	£550	80·00	
142		2½d. blue (5.2.80)	£175	10·00	15·00
		Plate			
		17 (1880)	£175	20·00	
		18 (1880)	£200	12·00	
		19 (1880)	£175	10·00	
		20 (1880)	£175	10·00	
		(*c*) *Wmk Spray, W* **33**			
143	**42**	3d. rose (5.7.73)	£200	12·00	35·00
144		3d. pale rose	£200	12·00	
		Plate			
		11 (1873)	£200	12·00	
		12 (1873)	£225	14·00	
		14 (1874)	£250	15·00	
		15 (1874)	£200	14·00	
		16 (1875)	£200	14·00	
		17 (1875)	£225	14·00	
		18 (1875)	£225	14·00	
		19 (1876)	£200	14·00	
		20 (1879)	£200	30·00	
145	**43**	6d. pale buff (Plate 13) (15.3.73)	*	£4500	
146		6d. deep grey (20.3.74) ..	£225	16·00	38·00
147		6d. grey	£225	16·00	
		Plate			
		13 (1874)	£225	18·00	
		14 (1875)	£225	18·00	
		15 (1876)	£225	16·00	
		16 (1878)	£225	16·00	
		17 (1880)	£300	35·00	
148	**44**	1s. deep green (1.9.73) ..	£325	32·00	
150		1s. pale green	£250	26·00	45·00
		Plate			
		8 (1873)	£325	32·00	
		9 (1874)	£325	32·00	
		10 (1874)	£300	32·00	
		11 (1875)	£300	32·00	
		12 (1875)	£250	26·00	
		13 (1876)	£250	26·00	
		14 (—)	*	£10000	
151		1s. orange-brown (Plate 13) (14.10.80)	£1100	£150	£250
		(*d*) *Wmk Large Garter, W* **17**			
152	**45**	4d. vermilion (1.3.76)	£600	£140	£275
		Plate			
		15 (1876)	£600	£140	
		16 (1877)	*	£10000	
153		4d. sage-green (12.3.77) ..	£400	85·00	£175
		Plate			
		15 (1877)	£450	90·00	
		16 (1877)	£400	85·00	
		17 (1877)	*	£6000	
154		4d. grey-brown (Plate 17) (15.8.80)	£600	£120	£170
		a. Imperf			
156	**46**	8d. orange (Plate 1) (11.9.76) ..	£550	£100	£200
★138/56		**For well-centred, lightly used** ..		+100%	

1876 (July). *Prepared for use but not issued.*

			Un
156*a*	**46**	8d. purple-brown (Plate 1) ..	£3000

49 Imperial Crown

3d
(**50**)

1880–83. *Wmk Imperial Crown, W* **49**.

			Un	★ Used	Used on cover
157	**41**	2½d. blue (23.3.81)	£175	8·00	20·00
		Plate			
		21 (1881)	£225	9·00	
		22 (1881)	£175	8·00	
		23 (1881)	£175	8·00	
158	**42**	3d. rose (1.81)	£180	25·00	28·00
		Plate			
		20 (1881)	£225	35·00	
		21 (1881)	£180	25·00	

			Un	Used	Used on cover
159	**42**	3d. on 3d. lilac (T **50**) (C.) (Plate 21) (1.1.83)	£225	65·00	£225
160	**45**	4d. grey-brown (8.12.80) ..	£175	25·00	60·00
		Plate			
		17 (1880)	£175	25·00	
		18 (1882)	£175	25·00	
161	**43**	6d. grey (1.1.81)	£150	20·00	40·00
		Plate			
		17 (1881)	£180	20·00	
		18 (1882)	£150	20·00	
162		6d. on 6d. lilac (as T **50**) (C.) (Plate 18) (1.1.83)	£200	60·00	£130
		a. Slanting dots (various) *from*	£250	75·00	
		b. Opt double	—	£3750	
163	**44**	1s. orange-brown (29.5.81) ..	£225	40·00	90·00
		Plate			
		13 (1881)	£275	40·00	
		14 (1881)	£225	40·00	
★157/63		**For well-centred, lightly used** ..		+75%	

The 1s. Plate 14 (line perf 14) exists in purple, but was not issued in this shade (*Price* £2500 *unused*). Examples were included in a few of the Souvenir Albums prepared for members of the "Stamp Committee of 1884".

52

53

54

55

56

1880–81. *Wmk Imperial Crown, W* **49**.

			Un	Used	★ Used on cover
164	**52**	½d. deep green (14.10.80) ..	15·00	3·00	6·00
		a. Imperf	£500		
165		½d. pale green	17·00	5·00	
166	**53**	1d. Venetian red (1.1.80) ..	4·00	2·00	4·00
		a. Imperf	£500		
167	**54**	1½d. Venetian red (14.10.80) ..	80·00	14·00	60·00
168	**55**	2d. pale rose (8.12.80) ..	90·00	30·00	60·00
168*a*		2d. deep rose	90·00	30·00	
169	**56**	5d. indigo (15.3.81)	£350	40·00	£120
		a. Imperf	£800		
★164/9		**For well-centred, lightly used** ..		+75%	

Die I

57

Die II

1881. *Wmk Imperial Crown, W* **49**. (*a*) 14 *dots in each corner, Die* I (12 July).

			Un	Used	★ Used on cover
170	**57**	1d. lilac	75·00	12·00	20·00
171		1d. pale lilac	75·00	12·00	

(*b*) 16 *dots in each corner, Die* II (12 December)

			Un	Used	Used on cover
172	**57**	1d. lilac	80	40	1·10
172*a*		1d. bluish lilac	£180	45·00	
173		1d. deep purple	1·00	30	
		a. Printed both sides	£400	†	
		b. Frame broken at bottom ..	£475	£175	
		c. Printed on gummed side ..	£375	†	
		d. Imperf three sides (pair) ..	£1750	†	
		e. Printed both sides but impression on back inverted	£400	†	
		f. No watermark	£250	†	
		g. Blued paper	£1500		
174		1d. mauve	80	30	
		a. Imperf (pair)	£800		
★170/4		**For well-centred, lightly used** ..		+50%	

1d. stamps with the words "PEARS SOAP" printed on back in *orange, blue* or *mauve* price *from* £300, *unused*.

The variety "frame broken at bottom" (No. 173b) shows a white space just inside the bottom frame-line from between the "N" and "E" of "ONE" to below the first "N" of "PENNY", breaking the pearls and cutting into the lower part of the oval below "PEN".

MINIMUM PRICE

The minimum price quote is 10p which represents a handling charge rather than a basis for valuing common stamps. For further notes about prices see introductory pages.

KEY TO SURFACE-PRINTED ISSUES 1880–1900

S.G. Nos.	*Description*	*Date of Issue*
164/5	½d. green ..	14.10.80
187	½d. slate-blue	1.4.84
197/d	½d. vermilion	1.1.87
213	½d. blue-green	17.4.1900
166	1d. Venetian red	1.1.80
170/1	1d. lilac, Die I	12.7.81
172/4	1d. lilac, Die II ..	12.12.81
167	1½d. Venetian red	14.10.80
188	1½d. lilac ..	1.4.84
198	1½d. purple and green	1.1.87
168/*a*	2d. rose ..	8.12.80
189	2d. lilac ..	1.4.84
199/200	2d. green and red	1.1.87
190	2½d. lilac ..	1.4.84
201	2½d. purple on blue paper	1.1.87
191	3d. lilac ..	1.4.84
202/4	3d. purple on yellow paper	1.1.87
192	4d. dull green	1.4.84
205/*a*	4d. green and brown	1.1.87
206	4½d. green and carmine ..	15.9.92
169	5d. indigo	15.3.81
193	5d. dull green	1.4.84
207	5d. purple and blue, Die I	1.1.87
207*a*	5d. purple and blue, Die II	—
194	6d. dull green	1.4.84
208/*a*	6d. purple on rose-red paper	1.1.87
195	9d. dull green	1.8.83
209	9d. purple and blue	1.1.87
210	10d. purple and carmine	24.2.90
196	1s. dull green	1.4.84
211	1s. green ..	1.1.87
214	1s. green and carmine ..	11.7.1900
175	2s. 6d. lilac on blued paper	2.7.83
178/9	2s. 6d. lilac	1884
176	5s. rose on blued paper ..	1.4.84
180/1	5s. rose	1884
177/*a*	10s. ultramarine on blued paper	1.4.84
182/3*a*	10s. ultramarine ..	1884
185	£1 brown-lilac, wmk Crowns ..	1.4.84
186	£1 brown-lilac, wmk Orbs	1.2.88
212	£1 green ..	27.1.91

Note that the £5 value used with the above series is listed as Nos. 133 and 137.

58

59

60

1883–84. *Coloured letters in the corners. Wmk Anchor, W* **40**.

(*a*) *Blued paper*

			Un	★ Used
175	**58**	2s. 6d. lilac (2.7.83)	£2000	£450
176	**59**	5s. rose (1.4.84)	£3500	£900
177	**60**	10s. ultramarine (1.4.84)	£12000	£1900
177*a*		10s. cobalt (5.84)	£14000	£3500

(*b*) *White paper*

			Un	Used
178	**58**	2s. 6d. lilac	£200	50·00
179		2s. 6d. deep lilac	£200	50·00
		a. Deep lilac, blued paper ..	£1600	£475
180	**59**	5s. rose	£400	70·00
181		5s. crimson	£400	70·00
182	**60**	10s. cobalt	£13000	£3250
183		10s. ultramarine	£700	£225
183*a*		10s. pale ultramarine	£700	£225
★175/83*a*		**For well-centred, lightly used** ..		+50%

For No. 180 perf 12 *see* second note below No. 196.

61

Broken frames, Plate 2

1884 (1 April). *Wmk Three Imperial Crowns, W* **49**.

			Un	★ Used
185	**61**	£1 brown-lilac	£10000	£850
		a. Frame broken	£20000	£1500

1888 (1 Feb). *Wmk Three Orbs, W* **48**.

			Un	Used
186	**61**	£1 brown-lilac	£16000	£1200
		a. Frame broken	£25000	£2250
★185/6*a*		**For well-centred, lightly used**		+50%

The broken-frame varieties, Nos. 185a and 186a, are on Plate 2 stamps JC and TA, as illustrated. *See also* No. 212a.

62

63

64

65

66

1883 (1 Aug) (*9d.*) *or* **1884** (1 April) (*others*). *Wmk Imperial Crown, W* **49** (*sideways on horiz designs*).

			Un	Used	★ Used on cover
187	**52**	½d. slate-blue	8·00	1·50	3·00
		a. Imperf	£350		
188	**62**	1½d. lilac	55·00	18·00	55·00
		a. Imperf	£350		
189	**63**	2d. lilac	70·00	25·00	50·00
		a. Imperf	£400		
190	**64**	2½d. lilac	40·00	5·00	12·00
		a. Imperf	£400		
191	**65**	3d. lilac	90·00	40·00	55·00
		a. Imperf	£400		
192	**66**	4d. dull green	£200	80·00	£130
		a. Imperf	£450		
193	**62**	5d. dull green	£200	80·00	£120
		a. Imperf	£450		
194	**63**	6d. dull green	£225	90·00	£140
		a. Imperf	£450		
195	**64**	9d. dull green (1.8.83) ..	£475	£200	£500
196	**65**	1s. dull green	£350	£130	£250
		a. Imperf	£1000		
★187/96		**For well-centred, lightly used** ..		+100%	

The above prices are for stamps in the true dull green colour. Stamps which have been soaked, causing the colour to run, are virtually worthless.

Stamps of the above set and No. 180 are also found perf 12; these are official perforations, but were never issued. A second variety of the 5d. is known with a line instead of a stop under the "d" in the value; this was never issued and is therefore only known *unused* (*Price* £5000).

71

72

73

74

75

76

77

78

79

80

81

82

Die I　　　　Die II

Die I: Square dots to right of "d".
Die II: Thin vertical lines to right of "d".

1887 (1 Jan)–**1892.** *"Jubilee" issue. New types. The bicoloured stamps have the value tablets, or the frames including the value tablets, in the second colour. Wmk Imperial Crown, W* **49** *(Three Crowns on £1).*

No.	Type		Un	Used	★ Used on cover
197	**71**	½d. vermilion	75	30	5·00
		a. Printed on gummed side	£700	†	
		b. Printed both sides			
		c. Doubly printed	£1750		
		d. Imperf	£475		
197*e*		½d. orange-vermilion	75	30	
198	**72**	1½d. dull purple and pale green	8·00	2·00	15·00
		a. Purple part of design double	—	£2500	
199	**73**	2d. green and scarlet	£275	£125	
200		2d. grey-green and carmine	13·00	4·00	15·00
201	**74**	2½d. purple/*blue*	8·00	40	4·00
		a. Printed on gummed side	—	†	
		b. Imperf three sides	£1200		
		c. Imperf			
202	**75**	3d. purple/*yellow*	13·00	1·00	20·00
		a. Imperf			
203		3d. deep purple/*yellow*	13·00	1·00	
204		3d. purple/*orange* (1890)	£400	£125	
205	**76**	4d. green and purple-brown	16·00	6·00	18·00
		aa. Imperf			
205*a*		4d. green and deep brown	16·00	6·00	
206	**77**	4½d. green and carmine (15.9.92)	3·75	20·00	55·00
206*a*		4½d. green & deep brt carmine	£450	£200	
207	**78**	5d. dull purple and blue (Die I)	£350	30·00	60·00
207*a*		5d. dull purple and blue (Die II)	18·00	3·50	20·00
208	**79**	6d. purple/*rose-red*	18·00	5·00	15·00
208*a*		6d. deep purple/*rose-red*	18·00	5·00	
209	**80**	9d. dull purple and blue	40·00	25·00	50·00
210	**81**	10d. dull purple and carmine (24.2.90)	35·00	22·00	60·00
		aa. Imperf	£3000		
210*a*		10d. dull purple and deep bright carmine	£350	£150	
211	**82**	1s. dull green	£125	30·00	75·00
212	**61**	£1 green (27.1.91)	£2000	£350	
		a. Frame broken	£4500	£800	
★197/212a		**For well-centred, lightly used**		+50%	

The broken-frame varieties, No. 212a, are on Plate 2 stamps JC or TA, as illustrated above No. 185.

½d. stamps with "PEARS SOAP" printed on the back in *orange, blue* or *mauve*, price *from* £300 each.

1900. *Colours changed. Wmk Imperial Crown, W* **49**.

No.	Type		Un	Used	★ Used on cover
213	**71**	½d. blue-green (17.4)	1·00	40	5·00
		a. Printed on gummed side	—	†	
		b. Imperf	£1500		
214	**82**	1s. green and carmine (11.7)	45·00	70·00	£225
197/214		*Set of* 14	£300	£180	
★213/14		**For well-centred, lightly used**		+50%	

The ½d. No. 213, in bright blue, is a colour changeling.

KING EDWARD VII
22 January 1901–6 May 1910

PRINTINGS. Distinguishing De La Rue printings from the provisional printings of the same values made by Harrison & Sons Ltd. or at Somerset House may prove difficult in some cases. For very full guidance Volume 2 of the Stanley Gibbons *Great Britain Specialised Catalogue* should prove helpful.

Note that stamps perforated 15 × 14 must be Harrison; the 2½d., 3d. and 4d. in this perforation are useful reference material, their shades and appearance in most cases matching the Harrison perf 14 printings.

Except for the 6d. value, all stamps on chalk-surfaced paper were printed by De La Rue.

Of the stamps on ordinary paper, the De La Rue impressions are usually clearer and of a higher finish than those of the other printers. The shades are markedly different except in some printings of the 4d., 6d. and 7d. and in the 5s., 10s. and £1.

Used stamps in good, clean, unrubbed condition and with dated postmarks can form the basis of a useful reference collection, the dates often assisting in the assignment to the printers.

USED STAMPS. For well-centred, lightly used examples of King Edward VII stamps, add the following percentages to the used prices quoted below:

De La Rue printings (Nos. 215/66)—3d. values +35%, 4d. orange +100%, 6d. +75%, 7d. and 1s. +25%, all other values +50%.

Harrison printings (Nos. 267/86)—all values and perforations +75%

Somerset House printings (Nos. 287/320)—1s. values +25%, all other values +50%.

83

84

85

86

87

88

89　　90

91

92　　93

94

95

96

97

(Des E. Fuchs)

1902 (1 Jan)–**10.** *Printed by De La Rue & Co. Wmk Imperial Crown (½d. to 1s.); Anchor (2s. 6d. to 10s.); Three Crowns (£1). P* 14.

O = "Ordinary" paper.　**C** = Chalk-surfaced paper

No.	Type		Un	Used	Used on cover
215	**83**	½d. dull blue-green, **O** (1.1.02)	60	30	60
216		½d. blue-green, **O**	60	30	
217		½d. pale yellowish green, **O** (26.11.04)	50	20	30
218		½d. yellowish green, **O**	50	20	
		a. Booklet pane. Five stamps plus St. Andrew's Cross label (6.06)	£200		
		b. Doubly printed (bottom row on one pane) (Control H9)	£9750		
219		1d. scarlet, **O** (1.1.02)	50	15	1·50
220		1d. bright scarlet, **O**	50	15	
		a. Imperf (pair)	£7500		
221	**84**	1½d. dull pur & grn, **O** (21.3.02)	15·00	6·00	
222		1½d. slate-purple and green, **O**	12·00	4·75	12·00
223		1½d. pale dull purple and green, **C** (8.05)	25·00	5·50	
224		1½d. slate-pur & bluish green, **C**	20·00	4·25	
225	**85**	2d. yellowish green & carmine-red, **O** (25.3.02)	18·00	4·00	12·00
226		2d. grey-green and carmine-red, **O** (1904)	18·00	4·00	
227		2d. pale grey-green & carmine-red, **C** (4.06)	22·00	6·00	
228		2d. pale grey-green and scarlet, **C** (1909)	25·00	6·00	
229		2d. dull blue-green and carmine, **C** (1907)	40·00	20·00	
230	**86**	2½d. ultramarine, **O** (1.1.02)	5·50	2·50	10·00
231		2½d. pale ultramarine, **O**	4·50	2·50	
232	**87**	3d. dull purple/*orange-yellow*, **O** (20.3.02)	18·00	2·50	20·00
232*a*		3d. dp purple/*orange-yellow*, **O**	20·00	2·50	
232*b*		3d. pale reddish purple/*orange-yellow*, **C** (3.06)	70·00	15·00	
233		3d. dull purple/*orange-yellow*, **C**	80·00	18·00	
233*a*		3d. dull reddish purple/*yellow* (*lemon* back), **C**	70·00	28·00	
233*b*		3d. pale purple/*lemon*, **C**	16·00	6·00	
234		3d. purple/*lemon*, **C**	13·00	6·00	
235	**88**	4d. grn & grey-brn, **O** (27.3.02)	30·00	11·00	
236		4d. green & chocolate-brn, **O**	30·00	12·00	
237		4d. green and chocolate-brown, **C** (1.06)	22·00	7·00	25·00
238		4d. dp grn & chocolate-brn, **C**	25·00	8·50	
239		4d. brown-orange, **O** (1.11.09)	£140	80·00	
240		4d. pale orange, **O** (12.09)	7·50	6·50	20·00
241		4d. orange-red, **O** (12.09)	9·00	7·00	
242	**89**	5d. dull purple and ultramarine, **O** (14.5.02)	20·00	6·00	30·00
243		5d. dull pur & ultram, **C** (5.06)	25·00	8·00	
244		5d. slate-purple & ultram, **C**	20·00	8·00	
245	**83**	6d. pale dull purple, **O** (1.1.02)	15·00	4·00	30·00
246		6d. slate-purple, **O**	15·00	4·00	
247		6d. pale dull purple, **C** (1.06)	22·00	4·00	
248		6d. dull purple, **C**	18·00	4·00	
249	**90**	7d. grey-black, **O** (4.5.10)	3·50	6·00	£120
249*a*		7d. deep grey-black, **O**	60·00	60·00	
250	**91**	9d. dull purple and ultramarine, **O** (7.4.02)	40·00	24·00	£120
251		9d. slate-purple & ultram, **O**	40·00	24·00	
252		9d. dull pur & ultram, **C** (6.05)	45·00	30·00	
253		9d. slate-purple & ultram, **C**	45·00	30·00	
254	**92**	10d. dull purple and carmine, **O** (3.7.02)	40·00	18·00	£120
		a. No cross on crown	£225	£100	
255		10d. slate-pur & carm, **C** (9.06)	40·00	28·00	
		a. No cross on crown	£200	90·00	
256		10d. dull pur & scar, **C** (9.10)	45·00	35·00	
		a. No cross on crown	£190	80·00	
257	**93**	1s. dull green and carmine, **O** (24.3.02)	35·00	8·50	80·00
258		1s. dull green & carm, **C** (9.05)	40·00	12·00	
259		1s. dull green & scar, **C** (9.10)	40·00	20·00	
260	**94**	2s. 6d. lilac, **O** (5.4.02)	£150	45·00	£500
261		2s. 6d. pale dull purple, **C** (7.10.05)	£140	80·00	
262		2s. 6d. dull purple, **C**	£160	55·00	
263	**95**	5s. bright carmine, **O** (5.4.02)	£200	55·00	£500
264		5s. deep bright carmine, **O**	£200	55·00	
265	**96**	10s. ultramarine, **O** (5.4.02)	£475	£200	
266	**97**	£1 dull blue-green, **O** (16.6.02)	£1100	£300	

97*a*

1910 (May). *Prepared for use, but not issued.*

No.	Type		Un
266*a*	**97*a***	2d. Tyrian plum	£12000

One example of this stamp is known used, but it was never issued to the public.

1911. *Printed by Harrison & Sons. "Ordinary" paper. Wmk Imperial Crown. (a) P* 14.

No.	Type		Un	Used	Used on cover
267	**83**	½d. dull yellow-green (3.5.11)	1·10	40	3·00
268		½d. dull green	1·75	40	
269		½d. deep dull green	8·00	2·00	
270		½d. pale bluish green	22·00	22·00	
		a. Booklet pane. Five stamps plus St. Andrew's Cross label	£250		
		b. Wmk sideways	—	£10000	
		c. Imperf (pair)	£5500		
271		½d. bright green (fine impression) (6.11)	£150	£110	
272		1d. rose-red (3.5.11)	1·75	4·00	6·00
		a. No wmk	75·00	35·00	
273		1d. deep rose-red	2·75	4·00	
274		1d. rose-carmine	35·00	9·00	
275		1d. aniline pink (5.11)	£250	£110	
275*a*		1d. aniline rose	£110	75·00	
276	**86**	2½d. bright blue (10.7.11)	22·00	10·00	18·00
277	**87**	3d. purple/*lemon* (12.9.11)	40·00	£120	£400
277*a*		3d. grey/*lemon*	£3750		
278	**88**	4d. bright orange (13.7.11)	45·00	40·00	£100
		(b) P 15 × 14			
279	**83**	½d. dull green (30.10.11)	20·00	25·00	65·00
279*a*		½d. deep dull green	24·00	20·00	
280		1d. rose-red (5.10.11)	18·00	10·00	
281		1d. rose-carmine	5·00	3·00	15·00
282		1d. pale rose-carmine	8·00	3·00	
283	**86**	2½d. bright blue (14.10.11)	11·00	5·00	12·00
284		2½d. dull blue	12·00	5·00	
285	**87**	3d. purple/*lemon* (22.9.11)	18·00	3·50	15·00
285*a*		3d. grey/*lemon*	£3000		
286	**88**	4d. bright orange (11.11.11)	13·00	6·00	40·00
279/86		*Set of* 5	60·00	35·00	

1911–13. *Printed at Somerset House. Ordinary paper, unless marked* **C** *(= chalk-surfaced paper). Wmk as 1902–10. P* 14.

No.	Type		Un	Used	Used on cover
287	**84**	1½d. reddish purple and bright green (13.7.11)	25·00	9·50	
288		1½d. dull purple and green	13·00	6·00	30·00
289		1½d. slate-purple & green (9.12)	18·00	10·00	
290	**85**	2d. dp dull green & red (8.8.11)	12·00	4·50	30·00
291		2d. deep dull green and carmine	10·00	4·50	
292		2d. grey-green and bright carmine (carmine shows clearly on back) (11.3.12)	10·00	6·00	
293	**89**	5d. dull reddish purple and bright blue (7.8.11)	15·00	4·75	50·00
294		5d. dp dull reddish pur & brt bl	11·00	4·75	
295	**83**	6d. royal purple (31.10.11)	35·00	40·00	
296		6d. brt magenta, **C** (31.10.11)	£2250		
297		6d. dull purple	18·00	6·00	60·00
298		6d. reddish purple (11.11)	18·00	8·00	
		a. No cross on crown (*various shades*)	£250		
299		6d. very deep reddish purple (11.11)	38·00	18·00	
300		6d. dark purple (3.12)	18·00	15·00	
301		6d. dull purple "Dickinson" coated paper* (3.13)	£110	80·00	
303		6d. deep plum, **C** (7.13)	14·00	35·00	
		a. No cross on crown	£300		
305	**90**	7d. slate-grey (1.8.12)	5·00	8·50	85·00
306	**91**	9d. reddish purple and light blue (24.7.11)	50·00	30·00	
306*a*		9d. deep dull reddish purple and deep bright blue (9.11)	60·00	32·00	
307		9d. dull reddish pur & bl (10.11)	40·00	22·00	85·00
307*a*		9d. deep plum and blue (7.13)	40·00	30·00	
308		9d. slate-pur & cobalt-bl (3.12)	60·00	35·00	
309	**92**	10d. dull purple & scar (9.10.11)	45·00	25·00	
310		10d. dull reddish purple and aniline pink	£160	£110	
311		10d. dull reddish pur & car (5.12)	35·00	20·00	85·00
		a. No cross on crown	£500		

312	**93**	1s.	dark green & scar (13.7.11)	60·00	25·00	
313		1s.	dp green & scarlet (9.10.11)	45·00	9·00	85·00
314		1s.	green and carmine (15.4.12)	28·00	8·00	
315	**94**	2s.	6d. dull greyish purple (27.9.11)	£250	£150	
316		2s.	6d. dull reddish pur (10.11)	£135	45·00	
317		2s.	6d. dark purple	£135	50·00	
318	**95**	5s.	carmine (29.2.12)	£200	55·00	
319	**96**	10s.	blue (14.1.12)	£475	£200	
320	**97**	£1	deep green (3.9.11) ..	£1100	£275	
215/314			*Set of* 15 (*to* 1*s. and inc* ½*d.* (2))	£190	85·00	

*No. 301 was on an experimental coated paper which does not respond to the silver test.

KING GEORGE V
6 May 1910–20 January 1936

Further detailed information on the issues of King George V will be found in Volume 2 of the Stanley Gibbons *Great Britain Specialised Catalogue*.

PRINTERS. Types **98** to **102** were typographed by Harrison & Sons Ltd, with the exception of certain preliminary printings made at Somerset House and distinguishable by the controls "A.11", B.11" or "B.12" (the Harrison printings do not have a full stop after the letter). The booklet stamps, Nos. 334/7, and 344/5 were printed by Harrisons only.

WATERMARK VARIETIES. Many British stamps to 1967 exist without watermark owing to misplacement of the paper, and with either inverted, reversed, or inverted and reversed watermarks. A proportion of the low-value stamps issued in booklets have the watermark inverted in the normal course of printing.

Low values with *watermark sideways* are normally from stamp rolls used in machines with sideways delivery or, from June 1940, certain booklets.

STAMPS WITHOUT WATERMARK. Stamps found without watermark, due to misplacement of the sheet in relation to the dandy roll, are not listed here, but will be found in the *Great Britain Specialised Catalogue*.

The 1½d. and 5d. 1912–22, and 2d. and 2½d., 1924–26, listed here, are from *whole* sheets completely without watermark.

98

99

For type differences with T **101/2** *see* notes below the latter.

Die A

Die B

Dies of Halfpenny

Die A. The three upper scales on the body of the right hand dolphin form a triangle; the centre jewel of the cross inside the crown is suggested by a comma.

Die B. The three upper scales are incomplete; the centre jewel is suggested by a crescent.

Die A

Die B

Dies of One Penny

Die A. The second line of shading on the ribbon to the right of the crown extends right across the wreath; the line nearest to the crown on the right hand ribbon shows as a short line at the bottom of the ribbon.

Die B. The second line of shading is broken in the middle; the first line is little more than a dot.

(Des Bertram Mackennal and G. W. Eve. Head from photograph by W. & D. Downey. Die eng J. A. C. Harrison)

1911–12. *Wmk Imperial Crown, W* **49.** *P* 15 × 14.

				Un	*Used*
321	**98**	½d.	pale green (Die A) (22.6.11) ..	3·25	85
322		½d.	green (Die A) (22.6.11)	2·25	75
		a.	Error. Perf 14	—	£250
323		½d.	bluish green (Die A)	£375	£125
324		½d.	yellow-green (Die B)	4·00	50
325		½d.	bright green (Die B)	3·75	50
		a.	Wmk sideways	—	£1700
326		½d.	bluish green (Die B)	£200	70·00
327	**99**	1d.	carmine-red (Die A) (22.6.11) ..	2·00	90
		a.	Error. Perf 14		
		b.	Experimental ptg on chalk-surfaced paper (Control A.11)	£225	
		c.	Wmk sideways	†	—
328		1d.	pale carmine (Die A) (22.6.11) ..	10·00	1·00
		a.	No cross on crown	£350	£150
329	**99**	1d.	carmine (Die B)	2·50	90
330		1d.	pale carmine (Die B)	2·75	90
		a.	No cross on crown	£450	£250
331		1d.	rose-pink (Die B)	70·00	18·00
332		1d.	scarlet (Die B) (6.12)	13·00	9·00
333		1d.	aniline scarlet (Die B)	£120	55·00

For note on the aniline scarlet No. 333 *see* below No. 343.

100 Simple Cypher

1912 (Aug). *Booklet stamps. Wmk Royal Cypher ("Simple"), W* **100.** *P* 15 × 14.

334	**98**	½d.	pale green (Die B)	28·00	22·00
335		½d.	green (Die B)	28·00	22·00
336	**99**	1d.	scarlet (Die B)	15·00	12·00
337		1d.	bright scarlet (Die B)	15·00	12·00

101

102

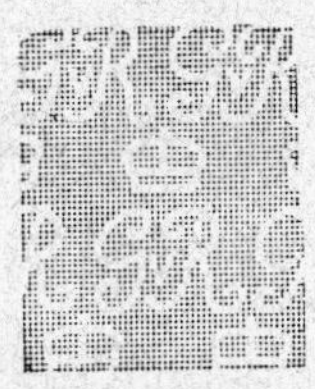
103 Multiple Cypher

Type differences

½d. In T **98** the ornament above "P" of "HALFPENNY" has two thin lines of colour and the beard is undefined. In T **101** the ornament has one thick line and the beard is well defined.

1d. In T **99** the body of the lion is unshaded and in T **102** it is shaded.

1912 (1 Jan). *Wmk Imperial Crown, W* **49.** *P* 15 × 14.

338	**101**	½d.	deep green	7·00	3·00
339		½d.	green	2·50	50
340		½d.	yellow-green	2·50	40
		a.	No cross on crown	60·00	12·00
341	**102**	1d.	bright scarlet	1·00	40
		a.	No cross on crown	45·00	12·00
		b.	Printed double, one albino ..	£125	
342		1d.	scarlet	1·00	35
343		1d.	aniline scarlet*	£120	55·00
		a.	No cross on crown	£750	

* Our prices for the aniline scarlet 1d. stamps, Nos. 333 and 343, are for specimens in which the colour is suffused on the surface of the stamp and shows through clearly on the back. Specimens without these characteristics but which show "aniline" reactions under the quartz lamp are relatively common.

1912 (Aug). *Wmk Royal Cypher ("Simple"), W* **100.** *P* 15 × 14.

344	**101**	½d.	green	3·00	60
		a.	No cross on crown	65·00	15·00
345	**102**	1d.	scarlet	1·50	40
		a.	No cross on crown	55·00	13·00

1912 (Sept–Oct). *Wmk Royal Cypher ("Multiple"), W* **103.** *P* 15 × 14.

346	**101**	½d.	green (Oct)	5·00	3·00
		a.	No cross on crown	65·00	20·00
		b.	Imperf	£110	
		c.	Wmk sideways	†	£800
		d.	Printed on gummed side	—	†
347		½d.	yellow-green	5·00	3·75
348		½d.	pale green	5·00	2·50
349	**102**	1d.	bright scarlet	6·50	4·00
350		1d.	scarlet	6·50	3·00
		a.	No cross on crown	70·00	16·00
		b.	Imperf	85·00	
		c.	Wmk sideways	£110	75·00
		d.	Wmk sideways. No cross on crown	£550	

104

105

106

No. 357a

No. 357ab

No. 357ac

107

108

Die I

Die II

Dies of 2d.

Die I.— Inner frame-line at top and sides close to solid of background. *Four* complete lines of shading between top of head and oval frame-line. These four lines do *not* extend to the oval itself. White line round "TWOPENCE" thin.

Die II.— Inner frame-line farther from solid of background. *Three* lines between top of head and extending to the oval. White line round "TWOPENCE" thicker.

(Des Bertram Mackennal (heads) and G. W. Eve (frames). Coinage head (½, 1½, 2, 3 and 4d.); large medal head (1d., 2½d.); intermediate medal head (5d. to 1s.); small medal head used for fiscal stamps. Dies eng J. A. C. Harrison)

(Typo by Harrison & Sons Ltd., except the 6d. printed by the Stamping Department of the Board of Inland Revenue, Somerset House. The latter also made printings of the following which can only be distinguished by the controls: ½d. B.13; 1½d. A.12; 2d. C.13; 2½d. A.12; 3d. A.12, B.13, C.13; 4d. B.13; 5d. B.13; 7d. C.13; 8d. C.13; 9d. agate B.13; 10d. C.13; 1s. C.13)

1912–24. *Wmk Royal Cypher, W* **100.** *P* 15 × 14.

351	**105**	½d.	green (1.13)	40	15
		a.	Doubly printed	£9500	
352		½d.	bright green	40	15
353		½d.	deep green	2·25	90
354		½d.	yellow-green	5·00	1·25
355		½d.	very yellow (Cyprus) green (1914)	£2500	
356		½d.	blue-green	32·00	12·00
357	**104**	1d.	bright scarlet (10.12)	25	15
		a.	"Q" for "O" (R.1/4) (Control E14)	£200	75·00
		ab.	"Q" for "O" (R.4/11) (Control T22)	£350	£100
		ac.	Reversed "Q" for "O" (R.15/9) (Control T22)	£400	£125
		ad.	Inverted "Q" for "O" (R.20/3) ..	£550	£150
		b.	*Tête-bêche* (pair)	—	†
358		1d.	vermilion	1·50	60
359		1d.	pale rose-red	6·00	40
360		1d.	carmine-red	7·00	2·25
361		1d.	scarlet-vermilion	70·00	20·00
		a.	Printed on back†	£200	†
362	**105**	1½d.	red-brown (10.12)	80	15
		a.	"PENCF" (R.15/12)	£225	90·00
		b.	Booklet pane. Four stamps plus two printed labels (2.24)	£225	
363		1½d.	chocolate-brown	1·00	35
		a.	Without wmk	£120	
364		1½d.	chestnut	1·25	25
		a.	"PENCF" (R.15/12)	£110	50·00
365		1½d.	yellow-brown	15·00	9·00
366	**106**	2d.	orange-yellow (Die I) (8.12) ..	3·00	1·50
367		2d.	reddish orange (Die I) (11.13) ..	1·00	35
368		2d.	orange (Die I)	90	35
369		2d.	bright orange (Die I)	1·10	55
370		2d.	orange (Die II) (9.21)	2·50	1·75
371	**104**	2½d.	cobalt-blue (10.12)	4·50	1·00
371*a*		2½d.	bright blue (1914)	4·00	1·00
372		2½d.	blue	4·00	1·00
373		2½d.	indigo-blue* (1920)	£900	£550
373*a*		2½d.	dull Prussian blue* (1921) ..	£600	£325
374	**106**	3d.	dull reddish violet (10.12) ..	7·00	1·00
375		3d.	violet	2·00	55
376		3d.	bluish violet (11.13)	2·50	90
377		3d.	pale violet	4·00	90
378		4d.	deep grey-green (1.13)	18·00	3·50
379		4d.	grey-green	4·50	60
380		4d.	pale grey-green	9·00	1·75
381	**107**	5d.	brown (6.13)	4·50	2·25
382		5d.	yellow-brown	4·50	2·25
		a.	Without wmk	£500	
383		5d.	bistre-brown	65·00	25·00
384		6d.	dull purple, **C** (8.13)	14·00	3·00
385		6d.	reddish purple, **C**	7·00	1·00
		a.	Perf 14 (10.20)	60·00	80·00
386		6d.	deep reddish purple, **C**	9·00	1·50
387		7d.	olive (8.13)	9·00	3·75
388		7d.	bronze-green (1915)	50·00	12·00
389		7d.	sage-green (1917)	25·00	6·00
390		8d.	black/*yellow* (8.13)	20·00	6·50
391		8d.	blk/*yell-buff* (*granite*) (5.17) ..	20·00	8·00
392	**108**	9d.	agate (6.13)	7·00	2·00
393		9d.	deep agate	12·00	2·75
393*a*		9d.	olive-green (9.22)	65·00	14·00
393*b*		9d.	pale olive-green	70·00	14·00
394		10d.	turquoise-blue (8.13)	13·00	11·00
394*a*		10d.	deep turquoise-blue	30·00	15·00
395		1s.	bistre (8.13)	7·50	75
396		1s.	bistre-brown	20·00	5·00
351/95			.. .. *Set of* 15	£130	38·00

Imperf stamps of this issue exist but may be war-time colour trials.

† The impression of No. 361a is set sideways and is very pale.

* No. 373 comes from Control O 20 and also exists on toned paper.

No. 373*a* comes from Control R 21 and also exists on toned paper, but both are unlike the rare Prussian blue shade of the 1935 2½d. Jubilee issue.

See also Nos. 418/29.

For the 2d., T **106** bisected, see note under Guernsey, War Occupation Issues.

1913 (Aug). *Wmk Royal Cypher ("Multiple"), W* **103**. *P* 15 × 14.

397	**105**	½d.	bright green	75·00	90·00
398	**104**	1d.	dull scarlet	£150	£130

Both these stamps were originally issued in rolls only. Subsequently sheets were found, so that horizontal pairs and blocks are known but are of considerable rarity.

109

A

110 Single Cypher

Major Re-entries on 2s. 6d.

Nos. 400a and 408a

No. 415b

(Des Bertram Mackennal. Dies eng J. A. C. Harrison. Recess)

High values, so-called "Sea Horses" design: T **109**. *Background around portrait consists of horizontal lines, Type* A. *Wmk Single Cypher, W* **110.** *P* 11 × 12.

1913 (30 June–Aug). *Printed by Waterlow Bros & Layton.*

399	2s. 6d.	deep sepia-brown	£175	65·00
400	2s. 6d.	sepia-brown	£175	60·00
	a.	Re-entry (R.2/1)	£900	£400
401	5s.	rose-carmine (4 July)	£300	£130
402	10s.	indigo-blue (1 Aug)	£500	£225
403	£1	green (1 Aug)	£1250	£600
404	£1	dull blue-green (1 Aug)	£1250	£650
★399/404		**For well-centred, lightly used**		+25%

1915 (Dec)–**18.** *Printed by De La Rue & Co.*

405	2s. 6d.	deep yellow-brown	£200	70·00
406	2s. 6d.	yellow-brown	£200	65·00
407	2s. 6d.	pale brown (worn plate)	£175	65·00
408	2s. 6d.	sepia (seal-brown)	£200	70·00
	a.	Re-entry (R.2/1)	£700	£400
409	5s.	bright carmine	£325	£140
410	5s.	pale carmine (worn plate)	£325	£140
411	10s.	deep blue	£1200	£300
412	10s.	blue	£950	£250
413	10s.	pale blue	£900	£250
★405/13		**For well-centred, lightly used**		+25%

1918 (Dec)–**19.** *Printed by Bradbury, Wilkinson & Co. Ltd.*

413*a*	2s. 6d.	olive-brown	70·00	25·00
414	2s. 6d.	chocolate-brown	90·00	30·00
415	2s. 6d.	reddish brown	95·00	30·00
415*a*	2s. 6d.	pale brown	80·00	25·00
	b.	Major re-entry (R.1/2)	£600	£250
416	5s.	rose-red (1.19)	£175	35·00
417	10s.	dull grey-blue (1.19)	£300	80·00
399/417		*Set of* 4	£1600	£575
★413*a*/17		**For well-centred, lightly used**		+25%

DISTINGUISHING PRINTINGS. Note that the £1 value was only printed by Waterlow.

Waterlow and De La Rue stamps measure exactly 22 mm vertically. In the De La Rue printings the gum is usually patchy and yellowish, and the colour of the stamp, particularly in the 5s., tends to show through the back. The holes of the perforation are smaller than those of the other two printers.

In the Bradbury Wilkinson printings the height of the stamp is 22¾ or 23 mm. On most of the 22¾ mm high stamps a minute coloured guide dot appears in the margin just above the middle of the upper frame-line.

For (1934) re-engraved Waterlow printings *see* Nos. 450/2.

111 Block Cypher 111*a*

The watermark Type **111***a*, as compared with Type **111**, differs as follows: Closer spacing of horizontal rows (12½ mm instead of 14½ mm). Letters shorter and rounder. Watermark thicker.

(Typo by Waterlow & Sons, Ltd (all values except 6d.) and later, 1934–35, by Harrison & Sons, Ltd (all values). Until 1934 the 6d. was printed at Somerset House where a printing of the 1½d. was also made in 1926 (identifiable only by control E.26). Printings by Harrisons in 1934–35 can be identified, when in mint condition, by the fact that the gum shows a streaky appearance vertically, the Waterlow gum being uniformly applied, but Harrisons also used up the balance of the Waterlow "smooth gum" paper)

1924 (Feb)–**26.** *Wmk Block Cypher, W* **111.** *P* 15 × 14.

418	**105**	½d.	green	15	15
		a.	Wmk sideways (5.24)	7·00	2·50
		b.	Doubly printed	£6500	
419	**104**	1d.	scarlet	25	25
		a.	Wmk sideways	16·00	10·00
		b.	Expermental paper, W **111***a* (10.24)	30·00	
		c.	Inverted "Q" for "O" (R.20/3)	£375	
420	**105**	1½d.	red-brown	20	20
		a.	*Tête-bêche* (pair)	£375	£500
		b.	Wmk sideways (8.24)	4·25	2·25
		c.	Printed on the gummed side	£425	†
		d.	Booklet pane. Four stamps plus two printed labels (6.24)	60·00	
		e.	Ditto. Wmk sideways	£2000	
		f.	Experimental paper. W **111***a* (10.24)	40·00	
		g.	Double impression	£4500	
421	**106**	2d.	orange (Die II) (9.24)	80	60
		a.	No wmk	£400	
		b.	Wmk sideways (7.26)	70·00	55·00
		c.	Doubly printed	£10000	
422	**104**	2½d.	blue (10.24)	4·50	90
		a.	No wmk	£550	
		b.	Wmk sideways	†	—
423	**106**	3d.	violet (10.24)	5·50	60
424		4d.	grey-green (11.24)	7·50	90
		a.	Printed on the gummed side	£1100	†
425	**107**	5d.	brown (11.24)	17·00	1·40
426		6d.	reddish purple, **C** (9.24)	5·00	1·50
426*a*		6d.	purple, **O** (6.26)	2·00	35
427	**108**	9d.	olive-green (12.24)	9·00	2·25
428		10d.	turquoise-blue (11.24)	24·00	16·00
429		1s.	bistre-brown (10.24)	16·00	75
418/29			*Set of* 12	75·00	20·00

There are numerous shades in this issue.

The 6d. on both chalky and ordinary papers was printed by both Somerset House and Harrisons. The Harrison printings have streaky gum, differ slightly in shade, and that on chalky paper is printed in a highly fugitive ink. The prices quoted are for the commonest (Harrison) printing in each case.

112

(Des H. Nelson. Eng J. A. C. Harrison. Recess Waterlow)

1924–25. *British Empire Exhibition. W* **111.** *P* 14.

(*a*) *Dated* "1924" (23.4.24)

430	**112**	1d.	scarlet	2·25	6·00
431		1½d.	brown	4·00	11·00

(*b*) *Dated* "1925" (9.5.25)

432	**112**	1d.	scarlet	7·50	15·00
433		1½d.	brown	23·00	50·00

113

114

115

B

117

(Des J. Farleigh (T **113** and **115**), E. Linzell (T **114**) and H. Nelson (T **116**). Eng C. G. Lewis (T **113**), T. E. Storey (T **115**), both at the Royal Mint; J. A. C. Harrison, of Waterlow (T **114** and **116**). Typo by Waterlow from plates made at the Royal Mint, except T **116**, recess by Bradbury, Wilkinson from die and plate of their own manufacture)

1929 (10 May). *Ninth U.P.U. Congress, London.*

(*a*) *W* **111.** *P* 15 × 14

434	**113**	½d.	green	50	90
		a.	Wmk sideways	45·00	32·00
435	**114**	1d.	scarlet	70	1·00
		a.	Wmk sideways	45·00	38·00
436		1½d.	purple-brown	60	90
		a.	Wmk sideways	22·00	21·00
		b.	Booklet pane. Four stamps plus two printed labels	£130	
437	**115**	2½d.	blue	5·00	9·00

(*b*) *W* **117.** *P* 12

438	**116**	£1	black	£650	£450
434/7			*Set of* 4 (*to* 2½*d.*)	6·00	11·00

123

PRINTERS. All subsequent issues were printed in photogravure by Harrison and Sons, Ltd, *except where otherwise stated.*

118

119

120

121

NINE PENCE
122

1934–36. *W* **111.** *P* 15 × 14.

439	**118**	½d.	green (19.11.34)	15	15
		a.	Wmk sideways	10·00	2·75
		b.	Imperf three sides	£750	
440	**119**	1d.	scarlet (24.9.34)	15	15
		a.	Imperf (pair)	£975	
		b.	Printed on the gummed side	£500	
		c.	Wmk sideways	10·00	3·25
		d.	Double impression	†	—
		e.	Imperf between (pair)	£1500	
		f.	Imperf three sides (pair)	£975	
441	**118**	1½d.	red-brown (20.8.34)	10	15
		a.	Imperf (pair)	£300	
		b.	Imperf three sides (lower stamp in vert pair)	£550	
		c.	Imperf between (horiz pair)		
		d.	Wmk sideways	6·00	2·00
		e.	Booklet pane. Four stamps plus two printed labels (1.35)	60·00	
442	**120**	2d.	orange (21.1.35)	30	30
		a.	Imperf (pair)	£1250	
		b.	Wmk sideways	60·00	35·00
443	**119**	2½d.	ultramarine (18.3.35)	1·10	60
444	**120**	3d.	violet (18.3.35)	1·00	50
445		4d.	deep grey-green (2.12.35)	1·50	55
446	**121**	5d.	yellow-brown (17.2.36)	5·00	1·50
447	**122**	9d.	deep olive-green (2.12.35)	9·00	1·60
448		10d.	turquoise-blue (24.2.36)	12·00	8·00
449		1s.	bistre-brown (24.2.36)	12·00	40
		a.	Double impression		
439/49			*Set of* 11	35·00	11·00

Owing to the need for wider space for the perforations the size of the designs of the ½d. and 2d. were once, and the 1d. and 1½d. twice reduced from that of the first printings.

There are also numerous minor variations, due to the photographic element in the process.

The ½d. imperf three sides, No. 439b, is known in a block of four, from a sheet, in which the bottom pair is imperf at top and sides.

For No. 442 bisected, see Guernsey, War Occupation Issues.

(Eng J. A. C. Harrison. Recess Waterlow)

1934 (Oct). *T* **109** *(re-engraved). Background around portrait consists of horizontal and diagonal lines, Type* B. *W* **110.** *P* 11 × 12.

450 **109** 2s. 6d. chocolate-brown .. .. .. 50·00 15·00
451 5s. bright rose-red .. .. £100 30·00
452 10s. indigo .. .. £200 40·00
450/2 .. .. *Set of* 3 £300 75·00

There are numerous other minor differences in the design of this issue.

(Des B. Freedman)

1935 (7 May). *Silver Jubilee. W* **111.** *P* 15 × 14.

453 **123** ½d. green 50 20
454 1d. scarlet 75 90
455 1½d. red-brown 50 20
456 2½d. blue .. .. 3·00 5·50
456*a* 2½d. Prussian blue £4000 £3750
453/6 .. .. *Set of* 4 4·25 6·00

The 1½d. and 2½d. values differ from T **123** in the emblem in the panel at right.

No. 456*a*, from three sheets printed with the wrong ink, was issued at a P.O. in Edmonton, North London.

KING EDWARD VIII
20 January–10 December 1936

Further detailed information on the stamps of King Edward VIII will be found in Volume 2 of the Stanley Gibbons *Great Britain Specialised Catalogue*.

124

125

(Des from photo by Hugh Cecil)

1936. *W* **125.** *P* 15 × 14.

457 **124** ½d. green (1.9.36) 20 15
a. Double impression .. ..
458 1d. scarlet (14.9.36) 50 20
459 1½d. red-brown (1.9.36) 25 15
a. Booklet pane. Four stamps plus two printed labels .. .. .. 35·00
460 2½d. bright blue (1.9.36) 25 50
457/60 .. .. *Set of* 4 90 85

KING GEORGE VI
11 December 1936–6 February 1952

Further detailed information on the stamps of King George VI will be found in Volume 2 of the Stanley Gibbons *Great Britain Specialised Catalogue*.

126 King George VI and Queen Elizabeth

(Des E. Dulac)

1937 (13 May). *Coronation. W* **127.** *P* 15 × 14.

461 **126** 1½d. maroon 40 25

127

128

129

130

King George VI and National Emblems

(Des T **128/9**, E. Dulac (head) and E. Gill (frames). T **130**, E. Dulac (whole stamp))

1937–47. *W* **127.** *P* 15 × 14.

462 **128** ½d. green (10.5.37) 10 15
a. Wmk sideways (1.38) 25 25
ab. Booklet pane of 4 .. .. .. 6·00
463 1d. scarlet (10.5.37) 10 15
a. Wmk sideways (2.38) .. .. .. 10·00 4·00
ab. Booklet pane of 4 .. .. .. 40·00
464 1½d. red-brown (30.7.37) 20 15
a. Wmk sideways (2.38) 90 70
b. Booklet pane. Four stamps plus two printed labels .. .. .. 35·00
c. Imperf three sides (pair) .. ..
465 **128** 2d. orange (31.1.38) .. .. .. 1·25 35
a. Wmk sideways (2.38) .. .. .. 60·00 25·00
b. Bisected (on cover) .. .. .. † 20·00
466 2½d. ultramarine (10.5.37) 25 15
a. Wmk sideways (6.40) .. .. .. 75·00 12·00
b. *Tête-bêche* (horiz pair) .. ..
467 3d. violet (31.1.38) .. .. .. 6·00 60
468 **129** 4d. grey-green (21.11.38) 35 30
a. Imperf (pair) £1200
b. Imperf three sides (pair) £1500
469 5d. brown (21.11.38) .. .. .. 2·50 35
a. Imperf (pair) £1250
b. Imperf three sides (pair) £1000
470 6d. purple (30.1.39) .. .. .. 1·75 25
471 **130** 7d. emerald-green (27.2.39) .. .. 4·50 35
a. Imperf three sides (pair) £1000
472 8d. bright carmine (27.2.39) .. .. 5·00 40
473 9d. deep olive-green (1.5.39) .. .. 6·50 40
474 10d. turquoise-blue (1.5.39) .. .. 5·00 45
aa. Imperf (pair) £2000
474*a* 11d. plum (29.12.47) .. .. .. 3·00 1·25
475 1s. bistre-brown (1.5.39) .. .. .. 5·00 25
462/75 .. .. *Set of* 15 38·00 5·00

For later printings of the lower values in apparently lighter shades and different colours, see Nos. 485/90 and 503/8.

No. 465b was authorised for use in Guernsey. See notes on War Occupation Issues.

131 King George VI

132 King George VI

133

(Des E. Dulac (T **131**) and Hon. G. R. Bellew (T **132**). Eng J. A. C. Harrison. Recess Waterlow)

1939–48. *W* **133.** *P* 14.

476 **131** 2s. 6d. brown (4.9.39) .. .. .. 45·00 9·00
476*a* 2s. 6d. yellow-green (9.3.42) .. .. 15·00 90
477 5s. red (21.8.39) .. .. .. 20·00 1·25
478 **132** 10s. dark blue (30.10.39) .. .. .. £175 18·00
478*a* 10s. ultramarine (30.11.42) .. .. 50·00 4·00
478*b* £1 brown (1.10.48) .. .. .. 25·00 22·00
476/8*b* .. .. *Set of* 6 £300 48·00

134 Queen Victoria and King George VI.

(Des H. L. Palmer)

1940 (6 May). *Centenary of First Adhesive Postage Stamps. W* **127.** *P* 14½ × 14.

479 **134** ½d. green 30 20
480 1d. scarlet 40 40
481 1½d. red-brown 30 30
482 2d. orange 50 40
a. Bisected (on cover) .. .. .. † 16·00
483 2½d. ultramarine .. .. 1·90 80
484 3d. violet .. .. 4·50 4·00
479/84 .. .. *Set of* 6 7·00 5·50

No. 482a was authorised for use in Guernsey. See notes on War Occupation Issues.

1941–42. *Head as Nos.* 462/7, *but lighter background. W* **127.** *P* 15 × 14.

485 **128** ½d. pale green (1.9.41) 15 10
a. *Tête-bêche* (horiz pair) £2500
b. Imperf (pair) £1200
486 1d. pale scarlet (11.8.41) 15 10
a. Wmk sideways (10.42) .. .. .. 4·50 6·00
b. Imperf (pair) £1250
c. Imperf three sides (pair) £1000
d. Imperf between (vert pair) .. ..
487 1½d. pale red-brown (28.9.42) 65 35
488 2d. pale orange (6.10.41) 50 25
a. Wmk sideways (6.42) .. .. .. 17·00 15·00
b. *Tête-bêche* (horiz pair) .. ..
c. Imperf (pair) £1500
d. Imperf pane* .. .. ..
489 2½d. light ultramarine (21.7.41) 15 10
a. Wmk sideways (8.42) .. .. .. 14·00 10·00
b. *Tête-bêche* (horiz pair) £1300
c. Imperf (pair) £2000
d. Imperf pane* £2500
490 3d. pale violet (3.11.41) .. .. .. 1·60 30
485/90 .. .. *Set of* 6 2·75 1·10

The *tête-bêche* varieties are from defectively made-up stamp booklets.

*BOOKLET ERRORS. Those listed as "imperf panes" show one row of perforations either at the top or at the bottom of the pane of 6.

WATERMARK VARIETIES. Please note that *inverted watermarks* are outside the scope of this Catalogue but are fully listed in the *Great Britain Specialised Catalogue*. See also the notes about watermarks at the beginning of the King George V section.

135

136 Symbols of Peace and Reconstruction

(Des H. L. Palmer (T **135**) and R. Stone (T **136**))

1946 (11 June). *Victory. W* **127.** *P* 15 × 14.

491 **135** 2½d. ultramarine 20 15
492 **136** 3d. violet 20 10

137

138 King George VI and Queen Elizabeth

(Des G. Knipe and Joan Hassall from photographs by Dorothy Wilding)

1948 (26 Apr). *Royal Silver Wedding. W* **127.** *P* 15 × 14 (2½*d.*) *or* 14 × 15 (£1).

493 **137** 2½d. ultramarine 20 20
494 **138** £1 blue .. .. 40·00 35·00

1948 (10 May). Stamps of 1d. and 2½d. showing seaweed-gathering were on sale at eight Head Post Offices in Great Britain, but were primarily for use in the Channel Islands and are listed there (see after Great Britain Postal Fiscals).

139 Globe and Laurel Wreath

140 "Speed"

141 Olympic Symbol

142 Winged Victory

(Des P. Metcalfe, A. Games, S. D. Scott and E. Dulac)

1948 (29 July). *Olympic Games. W* **127.** *P* 15 × 14.

495 **139** 2½d. ultramarine 10 10
496 **140** 3d. violet 30 20
497 **141** 6d. bright purple 50 20
498 **142** 1s. brown .. .. 1·60 1·25
495/8 .. .. *Set of* 4 2·25 1·50

143 Two Hemispheres

144 U.P.U. Monument, Berne

145 Goddess Concordia, Globe and Points of Compass

146 Posthorn and Globe

(Des Mary Adshead (T **143**), P. Metcalfe (T **144**), H. Fleury (T **145**) and Hon. G. R. Bellew (T **146**))

1949 (10 Oct). *75th Anniv of Universal Postal Union. W* **127.** *P* 15 × 14.

499	**143**	2½d. ultramarine	10	10
500	**144**	3d. violet	30	30
501	**145**	6d. bright purple	55	55
502	**146**	1s. brown	1·60	1·40
499/502 ..		.. .. .. *Set of* 4	2·25	2·00

1950–52. *4d. as Nos.* 468 *and others as Nos.* 485/9, *but colours changed.*

503	**128**	½d. pale orange (3.5.51)	10	15
		a. Imperf (pair)		
		b. *Tête-bêche* (horiz pair)	£2000	
		c. Imperf pane*		
504		1d. light ultramarine (3.5.51)	10	15
		a. Wmk sideways (5.51)	40	45
		b. Imperf (pair)	£1100	
		c. Imperf three sides (pair)	£1000	
		d. Booklet pane. Three stamps plus three printed labels (3.52) ..	14·00	
		e. Ditto. Partial *tête-bêche* pane ..	£1750	
505		1½d. pale green (3.5.51)	25	30
		a. Wmk sideways (9.51)	2·00	2·50
506		2d. pale red-brown (3.5.51)	25	20
		a. Wmk sideways (5.51)	80	1·10
		b. *Tête-bêche* (horiz pair)	£2000	
		c. Imperf three sides (pair)	£800	
507		2½d. pale scarlet (3.5.51)	20	15
		a. Wmk sideways (5.51)	80	90
		b. *Tête-bêche* (horiz pair)		
508	**129**	4d. light ultramarine (2.10.50) ..	1·40	1·10
		a. Double impression		
503/8 ..		.. .. .. *Set of* 6	2·00	1·75

*BOOKLET ERRORS. Those listed as "imperf panes" show one row of perforations either at the top or at the bottom of the pane of 6.

147 H.M.S. *Victory*

148 White Cliffs of Dover

149 St. George and the Dragon

150 Royal Coat of Arms

(Des Mary Adshead (T **147/8**), P. Metcalfe (T **149/50**). Recess Waterlow)

1951 (3 May). *W* **133.** *P* 11 × 12.

509	**147**	2s. 6d. yellow-green	12·00	75
510	**148**	5s. red	30·00	1·50
511	**149**	10s. ultramarine	20·00	6·00
512	**150**	£1 brown	38·00	16·00
509/12 ..		.. .. .. *Set of* 4	90·00	20·00

151 "Commerce and Prosperity"

152 Festival Symbol

(Des E. Dulac (T **151**), A. Games (T **152**))

1951 (3 May). *Festival of Britain. W* **127.** *P* 15 × 14.

513	**151**	2½d. scarlet	20	10
514	**152**	4d. ultramarine	40	35

QUEEN ELIZABETH II
6 February 1952

Further detailed information on the stamps of Queen Elizabeth II will be found in volumes 3, 4 and 5 of the Stanley Gibbons *Great Britain Specialised Catalogue.*

USED PRICES. For Nos. 515 onwards the used prices quoted are for examples with circular dated postmarks.

153 Tudor Crown

154

155

156

157

158

159

160

Queen Elizabeth II and National Emblems

I II

Types of 2½d. Type I:—In the frontal cross of the diadem, the top line is only half the width of the cross.

Type II:—The top line extends to the full width of the cross and there are signs of strengthening in other parts of the diadem.

(Des Enid Marx (T **154**), M. Farrar-Bell (T **155/6**), G. Knipe (T **157**), Mary Adshead (T **158**), E. Dulac (T **159/60**). Portrait by Dorothy Wilding)

1952–54. *W* **153.** *P* 15 × 14.

515	**154**	½d. orange-red (31.8.53)	10	15
516		1d. ultramarine (31.8.53)	20	20
		a. Booklet pane. Three stamps plus three printed labels	25·00	
517		1½d. green (5.12.52)	10	15
		a. Wmk sideways (15.10.54) ..	35	60
		b. Imperf pane*		
518		2d. red-brown (31.8.53)	20	15
		a. Wmk sideways (8.10.54)	80	1·25
519	**155**	2½d. carmine-red (Type I) (5.12.52) ..	10	15
		a. Wmk sideways (15.11.54) ..	10·00	7·50
		b. Type II (Booklets) (5.53)	80	60
520		3d. deep lilac (18.1.54)	1·00	30
521	**156**	4d. ultramarine (2.11.53)	2·50	80
522	**157**	5d. brown (6.7.53)	90	2·00
523		6d. reddish purple (18.1.54)	2·50	60
		a. Imperf three sides (pair)		
524		7d. bright green (18.1.54)	10·00	3·50
525	**158**	8d. magenta (6.7.53)	90	60
526		9d. bronze-green (8.2.54)	16·00	3·00
527		10d. Prussian blue (8.2.54)	12·00	3·00
528		11d. brown-purple (8.2.54)	30·00	16·00
529	**159**	1s. bistre-brown (6.7.53)	90	40
530	**160**	1s. 3d. green (2.11.53)	5·00	2·00
531	**159**	1s. 6d. grey-blue (2.11.53)	11·00	2·25
515/31		.. .. *Set of* 17	95·00	28·00

See also Nos. 540/56, 561/6, 570/94 and 599/618*a*.

*BOOKLET ERRORS.—This pane of 6 stamps is *completely* imperf (see No. 540*a*, etc.).

161

162

163

164

(Des E. Fuller (2½d.), M. Goaman (4d.), E. Dulac (1s. 3d.), M. Farrar-Bell (1s. 6d.), Portrait (except 1s. 3d.) by Dorothy Wilding)

1953 (3 June). *Coronation. W* **153.** *P* 15 × 14.

532	**161**	2½d. carmine-red	10	10
533	**162**	4d. ultramarine	30	70
534	**163**	1s. 3d. deep yellow-green	5·00	4·00
535	**164**	1s. 6d. deep grey-blue	8·00	7·00
532/5 ..		.. .. *Set of* 4	12·00	10·00

165 St. Edward's Crown

166 Carrickfergus Castle

167 Caernarvon Castle

168 Edinburgh Castle

169 Windsor Castle

(Des L. Lamb. Portrait by Dorothy Wilding. Recess Waterlow (until 31.12.57) and De La Rue (subsequently))

1955–58. *W* **165.** *P* 11 × 12.

536	**166**	2s. 6d. black-brown (23.9.55) ..	8·00	1·50
		a. De La Rue printing (17.7.58) ..	28·00	2·25
537	**167**	5s. rose-carmine (23.9.55)	40·00	3·00
		a. De La Rue printing (30.4.58) ..	85·00	6·00
538	**168**	10s. ultramarine (1.9.55)	£100	10·00
		a. De La Rue printing. *Dull ultramarine* (25.4.58)	£160	15·00
539	**169**	£1 black (1.9.55)	£160	25·00
		a. De La Rue printing (28.4.58) ..	£325	45·00
536/9 ..		.. .. .. *Set of* 4	£275	35·00
536a/9a ..		.. .. .. *Set of* 4	£550	60·00

See also Nos. 595/8a and 759/62.

On 1 January 1958, the contract for printing the high values, T **166** to **169** was transferred to De La Rue & Co, Ltd.

The work of the two printers is very similar, but the following notes will be helpful to those attempting to identify Waterlow and De La Rue stamps of the W **165** issue.

The De La Rue sheets are printed in pairs and have a ⊣ or ⊢ shaped guide-mark at the centre of one side-margin, opposite the middle row of perforations, indicating left- and right-hand sheets respectively.

The Waterlow sheets have a small circle (sometimes crossed) instead of a "⊢" and this is present in both side-margins opposite the 6th row of stamps, though one is sometimes trimmed off. Short dashes are also present in the perforation gutter between the marginal stamps marking the middle of the four sides and a cross is at the centre of the sheet. The four corners of the sheet have two lines forming a right-angle as trimming marks, but some are usually trimmed off. All these gutter marks and sheet-trimming marks are absent in the De La Rue printings.

De La Rue used the Waterlow die and no alterations were made to it, so that no difference exists in the design or its size, but the making of new plates at first resulted in slight but measurable variations in the width of the gutters between stamps, particularly the horizontal, as follows:

	W.	D.L.R.
Horiz gutters, mm	3.8 to 4.0	3.4 to 3.8

Later D.L.R. plates were however less distinguishable in this respect.

For a short time in 1959 the D.L.R. 2s. 6d. appeared with one dot in the bottom margin below the first stamp.

It is possible to sort singles with reasonable certainty by general characteristics. The individual lines of the D.L.R. impression are cleaner and devoid of the whiskers of colour of Waterlow's, and the whole impression lighter and softer.

Owing to the closer setting of the horizontal rows the strokes of the perforating comb are closer; this results in the topmost tooth on each side of De La Rue stamps being narrower than the corresponding teeth in Waterlow's which were more than normally broad.

Shades also help. The 2s. 6d. D.L.R. is a warmer, more chocolate shade than the blackish brown of W.; the 5s. a lighter red with less carmine than W's; the 10s. more blue and less ultramarine; the £1 less intense black.

The paper of D.L.R. printings is uniformly white, identical with that of W. printings from February 1957 onwards, but earlier W. printings are on paper which is creamy by comparison.

In this and later issues of T **166/9** the dates of issue given for changes of watermark or paper are those on which supplies were first sent by the Supplies Department to Postmasters.

1955–58. *W* **165**. *P* 15 × 14.

No.	Type	Description	Unused	Used
540	**154**	½d. orange-red (booklets 8.55, sheets 12.12.55)	10	15
		a. Part perf pane*	£800	
541		1d. ultramarine (19.9.55)	25	15
		a. Booklet pane. Three stamps plus three printed labels	11·00	
		b. *Tête-bêche* (horiz pair)	£500	
542		1½d. green (booklets 8.55, sheets 11.10.55)	10	15
		a. Wmk sideways (7.3.56)	15	75
		b. *Tête-bêche* (horiz pair)	£900	
543		2d. red-brown (6.9.55)	20	20
		aa. Imperf between (vert pair)	£1500	
		a. Wmk sideways (31.7.56)	20	60
		ab. Imperf between (wmk sideways) (horiz pair)	£1500	
543*b*		2d. light red-brown (17.10.56)	20	15
		ba. *Tête-bêche* (horiz pair)	£600	
		bb. Imperf pane*	£800	
		bc. Part perf pane*	£850	
		d. Wmk sideways (5.3.57)	9·00	5·50
544	**155**	2½d. carmine-red (Type I) (28.9.55)	15	15
		a. Wmk sideways (Type I) (23.3.56)	1·25	1·10
		b. Type II (booklets 9.55, sheets 1957)	20	40
		ba. *Tête-bêche* (horiz pair)	£750	
		bb. Imperf pane*	£900	
		bc. Part perf pane*	£750	
545		3d. deep lilac (17.7.56)	20	15
		aa. *Tête-bêche* (horiz pair)	£750	
		a. Imperf three sides (pair)	£500	
		b. Wmk sideways (22.11.57)	8·00	10·00
546	**156**	4d. ultramarine (14.11.55)	1·25	40
547	**157**	5d. brown (21.9.55)	5·50	2·75
548		6d. reddish purple (20.12.55)	5·00	75
		aa. Imperf three sides (pair)	£400	
		a. *Deep claret* (8.5.58)	2·50	80
		ab. Imperf three sides (pair)	£450	
549		7d. bright green (23.4.56)	38·00	7·50
550	**158**	8d. magenta (21.12.55)	6·50	1·00
551		9d. bronze-green (15.12.55)	12·00	1·50
552		10d. Prussian blue (22.9.55)	12·00	1·50
553		11d. brown-purple (28.10.55)	40	1·00
554	**159**	1s. bistre-brown (3.11.55)	11·00	40
555	**160**	1s. 3d. green (27.3.56)	15·00	1·25
556	**159**	1s. 6d. grey-blue (27.3.56)	20·00	1·00
540/56		*Set of* 18	£110	18·00

The dates given for Nos. 540/556 are those on which they were first issued by the Supplies Dept to postmasters.

In December 1956 a completely imperforate sheet of No. 543*b* was noticed by clerks in a Kent post office, one of whom purchased it against P.O. regulations. In view of this irregularity we do not consider it properly issued.

Types of 2½d. In this issue, in 1957, Type II formerly only found in stamps from booklets, began to replace Type I on sheet stamps.

*BOOKLET ERRORS. Those listed as "imperf panes" show one row of perforations either at top or bottom of the booklet pane; those as "part perf panes" have one row of 3 stamps imperf on three sides.

170 Scout Badge and "Rolling Hitch"

171 "Scouts coming to Britain"

172 Globe within a Compass

(Des Mary Adshead (2½d.), P. Keely (4d.), W. H. Brown (1s. 3d.))

1957 (1 Aug). *World Scout Jubilee Jamboree. W* **165**. *P* 15 × 14.

No.	Type	Description	Unused	Used
557	**170**	2½d. carmine-red	15	10
558	**171**	4d. ultramarine	50	40
559	**172**	1s. 3d. green	6·00	5·00
557/9		*Set of* 3	6·00	5·00

173

½d. to 1½d., 2½d., 3d. 2d.

Graphite-line arrangements (Stamps viewed from back)

1957 (12 Sept). *46th Inter-Parliamentary Union Conference. W* **165**. *P* 15 × 14.

No.	Type	Description	Unused	Used
560	**173**	4d. ultramarine	1·10	1·10

GRAPHITE-LINED ISSUES. These were used in connection with automatic sorting machinery, first introduced experimentally at Southampton in December 1957.

The graphite lines were printed in black on the back, beneath the gum; two lines per stamp, except for the 2d.

In November 1959 phosphor bands were introduced (see notes after No. 598).

1957 (19 Nov). *Graphite-lined issue. Two graphite lines on the back, except 2d. value, which has one line. W* **165**. *P* 15 × 14.

No.	Type	Description	Unused	Used
561	**154**	½d. orange-red	20	30
562		1d. ultramarine	20	35
563		1½d. green	40	1·25
		a. Both lines at left	£750	£350
564		2d. light red-brown	3·00	1·50
		a. Line at left	£500	£175
565	**155**	2½d. carmine-red (Type II)	7·00	8·00
566		3d. deep lilac	50	50
561/6		*Set of* 6	10·00	11·00

No. 564a results from a misplacement of the line and horizontal pairs exist showing one stamp without line. No. 563a results from a similar misplacement.

See also Nos. 587/94.

176 Welsh Dragon

177 Flag and Games Emblem

178 Welsh Dragon

(Des R. Stone (3d.), W. H. Brown (6d.), P. Keely (1s. 3d.))

1958 (18 July). *Sixth British Empire and Commonwealth Games, Cardiff. W* **165**. *P* 15 × 14.

No.	Type	Description	Unused	Used
567	**176**	3d. deep lilac	15	10
568	**177**	6d. reddish purple	25	20
569	**178**	1s. 3d. green	2·75	2·00
567/9		*Set of* 3	2·75	2·10

179 Multiple Crowns

1958–65. *W* **179**. *P* 15 × 14.

No.	Type	Description	Unused	Used
570	**154**	½d. orange-red (25.11.58)	10	10
		a. Wmk sideways (26.5.61)	10	15
		c. Part perf pane*	£800	
		k. Chalky paper (15.7.63)	2·00	2·25
		l. Booklet pane. No. 570k × 3 *se-tenant* with 574k	6·00	
		m. Booklet pane. No. 570a × 2 *se-tenant* with 574l × 2 (1.7.64)	1·25	
571		1d. ultramarine (booklets 11.58, sheets 24.3.59)	10	10
		aa. Imperf (vert pair from coil)	£900	
		a. Wmk sideways (26.5.61)	60	40
		b. Part perf pane*	£700	
		c. Imperf pane	£1100	
		l. Booklet pane. No. 571a × 2 *se-tenant* with 575a × 2 (16.8.65)	4·50	
572		1½d. green (booklets 12.58, sheets 30.8.60)	10	15
		a. Imperf three sides (horiz strip of 3)	£1200	
		b. Wmk sideways (26.5.61)	8·00	3·00
573		2d. light red-brown (4.12.58)	10	10
		a. Wmk sideways (3.4.59)	25	65
574	**155**	2½d. carmine-red (Type II) (booklets 11.58, sheets 15.9.59)	10	10
		aa. Imperf strip of 3	£225	
		ab. *Tête-bêche* (horiz pr)	£600	
		ac. Imperf pane	£1100	
		a. Wmk sideways (Type I) (10.11.60)	20	30
		b. Type I (wmk upright) (4.10.61)	15	35
		ba. Imperf strip of 6		
		k. Type II. Chalky paper (15.7.63)	20	45
		l. Wmk sideways (Type II) Ord paper (1.7.64)	40	75
575		3d. deep lilac (booklets 11.58, sheets 8.12.58)	10	10
		a. Wmk sideways (24.10.58)	15	25
		b. Imperf pane*	£850	
		c. Part perf pane*	£750	
		d. Phantom "R" (Cyl 41 no dot)	£250	
		e. Phantom "R" (Cyl 37 no dot)	25·00	
576	**156**	4d. ultramarine (29.10.58)	50	20
		a. Deep ultramarine†† (28.4.65)	15	10
		ab. Wmk sideways (31.5.65)	45	35
		ac. Imperf pane*	£950	
		ad. Part perf pane*	£650	
577		4½d. chestnut (9.2.59)	10	15
578	**157**	5d. brown (10.11.58)	20	20
579		6d. deep claret (23.12.58)	15	15
		a. Imperf three sides (pair)	£450	
		b. Imperf (pair)	£550	
580		7d. bright green (26.11.58)	30	20
581	**158**	8d. magenta (24.2.60)	45	15
582		9d. bronze-green (24.3.59)	35	15
583		10d. Prussian blue (18.11.58)	90	15
584	**159**	1s. bistre-brown (30.10.58)	30	15
585	**160**	1s. 3d. green (17.6.59)	25	15
586	**159**	1s. 6d. grey-blue (16.12.58)	4·00	40
570/86		*Set of* 17	6·00	2·10

*BOOKLET ERRORS. See note after No. 556.

†Booklet pane No. 571l comes in two forms, with the 1d. stamps on the left or on the right.

††This "shade" was brought about by making more deeply etched cylinders, resulting in apparent depth of colour in parts of the design. There is no difference in the colour of the ink.

Sideways watermark. The 2d., 2½d., 3d. and 4d. come from coils and the ½d., 1d., 1½d., 2½d., 3d. and 4d. come from booklets. In *coil* stamps the sideways watermark shows the top of the watermark to the left. In the *booklet* stamps it comes equally to the left or right.

Nos. 570k and 574k only come from 2s. "Holiday Resort" Experimental undated booklets issued in 1963, in which one page contained 1 × 2½d. *se-tenant* with 3 × ½d. (*See* No. 570l).

No. 574l comes from coils, and the "Holiday Resort" Experimental booklets dated "1964" comprising four panes each containing two of these 2½d. stamps *se-tenant* vertically with two ½d. No. 570a. (*See* No. 570m.)

2½d. imperf. No. 574aa comes from a booklet with watermark upright. No. 574ba is from a coil with sideways watermark.

No. 574b comes from *sheets* bearing cylinder number 42 and is also known on vertical delivery coils.

Nos. 575d and 615a occurred below the last stamp of the sheet from Cyl 41 (no dot), where an incomplete marginal rule revealed an "R". The cylinder was later twice retouched. The stamps listed show the original, unretouched "R". The rare variety, No. 575d, is best collected in a block of 4 or 6 with full margins in order to be sure that it is not No. 615a with phosphor lines removed.

No. 575e is a similar variety but from Cyl. 37 (no dot). The marginal rule is much narrower and only a very small part of the "R" is revealed. The cylinder was later retouched. The listed variety is for the original, unretouched state.

WHITER PAPER. On 18 May 1962 the Post Office announced that a whiter paper was being used for the current issue (including Nos. 595/8). This is beyond the scope of this catalogue, but the whiter papers are listed in Vol. 3 of the Stanley Gibbons *Great Britain Specialised Catalogue*.

1958 (24 Nov)–**61.** *Graphite-lined issue. Two graphite lines on the back, except 2d. value, which has one line. W* **179**. *P* 15 × 14.

No.	Type	Description	Unused	Used
587	**154**	½d. orange-red (15.6.59)	2·50	3·00
588		1d. ultramarine (18.12.58)	90	1·25
		a. Misplaced graphite lines (7.61)*	60	90
589		1½d. green (4.8.59)†	30·00	30·00
590		2d. light red-brown (24.11.58)	7·00	4·00
591	**155**	2½d. carmine-red (Type II) (9.6.59)	10·00	10·00
592		3d. deep lilac (24.11.58)	40	40
		a. Misplaced graphite lines (5.61)*	£375	£350
593	**156**	4d. ultramarine (29.4.59)	4·00	4·50
		a. Misplaced graphite lines (1961)*	£1400	
594		4½d. chestnut (3.6.59)	4·00	4·00
587/94		*Set of* 8	55·00	45·00

Nos. 587/9 were only issued in booklets or coils (587/8).

*No. 588a (in coils), and Nos. 592a and 593a (both in sheets) result from the use of a residual stock of graphite-lined paper. As the use of graphite lines had ceased, the register of the lines in relation to the stamps was of no importance and numerous misplacements occurred—two lines close together, one line only, etc. No. 588a refers to two lines at left or at right; No. 592a refers to stamps with two lines only at left and both clear of the perforations and No. 593a to stamps with two lines at left (with left line down perforations) and traces of a third line down the opposite perforations.

†The prices quoted are for stamps with the watermark inverted. (*Prices for upright watermark £85 un, £60 us.*)

(Recess D.L.R. (until 31.12.62), then B.W.)

1959–68. *W* **179.** *P* 11 × 12.

No.	Type	Value	Description	Unused	Used
595	**166**	2s.	6d. black-brown (22.7.59) ..	18·00	75
		a.	B.W. printing (1.7.63)	40	30
		k.	Chalk-surfaced paper (30.5.68) ..	40	1·10
596	**167**	5s.	scarlet-vermilion (15.6.59) ..	55·00	2·00
		a.	B.W. ptg. *Red* (*shades*) (3.9.63) ..	1·00	60
		ab.	Printed on the gummed side ..	£750	
597	**168**	10s.	blue (21.7.59)	40·00	5·00
		a.	B.W. ptg. *Bright ultram* (16.10.63)	2·25	3·00
598	**169**	£1	black (23.6.59)	£110	12·00
		a.	B.W. printing (14.11.63)	9·50	5·00
595/8			.. .. *Set of* 4	£200	17·00
595a/8a			.. .. *Set of* 4	12·00	8·00

The B.W. printings have a marginal Plate Number. They are generally more deeply engraved than the D.L.R., showing more of the Diadem detail and heavier lines on Her Majesty's face. The vertical perf is 11.9 to 12 as against D.L.R. 11.8.

See also Nos. 759/62.

PHOSPHOR BAND ISSUES. These are printed on the front and are wider than graphite lines. They are not easy to see but show as broad vertical bands at certain angles to the light.

Values representing the rate for printed papers (and when this was abolished in 1968 for second class mail) have one band and others two, three or four bands as stated, according to the size and format.

In the small size stamps the bands are on each side with the single band at left (*except where otherwise stated*). In the large-size commemorative stamps the single band may be at left, centre or right, varying in different designs. The bands are vertical on both horizontal and vertical designs *except where otherwise stated*.

The phosphor was originally applied typographically but later usually by photogravure and sometimes using flexography, a typographical process using rubber cylinders.

Three different types of phosphor have been used, distinguishable by the colour emitted under an ultra-violet lamp, the first being green, then blue and now violet. Different sized bands are also known. All these are fully listed in Vol. 3 of the Stanley Gibbons *Great Britain Specialised Catalogue*.

Varieties. Misplaced and missing phosphor bands are known but such varieties are beyond the scope of this Catalogue.

1959 (18 Nov). *Phosphor-Graphite issue. Two phosphor bands on front and two graphite lines on back, except 2d. value, which has one band on front and one line on back. P* 15 × 14. (*a*) *W* **165.**

No.	Type	Value	Description	Unused	Used
599	**154**	½d.	orange-red	3·50	5·00
600		1d.	ultramarine	3·50	4·50
601		1½d.	green	3·50	4·50
			(*b*) W **179**		
605	**154**	2d.	light red-brown (1 band)	5·00	4·50
		a.	Error. W **165**	£190	£150
606	**155**	2½d.	carmine-red (Type II)	15·00	11·00
607		3d.	deep lilac	11·00	7·50
608	**156**	4d.	ultramarine	12·00	27·00
609		4½d.	chestnut	30·00	18·00
599/609			.. .. *Set of* 8	75·00	75·00

1960 (22 June)–**67.** *Phosphor issue. Two phosphor bands on front, except where otherwise stated. W* **179.** *P* 15 × 14.

No.	Type	Value	Description	Unused	Used
610	**154**	½d.	orange-red	10	15
		a.	Wmk sideways (26.5.61)	9·00	8·00
611		1d.	ultramarine	10	10
		a.	Wmk sideways (14.7.61)	35	40
		l.	Booklet pane. No. 611a × 2 *se-tenant* with 615d × 2† (16.8.65) ..	7·50	
		m.	Booklet pane. No. 611a × 2 *se-tenant* with 615b × 2†† (11.67) ..	3·50	
612		1½d.	green	10	20
		a.	Wmk sideways (14.7.61)	9·00	9·00
613		2d.	light red-brown (1 band)	22·00	20·00
613*a*		2d.	lt red-brown (two bands) (4.10.61)	10	10
		aa.	Imperf three sides***		
		ab.	Wmk sideways (6.4.67)	12	60
614	**155**	2½d.	carmine-red (Type II) (2 bands)*	10	40
614*a*		2½d.	carmine-red (Type II) (1 band) (4.10.61)	40	75
614*b*		2½d.	carmine-red (Type I) (1 band) (7.11.61)	35·00	27·00
615		3d.	deep lilac (2 bands)	60	45
		a.	Phantom "R" (Cyl 41 no dot) ..	20·00	
		b.	Wmk sideways (14.7.61)	1·25	90
615*c*		3d.	deep lilac (1 side band) (29.4.65)	35	60
		d.	Wmk sideways (16.8.65)	4·50	3·50
		e.	One centre band (8.12.66) ..	25	40
		ea.	Wmk sideways (19.6.67)	25	60
616	**156**	4d.	ultramarine	3·00	2·50
		a.	*Deep ultramarine* (28.4.65) ..	15	15
		aa.	Part perf pane**	£650	
		ab.	Wmk sideways (16.8.65)	15	25
616*b*		4½d.	chestnut (13.9.61)	15	25
616*c*	**157**	5d.	brown (9.6.67)	20	25
617		6d.	deep claret (27.6.60)	40	20
617*a*		7d.	bright green (15.2.67)	60	25
617*b*	**158**	8d.	magenta (28.6.67)	20	25
617*c*		9d.	bronze-green (29.12.66)	60	25
617*d*		10d.	Prussian blue (30.12.66)	80	35
617*e*	**159**	1s.	bistre-brown (28.6.67)	40	20
618	**160**	1s.	3d. green	2·00	2·50
618*a*	**159**	1s.	6d. grey-blue (12.12.66)	1·60	1·00
610/618*a*			.. .. *Set of* 17	7·00	6·00

The automatic facing equipment was brought into use on 6 July 1960 but the phosphor stamps may have been released a few days earlier.

The stamps with watermark sideways are from booklets except Nos. 613ab and 615ea which are from coils. No. 616ab comes from both booklets and coils.

No. 615a. See footnote after No. 586.

*No. 614 with two bands on the creamy paper was originally from cylinder 50 dot and no dot. When the change in postal rates took place in 1965 it was reissued from cylinder 57 dot and no dot on the whiter paper. Some of these latter were also released in error in districts of S.E. London in September 1964. The shade of the reissue is slightly more carmine.

**Booklet error. Two stamps at bottom left imperf on three sides and the third imperf on two sides.

***This comes from the bottom row of a sheet which is imperf at bottom and both sides.

†Booklet pane No. 611l comes in two forms, with the 1d. stamps on the left or on the right. This was printed in this manner to provide for 3d. stamps with only one band.

††Booklet pane No. 611m comes from 2s. booklets of January and March 1968. The two bands on the 3d. stamp thus created are intentional because of the technical difficulty of producing a single band on one stamp *se-tenant* with a two-banded stamp, as this requires perfect registration of the bands.

Unlike previous one-banded phosphor stamps, No. 615c has a broad band extending over two stamps so that alternate stamps have the band at left or right (same prices either way).

180 Postboy of 1660

181 Posthorn of 1660

(Des R. Stone (3d.), Faith Jaques (1s. 3d.))

1960 (7 July). *Tercentenary of Establishment of General Letter Office. W* **179** (*sideways on* 1*s.* 3*d.*). *P* 15 × 14 (3*d.*) *or* 14 × 15 (1*s.* 3*d.*).

No.	Type	Value	Description	Unused	Used
619	**180**	3d.	deep lilac	20	10
620	**181**	1s.	3d. green	4·50	4·25

182 Conference Emblem

(Des R. Stone (emblem, P. Rahikainen))

1960 (19 Sept). *First Anniv of European Postal and Telecommunications Conference. Chalk-surfaced paper. W* **179.** *P* 15 × 14.

No.	Type	Value	Description	Unused	Used
621	**182**	6d.	bronze-green and purple	40	60
622		1s.	6d. brown and blue	6·50	5·50

183 Thrift Plant

184 "Growth of Savings"

185 Thrift Plant

(Des P. Gauld (2½d.), M. Goaman (others))

1961 (28 Aug). *Centenary of Post Office Saving Bank. Chalk-surfaced paper. W* **179** (*sideways on* 2½*d.*) *P* 14 × 15 (2½*d.*) *or* 15 × 14 (*others*).

I. "TIMSON" Machine

II. "THRISSELL" Machine

No.	Type	Value	Description	I Unused	I Used	II Unused	II Used
623	**183**	2½d.	black and red ..	10	10	2·00	1·75
		a.	Black omitted ..	£6000	—	†	
624	**184**	3d.	orange-brown & vio	10	10	25	25
		a.	Orange-brn omitted	£125	—	£250	—
		x.	Perf through side sheet margin ..	20·00	—	†	
		xa.	Orange-brn omitted	£400	—	†	
625	**185**	1s.	6d. red and blue ..	2·60	2·00	†	
623/5			.. .. .. *Set of* 3	2·60	2·00		

2½d. TIMSON. Cyls 1E–1F. Deeply shaded portrait (brownish black).

2½d. THRISSELL. Cyls 1D–1B or 1D (dot)–1B (dot). Lighter portrait (grey-black).

3d. TIMSON. Cyls 3D–3E. Clear, well-defined portrait with deep shadows and bright highlights.

3d. THRISSELL. Cyls 3C–3B or 3C (dot)–3B (dot). Dull portrait, lacking in contrast.

Sheet marginal examples *without* single extension perf hole on the short side of the stamp are always "Timson", as are those with large punch-hole *not* coincident with printed three-sided box guide mark.

The 3d. "Timson" perforated completely through the right-hand side margin comes from a relatively small part of the printing perforated on a sheet-fed machine.

Normally the "Timsons" were perforated in the reel, with three large punch-holes in both long margins and the perforations completely through both short margins. Only one punch-hole coincides with the guide-mark.

The "Thrissells" have one large punch-hole in one long margin, coinciding with guide-mark and one short margin imperf (except sometimes for encroachments).

186 C.E.P.T. Emblem

187 Doves and Emblem

188 Doves and Emblem

(Des M. Goaman (doves T. Kurpershoek))

1961 (18 Sept). *European Postal and Telecommunications* (*C.E.P.T.*) *Conference, Torquay. Chalk-surfaced paper. W* **179.** *P* 15 × 14.

No.	Type	Value	Description	Unused	Used
626	**186**	2d.	orange, pink and brown	10	10
627	**187**	4d.	buff, mauve and ultramarine ..	20	10
628	**188**	10d.	turquoise, pale green & Prussian bl	40	25
		a.	Pale green omitted	£2750	
		b.	Turquoise omitted	£2750	
626/8			.. .. *Set of* 3	60	40

189 Hammer Beam Roof, Westminster Hall

190 Palace of Westminster

(Des Faith Jaques)

1961 (25 Sept). *Seventh Commonwealth Parliamentary Conference. Chalk-surfaced paper. W* **179** (*sideways on* 1*s.* 3*d.*). *P* 15 × 14 (6*d.*) *or* 14 × 15 (1*s.* 3*d.*).

No.	Type	Value	Description	Unused	Used
629	**189**	6d.	purple and gold	25	20
		a.	Gold omitted	£500	
630	**190**	1s.	3d. green and blue	2·75	2·00
		a.	Blue (Queen's head) omitted ..	£3000	

191 "Units of Productivity"

192 "National Productivity"

193 "Unified Productivity"

(Des D. Gentleman)

1962 (14 Nov). *National Productivity Year. Chalk-surfaced paper. W* **179** (*inverted on* 2½*d. and* 3*d.*). *P* 15 × 14.

No.	Type	Value	Description	Unused	Used
631	**191**	2½d.	myrtle-green & carm-red (*shades*)	20	10
		p.	One phosphor band	1·00	40
632	**192**	3d.	light blue and violet (*shades*) ..	25	10
		a.	Light blue (Queen's head) omitted	£1100	
		p.	Three phosphor bands	1·00	50
633	**193**	1s.	3d. carmine, light blue & dp green	2·50	1·60
		a.	Light blue (Queen's head) omitted	£3500	
		p.	Three phosphor bands	28·00	21·00
631/3			.. .. *Set of* 3	2·75	1·60
631p/3p			.. .. *Set of* 3	28·00	21·00

NEW INFORMATION

The editor is always interested to correspond with people who have new information that will improve or correct the Catalogue.

194 Campaign Emblem and Family

195 Children of Three Races

(Des M. Goaman)

1963 (21 Mar). *Freedom from Hunger. Chalk-surfaced paper. W* **179** *(inverted). P* 15 × 14.

634	**194**	2½d. crimson and pink	10	10
		p. One phosphor band	1·00	1·00
635	**195**	1s. 3d. bistre-brown and yellow	2·75	2·50
		p. Three phosphor bands	26·00	22·00

196 "Paris Conference"

(Des R. Stone)

1963 (7 May). *Paris Postal Conference Centenary. Chalk-surfaced paper. W* **179** *(inverted). P* 15 × 14.

636	**196**	6d. green and mauve	60	40
		a. Green omitted	£2000	
		p. Three phosphor bands	7·50	6·50

197 Posy of Flowers

198 Woodland Life

(Des S. Scott (3d.), M. Goaman (4½d.))

1963 (16 May). *National Nature Week. Chalk-surfaced paper. W* **179.** *P* 15 × 14.

637	**197**	3d. yellow, green, brown and black	20	20
		p. Three phosphor bands	50	50
638	**198**	4½d. black, blue, yellow, mag & brn-red	40	40
		p. Three phosphor bands	3·50	3·00

199 Rescue at Sea

200 19th-century Lifeboat

201 Lifeboatmen

(Des D. Gentleman)

1963 (31 May). *Ninth International Lifeboat Conference, Edinburgh. Chalk-surfaced paper. W* **179.** *P* 15 × 14.

639	**199**	2½d. blue, black and red	10	10
		p. One phosphor band	40	50
640	**200**	4d. red, yellow, brown, black and blue	40	30
		p. Three phosphor bands	20	50
641	**201**	1s. 6d. sepia, yellow and grey-blue	4·50	4·00
		p. Three phosphor bands	32·00	28·00
639/41		*Set of 3*	4·50	4·00
639p/41p		*Set of 3*	32·00	28·00

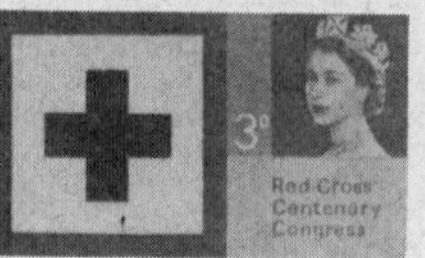

202 Red Cross

203

204

(Des H. Bartram)

1963 (15 Aug). *Red Cross Centenary Congress. Chalk-surfaced paper. W* **179.** *P* 15 × 14.

642	**202**	3d. red and deep lilac	10	10
		a. Red omitted	£2500	
		p. Three phosphor bands	60	60
		pa. Red omitted	£5500	
643	**203**	1s. 3d. red, blue and grey	3·25	2·75
		p. Three phosphor bands	45·00	35·00
644	**204**	1s. 6d. red, blue and bistre	3·25	2·75
		p. Three phosphor bands	30·00	20·00
642/4		*Set of 3*	6·00	5·00
642p/4p		*Set of 3*	70·00	50·00

205 Commonwealth Cable

(Des P. Gauld)

1963 (3 Dec). *Opening of COMPAC (Trans-Pacific Telephone Cable). Chalk-surfaced paper. W* **179.** *P* 15 × 14.

645	**205**	1s. 6d. blue and black	4·00	3·25
		a. Black omitted	£3250	
		p. Three phosphor bands	20·00	20·00

206 Puck and Bottom (*A Midsummer Night's Dream*)

207 Feste (*Twelfth Night*)

208 Balcony Scene (*Romeo and Juliet*)

209 "Eve of Agincourt" (*Henry V*)

210 Hamlet contemplating Yorick's Skull (*Hamlet*) and Queen Elizabeth II

(Des D. Gentleman. Photo Harrison & Sons (3d., 6d., 1s. 3d., 1s. 6d.). Des C. and R. Ironside. Recess B.W. (2s. 6d.))

1964 (23 April). *Shakespeare Festival. Chalk-surfaced paper. W* **179.** *P* 11 × 12 *(2s. 6d.) or* 15 × 14 *(others).*

646	**206**	3d. yell-bistre, blk & dp vio-bl (*shades*)	10	10
		p. Three phosphor bands	20	20
647	**207**	6d. yellow, orge, blk & yell-ol (*shades*)	20	20
		p. Three phosphor bands	60	40
648	**208**	1s. 3d. cerise, bl-grn, blk & sep (*shades*)	1·00	1·25
		p. Three phosphor bands	7·00	6·50
649	**209**	1s. 6d. violet, turq, blk & blue (*shades*)	1·25	1·25
		p. Three phosphor bands	12·00	6·50
650	**210**	2s. 6d. deep slate-purple (*shades*)	2·00	2·00
646/50		*Set of 5*	4·25	4·25
646p/9p		*Set of 4*	18·00	12·50

211 Flats near Richmond Park ("Urban Development")

212 Shipbuilding Yards, Belfast ("Industrial Activity")

213 Beddgelert Forest Park, Snowdonia ("Forestry")

214 Nuclear Reactor, Dounreay ("Technological Development")

(Des D. Bailey)

1964 (1 July). *20th International Geographical Congress, London. Chalk-surfaced paper. W* **179.** *P* 15 × 14.

651	**211**	2½d. blk, olive-yellow, ol-grey & turq-bl	10	10
		p. One phosphor band	50	40
652	**212**	4d. orge-brn, red-brn, rose, blk & vio	25	25
		a. Violet omitted	£200	
		b. Red-brown omitted		
		c. Violet and red-brown omitted	£200	
		p. Three phosphor bands	90	70
653	**213**	8d. yellow-brown, emerald, grn & blk	50	50
		a. Green (lawn) omitted	£3500	
		p. Three phosphor bands	2·00	1·75
654	**214**	1s. 6d. yell-brn, pale pink, blk & brn	4·00	3·75
		p. Three phosphor bands	28·00	25·00
651/4		*Set of 4*	4·50	4·25
651p/4p		*Set of 4*	28·00	25·00

215 Spring Gentian

216 Dog Rose

217 Honeysuckle

218 Fringed Water Lily

(Des M. and Sylvia Goaman)

1964 (5 Aug). *Tenth International Botanical Congress, Edinburgh. Chalk-surfaced paper.* *W* **179.** *P* 15 × 14.

655	**215**	3d. violet, blue and sage-green	10	10
		a. Blue omitted	£3500	
		p. Three phosphor bands	20	20
656	**216**	6d. apple-green, rose, scarlet and green	20	20
		p. Three phosphor bands	1·25	1·40
657	**217**	9d. lemon, green, lake and rose-red	2·25	2·25
		a. Green (leaves) omitted	£3500	
		p. Three phosphor bands	3·75	5·00
658	**218**	1s. 3d. yellow, emerald, reddish violet and grey-green	3·00	2·10
		a. Yellow (flowers) omitted	£7500	
		p. Three phosphor bands	26·00	26·00
655/8		*Set of* 4	5·00	4·25
655p/8p		*Set of* 4	28·00	28·00

219 Forth Road Bridge

220 Forth Road and Railway Bridges

(Des A. Restall)

1964 (4 Sept). *Opening of Forth Road Bridge. Chalk-surfaced paper.* *W* **179.** *P* 15 × 14.

659	**219**	3d. black, blue and reddish violet	15	10
		p. Three phosphor bands	50	50
660	**220**	6d. black, light blue and carmine-red	45	40
		a. Light blue omitted	£2500	£1500
		p. Three phosphor bands	5·00	5·50

221 Sir Winston Churchill

(Des D. Gentleman and Rosalind Dease, from photograph by Karsh)

1965 (8 July). *Churchill Commemoration. Chalk-surfaced paper.* *W* **179.** *P* 15 × 14.

I. "REMBRANDT" Machine

661	**221**	4d. black and olive-brown	15	10
		p. Three phosphor bands	30	30

II. "TIMSON" Machine

661*a*	**221**	4d. black and olive-brown	25	25

III. "L. & M. 4" Machine

662	–	1s. 3d. black and grey	45	30
		p. Three phosphor bands	4·00	3·50

The 1s. 3d. shows a closer view of Churchill's head.

4d. REMBRANDT. Cyls 1A–1B dot and no dot. Lack of shading detail on Churchill's portrait. Queen's portrait appears dull and coarse. This is a rotary machine which is sheet-fed.

4d. TIMSON. Cyls 5A–6B no dot. More detail on Churchill's portrait—furrow on forehead, his left eyebrow fully drawn and more shading on cheek. Queen's portrait lighter and sharper. This is a reel-fed, two-colour 12-in. wide rotary machine and the differences in impression are due to the greater pressure applied by this machine.

1s. 3d. Cyls 1A–1B no dot. The "Linotype and Machinery No. 4" machine is an ordinary sheet-fed rotary press machine. Besides being used for printing the 1s. 3d. stamps it was also employed for overprinting the phosphor bands on both values.

Two examples of the 4d. value exist with the Queen's head omitted, one due to something adhering to the cylinder and the other due to a paper fold. The stamp also exists with Churchill's head omitted, also due to a paper fold.

222 Simon de Montfort's Seal

223 Parliament Buildings (after engraving by Hollar, 1647)

(Des S. Black (6d.), R. Guyatt (2s. 6d.))

1965 (19 July). *700th Anniv of Simon de Montfort's Parliament. Chalk-surfaced paper.* *W* **179.** *P* 15 × 14.

663	**222**	6d. olive-green	10	10
		p. Three phosphor bands	40	40
664	**223**	2s. 6d. black, grey and pale drab	1·25	1·25

224 Bandsmen and Banner

225 Three Salvationists

(Des M. Farrar-Bell (3d.), G. Trenaman (1s. 6d.))

1965 (9 Aug). *Salvation Army Centenary. Chalk-surfaced paper.* *W* **179.** *P* 15 × 14.

665	**224**	3d. indigo, grey-blue, cerise, yell & brn	10	10
		p. One phosphor band	40	40
666	**225**	1s. 6d. red, blue, yellow and brown	1·00	1·00
		p. Three phosphor bands	4·00	4·25

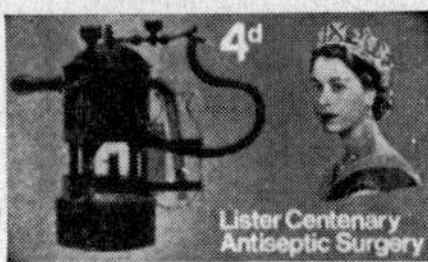

226 Lister's Carbolic Spray

227 Lister and Chemical Symbols

(Des P. Gauld (4d.), F. Ariss (1s.))

1965 (1 Sept). *Centenary of Joseph Lister's Discovery of Antiseptic Surgery. Chalk-surfaced paper.* *W* **179.** *P* 15 × 14.

667	**226**	4d. indigo, brown-red and grey-black	10	10
		a. Brown-red (tube) omitted	£200	75·00
		b. Indigo omitted	£1250	
		p. Three phosphor bands	15	20
		pa. Brown-red (tube) omitted	£950	
668	**227**	1s. black, purple and new blue	1·00	1·25
		p. Three phosphor bands	1·60	1·60

228 Trinidad Carnival Dancers

229 Canadian Folk-dancers

(Des D. Gentleman and Rosalind Dease)

1965 (1 Sept). *Commonwealth Arts Festival. Chalk-surfaced paper.* *W* **179.** *P* 15 × 14.

669	**228**	6d. black and orange	10	10
		p. Three phosphor bands	20	20
670	**229**	1s. 6d. black and light reddish violet	1·40	1·40
		p. Three phosphor bands	1·40	1·40

230 Flight of Spitfires

231 Pilot in Hurricane

232 Wing-tips of Spitfire and Messerschmitt "ME-109"

233 Spitfires attacking Heinkel "HE-111" Bomber

234 Spitfire attacking Stuka Dive-bomber

235 Hurricanes over Wreck of Dornier "DO-17z2" Bomber

236 Anti-aircraft Artillery in Action

237 Air-battle over St. Paul's Cathedral

(Des D. Gentleman and Rosalind Dease (4d. × 6 and 1s. 3d.), A. Restall (9d.))

1965 (13 Sept). *25th Anniv of Battle of Britain. Chalk-surfaced paper.* *W* **179.** *P* 15 × 14.

671	**230**	4d. yellow-olive and black	30	35
		a. Block of 6. Nos. 671/6	5·00	5·00
		p. Three phosphor bands	40	50
		pa. Block of 6. Nos. 671p/6p	8·50	8·00
672	**231**	4d. yellow-olive, olive-grey and black	30	35
		p. Three phosphor bands	40	50
673	**232**	4d. red, new blue, yell-ol, ol-grey & blk	30	35
		p. Three phosphor bands	40	50
674	**233**	4d. olive-grey, yellow-olive and black	30	35
		p. Three phosphor bands	40	50
675	**234**	4d. olive-grey, yellow-olive and black	30	35
		p. Three phosphor bands	40	50
676	**235**	4d. olive-grey, yell-olive, new blue & blk	30	35
		a. New blue omitted	—	£3000
		p. Three phosphor bands	40	50
677	**236**	9d. bluish violet, orange and slate-purple	1·25	1·25
		p. Three phosphor bands	80	80
678	**237**	1s. 3d. light grey, deep grey, black, light blue and bright blue	1·25	1·25
		p. Three phosphor bands	80	80
671/8		*Set of* 8	6·50	4·25
671p/8p		*Set of* 8	9·00	4·25

Nos. 671/6 were issued together *se-tenant* in blocks of 6 (3 × 2) within the sheet.

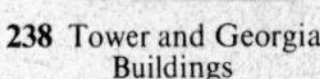

238 Tower and Georgian Buildings

239 Tower and "Nash" Terrace, Regent's Park

(Des C. Abbott)

1965 (8 Oct). *Opening of Post Office Tower. Chalk-surfaced paper.* *W* **179** *(sideways on 3d.). P* 14 × 15 *(3d.) or* 15 × 14 *(1s. 3d.).*

679	**238**	3d. olive-yell, new blue & bronze-green	10	10
		a. Olive-yellow (Tower) omitted	£1000	
		p. One phosphor band	10	10
680	**239**	1s. 3d. bronze-green, yellow-green & bl	65	75
		p. Three phosphor bands	50	50

The one phosphor band on No. 679p was produced by printing broad phosphor bands across alternate vertical perforations. Individual stamps show the band at right or left (same prices either way).

240 U.N. Emblem

241 I.C.Y. Emblem

(Des J. Matthews)

1965 (25 Oct). *20th Anniv of U.N.O. and International Co-operation Year. Chalk-surfaced paper. W* **179**. *P* 15 × 14.

681	**240**	3d. black, yellow-orange and light blue	15	20
		p. One phosphor band	15	20
682	**241**	1s. 6d. black, bright purple and lt blue	1·10	90
		p. Three phosphor bands	1·10	90

242 Telecommunications Network

243 Radio Waves and Switchboard

(Des A. Restall)

1965 (15 Nov). *I.T.U. Centenary. Chalk-surfaced paper. W* **179**. *P* 15 × 14.

683	**242**	9d. red, ultram, dp slate, vio, blk & pk	20	20
		p. Three phosphor bands	60	50
684	**243**	1s. 6d. red, greenish bl, ind, blk & lt pk	1·40	1·10
		a. Light pink omitted	£1500	
		p. Three phosphor bands	6·00	6·00

Originally scheduled for issue on 17 May 1965, supplies from the Philatelic Bureau were sent in error to reach a dealer on that date and another dealer received his supply on 27 May.

244 Robert Burns (after Skirving chalk drawing)

245 Robert Burns (after Nasmyth portrait)

(Des G. Huntly)

1966 (25 Jan). *Burns Commemoration. Chalk-surfaced paper. W* **179**. *P* 15 × 14.

685	**244**	4d. black, deep violet-blue and new blue	15	15
		p. Three phosphor bands	15	15
686	**245**	1s. 3d. black, slate-blue & yellow-orge	70	70
		p. Three phosphor bands	85	85

246 Westminster Abbey

247 Fan Vaulting, Henry VII Chapel

(Des Sheila Robinson. Photo Harrison (3d.). Des and eng Bradbury, Wilkinson. Recess (2s. 6d.))

1966 (28 Feb). *900th Anniv of Westminster Abbey. Chalk-surfaced paper (3d.). W* **179**. *P* 15 × 14 *(3d.) or* 11 × 12 *(2s. 6d.).*

687	**246**	3d. black, red-brown and new blue ..	15	10
		p. One phosphor band	30	30
688	**247**	2s. 6d. black	70	75

248 View near Hassocks, Sussex

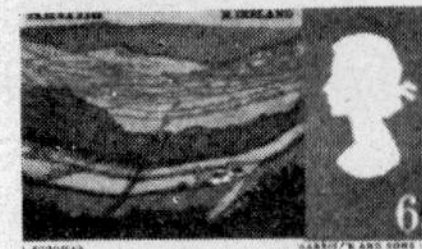

249 Antrim, Northern Ireland

250 Harlech Castle, Wales

251 Cairngorm Mountains, Scotland

(Des L. Rosoman. Queen's portrait, adapted by D. Gentleman from coinage)

1966 (2 May). *Landscapes. Chalk-surfaced paper. W* **179**. *P* 15 × 14.

689	**248**	4d. black, yellow-green and new blue	15	15
		p. Three phosphor bands	15	15
690	**249**	6d. black, emerald and new blue ..	15	15
		p. Three phosphor bands	25	25
691	**250**	1s. 3d. blk, greenish yell & greenish bl	35	35
		p. Three phosphor bands	35	35
692	**251**	1s. 6d. black, orange and Prussian blue	50	50
		p. Three phosphor bands	50	50
689/92 ..		.. .. *Set of* 4	1·00	1·00
689p/92p		.. .. *Set of* 4	1·00	1·00

252 Players with Ball

253 Goalmouth Mêlée

254 Goalkeeper saving Goal

(Des D. Gentleman (4d.), W. Kempster (6d.), D. Caplan (1s. 3d.). Queen's portrait adapted by D. Gentleman from coinage)

1966 (1 June). *World Cup Football Competition. Chalk-surfaced paper. W* **179** *(sideways on 4d.). P* 14 × 15 *(4d.) or* 15 × 14 *(others).*

693	**252**	4d. red, reddish pur, brt bl, flesh & blk	15	10
		p. Two phosphor bands	15	10
694	**253**	6d. black, sepia, red, apple-green & blue	20	20
		a. Black omitted	85·00	
		b. Apple-green omitted	£1500	
		c. Red omitted	£1750	
		p. Three phosphor bands	20	20
		pa. Black omitted	£600	
695	**254**	1s. 3d. black, blue, yell, red & lt yell-ol	50	50
		a. Blue omitted	£200	
		p. Three phosphor bands	50	50
693/5 ..		.. .. *Set of* 3	75	75
693p/5p ..		.. .. *Set of* 3	75	75

255 Black-headed Gull

256 Blue Tit

257 European Robin

258 Blackbird

(Des J. Norris Wood)

1966 (8 Aug). *British Birds. Chalk-surfaced paper. W* **179**. *P* 15 × 14.

696	**255**	4d. grey, black, red, emerald-green, brt blue, greenish yellow and bistre ..	10	15
		a. Block of 4. Nos. 696/9	90	90
		ab. Black (value), etc. omitted* (*block of four*)	£4000	
		ac. Black only omitted*		
		p. Three phosphor bands	10	15
		pa. Block of 4. Nos. 696p/9p	90	90
697	**256**	4d. black, greenish yellow, grey, emerald-green, bright blue and bistre ..	10	15
		p. Three phosphor bands	10	15
698	**257**	4d. red, greenish yellow, black, grey, bistre, reddish brown & emerald-grn	10	15
		p. Three phosphor bands	10	15
699	**258**	4d. black, reddish brown, greenish yellow, grey and bistre**	10	15
		p. Three phosphor bands	10	15
696/9 ..		.. .. *Set of* 4	90	50
696p/9p		.. .. *Set of* 4	90	50

Nos. 696/9 were issued together *se-tenant* in blocks of four within the sheet.

* In No. 696ab the blue, bistre and reddish brown are also omitted but in No. 696ac only the black is omitted.

** On No. 699 the black was printed over the bistre.

Other colours omitted, and the stamps affected:

d.	Greenish yellow (Nos. 696/9)	£150
e.	Red (Nos. 696 and 698)	£300
f.	Emerald-green (Nos. 696/8)	40·00
pf.	Emerald-green (Nos. 696p/8p)	40·00
g.	Bright blue (Nos. 696/7)	£110
pg.	Bright blue (Nos. 696p/7p)	£125
h.	Bistre (Nos. 696/9)	50·00
ph.	Bistre (Nos. 696p/9p)	50·00
j.	Reddish brown (Nos. 698/9)	50·00
pj.	Reddish brown (Nos. 698p/9p)	75·00

The prices quoted are for each stamp.

259 Cup Winners

1966 (18 Aug). *England's World Cup Football Victory. Chalk-surfaced paper. W* **179** *(sideways). P* 14 × 15.

700	**259**	4d. red, reddish pur, brt bl, flesh & blk	20	20

These stamps were only put on sale at post offices in England, the Channel Islands and the Isle of Man, and at the Philatelic Bureau in London and also, on 22 August, in Edinburgh on the occasion of the opening of the Edinburgh Festival as well as at Army post offices at home and abroad.

260 Jodrell Bank Radio Telescope

261 British Motor-cars

262 "SRN 6" Hovercraft

263 Windscale Reactor

(Des D. and A. Gillespie (4d., 6d.), A. Restall (others))

1966 (19 Sept). *British Technology. Chalk-surfaced paper. W* **179.** *P* 15 × 14.

No.	Type	Description	Unused	Used
701	**260**	4d. black and lemon	15	15
		p. Three phosphor bands	15	15
702	**261**	6d. red, deep blue and orange	15	15
		a. Red (Mini-cars) omitted	£3500	
		b. Deep blue (Jaguar and inscr) omitted	£3000	
		p. Three phosphor bands	15	15
703	**262**	1s. 3d. black, orange-red, slate and light greenish blue	30	40
		p. Three phosphor bands	35	40
704	**263**	1s. 6d. black, yellow-green, bronze-green, lilac and deep blue	40	45
		p. Three phosphor bands	45	50
701/4		*Set of* 4	90	1·00
701p/4p		*Set of* 4	1·00	1·10

264

265

266

267

268

269

All the above show battle scenes and they were issued together *se-tenant* in horizontal strips of six within the sheet.

270 Norman Ship

271 Norman Horsemen attacking Harold's Troops

(All the above are scenes from the Bayeux Tapestry)

(Des D. Gentleman. Photo, Queen's head die-stamped (6d., 1s. 3d.))

1966 (14 Oct). *900th Anniv of Battle of Hastings. Chalk-surfaced paper. W* **179** (*sideways on* 1*s.* 3*d.*). *P* 15 × 14.

No.	Type	Description	Unused	Used
705	**264**	4d. black, olive-green, bistre, deep blue, orange, mag, grn, blue and grey	10	15
		a. Strip of 6. Nos. 705/10	1·50	2·00
		p. Three phosphor bands	10	25
		pa. Strip of 6. Nos. 705p/10p	1·50	2·00
706	**265**	4d. black, olive-green, bistre, deep blue, orange, mag, grn, blue and grey	10	15
		p. Three phosphor bands	10	25
707	**266**	4d. black, olive-green, bistre, deep blue, orange, mag, grn, blue and grey	10	15
		p. Three phosphor bands	10	25
708	**267**	4d. black, olive-green, bistre, deep blue, magenta, green, blue and grey	10	15
		p. Three phosphor bands	10	25
709	**268**	4d. black, olive-green, bistre, deep blue, orange, mag, grn, blue and grey	10	15
		p. Three phosphor bands	10	25
710	**269**	4d. black, olive-green, bistre, deep blue, orange, mag, grn, blue and grey	10	15
		p. Three phosphor bands	10	25
711	**270**	6d. black, olive-grn, vio, bl, grn & gold	10	10
		p. Three phosphor bands	10	10
712	**271**	1s. 3d. black, lilac, bronze-green, rosine, bistre-brown and gold	20	20
		a. Lilac omitted	£450	
		p. Four phosphor bands	20	20
		pa. Lilac omitted	£650	
705/12		*Set of* 8	1·60	1·10
705p/12p		*Set of* 8	1·60	1·60

Other colours omitted on the 4d. values and the stamps affected:

	Description	Price
b.	Olive-green (Nos. 705/10)	25·00
pb.	Olive-green (Nos. 705p/10p)	25·00
c.	Bistre (Nos. 705/10)	25·00
pc.	Bistre (Nos. 705p/10p)	30·00
d.	Deep blue (Nos. 705/10)	35·00
pd.	Deep blue (Nos. 705p/10p)	35·00
e.	Orange (Nos. 705/7 and 709/10)	25·00
pe.	Orange (Nos. 705p/7p and 709p/10p)	20·00
f.	Magenta (Nos. 705/10)	30·00
pf.	Magenta (Nos. 705p/10p)	30·00
g.	Green (Nos. 705/10)	25·00
pg.	Green (Nos. 705p/10p)	25·00
h.	Blue (Nos. 705/10)	20·00
ph.	Blue (Nos. 705p/10p)	35·00
j.	Grey (Nos. 705/10)	20·00
pj.	Grey (Nos. 705p/10p)	20·00
pk.	Magenta and green (Nos. 705p/10p)	£200

The prices quoted are for each stamp.

Nos. 705 and 709, with grey and blue omitted, have been seen commercially used, posted from Middleton-in-Teesdale.

Three examples of No. 712 in a right-hand top corner block of 10 (2 × 5) are known with the Queen's head omitted as a result of a double paper fold prior to die-stamping. The perforation is normal. Of the other seven stamps, four have the Queen's head misplaced and three are normal.

MISSING GOLD HEADS. The 6d and 1s. 3d. were also issued with the die-stamped gold head omitted but as these can also be removed by chemical means we are not prepared to list them unless a way is found of distinguishing the genuine stamps from the fakes which will satisfy the Expert Committees.

The same remarks apply to Nos. 713/14.

272 King of the Orient **273** Snowman

(Des Tasveer Shemza (3d.), J. Berry (1s. 6d.) (winners of children's design competition). Photo, Queen's head die-stamped)

1966 (1 Dec). *Christmas. Chalk-surfaced paper. W* **179** (*sideways on* 3*d.*). *P* 14 × 15.

No.	Type	Description	Unused	Used
713	**272**	3d. black, blue, green, yell, red & gold	10	10
		a. Queen's head double		
		b. Green omitted	—	£150
		p. One phosphor band	10	10
714	**273**	1s. 6d. blue, red, pink, black and gold	35	35
		a. Pink (hat) omitted	£1250	
		p. Two phosphor bands	35	35

See note below Nos. 679/80 which also applies to No. 713p.

274 Sea Freight

275 Air Freight

(Des C. Abbott)

1967 (20 Feb). *European Free Trade Association (EFTA). Chalk-surfaced paper. W* **179.** *P* 15 × 14.

No.	Type	Description	Unused	Used
715	**274**	9d. deep blue, red, lilac, green, brown, new blue, yellow and black	15	15
		a. Black (Queen's head, etc.), brown, new blue and yellow omitted	£1000	
		b. Lilac omitted	60·00	
		c. Green omitted	40·00	
		d. Brown omitted	45·00	
		e. New blue omitted	42·00	
		f. Yellow omittted	42·00	
		p. Three phosphor bands	15	15
		pb. Lilac omitted	75·00	
		pc. Green omitted	45·00	
		pd. Brown omitted	45·00	
		pe. New blue omitted	45·00	
		pf. Yellow omitted	75·00	
716	**275**	1s. 6d. violet, red, deep blue, brown, green, blue-grey, new bl, yell & blk	30	30
		a. Red omitted		
		b. Deep blue omitted	£225	
		c. Brown omitted	45·00	
		d. Blue-grey omitted	45·00	
		e. New blue omitted	45·00	
		f. Yellow omitted	45·00	
		p. Three phosphor bands	30	30
		pa. Red omitted		
		pb. Deep blue omitted	£275	
		pc. Brown omitted	45·00	
		pd. Blue-grey omitted	45·00	
		pf. New blue omitted	45·00	

276 Hawthorn and Bramble

277 Larger Bindweed and Viper's Bugloss

278 Ox-eye Daisy, Coltsfoot and Buttercup

279 Bluebell, Red Campion and Wood Anemone

The above were issued together *se-tenant* in blocks of four within the sheet.

280 Dog Violet

281 Primroses

(Des Rev. W. Keble Martin (T **276/9**), Mary Grierson (others))

1967 (24 Apr). *British Wild Flowers. Chalk-surfaced paper. W* **179.** *P* 15 × 14.

No.	Type	Description	Unused	Used
717	**276**	4d. grey, lemon, myrtle-green, red, agate and slate-purple	15	10
		a. Block of 4. Nos. 717/20	1·00	1·10
		b. Grey double*		
		c. Red omitted	£850	
		p. Three phosphor bands	10	10
		pa. Block of 4. Nos. 717p/20p	70	80
		pd. Agate omitted	£450	
		pf. Slate-purple omitted	£150	

718 **277** 4d. grey, lemon, myrtle-green, red, agate and violet 15 10
b. Grey double* .. .. ..
p. Three phosphor bands 10 10
pd. Agate omitted £450
pe. Violet omitted .. .. ..
719 **278** 4d. grey, lemon, myrtle-green, red and agate 15 10
b. Grey double* .. .. ..
p. Three phosphor bands 10 10
pd. Agate omitted £450
720 **279** 4d. grey, lemon, myrtle-green, reddish purple, agate and violet 15 10
b. Grey double* .. .. ..
c. Reddish purple omitted £950
p. Three phosphor bands 10 10
pd. Agate omitted £450
pe. Violet omitted .. .. ..
721 **280** 9d. lavender-grey, green, reddish violet and orange-yellow 15 10
p. Three phosphor bands 10 10
722 **281** 1s. 9d. lavender-grey, green, greenish yellow and orange 20 20
p. Three phosphor bands 20 20
717/22 .. .. *Set of* 6 1·25 65
717p/22p .. .. *Set of* 6 90 65

* The double impression of the grey printing affects the Queen's head, value and inscription.

PHOSPHOR BANDS. Issues from No. 723 are normally with phosphor bands only, except for the high values. However, most stamps have appeared with the phosphor bands omitted in error, but they are outside the scope of this catalogue. They are listed in Volumes 3, 4 and 5 of the Stanley Gibbons *Great Britain Specialised Catalogue*. See also further notes after No. X1019.

PHOSPHORISED PAPER. Following the adoption of phosphor bands the Post Office started a series of experiments involving the addition of the phosphor to the paper coating before the stamps were printed. No. 743b was the first of these experiments to be issued for normal postal use. See also notes after No. X1019.

PVA GUM. Polyvinyl alcohol was introduced by Harrisons in place of gum Arabic in 1968. It is almost invisible except that a small amount of pale yellowish colouring matter was introduced to make it possible to see that the stamps had been gummed. Although this can be distinguished from gum arabic in unused stamps there is, of course, no means of detecting it in used examples. Such varieties are outside the scope of this catalogue, but they are listed in the *Great Britain Concise Catalogue*. See further notes *re* gum after Nos. 744 and 762.

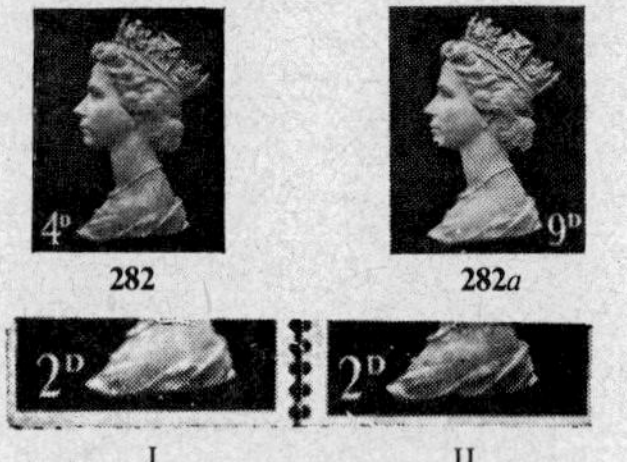

282 **282a**

I II

Two types of the 2d.

I. Value spaced away from left side of stamp (cylinders 1 no dot and dot).

II. Value close to left side from new multipositive used for cylinders 5 no dot and dot onwards. The portrait appears in the centre, thus conforming to the other values.

(Des after plaster cast by Arnold Machin)

1967 (5 June)–**70.** *Chalk-surfaced paper. Two phosphor bands except where otherwise stated. No wmk. P* 15 × 14.
723 **282** ½d. orange-brown (5.2.68) 10 20
724 1d. lt olive (*shades*) (2 bands) (5.2.68) 10 10
a. Imperf (coil strip)† £750
b. Part perf pane* .. ..
c. Imperf pane* .. ..
d. Uncoated paper (1970)** .. 85·00
l. Booklet pane. No. 724 × 2 *se-tenant* with 730 × 2 (6.4.68) .. 2·60
m. Booklet pane. No. 724 × 4 *se-tenant* with 734 × 2 (6.1.69) .. 3·25
n. Booklet pane. No. 724 × 6, 734 × 6 and 735 × 3 *se-tenant* (1.12.69) .. 11·00
na. Uncoated paper (1970)** .. £900
725 1d. yellowish olive (1 centre band) (16.9.68) 25 30
l. Booklet pane. No. 725 × 4 *se-tenant* with 732 × 2 .. .. 3·75
m. Coil strip. No. 728 × 2 *se-tenant* with 729, 725 and 733 (27.8.69) .. 1·25
726 2d. lake-brown (Type I) (2 bands) (5.2.68) 10 15
727 2d. lake-brown (Type II) (2 bands) (1969) 15 15
728 2d. lake-brown (Type II) (1 centre band) (27.8.69) 40 50
729 3d. violet (*shades*) (1 centre band) (8.8.67) 10 10
a. Imperf (pair) £475
730 3d. violet (2 bands) (6.4.68) .. 30 30
a. Uncoated paper** £900
731 4d. deep sepia (*shades*) (2 bands) .. 10 10
b. Part perf pane* £550
732 4d. deep olive-brown (*shades*) (1 centre band) (16.9.68) 10 10
a. Part perf pane* £450
l. Booklet pane. Two stamps plus two printed labels 75
733 4d. brt verm (1 centre band) (6.1.69) 10 10
a. *Tête-bêche* (horiz pair) £2500
b. Uncoated paper (1970)** .. 10·00
l. Booklet pane. Two stamps plus two printed labels (3.3.69) 80
734 **282** 4d. bright verm (1 side band) (6.1.69) 1·40 1·60
a. Uncoated paper (1970)** .. £150
735 5d. royal blue (*shades*) (1.7.68) .. 10 10
a. Imperf pane* £450
b. Part perf pane* £400
c. Imperf (pair)†† £100
d. Uncoated paper (1970)** .. 18·00
736 6d. brt reddish purple (*shades*) (5.2.68) 20 20
737 **282a** 7d. bright emerald (1.7.68) 40 30
738 8d. bright vermilion (1.7.68) 15 30
739 8d. light turquoise-blue (6.1.69) .. 45 50
740 9d. myrtle-green (8.8.67) 50 30
741 **282** 10d. drab (1.7.68) 45 50
a. Uncoated paper (1969)** .. 25·00
742 1s. light bluish violet (*shades*) .. 40 30
743 1s. 6d. greenish blue and deep blue (*shades*) (8.8.67) 50 30
a. Greenish blue omitted £100
c. Phosphorised paper. *Prussian blue and indigo* (10.12.69) 75 90
ca. Prussian blue omitted £225
744 1s. 9d. dull orange and black (*shades*) 40 30
723/44 .. .. *Set of* 16 3·00 3·25

*BOOKLET ERRORS. See note after No. 556.

** Uncoated paper. This does not respond to the chalky test, and may be further distinguished from the normal chalk-surfaced paper by the fibres which clearly show on the surface, resulting in the printing impression being rougher, and by the screening dots which are not so evident. The 1d., 4d. and 5d. come from the £1 "Stamps for Cooks" Booklet; the 3d. and 10d. from sheets. The 20p. and 50p. high values (Nos. 830/1) exist with similar errors.

† No. 724a occurs in a vertical strip of four, top stamp perforated on three sides, bottom stamp imperf three sides and the two middle stamps completely imperf.

†† No. 735c comes from the original state of cylinder 15 which is identifiable by the screening dots which extend through the gutters of the stamps and into the margins of the sheet. This must not be confused with imperforate stamps from cylinder 10, a large quantity of which was stolen from the printers early in 1970.

The 1d. with centre band (725) only came in the September 1968 booklets (PVA gum) and the coil strip (725m) (gum arabic); the 2d. with centre band (728) was only issued in the coil strip (725m); the 3d. (No. 730) appeared in booklets on 6.4.68, from coils during December 1968 and from sheets in January 1969; and the 4d. with one side band (734) only in 10s. and £1 booklets.

Gum. The 1d. (725), 3d. (729), 4d. (731 and 733), 9d., 1s., 1s. 6d. and 1s. 9d. exist with gum arabic as well as the PVA gum; the 2d. (728) and coil strip (725m) exist only with gum arabic; and the remainder exist with PVA gum only.

The 4d. (731) in shades of washed-out grey are colour changelings which we understand are caused by the concentrated solvents used in modern dry cleaning methods.

For decimal issue, see Nos. X841/1019.

283 "Master Lambton" (Sir Thomas Lawrence)

284 "Mares and Foals in a Landscape" (George Stubbs)

285 "Children Coming Out of School" (L. S. Lowry)

1967 (10 July). *British Paintings. Chalk-surfaced paper. Two phosphor bands. No wmk. P* 14 × 15 (4*d.*) *or* 15 × 14 (*others*).
748 **283** 4d. rose-red, lemon, brown, black, new blue and gold 10 10
a. Gold (value and Queen's head) omitted £175
b. New blue omitted £2500
749 **284** 9d. Venetian red, ochre, grey-black, new blue, greenish yellow and black 20 20
a. Black (Queen's head and value) omitted £550
b. Greenish yellow omitted £1200
750 **285** 1s. 6d. greenish yellow, grey, rose, new blue, grey-black and gold 35 25
a. Gold (Queen's head) omitted .. £750
b. New blue omitted £140
c. Grey omitted.. .. .. .. 85·00
748/50 .. .. *Set of* 3 50 50

286 *Gypsy Moth IV*

(Des M. and Sylvia Goaman)

1967 (24 July). *Sir Francis Chichester's World Voyage. Chalk-surfaced paper. Three phosphor bands. No wmk. P* 15 × 14.
751 **286** 1s. 9d. black, brown-red, lt emer & blue 25 25

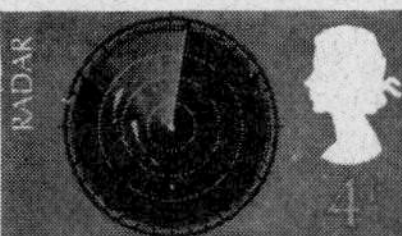

287 Radar Screen

288 Penicillin Mould

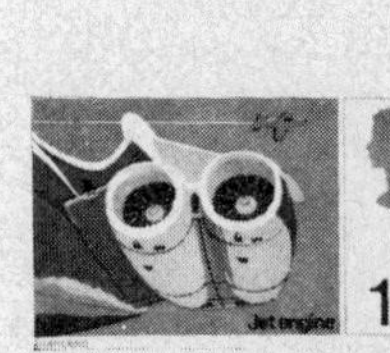

289 "VC-10" Jet Engines **290** Television Equipment

(Des C. Abbott (4d., 1s.), Negus-Sharland team (others))

1967 (19 Sept). *British Discovery and Invention. Chalk-surfaced paper. Three phosphor bands* (4*d.*) *or two phosphor bands* (*others*). *W* **179** (*sideways on* 1*s.* 9*d.*). *P* 14 × 15 (1*s.* 9*d.*) *or* 15 × 14 (*others*).
752 **287** 4d. greenish yellow, black and vermilion 10 10
753 **288** 1s. blue-green, light greenish blue, slate-purple and bluish violet 10 10
754 **289** 1s. 6d. black, grey, royal blue, ochre and turquoise-blue 25 15
755 **290** 1s. 9d. black, grey-blue, pale olive-grey, violet and orange 30 20
a. Grey-blue omitted .. .. ..
752/5 .. .. *Set of* 4 60 50

WATERMARK. All issues from this date are on unwatermarked paper.

291 "The Adoration of the Shepherds" (School of Seville) **292** "Madonna and Child" (Murillo)

293 "The Adoration of the Shepherds" (Louis le Nain)

1967. *Christmas. Chalk-surfaced paper. One phosphor band* (3*d.*) *or two phosphor bands* (*others*). *P* 15 × 14 (1*s.* 6*d.*) *or* 14 × 15 (*others*).
756 **291** 3d. ol-yell, rose, bl, blk & gold (27.11) 10 10
a. Gold (value and Queen's head) omitted .. .. 60·00
b. Printed on the gummed side .. £300
c. Rose omitted .. .. ..
757 **292** 4d. bright purple, greenish yellow, new blue, grey-black and gold (18.10) .. 10 10
a. Gold (value and Queen's head) omitted .. .. 60·00
b. Yellow (Child, robe and Madonna's face) omitted .. .. ..
758 **293** 1s. 6d. brt purple, bistre, lemon, black, orange-red, ultram & gold (27.11) 35 35
a. Gold (value and Queen's head) omitted £2000
b. Ultramarine omitted £450
756/8 .. .. *Set of* 3 50 50

Distinct shades exist of the 4d. value but are not listable as there are intermediate shades. Stamps emanating from one machine show a darker background and give the appearance of the yellow colour being omitted but this is not so and these should not be confused with the true missing yellow No. 757b.

(Recess Bradbury, Wilkinson)

1967–68. *No wmk. White paper. P* 11 × 12.
759 **166** 2s. 6d. black-brown (1.7.68) .. 40 50
760 **167** 5s. red (10.4.68) .. .. 1·00 1·00
761 **168** 10s. bright ultramarine (10.4.68) .. 5·00 5·50
762 **169** £1 black (4.12.67) .. .. 4·00 4·00
759/62 .. .. *Set of* 4 9·00 10·00

PVA GUM. All the following issues from this date have PVA gum *except where footnotes state otherwise.*

294 Tarr Steps, Exmoor

295 Aberfeldy Bridge

296 Menai Bridge

297 M4 Viaduct

(Des A. Restall (9d.), L. Rosoman (1s. 6d.), J. Matthews (others))

1968 (29 Apr). *British Bridges. Chalk-surfaced paper. Two phosphor bands. P* 15 × 14.

763	**294**	4d.	black, bluish violet, turq-bl & gold	10	10
			a. Printed on gummed side	25·00	
764	**295**	9d.	red-brown, myrtle-green, ultramarine, olive-brown, black and gold ..	10	10
			a. Gold (Queen's head) omitted ..	£180	
			b. Ultramarine omitted	†	£3000
765	**296**	1s.	6d. olive-brown, red-orange, bright green, turquoise-green and gold ..	20	15
			a. Gold (Queen's head) omitted ..	£180	
			b. Red-orange omitted	£225	
766	**297**	1s.	9d. olive-brown, greenish yellow, dull green, deep ultramarine & gold	25	30
			a. Gold (Queen's head) omitted ..	£275	
763/6			.. .. *Set of* 4	60	60

No. 764b is only known on first day covers posted from Canterbury.

298 "T U C" and Trades Unionists

299 Mrs. Emmeline Pankhurst (statute)

300 Sopwith "Camel" and "Lightning" Fighters

301 Captain Cook's *Endeavour* and Signature

(Des D. Gentleman (4d.), C. Abbott (others))

1968 (29 May). *British Anniversaries. Events described on stamps. Chalk-surfaced paper. Two phosphor bands. P* 15 × 14.

767	**298**	4d.	emerald, olive, blue and black ..	10	10
768	**299**	9d.	reddish violet, bluish grey and black	10	10
769	**300**	1s.	olive-brown, bl, red, slate-bl & blk	20	20
770	**301**	1s.	9d. yellow-ochre and blackish brown	25	25
767/70			.. .. *Set of* 4	60	60

302 "Queen Elizabeth I" (unknown artist)

303 "Pinkie" (Lawrence)

304 "Ruins of St. Mary Le Port" (Piper)

305 "The Hay Wain" (Constable)

1968 (12 Aug). *British Paintings. Queen's head embossed. Chalk-surfaced paper. Two phosphor bands. P* 15 × 14 (1*s.* 9*d.*) *or* 14 × 15 (*others*).

771	**302**	4d.	blk, verm, greenish yell, grey & gold	10	10
			a. Gold (value and Queen's head) omitted	£225	
			b. Vermilion omitted*	£200	
772	**303**	1s.	mauve, new blue, greenish yellow, black, magenta and gold	15	15
			a. Gold (value and Queen's head) omitted	£175	
773	**304**	1s.	6d. slate, orange, black, mauve, greenish yellow, ultramarine & gold	20	20
			a. Gold (value and Queen's head) omitted	£175	
774	**305**	1s.	9d. greenish yellow, black, new blue, red and gold	25	25
			a. Gold (value and Queen's head) and embossing omitted	£450	
			b. Red omitted		
771/4			.. .. *Set of* 4	60	60

*The effect of this is to leave the face and hands white and there is more yellow and olive in the costume.

The 4d. and 1s. are known with the embossing only omitted. No. 774a is only known with the phosphor also omitted. No. 772a exists both with or without embossing or phosphor bands.

306 Boy and Girl with Rocking Horse

307 Girl with Doll's House

308 Boy with Train Set

(Des Rosalind Dease. Head printed in gold and then embossed)

1968 (25 Nov). *Christmas. Chalk-surfaced paper. One centre phosphor band* (4*d.*) *or two phosphor bands* (*others*). *P* 15 × 14 (4*d.*) *or* 14 × 15 (*others*).

775	**306**	4d.	black, orange, vermilion, ultramarine, bistre and gold	10	10
			a. Gold omitted..	£1500	
			b. Vermilion omitted*	£140	
			c. Ultramarine omitted	£150	
776	**307**	9d.	yellow-olive, black, brown, yellow, magenta, orange, turq-green & gold	15	15
			a. Yellow omitted	60·00	
777	**308**	1s.	6d. ultramarine, yellow-orange, brt purple, blue-green, black and gold	25	25
775/7			.. .. *Set of* 3	50	50

*The effect of the missing vermilion is shown on the rocking horse, saddle and faces which appear orange instead of red.

A single used example of the 4d. exists with the bistre omitted.

No. 775c is only known with the phosphor also omitted. All values exist with the embossing of Queen's head omitted.

309 R.M.S. *Queen Elizabeth 2*

310 Elizabethan Galleon

311 East Indiaman

312 *Cutty Sark*

313 S.S. *Great Britain*

314 R.M.S. *Mauretania*

(Des D. Gentleman)

1969 (15 Jan). *British Ships. Chalk-surfaced paper. Two vertical phosphor bands at right* (1*s.*), *one horizontal phosphor band* (5*d.*) *or two phosphor bands* (9*d.*). *P* 15 × 14.

778	**309**	5d.	black, grey, red and turquoise ..	10	10
			a. Black (Queen's head, value, hull and inscr) omitted	£900	
			b. Grey (decks, etc.) omitted ..	£110	
			c. Red omitted	50·00	
779	**310**	9d.	red, blue, ochre, brown, blk & grey	10	15
			a. Strip of 3. Nos. 779/81	85	85
			ab. Red and blue omitted	£1250	
			ac. Blue omitted	£1250	
780	**311**	9d.	ochre, brown, black and grey ..	10	15
781	**312**	9d.	ochre, brown, black and grey ..	10	15
782	**313**	1s.	brn, black, grey, grn & greenish yell	25	25
			a. Pair. Nos. 782/3	90	85
			ab. Greenish yellow omitted	£2000	
783	**314**	1s.	red, black, brown, carmine and grey	25	25
			a. Carmine (hull overlay) omitted ..		
778/83			.. .. *Set of* 6	1·60	90

The 9d. and 1s. values were arranged in horizontal strips of three and pairs respectively throughout the sheet.

No. 779b is known only with the phosphor also omitted.

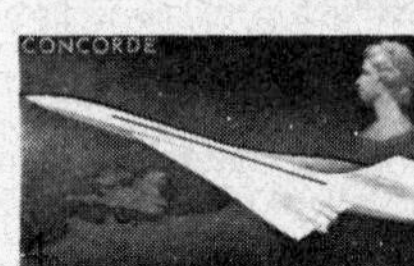

315 "Concorde" in Flight

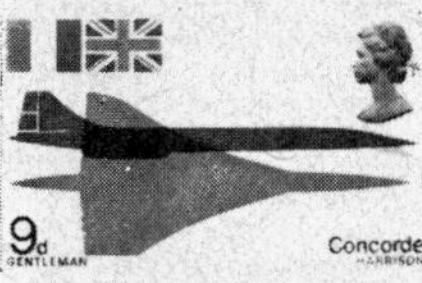

316 Plan and Elevation Views

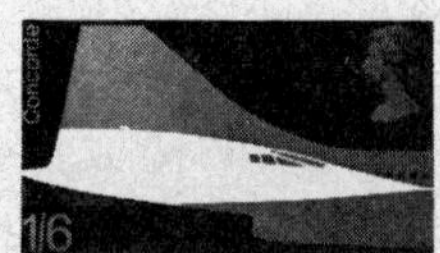

317 "Concorde's" Nose and Tail

(Des M. and Sylvia Goaman (4d.), D. Gentleman (9d., 1s. 6d.))

1969 (3 Mar). *First Flight of "Concorde". Chalk-surfaced paper. Two phosphor bands. P* 15 × 14.

784	**315**	4d. yellow-orange, violet, greenish blue, blue-green and pale green	10	10
		a. Violet (value, etc.) omitted ..	£300	
		b. Yellow-orange omitted	£125	
785	**316**	9d. ultramarine, emerald, red & grey-bl	20	20
786	**317**	1s. 6d. deep blue, silver-grey & lt blue	30	30
		a. Silver-grey omitted	£275	
784/6		.. .. *Set of* 3	50	50

No. 786a affects the Queen's head which appears in the light blue colour.

318 Queen Elizabeth II. (See also Type **357**)

(Des after plaster cast by Arnold Machin. Recess Bradbury, Wilkinson)

1969 (5 Mar). *P* 12.

787	**318**	2s. 6d. brown	50	30
788		5s. crimson-lake	2·00	60
789		10s. deep ultramarine	7·00	7·50
790		£1 bluish black	3·00	1·60
787/90		.. .. *Set of* 4	11·00	9·00

For decimal issue, see Nos. 829/31*b* and notes after No. 831*b*.

319 Page from *Daily Mail*, and Vickers "Vimy" Aircraft

320 Europa and CEPT Emblems

321 ILO Emblem

322 Flags of NATO Countries

323 Vickers "Vimy" Aircraft and Globe showing Flight

(Des P. Sharland (5d., 1s., 1s. 6d.), M. and Sylvia Goaman (9d., 1s. 9d.)

1969 (2 Apr). *Anniversaries. Events described on stamps. Chalk-surfaced paper. Two phosphor bands. P* 15 × 14.

791	**319**	5d. black, pale sage-grn, chest & new bl	10	10
792	**320**	9d. pale turq, dp bl, lt emer-green & blk	20	20
793	**321**	1s. bright purple, deep blue and lilac	20	20
794	**322**	1s. 6d. red, royal blue, yellow-green, black, lemon and new blue ..	20	20
		e. Black omitted	60·00	
		f. Yellow-green omitted	48·00	
795	**323**	1s. 9d. yellow-olive, greenish yellow and pale turquoise-green	25	25
		a. Uncoated paper*	£200	
791/5		.. .. *Set of* 5	85	85

*Uncoated paper. The second note after No. 744 also applies here.

324 Durham Cathedral

325 York Minster

326 St. Giles' Cathedral, Edinburgh

327 Canterbury Cathedral

328 St. Paul's Cathedral

329 Liverpool Metropolitan Cathedral

(Des P. Gauld)

1969 (28 May). *British Architecture. Cathedrals. Chalk-surfaced paper. Two phosphor bands. P* 15 × 14.

796	**324**	5d. grey-blk, orge, pale bluish vio & blk	10	10
		a. Block of 4. Nos. 796/9	85	1·00
		b. Pale bluish violet omitted	£1500	
797	**325**	5d. grey-black, pale bluish violet, new blue and black	10	10
		b. Pale bluish violet omitted	£1500	
798	**326**	5d. grey-black, purple, green and black	10	10
		c. Green omitted*	40·00	
799	**327**	5d. grey-black, green, new blue & black	10	10
800	**328**	9d. grey-blk, ochre, pale drab, vio & blk	15	15
		a. Black (value) omitted	£100	
801	**329**	1s. 6d. grey-black, pale turquoise, pale reddish violet, pale yellow-ol & blk	15	15
		a. Black (value) omitted	£2000	
		b. Black (value) double		
796/801		.. .. *Set of* 6	1·00	55

The 5d. values were issued together *se-tenant* in blocks of four throughout the sheet.

*The missing green on the roof top is known on R. 2/5, R. 8/5 and R. 10/5, but all from different sheets, and it only occurred in part of the printing, being "probably caused by a batter on the impression cylinder". Examples are also known with the green partly omitted.

330 The King's Gate, Caernarvon Castle

331 The Eagle Tower, Caernarvon Castle

332 Queen Eleanor's Gate, Caernarvon Castle

333 Celtic Cross, Margam Abbey

334 H.R.H. The Prince of Wales (after photo by G. Argent)

(Des D. Gentleman)

1969 (1 July). *Investiture of H.R.H. The Prince of Wales. Chalk-surfaced paper. Two phosphor bands. P* 14 × 15.

802	**330**	5d. deep olive-grey, light olive-grey, deep grey, light grey, red, pale turquoise-green, black and silver ..	10	10
		a. Strip of 3. Nos. 802/4	60	75
		b. Black (value and inscr) omitted ..	£325	
		c. Red omitted*	£200	
		d. Deep grey omitted**	£110	
		e. Pale turquoise-green omitted ..	£300	
803	**331**	5d. deep olive-grey, light olive-grey, deep grey, light grey, red, pale turquoise-green, black and silver ..	10	10
		b. Black (value and inscr) omitted ..	£325	
		c. Red omitted*	£200	
		d. Deep grey omitted**	£110	
		e. Pale turquoise-green omitted ..	£300	
804	**332**	5d. deep olive-grey, light olive-grey, deep grey, light grey, red, pale turquoise-green, black and silver ..	10	10
		b. Black (value and inscr) omitted ..	£325	
		c. Red omitted*	£200	
		d. Deep grey omitted**	£110	
		e. Pale turquoise-green omitted ..	£300	
805	**333**	9d. deep grey, light grey, black and gold	10	10
806	**334**	1s. blackish yellow-olive and gold ..	10	10
802/6		.. .. *Set of* 5	70	45

The 5d. values were issued together, *se-tenant*, in strips of three throughout the sheet.

*The 5d. value is also known with the red misplaced downwards and where this occurs the red printing does not take very well on the silver background and in some cases is so faint that it could be mistaken for a missing red. However, the red can be seen under a magnifying glass and caution should therefore be exercised when purchasing copies of Nos. 802/4c.

**The deep grey affects the dark portions of the windows and doors.

335 Mahatma Gandhi

(Des B. Mullick)

1969 (13 Aug). *Gandhi Centenary Year. Chalk-surfaced paper. Two phosphor bands. P* 15 × 14.

807	**335**	1s. 6d. black, green, red-orange & grey	30	30
		a. Printed on the gummed side ..	£275	

336 National Giro "G" Symbol

337 Telecommunications—International Subscriber Dialling

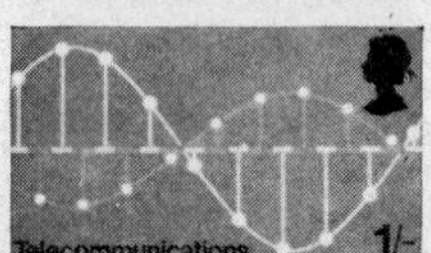

338 Telecommunications—Pulse Code Modulation

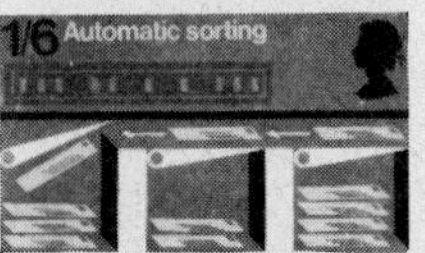

339 Postal Mechanisation—Automatic Sorting

(Des D. Gentleman. Litho De La Rue)

1969 (1 Oct). *Post Office Technology Commemoration. Chalk-surfaced paper. Two phosphor bands. P* $13\frac{1}{2} \times 14$.

No.	Type	Description	Unused	Used
808	**336**	5d. new bl, greenish bl, lavender & blk	10	10
809	**337**	9d. emerald, violet-blue and black ..	15	15
810	**338**	1s. emerald, lavender and black ..	15	15
811	**339**	1s. 6d. brt purple, lt blue, grey-bl & blk	40	40
808/11		.. .. *Set of* 4	70	70

340 Herald Angel

341 The Three Shepherds

342 The Three Kings

(Des F. Wegner. Queen's head (and stars 4d., 5d. and scroll-work 1s. 6d.) printed in gold and then embossed)

1969 (26 Nov). *Christmas. Chalk-surfaced paper. Two phosphor bands (5d., 1s. 6d.) or one centre band (4d.). P* 15×14.

No.	Type	Description	Unused	Used
812	**340**	4d. vermilion, new blue, orange, bright purple, light green, bluish violet, blackish brown and gold	10	10
		a. Gold (Queen's head etc.) omitted ..	£2500	
813	**341**	5d. magenta, light blue, royal blue, olive-brown, green, greenish yellow, red and gold	10	10
		a. Light blue (sheep, etc.) omitted ..	60·00	
		b. Red omitted*	£450	
		c. Gold (Queen's head) omitted ..	£400	
		d. Green omitted	£225	
814	**342**	1s. 6d. greenish yellow, bright purple, bluish violet, deep slate, orange, green, new blue and gold	30	30
		a. Gold (Queen's head etc.) omitted ..	£140	
		b. Deep slate (value) omitted	£350	
		c. Greenish yellow omitted	£125	
		d. Bluish violet omitted	£300	
		e. New blue omitted	£100	
812/14		.. .. *Set of* 3	45	45

*The effect of the missing red is shown on the hat, leggings and purse which appear as dull orange.

The 5d. and 1s. 6d. values are known with the embossing omitted.

Used copies of the 5d. have been seen with the olive-brown or greenish yellow omitted.

343 Fife Harling

344 Cotswold Limestone

345 Welsh Stucco

346 Ulster Thatch

(Des D. Gentleman (5d., 9d.), Sheila Robinson (1s., 1s. 6d.))

1970 (11 Feb). *British Rural Architecture. Chalk-surfaced paper. Two phosphor bands. P* 15×14.

No.	Type	Description	Unused	Used
815	**343**	5d. grey, grey-black, black, lemon, greenish bl, orge-brn, ultram & grn	10	10
		a. Lemon omitted	60·00	
		b. Grey (Queen's head and cottage shading) omitted	£4000	
816	**344**	9d. orange-brown, olive-yellow, bright green, black, grey-black and grey ..	20	20
817	**345**	1s. dp blue, reddish lilac, drab & new bl	20	20
		a. New blue omitted	45·00	
818	**346**	1s. 6d. greenish yell, blk, turq-bl & lilac	35	35
		a. Turquoise-blue omitted	£3500	
815/18		.. .. *Set of* 4	75	75

Used examples of the 5d. have been seen with the grey-black or greenish blue colours omitted.

347 Signing the Declaration of Arbroath

348 Florence Nightingale attending Patients

349 Signing of International Co-operative Alliance

350 Pilgrims and *Mayflower*

351 Sir William Herschel, Francis Baily, Sir John Herschel and Telescope

(Des F. Wegner (5d., 9d., and 1s. 6d.), Marjorie Saynor (1s., 1s. 9d.). Queen's head printed in gold and then embossed)

1970 (1 Apr). *Anniversaries. Events described on stamps. Chalk-surfaced paper. Two phosphor bands. P* 15×14.

No.	Type	Description	Unused	Used
819	**347**	5d. blk, yell-olive, blue, emer, greenish yellow, rose-red, gold & orange-red	10	10
		a. Gold (Queen's head) omitted ..	£400	
		b. Emerald omitted	50·00	
820	**348**	9d. ochre, deep blue, carmine, black, blue-green, yellow-olive, gold & bl	15	15
		a. Ochre omitted	£150	
821	**349**	1s. green, greenish yellow, brown, black, cerise, gold and light blue ..	15	15
		a. Gold (Queen's head) omitted ..	50·00	
		c. Green omitted	£110	
		d. Brown omitted	£125	
822	**350**	1s. 6d. greenish yellow, carmine, deep yellow-olive, emerald, black, blue gold and sage-green	30	30
		a. Gold (Queen's head) omitted ..	90·00	
		b. Emerald omitted	40·00	
823	**351**	1s. 9d. blk, slate, lemon, gold & brt pur	30	30
819/23		.. .. *Set of* 5	90	90

The 9d., 1s. and 1s. 6d. are known with the embossing omitted. No. 821c also exists with embossing omitted.

The 1s. 9d. with the lemon colour omitted has been seen used on a First Day Cover.

352 "Mr. Pickwick and Sam" (*Pickwick Papers*)

353 "Mr. and Mrs. Micawber" (*David Copperfield*)

354 "David Copperfield and Betsy Trotwood" (*David Copperfield*)

355 "Oliver asking for more" (*Oliver Twist*)

356 "Grasmere" (from engraving by J. Farrington, R.A.)

T **352/5** were issued together *se-tenant* in blocks of four throughout the sheet.

(Des Rosalind Dease. Queen's head printed in gold and then embossed)

1970 (3 June). *Literary Anniversaries. Death Centenary of Charles Dickens (novelist) (5d.* × *4) and Birth Bicentenary of William Wordsworth (poet) (1s. 6d.). Chalk-surfaced paper. Two phosphor bands. P* 14×15.

No.	Type	Description	Unused	Used
824	**352**	5d. black, orange, silver, gold and mag	10	10
		a. Block of 4. Nos. 824/7	90	90
		ab. Imperf (block of four)	£600	
825	**353**	5d. black, magenta, silver, gold & orge	10	10
826	**354**	5d. black, light greenish blue, silver, gold and yellow-bistre	10	10
		b. Yellow-bistre (value) omitted ..	£1200	
827	**355**	5d. black, yellow-bistre, silver, gold and light greenish blue	10	10
		b. Yellow-bistre (background) omitted	£3000	
		c. Light greenish blue (value) omitted*	£450	
828	**356**	1s. 6d. light yellow-olive, black, silver, gold and bright blue	20	20
		a. Gold (Queen's head) omitted ..	£225	
		b. Silver ("Grasmere") omitted ..	60·00	
824/8		.. .. *Set of* 5	1·00	55

*No 827c (unlike No. 827b) comes from a sheet on which the colour was only partially omitted so that, although No. 827 was completely without the light greenish blue colour, it was still partially present on No. 826.

The 1s. 6d. is known with embossing omitted.

357 (Value redrawn)

(Des after plaster cast by Arnold Machin. Recess B.W.)

1970 (17 June)–**72**. *Decimal Currency. Chalk-surfaced paper or phosphorised paper (10p.). P* 12.

No.	Type	Description	Unused	Used
829	**357**	10p. cerise	1·00	75
830		20p. olive-green	70	15
831		50p. deep ultramarine	1·40	40
831*b*		£1 bluish black (6.12.72)	2·75	75
829/31*b*		.. .. *Set of* 4	5·25	1·75

The 20p. and 50p. exist on thinner, uncoated paper and are listed in the *Great Britain Concise Catalogue*.

A whiter paper was introduced in 1973. The £1 appeared on 27 Sept. 1973, the 20p. on 30 Nov. 1973 and the 50p. on 20 Feb. 1974.

The 50p. was issued on 1 Feb. 1973 on phosphorised paper. This cannot be distinguished from No. 831 with the naked eye.

The £1, T **318**, was also issued, on 17 June 1970, in sheets of 100 (10 × 10) instead of panes of 40 (8 × 5) but it is not easy to distinguish from No. 790 in singles. It can be readily differentiated when in large strips or marginal pieces showing sheet markings or plate numbers.

358 Runners

359 Swimmers

360 Cyclists

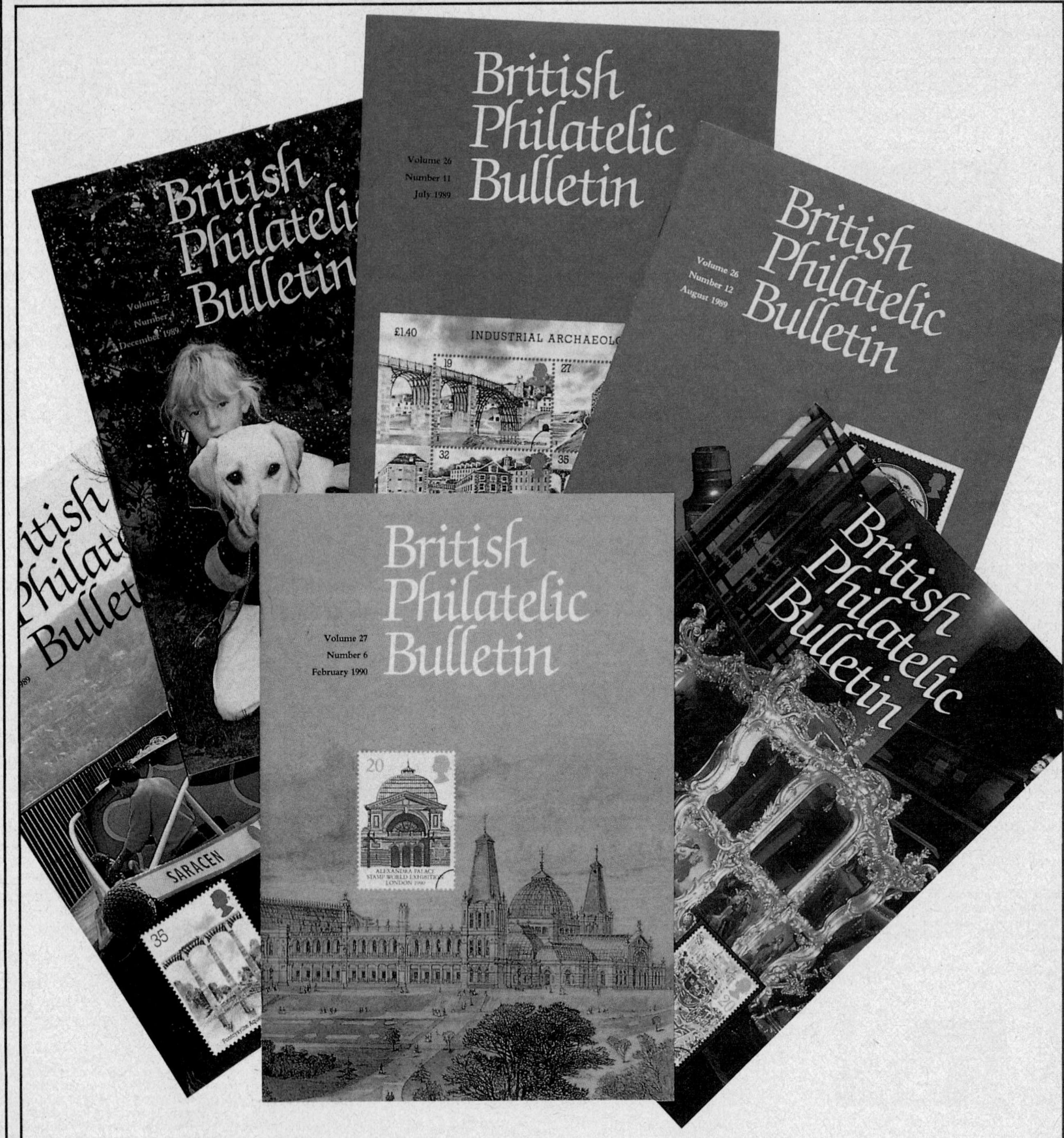
British Philatelic Bulletin
Volume 26
Number 11
July 1989
British Philatelic Bulletin
Volume 26
Number 12
August 1989
British Philatelic Bulletin
Volume 27
December 1989
British Philatelic Bulletin
Volume 27
Number 6
February 1990
British Philatelic Bulletin
INDUSTRIAL ARCHAEOLO
£1.40
SARACEN

(Des A. Restall. Litho D.L.R.)

1970 (15 July). *Ninth British Commonwealth Games. Chalk-surfaced paper. Two phosphor bands. P* 13½ × 14.

No.	Type	Description	Unused	Used
832	**358**	5d. pk, emer, greenish yell & dp yell-grn	10	10
		a. Greenish yellow omitted	£3000	
833	**359**	1s. 6d. light greenish blue, lilac, bistre-brown and Prussian blue	40	40
834	**360**	1s. 9d. yellow-orange, lilac, salmon and deep red-brown	40	40
832/4		.. .. *Set of* 3	80	80

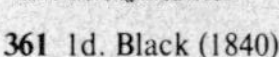

361 1d. Black (1840)

362 1s. Green (1847)

363 4d. Carmine (1855)

(Des D. Gentleman)

1970 (18 Sept). *"Philympia 70" Stamp Exhibition. Chalk-surfaced paper. Two phosphor bands. P* 14 × 14½.

No.	Type	Description	Unused	Used
835	**361**	5d. grey-black, brownish bistre, black and dull purple	10	10
836	**362**	9d. light drab, bluish green, stone, black and dull purple	35	35
837	**363**	1s. 6d. carmine, lt drab, blk & dull pur	40	40
835/7		.. .. *Set of* 3	75	75

364 Shepherds and Apparition of the Angel

365 Mary, Joseph, and Christ in the Manger

366 The Wise Men bearing gifts

(Des Sally Stiff after De Lisle Psalter. Queen's head printed in gold and then embossed)

1970 (25 Nov). *Christmas. Chalk-surfaced paper. One centre phosphor band (4d.) or two phosphor bands (others). P* 14 × 15.

No.	Type	Description	Unused	Used
838	**364**	4d. brown-red, turquoise-green, pale chestnut, brn, grey-blk, gold & verm	10	10
839	**365**	5d. emerald, gold, blue, brown-red, ochre, grey-black and violet ..	10	10
		a. Gold (Queen's head) omitted ..	†	£2500
		b. Emerald omitted	60·00	
		c. Imperf (pair)	£250	
840	**366**	1s. 6d. gold, grey-black, pale turq-grn, salmon, ultram, ochre & yellow-grn	35	35
		a. Salmon omitted	£125	
		b. Ochre omitted	65·00	
838/40		.. .. *Set of* 3	50	50

The 4d. and 5d. are known with embossing omitted, and the 1s. 6d. is known with embossing and phosphor omitted.

(New Currency. 100 new pence = £1)

"X" NUMBERS. The following definitive series has been allocated "X" prefixes to the catalogue numbers to avoid re-numbering all subsequent issues.

367

367*a*

NO VALUE INDICATED. Stamps as Types **367**/*a* inscribed "2nd" or "1st" are listed as Nos. 1445/52.

PRINTING PROCESSES

Litho   Photo

(*Illustrations enlarged* ×6)

Litho. Clear outlines to value and frame of stamp.
Photo. Uneven lines to value and frame formed by edges of screen.

Two types of the 3p., 10p. and 26p. (Nos. X930/c, X886/b and X967/a).

I   II

I   II

I   II

Figures of face value as I (all 3p., 10p. and 26p. sheet and booklet stamps except for multivalue coil, No. X930cl, 1984 "Christian Heritage" £4 booklet and 1987 £1.04 "window" booklet).

Figures of face value narrower as in II (from coil No. X930cl (3p.), 1984 "Christian Heritage" £4 booklet (10p.) or 1987 £1.04 "window" booklet (26p.)).

This catalogue includes changes of figure styles on those stamps where there is no other listable difference. Similar changes have also taken place on other values, but only in conjunction with listed colour, paper or perforation differences.

(Des from plaster cast by Arnold Machin)

1971 (15 Feb)–**90**. *Decimal Currency. T* **367**. *Chalk-surfaced paper.*

(*a*) *Photo Harrison* (*except for a printing of No.* X879 *in sheets produced by Enschedé in* 1979). *With phosphor bands. P* 15×14.

No.	Description	Unused	Used
X841	½p. turquoise-blue (2 bands)	10	10
	a. Imperf (pair)†	£900	
	l. Booklet pane. No. X841 × 2 *se-tenant* vert with X849 × 2	5·50	
	la. Ditto, *se-tenant* horiz (14.7.71) ..	75	
	m. Booklet pane. No. X841×5 plus label	2·25	
	n. Coil strip. No. X849, X841×2 and X844×2	35	
	o. Booklet pane. No. X841 × 3, X851 × 3 and X852 × 6 (24.5.72)	10·00	
	p. Booklet pane. No. X841 × 3, X842 and X852 × 2 (24.5.72)	70·00	
	q. Coil strip. No. X870, X849, X844 and X841 × 2 (3.12.75)	80	
	r. Booklet pane. No. X841 × 2, X844 × 3 and X870 (10.3.76)	65	
	s. Booklet pane. No. X841 × 2, X844 × 2, X873 × 2 and X881 × 4 (8½p. values at right) (26.1.77)	2·50	
	sa. Ditto. 8½p. values at left	2·25	
	t. Booklet pane. No. X841, X844, X894 × 3 and X902 (14p. value at right) (26.1.81)	2·25	
	ta. Ditto. 14p. value at left	2·25	
	u. Booklet pane. No. X841, X857 × 4 and X899 × 3 (12½p. values at left) (1.2.82)	2·75	
	ua. Ditto. 12½p. values at right	2·75	
X842	½p. turquoise-blue (1 side band) (24.5.72)	65·00	25·00
X843	½p. turquoise-bl (1 centre band) (14.12.77)	20	20
	l. Coil strip. No. X843 × 2, X875 and X845 × 2 (14.12.77)	55	
	m. Booklet pane. No. X843 × 2, X845 × 2 and X875 plus label (8.2.78) ..	65	
X844	1p. crimson (2 bands)	10	10
	a. Imperf (vert coil)		
	b. Pair, one imperf 3 sides (vert coil) ..		
	c. Imperf (pair)		
	l. Booklet pane. No. X844 × 2 *se-tenant* vert with X848 × 2	5·50	
	m. Ditto, *se-tenant* horiz (14.7.71) ..	75	
	n. Booklet pane. No. X844 × 2, X876 × 3 and X883 × 3 (9p. values at right) (13.6.77)	4·00	
	na. Ditto. 9p. values at left	2·75	
X845	1p. crimson (1 centre band) (14.12.77) ..	20	20
	l. Booklet pane. No. X879 and X845 × 2 plus label (17.10.79)	50	
	m. Coil strip. No. X879 and X845 × 2 plus 2 labels (16.1.80)	45	
	n. Booklet pane. No. X845 × 2, X860 and X898 each × 3 (5.4.83)	6·50	
	p. Booklet pane. No. X845× 3, X863 × 2 and X900 × 3 (3.9.84)	2·50	
	q. Booklet pane. No. X845 × 2 and X896 × 4 (29.7.86)	2·50	
	s. Booklet pane. No. X845, X867 × 2 and X900 × 3 (20.10.86)	3·25	
	sa. Ditto, but with vert sides of pane imperf (29.9.87)	2·50	
X846	1p. crimson ("all-over") (10.10.79) ..	20	20
X847	1p. crimson (1 side band) (20.10.86) ..	75	90
	l. Booklet pane. X847, X901 and X910 × 2	2·50	
	m. Booklet pane. No. X847, X901 × 2, X910 × 5 and X914 with margins all round (3.3.87)	7·50	
X848	1½p. black (2 bands)	20	15
	a. Uncoated paper (1971)*	£110	
	b. Imperf (pair)		
	c. Imperf 3 sides (horiz pair)		
X849	2p. myrtle-green (face value as T **367**) (2 bands)	20	10
	l. Booklet pane. No. X849 × 2, X880 × 2 and X886 × 3 plus label (10p. values at right) (28.8.79)	2·00	
	la. Ditto. 10p. values at left	2·00	
	m. Booklet pane. No. X849 × 3, X889 × 2 and X895 × 2 plus label (12p. values at right) (4.2.80)	2·75	
	ma. Ditto. 12p. values at left	2·75	
	n. Booklet pane. No. X849, X888 × 3, X889 and X895 × 4 with margins all round (16.4.80)	3·00	
	o. Booklet pane. No. X849 × 6 with margins all round (16.4.80)	60	
	p. Booklet pane. No. X849, X857, X898 and X899 × 6 with margins all round (19.5.82)	6·50	
X850	2p. myrtle-green (face value as T **367**) ("all-over") (10.10.79)	20	15
X851	2½p. magenta (1 centre band)	15	10
	a. Imperf (pair)†	£225	
	l. Booklet pane. No. X851 × 5 plus label	3·50	
	m. Booklet pane. No. X851 × 4 plus two labels	4·00	
	n. Booklet pane. No. X851 × 3, X852 × 3 and X855 × 6 (24.5.72)	10·00	
X852	2½p. magenta (1 side band)	1·75	1·75
	l. Booklet pane. No. X852 × 2 and X855 × 4	4·50	
X853	2½p. magenta (2 bands) (21.5.75) ..	20	30
X854	2½p. rose-red (2 bands) (26.8.81) ..	40	40
	l. Booklet pane. No. X854 × 3, X862 × 2 and X894 × 3 (11½p. values at left) ..	6·00	
	la. Ditto. 11½p. values at right	6·00	
X855	3p. ultramarine (2 bands)	20	10
	a. Imperf (coil strip of 5)	£1000	
	b. Imperf (pair)†	£225	
	c. Uncoated paper (1972)*	40·00	
	l. Booklet pane. No. X855 × 5 plus label	2·25	
X856	3p. ultramarine (1 centre band) (10.9.73)	20	25
	a. Imperf (pair)†	£250	
	b. Imperf between (vert pair)† ..	£375	
	c. Imperf horiz (vert pair)†	£150	
X857	3p. bright magenta (2 bands) (1.2.82) ..	30	25
X858	3½p. olive-grey (*shades*) (2 bands) ..	30	30
	a. Imperf (pair)	£350	
X859	3½p. olive-grey (1 centre band) (24.6.74) ..	30	15
X860	3½p. purple-brown (1 centre band) (5.4.83)	1·75	1·25
X861	4p. ochre-brown (2 bands)	20	20
	a. Imperf (pair)†	£450	
X862	4p. greenish blue (2 bands) (26.8.81) ..	2·00	1·75
X863	4p. greenish blue (1 centre band) (3.9.84)	75	75
X864	4p. greenish blue (1 side band) (8.1.85)	1·25	1·50
	l. Booklet pane. No. X864 × 2, X901 × 4, X909 × 2 and X916 with margins all round	6·50	
X865	4½p. grey-blue (2 bands) (24.10.73) ..	20	25
	a. Imperf (pair)	£250	
X866	5p. pale violet (2 bands)	20	10
X867	5p. claret (1 centre band) (20.10.86) ..	90	1·00
X868	5½p. violet (2 bands) (24.10.73) ..	25	25
X869	5½p. violet (1 centre band) (17.3.75) ..	20	20
	a. Uncoated paper*	£350	
X870	6p. light emerald (2 bands)	30	15
	a. Uncoated paper*	15·00	
X871	6½p. greenish blue (2 bands) (4.9.74) ..	45	45
X872	6½p. greenish blue (1 centre band) (24.9.75)	30	15
	a. Imperf (vert pair)	£300	
	b. Uncoated paper*	£160	
X873	6½p. greenish blue (1 side band) (26.1.77)	60	55
X874	7p. purple-brown (2 bands) (15.1.75) ..	35	25
	a. Imperf (pair)	£250	
X875	7p. purple-brown (1 centre band) (13.6.77)	35	20
	a. Imperf (pair)	£100	
	l. Booklet pane. No. X875 × 10 and X883 × 10 (15.11.78)	4·50	
X876	7p. purple-brown (1 side band) (13.6.77)	60	75
X877	7½p. pale chestnut (2 bands)	30	25
X878	8p. rosine (2 bands) (24.10.73) ..	25	20
	a. Uncoated paper*	10·00	
X879	8p. rosine (1 centre band) (20.8.79) ..	25	15
	a. Uncoated paper*	£550	
	b. Imperf (pair)	£550	
	l. Booklet pane. No. X879 and X886, each × 10 (14.11.79)	5·00	
X880	8p. rosine (1 side band) (29.8.79) ..	50	60

X881 8½p. light yellowish green (*shades*) (2 bands) (24.9.75) . . 35 20
a. Imperf (pair) . . £750
X882 9p. yellow-orange and black (2 bands) . . 60 30
X883 9p. deep violet (2 bands) (25.2.76) . . 45 25
a. Imperf (pair) . . £175
X884 9½p. purple (2 bands) (25.2.76) . . 45 30
X885 10p. orange-brown and chestnut (2 bands) (11.8.71) . . 40 30
a. Orange-brown omitted . . £150
b. Imperf (horiz pair) . . £2000
X886 10p. orange-brn (Type I) (2 bands) (25.2.76) 40 20
a. Imperf (pair) . . £250
b. Type II (4.9.84) . . 2·00 2·00
bl. Booklet pane. No. X886b, X901 and X909 × 7, with margins all round . . 6·50
X887 10p. orange-brown ("all-over") (3.10.79) . . 30 45
X888 10p. orange-brown (1 centre band) (4.2.80) 30 20
a. Imperf (pair) . . £225
l. Booklet pane. No. X888 × 9 with margins all round (16.4.80) . . 2·75
m. Booklet pane. No. X888 and X895, each × 10 (12.11.80) . . 6·50
X889 10p. orange-brown (1 side band) (4.2.80) 60 60
X890 10½p. yellow (2 bands) (25.2.76) . . 40 30
X891 10½p. deep dull blue (2 bands) (26.4.78) . . 60 45
X892 11p. brown-red (2 bands) (25.2.76) . . 40 25
a. Imperf (pair) . . £1500
X893 11½p. drab (1 centre band) (14.1.81) . . 45 30
a. Imperf (pair) . . £175
l. Booklet pane. No. X893 and X902, each × 10 (11.11.81) . . 8·50
X894 11½p. drab (1 side band) (26.1.81) . . 60 60
l. Booklet pane. No. X894 × 4 and X902 × 6 (6.5.81) . . 4·50
X895 12p. yellowish green (2 bands) (4.2.80) . . 45 40
l. Booklet pane. No. X895 × 9 with margins all round (16.4.80) . . 3·50
X896 12p. brt emerald (1 centre band) (29.10.85) 60 40
l. Booklet pane. No. X896 × 9 with margins all round (18.3.86) . . 4·50
X897 12p. bright emerald (1 side band) (14.1.86) 75 75
l. Booklet pane. No. X897 × 4 and X909 × 6 (12p. values at left) . . 5·50
la. Ditto. 12p. values at right . . 5·50
m. Booklet pane. No. X897 × 6, X909 × 2 and X915 with margins all round (18.3.86) . . 7·50
X898 12½p. light emerald (1 centre band) (27.1.82) 45 25
a. Imperf (pair) . . £100
l. Booklet pane. No. X898 and X907 each × 10 (10.11.82) . . 12·00
X899 12½p. light emerald (1 side band) (1.2.82) . . 60 60
l. Booklet pane. No. X899 × 4 and X907 × 6 (1.2.82) . . 5·00
m. Booklet pane. No. X899 × 6 with margins all round (19.5.82) . . 2·25
n. Booklet pane. No. X899 × 4 and X908 × 6 (12½p. values at left) (5.4.83) 10·00
na. Ditto. 12½p. values at right . . 10·00
X900 13p. pale chestnut (1 centre band) (28.8.84) 50 35
a. Imperf (pair) . . £400
l. Booklet pane. No. X900 × 9 with margins all round (8.1.85) . . 4·00
m. Booklet pane. No. X900 × 6 with margins all round (3.3.87) . . 2·50
n. Booklet pane. No. X900 × 4 with margins all round (4.8.87) . . 1·75
o. Booklet pane. No. X900 × 10 with margins all round (4.8.87) . . 4·00
X901 13p. pale chestnut (1 side band) (3.9.84) . . 60 60
l. Booklet pane. No. X901 × 4 and X909 × 6 (13p. values at left) . . 6·50
la. Ditto. 13p. values at right . . 6·50
m. Booklet pane. No. X901 × 6 with margins all round (4.9.84) . . 3·00
n. Booklet pane. No. X901 and X910 × 5 (20.10.86) . . 3·75
na. Ditto, but with vert sides of pane imperf (29.9.87) . . 2·75
X902 14p. grey-blue (2 bands) (26.1.81) . . 50 45
X903 14p. deep blue (1 centre band) (23.8.88) . . 25 30
a. Imperf (pair)
l. Booklet pane. No. X903 × 4 with margins all round . . 85
m. Booklet pane. No. X903 × 10 with margins all round . . 3·50
n. Booklet pane. No. X903 × 4 with horiz edges of pane imperf (11.10.88) . . 85
p. Booklet pane. No. X903 × 10 with horiz edges of pane imperf (11.10.88) . . 2·10
q. Booklet pane. No. X903 × 4 with three sides of pane imperf (24.1.89) . . 85
X904 14p. deep blue (1 side band) (5.9.88) . . 25 30
l. Booklet pane. No. X904 and X911×2 plus label . . 90
m. Booklet pane. No. X904×2 and X911×4 with vert sides of pane imperf 1·50
X905 15p. bright blue (1 centre band) (26.9.89) 25 20
a. Imperf (pair) . . £250
X906 15p. bright blue (1 side band) (2.10.89) . . 25 30
l. Booklet pane. No. X906 × 2 and X913 plus label . . 75
m. Booklet pane. No. X906, X913, X918, 1446, 1448, 1468, 1470 and 1472 (20.3.90) . . 5·00
X907 15½p. pale violet (2 bands) (1.2.82) . . 45 45
l. Booklet pane. No. X907 × 6 with margins all round (19.5.82) . . 3·00
m. Booklet pane. No. X907 × 9 with margins all round (19.5.82) . . 4·00
X908 16p. olive-drab (2 bands) (5.4.83) . . 1·50 1·75
X909 17p. grey-blue (2 bands) (3.9.84) . . 75 75
l. Booklet pane. No. X909 × 3 plus label (4.11.85) . . 2·25
X910 18p. deep olive-grey (2 bands) (20.10.86) 75 75
X911 19p. bright orange-red (2 bands) (5.9.88) 75 75
X912 20p. dull purple (2 bands) (25.2.76) . . 75 40
X913 20p. brownish black (2 bands) (2.10.89) . . 30 30
X914 26p. rosine (2 bands) (3.3.87) . . 3·50 3·50
X915 31p. purple (2 bands) (18.3.86) . . 3·50 3·50
X916 34p. ochre-brown (2 bands) (8.1.85) . . 3·50 3·50
X917 50p. ochre-brown (2 bands) (2.2.77) . . 1·75 40
X918 50p. ochre (2 bands) (20.3.90) . . 1·90 2·10

(*b*) *Photo Harrison. On phosphorised paper. P* 15×14.

X924 ½p. turquoise-blue (10.12.80) . . 10 10
a. Imperf (pair) . . £125
l. Coil strip. No. X924 and X932 × 3 (30.12.81) . . 45
X925 1p. crimson (12.12.79) . . 10 10
l. Coil strip. No. X925 and X932 × 3 (14.8.84) . . 20
X926 2p. myrtle-green (face value as T **367**) (12.12.79) . . 10 10
X927 2p. dp grn (face value as T **367***a*) (26.7.88) 10 10
X928 2p. myrtle-green (face value as T **367***a*) (5.9.88) . . 20 10
l. Coil strip. No. X928 and X932 × 3 . . 40
X929 2½p. rose-red (14.1.81) . . 20 20
l. Coil strip. No. X929 and X930 × 3 (6.81) . . 45
X930 3p. bright magenta (Type I) (22.10.80) . . 20 20
a. Imperf (horiz pair)
b. Booklet pane. No. X930, X931 × 2 and X947 × 6 with margins all round (14.9.83) . . 6·50
c. Type II (10.10.89) . . 20 25
cl. Coil strip. No. X930c and X933 × 3 . . 25
X931 3½p. purple-brown (30.3.83) . . 35 30
X932 4p. greenish blue (30.12.81) . . 25 20
X933 4p. new blue (26.7.88) . . 10 10
X934 5p. pale violet (10.10.79) . . 30 25
X935 5p. dull red-brown (26.7.88) . . 10 10
X936 7p. red (29.10.85) . . 2·00 1·50
X937 8½p. yellowish green (24.3.76) . . 30 55
X938 10p. orange-brown (11.79) . . 15 20
X939 11p. brown-red (27.8.80) . . 60 75
X940 11½p. ochre-brown (15.8.79) . . 50 45
X941 12p. yellowish green (30.1.80) . . 45 40
X942 13p. olive-grey (15.8.79) . . 60 45
X943 13½p. purple-brown (30.1.80) . . 65 60
X944 14p. grey-blue (14.1.81) . . 50 40
X945 15p. ultramarine (15.8.79) . . 50 40
X946 15½p. pale violet (14.1.81) . . 50 40
a. Imperf (pair) . . £300
X947 16p. olive-drab (30.3.83) . . 60 30
a. Imperf (pair) . . £160
l. Booklet pane. No. X947 × 9 with margins all round (14.9.83) . . 3·75
X948 16½p. pale chestnut (27.1.82) . . 85 75
X949 17p. light emerald (30.1.80) . . 70 40
X950 17p. grey-blue (30.3.83) . . 60 40
a. Imperf (pair) . . £225
l. Booklet pane. No. X950 × 6 with margins all round (4.9.84) . . 3·00
m. Booklet pane. No. X950 × 9 with margins all round (8.1.85) . . 4·50
X951 17½p. pale chestnut (30.1.80) . . 80 80
X952 18p. deep violet (14.1.81) . . 70 75
X953 18p. deep olive-grey (28.8.84) . . 70 60
a. Imperf (pair) . . £160
l. Booklet pane. No. X953 × 9 with margins all round (3.3.87) . . 5·50
m. Booklet pane. No. X953 × 4 with margins all round (4.8.87) . . 2·50
n. Booklet pane. No. X953 × 10 with margins all round (4.8.87) . . 5·50
X954 19p. bright orange-red (23.8.88) . . 30 35
a. Imperf (pair) . . £225
l. Booklet pane. No. X954 × 4 with margins all round . . 1·25
m. Booklet pane. No. X954 × 10 with margins all round . . 4·50
n. Booklet pane. No. X954 × 4 with horiz edges of pane imperf (11.10.88) . . 1·25
o. Booklet pane. No. X954 × 10 with horiz edges of pane imperf (11.10.88) 3·00
q. Booklet pane. No. X954 × 4 with three edges of pane imperf (24.1.89) . . 1·25
X955 19½p. olive-grey (27.1.82) . . 2·50 1·50
X956 20p. dull purple (10.10.79) . . 80 20
X957 20p. turquoise-green (23.8.88) . . 30 35
X958 20p. brownish black (26.9.89) . . 30 30
a. Imperf (pair)
l. Booklet pane. No. X958 × 5 plus label with vert sides of pane imperf (2.10.89) 1·50
X959 20½p. ultramarine (30.3.83) . . 1·10 85
a. Imperf (pair)
X960 22p. blue (22.10.80) . . 80 45
a. Imperf (pair) . . £150
X961 22p. yellow-green (28.8.84) . . 35 45
a. Imperf (horiz pair) . . £950
X962 23p. brown-red (30.3.83) . . 1·40 60
a. Imperf (horiz pair) . . £750
X963 23p. bright green (23.8.88) . . 35 40
X964 24p. violet (28.8.84) . . 75 60
X965 24p. Indian red (26.9.89) . . 40 45
X966 25p. purple (14.1.81) . . 90 90
X967 26p. rosine (Type I) (27.1.82) . . 90 30
a. Type II (4.8.87) . . 1·00 90
al. Booklet pane. No. X967a × 4 with margins all round . . 3·75
X968 27p. chestnut (23.8.88) . . 45 50
l. Booklet pane. No. X968 × 4 with margins all round . . 1·75
m. Booklet pane. No. X968 × 4 with horiz edges of pane imperf (11.10.88) . . 1·75
X969 28p. deep violet (30.3.83) . . 75 60
a. Imperf (pair) . . £975
X970 28p. ochre (23.8.88) . . 45 50
X971 29p. ochre-brown (27.1.82) . . 2·50 1·25
X972 29p. deep mauve (26.9.89) . . 45 50
X973 30p. deep olive-grey (26.9.89) . . 45 50
X974 31p. purple (30.3.83) . . 1·10 80
a. Imperf (pair) . . £975
X975 32p. greenish blue (23.8.88) . . 50 55
X976 34p. ochre-brown (28.8.84) . . 1·10 80
X977 34p. deep bluish grey (26.9.89) . . 55 55
X978 35p. sepia (23.8.88) . . 55 60
a. Imperf (pair)
X979 37p. rosine (26.9.89) . . 60 65

(*c*) *Photo Harrison. On ordinary paper. P* 15×14

X980 50p. ochre-brown (21.5.80) . . 75 45
a. Imperf (pair) . . £400
X981 50p. ochre (13.3.90) . . 75 45
X982 75p. grey-black (face value as T **367***a*) (26.7.88) . . 1·10 1·25

(*d*) *Litho J.W. P* 14

X996 4p. greenish blue (2 phosphor bands) (30.1.80) . . 20 25
X997 4p. greenish blue (phosphorised paper) (11.81) . . 20 20
X998 20p. dull pur (2 phosphor bands) (21.5.80) 75 40
X999 20p. dull pur (phosphorised paper) (11.81) 75 40

(*e*) *Litho Questa. P* 14 (*Nos.* X1000, X1003/4 *and* X1014) *or* 15×14 (*others*)

X1000 2p. emerald-green (face value as T **367**) (phosphorised paper) (21.5.80) . . 20 20
a. Perf 15×14 (10.7.84) . . 20 20
X1001 2p. bright green & dp green (face value as T **367***a*) (phosphorised paper) (23.2.88) 25 25
X1002 4p. greenish blue (phosphorised paper) (13.5.86) . . 15 20
X1003 5p. lt violet (phosphorised paper) (21.5.80) 20 20
X1004 5p. claret (phosphorised paper) (27.1.82) 40 20
a. Perf 15×14 (21.2.84) . . 25 25
X1005 13p. pale chestnut (1 centre band) (9.2.88) 60 60
l. Booklet pane. No. X1005 × 6 with margins all round . . 3·00
X1006 13p. pale chestnut (1 side band) (9.2.88) 60 60
l. Booklet pane. No. X1006 × 6, X1009 and X1012/13 with margins all round 11·00
X1007 14p. deep blue (1 centre band) (11.10.88) 60 50
X1008 18p. deep olive-grey (phosphorised paper) (9.2.88) . . 60 60
l. Booklet pane. No. X1008 × 9 with margins all round . . 4·50
m. Booklet pane. No. X1008 × 6 with margins all round . . 3·00
X1009 18p. dp ol-grey (2 phosphor bands) (9.2.88) 3·00 2·00
X1010 19p. bright orange-red (phosphorised paper) (11.10.88) . . 75 75
X1011 20p. dull pur (phosphorised paper) (13.5.86) 75 60
X1012 22p. yell-grn (2 phosphor bands) (9.2.88) 3·00 2·00
X1013 34p. ochre-brn (2 phosphor bands) (9.2.88) 3·00 2·00
X1014 75p. black (face value as T **367**) (ordinary paper) (30.1.80) . . 2·00 1·50
a. Perf 15×14 (21.2.84) . . 2·50 1·50
X1015 75p. brownish grey and black (face value as T **367***a*) (ordinary paper) (23.2.88) . . 3·00 1·75

(*e*) *Litho Walsall. P* 14

X1016 14p. deep blue (1 side band) (25.4.89) . . 75 75
l. Booklet pane. No. X1016 × 2 and X1017 × 4 with vert sides of pane imperf . . 2·50
X1017 19p. bright orange-red (2 phosphor bands) (25.4.89) . . 85 35
X1018 29p. dp mauve (2 phosphor bands) (2.10.89) 45 50
l. Booklet pane. No. X1018 × 4 with three sides of pane imperf . . 1·75
X1019 29p. dp mve (phosphorised paper) (17.4.90) 45 50
l. Booklet pane. No. X1019 × 4 with three sides of pane imperf . . 1·75

*See footnote after No. 744.

†These come from sheets with gum arabic.

Nos. X842, X847, X852, X854, X857, X860, X864, X867, X873, X876, X880, X889, X894/5, X897, X899, X901, X904, X906, X910/11, X913/17, X918, X1005/10, X1012/13 and X1016/19 come from booklets; Nos. X843 and X845 come from booklets or coils; Nos. X928 and X932 come from coils. Nos. X852, X864, X873, X876, X880, X889, X894, X897, X899, X901 and X1006 were each issued in equal quantities with the phosphor band at the right or the left. Nos. X847 and X906 also exist with phosphor band at left or right, but these come from different booklets.

Nos. X844a/b come from a strip of eight of the vertical coil. It comprises two normals, one imperforate at sides and bottom, one completely imperforate, one imperforate at top, left and bottom and partly perforated at right due to the bottom three stamps being perforated twice. No. X844b is also known from another strip having one stamp imperforate at sides and bottom.

Nos. X848b/c come from the same sheet, the latter having perforations at the foot of the stamps only.

Multi-value coil strips Nos. X924l, X925l, X928l and X929l were produced by the Post Office for a large direct mail marketing firm. Use of the first coil strip, No. X929l, is known from June 1981. From 2 September 1981 No. X929l was available from the Philatelic Bureau, Edinburgh and, subsequently, from a number of other Post Office counters.

Later coil strips were sold at the Philatelic Bureau and Post Office philatelic counters.

PART-PERFORATED SHEETS. Since the introduction of the "Jumelle" press in 1972 a number of part-perforated sheets, both definitive and commemoratives, have been discovered. It is believed that these occur when the operation of the press is interrupted. Such sheets invariably show a number of "blind" perforations, where the pins have failed to cut the paper. Our listings of imperforate errors from these sheets are for pairs showing no trace whatsoever of the perforations. Examples showing "blind" perforations are outside the scope of this catalogue.

In cases where perforation varieties affect *se-tenant* stamps fuller descriptions will be found in Vol. 4 of the *G.B. Specialised Catalogue*,

WHITE PAPER. From 1972 printings appeared on fluorescent white paper giving a stronger chalk reaction than the original ordinary cream paper.

GUM ARABIC. The following exist with gum arabic as well as PVA gum (with or without added dextrin): Nos. X841, X841n, X851, X855, X856, X861 and X870. See notes after No. 722.

DEXTRIN GUM. From 1973 printings appeared with PVA gum to which dextrin, a bluish green substance had been added, giving a very mottled appearance.

"ALL-OVER" PHOSPHOR. To improve mechanised handling most commemoratives from the 1972 Royal Silver Wedding 3p. value to the 1979 Rowland Hill Death Centenary set had the phosphor applied by printing cylinder across the entire surface of the stamp, giving a matt effect. Printing of the 1, 2 and 10p. definitives, released in October 1979, also had "all-over" phosphor, but these were purely a temporary expedient pending the adoption of phosphorised paper. Nos. X883, X890 and X914 have been discovered with "all-over" phosphor in addition to the normal phosphor bands. These errors are outside the scope of this catalogue.

PHOSPHORISED PAPER. Following the experiments on Nos. 743b and 829 a printing of the 4½p. definitive was issued on 13 November 1974, which had, in addition to the normal phosphor bands, phosphor included in the paper coating. Because of difficulties in identifying the phosphorised paper with the naked eye this printing is not listed separately in this catalogue.

No. X937 was the first value printed on phosphorised paper without phosphor bands and was a further experimental issue to test the efficacy of this system. From 15 August 1979 phosphorised paper was accepted for use generally, the paper replacing phosphor bands on values other than those required in the second-class rate.

Stamps on phosphorised paper show a shiny surface instead of the matt areas of those printed with phosphor bands.

VARNISH COATING. Nos. X841 and X883 exist with and without a varnish coating. This cannot easily be detected without the use of an ultra-violet lamp as it merely reduces the fluorescent paper reaction.

UNDERPRINTS. From 1982 various values appeared with underprints, printed on the reverse, in blue, over the gum. These were usually from special stamp booklets, sold at a discount by the Post Office, but in 1985 surplus stocks of such underprinted paper were used for other purposes.

The following Decimal Machin stamps exist with underprints:

12p. bright emerald (1 centre band)—double-lined star underprint from sheet printing (also exists without)
12½p. light emerald (1 centre band)—star with central dot underprint from booklet pane X898l
12½p. light emerald (1 centre band)—double-lined star underprint from booklet pane of 20
13p. pale chestnut (1 centre band)—double-lined star underprint from booklet pane of 10 (also exists without)
15½p. pale violet (2 bands)—star with central dot underprint from booklet pane X898l
16p. olive-drab (phosphorised paper)—double-lined D underprint from booklet pane of 10 (also exists without)
17p. grey-blue (2 bands)—double-lined star underprint from booklet pane X909l
17p. grey-blue (phosphorised paper)—double-lined D underprint from booklet pane of 10 (also exists without)

DECIMAL MACHIN CATALOGUE NUMBER CHANGES

1990 Edition	1991 Edition
X905/10	X907/12
X911/14	X914/17
X958/63	X959/64
X964/9	X966/71
X970/2	X974/6
X973	X978
X974	X980
X975	X982

368 "A Mountain Road" (T. P. Flanagan)

369 "Deer's Meadow" (Tom Carr)

370 "Slieve na brock" (Colin Middleton)

(Layout des Stuart Rose)

1971 (16 June). *"Ulster 1971" Paintings. Chalk-surfaced paper. Two phosphor bands. P* 15 × 14.

No.	Type		Description	Unused	Used
881	**368**	3p.	yellow-buff, pale yellow, Venetian red, black, blue and drab ..	10	10
882	**369**	7½p.	olive-brown, brownish grey, pale olive-grey, dp bl, cobalt & grey-bl	75	80
		a.	Pale olive-grey omitted*	60·00	
883	**370**	9p.	greenish yellow, orange, grey, lavender-grey, bistre, black, pale ochre-brown, and ochre-brown ..	75	80
		a.	Orange omitted	£500	
881/3			.. .. *Set of* 3	1·40	1·50

A used example of the 3p. has been seen with the Venetian red omitted.

371 John Keats (150th Death Anniv)

372 Thomas Gray (Death Bicentenary)

373 Sir Walter Scott (Birth Bicentenary)

(Des Rosalind Dease. Queen's head printed in gold and then embossed)

1971 (28 July). *Literary Anniversaries. Chalk-surfaced paper. Two phosphor bands. P* 15 × 14.

No.	Type		Description	Unused	Used
884	**371**	3p.	black, gold and greyish blue ..	10	10
		a.	Gold (Queen's head) omitted ..	75·00	
885	**372**	5p.	black, gold and yellow-olive ..	75	80
		a.	Gold (Queen's head) omitted ..	£160	
886	**373**	7½p.	black, gold and yellow-brown ..	75	80
884/6			.. .. *Set of* 3	1·40	1·50

The 7½p. exists with embossing omitted.

374 Servicemen and Nurse of 1921

375 Roman Centurion

376 Rugby Football, 1871

(Des F. Wegner)

1971 (25 Aug). *British Anniversaries. Events described on stamps. Chalk-surfaced paper. Two phosphor bands. P* 15 × 14.

No.	Type		Description	Unused	Used
887	**374**	3p.	red-orange, grey, deep blue, olive-grn, olive-brn, blk, rosine & vio-bl	10	10
		a.	Deep blue omitted*	£750	
		b.	Red-orange (nurse's cloak) omitted	£300	
		c.	Olive-brown (faces, etc.) omitted	£160	
		d.	Black omitted	£10000	
888	**375**	7½p.	grey, yellow-brown, vermilion, mauve, grey-black, black, silver, pale ochre and ochre	90	90
		a.	Grey omitted	75·00	
		b.	Pale ochre (shading on horse, walls, etc.) omitted		
889	**376**	9p.	new blue, myrtle-green, grey-blk, lemon, olive-brown, mag & yell-ol	1·00	1·00
		a.	Olive-brown omitted	£110	
		b.	New blue omitted	£1400	
		c.	Myrtle-green omitted	£1200	
887/9			.. .. *Set of* 3	1·75	1·75

*The effect of the missing deep blue is shown on the sailor's uniform, which appears as grey.

A used example has been seen of the 3p. with grey omitted.

377 Physical Sciences Building, University College of Wales, Aberystwyth

378 Faraday Building, Southampton University

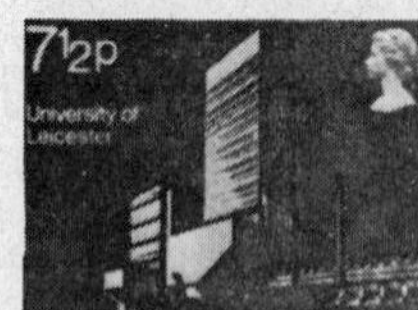

379 Engineering Department, Leicester University

380 Hexagon Restaurant, Essex University

(Des N. Jenkins)

1971 (22 Sept). *British Architecture. Modern University Buildings. Chalk-surfaced paper. Two phosphor bands. P* 15 × 14.

No.	Type		Description	Unused	Used
890	**377**	3p.	olive-brn, ochre, lem, blk & yell-ol	10	10
		a.	Lemon omitted		
		b.	Black (windows) omitted ..	£4500	
891	**378**	5p.	rose, black, chestnut and lilac ..	20	25
892	**379**	7½p.	ochre, black and purple-brown ..	80	80
893	**380**	9p.	pale lilac, black, sepia-brn & dp bl	1·60	1·60
890/3			.. .. *Set of* 4	2·50	2·60

381 "Dream of the Wise Men"

382 "Adoration of the Magi"

383 "Ride of the Magi"

(Des Clarke-Clements-Hughes design team, from stained-glass windows, Canterbury Cathedral. Queen's head printed in gold and then embossed)

1971 (13 Oct). *Christmas. Ordinary paper. One centre phosphor band (2½p.) or two phosphor bands (others). P* 15 × 14.

No.	Type		Description	Unused	Used
894	**381**	2½p.	new blue, black, lemon, emerald, reddish violet, carmine-red, carmine-rose and gold	10	10
		a.	Imperf (pair)	£450	
895	**382**	3p.	black, reddish violet, lemon, new bl, carm-rose, emer, ultram & gold	10	10
		a.	Gold (Queen's head) omitted ..	£350	
		b.	Carmine-rose omitted	£1500	
		c.	Lemon omitted	60·00	
		d.	New blue omitted	†	—
896	**383**	7½p.	black, lilac, lemon, emerald, new blue, rose, green and gold ..	90	1·00
		a.	Gold (Queen's head) omitted ..	90·00	
		b.	Lilac omitted	£500	
		c.	Emerald omitted	£200	
894/6			.. .. *Set of* 3	1·00	1·10

The 3p. exists with embossing omitted; used copies have been seen with reddish violet and embossing omitted, with lemon and carmine-rose omitted. The 7½p. is known with embossing omitted and embossing double.

WHITE CHALK-SURFACED PAPER. From No. 897 all issues, with the exception of Nos. 904/8, were printed on fluorescent white paper, giving a stronger chalk reaction than the original cream paper.

384 Sir James Clark Ross

385 Sir Martin Frobisher

386 Henry Hudson

387 Capt. Scott

(Des Marjorie Saynor. Queen's head printed in gold and then embossed)

1972 (16 Feb). *British Polar Explorers. Two phosphor bands. P* 14 × 15.

No.	Type		Description	Unused	Used
897	**384**	3p.	yellow-brown, indigo, slate-black, flesh, lemon, rose, brt blue & gold	10	10
		a.	Gold (Queen's head) omitted ..	60·00	
		b.	Slate-black (hair, etc.) omitted ..	£1500	
		c.	Lemon omitted		
898	**385**	5p.	salmon, flesh, purple-brown, ochre, black and gold	20	20
		a.	Gold (Queen's head) omitted ..	90·00	
899	**386**	7½p.	reddish violet, blue, deep slate, yellow-brown, buff, black and gold	65	65
		a.	Gold (Queen's head) omitted ..	£200	

900 **387** 9p. dull blue, ultramarine, black, greenish yell, pale pink, rose-red & gold 1·10 1·10
897/900 .. .. *Set of* 4 1·75 1·75

The 3p. and 5p. are known with embossing omitted and the 3p. also exists with gold and embossing omitted. An example of the 3p. is known used on piece with the flesh colour omitted.

388 Statuette of Tutankhamun

389 19th-century Coastguard

390 Ralph Vaughan Williams and Score

(Des Rosalind Dease (3p.), F. Wegner (7½p.), C. Abbott (9p.). Queen's head printed in gold and then embossed (7½p., 9p.))

1972 (26 Apr). *General Anniversaries. Events described on stamps. Two phosphor bands. P* 15 × 14.

901 **388** 3p. black, grey, gold, dull bistre-brown, blackish brn, pale stone & lt brn 10 10
902 **389** 7½p. pale yellow, new blue, slate-blue, violet-blue, slate and gold .. 70 80
903 **390** 9p. bistre-brown, black, sage-green, dp slate, yellow-ochre, brown & gold 70 65
a. Gold (Queen's head) omitted .. £1000
b. Brown (facial features) omitted .. £1500
c. Deep slate omitted £7500
901/3 .. .. *Set of* 3 1·25 1·40

The 7½p. exists with embossing omitted.

391 St. Andrew's, Greensted-juxta-Ongar, Essex

392 All Saints, Earls Barton, Northants

393 St. Andrew's, Letheringsett, Norfolk

394 St. Andrew's, Helpringham, Lincs

395 St. Mary the Virgin, Huish Episcopi, Somerset

(Des R. Maddox. Queen's head printed in gold and then embossed)

1972 (21 June). *British Architecture. Village Churches. Ordinary paper. Two phosphor bands. P* 14 × 15.

904 **391** 3p. violet-blue, black, lt yellow-olive, emerald-green, orange-verm & gold 10 10
a. Gold (Queen's head) omitted .. 75·00
905 **392** 4p. deep yellow-olive, black, emerald, violet-blue, orge-vermilion & gold 20 20
a. Gold (Queen's head) omitted .. £2500
b. Violet-blue omitted £110
906 **393** 5p. deep emerald, black, royal blue, lt yellow-olive, orange-verm & gold 20 25
a. Gold (Queen's head) omitted .. £150
907 **394** 7½p. orange-red, black, deep yellow-ol, royal blue, lt emerald & gold .. 1·40 1·50
908 **395** 9p. new blue, black, emerald-green, dp yellow-olive, orange-verm & gold 1·60 1·75
904/8 .. .. *Set of* 5 3·25 3·50

The 3p., 4p., 5p. and 9p. exist with embossing omitted.

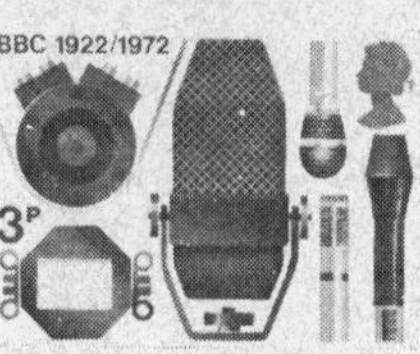

396 Microphones, 1924–69

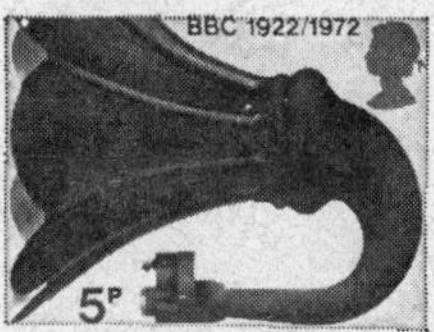

397 Horn Loudspeaker

398 T.V. Camera, 1972

399 Oscillator and Spark Transmitter, 1897

(Des D. Gentleman)

1972 (13 Sept). *Broadcasting Anniversaries. 75th Anniv of Marconi and Kemp's Radio Experiments* (9p.), *and 50th Anniv of Daily Broadcasting by the B.B.C.* (*others*). *Two phosphor bands. P* 15 × 14.

909 **396** 3p. pale brown, black, grey, greenish yellow and brownish slate .. 10 10
a. Greenish yellow (terminals) omitted £1200
910 **397** 5p. brownish slate, lake-brown, salmon, lt brown, black & red-brn 15 20
911 **398** 7½p. light grey, slate, brownish slate, magenta and black .. .. 1·00 1·00
a. Brownish slate (Queen's head) omitted .. .. † —
912 **399** 9p. lemon, brown, brownish slate, deep brownish slate, bluish slate & blk 1·00 1·00
a. Brownish slate (Queen's head) omitted £600
909/12 .. .. *Set of* 4 2·00 2·00

No. 911a is only known on first day covers posted from the Philatelic Bureau in Edinburgh.

400 Angel holding Trumpet

401 Angel playing Lute

402 Angel playing Harp

(Des Sally Stiff. Photo and embossed)

1972 (18 Oct). *Christmas. One centre phosphor band* (2½p.) *or two phosphor bands* (*others*). *P* 14 × 15.

913 **400** 2½p. cerise, pale reddish brown, yellow-orange, orange-vermilion, lilac, gold, red-brown and deep grey .. 10 15
a. Gold omitted £375
c. Deep grey omitted .. .. ..
914 **401** 3p. ultramarine, lavender, light turquoise-blue, bright green, gold, red-brown and bluish violet .. 10 15
a. Red-brown omitted £400
b. Bright green omitted .. .. 70·00
c. Bluish violet omitted .. .. 75·00
915 **402** 7½p. deep brown, pale lilac, light cinnamon, ochre, gold, red-brown and blackish violet 70 60
a. Ochre omitted .. .. .. 55·00
913/15 .. .. *Set of* 3 75 80

All three values exist with embossing omitted.

403 Queen Elizabeth and Duke of Edinburgh

404 "Europe"

(Des J. Matthews from photo by N. Parkinson)

1972 (20 Nov). *Royal Silver Wedding. "All-over" phosphor* (3p.) *or without phosphor* (20p.). *P* 14 × 15.

I. "REMBRANDT" Machine

916 **403** 3p. brownish black, dp blue & silver 20 20
a. Silver omitted £300
917 20p. brownish blk, reddish pur & silver 80 80

II. "JUMELLE" Machine

918 **403** 3p. brownish black, deep blue & silver 20 25

The 3p. "JUMELLE" has a lighter shade of the brownish black than the 3p. "Rembrandt". It also has the brown cylinders less deeply etched, which can be distinguished in the Duke's face which is slightly lighter, and in the Queen's hair where the highlights are sharper.

3p. "REMBRANDT". Cyls. 3A-1B-11C no dot. Sheets of 100 (10 × 10).

3p. "JUMELLE". Cyls. 1A–1B–3C dot and no dot. Sheets of 100 (two panes 5 × 10, separated by gutter margin).

(Des P. Murdoch)

1973 (3 Jan). *Britain's Entry into European Communities. Two phosphor bands. P* 14 × 15.

919 **404** 3p. dull orange, bright rose-red, ultramarine, light lilac and black .. 10 10
920 5p. new blue, bright rose-red, ultramarine, cobalt-blue and black 25 35
a. Pair. Nos. 920/1 .. .. .. 1·50 1·60
921 5p. light emerald-green, bright rose-red, ultramarine, cobalt-blue and black 25 35
919/21 .. .. *Set of* 3 1·50 70

Nos. 920/1 were printed horizontally *se-tenant* throughout the sheet.

405 Oak Tree

(Des D. Gentleman)

1973 (28 Feb). *Tree Planting Year. British Trees* (*1st issue*). *Two phosphor bands. P* 15 × 14.

922 **405** 9p. brownish black, apple-green, deep olive, sepia, blackish green and brownish grey 50 45
a. Brownish black (value and inscr) omitted £550
b. Brownish grey (Queen's head) omitted £400

See also No. 949.

CHALK-SURFACED PAPER. The following issues are printed on chalk-surfaced paper but where "all-over" phosphor has been applied there is no chalk reaction except in the sheet margins outside the phosphor area.

406 David Livingstone

407 H. M. Stanley

(T **406/7** were printed together, horizontally *se-tenant* within the sheet)

408 Sir Francis Drake

409 Walter Raleigh

410 Charles Sturt

(Des Marjorie Saynor. Queen's head printed in gold and then embossed)

1973 (18 Apr). *British Explorers. "All-over" phosphor. P* 14 × 15.

No.	Type		Description	Unused	Used
923	**406**	3p.	orange-yellow, light orange-brown, grey-black, light turquoise-blue, turquoise-blue and gold	25	20
		a.	Pair. Nos. 923/4	1·60	1·60
		b.	Gold (Queen's head) omitted	32·00	
		c.	Turquoise-blue (background and inscr) omitted	£450	
		d.	Light orange-brown omitted	£350	
924	**407**	3p.	orange-yellow, light orange-brown, grey-black, light turquoise-blue, turquoise-blue and gold	25	20
		b.	Gold (Queen's head) omitted	32·00	
		c.	Turquoise-blue (background and inscr) omitted	£450	
		d.	Light orange-brown omitted	£350	
925	**408**	5p.	light flesh, chrome-yellow, orange-yellow, sepia, brownish grey, grey-black, violet-blue and gold	30	30
		a.	Gold (Queen's head) omitted	90·00	
		b.	Grey-black omitted	£550	
		c.	Sepia omitted	£450	
926	**409**	7½p.	light flesh, reddish brown, sepia, ultram, grey-blk, brt lilac & gold	35	30
		a.	Gold (Queen's head) omitted	£1250	
		b.	Ultramarine (eyes) omitted		
927	**410**	9p.	flesh, pale stone, grey-blue, grey-black, brown-grey, Venetian red, brown-red and gold	40	40
		a.	Gold (Queen's head) omitted	90·00	
		b.	Brown-grey printing double *from*	£100	
		c.	Grey-black omitted	£1000	
923/7			*Set of* 5	2·50	1·25

Caution is needed when buying missing gold heads in this issue as they can be removed by using a hard eraser, etc., but this invariably affects the "all-over" phosphor. Genuine examples have the phosphor intact. Used examples off cover cannot be distinguished as much of the phosphor is lost in the course of floating.

In the 5p. value the missing grey-black affects the doublet, which appears as brownish grey, and the lace ruff, which is entirely missing. The missing sepia affects only Drake's hair, which appears much lighter.

The double printing of the brown-grey (cylinder 1F) on the 9p. is a most unusual type of error to occur in a multicoloured photogravure issue. Two sheets are known and it is believed that they stuck to the cylinder and went through a second time. This would result in the following two sheets missing the colour but at the time of going to press this error has not been reported. The second print is slightly askew and more prominent in the top half of the sheets. Examples from the upper part of the sheet showing a clear double impression of the facial features are worth a substantial premium over the price quoted.

The 3p values, the 5p. and the 9p. exist with embossing omitted.

411

412

413

(T **411/13** show sketches of W. G. Grace by Harry Furniss)

(Des E. Ripley. Queen's head printed in gold and then embossed)

1973 (16 May). *County Cricket* 1873–1973. *"All-over" phosphor. P* 14 × 15.

No.	Type		Description	Unused	Used
928	**411**	3p.	black, ochre and gold	10	10
		a.	Gold (Queen's head) omitted	£2500	
929	**412**	7½p.	black, light sage-green and gold	1·25	1·40
930	**413**	9p.	black, cobalt and gold	1·40	1·40
928/30			*Set of* 3	2·40	2·50

All three values exist with embossing omitted.

414 "Self-portrait" (Reynolds)

415 "Self-portrait" (Raeburn)

416 "Nelly O'Brien" (Reynolds)

417 "Rev. R. Walker (The Skater)" (Raeburn)

(Des S. Rose. Queen's head printed in gold and then embossed)

1973 (4 July). *British Paintings. 250th Birth Anniv of Sir Joshua Reynolds and 150th Death Anniv of Sir Henry Raeburn. "All-over" phosphor. P* 14 × 15.

No.	Type		Description	Unused	Used
931	**414**	3p.	rose, new blue, jet-black, magenta, greenish yellow, blk, ochre & gold	10	10
		a.	Gold (Queen's head) omitted	60·00	
932	**415**	5p.	cinnamon, greenish yellow, new blue, lt mag, blk, yell-olive & gold	20	25
		a.	Gold (Queen's head) omitted	75·00	
		b.	Greenish yellow omitted	£350	
933	**416**	7½p.	greenish yellow, new blue, light magenta, black, cinnamon and gold	70	70
		a.	Gold (Queen's head) omitted	75·00	
		b.	Cinnamon omitted	£3000	
934	**417**	9p.	brownish rose, black, dull rose, pale yell, brownish grey, pale bl & gold	90	90
		b.	Brownish rose omitted	30·00	
931/4			*Set of* 4	1·60	1·75

No. 931a is also known with the embossing also omitted or misplaced.

The 5p. and 7½p. are known with the embossing omitted.

The 9p. is known with the embossing and phosphor both omitted.

418 Court Masque Costumes

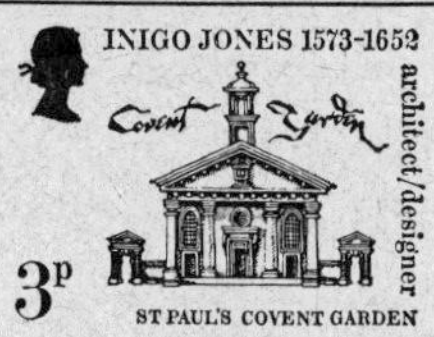

419 St. Paul's Church, Covent Garden

420 Prince's Lodging, Newmarket

421 Court Masque Stage Scene

T **418/19** and T **420/1** were printed horizontally *se-tenant* within the sheet

(Des Rosalind Dease. Litho and typo B.W.)

1973 (15 Aug). *400th Birth Anniv of Inigo Jones* (*architect and designer*). *"All-over" phosphor. P* 15 × 14.

No.	Type		Description	Unused	Used
935	**418**	3p.	deep mauve, black and gold	10	15
		a.	Pair. Nos. 935/6	35	40
936	**419**	3p.	deep brown, black and gold	10	15
937	**420**	5p.	blue, black and gold	40	45
		a.	Pair. Nos. 937/8	2·40	2·40
938	**421**	5p.	grey-olive, black and gold	40	45
935/8			*Set of* 4	2·50	1·10

422 Palace of Westminster seen from Whitehall

423 Palace of Westminster seen from Millbank

(Des R. Downer. Recess and typo B.W.)

1973 (12 Sept). *19th Commonwealth Parliamentary Conference. "All-over" phosphor. P* 15 × 14.

No.	Type		Description	Unused	Used
939	**422**	8p.	black, brownish grey and stone	50	60
940	**423**	10p.	gold and black	50	40

424 Princess Anne and Capt. Mark Phillips.

(Des C. Clements and E. Hughes from photo by Lord Litchfield)

1973 (14 Nov). *Royal Wedding. "All-over" phosphor. P* 15 × 14.

No.	Type		Description	Unused	Used
941	**424**	3½p.	dull violet and silver	10	10
		a.	Imperf (pair)	£900	
942		20p.	deep brown and silver	90	1·00
		a.	Silver omitted	£900	

425

426

427

428

429

T 425/9 depict the carol "Good King Wenceslas" and were printed horizontally *se-tenant* within the sheet.

430 "Good King Wenceslas, the Page and Peasant"

(Des D. Gentleman)

1973 (28 Nov). *Christmas. One centre phosphor band* (3p.) *or "all-over" phosphor* (3½p.). *P* 15 × 14.

943 **425** 3p. grey-black, blue, brownish grey, light brown, bright rose-red, turq-green, salmon-pink and gold .. 15 15
a. Strip of 5. Nos. 943/7 .. .. 3·00 2·75
b. Imperf (horiz strip of 5) .. .. †
944 **426** 3p. grey-black, violet-blue, slate, brown, rose-red, rosy mauve, turq-green, salmon-pink and gold .. 15 15
a. Rosy mauve omitted .. ..
945 **427** 3p. grey-black, violet-blue, slate, brown, rose-red, rosy mauve, turq-green, salmon-pink and gold .. 15 15
a. Rosy mauve omitted .. ..
946 **428** 3p. grey-black, violet-blue, slate, brown, rose-red, rosy mauve, turq-green, salmon-pink and gold .. 15 15
a. Rosy mauve omitted .. ..
947 **429** 3p. grey-black, violet-blue, slate, brown, rose-red, rosy mauve, turq-green, salmon-pink and gold .. 15 15
a. Rosy mauve omitted .. ..
948 **430** 3½p. salmon-pink, grey-black, red-brown, blue, turquoise-green, bright rose-red, rosy mauve, lavender-grey and gold 15 15
a. Imperf (pair) £450
b. Grey-black (value and inscr, etc) omitted .. .. 75·00
c. Salmon-pink omitted .. .. 70·00
d. Blue (leg, robes) omitted £125
e. Rosy mauve (robe at right) omitted 80·00
f. Blue and rosy mauve omitted .. £250
g. Bright rose-red (King's robe) omitted .. .. 75·00
h. Red-brown (logs, basket etc) omitted .. ..
943/8 .. .. *Set of* 6 3·00 80

An example of the 3½p. with the gold background colour omitted has been seen used on cover; another has been seen with the turquoise-green omitted (used on piece); and a pair with the lavender-grey omitted (used on piece).

The 3p. and 3½p. are normally with PVA gum with added dextrin but the 3½p. also exists with normal PVA gum and the 3p. with gum arabic.

431 Horse Chestnut

(Des. D. Gentleman)

1974 (27 Feb). *British Trees* (2*nd issue*). *"All-over" phosphor. P* 15 × 14.

949 **431** 10p. light emerald, bright green, greenish yellow, brown-olive, black and brownish grey 50 50

432 First Motor Fire-engine, 1904

433 Prize-winning Fire-engine, 1863

434 First Steam Fire-engine, 1830

435 Fire-engine, 1766

(Des D. Gentleman)

1974 (24 Apr). *Bicentenary of the Fire Prevention* (*Metropolis*) *Act. "All-over" phosphor. P* 15 × 14.

950 **432** 3½p. grey-black, orange-yellow, greenish yellow, dull rose, ochre and grey 10 10
a. Imperf (pair) £850
951 **433** 5½p. greenish yellow, deep rosy magenta, orange-yellow, light emerald, grey-black and grey 25 25
952 **434** 8p. greenish yellow, light blue-green, light greenish blue, light chestnut, grey-black and grey 60 65
953 **435** 10p. grey-black, pale reddish brown, lt brown, orange-yellow and grey .. 80 85
950/3 .. .. *Set of* 4 1·50 1·60

The 3½p. exists with ordinary PVA gum.

436 P & O Packet, *Peninsular*, 1888

437 Farman Biplane, 1911

438 Airmail-blue Van and Postbox, 1930

439 Imperial Airways "C" Class Flying-boat, 1937

(Des Rosalind Dease)

1974 (12 June). *Centenary of Universal Postal Union. "All-over" phosphor. P* 15 × 14.

954 **436** 3½p. deep brownish grey, bright mauve, grey-black and gold 10 10
955 **437** 5½p. pale orge, lt emer, grey-blk & gold 20 25
956 **438** 8p. cobalt, brown, grey-black and gold 30 35
957 **439** 10p. deep brownish grey, orange, grey-black and gold 50 40
954/7 .. .. *Set of* 4 1·00 1·00

440 Robert the Bruce **441** Owain Glyndŵr

442 Henry the Fifth **443** The Black Prince

(Des F. Wegner)

1974 (10 July). *Medieval Warriors. "All-over" phosphor. P* 15 × 14.

958 **440** 4½p. greenish yellow, vermilion, slate-blue, red-brown, reddish brown, lilac-grey and gold 10 10
959 **441** 5½p. lemon, vermilion, slate-blue red-brn, reddish brn, ol-drab & gold 20 25
960 **442** 8p. deep grey, vermilion, greenish yellow, new blue, red-brown, deep cinnamon and gold 85 90
961 **443** 10p. vermilion, greenish yellow, new blue, red-brown, reddish brown, light blue and gold 85 90
958/61 .. .. *Set of* 4 1·90 1·90

444 Churchill in Royal Yacht Squadron Uniform **445** Prime Minister, 1940

446 Secretary for War and Air, 1919 **447** War Correspondent, South Africa, 1899

(Des C. Clements and E. Hughes)

1974 (9 Oct). *Birth Centenary of Sir Winston Churchill. "All-over" phosphor. P* 14 × 15.

962 **444** 4½p. Prussian blue, pale turquoise-green and silver 15 15
963 **445** 5½p. sepia, brownish grey and silver .. 20 25
964 **446** 8p. crimson, light claret and silver .. 45 40
965 **447** 10p. light brown, stone and silver .. 45 45
962/5 .. .. *Set of* 4 1·10 1·10

448 "Adoration of the Magi" (York Minster, *circa* 1355)

449 "The Nativity" (St. Helen's Church, Norwich, *circa* 1480)

450 "Virgin and Child" (Ottery St. Mary Church, *circa* 1350)

451 "Virgin and Child" (Worcester Cathedral, *circa* 1224)

(Des Peter Hatch Partnership)

1974 (27 Nov). *Christmas. Church Roof Bosses. One phosphor band (3½p.) or "all-over" phosphor (others). P* 15 × 14.

No.	Type	Value	Description	Unused	Used
966	**448**	3½p.	gold, light new blue, light brown, grey-black and light stone	10	10
		a.	Light stone (background shading) omitted	£8000	
967	**449**	4½p.	gold, yellow-orange, rose-red, light brown, grey-black, & lt new blue	10	10
968	**450**	8p.	blue, gold, light brown, rose-red, dull green and grey-black	45	45
969	**451**	10p.	gold, dull rose, grey-black, light new blue, pale cinnamon and light brown	50	50
966/9			*Set of* 4	1·00	1·00

The phosphor band on the 3½p. was first applied down the centre of the stamp but during the printing this was deliberately placed to the right between the roof boss and the value; however, intermediate positions, due to shifts, are known.

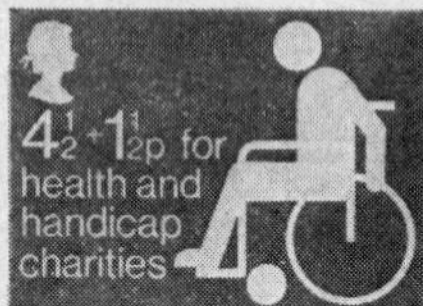

452 Invalid in Wheelchair

(Des P. Sharland)

1975 (22 Jan). *Health and Handicap Funds. "All-over" phosphor. P* 15 × 14.

No.	Type	Value	Description	Unused	Used
970	**452**	4½p. + 1½p.	azure and grey-blue	25	25

453 "Peace—Burial at Sea"

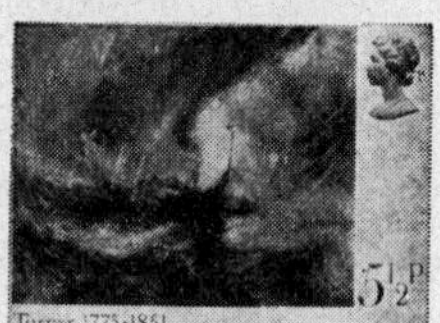

454 "Snowstorm—Steamer off a Harbour's Mouth"

455 "The Arsenal, Venice"

456 "St. Laurent"

(Des S. Rose)

1975 (19 Feb). *Birth Bicentenary of J. M. W. Turner (painter). "All-over" phosphor. P* 15 × 14.

No.	Type	Value	Description	Unused	Used
971	**453**	4½p.	grey-blk, salmon, stone, bl & grey	10	10
972	**454**	5½p.	cobalt, greenish yellow, light yellow-brown, grey-black and rose	15	15
973	**455**	8p.	pale yellow-orange, greenish yellow, rose, cobalt and grey-black	40	40
974	**456**	10p.	deep blue, light yellow-ochre, light brown, deep cobalt and grey-black	45	45
971/4			*Set of* 4	1·00	1·00

457 Charlotte Square, Edinburgh

458 The Rows, Chester

T **457/8** were printed horizontally *se-tenant* within the sheet.

459 Royal Observatory, Greenwich

460 St. George's Chapel, Windsor

461 National Theatre, London

(Des P. Gauld)

1975 (23 Apr). *European Architectural Heritage Year. "All-over" phosphor. P* 15 × 14.

No.	Type	Value	Description	Unused	Used
975	**457**	7p.	greenish yellow, bright orange, grey-black, red-brown, new blue, lavender and gold	30	20
		a.	Pair. Nos. 975/6	75	70
976	**458**	7p.	grey-black, greenish yellow, new blue, brt orange, red-brown & gold	30	20
977	**459**	8p.	magenta, deep slate, pale magenta, lt yellow-olive, grey-black & gold	20	25
978	**460**	10p.	bistre-brown, greenish yellow, deep slate, emer-green, grey-blk & gold	25	25
979	**461**	12p.	grey-blk, new bl, pale mag & gold	30	35
975/9			*Set of* 5	1·25	1·10

462 Sailing Dinghies

463 Racing Keel Yachts

464 Cruising Yachts

465 Multihulls

(Des A. Restall. Recess and photo)

1975 (11 June). *Sailing "All-over" phosphor. P* 15 × 14.

No.	Type	Value	Description	Unused	Used
980	**462**	7p.	black, bluish violet, scarlet, orange-vermilion, orange and gold	20	20
981	**463**	8p.	black, orange-vermilion, orange, lavender, bright mauve, bright blue, deep ultramarine and gold	20	20
		a.	Black omitted	55·00	
982	**464**	10p.	black, orange, bluish emerald, light olive-drab, chocolate and gold	25	25
983	**465**	12p.	black, ultramarine, turquoise-blue, rose, grey, steel-blue and gold	45	45
980/3			*Set of* 4	1·00	1·00

On No. 981a the recess-printed black colour is completely omitted.

466 Stephenson's *Locomotion*, 1825

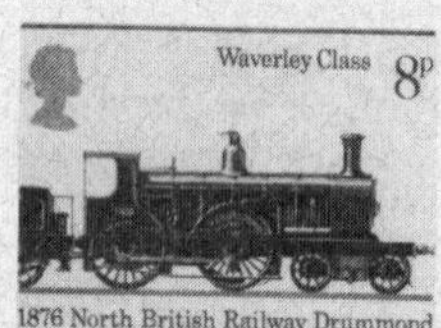

467 *Abbotsford*, 1876

468 *Caerphilly Castle*, 1923

469 High Speed Train, 1975

(Des B. Craker)

1975 (13 Aug). *150th Anniv of Public Railways. "All-over" phosphor. P* 15 × 14.

No.	Type	Value	Description	Unused	Used
984	**466**	7p.	red-brown, grey-black, greenish yellow, grey and silver	30	35
985	**467**	8p.	brown, orange-yellow, vermilion, grey-black, grey and silver	30	40
986	**468**	10p.	emerald-green, grey-black, yellow-orange, vermilion, grey and silver	40	45
987	**469**	12p.	grey-black, pale lemon, vermilion, blue, grey and silver	50	60
984/7			*Set of* 4	1·40	1·60

470 Palace of Westminster

(Des R. Downer)

1975 (3 Sept). *62nd Inter-Parliamentary Union Conference. "All-over" phosphor. P* 15 × 14.

No.	Type	Value	Description	Unused	Used
988	**470**	12p.	light new blue, black, brownish grey and gold	50	50

471 "Emma and Mr. Woodhouse" (*Emma*)

472 "Catherine Morland" (*Northanger Abbey*)

473 "Mr. Darcy" (*Pride and Prejudice*)

474 "Mary and Henry Crawford" (*Mansfield Park*)

(Des Barbara Brown)

1975 (22 Oct). *Birth Bicentenary of Jane Austen (novelist). "All-over" phosphor. P* 14 × 15.

989	**471**	8½p.	blue, slate, rose-red, light yellow, dull green, grey-black and gold ..	20	20
990	**472**	10p.	slate, bright magenta, grey, light yellow, grey-black and gold ..	25	25
991	**473**	11p.	dull blue, pink, olive-sepia, slate, pale greenish yell, grey-blk & gold	40	45
992	**474**	13p.	bright magenta, light new blue, slate, buff, dull blue-green, grey-black and gold	40	40
989/92			.. .. *Set of* 4	1·10	1·10

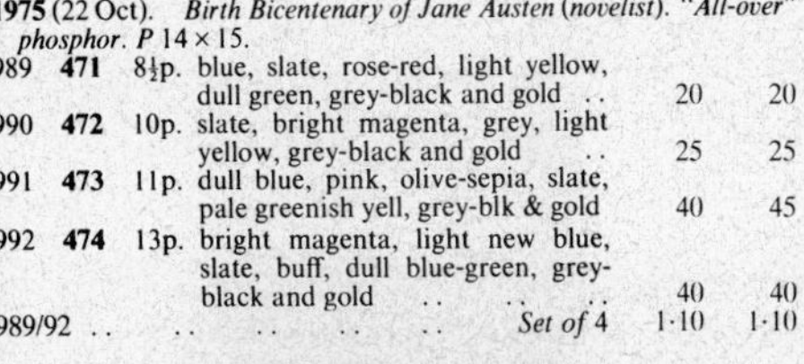

475 Angels with Harp and Lute

476 Angel with Mandolin

477 Angel with Horn

478 Angel with Trumpet

(Des R. Downer)

1975 (26 Nov). *Christmas. One phosphor band* (6½p.), *phosphor-inked background* (8½p.), *"all-over" phosphor (others). P* 15 × 14.

993	**475**	6½p.	bluish violet, bright reddish violet, light lavender and gold	20	15
994	**476**	8½p.	turquoise-green, bright emerald-green, slate, lt turq-green & gold	20	20
995	**477**	11p.	vermilion, cerise, pink and gold ..	40	50
996	**478**	13p.	drab, brn, brt orge, buff & gold ..	40	45
993/6			.. .. *Set of* 4	1·10	1·10

479 Housewife

480 Policeman

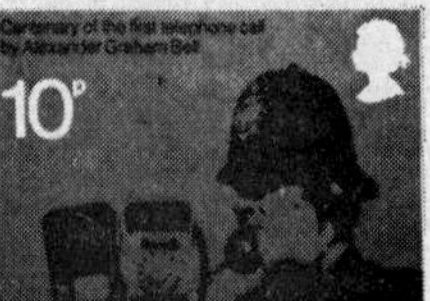

481 District Nurse

482 Industrialist

(Des P. Sharland)

1976 (10 Mar). *Telephone Centenary. "All-over" phosphor. P* 15 × 14.

997	**479**	8½p.	greenish blue, dp rose, black & bl	20	20
		a.	Deep rose omitted	£2250	
998	**480**	10p.	greenish blue, black & yellow-ol	25	25
999	**481**	11p.	greenish blue, deep rose, black and bright mauve	40	45
1000	**482**	13p.	olive-brn, dp rose, blk & orge-red	40	45
997/1000			.. .. *Set of* 4	1·10	1·10

483 Hewing Coal (Thomas Hepburn)

484 Machinery (Robert Owen)

485 Chimney Cleaning (Lord Shaftesbury)

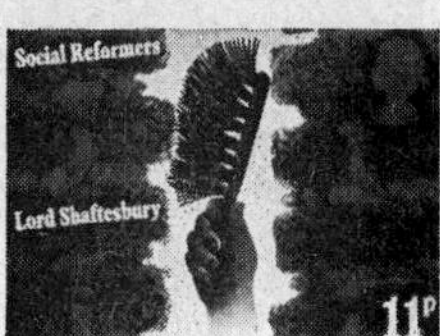

486 Hands clutching Prison Bars (Elizabeth Fry)

(Des D. Gentleman)

1976 (28 Apr). *Social Reformers. "All-over" phosphor. P* 15 × 14.

1001	**483**	8½p.	lavender-grey, grey-black, black and slate-grey	20	20
1002	**484**	10p.	lavender-grey, grey-black, grey and slate-violet	25	25
1003	**485**	11p.	black, slate-grey and drab ..	40	45
1004	**486**	13p.	slate-grey, black & deep dull grn	40	45
1001/4			.. .. *Set of* 4	1·10	1·10

NEW INFORMATION

The editor is always interested to correspond with people who have new information that will improve or correct the Catalogue.

487 Benjamin Franklin (bust by Jean-Jacques Caffieri)

(Des P. Sharland)

1976 (2 June). *Bicentenary of American Revolution. "All-over" phosphor. P* 14 × 15.

1005	**487**	11p	pale bistre, slate-violet, pale blue-green, black and gold	50	50

488 "Elizabeth of Glamis"

489 "Grandpa Dickson"

490 "*Rosa Mundi*"

491 "Sweet Briar"

(Des Kristin Rosenberg)

1976 (30 June). *Centenary of Royal National Rose Society. "All-over" phosphor. P* 14 × 15.

1006	**488**	8½p.	bright rose-red, greenish yellow, emerald, grey-black and gold ..	20	20
1007	**489**	10p.	greenish yellow, bright green, reddish brown, grey-black and gold	30	30
1008	**490**	11p.	bright magenta, greenish yellow, emerald, grey-blue, grey-black and gold	35	40
1009	**491**	13p.	rose-pink, lake-brown, yellow-green, pale greenish yellow, grey-black and gold	35	35
		a.	Value omitted*		
1006/9			.. .. *Set of* 4	1·10	1·10

*The value was obscured on one position of the cylinder during printing, but the error was discovered before issue and most examples were removed from the sheets.

492 Archdruid

493 Morris Dancing

494 Scots Piper

495 Welsh Harpist

(Des Marjorie Saynor)

1976 (4 Aug). *British Cultural Traditions. "All-over" phosphor. P* 14 × 15.

1010	**492**	8½p.	yellow, sepia, bright rose, dull ultramarine, black and gold ..	20	20
1011	**493**	10p.	dull ultramarine, bright rose-red, sepia, greenish yellow, blk & gold	30	30
1012	**494**	11p.	bluish green, yellow-brown, yell-orge, blk, brt rose-red & gold ..	35	35
1013	**495**	13p.	dull violet-blue, yellow-orange, yell-brn, blk, bluish grn & gold	35	35
1010/13			.. .. *Set of* 4	1·10	1·10

The 8½p. and 13p. commemorate the 800th Anniv of the Royal National Eisteddfod.

496 Woodcut from *The Canterbury Tales*

497 Extract from *The Tretyse of Love*

498 Woodcut from *The Game and Playe of Chesse*

499 Early Printing Press

(Des R. Gay. Queen's head printed in gold and then embossed)

1976 (29 Sept). *500th Anniv of British Printing. "All-over" phosphor. P* 14 × 15.

1014	**496**	8½p. black, light new blue and gold ..	20	20
1015	**497**	10p. black, olive-green and gold ..	25	30
1016	**498**	11p. black, brownish grey and gold ..	35	40
1017	**499**	13p. chocolate, pale ochre and gold ..	40	45
1014/17 ..		.. .. *Set of* 4	1·10	1·10

500 Virgin and Child

501 Angel with Crown

502 Angel appearing to Shepherds

503 The Three Kings

(Des Enid Marx)

1976 (24 Nov). *Christmas. English Medieval Embroidery. One phosphor band* (6½p.), *"all-over" phosphor* (*others*). *P* 15 × 14.

1018	**500**	6½p. bl, bistre-yell, brn & brt orange	15	15
		a. Imperf (pair)	£450	
1019	**501**	8½p. sage-green, yellow, brown-ochre, chestnut and olive-black	20	20
1020	**502**	11p. deep magenta, brown-orange, new blue, black and cinnamon ..	35	40
		a. Uncoated paper*	70·00	30·00
1021	**503**	13p. bright purple, new blue, cinnamon, bronze-green and olive-grey	40	40
1018/21 ..		.. .. *Set of* 4	1·10	1·00

* See footnote after No. 744.

504 Lawn Tennis

505 Table Tennis

506 Squash

507 Badminton

(Des A. Restall)

1977 (12 Jan). *Racket Sports. Phosphorised paper. P* 15 × 14.

1022	**504**	8½p. emer-grn, blk, grey & bluish grn	20	20
		a. Imperf (horiz pair)	£850	
1023	**505**	10p. myrtle-green, black, grey-black and deep blue-green	30	30
1024	**506**	11p. orange, pale yellow, black, slate-black and grey	35	40
1025	**507**	13p. brown, grey-black, grey and bright reddish violet	40	40
1022/5 ..		.. .. *Set of* 4	1·10	1·10

508

(Des after plaster cast by Arnold Machin)

1977 (2 Feb)–**87**. *P* 14 × 15.

1026	**508**	£1 bright yellow-green & blackish olive	2·50	20
		a. Imperf (pair)..	£650	
1026*b*		£1.30, pale drab and deep greenish blue (3.8.83)	10·00	7·50
1026*c*		£1.33, pale mve & grey-blk (28.8.84)	8·50	6·00
1026*d*		£1.41, pale drab and deep greenish blue (17.9.85)	9·00	5·00
1026*e*		£1.50, pale mauve & grey-blk (2.9.86)	4·50	3·00
1026*f*		£1.60 pale drab and deep greenish blue (15.9.87)	4·50	2·75
1027		£2 light emerald and purple-brown ..	5·00	75
1028		£5 salmon and chalky blue	12·00	3·50
1026/8 ..		.. .. *Set of* 8	55·00	18·00

509 Steroids—Conformational Analysis

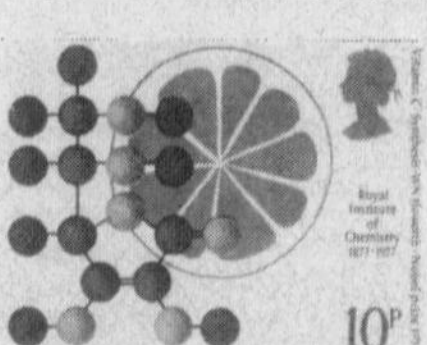

510 Vitamin C—Synthesis

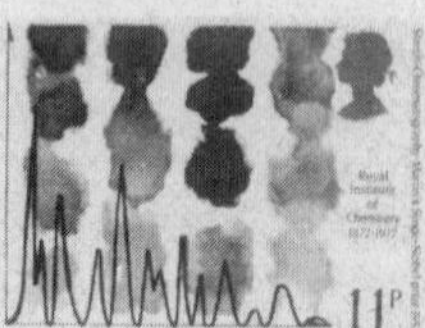

511 Starch—Chromatography

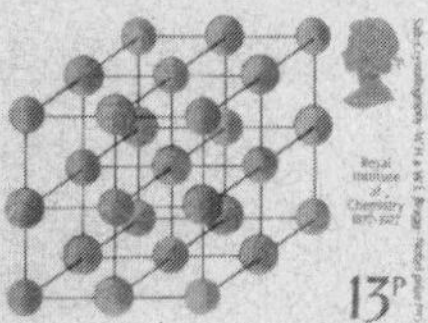

512 Salt—Crystallography

(Des J. Karo)

1977 (2 Mar). *Royal Institute of Chemistry Centenary. "All-over" phosphor. P* 15 × 14.

1029	**509**	8½p. rosine, new blue, olive-yellow, brt mauve, yellow-brown, blk & gold	20	20
		a. Imperf (horiz pair)	£850	
1030	**510**	10p. bright orange, rosine, new blue, bright blue, black and gold ..	30	30
1031	**511**	11p. rosine, greenish yellow, new blue, deep violet, black and gold ..	35	35
1032	**512**	13p. new blue, brt green, black & gold	40	40
1029/32		.. .. *Set of* 4	1·10	1·10

513

514

515

516

T **513/16** differ in the decorations of "ER".

(Des R. Guyatt)

1977 (11 May–15 June). *Silver Jubilee. "All-over" phosphor. P* 15 × 14.

1033	**513**	8½p. blackish green, black, silver, olive-grey and pale turquoise-green ..	20	20
		a. Imperf (pair)	£750	
1034		9p. maroon, black, silver, olive-grey and lavender (15 June)	25	25
1035	**514**	10p. blackish blue, black, silver, olive-grey and ochre	25	30
		a. Imperf (horiz pair)		
1036	**515**	11p. brown-purple, black, silver, olive-grey and rose-pink	30	35
		a. Imperf (horiz pair)	£1250	
1037	**516**	13p. sepia, black, silver, olive-grey and bistre-yellow	40	40
		a. Imperf (pair)	£1250	
1033/7 ..		.. .. *Set of* 5	1·25	1·40

517 "Gathering of Nations"

(Des P. Murdoch. Recess and photo)

1977 (8 June). *Commonwealth Heads of Government Meeting, London. "All-over" phosphor. P* 14 × 15.

1038	**517**	13p. black, blackish green, rose-car and silver	50	50

518 Hedgehog

519 Brown Hare

520 Red Squirrel

521 Otter

522 Badger

T **518/22** were printed horizontally *se-tenant* within the sheet.

(Des P. Oxenham)

1977 (5 Oct). *British Wildlife. "All-over" phosphor. P* 14 × 15.

1039 **518** 9p. reddish brown, grey-black, pale lemon, brt turq-bl, brt mag & gold .. 25 20
 a. Horiz strip of 5. Nos. 1039/43 .. 1·75 1·75
 b. Imperf (vert pair) .. ..
 c. Imperf (horiz pair, Nos. 1039/40) ..
1040 **519** 9p. reddish brown, grey-black, pale lemon, brt turq-bl, brt mag & gold 25 20
1041 **520** 9p. reddish brown, grey-black, pale lemon, brt turq-bl, brt mag & gold 25 20
1042 **521** 9p. reddish brown, grey-black, pale lemon, brt turq-bl, brt mag & gold 25 20
1043 **522** 9p. grey-black, reddish brown, pale lemon, brt turq-bl, brt mag & gold 25 20
1039/43 .. .. *Set of* 5 1·75 90

523 "Three French Hens, Two Turtle Doves and a Partridge in a Pear Tree"

524 "Six Geese a-laying, Five Gold Rings, Four Colly Birds"

525 "Eight Maids a-milking, Seven Swans a-swimming"

526 "Ten Pipers piping, Nine Drummers drumming"

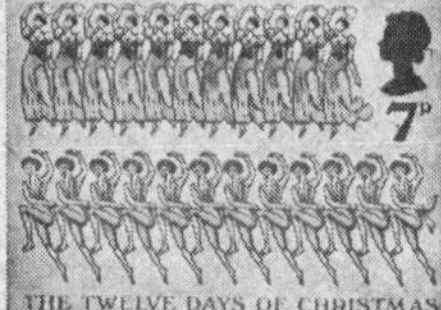

527 "Twelve Lords a-leaping, Eleven Ladies dancing"

T **523/7** depict the carol "The Twelve Days of Christmas" and were printed horizontally *se-tenant* within the sheet.

528 "A Partridge in a Pear Tree"

(Des D. Gentleman)

1977 (23 Nov). *Christmas. One centre phosphor band* (7*p.*) *or "all-over" phosphor* (9*p.*). *P* 15 × 14.

1044 **523** 7p. slate, grey, bright yellow-green, new blue, rose-red and gold 15 15
 a. Horiz strip of 5. Nos. 1044/8 .. 1·00 1·10
 ab. Imperf (strip of 5. Nos. 1044/8) .. £1100
1045 **524** 7p. slate, brt yellow-grn, new bl & gold 15 15
1046 **525** 7p. slate, grey, bright yellow-green, new blue, rose-red and gold 15 15
1047 **526** 7p. slate, grey, bright yellow-green, new blue, rose-red and gold 15 15
1048 **527** 7p. slate, grey, bright yellow-green, new blue, rose-red and gold 15 15
1049 **528** 9p. pale brown, pale orange, brt emer, pale greenish yell, slate-blk & gold 20 20
 a. Imperf (pair) £850
1044/9 .. .. *Set of* 6 1·10 85

529 Oil—North Sea Production Platform

530 Coal—Modern Pithead

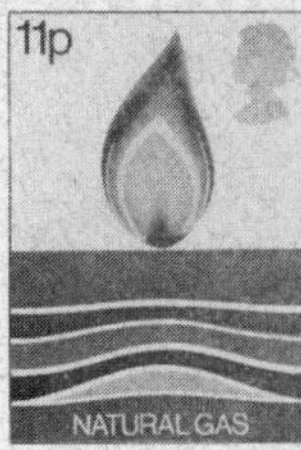

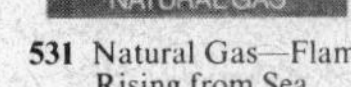

531 Natural Gas—Flame Rising from Sea

532 Electricity—Nuclear Power Station and Uranium Atom

(Des P. Murdoch)

1978 (25 Jan). *Energy Resources. "All-over" phosphor. P* 14 × 15.

1050 **529** 9p. deep brown, orange-vermilion, grey-black, greenish yellow, rose-pink, new blue and silver .. 25 20
1051 **530** 10½p. light emerald-green, grey-black, red-brown, slate-grey, pale apple-green and silver 25 35
1052 **531** 11p. greenish blue, bright violet, violet-blue, blackish brown, grey-black and silver 35 40
1053 **532** 13p. orange-vermilion, grey-black, deep brown, greenish yellow, light brown, light blue and silver .. 40 40
1050/3 .. .. *Set of* 4 1·10 1·10

533 The Tower of London

534 Holyroodhouse

535 Caernarvon Castle

536 Hampton Court Palace

(Des R. Maddox (stamps), J. Matthews (miniature sheet))

1978 (1 Mar). *British Architecture. Historic Buildings. "All-over" phosphor. P* 15 × 14.

1054 **533** 9p. black, olive-brown, new blue, brt green, lt yellow-olive & rose-red 25 20
1055 **534** 10½p. black, brown-olive, orange-yell, brt grn, lt yell-olive & vio-bl .. 25 30
1056 **535** 11p. black, brown-olive, violet-blue, brt green, lt yellow-olive & dull bl 35 35
1057 **536** 13p. black, orange-yellow, lake-brown, bright green and light yellow-olive 40 40
1054/7 .. .. *Set of* 4 1·10 1·10
MS1058 121 × 89 mm. Nos. 1054/7 (*sold at* 53½*p.*) 1·50 1·60
 a. Imperforate £5000
 b. Light yellow-olive (Queen's head) omitted £3000
 c. Rose-red (Union Jack on 9p.) omitted £1500
 d. Orange-yellow omitted £1500

The premium on No. **MS**1058 was used to support the London 1980 International Stamp Exhibition.

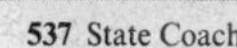

537 State Coach

538 St. Edward's Crown

539 The Sovereign's Orb

540 Imperial State Crown

(Des J. Matthews)

1978 (31 May). *25th Anniv of Coronation. "All-over" phosphor. P* 14 × 15.

1059 **537** 9p. gold and royal blue 20 20
1060 **538** 10½p. gold and brown-lake 25 30
1061 **539** 11p. gold and deep dull green .. 35 40
1062 **540** 13p. gold and reddish violet 40 40
1059/62 .. .. *Set of* 4 1·10 1·10

541 Shire Horse

542 Shetland Pony

543 Welsh Pony

544 Thoroughbred

(Des P. Oxenham)

1978 (5 July). *Horses. "All-over" phosphor. P* 15 × 14.

1063	**541**	9p.	black, pale reddish brown, grey-black, greenish yellow, light blue, vermilion and gold	20	25
1064	**542**	10½p.	pale chestnut, magenta, brownish grey, greenish yellow, greenish blue, grey-black and gold ..	25	30
1065	**543**	11p.	reddish brown, black, light green, greenish yellow, bistre, grey-black and gold	35	35
1066	**544**	13p.	reddish brown, pale reddish brown, emerald, greenish yellow, grey-black and gold	40	40
1063/6 ..			.. .. *Set of* 4	1·10	1·10

545 "Penny-farthing" and 1884 Safety Bicycle

546 1920 Touring Bicycles

547 Modern Small-wheel Bicycles

548 1978 Road-racers

(Des F. Wegner)

1978 (2 Aug). *Centenaries of Cyclists Touring Club and British Cycling Federation. "All-over" phosphor. P* 15 × 14.

1067	**545**	9p.	brown, deep dull blue, rose-pink, pale olive, grey-black and gold ..	20	20
		a.	Imperf (pair)	£350	
1068	**546**	10½p.	olive, pale yellow-orange, orange-vermilion, rose-red, light brown, grey-black and gold	25	35
1069	**547**	11p.	orange-vermilion, greenish blue, light brown, pale greenish yellow, deep grey, grey-black and gold ..	35	35
1070	**548**	13p.	new blue, orange-vermilion, light brn, olive-grey, grey-black & gold	40	40
		a.	Imperf (pair)	£750	
1067/70 ..			.. .. *Set of* 4	1·10	1·10

549 Singing Carols round the Christmas Tree

550 The Waits

551 18th-century Carol Singers

552 "The Boar's Head Carol"

(Des Faith Jaques)

1978 (22 Nov). *Christmas. One centre phosphor band* (7p.) *or "all-over" phosphor* (*others*). *P* 15 × 14.

1071	**549**	7p.	bright green, greenish yellow, magenta, new blue, black and gold	20	20
		a.	Imperf (vert pair)	£350	
1072	**550**	9p.	magenta, greenish yellow, new blue, sage-green, black and gold	25	25
		a.	Imperf (horiz pair)		
1073	**551**	11p.	magenta, new blue, greenish yellow, yellow-brown, black and gold	30	35
		a.	Imperf (horiz pair)		
1074	**552**	13p.	salmon-pink, new blue, greenish yellow, magenta, black and gold	35	35
1071/4 ..			.. .. *Set of* 4	1·00	1·00

553 Old English Sheepdog

554 Welsh Springer Spaniel

555 West Highland Terrier

556 Irish Setter

(Des P. Barrett)

1979 (7 Feb). *Dogs. "All-over" phosphor. P* 15 × 14.

1075	**553**	9p.	grey-black, sepia, turquoise-green, pale greenish yellow, pale greenish blue and grey	20	25
1076	**554**	10½p.	grey-black, lake-brown, apple-green, pale greenish yellow, pale greenish blue and grey	30	35
1077	**555**	11p.	grey-black, claret, yellowish grn, pale greenish yell, cobalt & grey	35	40
		a.	Imperf (horiz pair)	£850	
1078	**556**	13p.	grey-black, lake-brown, green, pale greenish yellow & dp turq-bl	40	40
1075/8 ..			.. .. *Set of* 4	1·10	1·25

557 Primrose

558 Daffodil

559 Bluebell

560 Snowdrop

(Des P. Newcombe)

1979 (21 Mar). *Spring Wild Flowers. "All-over" phosphor. P* 14 × 15.

1079	**557**	9p.	slate-black, deep brown, pale greenish yellow, deep olive, pale new blue and silver	20	20
		a.	Imperf (pair)	£400	
1080	**558**	10½p.	greenish yellow, grey-green, steel-blue, slate-blk, new blue & silver	30	35
		a.	Imperf (vert pair)	£1500	
1081	**559**	11p.	slate-black, deep brown, ultramarine, light greenish blue, pale greenish yellow and silver ..	35	40
		a.	Imperf (horiz pair)	£1200	
1082	**560**	13p.	slate-black, indigo, grey-green, sepia, ochre and silver	35	40
		a.	Imperf (horiz pair)	£750	
1079/82			.. .. *Set of* 4	1·10	1·10

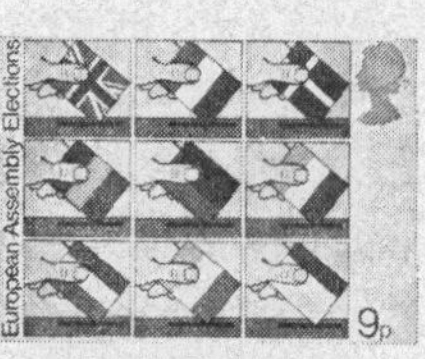

561

562

563

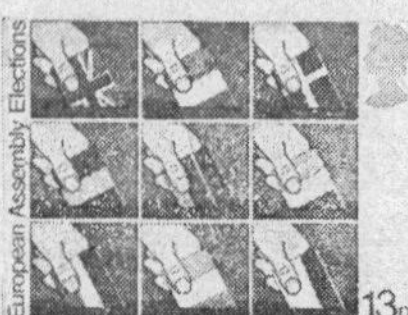

564

T **561/4** show Hands placing National Flags in Ballot Boxes.

(Des S. Cliff)

1979 (9 May). *First Direct Elections to European Assembly. Phosphorised paper.* P 15 × 14.

1083	**561**	9p.	grey-black, vermilion, cinnamon, pale greenish yellow, pale turq-green and dull ultramarine ..	20	20
1084	**562**	10½p.	grey-black, vermilion, cinnamon, pale greenish yellow, dull ultramarine, pale turq-grn & chestnut	30	35
1085	**563**	11p.	grey-black, vermilion, cinnamon, pale greenish yellow, dull ultramarine, pale turq-grn & grey-grn	35	40
1086	**564**	13p.	grey-black, vermilion, cinnamon, pale greenish yellow, dull ultramarine, pale turq-grn & brown	35	40
1083/6			.. .. *Set of* 4	1·10	1·10

565 "Saddling 'Mahmoud' for the Derby, 1936" (Sir Alfred Munnings)

566 "The Liverpool Great National Steeple Chase, 1839" (aquatint by F. C. Turner)

567 "The First Spring Meeting, Newmarket, 1793" (J. N. Sartorius)

568 "Racing at Dorsett Ferry, Windsor, 1684" (Francis Barlow)

(Des S. Rose)

1979 (6 June). *Horseracing Paintings. Bicentenary of the Derby* (9p.). *"All-over" phosphor.* P 15 × 14.

1087	**565**	9p.	light blue, red-brown, rose-pink, pale greenish yellow, grey-black and gold	25	25
1088	**566**	10½p.	bistre-yellow, slate-blue, salmon-pink, lt blue, grey-black and gold	30	30
1089	**567**	11p.	rose, vermilion, pale greenish yellow, new blue, grey-black and gold	35	50
1090	**568**	13p.	bistre-yellow, rose, turquoise, grey-black and gold	40	55
1087/90			.. .. *Set of* 4	1·10	1·40

569 *The Tale of Peter Rabbit* (Beatrix Potter) **570** *The Wind in the Willows* (Kenneth Grahame)

571 *Winnie-the-Pooh* (A. A. Milne) **572** *Alice's Adventures in Wonderland* (Lewis Carroll)

(Des E. Hughes)

1979 (11 July). *International Year of the Child. Children's Book Illustrations. "All-over" phosphor.* P 14 × 15.

1091	**569**	9p.	deep bluish green, grey-black, bistre-brown, bright rose, greenish yellow and silver	45	20
1092	**570**	10½p.	dull ultramarine, grey-black, olive-brown, bright rose, yellow-orge, pale greenish yellow and silver ..	50	35
1093	**571**	11p.	drab, grey-black, greenish yellow, new bl, yell-orge, agate & silver	55	50
1094	**572**	13p.	pale greenish yellow, grey-black, bright rose, deep bluish green, olive-brown, new blue and silver	60	55
1091/4			.. .. *Set of* 4	1·90	1·40

573 Sir Rowland Hill **574** Postman, *circa* 1839

575 London Postman, *circa* 1839 **576** Woman and Young Girl with Letters, 1840

(Des E. Stemp)

1979 (22 Aug–24 Oct). *Death Centenary of Sir Rowland Hill. "All-over" phosphor.* P 14 × 15.

1095	**573**	10p.	grey-black, brown-ochre, myrtle-green, pale greenish yellow, rosine, bright blue and gold ..	25	25
1096	**574**	11½p.	grey-black, brown-ochre, bright blue, rosine, bistre-brown, pale greenish yellow and gold ..	30	35
1097	**575**	13p.	grey-black, brown-ochre, bright blue, rosine, bistre-brown, pale greenish yellow and gold ..	35	40
1098	**576**	15p.	grey-black, brown-ochre, myrtle-green, bistre-brown, rosine, pale greenish yellow and gold	40	40
1095/8			.. .. *Set of* 4	1·10	1·25
MS1099			89 × 121 mm. Nos. 1095/8 (*sold at* 59½p.) (24 Oct)	1·10	1·25
		a.	Imperforate	£1100	
		b.	Brown-ochre (15p. background, etc) omitted	£950	
		c.	Gold (Queen's head) omitted ..	£225	
		d.	Brown-ochre, myrtle-green and gold omitted	£3000	
		e.	Bright blue (13p. background, etc) omitted	£950	
		f.	Myrtle-green (10p. (background), 15p.) omitted	£1250	
		g.	Pale greenish yellow omitted ..	£160	
		h.	Rosine omitted	£700	
		i.	Bistre-brown omitted	£900	

The premium on No. **MS**1099 was used to support the London 1980 International Stamp Exhibition.

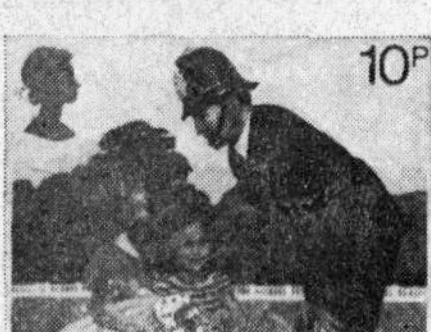

577 Policeman on the Beat

578 Policeman directing Traffic

579 Mounted Policeman

580 River Patrol Boat

(Des B. Sanders)

1979 (26 Sept). *150th Anniv of Metropolitan Police. Phosphorised paper.* P 15 × 14.

1100	**577**	10p.	grey-black, red-brown, emerald, greenish yellow, brt blue & mag	25	25
1101	**578**	11½p.	grey-black, bright orange, purple-brown, ultramarine, greenish yellow and deep bluish green ..	30	35
1102	**579**	13p.	grey-black, red-brown, magenta, ol-grn, greenish yell & dp dull bl	35	40
1103	**580**	15p.	grey-black, magenta, brown, slate-bl, dp brown & greenish blk	40	40
1100/3			.. .. *Set of* 4	1·10	1·25

581 The Three Kings

582 Angel appearing to the Shepherds

583 The Nativity

584 Mary and Joseph travelling to Bethlehem

585 The Annunciation

(Des F. Wegner)

1979 (21 Nov). *Christmas. One centre phosphor band* (8p.) *or phosphorised paper* (*others*). P 15 × 14.

1104	**581**	8p.	blue, grey-black, ochre, slate-violet and gold	20	20
		a.	Imperf (pair)	£550	
1105	**582**	10p.	bright rose-red, grey-black, chestnut, chrome-yell, dp vio & gold	25	25
		a.	Imperf between (vert pair) ..	£450	
		b.	Imperf (pair)	£600	
1106	**583**	11½p.	orange-vermilion, steel-bl, drab, grey-black, deep blue-grn & gold	30	35
1107	**584**	13p.	bright blue, orange-vermilion, bistre, grey-black and gold ..	40	40
1108	**585**	15p.	orange-vermilion, blue, bistre, grey-black, green and gold ..	40	45
1104/8			.. .. *Set of* 5	1·40	1·50

MINIMUM PRICE

The minimum price quote is 10p which represents a handling charge rather than a basis for valuing common stamps. For further notes about prices see introductory pages.

586 Common Kingfisher

587 Dipper

588 Moorhen

589 Yellow Wagtails

(Des M. Warren)

1980 (16 Jan). *Centenary of Wild Bird Protection Act. Phosphorised paper. P* 14 × 15.

1109 **586** 10p. bright blue, bright yellow-green, vermilion, pale greenish yellow, grey-black and gold 25 25
1110 **587** 11½p. sepia, grey-black, dull ultramarine, vermilion, grey-green, pale greenish yellow and gold .. 30 35
1111 **588** 13p. emerald-green, grey-black, bright bl, verm, pale greenish yell & gold 40 45
1112 **589** 15p. greenish yellow, brown, light green, slate-bl, grey-blk & gold 45 50
1109/12 .. .. *Set of* 4 1·25 1·40

590 "Rocket" approaching Moorish Arch, Liverpool

591 First and Second Class Carriages passing through Olive Mount cutting

592 Third Class Carriage and Cattle Truck crossing Chat Moss

593 Horsebox and Carriage Truck near Bridgewater Canal

594 Goods Truck and Mail-Coach at Manchester

T **590/4** were printed together, *se-tenant*, in horizontal strips of 5 throughout the sheet.

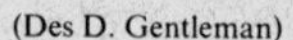
(Des D. Gentleman)

1980 (12 Mar). *150th Anniv of Liverpool and Manchester Railway. Phosphorised paper. P* 15 × 14.

1113 **590** 12p. lemon, light brown, rose-red, pale blue and grey-black 25 25
a. Strip of 5. Nos. 1113/17 .. .. 1·50 1·60
ab. Imperf (horiz strip of 5. Nos. 1113/17) £1200
ac. Lemon omitted (horiz strip of 5. Nos. 1113/17) .. .. ..
1114 **591** 12p. rose-red, light brown, lemon, pale blue and grey-black 25 25
1115 **592** 12p. pale blue, rose-red, lemon, light brown and grey-black 25 25
1116 **593** 12p. light brown, lemon, rose-red, pale blue and grey-black 25 25
1117 **594** 12p. light brown, rose-red, pale blue, lemon and grey-black 25 25
1113/17 .. .. *Set of* 5 1·50 1·10

595 Montage of London Buildings

(Des J. Matthews. Recess)

1980 (9 Apr–7 May). *"London 1980" International Stamp Exhibition. Phosphorised paper. P* 14½ × 14.

1118 **595** 50p. agate .. .. 1·50 1·50
MS1119 90 × 123 mm. No. 1118 (*sold at* 75*p.*) (7 May) .. .. 1·50 1·50
a. Error. Imperf £700

596 Buckingham Palace **597** The Albert Memorial

598 Royal Opera House

599 Hampton Court

600 Kensington Palace

(Des Sir Hugh Casson)

1980 (7 May). *London Landmarks. Phosphorised paper. P* 14 × 15.

1120 **596** 10½p. grey, pale blue, rosine, pale greenish yell, yellowish green & silver 25 25
1121 **597** 12p. grey-black, bistre, rosine, yellowish green, pale greenish yellow and silver 30 30
a. Imperf (vert pair) £550
1122 **598** 13½p. grey-black, pale salmon, pale olgreen, slate-blue and silver .. 35 35
a. Imperf (pair) £550
1123 **599** 15p. grey-black, pale salmon, slateblue, dull yellowish green, oliveyellow and silver 40 45
1124 **600** 17½p. grey, slate-blue, red-brown, sepia, yellowish green, pale greenish yellow and silver 50 55
a. Silver (Queen's head) omitted .. £250
1120/4 .. .. *Set of* 5 1·60 1·75

No. 1124a shows the Queen's head in pale greenish yellow, this colour being printed beneath the silver for technical reasons.

601 Charlotte Brontë (*Jane Eyre*)

602 George Eliot (*The Mill on the Floss*)

603 Emily Brontë (*Wuthering Heights*)

604 Mrs. Gaskell (*North and South*)

T **601/4** show authoresses and scenes from their novels. T **601/2** also include the "Europa" C.E.P.T. emblem.

(Des Barbara Brown)

1980 (9 July). *Famous Authoresses. Phosphorised paper. P* 15 × 14.

1125 **601** 12p. red-brown, bright rose, bright bl, greenish yellow, grey and silver 30 30
1126 **602** 13½p. red-brown, dull vermilion, pale blue, pale greenish yellow, grey and silver 35 35
a. Pale blue omitted £1500
1127 **603** 15p. red-brown, vermilion, blue, lemon, grey and silver 40 45
1128 **604** 17½p. dull vermilion, slate-blue, ultram, pale greenish yell, grey & silver 60 60
a. Imperf and slate-blue omitted (pair) £850
1125/8 .. .. *Set of* 4 1·50 1·50

605 Queen Elizabeth the Queen Mother

(Des J. Matthews from photograph by N. Parkinson)

1980 (4 Aug). *80th Birthday of Queen Elizabeth the Queen Mother. Phosphorised paper. P* 14 × 15.

1129 **605** 12p. bright rose, greenish yellow, new blue, grey and silver 50 50
a. Imperf (horiz pair) £1200

606 Sir Henry Wood

607 Sir Thomas Beecham

608 Sir Malcolm Sargent

609 Sir John Barbirolli

(Des P. Gauld)

1980 (10 Sept). *British Conductors. Phosphorised paper. P* 14 × 15.

1130	**606**	12p.	slate, rose-red, greenish yellow, bistre and gold	30	30
1131	**607**	13½p.	grey-black, vermilion, greenish yellow, pale carmine-rose and gold	35	40
1132	**608**	15p.	grey-black, bright rose-red, greenish yellow, turquoise-grn & gold	45	45
1133	**609**	17½p.	black, bright rose-red, greenish yellow, dull violet-blue and gold	55	50
1130/3			.. .. *Set of* 4	1·50	1·50

610 Running

611 Rugby

612 Boxing

613 Cricket

(Des R. Goldsmith. Litho Questa)

1980 (10 Oct). *Sport Centenaries. Phosphorised paper. P* 14 × 14½.

1134	**610**	12p.	pale new blue, greenish yellow, magenta, light brown, reddish purple and gold	30	30
		a.	Gold (Queen's head) omitted ..		
1135	**611**	13½p.	pale new blue, olive-yellow, bright purple, orange-vermilion, blackish lilac and gold	35	40
1136	**612**	15p.	pale new blue, greenish yellow, bright purple, chalky blue & gold	40	40
		a.	Gold (Queen's head) omitted ..		
1137	**613**	17½p.	pale new blue, greenish yellow, magenta, dp ol, grey-brn & gold	60	55
1134/7			.. .. *Set of* 4	1·50	1·50

Centenaries:—12p. Amateur Athletics Association; 13½p. Welsh Rugby Union; 15p. Amateur Boxing Association; 17½p. First England–Australia Test Match.

No. 1134a was caused by a paper fold.

614 Christmas Tree

615 Candles

616 Apples and Mistletoe

617 Crown, Chains and Bell

618 Holly

(Des J. Matthews)

1980 (19 Nov). *Christmas. One centre phosphor band* (10p.) *or phosphorised paper* (*others*). *P* 15 × 14.

1138	**614**	10p.	black, turquoise-green, greenish yellow, vermilion and blue ..	25	25
		a.	Imperf (horiz pair)		
1139	**615**	12p.	grey, magenta, rose-red, greenish grey and pale orange	30	35
1140	**616**	13½p.	grey-black, dull yellow-green, brown, greenish yellow and pale olive-bistre	35	40
1141	**617**	15p.	grey-black, bistre-yellow, bright orange, magenta and new blue ..	40	45
1142	**618**	17½p.	black, vermilion, dull yellowish green and greenish yellow ..	45	50
1138/42			.. .. *Set of* 5	1·60	1·75

619 St. Valentine's Day

620 Morris Dancers

621 Lammastide

622 Medieval Mummers

T **619/20** also include the "Europa" C.E.P.T. emblem.

(Des F. Wegner)

1981 (6 Feb). *Folklore. Phosphorised paper. P* 15 × 14.

1143	**619**	14p.	cerise, green, yellow-orange, salmon-pink, black and gold ..	35	35
1144	**620**	18p.	dull ultramarine, lemon, lake-brown, brt green, black & gold	45	50
1145	**621**	22p.	chrome-yellow, rosine, brown, new blue, black and gold ..	60	60
1146	**622**	25p.	brt blue, red-brown, brt rose-red, greenish yellow, black and gold	75	70
1143/6			.. .. *Set of* 4	2·00	2·00

623 Blind Man with Guide Dog

624 Hands spelling "Deaf" in Sign Language

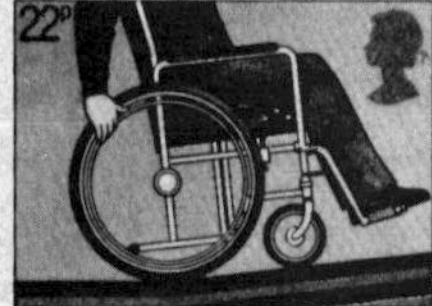

625 Disabled Man in Wheelchair

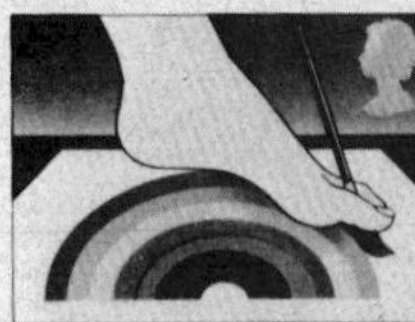

626 Disabled Artist painting with Foot

(Des J. Gibbs)

1981 (25 Mar). *International Year of the Disabled. Phosphorised paper. P* 15 × 14.

1147	**623**	14p.	drab, greenish yellow, bright rose-red, dull purple and silver ..	35	35
1148	**624**	18p.	deep blue-green, brt orange, dull vermilion, grey-black and silver	45	50
1149	**625**	22p.	brown-ochre, rosine, purple-brn, greenish blue, black and silver ..	60	60
1150	**626**	25p.	vermilion, lemon, pale salmon, olive-brn, new blue, blk & silver	75	70
1147/50			.. .. *Set of* 4	2·00	2·00

627 Small Tortoiseshell

628 Large Blue

629 Peacock

630 Chequered Skipper

(Des G. Beningfield)

1981 (13 May). *Butterflies. Phosphorised paper. P* 14 × 15.

1151	**627**	14p.	greenish yellow, yellow-green, brt rose, brt blue, emerald & gold ..	35	35
		a.	Imperf (pair)	£950	
1152	**628**	18p.	black, greenish yellow, dull yellowish green, bright mauve, bright blue, bright green and gold ..	50	50
1153	**629**	22p.	black, greenish yell, bronze-grn, rosine, ultramarine, lt grn & gold	60	65
1154	**630**	25p.	black, greenish yellow, bronze-green, bright rose-red, ultramarine, bright emerald and gold ..	70	75
1151/4			.. .. *Set of* 4	2·00	2·00

631 Glenfinnan, Scotland

632 Derwentwater, England

633 Stackpole Head, Wales

634 Giant's Causeway, Northern Ireland

635 St. Kilda, Scotland

(Des M. Fairclough)

1981 (24 June). *50th Anniv of National Trust for Scotland. British Landscapes. Phosphorised paper. P* 15 × 14.

1155	**631**	14p.	lilac, dull blue, reddish brown, bistre-yellow, black and gold ..	40	40
1156	**632**	18p.	bottle green, bright blue, brown, bistre-yellow, black and gold ..	50	55
1157	**633**	20p.	deep turq-blue, dull blue, greenish yellow, reddish brn, black & gold	55	60
1158	**634**	22p.	chrome-yellow, reddish brn, new blue, yellow-brown, black & gold	60	60
1159	**635**	25p.	ultramarine, new blue, olive-green, olive-grey and gold ..	75	70
1155/9			.. .. *Set of* 5	2·50	2·50

636 Prince Charles and Lady Diana Spencer

(Des J. Matthews from photograph by Lord Snowdon)

1981 (22 July). *Royal Wedding. Phosphorised paper. P* 14 × 15.

1160	**636**	14p.	grey-blk, greenish yellow, brt rose-red, ultram, pale bl, blue & silver	35	35
1161		25p.	drab, greenish yellow, bright rose-red, ultramarine, grey-brown, grey-black and silver	90	90

637 "Expeditions"

638 "Skills"

639 "Service"

640 "Recreation"

(Des P. Sharland. Litho J.W.)

1981 (12 Aug). *25th Anniv of Duke of Edinburgh Award Scheme. Phosphorised paper. P* 14.

1162	**637**	14p.	greenish yellow, magenta, pale new blue, black, emerald & silver	35	35
1163	**638**	18p.	greenish yellow, magenta, pale new blue, black, cobalt and gold	50	50
1164	**639**	22p.	greenish yellow, magenta, pale new blue, black, red-orge & gold	60	60
1165	**640**	25p.	bright orange, mauve, pale new blue, black, flesh and bronze ..	70	70
1162/5			.. .. *Set of* 4	2·00	2·00

641 Cockle-dredging

642 Hauling in Trawl Net

643 Lobster Potting

644 Hoisting Seine Net

(Des B. Sanders)

1981 (23 Sept). *Fishing Industry. Phosphorised paper. P* 15 × 14.

1166	**641**	14p.	slate, greenish yellow, magenta, new blue, orange-brown, olive-grey and bronze-green	35	35
1167	**642**	18p.	slate, greenish yellow, brt crimson, ultramarine, blk & greenish slate	50	50
1168	**643**	22p.	grey, greenish yellow, bright rose, dull ultram, reddish lilac & black	60	60
1169	**644**	25p.	grey, greenish yellow, bright rose, cobalt and black	70	65
1166/9			.. .. *Set of* 4	2·00	2·00

Nos. 1166/9 were issued on the occasion of the centenary of the Royal National Mission to Deep Sea Fishermen.

645 Father Christmas

646 Jesus Christ

647 Flying Angel

648 Joseph and Mary arriving at Bethlehem

649 Three Kings approaching Bethlehem

(Des Samantha Brown (11½p.), Tracy Jenkins (14p.), Lucinda Blackmore (18p.), Stephen Moore (22p.), Sophie Sharp (25p.))

1981 (18 Nov). *Christmas. Children's Pictures. One phosphor band* (11½*p.*) *or phosphorised paper* (*others*). *P* 15 × 14.

1170	**645**	11½p.	ultramarine, black, red, olive-bistre, bright green and gold ..	30	30
1171	**646**	14p.	bistre-yellow, brt magenta, blue, greenish blue, brt grn, blk & gold	40	40
1172	**647**	18p.	pale blue-green, bistre-yellow, brt magenta, ultramarine, blk & gold	50	50
1173	**648**	22p.	deep turquoise-blue, lemon, magenta, black and gold	60	60
1174	**649**	25p.	royal blue, lemon, bright magenta, black and gold	70	70
1170/4			.. .. *Set of* 5	2·25	2·25

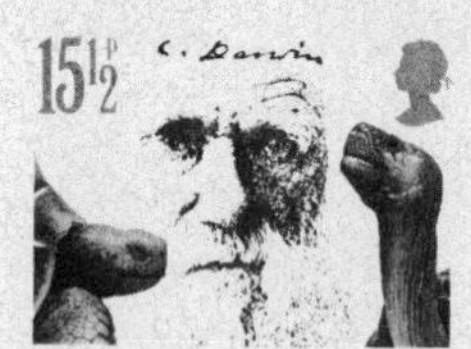

650 Charles Darwin and Giant Tortoises

651 Darwin and Marine Iguanas

652 Darwin, Cactus Ground Finch and Large Ground Finch

653 Darwin and Prehistoric Skulls

(Des D. Gentleman)

1982 (10 Feb). *Death Centenary of Charles Darwin. Phosphorised paper. P* 15 × 14.

1175	**650**	15½p.	dull purple, drab, bistre, black and grey-black	35	35
1176	**651**	19½p.	violet-grey, bistre-yellow, slate-black, red-brown, grey-blk & blk	60	60
1177	**652**	26p.	sage green, bistre-yellow, orange, chalky bl, grey-blk, red-brn & blk	70	70
1178	**653**	29p.	grey-brown, yellow-brn, brown-ochre, black and grey-black ..	75	75
1175/8			.. .. *Set of* 4	2·25	2·25

654 Boys' Brigade

655 Girls' Brigade

656 Boy Scout Movement **657** Girl Guide Movement

(Des B. Sanders)

1982 (24 Mar). *Youth Organizations. Phosphorised paper. P* 15 × 14.

1179	**654**	15½p.	gold, greenish yellow, pale orange, mauve, dull blue and grey-black	35	35
1180	**655**	19½p.	gold, greenish yellow, pale orange, bright rose, deep ultramarine, olive-bistre and grey-black ..	70	70
1181	**656**	26p.	gold, greenish yellow, olive-sepia, rosine, deep blue, deep dull green and grey-black	90	90
1182	**657**	29p.	gold, yellow, dull orange, cerise, dull ultram, chestnut & grey-blk	1·00	1·00
1179/82			.. .. *Set of* 4	2·75	2·75

Nos. 1179/82 were issued on the occasion of the 75th anniversary of the Boy Scout Movement; the 125th birth anniversary of Lord Baden-Powell and the centenary of the Boys' Brigade (1983).

658 Ballerina **659** "Harlequin"

660 "Hamlet" **661** Opera Singer

(Des A. George)

1982 (28 Apr). *Europa. British Theatre. Phosphorised paper. P* 15 × 14.

1183	**658**	15½p.	carm-lake, greenish bl, greenish yell, grey-blk, bottle grn & silver	35	35
1184	**659**	19½p.	rosine, new blue, greenish yellow, black, ultramarine and silver ..	70	70
1185	**660**	26p.	carmine-red, bright rose-red, greenish yellow, black, dull ultramarine, lake-brown and silver ..	90	90
1186	**661**	29p.	rose-red, greenish yellow, bright blue, grey-black and silver ..	1·00	1·00
1183/6			.. .. *Set of* 4	2·75	2·75

662 Henry VIII and *Mary Rose*

663 Admiral Blake and *Triumph*

664 Lord Nelson and H.M.S. *Victory*

665 Lord Fisher and H.M.S. *Dreadnought*

666 Viscount Cunningham and H.M.S *Warspite*

(Des Marjorie Saynor. Eng C. Slania. Recess and photo)

1982 (16 June). *Maritime Heritage. Phosphorised paper. P* 15 × 14.

1187	**662**	15½p.	black, lemon, bright rose, pale orange, ultramarine and grey ..	35	35
1188	**663**	19½p.	black, greenish yellow, bright rose-red, pale orange, ultram and grey	60	60
1189	**664**	24p.	black, orange-yellow, bright rose-red, lake-brown, dp ultram & grey	70	70
1190	**665**	26p.	black, orange-yellow, bright rose, lemon, ultramarine and grey ..	80	80
		a.	Imperf (pair)		
1191	**666**	29p.	black, olive-yellow, bright rose, orange-yellow, ultram & grey ..	90	80
1187/91			.. .. *Set of* 5	3·00	3·00

Nos. 1187/91 were issued on the occasion of Maritime England Year, the Bicentenary of the Livery Grant by City of London to Worshipful Company of Shipwrights and the raising of *Mary Rose* from Portsmouth Harbour.

Several used examples of the 15½p. have been seen with the black recess (ship and waves) omitted.

667 "Strawberry Thief" (William Morris) **668** Untitled (Steiner and Co)

669 "Cherry Orchard" (Paul Nash) **670** "Chevron" (Andrew Foster)

(Des Peter Hatch Partnership)

1982 (23 July). *British Textiles. Phosphorised paper. P* 14 × 15.

1192	**667**	15½p.	blue, olive-yellow, rosine, deep blue-green, bistre & Prussian blue	35	35
		a.	Imperf (horiz pair)	£950	
1193	**668**	19½p.	olive-grey, greenish yellow, bright magenta, dull grn, yell-brn & blk	70	70
		a.	Imperf (vert pair)	£1500	
1194	**669**	26p.	bright scarlet, dull mauve, dull ultramarine and bright carmine	70	70
1195	**670**	29p.	bronze-green, orange-yellow, turq-green, stone, chestnut & sage-grn	1·00	1·00
1192/5			.. .. *Set of* 4	2·50	2·50

Nos. 1192/5 were issued on the occasion of the 250th birth anniversary of Sir Richard Arkwright (inventor of spinning machine).

671 Development of Communications

672 Modern Technological Aids

(Des Delaney and Ireland)

1982 (8 Sept). *Information Technology. Phosphorised paper. P* 14 × 15.

1196	**671**	15½p.	black, greenish yellow, bright rose-red, bistre-brn, new bl & lt ochre	45	50
		a.	Imperf (pair)	£250	
1197	**672**	26p.	black, greenish yellow, bright rose-red, ol-bistre, new bl & lt ol-grey	80	85
		a.	Imperf (pair)	£1250	

673 Austin "Seven" and "Metro"

674 Ford "Model T" and "Escort"

675 Jaguar "SS 1" and "XJ6"

676 Rolls-Royce "Silver Ghost" and "Silver Spirit"

(Des S. Paine. Litho Questa)

1982 (13 Oct). *British Motor Cars. Phosphorised paper. P* 14½ × 14.

1198	**673**	15½p.	slate, orange-vermilion, bright orange, drab, yellow-green, olive-yellow, bluish grey and black ..	50	50
1199	**674**	19½p.	slate, brt orange, olive-grey, rose-red, dull vermilion, grey & black	1·00	1·10
1200	**675**	26p.	slate, red-brown, bright orange, turquoise-green, myrtle-green, dull blue-green, grey and olive ..	1·10	1·25
1201	**676**	29p.	slate, bright orange, carmine-red, reddish purple, grey and black ..	1·25	1·40
1198/201			.. .. *Set of* 4	3·50	3·75

677 "While Shepherds Watched"

678 "The Holly and the Ivy"

679 "I Saw Three Ships"

680 "We Three Kings"

681 "Good King Wenceslas"

(Des Barbara Brown)

1982 (17 Nov). *Christmas. Carols. One phosphor band* (12½p.) *or phosphorised paper* (*others*). *P* 15 × 14.

No.	Type	Value	Description	Unused	Used
1202	**677**	12½p.	black, greenish yellow, brt scarlet, steel blue, red-brown & gold ..	30	30
1203	**678**	15½p.	black, bistre-yellow, bright rose-red, brt blue, brt green & gold	55	55
1204	**679**	19½p.	black, bistre-yellow, brt rose-red, dull blue, deep brown and gold	80	80
			a. Imperf (pair)	£1250	
1205	**680**	26p.	black, bistre-yellow, brt magenta, brt blue, choc, gold & orange-red	80	80
1206	**681**	29p.	black, bistre-yellow, magenta, brt blue, chestnut, gold and brt mag	90	90
1202/6			.. .. *Set of* 5	3·00	3·00

682 Salmon

683 Pike

684 Trout

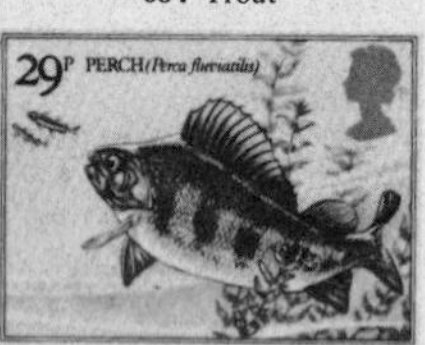

685 Perch

(Des A. Jardine)

1983 (26 Jan). *British River Fishes. Phosphorised paper. P* 15 × 14.

No.	Type	Value	Description	Unused	Used
1207	**682**	15½p.	grey-black, bistre-yellow, bright purple, new blue and silver ..	35	35
			a. Imperf (pair)	£1250	
1208	**683**	19½p.	black, bistre-yellow, olive-bistre, dp claret, silver & dp bluish green	70	70
1209	**684**	26p.	grey-black, bistre-yellow, chrome-yellow, magenta, silver & pale blue	80	80
1210	**685**	29p.	black, greenish-yellow, bright carmine, new blue and silver ..	90	90
1207/10			.. .. *Set of* 4	2·50	2·50

686 Tropical Island

687 Desert

688 Temperate Farmland **689** Mountain Range

(Des D. Fraser)

1983 (9 Mar). *Commonwealth Day. Geographical Regions. Phosphorised paper. P* 14 × 15.

No.	Type	Value	Description	Unused	Used
1211	**686**	15½p.	greenish blue, greenish yellow, bright rose, light brown, grey-black, deep claret and silver ..	35	35
1212	**687**	19½p.	brt lilac, greenish yell, mag, dull blue, grey-blk, dp dull-bl & silver	70	70
1213	**688**	26p.	lt blue, greenish yellow, brt mag, new blue, grey-blk, vio & silver	80	80
1214	**689**	29p.	dull vio-bl, reddish vio, slate-lilac, new blue, myrtle-grn, blk & silver	90	90
1211/14			.. .. *Set of* 4	2·50	2·50

690 Humber Bridge

691 Thames Flood Barrier

692 *Iolair* (oilfield emergency support vessel)

(Des. M. Taylor)

1983 (25 May). *Europa. Engineering Achievements. Phosphorised paper. P* 15 × 14.

No.	Type	Value	Description	Unused	Used
1215	**690**	16p.	silver, orange-yellow, ultramarine, black and grey	55	55
1216	**691**	20½p.	silver, greenish yellow, bright purple, blue, grey-black and grey ..	1·25	1·25
1217	**692**	28p.	silver, lemon, brt rose-red, chestnut, dull ultramarine, blk & grey	1·25	1·25
1215/17			.. .. *Set of* 3	2·75	2·75

693 Musketeer and Pikeman, The Royal Scots (1633)

694 Fusilier and Ensign, The Royal Welch Fusiliers (mid-18th century)

695 Riflemen, 95th Rifles (The Royal Green Jackets) (1805)

696 Sergeant (khaki service uniform) and Guardsman (full dress), The Irish Guards (1900)

697 Paratroopers, The Parachute Regiment (1983)

(Des E. Stemp)

1983 (6 July). *British Army Uniforms. Phosphorised paper. P* 14 × 15.

No.	Type	Value	Description	Unused	Used
1218	**693**	16p.	black, buff, deep brown, slate-black, rose-red, gold and new blue	40	40
1219	**694**	20½p.	black, buff, greenish yellow, slate-black, brown-rose, gold & brt bl	70	70
1220	**695**	26p.	black, buff, slate-purple, green, bistre and gold	80	80
1221	**696**	28p.	black, buff, light brown, grey, dull rose, gold and new blue	80	80
1222	**697**	31p.	black, buff, olive-yellow, grey, deep magenta, gold and new blue	90	90
1218/22			.. .. *Set of* 5	3·25	3·25

Nos. 1218/22 were issued on the occasion of the 350th anniversary of the Royal Scots, the senior line regiment of the British Army.

698 20th-century Garden, Sissinghurst

699 19th-century Garden, Biddulph Grange

700 18th-century Garden, Blenheim

701 17th-century Garden, Pitmedden

(Des Liz Butler, Litho J.W.)

1983 (24 Aug). *British Gardens. Phosphorised paper. P* 14.

No.	Type	Value	Description	Unused	Used
1223	**698**	16p.	greenish yellow, brt purple, new blue, black, bright green & silver	40	40
1224	**699**	20½p.	greenish yellow, brt purple, new blue, black, bright green & silver	50	55
1225	**700**	28p.	greenish yellow, brt purple, new blue, black, bright green & silver	85	90
1226	**701**	31p.	greenish yellow, brt purple, new blue, black, bright green & silver	90	90
1223/6			.. .. *Set of* 4	2·50	2·50

Nos. 1223/6 were issued on the occasion of the death bicentenary of "Capability" Brown (landscape gardener)

702 Merry-go-round

703 Big Wheel, Helter-Skelter and Performing Animals

704 Side Shows

705 Early Produce Fair

(Des A. Restall)

1983 (5 Oct). *British Fairs. Phosphorised paper. P* 15 × 14.

1227	**702**	16p.	grey-black, greenish yellow, orge-red, ochre & turquoise-blue ..	40	40
1228	**703**	20½p.	grey-black, yellow-ochre, yellow-orange, brt magenta, violet & blk	50	55
1229	**704**	28p.	grey-black, bistre-yellow, orange-red, violet and yellow-brown ..	85	90
1230	**705**	31p.	grey-black, greenish yellow, red, dp turq-green, slate-violet & brn	90	90
1227/30 ..			.. .. *Set of* 4	2·50	2·50

706 "Christmas Post" (pillar-box)

707 "The Three Kings" (chimney-pots)

708 "World at Peace" (Dove and Blackbird)

709 "Light of Christmas" (street lamp)

710 "Christmas Dove" (hedge sculpture)

(Des T. Meeuwissen)

1983 (16 Nov). *Christmas. One phosphor band* (12½p.) *or phosphorised paper* (*others*). *P* 15 × 14.

1231	**706**	12½p.	black, greenish yellow, bright rose-red, bright blue, gold and grey-black	30	30
		a.	Imperf (horiz pair)	£750	
1232	**707**	16p.	black, greenish yellow, bright rose, pale new blue, gold & brown-pur	45	45
		a.	Imperf (pair)	£850	
1233	**708**	20½p.	black, greenish yellow, bright rose, new blue, gold and blue	70	70
1234	**709**	28p.	black, lemon, bright carmine, bluish violet, gold, deep turquoise-green and purple	90	90
1235	**710**	31p.	black, greenish yellow, brt rose, new blue, gold, green & brn-olive	1·00	1·00
1231/5 ..			.. .. *Set of* 5	3·00	3·00

711 Arms of the College of Arms

712 Arms of King Richard III (founder)

713 Arms of the Earl Marshal of England

714 Arms of the City of London

(Des J. Matthews)

1984 (17 Jan). *500th Anniv of College of Arms. Phosphorised paper. P* 14½.

1236	**711**	16p.	black, chrome-yellow, reddish brown, scarlet-vermilion, bright blue and grey-black	40	40
1237	**712**	20½p.	black, chrome-yellow, rosine, bright blue and grey-black ..	70	70
1238	**713**	28p.	black, chrome-yellow, rosine, brt blue, dull green and grey-black ..	95	95
1239	**714**	31p.	black, chrome-yellow, rosine, bright blue and grey-black ..	1·00	1·00
1236/9 ..			.. .. *Set of* 4	2·75	2·75

715 Highland Cow

716 Chillingham Wild Bull

717 Hereford Bull

718 Welsh Black Bull

719 Irish Moiled Cow

(Des B. Driscoll)

1984 (6 Mar). *British Cattle. Phosphorised paper. P* 15 × 14.

1240	**715**	16p.	grey-black, bistre-yellow, rosine, yellow-orge, new bl & pale drab	40	40
1241	**716**	20½p.	grey-black, greenish yellow, magenta, bistre, dull blue-green, pale drab and light green	65	65
1242	**717**	26p.	black, chrome-yellow, rosine, reddish brown, new blue & pale drab	70	70
1243	**718**	28p.	black, greenish yellow, bright carmine, orange-brown, deep dull blue and pale drab	85	85
1244	**719**	31p.	grey-black, bistre-yellow, rosine, red-brown, light blue & pale drab	1·00	1·00
1240/4 ..			.. .. *Set of* 5	3·25	3·25

Nos. 1240/4 were issued on the occasion of the centenary of the Highland Cattle Society and the bicentenary of the Royal Highland and Agricultural Society of Scotland.

720 Liverpool Garden Festival Hall

721 Milburngate Centre, Durham

722 Bush House, Bristol

723 Commercial Street Development, Perth

(Des R. Maddox and Trickett and Webb Ltd)

1984 (10 Apr). *Urban Renewal. Phosphorised paper. P* 15 × 14.

1245	**720**	16p.	bright emerald, greenish yellow, cerise, steel-bl, blk, silver & flesh	40	40
1246	**721**	20½p.	bright orange, greenish yellow, deep dull blue, yellowish green, azure, black and silver	70	70
		a.	Imperf (horiz pair)..	£1000	
1247	**722**	28p.	rosine, greenish yellow, Prussian blue, pale blue-green, blk & silver	95	95
1248	**723**	31p.	blue, greenish yellow, cerise, grey-blue, bright green, black and silver	1·00	1·00
		a.	Imperf (vert pair)	£1000	
1245/8 ..			.. .. *Set of* 4	2·75	2·75

Nos. 1245/8 were issued on the occasion of 150th anniversaries of the Royal Institute of British Architects and the Chartered Institute of Building, and to commemorate the first International Gardens Festival, Liverpool.

ROYAL MAIL POSTAGE LABELS

These imperforate labels, printed in red on phosphorised paper with grey-green background design, were issued on 1 May 1984 as an experiment by the Post Office. Special microprocessor controlled machines were installed at post offices in Cambridge, London, Shirley, (Southampton) and Windsor to provide an after-hours sales service to the public. The machines printed and dispensed the labels according to the coins inserted and the buttons operated by the customer. Values were initially available in ½p steps to 16p and in addition, the labels were sold at philatelic counters in two packs containing either 3 values (3½, 12½, 16p) or 32 values (½p to 16p).

From 28 August 1984 the machines were adjusted to provide values up to 17p. After 31 December 1984 labels including ½p values were withdrawn. The machines were withdrawn from service on 30 April 1985.

724 C.E.P.T. 25th Aniversary Logo

725 Abduction of Europa

(Des J. Larrivière (T **724**), F. Wegner (T **725**))

1984 (15 May). *25th Anniv of C.E.P.T. ("Europa") (T* **724***) and Second Elections to European Parliament (T* **725***). Phosphorised paper. P* 15 × 14.

1249 **724** 16p. greenish slate, deep blue & gold .. 40 60
a. Horiz pair. Nos. 1249/50 .. 1·25 1·25
1250 **725** 16p. greenish slate, deep blue, black and gold 40 60
1251 **724** 20½p. Venetian red, dp magenta & gold 70 90
a. Horiz pair. Nos. 1251/2 .. .. 1·75 1·75
1252 **752** 20½p. Venetian, deep magenta, black and gold 70 90
1249/52 .. .. *Set of* 4 2·75 2·75

Nos. 1249/50 and 1251/2 were each printed together, *se-tenant*, in horizontal pairs throughout the sheets.

726 Lancaster House

(Des P. Hogarth)

1984 (5 June). *London Economic Summit Conference. Phosphorised paper. P* 14 × 15.

1253 **726** 31p. silver, bistre-yellow, brown-ochre, black, rosine, bright blue and reddish lilac .. .. 1·25 1·25

727 View of Earth from "Apollo 11"

728 Navigational Chart of English Channel

729 Greenwich Observatory

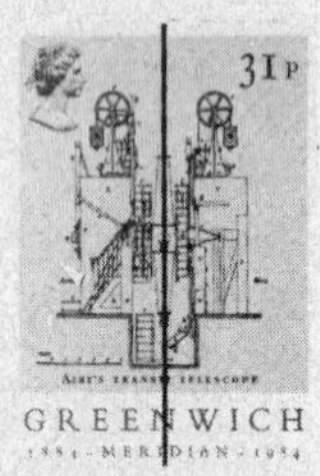

730 Sir George Airy's Transit Telescope

(Des. H. Waller. Litho Questa)

1984 (26 June). *Centenary of the Greenwich Meridian. Phosphorised paper. P* 14 × 14½.

1254 **727** 16p. new blue, greenish yellow, magenta, black, scarlet and blue-black 40 40
1255 **728** 20½p. olive-sepia, light brown, pale buff, black and scarlet 60 60
1256 **729** 28p. new blue, greenish yellow, scarlet, black and bright purple 95 95
1257 **730** 31p. deep blue, cobalt, scarlet and black .. 1·10 1·10
1254/7 .. .. *Set of* 4 2·75 2·75

On Nos. 1254/7 the Meridian is represented by a scarlet line.

731 Bath Mail Coach, 1784

732 Attack on Exeter Mail, 1816

733 Norwich Mail in Thunderstorm, 1827

734 Holyhead and Liverpool Mails leaving London, 1828

735 Edinburgh Mail Snowbound, 1831

(Des K. Bassford and S. Paine. Eng C. Slania. Recess and photo)

1984 (31 July). *Bicentenary of First Mail Coach Run Bath and Bristol to London. Phosphorised paper. P* 15 × 14.

1258 **731** 16p. pale stone, black, grey-black and bright scarlet 60 60
a. Horiz strip of 5 Nos. 1258/62 .. 2·75 2·75
1259 **732** 16p. pale stone, black, grey-black and bright scarlet 60 60
1260 **733** 16p. pale stone, black, grey-black and bright scarlet 60 60
1261 **734** 16p. pale stone, black, grey-black and bright scarlet 60 60
1262 **735** 16p. pale stone, black, grey-black and bright scarlet 60 60
1258/62 .. .. *Set of* 5 2·75 2·75

Nos. 1258/62 were printed together, *se-tenant*, in horizontal strips of 5 throughout the sheet.

736 Nigerian Clinic

737 Violinist and Acropolis, Athens

738 Building Project, Sri Lanka

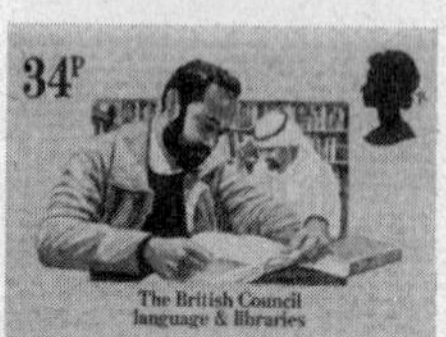

739 British Council Library, Middle East

(Des F. Newell and J. Sorrell)

1984 (25 Sept). *50th Anniv of the British Council. Phosphorised paper. P* 15 × 14.

1263 **736** 17p. grey-green, greenish yellow, bright purple, dull blue, black, pale green and yellow-green 50 50
1264 **737** 22p. crimson, greenish yellow, bright rose-red, dull green, black, pale drab and slate-purple 75 75
1265 **738** 31p. sepia, olive-bistre, red, black, pale stone and olive-brown .. .. 1·10 1·10
1266 **739** 34p. steel blue, yellow, rose-red, new blue, black, azure and pale blue .. .. 1·25 1·25
1263/6 .. .. *Set of* 4 3·25 3·25

740 The Holy Family

741 Arrival in Bethlehem

742 Shepherd and Lamb

743 Virgin and Child

744 Offering of Frankincense

(Des Yvonne Gilbert)

1984 (20 Nov). *Christmas. One phosphor band* (13*p.*) *or phosphorised paper (others). P* 15 × 14.

1267 **740** 13p. pale cream, grey-black, bistre-yellow, magenta, red-brown and lake-brown 30 30
1268 **741** 17p. pale cream, grey-black, yellow, magenta, dull blue and deep dull blue 40 45
1269 **742** 22p. pale cream, grey-black, olive-yellow, bright magenta, bright blue and brownish grey 55 60
1270 **743** 31p. pale cream, grey-black, bistre-yellow, magenta, dull blue and light brown 1·00 1·10
1271 **744** 34p. pale cream, olive-grey, bistre-yellow, magenta, turquoise-green and brown-olive .. .. 1·00 1·10
1267/71 .. .. *Set of* 5 3·00 3·25

Examples of No. 1267 from the Christmas £2.30 discount stamp booklet show a blue underprint of a double-lined star printed on the reverse over the gum.

745 "The Flying Scotsman"

746 "The Golden Arrow"

747 "The Cheltenham Flyer"

748 "The Royal Scot"

749 "The Cornish Riviera"

(Des T. Cuneo)

1985 (22 Jan). *Famous Trains. Phosphorised paper. P* 15 × 14.

1272 **745** 17p. black, lemon, magenta, dull glue, grey-black and gold 60 60
a. Imperf (pair) £1750
1273 **746** 22p. black, greenish yellow, bright rose, dp dull blue, grey-blk & gold 80 80
1274 **747** 29p. black, greenish yellow, magneta, blue, grey-black and gold .. 1·10 1·10
1275 **748** 31p. black, bistre-yellow, bright magenta, new blue slate-black & gold 1·10 1·10
1276 **749** 34p. black, greenish yellow, bright rose, blue, slate-black and gold .. 1·40 1·40
1272/6 .. .. *Set of* 5 4·50 4·50

Nos. 1272/6 were issued on the occasion of the 150th anniversary of the Great Western Railway Company.

750 Buff-tailed Bumble Bee

751 Seven-spotted Ladybird

752 Wart-biter Bush-cricket

753 Stag Beetle

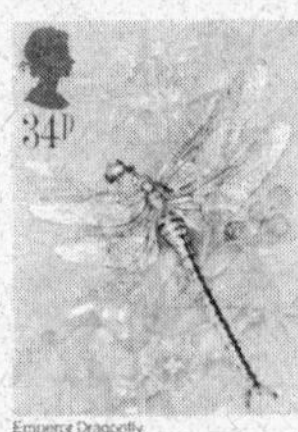

754 Emperor Dragonfly

(Des G. Beningfield)

1985 (12 Mar). *Insects. Phosphorised paper. P* 14 × 15.

1277 **750** 17p. black, greenish yellow, magenta, blue, azure, gold and slate-black 50 55
1278 **751** 22p. black, greenish yellow, bright rose-red, dull blue-green, slate-black and gold 70 70
1279 **752** 29p. black, greenish yellow, bright rose, greenish blue, grey-black, gold and bistre-yellow.. .. .. 90 90
1280 **753** 31p. black, greenish yellow, rose, pale new blue and gold .. .. .. 1·10 1·10
1281 **754** 34p. black, greenish yellow, magenta, greenish blue, grey-black and gold .. 1·10 1·10
1277/81 .. .. *Set of* 5 4·00 4·00

Nos. 1277/81 were issued on the occasion of the centenaries of the Royal Entomological Society of London's Royal Charter, and of the Selborne Society.

755 "Water Music" (George Frideric Handel

756 "The Planets" Suite (Gustav Holst)

757 "The First Cuckoo" (Frederick Delius)

758 "Sea Pictures" (Edward Elgar)

(Des W. McLean)

1985 (14 May). *Europa. European Music Year. British Composers. Phosphorised paper. P* 14 × 14½.

1282 **755** 17p. black, bright yellow-green, deep magenta, new blue, grey-black and gold 60 60
a. Imperf (vert pair) .. .. ..
1283 **756** 22p. black, greenish yellow, bright magenta, new blue, grey-black and gold 90 90
1284 **757** 31p. black, greenish yellow, magenta, greenish blue, grey-black and gold .. 1·25 1·25
1285 **758** 34p. black, olive-yellow, bistre, turquoise-blue, slate and gold .. .. .. 1·40 1·40
1282/5 .. .. *Set of* 4 3·75 3·75

Nos. 1282/5 were issued on the occasion of the 300th birth anniversary of Handel.

759 R.N.L.I. Lifeboat and Signal Flags

760 Beachy Head Lighthouse and Chart

761 "Marecs A" Communications Satellite and Dish Aerials

762 Buoys

(Des F. Newell and J. Sorrel. Litho J.W.)

1985 (18 June). *Safety at Sea. Phosphorised paper. P* 14.

1286 **759** 17p. black, azure, emerald, ultramarine, orange-yellow, vermilion, bright blue, and chrome-yellow 50 50
1287 **760** 22p. black, azure, emerald, ultramarine, orange-yellow, vermilion, bright blue and chrome-yellow 75 75
1288 **761** 31p. black, azure, emerald, ultramarine, orange-yellow, vermilion, and bright blue .. .. 1·10 1·10
1289 **762** 34p. black, azure, emerald, ultramarine, orange-yellow, vermilion, bright blue and chrome-yellow .. .. .. 1·25 1·25
1286/9 .. .. *Set of* 4 3·25 3·25

Nos. 1286/9 were issued on the occasion of the Bicentenary of the unimmersible lifeboat and the 50th anniversary of radar.

763 Datapost Motorcyclist, City of London

764 Rural Postbus

765 Parcel Delivery in Winter

766 Town Letter Delivery

(Des P. Hogarth)

1985 (30 July). 350 *Years of Royal Mail Public Postal Service. Phosphorised paper. P* 14 × 15.

1290 **763** 17p. black, greenish yellow, bright carmine, greenish blue, yellow-brown, grey-black and silver .. 50 50
a. Imperf on 3 sides (vert pair) .. £1250
1291 **764** 22p. black, greenish yellow, cerise, steel blue, lt grn, grey-blk & silver 75 75
1292 **765** 31p. black, greenish yellow, brt carm, dull blue, drab, grey-blk & silver 1·10 1·10
a. Imperf (vert pair).. .. ..
1293 **766** 34p. black, greenish yellow, cerise, ultram, lt brown, grey-blk & silver 1·25 1·25
1290/3 .. .. *Set of* 4 3·25 3·25

Examples of No. 1290 from the commemorative £1.53 discount stamp booklet show a blue underprint of a double-lined D printed on the reverse over the gum.

No. 1290a shows perforation indentations at right, but is imperforate at top, bottom and on the left-hand side.

767 King Arthur and Merlin

768 Lady of the Lake

769 Queen Guinevere and Sir Lancelot

770 Sir Galahad

(Des Yvonne Gilbert)

1985 (3 Sept). *Arthurian Legends. Phosphorised paper. P* 15 × 14.

1294	**767**	17p. grey-black, lemon, brown-lilac, ultramarine, grey-black and silver	50	50
		a. Imperf (pair)	£1750	
1295	**768**	22p. black, lemon, brown-lilac, pale blue, grey-black, silver & grey-blk	75	75
1296	**769**	31p. black, lemon, magenta, turquoise-blue, grey-black, silver & grey-blk	1·10	1·10
1297	**770**	34p. grey, lemon, magenta, new blue, grey-black, silver and grey-black..	1·25	1·25
1294/7		.. .. *Set of* 4	3·25	3·25

Nos. 1294/7 were issued on the occasion of the 500th anniversary of the printing of Sir Thomas Malory's *Morte d'Arthur*.

771 Peter Sellers (from photo by Bill Brandt)

772 David Niven (from photo by Cornell Lucas)

773 Charlie Chaplin (from photo by Lord Snowdon)

774 Vivien Leigh (from photo by Angus McBean)

775 Alfred Hitchcock (from photo by Howard Coster)

(Des K. Bassford)

1985 (8 Oct). *British Film Year. Phosphorised paper. P* 14½.

1298	**771**	17p. grey-black, ol-grey, gold & silver	40	40
1299	**772**	22p. black, brown, gold and silver ..	70	80
1300	**773**	29p. black, lavender, gold and silver ..	1·10	90
1301	**774**	31p. black, pink, gold and silver ..	1·10	1·10
1302	**775**	34p. black, greenish blue, gold & silver	1·10	1·10
1298/302		.. .. *Set of* 5	4·00	4·00

776 Principal Boy

777 Genie

778 Dame

779 Good Fairy

780 Pantomine Cat

(Des A. George)

1985 (19 Nov). *Christmas. Pantomine Characters. One phosphor band* (12*p*.) *or phosphorised paper* (*others*). *P* 15 × 14.

1303	**776**	12p. new blue, greenish yellow, bright rose, gold, grey-black and silver	35	35
		a. Imperf (pair)	£1250	
1304	**777**	17p. emerald, greenish yellow, bright rose, new blue, blk, gold & silver	45	50
		a. Imperf (pair)	£1750	
1305	**778**	22p. bright carmine, greenish yellow, pale new blue, grey, gold & silver	75	75
1306	**779**	31p. bright orange, lemon, rose, slate-purple, silver and gold	1·00	1·00
1307	**780**	34p. brt reddish violet, brt blue, brt rose, blk, grey-brn, gold & silver	1·10	1·10
1303/7		.. .. *Set of* 5	3·25	3·25

Examples of No. 1303 from the Christmas £2.40 stamp booklet show a blue underprint of a double-lined star printed on the reverse over the gum.

781 Light Bulb and North Sea Oil Drilling Rig (Energy)

782 Thermometer and Pharmaceutical Laboratory (Health)

783 Garden Hoe and Steelworks (Steel)

784 Loaf of Bread and Cornfield (Agriculture)

(Des K. Bassford. Litho Questa)

1986 (14 Jan). *Industry Year. Phosphorised paper. P* 14½ × 14.

1308	**781**	17p. gold, black, magenta, greenish yellow and new blue	45	45
1309	**782**	22p. gold, pale turquoise-green, black, magenta, greenish yellow and blue	70	70
1310	**783**	31p. gold, black, magenta, greenish yellow and new blue	1·10	1·10
1311	**784**	34p. gold, black, magenta, greenish yellow and new blue	1·10	1·10
1308/11		.. .. *Set of* 4	3·00	3·00

785 Dr. Edmond Halley as Comet

786 *Giotto* Spacecraft approaching Comet

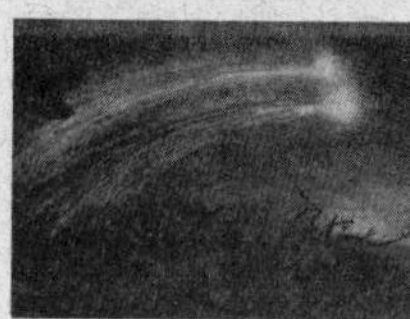

787 "Twice in a Lifetime"

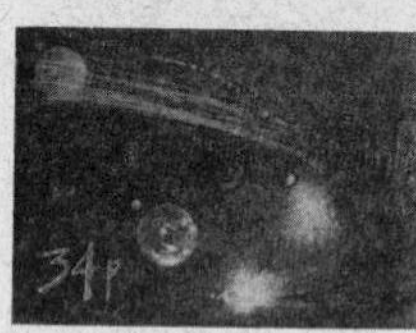

788 Comet orbiting Sun and Planets

(Des R. Steadman)

1986 (18 Feb). *Appearance of Halley's Comet. Phosphorised paper. P* 15 × 14.

1312	**785**	17p. black, bistre, rosine, blue, grey-black, gold and deep brown ..	45	45
1313	**786**	22p. orange-vermilion, greenish yellow, brt purple, new bl, blk & gold	90	90
1314	**787**	31p. black, greenish yellow, brt purple dp turquoise-blue, grey-blk & gold	1·25	1·25
1315	**788**	34p. blue, greenish yellow, magenta, deep turquoise-blue, black & gold	1·25	1·25
1312/15		.. .. *Set of* 4	3·50	3·50

789 Queen Elizabeth II in 1928, 1942 and 1952

790 Queen Elizabeth II in 1958, 1973 and 1982

(Des J. Matthews)

1986 (21 Apr). 60*th Birthday of Queen Elizabeth II. Phosphorised paper. P* 15 × 14.

1316	**789**	17p. grey-black, turquoise-green, bright green, green and dull blue..	60	60
		a. Horiz pair. Nos. 1316/17.. ..	1·60	1·60
1317	**790**	17p. grey-black, dull blue, greenish blue and indigo	60	50
1318	**789**	34p. grey-black, deep dull purple, yellow-orange and red	1·10	1·10
		a. Horiz pair. Nos. 1318/19.. ..	2·50	2·50
1319	**790**	34p. grey-black, olive-brown, yellow-brown, olive-grey and red ..	1·10	1·10
1316/19		.. .. *Set of* 4	3·75	3·75

Nos. 1316/17 and 1318/19 were printed together, *se-tenant*, in horizontal pairs throughout the sheets.

NEW INFORMATION

The editor is always interested to correspond with people who have new information that will improve or correct the Catalogue.

791 Barn Owl

792 Pine Marten

793 Wild Cat **794** Natterjack Toad

(Des K. Lilly)

1986 (20 May). *Europa. Nature Conservation. Endangered Species. Phosphorised paper. P* 14½ × 14.

1320	**791**	17p. gold, greenish yellow, rose, yellow-brown, olive-grey, new blue & blk	50	55
1321	**792**	22p. gold, greenish yellow, reddish brn, ol-yell, turq-bl, grey-blk & blk	90	80
1322	**793**	31p. gold, brt yellow-green, magenta, lt brown, ultramarine, ol-brn & blk	1·25	1·25
1323	**794**	34p. gold, greenish yellow, bright rose-red, brt green, grey-black & black	1·25	1·25
1320/3		*Set of* 4	3·50	3·50

795 Peasants working in Fields

796 Freemen working at Town Trades

797 Knight and Retainers

798 Lord at Banquet

(Des Tayburn Design Consultancy)

1986 (17 June). *900th Anniv of Domesday Book. Phosphorised paper. P* 15 × 14.

1324	**795**	17p. yell-brn, verm, lemon, brt emer, orge-brn, grey & brownish grey	50	50
1325	**796**	22p. yellow-ochre, red, greenish blue, chestnut, grey-blk & brownish grey	90	90
1326	**797**	31p. yellow-brown, verm, grn, Indian red, grey-blk & brownish grey	1·25	1·25
1327	**798**	34p. yellow-ochre, brt scar, grey-brn, new bl, lake-brn, grey-blk & grey	1·25	1·25
1324/7		*Set of* 4	3·50	3·50

MINIMUM PRICE

The minimum price quote is 10p which represents a handling charge rather than a basis for valuing common stamps. For further notes about prices see introductory pages.

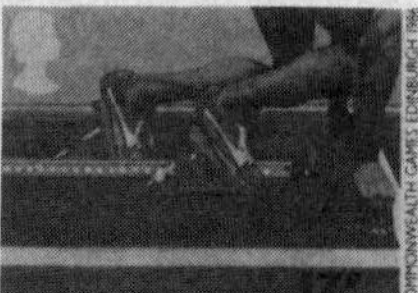

799 Athletics

800 Rowing

801 Weightlifting

802 Rifle Shooting

803 Hockey

(Des N. Cudworth)

1986 (15 July). *Thirteenth Commonwealth Games, Edinburgh and World Hockey Cup for Men, London* (34*p*.). *Phosphorised paper. P* 15 × 14.

1328	**799**	17p. black, greenish yellow, orange-vermilion, ultram, chestnut & emer	45	50
1329	**800**	22p. black, lemon, scarlet, new blue, royal blue, chestnut & dp ultram	90	60
1330	**801**	29p. grey-black, greenish yellow, scarlet, new blue, brown-ochre, brown-rose and pale chestnut	1·25	1·25
1331	**802**	31p. black, greenish yellow, rose, blue, dull yell-grn, chestnut & yell-grn	1·25	1·25
1332	**803**	34p. black, lemon, scarlet, brt blue, brt emerald, red-brown & vermilion	1·25	1·10
		a. Imperf (pair)	£1250	
1328/32		*Set of* 5	4·50	4·00

No. 1332 also commemorates the Centenary of the Hockey Association.

804 **805**
Prince Andrew and Miss Sarah Ferguson (from photo by Gene Nocon)

(Des J. Matthews)

1986 (22 July). *Royal Wedding. One phosphor band* (12*p*.) *or phosphorised paper* (17*p*.). *P* 14 × 15.

1333	**804**	12p. lake, greenish yellow, cerise, ultramarine, black and silver	60	60
1334	**805**	17p. steel blue, greenish yellow, cerise, ultramarine, black and gold	90	90
		a. Imperf (pair)	£850	

806 Stylised Cross on Ballot Paper

(Des J. Gibbs. Litho Questa)

1986 (19 Aug). *32nd Commonwealth Parliamentary Association Conference. Phosphorised paper. P* 14 × 14½.

1335	**806**	34p. pale grey-lilac, black, vermilion, yellow and ultramarine	1·50	1·50

807 Lord Dowding and Hawker "Hurricane" **808** Lord Tedder and Hawker "Typhoon"

809 Lord Trenchard and De Havilland "DH 9A" **810** Sir Arthur Harris and Avro "Lancaster"

811 Lord Portal and De Havilland "Mosquito"

(Des B. Sanders)

1986 (16 Sept). *History of the Royal Air Force. Phosphorised paper. P* 14½.

1336	**807**	17p. pale blue, greenish yellow, bright rose, blue, black and grey-black	40	40
1337	**808**	22p. pale turquoise-green, greenish yellow, mag, new bl, blk & grey-blk	90	90
		a. Face value omitted*	£400	
		b. Queen's head omitted*	£400	
1338	**809**	29p. pale drab, olive-yellow, magenta, blue, grey-black and black	1·10	1·10
1339	**810**	31p. pale flesh, greenish yellow, magenta, ultram, blk & grey-blk	1·25	1·25
1340	**811**	34p. buff, greenish yellow, magenta, blue, grey-black and black	1·25	1·25
1336/40		*Set of* 5	4·50	4·50

*Nos. 1337a/b come from three consecutive sheets on which the stamps in the first vertical row are without the face value and those in the second vertical row the Queen's head.

Nos. 1336/40 were issued to celebrate the 50th anniversary of the first R.A.F. Commands.

812 The Glastonbury Thorn

813 The Tanad Valley Plygain

814 The Hebrides Tribute

815 The Dewsbury Church Knell

816 The Hereford Boy Bishop

(Des Lynda Gray)

1986 (18 Nov–2 Dec). *Christmas. One phosphor band* (12*p*., 13*p*.) *or phosphorised paper* (*others*). *P* 15 × 14.

1341	**812**	12p.	gold, greenish yellow, vermilion, deep brown, emerald and deep blue (2.12)	75	75
1342		13p.	deep blue, greenish yellow, vermilion, deep brown, emerald and gold	40	40
1343	**813**	18p.	myrtle-green, yellow, vermilion, dp blue, black, reddish brn & gold	55	55
1344	**814**	22p.	vermilion, olive-bistre, dull blue, deep brown, deep green and gold	75	75
1345	**815**	31p.	deep brown, yellow, vermilion, violet, dp dull green, black & gold	1·00	1·00
1346	**816**	34p.	violet, lemon, vermilion, deep dull blue, reddish brown and gold ..	1·00	1·00
1341/6			.. .. *Set of* 6	4·00	4·00

No. 1341 represented a discount of 1p., available between 2 and 24 December 1986, on the current second class postage rate.

Examples of the 13p. value from special folders, containing 36 stamps and sold for £4.30, show a blue underprint of double-lined stars printed on the reverse over the gum.

817 North American Blanket Flower

818 Globe Thistle

819 *Echeveria*

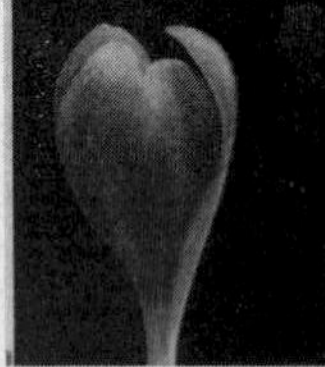

820 Autumn Crocus

(Adapted J. Matthews)

1987 (20 Jan). *Flower Photographs by Alfred Lammer. Phosphorised paper. P* 14½ × 14.

1347	**817**	18p.	silver, greenish yellow, rosine, deep green and black	50	50
1348	**818**	22p.	silver, greenish yellow, new blue, greenish blue and black	80	80
1349	**819**	31p.	silver, greenish yellow, scarlet, blue-green, deep green and black	1·10	1·10
			a. Imperf (pair)	£1600	
1350	**820**	34p.	silver, greenish yellow, magenta, dull blue, deep green and black ..	1·25	1·25
1347/50			.. .. *Set of* 4	3·25	3·25

OMNIBUS ISSUES

Details, together with prices for complete sets, of the various Omnibus issues from the 1935 Silver Jubilee series to date are included in a special section following Zululand at the end of the catalogue.

821 *The Principia Mathematica*

822 *Motion of Bodies in Ellipses*

823 *Optick Treatise*

824 *The System of the World*

(Des Sarah Godwin)

1987 (24 Mar). 300*th Anniv of* The Principia Mathematica *by Sir Isaac Newton. Phosphorised paper. P* 14 × 15.

1351	**821**	18p.	black, greenish yellow, cerise, blue-green, grey-black and silver ..	50	50
1352	**822**	22p.	black, greenish yellow, brt orange, blue, brt emer, silver & bluish vio	80	80
1353	**823**	31p.	black, greenish yellow, scar, new bl, bronze-grn, silver & slate-grn	1·10	1·10
1354	**824**	34p.	black, greenish yellow, red, bright blue, grey-black and silver ..	1·25	1·25
1351/4			.. .. *Set of* 4	3·25	3·25

825 Willis Faber & Dumas Building, Ipswich

826 Pompidou Centre, Paris

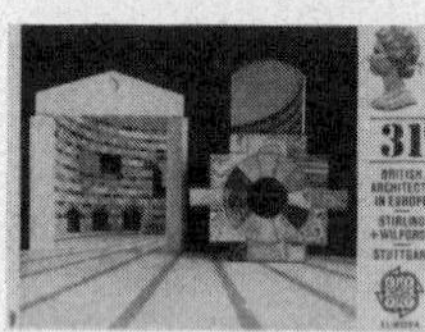

827 Staatsgalerie, Stuttgart

828 European Investment Bank, Luxembourg

(Des Brian Tattersfield)

1987 (12 May). *Europa. British Architects in Europe. Phosphorised paper. P* 15 × 14.

1355	**825**	18p.	black, bistre-yellow, cerise, bright blue, deep grey and grey-black ..	50	50
1356	**826**	22p.	black, greenish yellow, carmine, bright blue, dp grey & grey-black	80	80
1357	**827**	31p.	grey-black, bistre-yellow, cerise, brt blue, brt green, black & dull vio	1·10	1·10
			a. Imperf (horiz pair)		
1358	**828**	34p.	black, greenish yellow, cerise, bright blue, grey-black & deep grey	1·25	1·25
1355/8			.. .. *Set of* 4	3·25	3·25

829 Brigade Members with Ashford Litter, 1887

830 Bandaging Blitz Victim, 1940

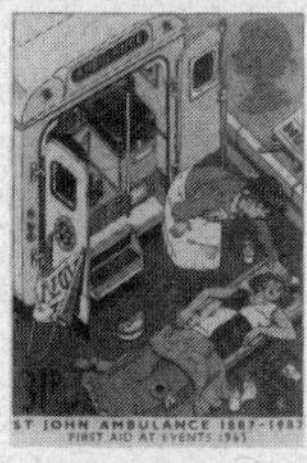

831 Volunteer with fainting Girl, 1965

832 Transport of Transplant Organ by Air Wing, 1987

(Des Debbie Cook. Litho Questa)

1987 (16 June). *Centenary of St. John Ambulance Brigade. Phosphorised paper. P* 14 × 14½.

1359	**829**	18p.	new blue, greenish yellow, magenta, black, silver and pink ..	50	50
1360	**830**	22p.	new blue, greenish yellow, magenta, black, silver and cobalt	80	80
1361	**831**	31p.	new blue, greenish yellow, magenta, black, silver & bistre-brn	1·10	1·10
1362	**832**	34p.	new blue, greenish yellow, mag, blk, silver & greenish grey	1·25	1·25
1359/62			.. .. *Set of* 4	3·25	3·25

833 Arms of the Lord Lyon King of Arms

834 Scottish Heraldic Banner of Prince Charles

835 Arms of Royal Scottish Academy of Painting, Sculpture and Architecture

836 Arms of Royal Society of Edinburgh

(Des J. Matthews)

1987 (21 July). 300*th Anniv of Revival of Order of the Thistle. Phosphorised paper. P* 14½.

1363	**833**	18p.	black, lemon, scarlet, blue, deep green, slate and brown	50	50
1364	**834**	22p.	black, greenish yellow, carmine, new blue, dp grn, grey & lake-brn	80	80
1365	**835**	31p.	black, greenish yellow, scarlet, new blue, dull grn, grey & grey-blk	1·10	1·10
1366	**836**	34p.	black, greenish yellow, scarlet, dp ultram, dull grn, grey & yell-brn	1·25	1·25
1363/6			.. .. *Set of* 4	3·25	3·25

837 Crystal Palace, "Monarch of the Glen" (Landseer) and Grace Darling

838 *Great Eastern, Beeton's Book of Household Management* and Prince Albert

839 Albert Memorial, Ballot Box and Disraeli

840 Diamond Jubilee Emblem, Newspaper Placard for Relief of Mafeking and Morse Key

(Des M. Dempsey. Eng C. Slania. Recess and photo)

1987 (8 Sept). *150th Anniv of Queen Victoria's Accession. Phosphorised paper. P* 15 × 14.

1367	**837**	18p.	pale stone, dp blue, lemon, rose, greenish bl, brn-ochre & grey-blk	50	50
1368	**838**	22p.	pale stone, deep brown, lemon, rose, grey-black and brown-ochre	80	80
1369	**839**	31p.	pale stone, dp lilac, lemon, cerise, brn-ochre, greenish bl & grey-blk	1·10	1·10
1370	**840**	34p.	pale stone, myrtle-green, yellow-ochre, reddish brown & brn-ochre	1·25	1·25
1367/70			.. .. *Set of* 4	3·25	3·25

841 Pot by Bernard Leach

842 Pot by Elizabeth Fritsch

843 Pot by Lucie Rie

844 Pot by Hans Coper

(Des T. Evans)

1987 (13 Oct). *Studio Pottery. Phosphorised paper. P* 14½ × 14.

1371	**841**	18p.	gold, lemon, light red-brown, chestnut, light grey and black ..	50	50
1372	**842**	26p.	blue over silver, yellow-orange, bright purple, lavender, bluish violet, grey-brown and black ..	80	80
1373	**843**	31p.	rose-lilac over silver, greenish yellow, cerise, new bl, grey-lilac & blk	1·10	1·10
1374	**844**	34p.	copper, yellow-brown, reddish brown, grey-lilac and black ..	1·25	1·25
1371/4			.. .. *Set of* 4	3·25	3·25

845 Decorating the Christmas Tree

846 Waiting for Father Christmas

847 Sleeping Child and Father Christmas in Sleigh

848 Child reading

849 Child playing Recorder and Snowman

(Des M. Foreman)

1987 (17 Nov). *Christmas. One phosphor band* (13*p.*) *or phosphorised paper* (*others*). *P* 15 × 14.

1375	**845**	13p.	gold, greenish yellow, rose, greenish blue and black	40	40
1376	**846**	18p.	gold, greenish yellow, bright purple, greenish blue, brt blue & blk	50	50
1377	**847**	26p.	gold, greenish yellow, bright purple, new blue, bright blue and black	75	75
1378	**848**	31p.	gold, greenish yellow, scarlet, brt mag, dull rose, greenish bl & blk	90	90
1379	**849**	34p.	gold, greenish yellow, dull rose, greenish blue, bright blue & black	1·00	1·00
1375/9			.. .. *Set of* 5	3·25	3·25

850 Bull-rout (Jonathan Couch)

851 Yellow Waterlily (Major Joshua Swatkin)

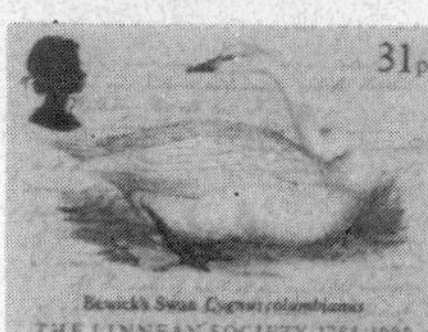

852 Bewick's Swan (Edward Lear)

853 *Morchella esculenta* (James Sowerby)

(Des E. Hughes)

1988 (19 Jan). *Bicentenary of Linnean Society. Archive Illustrations. Phosphorised paper. P* 15 × 14.

1380	**850**	18p.	grey-black, stone, orange-yellow, bright purple, olive-bistre & gold	45	45
1381	**851**	26p.	black, stone, bistre-yellow, dull orange, greenish bl, gold & pale bis	75	75
1382	**852**	31p.	black, stone, greenish yellow, rose-red, dp blue, gold & olive-bis	1·00	1·00
			a. Imperf (horiz pair)	£1250	
1383	**853**	34p.	black, stone, yellow, pale bistre, olive-grey, gold and olive-bistre..	1·10	1·10
1380/3			.. .. *Set of* 4	3·00	3·00

854 Revd William Morgan (Bible translator, 1588)

855 William Salesbury (New Testament translator, 1567)

856 Bishop Richard Davies (New Testament translator, 1567)

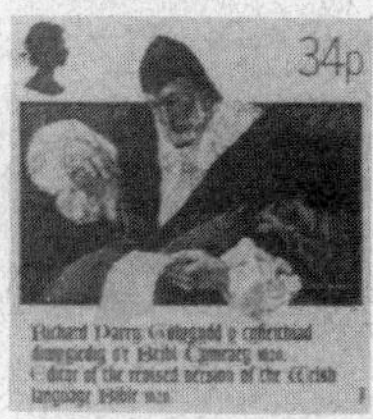

857 Bishop Richard Parry (editor of Revised Welsh Bible, 1620)

(Des K. Bowen)

1988 (1 Mar). *400th Anniv of Welsh Bible. Phosphorised paper. P* 14½ × 14.

1384	**854**	18p.	grey-black, greenish yellow, cerise, blue, black and emerald ..	45	45
			a. Imperf (pair)	£1250	
1385	**855**	26p.	grey-black, yellow, bright rose-red, turquoise-blue, black & orge	75	75
1386	**856**	31p.	black, chrome-yellow, carmine, new blue, grey-black and blue ..	1·00	1·00
1387	**857**	34p.	grey-black, greenish yellow, cerise, turquoise-grn, blk & brt vio	1·10	1·10
1384/7			.. .. *Set of* 4	3·00	3·00

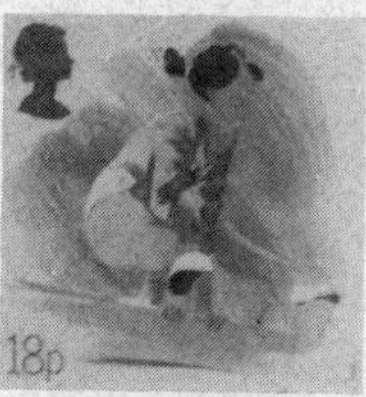

858 Gymnastics (Centenary of British Amateur Gymnastics Association)

859 Downhill Skiing (Ski Club of Great Britain)

860 Tennis (Centenary of Lawn Tennis Association)

861 Football (Centenary of Football League)

(Des J. Sutton)

1988 (22 Mar). *Sports Organizations. Phosphorised paper. P* 14½.

1388	**858**	18p.	violet-blue, greenish yellow, rosine, brt rose, new blue & silver	45	45
1389	**859**	26p.	violet-blue, greenish yellow, vermilion, carmine, yell-orge & silver	75	75
1390	**860**	31p.	violet-bl, greenish yell, rose, bl, pale greenish bl, silver & brt orge	1·00	1·00
1391	**861**	34p.	violet-blue, greenish yellow, vermilion, bl, brt emer, silver & pink	1·10	1·10
1388/91			.. .. *Set of* 4	3·00	3·00

862 *Mallard* and Mailbags on Pick-up Arms

863 Loading Transatlantic Mail on Liner *Queen Elizabeth*

864 Glasgow Tram No. 1173 and Pillar Box

865 Imperial Airways Handley Page "HP 24" and Airmail Van

(Des M. Dempsey)

1988 (10 May). *Europa. Transport and Mail Services in 1930's. Phosphorised paper. P* 15 × 14.

1392	**862**	18p. brown, yellow, rose-red, dull blue, dp brown, reddish vio & blk	50	50
1393	**863**	26p. brown, yellow, orange-vermilion, dull blue, violet-bl, brt emer & blk	70	70
1394	**864**	31p. brown, yellow-orange, carmine, dull purple, vio-bl, brt grn & blk	1·00	1·00
1395	**865**	34p. brown, orange-yellow, carmine-rose, bluish vio, brt bl, sepia & blk	1·10	1·10
1392/5		*Set of* 4	3·00	3·00

866 Early Settler and Sailing Clipper

867 Queen Elizabeth II with British and Australian Parliament Buildings

868 W. G. Grace (cricketer) and Tennis Racquet

869 Shakespeare, John Lennon (entertainer) and Sydney Landmarks

(Des G. Emery. Litho Questa)

1988 (21 June). *Bicentenary of Australian Settlement. Phosphorised paper. P* 14½.

1396	**866**	18p. deep ultramarine, orange-yellow, scarlet, black, bluish grey & emerald	50	35
		a. Horiz pair. Nos. 1396/7	1·10	1·10
1397	**867**	18p. deep ultramarine, orange-yellow, black, bluish grey and emerald	50	35
1398	**868**	34p. deep ultramarine, orange-yellow, scarlet, black, bluish grey & emerald	1·10	1·00
		a. Horiz pair. Nos. 1398/9	2·25	2·25
1399	**869**	34p. deep ultramarine, orange-yellow, black, bluish grey and emerald	1·10	1·00
1396/9		*Set of* 4	3·00	3·00

Nos. 1396/7 and 1398/9 were printed together, *se-tenant*, in horizontal pairs throughout the sheets, each pair showing a background design of the Australian flag.

Stamps in similar designs were also issued by Australia.

870 Spanish Galeasse off The Lizard

871 English Fleet leaving Plymouth

872 Engagement off Isle of Wight

873 Attack of English Fire-ships, Calais

874 Armada in Storm, North Sea

(Des G. Evernden)

1988 (19 July). *400th Anniv of Spanish Armada. Phosphorised paper. P* 15 × 14.

1400	**870**	18p. slate-black, yellow-orange, bright carm, brt bl, turq-bl, yell-grn & gold	65	65
		a. Horiz strip of 5. Nos. 1400/4	2·75	2·75
1401	**871**	18p. slate-black, yellow-orange, bright carm, brt bl, turq-bl, yell-grn & gold	65	65
1402	**872**	18p. slate-black, yellow-orange, bright carm, brt bl, turq-bl, yell-grn & gold	65	65
1403	**873**	18p. slate-black, yellow-orange, bright carm, brt bl, turq-bl, yell-grn & gold	65	65
1404	**874**	18p. slate-black, yellow-orange, bright carm, brt bl, turq-bl, yell-grn & gold	65	65
1400/4		*Set of* 5	2·75	2·75

Nos. 1400/4 were printed together, *se-tenant*, in horizontal strips of 5 throughout the sheet, forming a composite design.

875 "The Owl and the Pussy-cat"

876 "Edward Lear as a Bird" (self-portrait)

877 "Cat" (from alphabet book)

878 "There was a Young Lady whose Bonnet .." (limerick)

(Des M. Swatridge and S. Dew)

1988 (6–27 Sept). *Death Centenary of Edward Lear (artist and author). Phosphorised paper. P* 15 × 14.

1405	**875**	19p black, pale cream and carmine	50	50
1406	**876**	27p black, pale cream and yellow	85	80
1407	**877**	32p black, pale cream and emerald	1·00	1·00
1408	**878**	35p black, pale cream and blue	1·10	1·10
1405/8		*Set of* 4	3·00	3·00
MS1409		122 × 90 mm. Nos. 1405/8 (*sold at* £1.35) (27 Sept)	3·50	3·75

The premium on No. **MS**1409 was used to support the "Stamp World London 90" International Stamp Exhibition.

879 Carrickfergus Castle

880 Caernarfon Castle

881 Edinburgh Castle

882 Windsor Castle

(Des from photos by Prince Andrew, Duke of York. Eng C. Matthews. Recess Harrison)

1988 (18 Oct). *Ordinary paper. P* 15 × 14.

1410	**879**	£1 deep green	1·50	1·60
1411	**880**	£1.50, maroon	2·25	2·40
1412	**881**	£2 steel-blue	3·00	3·25
1413	**882**	£5 deep brown	7·50	7·75
1410/13		*Set of* 4	13·00	13·50

883 Journey to Bethlehem

884 Shepherds and Star

885 Three Wise Men

886 Nativity

887 The Annunciation

(Des L. Trickett)

1988 (15 Nov). *Christmas. Christmas Cards. One phosphor band (14p.) or phosphorised paper (others). P* 15 × 14.

1414 **883** 14p. gold, orange-yellow, bright mauve, bluish violet, brt blue & grey-black . . 35 35
a. Error. "13p." instead of "14p." . .
b. Imperf (pair) . . . .
1415 **884** 19p. gold, yell-orange, brt violet, ultram, rose-red, grey-black & bright blue . . 50 50
a. Imperf (pair) . . . .
1416 **885** 27p. gold, red, deep lavender, deep lilac, emerald, grey-black and bright blue 80 80
1417 **886** 32p. gold, orange-yellow, bright rose, dp mauve, violet, grey-black & brt blue 1·00 1·00
1418 **887** 35p. gold, green, reddish violet, bright blue, bright purple and grey-black . . 1·00 1·00
1414/18 . . . . *Set of* 5 3·25 3·25

Examples of No. 1414a were found in some 1988 Post Office Yearbooks.

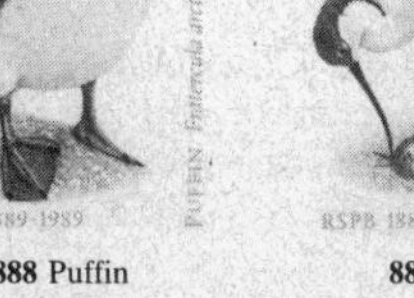

888 Puffin **889** Avocet

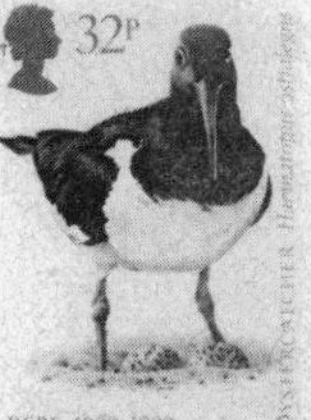

890 Oystercatcher **891** Gannet

(Des D. Cordery)

1989 (17 Jan). *Centenary of Royal Society for the Protection of Birds. Phosphorised paper. P* 14 × 15.

1419 **888** 19p. grey, orange-yellow, orange-red, dull ultramarine, grey-black and silver . . 50 50
1420 **889** 27p. grey, bistre, rose, steel-blue, lavender, silver and grey-black . . 75 75
1421 **890** 32p. grey, bistre, scarlet, orange-red, lavender, silver and black . . 90 90
1422 **891** 35p. grey, lemon, rose-carmine, green, new blue, silver and black 90 90
1419/22 . . . . *Set of* 4 2·75 2·75

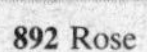

892 Rose **893** Cupid

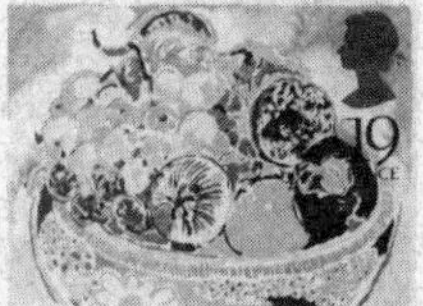

894 Yachts **895** Fruit

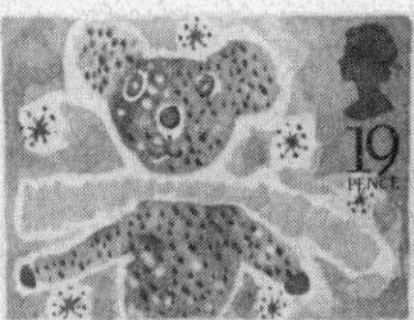

896 Teddy Bear

(Des P. Sutton)

1989 (31 Jan). *Greetings Stamps. Phosphorised paper. P* 15 × 14.

1423 **892** 19p. black, greenish yellow, bright rose, red, new blue, light green and gold . . 90 90
a. Booklet pane. Nos. 1423/7 × 2 plus 12 half stamp-size labels . . . . 9·00
1424 **893** 19p. black, greenish yellow, bright rose, red, new blue, light green and gold . . 90 90
1425 **894** 19p. black, greenish yellow, bright rose, red, new blue, light green and gold . . 90 90
1426 **895** 19p. black, greenish yellow, bright rose, red, new blue, light green and gold . . 90 90
1427 **896** 19p. black, greenish yellow, bright rose, red, new blue, light green and gold . . 90 90
1423/7 . . . . *Set of* 5 4·50 4·50

Nos. 1423/7 were only issued in £1.90 booklets.

897 Fruit and Vegetables **898** Meat Products

899 Dairy Produce **900** Cereal Products

(Des Sedley Place Ltd)

1989 (7 Mar). *Food and Farming Year. Phosphorised paper. P* 14 × 14½.

1428 **897** 19p. brownish grey, greenish yellow, rose, new blue, black, pale grey & emerald 50 50
1429 **898** 27p. brownish grey, greenish yellow, bright carmine, new blue, black, pale grey and bright orange 75 75
1430 **899** 32p. brownish grey, greenish yellow, rose-red, new blue, black, pale grey and bistre-yellow 90 90
1431 **900** 35p. brownish grey, greenish yellow, bright carmine, new blue, black, pale grey and brown-red 90 90
1428/31 . . . . *Set of* 4 2·75 2·75

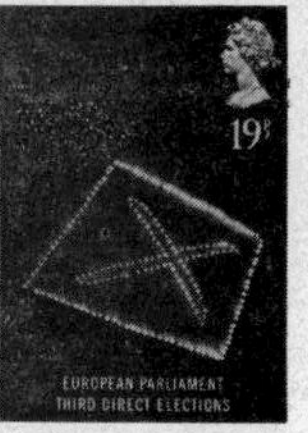

901 Mortar Board (150th Anniv of Public Education in England)

902 Cross on Ballot Paper (3rd Direct Elections to European Parliament)

903 Posthorn (26th Postal, Telegraph and Telephone International Congress, Brighton)

904 Globe(Inter–Parliamentary Union Centenary Conference, London)

(Des Lewis Moberly from firework set-pieces. Litho Questa)

1989 (11 Apr). *Anniversaries. Phosphorised paper. P* 14 × 14½.

1432 **901** 19p. new blue, greenish yellow, mag & blk 45 45
a. Horiz pair. Nos. 1432/3 . . . . 95 95
1433 **902** 19p. new blue, greenish yellow, mag & blk 45 45
1434 **903** 35p. new blue, greenish yellow, mag & blk 1·00 95
a. Horiz pair. Nos. 1434/5 . . . . 2·10 2·10
1435 **904** 35p. new blue, greenish yellow, mag & blk 1·00 95
1432/5 . . . . *Set of* 4 2·75 2·75

Nos. 1432/3 and 1434/5 were each printed together, *se-tenant*, in horizontal pairs throughout the sheets.

905 Toy Train and Airplane **906** Building Bricks

907 Dice and Board Games **908** Toy Robot, Boat and Doll's House

(Des D. Fern)

1989 (16 May). *Europa. Games and Toys. Phosphorised paper. P* 14 × 15.

1436 **905** 19p. black, greenish yellow, vermilion, blue-green, blue, gold and pale ochre 50 50
1437 **906** 27p. black, greenish yellow, reddish orange, blue-green, blue and gold . . 75 75
1438 **907** 32p. black, greenish yellow, orange-red, blue-green, blue, gold and pale ochre 90 90
1439 **908** 35p. black, greenish yellow, reddish orange, blue-green, bl, gold & stone 90 90
1436/9 . . . . *Set of* 4 2·75 2·75

909 Ironbridge, Shropshire **910** Tin Mine, St. Agnes Head, Cornwall

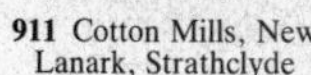

911 Cotton Mills, New Lanark, Strathclyde **912** Pontcysyllte Aqueduct, Clwyd

(Des R. Maddox)

1989 (4–25 July). *Industrial Archaeology. Phosphorised paper. P* 14×15.

1440 **909** 19p. black, bistre-yellow, rose-red, apple-green, lt blue, grey-black & emerald 50 50
1441 **910** 27p. black, bistre-yellow, rose-red, apple-green, lt blue, grey-black & dull blue 75 75
1442 **911** 32p. black, yellow-orange, apple-green, yellow, dull blue, grey-black and deep reddish violet 90 90
1443 **912** 35p. black, yellow, bright rose, apple-green, dull blue, grey-black & verm 90 90
1440/3 . . . . *Set of* 4 2·75 2·75
MS1444 122×90 mm. 19p., 27p., 32p., 35p. each black, olive-yellow, bright rose-red, dull blue, apple-green, grey-black and vermilion. P 15×14 (*sold at* £1.40) (25 July) . . . . 3·25 3·50

The stamps in No. **MS**1444 are horizontal versions of Nos. 1440/3 with each design continuing onto the sheet margins.

The premium on No. **MS**1444 was used to support "Stamp World London 90" International Stamp Exhibition.

913 **914**

1989 (22 Aug)–**90**. *Booklet Stamps.*

(*a*) *Photo Harrison. P* 15×14

1445 **913** (2nd) bright blue (1 centre band) .. 25 30
a. Booklet pane. No. 1445×10 with horiz edges of pane imperf .. 2·25
b. Booklet pane. No. 1445×4 with three edges of pane imperf (28.11.89) .. 90
1446 (2nd) bright blue (1 side band) (20.3.90) 30 35
1447 **914** (1st) brownish black (phosphorised paper) 30 35
a. Booklet pane. No. 1447×10 with horiz edges of pane imperf .. 3·00
b. Booklet pane. No. 1447×4 with three edges of pane imperf (5.12.89) .. 1·25
1448 (1st) brownish black (2 bands) (20.3.90) 40 45

(*b*) *Litho Walsall. P* 14

1449 **913** (2nd) bright blue (1 centre band) .. 25 30
a. Booklet pane. No. 1449×4 with three edges of pane imperf 90
1450 **914** (1st) blackish brown (2 bands) .. 30 35
a. Booklet pane. No. 1450×4 with three edges of pane imperf .. .. 1·25

(*c*) *Litho Questa. P* 15×14.

1451 **913** (2nd) bright blue (1 centre band) (19.9.89) 25 30
1452 **914** (1st) brownish black (phosphorised paper) (19.9.89) 30 35

Nos. 1445, 1447 and 1449/52 were initially sold at 14p (2nd) and 19p (1st), but these prices increased on 2 October 1989 to reflect the new postage rates of 15 and 20p.

Nos. 1446 and 1448 come from the *se-tenant* pane in the 1990 London Life £5 booklet. This pane is listed as No. X906m.

915 Snowflake (×10)

916 Blue Fly (×5)

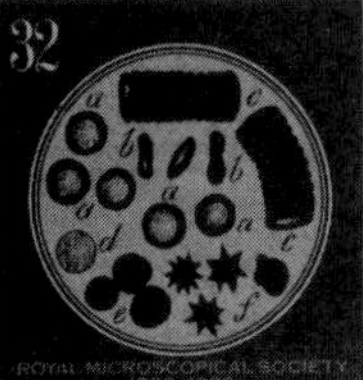

917 Blood Cells (×500)

918 Microchip (×600)

(Des K. Bassford. Litho Questa)

1989 (5 Sept). *150th Anniv of Royal Microscopical Society. Phosphorised paper. P* 14½×14.

1453 **915** 19p. gold, lemon, pale blue, grey, black and grey-black 30 35
1454 **916** 27p. gold, lemon, drab, black & grey-blk 45 50
1455 **917** 32p. gold, lemon, orange-vermilion, flesh, black and grey-black 50 55
1456 **918** 35p. gold, lemon, blk, brt grn & grey-blk 55 60
1453/6 .. .. *Set of* 4 1·60 1·75

919 Royal Mail Coach

920 Escort of Blues and Royals

921 Lord Mayor's Coach

922 Coach Team passing St. Pauls

923 Blues and Royals Drum Horse

(Des P. Cox)

1989 (17 Oct). *Lord Mayor's Show, London. Phosphorised paper. P* 14×15.

1457 **919** 20p. gold, lemon, rose, orge, pale bl & blk 30 35
a. Horiz strip of 5. Nos. 1457/61 .. 1·40 1·50
ab. Imperf (horiz strip of 5. Nos. 1457/61) .. ..
ac. Imperf (horiz strip of 4. Nos. 1457/60) .. ..
ad. Imperf (horiz strip of 3. Nos. 1457/9)
1458 **920** 20p. gold, lemon, rose, orge, pale bl & blk 30 35
1459 **921** 20p. gold, lemon, rose, orge, pale bl & blk 30 35
1460 **922** 20p. gold, lemon, rose, orge, pale bl & blk 30 35
1461 **923** 20p. gold, lemon, rose, orge, pale bl & blk 30 35
1457/61 .. .. *Set of* 5 1·40 1·50

This issue commemorates the 800th anniversary of the installation of the first Lord Mayor of London.

Nos. 1457/61 were printed together, *se-tenant*, in horizontal strips of 5 throughout the sheet.

Nos. 1457ab/ad come from a sheet partly imperforate at left.

924 14th-century Peasants from Stained-glass Window

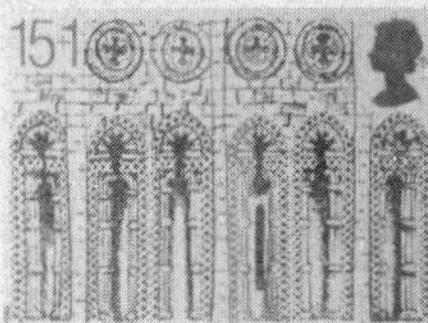

925 Arches and Roundels, West Front

926 Octagon Tower

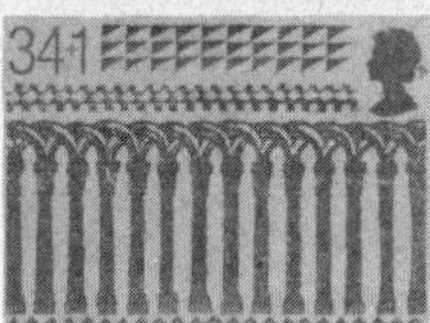

927 Arcade from West Transept

928 Triple Arch from West Front

(Des D. Gentleman)

1989 (14 Nov). *Christmas. 800th Anniversary of Ely Cathedral. One phosphor band* (*15p., 15p.+1p.*) *or phosphorised paper* (*others*). *P* 15×14.

1462 **924** 15p. gold, silver and blue 25 30
1463 **925** 15p. + 1p. gold, silver and blue .. 25 30
a. Imperf (pair) £1250
1464 **926** 20p. + 1p. gold, silver and rosine .. 35 40
a. Imperf (pair) £1250
1465 **927** 34p. + 1p. gold, silver and emerald 55 60
1466 **928** 37p. + 1p. gold, silver and yellow-olive 60 65
1462/6 .. .. *Set of* 5 1·75 2·00

929 Queen Victoria and Queen Elizabeth II

(Des J. Matthews (from plaster casts by Wyon and Machin))

1990 (10 Jan–17 Apr). *150th Anniv of the Penny Black.*

(*a*) *Photo Harrison. P* 15×14

1467 **929** 15p. bright blue (1 centre band) .. 25 30
l. Booklet pane. No. 1467×10 with horiz edges of pane imperf (30.1.90) 2·25
1468 15p. bright blue (1 side band) (30.1.90) 25 30
l. Booklet pane. No. 1468×2 and 1470 plus label 75
1469 20p. brownish black and cream (phosphorised paper) .. 30 35
l. Booklet pane. No. 1469×5 plus label with vert sides of pane imperf (30.1.90) .. .. .. 1·50
m. Booklet pane. No. 1469×10 with horiz edges of pane imperf (30.1.90) 3·00
n. Booklet pane. No. 1469×6 with margins all round (20.3.90) .. 1·75
r. Booklet pane. No. 1469×4 with three edges of pane imperf (17.4.90) .. 1·25
1470 20p. brownish black and cream (2 bands) (30.1.90) 30 35
1471 29p. deep mauve (phosphorised paper) 45 50
1472 29p. deep mauve (2 bands) (20.3.90) 1·10 1·25
1473 34p. dp bluish grey (phosphorised paper) 55 55
1474 37p. rosine (phosphorised paper) .. 60 65

(*b*) *Litho Walsall. P* 14

1475 **929** 15p. bright blue (1 centre band) (30.1.90) 25 30
l. Booklet pane. No. 1475×4 with three edges of pane imperf 90
1476 20p. brownish black & cream (phosphorised paper) (30.1.90) 30 35
l. Booklet pane. No. 1476×5 plus label with vertical sides of pane imperf .. 1·50
m. Booklet pane. No. 1476×4 with three edges of pane imperf .. .. 1·25

(*c*) *Litho Questa. P* 15×14

1477 **929** 15p. bright blue (1 centre band) (17.4.90) 25 30
1478 20p. brownish black (phosphorised paper) (17.4.90) 30 35

Nos. 1468, 1470, 1472 and 1475/8 come from booklets. No. 1468 exists with the phosphor band at left or right. Nos. 1468 (band at right), 1470 and 1472 occur in the *se-tenant* pane from the 1990 London Life £5 booklet. This pane is listed as No. X906m.

For No. 1469 in miniature sheet see No. **MS**1501.

930 Kitten

931 Rabbit

932 Duckling

933 Puppy

(Des T. Evans. Litho Questa)

1990 (23 Jan). *150th Anniv of Royal Society for Prevention of Cruelty to Animals. Phosphorised paper. P* 14×14½.

1479 **930** 20p. new blue, greenish yellow, bright magenta, black and silver 30 35
a. Silver (Queen's head and face value) omitted .. ..
1480 **931** 29p. new blue, greenish yellow, bright magenta, black and silver 45 50
a. Imperf (horiz pair) .. ..
1481 **932** 34p. new blue, greenish yellow, bright magenta, black and silver 55 60
1482 **933** 37p. new blue, greenish yellow, bright magenta, black and silver 60 65
1479/82 .. .. *Set of* 4 1·75 1·90

MINIMUM PRICE

The minimum price quote is 10p which represents a handling charge rather than a basis for valuing common stamps. For further notes about prices see introductory pages.

934 Teddy Bear

935 Dennis the Menace

936 Punch

937 Cheshire Cat

938 The Man in the Moon

939 The Laughing Policeman

940 Clown

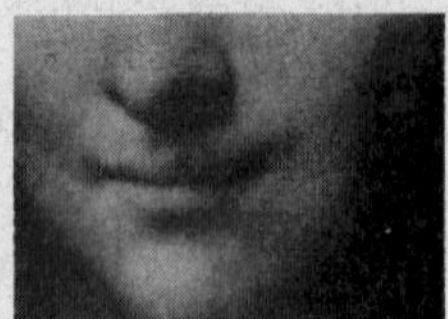
941 Mona Lisa

942 Queen of Hearts

943 Stan Laurel (comedian)

(Des Michael Peters and Partners Ltd)

1990 (6 Feb). *Greetings Stamps. "Smiles". Two phosphor bands. P* 15×14.

1483 **934** 20p. gold, greenish yellow, bright rose-red and grey-black 30 35
a. Booklet pane. Nos. 1483/92 with margins all round .. .. 3·00
1484 **935** 20p. gold, greenish yellow, brt rose-red, new blue, deep blue and grey-black 30 35
1485 **936** 20p. gold, greenish yellow, brt rose-red, new blue, deep blue and grey-black 30 35
1486 **937** 20p. gold, greenish yellow, brt rose-red, new blue and grey-black 30 35
1487 **938** 20p. gold, greenish yellow, brt rose-red, new blue and grey-black 30 35
1488 **939** 20p. gold, greenish yellow, brt rose-red, new blue and grey-black .. 30 35
1489 **940** 20p. gold, greenish yellow, brt rose-red, new blue and grey-black .. 30 35
1490 **941** 20p. gold, greenish yellow, bright rose-red, and grey-black 30 35
1491 **942** 20p. gold, greenish yellow, bright rose-red, new blue and grey-black .. 30 35
1492 **943** 20p. gold and grey-black 30 35
1483/92 .. .. *Set of* 10 3·00 3·50

Nos. 1483/92 were only issued in £2 booklets. The designs of Nos. 1483, 1485/6, 1489 and 1492 extend onto the pane margin.

944 Alexandra Palace ("Stamp World London 90" Exhibition)

945 Glasgow School of Art

946 British Philatelic Bureau, Edinburgh

947 Templeton Carpet Factory, Glasgow

(Des P. Hogarth)

1990 (6–20 Mar). *Europa (Nos.* 1493 *and* 1495) *and "Glasgow* 1990 *European City of Culture" (Nos.* 1494 *and* 1496). *Phosphorised paper. P* 14×15.

1493 **944** 20p. silver, lemon, flesh, grey-brown, blue, grey-black and black .. 30 35
a. Booklet pane. No. 1493×4 with margins all round (20 March) 1·25
1494 **945** 20p. silver, greenish yellow, dull orange, blue, grey-black and black .. 30 35
1495 **946** 29p. silver, stone, orange, olive-sepia, grey-blue, grey-black and black .. 45 50
1496 **947** 37p. silver, greenish yellow, brt emerald, salmon, olive-sepia, brt blue & black 60 65
1493/6 .. .. *Set of* 4 1·50 1·60

948 Export Achievement Award

949 Technological Achievement Award

(Des S. Broom. Litho Questa)

1990 (10 Apr). *25th Anniv of Queen's Awards for Export and Technology. Phosphorised paper. P* 14×14½.

1497 **948** 20p. new blue, greenish yellow, magenta, black and silver 30 35
a. Horiz pair. Nos. 1497/8 .. .. 60 70
1498 **949** 20p. new blue, greenish yellow, magenta, black and silver 30 35
1499 **948** 37p. new blue, greenish yellow, magenta, black and silver 60 65
a. Horiz pair. Nos. 1499/500 .. 1·25 1·25
1500 **949** 37p. new blue, greenish yellow, magenta, black and silver 60 65
1497/500 .. .. *Set of* 4 1·60 1·75

Nos. 1497/8 and 1499/500 were each printed together, *se-tenant*, in horizontal pairs throughout the sheets.

(Des J. Matthews and Sedley Place Design Ltd. Eng C. Matthews. Recess and photo)

1990 (3 May). *"Stamp World London 90" International Stamp Exhibition, London. Sheet,* 122×90 *mm., containing No.* 1469. *Phosphorised paper. P* 15×14.

MS1501 **929** 20p. brownish blk & cream (*sold at* £1) 1·50 1·75
a. Error. Imperf .. .. ..

The premium on No. **MS**1501 was used to support the "Stamp World London 90" International Stamp Exhibition.

950 Cycad and Sir Joseph Banks Building

951 Stone Pine and Princess of Wales Conservatory

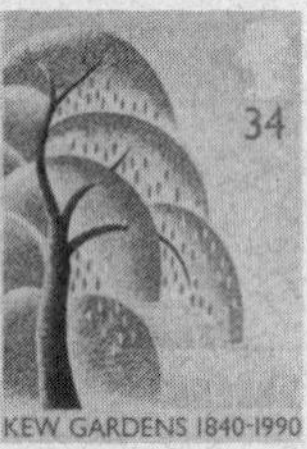

952 Willow Tree and Palm House

953 Cedar Tree and Pagoda

(Des P. Leith)

1990 (5 June). *150th Anniv of Kew Gardens. Phosphorised paper. P* 14×15.

1502 **950** 20p. black, brt emerald, pale turquoise-green, light brown and lavender .. 30 35
1503 **951** 29p. black, brt emerald, turquoise-green, reddish orange and grey-black .. 45 50
1504 **952** 34p. Venetian red, brt green, cobalt, dull purple, turquoise-grn & yellow-green 55 60
1505 **953** 37p. pale violet-blue, bright emerald, red-brown, steel-blue and brown-rose .. 60 65
1502/5 .. .. *Set of* 4 1·75 1·90

REGIONAL ISSUES

For Regional Issues of Guernsey, Jersey and the Isle of Man, *see* after Great Britain Postal Fiscals.

Printers (£ s. d. stamps of all regions):—Photo Harrison & Sons. Portrait by Dorothy Wilding Ltd.

DATES OF ISSUE. Conflicting dates of issue have been announced for some of the regional issues, partly explained by the stamps being released on different dates by the Philatelic Bureau in Edinburgh or the Philatelic Counter in London and in the regions. We have adopted the practice of giving the earliest known dates, since once released the stamps could have been used anywhere in the U.K.

I. NORTHERN IRELAND

N 1

N 2

N 3

(Des W. Hollywood (3d., 4d., 5d.), L. Pilton (6d., 9d.), T. Collins (1s. 3d., 1s. 6d.))

1958–67. *W* **179.** *P* 15 × 14.

No.	Type	Description	Unused	Used
NI1	N 1	3d. deep lilac (18.8.58)	20	10
		p. One centre phosphor band (9.6.67)	20	15
NI2		4d. ultramarine (7.2.66)	20	15
		p. Two phosphor bands (10.67)	20	15
NI3	N 2	6d. deep claret (29.9.58)	20	20
NI4		9d. bronze-green (2 phosphor bands) (1.3.67)	30	50
NI5	N 3	1s. 3d. green (29.9.58)	30	50
NI6		1s. 6d. grey-blue (2 phosphor bands) (1.3.67)	30	50

1968–69. *No wmk. Chalk-surfaced paper. One centre phosphor band (Nos.* NI8/9) *or two phosphor bands (others). P* 15 × 14.

No.	Type	Description	Unused	Used
NI 7	N 1	4d. deep bright blue (27.6.68)	20	15
NI 8		4d. olive-sepia (4.9.68)	20	15
NI 9		4d. bright vermilion (26.2.69)	20	20
NI10		5d. royal blue (4.9.68)	20	20
NI11	N 3	1s. 6d. grey-blue (20.5.69)	2·50	3·00

No. NI7 was only issued in Northern Ireland with gum arabic. After it had been withdrawn from Northern Ireland but whilst still on sale at the philatelic counters elsewhere, about fifty sheets with PVA gum were sold over the London Philatelic counter on 23 October 1968, and some were also on sale at the British Philatelic Exhibition Post Office in October, without any prior announcement. The other values exist with PVA gum only.

N 4

(Des J. Matthews after plaster cast by Arnold Machin)

1971 (7 July)–**89.** *Decimal Currency. Chalk-surfaced paper. Type* N **4.** (*a*) *Photo Harrison. With phosphor bands. P* 15×14.

No.	Type	Description	Unused	Used
NI12		2½p. bright magenta (1 centre band)	90	25
NI13		3p. ultramarine (2 bands)	40	15
NI14		3p. ultramarine (1 centre band) (23.1.74)	20	15
NI15		3½p. olive-grey (2 bands) (23.1.74)	20	20
NI16		3½p. olive-grey (1 centre band) (6.11.74)	20	25
NI17		4½p. grey-blue (2 bands) (6.11.74)	25	25
NI18		5p. reddish violet (2 bands)	1·50	1·50
NI19		5½p. violet (2 bands) (23.1.74)	20	20
NI20		5½p. violet (1 centre band) (21.5.75)	20	20
NI21		6½p. greenish blue (1 centre band) (14.1.76)	20	20
NI22		7p. purple-brown (1 centre band) (18.1.78)	25	25
NI23		7½p. chestnut (2 bands)	2·50	2·50
NI24		8p. rosine (2 bands) (23.1.74)	30	30
NI25		8½p. yellow-green (2 bands) (14.1.76)	30	30
NI26		9p. deep violet (2 bands) (18.1.78)	30	30
NI27		10p. orange-brown (2 bands) (20.10.76)	35	35
NI28		10p. orange-brown (1 centre band) (23.7.80)	35	35
NI29		10½p. steel-blue (2 bands) (18.1.78)	40	40
NI30		11p. scarlet (2 bands) (20.10.76)	40	40

(*b*) *Photo Harrison. On phosphorised paper. P* 15 × 14.

No.	Type	Description	Unused	Used
NI31		12p. yellowish green (23.7.80)	40	45
NI32		13½p. purple-brown (23.7.80)	60	70
NI33		15p. ultramarine (23.7.80)	45	50

(*c*) *Litho Questa. One side phosphor band* (11½*p.*, 12*p.*, 12½*p.*, 13*p.*), *one centre band* (14*p.* (*No.* NI39), 15*p.*) *or on phosphorised paper (others). P* 14 (11½*p.*, 12½*p.*, 14*p.* (*No.* NI38), 15½*p.*, 16*p.*, 18*p.* (*No.* NI44), 19½*p.*, 20½*p.*, 22*p.* (*No.* NI50), 26*p.*, 28*p.*) *or* 15×14 (*others*).

No.	Type	Description	Unused	Used
NI34		11½p. drab (8.4.81)	1·00	60
NI35		12p. bright emerald (7.1.86)	50	50
NI36		12½p. light emerald (24.2.82)	50	40
		a. Perf 15×14 (28.2.84)	4·00	4·00
NI37		13p. pale chestnut (23.10.84)	50	35
NI38		14p. grey-blue (8.4.81)	60	50
NI39		14p. deep blue (8.11.88)	25	30
NI40		15p. bright blue (28.11.89)	25	30
NI41		15½p. pale violet (24.2.82)	60	65
NI42		16p. drab (27.4.83)	1·00	1·00
		a. Perf 15×14 (28.2.84)	3·50	1·00
NI43		17p. grey-blue (23.10.84)	60	40
NI44		18p. deep violet (8.4.81)	80	80
NI45		18p. olive-grey (6.1.87)	60	45
NI46		19p. bright orange-red (8.11.88)	30	35
NI47		19½p. olive-grey (24.2.82)	2·00	2·00
NI48		20p. brownish black (28.11.89)	30	30
NI49		20½p. ultramarine (27.4.83)	1·60	1·50
NI50		22p. blue (8.4.81)	90	1·10
NI51		22p. yellow-green (23.10.84)	35	50
NI52		23p. bright green (8.11.88)	60	40
NI53		24p. Indian red (28.11.89)	40	45
NI54		26p. rosine (24.2.82)	80	80
		a. Perf 15×14 (27.1.87)	70	60
NI55		28p. deep violet-blue (27.4.83)	85	80
		a. Perf 15×14 (27.1.87)	45	65
NI56		31p. bright purple (23.10.84)	1·00	80
NI57		32p. greenish blue (8.11.88)	50	60
NI58		34p. deep bluish grey (28.11.89)	55	55

From 1972 printings were made on fluorescent white paper and from 1973 printings had dextrin added to the PVA gum (see notes after No. X1019 of Great Britain).

II. SCOTLAND

S 1

S 2

S 3

(Des G. Huntly (3d., 4d., 5d), J. Fleming (6d., 9d.), A. Imrie (1s. 3d., 1s. 6d.))

1958–67. *W* **179.** *P* 15 × 14.

No.	Type	Description	Unused	Used
S1	S 1	3d. deep lilac (18.8.58)	20	15
		p. Two phosphor bands (29.1.63)	17·00	1·00
		pa. One side phosphor band (30.4.65)	20	25
		pb. One centre phosphor band (9.11.67)	20	15
S2		4d. ultramarine (7.2.66)	20	10
		p. Two phosphor bands	20	20
S3	S 2	6d. deep claret (29.9.58)	20	15
		p. Two phosphor bands (29.1.63)	20	25
S4		9d. bronze-green (2 phosphor bands) (1.3.67)	30	30
S5	S 3	1s. 3d. green (29.9.58)	30	30
		p. Two phosphor bands (29.1.63)	30	30
S6		1s. 6d. grey-blue (2 phosphor bands) (1.3.67)	35	30

The one phosphor band on No. S1pa was produced by printing broad phosphor bands across alternate vertical perforations. Individual stamps show the band at right or left (same prices either way).

1967–70. *No wmk. Chalk-surfaced paper. One centre phosphor band* (S7, S9/10) *or two phosphor bands (others). P* 15 × 14.

No.	Type	Description	Unused	Used
S 7	S 1	3d. deep lilac (16.5.68)	10	15
S 8		4d. deep bright blue (28.11.67)	10	15
S 9		4d. olive-sepia (4.9.68)	10	10
S10		4d. bright vermilion (26.2.69)	10	10
S11		5d. royal blue (4.9.68)	20	10
S12	S 2	9d. bronze-green (28.9.70)	5·00	5·50
S13	S 3	1s. 6d. grey-blue (12.12.68)	1·40	1·00

Nos. S7/8 exist with both gum arabic and PVA gum; others with PVA gum only.

S 4

(Des J. Matthews after plaster cast by Arnold Machin)

1971 (7 July)–**89.** *Decimal Currency. Chalk-surfaced paper. Type* **S 4.**

(*a*) *Photo Harrison. With phosphor bands. P* 15 × 14

No.	Type	Description	Unused	Used
S14		2½p. bright magenta (1 centre band)	20	15
S15		3p. ultramarine (2 bands)	30	15
		a. Imperf (pair)†	£400	
S16		3p. ultramarine (1 centre band) (23.1.74)	15	15
S17		3½p. olive-grey (2 bands) (23.1.74)	20	20
S18		3½p. olive-grey (1 centre band) (6.11.74)	20	20
S19		4½p. grey-blue (2 bands) (6.11.74)	25	20
S20		5p. reddish violet (2 bands)	1·50	1·50
S21		5½p. violet (2 bands) (23.1.74)	20	20
S22		5½p. violet (1 centre band) (21.5.75)	20	20
		a. Imperf (pair)	£350	
S23		6½p. greenish blue (1 centre band) (14.1.76)	20	20
S24		7p. purple-brown (1 centre band) (18.1.78)	25	25
S25		7½p. chestnut (2 bands)	2·00	2·00
S26		8p. rosine (2 bands) (23.1.74)	30	40
S27		8½p. yellow-green (2 bands) (14.1.76)	30	30
S28		9p. deep violet (2 bands) (18.1.78)	30	30
S29		10p. orange-brown (2 bands) (20.10.76)	35	30
S30		10p. orange-brown (1 centre band) (23.7.80)	35	35
S31		10½p. steel-blue (2 bands) (18.1.78)	40	35
S32		11p. scarlet (2 bands) (20.10.76)	40	35

(*b*) *Photo Harrison. On phosphorised paper. P* 15 × 14

No.	Type	Description	Unused	Used
S33		12p. yellowish green (23.7.80)	40	30
S34		13½p. purple-brown (23.7.80)	60	65
S35		15p. ultramarine (23.7.80)	45	45

(*c*) *Litho J.W. One side phosphor band* (11½*p.*, 12*p.*, 12½*p.*, 13*p.*) *or phosphorised paper (others). P* 14

No.	Type	Description	Unused	Used
S36		11½p. drab (8.4.81)	75	60
S37		12p. bright emerald (7.1.86)	55	70
S38		12½p. light emerald (24.2.82)	40	40
S39		13p. pale chestnut (23.10.84)	40	30
S40		14p. grey-blue (8.4.81)	55	50
S41		15½p. pale violet (24.2.82)	60	65
S42		16p. drab (27.4.83)	55	45
S43		17p. grey-blue (23.10.84)	70	1·00
S44		18p. deep violet (8.4.81)	70	65
S45		19½p. olive-grey (24.2.82)	2·00	2·25
S46		20½p. ultramarine (27.4.83)	1·60	1·50
S47		22p. blue (8.4.81)	80	1·10
S48		22p. yellow-green (23.10.84)	80	80
S49		26p. rosine (24.2.82)	80	80
S50		28p. deep violet-blue (27.4.83)	85	80
S51		31p. bright purple (23.10.84)	80	90

(*d*) *Litho Questa. P* 15×14

No.	Type	Description	Unused	Used
S52		12p. bright emerald (1 side band) (29.4.86)	50	60
S53		13p. pale chestnut (1 side band) (4.11.86)	50	30
S54		14p. deep blue (1 centre band) (8.11.88)	25	30
		l. Booklet pane. No. S54 × 6 with margins all round (21.3.89)	1·50	
S55		14p. deep blue (1 side band) (21.3.89)	50	50
		l. Booklet pane. No. S55 × 5, S60 × 2, S64 and centre label with margins all round	3·00	
		la. Error. Booklet pane imperf		
S56		15p. bright blue (1 centre band) (28.11.89)	25	30
S57		17p. grey-bl (phosphorised paper) (29.4.86)	3·00	2·00
S58		18p. olive-grey (phosphorised paper) (6.1.87)	60	45
S59		19p. bright orange-red (phosphorised paper) (8.11.88)	30	35
		l. Booklet pane. No. S59 × 9 with margins all round (21.3.89)	2·75	
		m. Booklet pane. No. S59 × 6 with margins all round (21.3.89)	1·90	
S60		19p. bright orange-red (2 bands) (21.3.89)	1·00	1·00
S61		20p. brownish black (phosphorised paper) (28.11.89)	30	30
S62		22p. yell-grn (phosphorised paper) (27.1.87)	35	50
S63		23p. brt grn (phosphorised paper) (8.11.88)	35	40
S64		23p. bright green (2 bands) (21.3.89)	2·25	2·25
S65		24p. Indian red (phosphorised paper) (28.11.89)	40	45
S66		26p. rosine (phosphorised paper) (27.1.87)	80	80
S67		28p. dp vio-bl (phosphorised paper) (27.1.87)	45	65
S68		31p. brt pur (phosphorised paper) (29.4.86)	65	70
S69		32p. greenish blue (phosphorised paper) (8.11.88)	50	60
S70		34p. deep bluish grey (phosphorised paper) (28.11.89)	55	55

†Exists only with gum arabic.

Nos. S55, S60 and S64 were only issued in the £5 sponsored stamp booklet of 21 March 1989.

From 1972 printings were on fluorescent white paper. Nos. S14/15 exist with PVA and gum arabic and the remainder with PVA only. From 1973 printings had dextrin added (see notes after No. X1019 of Great Britain).

III. WALES

From the inception of the Regional stamps, the Welsh versions were tendered to members of the public at all Post Offices within the former County of Monmouthshire but the English alternatives were available on request. Offices with a Monmouthshire postal address but situated outside the County, namely Beachley, Brockweir, Redbrook, Sedbury, Tutshill, Welsh Newton and Woodcroft, were not supplied with the Welsh Regional stamps.

With the re-formation of Counties, Monmouthshire became known as Gwent and was also declared to be part of Wales. From 1 July 1974, therefore, except for the offices mentioned above, only Welsh Regional stamps were available at the offices under the jurisdiction of Newport, Gwent.

W 1

W 2 W 3

(Des R. Stone)

1958–67. *W* **179.** *P* 15 × 14.

No.	Type	Description	Unused	Used
W1	W 1	3d. deep lilac (18.8.58)	20	10
		p. One centre phosphor band (16.5.67)	20	15
W2		4d. ultramarine (7.2.66)	20	15
		p. Two phosphor bands (10.67)	20	15
W3	W 2	6d. deep claret (29.9.58)	40	20
W4		9d. bronze-green (2 phosphor bands) (1.3.67)	30	35
W5	W 3	1s. 3d. green (29.9.58)	30	30
W6		1s. 6d. grey-blue (2 phosphor bands) (1.3.67)	35	30

1967–69. *No wmk. Chalk-surfaced paper. One centre phosphor band* (W7, W9/10) *or two phosphor bands (others). P* 15 × 14.

No.	Type	Description	Unused	Used
W 7	W 1	3d. deep lilac (6.12.67)	20	10
W 8		4d. deep bright blue (21.6.68)	20	10
W 9		4d. olive-sepia (4.9.68)	20	10
W10		4d. bright vermilion (26.2.69)	20	20
W11		5d. royal blue (4.9.68)	20	10
W12	W 3	1s. 6d. grey-blue (1.8.69)	3·00	3·00

The 3d. exists with gum arabic only; the remainder with PVA gum only.

W 4

(Des J. Matthews after plaster cast by Arnold Machin)

1971 (7 July)–**89.** *Decimal Currency. Chalk-surfaced paper. Type* W **4.** (*a*) *Photo Harrison. With phosphor bands. P* 15×14.

No.	Type	Description	Unused	Used
W13		2½p. bright magenta (1 centre band)	20	15
W14		3p. ultramarine (2 bands)	25	15
W15		3p. ultramarine (1 centre band) (23.1.74)	20	20
W16		3½p. olive-grey (2 bands) (23.1.74)	20	25
W17		3½p. olive-grey (1 centre band) (6.11.74)	20	25
W18		4½p. grey-blue (2 bands) (6.11.74)	25	20
W19		5p. reddish violet (2 bands)	1·50	1·50
W20		5½p. violet (2 bands) (23.1.74)	20	25
W21		5½p. violet (1 centre band) (21.5.75)	20	25
		a. Imperf (pair)	£400	
W22		6½p. greenish blue (1 centre band) (14.1.76)	20	20
W23		7p. purple-brown (1 centre band) (18.1.78)	25	25
W24		7½p. chestnut (2 bands)	2·00	2·25
W25		8p. rosine (2 bands) (23.1.74)	30	30

W26	8½p.	yellow-green (2 bands) (14.1.76) ..	30	30
W27	9p.	deep violet (2 bands) (18.1.78) ..	30	30
W28	10p.	orange-brown (2 bands) (20.10.76) ..	35	30
W29	10p.	orange-brown (1 centre band) (23.7.80)	35	30
W30	10½p.	steel-blue (2 bands) (18.1.78)	40	35
W31	11p.	scarlet (2 bands) (20.10.76)	40	45

(*b*) *Photo Harrison. On phosphorised paper. P* 15 × 14

W32	12p.	yellowish green (23.7.80)	40	45
W33	13½p.	purple-brown (23.7.80)	60	70
W34	15p.	ultramarine (23.7.80)	45	50

(*c*) *Litho Questa. One side phosphor band* (11½*p*., 12*p*., 12½*p*., 13*p*.), *one centre band* (14*p*. (*No*. W40), 15*p*.) *or on phosphorised paper* (*others*). *P* 14 (11½*p*., 12½*p*., 14*p*. (*No*. W39), 15½*p*., 16*p*., 18*p*. (*No*. W45), 19½*p*., 20½*p*., 22*p*. (*No*. W51), 26*p*., 28*p*.) *or* 15×14 (*others*).

W35	11½p.	drab (8.4.81)	75	60
W36	12p.	bright emerald (7.1.86)	1·00	1·00
W37	12½p.	light emerald (24.2.82)	50	45
	a.	Perf 15×14 (10.1.84)	4·50	3·75
W38	13p.	pale chestnut (23.10.84)	40	35
W39	14p.	grey-blue (8.4.81)	55	50
W40	14p.	deep blue (8.11.88)	25	30
W41	15p.	bright blue (28.11.89)	25	30
W42	15½p.	pale violet (24.2.82)	60	65
W43	16p.	drab (27.4.83)	1·00	1·00
	a.	Perf 15×14 (10.1.84)	80	1·00
W44	17p.	grey-blue (23.10.84)	60	45
W45	18p.	deep violet (8.4.81)	70	75
W46	18p.	olive-grey (6.1.87)	60	45
W47	19p.	bright orange-red (8.11.88)	30	35
W48	19½p.	olive-grey (24.2.82)	2·00	2·00
W49	20p.	brownish black (28.11.89)	30	30
W50	20½p.	ultramarine (27.4.83)	1·60	1·50
W51	22p.	blue (8.4.81)	80	1·10
W52	22p.	yellow-green (23.10.84)	35	50
W53	23p.	bright green (8.11.88)	35	40
W54	24p.	Indian red (28.11.89)	40	45
W55	26p.	rosine (24.2.82)	80	80
	a.	Perf 15×14 (27.1.87)	1·00	60
W56	28p.	deep violet-blue (27.8.83)	85	80
	a.	Perf 15×14 (27.1.87)	70	65
W57	31p.	bright purple (23.10.84)	90	70
W58	32p.	greenish blue (8.11.88)	50	60
W59	34p.	deep bluish grey (28.11.89)	55	55

*Exists only with gum arabic.

From 1972 printings were on fluorescent white paper. Nos. W13/14 exist with PVA and gum arabic and the remainder with PVA only. From 1973 printings had dextrin added (see notes after No. X1019 of Great Britain).

KEY TO LINE-ENGRAVED ISSUES

S.G. Nos.	Description	Date	Wmk	Perf	Die	Alpha-bet
	THE IMPERFORATE ISSUES					
1/3	1d. black	6.5.40	SC	Imp	I	I
4/6	2d. no lines	8.5.40	SC	Imp	I	I
	PAPER MORE OR LESS BLUED					
7	1d. red-brown	10.2.41	SC	Imp	I	I
8/12	1d. red-brown	10.2.41	SC	Imp	I	I
8/12	1d. red-brown	6.2.52	SC	Imp	I	II
13/15	2d. white lines	13.3.41	SC	Imp	I	I
	THE PERFORATED ISSUES					
	ONE PENNY VALUE					
16*a*	1d. red-brown	1848	SC	Roul	I	I
16*b*	1d. red-brown	1850	SC	16	I	I
16*c*	1d. red-brown	1853	SC	16	I	II
16*d*	1d. red-brown	1854	SC	14	I	I
17/18	1d. red-brown	Feb 1854	SC	16	I	II
22	1d. red-brown	Jan 1855	SC	14	I	II
24/5	1d. red-brown	28.2.55	SC	14	II	II
21	1d. red-brown	1.3.55	SC	16	II	II
26	1d. red-brown	15.5.55	LC	16	II	II
29/33	1d. red-brown	Aug 1855	LC	14	II	III
	NEW COLOURS ON WHITE PAPER					
37/41	1d. rose-red	Nov 1856	LC	14	II	III
36	1d. rose-red	26.12.57	LC	16	II	III
42	1d. rose-red	1861	LC	14	II	IV
	TWO PENCE VALUE					
19, 20	2d. blue	1.3.54	SC	16	I	I
23	2d. blue	22.2.55	SC	14	I	I
23*a*	2d. blue	5.7.55	SC	14	I	II
20*a*	2d. blue	18.8.55	SC	16	I	II
27	2d. blue	20.7.55	LC	16	I	II
34	2d. blue	20.7.55	LC	14	I	II
35	2d. blue	2.7.57	LC	14	I	III
36*a*	2d. blue	1.2.58	LC	16	I	III
	LETTERS IN ALL FOUR CORNERS					
48/9	½d. rose-red	1.10.70	W **9**	14	—	
43/4	1d. rose-red	1.4.64	LC	14	II	
53*a*	1½d. rosy mauve	1860	LC	14	II	
51/3	1½d. rose-red	1.10.70	LC	14	II	
45	2d. blue	July 1858	LC	14	II	
46/7	2d. thinner lines	7.7.69	LC	14	II	

Watermarks: SC = Small Crown, T **2**.
LC = Large Crown, T **4**.
Dies: *See* notes above No. 17 in the catalogue.
Alphabets: *See* General Notes to this section.

3 White lines added

1841 (13 Mar). *White lines added. Wmk W* **2**. *Paper more or less blued. Imperf.*

			Un	Used	Used on cover
13	**3**	2d. pale blue	£1300	45·00	
14		2d. blue	£1000	35·00	£140
15		2d. deep full blue	£1300	50·00	
15*aa*		2d. violet-blue	£7000	£475	

The 2d. stamp with white lines was printed from Plates 3 and 4.

Plates of 2d. blue

Plate		Un	Used
3	*Shades from*	£1000	40·00
4	*Shades from*	£1200	35·00

Varieties of 2d. blue

		Un	Used
a.	Guide line in corner	—	38·00
b.	,, ,, through value	£1500	38·00
bb.	Double letter in corner	—	45·00
be.	Re-entry	£1800	60·00
c.	Ivory head	£1600	40·00
d.	Watermark inverted	£2250	£180
e.	Obliterated by Maltese Cross		
	In red	—	£3000
	In black	—	55·00
	In blue	—	£700
f.	Obliterated by Maltese Cross with number in centre		
	No. 1	—	£160
	No. 2	—	£160
	No. 3	—	£160
	No. 4	—	£150
	No. 5	—	£200
	No. 6	—	£150
	No. 7	—	£300
	No. 8	—	£200
	No. 9	—	£300
	No. 10	—	£350
	No. 11	—	£200
	No. 12	—	£110
g.	Obliterated by town postmark (without Maltese Cross)		
	In black *from*	—	£300
	In blue *from*	—	£550
h.	Obliterated by 1844 type postmark		
	In black *from*	—	35·00
	In blue *from*	—	£300
	In red *from*	—	£3500
	In green *from*	—	£400

1841 (April). *Trial printing (unissued) on Dickinson silk-thread paper. Imperf.*

16 **1** 1d. red-brown (Plate 11) £1500

Eight sheets were printed on this paper, six being gummed, two ungummed, but we have only seen examples without gum.

1848. *Rouletted approx* 11½ *by Henry Archer.*

16*a* **1** 1d. red-brown (Plates 70, 71) £3500

1850. *P* 16, *by Henry Archer.*

16*b* **1** 1d. red-brown (Alph 1) (from Plates 71, 79, 90–101, 105 and 107. Also Plate 8, unused only) .. .. .. *from* £500 £150

Stamp on cover, dated prior to February 1854 (*price* £350); dated February and after 1854 (*price* £250).

1853. *Government Trial Perforations.*

16*c*	**1**	1d. red-brown (*p* 16) (Alph II) (*on cover*)	†	£4500
16*d*		1d. red-brown (*p* 14) (Alph I)	£3500	

SEPARATION TRIALS. Although the various trials of machines for rouletting and perforating were unofficial, Archer had the consent of the authorities in making his experiments, and sheets so experimented upon were afterwards used by the Post Office.

As Archer ended his experiments in 1850 and plates with corner letters Alphabet II did not come into issue until 1852, perforated stamps with corner letters of Alphabet I may safely be assumed to be Archer productions, if genuine.

The Government trial perforations were done on Napier machines in 1853. As Alphabet II was by that time in use, the trials can only be distinguished from the perforated stamps listed below by being dated prior to 28 January 1854, the date when the perforated stamps were officially issued.

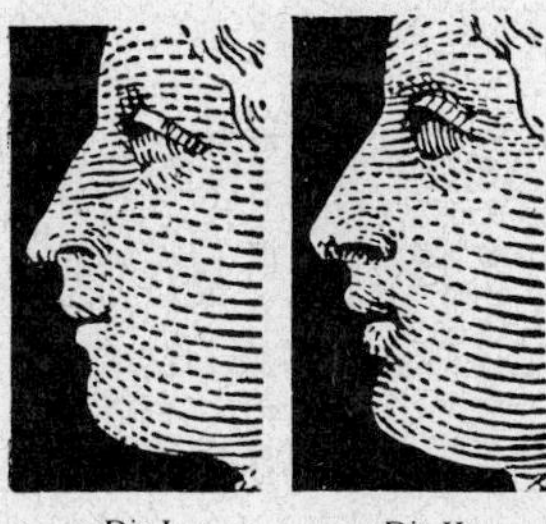

Die I

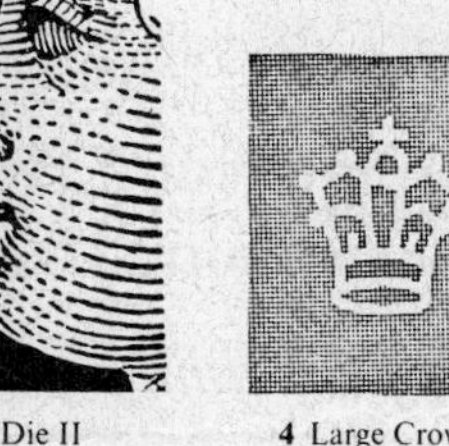

Die II

4 Large Crown

Die I: The features of the portrait are lightly shaded and consequently lack emphasis.

Die II (Die I retouched): The lines of the features have been deepened and appear stronger.

The eye is deeply shaded and made more lifelike. The nostril and lips are more clearly defined, the latter appearing much thicker. A strong downward stroke of colour marks the corner of the mouth. There is a deep indentation of colour between lower lip and chin. The band running from the back of the ear to the chignon has a bolder horizontal line below it than in Die I.

The original die (Die I) was used to provide roller dies for the laying down of all the line-engraved stamps from 1840 to 1855. In that year a new master die was laid down (by means of a Die I roller die) and the impression was retouched by hand engraving by William Humphrys. This retouched die, always known to philatelists as Die II, was from that time used for preparing all new roller dies.

One Penny. The numbering of the 1d. plates recommenced at 1 on the introduction of Die II. Plates 1 to 21 were Alphabet II from which a scarce plum shade exists. Corner letters of Alphabet III appear on Plate 22 and onwards.

As an experiment, the corner letters were engraved by hand on Plates 50 and 51 in 1856, instead of being punched (Alphabet IV), but punching was again resorted to from Plate 52 onwards. Plates 50 and 51 were not put into use until 1861.

Two Pence. Unlike the 1d. the old sequence of plate numbers continued. Plates 3 and 4 of the 2d. had corner letters of Alphabet I, Plate 5 Alphabet II and Plate 6 Alphabet III. In Plate 6 the white lines are thinner than before.

1854–57. *Paper more or less blued.* (*a*) *Wmk Small Crown, W* **2**. *P* 16.

			Un	Used	★ Used on cover
17	**1**	1d. red-brown (Die I) (2.54) ..	£120	3·00	10·00
18		1d. yellow-brown (Die I)	£140	8·00	
19	**3**	2d. deep blue (Plate 4) (1.3.54) ..	£1250	35·00	55·00
		a. Imperf three sides (horiz pair)	†	—	
20		2d. pale blue (Plate 4) ..	£1300	45·00	
20*a*		2d. blue (Plate 5) (18.8.55) ..	£1750	£130	£200
21	**1**	1d. red-brown (Die II) (1.3.55) ..	£130	10·00	20·00
		a. Imperf			
		(*b*) *Wmk Small Crown, W* **2**. *P* 14			
22	**1**	1d. red-brown (Die I) (1.55) ..	£250	16·00	30·00
23	**3**	2d. blue (Plate 4) (22.2.55) ..	£1750	£110	£150
23*a*		2d. blue (Plate 5) (5.7.55) ..	£1750	£110	£150
		b. Imperf (Plate 5)			
24	**1**	1d. red-brown (Die II) (28.2.55)	£225	15·00	22·00
24*a*		1d. deep red-brown (very blue paper) (Die II)	£225	18·00	
25		1d. orange-brown (Die II)	£550	45·00	
		(*c*) *Wmk Large Crown, W* **4**. *P* 16			
26	**1**	1d. red-brown (Die II) (15.5.55)	£400	28·00	40·00
		a. Imperf (Plate 7)			
27	**3**	2d. blue (Plate 5) (20.7.55) ..	£2000	£125	£200
		a. Imperf	—	£2500	
		(*d*) *Wmk Large Crown, W* **4**. *P* 14			
29	**1**	1d. red-brown (Die II) (18.8.55)	£100	80	5·50
		a. Imperf (*shades*) (Plates 22, 25, 43)	£900	£700	
30		1d. brick-red (Die II) ..	£130	12·00	
31	**1**	1d. plum (Die II) (2.56)	£750	£250	
32		1d. brown-rose (Die II)	£150	12·00	
33		1d. orange-brown (Die II) (3.57)	£225	15·00	
34	**3**	2d. blue (Plate 5) (20.7.55) ..	£1000	25·00	70·00
35		2d. blue (Plate 6) (2.7.57) ..	£1100	20·00	60·00
		a. Imperf	—	£2500	
★17/35a		**For well-centred, lightly used**	+125%		

1856–58. *Paper no longer blued.* (*a*) *Wmk Large Crown. W* **4**. *P* 16.

36	**1**	1d. rose-red (Die II) (26.12.57) ..	£500	20·00	35·00
36*a*	**3**	2d. blue (Plate 6) (1.2.58) ..	£3000	£125	£200
		(*b*) (Die II) *Wmk Large Crown, W* **4**. *P* 14			
37	**1**	1d. red-brown (11.56)	£225	50·00	
38		1d. pale red (9.4.57)	40·00	1·75	
		a. Imperf	£475	£400	
39		1d. pale rose (3.57)	40·00	6·00	
40		1d. rose-red (9.57)	25·00	60	1·00
		a. Imperf	£525	£400	
41		1d. deep-rose-red (7.57) ..	40·00	2·00	

1861. *Letters engraved on plate instead of punched (Alphabet IV).*

42	**1**	1d. rose-red (Die II) (Plates 50 and 51)	£100	7·00	20·00
		a. Imperf	—	£1750	
★36/42a		**For well-centred, lightly used** ..	+125%		

In both values, varieties may be found as described in the preceding issues—ivory heads, inverted watermarks, re-entries, and double letters in corners.

The change of perforation from 16 to 14 was decided upon late in 1854 since the closer holes of the former gauge tended to cause the sheets of stamps to break up when handled, but for a time both gauges were in concurrent use. Owing to faulty alignment of the impressions on the plates and to shrinkage of the paper when damped, badly perforated stamps are plentiful in the line-engraved issues.

5

6

Showing position of the plate number on the 1d. and 2d. values. (Plate 170 shown)

1858–79. *Letters in all four corners. Wmk Large Crown, W* **4**. *Die* II (*1d. and 2d.*). *P* 14.

			Un	Used	★ Used on cover
43	**5**	1d. rose-red (1.4.64)	9·00	60	1·25
44		1d. lake-red	9·00	60	
		a. Imperf. .. .. *from*	£850	£600	
★43/4a		**For well-centred, lightly used** ..	+125%		

Plate	Un	Used	*Plate*	Un	Used
71	22·00	3·00	133	90·00	9·00
72	35·00	3·50	134	9·00	60
73	25·00	3·00	135	£100	30·00
74	20·00	75	136	£100	20·00
76	40·00	75	137	15·00	1·25
77	£50000	£30000	138	9·00	60
78	£100	75	139	20·00	16·00
79	30·00	60	140	9·00	60
80	20·00	1·25	141	£150	9·00
81	60·00	1·50	142	50·00	25·00
82	£120	3·50	143	30·00	15·00
83	£140	6·00	144	£100	20·00
84	60·00	1·50	145	9·00	1·50
85	25·00	1·50	146	10·00	5·00
86	30·00	3·50	147	18·00	3·00
87	9·00	1·00	148	20·00	2·50
88	£160	8·00	149	15·00	5·00
89	40·00	75	150	9·00	60
90	28·00	75	151	25·00	9·00
91	40·00	5·00	152	18·00	4·50
92	15·00	75	153	70·00	8·00
93	40·00	75	154	15·00	60
94	40·00	4·00	155	16·00	1·00
95	25·00	75	156	15·00	75
96	28·00	60	157	15·00	75
97	15·00	2·50	158	9·00	75
98	15·00	5·00	159	9·00	75
99	25·00	4·00	160	9·00	60
100	35·00	1·75	161	29·00	6·00
101	50·00	8·00	162	16·00	6·00
102	20·00	80	163	15·00	2·00
103	19·00	2·00	164	15·00	3·00
104	28·00	4·00	165	20·00	75
105	65·00	6·00	166	15·00	5·00
106	30·00	80	167	10·00	70
107	40·00	5·50	168	12·00	7·00
108	30·00	1·50	169	30·00	6·00
109	75·00	2·50	170	11·00	60
110	19·00	8·00	171	9·00	60
111	35·00	1·50	172	9·00	1·25
112	60·00	1·50	173	50·00	9·00
113	15·00	11·00	174	9·00	60
114	£350	12·00	175	35·00	2·50
115	£100	1·50	176	25·00	1·25
116	75·00	9·00	177	10·00	75
117	16·00	60	178	15·00	3·00
118	25·00	75	179	16·00	1·50
119	10·00	1·00	180	16·00	4·00
120	9·00	60	181	15·00	75
121	40·00	9·00	182	£100	4·00
122	9·00	60	183	25·00	2·00
123	12·00	1·00	184	9·00	1·00
124	12·00	60	185	15·00	2·00
125	15·00	2·00	186	30·00	1·50
127	35·00	2·00	187	11·00	75
129	11·00	7·00	188	20·00	10·00
130	18·00	1·50	189	35·00	6·00
131	75·00	16·00	190	10·00	5·00
132	£100	24·00	191	9·00	6·00

Die 2. Ornaments small and always broken; clear line of shading under chin

Die 3. Ornaments larger and joined; line of shading under chin extended half way down neck

Die 4. Ornaments much larger; straight line of shading continued to bottom of neck

1867–81. *White to bluish paper. P* 14. (*a*) *W* **47** (*Small Anchor*).

F18	F **11**	1d. purple (1.9.67)	8·00	5·00	60·00
F19	F **12**	1d. purple (Die 1) (6.68)	1·75	1·50	40·00
F20		1d. purple (Die 2) (6.76)	10·00	10·00	£180
F21		1d. purple (Die 3) (3.77)	4·00	4·00	75·00
F22		1d. purple (Die 4) (7.78)	3·00	2·50	65·00
		(*b*) *W* **48** (*Orb*)			
F23	F **12**	1d. purple (Die 4) (1.81)	2·00	1·50	40·00

1881. *White to bluish paper. P* 14.

		(*a*) *W* **40** (*Anchor 18 mm high*) (Jan)			
F24	F **9**	3d. reddish lilac	£325	£200	£325
F25	F **10**	6d. reddish lilac	£170	50·00	£150
		(*b*) *W* **40** (*Anchor 20 mm high*) (May)			
F26	F **9**	3d. reddish lilac	£250	55·00	£150
F27	F **10**	6d. reddish lilac	£110	75·00	£250

ISSUES EMBOSSED IN COLOUR

(Made at Somerset House)

The embossed stamps were struck from dies not appropriated to any special purpose on paper which had the words "INLAND REVENUE" previously printed, and thus became available for payment of any duties for which no special stamps had been provided.

The die letters are included in the embossed designs and holes were drilled for the insertion of plugs showing figures indicating dates of striking.

F 13

F 14

INLAND REVENUE

(F 15)

INLAND REVENUE

(F 16)

1860 (3 Apr)–**71.** *Types* F **13/14** *and similar types embossed on bluish paper. Underprint Type* F **15.** *No wmk. Imperf.*

		Un	*Used*
F28	2d. pink (Die A) (1.1.71)	£120	£120
F29	3d. pink (Die C)	90·00	80·00
	a. *Tête-bêche* (vert pair)	£1000	
F30	3d. pink (Die D)	£325	
F31	6d. pink (Die T)	£650	
F32	6d. pink (Die U)	95·00	80·00
	a. *Tête-bêche* (vert pair)	£1200	
F33	9d. pink (Die C) (1.1.71)	£225	
F34	1s. pink (Die E) (28.6.61)	£325	£130
F35	1s. pink (Die F) (28.6.61)	£110	90·00
	a. *Tête-bêche* (vert pair)	£500	
F36	2s. pink (Die K) (6.8.61)	£250	£150
F37	2s. 6d. pink (Die N) (28.6.61)	£750	
F38	2s. 6d. pink (Die O) (28.6.61)	75·00	65·00

1861–71. *As last but perf* 12½.

F39	2d. pink (Die A) (8.71)	£225	£110
F40	3d. pink (Die C)		
F41	3d. pink (Die D)		
F42	9d. pink (Die C) (8.71)	£250	£120
F43	1s. pink (Die E) (8.71)	£190	£110
F44	1s. pink (Die F) (8.71)	£170	85·00
F45	2s. 6d. pink (Die O) (8.71)	£100	50·00

1874 (Nov). *Types as before embossed on white paper. Underprint Type* F **16**, *in green. W* **47** (*Small Anchor*). *P* 12½.

F46	2d. pink (Die A)	—	£150
F47	9d. pink (Die C)		
F48	1s. pink (Die F)	£170	90·00
F49	2s. 6d. pink (Die O)	—	£130

1875 (Nov)–**80.** *As last but colour changed and on white or bluish paper.*

F50	2d. vermilion (Die A) (1880)	£250	85·00
F51	9d. vermilion (Die C) (1876)	£250	£120
F52	1s. vermilion (Die E)	£150	55·00
F53	1s. vermilion (Die F)	£150	55·00
F54	2s. 6d. vermilion (Die O) (1878)	£190	85·00

1882 (Oct). *As last but W* **48** (*Orbs*).

F55	2d. vermilion (Die A)		
F56	9d. vermilion (Die C)		
F57	1s. vermilion (Die E)		
F58	2s. 6d. vermilion (Die O)	£400	£190

The sale of Inland Revenue stamps up to the 2s. value ceased from 30 December 1882 and stocks were called in and destroyed. The 2s. 6d. value remained on sale until 2 July 1883 when it was replaced by the 2s. 6d. "Postage & Revenue" stamp. Inland Revenue stamps still in the hands of the public continued to be accepted for revenue and postal purposes.

CONTROLS. Since the 1967 edition of the Part 1 Catalogue the priced lists of stamps with control letters have been transferred to Volumes 1 and 2 of the Stanley Gibbons *Great Britain Specialised Catalogue*.

TELEGRAPH STAMPS. A priced listing of the Post Office telegraph stamps appears in Volume 1 of the Stanley Gibbons *Great Britain Specialised Catalogue*. The last listing for the private telegraph companies in the Part 1 Catalogue was in the 1940 edition and for military telegraphs the 1941 edition.

ISLAND ISSUES

Several islands off the coast of Great Britain have issued local stamps (usually termed British Private Local Issues or Local Carriage Labels) ostensibly to cover the cost of ferrying mail to the nearest mainland post office. No official post offices operate on most of these islands. As these stamps are not recognised as valid for national or international mail they are not listed here. The following islands are known to operate (or have operated) a local postal service and issued stamps from the dates shown:
Bardsey, Gwynedd (from 1979); *Bernera*, Hebrides (from 1977); *Brecqhou*, Channel Is. (1969); *Caldey*, Dyfed (from 1973); *Calf of Man*, Isle of Man (1962–73); *Calve*, Hebrides (from 1984); *Canna*, Hebrides (from 1958); *Carn Iar*, Hebrides (1961–62); *Davaar*, Argyllshire (from 1964); *Drake's Island*, Devon (1973–82); *Easdale*, Argyllshire (from 1988); *Eynhallow*, Orkney (from 1973); *Gairsay*, Orkney (from 1980); *Grunay*, Shetland (from 1981); *Gugh*, Isles of Scilly (1972–80); *Herm*, Channel Is. (1949–69); *Heston*, Wigtownshire (1960s); *Hilbre*, Cheshire (1960s); *Inchcolm*, Fife (1961, unissued); *Jethou*, Channel Is. (1960–69); *Lihou*, Channel Is. (1966–69); *Lundy*, Devon (from 1929); *Pabay*, Skye (1962–70, 1972–81 and from 1982); *St. Kilda*, Hebrides (1968–71); *Sanda*, Argyllshire (from 1962); *Shuna*, Argyllshire (from 1949); *Soay*, Skye (1965–67); *Staffa*, Hebrides (from 1969); *Steep Holm*, Avon (1980–87); *Stroma*, Caithness (1962–70) and *Summer Isles*, Hebrides (from 1970). Those issued for Soay have been declared bogus by a committee of the Philatelic Traders Society.

Issues of the *Commodore Shipping Co* (1950–69), the *Alderney Shipping Co* (1969–75) and the *Isle of Sark Shipping Co* (from 1969) were/are for use on parcels carried by ship between Guernsey and Alderney and Sark. They are not valid for the carriage of letters and postcards.

Issues inscribed Alderney (1975–83) were issued in conjunction with an internal parcel delivery service. They were not valid for use on letters or postcards.

CHANNEL ISLANDS

GENERAL ISSUE

C **1** Gathering Vraic

C **2** Islanders gathering Vraic

(Des J. R. R. Stobie (1d.) or from drawing by E. Blampied (2½d.). Photo Harrison)

1948 (10 May). *Third Anniv of Liberation. W* **127** *of Great Britain. P* 15 × 14.

C1	C **1**	1d. scarlet	20	20
C2	C **2**	2½d. ultramarine	30	30

GUERNSEY

Further detailed information on the stamps of Guernsey will be found in the Stanley Gibbons *Channel Islands Specialised Catalogue*.

WAR OCCUPATION ISSUES

Stamps issued under British authority during the German Occupation

BISECTS. On 24 December 1940 authority was given, by Post Office notice, that prepayment of penny postage could be effected by using half a British 2d. stamp, diagonally bisected. Such stamps were first used on 27 December 1940.

The 2d. stamps generally available were those of the Postal Centenary issue, 1940 (S.G. 482) and the first colour of the King George VI issue (S.G. 465). These are listed under Nos. 482a and 465b. A number of the 2d. King George V, 1912–22, and of the King George V photogravure stamp (S.G. 442) which were in the hands of philatelists, were also bisected and used.

1

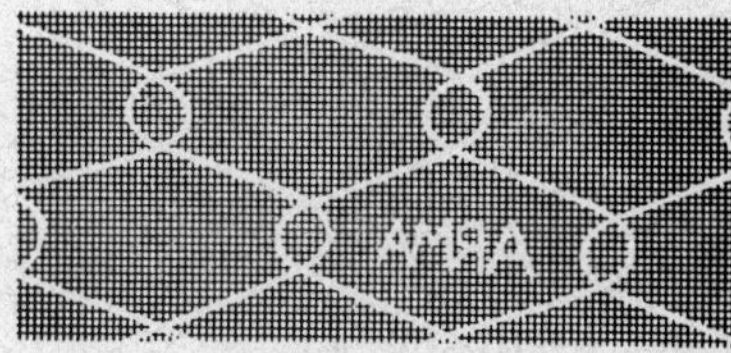

1*a* Loops (*half actual size*)

(Des E. W. Vaudin. Typo Guernsey Press Co Ltd)

1941–44. *Rouletted.* (*a*) *White paper. No wmk.*

1	**1**	½d. light green (7.4.41)	3·00	2·50
		a. Emerald-green (6.41)	2·50	2·50
		b. Bluish green (11.41)	45·00	28·00
		c. Bright green (2.42)	24·00	12·00
		d. Dull green (9.42)	4·50	3·50
		e. Olive-green (2.43)	20·00	22·00
		f. Pale yellowish green (7.43 and later) (*shades*)	2·50	2·50
		g. Imperf (pair)	£150	
		h. Imperf between (horiz pair)	£600	
		i. Imperf between (vert pair)	£700	
2		1d. scarlet (18.2.41)	2·25	1·25
		a. Pale vermilion (7.43) (etc.)	4·00	2·50
		b. Carmine (1943)	4·00	3·50
		c. Imperf (pair)	£150	75·00
		d. Imperf between (horiz pair)	£600	
		da. Imperf vert (centre stamp of horiz strip of 3)		
		e. Imperf between (vert pair)	£700	
		f. Printed double (scarlet shade)	75·00	
3		2½d. ultramarine (12.4.44)	6·00	6·00
		a. Pale ultramarine (7.44)	6·00	4·50
		b. Imperf (pair)	£350	
		c. Imperf between (horiz pair)	£800	
		(*b*) *Bluish French bank-note paper. W* **1a** (*sideways*)		
4	**1**	½d. bright green (11.3.42)	14·00	22·00
5		1d. scarlet (9.4.42)	8·00	22·00

The dates given for the shades of Nos. 1 and 2 are the months in which they were printed as indicated on the printer's imprints. Others are issue dates.

REGIONAL ISSUES

DATES OF ISSUE. Conflicting dates of issue have been announced for some of the regional issues, partly explained by the stamps being released on different dates by the Philatelic Bureau in Edinburgh or the Philatelic Counter in London and in the regions. We have adopted the practice of giving the earliest known dates, since once released the stamps could have been used anywhere in the U.K.

2

3

(Des E. A. Piprell. Portrait by Dorothy Wilding Ltd. Photo Harrison & Sons)

1958 (18 Aug)–**67.** *W* **179** *of Great Britain. P* 15 × 14.

6	**2**	2½d. rose-red (8.6.64)	35	40
7	**3**	3d. deep lilac	35	30
		p. One centre phosphor band (24.5.67)	20	20
8		4d. ultramarine (7.2.66)	25	30
		p. Two phosphor bands (24.10.67)	20	20
6/8p.		*Set of* 3	50	75

1968–69. *No wmk. Chalk-surfaced paper. PVA gum*. One centre phosphor band (Nos. 10/11) or two phosphor bands (others). P* 15 × 14.

9 **3** 4d. pale ultramarine (16.4.68) 10 25
10 4d. olive-sepia (4.9.68) 15 20
11 4d. bright vermilion (26.2.69) 15 30
12 5d. royal blue (4.9.68) 15 30
9/12 .. .. *Set of* 4 40 95

No. 9 was not issued in Guernsey until 22 April.
* PVA Gum. See note after No. 722 of Great Britain.

INDEPENDENT POSTAL ADMINISTRATION

4 Castle Cornet and Edward the Confessor

5 View of Sark

Two Types of 1d. and 1s. 6d.:

I. Latitude inscr "40° 30′ N".
II. Corrected to "49° 30′ N".

(Des R. Granger Barrett. Photo Harrison (½d. to 2s. 6d.); Delrieu (others))

1969 (1 Oct)–**70.** *Designs as T* **4/5.** *P* 14 (*½d. to* 2*s.* 6*d.*) *or* 12½ (*others*).

13 ½d. deep magenta and black 10 10
14 1d. bright blue and black (I) 10 10
14*b* 1d. bright blue and black (II) (12.12.69) .. 50 60
c. Booklet stamp with blank margins .. 55 55
15 1½d. yellow-brown and black 10 10
16 2d. gold, bright red, deep blue and black .. 10 10
17 3d. gold, pale greenish yellow, orge-red & blk 15 15
a. Error. Wmk w **12** £1100
18 4d. multicoloured 25 25
a. Booklet stamp with blank margins (12.12.69) 35 35
ab. Yellow omitted £225
ac. Emerald (stem) omitted £100
19 5d. gold, brt vermilion, bluish violet & black 25 15
a. Booklet stamp with blank margins (12.12.69) 35 35
b. Gold (inscr etc.) omitted (booklets) .. £450
20 6d. gold, pale greenish yellow, light bronze-green and black 30 35
21 9d. gold, bright red, crimson and black .. 70 60
22 1s. gold, bright vermilion, bistre and black 55 45
23 1s. 6d. turquoise-green and black (I) .. 40 50
23*b* 1s. 6d. turquoise-green and black (II) (4.2.70) 6·50 1·90
24 1s. 9d. multicoloured .. .. .. 2·50 2·50
a. Emerald (stem) omitted £300
25 2s. 6d. bright reddish violet and black .. 9·00 3·50
26 5s. multicoloured .. .. 3·75 4·00
27 10s. multicoloured .. .. 30·00 21·00
a. Perf 13 (4.3.70) .. .. .. 55·00 55·00
28 £1 multicoloured .. .. 6·00 6·00
a. Perf 13 (4.3.70) .. .. .. 2·00 2·00
13/28 .. .. *Set of* 16 45·00 30·00

Designs: *Horiz as T* **4**—1d. (*both*), 1s. 6d. (*both*), Map and William I; 1½d. Martello Tower and Henry II; 2d. Arms of Sark and King John; 3d. Arms of Alderney and Edward III; 4d. Guernsey Lily and Henry V; 5d. Arms of Guernsey and Elizabeth I; 6d. Arms of Alderney and Charles II; 9d. Arms of Sark and George III; 1s. Arms of Guernsey and Queen Victoria; 1s. 9d. Guernsey Lily and Elizabeth I; 2s. 6d. Martello Tower and King John. *Horiz as T* **5**—10s. View of Alderney; £1, View of Guernsey.

The booklet panes consist of single perforated stamps with wide margins all round intended to fit automatic machines designed for the Great Britain 2s. booklets. They are therefore found with three margins when detached from booklets or four margins when complete.

There was no postal need for the ½d. and 1½d. values as the ½d. coin had been withdrawn prior to their issue in anticipation of decimalisation. These values were only on sale at the Philatelic Bureau and the Crown Agents as well as in the U.S.A.

Nos. 14*b* and 23*b* are known only on thin paper and Nos. 13, 14, 16, 17, 20, 21, 22, 23, 24 and 25 also exist on thin paper.

19 Isaac Brock as Colonel

23 Landing Craft entering St. Peter's Harbour

(Litho Format)

1969 (1 Dec). *Birth Bicentenary of Sir Isaac Brock. T* **19** *and similar multicoloured designs. P* 13½ × 14 (2*s.* 6*d.*) *or* 14 × 13½ (*others*).

29 4d. Type **19** 30 30
30 5d. Sir Isaac Brock as Major-General .. 30 30
31 1s. 9d. Isaac Brock as Ensign .. .. 2·50 2·50
32 2s. 6d. Arms and flags (*horiz*) .. .. 2·50 2·50
29/32 .. .. *Set of* 4 5·00 5·00

(Des and photo Courvoisier)

1970 (9 May). *25th Anniv of Liberation. T* **23** *and similar designs. Granite paper. P* 11½.

33 4d. blue and pale blue 35 40
34 5d. brown-lake and pale grey 35 40
35 1s. 6d. bistre-brown and buff .. .. .. 4·75 2·50
33/5 .. .. *Set of* 3 5·00 3·00

Designs: *Horiz*—5d. British ships entering St. Peter's Port. *Vert*—1s. 6d. Brigadier Snow reading Proclamation.

BAILIWICK OF GUERNSEY
HORTICULTURE
4d
THE GUERNSEY "TOM"

26 Guernsey "Toms"

32 St. Peter Church, Sark

(Des and photo Courvoisier)

1970 (12 Aug). *Agriculture and Horticulture. T* **26** *and similar horiz designs. Multicoloured. Granite paper. P* 11½.

36 4d. Type **26** .. .. 1·00 30
37 5d. Guernsey Cow .. .. 1·10 30
38 9d. Guernsey Bull .. .. 14·00 3·25
39 1s. 6d. Freesias .. .. 16·00 3·75
36/9 .. .. *Set of* 4 28·00 7·00

(Des and photo Courvoisier)

1970 (11 Nov). *Christmas. Guernsey Churches (1st series). T* **32** *and similar multicoloured designs. Granite paper. P* 11½.

40 4d. St. Anne's Church, Alderney (*horiz*) .. 50 20
41 5d. St. Peter's Church (*horiz*) 50 25
42 9d. Type **32** .. .. 2·50 1·40
43 1s. 6d. St. Tugual Chapel, Herm .. .. 3·50 1·50
40/3 .. .. *Set of* 4 6·00 3·00

See also Nos. 63/6.

INVALIDATION. The regional issues for Guernsey were invalidated for use in Guernsey and Jersey on 1 November 1969 but remained valid for use in the rest of the United Kingdom. Nos. 13/43 (except Nos. 28/a) and Nos. D1/7 were invalidated on 14 February 1972.

34 Martello Tower and King John

(Photo Harrison (½p. to 10p.), Delrieu (others))

1971 (6 Jan)–**73.** *Decimal Currency. Designs as Nos.* 13/27 *but values inscr in decimal currency as in T* **34.** *Chalk-surfaced paper. P* 14 (*½p. to* 10*p.*) *or* 13 (20*p.*, 50*p.*).

44 ½p. deep magenta and black (15.2.71) .. 10 15
a. Booklet stamp with margins (*glazed, ordinary paper*) 15 20
ab. Ditto. Chalk-surfaced paper (2.4.73) .. 15 20
45 1p. bright blue and black (II) (15.2.71) .. 10 10
46 1½p. yellow-brown and black (15.2.71) .. 15 15
47 2p. multicoloured (15.2.71) 15 15
a. Booklet stamp with margins (*glazed, ordinary paper*) 20 20
ab. Ditto. Chalk-surfaced paper (2.4.73) .. 20 20
ac. Emerald (stem) omitted £1100
b. Glazed, ordinary paper (15.2.71) .. 20 20
48 2½p. gold, brt verm, bluish vio & blk (15.2.71) 15 10
a. Bright vermilion omitted £450
b. Booklet stamp with margins (*glazed, ordinary paper*) 20 20
ba. Ditto. Chalk-surfaced paper (2.4.73) .. 20 20
49 3p. gold, pale greenish yellow, orange-red and black (15.2.71) 20 20
50 3½p. mult (*glazed, ordinary paper*) (15.2.71) .. 25 25
51 4p. multicoloured (15.2.71) 35 25
52 5p. turquoise-green and black (II) (15.2.71) 30 25
53 6p. gold, pale greenish yellow, light bronze-green and black (15.2.71) 30 35
54 7½p. gold, brt verm, bistre & black (15.2.71) 40 45
55 9p. gold, brt red, crimson & black (15.2.71) 1·00 1·25
56 10p. bright reddish violet and black .. .. 1·60 2·00
a. Ordinary paper. *Bright reddish violet and deep black* (1.9.72) .. .. .. 1·00 1·50
57 20p. multicoloured (*glazed, ordinary paper*) .. 1·00 1·10
*a. Shade** (25.1.73) 80 75
58 50p. multicoloured (*glazed, ordinary paper*) .. 2·00 3·25
44/58 .. .. *Set of* 15 7·00 8·00

*No. 57 has the sky in a pale turquoise-blue; on No. 57*a* it is pale turquoise-green.

35 Hong Kong 2 c. of 1862

(Des and recess D.L.R.)

1971 (2 June). *Thomas De La Rue Commemoration. T* **35** *and similar horiz designs. P* 14 × 13½.

59 2p. dull purple to brown-purple* 50 30
60 2½p. carmine-red 50 30
61 4p. deep bluish green .. .. 5·00 3·00
62 7½p. deep blue .. .. 5·00 3·00
59/62 .. .. *Set of* 4 10·00 6·00

Designs: (each incorporating portraits of Queen Elizabeth II and Thomas De La Rue as in T **35**)—2½p. Great Britain 4d. of 1855–7; 4p. Italy 5 c. of 1862; 7½p. Confederate States 5 c. of 1862.

* These colours represent the extreme range of shades of this value. The majority of the printing, however, is in an intermediate shade.

36 Ebenezer Church, St. Peter Port

(Des and photo Courvoisier)

1971 (27 Oct). *Christmas. Guernsey Churches (2nd series). T* **36** *and similar multicoloured designs. Granite paper. P* 11½.

63 2p. Type **36** 45 25
64 2½p. Church of St. Pierre du Bois 50 25
65 5p. St. Joseph's Church, St. Peter Port (*vert*) 2·75 2·00
66 7½d. Church of St. Philippe de Torteval (*vert*) 3·00 2·00
63/6 .. .. *Set of* 4 6·00 4·00

37 *Earl of Chesterfield* (1794)

(Des and photo Courvoisier)

1972 (10 Feb). *Mail Packet Boats (1st series). T* **37** *and similar horiz designs. Multicoloured. Granite paper. P* 11½.

67 2p. Type **37** 25 15
68 2½p. *Dasher* (1827) 25 20
69 7½p. *Ibex* (1891) 75 75
70 9p. *Alberta* (1900) 90 85
67/70 .. .. *Set of* 4 1·90 1·75

See also Nos. 80/3

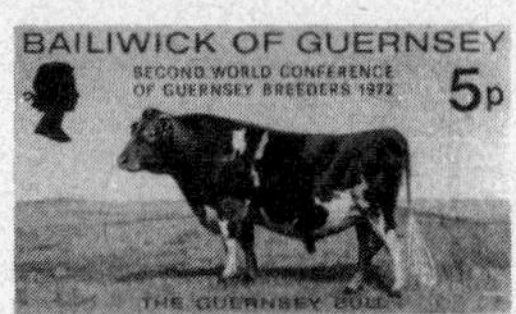

38 Guernsey Bull

(Photo Courvoisier)

1972 (22 May). *World Conference of Guernsey Breeders, Guernsey. Granite paper. P* 11½.

71 **38** 5p. multicoloured .. .. .. 1·00 1·00

39 Bermuda Buttercup **40** Angels adoring Christ

(Des and photo Courvoisier)

1972 (24 May). *Wild Flowers. T* **39** *and similar multicoloured designs. Granite paper. P* 11½.

72 2p. Type **39** 15 20
73 2½p. Heath Spotted Orchid (*vert*) 15 20
74 7½p. Kaffir Fig 80 80
75 9p. Scarlet Pimpernel (*vert*) .. .. 1·10 1·10
72/5 .. .. *Set of* 4 2·00 2·00

(Des and photo Courvoisier)

1972 (20 Nov). *Royal Silver Wedding and Christmas. T* **40** *and similar vert designs showing stained-glass windows from Guernsey Churches. Multicoloured. Granite paper. P* 11½.

76 2p. Type **40** 10 10
77 2½p. The Epiphany 15 15
78 7½p. The Virgin Mary 60 60
79 9p. Christ 70 70
76/9 .. .. *Set of* 4 1·40 1·40

See also Nos. 89/92.

(Des and photo Courvoisier)

973 (9 Mar). *Mail Packet Boats* (*2nd series*). *Multicoloured designs as T* **37**. *Granite paper. P* 11½.

0 2½p. *St. Julien* (1925) 10 10
1 3p. *Isle of Guernsey* (1930) 20 20
2 7½p. *St. Patrick* (1947) 55 60
3 9p. *Sarnia* (1961) 70 75
0/3 .. .. *Set of* 4 1·40 1·50

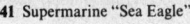

41 Supermarine "Sea Eagle" **42** "The Good Shepherd"

(Des and photo Courvoisier)

973 (4 July). *50th Anniv of Air Service. T* **41** *and similar horiz designs. Multicoloured. Granite paper. P* 11½.

4 2½p. Type **41** 10 10
5 3p. Westland "Wessex" 15 15
6 5p. De Havilland "Rapide" 25 25
7 7½p. Douglas "Dakota" 45 50
8 9p. Vickers "Viscount" 45 55
34/8 .. .. *Set of* 5 1·25 1·40

(Des and photo Courvoisier)

973 (24 Oct). *Christmas. T* **42** *and similar vert designs showing stained-glass windows from Guernsey Churches. Multicoloured. Granite paper. P* 11½.

9 2½p. Type **42** 10 10
0 3p. Christ at the well of Samaria 10 10
1 7½p. St. Dominic 30 30
2 20p. Mary and the Child Jesus 60 60
9/92 .. .. *Set of* 4 1·00 1·00

43 Princess Anne and Capt. Mark Phillips

(Des G. Anderson. Photo Courvoisier)

1973 (14 Nov). *Royal Wedding. Granite paper. P* 11½.

)3 **43** 25p. multicoloured 70 80

44 *John Lockett*, 1875

(Des and photo Courvoisier)

974 (15 Jan). *150th Anniv of Royal National Lifeboat Institution. T* **44** *and similar horiz designs. Multicoloured. Granite paper. P* 11½.

)4 2½p. Type **44** 10 10
)5 3p. *Arthur Lionel*, 1912 .. .. 10 10
)6 8p. *Euphrosyne Kendal*, 1954 .. .. .. 35 35
)7 10p. *Arun*, 1972 .. .. 35 35
)4/7 .. .. *Set of* 4 80 80

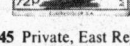

45 Private, East Regt, 1815 **46** Driver, Field Battery, Royal Guernsey Artillery, 1848

(Photo Courvoisier (½ to 10p.) or Delrieu (others))

974 (2 Apr)–**78.** *Designs as T* **45**/**6.** *Multicoloured.*

(*a*) *Vert designs as T* **45**. *Granite paper. P* 11½

98 ½p. Type **45** 10 10
a. Booklet strip of 8 (98 × 5 and 102 × 3)† 50
b. Booklet pane of 16 (98 × 4, 102 × 6 and 103 × 6)† .. .. 1·75
99 1p. Officer, 2nd North Regt, 1825 .. .. 10 10
a. Booklet strip of 8 (99 × 4, 103, 105 × 2 and 105*a*) (8.2.77)† 85
b. Booklet strip of 4 (99, 101 × 2 and 105*a*) (7.2.78)† 50
00 1½p. Gunner, Guernsey Artillery, 1787 .. 10 10
01 2p. Gunner, Guernsey Artillery, 1815 .. 10 10
02 2½p. Corporal, Royal Guernsey Artillery, 1868 .. .. 10 10
103 3p. Field Officer, Royal Guernsey Artillery, 1895 .. .. 10 10
104 3½p. Sergeant, 3rd Regt, 1867 .. .. 10 10
105 4p. Officer, East Regt, 1822 .. .. 15 15
105*a* 5p. Field Officer, Royal Guernsey Artillery, 1895 (29.5.76) 15 15
106 5½p. Colour-Sergeant of Grenadiers, East Regt, 1833 .. .. 20 25
107 6p. Officer, North Regt, 1832 .. .. 20 25
107*a* 7p. Officer, East Regt, 1822 (29.5.76) .. 25 25
108 8p. Field Officer, Rifle Company, 1868 .. 25 30
109 9p. Private, 4th West Regt, 1785 .. .. 30 35
110 10p. Field Officer, 4th West Regt, 1824 .. 30 35

(*b*) *Size as T* **46.** *P* 13 × 13½ (20, 50*p.*) *or* 13½ × 13 (£1)

111 20p. Type **46** (1.4.75) 55 55
112 50p. Officer, Field Battery, Royal Guernsey Artillery, 1868 (1.4.75) .. .. .. 1·50 1·40
113 £1 Cavalry Trooper, Light Dragoons, 1814 (*horiz*) (1.4.75) .. .. 3·00 2·75
98/113 .. .. *Set of* 18 6·75 6·75

The ½p. and 2½p. with the red colour omitted are chemically produced fakes.

† Nos. 98a/b come from special booklet sheets of 88 (8 × 11), and Nos. 99a/b from separate booklet sheets of 80 (2 panes 8 × 5). These sheets were put on sale in addition to the normal sheets. The strips and panes have the left-hand selvedge stuck into booklet covers, except for No. 99b which was loose, and then folded and supplied in plastic wallets.

47 Badge of Guernsey and U.P.U. Emblem

(Photo Courvoisier)

1974 (7 June). *U.P.U. Centenary. T* **47** *and similar horiz designs. Multicoloured. Granite paper. P* 11½.

114 2½p. Type **47** 10 10
115 3p. Map of Guernsey 10 10
116 8p. U.P.U. Building, Berne, and Guernsey flag 35 35
117 10p. "Salle des Etats" 40 40
114/17 .. .. *Set of* 4 80 80

48 "Cradle Rock" **49** Guernsey Spleenwort

(Des and photo Delrieu)

1974 (21 Sept). *Renoir Paintings. T* **48** *and similar multicoloured designs. P* 13.

118 3p. Type **48** 10 10
119 5½p. "Moulin Huet Bay" 15 15
120 8p. "Au Bord de la Mer" (*vert*) 30 25
121 10p. Self-portrait (*vert*) 35 30
118/21 .. .. *Set of* 4 80 70

(Des and photo Courvoisier)

1975 (7 Jan). *Guernsey Ferns. T* **49** *and similar vert designs. Multicoloured. Granite paper. P* 11½.

122 3½p. Type **49** 10 10
123 4p. Sand Quillwort 10 10
124 8p. Guernsey Quillwort 30 30
125 10p. Least Adder's Tongue 40 40
122/5 .. .. *Set of* 4 80 80

50 Victor Hugo House **51** Globe and Seal of Bailiwick

(Des and photo Courvoisier)

1975 (6 June). *Victor Hugo's Exile in Guernsey. T* **50** *and similar multicoloured designs. Granite paper. P* 11½.

126 3½p. Type **50** 10 10
127 4p. Candie Gardens (*vert*) 10 10
128 8p. United Europe Oak, Hauteville (*vert*) 30 30
129 10p. Tapestry Room, Hauteville 40 40
126/9 .. .. *Set of* 4 80 80
MS130 114 × 143 mm. Nos. 126/9 .. .. 75 1·00

(Des and photo Delrieu)

1975 (7 Oct). *Christmas. Multicoloured designs each showing Globe as T* **51.** *P* 13.

131 4p. Type **51** 10 10
132 6p. Guernsey flag 15 15
133 10p. Guernsey flag and Alderney shield (*horiz*) 35 25
134 12p. Guernsey flag and Sark shield (*horiz*) .. 50 40
131/4 .. .. *Set of* 4 1·00 80

52 Les Hanois

(Des and photo Courvoisier)

1976 (10 Feb). *Lighthouses. T* **52** *and similar horiz designs. Multicoloured. Granite paper. P* 11½.

135 4p. Type **52** 10 10
136 6p. Les Casquets 15 15
137 11p. Quesnard 40 25
138 13p. Point Robert 45 40
135/8 .. .. *Set of* 4 1·00 80

53 Milk Can

(Des and photo Courvoisier)

1976 (29 May). *Europa. T* **53** *and similar horiz design. Granite paper. P* 11½.

139 10p. chestnut and greenish black 30 30
140 25p. slate and deep dull blue 70 70

Design:—25p. Christening Cup.

54 Pine Forest, Guernsey

(Des and photo Courvoisier)

1976 (3 Aug). *Bailiwick Views. T* **54** *and similar multicoloured designs. Granite paper. P* 11½.

141 5p. Type **54** 15 10
142 7p. Herm and Jethou 15 15
143 11p. Grand Greve Bay, Sark (*vert*) 40 25
144 13p. Trois Vaux Bay, Alderney (*vert*) .. 40 40
141/4 .. .. *Set of* 4 1·00 80

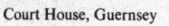

55 Royal Court House, Guernsey **56** Queen Elizabeth II

(Des and photo Courvoisier)

1976 (14 Oct). *Christmas. Buildings. T* **55** *and similar horiz designs. Multicoloured. Granite paper. P* 11½.

145 5p. Type **55** 15 10
146 7p. Elizabeth College, Guernsey 15 15
147 11p. La Seigneurie, Sark 40 25
148 13p. Island Hall, Alderney 40 40
145/8 .. .. *Set of* 4 1·00 80

(Des R. Granger Barrett. Photo Courvoisier)

1977 (8 Feb). *Silver Jubilee. T* **56** *and similar vert design. Multicoloured. Granite paper. P* 11½.

149 7p. Type **56** 20 20
150 35p. Queen Elizabeth (half-length portrait) 80 70

OMNIBUS ISSUES

Details, together with prices for complete sets, of the various Omnibus issues from the 1935 Silver Jubilee series to date are included in a special section following Zululand at the end of the catalogue.

57 Woodland, Talbot's Valley **58** Statue-menhir, Castel

(Des and photo Courvoisier)

1977 (17 May). *Europa. T* **57** *and similar horiz design. Multicoloured. Granite paper. P* 11½.
151 7p. Type **57** 25 15
152 25p. Pastureland, Talbot's Valley 75 55

(Des and photo Courvoisier)

1977 (2 Aug). *Prehistoric Monuments. T* **58** *and similar multicoloured designs. Granite paper. P* 11½.
153 5p. Type **58** 10 10
154 7p. Megalithic tomb, St. Saviour (*horiz*) .. 15 15
155 11p. Cist, Tourgis (*horiz*) 40 25
156 13p. Statue-menhir, St. Martin 50 40
153/6 .. .. *Set of* 4 1·00 80

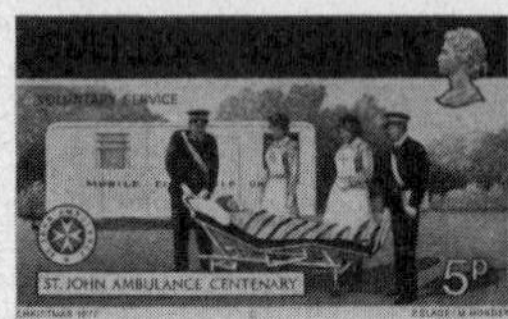

59 Mobile First Aid Unit

(Des P. Slade and M. Horder. Photo Courvoisier)

1977 (25 Oct). *Christmas and St. John Ambulance Centenary. T* **59** *and similar multicoloured designs. Granite paper. P* 11½.
157 5p. Type **59** 10 10
158 7p. Mobile radar unit 15 15
159 11p. Marine Ambulance *Flying Christine II* (*vert*) 40 25
160 13p. Cliff rescue (*vert*) 50 40
157/60 .. .. *Set of* 4 1·00 80

60 View from Clifton, *circa* 1830

(Des, recess and litho D.L.R.)

1978 (7 Feb). *Old Guernsey Prints* (*1st series*). *T* **60** *and similar horiz designs. P* 14 × 13½.
161 5p. black and pale apple-green 10 10
162 7p. black and stone 15 15
163 11p. black and light pink 40 25
164 13p. black and light azure 50 40
161/4 .. .. *Set of* 4 1·00 80

Designs:—7p. Market Square, St. Peter Port, *circa* 1838; 11p. Petit-Bo Bay, *circa* 1839; 13p. The Quay, St. Peter Port, *circa* 1830.

See also Nos. 249/52.

61 *Prosperity* Memorial **62** Queen Elizabeth II

(Des R. Granger Barrett. Litho Questa)

1978 (2 May). *Europa. T* **61** *and similar vert design. Multicoloured. P* 14½.
165 5p. Type **61** 25 15
166 7p. Victoria Monument 30 25

(Des R. Granger Barrett from bust by Arnold Machin. Photo Courvoisier)

1978 (2 May). *25th Anniv of Coronation. Granite paper. P* 11½.
167 **62** 20p. black, grey and bright blue 50 60

1978 (28 June). *Royal Visit. Design as No.* 167 *but inscr.* "VISIT OF H.M. THE QUEEN AND H.R.H. THE DUKE OF EDINBURGH JUNE 28–29, 1978 TO THE BAILIWICK OF GUERNSEY".
168 **62** 7p. black, grey and bright green 25 25

63 Northern Gannet

(Des J.W. Photo Courvoisier)

1978 (29 Aug). *Birds. T* **63** *and similar horiz designs. Multicoloured. Granite paper. P* 11½.
169 5p. Type **63** 15 15
170 7p. Firecrest 25 25
171 11p. Dartford Warbler 35 35
172 13p. Spotted Redshank 40 40
169/72 .. .. *Set of* 4 1·00 1·00

64 Solanum

(Des and photo Courvoisier)

1978 (31 Oct). *Christmas. T* **64** *and similar designs. Granite paper. P* 11½.
173 5p. multicoloured 10 10
174 7p. multicoloured 20 20
175 11p. multicoloured 40 30
176 13p. dp blue-green, grey & greenish yellow 50 40
173/6 .. .. *Set of* 4 1·10 90

Designs: *Horiz*—7p. Christmas Rose. *Vert*—11p. Holly; 13p. Mistletoe.

65 One Double Coin, 1830 **66** Ten Shillings William I Commemorative Coin, 1966

66a Seal of the Bailiwick

(Des R. Reed and Courvoisier (£5). Photo Courvoisier)

1979 (13 Feb)–**83**. *Designs as T* **65/66a**. *Granite paper. P* 11½.
177 ½p. multicoloured 10 10
a. Booklet pane of 10. Nos. 177 × 2, 178 × 3, 179 × 2, 181, 183 and 187 (6.5.80) .. 1·00
b. Booklet pane of 10. Nos. 177 × 2, 178, 179 × 2, 183 × 2 and 187 × 3 (6.5.80) .. 1·50
178 1p. multicoloured 10 10
a. Booklet strip of 4. Nos. 178 × 2, 179 and 182 40
179 2p. multicoloured 10 10
a. Booklet strip of 5. Nos. 179, 182 × 2 and 184 × 2 90
180 4p. multicoloured 10 10
a. Booklet pane of 10. Nos. 180 and 184, each × 5 (24.2.81) .. .. .. 1·75
b. Booklet pane of 15. Nos. 180, 184 and 190, each × 5 (24.2.81) .. .. .. 3·50
c. Booklet pane of 10. Nos. 180 × 2, 185 × 3 and 191 × 5 (14.3.83) .. .. .. 3·00
d. Booklet pane of 15. Nos. 180, 185 and 191 each × 5 (14.3.83) .. .. .. 4·50
181 5p. grey-black, silver & chestnut (*shades*) .. 15 10
b. Booklet pane. Nos. 181 × 5, 184 × 4 and 191 (2.2.82) .. .. 2·00
c. Booklet pane. Nos. 181, 184 and 191 each × 5 (2.2.82) .. .. 3·75
182 6p. grey-black, silver and brown-red .. 15 15
183 7p. grey-black, silver and green 15 20
184 8p. grey-black, silver and brown 20 20
185 9p. multicoloured 25 20
186 10p. multicoloured (green background) .. 50 50
187 10p. mult (orange background) (5.2.80) .. 25 30
188 11p. multicoloured 25 30
189 11½p. multicoloured (5.2.80) 25 30
190 12p. multicoloured 30 30
191 13p. multicoloured 30 30
192 14p. grey-black, silver and dull blue .. 30 30
193 15p. grey-black, silver and bistre 35 35
194 20p. grey-black, silver and dull brown .. 50 45
195 50p. grey-black, orange-red and silver (5.2.80) 1·25 1·25
196 £1 grey-blk, yellowish grn & silver (5.2.80) 2·40 2·40
197 £2 grey-black, new blue and silver (5.2.80) 4·75 4·75
198 £5 multicoloured (22.5.81) .. .. .. 9·00 9·50
177/98 .. .. *Set of* 22 19·50 20·00

Coins: *Vert as T* **65**—1p. Two doubles, 1899; 2p. Four doubles 1902; 4p. Eight doubles 1959; 5p. Three pence, 1956; 6p. Five new pence, 1968; 7p. Fifty new pence, 1969; 8p. Ten new pence, 1970 9p. Half new penny, 1971; 10p. (*both*), One new penny, 1971; 11p Two new pence, 1971; 11½p. Half penny, 1979; 12p. One penny 1977; 13p. Two pence, 1977; 14p. Five pence, 1977; 15p. Ten pence 1977; 20p. Twenty-five pence, 1972. *Horiz as T* **66**—£1 Silver Jubilee commemorative crown, 1977; £2 Royal Silver Wedding crown, 1972

Nos. 177a/b, 178a, 179a, 180a/d and 181b/c come from special booklet sheets of 40 (8 × 5) (Nos. 177a and 178a); 30 (6 × 5) (Nos 177b, 180a/b, 180d and 181 b/c), 25 (5 × 5) (No. 179a) or 20 (4 × 5 No. 180c). These were put on sale in addition to the normal sheets being first separated into strips, then folded and either affixed by the selvedge to booklet covers or supplied loose in plastic wallets.

67 Pillar-box and Postmark, 1853, Mail Van and Postmark, 1979 **68** Steam Tram, 1879

(Des R. Granger Barrett. Photo Courvoisier)

1979 (8 May). *Europa. Communications. T* **67** *and similar vert design Multicoloured. Granite paper. P* 11½.
201 6p. Type **67** 30 2
202 8p. Telephone, 1897 and telex machine, 1979 30 2

(Photo Courvoisier)

1979 (7 Aug). *History of Public Transport. T* **68** *and similar hori designs. Multicoloured. Granite paper. P* 11½.
203 6p. Type **68** 15 1
204 8p. Electric tram, 1896 .. .. 20 2
205 11p. Motor bus, 1911 .. .. 40 2
206 13p. Motor bus, 1979 .. .. 50 2
203/6 .. .. *Set of* 4 1·10 7

69 Bureau and Postal Headquarters **70** Major-General Le Marchant

(Des R. Granger Barrett. Photo Courvoisier)

1979 (1 Oct). *Christmas and 10th Anniv of Guernsey Postal Administration. T* **69** *and similar horiz designs. Multicoloured Granite paper. P* 11½.
207 6p. Type **69** 15 1
208 8p. "Mails and telegrams" 25 1
209 13p. "Parcels" 30 2
210 15p. "Philately" 40 2
207/10 .. .. *Set of* 4 1·00 7
MS211 120 × 80 mm. Nos. 207/10 .. .. .. 1·00 7

One copy of a pre-release sample as No. 210, but with a face value of 11p., is known. Such stamps were not sold for postal purposes.

(Des and photo Courvoisier)

1980 (6 May). *Europa. Personalities. T* **70** *and similar vert design Multicoloured. Granite paper. P* 11½.
212 10p. Type **70** 35 2
213 13½p. Admiral Lord De Saumarez 45 3

71 Policewoman with Lost Child

(Litho J.W.)

1980 (6 May). *60th Anniv of Guernsey Police Force. T* **71** *and simila horiz designs. Multicoloured. P* 13½ × 14.
214 7p. Type **71** 15 1
215 15p. Police motorcyclist escorting lorry .. 50 3
216 17½p. Police dog-handler 55 4
214/16 .. .. *Set of* 3 1·10 8

72 Golden Guernsey Goat

(Des P. Lambert. Photo Delrieu)

1980 (5 Aug). *Golden Guernsey Goats. T* **72** *and similar horiz designs showing goats. P* 13.

217	7p.	multicoloured	20	20
218	10p.	multicoloured	30	35
219	15p.	multicoloured	50	45
220	17½p.	multicoloured	60	60
217/20		*Set of* 4	1·40	1·40

73 "Sark Cottage"

(Photo Courvoisier)

1980 (15 Nov). *Christmas. Peter le Lievre Paintings. T* **73** *and similar multicoloured designs. Granite paper. P* 11½.

221	7p.	Type **73**	20	20
222	10p.	"Moulin Huet"	25	25
223	13½p.	"Boats at Sea"	30	30
224	15p.	"Cow Lane" (*vert*)	40	40
225	17½p.	"Peter le Lievre" (*vert*)	45	50
221/5		*Set of* 5	1·40	1·50

74 Common Blue

75 Sailors paying respect to "Le Petit Bonhomme Andriou" (rock resembling head of a man)

(Photo Harrison)

1981 (24 Feb). *Butterflies. T* **74** *and similar horiz designs. Multicoloured. P* 14.

226	8p.	Type **74**	25	25
227	12p.	Red Admiral	40	40
228	22p.	Small Tortoiseshell	65	70
229	25p.	Wall Brown	75	80
226/9		*Set of* 4	1·75	1·90

(Des C. Abbott. Litho Questa)

1981 (22 May). *Europa. Folklore. T* **75** *and similar vert design. P* 14½.

230	12p.	gold, red-brown and cinnamon	30	30
231	18p.	gold, indigo and azure	45	50

Design:—18p. Fairies and Guernsey Lily.

76 Prince Charles

77 Sark Launch

(Des C. Abbott. Litho Questa)

1981 (29 July). *Royal Wedding. T* **76** *and similar multicoloured designs. P* 14½.

232	8p.	Type **76**	20	20
		a. Horiz strip of 3. Nos. 232/4	75	75
233	8p.	Prince Charles and Lady Diana Spencer	20	20
234	8p.	Lady Diana	20	20
235	12p.	Type **76**	30	30
		a. Horiz strip of 3. Nos. 235/7	1·10	1·10
236	12p.	As No. 233	30	30
237	12p.	As No. 234	30	30
238	25p.	Royal family (49 × 32 *mm*)	75	75
232/8		*Set of* 7	2·40	2·40
MS239		104 × 127 mm. Nos. 232/8. P 14	2·60	2·60

The 8 and 12p. values were each printed together, *se-tenant*, in horizontal strips of 3 throughout the sheets.

(Des and photo Courvoisier)

1981 (25 Aug). *Inter-island Transport. T* **77** *and similar horiz designs. Multicoloured. Granite paper. P* 11½.

240	8p.	Type **77**	20	20
241	12p.	"Trislander" aeroplane	40	40
242	18p.	Hydrofoil	60	60
243	22p.	Herm catamaran	75	75
244	25p.	*Sea Trent* (coaster)	85	85
240/4		*Set of* 5	2·50	2·50

78 Rifle Shooting

79 Sir Edgar MacCulloch (founder-president) and Guille-Allès Library, St. Peter Port

(Des P. le Vasseur. Litho Questa)

1981 (17 Nov). *International Year for Disabled Persons. T* **78** *and similar horiz designs. Multicoloured. P* 14½.

245	8p.	Type **78**	20	20
246	12p.	Riding	40	40
247	22p.	Swimming	65	65
248	25p.	"Work"	70	70
245/8		*Set of* 4	1·75	1·75

(Des, recess and litho D.L.R.)

1982 (2 Feb). *Old Guernsey Prints* (2*nd series*). *Prints from sketches by T. Compton. Horiz designs as T* **60**. *P* 14 × 13½.

249	8p.	black and pale blue	20	20
250	12p.	black and pale turquoise-green	40	40
251	22p.	black and pale yellow-brown	65	65
252	25p.	black and pale rose-lilac	70	70
249/52		*Set of* 4	1·75	1·75

Designs:—8p. Jethou; 12p. Fermain Bay; 22p. The Terres; 25p. St. Peter Port.

(Des G. Drummond. Photo Courvoisier)

1982 (28 Apr). *Centenary of La Société Guernesiaise. T* **79** *and similar horiz designs. Multicoloured. Granite paper. P* 11½.

253	8p.	Type **79**	20	20
254	13p.	French invasion fleet crossing English Channel, 1066 ("History")	45	45
255	20p.	H.M.S. *Crescent*, 1793 ("History")	55	55
256	24p.	Dragonfly ("Entomology")	70	70
257	26p.	Common Snipe caught for ringing ("Ornithology")	75	75
258	29p.	Samian Bowl, 160–200 A.D. ("Archaeology")	80	80
253/8		*Set of* 6	3·25	3·25

The 13 and 20p. values also include the Europa C.E.P.T. emblem in the designs.

80 "Sea Scouts"

81 Midnight Mass

(Des W.L.G. Creative Services Ltd. Litho Questa)

1982 (13 July). *75th Anniv of Boy Scout Movement. T* **80** *and similar vert designs. Multicoloured. P* 14½ × 14.

259	8p.	Type **80**	20	25
260	13p.	"Scouts"	40	40
261	26p.	"Cub Scouts"	70	70
262	29p.	"Air Scouts"	85	85
259/62		*Set of* 4	2·00	2·00

(Des Lynette Hemmant. Photo Harrison)

1982 (12 Oct). *Christmas. T* **81** *and similar horiz designs. Multicoloured. P* 14½.

263	8p.	Type **81**	20	20
		a. Black (Queen's head, value and inscr) omitted		
264	13p.	Exchanging gifts	40	40
265	24p.	Christmas meal	70	70
266	26p.	Exchanging cards	75	75
267	29p.	Queen's Christmas message	85	85
263/7		*Set of* 5	2·60	2·60

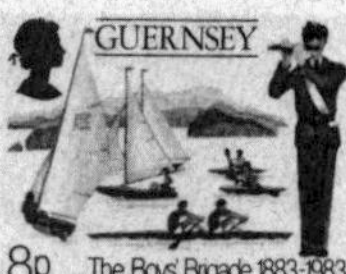

82 Flute Player and Boats

83 Building Albert Pier Extension, 1850s

(Des Sally Stiff. Photo Harrison)

1983 (18 Jan). *Centenary of Boys' Brigade. T* **82** *and similar horiz designs. Multicoloured. P* 14.

268	8p.	Type **82**	25	25
269	13p.	Cymbal player and tug 'o' war	45	45
270	24p.	Trumpet player and bible class	75	75
271	26p.	Drummer and cadets marching	85	85
272	29p.	Boys' Brigade band	95	95
268/72		*Set of* 5	3·00	3·00

(Des C. Abbott. Photo Courvoisier)

1983 (14 Mar). *Europa. Development of St. Peter Port Harbour. T* **83** *and similar horiz designs. Multicoloured. Granite paper. P* 11½.

273	13p.	Type **83**	35	35
		a. Horiz pair. Nos. 273/4	70	70
274	13p.	St. Peter Port Harbour, 1983	35	35
275	20p.	St. Peter Port, 1680	75	75
		a. Horiz pair. Nos. 275/6	1·50	1·50
276	20p.	Artist's impression of future development scheme	75	75
273/6		*Set of* 4	2·00	2·00

The two designs of each value were issued together, *se-tenant*, in horizontal pairs throughout the sheets.

84 "View at Guernsey" (Renoir)

(Des and photo Courvoisier)

1983 (6 Sept). *Centenary of Renoir's Visit to Guernsey. T* **84** *and similar multicoloured designs, showing paintings. Granite paper. P* 11 × 11½ (13*p*.) *or* 11½ (*others*).

277	9p.	Type **84**	25	25
278	13p.	"Children on the Seashore" (25 × 39 *mm*)	45	45
279	26p.	"Marine, Guernesey"	80	80
280	28p.	"La Baie du Moulin Huet à travers les Arbres"	85	85
281	31p.	"Brouillard à Guernesey"	95	95
277/81		*Set of* 5	3·00	3·00

85 Launching *Star of the West*, 1869, and Capt. J. Lenfestey

(Des R. Granger Barrett. Litho Questa)

1983 (15 Nov). *Guernsey Shipping* (1*st series*). *"Star of the West"* (*brigantine*). *T* **85** *and similar horiz designs. Multicoloured. P* 14.

282	9p.	Type **85**	25	25
283	13p.	Leaving St. Peter Port	40	40
284	26p.	Off Rio Grande Bar	80	80
285	28p.	Off St. Lucia	85	85
286	31p.	Map of 1879–80 voyage	95	95
282/6		*Set of* 5	3·00	3·00

See also Nos. 415/19.

86 Dame of Sark as Young Woman

(Des Jennifer Toombs. Litho Questa)

1984 (7 Feb). *Birth Centenary of Sibyl Hathaway, Dame of Sark. T* **86** *and similar horiz designs. Multicoloured. P* 14½.

287	9p.	Type **86**	25	25
288	13p.	German occupation, 1940–45	40	45
289	26p.	Royal Visit, 1957	80	80
290	28p.	Chief Pleas	85	85
291	31p.	The Dame of Sark rose	95	95
287/91		*Set of* 5	3·00	3·00

87 C.E.P.T. 25th Anniversary Logo

(Des J. Larrivière and C. Abbott. Litho Questa)

1984 (10 Apr). *Europa. P* 15 × 14½.

292	**87**	13p.	cobalt, dull ultramarine and black	50	50
293		20½p.	emerald, deep dull green and black	75	75

88 The Royal Court and St. George's Flag

89 St. Apolline Chapel

(Des C. Abbott. Litho Questa)

1984 (10 Apr). *Links with the Commonwealth. T* **88** *and similar horiz design. Multicoloured. P* 14 × 14½.

294	9p. Type **88**		30	30
295	31p. Castle Cornet and Union flag		1·10	1·10

(Des C. Abbott. Litho Questa

1984 (18 Sept)–**89**. *Views. T* **89** *and similar multicoloured designs. P* 14½.

296	1p. Little Chapel (23.7.85)		10	10
297	2p. Fort Grey (*horiz*) (23.7.85)		10	10
	a. Booklet pane. Nos. 297 × 2, 299 × 4, 300 × 2 and 305 × 2 (2.12.85)		1·60	
298	3p. Type **89**		10	10
	a. Booklet pane. Nos. 298, 299 × 2, 306 × 4 and 309 × 3 (30.3.87)		1·75	
299	4p. Petit Port (*horiz*)		10	10
	a. Booklet pane. Nos. 299 × 2, 304 × 3 and 307 × 5		4·00	
	b. Booklet pane. Nos. 299, 304 and 307, each × 5		4·50	
	c. Booklet pane. Nos. 299 × 4, 306*b* × 3 and 309*a* × 3 (28.3.88)		1·75	
	d. Booklet pane. Nos. 299, 301, 306*b* × 3 and 309*b* × 3 (28.2.89)		1·75	
300	5p. Little Russel (*horiz*) (23.7.85)		10	10
301	6p. The Harbour, Herm (*horiz*) (23.7.85)		10	10
	a. Booklet pane. Nos. 301 × 4, 308 × 4 and 310 × 2 (27.12.89)		2·10	
302	7p. Saints (*horiz*) (23.7.85)		10	15
303	8p. St. Saviour (23.7.85)		15	20
304	9p. New jetty (inscr "Cambridge Berth") (*horiz*)		15	20
	a. Booklet pane. Nos. 304 × 4 and 308 × 6 (19.3.85)		3·50	
	b. Booklet pane. Nos. 304 × 2 and 308 × 8 (19.3.85)		4·00	
305	10p. Belvoir, Herm (*horiz*)		20	25
	a. Booklet pane. Nos. 305 and 308, each × 5 (1.4.86)		2·10	
306	11p. La Seigneurie, Sark (*horiz*) (23.7.85)		20	25
	a. Booklet pane. Nos. 306 and 309, each × 5 (30.3.87)		2·25	
306*b*	12p. Petit Bot (28.3.88)		20	25
	ba. Booklet pane. Nos. 306*b* and 309*a*, each × 5		2·50	
	bb. Booklet pane. Nos. 306*b* and 309*b*, each × 4 (28.2.89)		2·10	
307	13p. St. Saviours reservoir (*horiz*)		25	30
308	14p. St. Peter Port		25	30
	a. Booklet pane. Nos. 308 and 310, each × 5 (27.12.89)		3·00	
309	15p. Havelet (23.7.85)		25	30
309*a*	16p. Hostel of St. John (*horiz*) (28.3.88)		30	35
309*b*	18p. Le Variouf (28.2.89)		30	35
310	20p. La Coupee, Sark (*horiz*)		35	40
311	30p. Grandes Rocques (*horiz*) (23.7.85)		50	55
312	40p. Torteval church		70	75
313	50p. Bordeaux (*horiz*)		90	95
314	£1 Albecq (*horiz*)		1·75	1·90
315	£2 L'Ancresse (*horiz*) (23.7.85)		3·50	3·75
296/315		*Set of* 23	9·25	10·00

Booklet panes Nos. 297a, 298a, 299a/c, 304a/b, 305a, 306a and 306ba have margins all round and were issued, folded and loose, within the booklet covers.

Booklet panes Nos. 299d, 301a, 306bb and 308a have the outer edges imperforate on three sides and were also issued loose within the booklet covers.

For 11p., 12p., 15p. and 16p. stamps in a smaller size see Nos. 398/9*a*.

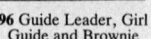

90 "A Partridge in a Pear Tree' **91** Sir John Doyle and Coat of Arms

(Des R. Downer. Litho Questa)

1984 (20 Nov). *Christmas. "The Twelve Days of Christmas". T* **90** *and similar vert designs. Multicoloured. P* 14½.

316	5p. Type **90**		20	20
	a. Sheetlet of 12. Nos. 316/27		2·25	
317	5p. "Two turtle doves"		20	20
318	5p. "Three French hens"		20	20
319	5p. "Four colly birds"		20	20
320	5p. "Five gold rings"		20	20
321	5p. "Six geese a-laying"		20	20
322	5p. "Seven swans a-swimming"		20	20
323	5p. "Eight maids a-milking"		20	20
324	5p. "Nine drummers drumming"		20	20
325	5p. "Ten pipers piping"		20	20
326	5p. "Eleven ladies dancing"		20	20
327	5p. "Twelve lords a-leaping"		20	20
316/27		*Set of* 12	2·25	2·25

Nos. 316/27 were printed, *se-tenant*, in sheetlets of 12.

(Des E. Stemp. Photo Courvoisier)

1984 (20 Nov). *150th Death Anniv of Lieut-General Sir John Doyle. T* **91** *and similar multicoloured designs. Granite paper. P* 11½.

328	13p. Type **91**		40	40
329	29p. Battle of Germantown, 1777 (*horiz*)		90	90
330	31p. Reclamation of Braye du Valle, 1806 (*horiz*)		1·00	1·00
331	34p. Mail for Alderney, 1812 (*horiz*)		1·10	1·10
328/31		*Set of* 4	3·00	3·00

NEW INFORMATION

The editor is always interested to correspond with people who have new information that will improve or correct the Catalogue.

92 Cuckoo Wrasse **93** Dove

(Des P. Barrett. Photo Courvoisier)

1985 (22 Jan). *Fishes. T* **92** *and similar horiz designs. Multicoloured. Granite paper. P* 11½.

332	9p. Type **92**		40	40
333	13p. Red Gurnard		60	60
334	29p. Red Mullet		1·10	1·10
335	31p. Mackerel		1·10	1·10
336	34p. Sunfish		1·25	1·25
332/6		*Set of* 5	4·00	4·00

(Des C. Abbott. Litho Questa)

1985 (9 May). *40th Anniv of Peace in Europe. P* 14 × 14½.

337 **93**	22p. multicoloured		1·00	1·00

94 I.Y.Y. Emblem and Young People of Different Races **95** Stave of Music enclosing Flags

(Des Suzanne Brehaut (9p.), Mary Harrison (31p.). Litho Questa)

1985 (14 May). *International Youth Year. T* **94** *and similar square design. Multicoloured. P* 14.

338	9p. Type **94**		40	40
339	31p. Girl Guides cooking over campfire		1·00	1·00

(Des Fiona Sloan (14p.), Katie Lillington (22p.). Litho Questa)

1985 (14 May). *Europa. European Music Year. T* **95** *and similar horiz design. Multicoloured. P* 14 × 14½.

340	14p. Type **95**		45	40
341	22p. Stave of music and musical instruments		85	80

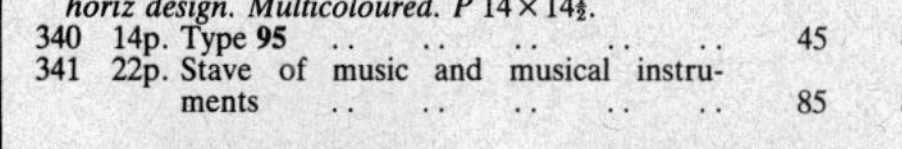

96 Guide Leader, Girl Guide and Brownie **97** Santa Claus

(Des Karon Mahy. Litho Questa)

1985 (14 May). *75th Anniv of Girl Guide Movement. P* 14.

342 **96**	34p. multicoloured		1·25	1·25

(Des C. Abbott. Photo Courvoisier)

1985 (19 Nov). *Christmas. Gift-bearers. T* **97** *and similar vert designs. Multicoloured. Granite paper. P* 12½.

343	5p. Type **97**		20	20
	a. Sheetlet of 12. Nos. 343/54		2·25	
344	5p. Lussibruden (Sweden)		20	20
345	5p. King Balthazar		20	20
346	5p. Saint Nicholas (Netherlands)		20	20
347	5p. La Befana (Italy)		20	20
348	5p. Julenisse (Denmark)		20	20
349	5p. Christkind (Germany)		20	20
350	5p. King Wenceslas (Czechoslovakia)		20	20
351	5p. Shepherd of Les Baux (France)		20	20
352	5p. King Caspar		20	20
353	5p. Baboushka (Russia)		20	20
354	5p. King Melchior		20	20
343/54		*Set of* 12	2·25	2·25

Nos. 343/54 were printed, *se-tenant*, in sheetlets of 12.

98 "Vraicing"

(Des and photo Harrison)

1985 (19 Nov). *Paintings by Paul Jacob Naftel. T* **98** *and similar horiz designs. Multicoloured. P* 15 × 14.

355	9p. Type **98**		25	25
356	14p. "Castle Cornet"		45	45
357	22p. "Rocquaine Bay"		75	75
358	31p. "Little Russel"		1·00	1·00
359	34p. "Seaweedgatherers"		1·10	1·10
355/9		*Set of* 5	3·25	3·25

99 Squadron off Nargue Island, 1809 **100** Profile of Queen Elizabeth II (after R. Maklouf)

(Des T. Thompson. Photo Courvoisier)

1986 (4 Feb). *150th Death Anniv of Admiral Lord De Saumarez. T* **99** *and similar horiz designs. Multicoloured. Granite paper. P* 11½.

360	9p. Type **99**		40	40
361	14p. Battle of the Nile, 1798		60	60
362	29p. Battle of St. Vincent, 1797		1·10	1·10
363	31p. H.M.S. *Crescent* off Cherbourg, 1793		1·10	1·10
364	34p. Battle of the Saints, 1782		1·25	1·25
360/4		*Set of* 5	4·00	4·00

(Des C. Abbott. Litho Questa)

1986 (21 Apr). *60th Birthday of Queen Elizabeth II. P* 14.

365 **100**	60p. multicoloured		2·00	2·00

101 Northern Gannet and Nylon Net ("Operation Gannet") **102** Prince Andrew and Miss Sarah Ferguson

(Des P. Newcombe. Photo Courvoisier)

1986 (22 May). *Europa. Nature and Environmental Protection. T* **101** *and similar vert designs. Multicoloured. Granite paper. P* 11½.

366	10p. Type **101**		35	35
367	14p. Loose-flowered Orchid		50	50
368	22p. Guernsey Elm		70	70
366/8		*Set of* 3	1·40	1·40

(Des C. Abbott. Litho Questa)

1986 (23 July). *Royal Wedding. T* **102** *and similar multicoloured design. P* 14 (14*p*.) *or* 13½ × 14 (34*p*.).

369	14p. Type **102**		55	55
370	34p. Prince Andrew and Miss Sarah Ferguson (*different*) (47 × 30 *mm*)		1·25	1·25

103 Bowls **104** Guernsey Museum and Art Gallery Candie Gardens

(Des R. Goldsmith. Litho Questa)

1986 (24 July). *Sport in Guernsey. T* **103** *and similar multicoloured designs. P* 14½.

371	10p. Type **103**		30	30
372	14p. Cricket		45	45
373	22p. Squash		65	65
374	29p. Hockey		90	90
375	31p. Swimming (*horiz*)		1·00	1·00
376	34p. Rifle-shooting (*horiz*)		1·10	1·10
371/6		*Set of* 6	4·00	4·00

(Des Sir Hugh Casson. Litho Questa)

1986 (18 Nov). *Centenary of Guernsey Museums. T* **104** *and similar horiz designs. Multicoloured. P* 14½.

377	14p. Type **104**		45	45
378	29p. Fort Grey Maritime Museum		1·00	90
379	31p. Castle Cornet		1·00	1·00
380	34p. National Trust of Guernsey Folk Museum		1·25	1·10
377/80		*Set of* 4	3·25	3·00

105 "While Shepherds Watched their Flocks by Night"

(Des Wendy Bramall. Photo Courvoisier)

986 (18 Nov). *Christmas. Carols. T* **105** *and similar vert designs. Multicoloured. Granite paper. P* 12½.

81 6p. Type **105** 20 20
a. Sheetlet of 12. Nos. 381/92 .. .. 2·00
82 6p. "In The Bleak Mid-Winter" 20 20
83 6p. "O Little Town of Bethlehem" 20 20
84 6p. "The Holly and the Ivy" 20 20
85 6p. "O Little Christmas Tree" 20 20
86 6p. "Away in a Manger" 20 20
87 6p. "Good King Wenceslas" 20 20
88 6p. "We Three Kings of Orient Are" .. 20 20
89 6p. "Hark the Herald Angels Sing" 20 20
90 6p. "I Saw Three Ships" 20 20
91 6p. "Little Donkey" 20 20
92 6p. "Jingle Bells" 20 20
81/92 .. .. *Set of* 12 2·00 2·00

Nos. 381/92 were printed, *se-tenant*, in sheetlets of 12.

106 Duke of Richmond and Portion of Map

(Des J. Cooter. Litho Questa)

987 (10 Feb). *Bicentenary of Duke of Richmond's Survey of Guernsey. Sheet* 134 × 103 *mm containing T* **106** *and similar horiz designs showing sections of map. Multicoloured. P* 14½ × 14.

MS393 14p. Type **106**; 29p. North-east; 31p. South-west; 34p. South-east .. .. 3·00 3·00

The stamps within No. **MS**393 show a composite design of the Duke of Richmond's map of Guernsey.

107 Post Office Headquarters **108** Sir Edmund Andros and La Plaiderie, Guernsey

(Des R. Reed. Litho Cartor, France)

1987 (5 Mar). *Europa. Modern Architecture. T* **107** *and similar vert designs. Multicoloured. P* 13 × 13½.

394 15p. Type **107** 40 45
a. Horiz pair. Nos. 394/5 .. .. .. 90 1·00
395 15p. Architect's elevation of Post Office Headquarters 40 45
396 22p. Guernsey Grammar School 70 75
a. Horiz pair. Nos. 396/7 .. .. .. 1·50 1·60
397 22p. Architect's elevation of Grammar School 70 75
394/7 .. .. *Set of* 4 2·25 2·40

Nos. 394/5 and 396/7 were each printed together, *se-tenant*, in horizontal pairs throughout the sheets.

(Photo Harrison)

1987 (15 May)–**88**. *Coil Stamps. Designs as Nos.* 306, 306*b and* 309/*a*, *but smaller. P* 14 × 14½ (11*p*., 16*p*.) *or* 14½ × 14 (12*p*., 15*p*.).

398 11p. La Seigneurie, Sark (22 × 18 *mm*) .. 20 25
398*a* 12p. Petit Bot (18 × 22 *mm*) (28.3.88) .. 20 25
399 15p. Havelet (18 × 22 *mm*) 25 30
399*a* 16p. Hospital of St. John (22 × 18 *mm*) (28.3.88) 30 35
398/9*a* .. .. *Set of* 4 85 1·00

(Des B. Sanders. Photo Courvoisier)

1987 (7 July). 350*th Birth Anniv of Sir Edmund Andros* (*colonial administrator*). *T* **108** *and similar horiz designs, each showing portrait. Multicoloured. Granite paper. P* 12.

400 15p. Type **108** 45 45
401 29p. Governor's Palace, Virginia 80 80
402 31p. Governor Andros in Boston .. .. 1·00 1·00
403 34p. Map of New Amsterdam (New York), 1661 .. .. 1·10 1·10
400/3 .. .. *Set of* 4 3·00 3·00

109 The Jester's Warning to Young William **110** John Wesley preaching on the Quay, Alderney

(Des P. le Vasseur. Litho Cartor, France)

1987 (9 Sept). 900*th Death Anniv of William the Conqueror. T* **109** *and similar vert designs. Multicoloured. P* 13½ × 14.

404 11p. Type **109** 35 35
405 15p. Hastings battlefield 40 40
a. Horiz pair. Nos. 405/6 .. .. .. 85 85
406 15p. Norman soldier with pennant 40 40
407 22p. William the Conqueror 70 70
a. Horiz pair. Nos. 407/8 .. .. .. 1·50 1·50
408 22p. Queen Matilda and Abbaye aux Dames, Caen 70 70
409 34p. William's Coronation regalia and Halley's Comet .. .. 1·10 1·10
404/9 .. .. *Set of* 6 3·50 3·50

Nos. 405/6 and 407/8 were each printed together, *se-tenant*, in horizontal pairs throughout the sheets.

(Des R. Geary. Litho Questa)

1987 (17 Nov). *Bicentenary of John Wesley's Visit to Guernsey. T* **110** *and similar horiz designs. Multicoloured. P* 14½.

410 7p. Type **110** 20 20
411 15p. Wesley preaching at Mon Plaisir, St. Peter Port 35 35
412 29p. Preaching at Assembly Rooms 90 90
413 31p. Wesley and La Ville Baudu (early Methodist meeting place) .. .. 1·00 1·00
414 34p. Wesley and first Methodist Chapel, St. Peter Port .. .. 1·10 1·10
410/14 .. .. *Set of* 5 3·50 3·50

111 *Golden Spur* off St. Sampson Harbour

(Des R. Granger Barrett. Litho B.D.T.)

1988 (9 Feb). *Guernsey Shipping* (2*nd series*). *"Golden Spur"* (*full-rigged ship*). *T* **111** *and similar horiz designs. Multicoloured. P* 13½.

415 11p. Type **111** 25 25
416 15p. *Golden Spur* entering Hong Kong harbour 35 35
417 29p. Anchored off Macao 90 90
418 31p. In China Tea Race 95 95
419 34p. *Golden Spur* and map showing voyage of 1872–74 .. .. 1·10 1·10
415/19 .. .. *Set of* 5 3·50 3·50

112 Rowing Boat and Bedford "Rascal" Mail Van **113** Frederick Corbin Lukis and Lukis House, St. Peter Port

(Des C. Abbott. Litho Questa)

1988 (10 May). *Europa. Transport and Communications. T* **112** *and similar horiz designs. Multicoloured. P* 14½.

420 16p. Type **112** 35 35
a. Horiz pair. Nos. 420/1 .. .. .. 75 75
421 16p. Rowing boat and "Viscount" mail plane .. 35 35
422 22p. Postman on bicycle and horse-drawn carriages, Sark 65 65
a. Horiz pair. Nos. 422/3 .. .. .. 1·40 1·40
423 22p. Postmen on bicycles and carriage .. 65 65
420/3 .. .. *Set of* 4 2·00 2·00

Nos. 420/1 and 422/3 were each printed together, *se-tenant*, in horizontal pairs throughout the sheets, the two stamps of each value forming a composite design.

(Des Wendy Bramall. Photo Courvoisier)

1988 (12 July). *Birth Bicentenary of Frederick Corbin Lukis* (*archaeologist*). *T* **113** *and similar horiz designs. Multicoloured. Granite paper. P* 12½.

424 12p. Type **113** 40 40
425 16p. Natural history books and reconstructed pot 50 50
426 29p. Lukis directing excavation of Le Creux ès Faies and prehistoric beaker 90 90
427 31p. Lukis House Observatory and garden .. 90 90
428 34p. Prehistoric artifacts .. .. .. 1·10 1·10
424/8 .. .. *Set of* 5 3·50 3·50

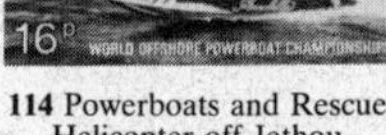

114 Powerboats and Rescue Helicopter off Jethou **115** Joshua Gosselin and Herbarium

(Des and photo Courvoisier)

1988 (6 Sept). *World Offshore Powerboat Championships. T* **114** *and similar multicoloured designs. Granite paper. P* 12.

429 16p. Type **114** 50 50
430 30p. Powerboats in Gouliot Passage 90 90
431 32p. Start of race at St. Peter Port (*vert*) .. 95 95
432 35p. Admiralty chart showing course (*vert*) .. 1·25 1·25
429/32 .. .. *Set of* 4 3·25 3·25

(Des M. Oxenham. Litho Cartor, France)

1988 (15 Nov). *Bicentenary of Joshua Gosselin's* Flora Sarniensis. *T* **115** *and similar vert designs. Multicoloured. P* 13½ × 14.

433 12p. Type **115** 40 40
434 16p. Hares-tail Grass 45 45
a. Horiz pair. Nos. 434/5 .. .. .. 95 95
435 16p. Dried Hares-tail Grass 45 45
436 23p. Variegated Catchfly 70 70
a. Horiz pair. Nos. 436/7 .. .. .. 1·40 1·40
437 23p. Dried Variegated Catchfly 70 70
438 35p. Rock Sea Lavender .. .. .. 1·10 1·10
433/8 .. .. *Set of* 6 3·50 3·50

Nos. 434/5 and 436/7 were each printed together, *se-tenant*, in horizontal pairs throughout the sheets.

116 Coutances Cathedral, France **117** Lé Cat (Tip Cat)

(Des R. Downer. Litho Questa)

1988 (15 Nov). *Christmas. Ecclesiastical Links. T* **116** *and similar vert designs. Multicoloured. P* 14½.

439 8p. Type **116** 20 20
a. Sheetlet of 12. Nos. 439/50 .. .. 2·75
440 8p. Interior of Notre Dame du Rosaire Church, Guernsey 20 20
441 8p. Stained glass, St. Sampson's Church, Guernsey 20 20
442 8p. Dol-de-Bretagne Cathedral, France .. 20 20
443 8p. Bishop's throne, Town Church, Guernsey 20 20
444 8p. Winchester Cathedral 20 20
445 8p. St. John's Cathedral, Portsmouth .. 20 20
446 8p. High altar, St. Joseph's Church, Guernsey 20 20
447 8p. Mont Saint-Michel, France 20 20
448 8p. Chancel, Vale Church, Guernsey .. 20 20
449 8p. Lychgate, Forest Church, Guernsey .. 20 20
450 8p. Marmoutier Abbey, France 20 20
439/50 .. .. *Set of* 12 2·75 2·75

Nos. 439/50 were printed, *se-tenant*, in sheetlets of 12.

(Des P. le Vasseur. Litho Cartor, France)

1989 (28 Feb). *Europa. Children's Toys and Games. T* **117** *and similar horiz designs. Multicoloured. P* 13½.

451 12p. Type **117** 30 30
452 16p. Girl with Cobo Alice doll 40 40
453 23p. Lé Colimachaön (hopscotch) 70 70
451/3 .. .. *Set of* 3 1·25 1·25

118 Outline Map of Guernsey **119** Guernsey Airways DH86 "Express" and Mail Van

(Photo Harrison)

1989 (3 Apr–27 Dec). *Coil Stamps. No value expressed. P* 14½ × 14.

454 **118** (–) ultramarine (27.12.89) 25 30
455 (–) emerald 30 35

No. 454 is inscribed "MINIMUM BAILIWICK POSTAGE PAID" and No. 455 "MINIMUM FIRST CLASS POSTAGE TO UK PAID". They were initially sold at 14p. and 18p., but it is intended that this will change in line with future postage rate rises.

(Des N. Foggo. Litho B.D.T.)

1989 (5 May). 50*th Annivs of Guernsey Airport* (*Nos.* 456, 458, *and* 460) *and* 201 *Squadron's Affiliation with Guernsey* (*Nos.* 457, 459 *and* 461). *T* **119** *and similar horiz designs. Multicoloured. P* 13½.

456 12p. Type **119** 30 30
a. Booklet pane. No. 456 × 6 .. .. 1·50
457 12p. Supermarine "Southampton" flying boat at mooring 30 30
458 18p. B.E.A. DH89 "Rapide" 45 45
a. Booklet pane. No. 458 × 6 .. .. 2·75
459 18p. Sunderland "Mk V" flying boat taking off 45 45
460 35p. Air U.K. BAe "146" 90 90
a. Booklet pane. No. 460 × 6 .. .. 5·50
461 35p. Shackleton "Mk 3" 90 90
456/61 .. .. *Set of* 6 3·00 3·00

Each booklet pane has margins all round with text printed at the foot.

120 "Queen Elizabeth II" (June Mendoza)

121 *Ibex* at G.W.R. Terminal, St. Peter Port

(Des A. Theobald. Litho B.D.T.)

1989 (23 May). *Royal Visit. P* 15 × 14.

462	**120**	30p. multicoloured	80	80

(Des C. Jaques. Litho B.D.T.)

1989 (5 Sept). *Centenary of Great Western Railway Steamer Service to Channel Islands. T* **121** *and similar horiz designs. Multicoloured. P* 13½.

463	12p. Type **121**	25	30
464	18p. *Great Western* (paddle-steamer) in Little Russel	35	40
465	29p. *St. Julien* passing Casquets Light ..	60	65
466	34p. *Roebuck* off Portland	70	75
467	37p. *Antelope* and boat train at Weymouth quay	75	80
463/7	.. .. *Set of* 5	2·40	2·50
MS468	115×117 mm. Nos. 463/7	2·50	2·75

122 Two-toed Sloth

123 Star

(Des Anne Farncombe. Litho Cartor, France)

1989 (17 Nov). *10th Anniv of Guernsey Zoological Trust. Animals of the Rainforest. T* **122** *and similar vert designs. Multicoloured. P* 13½×14.

469	18p. Type **122**	35	40
	a. Horiz strip of 5. Nos. 469/73 ..	2·75	
470	29p. Capuchin Monkey	60	65
471	32p. White-lipped Tamarin	65	70
472	34p. Common Squirrel-Monkey	70	75
473	37p. Common Gibbon	75	80
469/73	.. .. .. *Set of* 5	2·75	3·00

Nos. 469/73 were printed together, *se-tenant*, in horizontal strips of five throughout the sheet.

(Des Wendy Bramall. Litho B.D.T.)

1989 (17 Nov). *Christmas. Christmas Tree Decorations. T* **123** *and similar square designs. Multicoloured. P* 13.

474	10p. Type **123**	20	25
	a. Sheetlet. Nos. 474/85	2·25	
475	10p. Fairy	20	25
476	10p. Candles	20	25
477	10p. Bird	20	25
478	10p. Present	20	25
479	10p. Carol-singer	20	25
480	10p. Christmas cracker	20	25
481	10p. Bauble	20	25
482	10p. Christmas stocking	20	25
483	10p. Bell	20	25
484	10p. Fawn	20	25
485	10p. Church	20	25
474/85	.. .. .. *Set of* 12	2·25	2·75

Nos. 474/85 were printed, *se-tenant*, in sheetlets of 12.

124 Sark Post Office, *c.* 1890

(Des C. Abbott. Litho Enschedé)

1990 (27 Feb). *Europa. Post Office Buildings. T* **124** *and similar horiz designs. P* 13½×14.

486	20p. blackish brown, sepia and pale cinnamon	40	45
487	20p. multicoloured	40	45
488	24p. blackish brown, sepia and pale cinnamon	50	55
489	24p. multicoloured	50	55
486/9	.. .. .. *Set of* 4	1·60	1·75

Designs:—No. 487, Sark Post Office, 1990; 488, Arcade Post Office counter, St. Peter Port, *c.* 1840; 489, Arcade Post Office counter, St. Peter Port, 1990.

125 Penny Black and Mail Steamer off St. Peter Port, 1840

(Des Jennifer Toombs. Litho Questa)

1990 (3 May). *150th Anniv of the Penny Black. T* **125** *and similar horiz designs. Multicoloured. P* 14.

490	14p. Type **125**	30	35
491	20p. Penny Red, 1841, and pillar box of 1853	40	45
492	32p. Bisected 2d., 1940, and German Army band	65	70
493	34p. Regional 3d., 1958, and Guernsey emblems	70	75
494	37p. Independent postal administration 1½d., 1969, and queue outside Main Post Office	75	80
490/4	.. .. .. *Set of* 5	2·50	2·75
MS495	151×116 mm. Nos. 490/4	2·75	3·00

No. **MS**495 also commemorates "Stamp World London 90" International Stamp Exhibition.

POSTAGE DUE STAMPS

D 1 Castle Cornet

D 2 St. Peter Port

(Des R. Granger Barrett. Photo Delrieu)

969 (1 Oct). *Value in black; background colour given. No wmk. P* 12½ × 12.

1	D 1	1d. plum	2·50	1·25
2		2d. bright green	2·50	1·25
3		3d. vermilion	4·00	4·00
4		4d. ultramarine	5·00	5·00
5		5d. yellow-ochre	6·00	6·00
6		6d. turquoise-blue	9·00	8·00
7		1s. lake-brown	21·00	20·00
1/7		*Set of* 7	45·00	40·00

971 (15 Feb)–**76.** *As Type* **D 1** *but values in decimal currency.*

8	D 1	½p. plum	10	10
9		1p. bright green	10	10
10		2p. vermilion	10	10
11		3p. ultramarine	10	15
12		4p. yellow-ochre	15	15
13		5p. turquoise-blue	15	15
14		6p. violet (10.2.76)	20	20
15		8p. light yellow-orange (7.10.75)	25	20
16		10p. lake-brown	30	30
17		15p. grey (10.2.76)	40	40
8/17		*Set of* 10	1·50	1·60

(Photo Delrieu)

977 (2 Aug)–**80.** *Face value in black; background colour given. P* 13.

18	D 2	½p. lake-brown	10	10
19		1p. bright purple	10	10
20		2p. bright orange	10	10
21		3p. vermilion	10	10
22		4p. turquoise-blue	15	15
23		5p. yellow-green	15	15
24		6p. turquoise-green	20	20
25		8p. brown-ochre	25	25
26		10p. ultramarine	30	30
27		14p. green (5.2.80)	35	35
28		15p. bright violet	35	35
29		16p. rose-red (5.2.80)	45	45
18/29		*Set of* 12	2·10	2·10

D 3 Milking Cow

(Litho Questa)

982 (13 July). *Guernsey Scenes, circa* 1900. *Horiz designs as Type* D 3. *P* 14½.

30	1p. indigo, blue-black and bright green	10	10
31	2p. sepia, yellow-brown and azure	10	10
32	3p. blackish green, black and lilac	10	10
33	4p. bottle-green, black and dull orange	10	10
34	5p. dp violet-blue, blue-black & turq-grn	10	10
35	16p. deep grey-blue, deep blue and cobalt	30	35
36	18p. steel-blue, indigo and apple-green	30	35
37	20p. brown-olive, agate and pale blue	35	40
38	25p. Prussian blue, blue-black and rose-pink	45	50
39	30p. dp bluish grn, blackish ol & bistre-yell	50	55
40	50p. olive-brown, sepia and dull violet-blue	90	95
41	£1 light brown, brown and pale brown	1·75	1·90
30/41	*Set of* 12	4·25	4·75

Designs:—2p. Vale Mill; 3p. Sark cottage; 4p. Quay-side, St. Peter Port; 5p. Well, Water Lane, Moulin Huet; 16p. Seaweed gathering; 8p. Upper Walk, White Rock; 20p. Cobo Bay; 25p. Saint's Bay; 0p. La Coupee, Sark; 50p. Old Harbour, St. Peter Port; £1 Greenhouses, Doyle Road, St. Peter Port.

ALDERNEY

The following issues are provided by the Guernsey Post Office for use on Alderney. They are also valid for postal purposes throughout the rest of the Bailiwick of Guernsey.

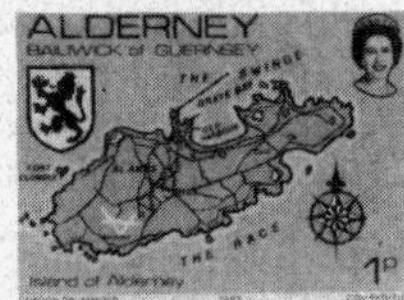

A 1 Island Map

(Des G. Drummond. Litho B.D.T. (20p.). Photo Courvoisier (others))

983 (14 June)–**89.** *Island Scenes. Type* A **1** *and similar horiz designs. Multicoloured. Granite paper* (*Nos.* A1/12). *P* 15×14 (20p.) *or* 11½ (*others*).

A 1	1p. Type **A 1**	10	10
A 2	4p. Hanging Rock	10	10
A 3	9p. States' Building, St. Anne	15	20
A 4	10p. St. Anne's Church	20	25
A 5	11p. Yachts in Braye Bay	20	25
A 6	12p. Victoria St., St. Anne	20	25
A 7	13p. Map of Channel	25	30
A 8	14p. Fort Clonque	25	30
A 9	15p. Corblets Bay and Fort	25	30
A10	16p. Old Tower, St. Anne	30	35
A11	17p. Golf course and Essex Castle	30	35
A12	18p. Old Harbour	30	35
A12*a*	20p. Quesnard Lighthouse (38 × 27 *mm*) (27.12.89)	35	40
A1/12*a*	*Set of* 13	2·50	3·00

A2 Oystercatcher

(Des and photo Harrison)

1984 (12 June). *Birds. Type* **A2** *and similar horiz designs. Multicoloured. P* 14½.

A13	9p. Type **A2**	2·00	1·75
A14	13p. Turnstone	2·75	2·50
A15	26p. Ringed Plover	8·00	5·00
A16	28p. Dunlin	8·50	5·50
A17	31p. Curlew	10·00	6·00
A13/17	*Set of* 5	28·00	18·00

A 3 Wessex Helicopter of the Queen's Flight

A 4 Royal Engineers, 1890

(Des A. Theobald. Photo Courvoisier)

1985 (19 Mar). *50th Anniv of Alderney Airport. Type* **A 3** *and similar horiz designs. Multicoloured. Granite paper. P* 11½.

A18	9p. Type A **3**	3·50	2·50
A19	13p. Britten-Norman "Trislander"	4·00	3·50
A20	29p. De Havilland "Heron"	8·00	4·75
A21	31p. De Havilland "Dragon Rapide"	8·50	8·50
A22	34p. Saro "Windhover"	9·50	6·00
	Set of 5	30·00	20·00

(Des E. Stemp. Litho Harrison)

1985 (24 Sept). *Regiments of the Alderney Garrison. Type* **A 4** *and similar vert designs. Multicoloured. P* 14½.

A23	9p. Type A **4**	1·25	75
A24	14p. Duke of Albany's Own Highlanders (72nd Highland Regt), 1856	2·00	1·25
A25	29p. Royal Artillery, 1855	2·75	2·50
A26	31p. South Hampshire Regiment, 1810	3·50	3·00
A27	34p. Royal Irish Regiment, 1782	4·00	3·50
A23/7	*Set of* 5	12·00	10·00

No. A24 shows the tartan and insignia of the 78th Highland Regiment in error.

A **5** Fort Grosnez

A **6** *Liverpool* (full-rigged ship) 1902

(Des R. Reed. Litho Cartor, France)

1986 (23 Sept). *Alderney Forts. Type* A **5** *and similar vert designs. Multicoloured. P* 13 × 13½.

A28	10p. Type A **5**	75	75
A29	14p. Fort Tourgis	1·25	1·25
A30	31p. Fort Clonque	2·75	2·75
A31	34p. Fort Albert	3·00	3·00
A28/31	*Set of* 4	7·00	7·00

(Des C. Jaques. Litho Questa)

1987 (5 May). *Alderney Shipwrecks. Type* A **6** *and similar horiz designs. Multicoloured. P* 14 × 14½.

A32	11p. Type A **6**	1·50	1·00
A33	15p. *Petit Raymond* (schooner), 1906	2·25	1·25
A34	29p. *Maina* (yacht), 1910	3·75	3·50
A35	31p. *Burton* (steamer), 1911	4·50	4·00
A36	34p. *Point Law* (oil tanker), 1975	5·25	4·75
A32/6	*Set of* 5	16·00	13·00

MINIMUM PRICE

The minimum price quote is 10p which represents a handling charge rather than a basis for valuing common stamps. For further notes about prices see introductory pages.

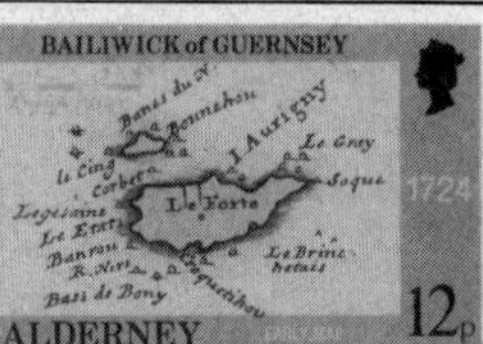

A 7 Moll's Map of 1724

(Des J. Cooter. Litho Enschedé)

1989 (7 July). *250th Anniv of Bastide's Survey of Alderney. Type* A **7** *and similar horiz designs. P* 13½×14.

A37	12p. multicoloured	35	35
A38	18p. black, greenish blue and orange-brown	45	45
A39	27p. black, greenish blue & dull yellow-green	75	75
A40	32p. black, greenish blue and bright rose-red	85	85
A41	35p. multicoloured	95	95
A37/41	*Set of* 5	3·00	3·00

Designs:—18p. Bastide's survey of 1739; 27p. Goodwin's map of 1831; 32p. General Staff map of 1943; 35p. Ordnance Survey map, 1988.

A **8** H.M.S. *Alderney* (bomb ketch), 1738

(Des A. Theobald. Litho B.D.T.)

1990 (3 May). *Royal Navy Ships named after Alderney. Type* A **8** *and similar horiz designs. P* 13½.

A42	14p. black and olive-bistre	30	35
A43	20p. black and orange-brown	40	45
A44	29p. black and cinnamon	60	65
A45	34p. black and pale turquoise-blue	70	75
A46	37p. black and cobalt	75	80
A42/6	*Set of* 5	2·50	2·75

Designs:—20p. H.M.S. *Alderney* (sixth rate), 1742; 29p. H.M.S. *Alderney* (sloop), 1755; 34p. H.M.S. *Alderney* (submarine), 1945; 37p. H.M.S. *Alderney* (fishery protection vessel), 1979.

ISLE OF MAN

REGIONAL ISSUES

Although specifically issued for use in the Isle of Man, these issues were also valid for use throughout Great Britain.

DATES OF ISSUE: The note at the beginning of Guernsey also applies here.

Nos. 8/11 and current stamps of Great Britain were withdrawn from sale on the island from 5 July 1973 when the independent postal administration was established but remained valid for use there for a time. They also remained on sale at the Philatelic Sales counters in the United Kingdom until 4 July 1974.

1

2

3

(Des J. Nicholson. Portrait by Dorothy Wilding Ltd. Photo Harrison)

1958 (18 Aug)–**68.** *W* **179.** *P* 15 × 14.

1	**1**	2½d. carmine-red (8.6.64)	45	80
2	**2**	3d. deep lilac	20	10
		a. Chalk-surfaced paper (17.5.63) ..	20·00	13·00
		p. One centre phosphor band (27.6.68)	20	30
3		4d. ultramarine (7.2.66)	1·50	1·10
		p. Two phosphor bands (5.7.67) ..	20	15
1/3p		.. .. *Set of* 3	55	90

No. 2a was released in London sometime after 17 May 1963, this being the date of issue in Douglas.

1968–69. *No wmk. Chalk-surfaced paper. PVA gum. One centre phosphor band* (*Nos.* 5/6) *or two phosphor bands* (*others*). *P* 15 × 14.

4	**2**	4d. blue (24.6.68)	20	25
5		4d. olive-sepia (4.9.68)	20	30
6		4d. bright vermilion (26.2.69)	45	60
7		5d. royal blue (4.9.68)	45	60
4/7		.. .. *Set of* 4	1·00	1·60

(Des J. Matthews. Portrait after plaster cast by Arnold Machin. Photo Harrison)

1971 (7 July). *Decimal Currency. Chalk-surfaced paper. One centre phosphor band* (2½*p.*) *or two phosphor bands* (*others*). *P* 15 × 14.

8	**3**	2½p. bright magenta	20	15
9		3p. ultramarine	20	15
10		5p. reddish violet	70	75
11		7½p. chestnut	70	90
8/11		.. .. *Set of* 4	1·50	1·60

All values exist with PVA gum on ordinary cream paper and the 2½p. and 3p. also on fluorescent white paper.

INDEPENDENT POSTAL ADMINISTRATION

4 Castletown

5 Manx Cat

(Des J. Nicholson. Photo Courvoisier)

1973 (5 July)–**75.** *Horiz designs as T* **4** (½*p. to* 9*p.*, 11*p. and* 13*p.*) *or vert designs as T* **5** (*others*). *Multicoloured. Granite paper. P* 11½.

12	½p.	Type **4**	10	10
13	1p.	Port Erin	10	10
14	1½p.	Snaefell	10	10
15	2p.	Laxey	10	10
16	2½p.	Tynwald Hill	10	10
17	3p.	Douglas Promenade	10	10
18	3½p.	Port St. Mary	15	15
19	4p.	Fairy Bridge	15	15
20	4½p.	As 2½p. (8.1.75)	20	20
21	5p.	Peel	20	20
22	5½p.	As 3p. (28.5.75)	25	25
23	6p.	Cregneish	25	25
24	7p.	As 2p. (28.5.75)	30	30
25	7½p.	Ramsey Bay	25	25
26	8p.	As 7½p. (8.1.75)	35	35
27	9p.	Douglas Bay	30	35
28	10p.	Type **5**	30	35
29	11p.	Monk's Bridge, Ballasalla (29.10.75) ..	45	50
30	13p.	Derbyhaven (29.10.75)	55	60
31	20p.	Manx Loaghtyn Ram	65	80
32	50p.	Manx Shearwater	1·60	1·90
33	£1	Viking longship	3·25	3·75
12/33		.. .. *Set of* 22	9·00	10·00

Some printings from late 1973 have invisible gum.

6 Viking landing on Man, A.D. 938

7 *Sutherland*

(Des J. Nicholson. Photo Harrison)

1973 (5 July). *Inauguration of Postal Independence. P* 14.

34	**6**	15p. multicoloured	80	80

(Des J. Nicholson. Photo Harrison)

1973 (4 Aug). *Steam Railway Centenary. T* **7** *and similar horiz designs showing steam locomotives. Multicoloured. P* 15 × 14.

35	2½p.	Type **7**	20	20
36	3p.	*Caledonia*	20	20
37	7½p.	*Kissack*	1·40	1·50
38	9p.	*Pender*	1·50	1·50
35/8		.. .. *Set of* 4	3·00	3·00

8 Leonard Randles, First Winner, 1923

(Des J. Nicholson. Litho J.W.)

1973 (4 Sept). *Golden Jubilee of the Manx Grand Prix. T* **8** *and similar horiz design. Multicoloured. P* 14.

39	3p.	Type **8**	30	20
40	3½p.	Alan Holmes, Double Winner, 1957 ..	30	20

9 Princess Anne and Capt. Mark Phillips

(Des A. Larkins. Recess and litho D.L.R.)

1973 (14 Nov). *Royal Wedding. P* 13½.

41	**9**	25p. multicoloured	1·00	90

10 Badge, Citation and Sir William Hillary (Founder)

(Des J. Nicholson. Photo Courvoisier)

1974 (4 Mar). 150*th Anniv of Royal National Lifeboat Institution. T* **10** *and similar horiz designs. Multicoloured. Granite paper. P* 11½.

42	3p.	Type **10**	10	10
43	3½p.	Wreck of *St. George*, 1830	15	15
44	8p.	R.N.L.B. *Manchester & Salford*, 1868–87	60	65
45	10p.	R.N.L.B. *Osman Gabriel*	60	65
42/5		.. .. *Set of* 4	1·25	1·40

11 Stanley Woods, 1935

(Des J. Nicholson. Litho D.L.R.)

1974 (29 May). *Tourist Trophy Motor-cycle Races* (1*st issue*). *T* **11** *and similar horiz designs. Multicoloured. P* 13 × 13½.

46	3p.	Type **11**	10	10
47	3½p.	Freddy Frith, 1937	10	10
48	8p.	Max Deubel and Emil Horner, 1961 ..	45	45
49	10p.	Mike Hailwood, 1961	55	45
46/9		.. .. *Set of* 4	1·10	1·00

See also Nos. 63/6.

12 Rushen Abbey and Arms

(Des J. Nicholson from ideas by G. Kneale. Litho Questa (3½p., 10p.) or J.W. (others))

1974 (18 Sept). *Historical Anniversaries. T* **12** *and similar horiz designs. Multicoloured. P* 14.

50	3½p.	Type **12**	10	10
51	4½p.	Magnus Haraldson rows King Edgar on the Dee	10	10
52	8p.	King Magnus and Norse fleet	40	40
53	10p.	Bridge at Avignon and bishop's mitre ..	50	50
50/3		.. .. *Set of* 4	1·00	1·00

Nos. 50 and 53 mark the 600th Death Anniv of William Russell Bishop of Sodor and Man, and Nos. 51/2 the 1000th Anniv of the rule of King Magnus Haraldson.

13 Churchill and Bugler Dunne at Colenso, 1899

(Des G. Kneale. Photo Courvoisier)

1974 (22 Nov). *Birth Centenary of Sir Winston Churchill. T* **13** *and similar horiz designs. Multicoloured. Granite paper. P* 11½.

54	3½p.	Type **13**	10	1
55	4½p.	Churchill and Government Buildings, Douglas	10	1
56	8p.	Churchill and Manx ack-ack crew ..	25	3
57	20p.	Churchill as Freeman of Douglas ..	65	5
54/7		.. .. *Set of* 4	1·00	1·0
MS58		121 × 91 mm. Nos. 54/7	90	9

No. **MS**58 is inscribed "30th Nov. 1974".

14 Cabin School and Names of Pioneers

(Des J. Nicholson. Photo Courvoisier)

1975 (14 Mar). *Manx Pioneers in Cleveland, Ohio. T* **14** *and similar horiz designs. Multicoloured. Granite paper. P* 11½.

59	4½p.	Type **14**	10	10
60	5½p.	Terminal Tower Building, J. Gill and R. Carran	15	10
61	8p.	Clague House Museum, and Robert and Margaret Clague	35	30
62	10p.	S.S. *William T. Graves* and Thomas Quayle	50	40
59/62		.. .. *Set of* 4	1·00	80

15 Tom Sheard, 1923

(Des J. Nicholson. Litho J.W.)

1975 (28 May). *Tourist Trophy Motor-cycle Races* (2*nd issue*). *T* **15** *and similar horiz designs. Multicoloured. P* 13½.

63	5½p.	Type **15**	10	15
64	7p.	Walter Handley, 1925	20	20
65	10p.	Geoff Duke, 1955	40	30
66	12p.	Peter Williams, 1973	40	35
63/6		.. .. *Set of* 4	1·00	90

16 Sir George Goldie and Birthplace

17 Title Page of Manx Bible

(Des G. Kneale. Photo Courvoisier)

1975 (9 Sept). 50*th Death Anniv of Sir George Goldie. T* **16** *and similar multicoloured designs. Granite paper. P* 11½.

67	5½p.	Type **16**	10	15
68	7p.	Goldie and map of Africa (*vert*) ..	20	20
69	10p.	Goldie as President of Geographical Society (*vert*)	40	30
70	12p.	River scene on the Niger	40	35
67/70		.. .. *Set of* 4	1·00	90

(Des J. Nicholson. Litho Questa)

1975 (29 Oct). *Christmas and Bicentenary of Manx Bible. T* **17** *and similar horiz designs. Multicoloured. P* 14.

71	5½p.	Type **17**	15	15
72	7p.	Rev. Philip Moore and Ballaugh Old Church	20	20
73	11p.	Bishop Hildesley and Bishops Court ..	40	35
74	13p.	John Kelly saving Bible manuscript ..	45	40
71/4		.. .. *Set of* 4	1·10	1·00

18 William Christian listening to Patrick Henry

19 First Horse Tram, 1876

(Des and litho J.W.)

1976 (12 Mar). *Bicentenary of American Revolution. T* **18** *and similar vert designs. Multicoloured. P* 13½.

75	5½p. Type **18**	..	15	15
76	7p. Conveying the Fincastle Resolutions	..	20	20
77	13p. Patrick Henry and William Christian	..	35	35
78	20p. Christian as an Indian fighter	..	50	50
75/8	..	*Set of* 4	1·10	1·10
MS79	153 × 89 mm. Nos. 75/8. P 14	..	1·90	2·50

(Des J. Nicholson. Photo Courvoisier)

1976 (26 May). *Douglas Horse Trams Centenary. T* **19** *and similar horiz designs. Multicoloured. Granite paper. P* 11½.

80	5½p. Type **19**	..	10	12
81	7p. "Toast-rack" tram, 1890	..	15	15
82	11p. Horse-bus, 1895	..	45	35
83	13p. Royal tram, 1972	..	50	45
80/3	..	*Set of* 4	1·10	1·00

20 Barroose Beaker

21 Diocesan Banner

(Des J. Nicholson. Photo Courvoisier)

1976 (28 July). *Europa. Ceramic Art. T* **20** *and similar multicoloured designs. Granite paper. P* 11½.

84	5p. Type **20**	..	20	25
	a. Strip of 3. Nos. 84/6	..	75	75
85	5p. Souvenir teapot	..	20	25
86	5p. Laxey jug	..	20	25
87	10p. Cronk Aust food vessel (*horiz*)	..	40	45
	a. Strip of 3. Nos. 87/9	..	1·50	1·50
88	10p. Sansbury bowl (*horiz*)	..	40	45
89	10p. Knox urn (*horiz*)	..	40	45
84/9	..	*Set of* 6	2·00	2·00

Nos. 84/6 and 87/9 were each printed in sheets of 9 (3 × 3) the three designs being horizontally and vertically *se-tenant*.

(Des G. Kneale. Litho Questa)

1976 (14 Oct). *Christmas and Centenary of Mothers' Union. T* **21** *and similar vert designs. Multicoloured. P* 14½.

90	6p. Type **21**	..	15	15
91	7p. Onchan banner	..	15	15
92	11p. Castletown banner	..	40	35
93	13p. Ramsey banner	..	40	45
90/3	..	*Set of* 4	1·00	1·00

22 Queen Elizabeth II

(Des A. Larkins. Litho and recess D.L.R.)

1977 (1 Mar). *Silver Jubilee. T* **22** *and similar multicoloured designs. P* 14 × 13 (*7p.*) *or* 13 × 14 (*others*).

94	6p. Type **22**	..	20	20
95	7p. Queen Elizabeth and Prince Philip (*vert*)		20	20
96	25p. Queen Elizabeth	..	80	70
94/6	..	*Set of* 3	1·10	1·00

The 25p. is similar to T **22** but has the portrait on the right.

23 Carrick Bay from "Tom-the-Dipper"

(Des J. Nicholson. Litho Questa)

1977 (26 May). *Europa. Landscapes. T* **23** *and similar horiz design. Multicoloured. P* 13½ × 14.

97	6p. Type **23**	..	20	20
98	10p. View from Ramsey	..	30	30

24 F. A. Applebee, 1912

(Des J. Nicholson. Litho J.W.)

1977 (26 May). *Linked Anniversaries. T* **24** *and similar horiz designs. Multicoloured. P* 13½.

99	6p. Type **24**	..	15	15
100	7p. St. John Ambulance Brigade at Governor's Bridge, *c.* 1938	..	15	20
101	11p. Scouts working scoreboard	..	40	40
102	13p. John Williams, 1976	..	40	40
99/102	..	*Set of* 4	1·00	1·00

The events commemorated are: 70th Anniv of Manx TT; 70th Anniv of Boy Scouts; Centenary of St John Ambulance Brigade.

25 Old Summer House, Mount Morrison, Peel

(Des and photo Courvoisier)

1977 (19 Oct). *Bicentenary of the First Visit of John Wesley. T* **25** *and similar horiz designs. Multicoloured. Granite paper. P* 11½.

103	6p. Type **25**	..	15	15
104	7p. Wesley preaching in Castletown Square		20	20
105	11p. Wesley preaching outside Braddan Church	..	35	35
106	13p. New Methodist Church, Douglas	..	40	40
103/6	..	*Set of* 4	1·00	1·00

Nos. 104/5 are larger, 38 × 26 mm.

26 H.M.S. *Ben-My-Chree* and Short "Type 184" Seaplane, 1915

(Des A. Theobald. Litho J.W.)

1978 (28 Feb). *R.A.F. Diamond Jubilee. T* **26** *and similar horiz designs. Multicoloured. P* 13½ × 14.

107	6p. Type **26**	..	15	15
108	7p. H.M.S. *Vindex* and Bristol "Scout", 1915		20	20
109	11p. Boulton Paul "Defiant" over Douglas Bay, 1941	..	40	35
110	13p. "Jaguar" over Ramsey, 1977	..	45	40
107/10	..	*Set of* 4	1·10	1·00

27 Watch Tower, Langness

27a Queen Elizabeth II

(Des J. Nicholson (½p. to £1), G. Kneale (£2). Litho Questa (½p. to 16p.). Photo Courvoisier (20p. to £2))

1978 (28 Feb)–**81**. *Various multicoloured designs.*

(*a*) *As T* **27**. A. *P* 14. B. *P* 14½

			A		B	
111	½p. Type **27**	..	10	10	40	40
112	1p. Jurby Church	..	10	10	30	30
113	6p. Government Buildings		25	25	†	
114	7p. Tynwald Hill	..	30	30	2·50	1·60
115	8p. Milner's Tower	..	30	30	50	30
116	9p. Laxey Wheel	..	35	35	50	30
117	10p. Castle Rushen	..	35	35	50	30
118	11p. St. Ninian's Church	..	40	40	50	40
119	12p. Tower of Refuge	..	45	45	30	30
120	13p. St. German's Cathedral		50	50	30	30
121	14p. Point of Ayre Lighthouse	..	50	50	40	40
122	15p. Corrin's Tower	..	60	60	40	30
123	16p. Douglas Head Lighthouse	..	65	65	25·00	20·00

(*b*) *As T* **27** *but size* 25 × 31 *mm. Granite paper. P* 11½ (18.10.78)

124	20p. Fuchsia	..	50	50
125	25p. Manx cat	..	65	65
126	50p. Chough	..	1·25	1·25
127	£1 Viking warrior	..	2·50	2·50

(*c*) *T* **27a**. *P* 11½ (29.9.81).

128	£2 multicoloured	..	3·50	3·75
111/28	..	*Set of* 18	12·00	12·00

The 1p., 7p., 10p., 12p. to 16p. are horiz designs.

28 Queen Elizabeth in Coronation Regalia

29 Wheel-headed Cross-slab

(Des G. Kneale. Litho Questa)

1978 (24 May). *25th Anniv of Coronation. P* 14½ × 14.

132	**28**	25p. multicoloured	..	75	75

(Des J. Nicholson. Photo Courvoisier)

1978 (24 May). *Europa. Sculpture. T* **29** *and similar vert designs showing Celtic and Norse Crosses. Multicoloured. Granite paper. P* 11½.

133	6p. Type **29**	..	15	15
	a. Strip of 3. Nos. 133/5	..	40	50
134	6p. Celtic wheel-cross	..	15	15
135	6p. Keeil Chiggyrt Stone	..	15	15
136	11p. Olaf Liotulfson Cross	..	25	30
	a. Strip of 3. Nos. 136/8	..	80	90
137	11p. Odd's and Thorleif's Crosses	..	25	30
138	11p. Thor Cross	..	25	30
133/8	..	*Set of* 6	1·10	1·25

Nos. 133/5 and 136/8 were each printed together, *se-tenant*, in horizontal and vertical strips of 3 throughout the sheet.

30 J. K. Ward and Ward Library, Peel

31 Hunt the Wren

(Des J.W. (7p.), G. Kneale (11p.), J. Nicholson (others). Litho J.W.)

1978 (10 June). *Anniversaries and Events. T* **30** *and similar horiz designs. Multicoloured. Invisible gum. P* 13½.

139	6p. Type **30**	..	15	15
140	7p. Swimmer, cyclist and walker (42 × 26 *mm*)	..	20	20
141	11p. American Bald Eagle, Manx arms and maple leaf (42 × 26 *mm*)	..	35	35
142	13p. Lumber camp at Three Rivers, Quebec		40	40
139/42	..	*Set of* 4	1·00	1·00

Commemorations:—6, 13p. James Kewley Ward (Manx pioneer in Canada); 7p. Commonwealth Games, Edmonton; 11p. 50th anniversary of North American Manx Association.

(Des J. Nicholson. Litho J.W.)

1978 (18 Oct). *Christmas. P* 13.

143	**31**	5p. multicoloured	..	30	25

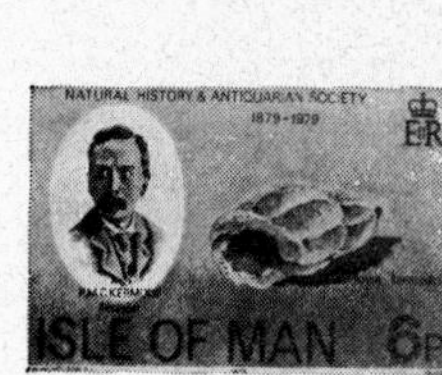

32 P. M. C. Kermode (founder) and *Nassa kermodei*

33 Postman, 1859

(Des J. Nicholson. Litho Questa)

1979 (27 Feb). *Centenary of Natural History and Antiquarian Society. T* **32** *and similar horiz designs. Multicoloured. P* 14.

144	6p. Type **32**	..	15	15
145	7p. Peregrine Falcon	..	20	20
146	11p. Fulmar	..	35	35
147	13p. *Epitriptus cowini*	..	40	40
144/7	..	*Set of* 4	1·00	1·00

(Des A. Theobald. Litho Questa)

1979 (16 May). *Europa. Communications. T* **33** *and similar vert design. Multicoloured. P* 14½.

148	6p. Type **33**	..	20	20
149	11p. Postman, 1979	..	30	30

34 Viking Longship Emblem

35 Viking Raid at Garwick

Two types of No. 150:

Type I. Wrongly inscribed "INSULAREM". "1979" imprint date.

Type II. Inscription corrected to "INSULARUM". "1980" imprint date.

(Des J. Nicholson. Litho Harrison (3, 4p.), J.W. (others))

1979 (16 May)–**80**. *Millenium of Tynwald. Multicoloured.*

(*a*) *Vert designs as T* **34**. *P* 14½ × 14

150	3p.	Type **34** (Type I)	15	15
		a. Booklet pane. Nos. 150 × 4, 151 × 2 (4p. stamps at top)	80	
		ab. Ditto (4p. stamps in centre)	1·00	
		b. Type II (29.9.80)	10	10
		ba. Booklet pane. Nos. 150b × 4, 151 × 2 (4p. stamps at bottom)	75	
151	4p.	"Three Legs of Man" emblem	15	15

(*b*) *Horiz designs as T* **35**. *P* 13

152	6p.	Type **35**	15	15
153	7p.	10th-century meeting of Tynwald ..	20	20
154	11p.	Tynwald Hill and St. John's Church ..	30	30
155	13p.	Procession to Tynwald Hill	35	35
150/5		.. .. *Set of* 6	1·10	1·10

See also Nos. 188/9.

The 3 and 4p. values were printed in sheets containing ten blocks of 6 and five blocks of 4 separated by blank margins. The blocks of 6 contained four 3p. values and two 4p., *se-tenant*, with the 4p. in either the top or centre rows. The blocks of 4 contain the 4p. value only.

For details of No. 150ba see after No. 189.

36 Queen and Court on Tynwald Hill

(Des G. Kneale. Litho Questa)

1979 (5 July). *Royal Visit. T* **36** *and similar horiz design. Multicoloured. P* 14½.

156	7p.	Type **36**	20	20
157	13p.	Queen and procession from St. John's Church to Tynwald Hill	30	40

37 *Odin's Raven*

(Des J. Nicholson. Litho Questa)

1979 (19 Oct). *Voyage of "Odin's Raven". P* 14 × 14½.

158	**37**	15p. multicoloured	40	40

38 John Quilliam seized by the Press Gang

39 Young Girl with Teddybear and Cat

(Des A. Theobald. Litho Questa)

1979 (19 Oct). *150th Death Anniv of Captain John Quilliam. T* **38** *and similar horiz designs. Multicoloured. P* 14.

159	6p.	Type **38**	15	15
160	8p.	Steering H.M.S. *Victory*, Battle of Trafalgar	20	20
161	13p.	Capt. John Quilliam and H.M.S. *Spencer*	35	40
162	15p.	Capt. John Quilliam (member of the House of Keys)	40	45
159/62		.. .. *Set of* 4	1·00	1·10

(Des Mrs E. Moore. Litho J.W.)

1979 (19 Oct). *Christmas. International Year of the Child. T* **39** *and similar vert design. Multicoloured. P* 13.

163	5p.	Type **39**	15	15
164	7p.	Father Christmas with young children	25	25

40 Conglomerate Arch, Langness

(Des J. Nicholson. Litho Questa)

1980 (5 Feb). *150th Anniv of Royal Geographical Society. T* **40** *and similar horiz designs. Multicoloured. P* 14½.

165	7p.	Type **40**	20	20
166	8p.	Braaid Circle	20	20
167	12p.	Cashtal-yn-Ard	30	30
168	13p.	Volcanic Rocks at Scarlett	35	40
169	15p.	Sugar-loaf Rock	40	45
165/9		.. .. *Set of* 5	1·25	1·40

41 *Mona's Isle I*

(Des J. Nicholson. Photo Courvoisier)

1980 (6 May). *150th Anniv of Isle of Man Steam Packet Company. T* **41** *and similar horiz designs. Multicoloured. Granite paper. P* 11½.

170	7p.	Type **41**	20	20
171	8p.	*Douglas I*	20	20
172	11½p.	H.M.S. *Mona's Queen II* sinking U-boat	30	30
173	12p.	H.M.S. *King Orry* at surrender of German fleet	30	30
174	13p.	*Ben-My-Chree IV*	35	35
175	15p.	*Lady of Mann II*	40	40
170/5		.. .. *Set of* 6	1·50	1·60
MS176		180 × 125 mm. Nos. 170/5	1·75	1·75

No. **MS**176 was issued to commemorate the "London 1980" International Stamp Exhibition.

42 Stained Glass Window, T. E. Brown Room, Manx Museum

(Des G. Kneale. Photo Courvoisier)

1980 (6 May). *Europa. Personalities. Thomas Edward Brown (poet and scholar) Commemoration. T* **42** *and similar horiz design. Multicoloured. Granite paper. P* 11½.

177	7p.	Type **42**	20	20
178	13½p.	Clifton College, Bristol	30	30

43 King Olav V

(Des J. Nicholson. Litho Questa)

1980 (13 June). *Visit of King Olav V of Norway. P* 14 × 14½.

179	**43**	12p. multicoloured	35	35
MS180		125 × 157 mm. Nos. 158 and 179	90	90

44 Winter Wren and View of Calf of Man

(Des J. Nicholson. Litho J.W.)

1980 (29 Sept). *Christmas and Wildlife Conservation Year. T* **44** *and similar horiz design. Multicoloured. P* 13½ × 14.

181	6p.	Type **44**	20	20
182	8p.	European Robin and view of Port Erin Marine Biological Station	25	30

45 William Kermode and Brig *Robert Quayle*, 1819

46 Peregrine Falcon

(Des A. Theobald. Litho Questa)

1980 (29 Sept). *Kermode Family in Tasmania Commemoration. T* **45** *and similar horiz designs. Multicoloured. P* 14½.

183	7p.	Type **45**	20	20
184	9p.	"Mona Vale", Van Diemen's Land, 1834	25	25
185	13½p.	Ross Bridge, Tasmania	30	35
186	15p.	"Mona Vale", Tasmania (completed 1868)	35	40
187	17½p.	Robert Q. Kermode and Parliament Buildings, Tasmania	40	45
183/7		.. .. *Set of* 5	1·40	1·50

(Des J. Nicholson. Litho Harrison)

1980 (29 Sept). *Booklet stamps. Vert designs as T* **46**. *Multicoloured. P* 14½ × 14.

188	1p.	Type **46**	10	10
		a. Booklet pane. Nos. 151, 188 and 189 each × 2	75	
189	5p.	Loaghtyn Ram	40	40

In addition to 40p. and 80p. booklets Nos. 188/9 also come from special booklet sheets of 60. These sheets contained No. 150ba and 188a, each × 5.

47 Luggers passing Red Pier, Douglas

(Des J. Nicholson. Litho Questa)

1981 (24 Feb). *Centenary of Royal National Mission to Deep Sea Fishermen. T* **47** *and similar horiz designs. Multicoloured. P* 14.

190	8p.	Type **47**	25	25
191	9p.	Peel Lugger *Wanderer* rescuing survivors from the *Lusitania*	30	30
192	18p.	Nickeys leaving Port St. Mary Harbour	45	45
193	20p.	Nobby entering Ramsey Harbour ..	45	50
194	22p.	Nickeys *Sunbeam* and *Zebra* at Port Erin	50	50
190/4		.. .. *Set of* 5	1·75	1·75

48 "Crosh Cuirn" Superstition

(Des J. Nicholson. Litho Questa)

1981 (22 May). *Europa. Folklore. T* **48** *and similar horiz design. Multicoloured. P* 14½.

195	8p.	Type **48**	25	25
196	18p.	"Bollan Cross" superstition	55	55

49 Lt. Mark Wilks (Royal Manx Fencibles) and Peel Castle

(Des A. Theobald. Litho Questa)

1981 (22 May). *150th Death Anniv of Colonel Mark Wilks. T* **49** *and similar horiz designs. Multicoloured. P* 14.

197	8p.	Type **49**	25	25
198	20p.	Ensign Mark Wilks and Fort St. George, Madras	50	50
199	22p.	Governor Mark Wilks and Napoleon, St. Helena	55	55
200	25p.	Col. Mark Wilks (Speaker of the House of Keys) and estate, Kirby	65	65
197/200 ..		.. .. *Set of* 4	1·60	1·75

50 Miss Emmeline Goulden (Mrs. Pankhurst) and Mrs. Sophia Jane Goulden

(Des A. Theobald. Litho Questa)

1981 (22 May). *Centenary of Manx Women's Suffrage. P* 14.

201	**50**	9p. black, olive-grey and stone	35	30

51 Prince Charles and Lady Diana Spencer

(Des G. Kneale. Litho Harrison)

1981 (29 July). *Royal Wedding. P* 14.

202	**51**	9p. black, bright blue and pale blue ..	25	25
203		25p. black, bright blue and pink ..	75	75
MS204		130 × 183 mm. Nos. 202/3 × 2	2·40	2·40

52 Douglas War Memorial, Poppies and Commemorative Inscription

(Des A. Theobald. Photo Courvoisier)

1981 (29 Sept). *60th Anniv of The Royal British Legion. T* **52** *and similar horiz designs. Multicoloured. Granite paper. P* 11½.

205	8p.	Type **52**	25	25
206	10p.	Major Robert Cain (war hero)	30	35
207	18p.	Festival of Remembrance, Royal Albert Hall	40	45
208	20p.	T.S.S. *Tynwald* at Dunkirk, May 1940	45	50
205/8 ..		.. .. *Set of* 4	1·25	1·40

53 Nativity Scene (stained-glass window, St. George's Church)

(Des J.W. (7p.), G. Kneale (9p.). Litho J.W.)

1981 (29 Sept). *Christmas. T* **53** *and similar multicoloured design. P* 14.

209	7p.	Type **53**	20	20
210	9p.	Children from Special School performing nativity play (48 × 30 *mm*) ..	25	25

The 7p. value also commemorates the bicentenary of St. George's Church, Douglas and the 9p. the International Year for Disabled Persons.

54 Joseph and William Cunningham (founders of Isle of Man Boy Scout Movement) and Cunningham House Headquarters

(Des G. Kneale. Litho Questa)

1982 (23 Feb). *75th Anniv of Boy Scout Movement and 125th Birth Anniv of Lord Baden-Powell. T* **54** *and similar multicoloured designs. P* 14 × 14½ (19½*p.*) *or* 13½ × 14 (*others*).

211	9p.	Type **54**	30	30
212	10p.	Baden-Powell visiting Isle of Man, 1911	30	30
213	19½p.	Baden-Powell and Scout emblem (40 × 31 *mm*)	55	55
214	24p.	Scouts and Baden-Powell's last message	75	75
215	29p.	Scout salute, handshake, emblem and globe	95	95
211/15 ..		.. .. *Set of* 5	2·50	2·50

55 *The Principals and Duties of Christianity* (Bishop T. Wilson) (first book printed in Manx, 1707)

(Des A. Theobald. Photo Courvoisier)

1982 (1 June). *Europa. Historic Events. T* **55** *and similar horiz design. Multicoloured. Granite paper. P* 12 × 12½.

216	9p.	Type **55**	25	25
217	19½p.	Landing at Derbyhaven (visit of Thomas, 2nd Earl of Derby, 1507) ..	50	50

56 Charlie Collier (first TT race (single cylinder) winner) and Tourist Trophy Race, 1907

(Des J. Nicholson. Litho Questa)

1982 (1 June). *75th Anniv of Tourist Trophy Motorcycle Racing. T* **56** *and similar horiz designs. Multicoloured. P* 14.

218	9p.	Type **56**	20	20
219	10p.	Freddie Dixon (Sidecar and Junior TT winner) and Junior TT race, 1927 ..	25	25
220	24p.	Jimmie Simpson (TT winner and first to lap at 60, 70 and 80 mph) and Senior TT, 1932	70	70
221	26p.	Mike Hailwood (winner of fourteen TT's) and Senior TT, 1961	80	80
222	29p.	Jock Taylor (Sidecar TT winner, 1978, 1980 and 1981) and Sidecar TT (with Benga Johansson), 1980	90	90
218/22 ..		.. .. *Set of* 5	2·50	2·50

57 *Mona I*

(Des J. Nicholson. Litho Questa)

1982 (5 Oct). *150th Anniv of Isle of Man Steam Packet Company Mail Contract. T* **57** *and similar horiz design. Multicoloured. P* 13½ × 14.

223	12p.	Type **57**	30	30
224	19½p.	*Manx Maid II*	60	60

58 Three Wise Men bearing Gifts

59 Princess Diana with Prince William

(Des and litho J.W.)

1982 (5 Oct). *Christmas. T* **58** *and similar multicoloured design. P* 13 × 13½ (8*p.*) *or* 13½ × 13 (11*p.*).

225	8p.	Type **58**	30	30
226	11p.	Christmas snow scene (*vert*)	40	40

(Des G. Kneale. Litho Questa)

1982 (12 Oct). *21st Birthday of Princess of Wales and Birth of Prince William. Sheet* 100 × 83 mm. *P* 14½ × 14.

MS227	**59**	50p. multicoloured	2·00	2·00

60 Opening of Salvation Army Citadel, and T.H. Cannell, J.P.

(Des A. Theobald. Photo Courvoisier)

1983 (15 Feb). *Centenary of Salvation Army in Isle of Man. T* **60** *and similar horiz designs. Multicoloured. Granite paper. P* 11½.

228	10p.	Type **60**	30	30
229	12p.	Early meeting place and Gen. William Booth	40	40
230	19½p.	Salvation Army band	60	60
231	26p.	Treating lepers and Lt.-Col. Thomas Bridson	90	90
228/31 ..		.. .. *Set of* 4	2·00	2·00

61 Atlantic Puffins

61a "Queen Elizabeth II" (Ricardo Macarron)

(Des Colleen Corlett (£5), J. Nicholson (others). Litho Questa)

1983 (15 Feb)–**85**. *Horiz designs as T* **61**, *showing sea birds, and T* **61a**. *Multicoloured. P* 14 (20*p.* to £1), 14 × 13½ (£5) *or* 14½ (*others*).

232	1p.	Type **61**	10	10
233	2p.	Northern Gannets	10	10
234	5p.	Lesser Black-backed Gulls	20	20
235	8p.	Common Cormorants	20	20
236	10p.	Kittiwakes	25	25
237	11p.	Shags	25	25
238	12p.	Grey Herons	30	30
239	13p.	Herring Gulls	30	30
240	14p.	Razorbills	30	30
241	15p.	Great Black-backed Gulls	35	35
242	16p.	Common Shelducks	35	35
243	18p.	Oystercatchers	40	40
244	20p.	Arctic Terns (14.9.83)	40	40
245	25p.	Common Guillemots (14.9.83)	60	60
246	50p.	Redshanks (14.9.83)	1·10	1·10
247	£1	Mute Swans (14.9.83)	2·25	2·25
248	£5	Type **61a** (31.1.85)	9·00	9·25
232/48 ..		.. .. *Set of* 17	15·00	15·00

Nos. 244/7 are larger, 39 × 26 mm.

62 Design Drawings by Robert Casement for the Great Laxey Wheel

(Des J. Nicholson. Litho Questa)

1983 (18 May). *Europa. The Great Laxey Wheel. T* **62** *and similar horiz design. P* 14.

249	10p.	black, azure and buff	40	35
250	20½p.	multicoloured	70	70

Design:—20½p. Robert Casement and the Great Laxey Wheel.

63 Nick Keig (international yachtsman) and Trimaran *Three Legs of Man III*

64 New Post Office Headquarters, Douglas

(Des J. Nicholson (10p., 31p.), Colleen Corlett (12p., 28p.). Photo Courvoisier)

1983 (18 May). *150th Anniv of King William's College. T* **63** *and similar horiz designs. Multicoloured. Granite paper. P* 11½.

251	10p.	Type **63**	30	30
252	12p.	King William's College, Castletown ..	40	40
253	28p.	Sir William Bragg (winner of Nobel Prize for Physics) and spectrometer ..	90	90
254	31p.	General Sir George White V.C. and action at Charasiah	1·10	1·10
251/4 ..		.. .. *Set of* 4	2·40	2·40

(Des Colleen Corlett (10p.), J. Nicholson (15p.). Litho Questa)

1983 (5 July). *World Communications Year and 10th Anniv of Isle of Man Post Office Authority. T* **64** *and similar vert design. Multicoloured. P* 14½.

255 10p. Type **64** 40 30
256 15p. As Type **6**, but inscr "POST OFFICE DECENNIUM 1983" 60 50

65 Shepherds

(Des Colleen Corlett. Litho J.W.)

1983 (14 Sept). *Christmas. T* **65** *and similar horiz design. Multicoloured. P* 13.

257 9p. Type **65** 40 30
258 12p. Three Kings 50 40

66 *Manx King* (full-rigged ship)

67 C.E.P.T. 25th Anniversary Logo

(Des J. Nicholson (10p. to 31p.); Colleen Corlett, J. Nicholson and J. Smith (miniature sheet). Litho Questa)

1984 (14 Feb). *The Karran Fleet. T* **66** *and similar horiz designs. Multicoloured. P* 14.

259 10p. Type **66** 35 35
260 13p. *Hope* (barque) 45 45
261 20½p. *Rio Grande* (brig) 70 70
262 28p. *Lady Elizabeth* (barque) 85 85
263 31p. *Sumatra* (barque) 95 95
259/63 .. .. *Set of* 5 3·00 3·00
MS264 103 × 94 mm. 28p. As No. 262, 31p. *Lady Elizabeth* (as shown on Falkland Islands No. 417) (*sold at* 60p.) .. .. 2·75 2·75

No. **MS**264 was issued to commemorate links bewtween the Isle of Man and Falkland Islands.

(Des J. Larrivière, adapted Colleen Corlett. Photo Courvoisier)

1984 (27 Apr). *Europa. Granite paper. P* 12 × 11½.

265 **67** 10p. dull orange, deep reddish brown and pale orange 35 35
266 20½p. light blue, deep blue and pale blue 70 70

68 Railway Air Services "D.H.84"

69 Window from Glencrutchery House, Douglas

(Des A. Theobald. Litho Questa)

1984 (27 Apr). (27 Apr). *50th Anniv of First Official Airmail to the Isle of Man and 40th Anniv of International Civil Aviation Organization. T* **68** *and similar horiz designs. Multicoloured. P* 14.

267 11p. Type **68** 35 35
268 13p. West Coast Air Services "D.H.86" 40 40
269 26p. B.E.A. "DC-3" 75 75
270 28p. B.E.A. Vickers "Viscount" 85 85
271 31p. Telair "Islander" 95 95
267/71 .. .. *Set of* 5 3·00 3·00

(Des D. Swinton. Litho J.W.)

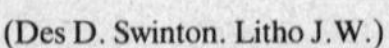

1984 (21 Sept). *Christmas. Stained-glass Windows. T* **69** *and similar vert design. Multicoloured. P* 14.

272 10p. Type **69** 40 40
273 13p. Window from Lonan Old Church 50 50

70 William Cain's Birthplace, Ballasalla

(Des J. Nicholson. Litho Questa)

1984 (21 Sept). *William Cain (civic leader, Victoria) Commemoration. T* **70** *and similar horiz designs. Multicoloured. P* 14½ × 14.

274 11p. Type **70** 30 30
275 22p. The *Anna* leaving Liverpool, 1852 .. 65 65
276 28p. Early Australian railway 90 90
277 30p. William Cain as Mayor of Melbourne, and Town Hall .. .. 1·00 1·00
278 33p. Royal Exhibition Building, Melbourne .. 1·10 1·10
274/8 .. .. *Set of* 5 3·50 3·50

71 Queen Elizabeth II and Commonwealth Parliamentary Association Badge

(Des and litho J.W.)

1984 (21 Sept). *Links with the Commonwealth. 30th Commonwealth Parliamentary Association Conference. T* **71** *and similar horiz design. Multicoloured. P* 14.

279 14p. Type **71** 45 45
280 33p. Queen Elizabeth II and Manx emblem .. 1·00 1·00

72 Cunningham House Headquarters, and Mrs. Willie Cunningham and Mrs. Joseph Cunningham (former Commissioners)

(Des Colleen Corlett. Photo Courvoisier)

1985 (31 Jan). *75th Anniv of Girl Guide Movement. T* **72** *and similar horiz designs. Multicoloured. Granite paper. P* 11½.

281 11p. Type **72** 35 35
282 14p. Princess Margaret, Isle of Man standard and guides 50 50
283 29p. Lady Olave Baden-Powell opening Guide Headquarters, 1955 .. .. 90 90
284 31p. Guide uniforms from 1910 to 1985 .. 1·00 1·00
285 34p. Guide handclasp, salute and early badge .. 1·10 1·10
281/5 .. .. *Set of* 5 3·50 3·50

73 Score of Manx National Anthem

(Des D. Swinton. Photo Courvoisier)

1985 (24 Apr). *Europa. European Music Year. T* **73** *and similar horiz designs. Granite paper. P* 11½.

286 12p. black, orange-brown and chestnut .. 25 30
a. Horiz pair. Nos. 286/7 .. .. .. 65 65
287 12p. black, orange-brown and chestnut .. 25 30
288 22p. black, bright new blue and new blue .. 60 65
a. Horiz pair. Nos. 288/9 .. .. .. 1·50 1·50
289 22p. black, bright new blue and new blue .. 60 65
286/9 .. .. *Set of* 4 1·90 1·90

Designs:—No. 287, William H. Gill (lyricist); 288, Score of hymn "Crofton"; 289, Dr. John Clague (composer).

Nos. 286/7 and 288/9 were printed together, *se-tenant*, in horizontal pairs throughout the sheets.

74 Charles Rolls in 20 h.p. Rolls-Royce (1906 Tourist Trophy Race)

(Des A. Theobald. Litho Questa)

1985 (25 May). *Century of Motoring. T* **74** *and similar horiz designs. Multicoloured. P* 14.

290 12p. Type **74** 25 30
a. Horiz pair. Nos. 290/1 .. .. .. 70 70
291 12p. W. Bentley in 3 litre Bentley (1922 Tourist Trophy Race) 25 30
292 14p. F. Gerrard in E.R.A. (1950 British Empire Trophy Race) 30 35
a. Horiz pair. Nos. 292/3 .. .. .. 90 90
293 14p. Brian Lewis in Alfa Romeo (1934 Mannin Moar Race) 30 35
294 31p. Jaguar "XJ-SC" ("Roads Open" car, 1984 Motor Cycle T.T. Races) 80 85
a. Horiz pair. Nos. 294/5 .. .. .. 2·25 2·25
295 31p. Tony Pond and Mike Nicholson in Vauxhall "Chevette" (1981 Rothmans International Rally) 80 85
290/5 .. .. *Set of* 6 3·50 3·50

Nos. 290/1, 292/3 and 294/5 were printed together, *se-tenant*, in horizontal pairs throughout the sheets.

75 Queen Alexandra and Victorian Sergeant with Wife

(Des Colleen Corlett. Litho Questa)

1985 (4 Sept). *Centenary of the Soldiers', Sailors' and Airmen's Families Association. T* **75** *and similar horiz designs showing Association Presidents. Multicoloured. P* 14.

296 12p. Type **75** 45 45
297 15p. Queen Mary and Royal Air Force family 55 55
298 29p. Earl Mountbatten and Royal Navy family 1·10 1·10
299 34p. Prince Michael of Kent and Royal Marine with parents, 1982 .. .. 1·25 1·25
296/9 .. .. *Set of* 4 3·00 3·00

76 Kirk Maughold (Birthplace)

(Des A. Theobald. Litho Questa)

1985 (2 Oct). *Birth Bicentenary of Lieutenant-General Sir Mark Cubbon (Indian administrator). T* **76** *and similar multicoloured designs. P* 14.

300 12p. Type **76** 35 35
301 22p. Lieutenant-General Sir Mark Cubbon (*vert*) 70 70
302 45p. Memorial Statue, Bangalore, India (*vert*) 1·60 1·60
300/2 .. .. *Set of* 3 2·40 2·40

77 St. Peter's Church, Onchan

(Des A. Theobald. Litho J.W.)

1985 (2 Oct). *Christmas. Manx Churches. T* **77** *and similar horiz designs. Multicoloured. P* 13 × 13½.

303 11p. Type **77** 35 35
304 14p. Royal Chapel of St. John, Tynwald .. 45 45
305 31p. Bride Parish Church .. .. 1·10 1·10
303/5 .. .. *Set of* 3 1·75 1·75

78 Swimming

(Des C. Abbott. Litho Questa)

1986 (5 Feb). *Commonwealth Games, Edinburgh. T* **78** *and similar horiz designs. Multicoloured. P* 14.

306 12p. Type **78** 40 40
307 15p. Race walking 50 50
308 31p. Rifle-shooting .. .. 1·25 1·25
309 34p. Cycling .. .. 1·25 1·25
306/9 .. .. *Set of* 4 3·00 3·00

No. 309 also commemorates the 50th anniversary of Manx International Cycling Week.

79 Viking Necklace and Peel Castle

80 Viking Longship

(Des J. Nicholson. Litho Questa)

1986 (5 Feb). *Centenary of the Manx Museum. T* **79** *and similar multicoloured designs. P* 14.

310 12p. Type **79** 35 35
311 15p. Meayll Circle, Rushen 40 40
312 22p. Skeleton of Great Deer and Manx Museum (*vert*) 70 70
313 26p. Viking longship model (*vert*) 80 80
314 29p. Open Air Museum, Cregneash 90 90
310/14 .. .. *Set of* 5 3·00 3·00

(Des Colleen Corlett. Litho Harrison)

1986 (10 Apr). *Manx Heritage Year. Booklet stamps. T* **80** *and similar vert design. P* 14½×14.

315 2p. multicoloured .. 25 25
a. Booklet pane. Nos. 315×2 and 316×4 .. 2·50
316 10p. black, apple green and brownish grey .. 75 75
a. Booklet pane. No. 316×3 and 3 stamp-size labels .. 2·50

Design:—10p. Celtic cross logo.

In addition to 50p. and £1.14 booklets Nos. 315/16 also come from special booklet sheets of 50 containing five each of Nos. 315a and 316a.

81 *Usnea articulata* (lichen) and *Neotinea intacta* (orchid), The Ayres

82 Ellanbane (home of Myles Standish)

(Des J. Nicholson and Nancy Corkish. Photo Courvoisier)

1986 (10 Apr). *Europa. Protection of Nature and the Environment. T* **81** *and similar horiz designs. Multicoloured. Granite paper. P* 11½.

317 12p. Type **81** .. 35 35
a. Horiz pair. Nos. 317/18 .. 70 70
318 12p. Hen Harrier, Calf of Man .. 35 35
319 22p. Manx Stoat, Eary Cushlin .. 70 70
a. Horiz pair. Nos. 319/20 .. 1·50 1·50
320 22p. *Stenobothus stigmaticus* (grasshopper), St. Michael's Isle .. 70 70
317/20 .. *Set of* 4 2·00 2·00

The two designs of each value were printed together, *se-tenant*, in horizontal pairs throughout the sheets.

(Des C. Abbott. Litho Cartor, France)

1986 (22 May). *"Ameripex '86" International Stamp Exhibition, Chicago. Captain Myles Standish of the "Mayflower". T* **82** *and similar vert designs. Multicoloured. P* 13½.

321 12p. Type **82** .. 35 35
322 15p. *Mayflower* crossing the Atlantic, 1620 .. 45 45
323 31p. Pilgrim Fathers landing at Plymouth, 1620 .. 1·00 1·00
324 34p. Captain Myles Standish .. 1·25 1·25
321/4 .. *Set of* 4 2·75 2·75
MS325 100×75 mm. Nos. 323/4. P 12½ .. 2·25 2·25

No. **MS**325 also commemorates the 75th anniversary of the World Manx Association.

83 Prince Andrew in Naval Uniform and Miss Sarah Ferguson

84 Prince Philip (from photo by Karsh)

(Des Colleen Corlett. Litho B.D.T.)

1986 (23 July). *Royal Wedding. T* **83** *and similar horiz design. Multicoloured. P* 15×14.

326 15p. Type **83** .. 60 60
327 40p. Engagement photograph .. 1·40 1·40

(Des Colleen Corlett. Photo Courvoisier)

1986 (28 Aug). *Royal Birthdays. T* **84** *and similar multicoloured designs. Granite paper. P* 11½.

328 15p. Type **84** .. 60 60
a. Horiz pair. Nos. 328/9 .. 1·25 1·25
329 15p. Queen Elizabeth II (from photo by Karsh) .. 60 60
330 34p. Queen Elizabeth and Prince Philip (from photo by Karsh) (48×35 *mm*) .. 1·40 1·40
328/30 .. *Set of* 3 2·50 2·50

Nos. 328/9 were printed together, *se-tenant*, in horizontal pairs throughout the sheet.

Nos. 328/30 also commemorate "Stockholmia '86" International Stamp Exhibition, Sweden and the 350th anniversary of the Swedish Post Office and are so inscribed on the margins of the sheet of twelve (Nos. 328/9) and six (No. 330).

85 European Robins on Globe and "Peace and Goodwill" in Braille

86 North Quay

(Des Colleen Corlett. Litho Questa)

1986 (25 Sept). *Christmas. International Peace Year. T* **85** *and similar vert designs. Multicoloured. P* 14.

331 11p. Type **85** .. 40 40
332 14p. Hands releasing peace dove .. 45 45
333 31p. Clasped hands and "Peace" in sign language .. 1·10 1·10
331/3 .. *Set of* 3 1·75 1·75

(Des A. Theobald. Litho Questa)

1987 (21 Jan–26 Mar). *Victorian Douglas. T* **86** *and similar horiz designs. Multicoloured. P* 14×14½.

334 2p. Type **86** .. 10 10
a. Booklet pane. Nos. 334×2, 335×2 and 336×4 (2p. stamps at top) (26.3) .. 1·40
ab. Ditto, but 2p. stamps at bottom (26.3) .. 1·40
b. Booklet pane. Nos. 334/7, each×2 (26.3) 1·75
335 3p. Old Fishmarket .. 10 10
336 10p. The Breakwater .. 35 35
337 15p. Jubilee Clock .. 50 50
338 31p. Loch Promenade .. 1·10 1·10
339 34p. Beach .. 1·25 1·25
334/9 .. *Set of* 6 3·00 3·00

87 "The Old Fishmarket and Harbour, Douglas"

(Des A. Theobald. Litho Cartor, France)

1987 (18 Feb). *Paintings by John Miller Nicholson. T* **87** *and similar horiz designs. Multicoloured. P* 13½.

340 12p. Type **87** .. 35 35
341 26p. "Red Sails at Douglas" .. 80 80
342 29p. "The Double Corner, Peel" .. 95 95
343 34p. "Peel Harbour" .. 1·25 1·25
340/3 .. *Set of* 4 3·00 3·00

88 Sea Terminal, Douglas

(Des R. Maddox. Litho B.D.T.)

1987 (29 Apr). *Europa. Architecture. T* **88** *and similar horiz designs. Multicoloured. P* 13½.

344 12p. Type **88** .. 40 40
a. Horiz pair. Nos. 344/5 .. 80 80
345 12p. Tower of Refuge, Douglas .. 40 40
346 22p. Gaiety Theatre, Douglas .. 80 80
a. Horiz pair. Nos. 346/7 .. 1·60 1·60
347 22p. Villa Marina, Douglas .. 80 80
344/7 .. *Set of* 4 2·25 2·25

Nos. 344/5 and 346/7 were each printed, *se-tenant*, in horizontal pairs throughout the sheets.

89 Supercharged BMW 500cc Motor Cycle, 1939

(Des B. Dix. Litho Cartor, France)

1987 (27 May). *80th Anniv of Tourist Trophy Motor Cycle Races. T* **89** *and similar horiz designs. Multicoloured. P* 13½×13.

348 12p. Type **89** .. 30 30
349 15p. Manx "Kneeler" Norton 350cc, 1953 .. 50 50
350 29p. MV Agusta 500cc 4, 1956 .. 90 90
351 31p. Guzzi 500cc V8, 1957 .. 1·00 1·00
352 34p. Honda 250cc 6, 1967 .. 1·25 1·25
348/52 .. *Set of* 5 3·50 3·50
MS353 150×140 mm. Nos. 348/52. P 14×13½ .. 3·50 3·50

Nos. 348/53 also commemorate the Centenary of the St. John Ambulance Brigade and the miniature sheet also carries the logo of "Capex '87" International Stamp Exhibition, Toronto, on its margin.

90 Fuchsia and Wild Roses

91 Stirring the Christmas Pudding

(Des Nancy Corkish. Litho Enschedé)

1987 (9 Sept). *Wild Flowers. T* **90** *and similar vert designs. Multicoloured. P* 14½×13.

354 16p. Type **90** .. 50 50
355 29p. Field Scabious and Ragwort .. 90 90
356 31p. Wood Anemone and Celandine .. 1·00 1·00
357 34p. Violets and Primroses .. 1·25 1·25
354/7 .. *Set of* 4 3·25 3·25

(Des Colleen Corlett. Litho Questa)

1987 (16 Oct). *Christmas. Victorian Scenes. T* **91** *and similar vert designs. Multicoloured. P* 14.

358 12p. Type **91** .. 50 50
359 15p. Bringing home the Christmas tree .. 65 65
360 31p. Decorating the Christmas tree .. 1·10 1·10
358/60 .. *Set of* 3 2·00 2·00

92 Russell Brookes in Vauxhall Opel (Manx Rally winner, 1985)

(Des C. Abbott. Litho Enschedé)

1988 (10 Feb). *Motor Sport. T* **92** *and similar horiz designs. Multicoloured. P* 13½×14½.

361 13p. Type **92** .. 45 45
362 26p. Ari Vatanen in Ford "Escort" (Manx Rally winner, 1976) .. 75 75
363 31p. Terry Smith in Repco "March 761" (Hill Climb winner, 1980) .. 85 85
364 34p. Nigel Mansell in Williams/Honda (British Grand Prix winner, 1986 and 1987) .. 95 95
361/4 .. *Set of* 4 2·75 2·75

93 Horse Tram Terminus, Douglas Bay Tramway

93*a* Queen Elizabeth II taking Salute at Trooping the Colour

(Des Colleen Corlett (£2), A. Theobald (others). Litho B.D.T. (1p. to 19p.), Questa (20p. to £2)

1988 (10 Feb)–**90**. *Manx Railways and Tramways. Horiz designs as T* **93**, *and T* **93*a***. *Multicoloured. P* 13 *(1p. to 19p.)*, 14½×15 *(20p. to £1) or* 14½ *(£2).*

365 1p. Type **93** .. 10 10
366 2p. Snaefell Mountain Railway .. 10 10
367 3p. Marine Drive Tramway .. 10 10
a. Booklet pane. Nos. 367 × 2, 370 and 373 × 2 (16.3.88) .. 90
b. Booklet pane. Nos. 367 × 2, 371 × 2 and 374 (16.10.89) .. 90
368 5p. Douglas Head Incline Railway .. 10 10
369 10p. Manx Electric Railway train at Maughold Head .. 20 25
370 13p. Douglas Cable Tramway .. 25 30
a. Booklet pane. Nos. 370 × 4 and 373 × 6 (16.3.88) .. 2·50
371 14p. Manx Northern Railway No. 4, *Caledonia*, at Gob-y-Deigan .. 25 30
a. Booklet pane. Nos. 371 × 4 and 374 × 6 (16.10.89) .. 3·75
372 15p. Laxey Mine Railway Lewin locomotive *Ant* .. 25 30
a. Booklet pane. Nos. 372 and 376×2 (14.2.90) .. 95
b. Booklet pane. Nos. 372×4 and 376×6 (14.2.90) .. 3·00
373 16p. Port Erin Breakwater Tramway locomotive *Henry B. Loch* .. 30 35
374 17p. Ramsey Harbour Tramway .. 30 35
375 18p. Locomotive No. 7, *Tynwald*, on Foxdale line .. 30 35
376 19p. Baldwin Reservoir Tramway steam locomotive *Injebreck* .. 35 40
377 20p. I.M.R. No. 13, *Kissack*, near St. Johns (21.9.88) .. 35 40
378 25p. I.M.R. No. 12, *Hutchinson*, leaving Douglas (21.9.88) .. 45 50
379 50p. Groudle Glen Railway locomotive *Polar Bear* (21.9.88) .. 90 1·00
380 £1 I.M.R. No. 11, *Maitland*, pulling Royal Train, 1963 (21.9.88) .. 1·75 2·00
380*a* £2 Type **93*a*** (14.2.90) .. 3·50 3·75
365/80*a* .. *Set of* 17 8·50 9·50

In addition to stamp booklets Nos. 367a/b, 370a, 371a and 372a/b also come from special booklet sheets of 50 containing either ten examples of the strips of five or five examples of the strips of ten.

MINIMUM PRICE

The minimum price quote is 10p which represents a handling charge rather than a basis for valuing common stamps. For further notes about prices see introductory pages.

94 Laying Isle of Man—U.K. Submarine Cable

(Des C. Abbott. Litho Cartor, France)

1988 (14 Apr). *Europa. Transport and Communications. T* **94** *and similar horiz designs. Multicoloured. P* 14 × 13½.

381 13p. Type **94** 35 35
 a. Horiz pair. Nos. 381/2 .. .. 70 70
382 13p. *Flex Service 3* (cable ship) 35 35
383 22p. Earth station, Braddan 60 60
 a. Horiz pair. Nos. 383/4 .. .. .. 1·25 1·25
384 22p. "INTELSAT 5" satellite 60 60
381/4 .. .. *Set of* 4 1·75 1·75

Nos. 381/2 and 383/4 were each printed together, *se-tenant*, in horizontal pairs throughout the sheets. Nos. 381/2 form a composite design.

95 *Euterpe* (full-rigged ship) off Ramsey, 1863

96 "Magellanica"

(Des J. Nicholson. Litho Questa)

1988 (11 May). *Manx Sailing Ships. T* **95** *and similar horiz designs. Multicoloured. P* 14.

385 16p. Type **95** 50 50
386 29p. *Vixen* (topsail schooner) leaving Peel for Australia, 1853 .. .. 85 85
387 31p. *Ramsey* (full-rigged ship) off Brisbane, 1870 .. .. 90 90
388 34p. *Star of India* (formerly *Euterpe*) (barque) off San Diego, 1976 .. .. .. 1·10 1·10
385/8 .. .. *Set of* 4 3·00 3·00
MS389 110 × 85 mm. Nos. 385 and 388 .. .. 1·50 1·50

Nos. 386/7 also commemorate the Bicentenary of Australian Settlement.

(Des Colleen Corlett. Litho Enschedé)

1988 (21 Sept). *50th Anniv of British Fuchsia Society. T* **96** *and similar vert designs. Multicoloured. P* 13½ × 14.

390 13p. Type **96** 40 40
391 16p. "Pink Cloud" 50 50
392 22p. "Leonora" 70 70
393 29p. "Satellite" 90 90
394 31p. "Preston Guild" 95 95
395 34p. "Thalia" .. .. 1·10 1·10
390/5 .. .. *Set of* 6 4·00 4·00

97 Long-eared Owl

(Des Audrey North. Litho Questa)

1988 (12 Oct). *Christmas. Manx Birds. T* **97** *and similar horiz designs. Multicoloured. P* 14.

396 12p. Type **97** 35 35
397 15p. European Robin 45 45
398 31p. Grey Partridge 90 90
396/8 .. .. *Set of* 3 1·50 1·50

98 Ginger Cat

99 Tudric Pewter Clock, *c.* 1903

(Des P. Layton. Litho Questa)

1989 (8 Feb). *Manx Cats. T* **98** *and similar horiz designs. Multicoloured. P* 14.

399 16p. Type **98** 40 40
400 27p. Black and white cat 75 75
401 30p. Tortoiseshell and white cat 85 85
402 40p. Tortoiseshell cat .. .. 1·10 1·10
399/402 .. .. *Set of* 4 2·75 2·75

(Des Colleen Corlett. Litho Cartor, France)

1989 (8 Feb). *125th Birth Anniv of Archibald Knox (artist and designer). T* **99** *and similar multicoloured designs. P* 13.

403 13p. Type **99** 35 35
404 16p. "Celtic Cross" watercolour 45 45
405 23p. Silver cup and cover, 1902-03 .. .. 65 65
406 32p. Gold and silver brooches from Liberty's Cymric range (*horiz*) 90 90
407 35p. Silver jewel box, 1900 (*horiz*) .. .. 1·00 1·00
403/7 .. .. *Set of* 5 3·00 3·00

100 William Bligh and Old Church, Onchan

(Des C. Abbott. Litho B.D.T.)

1989 (28 Apr). *Bicentenary of the Mutiny on the Bounty. T* **100** *and similar horiz designs. Multicoloured. P* 14.

408 13p. Type **100** 25 30
 a. Booklet pane. Nos. 408/10 and 412/14 .. 3·00
 b. Booklet pane. Nos. 408/9 and 411/14 .. 3·00
409 16p. Bligh and loyal crew cast adrift .. 30 35
410 23p. Pitcairn Islands 1989 Settlement Bicentary 90 c., No. 345 .. .. 80 85
 a. Booklet pane. Nos. 410/11, each × 3 .. 3·00
411 27p. Norfolk Island 1989 Bicentenary 39 c., No. 461 .. .. 90 95
412 30p. Midshipman Peter Heywood and Tahiti 60 65
413 32p. H.M.S. *Bounty* anchored off Pitcairn Island 65 70
414 35p. Fletcher Christian and Pitcairn Island .. 70 75
408/14 .. .. *Set of* 7 3·75 4·00
MS415 110 × 85 mm. Nos. 410/11 and 414 .. 2·25 2·25

Nos. 410/11 were only issued in £5.30 booklets and as part of No. **MS**415.

Booklet panes Nos. 408a/b and 410a each contain two vertical rows of three stamps, separated by a central gutter.

101 Skipping and Hopscotch

102 Atlantic Puffin

(Des Colleen Corlett. Litho Enschedé)

1989 (17 May). *Europa. Children's Games. T* **101** *and similar horiz designs. Multicoloured. P* 13½.

416 13p. Type **101** 40 40
 a. Horiz pair. Nos. 416/17 .. .. .. 85 85
417 13p. Wheelbarrow, leapfrog and piggyback .. 40 40
418 23p. Completing model house and blowing bubbles 70 70
 a. Horiz pair. Nos. 418/19 .. .. .. 1·40 1·40
419 23p. Girl with doll and doll's house 70 70
416/19 .. .. *Set of* 4 2·00 2·00

Nos. 416/17 and 418/19 were printed together, *se-tenant* as composite designs, in horizontal pairs throughout the sheets.

(Des W. Oliver. Litho Questa)

1989 (20 Sept). *Sea Birds. T* **102** *and similar vert designs. Multicoloured. P* 14.

420 13p. Type **102** 25 30
 a. Strip of 4. Nos. 420/3 90
421 13p. Black Guillemot 25 30
422 13p. Common Cormorant 25 30
423 13p. Kittiwake 25 30
420/3 .. .. *Set of* 4 90 1·10

Nos. 420/3 were printed together, *se-tenant*, in horizontal and vertical strips of 4 throughout the sheet. The sheet exists with or without perforations across the side margins.

103 Red Cross Cadets learning Resuscitation

104 Mother with Baby, Jane Crookall Maternity Home

(Des A. Theobald. Litho Questa)

1989 (16 Oct). *125th Anniversary of International Red Cross and Centenary of Noble's Hospital, Isle of Man. T* **103** *and similar horiz designs. P* 14.

424 14p. multicoloured 30 35
425 17p. grey and orange-vermilion 35 40
426 23p. multicoloured 45 50
427 30p. multicoloured 60 65
428 35p. multicoloured 70 75
424/8 .. .. *Set of* 5 2·10 2·40

Designs:—17p. Anniversary logo; 23p. Signing Geneva Convention, 1864; 30p. Red Cross ambulance; 35p. Henri Dunant (founder).

(Des Colleen Corlett. Litho Questa)

1989 (16 Oct). *Christmas. 50th Anniversary of Jane Crookall Maternity Home and 75th Anniversary of St. Ninian's Church, Douglas. T* **104** *and similar vert designs. Multicoloured. P* 14½.

429 13p. Type **104** 25 30
430 16p. Mother with child 30 35
431 34p. Madonna and Child 70 75
432 37p. Baptism, St. Ninian's Church 75 80
429/32 .. .. *Set of* 4 1·75 2·00

105 "The Isle of Man Express going up a Gradient"

(Des D. Swinton. Litho B.D.T.)

1990 (14 Feb). *Isle of Man Edwardian Postcards. T* **105** *and similar horiz designs. Multicoloured. P* 14.

433 15p. Type **105** 30 35
434 19p. "A way we have in the Isle of Man" .. 40 45
435 32p. "Douglas–waiting for the male boat" .. 65 70
436 34p. "The last toast rack home, Douglas Parade" 70 75
437 37p. "The last Isle of Man boat" 75 80
433/7 .. .. *Set of* 5 2·50 2·75

POSTAGE DUE STAMPS

D 1

D 2

D 3

(Litho Questa)

1973 (5 July). *P* 13½ × 14.

D1 **D 1** ½p. red, black and bistre-yellow .. 2·25 1·40
D2 1p. red, black and cinnamon 75 55
D3 2p. red, black and light apple-green .. 15 20
D4 3p. red, black and grey 25 25
D5 4p. red, black and carmine-rose .. 35 30
D6 5p. red, black and cobalt 40 35
D7 10p. red, black and light lavender .. 50 45
D8 20p. red, black and pale turquoise-green 90 70
D1/8 .. .. *Set of* 8 5·00 3·75

A second printing of all values was put on sale by the Philatelic Bureau from 1 September 1973. These can be distinguished by the addition of a small "A" after the date "1973" in the bottom left margin of the stamps. Spurious examples of the second printing exist with the "A" removed.

Prices quoted above are for the second printing. *Prices for set of* 8 *original printing £45 mint, £40 used.*

(Des and litho Questa)

1975 (8 Jan). *Arms and inscriptions in black and red; background colour given. P* 14 × 13½.

D 9 **D 2** ½p. greenish yellow 10 10
D10 1p. flesh 10 10
D11 4p. rose-lilac 10 10
D12 7p. light greenish blue 20 20
D13 9p. brownish grey 25 25
D14 10p. bright mauve 30 30
D15 50p. orange-yellow .. .. .. 1·40 1·40
D16 £1 turquoise-green .. .. .. 2·00 2·00
D9/16 .. .. .. *Set of* 8 4·00 4·00

(Litho B.D.T.)

1982 (5 Oct). *P* 15 × 14.

D17 **D 3** 1p. multicoloured 10 10
D18 2p. multicoloured 10 10
D19 5p. multicoloured 10 10
D20 10p. multicoloured 20 25
D21 20p. multicoloured 35 40
D22 50p. multicoloured .. .. .. 90 1·00
D23 £1 multicoloured .. .. .. 1·75 1·90
D24 £2 multicoloured .. .. .. 3·50 3·75
D17/24 .. .. .. *Set of* 8 6·00 6·75

MINIMUM PRICE

The minimum price quote is 10p which represents a handling charge rather than a basis for valuing common stamps. For further notes about prices see introductory pages.

JERSEY

Further detailed information on the stamps of Jersey will be found in the Stanley Gibbons *Channel Islands Specialised Catalogue*.

WAR OCCUPATION ISSUES

Stamps issued under British authority during the German Occupation

1

(Des Major N. V. L. Rybot. Typo *Evening Post*, Jersey)

1941–42. *White paper (thin to thick). No wmk. P* 11.
1 **1** ½d. bright green (29.1.42) .. .. 3·75 2·50
a. Imperf between (vert pair) £650
b. Imperf between (horiz pair) .. £550
c. Imperf (pair) £175
d. On greyish paper .. .. .. 5·50 6·50
2 1d. scarlet (1.4.41) .. .. .. 4·00 3·50
a. Imperf between (vert pair) £650
b. Imperf between (horiz pair) .. £550
c. Imperf (pair) £200
d. On chalk-surfaced paper .. .. 38·00 40·00
e. On greyish paper .. .. .. 4·25 6·50

2 Old Jersey Farm — 3 Portelet Bay

4 Corbière Lighthouse — 5 Elizabeth Castle

6 Mont Orgueil Castle — 7 Gathering Vraic (seaweed)

(Des E. Blampied. Eng H. Cortot. Typo French Govt Works, Paris)

1943–44. *No wmk. P* 13½.
3 **2** ½d. green (1 June) .. .. .. 7·00 3·75
a. Rough, grey paper (6.10.43) .. 8·50 11·00
4 **3** 1d. scarlet (1 June) .. .. .. 1·00 50
a. On newsprint (28.2.44) .. .. 2·00 2·75
5 **4** 1½d. brown (8 June) .. .. .. 3·00 3·00
6 **5** 2d. orange-yellow (8 June) .. .. 3·00 2·25
7 **6** 2½d. blue (29 June) .. .. .. 1·50 2·25
a. On newsprint (25.2.44) .. .. 1·00 2·00
ba. Thin paper* £175
8 **7** 3d. violet (29 June) .. .. .. 1·00 4·00
3/8 .. .. *Set of* 6 14·00 14·00

*On No. 7ba the design shows clearly through the back of the stamp.

REGIONAL ISSUES

DATES OF ISSUE. The note at the beginning of the Guernsey Regional Issues also applies here.

8 — 9

(Des E. Blampied (T **8**), W. Gardner (T **9**). Portrait by Dorothy Wilding Ltd. Photo Harrison & Sons)

1958 (18 Aug)–**67.** *W* **179** *of Great Britain. P* 15 × 14.
9 **8** 2½d. carmine-red (8.6.64) 35 50
a. Imperf three sides (pair) £1750
10 **9** 3d. deep lilac 35 30
p. One centre phosphor band (9.6.67) 20 20
11 4d. ultramarine (7.2.66) 25 30
p. Two phosphor bands (5.9.67) .. 20 25
9/11p .. .. *Set of* 3 60 85

1968–69. *No wmk. Chalk-surfaced paper. PVA gum**. *One centre phosphor band* (4*d. values*) *or two phosphor bands* (5*d.*). *P* 15 × 14.
12 **9** 4d. olive-sepia (4.9.68) 20 25
13 4d. bright vermilion (26.2.69) .. 20 30
14 5d. royal blue (4.9.68) 20 40
12/14 .. .. *Set of* 3 50 85

*PVA Gum. See note after No. 722 of Great Britain.

INDEPENDENT POSTAL ADMINISTRATION

10 Elizabeth Castle

11 Queen Elizabeth II (after Cecil Beaton) — **13** Queen Elizabeth II (after Cecil Beaton)

12 Jersey Airport

(Des V. Whiteley. Photo Harrison (½d. to 1s. 9d.); Courvoisier (others))

1969 (1 Oct). *T* **10/13** *and similar horiz designs as T* **10** (*½d. to* 1*s.* 6*d.*) *or T* **12** (5*s.*, 10*s.*, £1). *Multicoloured. Granite paper* (2*s.* 6*d. to* £1). *P* 14 (*½d. to* 1*s.* 9*d.*) *or* 12 (*others*).
15 ½d. Type **10** 10 60
16 1d. La Hougue Bie (prehistoric tomb) (*shades*) 15 20
a. Booklet stamp with blank margins .. 55 60
17 2d. Portelet Bay 10 15
18 3d. La Corbière Lighthouse 20 15
b. Orange omitted £110
19 4d. Mont Orgueil Castle by night 15 10
a. Booklet stamp with blank margins .. 30 35
20 5d. Arms and Royal Mace 15 10
21 6d. Jersey Cow 30 40
22 9d. Chart of English Channel 55 90
23 1s. Mont Orgueil Castle by day 90 90
24 1s. 6d. As 9d. .. .. 1·75 1·75
25 1s. 9d. Type **11** .. .. 1·75 1·75
26 2s. 6d. Type **12** .. .. 3·75 2·50
27 5s. Legislative Chamber .. .. .. 14·00 6·00
28 10s. The Royal Court .. .. .. 28·00 18·00
a. Error. Green border* £4000
29 £1 Type **13** (*shades*) .. .. .. 2·00 1·50
15/29 .. .. *Set of* 15 45·00 30·00

*During the final printing of the 10s. a sheet was printed in the colours of the 50p., No. 56, i.e. green border instead of slate.

The 3d. is known with the orange omitted.

There was no postal need for the ½d. value as the ½d. coin had been withdrawn prior to its issue in anticipation of decimalisation.

Nos. 16a and 19a come from 2s. booklets for the automatic machines formerly used for the Great Britain 2s. booklets (see also note after Guernsey No. 28).

Various papers were used by Harrisons. The ½d. and 1d. exist on much thicker paper from 2s. booklets and the 2d. to 1s. 9d. exist on thinner paper having white instead of creamy gum.

24 First Day Cover — **25** Lord Coutanche, former Bailiff of Jersey

(Des R. Sellar. Photo Harrison)

1969 (1 Oct). *Inauguration of Post Office. P* 14.
30 **24** 4d. multicoloured 25 30
31 5d. multicoloured 50 60
32 1s. 6d. multicoloured .. .. .. 2·00 5·00
33 1s. 9d. multicoloured .. .. .. 2·00 5·00
30/3 .. .. *Set of* 4 4·00 10·00

(Des Rosalind Pease. Photo Courvoisier)

1970 (9 May). 25*th Anniv of Liberation. T* **25** *and similar multicoloured designs. Granite paper P* 11½.
34 4d. Type **25** 25 25
35 5d. Sir Winston Churchill 35 25
36 1s. 6d. "Liberation" (Edmund Blampied) (*horiz*) .. .. 2·25 2·00
37 1s. 9d. S.S. *Vega* (*horiz*) .. .. 2·25 2·00
34/7 .. .. *Set of* 4 4·50 4·00

29 "A Tribute to Enid Blyton"

(Des Jennifer Toombs. Photo Courvoisier)

1970 (28 July). *"Battle of Flowers" Parade. T* **29** *and similar horiz designs. Multicoloured. Granite paper. P* 11½.
38 4d. Type **29** 25 35
39 5d. "Rags to Riches" (Cinderella and pumpkin) 30 45
40 1s. 6d. "Gourmet's Delight" (lobster and cornucopia) .. .. 12·00 3·50
41 1s. 9d. "We're the Greatest" (ostriches) .. 12·00 3·50
38/41 .. .. *Set of* 4 22·00 7·00

INVALIDATION. The regional issues for Jersey were invalidated for use in Jersey and Guernsey on 1 November 1969 but remained valid for use in the rest of the United Kingdom. Nos. 15/41 (except No. 29) and Nos. D1/6 were invalidated on 14 February 1972.

33 Jersey Airport

(Des V. Whiteley. Photo Harrison (½ to 9p.); Courvoisier (others))

1970 (1 Oct)–**74.** *Decimal Currency. Designs as Nos.* 15/28, *but with values inscr in decimal currency as in T* **33**, *and new horiz design as T* **10** (6*p.*). *Chalk-surfaced paper* (4½, 5½, 8*p.*), *granite paper* (10, 20, 50*p.*).
42 ½p. Type **10** (15.2.71) 10 10
a. Booklet stamp with blank margins .. 40 40
43 1p. La Corbière Lighthouse (*shades*) (15.2.71) 10 10
a. Orange omitted .. ..
44 1½p. Jersey Cow (15.2.71) 10 10
45 2p. Mont Orgueil Castle by night (15.2.71) 10 10
a. Booklet stamp with blank margins .. 1·10 1·10
46 2½p. Arms and Royal Mace (15.2.71) .. 10 10
a. Booklet stamp with blank margins .. 70 70
ab. Gold (Mace) omitted £350
ac. Gold (Mace) printed double £275
47 3p. La Hougue Bie (prehistoric tomb) (15.2.71) 10 10
a. Booklet stamp with blank margins (1.12.72) 90 60
48 3½p. Portelet Bay (15.2.71) 15 15
a. Booklet stamp with blank margins (1.7.74) 1·10 70
49 4p. Chart of English Channel (15.2.71) .. 15 15
49*a* 4½p. Arms and Royal Mace (1.11.74) .. 20 20
ab. Uncoated paper £350
50 5p. Mont Orgueil Castle by day (15.2.71) .. 10 15
50*a* 5½p. Jersey Cow (1.11.74) 40 25
51 6p. Martello Tower, Archirondel (15.2.71) 25 30
52 7½p. Chart of English Channel (15.2.71) .. 30 40
52*a* 8p. Mont Orgueil Castle by night (1.11.74) 25 25
53 9p. Type **11** (15.2.71) 30 30
54 10p. Type **33** 30 55
55 20p. Legislative Chamber 60 75
56 50p. The Royal Court .. .. 1·25 1·25
42/56 .. .. *Set of* 18 4·00 4·50

Original printings of the ½p. to 4p., 5p. and 6p. to 9p. were with PVA gum; printings from 1974 (including original printings of the 4½p. and 5½p.) have dextrin added (see notes after No. X1017 of Great Britain). The 10p. to 50p. have gum arabic.

The border of No. 56 has been changed from turquoise-blue to dull green.

34 White Eared-pheasant

(Des Jennifer Toombs. Photo Courvoisier)

1971 (12 Mar). *Wildlife Preservation Trust* (1*st series*). *T* **34** *and similar multicoloured designs. Granite paper. P* 11½.
57 2p. Type **34** 60 25
58 2½p. Thick-billed Parrot (*vert*) 60 25
59 7½p. Western Black and White Colobus Monkey (*vert*) .. .. 10·50 3·75
60 9p. Ring-tailed Lemur .. .. .. 10·50 3·75
57/60 .. .. *Set of* 4 20·00 7·25

See also Nos. 73/6, 217/21, 324/9 and 447/51.

35 Poppy Emblem and Field — **36** "Tante Elizabeth" (E. Blampied)

(Des G. Drummond. Litho Questa)

1971 (15 June). *50th Anniv of Royal British Legion. T* **35** *and similar horiz designs. Multicoloured. P* 14.

61 2p. Royal British Legion Badge 25 20
62 2½p. Type **35** 25 20
63 7½p. Jack Counter, V.C., and Victoria Cross 3·00 2·50
64 9p. Crossed Tricolour and Union Jack 3·25 2·75
61/4 *Set of* 4 6·00 5·00

(Des and photo Courvoisier)

1971 (5 Oct). *Paintings. T* **36** *and similar multicoloured designs. Granite paper. P* 11½.

65 2p. Type **36** 15 15
66 2½p. "English Fleet in the Channel" (P. Monamy) (*horiz*) 20 20
67 7½p. "The Boyhood of Raleigh" (Millais) (*horiz*) 3·00 2·50
68 9p. "The Blind Beggar" (W. W. Ouless) 3·25 2·75
65/8 *Set of* 4 6·00 5·00

See also Nos. 115/18 and 213/16.

37 Jersey Fern

38 Artillery Shako

(Des G. Drummond. Photo Courvoisier)

1972 (18 Jan). *Wild Flowers of Jersey. T* **37** *and similar vert designs. Multicoloured. Granite paper. P* 11½.

69 3p. Type **37** 15 15
70 5p. Jersey Thrift 50 50
71 7½p. Jersey Orchid 3·00 2·50
72 9p. Jersey Viper's Bugloss 3·00 2·50
69/72 *Set of* 4 6·00 5·00

(Des Jennifer Toombs. Photo Courvoisier)

1972 (17 Mar). *Wildlife Preservation Trust (2nd series). Multicoloured designs similar to T* **34**. *Granite paper. P* 11½.

73 2½p. Cheetah 50 20
74 3p. Rothschild's Mynah (*vert*) 30 25
75 7½p. Spectacled Bear 1·75 2·00
76 9p. Tuatara 1·90 2·00
73/6 *Set of* 4 4·00 4·00

(Des and photo Courvoisier)

1972 (27 June). *Royal Jersey Militia. T* **38** *and similar vert designs. Multicoloured. Granite paper. P* 11½.

77 2½p. Type **38** 15 20
78 3p. Shako (2nd North Regt) 20 20
79 7½p. Shako (5th South-West Regt) 1·10 1·25
80 9p. Helmet (3rd Jersey Light Infantry) 1·25 1·40
77/80 *Set of* 4 2·50 2·75

39 Princess Anne

40 Armorican Bronze Coins

(Des G. Drummond from photographs by D. Groves. Photo Courvoisier)

1972 (1 Nov). *Royal Silver Wedding. T* **39** *and similar multicoloured designs. Granite paper. P* 11½.

81 2½p. Type **39** 10 10
82 3p. Queen Elizabeth and Prince Philip (*horiz*) 10 10
83 7½p. Prince Charles 40 40
84 20p. The Royal Family (*horiz*) 50 50
81/4 *Set of* 4 1·00 1·00

(Des G. Drummond. Photo Courvoisier)

1973 (23 Jan). *Centenary of La Société Jersiaise. T* **40** *and similar multicoloured designs. Granite paper. P* 11½.

85 2½p. Silver cups 10 10
86 3p. Gold torque (*vert*) 10 10
87 7½p. Royal Seal of Charles II (*vert*) 50 40
88 9p. Type **40** 50 40
85/8 *Set of* 4 1·10 90

41 Balloon and Letter

42 *North Western*

(Des and photo Courvoisier)

1973 (16 May). *Jersey Aviation History* (*1st series*). *T* **41** *and similar horiz designs. Multicoloured. Granite paper. P* 11½.

89 3p. Type **41** 10 10
90 5p. Seaplane "Astra" 15 15
91 7½p. Supermarine "Sea Eagle" 50 60
92 9p. De Havilland "Express" 50 60
89/92 *Set of* 4 1·10 1·25

See also Nos. 340/3.

(Des G. Drummond. Photo Courvoisier)

1973 (6 Aug). *Centenary of Jersey Eastern Railway. T* **42** *and similar designs showing early locomotives. Multicoloured. Granite paper. P* 11½.

93 2½p. Type **42** 10 10
94 3p. *Calvados* 10 10
95 7½p. *Carteret* 50 40
96 9p. *Caesarea* 50 40
93/6 *Set of* 4 1·10 90

43 Princess Anne and Capt. Mark Phillips

(Des and photo Courvoisier)

1973 (14 Nov). *Royal Wedding. Granite paper. P* 11½.

97 **43** 3p. multicoloured 10 10
98 20p. multicoloured 80 60

44 Spider Crab

45 Freesias

(Des Jennifer Toombs. Photo Courvoisier)

1973 (15 Nov). *Marine Life. T* **44** *and similar horiz designs. Multicoloured. Granite paper. P* 11½.

99 2½p. Type **44** 10 10
100 3p. Conger eel 10 10
101 7½p. Lobster 35 25
102 20p. Ormer 55 40
99/102 *Set of* 4 90 70

(Des G. Drummond. Photo Courvoisier)

1974 (13 Feb). *Spring Flowers. T* **45** *and similar vert designs. Multicoloured. Granite paper. P* 11½.

103 3p. Type **45** 10 10
104 5½p. Anemones 10 10
105 8p. Carnations and Gladioli 30 25
106 10p. Daffodils and Iris 50 35
103/6 *Set of* 4 90 70

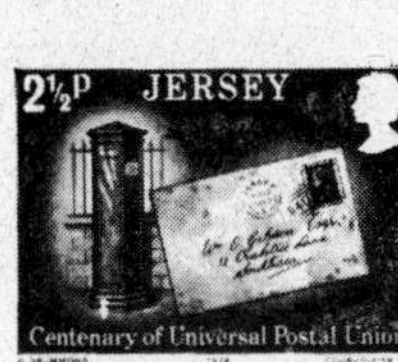

46 First Letter-Box and Contemporary Cover

47 John Wesley

(Des G. Drummond. Photo Courvoisier)

1974 (7 June). *U.P.U. Centenary. T* **46** *and similar horiz designs. Multicoloured. Granite paper. P* 11½.

107 2½p. Type **46** 10 10
108 3p. Postmen, 1862 and 1969 10 10
109 5½p. Letter-box and letter, 1974 25 30
110 20p. R.M.S. *Aquila* (1874) and aeroplane (1974) 70 60
107/10 *Set of* 4 1·00 90

(Des, recess and litho D.L.R.)

1974 (31 July). *Anniversaries. T* **47** *and similar vert designs. P* 13 × 14.

111 3p. agate and light cinnamon 10 10
112 3½p. blackish violet and light azure 10 10
113 8p. blue-black and pale rose-lilac 30 35
114 20p. black and pale buff 70 65
a. Pale buff (background) omitted
111/14 *Set of* 4 1·00 1·00

Portraits and events:—3p. Type **47** (Bicentenary of Methodism in Jersey); 3½p. Sir William Hillary, founder (150th Anniv of R.N.L.I.); 8p. Cannon Wace, poet and historian (800th Death Anniv); 20p. Sir Winston Churchill (Birth Centenary).

48 Royal Yacht

49 Potato Digger

(Des and photo Courvoisier)

1974 (22 Nov). *Marine Paintings by Peter Monamy. T* **48** *and similar multicoloured designs. Granite paper. P* 11½.

115 3½p. Type **48** 10 10
116 5½p. French two-decker 15 15
117 8p. Dutch vessel (*horiz*) 25 30
118 25p. Battle of Cap La Hague, 1692 (55 × 27 *mm*) 65 60
115/18 *Set of* 4 1·00 1·00

(Des G. Drummond. Photo Courvoisier)

1975 (25 Feb). *19th-Century Farming. T* **49** *and similar horiz designs. Multicoloured. Granite paper. P* 11½.

119 3p. Type **49** 10 10
120 3½p. Cider crusher 10 15
121 8p. Six-horse plough 35 25
122 10p. Hay cart 45 30
119/22 *Set of* 4 90 70

50 H.M. Queen Elizabeth, the Queen Mother (photograph by Cecil Beaton)

51 Shell

(Des and photo Courvoisier)

1975 (30 May). *Royal Visit. Granite paper. P* 11½.

123 **50** 20p. multicoloured 55 60

(Des A. Games. Photo Courvoisier)

1975 (6 June). *Jersey Tourism. T* **51** *and similar vert designs based on holiday posters. Multicoloured. Granite paper. P* 11½.

124 5p. Type **51** 10 10
125 8p. Parasol 15 15
126 10p. Deckchair 35 30
127 12p. Sandcastle with flags of Jersey and the U.K. 40 35
124/7 *Set of* 4 90 80
MS128 146 × 68 mm. Nos. 124/7 80 1·10

52 Common Tern

53 Siskin "3-A"

(Des Jennifer Toombs. Photo Courvoisier)

1975 (28 July). *Sea Birds. T* **52** *and similar vert designs. Multicoloured. Granite paper. P* 11½.

129 4p. Type **52** 15 15
130 5p. British Storm Petrel 15 15
131 8p. Brent Geese 30 35
132 25p. Shag 60 55
129/32 *Set of* 4 1·10 1·10

(Des A. Theobald. Photo Courvoisier)

1975 (30 Oct). *50th Anniv of Royal Air Forces Association, Jersey Branch. T* **53** *and similar horiz designs. Multicoloured. Granite paper. P* 11½.

133 4p. Type **53** 10 10
134 5p. "Southampton" flying-boat 15 15
135 10p. Mk. I "Spitfire" 30 30
136 25p. Folland "Gnat" 60 60
133/6 *Set of* 4 1·00 1·00

54 Map of Jersey Parishes

55 Parish Arms and Island Scene

(Des Courvoisier (£2). G. Drummond (others). Litho Questa (½ to 15p.). Photo Courvoisier (others))

1976–80. *Various multicoloured designs as T* **54/5**.

(*a*) *Parish Arms and Views as T* **54**. *P* 14½. (29 Jan)

137 ½p. Type **54** 10 10
138 1p. Zoological Park 10 10
a. Booklet pane of 2 plus 2 *se-tenant* labels (5.4.76) .. .. 1·75
b. Booklet pane of 4 (5.4.76) .. .. 1·50
139 5p. St. Mary's Church 15 15
a. Booklet pane of 4 (5.4.76) 60
140 6p. Seymour Tower 15 15
a. Booklet pane of 4 (28.2.78) .. .. 1·25
141 7p. La Corbière Lighthouse 20 20
a. Booklet pane of 4 (5.4.76) 75
142 8p. St. Saviour's Church 20 20
a. Booklet pane of 4 (28.2.78) .. .. 1·50
143 9p. Elizabeth Castle 25 25
a. Booklet pane of 4 (6.5.80) .. .. 1·25
144 10p. Gorey Harbour 25 25
145 11p. Jersey Airport 30 25
146 12p. Grosnez Castle 30 30
147 13p. Bonne Nuit Harbour 35 35
148 14p. Le Hocq Tower 35 40
149 15p. Morel Farm 40 45

(*b*) *Emblems as T* **55**. *Granite paper. P* 12 (20 Aug 1976–16 Nov 1977)

150 20p. Type **55** 50 50
151 30p. Flag and map 75 75
152 40p. Postal H.Q. and badge .. .. 1·00 1·00
153 50p. Parliament, Royal Court and arms .. 1·25 1·25
154 £1 Lieutenant-Governor's flag and Government House .. .. 2·50 2·50
155 £2 Queen Elizabeth II (photograph by Alex Wilson) (*vert*) (16.11.77) .. 3·50 3·75
137/55 .. *Set of* 19 12·00 12·00

Nos. 156/9 are vacant.

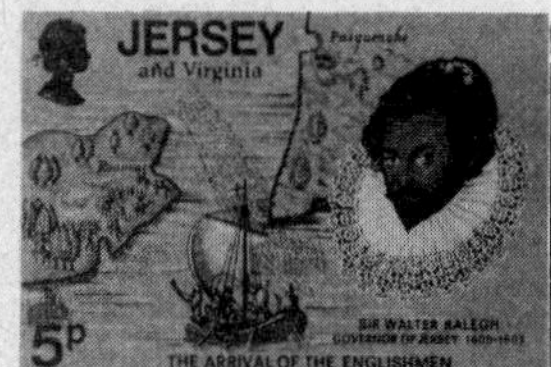

56 Sir Walter Ralegh and Map of Virginia

(Des M. Orbell. Photo Courvoisier)

1976 (29 May). *"Links with America". T* **56** *and similar horiz designs. Multicoloured. Granite paper. P* 11½.

160 5p. Type **56** 10 10
161 7p. Sir George Carteret and map of New Jersey 15 15
162 11p. Philippe Dauvergne and Long Island Landing 40 35
163 13p. John Copley and sketch 45 40
160/3 .. *Set of* 4 1·00 90

57 Dr. Grandin and Map of China

58 Coronation, 1953 (photographed by Cecil Beaton)

(Des Jennifer Toombs. Photo Courvoisier)

1976 (25 Nov). *Birth Centenary of Dr. Lilian Grandin (medical missionary). T* **57** *and similar horiz designs. Granite paper. P* 11½.

164 5p. multicoloured 10 10
165 7p. light yellow, yellow-brown and black .. 15 15
166 11p. multicoloured 40 35
167 13p. multicoloured 45 40
164/7 .. *Set of* 4 1·00 90

Designs:—7p. Sampan on the Yangtze; 11p. Overland trek; 13p. Dr. Grandin at work.

(Des G. Drummond. Photo Courvoisier)

1977 (7 Feb). *Silver Jubilee. T* **58** *and similar vert designs. Multicoloured. Granite paper. P* 11½.

168 5p. Type **58** 15 15
169 7p. Visit to Jersey, 1957 .. .. 30 20
170 25p. Queen Elizabeth II (photo by Peter Grugeon) 80 80
168/70 .. *Set of* 3 1·10 1·00

59 Coins of 1871 and 1877

(Des D. Henley. Litho Questa)

1977 (25 Mar). *Centenary of Currency Reform. T* **59** *and similar horiz designs. Multicoloured. P* 14.

171 5p. Type **59** 10 10
172 7p. One-twelfth shilling, 1949 .. .. 15 15
173 11p. Silver Crown, 1966 .. .. 40 35
174 13p. £2 piece, 1972 .. .. 45 40
171/4 .. *Set of* 4 1·00 90

60 Sir William Weston and *Santa Anna*, 1530

(Des A. Theobald. Litho Questa)

1977 (24 June). *St. John Ambulance Centenary. T* **60** *and similar horiz designs each showing a Grand Prior of the Order. Multicoloured. P* 14 × 13½.

175 5p. Type **60** 10 10
176 7p. Sir William Drogo and ambulance, 1877 15 15
177 11p. Duke of Connaught and ambulance, 1917 .. .. 40 35
178 13p. Duke of Gloucester and stretcher-team, 1977 .. .. 45 40
175/8 .. *Set of* 4 1·00 90

61 Arrival of Queen Victoria, 1846

(Des R. Granger Barrett. Litho Questa)

1977 (29 Sept). *125th Anniv of Victoria College. T* **61** *and similar multicoloured designs. P* 14½.

179 7p. Type **61** 20 20
180 10½p. Victoria College, 1852 .. .. 25 20
181 11p. Sir Galahad statue, 1924 (*vert*) .. 30 35
182 13p. College Hall (*vert*) 35 35
179/82 .. *Set of* 4 1·00 1·00

62 Harry Vardon Statuette and Map of Royal Jersey Course

(Des Jennifer Toombs. Litho Questa)

1978 (28 Feb). *Centenary of Royal Jersey Golf Club. T* **62** *and similar horiz designs. Multicoloured. P* 14.

183 6p. Type **62** 15 15
184 8p. Harry Vardon's grip and swing .. 20 20
185 11p. Harry Vardon's putt 35 35
186 13p. Golf trophies and book by Harry Vardon 40 40
183/6 .. *Set of* 4 1·00 1·00

63 Mont Orgueil Castle

64 "Gaspé Basin" (P. J. Ouless)

(Des from paintings by Thomas Phillips. Photo Courvoisier)

1978 (1 May). *Europa. Castles. T* **63** *and similar horiz designs. Multicoloured. Granite paper. P* 11½.

187 6p. Type **63** 20 15
188 8p. St. Aubin's Fort 30 25
189 10½p. Elizabeth Castle 50 35
187/9 .. *Set of* 3 90 70

(Des R. Granger Barrett. Litho Questa)

1978 (9 June). *Links with Canada. T* **64** *and similar horiz designs. Multicoloured. P* 14½.

190 6p. Type **64** 15 15
191 8p. Map of Gaspé Peninsula 20 20
192 10½p. *Century* (brigantine) 25 25
193 11p. Early map of Jersey 30 30
194 13p. St. Aubin's Bay, town and harbour .. 35 35
190/4 .. *Set of* 5 1·10 1·10

65 Queen Elizabeth and Prince Philip

66 Mail Cutter, 1778–1827

(Des and photo Courvoisier)

1978 (26 June). *25th Anniv of Coronation. T* **65** *and similar vert design. Granite paper. P* 11½.

195 8p. silver, black and cerise 30 20
196 25p. silver, black and new blue 70 60

Design:—25p. Hallmarks of 1953 and 1977.

(Des Jersey P.O. Litho Harrison)

1978 (18 Oct). *Bicentenary of England-Jersey Government Mail Packet Service. T* **66** *and similar horiz designs. P* 14½ × 14.

197 6p. black, yellow-brown and greenish yellow 15 15
198 8p. black, dull yellowish grn & pale yell-grn 20 20
199 10½p. black, ultramarine and cobalt 30 30
200 11p. black, purple and pale rose-lilac .. 35 35
201 13p. black, Venetian red and pink 45 45
197/201 .. *Set of* 5 1·25 1·25

Designs:—8p. *Flamer*, 1831–37; 10½p. *Diana*, 1877–90; 11p. *Ibex*, 1891–1925; 13p. *Caesarea*, 1960–75.

67 Jersey Calf

68 Jersey Pillar Box, *circa* 1860

(Des Jersey P.O. and Questa. Litho Questa)

1979 (1 Mar). *9th World Jersey Cattle Bureau Conference. T* **67** *and similar horiz design. Multicoloured. P* 13½.

202 6p. Type **67** 20 15
203 25p. "Ansom Designette" (cow presented to the Queen, 27 June 1978) (46 × 29 *mm*) 80 65

(Des Jennifer Toombs. Litho Questa)

1979 (1 Mar). *Europa. T* **68** *and similar vert designs. Multicoloured.* A. *P* 14. B. *P* 14½.

			A		B	
204	8p.	Type **68**	20	25	20	25
	a.	Horiz pair. Nos. 204/5	40	50	40	50
205	8p.	Clearing a modern Jersey post box ..	20	25	20	25
206	10½p.	Telephone switchboard, *circa* 1900 ..	25	30	25	30
	a.	Horiz pair, Nos. 206/7	55	65	55	65
207	10½p.	Modern S.P.C. telephone system ..	25	30	25	30
204/7 ..		*Set of* 4	1·00	1·10	1·00	1·10

Nos. 204/5 and 206/7 were each printed together, *se-tenant*, in horizontal pairs throughout the sheets.

69 Percival "Mew Gull"

70 "My First Sermon"

(Des A. Theobald. Photo Courvoisier)

1979 (24 Apr). *25th Anniv of International Air Rally. T* **69** *and similar horiz designs. Multicoloured. Granite paper. P* 11½.

208 6p. Type **69** 15 15
209 8p. De Havilland "Chipmunk" 20 20
210 10½p. Druine "Turbulent" 30 30
211 11p. De Havilland "Tiger Moth" 35 35
212 13p. North American "Harvard" Mk. 4 .. 40 40
208/12 .. *Set of* 5 1·25 1·25

(Des Jersey P.O. and Courvoisier. Photo Courvoisier)

1979 (13 Aug). *International Year of the Child and 150th Birth Anniv of Millais. Paintings. T* **70** *and similar multicoloured designs. Granite paper. P* 12 × 12½ (25*p.*) *or* 12 × 11½ (*others*).

213 8p. Type **70** 25 25
214 10½p. "Orphans" 30 30
215 11p. "The Princes in the Tower" 40 40
216 25p. "Christ in the House of His Parents" (50 × 32 *mm*) 65 65
213/16 .. *Set of* 4 1·40 1·40

(Des Jennifer Toombs. Photo Courvoisier)

1979 (8 Nov). *Wildlife Preservation Trust* (*3rd series*). *Multicoloured designs as T* **34**. *Granite paper. P* 11½.

217 6p. Pink Pigeon (*vert*) 15 15
218 8p. Orang-Utan (*vert*) 20 20
219 11½p. Waldrapp 40 35
220 13p. Lowland Gorilla (*vert*) 45 40
221 15p. Rodriguez Flying Fox (*vert*) 50 45
217/21 .. .. *Set of* 5 1·50 1·40

71 Plan of Mont Orgueil

(Litho Enschedé)

1980 (5 Feb). *Fortresses. T* **71** *and similar multicoloured designs showing drawings by Thomas Phillips. P* 13 × 13½ (25*p.*) *or* 13½ × 13 (*others*).

222 8p. Type **71** 25 25
223 11½p. Plan of La Tour de St. Aubin 30 30
224 13p. Plan of Elizabeth Castle 35 35
225 25p. Map of Jersey showing fortresses (38 × 27 *mm*) 70 70
222/5 .. .. *Set of* 4 1·40 1·40

72 Sir Walter Raleigh and Paul Ivy (engineer) discussing Elizabeth Castle

(Des Jersey Post Office and Questa. Litho Questa)

1980 (6 May). *Europa. Personalities. Links with Britain. T* **72** *and similar vert design. Multicoloured. P* 14.

226 9p.} Type **72** .. 20 20
227 9p.} .. 20 20
a. Horiz pair. Nos. 226/7 .. .. 50 50
228 13½p.} Sir George Carteret receiving rights .. 30 35
} to Smith's Island, Virginia from King ..
229 13½p.} Charles II .. 30 35
a. Horiz pair. Nos. 228/9 .. .. 70 70
226/9 .. .. *Set of* 4 1·10 1·10

Nos. 226/7 and 228/9 were each printed together, *se-tenant*, in horizontal pair throughout the sheet, forming composite designs.

73 Planting

74 Three Lap Event

(Des R. Granger Barrett. Litho Questa)

1980 (6 May). *Centenary of Jersey Royal Potato. T* **73** *and similar vert designs. Multicoloured. P* 14.

230 7p. Type **73** 15 15
231 15p. Digging 45 35
232 17½p. Weighbridge 65 50
230/2 .. .. *Set of* 3 1·10 90

(Des A. Theobald. Photo Courvoisier)

1980 (24 July). *60th Anniv of Jersey Motor-cycle and Light Car Club. T* **74** *and similar horiz designs. Multicoloured. Granite paper. P* 11½.

233 7p. Type **74** 25 25
234 9p. Jersey International Road Race .. 25 25
235 13½p. Scrambling 40 40
236 15p. Sand racing (saloon cars) 45 45
237 17½p. National Hill Climb 50 50
233/7 .. .. *Set of* 5 1·60 1·60

75 *Eye of the Wind*

76 Detail of "The Death of Major Peirson"

(Des G. Drummond. Litho Questa)

1980 (1 Oct). *"Operation Drake" Round the World Expedition and 150th Anniv of Royal Geographical Society* (14*p.*). *P* 14.

238 7p. Type **75** 20 20
239 9p. Diving from inflatable dinghy 25 25
240 13½p. Exploration of Papua New Guinea .. 45 35
241 14p. Captain Scott's *Discovery* 45 35
242 15p. Using aerial walkways, Conservation Project, Sulawesi 45 35
243 17½p. *Eye of the Wind* and Goodyear airship .. 45 45
238/43 .. .. *Set of* 6 2·00 1·75

(Photo Courvoisier)

1981 (6 Jan). *Bicentenary of Battle of Jersey. Painting "The Death of Major Peirson" by J. S. Copley. T* **76** *and similar vert designs showing details of the work. Granite paper. P* 12½ × 12.

244 7p. multicoloured 25 25
245 10p. multicoloured 30 30
246 15p. multicoloured 50 50
247 17½p. multicoloured 55 55
244/7 .. .. *Set of* 4 1·40 1·40
MS248 144 × 97 mm. Nos. 244/7 .. .. .. 1·75 1·50

Stamps from No. **MS**248 are without white margins.

77 De Bagot

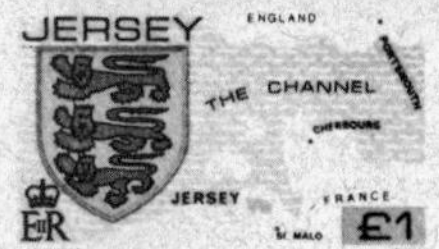

78 Jersey Crest and Map of Channel

78a "Queen Elizabeth II" (Norman Hepple)

(Des and photo Courvoisier (£5). Des G. Drummond. Litho Questa (others))

1981 (24 Feb)–**88**. *Arms of Jersey Families. T* **77** *and similar designs in black, silver and turquoise-green* (½*p.*), *black, silver and mauve* (4*p.*), *black, silver and chrome-yellow* (20*p.*), *black and dull blue* (25*p.*), *black, silver and carmine* (26*p.*) *or multicoloured* (*others*) *with T* **78/a**. *Granite paper* (£5). *P* 12½ × 12 (£5), 15 × 14 (16*p.*, 17*p.*, 18*p.*, 19*p.*, 26*p.*, 75*p.*) *or* 14 (*others*).

249 ½p. Type **77** 10 10
250 1p. De Carteret 10 10
a. Booklet pane of 6 20
b. Perf 15 × 14 (12.1.88) 10 10
251 2p. La Cloche 10 10
a. Booklet pane of 6 (1.12.81) 40
b. Perf 15 × 14 (15.11.84) 10 10
ba. Booklet pane of 6 (1.4.86) 20
252 3p. Dumaresq 10 10
a. Booklet pane of 6 55
b. Perf 15 × 14 (27.4.84) 10 10
ba. Booklet pane of 6 55
253 4p. Payn 15 15
a. Perf 15 × 14 (4.3.86) 10 10
ab. Booklet pane of 6 (6.4.87) 40
254 5p. Janvrin 15 15
a. Perf 15 × 14 (4.3.86) 10 10
255 6p. Poingdestre 20 20
a. Perf 15 × 14 (4.3.86) 10 10
256 7p. Pipon 15 15
a. Booklet pane of 6 .. .. 1·40
257 8p. Marett 15 20
a. Booklet pane of 6 (19.4.83) .. .. 1·50
258 9p. Le Breton 15 20
a. Perf 15 × 14 (27.4.84) 30 30
ab. Booklet pane of 6 .. .. 1·75
259 10p. Le Maistre 20 25
a. Booklet pane of 6 .. .. 1·75
b. Perf 15 × 14 (1.4.86) 20 25
ba. Booklet pane of 6 .. .. 1·10
260 11p. Bisson (28.7.81) 20 25
a. Booklet pane of 6 (19.4.83) .. .. 2·00
b. Perf 15 × 14 (6.4.87) 20 25
ba. Booklet pane of 6 .. .. 1·25
261 12p. Robin (28.7.81) 20 25
a. Perf 15 × 14 (27.4.84) 20 25
ab. Booklet pane of 6 .. .. 1·25
262 13p. Herault (28.7.81) 40 40
a. Perf 15 × 14 (15.11.84) 25 30
263 14p. Messervy (28.7.81) 45 45
a. Perf 15 × 14 (15.11.84) 25 30
ab. Booklet pane of 6 (1.4.86) .. .. 1·50
264 15p. Fiott (28.7.81) 45 45
a. Perf 15 × 14 (6.4.87) 25 30
ab. Booklet pane of 6 .. .. 1·60
265 16p. Malet (25.10.85) 30 35
a. Booklet pane of 6 (17.5.88) .. .. 1·75
266 17p. Mabon (25.10.85) 30 35
266*a* 18p. De St. Martin (26.4.88) 30 35
266*b* 19p. Hamptonne (26.4.88) 35 40
267 20p. Badier (28.7.81) 60 55
a. Perf 15 × 14 (4.3.86) 35 40
268 25p. L'Arbalestier (23.2.82) 45 50
268*a* 26p. Type **77** (26.4.88) 45 50
269 30p. Journeaux (23.2.82) 90 90
a. Perf 15 × 14 (4.3.86) 50 55
270 40p. Lempriere (23.2.82) .. .. .. 1·10 1·10
a. Perf 15 × 14 (6.4.87) 70 75
271 50p. D'Auvergene (23.2.82) .. .. .. 1·40 1·40
a. Perf 15 × 14 (6.4.87) 90 95
272 75p. Remon (23.4.87) .. .. 1·25 1·40
273 £1 Type **78** (23.2.82) .. .. 2·50 2·50
274 £5 Type **78a** (17.11.83) .. .. .. 9·00 9·50
249/74 .. .. *Set of* 29 18·00 19·00

No. 258a only occurs in the £2.16 stamp booklet issued 27 April 1984, No. 259b from the £3.12 booklet of 1 April 1986, No. 260b from the £3.60 booklet of 6 April 1987 and No. 261a from the £2.16 booklet of 27 April 1984 and the £3.84 booklet of 17 May 1988.

79 Knight of Hambye slaying Dragon

(Des Jennifer Toombs. Litho Questa)

1981 (7 Apr). *Europa. Folklore. T* **79** *and similar horiz designs. Multicoloured. P* 14½.

275 10p. Type **79** 25 25
a. Horiz pair. Nos. 275/6 .. .. .. 55 55
276 10p. Servant slaying Knight of Hambye, and awaiting execution 25 25
277 18p. St. Brelade celebrating Easter on island 50 50
a. Horiz pair. Nos. 277/8 .. .. .. 1·10 1·10
278 18p. Island revealing itself as a huge fish .. 50 50
275/8 .. .. *Set of* 4 1·50 1·50

Legends:—10p. (*both*), Slaying of the Dragon of Lawrence by the Knight of Hambye; 18p. (*both*), Voyages of St. Brelade.

Nos. 275/6 and 277/8 were each printed together, *se-tenant*, in horizontal pairs throughout the sheet.

80 The Harbour by Gaslight

81 Prince Charles and Lady Diana Spencer

(Des R. Granger Barrett. Photo Courvoisier)

1981 (22 May). *150th Anniv of Gas Lighting in Jersey. T* **80** *and similar horiz designs showing Jersey by gaslight. Multicoloured. Granite paper. P* 11½.

279 7p. Type **80** 25 25
280 10p. The Quay 30 30
281 18p. Royal Square 45 45
282 22p. Halkett Place 55 55
283 25p. Central Market 65 65
279/83 .. .. *Set of* 5 2·00 2·00

(Des Jersey P.O. and Courvoisier. Photo Courvoisier)

1981 (28 July). *Royal Wedding. Granite paper. P* 11½.

284 **81** 10p. multicoloured 55 50
285 25p. multicoloured .. .. 1·25 1·40

82 Christmas Tree in Royal Square

83 Jersey, 16,000 B.C.

(Des A. Copp. Litho Questa)

1981 (29 Sept). *Christmas. T* **82** *and similar vert designs. Multicoloured. P* 14½.

286 7p. Type **82** 25 25
287 10p. East window, Parish Church, St. Helier 40 40
288 18p. Boxing Day meet of Jersey Drag Hunt 60 60
286/8 .. .. *Set of* 3 1·10 1·10

(Des A. Copp. Litho Questa)

1982 (20 Apr). *Europa. Historic Events. Formation of Jersey. T* **83** *and similar multicoloured designs. P* 14½.

289 11p. Type **83** 30 30
290 11p. Jersey, 10,000 B.C. (*vert*) 30 30
291 19½p. 7,000 B.C. (*vert*) 60 60
292 19½p. 4,000 B.C. 60 60
289/92 .. .. *Set of* 4 1·60 1·60

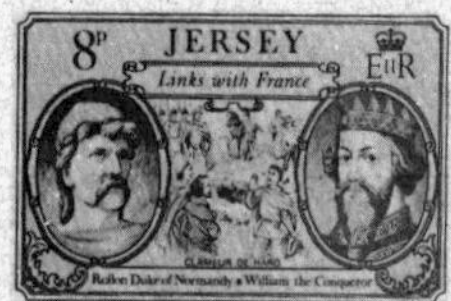

84 Duke Rollo of Normandy, William the Conqueror and "Clameur de Haro" (traditional procedure for obtaining justice)

(Des R. Granger Barrett. Litho Questa)

1982 (11 June–7 Sept). *Links with France. T* **84** *and similar horiz designs. Multicoloured. P* 14.

293	8p.	Type **84**	30	30
	a.	Horiz pair. Nos. 293/4	60	60
	b.	Booklet pane. Nos. 293 and 294 each × 2 (7 Sept)	1·40	
294	8p.	John of England, Philippe Auguste of France and Siege of Rouen	30	30
295	11p.	Jean Martell (brandy merchant), early still and view of Cognac	40	40
	a.	Horiz pair. Nos. 295/6	80	80
	b.	Booklet pane. Nos. 295 and 296 each × 2 (7 Sept)	1·60	
296	11p.	Victor Hugo, "Le Rocher des Proscrits" (rock where he used to meditate) and Marine Terrace	40	40
297	19½p.	Pierre Teilhard de Chardin (philosopher) and "Maison Saint Louis" (science institute)	70	70
	a.	Horiz pair. Nos. 297/8	1·40	1·40
	b.	Booklet pane. Nos. 297 and 298 each × 2 (7 Sept)	2·75	
298	19½p.	Père Charles Rey (scientist), anemotachymeter and The Observatory, St. Louis	70	70
293/8		*Set of* 6	2·50	2·50

The two designs of each value were printed together, *se-tenant*, in horizontal pairs throughout the sheet.

Nos. 293b, 295b and 297b were printed with either a French or an English inscription on the selvedge.

85 Sir William Smith, Founder of Boys' Brigade

86 H.M.S. *Tamar* with H.M.S. *Dolphin* at Port Egmont

(Des A. Theobald. Photo Courvoisier)

1982 (18 Nov). *75th Anniv of Boy Scout Movement (Nos. 301/3) and Centenary of Boys' Brigade (Nos. 299/301). T* **85** *and similar multicoloured designs. Granite paper. P* 11½.

299	8p.	Type **85**	25	25
300	11p.	Boys' Brigade "Old Boys" band, Liberation Parade, 1945 (*vert*)	35	35
301	24p.	William Smith and Lord Baden-Powell at Royal Albert Hall, 1903	75	75
302	26p.	Lord and Lady Baden-Powell in St. Helier, 1924 (*vert*)	90	90
303	29p.	Scouts at "Westward Ho" campsite, St. Ouen's Bay	1·10	1·10
299/303		*Set of* 5	3·00	3·00

(Des R. Granger Barrett. Litho Questa)

1983 (15 Feb). *Jersey Adventurers* (1*st series*). *250th Birth Anniv of Philippe de Carteret. T* **86** *and similar horiz designs. Multicoloured. P* 14 × 14½.

304	8p.	Type **86**	25	25
305	11p.	H.M.S. *Dolphin* and H.M.S. *Swallow* off Magellan Strait	35	35
306	19½p.	Discovering Pitcairn Island	60	60
307	24p.	Carteret taking possession of English Cove, New Ireland	85	85
308	26p.	H.M.S. *Swallow* sinking a pirate, Macassar Strait	90	90
309	29p.	H.M.S. *Endymion* leading convoy from West Indies	1·00	1·00
304/9		*Set of* 6	3·50	3·50

See also Nos. 417/21.

87 1969 5s. Legislative Chamber Definitive

(Des G. Drummond. Litho Questa)

1983 (19 Apr). *Europa. T* **87** *and similar multicoloured designs. P* 14½.

310	11p.	Type **87**	35	40
	a.	Horiz pair. Nos. 310/11	90	90
311	11p.	Royal Mace (23 × 32 *mm*)	35	40
312	19½p.	1969 10s. Royal Court definitive showing green border error	65	75
	a.	Horiz pair. Nos. 312/13	1·75	1·75
313	19½p.	Bailiff's Seal (23 × 32 *mm*)	65	75
310/13		*Set of* 4	2·50	2·50

The two designs of each value were issued together, *se-tenant*, in horizontal pairs throughout the sheets.

88 Charles Le Geyt and Battle of Minden (1759)

(Des A. Copp. Litho Questa)

1983 (21 June). *World Communications Year and 250th Birth Anniv of Charles Le Geyt (first Jersey postmaster). T* **88** *and similar horiz designs. Multicoloured. P* 14.

314	8p.	Type **88**	25	25
315	11p.	London to Weymouth mail coach	35	35
316	24p.	P.O. Mail Packet *Chesterfield* attacked by French privateer	75	75
317	26p.	Mary Godfray and the Hue Street Post Office	90	90
318	29p.	Mail steamer leaving St. Helier harbour	1·10	1·10
314/18		*Set of* 5	3·00	3·00

89 Assembly Emblem

90 "Cardinal Newman"

(Des A. Copp. Litho Questa)

1983 (21 June). *13th General Assembly of the A.I.P.L.F. (Association Internationale des Parlementaires de Langue Francaise), Jersey. P* 14½.

319	**89**	19½p. multicoloured	90	90

(Des and photo Courvoisier)

1983 (20 Sept). *50th Death Anniv of Walter Ouless (artist). T* **90** *and similar multicoloured designs, showing paintings. Granite paper. P* 11½.

320	8p.	Type **90**	25	25
321	11p.	"Incident in the French Revolution"	35	35
322	20½p.	"Thomas Hardy"	70	70
323	31p.	"David with the head of Goliath" (38 × 32 *mm*)	1·00	1·00
320/3		*Set of* 4	2·10	2·10

91 Golden Lion Tamarin

92 C.E.P.T. 25th Anniversary Logo

(Des W. Oliver. Litho Questa)

1984 (17 Jan). *Wildlife Preservation Trust* (4*th series*). *T* **91** *and similar vert designs. Multicoloured. P* 13½ × 14.

324	9p.	Type **91**	30	30
325	12p.	Snow Leopard	40	40
326	20½p.	Jamaican Boa	65	65
327	26p.	Round Island Gecko	80	80
328	28p.	Coscoroba Swan	90	90
329	31p.	St. Lucia Amazon	1·00	1·00
324/9		*Set of* 6	3·75	3·75

(Des J. Larrivière. Litho Questa)

1984 (12 Mar). *Europa. P* 14½ × 15.

330	**92**	9p. cobalt, dull ultramarine and black	30	30
331		12p. light green, green and black	40	40
332		20½p. rose-lilac, deep magenta and black	70	70
330/2		*Set of* 3	1·25	1·25

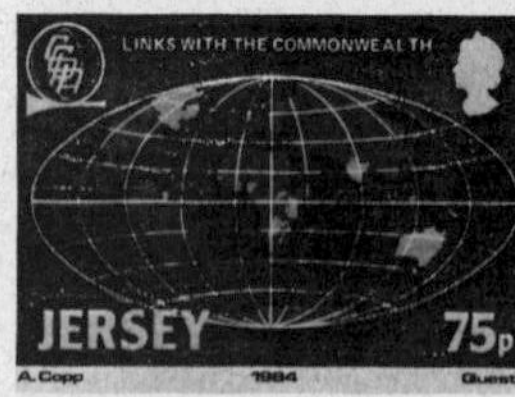

93 Map showing Commonwealth

(Des A. Copp. Litho Questa)

1984 (12 Mar). *Links with the Commonwealth. Sheet* 108 × 74 *mm. P* 15 × 14½.

MS333	**93**	75p. multicoloured	2·75	2·75

94 *Sarah Bloomshoft* at Demie de Pas Light, 1906

(Des G. Palmer. Litho Questa)

1984 (1 June). *Centenary of the Jersey R.N.L.I. Lifeboat Station T* **94** *and similar horiz designs showing famous rescues. Multicoloured. P* 14½.

334	9p.	Type **94**	30	30
335	9p.	*Hearts of Oak* and *Maurice Georges*, 1949	30	30
336	12p.	*Elizabeth Rippon* and *Hanna*, 1949	40	40
337	12p.	*Elizabeth Rippon* and *Santa Maria*, 1951	40	40
338	20½p.	*Elizabeth Rippon and Bacchus*, 1973	65	65
339	20½p.	*Thomas James King* and *Cythara*, 1983	65	65
334/9		*Set of* 6	2·50	2·50

95 Bristol "Type 170" Freighter

(Des G. Drummond. Litho Questa)

1984 (24 July). *Jersey Aviation History* (2*nd series*). *T* **95** *and similar horiz designs. Multicoloured. P* 14.

340	9p.	Type **95**	30	30
341	12p.	Airspeed "A.S.57 Ambassador 2"	40	40
342	26p.	De Havilland "D.H.114 Heron 1B"	90	90
343	31p.	De Havilland "D.H.89A Dragon Rapide"	1·10	1·10
340/3		*Set of* 4	2·50	2·50

96 "Robinson Crusoe leaves the Wreck"

97 "B.L.C. St Helier" Orchid

(Des R. Granger Barrett. Photo Courvoisier)

1984 (21 Sept). *Links with Australia. Paintings by John Alexander Gilfillan. T* **96** *and similar horiz designs. Multicoloured. Granite paper. P* 11½ × 12.

344	9p.	Type **96**	30	30
345	12p.	"Edinburgh Castle"	40	40
346	20½p.	"Maori Village"	65	65
347	26p.	"Australian Landscape"	80	80
348	28p.	"Waterhouse's Corner, Adelaide"	90	90
349	31p.	"Captain Cook at Botany Bay"	1·00	1·00
344/9		*Set of* 6	3·75	3·75

(Photo Courvoisier)

1984 (15 Nov). *Christmas. Jersey Orchids* (1*st series*). *T* **97** *and similar vert design. Multicoloured. Granite paper. P* 12 × 11½.

350	9p.	Type **97**	45	45
351	12p.	"Oda Mt Bingham"	75	75

See also Nos. 433/7.

98 "*Hebe* off Corbiere, 1874"

(Photo Harrison)

1985 (26 Feb). *Death Centenary of Philip John Ouless (artist). T* **98** *and similar horiz designs. Multicoloured. P* 14 × 15.

352	9p.	Type **98**	30	30
353	12p.	"The *Gaspe* engaging the *Diomede*"	40	40
354	22p.	"The Paddle-steamer *London* entering Naples, 1856"	80	80
355	31p.	"The *Rambler* entering Cape Town, 1840"	1·10	1·10
356	34p.	"St. Aubin's Bay from Mount Bingham, 1872"	1·25	1·25
352/6		*Set of* 5	3·50	3·50

99 John Ireland (composer) and Faldouet Dolmen

100 Girls' Brigade

(Des Jennifer Toombs. Litho Questa)

1985 (23 Apr). *Europa. European Music Year. T* **99** *and similar horiz designs. Multicoloured. P* 14.

357	10p.	Type **99**	40	45
358	13p.	Ivy St. Helier (actress) and His Majesty's Theatre, London	55	60
359	22p.	Claude Debussy (composer) and Elizabeth Castle	90	95
357/9		*Set of* 3	1·60	1·75

(Des A. Theobald. Litho Questa)

1985 (30 May). *International Youth Year. T* **100** *and similar vert designs. Multicoloured. P* 14½×14.
360 10p. Type **100** 30 30
361 13p. Girl Guides (75th anniversary) 50 50
362 29p. Prince Charles and Jersey Youth Service Activities Base .. .. 1·00 1·00
363 31p. Sea Cadet Corps .. .. 1·00 1·00
364 34p. Air Training Corps .. .. .. 1·10 1·10
360/4 .. .. *Set of* 5 3·50 3·50

101 *Duke of Normandy* at Cheapside

(Des G. Palmer. Photo Courvoisier)

1985 (16 July). *The Jersey Western Railway. T* **101** *and similar horiz designs. Multicoloured. Granite paper. P* 11½.
365 10p. Type **101** 40 40
366 13p. Saddletank at First Tower 50 50
367 22p. *La Moye* at Millbrook 90 90
368 29p. *St. Heliers* at St. Aubin .. .. .. 1·00 1·00
369 34p. *St. Aubyns* at Corbière .. .. .. 1·10 1·10
365/9 .. .. *Set of* 5 3·50 3·50

102 Memorial Window to Revd. James Hemery (former Dean) and St. Helier Parish Church

(Des R. Granger Barrett. Litho Questa)

1985 (10 Sept). *300th Anniv of Huguenot Immigration. T* **102** *and similar horiz designs. Multicoloured. P* 14.
370 10p. Type **102** 20 30
a. Booklet pane of 4 80
371 10p. Judge Francis Jeune, Baron St. Helier, and Houses of Parliament 20 30
a. Booklet pane of 4 80
372 13p. Silverware by Pierre Amiraux 25 45
a. Booklet pane of 4 .. .. 1·00
373 13p. Francis Voisin (merchant) and Russian port 25 45
a. Booklet pane of 4 .. .. 1·00
374 22p. Robert Brohier, Schweppes carbonation plant and bottles 45 75
a. Booklet pane of 4 .. .. 1·75
375 22p. George Ingouville, V.C., R.N., and attack on Viborg 45 75
a. Booklet pane of 4 .. .. 1·75
370/5 .. .. *Set of* 6 1·60 2·75

Each booklet pane has margins all round and text printed on the binding selvedge.

103 Howard Davis Hall, Victoria College

(Des A. Copp. Litho Cartor, France)

1985 (25 Oct). *Thomas Benjamin Davis (philanthropist) Commemoration. T* **103** *and similar horiz designs. Multicoloured. P* 13½.
376 10p. Type **103** 40 40
377 13p. Racing schooner *Westward* 60 60
378 31p. Howard Davis Park, St. Helier .. .. 1·10 1·10
379 34p. Howard Davis Experimental Farm, Trinity .. .. 1·25 1·25
376/9 .. .. *Set of* 4 3·00 3·00

104 "Amaryllis belladonna" (Pandora Sellars)

105 King Harold, William of Normandy and Halley's Comet, 1066 (from Bayeux Tapestry)

(Des C. Abbott. Litho Questa)

1986 (28 Jan). *Jersey Lilies. T* **104** *and similar multicoloured design. P* 15×14½.
380 13p. Type **104** 40 40
381 34p. "A Jersey Lily" (Lily Langtry) (Sir John Millais) (30×48 *mm*) .. .. .. 1·00 1·00
MS382 140×96 mm. Nos. 380×4 and 381 .. 2·75 2·75

(Des Jennifer Toombs. Litho Cartor, France)

1986 (4 Mar). *Appearance of Halley's Comet. T* **105** *and similar horiz designs. Multicoloured. P* 13½×13.
383 10p. Type **105** 30 30
384 22p. Lady Carteret, Edmond Halley, map and Comet 75 75
385 31p. Aspects of communications in 1910 and 1986 on TV screen .. .. .. 1·10 1·10
383/5 .. .. *Set of* 3 2·00 2·00

106 Dwarf Pansy

107 Queen Elizabeth II (from photo by Karsh)

(Des Pandora Sellars. Litho Questa)

1986 (21 Apr). *Europa. Environmental Conservation. T* **106** *and similar vert designs. Multicoloured. P* 14½×14.
386 10p. Type **106** 35 35
387 14p. Sea Stock 65 65
388 22p. Sand Crocus 95 95
386/8 .. .. *Set of* 3 1·75 1·75

(Photo Courvoisier)

1986 (21 Apr). *60th Birthday of Queen Elizabeth II. Granite paper. P* 11½.
389 **107** £1 multicoloured .. .. 1·75 1·90

No. 389 was retained in use as part of the current definitive series.

108 Le Rât Cottage

109 Prince Andrew and Miss Sarah Ferguson

(Des A. Copp. Litho Cartor, France)

1986 (17 June). *50th Anniv of National Trust for Jersey. T* **108** *and similar horiz designs. Multicoloured. P* 13½×13.
390 10p. Type **108** 30 30
391 14p. The Elms (Trust headquarters) 45 45
392 22p. Morel Farm 70 70
393 29p. Quétivel Mill 90 90
394 31p. La Vallette .. .. 1·00 1·00
390/4 .. .. *Set of* 5 3·00 3·00

(Des A. Copp. Litho Cartor, France)

1986 (23 July). *Royal Wedding. P* 13½.
395 **109** 14p. multicoloured 50 50
396 40p. multicoloured .. .. 1·50 1·50

110 "Gathering Vraic"

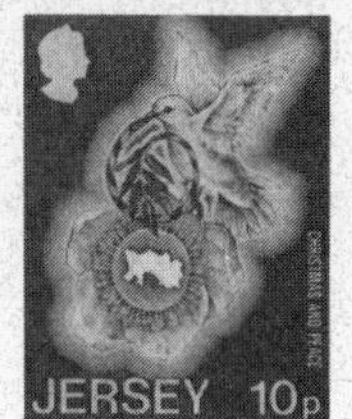

111 Island Map on Jersey Lily, and Dove holding Olive Branch

(Des A. Copp. Litho Questa)

1986 (28 Aug). *Birth Centenary of Edmund Blampied (artist). T* **110** *and similar vert designs. P* 14.
397 10p. multicoloured 30 30
398 14p. black, light blue and brownish grey .. 50 50
399 29p. multicoloured .. .. 1·00 1·00
400 31p. black, pale orange and brownish grey .. 1·10 1·10
401 34p. multicoloured .. .. 1·25 1·25
397/401 .. .. *Set of* 5 3·75 3·75

Designs:—14p. "Driving Home in the Rain"; 29p. "The Miller"; 31p. "The Joy Ride"; 34p. "Tante Elizabeth".

(Des G. Taylor. Litho Questa)

1986 (4 Nov). *Christmas. International Peace Year. T* **111** *and similar vert designs. Multicoloured. P* 14½.
402 10p. Type **111** 40 40
403 14p. Mistletoe wreath encircling robin and dove 60 60
404 34p. Christmas cracker releasing dove .. .. 1·25 1·25
402/4 .. .. *Set of* 3 2·00 2·00

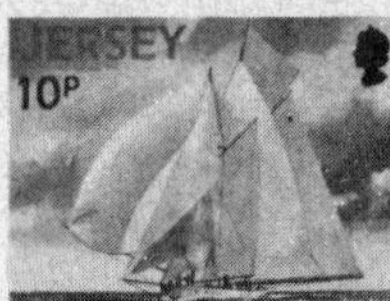

112 *Westward* under Full Sail

(Des A. Copp. Litho Cartor, France)

1987 (15 Jan). *Racing Schooner "Westward". T* **112** *and similar horiz designs. Multicoloured. P* 13½.
405 10p. Type **112** 40 40
406 14p. T. B. Davis at the helm 60 60
407 31p. *Westward* overhauling *Britannia* .. 1·10 1·10
408 34p. *Westward* fitting-out at St. Helier .. 1·25 1·25
405/8 .. .. *Set of* 4 3·00 3·00

113 De Havilland "DH86" *Belcroute Bay*

(Des G. Palmer. Litho Questa)

1987 (3 Mar). *50th Anniv of Jersey Airport. T* **113** *and similar horiz designs. Multicoloured. P* 14.
409 10p. Type **113** 30 30
410 14p. Boeing "757" and Douglas "DC 9" .. 40 40
411 22p. Britten Norman "Trislander" and "2A Islander" 70 70
412 29p. Short "SD330" and Vickers "Viscount 800" .. .. 1·00 1·00
413 31p. BAC "1-11" and HPR "7 Dart Herald" 1·25 1·25
409/13 .. .. *Set of* 5 3·25 3·25

114 St. Mary and St. Peter's Roman Catholic Church

(Des A. Copp. Litho Questa)

1987 (23 Apr). *Europa. Modern Architecture. T* **114** *and similar horiz designs. Multicoloured. P* 15×14.
414 11p. Type **114** 35 35
415 15p. Villa Devereux, St. Brelade 65 65
416 22p. Fort Regent Leisure Centre, St. Helier (57×29 *mm*) 90 90
414/16 .. .. *Set of* 3 1·75 1·75

115 H.M.S. *Racehorse* (bomb-ketch) trapped in Arctic

(Des R. Granger Barrett. Litho Questa)

1987 (9 July). *Jersey Adventurers (2nd series). Philippe D'Auvergne. T* **115** *and similar horiz designs. Multicoloured. P* 14.
417 11p. Type **115** 40 40
418 15p. H.M.S. *Alarm* on fire, Rhode Island .. 50 50
419 29p. H.M.S. *Arethusa* wrecked off Ushant .. 90 90
420 31p. H.M.S. *Rattlesnake* stranded on Isle de Trinidad .. .. 1·00 1·00
421 34p. Mont Orgueil Castle and fishing boats .. 1·10 1·10
417/21 .. .. *Set of* 5 3·50 3·50

See also Nos. 501/6.

116 Grant of Lands to Normandy, 911 and 933

(Des Jennifer Toombs. Litho Cartor, France)

1987 (9 Sept–16 Oct). *900th Death Anniv of William the Conqueror. T* **116** *and similar horiz designs. Multicoloured. P* 13½.
422 11p. Type **116** 40 40
a. Booklet pane of 4 (16 Oct) .. .. 1·60
423 15p. Edward the Confessor and Duke Robert I of Normandy landing on Jersey, 1030 .. 45 45
a. Booklet pane of 4 (16 Oct) .. .. 1·75

424 22p. King William's coronation, 1066, and fatal fall, 1087 .. .. 70 70
a. Booklet pane of 4 (16 Oct) .. .. 2·75
425 29p. Death of William Rufus, 1100, and Battle of Tinchebrai, 1106 .. .. .. 85 85
a. Booklet pane of 4 (16 Oct) .. .. 3·25
426 31p. Civil war between Matilda and Stephen, 1135–41 .. .. 95 95
a. Booklet pane of 4 (16 Oct) .. .. 3·75
427 34p. Henry inherits Normandy, 1151; John asserts ducal rights in Jersey, 1213 .. 1·10 1·10
a. Booklet pane of 4 (16 Oct) .. .. 4·25
422/7 .. .. *Set of* 6 4·00 4·00

Each booklet pane has margins all round and text printed on the binding selvedge.

117 "Grosnez Castle"

(Photo Courvoisier)

1987 (3 Nov). *Christmas. Paintings by John Le Capelain. T* **117** *and similar horiz designs. Multicoloured. Granite paper. P* 11½.
428 11p. Type **117** 40 40
429 15p. "St. Aubin's Bay" 60 60
430 22p. "Mont Orgueil Castle" 80 80
431 31p. "Town Fort and Harbour, St. Helier" .. 1·00 1·00
432 34p. "The Hermitage" .. .. 1·10 1·10
428/32 .. .. *Set of* 5 3·50 3·50

118 *Cymbidium pontac*

(Litho Questa)

1988 (12 Jan). *Jersey Orchids (2nd series). T* **118** *and similar multicoloured designs. P* 14.
433 11p. Type **118** 40 40
434 15p. *Odontioda Eric Young (vert)* 50 50
435 29p. *Lycaste auburn* "Seaford" and "Ditchling" 90 90
436 31p. *Odontoglossum St. Brelade (vert)* .. 1·00 1·00
437 34p. *Cymbidium mavourneen* "Jester" .. 1·10 1·10
433/7 .. .. *Set of* 5 3·50 3·50

119 Labrador Retriever

(Des P. Layton. Litho Questa)

1988 (2 Mar). *Centenary of Jersey Dog Club. T* **119** *and similar horiz designs. Multicoloured. P* 14.
438 11p. Type **119** 40 40
439 15p. Wire-haired Dachshund 60 60
440 22p. Pekinese 80 80
441 31p. Cavalier King Charles Spaniel .. .. 1·00 1·00
442 34p. Dalmatian .. .. 1·10 1·10
438/42 .. .. *Set of* 5 3·50 3·50

120 D.H. "Dash 7" Aircraft, London Landmarks and Jersey Control Tower

121 Rodriguez Fody

(Des A. Copp. Litho Cartor, France)

1988 (26 Apr). *Europa. Transport and Communications. T* **120** *and similar multicoloured designs. P* 14×13½ *(horiz) or* 13½×14 *(vert)*.
443 16p. Type **120** 50 50
444 16p. Weather radar and Jersey airport landing system (*vert*) 50 50
445 22p. Hydrofoil, St. Malo and Elizabeth Castle, St. Helier 80 80
446 22p. Port control tower and Jersey Radio maritime communication centre, La Moye (*vert*) 80 80
443/6 .. .. *Set of* 4 2·25 2·25

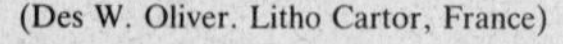

(Des W. Oliver. Litho Cartor, France)

1988 (6 July). *Wildlife Preservation Trust (5th series). T* **121** *and similar multicoloured designs. P* 13½ × 14 *(vert) or* 14 × 13½ *(horiz)*.
447 12p. Type **121** 40 40
448 16p. Volcano Rabbit (*horiz*) 50 50
449 29p. White-faced Marmoset 90 90
450 31p. Ploughshare Tortoise (*horiz*) .. .. 1·00 1·00
451 34p. Mauritius Kestrel .. .. 1·10 1·10
447/51 .. .. *Set of* 5 3·50 3·50

122 Rain Forest Leaf Frog, Costa Rica

123 St. Clement Parish Church

(Des V. Ambrus. Photo Courvoisier)

1988 (27 Sept). *Operation Raleigh. T* **122** *and similar horiz designs. Multicoloured. Granite paper. P* 12.
452 12p. Type **122** 45 45
453 16p. Archaelogical survey, Peru 55 55
454 22p. Climbing glacier, Chile 70 70
455 29p. Red Cross Centre, Solomon Islands .. 80 80
456 31p. Underwater exploration, Australia .. 85 85
457 34p. *Zebu* (brigantine) returning to St. Helier 1·10 1·10
452/7 .. .. *Set of* 6 4·00 4·00

(Des P. Layton. Litho B.D.T.)

1988 (15 Nov). *Christmas. Jersey Parish Churches (1st series). T* **123** *and similar horiz designs. Multicoloured. P* 13½.
458 12p. Type **123** 35 35
459 16p. St. Ouen 50 50
460 31p. St. Brelade 90 90
461 34p. St. Lawrence .. .. 1·00 1·00
458/61 .. .. *Set of* 4 2·50 2·50

124 Talbot "Type 4 CT Tourer", 1912

125 Belcroute Bay

(Des A. Copp. Litho Questa)

1989 (31 Jan). *Vintage Cars. T* **124** *and similar horiz designs. Multicoloured. P* 14.
462 12p. Type **124** 35 35
463 16p. De Dion "Bouton Type 1-D", 1920 .. 40 40
464 23p. Austin 7 "Chummy", 1926 .. .. 55 55
465 30p. Ford "Model T", 1926 .. .. .. 70 70
466 32p. Bentley 8 litre, 1930 .. .. .. 85 85
467 35p. Cadillac "452A -V16 Fleetwood Sports Phaeton", 1931 .. .. 95 95
462/7 .. .. *Set of* 6 3·50 3·50

(Des G. Drummond. Litho B.D.T.)

1989 (21 Mar)–**90**. *Jersey Scenes. T* **125** *and similar horiz designs. Multicoloured. P* 13×13½.
468 1p. **Type 125** 10 10
469 2p. **High Street, St. Aubin** 10 10
470 4p. Royal Jersey Golf Course 10 10
a. Booklet pane of 6 with margins all round (3.5.90) 40
471 5p. Portelet Bay 10 10
472 10p. **Les Charrières D'Anneport** 20 25
473 13p. **St. Helier Marina** 25 30
474 14p. Sand yacht racing, St. Ouen's Bay .. 25 30
a. Booklet pane of 6 with margins all round (3.5.90) .. .. 1·50
475 15p. Rozel Harbour 25 30
476 16p. **St. Aubin's Harbour** 30 35
477 17p. **Jersey Airport** 30 35
478 18p. Corbiere Lighthouse 30 35
a. Booklet pane of 6 with margins all round (3.5.90) .. .. 1·90
479 19p. Val de la Mare 35 40
480 20p. **Elizabeth Castle** 35 40
481 21p. Greve de Lecq (16.1.90) 35 40
482 22p. Samarès Manor (16.1.90) 40 45
483 23p. Bonne Nuit Harbour (16.1.90) 40 45
484 24p. Grosnez Castle (16.1.90) 40 45
485 25p. Augrès Manor (16.1.90) 45 50
486 26p. Central Market (16.1.90) 45 50
487 27p. St. Brelade's Bay (16.1.90) 45 50
488 30p. St. Ouen's Manor (13.3.90) 50 55
489 40p. La Hougue Bie (13.3.90) 70 75
490 50p. Mont Orgueil Castle (13.3.90) 90 95
491 75p. Royal Square, St. Helier (13.3.90) .. 1·25 1·40
468/91 .. .. *Set of* 24 8·00 9·00

MINIMUM PRICE

The minimum price quote is 10p which represents a handling charge rather than a basis for valuing common stamps. For further notes about prices see introductory pages.

126 Agile Frog

127 Toddlers' Toys

(Des W. Oliver. Litho Cartor, France)

1989 (25 Apr). *Endangered Jersey Fauna. T* **126** *and similar multicoloured designs. P* 13½×13 *(Nos.* 492 *and* 495*)*, 13×13½ *(No.* 493*) or* 13½×14 *(No.* 494*)*.
492 13p. Type **126** 25 35
493 13p. Large Chequered Skipper (*vert*) .. 25 35
494 17p. Barn Owl (*vert*) 35 50
495 17p. Green Lizard 35 50
492/5 .. .. *Set of* 4 1·50 1·50

(Des Clare Luke. Litho Questa)

1989 (25 Apr). *Europa. Children's Toys and Games. T* **127** *and similar square designs showing clay plaques. Multicoloured. P* 14.
496 17p. Type **127** 40 40
497 17p. Playground games 40 40
498 23p. Party games 70 70
499 23p. Teenage sports 70 70
496/9 .. .. *Set of* 4 2·00 2·00

128 Queen Elizabeth II and Royal Yacht *Britannia* in Elizabeth Harbour

(Des A. Copp. Litho Questa)

1989 (24 May). *Royal Visit. P* 14½.
500 **128** £1 multicoloured .. .. .. 2·50 2·50

129 Philippe D'Auvergne presented to Louis XVI, 1786

(Des V. Ambrus. Litho Cartor, France)

1989 (7 July). *Bicentenary of the French Revolution. Philippe D'Auvergne. T* **129** *and similar horiz designs. Multicoloured. P* 13½.
501 13p. Type **129** 35 35
a. Booklet pane of 4 .. .. .. 1·40
502 17p. Storming the Bastille, 1789 .. .. 45 45
a. Booklet pane of 4 .. .. .. 1·75
503 23p. Marie de Bouillon and revolutionaries, 1790 .. .. 55 55
a. Booklet pane of 4 .. .. .. 2·25
504 30p. Auvergne's headquarters at Mont Orgueil, 1795 .. .. 85 85
a. Booklet pane of 4 .. .. .. 3·25
505 32p. Landing arms for Chouan rebels, 1796 .. 85 85
a. Booklet pane of 4 .. .. .. 3·25
506 35p. The last Chouan revolt, 1799 .. .. 95 95
a. Booklet pane of 4 .. .. .. 3·75
501/6 .. .. *Set of* 6 3·50 3·50

Each booklet pane has margins all round and text printed on the binding selvedge.

130 *St. Helier* off Elizabeth Castle

(Des G. Palmer. Litho Questa)

1989 (5 Sept). *Centenary of Great Western Railway Steamer Service to Channel Islands. T* **130** *and similar horiz designs. Multicoloured. P* 13½×14.
507 13p. Type **130** 25 30
508 17p. *Caesarea II* off Corbière Lighthouse .. 35 40
509 27p. *Reindeer* in St. Helier harbour 55 60
510 32p. *Ibex* racing *Frederica* off Portelet .. 65 70
511 35p. *Lynx* off Noirmont 70 75
507/11 .. .. *Set of* 5 2·25 2·50

131 "Gorey Harbour"

132 Head Post Office, Broad Street, 1969

(Litho Enschedé)

1989 (24 Oct). *150th Birth Anniv of Sarah Louisa Kilpack (artist). T* **131** *and similar horiz designs. Multicoloured. P* 13×12½.

512	13p. Type **131**	25	30
513	17p. "La Corbière"	35	40
514	23p. "Grève de Lecq"	45	50
515	32p. "Bouley Bay"	65	70
516	35p. "Mont Orgueil"	70	75
512/16	*Set of* 5	2·25	2·40

(Des P. Layton. Litho Cartor, France)

1990 (13 Mar). *Europa. Post Office Buildings. T* **132** *and similar multicoloured designs. P* 13½×14 (*vert*) *or* 14×13½ (*horiz*).

517	18p. Type **132**	30	35
518	18p. Postal Headquarters, Mont Millais, 1990	30	35
519	24p. Hue Street Post Office, 1815 (*horiz*)	50	55
520	24p. Head Post Office, Halkett Place, 1890 (*horiz*)	50	55
517/20	*Set of* 4	1·40	1·50

133 "Battle of Flowers" Parade

(Des A. Copp. Litho Enschedé)

1990 (3 May). *Festival of Tourism. T* **133** *and similar vert designs. Multicoloured. P* 14×13½.

521	18p. Type **133**	35	40
522	24p. Sports	50	55
523	29p. Mont Orgueil Castle and German Underground Hospital Museum	60	65
524	32p. Salon Culinaire	65	70
521/4	*Set of* 4	1·90	2·10
MS525	151×100 mm. Nos. 521/4	2·10	2·25

POSTAGE DUE STAMPS

D 1

D 2 Map

(Des F. Guénier. Litho Bradbury, Wilkinson)

1969 (1 Oct). *P* 14×13½.

D1	**D 1**	1d. bluish violet	2·50	1·90
D2		2d. sepia	3·50	2·00
D3		3d. magenta	5·00	3·25
D4	**D 2**	1s. bright emerald	13·00	8·50
D5		2s. 6d. olive-grey	25·00	22·00
D6		5s. vermilion	35·00	40·00
D1/6		*Set of* 6	75·00	70·00

1971 (15 Feb)–**75**. *As Type* D **2** *but values in decimal currency.*

D 7	½p. black	10	10
D 8	1p. violet-blue	10	10
D 9	2p. olive-grey	10	10
D10	3p. reddish purple	10	10
D11	4p. pale red	10	10
D12	5p. bright emerald	15	15
D13	6p. yellow-orange (12.8.74)	15	15
D14	7p. bistre-yellow (12.8.74)	15	15
D15	8p. light greenish blue (1.5.75)	25	25
D16	10p. pale olive-grey	35	35
D17	11p. ochre (1.5.75)	35	40
D18	14p. violet	40	45
D19	25p. myrtle-green (12.8.74)	80	90
D20	50p. dull purple (1.5.75)	1·40	1·50
D7/20	*Set of* 14	4·00	4·25

D 3 Arms of St. Clement and Dovecote at Samares

D 4 St. Brelade

(Des G. Drummond. Litho Questa)

1978 (17 Jan). *Type* D **3** *and similar horiz designs showing the Parish Arms given. P* 14.

D21	1p. blue-green and black	10	10
D22	2p. orange-yellow and black (St. Lawrence)	10	10
D23	3p. lake-brown and black (St. John)	10	10
D24	4p. orange-vermilion and black (St. Ouen)	15	15
D25	5p. ultramarine and black (St. Peter)	15	20
D26	10p. brown-olive and black (St. Martin)	25	30
D27	12p. greenish blue and black (St. Helier)	30	35
D28	14p. red-orange and black (St. Saviour)	30	40
D29	15p. bright magenta and black (St. Brelade)	35	40
D30	20p. yellow-green and black (Grouville)	45	50
D31	50p. deep brown and black (St. Mary)	1·25	1·40
D32	£1 chalky blue and black (Trinity)	2·50	2·50
D21/32	*Set of* 12	5·25	6·00

Parish Views shown:—2p. Handois Reservoir; 3p. Sorel Point; 4p. Pinnacle Rock; 5p. Quetivel Mill; 10p. St. Catherine's Breakwater; 12p. St. Helier Harbour; 14p. Highlands College; 15p. Beauport Bay; 20p. La Hougue Bie; 50p. Perry Farm; £1 Bouley Bay.

(Des G. Drummond. Litho Questa)

1982 (7 Sept). *Type* D **4** *and similar vert designs depicting Jersey Harbours. P* 14.

D33	1p. bright turquoise-green and black	10	10
D34	2p. chrome-yellow and black	10	10
D35	3p. lake-brown and black	10	10
D36	4p. red and black	10	10
D37	5p. bright blue and black	10	10
D38	6p. yellow-olive and black	10	10
D39	7p. bright reddish mauve and black	10	15
D40	8p. bright orange-red and black	15	20
D41	9p. bright green and black	15	20
D42	10p. turquoise-blue and black	20	25
D43	20p. apple-green and black	35	40
D44	30p. bright purple and black	50	55
D45	40p. dull orange and black	70	75
D46	£1 bright reddish violet and black	1·75	1·90
D33/46	*Set of* 14	4·00	4·25

Designs:—2p. St. Aubin; 3p. Rozel; 4p. Greve de Lecq; 5p. Bouley Bay; 6p. St. Catherine; 7p. Gorey; 8p. Bonne Nuit; 9p. La Roque; 10p. St. Helier; 20p. Ronez; 30p. La Collette; 40p. Elizabeth Castle; £1 Upper Harbour Marina.

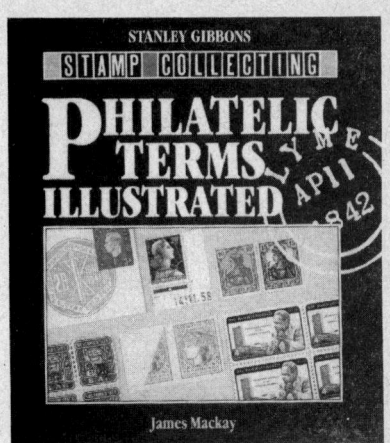

British Post Offices Abroad

The origins of the network of Post Offices, Postal Agencies and Packet Agents can be recognised from the 18th century, but the system did not become established until the expansion of trade, following the end of the Napoleonic Wars in 1815.

Many offices were provided in newly acquired dependent territories, and were then, eventually, transferred from the control of the British Post Office to the evolving local administrations.

Those in foreign countries, nearly always based on existing British Consular appointments, were mostly connected to the network of British Packet lines which had been re-established in 1814. They tended to survive until the country in which they were situated established its own efficient postal service or joined the U.P.U. The term "Post Office Agent" was employed by the British G.P.O. and "Packet Agent" by the shipping lines to describe similar functions.

Listed in this section are the Crowned-circle handstamps and G.B. stamps used in the Post Offices and Agencies situated in foreign countries. Those for the territories within the scope of this volume will be found under the following headings:

Prices. Catalogue prices quoted in this section, and throughout the volume, covering Crowned-circle handstamps and stamps of Great Britain used abroad are for fine used examples with the cancellation or handstamp clearly legible. Poor impressions of the cancellations and handstamps are worth much less than the prices quoted.

CROWNED-CIRCLE HANDSTAMPS

Following the introduction, in 1840, of adhesive stamps in Great Britain there was considerable pressure from a number of the dependent territories for the British Post Office to provide something similar for their use.

Such suggestions were resisted, however, because of supposed operational problems, but the decision was taken, in connection with an expansion of the Packet Service, to issue a uniform series of handstamps and date stamps to the offices abroad, both in the dependent territories and in foreign countries.

Under the regulations circulated in December 1841, letters and packets forwarded through these offices to the United Kingdom or any of its territories were to be sent unpaid, the postage being collected on delivery. Where this was not possible, for example from a British colony to a foreign country or between two foreign ports, then a *crowned-circle handstamp* was to be applied with the postage, paid in advance, noted alongside in manuscript.

Examples of these handstamps were supplied over twenty years from 1842, but many continued to fulfil other functions long after the introduction of adhesive stamps in the colony concerned.

Our listings cover the use of these handstamps for their initial purpose and the prices quoted are for examples used on cover during the pre-adhesive period.

In most instances the dates quoted are those on which the handstamp appears in the G.P.O. Record Books, but it seems to have been normal for the handstamps to be sent to the office concerned immediately following this registration.

Many of the handstamps were individually cut by hand, so that each has its own characteristics, but for the purposes of the listing they have been grouped into nine Types as shown in the adjacent column. No attempt has been made to identify them by anything but the most major differences, so that minor differences in size and in the type of the crown have been ignored.

DOUBLE CIRCLE

CC 1

CC 1a

Curved "PAID"

CC 1b

CC 1c

Curved "PAID"

CC 2

Straight "PAID"

SINGLE CIRCLE

CC 3

CC 4

Straight "PAID"

CC 5

Curved "PAID"

CC 6

Straight "PAID"

CC 7

Curved "PAID"

GREAT BRITAIN STAMPS USED ABROAD

Prices quoted are for single stamps not on cover unless otherwise stated. Stamps on cover are worth considerably more in most cases.

In many instances obliterators allocated to post offices abroad were, at a later date re-allocated to offices at home. Postmarks on issues later than those included in our lists can therefore safely be regarded as *not* having been "used abroad".

INDEX

TYPES OF OBLITERATOR FOR GREAT BRITAIN STAMPS USED ABROAD

HORIZONTAL OVAL

(1)

(2)

(3)

(4)

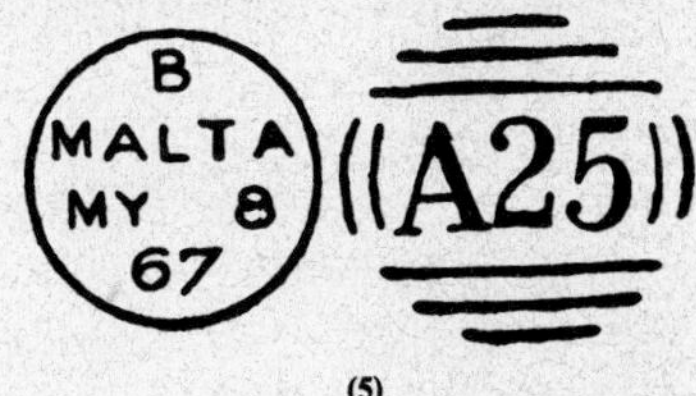

(5)

(6)

(7)

VERTICAL OVAL

(8)

(9)

(10)

(11)

(12)

(13)

(14)

(15)

CIRCULAR DATE STAMPS

(16)

(17)

(18)

(19)

(20)

ARGENTINE REPUBLIC

BUENOS AYRES

The first regular monthly British mail packet service was introduced in 1824, replacing a private arrangement which had previously existed for some years.

Great Britain stamps were used from 1860 until the office closed at the end of June 1873. Until 1878 the British Consul continued to sell stamps which were used in combination with an Argentine value prepaying the internal rate. The British stamps on such covers were cancelled on arrival in England.

CROWNED-CIRCLE HANDSTAMPS

CC1 CC 7 BUENOS AYRES (R.) (5.1.1851) *Price on cover* £650

Stamps of GREAT BRITAIN *cancelled* "B 32" *as in Types* **2, 12** *or* **13.**

1860 *to* **1873.**
Z 1 1d. rose-red (1857) .. ..
Z 2 1d. rose-red (1864) .. .. *From* 10·00
Plate Nos. 71, 72, 73, 74, 76, 78, 79, 80, 81, 82, 85, 87, 89, 90, 91, 92, 93, 94, 95, 96, 97, 99, 101, 103, 104, 107, 108, 110, 112, 113, 114, 117, 118, 119, 120, 121, 123, 125, 127, 129, 130, 131, 135, 136, 138, 139, 140, 142, 143, 145, 147, 149, 150, 151, 155, 159, 163, 164, 166, 169, 172.
Z 3 2d. blue (1858–69) .. .. *From* 20·00
Plate Nos. 8, 9, 12, 13, 14.
Z 4 3d. carmine-rose (1862) £150
Z 5 3d. rose (1865) (Plate No. 4) .. .. .. 45·00
Z 6 3d. rose (1867–73) .. .. *From* 20·00
Plate Nos. 4, 5, 6, 7, 8, 9, 10.
Z 7 4d. rose (1857) .. .. 38·00
Z 8 4d. red (1862) (Plate Nos. 3, 4) .. .. .. 48·00
Z 9 4d. vermilion (1865–73) .. .. .. *From* 24·00
Plate Nos. 7, 8, 9, 10, 11, 12, 13.
Z10 6d. lilac (1856) .. .. 50·00
Z11 6d. lilac (1862) (Plate Nos. 3, 4) .. .. ..
Z12 6d. lilac (1865–67) (Plate Nos. 5, 6) .. *From* 38·00
Z13 6d. lilac (1867) (Plate No. 6) .. .. .. 60·00
Z14 6d. violet (1867–70) (Plate Nos. 6, 8, 9) .. *From* 30·00
Z15 6d. buff (1872) (Plate No. 11) .. .. .. 60·00
Z16 6d. chestnut (1872) (Plate No. 11) .. .. .. 30·00
Z17 9d. bistre (1862) £200
Z18 9d. straw (1862) £140
Z19 9d. straw (1865) £250
Z20 9d. straw (1867) £150
Z21 10d. red-brown (1867) £175
Z22 1s. green (1856) .. .. 85·00
Z23 1s. green (1862) .. .. 60·00
Z24 1s. green (1865) (Plate No. 4) .. .. .. 40·00
Z25 1s. green (1867–73) (Plate Nos. 4, 5, 6, 7) .. *From* 18·00
Z26 1s. green (1873–77) (Plate No. 8) .. .. ..
Z27 2s. blue (1867) .. .. 95·00
Z28 5s. rose (1867) (Plate No. 1) £250

A "B 32" obliteration was later used by Mauritius on its own stamps.

AZORES

ST. MICHAELS (SAN MIGUEL)

A British Postal Agency existed at Ponta Delgada, the chief port of the island, to operate with the services of the Royal Mail Steam Packet Company.

CROWNED-CIRCLE HANDSTAMPS

CC1 CC **1b** ST. MICHAELS (27.5.1842) .. ..

BOLIVIA

COBIJA

It is believed that the British Postal Agency opened in 1852. The stamps of Great Britain were used between 1865 and 1878. The Agency closed in 1881, the town having been occupied by Chile in 1879.

CROWNED-CIRCLE HANDSTAMPS

CC1 CC 4 COBIJA (29.3.1862) .. .. *Price on cover* £4000

Stamps of GREAT BRITAIN *cancelled* "C 39" *as Types* **4, 8** *or* **12.**

1865 *to* **1878.**
Z 1 1d. rose-red (Plate Nos. 93, 95) .. .. ..
Z 2 2d. blue (1858–69) (Plate No. 14) .. .. ..
Z 3 3d. rose (1867–73) (Plate No. 6) .. .. ..
Z 4 3d. rose (1873–76) (Plate Nos. 16, 19) .. ..
Z 5 4d. sage-green (1877) (Plate No. 15) .. ..
Z 6 6d. violet (1867–70) (Plate No. 9) £350
Z 7 6d. buff (1872) (Plate No. 11) .. .. ..
Z 8 6d. grey (1874–76) (Plate Nos. 13, 14, 15, 16) .. £275
Z 9 1s. green (1867–73) (Plate Nos. 4, 5) .. ..
Z10 1s. green (1873–77) (Plate Nos. 10, 11, 12, 13) .. £275
Z11 2s. blue (1867) £450
Z12 5s. rose (1867–74) (Plate No. 2) .. .. ..

BRAZIL

The first British packets ran to Brazil in 1808 when the Portuguese royal family went into exile at Rio de Janeiro. The Agencies at Bahia and Pernambuco did not open until 1851. All three agencies used the stamps of Great Britain from 1866, and were closed in 1874.

BAHIA

CROWNED-CIRCLE HANDSTAMPS

CC1 CC 7 BAHIA (B., G. *or* R.) (6.1.1851) *Price on cover* £1500

Stamps of GREAT BRITAIN *cancelled* "C 81" *as Type* **12.**

1866 *to* **1874.**
Z 1 1d. rose-red (1864–79) .. .. .. *From* 30·00
Plate Nos. 90, 93, 96, 108, 113, 117, 135, 140, 147, 155.
Z 2 1½d. lake-red (1870–74) (Plate No. 3) .. .. 65·00
Z 3 2d. blue (1858–69) (Plate Nos. 9, 12, 13, 14) .. 50·00
Z 4 3d. rose (1865) (Plate No. 4) .. .. ..
Z 5 3d. rose (1867–73) (Plate Nos. 4, 6, 8, 9, 10) .. 30·00
Z 6 3d. rose (1873–79) (Plate No. 11) .. .. ..
Z 7 4d. vermilion (1865–73) .. .. .. *From* 20·00
Plate Nos. 8, 9, 10, 11, 12, 13.
Z 8 6d. lilac (1865–67) (Plate No. 5) .. .. ..
Z 9 6d. lilac (1867) (Plate No. 6) .. .. .. 40·00
Z10 6d. violet (1867–70) (Plate Nos. 6, 8, 9) .. *From* 35·00
Z11 6d. buff (1872–73) (Plate Nos. 11, 12) .. *From* 85·00
Z12 6d. chestnut (1872) (Plate No. 11) .. .. ..
Z13 6d. grey (1873) (Plate No. 12) .. .. ..
Z14 6d. grey (1874–76) (Plate No. 13) .. .. ..
Z15 9d. straw (1865) £300
Z16 9d. straw (1867) £100
Z17 1s. green (1865) (Plate No. 4) .. .. .. 30·00
Z18 1s. green (1867–73) (Plate Nos. 4, 5, 6, 7) .. *From* 20·00
Z19 1s. green (1873–77) (Plate Nos. 8, 9) .. *From* 25·00
Z20 2s. blue (1867) £175
Z21 5s. rose (1867) (Plate No. 1) £325

PERNAMBUCO

CROWNED-CIRCLE HANDSTAMPS

CC2 CC 7 PERNAMBUCO (Black *or* R.) (6.1.1851) *Price on cover* £1500

Stamps of GREAT BRITAIN *cancelled* "C 82" *as Type* **12.**

1866 *to* **1874.**
Z22 1d. rose-red (1864–79) .. .. .. *From* 30·00
Plate Nos. 85, 108, 111, 130, 131, 132, 149, 157, 159, 160, 187.
Z23 2d. blue (1858–69) (Plate Nos. 9, 12, 13, 14) *From* 35·00
Z24 3d. rose (1867–73) (Plate Nos. 4, 5, 6, 7, 10) .. 35·00
Z25 3d. rose (1873–77) (Plate No. 11) .. .. ..
Z26 4d. vermilion (1865–73) .. .. .. *From* 20·00
Plate Nos. 9, 10, 11, 12, 13, 14.
Z27 6d. lilac (1865–67) (Plate Nos. 5, 6) .. ..
Z28 6d. lilac (1867) (Plate No. 6) .. .. .. 40·00
Z29 6d. violet (1867–70) (Plate Nos. 8, 9) .. *From* 35·00
Z30 6d. buff (1872–73) (Plate Nos. 11, 12) .. .. 45·00
Z31 6d. chestnut (1872) (Plate No. 11) .. .. .. 35·00
Z32 6d. grey (1873) (Plate No. 12) .. .. ..
Z33 9d. straw (1865) £350
Z34 9d. straw (1867) £120
Z35 10d. red-brown (1867) £175
Z36 1s. green (1865) (Plate No. 4) .. .. .. 50·00
Z37 1s. green (1867–73) (Plate Nos. 4, 5, 6, 7) .. .. 28·00
Z38 2s. blue (1867) £225
Z39 5s. rose (1867–74) (Plate Nos. 1, 2) £400

RIO DE JANEIRO

CROWNED-CIRCLE HANDSTAMPS

CC3 CC 7 RIO DE JANEIRO (Black, B., G. *or* R.) (6.1.1851) .. .. .. *Price on cover* £400

Stamps of GREAT BRITAIN *cancelled* "C 83" *as Type* **12.**

1866 *to* **1874.**
Z40 1d. rose-red (1857) .. .. 38·00
Z41 1d. rose-red (1864–79) .. .. .. *From* 20·00
Plate Nos. 71, 76, 80, 82, 86, 94, 103, 113, 117, 119, 123, 130, 132, 134, 135, 146, 148, 159, 161, 166, 185, 200, 204.
Z42 2d. blue (1858–69) (Plate Nos. 9, 12, 13, 14) *From* 22·00
Z43 3d. rose (1867–73) (Plate Nos. 4, 5, 6, 7, 8) *From* 28·00
Z44 3d. rose (1873–77) (Plate No. 11) .. .. ..
Z45 4d. vermilion (1865–73) .. .. .. *From* 20·00
Plate Nos. 8, 9, 10, 11, 12, 13, 14.
Z46 6d. lilac (1865–67) (Plate No. 5) .. .. ..
Z47 6d. lilac (1867) (Plate No. 6) .. .. .. 30·00
Z48 6d. violet (1867–70) (Plate Nos. 6, 8, 9) .. *From* 28·00
Z49 6d. buff (1872) (Plate No. 11) .. .. .. 45·00
Z50 6d. chestnut (1872) (Plate No. 11) .. .. .. 35·00
Z51 6d. grey (1873) (Plate No. 12) .. .. ..
Z52 9d. straw (1865) £225
Z53 9d. straw (1867) £100
Z54 10d. red-brown (1867) £130
Z55 1s. green (1865) (Plate No. 4) .. .. .. 30·00
Z56 1s. green (1867–73) (Plate Nos. 4, 5, 6, 7) .. *From* 12·00
Z57 1s. green (1873–77) (Plate Nos. 8, 9) .. .. 20·00
Z58 2s. blue (1867) .. .. 80·00
Z59 5s. rose (1867–74) (Plate Nos. 1, 2) .. *From* £200

CAPE VERDE ISLANDS

The British Packet Agency at St. Vincent opened in 1851 as part of the revised service to South America. The agency was closed by 1880.

CROWNED-CIRCLE HANDSTAMPS

CC1 CC **6** ST. VINCENT C.DE.V. (6.1.1851) *Price on cover* £4000

CHILE

The British Postal Agency at Valparaiso opened in 1846, to be followed by further offices at Caldera (1862) and Coquimbo (1863). The stamps of Great Britain were introduced in 1865 and all three offices closed on 31 March 1881 when Chile joined the U.P.U.

CALDERA

Stamps of GREAT BRITAIN *cancelled* "C 37" *as in Type* **4.**

1865 *to* **1881.**
Z 1 1d. rose-red (1864–79) .. .. .. *From* 25·00
Plate Nos. 71, 72, 88, 90, 95, 160, 195.
Z 2 1½d. lake-red (1870–74) (Plate No. 3) .. ..
Z 3 2d. blue (1858–69) (Plate No. 9) .. .. 35·00
Z 4 3d. rose (1865) (Plate No. 4) .. .. .. 65·00
Z 5 3d. rose (1867–73) (Plate Nos. 5, 7) .. ..
Z 6 3d. rose (1873–76) .. .. .. *From* 25·00
Plate Nos. 11, 12, 16, 17, 18, 19.
Z 7 4d. red (1862) (Plate No. 4) .. .. ..
Z 8 4d. vermilion (1865–73) .. .. .. *From* 30·00
Plate Nos. 8, 12, 13, 14.
Z 9 4d. sage-green (1877) (Plate No. 16) .. ..
Z10 6d. lilac (1862) (Plate No. 4) .. .. .. 80·00
Z11 6d. lilac (1865–67) (Plate No. 6) .. .. ..
Z12 6d. violet (1867–70) (Plate Nos. 6, 8, 9) .. *From* 40·00
Z13 6d. buff (1872) (Plate No. 11) .. .. ..
Z14 6d. chestnut (1872) (Plate No. 11) .. .. ..
Z15 6d. grey (1873) (Plate No. 12) .. .. ..
Z16 6d. grey (1874–80) .. .. .. *From* 25·00
Plate Nos. 13, 14, 15, 16, 17.
Z17 8d. orange (1876) £225
Z18 9d. straw (1867) £125
Z19 10d. red-brown (1867) £175
Z20 1s. green (1865) (Plate No. 4) .. .. ..
Z21 1s. green (1867–73) (Plate Nos. 4, 5, 6) .. *From* 22·00
Z22 1s. green (1873–77) .. .. *From* 25·00
Plate Nos. 8, 10, 11, 12, 13.
Z23 2s. blue (1867) £200
Z24 2s. brown (1880) £1100
Z25 5s. rose (1867–74) (Plate No. 2) £400

COQUIMBO

Stamps of GREAT BRITAIN *cancelled* "C 40" *as in Type* **4.**

1865 *to* **1881.**
Z26 ½d. rose-red (1870–79) (Plate No. 14) .. ..
Z27 1d. rose-red (1857) .. ..
Z28 1d. rose-red (1864–79) (Plate Nos. 85, 204) ..
Z29 2d. blue (1858–69) (Plate Nos. 9, 14) .. ..
Z30 3d. rose (1865) .. ..
Z31 3d. rose (1872) (Plate No. 8) .. .. ..
Z32 3d. rose (1873–76) (Plate Nos. 18, 19) .. *From* 22·00
Z33 4d. red (1863) (Plate No. 4) .. .. .. 50·00
Z34 4d. vermilion (1865–73) (Plate Nos. 12, 14) ..
Z35 4d. sage-green (1877) (Plate Nos. 15, 16) £100
Z36 6d. lilac (1862) (Plate Nos. 3, 4) .. .. 50·00
Z37 6d. lilac (1865–67) (Plate No. 5) .. ..
Z38 6d. lilac (1867) (Plate No. 6) .. .. .. 50·00
Z39 6d. violet (1867–70) (Plate Nos. 6, 8, 9) .. *From* 30·00
Z40 6d. buff (1872–73) (Plate Nos. 11, 12) .. *From* 55·00
Z41 6d. chestnut (1872) (Plate No. 11) .. .. ..
Z42 6d. grey (1873) (Plate No. 12) .. .. .. 45·00
Z43 6d. grey (1874–76) (Plate Nos. 13, 14, 15, 16) *From* 22·00
Z44 8d. orange (1876) .. ..
Z45 9d. straw (1862) £200
Z46 9d. straw (1867) £125
Z47 10d. red-brown (1867) .. ..
Z48 1s. green (1865) (Plate No. 4) .. .. .. 50·00
Z49 1s. green (1867–73) (Plate Nos. 4, 5, 6) .. .. 22·00
Z50 1s. green (1873–77) .. .. *From* 28·00
Plate Nos. 8, 10, 11, 12, 13.
Z51 2s. blue (1867) £125
Z51*a* 2s. cobalt (1867) .. ..
Z52 2s. brown (1880) £1200
Z53 5s. rose (1867–74) (Plate Nos. 1, 2) £325

VALPARAISO

CROWNED-CIRCLE HANDSTAMPS

CC1 CC **2** VALPARAISO (R.) (13.1.1846) *Price on cover* £375
CC2 CC **1** VALPARAISO (R.) (16.7.1846) *Price on cover* £475

Stamps of GREAT BRITAIN *cancelled* "C 30", *as in Types* **12** *and* **14** *or circular date stamp as Type* **16.**

1865 *to* **1881.**
Z54 ½d. rose-red (1870–79) .. .. .. *From* 50·00
Plate Nos. 6, 11, 12, 13, 14.
Z55 1d. rose-red (1864–79) .. .. .. *From* 15·00
Plate Nos. 80, 84, 85, 89, 91, 101, 106, 113, 116, 122, 123, 138, 140, 141, 146, 148, 149, 152, 157, 158, 162, 167, 175, 178, 181, 185, 186, 187, 189, 190, 195, 197, 198, 199, 200, 201, 207, 209, 210, 211, 212, 213, 214, 215, 217.
Z56 1½d. lake-red (1870–74) (Plate Nos. 1, 3) .. *From* 55·00
Z57 2d. blue (1858–69) (Plate Nos. 9, 13, 14, 15) .. 35·00
Z58 2½d. rosy mauve (1875), white paper (Plate No. 2) 60·00
Z59 2½d. rosy mauve (1876) (Plate Nos. 4, 8) .. .. 50·00
Z60 3d. carmine-rose (1862) .. .. ..
Z61 3d. rose (1865) (Plate No. 4) .. .. ..
Z62 3d. rose (1867–73) .. .. .. *From* 20·00
Plate Nos. 5, 6, 7, 8, 9, 10.
Z63 3d. rose (1873–76) .. .. .. *From* 20·00
Plate Nos. 11, 12, 14, 16, 17, 18, 19.
Z63*a* 4d. red (1862) (Plate No. 4) .. .. ..
Z63*b* 4d. red (1863) (Plate No. 4) (*Hair lines*) ..
Z64 4d. vermilion (1865–73) .. .. .. *From* 22·00
Plate Nos. 9, 10, 11, 12, 13, 14.
Z65 4d. vermilion (1876) (Plate No. 15) £120
Z66 4d. sage-green (1877) (Plate Nos. 15, 16) .. .. 50·00
Z67 4d. grey-brown (1880) *wmk* Large Garter ..
Plate No. 17.
Z68 6d. lilac (1862) (Plate Nos. 3, 4) .. *From* 40·00
Z69 6d. lilac (1865) (Plate Nos. 5, 6) .. ..
Z70 6d. lilac (1867) (Plate No. 6) .. .. ..
Z71 6d. violet (1867–70) (Plate Nos. 6, 8, 9) .. *From* 30·00
Z72 6d. buff (1872–73) (Plate Nos. 11, 12) .. *From* 40·00
Z73 6d. chestnut (1872) (Plate Nos. 11, 12) .. .. 25·00
Z74 6d. grey (1873) (Plate No. 12) .. .. .. 40·00
Z75 6d. grey (1874–80) .. .. .. *From* 20·00
Plate Nos. 13, 14, 15, 16, 17.
Z76 6d. grey (1881) (Plate No. 17) .. ..
Z77 8d. orange (1876) £150
Z78 9d. straw (1862) .. ..
Z79 9d. straw (1865) .. ..
Z80 9d. straw (1867) £100
Z81 10d. red-brown (1867) £120
Z82 1s. geeen (1865) (Plate No. 4) .. ..
Z83 1s. green (1867–73) (Plate Nos. 4, 5, 6, 7) .. *From* 12·00
Z84 1s. green (1873–77) .. .. .. *From* 20·00
Plate Nos. 8, 9, 10, 11, 12, 13.
Z85 1s. orange-brown (1880) (Plate No. 13) £145
Z86 2s. blue (1867) .. .. 70·00
Z86*a* 2s. cobalt (1867) £800
Z87 2s. brown (1880) £1000
Z88 5s. rose (1867–74) (Plate Nos. 1, 2) .. *From* £180
Z89 10s. grey-green (1878) (*wmk* Cross) £1500
Z90 £1 brown-lilac (1878) (*wmk* Cross) £2500

1880.
Z91 1d. Venetian red .. ..
Z92 1½d. Venetian red .. ..

COLOMBIA

The system of British Postal Agencies in the area was inaugurated by the opening of the Carthagena office in 1825. In 1842 agencies at Chagres, Panama and Santa Martha were added to the system. A further office opened at Colon in 1852, this port also being known as Aspinwall. During 1872 the system was further enlarged by an office at Savanilla, although this agency was later, 1878, transferred to Barranquilla.

Stamps of Great Britain were supplied to Carthagena, Panama and Santa Martha in 1865, Colon in 1870 and Savanilla in 1872.

All offices, except Chagres which had ceased to operate in 1855, closed for public business on 30 June 1881. Colon and Panama continued to exist as transit offices to deal with the mail across the isthmus. Both finally closed on 31 March 1921.

CARTHAGENA

CROWNED-CIRCLE HANDSTAMPS

CC1	CC **1b** CARTHAGENA (R.) (15.1.1841)	*Price on cover* £750
CC2	CC **1** CARTHAGENA (1.7.1846)	*Price on cover* £650

Stamps of GREAT BRITAIN *cancelled* "C 56" *as in Type* **4**.

1865 *to* **1881.**

Z 1	½d. rose-red (1870–79) (Plate No. 10)	
Z 2	1d. rose-red (1864–79) *From* — Plate Nos. 78, 87, 100, 111, 113, 117, 119, 125, 172, 189, 217.	30·00
Z 3	2d. blue (1858–69) (Plate Nos. 9, 14) *From*	26·00
Z 4	3d. rose (1865) (Plate No. 4)	
Z 5	3d. rose (1865–68) (Plate Nos. 4, 5)	
Z 6	3d. rose (1873–79) (Plate Nos. 12, 17, 18) *From*	38·00
Z 7	4d. vermilion (1865–73) *From* — Plate Nos. 7, 8, 9, 10, 11, 12, 13, 14.	26·00
Z 8	4d. vermilion (1876) (Plate No. 15)	£150
Z 9	4d. sage-green (1877) (Plate Nos. 15, 16) *From*	£110
Z10	6d. lilac (1865–67) (Plate Nos. 5, 6)	
Z11	6d. violet (1867–70) (Plate Nos. 6, 8) *From*	42·00
Z12	6d. grey (1873) (Plate No. 12)	40·00
Z13	6d. grey (1874–76) (Plate Nos. 13, 14, 15, 16) *From*	30·00
Z14	8d. orange (1876)	£150
Z15	9d. straw (1865)	
Z16	1s. green (1865)	
Z17	1s. green (1867–73) (Plate Nos. 4, 5, 7)	32·00
Z18	1s. green (1873–77) (Plate Nos. 8, 9, 10, 11, 12, 13)	32·00
Z19	1s. orange-brown (1880)	
Z20	2s. blue (1867)	£170
Z21	5s. rose (1867) (Plate No. 1)	£325

Cancelled "C 65" (*incorrect handstamp, supplied in error*) *as T* **12.**

1866 *to* **1881.**

Z22	½d. rose-red (1870–79) (Plate No. 10)	
Z23	1d. rose-red (1864–79) (Plate Nos. 100, 106, 111, 123) *From*	40·00
Z23*a*	1½d. lake-red (1870) (Plate No. 3)	
Z24	2d. blue (1858–69) (Plate No. 9)	38·00
Z25	2d. rose (1880)	
Z26	2½d. blue (1880) (Plate No. 19)	
Z27	3d. rose (1867–73) (Plate No. 9)	
Z28	3d. rose (1873–79) (Plate Nos. 14, 17, 19, 20)	
Z29	4d. vermilion (1865–73) *From* — Plate Nos. 7, 8, 9, 11, 12, 13, 14.	35·00
Z30	4d. vermilion (1876) (Plate No. 15)	£175
Z31	4d. sage-green (1877) (Plate Nos. 15, 16) *From*	£130
Z32	6d. violet (1867–70) (Plate Nos. 6, 8)	80·00
Z33	6d. pale buff (1872) (Plate No. 11)	
Z34	6d. grey (1873) (Plate No. 12)	60·00
Z35	6d. grey (1874–80) (Plate Nos. 13, 15, 16, 17)	40·00
Z36	8d. orange (1876)	£250
Z37	9d. straw (1865)	£250
Z38	1s. green (1865) (Plate No. 4)	50·00
Z39	1s. green (1867) (Plate Nos. 4, 5, 6, 7)	28·00
Z40	1s. green (1873–77) (Plate Nos. 8, 11, 12, 13) *From*	32·00
Z41	1s. orange-brown (1880)	
Z42	2s. blue (1867)	£350
Z43	2s. brown (1880)	£1200
Z44	5s. rose (1867) (Plate Nos. 1, 2)	£375

CHAGRES

CROWNED-CIRCLE HANDSTAMPS

CC3	CC **1** CHAGRES (16.9.1846)	

COLON

CROWNED-CIRCLE HANDSTAMPS

CC4	CC **5** COLON (R.) (21.6.1854)	*Price on cover* £3250

Stamps of GREAT BRITAIN *cancelled* "E 88" *as in Type* **12.**

1870 *to* **1881.**

Z45	1d. rose-red (1864–79) *From* — Plate Nos. 107, 121, 122, 123, 125, 127, 130, 131, 133, 136, 138, 142, 150, 151, 152, 153, 155, 156, 157, 158, 160, 169, 170, 171, 174, 176, 178, 179, 184, 187, 188, 194, 195, 201, 209, 213, 214, 217.	23·00
Z46	1d. Venetian red (1880)	
Z47	1½d. lake-red (1870–74) (Plate No. 3)	90·00
Z48	2d. blue (1858–69) (Plate Nos. 14, 15)	28·00
Z49	2d. pale rose (1880)	
Z50	3d. rose (1867–73) (Plate Nos. 6, 9)	
Z51	3d. rose (1873–76) — Plate Nos. 11, 12, 16, 18, 19, 20.	35·00
Z52	4d. vermilion (1865–73) *From* — Plate Nos. 10, 11, 12, 13, 14.	30·00
Z53	4d. vermilion (1876) (Plate No. 15)	
Z54	4d. sage-green (1877) (Plate Nos. 15, 16)	£100
Z55	4d. grey-brown (1880) *wmk* Large Garter — Plate No. 17.	£120
Z56	4d. grey-brown (1880) *wmk* Crown (Plate No. 17)	
Z57	6d. violet (1867–70) (Plate Nos. 6, 8, 9)	
Z58	6d. buff (1872) (Plate No. 11)	
Z59	6d. chestnut (1872) (Plate No. 11)	50·00
Z60	6d. grey (1873) (Plate No. 12)	
Z61	6d. grey (1874–80) *From* — Plate Nos. 13, 14, 15, 16, 17.	26·00
Z62	8d. orange (1876)	
Z63	9d. straw (1867)	£130
Z63*a*	10d. red-brown (1867)	
Z64	1s. green (1867–73) (Plate Nos. 4, 5, 6, 7)	25·00
Z65	1s. green (1873–77) *From* — Plate Nos. 8, 9, 10, 11, 12, 13.	27·00
Z66	1s. orange-brown (1880) (Plate 13)	£200
Z67	1s. orange-brown (1881) (Plate 13)	60·00
Z68	2s. blue (1867)	£120
Z69	2s. brown (1880)	£1400
Z70	5s. rose (1867) (Plate Nos. 1, 2)	£350

PANAMA

CROWNED-CIRCLE HANDSTAMPS

CC5	CC **1** PANAMA (R.) (24.8.1846)	*Price on cover* £1000

Stamps of GREAT BRITAIN *cancelled* "C 35" *as in Types* **4, 11** *or* **14.**

1865 *to* **1881.**

Z 71	½d. rose-red (1870–79) *From* — Plate Nos. 10, 11, 12, 13, 14, 15, 19.	27·00
Z 72	1d. rose-red (1864–79) *From* — Plate Nos. 71, 72, 76, 81, 85, 87, 88, 89, 93, 95, 96, 101, 104, 114, 124, 130, 138, 139, 142, 159, 168, 171, 172, 174, 177, 179, 180, 184, 185, 187, 189, 191, 192, 193, 196, 197, 200, 203, 204, 205, 207, 208, 209, 210, 211, 213, 214, 215, 218, 224.	16·00
Z 73	1½d. lake-red (1870–74) (Plate No. 3)	40·00
Z 74	2d. blue (1858–69) *From* — Plate Nos. 9, 12, 13, 14, 15.	22·00
Z 75	2½d. rosy mauve (1875) (Plate No. 1)	
Z 76	2½d. rosy mauve (1876–80) (Plate Nos. 4, 12, 16)	
Z 77	2½d. blue (1880) (Plate No. 19)	
Z 78	2½d. blue (1881) (Plate Nos. 22, 23)	
Z 79	3d. carmine-red (1862)	£100
Z 80	3d. rose (1865) (Plate No. 4)	
Z 81	3d. rose (1867–73) *From* — Plate Nos. 4, 5, 6, 7, 8, 9.	20·00
Z 82	3d. rose (1873–76) *From* — Plate Nos. 12, 14, 15, 16, 17, 18, 19, 20.	20·00
Z 83	3d. rose (1881) (Plate Nos. 20, 21)	
Z 84	4d. red (1863) (Plate No. 4)	65·00
Z 85	4d. vermilion (1865–73) *From* — Plate Nos. 7, 8, 9, 10, 11, 12, 13, 14.	25·00
Z 86	4d. vermilion (1876) (Plate No. 15)	£140
Z 87	4d. sage-green (1877) (Plate Nos. 15, 16)	95·00
Z 88	4d. grey-brown (1880) *wmk* Crown *From* — Plate Nos. 17, 18.	28·00
Z 89	6d. lilac (1862) (Plate Nos. 3, 4) *From*	55·00
Z 90	6d. lilac (1865–67) (Plate Nos. 5, 6) *From*	30·00
Z 91	6d. lilac (1867) (Plate No. 6)	
Z 92	6d. violet (1867–70) (Plate Nos. 6, 8, 9)	28·00
Z 93	6d. buff (1872–73) (Plate Nos. 11, 12) *From*	42·00
Z 94	6d. chestnut (Plate No. 11)	25·00
Z 95	6d. grey (1873) (Plate No. 12)	40·00
Z 96	6d. grey (1874–80) *From* — Plate Nos. 13, 14, 15, 16, 17.	25·00
Z 97	6d. grey (1881) (Plate No. 17)	60·00
Z 98	8d. orange (1876)	£140
Z 99	9d. straw (1862)	£150
Z100	9d. straw (1867)	£120
Z101	10d. red-brown (1867)	£150
Z102	1s. green (1865) (Plate No. 4)	50·00
Z103	1s. green (1867–73) (Plate Nos. 4, 5, 6, 7) *From*	16·00
Z104	1s. green (1873–77) *From* — Plate Nos. 8, 9, 10, 11, 12, 13.	27·00
Z105	1s. orange-brown (1880) (Plate No. 13)	£175
Z106	1s. orange-brown (1881) (Plate No. 13)	50·00
Z107	2s. blue (1867)	70·00
Z108	2s. brown (1880)	£1200
Z109	5s. rose (1867–74) (Plate Nos. 1, 2) *From*	£250

1880.

Z110	1d. Venetian red	15·00
Z111	2d. rose	25·00
Z112	5d. indigo	75·00

Later stamps cancelled "C 35" are believed to originate from sailors' letters or other forms of maritime mail.

SANTA MARTHA

CROWNED-CIRCLE HANDSTAMPS

CC6	CC **1b** SANTA MARTHA (R.) (15.12.1841)	*Price on cover* £900

Stamps of GREAT BRITAIN *cancelled* "C 62" *as in Type* **4.**

1865 *to* **1881.**

Z113	½d. rose-red (1870–79) (Plate No. 6)	70·00
Z114	1d. rose-red (1864–79) (Plate No. 106)	50·00
Z115	2d. blue (1858–69) (Plate No. 9)	70·00
Z116	4d. vermilion (1865–73) *From* — Plate Nos. 7, 8, 9, 11, 12, 13, 14.	30·00
Z117	4d. sage-green (1877) (Plate No. 15)	£100
Z118	4d. grey-brown (1880) *wmk* Large Garter — Plate No. 17.	£100
Z119	4d. grey-brown (1880) *wmk* Crown (Plate No. 17)	55·00
Z120	6d. lilac (1865–67) (Plate No. 5)	55·00
Z121	6d. grey (1873) (Plate No. 12)	
Z122	6d. grey (1874–76) (Plate No. 14)	
Z123	8d. orange (1876)	£200
Z123*a*	9d. bistre (1862)	
Z124	1s. green (1865) (Plate No. 4)	60·00
Z125	1s. green (1867–73) (Plate Nos. 5, 7)	50·00
Z126	1s. green (1873–77) (Plate No. 8)	
Z127	2s. blue (1867)	£275
Z128	5s. rose (1867) (Plate No. 2)	£375

SAVANILLA (BARRANQUILLA)

Stamps of GREAT BRITAIN *cancelled* "F 69" *as in Type* **12.**

1872 *to* **1881.**

Z129	½d. rose-red (1870–79) (Plate No. 6)	55·00
Z130	1d. rose-red (1864–79) (Plate Nos. 122, 171)	50·00
Z131	1½d. lake-red (1870–74) (Plate No. 3)	90·00
Z132	3d. rose (1867–73) (Plate No. 7)	
Z133	3d. rose (1873–76) (Plate No. 20)	85·00
Z134	3d. rose (1881) (Plate No. 20)	85·00
Z135	4d. vermilion (1865–73) (Plate Nos. 12, 13, 14)	28·00
Z136	4d. vermilion (1876) (Plate No. 15)	£150
Z137	4d. sage-green (1877) (Plate Nos. 15, 16)	95·00
Z138	4d. grey-brown (1880) *wmk* Large Garter — Plate No. 17.	£110
Z139	4d. grey-brown (1880) *wmk* Crown (Plate No. 17)	50·00
Z140	6d. buff (1872) (Plate No. 11)	
Z141	6d. grey (1878) (Plate No. 16)	60·00
Z142	8d. orange (1876)	£200
Z143	1s. green (1867–73) (Plate Nos. 5, 7)	38·00
Z144	1s. green (1873–77) (Plate Nos. 8, 11, 12, 13)	40·00
Z145	1s. orange-brown (1880)	£150
Z146	2s. blue (1867)	£170
Z147	5s. rose (1867–74) (Plate No. 2)	£350

CUBA

The British Postal Agency at Havana opened in 1762, the island then being part of the Spanish Empire. A further office, at St. Jago de Cuba, was added around 1840.

Great Britain stamps were supplied to these offices in 1865 and continued in use until they closed on 30 May 1877.

HAVANA

CROWNED-CIRCLE HANDSTAMPS

CC1	CC **1b** HAVANA (13.11.1841)	*Price on cover* £850
CC2	CC **1c** HAVANA (1848)	*Price on cover* £850
CC3	CC **2** HAVANA (14.7.1848)	*Price on cover* £750

Stamps of GREAT BRITAIN *cancelled* "C 58" *as in Types* **4, 12** *or* **14.**

1865 *to* **1877.**

Z 1	½d. rose-red (1870) (Plate Nos. 6, 12)	50·00
Z 2	1d. rose-red (1864–79) — Plate Nos. 86, 90, 93, 115, 120, 123, 144, 146, 171, 174, 208.	30·00
Z 3	2d. blue (1858–69) (Plate Nos. 9, 14, 15)	35·00
Z 4	3d. rose (1867–73) (Plate No. 4)	75·00
Z 5	3d. rose (1873–76) (Plate Nos. 18, 19)	
Z 6	4d. vermilion (1865–73) *From* — Plate Nos. 7, 10, 11, 12, 13, 14.	30·00
Z 7	4d. vermilion (1876) (Plate No. 15)	
Z 8	6d. lilac (1865) (with hyphen) (Plate No. 5)	
Z 9	6d. grey (1874–76) (Plate No. 15)	
Z10	8d. orange (1876)	
Z11	9d. straw (1867)	£180
Z12	10d. red-brown (1867)	£250
Z13	1s. green (1865) (Plate No. 4)	50·00
Z14	1s. green (1867–73) (Plate Nos. 4, 5, 7) *From*	35·00
Z15	1s. green (1873–77) (Plate Nos. 10, 12, 13) *From*	38·00
Z16	2s. blue (1867)	£160
Z17	5s. rose (1867–74) (Plate Nos. 1, 2)	£375

ST. JAGO DE CUBA

CROWNED-CIRCLE HANDSTAMPS

CC4	CC **1b** ST. JAGO-DE-CUBA (R.) (15.12.1841)	*Price on cover* £4500

Stamps of GREAT BRITAIN *cancelled* "C 88" *as Type* **12.**

1865 *to* **1877.**

Z18	½d. rose-red (1870–79) (Plate Nos. 4, 6, 14)	
Z19	1d. rose-red (1864–79) *From* — Plate Nos. 100, 105, 106, 109, 111, 120, 123, 138, 144, 146, 147, 148, 171, 208.	55·00
Z20	1½d. lake-red (1870–74) (Plate No. 3)	
Z21	2d. blue (1858–69) (Plate Nos. 9, 12, 13, 14)	
Z22	3d. rose (1867) (Plate No. 5)	
Z23	4d. vermilion (1865–73) *From* — Plate Nos. 9, 10, 11, 12, 13, 14.	55·00
Z24	4d. vermilion (1876) (Plate No. 15)	£160
Z25	6d. violet (1867–70) (Plate Nos. 6, 8, 9) *From*	£180
Z26	6d. buff (Plate No. 11)	
Z27	9d. straw (1865)	
Z27*a*	9d. straw (1867)	
Z28	10d. red-brown (1867)	£250
Z29	1s. green (1867–73) (Plate Nos. 4, 5, 6) *From*	£180
Z30	1s. green (1873–77) (Plate Nos. 9, 10, 12, 13)	
Z31	2s. blue (1867)	
Z32	5s. rose (1867) (Plate 1)	

DANISH WEST INDIES

ST. THOMAS

The British Postal Agency at St. Thomas was opened *circa* 1843 and was the office around which many of the packet routes were organised.

Great Britain stamps were introduced on 3 July 1865, and the office closed in 1879.

CROWNED-CIRCLE HANDSTAMPS

CC1	CC **1** ST. THOMAS (R.) (*circa* 1850)	*Price on cover* £500
CC2	CC **6** ST. THOMAS (R.) (1.5.1855)	*Price on cover* £1000

Stamps of GREAT BRITAIN *cancelled* "C 51" *as in Types* **4, 12** *or* **14.**

1865 *to* **1879.**

Z 1	½d. rose-red (1870–79) — Plate Nos. 5, 6, 8, 10, 11, 12.	30·00
Z 2	1d. rose-red (1857)	
Z 3	1d. rose-red (1864–79) *From* — Plate Nos. 71, 72, 79, 81, 84, 85, 86, 87, 88, 89, 90, 93, 94, 95, 96, 97, 98, 99, 100, 101, 102, 105, 106, 107, 108, 109, 110, 111, 112, 113, 114, 116, 117, 118, 119, 120, 121, 122, 123, 124, 125, 127, 129, 130, 131, 133, 134, 136, 137, 138, 139, 140, 141, 142, 144, 145, 146, 147, 148, 149, 150, 151, 152, 154, 155, 156, 157, 158, 159, 160, 161, 162, 163, 164, 165, 166, 167, 169, 170, 171, 172, 173, 174, 175, 176, 177, 178, 179, 180, 181, 182, 184, 185, 186, 187, 189, 190, 197.	18·00
Z 4	1½d. lake-red (1870–74) (Plate Nos. 1, 3)	45·00
Z 5	2d. blue (1858–69) *From* — Plate Nos. 9, 12, 13, 14, 15.	25·00
Z 6	3d. rose (1865) (Plate No. 4)	50·00
Z 7	3d. rose (1867–73) *From* — Plate Nos. 4, 5, 6, 7, 8, 9, 10.	22·00
Z 8	3d. rose (1873–76) *From* — Plate Nos. 11, 12, 14, 15, 16, 17, 18, 19.	24·00
Z 9	4d. red (1862) (Plate Nos. 3, 4)	40·00
Z10	4d. vermilion (1865–73) *From* — Plate Nos. 7, 8, 9, 10, 11, 12, 13, 14.	28·00
Z11	4d. vermilion (1876) (Plate No. 15)	£140
Z12	4d. sage-green (1877) (Plate Nos. 15, 16) *From*	£100
Z13	4d. grey-brown (1880) *wmk* Large Garter — Plate No. 17.	£130
Z14	6d. lilac (1864) (Plate No. 4)	£100
Z15	6d. lilac (1865–67) (Plate Nos. 5, 6) *From*	35·00
Z16	6d. lilac (1867) (Plate No. 6)	32·00
Z17	6d. violet (1867–70) (Plate Nos. 6, 8, 9) *From*	30·00
Z18	6d. buff (1872–73) (Plate Nos. 11, 12) *From*	60·00
Z19	6d. chestnut (1872) (Plate No. 11)	26·00
Z20	6d. grey (1873) (Plate No. 12)	40·00
Z21	6d. grey (1874–76) (Plate Nos. 13, 14, 15, 16)	25·00
Z22	8d. orange (1876)	£150
Z23	9d. straw (1862)	£150
Z24	9d. bistre (1862)	£140
Z25	9d. straw (1865)	£250
Z26	9d. straw (1867)	£110
Z27	10d. red-brown (1867)	£150

Z28 1s. green (1865) (Plate No. 4) .. .. .. 40·00
Z29 1s. green (1867–73) (Plate Nos. 4, 5, 6, 7) .. *From* 17·00
Z30 1s. green (1873–77) .. .. *From* 24·00
Plate Nos. 8, 9, 10, 11, 12, 13.
Z31 2s. blue (1867) £120
Z32 5s. rose (1867–74) (Plate Nos. 1, 2) .. *From* £225

Stamps of GREAT BRITAIN *cancelled* "D 26" *as Type* **12** *(used in connection with the Spanish Mail Packets).*

1868 *to* **1871**.
Z33 1d. rose-red (1864) .. ..
Plate Nos. 98, 125.
Z34 4d. vermilion (1865–73) (Plate Nos. 9, 10, 11) .. £500
Z35 6d. violet (1867–70) (Plate No. 8) .. .. ..
Z36 1s. green (1867) (Plate No. 4) .. .. ..

DOMINICAN REPUBLIC

British Postal Agencies may have existed in the area before 1866, but it is only from that year that details can be found concerning offices at Porto Plata and St. Domingo.

Great Britain stamps were supplied in 1869, but both agencies did not operate between 1870 and 1876. Both finally closed in 1881.

PORTO PLATA

Stamps of GREAT BRITAIN *cancelled* "C 86" *or circular date stamp as in Types* **8** *or* **17**.

1869/70 *and* **1876** *to* **1881**.
Z 1 ½d. rose-red (1870–79) (Plate Nos. 10, 12, 14) *From* 50·00
Z 2 1d. rose-red (1864–79) .. .. .. *From* 30·00
Plate Nos. 123, 130, 136, 146, 151, 178, 199, 200, 205, 217.
Z 3 1½d. lake-red (1870–74) (Plate No. 3) .. .. 75·00
Z 4 2d. blue (1858–69) (Plate Nos. 14, 15) .. .. 35·00
Z 5 2½d. rosy mauve (1876–79) (Plate Nos. 13, 14) *From* £125
Z 6 3d. rose (1873–76) (Plate No. 18) .. .. .. 70·00
Z 7 4d. vermilion (1873) (Plate No. 14) .. .. 70·00
Z 8 4d. vermilion (1876) (Plate No. 15) £175
Z 9 4d. sage-green (1877) (Plate No. 15) £100
Z10 6d. violet (1867–70) (Plate No. 8) .. .. ..
Z11 6d. grey (1874–76) (Plate No. 15) .. .. 60·00
Z12 8d. orange (1876) £250
Z13 1s. green (1867–73) (Plate Nos. 4, 7) .. *From* 35·00
Z14 1s. green (1873–77) (Plate Nos. 11, 12, 13) *From* 30·00
Z15 2s. blue (1867) £180
Z15*a* 5s. rose (1867–83) (Plate No. 2) .. .. ..

ST. DOMINGO

Stamps of GREAT BRITAIN *cancelled* "C 87" *or circular date stamp as in Types* **12** *or* **16**.

1869/70 *and* **1876** *to* **1881**.
Z16 ½d. rose-red (1870–79) .. .. .. *From* 50·00
Plate Nos. 5, 6, 8, 10, 11, 13.
Z17 1d. rose-red (1864–79) .. .. .. *From* 38·00
Plate Nos. 146, 154, 171, 173, 174, 176, 178, 186, 190, 197, 220.
Z18 1½d. lake-red (1870–74) (Plate No. 3) .. .. 75·00
Z19 2d. blue (1858–69) (Plate Nos. 13, 14) .. .. 60·00
Z20 3d. rose (1873–76) (Plate No. 18) .. .. ..
Z21 4d. vermilion (1865–73) .. .. .. *From* 40·00
Plate Nos. 11, 12, 14.
Z22 4d. vermilion (1876) (Plate No. 15) £180
Z23 4d. sage-green (1877) (Plate No. 15) £125
Z24 6d. grey (1874–76) (Plate No. 15) .. .. ..
Z25 9d. straw (1867) .. ..
Z26 1s. green (1867) (Plate No. 4) .. .. ..
Z27 1s. green (1873–77) .. .. .. *From* 55·00
Plate Nos. 10, 11, 12, 13.
Z28 2s. blue (1867) .. ..

ECUADOR

GUAYAQUIL

The first British Postal Agent in Guayaquil was appointed during 1849.

Great Britain stamps were supplied in 1865 and continued to be used until the agency closed in 1880.

Stamps of GREAT BRITAIN *cancelled* "C 41" *as Type* **4**.

1865 *to* **1880**.
Z 1 ½d. rose-red (1870–79) (Plate Nos. 5, 6) .. .. 55·00
Z 2 1d. rose-red (1857) .. ..
Z 3 1d. rose-red (1864–79) .. .. .. *From* 27·00
Plate Nos. 74, 78, 85, 92, 94, 105, 110, 115, 133, 140, 145, 166, 174, 180, 216.
Z 4 1½d. lake-red (1870–74) (Plate No. 3) .. .. 75·00
Z 5 2d. blue (1858–69) (Plate Nos. 9, 13, 14) .. *From* 30·00
Z 6 3d. carmine-rose (1862) £150
Z 7 3d. rose (1865) (Plate No. 4) .. .. .. 40·00
Z 8 3d. rose (1867–73) (Plate Nos. 6, 7, 9, 10) .. *From* 22·00
Z 9 3d. rose (1873–76) .. .. *From* 22·00
Plate Nos. 11, 12, 15, 16, 17, 18, 19, 20.
Z10 4d. red (1862) (Plate Nos. 3, 4) .. .. 60·00
Z11 4d. vermilion (1865–73) .. .. .. *From* 26·00
Plate Nos. 7, 8, 9, 10, 11, 12, 13, 14.
Z12 4d. vermilion (1876) (Plate No. 15) £130
Z13 4d. sage-green (1877) (Plate Nos. 15, 16) £100
Z14 6d. lilac (1864) (Plate No. 4) .. .. .. 70·00
Z15 6d. lilac (1865–67) (Plate Nos. 5, 6) .. .. 32·00
Z16 6d. lilac (1867) (Plate No. 6) .. .. ..
Z17 6d. violet (1867–70) (Plate Nos. 6, 8, 9) .. *From* 30·00
Z18 6d. buff (1872–73) (Plate Nos. 11, 12) .. .. 70·00
Z19 6d. chestnut (1872) .. ..
Z20 6d. grey (1873) (Plate No. 12) .. .. ..
Z21 6d. grey (1874–76) (Plate Nos. 13, 14, 15, 16) *From* 26·00
Z22 8d. orange (1876) £175
Z23 9d. straw (1862) £190
Z24 9d. straw (1867) £120
Z25 10d. red-brown (1867) £150
Z26 1s. green (1865) (Plate No. 4) .. .. .. 40·00
Z27 1s. green (1867–73) (Plate Nos. 4, 5, 6, 7) .. *From* 24·00
Z28 1s. green (1873–77) .. .. *From* 30·00
Plate Nos. 8, 9, 10, 11, 12, 13.
Z29 2s. blue (1867) £120
Z30 2s. brown (1880) £1200
Z31 5s. rose (1867–74) (Plate Nos. 1, 2) .. *From* £350

FERNANDO PO

The British Consulate in this Spanish colony was a centre of British influence in the area before the growth of interest in Nigeria. The first British Post Office Agent (the resident Consul) was appointed in 1859.

Great Britain stamps were supplied in 1874 and the office remained open until 1877.

CROWNED-CIRCLE HANDSTAMPS

CC1 CC **4** FERNANDO-PO (R.) (19.2.1859)
Price on cover £3500

Stamps of GREAT BRITAIN *cancelled* "247" *as Type* **9**.

1874 *to* **1877**.
Z1 4d. vermilion (1865–72) (Plate Nos. 13, 14) .. £650
Z2 4d. vermilion (1876) (Plate No. 15) .. .. ..
Z3 6d. grey (1874–76) (Plate Nos. 13, 14, 15, 16) .. £550

GUADELOUPE

A British Packet Agency was established on Guadeloupe around 1841 and continued to function until 1 April 1882.

No. CC1 is often found used in conjunction with French Colonies (General Issues) adhesive stamps.

A similar packet agency existed on Martinique from 1848 until 1 April 1882, but no crowned-circle handstamp appears to have been issued for it.

CROWNED-CIRCLE HANDSTAMPS

CC1 CC **1** GUADALOUPE (R., B. *or* Black) (9.3.1849)
Price on cover £900

HAITI

The original British Postal Agencies in Haiti date from 1830 when it is known a Packet Agency was established at Jacmel. An office at Port-au-Prince followed in 1842, both these agencies remaining in operation until 30 June 1881.

During this period short-lived agencies also operated in the following Haitian towns: Aux Cayes (1859 to 1863), Cap Haitien (1842 to 1863), Gonaives (1849 to 1857) and St. Marc (1854 to 1861). A further agency may have operated at Le Mole around the year 1841.

Great Britain stamps were supplied to Jacmel in 1865 and to Port-au-Prince in 1869.

CAP HAITIEN

CROWNED-CIRCLE HANDSTAMPS

CC1 CC **1b** CAPE-HAITIEN (R.) (31.12.1841)
Price on cover £2750

JACMEL

CROWNED-CIRCLE HANDSTAMPS

CC2 CC **1b** JACMEL (R.) (29.6.1843) .. *Price on cover* £900

Stamps of GREAT BRITAIN *cancelled* "C 59" *as Type* **4**.

1865 *to* **1881**.
Z 1 ½d. rose-red (1870–79) .. .. .. *From* 32·00
Plate Nos. 4, 5, 6, 10, 11, 12, 14, 15.
Z 2 1d. rose-red (1864–79) .. .. .. *From* 25·00
Plate Nos. 74, 81, 84, 87, 95, 106, 107, 109, 122, 136, 137, 139, 148, 150, 151, 152, 156, 157, 159, 160, 162, 164, 166, 167, 170, 171, 179, 181, 183, 184, 186, 187, 189, 192, 194, 198, 200, 204, 206, 215, 219.
Z 3 1½d. lake-red (1870–74) (Plate No. 3) .. .. 48·00
Z 4 2d. blue (1858–69) (Plate Nos. 9, 13, 14, 15) .. 30·00
Z 5 2½d. rosy mauve (1876) (Plate No. 4) .. ..
Z 6 3d. rose (1867–73) (Plate Nos. 5, 6, 7, 8, 9, 10) *From* 30·00
Z 7 3d. rose (1873–76) .. .. 30·00
Plate Nos. 11, 12, 14, 16, 17, 18, 19.
Z 8 4d. red (1863) (Plate No. 4) (*Hair lines*) .. .. 75·00
Z 9 4d. vermilion (1865–73) .. .. .. *From* 27·00
Plate Nos. 7, 8, 9, 10, 11, 12, 13, 14.
Z10 4d. vermilion (1876) (Plate No. 15) £145
Z11 4d. sage-green (1877) (Plate Nos. 15, 16) £100
Z12 4d. grey-brown (1880) *wmk* Large Garter .. .. 95·00
Plate No. 17.
Z13 4d. grey-brown (1880) *wmk* Crown (Plate No. 17) 28·00
Z14 6d. lilac (1867) (Plate Nos. 5, 6) .. .. 35·00
Z15 6d. violet (1867–70) (Plate Nos. 8, 9) .. .. 30·00
Z16 6d. buff (1872–73) (Plate Nos. 11, 12) .. *From* 55·00
Z17 6d. chestnut (1872) (Plate No. 11) .. .. ..
Z18 6d. grey (1873) (Plate No. 12) .. .. ..
Z19 6d. grey (1874–76) .. .. *From* 25·00
Plate Nos. 13, 14, 15, 16, 17.
Z20 8d. orange (1876) £180
Z21 9d. straw (1862) £130
Z22 9d. straw (1867) £125
Z23 10d. red-brown (1867) £125
Z24 1s. green (1865) (Plate No. 4) .. .. .. 50·00
Z25 1s. green (1867–73) (Plate Nos. 4, 5, 6, 7) .. *From* 22·00
Z26 1s. green (1873–77) .. .. *From* 28·00
Plate Nos. 8, 9, 10, 11, 12, 13.
Z27 1s. orange-brown (1880) (Plate No. 13) £150
Z28 2s. blue (1867) .. .. 85·00
Z29 2s. brown (1880) £1200
Z30 5s. rose (1867–74) (Plate Nos. 1, 2) .. *From* £260

1880.
Z31 ½d. green (1880) .. .. 25·00
Z32 1d. Venetian red .. .. 22·00
Z33 1½d. Venetian red .. .. 38·00
Z34 2d. rose .. .. 48·00

PORT-AU-PRINCE

CROWNED-CIRCLE HANDSTAMPS

CC3 CC **1b** PORT-AU-PRINCE (R.) (29.6.1843)
Price on cover £1500

Stamps of GREAT BRITAIN *cancelled* "E 53" *as in Types* **8** *or* **12**.

1869 *to* **1881**.
Z35 ½d. rose-red (1870–79) .. .. .. *From* 37·00
Plate Nos. 5, 6, 10, 11, 12, 13, 14.
Z36 1d. rose-red (1864–79) .. .. .. *From* 24·00
Plate Nos. 87, 134, 154, 167, 171, 173, 174, 183, 187, 189, 193, 199, 200, 201, 202, 206, 209, 210, 218, 219.
Z37 1½d. lake-red (1870–74) (Plate No. 3) .. .. 48·00
Z38 2d. blue (1858–69) (Plate Nos. 9, 14, 15) .. .. 35·00
Z40 2½d. rosy mauve (1876–79) (Plate Nos. 3, 9) .. 70·00
Z41 3d. rose (1867–73) (Plate Nos. 6, 7) .. ..
Z42 3d. rose (1873–79) (Plate Nos. 17, 18, 20) .. 28·00
Z43 4d. vermilion (1865–73) .. .. .. *From* 27·00
Plate Nos. 11, 12, 13, 14.
Z44 4d. vermilion (1876) (Plate No. 15) £150
Z45 4d. sage-green (1877) (Plate Nos. 15, 16) .. *From* 95·00
Z46 4d. grey-brown (1880) *wmk* Large Garter £100
Plate No. 17.
Z47 4d. grey-brown (1880) *wmk* Crown (Plate No. 17) 25·00
Z48 6d. grey (1874–76) (Plate Nos. 15, 16) .. ..
Z49 8d. orange (1876) £170
Z50 1s. green (1867–73) (Plate Nos. 4, 5, 6, 7) .. *From* 22·00
Z51 1s. green (1873–77) .. .. *From* 32·00
Plate Nos. 8, 9, 10, 11, 12, 13.
Z52 1s. orange-brown (1880) (Plate No. 13) £150
Z53 1s. orange-brown (1881) (Plate No. 13) .. .. 50·00
Z54 2s. blue (1867) .. .. 95·00
Z55 2s. brown (1880) £1200
Z56 5s. rose (1867–74) (Plate Nos. 1, 2) £325
Z57 10s. greenish grey (1878) £1800

1880.
Z58 ½d. green .. .. 35·00
Z59 1d. Venetian red .. .. 26·00
Z60 1½d. Venetian red .. .. 38·00
Z61 2d. rose .. ..

MACAO

Some form of British Postal Agency was operating in this Portuguese territory as early as 1838, its existence being confirmed by a cover of that year. The Agency continued to function, in conjunction with the Hong Kong Post Office, until Portugal joined the U.P.U. in 1884.

CROWNED-CIRCLE HANDSTAMPS

CC1 CC **2** PAGO EM MACAO (1870) .. *Price on cover* £10000

What may be a locally-cut variation is known from the 1843–44 period. This shows a Crown over an oval 20 mm wide, inscribed "PAID AT MACAO". Three examples are said to exist, all struck in red (*Price* £14000).

MADEIRA

The British Packet Agency on this Portuguese island was opened in 1767 and was of increased importance from 1808 following the exile of the Portuguese royal family to Brazil. The South American packets ceased to call in 1858. It appears to have closed sometime before 1880.

CROWN-CIRCLE HANDSTAMPS

CC1 CC **1b** MADEIRA (R.) (28.2.1842) .. *Price on cover* £2500

MEXICO

The British Postal Agency at Vera Cruz opened in 1825, following the introduction of the Mexican Packet service. No handstamps were supplied, however, until 1842, when a similar agency at Tampico was set up.

Great Britain stamps were used at Tampico from 1867, but, apparently, were never sent to the Vera Cruz office. The Agency at Vera Cruz closed in 1874 and that at Tampico in 1876.

TAMPICO

CROWNED-CIRCLE HANDSTAMPS

CC1 CC **1b** TAMPICO (R.) (13.11.1841) .. *Price on cover* £1250

No. CC1 may be found on cover, used in conjunction with Mexico adhesive stamps.

Stamps of GREAT BRITAIN *cancelled* "C 63" *as Type* **4**.

1867 *to* **1876**.
Z 1 1d. rose-red (1864–79) .. .. .. *From* 80·00
Plate Nos. 81, 89, 103, 117, 139, 147.
Z 2 2d. blue (1858–69) (Plate Nos. 9, 14) £100
Z 3 4d. vermilion (1865–73) .. .. .. *From* 50·00
Plate Nos. 7, 8, 10, 11, 12, 13, 14.
Z 4 1s. green (1867–73) (Plate Nos. 4, 5, 7, 8) .. .. 70·00
Z 5 2s. blue (1867) £350

VERA CRUZ

CROWNED-CIRCLE HANDSTAMPS

CC2 CC **1b** VERA CRUZ (R.) (13.11.1841) *Price on cover* £1500
CC3 VERA CRUZ (Black) (*circa* 1845)
Price on cover £700

No. CC3 can also be found used in conjunction with Mexico adhesive stamps.

NICARAGUA

GREYTOWN

British involvement on the Mosquito Coast of Nicaragua dates from 1655 when contacts were first made with the indigenous Misquito Indians. A formal alliance was signed in 1740 and the area was considered as a British dependency until the Spanish authorities negotiated a withdrawal in 1786.

The Misquitos remained under British protection, however, and, following the revolutionary period in the Spanish dominions, this eventually led to the appropriation, by the Misquitos with British backing, of the town of San Juan del Norte, later renamed Greytown.

The port was included in the Royal West Indian Mail Steam Packet Company's mail network from January 1842, forming part of the Jamaica District. This arrangement only lasted until September of that year, however, although packets were once again calling at Greytown by November 1844. Following the discovery of gold in California the office increased in importance, owing to the overland traffic, although the first distinctive postmark is not recorded in use until February 1856.

A subsidiary agency, without its own postmark, operated at Bluefields from 1857 to 1863.

The British Protectorate over the Misquitos ended in 1860, but the British Post Office at Greytown continued to operate, being supplied with Great Britain stamps in 1865. These are occasionally found used in combination with Nicaragua issues, which had only internal validity.

The British Post Office at Greytown closed in May 1882 when the Republic of Nicaragua joined the U.P.U.

CROWNED-CIRCLE HANDSTAMPS

Z 1

CC1 **Z 1** GREYTOWN (R.) (14.4.1859) .. ..

Z 2 Z 4

Z 3

Stamps of GREAT BRITAIN *cancelled* "C 57" *as in Types* **Z 2** (*issued* 1865), **Z 3** (*issued* 1875), *or with circular postmark as Type* **Z 4** (*issued* 1864).

1865 *to* **1882**.
Z 1 ½d. rose-red (1870–79) (Plate Nos. 5, 10, 11) .. 50·00
Z 2 1d. rose-red (1864–79) (Plate Nos. 180, 197, 210) .. 30·00
Z 3 1½d. lake-red (1870) (Plate No. 3) .. .. 50·00
Z 4 2d. blue (1858–69) (Plate Nos. 9, 14, 15) .. ..
Z 5 3d. rose (1873–76) (Plate Nos. 17, 18, 19, 20) .. 40·00
Z 6 3d. rose (1881) (Plate No. 20) .. .. ..
Z 7 4d. vermilion (1865–73) .. .. .. *From* 32·00
Plate Nos. 8, 10, 11, 12, 13, 14.
Z 8 4d. vermilion (1876) (Plate No. 15) £150
Z 9 4d. sage-green (1877) (Plate Nos. 15, 16) .. .. 95·00
Z10 4d. grey-brown (1880) *wmk* Large Garter £110
Plate No. 17.
Z11 4d. grey-brown (1880) *wmk* Crown (Plate No. 17) 85·00
Z12 6d. grey (1874–76) (Plate Nos. 14, 15, 16) .. .. 50·00
Z13 8d. orange (1876) .. ..
Z14 1s. green (1865) (Plate No. 4) .. .. ..
Z15 1s. green (1867–73) (Plate Nos. 6, 7) .. ..
Z16 1s. green (1873–77) (Plate Nos. 8, 12, 13) .. 30·00
Z17 1s. orange-brown (1880) (Plate No. 13) .. £150
Z18 1s. orange-brown (1881) (Plate No. 13) .. 60·00
Z19 2s. blue (1867) £150
Z20 2s. brown (1880) £1200
Z21 5s. rose (1867–74) (Plate Nos. 1, 2) £250
Z22 5s. rose (1882) (Plate No. 4), blue *paper* .. £950
Z23 10s. greenish grey (1878) £1400

1880.
Z24 1d. Venetian red .. ..
Z25 1½d. Venetian red .. .. 38·00

PERU

British Agencies in Peru date from 1846 when offices were established at Arica and Callao. The network was later expanded to include agencies at Paita and Pisco (both 1848), and Iquique and Islay (both 1869). This last office was transferred to Mollendo in 1871.

It is believed that a further agency existed at Pisagua, but no details exist.

Great Britain stamps were supplied from 1865. The Postal Agency at Pisco closed in 1870 and the remainder in 1879, the towns of Arica, Iquique and Pisagua passing to Chile by treaty in 1883.

ARICA

CROWNED-CIRCLE HANDSTAMPS

CC1 **CC 1** ARICA (R.) (5.11.1850) .. *Price on cover* £2500

Stamps of GREAT BRITAIN *cancelled* "C 36" *as in Types* **4**, **12** *or* **14**.

1865 *to* **1879**.
Z 1 ½d. rose-red (1870–79) .. .. .. *From* 45·00
Plate Nos. 5, 6, 10, 11, 13.
Z 2 1d. rose-red (1864–79) .. .. .. *From* 30·00
Plate Nos. 102, 139, 140, 163, 167.
Z 3 1½d. lake-red (1870–74) (Plate No. 3) .. ..
Z 4 2d. blue (1858–69) (Plate No. 14) .. .. 65·00
Z 5 3d. rose (1867–73) (Plate Nos. 5, 9) .. ..
Z 6 3d. rose (1873–76) .. .. .. *From* 24·00
Plate Nos. 11, 12, 17, 18, 19.
Z 7 4d. vermilion (1865–73) .. .. .. *From* 27·00
Plate Nos. 10, 11, 12, 13, 14.
Z 8 4d. vermilion (1876) (Plate No. 15) .. ..
Z 9 4d. sage-green (1877) (Plate Nos. 15, 16) .. .. 95·00
Z10 6d. lilac (1862) (Plate Nos. 3, 4) .. ..
Z11 6d. lilac (1865–67) (Plate No. 5) .. ..
Z12 6d. violet (1867–70) (Plate Nos. 6, 8, 9) .. .. 30·00
Z13 6d. buff (1872) (Plate No. 11) .. .. 75·00
Z14 6d. chestnut (1872) (Plate No. 11) .. .. ..
Z15 6d. grey (1873) (Plate No. 12) .. .. 45·00
Z16 6d. grey (1874–76) (Plate Nos. 13, 14, 15, 16) *From* 24·00
Z17 8d. orange (1876) .. ..
Z18 9d. straw (1862) .. ..
Z19 9d. straw (1865) .. ..
Z20 9d. straw (1867) £125
Z21 10d. red-brown (1867) .. ..
Z22 1s. green (1862) .. ..
Z23 1s. green (1865) .. ..
Z24 1s. green (1867–73) (Plate Nos. 4, 5, 6, 7) .. *From* 20·00
Z25 1s. green (1873–77) .. .. .. *From* 28·00
Plate Nos. 8, 9, 10, 11, 12, 13.
Z26 2s. blue (1867) £150
Z27 5s. rose (1867–74) (Plate Nos. 1, 2) £300

CALLAO

CROWNED-CIRCLE HANDSTAMPS

CC2 **CC 2** CALLAO (R.) (13.1.1846) .. *Price on cover* £1100
CC3 **CC 1** CALLAO (R.) (16.7.1846) .. *Price on cover* £600

Stamps of GREAT BRITAIN *cancelled* "C 38" *as in Types* **4**, **12** *or with circular date stamp as Type* **5**.

1865 *to* **1879**.
Z28 ½d. rose-red (1870–79) .. .. .. *From* 30·00
Plate Nos. 5, 6, 10, 11, 12, 13, 14.
Z29 1d. rose-red (1864–79) .. .. .. *From* 14·00
Plate Nos. 74, 88, 89, 93, 94, 97, 108, 123, 127, 128, 130, 134, 137, 139, 140, 141, 143, 144, 145, 146, 148, 149, 156, 157, 160, 163, 167, 171, 172, 173, 175, 176, 180, 181, 182, 183, 185, 187, 190, 193, 195, 198, 199, 200, 201, 204, 206, 209, 210, 212, 213, 215.
Z30 1½d. lake-red (1870–74) (Plate No. 3) .. ..
Z31 2d. blue (1858–69) .. .. .. *From* 18·00
Plate Nos. 9, 12, 13, 14, 15.
Z32 3d. carmine-rose (1862) .. ..
Z33 3d. rose (1865) (Plate No. 4) .. .. .. 40·00
Z34 3d. rose (1867–73) .. .. .. *From* 22·00
Plate Nos. 5, 6, 7, 8, 9, 10.
Z35 3d. rose (1873–76) .. .. .. *From* 27·00
Plate Nos. 11, 12, 14, 15, 16, 17, 18, 19.
Z36 4d. red (1862) (Plate Nos. 3, 4) .. ..
Z37 4d. vermilion (1865–73) .. .. .. *From* 24·00
Plate Nos. 8, 10, 11, 12, 13, 14.
Z38 4d. vermilion (1876) (Plate No. 15) £140
Z39 4d. sage-green (1877) (Plate Nos. 15, 16) .. .. 95·00
Z40 6d. lilac (1862) (Plate Nos. 3, 4) .. ..
Z40*a* 6d. lilac (1865) (Plate No. 5) .. ..
Z41 6d. lilac (1867) .. ..
Z42 6d. violet (1867–70) (Plate Nos. 6, 8, 9) .. *From* 35·00
Z43 6d. buff (1872–73) (Plate Nos. 11, 12) .. *From* 48·00
Z44 6d. chestnut (1872) (Plate No. 11) .. .. 28·00
Z45 6d. grey (1873) (Plate No. 12) .. .. 50·00
Z46 6d. grey (1874–80) (Plate Nos. 13, 14, 15, 16) *From* 25·00
Z47 8d. orange (1876) £150
Z48 9d. straw (1862) .. ..
Z49 9d. straw (1865) £225
Z50 9d. straw (1867) £110
Z51 10d. red-brown (1867) £150
Z52 1s. green (1865) .. ..
Z53 1s. green (1867–73) (Plate Nos. 4, 5, 6, 7) .. *From* 17·00
Z54 1s. green (1873–77) .. .. .. *From* 24·00
Plate Nos. 8, 9, 10, 11, 12, 13.
Z55 2s. blue (1867) £100
Z56 5s. rose (1867–74) (Plate Nos. 1, 2) .. *From* £180

IQUIQUE

Stamps of GREAT BRITAIN *cancelled* "D 87" *as Type* **12**.

1865 *to* **1879**.
Z57 ½d. rose-red (1870–79) (Plate Nos. 5, 6, 13, 14) .. 60·00
Z58 1d. rose-red (1864–79) (Plate Nos. 76, 179, 185, 205) 40·00
Z59 2d. blue (1858–69) (Plate Nos. 9, 12, 13, 14) ..
Z60 3d. rose (1867–73) (Plate Nos. 5, 6, 7, 8, 9) *From* 38·00
Z61 3d. rose (1873–76) (Plate Nos. 12, 18, 19) .. .. 50·00
Z62 4d. vermilion (1865–73) (Plate Nos. 12, 13, 14) .. 34·00
Z63 4d. vermilion (1876) (Plate No. 15) £160
Z64 4d. sage-green (1877) (Plate Nos. 15, 16) .. *From* £110
Z65 6d. mauve (1869) (Plate Nos. 8, 9) .. ..
Z66 6d. buff (1872–73) (Plate Nos. 11, 12) .. *From* 80·00
Z67 6d. chestnut (1872) (Plate No. 11) .. ..
Z68 6d. grey (1873) (Plate No. 12) .. .. 65·00
Z69 6d. grey (1874–76) (Plate Nos. 13, 14, 15, 16) ..
Z70 8d. orange (1876) £200
Z71 9d. straw (1867) £130
Z72 10d. red-brown (1867) .. ..
Z73 1s. green (1867–73) (Plate Nos. 4, 6, 7) .. *From* 38·00
Z74 1s. green (1873–77) .. .. .. *From* 40·00
Plate Nos. 8, 9, 10, 11, 12, 13.
Z75 2s. blue (1867) .. ..

ISLAY (*later* MOLLENDO)

CROWNED-CIRCLE HANDSTAMPS

CC4 **CC 1** ISLAY (R.) (23.10.1850) .. .. ..

Stamps of GREAT BRITAIN *cancelled* "C 42" *as Types* **4** *or* **12**.

1865 *to* **1879**.
Z76 1d. rose-red (1864–79) .. .. .. *From* 30·00
Plate Nos. 78, 84, 87, 88, 96, 103, 125, 134.
Z77 1½d. lake-red (1870–74) (Plate No. 3) .. ..
Z78 2d. blue (1858–69) (Plate Nos. 9, 13, 15) .. .. 24·00
Z79 3d. carmine-rose (1862) .. ..
Z80 3d. rose (1865) .. .. 60·00
Z81 3d. rose (1867–73) (Plate Nos. 4, 5, 6, 10) .. .. 32·00
Z82 4d. red (1862) (Plate Nos. 3, 4) .. .. .. 60·00
Z83 4d. vermilion (1867–73) .. .. .. *From* 30·00
Plate Nos. 9, 10, 11, 12, 13.
Z84 4d. vermilion (1876) (Plate No. 15) .. ..
Z85 4d. sage-green (1877) (Plate Nos. 15, 16) .. .. 90·00
Z86 6d. lilac (1862) (Plate Nos. 3, 4) .. .. 80·00
Z87 6d. lilac (1865) (Plate No. 5) .. .. 50·00
Z88 6d. violet (1867–70) (Plate Nos. 6, 8, 9) .. *From* 40·00
Z89 6d. buff (1873) (Plate No. 12) .. ..
Z90 6d. grey (1873) (Plate No. 12) .. ..
Z91 6d. grey (1874–76) (Plate Nos. 13, 14, 15, 16) *From* 28·00
Z92 9d. straw (1865) £225
Z93 9d. straw (1867) £120
Z94 10d. red-brown (1867) £160
Z95 1s. green (1865) (Plate No. 4) .. ..
Z96 1s. green (1867–73) (Plate Nos. 4, 5, 6, 7) .. *From* 28·00
Z97 1s. green (1873–77) (Plate Nos. 8, 10, 12, 13) *From* 30·00
Z98 2s. blue (1867) .. ..
Z99 5s. rose (1867) (Plate No. 1) .. .. ..

PAITA

CROWNED-CIRCLE HANDSTAMPS

CC5 **CC 1** PAITA (Black *or* R.) (5.11.1850)
Price on cover £3500

Stamps of GREAT BRITAIN *cancelled* "C 43" *as Type* **4**.

1865 *to* **1879**.
Z100 1d. rose-red (1864–79) (Plate Nos. 127, 147) ..
Z101 2d. blue (1858–69) (Plate Nos. 9, 14) ..
Z102 3d. rose (1867–73) (Plate Nos. 5, 6) .. .. 38·00
Z103 3d. rose (1876) (Plate Nos. 17, 18, 19) .. .. 38·00
Z104 4d. vermilion (1865–73) .. .. .. *From* 34·00
Plate Nos. 10, 11, 12, 13, 14.
Z105 4d. sage-green (1877) (Plate No. 15) .. ..
Z106 6d. lilac (1862) (Plate No. 3) .. .. 70·00
Z107 6d. lilac (1865–67) (Plate Nos. 5, 6) .. .. 45·00
Z108 6d. violet (1867–70) (Plate Nos. 6, 8, 9) .. .. 40·00
Z109 6d. buff (1872–73) (Plate Nos. 11, 12) .. *From* 60·00
Z110 6d. chestnut (Plate No. 11) .. .. .. 37·00
Z111 6d. grey (1873) .. ..
Z112 6d. grey (1874–76) (Plate Nos. 13, 14, 15) ..
Z113 9d. straw (1862) .. ..
Z114 10d. red-brown (1867) £200
Z115 1s. green (1865) (Plate No. 4) .. ..
Z116 1s. green (1867–73) (Plate No. 4) .. .. 38·00
Z117 1s. green (1873–77) (Plate Nos. 8, 9, 10, 13) .. 38·00
Z118 2s. blue (1867) £150
Z119 5s. rose (1867) (Plate No. 1) £350

PISAGUA(?)

Stamp of GREAT BRITAIN *cancelled* "D 65" *as Type* **12**.

Z120 2s. blue (1867) .. ..

PISCO AND CHINCHA ISLANDS

Stamps of GREAT BRITAIN *cancelled* "D 74" *as Type* **12**.

1865 *to* **1870**.
Z121 2d. blue (1858–69) (Plate No. 9) .. ..
Z122 4d. vermilion (1865–73) (Plate Nos. 10, 12) .. £175
Z123 6d. violet (1868) (Plate No. 6) £700
Z124 1s. green (1867) (Plate No. 4) .. ..
Z125 2s. blue (1867) £600

PORTO RICO

A British Postal Agency operated at San Juan from 1844. In 1872 further offices were opened at Aguadilla, Arroyo, Mayaguez and Ponce, with Naguabo added three years later.

Great Britain stamps were used during 1865–66 and from 1873 to 1877. All the British Agencies closed in 1877.

AGUADILLA

Stamps of GREAT BRITAIN *cancelled* "F 84" *as Type* **8**.

1873 *to* **1877**.
Z 1 ½d. rose-red (1870) (Plate No. 6) .. .. 70·00
Z 2 1d. rose-red (1864–79) .. .. .. 40·00
Plate Nos. 119, 122, 139, 149, 156, 160.
Z 3 2d. blue (1858–69) (Plate No. 14) ..
Z 4 3d. rose (1867–73) (Plate Nos. 7, 8, 9) ..
Z 5 3d. rose (1873–76) (Plate No. 12) ..
Z 6 4d. vermilion (1865–73) (Plate Nos. 12, 13, 14) .. 40·00
Z 7 4d. vermilion (1876) (Plate No. 15) £160
Z 7*a* 6d. pale buff (1872–73) (Plate No. 11) ..
Z 8 6d. grey (1874–76) (Plate Nos. 13, 14) ..
Z 9 9d. straw (1867) £225
Z10 10d. red-brown (1867) £150
Z11 1s. green (1867–73) (Plate Nos. 4, 5, 6, 7) .. *From* 32·00
Z12 1s. green (1873–77) .. .. .. *From* 40·00
Plate Nos. 8, 9, 10, 11, 12.
Z13 2s. blue (1867) £225

ARROYO

Stamps of GREAT BRITAIN *cancelled* "F 83" *as Type* **8**.

1873 *to* **1877**.
Z14 ½d. rose-red (1870) (Plate No. 5) .. .. 55·00
Z15 1d. rose-red (1864–79) .. .. .. 45·00
Plate Nos. 149, 150, 151, 156, 164, 174, 175.
Z16 1½d. lake-red (1870) (Plate Nos. 1, 3) ..
Z17 2d. blue (1858–69) (Plate No. 14) ..
Z18 3d. rose (1867–73) (Plate Nos. 5, 7, 10) .. 40·00
Z19 3d. rose (1873–76) (Plate Nos. 11, 12, 14, 16, 18) .. 45·00
Z20 4d. vermilion (1865–73) (Plate Nos. 12, 13, 14) .. 38·00
Z21 4d. vermilion (1876) (Plate No. 15) £140
Z22 6d. chestnut (1872) (Plate No. 11) .. .. 50·00
Z23 6d. pale-buff (1872) (Plate No. 11) .. .. 55·00
Z23*a* 6d. grey (1873) (Plate No. 12) ..
Z24 6d. grey (1874–76) (Plate Nos. 13, 14, 15) .. 50·00
Z25 9d. straw (1867) £225
Z26 10d. red-brown (1867) £150
Z27 1s. green (1865) (Plate No. 4) .. ..
Z28 1s. green (1867–73) (Plate Nos. 4, 5, 6, 7) .. 40·00
Z29 1s. green (1873–77) .. .. .. 35·00
Plate Nos. 8, 9, 10, 11, 12, 13.
Z30 2s. blue (1867) £180
Z31 5s. rose (1867–74) (Plate No. 2) .. ..

MAYAGUEZ

Stamps of GREAT BRITAIN *cancelled* "F 85" *as Type* **8**.

1873 *to* **1877**.

Z32 ½d. rose-red (1870) .. .. *From* 45·00
Plate Nos. 4, 5, 6, 8, 10, 11.
Z33 1d. rose-red (1864–79) .. .. .. *From* 22·00
Plate Nos. 76, 120, 121, 122, 124, 134, 137, 140, 146, 149, 150, 151, 154, 155, 156, 157, 160, 167, 170, 171, 174, 175, 176, 178, 180, 182, 185, 186, 189.
Z34 1½d. lake-red (1870–74) (Plate Nos. 1, 3) .. .. 40·00
Z35 2d. blue (1858–69) (Plate Nos. 13, 14, 15) .. .. 38·00
Z36 3d. rose (1867–73) (Plate Nos. 7, 8, 9, 10) .. .. 28·00
Z37 3d. rose (1873–76) .. .. 28·00
Plate Nos. 11, 12, 14, 15, 16, 17, 18, 19.
Z38 4d. vermilion (1865–73) (Plate Nos. 11, 12, 13, 14) 30·00
Z39 4d. vermilion (1876) (Plate No. 15) £135
Z40 4d. sage-green (1877) (Plate No. 15) .. ..
Z41 6d. mauve (1870) (Plate No. 9) .. .. ..
Z42 6d. buff (1872) (Plate No. 11) .. .. .. 70·00
Z43 6d. chestnut (1872) (Plate No. 11) .. .. .. 60·00
Z44 6d. grey (1873) (Plate No. 12) .. .. ..
Z45 6d. grey (1874–80) (Plate Nos. 13, 14, 15, 16) .. 35·00
Z46 8d. orange (1876) £150
Z47 9d. straw (1867) £125
Z48 10d. red-brown (1867) £125
Z49 1s. green (1867–73) (Plate Nos. 4, 5, 6, 7) .. 25·00
Z50 1s. green (1873–77) .. .. .. *From* 30·00
Plate Nos. 8, 9, 10, 11, 12.
Z51 2s. blue (1867) £160
Z52 5s. rose (1867–74) (Plate Nos. 1, 2) .. ..

NAGUABO

Stamps of GREAT BRITAIN *cancelled* "582" *as Type* **9**.

1875 *to* **1877**.

Z53 ½d. rose-red (1870–79) (Plate Nos. 5, 12, 14) ..
Z54 1d. rose-red (1864–70) (Plate Nos. 159, 165) ..
Z55 3d. rose (1873–76) (Plate Nos. 17, 18) £375
Z56 4d. vermilion (1872–73) (Plate Nos. 13, 14) *From* £350
Z57 4d. vermilion (1876) (Plate No. 15) .. ..
Z58 6d. grey (1874–76) (Plate Nos. 14, 15) .. ..
Z59 9d. straw (1867) .. ..
Z60 10d. red-brown (1867) £700
Z61 1s. green (1873–77) (Plate Nos. 11, 12) .. ..
Z62 2s. dull blue (1867) (Plate No. 1) £550

PONCE

Stamps of GREAT BRITAIN *cancelled* "F 88" *as Type* **8**.

1873 *to* **1877**.

Z63 ½d. rose-red (1870) (Plate Nos. 5, 10, 12) .. .. 45·00
Z64 1d. rose-red (1864–79) .. .. .. *From* 22·00
Plate Nos. 120, 121, 122, 123, 124, 146, 148, 154, 156, 157, 158, 160, 167, 171, 174, 175, 179, 186, 187.
Z65 1½d. lake-red (1870–74) (Plate No. 3) £100
Z66 2d. blue (1858–69) (Plate Nos. 13, 14) .. .. 40·00
Z67 3d. rose (1867–73) (Plate Nos. 7, 8, 9) .. ..
Z68 3d. rose (1873–76) (Plate Nos. 12, 16, 17, 18, 19) .. 34·00
Z69 4d. vermilion (1865–73) .. .. .. *From* 32·00
Plate Nos. 8, 9, 12, 13, 14.
Z70 4d. vermilion (1876) (Plate No. 15) £140
Z71 4d. sage-green (1877) (Plate Nos. 15, 16) £100
Z72 6d. buff (1872–73) (Plate Nos. 11, 12) .. .. 65·00
Z73 6d. chestnut (1872) (Plate No. 11) .. .. .. 45·00
Z74 6d. grey (1873) (Plate No. 12) .. .. ..
Z75 6d. grey (1874–76) (Plate Nos. 13, 14, 15) .. *From* 35·00
Z76 9d. straw (1867) £175
Z77 10d. red-brown (1867) £130
Z78 1s. green (1867–73) (Plate Nos. 4, 6, 7) .. .. 28·00
Z79 1s. green (1873–77) .. .. .. *From* 26·00
Plate Nos. 8, 9, 10, 11, 12, 13.
Z80 2s. blue (1867) .. ..
Z81 5s. rose (1867–74) (Plate Nos. 1, 2) .. *From* £300

SAN JUAN

CROWNED-CIRCLE HANDSTAMPS

CC1 CC **1** SAN JUAN PORTO RICO (R. *or* Black) (25.5.1844) .. .. .. *Price on cover* £750

No. CC1 may be found on cover, used in conjunction with Spanish colonial adhesive stamps.

Stamps of GREAT BRITAIN *cancelled* "C 61" *as in Types* **4**, **8** *or* **14**.

1865 *to* **1866** *and* **1873** *to* **1877**.

Z 82 ½d. rose-red (1870) (Plate Nos. 5, 10, 15) .. *From* 30·00
Z 83 1d. rose-red (1857) .. ..
Z 84 1d. rose-red (1864–79) .. .. .. *From* 18·00
Plate Nos. 73, 74, 81, 84, 90, 94, 100, 101, 102, 107, 117, 122, 124, 125, 127, 130, 137, 138, 139, 140, 145, 146, 149, 153, 156, 159, 160, 162, 163, 169, 171, 172, 173, 174, 175, 179, 180, 182, 186.
Z 85 1½d. lake-red (1870–74) (Plate Nos. 1, 3) .. *From* 60·00
Z 86 2d. blue (1858–69) (Plate Nos. 9, 13, 14) .. *From* 25·00
Z 87 3d. rose (1865) (Plate No. 4) .. .. .. 50·00
Z 88 3d. rose (1867–73) .. .. .. *From* 25·00
Plate Nos. 5, 6, 7, 8, 9, 10.
Z 89 3d. rose (1873–76) .. .. .. *From* 25·00
Plate Nos. 11, 12, 14, 15, 16, 17, 18.
Z 90 4d. vermilion (1865–73) .. .. .. *From* 24·00
Plate Nos. 7, 8, 9, 10, 11, 12, 13, 14.
Z 91 4d. vermilion (1876) (Plate No. 15) £135
Z 92 6d. lilac (1865–67) (Plate Nos. 5, 6) .. *From* 35·00
Z 93 6d. lilac (1867) (Plate No. 6) .. .. .. 38·00
Z 94 6d. violet (1867–70) (Plate Nos. 6, 8, 9) .. *From* 30·00
Z 95 6d. buff (1872–73) (Plate Nos. 11, 12) .. .. 55·00
Z 96 6d. chestnut (1872) (Plate No. 11) .. .. .. 35·00
Z 97 6d. grey (1873) (Plate No. 12) .. .. ..
Z 98 6d. grey (1874–76) (Plate Nos. 13, 14, 15) .. *From* 24·00
Z 99 9d. straw (1862) £140
Z100 9d. straw (1865) £250
Z101 9d. straw (1867) £110
Z102 10d. red-brown (1867) £130
Z103 1s. green (1865) (Plate No. 4) .. .. .. 50·00
Z104 1s. green (1867–73) (Plate Nos. 4, 5, 6, 7) .. *From* 22·00
Z105 1s. green (1873–77) .. .. .. *From* 28·00
Plate Nos. 8, 9, 10, 11, 12, 13.
Z106 2s. blue (1867) £110
Z107 5s. rose (1867) (Plate Nos. 1, 2) .. .. *From* £260

SPAIN

Little is known about the operation of British Packet Agencies in Spain, other than the dates recorded for the various postal markings in the G.P.O. Proof Books. The Agency at Corunna is said to date from the late 17th century. Teneriffe became a port-of-call for the South American packets in 1817 and this arrangement continued until 1858.

Both appear to have closed by the late 1850s.

CORUNNA

CROWNED-CIRCLE HANDSTAMPS

CC1 CC **1b** CORUNNA (28.2.1842) .. .. ..

Although recorded in the G.P.O. Proof Books no example of No. CC1 on cover is known.

TENERIFFE (CANARY ISLANDS)

CROWNED-CIRCLE HANDSTAMPS

CC2 CC **7** TENERIFFE (6.1.1851) .. *Price on cover* £2500
CC3 CC **4** TENERIFFE (23.10.1857) .. *Price on cover* £2500

UNITED STATES OF AMERICA

The network of British Packet Agencies, to operate the trans-Atlantic Packet system, was re-established in 1814 after the War of 1812.

The New York Agency opened in that year to be followed by further offices at Boston, Charleston (South Carolina), New Orleans, Savannah (Georgia) (all in 1842), Mobile (Alabama) (1848) and San Francisco (1860). Of these agencies Charleston and Savannah closed the same year (1842) as did New Orleans, although the latter was re-activated from 1848 to 1850. Mobile closed 1850, Boston in 1865, New York in 1882 and San Francisco, for which no postal markings have been recorded, in 1883.

Although recorded in the G.P.O. Proof Books no actual examples of the Crowned-circle handstamps for Charleston, Mobile, New Orleans and Savannah are known on cover.

The G.P.O. proof books record, in error, a Crowned-circle handstamp for St. Michaels, Maryland. This handstamp was intended for the agency on San Miguel in the Azores.

CHARLESTON

CROWNED-CIRCLE HANDSTAMPS

CC1 CC **1b** CHARLESTON (15.12.1841) .. ..

MOBILE

CROWNED-CIRCLE HANDSTAMPS

CC2 CC **1b** MOBILE (15.12.1841) .. .. ..

NEW ORLEANS

CROWNED-CIRCLE HANDSTAMPS

CC3 CC **1b** NEW ORLEANS (15.12.1841) .. ..
CC4 CC **1** NEW ORLEANS (27.4.1848) .. ..

NEW YORK

CROWNED-CIRCLE HANDSTAMPS

CC5 CC **1b** NEW YORK (R.) (15.12.1841) *Price on cover* £8500

SAVANNAH

CROWNED-CIRCLE HANDSTAMPS

CC6 CC **1b** SAVANNAH (15.12.1841) .. ..

URUGUAY

MONTEVIDEO

British packets commenced calling at Montevideo in 1824 on passage to and from Buenos Aires.

Great Britain stamps were in use from 1864. The agency was closed by 1872.

CROWNED-CIRCLE HANDSTAMPS

CC1 CC **5** MONTEVIDEO (Black *or* R.) (6.1.1851) *Price on cover* £725

Stamps of GREAT BRITAIN *cancelled* "C 28" *as in Types* **4** *or* **12**.

1864 *to* **1872**.

Z 1 1d. rose-red (1864) .. .. 45·00
Plate Nos. 73, 92, 93, 94, 119, 148, 154, 157, 171.
Z 2 2d. blue (1858–69) (Plate Nos. 9, 13) .. .. 38·00
Z 3 3d. rose (1865) (Plate No. 4) .. .. ..
Z 4 3d. rose (1867–71) (Plate Nos. 4, 5, 7) .. .. 38·00
Z 6 4d. rose (1857) .. ..
Z 7 4d. red (1862) (Plate No. 4) .. ..
Z 8 4d. vermilion (1865–70) .. .. .. *From* 32·00
Plate Nos. 7, 8, 9, 10, 11, 12.
Z 9 6d. lilac (1856) .. ..
Z10 6d. lilac (1862) (Plate No. 4) .. .. ..
Z11 6d. lilac (1865–67) (Plate Nos. 5, 6) .. .. 48·00
Z12 6d. lilac (1867) (Plate No. 6) .. .. ..
Z13 6d. violet (1867–70) (Plate Nos. 8, 9) .. *From* 38·00
Z14 6d. buff (1872) .. ..
Z15 6d. chestnut (1872) .. ..
Z16 9d. straw (1862) .. ..
Z17 9d. straw (1865) .. ..
Z18 9d. straw (1867) £130
Z19 10d. red-brown (1867) £130
Z20 1s. green (1862) .. .. 80·00
Z21 1s. green (1865) (Plate No. 4) .. .. .. 38·00
Z22 1s. green (1867–73) (Plate Nos. 4, 5) .. .. 30·00
Z23 2s. blue (1867) .. .. 95·00
Z24 5s. rose (1867) (Plate No. 1) £250

VENEZUELA

British Postal Agencies were initially opened at La Guayra and Porto Cabello in 1841. Further offices were added at Maracaibo in 1842 and Ciudad Bolivar during 1868. All agencies closed in 1880.

Great Britain stamps were used at La Guayra from 1865 and at Ciudad Bolivar from its establishment in 1868.

CIUDAD BOLIVAR

Stamps of GREAT BRITAIN *cancelled* "D 22" *as Type* **12**, *or circular date stamp as Type* **17**.

1868 *to* **1880**.

Z 1 1d. rose-red (1864–79) (Plate No. 133) .. .. 75·00
Z 2 2d. blue (1858–69) (Plate No. 13) .. .. ..
Z 3 3d. rose (1867–73) (Plate No. 5) .. .. ..
Z 4 3d. rose (1873–79) (Plate No. 11) £125
Z 5 4d. vermilion (1865–73) (Plate Nos. 9, 12, 14) .. 45·00
Z 6 4d. sage-green (1877) (Plate Nos. 15, 16) .. *From* £125
Z 7 4d. grey-brown (1880) *wmk* Crown (Plate No. 17)
Z 8 9d. straw (1867) .. ..
Z 9 10d. red-brown (1867) .. ..
Z10 1s. green (1867–73) (Plate Nos. 4, 5, 7) .. *From* 95·00
Z11 1s. green (1873–77) (Plate Nos. 10, 12, 13) .. 70·00
Z12 2s. blue (1867) £300
Z13 5s. rose (1867–74) (Plate Nos. 1, 2) £400

LA GUAYRA

CROWNED-CIRCLE HANDSTAMPS

CC1 CC **1b** LA GUAYRA (R.) (15.12.1841) *Price on cover* £850

Stamps of GREAT BRITAIN *cancelled* "C 60" *as Type* **4**, *circular date stamp as Type* **16** *or with No.* CC1.

1865 *to* **1880**.

Z14 ½d. rose-red (1870) (Plate No. 6) .. .. ..
Z15 1d. rose-red (1864–79) .. .. .. *From* 35·00
Plate Nos. 81, 92, 96, 98, 111, 113, 115, 131, 138, 144, 145, 154, 177, 178, 180, 196.
Z16 1½d. lake-red (1870–74) (Plate No. 3) .. ..
Z17 2d. blue (1858–69) (Plate Nos. 13, 14) .. .. 40·00
Z18 3d. rose (1873–76) .. .. .. *From* 48·00
Plate Nos. 14, 15, 17, 18, 19.
Z19 4d. vermilion (1865–73) .. .. .. *From* 30·00
Plate Nos. 7, 9, 11, 12, 13, 14.
Z20 4d. vermilion (1876) (Plate No. 15) £140
Z21 4d. sage-green (1877) (Plate Nos. 15, 16) .. .. 95·00
Z22 6d. lilac (1865) (Plate No. 5) .. .. ..
Z23 6d. violet (1867–70) (Plate Nos. 6, 8) .. ..
Z24 6d. buff (1872–73) (Plate Nos. 11, 12) .. *From* 85·00
Z25 6d. grey (1873) (Plate No. 12) .. .. .. 50·00
Z26 6d. grey (1874–76) (Plate Nos. 13, 14, 15, 16) .. 40·00
Z27 8d. orange (1876) £170
Z28 9d. straw (1862) .. ..
Z29 9d. straw (1867) .. ..
Z30 10d. red-brown (1867) .. ..
Z31 1s. green (1865) (Plate No. 4) .. .. .. 55·00
Z32 1s. green (1867–73) (Plate Nos. 4, 7) .. ..
Z33 1s. green (1873–77) .. .. .. *From* 32·00
Plate Nos. 8, 9, 10, 11, 12, 13.
Z34 2s. blue (1867) £200
Z35 5s. rose (1867–74) (Plate No. 1, 2) .. .. *From* £350

MARACAIBO

CROWNED-CIRCLE HANDSTAMPS

CC2 CC **1b** MARACAIBO (31.12.1841) .. ..

No examples of No. CC2 on cover have been recorded.

PORTO CABELLO

CROWNED-CIRCLE HANDSTAMPS

CC3 CC **1b** PORTO-CABELLO (R.) (15.12.1841) *Price on cover* £1500

MAIL BOAT OBLITERATIONS

For many years it was supposed that obliterations numbered A 80 to A 99, B 03, B 12, B 56, B 57 and C 79 were used on mail boats or at Naval Stations abroad (the whereabouts of which were not known), owing to the fact that they are almost invariably found on sailors' letters.

It is definitely known that these obliterations were allotted to mail boats and they are therefore omitted from this Catalogue.

ARMY FIELD OFFICES

1854 *to* **1857. CRIMEA.**

Crown between Stars

Z 1 1d. red-brown (1841), *imperf* £325
Z 2 1d. red-brown (1854), Die I, *wmk* Small Crown, *perf* 16 .. ..
Z 3 1d. red-brown (1855), Die II, *wmk* Small Crown, *perf* 16 .. .. 80·00
Z 4 1d. red-brown, Die I, *wmk* Small Crown, *perf* 14 ..
Z 5 1d. red-brown (1855), Die II, Small Crown, *perf* 14
Z 6 2d. blue (1841) *imperf* £650
Z 7 2d. blue, Small Crown (1854), *perf* 16 (Plate No. 4)
Z 8 1s. green (1847), embossed £875

Star between Cyphers

Z 9 1d. red-brown (1841), *imperf* .. .. ..
Z10 1d. red-brown (1854), Die I, *wmk* Small Crown, *perf* 16 .. .. 40·00
Z11 1d. red-brown (1855), Die II, *wmk* Small Crown, *perf* 16 .. .. 40·00
Z12 1d. red-brown (1855), Die I, *wmk* Small Crown, *perf* 14 .. .. 40·00
Z13 1d. red-brown (1855), Die II, *wmk* Small Crown, *perf* 14 .. .. 40·00
Z14 1d. red-brown (1855), Die II, *wmk* Large Crown, *perf* 16 .. .. 60·00

Z15	1d.	red-brown (1855), Die II, *wmk* Large Crown, *perf* 14	22·00
Z16	2d.	blue (1841), *imperf*	£650
Z17	2d.	blue (1854) *wmk* Small Crown, *perf* 16 *From* Plate Nos. 4, 5.	80·00
Z18	2d.	blue (1855) *wmk* Small Crown, *perf* 14 Plate No. 4.	£100
Z19	2d.	blue (1855), *wmk* Large Crown, *perf* 16 Plate No. 5.	£150
Z20	2d.	blue (1855), *wmk* Large Crown, *perf* 14 Plate No. 5.	75·00
Z21	4d.	rose (1857)	£500
Z22	6d.	violet (1854), embossed	£675
Z23	1s.	green (1847), embossed	£750

1882. EGYPT. *Tel-el-Kebir Campaign.*

Z24	½d.	rose-red (Plate No. 20)	
Z25	½d.	green (1880)	£275
Z26	1d.	Venetian red (1880)	
Z27	1d.	lilac (1881)	£150
Z28	2½d.	blue (1881) (Plate Nos. 21, 22, 23)	80·00

1885. SUDAN. *Suakin Campaign.*

Z29	1d.	lilac (1881)	£250
Z30	2½d.	lilac (1884)	£180
Z31	5d.	green (1884)	£450

1899 *to* **1902. SOUTH AFRICA.**

Z32 *to* Z45*a*	½d., 1d., 1½d., 2d., 2½d., 3d., 4d., 4½d., 5d., 6d., 9d., 10d., 1s., 5s., £1 (1881–92) *From*	12·00
Z46–Z47	½d., 1s. (1900) *From*	18·00
Z48 *to* Z59	½d., 1d., 1½d., 2d., 2½d., 3d., 4d., 5d., 6d., 9d., 10d., 1s. (1902) *From*	14·00

Many types of cancellation exist besides those shown.

ARMY OFFICIAL

Z60	½d.	vermilion	80·00
Z61	½d.	green	80·00
Z62	1d.	lilac	70·00
Z63	6d.	purple/*red*	

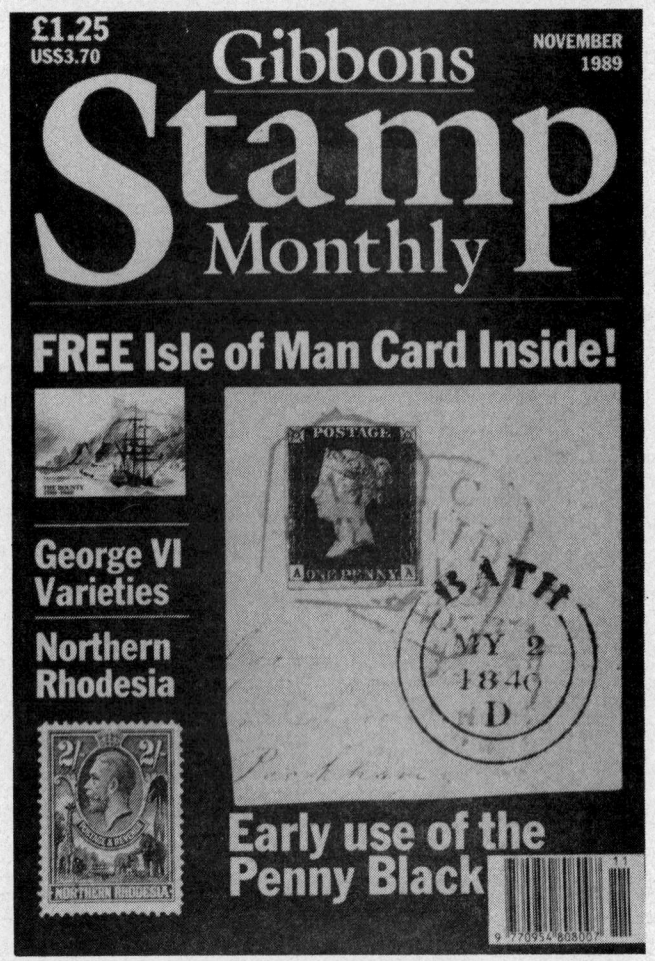

Abu Dhabi

Stamps of the BRITISH POSTAL AGENCIES IN EASTERN ARABIA were used by the British postal administration from 30 March 1963 until the introduction of Abu Dhabi issues in 1964. They can be found postmarked "ABU DHABI" or "DAS ISLAND"

An independent Arab Shaikhdom (one of the Trucial States), with a British postal administration until 31 December 1966.

1 Shaikh Shakhbut bin Sultan

3 Ruler's Palace

Des M. Farrar Bell. Photo Harrison (5 n.p. to 75 n.p.). Des C. T. Kavanagh (1, 2 r.), Miss P. M. Goth (5, 10 r.). Recess B.W.)

1964 (30 Mar). *T* **1**, **3** *and similar designs. P* 14½ (5 *to* 75 *n.p.*) *or* 13 × 13½ (*others*).

No.	Type	Description	Unused	Used
1	1	5 n.p. green	80	35
2		15 n.p. red-brown	1·25	35
3		20 n.p. ultramarine	1·40	35
4		30 n.p. red-orange	1·40	65
5	–	40 n.p. reddish violet	2·75	20
6	–	50 n.p. bistre	2·50	35
7	–	75 n.p. black	2·75	75
8	3	1 r. emerald	3·75	70
9		2 r. black	5·50	2·25
10	–	5 r. carmine-red	13·00	7·00
11	–	10 r. deep ultramarine	18·00	13·00
1/11		*Set of* 11	48·00	23·00

Designs: *As Type* 1 – 40, 50, 75 n.p. Mountain Gazelle. *As Type* 3 – 5, 10 r. Oil rig and camels.

5

6

7

Saker Falcon

(Des V. Whiteley. Photo Harrison)

1965 (30 Mar). *Falconry. P* 14½.

No.	Type	Description	Unused	Used
12	5	20 n.p. light brown and grey-blue	4·25	80
13	6	40 n.p. light brown and blue	6·00	2·00
14	7	2 r. sepia and turquoise-green	12·00	8·50
12/14		*Set of* 3	20·00	10·00

(New Currency. 1,000 fils = 1 dinar)

Fils فلس

(8)

1966 (1 Oct). *Nos.* 1/11 *such as T* 8 ("FILS" *only on* 40 *f. to* 70 *f.*) *with new value expressed on remainder), by Arabian Printing and Publishing House, Bahrain. P* 13 × 13½ (20 *f.*), *others as before.*

No.	Type	Description	Unused	Used
15	1	5 f. on 5 n.p. green	3·00	3·00
16		15 f. on 15 n.p. red-brown	3·00	1·75
17		20 f. on 20 n.p. ultramarine	3·00	2·50
		a. Surch inverted	£175	£250
		b. Perf 14½		
18		30 f. on 30 n.p. red-orange	4·25	4·50
		a. Arabic "2" for "3" in surch	£1600	
19	–	40 f. on 40 n.p. reddish violet	6·00	70
20	–	50 f. on 50 n.p. bistre	9·50	11·00
21	–	75 f. on 75 n.p. black	9·50	11·00
22	3	100 f. on 1 r. emerald	10·00	3·25
23		200 f. on 2 r. black	18·00	12·00
24	–	500 f. on 5 r. carmine-red	40·00	38·00
25	–	1 d. on 10 r. deep ultramarine	48·00	70·00
15/25		*Set of* 11	£140	£140

The Abu Dhabi Post Department took over the postal services on 1 January 1967. Later stamp issues will be found in Part 19 (*Middle East*) of this Catalogue.

Aden

The first post office in Aden opened during January 1839, situated in what became known as the Crater district. No stamps were initially available, but, after the office was placed under the Bombay Postal Circle, stocks of the 1854 ½ a. and 1 a. stamps were placed on sale in Aden from 10 October 1854. Supplies of the 2 a. and 4 a. values did not arrive until December. Most Indian issues from the 1854 lithographs up to 1935 Silver Jubilee set can be found with Aden postmarks.

During January 1858 a further office, Aden Steamer Point, was opened in the harbour area and much of the business was transferred to it by 1869. The original Aden post office, in Crater, was renamed Aden Cantonment, later to be changed again to Aden Camp.

The first cancellation used with the Indian stamps was a plain diamond of dots. This type was also used elsewhere so that attribution to Aden is only possible when on cover. Aden was assigned "124" in the Indian postal number system and this formed the main feature of marks from 1858, either on its own or as part of a duplex.

1858 "124" Cancellation

1870 Aden Duplex

1872 Aden Steamer Point Duplex

Both post offices used this number until 1871 when Aden Cantonment was assigned "125", only to have this swiftly amended to "124A" in the same year.

1871 Aden Cantonment "125" Cancellation

1871 Aden Cantonment "124A" Cancellation

Cancellations inscribed "Aden Steamer Point" disappear after 1874 and this office was then known simply as Aden. Following this change the office was given number "B-22" under the revised Indian P.O. scheme and this number appears as a major part of the cancellations from 1875 to 1886, either on its own or as part of a duplex, Aden Camp, the alternative name for the Cantonment office, became "B-22/1".

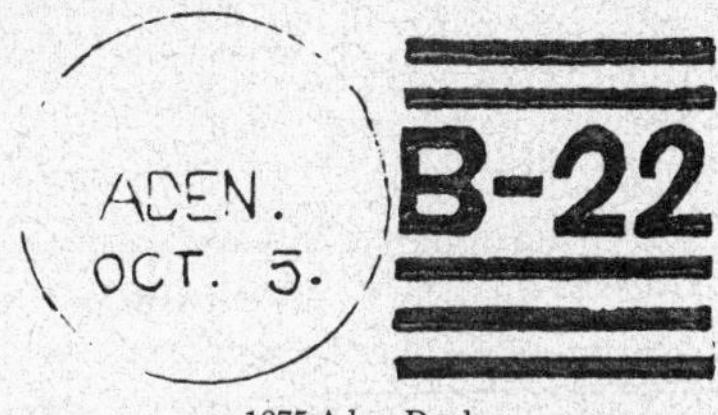

1875 Aden Duplex

Squared-circle types for Aden and Aden Cantonment were introduced in 1884 and 1888 to be in turn replaced by standard Indian double and single circle from 1895 onwards.

A number of other post offices were opened between 1891 and 1937:

Dthali (*opened* 1903, *initially using* "EXPERIMENTAL P.O. B-84" *postmark; closed* 1907)

Kamaran (*opened c* 1915, *but no civilian postmarks known before* 1925)

Khormaksar (*opened* 1892; *closed* 1915; *reopened* 1925)

Maalla (*opened* 1923; *closed* 1931)

Nobat-Dakim (*opened* 1904, *initially using* "EXPERIMENTAL P.O. B-84" *postmark; closed* 1905)

Perim (*opened* 1915; *closed* 1936)

Sheikh Othman (*opened* 1891; *closed* 1915; *reopened* 1922; *closed* 1937)

PRICES FOR STAMPS ON COVER TO 1945

Nos. 1/12	*from* × 4
Nos. 13/15	*from* × 5
Nos. 16/27	*from* × 3

1 Dhow

2 King George VI and Queen Elizabeth

(Recess D.L.R.)

1937 (1 Apr). *Wmk Mult Script CA sideways. P* 13 × 12.

No.	Type	Description	Unused	Used
1	1	½ a. yellow-green	2·25	1·00
2		9 p. deep green	2·25	1·10
3		1 a. sepia	2·25	40
4		2 a. scarlet	2·25	2·00
5		2½ a. bright blue	2·25	80
6		3 a. carmine	7·00	4·75
7		3½ a. grey-blue	3·25	2·00
8		8 a. pale purple	12·00	5·50
9		1 r. brown	15·00	7·00
10		2 r. yellow	35·00	16·00
11		5 r. deep purple	65·00	60·00
12		10 r. olive-green	£130	£130
1/12		*Set of* 12	£250	£200
1/12 Perf "Specimen"		*Set of* 12	£250	

(Des and recess D.L.R.)

1937 (12 May). *Coronation. Wmk Mult Script CA. P* 14.

No.	Type	Description	Unused	Used
13	2	1 a. sepia	50	50
14		2½ a. light blue	70	70
15		3½ a. grey-blue	95	1·25
13/15		*Set of* 3	2·00	2·25
13/15 Perf "Specimen"		*Set of* 3	50·00	

3 Aidrus Mosque, Crater

9 Houses of Parliament, London

(Recess Waterlow)

1939 (19 Jan)–**48**. *Horiz designs as T* **3**. *Wmk Mult Script CA. P* 12½.

No.	Type	Description	Unused	Used
16		½ a. yellowish green	25	40
		a. Bluish green (9.48)	70	1·75
17		¾ a. red-brown	25	60
18		1 a. pale blue	20	25
19		1½ a. scarlet	35	60
20		2 a. sepia	20	25
21		2½ a. deep ultramarine	20	25
22		3 a. sepia and carmine	50	25
23		8 a. red-orange	35	40
23*a*		14 a. sepia and light blue (15.1.45)	1·00	90
24		1 r. emerald-green	80	1·00
25		2 r. deep blue and magenta	3·75	1·50
26		5 r. red-brown and olive-green	7·50	5·00
27		10 r. sepia and violet	11·00	9·50
16/27		*Set of* 13	24·00	20·00
16/27 Perf "Specimen"		*Set of* 13	£150	

Designs:—½ a., 2 a., Type **3**; ¾ a., 5 r. Adenese Camel Corps; 1 a., 2 r. The Harbour; 1½ a., 1 r. Adenese Dhow; 2½ a., 8 a. Mukalla; 3 a., 14 a., 10 r. "Capture of Aden, 1839" (Capt. Rundle).

(Des and recess D.L.R.)

1946 (15 Oct). *Victory. Wmk Mult Script CA. P* 13½ × 14.

No.	Type	Description	Unused	Used
28	9	1½ a. carmine	15	35
29		2½ a. blue	15	20
28/9 Perf "Specimen"		*Set of* 2	50·00	

10

11

King George VI and Queen Elizabeth

(Des and photo Waterlow (T **10**). Design recess; name typo B. W. (T **11**))

1949 (17 Jan.). *Royal Silver Wedding. Wmk Mult Script CA.*

No.	Type	Description	Unused	Used
30	10	1½ a. scarlet (*p* 14 × 15)	40	50
31	11	10 r. mauve (*p* 11½ × 11)	22·00	24·00

1949 (10 Oct). *75th Anniv. of Universal Postal Union. As Nos.* 114/17 *of Antigua, surch with new values by Waterlow.*

No.	Type	Description	Unused	Used
32		2½ a. on 20 c. ultramarine	40	75
33		3 a. on 30 c. carmine-red	75	90
34		8 a. on 50 c. orange	1·50	1·00
35		1 r. on 1 s. blue	1·75	2·00
32/5		*Set of* 4	4·00	4·25

5
CENTS

(12)

13 Queen Elizabeth II

1951 (1 Oct). *Currency changed. Nos.* 18 *and* 20/7 *surch with new values, in cents or shillings, as T* **12**, *or in one line between bars* (30 *c.*) *by Waterlow.*

No.	Description	Unused	Used
36	5 c. on 1 a. pale blue	15	40
37	10 c. on 2 a. sepia	15	45
38	15 c. on 2½ a. deep ultramarine	20	75
	a. Surch double	£425	
39	20 c. on 3 a. sepia and carmine	25	40
40	30 c. on 8 a. red-orange (R.)	25	50
41	50 c. on 8 a. red-orange	25	35
42	70 c. on 14 a. sepia and light blue	35	65
43	1 s. on 1 r. emerald-green	35	30
44	2 s. on 2 r. deep blue and magenta	3·50	2·25
	a. Surch albino	£175	
45	5 s. on 5 r. red-brown and olive-green	8·50	3·25
46	10 s. on 10 r. sepia and violet	12·00	7·50
36/46	*Set of* 11	23·00	15·00

(Des and eng B. W. Recess D.L.R.)

1953 (2 June). *Coronation. Wmk Mult Script CA. P* 13½ × 13.

No.	Description	Unused	Used
47 **13**	15 c. black and green	25	85

14 Minaret

25 "Aden in 1572" (F. Hogenberg)

(Recess Waterlow, until 1961, then D.L.R.)

1953 (15 June)–**63**. *T* **14** *and similar designs, and T* **25**. *Wmk Mult Script CA. P* 13½ × 30 (*No.* 72), 12 × 13½ (*Nos.* 57, 64, 66, 68) *or* 12 (*others*).

No.	Description	Unused	Used
48	5 c. yellowish green	10	10
49	5 c. bluish green (1.6.55)	10	25
	a. Perf 12 × 13½ (12.4.56)	10	10
50	10 c. orange	10	10
51	10 c. vermilion (1.2.55)	10	10
52	15 c. blue-green	25	10
53	15 c. greenish grey (26.4.59)	40	70
	a. Deep greenish grey (16.1.62)	1·50	1·50
	b. Greenish slate (13.11.62)	1·75	1·90
54	25 c. carmine-red	15	10
55	25 c. deep rose-red (15.3.56)	25	15
	a. Rose-red (13.3.62)	1·00	45
56	35 c. deep ultramarine	80	60
57	35 c. deep blue (15.10.58)	60	60
	a. Violet-blue (17.2.59)	80	50
58	50 c. dull blue	15	10
59	50 c. deep blue (1.7.55)	20	45
	a. Perf 12 × 13½ (12.4.56)	15	10
60	70 c. brown-grey	15	10
61	70 c. black (20.9.54)	20	35
	a. Perf 12 × 13½ (12.4.56)	15	10
62	1 s. sepia and reddish violet	25	10
63	1 s. black and violet (1.7.55)	25	10
64	1 s. 25, blue and black (16.7.56)	2·00	40
	a. Dull blue and black (16.1.63)	3·50	50
65	2 s. sepia and rose-carmine	1·25	40
66	2 s. black and carmine-red (1.3.56)	1·75	40
	a. Black and carmine-rose (22.1.63)	5·00	2·75
67	5 s. sepia and dull blue	1·25	40
68	5 s. black and deep dull blue (11.4.56)	1·75	40
	a. Black and blue (11.12.62)	10·00	3·50
69	10 s. sepia and olive	1·75	8·00
70	10 s. black and bronze-green (20.9.54)	3·50	1·25
71	20 s. chocolate and reddish lilac	6·50	10·00
72	20 s. black and deep lilac (7.1.57)	26·00	12·00
	a. Deep black and deep lilac (14.5.58)	28·00	13·00
48/72	*Set of* 25	45·00	32·00

Designs: (*as Type* **14**). *Horiz*—10 c. Camel transport; 15 c. Crater; 25 c. Mosque; 1 s. Dhow building. *Vert*—35 c. Dhow; 50 c. Map; 70 c. Salt works; 1 s. 25 Colony's badge; 2 s. Aden Protectorate levy; 5 s. Crater Pass; 10 s. Tribesman.

On No. 70 the tribesman's skirt is shaded with cross-hatching instead of with mainly diagonal lines as in No. 69.

1954 (27 Apr). *Royal Visit. As No.* 62 *but inscr* "ROYAL VISIT 1954" *at top.*

No.	Description	Unused	Used
73	1 s. sepia and reddish violet	20	25

تعديل
الدستور
١٩٥٩

(26)

REVISED
CONSTITUTION
1959

(27)

1959 (26 Jan). *Revised Constitution. No.* 53 *optd with T* **26**, *and No.* 64 *optd with T* **27**, *in red, by Waterlow.*

No.	Description	Unused	Used
74	15 c. slate-green	15	40
75	1 s. 25, blue and black	15	50

28 Protein Foods

(Des M. Goaman. Photo Harrison)

1963 (4 June). *Freedom from Hunger. W* w **12**. *P* 14 × 14½.

No.	Description	Unused	Used
76 **28**	1 s. 25 c. bluish green	1·25	1·40

For Red Cross issue see under South Arabian Federation.

1964 (5 Feb)–**65**. *As Nos.* 48, *etc. but wmk* w **12**. *P* 12 (10 *c.*, 15 *c.*, 25 *c.*, 1 *s.*) *or* 12 × 13½ (*others*).

No.	Description	Unused	Used
77	5 c. green (16.2.65)	20	60
78	10 c. bright orange	20	25
79	15 c. greenish grey	25	40
80	25 c. carmine-red	25	25
81	35 c. indigo-violet	65	70
82	50 c. indigo-blue	20	15
	a. Pale indigo-blue (16.2.65)	30	30
83	70 c. black	25	45
	a. Brownish grey (16.2.65)	30	40
84	1 s. black and violet (10.3.64)	1·75	80
85	1 s. 25, ultramarine and black (10.3.64)	5·00	2·00
86	2 s. black and carmine-rose (16.2.65)	2·25	16·00
77/86	*Set of* 10	10·00	19·00

The stamps of Aden were withdrawn on 31 March 1965 and superseded by the stamps of the SOUTH ARABIAN FEDERATION.

KATHIRI STATE OF SEIYUN

The stamps of ADEN were used in Kathiri State of Seiyun from 22 May 1937 until 1942. A further office was opened at Tarim on 11 December 1940.

PRICES FOR STAMPS ON COVER TO 1945
Nos. 1/11 *from* × 10

1 Sultan of Seiyun

2 Seiyun

(Recess D.L.R.)

1942 (July–Oct). *Designs as T* **1**/**2**. *Wmk Mult Script CA. T* **1**, *perf* 14; *others, perf* 12 × 13 (*vert*) *or* 13 × 12 (*horiz*).

No.	Description	Unused	Used
1	½ a. blue-green	15	35
2	¾ a. brown	15	35
3	1 a. blue	15	35
4	1½ a. carmine	15	40
5	2 a. sepia	15	50
6	2½ a. blue	15	60
7	3 a. sepia and carmine	15	50
8	8 a. red	15	50
9	1 r. green	20	50
10	2 r. blue and purple	2·75	4·75
11	5 r. brown and green	6·50	8·00
1/11	*Set of* 11	9·50	15·00
1/11 Perf "Specimen"	*Set of* 11	£100	

Designs:—½ to 1 a. Type **1**. *Vert as T* **2**—2 a. Tarim; 2½ a. Mosque, Seiyun; 1 r. South Gate, Tarim; 5 r. Mosque entrance, Tarim. *Horiz as T* **2**—3 a. Fortress, Tarim; 8 a. Mosque, Seiyun; 2 r. A Kathiri house.

VICTORY
ISSUE
8TH JUNE 1946

(10)

1946 (15 Oct). *Victory. No.* 4 *optd with T* **10**, *and No.* 6 *optd similarly but in four lines, by De La Rue.*

No.	Description	Unused	Used
12	1½ a. carmine	10	10
13	2½ a. blue (R.)	10	10
	a. Opt inverted	£300	
12/13 Perf "Specimen"	*Set of* 2	50·00	

No. 13 is known with surcharge double but the second impression is almost coincident with the first.

1949 (17 Jan). *Royal Silver Wedding. As Nos.* 30/1 *of Aden.*

No.	Description	Unused	Used
14	1½ a. scarlet	20	30
15	5 r. green	6·50	8·00

1949 (10 Oct). *75th Anniv of U.P.U. As Nos.* 114/17 *of Antigua, but inscr* "ADEN KATHIRI STATE OF SEIYUN" *and surch with new values, by Waterlow.*

No.	Description	Unused	Used
16	2½ a. on 20 c. ultramarine	25	40
17	3 a. on 30 c. carmine-red	40	55
18	8 a. on 50 c. orange	40	60
19	1 r. on 1 s. blue	60	90
16/19	*Set of* 4	1·50	2·25

5 CTS

(11)

50 CENTS

(12)

5/-

(13)

1951 (1 Oct). *Currency changed. Nos.* 3 *and* 5/11 *surch as T* **1** (5 *c.*), **12** (10 *c.* ("CTS"), 15 *c.* ("CTS"), 20 *c. and* 50 *c.*) *or* **13** (1s *to* 5*s.*), *by Waterlow.*

No.	Description	Unused	Used
20	5 c. on 1 a. blue (R.)	15	2
21	10 c. on 2 a. sepia	15	2
22	15 c. on 2½ a. blue	15	2
23	20 c. on 3 a. sepia and carmine	15	2
24	50 c. on 8 a. red	15	2
25	1 s. on 1 r. green	20	2
26	2 s. on 2 r. blue and purple	1·75	5·5
27	5 s. on 5 r. brown and green	5·00	16·0
20/27	*Set of* 8	7·00	20·0

1953 (2 June). *Coronation. As No.* 47 *of Aden.*

No.	Description	Unused	Used
28	15 c. black and deep green	20	8

14 Sultan Hussein

15 Tarim

(Des Freya Stark and H. Ingram. Recess D.L.R.)

1954 (15 Jan). *As Nos.* 1/11 (*but with portrait of Sultan Hussei as in T* **14**/**15**). *Wmk Mult Script CA. T* **14**, *perf* 12½; *others, pe* 12 × 13 (*vert*) *or* 13 × 12 (*horiz*).

No.	Description	Unused	Used
29	5 c. sepia	10	1
30	10 c. deep blue	10	1
31	15 c. deep bluish green	15	1
32	25 c. carmine-red	15	1
33	35 c. deep blue	15	1
34	50 c. deep brown and carmine-red	15	1
35	1 s. brown-orange	15	1
36	2 s. deep yellow-green	1·50	1·2
37	5 s. deep blue and violet	1·75	3·0
38	10 s. yellow-brown and violet	2·50	6·5
29/38	*Set of* 10	6·00	10·0

16 Qarn Adh Dhabi

17 Seiyun

(Recess D.L.R.)

1964 (1 July). *Designs as T* **16**/**17**. *W* w **12**. *P* 12 × 13 (70 *c.*) *o* 13 × 12 (*others*).

No.	Description	Unused	Used
39	70 c. black	45	6
40	1 s. 25 c. blue-green	45	2·7
41	1 s. 50 c. deep reddish violet	50	2·7
39/41	*Set of* 3	1·25	5·5

Design: *Horiz as T* **17**—1 s. 50 c. Gheil Omer.

(New Currency. 1000 fils = 1 dinar)

SOUTH ARABIA
للجنوب العربي
5 ٥
FILS فلوس

19

SOUTH ARABIA
الجنوب العربي
500 ٥٠٠
FILS فلس

(20)

SOUTH ARABIA
الجنوب العربي
50 ٥٠
FILS فلسا

(21)

1966 (1 Apr). *New Currency. Nos.* 29/41 *surch as T* **19**/**21**.

No.	Description	Unused	Used
42	5 f. on 5 c. (**19**)	10	1(
	a. Surch quadruple, one inverted	45·00	
43	5 f. on 10 c. (**19**) (R.)	10	1(
44	10 f. on 15 c. (**21**) (R.)	10	1(
	a. Surch inverted	75·00	
45	15 f. on 25 c. (**20**)	15	1(
46	20 f. on 35 c. (**20**) (R.)	15	1(
47	25 f. on 50 c. (**21**) (R.)	15	15
48	35 f. on 70 c. (**20**) (R.)	15	4(
49	50 f. on 1 s. (**21**)	15	15
50	65 f. on 1 s. 25 (**21**)	15	15
51	75 f. on 1 s. 50 (**21**)	20	3(
52	100 f. on 2 s. (**20**) (R.)	12·00	16·0(
53	250 f. on 5 s. (**21**) (R.)	1·40	3·25
54	500 f. on 10 s. (**20**)	1·75	3·75
42/54	*Set of* 13	15·00	22·0(

SOUTH ARABIA
الجنوب العربي
5 FILS

(22)

SOUTH ARABIA
الجنوب العربي
50 FILS

(23)

SOUTH ARABIA
الجنوب العربي
15 FILS ١٥

(24)

66. *Nos.* 29/41 *surch with T* **22**/**4**.
5 f. on 5 c. (**22**) (B.) 15 10
a. Surch inverted 45·00
5 f. on 10 c. (**22**) (R.) 20 10
10 f. on 15 c. (**23**) (Y.) 20 10
a. Surch inverted 45·00
15 f. on 25 c. (**24**) (B.) 20 10
a. Surch inverted 45·00
20 f. on 35 c. (**24**) (Y.) 30 10
25 f. on 50 c. (**23**) (B.) 30 10
35 f. on 70 c. (**24**) (Br.) 30 20
50 f. on 1 s. (**23**) (G.) 30 20
a. Stop after "FILS" 9·50
65 f. on 1 s. 25 (**23**) (Y.) 30 45
75 f. on 1 s. 50 (**23**) (G.) 30 50
a. Surch inverted 45·00
100 f. on 2 s. (**24**) (Y.) 1·50 85
a. Surch inverted 30·00
250 f. on 5 s. (**23**) (Y.) 2·50 2·75
a. Surch inverted 50·00
500 f. on 10 s. (**24**) (G.) 2·75 5·00
/67 *Set of* 13 8·50 9·00

HELSINKI 1952

(25)

INTERNATIONAL COOPERATION THROUGH OLYMPICS

(26)

66. *History of Olympic Games. Nos.* 57, 59, 61/7 *Optd as T* **25**/**6** *in red.*
10 f. on 15 c. deep bluish green (**25** ("LOS ANGELES 1932")) 10 10
20 f. on 35 c. deep blue (**25** ("BERLIN 1936")) 15 15
35 f. on 70 c. black (**26**) 15 15
a. Opt T **26** inverted
50 f. on 1 s. brown-orange (**25** ("LONDON 1948")) 20 20
a. Stop after "FILS" 8·00
65 f. on 1 s. 25, blue-green (**25**) 30 30
75 f. on 1 s. 50, deep reddish violet (**25** ("MELBOURNE 1956")) 35 35
100 f. on 2 s. deep yellow-green (**25** ("ROME 1960")) 40 40
250 f. on 5 s. deep blue and violet (**25** ("TOKYO 1964")) 90 1·00
500 f. on 10 s. yellow-brown and violet (**25** ("MEXICO CITY 1968")) 1·25 2·00
3/76 *Set of* 9 3·50 4·25

CHAMPION: ENGLAND

(27)

FOOTBALL 1966

(28)

66 (19 Sept). *World Cup Football Championships. Nos.* 57, 59, 61/2, 65/7 *optd with T* **27**/**8**.
10 f. on 15 c. deep bluish green (**27**) 30 30
20 f. on 35 c. deep blue (**28**) 40 40
35 f. on 70 c. black (**28**) 50 40
50 f. on 1 s. brown-orange (**27**) 55 40
a. Stop after "FILS" 12·00
100 f. on 2 s. deep yellow-green (**28**) 2·50 1·75
250 f. on 5 s. deep blue and violet (**27**) 6·00 4·50
500 f. on 10 s. yellow-brown and violet (**28**) 8·00 7·00
7/83 *Set of* 7 16·00 13·50

29 "Telstar"

(Photo State Ptg Wks, Vienna)

966 (25 Oct). *I.T.U. Centenary* (1965). *T* **29** *and similar vert designs. P* 13½.
4 5 f. blackish green, black and reddish violet 70 25
5 10 f. maroon, black and bright green 90 30
6 15 f. Prussian blue, black and orange 1·25 40
7 25 f. blackish green, black and orange-red 1·75 50
8 35 f. maroon, black and deep olive-yellow 2·25 70
9 50 f. Prussian blue, black and orange-brown 2·75 1·10
0 65 f. blackish green, black and orange-yellow 3·50 1·25
4/90 *Set of* 7 12·00 4·00
Designs:—10, 35 f. "Relay"; 15, 50 f. "Ranger"; others, Type **29**.

32 Churchill at Easel

(Photo State Ptg Wks, Vienna)

1966 (Dec). *Sir Winston Churchill's Paintings. T* **32** *and similar designs in black and gold* (5 *f.*) *or multicoloured* (*others*). *P* 13½.
91 5 f. Type **32** 1·00 15
92 10 f. "Antibes" 1·25 15
93 15 f. "Flowers" (*vert*) 1·25 20
94 20 f. "Tapestries" 1·40 35
95 25 f. "Village, Lake Lugano" 1·60 35
96 35 f. "Church, Lake Como" (*vert*) 1·75 40
97 50 f. "Flowers at Chartwell" (*vert*) 2·25 65
98 65 f. Type **32** 2·75 90
91/8 *Set of* 8 12·00 2·75

WORLD PEACE PANDIT NEHRU

(39)

40 "Master Crewe as Henry VIII" (Sir Joshua Reynolds)

1967. *"World Peace". Nos.* 57, 59, 61/7 *optd as T* **39** *in various sizes of type.*
99 10 f. on 15 c. deep bluish green (Type **39**) (R.) 15 15
100 20 f. on 35 c. deep blue ("WINSTON CHURCHILL") (R.) 1·75 60
101 35 f. on 70 c. black ("DAG HAMMARSKJOLD") (B.) 40 40
102 50 f. on 1 s. brown-orange ("JOHN F. KENNEDY") (R.) 50 50
a. Stop after "FILS" 12·00
103 65 f. on 1 s. 25, blue-green ("LUDWIG ERHARD") (Pk.) 60 60
104 75 f. on 1 s. 50 dp reddish violet ("LYNDON JOHNSON") (B.) 70 70
105 100 f. on 2 s. deep yellow-green ("ELEANOR ROOSEVELT") (B.) 85 85
106 250 f. on 5 s. dp blue and violet ("WINSTON CHURCHILL") (R.) 6·50 4·50
107 500 f. on 10 s. yellow-brown & violet ("JOHN F. KENNEDY") (R.) 4·50 5·50
99/107 *Set of* 9 14·50 12·00

(Photo State Ptg Wks, Vienna)

1967. *Paintings. T* **40** *and similar multicoloured designs. P* 13½.
108 5 f. Type **40** 20 20
109 10 f. "The Dancer" (Degas) 25 25
110 15 f. "The Fifer" (Manet) 30 30
111 20 f. "Stag at Sharkey's" (boxing match, G. Burrows) 35 35
112 25 f. "Don Manuel Osorio" (Goya) 40 40
113 35 f. "St. Martin distributing his Cloak" (A. van Dyck) 55 55
114 50 f. "The Blue Boy" (Gainsborough) 65 65
115 65 f. "The White Horse" (Gauguin) 85 85
116 75 f. "Mona Lisa" (Da Vinci) (45 × 62 *mm.*) 1·00 1·00
108/16 *Set of* 9 4·00 4·00

SCOTT CARPENTER

(49)

50 Churchill Crown

1967. *American Astronauts. Nos.* 57, 59, 61/2 *and* 65/6 *optd as T* **49** *in various sizes of type, in red.*
117 10 f. on 15 c. deep bluish green ("ALAN SHEPARD, JR.") 30 40
118 20 f. on 35 c. dp blue ("VIRGIL GRISSOM") 45 50
119 35 f. on 70 c. black ("JOHN GLENN, JR.") 60 75
120 50 f. on 1 s. brown-orange (Type **49**) 60 75
a. Stop after "FILS" 13·00
121 100 f. on 2 s. deep yellow-green ("WALTER SCHIRRA, JR.") 1·50 2·25
122 250 f. on 5 s. deep blue & violet ("GORDON COOPER, JR.") 2·75 3·50
a. Opt (as T **49**) double 90·00
117/122 *Set of* 6 5·50 7·50

1967 (Mar). *Churchill Commemoration. Photo. P* 13½.
123 **50** 75 f. multicoloured 8·50 6·50

Later issues up to 1 October 1967 are recorded in the Appendix below.

Appendix

The following stamps have either been issued in excess of postal needs, or have not been made available to the public in reasonable quantities at face value. Miniature sheets, imperforate stamps etc., are excluded from this section.

1967

Hunting. 20 *f.*
Olympic Games, Grenoble. Postage 10, 25, 35, 50, 75 *f. Air* 100, 200 *f.*
Scout Jamboree, Idaho. Air 150 *f.*
Paintings by Renoir. Postage 10, 35, 50, 65, 75 *f. Air* 100, 200, 250 *f.*
Paintings by Toulouse-Lautrec. Postage 10, 35, 50, 65, 75 *f. Air* 100, 200, 250 *f.*

The National Liberation Front is said to have taken control on 1 October 1967 and full independence was granted by Great Britain on 30 November 1967. Stamps issued after independence will be found listed under YEMEN (PEOPLE'S DEMOCRATIC REPUBLIC) in Part 19 (*Middle East*) of this catalogue.

QU'AITI STATE IN HADHRAMAUT

The stamps of ADEN were used in Qu'aiti State in Hadhramaut from 22 April 1937 until 1942. The main post office was at Mukalla. Other offices existed at Du'an (*opened* 1940), Gheil Ba Wazir (*opened* 1942), Haura (*opened* 1940), Shibam (*opened* 1940) and Shihr (*opened* 1939).

PRICES FOR STAMPS ON COVER TO 1945
Nos. 1/11 *from* × 6

I. Issues inscr "SHIHR and MUKALLA"

1 Sultan of Shihr and Mukalla

2 Mukalla Harbour

VICTORY ISSUE 8TH JUNE 1946

(10)

(Recess D.L.R.)

1942 (July)–**46**. *Wmk Mult Script CA. Designs as T* **1** (½ *to* 1 *a.*) *or T* **2** (*others*). *P* 14 (½ *to* 1 *a.*), 12 × 13 (1½, 2, 3 *a. and* 1 *r.*) *or* 13 × 12 (*others*).
1 ½ a. blue-green 15 25
a. Olive-green (12.46) 9·00 14·00
2 ¾ a. brown 15 25
3 1 a. blue 15 25
4 1½ a. carmine 15 20
5 2 a. sepia 15 25
6 2½ a. blue 15 20
7 3 a. sepia and carmine 15 25
8 8 a. red 15 40
9 1 r. green 25 50
10 2 r. blue and purple 3·50 4·00
11 5 r. brown and green 4·25 5·50
1/11 *Set of* 11 8·50 11·00
1/11 Perf "Specimen" *Set of* 11 £100
Designs: *Vert*—2 a. Gateway of Shihr; 3 a. Outpost of Mukalla; 1 r. Du'an. *Horiz*—2½ a. Shibam; 8 a. 'Einat; 2 r. Mosque in Hureidha; 5 r. Meshhed.

1946 (15 Oct). *Victory. No.* 4 *optd. with T* **10** *and No.* 6 *optd similarly, but in three lines, by De La Rue.*
12 1½ a. carmine 10 10
13 2½ a. blue (R.) 10 10
12/13 Perf "Specimen" *Set of* 2 55·00

1949 (17 Jan). *Royal Silver Wedding. As Nos.* 30/1 *of Aden.*
14 1½ a. scarlet 20 30
15 5 r. green 6·00 8·00

1949 (10 Oct). *75th Anniv of Universal Postal Union. As Nos.* 114/17 *of Antigua, but surch with new values, by Waterlow.*
16 2½ a. on 20 c. ultramarine 20 20
17 3 a. on 30 c. carmine-red 55 50
18 8 a. on 50 c. orange 55 60
19 1 r. on 1s. blue 60 50
a. Surch omitted £750
16/19 *Set of* 4 1·75 1·60

1951 (1 Oct). *Currency changed. Surch with new values in cents or shillings as T* **11** (5 *c.*), **12** (10 *c.* ("CTS"), 15 *c.*, 20 *c. and* 50 *c.*) *or* **13** (1 *s. to* 5 *s.*) *of Seiyun, by Waterlow.*
20 5 c. on 1 a. blue (R.) 15 15
21 10 c. on 2 a. sepia 15 15
22 15 c. on 2½ a. blue 15 15
23 20 c. on 3 a. sepia and carmine 15 20
a. Surch double, one albino 65·00
24 50 c. on 8 a. red 15 40
25 1 s. on 1 r. green 20 25
26 2 s. on 2 r. blue and purple 1·75 4·50
27 5 s. on 5 r. brown and green 2·75 6·50
20/27 *Set of* 8 5·00 11·00

1953 (2 June). *Coronation. As No.* 47 *of Aden.*
28 15 c. black and deep blue 20 55

II. Issues inscr "HADHRAMAUT"

11 Metal Work

22 Metal Work

(Des Mme M. de Sturler Raemaekers. Recess D.L.R.)

1955 (1 Sept)–**63**. *T* **11** *and similar designs. Wmk Mult Script CA. P* 11½ × 13–13½ *(vert) or* 14 *(horiz).*

29 5 c. greenish blue 10 10
30 10 c. grey-black 15 10
31 15 c. deep green 15 10
a. Bronze-green (9.3.63) 15 20
32 25 c. carmine-red 15 10
33 35 c. blue 15 10
34 50 c. orange-red 15 10
a. Red-orange (9.3.63) 30 30
35 90 c. sepia 15 15
36 1 s. black and deep lilac 20 10
37 1 s. 25, black and red-orange 30 45
38 2 s. black and indigo 80 60
39 5 s. black and bluish green . . . . 1·75 1·25
40 10 s. black and lake . . . . 2·25 2·00
29/40 . . . . *Set of* 12 5·75 4·50

Designs: *Vert*—10 c. Mat-making; 15 c. Weaving; 25 c. Pottery; 35 c. Building; 50 c. Date cultivation; 90 c. Agriculture. *Horiz*—1 s. Fisheries; 1 s. 25, 10 s. Lime-burning; 2 s. Dhow building; 5 s. Agriculture.

1963 (20 Oct). *As Nos.* 29/40 *but with inset portrait of Sultan Awadh bin Saleh el-Qu'aiti as in T* **22** *and wmk* w **12**.

41 5 c. greenish blue 10 10
42 10 c. grey-black 10 10
43 15 c. bronze-green 10 10
44 25 c. carmine-red 10 10
45 35 c. blue 10 10
46 50 c. red-orange 10 10
47 70 c. deep brown (as 90 c.) 15 20
48 1 s. black and deep lilac 20 10
49 1 s. 25, black and red-orange 35 65
50 2 s. black and indigo-blue . . . . 1·00 1·00
51 5 s. black and bluish green . . . . 3·25 4·50
52 10 s. black and lake . . . . 3·50 6·50
41/52 . . . . *Set of* 12 8·00 12·00

(New Currency. 1000 fils = 1 dinar)

1966 (1 Apr). *New currency. Nos.* 41/52 *surch as T* **20**/**21** *of Kathiri State of Seiyun.*

53 5 f. on 5 c. greenish blue (**20**) (R.) 10 15
54 5 f. on 10 c. grey-black (**20**) (R.) 10 15
55 10 f. on 15 c. bronze-green (**20**) (R.) 10 10
56 15 f. on 25 c. carmine-red (**20**) 10 15
57 20 f. on 35 c. blue (**20**) (R.) 10 20
58 25 f. on 50 c. red-orange (**20**) 10 15
59 35 f. on 70 c. deep brown (**20**) (R.) 10 20
60 50 f. on 1 s. black and deep lilac (**21**) (R.) . . 10 15
61 65 f. on 1 s. 25, black and red-orange (**21**) (R.) . . 25 25
62 100 f. on 2 s. black and indigo-blue (**21**) (R.) . . 45 75
63 250 f. on 5 s. black and bluish green (**21**) (R.) . . 1·00 1·50
64 500 f. on 10 s. black and lake (**21**) (R.) . . 8·00 3·00
53/64 . . . . *Set of* 12 9·00 6·00

1874–1965 WINSTON CHURCHILL (23)

1917-1963 JOHN F. KENNEDY (24)

1966. *Churchill Commemoration. Nos.* 54/6 *optd with T* **23**.

65 5 f. on 10 c. grey-black (R.) . . . . 3·00 3·75
66 10 f. on 15 c. bronze-green (R.) . . . . 3·50 4·00
a. Opt T 23 inverted . . . . 95·00
67 15 f. on 25 c. carmine-red (B.) . . . . 4·50 5·50
65/7 . . . . *Set of* 3 10·00 12·00

1966. *President Kennedy Commemoration. Nos.* 57/9 *optd with T* **24**.

68 20 f. on 35 c. blue (R.) . . . . 1·00 2·00
69 25 f. on 50 c. red-orange (B.) . . . . 1·40 2·75
70 35 f. on 70 c. deep brown (B.) . . . . 2·00 3·50
68/70 . . . . *Set of* 3 4·00 7·50

25 World Cup Emblem

(Photo State Ptg Wks. Vienna)

1966. *World Cup Football Championship, England. T* **25** *and similar diamond-shaped designs. P* 13½.

71 5 f. maroon and yellow-orange . . . . 1·00 25
72 10 f. slate-violet and light green . . . . 1·40 25
73 15 f. maroon and yellow-orange . . . . 1·60 30
74 20 f. slate-violet and light green . . . . 1·75 40
75 25 f. blackish green and orange-red . . . . 2·00 55
76 35 f. blue and yellow . . . . 2·50 80
77 50 f. blackish green and orange-red . . . . 3·00 1·10
78 65 f. blue and yellow . . . . 3·50 1·40
71/78 . . . . *Set of* 8 15·00 4·50

Designs:—10, 35 f. Wembley Stadium; 15, 50 f. Footballers; 20 f. Jules Rimet Cup and football; 25, 65 f. Type **25**.

29 Mexican Hat and Blanket

(Photo State Ptg Wks, Vienna)

1966 (25 Oct). *Pre-Olympic Games, Mexico* (1968). *P* 13½.

79 **29** 75 f. sepia and light yellow-green . . . . 1·25 1·25

30 Telecommunications Satellite

(Photo State Ptg Wks, Vienna)

1966 (Dec). *International Co-operation Year* (1965). *T* **30** *and similar horiz designs. P* 13½.

80 5 f. maroon, bright purple and emerald . . 1·25 25
81 10 f. violet, orange, blue-green and new blue 1·40 25
82 15 f. maroon, new blue and red . . . . 1·75 30
83 20 f. Prussian blue, purple and red . . 2·00 35
84 25 f. violet, olive-yellow, red and emerald . . 2·25 40
85 35 f. maroon, rose-red and new blue . . 3·25 70
a. New blue (face values) omitted . . £150
86 50 f. maroon, green and red . . . . 4·00 1·00
87 65 f. chocolate, bluish violet and red . . 4·50 1·50
80/87 . . . . *Set of* 8 18·00 4·25

Designs:—10, 25 f. Olympic runner (inscribed "ROME 1960"); 15 f. Fishes; 50 f. Tobacco plant; others, Type **30**.

Later issues up to 17 September 1967 are recorded in the Appendix below.

Appendix

The following stamps have either been issued in excess of postal needs, or have not been made available to the public in reasonable quantities at face value. Miniature sheets, imperforate stamps etc. are excluded from this section.

1967

Stampex Stamp Exhibition, London. Postage 5, 10, 15, 20, 25 *f. Air* 50, 65 *f.*
Amphilex International Stamp Exhibition, Amsterdam. Air 75 *f.*
Olympic Games, Mexico (1968), 75 *f.*
Paintings. Postage 5, 10, 15, 20, 25 *f. Air* 50, 65 *f.*
Scout Jamboree, Idaho. Air 35 *f.*
Space Research. Postage 10, 25, 35, 50, 75 *f. Air* 100, 250 *f.*

The National Liberation Front is said to have taken control on 17 September 1967 and full independence was granted by Great Britain on 30 November 1967. Stamps issued after independence, will be found listed under YEMEN (PEOPLE'S DEMOCRATIC REPUBLIC) in Part 19 (*Middle East*) of this catalogue.

MAHRA SULTANATE OF QISHN AND SOCOTRA

(Currency. 1000 fils = 1 dinar)

1 Mahra Flag

(Des and litho Harrison)

1967 (12 Mar). *Flag in green, black and vermilion; inscriptions black; background colours given. P* 14 × 14½.

1 **1** 5 f. mauve 95
2 10 f. buff 95
3 15 f. sage-green 95
4 20 f. red-orange 95
5 25 f. yellow-brown 95
6 35 f. turquoise-green 95
7 50 f. new blue 95
8 65 f. blackish brown 95
9 100 f. violet . . . . 1·00
10 250 f. rose-red . . . . 1·25
11 500 f. grey-green . . . . 1·50
1/11 . . . . *Set of* 11 10·00 2·

Later issues up to 1 October 1967 are recorded in the Appenc below.

Appendix

The following stamps have either been issued in excess of pos needs, or have not been made available to the public in reasonal quantities at face value. Miniature sheets, imperforate stamps e are excluded from this section.

1967

Scout Jamboree, Idaho. 15, 75, 100, 150 *f.*
President Kennedy Commemoration. Postage 10, 15, 25, 50, 75, 10 150 *f. Air* 250, 500 *f.*
Olympic Games, Mexico (1968). *Postage* 10, 25, 50 *f. Air* 250, 500

The National Liberation Front is said to have taken control or October 1967 and full independence was granted by Great Brita on 30 November 1967. Stamps issued after independence, will found listed under YEMEN (PEOPLE'S DEMOCRAT REPUBLIC) in Part 19 (*Middle East*) of this catalogue.

Anguilla

St. Christopher, Nevis and Anguilla were granted Associat Statehood on 27 February 1967, but, following a referendu Anguilla declared her independence on 30 May 1967 and the S Christopher authorities withdrew. The following stamps we issued by the governing Council and have been accepted for inte national mail. On 7 July 1969 the Anguilla post office was official recognised by the Government of St. Christopher, Nevis and A guilla and normal postal communications via St. Christopher we resumed. By the Anguilla Act of 27 July 1971, Anguilla w restored to direct British control.

A degree of internal self-government with an Executive Counc was introduced on 10 February 1976 and the links with St. Kitt Nevis were officially severed on 18 December 1980.

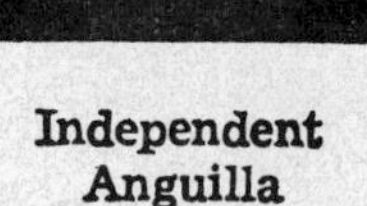
Independent Anguilla
(1)

2 Mahogany Tree, The Quarter

1967 (4 Sept). *Nos.* 129/44 *of St. Christopher, Nevis and Anguill optd as T* **1**, *by Island Press Inc, St. Thomas, U.S. Virgin Island*

1 ½ c. New lighthouse, Sombrero . . 18·00 18·0
2 1 c. Loading sugar cane, St. Kitts . . 20·00 6·5
3 2 c. Pall Mall Square, Basseterre . . 22·00 1·2
4 3 c. Gateway, Brimstone Hill Fort, St. Kitts 22·00 4·5
5 4 c. Nelson's Spring, Nevis . . 22·00 5·5
6 5 c. Grammar School, St. Kitts . . 80·00 18·0
7 6 c. Crater, Mt. Misery, St. Kitts . . 35·00 9·0
8 10 c. Hibiscus . . . . 22·00 6·5
9 15 c. Sea Island cotton, Nevis . . 45·00 11·0
10 20 c. Boat building, Anguilla . . 75·00 12·0
11 25 c. White-crowned Pigeon . . 60·00 20·0
12 50 c. St. George's Church Tower, Basseterre — £45
13 60 c. Alexander Hamilton . . — £85
14 $1 Map of St. Kitts-Nevis . . — £40
15 $2.50, Map of Anguilla . . — £30
16 $5 Arms of St. Christopher, Nevis and Anguilla . . — £30
1/16 . . . . *Set of* 16 £8000 £225

Owing to the limited stocks available for overprinting, the sal of the above stamps was personally controlled by the Postmaste and no orders from the trade were accepted.

(Des John Lister Ltd. Litho A. & M.)

1967 (27 Nov)–**68**. *T* **2** *and similar horiz designs. P* 12½ × 13.

17 1 c. dull green, bistre-brown and pale orange 10 1
18 2 c. bluish green and black (21.3.68) . . 10 1
19 3 c. black and light emerald (10.2.68) 10 1
20 4 c. cobalt-blue and black (10.2.68) . . 10 1
21 5 c. multicoloured 10 1
22 6 c. light vermilion and black (21.3.68) . . 10 1
23 10 c. multicoloured 15 1
24 15 c. multicoloured (10.2.68) . . 30 2
25 20 c. multicoloured 40 2
26 25 c. multicoloured 50 2
27 40 c. apple green, light greenish blue and black 80 2
28 60 c. multicoloured (10.2.68) . . 1·50 1·2

$1 multicoloured (10.2.68) .. .. .. 1·75 1·75
$2.50, multicoloured (21.3.68) .. .. 2·00 2·00
$5 multicoloured (10.2.68) .. .. .. 3·50 3·75
'31 .. .. *Set of* 15 10·00 9·00

Designs:—2 c. Sombrero Lighthouse; 3 c. St. Mary's Church; 4 c. ·lley Police Station; 5 c. Old Plantation House, Mt. Fortune; 6 c. ·lley Post Office; 10 c. Methodist Church, West End; 15 c. Wall-ake Airport; 20 c. Aircraft over Sandy Ground; 25 c. Island ·rbour; 40 c. Map of Anguilla; 60 c. Hermit Crab and Starfish; $1 biscus; $2.50, Local scene; $5, Spiny Lobster.

On 9 January 1969 Anguilla reaffirmed her independence from Kitts and issued Nos. 17/31 overprinted in black "INDEPEN-ENCE JANUARY 1969" in two lines. These are outside the scope this catalogue.

17 Yachts in Lagoon **18** Purple-throated Carib

(Des John Lister Ltd. Litho A. & M.)

·68 (11 May). *Anguillan Ships. T* **17** *and similar horiz designs. Multicoloured. P* 14.
· 10 c. Type **17** 15 10
· 15 c. Boat on beach 20 10
· 25 c. *Warspite* (schooner) 30 15
· 40 c. *Atlantic Star* (schooner) 35 20
·/5 .. .. *Set of* 4 90 40

(Des John Lister Ltd. Litho A. & M.)

·68 (8 July). *Anguillan Birds. T* **18** *and similar multicoloured designs. P* 14.
· 10 c. Type **18** 75 15
· 15 c. Bananaquit 95 20
· 25 c. Black-necked Stilt (*horiz*) .. .. 1·25 20
· 40 c. Royal Tern (*horiz*) .. .. .. 1·50 30
·/9 .. .. *Set of* 4 4·00 75

19 Guides' Badge and Anniversary Years

(Des John Lister Ltd. Litho A. & M.)

·968 (14 Oct). *35th Anniv of Anguillan Girl Guides. T* **19** *and similar multicoloured designs. P* 13 × 13½ (10, 25 *c.*) *or* 13½ × 13 (*others*).
·0 10 c. Type **19** 10 10
·1 15 c. Badge and silhouettes of Guides (*vert*) .. 15 10
·2 25 c. Guides' badge and Headquarters .. 20 15
·3 40 c. Association and Proficiency badges (*vert*) 25 15
·0/3 .. .. *Set of* 4 65 35

20 The Three Kings

(Des John Lister Ltd. Litho A. & M.)

·968 (18 Nov). *Christmas. T* **20** *and similar designs. P* 13.
·4 1 c. black and cerise 10 10
·5 10 c. black and light greenish blue 10 10
·6 15 c. black and chestnut 10 10
·7 40 c. black and blue 15 10
·8 50 c. black and dull green 15 15
·4/8 .. .. *Set of* 5 45 30

Designs: *Vert*—10 c. The Wise Men; 15 c. Holy Family and ·anger. *Horiz*—40 c. The Shepherds; 50 c. Holy Family and ·onkey.

21 Bagging Salt **22** "The Crucifixion" (Studio of Massys)

(Des John Lister Ltd. Litho A. & M.)

1969 (4 Jan). *Anguillan Salt Industry. T* **21** *and similar horiz designs. Multicoloured. P* 13.
49 10 c. Type **21** 10 10
50 15 c. Packing salt 10 10
51 40 c. Salt pond 15 10
52 50 c. Loading salt 15 10
49/52 .. .. *Set of* 4 35 25

(Des John Lister Ltd. Litho Format)

1969 (31 Mar). *Easter Commemoration. T* **22** *and similar vert design. P.* 13½.
53 25 c. multicoloured 15 10
54 40 c. multicoloured 20 15

Design:—40 c. "The Last Supper" (ascribed to Roberti).

23 Amaryllis

(Des John Lister Ltd. Litho Format)

1969 (10 June). *Flowers of the Caribbean. T* **23** *and similar horiz designs. Multicoloured. P* 14.
55 10 c. Type **23** 15 10
56 15 c. Bougainvillea 15 10
57 40 c. Hibiscus 30 10
58 50 c. *Cattleya* orchid 45 20
55/8 .. .. *Set of* 4 95 35

24 Turbans and Star Shells

(Des John Lister Ltd. Litho A. & M.)

1969 (22 Sept). *Sea Shells. T* **24** *and similar horiz designs. Multicoloured. P* 14.
59 10 c. Type **24** 20 10
60 15 c. Spiny oysters 20 10
61 40 c. Scotch, Royal and Smooth Scotch bonnets 30 15
62 50 c. Triton trumpet 40 20
59/62 .. .. *Set of* 4 1·00 45

(25)

(26)

(27)

(28)

(29)

1969 (Oct). *Christmas. Nos.* 17, 25/8 *optd with T* **25/29**.
63 1 c. dull green, bistre-brown & light orange 10 10
64 20 c. multicoloured 20 10
65 25 c. multicoloured 20 10
66 40 c. apple-green, light greenish blue & black 25 15
67 60 c. multicoloured 40 20
63/7 .. .. *Set of* 4 1·00 45

30 Red Goatfish **31** "Morning Glory"

(Des John Lister Ltd. Litho A. & M.)

1969 (1 Dec). *Fishes. T* **30** *and similar horiz designs. Multicoloured. P* 14.
68 10 c. Type **30** 30 15
69 15 c. Blue Striped grunts 45 15
70 40 c. Mutton grouper 55 20
71 50 c. Banded Butterfly fish 65 20
68/71 .. .. *Set of* 4 1·75 65

(Des John Lister Ltd. Litho A. & M.)

1970 (23 Feb). *Flowers. T* **31** *and similar vert designs. Multicoloured, P* 14.
72 10 c. Type **31** 25 10
73 15 c. Blue Petrea 40 10
74 40 c. Hibiscus 60 15
75 50 c. "Flame Tree" 70 20
72/5 .. .. *Set of* 4 1·75 45

32 "Deposition" (Rosso Fiorentino) **33** Scout Badge and Map

(Des John Lister Ltd. Litho Format)

1970 (26 Mar). *Easter. T* **32** *and similar multicoloured designs. P* 13½.
76 10 c. "The Ascent to Calvary" (Tiepolo) (*horiz*) 10 10
77 20 c. "The Crucifixion" (Masaccio) 15 10
78 40 c. Type **32** 20 15
79 60 c. "The Ascent to Calvary" (Murillo) (*horiz*) 25 15
76/9 .. .. *Set of* 4 65 40

(Des John Lister Ltd. Litho A. & M.)

1970 (10 Aug). *40th Anniv of Scouting in Anguilla. T* **33** *and similar horiz designs. Multicoloured. P* 13.
80 10 c. Type **33** 15 10
81 15 c. Scout camp and cubs practising first-aid 20 10
82 40 c. Monkey Bridge 25 15
83 50 c. Scout H.Q. Building and Lord Baden-Powell 35 15
80/3 .. .. *Set of* 4 85 45

34 Boatbuilding

(Des John Lister Ltd. Litho Format)

1970 (23 Nov). *Various horiz designs as T* **34**. *Multicoloured. P* 14.
84 1 c. Type **34** 10 10
85 2 c. Road Construction 10 10
86 3 c. Quay, Blowing Point 10 10
87 4 c. Broadcaster, Radio Anguilla 10 20
88 5 c. Cottage Hospital Extension 10 20
89 6 c. Valley Secondary School 10 20
90 10 c. Hotel Extension 15 20
91 15 c. Sandy Ground 20 25
92 20 c. Supermarket and Cinema 25 30
93 25 c. Bananas and Mangoes 35 50
94 40 c. Wall Blake Airport 45 60
95 60 c. Sandy Ground Jetty 65 80
96 $1 Administration Buildings .. .. 1·25 1·40
97 $2.50, Livestock .. .. 1·50 2·75
98 $5 Sandy Hill Bay .. .. 2·50 3·75
84/98 .. .. *Set of* 15 7·00 10·00

35 "The Adoration of the Shepherds" (Reni) **36** "Ecce Homo" (detail, Correggio)

(Des John Lister Ltd. Litho Questa)

1970 (11 Dec). *Christmas. T* **35** *and similar vert designs. Multicoloured. P* 13½.
99 1 c. Type **35** 10 10
100 20 c. "The Virgin and Child" (Gozzoli) .. 15 10
101 25 c. "Mystic Nativity" (detail, Botticelli) .. 15 10
102 40 c. "The Santa Margherita Madonna" (detail, Mazzola) 20 15
103 50 c. "The Adoration of the Magi" (detail, Tiepolo) 25 15
99/103 .. .. *Set of* 5 70 40

(Des John Lister Ltd. Litho Format)

1971 (29 Mar). *Easter. T* **36** *and similar designs. P* 13½.
104 10 c. multicoloured 15 10
105 15 c. multicoloured 20 10
106 40 c. multicoloured 25 10
107 50 c. multicoloured 25 15
104/7 .. .. *Set of* 4 75 25

Designs: *Vert*—15 c. "Christ appearing to St. Peter" (detail, Carracci). *Horiz*—40 c. "Angels weeping over the Dead Christ" (detail, Guercino); 50 c. "The Supper at Emmaus" (detail, Caravaggio).

37 *Hypolimnas misippus*

38 *Magnanime* and *Amiable* in Battle

(Des John Lister Ltd. Litho Questa)

1971 (21 June). *Butterflies. T* **37** *and similar horiz designs. Multicoloured. P* 14 × 14½.
108 10 c. Type **37** 80 70
109 15 c. *Junonia lavinia* .. .. 1·00 80
110 40 c. *Agraulis vanillae* .. .. 1·60 1·25
111 50 c. *Danaus plexippus* .. .. 1·90 1·50
108/11 .. .. *Set of* 4 4·75 3·75

(Des John Lister Ltd. Litho Format)

1971 (30 Aug). *Sea-battles of the West Indies. T* **38** *and similar vert designs. Multicoloured. P* 14.
112 10 c. Type **38** 60 60
a. Horiz strip of 5. Nos. 112/16 .. .. 4·75
113 15 c. H.M.S. *Duke*, *Glorieux* and H.M.S. *Agamemnon* 75 75
114 25 c. H.M.S. *Formidable* and H.M.S. *Namur* against *Ville de Paris* .. .. .. 1·00 1·00
115 40 c. H.M.S. *Canada* .. .. 1·25 1·25
116 50 c. H.M.S. *St. Albans* and wreck of *Hector* 1·50 1·50
112/16 .. .. *Set of* 5 4·75 4·75

Nos. 112/16 were issued in horizontal *se-tenant* strips within the sheet, to form a composite design in the order listed.

ADMINISTRATION BY BRITISH COMMISSION

39 "The Ansidei Madonna" (detail, Raphael)

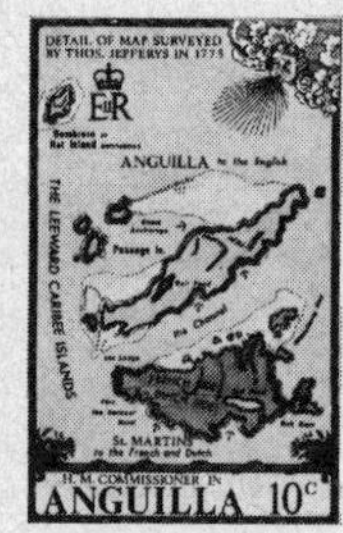

40 Map of Anguilla and St. Martins by Thomas Jefferys (1775)

(Des John Lister Ltd. Litho Questa)

1971 (29 Nov). *Christmas. T* **39** *and similar vert designs. P* 13½.
117 20 c. multicoloured 10 10
118 25 c. multicoloured 10 10
119 40 c. multicoloured 15 15
120 50 c. multicoloured 20 20
117/20 .. .. *Set of* 4 40 40

Designs:—25 c. "Mystic Nativity" (detail, Botticelli); 40 c. "Adoration of the Shepherds" (detail; ascr to Murillo); 50 c. "The Madonna of the Iris" (detail; ascr to Dürer).

(Litho Format)

1972 (24 Jan). *Maps. T* **40** *and similar multicoloured designs showing maps by the cartographers given. P* 14.
121 10 c. Type **40** 15 10
122 15 c. Samuel Fahlberg (1814) 25 15
123 40 c. Thomas Jefferys (1775) (*horiz*) 30 25
124 50 c. Capt. E. Barnett (1847) (*horiz*) 35 25
121/4 .. .. *Set of* 4 95 65

PRICES OF SETS

Set prices are given for many issues, generally those containing three stamps or more. Definitive sets include one of each value or major colour change, but do not cover different perforations, die types or minor shades. Where a choice is possible the set prices are based on the cheapest versions of the stamps included in the listings.

41 "Jesus Buffeted"

42 Loblolly Tree

(Des John Lister Ltd. Litho Format)

1972 (14 Mar). *Easter. Stained Glass Windows from Church of St. Michael, Bray, Berkshire. T* **41** *and similar vert designs. Multicoloured. P* 14 × 13½.
125 10 c. Type **41** 25 25
a. Horiz strip of 5. Nos. 125/9 .. .. 1·40
126 15 c. "The Way of Sorrows" 30 30
127 25 c. "The Crucifixion" 30 30
128 40 c. "Descent from the Cross" 35 35
129 50 c. "The Burial" 40 40
125/9 .. .. *Set of* 5 1·40 1·40

Nos. 125/9 were printed horizontally *se-tenant* within the sheet.

(Litho Questa ($10), Format (others))

1972 (30 Oct)–**75**. *T* **42** *and similar multicoloured designs (horiz, except 2, 4 and 6 c.). P* 13½.
130 1 c. Spear fishing 10 15
131 2 c. Type **42** 10 15
132 3 c. Sandy Ground 10 15
133 4 c. Ferry at Blowing Point 15 15
134 5 c. Agriculture 15 15
135 6 c. St. Mary's Church 25 15
136 10 c. St. Gerard's Church 25 25
137 15 c. Cottage Hospital extension 25 25
138 20 c. Public library 30 30
139 25 c. Sunset at Blowing Point 40 40
140 40 c. Boat building .. .. 1·50 1·50
141 60 c. Hibiscus .. .. 3·50 2·75
142 $1 Magnificent Frigate Bird .. .. 6·00 3·75
143 $2.50, Frangipani .. .. 5·50 5·50
144 $5 Brown Pelican .. .. 11·00 10·00
144*a* $10 Green-back turtle (20.5.75) .. .. 18·00 18·00
130/44*a* .. .. .. *Set of* 16 42·00 38·00

43 *Malcolm Miller* (schooner) and Common Dolphin

(Des (from photograph by D. Groves) and photo Harrison)

1972 (20 Nov). *Royal Silver Wedding. Multicoloured; background colour given. W w* **12**. *P* 14 × 14½.
145 **43** 25 c. yellow-olive (*shades*) .. .. 1·00 1·50
146 40 c. chocolate .. .. 1·10 1·75

44 Flight into Egypt

45 "The Betrayal of Christ"

(Des John Lister Ltd. Litho Questa)

1972 (4 Dec). *Christmas. T* **44** *and similar vert designs. Multicoloured. P* 13½.
147 1 c. Type **44** 10 10
148 20 c. Star of Bethlehem 20 20
a. Vert strip of 4. Nos. 148/51 85
149 25 c. Holy Family 20 20
150 40 c. Arrival of the Magi 25 25
151 50 c. Adoration of the Magi 25 25
147/51 .. .. *Set of* 5 85 85

Nos. 148/51 were printed vertically *se-tenant* within a sheet of 20 stamps.

(Des John Lister Ltd. Litho Questa)

1973 (26 Mar). *Easter. T* **45** *and similar vert designs. Multicoloured; bottom panel in gold and black. P* 13½.
152 1 c. Type **45** 10 10
153 10 c. "The Man of Sorrows" 10 10
a. Vert strip of 5. Nos. 153/7 70
154 20 c. "Christ bearing the Cross" 15 15
155 25 c. "The Crucifixion" 15
156 40 c. "The Descent from the Cross" 15
157 50 c. "The Resurrection" 20
152/7 .. .. *Set of* 6 70
MS158 140 × 141 mm. Nos. 152/7. Bottom panel in gold and mauve 70

Nos. 153/7 were printed within one sheet, vertically *se-tenant*.

46 *Santa Maria*

47 Princess Anne an[d] Captain Mark Phillip[s]

(Des John Lister Ltd. Litho Questa)

1973 (10 Sept). *Columbus Discovers the West Indies. T* **46** *a[nd] similar horiz designs. Multicoloured. P* 13½.
159 1 c. Type **46** 10
160 20 c. Early map 75
a. Horiz strip of 4. Nos. 160/3 .. .. 5·00
161 40 c. Map of voyages 90
162 70 c. Sighting land .. .. 1·50 1·
163 $1.20, Landing of Columbus .. .. .. 2·25 2·
159/63 .. .. *Set of* 5 5·00 5·
MS164 193 × 93 mm. Nos. 159/63 .. .. .. 6·00 7·

Nos. 160/3 were printed horizontally *se-tenant* within the shee[t].

(Des PAD Studio. Litho Questa)

1973 (14 Nov). *Royal Wedding. Centre multicoloured. W w* 1 (*sideways*). *P* 13½.
165 **47** 60 c. turquoise-green 20
166 $1.20, deep mauve 30

48 "The Adoration of the Shepherds" (Reni)

49 "The Crucifixion" (Raphael)

(Des John Lister Ltd. Litho Questa)

1973 (2 Dec). *Christmas. T* **48** *and similar horiz designs. Mult[i]coloured. P* 13½.
167 1 c. Type **48** 10
168 10 c. "The Madonna and Child with Saints Jerome and Dominic" (Lippi) 10 1
a. Horiz strip of 5. Nos. 168/72 75
169 20 c. "The Nativity" (Master of Brunswick) .. 15 1
170 25 c. "Madonna of the Meadow" (Bellini) .. 15 1
171 40 c. "Virgin and Child" (Cima) 20 2
172 50 c. "Adoration of the Kings" (Geertgen) .. 20 2
167/72 .. .. *Set of* 6 75 7
MS173 148 × 149 mm. Nos. 167/72 .. .. 80 1·4

Nos. 168/72 were printed within the sheet, horizontally *se-tenant*.

(Des John Lister Ltd. Litho Questa)

1974 (30 Mar). *Easter. T* **49** *and similar vert designs showin[g] various details of Raphael's "Crucifixion". P* 13½.
174 1 c. multicoloured 10 1
175 15 c. multicoloured 10 1
a. Vert strip of 5. Nos. 175/9 70
176 20 c. multicoloured 15 1
177 25 c. multicoloured 15 1
178 40 c. multicoloured 15 1
179 $1 multicoloured 25 2
174/9 .. .. *Set of* 6 70 7
MS180 123 × 141 mm. Nos. 174/9 .. .. 80 1·2

Nos. 175/9 were printed vertically *se-tenant* within one sheet.

50 Churchill making "Victory" Sign

(Des John Lister Ltd. Litho Questa)

1974 (24 June). *Birth Centenary of Sir Winston Churchill. T* **50** *and similar horiz designs. Multicoloured. P* 13½.
181 1 c. Type **50** 10 1
182 20 c. Churchill with Roosevelt 30 2
a. Horiz strip of 5. Nos. 182/6 .. .. 2·00
183 25 c. Wartime broadcast 30 2
184 40 c. Birthplace, Blenheim Palace 40 3

85 60 c. Churchill's statue 50 35
86 $1.20, Country residence, Chartwell .. 70 55
81/6 .. .. *Set of* 6 2·00 1·50
IS187 195 × 96 mm. Nos. 181/6 .. .. .. 2·25 2·25
Nos. 182/6 were printed horizontally *se-tenant* within the sheet.

51 U.P.U. Emblem

(Des John Lister Ltd. Litho Questa)

974 (27 Aug). *Centenary of Universal Postal Union. P* 13½*.
88 **51** 1 c. black and bright blue 10 10
89 20 c. black and pale orange 15 15
a. Horiz strip of 5. Nos. 189/93 .. 1·40
90 25 c. black and light yellow 15 15
91 40 c. black and bright mauve 25 25
92 60 c. black and light emerald 40 40
93 $1.20, black and light blue 60 60
88/93 .. .. *Set of* 6 1·40 1·40
IS194 195 × 96 mm. Nos. 188/93 .. .. .. 1·60 1·90
Nos. 189/93 were printed horizontally *se-tenant* within the sheet.
*In No. **MS**194 the lower row of three stamps, 40 c., 60 c. and 1.20 values, are line-perforated 15 at foot, the remaining 3 stamps eing comb-perforated 13½.

52 Anguillan pointing to Star

53 "Mary, John and Mary Magdalene" (Matthias Grünewald)

(Litho Questa)

1974 (16 Dec). *Christmas. T* **52** *and similar horiz designs. Multicoloured. P* 14.
95 1 c. Type **52** 10 10
96 20 c. Child in Manger 15 15
a. Horiz strip of 5. Nos. 196/200 95
97 25 c. King's offering 15 15
98 40 c. Star over Map of Anguilla 15 15
99 60 c. Family looking at star 20 20
200 $1.20, Angels of Peace 30 30
195/200 .. .. *Set of* 6 95 95
MS201 177 × 85 mm. Nos. 195/200 .. .. .. 1·40 1·75
Nos. 196/200 were printed horizontally *se-tenant* within the sheet.

(Litho Questa)

1975 (25 Mar). *Easter. T* **53** *and similar multicoloured designs showing details of the Isenheim altarpiece. P* 14.
202 1 c. Type **53** 10 10
203 10 c. "The Crucifixion" 10 10
a. Horiz strip of 5. Nos. 203/7 85
204 15 c. "St. John the Baptist" 10 10
205 20 c. "St. Sebastian and Angels" 15 15
206 $1 "The Entombment" 25 25
207 $1.50, "St. Anthony the Hermit" 35 35
202/7 .. .. *Set of* 6 85 85
MS208 134 × 127 mm. Nos. 202/7. Imperf. .. 1·00 1·75
Nos. 203/7 were printed horizontally *se-tenant* within the sheet.

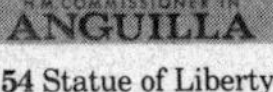

54 Statue of Liberty

55 "Madonna, Child and the Infant John the Baptist" (Raphael)

(Des John Lister Ltd. Litho Questa)

1975 (10 Nov). *Bicentenary of American Revolution. T* **54** *and similar horiz designs. Multicoloured. P* 13½*.
209 1 c. Type **54** 10 10
210 10 c. The Capitol 10 10
a. Horiz strip of 5. Nos. 210/14 .. .. 1·25
211 15 c. "Congress voting for Independence" (Pine and Savage) 15 15
212 20 c. Washington and map 15 15
213 $1 Boston Tea Party 40 40
214 $1.50, Bicentenary logo 60 60
209/14 .. .. *Set of* 6 1·25 1·25
MS215 198 × 97 mm. Nos. 209/14 .. .. .. 2·00 2·50
Nos. 210/14 were printed horizontally *se-tenant* within the sheet.
*In No. **MS**215 the lower row of three stamps, 20 c., $1 and $1.50 values, are line-perforated 15 at foot, the remaining 3 stamps being comb-perforated 13½.

(Des John Lister Ltd. Litho Questa)

1975 (8 Dec). *Christmas. T* **55** *and similar vert designs showing the "Madonna and Child". Multicoloured. P* 13½.
216 1 c. Type **55** 10 10
217 10 c. Cima 10 10
a. Horiz strip of 5. Nos. 217/21 90
218 15 c. Dolci 15 15
219 20 c. Dürer 15 15
220 $1 Bellini 25 25
221 $1.50, Botticelli 35 35
216/21 .. .. *Set of* 6 90 90
MS222 130 × 145 mm. Nos. 216/21 .. .. 1·25 2·00
Nos. 217/21 were printed horizontally *se-tenant* within the sheet.

EXECUTIVE COUNCIL

NEW CONSTITUTION 1976

(56)

57 Almond

TION

Italic second "O" in "CONSTITUTION". Occurs on Row 2/2 (Nos. 226, 228, 232, 235, 239), Row 3/2 (Nos. 230/1, 233/4, 236/8), Row 4/5 (Nos. 223/4, 240) or Row 5/2 (Nos. 225, 227, 229).

1976 (10 Feb–1 July). *New Constitution. Nos. 130 etc. optd with T* **56** *or surch also.*
223 1 c. Spear fishing 15 15
a. Italic "O" .. .. 1·00
224 2 c. on 1 c. Spear fishing 15 15
a. Italic "O" .. .. 1·10
225 2 c. Type **42** (1.7.76) .. .. .. 1·75 90
a. Italic "O" .. .. 5·00
226 3 c. on 40 c. Boat building 15 20
a. "3 c" omitted .. ..
b. Typo. "3 c"* .. .. 2·75 3·50
c. Italic "O" .. .. 1·10
227 4 c. Ferry at Blowing Point 15 20
a. Italic "O" .. .. 1·10
228 5 c. on 40 c. Boat building 15 20
a. Italic "O" .. .. 1·10
229 6 c. St. Mary's Church 15 20
a. Italic "O" .. .. 1·25
230 10 c. on 20 c. Public Library 15 20
a. Italic "O" .. .. 1·40
231 10 c. St. Gerard's Church (1.7.76) .. .. 2·00 1·00
a. Italic "O" .. .. 5·50
232 15 c. Cottage Hospital extension 25 35
a. Italic "O" .. .. 1·50
233 20 c. Public Library 25 35
a. Italic "O" .. .. 1·75
234 25 c. Sunset at Blowing Point 25 35
a. Italic "O" .. .. 2·40
235 40 c. Boat building 45 60
a. Italic "O" .. .. 2·40
236 60 c. Hibiscus 70 70
a. Italic "O" .. .. 3·00
237 $1 Magnificent Frigate Bird .. .. 2·75 2·00
a. Italic "O" .. .. 7·50
238 $2.50, Frangipani .. .. 2·25 2·25
a. Italic "O" .. .. 8·00
239 $5 Brown Pelican .. .. 4·50 5·50
a. Italic "O" .. .. 15·00
240 $10 Green-back turtle .. .. .. 4·00 6·00
a. Italic "O" .. .. 15·00
223/40 .. .. *Set of* 18 17·00 19·00
*No. 226a/b occur on R. 5/2, the "3 c" having been omitted during the normal litho surcharging.

(Des John Lister Ltd. Litho Questa)

1976 (16 Feb). *Flowering Trees. T* **57** *and similar horiz designs. Multicoloured. P* 13½.
241 1 c. Type **57** 10 10
242 10 c. Autograph 10 10
a. Horiz strip of 5. Nos. 242/6 .. .. 1·10
243 15 c. Calabash 15 15
244 20 c. Cordia 15 15
245 $1 Papaya 35 45
246 $1.50, Flamboyant 45 55
241/6 .. .. *Set of* 6 1·10 1·25
MS247 194 × 99 mm. Nos. 241/6 .. .. .. 1·50 2·00
Nos. 242/6 were printed horizontally *se-tenant* within the sheet.

58 The Three Marys

59 French Ships approaching Anguilla

(Litho Questa)

1976 (5 Apr). *Easter. T* **58** *and similar multicoloured designs showing portions of the Altar Frontal Tapestry, Rheinau. P* 13½.
248 1 c. Type **58** 10 10
249 10 c. The Crucifixion 10 10
a. Horiz strip of 5. Nos. 249/53 .. .. 1·75
250 15 c. Two Soldiers 15 15
251 20 c. The Annunciation 15 15
252 $1 The complete tapestry (*horiz*) 65 65
253 $1.50, The Risen Christ 80 80
248/53 .. .. *Set of* 6 1·75 1·75
MS254 138 × 130 mm. Nos. 248/53. Imperf .. 1·75 2·10
Nos. 249/53 were printed horizontally *se-tenant* within the sheet.

(Des John Lister Ltd. Litho Questa)

1976 (8 Nov). *Battle for Anguilla, 1796. T* **59** *and similar horiz designs. Multicoloured. P* 13½.
255 1 c. Type **59** 10 10
256 3 c. Sailing boat leaving Anguilla 35 35
a. Horiz strip of 5. Nos. 256/60 .. .. 4·25
257 15 c. Capture of *Le Desius* 55 55
258 25 c. *La Vaillante* forced aground 80 80
259 $1 H.M.S. *Lapwing* .. .. 1·25 1·25
260 $1.50, *Les Desius* burning .. .. .. 1·75 1·75
255/60 .. .. *Set of* 6 4·25 4·25
MS261 205 × 103 mm. Nos. 255/60 .. .. 5·50 6·00
Nos. 256/60 were printed horizontally *se-tenant* within the sheet.

60 "Christmas Carnival" (A. Richardson)

(Litho Questa)

1976 (22 Nov). *Christmas. T* **60** *and similar horiz designs showing children's paintings. Multicoloured. P* 13½.
262 1 c. Type **60** 10 10
263 3 c. "Dreams of Christmas Gifts" (J. Connor) 10 10
a. Horiz strip of 5, Nos. 263/7 .. .. 1·25
264 15 c. "Carolling" (P. Richardson) 15 15
265 25 c. "Candle-light Procession" (A. Mussington) 20 20
266 $1 "Going to Church" (B. Franklin) 40 30
267 $1.50, "Coming Home for Christmas" (E. Gumbs) 50 40
262/7 .. .. *Set of* 6 1·25 1·10
MS268 232 × 147 mm. Nos. 262/7 .. .. 1·50 1·75
Nos. 263/7 were printed horizontally *se-tenant* within the sheet.

61 Prince Charles and H.M.S. *Minerva*

(Des John Lister Ltd. Litho Questa)

1977 (9 Feb). *Silver Jubilee. T* **61** *and similar horiz designs. Multicoloured. P* 13½.
269 25 c. Type **61** 15 10
270 40 c. Prince Philip landing at Road Bay, 1964 20 15
271 $1.20, Coronation scene 35 25
272 $2.50, Coronation regalia and map of Anguilla 50 40
269/72 .. .. *Set of* 4 1·10 80
MS273 145 × 96 mm. Nos. 269/72 .. .. .. 1·10 1·50

62 Yellow-crowned Night Heron

(Des John Lister Ltd. Litho Questa)

1977 (18 Apr)–**78**. *T* **62** *and similar horiz designs. Multicoloured. P* 13½.
274 1 c. Type **62** 15 10
275 2 c. Great Barracuda 15 10
276 3 c. Queen Conch 15 10
277 4 c. Spanish Bayonet 15 15
278 5 c. Trunkfish 15 10
279 6 c. Cable and Wireless Building 15 10
280 10 c. American Kestrel (20.2.78) .. .. 1·50 45
281 15 c. Ground orchid (20.2.78) .. .. .. 1·50 70
282 20 c. Parrotfish (20.2.78) .. .. .. 1·50 75
283 22 c. Lobster fishing boat (20.2.78) 35 35
284 35 c. Boat race (20.2.78) 40 35
285 50 c. Sea Bean (20.2.78) 55 35
286 $1 Sandy Island (20.2.78) 60 45
287 $2.50, Manchineel (20.2.78) .. .. .. 1·00 1·00
288 $5 Ground Lizard (20.2.78) .. .. .. 2·00 1·75
289 $10 Red-billed Tropic Bird .. .. .. 6·50 4·25
274/89 .. .. *Set of* 16 15·00 10·00

NEW INFORMATION

The editor is always interested to correspond with people who have new information that will improve or correct the Catalogue.

63 "The Crucifixion" (Massys)

(Des John Lister Ltd. Litho Questa)

1977 (25 Apr). *Easter. T* **63** *and similar horiz designs showing paintings by Castagno* ($1.50) *or Ugolino (others). Multicoloured. P* 13½.

291 1 c. Type **63** 10 10
292 3 c. "The Betrayal" 10 10
a. Horiz strip of 5. Nos. 292/6 .. .. 1·60
293 22 c. "The Way to Calvary" 20 20
294 30 c. "The Deposition" 25 25
295 $1 "The Resurrection" 50 50
296 $1.50, "The Crucifixion" 65 65
291/6 .. .. *Set of* 6 1·60 1·60
MS297 192 × 126 mm. Nos. 291/6 .. .. .. 1·60 1·75

Nos. 292/6 were printed horizontally *se-tenant* within the sheet.

ROYAL VISIT
TO WEST INDIES

(**64**)

65 "Le Chapeau de Paille"

1977 (26 Oct). *Royal Visit. Nos.* 269/**MS**273 *optd with T* **64**.

298 25 c. Type **61** 15 10
299 40 c. Prince Philip landing at Road Bay, 1964 20 20
300 $1.20, Coronation scene 30 30
301 $2.50, Coronation regalia and map of Anguilla 50 50
298/301 .. .. *Set of* 4 1·00 1·00
MS302 145 × 96 mm. Nos. 298/301 .. .. 1·00 1·75

(Des John Lister Ltd. Litho Questa)

1977 (1 Nov). *400th Birth Anniv of Rubens. T* **65** *and similar vert designs. Multicoloured. P* 13½.

303 25 c. Type **65** 15 15
304 40 c. "Hélène Fourment and her Two Children" 20 25
305 $1.20, "Rubens and his Wife" 60 65
306 $2.50, "Marchesa Brigida Spinola-Doria" .. 75 95
303/6 .. .. *Set of* 4 1·50 1·75
MS307 93 × 145 mm. Nos. 303/6 .. .. .. 1·75 2·10

Each value was issued in sheets of 5 stamps and 1 label.

EASTER 1978

(**66**) (**67**)

1977 (14 Nov). *Christmas. Nos.* 262/8 *with old date blocked out and additionally inscr* "1977", *some surch also as T* **66**.

308 1 c. Type **60** 10 10
309 5 c. on 3 c. "Dreams of Christmas Gifts" .. 10 10
a. Horiz strip of 5. Nos. 309/13 .. .. 1·75
310 12 c. on 15 c. "Carolling" 15 15
311 18 c. on 25 c. "Candle-light Procession" .. 20 20
312 $1 "Going to Church" 45 45
313 $2.50 on $1.50, "Coming Home for Christmas" 90 90
308/13 .. .. *Set of* 6 1·75 1·75
MS314 232 × 147 mm. Nos. 308/13 .. .. 2·50 3·00

1978 (6 Mar). *Easter. Nos.* 303/7 *optd with T* **67**, *in gold*.

315 25 c. Type **65** 20 20
316 40 c. "Hélène Fourment and her Two Children" 25 25
317 $1.20, "Rubens and his Wife" 50 50
318 $2.50, "Marchesa Brigida Spinola-Doria" .. 85 85
315/18 .. .. *Set of* 4 1·60 1·60
MS319 93 × 145 mm. Nos. 315/18 .. .. 1·75 2·00

68 Coronation Coach at Admiralty Arch

VALLEY
SECONDARY
SCHOOL
1953-1978

(**69**)

(**70**)

(Des John Lister Ltd. Litho Questa)

1978 (6 Apr). *25th Anniv of Coronation. T* **68** *and similar horiz designs. Multicoloured. P* 14.

320 22 c. Buckingham Palace 10 10
321 50 c. Type **68** 15 15
322 $1.50, Balcony scene 25 20
323 $2.50, Royal coat of arms 40 30
320/3 .. .. *Set of* 4 80 60
MS324 138 × 92 mm. Nos. 320/3 .. .. .. 80 1·00

1978 (14 Aug). *Anniversaries. Nos.* 283/8 *optd as T* **69** *or surch as T* **70**.

325 22 c. Lobster fishing boat 20 15
a. Opt double £125
b. "C" omitted from "SECONDARY" .. 3·00
326 35 c. Boat race 30 20
a. "C" omitted from "SECONDARY" .. 3·00
327 50 c. Sea Bean 40 30
a. "I" omitted from "METHODIST" .. 3·25
328 $1 Sandy Island 50 40
a. "I" omitted from "METHODIST" .. 3·50
329 $1.20 on $5 Ground Lizard 60 45
a. "I" omitted from "METHODIST" .. 4·00
330 $1.50 on $2.50, Manchineel 75 55
a. "C" omitted from "SECONDARY" .. 5·00
325/30 .. .. *Set of* 6 2·50 1·75

The 22, 35 c. and $1.50 values commemorate the 25th anniversary of Valley Secondary School; the other values commemorate the Centenary of Road Methodist Church.

Nos. 325b, 326a and 330a occur on R. 4/1 and Nos. 327a, 328a and 329a on R. 2/4.

71 Mother and Child

(Des and litho Questa)

1978 (11 Dec). *Christmas. Children's Paintings. T* **71** *and similar horiz designs. Multicoloured. P* 13½.

331 5 c. Type **71** 10 10
332 12 c. Christmas masquerade 10 10
333 18 c. Christmas dinner 10 10
334 22 c. Serenading 10 10
335 $1 Child in manger 45 20
336 $2.50, Family going to church 90 40
331/6 .. .. *Set of* 6 1·40 70
MS337 191 × 101 mm. Nos. 331/6 .. .. 1·60 1·75

1979 (15 Jan). *International Year of the Child. As Nos.* 331/7 *but additionally inscr with emblem and* "1979 INTERNATIONAL YEAR OF THE CHILD". *Borders in different colours*.

338 5 c. Type **71** 10 10
339 12 c. Christmas masquerade 10 10
340 18 c. Christmas dinner 15 15
341 22 c. Serenading 15 15
342 $1 Child in manger 60 60
343 $2.50, Family going to church 90 90
338/43 .. .. *Set of* 6 1·75 1·75
MS344 205 × 112 mm. Nos. 338/43 .. .. 2·25 2·50

(**72**)

73 Valley Methodist Church

1979 (12 Feb). *Nos.* 274/7 *and* 279/80 *surch as T* **72**.

345 12 c. on 2 c. Great Barracuda 40 25
346 14 c. on 4 c. Spanish Bayonet 40 25
a. Surch inverted .. .. 45·00
347 18 c. on 3 c. Queen Conch 50 30
348 25 c. on 6 c. Cable and Wireless Building .. 55 35
349 38 c. on 10 c. American Kestrel 75 40
350 40 c. on 1 c. Type **62** 75 40
345/50 .. .. *Set of* 6 3·00 1·75

(Des John Lister Ltd. Litho Questa)

1979 (30 Mar). *Easter. Church Interiors. T* **73** *and similar horiz designs. Multicoloured. P* 14.

351 5 c. Type **73** 10 10
a. Horiz strip of 6. Nos. 351/6 .. .. 1·60
352 12 c. St. Mary's Anglican Church, The Valley 10 10
353 18 c. St. Gerard's Roman Catholic Church, The Valley 15 15
354 22 c. Road Methodist Church 15 15
355 $1.50, St. Augustine's Anglican Church, East End 60 60
356 $2.50, West End Methodist Church 75 75
351/6 .. .. *Set of* 6 1·60 1·60
MS357 190 × 105 mm. Nos. 351/6 .. .. 1·75 2·25

Nos. 351/6 were printed together horizontally *se-tenant*, within the sheet.

74 Cape of Good Hope 1d. "Woodblock" of 1881

(Des Stanley Gibbons Ltd. Litho Questa)

1979 (23 Apr). *Death Centenary of Sir Rowland Hill. T* **74** *and similar horiz designs showing stamps. Multicoloured. P* 14.

358 1 c. Type **74** 10 1
359 1 c. U.S.A. "inverted Jenny" of 1918 .. .. 10 1
360 22 c. Penny Black ("V.R. Official") 15 1
361 35 c. Germany 2 m. *Graf Zeppelin* of 1928 .. 20 2
362 $1.50, U.S.A. $5 Columbus of 1893 .. .. 60 6
363 $2.50, Great Britain £5 orange of 1882 .. 95 9
358/63 .. .. *Set of* 6 1·75 1·7
MS364 187 × 123 mm. Nos. 358/63 .. .. 1·75 2·1

75 Wright *Flyer I* (1st powered flight, 1903)

(Des John Lister Ltd. Litho Questa)

1979 (21 May). *History of Powered Flight. T* **75** *and similar horiz designs. Multicoloured. P* 14.

365 5 c. Type **75** 10 10
366 12 c. Louis Blériot at Dover after Channel crossing, 1909 .. .. 15 10
367 18 c. Vickers "Vimy" (1st non-stop crossing of Atlantic, 1919) 20 15
368 22 c. *Spirit of St. Louis* (1st solo Atlantic flight by Charles Lindbergh, 1927) 20 20
369 $1.50, "LZ 127" *Graf Zeppelin*, 1928 .. .. 70 60
370 $2.50, "Concorde", 1979 .. .. .. 1·50 90
365/70 .. .. *Set of* 6 2·50 1·75
MS371 200 × 113 mm. Nos. 365/70 .. .. 2·50 2·50

76 Sombrero Island

(Des John Lister Ltd. Litho Questa)

1979 (20 Aug). *Outer Islands. T* **76** *and similar horiz designs. Multicoloured. P* 14.

372 5 c. Type **76** 10 10
373 12 c. Anguillita Island 10 10
374 18 c. Sandy Island 15 15
375 25 c. Prickly Pear Cays 20 20
376 $1 Dog Island 45 45
377 $2.50, Scrub Island 85 85
372/7 .. .. *Set of* 6 1·60 1·60
MS378 180 × 91 mm. Nos. 372/7 .. .. 1·75 2·00

77 Red Poinsettia

(Des John Lister Ltd. Litho Format)

1979 (22 Oct). *Christmas. Flowers. T* **77** *and similar diamond-shaped designs. Multicoloured. P* 14½.

379 22 c. Type **77** 30 30
380 35 c. Kalanchoe 40 40
381 $1.50, Cream Poinsettia 80 80
382 $2.50, White Poinsettia .. .. .. 1·25 1·25
379/82 .. .. *Set of* 4 2·50 2·50
MS383 146 × 164 mm. Nos. 379/82 .. .. 3·00 3·25

78 Exhibition Scene

(Des R. Granger Barrett. Litho Format)

1979 (10 Dec). "*London* 1980" *International Stamp Exhibition (1st issue). T* **78** *and similar horiz designs. Multicoloured. A. P* 13 *(from sheets of* 20). B. *P* 14½ *(from booklets except* **MS**388B)

		A		B	
384	35 c. Type **78**	15	20	15	20
385	50 c. Earls Court Exhibition Centre	20	25	20	25

386	$1.50, Penny Black and Two-penny Blue stamps	55	60	55	60
387	$2.50, Exhibition logo	90	95	90	95
384/7	*Set of* 4	1·60	1·75	1·60	1·75
MS388	150 × 94 mm. Nos. 384/7	2·25	2·40	2·25	2·40

Nos. 384B/7B also exist from uncut booklet sheets of 10.
See also Nos. 407/10.

79 Games Site

(Des John Lister Ltd. Litho Format)

1980 (14 Jan). *Winter Olympic Games, Lake Placid, U.S.A. T* **79** *and similar horiz designs. Multicoloured. P* 13.

389	5 c. Type **79**	10	10
390	18 c. Ice-hockey	10	10
391	35 c. Ice-skating	15	20
392	50 c. Bobsleighing	20	25
393	$1 Skiing	40	45
394	$2.50, Luge-tobogganing	90	95
389/94	*Set of* 6	1·60	1·90
MS395	136 × 128 mm. Nos. 389/94	1·90	2·00

Nos. 389/94 also exist perforated 14½ (*Price for set of* 6 £1.60 *mint*, £1.90 *used*) from additional sheetlets of 10. Stamps perforated 13 are from normal sheets of 40.

80 Salt ready for Reaping

50th Anniversary Scouting 1980 (**81**)

75th Anniversary Rotary 1980 (**82**)

(Des John Lister Ltd. Litho Questa)

1980 (14 Apr). *Salt Industry. T* **80** *and similar horiz designs. Multicoloured. P* 14.

396	5 c. Type **80**	10	10
397	12 c. Tallying salt	10	10
398	18 c. Unloading salt flats	10	10
399	22 c. Salt storage heap	10	10
400	$1 Salt for bagging and grinding	30	30
401	$2.50, Loading salt for export	55	55
396/401	*Set of* 6	90	90
MS402	180 × 92 mm. Nos. 396/401	1·25	1·75

Nos. 396/7, 398/9 and 400/1 were each printed in the same sheet, but with the values in separate panes.

1980 (16 Apr). *Anniversaries. Nos.* 280, 282 *and* 287/8 *optd with T* **81** (10 *c.*, $2.50) *or* **82** (*others*).

403	10 c. American Kestrel	30	10
404	20 c. Parrotfish	35	15
405	$2.50, Manchineel	1·25	1·00
406	$5 Ground Lizard	2·00	1·90
403/6	*Set of* 4	3·50	2·75

Commemorations:—10 c., $2.50, 50th anniversary of Anguilla Scout Movement; others, 75th anniversary of Rotary International.

83 Palace of Westminster and Great Britain 1970 9d. "Philympia" Commemorative

84 Queen Elizabeth the Queen Mother

(Des Stamp Magazine. Litho Rosenbaum Bros, Vienna)

1980 (6 May). *"London 1980" International Stamp Exhibition (2nd issue). T* **83** *and similar horiz designs showing famous landmarks and various international stamp exhibition commemorative stamps. Multicoloured. P* 13½.

407	50 c. Type **83**	25	30
408	$1.50, City Hall, Toronto and Canada 1978 $1.50, "CAPEX"	50	55
409	$2.50, Statue of Liberty and U.S.A. 1976 13 c. "Interphil"	75	85
407/9	*Set of* 3	1·40	1·50
MS410	157 × 130 mm. Nos. 407/9	1·40	1·75

(Des R. Granger Barrett from photograph by N. Parkinson. Litho Rosenbaum Bros, Vienna)

1980 (4 Aug). *80th Birthday of Queen Elizabeth the Queen Mother. P* 13½.

411	**84**	35 c. multicoloured	25	20
412		50 c. multicoloured	35	25
413		$1.50, multicoloured	75	65
414		$3 multicoloured	2·75	1·40
411/14		*Set of* 4	3·50	2·25
MS415		160 × 110 mm. Nos. 411/14	4·00	3·00

85 Brown Pelicans

SEPARATION 1980

(**86**)

(Des John Lister Ltd. Litho Questa)

1980 (13 Nov). *Christmas. Birds. T* **85** *and similar vert designs. Multicoloured. P* 13½.

416	5 c. Type **85**	30	10
417	22 c. Great Blue Heron	75	20
418	$1.50, Barn Swallow	1·75	60
419	$3 Ruby-throated Hummingbird	2·25	1·40
416/19	*Set of* 4	4·50	2·10
MS420	126 × 160 mm. Nos. 416/19	4·50	3·25

1980 (18 Dec). *Separation of Anguilla from St. Kitts-Nevis. Nos.* 274, 277, 279/89, 341 *and* 418/19 *optd as T* **86** *or surch also.*

421	1 c. Type **62**	10	10
422	2 c. on 4 c. Spanish Bayonet	10	10
423	5 c. on 15 c. Ground orchid	15	15
424	5 c. on $1.50, Barn Swallow	15	15
425	5 c. on $3 Ruby-throated Hummingbird	15	15
426	10 c. American Kestrel	20	20
427	12 c. on $1 Sandy Island	20	20
428	14 c. on $2.50, Manchineel	20	20
429	15 c. Ground orchid	25	25
430	18 c. on $5 Ground Lizard	25	25
431	20 c. Parrotfish	25	25
432	22 c. Lobster fishing boat	25	25
433	25 c. on 15 c. Ground orchid	30	30
434	35 c. Boat race	30	30
435	38 c. on 22 c. Serenading	30	30
436	40 c. on 1 c. Type **62**	30	30
437	50 c. Sea Bean	35	35
438	$1 Sandy Island	50	50
439	$2.50, Manchineel	1·00	85
440	$5 Ground Lizard	2·25	2·00
441	$10 Red-billed Tropic Bird	5·00	4·25
442	$10 on 6 c. Cable and Wireless Building	5·00	4·25
421/42	*Set of* 22	16·00	14·00

87 First Petition for Separation, 1825

(Des John Lister Ltd. Litho Format)

1980 (18 Dec). *Separation of Anguilla from St. Kitts-Nevis. T* **87** *and similar horiz designs. Multicoloured. P* 14.

443	18 c. Type **87**	10	10
444	22 c. Referendum ballot paper, 1967	10	10
445	35 c. Airport blockade, 1967	15	15
446	50 c. Anguilla flag	20	20
447	$1 Separation celebrations, 1980	35	35
443/7	*Set of* 5	85	85
MS448	178 × 92 mm. Nos. 443/7	90	1·25

Nos. 443/4 and 445/6 were each printed in the same sheet with the two values in separate panes.

ANGUILLA 1¢ EASTER 1981

88 "Nelson's Dockyard" (R. Granger Barrett)

89 Minnie Mouse being chased by Bees

(Litho Rosenbaum Bros, Vienna)

1981 (2 Mar). *175th Death Anniv of Lord Nelson. Paintings. T* **88** *and similar horiz designs. Multicoloured. P* 14.

449	22 c. Type **88**	35	15
450	35 c. "Ships in which Nelson served" (Nicholas Pocock)	45	25
451	50 c. "H.M.S. *Victory*" (Monamy Swaine)	55	30
452	$3 "Battle of Trafalgar" (Clarkson Stanfield)	1·75	1·50
449/52	*Set of* 4	2·75	2·00
MS453	82 × 63 mm. $5 "Horatio Nelson" (L. F. Abbott) and coat of arms	2·75	3·00

(Litho Questa)

1981 (30 Mar). *Easter. Walt Disney Cartoon Characters. T* **89** *and similar vert designs. Multicoloured. P* 13½ × 14.

454	1 c. Type **89**	10	10
455	2 c. Pluto laughing at Mickey Mouse	10	10
456	3 c. Minnie Mouse tying ribbon round Pluto's neck	10	10
457	5 c. Minnie Mouse confronted by love-struck bird who fancies her bonnet	10	10
458	7 c. Dewey and Huey admiring themselves in mirror	10	10
459	9 c. Horace Horsecollar and Clarabelle Cow out for a stroll	10	10
460	10 c. Daisy Duck with hat full of Easter eggs	10	10
461	$2 Goofy unwrapping Easter hat	1·75	1·40
462	$3 Donald Duck in his Easter finery	1·90	1·60
454/62	*Set of* 9	3·50	3·00
MS463	134 × 108 mm. $5 Chip and Dale making off with hat	2·75	2·75

90 Prince Charles, Lady Diana Spencer and St. Paul's Cathedral

Extra flagstaff at right of Windsor Castle (R. 1/5).

(Des R. Granger Barrett. Litho Rosenbaum Bros, Vienna)

1981 (15 June). *Royal Wedding. T* **90** *and similar horiz designs showing Prince Charles, Lady Diana Spencer and buildings. Multicoloured. P* 14. (*a*) *No wmk.*

464	50 c. Type **90**	25	25
465	$2.50, Althorp	75	75
466	$3 Windsor Castle	90	90
	a. Extra flagstaff	8·50	
464/6	*Set of* 3	1·75	1·75
MS467	90 x 72 mm. $5 Buckingham Palace	1·50	1·75

(*b*) *Booklet stamps. W w* **15** (*sideways*)

468	50 c. Type **90**	25	45
	a. Booklet pane of 4	90	
	ab. Black printed twice	7·00	
469	$3 As No. 466	1·25	1·75
	a. Booklet pane of 4	4·50	
	ab. Black printed twice	7·00	

Nos. 464/6 also exist from additional sheetlets of two stamps and one label with changed background colours (*Price for set of* 3 £4 *mint or used*).

Nos. 468/9 come from $14 stamp booklets.

Nos. 468ab and 469ab show the black features of the portraits strengthened by a further printing applied by typography. This is particularly visible on the Prince's suit and on the couple's hair.

91 Children playing in Tree

(Des Susan Csomer. Litho Rosenbaum Bros, Vienna)

1981 (31 July–30 Sept). *35th Anniv of U.N.I.C.E.F. T* **91** *and similar horiz designs. Multicoloured. P* 14.

470	5 c. Type **91**	10	10
471	10 c. Children playing by pool	10	10
472	15 c. Children playing musical instruments	10	10
473	$3 Children playing with pets (30 Sept)	1·40	1·40
470/3	*Set of* 4	1·40	1·40
MS474	78 × 106 mm. $4 Children playing football (*vert*) (30 Sept)	1·90	1·90

(Litho Questa)

1981 (2 Nov). *Christmas. Horiz designs as T* **89** *showing scenes from Walt Disney's cartoon film "The Night before Christmas". P* 13½.

475	1 c. multicoloured	10	10
476	2 c. multicoloured	10	10
477	3 c. multicoloured	10	10
478	5 c. multicoloured	10	10
479	7 c. multicoloured	10	10
480	10 c. multicoloured	10	10
481	12 c. multicoloured	10	10
482	$2 multicoloured	1·75	1·25
483	$3 multicoloured	1·75	1·60
475/83	*Set of* 9	3·25	2·75
MS484	130 × 105 mm. $5 multicoloured	2·75	2·75

NEW INFORMATION

The editor is always interested to correspond with people who have new information that will improve or correct the Catalogue.

92 Red Grouper (93)

(Des R. Granger Barrett. Litho Questa)

1982 (1 Jan). *Horiz designs as T* **92**. *Multicoloured. P* 13½ × 14.

485	1 c. Type **92**	15	10
486	5 c. Ferry service, Blowing Point	15	10
487	10 c. Racing boats	15	10
488	15 c. Majorettes	15	10
489	20 c. Launching boat, Sandy Hill	20	10
490	25 c. Corals	45	20
491	30 c. Little Bay cliffs	25	15
492	35 c. Fountain Cave interior	80	40
493	40 c. Sunset over Sandy Island	30	20
494	45 c. Landing at Sombrero	50	35
495	60 c. Seine fishing	1·40	60
496	75 c. Boat race at sunset, Sandy Ground	60	40
497	$1 Bagging lobster at Island Harbour	1·50	75
498	$5 Brown Pelicans	8·50	4·50
499	$7.50, Hibiscus	7·50	4·25
500	$10 Queen Triggerfish	9·00	8·00
485/500	*Set of* 16	28·00	18·00

1982 (22 Mar). *No.* 494 *surch with T* **93**.

501	50 c. on 45 c. Landing at Sombrero	35	35

94 Anthurium and Zebra — **95** Lady Diana Spencer in 1961

(Des R. Granger Barrett. Litho Questa)

1982 (5 Apr). *Easter. Flowers and Butterflies. T* **94** *and similar vert designs. Multicoloured. P* 14.

502	10 c. Type **94**	15	10
503	35 c. Bird of Paradise and Caribbean Buckeye	25	20
504	75 c. Allamanda and Monarch	45	40
505	$3 Orchid Tree and Red Rim	1·60	1·60
502/5	*Set of* 4	2·25	2·10
MS506	65 × 79 mm. $5 Amaryllis and Flambeau	2·75	3·00

(Des R. Granger Barrett. Litho C. Ueberreuter Security Printing, Vienna)

1982 (17 May–30 Aug). *21st Birthday of Princess of Wales. T* **95** *and similar vert designs. Multicoloured. P* 14.

507	10 c. Type **95**	10	10
	a. Booklet pane of 4 (30 Aug)	40	
508	30 c. Lady Diana Spencer in 1968	20	20
509	40 c. Lady Diana in 1970	25	25
	a. Booklet pane of 4 (30 Aug)	1·00	
510	60 c. Lady Diana in 1974	35	35
	a. Booklet pane of 4 (30 Aug)	1·40	
511	$2 Lady Diana in 1981	1·10	1·10
	a. Booklet pane of 4 (30 Aug)	4·25	
512	$3 Lady Diana in 1981 (*different*)	1·40	1·40
507/12	*Set of* 6	3·00	3·00
MS513	72 × 90 mm. $5 Princess of Wales	2·75	3·00
MS514	125 × 125 mm. As Nos. 507/12, but with buff borders	3·00	3·50

96 Pitching Tent

(Litho C. Ueberreuter Security Printing, Vienna)

1982 (5 July). *75th Anniv of Boy Scout Movement. T* **96** *and similar horiz designs. Multicoloured. P* 14.

515	10 c. Type **96**	35	15
516	35 c. Scout band	70	40
517	75 c. Yachting	95	75
518	$3 On parade	2·50	2·50
515/18	*Set of* 4	4·00	3·50
MS519	90 × 72 mm. $5 Cooking	3·50	4·00

(Litho Format)

1982 (3 Aug). *World Cup Football Championship, Spain. Horiz designs as T* 89 *showing scenes from Walt Disney's cartoon film "Bedknobs and Broomsticks". P* 11.

520	1 c. multicoloured	10	10
521	3 c. multicoloured	10	10
522	4 c. multicoloured	10	10
523	5 c. multicoloured	10	10
524	7 c. multicoloured	10	10
525	9 c. multicoloured	10	10
526	10 c. multicoloured	10	10
527	$2.50 multicoloured	1·25	1·25
528	$3 multicoloured	1·50	1·50
520/8	*Set of* 9	2·75	2·75
MS529	126 × 101 mm. $5 multicoloured. P 14 × 13½	2·50	2·75

COMMONWEALTH GAMES 1982

(97)

1982 (18 Oct). *Commonwealth Games, Brisbane. Nos.* 487, 495/6 *and* 498 *optd with T* **97**.

530	10 c. Racing boats	10	10
	a. "S" omitted from "GAMES"	1·00	
531	60 c. Seine fishing	35	35
	a. "S" omitted from "GAMES"	1·50	
532	75 c. Boat race at sunset, Sandy Ground	45	45
	a. "S" omitted from "GAMES"	1·50	
533	$5 Brown Pelicans	2·75	2·75
	a. "S" omitted from "GAMES"	4·50	
530/3	*Set of* 4	3·25	3·25

The "S" omitted variety occurs on R.2/2 of the right-hand pane for all values.

(Litho Questa)

1982 (29 Nov). *Birth Centenary of A. A. Milne (author). Horiz designs as T* 89 *showing scenes from various "Winnie the Pooh" stories. P* 14 × 13½.

534	1 c. multicoloured	10	10
535	2 c. multicoloured	10	10
536	3 c. multicoloured	10	10
537	5 c. multicoloured	10	10
538	7 c. multicoloured	15	10
539	10 c. multicoloured	20	10
540	12 c. multicoloured	20	10
541	20 c. multicoloured	25	15
542	$5 multicoloured	3·25	2·75
534/42	*Set of* 9	3·75	3·00
MS543	120 × 93 mm. $5 multicoloured	3·00	3·00

98 Culture — **99** "I am the Lord Thy God"

(Des R. Granger Barrett. Litho Ueberreuter)

1983 (28 Feb). *Commonwealth Day. T* **98** *and similar horiz designs. Multicoloured. P* 14.

544	10 c. Type **98**	10	10
545	35 c. Anguilla and British flags	30	30
546	75 c. Economic co-operation	60	50
547	$2.50, Salt industry (salt pond)	3·00	1·75
544/7	*Set of* 4	3·50	2·40
MS548	76 × 61 mm. $5 World map showing position of Commonwealth countries	4·00	3·00

(Litho Questa)

1983 (31 Mar). *Easter. The Ten Commandments. T* **99** *and similar vert designs. Multicoloured. P* 14.

549	1 c. Type **99**	10	10
550	2 c. "Thou shalt not make any graven image"	10	10
551	3 c. "Thou shalt not take My Name in vain"	10	10
552	10 c. "Remember the Sabbath Day"	10	10
553	35 c. "Honour thy father and mother"	20	20
554	60 c. "Thou shalt not kill"	35	35
555	75 c. "Thou shalt not commit adultery"	40	40
556	$2 "Thou shalt not steal"	1·00	1·00
557	$2.50, "Thou shalt not bear false witness"	1·25	1·25
558	$5 "Thou shalt not covet"	2·50	2·50
549/58	*Set of* 10	5·50	5·50
MS559	126 × 102 mm. $5 "Moses receiving the Tablets" (16th-century woodcut)	2·50	2·50

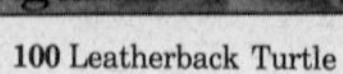

100 Leatherback Turtle — **101** Montgolfier Hot Air Balloon, 1783

(Des R. Granger Barrett. Litho Questa)

1983 (10 Aug). *Turtles. T* **100** *and similar horiz designs. Multicoloured. A. P* 13½. *B. P* 12.

		A		B	
560	10 c. Type **100**	25	15	25	15
561	35 c. Hawksbill Turtle	50	30	60	45
562	75 c. Green Turtle	75	45	1·00	70
563	$1 Loggerhead Turtle	1·00	70	1·25	85
560/3	*Set of* 4	2·25	1·40	2·75	1·90
MS564	93 × 72 mm. $5 Leatherback Turtle (*different*)	2·50	2·75	†	

(Des R. Granger Barrett. Litho Questa)

1983 (22 Aug). *Bicentenary of Manned Flight. T* **101** *and similar vert designs. Multicoloured. P* 13½.

565	10 c. Type **101**	20	10
566	60 c. Blanchard and Jeffries crossing English Channel by balloon, 1785	55	35
567	$1 Henri Giffard's steam driven airship, 1852	70	50
568	$2.50, Otto Lilienthal and glider, 1890–96	1·60	1·25
565/8	*Set of* 4	2·75	2·00
MS569	72 × 90 mm. $5 Wilbur Wright flying round Statue of Liberty, 1909	2·50	3·00

102 Boys' Brigade Band and Flag

(Des R. Granger Barrett. Litho Questa)

1983 (12 Sept). *Centenary of Boys' Brigade. T* **102** *and similar horiz design. Multicoloured. P* 13½.

570	10 c. Type **102**	15	15
571	$5 Brigade members marching	2·75	2·75
MS572	96 × 115 mm. Nos. 570/1	2·75	3·25

150TH ANNIVERSARY ABOLITION OF SLAVERY ACT

(103)

1983 (24 Oct). *150th Anniv of the Abolition of Slavery. Nos.* 487, 493 *and* 497/8 *optd with T* **103**.

573	10 c. Racing boats	10	10
	a. Opt inverted	35·00	
574	40 c. Sunset over Sandy Island	20	25
575	$1 Bagging lobster at Island Harbour	45	50
576	$5 Brown Pelicans	2·50	2·75
573/6	*Set of* 4	2·75	3·25

104 Jiminy on Clock (*Cricket on the Hearth*)

(Litho Format)

1983 (14 Nov). *Christmas. Walt Disney Cartoon Characters. T* **104** *and similar vert designs depicting scenes from Dickens' Christmas stories. Multicoloured. P* 13½.

577	1 c. Type **104**	10	10
578	2 c. Jiminy with fiddle (*Cricket on the Hearth*)	10	10
579	3 c. Jiminy among toys (*Cricket on the Hearth*)	10	10
580	4 c. Mickey as Bob Cratchit (*A Christmas Carol*)	10	10
581	5 c. Donald Duck as Scrooge (*A Christmas Carol*)	10	10
582	6 c. Mini and Goofy in *The Chimes*	10	10
583	10 c. Goofy sees an imp appearing from bells (*The Chimes*)	10	10
584	$2 Donald Duck as Mr. Pickwick (*The Pickwick Papers*)	1·75	1·25
585	$3 Disney characters as Pickwickians (*The Pickwick Papers*)	2·00	1·60
577/85	*Set of* 9	3·75	3·00
MS586	130 × 104 mm. $5 Donald Duck as Mr. Pickwick with gifts (*The Pickwick Papers*)	3·25	3·50

105 100 Metres Race

(Litho Questa)

1984 (20 Feb–24 Apr). *Olympic Games, Los Angeles. T* **105** *and similar horiz designs showing Mickey Mouse in Decathlon events. Multicoloured. A. Inscr.* "1984 Los Angeles". *P* 14 × 13½. *B. Inscr.* "1984 Olympics Los Angeles" *and Olympic emblem. P* 14 × 13½ (**MS**596B) *or* 12 (*others*) (24 April).

		A		B	
587	1 c. Type **105**	10	10	10	10
588	2 c. Long jumping	10	10	10	10
589	3 c. Shot-putting	10	10	10	10

590 4 c. High jumping 10 10 10 10
591 5 c. 400 metres race 10 10 10 10
592 6 c. Hurdling 10 10 10 10
593 10 c. Discus-throwing 10 10 10 10
594 $1 Pole-vaulting 85 60 85 60
595 $4 Javelin-throwing .. .. 2·75 2·25 2·75 2·25
587/95 .. .. .. Set of 9 3·50 3·00 3·50 3·00
MS596 117 × 93 mm. $5 1500 metres race .. .. 2·50 2·75 2·50 2·75

Nos. 587B/95B were each printed in small sheets of 6 stamps including one *se-tenant* stamp-size label in position 2.

35c

106 "Justice" (107)

(Des and litho Questa)

1984 (19 Apr). *Easter. T* **106** *and similar vert designs showing details from "La Stanza della Segnatura" by Raphael. Multi-coloured. P* 13½ × 14.
597 10 c. Type **106** 10 10
598 25 c. "Poetry" 15 20
599 35 c. "Philosophy" 25 30
600 40 c. "Theology" 25 30
601 $1 "Abraham and Paul" 65 70
602 $2 "Moses and Matthew" .. .. .. 1·25 1·40
603 $3 "John and David" .. .. .. 1·75 1·90
604 $4 "Peter and Adam" .. .. .. 2·00 2·25
597/604 .. .. Set of 8 5·75 6·50
MS605 83 × 110 mm. $5 "Astronomy" .. .. 2·50 3·00

1984 (24 Apr–17 May). *Nos.* 485, 491 *and* 498/500 *surch as T* **107**.
606 25 c. on $7.50, Hibiscus (17 May) 20 20
607 35 c. on 30 c. Little Bay cliffs 25 25
608 60 c. on 1 c. Type **92** 45 45
609 $2.50 on $5 Brown Pelicans .. .. 1·40 1·50
a. Surch at left with decimal point* .. 18·00
610 $2.50 on $10 Queen Triggerfish .. .. 1·40 1·50
a. Surch at right without decimal point* .. 18·00
606/10 .. .. Set of 5 3·25 3·50

*The surcharge on No. 609 shows the figures at right of the design and without a decimal point. On No. 610 they are to the left and include a decimal point. No 609a shows, in error, the surcharge for No. 610 and No. 610a that intended for No. 609.

108 Australia 1913 1d. Kangaroo Stamp

(Des K. Cato. Litho Leigh-Mardon Ltd, Melbourne)

1984 (16 July). *"Ausipex 84" International Stamp Exhibition, Melbourne. T* **108** *and similar horiz designs showing Australian stamps. Multicoloured. P* 13½ × 14.
611 10 c. Type **108** 10 10
612 75 c. 1914 6d. Laughing Kookaburra 60 50
613 $1 1932 2d. Sydney Harbour Bridge .. 80 65
614 $2.50, 1938 10s. King George VI .. .. 1·75 1·60
611/14 .. .. Set of 4 3·00 2·50
MS615 95 × 86 mm. $5 £1 Bass and £2 Admiral King .. .. 2·75 3·25

109 Thomas Fowell Buxton

(Des R. Granger Barrett. Litho Questa)

1984 (1 Aug). *150th Anniv of Abolition of Slavery. T* **109** *and similar horiz designs. Multicoloured. P* 14.
616 10 c. Type **109** 10 10
617 25 c. Abraham Lincoln 25 25
618 35 c. Henri Christophe 35 35
619 60 c. Thomas Clarkson 50 50
620 75 c. William Wilberforce 60 60
621 $1 Olaudah Equiano 70 70
622 $2.50, General Charles Gordon .. .. 1·60 1·60
623 $5 Granville Sharp .. .. 3·00 3·00
616/23 .. .. Set of 8 6·50 6·50
MS624 150 × 121 mm. Nos. 616/23. P 12 .. .. 6·50 7·50

U.P.U. CONGRESS
HAMBURG 1984

(110)

PRINCE HENRY
BIRTH 15.9.84

(111)

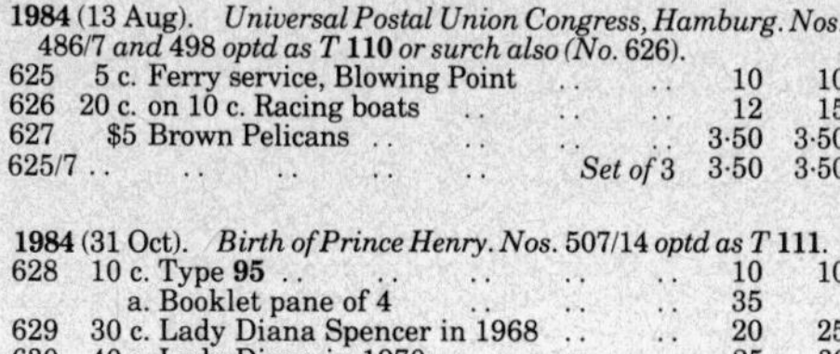

1984 (13 Aug). *Universal Postal Union Congress, Hamburg. Nos.* 486/7 *and* 498 *optd as T* **110** *or surch also* (*No.* 626).
625 5 c. Ferry service, Blowing Point 10 10
626 20 c. on 10 c. Racing boats 12 15
627 $5 Brown Pelicans .. .. 3·50 3·50
625/7 .. .. Set of 3 3·50 3·50

1984 (31 Oct). *Birth of Prince Henry. Nos.* 507/14 *optd as T* **111**.
628 10 c. Type **95** 10 10
a. Booklet pane of 4 35
629 30 c. Lady Diana Spencer in 1968 .. .. 20 25
630 40 c. Lady Diana in 1970 .. .. .. 25 30
a. Booklet pane of 4 .. .. .. 1·00
631 60 c. Lady Diana in 1974 .. .. .. 40 45
a. Booklet pane of 4 .. .. .. 1·60
632 $2 Lady Diana in 1981 .. .. .. 1·25 1·40
a. Booklet pane of 4 .. .. .. 5·00
633 $3 Lady Diana in 1981 (*different*) .. 2·00 2·25
628/33 .. .. Set of 6 3·75 4·25
MS634 72 × 90 mm. $5 Princess of Wales .. 3·25 3·50
MS635 125 × 125 mm. As Nos. 628/33, but with buff borders .. .. 7·50 8·00

On No. **MS**634 the lines of overprint are larger, being placed vertically each side of the portrait.

112 Christmas in Sweden

(Litho Questa)

1984 (12 Nov). *Christmas. Walt Disney Cartoon Characters. T* **112** *and similar horiz designs showing national scenes. Multi-coloured. P* 12 (*$2*) *or* 14 × 13½ (*others*).
636 1 c. Type **112** 10 10
637 2 c. Italy 10 10
638 3 c. Holland 10 10
639 4 c. Mexico 10 10
640 5 c. Spain 10 10
641 10 c. Disneyland, U.S.A. 10 10
642 $1 Japan .. .. 1·25 65
643 $2 Anguilla .. .. 1·75 1·10
644 $4 Germany .. .. 3·00 2·25
636/44 .. .. Set of 9 5·75 3·75
MS645 126 × 102 mm. $5 England .. .. 3·50 3·50

No. 643 was printed in sheetlets of 8 stamps.

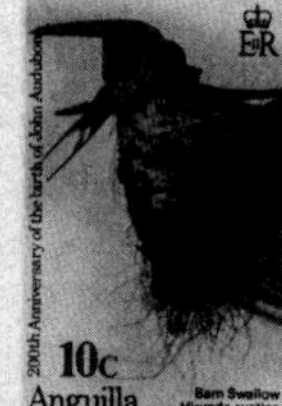

113 Icarus in Flight 114 Barn Swallow

(Des H. Herni (60 c.), S. Diouf (75 c.), adapted R. Granger Barrett. Litho Ueberreuter)

1984 (3 Dec). *40th Anniv of International Civil Aviation Organization. T* **113** *and similar multicoloured designs. P* 14.
646 60 c. Type **113** 35 40
647 75 c. "Solar Princess" (abstract) 45 50
648 $2.50, I.C.A.O. emblem (*vert*) .. .. 1·50 1·60
646/8 .. .. Set of 3 2·10 2·25
MS649 65 × 49 mm. $5 Map of air routes serving Anguilla .. .. 3·00 3·50

(Litho Questa)

1985 (29 Apr). *Birth Bicentenary of John J. Audubon* (*ornithologist*). *T* **114** *and similar multicoloured designs. P* 14.
650 10 c. Type **114** 15 10
651 60 c. American Wood Stork 45 40
652 75 c. Roseate Tern 50 45
653 $5 Osprey .. .. 2·75 3·00
650/3 .. .. Set of 4 3·50 3·50
MS654 Two sheets, each 73 × 103 mm. (a) $4 Western Tanager (*horiz*); (b) $4 Solitary Vireo (*horiz*) .. .. .. Set of 2 sheets 4·50 5·00

Nos. 650/3 were each issued in sheetlets of five stamps and one stamp-size label, which appears in the centre of the bottom row.

115 The Queen Mother visiting King's College Hospital, London 116 White-tailed Tropic Bird

(Des J.W. Litho Questa)

1985 (2 July). *Life and Times of Queen Elizabeth the Queen Mother. T* **115** *and similar vert designs. Multicoloured. P* 14.
655 10 c. Type **115** 10 10
656 $2 The Queen Mother inspecting Royal Marine Volunteer Cadets, Deal .. .. 1·10 1·25
657 $3 The Queen Mother outside Clarence House .. .. 1·60 1·75
655/7 .. .. Set of 3 2·50 2·75
MS658 56 × 85 mm. $5 At Ascot, 1979 .. .. 2·75 3·00

Nos. 655/7 also exist perforated 12 × 12½ from additional sheetlets of five stamps and one label (*Price for set of* 3 *£2.50 mint, £2.75 used*).

(Des R. Granger Barrett. Litho Questa)

1985 (22 July)–**86**. *Birds. T* **116** *and similar horiz designs. Multicoloured. P* 13½ × 14.
659 5 c. Brown Pelican (11.11.85) 10 10
660 10 c. Mourning Dove (11.11.85) 10 10
661 15 c. Magnificent Frigate Bird (inscr "Man-o-War") (11.11.85) 10 10
662 20 c. Antillean Crested Hummingbird (11.11.85) 10 10
663 25 c. Type **116** 10 10
664 30 c. Caribbean Elaenia (11.11.85) 10 15
665 35 c. Black-whiskered Vireo (11.11.85) .. 90 60
665*a* 35 c. Lesser Antillean Bullfinch (10.3.86) .. 15 20
666 40 c. Yellow-crowned Night Heron (11.11.85) 15 20
667 45 c. Pearly-eyed Thrasher (30.9.85) .. 20 25
668 50 c. Laughing Gull (30.9.85) 20 25
669 65 c. Brown Booby 25 30
670 80 c. Grey Kingbird (30.9.85) 30 35
671 $1 Audubon's Shearwater (30.9.85) .. 40 45
672 $1.35, Roseate Tern 55 60
673 $2.50, Bananaquit (11.11.85) .. .. 1·00 1·10
674 $5 Belted Kingfisher .. .. .. 2·10 2·25
675 $10 Green Heron (30.9.85) .. .. 4·00 4·25
659/75 .. .. Set of 18 9·75 10·50

GIRL GUIDES 75TH ANNIVERSARY
1910–1985

(117)

1985 (14 Oct). *75th Anniv of Girl Guide Movement. Nos.* 486, 491, 496 *and* 498 *optd with T* **117**.
676 5 c. Ferry service, Blowing Point 10 10
677 30 c. Little Bay cliffs 30 25
678 75 c. Boat race at sunset, Sandy Ground .. 60 50
679 $5 Brown Pelicans .. .. 3·50 3·50
a. Opt double .. .. 85·00
676/9 .. .. Set of 4 4·00 4·00

118 Goofy as Huckleberry Finn Fishing

(Des Walt Disney Productions. Litho Questa)

1985 (11 Nov). *150th Birth Anniv of Mark Twain* (*author*). *T* **118** *and similar horiz designs showing Walt Disney cartoon characters in scenes from "Huckleberry Finn". Multicoloured. P* 12 (*$1*) *or* 14 × 13½ (*others*).
680 10 c. Type **118** 10 10
681 60 c. Pete as Pap surprising Huck 50 50
682 $1 "Multiplication tables" 75 75
683 $3 The Duke reciting Shakespeare .. 2·00 2·00
680/3 .. .. Set of 4 3·00 3·00
MS684 127 × 102 mm. $5 "In school but out" 3·00 3·50

No. 682 was printed in sheetlets of 8 stamps.

119 Hansel and Gretel (Mickey and Minnie Mouse) awakening in Forest

(Des Walt Disney Productions. Litho Questa)

1985 (11 Nov). *Birth Bicentenaries of Grimm Brothers* (*folklorists*). *T* **119** *and similar horiz designs showing Walt Disney cartoon characters in scenes from "Hansel and Gretel". Multi-coloured. P* 12 (*90 c.*) *or* 14 × 13½ (*others*).
685 5 c. Type **119** 10 10
686 50 c. Hansel and Gretel find the gingerbread house 25 30
687 90 c. Hansel and Gretel meeting the Witch .. 45 50
688 $4 Hansel and Gretel captured by the Witch .. .. 2·00 2·10
685/8 .. .. Set of 4 2·50 2·75
MS689 126 × 101 mm. $5 Hansel and Gretel riding on swan .. .. 2·50 3·00

No. 687 was printed in sheetlets of 8 stamps.

120 Statue of Liberty and *Danmark* (Denmark)

(Litho Format)

1985 (14 Nov). *Centenary of the Statue of Liberty* (1986). *T* **120** *and similar multicoloured designs showing the Statue of Liberty and cadet ships. P* 15.

690 10 c. Type **120** 30 30
691 20 c. *Eagle* (U.S.A.) 40 40
692 60 c. *Amerigo Vespucci* (Italy) 80 80
693 75 c. *Sir Winston Churchill* (Great Britain) .. 90 90
694 $2 *Nippon Maru* (Japan) .. .. 1·75 1·75
695 $2.50, *Gorch Fock* (West Germany) .. .. 1·90 1·90
690/5 .. .. *Set of* 6 5·50 5·50
MS696 96×69 mm. $5 Statue of Liberty (*vert*) .. 3·75 4·25

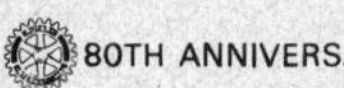
80TH ANNIVERSARY ROTARY 1985

(**121**)

INTERNATIONAL YOUTH YEAR

(**122**)

1985 (18 Nov). *80th Anniv of Rotary* (10, 35 c.) *and International Youth Year* (*others*). *Nos.* 487, 491 *and* 497 *surch or optd as T* **121** (10 *c.*, 35 *c.*) *or* **122** (*others*).

697 10 c. Racing boats 10 10
698 35 c. on 30 c. Little Bay cliffs 25 25
699 $1 Bagging lobster at Island Harbour 70 70
700 $5 on 30 c. Little Bay cliffs .. .. .. 3·50 3·50
697/700 .. .. *Set of* 4 4·00 4·00

123 Johannes Hevelius (astronomer) and Mayan Temple Observatory

124 The Crucifixion

(Des W. Hanson. Litho Questa)

1986 (17 Mar). *Appearance of Halley's Comet. T* **123** *and similar horiz designs. Multicoloured. P* 14.

701 5 c. Type **123** 10 10
702 10 c. "Viking Lander" space vehicle on Mars, 1976 .. .. 10 10
703 60 c. Comet in 1664 (from *Theatri Cosmicum*, 1668) 45 45
704 $4 Comet over Mississippi riverboat, 1835 (150th birth anniv of Mark Twain) .. 2·50 2·50
701/4 .. .. *Set of* 4 2·75 2·75
MS705 101×70 mm. $5 Halley's Comet over Anguilla .. .. 2·50 3·00

(Des R. Granger Barrett. Litho Questa)

1986 (27 Mar). *Easter. T* **124** *and similar designs showing stained glass windows from Chartres Cathedral. P* 14×13½.

706 10 c. multicoloured 10 10
707 25 c. multicoloured 20 20
708 45 c. multicoloured 40 40
709 $4 multicoloured .. .. 2·50 2·50
706/9 .. .. *Set of* 4 2·75 2·75
MS710 93×75 mm. $5 multicoloured (*horiz*). P 13½×14 .. .. 3·25 3·50

125 Princess Elizabeth inspecting Guards, 1946

AMERIPEX 1986

(**126**)

(Litho Questa)

1986 (21 Apr). *60th Birthday of Queen Elizabeth II. T* **125** *and similar vert designs. P* 14.

711 20 c. black and yellow 15 15
712 $2 multicoloured .. .. 1·25 1·25
713 $3 multicoloured .. .. 1·75 1·75
711/13 .. .. *Set of* 3 2·75 2·75
MS714 120×85 mm. $5 black and grey-brown .. 2·75 3·25

Designs:—$2 Queen at Garter Ceremony; $3 At Trooping the Colour; $5 Duke and Duchess of York with baby Princess Elizabeth, 1926.

1986 (22 May). *"Ameripex" International Stamp Exhibition, Chicago. Nos.* 659, 667, 671, 673 *and* 675 *optd with T* **126**.

715 5 c. Brown Pelican 10 10
716 45 c. Pearly-eyed Thrasher 35 35
717 $1 Audubon's Shearwater 65 65
718 $2.50, Bananaquit .. .. 1·50 1·50
719 $10 Green Heron .. .. 5·50 5·50
715/19 .. .. *Set of* 5 7·25 7·25

127 Prince Andrew and Miss Sarah Ferguson

INTERNATIONAL
YEAR OF
PEACE

(**128**)

(Des and litho Questa)

1986 (23 July). *Royal Wedding. T* **127** *and similar vert designs. Multicoloured. A. P* 14. *B. P* 12.

		A		B	
720	10 c. Type **127**	10	10	10	10
721	35 c. Prince Andrew	20	25	20	25
722	$2 Miss Sarah Ferguson ..	1·00	1·10	1·00	1·10
723	$3 Prince Andrew and Miss Sarah Ferguson (*different*)	1·50	1·60	1·50	1·60
720/3	.. .. .. *Set of* 4	2·50	2·75	2·50	2·75
MS724	119×90 mm. $6 Westminster Abbey	3·00	3·25	3·00	3·25

1986 (29 Sept). *International Peace Year. Nos.* 616/24 *optd with T* **128**.

725 10 c. Type **109** 10 10
726 25 c. Abraham Lincoln 20 20
727 35 c. Henri Christophe 30 30
728 60 c. Thomas Clarkson 45 45
729 75 c. William Wilberforce 50 50
730 $1 Olaudah Equiano 65 65
731 $2.50, General Gordon .. .. 1·50 1·50
732 $5 Granville Sharp .. .. 2·75 2·75
725/32 .. .. *Set of* 8 5·75 5·75
MS733 150×121 mnm. Nos. 725/32 .. .. 5·75 6·50

129 Trading Sloop

130 Christopher Columbus with Astrolabe

(Des R. Granger Barrett. Litho Questa)

1986 (25 Nov). *Christmas. Ships. T* **129** *and similar multicoloured designs. P* 14.

734 10 c. Type **129** 20 20
735 45 c. *Lady Rodney* (cargo liner) 65 65
736 80 c. *West Derby* (19th-century sailing ship) .. 80 80
737 $3 *Warspite* (local sloop) .. .. .. 2·50 2·50
734/7 .. .. *Set of* 4 3·75 3·75
MS738 130×100 mm. $6 Boat race day (*vert*) .. 4·25 4·75

(Des Mary Walters. Litho Questa)

1986 (22 Dec). *500th Anniv of Discovery of America* (1992). *T* **130** *and similar multicoloured designs. P* 14.

739 5 c. Type **130** 10 10
740 10 c. Columbus on board ship 10 10
741 35 c. *Santa Maria* 40 40
742 80 c. King Ferdinand and Queen Isabella of Spain (*horiz*) 60 60
743 $4 Caribbean Indians smoking tobacco (*horiz*) .. .. 2·40 2·40
739/43 .. .. *Set of* 5 3·25 3·25
MS744 Two sheets, each 96×66 mm. (a) $5 Caribbean Manatee (*horiz*). (b) $5 Dragon Tree .. .. *Set of* 2 *sheets* 7·00 7·50

NEW INFORMATION

The editor is always interested to correspond with people who have new information that will improve or correct the Catalogue.

131 Monarch

(Des R. Vigurs. Litho Questa)

1987 (14 Apr). *Easter. Butterflies. T* **131** *and similar horiz designs. Multicoloured. P* 14.

745 10 c. Type **131** 15 15
746 80 c. White Peacock 60 60
747 $1 Zebra 75 75
748 $2 Caribbean Buckeye .. .. 1·40 1·40
745/8 .. .. *Set of* 4 2·75 2·75
MS749 90×69 mm. $6 Flambeau .. .. .. 3·75 4·25

132 Old Goose Iron and Modern Electric Iron

CAPEX'87

(**133**)

(Des R. Vigurs. Litho Questa)

1987 (25 May). *20th Anniv of Separation from St. Kitts–Nevis. T* **132** *and similar horiz designs. Multicoloured. P* 14.

750 10 c. Type **132** 10 10
751 35 c. Old East End School and Albena Lake-Hodge Comprehensive College 15 20
752 45 c. Past and present markets 20 25
753 80 c. Previous sailing ferry and new motor ferry, Blowing Point 35 40
754 $1 Original mobile office and new telephone exchange 45 50
755 $2 Open-air meeting, Burrowes Park, and House of Assembly in session 90 95
750/5 .. .. *Set of* 6 1·90 2·10
MS756 159×127 mm. Nos. 750/5 .. .. .. 2·10 2·40

1987 (13 June). *"Capex '87" International Stamp Exhibition, Toronto. Nos.* 665a, 667, 670 *and* 675 *optd with T* **133** *in red.*

757 35 c. Lesser Antillean Bullfinch 15 20
758 45 c. Pearly-eyed Thrasher 20 25
759 80 c. Grey Kingbird 35 40
760 $10 Green Heron .. .. 4·50 5·00
757/60 .. .. *Set of* 4 4·75 5·25

20 YEARS OF PROGRESS

1967 - 1987

(**134**)

1987 (4 Sept). *20th Anniv of Independence. Nos.* 659, 661/4 *and* 665a/75 *optd as T* **134** *in red or surch additionally in black* (*No.* 762).

761 5 c. Brown Pelican 10 10
762 10 c. on 15 c. Magnificent Frigate Bird 10 10
763 15 c. Magnificent Frigate Bird 10 10
764 20 c. Antillean Crested Hummingbird 15 15
765 25 c. Type **116** 15 15
766 30 c. Caribbean Elaenia 20 20
767 35 c. Lesser Antillean Bullfinch 25 25
768 40 c. Yellow-crowned Night Heron 25 25
769 45 c. Pearly-eyed Thrasher 30 30
a. Opt double, one albino .. .. .. 40·00
770 50 c. Laughing Gull 30 30
771 65 c. Brown Booby 35 35
772 80 c. Grey Kingbird 45 45
773 $1 Audubon's Shearwater 55 55
774 $1.35, Roseate Tern 70 70
775 $2.50, Bananaquit .. .. 1·25 1·25
776 $5 Belted Kingfisher .. .. 2·50 2·50
777 $10 Green Heron .. .. 4·75 4·75
761/77 .. .. *Set of* 17 11·00 11·00

135 Wicket Keeper and Game in Progress

(Des R. Granger Barrett. Litho Questa)

1987 (5 Oct). *Cricket World Cup. T* **135** *and similar horiz designs. Multicoloured. P* 13½×14.

778 10 c. Type **135** 15 15
779 35 c. Batsman and local Anguilla team 30 30
780 45 c. Batsman and game in progress 40 40
781 $2.50, Bowler and game in progress .. .. 1·50 1·50
778/81 .. .. *Set of* 4 2·10 2·10
MS782 100×75 mm. $6 Batsman and game in progress (*different*) .. .. 4·00 4·25

136 West Indian Top Shell

(Des R. Granger Barrett. Litho Questa)

1987 (2 Nov). *Christmas. Sea Shells and Crabs. T* **136** *and similar horiz designs. Multicoloured. P* 13½×14.

783	10 c. Type **136**	10	10
784	35 c. Ghost Crab	15	20
785	50 c. Spiny Caribbean Vase	25	30
786	$2 Great Land Crab	90	95
783/6	*Set of* 4	1·25	1·40
MS787	101×75 mm. $6 Queen Conch	2·75	3·00

40TH WEDDING ANNIVERSARY

H.M. QUEEN ELIZABETH II

H.R.H. THE DUKE OF EDINBURGH

(**137**)

1987 (16 Dec). *Royal Ruby Wedding. Nos.* 665a, 671/2 *and* 675 *optd with T* **137** *in carmine.*

788	35 c. Lesser Antillean Bullfinch	15	20
789	$1 Audubon's Shearwater	45	50
790	$1.35, Roseate Tern	60	65
791	$10 Green Heron	4·50	4·75
788/91	*Set of* 4	5·00	5·50

138 *Crinum erubescens*

139 Relay Racing

(Des R. Vigurs. Litho Questa)

1988 (28 Mar). *Easter. Lilies. T* **138** *and similar vert designs. Multicoloured. P* 14×13½.

792	30 c. Type **138**	15	15
793	45 c. Spider Lily	25	25
794	$1 *Crinum macowanii*	50	50
795	$2.50, Day Lily	1·25	1·25
792/5	*Set of* 4	1·90	1·90
MS796	100×75 mm. $6 Easter Lily	2·75	3·00

(Des R. Vigurs. Litho Questa)

1988 (25 July). *Olympic Games, Seoul. T* **139** *and similar vert designs. Multicoloured. P* 14×13½.

797	35 c. Type **139**	25	25
798	45 c. Windsurfing	35	35
799	50 c. Tennis	40	40
800	80 c. Basketball	55	55
797/800	*Set of* 4	1·40	1·40
MS801	104×78 mm. $6 Athletics	3·00	3·50

140 Common Sea Fan

(Des R. Vigurs. Litho Questa)

1988 (28 Nov). *Christmas. Marine Life. T* **140** *and similar horiz designs. Multicoloured. P* 13½ × 14.

802	35 c. Type **140**	15	20
803	80 c. Coral Crab	40	45
804	$1 Grooved Brain Coral	45	50
805	$1.60, Queen Triggerfish	65	70
802/5	*Set of* 4	1·50	1·60
MS806	103 x 78 mm. $6 West Indies Spiny Lobster	2·50	2·75

H.R.H. PRINCESS

ALEXANDRA'S

VISIT NOVEMBER 1988

(**141**)

1988 (14 Dec). *Visit of Princess Alexandra. Nos.* 665a, 670/1 *and* 673 *optd with T* **141**.

807	35 c. Lesser Antillean Bullfinch	15	20
808	80 c. Grey Kingbird	40	45
809	$1 Audubon's Shearwater	45	50
810	$2.50, Bananaquit	1·00	1·10
807/10	*Set of* 4	1·75	2·00

142 Wood Slave

143 "Christ Crowned with Thorns" (detail) (Bosch)

(Des R. Vigurs. Litho Questa)

1989 (20 Feb). *Lizards. T* **142** *and similar horiz designs. Multicoloured. P* 13½ × 14.

811	45 c. Type **142**	20	25
812	80 c. Slippery Back	40	45
813	$2.50, *Iguana delicatissima*	1·25	1·40
811/13	*Set of* 3	1·60	1·90
MS814	101 × 75 mm. $6 Tree Lizard	2·75	3·00

(Des R. Vigurs. Litho Questa)

1989 (23 Mar). *Easter. Religious Paintings. T* **143** *and similar vert designs. Multicoloured. P* 14 × 13½.

815	35 c. Type **143**	15	20
816	80 c. "Christ bearing the Cross" (detail) (Gerard David)	40	45
817	$1 "The Deposition" (detail) (Gerard David)	45	50
818	$1.60, "Pietà" (detail) (Rogier van der Weyden)	75	80
815/18	*Set of* 4	1·60	1·75
MS819	103 × 77 mm. $6 "Crucified Christ with the Virgin Mary and Saints" (detail) (Raphael)	2·75	3·00

144 University Arms

20th
ANNIVERSARY
MOON
LANDING

(**145**)

(Des R. Vigurs. Litho Questa)

1989 (24 Apr). *40th Anniv of University of the West Indies. P* 14 × 13½.

820	**144** $5 multicoloured	2·40	2·50

1989 (31 July). *20th Anniv of First Manned Landing on Moon. Nos.* 670/2 *and* 674 *optd with T* **145**.

821	80 c. Grey Kingbird	40	45
822	$1 Audubon's Shearwater	45	50
823	$1.35, Roseate Tern	65	70
824	$5 Belted Kingfisher	2·40	2·50
821/4	*Set of* 4	3·50	3·75

146 Lone Star House, 1930

(Des J. Vigurs. Litho Questa)

1989 (11 Dec). *Christmas. Historic Houses. T* **146** *and similar horiz designs. Multicoloured. P* 13½×14.

825	5 c. Type **146**	10	10
826	35 c. Whitehouse, 1906	15	20
827	45 c. Hodges House	20	25
828	80 c. Warden's Place	40	45
825/8	*Set of* 4	75	90
MS829	102×77 mm. $6 Wallblake House, 1787	2·75	3·00

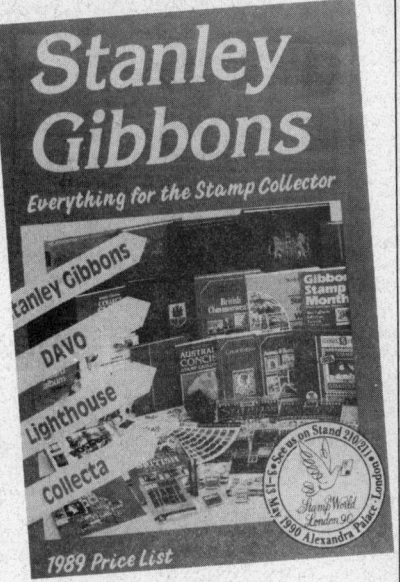

Antigua

A branch office of the British G.P.O. was opened at St. John's, the capital, in 1850, to be followed by a second, at English Harbour, in 1857. Mail before 1850 was carried by packet or merchant ships usually via Jamaica, and often did not show local postal markings. Examples of a straight line mark are, however, known from 1796.

The stamps of Great Britain were used between May 1858 and March 1860, when the island postal service became the responsibility of the local colonial authorities. In the interim period, between the take-over and the appearance of Antiguan stamps, the crowned-circle handstamps were again utilised and can be found used as late as 1869.

For illustrations of the handstamp and postmark types see BRITISH POST OFFICES ABROAD notes, following GREAT BRITAIN.

ST. JOHN'S

CROWNED-CIRCLE HANDSTAMPS

CC1 CC 1 ANTIGUA (St. John's) (9.3.1850)(R.)
Price on cover £500

Stamps of GREAT BRITAIN *cancelled* "A 02" *as Type* **2**.

1858 *to* **1860**.
Z1 1d. rose-red (1857), *perf* 14 .. .. .. £450
Z2 2d. blue (1855), *perf* 14 (Plate No. 6) £900
Z3 2d. blue (1858) (Plate Nos. 7, 8, 9) £550
Z4 4d. rose (1857) £450
Z5 6d. lilac (1856) £160
Z6 1s. green (1856) £1400

ENGLISH HARBOUR

CROWNED-CIRCLE HANDSTAMPS

CC2 CC 3 ENGLISH HARBOUR (10.12.1857)
Price on cover £4000

Stamps of GREAT BRITAIN *cancelled* "A 18" *as Type* **2**.

1858 to **1860**.
Z7 2d. blue (1858) (Plate No. 7) £5000
Z8 4d. rose (1857) £5000
Z9 6d. lilac £2000
Z10 1s. green (1856) .. ..

PRICES FOR STAMPS ON COVER TO 1945	
No. 1	*from* × 5
Nos. 2/4	†
Nos. 5/30	*from* × 8
Nos. 31/51	*from* × 3
Nos. 52/4	*from* × 5
Nos. 55/61	*from* × 4
Nos. 62/80	*from* × 3
Nos. 81/90	*from* × 4
Nos. 91/4	*from* × 3
Nos. 95/7	*from* × 4
Nos. 98/109	*from* × 3

CROWN COLONY

1

3 (Die I)

(Des E. H. Corbould, probably eng C. H. Jeens. Recess P.B.)

1862 (Aug). *No wmk*. (*a*) *Rough perf* 14 *to* 16.
1 1 6d. blue-green £800 £500

(*b*) *P* 11 *to* 12½
2 1 6d. blue-green £3250

(*c*) *P* 14 *to* 16 × 11 *to* 12½
3 1 6d. blue-green £2250

(*d*) *P* 14 *to* 16 *compound with* 11 *to* 12½
4 1 6d. blue-green £2750
Nos. 2 to 4 have not been found used.

1863 (Jan)–**1867**. *Wmk Small Star*. *W* w **2**. *Rough perf* 14 *to* 16.
5 1 1d. rosy mauve .. .. .. £100 35·00
6 1d. dull rose (1864) .. .. .. 80·00 35·00
a. Imperf between (vert pair) £9000
7 1d. vermilion (1867) .. .. .. 80·00 22·00
a. Imperf between (pair) £9000
8 6d. green (*shades*) .. .. .. £250 22·00
9 6d. dark green .. .. .. £150 22·00
10 6d. yellow-green .. .. .. £2500 60·00

Caution is needed in buying No. 10 as some of the shades of No. 8 verge on yellow-green.

The 1d. rosy mauve exists perf compound of 11, 12 and 14 to 16. This is believed to be a trial perforation and it is not known used.

(Recess D.L.R. from P.B. plates)

1872. *Wmk Crown CC*. *P* 12½.
13 1 1d. lake .. .. .. 70·00 15·00
14 1d. scarlet .. .. .. 85·00 15·00
15 6d. blue-green .. .. .. £500 6·00

1876. *Wmk Crown CC*. *P* 14.
16 1 1d. lake .. .. .. 70·00 9·00
a. Bisected (½d.) (1883) (on cover) .. † £1800
17 1d. lake-rose .. .. .. 70·00 9·00
18 6d. blue-green .. .. .. £300 11·00

(Recess (T 1); typo (T 3) De La Rue & Co)

1879. *Wmk Crown CC*. *P* 14.
19 3 2½d. red-brown £600 £160
a. Large "2" in "2½" with slanting foot £6000 £1800
20 4d. blue .. .. .. £275 14·00

1882. *Wmk Crown CA*. *P* 14.
21 3 ½d. dull green .. .. .. 1·40 10·00
22 2½d. red-brown .. .. .. £120 40·00
a. Large "2" in "2½" with slanting foot £1700 £850
23 4d. blue .. .. .. £250 15·00

1884. *Wmk Crown CA*. *P* 12.
24 1 1d. carmine-red .. .. .. 40·00 15·00
The 1d. scarlet is a colour changeling.

1884–86. *Wmk Crown CA*. *P* 14.
25 1 1d. carmine-red .. .. .. 80 2·25
26 1d. rose .. .. .. 40·00 12·00
27 3 2½d. ultramarine (1886) .. .. 5·00 11·00
a. Large "2" in "2½" with slanting foot £140 £190
28 4d. chestnut (1886) .. .. 1·25 2·00
29 1 6d. deep green .. .. .. 45·00 £110
30 3 1s. mauve (1886) £160 £120
27/28, 30 Optd "Specimen" .. *Set of* 3 £150

Nos. 25 and 26 postmarked "A 12" in place of "A 02" were used in St. Christopher.

2½ 2½ 2½
A B C

The variety "Large '2' in '2½' with slanting foot" occurs on the first stamp of the seventh row in both left (A) and right (B) panes (in which positions the "NN" of "PENNY" have three vertical strokes shortened) and on the first stamp of the third row of the right-hand pane (C). The "2" varies slightly in each position.

From 31 October 1890 until 1903 Leeward Islands general issues were used. Subsequently both general issues and the following separate issues were in concurrent use, until 1 July 1956, when the general Leeward Island stamps were withdrawn.

4

5

(Typo D.L.R.)

1903–9. *T* 4 *and* 5 (5s.). *Wmk Crown CC*. *P* 14.
31 ½d. grey-black and grey-green, O .. .. 2·00 3·25
32 1d. grey-black and rose-red, O .. .. 3·75 40
a. Blue paper (1909) .. .. 60·00 60·00
33 2d. dull purple and brown, O .. .. 6·00 22·00
34 2½d. grey-black and blue, OC .. .. 8·00 10·00
35 3d. grey-green and orange-brown, O .. 9·50 20·00
36 6d. purple and black, O .. .. 22·00 42·00
37 1s. blue and dull purple, OC .. .. 19·00 35·00
38 2s. grey-green and pale violet, O .. .. 42·00 55·00
39 2s. 6d. grey-black and purple, O .. .. 16·00 38·00
40 5s. grey-green and violet, OC .. .. 55·00 65·00
31/40 .. .. .. *Set of* 10 £150 £250
31/40 Optd "Specimen" .. *Set of* 10 £150

1908–17. *T* 4. *Wmk Mult Crown CA*. *P* 14.
41 ½d. green, O .. .. .. 1·00 2·00
42 ½d. blue-green, O (1917) .. .. 1·50 3·25
43 1d. red, O .. .. .. 2·25 1·40
44 1d. scarlet, O (5.8.15) .. .. 2·25 2·50
45 2d. dull purple and brown, C (1912) .. 3·00 14·00
46 2½d. ultramarine, O .. .. .. 6·00 12·00
a. *Blue*, O .. .. .. 10·00 17·00
47 3d. grey-green and orange-brown, C (1912) 6·00 14·00
48 6d. purple and black, C (1911) .. 7·50 22·00
49 1s. blue and dull purple, C .. .. 14·00 45·00
50 2s. grey-green and violet, C (1912) .. 42·00 55·00
41/50 .. .. .. *Set of* 8 75·00 £140
41, 43, 46 Optd "Specimen" .. *Set of* 3 65·00

1913. *As T* 5, *but portrait of King George V*. *Wmk Mult Crown CA*. *P* 14.
51 5s. grey-green and violet, C (Optd S. £60) 60·00 80·00

WAR STAMP
(7)

8

1916 (Sept)–**17**. *No*. 41 *optd in London with T* 7.
52 4 ½d. deep green (Bk.) 40 60
53 ½d. green (R.) (1.10.17) 40 60

1918. *Optd with T* 7. *Wmk Mult Crown CA*. *P* 14.
54 4 1½d. orange 35 60
52/4 Optd "Specimen" .. *Set of* 3 70·00

(Typo D.L.R.)

1921–29. *T* 8. *P* 14. (*a*) *Wmk Mult Crown CA*.
55 3d. purple/*pale yellow*, C .. .. 3·50 11·00
56 4d. grey-black & red/*pale yellow*, C (Jan 1922) 1·25 5·00
57 1s. black/*emerald*, C .. .. 3·75 4·50
58 2s. purple and blue/*blue*, C .. .. 7·50 16·00
59 2s. 6d. black and red/*blue*, C .. .. 11·00 26·00
60 5s. green and red/*pale yellow*, C (Jan, 1922) 8·00 25·00
61 £1 purple and black/*red*, C (1922) £160 £225
55/61 .. .. .. *Set of* 7 £175 £275
55/61 Optd "Specimen" .. *Set of* 7 £225

(*b*) *Wmk Mult Script CA*
62 ½d. dull green, O 35 20
63 1d. carmine-red, O 75 20
64 1d. bright scarlet, O (1929) .. .. 1·50 70
65 1d. bright violet, O .. .. .. 1·25 1·50
66 1d. mauve, O .. .. .. 4·75 4·75
67 1½d. dull orange, O (1922) .. .. 1·50 7·00
68 1½d. carmine-red, O (1926) .. .. 1·00 1·75
69 1½d. pale red-brown, O (1929) .. .. 1·50 60
70 2d. grey, O .. .. .. 1·00 75
a. Wmk sideways .. ..
71 2½d. bright blue, O .. .. .. 6·00 11·00
72 2½d. ultramarine, O (1927) .. .. 3·00 5·50
73 2½d. orange-yellow, O .. .. .. 1·25 12·00
74 3d. purple/*pale yellow*, C (1925) .. .. 4·00 8·50
75 6d. dull and bright purple, C .. .. 2·75 5·00
76 1s. black/*emerald*, C (1929) .. .. 7·00 8·00
77 2s. purple and blue/*blue*, C (1927) .. .. 10·00 24·00
78 2s. 6d. black and red/*blue*, C (1927) .. 15·00 20·00
79 3s. green and violet, C (1922) .. .. 18·00 38·00
80 4s. grey-black and red, C (1922) .. .. 40·00 48·00
62/80 .. .. .. *Set of* 16 90·00 £150
62/80 Optd/Perf "Specimen" .. *Set of* 18 £300

9 Old Dockyard, English Harbour

10 Government House, St. John's

(Des Mrs. J. Goodwin (5s.), Waterlow (others). Recess Waterlow)

1932 (27 Jan). *Tercentenary*. *T* **9/10** *and similar designs*. *Wmk Mult Script CA*. *P* 12½.
81 9 ½d. green .. .. .. 1·50 3·50
82 1d. scarlet .. .. .. 2·00 2·00
83 1½d. brown .. .. .. 3·00 3·75
84 10 2d. grey .. .. .. 3·75 12·00
85 2½d. deep blue .. .. .. 3·75 7·50
86 3d. orange .. .. .. 3·75 12·00
87 – 6d. violet .. .. .. 11·00 12·00
88 – 1s. olive-green .. .. .. 14·00 22·00
89 – 2s. 6d. claret .. .. .. 40·00 48·00
90 – 5s. black and chocolate .. .. 80·00 £110
81/90 .. .. .. *Set of* 10 £140 £200
81/90 Perf "Specimen" .. *Set of* 10 £300

Designs: *Horiz*—6d., 1s., 2s. 6d. Nelson's *Victory*. *Vert*—5s. Sir Thomas Warner's *Concepcion*.

13 Windsor Castle

(Des H. Fleury. Recess D.L.R.)

1935 (6 May). *Silver Jubilee*. *Wmk Mult Script CA*. *P* 13½ × 14.
91 13 1d. deep blue and carmine .. .. 1·50 1·00
f. Diagonal line by turret .. .. 30·00
92 1½d. ultramarine and grey .. .. 1·50 45
93 2½d. brown and deep blue .. .. 2·75 1·00
g. Dot to left of chapel .. .. 40·00
94 1s. slate and purple .. .. 7·50 11·00
91/4 .. .. .. *Set of* 4 12·00 12·00
91/4 Perf "Specimen" .. *Set of* 4 60·00

For illustrations of plate varieties see Omnibus section following Zululand.

1937 (12 May). *Coronation*. *As Nos*. 13/15 *of Aden*, *but ptd by B.W.* *P* 11 × 11½.
95 1d. carmine 50 35
96 1½d. yellow-brown 60 30
97 2½d. blue .. .. .. 1·75 75
95/7 .. .. .. *Set of* 3 2·50 1·25
95/7 Perf "Specimen" .. *Set of* 3 45·00

14 English Harbour

16 Nelson's Dockyard

(Recess Waterlow)

1938 (15 Nov)–**51**. *T* **14**, **16** *and similar designs*. *Wmk Mult Script CA*. *P* 12½.
98 14 ½d. green 15 35
99 16 1d. scarlet 70 60
a. *Red* (8.42 and 11.47) 40 35
100 1½d. chocolate-brown .. .. 1·50 40
a. *Dull reddish brown* (12.43) 70 75
b. *Lake-brown* (7.49) .. .. 12·00 12·00
101 14 2d. grey 25 20
a. *Slate-grey* (6.51) .. .. 1·50 1·25

102 16 2½d. deep ultramarine 25 25
103 – 3d. orange 25 20
104 – 6d. violet 60 20
105 – 1s. black and brown .. .. 1·00 45
a. *Black and red-brown* (7.49) .. .. 15·00 9·50
ab. Frame ptd double, once albino .. £1400
106 – 2s. 6d. brown-purple .. .. 12·00 4·50
a. *Maroon* (8.42) .. .. 11·00 3·75
107 – 5s. olive-green .. .. 10·00 7·00
108 16 10s. magenta (April 1948) .. .. .. 16·00 22·00
109 – £1 slate-green (April 1948) .. .. .. 22·00 27·00
98/109 .. .. *Set of* 12 55·00 55·00
98/109 Perf "Specimen" .. .. *Set of* 12 £200

Designs: *Horiz*—3d., 2s. 6d., £1 Fort James. *Vert*—6d., 1s., 5s. St. John's Harbour.

1946 (1 Nov). *Victory. As Nos. 28/9 of Aden.*
110 1½d. brown 15 10
111 3d. red-orange 15 15
110/111 Perf "Specimen" .. .. *Set of* 2 40·00

1949 (3 Jan). *Royal Silver Wedding. As Nos. 30/1 of Aden.*
112 2½d. ultramarine 20 20
113 5s. grey-olive .. .. 7·50 3·50

18 Hermes, Globe and Forms of Transport

19 Hemispheres, Aeroplane and Steamer

20 Hermes and Globe

21 U.P.U. Monument

(Recess, Waterlow (T **18**, **21**). Design recess, name typo, B.W. (T **19**, **20**))

1949 (10 Oct). *75th Anniv of Universal Postal Union. Wmk Mult Script CA.*
114 18 2½d. ultramarine (*p* 13½–14) 40 40
115 19 3d. orange (*p* 11 × 11½) 80 65
116 20 6d. purple (*p* 11 × 11½) 80 65
117 21 1s. red-brown (*p* 13½–14) 80 65
114/17 .. .. *Set of* 4 2·50 2·10

(New Currency. 100 cents = 1 dollar)

22 Arms of University

23 Princess Alice

(Recess Waterlow)

1951 (16 Feb). *Inauguration of B.W.I. University College. Wmk Mult Script CA. P* 14 × 14½.
118 22 3 c. black and brown 30 15
119 23 12 c. black and violet 45 30

1953 (2 June). *Coronation. As No. 47 of Aden.*
120 2 c. black and deep yellow-green 10 30

ALTERED CATALOGUE NUMBERS

Any Catalogue numbers altered from the last edition are shown as a list in the introductory pages.

24 Martello Tower

25 Federation Map

(Recess Waterlow until 1961, then D.L.R.)

1953 (2 Nov)–**62**. *Designs previously used for King George VI issue, but with portrait of Queen Elizabeth II, as in T* **24**. *Wmk Mult Script CA. P* 13 × 13½ (*horiz*) *or* 13½ × 13 (*vert*).
120*a* – ½ c. brown (3.7.56) 10 20
121 – 1 c. slate-grey 10 10
a. Slate (7.11.61) 20 20
122 – 2 c. green 10 10
123 – 3 c. black and orange-yellow 10 10
a. Black and yellow-orange (5.12.61) .. 40 40
124 – 4 c. scarlet 20 10
a. Brown-red (11.12.62) 20 10
125 – 5 c. black and slate-lilac 35 10
126 – 6 c. yellow-ochre 30 10
a. Dull yellow-ochre (5.12.61) 80 40
127 24 8 c. deep blue 45 10
128 – 12 c. violet 45 10
129 – 24 c. black and chocolate 70 15
130 24 48 c. purple and deep blue .. .. .. 2·50 1·25
131 – 60 c. maroon .. .. 3·25 80
132 – $1.20, olive-green .. .. 1·75 70
a. Yellowish olive (10.8.55) .. .. 1·50 70
133 – $2.40, bright reddish purple .. .. 7·50 12·00
134 – $4.80, slate-blue .. .. 8·50 14·00
120a/134 .. .. *Set of* 15 23·00 28·00

Designs: *Horiz*—½ c., 6 c., 60 c., $4.80, Fort James; 2 c., 3 c., 5 c., $2.40, Nelson's Dockyard. *Vert*—1 c., 4 c., English Harbour; 12 c., 24 c., $1.20, St. John's Harbour.

See also Nos. 149/58.

(Recess B.W.)

1958 (22 Apr). *Inauguration of British Caribbean Federation. W w* **12**. *P* 11½ × 11.
135 25 3 c. deep green 40 25
136 6 c. blue 60 70
137 12 c. scarlet 70 40
135/7 .. .. *Set of* 3 1·50 1·25

MINISTERIAL GOVERNMENT

COMMEMORATION
ANTIGUA
CONSTITUTION
1960

(26)

27 Nelson's Dockyard and Admiral Nelson

1960 (1 Jan). *New Constitution. Nos. 123 and 128 optd with T* **26**.
138 3 c. black and orange-yellow (R.) 10 10
139 12 c. violet 15 10

(Recess B.W.)

1961 (14 Nov). *Restoration of Nelson's Dockyard. W w* **12**. *P* 11½ × 11.
140 27 20 c. purple and brown 25 15
141 30 c. green and blue 30 15

28 Stamp of 1862 and R.M.S.P. *Solent* at English Harbour

(Des A. W. Morley. Recess B.W.)

1962 (1 Aug). *Stamp Centenary. W w* **12**. *P* 13½.
142 28 3 c. purple and deep green 15 10
143 10 c. blue and deep green 25 10
144 12 c. deep sepia and deep green 25 10
145 50 c. orange-brown and deep green 60 40
142/5 .. .. *Set of* 4 1·10 55

1963 (4 June). *Freedom from Hunger. As No. 76 of Aden.*
146 12 c. bluish green 15 15

29 Red Cross Emblem

(Des V. Whiteley. Litho B.W.)

1963 (2 Sept). *Red Cross Centenary. W w* **12**. *P* 13½.
147 3 c. red and black 20 25
148 12 c. red and blue 50 60

(Recess D.L.R.)

1963 (16 Sept)–**65**. *As 1953–61 but wmk w* **12**.
149 – ½ c. brown (13.4.65) 25 50
150 – 1 c. slate (13.4.65) 50 75
151 – 2 c. green 15 10
152 – 3 c. black and yellow-orange 15 15
153 – 4 c. brown-red 15 10
154 – 5 c. black and slate-lilac 20 10
a. Black and reddish violet (15.1.65) .. 15 10
155 – 6 c. yellow-ochre 30 30
156 24 8 c. deep blue 30 15
157 – 12 c. violet 25 15
158 – 24 c. black and deep chocolate 60 60
a. Black and chocolate-brown (28.4.65) 1·50 1·50
149/158 .. .. *Set of* 10 2·50 2·50

30 Shakespeare and Memorial Theatre, Stratford-upon-Avon

= =
15c.

(31)

(Des R. Granger Barrett. Photo Harrison)

1964 (23 April). *400th Birth Anniv of William Shakespeare. W w* **12**. *P* 14 × 14½.
164 30 12 c. orange-brown 15 10

1965 (1 April). *No. 157 surch with T* **31**.
165 15 c. on 12 c. violet 10 10

32 I.T.U. Emblem

(Des M. Goaman. Litho Enschedé)

1965 (17 May). *I.T.U. Centenary. W w* **12**. *P* 11 × 11½.
166 32 2 c. light blue and light red 20 15
167 50 c. orange-yellow and ultramarine .. 1·25 80

33 I.C.Y. Emblem

(Des V. Whiteley. Litho Harrison)

1965 (25 Oct). *International Co-operation Year. W w* **12**. *P* 14½.
168 33 4 c. reddish purple and turquoise-green 15 10
169 15 c. deep bluish green and lavender .. 25 20

34 Sir Winston Churchill, and St. Paul's Cathedral in Wartime

(Des Jennifer Toombs. Photo Harrison)

1966 (24 Jan). *Churchill Commemoration. Printed in black, cerise and gold and with background in colours stated. W w* **12**. *P* 14.
170 34 ½ c. new blue 10 10
a. Value omitted £250
171 4 c. deep green 30 10
172 25 c. brown 65 30
173 35 c. bluish violet 75 40
170/3 .. .. *Set of* 4 1·60 75

No. 170a was caused by misplacement of the gold and also shows "ANTIGUA" moved to the right.

35 Queen Elizabeth II and Duke of Edinburgh

(Des H. Baxter. Litho B.W.)

1966 (4 Feb). *Royal Visit. W w* **12**. *P* 11 × 12.
174 35 6 c. black and ultramarine .. .. .. 1·50 1·10
175 15 c. black and magenta .. .. .. 2·00 1·40

36 Footballer's Legs, Ball and Jules Rimet Cup

(Des V. Whiteley. Litho Harrison)

1966 (1 July). *World Football Cup Championships. W w* **12** *(sideways). P* 14.
176 **36** 6 c. violet, yellow-green, lake & yell-brn 15 15
177 35 c. chocolate, blue-grn, lake & yell-brn 50 25

37 W.H.O. Building

(Des M. Goaman. Litho Harrison)

1966 (20 Sept). *Inauguration of W.H.O. Headquarters, Geneva. W* w **12** *(sideways). P* 14.
178 **37** 2 c. black, yellow-green and light blue 15 15
179 15 c. black, light purple and yellow-brown 70 25

38 Nelson's Dockyard

(Des, eng and recess B.W.)

1966 (1 Nov)–**68**. *Horiz designs as T* **38**. *W* w **12**. *P* 11½ × 11.
180 ½ c. green and turquoise-blue 10 15
181 1 c. purple and cerise 10 15
182 2 c. slate-blue and yellow-orange 10 15
183 3 c. rose-red and black 10 15
184 4 c. slate-violet and brown 15 10
185 5 c. ultramarine and yellow-olive 10 10
186 6 c. salmon and purple 15 10
187 10 c. emerald and rose-red 15 10
188 15 c. brown and new blue 25 10
189 25 c. slate-blue and sepia 35 20
190 35 c. cerise and blackish brown 1·50 55
191 50 c. dull green and black 1·50 2·25
192 75 c. greenish blue and ultramarine 1·50 2·50
193 $1 cerise and yellow-olive 2·00 2·50
a. *Carmine and yellow-olive* (14.5.68) 4·50 5·00
194 $2.50, black and cerise 2·50 4·25
195 $5 olive-green and slate-violet 4·50 6·50
180/195 *Set of* 16 13·50 18·00

Designs:—1 c. Old Post Office, St. John's; 2 c. Health Centre; 3 c. Teachers' Training College; 4 c. Martello Tower, Barbuda; 5 c. Ruins of Officers' Quarters, Shirley Heights; 6 c. Government House, Barbuda; 10 c. Princess Margaret School; 15 c. Air Terminal building; 25 c. General Post Office; 35 c. Clarence House; 50 c. Government House, St. John's; 75 c. Administration Building; $1, Courthouse, St. John's; $2.50, Magistrates' Court; $5, St. John's Cathedral.

See also Nos. 234/48.

54 "Education"

55 "Science"

56 "Culture"

(Des Jennifer Toombs. Litho Harrison)

1966 (1 Dec). *20th Anniv of U.N.E.S.C.O. W* w **12** *(sideways). P* 14.
196 **54** 4 c. slate-violet, red, yellow and orange 15 10
197 **55** 25 c. orange-yellow, violet and deep olive 35 10
198 **56** $1 black, bright purple and orange 1·75 1·75
196/8 *Set of* 3 2·00 1·75

NEW INFORMATION

The editor is always interested to correspond with people who have new information that will improve or correct the Catalogue.

ASSOCIATED STATEHOOD

57 State Flag and Maps

(Des W. D. Cribbs. Photo Harrison)

1967 (27 Feb). *Statehood. T* **57** *and similar horiz designs. Multicoloured. W* w **12** *(sideways). P* 14.
199 4 c. Type **57** 10 10
200 15 c. State Flag 10 10
201 25 c. Premier's Office and State Flag 10 10
202 35 c. As 15 c. 15 15
199/202 *Set of* 4 25 20

60 Gilbert Memorial Church

(Des G. Drummond (from sketches by W. D. Cribbs). Photo Harrison)

1967 (18 May). *Attainment of Autonomy by the Methodist Church. T* **60** *and similar horiz designs. W* w **12**. *P* 14½ × 13½.
203 4 c. black and orange-red 10 10
204 25 c. black and bright green 10 10
205 35 c. black and bright blue 15 15
203/5 *Set of* 3 25 25

Designs:—25 c. Nathaniel Gilbert's House; 35 c. Caribbean and Central American map.

63 Coat of Arms **64** Settlers' Ship

(Des V. Whiteley (from sketches by W. D. Cribbs). Photo Harrison)

1967 (21 July). *300th Anniv of Treaty of Breda and Grant of New Arms. W* w **12** *(sideways). P* 14½ × 14.
206 **63** 15 c. multicoloured 10 10
207 35 c. multicoloured 15 10

(Des and recess B.W.)

1967 (14 Dec). *300th Anniv of Barbuda Settlement. T* **64** *and similar horiz design. W* w **12**. *P* 11½ × 11.
208 **64** 4 c. deep ultramarine 10 10
209 – 6 c. purple 10 10
210 **64** 25 c. emerald 15 10
211 – 35 c. black 15 15
208/11 *Set of* 4 45 25

Design:—6, 35 c. Blaeu's map of 1665.

66 Tracking Station **70** Limbo-dancing

(Des G. Vasarhelyi. Photo Harrison)

1968 (29 Mar). *N.A.S.A. Apollo Project. Inauguration of Dow Hill Tracking Station. T* **66** *and similar vert designs in deep blue, orange-yellow and black. W* w **12** *(sideways). P* 14½ × 14.
212 4 c. Type **66** 10 10
213 15 c. Antenna and spacecraft taking off 10 10
214 25 c. Spacecraft approaching Moon 10 10
215 50 c. Re-entry of space capsule 20 20
212/15 *Set of* 4 40 25

(Des and photo Harrison)

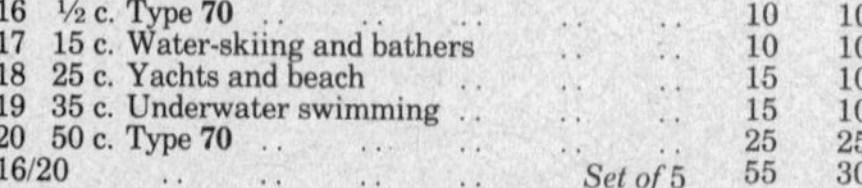

1968 (1 July). *Tourism. T* **70** *and similar horiz designs. Multicoloured. W* w **12**. *P* 14½ × 14.
216 ½ c. Type **70** 10 10
217 15 c. Water-skiing and bathers 10 10
218 25 c. Yachts and beach 15 10
219 35 c. Underwater swimming 15 10
220 50 c. Type **70** 25 25
216/20 *Set of* 5 55 30

74 Old Harbour in 1768

(Des R. Granger Barrett. Recess B.W.)

1968 (31 Oct). *Opening of St. John's Deep Water Harbour. T* **74** *and similar horiz designs. W* w **12**. *P* 13.
221 2 c. light blue and carmine 10 10
222 15 c. light yellow-green and sepia 15 10
223 25 c. olive-yellow and blue 20 10
224 35 c. salmon and emerald 25 10
225 $1 black 55 30
221/5 *Set of* 5 1·10 40

Designs:—15 c. Old Harbour in 1829; 25 c. Freighter and chart of New Harbour; 35 c. New Harbour, 1968; $1, Type **74**.

78 Parliament Buildings

(Des R. Granger Barrett. Photo Harrison)

1969 (3 Feb). *Tercentenary of Parliament. T* **78** *and similar square designs. Multicoloured. W* w **12** *(sideways). P* 12½.
226 4 c. Type **78** 10 10
227 15 c. Antigua Mace and bearer 10 10
228 25 c. House of Representatives' Room 10 10
229 50 c. Coat of arms and Seal of Antigua 20 25
226/9 *Set of* 4 35 35

82 Freight Transport

(Des Jennifer Toombs. Litho D.L.R.)

1969 (14 Apr). *1st Anniv of CARIFTA (Caribbean Free Trade Area). T* **82** *and similar design. W* w **12** *(sideways on 4 c., 15 c). P* 13.
230 4 c. black and reddish purple 10 10
231 15 c. black and turquoise-blue 10 10
232 25 c. chocolate, black and yellow-ochre 10 10
233 35 c. chocolate, black and yellow-brown 15 15
230/3 *Set of* 4 30 20

Designs: *Horiz*—4, 15 c. Type **82**. *Vert*—25, 35 c. Crate of cargo.

1969–70. *As Nos. 180/91 and 193/5 but perf 13½.*
A. *Ordinary paper* (24.6.69).
B. *Glazed paper* (30.9.69 *or* 6.4.70 (4 c.))

		A		B	
234	½ c. green and turquoise-blue	10	10	†	
235	1 c. purple and cerise	10	10	15	15
236	2 c. slate-blue & yellow-orange	10	10	15	10
237	3 c. rose-red and black	15	15	†	
238	4 c. slate-violet and brown	15	15	9·00	9·00
239	5 c. ultramarine & yellow-olive	15	10	15	10
240	6 c. salmon and purple	15	15	†	
241	10 c. emerald and rose-red	15	15	30	15
242	15 c. brown and new blue	†		55	35
243	25 c. slate-blue and sepia	†		45	35
244	35 c. cerise & blackish brown	†		60	1·00
245	50 c. dull green and black	†		70	1·60
246	$1 cerise and yellow-olive	†		1·25	3·25
247	$2.50, black and cerise	†		2·00	7·00
248	$5 olive-green & slate-violet	†		14·00	22·00
234/41A	*Set of* 8	90	80	†	
235/48B	*Set of* 12	†		27·00	42·00

84 Island of Redonda (Chart)

(Des R. Granger Barrett. Photo Enschedé)

1969 (1 Aug). *Centenary of Redonda Phosphate Industry. T* **84** *and similar horiz design. W* w **12** *(sideways). P* 13 × 13½.
249 15 c. Type **84** 15 10
250 25 c. Redonda from the sea 15 10
251 50 c. Type **84** 35 30
249/51 *Set of* 3 60 35

20¢

86 "The Adoration of the Magi" (Marcillat) (88)

(Des adapted by V. Whiteley. Litho Enschedé)

1969 (15 Oct). *Christmas. Stained-glass Windows. T* **86** *and similar vert design. Multicoloured.* W w **12** (*sideways*). *P* 13 × 14.
252 6 c. Type **86** 10 10
253 10 c. "The Nativity" (unknown German artist, 15th-century) 10 10
254 35 c. Type **86** 10 10
255 50 c. As 10 c. 25 30
252/5 .. .. *Set of* 4 40 45

1970 (2 Jan). *No.* 189 *surch with T* **88**.
256 20 c. on 25 c. slate-blue and sepia 10 10

89 Coat of Arms **90** Sikorsky "S–38"

(Des and photo Harrison)

1970–73. *Coil Stamps.* W w **12**. *P* 14½ × 14.
A. *Chalk-surfaced paper. Wmk upright* (30.1.70).
B. *Glazed paper. Wmk sideways* (8.3.73).

			A		B	
257	**89**	5 c. blue ..	10	10	15	20
258		10 c. emerald ..	10	15	20	35
259		25 c. crimson ..	20	25	40	60
257/9		.. *Set of* 3	35	45	70	1·10

For 10 c. with watermark W w **14** (inverted), see No. 541*a*.

(Des R. Granger Barrett. Litho J.W.)

1970 (16 Feb). *40th Anniv of Antiguan Air Services. T* **90** *and similar designs. Multicoloured.* W w **12** (*sideways*). *P* 14½.
260 5 c. Type **90** 15 10
261 20 c. Dornier "DO–X" 25 10
262 35 c. Hawker Siddeley "HS–748" 35 10
263 50 c. Douglas "C–124C Globemaster II" .. 50 50
264 75 c. Vickers "VC–10" 70 90
260/4 .. .. *Set of* 5 1·75 1·40

91 Dickens and Scene from *Nicholas Nickleby*

(Des Jennifer Toombs. Litho Walsall Security Printers Ltd)

1970 (19 May). *Death Centenary of Charles Dickens. T* **91** *and similar horiz designs.* W w **12** (*sideways*). *P* 14.
265 5 c. bistre, sepia and black 10 10
266 20 c. light turquoise-blue, sepia and black .. 10 10
267 35 c. violet-blue, sepia and black 15 10
268 $1 rosine, sepia and black 35 50
265/8 .. .. *Set of* 4 55 60

Designs:—20 c. Dickens and Scene from *Pickwick Papers*; 35 c. Dickens and Scene from *Oliver Twist*; $1 Dickens and Scene from *David Copperfield*.

92 Carib Indian and War Canoe **93** "The Small Passion" (detail) (Dürer)

(Des J. W. Litho Questa)

1970 (19 Aug)–**75**. *Horiz designs as T* **92**. *Multicoloured. Toned paper.* W w **12** (*sideways*). *P* 14.
269 ½ c. Type **92** 10 20
270 1 c. Columbus and *Nina* 25 15
271 2 c. Sir Thomas Warner's emblem and *Concepcion* 40 15
a. Whiter paper (20.10.75) .. .. 1·50 2·50
272 3 c. Viscount Hood and H.M.S. *Barfleur* .. 40 20
273 4 c. Sir George Rodney and H.M.S. *Formidable* 40 25
274 5 c. Nelson and H.M.S. *Boreas* 50 20
275 6 c. William IV and H.M.S. *Pegasus* 50 25
276 10 c. "Blackbeard" and pirate ketch 65 35
277 15 c. Captain Collingwood and H.M.S. *Pelican* 1·75 1·00
278 20 c. Nelson and H.M.S. *Victory* .. .. 1·25 60
279 25 c. R.M.S.P. *Solent* .. .. 1·25 60
280 35 c. George V (when Prince George) and H.M.S. *Canada* .. .. 1·60 70
281 50 c. H.M.S. *Renown* (battle cruiser) .. 2·50 1·50
282 75 c. *Federal Maple* (freighter) .. .. 3·75 3·50
283 $1 *Sol Quest* (yacht) and class emblem .. 4·00 2·00
284 $2.50, H.M.S. *London* (destroyer) .. .. 4·50 5·50
285 $5 *Pathfinder* (tug) .. .. 7·00 7·50
269/85 .. .. *Set of* 17 27·00 22·00

See also Nos. 323/34 and 426.

(Des G. Drummond. Recess and litho D.L.R.)

1970 (28 Oct). *Christmas. T* **93** *and similar vert design.* W w **12**. *P* 13½ × 14.
286 **93** 3 c. black and turquoise-blue 10 10
287 – 10 c. dull purple and pink 10 10
288 **93** 35 c. black and rose-red 15 10
289 – 50 c. black and lilac 25 30
286/9 .. .. *Set of* 4 40 35

Design:—10 c., 50 c. "Adoration of the Magi" (detail) (Dürer).

94 4th King's Own Regt, 1759 **95** Market Woman casting Vote

(Des P. W. Kingsland. Litho Questa)

1970 (14 Dec). *Military Uniforms* (1*st series*). *T* **94** *and similar vert designs. Multicoloured.* W w **12**. *P* 14 × 13½.
290 ½ c. Type **94** 10 10
291 10 c. 4th West India Regiment, 1804 .. .. 50 10
292 20 c. 60th Regiment, The Royal American, 1809 .. .. 90 25
293 35 c. 93rd Regiment, Sutherland Highlanders, 1826–34 .. .. 1·25 30
294 75 c. 3rd West India Regiment, 1851 .. .. 2·25 2·25
290/4 .. .. *Set of* 5 4·50 2·50
MS295 128 × 146 mm. Nos. 290/4 .. .. 7·50 11·00

See also Nos. 303/8, 313/18, 353/8 and 380/5.

(Des Sylvia Goaman. Photo Harrison)

1971 (1 Feb). *20th Anniversary of Adult Suffrage. T* **95** *and similar vert designs.* W w **12** (*sideways*). *P* 14½ × 14.
296 5 c. brown 10 10
297 20 c. deep olive 10 10
298 35 c. reddish purple 10 10
299 50 c. ultramarine 15 30
296/9 .. .. *Set of* 4 30 40

People voting:—20 c. Executive; 35 c. Housewife; 50 c. Artisan.

96 "The Last Supper" **97** "Madonna and Child" (detail, Veronese)

(Des Jennifer Toombs. Litho Questa)

1971 (7 Apr). *Easter. Works by Dürer. T* **96** *and similar vert designs.* W w **12**. *P* 14 × 13½.
300 5 c. black, grey and scarlet 10 10
301 35 c. black, grey and bluish violet 10 10
302 75 c. black, grey and gold 15 30
300/2 .. .. *Set of* 3 25 35

Designs:—35 c. The Crucifixion; 75 c. The Resurrection.

(Des J. W. Litho Questa)

1971 (12 July). *Military Uniforms* (2*nd series*). *Multicoloured designs as T* **94**. W w **12**. *P* 13½.
303 ½ c. Private, 12th Regiment, The Suffolk (1704) 10 10
304 10 c. Grenadier, 38th Regiment, South Staffs (1751) 35 15
305 20 c. Light Company, 5th Regiment, Royal Northumberland Fusiliers (1778) .. 55 20
306 35 c. Private, 48th Regiment, The Northamptonshire (1793) .. 1·00 40
307 75 c. Private, 15th Regiment, East Yorks (1805) .. .. 2·25 2·75
303/7 .. .. *Set of* 5 3·75 3·25
MS308 127 × 144 mm. Nos. 303/7 .. .. 5·50 6·50

(Des Jennifer Toombs. Litho Questa)

1971 (4 Oct). *Christmas. T* **97** *and similar vert design. Multicoloured.* W w **12**. *P* 13½.
309 3 c. Type **97** 10 10
310 5 c. "Adoration of the Shepherds" (detail, Veronese) 10 10
311 35 c. Type **97** 15 10
312 50 c. As 5 c. 25 30
309/12 .. .. *Set of* 4 45 40

(Des J.W. Litho Questa)

1972 (1 July). *Military Uniforms* (3*rd series*). *Multicoloured designs as T* **94**. W w **12** (*sideways*). *P* 14 × 13½.
313 ½ c. Battalion Company Officer, 25th Foot, 1815 .. .. 10 10
314 10 c. Sergeant, 14th Foot, 1837 .. .. 30 10
315 20 c. Private, 67th Foot, 1853 .. .. 50 15
316 35 c. Officer, Royal Artillery, 1854 .. .. 90 20
317 75 c. Private, 29th Foot, 1870 .. .. 1·50 1·75
313/17 .. .. *Set of* 5 3·00 2·00
MS318 125 × 141 mm. Nos. 313/17 .. .. 7·00 8·00

98 Cowrie-Helmet

(Des J.W. Litho Questa)

1972 (1 Aug). *Shells. T* **98** *and similar horiz designs. Multicoloured.* W w **12** (*sideways*). *P* 14½.
319 3 c. Type **98** 15 10
320 5 c. Measled Cowrie 15 10
321 35 c. West Indian Fighting Conch 35 10
322 50 c. Hawk-wing Conch 80 85
319/22 .. .. *Set of* 4 1·60 95

1972–74. *As No.* 269 *etc., but* W w **12** (*upright*) *and whiter paper.*
323 ½ c. Type **92** 15 25
324 1 c. Columbus and *Nina* 30 25
325 3 c. Viscount Hood and H.M.S. *Barfleur* .. 35 20
326 4 c. Sir George Rodney and H.M.S. *Formidable* 35 25
327 5 c. Nelson and H.M.S. *Boreas* 50 25
328 6 c. William IV and H.M.S. *Pegasus* 50 35
329 10 c. "Blackbeard" and pirate ketch 55 20
330 15 c. Collingwood and H.M.S. *Pelican* .. 2·50 65
331 75 c. *Federal Maple* (freighter) .. .. 4·50 3·00
332 $1 *Sol Quest* (yacht) and class emblem .. 4·25 1·75
333 $2.50, H.M.S. *London* (destroyer) .. .. 4·50 6·50
334 $5 *Pathfinder* (tug) .. .. 6·50 11·00
323/34 .. .. *Set of* 12 22·00 22·00

Dates of issue:—2.11.72, ½ c., 15 c., 75 c., $1, $5; 2.1.74, 1 to 10 c.; 25.2.74, $2.50.

See also No. 426.

99 St. John's Cathedral, Side View

(Des J.W. Litho Format)

1972 (6 Nov). *Christmas and 125th Anniversary of St. John's Cathedral. T* **99** *and similar horiz designs. Multicoloured.* W w **12**. *P* 14.
335 35 c. Type **99** 20 10
336 50 c. Cathedral interior 25 20
337 75 c. St. John's Cathedral 30 50
335/7 .. .. *Set of* 3 65 65
MS338 165 × 102 mm. Nos. 335/7. P 15 .. .. 65 1·00

100 Floral Pattern

(Des (from photograph by D. Groves) and photo Harrison)

1972 (20 Nov). *Royal Silver Wedding. Multicoloured; background colour given.* W w **12**. *P* 14 × 14½.
339 **100** 20 c. bright blue 10 10
340 35 c. turquoise-blue 15 10

101 Batsman and Map

(Des G. Vasarhelyi. Litho Questa)

1972 (15 Dec). *50th Anniv of Rising Sun Cricket Club. T* **101** *and similar horiz designs. Multicoloured. W w* **12.** *P* 13½.
341 5 c. Type **101** 45 25
342 35 c. Batsman and wicket-keeper . . 1·40 1·25
343 $1 Club badge . . . . 2·75 3·50
341/3 . . *Set of* 3 4·25 4·50
MS344 88 × 130 mm. Nos. 341/3 . . 5·50 7·50

102 Yacht and Map

103 "Episcopal Coat of Arms"

(Des M. and G. Shamir. Litho Format)

1972 (29 Dec). *Sailing Week and Inauguration of Tourist Office, New York. T* **102** *and similar square designs. Multicoloured. W w* **12.** *P* 14½.
345 35 c. Type **102** 15 10
346 50 c. Yachts 20 15
347 75 c. St. John's G.P.O. 25 30
348 $1 Statue of Liberty 30 35
345/8 . . *Set of* 4 80 75
MS349 100 × 94 mm. Nos. 346, 348 . . 1·00 1·50

(Des PAD Studio. Litho Format)

1973 (16 Apr). *Easter. T* **103** *and similar vert designs showing stained-glass windows from St. John's Cathedral. Multicoloured. W w* **12** *(sideways). P* 13½.
350 5 c. Type **103** 10 10
351 35 c. "The Crucifixion" 10 10
352 75 c. "Arms of 1st Bishop of Antigua" . . 20 30
350/2 . . *Set of* 3 30 35

(Des J.W. Litho Questa)

1973 (1 July). *Military Uniforms (4th series). Multicoloured designs as T* **94.** *W w* **12** *(sideways). P* 13½.
353 ½ c. Private, Zacharia Tiffin's Regiment of Foot, 1701 . . 10 10
354 10 c. Private, 63rd Regiment of Foot, 1759 . . 20 10
355 20 c. Light Company Officer, 35th Regiment of Foot, 1828 . . 30 15
356 35 c. Private, 2nd West India Regiment, 1853 55 15
357 75 c. Sergeant, 49th Regiment, 1858 . . 1·25 1·00
353/7 . . *Set of* 5 2·10 1·25
MS358 127 × 145 mm. Nos. 353/7 . . 2·75 3·25

104 Butterfly Costumes

(Des G. Vasarhelyi. Litho Format)

1973 (30 July). *Carnival. T* **104** *and similar horiz designs. Multicoloured. P* 13½.
359 5 c. Type **104** 10 10
360 20 c. Carnival street scene . . 10 10
361 35 c. Carnival troupe . . 15 10
362 75 c. Carnival Queen . . 25 30
359/62 . . *Set of* 4 40 35
MS363 134 × 95 mm. Nos. 359/62 . . 55 1·00

105 "Virgin of the Milk Porridge" (Gerard David)

106 Princess Anne and Captain Mark Phillips

(Des G. Vasarhelyi. Litho Format)

1973 (15 Oct). *Christmas. T* **105** *and similar vert designs. Multicoloured. P* 14½.
364 3 c. Type **105** 10 10
365 5 c. "Adoration of the Magi" (Stomer) . . 10 10
366 20 c. "The Granducal Madonna" (Raphael) . . 10 10
367 35 c. "Nativity with God the Father and Holy Ghost" (Battista) . . 15 10
368 $1 "Madonna and Child" (Murillo) . . 35 45
364/8 . . *Set of* 5 55 50
MS369 130 × 128 mm. Nos. 364/8 . . 90 1·75

(Des G. Drummond. Litho Format)

1973 (14 Nov). *Royal Wedding. T* **106** *and similar horiz design. P* 13½.
370 **106** 35 c. multicoloured . . 15 10
371 – $2 multicoloured . . 35 25
MS372 78 × 100 mm. Nos. 370/1 . . 50 40

The $2 is as T **106** but has a different border.

Nos. 370/1 were each issued in small sheets of five stamps and one stamp-size label.

HONEYMOON VISIT

DECEMBER 16th 1973

(107)

1973 (15 Dec). *Honeymoon Visit of Princess Anne and Captain Phillips. Nos. 370/***MS***372 optd with T* **107** *by lithography.**
373 **106** 35 c. multicoloured . . 15 10
a. Typo opt . . 95 95
374 – $2 multicoloured . . 40 40
a. Typo opt . . 2·75 2·75
MS375 78 × 100 mm. Nos. 373/4 . . 55 55
a. Typo opt . . 7·00 9·00

*The litho overprints can be distinguished from the typo by the latter being less clear, less intense, and showing through on the reverse.

108 Coats of Arms of Antigua and University

(Des PAD Studio. Litho D.L.R.)

1974 (18 Feb). *25th Anniv of University of West Indies. T* **108** *and similar horiz designs. Multicoloured. W w* **12.** *P* 13.
376 5 c. Type **108** 10 10
377 20 c. Extra-mural art . . 10 10
378 35 c. Antigua campus . . 10 10
379 75 c. Antigua chancellor . . 20 25
376/9 . . *Set of* 4 30 30

(Des J.W. Litho Questa)

1974 (1 May). *Military Uniforms (5th series). Multicoloured designs as T* **94.** *W w* **12** *(sideways). P* 13½.
380 ½ c. Officer, 59th Foot, 1797 . . 10 10
381 10 c. Gunner, Royal Artillery, 1800 . . 20 10
a. Error. Wmk T **55** of Malawi . . 90·00
382 20 c. Private, 1st West India Regiment, 1830 25 10
383 35 c. Officer, 92nd Foot, 1843 . . 30 10
384 75 c. Private, 23rd Foot, 1846 . . 60 60
380/4 . . *Set of* 5 1·25 80
MS385 127 × 145 mm. Nos. 380/4 . . 1·60 2·00

109 English Postman, Mailcoach and Helicopter

110 Traditional Player

(Des G. Vasarhelyi. Litho Format)

1974 (15 July). *Centenary of Universal Postal Union. T* **109** *and similar horiz designs. Multicoloured. P* 14½.
386 ½ c. Type **109** 10 10
387 1 c. Bellman, mail steamer *Orinoco* and satellite . . 10 10
388 2 c. Train guard, post-bus and hydrofoil . . 10 10
389 5 c. Swiss messenger, Wells Fargo coach and "Concorde" . . 10 10
390 20 c. Postillion, Japanese postmen and carrier pigeon . . 30 10
391 35 c. Antiguan postman, flying-boat and tracking station . . 45 15
392 $1 Medieval courier, American express train and Boeing "747" . . 1·50 1·10
386/92 . . *Set of* 7 2·25 1·25
MS393 141 × 164 mm. Nos. 386/92 plus label. P 13 2·25 2·50

On the ½ c. "English" is spelt "Enlish", and on the 2 c. "Postal" is spelt "Fostal".

(Des C. Abbott. Litho Questa)

1974 (1 Aug). *Antiguan Steel Bands. T* **110** *and similar designs. W w* **12** *(sideways on 5 c., 75 c. and* **MS**398*). P* 13.
394 5 c. rose-red, carmine and black . . 10 10
395 20 c. brown-ochre, chestnut and black . . 10 10
396 35 c. light sage-green, blue-green and black . . 10 10
397 75 c. dull blue, dull ultramarine and black . . 20 20
394/7 . . *Set of* 4 30 25
MS398 115 × 108 mm. Nos. 394/7 . . 35 65

Designs: *Horiz*—20 c. Traditional band; 35 c. Modern band. *Vert*—75 c. Modern player.

111 Footballers

EARTHQUAKE RELIEF

(112)

(Des G. Vasarhelyi. Litho Format)

1974 (23 Sept). *World Cup Football Championships. T* **111** *and similar vert designs showing footballers. P* 14½.
399 **111** 5 c. multicoloured . . 10 10
400 – 35 c. multicoloured . . 10 10
401 – 75 c. multicoloured . . 25 30
402 – $1 multicoloured . . 30 40
399/402 . . *Set of* 4 55 70
MS403 135 × 130 mm. Nos. 399/402 plus two labels. P 13 . . 60 90

1974 (16 Oct). *Earthquake Relief Fund. Nos. 400/2 and 397 optd with T* **112**, *No. 397 surch also.*
404 35 c. multicoloured . . 20 10
405 75 c. multicoloured . . 30 25
406 $1 multicoloured . . 40 30
407 $5 on 75 c. dull blue, dull ultram & black 1·50 2·00
404/7 . . *Set of* 4 2·25 2·40

113 Churchill as Schoolboy and School College Building, Harrow

114 "Madonna of the Trees" (Bellini)

(Des V. Whiteley. Litho Format)

1974 (20 Oct). *Birth Centenary of Sir Winston Churchill. T* **113** *and similar horiz designs. Multicoloured. P* 14½.
408 5 c. Type **113** 10 10
409 35 c. Churchill and St. Paul's Cathedral . . 20 10
410 75 c. Coat of arms and catafalque . . 30 35
411 $1 Churchill, "reward" notice and South African escape route . . 50 60
408/11 . . *Set of* 4 1·00 1·00
MS412 1007 × 82 mm. Nos. 408/11. P 13 . . 1·00 1·50

(Des M. Shamir. Litho Format)

1974 (18 Nov). *Christmas. T* **114** *and similar vert designs showing "Madonna and Child" by the artists given. Multicoloured. P* 14½.
413 ½ c. Type **114** 10 10
414 1 c. Raphael . . 10 10
415 2 c. Van der Weyden . . 10 10
416 3 c. Giorgione . . 10 10
417 5 c. Mantegna . . 10 10
418 20 c. Vivarini . . 10 10
419 35 c. Montagna . . 20 10
420 75 c. Lorenzo Costa . . 40 60
413/20 . . *Set of* 8 85 90
MS421 139 × 126 mm. Nos. 417/20. P 13 . . 85 1·40

(115)

116 Carib War Canoe, English Harbour, 1300

1975 (14 Jan). *Nos. 331 and 390/2 surch as T* **115.**
422 50 c. on 20 c. multicoloured . . 1·50 2·00
423 $2.50, on 35 c. multicoloured . . 3·50 6·00
424 $5 on $1 multicoloured . . 5·00 8·00
425 $10 on 75 c. multicoloured . . 5·50 8·50
422/5 . . *Set of* 4 14·00 22·00

1975 (21 Jan). *As No. 334 but W w* **14.**
426 $5 *Pathfinder* (tug) . . 4·50 10·00

(Des G. Drummond. Litho Format)

1975 (17 Mar). *Nelson's Dockyard. T* **116** *and similar horiz designs. Multicoloured. P* 14½.
427 5 c. Type **116** 15 10
428 15 c. Ship of the line, English Harbour, 1770 25 10
429 35 c. H.M.S. *Boreas* at anchor, and Lord Nelson, 1787 . . 50 15
430 50 c. Yachts during "Sailing Week", 1974 . . 70 40
431 $1 Yacht Anchorage, Old Dockyard, 1970 . . 1·10 1·10
427/31 . . *Set of* 5 2·40 1·75
MS432 130 × 134 mm. As Nos. 427/31, but in larger format, 43 × 28 mm. P 13½ . . 2·50 2·50

117 Lady of the Valley Church

(Des R. Vigurs. Litho Format)

1975 (19 May). *Antiguan Churches. T* **117** *and similar horiz designs. Multicoloured. P* 14½.

433	5 c. Type **117**	10	10
434	20 c. Gilbert Memorial	10	10
435	35 c. Grace Hill Moravian	15	10
436	50 c. St. Phillips	20	20
437	$1 Ebenezer Methodist	35	50
433/7	*Set of* 5	65	75
MS438	91 × 101 mm. Nos. 435/7. P 13	65	1·25

118 Map of 1721 and Sextant of 1640

(Des PAD Studio. Litho Questa)

1975 (21 July). *Maps of Antigua. T* **118** *and similar horiz designs. Multicoloured. W w* **14** *(sideways). P* 14.

439	5 c. Type **118**	10	10
440	20 c. Map of 1775 and galleon	20	10
441	35 c. Maps of 1775 and 1955	30	15
442	$1 1973 maps of Antigua and English Harbour	80	1·00
439/42	*Set of* 4	1·25	1·10
MS443	130 × 89 mm. Nos. 439/42	1·25	1·50

119 Scout Bugler

(Des G. Vasarhelyi. Litho Questa)

1975 (26 Aug). *World Scout Jamboree, Norway. T* **119** *and similar horiz designs. Multicoloured. P* 14.

444	15 c. Type **119**	25	15
445	20 c. Scouts in camp	30	15
446	35 c. "Lord Baden-Powell" (D. Jagger)	50	20
447	$2 Scout dancers from Dahomey	1·50	1·75
444/7	*Set of* 4	2·25	2·00
MS448	145 × 107 mm. Nos. 444/7	2·50	3·00

120 *Eurema elathea*

121 "Madonna and Child" (Correggio)

(Des. G. Vasarhelyi. Litho Questa)

1975 (30 Oct). *Butterflies. T* **120** *and similar horiz designs. Multicoloured. P* 14.

449	½ c. Type **120**	10	10
450	1 c. *Danaus plexippus*	10	10
451	2 c. *Phoebis philea*	10	10
452	5 c. *Hypolimnas misippus*	15	10
453	35c. *Eurema proterpia*	60	60
454	35 c. *Papilio polydamas*	90	90
455	$2 *Vanessa cardui*	4·00	5·50
449/55	*Set of* 7	5·50	6·50
MS456	147 × 94 mm. Nos. 452/5	6·00	7·00

No. 452 is incorrectly captioned "Marpesia petreus thetys".

(Des G. Vasarhelyi. Litho Questa)

1975 (17 Nov). *Christmas. T* **121** *and similar vert designs showing "Madonna and Child". Multicoloured. P* 14.

457	½ c. Type **121**	10	10
458	1 c. El Greco	10	10
459	2 c. Dürer	10	10
460	3 c. Antonello	10	10
461	5 c. Bellini	10	10
462	10 c. Dürer (*different*)	10	10
463	35 c. Bellini (*different*)	15	10
464	$2 Dürer (*different*)	55	70
457/64	*Set of* 8	85	85
MS465	138 × 119 mm. Nos. 461/4	1·10	1·60

122 Vivian Richards

123 Antillean Crested Hummingbird

(Des G. Vasarhelyi. Litho Format)

1975 (15 Dec). *World Cup Cricket Winners. T* **122** *and similar multicoloured designs. P* 13½.

466	5 c. Type **122**	70	15
467	35 c. Andy Roberts	1·60	60
468	$2 West Indies team (*horiz*)	4·25	4·75
466/8	*Set of* 3	6·00	5·00

(Des G. Vasarhelyi. Litho Format)

1976 (19 Jan)–**78.** *Various multicoloured designs as T* **123**. A. *Without imprint* (19.1.76). B. *With imprint date at foot* (1978).

		A		B	
	(*a*) *Size as T* **123**. *P* 14½				
469	½ c. Type **123**	15	15	30	25
470	1 c. Imperial Amazon	20	15	35	20
471	2 c. Zenaida Dove	20	15	35	20
472	3 c. Loggerhead Kingbird	20	15	35	20
473	4 c. Red-necked Pigeon	20	15	35	20
474	5 c. Rufous-throated Solitaire	25	10	35	20
475	6 c. Orchid Tree	20	15	20	15
476	10 c. Bougainvillea	20	10	25	20
477	15 c. Geiger Tree	35	10	30	20
478	20 c. Flamboyant	35	15	30	20
479	25 c. Hibiscus	40	15	35	20
480	35 c. Flame of the Wood	40	20	35	25
481	50 c. Cannon at Fort James	55	30	50	45
482	75 c. Premier's Office	60	50	55	65
483	$1 Potworks Dam	75	70	75	75
	(*b*) *Size* 44 × 28 *mm. P* 13½				
484	$2.50, Irrigation Scheme, Diamond Estate	2·00	2·00	3·75	4·00
485	$5 Government House	3·00	3·50	3·75	4·25
486	$10 Coolidge Airport	4·50	5·50	8·50	8·50
469/86	*Set of* 18	13·00	13·00	19·00	19·00

124 Privates, Clark's Illinois Regt

125 High Jump

(Des J.W. Litho Format)

1976 (17 Mar). *Bicentenary of American Revolution. T* **124** *and similar vert designs. Multicoloured. P* 14½.

487	½ c. Type **124**	10	10
488	1 c. Riflemen, Pennsylvania Militia	10	10
489	2 c. Powder horn	10	10
	a. Imperf (pair)	£225	
490	5 c. Water bottle	10	10
491	35 c. American flags	35	10
492	$1 Privateer *Montgomery*	1·00	55
493	$5 Sloop *Ranger*	3·50	3·50
487/93	*Set of* 7	4·50	3·75
MS494	71 × 84 mm. $2.50 Congress flag. P 13	2·25	3·00

(Des J.W. Litho Format)

1976 (17 July). *Olympic Games, Montreal. T* **125** *and similar horiz designs. P* 14½.

495	½ c. orange-brown, bistre-yellow and black	10	10
496	1 c. light reddish violet, bright blue & black	10	10
497	2 c. light green and black	10	10
498	15 c. bright blue and black	10	10
499	30 c. olive-brown, yellow-ochre and black	15	15
500	$1 red-orange, Venetian red and black	40	40
501	$2 rosine and black	70	80
495/501	*Set of* 7	1·25	1·40
MS502	88 × 138 mm. Nos. 498/501. P 13½	1·75	2·25

Designs:—1 c. Boxing; 2 c. Pole vault; 15 c. Swimming; 30 c. Running; $1 Cycling; $2 Shot put.

126 Water Skiing

(Des J.W. Litho Questa)

1976 (26 Aug). *Water Sports. T* **126** *and similar horiz designs. Multicoloured. P* 14.

503	½ c. Type **126**	10	10
504	1 c. Sailing	10	10
505	2 c. Snorkeling	10	10
506	20 c. Deep sea fishing	15	10
507	50 c. Scuba diving	35	35
508	$2 Swimming	1·00	1·25
503/8	*Set of* 6	1·40	1·60
MS509	89 × 114 mm. Nos. 506/8	1·40	1·75

127 French Angelfish

128 The Annunciation

(Des G. Drummond. Litho Questa)

1976 (4 Oct). *Fishes. T* **127** *and similar horiz designs. Multicoloured. W w* **14** *(sideways). P* 13½.

510	15 c. Type **127**	25	15
511	30 c. Yellowfin Grouper	40	30
512	50 c. Yellowtail Snappers	55	50
513	90 c. Shy Hamlet	80	80
510/13	*Set of* 4	1·75	1·60

(Des J.W. Litho Walsall)

1976 (15 Nov). *Christmas. T* **128** *and similar vert designs. Multicoloured. P* 13½.

514	8 c. Type **128**	10	10
515	10 c. The Holy Family	10	10
516	15 c. The Magi	10	10
517	50 c. The Shepherds	20	25
518	$1 Epiphany scene	30	50
514/18	*Set of* 5	60	75

129 Mercury and U.P.U. Emblem

130 Royal Family

(Des BG Studio. Litho Questa)

1976 (28 Dec). *Special Events, 1976. T* **129** *and similar horiz designs. Multicoloured. P* 14.

519	½ c. Type **129**	10	10
520	1 c. Alfred Nobel	10	10
521	10 c. Space satellite	20	10
522	50 c. Viv Richards and Andy Roberts	1·25	90
523	$1 Bell and telephones	1·50	1·50
524	$2 Yacht *Freelance*	2·25	2·25
519/24	*Set of* 6	4·75	4·25
MS525	127 × 101 mm. Nos. 521/4	5·50	7·50

Events:—½ c. 25th Anniv of U.N. Postal Administration; 1 c. 75th Anniv of Nobel Prize; 10 c. "Viking" Space Mission; 50 c. Cricketing achievements; $1 Telephone Centenary; $2 "Operation Sail", U.S. Bicentennial.

(Des J. W. Litho Questa (Nos. 526/31); Manufactured by Walsall (Nos. 532/3))

1977 (7 Feb–26 Sept). *Silver Jubilee. T* **130** *and similar vert designs. Multicoloured.* (*a*) *Sheet stamps. P* 14 (7 Feb).

526	10 c. Type **130**	10	10
527	30 c. Royal Visit, 1966	10	10
528	50 c. The Queen enthroned	15	15
529	90 c. The Queen after Coronation	25	20
530	$2.50, Queen and Prince Charles	45	35
526/30	*Set of* 5	75	70
MS531	116×78 mm. $5 Queen and Prince Philip	1·00	1·10
	a. Error. Imperf	£350	
	(*b*) *Booklet stamps. Roul* 5 × *imperf* (50 c.) *or imperf* ($5).* *Self-adhesive* (26 Sept)		
532	50 c. Design as No. 529 (24 × 42 *mm*)	35	60
	a. Booklet pane of 6	1·90	
533	$5 Design as stamp from No. **MS**531 (24 × 42 *mm*)	2·50	3·50
	a. Booklet pane of 1	2·50	

*No. 532 was separated by various combinations of rotary knife (giving a straight edge) and roulette. No. 533 exists only with straight edges.

Stamps as Nos. 526/30 but perforated 11½ × 12, come from sheets of 5 stamps and 1 label. These were not placed on sale by the Antigua Post Office.

MINIMUM PRICE

The minimum price quote is 10p which represents a handling charge rather than a basis for valuing common stamps. For further notes about prices see introductory pages.

131 Making Camp **132** Carnival Costume

(Des J.W. Litho Questa)

1977 (23 May). *Caribbean Scout Jamboree, Jamaica. T* **131** *and similar horiz designs. Multicoloured. P* 14.

534 ½ c. Type **131** 10 10
535 1 c. Hiking 10 10
536 2 c. Rock-climbing 10 10
537 10 c. Cutting logs 10 10
538 30 c. Map and sign reading 20 10
539 50 c. First aid 35 20
540 $2 Rafting .. .. 1·50 1·50
534/40 .. *Set of* 7 2·00 1·75
MS541 127 × 114 mm. Nos. 538/40 .. 2·25 2·75

1977. *Coil Stamp. W w* **14** (*inverted*). *P* 14½ × 14.
541*a* **89** 10 c. emerald .. .. — 15

(Des C. Abbott. Litho Walsall)

1977 (18 July). *21st Anniv of Carnival. T* **132** *and similar vert designs. Multicoloured. P* 14.

542 10 c. Type **132** 10 10
543 30 c. Carnival Queen 15 10
544 50 c. Butterfly costume 20 15
545 90 c. Queen of the band 30 25
546 $1 Calypso King and Queen 30 30
542/6 .. *Set of* 5 90 70
MS547 140 × 120 mm. Nos. 542/6 .. 1·00 1·60

ROYAL VISIT
28th OCTOBER 1977

(**133**)

134 "Virgin and Child Enthroned" (Tura)

1977 (17 Oct). *Royal Visit. Nos.* 526/531 *optd with T* **133.** *P* 14.

548 10 c. Type **130**.. .. 10 10
549 30 c. Royal Visit, 1966 .. .. 10 10
550 50 c. The Queen enthroned 15 10
551 90 c. The Queen after Coronation 25 20
552 $2.50, Queen and Prince Charles.. .. 45 35
548/52 .. *Set of* 5 80 65
MS553 116 × 78 mm. $5 Queen and Prince Philip 1·00 1·25
a. Opt double .. 50·00

Nos. 548/52 also exist perf 11½ × 12 (*Price for set of* 5 £1 *mint or used*) from additional sheetlets of five stamps and one label.

(Des M. Shamir. Litho Questa)

1977 (21 Nov). *Christmas. T* **134** *and similar vert designs showing "Virgin and Child" by the artists given. Multicoloured. P* 14.

554 ½ c. Type **134** 10 10
555 1 c. Crivelli 10 10
556 2 c. Lotto 10 10
557 8 c. Pontormo.. .. 10 10
558 10 c. Tura (*different*) 10 10
559 25 c. Lotto (*different*) 10 10
560 $2 Crivelli (*different*) 50 60
554/60 .. *Set of* 7 70 75
MS561 144 × 118 mm. Nos. 557/60 .. 85 1·40

135 Pineapple

(Des and litho J.W.)

1977 (29 Dec). *Tenth Anniv of Statehood. T* **135** *and similar horiz designs. Multicoloured. P* 13.

562 10 c. Type **135** 10 10
563 15 c. State flag.. .. 10 10
564 50 c. Police band 20 10
565 90 c. Premier V. C. Bird 25 15
566 $2 State Coat of Arms 40 45
562/6 .. *Set of* 5 80 70
MS567 126 × 99 mm. Nos. 563/6. P 14 .. 85 1·60

136 *Glider III*, 1902

(Des PAD Studio. Litho Questa)

1978 (23 Mar). *75th Anniv of Powered Flight. T* **136** *and similar multicoloured designs. P* 14.

568 ½ c. Type **136** 10 10
569 1 c. *Flyer I*, 1903 .. .. 10 10
570 2 c. Launch system and engine 10 10
571 10 c. Orville Wright (*vert.*) 10 10
572 50 c. *Flyer III*, 1905 .. .. 30 15
573 90 c. Wilbur Wright (*vert*) 45 30
574 $2 Wright "Model B", 1910.. .. 80 80
568/74 .. *Set of* 7 1·60 1·25
MS575 90 × 75 mm. $2.50, *Flyer I* on launch system .. 1·60 2·25

137 Sunfish Regatta

(Des G. Drummond. Litho Format)

1978 (27 Apr). *Sailing Week. T* **137** *and similar horiz designs. Multicoloured. P* 15.

576 10 c. Type **137** 15 10
577 50 c. Fishing and work boat race 35 20
578 90 c. Curtain Bluff race 60 35
579 $2 Power boat rally.. .. 1·25 1·25
576/9 .. *Set of* 4 2·10 1·75
MS580 110 × 77 mm. $2.50, Guadeloupe–Antigua race .. 1·90 2·50

138 Queen Elizabeth and Prince Philip **139** Glass Coach

(Des J.W. Litho Questa (Nos. 581/6); Manufactured by Walsall (Nos. 587/9))

1978 (2 June). *25th Anniv of Coronation. Multicoloured.* (*a*) *Sheet stamps. Vert designs as T* **138**. *P* 14.

581 10 c. Type **138** 10 10
582 30 c. Crowning 10 10
583 50 c. Coronation procession 15 10
584 90 c. Queen seated in St. Edward's Chair .. 20 15
585 $2.50, Queen wearing Imperial State Crown 40 40
581/5 .. *Set of* 5 65 65
MS586 114 × 104 mm. $5 Queen and Prince Philip 1·00 1·10

(*b*) *Booklet stamps. Horiz design as T* **139** *showing State Coaches. Imperf* ($5) *or roul* 5 × *imperf*. Self-adhesive.*

587 25 c. Type **139** 15 30
a. Booklet pane. Nos. 587/8 × 3 .. 1·25
588 50 c. Irish State Coach 25 50
589 $5 Coronation Coach .. .. 2·50 3·00
a. Booklet pane of 1.. .. 2·50
587/9 .. *Set of* 3 2·50 3·50

Nos. 581/5 also exist perf 12 (*Price for set of* 5 £1 *mint or used*) from additional sheetlets of three stamps and one label. These stamps have changed background colours.

*Nos. 587/8 were separated by various combinations of rotary-knife (giving a straight edge) and roulette. No. 589 exists only with straight edges.

140 Player running with Ball **141** Petrea

(Des BG Studio. Litho Format)

1978 (17 Aug). *World Cup Football Championship, Argentina. T* **140** *and similar vert designs. Multicoloured. P* 14½.

590 10 c. Type **140** 10 10
591 15 c. Players in front of goal 10 10
592 $3 Referee and player .. .. 1·75 1·75
590/2 .. *Set of* 3 1·75 1·75
MS593 126 × 88 mm. 25 c. Player crouching with ball; 30 c. Players heading ball; 50 c. Players running with ball; $2 Goalkeeper diving. (*All horiz*) .. 1·90 2·25

Nos. 590/2 were each printed in small sheets of 6 including 1 *se-tenant* stamp-size label.

(Des G. Drummond. Litho Questa)

1978 (5 Oct). *Flowers. T* **141** *and similar vert designs. Multicoloured. P* 14.

594 25 c. Type **141** 20 10
595 50 c. Sunflower 30 20
596 90 c. Frangipani 50 30
597 $2 Passion Flower .. .. 1·10 1·10
594/7 .. *Set of* 4 1·90 1·40
MS598 118 × 85 mm. $2.50, Hibiscus .. 1·40 1·60

142 "St Ildefonso receiving the Chasuble from the Virgin" (Rubens) **143** 1d. Stamp of 1863

(Des BG Studio. Litho Questa)

1978 (30 Oct). *Christmas Paintings. T* **142** *and similar horiz designs. Multicoloured. P* 14.

599 8 c. Type **142** 10 10
600 25 c. "The Flight of St. Barbara" (Rubens) .. 15 10
601 $2 "Madonna and Child, with St. Joseph, John the Baptist and Donor" (Sebastiano del Piombo*) .. 65 55
599/601 .. *Set of* 3 75 60
MS602 170 × 113 mm. $4 "The Annunciation" (Rubens) .. 2·00 2·75

*The work is incorrectly attributed to Rubens on the stamp.

(Des G. Vasarhelyi. Litho Questa)

1979 (12 Feb). *Death Centenary of Sir Rowland Hill. T* **143** *and similar vert designs. Multicoloured. P* 14.

603 25 c. Type **143** 10 10
604 50 c. Penny Black 25 15
605 $1 Stage-coach and woman posting letter, *circa* 1840 .. 45 30
606 $2 Modern mail transport .. .. 1·00 75
603/6 .. *Set of* 4 1·60 1·10
MS607 108 × 82 mm. $2.50, Sir Rowland Hill .. 80 90

Nos. 603/6 also exist perf 12 (*Price for set of* 4 £1.60 *mint or used*) from additional sheetlets of five stamps and one label.

Antigua 25c
International Year Of The Child 1979

144 "The Deposition from the Cross" (painting) **145** Toy Yacht and Child's Hand

(Des BG Studio. Litho Questa)

1979 (15 Mar). *Easter. Works by Dürer. T* **144** *and similar vert designs. P* 14.

608 10 c. multicoloured 10 10
609 50 c. multicoloured 20 20
610 $4 black, magenta and greenish yellow .. 90 90
608/10 .. *Set of* 3 1·00 1·00
MS611 114 × 99 mm. $2.50, multicoloured .. 65 80

Designs:—50 c., $2.50, "Christ on the Cross—The Passion" (wood engravings) (*both different*); $4 "Man of Sorrows with Hands Raised" (wood engraving).

(Des M. Rubin. Litho Questa)

1979 (9 Apr). *International Year of the Child. T* **145** *and similar vert designs showing toys and hands of children of different races. Multicoloured. P* 14.

612 25 c. Type **145** 10 10
613 50 c. Rocket 25 15
614 90 c. Car 40 25
615 $2 Train .. .. 1·00 90
612/15 .. *Set of* 4 1·60 1·25
MS616 80 × 112 mm. $5 Aeroplane .. 1·75 2·00

NEW INFORMATION

The editor is always interested to correspond with people who have new information that will improve or correct the Catalogue.

146 Yellowjack　　**147** Cook's Birthplace, Marton

(Des P. Powell. Litho Questa)

1979 (14 May). *Fishes. T* **146** *and similar horiz designs. Multi-coloured. P* 14½ × 14.
617　30 c. Type **146** .. .. 15　15
618　50 c. Bluefin Tuna .. .. 25　25
619　90 c. Sailfish .. .. 40　40
620　$3 Wahoo .. .. 1·75　1·75
617/20 .. .. *Set of* 4　2·25　2·25
MS621　122 × 75 mm. $2.50, Barracuda .. .. 1·25　1·40

(Des J.W. Litho Questa)

1979 (2 July). *Death Bicentenary of Captain Cook. T* **147** *and similar vert designs. Multicoloured. P* 14.
622　25 c. Type **147** .. .. 45　30
623　50 c. H.M.S. *Endeavour* .. .. 65　50
624　90 c. Marine chronometer .. .. 80　80
625　$3 Landing at Botany Bay .. .. 2·00　2·00
622/5 .. .. *Set of* 4　3·50　3·25
MS626　110 × 85 mm. $2.50, H.M.S. *Resolution* .. 2·25　2·50

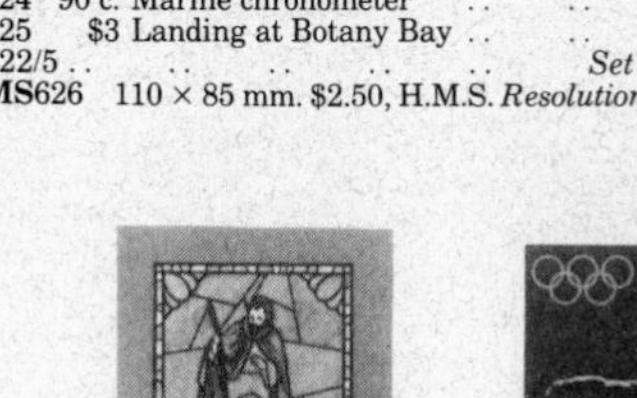

148 The Holy Family　　**149** Javelin Throwing

(Des J.W. Litho Questa)

1979 (1 Oct). *Christmas. T* **148** *and similar vert designs. Multi-coloured. P* 14.
627　8 c. Type **148** .. .. 10　10
628　25 c. Virgin and Child on Ass .. .. 10　10
629　50 c. Shepherd and star .. .. 20　20
630　$4 Wise Men with gifts .. .. 1·25　1·60
627/30 .. .. *Set of* 4　1·40　1·75
MS631　113 × 94 mm. $3 Angel with trumpet. P 12　1·00　1·50

(Des Design Images Inc. Litho Questa)

1980 (18 Feb). *Olympic Games, Moscow. T* **149** *and similar multi-coloured designs. P* 14.
632　10 c. Type **149** .. .. 10　10
633　25 c. Running .. .. 10　10
634　$1 Pole vaulting .. .. 30　30
635　$2 Hurdling .. .. 55　65
632/5 .. .. *Set of* 4　90　95
MS636　127 × 96 mm. $3 Boxing (*horiz*) .. .. 65　90

150 Mickey Mouse and Aeroplane　　LONDON 1980 (**151**)

(Litho Format)

1980 (24 Mar). *International Year of the Child* (1979). *Walt Disney Cartoon Characters. T* **150** *and similar multicoloured designs showing characters and transport. P* 11.
637　½ c. Type **150** .. .. 10　10
638　1 c. Donald Duck driving car .. .. .. 10　10
639　2 c. Goofy driving taxi .. .. 10　10
640　3 c. Mickey Mouse on motorcycle with Minnie Mouse in sidecar .. .. 10　10
641　4 c. Huey, Dewey and Louie riding cycle .. 10　10
642　5 c. Grandma Duck, chickens and pickup truck .. .. 10　10
643　10 c. Mickey Mouse driving jeep (*vert*) .. 10　10
644　$1 Chip and Dale in sailing boat .. .. 1·00　75
645　$4 Donald Duck riding toy train (*vert*) .. 3·00　2·75
637/45 .. .. *Set of* 9　4·00　3·50
MS646　101 × 127 mm. $2.50, Goofy flying biplane. P 14 × 13½ .. .. 2·25　2·00
See also Nos. 671/80.

1980 (6 May). *"London 1980" International Stamp Exhibition. Nos. 603/6 optd with T* **151**. *P* 12.
647　25 c. Type **143** .. .. 15　15
648　50 c. Penny Black .. .. 25　20
649　$1 Stage-coach and woman posting letter, *circa* 1840 .. .. 45　40
650　$2 Modern mail transport .. .. 1·25　1·25
647/50 .. .. *Set of* 4　1·90　1·75

152 "David" (statue, Donatello)　　**153** Rotary International 75th Anniversary Emblem and Headquarters, U.S.A.

(Des J.W. Litho Questa)

1980 (23 June). *Famous Works of Art. T* **152** *and similar multi-coloured designs. P* 13½.
651　10 c. Type **152** .. .. 10　10
652　30 c. "The Birth of Venus" (painting, Sandro Botticelli) (*horiz*) .. .. 15　15
653　50 c. "Reclining Couple" (sarcophagus), Cerveteri (*horiz*) .. .. 25　25
654　90 c. "The Garden of Earthly Delights" (painting, Hieronymus Bosch) (*horiz*) .. 40　40
655　$1 "Portinari Altarpiece" (painting, Hugo van der Goes) (*horiz*) .. .. .. 45　45
656　$4 "Eleanora of Toledo and her Son Giovanni de'Medici" (painting, Agnolo Bronzino) .. 1·60　1·60
651/6 .. .. *Set of* 6　2·50　2·50
MS657　99 × 124 mm. $5 "The Holy Family" (painting, Rembrandt) .. .. 2·00　2·25

(Des G. Vasarhelyi. Litho Questa)

1980 (21 July). *75th Anniv of Rotary International. T* **153** *and similar horiz designs. Multicoloured. P* 14.
658　30 c. Type **153** .. .. 20　20
659　50 c. Rotary anniversary emblem and Antigua Rotary Club banner .. .. 25　25
660　90 c. Map of Antigua and Rotary emblem .. 40　40
661　$3 Paul P. Harris (founder) and Rotary emblem .. .. 1·40　1·50
658/61 .. .. *Set of* 4　2·00　2·10
MS662　102 × 78 mm. $5 Antiguan flags and Rotary emblems .. .. 2·00　2·50

154 Queen Elizabeth the Queen Mother　　**155** Ringed Kingfisher

(Des G. Vasarhelyi. Litho Questa)

1980 (4 Aug). *80th Birthday of Queen Elizabeth the Queen Mother. P* 14.
663　**154**　10 c. multicoloured .. .. 15　10
664　$2.50, multicoloured .. .. 1·75　1·75
MS665　68 × 90 mm. **154** $3 multicoloured. P 12 .. 2·00　2·25

(Des Jennifer Toombs. Litho Questa)

1980 (3 Nov). *Birds. T* **155** *and similar vert designs. Multi-coloured. P* 14.
666　10 c. Type **155** .. .. 20　10
667　30 c. Plain Pigeon .. .. 35　25
668　$1 Green-throated Carib .. .. 90　75
669　$2 Black-necked Stilt .. .. 1·40　1·00
666/9 .. .. *Set of* 4　2·50　1·90
MS670　73 × 73 mm. $2.50, Roseate Tern .. .. 3·50　2·75

(Litho Format)

1980 (23 Dec). *Christmas. Scenes from Walt Disney's Cartoon Film "Sleeping Beauty". Horiz designs as T* **150**. *P* 11.
671　½ c. multicoloured .. .. 10　10
672　1 c. multicoloured .. .. 10　10
673　2 c. multicoloured .. .. 10　10
674　4 c. multicoloured .. .. 10　10
675　8 c. multicoloured .. .. 10　10
676　10 c. multicoloured .. .. 10　10
677　25 c. multicoloured .. .. 15　15
678　$2 multicoloured .. .. 1·60　1·50
679　$2.50, multicoloured .. .. 1·90　1·75
671/9 .. .. *Set of* 9　3·50　3·25
MS680　126 × 101 mm. $4 multicoloured (*vert*) P 13½ × 14 .. .. 3·00　2·50

156 Diesel Locomotive No. 15

(Des G. Drummond. Litho Questa)

1981 (12 Jan). *Sugar Cane Railway Locomotives. T* **156** *and similar horiz designs. Multicoloured. P* 14.
681　25 c. Type **156** .. .. 15　15
682　50 c. Narrow-gauge steam locomotive .. .. 30　30
683　90 c. Diesel locomotives Nos. 1 and 10 .. 55　55
684　$3 Steam locomotive hauling sugar cane .. 2·00　2·00
681/4 .. .. *Set of* 4　2·75　2·75
MS685　82 × 111 mm. $2.50, Antigua sugar factory, railway yard and sheds .. .. 1·75　1·75

"INDEPENDENCE 1981" (**157**)　　**158** "Pipes of Pan"

1981 (31 Mar). *Independence. Optd with T* **157**. A. *On Nos.* 475A, 478A, 480A *and* 484A/6A. B. *On Nos.* 475B/6B *and* 478B/86B.

		A		B	
686	6 c. Orchid Tree	35	35	10	10
687	10 c. Bougainvillea	†		10	10
688	20 c. Flamboyant	35	35	10	10
689	25 c. Hibiscus	†		15	15
690	35 c. Flame of the Wood	70	70	20	20
691	50 c. Cannon at Fort James	†		35	35
692	75 c. Premier's Office	†		40	40
693	$1 Potworks Dam	†		55	55
694	$2.50, Irrigation Scheme, Diamond Estate	2·00	2·25	1·25	1·25
695	$5 Government House	4·00	4·25	2·50	2·50
696	$10 Coolidge Airport	7·50	8·00	4·50	5·00
686A/96A	*Set of* 6	13·50	14·50	†	
686B/96B	*Set of* 11	†		9·00	9·50

(Des J.W. Litho Questa)

1981 (5 May). *Birth Centenary of Picasso. T* **158** *and similar vert designs. Multicoloured. P* 14.
697　10 c. Type **158** .. .. 10　10
698　50 c. "Seated Harlequin" .. .. 30　30
699　90 c. "Paulo as Harlequin" .. .. 55　55
700　$4 "Mother and Child" .. .. 2·50　2·50
697/700 .. .. *Set of* 4　3·00　3·00
MS701　115 × 140 mm. $5 "Three Musicians" (detail) .. .. 2·75　2·75

159 Prince Charles and Lady Diana Spencer　　**160** Prince of Wales at Investiture, 1969

(Des J.W. Litho Questa)

1981 (23 June). *Royal Wedding. T* **159** *and similar vert designs. Multicoloured. P* 14.
702　25 c. Type **159** .. .. 15　10
703　50 c. Glamis Castle .. .. 25　20
704　$4 Prince Charles skiing .. .. 1·25　1·40
702/4 .. .. *Set of* 3　1·50　1·50
MS705　96 × 82 mm. $5 Glass Coach .. .. 1·40　1·75
Nos. 702/4 also exist perforated 12 (*Price for set of* 3 £1·50 *mint or used*) from additional sheetlets of five stamps and one label. These stamps have changed background colours.

(Manufactured by Walsall)

1981 (23 June). *Royal Wedding. Booklet stamps. T* **160** *and similar vert designs. Multicoloured* ($5) *or black and flesh* (*others*). *Roul* 5 × *imperf**. *Self-adhesive.*
706　25 c. Type **160** .. .. 20　20
　a. Booklet pane. Nos. 706/11 .. .. .. 2·50
707　25 c. Prince Charles as baby, 1948 .. .. 20　20
708　$1 Prince Charles at R.A.F. College, Cranwell, 1971 .. .. 40　40
709　$1 Prince Charles attending Hill House School, 1956 .. .. 40　40
710　$2 Prince Charles and Lady Diana Spencer　75　75
711　$2 Prince Charles at Trinity College, 1967　75　75
712　$5 Prince Charles and Lady Diana (*different*)　1·50　1·50
　a. Booklet pane of 1 .. .. 1·50
706/12 .. .. *Set of* 7　3·50　3·50
*The 25 c. to $2 values were each separated by various combinations of rotary knife (giving a straight edge) and roulette. The $5 value exists only with straight edges.

161 Irene Joshua (founder)

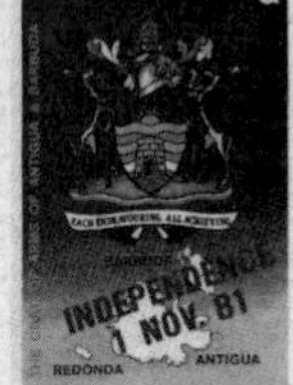

162 Antigua and Barbuda Coat of Arms

(Des M. Diamond. Litho Format)

1981 (28 Oct). *50th Anniv of Antigua Girl Guide Movement. T* **161** *and similar horiz designs. Multicoloured. P* 14½.

713 10 c. Type **161** 10 10
714 50 c. Campfire sing-song 35 35
715 90 c. Sailing 65 65
716 $2.50, Animal tending .. .. 1·75 1·75
713/16 .. .. *Set of* 4 2·50 2·50
MS717 110 × 85 mm. $5 Raising the flag .. .. 3·50 3·50

INDEPENDENT

Nos. 718/22 and 733 onwards are inscribed "ANTIGUA & BARBUDA".

(Des E. Henry. Litho Format)

1981 (1 Nov). *Independence. T* **162** *and similar multicoloured designs. P* 14½.

718 10 c. Type **162** 10 10
719 50 c. Pineapple, Antigua flag and map .. 25 15
720 90 c. Prime Minister Vere Bird 50 30
721 $2.50, St. John's Cathedral (38 × 25 *mm*) .. 1·00 1·40
718/21 .. .. *Set of* 4 1·75 1·75
MS722 105 × 79 mm. $5 Map of Antigua and Barbuda (42 × 42 *mm*) .. .. 2·75 2·75

163 "Holy Night" (Jacques Stella)

164 Swimming

(Des Clover Mill. Litho Format)

1981 (16 Nov). *Christmas. Paintings. T* **163** *and similar vert designs. Multicoloured. P* 14½.

723 8 c. Type **163** 10 10
724 30 c. "Mary with Child" (Julius Schnorr von Carolfeld) 15 15
725 $1 "Virgin and Child" (Alonso Cano) .. 55 55
726 $3 "Virgin and Child" (Lorenzo di Credi) .. 1·75 2·00
723/6 .. .. *Set of* 4 2·25 2·50
MS727 77 × 111 mm. $5 "Holy Family" (Pieter von Avon) .. .. 3·00 3·00

(Des M. Diamond. Litho Format)

1981 (1 Dec). *International Year for Disabled Persons. Sport for the Disabled. T* **164** *and similar horiz designs. Multicoloured. P* 15.

728 10 c. Type **164** 10 10
729 50 c. Discus throwing 30 30
730 90 c. Archery 55 55
731 $2 Baseball .. .. 1·40 1·40
728/31 .. .. *Set of* 4 2·10 2·10
MS732 108 × 84 mm. $4 Basketball .. .. 3·00 2·75

165 Scene from Football Match

166 European "A-300 (Airbus)"

(Des Clover Mill. Litho Questa)

1982 (15 Apr). *World Cup Football Championship, Spain. T* **165** *and similar horiz designs showing scenes from different matches. P* 14.

733 10 c. multicoloured 10 10
734 50 c. multicoloured 30 30
735 90 c. multicoloured 55 55
736 $4 multicoloured .. .. 2·50 2·50
733/6 .. .. *Set of* 4 3·00 3·00
MS737 75 × 92 mm. $5 multicoloured .. .. 3·00 3·00

Nos. 733/6 also exist perforated 12 (*Price for set of* 4, £3 *mint or used*) from additional sheetlets of five stamps and one label. These stamps have changed inscription colours.

(Des Clover Mill. Litho Format)

1982 (17 June). *Coolidge International Airport. T* **166** *and similar multicoloured designs. P* 14½.

738 10 c. Type **166** 10 10
739 50 c. Hawker-Siddeley "748" 30 30
740 90 c. De Havilland "DCH6 (Twin Otter)" .. 60 60
741 $2.50, Britten-Norman "Islander" .. .. 1·50 1·50
738/41 .. .. *Set of* 4 2·25 2·25
MS742 99 × 73 mm. $5 Boeing "747 (Jumbo Jet)" (*horiz*) .. .. 3·75 3·50

167 Cordia

(Des G. Drummond. Litho Questa)

1982 (28 June). *Death Centenary of Charles Darwin. Fauna and Flora. T* **167** *and similar multicoloured designs. P* 15.

743 10 c. Type **167** 15 10
744 50 c. Small Indian Mongoose (*horiz*) .. 45 35
745 90 c. Corallita 75 60
746 $3 Mexican Bulldog Bat (*horiz*) .. .. 2·00 2·25
743/6 .. .. *Set of* 4 3·00 3·00
MS747 107 × 85 mm. $5 Caribbean Monk Seal 4·75 5·00

168 Queen's House, Greenwich

169 Princess of Wales

(Des PAD Studio. Litho Questa)

1982 (1 July). *21st Birthday of Princess of Wales. T* **168/9** *and similar vert design. Multicoloured. P* 14½ × 14.

748 90 c. Type **168** 45 45
749 $1 Prince and Princess of Wales 50 50
750 $4 Princess Diana (*different*) .. .. 2·00 2·00
748/50 .. .. *Set of* 3 2·75 2·75
MS751 102 × 75 mm. $5 Type **169** .. .. 2·40 2·50

Nos. 748/50 also exist in sheetlets of 5 stamps and 1 label.

170 Boy Scouts decorating Streets for Independence Parade

ROYAL BABY
21.6.82
(**171**)

(Des J.W. Litho Questa)

1982 (15 July). *75th Anniv of Boy Scout Movement. T* **170** *and similar horiz designs. Multicoloured. P* 14.

752 10 c. Type **170** 15 10
753 50 c. Boy Scout giving helping hand during street parade 40 35
754 90 c. Boy Scouts attending Princess Margaret at Independence Ceremony 75 65
755 $2.20, Cub Scout giving directions to tourists 1·75 1·75
752/5 .. .. *Set of* 4 2·75 2·50
MS756 102 × 72 mm. $5 Lord Baden-Powell .. 4·25 3·75

1982 (30 Aug). *Birth of Prince William of Wales. Nos.* 748/51 *optd with T* **171**.

757 90 c. Type **168** 45 45
758 $1 Prince and Princess of Wales 50 50
759 $4 Princess Diana (*different*) .. .. 2·00 2·00
757/9 .. .. *Set of* 3 2·75 2·75
MS760 102 × 75 mm. $5 Type **169** .. .. 2·40 2·50

Nos. 757/9 also exist in sheetlets of 5 stamps and 1 label.

172 Roosevelt in 1940

(Des PAD Studio. Litho Format)

1982 (20 Sept). *Birth Centenary of Franklin D. Roosevelt (Nos.* 761, 763, 765/6 *and* **MS**767) *and 250th Birth Anniv of George Washington (others). T* **172** *and similar multicoloured designs. P* 15.

761 10 c. Type **172** 10 10
762 25 c. Washington as blacksmith 20 15
763 45 c. Churchill, Roosevelt and Stalin at Yalta Conference 45 25
764 60 c. Washington crossing the Delaware (*vert*) 50 35
765 $1 "Roosevelt Special" train (*vert*) 80 55
766 $3 Portrait of Roosevelt (*vert*) .. .. 1·75 1·75
761/6 .. .. *Set of* 6 3·50 2·75
MS767 92 × 87 mm. $4 Roosevelt and Wife .. 2·50 2·25
MS768 92 × 87 mm. $4 Portrait of Washington (*vert*) .. .. 2·50 2·25

173 "Annunciation"

(Des Design Images. Litho Questa)

1982 (Nov). *Christmas. Religious Paintings by Raphael. T* **173** *and similar horiz designs. Multicoloured. P* 14 × 13½.

769 10 c. Type **173** 10 10
770 30 c. "Adoration of the Magi" 15 15
771 $1 "Presentation at the Temple" 50 50
772 $4 "Coronation of the Virgin" .. .. 2·10 2·25
769/72 .. .. *Set of* 4 2·50 2·75
MS773 95 × 124 mm. $5 "Marriage of the Virgin" 2·50 2·50

174 Tritons and Dolphins

175 Pineapple Produce

(Des Design Images. Litho Format)

1983 (28 Jan). *500th Birth Anniv of Raphael. Details from "Galatea" Fresco. T* **174** *and similar multicoloured designs. P* 14½.

774 45 c. Type **174** 20 25
775 50 c. Sea Nymph carried off by Triton .. 25 30
776 60 c. Winged angel steering Dolphins (*horiz*) 30 35
777 $4 Cupids shooting arrows (*horiz*) .. .. 1·90 2·00
774/7 .. .. *Set of* 4 2·40 2·50
MS778 101 × 125 mm. $5 Galatea pulled along by Dolphins .. .. 2·50 2·75

(Des Artists International. Litho Questa)

1983 (14 Mar). *Commonwealth Day. T* **175** *and similar horiz designs. Multicoloured. P* 14.

779 25 c. Type **175** 15 15
780 45 c. Carnival 20 25
781 60 c. Tourism 30 35
782 $3 Airport .. .. 1·25 1·50
779/82 .. .. *Set of* 4 1·75 2·00

176 T.V. Satellite Coverage of Royal Wedding

(Des PAD Studio. Litho Questa)

1983 (5 Apr). *World Communications Year. T* **176** *and similar horiz designs. Multicoloured. P* 14.

783 15 c. Type **176** 25 10
784 50 c. Police communications 90 50
785 60 c. House-to-train telephone call 90 50
786 $3 Satellite earth station with planets Jupiter and Saturn .. .. 3·00 3·00
783/6 .. .. *Set of* 4 4·50 3·75
MS787 100 × 90 mm. $5 "Comsat" satellite over West Indies .. .. 3·25 3·75

177 Bottle-nosed Dolphin

(Des D. Miller. Litho Format)

1983 (9 May). *Whales. T* **177** *and similar horiz designs. Multicoloured. P* 14½.

788	15 c. Type **177** ..	40	10
789	50 c. Fin Whale	75	40
790	60 c. Bowhead Whale ..	85	55
791	$3 Spectacled Porpoise	2·50	2·75
788/91	*Set of* 4	4·00	3·50
MS792	122×101 mm. $5 Narwhal	5·00	5·00

178 Cashew Nut

(Des J.W. Litho Questa)

1983 (11 July)–**85**. *Fruits and Flowers. T* **178** *and similar horiz designs. Multicoloured.* A. *P* 14. B. *P* 12.

		A		B	
793	1 c. Type **178** ..	10	10	10	10
794	2 c. Passion Fruit	10	10	10	10
795	3 c. Mango	10	10	10	10
796	5 c. Grapefruit	10	10	10	10
797	10 c. Pawpaw	15	10	15	10
798	15 c. Breadfruit	20	10	20	10
799	20 c. Coconut	25	10	20	10
800	25 c. Oleander ..	35	15	25	10
801	30 c. Banana	40	20	30	15
802	40 c. Pineapple ..	45	25	30	20
803	45 c. Cordia	50	30	40	25
804	50 c. Cassia	60	35	45	25
805	60 c. Poui	80	55	55	30
806	$1 Frangipani	1·25	70	75	45
807	$2 Flamboyant	2·25	1·25	1·50	1·00
808	$2.50, Lemon	2·50	2·25	1·75	1·25
809	$5 Lignum Vitae	4·25	4·25	3·50	2·75
810	$10 National flag and coat of arms	7·00	8·50	6·00	7·00
793A/810A	*Set of* 18	19·00	17·00		
793B/810B	*Set of* 18			15·00	13·00

Dates of issue: 11.7.83, Nos. 793A/810A; 3.85, Nos. 793B/806B, 810B; 12.85, 807B/9B.

179 Dornier "Do X" Flying Boat

(Des W. Wright. Litho Format)

1983 (15 Aug). *Bicentenary of Manned Flight. T* **179** *and similar horiz designs. Multicoloured. P* 14½.

811	30 c. Type **179** ..	45	20
812	50 c. Supermarine "S.6B" seaplane	55	35
813	60 c. Curtiss "9C" biplane and airship U.S.S. *Akron*	70	45
814	$4 *Pro Juventute* balloon	2·75	3·00
811/14	*Set of* 4	4·00	3·50
MS815	80 × 105 mm. $5 *Graf Zeppelin*	3·00	3·25

180 "Sibyls and Angels" (detail) (Raphael)

(Des W. Wright. Litho Format)

1983 (4 Oct). *Christmas. 500th Birth Anniv of Raphael. T* **180** *and similar designs. P* 13½.

816	10 c. multicoloured	20	15
817	30 c. multicoloured	35	20
818	$1 multicoloured	80	60
819	$4 multicoloured	2·75	3·00
816/19	*Set of* 4	3·75	3·50
MS820	101 × 131 mm. $5 multicoloured ..	2·75	3·25

Designs: *Horiz*—10 c. to $4 Different details from "Sibyls and Angels". *Vert*—$5 "The Vision of Ezekiel".

181 John Wesley (founder)

182 Discus

(Des M. Diamond. Litho Questa)

1983 (7 Nov). *Bicentenary of Methodist Church* (1984). *T* **181** *and similar vert designs. Multicoloured. P* 14.

821	15 c. Type **181** ..	15	10
822	50 c. Nathaniel Gilbert (founder in Antigua)	40	30
823	60 c. St. John Methodist Church steeple	45	40
824	$3 Ebenezer Methodist Church, St. John's ..	2·00	2·50
821/4	*Set of* 4	2·75	3·00

(Des Artists International. Litho Format)

1984 (9 Jan). *Olympic Games, Los Angeles. T* **182** *and similar vert designs. Multicoloured. P* 14½.

825	25 c. Type **182** ..	15	15
826	50 c. Gymnastics	30	30
827	90 c. Hurdling ..	55	55
828	$3 Cycling	1·75	2·00
825/8	*Set of* 4	2·50	2·75
MS829	82 × 67 mm. $5 Volleyball	2·75	3·00

183 *Booker Vanguard* (freighter)

184 Chenille

(Des Artists International. Litho Format)

1984 (14 June). *Ships. T* **183** *and similar multicoloured designs. P* 15.

830	45 c. Type **183** ..	75	45
831	50 c. S.S. *Canberra* (liner)	85	50
832	60 c. Sailing boats	95	60
833	$4 *Fairwind* (liner) ..	3·75	4·00
830/3	*Set of* 4	5·75	5·00
MS834	107 × 80 mm. $5 Eighteenth-century British man-of-war (*vert*) ..	4·50	4·75

(Des J.W. Litho Format)

1984 (19 June). *Universal Postal Union Congress, Hamburg. T* **184** *and similar vert designs showing flowers. Multicoloured. P* 15.

835	15 c. Type **184** ..	25	15
836	50 c. Shell Flower	60	40
837	60 c. Anthurium	70	50
838	$3 Angels Trumpet ..	3·25	3·50
835/8	*Set of* 4	4·25	4·00
MS839	100 × 75 mm. $5 Crown of Thorns	3·75	4·25

$2

$2 $2

(185) (186)

1984 (25 June). (*a*) *Nos.* 702/5 *surch with T* **185**

840	$2 on 25 c. Type **159** ..	5·00	5·00
841	$2 on 50 c. Glamis Castle	5·00	5·00
842	$2 on $4 Prince Charles skiing	5·00	5·00
840/2	*Set of* 3	13·50	13·50
MS843	96 × 82 mm. $2 on $5 Glass Coach	8·00	8·00
	(*b*) *Nos.* 748/51 *surch with T* **186**		
844	$2 on 90 c. Type **168** (Gold)*	4·00	3·00
845	$2 on $1 Prince and Princess of Wales (Gold)*	4·00	3·00
846	$2 on $4 Princess Diana (*different*) (Gold)*	4·00	3·00
844/6	*Set of* 3	11·00	8·00
MS847	102 × 75 mm. $2 on $5 Type **169** (Gold)	7·50	7·50
	(*c*) *Nos.* 757/60 *surch with T* **186**		
848	$2 on 90 c. Type **168** (Gold)*	4·00	3·00
849	$2 on $1 Prince and Princess of Wales (Gold)*	4·00	3·00
850	$2 on $4 Princess Diana (*different*) (Gold)*	4·00	3·00
848/50	*Set of* 3	11·00	8·00
MS851	102 × 75 mm. $2 on $5 Type **169** (Gold)	7·50	7·50
	(*d*) *Nos.* 779/82 *surch as T* **185**		
852	$2 on 25 c. Type **175** ..	1·25	1·25
853	$2 on 45 c. Carnival ..	1·25	1·25
854	$2 on 60 c. Tourism ..	1·25	1·25
855	$2 on $3 Airport	1·25	1·25
852/5	*Set of* 4	4·50	4·50

*Nos. 844/6 and 848/50 also exist with similar surcharges in gold or silver on the sheetlets of 5 stamps and 1 label (*price for set of 3 as Nos.* 844/6, £12 *mint or used*) (*price for set of 3 as Nos.* 848/50, £12 *mint or used*).

MINIMUM PRICE

The minimum price quote is 10p which represents a handling charge rather than a basis for valuing common stamps. For further notes about prices see introductory pages.

187 Abraham Lincoln

188 View of Moravian Mission

(Des Liane Fried. Litho Questa)

1984 (18 July). *Presidents of the United States of America. T* **187** *and similar vert designs. Multicoloured. P* 14.

856	10 c. Type **187** ..	10	10
857	20 c. Harry Truman	15	15
858	30 c. Dwight Eisenhower	20	25
859	40 c. Ronald Reagan	25	30
860	90 c. Gettysburg Address, 1863	60	65
861	$1.10, Formation of N.A.T.O., 1949 ..	70	75
862	$1.50, Eisenhower during Second World War	1·00	1·10
863	$2 Reagan and Caribbean Basin Initiative	1·25	1·40
856/63	*Set of* 8	3·75	4·00

(Des and litho Questa)

1984 (1 Aug). *150th Anniv of Abolition of Slavery. T* **188** *and similar horiz designs. Multicoloured. P* 14.

864	40 c. Type **188** ..	60	40
865	50 c. Antigua Courthouse, 1823	70	45
866	60 c. Planting sugar-cane, Monks Hill	75	55
867	$3 Boiling house, Delaps' estate	3·00	3·50
864/7	*Set of* 4	4·50	4·50
MS868	95 × 70 mm. $5 Loading sugar, Willoughby Bay	4·50	4·75

189 Rufous-sided Towhee

190 Grass-skiing

(Des Jennifer Toombs. Litho Questa)

1984 (15 Aug). *Songbirds. T* **189** *and similar vert designs. Multicoloured. P* 15.

869	40 c. Type **189** ..	60	40
870	50 c. Parula Warbler	70	50
871	60 c. House Wren	80	60
872	$2 Ruby-crowned Kinglet	1·75	2·00
873	$3 Common Flicker	2·75	3·00
869/73	*Set of* 5	6·00	6·00
MS874	76 × 76 mm. $5 Yellow-breasted Chat ..	5·00	5·00

(Des Bonny Redecker. Litho Questa)

1984 (21 Sept). *"Ausipex" International Stamp Exhibition, Melbourne. Australian Sports. T* **190** *and similar vert designs. Multicoloured. P* 14½.

875	$1 Type **190** ..	1·00	1·00
876	$5 Australian Football	4·00	4·50
MS877	108 × 78 mm. $5 Boomerang-throwing ..	3·50	4·00

191 "The Virgin and Infant with Angels and Cherubs" (Correggio)

192 "The Blue Dancers" (Degas)

(Litho Format)

1984 (4 Oct). *450th Death Anniv of Correggio (painter). T* **191** *and similar vert designs. Multicoloured. P* 15.

878	25 c. Type **191** ..	20	20
879	60 c. "The Four Saints"	50	50
880	90 c. "St. Catherine" ..	75	75
881	$3 "The Campori Madonna"	2·50	2·75
878/81	*Set of* 4	3·50	3·75
MS882	90 × 60 mm. $5 "St. John the Baptist" ..	3·25	3·50

(Litho Format)

1984 (4 Oct). *150th Birth Anniv of Edgar Degas (painter). T* **192** *and similar multicoloured designs. P* 15.

883	15 c. Type **192** ..	20	15
884	50 c. "The Pink Dancers"	50	50
885	70 c. "Two Dancers" ..	65	65
886	$4 "Dancers at the Bar"	3·00	3·25
883/6	*Set of* 4	4·00	4·00
MS887	90 × 60 mm. $5 "The Folk Dancers" (40 × 27 *mm*)	3·25	3·50

193 Sir Winston Churchill **194** Donald Duck fishing

(Des J. Iskowitz. Litho Format)

1984 (19 Nov). *Famous People. T* **193** *and similar multicoloured designs. P* 15.

888 60 c. Type **193** .. .. 1·25 90
889 60 c. Mahatma Gandhi .. .. 1·25 90
890 60 c. John F. Kennedy .. .. 1·25 90
891 60 c. Mao Tse-tung .. .. 1·25 90
892 $1 Churchill with General De Gaulle, Paris, 1944 (*horiz*) .. .. 1·75 1·50
893 $1 Gandhi leaving London by train, 1931 (*horiz*) .. .. 1·75 1·50
894 $1 Kennedy with Chancellor Adenauer and Mayor Brandt, Berlin, 1963 (*horiz*) .. .. 1·75 1·50
895 $1 Mao Tse-tung with Lin Piao, Peking, 1969 (*horiz*) .. .. 1·75 1·50
888/95 .. .. *Set of* 8 11·00 8·50
MS896 114×80 mm. $5 Flags of Great Britain, India, the United States and China .. .. 4·50 4·50

(Litho Format)

1984 (26 Nov). *Christmas. Walt Disney Cartoon Characters. T* **194** *and similar multicoloured designs. P* 11.

897 1 c. Type **194** 10 10
898 2 c. Donald Duck lying on beach 10 10
899 3 c. Donald Duck and nephews with fishing rods and fishes 10 10
900 4 c. Donald Duck and nephews in boat .. 10 10
901 5 c. Wearing diving masks 10 10
902 10 c. In deckchairs reading books 10 10
903 $1 With toy shark's fin .. .. 1·10 1·10
904 $2 In sailing boat .. .. 1·90 1·90
905 $5 Attempting to propel boat .. .. 4·00 4·00
897/905 .. .. *Set of* 9 6·50 6·50
MS906 Two sheets, each 125×100 mm. (a) $5 Nephews with crayon and paintbrushes (*horiz*). P 14×13½. (b) $5 Donald Duck in deckchair. P 13½×14 .. .. *Set of* 2 *sheets* 7·50 7·50

No. 904 was printed in sheetlets of 8 stamps.

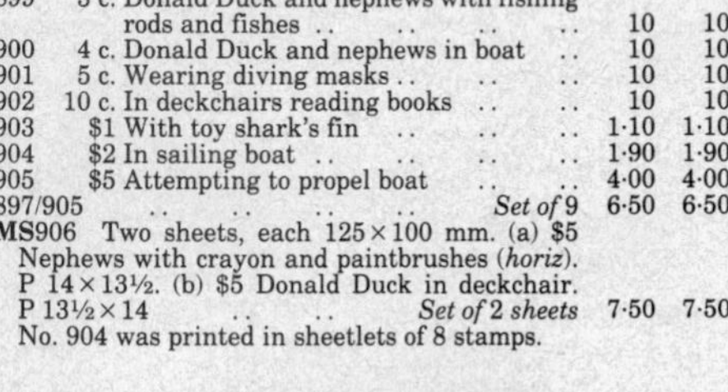

195 Torch from Statue in Madison Square Park, 1885

(Des J. Iskowitz. Litho Format)

1985 (7 Jan). *Centenary of the Statue of Liberty* (1986) (1*st issue*). *T* **195** *and similar multicoloured designs. P* 15.

907 25 c. Type **195** 20 20
908 30 c. Statue of Liberty and scaffolding ("Restoration and Renewal") (*vert*) .. 20 20
909 50 c. Frederic Bartholdi (sculptor) supervising construction, 1876 .. .. 30 30
910 90 c. Close-up of Statue 55 55
911 $1 Statue and sailing ship ("Operation Sail", 1976) (*vert*) 60 60
912 $3 Dedication ceremony, 1886 .. .. 1·75 1·75
907/12 .. .. *Set of* 6 3·00 3·00
MS913 110×80 mm. $5 Port of New York .. 4·00 3·50

See also Nos. 1110/19.

196 Arawak Pot Sherd and Indians making Clay Utensils

(Des N. Waldman. Litho Format)

1985 (21 Jan). *Native American Artefacts. T* **196** *and similar designs. Multicoloured. P* 15.

914 15 c. Type **196** 15 10
915 50 c. Arawak body design and Arawak Indians tattooing 30 30
916 60 c. Head of the god "Yocahu" and Indians harvesting manioc 40 40
917 $3 Carib war club and Carib Indians going into battle .. .. 1·75 2·00
914/17 .. .. *Set of* 4 2·40 2·50
MS918 97×68 mm. $5 Taino Indians worshipping stone idol .. .. 3·00 3·50

197 Triumph 2hp "Jap", 1903

(Des BG Studio. Litho Questa)

1985 (7 Mar). *Centenary of the Motorcycle. T* **197** *and similar horiz designs. Multicoloured. P* 14.

919 10 c. Type **197** 40 10
920 30 c. Indian "Arrow", 1949 .. .. 60 20
921 60 c. BMW "R100RS", 1976 .. .. 85 40
922 $4 Harley-Davidson "Model II", 1916 .. 3·50 3·25
919/22 .. .. *Set of* 4 4·75 3·50
MS923 90×93 mm. $5 Laverda "Jota", 1975 .. 3·50 4·00

198 Slavonian Grebe

(Litho Questa)

1985 (25 Mar). *Birth Bicentenary of John J. Audubon (ornithologist)* (1*st issue*). *T* **198** *and similar multicoloured designs showing original paintings. P* 14.

924 90 c. Type **198** 80 55
925 $1 British Storm Petrel 90 60
926 $1.50, Great Blue Heron .. .. 1·10 85
927 $3 Double-crested Cormorant .. .. 2·25 2·00
924/7 .. .. *Set of* 4 4·50 3·50
MS928 103×72 mm. $5 White-tailed Tropic Bird (*vert*) .. .. 4·00 3·75

Nos. 924/7 were each issued in sheetlets of five stamps and one stamp-size label, which appears in the centre of the bottom row.

See also Nos. 990/4.

199 *Polygrapha cyanea*

(Des R. Sauber. Litho Questa)

1985 (16 Apr). *Butterflies. T* **199** *and similar horiz designs. Multicoloured. P* 14.

929 25 c. Type **199** 60 25
930 60 c. *Leodonta dysoni* .. .. 1·00 55
931 90 c. *Junea doraete* .. .. 1·50 70
932 $4 *Prepona xenagoras* .. .. 4·00 3·50
929/32 .. .. *Set of* 4 6·50 4·50
MS933 132×105 mm. $5 *Caerois gerdrudtus* .. 4·50 4·75

200 Cessna "172" **201** Maimonides

(Des A. DiLorenzo. Litho Questa)

1985 (30 Apr). *40th Anniv of International Civil Aviation Organization. T.* **200** *and similar horiz designs. Multicoloured. P* 14.

934 30 c. Type **200** 65 25
935 90 c. Fokker "DVII" .. .. 1·40 70
936 $1.50, Spad "VII" .. .. 2·00 1·10
937 $3 Boeing "747" .. .. 3·50 3·00
934/7 .. .. *Set of* 4 6·75 4·50
MS938 97×83 mm. $5 Twin "Otter" .. .. 4·50 5·00

(Des and litho Questa)

1985 (17 June). *850th Birth Anniv of Maimonides (physician, philosopher and scholar). P* 14.

939 **201** $2 bright green .. .. 1·25 1·25
MS940 70×84 mm. **201** $5 reddish brown .. 3·75 3·50

No. 939 was printed in sheetlets of 6 stamps.

ALTERED CATALOGUE NUMBERS

Any Catalogue numbers altered from the last edition are shown as a list in the introductory pages.

202 Young Farmers with Produce **203** The Queen Mother attending Church

(Des Susan David. Litho Questa)

1985 (1 July). *International Youth Year. T* **202** *and similar horiz designs. Multicoloured. P* 14.

941 25 c. Type **202** 15 20
942 50 c. Hotel management trainees 25 30
943 60 c. Girls with goat and boys with football ("Environment") 35 40
944 $3 Windsurfing ("Leisure") .. .. 1·60 1·75
941/4 .. .. *Set of* 4 2·10 2·40
MS945 102×72 mm. $5 Young people with Antiguan flags .. .. 2·75 3·00

(Des J.W. Litho Questa)

1985 (10 July). *Life and Times of Queen Elizabeth the Queen Mother. T* **203** *and similar vert designs. Multicoloured. P* 14.

946 $1 Type **203** 55 60
947 $1.50, Watching children playing in London garden 80 85
948 $2.50, The Queen Mother in 1979 .. .. 1·25 1·40
946/8 .. .. *Set of* 3 2·40 2·50
MS949 56×85 mm. $5 With Prince Edward at Royal Wedding, 1981 .. .. 3·00 3·00

Stamps as Nos. 946/8, but with face values of 90 c., $1 and $3, exist from additional sheetlets of 5 plus a label issued 13 January 1986. These also have changed background colours and are perforated 12×12½ (*price for set of* 3 *stamps* £2.40 *mint*).

204 Magnificent Frigate Bird **205** Girl Guides Nursing

(Des Mary Walters. Litho Questa)

1985 (1 Aug). *Marine Life. T* **204** *and similar vert designs. Multicoloured. P* 14.

950 15 c. Type **204** 40 10
951 45 c. Brain Coral 70 35
952 60 c. Cushion Star 90 45
953 $3 Spotted Moray Eel .. .. 3·00 3·00
950/3 .. .. *Set of* 4 4·50 3·50
MS954 110×80 mm. $5 Elkhorn Coral .. .. 4·25 4·50

(Des Y. Berry. Litho Questa)

1985 (22 Aug). *75th Anniv of Girl Guide Movement. T* **205** *and similar horiz designs. Multicoloured. P* 14.

955 15 c. Type **205** 40 10
956 45 c. Open-air Girl Guide meeting 70 35
957 60 c. Lord and Lady Baden-Powell 90 45
958 $3 Girl Guides gathering flowers .. .. 2·75 2·50
955/8 .. .. *Set of* 4 4·25 3·00
MS959 67× 96 mm. $5 Barn Swallow (Nature study) .. .. 4·25 5·00

206 Bass Trombone **207** Flags of Great Britain and Antigua

(Des Susan David. Litho Questa)

1985 (26 Aug). *300th Birth Anniv of Johann Sebastian Bach (composer). T* **206** *and similar vert designs. P* 14.

960 25 c. multicoloured 65 25
961 50 c. multicoloured .. .. 1·00 40
962 $1 multicoloured .. .. 1·60 80
963 $3 multicoloured .. .. 3·50 3·00
960/3 .. .. *Set of* 4 6·00 4·00
MS964 104×73 mm. $5 black and brownish grey .. .. 4·50 4·75

Designs:—50 c. English horn; $1 Violino piccolo; $3 Bass rackett; $5 Johann Sebastian Bach.

(Des Mary Walters. Litho Format)

1985 (24 Oct). *Royal Visit. T* **207** *and similar multicoloured designs. P* 14½.
965 60 c. Type **207** 70 45
966 $1 Queen Elizabeth II (*vert*) . . 1·10 80
967 $4 Royal Yacht *Britannia* . . 3·50 3·50
965/7 . . *Set of* 3 4·75 4·25
MS968 110×83 mm. $5 Map of Antigua . . 3·75 4·00

(Des Walt Disney Productions. Litho Questa)

1985 (4 Nov). *150th Birth Anniv of Mark Twain (author). Horiz designs as T* **118** *of Anguilla showing Walt Disney cartoon characters in scenes from "Roughing It". Multicoloured. P* 14×13½.
969 25 c. Donald Duck and Mickey Mouse meeting Indians . . 20 20
970 50 c. Mickey Mouse, Donald Duck and Goofy canoeing . . 35 35
971 $1.10, Goofy as Pony Express rider . . 70 70
972 $1.50, Donald Duck and Goofy hunting buffalo . . 95 95
973 $2 Mickey Mouse and silver mine . . 1·40 1·40
969/73 . . *Set of* 5 3·25 3·25
MS974 127×101 mm. $5 Mickey Mouse driving stagecoach . . 3·25 3·50

(Des Walt Disney Productions. Litho Questa)

1985 (11 Nov). *Birth Bicentenaries of Grimm Brothers (folklorists). Horiz designs as T* **119** *of Anguilla showing Walt Disney cartoon characters in scenes from "Spindle, Shuttle and Needle". Multicoloured. P* 14×13½.
975 30 c. The Prince (Mickey Mouse) searches for a bride . . 40 20
a. Error. Wmk w **16** . . £120
976 60 c. The Prince finds the Orphan Girl (Minnie Mouse) . . 65 40
977 70 c. The Spindle finds the Prince . . 75 45
978 $1 The Needle tidies the Girl's House . . 1·00 75
979 $3 The Prince proposes . . 2·75 3·00
975/9 . . *Set of* 5 5·00 4·25
MS980 125×101 mm. $5 The Orphan Girl and spinning wheel on Prince's horse . . 3·75 4·50

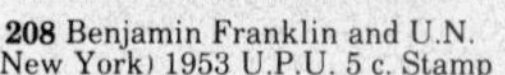

208 Benjamin Franklin and U.N. (New York) 1953 U.P.U. 5 c. Stamp

209 "Madonna and Child" (De Landi)

(Litho Walsall)

1985 (18 Nov). *40th Anniv of United Nations Organization. T* **208** *and similar multicoloured designs showing United Nations (New York) stamps. P* 13½×14.
981 40 c. Type **208** . . 55 35
982 $1 George Washington Carver (agricultural chemist) and 1982 Nature Conservation 28 c. stamp . . 1·25 1·00
983 $3 Charles Lindbergh (aviator) and 1978 I.C.A.O. 25 c. stamp . . 3·00 3·00
981/3 . . *Set of* 3 4·25 4·00
MS984 101×77 mm. $5 Marc Chagall (artist) (*vert*). P 14×13½ . . 4·00 4·25

(Des Mary Walters. Litho Format)

1985 (30 Dec). *Christmas. Religious Paintings. T* **209** *and similar vert designs. Multicoloured. P* 15.
985 10 c. Type **209** . . 15 10
986 25 c. "Madonna and Child" (Berlinghiero) 30 20
987 60 c. "The Nativity" (Fra Angelico) . . 55 40
988 $4 "Presentation in the Temple" (Giovanni di Paolo) . . 3·25 3·50
985/8 . . *Set of* 4 3·75 3·75
MS989 113×81 mm. $5 "The Nativity" (Antoniazzo Romano) . . 3·75 4·25

(Litho Questa)

1986 (6 Jan). *Birth Bicentenary of John J. Audubon (ornithologist) (2nd issue). Horiz designs as T* **198** *showing original paintings. Multicoloured. P* 12.
990 60 c. Mallard . . 80 45
991 90 c. North American Black Duck . . 1·00 70
992 $1.50, Pintail . . 1·75 1·60
993 $3 American Wigeon . . 2·50 2·75
990/3 . . *Set of* 4 5·50 5·00
MS994 102×73 mm. $5 American Eider. P 14 . . 4·25 4·50
Nos. 990/3 were issued in sheetlets of 5 as Nos. 924/7.

210 Football, Boots and Trophy

211 Tug

(Des M. Donk. Litho Questa)

1986 (17 Mar). *World Cup Football Championship, Mexico. T* **210** *and similar multicoloured designs. P* 14.
995 30 c. Type **210** . . 40 20
996 60 c. Goalkeeper (*vert*) . . 55 35
997 $1 Referee blowing whistle (*vert*) . . 90 80
998 $4 Ball in net . . 2·75 3·00
995/8 . . *Set of* 4 4·25 4·00
MS999 87×76 mm. $5 Two players competing for ball . . 4·00 4·50

(Des W. Hanson. Litho Questa)

1986 (24 Mar). *Appearance of Halley's Comet (1st issue). Horiz designs as T* **123** *of Anguilla. Multicoloured. P* 14.
1000 5 c. Edmond Halley and Old Greenwich Observatory . . 10 10
1001 10 c. "Me 163B Komet" (fighter aircraft), 1944 . . 15 10
1002 60 c. Montezuma (Aztec Emperor) and Comet in 1517 (from "Historias de las Indias de Neuva Espana") . . 50 35
1003 $4 Pocahontas saving Capt. John Smith and Comet in 1607 . . 2·50 2·75
1000/3 . . *Set of* 4 3·00 3·00
MS1004 101×70 mm. $5 Halley's Comet over English Harbour, Antigua . . 3·00 3·75
See also Nos. 1047/51.

(Litho Questa)

1986 (21 Apr). *60th Birthday of Queen Elizabeth II. Vert designs as T* **125** *of Anguilla. P* 14.
1005 60 c. black and yellow . . 35 35
1006 $1 multicoloured . . 55 55
1007 $4 multicoloured . . 2·10 2·10
1005/7 . . *Set of* 3 2·75 2·75
MS1008 120×85 mm. $5 black and grey-brown . . 3·00 3·25
Designs:—60 c. Wedding photograph, 1947; $1 Queen at Trooping the Colour; $4 In Scotland; $5 Queen Mary and Princess Elizabeth, 1927.

(Des A. DiLorenzo. Litho Questa)

1986 (15 May). *Local Boats. T* **211** *and similar vert designs. Multicoloured. P* 14.
1009 30 c. Type **211** . . 25 20
1010 60 c. Game fishing boat . . 45 35
1011 $1 Yacht . . 75 60
1012 $4 Lugger with auxiliary sail . . 2·50 3·00
1009/12 . . *Set of* 4 3·50 3·75
MS1013 108×78 mm. $5 Boats under construction . . 3·00 3·75

212 "Hiawatha Express"

213 Prince Andrew and Miss Sarah Ferguson

(Des W. Wright. Litho Format)

1986 (22 May). *"Ameripex '86" International Stamp Exhibition, Chicago. Famous American Trains. T* **212** *and similar horiz designs. Multicoloured. P* 15.
1014 25 c. Type **212** . . 35 20
1015 50 c. "Grand Canyon Express" . . 55 35
1016 $1 "Powhattan Arrow Express" . . 1·00 70
1017 $3 "Empire State Express" . . 2·75 2·75
1014/17 . . *Set of* 4 4·25 3·50
MS1018 116×87 mm. $5 "Daylight Express" . . 4·00 4·50

(Des and litho Questa)

1986 (1 July). *Royal Wedding. T* **213** *and similar vert designs. Multicoloured. P* 14.
1019 45 c. Type **213** . . 30 30
1020 60 c. Prince Andrew . . 35 35
1021 $4 Prince Andrew with Prince Philip . . 2·10 2·10
1019/21 . . *Set of* 3 2·50 2·50
MS1022 88×88 mm. $5 Prince Andrew and Miss Sarah Ferguson (*different*) . . 3·00 3·25

214 Fly-specked Cerith

215 *Nymphaea ampla* (Water Lily)

(Des L. Birmingham. Litho Format)

1986 (6 Aug). *Sea Shells. T* **214** *and similar multicoloured designs. P* 15.
1023 15 c. Type **214** . . 30 10
1024 45 c. Smooth Scotch Bonnet . . 65 40
1025 60 c. West Indian Crown Conch . . 80 55
1026 $3 Murex Ciboney . . 3·25 3·00
1023/6 . . *Set of* 4 4·50 3·50
MS1027 109×75 mm. $5 Colourful Atlantic Natica (*horiz*) . . 4·50 5·00

(Des Mary Walters. Litho Format)

1986 (25 Aug). *Flowers. T* **215** *and similar horiz designs. Multicoloured. P* 15.
1028 10 c. Type **215** . . 10 10
1029 15 c. Queen of the Night . . 15 10
1030 50 c. Cup of Gold . . 40 30
1031 60 c. Beach Morning Glory . . 50 35
1032 70 c. Golden Trumpet . . 60 40
1033 $1 Air Plant . . 85 65
1034 $3 Purple Wreath . . 2·25 2·00
1035 $4 Zephyr Lily . . 2·75 2·75
1028/35 . . *Set of* 8 7·00 6·00
MS1036 Two sheets, each 102×72 mm. (a) $4 Dozakie. (b) $5 Four O'Clock Flower *Set of 2 sheets* 6·00 7·00

WINNERS
Argentina 3
W.Germany 2

(**216**)

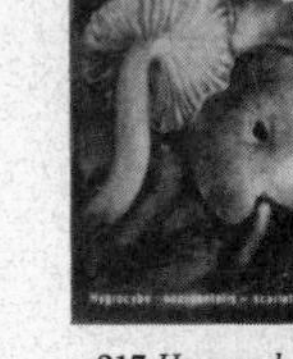

217 *Hygrocybe occidentalis*

1986 (15 Sept). *World Cup Football Championship Winners, Mexico. Nos.* 995/9 *optd as T* **216** *in gold.*
1037 30 c. Type **210** . . 25 25
1038 60 c. Goalkeeper (*vert*) . . 45 45
1039 $1 Referee blowing whistle (*vert*) . . 65 65
1040 $4 Ball in net . . 2·50 2·75
1037/40 . . *Set of* 4 3·50 3·75
MS1041 87×76 mm. $5 Two players competing for ball . . 3·00 3·50
The overprint on the horizontal designs is in two lines.

(Litho Format)

1986 (15 Sept). *Mushrooms. T* **217** *and similar vert designs. Multicoloured. P* 15.
1042 10 c. Type **217** . . 20 10
1043 50 c. *Trogia buccinalis* . . 55 40
1044 $1 *Collybia subpruinosa* . . 95 75
1045 $4 *Leucocoprinus brebissonii* . . 3·25 3·50
1042/5 . . *Set of* 4 4·50 4·25
MS1046 102×82 mm $5 *Pyrrhoglossum pyrrhum* 5·00 5·00

(**218**)

219 Auburn "Speedster" (1933)

1986 (15 Oct). *Appearance of Halley's Comet (2nd issue). Nos.* 1000/4 *optd with T* **218** (*in silver on* $5).
1047 5 c. Edmond Halley and Old Greenwich Observatory . . 10 10
1048 10 c. "Me 163B Komet" (fighter aircraft), 1944 . . 10 10
1049 60 c. Montezuma (Aztec Emperor) and Comet in 1517 (from "Historias de las Indias de Neuva Espana") . . 45 45
1050 $4 Pocahontas saving Capt. John Smith and Comet in 1607 . . 2·50 2·50
1047/50 . . *Set of* 4 2·75 2·75
MS1051 101×70 mm. $5 Halley's Comet over English Harbour, Antigua . . 3·75 4·50

(Des J. Martin. Litho Questa)

1986 (20 Oct). *Centenary of First Benz Motor Car. T* **219** *and similar horiz designs. Multicoloured. P* 14.
1052 10 c. Type **219** . . 10 10
1053 15 c. Mercury "Sable" (1986) . . 15 10
1054 50 c. Cadillac (1959) . . 40 30
1055 60 c. Studebaker (1950) . . 45 35
1056 70 c. Lagonda "V-12" (1939) . . 55 40
1057 $1 Adler "Standard" (1930) . . 75 65
1058 $3 DKW (1956) . . 2·00 2·00
1059 $4 Mercedes "500K" (1936) . . 2·50 2·75
1052/9 . . *Set of* 8 6·25 6·00
MS1060 Two sheets, each 99×70 mm. (a) $5 Daimler (1896). (b) $5 Mercedes "Knight" (1921) *Set of 2 sheets* 5·50 6·50

220 Young Mickey Mouse playing Santa Claus

221 Arms of Antigua

(Des Walt Disney Co. Litho Format)

1986 (4 Nov). *Christmas. T* **220** *and similar horiz designs showing Walt Disney cartoon characters as babies. Multicoloured. P* 11.
1061 25 c. Type **220** 25 25
1062 30 c. Mickey and Minnie Mouse building snowman 30 30
1063 40 c. Aunt Matilda and Goofy baking .. 35 35
1064 60 c. Goofy and Pluto 55 55
1065 70 c. Pluto, Donald and Daisy Duck carol singing 60 60
1066 $1.50, Donald Duck, Mickey Mouse and Pluto stringing popcorn .. .. 1·00 1·00
1067 $3 Grandma Duck and Minnie Mouse .. 1·90 1·90
1068 $4 Donald Duck and Pete .. .. 2·40 2·40
1061/8 .. .. *Set of* 8 6·50 6·50
MS1069 Two sheets, each 127 × 102 mm. P 14 × 13½. (a) $5 Goofy, Donald Duck and Minnie Mouse playing reindeer. (b) $5 Mickey Mouse, Donald and Daisy Duck playing with toys. *Set of* 2 *sheets* 7·50 7·50

1986 (25 Nov). *Coil stamps. T* **221** *and similar vert design. Litho. P* 14.
1070 10 c. new blue 10 10
1071 25 c. orange-vermilion 10 15
Design:—25 c. Flag of Antigua.

222 *Canada I* (1981)

223 Bridled Burrfish

(Des J. Iskowitz. Litho Format)

1987 (5 Feb). *America's Cup Yachting Championship. T* **222** *and similar multicoloured designs. P* 15.
1072 30 c. Type **222** 20 20
1073 60 c. *Gretel II* (1970) 35 35
1074 $1 *Sceptre* (1958) 65 65
1075 $3 *Vigilant* (1893) .. .. 1·75 1·75
1072/5 .. .. *Set of* 4 2·75 2·75
MS1076 113 × 84 mm. $5 *Australia II* defeating *Liberty* (1983) (*horiz*) .. .. .. 3·00 3·50

(Des G. Drummond. Litho Questa)

1987 (23 Feb). *Marine Life. T* **223** *and similar horiz designs. Multicoloured. P* 14.
1077 15 c. Type **223** 25 10
1078 30 c. Common Noddy 30 15
1079 40 c. Nassau Grouper 45 30
1080 50 c. Laughing Gull 60 40
1081 60 c. French Angelfish 60 50
1082 $1 Porkfish 90 80
1083 $2 Royal Tern .. .. 1·75 1·75
1084 $3 Sooty Tern .. .. 2·25 2·50
1077/84 .. .. *Set of* 8 6·50 6·00
MS1085 Two sheets, each 120 × 94 mm. (a) $5 Banded Butterflyfish. (b) $5 Brown Booby *Set of* 2 *sheets* 6·00 7·00
Nos. 1078, 1080 and 1083/5 are without the World Wildlife Fund logo shown on Type **223**.

224 Handball

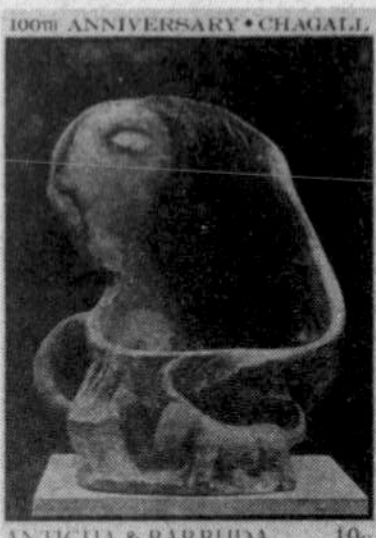

225 "The Profile"

(Litho Questa)

1987 (23 Mar). *Olympic Games, Seoul* (1988) (1*st issue*). *T* **224** *and similar horiz designs. Multicoloured. P* 14.
1086 10 c. Type **224** 10 10
1087 60 c. Fencing 25 30
1088 $1 Gymnastics 45 50
1089 $3 Football .. .. 1·40 1·50
1086/9 .. .. *Set of* 4 1·90 2·10
MS1090 100 × 72 mm. $5 Boxing gloves .. .. 2·25 2·40
See also Nos. 1222/6.

(Litho Questa)

1987 (30 Mar). *Birth Centenary of Marc Chagall* (*artist*). *T* **225** *and similar multicoloured designs. P* 13½ × 14.
1091 10 c. Type **225** 10 10
1092 30 c. "Portrait of the Artist's Sister" .. 15 15
1093 40 c. "Bride with Fan" 20 25
1094 60 c. "David in Profile" 25 30
1095 90 c. "Fiancee with Bouquet" 40 45
1096 $1 "Self Portrait with Brushes" 45 50
1097 $3 "The Walk" .. .. 1·40 1·50
1098 $4 "Three Candles" .. .. .. 1·75 1·90
1091/8 .. .. *Set of* 8 4·25 4·50
MS1099 Two sheets, each 110 × 95 mm. (a) $5 "Fall of Icarus" (104 × 89 *mm*). (b) $5 "Myth of Orpheus" (104 × 89 *mm*). Imperf *Set of* 2 *sheets* 4·50 4·75

226 *Spirit of Australia* (fastest powerboat), 1978

227 Lee Iacocca at Unveiling of Restored Statue

(Des W. Wright. Litho Format)

1987 (9 Apr). *Milestones of Transportation. T* **226** *and similar horiz designs. Multicoloured. P* 15.
1100 10 c. Type **226** 15 10
1101 15 c. Siemen's electric locomotive, 1879 .. 20 10
1102 30 c. U.S.S. *Triton* (first submerged circumnavigation), 1960 .. .. .. 25 15
1103 50 c. Trevithick's steam carriage (first passenger-carrying vehicle), 1801 .. 40 30
1104 60 c. U.S.S. *New Jersey* (battleship), 1942 .. 45 30
1105 70 c. Draisaine bicycle, 1818 .. .. 45 35
1106 90 c. S.S. *United States* (holder of Blue Riband), 1952 .. .. 65 45
1107 $1.50, Cierva "C.4" (first autogiro), 1923 85 85
1108 $2 Curtiss "NC.4" (first transatlantic flight), 1919 .. .. 1·10 1·10
1109 $3 *Queen Elizabeth 2* (liner), 1969 .. 1·75 1·75
1100/9 .. .. *Set of* 10 5·50 4·75

(Litho Questa)

1987 (23 Apr). *Centenary of Statue of Liberty* (1986) (2*nd issue*). *T* **227** *and similar multicoloured designs. P* 14.
1110 15 c. Type **227** 10 10
1111 30 c. Statue at sunset (side view) 15 15
1112 45 c. Aerial view of head 25 25
1113 50 c. Lee Iacocca and torch 30 30
1114 60 c. Workmen inside head of Statue (*horiz*) 30 30
1115 90 c. Restoration work (*horiz*) 40 45
1116 $1 Head of Statue 45 50
1117 $2 Statue at sunset (front view) 90 95
1118 $3 Inspecting restoration work (*horiz*) 1·40 1·60
1119 $5 Statue at night .. .. .. 2·25 2·75
1110/19 .. .. *Set of* 10 6·00 6·50

228 Grace Kelly

229 Scouts around Camp Fire and Red Kangaroo

(Des Lynda Bruscheni. Litho Questa)

1987 (11 May). *Entertainers. T* **228** *and similar vert designs. Multicoloured. P* 14.
1120 15 c. Type **228** 15 10
1121 30 c. Marilyn Monroe 20 15
1122 45 c. Orson Welles 30 25
1123 50 c. Judy Garland 35 30
1124 60 c. John Lennon 40 30
1125 $1 Rock Hudson 60 50
1126 $2 John Wayne .. .. 1·10 1·10
1127 $3 Elvis Presley .. .. 1·75 1·75
1120/7 .. .. *Set of* 8 4·25 4·00

(Litho Format)

1987 (25 May). 16*th World Scout Jamboree, Australia. T* **229** *and similar horiz designs. Multicoloured. P* 15.
1128 10 c. Type **229** 20 10
1129 60 c. Scouts canoeing and Blue-winged Kookaburra 50 40
1130 $1 Scouts on assault course and Ring-tailed Rock Wallaby 90 80
1131 $3 Field kitchen and Koala .. .. 2·00 2·25
1128/31 .. .. *Set of* 4 3·25 3·00
MS1132 103 × 78 mm. $5 Flags of Antigua, Australia and Scout Movement .. .. .. 2·50 3·00

230 Whistling Frog

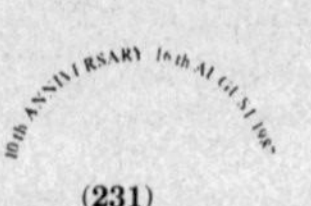

(**231**)

NEW INFORMATION

The editor is always interested to correspond with people who have new information that will improve or correct the Catalogue.

(Des B. Bundock. Litho Questa)

1987 (15 June). *"Capex '87" International Stamp Exhibition, Toronto. Reptiles and Amphibians. T* **230** *and similar horiz designs. Multicoloured. P* 14.
1133 30 c. Type **230** 15 15
1134 60 c. Croaking Lizard 25 30
1135 $1 Antiguan Anole 45 50
1136 $3 Red-footed Tortoise .. .. .. 1·40 1·75
1133/6 .. .. *Set of* 4 2·00 2·40
MS1137 106 × 76 mm. $5 Ground Lizard .. 2·25 2·75

1987 (9 Sept). 10*th Death Anniv of Elvis Presley* (*entertainer*). *No.* 1127 *optd with T* **231**.
1138 $3 Elvis Presley .. .. 1·75 2·00

232 House of Burgesses, Virginia ("Freedom of Speech")

233 "Madonna and Child" (Bernardo Daddi)

(Des and litho Questa)

1987 (16 Nov). *Bicentenary of U.S. Constitution. T* **232** *and similar multicoloured designs. P* 14.
1139 15 c. Type **232** 10 10
1140 45 c. State Seal, Connecticut 20 25
1141 60 c. State Seal, Delaware 25 30
1142 $4 Gouverneur Morris (Pennsylvania delegate) (*vert*) .. .. 1·75 1·90
1139/42 .. .. *Set of* 4 2·10 2·25
MS1143 105 × 75 mm. $5 Roger Sherman (Connecticut delegate) (*vert*) .. .. .. 2·25 2·75
Nos. 1139/42 were each issued in sheetlets of five stamps and one stamp-size label, which appears in the centre of the bottom row.

(Litho Questa)

1987 (1 Dec). *Christmas. Religious Paintings. T* **233** *and similar vert designs. Multicoloured. P* 14.
1144 45 c. Type **233** 20 25
1145 60 c. "St. Joseph" (detail, "The Nativity" (Sano di Pietro)) 25 30
1146 $1 "Virgin Mary" (detail, "The Nativity" (Sano di Pietro)) 45 50
1147 $4 "Music-making Angel" (Melozzo da Forli) .. .. 1·75 2·25
1144/7 .. .. *Set of* 4 2·40 3·00
MS1148 99 × 70 mm. $5 "The Flight into Egypt" (Sano di Pietro) .. .. 2·25 2·75

234 Wedding Photograph, 1947

235 Great Blue Heron

(Des and litho Questa)

1988 (8 Feb). *Royal Ruby Wedding. T* **234** *and similar vert designs. P* 14.
1149 25 c. deep brown, black and bright new blue 15 15
1150 60 c. multicoloured 30 30
1151 $2 deep brown, black and light green .. 90 95
1152 $3 multicoloured .. .. 1·40 1·50
1149/52 .. .. *Set of* 4 2·50 2·75
MS1153 102 × 77 mm. $5 multicoloured .. .. 2·25 2·75
Designs:—60 c. Queen Elizabeth II; $2 Princess Elizabeth and Prince Philip with Prince Charles at his christening, 1948; $3 Queen Elizabeth (from photo by Tim Graham), 1980; $5 Royal Family, 1952.

(Des W. Wright. Litho Questa)

1988 (1 Mar). *Birds of Antigua. T* **235** *and similar multicoloured designs. P* 14.
1154 10 c. Type **235** 15 10
1155 15 c. Ringed Kingfisher (*horiz*) 15 10
1156 50 c. Bananaquit (*horiz*) 35 30
1157 60 c. Purple Gallinule (*horiz*) 35 30
1158 70 c. Blue-hooded Euphonia (*horiz*) .. 40 35
1159 $1 Brown-throated Conure ("Caribbean Parakeet") 55 55
1160 $3 Troupial (*horiz*) .. .. .. 1·75 1·90
1161 $4 Purple-throated Carib (*horiz*) .. 2·00 2·50
1154/61 .. .. *Set of* 8 5·00 5·50
MS1162 Two sheets, each 115 × 86 mm. (a) $5 Greater Flamingo. (b) $5 Brown Pelican *Set of* 2 *sheets* 4·50 5·50

236 First Aid at Daycare Centre, Antigua

(Des G. Vasarhelyi. Litho Format)

1988 (10 Mar). *Salvation Army's Community Service. T* **236** *and similar horiz designs. Multicoloured. P* 14×13½.

1163 25 c. Type **236** 15 15
1164 30 c. Giving penicillin injection, Indonesia 15 15
1165 40 c. Children at daycare centre, Bolivia .. 25 25
1166 45 c. Rehabilitation of the handicapped, India 25 25
1167 50 c. Training blind man, Kenya 30 30
1168 60 c. Weighing baby, Ghana 30 30
1169 $1 Training typist, Zambia 55 55
1170 $2 Emergency food kitchen, Sri Lanka .. 1·25 1·40
1163/70 .. .. *Set of* 8 2·75 3·00
MS1171 152×83 mm. $5 General Eva Burrows 2·25 2·75

237 Columbus' Second Fleet, 1493

238 "Bust of Christ"

(Des I. MacLaury. Litho Questa)

1988 (16 Mar–16 May). *500th Anniv of Discovery of America by Columbus* (1992). *T* **237** *and similar horiz designs. Multicoloured. P* 14.

1172 10 c. Type **237** 15 10
1173 30 c. Painos Indian village and fleet (16.5) 20 15
1174 45 c. *Santa Mariagalante* (flagship) and Painos village (16.5) 25 25
1175 60 c. Painos Indians offering Columbus fruit and vegetables (16.5) 30 30
1176 90 c. Painos Indian and Columbus with parrot 45 45
1177 $1 Columbus landing on island 50 50
1178 $3 Spanish soldier and fleet .. .. 1·40 1·50
1179 $4 Fleet under sail (16.5) .. .. 1·75 2·00
1172/9 .. .. *Set of* 8 4·50 4·75
MS1180 Two sheets, each 110×80 mm. (a) $5 Queen Isabella's cross. (b) $5 Gold coin of Ferdinand and Isabella (16.5) *Set of* 2 *sheets* 4·50 5·50

(Litho Questa)

1988 (11 Apr). *500th Birth Anniv of Titian. T* **238** *and similar vert designs showing paintings. Multicoloured. P* 13½×14.

1181 30 c. Type **238** 15 15
1182 40 c. "Scourging of Christ" 20 25
1183 45 c. "Madonna in Glory with Saints" .. 20 25
1184 50 c. "The Averoldi Polyptych" (detail) .. 25 30
1185 $1 "Christ Crowned with Thorns" .. 45 50
1186 $2 "Christ Mocked" 90 95
1187 $3 "Christ and Simon of Cyrene" .. 1·40 1·50
1188 $4 "Crucifixion with Virgin and Saints" 1·75 2·00
1181/8 .. .. *Set of* 8 4·75 5·25
MS1189 Two sheets, each 110×95 mm. (a) $5 "Ecce Homo" (detail). (b) $5 "Noli me Tangere" (detail) *Set of* 2 *sheets* 4·50 5·00

239 Two Yachts rounding Buoy

(Des G. Drummond. Litho Format)

1988 (18 Apr). *Sailing Week. T* **239** *and similar horiz designs. Multicoloured. P* 15.

1190 30 c. Type **239** 20 15
1191 60 c. Three yachts 30 30
1192 $1 British yacht under way 50 50
1193 $3 Three yachts (*different*) .. .. 1·40 1·50
1190/3 .. .. .. *Set of* 4 2·25 2·25
MS1194 103×92 mm. $5 Two yachts .. .. 2·25 2·75

NEW INFORMATION

The editor is always interested to correspond with people who have new information that will improve or correct the Catalogue.

240 Mickey Mouse and Diver with Porpoise

(**241**)

(Des Walt Disney Co. Litho Questa)

1988 (3 May). *Disney EPCOT Centre, Orlando, Florida. T* **240** *and similar multicoloured designs showing cartoon characters and exhibits. P* 14×13½ *(horiz) or* 13½×14 *(vert)*.

1195 1 c. Type **240** 10 10
1196 2 c. Goofy and Mickey Mouse with futuristic car (*vert*) 10 10
1197 3 c. Mickey Mouse and Goofy as Atlas (*vert*) 10 10
1198 4 c. Mickey Mouse and prehistoric reptile 10 10
1199 5 c. Mickey Mouse at Journey into Imagination exhibit 10 10
1200 10 c. Mickey Mouse collecting vegetables (*vert*) 10 10
1201 25 c. Type **240** 15 15
1202 30 c. As 2 c. 15 15
1203 40 c. As 3 c. 20 25
1204 60 c. As 4 c. 25 30
1205 70 c. As 5 c. 30 35
1206 $1.50, As 10 c. 70 75
1207 $3 Goofy and Mickey Mouse with robot (*vert*) .. .. 1·40 1·50
1208 $4 Mickey Mouse and Clarabelle at Horizons exhibit .. .. .. 1·75 1·90
1195/1208 .. .. .. *Set of* 14 4·75 5·00
MS1209 Two sheets, each 125×99 mm. (a) $5 Mickey Mouse and monorail (*vert*). (b) $5 Mickey Mouse flying over EPCOT Centre *Set of* 2 *sheets* 4·50 5·00

1988 (9 May). *Stamp Exhibitions. Nos.* 1083/5 *optd as T* **241** *showing various emblems.*

1210 $2 Royal Tern (optd T **241**, Prague) .. 90 95
1211 $3 Sooty Tern (optd "INDEPENDENCE 40", Israel) .. .. 1·40 1·50
MS1212 Two sheets, each 120×94 mm. (a) $5 Banded Butterflyfish (optd "OLYMPHILEX '88", Seoul). (b) $5 Brown Booby (optd "FINLANDIA 88", Helsinki) *Set of* 2 *sheets* 4·50 5·00

242 Jacaranda

243 Gymnastics

(Des Mary Walters. Litho Questa)

1988 (16 May). *Flowering Trees. T* **242** *and similar vert designs. Multicoloured. P* 14.

1213 10 c. Type **242** 15 10
1214 30 c. Cordia 20 15
1215 50 c. Orchid Tree 30 30
1216 90 c. Flamboyant 40 45
1217 $1 African Tulip Tree 45 50
1218 $2 Potato Tree 90 95
1219 $3 Crepe Myrtle .. .. 1·40 1·60
1220 $4 Pitch Apple .. .. 1·75 2·25
1213/20 .. .. *Set of* 8 5·00 5·50
MS1221 Two sheets, each 106×76 mm. (a) $5 Cassia. (b) $5 Chinaberry *Set of* 2 *sheets* 4·50 5·00

(Des J. Martin. Litho Questa)

1988 (10 June). *Olympic Games, Seoul (2nd issue). T* **243** *and similar multicoloured designs. P* 14.

1222 40 c. Type **243** 20 25
1223 60 c. Weightlifting 25 30
1224 $1 Water polo (*horiz*) 45 50
1225 $3 Boxing (*horiz*) .. .. 1·40 1·50
1222/5 .. .. *Set of* 4 2·10 2·25
MS1226 114×80 mm. $5 Runner with Olympic torch .. .. 2·25 2·75

244 Monarch

(Des S. Heimann. Litho Questa)

1988 (29 Aug). *Caribbean Butterflies. T* **244** *and similar horiz designs. Multicoloured. P* 14.

1227 1 c. Type **244** 10 10
1228 2 c. Jamaican Clearwing 10 10
1229 3 c. Yellow-barred Ringlet 10 10
1230 5 c. Cracker 10 10
1231 10 c. Jamaican Mestra 10 10
1232 15 c. Mimic 10 10
1233 20 c. Silver Spot 10 10
1234 25 c. Zebra 10 10
1235 30 c. Fiery Sulphur 10 15
1236 40 c. Androgeus Swallowtail 15 20
1237 45 c. Giant Brimstone 20 25
1238 50 c. Orbed Sulphur 20 25
1239 60 c. Blue-backed Skipper 25 30
1240 $1 Common White Skipper 40 45
1241 $2 Baracoa Skipper 80 85
1242 $2.50, Mangrove Skipper .. .. .. 1·00 1·10
1243 $5 Silver King .. .. 2·10 2·25
1244 $10 Pygmy Skipper .. .. 4·00 4·25
1227/44 .. .. *Set of* 18 9·00 9·75

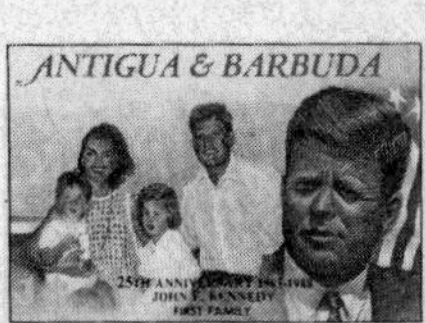

245 President Kennedy and Family

246 Minnie Mouse carol singing

(Des J. Iskowitz. Litho Questa)

1988 (23 Nov). *25th Death Anniv of John F. Kennedy (American statesman). T* **245** *and similar horiz designs, each showing different inset portrait. Multicoloured. P* 14.

1245 1 c. Type **245** 10 10
1246 2 c. Kennedy commanding *PT109* .. 10 10
1247 3 c. Funeral cortege 10 10
1248 4 c. In motorcade, Mexico City 10 10
1249 30 c. As 1 c. 15 15
1250 60 c. As 4 c. 25 30
1251 $1 As 3 c. 45 50
1252 $4 As 2 c. .. .. 1·60 1·75
1245/52 .. .. *Set of* 8 2·40 2·50
MS1253 105 × 75 mm. $5 Kennedy taking presidential oath of office .. .. .. 2·25 2·50

(Des Walt Disney Co. Litho Questa)

1988 (1 Dec). *Christmas. "Mickey's Christmas Chorale". T* **246** *and similar multicoloured designs showing Walt Disney cartoon characters. P* 13½ × 14.

1254 10 c. Type **246** 10 10
1255 25 c. Pluto 15 15
1256 30 c. Mickey Mouse playing ukelele 15 15
1257 70 c. Donald Duck and nephew 35 35
1258 $1 Mordie and Ferdie carol singing .. 45 50
a. Sheetlet. Nos. 1258/65 .. .. 3·50
1259 $1 Goofy carol singing 45 50
1260 $1 Chip n'Dale sliding off roof 45 50
1261 $1 Two of Donald Duck's nephews at window 45 50
1262 $1 As 10 c. 45 50
1263 $1 As 25 c. 45 50
1264 $1 As 30 c. 45 50
1265 $1 As 70 c. 45 50
1254/65 .. .. *Set of* 12 3·75 4·25
MS1266 Two sheets, each 127 × 102 mm. (a) $7 Donald Duck playing trumpet and Mickey and Minnie Mouse in carriage. P 13½ × 14. (b) $7 Mickey Mouse and friends singing carols on roller skates (*horiz*). P 14 × 13½ *Set of* 2 *sheets* 6·00 6·50

Nos. 1258/65 were printed together, *se-tenant* as a composite design, in sheetlets of eight.

247 Arawak Warriors

248 De Havilland "Comet 4" Airliner

(Des D. Miller. Litho Questa)

1989 (16 May). *500th Anniv of Discovery of America by Colombus* (1992) *(2nd issue). Pre-Columbian Arawak Society. T* **247** *and similar vert designs. Multicoloured. P* 14.

1267 $1.50, Type **247** 70 75
a. Horiz strip of 4. Nos. 1267/70 .. 2·50
1268 $1.50, Whip dancers 70 75
1269 $1.50, Whip dancers and chief with pineapple 70 75
1270 $1.50, Family and camp fire 70 75
1267/70 .. .. *Set of* 4 2·50 2·75
MS1271 71 × 84 mm. $6 Arawak chief .. 2·75 3·00

Nos. 1267/70 were printed together, *se-tenant*, in horizontal strips of 4 throughout the sheet, each strip forming a composite design.

(Des W. Wright. Litho Questa)

1989 (29 May). *50th Anniv of First Jet Flight. T* **248** *and similar horiz designs. Multicoloured. P* 14.

1272 10 c. Type **248** 10 10
1273 30 c. Messerschmitt "Me 262" fighter .. 15 20
1274 40 c. Boeing "707" airliner 20 25
1275 60 c. Canadair "F-86 Sabre" fighter .. 30 35
1276 $1 Lockheed "F-104 Starfighter" fighters 45 50
1277 $2 McDonnell Douglas "DC-10" airliner 95 1·00
1278 $3 Boeing "747" airliner .. .. 1·50 1·60
1279 $4 McDonnell "F-4 Phantom" fighter .. 1·90 2·00
1272/9 .. .. *Set of* 8 5·00 5·50
MS1280 Two sheets, each 114 × 83 mm. (a) $7 Grumman "F-14 Tomcat" fighter. (b) $7 "Concorde" airliner *Set of* 2 *sheets* 6·50 6·75

249 *Festivale*

(Des W. Wright. Litho Questa)

1989 (20 June). *Caribbean Cruise Ships. T* **249** *and similar horiz designs. Multicoloured. P* 14.

1281 25 c. Type **249** 10 15
1282 45 c. *Southward* 20 25
1283 50 c. *Sagafjord* 25 30
1284 60 c. *Daphne* 30 35
1285 75 c. *Cunard Countess* 35 40
1286 90 c. *Song of America* 40 45
1287 $3 *Island Princess* .. .. .. 1·50 1·60
1288 $4 *Galileo* .. .. 1·90 2·00
1281/8 .. .. *Set of* 8 4·50 5·00
MS1289 (a) 113 × 87 mm. $6 *Norway*. (b) 111 × 82 mm. $6 *Oceanic* *Set of* 2 *sheets* 5·50 5·75

250 "Fish swimming by Duck half-submerged in Stream"

(Litho Questa)

1989 (1 July). *Japanese Art. Paintings by Hiroshige. T* **250** *and similar horiz designs. Multicoloured. P* 14 × 13½.

1290 25 c. Type **250** 10 15
1291 45 c. "Crane and Wave" 20 25
1292 50 c. "Sparrows and Morning Glories" 25 30
1293 60 c. "Crested Blackbird and Flowering Cherry" 30 35
1294 $1 "Great Knot sitting among Water Grass" 45 50
1295 $2 "Goose on a Bank of Water" .. 95 1·00
1296 $3 "Black Paradise Flycatcher and Blossoms" .. .. 1·50 1·60
1297 $4 "Sleepy Owl perched on a Pine Branch" .. .. 1·90 2·00
1290/7 .. .. *Set of* 8 5·00 5·50
MS1298 Two sheets, each 102 × 75 mm. (a) $5 "Bullfinch flying near a Clematis Branch". (b) $5 "Titmouse on a Cherry Branch" *Set of* 2 *sheets* 4·75 5·00

Nos. 1290/7 were each printed in sheetlets of 10 containing two horizontal strips of 5 stamps separated by printed labels commemorating Emperor Hirohito.

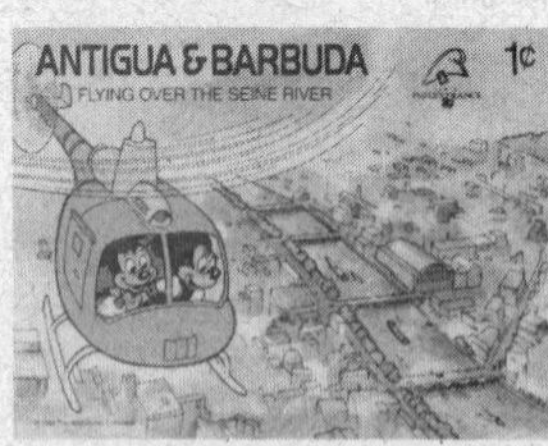

251 Mickey and Minnie Mouse in Helicopter over River Seine

(Des Walt Disney Company. Litho Questa)

1989 (7 July). *"Philexfrance 89" International Stamp Exhibition, Paris. T* **251** *and similar multicoloured designs showing Walt Disney cartoon characters in Paris. P* 14 × 13½.

1299 1 c. Type **251** 10 10
1300 2 c. Goofy and Mickey Mouse passing Arc de Triomphe 10 10
1301 3 c. Mickey Mouse painting picture of Notre Dame 10 10
1302 4 c. Mickey and Minnie Mouse with Pluto leaving Metro station 10 10
1303 5 c. Minnie Mouse as model in fashion show 10 10
1304 10 c. Daisy Duck, Minnie Mouse and Clarabelle as Folies Bergere dancers 10 10
1305 $5 Mickey and Minnie Mouse shopping in street market .. .. .. 2·40 2·50
1306 $6 Mickey and Minnie Mouse, Jose Carioca and Donald Duck at pavement cafe .. .. .. 2·75 3·00
1299/1306 .. .. *Set of* 8 4·75 5·00
MS1307 Two sheets, each 127 × 101 mm. (a) $5 Mickey and Minnie Mouse in hot air balloon. P 14 × 13½. (b) $5 Mickey Mouse at Pompidou Centre cafe (*vert*). P 13½ × 14 *Set of* 2 *sheets* 4·75 5·00

252 Goalkeeper **253** Lilac Fairy Helmet

(Des D. Bruckner. Litho B.D.T.)

1989 (21 Aug). *World Cup Football Championship, Italy* (1990). *T* **252** *and similar multicoloured designs. P* 14.

1308 15 c. Type **252** 10 10
1309 25 c. Goalkeeper moving towards ball .. 10 15
1310 $1 Goalkeeper reaching for ball .. 45 50
1311 $4 Goalkeeper saving goal .. .. 1·90 2·00
1308/11 .. .. *Set of* 4 2·25 2·40
MS1312 Two sheets, each 75 × 105 mm. (a) $5 Three players competing for ball (*horiz*). (b) $5 Ball and players' legs (*horiz*) *Set of* 2 *sheets* 4·75 5·00

(Litho Questa)

1989 (12 Oct). *Fungi. T* **253** *and similar multicoloured designs. P* 14.

1313 10 c. Type **253** 10 10
1314 25 c. Rough Psathyrella (*vert*) 10 15
1315 50 c. Golden Tops 25 30
1316 60 c. Blue Cap (*vert*) 30 35
1317 75 c. Brown Cap (*vert*) 35 40
1318 $1 Green Gill (*vert*) 45 50
1319 $3 Red Pinwheel .. .. .. 1·50 1·60
1320 $4 Red Chanterelle .. .. .. 1·90 2·00
1313/20 .. .. *Set of* 8 4·50 4·75
MS1321 Two sheets, each 88 x 62 mm. (a) $6 Slender Stalk (*vert*). (b) $6 Paddy Straw Mushroom *Set of* 2 *sheets* 5·50 5·75

254 Desmarest's Hutia **255** Goofy and Old Printing Press

(Des J. Barbaris. Litho B.D.T.)

1989 (19 Oct). *Local Fauna. T* **254** *and similar multicoloured designs. P* 14.

1322 25 c. Type **254** 10 15
1323 45 c. Caribbean Monk Seal 20 25
1324 80 c. Mustache Bat (*vert*) 40 45
1325 $4 American Manatee (*vert*) .. 1·90 2·00
1322/5 .. .. *Set of* 4 2·40 2·50
MS1326 113 x 87 mm. $5 West Indies Giant Rice Rat .. .. 2·40 2·50

(Des Walt Disney Co. Litho Questa)

1989 (2 Nov). *"American Philately". T* **255** *and similar multicoloured designs, each showing Walt Disney cartoon characters with stamps and the logo of the American Philatelic Society. P* 13½×14.

1327 1 c. Type **255** 10 10
1328 2 c. Donald Duck cancelling first day cover for Mickey Mouse 10 10
1329 3 c. Donald Duck's nephews reading recruiting poster for Pony Express riders 10 10
1330 4 c. Morty and Ferdie as early radio broadcasters 10 10
1331 5 c. Donald Duck and water buffalo watching television 10 10
1332 10 c. Donald Duck with stamp album .. 10 10
1333 $4 Daisy Duck with computer system .. 1·90 2·00
1334 $6 Donald's nephews with stereo radio, trumpet and guitar .. .. .. 2·75 3·00
1327/34 .. .. *Set of* 8 4·50 4·75
MS1335 Two sheets, each 127×102 mm. (a) $5 Donald's nephews donating stamps to charity. P 13½×14. (b) $5 Minnie Mouse flying mailplane upside down (*horiz*). P 14×13½ Set of 2 *sheets* 4·75 5·00

256 Mickey Mouse and Donald Duck with Locomotive *John Bull*, 1831

(Des Walt Disney Co. Litho Questa)

1989 (17 Nov). *"World Stamp Expo '89" International Stamp Exhibition, Washington (1st issue). T* **256** *and similar multicoloured designs showing Walt Disney cartoon characters and locomotives. P* 14×13½.

1336 25 c. Type **256** 10 15
1337 45 c. Mickey Mouse and friends with *Atlantic*, 1832 .. .. 20 25
1338 50 c. Mickey Mouse and Goofy with *William Crooks*, 1861 .. .. .. 25 30
1339 60 c. Mickey Mouse and Goofy with *Minnetonka*, 1869 .. .. .. 30 35
1340 $1 Chip n'Dale with *Thatcher Perkins*, 1863 .. .. 45 50
1341 $2 Mickey and Minnie Mouse with *Pioneer*, 1848 .. .. 95 1·00
1342 $3 Mickey Mouse and Donald Duck with cog railway locomotive *Peppersass*, 1869 .. .. 1·50 1·60
1343 $4 Mickey Mouse with Huey, Dewey and Louie aboard N.Y. World's Fair *Gimbels Flyer*, 1939 .. .. .. 1·90 2·00
1336/43 .. .. *Set of* 8 5·00 5·50
MS1344 Two sheets, each 127×101 mm. (a) $6 Mickey Mouse and Thomas Jefferson, 1835 (*vert*). P 13½×14. (b) $6 Mickey Mouse and friends at "Golden Spike" ceremony, 1869. P 14×13½ .. .. *Set of* 2 *sheets* 5·50 5·75

257 Smithsonian Institution, Washington **258** Launch of "Apollo 11"

(Des Design Element. Litho Questa)

1989 (17 Nov). *"World Stamp Expo '89" International Stamp Exhibition, Washington (2nd issue). Sheet* 78×61 *mm. P* 14.

MS1345 **257** $4 multicoloured .. .. .. 1·90 2·00

(Des J. Iskowitz. Litho B.D.T.)

1989 (24 Nov). *20th Anniv of First Manned Landing on Moon. T* **258** *and similar multicoloured designs. P* 14.

1346 10 c. Type **258** 10 10
1347 45 c. Aldrin on Moon 20 25
1348 $1 Module *Eagle* over Moon (*horiz*) .. 45 50
1349 $4 Recovery of "Apollo 11" crew after splashdown (*horiz*) .. .. .. 1·90 2·00
1346/9 .. .. *Set of* 4 2·40 2·50
MS1350 107×77 mm. $5 Astronaut Neil Armstrong .. .. 2·40 2·50

BARBUDA

DEPENDENCY OF ANTIGUA

PRICES FOR STAMPS ON COVER TO 1945
Nos. 1/11 *from* × 3

BARBUDA

(1)

1922 (13 July). *Stamps of Leeward Islands optd with T* 1. *All Die II.*

(a) Wmk Mult Script CA

1 **11** ½d. deep green, O .. .. .. 1·00 7·50
2 1d. bright scarlet, O .. .. .. 1·00 6·50
3 **10** 2d. slate-grey, O .. .. .. 1·00 7·00
4 **11** 2½d. bright blue, O .. .. .. 1·00 7·50
5 6d. dull and bright purple, C .. .. 1·50 14·00
6 **10** 2s. purple and blue/*blue*, C .. .. 8·50 32·00
7 3s. bright green and violet, C .. .. 27·00 65·00
8 4s. black and red, C (R.) .. .. 35·00 65·00

(b) Wmk Mult Crown CA

9 **10** 3d. dull purple/*pale yellow*, C .. .. 1·00 8·00
10 **12** 1s. black/*emerald*, C (R.) .. .. 1·50 8·00
11 5s. green and red/*pale yellow*, C .. 65·00 £110
1/11 .. .. *Set of* 11 £130 £275
1/11 Optd "Specimen" .. .. *Set of* 11 £250

The postage stamps of Antigua were used in Barbuda until 1968.
The following issues of Barbuda were also valid for use in Antigua.

2 Map of Barbuda **3** Great Amberjack

(Des R. Granger Barrett. Litho Format)

1968 (19 Nov)–**70**. *Designs as T* **2**/**3**. *P* 14.

12 ½ c. brown, black and pink 10 10
13 1 c. orange, black and flesh 10 10
14 2 c. blackish brown, rose-red and rose .. 10 10
15 3 c. blackish brown, orange-yellow and lemon 10 10
16 4 c. black, bright green and apple-green .. 10 10
17 5 c. blue-green, black and pale blue-green .. 10 10
18 6 c. black, bright purple and pale lilac .. 10 10
19 10 c. black, ultramarine and cobalt 10 10
20 15 c. black, blue-green and turquoise-green .. 15 15
20*a* 20 c. multicoloured (22.7.70) .. .. .. 1·50 2·00
21 25 c. multicoloured (5.2.69) 25 25
22 35 c. multicoloured (5.2.69) 30 25
23 50 c. multicoloured (5.2.69) 40 45
24 75 c. multicoloured (5.2.69) 70 80
25 $1 multicoloured (6.3.69) .. .. .. 85 2·00
26 $2.50, multicoloured (6.3.69) .. .. 1·50 5·00
27 $5 multicoloured (6.3.69) .. .. .. 3·75 7·50
12/27 .. .. *Set of* 17 9·00 17·00

Designs:—½ to 15 c. Type **2**. *Horiz as T* **3**—20 c. Great Barracuda; 35 c. French Angelfish; 50 c. Porkfish; 75 c. Striped Parrotfish; $1, Longspine Squirrelfish; $2.50, Catalufa; $5, Blue Chromis.

10 Sprinting and Aztec Sun-stone **14** "The Ascension" (Orcagna)

(Des R. Granger Barrett. Litho Format)

1968 (20 Dec). *Olympic Games, Mexico. T* **10** *and similar horiz designs. Multicoloured. P* 14.

28 25 c. Type **10** 20 25
29 35 c. High-jumping and Aztec statue 25 25
30 75 c. Yachting and Aztec lion mask 40 45
28/30 .. .. *Set of* 3 75 85
MS31 85 × 76 mm. $1 Football and engraved plate 1·00 3·25

(Des R. Granger Barret. Litho Format)

1969 (24 Mar). *Easter Commemoration. P* 14.

32 **14** 25 c. black and light blue 15 45
33 35 c. black and deep carmine 15 50
34 75 c. black and bluish lilac 15 55
32/4 .. .. *Set of* 3 40 1·40

15 Scout Enrolment Ceremony **18** "Sistine Madonna" (Raphael)

(Des R. Granger Barrett. Litho Format)

1969 (7 Aug). *3rd Caribbean Scout Jamboree. T* **15** *and similar horiz designs. Multicoloured. P* 14.

35 25 c. Type **15** 25 55
36 35 c. Scouts around camp fire 35 65
37 75 c. Sea Scouts rowing boat 45 85
35/7 .. .. *Set of* 3 95 1·90

(Des. R. Granger Barrett. Litho Format)

1969 (20 Oct). *Christmas. P* 14.

38 **18** ½ c. multicoloured 10 10
39 25 c. multicoloured 10 15
40 35 c. multicoloured 10 20
41 75 c. multicoloured 20 35
38/41 .. .. *Set of* 4 30 60

19 William I (1066–87) **(20)**

(Des R. Granger Barrett. Litho Format (Nos. 42/9) or Questa (others))

1970–71. *English Monarchs. T* **19** *and similar vert designs. Multicoloured. P* 14½ × 14.

42 35 c. Type **19** (16.2.70) 30 15
43 35 c. William II (2.3.70) 15 15
44 35 c. Henry I (16.3.70) 15 15
45 35 c. Stephen (1.4.70) 15 15
46 35 c. Henry II (15.4.70) 15 15
47 35 c. Richard I (1.5.70) 15 15
48 35 c. John (15.5.70) 15 15
49 35 c. Henry III (1.6.70) 15 15
50 35 c. Edward I (15.6.70) 15 15
51 35 c. Edward II (1.7.70) 15 15
52 35 c. Edward III (15.7.70) 15 15
53 35 c. Richard II (1.8.70) 15 15
54 35 c. Henry IV (15.8.70) 15 15
55 35 c. Henry V (1.9.70) 15 15
56 35 c. Henry VI (15.9.70) 15 15
57 35 c. Edward IV (1.10.70) 15 15
58 35 c. Edward V (15.10.70) 15 15
59 35 c. Richard III (2.11.70) 15 15
60 35 c. Henry VII (16.11.70) 15 15
61 35 c. Henry VIII (1.12.70) 15 15
62 35 c. Edward VI (15.12.70) 15 15
63 35 c. Lady Jane Grey (2.1.71) 15 15
64 35 c. Mary I (15.1.71) 15 15
65 35 c. Elizabeth I (1.2.71) 15 15
66 35 c. James I (15.2.71) 15 15
67 35 c. Charles I (1.3.71) 15 15
68 35 c. Charles II (15.3.71) 15 15
69 35 c. James II (1.4.71) 15 15
70 35 c. William III (15.4.71) 15 15
71 35 c. Mary II (1.5.71) 15 15
72 35 c. Anne (15.5.71) 15 15
73 35 c. George I (1.6.71) 15 15
74 35 c. George II (15.6.71) 15 15
75 35 c. George III (1.7.71) 15 15
76 35 c. George IV (15.7.71) 15 15
77 35 c. William IV (2.8.71) 15 15
78 35 c. Victoria (16.8.71) 15 15
42/78 .. .. *Set of* 37 5·00 5·00

See also Nos. 710/15.

1970 (26 Feb). *No. 12 surch with T* **20**.

79 **2** 20 c. on ½ c. brown, black and pink .. 10 20
a. Surch inverted .. .. .. 50·00
b. Surch double .. .. .. 50·00

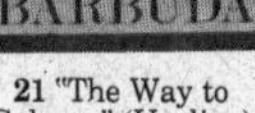

21 "The Way to Calvary" (Ugolino) **22** Oliver is introduced to Fagin (*Oliver Twist*)

(Des R. Granger Barrett. Litho Questa)

1970 (16 Mar). *Easter Paintings. T* **21** *and similar vert designs. Multicoloured P* 14.

80 25 c. Type **21** 15 30
a. Horiz strip of 3. Nos. 80/2 40
81 35 c. "The Deposition from the Cross" (Ugolino) 15 30
82 75 c. Crucifix (The Master of St. Francis) .. 15 35
80/2 .. .. *Set of* 3 40 85

Nos. 80/2 were printed together, *se-tenant*, in horizontal strips of 3 throughout the sheet.

(Des R. Granger Barrett. Litho Questa)

1970 (10 July). *Death Centenary of Charles Dickens. T* **22** *and similar horiz design. Multicoloured. P* 14.

83 20 c. Type **22** 10 15
84 75 c. Dickens and Scene from *The Old Curiosity Shop* 20 40

23 "Madonna of the Meadow" (Bellini) **24** Nurse with Patient in Wheelchair

(Des R. Granger Barrett. Litho Questa)

1970 (15 Oct). *Christmas. T* **23** *and similar horiz designs. Multicoloured. P* 14.

85 20 c. Type **23** 10 25
86 50 c. "Madonna, Child and Angels" (from Wilton diptych) 15 30
87 75 c. "The Nativity" (della Francesca) .. 15 35
85/7 .. .. *Set of* 3 30 80

(Des R. Granger Barrett. Litho Questa)

1970 (21 Dec). *Centenary of British Red Cross. T* **24** *and similar multicoloured designs. P* 14.

88 20 c. Type **24** 15 30
89 35 c. Nurse giving patient magazines (*horiz*) 20 40
90 75 c. Nurse and mother weighing baby (*horiz*) 25 70
88/90 .. .. *Set of* 3 55 1·25

25 Angel with Vases **26** Martello Tower

(Des R. Granger Barrett. Litho Questa)

1971 (7 Apr). *Easter. Details of the "Mond" Crucifixion by Raphael. T* **25** *and similar vert designs. Multicoloured. P* 14.

91 35 c. Type **25** 15 65
a. Horiz strip of 3. Nos. 91/3 40
92 50 c. Christ crucified 15 75
93 75 c. Angel with vase 15 80
91/3 .. .. *Set of* 3 40 2·00

Nos. 91/3 were issued horizontally *se-tenant* within the sheet.

(Des R. Granger Barrett. Litho Questa)

1971 (10 May). *Tourism. T* **26** *and similar horiz designs. Multicoloured. P* 14.

94 20 c. Type **26** 10 25
95 25 c. Sailing boats 10 30
96 50 c. Hotel bungalows 15 35
97 75 c. Government House and Mystery Stone 20 40
94/7 .. .. *Set of* 4 40 1·10

B A R B U D A B A R B U D A

27 "The Granducal Madonna" (Raphael) (28)

(Des R. Granger Barrett. Litho Questa)

1971 (4 Oct). *Christmas. T* **27** *and similar vert designs. Multicoloured. P* 14.

98 ½ c. Type **27** 10 10
99 35 c. "The Ansidei Madonna" (Raphael) .. 10 20
100 50 c. "The Madonna and Child" (Botticelli) .. 15 25
101 75 c. "The Madonna of the Trees" (Bellini) .. 15 30
98/101 .. .. *Set of* 4 35 65

The contract with the agency for the distribution of Barbuda stamps was cancelled by the Antiguan Government on 15 August 1971 but the above issue was duly authorised. Four stamps (20, 35, 50 and 70 c.) were prepared to commemorate the 500th anniversary of the birth of Albrecht Dürer but their issue was not authorised.

Barbuda ceased to have separate stamps issues in 1972 but again had stamps of her own on 14 November 1973 with the following issue.

1973 (14 Nov). *Royal Wedding. Nos.* 370/1 *of Antigua optd with T* **28**.
102 35 c. multicoloured .. .. 10·00 4·25
a. Opt inverted £100
103 $2 multicoloured .. .. 5·00 2·25
a. Opt inverted £120

No. **MS**372 of Antigua also exists with this overprint, but was not placed on sale at post offices. Examples of this sheet are known with "Specimen" overprint (*Price* £120).

BARBUDA (29) — B A R B U D A (30) — B A R B U D A (30*a*) — B A R B U D A (31)

1973 (26 Nov)–**74**. *T* **92** *etc. of Antigua optd with T* **29**.

(*a*) *On Nos.* 270 *etc. W w* **12** (*sideways*)
104 1 c. Columbus and *Nina* 15 15
105 2 c. Sir Thomas Warner's emblem and *Concepcion* 25 25
106 4 c. Sir George Rodney and H.M.S. *Formidable* 30 30
107 5 c. Nelson and H.M.S. *Boreas* 40 40
108 6 c. William IV and H.M.S. *Pegasus*.. .. 40 40
109 10 c. "Blackbeard" and pirate ketch 45 45
110 20 c. Nelson and H.M.S. *Victory* 55 60
111 25 c. R.M.S.P. *Solent* 55 60
112 35 c. George V (when Prince George) and H.M.S. *Canada* 55 70
113 50 c. H.M.S. *Renown* (battle cruiser) .. 55 70
114 75 c. *Federal Maple* (freighter) 55 70
115 $2.50, H.M.S. *London* (destroyer) (18.2.74) 1·50 1·50

(*b*) *On Nos.* 323 *etc. W w* **12** (*upright*). *White paper*
116 ½ c. Type **92** (11.12.73) 15 20
117 3 c. Viscount Hood and H.M.S. *Barfleur* (11.12.73).. .. .. .. 25 25
118 15 c. Captain Collingwood and H.M.S. *Pelican* (11.12.73).. .. .. 35 50
119 $1 *Sol Quest* (yacht) and class emblem (11.12.73) 55 70
120 $2.50, H.M.S. *London* (destroyer) (18.2.74) 9·00 10·00
121 $5 *Pathfinder* (tug) (26.11.73) .. .. 1·75 2·50
104/21 .. .. *Set of* 18 16·00 18·00

1973 (26 Nov). *Commemorative stamps of Antigua optd.*

(*a*) *Nos.* 353, 355 *and* 357/8 *optd with T* **30**
122 ½ c. Private, Zacharia Tiffin's Regt of Foot, 1701 .. .. 10 10
123 20 c. Light Company Officer, 35th Regt of Foot, 1828 .. .. 10 10
a. Optd with T **30***a* 85 90
124 75 c. Sergeant, 49th Regt, 1858 .. .. 30 15
122/4 .. .. *Set of* 3 40 25
MS125 127 × 145 mm .. .. 2·00 3·50

(*b*) *Nos* 360/3 *optd with T* **31**, *in red*
126 20 c. Carnival street scene 10 10
127 35 c. Carnival troupe 10 10
a. Opt inverted .. .. 30·00
128 75 c. Carnival Queen 20 25
126/8 .. .. *Set of* 3 30 40
MS129 134 × 95 mm .. .. 1·25 2·25
a. Albino opt .. ..
b. Opt double £275

Type **30***a* is a typographical overprint, applied locally.

B A R B U D A (32) — BARBUDA (33) — B A R B U D A (34) — B A R B U D A (35)

1973 (11 Dec). *Christmas. Nos.* 364/9 *of Antigua optd with T* **32**.
130 3 c. Type **105** (Sil.) 10 10
a. Opt inverted .. .. 28·00
b. "BABRUDA" (R.4/2) .. .. .. 5·50 5·50
131 5 c. "Adoration of the Magi" (Stomer) (Sil.) 10 10
a. "BABRUDA" (R.4/2) .. .. .. 7·00 7·00
132 20 c. "Granducal Madonna" (Raphael) (Sil.) .. 10 10
a. "BABRUDA" (R.4/2) .. .. .. 9·00 9·00
133 35 c. "Nativity with God the Father and Holy Ghost" (Battista) (R.) 15 15
134 $1 "Madonna and Child" (Murillo) (R.) .. 30 30
a. Opt inverted .. .. 45·00
130/4 .. .. *Set of* 5 60 60
MS135 130 × 128 mm. Nos. 130/4 (Sil.) .. .. 6·00 12·00

1973 (15 Dec). *Honeymoon Visit of Princess Anne and Capt. Phillips. Nos.* 373/5 *of Antigua further optd with T* **33**.
136 35 c. multicoloured 40 20
a. Opt double, one albino .. .. 65·00
b. Optd on Antigua No. 373a .. ..
137 $2 multicoloured .. .. 1·25 60
a. Optd on Antigua No. 374a .. ..
MS138 78 × 100 mm. Nos. 136/7 .. .. .. 5·00 7·50

1974 (18 Feb). *25th Anniv of University of West Indies. Nos.* 376/9 *of Antigua optd with T* **34**.
139 5 c. Coat of arms 10 10
140 20 c. Extra-mural art 10 10
141 35 c. Antigua campus 15 15
a. Opt double .. ..
142 75 c. Antigua Chancellor 15 15
139/42 .. .. *Set of* 4 30 30

1974 (1 May). *Military Uniforms. Nos.* 380/4 *of Antigua optd with T* **35**.
143 ½ c. Officer, 59th Foot, 1797 .. .. .. 10 10
144 10 c. Gunner, Royal Artillery, 1800 .. .. 10 10
a. Horiz pair, left-hand stamp without opt £120
145 20 c. Private, 1st West India Regt, 1830 .. 20 10
a. Horiz pair, left-hand stamp without opt £120
146 35 c. Officer, 92nd Foot, 1843 .. .. .. 25 10
a. Opt inverted .. .. 50·00
147 75 c. Private, 23rd Foot, 1846.. .. .. 45 25
a. Horiz pair, left-hand stamp without opt
143/7 .. .. *Set of* 5 90 45

Nos. 144a, 145a and 147a come from sheets on which the overprint was so misplaced as to miss the first vertical row completely. Other stamps in these sheets show the overprint at left instead of right.

No. **MS**385 of Antigua also exists with this overprint, but was not placed on sale at post offices.

BARBUDA 13 JULY 1922 (**36**) — BARBUDA 15 SEPT. 1874 G.P.U. (**37** "General Postal Union") — BARBUDA (**38**)

1974 (15 July). *Centenary of Universal Postal Union* (*1st issue*). *Nos.* 386/92 *of Antigua optd with T* **36** (*Nos.* 148, 150, 152, 154, 156, 158 *and* 160) *or T* **37** (*others*), *in red.*
148 ½ c. English postman, mailcoach and helicopter 10 10
149 ½ c. English postman, mailcoach and helicopter 10 10
150 1 c. Bellman, mail steamer *Orinoco* and satellite 10 10
151 1 c. Bellman, mail steamer *Orinoco* and satellite 10 10
152 2 c. Train guard, post-bus and hydrofoil .. 15 15
153 2 c. Train guard, post-bus and hydrofoil .. 15 15
154 5 c. Swiss messenger, Wells Fargo coach and "Concorde" 15 15
155 5 c. Swiss messenger, Wells Fargo coach and "Concorde" 15 15
156 20 c. Postillion, Japanese postmen and carrier pigeon 40 70
157 20 c. Postillion, Japanese postmen and carrier pigeon 40 70
158 35 c. Antiguan postman, flying-boat and tracking station .. .. .. 80 1·50
159 35 c. Antiguan postman, flying-boat and tracking station .. .. .. 80 1·50
160 $1 Medieval courier, American express train and Boeing "747" .. .. .. 2·25 4·00
161 $1 Medieval courier, American express train and Boeing "747" .. .. .. 2·25 4·00
148/61 .. .. *Set of* 14 7·00 12·00
MS162 141 × 164 mm. No. **MS**393 of Antigua overprinted with T **38**, in red .. .. .. 3·00 6·00
a. Albino opt .. ..

Nos. 148/9, 150/1, 152/3, 154/5, 156/7, 158/9 and 160/1 were each printed together, *se-tenant*, in horizontal pairs throughout the sheet.

See also Nos. 177/80.

1974 (14 Aug). *Antiguan Steel Bands. Nos.* 394/8 *of Antigua optd with T* **38**.
163 5 c. rose-red, carmine and black 10 10
164 20 c. brown-ochre, chestnut and black .. 10 10
165 35 c. light sage-green, blue-green and black .. 10 10
166 75 c. dull blue, dull ultramarine and black .. 20 20
163/6 .. .. *Set of* 4 35 35
MS167 115×108 mm. Nos. 163/6 .. .. 65 80

39 Footballers

B A R B U D A (**40**)

(Des G. Drummond. Litho Format)

1974 (2 Sept). *World Cup Football Championships* (*1st issue*). *Various horiz designs as T* **39** *each showing footballers in action. P* 14.
168 **39** 35 c. multicoloured 10 10
169 $1.20, multicoloured 25 35
170 $2.50, multicoloured 35 50
168/70 .. .. *Set of* 3 60 75
MS171 70 × 128 mm. Nos. 168/70 .. .. 85 90

1974 (23 Sept). *World Cup Football Championships* (*2nd issue*). *Nos.* 399/403 *of Antigua optd with T* **40**.
172 5 c. multicoloured 10 10
173 35 c. multicoloured 10 10
174 75 c. multicoloured 15 15
175 $1 multicoloured 20 25
172/5 .. .. *Set of* 4 35 45
MS176 135×130 mm. Nos. 172/5 .. .. 60 90

41 Ship Letter of 1833

42 Great Amberjack

(Des G. Drummond. Litho Questa)

1974 (30 Sept). *Centenary of Universal Postal Union* (*2nd issue*). *T* **41** *and similar vert designs. Multicoloured. P* 13½.
177 35 c. Type **41** 15 15
178 $1.20, Stamps and postmark of 1922 .. 50 75
179 $2.50, Mailplane over map of Barbuda .. 75 1·25
177/9 .. .. *Set of* 3 1·25 2·00
MS180 128 × 97 mm. Nos. 177/9 .. .. 2·00 2·75

(Des G. Drummond. Litho Questa)

1974 (15 Oct)–**75**. *Multicoloured designs as T* **42**. *P* 14 × 14½ (½ *c. to* 3 *c.,* 25 *c.*), 14½ × 14 (4 *c. to* 20 *c.,* 35 *c.*), 14 (50 *c. to* $1) *or* 13½ (*others*).
181 ½ c. Oleander, Rose Bay (6.1.75) 10 20
182 1 c. Blue Petrea (6.1.75) 10 20
183 2 c. Poinsettia (6.1.75) 10 20
184 3 c. Cassia tree (6.1.75) 10 20
185 4 c. Type **42** 10 20
186 5 c. Holy Trinity School 15 15
187 6 c. Snorkeling 15 15
188 10 c. Pilgrim Holiness Church 15 15
189 15 c. New Cottage Hospital 15 15
190 20 c. Post Office and Treasury 15 15
191 25 c. Island jetty and boats 30 25
192 35 c. Martello Tower 30 25
193 50 c. Warden's House (6.1.75).. .. .. 30 30
194 75 c. Inter-island aircraft .. .. .. 75 1·00
195 $1 Tortoise (6.1.75) 70 80
196 $2.50, Spiny lobster (6.1.75).. .. .. 1·50 1·75
197 $5 Magnificent Frigate Bird (6.1.75) .. 7·00 5·50
a. Perf 14 × 14½ (24.7.75)* .. .. 11·00 17·00
197*b* $10 Hibiscus (19.9.75) .. .. .. 9·00 9·50
181/97*b* .. .. *Set of* 18 19·00 19·00

*See footnote below Nos. 227/8.

The 50 c. to $1 are larger, 39 × 25 mm; the $2.50 and $5 are 45 × 29 mm; the $10 is 34 × 48 mm and the ½ c. to 3c. 25 c. and $10 are vert designs.

1974 (15 Oct). *Birth Centenary of Sir Winston Churchill* (*1st issue*). *Nos.* 408/12 *of Antigua optd with T* **38** *in red.*
198 5 c. Churchill as schoolboy, and school college building, Harrow 10 10
a. Opt inverted .. .. 60·00
199 35 c. Churchill and St. Paul's Cathedral .. 20 15
200 75 c. Coat of arms and catafalque 35 45
201 $1 Churchill, "reward" notice and South African escape route 55 70
a. Opt inverted .. .. 60·00
198/201 .. .. *Set of* 4 1·10 1·25
MS202 107 × 82 mm. Nos. 198/201 .. .. 8·00 13·00

43 Churchill making Broadcast

BARBUDA (**44**)

(Des G. Drummond. Litho Questa)

1974 (20 Nov). *Birth Centenary of Sir Winston Churchill* (*2nd issue*). *T* **43** *and similar horiz designs. Multicoloured. P* 13½ × 14.
203 5 c. Type **43** 10 10
204 35 c. Churchill and Chartwell 10 10
205 75 c. Churchill painting 20 20
206 $1 Churchill making "V" sign 25 30
203/6 .. .. *Set of* 6 55 60
MS207 146 × 95 mm. Nos. 203/6 .. .. 1·40 2·50

1974 (25 Nov). *Christmas. Nos.* 413/21 *of Antigua optd with T* **33**.
208 ½ c. Bellini 10 10
a. Opt inverted .. .. 45·00
209 1 c. Raphael 10 10
210 2 c. Van der Weyden 10 10
211 3 c. Giorgione 10 10
212 5 c. Mantegna 10 10
213 20 c. Vivarini 10 10
214 35 c. Montagna 15 15
215 75 c. Lorenzo Costa 30 30
208/15 .. .. *Set of* 8 60 60
MS216 139 × 126 mm. Nos. 208/15 .. .. 80 1·40

1975 (17 Mar). *Nelson's Dockyard. Nos.* 427/32 *of Antigua optd with T* **44**.
217 5 c. Carib war canoe, English Harbour, 1300 15 15
218 15 c. Ship of the line, English Harbour, 1770 25 25
219 35 c. H.M.S. *Boreas* at anchor, and Lord Nelson, 1787 .. .. 35 35
220 50 c. Yachts during "Sailing Week", 1974 .. 50 50
221 $1 Yacht Anchorage, Old Dockyard, 1970 .. 80 80
217/21 .. .. *Set of* 5 1·75 1·75
MS222 130 × 134 mm. As Nos. 217/21, but in larger format; 43 × 28 mm .. .. 2·25 2·75

45 Battle of the Saints, 1782

(Des G. Vasarhelyi. Litho Format)

1975 (30 May). *Sea Battles. T* **45** *and similar horiz designs showing scenes from the Battle of the Saints,* 1782. *Multicoloured. P* 13½.

223	35 c. Type **45**	2·00	85
224	50 c. H.M.S. *Ramillies*	2·00	1·00
225	75 c. Ships firing broadsides	2·25	1·25
226	95 c. Sailors fleeing burning ship	2·50	1·50
223/6	.. .. *Set of* 4	8·00	4·25

(**46**)

1975 (24 July). *"Apollo-Soyuz" Space Project. No.* 197a *optd with T* **46** *and similar ("Soyuz") opt.*

227	$5 Magnificent Frigate Bird ("Apollo") ..	6·50	9·00
	a. *Se-tenant* strip of 3. Nos. 227/8 and 197a	42·00	
228	$5 Magnificent Frigate Bird ("Soyuz") ..	6·50	9·00

Nos. 227/8 were issued together *se-tenant* in sheets of 25 (5 × 5), with the "Apollo" opts in the first and third vertical rows and the "Soyuz" opts in the second and fourth vertical rows, the fifth vertical row comprising five unoverprinted stamps (No. 197a).

47 Officer, 65th Foot, 1763

30TH ANNIVERSARY
UNITED NATIONS
1945 — 1975

(**48**)

(Des G. Drummond. Litho Questa)

1975 (17 Sept). *Military Uniforms. T* **47** *and similar vert designs. Multicoloured. P* 13½.

229	35 c. Type **47**	75	75
230	50 c. Grenadier, 27th Foot, 1701–10	90	90
231	75 c. Officer, 21st Foot, 1793–6	1·00	1·00
232	95 c. Officer, Royal Regt of Artillery, 1800 ..	1·25	1·25
229/32	.. .. *Set of* 4	3·50	3·50

1975 (24 Oct). *30th Anniv of United Nations. Nos.* 203/6 *optd with T* **48**.

233	5 c. Churchill making broadcast	10	10
234	35 c. Churchill and Chartwell	10	15
235	75 c. Churchill painting	15	20
236	$1 Churchill making "V" sign	20	30
233/6	.. .. *Set of* 4	40	60

BARBUDA (**49**)　　BARBUDA (**50**)

1975 (17 Nov). *Christmas. Nos.* 457/65 *of Antigua optd with T* **49**.

237	½ c. Correggio	10	10
238	1 c. El Greco	10	10
239	2 c. Dürer	10	10
240	3 c. Antonello	10	10
241	5 c. Bellini	10	10
242	10 c. Dürer	10	10
243	25 c. Bellini	15	20
244	$2 Dürer	60	1·00
237/44	.. .. *Set of* 8	95	1·50
MS245	138 × 119 mm. Nos. 241/4	1·50	2·25

1975 (15 Dec). *World Cup Cricket Winners. Nos.* 466/8 *of Antigua optd with T* **50**.

246	5 c. Vivian Richards	75	75
247	35 c. Andy Roberts	1·50	1·50
248	$2 West Indies team	3·25	3·25
246/8	.. .. *Set of* 3	5·00	5·00

51 "Surrender of Cornwallis at Yorktown" (Trumbull)

(Des G. Vasarhelyi. Litho Format)

1976 (8 Mar). *Bicentenary of American Revolution. T* **51** *and similar horiz designs. Multicoloured. P* 13½ × 13.

249	15 c. }	15	15
250	15 c. } Type **51**	15	15
251	15 c. }	15	15
252	35 c. }	30	30
253	35 c. } "The Battle of Princeton"	30	30
254	35 c. }	30	30
255	$1 }	60	50
256	$1 } "Surrender of General Burgoyne at Saratoga" (W. Mercer)	60	50
257	$1 }	60	50
258	$2 }	90	80
259	$2 } "The Declaration of Independence" (Trumbull)	90	80
260	$2 }	90	80
249/60	.. .. *Set of* 12	5·00	4·50
MS261	140 × 70 mm. Nos. 249/54 and 255/60 (*two sheets*)	5·00	9·00

The three designs of each value were printed horizontally *se-tenant* within the sheet to form the composite designs listed. Type **51** shows the left-hand stamp of the 15 c. design.

52 Bananaquits

(Des G. Drummond. Litho Format)

1976 (30 June). *Birds. T* **52** *and similar horiz designs. Multicoloured. P* 13½.

262	35 c. Type **52**	2·25	70
263	50 c. Blue-hooded Euphonia	2·50	80
264	75 c. Royal Tern	2·75	90
265	95 c. Killdeer	3·00	1·25
266	$1.25, Common Cowbird	4·00	1·50
267	$2 Purple Gallinule	5·50	2·25
262/7	.. .. *Set of* 6	18·00	6·50

1976 (12 Aug). *Royal Visit to the U.S.A. As Nos.* 249/60 *but redrawn and inscr at top* "H.M. QUEEN ELIZABETH ROYAL VISIT 6TH JULY 1976 H.R.H. DUKE OF EDINBURGH".

268	15 c. }	15	15
269	15 c. } As Type **51**	15	15
270	15 c. }	15	15
271	35 c. }	30	30
272	35 c. } As Nos. 252/4	30	30
273	35 c. }	30	30
274	$1 }	60	60
275	$1 } As Nos. 255/7	60	60
276	$1 }	60	60
277	$2 }	90	90
278	$2 } As Nos. 258/60	90	90
279	$2 }	90	90
268/79	.. .. *Set of* 12	5·00	5·00
MS280	143 × 81 mm. Nos. 268/73 and 274/9 (*two sheets*)	5·50	8·50

The three designs of each value were printed horizontally *se-tenant*, imperf between.

BARBUDA (**53**)　　**BARBUDA** (**54**)

1976 (2 Dec). *Christmas. Nos.* 514/18 *of Antigua optd with T* **53**.

281	8 c. The Annunciation	10	10
282	10 c. The Holy Family	10	10
283	15 c. The Magi	10	10
284	50 c. The Shepherds	15	15
285	$1 Epiphany scene	25	30
281/5	.. .. *Set of* 5	45	55

1976 (28 Dec). *Olympic Games, Montreal. Nos.* 495/502 *of Antigua optd with T* **54**.

286	½ c. High-jump	10	10
287	1 c. Boxing	10	10
288	2 c. Pole-vault	10	10
289	15 c. Swimming	10	10
290	30 c. Running	10	10
291	$1 Cycling	20	20
292	$2 Shot put	35	35
286/92	.. .. *Set of* 7	60	60
MS293	88 × 138 mm. Nos. 289/92	1·50	2·40

55 Post Office Tower, Telephones and Alexander Graham Bell

(Des G. Vasarhelyi. Litho Format)

1977 (31 Jan). *Telephone Centenary* (1976). *T* **55** *and similar horiz designs. Multicoloured. P* 13½.

294	75 c. Type **55**	30	35
295	$1.25, Dish aerial and television	45	55
296	$2 Globe and satellites	65	75
294/6	.. .. *Set of* 3	1·25	1·50
MS297	96 × 144 mm. Nos. 294/6. P 15	1·40	3·00

56 St. Margaret's Church, Westminster

1977 (7 Feb). *Silver Jubilee* (*1st issue*). *T* **56** *and similar horiz designs. Multicoloured. Litho. P* 13½ × 13.

298	75 c. Type **56**	15	15
299	75 c. Entrance, Westminster Abbey	15	15
300	75 c. Westminster Abbey	15	15
301	$1.25, Household Cavalry	25	25
302	$1.25, Coronation Coach	25	25
303	$1.25, Team of Horses	25	25
298/303	.. .. *Set of* 6	1·10	1·10
MS304	148 × 83 mm. Nos. 298/303. P 15	1·10	1·75

Nos. 298/300 and 301/3 were printed horizontally *se-tenant*, forming composite designs.

See also Nos. 323/30 and 375/8.

1977 (4 Apr). *Nos.* 469A/86A *of Antigua optd with T* **54**.

305	½ c. Antillean Crested Hummingbird ..	20	20
306	1 c. Imperial Amazon	30	20
307	2 c. Zenaida Dove	30	20
308	3 c. Loggerhead Kingbird	30	20
309	4 c. Red-necked Pigeon	30	20
310	5 c. Rufous-throated Solitaire	30	20
311	6 c. Orchid Tree	25	20
312	10 c. Bougainvillea	25	20
313	15 c. Geiger Tree	25	25
314	20 c. Flamboyant	30	25
315	25 c. Hibiscus	30	25
316	35 c. Flame of the Wood	35	30
317	50 c. Cannon at Fort James	40	40
318	75 c. Premier's Office	40	40
319	$1 Potworks Dam	50	60
320	$2.50, Irrigation scheme	1·25	1·60
321	$5 Government House	2·75	3·25
322	$10 Coolidge Airport	5·50	7·50
305/22	.. .. *Set of* 18	13·00	15·00

BARBUDA (**57**)　　B A R B U D A (**58**)　　**BARBUDA** (**59**)

1977 (4 Apr–20 Dec). *Silver Jubilee* (*2nd issue*).

(*a*) *Sheet stamps. Nos.* 526/31 *of Antigua optd with T* **57**

323	10 c. Royal Family	20	25
324	30 c. Royal Visit, 1966	40	45
325	50 c. Queen enthroned	60	70
326	90 c. Queen after Coronation	1·10	1·40
327	$2.50, Queen and Prince Charles	3·00	3·75
323/7	.. .. *Set of* 5	4·75	6·00
MS328	116×78 mm. $5 Queen Elizabeth and Prince Philip	3·25	4·00
	a. Error. Imperf	£600	
	b. Opt albino	25·00	
	c. Opt double		

(*b*) *Booklet stamps. Nos.* 532/3 *of Antigua optd with T* **58** *in silver* (50 *c.*) *or T* **59** *in gold* ($5) (20 Dec)

329	50 c. Queen after Coronation	1·00	1·50
	a. Booklet pane of 6	6·00	
330	$5 The Queen and Prince Philip	14·00	16·00
	a. Booklet pane of 1	14·00	

BARBUDA (**60**)

61 Royal Yacht *Britannia*

1977 (13 June). *Caribbean Scout Jamboree, Jamaica. Nos.* 534/41 *of Antigua optd with T* **60**.

331	½ c. Making camp	10	10
332	1 c. Hiking	10	10
333	2 c. Rock-climbing	10	10
334	10 c. Cutting logs	10	10
335	30 c. Map and sign reading	40	40
336	50 c. First aid	55	55
337	$2 Rafting	2·00	2·00
331/37	.. .. *Set of* 7	2·75	2·75
MS338	127 × 114 mm. Nos. 335/7	3·25	4·00

1977 (12 Aug). *21st Anniv of Carnival. Nos.* 542/7 *of Antigua optd with T* **60**.

339	10 c. Carnival costume	10	10
340	30 c. Carnival Queen	10	10
341	50 c. Butterfly costume	15	20
342	90 c. Queen of the band	20	30
343	$1 Calypso King and Queen	25	40
339/43	.. .. *Set of* 5	65	90
MS344	140 × 120 mm. Nos. 339/43	1·00	1·75

(Des G. Drummond. Litho Format)

1977 (27 Oct). *Royal Visit* (*1st issue*). *T* **61** *and similar horiz designs. Multicoloured. P* 14½.

345	50 c. Type **61**	25	20
346	$1.50, Jubilee emblem	40	35
347	$2.50, Union Jack and flag of Antigua ..	60	50
345/7	.. .. *Set of* 3	1·10	95
MS348	77 × 124 mm. Nos. 345/7	1·60	2·75

BARBUDA (62) **BARBUDA** (63) 64 Zeppelin "LZ1"

1977 (28 Nov–20 Dec). *Royal Visit* (2*nd issue*). Nos. 548/**MS**553 *of Antigua optd*. A. *With T* **57**. *P* 14 (28 Nov). B. *With T* **62**. *P* 11½ × 12 (20 Dec).

		A.		B.	
349	10 c. Royal Family	25	10	15	10
	a. Blue opt	†		35	35
350	30 c. Royal Visit, 1966	45	20	30	15
	a. Blue opt	†		90	95
351	50 c. Queen enthroned	65	35	40	20
	a. Blue opt	†		2·75	1·90
352	90 c. Queen after Coronation	1·25	60	70	30
	a. Blue opt	†		5·00	3·50
353	$2.50, Queen and Prince Charles	3·25	2·25	1·75	80
	a. Blue opt	†		11·00	9·50
349/53	*Set of* 5	5·25	3·25	3·00	1·40
MS354	116 × 78 mm. $5 Queen and Prince Philip	4·75	5·50	†	

Nos. 349B/53B were each printed in small sheets of 6 including one *se-tenant* stamp-size label.

1977 (28 Nov). *Christmas. Nos.* 554/61 *of Antigua optd with T* **63**. *"Virgin and Child" paintings by the artists given.*

355	½ c. Tura	10	10
356	1 c. Crivelli	10	10
357	2 c. Lotto	10	10
358	8 c. Pontormo	10	10
359	10 c. Tura	10	10
360	25 c. Lotto	15	10
361	$2 Crivelli	45	45
355/61	*Set of* 7	70	65
MS362	144 × 118 mm. Nos. 358/61	1·00	1·75

(Des I. Oliver. Litho Format)

1977 (29 Dec). *Special Events*, 1977. *T* **64** *and similar horiz designs. Multicoloured. P* 14.

363	75 c. Type **64**	40	35
	a. Nos 363/6 in *se-tenant* block	1·60	
364	75 c. German battleship and naval airship "L 31"	40	35
365	75 c. *Graf Zeppelin* in hangar	40	35
366	75 c. Military airship gondola	40	35
367	95 c. "Sputnik 1"	60	35
	a. Nos. 367/70 in *se-tenant* block	2·25	
368	95 c. "Vostok"	60	35
369	95 c. "Voskhod"	60	35
370	95 c. Space walk	60	35
371	$1.25, Fuelling for flight	75	45
	a. Nos. 371/4 in *se-tenant* block	3·00	
372	$1.25, Leaving New York	75	45
373	$1.25, *Spirit of St. Louis*	75	45
374	$1.25, Welcome in England	75	45
375	$2 Lion of England	1·75	70
	a. Nos. 375/8 in *se-tenant* block	7·00	
376	$2 Unicorn of Scotland	1·75	70
377	$2 Yale of Beaufort	1·75	70
378	$2 Falcon of Plantagenets	1·75	70
379	$5 "Daniel in the Lion's Den" (Rubens)	2·75	2·00
380	$5	2·75	2·00
381	$5	2·75	2·00
382	$5	2·75	2·00
	a. Nos. 379/82 in *se-tenant* block	11·00	
363/82	*Set of* 20	22·00	14·00
MS383	132 × 156 mm. Nos. 363/82	22·00	30·00

Events:—75 c. 75th Anniv of Navigable Airships; 95 c. 20th Anniv of U.S.S.R. Space Programme; $1.25, 50th Anniv of Lindbergh's Transatlantic Flight; $2 Silver Jubilee of Queen Elizabeth II; $5 400th Birth Anniv of Rubens.

Nos. 363/66, 367/70, 371/74, 375/78 and 379/82 were printed in *se-tenant* blocks of four within the sheet.

BARBUDA (65) 66 "Pieta" (sculpture) (detail)

1978 (15 Feb). *Tenth Anniv of Statehood. Nos.* 562/7 *of Antigua optd with T* **65**.

384	10 c. Pineapple	10	10
385	15 c. State flag	10	10
386	50 c. Police band	20	15
387	90 c. Premier V. C. Bird	20	20
388	$2 State Coat of Arms	40	40
384/8	*Set of* 5	80	75
MS389	126 × 99 mm. Nos. 385/88. P 14	1·60	2·00

(Des G. Vasarhelyi. Litho Format)

1978 (23 Mar). *Easter. Works by Michelangelo. T* **66** *and similar horiz designs. Multicoloured. P* 13½ × 14.

390	75 c. Type **66**	15	15
391	95 c. "The Holy Family" (painting)	20	20
392	$1.25, "Libyan Sibyl" from Sistine Chapel, Rome	25	25
393	$2 "The Flood" from Sistine Chapel	35	35
390/3	*Set of* 4	85	85
MS394	117 × 85 mm. Nos. 390/3	1·60	2·00

BARBUDA (67) 68 St. Edward's Crown

1978 (28 Mar). *75th Anniv of Powered Flight. Nos.* 568/75 *of Antigua optd with T* **67**.

395	½ c. *Glider III*, 1902	10	10
396	1 c. *Flyer I*, 1903	10	10
397	2 c. Launch system and engine	10	10
398	10 c. Orville Wright	10	10
399	50 c. *Flyer III*, 1905	25	15
400	90 c. Wilbur Wright	35	15
401	$2 Wright "Model B", 1910	60	45
395/401	*Set of* 7	1·25	75
MS402	90 × 75 mm. $2.50, *Flyer I* on launch system	1·25	1·75

1978 (22 May). *Sailing Week. Nos.* 576/80 *of Antigua optd with T* **67**.

403	10 c. Sunfish regatta	15	10
404	50 c. Fishing and work boat race	35	25
405	90 c. Curtain Bluff race	40	35
406	$2 Power boat rally	75	75
403/6	*Set of* 4	1·50	1·25
MS407	110 × 77 mm. $2.50, Guadeloupe–Antigua race	1·25	1·60
	a. Albino opt	†	—

(Des J. Cooter. Litho)

1978 (2 June). *25th Anniv of Coronation* (1*st issue*). *T* **68** *and similar vert designs. Multicoloured. P* 15.

408	75 c. Type **68**	15	15
409	75 c. Imperial State Crown	15	15
410	$1.50, Queen Mary's Crown	25	25
411	$1.50, Queen Mother's Crown	25	25
412	$2.50, Queen Consort's Crown	45	45
413	$2.50, Queen Victoria's Crown	45	45
408/413	*Set of* 6	1·50	1·50
MS414	123 × 117 mm. Nos. 408/13. P 14½	2·00	2·75

The two designs for each value were issued as two *se-tenant* pairs, together with 2 labels, in small sheets of 6.

1978 (2 June–12 Oct). *25th Anniv of Coronation* (2*nd issue*).

(*a*) *Sheet stamps. Nos.* 581/6 *of Antigua optd with T* **67**. *P* 14 (2.6)

415	10 c. Queen Elizabeth and Prince Philip	10	10
416	30 c. Crowning	10	10
417	50 c. Coronation procession	15	15
418	90 c. Queen seated in St. Edward's Chair	20	20
	a. Opt triple	85·00	
419	$2.50, Queen wearing Imperial State Crown	50	60
415/19	*Set of* 5	85	1·00
MS420	114 × 103 mm. $5 Queen and Prince Philip (17.7)	1·50	2·00
	a. Albino opt	£250	

(*b*) *Booklet stamps. Horiz designs as Nos.* 587/9 *of Antigua but additionally inscr* "BARBUDA". *Multicoloured. Roul* 5 × *imperf**. *Self-adhesive* (12.10)

421	25 c. Glass Coach	1·25	1·75
	a. Booklet pane. Nos. 421/2 × 3	6·50	
422	50 c. Irish State Coach	1·25	1·75
423	$5 Coronation Coach	3·50	4·00
	a. Booklet pane of 1	3·50	
421/3	*Set of* 3	5·50	6·75

Nos. 415/19 also exist perf 12 (*Price for set of* 5 £1 *mint or used*) from additional sheetlets of three stamps and one label, issued 12 October 1978. These stamps have different background colours from Nos. 415/19.

*The 25 and 50 c. values were separated by various combinations of rotary knife (giving a straight edge) and roulette. The $5 value exists only with straight edges.

1978 (12 Sept). *World Cup Football Championship, Argentina. Nos.* 590/3 *of Antigua optd with T* **67**.

424	10 c. Player running with ball	10	10
425	15 c. Players in front of goal	10	10
426	$3 Referee and player	1·00	1·25
424/6	*Set of* 3	1·00	1·25
MS427	126 × 88 mm. 25 c. Player crouching with ball; 30 c. Players heading ball; 50 c. Players running with ball; $2 Goalkeeper diving	80	90

BARBUDA (69) 70 Blackbar Soldierfish

1978 (20 Nov). *Flowers. Nos.* 594/8 *of Antigua optd with T* **69**.

428	25 c. Petrea	25	25
429	50 c. Sunflower	50	50
430	90 c. Frangipani	70	70
431	$2 Passion Flower	1·25	1·25
428/31	*Set of* 4	2·40	2·40
MS432	118 × 85 mm. $2.50, Hibiscus	1·50	2·25

1978 (20 Nov). *Christmas. Paintings. Nos.* 599/602 *optd with T* **69** *in silver.*

433	8 c. "St. Ildefonso receiving the Chasuble from the Virgin"	10	10
434	25 c. "The Flight of St. Barbara"	15	10
435	$2 "Madonna and Child, with St. Joseph, John the Baptist and Donor"	60	85
433/5	*Set of* 3	75	90
MS436	170 × 113 mm. $4 "The Annunciation"	1·75	2·25

(Litho Format)

1978 (20 Nov). *Flora and Fauna. T* **70** *and similar horiz designs. Multicoloured. P* 14½.

437	25 c. Type **70**	1·00	75
438	50 c. Painted Lady butterfly	1·75	1·40
439	75 c. Dwarf Poinciana	2·25	1·75
440	95 c. Zebra butterfly	3·00	2·25
441	$1.25, Bougainvillea	3·00	2·50
437/41	*Set of* 5	10·00	8·00

71 Footballers and World Cup

72 Sir Rowland Hill

(Des J. Cooter. Litho Format)

1978 (29 Dec). *Anniversaries and Events. T* **71** *and similar multicoloured designs. P* 14.

442	75 c. Type **71**	45	45
443	95 c. Wright brothers and *Flyer I* (*horiz*)	55	55
444	$1.25, *Double Eagle II* and map of Atlantic (*horiz*)	70	70
445	$2 Prince Philip paying homage to the newly crowned Queen	2·25	2·25
442/5	*Set of* 4	3·50	3·50
MS446	122 × 90 mm. Nos. 442/5. Imperf	5·50	5·50

Events:—75 c. Argentina—Winners of World Cup Football Championship; 95 c. 75th anniversary of powered flight; $1.25 1st Atlantic crossing by balloon; $2 25th anniversary of Coronation.

(Des J. Cooter. Litho Format)

1979 (4 Apr). *Death Centenary of Sir Rowland Hill* (1*st issue*). *T* **72** *and similar multicoloured designs. P* 14.

447	75 c. Type **72**	45	50
448	95 c. Mail coach, 1840 (*horiz*)	55	60
449	$1.25, London's first pillar box, 1855 (*horiz*)	60	70
450	$2 Mail leaving St. Martin's Le Grand Post Office, London	90	95
447/50	*Set of* 4	2·25	2·50
MS451	129 × 104 mm. Nos. 447/50 Imperf	2·25	2·75

Nos. 447/50 were each printed in small sheets of 4 including one *se-tenant* stamp-size label.

BARBUDA (73) 74 Passengers alighting from British Airways Boeing "747"

1979 (4 Apr). *Death Centenary of Sir Rowland Hill* (2*nd issue*). *Nos.* 603/7 *of Antigua optd with T* **73** *in blue. P* 14.

452	25 c. Antigua 1863 1d. stamp	15	15
453	50 c. Penny Black stamp	20	20
454	$1 Stage-coach and woman posting letter, *circa* 1840	35	30
455	$2 Modern mail transport	80	60
452/5	*Set of* 4	1·40	1·10
MS456	108 × 82 mm. $2.50, Sir Rowland Hill	75	80

Nos. 452/5 also exist perf 12 (*Price for set of* 4 £1.75 *mint or used*) from additional sheetlets of four stamps and one label, issued 28 December 1979.

1979 (12 Apr). *Easter. Works by Dürer. Nos.* 608/11 *of Antigua optd with T* **67**.

457	10 c. multicoloured	10	10
458	50 c. multicoloured	20	20
459	$4 black, magenta and greenish yellow	90	1·10
457/9	*Set of* 3	1·00	1·25
MS460	114 × 99 mm. $2.50, multicoloured	55	75

(Litho Format)

1979 (24 May). *30th Anniv of International Civil Aviation Organisation. T* **74** *and similar horiz designs. Multicoloured. P* 13½ × 14.

461	75 c. Type **74**	45	60
	a. Block of 4. Nos. 461/3 plus label	1·40	
462	95 c. Air traffic control	50	70
463	$1.25, Ground crew-man directing Boeing "707" on runway	60	85
461/3	*Set of* 3	1·40	2·00

Nos. 461/3 were either printed in separate sheets, or together with a stamp-size label, *se-tenant*, in blocks of 4, each block divided in the sheet by margins.

1979 (24 May). *International Year of the Child* (1*st issue*). *Nos.* 612/16 *of Antigua optd with T* **67**.

464	25 c. Yacht	20	15
465	50 c. Rocket	35	25
466	90 c. Car	50	35
467	$2 Train	1·25	60
464/7	*Set of* 4	2·10	1·25
MS468	80 × 112 mm. $5 Aeroplane	2·00	2·00

ALTERED CATALOGUE NUMBERS

Any Catalogue numbers altered from the last edition are shown as a list in the introductory pages.

BARBUDA (75) **BARBUDA** (76)

979 (1 Aug). *Fishes. Nos.* 617/21 *of Antigua optd with T* **75**.
69 30 c. Yellowjack 20 15
70 50 c. Bluefin Tuna 30 20
71 90 c. Sailfish 40 30
72 $3 Wahoo .. .. 1·10 1·10
69/72 .. .. *Set of* 4 1·75 1·60
MS473 122 × 75 mm. $2.50, Barracuda (overprinted with T **73**) .. .. 1·00 1·25
a. Albino opt .. .. ..

979 (1 Aug). *Death Bicentenary of Captain Cook. Nos.* 622/6 *of Antigua optd with T* **76**.
74 25 c. Cook's Birthplace, Marton 30 30
75 50 c. H.M.S. *Endeavour* 50 45
76 90 c. Marine chronometer 65 60
77 $3 Landing at Botany Bay .. .. .. 1·75 1·50
74/7 .. .. *Set of* 4 2·75 2·50
MS478 110 × 85 mm. $2.50, H.M.S. *Resolution* (overprinted with T **82**) .. .. 1·25 1·50
a. Albino opt .. ..

77 "Virgin with the Pear" **BARBUDA** (**78**)

(Des G. Vasarhelyi. Litho Format)

979 (24 Sept). *International Year of the Child (2nd issue). Details of Paintings by Dürer, showing the infant Jesus. T* **77** *and similar vert designs. Multicoloured. P* 14 × 13½.
79 25 c. Type **77** 15 15
80 50 c. "Virgin with the Pink" 25 25
81 75 c. "Virgin with the Pear" (*different*) .. 30 30
82 $1.25, "Nativity" 40 40
79/82 .. .. *Set of* 4 1·00 1·00
MS483 86 × 118 mm. Nos. 479/82 .. .. .. 1·25 1·75

979 (21 Nov). *Christmas. Nos.* 627/31 *of Antigua optd with T* **78**.
84 8 c. The Holy Family 10 10
85 25 c. Virgin and Child on Ass 15 10
86 50 c. Shepherd and star 25 15
87 $4 Wise Men with gifts .. .. .. 1·10 80
84/7 .. .. *Set of* 4 1·40 1·00
MS488 113 × 94 mm. $3 Angel with trumpet .. 80 1·10

980 (18 Mar). *Olympic Games, Moscow. Nos.* 632/6 *of Antigua optd with T* **67**.
89 10 c. Javelin throwing 10 10
90 25 c. Running 10 10
91 $1 Pole vaulting 30 20
92 $2 Hurdling 55 40
89/92 .. .. *Set of* 4 90 65
MS493 127 × 96 mm. $3 Boxing .. .. .. 70 1·10

LONDON 1980 (**79**)

80 "Apollo 11" Crew Badge

1980 (6 May). *"London 1980" International Stamp Exhibition. As Nos.* 452/5 *optd with T* **79** *in blue. P* 12.
494 25 c. Antigua 1863 1d. stamp 25 15
495 50 c. Penny Black stamp 35 30
496 $1 Mail coach and woman posting letter, *circa* 1840 .. .. 70 55
497 $2 Modern mail transport .. .. .. 2·00 1·10
494/7 .. .. *Set of* 4 3·00 1·90

(Litho Format)

1980 (21 May). *10th Anniv of Moon Landing. T* **80** *and similar horiz designs. Multicoloured. P* 13½ × 14.
498 75 c. Type **80** 25 25
499 95 c. Plaque left on Moon 30 30
500 $1.25, Rejoining mother ship 40 40
501 $2 Lunar Module 65 65
498/501 .. .. *Set of* 4 1·40 1·40
MS502 118 × 84 mm. Nos. 498/501 .. .. .. 1·75 2·50

81 American Wigeon

(Litho Questa)

1980 (16 June). *Birds. Multicoloured designs as T* **81**. *P* 14.
503 1 c. Type **81** 20 15
504 2 c. Snowy Plover 25 15
505 4 c. Rose-breasted Grosbeak 30 20
506 6 c. Mangrove Cuckoo 30 20
507 10 c. Adelaide's Warbler 30 20
508 15 c. Scaly-breasted Thrasher 35 25
509 20 c. Yellow-crowned Night Heron 35 25
510 25 c. Bridled Quail Dove 35 25
511 35 c. Carib Grackle 40 30
512 50 c. Pintail 50 35
513 75 c. Black-whiskered Vireo 60 45
514 $1 Blue-winged Teal 75 70
515 $1.50, Green-throated Carib (*vert*) .. .. 1·00 80
516 $2 Red-necked Pigeon (*vert*) .. .. 1·75 1·25
517 $2.50, Wied's Crested Flycatcher (*vert*) .. 2·00 1·50
518 $5 Yellow-bellied Sapsucker (*vert*) .. .. 2·50 2·50
519 $7.50, Caribbean Elaenia (*vert*) .. .. 4·00 4·00
520 $10 Great Egret (*vert*) .. .. .. 5·00 5·00
503/20 .. .. *Set of* 18 19·00 17·00

1980 (29 July). *Famous Works of Art. Nos.* 651/7 *of Antigua optd with T* **67**.
521 10 c. "David" (statue, Donatello) 10 10
522 30 c. "The Birth of Venus" (painting, Sandro Botticelli) 15 15
523 50 c. "Reclining Couple" (sarcophagus), Cerveteri 20 20
524 90 c. "The Garden of Earthly Delights" (painting, Hieronymus Bosch) 25 25
525 $1 "Portinari Altarpiece" (painting, Hugo van der Goes) 25 25
526 $4 "Eleanora of Toledo and her Son Giovanni de' Medici" (painting, Agnolo Bronzino) 80 80
521/6 .. .. *Set of* 6 1·50 1·50
MS527 99 × 124 mm. $5 "The Holy Family" (painting, Rembrandt) .. .. 1·50 1·75

1980 (8 Sept). *75th Anniv of Rotary International. Nos.* 658/62 *of Antigua optd with T* **67**.
528 30 c. Rotary anniversary emblem and headquarters, U.S.A. 15 15
529 50 c. Rotary anniversary emblem and Antigua Rotary Club banner 20 20
530 90 c. Map of Antigua and Rotary emblem .. 25 25
531 $3 Paul P. Harris (founder) and Rotary emblem 65 65
528/31 .. .. *Set of* 4 1·10 1·10
MS532 102 × 77 mm. $5 Antigua flags and Rotary emblems .. .. 1·50 2·25

BARBUDA (**82**) **BARBUDA** (**83**)

1980 (6 Oct). *80th Birthday of Queen Elizabeth the Queen Mother. Nos.* 663/5 *of Antigua optd with T* **82**.
533 10 c. multicoloured 30 15
a. Opt inverted .. .. 38·00
b. Opt double .. .. 40·00
534 $2.50, multicoloured .. .. 3·00 1·50
MS535 68 × 88 mm. $3 multicoloured .. .. 1·75 1·75

1980 (8 Dec). *Birds. Nos.* 666/70 *of Antigua optd with T* **83**.
536 10 c. Ringed Kingfisher 40 20
537 30 c. Plain Pigeon 65 30
538 $1 Green-throated Carib .. .. .. 1·25 80
539 $2 Black-necked Stilt .. .. .. 1·90 1·50
536/9 .. .. *Set of* 4 3·75 2·50
MS540 73 × 73 mm. $2.50, Roseate Tern .. .. 1·60 1·75

1981 (26 Jan). *Sugar Cane Railway Locomotives. Nos.* 681/5 *of Antigua optd with T* **67**.
541 25 c. Diesel Locomotive No. 15 .. .. 50 20
542 50 c. Narrow-gauge steam locomotive 65 30
543 90 c. Diesel locomotives Nos. 1 and 10 .. 80 40
544 $3 Steam locomotive hauling sugar cane .. 2·00 1·40
541/4 .. .. *Set of* 4 3·50 2·10
MS545 82 × 111 mm. $2.50, Antigua sugar factory, railway yard and sheds .. .. 1·50 1·75

84 Florence Nightingale **85** Goofy in Motor-boat

(Litho Format)

1981 (9 Mar). *Famous Women. T* **84** *and similar vert designs. P* 14 × 13½.
546 50 c. multicoloured 30 30
547 90 c. multicoloured 55 55
548 $1 multicoloured 60 60
549 $4 black, yellow-brown and rose-lilac .. 1·75 1·75
546/9 .. .. *Set of* 4 2·75 2·75
Designs:—90 c. Marie Curie; $1 Amy Johnson; $4 Eleanor Roosevelt.

(Litho Format)

1981 (15 May). *Walt Disney Cartoon Characters. T* **85** *and similar vert designs showing characters afloat. Multicoloured. P* 13½.
550 10 c. Type **85** 15 10
551 20 c. Donald Duck reversing car into sea .. 20 15
552 25 c. Mickey Mouse asking tug-boat to take on more than it can handle 25 20
553 30 c. Porpoise turning the tables on Goofy .. 35 25
554 35 c. Goofy in sailing boat 35 25
555 40 c. Mickey Mouse and boat being lifted out of water by fish 40 30
556 75 c. Donald Duck fishing for flying-fish with butterfly net 55 45
557 $1 Minnie Mouse in brightly decorated sailing boat 65 55
558 $2 Chip and Dale on floating ship-in-bottle 1·25 1·10
550/8 .. .. *Set of* 9 3·75 3·00
MS559 127 × 101 mm. $2.50, Donald Duck .. 2·50 2·25

BARBUDA (**86**)

1981 (9 June). *Birth Centenary of Picasso. Nos.* 697/701 *of Antigua optd with T* **86**.
560 10 c. "Pipes of Pan" 10 10
561 50 c. "Seated Harlequin" 25 25
562 90 c. "Paulo as Harlequin" 45 45
563 $4 "Mother and Child" .. .. .. 1·60 1·60
560/3 .. .. *Set of* 4 2·10 2·10
MS564 115 × 140 mm. $5 "Three Musicians" (detail) .. .. 2·25 2·75

87 Buckingham Palace **88**

(Des G. Drummond. Litho Format)

1981 (27 July). *Royal Wedding (1st issue). Buildings. T* **87/8** *and similar horiz designs. Each bicoloured*. P* 11 × 11½.
565 $1 Type **87** 70 70
566 $1 Type **88** 70 70
a. Sheetlet. Nos. 565/70 .. .. .. 6·50
b. Booklet pane. Nos. 565/6 × 2 in imperf between horiz pairs .. .. .. 2·50
567 $1.50 } Caernarvon Castle 85 85
568 $1.50 } 85 85
b. Booklet pane. Nos. 567/8 × 2 in imperf between horiz pairs .. .. .. 3·00
569 $4 } Highgrove House .. .. 1·75 1·75
570 $4 } .. .. 1·75 1·75
b. Booklet pane. Nos. 569/70 × 2 in imperf between horiz pairs .. .. .. 7·00
565/70 .. .. *Set of* 6 6·00 6·00
MS571 75 × 90 mm. $5 black and olive-yellow (St. Paul's Cathedral—26 × 32 *mm*). P 11½ × 11 .. 1·50 2·00
*Nos. 565/70 each exist printed in black with three different background colours, rose-pink, turquoise-green and lavender.
No. 566b was printed only in black and rose-pink. No. 568b black and turquoise-green and No. 570b black and lavender.
Nos. 565/70 were printed together, *se-tenant*, in sheetlets of 6, the two versions of each value forming a composite design.

1981 (14 Aug). *Royal Wedding (2nd issue). Nos.* 702/5 *of Antigua optd with T* **86**.
572 25 c. Prince Charles and Lady Diana Spencer 25 25
573 50 c. Glamis Castle 35 35
a. Opt double .. .. 35·00
574 $4 Prince Charles skiing .. .. .. 1·40 1·40
a. Error. Optd on unissued Uganda 20s. as No. 343 .. .. 60·00
572/4 .. .. *Set of* 3 1·75 1·75
MS575 95 × 85 mm. $5 Glass Coach .. .. 2·00 2·50
Nos. 572/4 also exist perforated 12 (*Price for set of* 3 £2 *mint or used*) from additional sheetlets of five stamps and one label. These stamps have changed background colours. One sheetlet of the 25 c. is known with the overprints inverted.

89 "Integration and Travel"

(Litho Format)

1981 (14 Sept). *International Year for Disabled Persons. T* **89** *and similar horiz designs. P* 14.
576 50 c. multicoloured 55 25
577 90 c. black, red-orange and blue-green .. 75 40
578 $1 black, light blue and bright green .. 85 45
579 $4 black, yellow-ochre and orange-brown .. 2·40 1·75
576/9 .. .. *Set of* 4 4·00 2·50
Designs:—90 c. Braille and sign language; $1 "Helping hands"; $4 "Mobility aids for disabled".

BARBUDA (**90**)

1981 (12 Oct). *Royal Wedding (3rd issue). Booklet stamps. Nos.* 706/12 *of Antigua optd with T* **90** *in silver.*
580 25 c. Prince of Wales at Investiture, 1969 .. 25 25
a. Booklet pane. Nos. 580/5 .. .. 2·75
581 25 c. Prince Charles as baby, 1948 .. .. 25 25
582 $1 Prince Charles at R.A.F. College, Cranwell, 1971 .. .. 45 45
583 $1 Prince Charles attending Hill House School, 1956 .. .. 45 45

584 $2 Prince Charles and Lady Diana Spencer .. 80 80
585 $2 Prince Charles at Trinity College, 1967 .. 80 80
586 $5 Prince Charles and Lady Diana .. .. 3·00 3·00
a. Booklet pane of 1 .. .. 3·00
580/6 .. .. *Set of* 7 5·50 5·50

1981 (1 Nov). *Independence. Nos. 686B/96B of Antigua additionally optd with T* **86**.
587 6 c. Orchid Tree 30 10
588 10 c. Bougainvillea 35 15
589 20 c. Flamboyant 50 20
590 25 c. Hibiscus 55 25
591 35 c. Flame of the Wood 65 30
592 50 c. Cannon at Fort James 70 35
593 75 c. Premier's Office 80 45
594 $1 Potworks Dam .. .. 1·00 55
595 $2.50, Irrigation scheme, Diamond Estate .. 2·75 1·50
596 $5 Government House .. .. .. 3·75 2·50
597 $10 Coolidge International Airport .. .. 5·50 4·75
587/97 .. .. *Set of* 11 15·00 10·00

BARBUDA (91) BARBUDA (92)

1981 (14 Dec). *50th Anniv of Antigua Girl Guide Movement. Nos. 713/17 of Antigua optd with T* **83** *(No.* **MS602**) *or T* **91** *(others).*
598 10 c. Irene Joshua (founder) 40 10
599 50 c. Campfire sing-song 80 30
600 90 c. Sailing .. .. 1·10 45
601 $2.50, Animal tending .. .. .. 2·50 1·40
598/601 .. .. .. *Set of* 4 4·25 2·00
MS602 110 × 85 mm. $5 Raising the flag .. .. 3·00 3·50

1981 (14 Dec). *International Year for Disabled Persons. Sport for the Disabled. Nos. 728/32 of Antigua optd with T* **83** *(No.* **MS**607) *or T* **91** *(others).*
603 10 c. Swimming 20 15
604 50 c. Discus throwing 45 35
605 90 c. Archery 65 60
606 $2 Baseball .. .. 1·50 1·60
603/6 .. .. *Set of* 4 2·50 2·40
MS607 108 × 84 mm. $4 Basketball .. .. 2·50 2·75

1981 (22 Dec). *Christmas. Paintings. Nos. 723/7 of Antigua optd with T* **92**.
608 8 c. "Holy Night" (Jacques Stella) 10 10
609 30 c. "Mary with Child" (Julius Schnorr von Carolfeld) 20 20
610 $1 "Virgin and Child" (Alonso Cano) (S.) .. 40 40
611 $3 "Virgin and Child" (Lorenzo di Credi) .. 1·10 1·10
608/11 .. .. *Set of* 4 1·60 1·60
MS612 77 × 111 mm. $5 "Holy Family" (Pieter von Avon) .. .. 1·75 2·25

93 Princess of Wales

S. Atlantic Fund + 50c. (94)

(Des G. Drummond. Litho Format)

1982 (21 June). *Birth of Prince William of Wales (1st issue). T* **93** *and similar vert portraits. W w* **15**. *P* 14.
613 $1 multicoloured 50 50
614 $2.50, multicoloured .. .. 1·10 1·10
a. Reddish violet (top inscr) omitted .. £175
615 $5 multicoloured .. .. 2·25 2·25
613/15 .. .. .. *Set of* 3 3·50 3·50
MS616 88 × 108 mm. $4 multicoloured. No wmk .. 2·00 2·10

Nos. 613/15 were issued in sheets of 10 stamps with 2 undenominated black prints, in positions 9 and 13, and 9 blank labels. These sheets exist in two different formats, with all stamps upright or with 6 stamps and one black print inverted.

1982 (28 June). *South Atlantic Fund. Booklet stamps. Nos. 580/6 surch as T* **94**.
617 25 c. +50 c. Prince of Wales at Investiture, 1969 .. .. 20 20
a. Booklet pane. Nos. 617/22 .. .. 2·50
b. Surch double .. .. 20·00
618 25 c. +50 c. Prince Charles as baby, 1948 .. 20 20
b. Surch double .. .. 20·00
619 $1 +50 c. Prince Charles at R.A.F. College, Cranwell, 1971 .. .. 45 45
b. Surch double .. .. 20·00
620 $1 +50 c. Prince Charles attending Hill House School, 1956 .. .. .. 45 45
b. Surch double .. .. 20·00
621 $2 +50 c. Prince Charles and Lady Diana Spencer 75 75
b. Surch double .. .. 20·00
622 $2 +50 c. Prince Charles at Trinity College, 1967 .. .. 75 75
b. Surch double .. .. 20·00
623 $5 +50 c. Prince Charles and Lady Diana 2·00 2·00
a. Booklet pane of 1 .. .. 2·00
b. Surch double £150
617/23 .. .. *Set of* 7 4·00 4·00

(Des G. Drummond. Litho Format)

1982 (1 July). *21st Birthday of Princess of Wales (1st issue). As Nos. 613/16 but inscribed "Twenty First Birthday Greetings to H.R.H. The Princess of Wales". W w* **15**. *P* 14.
624 $1 multicoloured 45 45
625 $2.50, multicoloured .. .. 1·25 1·25
626 $5 multicoloured .. .. 2·40 2·40
624/6 .. .. *Set of* 3 3·75 3·75
MS627 88 × 108 mm. $4 multicoloured. No wmk .. 2·25 2·25

See note beneath Nos. 613/16.

BARBUDA MAIL (95) BARBUDA MAIL (96)

1982 (30 Aug). *21st Birthday of Princess of Wales (2nd issue). Nos. 748/51 of Antigua optd as T* **95**, *in silver (No. 629) or black (others).*
628 90 c. Queen's House, Greenwich 45 45
629 $1 Prince and Princess of Wales 50 50
630 $4 Princess of Wales .. .. .. 1·50 1·50
628/30 .. .. *Set of* 3 2·25 2·25
MS631 102 × 75 mm. $5 Princess of Wales (*different*) .. .. 2·25 2·50

The overprint on No. **MS**631 measures 18 × 6 mm.

Nos. 628/30 also exist from additional sheetlets of 5 stamps and 1 label overprinted with a larger overprint, 18 × 6 mm long (*price for set of 3 £3 mint or used*). On the $1 and $4 values the second line of overprint aligns to left.

1982 (12 Oct). *Birth of Prince William of Wales (2nd issue). Nos. 757/60 of Antigua further optd with T* **95**, *in silver ($1, $4) or black (others).*
632 90 c. Queen's House, Greenwich 45 45
633 $1 Prince and Princess of Wales 50 50
634 $4 Princess of Wales .. .. .. 1·50 1·50
632/4 .. .. *Set of* 3 2·75 2·75
MS635 102 × 75 mm. $5 Princess of Wales (*different*) .. .. 2·40 2·50

The overprint on No. **MS**635 measures 18 × 6 mm.

1982 (6 Dec). *Birth Centenary of Franklin D. Roosevelt (Nos. 636, 638, 640/2) and 250th Birth Anniv of George Washington (others). Nos. 761/8 of Antigua optd as T* **95** *(second line ranged left on No.* **MS**642).
636 10 c. Roosevelt in 1940 .. .. .. 15 10
637 25 c. Washington as blacksmith 20 15
638 45 c. Churchill, Roosevelt and Stalin at Yalta conference 35 25
639 60 c. Washington crossing the Delaware .. 45 35
640 $1 "Roosevelt Special" train 65 55
641 $3 Portrait of Roosevelt .. .. .. 1·75 1·75
636/41 .. .. *Set of* 6 3·00 2·75
MS642 92 × 87 mm. $4 Roosevelt and wife .. 2·00 2·75
MS643 92 × 87 mm. $4 Portrait of Washington .. 2·00 2·75

1982 (6 Dec). *Christmas. Religious Paintings by Raphael. Nos. 769/73 of Antigua optd with T* **96**.
644 10 c. "Annunciation" 10 10
645 30 c. "Adoration of the Magi" 15 15
646 $1 "Presentation at the Temple" 40 40
647 $4 "Coronation of the Virgin" .. .. 1·75 1·75
644/7 .. .. *Set of* 4 2·25 2·25
MS648 95 × 124 mm. $5 "Marriage of the Virgin" 2·00 2·75

1983 (14 Mar). *500th Birth Anniv of Raphael. Details from "Galatea" Fresco. Nos. 774/8 of Antigua optd as T* **95** *(45, 50 c. and larger (18 × 6 mm) on* **MS**653) *or T* **96** *(others).*
649 45 c. Tritons and Dolphins 20 20
650 50 c. Sea Nymph carried off by Triton 25 25
651 60 c. Winged angel steering Dolphins (*horiz*) .. 30 30
652 $4 Cupids shooting arrows (*horiz*) .. .. 1·60 1·60
649/52 .. .. *Set of* 4 2·10 2·10
MS653 101 × 126 mm. $5 Galatea pulled along by Dolphins .. .. 2·25 2·75

1983 (14 Mar). *Commonwealth Day. Nos. 779/82 of Antigua optd as T* **96**.
654 25 c. Pineapple produce 25 25
655 45 c. Carnival 45 45
656 60 c. Tourism 55 55
657 $3 Airport .. .. 1·75 2·25
654/7 .. .. *Set of* 4 2·75 3·25

1983 (12 Apr). *World Communications Year. Nos. 783/7 of Antigua optd as T* **96** *(Nos. 658/61) or as T* **95** *with second line ranged left (No.* **MS**662).
658 15 c. T.V. satellite coverage of Royal Wedding 20 10
659 50 c. Police communications 60 30
660 60 c. House-to-train telephone call 60 35
661 $3 Satellite earth station with planets Jupiter and Saturn .. .. .. 2·00 1·50
658/61 .. .. *Set of* 4 3·00 2·00
MS662 100 × 90 mm. $5 "Comsat" satellite over West Indies .. .. 2·75 3·00

97 Vincenzo Lunardi's Balloon Flight, London, 1785

= 45c (98)

(Des G. Drummond. Litho)

1983 (13 June). *Bicentenary of Manned Flight (1st issue). T* **97** *and similar vert designs. Multicoloured. P* 14.
663 $1 Type **97** 50 50
664 $1.50, Montgolfier brothers' balloon flight, Paris, 1783 .. .. 75 75
665 $2.50, Blanchard and Jeffries' Cross-Channel balloon flight, 1785 .. .. .. 1·25 1·25
663/5 .. .. *Set of* 3 2·25 2·25
MS666 111 × 111 mm. $5 Maiden flight of *Graf Zeppelin*, 1928 .. .. 2·50 2·75

1983 (4 July). *Whales. Nos. 788/92 of Antigua optd as T* **95** *(No. 667/70) or larger, 17 × 5½ mm (No.* **MS**671), *each with the second line ranged left.*
667 15 c. Bottle-nosed Dolphin 45 2
668 50 c. Fin Whale .. .. 1·00 5
669 60 c. Bowhead Whale .. .. 1·10 6
670 $3 Spectacled Porpoise .. .. .. 3·50 2·2
667/70 .. .. *Set of* 4 5·50 3·2
MS671 122 × 101 mm. $5 Narwhal .. .. 3·75 4·5

1983 (12 Sept). *Bicentenary of Manned Flight (2nd issue). Nos. 811/15 of Antigua optd as T* **96**.
672 30 c. Dornier "Do X" flying boat 35 2
673 50 c. Supermarine "S.6B" seaplane 45 3
674 60 c. Curtiss "9C" biplane and airship U.S.S. *Akron* 50 4
675 $4 *Pro Juventute* balloon .. .. .. 3·00 3·2
672/5 .. .. *Set of* 4 4·00 4·0
MS676 80 × 105 mm. $5 *Graf Zeppelin* .. .. 3·50 4·2

1983 (21 Oct). *Nos. 565/70 surch as T* **98**. A. *P* 11 × 11½. B. *P* 14½.

		A		B	
677	45 c. on $1 Type **87**	45	45	2·25	2·2
	a. Sheetlet. Nos. 677/82	3·00		12·00	
	b. Error. 50 c. on $1 ..		†	7·50	—
	c. Surch omitted ..		†	35·00	—
678	45 c. on $1 Type **88** ..	45	45	2·25	2·2
	b. Error. 50 c. on $1 ..		†	7·50	—
	c. Surch omitted ..		†	35·00	—
679	50 c. on $1.50, Caernarvon Castle (*left*) ..	50	50	2·25	2·2
	b. Error. 45 c. on $1.50		†	7·50	—
	c. Surch omitted ..		†	35·00	—
680	50 c. on $1.50, Caernarvon Castle (*right*) ..	50	50	2·25	2·2
	b. Error. 45 c. on $1.50		†	7·50	—
	c. Surch omitted ..		†	35·00	—
681	60 c. on $4 Highgrove House (*left*)	60	60	2·25	2·2
	c. Surch omitted ..		†	35·00	—
682	60 c. on $4 Highgrove House (*right*) ..	60	60	2·25	2·2
	c. Surch omitted ..		†	35·00	—
677/82 ..	*Set of* 6	3·00	3·00	12·00	12·0

Nos. 677b, 678b, 679b and 680b occur on the 14½ perforated sheetlets with rose-pink background.

1983 (28 Oct). *Nos. 793A/810A of Antigua optd with T* **96**.
683 1 c. Cashew Nut 10 1
684 2 c. Passion Fruit 10 1
685 3 c. Mango 10 1
686 5 c. Grapefruit 10 1
687 10 c. Pawpaw 10 1
688 15 c. Breadfruit 15 1
689 20 c. Coconut 20 1
690 25 c. Oleander 20 1
691 30 c. Banana 25 2
692 40 c. Pineapple 30 2
693 45 c. Cordia 35 3
694 50 c. Cassia 40 3
695 60 c. Poui 40 3
696 $1 Frangipani 60 5
697 $2 Flamboyant .. .. 1·25 1·25
698 $2.50, Lemon .. .. 1·75 1·75
699 $5 Lignum Vitae .. .. 2·75 2·75
700 $10 National flag and coat of arms .. 5·00 5·50
683/700 .. .. .. *Set of* 18 12·50 12·00

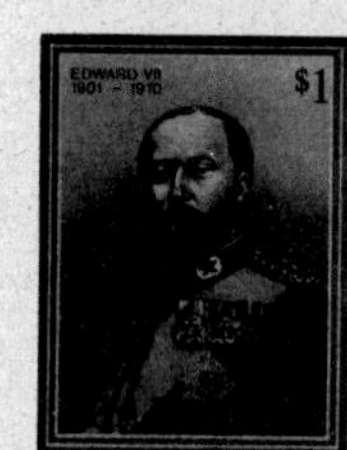

BARBUDA MAIL (99)

100 Edward VII

1983 (28 Oct). *Christmas. 500th Birth Anniv of Raphael. Nos. 816/20 of Antigua optd with T* **99** *or slightly smaller (29 × 4 mm) (*MS*705).*
701 10 c. multicoloured 10 10
702 30 c. multicoloured 15 20
703 $1 multicoloured 45 50
704 $4 multicoloured .. .. 1·50 1·75
701/4 .. .. *Set of* 4 1·90 2·25
MS705 101 × 131 mm. $5 multicoloured .. .. 2·25 2·75

1983 (14 Dec). *Bicentenary of Methodist Church (1984). Nos. 821/4 of Antigua optd with T* **94** *(in silver on 15 c. and 50 c.).*
706 15 c. John Wesley (founder) 20 15
707 50 c. Nathaniel Gilbert (founder in Antigua) 40 30
708 60 c. St. John Methodist Church steeple .. 45 35
709 $3 Ebenezer Methodist Church, St. John's 1·75 1·75
706/9 .. .. *Set of* 4 2·50 2·25

(Des G. Drummond. Litho Format)

1984 (14 Feb). *Members of British Royal Family. T* **100** *and similar vert portraits. Multicoloured. P* 14½.
710 $1 Type **100** 85 85
711 $1 George V 85 85
712 $1 George VI 85 85
713 $1 Elizabeth II 85 85
714 $1 Charles, Prince of Wales 85 85
715 $1 Prince William of Wales 85 85
710/15 .. .. *Set of* 6 4·50 4·50

1984 (26 Apr). *Olympic Games, Los Angeles (1st issue). Nos. 825/9 of Antigua optd as T* **99** *(23 × 3 mm in size on Nos. 716/19).*
716 25 c. Discus 15 20
717 50 c. Gymnastics 35 40
718 90 c. Hurdling 50 60
719 $3 Cycling .. .. 1·25 1·50
716/19 .. .. *Set of* 4 2·00 2·40
MS720 82 × 67 mm. $5 Volleyball .. .. 2·75 3·25

84 (12 July). *Ships. Nos. 830/4 of Antigua optd with T* **95** *(MS725) or T* **99** *(others).*
1 45 c. *Booker Vanguard* (freighter) 75 45
2 50 c. S.S. *Canberra* (liner) 85 50
3 60 c. Sailing boats 95 60
4 $4 *Fairwind* (liner) 3·25 2·75
1/4 *Set of* 4 5·25 3·75
S725 107 × 80 mm. $5 Eighteenth-century British man-of-war (*vert*) 4·25 4·50

984 (12 July). *Universal Postal Union Congress, Hamburg. Nos. 835/9 of Antigua optd with T* **95**.
26 15 c. Chenille 15 10
27 50 c. Shell Flower 45 40
28 60 c. Anthurium 50 45
29 $3 Angels Trumpet 1·60 1·75
26/9 *Set of* 4 2·40 2·40
S730 100 × 75 mm. $5 Crown of Thorns 3·25 3·50

BARBUDA MAIL

101 Olympic Stadium, Athens, 1896 (**102**)

(Litho Format)

84 (27 July). *Olympic Games, Los Angeles (2nd issue). T* **101** *and similar horiz designs. Multicoloured. P* 13½.
31 $1.50, Type **101** 1·00 1·10
32 $2.50, Olympic stadium, Los Angeles, 1984 1·50 1·75
33 $5 Athlete carrying Olympic torch 2·50 2·75
31/3 *Set of* 3 4·50 5·00
S734 121 × 95 mm. No. 733. P 15 2·75 3·50

984 (1 Oct). *Presidents of the United States of America. Nos. 856/63 of Antigua optd with T* **95** *(in silver on* 10, 90 *c.,* $1.10 *and* $1.50*).*
35 10 c. Abraham Lincoln 10 10
36 20 c. Harry Truman 12 15
37 30 c. Dwight Eisenhower 20 25
38 40 c. Ronald Reagan 25 30
39 90 c. Gettysburg Address, 1863 50 55
40 $1.10, Formation of N.A.T.O., 1949 60 65
41 $1.50, Eisenhower during Second World War 80 85
42 $2 Reagan and Caribbean Basin Initiative 1·00 1·25
35/42 *Set of* 8 3·25 3·75

984 (1 Oct). *150th Anniv of Abolition of Slavery. Nos. 864/8 of Antigua optd with T* **96** *(Nos. 743/6) or as T* **95**, *but* 18 × 6½ *mm (No.* **MS**747*).*
43 40 c. View of Moravian Mission 30 30
44 50 c. Antigua Courthouse, 1823 40 40
45 60 c. Planting sugar-cane, Monks Hill 45 45
46 $3 Boiling house, Delaps' Estate 1·90 1·90
43/6 *Set of* 4 2·75 2·75
1S747 95 × 70 mm. $5 Loading sugar, Willoughby Bay 3·50 4·00

984 (21 Nov). *Songbirds. Nos. 869/74 of Antigua optd with T* **95** *or larger (18 × 7 mm) (No.* **MS**753*).*
48 40 c. Rufous-sided Towhee 45 45
49 50 c. Parula Warbler 50 50
50 60 c. House Wren 55 55
51 $2 Ruby-crowned Kinglet 1·50 1·50
52 $3 Common Flicker 2·25 2·25
48/52 *Set of* 5 4·75 4·75
1S753 76 × 76 mm. $5 Yellow-breasted Chat 4·00 4·50

984 (21 Nov). *450th Death Anniv of Correggio (painter). Nos. 878/82 of Antigua optd with T* **95** *or larger (18 × 7 mm) No.* **MS**758*), all in silver.*
54 25 c. "The Virgin and Infant with Angels and Cherubs" 15 20
55 60 c. "The Four Saints" 40 45
56 90 c. "St. Catherine" 60 65
57 $3 "The Campori Madonna" 1·75 2·25
54/7 *Set of* 4 2·50 3·25
1S758 90 × 60 mm. $5 "St. John the Baptist" 2·75 3·75

984 (30 Nov). *"Ausipex" International Stamp Exhibition, Melbourne. Australian Sports. Nos. 875/7 of Antigua optd with T* **95** *or larger (18 × 7 mm) (No.* **MS**761*).*
59 $1 Grass-skiing 70 75
60 $5 Australian Football 3·00 3·75
1S761 108 × 78 mm. $5 Boomerang-throwing 3·00 3·75

984 (30 Nov). *150th Birth Anniv of Edgar Degas (painter). Nos. 883/7 of Antigua optd with T* **95** *(Nos. 762/5) or T* **99** *(No.* **MS**766*), all in silver.*
62 15 c. "The Blue Dancers" 10 10
63 50 c. "The Pink Dancers" 30 35
64 70 c. "Two Dancers" 45 50
65 $4 "Dancers at the Bar" 2·40 2·75
62/5 *Set of* 4 3·00 3·25
1S766 90 × 60 mm. $5 "The Folk Dancers" (40 × 27 *mm*) 2·75 3·25

985 (18 Feb). *Famous People. Nos. 888/96 of Antigua optd with T* **102** *(horizontally on Nos. 771/5).*
767 60 c. Winston Churchill 80 50
768 60 c. Mahatma Gandhi 80 50
769 60 c. John F. Kennedy 80 50
770 60 c. Mao Tse-tung 80 50
771 $1 Churchill with General De Gaulle, Paris, 1944 (*horiz*) 1·25 75
772 $1 Gandhi leaving London by train, 1931 (*horiz*) 1·25 75
773 $1 Kennedy with Chancellor Adenauer and Mayor Brandt, Berlin, 1963 (*horiz*) 1·25 75
774 $1 Mao Tse-tung with Lin Piao, Peking, 1969 (*horiz*) 1·25 75
767/74 *Set of* 8 7·50 4·50
MS775 114×80 mm. $5 Flags of Great Britain, India, the United States and China 3·00 3·25

103 Lady Elizabeth Bowes-Lyon, 1907, and Camellias **104** Roseate Tern

(Des G. Drummond. Litho Format)

1985 (26 Feb). *Life and Times of Queen Elizabeth the Queen Mother (1st issue). T* **103** *and similar vert designs. Multicoloured. P* 14 × 14½.
776 15 c. Type **103** 10 10
777 45 c. Duchess of York, 1926, and "Elizabeth of Glamis" roses 25 30
778 50 c. The Queen Mother after the Coronation, 1937 25 30
779 60 c. In Garter robes, 1971, and Dog Roses 35 40
780 90 c. Attending Royal Variety show, 1967, and red Hibiscus 50 55
781 $2 The Queen Mother in 1982, and blue Plumbago 1·10 1·25
782 $3 Receiving 82nd birthday gifts from children, and Morning Glory 1·60 1·75
776/82 *Set of* 7 3·75 4·00
See also Nos. 826/9.

(Des G. Drummond. Litho Format)

1985 (4 Apr). *Birth Bicentenary of John J. Audubon (ornithologist) (1st issue). T* **104** *and similar vert designs showing original paintings. Multicoloured. P* 14.
783 45 c. Type **104** 35 30
784 50 c. Mangrove Cuckoo 35 30
785 60 c. Yellow-crowned Night Heron 45 40
786 $5 Brown Pelican 3·00 3·25
783/6 *Set of* 4 3·75 3·75
See also Nos. 794/8 and 914/17.

1985 (10 May). *Centenary of the Statue of Liberty* (1986). *Nos. 907/13 of Antigua optd horizontally with T* **102**.
787 25 c. Torch from Statue in Madison Square Park, 1885 15 20
788 30 c. Statue of Liberty and scaffolding ("Restoration and Renewal") (*vert*) 15 20
789 50 c. Frederic Bartholdi (sculptor) supervising construction, 1876 25 30
790 90 c. Close-up of Statue 50 55
791 $1 Statue and sailing ship ("Operation Sail", 1976) (*vert*) 55 60
792 $3 Dedication ceremony, 1886 (*vert*) 1·60 1·75
787/92 *Set of* 6 2·75 3·00
MS793 110×80 mm. $5 Port of New York 2·75 3·00

BARBUDA MAIL BARBUDA MAIL 4TH AUG 1900–1985

(**105**) (**106**) (**107**)

1985 (18 July). *Birth Bicentenary of John J. Audubon (ornithologist) (2nd issue). Nos. 924/8 of Antigua optd with T* **105**.
794 90 c. Slavonian Grebe 1·00 75
795 $1 British Storm Petrel 1·10 85
796 $1.50, Great Blue Heron 1·75 1·25
797 $3 Double-crested Cormorant 2·50 2·25
794/7 *Set of* 4 5·75 4·50
MS798 103×72 mm. $5 White-tailed Tropic Bird (*vert*) 5·00 4·75

1985 (18 July). *Butterflies. Nos. 929/33 of Antigua optd with T* **106**.
799 25 c. *Polygrapha cyanea* 75 45
800 60 c. *Leodonta dysoni* 1·25 75
801 90 c. *Junea doraete* 1·50 95
802 $4 *Prepona xenagoras* 4·00 3·75
799/802 *Set of* 4 6·75 5·50
MS803 132×105 mm. $5 *Caerois gerdrudtus* 5·00 5·50

1985 (2 Aug). *Centenary of the Motorcycle. Nos. 919/23 of Antigua optd with T* **106**.
804 10 c. Triumph 2hp "Jap", 1903 30 10
805 30 c. Indian "Arrow", 1949 50 20
806 60 c. BMW "R100RS", 1976 75 40
807 $4 Harley-Davidson "Model II", 1916 3·00 2·75
804/7 *Set of* 4 4·00 3·00
MS808 90×93 mm. $5 Laverda "Jota", 1975 3·50 4·00

1985 (2 Aug). *85th Birthday of Queen Elizabeth the Queen Mother. Nos. 776/82 optd with T* **107**.
809 15 c. Type **103** 15 10
a. Red (frame, flowers, etc) omitted 32·00
810 45 c. Duchess of York, 1926, and "Elizabeth of Glamis" roses 40 30
811 50 c. The Queen Mother after the Coronation, 1937 40 30
812 60 c. In Garter robes, 1971, and Dog Roses 50 40
813 90 c. Attending Royal Variety show, 1967, and red Hibiscus 65 55
814 $2 The Queen Mother in 1982, and blue Plumbago 1·40 1·25
815 $3 Receiving 82nd birthday gifts from children, and Morning Glory 2·00 1·75
809/15 *Set of* 7 5·00 4·00

1985 (30 Aug). *Native American Artefacts. Nos. 914/18 of Antigua optd horizontally with T* **102**.
816 15 c. Arawak pot sherd and Indians making clay utensils 15 10
817 50 c. Arawak body design and Arawak Indians tattooing 30 30
818 60 c. Head of the god "Yocahu" and Indians harvesting manioc 40 40
819 $3 Carib war club and Carib Indians going into battle 1·60 1·75
816/19 *Set of* 4 2·25 2·25
MS820 97×68 mm. $5 Taino Indians worshipping stone idol 3·00 3·50

1985 (30 Aug). *40th Anniv of International Civil Aviation Organization. Nos. 934/8 of Antigua optd with T* **106**.
821 30 c. Cessna "172" 20 20
822 90 c. Fokker "DVII" 55 55
823 $1.50, Spad "VII" 85 85
824 $3 Boeing "747" 1·75 1·75
821/4 *Set of* 4 3·00 3·00
MS825 97×83 mm. $5 Twin "Otter" 3·00 3·50

1985 (8 Nov). *Life and Times of Queen Elizabeth the Queen Mother (2nd issue). Nos. 946/9 of Antigua optd with T* **95** *(in silver on Nos. 826/7 and* **MS**829*).*
826 $1 The Queen Mother attending church 1·00 1·00
827 $1.50, Watching children playing in London garden 1·25 1·25
828 $2.50, The Queen Mother in 1979 1·90 1·90
826/8 *Set of* 3 3·75 3·75
MS829 56×85 mm. $5 With Prince Edward at Royal Wedding, 1981 3·50 4·00
Nos. 826/7 also exist with black and No. 828 with silver overprints (*Price for set of* 3 £50 *mint*).
The stamps from the sheetlets mentioned beneath Antigua No. **MS**949 also exist overprinted with Type **95**.

1985 (25 Nov). *850th Birth Anniv of Maimonides (physician, philosopher and scholar). Nos. 939/40 of Antigua optd with T* **95**.
830 $2 bright green 1·75 1·75
MS831 70×84 mm. $5 reddish brown 3·00 3·50

1985 (25 Nov). *Marine Life. Nos. 950/4 of Antigua optd with T* **95** *(in silver on* 15 *c. and* $3*).*
832 15 c. Magnificent Frigate Bird 35 20
833 45 c. Brain Coral 60 45
834 60 c. Cushion Star 75 60
835 $3 Spotted Moray Eel 2·75 2·50
832/5 *Set of* 4 4·00 3·25
MS836 110×80 mm. $5 Elkhorn Coral 4·00 4·50

1986 (17 Feb). *International Youth Year. Nos. 941/5 of Antigua optd with T* **95**.
837 25 c. Young farmers with produce 15 15
838 50 c. Hotel management trainees 25 30
839 60 c. Girls with goat and boys with football ("Environment") 30 35
840 $3 Windsurfing ("Leisure") 1·50 1·60
837/40 *Set of* 4 2·00 2·10
MS841 102×72 mm. $5 Young people with Antiguan flags 2·75 3·25

1986 (17 Feb). *Royal Visit. Nos. 965/8 of Antigua optd with T* **106**.
842 60 c. Flags of Great Britain and Antigua 30 35
843 $1 Queen Elizabeth II (*vert*) 50 55
844 $4 Royal Yacht *Britannia* 2·00 2·10
842/4 *Set of* 3 2·50 2·75
MS845 110×83 mm. $5 Map of Antigua 2·50 3·00

1986 (10 Mar). *75th Anniv of Girl Guide Movement. Nos. 955/9 of Antigua optd with T* **95**.
846 15 c. Girl Guides nursing 35 35
847 45 c. Open-air Girl Guide meeting 75 75
848 60 c. Lord and Lady Baden-Powell 95 95
849 $3 Girl Guides gathering flowers 3·25 3·25
846/9 *Set of* 4 4·75 4·75
MS850 67×96 mm. $5 Barn Swallow (Nature study) 5·50 5·50

1986 (10 Mar). *300th Birth Anniv of Johann Sebastian Bach (composer). Nos. 960/4 of Antigua optd with T* **95**.
851 25 c. multicoloured 45 45
852 50 c. multicoloured 75 75
853 $1 multicoloured 1·25 1·25
854 $3 multicoloured 2·75 2·75
851/4 *Set of* 4 4·75 4·75
MS855 104×73 mm. $5 black and brownish grey 5·00 5·50

1986 (4 Apr). *Christmas. Religious Paintings. Nos. 985/9 of Antigua optd with T* **106**.
856 10 c. "Madonna and Child" (De Landi) 20 15
857 25 c. "Madonna and Child" (Berlinghiero) 40 30
858 60 c. "The Nativity" (Fra Angelico) 75 60
859 $4 "Presentation in the Temple" (Giovanni di Paolo) 3·00 3·25
856/9 *Set of* 4 4·00 4·00
MS860 113×81 mm. $5 "The Nativity" (Antoniazzo Romano) 4·00 4·75

108 Queen Elizabeth II meeting Members of Legislature

(Litho Format)

1986 (21 Apr). *60th Birthday of Queen Elizabeth II* (*1st issue*). *T* **108** *and similar horiz designs. Multicoloured. P* 15.
861 $1 Type **108** .. .. 1·00 1·00
862 $2 Queen with Headmistress of Liberta School .. .. 1·50 1·50
863 $2.50, Queen greeted by Governor-General of Antigua .. .. 1·75 1·75
861/3 .. .. *Set of* 3 3·75 3·75
MS864 95×75 mm. $5 Queen Elizabeth in 1928 and 1986 (33×27 *mm*). P 13½×14 .. .. 3·50 4·00
See also Nos. 872/5.

109 Halley's Comet over Barbuda Beach

(Des and litho Format)

1986 (10 July). *Appearance of Halley's Comet* (*1st issue*). *T* **109** *and similar multicoloured designs. P* 15.
865 $1 Type **109** .. .. 1·25 1·25
866 $2.50, Early telescope and dish aerial (*vert*) .. 2·50 2·50
867 $5 Comet and World map .. .. .. 4·00 4·00
865/7 .. .. *Set of* 3 7·00 7·00
See also Nos. 886/90.

1986 (12 Aug). *40th Anniv of United Nations Organization. Nos.* 981/4 *of Antigua optd with T* **96** (*Nos.* 868/70) *or T* **95** (*No.* **MS**871).
868 40 c. Benjamin Franklin and U.N. (New York) 1953 U.P.U. 5 c. stamp .. 55 55
869 $1 George Washington Carver (agricultural chemist) and 1982 Nature Conservation 28 c. stamp .. .. 1·00 1·00
870 $3 Charles Lindbergh (aviator) and 1978 I.C.A.O. 25 c. stamp .. .. 2·25 2·25
868/70 .. .. *Set of* 3 3·50 3·50
MS871 101×77 mm. $5 Marc Chagall (artist) (*vert*) .. .. 4·50 5·50

1986 (12 Aug). *60th Birthday of Queen Elizabeth II* (*2nd issue*). *Nos.* 1005/8 *of Antigua optd with T* **95** *in black* (*No.* **MS**875) *or silver* (*others*)
872 60 c. black and yellow 55 55
873 $1 multicoloured 90 90
874 $4 multicoloured .. .. 2·75 2·75
872/4 .. .. *Set of* 3 3·75 3·75
MS875 120×85 mm. $5 black and grey-brown .. 3·50 4·00

1986 (28 Aug). *World Cup Football Championship, Mexico. Nos.* 995/9 *of Antigua optd with T* **96** (30 *c.*, $4) *or T* **95** (*others*).
876 30 c. Football, boots and trophy 40 40
877 60 c. Goalkeeper (*vert*) 70 70
878 $1 Referee blowing whistle (*vert*) .. .. 1·00 1·00
879 $4 Ball in net .. .. 2·75 2·75
876/9 .. .. *Set of* 4 4·25 4·25
MS880 87×76 mm. $5 Two players competing for ball .. .. 3·50 4·25

1986 (28 Aug). *"Ameripex '86" International Stamp Exhibition, Chicago. Famous American Trains. Nos.* 1014/18 *of Antigua optd with T* **106**.
881 25 c. "Hiawatha Express" 45 45
882 50 c. "Grand Canyon Express" 70 70
883 $1 "Powhattan Arrow Express" .. .. 1·25 1·25
884 $3 "Empire State Express" .. .. 2·75 2·75
881/4 .. .. *Set of* 4 4·50 4·50
MS885 116×87 mm. $5 "Daylight Express" .. 4·75 5·50

1986 (22 Sept). *Appearance of Halley's Comet* (*2nd issue*). *Nos.* 1000/4 *of Antigua optd with T* **96** (*Nos.* 886/9) *or T* **95** (**MS**890).
886 5 c. Edmond Halley and Old Greenwich Observatory 15 15
887 10 c. "Me 163B Komet" (fighter aircraft), 1944 .. .. 15 15
888 60 c. Montezuma (Aztec Emperor) and Comet in 1517 (from "Historias de las Indias de Neuva Espana") 80 80
889 $4 Pocahontas saving Capt. John Smith and Comet in 1607 .. .. .. 3·50 3·50
886/9 .. .. *Set of* 4 4·25 4·25
MS890 101×70 mm. $5 Halley's Comet over English Harbour, Antigua .. .. .. 3·50 4·25

1986 (22 Sept). *Royal Wedding. Nos.* 1019/22 *of Antigua optd with T* **95** *in silver.*
891 45 c. Prince Andrew and Miss Sarah Ferguson 45 45
892 60 c. Prince Andrew 55 55
893 $4 Prince Andrew with Prince Philip .. 2·75 2·75
891/3 .. .. *Set of* 3 3·25 3·25
MS894 88×88 mm. $5 Prince Andrew and Miss Sarah Ferguson (*different*) .. .. .. 3·75 4·25

1986 (10 Nov). *Sea Shells. Nos.* 1023/7 *of Antigua optd with T* **106** (*in silver on* 15 *c. to* $3).
895 15 c. Fly-specked Cerith 45 45
896 45 c. Smooth Scotch Bonnet 80 80
897 60 c. West Indian Crown Conch .. .. 1·00 1·00
898 $3 Murex Ciboney .. .. 3·00 3·00
895/8 .. .. *Set of* 4 4·75 4·75
MS899 109×75 mm. $5 Colourful Atlantic Natica (*horiz*) .. .. 5·50 6·00

1986 (10 Nov). *Flowers. Nos.* 1028/36 *of Antigua optd with T* **106**.
900 10 c. *Nymphaea ampla* (water lily) 20 20
901 15 c. Queen of the Night 30 30
902 50 c. Cup of Gold 50 50
903 60 c. Beach Morning Glory 55 55
904 70 c. Golden Trumpet 70 70
905 $1 Air Plant 85 85
906 $3 Purple Wreath .. .. 2·25 2·25
907 $4 Zephyr Lily .. .. 2·75 2·75
900/7 .. .. *Set of* 8 7·50 7·50
MS908 Two sheets, each 102×72 mm. (a) $4 Dozakie. (b) $5 Four O'Clock Flower *Set of* 2 *sheets* 8·00 9·00

1986 (28 Nov). *Mushrooms. Nos.* 1042/6 *of Antigua optd with T* **106**.
909 10 c. *Hygrocybe occidentalis* 30 30
910 50 c. *Trogia buccinalis* 60 60
911 $1 *Collybia subpruinosa* .. .. .. 1·00 1·00
912 $4 *Leucocoprinus brebissonii* .. .. 3·00 3·00
909/12 .. .. *Set of* 4 4·50 4·50
MS913 102×82 mm. $5 *Pyrrhoglossum pyrrhum* 5·00 5·50

1986 (Dec). *Birth Bicentenary of John J. Audubon* (*ornithologist*) (*3rd issue*). *Nos.* 990/3 *of Antigua optd with T* **96** (*in silver on* 60, 90 *c.*).
914 60 c. Mallard 40 40
915 90 c. North American Black Duck 60 60
916 $1.50, Pintail .. .. 1·00 1·00
917 $3 American Wigeon .. .. .. 1·75 1·75
914/17 .. .. *Set of* 4 3·25 3·25

1987 (12 Jan). *Local Boats. Nos.* 1009/13 *of Antigua optd with T* **95**.
918 30 c. Tugboat 25 25
919 60 c. Game fishing boat 40 40
920 $1 Yacht 65 65
921 $4 Lugger with auxiliary sail .. .. 2·25 2·25
918/21 .. .. *Set of* 4 3·25 3·25
MS922 108×78 mm. $5 Boats under construction 3·75 4·25

1987 (12 Jan). *Centenary of First Benz Motor Car. Nos.* 1052/60 *of Antigua optd with T* **95** (*No.* **MS**931) *or T* **96** (*others*).
923 10 c. Auburn "Speedster" (1933) 10 10
924 15 c. Mercury "Sable" (1986) 15 15
925 50 c. Cadillac (1959) 35 35
926 60 c. Studebaker (1950) 35 35
927 70 c. Lagonda "V-12" (1939) 40 40
928 $1 Adler "Standard" (1930) 55 55
929 $3 DKW (1956) .. .. 1·60 1·60
930 $4 Mercedes "500K" (1936) .. .. 2·00 2·00
923/30 .. .. *Set of* 8 5·00 5·00
MS931 Two sheets, each 99×70 mm. (a) $5 Daimler (1896). (b) $5 Mercedes "Knight" (1921) *Set of* 2 *sheets* 5·50 6·50

1987 (10 Mar). *World Cup Football Championship Winners, Mexico. Nos.* 1037/40 *of Antigua optd with T* **95** (60 *c.*, $1) *or T* **96** (30 *c.*, $4).
932 30 c. Football, boots and trophy 20 20
933 60 c. Goalkeeper (*vert*) 35 35
934 $1 Referee blowing whistle (*vert*) 60 60
935 $4 Ball in net .. .. 2·00 2·00
932/5 .. .. *Set of* 4 2·75 2·75

1987 (23 Apr). *America's Cup Yachting Championship. Nos.* 1072/6 *of Antigua optd horizontally as T* **102**.
936 30 c. *Canada I* (1981) 20 20
937 60 c. *Gretel II* (1970) 35 35
938 $1 *Sceptre* (1958) 60 60
939 $3 *Vigilant* (1893) .. .. 1·75 1·75
936/9 .. .. *Set of* 4 2·75 2·75
MS940 113×84 mm. $5 *Australia II* defeating *Liberty* (1983) (*horiz*) .. .. 2·75 3·50

1987 (1 July). *Marine Life. Nos.* 1077/85 *of Antigua optd with T* **95** (*No.* **MS**949) *or T* **96** (*others*).
941 15 c. Bridled Burrfish 15 15
942 30 c. Common Noddy 25 25
943 40 c. Nassau Grouper 30 30
944 50 c. Laughing Gull 40 40
945 60 c. French Angelfish 40 40
946 $1 Porkfish 55 55
947 $2 Royal Tern .. .. 1·25 1·25
948 $3 Sooty Tern .. .. 1·75 1·75
941/8 .. .. *Set of* 8 4·50 4·50
MS949 Two sheets, each 120×94 mm. (a) $5 Banded Butterflyfish. (b) $5 Brown Booby *Set of* 2 *sheets* 6·00 7·50

1987 (28 July). *Milestones of Transportation. Nos.* 1100/9 *of Antigua optd with T* **106**.
950 10 c. *Spirit of Australia* (fastest powerboat), 1978 .. .. 15 15
951 15 c. Siemen's electric locomotive, 1879 .. 20 20
952 30 c. U.S.S. *Triton* (first submerged circumnavigation), 1960 .. .. .. 30 30
953 50 c. Trevithick's steam carriage (first passenger-carrying vehicle), 1801 .. .. 45 45
954 60 c. U.S.S. *New Jersey* (battleship), 1942 .. 45 45
955 70 c. Draisine bicycle, 1818 .. .. .. 50 50
956 90 c. S.S. *United States* (holder of Blue Riband), 1952 .. .. 65 65
957 $1.50, Cierva "C.4" (first autogiro), 1923 .. 1·00 1·00
958 $2 Curtiss "NC.4" (first transatlantic flight), 1919 .. .. 1·40 1·40
959 $3 *Queen Elizabeth 2* (liner), 1969 .. 1·90 1·90
950/9 .. .. *Set of* 10 6·25 6·25

110 Shore Crab

(Litho Format)

1987 (15 Sept). *Marine Life. T* **110** *and similar multicolour[ed] designs. P* 15.
960 5 c. Type **110** 10
961 10 c. Sea Cucumber 10
962 15 c. Stop Light Parrotfish 10
963 25 c. Banded Coral Shrimp 10
964 35 c. Spotted Drum 15
965 60 c. Thorny Starfish 25
966 75 c. Atlantic Trumpet Triton 30
967 90 c. Feather Star and Yellow Beaker Sponge 35
968 $1 Blue Gorgonian (*vert*) 40
969 $1.25, Slender Filefish (*vert*) 50
970 $5 Barred Hamlet (*vert*) .. .. .. 2·10
971 $7.50, Fairy Basslet (*vert*) .. .. 3·00
972 $10 Fire Coral and Butterfly Fish (*vert*) .. 4·00
960/72 .. .. *Set of* 13 10·00

1987 (12 Oct). *Olympic Games, Seoul* (1988). *Nos.* 1086/90 [*of*] *Antigua optd with T* **95** (*No.* **MS**977) *or T* **96** *in silver* (*others*).
973 10 c. Handball 10
974 60 c. Fencing 25
975 $1 Gymnastics 45
976 $3 Football .. .. 1·40
973/6 .. .. *Set of* 4 1·90
MS977 100×72 mm. $5 Boxing gloves .. .. 2·25

1987 (12 Oct). *Birth Centenary of Marc Chagall* (*artist*). *No[s.]* 1091/9 *of Antigua optd as T* **95** (*in silver on Nos.* 983, **MS**986b
978 10 c. "The Profile" 10
979 30 c. "Portrait of the Artist's Sister" .. 15
980 40 c. "Bride with Fan" 20
981 60 c. "David in Profile" 25
982 90 c. "Fiancee with Bouquet" 40
983 $1 "Self Portrait with Brushes" 45
984 $3 "The Walk" .. .. 1·40
985 $4 "Three Candles" .. .. 1·75
978/85 .. .. *Set of* 8 4·25
MS986 Two sheets, each 110×95 mm. (a) $5 "Fall of Icarus" (104×89 *mm*). (b) $5 "Myth of Orpheus" (104×89 *mm*) *Set of* 2 *sheets* 4·50

1987 (5 Nov). *Centenary of Statue of Liberty* (1986) (*2nd issue*). *Nos* 1110/19 *of Antigua optd with T* **95** (15, 30, 45, 50 *c.*, $1, $2, $5) *or T* **96** (60, 90 *c.*, $3), *in black* (50 *c.*, $3) *or silver* (*others*).
987 15 c. Lee Iacocca at unveiling of restored Statue 10
988 30 c. Statue at sunset (side view) 15
989 45 c. Aerial view of head 20
990 50 c. Lee Iacocca and torch 25
991 60 c. Workmen inside head of Statue (*horiz*) 25
992 90 c. Restoration work (*horiz*) 40
993 $1 Head of Statue 45
994 $2 Statue at Sunset (front view) 90
995 $3 Inspecting restoration work (*horiz*) .. 1·40
996 $5 Statue at night .. .. 2·25
987/96 .. .. *Set of* 10 5·75

1987 (5 Nov). *Entertainers. Nos.* 1120/7 *of Antigua optd with T* **95** (*in silver on* $3).
997 15 c. Grace Kelly 15
998 30 c. Marilyn Monroe 20
999 45 c. Orson Welles 35
1000 50 c. Judy Garland 40
1001 60 c. John Lennon 45
1002 $1 Rock Hudson 65
1003 $2 John Wayne .. .. 1·25
1004 $3 Elvis Presley .. .. 1·75
997/1004 .. .. *Set of* 8 4·75

1987 (5 Nov). *"Capex '87" International Stamp Exhibition, Toronto. Reptiles and Amphibians. Nos.* 1133/7 *of Antigua optd with T* **95** (*No.* **MS**1009) *or T* **96** (*others*).
1005 30 c. Whistling Frog 15
1006 60 c. Croaking Lizard 25
1007 $1 Antiguan Anole 45
1008 $3 Red-footed Tortoise .. .. .. 1·40
1005/8 .. .. *Set of* 4 1·90
MS1009 106×76 mm. $5 Ground Lizard .. 2·25

1988 (12 Jan). *Christmas. Religious Paintings. Nos.* 1144/8 *of Antigua optd with T* **95**.
1010 45 c. "Madonna and Child" (Bernardo Daddi) 20
1011 60 c. "St. Joseph" (detail, "The Nativity" (Sano di Pietro)) 25
1012 $1 "Virgin Mary" (detail, "The Nativity" (Sano di Pietro)) 45
1013 $4 "Music-making Angel" (Melozzo da Forli) .. .. 1·75
1010/13 .. .. *Set of* 4 2·40
MS1014 99×70 mm. $5 "The Flight into Egypt" (Sano di Pietro) .. .. 2·25

1988 (25 Mar). *Salvation Army's Community Service. Nos.* 1163/71 *of Antigua optd with T* **106**.
1015 25 c. First aid at daycare centre, Antigua .. 15 15
1016 30 c. Giving penicillin injection, Indonesia 15 15
1017 40 c. Children at daycare centre, Bolivia .. 25 25
1018 45 c. Rehabilitation of the handicapped, India 25 25
1019 50 c. Training blind man, Kenya 30 30
1020 60 c. Weighing baby, Ghana 30 30
1021 $1 Training typist, Zambia 50 50
1022 $2 Emergency food kitchen, Sri Lanka .. 95 95
1015/22 .. .. *Set of* 8 2·50 2·50
MS1023 152×83 mm. $5 General Eva Burrows 2·25 2·75

88 (6 May). *Bicentenary of U.S. Constitution. Nos.* 1139/43 *of Antigua optd with T* **95** *($4, $5) or T* **96** *(others), all in silver.*

24 15 c. House of Burgesses, Virginia ("Freedom of Speech") 10 10
25 45 c. State Seal, Connecticut 20 25
26 60 c. State Seal, Delaware 25 30
27 $4 Gouverneur Morris (Pennsylvania delegate) (*vert*) .. .. 1·75 1·90
024/7 .. .. *Set of* 4 2·10 2·25
S1028 105×75 mm. $5 Roger Sherman (Connecticut delegate) (*vert*) .. .. 2·25 2·75

88 (4 July). *Royal Ruby Wedding. Nos.* 1149/53 *of Antigua optd with T* **95.**

29 25 c. deep brown, black and bright new blue 15 15
30 60 c. multicoloured 25 30
31 $2 deep brown, black and light green .. 90 95
32 $3 multicoloured .. .. .. 1·40 1·50
029/32 .. .. *Set of* 4 2·40 2·50
S1033 102×77 mm. $5 multicoloured .. 2·25 2·75

88 (4 July). *Birds of Antigua. Nos.* 1154/62 *of Antigua optd with T* **95** *(10 c., $1, $5) or T* **96** *(others).*

34 10 c. Great Blue Heron 15 15
35 15 c. Ringed Kingfisher (*horiz*) 15 15
36 50 c. Bananaquit (*horiz*) 35 35
37 60 c. Purple Gallinule (*horiz*) 35 35
38 70 c. Blue-hooded Euphonia (*horiz*) .. 40 40
39 $1 Brown-throated Conure ("Caribbean Parakeet") 60 60
040 $3 Troupial (*horiz*) .. .. .. 1·60 1·60
041 $4 Purple-throated Carib (*horiz*) .. 2·00 2·00
034/41 .. .. *Set of* 8 5·00 5·00
S1042 Two sheets, each 115×86 mm. (a) $5 Greater Flamingo. (b) $5 Brown Pelican *Set of* 2 *sheets* 5·00 6·00

88 (25 July–8 Dec). *500th Anniv of Discovery of America by Columbus* (1992) (*1st issue*). *Nos.* 1172/80 *of Antigua optd with T* **96** (*Nos.* 1043/50) *or T* **95** (*No.* **MS**1051).

043 10 c. Columbus' second fleet, 1493 .. 10 10
044 30 c. Painos Indian village and fleet .. 15 15
045 45 c. *Santa Mariagalante* (flagship) and Painos village 25 25
046 60 c. Painos Indians offering Columbus fruit and vegetables 30 30
047 90 c. Painos Indian and Columbus with parrot 45 45
048 $1 Columbus landing on island 50 50
049 $3 Spanish soldier and fleet .. .. 1·50 1·50
050 $4 Fleet under sail .. .. .. 2·00 2·00
043/50 .. .. *Set of* 8 4·75 4·75
MS1051 Two sheets, each 110×80 nn. (a) $5 Queen Isabella's cross. (b) $5 Gold coin of Ferdinand and Isabella (8 Dec) *Set of* 2 *sheets* 4·25 4·50
See also Nos. 1112/16.

988 (25 July). *500th Birth Anniv of Titian. Nos.* 1181/9 *of Antigua optd with T* **96** (*Nos.* 1052/9) *or T* **95** (*No.* **MS**1060), *all in silver.*

052 30 c. "Bust of Christ" 15 15
053 40 c. "Scourging of Christ" 20 25
054 45 c. "Madonna in Glory with Saints" .. 20 25
055 50 c. "The Averoldi Polyptych" (detail) .. 25 30
056 $1 "Christ Crowned with Thorns" .. 45 50
057 $2 "Christ Mocked" 90 95
058 $3 "Christ and Simon of Cyrene" .. 1·40 1·50
059 $4 "Crucifixion with Virgin and Saints" 1·75 2·00
052/9 .. .. *Set of* 8 4·75 5·25
MS1060 Two sheets, each 110×95 mm. (a) $5 "Ecce Homo" (detail). (b) $5 "Noli me Tangere" (detail) *Set of* 2 *sheets* 4·50 5·50

1988 (25 Aug). *16th World Scout Jamboree, Australia. Nos.* 1128/32 *of Antigua optd with T* **95** (*No.* **MS**1064) *or T* **96** (*others*).

1061 10 c. Scouts around camp fire and Red Kangaroo 10 10
1062 60 c. Scouts canoeing and Blue-winged Kookaburra 35 35
1063 $1 Scouts on assault course and Ring-tailed Rock Wallaby 60 60
1064 $3 Field kitchen and Koala .. .. 1·60 1·60
1061/4 .. .. *Set of* 4 2·40 2·40
MS1065 103 × 78 mm. $5 Flags of Antigua, Australia and Scout Movement .. .. 2·50 3·00

1988 (25 Aug–8 Dec). *Sailing Week. Nos.* 1190/4 *of Antigua optd with T* **95** (*No.* **MS**1070) *or T* **96** (*others*).

1066 30 c. Two yachts rounding buoy 15 15
1067 60 c. Three yachts 35 35
1068 $1 British yacht under way 60 60
1069 $3 Three yachts (*different*) .. .. 1·40 1·40
1066/9 .. .. *Set of* 4 2·25 2·25
MS1070 103 × 92 mm. $5 Two yachts (8 Dec) 2·50 3·00

1988 (16 Sept). *Flowering Trees. Nos.* 1213/21 *of Antigua optd with T* **95.**

1071 10 c. Jacaranda 10 10
1072 30 c. Cordia 15 15
1073 50 c. Orchid Tree 20 25
1074 90 c. Flamboyant 40 45
1075 $1 African Tulip Tree 45 50
1076 $2 Potato Tree 80 85
1077 $3 Crepe Myrtle .. .. .. 1·25 1·40
1078 $4 Pitch Apple .. .. .. 1·60 1·75
1071/8 .. .. *Set of* 8 4·50 5·00
MS1079 Two sheets, each 106 × 76 mm. (a) $5 Cassia. (b) $5 Chinaberry .. *Set of* 2 *sheets* 4·25 5·00

1988 (16 Sept). *Olympic Games, Seoul. Nos.* 1222/6 *of Antigua optd with T* **95** (*Nos.* 1080/1, **MS**1084) *or T* **96** (*Nos.* 1082/3).

1080 40 c. Gymnastics 20 25
1081 60 c. Weightlifting 25 30
1082 $1 Water polo (*horiz*) 45 50
1083 $3 Boxing (*horiz*) .. .. .. 1·25 1·40
1080/3 .. .. *Set of* 4 1·90 2·25
MS1084 114 × 80 mm. $5 Runner with Olympic torch .. .. 2·10 2·40

1988 (8 Dec). *Caribbean Butterflies. Nos.* 1227/44 *of Antigua optd with T* **96.**

1085 1 c. Monarch 10 10
1086 2 c. Jamaican Clearwing 10 10
1087 3 c. Yellow-barred Ringlet 10 10
1088 5 c. Cracker 10 10
1089 10 c. Jamaican Mestra 10 10
1090 15 c. Mimic 10 10
1091 20 c. Silver Spot 10 10
1092 25 c. Zebra 10 10
1093 30 c. Fiery Sulphur 10 15
1094 40 c. Androgeus Swallowtail 15 20
1095 45 c. Giant Brimstone 20 25
1096 50 c. Orbed Sulphur 20 25
1097 60 c. Blue-backed Skipper 25 30
1098 $1 Common White Skipper 40 45
1099 $2 Baracoa Skipper 80 85
1100 $2.50, Mangrove Skipper .. .. 1·00 1·10
1101 $5 Silver King .. .. .. 2·10 2·25
1102 $10 Pygmy Skipper .. .. .. 4·00 4·25
1085/102 .. .. .. *Set of* 18 9·00 9·75

BARBUDA MAIL (111) BARBUDA MAIL (112)

1989 (28 Apr). *25th Death Anniv of John F. Kennedy (American statesman). Nos.* 1245/53 *of Antigua optd with T* **96** (*Nos.* 1103/10) *or T* **111** (*No.* **MS**1111).

1103 1 c. President Kennedy and family .. 10 10
1104 2 c. Kennedy commanding *PT109* .. 10 10
1105 3 c. Funeral cortege 10 10
1106 4 c. In motorcade, Mexico City 10 10
1107 30 c. As 1 c. 15 20
1108 60 c. As 4 c. 30 35
1109 $1 As 3 c. 45 50
1110 $4 As 2 c. .. .. 1·90 2·00
1103/10 .. .. .. *Set of* 8 2·75 3·00
MS1111 105 × 75 mm. $5 Kennedy taking presidential oath of office .. .. 2·40 2·75

1989 (24 May). *500th Anniv of Discovery of America by Columbus* (1992) (*2nd issue*). *Pre-Columbian Arawak Society. Nos.* 1267/71 *of Antigua optd with T* **112.**

1112 $1.50, Arawak warriors 70 75
a. Horiz strip of 4. Nos. 1112/15 .. 2·50
1113 $1.50, Whip dancers 70 75
1114 $1.50, Whip dancers and chief with pineapple 70 75
1115 $1.50, Family and camp fire 70 75
1112/15 .. .. .. *Set of* 4 2·50 2·75
MS1116 71 × 84 mm. $6 Arawak chief .. 2·75 3·00

REDONDA

DEPENDENCY OF ANTIGUA

Appendix

The following stamps were issued in anticipation of commercial and tourist development, philatelic mail being handled by a bureau in Antigua. Since at the present time the island is uninhabited, we do not list or stock these items. It is understood that the stamps are valid for the prepayment of postage in Antigua. Miniature sheets, imperforate stamps etc., are excluded from this section.

1979

Antigua 1976 *definitive issue optd* "REDONDA". 3, 5, 10, 25, 35, 50, 75 c., $1, $2.50, $5, $10.
Antigua Coronation Anniversary issue optd "REDONDA". 10, 30, 50, 90 c., $2.50.
Antigua World Cup Football Championship issue optd "REDONDA". 10, 15 c., $3.
Death Centenary of Sir Rowland Hill. 50, 90 c., $2.50, $3.
International Year of the Child. 25, 50 c., $1, $2.
Christmas. Paintings. 8, 50, 90 c., $3.

1980

Marine Life. 8, 25, 50 c., $4.
75th Anniv of Rotary International. 25, 50 c., $1, $2.
Birds of Redonda. 8, 10, 15, 25, 30, 50 c., $1, $2, $5.
Olympic Medal Winners, Lake Placid and Moscow. 8, 25, 50 c., $3.
80th Birthday of Queen Elizabeth the Queen Mother. 10 c., $2.50.
Christmas. Paintings. 8, 25, 50 c., $4.

1981

Royal Wedding. 25, 55 c., $4.
Christmas. Walt Disney Cartoon Characters. ½, 1, 2, 3, 4, 5, 10 c., $2.50, $3.
World Cup Football Championship, Spain (1982). 30 c. × 2, 50 c. × 2, $1 × 2, $2 × 2.

1982

Boy Scout Anniversaries. 8, 25, 50 c., $3, $5.
Butterflies. 8, 30, 50 c., $2.
21st Birthday of Princess of Wales. $2, $4.
Birth of Prince William of Wales. Optd on 21st Birthday of Princess of Wales issue. $2, $4.
Christmas. Walt Disney's "One Hundred and One Dalmatians". ½, 1, 2, 3, 4, 5, 10 c., $2.50, $3.

1983

Easter. 500th Birth Anniv of Raphael. 10, 50, 90 c., $4.
Bicentenary of Manned Flight. 10, 50, 90 c., $2.50.
Christmas. Walt Disney Cartoon Characters. "Deck the Halls". ½, 1, 2, 3, 4, 5, 10 c., $2.50, $3.

1984

Easter. Walt Disney Cartoon Characters. ½, 1, 2, 3, 4, 5, 10 c., $2, $4.
Olympic Games, Los Angeles. 10, 50, 90 c., $2.50.
Christmas. 50th Birthday of Donald Duck. 45, 60, 90 c., $2, $4.

1985

Birth Bicentenary of John J. Audubon (ornithologist) (1st issue). 60, 90 c., $1, $3.
Life and Times of Queen Elizabeth the Queen Mother. $1, $1.50, $2.50.
Royal Visit. 45 c., $1, $4.
150th Birth Anniv of Mark Twain (author). 25, 50 c., $1.50, $3.
Birth Bicentenaries of Grimm Brothers (folklorists). Walt Disney Cartoon Characters. 30, 60, 70 c., $4.

1986

Birth Bicentenary of John J. Audubon (ornithologist) (2nd issue). 90 c., $1, $1.50, $3.
Appearance of Halley's Comet. 5, 15, 55 c., $4.
Centenary of Statue of Liberty (1st issue). 20, 25, 30 c., $4.
60th Birthday of Queen Elizabeth II. 50, 60 c., $4.
Royal Wedding. 60 c., $1, $4.
Christmas (1st issue). Disney characters in Hans Andersen Stories. 30, 60, 70 c., $4.
Christmas (2nd issue). "Wind in the Willows" (Kenneth Grahame). 25, 50 c., $1.50, $3.

1987

"Capex '87" International Stamp Exhibition, Toronto. Disney characters illustrating Art of Animation. 25, 30, 50, 60, 70 c., $1.50, $3, $4.
Birth Centenary of Marc Chagall (artist). 10, 30, 40, 60, 90 c., $1, $3, $4.
Centenary of Statue of Liberty (2nd issue). 10, 15, 25, 30, 40, 60, 70, 90 c., $1, $2, $3, $4.
250th Death Anniv of Sir Isaac Newton (scientist). 20 c., $2.50.
750th Anniv of Berlin. $1, $4.
Bicentenary of U.S. Constitution. 30 c., $3.
16th World Scout Jamboree, Australia. 10 c., $4.

1988

500th Anniv of Discovery of America by Columbus (1992) (*1st issue*). 15, 30, 45, 60, 90 c., $1, $2, $3.
"Finlandia '88" International Stamp Exhibition, Helsinki. Disney characters in Finnish scenes. 1, 2, 3, 4, 5, 6 c., $5, $6.
Olympic Games, Seoul. 25, 60 c., $1.25, $3.
500th Birth Anniv of Titian. 10, 25, 40, 70, 90 c., $2, $3, $4.

1989

20th Anniv of First Manned Landing on Moon. Disney characters on Moon. ½, 1, 2, 3, 4, 5 c., $5, $6.
500th Anniv of Discovery of America by Columbus (1992) (*2nd issue*). *Pre-Columbian Societies*. 15, 45 c., $2, $3.

Ascension

DEPENDENCY OF ST. HELENA

Ascension, first occupied in 1815, was retained as a Royal Iavy establishment from 1816 until 20 October 1922 when it ecame a dependency of St. Helena by Letters Patent.

Under Post Office regulations of 1850 (ratings) and 1854 officers) mail from men of the Royal Navy serving abroad had he postage prepaid in Great Britain stamps, supplies of which vere issued to each ship. Great Britain stamps used on scension before 1860 may have been provided by the naval fficer in charge of the postal service.

The British G.P.O. assumed responsibility for such matters in 860, but failed to send any stamps to the island until 1867.

Until about 1880 naval mail, which made up most early orrespondence, did not have the stamps cancelled until arrival n England. The prices quoted for Nos. Z1/3 and Z6 are for xamples on cover or large piece showing the Great Britain tamps cancelled on arrival and an Ascension postmark struck lsewhere on the front of the envelope.

The use of British stamps ceased in December 1922.

The following postmarks were used on Great Britain stamps rom Ascension:

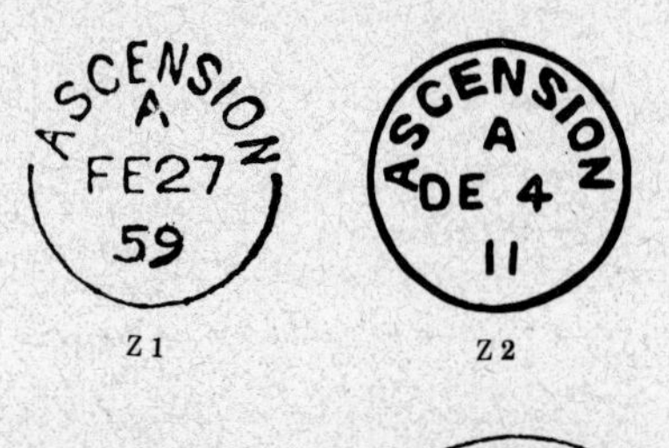

Z 1 Z 2

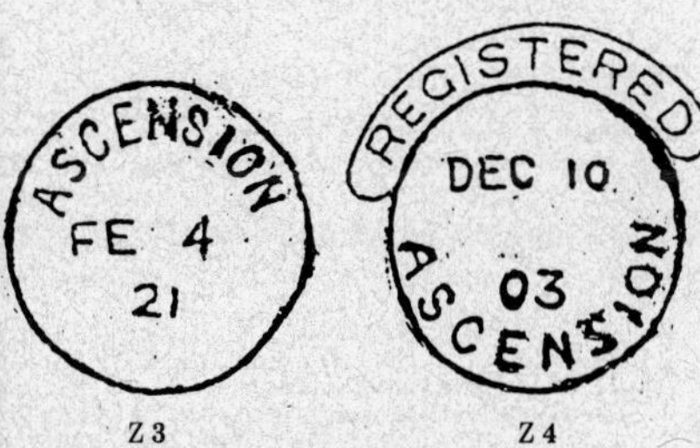

Z 3 Z 4

Z 5

Postmark Type	*Approx Period of Use*	*Diameter*	*Index Letter*
Z 1	1858–1862	20 mm	A
Z 2	1864–1872	20 mm	A
	1872–1878	21½ mm	A
	1879–1889	19½ mm	A
	1891–1894	21½ mm	C
	1894–1902	22 mm	A
	1903–1907	20½ mm	A
	1908–1920	21 mm	A or none
	1909–1920	23 mm	C sideways (1909), none (1910–11), B (1911–20)
Z 3	1920–1922	24 mm	none
Z 4	1897–1903 Registered	23 mm	none
Z 5	1900–1902 Registered	28 mm	C
	1903–1904 Registered	29 mm	A

Forged postmarks exist. Those found most frequently are genuine postmarks of the post-1922 period with earlier date slugs fraudulently inserted, namely a 20 mm postmark as Type Z 2 (because of the shape of the "O" in "ASCENSION" this is often known as the Square O postmark) and a 24 mm postmark as Type Z 3 but with the index letter A.

Stamps of GREAT BRITAIN *cancelled with Types* Z 1/5.

Line-engraved issues.

Z 1 1d. red-brown (1855) £1400
Z 2 1d. rose-red (1864–79) .. .. .. *From* £850
Plate Nos. 71, 74, 78, 83, 85, 96, 100, 102, 103, 104, 122, 134, 138, 154, 155, 157, 160, 168, 178

Surface-printed issues (1856–1883).

Z 2*a* 6d. lilac (1856) .. ..
Z 3 6d. lilac (1865) (Plate No. 5) £1600
Z 4 1s. green (1865) (Plate No. 4) .. .. ..
Z 5 1s. green (1867) (Plate No. 7) .. .. ..
Z 6 6d. grey (1874) (Plate Nos. 15, 16, 17) £1300
Z 6*a* 6d. on 6d. lilac (1883) .. ..
Z 7 1d. lilac (1881) (16 *dots*) .. .. .. 20·00

1887–92.

Z 8 ½d. vermilion .. .. 25·00
Z 9 1½d. purple and green .. .. 60·00
Z10 2d. green and carmine .. .. 65·00
Z11 2½d. purple/*blue* .. .. 25·00
Z12 3d. purple/*yellow* .. .. 80·00
Z13 4d. green and brown .. .. 85·00
Z14 4½d. green and carmine £275
Z15 5d. dull purple and blue .. .. 90·00
Z16 6d. purple/*rose-red* .. .. 85·00
Z17 9d. purple and blue £120
Z17*a* 10d. dull purple and carmine £200
Z18 1s. green £140

1900.

Z19 ½d. blue-green .. .. 22·00
Z20 1s. green and carmine £140

King Edward VII issues (1902–1911).

Z21 ½d. green .. .. 16·00
Z22 1d. red .. .. 15·00
Z23 1½d. purple and green .. .. 45·00
Z24 2d. green and carmine .. .. 42·00
Z25 2½d. blue .. .. 42·00
Z26 3d. purple/*yellow* .. .. 55·00
Z27 4d. green and brown £140
Z28 4d. orange (1909) .. .. 90·00
Z29 5d. purple and blue .. .. 90·00
Z30 6d. purple .. .. 90·00
Z31 7d. grey-black (1910) £225
Z32 9d. purple and blue (1910) £100
Z32*a* 10d. dull purple and scarlet £160
Z33 1s. green and carmine .. .. 55·00
Z33*a* 2s. 6d. dull reddish purple (1911) £500
Z34 5s. carmine £700
Z35 10s. ultramarine £1100
Z35*a* £1 green £2250

1911–12. *T* **98/9** *of Great Britain.*

Z36 ½d. green (Die A) .. .. 55·00
Z37 ½d. yellow-green (Die B) .. .. 20·00
Z38 1d. scarlet (Die B) .. .. 55·00

1912. *T* **101/2** *of Great Britain.*

Z38*a* ½d. green .. .. 55·00
Z38*b* 1d. scarlet .. .. 55·00

1912–22.

Z39 ½d. green (1913) .. .. 16·00
Z40 1d. scarlet .. .. 14·00
Z41 1½d. red-brown .. .. 20·00
Z42 2d. orange (Die I) .. .. 20·00
Z42*a* 2d. orange (Die II) (1921) .. .. 70·00
Z43 2½d. blue .. .. 24·00
Z44 3d. violet .. .. 27·00
Z45 4d. grey-green (1913) .. .. 35·00
Z46 5d. brown (1913) .. .. 32·00
Z47 6d. purple (1913) .. .. 32·00
Z47*a* 7d. green (1913) £250
Z47*b* 8d. black/*yellow* (1913) £200
Z48 9d. agate (1913) £110
Z49 9d. olive-green (1922) £160
Z50 10d. turquoise-blue (1913) £150
Z51 1s. bistre (1913) £110
Z52 2s. 6d. brown (1918) £600

Supplies of some values do not appear to have been sent to the island, known examples originating from maritime or philatelic mail.

PRICES FOR STAMPS ON COVER TO 1945
Nos. 1/34 *from* × 4
Nos. 35/7 *from* × 8
Nos. 38/47 *from* × 5

ASCENSION

(1)

Line through "P" of "POSTAGE" (R. 3/6)

1922 (2 Nov). *Stamps of St. Helena, optd with T* **1** *by D.L.R.*

(*a*) *Wmk Mult Script CA*

1 **16** ½d. black and green .. .. .. 2·75 7·00
2 **17** 1d. green .. .. 3·00 8·00
3 1½d. rose-scarlet .. .. 12·00 25·00
4 **16** 2d. black and grey .. .. .. 10·00 10·00
a. Line through "P" of "POSTAGE" .. £120
5 3d. bright blue .. .. 10·00 14·00
6 **17** 8d. black and dull purple .. .. 24·00 28·00
7 2s. black and blue/*blue* £100 £110
8 3s. black and violet £150 £170

(*b*) *Wmk Mult Crown CA*

9 **16** 1s. black/*green* (R.) .. .. .. 24·00 27·00
1/9 .. .. *Set of* 9 £300 £350
1/9 Optd "Specimen" .. .. .. *Set of* 9 £600

PLATE FLAWS ON THE 1924–33 ISSUE. Many constant plate varieties exist on both the vignette and duty plates of this issue.

The three major varieties are illustrated and listed below with prices for mint examples. Fine used stamps showing these flaws are worth a considerable premium over the mint prices quoted.

This issue utilised the same vignette plate as the St. Helena 1922–36 set so that these flaws occur there also.

2 Badge of St. Helena

Broken mainmast. Occurs on R.2/1 of all values.

Torn flag. Occurs on R.4/6 of all values except the 5d. Retouched on sheets of ½d. and 1d. printed after 1927.

Cleft rock. Occurs on R.5/1 of all values.

(Typo D.L.R.)

1924 (20 Aug)–**33.** *T* **2**. *Wmk Mult Script CA. P* 14.

10 ½d. grey-black and black, **C** .. .. .. 1·50 4·00
a. Broken mainmast .. .. .. 30·00
b. Torn flag .. .. 32·00
c. Cleft rock .. .. 26·00
11 1d. grey-black and deep blue-green, **C** .. 2·50 4·00
a. Broken mainmast .. .. .. 32·00
b. Torn flag .. .. 35·00
c. Cleft rock .. .. 27·00
11*d* 1d. grey-black & bt blue-green, **C** (1933) .. 65·00 £250
da. Broken mainmast £200
dc. Cleft rock £190
12 1½d. rose-red, **C** .. .. 4·00 11·00
a. Broken mainmast .. .. .. 42·00
b. Torn flag .. .. 42·00
c. Cleft rock .. .. 38·00
13 2d. grey-black and grey, **C** .. .. .. 4·00 3·00
a. Broken mainmast .. .. .. 45·00
b. Torn flag .. .. 45·00
c. Cleft rock .. .. 40·00
14 3d. blue, **C** .. .. 3·75 7·50
a. Broken mainmast .. .. .. 50·00
b. Torn flag .. .. 50·00
c. Cleft rock .. .. 45·00
15 4d. grey-black and black/*yellow*, **C** .. .. 27·00 48·00
a. Broken mainmast £100
b. Torn flag £100
c. Cleft rock .. .. 90·00
15*d* 5d. purple and olive-green, **C** (8.27) .. .. 9·50 16·00
da. Broken mainmast .. .. .. 70·00
dc. Cleft rock .. .. 60·00
16 6d. grey-black and bright purple, **C** .. .. 38·00 60·00
a. Broken mainmast £150
b. Torn flag £150
c. Cleft rock £130
17 8d. grey-black and bright violet, **C** .. .. 10·00 23·00
a. Broken mainmast .. .. .. 75·00
b. Torn flag .. .. 75·00
c. Cleft rock .. .. 65·00
18 1s. grey-black and brown, **C** .. .. .. 16·00 26·00
a. Broken mainmast .. .. .. 80·00
b. Torn flag .. .. 80·00
c. Cleft rock .. .. 70·00
19 2s. grey-black and blue/*blue*, **C** .. .. 55·00 70·00
a. Broken mainmast £200
b. Torn flag £200
c. Cleft rock £180

20 3s. grey-black and black/*blue*, C .. .. 80·00 85·00
a. Broken mainmast £325
b. Torn flag £325
c. Cleft rock £300
10/20 .. .. *Set of* 12 £225 £325
10/20 Optd "Specimen" .. .. *Set of* 12 £500

3 Georgetown

4 Ascension Island

(Des and recess D.L.R.)

1934 (2 July). *T* **3/4** *and similar designs. Wmk Mult Script CA. P* 14.
21 3 ½d. black and violet 45 80
22 4 1d. black and emerald .. .. .. 1·40 1·25
23 – 1½d. black and scarlet .. .. .. 1·50 1·75
24 4 2d. black and orange .. .. .. 1·75 1·75
25 – 3d. black and ultramarine .. .. 1·75 1·50
26 – 5d. black and blue .. .. .. 2·00 3·00
27 4 8d. black and sepia .. .. .. 4·00 4·75
28 – 1s. black and carmine .. .. .. 12·00 6·00
29 4 2s. 6d. black and bright purple .. 25·00 32·00
30 – 5s. black and brown .. .. .. 45·00 55·00
21/30 .. .. *Set of* 10 85·00 £100
21/30 Perf "Specimen" .. .. *Set of* 10 £200
Designs: *Horiz*—1½d. The Pier; 3d. Long Beach; 5d. Three Sisters; 1s. Sooty Tern and Wideawake Fair; 5s. Green Mountain.

1935 (6 May). *Silver Jubilee. As Nos.* 91/4 *of Antigua, but ptd by Waterlow. P* 11 × 12.
31 1½d. deep blue and scarlet .. .. .. 3·50 3·50
k. Kite and horizontal log .. .. .. 40·00
32 2d. ultramarine and grey .. .. .. 7·50 10·00
k. Kite and horizontal log .. .. .. 60·00
33 5d. green and indigo .. .. .. 10·00 11·00
j. Kite and vertical log .. .. .. 80·00
k. Kite and horizontal log .. .. .. 80·00
34 1s. slate and purple .. .. 18·00 25·00
31/4 .. .. *Set of* 4 35·00 45·00
31/4 Perf "Specimen" .. .. *Set of* 4 95·00
For illustrations of plate varieties see Omnibus section following Zululand.

1937 (19 May). *Coronation. As Nos.* 13/15 *of Aden. P* 14.
35 1d. green 50 50
36 2d. orange 90 40
37 3d. bright blue .. .. 1·50 50
35/7 .. .. *Set of* 3 2·50 1·25
35/7 Perf "Specimen" .. .. *Set of* 3 85·00

10 The Pier

Long centre bar to "E" in "GEORGETOWN" (R. 2/3)

"Davit" flaw (R. 5/1) (all ptgs of 1½d. and 2s. 6d.)

(Recess D.L.R.)

1938 (12 May)–**53**. *Horiz designs as King George V issue, but modified and with portrait of King George VI as in T* **10**. *Wmk Mult Script CA. P* 13½.
38 3 ½d. black and violet 55 40
a. Long centre bar to E .. .. 10·00
b. Perf 13. *Black and bluish violet* (17.5.44) 20 40
ba. Long centre bar to E .. .. 7·00
39 – 1d. black and green .. .. .. 48·00 8·00
39*a* – 1d. black and yellow-orange (8.7.40) .. 6·00 11·00
b. Perf 13 (5.42) 25 40
c. Perf 14 (17.2.49) .. .. .. 70 7·00
39*d* – 1d. black and green, *p* 13 (1.6.49) .. 20 30
40 10 1½d. black and vermilion .. .. 1·50 1·40
a. Davit flaw .. .. 35·00
b. Perf 13 (17.5.44) 70 80
ba. Davit flaw .. .. 18·00
c. Perf 14 (17.2.49) .. .. .. 3·50 13·00
ca. Davit flaw .. .. 40·00
40*d* 1½d. black and rose-carmine, *p* 14 (1.6.49) 45 80
da. Davit flaw .. .. 15·00
db. *Black and carmine* .. .. .. 4·00 5·00
dba. Davit flaw .. .. 40·00
e. Perf 13 (25.2.53) .. .. .. 45 5·00
ea. Davit flaw .. .. 15·00
41 – 2d. black and red-orange 85 60
a. Perf 13 (17.5.44) 80 40
b. Perf 14 (17.2.49) .. .. .. 5·00 24·00
41*c* – 2d. black and scarlet, *p* 14 (1.6.49) .. 35 30
42 – 3d. black and ultramarine .. .. 95·00 26·00
42*a* – 3d. black and grey (8.7.40) .. .. 2·75 90
b. Perf 13 (17.5.44) 50 40
42*c* – 4d. black and ultramarine (8.7.40) .. 1·75 1·00
d. Perf 13 (17.5.44) .. .. .. 1·50 1·00
43 – 6d. black and blue .. .. .. 1·75 40
a. Perf 13 (17.5.44) .. .. .. 4·50 1·75
44 3 1s. black and sepia .. .. .. 3·25 70
a. Perf 13 (17.5.44) .. .. .. 1·75 1·25
45 10 2s. 6d. black and deep carmine .. 15·00 7·00
a. Frame printed double, once albino
b. Davit flaw .. .. 85·00
c. Perf 13 (17.5.44) .. .. .. 15·00 24·00
ca. Davit flaw .. .. 85·00
46 – 5s. black and yellow-brown .. .. 40·00 7·00
a. Perf 13 (17.5.44) .. .. .. 17·00 20·00
47 – 10s. black and bright purple .. .. 65·00 30·00
a. Perf 13 (17.5.44) .. .. .. 42·00 40·00
38/47a .. .. *Set of* 16 £200 75·00
38/47 Perf "Specimen" .. .. *Set of* 13 £325
Designs: *Horiz*—1d. (Nos. 39/*c*), 2d., 4d. Green Mountain; 1d. (No. 39*d*), 6d., 10s. Three Sisters; 3d., 5s. Long Beach.

1946 (21 Oct). *Victory. As Nos.* 28/9 *of Aden.*
48 2d. red-orange 40 25
49 4d. blue 40 25
48/9 Perf "Specimen" .. .. *Set of* 2 70·00

1948 (20 Oct). *Royal Silver Wedding. As Nos.* 30/1 *of Aden.*
50 3d. black 50 30
51 10s. bright purple .. .. 42·00 35·00

1949 (10 Oct). 75*th Anniv of Universal Postal Union. As Nos.* 114/17 *of Antigua.*
52 3d. carmine .. .. 1·40 1·00
53 4d. deep blue .. .. 4·50 1·10
54 6d. olive .. .. 5·50 2·00
55 1s. blue-black .. .. 6·00 1·50
52/5 .. .. *Set of* 4 16·00 5·00

1953 (2 June). *Coronation. As No.* 47 *of Aden.*
56 3d. black and grey-black .. .. .. 1·25 1·50

15 Water Catchment

(Recess B.W.)

1956 (19 Nov). *T* **15** *and similar horiz designs. Wmk Mult Script CA. P* 13.
57 ½d. black and brown 10 25
58 1d. black and magenta 45 30
59 1½d. black and orange 30 30
60 2d. black and carmine-red 50 40
61 2½d. black and orange-brown 50 45
62 3d. black and blue .. .. .. 2·00 1·00
63 4d. black and deep turquoise-green .. 1·25 1·00
64 6d. black and indigo .. .. .. 1·25 90
65 7d. black and deep olive .. .. 1·00 1·00
66 1s. black and vermilion .. .. .. 1·00 90
67 2s. 6d. black and deep dull purple .. 20·00 6·50
68 5s. black and blue-green .. .. 26·00 13·00
69 10s. black and purple .. .. .. 42·00 28·00
57/69 .. .. *Set of* 13 85·00 48·00
Designs:—1d. Map of Ascension; 1½d. View of Georgetown; 2d. Map showing cable network; 2½d. Mountain road; 3d. White-tailed Tropic Bird; 4d. Long-finned Tunny; 6d. Rollers on the seashore; 7d. Young turtles; 1s. Land Crab; 2s. 6d. Sooty Tern; 5s. Perfect Crater; 10s. View of Ascension from North-west.

28 Brown Booby

42 Satellite Station

(Des after photos by N. P. Ashmole. Photo Harrison)

1963 (23 May). *T* **28** *and similar horiz designs. W* w **12**. *P* 14 × 14½.
70 1d. black, lemon and new blue 10 10
71 1½d. black, cobalt and ochre 20 10
a. Cobalt omitted .. .. 50·00
72 2d. black, grey and bright blue 20 10
73 3d. black, magenta and turquoise-blue .. 25 15
74 4½d. black, bistre-brown and new blue .. 30 20
75 6d. bistre, black and yellow-green .. 30 20
76 7d. black, brown and reddish violet .. 35 20
77 10d. black, greenish yellow and blue-green .. 45
78 1s. multicoloured 50
79 1s. 6d. multicoloured .. .. .. 3·25
80 2s. 6d. multicoloured .. .. .. 4·25
81 5s. multicoloured .. .. 6·00
82 10s. multicoloured .. .. 12·00
83 £1 multicoloured .. .. 22·00
70/83 .. .. *Set of* 14 45·00
Designs:—1½d. White-capped Noddy; 2d. White Tern; 3d. Re[d-]billed Tropic Bird; 4½d. Common Noddy; 6d. Sooty Tern; 7[d.] Ascension Frigate Bird; 10d. Blue-faced Booby; 1s. White-tail[ed] Tropic Bird; 1s. 6d. Red-billed Tropic Bird; 2s. 6d. Madeiran Stor[m] Petrel; 5s. Red-footed Booby (brown phase); 10s. Ascension Friga[te] Birds; £1 Red-footed Booby (white phase).

1963 (4 June). *Freedom from Hunger. As No.* 76 *of Aden.*
84 1s. 6d. carmine .. .. 3·00

1963 (2 Sept). *Red Cross Centenary. As Nos.* 147/8 *of Antigua.*
85 3d. red and black .. .. 2·25
86 1s. 6d. red and blue .. .. 4·75

1965 (17 May). *I.T.U. Centenary. As Nos.* 166/7 *of Antigua.*
87 3d. magenta and bluish violet .. .. 1·25
88 6d. turquoise-blue and light chestnut .. 1·50

1965 (25 Oct). *International Co-operation Year. As Nos.* 168/9 [of] *Antigua.*
89 1d. reddish purple and turquoise-green .. 50
90 6d. deep bluish green and lavender .. .. 1·50

1966 (24 Jan). *Churchill Commemoration. As Nos.* 170/3 [of] *Antigua.*
91 1d. new blue 50
92 3d. deep green .. .. 2·75
93 6d. brown .. .. 3·50
94 1s. 6d. bluish violet .. .. 4·50
91/4 .. .. *Set of* 4 10·00

1966 (1 July). *World Cup Football Championships. As Nos.* 176[/7] *of Antigua.*
95 3d. violet, yellow-green, lake and yell-brn .. 1·25
96 6d. chocolate, blue-green, lake & yellow-brn 1·50

1966 (20 Sept). *Inauguration of W.H.O. Headquarters, Geneva. A[s] Nos.* 178/9 *of Antigua.*
97 3d. black, yellow-green and light blue .. 1·75
98 1s. 6d. black, light purple and yellow-brown 4·25

(Des V. Whiteley. Photo Harrison)

1966 (7 Nov). *Opening of Apollo Communications Satellite Eart[h] Station. W* w **12**. (*sideways*). *P* 14 × 14½.
99 42 4d. black and reddish violet 15
100 8d. black and deep bluish green 20
101 1s. 3d. black and olive-brown 25
102 2s. 6d. black and turquoise-blue 35
99/102 .. .. *Set of* 4 85

43 B.B.C. Emblem

44 Human Rights Emblem and Chain Links

(Des B.B.C. staff. Photo, Queen's head and emblem die-stamped Harrison)

1966 (1 Dec). *Opening of B.B.C. Relay Station. W* w **12.** *P* 14½.
103 43 1d. gold and ultramarine 10
104 3d. gold and myrtle-green 10
105 6d. gold and reddish violet 15
106 1s. 6d. gold and red 20
103/6 .. .. *Set of* 4 50

1967 (1 Jan). 20*th Anniv of U.N.E.S.C.O. As Nos.* 196/8 [of] *Antigua.*
107 3d. slate-violet, red, yellow and orange .. 2·25
108 6d. orange-yellow, violet and deep olive .. 3·50
109 1s. 6d. black, bright purple and orange .. 5·50
107/9 .. .. *Set of* 3 10·00

(Des and litho Harrison)

1968 (8 July). *Human Rights Year. W* w **12** (*sideways*). *P* 14½ × 14.
110 44 6d. light orange, red and black 20
111 1s. 6d. light grey-blue, red and black .. 30
112 2s. 6d. light green, red and black .. 35
110/12 .. .. *Set of* 3 75

45 Ascension Black-Fish

46 H.M.S. *Rattlesnake*

(Des M. Farrar Bell. Litho D.L.R.)

1968 (23 Oct). *Fishes (1st series). T* **45** *and similar horiz designs. W* w **12** *(sideways). P* 13.

113	4d. black, slate and turquoise-blue	60	20
114	8d. multicoloured	75	35
115	1s. 9d. multicoloured	1·00	40
116	2s. 3d. multicoloured	1·25	45
113/16	*Set of* 4	3·25	1·25

Designs:—8d. Leather-jacket; 1s. 9d. Tunny; 2s. 3d. Mako Shark.
See also Nos. 117/20 and 126/9.

(Des M. Farrar Bell. Litho D.L.R.)

1969 (3 Mar). *Fishes (2nd series). Horiz designs as T* **45**. *Multicoloured. W* w **12** *(sideways). P* 13.

117	4d. Sailfish	90	55
118	6d. Old Wife	1·25	70
119	1s. 6d. Yellowtail	2·00	1·25
120	2s. 11d. Jack	3·75	2·25
117/20	*Set of* 4	7·00	4·25

(Des L. Curtis. Photo Harrison)

1969 (1 Oct). *Royal Naval Crests (1st series). T* **46** *and similar vert designs. W* w **12** *(sideways). P* 14 × 14½.

121	4d. multicoloured	50	15
122	9d. multicoloured	70	15
123	1s. 9d. deep blue, pale blue and gold	1·25	25
124	2s. 3d. multicoloured	1·50	30
121/4	*Set of* 4	3·50	75
MS125	165 × 105 mm. Nos. 121/4. P 14½	7·50	6·50

Designs:—9d. H.M.S. *Weston*; 1s. 9d. H.M.S. *Undaunted*; 2s. 3d. H.M.S. *Eagle*.
See also Nos. 130/4, 149/53, 154/8 and 166/70.

(Des M. Farrar Bell. Litho D.L.R.)

1970 (6 Apr). *Fishes (3rd series). Horiz designs as T* **45**. *Multicoloured. W* w **12** *(sideways). P* 14.

126	4d. Wahoo	2·50	1·25
127	9d. Coal-fish	2·75	1·50
128	1s. 9d. Dolphin	3·25	2·00
129	2s. 3d. Soldier Fish	3·75	2·25
126/9	*Set of* 4	11·00	6·25

(Des L. Curtis. Photo D.L.R.)

1970 (7 Sept). *Royal Naval Crests (2nd series). Designs as T* **46**. *Multicoloured. W* w **12**. *P* 12½.

130	4d. H.M.S. *Penelope*	75	35
131	9d. H.M.S. *Carlisle*	1·00	60
132	1s. 6d. H.M.S. *Amphion*	1·75	85
133	2s. 6d. H.M.S. *Magpie*	2·00	1·25
130/3	*Set of* 4	5·00	2·75
MS134	153 × 96 mm. Nos. 130/3	8·00	8·00

50 Early Chinese Rocket   **51** Course of the *Quest*

(Des V. Whiteley. Litho Format)

1971 (15 Feb). *Decimal Currency. The Evolution of Space Travel. T* **50** *and similar multicoloured designs. W* w **12** *(sideways on horiz designs). P* 14.

135	½p. Type **50**	15	15
136	1p. Medieval Arab Astronomers	20	15
137	1½p. Tycho Brahe's Observatory, Quadrant and Supernova	25	25
138	2p. Galileo, Moon and Telescope	40	30
139	2½p. Isaac Newton, Instruments and Apple	45	40
140	3½p. Harrison's Chronometer and Ship	55	45
141	4½p. Space Rocket taking-off	85	50
142	5p. World's Largest Telescope, Palomar	1·00	60
143	7½p. World's largest Radio Telescope, Jodrell Bank	3·25	1·40
144	10p. Mariner VII and Mars	3·25	1·60
145	12½p. Sputnik II and Space Dog, Laika	4·50	2·00
146	25p. Walking in Space	5·50	2·25
147	50p. Apollo XI Crew on Moon	4·50	2·50
148	£1 Future Space Research Station	5·50	4·00
135/48	*Set of* 14	27·00	15·00

The ½p., 1p., 4½p. and 25p. are vertical, and the remainder are horizontal.

(Des L. Curtis. Photo D.L.R.)

1971 (15 Nov). *Royal Naval Crests (3rd series). Designs as T* **46**. *Multicoloured. W* w **12**. *P* 13.

149	2p. H.M.S. *Phoenix*	70	30
150	4p. H.M.S. *Milford*	1·25	55
151	9p. H.M.S. *Pelican*	1·40	80
152	15p. H.M.S. *Oberon*	1·75	1·00
149/52	*Set of* 4	4·50	2·40
MS153	151 × 104 mm. Nos. 149/52	7·50	9·00

(Des L. Curtis. Litho Questa)

1972 (29 May). *Royal Naval Crests (4th series). Multicoloured designs as T* **46**. *W* w **12** *(sideways). P* 14.

154	1½p. H.M.S. *Lowestoft*	50	50
155	3p. H.M.S. *Auckland*	75	75
156	6p. H.M.S. *Nigeria*	90	1·25
157	17½p. H.M.S. *Bermuda*	2·00	2·50
154/7	*Set of* 4	3·75	4·50
MS158	157 × 93 mm. Nos. 154/7	3·75	7·00

(Des J. Cooter. Litho Questa)

1972 (2 Aug). *50th Anniv of Shackleton's Death. T* **51** *and similar multicoloured designs. W* w **12** *(sideways on 4 and 7½p.). P* 14.

159	2½p. Type **51**	1·00	60
160	4p. Shackleton and *Quest* (*horiz*)	1·10	70
161	7½p. Shackleton's cabin and *Quest* (*horiz*)	1·25	75
162	11p. Shackleton's statue and memorial	1·40	1·00
159/62	*Set of* 4	4·25	2·75
MS163	139 × 114 mm. Nos. 159/62 (wmk sideways)	4·50	6·00

52 Land Crab and Mako Shark

(Des (from photograph by D. Groves) and photo Harrison)

1972 (20 Nov). *Royal Silver Wedding. Multicoloured; background colour given. W* w **12**. *P* 14 × 14½.

164 **52**	2p. bright bluish violet	15	10
165	16p. rose-carmine	35	30

(Des L. Curtis. Litho J.W.)

1973 (28 May). *Royal Naval Crests (5th series). Multicoloured designs as T* **46**. *W* w **12** *(sideways). P* 14.

166	2p. H.M.S. *Birmingham*	2·25	1·00
167	4p. H.M.S. *Cardiff*	2·75	1·00
168	9p. H.M.S. *Penzance*	3·75	1·25
169	13p. H.M.S. *Rochester*	4·00	1·50
166/9	*Set of* 4	11·50	4·25
MS170	109 × 152 mm. Nos. 166/9	19·00	10·00

53 Green Turtle

(Des V. Whiteley Studio. Litho Enschedé)

1973 (28 Aug). *Turtles. T* **53** *and similar triangular designs. Multicoloured. W* w **12**. *P* 13½.

171	4p. Type **53**	2·75	1·00
172	9p. Loggerhead turtle	3·25	1·50
173	12p. Hawksbill turtle	3·50	1·50
171/3	*Set of* 3	8·50	3·50

54 Sergeant, R.M. Light Infantry, 1900   **55** Letter and H.Q., Berne

(Des G. Drummond from paintings by C. Stadden. Litho Walsall)

1973 (31 Oct). *50th Anniv of Departure of Royal Marines from Ascension. T* **54** *and similar vert designs. Multicoloured. W* w **12** *(sideways). P* 14.

174	2p. Type **54**	2·50	1·25
175	6p. R.M. Private, 1816	3·50	1·75
176	12p. R.M. Light Infantry Officer, 1880	4·00	2·25
177	20p. R.M. Artillery Colour Sergeant, 1910	4·50	2·50
174/7	*Set of* 4	13·00	7·00

1973 (14 Nov). *Royal Wedding. As Nos. 165/6 of Anguilla. Centre multicoloured. W* w **12** *(sideways). P* 13½.

178	2p. ochre	15	10
179	18p. dull blue-green	25	15

(Des PAD Studio. Litho Questa)

1974 (27 Mar). *Centenary of U.P.U. T* **55** *and similar horiz design. Multicoloured. W* w **12**. *P* 14½ × 14.

180	2p. Type **55**	25	30
181	9p. Hermes and U.P.U. monument	40	45

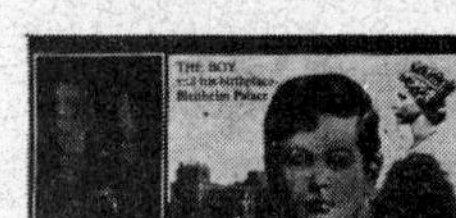

56 Churchill as a Boy, and Birthplace, Blenheim Palace

(Des J.W. Litho Questa)

1974 (30 Nov). *Birth Centenary of Sir Winston Churchill. T* **56** *and similar horiz design. Multicoloured. No wmk. P* 14.

182	5p. Type **56**	40	40
183	25p. Churchill as statesman, and U.N. Building	1·00	1·00
MS184	93 × 87 mm. Nos. 182/3	2·00	2·50

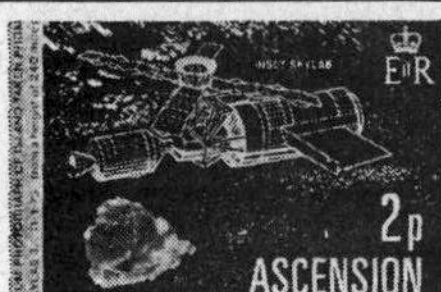

57 "Skylab 3" and Photograph of Ascension

(Des PAD Studio. Litho Questa)

1975 (20 Mar). *Space Satellites. T* **57** *and similar horiz design. Multicoloured. W* w **12** *(sideways). P* 14.

185	2p. Type **57**	20	25
186	18p. "Skylab 4" command module and photograph	30	40

The date "11.1.73" given on the 2p. is incorrect, "Skylab 3" was launched in July 1973 and returned to Earth in September 1973.

The date on the 18p. is also incorrect. The photograph was taken on 6 January 1974, three days later than the date given in the caption.

58 U.S.A.F. "Starlifter"

APOLLO-SOYUZ
LINK
1975

(**59**)

(Des R. Granger Barrett. Litho Questa)

1975 (19 June). *Wideawake Airfield. T* **58** *and similar horiz designs. Multicoloured. W* w **12** *(sideways). P* 13½.

187	2p. Type **58**	90	55
188	5p. R.A.F. "Hercules"	1·25	75
189	9p. Vickers "VC-10"	1·60	1·25
190	24p. U.S.A.F. "Galaxy"	2·50	2·50
187/90	*Set of* 4	5·75	4·50
MS191	144 × 99 mm. Nos. 187/90	8·50	11·00

1975 (18 Aug). *"Apollo–Soyuz" Space Link. Nos. 141 and 145/6 optd with T* **59**.

192	4½p. Space rocket taking-off	10	15
193	12½p. Sputnik II and Space Dog, Laika	20	20
194	25p. Walking in Space	40	35
192/4	*Set of* 3	60	65

60 Arrival of Royal Navy, 1815

(Des J.W. from paintings by Isobel McManus. Litho Walsall)

1975 (22 Oct). *160th Anniv of Occupation. T* **60** *and similar horiz designs. Multicoloured. W* w **14** *(sideways). P* 14.

195	2p. Type **60**	35	25
196	5p. Water Supply, Dampiers Drip	50	40
197	9p. First landing, 1815	60	60
198	15p. The garden on Green Mountain	75	85
195/8	*Set of* 4	2·00	1·90

61 Yellow Canary

62 Boatswain Bird Island Sanctuary

(Des J.W. Litho Questa)

1976 (26 Apr). *Multicoloured designs as T* **61** *and T* **62**. *W* w **14** *(sideways on horiz designs). P* 13½ (£2) *or* 14 (*others*).

199	1p. Type **61**	25	25
200	2p. White Tern	30	25
201	3p. Common Waxbill	30	30
202	4p. White-capped Noddy	30	30
203	5p. Common Noddy	30	30
204	6p. Common Mynah	35	35
205	7p. Madeiran Storm Petrel	45	45

206 8p. Sooty Tern 50 50
207 9p. Blue-faced Booby 55 55
208 10p. Red-footed Booby 60 60
209 15p. Bare-throated Francolin .. .. .. 1·25 1·25
210 18p. Brown Booby .. .. 1·25 1·25
211 25p. Red-billed Tropic Bird .. .. .. 1·40 1·40
212 50p. White-tailed Tropic Bird .. .. .. 2·25 2·50
213 £1 Ascension Frigate Bird .. .. .. 2·75 3·25
214 £2 Type **62** .. .. 5·00 6·00
199/214 .. .. *Set of* 16 16·00 18·00

The 2, 4, 7, 9, 15, 18p. and £1 are vertical designs.

63 G.B. Penny Red with Ascension Postmark

(Des C. Abbott. Litho J.W.)

1976 (4 May). *Festival of Stamps, London. T* **63** *and similar designs. W w* **14** (*sideways on 5 and 25p.*). *P* 13½.
215 5p. rose-red, black and cinnamon 20 15
216 9p. green, black and greenish stone 30 20
217 25p. multicoloured 50 45
215/17 .. .. *Set of* 3 90 70
MS218 133 × 121 mm. No. 217 with St. Helena 318 and Tristan da Cunha 206 (wmk sideways). P 13 1·50 2·00

Designs: *Vert*—9p. ½d. stamp of 1922. *Horiz*—25p. *Southampton Castle* (liner).

No. **MS**218 was postally valid on each island to the value of 25p.

64 U.S. Base, Ascension

65 Visit of Prince Philip, 1957

(Des V. Whiteley Studio. Litho J.W.)

1976 (4 July). *Bicentenary of American Revolution. T* **64** *and similar horiz designs. Multicoloured. W w* **14** (*sideways*). *P* 13.
219 8p. Type **64** 65 40
220 9p. NASA Station at Devils Ashpit 70 45
221 25p. "Viking" landing on Mars .. .. 1·25 80
219/21 .. .. *Set of* 3 2·40 1·50

(Des J. Cooter. Litho Walsall)

1977 (7 Feb). *Silver Jubilee. T* **65** *and similar horiz designs. Multicoloured. W w* **14** (*sideways on 12 and 25p.*). *P* 13½.
222 8p. Type **65** 15 15
223 12p. Coronation Coach leaving Buckingham Palace 25 20
224 25p. Coronation Coach 45 40
222/4 .. .. *Set of* 3 75 65

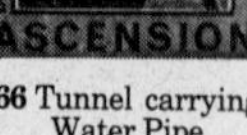

66 Tunnel carrying Water Pipe

67 Mars Bay Location, 1877

(Des G. Drummond. Litho Harrison)

1977 (27 June). *Water Supplies. T* **66** *and similar multicoloured designs. W w* **14** (*sideways on 12 and 25p.*). *P* 14.
225 3p. Type **66** 20 15
226 5p. Breakneck Valley wells 30 20
227 12p. Break tank (*horiz*) 55 35
228 25p. Water catchment (*horiz*) 90 65
225/8 .. .. *Set of* 4 1·75 1·25

(Des J.W. Litho Questa)

1977 (3 Oct). *Centenary of Visit of Professor Gill (astronomer). T* **67** *and similar horiz designs. Multicoloured. W w* **14** (*sideways*). *P* 13½.
229 3p. Type **67** 25 20
230 8p. Instrument sites, Mars Bay 35 25
231 12p. Sir David and Lady Gill 55 40
232 25p. Maps of Ascension 90 70
229/32 .. .. *Set of* 4 1·90 1·40

68 Lion of England

69 Queen Elizabeth II

(Des C. Abbott. Litho Questa)

1978 (2 June). *25th Anniv of Coronation. T* **68/9** *and similar vert design. P* 15.
233 **68** 25p. yellow, sepia and silver 60 65
a. Sheetlet. Nos. 233/5 × 2 .. .. 3·25
234 **69** 25p. multicoloured 60 65
235 – 25p. yellow, sepia and silver 60 65
233/5 .. .. *Set of* 3 1·60 1·75

Design:—No. 235, Green Turtle.

Nos. 233/5 were printed together in small sheets of 6, containing two *se-tenant* strips of 3 with horizontal gutter margin between.

70 Flank of Sisters, Sisters' Red Hill and East Crater

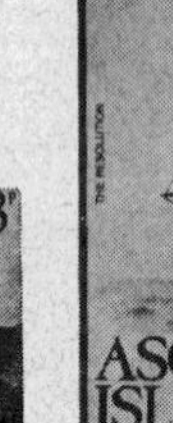

71 "*The Resolution*" (H. Roberts).

(Des J.W. Litho Questa)

1978 (4 Sept). *Volcanic Rock Formations of Ascension. T* **70** *and similar horiz designs. Multicoloured. W w* **14**. *P* 14½.
236 3p. Type **70** 20 20
a. Horiz strip of 5. Nos. 236/40 .. .. 1·60
237 5p. Holland's Crater (Hollow Tooth) .. 30 30
238 12p. Street Crater, Lower Valley Crater and Bear's Back 40 40
239 15p. Butt Crater, Weather Post and Green Mountain 45 45
240 25p. Flank of Sisters, Thistle Hill and Two Boats Village 50 50
236/40 .. .. *Set of* 5 1·60 1·60
MS241 185 × 100 mm. Nos. 236/40, each × 2 .. 3·75 4·25
a. Blue ("Ascension Island") omitted .. £3000

Nos. 236/40 were printed together, *se-tenant*, in horizontal strips of 5 throughout the sheet forming a composite design.

(Des and litho (25p. also embossed) Walsall)

1979 (19 Feb*). *Bicentenary of Captain Cook's Voyages*, 1768–79. *T* **71** *and similar vert designs. Multicoloured. P* 11.
242 3p. Type **71** 45 25
243 8p. Chronometer 65 40
244 12p. Green Turtle 75 50
245 25p. Flaxman/Wedgwood medallion of Captain Cook .. .. 1·00 70
242/5 .. .. *Set of* 4 2·50 1·75

*This is the local date of issue; the stamps were released in London on 8 January.

72 St. Mary's Church, Georgetown

73 Landing Cable, Comfortless Cove

(Des Walsall. Litho Format)

1979 (24 May). *Ascension Day. T* **72** *and similar vert designs. Multicoloured. W w* **14**. *P* 14.
246 8p. Type **72** 30 20
247 12p. Map of Ascension 40 30
248 50p. "The Ascension" (painting by Rembrandt) 1·00 90
246/8 .. .. *Set of* 3 1·50 1·25

(Des G. Vasarhelyi. Litho Walsall)

1979 (15 Sept). *80th Anniv of Eastern Telegraph Company's Arrival on Ascension. T* **73** *and similar designs. W w* **14** (*inverted on 12p. or sideways on others*). *P* 14.
249 3p. black and carmine 15 10
250 8p. black and yellowish green 25 20
251 12p. black and yellow 30 25
252 15p. black and bright violet 35 35
253 25p. black and orange-brown 50 50
249/53 .. .. *Set of* 5 1·40 1·25

Designs: *Horiz*—8p. C.S. *Anglia*; 15p. C.S. *Seine*; 25p. Cable and Wireless earth station. *Vert*—12p. Map of Atlantic cable network.

74 1938 6d. Stamp

(Des BG Studio. Litho Questa)

1979 (12 Dec). *Death Centenary of Sir Rowland Hill. T* **74** *and similar designs. W w* **14** (*sideways on 3 and 8p.*). *P* 14.
254 3p. black, new blue and deep turquoise-blue 10 10
255 8p. black, blue-green and light green .. 20 20
256 12p. black, bright blue and turquoise-blue .. 25 25
257 50p. black, brownish grey and red 90 90
254/7 .. .. *Set of* 4 1·25 1·25

Designs: *Horiz*—8p. 1956 5s. definitive stamp. *Vert*—12p. 1924 3s. stamp; 50p. Sir Rowland Hill.

75 *Anogramma ascensionis*

76 17th-century Bottle Post

(Des J. Cooter. Litho Format)

1980 (18 Feb). *Ferns and Grasses. T* **75** *and similar multicoloured designs. W w* **14** (*sideways on 12 to 24p.*). *P* 14½ × 14 (3 *to* 8*p.*) *or* 14 × 14½ (12 *to* 24*p.*).
258 3p. Type **75** 10 10
259 6p. *Xiphopteris ascensionense* 20 15
260 8p. *Sporobolus caespitosus* 20 15
261 12p. *Sporobolus durus* (*vert*) 30 25
262 18p. *Dryopteris ascensionis* (*vert*) 40 35
a. Brown (thorns) omitted .. .. 50·00
263 24p. *Marattia purpurascens* (*vert*) 50 50
258/63 .. .. *Set of* 6 1·50 1·25

(Des L. Curtis. Litho Format)

1980 (1 May). *"London 1980" International Stamp Exhibition. T* **76** *and similar horiz designs. Multicoloured. W w* **14** (*sideways*). *P* 13½.
264 8p. Type **76** 25 20
265 12p. 19th-century chance calling ship .. 35 25
266 15p. *Garthcastle II* (regular mail service from 1863) 40 30
267 50p. *St. Helena* (mail services, 1980) .. 1·00 90
264/7 .. .. *Set of* 4 1·75 1·50
MS268 102 × 154 mm. Nos. 264/7 .. .. 1·90 2·40

77 Queen Elizabeth the Queen Mother

78 Lubbock's Yellowtail

(Des Harrison. Litho Questa)

1980 (11 Aug)*. *80th Birthday of Queen Elizabeth the Queen Mother. W w* **14** (*sideways*). *P* 14.
269 **77** 15p. multicoloured 40 40

*This was the local release date. The Crown Agents placed stocks on sale in London on 4 August.

(Des G. Drummond. Litho Enschedé)

1980 (15 Sept). *Fishes. T* **78** *and similar horiz designs. Multicoloured. W w* **14** (*sideways*). *P* 13 × 13½.
270 3p. Type **78** 20 15
271 10p. Resplendent Angelfish 35 25
272 25p. Hedgehog Butterflyfish 60 50
273 40p. Marmalade Razorfish 80 65
270/3 .. .. *Set of* 4 1·75 1·40

79 H.M.S. *Tortoise*

(Des D. Bowen. Litho Rosenbaum Bros, Vienna)

1980 (17 Nov). *150th Anniv of Royal Geographical Society. T* **79** *and similar multicoloured designs. W w* **14** (*sideways*). *P* 14 (60*p.*) *or* 13½ (*others*).
274 10p. Type **79** 45 40
275 15p. "Wideawake Fair" 55 45
276 60p. Mid-Atlantic Ridge (38 × 48 *mm*) .. 1·10 1·25
274/6 .. .. *Set of* 3 1·90 2·00

80 Green Mountain Farm, 1881

(Des C. Abbott. Litho Format)

1981 (15 Feb). *Green Mountain Farm. T* **80** *and similar horiz designs. Multicoloured. W* w **14** *(sideways). P* 13½ × 14.

277	12p. Type **80**	45	35
278	15p. Two Boats, 1881	50	40
279	20p. Green Mountain and Two Boats, 1981	60	50
280	30p. Green Mountain Farm, 1981	80	70
277/80	*Set of* 4	2·10	1·75

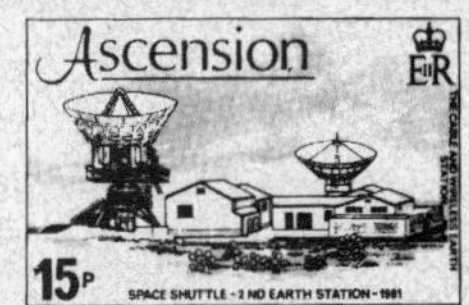

81 Cable and Wireless Earth Station

(Des G. Vasarhelyi and Walsall. Litho Walsall)

1981 (27 Apr). *"Space Shuttle" Mission and Opening of 2nd Earth Station. W* w **14** *(sideways). P* 14.

281	**81**	15p. black, bright blue and pale blue	30	35

82 Poinsettia

83 Solanum

(Des J. Cooter. Litho J.W.)

1981 (11 May)–**82**. *Flowers. Designs as T* **82** *(1 to 40p.) or vert as T* **83** *(50p. to £2). Multicoloured. W* w **14** *(sideways on* 1, 2, 4, 5, 8, 15, 20, 40, 50p., £1 *and* £2). *P* 13½. A. *Without imprint date.* B. *With imprint date* ("1982") (27.8.82).

		A		B	
282	1p. Type **82**	30	15	†	
283	2p. Clustered Wax Flower	40	15	35	35
284	3p. Kolanchoe (*vert*)	40	15	35	35
285	4p. Yellow Pops	40	20	†	
286	5p. Camels Foot Creeper	40	20	†	
287	8p. White Oleander	50	30	†	
288	10p. Ascension Lily (*vert*)	70	30	45	45
289	12p. Coral Plant (*vert*)	60	35	†	
290	15p. Yellow Allamanda	70	40	50	50
291	20p. Ascension Euphorbia	75	50	60	60
292	30p. Flame of the Forest (*vert*)	90	70	†	
293	40p. Bougainvillea "King Leopold"	1·25	90	†	
294	50p. Type **83**	1·25	1·50	†	
295	£1 Ladies Petticoat	2·00	2·75	2·00	2·75
296	£2 Red Hibiscus	3·75	4·50	†	
282A/96A	*Set of* 15	13·00	12·00	†	
283B/95B	*Set of* 6	†		3·75	4·50

Nos. 283B/95B had the imprint dates printed on the stamps by typography.

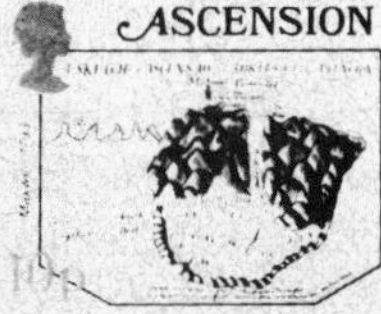

84 Map by Maxwell, 1793

(Des L. Curtis. Litho Walsall)

1981 (22 May). *Early Maps of Ascension. T* **84** *and similar horiz designs. W* w **14** *(sideways). P* 14 × 14½.

297	10p. black, gold and pale blue	40	35
298	12p. black, gold and apple-green	45	35
299	15p. black, gold and stone	50	40
300	40p. black, gold and pale greenish yellow	85	85
297/300	*Set of* 4	2·00	1·75
MS301	79 × 64 mm. 5p. × 4, multicoloured	60	60

Designs:—12p. Maxwell, 1793 (*different*); 15p. Ekeberg and Chapman, 1811; 40p. Campbell, 1819; miniature sheet, Linschoten, 1599.

Stamps from No. **MS**301 form a composite design.

85 Wedding Bouquet from Ascension

86 Prince Charles and Lady Diana Spencer

(Des J.W. Litho Questa)

1981 (22 July). *Royal Wedding. T* **85/6** *and similar vert design. Multicoloured. W* w **14**. *P* 14.

302	10p. Type **85**	25	25
303	15p. Prince Charles in Fleet Air Arm flying kit	30	30
304	50p. Type **86**	85	85
302/4	*Set of* 3	1·25	1·25

87 "Interest"

88 Scout crossing Rope Bridge

(Des BG Studio. Litho Questa)

1981 (14 Sept). *25th Anniv of Duke of Edinburgh Award Scheme. T* **87** *and similar vert designs. Multicoloured. W* w **14**. *P* 14.

305	5p. Type **87**	15	15
306	10p. "Physical activities"	20	20
307	15p. "Service"	25	25
308	40p. Duke of Edinburgh	70	70
305/8	*Set of* 4	1·10	1·10

(Des A. Theobald. Litho Format)

1982 (22 Feb). *75th Anniv of Boy Scout Movement. T* **88** *and similar designs. W* w **14** *(sideways). P* 14.

309	10p. black, bright blue and azure	45	35
310	15p. black, orange-brown and greenish yellow	55	50
311	25p. black, bright mauve and pale mauve	75	60
312	40p. black, rosine and pale orange	1·10	85
309/12	*Set of* 4	2·50	2·10
MS313	121 × 121 mm. 10p., 15p., 25p., 40p. As Nos. 309/12 (*each diamond*, 40 × 40 *mm*). *P* 14½	2·50	2·50

Designs:—15p. 1st Ascension Scout Group flag; 25p. Scouts learning to use radio; 40p. Lord Baden-Powell.

Stamps from No. **MS**313 have an overall design showing a flag printed on the reverse beneath the gum.

89 Charles Darwin

(Des L. Curtis. Litho Questa)

1982 (19 Apr). *150th Anniv of Charles Darwin's Voyage. T* **89** *and similar horiz designs. Multicoloured. W* w **14** *(sideways). P* 14.

314	10p. Type **89**	50	40
315	12p. Darwin's pistols	55	50
316	15p. Rock Crab	60	55
317	40p. H.M.S. *Beagle*	1·10	95
314/17	*Set of* 4	2·50	2·25

90 Fairey "Swordfish"

(Des A. Theobald. Litho Walsall)

1982 (15 June). *40th Anniv of Wideawake Airfield. T* **90** *and similar horiz designs. Multicoloured. W* w **14** *(sideways). P* 14.

318	5p. Type **90**	40	35
319	10p. North American "B-25C (Mitchell)"	60	40
320	15p. Boeing "EC-135N (Aria)"	75	55
321	50p. Lockheed "Hercules"	1·25	1·10
318/21	*Set of* 4	2·75	2·25

91 Ascension Coat of Arms

92 Formal Portrait

(Des Jennifer Toombs. Litho Questa)

1982 (1 July). *21st Birthday of Princess of Wales. T* **91/2** *and similar vert designs. Multicoloured. W* w **14**. *P* 14 × 14½.

322	12p. Type **91**	30	30
323	15p. Lady Diana Spencer in Music Room, Buckingham Palace	35	35
324	25p. Bride and Earl Spencer leaving Clarence House	55	55
325	50p. Type **92**	1·00	1·00
322/5	*Set of* 4	2·00	2·00

1st PARTICIPATION
COMMONWEALTH GAMES 1982
(**93**)

94 Bush House, London

1982 (29 Oct). *Commonwealth Games, Brisbane. Nos.* 290B/1B *optd with T* **93**.

326	15p. Yellow Allamanda	30	40
327	20p. Ascension Euphorbia	40	45

(Des A. Theobald. Litho Questa)

1982 (1 Dec). *50th Anniv of B.B.C. External Broadcasting. T* **94** *and similar horiz designs. Multicoloured. W* w **14** *(sideways). P* 14.

328	5p. Type **94**	25	25
329	10p. Atlantic relay station	35	35
330	25p. Lord Reith, first director-general	75	75
331	40p. King George V making his first Christmas broadcast, 1932	1·00	1·00
328/31	*Set of* 4	2·10	2·10

95 *Manismius echinosphaerus*

96 Aerial View of Georgetown

(Des Harrison. Litho Questa)

1983 (1 Mar). *Fungi. T* **95** *and similar vert designs. Multicoloured. W* w **14**. *P* 14.

332	7p. Type **95**	25	25
333	12p. *Chlorophyllum molybditus*	35	35
334	15p. *Leucocoprinus cepaestipes*	40	40
335	20p. *Lycoperdon marginatum*	50	50
336	50p. *Marasmiellus distantifolius*	1·00	1·00
332/6	*Set of* 5	2·25	2·25

(Des Jennifer Toombs. Litho Format)

1983 (12 May). *Island Views* (1*st series*) *T* **96** *and similar horiz designs. Multicoloured. W* w **14** *(sideways). P* 14 × 13½.

337	12p. Type **96**	25	30
338	15p. Green Mountain farm	30	35
339	20p. Boatswain Bird Island	40	45
340	60p. Telemetry Hill by night	1·25	1·40
337/40	*Set of* 4	2·00	2·25

See also Nos. 367/70.

97 "Wessex 5" Helicopter of No. 845 Naval Air Squadron

(Des D. Hartley-Marjoram. Litho Questa)

1983 (1 Aug). *Bicentenary of Manned Flight. British Military Aircraft. T* **97** *and similar horiz designs. Multicoloured. W w* **14** *(sideways). P* 13½.

341	12p. Type **97**	40	35
342	15p. "Vulcan B2" of No. 44 Squadron	50	40
343	20p. "Nimrod MR2P" of No. 120 Squadron	65	50
344	60p. "Victor K2" of No. 55 Squadron	1·60	1·60
341/4	*Set of* 4	2·75	2·50

98 Iguanid

(Des D. Nockles. Litho Questa)

1983 (20 Sept). *Introduced Species. T* **98** *and similar horiz designs. Multicoloured. W w* **14** *(sideways). P* 14.

345	12p. Type **98**	30	30
346	15p. Rabbit	35	35
347	20p. Cat	45	45
348	60p. Donkey	1·40	1·40
345/8	*Set of* 4	2·25	2·25

99 *Tellina antonii philippi* 100 1922 1½d. Stamp

(Des G. Wilby. Litho Format)

1983 (28 Nov). *Sea Shells. T* **99** *and similar horiz designs. Multicoloured. W w* **14** *(sideways). P* 14½ × 14.

349	7p. Type **99**	20	20
350	12p. *Nodipecten nodosus (Linne)*	30	30
351	15p. *Cypraea lurida oceanica sch*	35	35
352	20p. *Nerita ascensionis gmelin*	45	45
353	50p. *Micromelo undatus (bruguiere)*	1·10	1·10
349/53	*Set of* 5	2·25	2·25

(Des C. Abbott. Litho Questa)

1984 (3 Jan). *150th Anniv of St. Helena as a British Colony. T* **100** *and similar vert designs showing stamps of the 1922 issue overprinted on St. Helena. Multicoloured. W w* **14**. *P* 14.

354	12p. Type **100**	30	35
355	15p. 1922 2d. stamp	35	40
356	20p. 1922 8d. stamp	40	45
357	60p. 1922 1s. stamp	1·25	1·40
354/7	*Set of* 4	2·10	2·40

101 Prince Andrew 102 Naval Semaphore

(Des L. Curtis. Litho Questa)

1984 (10 Apr). *Visit of Prince Andrew. Sheet, 124 × 90 mm, containing vert designs as T* **101**. *W w* **14**. *P* 14½ × 14.

MS358	12p. Type **101**; 70p. Prince Andrew in naval uniform	1·75	1·90

(Des D. Hartley-Marjoram. Litho Questa)

1984 (28 May). *250th Anniv of "Lloyd's List" (newspaper). T* **102** *and similar vert designs. Multicoloured. W w* **14**. *P* 14½ × 14.

359	12p. Type **102**	30	30
360	15p. *Southampton Castle* (liner)	35	35
361	20p. Pier Head	45	45
362	70p. *The Dane* (mail ship)	1·50	1·50
359/62	*Set of* 4	2·40	2·40

103 Penny Coin and Yellowfin Tuna 104 Bermuda Cypress

(Des G. Drummond. Litho Questa)

1984 (26 July). *New Coinage. T* **103** *and similar horiz designs. Multicoloured. W w* **14** *(sideways). P* 14.

363	12p. Type **103**	40	35
364	15p. Twopenny coin and donkey	50	40
365	20p. Fifty pence coin and Green Turtle	65	50
366	70p. Pound coin and Sooty Tern	1·75	1·75
363/6	*Set of* 4	3·00	2·75

(Des Jennifer Toombs. Litho B.D.T.)

1984 (26 Oct). *Island Views (2nd series). Horiz designs as T* **96**. *Multicoloured. W w* **14** *(sideways). P* 13½.

367	12p. The Devil's Riding-school	30	30
368	15p. St. Mary's Church	35	35
369	20p. Two Boats Village	45	45
370	70p. Ascension from the sea	1·50	1·50
367/70	*Set of* 4	2·40	2·40

(Des N. Shewring. Litho Questa)

1985 (8 Mar). *Trees. T* **104** *and similar vert designs. Multicoloured. W w* **14**. *P* 14½.

371	7p. Type **104**	25	20
372	12p. Norfolk Island Pine	35	30
373	15p. Screwpine	40	35
374	20p. Eucalyptus	55	45
375	65p. Spore Tree	1·60	1·40
371/5	*Set of* 5	2·75	2·40

105 The Queen Mother with Prince Andrew at Silver Jubilee Service 106 32 Pdr. Smooth Bore Muzzle-loader, c 1820, and Royal Marine Artillery Hat Plate, *c* 1816

(Des A. Theobald (75p.), C. Abbott (others). Litho Questa)

1985 (7 June). *Life and Times of Queen Elizabeth the Queen Mother. T* **105** *and similar vert designs. Multicoloured. W w* **16**. *P* 14½ × 14.

376	12p. With the Duke of York at Balmoral, 1924	30	30
377	15p. Type **105**	35	35
378	20p. The Queen Mother at Ascot	45	45
379	70p. With Prince Henry at his christening (from photo by Lord Snowdon)	1·50	1·50
376/9	*Set of* 4	2·40	2·40
MS380	91 × 73 mm. 75p. Visiting the *Queen Elizabeth 2* at Southampton, 1968. Wmk sideways	1·50	1·60

(Des W. Fenton. Litho Walsall)

1985 (19 July). *Guns on Ascension Island. T* **106** *and similar horiz designs. Multicoloured. W w* **14** *(sideways). P* 14 × 14½.

381	12p. Type **106**	40	35
382	15p. 7 inch rifled muzzle-loader, *c* 1866, and Royal Cypher on barrel	50	40
383	20p. 7 pdr. rifled muzzle-loader, *c* 1877, and Royal Artillery badge	60	50
384	70p. 5·5 inch gun, 1941, and crest from H.M.S. *Hood*	1·75	1·75
381/4	*Set of* 4	3·00	2·75

107 Guide Flag 108 *Clerodendrum fragrans*

(Des N. Shewring. Litho Questa)

1985 (4 Oct). *75th Anniv of Girl Guide Movement and International Youth Year. T* **107** *and similar vert designs. Multicoloured. W w* **14**. *P* 14½ × 14.

385	12p. Type **107**	45	45
386	15p. Practising first aid	55	55
387	20p. Camping	65	65
388	70p. Lady Baden-Powell	2·00	2·00
385/8	*Set of* 4	3·25	3·25

(Des Josephine Martin. Litho Questa)

1985 (6 Dec). *Wild Flowers. T* **108** *and similar vert designs. Multicoloured. W w* **16**. *P* 14.

389	12p. Type **108**	45	35
390	15p. Shell Ginger	55	40
391	20p. Cape Daisy	65	50
392	70p. Ginger Lily	2·00	1·75
389/92	*Set of* 4	3·25	2·75

109 Newton's Reflector Telescope 110 Princess Elizabeth in 1926

(Des D. Hartley. Litho B.D.T.)

1986 (7 Mar). *Appearance of Halley's Comet. T* **109** *and similar vert designs. Multicoloured. W w* **16**. *P* 14.

393	12p. Type **109**	40	40
394	15p. Edmond Halley and Old Greenwich Observatory	45	45
395	20p. Short's Gregorian telescope and comet, 1759	55	55
396	70p. Ascension satellite tracking station and ICE spacecraft	1·75	1·75
393/6	*Set of* 4	2·75	2·75

(Des A. Theobald. Litho Format)

1986 (21 Apr). *60th Birthday of Queen Elizabeth II. T* **110** *and similar vert designs. Multicoloured. W w* **16**. *P* 14 × 14½.

397	7p. Type **110**	15	20
398	15p. Queen making Christmas broadcast, 1952	30	35
399	20p. At Garter ceremony, Windsor Castle, 1983	40	45
400	35p. In Auckland, New Zealand, 1981	70	75
401	£1 At Crown Agents' Head Office, London, 1983	2·00	2·10
397/401	*Set of* 5	3·25	3·50

111 1975 Space Satellites 2p. Stamp 112 Prince Andrew and Miss Sarah Ferguson

(Des L. Curtis. Litho Walsall)

1986 (22 May). *"Ameripex '86" International Stamp Exhibition, Chicago. T* **111** *and similar horiz designs showing previous Ascension stamps. Multicoloured. W w* **16** *(sideways). P* 14 × 14½.

402	12p. Type **111**	25	30
403	15p. 1980 "London 1980" International Stamp Exhibition 50p.	30	35
404	20p. 1976 Bicentenary of American Revolution 8p.	40	45
405	70p. 1982 40th Anniv of Wideawake Airfield 10p.	1·40	1·50
402/5	*Set of* 4	2·10	2·40
MS406	60 × 75 mm. 75p. Statue of Liberty	1·50	1·60

(Des D. Miller. Litho Questa)

1986 (23 July). *Royal Wedding. T* **112** *and similar square design. Multicoloured. W w* **16**. *P* 14.

407	15p. Type **112**	35	35
408	35p. Prince Andrew aboard H.M.S. *Brazen*	75	75

113 H.M.S. *Ganymede* (c 1811)

(Des E. Nisbet. Litho Questa)

1986 (14 Oct). *Ships of the Royal Navy. T* **113** *and similar horiz designs. Multicoloured. W w* **16** *(sideways). P* 14½.

409	1p. Type **113**	10	10
410	2p. H.M.S. *Kangaroo* (c 1811)	10	10
411	4p. H.M.S. *Trinculo* (c 1811)	10	10
412	5p. H.M.S. *Daring* (c 1811)	10	10
413	9p. H.M.S. *Thais* (c 1811)	15	20
414	10p. H.M.S. *Pheasant* (1819)	20	25
415	15p. H.M.S. *Myrmidon* (1819)	25	30
416	18p. H.M.S. *Atholl* (1825)	30	35
417	20p. H.M.S. *Medina* (1830)	35	40
418	25p. H.M.S. *Saracen* (1840)	45	50
419	30p. H.M.S. *Hydra* (c 1845)	50	55
420	50p. H.M.S. *Sealark* (1849)	90	95
421	70p. H.M.S. *Rattlesnake* (1868)	1·25	1·40
422	£1 H.M.S. *Penelope* (1889)	1·75	1·90
423	£2 H.M.S. *Monarch* (1897)	3·50	3·75
409/23	*Set of* 15	9·00	9·75

COVER PRICES

Cover factors are quoted at the beginning of each country for most issues to 1945. An explanation of the system can be found on page x. The factors quoted do not, however, apply to philatelic covers.

114 Cape Gooseberry

115 Ignition of Rocket Motors

(Des R. Gorringe. Litho Walsall)

1987 (29 Jan). *Edible Bush Fruits. T* **114** *and similar horiz designs. Multicoloured. W w* **16** *(sideways). P* 14.

424 12p. Type **114** 45 45
425 15p. Prickly Pear 50 50
426 20p. Guava 60 60
427 70p. Loquat . . . . 1·75 1·75
424/7 . . . . *Set of* 4 3·00 3·00

(Des D. Hartley. Litho Questa)

1987 (30 Mar). *25th Anniv of First American Manned Earth Orbit. T* **115** *and similar vert designs. Multicoloured. W w* **16**. *P* 14.

428 15p. Type **115** 45 45
429 18p. Lift-off 50 50
430 25p. Re-entry 65 65
431 £1 Splashdown . . . . 2·25 2·25
428/31 . . . . *Set of* 4 3·50 3·50
MS432 92×78 mm. 70p. "Friendship 7" capsule 1·75 2·00

116 Captains in Full Dress raising Red Ensign

117 Painted Lady

(Des C. Collins. Litho Format)

1987 (29 June). *19th-century Uniforms (1st series). Royal Navy, 1815–20. T* **116** *and similar vert designs. Multicoloured. W w* **16**. *P* 14.

433 25p. Type **116** 60 60
a. Horiz strip of 5. Nos. 433/7 . . 2·75
434 25p. Surgeon and seamen 60 60
435 25p. Seaman with water-carrying donkey . . 60 60
436 25p. Midshipman and gun 60 60
437 25p. Commander in undress uniform surveying 60 60
433/7 . . . . *Set of* 5 2·75 2·75

Nos. 433/7 were printed together, *se-tenant*, in horizontal strips of five throughout the sheet.

See also Nos. 478/82.

(Des I. Loe. Litho Questa)

1987 (10 Aug). *Insects (1st series). Butterflies. T* **117** *and similar horiz designs. Multicoloured. W w* **16** *(sideways). P* 14×14½.

438 15p. Type **117** 55 55
439 18p. Monarch 60 60
440 25p. Diadem 75 75
441 £1 Long-tailed Blue . . . . 2·25 2·25
438/41 . . . . *Set of* 4 3·75 3·75

See also Nos. 452/5 and 483/6.

118 Male Ascension Frigate Birds

40TH WEDDING ANNIVERSARY

(119)

(Des N. Arlott. Litho B.D.T.)

1987 (8 Oct). *Sea Birds (1st series). T* **118** *and similar vert designs. Multicoloured. W w* **16**. *P* 14.

442 25p. Type **118** 70 70
a. Horiz strip of 5. Nos. 442/6 . . 3·25
443 25p. Juvenile Ascension Frigate Bird, Brown Booby and White Boobies . . 70 70
444 25p. Male Ascension Frigate Bird and White Boobies . . 70 70
445 25p. Female Ascension Frigate Bird . . 70 70
446 25p. Adult male feeding juvenile Ascension Frigate Bird . . 70 70
442/6 . . . . *Set of* 5 3·25 3·25

Nos. 442/6 were printed together, *se-tenant*, in horizontal strips of five throughout the sheet, forming a composite design.

See also Nos. 469/73.

1987 (9 Dec). *Royal Ruby Wedding. Nos.* 397/401 *optd with T* **119** *in silver.*

447 7p. Type **110** 15 20
448 15p. Queen making Christmas broadcast, 1952 . . . . 30 35
449 20p. At Garter ceremony, Windsor Castle, 1983 . . . . 40 45
a. Opt double . . . . 75·00
450 35p. In Auckland, New Zealand, 1981 . . 70 75
451 £1 At Crown Agents' Head Office, London, 1983 . . . . 2·00 2·10
447/51 . . . . *Set of* 5 3·25 3·50

(Des I. Loe. Litho Questa)

1988 (18 Jan). *Insects (2nd series). Horiz designs as T* **117**. *Multicoloured. W w* **16** *(sideways). P* 14×14½.

452 15p. *Gryllus bimaculatus* (field cricket) . . 50 50
453 18p. *Ruspolia differens* (bush cricket) . . 55 55
454 25p. *Chilomenes lunata* (ladybird) . . 70 70
455 £1 Burnished Brass Moth . . . . 2·25 2·25
452/5 . . . . *Set of* 4 3·50 3·50

120 Bate's Memorial, St. Mary's Church

(Des S. Noon. Litho Questa)

1988 (14 Apr). *150th Death Anniv of Captain William Bate (garrison commander, 1828–38). T* **120** *and similar horiz designs. Multicoloured. W w* **16** *(sideways). P* 14.

456 9p. Type **120** 35 35
457 15p. Commodore's Cottage 45 45
458 18p. North East Cottage 50 50
459 25p. Map of Ascension 70 70
460 70p. Captain Bate and marines . . . . 1·75 1·75
456/60 . . . . *Set of* 5 3·25 3·25

121 H.M.S. *Resolution* (ship of the line), 1667

(Des E. Nisbet. Litho Questa)

1988 (23 June). *Bicentenary of Australian Settlement. Ships of the Royal Navy. T* **121** *and similar diamond-shaped designs. Multicoloured. W w* **16** *(sideways). P* 14.

461 9p Type **121** 35 35
462 18p H.M.S. *Resolution* (Captain Cook), 1772 . . . . 55 55
463 25p H.M.S. *Resolution* (battleship), 1892 . . 75 75
464 65p H.M.S. *Resolution* (battleship), 1916 . . 1·50 1·50
461/4 . . . . *Set of* 4 2·75 2·75

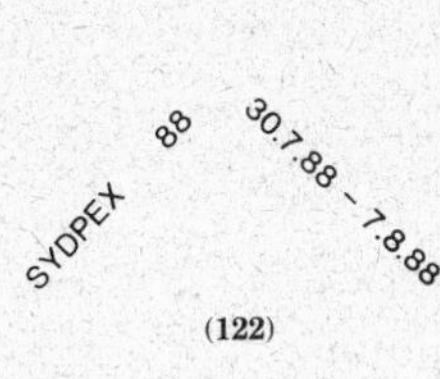

(122)

123 Lloyd's Coffee House, London, 1688

1988 (30 July). *"Sydpex '88" National Stamp Exhibition, Sydney. Nos.* 461/4 *optd with T* **122**.

465 9p Type **121** 25 25
466 18p H.M.S. *Resolution* (Captain Cook), 1772 . . . . 40 40
467 25p H.M.S. *Resolution* (battleship), 1892 . . 55 55
468 65p H.M.S. *Resolution* (battleship), 1916 . . 1·40 1·40
465/8 . . . . *Set of* 4 2·40 2·40

(Des N. Arlott. Litho Questa)

1988 (15 Aug). *Sea Birds (2nd series). Sooty Tern. Vert designs as T* **118**. *Multicoloured. W w* **16**. *P* 14.

469 25p. Pair displaying 70 70
a. Horiz strip of 5. Nos. 469/73 . . 3·25
470 25p. Turning egg 70 70
471 25p. Incubating egg 70 70
472 25p. Feeding chick 70 70
473 25p. Immature Sooty Tern 70 70
469/73 . . . . *Set of* 5 3·25 3·25

Nos. 469/73 were printed together, *se-tenant*, in horizontal strips of five throughout the sheet, forming a composite design of a nesting colony.

(Des E. Nisbet and D. Miller (8p., 25p.), D. Miller (others). Litho Questa)

1988 (17 Oct). *300th Anniv of Lloyd's of London. T* **123** *and similar multicoloured designs. W w* **14** *(sideways on 18, 25p.). P* 14.

474 8p. Type **123** 25 25
475 18p. *Alert* (cable ship) *(horiz)* . . 50 50
476 25p. Satellite recovery in space *(horiz)* . . 70 70
477 65p. *Good Hope Castle* on fire off Ascension, 1973 . . . . 1·50 1·50
474/7 . . . . *Set of* 4 2·75 2·75

(Des C. Collins. Litho B.D.T.)

1988 (21 Nov). *19th-century Uniforms (2nd series). Royal Marines, 1821–34. Vert designs as T* **116**. *Multicoloured. W w* **14**. *P* 14.

478 25p. Marines landing on Ascension, 1821 . . 70 70
a. Horiz strip of 5. Nos. 478/82 . . 3·25
479 25p. Officer and Marine at semaphore station, 1829 . . . . 70 70
480 25p. Sergeant and Marine at Octagonal Tank, 1831 . . . . 70 70
481 25p. Officers at water pipe tunnel, 1833 . . 70 70
482 25p. Officer supervising construction of barracks, 1834 . . . . 70 70
478/82 . . . . *Set of* 5 3·25 3·25

Nos. 478/82 were printed together, *se-tenant*, in horizontal strips of five throughout the sheet.

(Des I. Loe. Litho Questa)

1989 (16 Jan). *Insects (3rd series). Horiz designs as T* **117**. *Multicoloured. W w* **16** *(sideways). P* 14×14½.

483 15p. *Trichoptilus wahlbergi* (plume moth) 40 35
484 18p. *Lucilia sericata* (green bottle) . . 45 40
485 25p. *Alceis ornatus* (weevil) . . 60 55
486 £1 *Polistes fuscatus* (paper wasp) . . 2·40 2·10
483/6 . . . . *Set of* 4 3·50 3·00

124 Two Land Crabs

125 1949 75th Anniversary of U. P. U. 1s. Stamp

(Des Doreen McGuiness. Litho Questa)

1989 (17 Apr). *Ascension Land Crabs* (Gecarcinus lagostoma). *T* **124** *and similar vert designs. Multicoloured. W w* **16**. *P* 14.

487 15p. Type **124** 40 40
488 18p. Crab with claws raised . . 45 45
489 25p. Crab on rock 60 60
490 £1 Crab in surf . . . . 2·25 2·25
487/90 . . . . *Set of* 4 3·25 3·25
MS491 98 × 101 mm. Nos. 487/90 . . 3·50 3·75

(Des D. Miller. Litho Walsall)

1989 (7 July). *"Philexfrance 89" International Stamp Exhibition, Paris, and "World Stamp Expo '89", Washington. Sheet* 104 × 86 *mm. W w* **16**. *P* 14 × 13½.

MS492 **125** 75p. multicoloured . . . . 1·50 1·75

126 "Apollo 7" Tracking Station, Ascension

127 *Queen Elizabeth 2* and Aircraft Carrier in New York Harbour

(Des A. Theobald (£1), D. Miller (others). Litho Questa)

1989 (20 July). *20th Anniv of First Manned Landing on Moon. T* **126** *and similar multicoloured designs. W w* **16** *(sideways on 18, 25p). P* 14 × 13½ *(15, 70p.) or* 14 *(others).*

493 15p. Type **126** 30 35
494 18p. Launch of "Apollo 7" (30 × 30 *mm*) . . 35 40
495 25p. "Apollo 7" emblem (30 × 30 *mm*) . . 50 55
496 70p. "Apollo 7" jettisoning expended Saturn rocket . . . . 1·40 1·50
493/6 . . . . *Set of* 4 2·25 2·50
MS497 101 × 83 mm. £1 Diagram of "Apollo 11" mission. P 14 × 13½ . . . . 2·00 2·10

(Des D. Miller. Litho Walsall)

1989 (21 Aug). *"Philexfrance 89" International Stamp Exhibition, Paris, and "World Stamp Expo '89", Washington. T* **127** *and similar vert designs showing Statue of Liberty and Centenary celebrations. Multicoloured. W* w **14**. *P* 14 × 13½.

498	15p. Type **127**	30	35
	a. Sheetlet. Nos. 498/503	1·60	
499	15p. Cleaning Statue	30	35
500	15p. Statue of Liberty	30	35
501	15p. Crown of Statue	30	35
502	15p. Warships and New York skyline	30	35
503	15p. French warship and skyscrapers	30	35
498/503	*Set of* 6	1·60	1·90

Nos. 498/503 were printed, *se-tenant*, in sheetlets of 6.

128 Devil's Ashpit Tracking Station

(Des D. Miller. Litho Questa)

1989 (30 Sept). *Closure of Devil's Ashpit Tracking Station, Ascension. T* **128** *and similar horiz design. Multicoloured. W* w **16** *(sideways). P* 14.

504	18p. Type **128**	35	40
	a. Sheetlet. Nos. 504/5, each × 5	4·25	
505	25p. Launch of shuttle *Atlantis*	50	55

Nos. 504/5 were issued in sheetlets of ten containing vertical strips of five of each design, separated by a central inscribed gutter.

129 *Strombus latus*

130 Donkeys

(Des I. Loe. Litho Questa)

1989 (2 Nov). *Sea Shells. T* **129** *and similar horiz designs. Multicoloured. W* w **16** *(sideways). P* 14.

506	8p. Type **129**	15	20
507	18p. *Tonna galea*	35	40
508	25p. *Harpa doris*	50	55
509	£1 *Charonia variegata*	2·00	2·10
506/9	*Set of* 4	2·75	3·00

(Des G. Drummond, adapted N. Harvey. Litho Walsall)

1989 (17 Nov). *Booklet stamps. T* **130** *and similar vert design. Multicoloured. W* w **16** *(sideways). P* 14.

510	18p. Type **130**	30	35
	a. Booklet pane. No. 510×6	1·75	
511	25p. Green Turtle	45	50
	a. Booklet pane. No. 511×4	1·75	

Nos. 510/11 come with either the left or right-hand side imperforate.

POSTAGE DUE STAMPS

D 1 Outline Map of Ascension

(Des L. Curtis. Litho Questa)

1986 (9 June). *W* w **16**. *P* 14½ × 14.

D1	D 1	1p. deep brown and cinnamon	10	10
D2		2p. deep brown and bright orange	10	10
D3		5p. deep brown and orange-vermilion	10	10
D4		7p. black and bright reddish violet	10	15
D5		10p. black and violet-blue	20	25
D6		25p. black and pale emerald	45	50
D1/6		*Set of* 6	90	1·10

Australia

AUSTRALIAN STATES. The following States combined to form the Commonwealth of Australia and their issues are listed in alphabetical order in this Catalogue:—

NEW SOUTH WALES QUEENSLAND

SOUTH AUSTRALIA TASMANIA

VICTORIA WESTERN AUSTRALIA

PRICES FOR STAMPS ON COVER TO 1945	
Nos. 1/27	*from* × 4
Nos. 29/34	*from* × 2
Nos. 35/50*d*	*from* × 3
Nos. 51/3	*from* × 4
Nos. 56/75	*from* × 3
Nos. 76/84	*from* × 4
Nos. 85/104	*from* × 3
Nos. 105/6	*from* × 4
Nos. 107/15	*from* × 3
No. 116	*from* × 5
Nos. 117/20	*from* × 4
Nos. 121/39*a*	*from* × 2
Nos. 140/*a*	*from* × 5
Nos. 141/4	*from* × 3
No. 146	*from* × 6
Nos. 147/53	*from* × 3
Nos. 153*a*/*b*	*from* × 2
Nos. 154/63	*from* × 3
Nos. 164/211	*from* × 2
Nos. D1/118	*from* × 8
Nos. O1/18	*from* × 5

PRINTERS. Except where otherwise stated, all Commonwealth stamps to No. 581 were printed under Government authority at Melbourne. Until 1918 there were two establishments (both of the Treasury Dept)—the Note Printing Branch and the Stamp Printing Branch. The former printed T **3** and **4**.

In 1918 the Stamp Printing Branch was closed and all stamps were printed by the Note Printing Branch. In 1926 control was transferred from the Treasury to the Commonwealth Bank of Australia, and on 14 January 1960 the branch was attached to the newly established Reserve Bank of Australia.

Until 1942 stamps bore in the sheet margin the initials or names of successive managers and from 1942 to March 1952 the imprint "Printed by the Authority of the Government of the Commonwealth of Australia". After November 1952 (or Nos. D129/31 for Postage Dues) imprints were discontinued.

SPECIMEN OVERPRINTS. These come from Specimen sets, first produced in 1913. In these sets the lower values were cancelled-to-order, but stamps with a face value of 7s. 6d. or 75 c. were overprinted "Specimen" in different types. These overprints are listed as they could be purchased from the Australian Post Office.

It is, however, believed that examples of No. 112 overprinted "Specimen" were distributed by the U.P.U. in 1929. Supplies of the 1902 and 1902–04 postage due stamps overprinted "Specimen" were supplied to the U.P.U. by some of the states.

The sale of the cancelled-to-order sets ceased after 1966, but high value "Specimen" overprints were retained to support philatelic funds.

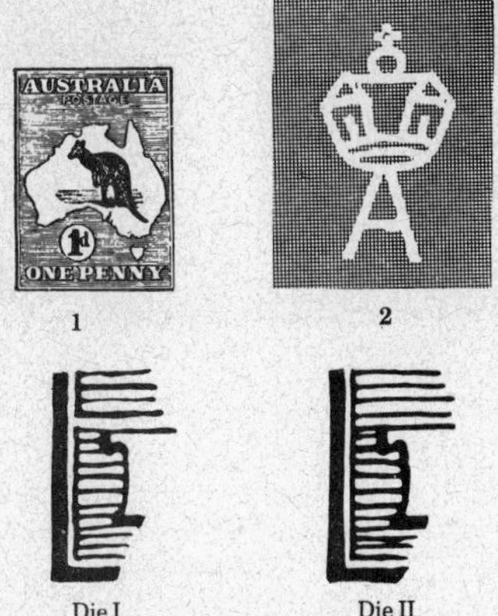

1 2

Die I Die II

Dies of Type **1** (mono-coloured values only):—

Die I. Break in inner frame line at lower left level with top of words of value.

Die II. Die repaired showing no break.

Die I was only used for the ½d., 1d., 2d. and 3d. Several plates were produced for each except the 3d. When the second plate of the 3d. was being prepared the damage became aggravated after making 105 out of the 120 units when the die was returned for repair. This gave rise to the *se-tenant* pairs showing the two states of the die.

Die II was used until 1945 and deteriorated progressively with damage to the frame lines and rounding of the corners.

Specialists recognise seven states of this die, but we only list the two most major of the later versions.

Die IIA. This state is as Die II, but, in addition, shows a break in the inner left-hand frame line, 9 mm from the top of the design.

Die IIB. As Die IIA, but now also showing break in outer frame line above "ST", and (not illustrated) an incomplete corner to the inner frame line at top right.

(Des B. Young. Eng S. Reading. Typo J. B. Cooke)

1913 (Jan–Apr). *W* **2.** *P* 12.

No.	Type	Description		
1	**1**	½d. green (Die I) (16 Jan)	5·00	1·50
		a. Wmk sideways	†	—
2		1d. red (Die I) (2 Jan)	6·50	40
		a. Wmk sideways	£700	£100
		b. Carmine	6·50	40
		c. Die II. *Red*	6·50	40
		ca. Wmk sideways	£750	£100
		cb. Carmine	6·50	40
		d. Die IIA. *Red*	6·00	30
		da. Wmk sideways	£700	£100
		db. Carmine	6·00	30
3		2d. grey (Die I) (11 Jan)	24·00	2·75
4		2½d. indigo (Die II) (27 Jan)	26·00	10·00
5		3d. olive (Die I) (22 Jan)	40·00	5·50
		a. Imperf three sides (pair)	£10000	
		b. In pair with Die II	£375	£130
		c. Yellow-olive	40·00	6·00
		ca. In pair with Die II	£375	£130
		d. Die II. *Olive*	£140	35·00
		da. Yellow-olive	£140	35·00
6		4d. orange (Die II) (12 Feb)	48·00	22·00
		a. Orange-yellow	£170	48·00
8		5d. chestnut (Die II) (16 Jan)	40·00	28·00
9		6d. ultramarine (Die II) (11 Jan) ..	48·00	22·00
		a. Retouched "E"	£1500	£500
		b. Die I'A	£850	£225
10		9d. violet (Die II) (29 Jan)	45·00	18·00
11		1s. emerald (Die II) (21 Jan)	45·00	11·00
		a. Blue-green	45·00	11·00
12		2s. brown (Die II) (25 Jan)	£140	45·00
13		5s. grey and yellow (20 March) ..	£250	£100
14		10s. grey and pink (20 March)	£500	£300
15		£1 brown and blue (20 March) ..	£1100	£1000
16		£2 black and rose (8 April)	£2100	£1500
1/16		.. .. *Set of* 15	£4000	£2750
14/16 Optd "Specimen"		.. .. *Set of* 3	£550	

No. 9a shows a badly distorted second "E" in "PENCE", which is unmistakable. It occurs on the last stamp in the sheet and was replaced by a substitute cliché in Type IIA (No. 9b).

For the previous No. 12a see No. O11a.

See also Nos. 20/27 (*W* **5**), 35/45*b* (*W* **6**), 73/5 (*W* **6**, new colours), 107/14 (*W* **7**), 132/8 (*W* **15**), 212 (2s. re-engraved).

INVERTED WATERMARKS are met with in some values in this and subsequent issues.

3 4 Laughing Kookaburra

(Des R. A. Harrison. Eng and recess T. S. Harrison)

1913 (8 Dec)–**14.** *No wmk. P* 11.

No.	Type	Description		
17	**3**	1d. red	1·75	4·00
		a. Pale rose-red	6·50	10·00
		b. Imperf horiz (vert pair)	£1500	
19	**4**	6d. claret (26.8.14)	70·00	38·00

All printing from Plate 1 of the 1d. were in the shade of No. 17*a*. This plate shows many retouches.

5 5*a*

(Typo J. B. Cooke)

1915. *W* 5. *P* 12.

No.	Type	Description		
20	**1**	2d. grey (Die I) (2 Jan)	50·00	10·00
21		2½d. indigo (Die II) (July)	50·00	25·00
23		6d. ultramarine (Die II) (April) ..	£130	22·00
		a. Bright blue	£170	45·00
		b. Die IIA. *Ultramarine*	£900	£200
		ba. Bright blue	£1100	£250
24		9d. violet (Die II) (9 July)	£130	26·00
25		1s. blue-green (Die II) (Aug)	£140	20·00
26		2s. brown (Die II) (April)	£400	70·00
27		5s. grey and yellow (12 Feb)	£600	£200
		a. Yellow portion doubly printed ..	£5500	£1000
20/27		.. .. *Set of* 7	£1400	£325

The watermark in this issue is often misplaced as the paper was made for the portrait stamps.

Die II Die III

Die II. The flaw distinguishing the so-called Die II is now known to be due to a defective roller-die and occurs in 18 impressions on one of the plates. It appears as a white upward projection to right of the base of figure "1" in the shield containing value at left, as shown in the illustration.

Die III. In 1918 a printing (in sheets of 120) was made on paper prepared for printing War Savings Stamps, with wmk T **5**. A special plate was made for this printing, differing in detail from those previously used. The shading round the head is even; the solid background of the words "ONE PENNY" is bounded at each end by a *white* vertical line; and there is a horizontal white line cutting the vertical shading lines at left on the King's neck. *See* Nos. 55*b*/*c*.

(Dies eng P. B. Typo J. B. Cooke until 1918, then T. S. Harrison)

1914–21. *W* **5.** *P* 14.

No.	Type	Description		
29	**5*a***	½d. bright green (22.2.15)	3·00	60
		a. Green (13.5.16)	2·75	50
		b. Yellow-green (8.16)	20·00	5·00
		c. Thin "1" in fraction at right ..	£1000	£500
30		1d. carmine-red (*shades*) (I) (17.7.14) ..	6·00	20
		a. Rusted cliché (2 vars)*	£4000	£400
		b. Substituted cliché	£1300	50·00
		c. Pale carmine (*shades*)	14·00	20
		d. Carmine-pink (1.18)	90·00	2·50
		e. Rose-red (3.18)	10·00	1·50
		f. Carmine (*aniline*) (1921)	15·00	1·75
31		1d. carmine-red (*shades*) (II) (1914) ..	£400	6·00
		a. Substituted cliché	£1300	50·00
		b. Pale red (*shades*)	£350	6·00
32		4d. orange (6.1.15)	38·00	2·25
		a. Yellow-orange	38·00	3·25
		b. Pale orange-yellow (10.15)	65·00	9·00
		c. Lemon-yellow (1916)	£120	14·00
		d. Dull orange	42·00	3·25
		e. Line through "FOUR PENCE" (*all shades*) .. .. .. *From*	£550	£110
34		5d. brown (22.2.15)	15·00	1·25
		a. Yellow-brown (1920)	25·00	1·50

The variety No. 29c was caused by the engraving of a new fraction in a defective electro.

*The two varieties listed under No. 30a were caused by rusting of the steel plate and show as white patches on the back of King's neck and on, and beside, the top of the right frame (upper left pane, No. 34); and on the left frame, wattles, head and ears of kangaroo (upper left pane, No. 35). These were noticed in late 1916 when the damaged impressions were removed and replaced by a pair of copper electros (Die II for No. 34 and Die I for No. 35), showing rounded corners and some frame damage, the former also showing a white spot under tail of emu. In time the tops of the crown quickly wore away. These substituted clichés (Nos. 30b and 31a) were formerly described as "Top of crown missing".

The 5d. is known printed on the gummed side of the paper.

Two machines were used for the 14 perforation, one an old single line, converted to that gauge, the other a new comb-machine. The former was used mainly for early printings of the 1d. and 5d. and very rarely for later printings of the ½d. and 1d.

See also Nos. 47/50*b* (*W* **5**, rough paper), 55*b*/*c* (1d. Die III), 51/5*a* (*W* **6***a*), 56/66*b* and 76/84 (*W* **5**, new colours), 85/104 (*W* **7**), 124/31 (*W* **15**).

6 6*a*

Nos. 38ca and 73a
(R. 1/6, lower plate)

Australasia

★ **For over 20 years, the source for Australasian scarce to rare stamps, postal history and cancellations, essays, proofs and specimens.**

★ **Leading specialists worldwide take advantage of our auction and private treaty facilities.**

If you would like to see either . . .

— OUR CURRENT AUCTION CATALOGUE

— DETAILS OF HOW WE CAN HELP YOU, THE PROSPECTIVE VENDOR

Then write, phone or fax us, giving details of your philatelic interests and we shall be delighted to help you in any way possible.

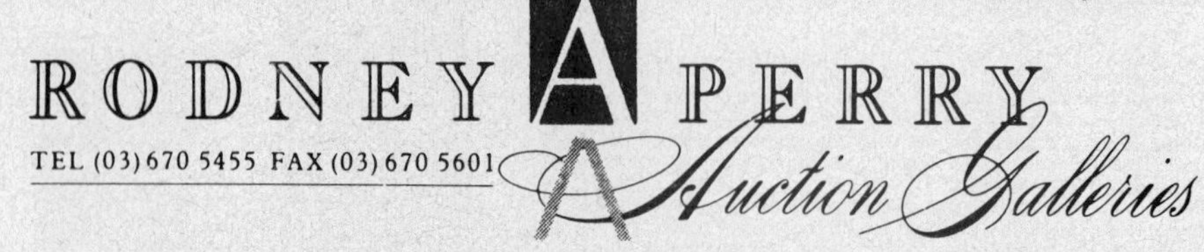

(Typo J. B. Cooke (to May 1918), T. S. Harrison (to February 1926), A. J. Mullett (to January 1927) and thereafter J. Ash)

1915–28. W 6 (*narrow Crown*). *P* 12.

35 1 2d. grey (Die I) (11.15) .. .. 28·00 3·75
a. In pair with Die IIA (1917)* .. £650 £225
b. Silver-grey (shiny paper) (2.18) .. 28·00 4·00
c. Die II. *Grey* (1918) .. .. 32·00 5·50
ca. Silver-grey (shiny paper) (2.18) .. 30·00 5·50
36 2½d. deep blue (Die II) (9.17) .. .. 22·00 6·50
a. Deep indigo (1920) .. .. 26·00 8·00
ab. "1" of fraction omitted £9000 £3000
37 3d. yellow-olive (Die I) (12.10.15) .. 27·00 3·00
a. In pair with Die II .. .. £225 75·00
b. Olive-green (1917) .. .. 30·00 3·00
ba. In pair with Die II .. .. £225 75·00
c. Die II. *Yellow-olive* .. .. 90·00 22·00
ca. Olive-green .. .. 90·00 22·00
d. Die IIB. *Light olive* (1923) .. 38·00 11·00
38 6d. ultramarine (Die II) (15.12.15) .. 48·00 6·00
a. Die IIA (substituted cliché) .. £650 £150
b. Dull blue .. .. 55·00 7·00
ba. Die IIA (substituted cliché) .. £750 £150
c. Die IIB. *Bright ultramarine* (23.7.21) .. .. 48·00 6·00
ca. Leg of kangaroo broken .. £2500 £500
39 9d. violet (Die II) (29.7.16) .. 38·00 4·75
a. Die IIB. *Violet* (16.4.19) .. 35·00 4·25
40 1s. blue-green (Die II) (6.16) .. 35·00 2·75
a. Die IIB (9.12.20) .. .. 35·00 2·50
b. Wmk sideways (1927) .. 80·00 £100
41 2s. brown (Die II) (6.16) .. .. £150 11·00
a. Imperf three sides (pair) .. £12000
b. Red-brown (aniline) .. .. £400 38·00
42 5s. grey and yellow (4.18) .. £175 55·00
a. Grey and orange (1920) .. £175 55·00
b. Grey and deep yellow .. £175 55·00
ba. Wmk sideways £2250 £1600
c. Grey and pale yellow (1928) £175 55·00
43 10s. grey and pink (5.2.17) .. £400 £140
a. Grey and bright aniline pink £350 £140
ab. Wmk sideways £2750 £1500
b. Grey and pale aniline pink (1928) £425 £140
44 £1 chocolate and dull blue (7.16) .. £1300 £650
a. Chestnut and bright blue (1917) .. £1400 £700
b. Bistre-brown and bright blue .. £1300 £650
ba. Wmk sideways £4500 £1800
45 £2 black and rose (12.19) .. £2100 £1100
a. Grey and crimson (1920) .. £2000 £1100
b. Purple-black and pale rose (1924) £1800 £1100
35/45*b* .. .. .. *Set of* 11 £3500 £1700
43/45 Optd "Specimen" .. .. *Set of* 3 £500

*The Die II of No. 35a is a substituted cliché introduced to replace a cracked plate which occurred on No. 55 of the upper left pane (Row 10, No. 1). The Die IIA characteristics are more pronounced in this cliché than on the sheet stamps from this die. The break at left, for instance, extends to the outer, in addition to the inner, frame line.

All values were printed by both Cooke and Harrison, and the 9d., 1s. and 5s. were also printed by Mullett and Ash.

1916–18. W 5. *Rough paper, locally gummed. P* 14.

47 5*a* 1d. scarlet (I) (14.12.16) .. .. 22·00 1·25
48 1d. deep red (I) (1917) .. .. 22·00 1·00
49 1d. rose-red (I) (1918) .. .. 32·00 1·50
a. Substituted cliché .. .. £1300 75·00
49*b* 1d. rosine (I) (1918) .. .. 85·00 8·00
c. Substituted cliché £1600 £110
50 1d. rose-red (II) (1918) .. .. £275 20·00
aa. Substituted cliché .. .. £1300 75·00
50*a* 1d. rosine (II) (1918) .. .. £600 50·00
ab. Substituted cliché £1600 £110

For explanations of substituted cliché varieties, see 2nd paragraph of note below No. 34*a*.

For illustrations and descriptions of Dies II and III, see after T 5*a*.
For the previous No. 50*b* see No. O60.

(Typo J. B. Cooke or T. S. Harrison)

1918–20. W 6*a* (*Mult*). *P* 14.

51 5*a* ½d. green (*shades*) (8.1.18) .. .. 4·00 1·50
a. "1" in fraction at right thinner .. £100 40·00
b. Wmk sideways .. .. † £1500
52 1d. carmine-pink (I) (23.1.18) .. .. £120 40·00
a. Deep red (I) (1918) £750 £140
53 1d. carmine (I) (10.12.19) .. .. 32·00 5·00
a. Deep red (aniline) (I) (1920) .. £140 35·00
54 1½d. black-brown (30.1.19) .. .. 5·00 1·50
a. Very thin paper (3.19) .. .. 28·00 10·00
55 1½d. red-brown (4.19) .. .. 8·50 1·25
a. Chocolate .. .. .. 8·50 1·25

No. 51 was printed by Cooke and Harrison, Nos. 52/*a* by Cooke only and Nos. 53/55*a* by Harrison only. Nos. 52/*a* have rather yellowish gum, that of No. 53 being pure white.

1918 (June). *Printed from a new plate* (Die III) *on white unsurfaced paper, locally gummed.* W 5. *P* 14.

55*b* 5*a* 1d. rose-red (III) .. .. 60·00 24·00
55*c* 1d. rose-carmine (III) .. .. 60·00 24·00

(Typo T. S. Harrison and also A. J. Mullett for 1s. 4d. from March 1926)

1918–23. W 5. *P* 14.

56 5*a* ½d. orange (9.11.23) .. .. 2·50 90
57 1d. violet (*shades*) (13.2.22) .. 4·50 60
a. Imperf three sides (pair) .. £7000
b. Red-violet .. .. 5·50 70
58 1½d. black-brown (9.11.18) .. 7·00 55
59 1½d. deep red-brown (4.19) .. 4·00 25
a. Chocolate .. .. 4·25 30
60 1½d. bright red-brown (20.1.22) .. 10·00 1·50
61 1½d. green (7.3.23) .. .. 2·00 20
a. Rough unsurfaced paper .. 90·00 35·00
62 2d. dull orange (5.10.20) .. 14·00 30
a. Brown-orange .. .. 14·00 30
63 2d. bright rose-scarlet (17.2.22) .. 6·50 40
a. Dull rose-scarlet .. .. 6·50 40
64 4d. violet (21.6.21) .. .. 9·00 10·00
a. Line through "FOUR PENCE" £7000 £3500
b. "FOUR PENCE" in thinner letters £600 £225
65 5*a* 4d. ultramarine (*shades*) (23.3.22) .. 48·00 5·00
a. "FOUR PENCE" in thinner letters £750 £150
b. Pale milky blue .. .. 55·00 8·00
66 1s. 4d. pale blue (2.12.20) .. 65·00 18·00
a. Dull greenish blue (1923) .. 65·00 18·00
b. Deep turquoise .. .. £550 80·00
56/66 .. .. *Set of* 11 £160 40·00

In addition to a number of mint pairs a single used example of No. 57 imperforate on three sides is known.

The 4d. ultramarine was originally printed by Cooke but the plates were worn in mid-1923 and Harrison prepared a new pair of plates. Stamps from these plates can only be distinguished by the minor flaws which are peculiar to them.

The variety of Nos. 64 and 65 with "FOUR PENCE" thinner, was caused by the correction of a defective cliché (No. 6, 2nd row, right-hand pane), which showed a line running through these words.

No. 61a was printed on a small residue of paper which had been employed for Nos. 47/50*d*.

(Typo T. S. Harrison (to February 1926), A. J. Mullett (to June 1927), thereafter J. Ash)

1923–24. W 6. *P* 12.

73 1 6d. chestnut (Die IIB) (6.12.23) .. 20·00 1·00
a. Leg of kangaroo broken .. £100 50·00
74 2s. maroon (Die II) (1.5.24) .. 50·00 15·00
75 £1 grey (Die IIB) (1.5.24) (Optd S. £75) £500 £175

The 6d. and 2s. were printed by all three printers, but the £1 only by Harrison.

(Typo T. S. Harrison (to February 1926), thereafter A. J. Mullett)

1924. *P* 14. (*a*) W 5 (1 May).

76 5*a* 1d. sage-green .. .. .. 2·25 25
77 1½d. scarlet (*shades*) .. .. 2·00 20
a. Very thin paper .. .. 40·00 12·00
b. "HALEPENCE" .. .. 35·00 15·00
c. "RAL" of "AUSTRALIA" thin .. 35·00 15·00
d. Curved "1" and thin fraction at left 32·00 15·00
78 2d. red-brown .. .. .. 18·00 5·00
a. Bright red-brown .. .. 26·00 7·50
79 3d. dull ultramarine .. .. 24·00 1·25
a. Imperf three sides (pair) .. £6500
80 4d. olive-yellow .. .. .. 26·00 2·00
a. Olive-green .. .. .. 28·00 2·00
81 4½d. violet .. .. .. 23·00 2·00

(*b*) W 6*a*

82 5*a* 1d. sage-green (20 May) .. .. 8·00 5·50

(*c*) *No wmk*

83 5*a* 1d. sage-green (18 August) .. .. 4·75 7·50
84 1½d. scarlet (14 August) .. .. 8·50 8·50
76/84 .. .. *Set of* 9 £100 29·00

Nos. 78/*a* and 82/4 were printed by Harrison only but the remainder were printed by both Harrison and Mullett.

In the semi-transparent paper of Nos. 54a and 77a the watermark is almost indistinguishable. Nos. 77b, 77c and 77d are typical examples of retouching of which there are many others in these issues. In No. 77c the letters "RAL" differ markedly from the normal. There is a white stroke cutting the oval frame-line above the "L", and the right-hand outer line of the Crown does not cut the white frame-line above the "A". No. 77b occurs on the row above No. 77c in the sheet, so that the varieties may be found *se-tenant*.

7

I

II

New Dies

1d. For differences see note after No. 27a.
1½d. From new steel plates made from a new die. Nos. 88 and 98 are the Ash printings, the ink of which is shiny.
2d. Die I. Height of frame 25.6 mm. Left-hand frame-line thick and uneven behind Kangaroo. Pearls in Crown vary in size.
Die II. Height of frame 25.6 mm. Left-hand frame-line thin and even. Pearls in Crown are all the same size.
Die III. Height 25.1 mm; lettering and figures of value bolder than Die I.
3d. Die II has bolder letters and figures than Die I, as illustrated above.
5d. Die II has a bolder figure "5" with flat top compared with Die I of the earlier issues.

(Typo by A. J. Mullett or J. Ash)

1926–30. W 7. (*a*) *P* 14.

85 5*a* ½d. orange (10.3.27) .. .. 7·00 5·50
86 1d. sage-green (23.10.26) .. .. 3·75 75
87 1½d. scarlet (5.11.26) .. .. 5·50 70
88 1½d. golden scarlet (1927) .. .. 8·00 1·75
89 2d. red-brown (Die I) (17.8.27) .. 28·00 26·00
90 3d. dull ultramarine (12.26) .. 22·00 4·00
91 4d. yellow-olive (17.1.28) .. .. 48·00 26·00
92 4½d. violet (26.10.27) .. .. 14·00 2·75
93 1s. 4d. pale greenish blue (6.9.27) .. £150 75·00
85/93 .. .. *Set of* 8 £250 £120

(*b*) *P* 13½ × 12½

94 5*a* ½d. orange (21.11.28) .. .. 1·50 75
95 1d. sage-green (Die I) (23.12.26) .. 1·60 20
96 1d. sage-green (Die II) .. .. 60·00 75·00
97 1½d. scarlet (14.1.27) .. .. 1·50 25
98 1½d. golden scarlet .. .. 2·00 35
98*a* 1½d. red-brown (16.9.30) .. .. 4·50 5·50
99 2d. red-brown (Die II) (28.4.28) .. 7·00 7·00
99*a* 2d. golden scarlet (Die II) (2.8.30) .. 7·50 90
99*b* 2d. golden scarlet (Die III) (9.9.30) .. 7·00 40
c. No wmk £950 £400
d. Tête-bêche (pair) £28000
100 3d. dull ultramarine (Die I) (23.2.28) 45·00 4·25
101 3d. deep ultramarine (Die II) (28.9.29) 23·00 1·25
102 4d. yellow-olive (4.29) .. .. 23·00 2·00
103 4½d. violet (11.28) .. .. 48·00 16·00
103*a* 5d. orange-brown (Die II) (27.8.30) .. 17·00 2·00
104 1s. 4d. turquoise (30.9.28) .. .. 80·00 20·00
94/104 .. .. *Set of* 11 £190 48·00

Owing to defective manufacture, part of a sheet of the 2d. (Die III) escaped unwatermarked; while the watermark in other parts of the same sheet was faint or normal.

Only one example of No. 99d is known.

8 Parliament House, Canberra

9 "DH66" Biplane and Pastoral Scene

(Des R. A. Harrison. Die eng by Waterlow. Plates and printing by A. J. Mullett)

1927 (9 May). *Opening of Parliament House, Canberra. No wmk. P* 11.

105 8 1½d. brownish lake 50 50
a. Imperf between (pair) £2750 £1900

(Eng T. S. Harrison. Recess J. Ash)

1928 (29 Oct). *National Stamp Exhibition, Melbourne. As T* 4. *No wmk. P* 11.

106 3d. blue .. .. 4·25 4·00
a. Pane of four with margins .. £175 £225
ab. Imperf (pane of four) £15000

No. 106a comes from special sheets of 60 stamps divided into 15 blocks of 4 (5 × 3) and separated by wide gutters perforated down the middle, printed and sold at the Exhibition.

(Typo J. Ash)

1929–30. W 7. *P* 12.

107 1 6d. chestnut (Die IIB) (25.9.29) .. 22·00 4·00
108 9d. violet (Die IIB) (2.29) .. .. 30·00 8·50
109 1s. blue-green (Die IIB) (12.6.29) .. 40·00 4·50
110 2s. maroon (Die II) (3.29) .. .. 48·00 12·00
111 5s. grey and yellow (30.11.29) .. £190 75·00
112 10s. grey and pink (2.29) £350 £250
114 £2 black and rose (11.30) £1800 £350
107/114 .. .. .. *Set of* 7 £2250 £650
112/114 Optd "Specimen" .. *Set of* 2 £300

(Des R. A. Harrison and H. Herbert. Eng A. Taylor. Recess J. Ash)

1929 (20 May). *Air. No wmk. P* 11.

115 9 3d. green (*shades*) .. .. .. 10·00 3·25

Variations of up to ¾ mm in the design size of No. 115 are due to paper shrinkage; the stamps having been printed by a "wet" process.

10 Black Swan

11 Capt. Charles Sturt

(Des Pitt Morison. Eng F. D. Manley. Recess J. Ash)

1929 (28 Sept). *Centenary of Western Australia. No wmk. P* 11.

116 10 1½d. dull scarlet .. .. .. 1·00 1·00
a. Re-entry ("T" of "AUSTRALIA" clearly double) .. .. 55·00 35·00

(Des R. A. Harrison. Eng F. D. Manley. Recess J. Ash)

1930 (2 June). *Centenary of Exploration of River Murray by Capt. Sturt. No wmk. P* 11.

117 11 1½d. scarlet .. .. 1·00 45
118 3d. blue .. .. 3·75 5·00

No. 117 with manuscript surcharge of "2d. paid P M L H I" was issued by the Postmaster of Lord Howe Island during a shortage of 2d. stamps between August and October 1930. A few copies of the 1½d. value No. 98 were also endorsed. These provisionals are not recognized by the Australian postal authorities. (*Price £550 un. or us., either stamp.*)

TWO

PENCE

(12)

13 The *Southern Cross* above hemispheres

1930 (1 Aug). *T* **5a** *surch as T* **12**. *W* **7**. *P* 13½ × 12½.

119		2d. on 1½d. golden scarlet	80	40
120		5d. on 4½d. violet	7·00	7·00

No. 120 is from a redrawn die in which the words "FOURPENCE HALFPENNY" are noticeably thicker than in the original die and the figure "4" has square instead of tapering serifs.

Stamps from the redrawn die without the surcharge were printed, but not issued thus. Some stamps, *cancelled to order*, were included in sets supplied by the post office. A few mint copies, which escaped the cancellation were found and some may have been used postally (*Price* £38 *used c.t.o.*).

(Des and eng F. D. Manley. Recess John Ash)

1931 (19 Mar). *Kingsford Smith's flights. No wmk. P* 11. (*a*) *Postage*.

121	**13**	2d. rose-red	75	35
122		3d. blue	5·00	4·00
		(*b*) *Air. Inscr* "AIR MAIL SERVICE"		
123	**13**	6d. violet	10·00	10·00
		a. Re-entry ("FO" and "LD" double)	80·00	65·00
121/3		*Set of* 3	14·00	13·00

15

17 Superb Lyrebird

(Typo John Ash)

1931–36. *W* **15**. (*a*) *P* 13½ × 12½.

124	**5a**	½d. orange (2.33)	2·75	4·00
125		1d. green (Die I) (10.31)	1·00	10
126		1½d. red-brown (10.36)	5·00	7·00
127		2d. golden scarlet (Die III) (18.12.31)	1·75	10
128		3d. ultramarine (Die II) (30.9.32)	15·00	45
129		4d. yellow-olive (2.33)	16·00	60
130		5d. orange-brown (Die II) (25.2.32)	14·00	15
131		1s. 4d. turquoise (18.8.32)	70·00	3·25
124/131		*Set of* 8	£110	14·00
		(*b*) *P* 12		
132	**1**	6d. chestnut (Die IIB) (20.4.32)	20·00	22·00
133		9d. violet (Die IIB) (20.4.32)	18·00	75
134		2s. maroon (Die II) (6.8.35)	5·00	45
135		5s. grey and yellow (12.32)	£100	9·50
136		10s. grey and pink (31.7.32)	£250	90·00
137		£1 grey (Die IIB) (11.35)	£425	£140
138		£2 black and rose (6.34)	£1500	£225
132/138		*Set of* 7	£2000	£450
136/138 Optd "Specimen"		*Set of* 3	85·00	

Stamps as No. 127, without wmk and perf 11 are forgeries made in 1932 to defraud the P.O.

For re-engraved type of No. 134, see No. 212.

(Recess John Ash)

1931 (4 Nov). *Air Stamp. As T* **13** *but inscr* "AIR MAIL SERVICE" *in bottom tablet. No wmk. P* 11.

139		6d. sepia	16·00	12·00

1931 (17 Nov). *Air. No.* 139 *optd with Type* O **4**.

139a		6d. sepia	40·00	40·00

This stamp was not restricted to official use but was on general sale to the public.

(Des F. D. Manley. Recess John Ash)

1932 (15 Feb). *No wmk. P* 11.

140	**17**	1s. green	60·00	1·00
140a		1s. yellow-green	65·00	1·40

18 Sydney Harbour Bridge

19 Laughing Kookaburra

(Des R. A. Harrison. Eng F. D. Manley. Printed John Ash)

1932 (14 Mar). (*a*) *Recess. No wmk. P* 11.

141	**18**	2d. scarlet	2·25	2·50
142		3d. blue	4·00	6·50
143		5s. blue-green	£375	£180
		(*b*) *Typo. W* **15**. *P* 10½.		
144	**18**	2d. scarlet	2·50	75
141/4		*Set of* 4	£375	£180

Stamps as No. 144 without wmk and perf 11 are forgeries made in 1932 to defraud the P.O.

(Typo John Ash)

1932 (1 June). *W* **15**. *P* 13½ × 12½.

146	**19**	6d. red-brown	25·00	45

20 Melbourne and R. Yarra

21 Merino Ram

(Des and eng F. D. Manley. Recess John Ash)

1934 (2 July). *Centenary of Victoria. W* **15**.

			I. *P* 10½.		II. *P* 11½.	
147	**20**	2d. orange-vermilion	2·00	1·00	4·00	1·25
148		3d. blue	6·00	5·50	7·00	7·00
149		1s. black	42·00	12·00	42·00	12·00
147/9		*Set of* 3	45·00	17·00	48·00	18·00

(Des and eng F. D. Manley. Recess John Ash)

1934 (1 Nov). *Death Centenary of Capt. John Macarthur. W* **15**. *P* 11½.

150	**21**	2d. carmine-red (A)	3·25	1·00
150a		2d. carmine-red (B)	32·00	2·75
151		3d. blue	8·00	8·00
152		9d. bright purple	35·00	30·00
150/2		*Set of* 3	42·00	35·00

Type A of the 2d. shows shading on the hill in the background varying from light to dark (as illustrated). Type B has the shading almost uniformly dark.

22 Hermes

23 Cenotaph, Whitehall

(Des F. D. Manley. Eng E. Broad and F. D. Manley. Recess John Ash until April 1940; W. C. G. McCracken thereafter)

1934–48. (*a*) *No wmk. P* 11.

153	**22**	1s. 6d. dull purple (1.12.34)	32·00	90
		(*b*) *W* **15**. *P* 13½ × 14		
153a	**22**	1s. 6d. dull purple (22.10.37)	7·50	30
		b. Thin rough paper (12.2.48)	7·00	40

(Des B. Cottier; adapted and eng F. D. Manley. Recess John Ash)

1935 (18 Mar). *20th Anniv of Gallipoli Landing. W* **15**. *P* 13½ × 12½ *or* 11 (1s.).

154	**23**	2d. scarlet	80	25
155		1s. black (*chalk-surfaced*)	48·00	38·00
		a. Perf 13½×12½	£1500	

24 King George V on "Anzac"

25 Amphitrite and Telephone Cable

(Des and eng F. D. Manley. Recess John Ash)

1935 (2 May). *Silver Jubilee. Chalk-surfaced paper. W* **15** (*sideways*). *P* 11½.

156	**24**	2d. scarlet	1·00	30
157		3d. blue	6·00	6·00
158		2s. bright violet	45·00	38·00
156/8		*Set of* 3	48·00	40·00

(Des and eng F. D. Manley. Recess John Ash)

1936 (1 Apr). *Opening of Submarine Telephone Link to Tasmania. W* **15**. *P* 11½.

159	**25**	2d. scarlet	60	35
160		3d. blue	2·50	3·25

26 Site of Adelaide, 1836; Old Gum Tree, Glenelg; King William St., Adelaide

(Des and eng F. D. Manley. Recess John Ash)

1936 (3 Aug). *Centenary of South Australia. W* **15**. *P* 11½.

161	**26**	2d. carmine	90	25
162		3d. blue	5·00	4·00
163		1s. green	10·00	7·00
161/3		*Set of* 3	14·00	10·00

27 Wallaroo

28 Queen Elizabeth

29 King George VI

30 King George VI

31

32 Koala

Die I Die Ia Die II

33 Merino Ram

34 Laughing Kookaburra

35 Platypus

36 Superb Lyrebird

38 Queen Elizabeth

39 King George VI

40 King George VI and Queen Elizabeth

40a

40b (Background evenly shaded, lettering strengthened)

(Des R. A. Harrison (T **28/30**), F. D. Manley (T **27, 31/6**), H. Barr (T **38/9**), H. Barr and F. D. Manley (T **40**). Eng. F. D. Manley and T. C. Duffell (T **34**), T. C. Duffell (revised lettering for T **40***a*/*b*), F. D. Manley (others). All recess with John Ash, W. C. G. McCracken or "By Authority . . ." imprints)

1937–49. *W* **15** (*sideways on* 5*d*., 9*d*., 5*s*. *and* 10*s*.).

		(*a*) *P* 13½ × 14 (*vert designs*) *or* 14 × 13½ (*horiz*)		
164	**27**	½d. orange (3.10.38)	2·00	45
165	**28**	1d. emerald-green (10.5.37)	30	10
166	**29**	1½d. maroon (20.4.38)	9·00	2·50
167	**30**	2d. scarlet (10.5.37)	30	10
167a	**31**	3d. blue (Die I, 1st ptg) (2.8.37)	£110	55·00
168		3d. blue (Die I) (2.8.37)	45·00	7·50
168a		3d. blue (Die Ia) (1937)	£110	6·50
168b		3d. blue (Die II) (1938)	45·00	2·75
169		3d. bright blue, *thin paper* (Die II) (21.12.38)	42·00	2·00
170	**32**	4d. green (1.2.38)	9·00	30
171	**33**	5d. purple (1.12.38)	4·00	40
172	**34**	6d. purple-brown (2.8.37)	24·00	80
173	**35**	9d. chocolate (1.9.38)	9·00	90
174	**36**	1s. grey-green (2.8.37)	55·00	1·90
175	**31**	1s. 4d. deep magenta (3.10.38)	2·50	1·75
		a. Pale magenta	1·50	1·50
		(*b*) *P* 13½		
176	**38**	5s. claret **C** (1.4.38)	10·00	75
		a. Thin rough paper **O** (4.2.48)	7·00	1·50
177	**39**	10s. dull purple **C** (1.4.38) (Optd S. £30)	28·00	10·00
		a. Thin rough paper **O** (11.48)	55·00	20·00
178	**40**	£1 blue-slate **C** (1.11.38) (Optd S. £400)	60·00	28·00
		a. Thin rough paper **O** (4.4.49)	£110	60·00
164/178		*Set of* 14	£225	45·00
		(*c*) *P* 15 × 14 (*vert designs*) *or* 14 × 15 (*horiz*)		
179	**27**	½d. orange (28.1.42)	45	10
		a. Coil pair	10·00	12·00
180	**40a**	1d. emerald-green (1.8.38)	1·25	10
181		1d. maroon (10.12.41)	1·25	10
		a. Coil pair	12·00	14·00
182	**29**	1½d. maroon (21.11.41)	4·50	7·50
183		1½d. emerald-green (10.12.41)	1·00	25
184	**40b**	2d. scarlet (11.7.38)	2·25	10
		a. Coil pair	£275	£275
185		2d. bright purple (10.12.41)	50	40
		a. Coil pair	22·00	24·00
186	**31**	3d. bright blue (10.40)	38·00	2·00
187		3d. purple-brown (10.1.42)	20	10
188	**32**	4d. green (10.42)	1·50	10
188a	**33**	5d. purple (5.46)	45	1·50
189	**34**	6d. red-brown (5.42)	2·00	10
		a. Purple-brown (1944)	1·75	10
190	**35**	9d. chocolate (1943)	80	10
191	**36**	1s. grey-green (3.41)	1·00	10
179/191		*Set of* 14	50·00	11·00

For unwmkd issue, see Nos. 228/30*d*.

Dies of the 3*d*. In Die I the letters "TA" of "POSTAGE" at right are joined by a white flaw; the outline of the chin consists of separate strokes.

Die Ia is similar, but "T" and "A" have been clearly separated by retouches made on the plate.

In Die II "T" and "A" are separate and a continuous line has been added to the chin. The outline of the cheek extends to about 1 mm above the lobe of the King's right ear.

No. 167a is a preliminary printing made with unsuitable ink and may be detected by the absence of finer details; the King's face

appears whitish and the wattles are blank. The greater part of this printing was distributed to the Press with advance notices of the issue.

No. 186 is re-engraved and differs from Nos. 167*a* to 169 in the King's left eyebrow which is shaded downwards from left to right instead of from right to left.

Thin paper. Nos. 176a, 177a, 178a. In these varieties the watermark is more clearly visible on the back and the design is much less sharp. Early printings of No. 176a have tinted paper.

SPECIAL COIL PERFORATION. This special perforation of large and small holes on the narrow sides of the stamps is intended for stamps issued in coils, to facilitate separation. When they exist we list them as "Coil pairs".

The following with "special coil" perforation were placed on sale in *sheets*: Nos. 204ba, 222*a* (1952), 228, 230, 237, 262 (1953), 309, 311, and 314. These are listed as "Coil blocks of four".

Coils with "normal" perforations also exist for some values.

41 "Governor Phillip at Sydney Cove" (J. Allcot)

"Tail" flaw (Left pane R. 7/1)

(Des and eng E. Broad and F. D. Manley. Recess J. Ash)

1937 (1 Oct). *150th Anniv of Foundation of New South Wales*. *W* **15**. *P* 13½ × 14.

193	**41**	2d. scarlet	1·50	10
		a. "Tail" flaw	£170	40·00
194		3d. bright blue	10·00	1·75
195		9d. purple	22·00	7·00
193/5		*Set of* 3	30·00	8·00

42 A.I.F. and Nurse

(Des and eng F. D. Manley from drawing by Virgil Reilly. Recess W. C. G. McCracken)

1940 (15 July). *Australian Imperial Forces*. *W* **15** (*sideways*). *P* 14 × 13½.

196	**42**	1d. green	1·50	60
197		2d. scarlet	1·50	15
198		3d. blue	7·00	5·00
199		6d. brown-purple	20·00	9·00
196/9		*Set of* 4	27·00	13·50

(43) (44) (45)

(Opts designed by F. D. Manley)

1941 (10 Dec). *Nos.* 184, 186 *and* 171 *surch with T* **43/5**.

200	**40*b***	2½d. on 2d. (V.)	1·25	20
201	**31**	3½d. on 3d. (Y. on Black)	1·50	1·25
202	**33**	5½d. on 5d. (V.)	7·50	2·50
200/2		*Set of* 3	9·00	3·75

46 Queen Elizabeth **46*a*** **47** King George VI

48 King George VI **49** King George VI **50** Emu

(Des and eng F. D. Manley)

1942–44. *Recess*. *W* **15**. *P* 15 × 14.

203	**46**	1d. brown-purple (1.1.43)	20	10
		a. Coil pair	10·00	13·00
204	**46*a***	1½d. green (1.12.42)	20	10
204*a*	**47**	2d. bright purple (4.12.44)	40	25
		b. Coil pair	40·00	45·00
		ba. Coil block of four		
205	**48**	2½d. scarlet (7.1.42)	20	10
		a. Imperf (pair)*	£1300	
206	**49**	3½d. bright blue (3.42)	25	10
		a. Deep blue	50	15
207	**50**	5½d. slate-blue (12.2.42)	65	10
203/207		*Set of* 6	1·75	35

*No. 205*a* is in pair with stamp which only has the right-hand side imperf.

For stamps as Nos. 204/*a* but without watermark see Nos. 229/30.

52 Duke and Duchess of Gloucester

(Des and eng F. D. Manley. Recess)

1945 (19 Feb). *Arrival of Duke and Duchess of Gloucester in Australia*. *W* **15**. *P* 14½.

209	**52**	2½d. lake	10	10
210		3½d. ultramarine	15	25
211		5½d. indigo	20	30
209/11		*Set of* 3	40	55

A

B

1946 (3 Jan). *Kangaroo type, as No.* 134, *but re-engraved as* B. *W* **15**. *P* 12.

212	**1**	2s. maroon	3·25	3·75

No. 134 has two background lines between the value circle and "TWO SHILLINGS"; No. 212 has only one line in this position. There are also differences in the shape of the letters.

53 Star and Wreath

56 Sir Thos. Mitchell and Queensland

(Des F. D. Manley (2½d.), F. D. Manley and G. Lissenden (3½d.), G. Lissenden (5½d.). Eng F. D. Manley. Recess)

1946 (18 Feb). *Victory Commemoration*. *T* **53** *and similar designs*. *W* **15** (*sideways on* 5½*d*.). *P* 14½.

213	2½d. scarlet	10	10
214	3½d. blue	25	65
215	5½d. green	30	45
213/15	*Set of* 3	60	1·10

Designs: *Horiz*—3½d. Flag and dove. *Vert*—5½d. Angel.

(Des and eng F. D. Manley. Recess)

1946 (14 Oct). *Centenary of Mitchell's Exploration of Central Queensland*. *W* **15**. *P* 14½.

216	**56**	2½d. scarlet	10	10
217		3½d. blue	15	50
218		1s. grey-olive	20	20
216/18		*Set of* 3	40	65

57 Lt. John Shortland R.N.

58 Steel Foundry

59 Coal Carrier Cranes

(Des G. Lissenden, eng G. Lissenden and F. D. Manley (5½d.); des and eng F. D. Manley (others). Recess)

1947 (8 Sept). *Sesquicentenary of City of Newcastle, New South Wales*. *W* **15** (*sideways on* 3½*d*.). *P* 14½ *or* 15 × 14 (2½*d*.).

219	**57**	2½d. lake	10	10
		a. Imperf three sides	£700	
220	**58**	3½d. blue	15	40
221	**59**	5½d. green	15	30
219/21		*Set of* 3	35	65

The following items are understood to have been the subject of unauthorised leakages from the Commonwealth Note and Stamp Printing Branch and are therefore not listed by us.

It is certain that none of this material was distributed to post offices for issue to the public.

Imperforate all round. 1d. Princess Elizabeth; 1½d. Queen; 2½d. King; 4d. Koala; 6d. Kookaburra; 9d. Platypus; 1s. Lyre-bird (small); 1s. 6d. Air Mail (Type **22**); 2½d. Newcastle.

Also 2½d. Peace, unwatermarked; 2½d. King, *tête-bêche*; 3½d. Newcastle, in dull ultramarine; 2½d. King on "toned" paper.

60 Queen Elizabeth II when Princess

(Des R. A. Harrison. Eng F. D. Manley. Recess)

1947 (20 Nov)–**48**. *Marriage of Princess Elizabeth*. *P* 14 × 15.

(*a*) *W* **15** (*sideways*)

222	**60**	1d. purple	10	10

(*b*) *No wmk*

222*a*	**60**	1d. purple (8.48)	10	10
		b. Coil pair	2·00	4·50
		c. Coil block of four	4·00	

61 Hereford Bull

61*a* Hermes and Globe

62 Aboriginal Art

62*a* Commonwealth Coat of Arms

(Des G. Sellheim (T **62**), F. D. Manley (others). Eng F. D. Manley and G. Lissenden (T **62**), F. D. Manley (others). Recess)

1948 (16 Feb)–**56**. (*a*) *W* **15** (*sideways*). *P* 14½.

223	**61**	1s. 3d. brown-purple	1·75	75
223*a*	**61*a***	1s. 6d. blackish brown (1.9.49)	1·75	10
224	**62**	2s. chocolate	2·00	10

(*b*) *W* **15**. *P* 14½ × 13½

224*a*	**62*a***	5s. claret (11.4.49)	7·00	15
		ab. Thin paper	20·00	65
224*b*		10s. purple (3.10.49)	30·00	35
224*c*		£1 blue (28.11.49)	48·00	2·75
224*d*		£2 green (16.1.50)	£100	13·00
224*b/d*		Optd "Specimen" *Set of* 3	£150	

(*c*) *No wmk*. *P* 14½

224*e*	**61*a***	1s. 6d. blackish brown (6.12.56)	18·00	60
224*f*	**62**	2s. chocolate (21.7.56)	20·00	45
223/224*f*		*Set of* 9	£200	16·00

No. 224ab is an emergency printing on white Harrison paper instead of the toned paper used for No. 224*a*.

63 William J. Farrer

64 F. von Mueller

65 Boy Scout

(Des and eng F. D. Manley. Recess)

1948 (12 July). *William J. Farrer (wheat research)*. *W* **15**. *P* 15 × 14.

225	**63**	2½d. scarlet	10	10

(Des and eng F. D. Manley. Recess)

1948 (13 Sept). *Sir Ferdinand von Mueller (botanist)*. *W* **15**. *P* 15 × 14.

226	**64**	2½d. lake	10	10

(Des and eng F. D. Manley. Recess)

1948 (15 Nov). *Pan-Pacific Scout Jamboree, Wonga Park*. *W* **15** (*sideways*). *P* 14 × 15.

227	**65**	2½d. lake	10	10

See also No. 254.

MINIMUM PRICE

The minimum price quote is 10p which represents a handling charge rather than a basis for valuing common stamps. For further notes about prices see introductory pages.

Sky retouch (normally unshaded near hill)

"Green mist" retouch. A large area to the left of the bird's feathers is recut (upper plate left pane R. 9/3)

1948–56. *No wmk. P* 15 × 14 *or* 14 × 15 (9*d.*).

228 27	½d. orange (9.49)		20	10
	aa. Sky retouch (Rt. pane, R. 6/8)		6·00	
	a. Coil pair		75	2·00
	ab. Sky retouch (in pair)		70·00	
	b. Coil block of four		2·00	
229 46*a*	1½d. green (29.8.49)		90	45
230 47	2d. bright purple (12.48)		70	35
	aa. Coil pair		3·00	4·50
	ab. Coil block of four		15·00	
230*a* 32	4d. green (18.8.56)		2·00	40
230*b* 34	6d. purple-brown (18.8.56)		3·50	30
230*c* 35	9d. chocolate (13.12.56)		16·00	1·00
230*d* 36	1s. grey-green (13.12.56)		12·00	40
	da. "Green mist" retouch		£550	
228/230*d*		*Set of* 7	32·00	2·75

66 "Henry Lawson" (Sir Lionel Lindsay)

67 Mounted Postman and Aeroplane

(Des F. D. Manley. Eng E. R. M. Jones. Recess)

1949 (17 June). *Anniv of Birth of Henry Lawson (poet). P* 15 × 14.

231 66	2½d. maroon	15	10

(Des Sir Daryl Lindsay and F. D. Manley. Eng F. D. Manley. Recess)

1949 (10 Oct). *75th Anniv of Founding of U.P.U. P* 15 × 14.

232 67	3½d. ultramarine	20	25

68 Lord Forrest of Bunbury

69 King George VI

70 Queen Elizabeth

(Des and eng F. D. Manley. Recess)

1949 (28 Nov). *Lord Forrest of Bunbury (explorer and politician). W* 15. *P* 15 × 14.

233 68	2½d. lake	15	10

(Des and eng F. D. Manley. Recess)

1950–51. *P* 15 × 14. (*a*) *W* 15.

234 69	2½d. scarlet (12.4.50)		10	10
235	3d. scarlet (28.2.51)		15	10
	aa. Coil pair		9·00	12·00
	(*b*) *No wmk*			
235*a* 69	2½d. purple-brown (23.5.51)		15	15
235*b*	3d. grey-green (14.11.51)		15	10
	c. Coil pair		16·00	24·00
234/5*b*		*Set of* 4	50	30

On 1 December 1951 No. 235 was placed on sale in sheets of 144 originally intended for use in stamp booklets. These sheets contain 3 panes of 48 (16 × 3) with horizontal gutter margin between.

(Des and eng F. D. Manley. Recess)

1950–51. *P* 15 × 14.

236 70	1½d. green (19.6.50)	15	10
237	2d. yellow-green (28.3.51)	15	10
	a. Coil pair	3·50	6·00
	b. Coil block of four	7·00	

71 Aborigine

72, 73 Reproductions of First Stamps of New South Wales and Victoria

(Des F. D. Manley. Eng E. R. M. Jones. Recess)

1950 (14 Aug). *W* 15. *P* 15 × 14.

238 71	8½d. brown	15	40

For T 71 in a larger size, see Nos. 253/*b*.

(Des and eng E. R. M. Jones (T 72); des and eng G. Lissenden (T 73). Recess)

1950 (27 Sept). *Centenary of First Adhesive Postage Stamps in Australia. P* 15 × 14.

239 72	2½d. maroon	10	10
	a. Horiz pair. Nos. 239/40	20	55
240 73	2½d. maroon	10	10

Nos. 239/40 were printed alternately in vertical columns throughout the sheet.

74 Sir Edmund Barton

75 Sir Henry Parkes

76 "Opening First Federal Parliament" (T. Roberts)

77 Federal Parliament House, Canberra

(Des and eng F. D. Manley. Recess)

1951 (1 May). *Golden Jubilee of Commonwealth of Australia. P* 15 × 14.

241 74	3d. lake		30	10
	a. Horiz pair. Nos. 241/2		1·50	1·75
242 75	3d. lake		30	10
243 76	5½d. blue		20	1·50
244 77	1s. 6d. purple-brown		35	50
241/4		*Set of* 4	1·75	2·00

Nos. 241/2 are printed alternately in vertical columns throughout the sheet.

78 E. H. Hargraves

79 C. J. Latrobe

80 King George VI

(Des and eng F. D. Manley. Recess)

1951 (2 July). *Centenary of Discovery of Gold in Australia. P* 15 × 14.

245 78	3d. maroon	20	10
	a. Horiz pair. Nos. 245/6	50	95

(Des and eng F. D. Manley. Recess)

1951 (2 July). *Centenary of Responsible Government in Victoria. P* 15 × 14.

246 79	3d. maroon	20	10

Nos. 245/6 were printed alternately in vertical columns throughout the sheet.

(Des and eng E. R. M. Jones. Recess)

1951 (31 Oct). *W* 15. *P* 15 × 14.

247 80	7½d. blue	15	40
	a. Imperf 3 sides (vert pr)	£1500	

81 King George VI

82 King George VI

(Des F. D. Manley. Eng G. Lissenden. Recess)

1951–52. *W* 15. *P* 15 × 14.

248 81	3½d. brown-purple (28.11.51)		10	10
249	4½d. scarlet (20.2.52)		15	50
250	6½d. brown (20.2.52)		15	45
251	6½d. emerald-green (9.4.52)		10	15
248/51		*Set of* 4	45	1·10

(Des F. D. Manley. Eng D. Cameron (No. 252), E. R. M. Jones (Nos. 253/*b*). Recess)

1952 (19 Mar)–**65.** *P* 14½. (*a*) *W* 15 (*sideways*).

252 82	1s. 0½d. indigo	35	30
253 –	2s. 6d. deep brown	2·50	25
	(*b*) *No wmk*		
253*a* –	2s. 6d. deep brown (30.1.57)	5·00	30
	b. Sepia (10.65)	14·00	8·50

Design:—2s. 6d. As T 71 but larger (21 × 25½ *mm*).

No. 253*b* was an emergency printing and can easily be distinguished from No. 253*a* as it is on white Harrison paper, No. 253*a* being on toned paper.

(Des and eng F. D. Manley. Recess)

1952 (19 Nov). *Pan-Pacific Scout Jamboree, Greystanes. As T* 65, *but inscr* "1952–53". *W* 15 (*sideways*). *P* 14 × 15.

254	3½d. brown-lake	10	10

83 Butter

84 Wheat

85 Beef

(Des P.O. artists; adapted G. Lissenden. Typo)

1953 (11 Feb). *Food Production. P* 14½.

255 83	3d. emerald		30	10
	a. Strip of 3. Nos. 255/7		2·75	
256 84	3d. emerald		30	10
257 85	3d. emerald		30	10
258 83	3½d. scarlet		30	10
	a. Strip of 3. Nos. 258/60		2·75	
259 84	3½d. scarlet		30	10
260 85	3½d. scarlet		30	10
255/60		*Set of* 6	5·00	40

The three designs in each denomination appear in rotation, both horizontally and vertically, throughout the sheet.

86 Queen Elizabeth II

87 Queen Elizabeth II

(Des F. D. Manley from photograph by Dorothy Wilding Ltd. Eng D. Cameron. Recess)

1953–56. *P* 15 × 14. (*a*) *No wmk.*

261 86	1d. purple (19.8.53)		15	10
261*a*	2½d. blue (23.6.54)		20	10
262	3d. deep green (17.6.53)		20	10
	aa. Coil pair		4·50	5·50
	ab. Coil block of four		9·00	
262*a*	3½d. brown-red (2.7.56)		2·25	10
262*b*	6½d. orange (9.56)		2·75	70
	(*b*) *W* 15			
263 86	3½d. brown-red (21.4.53)		20	10
263*a*	6½d. orange (23.6.54)		1·50	10
261/3*a*		*Set of* 7	6·50	95

(Des and eng F. D. Manley. Recess)

1953 (25 May). *Coronation. P* 15 × 14.

264 87	3½d. scarlet		35	10
265	7½d. violet		1·50	55
266	2s. dull bluish green		5·50	30
264/6		*Set of* 3	6·50	75

88 Young Farmers and Calf

(Des P.O. artist; adapted P. E. Morriss. Eng E. R. M. Jones. Recess)

1953 (3 Sept). *25th Anniv of Australian Young Farmers' Clubs. P* 14½.

267 88	3½d. red-brown and deep green	10	10

89 Lt.-Gov. D. Collins

90 Lt.-Gov. W. Paterson

91 Sullivan Cove, Hobart, 1804

(Des E. R. M. Jones, eng D. Cameron (T **89/90**); des and eng G. Lissenden (T **91**). Recess)

1953 (23 Sept). *150th Anniv of Settlement in Tasmania. P* 15 × 14.
268 **89** 3½d. brown-purple 30 10
a. Horiz pair. Nos. 268/9 .. .. 80 1·25
269 **90** 3½d. brown-purple 30 10
270 **91** 2s. green .. .. .. 2·00 2·50
268/70 .. .. *Set of* 3 2·50 2·50

Nos. 268/9 were printed alternately in vertical columns throughout the sheet.

92 Stamp of 1853

(Des R. L. Beck; eng G. Lissenden. Recess)

1953 (11 Nov). *Tasmanian Postage Stamp Centenary. P* 14½.
271 **92** 3d. rose-red 10 10

93 Queen Elizabeth II and Duke of Edinburgh

94 Queen Elizabeth II

Re-entry (R. 8/2)

(Des and eng F. D. Manley; border and lettering on 7½d. des by R. M. Warner. Recess)

1954 (2 Feb). *Royal Visit. P* 14.
272 **93** 3½d. scarlet 20 10
a. Re-entry .. .. .. 25·00 3·75
273 **94** 7½d. purple 35 50
274 **93** 2s. dull bluish green 85 30
272/4 .. .. *Set of* 3 1·25 75

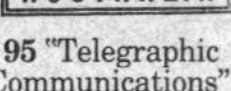

95 "Telegraphic Communications"

96 Red Cross and Globe

(Des R. M. Warner. Eng P. E. Morriss. Recess)

1954 (7 Apr). *Australian Telegraph System Centenary. P* 14.
275 **95** 3½d. brown-red 10 10

(Des B. Stewart. Eng P. E. Morriss. Design recess; cross typo)

1954 (9 June). *40th Anniv of Australian Red Cross Society. P* 14½.
276 **96** 3½d. ultramarine and scarlet 10 10

97 Black Swan **98** Locomotives of 1854 and 1954

(Des R. L. Beck. Eng G. Lissenden. Recess)

1954 (2 Aug). *Western Australian Postage Stamp Centenary. P* 14½.
277 **97** 3½d. black 10 10

(Des R. M. Warner. Eng G. Lissenden. Recess)

1954 (13 Sept). *Australian Railways Centenary. P* 14.
278 **98** 3½d. purple-brown 15 10

99 Territory Badge  **100** Olympic Games Symbol

(Des F. D. Manley. Eng G. Lissenden. Recess)

1954 (17 Nov). *Australian Antarctic Research. P* 14½ × 13½.
279 **99** 3½d. grey-black 15 10

(Des R. L. Beck. Eng P. E. Morriss. Recess)

1954–55. *Olympic Games Propaganda. P* 14.
280 **100** 2s. deep bright blue (1.12.54) 70 40
280*a* 2s. deep bluish green (30.11.55) .. 1·75 75

101 Rotary Symbol, Globe and Flags  **102** Queen Elizabeth II

(Des and eng D. Cameron. Recess)

1955 (23 Feb). *50th Anniv of Rotary International. P* 14 × 14½.
281 **101** 3½d. carmine 10 10

(Des F. D. Manley from bas-relief by W. L. Bowles. Eng G. Lissenden. Recess)

1955 (9 Mar)–**57.** *P* 14½. (*a*) *W* **15** (*sideways*).
282 **102** 1s. 0½d. deep blue .. .. .. 3·00 30

(*b*) *No wmk*
282*a* **102** 1s. 7d. red-brown (13.3.57) .. .. 3·50 10

103 American Memorial, Canberra **104** Cobb & Co. Coach (from dry-print by Sir Lionel Lindsay)

(Des R. L. Beck (head by F. D. Manley). Eng F. D. Manley. Recess)

1955 (4 May). *Australian–American Friendship. P* 14 × 14½.
283 **103** 3½d. violet-blue 10 10

(Design adapted and eng by F. D. Manley. Recess)

1955 (6 July). *Mail-coach Pioneers Commemoration. P* 14½ × 14.
284 **104** 3½d. blackish brown 25 10
285 2s. reddish brown .. .. .. 75 1·25

105 Y.M.C.A. Emblem and Map of the World **106** Florence Nightingale and Young Nurse

(Des E. Thake. Eng P. E. Morriss. Design recess; emblem typo)

1955 (10 Aug). *World Centenary of Y.M.C.A. P* 14½ × 14.
286 **105** 3½d. deep bluish green and red .. 10 10
a. Red (emblem) omitted £4000

(Des and eng F. D. Manley. Recess)

1955 (21 Sept). *Nursing Profession Commemoration. P* 14 × 14½.
287 **106** 3½d. reddish violet 10 10

107 Queen Victoria **108** Badges of New South Wales, Victoria and Tasmania

(Des and eng D. Cameron. Recess)

1955 (17 Oct). *Centenary of First South Australian Postage Stamps. P* 14½.
288 **107** 3½d. green 10 10

(Des and eng F. D. Manley. Recess)

1956 (26 Sept). *Centenary of Responsible Government in New South Wales, Victoria and Tasmania. P* 14½ × 14.
289 **108** 3½d. brown-lake 10 10

109 Arms of Melbourne **110** Olympic Torch and Symbol

111 Collins Street, Melbourne **112** Melbourne across R. Yarra

(Des P. E. Morriss; eng F. D. Manley (4d.). Des and eng F. D. Manley (7½d.). Recess. Des and photo Harrison from photographs by M. Murphy and sketches by L. Coles (1s.). Des and photo Courvoisier from photographs by M. Murphy (2s.))

1956 (31 Oct). *Olympic Games, Melbourne. P* 14½ (*4d.*), 14 × 14½ (*7½d., 1s.*) *or* 11½ (*2s.*).
290 **109** 4d. carmine-red 25 10
291 **110** 7½d. deep bright blue 40 60
292 **111** 1s. multicoloured 40 20
293 **112** 2s. multicoloured 50 60
290/3 .. .. *Set of* 4 1·40 1·25

113 Queen Elizabeth II **114** Queen Elizabeth II **115** South Australia Coat of Arms

(Des F. D. Manley from bas-relief by W. L. Bowles. Eng G. Lissenden. Recess)

1957 (6 Mar–13 Nov). *P* 15 x 14.
294 **113** 4d. lake (13 Mar) 30 10
294*a* **114** 7½d. violet (13 Nov) .. .. .. 1·25 85
ab. Double print £550
295 **113** 10d. deep grey-blue .. .. .. 1·50 30

The 4d. exists in booklet panes of six stamps, with imperf outer edges, producing single stamps with one or two adjacent sides imperf.

(Des and eng P. E. Morriss. Recess)

1957 (17 Apr). *Centenary of Responsible Government in South Australia. P* 14½.
296 **115** 4d. red-brown 10 10

116 Map of Australia and Caduceus

(Des J. E. Lyle; adapted B. Stewart. Eng D. Cameron. Recess)

1957 (21 Aug). *Flying Doctor Service. P* 14½ × 14.
297 **116** 7d. ultramarine 15 10

117 "The Spirit of Christmas"

Re-entry (Row 10/1)

(Des and eng D. Cameron from a painting by Sir Joshua Reynolds. Recess)

1957 (6 Nov). *Christmas. P* 14½ × 14.

298	**117**	3½d. scarlet	10	10
		a. Re-entry	5·00	2·75
299		4d. purple	10	10

118 Super-Constellation Airliner

(Des and eng P. E. Morriss. Recess)

1958 (6 Jan). *Inauguration of Australian "Round the World" Air Service. P* 14½ × 14.

301	**118**	2s. deep blue	50	75

119 Hall of Memory, Sailor and Airman

120 Sir Charles Kingsford Smith and *Southern Cross*

(Des and eng G. Lissenden. Recess)

1958 (10 Feb). *T* **119** *and similar horiz design. P* 14½ × 14.

302	**119**	5½d. brown-red	55	25
		a. Horiz pair. Nos. 302/3	1·10	5·00
303	–	5½d. brown-red	55	25

No. 303 shows a soldier and service-woman respectively in place of the sailor and airman. Nos. 302/3 are printed alternately in vertical columns throughout the sheet.

(Des J. E. Lyle. Eng F. D. Manley. Recess)

1958 (27 Aug). *30th Anniv of First Air Crossing of the Tasman Sea. P* 14 × 14½.

304	**120**	8d. deep ultramarine	60	70

121 Silver Mine, Broken Hill

122 The Nativity

(Des R. H. Evans; adapted and eng F. D. Manley. Recess)

1958 (10 Sept). *75th Anniv of Founding of Broken Hill. P* 14½ × 14.

305	**121**	4d. chocolate	15	10

(Des D. Cameron. Eng P. E. Morriss. Recess)

1958 (5 Nov). *Christmas. P* 14½ × 15.

306	**122**	3½d. deep scarlet	10	10
307		4d. deep violet	10	10

PHOSPHOR STAMPS ("Helecon"). "Helecon", a chemical substance of the zinc sulphide group, has been incorporated in stamps in two different ways, either in the ink with which the stamps are printed, or included in the surface coating of the stamp paper.

Owing to the difficulty of identification without the use of a U.V. lamp we do not list the helecon stamps separately but when in stock can supply them after testing under the lamp.

The first stamp to be issued was the 11d. Bandicoot from an experimental printing of four millions on helecon paper released to the public in December 1963. The next printing on ordinary paper was released in September 1964. The experimental printing was coarse, showing a lot of white dots and the colour is slate-blue, differing from both the ordinary and the later helecon paper.

The following helecon printings have been reported: 2d. and 3d. (sheets, coils and coil sheets) and 5d. (No. 354) Queen Elizabeth II; 8d. Tiger Cat; 11d. Bandicoot; 1s. Colombo Plan; 1s. 2d. Tasmanian Tiger; 2s. 3d. Wattle (No. 324*a*); and 6d. (No. 363*a*), 9d. and 1s. 6d. Birds (the 2s., 2s. 6d. and 3s. Birds were only issued on helecon paper). The 5d. Queen Elizabeth II in red (No. 354*b*) exists ordinary and with helecon ink. The coil pair was only issued with helecon ink; the booklet is normally with helecon ink but some were printed with ordinary ink by mistake. The Churchill stamp was printed on ordinary and helecon paper. The I.T.U. Centenary, Monash and later commemorative stamps were printed on helecon paper and all issues from No. 382 onwards were on helecon paper or paper coated with Derby Luminescence.

In 1982 a series of booklet stamps, Nos. 870/4, were printed by Enschedé on Harrison paper which gives a bluish white reaction under u.v. light.

123

124

126

127

128

129

Queen Elizabeth II

DIE I
Short break in outer line to bottom right of "4"

DIE II
Line unbroken

DIE A
Four short lines inside "5"

DIE B
Five short lines inside "5"

(Des G. Lissenden from photographs by Baron Studios. Eng F. D. Manley (2d.), D. Cameron (3d.). P. E. Morriss (others). Recess)

1959–62. *P* 14 × 15 (*horiz*), 15 × 14 (*vert*).

308	**123**	1d. deep slate-purple (2.2.59)	10	10
		a. Deep slate-lilac	40	20
309	**124**	2d. brown (21.3.62)	30	10
		a. Coil pair (1962)	3·75	4·25
		b. Coil block of four	7·50	
311	**126**	3d. blue-green (20.5.59)	15	10
		a. Coil pair (8.60)	3·50	4·00
		b. Coil block of four	7·00	
312	**127**	3½d. deep green (18.3.59)	15	10
313	**128**	4d. carmine-lake (Die I) (2.2.59)	1·25	10
		a. Carmine-red	1·25	10
		b. Die II	1·25	10
		ba. Carmine-red	1·25	10
314	**129**	5d. deep blue (Die A or B) (1.10.59)	70	10
		a. Vert *se-tenant* pair (A and B)	1·40	2·00
		b. Coil pair (early 1960)	6·00	7·00
		c. Coil block of four	12·00	
308/14		*Set of* 6	2·40	25

No. 313. Die I occurs in the upper pane and Die II in the lower pane of the sheet.

No. 314. Both dies occur in alternate horizontal rows in the sheet (Die A in Row 1, Die B in Row 2, and so on), and their value is identical.

Nos. 309a/b, 311a/b and 314b/c have horizontal coil perforations as described after No. 191.

The Note after No. 295 also applies to Nos. 313/14.

131 Numbat

137 Christmas Bells

142 Aboriginal Stockman

(Des Eileen Mayo (6d., 8d., 9d., 11d., 1s., 1s. 2d.), B. Stewart (5s.), Margaret Stones (others). Eng P. Morriss (11d.), F. D. Manley (1s.), B. Stewart (others). Recess)

1959–64. *T* **131, 137, 142** *and similar designs. W* **15** (5s.), *no wmk* (*others*). *P* 14 × 15 (1s. 2d.), 15 × 14 (6d. *to* 1s.), 14½ × 14 (5s.) *or* 14½ (*others*).

316		6d. brown (30.9.60)	1·75	10
317		8d. red-brown (11.5.60)	75	10
		a. Pale red-brown (1961)	75	10
318		9d. deep sepia (21.10.59)	2·50	30
319		11d. deep blue (3.5.61)	1·00	10
320		1s. deep green (9.9.59)	3·50	20
321		1s. 2d. deep purple (21.3.62)	1·00	10
322		1s. 6d. crimson/*yellow* (3.2.60)	2·25	70
323		2s. grey-blue (8.4.59)	1·25	10
324		2s. 3d. green/*maize* (9.9.59)	1·75	10
324*a*		2s. 3d. yellow-green (28.10.64)	7·50	1·50
325		2s. 5d. brown/*yellow* (16.3.60)	6·50	35
326		3s. scarlet (15.7.59)	1·75	10
327		5s. red-brown (26.7.61)	25·00	75
		a. White paper. *Brown-red* (17.6.64)	£160	5·00
316/327		*Set of* 13	50·00	4·00

Designs: (*As T* **131**) *Vert*—8d. Tiger Cat; 9d. Eastern Grey Kangaroos; 11d. Common Rabbit-Bandicoot; 1s. Platypus. *Horiz*—1s. 2d. Thylacine. (*As T* **137**) *Vert*—2s. Flannel Flower; 2s. 3d. Wattle; 2s. 5d. Banksia; 3s. Waratah.

No. 327 is on toned paper. No. 327a was a late printing on the white paper referred to in the note below No. 360.

See notes after No. 307 *re* helecon ink.

143 Postmaster Isaac Nichols boarding the brig *Experiment*

144 Parliament House, Brisbane, and Arms of Queensland

(Des R. Shackel; adapted and eng F. D. Manley. Recess)

1959 (22 Apr). *150th Anniv of the Australian Post Office. P* 14½ × 14.

331	**143**	4d. slate	15	10

(Des and eng G. Lissenden. Recess and typo)

1959 (5 June). *Centenary of Self-Government in Queensland. P* 14 × 14½.

332	**144**	4d. lilac and green	10	10

145 "The Approach of the Magi"

146 Girl Guide and Lord Baden-Powell

(Des and eng F. D. Manley. Recess)

1959 (4 Nov). *Christmas. P* 15 × 14.

333	**145**	5d. deep reddish violet	10	10

(Des and eng B. Stewart. Recess)

1960 (18 Aug). *Golden Jubilee of Girl Guide Movement. P* 14½ × 14.

334	**146**	5d. deep ultramarine	30	10

147 "The Overlanders" (Sir Daryl Lindsay)

148 "Archer" and Melbourne Cup

Two types:

I Mane rough

II Mane smooth

Type II occurs on Pane A, Row 2 Nos. 8 and 9, Row 4 Nos. 1 to 12, Row 5 Nos. 10 to 12, and on Pane C, Row 4 Nos. 5 to 12, Row 5 Nos. 1 to 9, and Rows 6 to 10 inclusive: the stamps in Row 4 Nos. 5 to 12 and Row 5 Nos. 1 to 9 are considered to be of an intermediate type with the mane as in Type II but the ear and rein being as in Type I. All the rest are Type I.

(Adapted and eng P. E. Morriss. Recess)

1960 (21 Sept). *Centenary of Northern Territory Exploration. P* 15 × 14½.

335	**147**	5d. magenta (I)	15	10
		a. Type II	70	15

(Des F. D. Manley. Eng G. Lissenden. Recess)

1960 (12 Oct). *100th Melbourne Cup Race Commemoration. P* 14½.

336	**148**	5d. sepia	15	10

149 Queen Victoria **150** Open Bible and Candle

(Des F. D. Manley. Eng B. Stewart. Recess)

1960 (2 Nov). *Centenary of First Queensland Postage Stamp. P* 14½ × 15.
337 **149** 5d. deep myrtle-green 25 10

(Des K. McKay. Adapted and eng B. Stewart. Recess)

1960 (9 Nov). *Christmas. P* 15 × 14½.
338 **150** 5d. carmine-red 10 10

151 Colombo Plan Bureau Emblem **152** Melba (after bust by Sir Bertram Mackennal)

(Des and eng G. Lissenden. Recess)

1961 (30 June). *Colombo Plan. P* 14 × 14½.
339 **151** 1s. red-brown 10 10
See notes after No. 307 *re* helecon ink.

(Des and eng B. Stewart. Recess)

1961 (20 Sept). *Centenary of Birth of Dame Nellie Melba (singer). P* 14½ × 15.
340 **152** 5d. blue 20 10

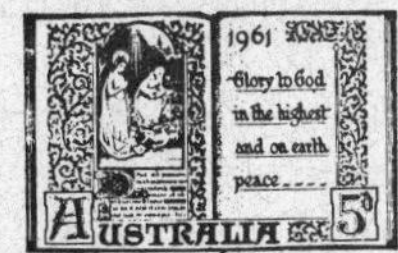

153 Open Prayer Book and Text

(Des G. Lissenden. Eng P. E. Morriss. Recess)

1961 (8 Nov). *Christmas. P* 14½ × 14.
341 **153** 5d. brown 10 10

154 J. M. Stuart **155** Flynn's Grave and Nursing Sister

(Des W. Jardine. Eng P. E. Morriss. Recess)

1962 (25 July). *Centenary of Stuart's Crossing of Australia from South to North. P* 14½ × 15.
342 **154** 5d. brown-red 15 10

(Des F. D. Manley. Photo)

1962 (5 Sept). *50th Anniv of Australian Inland Mission. P* 13½.
343 **155** 5d. multicoloured 25 10
a. Red omitted.. .. .. .. £350 £250
The note below No. 372b also applies to No. 343a.

156 "Woman" **157** "Madonna and Child"

(Des D. Dundas. Eng G. Lissenden. Recess)

1962 (26 Sept). *"Associated Country Women of the World" Conference, Melbourne. P* 14 × 14½.
344 **156** 5d. deep green 10 10

(Des and eng G. Lissenden. Recess)

1962 (17 Oct). *Christmas. P* 14½.
345 **157** 5d. violet 15 10

158 Perth and Kangaroo Paw (plant) **159** Arms of Perth and Running Track

(Des R. M. Warner (5d.), G. Hamori (2s. 3d.). Photo Harrison)

1962 (1 Nov). *Seventh British Empire and Commonwealth Games, Perth. P* 14 (5d.) *or* 14½ × 14 (2s. 3d.).
346 **158** 5d. multicoloured 40 10
a. Red omitted.. .. .. £375
347 **159** 2s. 3d. black, red, blue and green .. 2·50 2·50

160 Queen Elizabeth II. **161** Queen Elizabeth II and Duke of Edinburgh

(Des and eng after portraits by Anthony Buckley, P. E. Morriss (5d.), B. Stewart (2s. 3d.). Recess)

1963 (18 Feb). *Royal Visit. P* 14½.
348 **160** 5d. deep green 35 10
349 **161** 2s. 3d. brown-lake .. .. 1·90 3·00

162 Arms of Canberra and W. B. Griffin (architect) **163** Centenary Emblem

(Des and eng B. Stewart. Recess)

1963 (8 Mar). *50th Anniv of Canberra. P* 14½ × 14.
350 **162** 5d. deep green 15 10

(Des G. Hamori. Photo)

1963 (8 May). *Red Cross Centenary. P* 13½ × 13.
351 **163** 5d. red, grey-brown and blue 25 10

164 Blaxland, Lawson and Wentworth on Mt. York

(Des T. Alban. Eng P. E. Morriss. Recess)

1963 (28 May). *150th Anniv of First Crossing of Blue Mountains. P* 14½ × 14.
352 **164** 5d. ultramarine 15 10

165 "Export" **166** Queen Elizabeth II

(Des and eng B. Stewart. Recess)

1963 (28 Aug). *Export Campaign. P* 14½ × 14.
353 **165** 5d. red 10 10

(Des and eng P. E. Morriss from photograph by Anthony Buckley. Recess)

1963 (9 Oct)–**65**. *P* 15 × 14.
354 **166** 5d. deep green 45 10
a. Imperf between (horiz pair) (31.7.64) 1·75 2·50
354*b* 5d. red (30.6.65) 40 10
c. Coil pair (30.6.65) .. .. .. 14·00 18·00
See notes after No. 307 *re* helecon ink.
The above exist in booklet panes of six stamps, with imperf outer edges, producing single stamps with one or two adjacent sides imperf.

PRICES OF SETS

Set prices are given for many issues, generally those containing three stamps or more. Definitive sets include one of each value or major colour change, but do not cover different perforations, die types or minor shades. Where a choice is possible the set prices are based on the cheapest versions of the stamps included in the listings.

No. 354a comes from sheets of uncut booklet panes containing 288 stamps (16 × 18) with wide margins intersecting the sheet horizontally below each third row, alternate rows of stamps imperforate between vertically and the outer left, right and bottom margins imperforate. This means that in each sheet there are 126 pairs of stamps imperf between vertically, plus a number with wide imperforate margins attached, as shown in the illustration.

167 Tasman and *Heemskerk* **168** Dampier and *Roebuck*

(Des W. Jardine. Eng B. Stewart (4s., £1). E. R. M. Jones (10s.), P. E. Morriss (others). Recess)

1963–65. *T* **167/8** *and similar designs. No wmk* (4s.) *or W* **15** (*others*), (*sideways on* 5s., £1). *P* 14 *or* 14½ (5s., £1, £2).
355 4s. ultramarine (9.10.63) .. .. .. 4·50 40
356 5s. red-brown (25.11.64) .. .. .. 6·00 60
357 7s. 6d. olive (26.8.64) .. .. .. 17·00 14·00
358 10s. brown-purple (26.2.64) .. .. .. 42·00 3·75
a. White paper. *Deep brown-purple* (14.1.65) 55·00 6·00
359 £1 deep reddish violet (26.2.64) .. .. 48·00 12·00
a. White paper. *Deep bluish violet* (16.11.64) 70·00 20·00
360 £2 sepia (26.8.64) .. .. 70·00 60·00
355/360 .. .. *Set of* 6 £170 80·00
357/60 Optd "Specimen" .. .. *Set of* 4 £450
Designs: *As T* **167**—7s. 6d. Captain Cook; 10s. Flinders and *Investigator*. *As T* **168**—£1 Bass and whaleboat; £2 Admiral King and *Mermaid*.
Nos. 358 and 359 were printed on a toned paper but all the other values are on white paper, the 4s. being on rather thicker paper.

173 "Peace on Earth . . ." **174** "Commonwealth Cable"

(Des R. M. Warner. Eng B. Stewart. Recess)

1963 (25 Oct). *Christmas. P* 14½.
361 **173** 5d. greenish blue 10 10

(Des P. E. Morriss. Photo)

1963 (3 Dec). *Opening of COMPAC (Trans-Pacific Telephone Cable). Chalky paper. P* 13½.
362 **174** 2s. 3d. red, blue, black and pale blue 3·00 3·50

175 Yellow-tailed Thornbill **176** Black-backed Magpie

(Des Mrs. H. Temple-Watts. Photo)

1964 (11 Mar)–**65**. *T* **175/6** *and similar designs showing birds. Chalky paper (except No. 367a). P* 13½.

363 6d. brown, yellow, black and bluish green (19.8.64) .. 50 25
 a. *Brown, yellow, black and emerald-green* (12.65) .. 2·50 1·75
364 9d. black, grey and pale green .. 1·50 3·25
365 1s. 6d. pink, grey, dull purple and black .. 1·00 1·25
366 2s. yellow, black and pink (21.4.65) .. 2·50 50
367 2s. 5d. deep royal blue, light violet-blue, yellow-orange, grey and black .. 7·00 3·00
367*a* 2s. 5d. deep blue, light blue, orange-brown, blue-grey and black (8.65) .. 24·00 12·00
368 2s. 6d. black, red, grey and green (21.4.65) .. 3·75 2·50
 a. Red omitted (white breast) .. £650
369 3s. black, red, buff and yellow-green (21.4.65) 3·75 1·50
363/369 .. *Set of* 8 40·00 22·00

Designs: *Vert*—1s. 6d. Galah; 2s. Golden Whistler; 2s. 5d. Blue Wren; 3s. Straw-necked Ibis. *Horiz*—2s. 6d. Scarlet Robin.

No. 367*a* is from a printing on unsurfaced Wiggins Teape paper, the rest of the set being on chalk-surfaced Harrison paper. Apart from the differences in shade, the inscriptions, particularly "BLUE WREN", stand out very much more clearly on No. 367*a*. Although two colours are apparent in both stamps, the grey and black were printed from one plate.

See notes after No. 307 *re* helecon ink.

182 "Bleriot" Aircraft (type flown by M. Guillaux, 1914)

Re-entry (upper plate, R. 4/4)

(Des K. McKay. Adapted and eng P. E. Morriss. Recess)

1964 (1 July). *50th Anniv of First Australian Airmail Flight. P* 14½ × 14.

370 **182** 5d. olive-green .. 40 10
 a. Re-entry .. 75·00 40·00
371 2s. 3d. scarlet .. 2·25 2·00

183 Child looking at Nativity Scene

184 "Simpson and his Donkey"

(Des P. E. Morriss and J. Mason. Photo)

1964 (21 Oct). *Christmas. Chalky paper. P* 13½.

372 **183** 5d. red, blue, buff and black .. 10 10
 a. Red omitted .. £250
 b. Black omitted .. £250

The red ink is soluble and can be removed by bleaching and it is therefore advisable to obtain a certificate from a recognised expert committee before purchasing No. 372a.

(Des C. Andrew (after statue, Shrine of Remembrance, Melbourne). Eng E. R. M. Jones. Recess)

1965 (14 Apr). *50th Anniv of Gallipoli Landing. P* 14 × 14½.

373 **184** 5d. drab .. 40 10
374 8d. blue .. 70 1·50
375 2s. 3d. reddish purple .. 1·25 1·75
373/5 .. *Set of* 3 2·10 3·00

185 "Telecommunications"

186 Sir Winston Churchill

(Des J. McMahon and G. Hamori. Photo)

1965 (10 May). *I.T.U. Centenary. P* 13½.

376 **185** 5d. black, brown, orange-brown & bl .. 25 10
 a. Black (value and pylon) omitted .. £425

(Des P. E. Morriss from photo by Karsh. Photo)

1965 (24 May). *Churchill Commemoration. Chalky paper. P* 13½.

377 **186** 5d. black, pale grey and light blue .. 15 10
 a. Pale grey ("AUSTRALIA") omitted £350 £200

About half the printing was on helecon impregnated paper, differing slightly in the shade of the blue.

187 General Monash

188 Hargrave and "Seaplane" (1902)

(Des O. Foulkes and W. Walters. Photo)

1965 (23 June). *Birth Centenary of General Sir John Monash (engineer and soldier). Chalky paper. P* 13½.

378 **187** 5d. multicoloured .. 15 10

(Des G. Hamori. Photo)

1965 (4 Aug). *50th Death Anniv of Lawrence Hargrave (aviation pioneer). Chalky paper. P* 13½.

379 **188** 5d. purple-brown, blk, yell-ochre & pur 15 10
 a. Purple (value) omitted .. £150

189 I.C.Y. Emblem

190 "Nativity Scene"

(Des H. Fallu from U.N. theme. Photo)

1965 (1 Sept). *International Co-operation Year. Chalky paper. P* 13½.

380 **189** 2s. 3d. emerald and light blue .. 1·75 2·00

(Des J. Mason. Photo)

1965 (20 Oct). *Christmas. P* 13½.

381 **190** 5d. multicoloured .. 15 10
 a. Gold omitted .. £250
 b. Blue omitted .. £225

No. 381a comes from the bottom row of a sheet in which the gold is completely omitted, the background appearing as black with "CHRISTMAS 1965" and "AUSTRALIA" omitted. The row above had the black missing from the lower two-fifths of the stamp.

(New Currency. 100 cents = 1 dollar)

191 Queen Elizabeth II

192 Blue-faced Honeyeater

193 Humbug Fish

Nos. 401 (top), 401a (centre) and 401b (bottom). No. 401b shows the final form of the variety with a plate crack visible in sky and across sail (Lower sheet left pane. R. 10/1)

(Des Mrs. H. Temple-Watts (6 c. (No. 387), 13 c., 24 c.), Eileen Mayo (7 c. (No. 388) to 10 c.). Recess (T **191**, 40 c. to $4). Photo Chalky paper (others))

1966 (14 Feb)–**73**. *Decimal currency. T* **191/3** *and similar designs, some reused from previous issues. No wmk. P* 15 × 14 (*T* **191**), 14 (*40 c., 75 c.,* $1), 14½ (*50 c.,* $2, $4) *or* 13½ (*others*).

382 **191** 1 c. deep red-brown .. 25 10
383 2 c. olive-green .. 90 10
384 3 c. slate-green .. 90 10
385 4 c. red .. 20 10
 a. Booklet pane. Five stamps plus one printed label .. 35·00
386 **175** 5 c. brown, yellow, black & emer-grn 25 10
 a. Brown (plumage) omitted .. £400
 b. *Brown, yellow, blk & bl-grn* (1.67) 25 10
386*c* **191** 5 c. deep blue (29.9.67) .. 2·50 10
 ca. Booklet pane. Five stamps plus one printed label .. 8·00
 cb. Imperf in horiz strip of 3* .. £550
387 **192** 6 c. olive-yellow, blk, blue & pale grey 70 40
 aa. Blue (eye markings) omitted .. 90·00
387*a* **191** 6 c. orange (28.9.70) .. 35 10
388 **193** 7 c. black, grey, salmon and brown .. 1·50 10
388*a* **191** 7 c. purple (1.10.71) .. 1·10 10
389 – 8 c. red, yell, bl-grn & blackish green 1·50 15
390 – 9 c. brown-red, purple-brown, black and light yellow-olive .. 1·50 10
391 – 10 c. orange, blackish brown, pale turquoise-blue and olive-brown .. 1·50 10
392 – 13 c. red, black, grey & light turq-green 3·25 25
 a. Red omitted .. £325
 b. Grey (plumage and legs) omitted £275
393 – 15 c. rose-carmine, black, grey and light bluish green .. 2·50 50
 a. Rose-carmine omitted .. £850
394 – 20 c. yellow, black and pink .. 7·50 15
 a. Yellow (plumage) omitted .. £325
395 – 24 c. ultramarine, yellow, blk & lt brn 90 55
396 – 25 c. black, red, grey and green .. 5·00 20
 a. Red omitted .. £500
397 – 30 c. black, red, buff & lt yellow-green 23·00 30
 a. Red omitted .. £450
398 **167** 40 c. ultramarine .. 12·00 10
399 **168** 50 c. red-brown .. 15·00 10
400 – 75 c. olive .. 1·00 1·50
401 – $1 brown-purple (*shades*) .. 3·75 10
 a. Recut lines in sky .. 20·00
 b. Recut lines and plate crack .. 27·00
 c. Perf 15 × 14† (1973) .. 95·00 17·00
402 – $2 deep reddish violet .. 10·00 30
403 – $4 sepia .. 8·00 4·50
382/403 .. *Set of* 25 90·00 8·00
400/3 Optd "Specimen" .. *Set of* 4 90·00

Designs: *Vert* (*as T* **193**)—8 c. Coral Fish; 9 c. Hermit Crab; 10 c. Anemone Fish. (*as T* **192**)—13 c. Red-necked Avocet; 15 c. Galah; 20 c. Golden Whistler; 30 c. Straw-necked Ibis. *Horiz* (*as T* **192**)—24 c. Azure Kingfisher; 25 c. Scarlet Robin. *As T* **167**—75 c. Captain Cook; $1 Flinders and *Investigator*. *As T* **168**—$2 Bass and whaleboat; $4 Admiral King and *Mermaid*.

*This comprises two stamps imperf all round and one imperf on three sides.

†The note below No. 553 also applies to No. 401c, its exact gauge being 14·9 × 14·1. No. 401 is 14·25 × 13·95.

No. 385 is normally printed with helecon ink, the rest being on helecon paper. Early in 1967 experimental printings of No. 385 on different kinds of paper coated with helecon or Derby Luminescents phosphor were put on sale. They cannot be distinguished by the naked eye.

199 Queen Elizabeth II

200 "Saving Life"

1966 (14 Feb)–**67**. *Coil stamps. Photo. P* 15 × *imperf*.

404 **199** 3 c. black, light brown and green .. 20 40
405 4 c. black, light brown & lt vermilion .. 45 20
405*a* 5 c. black, light brown and new blue (29.9.67) .. 60 10
404/5*a* .. *Set of* 3 1·10 60

(Des L. Mason. Photo)

1966 (6 July). *75th Anniv of Royal Life Saving Society. P* 13½.

406 **200** 4 c. black, bright blue and blue .. 15 10

201 "Adoration of the Shepherds"

202 *Eendracht*

(Des L. Stirling, after medieval engraving. Photo)

1966 (19 Oct). *Christmas. P* 13½.

407 **201** 4 c. black and yellow-olive .. 10 10
 a. Value omitted .. £700

No. 407a was caused by a shift of the yellow-olive which covered the white face value.

(Des F. Eidlitz. Photo)

1966 (24 Oct). *350th Anniv of Dirk Hartog's Landing in Australia. P* 13½.

408 **202** 4 c. multicoloured .. 10 10
 a. Red (sphere) omitted .. £800

203 Open Bible

204 Ancient Keys and Modern Lock

(Des L. Stirling. Photo)

1967 (7 Mar). *150th Anniv of British and Foreign Bible Society in Australia. P* 13½.

409 **203** 4 c. multicoloured .. 10 10

(Des G. Andrews. Photo)

1967 (5 Apr). *150th Anniv of Australian Banking. P* 13½.

410 **204** 4 c. black, light blue and emerald .. 10 10

205 Lions Badge and 50 Stars 206 Y.W.C.A. Emblem

(Des M. Ripper. Photo)

1967 (7 June). *50th Anniv of Lions International. P* 13½.
411 **205** 4 c. black, gold and blue 10 10

(Des H. Williamson. Photo)

1967 (21 Aug). *World Y.W.C.A. Council Meeting. Monash University, Victoria. P* 13½.
412 **206** 4 c. dp blue, ultramarine, lt pur & lt bl 10 10

5c

207 Anatomical Figures (208)

(Des R. Ingpen. Photo)

1967 (20 Sept). *Fifth World Gynaecology and Obstetrics Congress, Sydney. P* 13½.
413 **207** 4 c. black, blue and light reddish violet 10 10

1967 (29 Sept). *No. 385 surch with T* **208**.
414 **191** 5 c. on 4 c. red 70 10
a. Booklet pane. Five stamps plus one printed label .. .. 3·25

No. 414 was only issued in booklets and so only occurs with one or two adjacent sides imperforate. It only exists printed with helecon ink on normal paper.

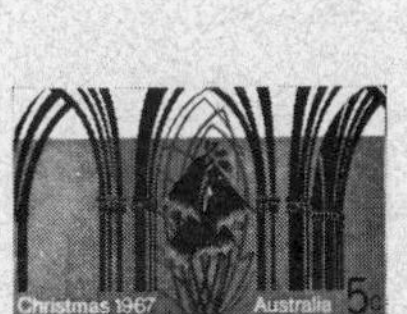

209 Christmas Bells and Gothic Arches 210 Religious Symbols

(Des M. Ripper (5 c.), Erica McGilchrist (25 c.). Photo)

1967. *Christmas. P* 13½.
415 **209** 5 c. multicoloured (18.10.67) 20 10
a. Imperf three sides £800
416 **210** 25 c. multicoloured (27.11.67) .. .. 1·25 1·75

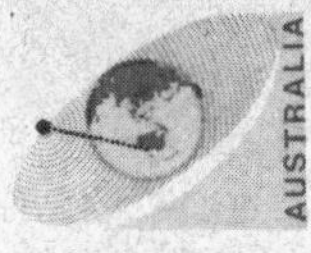

211 Satellite in Orbit 212 World Weather Map

(Des J. Mason. Photo)

1968 (20 Mar). *World Weather Watch. P* 13½.
417 **211** 5 c. orange-brown, pl blue, blk & ochre 30 10
418 **212** 20 c. orange-brown, blue and black .. 1·75 3·25
a. White (radio waves) omitted .. £300
b. Orange-brown (triangle) omitted £900

213 Radar Antenna 214 Kangaroo Paw (Western Australia)

(Des R. Ingpen. Photo)

1968 (20 Mar). *World Telecommunications Intelsat II. P* 13½.
419 **213** 25 c. greenish blue, black & lt blue-green 2·75 5·00

(Des Nell Wilson (6c., 30 c.); R. and P. Warner (13 c., 25 c.); Dorothy Thornhill (15 c., 20 c.). Photo)

1968 (10 July)–**71**. *State Floral Emblems. T* **214** *and similar vert designs. Multicoloured. P* 13½.
420 6 c. Type **214** 40 35
421 13 c. Pink Heath (Victoria) 50 20
422 15 c. Tasmanian Blue Gum (Tasmania) .. 2·00 20
423 20 c. Sturt's Desert Pea (South Australia) .. 9·00 30
424 25 c. Cooktown Orchid (Queensland) .. 4·50 45
425 30 c. Waratah (New South Wales) (Type I) 1·00 10
a. Green (leaves) omitted £350
b. Type II (29.6.71) .. .. .. 4·50 1·50
420/5 .. .. *Set of* 6 16·00 1·40

The 30 c. was reprinted in 1971 from new cylinders so that Type II shows greater areas of white in the pink tones of the petals.

220 Soil Sample Analysis

(Des R. Ingpen. Photo)

1968 (6 Aug). *International Soil Science Congress and World Medical Association Assembly. T* **220** *and similar horiz design. P* 13½.
426 **220** 5 c. orange-brn, stone, greenish bl & blk 10 10
a. Nos. 426/7 *se-tenant* with gutter margin between .. .. 17·00 17·00
427 – 5 c. greenish blue, dull ol-yell, rose & blk 10 10

Design:—No. 427, Rubber-gloved hands, syringe and head of Hippocrates.

The above were printed in sheets of 100 containing a pane of 50 of each design.

The major shades formerly listed have been deleted as there is a range of intermediate shades.

222 Athlete carrying Torch, and Sunstone Symbol 223 Sunstone Symbol and Mexican Flag

(Des H. Williamson. Photo)

1968 (2 Oct). *Olympic Games, Mexico City. P* 13½.
428 **222** 5 c. multicoloured 20 10
429 **223** 25 c. multicoloured .. .. .. 35 1·50

224 Houses and Dollar Signs 225 Church Window and View of Bethlehem

(Des Erica McGilchrist. Photo)

1968 (16 Oct). *Building and Savings Societies Congress. P* 13½.
430 **224** 5 c. multicoloured 10 20

(Des G. Hamori. Photo)

1968 (23 Oct). *Christmas. P* 13½.
431 **225** 5 c. multicoloured 10 10
a. Green window (gold omitted) .. £250
b. Red (inscr) omitted £275

226 Edgeworth David (geologist)

(Des Note Ptg Branch (Nos. 432, 434), A. Cook (others). Recess, background litho)

1968 (6 Nov). *Famous Australians (1st series). T* **226** *and similar vert portraits. P* 15 × 14.
432 5 c. myrtle-green/*pale green* 75 15
a. Booklet pane. Five stamps plus one printed label .. .. 3·75
433 5 c. black/*pale blue* 75 15
a. Booklet pane. Five stamps plus one printed label .. .. 3·75
434 5 c. blackish brown/*pale buff* 75 15
a. Booklet pane. Five stamps plus one printed label .. .. 3·75
435 5 c. deep violet/*pale lilac* 75 15
a. Booklet pane. Five stamps plus one printed label .. .. .. 3·75
432/5 .. .. *Set of* 4 2·75 55

Designs:—No. 432, Type **226**; No. 433, A. B. Paterson (poet); No. 434, Albert Namatjira (artist); No. 435, Caroline Chisholm (social worker).

Nos. 432/5 were only issued in booklets and only exist with one or two adjacent sides imperf.

See also Nos. 446/9, 479/82, 505/8, 537/40, 590/5, 602/7 and 637/40.

230 Macquarie Lighthouse 231 Pioneers and Modern Building, Darwin

(Des and eng Note Ptg Branch. Recess; background litho)

1968 (27 Nov). *150th Anniv of Macquarie Lighthouse. P* 14½ × 13½.
436 **230** 5 c. black/*pale yellow* 10 15

Used examples are known with the pale yellow background colour omitted.

(Des Mrs. M. Lyon. Photo)

1969 (5 Feb). *Centenary of Northern Territory Settlement. P* 13½.
437 **231** 5 c. blackish brown, yellow-olive and yellow-ochre 10 10

232 Melbourne Harbour 233 Concentric Circles (symbolising Management, Labour and Government)

(Des J. Mason. Photo)

1969 (26 Feb). *Sixth Biennial Conference of International Association of Ports and Harbours. P* 13½.
438 **232** 5 c. multicoloured 15 10

(Des G. Hamori. Photo.)

1969 (4 June). *50th Anniv of International Labour Organisation. P* 13½.
439 **233** 5 c. multicoloured 15 10
a. Gold (middle circle) omitted .. £350

234 Sugar Cane 238 "The Nativity" (stained-glass window) 240 Edmund Barton

(Des R. Ingpen. Photo)

1969 (17 Sept). *Primary Industries. T* **234** *and similar vert designs. Multicoloured. P* 13½.
440 7 c. Type **234** .. .. 1·25 2·00
441 15 c. Timber .. .. 4·00 6·00
a. Black ("Australia" and value) omitted .. £475
442 20 c. Wheat .. .. 1·25 80
443 25 c. Wool .. .. 2·50 2·00
440/3 .. .. *Set of* 4 8·00 9·75

(Des G. Hamori (5 c.), J. Coburn (25 c.). Photo)

1969 (15 Oct). *Christmas. T* **238** *and similar multicoloured designs. P* 13½.
444 5 c. Type **238** 20 10
a. Magenta (robe) omitted £250
b. Yellow omitted £250
445 25 c. "Tree of Life", Christ in Crib and Christmas Star (abstract) .. .. 1·00 1·50

(Des from drawings by J. Santry. Recess, background litho)

1969 (22 Oct). *Famous Australians (2nd series). Prime Ministers. T* **240** *and similar vert designs each black on pale green. P* 15 × 14.
446 5 c. Type **240** 75 15
a. Booklet pane. Five stamps plus one printed label .. .. .. 3·75
447 5 c. Alfred Deakin 75 15
a. Booklet pane. Five stamps plus one printed label .. .. .. 3·75

448 5 c. J. C. Watson 75 15
a. Booklet pane. Five stamps plus one printed label .. .. 3·75
449 5 c. G. H. Reid 75 15
a. Booklet pane. Five stamps plus one printed label .. .. 3·75
446/9 .. .. *Set of* 4 2·75 55

Nos. 446/9 were only issued in booklets and only exist with one or two adjacent sides imperf.

244 Capt. Ross Smith's Vickers "Vimy", 1919

247 Symbolic Track and Diesel Locomotive

(Des E. Thake. Photo)

1969 (12 Nov). *50th Anniv of First England–Australia Flight. T* **244** *and similar horiz designs. P* 13½.
450 5 c. olive-green, pale blue, black and red .. 15 10
a. Strip of 3. Nos. 450/2 .. .. 1·50
451 5 c. black, red and olive-green 15 10
452 5 c. olive-green, black, pale blue and red .. 15 10
450/2 .. .. *Set of* 3 1·50 25

Designs:—No. 450, Type **244**; No. 451, Lt. H. Fysh and Lt. P. McGinness on 1919 survey with Ford car; No. 452, Capt. Wrigley and Sgt. Murphy in "BE 2E" taking off to meet the Smiths.

The three designs appear *se-tenant*, both horizontally and vertically, throughout the sheet.

(Des B. Sadgrove. Photo)

1970 (11 Feb). *Sydney–Perth Standard Gauge Railway Link. P* 13½.
453 **247** 5 c. multicoloured 15 10

248 Australian Pavilion, Osaka

251 Australian Flag

(Des J. Copeland (5 c.), A. Leydin (20 c.). Photo)

1970 (16 Mar). *World Fair, Osaka. T* **248** *and similar horiz design. P* 13½.
454 5 c. multicoloured 15 10
455 20 c. orange-red and black 35 65

Design:—20 c. "Southern Cross" and "from the Country of the South with warm feelings" (message).

(Des P.O. Artists (5 c.), J. Mason (30 c.). Photo)

1970 (31 Mar). *Royal Visit. T* **251** *and similar horiz design. P* 13½.
456 5 c. black and deep ochre 25 15
457 30 c. multicoloured .. .. 75 2·00

Design:—5 c. Queen Elizabeth II and Prince Philip.

252 Lucerne Plant, Bull and Sun

253 Captain Cook and H.M.S. *Endeavour*

(Des R. Ingpen. Photo)

1970 (13 Apr). *Eleventh International Grasslands Congress. P* 13½.
458 **252** 5 c. multicoloured 10 25

(Des R. Ingpen and "Team" (T. Keneally, A. Leydin, J. R. Smith). Photo)

1970 (20 Apr). *Bicentenary of Captain Cook's Discovery of Australia's East Coast. T* **253** *and similar multicoloured designs. P* 13½.
459 5 c. Type **253** 30 10
a. Strip of 5. Nos. 459/63 .. .. .. 2·00
460 5 c. Sextant and H.M.S. *Endeavour* 30 10
461 5 c. Landing at Botany Bay 30 10
462 5 c. Charting and exploring 30 10
463 5 c. Claiming possession 30 10
464 30 c. Captain Cook, H.M.S. *Endeavour*, sextant, aborigines and kangaroo (63 × 30 *mm*) .. .. 1·50 2·75
459/64 .. .. *Set of* 6 3·25 3·00
MS465 157 × 129 mm. Nos. 459/64. Imperf .. 13·00 15·00

The 5 c. stamps were issued horizontally *se-tenant* within the sheet, to form a composite design in the order listed.

50,000 miniature sheets were made available by the Post Office to the organisers of the Australian National Philatelic Exhibition which overprinted them in the white margin at each side of the 30 c. stamp with "Souvenir Sheet AUSTRALIAN NATIONAL PHILATELIC EXHIBITION" at left and "ANPEX 1970 SYDNEY 27 APRIL–1 MAY" at right in light red-brown and they were also serially numbered. These were put on sale at the exhibition on the basis of one sheet to each visitor paying 30 c. for admission. Although still valid for postage, since the stamps themselves had not been defaced, these sheets were not sold at post offices.

Subsequently further supplies were purchased and similarly overprinted and numbered by a private firm without the authority of the Post Office and ANPEX took successful legal action to stop their further sale to the public. This firm also had the unoverprinted sheets rouletted in colour between the stamps whilst further supplies of the normal sheets were overprinted with reproductions of old coins and others with an inscription commemorating the opening of Melbourne Airport on 1st July 1970, but all these are private productions. Further private productions have been reported.

259 Sturt's Desert Rose

AUSTRALIA AUSTRALIA
I. II.

Two types of 2 c.

I. "AUSTRALIA" thin: "2c" thin; flower name lightly printed.
II. Redrawn. "AUSTRALIA" thicker; "2c" much more heavily printed; flower name thicker and bolder.

(Des Note Ptg Branch. Photo)

1970–75. *Coil Stamps. Vert designs as T* **259**. *Multicoloured. Perf* 15 × *imperf.*
465*a* 2 c. Type **259** (I) (1.10.71) 25 20
ab. Type II (1973) 25 10
466 4 c. Type **259** (27.4.70) .. .. .. 70 1·25
467 5 c. Golden Wattle (27.4.70) 20 10
468 6 c. Type **259** (28.9.70) .. .. .. 1·25 1·00
a. Green (leaves) omitted £200
468*b* 7 c. Sturt's Desert Pea (1.10.71) 25 20
c. Green (leaves) omitted .. .. .. 75·00
468*d* 10 c. As 7 c. (15.1.75) 25 15
465*a*/8*d* .. .. *Set of* 6 2·50 2·50

Nos. 465*a*/8*d* have horizontal coil perforations described after No. 191.

The 2 c. (No. 465*a*), 5 c. and 7 c. also exist on fluorescent paper; the 2 c. (No. 465ab) and 10 c. exist only on fluorescent paper (see note after No. 504).

264 Snowy Mountains Scheme

265 Rising Flames

(Des L. Mason (7 c.), R. Ingpen (8 c., 9 c.), B. Sadgrove (10 c.). Photo)

1970 (31 Aug). *National Development (1st series). T* **264** *and similar horiz designs. Multicoloured. P* 13½.
469 7 c. Type **264** 30 55
470 8 c. Ord River Scheme 15 15
471 9 c. Bauxite to aluminium 15 15
472 10 c. Oil and Natural Gas 40 10
469/72 .. .. *Set of* 4 90 85

See also Nos. 541/4.

(Des G. Hamori. Photo)

1970 (2 Oct). *16th Commonwealth Parliamentary Association Conference, Canberra. P* 13½.
473 **265** 6 c. multicoloured 10 10

266 Milk Analysis and Dairy Herd

267 "The Nativity"

(Des R. Honisett. Photo)

1970 (7 Oct). *18th International Dairy Congress, Sydney. P* 13½.
474 **266** 6 c. multicoloured 10 10

(Des W. Beasley. Photo)

1970 (14 Oct). *Christmas. P* 13½.
475 **267** 6 c. multicoloured 10 10

ALTERED CATALOGUE NUMBERS

Any Catalogue numbers altered from the last edition are shown as a list in the introductory pages.

268 U.N. "Plant" and Dove of Peace

269 Boeing "707" and Avro "504"

(Des Monad Ltd. Photo)

1970 (19 Oct). *25th Anniv of United Nations. P* 13½.
476 **268** 6 c. multicoloured 10 10

(Des G. Hamori. Photo)

1970 (2 Nov). *50th Anniv of QANTAS Airline. T* **269** *and similar horiz design. Multicoloured. P* 13½.
477 6 c. Type **269** 25 10
478 30 c. Avro "504" and Boeing "707" .. .. 75 1·25

270 The Duigan Brothers (Pioneer Aviators)

271 "Theatre"

(Des A. Cook (No. 480), T. Adams (No. 482), Note Ptg Branch (others). Recess (background litho))

1970 (16 Nov). *Famous Australians* (3*rd series*). *T* **270** *and similar vert designs. P* 15 × 14.
479 6 c. blue .. .. 1·25 20
a. Booklet pane. Five stamps plus one printed label .. .. 6·00
480 6 c. black/*flesh* .. .. 1·25 20
a. Booklet pane. Five stamps plus one printed label .. .. 6·00
481 6 c. purple/*pink* .. .. 1·25 20
a. Booklet pane. Five stamps plus one printed label .. .. 6·00
482 6 c. brown-lake/*pink* .. .. 1·25 20
a. Booklet pane. Five stamps plus one printed label .. .. 6·00
479/82 .. .. *Set of* 4 4·50 75

Designs:—No. 479 Type **270**; No. 480 Lachlan Macquarie (Governor of N.S.W.); No. 481 Adam Lindsay Gordon (poet); No. 482 E. J. Eyre (explorer).

Nos. 479/82 were only issued in booklets and only exist with one or two adjacent sides imperf.

(Des D. Annand. Photo)

1971 (6 Jan). *"Australia–Asia". T* **271** *and similar horiz designs. Multicoloured. P* 13½.
483 7 c. Type **271** 35 50
484 15 c. "Music" 60 90
485 20 c. "Sea Craft" 55 80
483/5 .. .. *Set of* 3 1·40 2·00

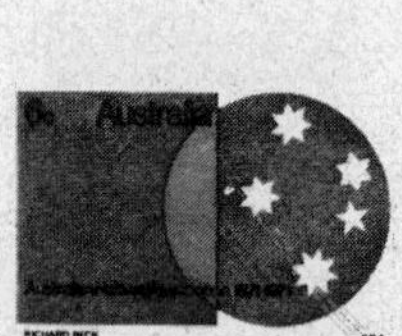

272 The Southern Cross

273 Market "Graph"

(Des R. Beck. Photo)

1971 (21 Apr). *Centenary of Australian Natives' Association. P* 13½.
486 **272** 6 c. black, vermilion and bright blue .. 10 10

(Des Monad Ltd. Photo)

1971 (5 May). *Centenary of Sydney Stock Exchange. P* 13½.
487 **273** 6 c. multicoloured 10 10

274 Rotary Emblem

275 "Mirage" Jets and "D.H.9a" Biplane

(Des H. Williamson. Photo)

1971 (17 May). *50th Anniv of Rotary International in Australia. P* 13½.
488 **274** 6 c. multicoloured 15 10

(Des R. Honisett. Photo)

1971 (9 June). *50th Anniv of R.A.A.F. P* 13½.
489 **275** 6 c. multicoloured 15 10
a. Black (face value and inscr) omitted £350

276 Draught-horse, Cat and Dog **277** Bark Painting

(Des R. Ingpen. Photo)

1971 (5 July). *Animals. T* **276** *and similar vert designs. Multicoloured. P* 13½.
490 6 c. Type **276** 20 10
491 12 c. Vet and lamb ("Animal Science") .. 45 40
492 18 c. Red Kangaroo ("Fauna Conservation") .. 60 75
493 24 c. Guide-dog ("Animals Aid to Man") .. 1·00 1·75
490/3 .. .. *Set of* 4 2·00 2·75

The 6 c. commemorated the Centenary of the Australian R.S.P.C.A., and the others were short-term definitives.

(Des J. Mason. Photo)

1971 (29 Sept). *Aboriginal Art. T* **277** *and similar multicoloured designs. P* 13½.
494 20 c. Type **277** 20 20
495 25 c. Body decoration 20 30
a. Black omitted* £300
496 30 c. Cave painting (*vert*) 30 20
497 35 c. Grave posts (*vert*) 30 15
494/7 .. .. *Set of* 4 90 75

*The omission of the black results in the stamp being without face-value and "AUSTRALIA".

Nos. 494/7 also exist on fluorescent paper and the 35 c. exists with both PVA gum and gum arabic.

278 The Three Kings and the Star **279** Andrew Fisher

(Des J. Lee. Photo)

1971 (13 Oct). *Christmas. Colours of star and colour of "AUSTRALIA" given. P* 13½.
498 **278** 7 c. royal blue, pl mauve & pl lake-brn 1·00 15
a. Block of 7. Nos. 498/504 .. .. 38·00
499 7 c. pale mauve, pl lake-brown & white 1·00 15
500 7 c. pale mauve, white and black .. 7·00 80
501 7 c. black, green and black .. .. 1·00 15
502 7 c. lilac, green and lilac .. .. 1·00 15
503 7 c. black, pale lake-brown and white .. 1·00 15
504 7 c. royal blue, pale mauve and green .. 30·00 2·25
498/504 .. .. *Set of* 7 38·00 3·50

Nos. 498/504, which also exist on fluorescent paper, were issued in sheets having two panes of 50 stamps. Each half pane had its stamps arranged thus:—

498	499	500	499	498
503	502	501	502	503
504	501	500	501	504
503	502	501	502	503
498	499	500	499	498

FLUORESCENT VERY WHITE CHALKY PAPER. As an experiment 10% of the above issue was printed on very white paper which fluoresces back and front under an ultraviolet lamp; it also has a strong coating of chalk on the surface. Late in 1972 this paper began to be introduced more generally and a number of stamps exist on both types of paper. The normal helecon paper does not fluoresce under the lamp but does react to the chalky test to a lesser degree.

Stamps reprinted on the white fluorescent paper are recorded below in footnotes and are listed in the *Elizabethan Catalogue*.

(Des J. Sandry. Recess)

1972 (8 Mar). *Famous Australians* (4*th series*). *Prime Ministers. T* **279** *and similar vert designs. P* 15 × 14.
505 7 c. ultramarine (Type **279**) 60 15
a. Booklet pane. Five stamps plus one printed label .. .. 2·75
506 7 c. ultramarine. (W. M. Hughes) .. 60 15
a. Booklet pane. Five stamps plus one printed label .. .. 2·75
507 7 c. red (Joseph Cook) 60 15
a. Booklet pane. Five stamps plus one printed label .. .. 2·75
508 7 c. red (S. M. Bruce) 60 15
a. Booklet pane. Five stamps plus one printed label .. .. 2·75
505/8 .. .. *Set of* 4 2·10 55

Nos. 505/8 were issued only in booklets and exist with one or two adjacent sides imperf.

280 Cameo Brooch **281** Fruit

(Des Mrs. V. Mason. Photo)

1972 (18 Apr). *50th Anniv of Country Women's Association. P* 13½.
509 **280** 7 c. multicoloured 20 10

(Des D. Annand. Photo)

1972 (14 June). *Primary Industries. T* **281** *and similar horiz designs. Multicoloured. P* 13½.
510 20 c. Type **281** .. .. 3·50 4·50
511 25 c. Rice .. .. 3·50 5·50
512 30 c. Fish .. .. 3·50 3·50
513 35 c. Beef .. .. 8·00 2·00
510/13 .. .. *Set of* 4 17·00 14·00

282 Worker in Wheelchair **283** Telegraph Line

(Des from photographs by Barbara Ardizzone. Photo)

1972 (2 Aug). *Rehabilitation of the Disabled. T* **282** *and similar designs. P* 13½.
514 12 c. yellow-brown and emerald 10 10
515 18 c. sage-green and yellow-orange 40 25
516 24 c. blue and yellow-brown 15 10
514/16 .. .. *Set of* 3 50 40

Designs: *Horiz*—18 c. Patient and teacher. *Vert*—24 c. Boy playing with ball.

The 12 c. and 24 c. also exist on fluorescent paper.

(Des J. Copeland. Photo)

1972 (22 Aug). *Centenary of Overland Telegraph Line. P* 13½.
517 **283** 7 c. multicoloured 15 10

284 Athletics **285** Numerals and Computer Circuit

(Des B. Sadgrove. Photo)

1972 (28 Aug). *Olympic Games, Munich. T* **284** *and similar vert designs. Multicoloured. P* 13½.
518 7 c. Type **284** 25 20
519 7 c. Rowing 25 20
520 7 c. Swimming 25 20
521 35 c. Equestrian .. .. 2·25 4·00
518/21 .. .. *Set of* 4 2·75 4·00

(Des G. Andrews. Photo)

1972 (16 Oct). *Tenth International Congress of Accountants, Sydney. P* 13½.
522 **285** 7 c. multicoloured 15 10

286 Australian-build Harvester

(Des R. Ingpen. Photo)

1972 (15 Nov). *Pioneer Life. T* **286** *and similar multicoloured designs. P* 13½.
523 5 c. Pioneer family (*vert*) 15 10
524 10 c. Water-pump (*vert*) 40 10
525 15 c. Type **286** 15 10
a. Black (face value and inscr) omitted £250
526 40 c. House 30 40
527 50 c. Stage-coach 80 20
528 60 c. Morse key (*vert*) 50 75
529 80 c. *Gem* (paddle-steamer) 60 75
a. Black (face value and inscr) omitted £375
523/9 .. .. *Set of* 7 2·50 2·00

All values also exist on fluorescent paper and the 15 c. exists with both PVA gum and gum arabic.

287 Jesus with Children **288** "Length"

(Des from drawing by Wendy Tamlyn (7 c.), L. Stirling (35 c.). Photo)

1972 (29 Nov). *Christmas. T* **287** *and similar vert design. Multicoloured. P* 15 × 14 (7 c.) *or* 13½ (35 c).
530 7 c. Type **287** 25 10
a. Brown-red ("Australia 7c") omitted .. £250
b. Red-brown (inscr) omitted £250
531 35 c. Dove and spectrum motif .. .. 6·50 8·00

(Des Weatherhead & Stitt Pty. Ltd. Photo)

1973 (7 Mar). *Metric Conversion. T* **288** *and similar multicoloured designs. P* 15 × 14. (*No.* 535) *or* 14 × 15 (*others*).
532 7 c. Type **288** 40 35
533 7 c. "Volume" 40 35
a. Yellow-olive omitted* £250
534 7 c. "Mass" 40 35
535 7 c. "Temperature" (*horiz*) 40 35
532/5 .. .. *Set of* 4 1·40 1·25

*This results in the man's drink and shorts appearing white, and the colour of the stool being the same as the background.

289 Caduceus and Laurel Wreath **290** William Wentworth (statesman and explorer)

(Des H. Williamson. Photo)

1973 (4 Apr). *25th Anniv of W.H.O. P* 15 × 14.
536 **289** 7 c. multicoloured 20 10

(Des J. Santry. Recess and litho)

1973 (16 May). *Famous Australians* (5*th series*). *T* **290** *and similar vert designs. P* 15 × 14.
537 7 c. yellow-bistre and black 40 20
a. Block of 4. Nos. 537/40 .. .. 2·50
538 7 c. lilac and black 40 20
539 7 c. yellow-bistre and black 40 20
540 7 c. lilac and black 40 20
537/40 .. .. *Set of* 4 2·50 70

Designs:—No. 537, Type **290**; No. 538, Isaac Isaacs (first Australian-born Governor-General); No. 539, Mary Gilmore (writer); No. 540, Marcus Clarke (author).

Nos. 537/40 were printed in *se-tenant* blocks of four within the sheet. They also exist on fluorescent paper.

291 Shipping **292** Banded Coral Shrimp

(Des J. Copeland. Photo)

1973 (6 June). *National Development* (2*nd series*). *T* **291** *and similar vert designs. Multicoloured. P* 13½.
541 20 c. Type **291** .. .. 4·00 4·00
542 25 c. Iron ore and steel .. .. .. 4·00 4·00
543 30 c. Beef roads .. .. 4·75 4·50
544 35 c. Mapping .. .. 4·00 4·50
541/4 .. .. *Set of* 4 15·00 15·00

(Des Printing Bureau artists (1 to 4 c.), J. Mason (others). Photo)

1973 (11 July)–74. *Marine Life and Gemstones. T* **292** *and similar multicoloured designs. P* 14 × 15 (1 *to* 4 *c.*) *or* 15 × 14 (*others*).
545 1 c. Type **292** 10 10
a. Black (inscr and face value) omitted .. 90·00
b. Yellow-brown omitted £225
546 2 c. Fiddler crab 10 10
547 3 c. Coral crab 10 10
a. Black (inscr and value) omitted .. £300
548 4 c. Mauve stinger 20 30
a. Black (face value and inscr) omitted .. £250
549 6 c. Chrysoprase (*vert*) 20 10
550 7 c. Agate (*vert*) 20 10
a. Black (value and "agate") omitted .. 90·00
551 8 c. Opal (*vert*) 20 10
a. Black (face value and inscr) omitted .. £100
552 9 c. Rhodonite (*vert*) 25 10
552*a* 10 c. Star sapphire (*vert*) (16.10.74) .. 20 10
ab. Black (value, inscr, etc.) omitted .. £100
ac. Turquoise-blue omitted* .. .. 10·00
545/52*a* .. .. *Set of* 9 1·40 70

*The turquoise-blue occurs on the gemstones, and is normally partly covered by the black.

The 1, 3, 7 and 10 c. exist with PVA gum as well as gum arabic.

293 Children at Play **294** John Baptising Jesus

(Des G. Hamori. Photo)

1973 (5 Sept). *50th Anniv of Legacy (Welfare Organisation). P* 13½.
553 **293** 7 c. cinnamon, deep claret and emerald 20 10

PERFORATIONS. From 1973 to 1975 two different perforating machines were used for some issues, giving gauges of 14½ × 14 or 15 × 14 (on horizontal stamps), the exact measurement being 14.4 × 14.1 or 14.9 × 14.1. The latter gauge was also used for a reprint of the $1 definitive (No. 401c).

(Des G. Hamori. Photo)

1973 (3 Oct). *Christmas. T* **294** *and similar vert design. Multicoloured. P* 14 × 14½ *(7 c.) or* 13½ *(30 c.).*
554 7 c. Type **294** .. 30 10
 a. Perf 14 × 15 .. 2·50 55
555 30 c. The Good Shepherd .. 1·10 1·50

295 Sydney Opera House **296** Wireless Receiver and Speaker

(Des A. Leydin. Photo)

1973 (17 Oct). *Architecture. T* **295** *and similar designs. P* 14½ × 14 *(7, 10 c.) or* 13½ *(40, 50 c.).*
556 7 c. pale turquoise-blue and new blue .. 25 10
 a. Perf 15 × 14 .. 2·50 1·25
557 10 c. light ochre and sepia .. 80 70
558 40 c. black, drab and dull mauve .. 1·00 1·50
 a. Dull mauve (background) omitted .. £700
559 50 c. multicoloured .. 1·25 2·25
556/9 .. *Set of* 4 3·00 4·00
Designs: *Horiz*—10 c. Buchanan's Hotel, Townsville; 40 c. Como House, Melbourne. *Vert*—50 c. St. James' Church, Sydney.

(Des E. Thake. Photo)

1973 (21 Nov). *50th Anniv of Regular Radio Broadcasting. P* 13½.
560 **296** 7 c. lt turquoise-blue, brown-red & blk 15 10

297 Common Wombat **298** "Sergeant of Light Horse" (G. Lambert)

(Des R. Bates. Photo)

1974 (13 Feb). *Animals. T* **297** *and similar vert designs. Multicoloured. P* 14 × 15 *(20, 30 c.) or* 13½ *(others).*
561 20 c. Type **297** .. 35 10
562 25 c. Short-nosed Echidna .. 75 50
563 30 c. Brush-tailed Possum .. 40 15
 a. Carmine-red (face-value, etc) omitted .. £325
564 75 c. Pygmy Glider .. 85 75
561/4 .. *Set of* 4 2·10 1·25
The 20 c. exists with gum arabic as well as PVA gum.

(Des P.O. artists. Litho Asher & Co, Melbourne ($5, $10). Photo R.B.A. (others))

1974 (24 Apr)–**79**. *Paintings. Multicoloured designs as T* **298**. *P* 13½ *($1, $2, $4) or* 14½ *(others).*
565 $1 Type **298** .. 1·00 10
 a. Flesh omitted† ..
566 $2 "Red Gums of the Far North" (H. Heysen) (*horiz*) .. 1·50 25
566*a* $4 "Shearing the Rams" (Tom Roberts) (*horiz*) .. 3·00 2·00
567 $5 "McMahon's Point" (Sir Arthur Streeton) (14.3.79) .. 5·50 2·75
567*a* $10 "Coming South" (Tom Roberts) (19.10.77) 8·50 4·00
565/7*a* .. *Set of* 5 18·00 8·00
567/*a*, 778 Optd "Specimen" .. *Set of* 3 9·00
†The omission of the flesh colour results in much of the design appearing in different shades, most notably the shirt, which appears green (especially the folds), the hillside, which is green, and the man's skin, which has highlights in yellow.
The $1 and $2 exist with PVA gum as well as gum arabic.
Nos. 567/*a* and 778 optd "Specimen" come from a special "Ausipex 84" Presentation Pack issued on 9 February 1983.

299 Supreme Court Judge **300** Rugby Football

(Des T. Thompson. Photo)

1974 (15 May). *150th Anniv of Australia's Third Charter of Justice. P* 14 × 15.
568 **299** 7 c. multicoloured .. 20 10

(Des A. Leydin from drawings by D. O'Brien. Photo)

1974 (24 July). *Non-Olympic Sports. T* **300** *and similar multicoloured designs. P* 15 × 14 *(Nos. 569/70) or* 14 × 15 *(others).*
569 7 c. Type **300** .. 50 30
570 7 c. Bowls .. 50 30
571 7 c. Australian football (*vert*) .. 50 30
572 7 c. Cricket (*vert*) .. 50 30
573 7 c. Golf (*vert*) .. 50 30
574 7 c. Surfing (*vert*) .. 50 30
575 7 c. Tennis (*vert*) .. 50 30
569/75 .. *Set of* 7 3·00 1·90

301 "Transport of Mails" **302** Letter "A" and W. C. Wentworth (co-founder)

(Des J. Copeland. Photo)

1974 (9 Oct). *Centenary of Universal Postal Union. T* **301** *and similar vert designs. Multicoloured. P* 15 × 14 *(7 c.) or* 13½ *(30 c.).*
576 7 c. Type **301** .. 30 15
 a. Perf 14½ × 14 .. 50 25
577 30 c. Three-part version of Type **301** .. 1·10 1·75

(Des I. Dalton. Typo and litho)

1974 (9 Oct). *150th Anniv of First Independent Newspaper, "The Australian". P* 14 × 15.
578 **302** 7 c. black/*light cinnamon* .. 30 20
 a. Perf 14 × 14½ .. 60 35

9c
(**303**)

304 "The Adoration of the Magi"

1974 (16 Oct). *No. 551 surch with T* **303**, *in red.*
579 9 c. on 8 c. Opal .. 15 15

(Des and recess R.B.A.)

1974 (13 Nov). *Christmas. Woodcuts by Dürer. T* **304** *and similar vert design. P* 14 × 15.
580 10 c. black/*cream* .. 25 10
581 35 c. black/*cream* .. 80 1·00
Design:—35 c. "The Flight into Egypt".

PROCESS. All the following issues to No. 772 were printed in photogravure, *except where otherwise stated.*

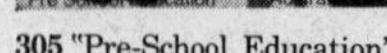

305 "Pre-School Education" **306** "Road Safety"

(Des Vivienne Binns (5 c.), Erica McGilchrist (11 c.), E. Tanner (15 c.), J. Meldrum (60 c.))

1974 (20 Nov). *Education in Australia. T* **305** *and similar multicoloured designs. P* 13½.
582 5 c. Type **305** .. 50 40
583 11 c. "Correspondence Schools" .. 50 20
584 15 c. "Science Education" .. 80 40
585 60 c. "Advanced Education" (*vert*) .. 1·75 2·50
582/5 .. *Set of* 4 3·25 3·25

(Des G. Andrews)

1975 (29 Jan). *Environment Dangers. T* **306** *and similar horiz designs. Multicoloured. P* 14 × 14½ *(No. 586) or* 14½ × 14 *(others).*
586 10 c. Type **306** .. 40 25
587 10 c. "Pollution" .. 40 25
 a. Perf 15 × 14 .. 9·00 3·00
588 10 c. "Bush Fires" .. 40 25
 a. Perf 15 × 14 .. 1·00 75
586/8 .. *Set of* 3 1·10 65

307 Australian Women's Year Emblem **308** J. H. Scullin

(Des Leonora Howlett)

1975 (12 Mar). *International Women's Year. P* 14 × 15.
589 **307** 10 c. dp violet-blue, green & bluish vio .. 20 15
This stamp exists with PVA gum as well as gum arabic.

(Des B. Dunlop)

1975 (26 Mar). *Famous Australians (6th series). Prime Ministers. T* **308** *and similar vert designs. Multicoloured. P* 14 × 15.
590 10 c. Type **308** .. 20 25
591 10 c. J. A. Lyons .. 20 25
592 10 c. Earle Page .. 20 25
593 10 c. Arthur Fadden .. 20 25
594 10 c. John Curtin .. 20 25
595 10 c. J. B. Chifley .. 20 25
590/5 .. *Set of* 6 1·00 1·40
Nos 591/2 and 594 exist with both PVA gum and gum arabic.

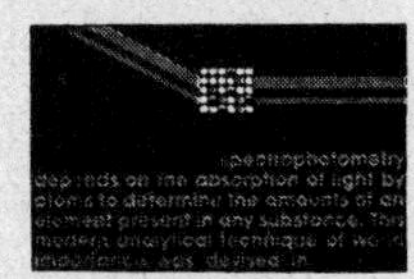

309 Atomic Absorption Spectrophotometry **310** Logo of Australian Postal Commission

(Des Weatherhead & Stitt)

1975 (14 May). *Scientific Development. T* **309** *and similar horiz designs. Multicoloured. P* 13½.
596 11 c. Type **309** .. 50 30
597 24 c. Radio astronomy .. 1·25 1·75
598 33 c. Immunology .. 1·50 2·00
599 48 c. Oceanography .. 2·00 2·50
596/9 .. *Set of* 4 4·75 6·00

(Des P. Huveneers)

1975 (1 July). *Inauguration of Australian Postal and Telecommunications Commissions. T* **310** *and similar horiz design. P* 14½ × 14.
600 10 c. black, rosine and pale grey .. 20 10
 a. Pair. Nos. 600/1 .. 1·50 1·50
 b. Perf 15 × 14 .. 20 10
 ba. Pair. Nos. 600b/1b .. 1·50 1·50
601 10 c. black, orange-yellow and pale grey .. 20 10
 b. Perf 15 × 14 .. 20 10
Design:—No. 601, Logo of Australian Telecommunications Commission.
Nos. 600/1 were printed together, *se-tenant* in horizontal and vertical pairs throughout the sheet.

311 Edith Cowan **312** *Helichrysum thomsonii* **313** "Tambaran" House and Sydney Opera House

(Des D. and J. O'Brien)

1975 (6 Aug). *Famous Australians (7th series). Australian Women. T* **311** *and similar vert designs. Multicoloured.* A. *P* 14 × 14½. B. *P* 14 × 15.

	A.		B.	
602 10 c. Type **311** ..	30	30	30	30
603 10 c. Louisa Lawson ..	30	30	60	30
604 10 c. Ethel Richardson ..	30	30	60	30
605 10 c. Catherine Spence ..	30	30	45	30
606 10 c. Constance Stone ..	45	30	30	30
607 10 c. Truganini ..	30	30	40	30
602/7 .. *Set of* 6	1·75	1·60	2·40	1·60

No. 604 is inscribed with the *nom de plume* "Henry Handel Richardson".

(Des F. Knight)

1975 (27 Aug). *Wild Flowers. T* **312** *and similar multicoloured design. P* 15 × 14 (18 *c.*) *or* 14 × 15 (45 *c.*).
608 18 c. Type **312** .. 25 10
a. Black omitted .. 25·00
b. Grey (stem, etc) omitted .. 20·00
609 45 c. *Callistemon teretifolius* (*horiz*) .. 50 10
a. Black (face value and inscr) omitted .. £200
b. Yellow-green (twigs) omitted .. £100
The 18 c. exists with both PVA gum and gum arabic.

(Des D. Annand (18 c.) or G. Hamori (25 c.))

1975 (16 Sept). *Papua New Guinea Independence. T* **313** *and similar horiz design. Multicoloured. P* 13½.
610 18 c. Type **313** .. 30 10
611 25 c. "Freedom" (bird in flight) .. 70 1·00

314 Epiphany Scene **315** Australian Coat of Arms

(Des D. O'Brien (15 c.) or J. Milne (45 c.))

1975 (29 Oct). *Christmas. T* **314** *and similar horiz design. P* 14 × 15 (15 *c.*) *or* 13½ (45 *c.*).
612 15 c. multicoloured .. 25 10
613 45 c. reddish violet, greenish blue and silver 1·00 2·25
Design:—45 c. "Shining Star".

I II

Two types of No. 614:
I. Emu's legs without toes.
II. Emu showing toes.
Other minor differences also occur.

(Des J. Spatchurst)

1976 (5 Jan). *75th Anniv of Nationhood. P* 15 x 14.
614 **315** 18 c. multicoloured (I) .. 35 20
a. Buff (supporters) omitted .. £275
b. Type II .. 75 30
ba. Gold (shield and star) omitted £120

316 Telephone-user, *circa* 1878 **317** John Oxley

(Des R. Ingpen)

1976 (10 Mar). *Telephone Centenary. P* 13½.
615 **316** 18 c. multicoloured .. 20 15

(Des B. Dunlop)

1976 (9 June). *19th Century Explorers. T* **317** *and similar horiz designs. Multicoloured. P* 13½.
616 18 c. Type **317** .. 35 35
617 18 c. Hume and Hovell .. 35 35
618 18 c. John Forrest .. 35 35
619 18 c. Ernest Giles .. 35 35
620 18 c. William Gosse .. 35 35
621 18 c. Peter Warburton .. 35 35
616/21 .. *Set of* 6 1·90 1·90

318 Measuring Stick, Graph and Computer Tape **319** Football

(Des R. Ingpen)

1976 (15 June). *50th Anniv of Commonwealth Scientific and Industrial Research Organisation. P* 15 × 14.
622 **318** 18 c. multicoloured .. 20 15

(Des A. Leydin)

1976 (14 July). *Olympic Games, Montreal. T* **319** *and similar multicoloured designs. P* 13½.
623 18 c. Type **319** .. 30 20
624 18 c. Gymnastics (*vert*) .. 30 20
625 25 c. Diving (*vert*) .. 50 50
626 40 c. Cycling .. 70 70
623/6 .. *Set of* 4 1·60 1·40
The 25 c. exists with gum arabic as well as PVA gum.

320 Richmond Bridge, Tasmania  **321** Blamire Young (designer of first Australian stamp)

(Des O. Borchert)

1976 (23 Aug). *Australian Scenes. T* **320** *and similar designs. Multicoloured. P* 14 × 15 (50 *c.*) *or* 15 × 14 (*others*).
627 5 c. Type **320** .. 15 10
628 25 c. Broken Bay, N.S.W. .. 40 20
629 35 c. Wittenoom Gorge, W.A. .. 35 20
630 50 c. Mt. Buffalo, Victoria (*vert*) .. 60 30
631 70 c. Barrier Reef .. 80 1·25
632 85 c. Ayers Rock, N.T. .. 1·00 1·75
627/32 .. *Set of* 6 3·00 3·50

(Des R. Honisett)

1976 (27 Sept). *National Stamp Week. P* 13½.
633 **321** 18 c. multicoloured .. 15 15
MS634 101 × 112 mm. No. 633 × 4 .. 1·25 2·00
MS634 contains one stamp coloured as No. 633; the others, showing the different colour separations used in the printing, are each differently coloured.
The miniature sheet exists with "AUSTRALIAN STAMP PROMOTION COUNCIL" overprinted in red on the margin from a privately produced booklet.

322 "Virgin and Child" (detail, Simone Cantarini)  **323** John Gould

(Des C. Medlycott (15 c.), Wendy Tamlyn (45 c.))

1976 (1 Nov). *Christmas. T* **322** *and similar horiz design. P* 15 × 14 (15 *c.*) *or* 13½ (45 *c.*).
635 15 c. bright magenta and light azure .. 20 10
636 45 c. multicoloured .. 60 80
Design:—45 c. Toy koala bear and decorations.

(Des B. Weatherhead)

1976 (10 Nov). *Famous Australians* (8*th series*). *T* **323** *and similar horiz designs. Multicoloured. P* 15 × 14.
637 18 c. Type **323** .. 40 35
638 18 c. Thomas Laby .. 40 35
a. Red-brown ("AUSTRALIA" etc.) omitted £140
639 18 c. Sir Baldwin Spencer .. 40 35
640 18 c. Griffith Taylor .. 40 35
637/40 .. *Set of* 4 1·40 1·25

324 "Music" **325** Queen Elizabeth II

1977 (19 Jan). *Performing Arts. T* **324** *and similar vert designs. Multicoloured. P* 14 × 15.
641 20 c. Type **324** .. 25 25
642 30 c. Drama .. 40 30
643 40 c. Dance .. 55 35
644 60 c. Opera .. 1·00 1·60
641/4 .. *Set of* 4 2·00 2·25

(Des P.O. Artists. Litho Govt Printer, Sydney (2% of supplies) or by Norman J. Field, Melbourne)

1977 (2 Feb). *Silver Jubilee. T* **325** *and similar vert design. Multicoloured. P* 14 × 15.
645 18 c. Type **325** .. 20 10
646 45 c. The Queen and Prince Philip .. 50 70

326 Fielder and Wicket Keeper **327** Parliament House

(Des B. Weatherhead)

1977 (9 Mar). *Australia–England Test Cricket Centenary. T* **326** *and similar vert designs. Multicoloured. P* 13½.
647 18 c. Type **326** .. 35 35
a. Horiz strip of 5. Nos. 647/51 .. 2·00
648 18 c. Umpire, batsman and scoreboard .. 35 35
649 18 c. Fielders .. 35 35
650 18 c. Batsman and umpire .. 35 35
651 18 c. Bowler and fielder .. 35 35
652 45 c. Batsman awaiting delivery .. 75 75
647/52 .. *Set of* 6 2·50 2·50
Nos. 647/51 were printed together, *se-tenant*, in horizontal strips of 5 throughout the sheet, forming a composite design.

(Des R.B.A.)

1977 (13 Apr). *50th Anniv of Opening of Parliament House, Canberra. P* 15 × 14.
653 **327** 18 c. multicoloured .. 15 10

328 Trade Unions Workers **329** Surfing Santa

(Des D. Lanyon; adapted B. Sadgrove)

1977 (9 May). *50th Anniv of Australian Council of Trade Unions. P* 13½.
654 **328** 18 c. multicoloured .. 15 10

(Des R. Roberts (15 c.), J. O'Brien (45 c.))

1977 (31 Oct). *Christmas. T* **329** *and similar vert design. Multicoloured. P* 14 × 15 (15 *c.*) *or* 13½ (45 *c.*).
655 15 c. Type **329** .. 25 10
656 45 c. Madonna and Child .. 1·00 80

330 National Flag **331** Harry Hawker and Sopwith "Camel"

(Des Cato Hibberd Design)

1978 (26 Jan). *Australia Day. P* 13½.
657 **330** 18 c. multicoloured .. 20 15

(Litho Asher and Co, Melbourne)

1978 (19 Apr). *Early Australian Aviators. T* **331** *and similar horiz designs. Multicoloured. P* 15½.
658 18 c. Type **331** .. 35 35
a. Imperf (horiz pair) .. £200
659 18 c. Bert Hinkler and Avro "Avian" .. 35 35
a. Imperf (horiz pair) .. £275
660 18 c. Sir Charles Kingsford Smith and *Southern Cross* .. 35 35
a. Imperf (pair) .. £150
661 18 c. Charles Ulm and *Southern Cross* .. 35 35
658/61 .. *Set of* 4 1·25 1·25
MS662 100 × 112 mm. Nos. 660/1 × 2. Imperf .. 1·50 1·75

332 Beechcraft "Baron" landing at Station Airstrip **333** Illawarra Flame Tree

1978 (15 May). *50th Anniv of Royal Flying Doctor Service. P* 13½.
663 **332** 18 c. multicoloured .. 15 15

(Des D. Rose)

1978 (1 June). *Trees. T* **333** *and similar vert designs. Multicoloured. P* 14 × 15 (18 *c.*) *or* 13½ (*others*).
664 18 c. Type **333** .. 25 10
665 25 c. Ghost Gum .. 55 1·25
666 40 c. Grass Tree .. 90 1·75
667 45 c. Cootamundra Wattle .. 90 1·25
664/7 .. *Set of* 4 2·40 4·00

334 Sturt's Desert Rose and Map **335** Hooded Plover

(Des D. Pitt. Litho Asher and Co, Melbourne)

1978 (19 June). *Establishment of State Government for the Northern Territory. P* 15½.
668 **334** 18 c. multicoloured 20 15

(Des Kay Breeden-Williams. Photo)

1978 (3 July)–**80**. *Birds* (1*st series*). *Multicoloured designs as T* **335**. *P* 15 × 14 (20 *c.* (*both*)), 14 × 15 (22 *c.*) *or* 13½ (*others*).
669 1 c. Spotted-sided Finch (17.9.79) 10 10
670 2 c. Crimson Finch (17.9.79) 10 10
671 5 c. Type **335** (17.7.78) 15 10
a. Grey-brown (bird's back) omitted .. £100
672 15 c. Forest Kingfisher (*vert*) (17.9.79) 20 10
673 20 c. Australian Dabchick ("Little Grebe") .. 45 10
a. Yellow (beak and eye) omitted .. 30·00
674 20 c. Eastern Yellow Robin (17.9.79) 20 10
675 22 c. White-tailed Kingfisher (22 × 29 *mm*) (31.3.80) 30 10
676 25 c. Masked Plover (17.7.78) 50 20
677 30 c. Oystercatcher (17.7.78) 65 25
678 40 c. Variegated Wren (*vert*) (17.9.79) .. 30 25
679 50 c. Flame Robin (*vert*) (17.9.79) 40 40
680 55 c. Comb-crested Jacana ("Lotus-bird") .. 85 60
669/80 .. .. *Set of* 12 3·75 2·00

See also Nos. 734/40.

336 1928 3d. "National Stamp Exhibition" Commemorative

337 "The Madonna and Child" (after van Eyck)

(Des Cato Hibberd Design. Litho Asher and Co, Melbourne)

1978 (25 Sept). *National Stamp Week. 50th Anniv of National Stamp Exhibition, Melbourne. P* 15½.
694 **336** 20 c. multicoloured 15 15
MS695 78 × 113 mm. No. 694 × 4 .. .. 1·40 1·75

(Litho Asher and Co, Melbourne)

1978 (3 Oct–1 Nov). *Christmas. Paintings. T* **337** *and similar vert designs. Multicoloured. P* 14½.
696 15 c. Type **337** (1.11) 25 10
697 25 c. "The Virgin and Child" (Marmion) .. 35 50
698 55 c. "The Holy Family" (del Vaga) (1.11) .. 60 85
696/8 .. .. *Set of* 3 1·10 1·25

338 "Tulloch"

339 Raising the Flag, Sydney Cove, 26 January 1788

(Des B. Clinton)

1978 (18 Oct). *Race-horses. T* **338** *and similar multicoloured designs. P* 15 × 14 (20 *c.*) *or* 13½ (*others*).
699 20 c. Type **338** 30 10
700 35 c. "Bernborough" (*vert*) 50 70
701 50 c. "Phar Lap" (*vert*) .. .. .. 75 1·00
702 55 c. "Peter Pan" .. .. 80 1·00
699/702 .. .. *Set of* 4 2·10 2·50

(Des B. Clinton. Litho Asher and Co, Melbourne)

1979 (26 Jan). *Australia Day. P* 15½.
703 **339** 20 c. multicoloured 15 15
a. Yellow omitted .. .. ..

340 P.S. *Canberra*

341 Port Campbell, Victoria

(Des O. Borchert)

1979 (14 Feb). *Ferries and Murray River Steamers. T* **340** *and similar horiz designs. Multicoloured. P* 15 × 14 (20 *c.*) *or* 13½ (*others*).
704 20 c. Type **340** 25 10
705 35 c. M.V. *Lady Denman* 50 75
706 50 c. P.S. *Murray River Queen* .. .. 70 1·10
707 55 c. H.V. *Curl Curl* .. .. .. 80 1·10
704/7 .. .. *Set of* 4 2·00 2·75

(Des M. Robinson. Litho Asher and Co. Melbourne)

1979 (9 Apr). *National Parks. T* **341** *and similar multicoloured designs. P* 15½.
708 20 c. Type **341** 25 25
a. Horiz strip of 5. Nos. 708/12 .. .. 1·10
709 20 c. Uluru, Northern Territory 25 25
710 20 c. Royal, New South Wales 25 25
711 20 c. Flinders Ranges, South Australia .. 25 25
712 20 c. Nambung, Western Australia 25 25
713 20 c. Girraween, Queensland (*vert*) 25 25
a. Horiz pair. Nos. 713/14 .. .. 50 50
ab. Imperf (horiz pair)* £275
714 20 c. Mount Field, Tasmania (*vert*) 25 25
708/14 .. .. *Set of* 7 1·40 1·40

Nos. 708/14 were printed together, *se-tenant*; Nos. 708/12 in horizontal strips of 5 and Nos. 713/14 in horizontal pairs, throughout separate sheets.

*The imperforate error, No. 713ab, involves the two right-hand vertical columns of the sheet only, the left-hand stamp having vertical perforations at left.

342 "Double Fairlie" Type Locomotive, Western Australia

343 Symbolic Swan

(Des R. Honisett)

1979 (16 May). *Steam Railways. T* **342** *and similar horiz designs. Multicoloured. P* 14 × 15 (20 *c.*) *or* 13½ (*others*).
715 20 c. Type **342** 30 10
716 35 c. Locomotive, "Puffing Billy" Line, Victoria 55 65
717 50 c. Locomotive, Pichi Richi Line, South Australia .. .. 80 1·00
718 55 c. Locomotive, Zig Zag Railway, New South Wales .. .. 90 1·10
715/18 .. .. *Set of* 4 2·25 2·50

(Des B. Weatherhead)

1979 (6 June). *150th Anniv of Western Australia. P* 13½.
719 **343** 20 c. multicoloured 15 15

344 Children playing on Slide

345 Letters and Parcels

(Des Wendy Tamlyn. Litho Asher and Co, Melbourne)

1979 (13 Aug). *International Year of the Child. P* 13½ × 13.
720 **344** 20 c. multicoloured 15 10

(Des A. Collins. Litho Asher and Co, Melbourne)

1979 (24 Sept–1 Nov). *Christmas. T* **345** *and similar vert designs. Multicoloured. P* 13 × 13½.
721 15 c. Christ's Nativity (Eastern European icon) (1.11.79) 15 10
722 25 c. Type **345** 20 40
723 55 c. "Madonna and Child" (Buglioni) (1.11.79) 40 60
721/3 .. .. *Set of* 3 65 1·00

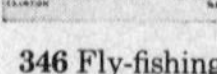

346 Fly-fishing

347 Matthew Flinders

(Des B. Clinton)

1979 (24 Oct). *Fishing. T* **346** *and similar vert designs. P* 14 × 15 (20 *c.*) *or* 13½ (*others*).
724 20 c. multicoloured 15 10
725 35 c. black, deep grey-blue and violet-blue .. 30 60
726 50 c. multicoloured 35 80
727 55 c. multicoloured 40 75
724/7 .. .. *Set of* 4 1·10 2·00

Designs:—35 c. Spinning; 50 c. Deep sea game-fishing; 55 c. Surf-fishing.

(Des B. Weatherhead. Litho Asher and Co, Melbourne)

1980 (23 Jan). *Australia Day. P* 13½ × 13.
728 **347** 20 c. multicoloured 20 10

348 Dingo

349 Queen Elizabeth II

(Des Marg Towt. Litho Asher and Co, Melbourne)

1980 (20 Feb). *Dogs. T* **348** *and similar horiz designs. Multicoloured. P* 13½ × 13.
729 20 c. Type **348** 35 10
730 25 c. Border Collie 35 35
731 35 c. Australian Terrier 55 65
732 50 c. Australian Cattle Dog .. .. .. 1·25 1·50
733 55 c. Australian Kelpie .. .. .. 1·00 1·25
729/33 .. .. *Set of* 5 3·25 3·50

(Des Kay Breeden-Williams. Litho Asher and Co, Melbourne)

1980 (31 Mar)–**83**. *Birds* (2*nd series*). *Multicoloured designs as T* **335**. *P* 12½.
734 10 c. Golden-shouldered Parrot (*vert*) (1.7.80) 30 10
a. Perf 14½ × 14 (5.83) .. .. .. 1·40 35
734*b* 18 c. Spotted Catbird (*vert*) (17.11.80) .. 35 60
735 28 c. Australian Bee Eater ("Rainbow Bird") (*vert*) 50 25
736 35 c. Regent Bowerbird (*vert*) (1.7.80) .. 35 10
737 45 c. Masked Wood Swallow (1.7.80) .. 40 10
a. Perf 14 × 14½ (5.83) .. .. 2·50 40
738 60 c. Australian King Parrot (*vert*) 50 15
739 80 c. Rainbow Pitta (1.7.80) 85 40
740 $1 Black-backed Magpie (*vert*) (1.7.80) .. 85 10
734/40 .. .. *Set of* 8 3·75 1·60

Designs of Nos. 734/40 measure 22 × 29 mm (vert) or 29 × 22 mm (horiz).

(Des B. Weatherhead. Litho Asher and Co, Melbourne)

1980 (21 Apr). *Queen Elizabeth II's Birthday. P* 13 × 13½.
741 **349** 22 c. multicoloured 20 20

350 "Once a jolly Swagman camp'd by a Billabong"

351 High Court Buildings

(Des R. Roberts. Litho Asher and Co, Melbourne)

1980 (7 May). *Folklore. Scenes and Verses from the Folksong "Waltzing Matilda". T* **350** *and similar vert designs. Multicoloured. P* 13 × 13½.
742 22 c. Type **350** 40 10
a. Horiz strip of 5. Nos. 742/6 .. .. 1·75
743 22 c. "And he sang as he shoved that Jumbuck in his Tuckerbag" 40 10
744 22 c. "Up rode the Squatter, mounted on his Thoroughbred" 40 10
745 22 c. "Down came the Troopers one, two, three" 40 10
746 22 c. "And his Ghost may be heard as you pass by that Billabong" 40 10
742/6 .. .. *Set of* 5 1·75 45

Nos. 742/6 were printed together, *se-tenant*, in horizontal strips of 5 throughout the sheet, forming a composite design.

(Des Cato Hibberd Design. Litho Asher and Co, Melbourne)

1980 (19 May). *Opening of High Court Building, Canberra. P* 13 × 13½.
747 **351** 22 c. multicoloured 20 20

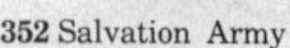

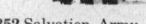

352 Salvation Army

353 Postbox, *circa* 1900

(Des J. Spatchurst. Litho Asher and Co, Melbourne)

1980 (11 Aug). *Community Welfare. T* **352** *and similar multicoloured designs. P* 13½ × 13 (*Nos.* 748, 751) *or* 13 × 13½ (*others*).
748 22 c. Type **352** 30 30
749 22 c. St. Vincent de Paul Society (*vert*) .. 30 30
750 22 c. Meals on Wheels (*vert*) 30 30
751 22 c. "Life. Be in it" 30 30
748/51 .. .. *Set of* 4 1·10 1·10

(Des B. Weatherhead. Litho Asher and Co, Melbourne)

980 (29 Sept). *National Stamp Week. T* **353** *and similar vert designs showing postal history, circa* 1900. *Multicoloured. P* 13 × 13½.

52 22 c. Type **353**.. .. .. 30 10
a. Horiz strip of 5. Nos. 752/6 .. .. 1·40
53 22 c. Postman (facing left) 30 10
54 22 c. Mail van.. .. .. 30 10
55 22 c. Postman and postbox 30 10
56 22 c. Postman (facing right).. .. .. 30 10
52/6 .. .. *Set of* 5 1·40 45
1S757 95 × 130 mm. Nos. 752, 754 and 756 .. 1·10 1·25
a. Error. Imperf .. ..

Nos. 752/6 were printed together, *se-tenant*, in horizontal strips f 5 throughout the sheet.

Stamps from No. **MS**757 have different backgrounds to the tamps from normal sheets.

354 "Holy Family" (painting, Prospero Fontana)   **355** "Wackett", 1941

(Des B. Weatherhead. Litho Asher and Co, Melbourne)

1980 (1 Oct–3 Nov). *Christmas. Works of Art. T* **354** *and similar vert designs. Multicoloured. P* 13 × 13½.

758 15 c. "The Virgin Enthroned" (detail of painting by Justin O'Brien) (3.11) .. 15 10
759 28 c. Type **354** 20 40
760 60 c. "Madonna and Child" (sculpture by School of M. Zuern) (3.11) 45 90
758/60 .. .. *Set of* 3 70 1·25

(Des O. Borchert. Litho Victorian Government Printer, Melbourne (22 c.), Asher and Co, Melbourne (others))

1980 (19 Nov). *Aircraft. T* **355** *and similar horiz designs. Multicoloured. P* 13½ × 14 (22 *c.*) *or* 13½ × 13 (*others*).

761 22 c. Type **355**.. .. .. 35 10
762 40 c. "Winjeel", 1955 .. .. 50 75
763 45 c. "Boomerang", 1944 .. .. 60 85
764 60 c. "Nomad", 1975 .. .. 80 1·10
761/4 .. .. *Set of* 4 2·00 2·50

356 Flag in shape of Australia   **357** Caricature of Darby Munro (jockey)

(Des B. Weatherhead. Litho Asher and Co, Melbourne)

1981 (21 Jan). *Australia Day. P* 13½ × 13.

765 **356** 22 c. multicoloured 20 20

(Des T. Rafty. Litho Cambec Press, Melbourne)

1981 (18 Feb). *Sports Personalities. T* **357** *and similar vert designs showing caricatures. Multicoloured. P* 14 × 13½.

766 22 c. Type **357** 30 10
767 35 c. Victor Trumper (cricketer) 55 65
768 55 c. Sir Norman Brookes (tennis player) .. 75 85
769 60 c. Walter Lindrum (billiards player) .. 80 90
766/9 .. .. *Set of* 4 2·25 2·25

358 1931 Kingsford Smith's Flights 6d. Commemorative   **359** Apex Emblem and Map of Australia

(Des Cato Hibberd Design. Litho Asher and Co, Melbourne)

1981 (25 Mar). *50th Anniv of Official Australia–U.K. Airmail Service. T* **358** *and similar horiz design showing* 1931 *Kingsford Smith's Flights* 6d. *commemorative. P* 13 × 13½ (22 *c.*) *or* 13½ × 13 (60 *c.*).

770 22 c. blackish lilac, rosine and bright blue .. 20 10
771 60 c. blackish lilac, rosine and ultramarine .. 50 90

(Des P. Clark)

1981 (6 Apr). *50th Anniv of Apex (young men's service club). P* 13½.

772 **359** 22 c. multicoloured 20 20

ASHER AND CO. From April 1981 this firm was known as Leigh-Mardon Ltd, Melbourne.

360 Queen's Personal Standard for Australia   **361** "Licence Inspected"

(Litho Leigh-Mardon Ltd, Melbourne)

1981 (21 Apr). *Queen Elizabeth II's Birthday. P* 13½ × 13.

773 **360** 22 c. multicoloured 20 20

(Des B. Weatherhead. Litho Leigh-Mardon Ltd, Melbourne)

1981 (20 May). *Gold Rush Era. Sketches by S. T. Gill. T* **361** *and similar vert designs. Multicoloured. P* 13 × 13½.

774 22 c. Type **361** 20 25
775 22 c. "Puddling" 20 25
776 22 c. "Quality of washing stuff" 20 25
777 22 c. "On route to deposit gold" 20 25
774/7 .. .. *Set of* 4 70 90

362 "On the Wallaby Track" (Fred McCubbin)

(Litho Leigh-Mardon Ltd, Melbourne)

1981 (17 June)–**84**. *Paintings. T* **362** *and similar horiz design. Multicoloured. P* 15 × 14½.

778 $2 Type **362** .. .. 1·75 30
779 $5 "A Holiday at Mentone, 1888" (Charles Conder) (4.4.84) (Optd S. £2·75) .. .. 4·75 1·50

For No. 778 overprinted "Specimen" see after No. 567*a*.

363 Thylacine   **363*a*** Blue Mountain Tree-Frog

363*b* Ulysses (butterfly)

(Des C. McCubbin (4, 10, 20, 27 c. (No. 791), 30 c. (No. 792*a*), 35, 45, 60, 80 c., $1), F. Knight (5, 24, 25, 30 c. (No. 792), 50, 55 c.) or Beverley Bruen (others). Photo Note Ptg Branch, Reserve Bank of Australia and litho Leigh-Mardon (early ptgs of 24 c.), litho Leigh-Mardon (3, 5, 15, 24, 25, 27 c. (both), 30 c. (both), 40, 50, 55, 65, 75, 90 c.) or Cambec Press (others))

1981 (19 July)–**84**. *Wildlife. Multicoloured designs as T* **363** (5, 24, 25, 30, 50, 55 *c.*), *T* **363*a*** (1, 3, 5, 27 (No. 790), 40, 65, 70, 75, 85, 90, 95 *c.*) *or vert as T* **363*b*** (*others*). *P* 13½ (1, 4, 10, 20, 24, 35, 45, 60, 70, 80, 85, 95 *c.*, $1), 14½ × 14 (27 *c.* (*No.* 791), 30 *c.* (*No.* 792*a*)) *or* 12½ (*others*).

781 1 c. Lace Monitor (2.2.83) 10 10
782 3 c. Corroboree Frog (19.4.82) 10 10
a. Perf 14 × 14½ (9.84) 40 10
783 4 c. Regent Skipper (butterfly) (*vert*) (15.6.83) 40 15
784 5 c. Queensland Hairy-nosed Wombat (*vert*) (15.7.81) 10 10
a. Perf 14½ × 14 (3.84) 60 10
785 10 c. Cairns Birdwing (butterfly) (*vert*) (15.6.83) 40 10
786 15 c. Eastern Snake-necked Tortoise (16.6.82) 20 25
a. Perf 14 × 14½ (3.84) 50 30
787 20 c. Macleay's Swallowtail (butterfly) (*vert*) (15.6.83) 50 20
788 24 c. Type **363** 35 10
a. Imperf (pair) £200
789 25 c. Common Rabbit-Bandicoot (*vert*) (15.7.81) 35 10
a. Perf 14 × 14½ (5.83) 80 25
790 27 c. Type **363*a*** (19.4.82) 35 15
a. Perf 14 × 14½ (6.82) 60 10
791 27 c. Type **363*b*** (15.6.83) 75 15
a. Imperf (pair) £300
792 30 c. Bridle Nail-tailed Wallaby (*vert*) (15.7.81) 40 15
792*a* 30 c. Chlorinda Hairstreak (butterfly) (*vert*) (24.10.83) 75 20
793 35 c. Blue Tiger (butterfly) (*vert*) (15.6.83) .. 60 20
794 40 c. Smooth Knob-tailed Gecko (16.6.82) .. 45 45
a. Perf 14 × 14½ (3.84) .. .. .. 1·50 75
795 45 c. Big Greasy (butterfly) (*vert*) (15.6.83) .. 60 25
796 50 c. Leadbeater's Possum (15.7.81) 50 10
a. Perf 14 × 14½ (1983) 70 30
797 55 c. Stick-nest Rat (*vert*) (15.7.81) 50 20
798 60 c. Wood White (butterfly) (*vert*) (15.6.83) .. 75 25
799 65 c. Yellow-faced Whip Snake (19.4.82) .. 80 30
a. Perf 14 × 14½ (3.84) 75 55
800 70 c. Crucifix Toad (2.2.83) 65 80
801 75 c. Eastern Water Dragon (19.4.82) 80 25
a. Perf 14 × 14½ (3.84) .. .. .. 1·25 75
802 80 c. Amaryllis Azure (butterfly) (*vert*) (15.6.83) .. .. 1·60 90
803 85 c. Centralian Blue-tongued Lizard (2.2.83) 1·10 90
804 90 c. Freshwater Crocodile (16.6.82) .. .. 1·10 90
805 95 c. Thorny Devil (2.2.83) .. .. .. 1·00 90
806 $1 Sword Grass Brown (butterfly) (*vert*) (15.6.83) .. .. 1·60 20
781/806 .. .. *Set of* 27 15·00 8·00

364 Prince Charles and Lady Diana Spencer   **365** *Cortinarius cinnabarinus*

(Des B. Clinton. Litho Leigh-Mardon Ltd, Melbourne)

1981 (29 July). *Royal Wedding. P* 13½ × 13.

821 **364** 24 c. multicoloured 25 10
822 60 c. multicoloured .. .. 75 1·00

(Des Celia Rosser. Litho Leigh-Mardon Ltd, Melbourne)

1981 (19 Aug). *Australian Fungi. T* **365** *and similar vert designs. Multicoloured. P* 13 × 13½.

823 24 c. Type **365** 35 10
824 35 c. *Coprinus comatus* 50 50
825 55 c. *Armillaria luteobubalina* 70 70
826 60 c. *Cortinarius austro-venetus* 80 80
823/6 .. .. *Set of* 4 2·10 1·90

366 Disabled People playing Basketball   **367** "Christmas Bush for His Adorning"

(Des J. Spatchurst. Litho Cambec Press, Melbourne)

1981 (16 Sept). *International Year for Disabled Persons. P* 14 × 13½.

827 **366** 24 c. multicoloured 20 20

(Des F. Beck. Litho Leigh-Mardon Ltd, Melbourne)

1981 (28 Sept–2 Nov). *Christmas. Scenes and Verses from Carols by W. James and J. Wheeler. T* **367** *and similar vert designs. Multicoloured. P* 13 × 13½.

828 18 c. Type **367** (2 Nov).. .. .. .. 20 10
829 30 c. "The Silver Stars are in the Sky" .. 30 25
830 60 c. "Noeltime" (2 Nov) 50 70
828/30 .. .. *Set of* 3 90 90

368 Globe depicting Australia   **369** Ocean Racing Yacht

(Des B. Weatherhead. Litho Leigh-Mardon Ltd, Melbourne)

1981 (30 Sept). *Commonwealth Heads of Government Meeting, Melbourne. P* 13 × 13½.

831 **368** 24 c. black, pale blue and gold 20 10
832 60 c. black, pale blue and silver 50 75

(Des R. Fletcher. Litho Leigh-Mardon Ltd, Melbourne)

1981 (14 Oct). *Yachts. T* **369** *and similar vert designs. Multicoloured. P* 13 × 13½.

833 24 c. Type **369**.. .. .. 35 10
834 35 c. "Sharpie" 50 50
835 55 c. "12 Metre" 75 85
836 60 c. "Sabot" .. .. 1·00 1·00
833/6 .. .. *Set of* 4 2·40 2·25

370 Aborigine, Governor Phillip (founder of N.S.W., 1788) and Post World War II Migrant

371 Humpback Whale

(Des B. Clinton. Litho Cambec Press, Melbourne)

1982 (20 Jan). *Australia Day. "Three Great Waves of Migration". P* 13½ × 14.
837 **370** 24 c. multicoloured 35 25

(Des R. and Katrina Ingpen. Litho Cambec Press, Melbourne)

1982 (17 Feb). *Whales. T* **371** *and similar multicoloured designs. P* 13½ × 14 (24, 60 c.) *or* 14 × 13½ (*others*).
838 24 c. Sperm Whale 40 10
839 35 c. Black Right Whale (*vert*) 60 60
840 55 c. Blue Whale (*vert*) .. .. .. 1·10 1·10
841 60 c. Type **371** (new blue background) .. 1·25 1·25
a. Solid greenish blue background .. £250
838/41 .. .. *Set of* 4 3·00 2·75

No. 841a comes from a small trial printing, some sheets of which were included amongst normal stock by mistake. The correct version of the 60 c. value shows the new blue background streaked with white at top left. On No. 841a the background is in greenish blue and is without the white streaks.

372 Queen Elizabeth II

373 "Marjorie Atherton"

(Des R. Honisett. Litho Cambec Press, Melbourne)

1982 (21 Apr). *Queen Elizabeth II's Birthday. P* 14 × 13½.
842 **372** 27 c. multicoloured 30 15

(Des Betty Conabere. Litho Leigh-Mardon Ltd, Melbourne)

1982 (19 May). *Roses. T* **373** *and similar vert designs. Multicoloured. P* 13 × 13½.
843 27 c. Type **373** 40 15
844 40 c. "Imp" 55 50
845 65 c. "Minnie Watson" 95 80
846 75 c. "Satellite" .. .. 1·10 1·00
843/6 .. .. *Set of* 4 2·75 2·25

374 Radio Announcer and 1930-style Microphone

375 Forbes Post Office

(Des Cato Hibberd Design. Litho Leigh-Mardon Ltd, Melbourne)

1982 (16 June). *50th Anniv of ABC (Australian Broadcasting Commission). T* **374** *and similar horiz design. Multicoloured. P* 13½ × 13.
847 27 c. Type **374** 30 40
a. Pair. Nos. 847/8 .. .. 60 80
848 27 c. ABC logo 30 40

Nos. 847/8 were printed together, *se-tenant*, in horizontal and vertical pairs throughout the sheet.

(Des F. Beck. Litho Cambec Press, Melbourne)

1982 (4 Aug). *Historic Australian Post Offices. T* **375** *and similar multicoloured designs. P* 14 × 13½ (*vert*) *or* 13½ × 14 (*horiz*).
849 27 c. Type **375** 40 30
850 27 c. Flemington Post Office 40 30
851 27 c. Rockhampton Post Office 40 30
852 27 c. Kingston S.E. Post Office (*horiz*) .. 40 30
853 27 c. York Post Office (*horiz*) 40 30
854 27 c. Launceston Post Office 40 30
855 27 c. Old Post and Telegraph Station, Alice Springs (*horiz*) 40 30
849/55 .. .. *Set of* 7 2·50 1·90

376 Early Australian Christmas Card

377 Boxing

(Des B. Weatherhead. Litho Leigh-Mardon Ltd, Melbourne)

1982 (15 Sept–1 Nov). *Christmas. T* **376** *and similar multicoloured designs. P* 14½.
856 21 c. Bushman's Hotel, with Cobb's coach arriving (*horiz*) (1.11.82) 30 10
857 35 c. Type **376** 40 50
858 75 c. Little girl offering Christmas pudding to swagman (1.11.82) .. .. .. 75 1·25
856/8 .. .. *Set of* 3 1·25 1·60

(Des R. Carnielye. Litho Leigh-Mardon Ltd, Melbourne)

1982 (22 Sept). *Commonwealth Games, Brisbane. T* **377** *and similar horiz designs. P* 14½.
859 27 c. stone, lemon and bright carmine .. 25 20
860 27 c. lemon, stone and emerald 25 20
861 27 c. stone, lemon and yellow-brown 25 20
862 75 c. multicoloured 75 90
859/62 .. .. *Set of* 4 1·40 1·40
MS863 130 × 95 mm. Nos. 859/61. P 13½ × 13 .. 1·10 1·25

Designs:—No. 859, Type **377**; No. 860, Archery; No. 861, Weightlifting; No. 862, Pole-vaulting.

378 Sydney Harbour Bridge 5s. Stamp of 1932

379 "Yirawala" Bark Painting

(Des Cato Hibberd Design. Litho Cambec Press, Melbourne)

1982 (27 Sept). *National Stamp Week. P* 13½ × 14.
864 **378** 27 c. multicoloured 30 25

(Des Australia Post Graphic Design Section. Litho Leigh-Mardon Ltd, Melbourne)

1982 (12 Oct). *Opening of Australian National Gallery. P* 14½.
865 **379** 27 c. multicoloured 30 25

380 Mimi Spirits Dancing

381 *Eucalyptus calophylla* "Rosea"

(Des D. Milaybuma (27 c.), L. Nabardayal (40 c.), J. Galareya (65 c.), D. Nguleingulei-Murrumurru (75 c.). Litho Cambec Press, Melbourne)

1982 (17 Nov). *Aboriginal Culture. Music and Dance. T* **380** *and similar horiz designs depicting Aboriginal Bark Paintings of Mimi Spirits. P* 13½ × 14.
866 27 c. multicoloured 25 10
867 40 c. multicoloured 40 50
868 65 c. multicoloured 70 80
869 75 c. multicoloured .. .. 80 1·10
866/9 .. .. *Set of* 4 2·00 2·25

(Des Elizabeth Conabere. Photo Enschedé)

1982 (17 Nov). *Booklet stamps. Eucalyptus Flowers. T* **381** *and similar horiz designs. Multicoloured. P* 12½ × 13½.
870 1 c. Type **381** 10 10
a. Booklet pane. Nos. 870/1 and 874 each × 2 80
b. Booklet pane. Nos. 870/1 each × 2, 872/3 and 874 × 3 .. .. 2·00
871 2 c. *Eucalyptus casia* 10 10
872 3 c. *Eucalyptus ficifolia* 25 20
873 10 c. *Eucalyptus globulus* 25 20
874 27 c. *Eucalyptus forrestiana* 30 30
870/4 .. .. *Set of* 5 90 80

Nos. 870/4 only exist from 60 c. (pane No. 870a) and $1 (pane No. 870b) stamp booklets and the stamps have one or two adjacent sides imperforate.

382 Shand Mason Steam Fire Engine, 1891

383 H.M.S. *Sirius*

(Des A. Puckett. Litho Cambec Press, Melbourne)

1983 (12 Jan). *Historic Fire Engines. T* **382** *and similar horiz designs. Multicoloured. P* 13½ × 14.
875 27 c. Type **382** 30 1
876 40 c. Hotchkiss fire engine, 1914 .. .. 45 5
877 65 c. Ahrens-Fox PS2 fire engine, 1929 .. 80 1·0
878 75 c. Merryweather manual fire appliance, 1851 .. .. 90 1·2
875/8 .. .. *Set of* 4 2·25 2·5

(Des J. Spatchurst. Litho Leigh-Mardon Ltd, Melbourne)

1983 (26 Jan). *Australia Day. T* **383** *and similar horiz design. Multicoloured. P* 14½.
879 27 c. Type **383** 30 40
a. Pair. Nos. 879/80 .. .. 60 8
880 27 c. H.M.S. *Supply* 30 40

Nos. 879/80 were printed together, *se-tenant*, in horizontal an vertical pairs throughout the sheet.

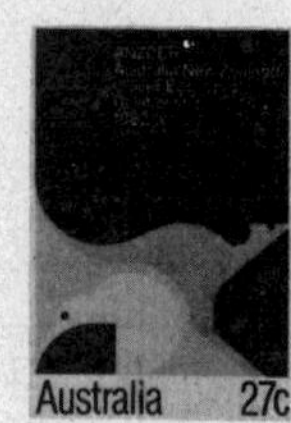

384 Stylised Kangaroo and Kiwi

385 Equality and Dignity

(Des G. Emery. Litho Cambec Press, Melbourne)

1983 (2 Feb). *Closer Economic Relationship Agreement with New Zealand. P* 14 × 13½.
881 **384** 27 c. multicoloured 30 25

(Des G. Emery. Litho Leigh-Mardon Ltd, Melbourne)

1983 (9 Mar). *Commonwealth Day. T* **385** *and similar vert designs. Multicoloured. P* 14½.
882 27 c. Type **385** 25 2
883 27 c. Liberty and Freedom 25 2
884 27 c. Social Justice and Co-operation 25 2
885 75 c. Peace and Harmony .. .. .. 70 1·10
882/5 .. .. *Set of* 4 1·25 1·75

386 R.Y. *Britannia* passing Sydney Opera House

387 "Postal and Telecommunications Services"

(Des J. Richards. Litho Leigh-Mardon Ltd, Melbourne)

1983 (20 Apr). *Queen Elizabeth II's Birthday. P* 14½.
886 **386** 27 c. multicoloured 40 25

(Des B. Sadgrove. Litho Cambec Press, Melbourne)

1983 (18 May). *World Communications Year. P* 13 × 13½.
887 **387** 27 c. multicoloured 30 25

388 Badge of the Order of St. John

389 Jaycee Members and Badge

(Des T. McCauley. Litho Cambec Press, Melbourne)

1983 (8 June). *Centenary of St. John Ambulance in Australia. P* 14 × 13½.
888 **388** 27 c. black and deep turquoise-blue .. 30 25

(Des B. Clinton. Litho Cambec Press, Melbourne)

1983 (8 June). *50th Anniv of Australian Jaycees. P* 13½ × 14.
889 **389** 27 c. multicoloured 30 25

390 "The Bloke"

391 Nativity Scene

(Des B. Clinton. Litho Leigh-Mardon Ltd, Melbourne)

1983 (3 Aug). *Folklore. "The Sentimental Bloke" (humorous poem by C. J. Dennis). T* **390** *and similar vert designs. Multicoloured. P* 14½.
890 27 c. Type **390** 40 40
a. Horiz strip of 5. Nos. 890/4 .. .. 1·75
891 27 c. "Doreen—The Intro" 40 40
892 27 c. "The Stror' at Coot" 40 40
893 27 c. "Hitched" 40 40
894 27 c. "The Mooch o'Life" 40 40
890/4 .. .. *Set of* 5 1·75 1·75
Nos. 890/4 were printed together, *se-tenant*, in horizontal strips of 5 throughout the sheet.

(Des Holly Alvarez (24 c.), Deanne Head (35 c.), Justine Jacobi (85 c.). Litho Cambec Press, Melbourne)

1983 (14 Sept–2 Nov). *Christmas. Children's Paintings. T* **391** *and similar horiz designs. Multicoloured. P* 13½ × 14.
895 24 c. Type **391** (2 November) 20 10
896 35 c. Kookaburra 35 45
897 85 c. Father Christmas in sleigh over beach (2 November) .. .. 90 1·10
895/7 .. .. *Set of* 3 1·25 1·50

392 Sir Paul Edmund de Strzelecki

393 Cook Family Cottage, Melbourne

(Des Dianne Quinn. Litho Leigh-Mardon Ltd, Melbourne)

1983 (26 Sept). *Explorers of Australia. T* **392** *and similar vert designs. Multicoloured. P* 14½.
898 30 c. Type **392** 35 40
899 30 c. Ludwig Leichardt 35 40
900 30 c. William John Wills and Robert O'Hara Burke 35 40
901 30 c. Alexander Forrest 35 40
898/901 .. .. *Set of* 4 1·25 1·40

(Des J. Quinn. Litho Cambec Press, Melbourne)

1984 (26 Jan). *Australia Day. P* 13½ × 14.
902 **393** 30 c. black and stone 30 35

MACHINE LABELS. From 22 February 1984 gummed labels in the above design, ranging in value from 1 c. to $9.99, were available from seven automatic machines. The number at the top of the label indicates the location of the machine from which it was issued: 2000, Sydney; 2601, Canberra; 3000, Melbourne; 4000, Brisbane; 5000, Adelaide; 6000, Perth; 7000, Hobart.

These were replaced by a further series, with a background pattern of kangaroos, on 22 October 1985. This second series included 5790 (later 0800) Darwin and labels without code number.

On 25 August 1986 a further series, with a background pattern of platypuses, was issued. These exist either without code or with one of the eight numbers introduced for the earlier issues. The design was again changed on 2 September 1987 to show Echidnas, to be followed by Ringtail Possums on 28 September 1988 and Frill-necked Lizards on 1 September 1989.

394 Charles Ulm, *Faith in Australia* and Trans-Tasman Cover

(Des G. Beck and J. Quinn. Litho Cambec Press, Melbourne)

1984 (22 Feb). *50th Anniv of First Official Airmail Flights, New Zealand–Australia and Australia–Papua New Guinea. T* **394** *and similar horiz designs. Multicoloured. P* 13½.
903 45 c. Type **394** 65 75
a. Horiz pair. Nos. 903/4 .. .. .. 1·25 1·50
904 45 c. As Type **394** but showing flown cover to Papua New Guinea 65 75
Nos. 903/4 were printed together, *se-tenant*, in horizontal pairs throughout the sheet.

NEW INFORMATION

The editor is always interested to correspond with people who have new information that will improve or correct the Catalogue.

395 Thomson "Steamer", 1898

396 Queen Elizabeth II

(Des A. Puckett. Litho Leigh-Mardon Ltd, Melbourne)

1984 (14 Mar). *Veteran and Vintage Cars. T* **395** *and similar horiz designs. Multicoloured. P* 14½.
905 30 c. Type **395** 45 45
a. Vert strip of 5. Nos. 905/9 .. .. 2·00
906 30 c. Tarrant, 1906 .. .. 45 45
907 30 c. Gordon & Co "Australian Six", 1919 .. 45 45
908 30 c. Summit, 1923 .. .. 45 45
909 30 c. Chic, 1924 .. .. 45 45
905/9 .. .. *Set of* 5 2·00 2·00
Nos. 905/9 were printed together, *se-tenant*, in vertical strips of 5 throughout the sheet.

(Des B. Weatherhead. Litho Leigh-Mardon Ltd, Melbourne)

1984 (18 Apr). *Queen Elizabeth II's Birthday. P* 14½.
910 **396** 30 c. multicoloured 30 35
a. Dull mauve (background) omitted £325

397 *Cutty Sark*

398 Freestyle

(Des J. Earl and J. Quinn. Litho Cambec Press, Melbourne)

1984 (23 May). *Clipper Ships. T* **397** *and similar multicoloured designs. P* 14 × 13½ (30 c., 85 c.) *or* 13½ × 14 (*others*).
911 30 c. Type **397** 40 25
912 45 c. *Orient* (*horiz*) 70 70
913 75 c. *Sobraon* (*horiz*) .. .. 1·25 1·25
914 85 c. *Thermopylae* .. .. 1·25 1·25
911/14 .. .. 3·25 3·00

(Des B. Clinton. Litho Leigh-Mardon Ltd, Melbourne)

1984 (6 June). *Skiing. T* **398** *and similar multicoloured designs. P* 14½.
915 30 c. Type **398** 40 45
916 30 c. Downhill racer 40 45
917 30 c. Slalom (*horiz*) 40 45
918 30 c. Nordic (*horiz*) 40 45
915/18 .. .. *Set of* 4 1·50 1·75

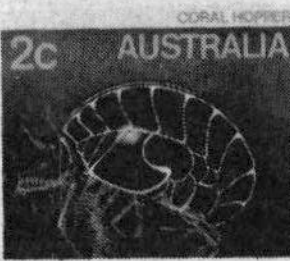

399 Coral Hopper

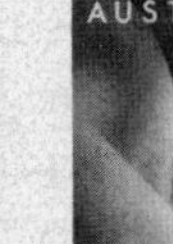

400 Before the Event

(Des G. Ryan and R. Fletcher (2, 25, 30, 50, 55, 85 c.) or G. Ryan (others). Litho Leigh-Mardon Ltd, Melbourne (30, 33 c.) or Cambec Press, Melbourne (others))

1984 (18 June)–**86**. *Marine Life. T* **399** *and similar horiz designs. Multicoloured. P* 14×14½ (30 c., 33 c.) *or* 13½ (*others*).
919 2 c. Type **399** 10 10
920 3 c. Jimble (11.6.86) 10 10
921 5 c. Tasselled Anglerfish (12.6.85) 10 10
922 10 c. Stonefish (11.6.86) 20 10
923 20 c. Red Handfish (12.6.85) 45 20
924 25 c. Orange-tipped Cowrie 45 15
925 30 c. Choat's Wrasse 45 15
926 33 c. Leafy Sea-dragon (20.3.85) 35 10
927 40 c. Red Velvet Fish (12.6.85) 65 40
928 45 c. Textile Cone (11.6.86) 80 25
929 50 c. Blue-lined Surgeonfish 80 35
930 55 c. Bennett's Nudibranch 80 50
a. New blue ("BENNETT'S NUDIBRANCH") omitted .. .. .. † –
931 60 c. Lionfish (11.6.86) 90 50
932 65 c. Stingaree (11.6.86) 90 55
933 70 c. Blue-ringed Octopus (11.6.86) 90 60
934 80 c. Pineapple Fish (12.6.85) .. .. .. 1·25 65
935 85 c. Regal Angelfish 90 50
936 90 c. Crab-eyed Goby (12.6.85) .. .. .. 1·00 75
937 $1 Crown of Thorns Starfish (11.6.86) (Optd S. 50p.) .. .. 1·50 80
919/37 .. .. *Set of* 19 11·00 6·00
No. 930a only exists used on maximum card.

(Des O. Schmidinger and Christine Stead. Litho Cambec Press, Melbourne)

1984 (25 July). *Olympic Games, Los Angeles. T* **400** *and similar multicoloured designs. P* 14 × 13½ (*No.* 943) *or* 13½ × 14 (*others*).
941 30 c. Type **400** 35 35
942 30 c. During the event 35 35
943 30 c. After the event (*vert*) 35 35
941/3 .. .. *Set of* 3 95 95

401 Australian 1913 1d. Kangaroo Stamp

402 "Angel" (stained-glass window, St. Francis' Church, Melbourne)

(Des Ken Cato Design Studio. Litho Cambec Press, Melbourne)

1984 (22 Aug–21 Sept). *"Ausipex" International Stamp Exhibition, Melbourne. T* **401** *and similar vert designs. Multicoloured. P* 14½.
944 30 c. Type **401** 35 30
MS945 126 × 175 mm. 30 c. × 7, Victoria 1850 3d. "Half Length"; New South Wales 1850 1d. "Sydney View"; Tasmania 1853 1d.; South Australia 1855 1d.; Western Australia 1854 1d. "Black Swan"; Queensland 1860 6d.; Type **401** (21 Sept) .. .. 3·00 3·50
On No. **MS**945 the emblem and inscription on the sheet margin are embossed.

(Des Ken Cato Design Studio. Litho Cambec Press, Melbourne)

1984 (17 Sept–31 Oct). *Christmas. Stained-glass Windows. T* **402** *and similar vert designs. Multicoloured. P* 14 × 13½.
946 24 c. "Angel and Child" (Holy Trinity Church, Sydney) (31.10.84) 40 20
947 30 c. "Veiled Virgin and Child" (St. Mary's Catholic Church, Geelong) (31.10.84) .. 55 20
948 40 c. Type **402** 70 60
949 50 c. "Three Kings" (St. Mary's Cathedral, Sydney) (31.10.84) 90 80
950 85 c. "Madonna and Child" (St. Bartholomew's Church, Norwood) (31.10.84) .. .. 1·25 1·25
946/50 .. .. *Set of* 5 3·50 2·75

403 "Stick Figures" (Cobar Region)

404 Yellow-tufted Honeyeater

(Des Elizabeth Innes. Litho Leigh-Mardon Ltd, Melbourne)

1984 (7 Nov). *Bicentenary of Australian Settlement* (1988) (*1st issue*). *The First Australians. T* **403** *and similar square designs showing aborigine rock paintings. Multicoloured. P* 14½.
951 30 c. Type **403** 45 45
952 30 c. "Bunjil" (large figure), Grampians .. 45 45
953 30 c. "Quikans" (tall figures), Cape York .. 45 45
954 30 c. "Wandjina Spirit and Baby Snakes" (Gibb River) 45 45
955 30 c. "Rock Python" (Gibb River) 45 45
956 30 c. "Silver Barramundi" (fish) (Kakadu National Park) 45 45
957 30 c. Bicentenary emblem 45 45
958 85 c. "Rock Possum" (Kakadu National Park) 1·10 1·25
951/8 .. .. *Set of* 8 3·75 4·00
See also Nos. 972/6, 993/6, 1002/7, 1019/22, 1059/63, 1064/6, 1077/81, 1090/2, 1105/9, 1110, 1137/41, 1145/8 and 1149.

(Des. G. Emery. Litho Leigh-Mardon Ltd, Melbourne)

1984 (19 Nov). *150th Anniv of Victoria. T* **404** *and similar vert design. Multicoloured. P* 14½.
959 30 c. Type **404** 35 40
a. Pair. Nos. 959/60 .. .. 70 80
960 30 c. Leadbeater's Possum 35 40
Nos. 959/60 were printed together, *se-tenant*, in horizontal and vertical pairs throughout the sheet.

405 "Musgrave Ranges" (Sidney Nolan)

406 Young People of Different Races, and Sun

(Des Sue Titcher. Litho Leigh-Mardon Ltd, Melbourne)

1985 (25 Jan). *Australia Day. Birth Centenary of Dorothea Mackellar (author of poem "My Country"). T* **405** *and similar horiz design. Multicoloured. P* 14½.
961 30 c. Type **405** 35 45
a. *Tête-bêche* (vert pair) 70 90
b. Vert pair. Nos. 961/2 .. .. .. 70 90
962 30 c. "The Walls of China" (Russell Drysdale) .. 35 45
a. *Tête-bêche* (vert pair) 70 90
Nos. 961/2 were printed together, *se-tenant*, within the same sheet. In each pane of 25 No. 961 occurs in horizontal rows 1, 4, 5, 8 and 9, and No. 962 in rows 2, 3, 6, 7 and 10. Horizontal rows 3/4 and 7/8 are inverted forming *tête-bêche* pairs of the same design in addition to the vertical *se-tenant* pairs containing both designs.

(Des Derryn Vogelnest. Litho Cambec Press, Melbourne)

1985 (13 Feb). *International Youth Year. P* 14 × 13½.
963 **406** 30 c. multicoloured 35 30

407 Royal Victorian Volunteer Artillery

408 District Nurse of early 1900's

(Des Pam Andrews. Litho Leigh-Mardon Ltd, Melbourne)

1985 (25 Feb). *19th-Century Australian Military Uniforms. T* **407** *and similar vert designs. Multicoloured. P* 14½.
964 33 c. Type **407** 50 50
a. Horiz strip of 5. Nos. 964/8 .. .. 2·25
965 33 c. Western Australian Pinjarrah Cavalry .. 50 50
966 33 c. New South Wales Lancers 50 50
967 33 c. New South Wales Contingent to the Sudan 50 50
968 33 c. Victorian Mounted Rifles 50 50
964/8 .. .. *Set of* 5 2·25 2·25
Nos. 964/8 were printed together, *se-tenant*, in horizontal strips of 5 throughout the sheet.

(Des Wendy Tamlyn. Litho Leigh-Mardon Ltd, Melbourne)

1985 (13 Mar). *Centenary of District Nursing Services. P* 14½.
969 **408** 33 c. multicoloured 40 35

409 Sulphur-crested Cockatoos

(Des R. Bevers. Litho Leigh-Mardon Ltd, Melbourne)

1985 (13 Mar). *Booklet stamps. Multicoloured, background colour given. P* 14½ × *imperf.*
970 **409** 1 c. flesh .. .. 70 1·00
a. Booklet pane. Nos. 970, and 971×3 2·00
971 33 c. pale turquoise-green 45 55
Nos. 970/1 only exist from $1 stamp booklets. As stamps from these booklets have their outer edges imperforate, the end example of No. 971 is only perforated along one side.

410 Abel Tasman and Journal Entry

411 Sovereign's Badge of Order of Australia

(Des G. Emery. Litho Cambec Press, Melbourne)

1985 (10 Apr). *Bicentenary of Australian Settlement* (1988) (*2nd issue*). *Navigators. T* **410** *and similar square designs. Multicoloured. P* 13.
972 33 c. Type **410** 45 35
973 33 c. Dirk Hartog's *Eendracht* (detail, Aert Anthonisz) 45 35
974 33 c. "William Dampier" (detail, T. Murray) 45 35
975 90 c. Globe and hand with extract from Dampier's journal .. .. 1·10 1·50
972/5 .. .. *Set of* 4 2·25 2·25
MS976 150×115 mm. As Nos. 972/5, but with cream-coloured margins .. .. 3·00 3·00

(Des Elizabeth Innes. Litho Cambec Press, Melbourne)

1985 (22 Apr). *Queen Elizabeth II's Birthday. P* 14 × 13½.
977 **411** 33 c. multicoloured 35 30

412 Tree, and Soil running through Hourglass ("Soil")

413 *Elves and Fairies* (Annie Rentoul and Ida Rentoul Outhwaite)

(Des L. Whaite and G. Jorgensen. Litho Cambec Press, Melbourne)

1985 (15 May). *Conservation. T* **412** *and similar vert designs. Multicoloured. P* 14 × 13½.
978 33 c. Type **412** 45 20
979 50 c. Washing on line and smog ("air") .. 70 85
980 80 c. Tap and flower ("water") .. .. 1·10 1·40
981 90 c. Chain encircling flames ("energy") .. 1·25 1·75
978/81 .. .. *Set of* 4 3·25 3·75

(Des P. Leuver. Litho Leigh-Mardon Ltd, Melbourne)

1985 (17 July). *Classic Australian Children's Books. T* **413** *and similar vert designs. Multicoloured. P* 14½.
982 33 c. Type **413** 50 50
a. Horiz strip of 5. Nos. 982/6 .. .. 2·25
983 33 c. *The Magic Pudding* (Norman Lindsay) 50 50
984 33 c. *Ginger Meggs* (James Charles Bancks) 50 50
985 33 c. *Blinky Bill* (Dorothy Wall) 50 50
986 33 c. *Snugglepot and Cuddlepie* (May Gibbs) 50 50
982/6 .. .. *Set of* 5 2·25 2·25
Nos. 982/6 were printed together, *se-tenant*, in horizontal strips of 5 throughout the sheet.

414 Dish Aerials

415 Angel in Sailing Ship

(Des J. Ostoja-Kotkowski. Litho Leigh-Mardon Ltd, Melbourne)

1985 (18 Sept). *Electronic Mail Service. P* 14½.
987 **414** 33 c. multicoloured 35 30

(Des S. Hartshorne. Litho Leigh-Mardon Ltd, Melbourne)

1985 (18 Sept–1 Nov). *Christmas. T* **415** *and similar horiz designs. Multicoloured. P* 14½.
988 27 c. Angel with holly wings (1.11) 30 15
989 33 c. Angel with bells (1.11) 35 15
990 45 c. Type **415** 50 50
991 55 c. Angel with star (1.11) 65 70
992 90 c. Angel with Christmas tree bauble (1.11) .. .. 1·00 1·25
988/92 .. .. *Set of* 5 2·50 2·50

416 Astrolabe (*Batavia*, 1629)

417 Aboriginal Wandjina Spirit, Map of Australia and Egg

(Des G. Emery. Litho Cambec Press, Melbourne)

1985 (2 Oct). *Bicentenary of Australian Settlement* (1988) (*3rd issue*). *Relics from Early Shipwrecks. T* **416** *and similar square designs. Multicoloured. P* 13.
993 33 c. Type **416** 40 15
994 50 c. German beardman jug (*Vergulde Draeck*, 1656) 70 70
995 90 c. Wooden bobbins (*Batavia*, 1629) and encrusted scissors (*Zeewijk*, 1727) .. 1·40 1·25
996 $1 Silver and brass buckle (*Zeewijk*, 1727) 1·60 1·50
993/6 .. .. *Set of* 4 3·75 3·25

(Des R. Meeks. Litho Leigh-Mardon Ltd, Melbourne)

1986 (24 Jan). *Australia Day. P* 14½.
997 **417** 33 c. multicoloured 40 30

418 AUSSAT Satellite, Moon and Earth's Surface

419 H.M.S. *Buffalo*

(Des O. Schmidinger and Christine Stead. Litho Leigh-Mardon Ltd, Melbourne)

1986 (24 Jan). *AUSSAT National Communications Satellite System. T* **418** *and similar vert design. Multicoloured. P* 14½.
998 33 c. Type **418** 50 15
999 80 c. AUSSAT satellite in orbit .. .. 1·50 1·50

(Des I. Kidd. Litho Cambec Press, Melbourne)

1986 (12 Feb). *150th Anniv of South Australia. T* **419** *and similar horiz design. Multicoloured. P* 13½ × 14.
1000 33 c. Type **419** 50 5
a. Pair. Nos. 1000/1 .. .. .. 1·00 1·1
1001 33 c. "City Sign" sculpture (Otto Hajek), Adelaide 50 5
Nos. 1000/1 were printed together, *se-tenant*, in horizontal and vertical pairs throughout the sheet, the background of each horizontal pair showing an extract from the colony's Letter Patent of 1836.

420 *Banksia serrata*

421 Radio Telescope, Parkes, and Diagram of Comet's Orbit

(Des Sue Titcher. Litho Cambec Press, Melbourne)

1986 (12 Mar). *Bicentenary of Australian Settlement* (1988) (*4th issue*). *Cook's Voyage to New Holland. T* **420** *and similar horiz designs. Multicoloured. P* 13.
1002 33 c. Type **420** 60 35
1003 33 c. *Hibiscus meraukensis* 60 35
1004 50 c. *Dillenia alata* 90 80
1005 80 c. *Correa reflexa* .. .. 1·60 1·50
1006 90 c. "Joseph Banks" (botanist) (Reynolds) and Banks with Dr. Solander .. 2·00 1·75
1007 90 c. "Sydney Parkinson" (self-portrait) and Parkinson drawing .. .. 2·00 1·75
1002/7 .. .. *Set of* 6 7·00 6·00

(Des J. Passmore. Litho Cambec Press, Melbourne)

1986 (9 Apr). *Appearance of Halley's Comet. P* 14 × 13½.
1008 **421** 33 c. multicoloured 50 35

422 Queen Elizabeth II

423 Brumbies (wild horses)

(Des Fay Plamka. Litho Leigh-Mardon Ltd, Melbourne)

1986 (21 Apr). *60th Birthday of Queen Elizabeth II. P* 14½.
1009 **422** 33 c. multicoloured 45 35

(Des R. Ingpen. Litho Leigh-Mardon Ltd, Melbourne)

1986 (21 May). *Australian Horses. T* **423** *and similar horiz designs. Multicoloured. P* 14½.
1010 33 c. Type **423** 60 15
1011 80 c. Mustering .. .. 1·50 1·50
1012 90 c. Show-jumping .. .. 1·75 1·75
1013 $1 Child on pony .. .. 2·00 2·00
1010/13 .. .. *Set of* 4 5·25 5·00

424 "The Old Shearer stands"

425 "King George III" (A. Ramsay) and Convicts

(Des R. Ingpen. Litho Leigh-Mardon Ltd, Melbourne)

1986 (21 July). *Folklore. Scenes and Verses from the Folksong "Click go the Shears". T* **424** *and similar vert designs. Multicoloured. P* 14½.
1014 33 c. Type **424** 55 55
a. Horiz strip of 5. Nos. 1014/18 .. 2·50
1015 33 c. "The ringer looks around" 55 55
1016 33 c. "The boss of the board" 55 55
1017 33 c. "The tar-boy is there" 55 55
1018 33 c. "Shearing is all over" 55 55
1014/18 .. .. *Set of* 5 2·50 2·50
Nos. 1014/18 were printed together, *se-tenant*, in horizontal strips of 5 throughout the sheet, forming a composite design.

(Des D. Lancashire. Litho Cambec Press, Melbourne)

1986 (6 Aug). *Bicentenary of Australian Settlement* (1988) (*5th issue*). *Convict Settlement in New South Wales. T* **425** *and similar horiz designs. Multicoloured. P* 13.

1019	33 c. Type **425**	70	40
1020	33 c. "Lord Sydney" (Gilbert Stuart) and convicts	70	40
1021	33 c. "Captain Arthur Phillip" (F. Wheatley) and ship	70	40
1022	$1 "Captain John Hunter" (W. B. Bennett) and aborigines	2·75	2·50
1019/22	*Set of* 4	4·25	3·25

426 Red Kangaroo

427 Royal Bluebell

428 Pink Enamel Orchid

(Des D. Higgins. Litho Leigh-Mardon Ltd, Melbourne)

1986 (13 Aug). *Australian Wildlife* (*1st series*). *T* **426** *and similar vert designs. Multicoloured. P* 14½ × 14.

1023	36 c. Type **426**	55	55
	a. Horiz strip of 5. Nos. 1023/7	2·50	
1024	36 c. Emu	55	55
1025	36 c. Koala	55	55
1026	36 c. Laughing Kookaburra	55	55
1027	36 c. Platypus	55	55
1023/7	*Set of* 5	2·50	2·50

Nos. 1023/7 were printed together, *se-tenant*, in horizontal strips of 5 throughout the sheet.

For 37 c. values see Nos. 1072/6.

(Des Betty Conabere. Litho Mercury-Walch Pty, Hobart)

1986 (25 Aug). *Booklet stamps. Alpine Wildflowers. T* **427** *and similar vert designs. Multicoloured. Roul.*

1028	3 c. Type **427**	20	20
	a. Booklet pane. Nos. 1028, 1029 and 1031 × 2	1·40	
	b. Booklet pane. Nos. 1028, 1030 and 1031 × 2	1·50	
1029	5 c. Alpine Marsh Marigold	40	50
1030	25 c. Mount Buffalo Sunray	50	60
1031	36 c. Silver Snow Daisy	50	30
1028/31	*Set of* 4	1·40	1·40

Nos. 1028/31 only exist from 80 c. (pane No. 1028a) and $1 (pane No. 1028b) stamp booklets. The outer edges of the booklet panes are imperforate.

(Des O. Schmidinger and Christine Stead. Litho Leigh-Mardon Ltd, Melbourne)

1986 (18 Sept). *Native Australian Orchids. T* **428** *and similar vert designs. Multicoloured. P* 14½.

1032	36 c. Type **428**	70	20
1033	55 c. *Dendrobium nindii*	1·25	85
1034	90 c. Duck Orchid	1·90	1·75
1035	$1 Queen of Sheba Orchid	2·00	1·75
1032/5	*Set of* 4	5·25	4·00

429 *Australia II* crossing Finishing Line

430 Dove with Olive Branch and Sun

(Des J. Passmore and G. Rowan. Litho Cambec Press, Melbourne)

1986 (26 Sept). *Australian Victory in America's Cup*, 1983. *T* **429** *and similar vert designs. Multicoloured. P* 14 × 13½.

1036	36 c. Type **429**	65	45
1037	36 c. Boxing kangaroo flag of winning syndicate	65	45
	a. Grey (inscr and face value) omitted	£150	
1038	36 c. America's Cup trophy	65	45
	a. Grey (inscr and face value) omitted	£150	
1036/8	*Set of* 3	1·75	1·25

(Des K. Cato. Litho Cambec Press, Melbourne)

1986 (22 Oct). *International Peace Year. P* 14 × 13½.

1039	**430** 36 c. multicoloured	65	35

Examples with the gutter margin overprinted to commemorate the Papal visit in November 1986 were not produced by the Australian Post Office.

431 Mary and Joseph

432 Australian Flag on Printed Circuit Board

(Des B. Clinton. Litho Leigh-Mardon Ltd, Melbourne)

1986 (3 Nov–Dec). *Christmas. T* **431** *and similar multicoloured designs showing scenes from children's nativity play. P* 14½.

1040	30 c. Type **431**	40	30
	a. Perf 14 × 13½ (12.86)	30	30
1041	36 c. Three Wise Men leaving gifts	50	35
1042	60 c. Angels (*horiz*)	90	1·25
1040/2	*Set of* 3	1·60	1·75
MS1043	147 × 70 mm. 30 c. Three angels and shepherd (*horiz*); 30 c. Kneeling shepherds (*horiz*); 30 c. Mary, Joseph and three angels; 30 c. Innkeeper and two angels; 30 c. Three Wise Men (*horiz*)	1·90	2·25

No. 1040a was printed by Cambec Press after stocks of the original printing by Leigh-Mardon Ltd ran short. It is believed that this Cambec Press printing was only distributed in New South Wales, Tasmania and Victoria.

(Des J. Passmore. Litho CPE Australia Ltd, Melbourne)

1987 (23 Jan). *Australia Day. T* **432** *and similar horiz design. Multicoloured. P* 13½ × 14.

1044	36 c. Type **432**	35	35
1045	36 c. "Australian Made" Campaign logos	35	35

433 Aerial View of Yacht

434 Grapes and Melons

(Des O. Schmidinger and Christine Stead. Litho Leigh-Mardon Ltd, Melbourne)

1987 (28 Jan). *America's Cup Yachting Championship. T* **433** *and similar vert designs. Multicoloured. P* 14½.

1046	36 c. Type **433**	40	20
1047	55 c. Two yachts tacking	80	80
1048	90 c. Two yachts turning	1·25	1·25
1049	$1 Two yachts under full sail	1·40	1·40
1046/9	*Set of* 4	3·50	3·00

(Des Susan Tilley. Litho CPE Australia Ltd, Melbourne)

1987 (11 Feb). *Australian Fruit. T* **434** *and similar vert designs. Multicoloured. P* 14 × 13½.

1050	36 c. Type **434**	40	20
1051	65 c. Tropical and sub-tropical fruits	85	85
1052	90 c. Citrus fruit, apples and pears	1·25	1·25
1053	$1 Stone and berry fruits	1·40	1·40
1050/3	*Set of* 4	3·50	3·25

435 Livestock

436 Queen Elizabeth in Australia, 1986

(Des D. Lancashire. Litho CPE Australia Ltd, Melbourne)

1987 (10 Apr). *Agricultural Shows. T* **435** *and similar vert designs. Multicoloured. P* 14 × 13½.

1054	36 c. Type **435**	50	20
1055	65 c. Produce	1·00	1·00
1056	90 c. Sideshows	1·60	1·60
1057	$1 Competitions	1·75	1·75
1054/7	*Set of* 4	4·25	4·00

(Des Janet Boschen. Litho CPE Australia Ltd, Melbourne)

1987 (21 Apr). *Queen Elizabeth II's Birthday. P* 13½ × 14.

1058	**436** 36 c. multicoloured	45	35

MINIMUM PRICE

The minimum price quote is 10p which represents a handling charge rather than a basis for valuing common stamps. For further notes about prices see introductory pages.

437 Convicts on Quay

438 "At the Station"

(Des Sue Passmore. Litho CPE Australia Ltd, Melbourne)

1987 (13 May). *Bicentenary of Australian Settlement* (1988) (*6th issue*). *Departure of the First Fleet. T* **437** *and similar square designs. Multicoloured. P* 13.

1059	36 c. Type **437**	65	65
	a. Horiz strip of 5. Nos. 1059/63	3·00	
1060	36 c. Royal Marines officer and wife	65	65
1061	36 c. Sailors loading supplies	65	65
1062	36 c. Officers being ferried to ships	65	65
1063	36 c. Fleet in English Channel	65	65
1059/63	*Set of* 5	3·00	3·00

Nos. 1059/63 were printed together, *se-tenant*, in horizontal strips of 5 throughout the sheet.

See also Nos. 1064/6, 1077/81, 1090/2 and 1105/9.

(Des Sue Passmore. Litho CPE Australia Ltd, Melbourne)

1987 (3 June). *Bicentenary of Australian Settlement* (1988) (*7th issue*). *First Fleet at Tenerife. Square designs as T* **437**. *Multicoloured. P* 13.

1064	36 c. Ferrying supplies, Santa Cruz	50	50
	a. Horiz pair. Nos. 1064/5	1·00	1·00
1065	36 c. Canary Islands fishermen and departing fleet	50	50
1066	$1 Fleet arriving at Tenerife (Optd S. 50p)	1·25	1·25
1064/6	*Set of* 3	2·00	2·00

Nos. 1064/5 were printed together, *se-tenant*, in horizontal pairs throughout the sheet, forming a composite design.

(Des C. Lee. Litho CPE Australia Ltd, Melbourne)

1987 (24 June). *Folklore. Scenes and Verses from Poem "The Man from Snowy River". T* **438** *and similar vert designs. Multicoloured. P* 14 × 13½.

1067	36 c. Type **438**	60	60
	a. Horiz strip of 5. Nos. 1067/71	2·75	
1068	36 c. "Mountain bred"	60	60
1069	36 c. "That terrible descent"	60	60
1070	36 c. "At their heels"	60	60
1071	36 c. "Brought them back"	60	60
1067/71	*Set of* 5	2·75	2·75

Nos. 1067/71 were printed together, *se-tenant*, in horizontal strips of five throughout the sheet, forming a composite background design of mountain scenery.

(Des D. Higgins. Litho Leigh-Mardon Ltd, Melbourne)

1987 (1 July). *Australian Wildlife* (*2nd series*). *Vert designs as T* **426**. *Multicoloured. P* 14½ × 14.

1072	37 c. Common Brushtail Possum	35	35
	a. Horiz strip of 5. Nos. 1072/6	1·60	
1073	37 c. Sulphur-crested Cockatoo	35	35
1074	37 c. Common Wombat	35	35
1075	37 c. Crimson Rosella	35	35
1076	37 c. Echidna	35	35
1072/6	*Set of* 6	1·60	1·60

Nos. 1072/6 were printed together, *se-tenant*, in horizontal strips of 5 throughout the sheet.

(Des Sue Passmore. Litho CPE Australia Ltd, Melbourne)

1987 (6 Aug). *Bicentenary of Australian Settlement* (1988) (*8th issue*). *First Fleet at Rio de Janeiro. Square designs as T* **437**. *Multicoloured. P* 13.

1077	37 c. Sperm Whale and fleet	55	55
	a. Horiz strip of 5. Nos. 1077/81	2·50	
1078	37 c. Brazilian coast	55	55
1079	37 c. British officers in market	55	55
1080	37 c. Religious procession	55	55
1081	37 c. Fleet leaving Rio	55	55
1077/81	*Set of* 5	2·50	2·50

Nos. 1077/81 were printed together, *se-tenant*, in horizontal strips of 5, forming a composite design.

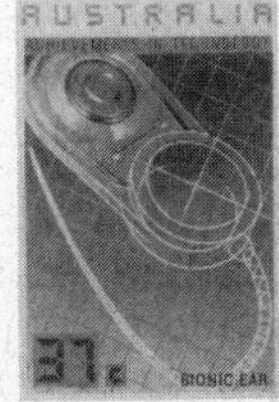
439 Bionic Ear

440 Catching Crayfish

(Des. O. Schmidinger and Christine Stead. Litho Leigh-Mardon Ltd, Melbourne)

1987 (19 Aug). *Australian Achievements in Technology. T* **439** *and similar vert designs. Multicoloured. P* 14½.

1082	37 c. Type **439**	40	35
1083	53 c. Microchips	65	60
1084	63 c. Robotics	75	70
1085	68 c. Ceramics	80	75
1082/5	*Set of* 4	2·40	2·25

(Des Elizabeth Honey. Litho Leigh-Mardon Ltd, Melbourne)

1987 (16 Sept). *"Aussie Kids". T* **440** *and similar horiz designs. Multicoloured. P* 14½.

1086 37 c. Type **440** 35 35
1087 55 c. Playing cat's cradle 65 65
1088 90 c. Young football supporters 95 95
1089 $1 Children with kangaroo (Optd S. 50p) .. .. 1·10 1·10
1086/9 .. .. *Set of* 4 2·75 2·75

(Des Sue Passmore. Litho CPE Australia Ltd, Melbourne)

1987 (13 Oct). *Bicentenary of Australian Settlement* (1988) (*9th issue*). *First Fleet at Cape of Good Hope. Square designs as T* **437**. *Multicoloured. P* 13.

1090 37 c. Marine checking list of livestock .. 50 50
a. Horiz pair. Nos. 1090/1 .. .. 1·00 1·00
1091 37 c. Loading livestock 50 50
1092 $1 First Fleet at Cape Town (Optd S. 50p) .. .. 1·25 1·25
1090/2 .. .. *Set of* 3 2·00 2·00

Nos. 1090/1 were printed together, *se-tenant*, in horizontal and vertical pairs throughout the sheet, the former showing a composite design.

441 Detail of Spearthrower, Western Australia

442 Grandmother and Granddaughters with Candles

(Des J. Passmore. Litho Leigh-Mardon Ltd, Melbourne)

1987 (13 Oct). *Booklet stamps. Aboriginal Crafts. T* **441** *and similar horiz designs. Multicoloured. P* 15½ × *imperf.*

1093 3 c. Type **441** 15 15
a. Booklet pane. Nos. 1093 and 1095, each × 2 85
1094 15 c. Shield pattern, New South Wales .. 25 35
a. Booklet pane. Nos. 1094, 1096 × 3 and 1097 × 2 .. .. 2·10
1095 37 c. Basket weave, Queensland 40 45
1096 37 c. Bowl design, Central Australia .. 40 45
1097 37 c. Belt pattern, Northern Territory .. 40 45
1093/7 .. .. *Set of* 5 1·40 1·75

Nos. 1093/7 only exist from 80 c. (pane No. 1093a) and $2 (pane No. 1094a) stamp booklets. The vertical edges of the booklet panes are imperforate.

(Des B. Clinton. Litho Leigh-Mardon Ltd, Melbourne (30 c.) or CPE Australia Ltd, Melbourne (37 c., 63 c.))

1987 (2 Nov). *Christmas. T* **442** *and similar multicoloured designs showing carol singing by candlelight. P* 14½ (30 *c.*) *or* 13½ × 14 (37 *c.*, 63 *c.*).

1098 30 c. Type **442** 40 40
a. Horiz strip of 5. Nos. 1098/102 .. 1·75
1099 30 c. Father and daughters 40 40
1100 30 c. Four children 40 40
1101 30 c. Family 40 40
1102 30 c. Six teenagers 40 40
1103 37 c. Choir (*horiz*) 45 45
1104 63 c. Father and two children (*horiz*) .. 75 75
1098/104 .. .. *Set of* 7 2·75 2·75

Nos. 1098/1102 were printed together, *se-tenant*, in horizontal strips of five throughout the sheet.

(Des Sue Passmore. Litho CPE Australia Ltd, Melbourne)

1988 (26 Jan). *Bicentenary of Australian Settlement* (*10th issue*). *Arrival of First Fleet. Square designs as T* **437**. *Multicoloured. P* 13.

1105 37 c. Aborigines watching arrival of Fleet, Botany Bay 55 55
a. Horiz strip of 5. Nos. 1105/9 .. .. 2·50
1106 37 c. Aborigine family and anchored ships 55 55
1107 37 c. Fleet arriving at Sydney Cove .. 55 55
1108 37 c. Ship's boat 55 55
1109 37 c. Raising the flag, Sydney Cove, 26 January 1788 .. .. 55 55
1105/9 .. .. *Set of* 5 2·50 2·50

Nos. 1105/9 were printed together, *se-tenant*, in horizontal strips of five throughout the sheet, forming a composite design.

443 Koala with Stockman's Hat and Eagle dressed as Uncle Sam

444 "Religion" (A. Horner)

(Des R. Harvey. Litho CPE Australia Ltd, Melbourne)

1988 (26 Jan). *Bicentenary of Australian Settlement* (*11th issue*). *Joint issue with U.S.A. P* 13.

1110 **443** 37 c. multicoloured 55 35

(Litho Leigh-Mardon Ltd, Melbourne (4, 5, 20, 25, 30, 37, 39, 40, 50, 53, 70, 80, 90 c., $1) or CPE Australia Ltd, Melbourne (others))

1988 (17 Feb–28 Sept). *"Living Together". T* **444** *and similar square designs showing cartoons. Multicoloured* (*except* 30 *c.*). *P* 14.

1111 1 c. Type **444** (16.3) 10 10
1112 2 c. "Industry" (P. Nicholson) (16.3) .. 10 10
1113 3 c. "Local Government" (A. Collette) (16.3) 10 10
1114 4 c. "Trade Unions" (Liz Honey) .. 10 10
1115 5 c. "Parliament" (Bronwyn Halls) (16.3) 10 10
1116 10 c. "Transport" (Meg Williams) .. 10 10
1117 15 c. "Sport" (G. Cook) 10 15
1118 20 c. "Commerce" (M. Atcherson) .. 15 20
1119 25 c. "Housing" (C. Smith) 20 25
1120 30 c. "Welfare" (R. Tandberg) (black and pale rose-lilac) (16.3) 25 30
1121 37 c. "Postal Services" (P. Viska) .. 30 35
a. Booklet pane. No. 1121 × 10 (pane imperf at top and bottom) (1.7.) .. 3·00
1121*b* 39 c. "Tourism" (J. Spooner) (28.9) .. 40 35
ba. Booklet pane. No. 1121*b* × 10 .. 3·00
1122 40 c. "Recreation" (R. Harvey) (16.3) .. 35 40
1123 45 c. "Health" (Jenny Coopes) 35 40
1124 50 c. "Mining" (G. Haddon) 40 45
1125 53 c. "Primary Industry" (S. Leahy) .. 60 50
1126 55 c. "Education" (Victoria Roberts) (16.3) 60 50
1127 60 c. "Armed Forces" (B. Green) (16.3) .. 50 55
1128 63 c. "Police" (J. Russell) (16.3) 70 55
1129 65 c. "Telecommunications" (B. Petty) (16.3) 55 60
1130 68 c. "The Media" (A. Langoulant) (16.3) 75 60
1131 70 c. "Science and Technology" (J. Hook) .. 80 65
1132 75 c. "Visual Arts" (G. Dazeley) (16.3) .. 60 65
1133 80 c. "Performing Arts" (A. Stitt) .. 65 70
1134 90 c. "Banking" (S. Billington) 75 80
1135 95 c. "Law" (C. Aslanis) (16.3) 80 85
1136 $1 "Rescue and Emergency" (M. Leunig) (Optd S. 50p.) 85 90
1111/36 .. .. *Set of* 27 10·00 10·00

Although Leigh-Mardon printed the 37 c. sheet stamps, and some of the booklets, No. 1121a was produced by CPE in $3.70 stamp booklets with the upper and lower edges of the pane imperforate, producing stamps imperforate at top or bottom.

No. 1121ba has the top and bottom edges of the pane imperforate.

445 "Government House, Sydney, 1790" (George Raper)

446 Queen Elizabeth II (from photo by Tim Graham)

(Des J. Passmore. Litho CPE Australia Ltd, Melbourne)

1988 (13 Apr). *Bicentenary of Australian Settlement* (*12th issue*). *"The Early Years, 1788–1809". T* **445** *and similar square designs showing paintings. Multicoloured. P* 13.

1137 37 c. Type **445** 45 45
a. Horiz strip of 5. Nos. 1137/41 .. 2·00
1138 37 c. "Government Farm, Parramatta, 1791" ("The Port Jackson Painter") .. 45 45
1139 37 c. "Parramatta Road, 1796" (attr Thomas Watling) 45 45
1140 37 c. "View of Sydney Cove, *c.* 1800" (detail) (Edward Dayes) 45 45
1141 37 c. "Sydney Hospital, 1803", (detail) (George William Evans) 45 45
1137/41 .. .. *Set of* 5 2·00 2·00

Nos. 1137/41 were printed together, *se-tenant*, in horizontal strips of 5 throughout the sheet, each strip forming a composite background design from the painting, "View of Sydney from the East Side of the Cove, *c.* 1808" by John Eyre.

(Des Sandra Baker. Litho Leigh-Mardon Ltd, Melbourne)

1988 (21 Apr). *Queen Elizabeth II's Birthday. P* 14½.

1142 **446** 37 c. multicoloured 35 40

447 Expo '88 Logo

448 New Parliament House

(Des G. Emery. Litho CPE Australia Ltd, Melbourne)

1988 (29 Apr). *"Expo '88" World Fair, Brisbane. P* 13.

1143 **447** 37 c. multicoloured 35 40

(Des B. Sadgrove. Litho Leigh-Mardon Ltd, Melbourne)

1988 (9 May). *Opening of New Parliament House, Canberra. P* 14½.

1144 **448** 37 c. multicoloured 35 40

449 Early Settler and Sailing Clipper

450 Kiwi and Koala at Campfire

(Des G. Emery. Litho CPE Australia Ltd, Melbourne)

1988 (21 June). *Bicentenary of Australian Settlement* (*13th issue*). *T* **449** *and similar square designs. Multicoloured. P* 13.

1145 37 c. Type **449** 45 45
a. Pair. Nos. 1145/6 .. .. .. 90 90
1146 37 c. Queen Elizabeth II with British and Australian Parliament Buildings .. 45 45
1147 $1 W. G. Grace (cricketer) and tennis racquet .. .. 1·25 1·25
a. Pair. Nos. 1147/8 .. .. .. 2·50 2·50
1148 $1 Shakespeare, John Lennon (entertainer) and Sydney Opera House .. 1·25 1·25
1145/8 .. .. *Set of* 4 3·00 3·00

Nos. 1145/6 and 1147/8 were printed together, *se-tenant*, in horizontal and vertical pairs throughout the sheets, each horizontal pair showing a background design of the Australian flag.

Stamps in similar designs were also issued by Great Britain.

(Des R. Harvey. Litho Leigh-Mardon Ltd, Melbourne)

1988 (21 June). *Bicentenary of Australian Settlement* (*14th issue*). *P* 14½.

1149 **450** 37 c. multicoloured 45 40

A stamp in a similar design was also issued by New Zealand.

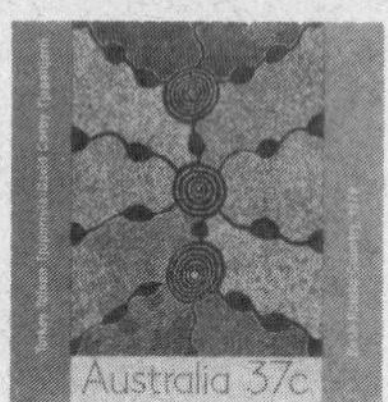

451 "Bush Potato Country" (Turkey Tolsen Tjupurrula and David Corby Tjapaltjarri)

452 Basketball

(Des Janet Boschen. Litho CPE Australia Ltd, Melbourne)

1988 (1 Aug). *Art of the Desert. Aboriginal Paintings from Central Australia. T* **451** *and similar square designs. Multicoloured. P* 13.

1150 37 c. Type **451** 35 40
1151 55 c. "Courtship Rejected" (Limpi Puntungka Tjapangati) 55 60
1152 90 c. "Medicine Story" (artist unknown) .. 90 1·10
1153 $1 "Ancestor Dreaming" (Tim Leura Tjapaltjarri) .. .. 95 1·25
1150/3 .. .. *Set of* 4 2·50 3·00

(Des Sue Passmore. Litho Leigh-Mardon Ltd, Melbourne)

1988 (14 Sept). *Olympic Games, Seoul. T* **452** *and similar horiz designs. Multicoloured. P* 14½.

1154 37 c. Type **452** 35 40
1155 65 c. Athlete crossing finish line 60 65
1156 $1 Gymnast with hoop .. .. .. 95 1·00
1154/6 .. .. *Set of* 3 1·75 1·90

453 Rod and Mace

(Des K. Christos. Litho Leigh-Mardon Ltd, Melbourne)

1988 (19 Sept). *34th Commonwealth Parliamentary Conference, Canberra. P* 14½.

1157 **453** 37 c. multicoloured 35 40

454 Necklace by Peter Tully

(Des K. Christos. Litho Mercury-Walch Pty, Hobart)

988 (28 Sept). *Booklet stamps. Australian Crafts. T* **454** *and similar horiz designs. Multicoloured. Roul × imperf.*
158 2 c. Type **454** 15 20
a. Booklet pane. Nos. 1158 and 1160 × 2 85
159 5 c. Vase by Colin Levy 15 20
a. Booklet pane. Nos. 1159 and 1160 × 5 2·00
160 39 c. Teapot by Frank Bauer 40 35
158/60 .. .. *Set of* 3 65 65

Nos. 1158/60 only exist from 80 c. (pane No. 1158a) and $2 pane No. 1159a) stamp booklets. The vertical edges of the booklet panes are imperforate.

455 Pinnacles Desert

456 "The Nativity" (Danielle Hush)

(Des K. Christos. Litho CPE Australia Ltd, Melbourne)

988 (17 Oct). *Panorama of Australia. T* **455** *and similar horiz designs. Multicoloured. P* 13.
161 39 c. Type **455** 35 40
162 55 c. Flooded landscape, Arnhem Land .. 50 55
163 65 c. Twelve Apostles, Victoria 60 65
164 70 c. Mountain Ash wood 65 70
161/4 .. .. *Set of* 4 1·90 2·10

Des Sandra Baker. Litho CPE Australia Ltd, Melbourne (32, 39 c.) or Leigh-Mardon Ltd, Melbourne (63 c.))

1988 (31 Oct). *Christmas. T* **456** *and similar square designs. Multicoloured. P* 14½ *(63 c.) or* 13 *(others).*
1165 32 c. Type **456** 30 35
1166 39 c. "Koala as Father Christmas" (Kylie Courtney) 35 40
1167 63 c. "Christmas Cockatoo" (Benjamin Stevenson) 60 65
1165/7 .. .. *Set of* 3 1·10 1·25

457 Sir Henry Parkes

458 Bowls

(Des R. Bevers. Litho CPE Australia Ltd, Melbourne)

1989 (25 Jan). *Australia Day. Centenary of Federation Speech by Sir Henry Parkes (N.S.W. Prime Minister). P* 14 × 13½.
1168 **457** 39 c. multicoloured 35 40

(Des Sue Passmore (41 c.), G. Cook (others). Litho Leigh-Mardon Ltd, Melbourne)

1989 (13 Feb–23 Aug). *Sports. T* **458** *and similar horiz designs. Multicoloured. P* 14 × 14½.
1169 1 c. Type **458** 10 10
1170 2 c. Tenpin-bowling 10 10
1171 3 c. Australian football 10 10
1179 39 c. Fishing 30 35
a. Booklet pane. No. 1179 × 10 .. 3·00
1180 41 c. Cycling (23.8) 35 40
1184 55 c. Kite-flying 45 50
1189 70 c. Cricket 60 65
1194 $1.10, Golf (Optd S. 70p.) 90 95
1169/94 .. .. .. *Set of* 8 2·50 2·75

The upper and lower edges of booklet pane No. 1179a are imperforate, producing stamps imperforate at top or bottom, and there are margins at left and right.

459 Merino

(Des K. McEwan. Litho CPE Australia Ltd, Melbourne)

1989 (27 Feb). *Sheep in Australia. T* **459** *and similar horiz designs. Multicoloured. P* 13½ × 14.
1195 39 c. Type **459** 35 40
1196 39 c. Poll Dorset 35 40
1197 85 c. Polwarth 80 85
1198 $1 Corriedale (Optd S. 70p.) .. .. 95 1·00
1195/8 .. .. *Set of* 4 1·25 1·40

COVER PRICES

Cover factors are quoted at the beginning of each country for most issues to 1945. An explanation of the system can be found on page x. The factors quoted do not, however, apply to philatelic covers.

460 Adelaide Botanic Garden

(Des J. Passmore. Eng B. Stewart. Litho CPE Australia Ltd, Melbourne, and recess Note Ptg Branch, Reserve Bank of Australia)

1989 (12 Apr–13 Sept). *Botanic Gardens. T* **460** *and similar horiz designs. Multicoloured. P* 14.
1199 $2 Nooroo, New South Wales (13.9) .. 1·60 1·75
1200 $5 Mawarra, Victoria (13.9) .. .. 4·25 4·50
1201 $10 Type **460** .. .. 8·50 9·00
1199/1201 .. .. .. *Set of* 3 13·00 13·50

461 "Queen Elizabeth II" (sculpture, John Dowie)

462 Arrival of Immigrant Ship, 1830's

(Des Sandra Baker. Litho Leigh-Mardon Ltd, Melbourne)

1989 (21 Apr). *Queen Elizabeth II's Birthday. P* 14½.
1202 **461** 39 c. multicoloured 35 40

(Des D. Lancashire. Litho Leigh-Mardon Ltd, Melbourne)

1989 (10 May). *Colonial Development (1st issue). Pastoral Era 1810–1850. T* **462** *and similar square designs. Multicoloured. P* 14½.
1203 39 c. Type **462** 35 40
a. Horiz strip of 5. Nos. 1203/7 .. .. 1·60
1204 39 c. Pioneer cottage and wool dray .. 35 40
1205 39 c. Squatter's homestead 35 40
1206 39 c. Shepherd with flock (from Joseph Lycett's "Views of Australia") .. 35 40
1207 39 c. Explorer in desert (after watercolour by Edward Frome) 35 40
1203/7 .. .. *Set of* 5 1·60 1·75

Nos. 1203/7 were printed together, *se-tenant*, in horizontal strips of five throughout the sheet.

463 Gladys Moncrieff and Roy Rene

464 "Impression" (Tom Roberts)

(Des Sue Passmore. Litho Leigh-Mardon Ltd, Melbourne)

1989 (12 July). *Australian Stage and Screen Personalities. T* **463** *and similar vert designs. Multicoloured. P* 14½.
1208 39 c. Type **463** 35 40
a. Perf 14 × 13½ .. .. .. 3·50 3·25
1209 85 c. Charles Chauvel and Chips Rafferty 80 85
1210 $1 Nellie Stewart and J. C. Williamson .. 95 1·00
1211 $1.10, Lottie Lyell and Raymond Longford .. .. 1·00 1·10
1208/11 .. .. .. *Set of* 4 2·75 3·00
1208/11 Optd "Specimen" .. .. *Set of* 2 1·40

No. 1208a was from a small first printing produced at the CPE Australia Ltd plant and used in presentation packs or on first day covers.

(Des K. Christos. Litho Leigh-Mardon Ltd, Melbourne)

1989 (23 Aug). *Australian Impressionist Paintings. T* **464** *and similar multicoloured designs. P* 14 × 13½ *(No. 1214) or* 13½ × 14 *(others).*
1212 41 c. Type **464** 40 45
1213 41 c. "Impression for Golden Summer" (Sir Arthur Streeton) 40 45
1214 41 c. "All on a Summer's Day" (Charles Conder) (*vert*) 40 45
1215 41 c. "Petit Déjeuner" (Frederick McCubbin) 40 45
1212/15 .. .. *Set of* 4 1·40 1·60

465 Freeways

(Des Sally Newell and Carolyn Limonta. Litho Leigh-Mardon Ltd, Melbourne)

1989 (1 Sept). *Booklet stamps. The Urban Environment. T* **465** *and similar horiz designs. P* 15½×*imperf.*
1216 41 c. black, maroon and blue-green .. 40 45
a. Booklet pane. Nos. 1216×2, 1217×3 and 1218×2 .. .. 2·75
1217 41 c. black, maroon and magenta .. 40 45
1218 41 c. black, maroon and bright blue .. 40 45
1216/18 .. .. *Set of* 3 1·10 1·25

Designs:—No. 1217, City buildings, Melbourne; No. 1218, Commuter train at platform.

Nos. 1216/18 only exist from $3 stamp booklets in which the vertical edges of the pane are imperforate.

466 Hikers outside Youth Hostel

467 Horse Tram, Adelaide, 1878

(Des Priscilla Cutter. Litho Leigh-Mardon Ltd, Melbourne)

1989 (13 Sept). *50th Anniv of Australian Youth Hostels. P* 14½.
1219 **466** 41 c. multicoloured 40 45

(Des I. McKellar. Litho Leigh-Mardon Ltd, Melbourne)

1989 (11 Oct). *Historic Trams. T* **467** *and similar horiz designs. Multicoloured. P* 13½×14.
1220 41 c. Type **467** 40 45
1221 41 c. Steam tram, Sydney, 1884 .. .. 40 45
1222 41 c. Cable tram, Melbourne, 1886 .. 40 45
a. Perf 14½ 40 45
ab. Booklet pane. No. 1222a×10 .. 7·50
1223 41 c. Double-deck electric tram, Hobart, 1893 .. .. 40 45
1224 41 c. Combination electric tram, Brisbane, 1901 .. .. 40 45
1220/4 .. .. *Set of* 5 1·75 2·00

The upper and lower edges of booklet pane No. 1222ab are imperforate.

468 "Annunciation" (15th-century Book of Hours)

(Des Lynette Brown. Litho Leigh-Mardon Ltd, Melbourne)

1989 (1 Nov). *Christmas. Illuminated Manuscripts. T* **468** *and similar vert designs. Multicoloured. P* 14×13½ *(36 c.) or* 14½ *(others).*
1225 36 c. Type **468** 35 40
a. Booklet pane. No. 1225×10 .. 3·50
1226 41 c. "Annunciation to the Shepherds" (Wharncliffe Book of Hours, c. 1475) 40 45
1227 80 c. "Adoration of the Magi" (15th-century Parisian Book of Hours) 75 80
1225/7 .. .. *Set of* 3 1·40 1·50

The vertical sides of booklet pane No. 1225a are imperforate.

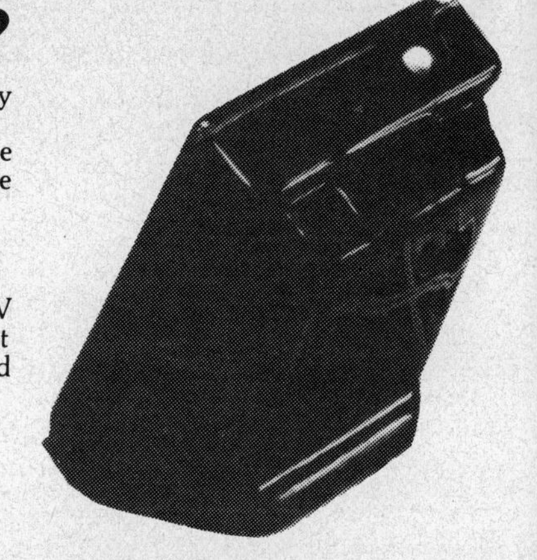

LONDON

MELBOURNE

NEW YORK

Index to Australian Stamp Designs from 1942

The following index is intended to facilitate the identification of all Australian stamps from 1942 onwards. Portrait stamps are usually listed under surnames only, views under the name of the town or city and other issues under the main subject or a prominent word and date chosen from the inscription. Simple abbreviations have occasionally been resorted to and when the same design or subject appears on more than one stamp, only the first of each series is indicated.

POSTAGE DUE STAMPS

POSTAGE DUE PRINTERS. Nos. D1/62 were typographed at the New South Wales Government Printing Office, Sydney.

D 1

D 2

D 3

Type D 1 adapted from plates of New South Wales Type D 1. No letters at foot.

1902 (From July). *Chalk-surfaced paper. Wmk Type* D **2**.

(*a*) *P* 11½, 12

D 1 D 1 ½d. emerald-green 2·75 3·00
D 2 1d. emerald-green 7·00 3·00
D 3 2d. emerald-green 20·00 3·50
D 4 3d. emerald-green 35·00 16·00
D 5 4d. emerald-green 35·00 10·00
D 6 6d. emerald-green 50·00 9·00
D 7 8d. emerald-green 95·00 55·00
D 8 5s. emerald-green £175 70·00
D1/8 *Set of* 8 £375 £150
D1/7 Optd "Specimen" *Set of* 7 £200

(*b*) *P* 11½, 12, *compound with* 11

D 9 D 1 1d. emerald-green 55·00 11·00
D10 2d. emerald-green 50·00 8·50

(*c*) *P* 11

D12 D 1 1d. emerald-green £150 75·00

The ½d., 6d. and 8d. exist in dull green.

Stamps may be found showing portions of the letters "N S W" at foot.

1902–4. *Type* D 3, *space at foot filled in. Chalky paper. Wmk Type* D **2**.

(*a*) *P* 11½, 12

D13 1d. emerald-green 45·00 25·00
D14 2d. emerald-green 45·00 20·00
D15 3d. emerald-green 60·00 20·00
D17 5d. emerald-green 27·00 9·00
D18 10d. emerald-green 50·00 12·00
D19 1s. emerald-green 50·00 9·00
D20 2s. emerald-green 85·00 16·00
D21 5s. emerald-green £300 75·00

(*b*) *P* 11½, 12, *compound with* 11

D22 ½d. emerald-green 3·25 3·00
D23 1d. emerald-green 3·75 1·25
D24 2d. emerald-green 17·00 2·50
D25 3d. emerald-green 26·00 4·00
D26 4d. emerald-green 26·00 3·50
D27 5d. emerald-green 48·00 9·00
D28 6d. emerald-green 42·00 8·50
D29 8d. emerald-green 75·00 22·00
D30 10d. emerald-green 80·00 16·00
D31 1s. emerald-green 80·00 9·00
D32 2s. emerald-green £110 22·00
D33 5s. emerald-green £130 14·00

(*c*) *P* 11

D34 ½d. emerald-green 45·00 32·00
D35 1d. emerald-green 26·00 3·50
D36 2d. emerald-green 45·00 4·00
D37 3d. emerald-green 38·00 8·50
D38 4d. emerald-green 45·00 9·00
D39 5d. emerald-green 65·00 9·00
D40 6d. emerald-green 45·00 12·00
D41 1s. emerald-green 80·00 22·00
D42 5s. emerald-green £225 42·00
D43 10s. emerald-green £1400 £750
D44 20s. emerald-green £2750 £1400
D13/44 *Set of* 14 £4250 £2000
D13/44 Optd "Specimen" *Set of* 14 £550

Most values exist in dull green.

D 4

D 6

1906 (From Jan)–**08.** *Chalky paper. Wmk Type* D **4**.

(*a*) *P* 11½, 12, *compound with* 11

D45 D 3 ½d. green (1907) 5·00 3·50
D46 1d. green 6·50 2·25
D47 2d. green 16·00 3·25
D48 3d. green £180 90·00
D49 4d. green (1907) 45·00 20·00
D50 6d. green (1908) 60·00 30·00
D45/50 *Set of* 6 £275 £130

(*b*) *P* 11

D51 D 3 1d. dull green £100 30·00
D52 4d. dull green £150 70·00

Shades exist.

1907 (From July). *Chalky paper. Wmk Type* w **11** (*see Introduction*). *P* 11½ × 11.

D53 D 3 ½d. dull green 18·00 35·00
D54 1d. dull green 35·00 15·00
D55 2d. dull green 75·00 60·00
D56 4d. dull green £140 75·00
D57 6d. dull green £160 75·00
D53/7 *Set of* 5 £375 £225

1908 (Sept)–**09.** *Stroke after figure of value. Chalky paper. Wmk Type* D **4**.

(*a*) *P* 11½ × 11

D58 D 6 1s. dull green (1909) 70·00 8·00
D59 5s. dull green £200 48·00

(*b*) *P* 11

D60 D 6 2s. dull green £650 £500
D61 10s. dull green £1600 £900
D62 20s. dull green £4000 £2500
D58/62 *Set of* 5 £6000 £3500

Nos. D1/62 were not for use in Victoria.

D 7

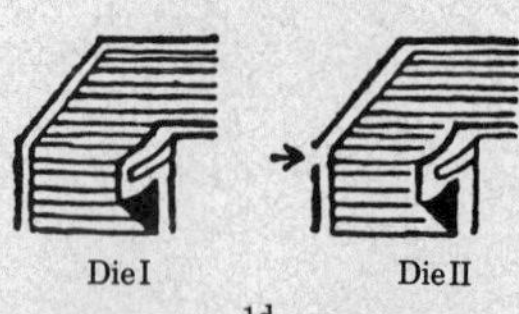
Die I Die II

1d.

Die I Die II

2d.

(Typo J. B. Cooke, Melbourne)

1909 (July)–**1911.** *Type* D **7**. *Wmk Crown over A, Type* w **11**.

(*a*) *P* 12 × 12½ (*comb*) *or* 12½ (*line*)

D63 ½d. rosine and yellow-green 9·00 12·00
D64 1d. rosine and yellow-green (I) 13·00 3·25
a. Die II (1911) 6·50 60
D65 2d. rosine and yellow-green (I) 24·00 3·50
a. Die II (7.10) 6·50 65
D66 3d. rosine and yellow-green 18·00 8·50
D67 4d. rosine and yellow-green 18·00 4·50
D68 6d. rosine and yellow-green 25·00 7·00
D69 1s. rosine and yellow-green 30·00 4·00
D70 2s. rosine and yellow-green 70·00 16·00
D71 5s. rosine and yellow-green 75·00 20·00
D72 10s. rosine and yellow-green £200 £120
D73 £1 rosine and yellow-green £350 £180

(*b*) *P* 11

D74 1d. rose and yellow-green (II) (1911) £300 £150
D74*a* 2d. rose and yellow-green (II) (7.10)
D75 6d. rose and yellow-green £1500 £650
D63/75 *Set of* 11 £750 £350

Only one example, unused without gum, is known of No. D74*a*.

The 1d. of this printing is distinguishable from No. D78 by the colours, the green being very yellow and the rose having less of a carmine tone. The paper is thicker and slightly toned, that of No. D78 being pure white; the gum is thick and yellowish, No. D78 having thin white gum.

All later issues of the 1d. and 2d. are Die II.

(Typo J. B. Cooke and T. S. Harrison (from May 1918))

1912–23. *Type* D **7**. *Thin paper. White gum.* W w **11**. (*a*) *P* 12½.

D76 ½d. scarlet and pale yellow-green (12.12) 17·00 18·00

(*b*) *P* 11

D77 ½d. rosine and bright apple-green (11.14) 3·50 4·50
a. Wmk sideways 3·25 4·50
D78 1d. rosine and bright apple-green (1913) 2·00 55
a. Wmk sideways 5·00 90

(*c*) *P* 14

D79 ½d. rosine and bright apple-green (1916) 60·00 35·00
a. Carmine and apple-green (Harrison) (1918) 9·00 14·00
D80 1d. rosine and bright apple-green (10.14) 55·00 10·00
a. Scarlet and pale yellow-green (1916) 16·00 3·50
b. Carmine and apple-green (Harrison) (1918) 6·50 2·25
D81 2d. scarlet and pale yellow-green (1915) 17·00 6·00
a. Carmine and apple-green (Harrison) (1918) 10·00 3·00
D82 3d. rosine and apple-green (5.16) 55·00 22·00
a. Wmk sideways £300 £225
D83 4d. rosine and apple-green (1916) 80·00 45·00
a. Wmk sideways £275 £180
b. Carmine and apple-green (Harrison) (1918) 55·00 35·00
c. Carmine and pale yellow-green (Harrison) (26.4.21) 45·00 35·00
D85 1s. scarlet and pale yellow-green (7.23) 25·00 10·00
D86 10s. scarlet and pale yellow-green (5.21) £400 £400
D87 £1 scarlet and pale yellow-green (5.21) £550 £500
D76/87 *Set of* 8 £1000 £900

Although printed by Cooke, the three higher values were not issued until some years later.

(Typo T. S. Harrison (to Feb. 1926), A. J. Mullet (to June 1927) and J. Ash (later))

1919–30. *Type* D **7**. W **6**. (*a*) *P* 14.

D91 ½d. carmine and yellow-green (7.23) 3·75 4·50
D92 1d. carmine and yellow-green (28.3.22) 3·00 65
D93 1½d. carmine and yellow-green (3.25) 1·75 9·00
D94 2d. carmine and yellow-green (20.3.22) 3·50 1·75
D95 3d. carmine and yellow-green (12.11.19) 9·50 3·50
D96 4d. carmine and yellow-green (13.2.22) 30·00 10·00
D97 6d. carmine and yellow-green (13.2.22) 30·00 11·00

(*b*) *P* 11

D98 4d. carmine and yellow-green (10.30) 4·00 3·75
D91/8 *Set of* 8 75·00 40·00

All values perf 14 were printed by Harrison and all except the 4d. by Mullett and Ash. There is a wide variation of shades in this issue.

(Typo J. Ash)

1931–37. *Type* D **7**. W **15**. (*a*) *P* 14.

D100 1d. carmine and yellow-green (10.31) 8·50 10·00
D102 2d. carmine and yellow-green (19.10.31) 8·50 10·00

(*b*) *P* 11

D105 ½d. carmine and yellow-green (4.34) 7·00 14·00
D106 1d. carmine and yellow-green (1.33) 4·00 60
D107 2d. carmine and yellow-green (29.9.32) 4·00 60
D108 3d. carmine and yellow-green (4.37) 70·00 60·00
D109 4d. carmine and yellow-green (26.7.34) 3·75 2·00
D110 6d. carmine and yellow-green (4.36) £300 £200
D111 1s. carmine and yellow-green (8.34) 45·00 32·00
D105/11 *Set of* 7 £375 £275

D 8 D 9

A B C

The differences are found in the middle of the "D"

D E

Type E. Larger "1" with only three background lines above; hyphen more upright.

(Frame recess. Value typo J. Ash)

1938. W **15**. *P* 14½ × 14.

D112 D 8 ½d. carmine and green (A) 2·00 2·00
D113 1d. carmine and green (A) 3·50 30
D114 2d. carmine and green (A) 4·75 1·00
D115 3d. carmine and green (B) 11·00 12·00
D116 4d. carmine and green (A) 6·00 30
D117 6d. carmine and green (A) 32·00 26·00
D118 1s. carmine and green (D) 45·00 12·00
D112/18 *Set of* 7 95·00 48·00

Shades exist.

1946–57. *Redrawn as Type* C *and* E (1*s.*). W **15**. *P* 14½ × 14.

D119 D 9 ½d. carmine and green (9.56) 60 3·00
D120 1d. carmine and green (11.1.47) 60 60
D121 2d. carmine and green (9.46) 3·25 80
D122 3d. carmine and green (25.9.46) 4·25 75
D123 4d. carmine and green (11.52) 4·50 1·50
D124 5d. carmine and green (12.48) 5·00 2·50
D125 6d. carmine and green (9.47) 8·00 1·25
D126 7d. carmine and green (26.8.53) 3·75 7·50
D127 8d. carmine and green (24.4.57) 10·00 22·00
D128 1s. carmine and green (9.47) 13·00 1·25
D119/28 *Set of* 10 48·00 38·00

There are many shades in this issue.

D 10

1953 (26 Aug)–**60.** W **15**. *P* 14½ × 14.

D129 D 10 1s. carmine & yellow-grn (17.2.54) 4·75 3·00
a. Carmine and deep green 9·00 6·50
D130 2s. carmine and yellow-green 18·00 9·00
a. Carmine and deep green 65·00 16·00
D131 5s. carmine and green 18·00 6·00
a. Carmine and deep green (1960) 12·00 70
D129/31 *Set of* 3 35·00 16·00
D129*a*/31*a* *Set of* 3 75·00 21·00

A new die was introduced for No. D131*a*. This differs from the original in having a distinct gap between the two arms of the "5". On No. D131 these two features are joined.

I

II

Type I. Numeral, "D" and stop, generally unoutlined.

Type II. Clear white line separates numeral, etc. from background.

1958–60. *No wmk. P* 14½ × 14.

D132 **D 9** ½d. carmine and deep green (II) (27.2.58) . . 1·00 1·75
D133 1d. carmine and deep green (I) (25.2.58) . . 3·00 3·25
a. Type II (1959) . . 1·00 65
D134 3d. carmine and deep green (II) (25.5.60) . . 1·75 2·50
D135 4d. carmine and deep green (I) (27.2.58) . . 3·75 7·50
a. Type II (12.59) . . 3·00 8·50
D136 5d. carmine and deep green (I) (27.2.58) . . 8·50 13·00
a. Type II (10.59) . . 60·00 75·00
D137 6d. carmine and deep green (II) (25.5.60) . . 2·75 2·75
D138 8d. carmine and deep green (II) (25.2.58) . . 10·00 32·00
D139 10d. carmine and deep green (II) (9.12.59) . . 5·50 3·25
D140 **D 10** 1s. carmine and deep green (8.9.58) 3·00 3·50
a. Deep carmine & deep green (1960) 4·00 4·00
D141 2s. deep carmine and deep green (8.3.60) . . 20·00 22·00
D132/41 *Set of* 10 50·00 80·00

Nos. D140*a* and D141. Value tablets are re-engraved and have thicker and sharper printed lines than before.

The use of Postage Due stamps ceased on 13 January 1963.

OFFICIAL STAMPS

From 1902 the departments of the Commonwealth government were issued with stamps of the various Australian States perforated "OS" to denote official use. These were replaced in 1913 by Commonwealth of Australia issues with similar perforated initials as listed below.

During the same period the administrations of the Australian States used their own stamps and those of the Commonwealth perforated with other initials for the same purpose. These States issues are outside the scope of this catalogue.

Most shades listed under the postage issues also exist perforated "OS". Only those which are worth more than the basic colours are included below.

(O 1) (O 2) (O 3)

1913 (Jan–Apr). *Nos. 1/16 punctured as Type* O **1**. *W* **2**. *P* 12.

O1 **1** ½d. green (Die I) . . 6·00 2·50
O2 1d. red (Die I) . . 8·00 1·00
a. Wmk sideways . . £200 35·00
c. Die II . . 8·00 1·00
ca. Wmk sideways . . £200 35·00
d. Die IIA . . 8·00 1·00
da. Wmk sideways . . £200 35·00
O3 2d. grey (Die I) . . 22·00 4·00
O4 2½d indigo (Die II) . . £100 40·00
O5 3d. olive (Die I) . . 32·00 5·00
d. Die II . . £125 20·00
O6 4d. orange (Die II) . . 45·00 13·00
a. Orange-yellow . . 75·00 20·00
O7 5d. chestnut (Die II) . . 45·00 18·00
O8 6d. ultramarine (Die II) . . 45·00 10·00
O9 9d. violet (Die II) . . 45·00 9·00
O10 1s. emerald (Die II) . . 45·00 8·00
O11 2s. brown (Die II) . . £125 40·00
a. Double print . . † —
O12 5s. grey and yellow . . £250 £100
O13 10s. grey and pink . . £500 £275
O14 £1 brown and blue . . £1000 £800
O15 £2 black and rose . . £2000 £1400
O1/15 *Set of* 15 £3750 £2400

1913 (June onwards). *Nos. 1/16 punctured as Type* O **2**. *W* **2**. *P* 12.

O16 **1** ½d. green (Die I) . . 7·00 1·50
O17 1d. red (Die I) . . 8·00 1·25
a. Wmk sideways . . £200 35·00
c. Die II . . 8·00 1·25
ca. Wmk sideways . . £200 35·00
d. Die IIA . . 8·00 1·25
da. Wmk sideways . . £200 35·00
O18 2d. grey (Die I) . . 22·00 4·00
O19 2½d. indigo (Die II) . . 60·00 30·00
O20 3d. olive (Die I) . . 30·00 4·00
d. Die II . . £100 15·00
O21 4d. orange (Die II) . . 60·00 40·00
a. Orange-yellow . . £100 60·00
O22 5d. chestnut (Die II) . . 45·00 18·00
O23 6d. ultramarine (Die II) . . 40·00 10·00
O24 9d. violet (Die II) . . 45·00 9·00
O25 1s. emerald (Die II) . . 45·00 8·00
O26 2s. brown (Die II) . . £130 25·00
O27 5s. grey and yellow . . £250 £100
O28 10s. grey and pink . . £500 £275
O29 £1 brown and blue . . £1000 £800
O30 £2 black and rose . . £2000 £1400
O16/30 *Set of* 15 £3750 £2400

1915. *Nos. 20 and 23/7 punctured as Type* O **2**. *W* **5**. *P* 12.

O31 **1** 2d. grey (Die I) . . 45·00 8·50
O33 6d. ultramarine (Die II) . . 85·00 12·00
b. Die IIA . . £700 £110
O34 9d. violet (Die II) . . £100 20·00
O35 1s. blue-green (Die II) . . £100 20·00
O36 2s. brown (Die II) . . £350 40·00
O37 5s. grey and yellow . . £350 75·00

1914–21. *Nos. 29/34 punctured as Type* O **2**. *W* **5**. *P* 14.

O38 **5a** ½d. bright green . . 4·00 1·00
O39 1d. carmine-red (I) . . 4·50 15
O40 1d. carmine-red (II) . . £250 4·00
O41 4d. orange . . 27·00 2·75
a. Yellow-orange . . 27·00 5·00
b. Pale orange-yellow . . 40·00 12·00
c. Lemon-yellow . . £100 20·00
O42 5d. brown . . 27·00 2·00

1915–28. *Nos. 35/45 punctured as Type* O **2**. *W* **6**. *P* 12.

O43 **1** 2d. grey (Die I) . . 15·00 2·00
c. Die II . . 15·00 2·00
O44 2½d. deep blue (Die II) . . 15·00 4·00
O45 3d. yellow-olive (Die I) . . 18·00 2·00
c. Die II . . 50·00 12·00
d. Die IIB . . 22·00 3·00
O46 6d. ultramarine (Die II) . . 30·00 3·00
a. Die IIA . . £400 £100
c. Die IB . . 30·00 3·00
O47 9d. violet (Die II) . . 20·00 2·75
a. Die IIB . . 20·00 2·75
O48 1s. blue-green (Die II) . . 23·00 1·75
a. Die IIB . . 23·00 1·75
O49 2s. brown (Die II) . . 90·00 9·50
a. Red-brown (aniline) . . £225 35·00
O50 5s. grey and yellow . . £125 30·00
O51 10s. grey and pink . . £200 60·00
O52 £1 chocolate and dull blue . . £1100 £550
ba. Wmk sideways . . — £1200
O53 £2 black and rose . . £1800 £750
O43/53 *Set of* 11 £3000 £1250

1916–18. *Nos. 47/50a and 5d. as No. 34 punctured as Type* O **2**. *W* **5**. *Rough paper. P* 14.

O54 **5a** 1d. scarlet . . 12·00 35
O55 1d. deep red (I) . . 12·00 35
O56 1d. rose-red (I) . . 14·00 35
O57 1d. rosine (I) . . 55·00 4·00
O58 1d. rose-red (II) . . £200 10·00
O59 1d. rosine (II) . . £400 25·00
O60 5d. bright chestnut (1918) . . £1100 95·00

All examples of the 5d. on this paper were perforated "OS".

1918–20. *Nos. 51 and 53/5 punctured as Type* O **2**. *W* **6a**. *P* 14.

O61 **5a** ½d. green . . 7·00 60
O63 1d. carmine (I) . . 11·00 1·75
O64 1½d. black-brown . . 8·00 70
a. Very thin paper . . 12·00 4·00
O65 1½d. red-brown . . 8·50 60
O61/5 *Set of* 4 30·00 3·00

1918–23. *Nos. 56/9 and 61/6 punctured as Type* O **2**. *W* **5**. *P* 14.

O66 **5a** ½d. orange . . 13·00 2·50
O67 1d. violet . . 17·00 70
O68 1½d. black-brown . . 13·00 1·00
O69 1½d. deep red-brown . . 10·00 60
O70 1½d. green . . 7·00 50
O71 2d. dull orange . . 12·00 40
O72 2d. bright rose-scarlet . . 7·50 40
O73 4d. violet . . 22·00 8·50
O74 4d. ultramarine . . 38·00 6·50
O75 1s. 4d. pale blue . . 50·00 15·00
b. Deep turquoise . . — £100
O66/75 *Set of* 10 £170 32·00

1923–24. *Nos. 73/5 punctured as Type* O **2**. *W* **6**. *P* 12.

O76 **1** 6d. chestnut (Die IIB) . . 15·00 1·50
O77 2s. maroon (Die II) . . 40·00 8·00
O78 £1 grey (Die IIB) . . £400 £150
O76/8 *Set of* 3 £425 £150

1924. *Nos. 76/84 punctured as Type* O **2**. *P* 14. *(a)* W **5**.

O79 **5a** 1d. sage-green . . 4·00 25
O80 1½d. scarlet . . 1·00 20
O81 2d. red-brown . . 20·00 3·25
a. Bright red-brown . . 25·00 6·00
O82 3d. dull ultramarine . . 25·00 70
O83 4d. olive-yellow . . 25·00 75
O84 4½d. violet . . 30·00 2·50

(b) W **6a**

O85 **5a** 1d. sage-green . . 9·00 3·25

(c) No wmk

O86 **5a** 1d. sage-green . . 25·00 11·00
O87 1½d. scarlet . . 45·00 15·00
O79/87 *Set of* 9 £160 32·00

1926–30. *Nos. 85/104 punctured as Type* O **2**. *W* **7**. *(a) P* 14.

O88 **5a** ½d. orange . . 65·00 25·00
O89 1d. sage-green . . 3·75 50
O90 1½d. scarlet . . 4·75 30
O91 1½d. golden scarlet . . 7·00 90
O92 2d. red-brown (Die I) . . 45·00 20·00
O93 3d. dull ultramarine . . 20·00 1·50
O94 4d. yellow-olive . . 40·00 7·00
O95 4½d. violet . . 30·00 6·00
O96 1s. 4d. pale greenish blue . . £120 40·00
O88/96 *Set of* 8 £300 90·00

(b) P 13½ × 12½

O97 **5a** ½d. orange . . 2·25 25
O98 1d. sage-green (Die I) . . 2·00 15
O99 1d. sage-green (Die II) . . 40·00 35·00
O100 1½d. scarlet . . 1·75 15
O101 1½d. golden scarlet . . 1·75 15
O102 1½d. red-brown . . 3·75 1·00
O103 2d. red-brown (Die II) . . 9·00 1·50
O104 2d. golden scarlet (Die II) . . 7·00 15
O105 2d. golden scarlet (Die III) . . 3·75 15
O106 3d. dull ultramarine (Die I) . . 22·00 1·00
O107 3d. dull ultramarine (Die II) . . 14·00 70
O108 4d. yellow-olive . . 17·00 1·00
O109 4½d. violet . . 45·00 10·00
O110 5d. orange-brown (Die II) . . 38·00 1·25
O111 1s. 4d. turquoise . . 85·00 14·00
O97/111 *Set of* 11 £200 27·00

1927 (9 May). *Opening of Parliament House, Canberra. No. 105 punctured as Type* O **3**.

O112 **8** 1½d. brownish lake . . 12·00 9·00

1928 (29 Oct). *National Stamp Exhibition, Melbourne. No. 106 punctured as Type* O **2**.

O113 3d. blue . . 13·00 9·00

1929–30. *Nos. 107/14 punctured as Type* O **2**. *W* **7**. *P* 12.

O114 **1** 6d. chestnut (Die IIB) . . 15·00 2·00
O115 9d. violet (Die IIB) . . 18·00 4·00
O116 1s. blue-green (Die IIB) . . 22·00 2·00
O117 **1** 2s. maroon (Die II) . . 45·00 7·00
O118 5s. grey and yellow . . £125 40·00
O118*a* 10s. grey and pink . . £400 £300
O118*b* £2 black and rose . . £1800 £600

1929 (20 May). *Air. No. 115 punctured as Type* O **3**.

O119 **9** 3d. green . . 20·00 12·00

1929 (28 Sept). *Centenary of Western Australia. No. 116 punctured as Type* O **3**.

O120 **10** 1½d. dull scarlet . . 12·00 8·50

1930 (2 June). *Centenary of Exploration of River Murray by Capt. Sturt. Nos. 117/18 punctured as Type* O **2**.

O121 **11** 1½d. scarlet . . 6·00 4·00
O122 3d. blue . . 12·00 9·00

O S

(O 4)

1931 (4 May). Nos. 121/2 *optd with Type* O 4.

O123 **13** 2d. rose-red . . 55·00 16·00
O124 3d. blue . . £200 38·00

For No. 139 overprinted with Type O 4, see No. 139*a*.

1932–33. *Optd as Type* O **4**. *(a) W* **7**. (i) *P* 13½ × 12½.

O125 **5a** 2d. golden-scarlet (Die III) . . 6·00 70
O126 4d. yellow-olive . . 40·00 3·75

(ii) *P* 12

O127 **1** 6d. chestnut . . 80·00 65·00

(b) W **15**. (i) *P* 13½ × 12½

O128 **5a** ½d. orange . . 9·00 1·50
a. Opt inverted . . £2000 £1100
O129 1d. green . . 4·00 45
O130 2d. golden scarlet (Die III) . . 6·00 55
a. Opt inverted . . — £1500
O131 3d. ultramarine (Die II) (3.33) . . 7·50 5·00
O132 5d. orange-brown . . 65·00 38·00

(ii) *P* 12

O133 **1** 6d. chestnut . . 40·00 30·00

(c) Recess. No wmk. P 11

O134 **18** 2d. scarlet . . 8·00 2·00
O135 3d. blue . . 20·00 5·50
O136 **17** 1s. green . . 80·00 35·00

Issue of overprinted official stamps ceased in February 1933 and thereafter mail from the federal administration was carried free.

BRITISH COMMONWEALTH OCCUPATION FORCE (JAPAN)

Nos. J1/7 were used by the Australian forces occupying Japan after the Second World War. Initially their military post offices supplied unoverprinted Australian stamps, but it was decided to introduce the overprinted issue to prevent currency speculation.

B.C.O.F. JAPAN 1946 (1)

B.C.O.F JAPAN 1946 (2)

1946 Wrong fount "6" (left pane R. 9/4)

1946 (11 Oct)–**48**. *Stamps of Australia optd as T* **1** *(1d., 3d.) or T* **2** *(others) at British Commonwealth Command Headquarters, Kure, Japan.*

J1 **27** ½d. orange (No. 179) . . 2·00 2·50
a. Wrong fount "6" . . 25·00 28·00
J2 **46** 1d. brown-purple (No. 203) . . 2·00 1·50
a. Error. Blue overprint . . 70·00 90·00
J3 **31** 3d. purple-brown (No. 187) . . 1·25 1·50
J4 **34** 6d. purple-brown (No. 189*a*) (8.5.47) . 10·00 7·50
a. Wrong fount "6" . . 70·00 65·00
b. Stop after "JAPAN" (right pane R. 5/5) . 70·00 65·00
J5 **36** 1s. grey-green (No. 191) (8.5.47) . 10·00 8·50
a. Wrong fount "6" . . £100 80·00
b. Stop after "JAPAN" (right pane R. 5/5) . . £100 80·00
J6 **1** 2s. maroon (No. 212) (8.5.47) . . 38·00 42·00
J7 **38** 5s. claret (No. 176) (8.5.47) . . £110 £130
a. Thin rough paper (No. 176a) (1948) £130 £150
J1/7 *Set of* 7 £150 £170

The ½d., 1d. and 3d. values were first issued on 11 October 1946, and withdrawn two days later, but were re-issued together with the other values on 8 May 1947.

The following values with T **2** opt in the colours given were from proof sheets which, however, were used for postage: ½d. (red), 1d. (red or black) and 3d. (gold, red or black). (*Price from* £300 *un.*)

The use of B.C.O.F. stamps ceased on 12 February 1949.

PRICES OF SETS

Set prices are given for many issues, generally those containing three stamps or more. Definitive sets include one of each value or major colour change, but do not cover different perforations, die types or minor shades. Where a choice is possible the set prices are based on the cheapest versions of the stamps included in the listings.

AUSTRALIAN ANTARCTIC TERRITORY

VALIDITY. All Antarctic Territory stamps are also valid for use in Australia, where they are put on sale for a limited period when first issued.

DATES OF ISSUE. The dates given refer to release dates in Australia. Local release dates are usually later and where known they are given in footnotes.

1 1954 Expedition at Vestfold Hills and Map

(Des. T. Lawrence: adapted by artist of the Printing Branch. Recess)

1957 (27 Mar). *P* 14½.
1 **1** 2s. ultramarine .. .. 1·75 60
Issued Macquarie Island 11.12.57, Davis 6.2.58, Mawson 18.2.58, Wilkes 1.2.59.

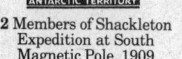

2 Members of Shackleton Expedition at South Magnetic Pole, 1909 — **3** Weazel and Team

1959 (16 Dec). *T* **2** *and designs as T* **3**. *Recess; new values surch typo* (5*d.*, 8*d.*). *P* 14½ (5*d.*), 14½ × 14 (8*d.*) *or* 14 × 14½ (*others*).
2 5d. on 4d. black and sepia 60 15
3 8d. on 7d. black and indigo .. .. .. 4·50 2·00
4 1s. deep green .. .. 4·50 1·75
5 2s. 3d. green .. .. 10·00 4·00
2/5 .. .. *Set of* 4 18·00 7·00
Designs: *Vert*—1s. Dog-team and iceberg; 2s. 3d. Map of Antarctica and Emperor Penguins. Issued Macquarie Island 26.12.59, Davis 30.1.60, Mawson 10.2.60, Wilkes 13.2.60.

6 — 7 Sir Douglas Mawson (Expedition leader)

1961 (5 July). *Recess. P* 14½.
6 **6** 5d. deep blue .. .. 1·50 15
Issued Macquarie Island 6.12.61, Wilkes 10.1.62, Davis 20.1.62, Mawson 30.1.62.

1961 (18 Oct). 50*th Anniv of* 1911–14 *Australasian Antarctic Expedition. Recess. P* 14½.
7 **7** 5d. myrtle-green 35 15
Issued Macquarie Island 6.12.61, Wilkes 10.1.62, Davis 20.1.62, Mawson 30.1.62.

(New Currency. 100 cents = 1 Australian dollar)

8 Aurora and Camera Dome — 9 Helicopter

(Des J. Mason. Photo)

1966 (28 Sept)–**68**. *T* **8/10** *and similar multicoloured designs. P* 13½.
8 1 c. Type **8** (*shades*) 70 30
9 2 c. Banding penguins (*shades*) .. .. 2·25 40
10 4 c. Ship and iceberg 70 50
11 5 c. Banding Elephant-seals (25.9.68) .. 2·50 1·75
12 7 c. Measuring snow strata 80 45
13 10 c. Wind gauges .. .. 1·00 60
14 15 c. Weather balloon .. .. 4·00 2·00
15 20 c. Type **9** .. .. 4·25 2·25
16 25 c. Radio operator .. .. 5·00 3·75
17 50 c. Ice compression tests .. .. .. 17·00 9·00
18 $1 Parahelion ("mock sun") .. .. .. 42·00 15·00
8/18 .. .. *Set of* 11 70·00 32·00
The 1 c. to 15 c. are vert as Type **8**; the 25 c., 50 c. and $1 are horiz as Type **9**.
Nos. 8/10 and 12/18 placed on sale locally at Macquarie Island on 11.12.66, Wilkes 9.2.67 and Mawson 16.2.67.
No. 11 issued Macquarie Island 4.12.68, Mawson 13.1.69, Wilkes/Casey 9.2.69 and Davis 20.2.69.

11 Sastrugi (Snow Ridges) — 12 Capt. Cook, Sextant and Compass

(Des J. Mason. Photo)

1971 (23 June). *Tenth Anniv of Antarctic Treaty. T* **11** *and similar horiz design. P* 13½.
19 6 c. blue and black .. .. 1·25 1·00
20 30 c. multicoloured (Pancake ice) .. .. 6·50 6·50
Issued Macquarie Island 23.11.71, Mawson 27.12.71, Davis 13.1.72 and Casey 17.1.72.

(Des J. Mason. Photo)

1972 (13 Sept). *Bicentenary of Cook's Circumnavigation of Antarctica. T* **12** *and similar horiz design. Multicoloured. P* 13½.
21 7 c. Type **12** .. .. 2·00 75
22 35 c. Chart and H.M.S. *Resolution* .. .. 8·00 6·00
Issued Macquarie Island 19.11.72, Mawson 24.12.72, Davis 3.1.73 and Casey 22.1.73.

13 Plankton — 14 Admiral Byrd (expedition leader), Aircraft and Map of South Pole

(Des G. Browning (1, 7, 9, 10, 20 c., $1), R. Honisett (others). Photo)

1973 (5 Aug). *T* **13** *and similar multicoloured designs. P* 13½.
23 1 c. Type **13** 20 15
24 5 c. Mawson's "Gipsy Moth", 1931 .. .. 30 20
25 7 c. Adélie Penguin .. .. 2·00 50
26 8 c. Rymill's "Fox Moth", 1934–7 .. .. 30 30
27 9 c. Leopard Seal (*horiz*) 30 30
28 10 c. Killer Whale (*horiz*) .. .. .. 5·00 1·00
a. Buff (overlay on seals) omitted £600
29 20 c. Wandering Albatross (*horiz*) 90 60
30 25 c. Wilkins' Lockheed "Vega", 1928 (*horiz*) 40 60
31 30 c. Ellsworth's Northrop "Gamma", 1935 .. 40 60
32 35 c. Christensen's Avro "Avian", 1934 (*horiz*) 40 60
33 50 c. Byrd's "Tri-Motor", 1929 .. .. 50 60
34 $1 Sperm Whale .. .. 80 1·40
23/34 .. .. *Set of* 12 10·00 6·25
Issued Macquarie Island 29.11.73, Mawson 30.12.73, Davis 10.1.74 and Casey 31.1.74.

(Des R. Honisett. Litho Asher and Co, Melbourne)

1979 (20 June). 50*th Anniv of First Flight over South Pole. T* **14** *and similar horiz design. Multicoloured. P* 15½.
35 20 c. Type 14 .. .. 50 40
36 55 c. Admiral Byrd, aircraft and Antarctic terrain .. .. 1·25 1·40
Issued Macquarie Island 24.10.79, Davis 3.1.80, Mawson 13.1.80 and Casey 9.2.80.

15 M.V. *Thala Dan* — 16 Sir Douglas Mawson in Antarctic Terrain

(Des R. Honisett, Litho Asher and Co, Melbourne)

1979 (29 Aug)–**81**. *Ships. Multicoloured designs as T* **15**. *P* 13½ × 13 (*horiz*) *or* 13 × 13½ (*vert*).
37 1 c. S.Y. *Aurora* (*horiz*) (21.5.80) 10 10
38 2 c. R.Y. *Penola* (9.9.81) 10 10
39 5 c. Type **15** 15 15
40 10 c. H.M.S. *Challenger* (*horiz*) (9.9.81) .. 20 10
41 15 c. S.S. *Morning** (bow view) (*horiz*) (21.5.80) 1·40 2·25
42 15 c. S.Y. *Nimrod* (stern view) (*horiz*) (9.9.81) 50 20
43 20 c. R.R.S. *Discovery II* (*horiz*) 40 50
44 22 c. R.Y.S. *Terra Nova* (21.5.80) 60 70
45 25 c. S.S. *Endurance* 60 70
46 30 c. S.S. *Fram* (*horiz*) 60 70
47 35 c. M.S. *Nella Dan* (*horiz*) (21.5.80) .. 70 70
48 40 c. M.S. *Kista Dan* (9.9.81) 70 45
49 45 c. *L'Astrolabe* (*horiz*) (9.9.81) 70 50
50 50 c. S.S. *Norvegia* (*horiz*) (9.9.81) 70 55
51 55 c. S.Y. *Discovery* .. .. 85 1·40
52 $1 H.M.S. *Resolution* (21.5.80) .. .. 1·50 2·00
37/52 .. .. *Set of* 16 8·75 9·00
*No. 41 is incorrectly inscribed "S.Y. *Nimrod*".
On No. 46 the S.S. *Fram* is shown flying the Icelandic ensign, instead of the Norwegian.
Nos. 37, 41, 44, 47 and 52 issued Macquarie Island 27.10.80, Casey 1.12.80, Mawson 5.12.80 and Davis 11.12.80.
Nos. 38, 40, 42 and 48/50 issued Macquarie Island 21.10.81, Mawson 25.11.81, Davis 11.1.82 and Casey 25.1.82.
Nos. 39, 43, 45/6 and 51 issued Macquarie Island 24.10.79, Davis 3.1.80, Mawson 13.1.80 and Casey 9.2.80.

(Des R. Honisett. Litho Cambec Press, Melbourne)

1982 (5 May). *Birth Centenary of Sir Douglas Mawson (Antarctic explorer). T* **16** *and similar vert design. Multicoloured. P* 14 × 13½.
53 27 c. Type **16** 50 30
54 75 c. Sir Douglas Mawson and map of Australian Antarctic Territory .. .. 1·50 2·00
Issued Macquarie Island 26.10.82, Casey 16.1.83, Davis 10.2.83 and Mawson 2.3.83.

17 Light-mantled Sooty Albatross — 18 Antarctic Scientist

(Des R. Honisett. Litho Leigh-Mardon Ltd, Melbourne)

1983 (6 Apr). *Regional Wildlife. T* **17** *and similar vert designs. Multicoloured. P* 14½.
55 27 c. Type **17** 70 70
a. Horiz strip of 5. Nos. 55/9 .. .. 3·25
56 27 c. King Cormorant 70 70
57 27 c. Southern Elephant-Seal 70 70
58 27 c. Royal Penguin 70 70
59 27 c. Dove Prion 70 70
55/9 .. .. *Set of* 5 3·25 3·25
Nos. 55/9 were issued together, *se-tenant*, in horizontal strips of five, forming a composite design.
Issued Macquarie Island 21.10.83, Mawson 9.12.83, Casey 1.1.84 and Davis 2.1.84.

(Des R. Honisett. Litho Leigh-Mardon Ltd, Melbourne)

1983 (17 Sept). 12*th Antarctic Treaty Consultative Meeting, Canberra. P* 14½.
60 **18** 27 c. multicoloured 60 45
Issued Macquarie Island 21.10.83, Mawson 9.12.83, Casey 1.1.84 and Davis 2.1.84.

19 Prismatic Compass and Lloyd-Creak Dip Circle — 20 Dog Team pulling Sledge

(Des R. Fletcher. Litho Leigh-Mardon Ltd, Melbourne)

1984 (16 Jan). 75*th Anniv of Magnetic Pole Expedition. T* **19** *and similar horiz design. Multicoloured. P* 14½.
61 30 c. Type **19** 75 40
62 85 c. Aneroid barometer and theodolite .. 1·75 1·25
Issued Macquarie Island 23.10.84, Mawson 15.11.84, Casey 16.11.84 and Davis 1.2.85.

(Des G. Emery. Litho Cambec Press, Melbourne)

1984 (18 July)–**87**. *Antarctic Scenes. T* **20** *and similar multicoloured designs. P* 14½ (2 *c.*, 10 *c.*, 20 *c.*, 36 *c.*, 60 *c.*), 14 × 13½ (45 *c.*, 90 *c.*) *or* 13½ × 14 (*others*).
63 2 c. Summer afternoon, Mawson Station (11.3.87) 10 10
64 5 c. Type **20** 10 10
65 10 c. Late summer evening, MacRobertson Land (11.3.87) 10 10
66 15 c. Prince Charles Mountains (7.8.85) .. 10 15
67 20 c. Summer morning, Wilkes Land (11.3.87) 15 20
68 25 c. Sea-ice and iceberg 20 25
69 30 c. Mount Coates 25 30
70 33 c. "Iceberg Alley", Mawson (7.8.85) .. 25 30
71 36 c. Early winter evening, Casey Station (11.3.87) 30 35
72 45 c. Brash ice (*vert*) (7.8.85) 35 40
73 60 c. Midwinter shadows, Casey Station (11.3.87) 50 55
74 75 c. Coastline 60 65
75 85 c. Landing strip 70 75
76 90 c. Pancake ice (*vert*) (7.8.85) 75 80
77 $1 Emperor Penguins (7.8.85) (Optd S. 50p) 85 90
64/77 .. .. *Set of* 15 4·75 5·25
Nos. 64, 68/9 and 74/5 issued Macquarie Island 23.10.84, Mawson 15.11.84, Casey 16.11.84 and Davis 1.2.85.

21 Prince Charles Mountains near Mawson Station — 22 Hourglass Dolphins and *Nella Dan*

(Des A. McGregor. Litho Cambec Press, Melbourne)

1986 (17 Sept). 25*th Anniv of Antarctic Treaty. P* 14 × 13½.
78 **21** 36 c. multicoloured 85 35

(Des Trish Hart. Litho CPE Australia Ltd, Melbourne)

1988 (20 July). *Environment, Conservation and Technology. T* **22** *and similar square designs. Multicoloured. P* 13.

79	37 c. Type **22**	.. ..	55	60
	a. Horiz strip of 5. Nos. 79/83	.. ..	2·50	
80	37 c. Emperor Penguins and Davis Station	..	55	60
81	37 c. Crabeater Seal and helicopter	.. ..	55	60
82	37 c. Adelie Penguins and tracked vehicle	..	55	60
83	37 c. Grey-headed Albatross and photographer	.. ..	55	60
79/83	.. ..	*Set of* 5	2·50	2·75

Nos. 79/83 were printed together, *se-tenant*, in horizontal strips of five throughout the sheet.

23 "Antarctica"

(Des Janet Boschen. Litho CPE Australia Ltd, Melbourne)

1989 (14 June). *Antarctic Landscape Paintings by Sir Sidney Nolan. T* **23** *and similar vert designs. Multicoloured. P* 14 × 13½.

84	39 c. Type **23**	.. ..	50	50
85	39 c. "Iceberg Alley"	.. ..	50	50
86	60 c. "Glacial Flow"	.. ..	75	75
87	80 c. "Frozen Sea"	.. ..	1·00	1·00
84/7	.. ..	*Set of* 4	2·50	2·50

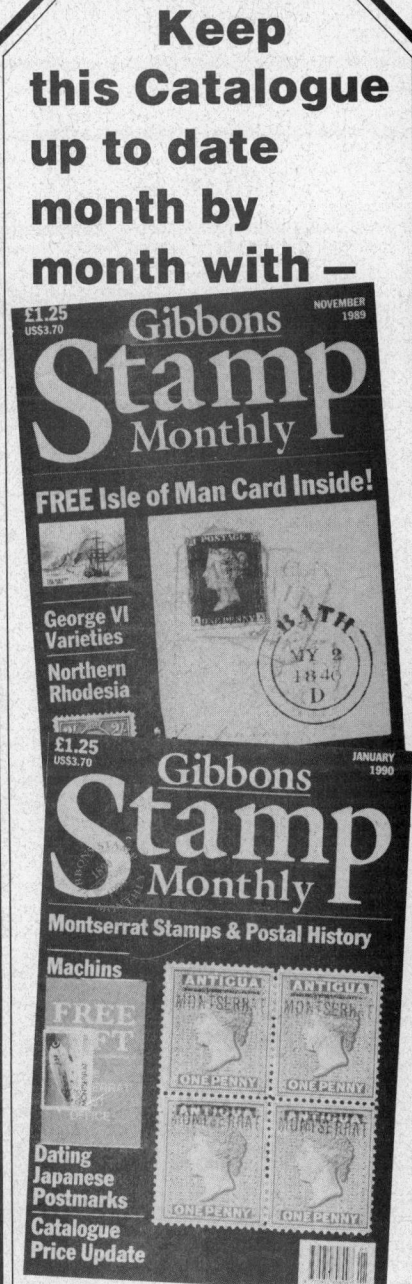

Baghdad *see* Iraq

Bahamas

The British Post Office at Nassau was established during the early days of the West Indies packet system, and was certainly operating by 1733. The first known local postmark dates from 1802.

The crowned-circle handstamps Nos. CC1/2 were issued in 1846 and were generally replaced, for the public mails, by various stamps of Great Britain in 1858.

Local mail deliveries were rudimentary until 1859 when Nos. 1/2 were issued by the colonial authorities for interisland mails. Examples used for this purpose are usually cancelled in manuscript or with a "27" postmark. The "local" 1d. stamp became valid for overseas mails in May, 1860, when the colonial authorities took over this service from the British G.P.O.

For illustrations of the handstamp and postmark types see BRITISH POST OFFICES ABROAD notes, following GREAT BRITAIN.

NASSAU

CROWNED-CIRCLE HANDSTAMPS

CC1 CC1 BAHAMAS (Nassau) (18.5.1846) (R.)
Price on cover £1400

No. CC1 was later struck in black and used as an Official Paid mark between July 1899 and September 1935. Handstamps as Types CC 2 and CC 3 (only three known) struck in black were used for the same purpose from 1933 until 1953; but it is believed that these were never employed during the pre-stamp period. *Price on cover from* £50.

Stamps of GREAT BRITAIN *cancelled* "A 05" *as Type* **2**.

1858 *to* **1860.**
Z1 1d. rose-red (1857), *perf* 14 .. £1500
Z2 2d. blue (1858) (Plate Nos. 7, 8) .. £1200
Z3 4d. rose (1857) .. £425
Z4 6d. lilac (1856) .. £350
Z5 1s. green (1856) .. £1700

PRICES FOR STAMPS ON COVER TO 1945	
Nos. 1/19*a*	*from* × 5
Nos. 20/44	*from* × 3
Nos. 45/57	*from* × 4
Nos. 58/99	*from* × 2
Nos. 100/36	*from* × 3
Nos. 137/8	*from* × 10
Nos. 139/44	*from* × 2
No. 145	*from* × 4
Nos. 146/8	*from* × 6
Nos. 149/57	*from* × 3
Nos. 158/60	*from* × 4
No. 161	*from* × 8
Nos. 162/75	*from* × 5
No. S1	*from* × 30
Nos. S2/3	*from* × 20

CROWN COLONY

1

2

3

(Eng and recess P.B.)

1859 (10 June). *No wmk. Imperf. (a) Thick paper.*
1 1 1d. reddish lake .. £4500 £2250
a. Brown-lake .. £4500 £2250

(b) Thin paper
2 1 1d. dull lake .. 30·00 £1500

Collectors are warned against false postmarks upon the remainder stamps of 1d., imperf, on thin paper.

1860 (Oct). *No wmk. Clean-cut perf* 14 *to* 16.
3 1 1d. lake .. £2000 £650

1861 (June–Dec). *No wmk. (a) Rough perf* 14 *to* 16.
4 1 1d. lake .. £700 £300
5 2 4d. dull rose (Dec, 1861) .. £1400 £325
a. Imperf between (pair) .. £9000
6 6d. grey-lilac (Dec, 1861) .. £2500 £450
a. Pale dull lilac .. £2500 £450

(b) P 11 *to* 12½
7 1 1d. lake .. £2000

No. 7 was not sent out to the Colony. It is also known part perforated.

(Recess D.L.R.)

1862. *No wmk.* (a) P* 11½, 12.
8 1 1d. carmine-lake .. £600 £120
9 1d. lake .. £600 £130
10 2 4d. dull rose .. £2500 £200
11 6d. lavender-grey .. £2750 £300

(b) P 11½, 12, *compound with* 11
12 1 1d. carmine-lake .. £1500 £850
13 1d. lake .. £1500 £850
14 2 4d. dull rose .. £7500 £1700
15 6d. lavender-grey .. £8500 £1300

(c) P 13
16 1 1d. lake .. £600 £140
17 1d. brown-lake .. £600 £120
18 2 4d. dull rose .. £2000 £300
19 6d. lavender-grey .. £2750 £275
a. Lilac .. £2500 £500

*Stamps exist with part of papermaker's sheet wmk ("T. H. SAUNDERS" and date).

(T 3 Typo D.L.R.)

1863–80. *Wmk Crown CC. (a) P* 12½.
20 1 1d. brown-lake .. 85·00 55·00
21 1d. carmine-lake .. 90·00 60·00
22 1d. carmine-lake (aniline) .. 95·00 60·00
23 1d. rose-red .. 55·00 40·00
24 1d. red .. 60·00 40·00
25 1d. vermilion .. 60·00 40·00
26 2 4d. dull rose .. £300 60·00
27 4d. bright rose .. £200 60·00
28 4d. brownish rose .. £350 80·00
28*a* 6d. rose-lilac .. £4000
29 6d. lilac (*shades*) .. £250 60·00
30 6d. deep violet .. £160 60·00
31 6d. violet (aniline) .. £250 90·00
32 3 1s. green (1865) .. £2250 £300

No. 28*a*, believed to be the shade of the first printing only, is a very rare stamp, not to be confused with No. 29.

(b) P 14
33 1 1d. scarlet-vermilion .. 35·00 15·00
34 1d. scarlet (or scarlet-vermilion) (aniline) £1400 †
35 2 4d. bright rose .. £350 40·00
36 4d. dull rose .. £1500 40·00
37 4d. rose-lake .. £350 40·00
38 3 1s. dark green (1863) .. 90·00 35·00
39 1s. green (thick paper) (1880?) .. 6·00 7·00

No. 34 is not known postally used, although manuscript fiscal cancellations are recorded on this shade.

1882 (March). *Wmk Crown CA. (a) P* 12.
40 1 1d. scarlet-vermilion .. 35·00 12·00
41 2 4d. rose .. £550 45·00

(b) P 14
42 1 1d. scarlet-vermilion .. £350 55·00
43 2 4d. rose .. £700 55·00
44 3 1s. green .. 30·00 14·00

See also No. 55.

FOURPENCE
(4)

5

Malformed "E"

1883. *No.* 30 *surch with T* **4**.
45 2 4d. on 6d. deep violet .. £500 £375
a. Surch inverted .. £4000 £2500

Type 4 was applied by handstamp and occurs in various positions.

Caution is needed in buying Nos. 45 and 45a.

(Typo D.L.R.)

1884–98. *Wmk Crown CA. P* 14.
47 5 1d. pale rose .. 20·00 9·00
48 1d. carmine-rose .. 3·50 1·50
49 1d. bright carmine (aniline) .. 2·75 5·50
50 2½d. dull blue (1888) .. 24·00 15·00
51 2½d. blue .. 20·00 7·00
52 2½d. ultramarine .. 7·00 1·50
53 4d. deep yellow .. 8·00 3·75
54 6d. mauve (1890) .. 4·00 16·00
a. Malformed "E" (R.6/6) .. £110 £180
55 3 1s. blue-green (1898) .. 32·00 20·00
56 5 5s. sage-green .. 55·00 55·00
57 £1 Venetian red .. £300 £225
47/57 .. *Set of* 7 £350 £300
50 & 54 Optd "Specimen" .. *Set of* 2 £120

6 Queen's Staircase, Nassau

7

8

(Recess D.L.R.)

1901–10. *P* 14. *(a) Wmk Crown CC* (Sept 1901).
58 6 1d. black and red (Optd S. £30) .. 5·50 2·50

(b) Wmk Mult Crown CA (1910)
59 6 1d. black and red .. 7·00 2·00

For later shades, see Nos. 93/4 and 122.

(Typo D.L.R.)

1902 (Dec). *Wmk Crown CA. P* 14.
60 7 1d. carmine .. 1·50 90
61 2½d. ultramarine .. 6·50 1·25
62 4d. orange .. 11·00 26·00
63 4d. deep yellow .. 13·00 28·00
64 7 6d. brown .. 5·50 12·00
a. Malformed "E" (R.6/6) .. 95·00 £150
65 1s. grey-black and carmine .. 11·00 25·00
66 1s. brownish grey and carmine .. 11·00 25·00
67 5s. dull purple and blue .. 45·00 55·00
68 £1 green and black .. £250 £300
60/8 .. *Set of* 7 £300 £375
60/68 Optd "Specimen" .. *Set of* 7 £300

1903. *Wmk Crown CC. P* 14.
69 6 5d. black and orange .. 8·00 32·00
70 2s. black and blue .. 15·00 38·00
71 3s. black and green .. 18·00 38·00
69/71 .. *Set of* 3 38·00 95·00
69/71 Optd "Specimen" .. *Set of* 3 90·00

1906–11. *Wmk Mult Crown CA. P* 14.
72 7 ½d. pale green (Optd S. £50) .. 3·25 1·00
73 1d. carmine-rose .. 7·50 90
74 2½d. ultramarine (1907) .. 16·00 24·00
75 6d. bistre-brown (1911) .. 16·00 48·00
a. Malformed "E" (R.6/6) .. £200 £450
72/5 .. *Set of* 4 38·00 65·00

(Typo D.L.R.)

1912–19. *Wmk Mult Crown CA. P* 14.
76 8 ½d. green, **O** .. 80 4·00
77 ½d. yellow-green, **O** .. 1·50 5·00
78 1d. carmine (aniline), **O** .. 80 30
79 1d. deep rose, **O** .. 2·50 1·25
80 1d. rose, **O** .. 5·50 2·00
81 2d. grey, **O** (1919) .. 2·25 3·00
82 2½d. ultramarine, **O** .. 4·00 11·00
83 2½d. deep dull blue, **O** .. 9·00 16·00
84 4d. orange-yellow, **O** .. 4·50 13·00
85 4d. yellow, **O** .. 2·00 7·50
86 6d. bistre-brown, **O** .. 1·75 4·00
a. Malformed "E" (R.6/6) .. 38·00 55·00
87 1s. grey-black and carmine, **C** .. 1·75 7·00
88 1s. jet-black and carmine, **C** .. 9·50 15·00
89 5s. dull purple and blue, **C** .. 22·00 45·00
90 5s. pale dull purple and deep blue, **C** .. 27·00 50·00
91 £1 dull green and black, **C** .. £140 £240
92 £1 green and black, **C** .. £170 £250
76/91 .. *Set of* 9 £160 £300
76/91 Optd "Specimen" .. *Set of* 9 £300

1916–19. *Wmk Mult Crown CA. P* 14.
93 6 1d. grey-black and scarlet (1916) .. 1·75 2·50
94 1d. grey-black and deep carmine-red (1919) .. 2·50 3·75
95 3d. purple/*yellow* (*thin*) (1917) .. 3·50 14·00
96 3d. reddish purple/*buff* (*thick*) (1.19) .. 3·00 4·50
97 5d. black and mauve (18.5.17) .. 2·25 5·50
98 2s. black and blue (11.16) .. 18·00 35·00
99 3s. black and green (8.17) .. 35·00 40·00
93/9 .. *Set of* 5 50·00 80·00
95 & 97 Optd "Specimen" .. *Set of* 2 60·00

1.1.17.
(9)

WAR TAX
(10)

1917 (18 May). *No.* 59 *optd with T* **9**.
100 6 1d. black and red (R.) (Optd S. £60) .. 25 85
a. Long stroke to "7" .. 45·00 65·00

The above stamps were to have been on sale on 1 January 1917, but owing to delay in shipment they were not issued till May 1917.

1918 (21 Feb). *Optd at Nassau with T* **10**.
101 8 ½d. green .. 4·50 14·00
a. Opt double .. £700 £700
b. Opt inverted .. £700
102 1d. carmine .. 30 50
a. Opt double .. £700 £700
b. Opt inverted .. £700
103 6 3d. purple/*yellow* .. 2·00 2·25
a. Opt double .. £850 £750
b. Opt inverted .. £750 £750
104 8 1s. grey-black and carmine .. 65·00 95·00
a. Opt double .. £1800
101/4 .. *Set of* 4 65·00 £100

1918 (10 July). *Wmk Mult Crown CA. Optd with T* **10**.
105 6 1d. black and red .. 1·60 2·50
a. Opt double, one inverted .. £650
b. Opt double .. £1000
c. Opt inverted .. £850 £900

No. 105a is from a sheet in which the top row was normal and the other four showed this error. No. 105 was on sale for ten days.

WAR TAX
(11)

WAR TAX
(12)

WAR CHARITY 3.6.18.
(13)

1918 (1 June–20 July). *Optd in London with T* **11** *or* **12** (3*d*.).
106 8 ½d. green .. 20 1·40
107 1d. carmine .. 20 35
a. Wmk sideways .. £550
108 6 3d. purple/*yellow* (20 July) .. 40 1·50
109 8 1s. grey-black and carmine (R.) .. 1·75 2·75
106/9 .. *Set of* 4 2·25 5·50
106/9 Optd "Specimen" .. *Set of* 4 £130

1919 (21 Mar). *Colour changed. Wmk Mult Crown CA. P* 14.
110 6 3d. black and brown (Optd S. £45) .. 40 2·25

1919 (21 Mar). *No. 110 optd with T* **12**.
111 **6** 3d. black and brown (Optd S. £45) .. 25 4·00
a. "C" and "A" missing from wmk ..

No. 111a shows the "C" omitted from one impression and the "A" missing from the next one to the right (as seen from the front of the stamp). The "C" is badly distorted in the second watermark.

1919 (1 Jan). *No. 59 optd with T* **13**.
112 **6** 1d. black and red (R.) (Optd S. £50) .. 20 2·25
a. Opt double £1200

The date is that originally fixed for the issue of the stamp. The year 1918 was also the bicentenary of the appointment of the first Royal governor.

WAR WAR

TAX TAX

(14) (15)

1919 (14 July). (*a*) *Optd with T* **14**.
113 **8** ½d. green (R.) .. .. 20 1·25
114 1d. carmine .. .. 20 1·50
115 1s. grey-black and carmine (R.) .. 4·75 17·00
(*b*) *No. 110 optd with T* **15**
116 **6** 3d. black and brown .. .. .. 30 5·00
113/16 .. .. .. *Set of* 4 5·00 22·00
113/16 Optd "Specimen" .. .. *Set of* 4 £120

16

17

(Recess D.L.R.)

1920 (1 Mar). *Peace Celebration. Wmk Mult Crown CA (sideways). P* 14.
117 **16** ½d. green .. .. 55 3·25
118 1d. carmine .. .. 2·50 70
119 2d. slate-grey .. .. 2·50 6·50
120 3d. deep brown .. .. 2·50 8·50
121 1s. deep myrtle-green .. .. .. 10·00 27·00
117/21 .. .. .. *Set of* 5 16·00 42·00
117/21 Optd "Specimen" .. .. *Set of* 5 £150

1921–29. *Wmk Mult Script CA. P* 14. (*a*) *Staircase type.*
122 **6** 1d. grey and rose-red (29.3.21) .. 70 1·00
122*a* 5d. black and purple (1929) .. .. 2·75 18·00
123 2s. black and blue (1922) .. .. 15·00 28·00
123*a* 3s. black and green (1924) .. .. 26·00 45·00
122/23*a* .. .. .. *Set of* 4 40·00 80·00
122/23*a* Optd/Perf "Specimen" .. *Set of* 4 £140
(*b*) *King George V type*
124 **8** ½d. green, **O** (1924) 20 40
125 1d. carmine, **O** (8.9.21) 40 15
125*a* 2d. grey, **O** (1927) .. .. .. 80 2·75
126 2½d. ultramarine, **O** (1922) .. .. 70 2·75
127 4d. orange-yellow, **O** (1924) .. .. 70 5·00
128 6d. bistre-brown, **O** (1922) .. .. 60 1·25
a. Malformed "E" (R.6/6) .. .. 35·00 50·00
129 1s. black and carmine, **C** (1926) .. 2·50 5·50
130 5s. dull purple and blue, **C** (1924) .. 27·00 38·00
131 £1 green and black, **C** (1926) .. £150 £225
124/131 .. .. .. *Set of* 9 £160 £250
124/31 Optd "Specimen" .. .. *Set of* 9 £300

(Recess B. W.)

1930 (2 Jan). *Tercentenary of Colony. Wmk Mult Script CA. P* 12.
132 **17** 1d. black and scarlet .. .. .. 1·50 2·50
133 3d. black and deep brown .. .. 3·00 10·00
134 5d. black and deep purple .. .. 3·00 11·00
135 2s. black and deep blue .. .. 18·00 35·00
136 3s. black and green .. .. .. 30·00 45·00
132/6 .. .. .. *Set of* 5 50·00 95·00
132/6 Perf "Specimen" .. .. *Set of* 5 £150

18

(Recess B.W.)

1931. *Wmk Mult Script CA. P* 12.
137 **18** 2s. black and deep blue 90 50
a. Slate-purple and deep blue .. 13·00 11·00
138 3s. black and green 90 85
a. Slate-purple and green .. .. 13·00 11·00
137/8 Perf "Specimen" .. .. *Set of* 2 65·00

1931–7. *Wmk Mult Script CA. P* 14.
139 **8** 1½d. red-brown, **O** (1934) .. .. 85 1·00
140 3d. purple/*pale yellow*, **C** (1931) .. 4·50 13·00
a. *Purple/orange-yellow*, **C** (1937) .. 4·50 14·00
139/40 Perf "Specimen" .. .. *Set of* 2 55·00

1935 (6 May). *Silver Jubilee. As Nos.* 91/4 *of Antigua. P* 13½ × 14.
141 1½d. deep blue and carmine.. .. .. 70 70
h. Dot by flagstaff.. .. .. .. 25·00
i. Dash by turret .. .. 35·00
142 2½d. brown and deep blue .. .. .. 1·75 2·50
f. Diagonal line by turret .. .. 45·00
g. Dot to left of chapel .. .. .. 35·00
143 6d. light blue and olive-green .. .. 4·00 6·50
g. Dot to left of chapel .. .. .. 50·00
144 1s. slate and purple .. .. .. 6·00 8·00
h. Dot by flagstaff.. .. .. .. 70·00
141/4 .. .. *Set of* 4 11·00 16·00
141/4 Perf "Specimen" .. .. *Set of* 4 75·00

For illustrations of plate varieties see Omnibus section following Zululand.

19 Greater Flamingos in flight

20 King George VI

(Recess Waterlow)

1935 (22 May). *Wmk Mult Script CA. P* 12½.
145 **19** 8d. ultramarine and scarlet .. .. 4·50 2·75
145 Perf "Specimen" .. .. 40·00

1937 (12 May). *Coronation. As Nos.* 13/15 *of Aden. P* 14.
146 ½d. green 15 15
147 1½d. yellow-brown 30 40
148 2½d. bright blue 50 60
146/8 .. .. *Set of* 3 85 1·00
146/8 Perf "Specimen" .. .. *Set of* 3 55·00

F PENN

Elongated "E" (left pane R. 9/6)

Short "T" in "TWO" (right pane R. 3/6) (Retouched on No. 152*c*, although bottom of letter is still pointed)

(Typo D.L.R.)

1938–52. *Wmk Mult Script CA. P* 14.
149 **20** ½d. bluish green (11.3.38) 15 60
a. Elongated "E" .. .. .. 10·00
b. Myrtle-green (11.12.46) 75 85
ba. Elongated "E" .. .. .. 24·00
149*c* ½d. brown-purple (18.2.52) .. .. 30 2·00
ca. Error. Crown missing £1500
cb. Error. St. Edward's Crown .. £950
cc. Elongated "E" .. .. .. 15·00
150 1d. carmine (11.3.38).. .. .. 8·50 4·75
150*a* 1d. grey (17.9.41) 20 30
151 1½d. red-brown (19.4.38) 40 55
a. Pale red-brown (19.4.48) .. 80 90
152 2d. grey (19.4.38) .. .. .. 13·00 9·00
a. Short T £100
152*b* 2d. scarlet (17.9.41) 30 55
ba. Short T .. .. 25·00
bb. "TWO PENCE" printed double .. † £2000
152*c* 2d. green (1.5.51) 30 80
153 2½d. blue (11.3.38) .. .. .. 3·00 2·00
153*a* 2½d. violet (1.7.43) 30 55
154 3d. violet (19.4.38) .. .. .. 9·00 5·00
154*a* 3d. blue (1943) 30 90
154*b* 3d. scarlet (1.2.52) .. .. .. 50 2·75
154*c* 10d. yellow-orange (18.11.46) 90 20
155 1s. black and carmine, **CO** (15.9.38).. 90 25
156 5s. lilac and blue, **C** (19.4.38) .. £120 90·00
a. Purple and blue, **O** (9.42) .. 20·00 7·50
b. Deep purple & brt bl, **C** (19.4.48) 18·00 5·00
157 £1 green and black, **C** (15.9.38) .. £140 £110
a. Blue-green and black, **O** (5.43) .. 40·00 32·00
149/157*a* .. .. .. *Set of* 17 85·00 60·00
149/57 Perf "Specimen" .. .. *Set of* 14 £350

No. 149cb. occurs on a row in the watermark in which the crowns and letters "C A" alternate.

The ordinary paper of Nos. 155/7 is thick, smooth and opaque, and first appeared in 1942 as a substitute for chalk-surfaced paper.

21 Sea Garden, Nassau

22 Fort Charlotte

23 Greater Flamingos in Flight

(Recess Waterlow)

1938 (1 July). *Wmk Mult Script CA. P* 12½.
158 **21** 4d. light blue and red-orange 80 30
159 **22** 6d. olive-green and light blue 60 25
160 **23** 8d. ultramarine and scarlet .. .. 2·00 90
158/60 .. .. .. *Set of* 3 3·00 1·25
158/60 Perf "Specimen" .. .. *Set of* 3 80·00

3d.

(24)

1492 LANDFALL OF COLUMBUS 1942

(25)

1940 (28 Nov). *No.* 153 *surcharged with T* **24**.
161 **20** 3d. on 2½d. blue 15 40

1942 (12 Oct). *450th Anniv of Landing of Columbus in New World. Optd locally with T* **25**.
162 **20** ½d. bluish green 20 60
a. Elongated "E" .. .. .. 14·00
163 1d. grey 20 60
164 1½d. red-brown 25 50
165 2d. scarlet 25 65
a. Short T .. .. 25·00
166 2½d. blue 25 65
167 3d. blue 25 65
168 **21** 4d. light blue and red-orange 40 90
a. "COIUMBUS" £190 £190
169 **22** 6d. olive-green and light blue .. .. 40 1·75
a. "COIUMBUS" £190 £190
170 **23** 8d. ultramarine and scarlet 55 70
a. "COIUMBUS" £500 £500
171 **20** 1s. black and carmine, **CO** 55 80
172 **18** 2s. black and deep blue .. .. 6·00 8·00
a. Slate-purple and deep blue .. 13·00 13·00
173 3s. black and green .. .. .. 18·00 18·00
a. Slate-purple and green .. .. 3·25 6·00
174 **20** 5s. purple and blue, **CO** .. .. 5·50 8·00
175 £1 green and black, **C** .. .. 28·00 26·00
a. Blue-green and black, **O** .. .. 22·00 18·00
162/175 .. .. .. *Set of* 14 35·00 42·00
162/75 Perf "Specimen" .. .. *Set of* 14 £325

The "COIUMBUS" error (Nos. 168a, 169a, 170a) occurs on R.5/2.

1946 (11 Nov). *Victory. As Nos.* 28/9 *of Aden.*
176 1½d. brown 10 10
177 3d. blue 10 10
176/7 Perf "Specimen" .. .. *Set of* 2 50·00

26 Infant Welfare Clinic

(Recess C.B.N.)

1948 (11 Oct). *Tercentenary of Settlement of Island of Eleuthera. T* **26** *and similar horiz designs. P* 12.
178 ½d. orange 20 50
179 1d. sage-green 20 35
180 1½d. yellow 25 70
181 2d. scarlet 30 40
182 2½d. brown-lake 35 60
183 3d. ultramarine 40 75
184 4d. black 40 70
185 6d. emerald-green 80 70
186 8d. violet 35 70
187 10d. carmine 35 35
188 1s. sepia 60 30
189 2s. magenta .. .. 4·00 7·00
190 3s. blue .. .. 5·00 7·00
191 5s. mauve .. .. 3·75 4·00
192 10s. grey .. .. 4·00 7·50
193 £1 vermilion .. .. 6·50 8·50
178/93 .. .. .. *Set of* 16 25·00 35·00

Designs:—1d. Agriculture (combine harvester); 1½d. Sisal; 2d. Straw work; 2½d. Dairy farm; 3d. Fishing fleet; 4d. Island settlement; 6d. Tuna fishing; 8d. Paradise Beach; 10d. Modern hotels; 1s. Yacht racing; 2s. Water sports (skiing); 3s. Shipbuilding; 5s. Transportation; 10s. Salt production; £1, Parliament Buildings.

1948 (1 Dec). *Royal Silver Wedding. As Nos.* 30/1 *of Aden.*
194 1½d. red-brown 15 25
195 £1 slate-green .. .. 26·00 26·00

1949 (10 Oct). *75th Anniv of Universal Postal Union. As Nos.* 114/17 *of Antigua.*
196 2½d. violet 35 40
197 3d. deep blue .. .. 70 1·00
198 6d. greenish blue .. .. 80 1·00
199 1s. carmine 80 75
196/9 .. .. *Set of* 4 2·40 2·75

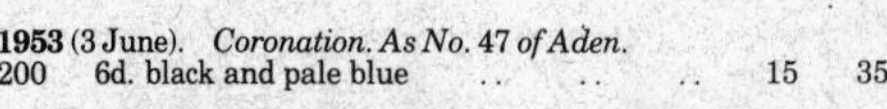

1953 (3 June). *Coronation. As No.* 47 *of Aden.*
200 6d. black and pale blue 15 35

42 Infant Welfare Clinic

43 Queen Elizabeth II

(Recess B.W.)

1954 (1 Jan)–**63**. *Designs previously used for King George VI issue, but with portrait of Queen Elizabeth II as in T* **42**, *and commemorative inscr omitted. Wmk Mult Script CA. P* 11 × 11½.
201 ½d. black and red-orange 10 40
202 1d. olive-green and brown 10 10
203 1½d. blue and black 15 40
204 2d. yellow-brown and myrtle-green .. 15 15
a. Yellow-brn & dp myrtle-grn (23.1.62) 70 80
205 3d. black and carmine-red 20 25

206 4d. turquoise-green & deep reddish purple 20 25
a. Turq-blue & dp reddish pur (23.1.62) 1·75 2·00
207 5d. red-brown and deep bright blue .. 90 2·25
208 6d. light blue and black 20 10
209 8d. black and reddish lilac 20 25
a. Black and deep reddish lilac (21.11.56) 50 70
210 10d. black and ultramarine 20 10
a. Black and deep ultramarine (8.1.63) .. 1·50 1·00
211 1s. ultramarine and olive-brown 35 10
a. Ultramarine & dp olive-sepia (19.2.58) 60 10
212 2s. orange-brown and black .. .. 1·75 70
a. Chestnut and black (19.2.58) .. 3·00 1·50
213 2s. 6d. black and deep blue .. .. 3·00 1·50
214 5s. bright emerald and orange .. .. 8·00 75
a. Brt emerald & reddish orange (14.1.59) 13·00 3·50
215 10s. black and slate-black .. .. 6·00 1·75
216 £1 slate-black and violet .. .. 10·00 5·00
201/216 .. .. *Set of* 16 28·00 12·00

Designs:—1d. Agriculture (combine harvester); 1½d. Island settlement; 2d. Straw work; 3d. Fishing fleet; 4d. Water sports (skiing); 5d. Dairy farm; 6d. Transportation; 8d. Paradise Beach; 10d. Modern hotels; 1s. Yacht racing; 2s. Sisal; 2s. 6d. Shipbuilding; 5s. Tuna fishing; 10s. Salt production; £1 Parliament Buildings.

See also No. 246.

(Recess Waterlow)

1959 (10 June). *Centenary of First Bahamas Postage Stamp. W w* **12**. *P* 13½.
217 **43** 1d. black and scarlet 10 10
218 2d. black and blue-green 15 30
219 6d. black and blue 15 20
220 10d. black and chocolate.. .. .. 20 35
217/20 .. .. *Set of* 4 55 85

44 Christ Church Cathedral

(Photo Enschedé)

1962 (30 Jan). *Nassau Centenary. T* **44** *and similar horiz design. P* 14 × 13.
221 8d. green 15 20
222 10d. bluish violet 15 15
Design:—10d. Nassau Public Library.

1963 (4 June). *Freedom from Hunger. As No.* 76 *of Aden.*
223 8d. sepia 40 35
a. Name and value omitted £800

BAHAMAS TALKS
1962
(46)

NEW CONSTITUTION
1964
(47)

1963 (15 July). *Bahamas Talks*, 1962. *Nos.* 209/10 *optd with T* **46**.
224 8d. black and reddish lilac 30 35
225 10d. black and deep ultramarine 40 40

1963 (2 Sept). *Red Cross Centenary. As Nos.* 147/8 *of Antigua.*
226 1d. red and black 25 25
227 10d. red and blue .. .. 1·25 1·50

SELF GOVERNMENT

1964 (7 Jan). *New Constitution. As Nos.* 201/16 *but W w* **12**, *optd with T* **47**, *by B.W.*
228 ½d. black and red-orange 10 25
229 1d. olive-green and brown 10 15
230 1½d. blue and black 20 30
231 2d. yellow-brown and deep myrtle-green .. 10 20
232 3d. black and carmine-red 25 30
233 4d. turquoise-blue and deep reddish purple 25 45
234 5d. red-brown and deep bright blue .. 20 55
235 6d. light blue and black 20 30
236 8d. black and reddish lilac 25 30
237 10d. black and deep ultramarine 20 15
238 1s. ultramarine and olive-brown 30 15
239 2s. chestnut and black .. .. .. 1·50 1·75
240 2s. 6d. black and deep blue.. .. .. 2·00 2·50
241 5s. bright emerald and orange .. .. 3·75 3·25
242 10s. black and slate black .. .. 4·00 5·50
243 £1 slate-black and violet .. .. 7·50 11·00
228/243 .. .. *Set of* 16 18·00 24·00

1964 (23 April). *400th Birth Anniv of William Shakespeare. As No.* 164 *of Antigua.*
244 6d. turquoise 10 10

8d
(48)

1964 (1 Oct). *Olympic Games, Tokyo. As No.* 211 *but W w* **12**, *surch with T* **48**.
245 8d. on 1s. ultramarine and olive-brown .. 10 10

1964 (6 Oct). *As No.* 204, *but wmk w* **12**.
246 2d. yellow-brown and deep myrtle-green 20 20

49 Colony's Badge (64)

(Queen's portrait by Anthony Buckley. Litho and recess (portrait and "BAHAMAS") B.W.)

1965 (7 Jan–14 Sept). *Horiz designs as T* **49**. *W w* **12**. *P* 13½.
247 ½d. multicoloured 15 40
248 1d. slate, light blue and orange 15 10
249 1½d. rose-red, green and brown 15 50
250 2d. slate, green and turquoise-blue .. 15 10
251 3d. red, light blue and purple 40 20
252 4d. green, blue and orange-brown 55 70
253 6d. dull green, light blue and rose 30 10
254 8d. reddish purple, light blue & bronze-green 50 30
255 10d. orange-brown, green and violet .. 25 10
256 1s. red, yellow, turquoise-blue & deep emer 50 10
a. Red, yellow, dull blue & emer (14.9.65) 25 10
257 2s. brown, light blue and emerald .. .. 1·00 1·00
258 2s. 6d. yellow-olive, blue and carmine .. 1·75 1·75
259 5s. orange-brown, ultramarine and green .. 2·00 1·00
260 10s. rose, blue and chocolate .. .. 4·00 2·25
261 £1 chestnut, blue and rose-red .. .. 7·00 4·50
247/261 .. .. .. *Set of* 15 17·00 12·00

Designs:—1d. Out Island Regatta; 1½d. Hospital; 2d. High School; 3d. Greater Flamingo; 4d. R.M.S. *Queen Elizabeth*; 6d. "Development"; 8d. Yachting; 10d. Public Square; 1s. Sea Garden; 2s. Old Cannons at Fort Charlotte; 2s. 6d. Sikorsky "S-38" seaplane, 1929 and Boeing "707" airliner; 5s. Williamson film project, 1914 and Undersea Post Office, 1939; 10s. Conch shell; £1, Columbus' flagship.

Nos. 247/8, 251, 253 and 256 exist in coils, constructed from normal sheets.

1965 (17 May). *I.T.U. Centenary. As Nos.* 166/7 *of Antigua.*
262 1d. light emerald and orange 15 10
263 2s. purple and yellow-olive 65 35

1965 (12 July). *No.* 254 *surch with T* **64**.
264 9d. on 8d. reddish purple, light blue and bronze-green 15 10

1965 (25 Oct). *International Co-operation Year. As Nos.* 168/9 *of Antigua.*
265 ½d. reddish purple and turquoise-green .. 10 10
266 1s. deep bluish green and lavender 30 35

1966 (24 Jan). *Churchill Commemoration. As Nos.* 170/3 *of Antigua.*
267 ½d. new blue 10 10
268 2d. deep green 30 30
269 10d. brown 65 85
270 1s. bluish violet .. .. 75 1·25
267/70 .. .. *Set of* 4 1·60 2·25

1966 (4 Feb). *Royal Visit. As Nos.* 174/5 *of Antigua, but inscr "to the Caribbean" omitted.*
271 6d. black and ultramarine 90 50
272 1s. black and magenta .. .. .. 1·60 1·25

(New Currency. 100 cents = 1 dollar.)

(65) (66)

1966 (25 May). *Decimal Currency. Nos.* 247/61 *variously surch as T* **65/6**, *by B.W.*
273 1 c. on ½d. multicoloured 10 10
274 2 c. on 1d. slate, light blue and orange .. 10 10
275 3 c. on 2d. slate, green and turquoise-blue .. 10 10
276 4 c. on 3d. red, light blue and purple .. 15 10
277 5 c. on 4d. green, blue and orange-brown .. 15 15
a. Surch omitted (vert strip of 10) £2750
278 8 c. on 6d. dull green, light blue and rose .. 15 20
279 10 c. on 8d. reddish purple, light blue and bronze-green 25 30
280 11 c. on 1½d. rose-red, green and brown .. 15 15
281 12 c. on 10d. orange-brown, green and violet 15 10
282 15 c. on 1s. multicoloured 25 10
283 22 c. on 2s. brown, light blue and emerald .. 60 80
284 50 c. on 2s. 6d. yellow-olive, blue and carmine 90 90
285 $1 on 5s. orange-brown, ultram & green .. 1·25 1·50
286 $2 on 10s. rose, blue and chocolate .. .. 3·00 3·00
287 $3 on £1 chestnut, blue and rose-red .. 5·00 4·00
273/287 .. .. *Set of* 15 11·00 10·00

The above were made on new printings some of which vary slightly in shade and in No. 273 the shield appears as vermilion and green instead of carmine and blue-green due to a different combination of the printing colours.

No. 277a. One sheet exists and the stamp can be distinguished from No. 252 when in a vertical strip of ten as these were printed in sheets of 100 whereas No. 252 was printed in sheets of 60 (six rows of ten across).

1966 (1 July). *World Cup Football Championships. As Nos.* 176/7 *of Antigua.*
288 8 c. violet, yellow-green, lake & yell-brown 15 15
289 15 c. chocolate, blue-green, lake & yell-brown 25 25

1966 (20 Sept). *Inauguration of W.H.O. Headquarters, Geneva. As Nos.* 178/9 *of Antigua.*
290 11 c. black, yellow-green and light blue .. 25 20
291 15 c. black, light purple and yellow-brown .. 30 25

1966 (1 Dec). *20th Anniv of U.N.E.S.C.O. As Nos.* 196/8 *of Antigua.*
292 3 c. slate-violet, red, yellow and orange .. 15 10
293 15 c. orange-yellow, violet and deep olive .. 35 30
294 $1 black, bright purple and orange .. 1·50 2·25
292/4 .. .. *Set of* 3 1·75 2·40

67 *Oceanic*

68 Conch Shell

(Portrait by Anthony Buckley. Litho and recess (portrait, "BAHAMAS" and value), B.W.)

1967 (25 May)–**71**. *T* **67/8** *or designs as Nos.* 247/51, 253/9 *and* 261 *but values in decimal currency and colours changed. Toned paper. W w* **12**. *P* 13½.
295 1 c. multicoloured (as ½d.) 10 30
a. Whiter paper (1970) 20 40
296 2 c. slate, light blue & deep emerald (as 1d.) 15 10
a. Whiter paper (1970) 75 75
297 3 c. slate, green and violet (as 2d.) 10 10
a. Whiter paper (1970) .. .. .. 50·00 3·75
298 4 c. red, light blue and ultramarine (as 3d.) 1·25 10
a. Whiter paper (9.70*) .. .. 9·00 9·00
299 5 c. black, greenish blue and purple .. 60 20
a. Whiter paper (1970) 95 90
300 8 c. dull green, light blue and sepia (as 6d.) 25 10
a. Whiter paper (1970) .. .. .. £100 16·00
301 10 c. reddish pur, greenish bl & carm (as 8d.) 30 20
a. Whiter paper (1970) 80 90
302 11 c. rose-red, green and blue (as 1½d.) .. 25 20
a. Whiter paper (1970) 80 90
303 12 c. orange-brown, green and olive (as 10d.) 25 10
a. Whiter paper (4.71) .. .. .. 9·00 18·00
304 15 c. red, yellow, turquoise-bl & carm (as 1s.) 55 10
a. Whiter paper (1970) .. .. .. £150 20·00
305 22 c. brown, new blue and rose-red (as 2s.) .. 70 65
a. Whiter paper (1970) .. .. .. 1·75 2·25
306 50 c. yellow-olive, new bl & emer (as 2s. 6d.) 2·00 75
a. Whiter paper (1970) .. .. .. 2·25 2·50
307 $1 orange-brown, ultram & slate-pur (as 5s.) 2·00 60
a. Whiter paper (4.71) .. .. .. 19·00 35·00
308 $2 multicoloured .. .. 5·00 2·00
a. Whiter paper (4.71) .. .. .. 30·00 48·00
309 $3 chestnut, new blue and purple (as £1) 3·75 2·00
a. Whiter paper (4.71) .. .. .. 30·00 48·00
295/309 .. .. *Set of* 15 14·00 6·50
295a/309a .. .. *Set of* 15 (whiter paper) £350 £190

*This is the earliest known date recorded in the Bahamas.

The 3 c. has the value at right instead of at left as on No. 250.

The 1970–71 printings on whiter paper were released as needed, the 12 c., $1, $2 and $3 only a week or two before the issue was withdrawn. Due to the marked difference in paper and the use of some new plates there are marked differences in shade in nearly all values.

69 Bahamas Crest

(Des R. Granger Barrett. Photo J. Enschedé)

1967 (1 Sept). *Diamond Jubilee of World Scouting. T* **69** *and similar horiz design. Multicoloured. W w* **12** *(sideways). P* 14 × 13.
310 3 c. Type **69** 10 10
311 15 c. Scout badge 15 10

71 Globe and Emblem

74 Golf

(Des R. Granger Barrett, Litho D.L.R.)

1968 (13 May). *Human Rights Year. T* **71** *and similar horiz designs. Multicoloured. W w* **12** *(sideways). P* 14 × 13½.
312 3 c. Type **71** 10 10
313 12 c. Scales of Justice and emblem 20 10
314 $1 Bahamas Crest and emblem 60 80
312/14 .. .. *Set of* 3 80 85

(Litho B.W.)

1968 (20 Aug). *Tourism. T* **74** *and similar vert designs. Multicoloured. P* 13.

315	5 c. Type **74**	35	20
316	11 c. Yachting	60	30
317	15 c. Horse-racing	60	35
318	50 c. Water-skiing	1·50	2·00
315/18	*Set of* 4	2·75	2·50

78 Racing Yacht and Olympic Monument

(Photo Harrison)

1968 (29 Sept). *Olympic Games, Mexico City. T* **78** *and similar horiz designs. No wmk. P* 14½ × 13½.

319	5 c. red-brown, orange-yellow & blue-green	25	15
320	11 c. multicoloured	35	25
321	50 c. multicoloured	80	1·40
322	$1 olive-grey, greenish blue and violet	1·75	3·00
319/22	*Set of* 4	2·75	4·25

Designs:—11 c. Long-jumping and Olympic Monument; 50 c. Running and Olympic Monument; $1, Type **78**.

It is understood that the above were released by the Philatelic Agency in the U.S.A. on 1st September.

81 Legislative Building

(Des J. Cooter, Litho Format)

1968 (1 Nov). *14th Commonwealth Parliamentary Conference. T* **81** *and similar multicoloured designs. P* 14.

323	3 c. Type **81**	10	10
324	10 c. Bahamas Mace and Westminster Clock-Tower (*vert*)	15	15
325	12 c. Local straw market (*vert*)	15	20
326	15 c. Horse-drawn Surrey	20	25
323/6	*Set of* 4	55	65

85 Obverse and reverse of $100 Gold Coin

(Recess D.L.R.)

1968 (2 Dec). *Gold Coins commemorating the first General Election under the New Constitution. T* **85** *and similar "boomerang" shaped designs. P* 13½.

327	3 c. red/*gold*	20	25
328	12 c. blue-green/*gold*	35	50
329	15 c. dull purple/*gold*	40	60
330	$1 black/*gold*	1·75	2·50
327/30	*Set of* 4	2·40	3·50

Designs:—12 c. Obverse and reverse of $50 gold coin; 15 c. Obverse and reverse of $20 gold coin; $1, Obverse and reverse of $10 gold coin.

89 First Flight Postcard of 1919

90 Sikorsky "S–38" Seaplane of 1929

(Des V. Whiteley. Litho Format)

1969 (30 Jan). *50th Anniv of Bahamas Airmail Service. P* 14.

331	**89**	12 c. multicoloured	30	35
332	**90**	15 c. multicoloured	35	55

91 Game-fishing Boats

92 "The Adoration of the Shepherds" (Louis le Nain)

(Des J. Cooter. Litho Format)

1969 (26 Aug). *Tourism. One Millionth Visitor to Bahamas. T* **91** *and similar horiz designs. Multicoloured. W* w **12** (*sideways*). *P* 14½.

333	3 c. Type **91**	20	10
334	11 c. Paradise Beach	40	15
335	12 c. "Sunfish" sailing boats	40	15
336	15 c. Rawson Square and Parade	45	25
333/6	*Set of* 4	1·25	60
MS337	130 × 96 mm. Nos. 333/6	2·50	3·00

(Des G. Drummond. Litho D.L.R.)

1969 (15 Oct). *Christmas. T* **92** *and similar vert designs. W* w **12**. *P* 12.

338	3 c. Type **92**	10	10
339	11 c. "The Adoration of the Shepherds" (Poussin)	15	15
340	12 c. "The Adoration of the Kings" (Gerard David)	15	15
341	15 c. "The Adoration of the Kings" (Vincenzo Foppa)	20	25
338/41	*Set of* 4	55	55

93 Badge of Girl Guides

(Des Mrs. R. Sands. Litho Harrison)

1970 (23 Feb). *Girl Guides Diamond Jubilee. T* **93** *and similar designs. Multicoloured. W* w **12**. *P* 14½.

342	3 c. Type **93**	15	10
343	12 c. Badge of Brownies	25	20
344	15 c. Badge of Rangers	30	35
342/4	*Set of* 3	65	55

94 U.P.U. Headquarters and Emblem

(Des L. Curtis, Litho J.W.)

1970 (20 May). *New U.P.U. Headquarters Building. W* w **12** (*sideways*). *P* 14.

345	**94**	3 c. multicoloured	10	10
346		15 c. multicoloured	20	30

95 Coach and Globe

(Des G. Drummond. Litho B.W.)

1970 (14 July). *"Goodwill Caravan". T* **95** *and similar horiz designs. Multicoloured. W* w **12** (*sideways*). *P* 13½ × 13.

347	3 c. Type **95**	25	10
348	11 c. Train and globe	70	20
349	12 c. *Canberra* (liner), yacht and globe	70	25
350	15 c. Airliner and globe	70	55
347/50	*Set of* 4	2·10	1·00
MS351	165 × 125 mm Nos. 347/50	6·00	9·50

96 Nurse, Patients and Greater Flamingo

97 "The Nativity" (detail, Pittoni)

(Photo Harrison)

1970 (1 Sept). *Centenary of British Red Cross. T* **96** *and similar horiz design. Multicoloured. W* w **12** (*sideways*). *P* 14½.

352	3 c. Type **96**	15	10
	a. Gold ("EIIR", etc.) omitted	£150	
353	15 c. Hospital and Dolphin	25	40

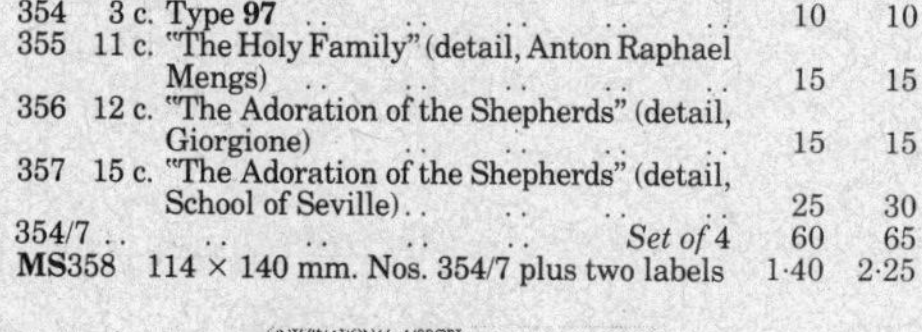

(Des G. Drummond. Litho D.L.R.)

1970 (3 Nov). *Christmas. T* **97** *and similar vert designs. Multicoloured. W* w **12**. *P* 13.

354	3 c. Type **97**	10	10
355	11 c. "The Holy Family" (detail, Anton Raphael Mengs)	15	15
356	12 c. "The Adoration of the Shepherds" (detail, Giorgione)	15	15
357	15 c. "The Adoration of the Shepherds" (detail, School of Seville)	25	30
354/7	*Set of* 4	60	65
MS358	114 × 140 mm. Nos. 354/7 plus two labels	1·40	2·25

98 International Airport

(Des Mrs. W. Wasile. Litho Format)

1971 (27 Apr–1 Sept). *Multicoloured designs as T* **98**. *W* w **12** (*sideways on* $1 *to* $3). *P* 14½ × 14 (1 *to* 50 c.) *or* 14 × 14½ ($1 *to* $3).

359	1 c. Type **98**	10	30
360	2 c. Breadfruit	15	35
361	3 c. Straw market	15	25
362	4 c. Hawksbill turtle	1·00	2·50
363	5 c. Grouper	35	35
364	6 c. As 4 c. (21.9.71)	35	50
365	7 c. Hibiscus (21.9.71)	75	85
366	8 c. Yellow Elder	60	1·50
367	10 c. Bahamian sponge boat	40	30
368	11 c. Greater Flamingos	60	50
369	12 c. As 7 c	2·00	3·00
370	15 c. Bonefish	40	55
371	18 c. Royal Poinciana (21.9.71)	55	65
372	22 c. As 18 c.	2·75	4·50
373	50 c. Post Office, Nassau	1·40	2·25
374	$1 Pineapple (*vert*)	4·25	3·00
375	$2 Crawfish (*vert*)	4·50	6·00
376	$3 Junkanoo (*vert*)	5·00	10·00
359/376	*Set of* 18	22·00	32·00

See also Nos. 395/400, 460/73 and 518/25.

99 Snowflake

(Litho (15 c. additionally die-stamped in gold) Walsall)

1971 (19 Oct). *Christmas. T* **99** *and similar horiz designs. W* w **12**. *P* 14 × 14½.

377	3 c. deep reddish purple, orange and gold	10	10
378	11 c. light ultramarine and gold	20	15
379	15 c. multicoloured	20	20
380	18 c. bluish green, royal blue and gold	25	25
377/80	*Set of* 4	65	60
MS381	126 × 95 mm. Nos. 377/80. P 15	1·00	1·50

Designs:—11 c. "Peace on Earth" (doves); 15 c. Arms of Bahamas and holly; 18 c. Starlit lagoon.

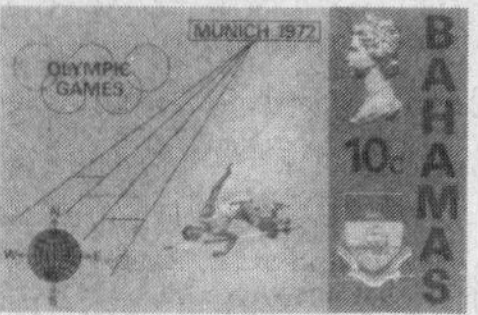

100 High jumping

(Des J. W. Litho B.W.)

1972 (11 July). *Olympic Games, Munich. T* **100** *and similar horiz designs. Multicoloured. W* w **12**. *P* 13½.

382	10 c. Type **100**	20	25
383	11 c. Cycling	25	30
384	15 c. Running	30	45
385	18 c. Sailing	50	70
382/5	*Set of* 4	1·10	1·50
MS386	127 × 95 mm. Nos. 382/5	1·40	2·00

101 Shepherd 102 Northerly Bahama Islands

(Des Jennifer Toombs. Litho (15 c. additionally embossed) J.W.)

1972 (3 Oct). *Christmas. T* **101** *and similar vert designs. Multicoloured.* W w **12** (*sideways on* 6 *and* 20 c.) *P* 14.

387 3 c. Type **101** 10 10
388 6 c. Bells 10 10
389 15 c. Holly and Cross 15 20
390 20 c. Poinsettia 25 45
387/90 .. .. *Set of* 4 50 70
MS391 108 × 140 mm. Nos. 387/90 (wmk sideways) 80 1·25

(Des M. Shamir. Litho Format)

1972 (1 Nov). *Tourism Year of the Americas. Sheet* 133 × 105 *mm, containing T* **102** *and similar vert designs. P* 15.

MS392 11, 15, 18 and 50 c. multicoloured .. 2·25 3·25

The four designs are printed horizontally *se-tenant* in **MS**392, forming a composite map design of the Bahamas.

103 Mace and Galleon

(Des (from photograph by D. Groves) and photo Harrison)

1972 (13 Nov). *Royal Silver Wedding. Multicoloured; background colour given.* W w **12**. *P* 14 × 14½.

393 **103** 11 c. rose 15 15
394 18 c. bluish violet 15 20

1972 (23 Nov)–**73**. *As Nos.* 363, 366 *and* 373/6 *but wmk sideways on* 5 *to* 50 *c.; upright on* $1 *to* $3.

395 5 c. Grouper .. .. 1·25 45
396 8 c. Yellow Elder (25.7.73) .. .. 1·50 95
397 50 c. Post Office, Nassau (25.7.73) .. .. 1·75 2·50
398 $1 Pineapple (25.7.73) .. .. 3·25 4·00
399 $2 Crawfish (25.7.73) .. .. 4·00 7·00
400 $3 Junkanoo (1973) .. .. 8·00 14·00
395/400 .. .. *Set of* 6 18·00 26·00

Nos. 401/9 vacant.

104 Weather Satellite

(Des C. Abbott. Litho Questa)

1973 (3 Apr). *I.M.O./W.M.O. Centenary. T* **104** *and similar horiz design. Multicoloured.* W w **12**. *P* 14.

410 15 c. Type **104** 20 25
411 18 c. Weather radar 25 35

INDEPENDENT

105 C. A. Bain (national hero) **106** "The Virgin in Prayer" (Sassoferrato)

(Des PAD Studio. Litho Questa)

1973 (10 July–1 Aug). *Independence. T* **105** *and similar vert designs. Multicoloured.* W w **12** (*sideways*). *P* 14½ × 14.

412 3 c. Type **105** 10 10
413 11 c. Coat of arms 10 10
414 15 c. Bahamas flag 15 15
415 $1 Governor-General, M. B. Butler (1 Aug) 75 1·00
412/15 .. .. *Set of* 4 95 1·10
MS416 86 × 121 mm. Nos. 412/15 (1 Aug) .. 1·00 1·75

(Des C. Abbott. Litho Format)

1973 (16 Oct). *Christmas. T* **106** *and similar vert designs. Multicoloured.* W w **12** (*sideways*). *P* 14.

417 3 c. Type **106** 10 10
418 11 c. "Virgin and Child with St. John" (Filippino Lippi) 15 15
419 15 c. "A Choir of Angels" (Simon Marmion) .. 15 15
420 18 c. "The Two Trinities" (Murillo) 25 25
417/20 .. .. *Set of* 4 60 55
MS421 120 × 99 mm. Nos. 417/20 .. .. .. 90 1·40

107 "Agriculture and Sciences"

(Des C. Abbott. Litho Questa)

1974 (5 Feb). *25th Anniv of University of West Indies. T* **107** *and similar horiz design. Multicoloured.* W w **12**. *P* 13½.

422 15 c. Type **107** 20 25
423 18 c. "Arts, Engineering and General Studies" 25 30

108 U.P.U. Monument, Berne

(Des P. Powell. Litho Questa)

1974 (23 Apr). *Centenary of Universal Postal Union. Designs as T* **108** *showing different arrangements of the U.P.U. Monument.* W w **12** (*upright on* 3 *c.,* 14 *c. and* **MS**428; *sideways on others*). *P* 14.

424 **108** 3 c. multicoloured 10 10
425 – 13 c. multicoloured (*vert*) 20 25
426 – 14 c. multicoloured 20 30
427 – 18 c. multicoloured (*vert*) 25 35
424/7 .. .. *Set of* 4 65 90
MS428 128 × 95 mm. Nos. 424/7 .. .. .. 80 1·40

109 Roseate Spoonbills

(Des G. Drummond. Litho Questa)

1974 (10 Sept). *15th Anniv of Bahamas National Trust. T* **109** *and similar horiz designs. Multicoloured.* W w **12** (*sideways*). *P* 13½.

429 13 c. Type **109** 85 65
430 14 c. White-crowned Pigeon 85 65
431 21 c. White-tailed Tropic Birds .. .. .. 1·25 1·00
432 36 c. Cuban Amazon .. .. 1·60 1·60
429/32 .. .. *Set of* 4 4·00 3·50
MS433 123 × 120 mm. Nos. 429/32 .. .. 4·00 5·00

110 "The Holy Family" (Jacques de Stella)

(Des J. W. Litho Enschedé)

1974 (29 Oct). *Christmas. T* **110** *and similar horiz designs. Multicoloured.* W w **12** (*sideways*). *P* 13 × 13½.

434 8 c. Type **110** 10 10
435 10 c. "Madonna and Child" (16th-cent Brescian School) 15 15
436 12 c. "Virgin and Child with St. John the Baptist and St. Catherine" (Previtali) .. 15 15
437 21 c. "Virgin and Child with Angels" (Previtali) 25 30
434/7 .. .. *Set of* 4 60 60
MS438 126 × 105 mm. Nos. 434/7 .. .. .. 80 1·40

111 *Anteos maerula*

(Des PAD Studio. Litho D.L.R.)

1975 (4 Feb). *Butterflies. T* **111** *and similar horiz designs. Multicoloured.* W w **12**. *P* 14 × 13½.

439 3 c. Type **111** 25 15
440 14 c. *Eurema nicippe* 80 50
441 18 c. *Papilio andraemon bonhotei* 95 65
442 21 c. *Euptoieta hegesia* .. .. 1·10 85
439/42 .. .. *Set of* 4 2·75 2·00
MS443 119 × 94 mm. Nos. 439/42 .. .. 3·50 3·00

112 Sheep Husbandry 113 Rowena Rand (evangelist)

(Des Daphne Padden. Litho Questa)

1975 (27 May). *Economic Diversification. T* **112** *and similar multicoloured designs. P* 14.

444 3 c. Type **112** 10 10
445 14 c. Electric-reel fishing (*vert*) 15 15
446 18 c. Farming 20 20
447 21 c. Oil Refinery (*vert*) 35 35
444/7 .. .. *Set of* 4 70 65
MS448 127 × 94 mm. Nos. 444/7 .. .. .. 85 1·50

(Des Jennifer Toombs. Litho Questa)

1975 (22 July). *International Women's Year. T* **113** *and similar vert design.* W w **14** (*sideways*). *P* 14.

449 14 c. bistre-brown, lt turquoise-blue & ultram 20 25
450 18 c. lemon, bright yellow-green and sepia .. 25 30

Design:—18 c. I.W.Y. symbol and Harvest symbol.

114 "Adoration of the Shepherds" (Perugino)

(Des Jennifer Toombs. Litho J.W.)

1975 (2 Dec). *Christmas. T* **114** *and similar horiz design. Multicoloured.* W w **14** (*sideways*). *P* 13.

451 3 c. Type **114** 10 10
452 8 c. "Adoration of the Magi" (Ghirlandaio) .. 15 10
453 18 c. As 8 c. 25 40
454 21 c. Type **114** 30 60
451/4 .. .. *Set of* 4 70 1·00
MS455 142 × 107 mm. Nos. 451/4. P 13½ .. 1·25 1·75

115 Telephones, 1876 and 1976

(Des G. Vasarhelyi. Litho D.L.R.)

1976 (23 Mar). *Telephone Centenary. T* **115** *and similar horiz designs. Multicoloured.* W w **14** (*sideways*). *P* 14.

456 3 c. Type **115** 10 10
457 16 c. Radio-telephone link, Deleporte 25 30
458 21 c. Alexander Graham Bell 35 45
459 25 c. Satellite 40 55
456/9 .. .. *Set of* 4 1·00 1·25

1976 (30 Mar)–**79**. *Designs as Nos.* 359/63, 365/7 *and* 373/6 (*some with new face values*). W w **14** (*sideways on* $1 *to* $3). *Ordinary paper.*

460 1 c. Type **98** (1.11.76) 90 90
a. Chalk-surfaced paper (1979) .. .. 5·50 6·00
461 2 c. Breadfruit 60 25
462 3 c. Straw market (1.11.76) .. .. .. 1·00 30
a. Chalk-surfaced paper (1979) 60 60
463 5 c. Grouper (1.11.76) .. .. 1·25 55
a. Chalk-surfaced paper (1979) 70 70
464 8 c. Yellow Elder 90 30
465 10 c. Bahamian sponge boat 80 30
466 16 c. As 7 c. (2.11.76) 70 35
a. Chalk-surfaced paper (1979) 70 80
467 21 c. As 2 c. (2.11.76) 80 70
a. Chalk-surfaced paper (1979) .. .. 80 1·25
468 25 c. As 4 c. (2.11.76) 75 40
a. Chalk-surfaced paper (1979) .. .. 90 2·00
469 40 c. As 10 c. (2.11.76) .. .. 1·00 75
470 50 c. Post Office, Nassau .. .. 1·75 1·75
471 $1 Pineapple .. .. 2·25 2·50
472 $2 Crawfish (2.5.76) .. .. 3·75 5·50
a. Chalk-surfaced paper (1979) .. .. 15·00 18·00
473 $3 Junkanoo (1.11.76) .. .. 5·00 9·00
460/73 .. .. *Set of* 14 19·00 21·00
460a72a .. .. *Set of* 7 22·00 26·00

No. 474 vacant.

116 Map of North America

(Des and litho Walsall)

1976 (1 June). *Bicentenary of American Revolution. T* **116** *and similar horiz design. Multicoloured. W* w **14** (*sideways*). *P* 14.

475 16 c. Type **116** 30 30
476 $1 John Murray, Earl of Dunmore .. .. 1·50 1·75
MS477 127 × 100 mm. No. 476 × 4 .. .. 5·50 7·50

117 Cycling

118 "Virgin and Child" (detail, Lippi)

1976 (13 July). *Olympic Games, Montreal. T* **117** *and similar vert designs. W* w **14**. *P* 14.

478 8 c. magenta, blue and pale cobalt 10 10
479 16 c. orange, brown and pale cobalt 15 15
480 25 c. blue, deep magenta and pale cobalt .. 25 35
481 40 c. brown, orange and pale cobalt 30 55
478/81 .. .. *Set of* 4 70 1·00
MS482 100 × 126 mm. Nos. 478/81 .. .. 1·00 1·75
Designs:—16 c. Jumping; 25 c. Sailing; 40 c. Boxing.

(Des G. Drummond. Litho Questa)

1976 (5 Oct). *Christmas. T* **118** *and similar vert designs. Multicoloured. W* w **14**. *P* 14.

483 3 c. Type **118** 10 10
484 21 c. "Adoration of the Shepherds" (School of Seville) 15 15
485 25 c. "Adoration of the Kings" (detail, Foppa) 15 20
486 40 c. "Virgin and Child" (detail, Vivarini) .. 25 40
483/6 .. .. *Set of* 4 60 75
MS487 107 × 127 mm. Nos. 483/6 .. .. 1·00 1·50

119 Queen beneath Cloth of Gold Canopy

(Des G. Vasarhelyi. Litho Cartor S.A., France)

1977 (7 Feb). *Silver Jubilee. T* **119** *and similar horiz designs. Multicoloured. No wmk. P* 12.

488 8 c. Type **119** 10 10
489 16 c. The Crowning 15 15
490 21 c. Taking the Oath 15 15
491 40 c. Queen with sceptre and orb 25 30
488/91 .. .. *Set of* 4 60 60
MS492 122 × 90 mm. Nos. 488/91 .. .. 80 1·25

120 Featherduster

(Des BG Studio. Litho J.W.)

1977 (24 May). *Marine Life. T* **120** *and similar designs. Multicoloured. W* w 14 (*sideways*). *P* 13½.

493 3 c. Type **120** 15 15
494 8 c. Pork Fish and cave 30 20
495 16 c. Elkhorn Coral 55 40
496 21 c. Soft Coral and sponge 65 55
493/6 .. .. *Set of* 4 1·50 1·10
MS497 119 × 93 mm. Nos. 493/6. P 14½ .. .. 2·50 3·00

121 Scouts around Campfire and Home-made Shower

Royal Visit
October 1977
(122)

(Des Harrison. Litho J.W.)

1977 (27 Sept). *Sixth Caribbean Scout Jamboree. T* **121** *and similar horiz design. Multicoloured. W* w **14** (*sideways*). *P* 13½.

498 16 c. Type **121** 30 20
499 21 c. Boating scenes 40 25
One used example of No. 498 is known with the mauve (face value and inscription) omitted.

1977 (19 Oct). *Royal Visit. As Nos.* 488/492, *but W* w **14** (*sideways*), *optd with T* **122**.

500 8 c. Type **119** 15 10
501 16 c. The Crowning 20 15
502 21 c. Taking the Oath 25 20
503 40 c. Queen with sceptre and orb 30 40
500/3 .. .. *Set of* 4 80 75
MS504 122 × 90 mm. Nos. 500/3 .. .. .. 1·00 1·40

123 Virgin and Child

124 Public Library, Nassau (Colonial)

(Des and litho J.W.)

1977 (25 Oct). *Christmas. T* **123** *and similar vert designs. Multicoloured. W* w **14**. *P* 13½.

505 3 c. Type **123** 10 10
506 16 c. The Magi 20 25
507 21 c. Nativity scene 25 40
508 25 c. The Magi and star 30 45
505/8 .. .. *Set of* 4 75 1·10
MS509 136 × 74 mm. Nos. 505/8. P 14 .. .. 75 1·40

(Des G. Drummond. Litho Questa)

1978 (28 Mar). *Architectural Heritage. T* **124** *and similar vert designs. W* w **14**. *P* 14½ × 14.

510 3 c. black and apple-green 10 10
511 8 c. black and pale greenish blue 10 10
512 16 c. black and mauve 15 20
513 18 c. black and salmon-pink 20 30
510/13 .. .. *Set of* 4 50 65
MS514 91 × 91 mm. Nos. 510/13 .. .. .. 60 1·00
Designs:—8 c. St. Matthew's Church (Gothic); 16 c. Government House (Colonial); 18 c. Hermitage, Cat Island (Spanish).

125 Sceptre, St. Edward's Crown and Orb

126 Coat of Arms within Wreath and Three Ships

(Des BG Studio. Litho Enschedé)

1978 (27 June). *25th Anniv of Coronation. T* **125** *and similar vert design. Multicoloured. W* w **14**. *P* 14 × 13½.

515 16 c. Type **125** 15 10
516 $1 Queen in Coronation regalia 50 65
MS517 147 × 96 mm. Nos. 515/16 .. .. 1·25 1·50

1978 (June). *As Nos.* 359/76, *but no wmk.*

518 1 c. Type **98** 25 60
519 5 c. Grouper 50 50
520 16 c. Hibiscus .. .. 1·00 90
521 25 c. Hawksbill Turtle .. .. 1·25 1·50
522 50 c. Post Office, Nassau .. .. .. 1·75 2·50
523 $1 Pineapple .. .. 2·50 3·00
524 $2 Crawfish .. .. 3·75 6·50
525 $3 Junkanoo .. .. 4·50 6·50
518/25 .. .. *Set of* 8 14·00 20·00
Nos. 526/31 vacant.

(Des Jennifer Toombs. Litho Questa)

1978 (14 Nov). *Christmas. T* **126** *and similar horiz design. W* w **14** (*sideways*). *P* 14 × 14½.

532 5 c. gold, bright crimson and bright rose .. 10 10
533 21 c. gold, deep ultramarine and violet-blue .. 25 25
MS534 95 × 95 mm. Nos. 532/3 .. .. .. 1·50 2·25
Design:—21 c. Three angels with trumpets.

ALTERED CATALOGUE NUMBERS

Any Catalogue numbers altered from the last edition are shown as a list in the introductory pages.

127 Child reaching for Adult

128 Sir Rowland Hill and Penny Black

(Litho J.W.)

1979 (15 May). *International Year of the Child. T* **127** *and similar vert designs. Multicoloured. W* w **14**. *P* 13.

535 5 c. Type **127** 10 10
536 16 c. Boys playing leap-frog 20 25
537 21 c. Girls skipping 25 30
538 25 c. Bricks with I.Y.C. emblem 25 30
535/8 .. .. *Set of* 4 70 85
MS539 101 × 125 mm. Nos. 535/8. P 14 .. .. 75 1·00

(Des J. Cooter. Litho Walsall)

1979 (14 Aug). *Death Centenary of Sir Rowland Hill. T* **128** *and similar horiz designs. Multicoloured. W* w **14** (*sideways*). *P* 13½ × 14.

540 10 c. Type **128** 15 10
541 21 c. Printing press, 1840 and 6d. stamp of 1862 25 30
542 25 c. Great Britain 6d. stamp of 1856 with "A 05" (Nassau) cancellation and Two-penny blue 30 35
543 40 c. Early mailboat and 1d. stamp of 1859 .. 40 45
540/3 .. .. *Set of* 4 1·00 1·10
MS544 115 × 80 mm. Nos. 540/3 .. .. .. 1·25 1·60

129 Commemorative Plaque and Map of Bahamas

130 Goombay Carnival Headdress

(Des G. Drummond. Litho Secura, Singapore)

1979 (27 Sept). *250th Anniv of Parliament. T* **129** *and similar horiz designs. Multicoloured. W* w **14** (*sideways*). *P* 13½.

545 16 c. Type **129** 15 10
546 21 c. Parliament buildings 20 15
547 25 c. Legislative Chamber 20 15
548 $1 Senate Chamber 70 80
545/8 .. .. *Set of* 4 1·10 1·00
MS549 116 × 89 mm. Nos. 545/8 (wmk upright) 1·75 2·10

(Des BG Studio. Litho J.W.)

1979 (6 Nov). *Christmas. T* **130** *and similar vert designs showing Goombay Carnival headdresses. W* w **14**. *P* 13.

550 5 c. multicoloured 10 10
551 10 c. multicoloured 10 10
552 16 c. multicoloured 15 10
553 21 c. multicoloured 20 20
554 25 c. multicoloured 20 20
555 40 c. multicoloured 30 35
550/5 .. .. *Set of* 6 90 85
MS556 50 × 88 mm. Nos. 550/5 (wmk sideways). P 13½ .. .. 1·25 1·40

131 Landfall of Columbus, 1492

132 Virgin and Child

(Des J. W. Litho Format)

1980 (9 July). *Horiz designs as T* **131**. *Multicoloured. W* w **14**. *P* 14½.

557 1 c. Type **131** 15 20
558 3 c. Blackbeard the Pirate, 1718 .. .. 15 15
559 5 c. Eleutheran Adventurers (Articles and Orders, 1647) 20 10
560 10 c. Ceremonial Mace 15 15
561 12 c. The Loyalists, 1783–88 (Colonel Andrew Deveaux) 20 25
562 15 c. Slave Trading, Vendue House .. .. 1·00 25
563 16 c. Wrecking in the 1800's 30 25
564 18 c. Blockade running (American Civil War) 40 40
565 21 c. Bootlegging, 1919–29 .. .. .. 40 40
566 25 c. Pineapple cultivation 40 45
567 40 c. Sponge clipping 70 75
568 50 c. Tourist development 75 75
569 $1 Modern agriculture .. .. .. 1·40 1·75
570 $2 Modern air and sea transport .. .. 3·00 3·00
571 $3 Banking in the Bahamas (Central Bank) 3·50 4·00
572 $5 Independence, 10 July 1973 (Prince of Wales and Prime Minister L.O. Pindling) 5·50 6·00
557/72 .. .. *Set of* 16 16·00 17·00
See also Nos. 720/6 for stamps watermarked w **16**.

(Des B. Malone. Litho Walsall)

1980 (28 Oct). *Christmas. Straw-work. T* **132** *and similar vert designs. Multicoloured.* W w **14**. P 14½ × 14.

573 5 c. Type **132** 10 10
574 21 c. Three Kings 20 10
575 25 c. Angel 20 15
576 $1 Christmas Tree 65 70
573/6 .. .. *Set of* 4 1·00 80
MS577 168 × 105 mm. Nos. 573/6 .. .. 1·00 1·60

133 Disabled Person with Walking-stick

(Des and litho Walsall)

1981 (10 Feb). *International Year for Disabled Persons. T* **133** *and similar horiz design. Multicoloured.* W w **14** (*sideways*). P 14½ × 14.

578 5 c. Type **133** 10 10
579 $1 Disabled person in wheelchair .. .. 1·25 1·25
MS580 120 × 60 mm. Nos. 578/9 .. .. .. 1·40 2·00

134 Grand Bahama Tracking Site

135 Prince Charles and Lady Diana Spencer

(Litho Enschedé)

1981 (21 Apr). *Space Exploration. T* **134** *and similar multicoloured designs.* W w **14** (*sideways on* 10 *and* 25 *c.*). P 13½.

581 10 c. Type **134** 15 15
582 20 c. Satellite view of Bahamas (*vert*) .. 35 35
583 25 c. Satellite view of Eleuthera 40 40
584 50 c. Satellite view of Andros and New Providence (*vert*) 65 65
581/4 .. .. *Set of* 4 1·40 1·40
MS585 115 × 99 mm. Nos. 581/4 (wmk sideways) 1·40 1·75

(Des C. Abbott. Litho Questa)

1981 (22 July). *Royal Wedding. T* **135** *and similar horiz design. Multicoloured.* W w **14** (*sideways*). P 14 × 14½.

586 30 c. Type **135** 75 25
587 $2 Prince Charles and Prime Minister Pindling .. .. 3·75 1·75
MS588 142 × 120 mm. Nos. 586/7 .. .. 5·00 2·50
a. Upper stamp in miniature sheet imperf on 3 sides £600

No. **MS**588a shows the upper stamp in the miniature sheet perforated at foot only.

136 Bahama Pintail

(Des Walsall. Litho Questa)

1981 (25 Aug). *Wildlife* (1*st series*). *Birds. T* **136** *and similar horiz designs. Multicoloured.* W w **14** (*sideways*). P 14.

589 5 c. Type **136** 30 10
590 20 c. Reddish Egret 55 35
591 25 c. Brown Booby 60 40
592 $1 Black-billed Whistling Duck .. .. 1·75 2·50
589/92 .. .. *Set of* 4 3·00 3·00
MS593 100 × 74 mm. Nos. 589/92 .. .. 3·00 3·50

See also Nos. 626/30, 653/7 and 690/4.

21 - 23 SEPTEMBER 1981

COMMONWEALTH FINANCE MINISTERS' MEETING

(137)

1981 (21 Sept). *Commonwealth Finance Ministers' Meeting. Nos.* 559/60, 566 *and* 568 *optd with T* **137**.

594 5 c. Eleutheran Adventurers (Articles and Orders, 1647) 10 15
a. Opt inverted .. .. 80·00
595 10 c. Ceremonial Mace 15 20
596 25 c. Pineapple cultivation 40 50
597 50 c. Tourist development .. .. .. 75 1·00
594/7 .. .. *Set of* 4 1·25 1·75

138 Poultry

139 Father Christmas

(Des L. McCombie. Litho J.W.)

1981 (16 Oct). *World Food Day. T* **138** *and similar horiz designs. Multicoloured.* W w **14** (*sideways*). P 13.

598 5 c. Type **138** 10 10
599 20 c. Sheep 30 35
600 30 c. Lobsters 40 50
601 50 c. Pigs .. .. 75 1·25
598/601 .. .. *Set of* 4 1·40 2·00
MS602 115 × 63 mm. Nos. 598/601. P 14 .. 1·50 2·50

(Des local artists. Litho Format)

1981 (24 Nov). *Christmas. T* **139** *and similar vert designs. Multicoloured.* W w **14**. P 13½ × 14.

603 5 c. Type **139** 15 15
a. Sheetlet of 9. Nos. 603/11 .. .. 3·00
604 5 c. Mother and child 15 15
605 5 c. St. Nicholas, Holland 15 15
606 25 c. Lussibruden, Sweden 40 40
607 25 c. Mother and child (*different*) 40 40
608 25 c. King Wenceslas, Czechoslovakia .. 40 40
609 30 c. Mother with child on knee 40 40
610 30 c. Mother carrying child 40 40
611 $1 Christkindl Angel, Germany .. .. 1·00 1·00
603/11 .. .. *Set of* 9 3·00 3·00

Nos. 603/11 were printed together, *se-tenant*, in a sheetlet of 9.

140 Robert Koch

141 Male Flamingo (*Phoenicopterus ruber*)

(Des A. Theobald. Litho Harrison)

1982 (3 Feb). *Centenary of Discovery of Tubercle Bacillus by Robert Koch. T* **140** *and similar horiz designs.* W w **14** (*sideways*). P 14.

612 5 c. black, red-brown and rose-lilac 20 10
613 16 c. black, drab and dull orange 45 35
614 21 c. multicoloured 50 40
615 $1 multicoloured .. .. 2·00 2·50
612/15 .. .. *Set of* 4 2·75 3·00
MS616 94 × 97 mm. Nos. 612/15. P 14½ .. 3·00 3·75

Designs:—16 c. Stylised infected person; 21 c. Early and modern microscopes; $1 Mantoux test.

(Des N. Arlott. Litho Questa)

1982 (28 Apr). *Greater Flamingos. T* **141** *and similar vert designs. Multicoloured.* W w **14**. P 14 × 13½.

617 25 c. Type **141** 60 65
a. Horiz strip of 5. Nos. 617/21 .. .. 2·75
618 25 c. Female 60 65
619 25 c. Female with nestling 60 65
620 25 c. Juvenile 60 65
621 25 c. Immature bird 60 65
617/21 .. .. *Set of* 5 2·75 3·00

Nos. 617/21 were printed together, *se-tenant*, in horizontal strips of 5 throughout the sheet, forming a composite design.

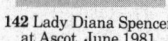

142 Lady Diana Spencer at Ascot, June 1981

143 House of Assembly Plaque

(Des C. Abbott. Litho Format)

1982 (1 July). 21*st Birthday of Princess of Wales. T* **142** *and similar vert designs. Multicoloured.* W w **14**. P 13½ × 14 (16 *c.*, $1) *or* 13½ (*others*).

622 16 c. Bahamas coat of arms 20 10
a. Perf 13½ .. .. 1·00 1·00
623 25 c. Type **142** 35 15
624 40 c. Bride and Earl Spencer arriving at St. Paul's 50 20
625 $1 Formal portrait .. .. 1·00 1·25
622/5 .. .. *Set of* 4 1·90 1·40

(Des Walsall. Litho Questa)

1982 (18 Aug). *Wildlife* (2*nd series*). *Mammals. Horiz designs as T* **136**. *Multicoloured.* W w **14** (*sideways*). P 14.

626 10 c. Buffy Flower Bat 25 15
627 16 c. Bahaman Hutia 40 25
628 21 c. Common Racoon 55 35
629 $1 Common Dolphin .. .. 1·75 1·75
626/9 .. .. *Set of* 4 2·75 2·25
MS630 115 × 76 mm. Nos. 626/9 .. .. .. 2·75 3·00

(Des and litho Walsall)

1982 (16 Oct). 28*th Commonwealth Parliamentary Association Conference. T* **143** *and similar vert designs. Multicoloured.* W w **14**. P 14 × 13½.

631 5 c. Type **143** 15 10
632 25 c. Association coat of arms 45 35
633 40 c. Coat of arms 70 60
634 50 c. House of Assembly 85 75
631/4 .. .. *Set of* 4 1·90 1·60

144 Wesley Methodist Church, Baillou Hill Road

(Des Jennifer Toombs. Litho Format)

1982 (3 Nov). *Christmas. Churches. T* **144** *and similar horiz designs. Multicoloured.* W w **14** (*sideways*). P 14.

635 5 c. Type **144** 10 10
636 12 c. Centreville Seventh Day Adventist Church 20 20
637 15 c. The Church of God of Prophecy, East Street 25 25
638 21 c. Bethel Baptist Church, Meeting Street 30 30
639 25 c. St. Francis Xavier Catholic Church, Highbury Park 35 40
640 $1 Holy Cross Anglican Church, Highbury Park .. .. 1·50 2·25
635/40 .. .. *Set of* 6 2·50 3·25

145 Prime Minister Lynden O. Pindling

(Des Walsall. Litho Questa)

1983 (14 Mar). *Commonwealth Day T* **145** *and similar horiz designs. Multicoloured.* W w **14** (*sideways*). P 14.

641 5 c. Type **145** 10 10
642 25 c. Bahamian and Commonwealth flags .. 40 40
643 35 c. Map showing position of Bahamas .. 50 50
644 $1 Ocean liner .. .. 1·40 1·40
641/4 .. .. *Set of* 4 2·10 2·10

═ **20c**

(146)

1983 (5 Apr). *Nos.* 562/5 *surch as T* **146**.

645 20 c. on 15 c. Slave Trading, Vendue House .. 35 35
646 31 c. on 21 c. Bootlegging, 1919–29 .. .. 55 55
647 35 c. on 16 c. Wrecking in the 1800's 60 60
648 80 c. on 18 c. Blockade running (American Civil War) .. .. 1·40 1·40
645/8 .. .. *Set of* 4 2·50 2·50

147 Customs Officers and Liner

148 Raising the National Flag

(Des Walsall. Litho Harrison)

1983 (31 May). 30*th Anniv of Customs Co-operation Council. T* **147** *and similar vert design. Multicoloured.* W w **14**. P 13½ × 13.

649 31 c. Type **147** 75 45
650 $1 Customs officers and airliner .. .. 2·00 2·00

(Des L. Curtis. Litho Questa)

1983 (6 July). 10*th Anniv of Independence.* W w **14**. P 14.

651 **148** $1 multicoloured .. .. 1·25 1·40
MS652 105 × 65 mm. No. 651. P 12 .. .. 1·25 1·40

(Des F. Solomon, adapted N. Arlott. Litho Harrison)

1983 (24 Aug). *Wildlife (3rd series). Butterflies. Horiz designs as T* **136**. *W* w **14** *(sideways). P* 14½ × 14.

653 5 c. multicoloured 25 10
654 25 c. multicoloured 65 40
655 31 c. black, bistre-yellow and bright rose-red 75 45
656 50 c. multicoloured 90 70
653/6 .. .. *Set of* 4 2·25 1·50
MS657 120 × 80 mm. Nos. 653/6 .. .. .. 2·25 2·50
a. Perf 14 .. .. 2·50 3·00

Designs:—5 c. Carter's Skipper; 25 c. Great Southern White; 31 c. Large Orange Sulphur; 50 c. The Flambeau.

No. **MS**657a was perforated by Questa, the remainder of the issue by Harrison.

149 "Loyalist Dreams" **150** Consolidated "Catalina"

(Des A. Lowe; adapted C. Abbott. Litho Questa)

1983 (28 Sept). *Bicentenary of Arrival of American Loyalists in the Bahamas. T* **149** *and similar multicoloured designs. W* w **14** *(sideways on* 31 *c.,* 35 *c.). P* 14.

658 5 c. Type **149** 10 10
659 31 c. New Plymouth, Abaco (*horiz*) 45 50
660 35 c. New Plymouth Hotel (*horiz*) 50 70
661 50 c. "Island Hope" 65 90
658/61 .. .. *Set of* 4 1·50 2·00
MS662 111 × 76 mm. Nos. 658/61. Wmk sideways 1·50 2·25

(Des and litho Harrison)

1983 (13 Oct). *Air Bicentenary of Manned Flight. T* **150** *and similar horiz designs. Multicoloured. W* w **14** *(sideways). P* 14.

663 10 c. Type **150** 15 15
664 25 c. Avro "Tudor IV" 35 40
665 31 c. Avro "Lancastrian" 40 45
666 35 c. Consolidated "Commodore" 45 50
663/6 .. .. *Set of* 4 1·25 1·40

For these stamps without the Manned Flight logo see Nos. 699/702.

151 "Christmas Bells" (Monica Pinder) **152** 1861 4d. Stamp

(Des local children, adapted G. Vasarhelyi. Litho Walsall)

1983 (1 Nov). *Christmas. Children's Paintings. T* **151** *and similar multicoloured designs. W* w **14** *(sideways on* 31 *c. and* 50 *c.). P* 14.

667 5 c. Type **151** 10 10
668 20 c. "Flamingo" (Cory Bullard) 25 30
669 25 c. "Yellow Hibiscus with Christmas Candle" (Monique Bailey) 35 40
670 31 c. "Santa goes a Sailing" (Sabrina Seiler) (*horiz*) 40 45
671 35 c. "Silhouette scene with Palm Trees" (James Blake) 45 50
672 50 c. "Silhouette scene with Pelicans" (Erik Russell) (*horiz*) 65 70
667/72 .. .. *Set of* 6 1·90 2·25

(Des D. Miller. Litho Format)

1984 (22 Feb). *125th Anniv of First Bahamas Postage Stamp. T* **152** *and similar vert design. Multicoloured. W* w **14**. *P* 14.

673 5 c. Type **152** 10 10
674 $1 1859 1d. stamp .. .. 1·40 1·50

153 R.M.S. *Trent* **154** Running

(Des L. Curtis. Litho Questa)

1984 (25 Apr). *250th Anniv of "Lloyd's List" (newspaper). T* **153** *and similar vert designs. Multicoloured. W* w **14**. *P* 14½ × 14.

675 5 c. Type **153** 10 10
676 31 c. R.M.S. *Orinoco* 55 60
677 35 c. Nassau harbour 60 65
678 50 c. M.V. *Oropesa* (container ship) 90 95
675/8 .. .. *Set of* 4 1·90 2·10

(Des McCombie Skinner Studio. Litho Questa)

1984 (20 June). *Olympic Games, Los Angeles. T* **154** *and similar horiz designs. W* w **14** *(sideways). P* 14 × 14½.

679 5 c. green, black and gold 10 10
680 25 c. new blue, black and gold 45 50
681 31 c. brown-lake, black and gold 55 60
682 $1 sepia, black and gold .. .. .. 1·75 2·00
679/82 .. .. *Set of* 4 2·50 2·75
MS683 115 × 80 mm. Nos. 679/82 .. .. 2·75 3·25

Designs:— 25 c. Shot-putting; 31 c. Boxing; $1 Basketball.

155 Bahamas and Caribbean Community Flags **156** Bahama Woodstar

(Des McCombie Skinner Studio. Litho Questa)

1984 (4 July). *5th Conference of Caribbean Community Heads of Government. W* w **14**. *P* 14.

684 **155** 50 c. multicoloured 90 95

(Des N. Arlott. Litho Questa)

1984 (15 Aug). *25th Anniv of National Trust. T* **156** *and similar vert designs. Multicoloured. W* w **14**. *P* 14.

685 31 c. Type **156** 65 80
a. Horiz strip of 5. Nos. 685/9 .. .. 3·00
686 31 c. Belted Kingfishers, Greater Flamingos and *Eleutherodactylus planirostris* (frog) 65 80
687 31 c. Black-necked Stilts, Greater Flamingos and *Phoebis sennae* (butterfly) .. 65 80
688 31 c. *Urbanis proteus* (butterfly) and *Chelonia mydas* (turtle) 65 80
689 31 c. Osprey and Greater Flamingos 65 80
685/9 .. .. *Set of* 5 3·00 3·50

Nos. 685/9 were printed together, *se-tenant*, in horizontal strips of 5 throughout the sheet, forming a composite design.

(Des N. Arlott. Litho Questa)

1984 (18 Sept). *Wildlife (4th series). Reptiles and Amphibians. Horiz designs as T* **136**. *W* w **14** *(sideways). P* 14.

690 5 c. Allen's Cay Iguana 20 10
691 25 c. Curly-tailed Lizard 65 50
692 35 c. Greenhouse Frog 75 65
693 50 c. Atlantic Green Turtle .. .. .. 1·10 95
690/3 .. .. *Set of* 4 2·40 2·00
MS694 112 × 82 mm. Nos. 690/3 .. .. 2·25 3·00

157 "The Holy Virgin with Jesus and Johannes" (19th-century porcelain plaque after Titian) **158** Brownie Emblem and Conch

(Des D. Slater. Litho J.W.)

1984 (7 Nov). *Christmas. Religious Paintings. T* **157** *and similar vert designs. Multicoloured. W* w **14**. *P* 13½.

695 5 c. Type **157** 10 10
696 31 c. "Madonna with Child in Tropical Landscape" (aquarelle, Anais Colin) 55 60
697 35 c. "The Holy Virgin with the Child" (miniature on ivory, Elena Caula) 60 65
695/7 .. .. *Set of* 3 1·10 1·25
MS698 116 × 76 mm. Nos. 695/7. P 14. .. .. 1·25 1·75

1985 (2 Jan). *Air. As Nos.* 663/6, *but without Manned Flight logo. W* w **14** *(sideways). P* 14.

699 10 c. Type **150** 20 20
700 25 c. Avro "Tudor IV" 40 40
701 31 c. Avro "Lancastrian" 40 45
702 35 c. Consolidated "Commodore" 40 45
699/702 .. .. *Set of* 4 1·25 1·40

See also Nos. 752/3 for stamps watermarked w **16** (sideways).

(Des Berta Dallen Sands. Litho Walsall)

1985 (22 Feb). *International Youth Year. 75th Anniv of Girl Guide Movement. T* **158** *and similar horiz designs. Multicoloured. W* w **14** *(sideways). P* 14.

703 5 c. Type **158** 15 10
704 25 c. Tents and coconut palm 50 50
705 31 c. Guide salute and Greater Flamingos .. 60 60
706 35 c. Ranger emblem and marlin 65 65
703/6 .. .. *Set of* 4 1·75 1·75
MS707 95 × 74 mm. Nos. 703/6 .. .. .. 1·75 2·25

159 Killdeer **160** The Queen Mother at the Christening of Peter Phillips, 1977

(Des Josephine Martin. Litho Walsall)

1985 (24 Apr). *Birth Bicentenary of John J. Audubon (ornithologist). T* **159** *and similar multicoloured designs. W* w **14** *(sideways on* 5 *c.,* $1*). P* 14.

708 5 c. Type **159** 25 10
709 31 c. Mourning Dove (*vert*) 65 55
710 35 c. "Mourning Dove" (John J. Audubon) (*vert*) 70 60
711 $1 "Killdeer" (John J. Audubon) .. .. 1·50 1·60
708/11 .. .. *Set of* 4 2·75 2·50

(Des A. Theobald ($1.25), C. Abbott (others). Litho Questa)

1985 (7 June). *Life and Times of Queen Elizabeth the Queen Mother. T* **160** *and similar vert designs. Multicoloured. W* w **16**. *P* 14½ × 14.

712 5 c. Visiting Auckland, New Zealand, 1927 .. .. 10 10
713 25 c. Type **160** 40 40
714 35 c. The Queen Mother attending church .. 55 55
715 50 c. With Prince Henry at his christening (from photo by Lord Snowdon) 75 75
712/15 .. .. *Set of* 4 1·60 1·60
MS716 91 × 73 mm. $1.25, In horse-drawn carriage, Sark. Wmk sideways .. .. .. 1·75 1·90

161 Ears of Wheat and Emblems **162** Queen Elizabeth II

(Des A. Theobald. Litho Questa)

1985 (26 Aug). *40th Anniv of United Nations and F.A.O. (Food and Agriculture Organization). W* w **16** *(sideways). P* 14.

717 **161** 25 c. multicoloured 35 40

(Des L. Curtis. Litho Walsall)

1985 (16 Oct). *Commonwealth Heads of Government Meeting, Nassau. T* **162** *and similar vert design. Multicoloured. W* w **16**. *P* 14½.

718 31 c. Type **162** 70 65
719 35 c. Bahamas Prime Minister's flag and Commonwealth emblem 80 85

1985 (6 Nov). *As Nos.* 557/8, 560 *and* 566, *but W* w **16**. *P* 14½.

720 1 c. Type **131** 40 60
721 3 c. Blackbeard the Pirate, 1718 .. .. 55 60
723 10 c. Ceremonial Mace .. .. 1·00 50
726 25 c. Pineapple cultivation .. .. .. 2·50 2·50
720/6 .. .. *Set of* 4 4·00 3·75

163 "Grandma's Christmas Bouquet" (Alton Roland Lowe)

(Des D. Miller. Litho J.W.)

1985 (12 Nov). *Christmas. Paintings by Alton Roland Lowe. T* **163** *and similar multicoloured designs. W* w **16** *(sideways on* 5, 35 *c.). P* 13 × 13½ (5, 35 c.) *or* 13½ × 13 (*others*).

736 5 c. Type **163** 15 10
737 25 c. "Junkanoo Romeo and Juliet" (*vert*) .. 50 50
738 31 c. "Bunce Gal" (*vert*) 60 60
739 35 c. "Home for Christmas" 70 70
736/9 .. .. *Set of* 4 1·75 1·75
MS740 110 × 68 mm. Nos. 736/9. Wmk sideways. P 14 .. .. 1·40 1·90

(Des A. Theobald. Litho Harrison)

1986 (21 Apr). *60th Birthday of Queen Elizabeth II. Vert designs as T* **110** *of Ascension. Multicoloured. W* w **16**. *P* 14½ × 14.

741 10 c. Princess Elizabeth aged one, 1927 .. 15 20
742 25 c. The Coronation, 1953 .. .. .. 35 40
743 35 c. Queen making speech at Commonwealth Banquet, Bahamas, 1985 .. 50 55
744 40 c. In Djakova, Yugoslavia, 1972 .. .. 55 60
745 $1 At Crown Agents Head Office, London, 1983 .. .. 1·40 1·50
741/5 .. .. *Set of* 5 2·75 3·00

164 1980 1 c. and 18 c. Definitive Stamps

(Des G. Drummond. Litho Walsall)

1986 (19 May). *"Ameripex '86" International Stamp Exhibition, Chicago. T* **164** *and similar designs. W w* **16** *(sideways on* 5 to 50 c). *P* 14.

746 5 c. multicoloured 10 10
747 25 c. multicoloured 35 40
748 31 c. multicoloured 40 45
749 50 c. multicoloured 70 75
750 $1 black, emerald and pale blue .. .. 1·40 1·75
746/50 .. .. *Set of* 5 2·50 3·00
MS751 80×80 mm. No. 750 .. .. 1·40 1·50

Designs: *Horiz* (showing Bahamas stamps)—25 c. 1969 50th Anniversary of Bahamas Airmail Service pair; 31 c. 1976 Bicentenary of American Revolution 16 c.; 50 c. 1981 Space Exploration miniature sheet. *Vert*—$1 Statue of Liberty.

Nos. 750/1 also commemorate the Centenary of the Statue of Liberty.

1986 (17 June). *Air. As Nos.* 699/700, *but W w* **16** *(sideways)*. *P* 14.

752 10 c. Type **150**.. .. .. 20 15
753 25 c. Avro "Tudor IV" 45 50

(Des D. Miller. Litho Walsall)

1986 (23 July). *Royal Wedding. Square designs as T* **112** *of Ascension. Multicoloured. W w* **16**. *P* 14½×14.

756 10 c. Prince Andrew and Miss Sarah Ferguson 20 20
757 $1 Prince Andrew .. .. 1·60 1·60

165 Rock Beauty (juvenile)

166 Christ Church Cathedral, Nassau, 1861

(Des Harrison Studio. Litho Questa)

1986 (5 Aug)–**87**. *Fishes. T* **165** *and similar horiz designs. Multicoloured. W w* **16**. *P* 14.

758 5 c. Type **165**.. .. .. 15 15
759 10 c. Stoplight Parrotfish 25 20
760 15 c. Jackknife Fish 40 35
761 20 c. Flamefish 20 25
762 25 c. Swissguard Basslet 25 30
763 30 c. Spotfin Butterflyfish 35 40
764 35 c. Queen Triggerfish 40 45
765 40 c. Four-eyed Butterflyfish 60 60
766 45 c. Fairy Basslet 80 80
767 50 c. Queen Angelfish 85 85
768 60 c. Blue Chromis .. .. 1·00 1·00
769 $1 Spanish Hogfish .. .. 1·25 1·25
770 $2 Harlequin Bass .. .. 2·75 2·75
771 $3 Blackbar Soldier Fish .. .. 3·25 3·50
772 $5 Pygmy Angelfish .. .. 5·50 5·75
773 $10 Red Hind (2.1.87) .. .. 11·00 11·50
758/73 .. .. *Set of* 16 26·00 27·00

Nos. 765 and 769/70 exist with different imprint dates below the designs.

For these designs watermarked w 14 see Nos. 791/9.

(Des L. Curtis. Litho Walsall)

1986 (16 Sept). *125th Annivs of City of Nassau, Diocese and Cathedral. T* **166** *and similar vert design. Multicoloured. W w* **16**. *P* 14½×14.

774 10 c. Type **166**.. .. .. 15 20
775 40 c. Christ Church Cathedral, 1986 .. .. 55 60
MS776 75×100 mm. Nos. 774/5 .. .. 70 1·00

167 Man and Boy looking at Crib

168 Great Isaac Lighthouse

(Des Jennifer Toombs. Litho Questa)

1986 (4 Nov). *Christmas. International Peace Year. T* **167** *and similar horiz designs. Multicoloured. W w* **16** *(sideways)*. *P* 14.

777 10 c. Type **167**.. .. .. 15 20
778 40 c. Mary and Joseph journeying to Bethlehem 55 60
779 45 c. Children praying and Star of Bethlehem 65 80
780 50 c. Children exchanging gifts 70 85
777/80 .. .. *Set of* 4 1·90 2·25
MS781 95×90 mm. Nos. 777/80 .. .. 2·25 2·75

(Des A. Lowe, adapted L. Curtis. Litho Walsall)

1987 (31 Mar). *Lighthouses. T* **168** *and similar horiz designs. Multicoloured. W w* **16** *(sideways)*. *P* 14×14½.

782 10 c. Type **168**.. .. .. 30 15
783 40 c. Bird Rock Lighthouse .. .. 1·25 70
784 45 c. Castle Island Lighthouse .. .. .. 1·25 75
785 $1 "Hole in the Wall" Lighthouse .. .. 2·00 2·50
782/5 .. .. *Set of* 4 4·25 3·75

169 Anne Bonney

170 Bahamasair Boeing "737"

(Des D. and Jane Hartley. Litho Questa)

1987 (2 June). *Pirates and Privateers of the Caribbean. T* **169** *and similar vert designs. Multicoloured. W w* **16**. *P* 14½.

786 10 c. Type **169**.. .. .. 25 15
787 40 c. Edward Teach ("Blackbeard") 80 55
788 45 c. Captain Edward England 85 60
789 50 c. Captain Woodes Rogers 90 65
786/9 .. .. *Set of* 4 2·50 1·75
MS790 75×95 mm. $1.25, Map of Bahamas and colonial coat of arms .. .. 1·90 2·00

1987 (25 June). *As Nos.* 758/60 *and* 765/70, *but W w* **14** *and with imprint date*. *P* 14.

791 5 c. Type **165**.. .. .. 10 10
792 10 c. Stoplight Parrotfish 10 15
793 15 c. Jackknife Fish 15 20
794 40 c. Four-eyed Butterflyfish 45 50
795 45 c. Fairy Basslet 50 55
796 50 c. Queen Angelfish 55 60
797 60 c. Blue Chromis 65 70
798 $1 Spanish Hogfish .. .. 1·10 1·25
799 $2 Harlequin Bass .. .. 2·25 2·40
791/9 .. .. *Set of* 9 5·25 5·75

The 5 c. and 10 c. exist with different imprint dates below the design.

(Des A. Theobald. Litho Questa)

1987 (7 July). *Air. Aircraft. T* **170** *and similar horiz designs. Multicoloured. W w* **16**. *P* 14.

800 15 c. Type **170**.. .. .. 15 20
801 40 c. Eastern Airlines Boeing "757" 45 50
802 45 c. Pan Am Airbus "A300" 50 55
803 50 c. British Airways Boeing "747" 55 60
800/3 .. .. *Set of* 4 1·50 1·60

171 Cruise Liner and Catamaran

172 *Cattleyopsis lindenii*

(Des A. Theobald. Litho Questa)

1987 (26 Aug). *Tourist Transport. T* **171** *and similar vert designs. Multicoloured. W w* **16**. *P* 14.

804 40 c. Type **171**.. .. .. 50 55
a. Horiz strip of 5. Nos. 804/8 .. .. 2·50
805 40 c. Liners and speedboat 50 55
806 40 c. Game fishing boat and cruising yacht .. 50 55
807 40 c. Game fishing boat and racing yachts .. 50 55
808 40 c. Fishing boat and schooner 50 55
809 40 c. Bahamasair airliner 50 55
a. Horiz strip of 5. Nos. 809/13 .. .. 2·50
810 40 c. Bahamasair and Pan Am Boeing airliners 50 55
811 40 c. Light aircraft and radio beacon 50 55
812 40 c. Aircraft and Nassau control tower .. 50 55
813 40 c. Helicopter and parked aircraft 50 55
804/13 .. .. *Set of* 10 4·50 5·00

Nos. 804/8 and 809/13 were each printed together, *se-tenant*, in horizontal strips of 5 throughout the sheets, each strip forming a composite design.

(Des. A. Lowe; adapted L. Curtis. Litho Questa)

1987 (20 Oct). *Christmas. Orchids. T* **172** *and similar horiz designs. Multicoloured. W w* **16** *(sideways)*. *P* 14×14½.

814 10 c. Type **172**.. .. .. 20 10
815 40 c. *Encyclia lucayana* 70 60
816 45 c. *Encyclia hodgeana* 80 70
817 50 c. *Encyclia lleidae* 90 80
814/17 .. .. *Set of* 4 2·40 2·00
MS818 120×92 mm. Nos. 814/17 .. .. .. 2·40 2·50

NEW INFORMATION

The editor is always interested to correspond with people who have new information that will improve or correct the Catalogue.

173 King Ferdinand and Queen Isabella of Spain

174 Whistling Ducks in Flight

(Des L. Curtis. Litho Format)

1988 (24 Feb). *500th Anniv of Discovery of America by Columbus* (1992) *(1st issue). T* **173** *and similar vert designs. Multicoloured. W w* **14**. *P* 14×14½.

819 10 c. Type **173**.. .. .. 20 15
820 40 c. Columbus before Talavera Committee .. 65 55
821 45 c. Lucayan village.. .. .. 70 60
822 50 c. Lucayan potters.. .. .. 75 65
819/22 .. .. *Set of* 4 2·10 1·75
MS823 65×50 mm. $1.50, Map of Antilles, c. 1500. Wmk sideways .. .. 1·75 1·90

See also Nos. 844/8.

(Des W. Oliver. Litho Walsall)

1988 (29 Apr). *Black-billed Whistling Duck. T* **174** *and similar horiz designs. Multicoloured. W w* **14** *(sideways)*. *P* 14×14½.

824 5 c. Type **174** 15 10
825 10 c. Whistling Duck in reeds 25 15
826 20 c. Pair with brood 45 35
827 45 c. Pair wading 90 75
824/7 .. .. *Set of* 4 1·60 1·25

175 Grantstown Cabin, c. 1820

176 Olympic Flame, High Jumping, Hammer throwing, Basketball and Gymnastics

(Des N. Shewring. Litho B.D.T.)

1988 (9 Aug). *150th Anniv of Abolition of Slavery. T* **175** *and similar horiz design. Multicoloured. W w* **14** *(sideways)*. *P* 13½.

828 10 c. Type **175** 15 15
829 40 c. Basket-making, Grantstown 50 55

(Des D. Miller. Litho Walsall)

1988 (30 Aug). *Olympic Games, Seoul. T* **176** *and similar horiz designs taken from painting by James Martin. Multicoloured. W w* **16** *(sideways)*. *P* 14.

830 10 c. Type **176** 15 15
831 40 c. Athletics, archery, swimming, long jumping, weightlifting and boxing 50 55
832 45 c. Javelin throwing, gymnastics, hurdling and shot put 55 60
833 $1 Athletics, hurdling, gymnastics and cycling .. .. 1·25 1·40
830/3 .. .. *Set of* 4 2·00 2·25
MS834 113×85 mm. Nos. 830/3. W w 14 (sideways) .. .. 2·25 2·40

(Des O. Bell and D. Miller (40 c.), E. Nisbet and D. Miller ($1), D. Miller (others). Litho Format)

1988 (4 Oct). *300th Anniv of Lloyd's of London. Multicoloured designs as T* **123** *of Ascension. W w* **14** *(sideways on* 40, 45 *c.)*. *P* 14.

835 10 c. Lloyd's List of 1740 .. .. 20 15
836 40 c. Freeport Harbour *(horiz)* 60 55
837 45 c. Space shuttle over Bahamas *(horiz)* .. 65 60
838 $1 *Yarmouth Castle* on fire .. .. .. 1·40 1·40
835/8 .. .. *Set of* 4 2·50 2·40

177 "Oh Little Town of Bethlehem"

178 Cuban Emerald

(Des Josephine Martin. Litho Questa)

1988 (21 Nov). *Christmas. Carols. T* **177** *and similar vert designs. Multicoloured. W w* **16**. *P* 14½×14.

839 10 c. Type **177** 15 15
840 40 c. "Little Donkey" 50 55
841 45 c. "Silent Night" 55 60
842 50 c. "Hark the Herald Angels Sing" 60 65
839/42 .. .. *Set of* 4 1·50 1·60
MS843 88×108 mm. Nos. 839/42. W w 14 .. 1·60 1·75

(Des A. Lowe (50 c.), L. Curtis (others). Litho Questa)

1989 (25 Jan). *500th Anniv of Discovery of America by Columbus (1992) (2nd issue). Vert designs as T* **173**. *Multicoloured. W w* **16**. *P* 14½×14.

844	10 c. Columbus drawing chart	15	15
845	40 c. Types of caravel	60	60
846	45 c. Early navigational instruments	65	65
847	50 c. Arawak artefacts	70	70
844/7	*Set of* 4	1·90	1·90
MS848	64×64 mm. $1.50, Caravel under construction (from 15th-cent *Nuremburg Chronicles*)	1·75	1·90

(Des N. Shewring. Litho Questa)

1989 (29 Mar). *Hummingbirds. T* **178** *and similar vert designs. Multicoloured. W w* **16**. *P* 14½ × 14.

849	10 c. Type **178**	25	15
850	40 c. Ruby-throated Hummingbird	70	75
851	45 c. Bahama Woodstar	75	80
852	50 c. Rufous Hummingbird	85	90
849/52	*Set of* 4	2·25	2·40

179 Teaching Water Safety

180 Church of the Nativity, Bethlehem

(Des S. Noon. Litho Questa)

1989 (31 May). *125th Anniv of International Red Cross. T* **179** *and similar horiz design. Multicoloured. W w* **16** *(sideways). P* 14×14½.

853	10 c. Type **179**	25	20
854	$1 Henri Dunant (founder) and Battle of Solferino	1·75	1·90

(Des A. Theobald ($2), D. Miller (others). Litho Questa)

1989 (20 July). *20th Anniv of First Manned Landing on Moon. Multicoloured designs as T* **126** *of Ascension. W w* **16** *(sideways on* 40, 45 *c.). P* 14×13½ *(*10 *c.*, $1*) or* 14 *(others).*

855	10 c. "Apollo 8" Communications Station, Grand Bahama	15	20
856	40 c. Crew of "Apollo 8" (30×30 *mm*)	50	55
857	45 c. "Apollo 8" emblem (30×30 *mm*)	55	60
858	$1 The Earth seen from "Apollo 8"	1·25	1·40
855/8	*Set of* 4	2·25	2·50
MS859	100×83 mm. $2 "Apollo 11" astronauts in training, Manned Spacecraft Centre, Houston. P 14×13½	2·50	2·75

(Des E. Weishoff. Litho Questa)

1989 (16 Oct). *Christmas. Churches of the Holy Land. T* **180** *and similar vert designs. Multicoloured. W w* **14**. *P* 14½×14.

860	10 c. Type **180**	15	20
861	40 c. Basilica of the Annunciation, Nazareth	50	55
862	45 c. Tabgha Church, Galilee	55	60
863	$1 Church of the Holy Sepulchre, Jerusalem	1·25	1·40
860/3	*Set of* 4	2·25	2·50
MS864	92×109 mm. Nos. 860/3. Wmk sideways	2·40	2·50

181 1974 U.P.U. Centenary 13 c. Stamp and Globe

(Des J. Sayer. Litho Questa)

1989 (17 Nov). *"World Stamp Expo '89" International Stamp Exhibition, Washington. T* **181** *and similar multicoloured designs. W w* **16** *(sideways). P* 14.

865	10 c. Type **181**	15	20
866	40 c. 1970 New U.P.U. Headquarters Building 3 c. and building	50	55
867	45 c. 1986 "Ameripex '86" $1 and Capitol, Washington	55	60
868	$1 1949 75th anniversary of U.P.U. 2½d. and Bahamasair airliner	1·25	1·40
865/8	*Set of* 4	2·25	2·50
MS869	107×80 mm. $2 Map showing route of Columbus, 1492 (30×38 mm). P 14½	2·50	2·75

SPECIAL DELIVERY STAMPS

SPECIAL DELIVERY

(S 1)

1916 (1 May). *No.* 69 *(wmk Crown CC) optd with Type* S 1 *by* The Nassau Guardian.

S1	**6**	5d. black and orange	5·00	20·00
		a. Opt double	£800	£1200
		b. Opt double, one inverted	£950	£1300
		c. Opt inverted	£1200	£1200
		d. Pair, one without opt	£12000	£17000

There were three printings from similar settings of 30, and each sheet had to pass through the press twice. The first printing of 600 was on sale from 1 May 1916 in Canada at Ottawa, Toronto, Westmount (Montreal) and Winnipeg; and under an agreement with the Canadian P.O. were used in combination with Canadian stamps and were cancelled in Canada. The second printing (number unknown) was made about the beginning of December 1916, and the third of 6000, issued probably on 1 March 1917, were on sale only in the Bahamas. These printings caused the revocation, in mid-December 1916, of the agreement by Canada, which no longer accepted the stamps as payment of the special delivery fee and left them to be cancelled in the Bahamas.

It is not possible to identify the printings of the normal stamps without plating both the basic stamp and the overprint, though, in general, the word "SPECIAL" is further to the right in relation to "DELIVERY" in the third printing than in the first or second. Our prices for No. S1 are for the third printing and any stamps which can be positively identified as being from the first or second printings would be worth about eight times as much unused, and any on cover are very rare. All the errors appear to be from the third printing.

SPECIAL DELIVERY (S 2)

SPECIAL DELIVERY (S 3)

1917 (2 July). *As No.* 69, *but Wmk Mult Crown CA. Optd in London with Type* S **2**.

S2	**6**	5d. black and orange (Optd S. £75)	45	4·00

1918. *No.* 97 *optd in London with Type* S **3**.

S3	**6**	5d. black and mauve (R.) (Optd S. £75)	30	1·25

Nos. S2/3 were only on sale in the Bahamas.

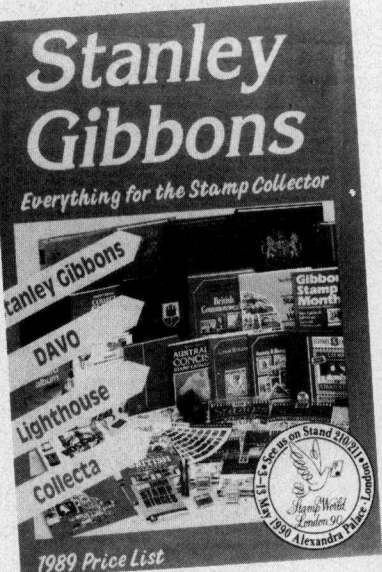

Bahrain

An independent shaikhdom, with an Indian postal administration from 1884. A British postal administration operated from 1 April 1948 to 31 December 1965.

The first, and for 62 years the only, post office in Bahrain opened at the capital, Manama, on 1 August 1884 as a sub-office of the Indian Post Office at Bushire (Iran), both being part of the Bombay Postal Circle.

Unoverprinted postage stamps of India were supplied to the new office, continuing on sale there until 1933. Examples of the lower values can sometimes be found postmarked at Bahrain, but such cancellations on values over 4 a. are decidedly scarce. The occasional Official stamp can also be discovered, possibly used by the office of the Indian Political Agent.

The initial cancellation supplied showed a "B" against a circular background of horizontal lines, this being used in conjunction with a single ring date-stamp without any indication of the year of use.

1884 Cancellation and Date-stamp

This was followed by a squared-circle type, first seen in 1886, which was used into the early years of the 20th century. Its replacement was a single ring date-stamp, succeeded in turn by the first of a considerable number of Indian-style double-circle postmarks, all inscribed "BAHRAIN".

1886 Squared-circle

PRICES FOR STAMPS ON COVER TO 1945	
Nos. 1/4	*from* × 5
Nos. 15/19	*from* × 6
Nos. 20/37	*from* × 2
Nos. 38/50	*from* × 6

BAHRAIN (1) BAHRAIN (2)

Stamps of India overprinted with T 1 or T 2 (rupee values)

1933 (10 Aug–Dec). *King George V. Wmk Mult Star, T* **69**.

No.	Type	Description	Unused	Used
1	**55**	3 p. slate (12.33)	1·25	45
2	**56**	½ a. green	4·50	3·25
3	**80**	9 p. deep green	3·25	80
4	**57**	1 a. chocolate	4·50	2·50
5	**82**	1 a. 3 p. mauve	2·50	45
6	**70**	2 a. vermilion	6·00	4·50
7	**62**	3 a. blue	18·00	27·00
8	**83**	3 a. 6 p. ultramarine	2·50	30
9	**71**	4 a. sage-green	17·00	26·00
10	**65**	8 a. reddish purple	2·50	25
11	**66**	12 a. claret	3·25	60
12	**67**	1 r. chocolate and green	13·00	7·50
13		2 r. carmine and orange	25·00	35·00
14		5 r. ultramarine and purple	85·00	£110
1/14		*Set of* 14	£160	£200

The 9 p. exists both offset-litho and typo.

1934–37. *King George V. Wmk Mult Star, T* **69**.

No.	Type	Description	Unused	Used
15	**79**	½ a. green (1935)	2·50	55
16	**81**	1 a. chocolate (1935)	4·00	40
17	**59**	2 a. vermilion (1935)	15·00	7·50
17*a*		2 a. vermilion (*small die*) (1937)	23·00	25
18	**62**	3 a. carmine	4·75	30
19	**63**	4 a. sage-green (1935)	3·00	30
15/19		*Set of* 6	48·00	8·50

1938–41. *King George VI.*

No.	Type	Description	Unused	Used
20	**91**	3 p. slate (5.38)	2·75	85
21		½ a. red-brown (5.38)	40	10
22		9 p. green (5.38)	85	30
23		1 a. carmine (5.38)	60	10
24	**92**	2 a. vermilion (1939)	2·00	40
26	–	3 a. yellow-green (1941)	24·00	2·00
27	–	3½ a. bright blue (7.38)	2·50	1·75
28	–	4 a. brown (1941)	95·00	40·00
30	–	8 a. slate-violet (1940)	£110	35·00
31	–	12 a. lake (1940)	90·00	48·00
32	**93**	1 r. grey and red-brown (1940)	2·50	1·25
33		2 r. purple and brown (1940)	15·00	1·75
34		5 r. green and blue (1940)	30·00	13·00
35		10 r. purple and claret (1941)	65·00	16·00
36		15 r. brown and green (1941)	42·00	35·00
37		25 r. slate-violet and purple (1941)	95·00	65·00
20/37		*Set of* 16	£550	£225

1942–45. *King George VI on white background.*

No.	Type	Description	Unused	Used
38	**100*a***	3 p. slate	30	20
39		½ a. purple	70	40
40		9 p. green	1·75	2·00
41		1 a. carmine	80	20
42	**101**	1 a. 3 p. bistre	1·25	3·50
43		1½ a. dull violet	1·75	75
44		2 a. vermilion	1·00	60
45		3 a. bright violet	2·75	2·50
46		3½ a. bright blue	2·50	4·00
47	**102**	4 a. brown	1·25	50
48		6 a. turquoise-green	6·50	5·50
49		8 a. slate-violet	1·00	75
50		12 a. lake	2·00	1·50
38/50		*Set of* 13	22·00	20·00

Stamps of Great Britain surcharged

For similar surcharges without the name of the country, see BRITISH POSTAL AGENCIES IN EASTERN ARABIA.

BAHRAIN 1 ANNA (3) BAHRAIN 5 RUPEES (4)

1948 (1 Apr)–**49**. *Surch as T* **3**, **4** (2 *r. and* 5 *r.*) *or similar surch with bars at foot* (10 *r.*).

No.	Type	Description	Unused	Used
51	**128**	½ a. on ½d. pale green	25	20
52		1 a. on 1d. pale scarlet	25	30
53		1½ a. on 1½d. pale red-brown	25	40
54		2 a. on 2d. pale orange	25	20
55		2½ a. on 2½d. light ultramarine	50	70
56		3 a. on 3d. pale violet	25	10
57	**129**	6 a. on 6d. purple	25	10
58	**130**	1 r. on 1s. bistre-brown	90	10
59	**131**	2 r. on 2s. 6d. yellow-green	2·00	3·75
60		5 r. on 5s. red	3·75	4·50
60*a*	**132**	10 r. on 10s. ultramarine (4.7.49)	48·00	40·00
51/60*a*		*Set of* 11	50·00	45·00

BAHRAIN 2½ ANNAS (5) BAHRAIN 15 RUPEES (6)

1948 (26 Apr). *Silver Wedding, surch as T* **5** *or* **6**.

No.	Type	Description	Unused	Used
61	**137**	2½ a. on 2½d. ultramarine	25	30
62	**138**	15 r. on £1 blue	32·00	40·00

1948 (29 July). *Olympic Games, surch as T* **5**, *but in one line* (6 *a.*) *or two lines (others); the* 1 *r. also has a square of dots as T* **7**.

No.	Type	Description	Unused	Used
63	**139**	2½ a. on 2½d. ultramarine	25	55
		a. Surch double	£500	£850
64	**140**	3 a. on 3d. violet	35	75
65	**141**	6 a. on 6d. bright purple	45	1·25
66	**142**	1 r. on 1s. brown	90	2·00
63/6		*Set of* 4	1·75	4·00

Twelve used examples of No. 63a are known, postmarked at Experimental P.O. K-121 (Muharraq).

BAHRAIN 3 ANNAS

(7)

1949 (10 Oct). *75th Anniv of U.P.U., surch as T* **7**, *in one line* (2½ *a.*) *or in two lines (others).*

No.	Type	Description	Unused	Used
67	**143**	2½ a. on 2½d. ultramarine	35	80
68	**144**	3 a. on 3d. violet	65	1·25
69	**145**	6 a. on 6d. bright purple	65	1·50
70	**146**	1 r. on 1s. brown	1·10	1·50
67/70		*Set of* 4	2·50	4·50

BAHRAIN 2 RUPEES (7*a*) BAHRAIN 2 RUPEES (7*b*)

"2" level with "RUPEES". "BAHRAIN" sharp

"2" raised "BAHRAIN" worn

The third type (No. 77b) is as Type II but the vertical distance between "BAHRAIN" and "2 RUPEES" is 16 mm. instead of 15 mm. and the value is set more to the left of "BAHRAIN".

BAHRAIN

Extra bar (R. 6/1)

1950 (2 Oct)–**55**. *Surch as T* **3** *or* **7*a*** *(rupee values).*

No.	Type	Description	Unused	Used
71	**128**	½ a. on ½d. pale orange (3.5.51)	20	20
72		1 a. on 1d. light ultramarine (3.5.51)	25	10
73		1½ a. on 1½d. pale green (3.5.51)	30	2·75
74		2 a. on 2d. pale red-brown (3.5.51)	25	25
75		2½ a. on 2½d. pale scarlet (3.5.51)	25	3·50
76	**129**	4 a. on 4d. light ultramarine	30	55
77	**147**	2 r. on 2s. 6d. yellow-green (3.5.51)	11·00	3·50
		a. Surch with Type 7*b* (1955)	50·00	25·00
		b. Third type (1955)	£250	55·00
		ba. "I" inverted and raised	£750	£200
78	**148**	5 r. on 5s. red (3.5.51)	12·00	3·50
		a. Extra bar	£175	
79	**149**	10 r. on 10s. ultramarine (3.5.51)	22·00	6·00
71/79		*Set of* 9	42·00	20·00

1952 (5 Dec)–**54**. *Q.E. II* (*W* **153**), *surch as T* **3** (*in two lines on* 2½ *and* 6 *a.*).

No.	Type	Description	Unused	Used
80	**154**	½ a. on ½d. orange-red (31.8.53)	10	10
		a. Fraction "½" omitted	90·00	£120
81		1 a. on 1d. ultramarine (31.8.53)	10	10
82		1½ a. on 1½d. green	10	10
83		2 a. on 2d. red-brown (31.8.53)	10	10
84	**155**	2½ a. on 2½d. carmine-red	20	15
85		3 a. on 3d. deep lilac (B.) (18.1.54)	20	10
86	**156**	4 a. on 4d. ultramarine (2.11.53)	3·50	20
87	**157**	6 a. on 6d. reddish purple (18.1.54)	2·00	10
88	**160**	12 a. on 1s. 3d. green (2.11.53)	3·00	20
89	**159**	1 r. on 1s. 6d. grey-blue (2.11.53)	3·00	10
80/89		*Set of* 10	11·00	80

The word BAHRAIN is in taller letters on the 1½ a., 2½a., 3 a. and 6 a.

2½ ANNAS BAHRAIN (8)

1953 (3 June). *Coronation. Surch as T* **8**, *or similarly.*

No.	Type	Description	Unused	Used
90	**161**	2½ a. on 2½d. carmine-red	1·25	75
91	**162**	4 a. on 4d. ultramarine	2·25	1·50
92	**163**	12 a. on 1s. 3d. deep yellow-green	2·50	1·50
93	**164**	1 r. on 1s. 6d. deep grey-blue	5·00	50
90/3		*Set of* 4	10·00	3·75

BAHRAIN 2 RUPEES I

BAHRAIN 2 RUPEES II

BAHRAIN 2 RUPEES III

(9)

BAHRAIN 5 RUPEES I

BAHRAIN 5 RUPEES II

(10)

BAHRAIN 10 RUPEES I

BAHRAIN 10 RUPEES II

(11)

TYPE I (T 9/11). Type-set opt. Bold thick letters with sharp corners and straight edges.

TYPE II (T 9/11). Plate-printed opt. Thinner letters, rounded corners and rough edges. Bars wider apart.

TYPE III (T 9). Plate-printed opt. Similar to Type II as regards the position of the bars on all 40 stamps of the sheet, but the letters are thinner and with more rounded corners than in II, while the ink of the surcharge is less black.

The general characteristics of Type II of the 2 r. are less pronounced than in the other values, but a distinguishing test is in the relative position of the bars and the "U" of "RUPEES". In Type II (except for the 1st stamp, 5th row) the bars start immediately beneath the left-hand edge of the "U". In Type I they start more to the right.

In the 10 r. the "1" and the "0" are spaced 0.9 mm in Type I and only 0.6 mm in Type II.

1955 (23 Sept)–**60**. *T* **166/8** *(Waterlow ptgs) surch as T* **9/11**.

No.	Type	Description	Unused	Used
94	**166**	2 r. on 2s. 6d. black-brown (Type I)	5·50	1·25
		a. Type II (13.5.58)	9·00	7·50
		b. Type III (No. 536a, D.L.R.) (29.1.60)	25·00	45·00
95	**167**	5 r. on 5s. rose-red (Type I)	11·00	2·75
		a. Type II (19.8.57)	11·00	7·50
96	**168**	10 r. on 10s. ultramarine (Type I)	23·00	2·75
		a. Type II (13.5.58)	55·00	90·00
		ab. Type II. Surch on No. 538a (D.L.R. ptg)	£200	
94I/6I		*Set of* 3	35·00	6·00
94II/6II		*Set of* 3	65·00	95·00

1956–7. *Q.E. II* (*W* **165**), *surch as T* **3** (*in two lines on* 6 *a.*).

No.	Type	Description	Unused	Used
97	**154**	½ a. on ½d. orange-red (1.57)	10	15
98	**156**	4 a. on 4d. ultramarine (8.6.56)	5·50	10·00
99	**157**	6 a. on 6d. reddish purple (5.12.56)	50	40
100	**160**	12 a. on 1s. 3d. green (2.8.56)	7·50	11·00
101	**159**	1 r. on 1s. 6d. grey-blue (4.3.57)	2·75	10
		a. Surch double		£1100
97/101		*Set of* 5	14·00	19·00

(New Currency. 100 naye paise = 1 rupee)

BAHRAIN NP 1 NP (12) BAHRAIN 3 NP (13) BAHRAIN 75 NP (14)

1957 (1 Apr)–**59.** *Q.E. II* (*W* **165**), *surch as T* **12** (1 *n.p.*, 15 *n.p.*, 25 *n.p.*, 40 *n.p.*, *and* 50 *n.p.*), *T* **14** (75 *n.p.*) *or T* **13** (*others*).

102	**157**	1 n.p. on 5d. brown	10	10
103	**154**	3 n.p. on ½d. orange-red	25	20
104		6 n.p. on 1d. ultramarine	25	20
105		9 n.p. on 1½d. green	25	15
106		12 n.p. on 2d. light red-brown	30	20
107	**155**	15 n.p. on 2½d. carmine-red (Type I)	25	15
		a. Type II (1959)	55	20
108		20 n.p. on 3d. deep lilac (B.)	20	10
109	**156**	25 n.p. on 4d. ultramarine	75	75
110	**157**	40 n.p. on 6d. reddish purple	40	10
		a. Deep claret (1959)	55	10
111	**158**	50 n.p. on 9d. bronze-green	3·25	2·50
112	**160**	75 n.p. on 1s. 3d. green	2·25	50
102/112		*Set of* 11	7·25	4·25

BAHRAIN
15 NP

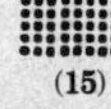

(15)

1957 (1 Aug). *World Scout Jubilee Jamboree. Surch in two lines as T* **15** (15 *n.p.*), *or in three lines* (*others*).

113	**170**	15 n.p. on 2½d. carmine-red	25	35
114	**171**	25 n.p. on 4d. ultramarine	30	35
115	**172**	75 n.p. on 1s. 3d. green	40	45
113/15		*Set of* 3	85	1·00

1960 (24 May). *Q.E. II* (*W* **179**), *surch as T* **12**.

116	**155**	15 n.p. on 2½d. carmine-red (Type II)	2·75	10·00

16 **17**
Shaikh Sulman bin Hamed al-Khalifa

(Des M. Farrar Bell. Photo Harrison (T **16**). Des O. C. Meronti. Recess D.L.R. (T **17**))

1960 (1 July). *P* 15 × 14 (*T* **16**) *or* 13½ × 13 (*T* **17**).

117	**16**	5 n.p. bright blue	10	10
118		15 n.p. red-orange	10	10
119		20 n.p. reddish violet	10	10
120		30 n.p. bistre-brown	10	10
121		40 n.p. grey	15	10
122		50 n.p. emerald-green	15	10
123		75 n.p. chocolate	25	15
124	**17**	1 r. black	1·00	20
125		2 r. rose-red	2·75	40
126		5 r. deep blue	4·50	1·25
127		10 r. bronze-green	11·00	1·75
117/127		*Set of* 11	18·00	3·50

18 Shaikh Isa bin Sulman al-Khalifa

19 Air Terminal, Muharraq

20 Deep Water Harbour

(Des M. Farrar Bell. Photo Harrison (5 to 75 n.p.). Des D. C. Rivett. Recess B.W. (others))

1964 (22 Feb). *P* 15 × 14 (*T* **18**) *or* 13½ × 13 (*T* **19/20**).

128	**18**	5 n.p. bright blue	10	10
129		15 n.p. orange red	10	10
130		20 n.p. reddish violet	10	10
131		30 n.p. olive-brown	10	10
132		40 n.p. slate	15	10
133		50 n.p. emerald-green	15	10
134		75 n.p. brown	25	10
135	**19**	1 r. black	1·25	15
136		2 r. carmine-red	5·00	35
137	**20**	5 r. ultramarine	7·00	3·75
138		10 r. myrtle-green	10·00	4·75
128/138		*Set of* 11	22·00	8·50

MINIMUM PRICE

The minimum price quote is 10p which represents a handling charge rather than a basis for valuing common stamps. For further notes about prices see introductory pages.

LOCAL STAMPS

The following stamps were issued primarily for postage within Bahrain, but apparently also had franking value when used on external mail.

L 1 Shaikh Sulman bin Hamed L 2 al-Khalifa

(Types L 1/2. Recess D.L.R.)

1953–56. *P* 12 × 12½.

L1	**L 1**	½ a. deep green (1.10.56)	1·75	45
L2		1 a. deep blue (1.10.56)	1·75	45
L3		1½ a. carmine (15.2.53)	50	70
L1/3		*Set of* 3	3·50	1·40

1957 (16 Oct). *As Nos.* L 1/3 *but values in new currency.*

L4		3 p. deep green	3·50	40
L5		6 p. carmine	3·50	40
L6		9 p. deep blue	3·50	40
L4/6		*Set of* 3	9·50	1·10

1961 (20 Mar). *P* 12 × 12½.

L 7	**L 2**	5 p. green	65	20
L 8		10 p. carmine-red	60	20
L 9		15 p. grey	50	15
L10		20 p. blue	60	15
L11		30 p. sepia	50	15
L12		40 p. ultramarine	60	20
L7/12		*Set of* 6	3·00	95

The Bahrain Post Department took over the postal services on 1 January 1966. Later stamp issues will be found in Part 19 (*Middle East*) of the Stanley Gibbons catalogue.

Bangkok
***see* British Post Office in Siam**

Bangladesh

Prior to the issue of these stamps, various Pakistan issues were overprinted by local postmasters, mainly using handstamps. These are of philatelic interest, but are outside the scope of the catalogue.

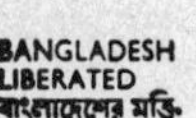

1 Map of Bangladesh (**2**)

(Des B. Mullick. Litho Format)

1971 (29 July). *Vert designs as T* **1**. *P* 14 × 14½.

1	10 p. indigo-blue, red-orange and pale blue	10	10
2	20 p. multicoloured	10	10
3	50 p. multicoloured	10	10
4	1 r. multicoloured	10	10
5	2 r. deep greenish blue, light new blue and rose-magenta	25	30
6	3 r. apple-green, dull yellowish green and greenish blue	30	40
7	5 r. multicoloured	50	60
8	10 r. gold, rose-magenta & deep greenish blue	1·00	1·50
1/8	*Set of* 8	2·00	2·75

Designs:—20 p. "Dacca University Massacre"; 50 p. "75 Million People"; 1 r. Flag of Independence; 2 r. Ballot box; 3 r. Broken chain; 5 r. Shaikh Mujibur Rahman; 10 r. "Support Bangla Desh" and map.

1971 (20 Dec). *Liberation. Nos.* 1 *and* 7/8 *optd with T* **2**.

9	10 p. indigo-blue, red-orange and pale blue	10	10
10	5 r. multicoloured (O.)	1·50	1·50
11	10 r. gold, rose-magenta & deep greenish blue	2·00	2·25
9/11	*Set of* 3	3·25	3·50

The remaining values of the original issue were also overprinted and placed on sale in Great Britain but were not issued in Bangladesh. (*Price for the complete set* £3 *un.*)

On 1 February 1972 the Agency placed on sale a further issue in the flag, map and Shaikh Mujibur designs in new colours and new currency (100 paisas = 1 taka). This issue proved to be unacceptable to the Bangladesh authorities who declared them to be invalid for postal purposes, no supplies being sold within Bangladesh. The values comprise 1, 2, 3, 5, 7, 10, 15, 20, 25, 40, 50, 75 p. and 1, 2 and 5 t. (*Price for set of* 14 *un.*, £1.)

(New Currency. 100 paisa = 1 taka)

3 "Martyrdom" **4** Flames of Independence

(Des and photo Indian Security Printing Press, Nasik)

1972 (21 Feb). *In Memory of the Martyrs. P* 13.

12	**3**	20 p. dull green and rose-red	10	10

(Des N. Kundu. Photo Indian Security Printing Press, Nasik)

1972 (26 Mar). *First Anniv of Independence. P* 13.

13	**4**	20 p. brown-lake and red	10	10
14		60 p. dull ultramarine and red	10	15
15		75 p. reddish violet and red	15	20
13/15		*Set of* 3	25	35

5 Doves of Peace **6** "Homage to Martyrs"

(Litho B.W.)

1972 (16 Dec). *Victory Day. P* 13½.

16	**5**	20 p. multicoloured	10	10
17		60 p. multicoloured	15	15
18		75 p. multicoloured	15	15
16/18		*Set of* 3	30	30

(Des K. G. Mustafa. Litho B.W.)

1973 (25 Mar). *In Memory of the Martyrs. P* 13½.

19	**6**	20 p. multicoloured	10	10
20		60 p. multicoloured	15	20
21		1 t. 35, multicoloured	30	40
19/21		*Set of* 3	45	60

7 Embroidered Quilt **8** Court of Justice

(Litho B.W.)

1973 (30 Apr). *T* **7/8** *and similar designs. P* 14½ × 14 (50 *p.*, 1 *t.*, 5 *t.*, 10 *t.*) *or* 14 × 14½ (*others*).

22	2 p. black	10	10
23	3 p. blue-green	10	10
	a. Imperf (pair)		
24	5 p. light brown	10	10
25	10 p. slate-black	10	10
26	20 p. yellow-green	30	10
27	25 p. bright reddish mauve	75	10
28	50 p. bright purple	50	10
29	60 p. greenish slate	40	10
30	75 p. yellow-orange	45	10
31	90 p. orange-brown	55	10
32	1 t. light violet	1·75	10
33	2 t. olive-green	2·50	40
34	5 t. grey-blue	2·75	90
35	10 t. rose	3·50	2·00
22/35	*Set of* 14	12·50	3·75

Designs: *As T* **7**—3 p. Jute field; 5 p. Jack fruit; 10 p. Bullocks ploughing; 20 p. Rakta jaba (flower); 25 p. Tiger; 60 p. Bamboo grove; 75 p. Plucking tea; 90 p. Handicrafts. *Horiz* (28 × 22 *mm*)—50 p. Hilsa (fish). *Horiz as T* **8**—5 t. Fishing boat; 10 t. Sixty-dome mosque, Bagerhat. *Vert as T* **8**—2 t. Date tree.

See also Nos. 49/51*a* and 64/75.

9 Flame Emblem **10** Family, Map and Graph

(Des A. F. Karim. Litho B.W.)

1973 (10 Dec). *5th Anniv of Declaration of Human Rights. P* 13½.
36 **9** 10 p. multicoloured 10 10
37 1 t. 25, multicoloured 15 20

(Des A. F. Karim. Litho B.W.)

1974 (10 Feb). *First Population Census. P* 13½.
38 **10** 20 p. multicoloured 10 10
39 25 p. multicoloured 10 10
40 75 p. multicoloured 15 20
38/40 .. .. *Set of* 3 25 30

11 Copernicus and Heliocentric System **12** U.N. H.Q. and Bangladesh Flag

(Des K. G. Mustafa. Litho B.W.)

1974 (22 July). *500th Birth Anniv of Copernicus. P* 13½.
41 **11** 25 p. yellow-orange, bluish violet & blk 10 10
a. Imperf (pair) .. .. 22·00
42 75 p. orange, yellow-green and black .. 25 35

(Des A. F. Karim. Litho B.W.)

1974 (25 Sept). *Bangladesh's Admission to the U.N. Multi-coloured; frame colour given. P* 13½.
43 **12** 25 p. light lilac 10 10
44 1 t. light greenish blue 15 25

13 U.P.U. Emblem **14** Courts of Justice

(Des K. G. Mustafa. Litho B.W.)

1974 (9 Oct). *Centenary of Universal Postal Union. T* **13** *and similar vert design. Multicoloured; country name on a yellow background (Nos. 45/6) or a blue background (Nos. 47/8). P* 13½.
45 25 p. Type **13** 10 10
46 1 t. 25, Mail runner 15 15
47 1 t. 75, Type **13** 20 20
48 5 t. As 1 t. 25 .. .. 80 1·10
45/8 .. .. *Set of* 4 1·10 1·40
The above exist imperforate in a miniature sheet from a restricted printing.

1974–76. *Nos. 32/5 redrawn with revised value inscriptions as T* **14**.
49 1 t. light violet .. .. 1·50 10
50 2 t. olive .. .. 1·75 60
51 5 t. grey-blue (1975) .. .. 1·50 70
51*a* 10 t. rose (1976) .. .. 4·00 2·25
49/51*a* .. .. *Set of* 4 8·00 3·25

15 Royal Bengal Tiger **16** Symbolic Family

(Des and litho B.W.)

1974 (4 Nov). *Wildlife Preservation. T* **15** *and similar vert designs. Multicoloured. P* 13½.
52 25 p. Type **15** 35 10
53 50 p. Tiger whelp 80 45
54 2 t. Tiger in stream .. .. 2·50 3·00
52/4 .. .. *Set of* 3 3·25 3·25

(Des A. F. Karim. Litho B.W.)

1974 (30 Dec). *World Population Year. "Family Planning for All". T* **16** *and similar multicoloured designs. P* 14.
55 25 p. Type **16** 15 10
56 70 p. Village family 25 35
57 1 t. 25, Heads of family (*horiz*) 40 70
55/7 .. .. *Set of* 3 70 1·00
The Bengali numerals on the 70 p. resemble "90".

17 Radar Antenna **18** Woman's Head

(Des and litho B.W.)

1975 (14 June). *Inauguration of Betbunia Satellite Earth Station. P* 13½.
58 **17** 25 p. black, silver and dull red 10 10
59 1 t. black, silver and ultramarine 20 30

(Des A. F. Karim. Litho Asher & Co., Melbourne)

1975 (31 Dec). *International Women's Year. P* 15.
60 **18** 50 p. multicoloured 10 10
61 2 t. multicoloured 25 45
a. Vert pair, bottom stamp imperf .. 65·00

(Litho Asher & Co., Melbourne)

1976 (15 Jan)–**77**. *As Nos. 24/31 and 49/51a but redrawn in smaller size and colours changed* (5, 75*p*.). *P* 14½×15 (50 *p*.), 14½ (1 *to* 10 *t*.) *or* 15×14½ (*others*). (*a*) 23×18 *mm* (50 *p*.) *or* 18×23 *mm* (*others*).
64 5 p. deep yellow-green (11.2.76) 10 10
a. Imperf (pair) .. .. 10·00
65 10 p. slate-black (28.4.76) 15 10
66 20 p. yellow-green 30 10
a. Imperf (pair) .. .. 10·00
67 25 p. bright reddish mauve 60 10
a. Imperf (pair) .. .. 10·00
68 50 p. light purple (8.6.76) 70 10
69 60 p. greenish slate (10.11.76) 30 10
70 75 p. yellow-olive (10.11.76) 70 15
71 90 p. orange-brown (10.11.76) 35 10
(*b*) 20×32 *mm* (2 *t*.) *or* 32×20 *mm* (*others*)
72 1 t. light violet .. .. 1·50 10
73 2 t. olive-green (8.6.76) .. .. .. 1·75 10
a. Imperf (pair) .. ..
74 5 t. grey-blue (10.11.76) .. .. .. 2·00 50
75 10 t. rose (25.2.77) .. .. 2·50 90
64/75 .. .. *Set of* 12 10·00 1·90

19 Telephones, 1876 and 1976 **20** Eye and Nutriments

(Des A. F. Karim. Litho Asher & Co., Melbourne)

1976 (10 Mar). *Telephone Centenary. T* **19** *and similar vert design. P* 15.
76 2 t. 25, multicoloured 25 20
77 5 t. dull vermilion, apple-green and black .. 55 65
Design:— 5 t. Alexander Graham Bell.

(Des A. F. Karim. Litho Asher & Co., Melbourne)

1976 (17 Apr). *Prevention of Blindness. P* 15.
78 **20** 30 p. multicoloured 10 10
79 2 t. 25, multicoloured 30 45

21 Liberty Bell **22** Industry, Science, Agriculture and Education

(Des E. W. Roberts. Photo Heraclio Fournier)

1976 (29 May). *Bicentenary of American Revolution. T* **21** *and similar horiz designs. Multicoloured. P* 14.
80 30 p. Type **21** 10 10
81 2 t. 25, Statue of Liberty 25 25
82 5 t. *Mayflower* 65 50
83 10 t. Mount Rushmore 80 80
80/3 .. .. *Set of* 4 1·60 1·40
MS84 167 × 95 mm. Nos. 80/3 .. .. .. 2·50 3·00
No. **MS**84 also exists imperforate from a restricted printing.

(Des K. G. Mustafa. Litho Asher & Co., Melbourne)

1976 (29 July). *25th Anniv of the Colombo Plan. P* 15.
85 **22** 30 p. multicoloured 10 10
86 2 t. 25, multicoloured 25 30

23 Hurdling **24** The Blessing

(Des K. G. Mustafa. Litho Asher & Co., Melbourne)

1976 (29 Nov). *Olympic Games, Montreal. T* **23** *and similar multi-coloured designs. P* 14½.
87 25 p. Type **23** 10 10
88 30 p. Running (*horiz*) 10 10
a. Imperf (pair) .. ..
89 1 t. Pole vault 10 10
90 2 t. 25, Swimming (*horiz*) 25 25
91 3 t. 50, Gymnastics 45 45
92 5 t. Football 60 60
87/92 .. .. *Set of* 6 1·40 1·40

(Des and litho Harrison)

1977 (7–17 Feb). *Silver Jubilee. T* **24** *and similar vert designs. Multicoloured. P* 14 × 14½.
93 30 p. Type **24** 10 10
94 2 t. 25, Queen Elizabeth II 35 35
95 10 t. Queen Elizabeth and Prince Philip .. 1·00 1·00
93/5 .. .. *Set of* 3 1·25 1·25
MS96 114 × 127 mm. Nos. 93/5. P 14½ (17 Feb) 1·50 2·00

25 Qazi Nazrul Islam (poet)

(Des K. G. Mustafa. Litho Harrison)

1977 (29 Aug). *Qazi Nazrul Islam Commemoration. T* **25** *and similar design. P* 14.
97 40 p. blue-green and black 10 10
98 2 t. 25, sepia, stone and chestnut 25 25
Design: *Horiz*—2 t. 25, Head and shoulders portrait.

26 Bird with Letter

(Des A. F. Karim. Litho Harrison)

1977 (29 Sept). *15th Anniv of Asian-Oceanic Postal Union. P* 14.
99 **26** 30 p. light rose, new blue and dull green 10 10
100 2 t. 25, light rose, new blue and light grey 20 25

27 Sloth Bear **28** Camp Fire and Tent

(Des K. G. Mustafa. Litho Harrison)

1977 (9 Nov). *Animals. T* **27** *and similar multicoloured designs. P* 13.
101 40 p. Type **27** 15 10
102 1 t. Spotted Deer 25 10
103 2 t. 25, Leopard (*horiz*) 60 20
104 3 t. 50, Gaur (*horiz*) 70 35
105 4 t. Indian Elephant (*horiz*) .. .. 1·00 50
106 5 t. Tiger (*horiz*) .. .. 1·10 75
101/6 .. .. *Set of* 6 3·50 1·75
The Bengali numerals on the 40 p. resemble "80", and that on the 4 t. resembles "8".

(Des A. F. Karim. Litho Harrison)

1978 (22 Jan). *First National Scout Jamboree. T* **28** *and similar designs. P* 13.
107 40 p. red, deep blue and light blue 15 10
108 3 t. 50, carmine, deep blue and green .. 60 30
109 5 t. reddish lilac, deep blue and bright green 75 45
107/9 .. .. *Set of* 3 1·40 70
Designs: *Horiz*—3 t. 50, Scout stretcher-team. *Vert*—5 t. Scout salute.

29 *Michelia champaca*

(Des and litho Harrison)

1978 (29 Apr). *Flowers. T* **29** *and similar horiz designs. Multicoloured. P* 14.
110 40 p. Type **29** 20 10
111 1 t. *Cassia fistula* 30 10
112 2 t. 25, *Delonix regia* 50 20
113 3 t. 50, *Nymphaea nouchali* 70 40
114 4 t. *Butea monosperma* 80 55
115 5 t. *Anthocephalus indicus* 85 65
110/15 .. .. *Set of* 6 3·00 1·75

30 St. Edward's Crown and Sceptres — 31 Sir Alan Cobham's "DH50"

(Des and litho Harrison)

1978 (20 May). *25th Anniv of Coronation. T* **30** *and similar vert designs. Multicoloured. P* 14.
116 40 p. Type **30** 10 10
117 3 t. 50, Balcony scene 25 35
118 5 t. Queen Elizabeth and Prince Philip .. 40 55
119 10 t. Coronation portrait by Cecil Beaton .. 80 1·00
116/19 .. .. *Set of* 4 1·40 1·75
MS120 89×121 mm. Nos. 116/19. P 14½ .. 1·60 2·00

(Des and litho Harrison)

1978 (15 June). *75th Anniv of Powered Flight. T* **31** *and similar horiz designs. P* 13.
121 40 p. multicoloured 10 10
122 2 t. 25, blackish brown and light new blue .. 40 35
123 3 t. 50, blackish brown and yellow 55 55
124 5 t. multicoloured .. .. 2·00 1·75
121/4 .. .. *Set of* 4 2·75 2·50
Designs:—2 t. 25, Captain Hans Bertram's seaplane *Atlantis*; 3 t. 50, Wright brothers' *Flyer I*, 5 t. "Concorde".

32 Fenchuganj Fertilizer Factory — 33 Tawaf-E-Ka'aba, Mecca

(Des P. Mandal (5 p.), A. F. Karim (10 p.), Harrison (30, 50 p., 1 t.). Photo Harrison)

1978 (6 Nov)–**82**. *Designs as T* **32**. *P* 14½.
125 5 p. deep brown (25.3.79) 10 10
126 10 p. turquoise-blue 10 10
127 15 p. orange (1.8.80) 10 10
128 20 p. brown-red (15.12.79) 10 10
129 25 p. grey-blue (1982) 10 10
130 30 p. deep green (10.12.80) 25 10
131 40 p. maroon (15.12.79) 15 10
132 50 p. black (1981) 50 15
134 80 p. brown (1.8.80) 15 10
136 1 t. reddish violet (6.81) 40 10
137 2 t. dull ultramarine (21.10.81) 20 20
125/37 .. .. *Set of* 11 1·75 75
Designs: *Horiz*—5 p. Lalbag Fort; 25 p. Jute on a boat; 40 p., 50 p. Baital Mukarram Mosque; 1 t. Dotara (musical instrument); 2 t. Karnaphuli Dam. *Vert*—15 p. Pineapple; 20 p. Bangladesh gas; 30 p. Banana Tree; 80 p. Mohastan Garh.

(Des A. F. Karim. Litho J.W.)

1978 (9 Nov). *Holy Pilgrimage to Mecca. T* **33** *and similar multicoloured design. P* 13.
140 40 p. Type **33** 10 10
141 3 t. 50, Pilgrims in Wuquf, Arafat (*horiz*) .. 30 30

34 Jasim Uddin

(Des P. Mandal. Litho J.W.)

1979 (14 Mar). *3rd Death Anniv of Jasim Uddin (poet). P* 14.
142 **34** 40 p. multicoloured 10 10

35 Moulana Abdul Hamid Khan Bhashani — 36 Sir Rowland Hill

(Des P. Mandal. Litho Harrison)

1979 (17 Nov). *3rd Death Anniv of Moulana Abdul Hamid Khan Bhashani (national leader). P* 12½.
143 **35** 40 p. multicoloured 10 10

(Des A. F. Karim. Litho Harrison)

1979 (26 Nov). *Death Centenary of Sir Rowland Hill. T* **36** *and similar designs. P* 14.
144 40 p. turquoise-blue, Venetian red and pale turquoise-blue 10 10
145 3 t. 50, multicoloured 35 30
146 10 t. multicoloured .. .. 80 1·00
144/6 .. .. *Set of* 3 1·10 1·25
MS147 176 × 96 mm. Nos. 144/6 .. .. 1·25 1·40
Designs: *Horiz*—3 t. 50, 1971 10 p. definitive stamp and Sir Rowland Hill; 10 t. 1974 1 t. 25, Centenary of U.P.U. commemorative stamp and Sir Rowland Hill.

37 Children with Hoops — 38 Rotary International Emblem

(Des P. Mandal. Litho Harrison)

1979 (17 Dec). *International Year of the Child. T* **37** *and similar vert designs. Multicoloured. P* 14 × 14½.
148 40 p. Type **37** 10 10
149 3 t. 50, Child with kite 30 35
150 5 t. Children playing 45 50
148/50 .. .. *Set of* 3 70 80
MS151 170 × 120 mm. Nos. 148/50. P 14½ .. 1·90 1·90

(Des P. Mandal. Litho Rosenbaum Bros, Vienna)

1980 (23 Feb). *75th Anniv of Rotary International. T* **38** *and similar vert design showing club emblem. P* 13½×14.
152 40 p. black, vermilion and bistre-yellow .. 10 10
153 5 t. gold and bright blue 45 45

39 Canal Digging — 40 A. K. Fazlul Huq

(Des A. F. Karim. Litho Rosenbaum Bros, Vienna)

1980 (27 Mar). *Mass Participation in Canal Digging. P* 14×13½.
154 **39** 40 p. multicoloured 10 10

(Des P. Mandal. Litho Rosenbaum Bros, Vienna)

1980 (27 Apr). *18th Death Anniv of A. K. Fazlul Huq (national leader). P* 13½×14.
155 **40** 40 p. multicoloured 10 10
On the face value the Bengali numerals resemble "80".

41 Early forms of Mail Transport — 42 Dome of the Rock

(Des A. F. Karim. Litho Rosenbaum Bros, Vienna)

1980 (5 May). *"London 1980" International Stamp Exhibition. T* **41** *and similar horiz design. Multicoloured. P* 14×13½.
156 1 t. Type **41** 10 1
157 10 t. Modern forms of mail transport .. 80 8
MS158 140 × 95 mm. Nos. 156/7 .. .. .. 1·00 1·2

(Des A. F. Karim. Litho Harrison)

1980 (21 Aug). *Palestinian Welfare. P* 14½.
159 **42** 50 p. deep mauve 20 10

43 Outdoor Class

(Des P. Mandal. Litho Rosenbaum Bros, Vienna)

1980 (23 Aug). *Education. P* 13½×14.
160 **43** 50 p. multicoloured 10 10

44 Beach Scene — 45 Mecca

(Des A. F. Karim. Litho Rosenbaum Bros, Vienna)

1980 (27 Sept). *World Tourism Conference, Manila. T* **44** *and similar horiz design showing different beach scene. P* 14.
161 50 p. multicoloured 10 10
a. Horiz pair. Nos. 161/2 .. .. .. 60 60
162 5 t. multicoloured 50 50
MS163 140 × 88 mm. Nos. 161/2 .. .. .. 75 75
Nos. 161/2 were printed together, *se-tenant*, in horizontal pairs throughout the sheet.

(Des A. F. Karim. Litho Rosenbaum Bros, Vienna)

1980 (11 Nov). *Moslem Year 1400 A.H. Commemoration. P* 14 × 13½.
164 **45** 50 p. multicoloured 10 10

46 Begum Roquiah — 47 Spotted Deer and Scout Emblem

(Des A. F. Karim. Litho Rosenbaum Bros, Vienna)

1980 (9 Dec). *Birth Centenary of Begum Roquiah (campaigner for women's rights). P* 14.
165 **45** 50 p. multicoloured 10 10
166 2 t. multicoloured 15 20

(Des A. F. Karim. Litho Rosenbaum Bros, Vienna)

1981 (1 Jan). *5th Asia–Pacific/2nd Bangladesh Scout Jamboree. P* 13½×14.
167 **47** 50 p. multicoloured 10 10
168 5 t. multicoloured 40 45

2nd.
CENSUS
1981
(48)

49 Queen Elizabeth the Queen Mother

1981 (6 Mar). *Second Population Census. Nos.* 38/40 *optd with T* **48**.

169	**10**	20 p. multicoloured	10	10
170		25 p. multicoloured	10	10
171		75 p. multicoloured	10	10
169/71		*Set of* 3	15	15

(Des R. Granger Barrett. Litho Rosenbaum Bros, Vienna)

1981 (16 Mar). *80th Birthday of Queen Elizabeth the Queen Mother. P* 13½×14.

172	**49**	1 t. multicoloured	10	10
173		15 t. multicoloured	3·00	2·00
MS174		95 × 73 mm. Nos. 172/3	3·00	2·50

50 Revolutionary with Flag and Sub-machine-gun
51 Bangladesh Village and Farm Scenes

(Des P. Mandal. Litho Rosenbaum Bros, Vienna)

1981 (26 Mar). *Tenth Anniv of Independence. T* **50** *and similar vert design. Multicolourd. P* 13½×14.

175	50 p. Type **50**	10	10
176	2 t. Figures on map symbolising Bangladesh life-style	15	20

(Des A. F. Karim. Litho Rosenbaum Bros, Vienna)

1981 (1 Sept). *U.N. Conference on Least Developed Countries, Paris. P* 14 × 13½.

177	**51**	50 p. multicoloured	15	10

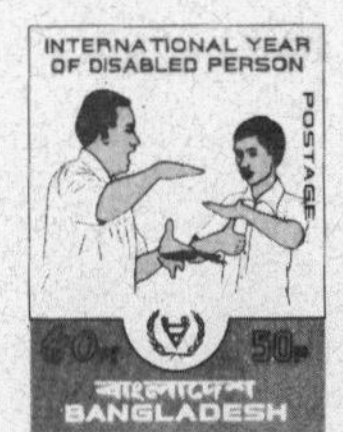

52 Kemal Atatürk in Civilian Dress
53 Deaf People using Sign Language

(Des F. Karim and P. Mandal. Litho Rosenbaum Bros, Vienna)

1981 (10 Nov). *Birth Centenary of Kemal Atatürk (Turkish statesman). T* **52** *and similar vert design. Multicoloured. P* 13½×14.

178	50 p. Type **52**	10	10
179	1 t. Kemal Atatürk in uniform	15	10

(Des F. Karim. Litho Ueberreuter, Austria)

1981 (26 Dec). *International Year for Disabled Persons. T* **53** *and similar multicoloured design. P* 13½ × 14 (50 *p.*) *or* 14 × 13½ (2 *t.*).

180	50 p. Type **53**	10	10
181	2 t. Disabled person writing (*horiz*)	35	20

54 Farm Scene and Wheat Ear
55 River Scene

(Des F. Karim. Litho Ueberreuter, Austria)

1981 (31 Dec). *World Food Day. P* 13½ × 14.

182	**54**	50 p. multicoloured	20	10

(Des P. Mandal. Litho Ueberreuter, Vienna)

1982 (22 May). *10th Anniv of Human Environment Conference. P* 13½ × 14.

183	**55**	50 p. multicoloured	20	10

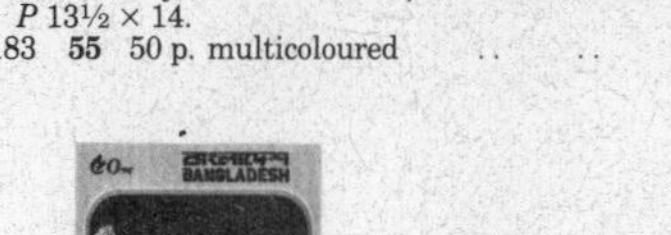

56 Dr. M. Hussain
57 Knotted Rope surrounding Bengali "75"

(Des F. Karim. Litho Ueberreuter, Vienna)

1982 (9 Oct). *Dr. M. Hussain Commemoration. P* 13½.

184	**56**	50 p. multicoloured	15	10

(Des F. Karim and P. Mandal. Litho Ueberreuter, Vienna)

1982 (21 Oct). *75th Anniv of Boy Scout Movement and 125th Birth Anniv of Lord Baden-Powell. T* **57** *and similar multicoloured design. P* 14×13½ (50 *p.*) *or* 13½×14 (2 *t.*).

185	50 p. Type **57**	20	10
186	2 t. Lord Baden-Powell (*vert*)	70	60

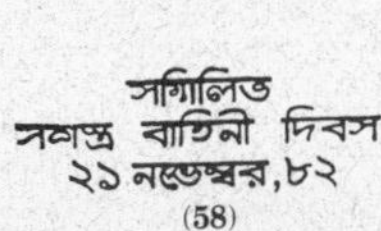
(58)

59 Capt. Mohiuddin Jahangir

1982 (21 Nov). *Armed Forces' Day. No.* 175 *optd with T* **58**.

187	50 p. Type **50**	35	20

(Litho Ueberreuter, Vienna)

1982 (16 Dec). *Heroes and Martyrs of the Liberation. T* **59** *and similar horiz designs. Multicoloured: background colours of commemorative plaque given. P* 14×13½.

188	50 p. Type **59** (pale orange)	15	15
	a. Horiz strip of 7. Nos. 188/94	95	
189	50 p. Sepoy Hamidur Rahman (apple-green)	15	15
190	50 p. Sepoy Mohammed Mustafa Kamal (dull claret)	15	15
191	50 p. Muhammed Ruhul Amin (bistre-yellow)	15	15
192	50 p. Flt. Lt. M. Matiur Rahman (olive-bistre)	15	15
193	50 p. Lance-Naik Munshi Abdur Rob (chestnut)	15	15
194	50 p. Lance-Naik Nur Mouhammad (bright green)	15	15
188/94	*Set of* 7	95	95

Nos. 188/94 were printed together, *se-tenant*, in horizontal strips of 7 throughout the sheet.

60 Metric Scales
61 Dr. Robert Koch

(Des F. Karim. Litho Ueberreuter, Vienna)

1983 (10 Jan). *Introduction of Metric Weights and Measures. T* **60** *and similar multicoloured design. P* 13½×14 (50 *p.*) *or* 14×13½ (2 *t.*).

195	50 p. Type **60**	10	10
196	2 t. Weights, jug and tap measure (*horiz*)	20	30

(Des F. Karim. Litho Ueberreuter, Vienna)

1983 (20 Feb). *Centenary* (1982) *of Robert Koch's Discovery of Tubercle Bacillus. T* **61** *and similar vert design. Multicoloured. P* 13½×14.

197	50 p. Type **61**	15	10
198	1 t. Microscope, slide and X-ray	25	30

62 Open Stage Theatre
63 Dr. Muhammed Shahidulla

(Des F. Karim and P. Mandal. Litho Ueberreuter, Vienna)

1983 (14 Mar). *Commonwealth Day. T* **62** *and similar horiz designs. Multicoloured. P* 14.

199	1 t. Type **62**	10	10
200	3 t. Boat race	20	25
201	10 t. Snake dance	55	70
202	15 t. Picking tea	80	1·25
199/202	*Set of* 4	1·50	2·00

(Litho Ueberreuter, Vienna)

1983 (10 July). *Dr. Muhammed Shahidulla (Bengali scholar) Commemoration. P* 13½×14.

203	**63**	50 p. multicoloured	15	10

64 Magpie Robin

(Des F. Karim and P. Mandal. Litho Ueberreuter, Vienna)

1983 (17 Aug). *Birds of Bangladesh. T* **64** *and similar multicoloured designs. P* 14×13½ (50 *p.*, 5 *t.*) *or* 13½×14 (2 *t.*, 3 *t.* 75).

204	50 p. Type **64**	40	15
205	2 t. White-brested Kingfisher (*vert*)	75	65
206	3 t. 75 Lesser Golden-backed Woodpecker (*vert*)	1·00	80
207	5 t. White-winged Wood Duck	1·40	1·40
204/7	*Set of* 4	3·25	2·75
MS208	165×110 mm. Nos. 204/7 (*sold at* 13 *t.*)	3·00	3·25

65 *Macrobrachium rosenbergii*

Visit of Queen
Nov. '83
(66)

(Litho Ueberreuter, Vienna)

1983 (31 Oct). *Fishes. T* **65** *and similar horiz designs. Multicoloured. P* 14×13½.

209	50 p. Type **65**	25	15
210	2 t. *Stromateus cinereus*	55	45
211	3 t. 75, *Labeo rohita*	75	60
212	5 t. *Anabas testudineus*	1·00	80
209/12	*Set of* 4	2·25	1·75
MS213	119×98 mm. Nos. 209/13. Imperf (*sold at* 13 *t.*)	2·25	2·50

1983 (14 Nov). *Visit of Queen Elizabeth II. No.* 95 *optd with T* **66** *in red.*

214	10 t. Queen Elizabeth and Prince Philip	1·25	1·40
	a. Optd "Nov '33" (R. 3/10)		

67 Conference Hall, Dhaka
68 Early Mail Runner

(Des M. Begum and M. Shamim. Litho Ueberreuter, Vienna)

1983 (5 Dec). *14th Islamic Foreign Ministers' Conference, Dhaka. T* **67** *and similar horiz design. Multicoloured. P* 14×13½.

215	50 p. Type **67**	10	10
216	5 t. Old Fort, Dhaka	35	50

(Litho Ueberreuter, Vienna)

1983 (21 Dec). *World Communications Year. T* **68** *and similar multicoloured designs. P* 14×13½ (10 *t.*) *or* 13½×14 (*others*).

217	50 p. Type **68**	10	10
218	5 t. Sailing ship, steam train and jet airliner	75	50
219	10 t. Mail runner and dish aerial (*horiz*)	1·40	1·00
217/19	*Set of* 3	2·00	1·40

69 Carrying Mail by Boat

প্রথম বাংলাদেশ জাতীয় ডাকটিকিট প্রদর্শনী-১৯৮৪
(70)

(Des M. Akond, P. Mandal and M. Shamim. Litho State Ptg Wks, Moscow)

1983 (21 Dec)–**86**. *Postal Communications. T* **69** *and similar designs. P* 11½×12½ (5, 25 *p.*), 12×11½ (1, 2, 3, 5 *t.*) *or* 12½×11½ (*others*).

220	5 p. turquoise-blue	10	10
221	10 p. purple	10	10
222	15 p. new blue	10	10
223	20 p. grey-black	10	10
224	25 p. slate	10	10
225	30 p. brown	10	10
226	50 p. light brown	10	10
227	1 t. dull ultramarine	10	10
228	2 t. deep bluish green	10	10
228*a*	3 t. bistre (11.1.86)	10	10
229	5 t. bright purple	20	25
220/9	*Set of* 11	1·10	1·10

Designs: *Horiz* (22 × 17 *mm*)—10 p. Counter, Dhaka G.P.O.; 15 p. I.W.T.A. Terminal, Dhaka; 20 p. Inside railway travelling post office; 30 p. Emptying pillar box; 50 p. Mobile post office van. (30 × 19 *mm*)—1 t. Kamalapur Railway Station, Dhaka; 2 t. Zia International Airport; 3 t. Sorting mail by machine; 5 t. Khulna G.P.O. *Vert* (17 × 22 *mm*)—25 p. Delivering a letter.

1984 (1 Feb). *1st National Stamp Exhibition* (*1st issue*). *Nos.* 161/2 *optd with T* 70 (5 *t.*) *or* "First Bangladesh National Philatelic Exhibition–1984" (50 *p.*), *both in red.*

230	**44**	50 p. multicoloured	10	15
		a. Horiz pair. Nos. 230/1	40	55
231	–	5 t. multicoloured	30	40

71 Girl with Stamp Album

(Des P. Mandal. Litho Harrison)

1984 (12 May). *1st National Stamp Exhibition* (*2nd issue*). *T* **71** *and similar triangular design. Multicoloured. P* 14.

232	50 p. Type **71**	10	15
	a. Pair. Nos. 232/3	60	75
233	7 t. 50, Boy with stamp album	50	60
MS234	98×117 mm. Nos. 232/3 (*sold at* 10 *t.*)	75	1·00

Nos. 232/3 were printed together, *se-tenant*, in pairs throughout the sheet.

72 Sarus Crane and Gavial

73 Eagle attacking Hen with Chicks

(Des P. Mandal and M. Akond. Litho Ueberreuter, Vienna)

1984 (17 July). *Dhaka Zoo. T* **72** *and similar vert design. Multicoloured. P* 13½×14.

235	1 t. Type **72**	25	15
236	2 t. Common Peafowl and Tiger	40	55

(Des K. Mostafa. Litho Harrison)

1984 (3 Dec). *Centenary of Postal Life Insurance. T* **73** *and similar vert design. Multicoloured. P* 14.

237	1 t. Type **73**	15	15
238	5 t. Bangladesh family and postman's hand with insurance cheque	45	45

74 Abbasuddin Ahmad

খুলনাপেক্স—৮৪

(**75**)

(Des K. Mostafa. Litho Harrison)

1984 (24 Dec). *Abbasuddin Ahmad* (*singer*) *Commemoration. P* 14.

239	**74**	3 t. multicoloured	20	25

1984 (29 Dec). *"Khulnapex-84" Stamp Exhibition. No.* 86 *optd with T* **75**.

240	**22**	2 t. 25, multicoloured	20	20

76 Cycling

(Des M. Shamim. Litho Harrison)

1984 (31 Dec). *Olympic Games, Los Angeles. T* **76** *and similar horiz designs. Multicoloured. P* 14.

241	1 t. Type **76**	15	15
242	5 t. Hockey	45	45
243	10 t. Volleyball	75	75
241/3	*Set of* 3	1·25	1·25

77 Farmer with Rice and Sickle

78 Mother and Baby

(Des M. Shamim. Litho Harrison)

1985 (2 Feb). *9th Annual Meeting of Islamic Development Bank, Dhaka. T* **77** *and similar horiz design. Multicoloured. P* 14.

244	1 t. Type **77**	10	10
245	5 t. Citizens of four races	30	35

(Des M. Akond. Litho Harrison)

1985 (14 Mar). *Child Survival Campaign. T* **78** *and similar vert design. Multicoloured. P* 14.

246	1 t. Type **78**	10	10
247	10 t. Young child and growth graph	60	65

উপজেলা নির্বাচন ১৯৮৫

(**79**)

1985 (16 May). *Local Elections. Nos.* 110/15 *optd with T* **79**.

248	40 p. Type **29**	10	10
249	1 t. *Cassia fistula*	10	10
250	2 t. 25, *Delonix regia*	15	30
251	3 t. 50, *Nymphaea nouchali*	20	35
252	4 t. *Butea monosperma*	20	35
253	5 t. *Anthocephalus indicus*	30	45
248/53	*Set of* 6	85	1·40

80 Women working at Traditional Crafts

81 U.N. Building, New York, Peace Doves and Flags

(Des M. Akond. Litho Harrison)

1985 (18 July). *United Nations Decade for Women. T* **80** *and similar vert design. Multicoloured. P* 14.

254	1 t. Type **80**	10	10
255	10 t. Women with microscope, computer terminal and in classroom	60	65

(Des M. Akond. Litho Harrison)

1985 (14 Sept). *40th Anniv of United Nations Organization and 11th Anniv of Bangladesh Membership. T* **81** *and similar horiz design. Multicoloured. P* 14.

256	1 t. Type **81**	10	10
257	10 t. Map of world and Bangladesh flag	60	65

82 Head of Youth, Flowers and Symbols of Commerce and Agriculture

83 Emblem and Seven Doves

(Des M. Shamim. Litho Harrison)

1985 (2 Nov). *International Youth Year. T* **82** *and similar vert design. Multicoloured. P* 14.

258	1 t. Type **82**	10	10
259	5 t. Head of youth, flowers and symbols of industry	30	35

(Des M. Akond. Litho Harrison)

1985 (3 Dec). *1st Summit Meeting of South Asian Association for Regional Co-operation, Dhaka. T* **83** *and similar vert design. Multicoloured. P* 14.

260	1 t. Type **83**	10	10
261	5 t. Flags of member nations and lotus blossom	30	35

84 Zainul Abedin

তৃতীয় বাংলাদেশ
জাতীয় জাম্বুরী
১৯৮৫-৮৬

(**85**)

(Des P. Mandal. Litho Harrison)

1985 (28 Dec). *10th Death Anniv of Zainul Abedin* (*artist*). *P* 14.

262	**84**	3 t. multicoloured	15	20

1985 (29 Dec). *3rd National Scout Jamboree. No.* 109 *optd with T* **85**.

263	5 t. reddish lilac, deep blue and bright green	30	35

86 "Fishing Net" (Safiuddin Ahmed)

(Litho Harrison)

1986 (6 Apr). *Bangladesh Paintings. T* **86** *and similar horiz designs. Multicoloured. P* 14.

264	1 t. Type **86**	10	10
265	5 t. "Happy Return" (Quamrul Hassan)	30	35
266	10 t. "Levelling the Ploughed Field" (Zainul Abedin)	55	60
264/6	*Set of* 3	80	95

87 Two Players competing for Ball

88 General M. A. G. Osmani

(Des K. Mostafa. Litho Harrison)

1986 (29 June). *World Cup Football Championship, Mexico. T* **87** *and similar horiz design. Multicoloured. P* 15×14.

267	1 t. Type **87**	10	10
268	10 t. Goalkeeper and ball in net	55	60
MS269	105×75 mm. 20 t. Four players (60×44 *mm*). Imperf.	1·10	1·25

(Des P. Mandal. Litho Harrison)

1986 (18 Sept). *General M. A. G. Osmani* (*army commander-in-chief*) *Commemoration. P* 14.

270	**88**	3 t. multicoloured	15	20

SAARC SEMINAR '86

(**89**)

90 Butterflies and Nuclear Explosion

1986 (3 Dec). *South Asian Association for Regional Co-operation Seminar. No.* 183 *optd with T* **89**.

271	**55**	50 p. multicoloured	15	10

(Des M. Shamim. Litho State Ptg Wks, Moscow)

1986 (29 Dec). *International Peace Year. T* **90** *and similar vert designs. Multicoloured. P* 12 × 12½.

272 1 t. Type **90** 15 15
273 10 t. Flowers and ruined buildings 60 60
MS274 109 × 80 mm. 20 t. Peace dove and soldier 1·00 1·10

TK. 1.00

CONFERENCE FOR
DEVELOPMENT '87

(**91**)

1987 (12 Jan). *Conference for Development. Nos.* 152/3 *surch or optd as T* **91**.

275 **38** 1 t. on 40 p. black, vermilion & bistre-yell 10 10
a. Surch double .. .. ..
b. Surch triple .. ..
c. Surch sideways .. .. ..
d. Surch inverted .. .. ..
276 – 5 t. gold and bright blue 20 30
a. Opt double .. ..
b. Opt double, one inverted .. ..
c. Opt inverted .. ..

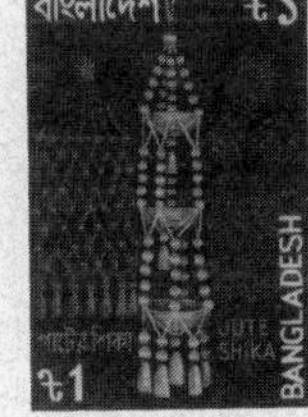

92 Demonstrators with Placards **93** Nurse giving Injection

(Des B. Sardar. Litho State Ptg Wks, Moscow)

1987 (21 Feb). *35th Anniv of Bangla Language Movement. T* **92** *and similar horiz design. Multicoloured. P* 12½ × 12.

277 3 t. Type **92** 15 25
a. Horiz pair. Nos. 277/8 .. .. .. 30 50
278 3 t. Martyrs' Memorial 15 25

Nos. 277/8 were printed together, *se-tenant*, in horizontal pairs throughout the sheet, each pair forming a composite design.

(Litho State Ptg Wks, Moscow)

1987 (7 Apr). *World Health Day. P* 11½ × 12.

279 **93** 1 t. blue-black and deep blue 15 15

See also No. 295.

94 Pattern and Bengali Script **95** Jute Shika

(Des M. Akond. Litho State Ptg Wks, Moscow)

1987 (16 Apr). *Bengali New Year. T* **94** *and similar vert design. Multicoloured. P* 12 × 12½.

280 1 t. Type **94** 10 10
281 10 t. Bengali woman 40 45

(Des P. Mandal, K. Mustafa and M. Akond. Photo State Ptg Wks, Moscow)

1987 (18 May). *Export Products. T* **95** *and similar multi-coloured designs. P* 12½ × 12 (5 *t.*) *or* 12 × 12½ (*others*).

282 1 t. Type **95** 10 10
283 5 t. Jute carpet (*horiz*) 20 25
284 10 t. Cane table lamp 40 45
282/4 .. .. *Set of* 3 60 70

96 Ustad Ayet Ali Khan and Surbahar **97** Palanquin

(Litho State Ptg Wks, Moscow)

1987 (2 Sept). *20th Death Anniv of Ustad Ayet Ali Khan (musician and composer). P* 12 × 12½.

285 **96** 5 t. multicoloured 20 25

(Litho State Ptg Wks, Moscow)

1987 (24 Oct). *Transport. T* **97** *and similar horiz designs. Multicoloured. P* 12½ × 12.

286 2 t. Type **97** 15 15
287 3 t. Bicycle rickshaw 20 20
288 5 t. River steamer 30 30
289 7 t. Express diesel train 40 40
290 10 t. Bullock cart 45 60
286/90 .. .. *Set of* 5 1·40 1·50

98 H. S. Suhrawardy **99** Villagers fleeing from Typhoon

(Des P. Mandal. Litho State Ptg Wks, Moscow)

1987 (5 Dec). *Hossain Shahid Suhrawardy (politician) Commem. P* 12 × 12½.

291 **98** 3 t. multicoloured 15 20

(Des M. Akond. Litho State Ptg Wks, Moscow)

1987 (15 Dec). *International Year of Shelter for the Homeless. T* **99** *and similar horiz design. Multicoloured. P* 12½ × 12.

292 5 t. Type **99** 20 30
a. Horiz pair. Nos. 292/3 .. .. .. 40 60
293 5 t. Villagers and modern houses 20 30

Nos. 292/3 were printed together, *se-tenant*, in horizontal pairs throughout the sheet.

100 President Ershad addressing Parliament

(Des K. Mustafa. Litho State Ptg Wks, Moscow)

1987 (31 Dec). *1st Anniv of Return to Democracy. P* 12½ × 12.

294 **100** 10 t. multicoloured 40 50

(Litho State Ptg Wks, Moscow)

1988 (16 Jan). *World Health Day. Vert design as T* **93**. *P* 11½ × 12.

295 25 p. brown 15 10

Design:—25 p. Oral rehydration.

101 Woman Planting Palm Saplings

(Des K. Mustafa. Litho State Ptg Wks, Moscow)

1988 (26 Jan). *I.F.A.D. Seminar on Agricultural Loans for Rural Women. T* **101** *and similar horiz design. Multicoloured. P* 12½ × 12.

296 3 t. Type **101** 15 15
297 5 t. Village woman milking cow 20 25

102 Basketball

(Litho State Ptg Wks, Moscow)

1988 (20 Sept). *Olympic Games, Seoul. T* **102** *and similar diamond-shaped designs. Multicoloured. P* 11½.

298 5 t. Type **102** 20 25
a. Strip of 5. Nos. 298/302 90
299 5 t. Weightlifting 20 25
300 5 t. Tennis 20 25
301 5 t. Rifle-shooting 20 25
302 5 t. Boxing 20 25
298/302 .. .. *Set of* 5 90 1·10

Nos. 298/302 were printed together, *se-tenant*, in horizontal and vertical strips of five throughout the sheet.

103 Interior of Shait Gumbaz Mosque, Bagerhat **104** Henri Dunant (founder), Red Cross and Crescent

(Litho State Ptg Wks, Moscow)

1988 (9 Oct). *Historical Buildings. T* **103** *and similar horiz designs. Multicoloured. P* 12½ × 12.

303 1 t. Type **103** 10 10
304 4 t. Paharpur Monastery 10 10
305 5 t. Kantanagar Temple, Dinajpur 10 10
306 10 t. Lalbag Fort, Dhaka 15 15
303/6 .. .. *Set of* 4 30 30

(Litho State Ptg Wks, Moscow)

1988 (26 Oct). *125th Anniv of International Red Cross and Red Crescent. T* **104** *and similar vert design. Multicoloured. P* 12 × 12½.

307 5 t. Type **104** 20 25
308 10 t. Red Cross workers with patient 40 45

105 Dr. Qudrat-i-Khuda in Laboratory **106** Wicket-keeper

(Litho State Ptg Wks, Moscow)

1988 (3 Nov). *Dr. Qudrat-i-Khuda (scientist) Commemoration. P* 12 × 12½.

309 **105** 5 t. multicoloured 20 25

(Litho State Ptg Wks, Moscow)

1988 (27 Nov). *Asia Cup Cricket. T* **106** *and similar vert designs. Multicoloured. P* 12 × 12½.

310 1 t. Type **106** 15 15
a. Horiz strip of 3. Nos. 310/12 80
311 5 t. Batsman 30 30
312 10 t. Bowler 45 45
310/12 .. .. *Set of* 3 80 80

Nos. 310/12 were printed together, *se-tenant*, in horizontal strips of three throughout the sheet.

107 Labourers, Factory and Technician

(Litho State Ptg Wks, Moscow)

1988 (29 Nov). *32nd Meeting of Colombo Plan Consultative Committee, Dhaka. P* 12 × 12½.

313 **107** 3 t. multicoloured 10 10
314 10 t. multicoloured 40 45

MINIMUM PRICE

The minimum price quote is 10p which represents a handling charge rather than a basis for valuing common stamps. For further notes about prices see introductory pages.

108 Dhaka G.P.O. Building

(Litho State Ptg Wks, Moscow)

1988 (6 Dec). *25th Anniv of Dhaka G.P.O. Building.* T **108** *and similar horiz design. Multicoloured. P* 12.

315	1 t. Type **108**	10	10
316	5 t. Post Office counter	20	25

৫ম জাতীয় রোভার মুট
১৯৮৮-৮৯

(109)

চতুর্থ দ্বিবার্ষিক এশীয়
চারুকলা প্রদর্শনী
বাংলাদেশ ১৯৮৯

(110)

1988 (29 Dec). *5th National Rover Scout Moot. No.* 168 *optd with T* **109**.

317 **47**	5 t. multicoloured	20	25
	a. Opt inverted		

1989 (1 Mar). *4th Biennial Asian Art Exhibition. No.* 266 *optd with T* **110**.

318	10 t. "Levelling the Ploughed Field" (Zainul Abedin)	40	45

111 Irrigation Methods and Student with Telescope

112 Academy Logo

(Litho State Ptg Wks, Moscow)

1989 (7 Mar). *12th National Science and Technology Week. P* 12×12½.

319 **111**	10 t. multicoloured	40	45

(Litho State Ptg Wks, Moscow)

1989 (13 Mar). *75th Anniv of Police Academy, Sardah. P* 12×12½.

320 **112**	10 t. multicoloured	40	45

113 Rejoicing Crowds, Paris, 1789

(Litho Harrison)

1989 (12 July). *Bicentenary of French Revolution. T* **113** *and similar horiz design. Multicoloured. P* 14×14½.

321	17 t. Type **113**	70	75
	a. Horiz pair. Nos. 321/2 plus label	1·40	
322	17 t. Storming the Bastille, 1789	70	75

Nos. 321/2 were printed in sheets of 30 (6 × 5) with No. 321 in vertical columns one and four, labels showing the Bicentenary emblem in columns two and five, and No. 322 in columns three and six.

OFFICIAL STAMPS

SERVICE (O 1)   SERVICE (O 2)   SERVICE (O 3)

1973 (30 Apr). *Nos.* 22/7, 29/30, 32 *and* 34 *optd with Type* O **1**.

O 1	**7**	2 p. black (R.)	10	10
O 2	–	3 p. blue-green	10	10
O 3	–	5 p. light brown	15	10
O 4	–	10 p. slate-black (R.)	15	10
O 5	–	20 p. yellow-green	35	10
O 6	–	25 p. bright reddish mauve	75	10
O 7	–	60 p. greenish slate (R.)	1·00	15
O 8	–	75 p. yellow-orange	45	10
O 9	**8**	1 t. light violet	4·50	2·50
O10	–	5 t. grey-blue	3·25	2·75
O1/10		*Set of* 10	9·50	5·00

1974–75. *Nos.* 49/51 *optd with Type* O **1**.

O11	**14**	1 t. light violet	1·25	15
O12	–	2 t. olive	1·75	60
O13	–	5 t. grey-blue (1975)	2·75	1·75
O11/13		*Set of* 3	5·25	2·25

1976. *Nos.* 64/70 *optd with Type* O **2** *and Nos.* 72/4 *optd with Type* O **3**.

O14	5 p. deep yellow-green (11.2.76)	10	10
O15	10 p. slate-black (R.) (28.4.76)	20	10
O16	20 p. yellow-green (1.76)	30	10
O17	25 p. bright reddish mauve (1.76)	80	10
O18	50 p. light purple (8.6.76)	70	10
O19	60 p. greenish slate (R.) (10.11.76)	10	10
O20	75 p. yellow-olive (10.11.76)	10	10
O21	1 t. ultramarine (1.76)	60	10
O22	2 t. olive-green (8.6.76)	25	25
O23	5 t. grey-blue (10.11.76)	60	60
O14/23	*Set of* 10	3·25	1·25

1979–82. *Nos.* 128/37 *optd with Type* O **1**.

O24	5 p. deep brown	10	10
O25	10 p. turquoise-blue	10	10
O26	15 p. orange (1980)	10	10
O27	20 p. brown-red	15	10
O28	25 p. grey-blue (1982)	20	15
O30	40 p. maroon	25	10
O31	50 p. black (24.9.81)	15	10
O32	80 p. brown	25	10
O33	1 t. reddish violet (24.9.81)	15	10
O34	2 t. dull ultramarine (21.10.81)	20	30
O24/34	*Set of* 10	1·40	75

Service

(O 4)

1983 (21 Dec). *Nos.* 220/8 *optd as Type* O **4** *in red, diagonally on* 1 *t. and* 2 *t.*

O35	5 p. turquoise-blue	10	10
O36	10 p. purple	10	10
O37	15 p. new blue	10	10
O38	20 p. grey-black	10	10
O39	25 p. slate	10	10
O40	30 p. brown	10	10
O41	50 p. light brown	10	10
O42	1 t. dull ultramarine	10	10
O43	2 t. deep bluish green	10	10
O35/43	*Set of* 9	80	80

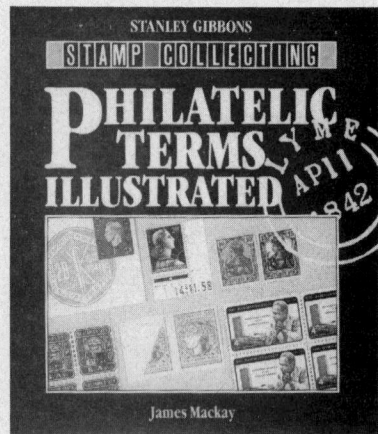

Barbados

Regular mails between Barbados and Great Britain were established at an early date in the island's development and it is believed that the British Mail Packet Agency at Bridgetown was opened in 1688 as part of the considerable expansion of the Packet Service in that year.

From 1 August 1851 the colonial authorities were responsible for the internal post system, but the British G.P.O. did not relinquish control of the overseas post until 1858.

For illustrations of the handstamp types see BRITISH POST OFFICES ABROAD notes, following GREAT BRITAIN.

CROWNED-CIRCLE HANDSTAMPS

CC1 CC 1 BARBADOES (3.10.1849) (R.) *Price on cover* £400

Combination covers exist with the local postage paid by a Barbados 1d. stamp and the overseas fee by an example of No. CC1.

During shortages of ½d. stamps in 1893 (17 February to 15 March) and of the ¼d. in 1896 (23 January to 4 May) No. CC1 was utilised, struck in black, on local mail. *Price on cover from* £95.

PRICES FOR STAMPS ON COVER TO 1945	
Nos. 1/35	*from* × 5
Nos. 43/63	*from* × 4
Nos. 64/6	*from* × 10
Nos. 67/83	*from* × 5
Nos. 86/8	*from* × 3
Nos. 89/103	*from* × 4
No. 104	*from* × 20
Nos. 105/15	*from* × 4
Nos. 116/24	*from* × 8
Nos. 125/33	*from* × 5
Nos. 135/44	*from* × 4
Nos. 145/52	*from* × 6
No. 153	*from* × 8
Nos. 158/62	*from* × 5
Nos. 163/9	*from* × 3
Nos. 170/96	*from* × 4
Nos. 197/8	*from* × 10
Nos. 199/212	*from* × 6
Nos. 213/39	*from* × 3
No. 240	*from* × 10
Nos. 241/4	*from* × 5
Nos. 245/7	*from* × 6
Nos. 248/56a	*from* × 4
Nos. 257/61	*from* × 5
Nos. D1/3	*from* × 25

CROWN COLONY

1 Britannia 2

(Recess Perkins, Bacon & Co)

1852 (15 April)–**55.** *Paper blued. No wmk. Imperf.*

1 1 (½d.) yellow-green .. — £700
2 (½d.) deep green .. 80·00 £300
3 (1d.) blue .. 21·00 £190
4 (1d.) deep blue .. 11·00 65·00
4a (2d.) greyish slate .. £250 £1100
b. Bisected (1d.) (on cover) (1854) .. † £6500
5 (4d.) brownish red (1855) .. 38·00 £350

The bisect, No. 4b, was authorised for use between 4 August and 21 September 1854 during a shortage of 1d. stamps.

Nos. 5*a*/*b* were never sent to Barbados and come from the Perkins Bacon remainders sold in the 1880's.

Apart from the shade, which is distinctly paler, No. 4*a* can be distinguished from No. 5*b* by the smooth even gum, the gum of No. 5*b* being yellow and patchy, giving a mottled appearance to the back of the stamp. No. 5*a* also has the latter gum.

Prepared for use but not issued

5a 1 (No value), slate-blue (*shades*) .. 12·00
5b (No value), deep slate .. £400

1855–58. *White paper. No wmk. Imperf.*

7 1 (½d.) yellow-green (1857) .. £475 £130
8 (½d.) green (1858) .. 95·00 £250
9 (1d.) pale blue .. 70·00 70·00
10 (1d.) deep blue .. 17·00 60·00

1858 (10 Nov). *No wmk. Imperf.*

11 2 6d. pale rose-red .. £850 £140
11a 6d. deep rose-red .. £700 £250
12 1s. brown-black .. £200 £110
12a 1s. black .. £130 70·00

1860. *No wmk.* (a) *Pin-perf* 14.

13 1 (½d.) yellow-green .. £1500 £375
14 (1d.) pale blue .. £1500 £150
15 (1d.) deep blue .. £1500 £150

(b) *Pin-perf* 12½

16 1 (½d.) yellow-green .. £3750 £700
16a (1d.) blue .. — £1200

(c) *Pin-perf* 14 × 12½

16b 1 (½d.) yellow-green .. — £3000

1861. *No wmk. Clean-cut perf* 14 *to* 16.

17 1 (½d.) deep green .. 50·00 7·50
18 (1d.) pale blue .. £500 25·00
19 (1d.) blue .. £650 25·00
a. Bisected (½d.) (on cover) .. † £2500

1861–70. *No wmk.* (a) *Rough perf* 14 *to* 16.

20 1 (½d.) deep green .. 12·00 11·00
21 (½d.) green .. 6·00 7·50
21a (½d.) blue-green .. 50·00 75·00
b. Imperf (pair) .. £450
22 (½d.) grass-green .. 20·00 10·00
a. Imperf (pair) .. £550
23 (1d.) blue (1861) .. 26·00 1·00
a. Imperf (pair) .. £450
24 (1d.) deep blue .. 16·00 3·00
a. Bisected diag (½d.) (on cover) (1863) † £1400
25 (4d.) dull rose-red (1861) .. 48·00 22·00
a. Imperf (pair) .. £575
26 (4d.) dull brown-red (1865) .. 70·00 30·00
a. Imperf (pair) .. £850
27 (4d.) lake-rose (1868) .. 50·00 40·00
a. Imperf (pair) .. £850
28 (4d.) dull vermilion (1869) .. £130 48·00
a. Imperf (pair) .. £850
29 2 6d. rose-red (1861) .. £160 11·00
30 6d. orange-red (1864) .. 60·00 13·00
31 6d. bright orange-vermilion (1868) .. 48·00 13·00
32 6d. dull orange-vermilion (1870) .. 48·00 11·00
a. Imperf (pair) .. £350
33 6d. orange (1870) .. 65·00 18·00
34 1s. brown-black (1863) .. 32·00 4·00
a. Error. Blue .. £12000
35 1s. black (1866) .. 25·00 6·00
a. Imperf between (horiz pair) .. £5000

(b) *Prepared for use, but not issued. P* 11 *to* 12

36 1 (½d.) green .. £5500
37 (1d.) blue .. £2250

The bisect, No. 24a, was authorised for use in April 1863 and November 1866 during shortages of ½d. stamps.

No. 34a was an error on the part of the printer who supplied the first requisition of the 1s. value in the colour of the 1d. The 1s. blue stamps were never placed on sale, but the Barbados Colonial Secretary circulated some samples which were defaced by a manuscript corner-to-corner cross. A number of these samples subsequently had the cross removed.

Nos. 36/7 were never sent to Barbados and come from the Perkins Bacon remainders. It is believed that the imperforate pairs came from the same source.

1870. *Wmk Large Star, Type* w **1**. *Rough perf* 14 *to* 16.

43 1 (½d.) green .. 55·00 4·50
a. Imperf (pair) .. £500
43b (½d.) yellow-green .. 85·00 40·00
44 (1d.) blue .. £800 28·00
a. Blue paper .. — 60·00
45 (4d.) dull vermilion .. £600 45·00
46 2 6d. orange-vermilion .. £450 30·00
47 1s. black .. £180 16·00

1871. *Wmk Small Star, Type* w **2**. *Rough perf* 14 *to* 16.

48 1 (1d.) blue .. 60·00 1·25
49 (4d.) dull rose-red .. £550 24·00
50 2 6d. orange-vermilion .. £250 11·00
51 1s. black .. 90·00 7·50

1872. *Wmk Small Star, Type* w **2**. (a) *Clean-cut perf* 14½ *to* 15½.

52 1 (1d.) blue .. £160 90
a. Bisected diag (½d.) (on cover) .. † £1200
53 2 6d. orange-vermilion .. £400 32·00
54 1s. black .. 70·00 6·00

(b) *P* 11 *to* 13 × 14½ *to* 15½

56 1 (½d.) green .. £160 14·00
57 (4d.) dull vermilion .. £250 48·00

1873. *Wmk Large Star, Type* w 1. (a) *Clean-cut perf* 14½ *to* 15½.

58 1 (½d.) green .. £140 10·00
59 (4d.) dull rose-red .. £550 75·00
60 2 6d. orange-vermilion .. £450 50·00
a. Imperf between (horiz pair) .. £3000
b. Imperf (pair) .. 85·00
61 1s. black .. 75·00 4·50
a. Imperf between (horiz pair) .. £4500

(b) *Prepared for use, but not issued. P* 11 *to* 12

62 2 6d. orange-vermilion

Only eight mint examples, in two strips of four, are known of No. 62.

Two used singles of No. 60b have been seen.

1873 (June). *Wmk Small Star, Type* w **2** *(sideways = two points upwards). P* 14.

63 2 3d. brown-purple .. £325 £110

3

1873 (June). *Wmk Small Star, Type* w **2** *(sideways). P* 15½×15.

64 3 5s. dull rose (H/S S. £300) .. £950 £300

1874 (May). *Wmk Large Star, Type* w **1**. (a) *Perf* 14.

65 2 ½d. deep green .. 13·00 3·25
66 1d. deep blue .. 48·00 75

(b) *Clean-cut perf* 14½ *to* 15½

66a 2 1d. deep blue .. — £2250
b. Imperf (pair)

(Recess D.L.R.)

1875–80. *Wmk Crown CC (sideways on 6d., 1s.)* (a) *P* 12½.

67 2 ½d. bright green .. 17·00 1·50
68 4d. deep red .. £150 7·00
69 6d. bright yellow (aniline) .. £900 70·00
70 6d. chrome-yellow .. £550 65·00
a. Wmk upright .. † —
71 1s. violet (aniline) .. £500 7·00

(b) *P* 14

72 2 ½d. bright green (1876) .. 5·50 50
73 1d. dull blue .. 18·00 30
a. Bisected (½d.) (on cover) (1877) .. † £1100
74 1d. grey-blue .. 18·00 30
a. Wmk sideways .. — £1000
75 3d. mauve-lilac (1878) .. 75·00 3·50
76 4d. red (1878) .. 70·00 7·00
77 4d. carmine .. £120 1·75
78 4d. crimson-lake .. £375 2·50
79 6d. chrome-yellow (1876) .. 90·00 1·00
80 6d. yellow .. £250 5·00
81 1s. purple (1876) .. £100 2·75
82 1s. violet (aniline) .. £1500 30·00
83 1s. dull mauve .. £250 1·50
a. Bisected (6d.) (on cover) (1.80) .. † £3250

(c) *P* 14 × 12½

84 2 4d. red .. £8500

72/3 (in red), 75/6, 79, 81 (in red) Handstamped "Specimen" .. *Set of* 6 £500

72/3 (in black) H/S "Specimen" .. *Set of* 2 £150

Very few examples of No. 84 have been found unused and only one used specimen is known.

1D. 1D. 1D.
(A) (B) (C)

1878 (March). *No.* 64 *with lower label removed, divided vertically by* 11½ *to* 13 *perforation, and each half surch sideways in black by West Indian Press.*

(A) *Large numeral "1", 7 mm high with curved serif, and large letter "D", 2¾ mm high.*

86 3 1d. on half 5s. dull rose .. £2750 £600
a. No stop after "D" ..
b. Unsevered pair (both No. 86) .. £9000 £1800
c. Ditto, Nos. 86 and 87 .. — £3500
ca. Pair without dividing perf .. — £12000
d. Ditto, Nos. 86 and 88 .. £18000 £5500

(B) *As last, but numeral with straight serif.*

87 3 1d. on half 5s. dull rose .. £3000 £700
a. Unsevered pair .. — £2500

(C) *Smaller numeral "1", 6 mm high and smaller "D", 2½ mm high.*

88 3 1d. on half 5s dull rose .. £3500 £800
a. Unsevered pair .. £9500 £3500

All types of the surcharge are found reading upwards as well as downwards, and there are minor varieties of the type.

4

HALF-PENNY
(5)

(Typo D.L.R.)

1882 (28 Aug)–**86.** *Wmk Crown CA. P* 14.

89 4 ½d. dull green (1882) .. 3·50 80
90 ½d. green .. 3·00 80
91 1d. rose (1882) .. 14·00 1·25
a. Bisected (½d.) (on cover) .. † £650
92 1d. carmine .. 2·25 25
93 2½d. ultramarine (1882) .. 32·00 70
94 2½d. deep blue .. 38·00 50
95 3d. deep purple (1885) .. 80·00 24·00
96 3d. reddish purple .. 3·25 8·50
97 4d. grey (1882) .. £140 2·00
98 4d. pale brown (1885) .. 2·75 1·50
99 4d. deep brown .. 2·75 60
100 6d. olive-black (1886) .. 40·00 22·00
102 1s. chestnut (1886) .. 16·00 21·00
103 5s. bistre (1886) .. £140 £170
89/103 .. *Set of* 9 £325 £200
95/103, except 97, Optd "Specimen" *Set of* 5 £350

1892 (July). *No.* 99 *surch with T* 5 *by West Indian Press.*

104 4 ½d. on 4d. deep brown .. 30 1·00
a. No hyphen .. 4·00 5·00
b. Surch double (R. + Bk.) .. £600 £900
ba. Surch double (R. + Bk.) both without hyphen .. £1300 £1300
c. Surch double, one albino ..
d. Surch "PENNY HALF" ..

Nos. 104b/ba come from a sheet with a trial surcharge in red which was subsequently surcharged again in black and put back into stock.

No. 104c is known in a horizontal pair with the left hand stamp showing the first two letters of the second impression inked. The right hand stamp shows a complete albino surcharge.

6 Seal of Colony

7

(Typo D.L.R.)

1892 (July)–**1903**. *Wmk Crown CA. P* 14.
105 **6** ¼d. slate-grey and carmine (5.5.96) .. 30 10
106 ½d. dull green 20 10
107 1d. carmine 85 10
108 2d. slate-black and orange (5.99) .. 6·00 65
109 2½d. ultramarine .. .. 4·75 20
110 5d. grey-olive .. .. 4·50 4·50
111 6d. mauve and carmine .. .. 4·50 2·00
112 8d. orange and ultramarine .. .. 2·50 11·00
113 10d. dull blue-green and carmine .. 4·50 6·50
114 2s. 6d. blue-black and orange .. 26·00 30·00
115 2s. 6d. violet and green (29.5.03) .. 42·00 48·00
105/15 .. .. *Set of* 11 85·00 95·00
105/15 Optd "Specimen" .. *Set of* 11 £160
See also Nos. 135/44 and 163/9.

(Typo D.L.R.)

1897 (Dec)–**98**. *Diamond Jubilee. T* **7**. *Wmk Crown CC. P* 14.

(a) White paper
116 ¼d. grey and carmine 35 15
117 ½d. dull green .. .. 1·50 15
118 1d. rose .. .. 2·25 10
119 2½d. ultramarine .. .. 3·75 25
120 5d. olive-brown .. .. 7·50 10·00
121 6d. mauve and carmine .. .. .. 11·00 11·00
122 8d. orange and ultramarine .. .. 4·75 11·00
123 10d. blue-green and carmine .. .. 22·00 26·00
124 2s. 6d. blue-black and orange .. .. 26·00 32·00
116/124 .. .. .. *Set of* 9 70·00 80·00
116/124 Optd "Specimen" .. *Set of* 9 £150

(b) Paper blued
125 ¼d. grey and carmine .. .. .. 26·00 30·00
126 ½d. dull green .. .. 27·00 30·00
127 1d. carmine .. .. 35·00 40·00
128 2½d. ultramarine .. .. 38·00 45·00
129 5d. olive-brown £225 £250
130 6d. mauve and carmine .. .. .. 95·00 £100
131 8d. orange and ultramarine .. .. 80·00 £100
132 10d. dull green and carmine £120 £140
133 2s. 6d. blue-black and orange .. .. 85·00 90·00

1905. *Wmk Mult Crown CA. P* 14.
135 **6** ¼d. slate-grey and carmine .. .. 2·25 45
136 ½d. dull green.. .. .. .. 3·00 10
137 1d. carmine .. .. 1·75 10
139 2½d. blue .. .. 4·50 15
141 6d. mauve and carmine .. .. 10·00 10·00
142 8d. orange and ultramarine .. .. 18·00 32·00
144 2s. 6d. violet and green .. .. 22·00 40·00
135/144 .. .. .. *Set of* 7 55·00 75·00
See also Nos. 163/9.

8 Nelson Monument

(Des Mrs. G. Goodman. Recess D.L.R.)

1906 (1 Mar). *Nelson Centenary. Wmk Crown CC. P* 14.
145 **8** ¼d. black and grey .. .. .. 1·25 30
146 ½d. black and pale green .. .. 3·25 15
147 1d. black and red .. .. .. 2·50 15
148 2d. black and yellow .. .. .. 1·75 3·50
149 2½d. black and bright blue .. .. 3·75 1·00
150 6d. black and mauve .. .. .. 15·00 17·00
151 1s. black and rose .. .. .. 16·00 26·00
145/151 .. .. .. *Set of* 7 40·00 45·00
145/51 Optd "Specimen" .. *Set of* 7 £125
Two sets may be made of the above: one on thick, opaque, creamy white paper; the other on thin, rather transparent, bluish white paper.
See also Nos. 158/62*a*.

9 *Olive Blossom*, 1605

Kingston Relief Fund. 1d.

(10)

(Des Lady Carter. Recess D.L.R.)

1906 (15 Aug). *Tercentenary of Annexation. Wmk Multiple Crown CA (sideways). P* 14.
152 **9** 1d. black, blue and green .. .. 7·50 25
152 Optd "Specimen" .. .. 65·00

1907 (25 Jan). *Kingston Relief Fund. No.* 108 *surch with T* **10** *by T. E. King & Co., Barbados.*
153 **6** 1d. on 2d. slate-black and orange (R.) .. 1·25 4·25
a. Surch inverted (25.2.07) .. .. 1·25 6·00
b. Surch double £550 £600
c. Surch double, both inverted .. £550
d. Surch *tête-bêche* (pair) £650
e. No stop after "1d." .. .. 17·00 26·00
ea. Do., surch, inverted (25.2.07) .. 17·00 28·00
f. Vert pair, one normal, one surch double
The above stamp was sold for 2d. of which 1d. was retained for the postal revenue, and the other 1d. given to a fund for the relief of the sufferers by the earthquake in Jamaica.
An entire printing as No. 153a was created after a sheet of inverted surcharges was found in the initial supply.

1907 (6 July). *Nelson Centenary. Wmk Mult Crown CA. P* 14.
158 **8** ¼d. black and grey .. .. .. 2·25 2·75
161 2d. black and yellow .. .. .. 10·00 15·00
162 2½d. black and bright blue .. .. 10·00 13·00
a. Black and indigo £1000 £1100
158/62 .. .. *Set of* 3 20·00 28·00

1909 (July)–**10**. *Wmk Mult Crown CA. P* 14.
163 **6** ¼d. brown 25 30
164 ½d. blue-green .. .. 3·75 50
165 1d. red .. .. 1·00 10
166 2d. greyish slate (8.10) .. .. 3·75 8·00
167 2½d. bright blue (1910) .. .. 11·00 3·50
168 6d. dull and bright purple (1910) .. 4·00 13·00
169 1s. black/*green* (8.10) .. .. 7·50 14·00
163/9 .. .. *Set of* 7 28·00 35·00
163, 165/6, 168/9 Optd "Specimen" *Set of* 5 £100

11

12

13

(Typo D.L.R.)

1912 (23 July)–**16**. *Wmk Mult Crown CA. P* 14.
170 **11** ¼d brown 15 15
a. Pale brown (1916) 45 30
171 ½d. green 50 10
172 1d. red (13.8.12) 90 10
a. Scarlet (1915) .. .. .. 5·50 90
173 2d. greyish slate (13.8.12) .. .. 2·00 7·50
174 2½d. bright blue (13.8.12) .. .. 1·25 30
175 **12** 3d. purple/*yellow* (13.8.12) .. .. 1·25 5·00
176 4d. red and black/*yellow* (13.8.12) .. 1·25 7·50
177 6d. purple and dull purple (13.8.12) .. 4·00 6·50
178 **13** 1s. black/*green* (13.8.12) .. .. 4·00 7·00
179 2s. blue and purple/*blue* (13.8.12) .. 24·00 38·00
180 3s. violet and green (13.8.12) .. 42·00 45·00
170/80 .. .. *Set of* 11 70·00 £110
170/80 Optd "Specimen" .. *Set of* 11 £130

14

WAR TAX

(15)

(Recess D.L.R.)

1916 (16 June)–**19**. *Wmk Mult Crown CA. P* 14.
181 **14** ¼d. deep brown 35 15
a. Chestnut-brown (9.17) 50 35
b. Sepia-brown (4.18) .. .. 1·25 1·50
182 ½d. green .. .. 1·10 15
a. Deep green (9.17) .. .. .. 1·10 15
b. Pale green (4.18) .. .. .. 1·40 80
183 1d. deep red .. .. 6·50 4·00
a. Bright carmine-red (4.17) .. .. 2·00 15
b. Pale carmine-red (9.17) .. .. 3·25 65
184 2d. grey .. .. 3·50 7·50
a. Grey-black (9.19) .. .. ..
185 2½d. deep ultramarine 70 50
a. Royal blue (11.17) 70 50
186 3d. purple/*yellow* (thin paper) .. 1·50 2·50
a. Deep purple/yellow (thick paper) (9.19) .. .. 15·00 18·00
187 4d. red/*yellow* .. .. 70 6·00
188 6d. purple .. .. 1·75 3·25
189 1s. black/*green* .. .. .. 6·00 5·50
190 2s. purple/*blue* .. .. .. 12·00 7·50
191 3s. deep violet .. .. .. 25·00 55·00
181/91 .. .. *Set of* 11 48·00 80·00
181/91 Optd "Specimen" .. *Set of* 11 £180
Dates quoted for shades are those of despatch from Great Britain.
Examples of the ½d. and 1d. values can be found perforated either by line or by comb machines.
See also Nos. 199/200*a*.

1917 (10 Oct)–**18**. *War Tax. Optd in London with T* **15**.
197 **11** 1d. bright red (Optd S. £55) 15 15
198 1d. pale red (*thicker bluish paper*) (4.18) 75 40

1918 (18 Feb)–**20**. *Colours changed. Wmk Mult Crown CA. P* 14.
199 **14** 4d. black and red .. .. .. 50 2·75
200 3s. green and deep violet .. .. 15·00 28·00
a. Green and bright violet (1920) .. £120 £160
199/200 Optd "Specimen" .. *Set of* 2 £120
The centres of these are from a new die having no circular border line.

OMNIBUS ISSUES

Details, together with prices for complete sets, of the various Omnibus issues from the 1935 Silver Jubilee series to date are included in a special section following Zululand at the end of the catalogue.

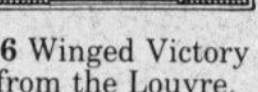

16 Winged Victory from the Louvre.

17 Victory from Victoria Memorial, London

(Recess D.L.R.)

1920 (9 Sept)–**21**. *Victory. P* 14.

(a) Wmk Mult Crown CA (sideways on T **17**)
201 **16** ¼d. black and bistre-brown 20 50
a. "C" missing from wmk .. ..
202 ½d. black and bright yellow-green .. 50 15
a. "C" missing from wmk .. ..
b. "A" missing from wmk .. ..
203 1d. black and vermilion 50 10
204 2d. black and grey .. .. .. 1·75 6·00
205 2½d. indigo and ultramarine .. .. 2·75 6·50
a. "C" missing from wmk .. ..
206 3d. black and purple .. .. .. 1·60 2·75
207 4d. black and blue-green .. .. 1·75 3·50
208 6d. black and brown-orange .. .. 2·50 5·50
209 **17** 1s. black and bright green .. .. 6·00 11·00
210 2s. black and brown .. .. .. 9·00 12·00
211 3s. black and dull orange .. .. 11·00 18·00
a. "C" missing from wmk .. ..

(b) Wmk Mult Script CA
212 **16** 1d. black and vermilion (22.8.21) .. 9·00 25
201/12 .. .. *Set of* 12 40·00 60·00
201/12 Optd "Specimen" .. *Set of* 12 £200

18

19

(Recess D.L.R.)

1921 (14 Nov)–**24**. *P* 14. *(a) Wmk Mult Crown CA*.
213 **18** 3d. purple/*pale yellow* .. .. .. 80 3·75
214 4d. red/*pale yellow* .. .. .. 1·75 3·75
215 1s. black/*emerald* .. .. .. 4·25 11·00

(b) Wmk Mult Script CA
217 **18** ¼d. brown 15 10
219 ½d. green 40 10
220 1d. red 70 10
a. Bright rose-carmine .. .. 3·25 1·00
221 2d. grey .. .. 1·60 20
222 2½d. ultramarine .. .. .. 1·25 3·25
225 6d. reddish purple .. .. .. 2·00 4·50
226 1s. black/*emerald* (18.9.24) .. .. 28·00 40·00
227 2s. purple/*blue* .. .. .. 10·00 18·00
228 3s. deep violet .. .. .. 13·00 27·00
213/228 .. .. *Set of* 12 55·00 £100
213/28 Optd "Specimen" .. *Set of* 12 £150

1925 (1 Apr)–**35**. *Wmk Mult Script CA. P* 14.
229 **19** ¼d. brown 10 10
230 ½d. green 10 10
a. Perf 13½×12½ (2.32) 40 10
231 1d. scarlet 15 10
a. Perf 13½×12½ (2.32) 60 15
231*b* 1½d. orange (1933) .. .. .. 3·00 70
ba. Perf 13½×12½ (15.8.32) 60 35
232 2d. grey .. .. 40 1·75
233 2½d. blue 50 40
a. Bright ultramarine (1933) .. .. 3·75 25
ab. Perf 13½×12½ (2.32) .. .. 3·75 80
234 3d. purple/*pale yellow* 40 35
a. Reddish purple/yellow (1935) .. 2·75 3·50
235 4d. red/*pale yellow* 50 75
236 6d. purple 50 50
237 1s. black/*emerald* .. .. .. 1·50 3·25
a. Perf 13½×12½ (8.32) .. .. 13·00 15·00
b. Brownish black/bright yellow-green (1934) .. .. .. 2·00 8·50
238 2s. purple/*blue* .. .. .. 4·75 6·50
238*a* 2s. 6d. carmine/*blue* (1.9.32) .. .. 15·00 20·00
239 3s. deep violet .. .. .. 8·50 13·00
229/39 .. .. *Set of* 13 30·00 45·00
229/39 Optd/Perf "Specimen" *Set of* 13 £170
Nos. 230/1 exist in coils constructed from normal sheets.

20 King Charles I and King George V

21 Badge of the Colony

(Recess B.W.)

1927 (17 Feb). *Tercentenary of Settlement of Barbados. Wmk Mult Script CA. P* 12½.
240 **20** 1 d. carmine (Optd S. £40) 40 25

1935 (6 May). *Silver Jubilee. As Nos.* 91/4 *of Antigua, but ptd by Waterlow. P* 11 × 12.
241 1d. deep blue and scarlet 25 20
242 1½d. ultramarine and grey .. .. .. 1·25 1·00
243 2½d. brown and deep blue .. .. .. 1·75 75
244 1s. slate and purple .. .. .. 7·00 13·00
k. Kite and horizontal log .. .. 55·00
241/4 .. .. *Set of* 4 9·00 13·50
241/4 Perf "Specimen" .. .. *Set of* 4 60·00
For illustration of plate variety see Omnibus section following Zululand.

1937 (14 May). *Coronation. As Nos.* 13/15 *of Aden. P* 14.
245 1d. scarlet 30 15
246 1½d. yellow-brown 40 25
247 2½d. bright blue 70 40
245/7 .. .. *Set of* 3 1·25 70
245/7 Perf "Specimen" .. .. *Set of* 3 45·00

Vertical line over horse's head (R. 4/10) (corrected on Dec 1947 ptg)

"Flying mane" (R. 4/1) (corrected on Dec 1947 ptg)

Curved line at top right (R. 7/8)

(Recess D.L.R.)

1938 (3 Jan)–**47**. *Wmk Mult Script CA. P* 13½×13.
248 **21** ½d. green .. .. 1·50 15
a. Perf 14 (8.42) .. .. .. 45·00 1·25
248*b* ½d. yellow-bistre (16.10.42) 10 15
249 1d. scarlet (1941) .. .. .. 90·00 1·25
a. Perf 14 (3.1.38) .. .. .. 8·00 10
249*b* 1d. blue-green (1943) 90 15
c. Perf 14 (16.10.42) 10 10
250 1½d. orange 10 10
a. Perf 14 (11.41) .. .. .. 1·50 15
250*b* 2d. claret (3.6.41) 35 80
250*c* 2d. carmine (20.9.43) 10 10
d. Perf 14 (11.9.44) 10 15
251 2½d. ultramarine 50 30
a. Blue (17.2.44) .. .. .. 40 2·50
252 3d. brown 20 90
a. Vertical line over horse's head .. 32·00
b. Perf 14 (4.41) 15 20
ba. Vertical line over horse's head .. 32·00
252*c* 3d. blue (1.4.47) 10 40
ca. Vertical line over horse's head .. 28·00
253 4d. black 15 10
a. Flying mane .. .. .. 40·00
b. Curved line at top right .. .. 30·00
c. Perf 14 (11.9.44) 10 75
ca. Flying mane .. .. .. 38·00
cb. Curved line at top right .. .. 30·00
254 6d. violet 15 10
254*a* 8d. magenta (9.12.46) 45 80
255 1s. olive-green .. .. .. 7·00 1·25
a. Deep brown-olive (19.11.45) .. 20 10
256 2s. 6d. purple .. .. 2·25 85
256*a* 5s. indigo (3.6.41) .. .. .. 2·50 2·25
248/56*a* .. .. .. *Set of* 16 14·50 6·00
248/56*a* Perf "Specimen" .. .. *Set of* 16 £170
No. 249a was perforated by two machines, one gauging 13.8×14.1 (1938), the other 14.1 (1939).
Nos. 248/*b* and 249/*c* exist in coils constructed from normal sheets.

22 Kings Charles I, George VI, Assembly Chamber and Mace

(Recess D.L.R.)

1939 (27 June). *Tercentenary of General Assembly. Wmk Mult Script CA. P* 13½ × 14.
257 **22** ½d. green 75 25
258 1d. scarlet 90 25
259 1½d. orange 80 60
260 2½d. bright ultramarine .. .. .. 90 1·25
261 3d. brown .. .. 1·25 2·00
257/61 .. .. *Set of* 5 4·25 4·00
257/61 Perf "Specimen" .. .. *Set of* 5 £140

Two flags on tug (R. 5/2)

1946 (18 Sept). *Victory. As Nos.* 28/9 *of Aden.*
262 1½d. red-orange 10 10
a. Two flags on tug .. .. .. 7·00
263 3d. brown 10 10
262/3 Perf "Specimen" .. .. *Set of* 2 48·00

ONE
PENNY
(23)

NY PEN

Short "Y" (R. 6/2) Broken "E" (R. 7/4 and 11/4)

(Surch by Barbados Advocate Co)

1947 (21 Apr). *Surch with T* **23**. (*a*) *P* 14.
264 **21** 1d. on 2d. carmine 15 35
a. Short "Y" .. .. .. 8·00
b. Broken "E" .. .. .. 6·00
(*b*) *P* 13½×13
264*c* **21** 1d. on 2d. carmine .. .. .. 85 1·75
ca. Short "Y" .. .. .. 25·00
cb. Broken "E" .. .. .. 18·00
The relationship of the two words in the surcharge differs on each position of the sheet.

1948 (24 Nov). *Royal Silver Wedding. As Nos.* 30/1 *of Aden.*
265 1½d. orange 15 10
266 5s. indigo .. .. 8·50 4·50

1949 (10 Oct). *75th Anniv of Universal Postal Union. As Nos.* 114/17 *of Antigua.*
267 1½d. red-orange 25 25
268 3d. deep blue 40 35
269 4d. grey 60 50
270 1s. olive 80 60
267/70 .. .. *Set of* 4 1·90 1·50

(New Currency. 100 cents = 1 Barbados dollar)

24 Dover Fort

27 Statue of Nelson

(Recess B.W.)

1950 (1 May). *T* **24, 27** *and similar designs. Wmk Mult Script CA. P* 11 × 11½ (*horiz*), 13½ (*vert*).
271 1 c. indigo 15 60
272 2 c. emerald-green 15 25
273 3 c. reddish brown and blue-green 15 60
274 4 c. carmine 15 20
275 6 c. light blue 15 40
276 8 c. bright blue and purple-brown 55 45
277 12 c. greenish blue and brown-olive 90 25
278 24 c. scarlet and black 70 25
279 48 c. violet .. .. 3·25 3·25
280 60 c. green and claret .. .. .. 5·00 3·25
281 $1.20, carmine and olive-green .. .. 5·50 2·50
282 $2.40, black .. .. 9·50 5·50
271/282 .. .. *Set of* 12 23·00 15·00
Designs: *Horiz*—2 c. Sugar cane breeding; 3 c. Public buildings; 6 c. Casting net; 8 c. *Frances W. Smith* (schooner); 12 c. Flying fish; 24 c. Old Main Guard Garrison; 60 c. Careenage; $2.40, Seal of Barbados. *Vert*—48 c. St. Michael's Cathedral; $1.20, Map of Barbados and wireless mast.

1951 (16 Feb). *Inauguration of B.W.I. University College. As Nos.* 118/19 *of Antigua.*
283 3 c. brown and blue-green 15 15
284 12 c. blue-green and brown-olive 30 25

36 King George VI and Stamp of 1852

(Recess Waterlow)

1952 (15 Apr). *Barbados Stamp Centenary. Wmk Mult Script CA. P* 13½.
285 **36** 3 c. green and slate-green 15 20
286 4 c. blue and carmine 15 20
287 12 c. slate-green and bright green 15 20
288 24 c. red-brown and brownish black 15 20
285/8 .. .. *Set of* 4 55 70

37 Harbour Police

(Recess B.W.)

1953 (13 Apr)–**61**. *Designs previously used for King George VI issue, but with portrait or cypher* ($2.40) *of Queen Elizabeth II, as in T* **37**. *Wmk Mult Script CA. P* 11×11½ (*horiz*) *or* 13½ (*vert*).
289 1 c. indigo 10 10
290 2 c. orange and deep turquoise (15.4.54) .. 10 10
291 3 c. black and emerald (15.4.54) 15 10
292 4 c. black and orange (15.4.54) 20 10
a. Black and reddish orange (18.3.59) .. 70 45
293 5 c. blue and deep carmine-red (4.1.54) .. 20 10
294 6 c. red-brown (15.4.54) 15 10
295 8 c. black and blue (15.4.54) 60 10
296 12 c. turquoise-blue & brown-olive (15.4.54) 1·00 10
a. Turquoise-grn & brown-olive (18.3.59) 2·50 60
b. Turquoise-blue & bronze-grn (13.6.61) 1·75 40
297 24 c. rose-red and black (2.3.56) 45 10
298 48 c. deep violet (2.3.56) .. .. .. 2·00 65
299 60 c. blue-green and brown-purple (3.4.56) 4·50 1·25
a. Blue-green and pale maroon (17.5.60) 8·00 3·00
300 $1.20, carmine and bronze-green (3.4.56) 8·50 1·25
301 $2.40, black (1.2.57) .. .. .. 7·50 1·25
289/301 .. .. *Set of* 13 23·00 4·50
Designs: *Horiz*—1 c. Dover Fort; 2 c. Sugar cane breeding; 3 c. Public buildings; 6 c. Casting net; 8 c. *Frances W. Smith* (schooner); 12 c. Flying fish; 24 c. Old Main Guard Garrison; 60 c. Careenage; $2.40, Seal of Barbados. *Vert*—4 c. Statue of Nelson; 48 c. The Cathedral; $1.20, Map of Barbados and wireless mast.
See also Nos. 312/19.

1953 (4 June). *Coronation. As No.* 47 *of Aden.*
302 4 c. black and red-orange 10 10

1958 (23 Apr). *Inauguration of British Caribbean Federation. As Nos.* 135/7 *of Antigua.*
303 3 c. deep green 20 15
304 6 c. blue 30 50
305 12 c. scarlet 35 15
303/5 .. .. *Set of* 3 75 70

38 Deep Water Harbour, Bridgetown

(Recess B.W.)

1961 (6 May). *Opening of Deep Water Harbour, Bridgetown. W w* **12**. *P* 11 × 12.
306 **38** 4 c. black and red-orange 10 10
307 8 c. black and blue 10 10
308 24 c. carmine-red and black 15 15
306/8 .. .. *Set of* 3 30 25

SELF-GOVERNMENT

39 Scout Badge and Map of Barbados

40 Deep Sea Coral

(Recess B.W.)

1962 (9 Mar). *Golden Jubilee of Barbados Boy Scout Association. W w* **12**. *P* 11½ × 11.
309 **39** 4 c. black and orange 15 10
310 12 c. blue and olive-brown 30 15
311 $1.20, carmine and olive-green .. .. 90 1·10
309/11 .. .. *Set of* 3 1·25 1·25

1964 (14 Jan)–**65**. *As Nos.* 289, *etc., but wmk w* **12**.
312 1 c. indigo (6.10.64) 50 75
313 4 c. black and orange 40 50
314 8 c. black and blue (29.6.65) 60 35
315 12 c. turquoise-blue and brown-olive (29.6.65) 60 50
316 24 c. rose-red and black (6.10.64) 50 35
317 48 c. deep violet .. .. .. 1·50 2·00
318 60 c. blue-green and brown-purple (6.10.64) .. 5·00 4·00
319 $2.40, black (29.6.65) .. .. .. 2·75 2·75
312/19 .. .. *Set of* 8 10·50 10·00
The above dates are for Crown Agents releases. The 14.1.64 printings were not released in Barbados until April 1964, the 6.10.64 printings until December 1964 and of the 29.6.65 printings the 8 c. and $2.40 were released from about 15 June 1965 but the 12 c. value was never put on sale in Barbados.

1965 (17 May). *I.T.U. Centenary. As Nos.* 166/7 *of Antigua.*
320 2 c. lilac and red 25 15
321 48 c. yellow and grey-brown .. .. .. 1·00 1·00

(Des V. Whiteley, from drawings by Mrs. J. Walker. Photo Harrison)

1965 (15 July). *Marine Life. Horiz designs as T* **40**. *W w* **12** (*upright*). *P* 14 × 13½.
322 1 c. black, pink and blue 10 15
323 2 c. olive-brown, yellow and magenta 10 15
324 3 c. olive-brown and orange 45 30
325 4 c. deep blue and olive-green 15 10
a. Imperf (pair) £200 £100
326 5 c. sepia, rose and lilac 20 10
327 6 c. multicoloured 45 10

328	8 c. multicoloured	25	10
329	12 c. multicoloured	35	10
	a. Grey printing double	35·00	
330	15 c. black, greenish yellow and red	50	45
331	25 c. ultramarine and yellow-ochre	95	50
332	35 c. brown-red and deep green	1·25	15
333	50 c. bright blue and apple-green	1·75	40
334	$1 multicoloured	2·50	1·25
335	$2.50, multicoloured	2·50	1·25
322/35	.. .. *Set of* 14	10·00	4·50

Designs:—2 c. Lobster; 3 c. Sea Horse; 4 c. Sea Urchin; 5 c. Staghorn Coral; 6 c. Butterfly Fish; 8 c. File Shell; 12 c. Balloon Fish; 15 c. Angel Fish; 25 c. Brain Coral; 35 c. Brittle Star; 50 c. Flying Fish; $1 Queen Conch Shell; $2.50, Fiddler Crab.

The 3 c. value is wrongly inscribed "Hippocanpus", the correct spelling being Hippocampus.

See also Nos. 342, etc.

1966 (24 Jan). *Churchill Commemoration. As Nos.* 170/3 *of Antigua.*

336	1 c. new blue	10	10
337	4 c. deep green	30	10
338	25 c. brown	70	40
339	35 c. bluish violet	80	60
336/9	.. .. *Set of* 4	1·75	1·10

1966 (4 Feb). *Royal Visit. As Nos.* 174/5 *of Antigua.*

340	3 c. black and ultramarine	40	25
341	35 c. black and magenta	1·60	80

41 Dolphin

54 Arms of Barbados

1966 (15 Mar)–**69**. *As Nos.* 322/35 *but wmk* w **12** *(sideways). New value and design (as T* **41**).

342	1 c. black, pink and blue	10	10
343	2 c. olive-brown, yellow & magenta (16.5.67)	20	10
344	3 c. olive-brown and orange (4.12.67) ..	30	30
345	4 c. deep blue and olive-green	40	10
346	5 c. sepia, rose and lilac (23.8.66)	30	10
347	6 c. multicoloured (31.1.67)	45	10
348	8 c. multicoloured (19.9.67)	50	10
349	12 c. multicoloured (31.1.67)	35	10
350	15 c. black, greenish yellow and red ..	1·25	10
351	25 c. ultramarine and yellow-ochre ..	1·50	25
	a. Deep ultram & yellow-ochre (26.9.66)	2·50	90
352	35 c. brown-red and deep green (23.8.66)	1·50	25
	a. Chestnut and deep green (26.11.68) ..	3·00	1·50
353	50 c. bright blue and apple-green ..	1·40	70
354	$1 multicoloured (23.8.66)	2·75	80
355	$2.50, multicoloured (23.8.66)	4·50	3·00
355*a*	$5 multicoloured (9.1.69)	8·50	7·00
342/55*a*	.. .. *Set of* 15	21·00	11·50

The 3 c. value is correctly inscribed "Hippocampus".

All values except the 50 c. exist with PVA gum as well as gum arabic but the $5 exists with PVA gum only.

The $5 was released by the Crown Agents on 6 January but was not put on sale locally until 9 January.

INDEPENDENT

(Des. V. Whiteley. Photo Harrison)

1966 (2 Dec). *Independence. T* **54** *and similar multicoloured designs. P* 14.

356	4 c. Type **54**	10	10
357	25 c. Hilton Hotel *(horiz)*	10	10
358	35 c. G. Sobers (Test cricketer)	40	15
359	50 c. Pine Hill Dairy *(horiz)*	40	15
356/9	.. .. *Set of* 4	85	35

1967 (6 Jan). *20th Anniv of U.N.E.S.CO. As Nos.* 196/8 *of Antigua.*

360	4 c. slate-violet, red, yellow and orange ..	30	10
361	12 c. orange-yellow, violet and deep olive ..	70	45
362	25 c. black, bright purple and orange	1·00	85
360/2	.. .. *Set of* 3	1·75	1·25

58 Policeman and Anchor

62 Governor-General Sir Winston Scott, G.C.M.G.

(Des V. Whiteley. Litho D.L.R.)

1967 (16 Oct). *Centenary of Harbour Police. T* **58** *and similar multicoloured designs. P* 14.

363	4 c. Type **58**	10	10
364	25 c. Policeman with telescope	20	10
365	35 c. *BP1* (police launch) *(horiz)*	20	10
366	50 c. Policeman outside H.Q.	25	15
363/6	.. .. *Set of* 4	65	30

(Des V. Whiteley. Photo Harrison)

1967 (4 Dec). *First Anniv of Independence. T* **62** *and similar multicoloured designs. P* 14½ × 14 *(4 c.) or* 14 × 14½ *(others).*

367	4 c. Type **62**	10	10
368	25 c. Independence Arch *(horiz)*	10	10
369	35 c. Treasury Building *(horiz)*	10	10
370	50 c. Parliament Building *(horiz)*	15	15
367/70	.. .. *Set of* 4	30	20

66 U.N. Building, Santiago, Chile

67 Radar Antenna

(Des G. Vasarhelyi. Photo Harrison)

1968 (27 Feb). *20th Anniv of the Economic Commission for Latin America. P* 14½.

371	**66** 15 c. multicoloured	10	10

(Des G. Vasarhelyi. Photo Harrison)

1968 (4 June). *World Meteorological Day. T* **67** *and similar multicoloured designs. P* 14 × 14½ *(25 c.) or* 14½ × 14 *(others).*

372	3 c. Type **67**	10	10
373	25 c. Meteorological Institute *(horiz)* ..	15	10
374	50 c. Harp Gun and coat of arms	20	10
372/4	.. .. *Set of* 3	35	15

70 Lady Baden-Powell, and Guide at Camp Fire

(Des V. Whiteley (from local designs). Photo Harrison)

1968 (29 Aug). *50th Anniv of Girl Guiding in Barbados. T* **70** *and similar horiz designs. P* 14.

375	3 c. ultramarine, black and gold	10	10
376	25 c. turquoise-blue, black and gold	25	10
377	35 c. orange-yellow, black and gold	35	10
375/7	.. .. *Set of* 3	60	20

Designs:—25 c. Lady Baden-Powell and Pax Hill; 35 c. Lady Baden-Powell and Guide badge.

73 Hands breaking Chain, and Human Rights Emblem

(Des V. Whiteley. Litho B.W.)

1968 (10 Dec).* *Human Rights Year. T* **73** *and similar horiz designs. P* 11 × 12.

378	4 c. violet, brown and light green	10	10
379	25 c. black, blue and orange-yellow	10	10
380	35 c. multicoloured	10	10
378/80	.. .. *Set of* 3	15	15

Designs:—25 c. Human Rights emblem and family enchained; 35 c. Shadows of refugees beyond opening fence.

*This was the local release date but the Crown Agents issued the stamps on 29 October.

76 Racehorses in the Paddock

(Des J. Cooter. Litho Format)

1969 (20 Mar).* *Horse-Racing. T* **76** *and similar horiz designs. Multicoloured. P* 14.

381	4 c. Type **76**	10	10
382	25 c. Starting-gate	20	10
383	35 c. On the flat	20	10
384	50 c. Winning post	30	20
381/4	.. .. *Set of* 4	70	30
MS385	117 × 85 mm. Nos. 381/4	2·25	2·75

*This was the local release date but the Crown Agents issued the stamps on 15 March.

COVER PRICES

Cover factors are quoted at the beginning of each country for most issues to 1945. An explanation of the system can be found on page x. The factors quoted do not, however, apply to philatelic covers.

80 Map showing "CARIFTA" Countries

81 "Strength in Unity"

(Des J. Cooter. Photo Harrison)

1969 (6 May). *First Anniv of CARIFTA (Caribbean Free Trade Area). W* w **12** *(sideways on T* **80**). *P* 14.

386	**80**	5 c. multicoloured	10	10
387	**81**	12 c. multicoloured	10	10
388	**80**	25 c. multicoloured	10	10
389	**81**	50 c. multicoloured	15	10
386/9		.. .. .. *Set of* 4	25	15

82 I.L.O. Emblem and "1919-1969".

ONE CENT
(83)

(Des Sylvia Goaman. Litho Enschedé)

1969 (12 Aug). *50th Anniv of International Labour Organisation. P* 14 × 13.

390	**82**	4 c. black, emerald and turquoise-blue	10	10
391		25 c. black, cerise and brown-red ..	10	10

Although released by the Crown Agents on 5 August, the above were not put on sale in Barbados until 12 August.

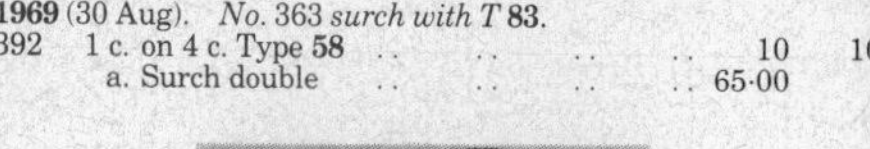

1969 (30 Aug). *No.* 363 *surch with T* **83**.

392	1 c. on 4 c. Type **58**	10	10
	a. Surch double	65·00	

84 National Scout Badge

(Des J. Cooter. Litho Enschedé)

1969 (16 Dec). *Independence of Barbados Boy Scouts Association and 50th Anniv of Barbados Sea Scouts. T* **84** *and similar horiz designs. Multicoloured. P* 13 × 13½.

393	5 c. Type **84**	10	10
394	25 c. Sea Scouts rowing	35	10
395	35 c. Scouts around camp fire	45	10
396	50 c. Scouts and National Scout Headquarters	60	40
393/6	.. .. *Set of* 4	1·40	55
MS397	155 × 115 mm. Nos. 393/6	9·50	12·00

4 X
(88)

89 Lion at Gun Hill

1970 (11 Mar). *No.* 346 *surch locally with T* **88**.

398	4 c. on 5 c. sepia, rose and lilac	10	10
	a. Vert pair, one without surch	35·00	
	b. Surch double	25·00	
	c. Vert pair, one normal, one surch double		
	d. Surch triple		
	e. Surch normal on front, inverted on back	12·00	
	f. Surch omitted on front, inverted on back	16·00	

(Des J. W. Photo D.L.R.)

1970–71. *Multicoloured designs as T* **89**. *W* w **12** *(sideways on 12 c. to $5). P* 12½. *A. Chalk-surfaced paper* (4.5.70) *B. Glazed, ordinary paper* (13.12.71, 12 *c.*, 15 *c. and* $2.50; 15.3.71, *others*).

		A		B	
399	1 c. Type **89**	10	10	10	15
400	2 c. Trafalgar Fountain ..	10	15	10	20
401	3 c. Montefiore Drinking Fountain	10	20	10	25
402	4 c. St. James' Monument ..	10	10	10	10
403	5 c. St. Anne's Fort	10	10	10	10
404	6 c. Old Sugar Mill, Morgan Lewis	35	70	†	
405	8 c. Cenotaph	10	10	10	10
406	10 c. South Point Lighthouse ..	50	15	50	15
407	12 c. Barbados Museum ..	20	10	30	20
408	15 c. Sharon Moravian Church	20	15	60	30
409	25 c. George Washington House	25	15	50	35
410	35 c. Nicholas Abbey	30	50	45	65

411 50 c. Bowmanston Pumping Station .. .. .. 40 75 70 1·25
412 $1 Queen Elizabeth Hospital 70 2·00 2·75 3·50
413 $2.50, Modern sugar factory .. 2·00 4·00 11·00 12·00
414 $5 Seawell International Airport .. .. .. 5·00 9·00 10·00 14·00
399/414A .. .. *Set of* 16 9·00 16·00
399B/414B .. .. *Set of* 15 25·00 29·00

The 2 to 10 c. values are vertical; the 12 c. to $5 horizontal.

See also Nos. 455/67.

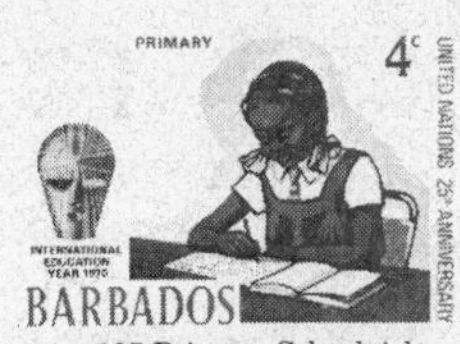

105 Primary Schoolgirl

(Des V. Whiteley. Litho J.W.)

1970 (26 June). *25th Anniv of United Nations. T* **105** *and similar horiz designs. Multicoloured. W* w **12.** *P* 14.

415 4 c. Type **106** 10 10
416 5 c. Secondary Schoolboy 10 10
417 25 c. Technical Student 30 10
418 50 c. University Buildings 45 35
415/18 .. .. *Set of* 4 75 40

106 Minnie Root

107 "Via Dolorosa" (Window, St. Margaret's Church, St. John)

(Des and litho J.W.)

1970 (24 Aug). *Flowers of Barbados. T* **106** *and similar designs. Multicoloured. W* w **12** *(sideways on horiz designs). P* 14½.

419 1 c. Barbados Easter Lily (*vert*) 10 10
420 5 c. Type **106** 15 10
421 10 c. Eyelash Orchid 40 10
422 25 c. Pride of Barbados (*vert*) 50 50
423 35 c. Christmas Hope 65 65
419/23 .. .. *Set of* 5 1·60 1·25
MS424 162 × 101 mm. Nos. 419/23. Imperf .. 1·75 2·00

(Des Jennifer Toombs. Litho J.W.)

1971 (7 Apr). *Easter. T* **107** *and similar vert design. Multicoloured. W* w **12.** *P* 14.

425 4 c. Type **107** 10 10
426 10 c. "The Resurrection" (Benjamin West) .. 10 10
427 35 c. Type **107** 15 10
428 50 c. As 10 c. 30 50
425/8 .. .. *Set of* 4 45 60

108 Sail-fish Craft

(Des and litho Harrison)

1971 (17 Aug). *Tourism. T* **108** *and similar horiz designs. Multicoloured. W* w **12** *(sideways on 5 c. and 25 c.). P* 14.

429 1 c. Type **108** 10 10
430 5 c. Tennis 15 10
431 12 c. Horse-riding 25 10
432 25 c. Water-skiing 30 20
433 50 c. Scuba-diving 50 65
429/33 .. .. *Set of* 5 1·10 90

109 S. J. Prescod (politician)

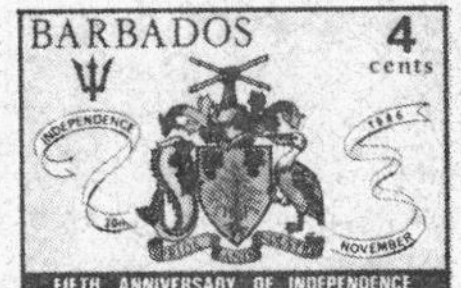

110 Arms of Barbados

(Des J.W. litho Questa)

1971 (28 Sept).* *Death Centenary of Samuel Jackman Prescod. W* w **12.** *P* 14.

434 **109** 3 c. multicoloured 10 10
435 35 c. multicoloured 15 10

*This is the local date but the Crown Agents released the stamps two days earlier.

(Des G. Drummond. Litho Questa)

1971 (23 Nov). *Fifth Anniv of Independence. T* **110** *and similar horiz design. Multicoloured. W* w **12** *(sideways). P* 14.

436 4 c. Type **110** 10 10
437 15 c. National flag and map 10 10
438 25 c. Type **110** 20 10
439 50 c. As 15 c. 45 55
436/9 .. .. *Set of* 4 70 60

111 Transmitting "Then and Now"

112 Map and Badge

(Des Cable & Wireless Ltd. Litho J.W.)

1972 (28 Mar). *Cable Link Centenary. T* **111** *and similar horiz designs. Multicoloured. W* w **12** *(sideways). P* 14.

440 4 c. Type **111** 10 10
441 10 c. *Stanley Angwin* (cable ship) 15 10
442 35 c. Barbados Earth Station and "Intelsat 4" 35 15
443 50 c. Mt. Misery and Tropospheric Scatter Station 50 80
440/3 .. .. *Set of* 4 95 90

(Des Mrs. C. Barrow (50 c.), Major L. Quintyne (others) and adapted by G. Drummond. Litho Questa)

1972 (1 Aug). *Diamond Jubilee of Scouts. T* **112** *and similar horiz designs. Multicoloured. W* w **12** *(sideways on 5 c.). P* 14.

444 5 c. Type **112** 10 10
445 15 c. Pioneers of scouting 15 10
446 25 c. Scouts 30 15
447 50 c. Flags 50 75
444/7 .. .. *Set of* 4 90 90

113 Mobile Library

(Des PAD Studio. Litho Harrison)

1972 (31 Oct). *International Book Year. T* **113** *and similar horiz designs. Multicoloured. W* w **12.** *P* 14.

448 4 c. Type **113** 10 10
449 15 c. Visual-aids van 15 10
450 25 c. Public library 20 10
451 $1 Codrington College .. .. .. 1·25 1·50
448/51 .. .. *Set of* 4 1·50 1·50

1972 (17 Nov)–**74**. *As Nos.* 402B/14B, *but W* w **12** *(sideways on 4 to 10 c.; upright on 12 c. to $5).*

455 4 c. St. James' Monument 80 60
456 5 c. St. Anne's Fort .. .. 1·00 70
457 6 c. Old Sugar Mill, Morgan Lewis .. 2·75 3·00
458 8 c. Cenotaph 90 60
459 10 c. South Point Lighthouse (21.1.74) .. 2·50 3·00
460 12 c. Barbados Museum .. .. .. 1·75 1·25
461 15 c. Sharon Moravian Church 75 60
462 25 c. George Washington House .. .. 2·00 1·00
463 35 c. Nicholas Abbey .. .. 2·25 70
464 50 c. Bowmanston Pumping Station .. 3·50 1·00
465 $1 Queen Elizabeth Hospital .. .. 4·50 2·50
466 $2.50, Modern sugar factory (2.10.73) .. 3·50 5·50
467 $5 Seawell International Airport (2.10.73) 4·00 5·50
455/67 .. .. .. *Set of* 13 27·00 23·00

114 Potter's Wheel

(Des PAD Studio. Litho Questa)

1973 (1 Mar). *Pottery in Barbados. T* **114** *and similar horiz designs. Multicoloured. W* w **12.** *P* 14.

468 5 c. Type **114** 10 10
469 15 c. Kilns 15 10
470 25 c. Finished products 20 10
471 $1 Market scene .. .. 85 1·10
468/71 .. .. *Set of* 4 1·10 1·25

115 First Flight, 1911

(Des C. Abbott. Litho Enschedé)

1973 (25 July). *Aviation. T* **115** *and similar horiz designs. W* w **12** *(sideways). P* 12½ × 12.

472 5 c. multicoloured 15 10
473 15 c. multicoloured 60 10
474 25 c. grey-blue, black and cobalt 85 20
475 50 c. multicoloured .. .. 1·50 1·50
472/5 .. .. *Set of* 4 2·75 1·75

Designs:–15 c. First flight to Barbados, 1928; 25 c. Passenger aircraft, 1939; 50 c. "VC-10" airliner, 1973.

116 University Chancellor (**117**)

(Des J. W. Litho Enschedé)

1973 (11 Dec). *25th Anniv of University of West Indies. T* **116** *and similar horiz designs. Multicoloured. W* w **12.** *P* 13 × 14.

476 5 c. Type **116** 10 10
477 25 c. Sherlock Hall 20 15
478 35 c. Cave Hill Campus 25 25
476/8 .. .. *Set of* 3 45 40

1974 (30 Apr). *No.* 462 *surch with T* **117.**

479 4 c. on 25 c. George Washington House .. 10 10
a. "4c." omitted .. .. 15·00

No. 479a occurs on R. 10/1, the overprint being applied to sheets consisting of two horizontal panes, 5 × 5. The variety occurs on plate 1A, and shows a clear albino impression of the "4c." on the reverse.

118 Old Sail Boat

(Des J. Cooter. Litho Questa)

1974 (11 June). *Fishing Boats of Barbados. T* **118** *and similar diamond-shaped designs. Multicoloured. W* w **12.** *P* 14.

480 15 c. Type **118** 20 15
481 35 c. Rowing-boat 45 25
482 50 c. Motor fishing-boat 60 60
483 $1 *Calamar* (fishing boat) .. .. .. 1·00 1·10
480/3 .. .. *Set of* 4 2·00 1·90
MS484 140 × 140 mm. Nos. 480/3 .. .. .. 2·50 3·00

119 *Cattleya Gaskelliana Alba*

(Des PAD Studio. Photo Harrison)

1974 (16 Sept)–**77**. *Orchids. T* **119** *and similar multicoloured designs. W* w **12** *(upright on* 1, 20, 25 c., $1 *and* $10; *sideways on others). P* 14½ × 14 ($1, $10) 14 × 14½ ($2.50, $5) *or* 14 (*others*).

485 1 c. Type **119** 15 25
486 2 c. *Renanthera storiei* 20 25
487 3 c. *Dendrobium* "Rose Marie" 20 20
488 4 c. *Epidendrum ibaguense* 75 40
489 5 c. *Schomburgkia humboldtii* 35 15
490 8 c. *Oncidium ampliatum* 55 25
491 10 c. *Arachnis maggie oei* 45 15
492 12 c. *Dendrobium aggregatum* 45 20
493 15 c. *Paphiopedilum puddle* 45 25
493*a* 20 c. *Spathoglottis* "The Gold" (3.5.77) .. 3·50 3·00
494 25 c. *Epidendrum ciliare* (Eyelash) 55 50
495 35 c. *Bletia patula* .. .. 1·75 50
495*a* 45 c. *Phalaenopsis schilleriana* "Sunset Glow" (3.5.77) .. .. 3·50 3·00
496 50 c. As 45 c. .. .. 2·00 1·00
497 $1 *Ascocenda* "Red Gem" .. .. .. 3·00 3·00
498 $2.50, *Brassolaeliocattleya* "Nugget" .. 3·25 3·25
499 $5 *Caularthron bicornutum* .. .. 3·50 6·00
500 $10 *Vanda* "Josephine Black" .. .. 4·00 11·00
485/500 .. .. .. *Set of* 18 26·00 30·00

The 1 c., 20 c., 25 c., $2.50 and $5 are horiz designs and the remainder are vert.

See also Nos. 510/24 and 543/51.

120 4d. Stamp of 1882, and U.P.U. Emblem

(Des Harrison. Litho Questa)

1974 (9 Oct). *Centenary of Universal Postal Union*. *T* **120** *and similar horiz designs*. W w **12** (*sideways*). *P* 14.

501 8 c. magenta, light orange & lt grey-green .. 10 10
502 35 c. dp rose-red, dull orange & bistre-brown 20 10
503 50 c. ultramarine, cobalt and silver 25 30
504 $1 bright blue, dull brown and grey-black .. 55 80
501/4 .. .. *Set of* 4 1·00 1·10
MS505 126 × 101 mm. Nos. 501/4 .. .. .. 1·25 2·25

Designs:—35 c. Letters encircling the globe; 50 c. U.P.U. emblem and arms of Barbados; $1 Map of Barbados, sailing-ship and aeroplane.

121 Royal Yacht *Britannia*

(Des Jennifer Toombs. Litho Harrison)

1975 (18 Feb). *Royal Visit. T* **121** *and similar horiz design. Multicoloured*. W w **12** (*sideways on* 8 *and* 25 *c*.) *P* 14.

506 8 c. Type **121** 20 15
507 25 c. Type **121** 50 25
508 35 c. Sunset and palms 60 30
509 $1 As 35 c. .. .. 1·75 2·00
506/9 .. .. *Set of* 4 2·75 2·40

1975 (30 Apr)–**79**. *As Nos*. 485/9, 491/3, 494 *and* 495*a*/500 *but* W w **14** (*sideways on* 1, 25 *c*., $1 *and* $10).

510 1 c. Type **119** 10 15
511 2 c. *Renanthera storiei* 10 15
512 3 c. *Dendrobium* "Rose Marie" 15 15
513 4 c. *Epidendrum ibaguense* 25 80
514 5 c. *Schomburgkia humboldtii* (19.10.77) .. 35 10
515 10 c. *Arachnis maggie oei* (19.10.77) 35 10
516 12 c. *Dendrobium aggregatum* (19.10.77) .. 3·25 15
517 15 c. *Paphiopedilum puddle* 70 15
518 25 c. *Epidendrum ciliare* (Eyelash) (27.3.79) 60 10
519 45 c. *Phalaenopsis schilleriana* "Sunset Glow" (25.5.78) 60 15
520 50 c. As 45 c. (23.8.79) .. .. 2·75 2·75
521 $1 *Ascocenda* "Red Gem" .. .. .. 5·50 6·00
522 $2.50, *Brassolaeliocattleya* "Nugget" .. 7·00 3·75
523 $5 *Caularthron bicornutum* .. .. .. 8·50 6·00
524 $10 *Vanda* "Josephine Black" .. .. 11·00 11·00
a. Dull green (stems) omitted .. .. 95·00
510/24 .. .. *Set of* 15 38·00 28·00

No. 525 vacant.

122 St. Michael's Cathedral

123 Pony Float

(Des R. Granger Barrett. Litho Questa)

1975 (29 July). *150th Anniv of Anglican Diocese*. *T* **122** *and similar square designs. Multicoloured*. W w **12** (*sideways*). *P* 13½.

526 5 c. Type **122** 10 10
527 15 c. Bishop Coleridge 15 10
528 50 c. All Saints' Church 45 50
529 $1 "Archangel Michael and Satan" (stained-glass window, St. Michael's Cathedral, Bridgetown) 70 80
526/9 .. .. *Set of* 4 1·25 1·25
MS530 95 × 96 mm. Nos. 526/9 (wmk upright) .. 1·40 2·00

(Des R. Granger Barrett. Litho Questa)

1975 (18 Nov). *Crop-over Festival*. *T* **123** *and similar horiz designs. Multicoloured*. W w **14** (*sideways*). *P* 14.

531 8 c. Type **123** 10 10
532 25 c. Man on stilts 10 10
533 35 c. Maypole dancing 15 10
534 50 c. Cuban dancers 30 45
531/4 .. .. *Set of* 4 55 60
MS535 127 × 85 mm. Nos. 531/4 .. .. .. 90 1·60

124 Barbados Coat of Arms

125 17th-Century Sailing Ship

(Des and litho Harrison)

1975 (15 Dec). *Coil Definitives*. W w 12 *P* 15 × 14.

536 **124** 5 c. greenish blue 10 15
537 25 c. bluish violet 15 20

For 5 c. in this design, but watermarked W w 14, see No. 743.

(Des PAD Studio. Litho J.W.)

1975 (17 Dec). *350th Anniv of First Settlement*. *T* **125** *and similar vert designs. Multicoloured*. W w **14**. *P* 13½.

538 4 c. Type **125** 25 10
539 10 c. Bearded fig tree and fruit 30 15
540 25 c. Ogilvy's 17th-century map 50 30
541 $1 Captain John Powell .. .. .. 2·00 3·00
538/41 .. .. *Set of* 4 2·75 3·25
MS542 105 × 115 mm. Nos. 538/41. *P* 14 × 14½ 3·25 3·50

1976 (20 Feb). *As Nos*. 485 *etc., but* W w **12** (*sideways on* 1 *c*., 25 *c*., $1) *or upright* (*others*).

543 1 c. Type **119** 35 50
544 2 c. *Renanthera storiei* 60 60
545 3 c. *Dendrobium* "Rose Marie" 55 70
546 4 c. *Epidendrum ibaguense* 45 80
547 10 c. *Arachnis maggie oei* 85 70
548 15 c. *Paphiopedilum puddle* 75 80
549 25 c. *Epidendrum ciliare* "Eyelash" .. .. 1·50 90
550 35 c. *Bletia patula* .. .. 1·60 1·50
551 $1 *Ascocenda* "Red Gem" .. .. .. 3·50 4·00
543/51 .. .. *Set of* 9 9·00 9·50

Nos. 552/8 vacant.

126 Map of the Caribbean

(Des PAD Studio. Litho Questa)

1976 (7 July). *West Indian Victory in World Cricket Cup*. *T* **126** *and similar design. No wmk*. *P* 14.

559 25 c. multicoloured .. .. 1·00 75
560 45 c. black and magenta .. .. 1·25 1·25

Design: *Vert*—45 c. The Prudential Cup.

127 Flag and Map of S. Carolina

(Des G. Vasarhelyi. Litho Walsall)

1976 (17 Aug). *Bicentenary of American Revolution*. *T* **127** *and similar horiz designs. Multicoloured*. W w **14** (*sideways*). *P* 13½.

561 15 c. Type **127** 25 15
562 25 c. George Washington and map of Bridgetown 30 15
563 50 c. Independence Declaration 40 50
564 $1 Prince Hall .. .. 60 1·00
561/4 .. .. *Set of* 4 1·40 1·60

128 Early Postman

(Des Jennifer Toombs. Litho Questa)

1976 (19 Oct). *125th Anniv of Post Office Act*. *T* **128** *and similar horiz designs. Multicoloured*. W w **14** (*sideways*) *P* 14.

565 8 c. Type **128** 10 10
566 35 c. Modern postman 25 10
567 50 c. Early letter 30 25
568 $1 Delivery van 50 75
565/8 .. .. *Set of* 4 1·00 1·00

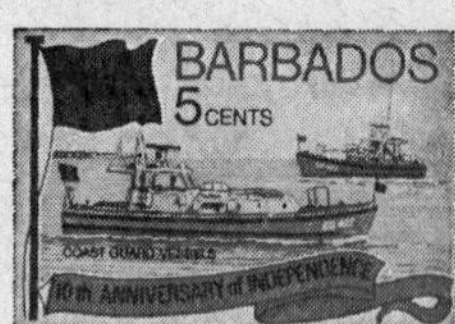

129 Coast Guard Vessels

(Des PAD Studio. Litho J.W.)

1976 (1 Dec).* *Tenth Anniv of Independence*. *T* **129** *and similar horiz designs. Multicoloured*. W w **14** (*sideways*). *P* 13 × 13½.

569 5 c. Type **129** 15 10
570 15 c. Reverse of currency note 15 10
571 25 c. National anthem 20 20
572 $1 Independence Day parade .. .. .. 55 1·10
569/72 .. .. *Set of* 4 95 1·25
MS573 90 × 125 mm. Nos. 569/72. *P* 14 .. .. 1·75 2·10

*This is the local date of issue; the Crown Agents released the stamps a day earlier.

NEW INFORMATION

The editor is always interested to correspond with people who have new information that will improve or correct the Catalogue.

130 Arrival of Coronation Coach at Westminster Abbey

131 Underwater Park

(Des C. Abbott. Litho Walsall)

1977 (7 Feb). *Silver Jubilee*. *T* **130** *and similar vert designs. Multicoloured* W w **14**. *P* 13½.

574 15 c. Garfield Sobers being knighted, 1975 .. 60 25
575 50 c. Type **130** 75 40
576 $1 Queen entering abbey .. .. .. 1·10 70
574/6 .. .. *Set of* 3 2·25 1·25

For the above with different inscription, see Nos. 590/2.

(Des R. Granger Barrett. Litho Questa)

1977 (3 May). *Natural Beauty of Barbados*. *T* **131** *and similar multicoloured designs*. W w **14** (*sideways on Nos*. 577 *and* 579). *P* 14.

577 5 c. Type **131** 15 10
578 35 c. Royal Palms (*vert*) 30 10
579 50 c. Underwater caves 40 35
580 $1 Stalagmite in Harrison's Cave (*vert*) .. 70 1·00
577/80 .. .. *Set of* 4 1·40 1·40
MS581 138 × 92 mm. Nos. 577/80 (wmk sideways) 2·00 2·75

132 Maces of the House of Commons

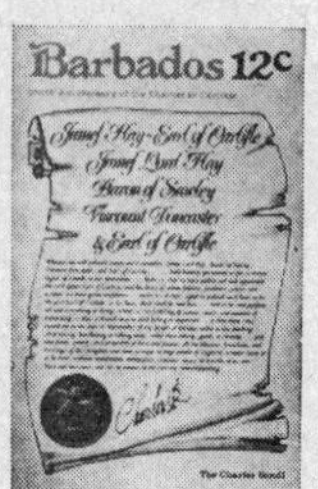

133 The Charter Scroll

(Des C. Abbott. Litho J. W.)

1977 (2 Aug). *13th Regional Conference of the Commonwealth Parliamentary Association*. *T* **132** *and similar designs*. W w **14** (*sideways on* $1). *P* 13½.

582 10 c. pale orange, yellow and lake-brown .. 10 10
583 25 c. apple-green, orange and deep green .. 10 10
584 50 c. multicoloured 20 20
585 $1 pale blue, orange and deep violet-blue .. 55 75
582/5 .. .. *Set of* 4 80 95

Designs: *Vert*.—25 c. Speaker's Chair; 50 c. Senate Chamber. *Horiz*—$1 Sam Lord's Castle.

(Des Walsall. Litho J.W.)

1977 (11 Oct). *350th Anniv of Granting of Charter to Earl of Carlisle*. *T* **133** *and similar multicoloured designs*. W w **14** (*sideways on* 45 *c*. *and* $1). *P* 13.

586 12 c. Type **133** 15 10
587 25 c. The earl receiving charter 15 10
588 45 c. The earl and Charles I (*horiz*) 30 35
589 $1 Ligon's map, 1657 (*horiz*) .. .. .. 50 1·00
586/9 .. .. *Set of* 4 1·00 1·40

(Des C. Abbott. Litho Walsall)

1977 (31 Oct). *Royal Visit. As Nos*. 574/6 *but inscr at top* "SILVER JUBILEE ROYAL VISIT". W w 14. *Roul* 5. *Self-adhesive*.

590 15 c. Garfield Sobers being knighted, 1975 .. 40 40
591 50 c. Type **130** 60 50
592 $1 Queen entering abbey 90 75
590/2 .. .. *Set of* 3 1·75 1·50

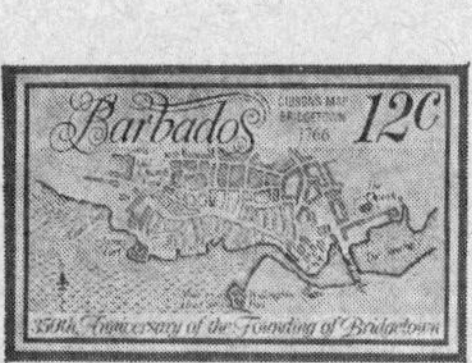

134 Gibson's Map of Bridgetown, 1766

135 Pelican

(Des J. W. Litho Questa)

1978 (1 Mar). *350th Anniv of Founding of Bridgetown*. *T* **134** *and similar horiz designs*. W w **14** (*sideways*). *P* 14.

593 12 c. multicoloured 15 10
594 25 c. black, light green and gold 20 10
595 45 c. multicoloured 25 15
596 $1 multicoloured 40 60
593/6 .. .. *Set of* 4 90 80

Designs:—25 c. "A Prospect of Bridgetown in Barbados" (engraving by S. Copens, 1695); 45 c. "Trafalgar Square, Bridgetown" (drawing by J. M. Carter, 1835); $1 The Bridges, 1978.

(Des C. Abbott. Litho Questa)

1978 (21 Apr). *25th Anniv of Coronation. T* **135** *and similar vert designs. P* 15.
597 50 c. yellow-olive, black and blue 25 40
a. Sheetlet. Nos. 597/9 × 2 .. .. 1·25
598 50 c. multicoloured 25 40
599 50 c. yellow-olive, black and blue 25 40
597/9 .. .. *Set of* 3 65 1·10

Designs:—No. 597, Griffin of Edward III; No. 598, Queen Elizabeth II; No. 599, Type **135**.

Nos. 597/9 were printed together in small sheets of 6 containing two *se-tenant* strips of 3, with horizontal gutter margin between.

136 Barbados Bridge League Logo

(Des J. W. Litho Questa)

1978 (6 June). *7th Regional Bridge Tournament, Barbados. T* **136** *and similar horiz designs. Multicoloured. W* w **14** *(sideways). P* 14½.
600 5 c. Type **136** 10 10
601 10 c. Emblem of World Bridge Federation .. 15 10
602 45 c. Central American and Caribbean Bridge Federation emblem 20 10
603 $1 Playing cards on map of Caribbean .. 35 60
600/3 .. .. *Set of* 4 70 75
MS604 134 × 83 mm. Nos. 600/3 .. .. 1·25 1·75

137 Camp Scene

(Des and litho Harrison)

1978 (1 Aug). *Diamond Jubilee of Guiding. T* **137** *and similar diamond-shaped designs. Multicoloured. W* w **14** *(sideways on* 12, 28 *c.). P* 13½.
605 12 c. Type **137** 20 15
606 28 c. Community work 30 15
607 50 c. Badge and "60" *(vert)* 40 20
608 $1 Guide badge *(vert)* 60 60
605/8 .. .. *Set of* 4 1·40 1·00

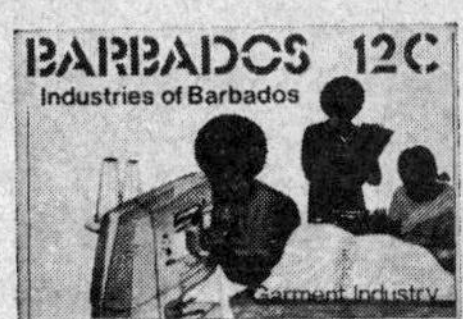

138 Garment Industry

(Des Walsall. Litho Harrison)

1978 (14 Nov). *Industries. T* **138** *and similar multicoloured designs. W* w **14** *(sideways on* 12 *and* 50 *c.). P* 14.
609 12 c. Type **138** 10 10
610 28 c. Cooper *(vert)* 15 20
611 45 c. Blacksmith *(vert)* 20 40
612 50 c. Wrought iron working 25 40
609/12 .. .. *Set of* 4 60 1·00

139 Early Mail Steamer

(Des J. Cooter. Litho J. W.)

1979 (8 Feb). *Ships. T* **139** *and similar horiz designs. Multicoloured. W* w **14** *(sideways). P* 13.
613 12 c. Type **139** 20 10
614 25 c. *Queen Elizabeth 2* in Deep Water Harbour 30 15
615 50 c. *Ra II* nearing Barbados 45 40
616 $1 Early mail steamer *(different)* .. .. 70 1·00
613/16 .. .. *Set of* 4 1·50 1·50

140 1953 1 c. Definitive Stamp

(Des J.W. Litho Format)

1979 (8 May). *Death Centenary of Sir Rowland Hill. T* **140** *and similar multicoloured designs showing stamps. W* w **14** *(sideways on* 12 *c.). P* 14.
617 12 c. Type **140** 15 15
618 28 c. 1975 350th anniv of first settlement 25 c. commemorative *(vert)* 20 25
619 45 c. Penny Black with Maltese Cross postmark *(vert)* 30 35
617/19 .. .. *Set of* 3 60 60
MS620 137 × 90 mm 50 c. Unissued "Britannia" blue (wmk sideways) 35 40

All examples of No. 618 show anniversary spelt as "anniverary".

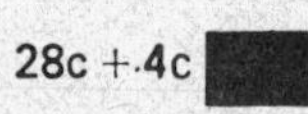

ST. VINCENT RELIEF FUND

(**141**)

142 Grassland Yellow Finch

1979 (29 May). *St Vincent Relief Fund. No.* 495 *surch with T* **141**.
621 28 c. + 4 c. on 35 c. *Bletia patula* 15 20

(Des J.W. Photo Harrison)

1979 (7 Aug)–**82**. *Birds. Vert designs as T* **142**. *Multicoloured. W* w **14** *(sideways on* 1, 5, 10, 12, 15, 20, 25, 28, 40, 50, 55, 60, 70 *c. and* $1). *P* 14.
622 1 c. Type **142** 10 15
623 2 c. Grey Kingbird 10 15
624 5 c. Lesser Antillean Bullfinch 10 15
625 8 c. Magnificent Frigate Bird 10 15
626 10 c. Cattle Egret (deep slate inscr) 10 15
a. Slate-blue inscr 20 20
627 12 c. Green Heron 15 15
627*a* 15 c. Carib Grackle (1.3.82) .. .. .. 1·50 60
628 20 c. Antillean Crested Hummingbird 20 20
629 25 c. Scaly-breasted Ground Dove 20 25
630 28 c. As 15 c. 25 35
631 35 c. Green-throated Carib 30 40
a. Yellow omitted £175
631*b* 40 c. Red-necked Pigeon (1.3.82) .. .. 2·00 70
632 45 c. Zenaida Dove 35 45
633 50 c. As 40 c. 45 55
633*a* 55 c. American Golden Plover (1.9.81) .. 2·00 60
633*b* 60 c. Bananaquit (1.3.82) .. .. .. 2·25 1·00
634 70 c. As 60 c. 55 70
635 $1 Caribbean Elaenia 75 90
636 $2.50, American Redstart .. .. .. 2·00 2·75
637 $5 Belted Kingfisher .. .. .. 3·25 4·75
638 $10 Moorhen .. .. 6·50 10·00
622/38 .. .. *Set of* 21 21·00 22·00

No. 626*a* occurred in the initial supply sent to Barbados.

No. 631*a* shows the birds' plumage in blue instead of green and has the background flowers omitted.

143 Gun aboard Landing Craft at Foul Bay

144 Family

(Des G. Vasarhelyi. Litho Format)

1979 (9 Oct). *Space Project Commemorations. T* **143** *and similar multicoloured designs. W* w **14** *(sideways on* 10, 28 *and* 45 *c.). P* 14.
639 10 c. Type **143** 10 10
640 12 c. Transporting launcher through Barbados *(vert)* 20 15
641 20 c. Firing of 16" launcher in daylight *(vert)* 15 15
642 28 c. Bath Earth Station and "Intelsat IV A" 25 25
643 45 c. "Intelsat V" over the Caribbean 35 35
644 50 c. "Intelsat IV A" over Atlantic *(vert)* .. 35 35
639/44 .. .. *Set of* 6 1·10 1·10
MS645 118 × 90 mm. $1 Lunar module descending on to Moon (wmk sideways) 65 80

Commemorations:—10 to 20 c. H.A.R.P. Gun experiment: 28 to 50 c. First use of "Intelsat" satellites; $1, 10th anniversary of Moon landing.

(Des R. Granger Barrett. Litho Questa)

1979 (27 Nov). *International Year of the Child. T* **144** *and similar vert designs. Multicoloured. W* w **14**. *P* 14.
646 12 c. Type **144** 10 10
647 28 c. Ring of children and map of Barbados .. 15 15
648 45 c. Child with teacher 20 20
649 50 c. Children playing 20 20
650 $1 Children and kite 35 45
646/50 .. .. *Set of* 5 80 90

MINIMUM PRICE

The minimum price quote is 10p which represents a handling charge rather than a basis for valuing common stamps. For further notes about prices see introductory pages.

145 Map of Barbados

146 Private, Artillery Company, Barbados Volunteer Force, *circa* 1909

(Des G. Hutchins. Litho Security Printers (M), Malaysia)

1980 (19 Feb). *75th Anniv of Rotary International. T* **145** *and similar horiz designs. Multicoloured. W* w **14** *(sideways). P* 13.
651 12 c. Type **145** 10 10
652 28 c. Map of Caribbean 15 15
653 50 c. Rotary anniversary emblem 20 25
654 $1 Paul P. Harris (founder) 35 60
651/4 .. .. *Set of* 4 70 1·00

(Des J.W. Litho Questa)

1980 (8 Apr). *75th Anniv of Barbados Regiment. T* **146** *and similar vert designs. Multicoloured. W* w **14**. *P* 14 × 14½.
655 12 c. Type **146** 10 10
656 35 c. Drum Major, Zouave Uniform 30 15
657 50 c. Sovereign's and Regimental colours .. 40 30
658 $1 Barbados Regiment Women's Corps .. 65 70
655/8 .. .. *Set of* 4 1·25 1·10

147 Early Postman **148** Underwater Scenery

(Des. V. Whiteley Studio. Litho Walsall)

1980 (6 May). *"London 1980" International Stamp Exhibition. Two sheets each* 122 × 125 *mm containing T* **147** *or similar vert design. Multicoloured. W* w **14**. *P* 14 × 13½.
MS659 (a) 28 c. × 6, Type **147** .. .. .. } 1·75 2·25
(b) 50 c. × 6, Modern Postwoman and Inspector .. .. }

The two sheets each contain the stamp in full colour and in five different colour separations.

(Des G. Drummond. Litho Security Printers (M), Malaysia)

1980 (30 Sept). *Underwater Scenery. T* **148** *and similar horiz designs. W* w **14** *(sideways). P* 13½.
660 12 c. multicoloured 10 10
661 28 c. multicoloured 20 15
662 50 c. multicoloured 30 25
663 $1 multicoloured 55 70
660/3 .. .. *Set of* 4 1·00 1·00
MS664 136 × 110 mm. Nos. 660/3 (wmk upright) 1·25 1·75

149 Bathsheba Railway Station

(Des J. W. Litho Questa)

1981 (13 Jan). *Early Transport. T* **149** *and similar horiz designs. Multicoloured. W* w **14** *(sideways). P* 14½ × 14.
665 12 c. Type **149** 10 10
666 28 c. Cab stand at The Green 20 15
667 45 c. Animal-drawn tram 30 25
668 70 c. Horse-drawn bus 45 50
669 $1 Railway station in Fairchild Street .. 60 85
665/9 .. .. *Set of* 5 1·50 1·75

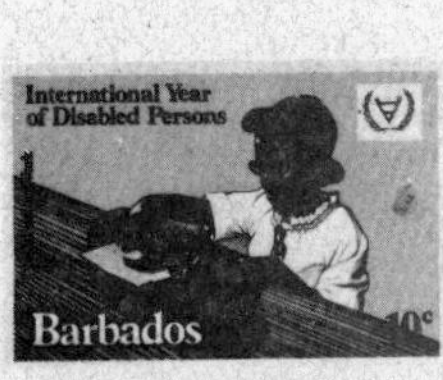

150 "The Blind at Work"

151 Prince Charles dressed for Polo

(Des BG Studio. Litho Walsall)

1981 (19 May). *International Year for Disabled Persons. T* **150** *and similar multicoloured designs. W w* **14** (*sideways on* 10 c. *and* $2.50). *P* 14.

670 10 c. Type **150** 10 10
671 25 c. Sign language (*vert*) 25 20
672 45 c. "Be alert to the white cane" (*vert*) .. 45 35
673 $2.50, Children at play .. .. 1·75 2·50
670/3 .. .. *Set of* 4 2·25 2·75

(Des and litho J.W.)

1981 (22 July). *Royal Wedding. T* **151** *and similar vert designs. Multicoloured. W w* **14**. *P* 13½ × 13.

674 28 c. Wedding bouquet from Barbados .. 20 10
675 50 c. Type **151** 25 15
676 $2.50, Prince Charles and Lady Diana Spencer .. .. 80 1·25
674/6 .. .. *Set of* 3 1·10 1·25

152 Landship Manoeuvre (**153**)

(Des C. Abbott. Litho Harrison)

1981 (11 Aug). *Carifesta* (*Caribbean Festival of Arts*), *Barbados. T* **152** *and similar vert designs. Multicoloured. W w* **14**. *P* 14½ × 14.

677 15 c. Type **152** 15 15
678 20 c. Yoruba dancers 15 15
679 40 c. Tuk band 25 25
680 55 c. Sculpture of Frank Collymore .. 35 35
681 $1 Harbour scene 60 75
677/81 .. .. *Set of* 5 1·40 1·50

1981 (1 Sept). *Nos.* 630, 632 *and* 634 *surch as T* **153**.

682 15 c. on 28 c. Carib Grackle 15 15
683 40 c. on 45 c. Zenaida Dove 20 30
684 60 c. on 70 c. Bananaquit 30 40
682/4 .. .. *Set of* 3 60 75

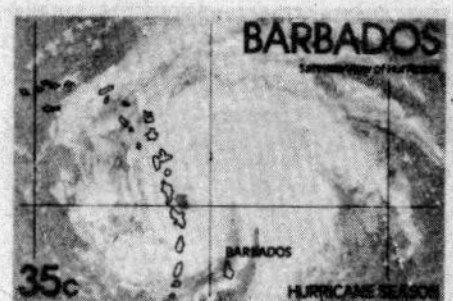

154 Satellite view of Hurricane

(Des A. Theobald. Litho Walsall)

1981 (29 Sept). *Hurricane Season. T* **154** *and similar horiz designs. W w* **14** (*sideways*). *P* 14.

685 35 c. black and blue 30 20
686 50 c. multicoloured 40 35
687 60 c. multicoloured 50 50
688 $1 multicoloured 75 90
685/8 .. .. *Set of* 4 1·75 1·75

Designs:—50 c. Hurricane "Gladys" from "Apollo 7"; 60 c. Police Department on hurricane watch; $1 Hurricane hunter (McDonnell "F2H-2P (Banshee)" jet aircraft).

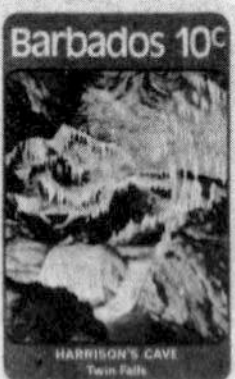

155 Twin Falls **156** Black Belly Ram

(Des. L. Curtis. Litho Format)

1981 (1 Dec.) *Harrison's Cave. T* **155** *and similar vert designs. Multicoloured. W w* **14**. *P* 14 × 14½.

689 10 c. Type **155** 10 10
690 20 c. Stream in Rotunda Room 20 15
691 55 c. Formations in Rotunda Room 40 40
692 $2.50, Cascade Pool .. .. 1·25 1·75
689/92 .. .. *Set of* 4 1·75 2·25

(Des BG Studio. Litho Format)

1982 (9 Feb). *Black Belly Sheep. T* **156** *and similar horiz designs. Multicoloured. W w* **14** (*sideways*). *P* 14.

693 40 c. Type **156** 30 30
694 50 c. Black Belly ewe 30 30
695 60 c. Ewe with lambs 40 50
696 $1 Ram and ewe, with map of Barbados .. 65 1·25
693/6 .. .. *Set of* 4 1·50 2·00

COVER PRICES

Cover factors are quoted at the beginning of each country for most issues to 1945. An explanation of the system can be found on page x. The factors quoted do not, however, apply to philatelic covers.

157 Barbados Coat of Arms and Flag

(Des Harrison. Litho Format)

1982 (8 Apr). *President Reagan's Visit. T* **157** *and similar horiz design. Multicoloured. W w* **14** (*sideways*). *P* 14.

697 20 c. Type **157** 40 45
a. Pair. Nos. 697/8 .. .. 80 90
698 20 c. U.S.A. coat of arms and flag 40 45
699 55 c. Type **157** 80 90
a. Pair. Nos. 699/700 .. .. 1·60 1·75
700 55 c. As No. 698 .. .. 80 90
697/700 .. .. *Set of* 4 2·40 2·50

The two designs of each value were printed together, *se-tenant*, in horizontal and vertical pairs within small sheets of 8 stamps.

158 Lighter **159** Bride and Earl Spencer proceeding up Aisle

(Des J.W. Litho Harrison)

1982 (4 May). *Early Marine Transport. T* **158** *and similar horiz designs. Multicoloured. W w* **14** (*sideways*). *P* 14½.

701 20 c. Type **158** 20 15
702 35 c. Rowing boat 35 25
703 55 c. Speightstown schooner 50 40
704 $2.50, Inter-colonial schooner .. .. 2·00 2·25
701/4 .. .. *Set of* 4 2·75 2·75

(Des Jennifer Toombs. Litho Questa)

1982 (1 July). *21st Birthday of Princess of Wales. T* **159** *and similar vert designs. Multicoloured W w* **14**. *P* 14½ × 14.

705 20 c. Barbados coat of arms 20 15
706 60 c. Princess at Llanelwedd, October 1981 .. 55 50
707 $1.20, Type **159** .. .. 90 1·10
708 $2.50, Formal portrait .. .. 1·50 1·90
705/8 .. .. *Set of* 4 2·75 3·25

160 "To Help other People" **161** Arms of George Washington

(Des G. Drummond. Litho Format)

1982 (7 Sept). *75th Anniv of Boy Scout Movement. T* **160** *and similar multicoloured designs. W w* **14** (*sideways on Nos.* 710/11). *P* 14.

709 15 c. Type **160** 40 10
710 40 c. "I Promise to do my Best" (*horiz*) .. 70 25
711 55 c. "To do my Duty to God, the Queen and my Country" (*horiz*) 90 40
712 $1 National and Troop flags .. .. 1·25 1·25
709/12 .. .. *Set of* 4 3·00 1·75
MS713 119 × 93 mm. $1.50, The Scout Law .. 2·50 2·75

(Des and litho J.W.)

1982 (2 Nov). *250th Birth Anniv of George Washington. T* **161** *and similar vert designs. Multicoloured. W w* **14**. *P* 13½ × 13.

714 10 c. Type **161** 10 10
715 55 c. Washington House, Barbados 45 45
716 60 c. Washington with troops 50 50
717 $2.50, Washington taking Oath .. .. 1·60 1·60
714/17 .. .. *Set of* 4 2·40 2·40

162 Gulf Fritillary

(Des I. Loe. Litho J.W.)

1983 (8 Feb). *Butterflies. T* **162** *and similar horiz designs. Multicoloured. W w* **14** (*sideways*). *P* 13 × 13½.

718 20 c. Type **162** 45 15
719 40 c. Monarch 60 40
720 55 c. Mimic 75 45
721 $2.50, Hanno Blue .. .. 2·00 2·00
718/21 .. .. *Set of* 4 3·50 2·75

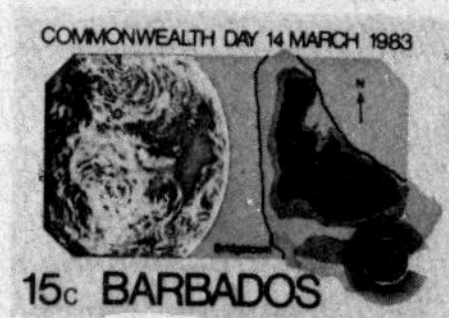

163 Map of Barbados and Satellite View

(Des D. Bowen. Litho J.W.)

1983 (14 Mar). *Commonwealth Day. T* **163** *and similar horiz designs. Multicoloured. W w* **14** (*sideways*). *P* 13.

722 15 c. Type **163** 25 10
723 40 c. Tourist beach 40 20
724 60 c. Sugar cane harvesting 60 40
725 $1 Cricket match .. .. 1·50 1·10
722/5 .. .. *Set of* 4 2·50 1·60

164 U.S. Navy Dirigible

(Des L. Curtis. Litho Format)

1983 (14 June). *Bicentenary of Manned Flight. T* **164** *and similar horiz designs. Multicoloured. W w* **14** (*sideways*). *P* 14.

726 20 c. Type **164** 35 10
727 40 c. Douglas "DC3" 50 25
728 55 c. Vickers "Viscount" 60 40
729 $1 Lockheed "Tristar" .. .. 1·00 90
726/9 .. .. *Set of* 4 2·25 1·50

165 Nash "600", 1941 **166** Game in Progress

(Des and litho Harrison)

1983 (9 Aug). *Classic Cars. T* **165** *and similar horiz designs. Multicoloured. W w* **14** (*sideways*). *P* 14.

730 25 c. Type **165** 30 20
731 45 c. Dodge, 1938 .. .. 40 30
732 75 c. Ford "Model AA", 1930 .. .. 60 55
733 $2.50, Dodge "Four", 1918 .. .. 1·75 2·00
730/3 .. .. *Set of* 4 2·75 2·75

(Des L. Curtis. Litho Questa)

1983 (30 Aug). *Table Tennis World Cup Competition. T* **166** *and similar vert designs. Multicoloured. W w* **14**. *P* 14.

734 20 c. Type **166** 25 20
735 65 c. Map of Barbados 50 45
736 $1 World Table Tennis Cup 75 85
734/6 .. .. *Set of* 3 1·40 1·40

167 Angel playing Lute (detail "The Virgin and Child") (Masaccio)) **168** Track and Field Events

(Des D. Miller. Litho Questa)

1983 (1 Nov). *Christmas. 50th Anniv of Barbados Museum. T* **167** *and similar multicoloured designs. W w* **14** (*sideways on* 45 c., 75 c. *and* $2.50). *P* 14.

737 10 c. multicoloured 15 10
738 25 c. multicoloured 30 20
739 45 c. multicoloured 45 30
740 75 c. black and gold 75 65
741 $2.50, multicoloured .. .. 2·40 2·75
737/41 .. .. *Set of* 5 3·50 3·50
MS742 59 × 98 mm. $2 multicoloured .. 1·75 2·00

Designs: *Horiz*—45 c. "The Barbados Museum" (Richard Day); 75 c. "St. Ann's Garrison" (W. S. Hedges); $2.50, Needham's Point, Carlisle Bay. *Vert*—25 c., $2 Different details from "The Virgin and Child" (Masaccio).

1983 (Dec). *Coil Definitive. As No. 536 but W* w **14**.
743 **124** 5 c. greenish blue 20 20
No. 743 was also available from sheets.

(Des McCombie Skinner Studio. Litho Walsall)

1984 (28 Mar). *Olympic Games, Los Angeles. T* **168** *and similar horiz designs. W* w **14** (*sideways*). *P* 14.
745 50 c. bright green, black and olive-sepia .. 50 45
746 65 c. dull orange, black and drab .. 65 60
747 75 c. greenish blue, black and deep cobalt .. 70 70
748 $1 light brown, black and yellow-ochre .. 90 90
745/8 .. .. *Set of* 4 2·50 2·40
MS749 115 × 97 mm. Nos. 745/8 .. .. .. 2·75 3·25
Designs:—65 c. Shooting; 75 c. Sailing; $1 Cycling.

169 Global Coverage **170** U.P.U. 1943 3d. Stamp and Logo

(Des C. Abbott. Litho Questa)

1984 (25 Apr). *250th Anniv of Lloyd's List (newspaper). T* **169** *and similar vert designs. Multicoloured. W* w **14**. *P* 14½ × 14.
750 45 c. Type **169** 65 40
751 50 c. Bridgetown harbour 70 50
752 75 c. *Philosopher*, 1857 .. .. .. 95 70
753 $1 *Sea Princess*, 1984 .. .. .. 1·10 95
750/3 .. .. *Set of* 4 3·00 2·25

(Des McCombie Skinner Studio. Litho J.W.)

1984 (6 June). *Universal Postal Union Congress, Hamburg. Sheet* 90 × 75 *mm. W* w **14** (*sideways*). *P* 13½.
MS754 **170** $2 multicoloured .. .. .. 2·25 2·50

171 Local Junior Match **172** Poinsettia

(Des L. Curtis. Litho Walsall)

1984 (8 Aug). *60th Anniv of World Chess Federation. T* **171** *and similar horiz designs. Multicoloured. W* w **14** (*sideways*). *P* 14½.
755 25 c. Type **171** 70 25
756 45 c. Staunton and 19th-century Knight .. 95 45
757 65 c. Staunton and 18th-century Queen .. 1·25 70
758 $2 Staunton and 17th-century Castle .. 2·75 3·00
755/8 .. .. *Set of* 4 5·00 4·00

(Des I. Loe. Litho Questa)

1984 (24 Oct). *Christmas. Flowers. T* **172** *and similar vert designs. Multicoloured. W* w **14**. *P* 14.
759 50 c. Type **172** 85 50
760 65 c. Snow-on-the-Mountain 95 60
761 75 c. Christmas Candle .. .. .. 1·10 95
762 $1 Christmas Hope .. .. 1·40 1·75
759/62 .. .. *Set of* 4 4·00 3·50

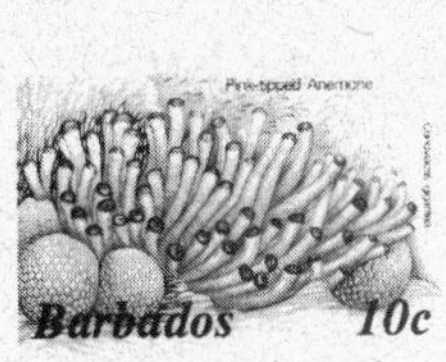

173 Pink-tipped Anemone **174** The Queen Mother at the Docks

(Des I. Loe. Litho Questa)

1985 (26 Feb)–**87**. *Marine Life. T* **173** *and similar horiz designs. Multicoloured. W* w **14** (*sideways*). *P* 14. *A. Without imprint date at foot. B. With imprint date* ("1987").

		A		B	
763	1 c. Bristle Worm	15	15	20	25
764	2 c. Spotted Trunkfish ..	15	15	20	25
765	5 c. Coney	15	15	†	
766	10 c. Type **173**	25	15	†	
767	20 c. Christmas Tree Worm ..	50	25	65	50
768	25 c. Hermit Crab	60	30	†	
769	35 c. Animal Flower	65	30	†	
770	40 c. Vase Sponge	70	45	†	
771	45 c. Spotted Moray	70	40	†	
772	50 c. Ghost Crab	1·25	60	1·50	1·00
773	65 c. Flamingo Tongue Snail ..	1·00	50	†	
774	75 c. Sergeant Major	1·25	60	1·75	1·25
775	$1 Caribbean Warty Anemone	1·75	65	†	
776	$2.50, Green Turtle	3·75	3·00	3·75	3·50
777	$5 Rock Beauty (fish) ..	6·50	5·50	6·50	6·50
778	$10 Elkhorn Coral	8·50	8·50	†	
763/78A	.. .. *Set of* 16	25·00	19·00	†	
763/78B	.. .. *Set of* 7	†		13·00	12·00

Dates of issue:—26.2.85, Nos. 766A/8A, 772A, 776A/7A; 9.4.85, Nos. 765A, 769A/70A, 773A, 778A; 7.5.85, Nos. 763A/4A, 771A, 774A/5A; 15.9.87, 763B/77B.
For these designs watermarked w **16** (sideways) see Nos. 794/809.

(Des A. Theobald ($2), C. Abbott (others). Litho Questa)

1985 (7 June). *Life and Times of Queen Elizabeth the Queen Mother. T* **174** *and similar vert designs. Multicoloured. W* w **16**. *P* 14½ × 14.
779 25 c. In the White Drawing Room, Buckingham Palace, 1930s 15 20
780 65 c. With Lady Diana Spencer at Trooping the Colour, 1981 .. .. .. 45 50
781 75 c. Type **174**.. .. .. 55 60
782 $1 With Prince Henry at his christening (from photo by Lord Snowdon).. .. 70 75
779/82 .. .. *Set of* 4 1·60 1·90
MS783 91 × 73 mm. $2 In Land Rover opening Syon House Garden Centre. Wmk sideways .. 1·40 1·50

175 Peregrine Falcon

(Des D. Miller. Litho Walsall)

1985 (6 Aug). *Birth Bicentenary of John J. Audubon (ornithologist). T* **175** *and similar multicoloured designs showing original paintings. W* w **14** (*sideways on* 45 c.). *P* 14.
784 45 c. Type **175**.. .. .. 80 45
785 65 c. Prairie Warbler (*vert*) 85 65
786 75 c. Great Blue Heron (*vert*) .. .. 1·00 90
787 $1 Yellow Warbler (*vert*) .. .. .. 1·40 1·25
784/7 .. .. *Set of* 4 3·50 3·00

176 Intelsat Satellite orbitting Earth **177** Traffic Policeman

(Des L. Curtis. Litho Harrison)

1985 (10 Sept). *20th Anniv of Intelsat Satellite System. W* w **14** (*sideways*). *P* 14.
788 **176** 75 c. multicoloured 60 60

(Des L. Curtis. Litho Format)

1985 (19 Nov). *150th Anniv of Royal Barbados Police. T* **177** *and similar multicoloured designs. W* w **16**. *P* 14.
789 25 c. Type **177**.. .. .. 50 20
790 50 c. Police Band on bandstand 80 40
791 65 c. Dog handler .. .. 1·10 70
792 $1 Mounted policeman in ceremonial uniform .. .. 1·50 1·50
789/92 .. .. *Set of* 4 3·50 2·50
MS793 85 × 60 mm. $2 Police Band on parade (*horiz*). Wmk sideways .. .. .. 2·25 2·50

1986 (6 Jan)–**87**. *As Nos. 763/78 but W* w **16** (*sideways*). *P* 14. A. *Without imprint date at foot.* B. *With imprint date.*

		A		B	
794	1 c. Bristle Worm	†		15	20
795	2 c. Spotted Trunkfish ..	†		15	20
796	5 c. Coney	20	15	20	15
797	10 c. Type **173**	30	15	20	15
798	20 c. Christmas Tree Worm ..	60	25	30	20
799	25 c. Hermit Crab	60	30	40	25
800	35 c. Animal Flower	60	35	50	35
801	40 c. Vase Sponge	†		50	40
802	45 c. Spotted Moray	†		50	40
803	50 c. Ghost Crab	1·25	75	60	45
804	65 c. Flamingo Tongue Snail ..	†		65	50
805	75 c. Sergeant Major	†		70	60
806	$1 Caribbean Warty Anemone	†		85	65
807	$2.50, Green Turtle	3·50	3·50	2·00	1·50
808	$5 Rock Beauty (fish) ..	6·00	6·00	3·75	3·00
809	$10 Elkhorn Coral	10·00	10·00	9·00	7·00
794/809A	.. .. *Set of* 9	21·00	19·00	†	
794/809B	.. .. *Set of* 16	†		18·00	14·50

Dates of issue:—6.1.86, Nos. 796A/800A, 803A, 807A/9A; 23.7.86, Nos. 794B/5B, 801B/2B; 18.8.86, Nos. 797B/9B, 803B/9B; 15.9.87, Nos. 796B, 800B.
Nos. 797B, 799B, 801B/2B, 804B, 806B and 809B exist with different imprint dates below the designs.

(Des A. Theobald. Litho Format)

1986 (21 Apr). *60th Birthday of Queen Elizabeth II. Vert designs as T* **110** *of Ascension. Multicoloured. W* w **16**. *P* 14 × 14½.
810 25 c. Princess Elizabeth aged two, 1928 .. 15 20
811 50 c. At University College of West Indies, Jamaica, 1953 .. .. 35 40
812 65 c. With Duke of Edinburgh, Barbados, 1985 .. .. 45 50
a. Silver (logo) omitted £300
813 75 c. At banquet in Sao Paulo, Brazil, 1968 .. 55 60
814 $2 At Crown Agents Head Office, London, 1983 .. .. 1·40 1·50
810/14 .. .. *Set of* 5 2·50 3·00

178 Trans-Canada "North Star DC-472" Airliner

(Des L. Curtis. Litho Format)

1986 (2 May). *"Expo '86" World Fair, Vancouver. T* **178** *and similar horiz design. Multicoloured. W* w **16** (*sideways*). *P* 14.
815 50 c. Type **178**.. .. .. 35 40
816 $2.50, *Lady Nelson* (liner) .. .. 1·75 1·90

(Des D. Miller. Litho Walsall)

1986 (22 May). *"Ameripex '86" International Stamp Exhibition, Chicago. Horiz designs as T* **164** *of Bahamas, showing Barbados stamps* (*Nos.* 817/20). *Multicoloured. W* w **16** (*sideways*). *P* 14.
817 45 c. 1976 Bicentenary of American Revolution 25 c... .. .. 40 35
818 50 c. 1976 Bicentenary of American Revolution 50 c... .. .. 45 40
819 65 c. 1981 Hurricane Season $1 .. .. 55 50
820 $1 1982 Visit of President Reagan 55 c. pair.. .. .. 75 75
817/20 .. .. *Set of* 4 2·00 1·75
MS821 90 × 80 mm. $2 Statue of Liberty and liner *Queen Elizabeth 2* .. .. .. 2·00 2·50
No. **MS**821 also commemorates the Centenary of the Statue of Liberty.

(Des D. Miller. Litho Walsall)

1986 (23 July). *Royal Wedding. Square designs as T* **112** *of Ascension. Multicoloured. W* w **16**. *P* 14½ × 14.
822 45 c. Prince Andrew and Miss Sarah Ferguson 45 35
823 $1 Prince Andrew in Midshipman's uniform 95 75

179 Transporting Electricity Poles, 1923 **180** *Alpinia purpurata* and Church Window

(Des A. Theobald. Litho B.D.T.)

1986 (16 Sept). *75th Anniv of Electricity in Barbados. T* **179** *and similar multicoloured designs. W* w **16** (*sideways on* 10, 65 c.). *P* 13½.
824 10 c. Type **179**.. .. .. 15 10
825 25 c. Heathman Ladder, 1935 (*vert*).. .. 25 20
826 65 c. Transport fleet, 1941 .. .. .. 60 50
827 $2 Bucket truck, 1986 (*vert*) .. .. 1·60 1·75
824/7 .. .. *Set of* 4 2·40 2·25

(Des A. Atkinson. Litho Questa)

1986 (28 Oct). *Christmas. T* **180** *and similar vert designs showing flowers and church windows. Multicoloured. W* w **14**. *P* 14.
828 25 c. Type **180**.. .. .. 20 20
829 50 c. *Anthurium andraeanum* 45 40
830 75 c. *Heliconia rostrata* 70 60
831 $2 *Heliconia x psittacorum* .. .. 1·50 2·00
828/31 .. .. *Set of* 4 2·50 3·00

181 Shot Putting **182** Barn Swallow

(Des G. Vasarhelyi. Litho Format)

1987 (27 Mar). *10th Anniv of Special Olympics. T* **181** *and similar horiz designs. Multicoloured. W* w **14** *(sideways). P* 14.
832 15 c. Type **181** 15 15
833 45 c. Wheelchair racing 30 30
834 65 c. Long jumping 45 45
835 $2 Logo and slogan . . . . . . 1·40 1·75
832/5 . . . . *Set of* 4 2·10 2·40

(Des P. Broadbent. Litho Walsall)

1987 (12 June). *"Capex '87" International Stamp Exhibition, Toronto. Birds. T* **182** *and similar vert designs. Multicoloured. W* w **16**. *P* 14.
836 25 c. Type **182** 45 30
837 50 c. Yellow Warbler 60 45
838 65 c. Audubon's Shearwater 75 65
839 75 c. Black-whiskered Vireo 85 75
840 $1 Scarlet Tanager . . . . . . 1·10 1·25
836/40 . . . . *Set of* 5 3·25 3·00

183 Sea Scout saluting

184 Bridgetown Synagogue

(Des L. Curtis. Litho Format)

1987 (24 July). *75th Anniv of Scouting in Barbados. T* **183** *and similar vert designs. Multicoloured. W* w **16**. *P* 14.
841 10 c. Type **183** 20 10
842 25 c. Scout jamboree 30 20
843 65 c. Scout badges 65 45
844 $2 Scout band . . . . 1·60 1·75
841/4 . . . . *Set of* 4 2·50 2·25

(Des R. Edge. Litho Questa)

1987 (6 Oct). *Restoration of Bridgetown Synagogue. T* **184** *and similar multicoloured designs. W* w **16** *(sideways on* 50, 65 *c.). P* 14 × 14½ *(horiz) or* 14½ × 14 *(vert).*
845 50 c. Type **184** 60 45
846 65 c. Interior of Synagogue 70 55
847 75 c. Ten Commandments (*vert*) . . 85 75
848 $1 Marble laver (*vert*) . . . . . . 1·25 1·40
845/8 . . . . *Set of* 4 3·00 2·75

185 Arms and Colonial Seal

(Des D. Hartley. Litho Walsall)

1987 (24 Nov). *21st Anniv of Independence. T* **185** *and similar multicoloured designs. W* w **16** *(sideways). P* 14 × 14½.
849 25 c. Type **185** 15 20
850 45 c. Flags of Barbados and Great Britain . . 25 30
851 65 c. Silver dollar and one penny coins . . 40 45
852 $2 Colours of Barbados Regiment . . 1·25 1·40
849/52 . . . . *Set of* 4 1·90 2·10
MS853 94 × 56 mm. $1.50, Prime Minister E. W. Barrow (*vert*). Wmk upright. P 14½ × 14 . . 90 95

186 E. A. (Manny) Martindale

187 *Kentropyx borckianus*

(Des D. Hartley. Litho Walsall)

1988 (6 June–11 July). *West Indian Cricket. T* **186** *and similar horiz designs, each showing portrait, cricket equipment and early belt buckle. Multicoloured. W* w **14** *(sideways). P* 14.
854 15 c. Type **186** 25 15
855 45 c. George Challenor 55 30
856 50 c. Herman C. Griffith (11.7) . . 65 45
857 75 c. Harold Austin 80 50
858 $2 Frank Worrell . . . . 1·75 1·40
854/8 . . . . *Set of* 5 3·50 2·50

(Des Doreen McGuinness. Litho B.D.T.)

1988 (13 June). *Lizards of Barbados. T* **187** *and similar vert designs. Multicoloured. W* w **14**. *P* 14.
859 10 c. Type **187** 15 10
860 50 c. *Hemidactylus mabouia* 50 35
861 65 c. *Anolis extremus* 60 45
862 $2 *Gymnophthalmus underwoodii* . . 1·60 1·75
859/62 . . . . *Set of* 4 2·50 2·40

188 Cycling

189 Harry Bayley and Observatory

(Des A. Edmonston. Litho Walsall)

1988 (2 Aug). *Olympic Games, Seoul. T* **188** *and similar vert designs. Multicoloured. W* w **14**. *P* 14½ × 14.
863 25 c. Type **188** 15 20
864 45 c. Athletics 25 30
865 75 c. Relay swimming 45 50
866 $2 Yachting . . . . 1·25 1·40
863/6 . . . . *Set of* 4 1·90 2·10
MS867 144×63 mm. Nos. 863/6. W w **16** . . 2·10 2·40

(Des S. Noon and D. Miller (50, 65 c.), D. Miller (others). Litho Questa)

1988 (18 Oct). *300th Anniv of Lloyd's of London. Designs as T* **123** *of Ascension. W* w **14** *(sideways on* 50, 65 *c.). P* 14.
868 40 c. multicoloured 25 30
869 50 c. multicoloured 30 35
870 65 c. multicoloured 40 45
871 $2 steel-blue and brown-lake . . . . 1·25 1·40
868/71 . . . . *Set of* 4 2·00 2·25
Designs: *Vert*—40 c. Royal Exchange, 1774; $2 Sinking of *Titanic*, 1912. *Horiz*—50 c. Early sugar mill; 65 c. *Author* (container ship).

(Des Josephine Martin. Litho Walsall)

1988 (28 Nov). *25th Anniv of Harry Bayley Observatory. T* **189** *and similar horiz designs. Multicoloured. W* w **16** *(sideways). P* 14 × 14½.
872 25 c. Type **189** 20 20
873 65 c. Observatory with North Star and Southern Cross constellations . . 45 45
874 75 c. Andromeda galaxy 50 50
875 $2 Orion constellation . . . . . . 1·40 1·60
872/5 . . . . *Set of* 4 2·25 2·50

190 LIAT BAe "748"

191 Assembly Chamber

(Des A. Theobald. Litho Walsall)

1989 (20 Mar). *50th Anniv of Commercial Aviation in Barbados. T* **190** *and similar horiz designs. Multicoloured. W* w **16** *(sideways). P* 14.
876 25 c. Type **190** 20 20
877 65 c. Panam Douglas "DC-8" 45 45
878 75 c. British Airways "Concorde" at Grantley Adams Airport 50 50
879 $2 Caribbean Air Cargo Boeing "707-351c" . . . . 1·40 1·60
876/9 . . . . *Set of* 4 2·25 2·50

(Des A. Edmonston. Litho B.D.T.)

1989 (19 July). *350th Anniv of Parliament. T* **191** *and similar square designs. W* w **16**. *P* 13½.
880 25 c. multicoloured 15 20
881 50 c. multicoloured 30 35
882 75 c. deep slate-blue and brownish black . . 45 50
883 $2.50, multicoloured . . . . . . 1·50 1·60
880/3 . . . . *Set of* 4 2·10 2·50
Designs:—50 c. The Speaker; 75 c. Parliament Buildings, *c.* 1882; $2.50, Queen Elizabeth II and Prince Philip in Parliament.

192 Brown Hare

193 Bread 'n Cheese

(Des R. Suffolk. Litho Questa)

1989 (1 Aug). *Wildlife Preservation. T* **192** *and similar multicoloured designs. W* w **16** *(sideways on* 50 *c.,* $2*). P* 14 × 13½ *(vert) or* 13½ × 14 *(horiz).*
884 10 c. Type **192** 10 10
885 50 c. Red-footed Tortoise (*horiz*) . . 30 35
886 65 c. Savanna ("Green") Monkey . . 40 45
887 $2 *Bufo marinus* (toad) (*horiz*) . . 1·25 1·40
884/7 . . . . *Set of* 4 1·90 2·10
MS888 87×97 mm. $1 Small Indian Mongoose . . 60 65

(Des A. Edmonston. Litho B.D.T.)

1989 (9 Oct). *35th Commonwealth Parliamentary Conference. Square design as T* **191**. *Multicoloured. W* w **14**. *P* 13½.
MS889 108×69 mm. $1 Barbados Mace . . 60 65

(Des Rosanne Sanders. Litho Questa)

1989 (1 Nov). *Wild Plants. T* **193** *and similar vert designs. Multicoloured. W* w **14**. *P* 14½.
890 2 c. Type **193** 10 10
891 5 c. Scarlet Cordia 10 10
892 10 c. Columnar Cactus 10 10
893 20 c. Spiderlily 10 10
894 25 c. Rock Balsam 15 20
895 30 c. Hollyhock 15 20
896 45 c. Yellow Shak-shak 25 30
897 50 c. Whitewood 25 30
898 55 c. Bluebell 30 35
899 65 c. Prickly Sage 35 40
900 70 c. Seaside Samphire 35 40
901 80 c. Flat-hand Dildo 40 45
902 $1.10, Lent Tree 60 65
903 $2.50, Rodwood . . . . 1·25 1·40
904 $5 Cowitch . . . . 2·50 2·75
905 $10 Maypole . . . . 5·25 5·50
890/905 . . . . *Set of* 16 11·00 12·00

194 Water Skiing

(Des C. Burke. Litho Harrison)

1989 (17 Nov). *"World Stamp Expo '89" International Stamp Exhibition, Washington. Watersports. T* **194** *and similar vert designs. Multicoloured. W* w **16**. *P* 14.
906 25 c. Type **194** 15 20
907 50 c. Yachting 30 35
908 65 c. Scuba diving 40 45
909 $2.50, Surfing . . . . 1·50 1·60
906/9 . . . . *Set of* 4 2·10 2·40

POSTAGE DUE STAMPS

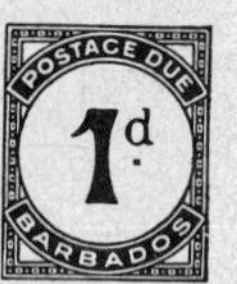

D 1

D 2

(Typo D.L.R.)

1934 (2 Jan)–**47**. *Wmk Mult Script CA. P* 14.
D1 D 1 ½d. green (10.2.35) . . . . . . 50 1·25
D2 1d. black 70 70
a. Bisected (½d.) (on cover) . . . . † £450
D3 3d. carmine (13.3.47) . . . . . . 14·00 16·00
D1/3 . . . . *Set of* 3 14·00 16·00
D1/3 Perf "Specimen" . . . . *Set of* 3 65·00
The bisected 1d. was officially authorised for use between March 1934 and February 1935. Some specimens had the value "½d." written across the half stamp in red or black ink (*Price on cover* £600).

(Typo D.L.R.)

1950 (8 Dec)–**53**. *Values in cents. Wmk Mult Script CA. P* 14.
D4 D 1 1 c. green, **O** . . . . 1·50 3·50
a. Deep green, **C** (29.11.51) . . . . 30 1·25
b. Error. Crown missing, W **9a**, **C** . . 90·00
c. Error. St. Edward's Crown, W **9b**, **C** 70·00
D5 2 c. black, **O** . . . . 2·50 5·00
a. Chalky paper (20.1.53) . . . . 40 1·50
c. Error. St. Edward's Crown, W **9b**, **C** 80·00
D6 6 c. carmine, **O** . . . . 8·50 12·00
a. Chalky paper (20.1.53) . . . . 1·50 5·50
b. Error. Crown missing, W **9a**, **C** . . 85·00
c. Error. St. Edward's Crown, W **9b**, **C** 70·00
D4/6 . . . . *Set of* 3 11·00 18·00
D4a/6a . . . . *Set of* 3 2·00 7·50
The 1 c. stamps have no dot below "c".

1965 (3 Aug)–**68**. *As Nos.* D4/6 *but wmk* w **12** *(upright). Chalky paper.*
D7 D 1 1 c. deep green . . . . 30 1·50
a. Green . . . . 55 2·00
D8 2 c. black . . . . 30 1·75
D9 6 c. carmine . . . . 50 2·00
a. Carmine-red (14.5.68) . . . . 1·40 4·50
D7/9 . . . . *Set of* 3 1·00 4·75
The 1 c. has no dot below "c".

1974 (4 Feb). *As No.* D9 *but* W w **12** *(sideways). Glazed, ordinary paper. P* 14 × 13½.
D10 D 1 6 c. carmine . . . . 4·75 8·50

1974 (4 Dec). *W* w **12** *(sideways). P* 13.
D12 D 1 2 c. black . . . . 3·00 7·00
D13 6 c. carmine . . . . 3·00 8·00

(Des Jennifer Toombs. Litho Questa)

1976 (12 May)–**85**. *Different floral backgrounds as Type* D **2**. *W* w **14**. *P* 14.

D14	1 c. deep mauve and light pink	10	15
	a. Perf 15 × 14 (7.85)	10	10
D15	2 c. ultramarine and light cobalt	10	15
	a. Perf 15 × 14 (7.85)	10	10
D16	5 c. reddish brown and yellow	15	20
	a. Perf 15 × 14 (7.85)	10	10
D17	10 c. royal blue and light lilac	15	35
	a. Perf 15 × 14 (7.85)	10	10
D18	25 c. deep green and bright yellow-green ..	20	50
	a. Perf 15 × 14 (7.85)	15	20
D19	$1 rose-carmine and rose	55	80
D14/19	.. .. *Set of* 6	1·10	2·00
D14a/18a	.. .. *Set of* 5	50	55

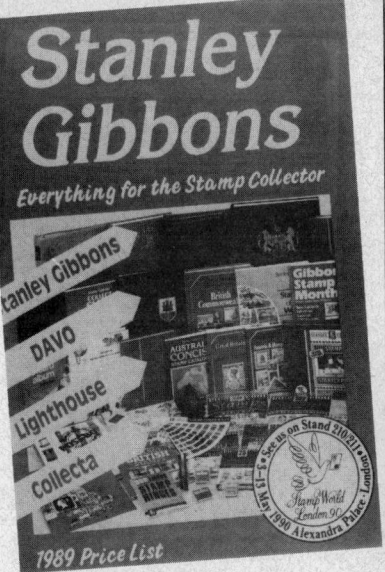

Barbuda
(*see after* Antigua)

Basutoland

Stamps of CAPE OF GOOD HOPE were used in Basutoland from about 1876, initially cancelled by upright oval with framed number type postmarks of that colony. Cancellation numbers known to have been used in Basutoland are 133 (Quthing), 156 (Mafeteng), 210 (Mohaleshoek), 277 (Morija), 281 (Maseru), 317 (Thlotse Heights) and 688 (Teyateyaneng).

From 1910 until 1933 the stamps of SOUTH AFRICA were in use. Stamps of the Union provinces are also known used in Basutoland during the early years of this period and can also be found cancelled-to-order during 1932–33.

The following post offices and postal agencies existed in Basutoland before December 1933. Stamps of Cape of Good Hope or South Africa with recognisable postmarks from them are worth a premium. For a few of the smaller offices or agencies there are, as yet, no actual examples recorded. Dates given are those generally accepted as the year in which the office was first opened.

Bokong (1931)	Motsekuoa (1915)
Butha Buthe (1907)	Mount Morosi (1918)
Jonathan's (1927)	Mphotos (1914)
Khabos (1927)	Peka (1908)
Khetisas (1930)	Phamong (1932)
Khukhune (1933)	Pitseng (1921)
Kolonyama (1914)	Qachasnek (1895)
Kueneng (1914)	Qalo (1923?)
Leribe (1890)	Quthing (1882)
Mafeteng (1874)	Rankakalas (1933)
Majara (1912)	Roma Mission (1913)
Makhoa (1932)	Sebapala (1930)
Makoalis (1927)	Seforong (1924)
Mamathes (1919)	Sehlabathebe (1921)
Mapoteng (1925)	Sekake (1931)
Marakabeis (1932)	Teyateyaneng (1886)
Maseru (1872)	Thaba Bosigo (1913)
Maseru Rail (1915?)	Thabana Morena (1922)
Mashai (1929)	Thabaneng (1914)
Matsaile (1930)	Thaba Tseka (1929)
Mekading (1914)	Thlotse Heights (1872)
Mofokas (1915)	Tsepo (1923)
Mohaleshoek (1873)	Tsoelike (1927)
Mokhotlong (1921)	Tsoloane (1918)
Morija (1884)	

For further details of the postal history of Basutoland see *The Cancellations and Postal Markings of Basutoland/Lesotho* by A. H. Scott, published by Collectors Mail Auctions (Pty) Ltd, Cape Town, from which the above has been, with permission, extracted.

PRICES FOR STAMPS ON COVER TO 1945

Nos. 1/19	*from* × 5
Nos. 11/14	*from* × 6
Nos. 15/17	*from* × 10
Nos. 18/28	*from* × 6
Nos. 29/31	*from* × 10
Nos. O1/4	*from* × 4
Nos. D1/2	*from* × 25

CROWN COLONY

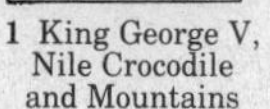

1 King George V, Nile Crocodile and Mountains

2 King George VI, Nile Crocodile and Mountains

(Recess Waterlow)

1933 (1 Dec). *Wmk Mult Script CA. P* 12½.

No.	Type	Description		
1	1	½d. emerald	60	75
2		1d. scarlet	60	35
3		2d. bright purple	70	35
4		3d. bright blue	70	60
5		4d. grey	2·50	6·50
6		6d. orange-yellow	3·00	1·50
7		1s. red-orange	3·75	4·50
8		2s. 6d. sepia	20·00	35·00
9		5s. violet	40·00	55·00
10		10s. olive-green	£100	£110
1/10		*Set of* 10	£150	£190
1/10 Perf "Specimen"		*Set of* 10	£250	

1935 (4 May). *Silver Jubilee. As Nos.* 91/4 *of Antigua. P* 13½ × 14.

No.	Description		
11	1d. deep blue and carmine	45	25
12	2d. ultramarine and grey	55	75
	f. Diagonal line by turret	25·00	
	g. Dot to left of chapel	25·00	
13	3d. brown and deep blue	2·75	1·00
	g. Dot to left of chapel	40·00	
	h. Dot by flagstaff	40·00	
14	6d. slate and purple	3·75	1·25
	g. Dot to left of chapel	50·00	
	h. Dot by flagstaff	50·00	
	i. Dash by turret	50·00	
11/14	*Set of* 4	6·75	3·00
11/14 Perf "Specimen"	*Set of* 4	65·00	

For illustrations of plate varieties see Omnibus section following Zululand.

1937 (12 May). *Coronation. As Nos* 13/15 *of Aden. P* 14.

No.	Description		
15	1d. scarlet	35	10
16	2d. bright purple	40	55
17	3d. bright blue	55	75
15/17	*Set of* 3	1·10	1·10
15/17 Perf "Specimen"	*Set of* 3	50·00	

Tower flaw (R. 2/4)

(Recess Waterlow)

1938 (1 Apr). *Wmk Mult Script CA. P* 12½.

No.	Type	Description		
18	2	½d. green	20	20
19		1d. scarlet	40	15
		a. Tower flaw	25·00	
20		1½d. light blue	40	15
21		2d. bright purple	25	25
22		3d. bright blue	25	50
23		4d. grey	80	1·75
24		6d. orange-yellow	40	50
25		1s. red-orange	40	30
26		2s. 6d. sepia	5·00	4·00
27		5s. violet	9·50	8·50
28		10s. olive-green	12·00	14·00
18/28		*Set of* 11	27·00	27·00
18/28 Perf "Specimen"		*Set of* 11	£150	

Basutoland
(3)

1945 (3 Dec). *Victory. Stamps of South Africa, optd with T* **3**, *inscr alternately in English and Afrikaans.*

No.	Type	Description	*Un. pair*	*Used pair*
29	**55**	1d. brown and carmine	20	25
30	**56**	2d. slate-blue and violet	20	30
31	**57**	3d. deep blue and blue	20	50
29/31		*Set of* 3 *pairs*	55	95

4 King George VI

5 King George VI and Queen Elizabeth

6 Queen Elizabeth II as Princess, and Princess Margaret

7 The Royal Family

(Recess Waterlow)

1947 (17 Feb). *Royal Visit. Wmk Mult Script CA. P* 12½.

No.	Type	Description		
32	4	1d. scarlet	10	10
33	5	2d. green	10	10
34	6	3d. ultramarine	10	10
35	7	1s. mauve	10	10
32/5		*Set of* 4	35	25
32/5 Perf "Specimen"		*Set of* 4	80·00	

1948 (1 Dec). *Royal Silver Wedding. As Nos.* 30/1 *of Aden.*

No.	Description		
36	1½d. ultramarine	10	10
37	10s. grey-olive	23·00	20·00

1949 (10 Oct). *75th Anniv of Universal Postal Union. As Nos.* 114/17 *of Antigua.*

No.	Description		
38	1½d. blue	30	25
39	3d. deep blue	75	50
40	6d. orange	85	70
41	1s. red-brown	95	80
38/41	*Set of* 4	2·50	2·00

1953 (3 June). *Coronation. As No.* 47 *of Aden.*

No.	Description		
42	2d. black and reddish purple	10	20

8 Qiloane

9 Mohair (Shearing Angora Goats)

(Recess D.L.R.)

1954 (18 Oct)–**58**. *Designs as T* **8/9**. *Wmk Mult Script CA. P* 11½ (10*s.*) *or* 13½ (*others*).

No.	Description		
43	½d. grey-black and sepia	10	10
44	1d. grey-black and bluish green	10	10
45	2d. deep bright blue and orange	50	10
46	3d. yellow-green and deep rose-red	70	10
	a. Yellow-green and rose (27.11.58)	90	25
47	4½d. indigo and deep ultramarine	60	15
48	6d. chestnut and deep grey-green	80	10
49	1s. bronze-green and purple	80	20
50	1s. 3d. brown and turquoise-green	4·50	3·50
51	2s. 6d. deep ultramarine and crimson	4·50	5·50
	a. Brt ultram & crimson-lake (27.11.58)	10·00	10·00
52	5s. black and carmine-red	4·75	7·50
53	10s. black and maroon	14·00	18·00
43/53	*Set of* 11	28·00	30·00

Designs: *Horiz as T* **8**—1d. Orange River; 2d Mosuto horseman; 3d. Basuto household; 4½d. Maletsunyane Falls; 6d. Herd-boy with Lesiba. 1s. Pastoral scene; 1s. 3d. Aeroplane over Lancers' Gap; 2s. 6d. Old Fort Leribe; 5s. Mission Cave House.

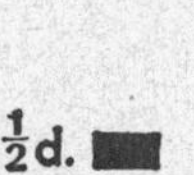

(19)

20 "Chief Moshoeshoe I" (engraving by Delangle)

1959 (1 Aug). *No.* 45 *surch with T* **19**, *by South African Govt Ptr, Pretoria.*

No.	Description		
54	½d. on 2d. deep bright blue and orange	10	10

(Des from drawings by James Walton. Recess Waterlow)

1959 (15 Dec). *Basutoland National Council. T* **20** *and similar vert designs. W w* **12**. *P* 13 × 13½.

No.	Description		
55	3d. black and yellow-olive	10	10
56	1s. carmine and yellow-green	10	10
57	1s. 3d. ultramarine and red-orange	15	25
55/7	*Set of* 3	30	35

Designs:—1s. Council house; 1s. 3d. Mosuto horseman.

(New Currency. 100 cents = 1 rand)

½c. (23) 1c. (24) 2c (25)

2½c (I) 2½c (II) 3½c (I) 3½c (II)

5c (I) 5c (II) 10c (I) 10c (II)

12½c (I) 12½c (II) 50c (I) 50c (II)

25c (I) 25c (II) 25c (III)

R1 (I) R1 (II) R1 (III)

1961 (14 Feb). *Nos. 43/53 surch with T* **23** (½ c.), **24** (1 c.) *or as T* **25** *(others) by South African Govt Printer, Pretoria*
58 ½ c. on ½d. grey-black and sepia .. 10 10
a. Surch double .. £225
59 1 c. on 1d. grey-black and bluish green .. 10 10
60 2 c. on 2d. deep bright blue and orange .. 10 10
a. Surch inverted .. 90·00
61 2½ c. on 3d. yellow-green and rose (Type I) .. 10 10
a. Type II .. 10 10
b. Type II inverted .. — £900
62 3½ c. on 4½d. indigo & deep ultram (Type I) .. 10 10
a. Type II .. 2·00 2·50
63 5 c. on 6d. chestnut & dp grey-green (Type I) 10 10
a. Type II 15 10
64 10 c. on 1s. bronze-green and purple (Type I) .. 10 10
a. Type II .. 55·00 55·00
65 12½ c. on 1s. 3d. brown & turq-green (Type I) .. 15 20
a. Type II .. 20 10
66 25 c. on 2s. 6d. bright ultramarine and crimson-lake (Type I) .. 15 30
a. Type II .. 15·00 7·00
b. Type III .. 25 50
67 50 c. on 5s. black and carmine-red (Type I) .. 1·75 2·50
a. Type II .. 90 1·25
68 1 r. on 10s. black and maroon (Type I) .. 15·00 3·75
a. Type II .. 8·50 18·00
b. Type III .. 2·00 3·50
58/68b .. *Set of* 11 3·50 4·75

There were two printings of the 2½ c. Type II, differing in the position of the surcharge on the stamps.

Examples of the 2 c. surcharge are known in a fount similar to Type **24**.

26 Basuto Household

(Recess D.L.R.)

1961–63. *As Nos. 43/53 but values in cents as in T* **26**. *Wmk Mult Script CA. P* 13½ *or* 11½ *(1 r.).*
69 ½ c. grey-black and sepia (as ½d.) (25.9.62) 10 15
a. Imperf (pair) .. £150
70 1 c. grey-blk & bluish grn (as 1d.) (25.9.62) 10 20
71 2 c. dp brt blue & orange (as 2d.) (25.9.62) 30 50
72 2½ c. yellow-green & deep rose-red (14.2.61) 40 10
a. Pale yellow-green & rose-red (22.5.62) 45 15
73 3½ c. indigo & dp ultram (as 4½d.) (25.9.62) 25 80
74 5 c. chestnut and deep grey-green (as 6d.) (10.8.62) .. 30 35
75 10 c. bronze-green & pur (as 1s.) (22.10.62) 20 20
76 12½ c. brown and turquoise-green (as 1s. 3d.) (17.12.62) .. 4·00 4·75
77 25 c. deep ultramarine and crimson (as 2s. 6d.) (25.9.62) .. 2·25 5·00
78 50 c. black & carmine-red (as 5s.) (22.10.62) 4·25 6·50
79 1 r. black and maroon (as 10s.) (4.2.63) .. 10·00 8·50
a. Black and light maroon (16.12.63) .. 12·00 10·00
69/79 .. *Set of* 11 20·00 24·00

1963 (4 June). *Freedom from Hunger. As No. 76 of Aden.*
80 12½ c. reddish violet .. 40 15

1963 (2 Sept). *Red Cross Centenary. As Nos. 147/8 of Antigua.*
81 2½ c. red and black .. 20 10
82 12½ c. red and blue .. 60 50

1964. *As Nos.* 70, 72, 74, 76 *and* 78, *but W w* **12**.
84 1 c. grey-black and bluish green (11.8.64) .. 10 20
86 2½ c. pale yellow-green and rose-red (10.3.64) 15 15
88 5 c. chestnut and deep grey-green (10.11.64) 30 40
90 12½ c. brown and turquoise-green (10.11.64) .. 2·00 1·25
92 50 c. black and carmine-red (29.9.64) .. 4·50 8·50
84/92 .. *Set of* 5 6·25 9·50

SELF-GOVERNMENT

27 Mosotho Woman and Child

28 Maseru Border Post

1965 (10 May). *New Constitution. T* **27/28** *and horiz designs similar to T* **28**. *Multicoloured. W w* **12**. *P* 14 × 13½.
94 2½ c. Type **27** .. 10 10
95 3½ c. Type **28** .. 10 10
96 5 c. Mountain scene .. 10 10
97 12½ c. Legislative Buildings .. 10 15
94/7 .. *Set of* 4 20 30

1965 (17 May). *I.T.U. Centenary. As Nos. 166/7 of Antigua.*
98 1 c. orange-red and bright purple .. 15 10
99 20 c. light blue and orange-brown .. 35 30

1965 (25 Oct). *International Co-operation Year. As Nos. 168/9 of Antigua.*
100 ½ c. reddish purple and turquoise-green .. 10 10
101 12½ c. deep bluish green and lavender .. 45 35

1966 (24 Jan). *Churchill Commemoration. As Nos. 170/3 of Antigua.*
102 1 c. new blue .. 15 15
103 2½ c. deep green .. 40 10
104 10 c. brown .. 60 25
105 22½ c. bluish violet .. 80 50
102/5 .. *Set of* 4 1·75 90

OFFICIAL STAMPS

OFFICIAL

(O 1)

1934 (4 May). *Nos. 1/3 and 6 optd with Type* O **1**.
O1 **1** ½d. emerald .. £2000 £2000
O2 1d. scarlet .. £1250 £1000
O3 2d. bright purple .. £750 £550
O4 6d. orange-yellow .. £10000 £4500
O1/4 .. *Set of* 4 £13000 £7000

Collectors are advised to buy these stamps only from reliable sources. They were not sold to the public.

POSTAGE DUE STAMPS

D 1

D 2

(Typo D.L.R.)

1933 (1 Dec)–**1952**. *Wmk Mult Script CA. P* 14.
D1 D **1** 1d. carmine, **O** .. 1·75 3·25
a. Scarlet, **O** (1938) .. 17·00 20·00
b. Deep-carmine, **C** (24.10.51) .. 30 50
c. Error. Crown missing. W9*a*, **C** .. 80·00
d. Error. St. Edward's Crown, W9*b*, **C** 45·00
D2 2d. violet, **O** .. 3·00 3·75
a. Chalky paper (6.11.52) .. 25 1·00
b. Error. Crown missing. W9*a*, **C** .. 85·00
c. Error. St. Edward's Crown, W9*b*, **C** 45·00
D1/2 Perf "Specimen" .. *Set of* 2 40·00

(Typo D.L.R.)

1956 (1 Dec). *Wmk Mult Script CA. P* 14.
D3 D **2** 1d. carmine .. 15 1·25
D4 2d. deep reddish violet .. 15 1·40

5c 5c
(I) (II)

1961 (14 Feb). *Surch as T* **24**, *but without stop.*
D5 D **2** 1 c. on 1d. carmine .. 10 25
D6 1 c. on 2d. deep reddish violet .. 10 25
D7 5 c. on 2d. deep reddish violet (Type I) .. 10 25
a. Type II .. 15·00 32·00
D5/7 .. *Set of* 3 25 70

1961 (June). *No. D2a surch as T* **24** *(without stop).*
D8 D **1** 5 c. on 2d. violet .. 1·50 4·50
a. Error. Missing Crown, W9*a* .. £950
b. Error. St. Edwards Crown, W9*b* .. £225

1964. *As No. D3/4 but values in cents and W w* **12** *(sideways on* 1 c.).
D9 D **2** 1 c. carmine .. 90 3·00
D10 5 c. deep reddish violet .. 90 3·00

POSTAL FISCAL

In July 1961 the 10s. stamp, T **9**, surcharged "R1 Revenue", was used for postage at one post office at least, but such usage was officially unauthorised.

Basutoland attained independence on 4 October 1966, and her stamps were withdrawn on 31 October 1966. For later issues see LESOTHO.

Batum

Batum, a Russian port on the Black Sea, had been taken by Turkish troops during the First World War. Following the Armistice British forces occupied the town on 1 December 1918.

BRITISH OCCUPATION

PRICES FOR STAMPS ON COVER

Nos. 1/6	*from* × 40
Nos. 7/10	*from* × 10
Nos. 11/12	*from* × 12
Nos. 13/20	*from* × 60
Nos. 21/45	*from* × 10
Nos. 46/51	*from* × 20
Nos. 52/60	*from* × 60

1

БАТУМ. ОБ.
Руб 10 Руб
(2)

1919 (4 Apr). *Litho. Imperf.*
1 **1** 5 k. green .. 1·75 2·50
2 10 k. ultramarine .. 1·75 2·50
3 50 k. yellow .. 45 55
4 1 r. chocolate .. 70 85
5 3 r. violet .. 3·00 3·00
6 5 r. brown .. 4·00 4·00
Nos. 1/6 were printed in sheets of 198 (11 × 18).

1919 (13 Apr). *Russian stamps (Arms types) surch with T* **2**.
7 10 r. on 1 k. orange *(imperf)* .. 13·00 16·00
8 10 r. on 3 k. carmine-red *(imperf)* .. 7·00 9·00
9 10 r. on 5 k. brown-lilac *(perf)* .. 80·00 80·00
10 10 r. on 10 on 7 k. deep blue *(perf)* .. 75·00 75·00

БАТУМ ОБЛ.
Р 10 Р.
BRITISH
OCCUPATION
(3)

БАТУМЪ
BRITISH
Р.15 Р.
OCCUPATION
ОБЛ.
(4)

1919 (Nov.) *Russian stamps (Arms types) surch with T* **3** *or* **4**. *Imperf.*
11 10 r. on 3 k. carmine-red .. 6·00 7·00
12 15 r. on 1 k. orange .. 17·00 18·00
a. Surch in red .. 15·00 16·00
ab. Surch double
b. Surch in violet .. 18·00 19·00

BRITISH
OCCUPATION
(5)

БАТУМ.ОБЛ.
Р.50Р.
BRITISH
OCCUPATION
(6)

1919 (10 Nov.) *T* **1**, *new colours etc., optd with T* **5**.
13 5 k. yellow-green .. 2·50 3·25
14 10 k. bright blue .. 2·50 3·25
15 25 k. orange-yellow .. 2·50 3·25
16 1 r. pale blue .. 1·40 2·00
17 2 r. pink .. 45 55
18 3 r. bright violet .. 50 70
19 5 r. brown .. 70 80
a. "CCUPATION" ..
20 7 r. brownish red .. 1·40 1·75
Nos. 13/20 were printed in sheets of 432 (18 × 24).

1920 (Jan–Apr). *Russian stamps (Arms types) surch as T* **6**.

(a) Perf
21 25 r. on 5 k. brown-lilac .. 10·00 11·00
22 25 r. on 5 k. brown-lilac (B.) .. 11·00 12·00
23 25 r. on 10 on 7 k. deep blue .. 25·00 25·00
24 25 r. on 10 on 7 k. deep blue (B.) .. 17·00 17·00
25 25 r. on 20 on 14 k. deep carmine and blue .. 18·00 18·00
26 25 r. on 20 on 14 k. deep carmine and blue (B.) 17·00 17·00
27 25 r. on 25 k. deep violet and light green (B.) 23·00 23·00
28 25 r. on 25 k. deep violet and light green .. 25·00 25·00
29 25 r. on 50 k. green and copper-red .. 17·00 17·00
30 25 r. on 50 k. green and copper-red (B.) .. 18·00 18·00
31 50 r. on 2 k. yellow-green .. 23·00 23·00
32 50 r. on 3 k. carmine-red .. 23·00 23·00
33 50 r. on 4 k. red .. 22·00 22·00
34 50 r. on 5 k. brown-lilac .. 18·00 18·00

(b) Imperf
35 50 r. on 2 k. yellow-green .. 60·00 60·00
36 50 r. on 3 k. carmine-red .. 65·00 65·00
37 50 r. on 5 k. brown-lilac .. £250 £250

1920. *Romanov issue, as T* **25** *of Russia, surch with T* **6**.
38 50 r. on 4 k. rose-carmine (B.) .. 16·00 18·00

1920 (12 Jan). *Russian stamps (Arms types) surch as T* **3**.

(a) Imperf
39 50 r. on 1 k. orange .. 60·00 60·00
40 50 r. on 2 k. yellow-green .. £100 £100

(b) Perf
41 50 r. on 2 k. yellow-green .. 90·00 90·00
42 50 r. on 3 k. carmine-red .. £180 £180
43 50 r. on 4 k. red .. £120 £120
44 50 r. on 5 k. brown-lilac .. 90·00 90·00
44*a* 50 r. on 10 k. deep blue (C.) .. £275 £275
45 50 r. on 15 k. blue and red-brown .. 90·00 90·00

РУБ25ЛЕЙ
25РУБ.25
(7)

R.50R.
BRITISH
OCCUPATION
РУБ.
(8)

1920 (1 Apr). *Nos. 13 and 15 surch with T* **7**.
46 25 r. on 5 k. yellow-green .. 9·00 9·00
47 25 r. on 5 k. yellow-green (B.) .. 10·00 10·00
48 25 r. on 25 k. orange-yellow .. 7·00 7·00
49 25 r. on 25 k. orange-yellow (B.) .. 24·00 24·00

1920 (1 Apr). *No. 3 surch with T* **8**.

50	50 r. on 50 k. yellow	6·00	6·00
51	50 r. on 50 k. yellow (B.)	26·00	26·00

1920 (22 June). *T* **1** (*new colours etc.*) *optd with T* **5**. *Imperf.*

A. *Normal.* B. *Error* "BPITISH"

		A		B	
52	1 r. chestnut	25	40	20·00	—
53	2 r. pale blue	20	40	20·00	—
54	3 r. pink	25	40	20·00	—
55	5 r. black-brown	20	40	20·00	—
56	7 r. yellow	25	40	20·00	—
57	10 r. myrtle-green	25	45	25·00	—
58	15 r. violet	40	55	35·00	—
59	25 r. scarlet	45	65	45·00	—
60	50 r. deep blue	50	75	50·00	—

Nos. 52/60 were printed in sheets of 308 (22 × 14). The "BPITISH" error occurs on R. 1/19.

Batum was handed over to the National Republic of Georgia on 7 July 1920.

Bechuanaland

PRICES FOR STAMPS ON COVER TO 1945

Nos. 1/8	*from* × 8
No. 9	*from* × 50
Nos. 10/21	*from* × 5
Nos. 22/8	*from* × 8
No. 29	*from* × 10
No. 30	*from* × 8
Nos. 31/2	*from* × 10
Nos. 33/7	*from* × 12
Nos. 38/9	*from* × 20
Nos. 40/51	*from* × 6
Nos. 52/8	*from* × 5
Nos. 59/71	*from* × 6
Nos. 72/82	*from* × 5
Nos. 83/98	*from* × 4
Nos. 99/110	*from* × 6
Nos. 111/17	*from* × 10
Nos. 118/28	*from* × 4
Nos. 129/31	*from* × 10
Nos. D1/3	*from* × 50
Nos. D4/6	*from* × 60
No. F1	*from* × 5
No. F2	–
No. F3	*from* × 5

A. BRITISH BECHUANALAND

CROWN COLONY

British Bechuanaland was proclaimed a Crown Colony on 30 September 1885.

British Bechuanaland (1)

BRITISH BECHUANALAND (2)

1885 (Dec)–**87**. *Stamps of Cape of Good Hope ("Hope" seated) optd with T* **1**, *by W. A. Richards & Sons, Cape Town.*

(*a*) *Wmk Crown CC (No. 3) or Crown CA (others)*

1	**6**	½d. slate (R.)	11·00	11·00
		a. Opt in lake		
		b. Opt double (Lake + Black)	£550	
2		3d. claret	25·00	32·00
3		4d. blue (12.86?)	50·00	55·00

(*b*) *Wmk Anchor (Cape, T* **13**)

4	**6**	½d. grey-black (3.87?)	6·00	11·00
		a. Error "ritish"	£1300	
		b. Opt double	£600	
5		1d. pale rose-red	8·00	8·00
		a. Error "ritish"	£1500	£1300
		b. Opt double	—	£1500
6		2d. bistre	28·00	12·00
		a. Error "ritish"	£3000	£2750
		b. Opt double	—	£1000
7	**4**	6d. purple	55·00	28·00
8		1s. green (11.86?)	£200	£125
		a. Error "ritish"	£6500	£4500

Overprints with stop after "Bechuanaland" are forged.

1887 (1 Nov). *Stamp of Gt. Britain optd with T* **2**, *by D.L.R.*

9	**71**	½d. vermilion (H/S S. £80)	60	90
		a. Opt double	£1400	

3

4

5

(Typo D.L.R.)

1887 (1 Nov). *P* 13½, 14. (*a*) *Wmk Orb (G.B.T.* **48**).

10	**3**	1d. lilac and black	12·00	1·25
11		2d. lilac and black	32·00	80
		a. Pale dull lilac and black	35·00	19·00
12		3d. lilac and black	3·25	4·75
		a. Pale reddish lilac and black	38·00	11·00
13		4d. lilac and black	38·00	2·75
14		6d. lilac and black	42·00	3·25

(*b*) *Wmk Script "V R" sideways, reading up*

15	**4**	1s. green and black	28·00	4·50
16		2s. green and black	45·00	35·00
17		2s. 6d. green and black	60·00	38·00
18		5s. green and black	£100	£100
19		10s. green and black	£200	£250

(*c*) *Wmk two orbs, sideways*

20	**5**	£1 lilac and black	£1000	£800
21		£5 lilac and black	£2750	£1300
10/21 H/S "Specimen"		*Set of* 12	£1000	

Several values of the above series are known on blued paper. No. 11*a* is the first printing of the 2d. (on safety paper?) and has a faded appearance.

When purchasing Nos. 20/21 in used condition beware of copies with fiscal cancellations cleaned off and bearing forged postmarks.

For No. 15 surcharged "£5" see No. F2.

1d. (6)

1s. (7)

One Half-Penny (8)

1888 (7 Aug). *Surch as T* **6** *or* **7**, *by P. Townshend & Co, Vryburg.*

22	**3**	1d. on 1d. lilac and black	7·50	5·00
23		2d. on 2d. lilac and black (R.)	12·00	2·50
		a. Pale dull lilac and black	60·00	40·00
		b. Curved foot to "2"	£200	£150
24		2d. on 2d. lilac and black (G.)	—	£1400
25		4d. on 4d. lilac and black (R.)	£140	£120
26		6d. on 6d. lilac and black	65·00	17·00
27		6d. on 6d. lilac and black (B.)	—	£1600
28	**4**	1s. on 1s. green and black	95·00	55·00

1888 (Dec.) *No.* 12*a surch with T* **8**, *by P. Townshend & Co, Vryburg.*

29	**3**	½d. on 3d. pale reddish lilac and black	90·00	£100
		a. Broken "f" in "Half"	£3500	

No. 29a shows the letter "f" almost completely missing. Four examples are known, one being in the Royal collection.

British Bechuanaland. (9)

British Bechuanaland. (10)

BRITISH BECHUANALAND (11)

1889 (Jan). *T* **6** *of Cape of Good Hope (wmk Anchor) optd with T* **9**, *by P. Townshend & Co, Vryburg.*

30		½d. slate (G.)	3·25	16·00
		b. Opt double, one inverted	£425	
		c. Opt double, one vertical	£425	
		ca. *Se-tenant* with stamp without opt	£1200	
		e. "British" omitted	£1700	

1891 (Nov). *T* **6** *of Cape of Good Hope (wmk Anchor), optd with T* **10**, *reading upwards.*

31		1d. rose-red	9·00	8·00
		a. Pair, one without opt		
		b. "British" omitted	—	£180
		c. "Bechuanaland" omitted	£375	
32		2d. bistre	3·25	2·25
		a. No stop after "Bechuanaland"	£140	
31/32 H/S "Specimen"		*Set of* 2	£150	

See also Nos. 38 and 39.

1891 (Dec)–**1894**. *Stamps of Great Britain optd with T* **11**, *by D.L.R.*

33	**57**	1d. lilac	3·75	60
34	**73**	2d. green and carmine	3·25	2·00
35	**76**	4d. green and purple-brown	2·50	50
		a. Bisected (2d.) (on cover)	†	£1200
36	**79**	6d. purple/*rose-red*	3·00	1·75
37	**82**	1s. green (July, 1894)	12·00	16·00
		a. Bisected (6d.) (on cover)	†	—
33/7		*Set of* 5	22·00	19·00
33/36 H/S "Specimen"		*Set of* 4	£200	

1893–95. *As Nos.* 31 *and* 32, *but T* **10** *reads downwards.*

38	1d. rose-red (12.93)	1·60	2·00
	a. Pair, one without opt		
	b. "British" omitted	£225	
	c. Optd "Bechuanaland. British"		
	d. No dots to "i" of "British"	70·00	70·00
	e. Opt reading up, no dots to "i" of "British"	£275	
39	2d. bistre (15.3.95)	3·50	2·00
	a. Opt double	£600	£550
	b. "British" omitted	£275	£275
	c. Optd "Bechuanaland. British"	—	£110
	d. No dots to "i" of British"	£100	£100

No. 38e was formerly listed as No. 31a but it does not occur on that setting and only exists from sheets fed the wrong way in the 1893 issue.

On 16 November 1895 British Bechuanaland was annexed to the Cape of Good Hope and ceased to have its own stamps, but they remained in use in the Protectorate until superseded in 1897.

B. BECHUANALAND PROTECTORATE

This large area north of the Molopo River was proclaimed a British Protectorate on 30 September 1885 at the request of the native chiefs.

A postal service using runners was inaugurated in August 1888 and Nos. 40 to 55 were issued as a temporary measure with the object of assessing the cost of this service.

Protectorate (12) 15½ mm

Protectorate 1d (13)

(Types 12/17 were applied by P. Townshend & Co. Vryburg)

1888 (7 Aug). *No.* 9 *optd with T* **12** *and Nos.* 10/19 *surch or optd only as T* **13**.

40	**71**	½d. vermilion (H/S S. £60)	2·75	18·00
		a. "Protectorate" double	£300	
41	**3**	1d. on 1d. lilac and black	4·50	10·00
		a. Small figure "1"	£225	£250
42		2d. on 2d. lilac and black	16·00	17·00
		b. Curved foot to "2"	£200	£200
43		3d. on 3d. pale reddish lilac and black	75·00	£100
44		4d. on 4d. lilac and black	£130	£130
		a. Small figure "4"		
45		6d. on 6d. lilac and black	45·00	40·00
46	**4**	1s. green and black (H/S S. £80)	55·00	45·00
		a. First "o" omitted	£2250	£2250
47		2s. green and black	£250	£325
		a. First "o" omitted	£3000	
48		2s. 6d. green and black	£500	£600
		a. First "o" omitted	£3500	
49		5s. green and black	£1100	£1400
		a. First "o" omitted	£4000	
50		10s. green and black	£3000	£3500
		a. First "o" omitted	£8000	

See also Nos. 54/5

1888 (Dec). *No.* 25 *optd with T* **12**.

51	**3**	4d. on 4d. lilac and black	55·00	32·00

Bechuanaland Protectorate. (14)

Protectorate Fourpence (15)

1889 (Jan). *T* **6** *of Cape of Good Hope (wmk Anchor), optd with T* **14**.

52	½d. slate (G.)	2·75	18·00
	a. Opt double	£300	£350
	ab. Ditto, one reading "Protectorate Bechuanaland"	£450	
	b. "Bechuanaland" omitted	£450	
	c. Optd "Protectorate Bechuanaland"	£150	£200

1889 (Aug). *No.* 9 *surch with T* **15**.

53	**71**	4d. on ½d. vermilion (H/S S. £100)	8·00	2·25
		a. Surch (T **15**) inverted	—	£2750

Protectorate (16) 15 mm

Protectorate (17)

1890. *No.* 9 *optd.*

54	**16**	½d. vermilion	75·00	80·00
		a. Type **16** inverted	70·00	85·00
		b. Type **16** double	75·00	85·00
		c. Type **16** double and inverted	£450	£450
		d. Error. "Portectorate" and opt inverted		
55	**17**	½d. vermilion	85·00	95·00
		a. Type **17** double	£400	
		b. Error. "Protectorrte"		

These were trial printings made in 1888 which were subsequently issued.

In June 1890 the Bechuanaland Protectorate and the Colony of British Bechuanaland came under one postal administration and the stamps of British Bechuanaland were used in the Protectorate until 1897.

BRITISH BECHUANALAND (18)

BECHUANALAND PROTECTORATE (19)

1897. *T* **6** *of Cape of Good Hope (wmk Anchor), optd as T* **18**.

(*a*) *Lines 13 mm apart, bottom line 16 mm long, by Taylor & Marshall, Cape Town*

56	½d. yellow-green (July?)	1·90	5·50

(*b*) *Lines 13½ mm apart, bottom line 15 mm long, by P. Townshend & Co, Vryburg*

57	½d. yellow-green (April)	14·00	48·00

(*c*) *Lines 10½ mm apart, bottom line 15 mm long, by W. A. Richards & Sons, Cape Govt Printers*

58	½d. yellow-green (July?)	6·50	24·00

Although issued only in the Protectorate, the above were presumably overprinted "BRITISH BECHUANALAND" because stamps bearing this inscription were in use there at the time.

1897 (Oct)–**1902**. *Stamps of Great Britain (Queen Victoria) optd with T* **19** *by D.L.R.*
59 **71** ½d. vermilion .. .. 60 1·50
60 ½d. blue-green (25.2.02) .. .. 1·25 2·00
61 **57** 1d. lilac .. .. 2·25 45
62 **73** 2d. green and carmine .. .. .. 2·25 4·50
63 **75** 3d. purple/*yellow* (12.97) .. .. 5·50 8·50
64 **76** 4d. green and purple-brown .. .. 10·00 11·00
65 **79** 6d. purple/*rose-red* .. .. .. 16·00 11·00
59/65 .. .. *Set of* 7 35·00 35·00
59/65 Optd "Specimen" .. .. *Set of* 7 £250

BECHUANALAND PROTECTORATE
(20)

BECHUANALAND PROTECTORATE
(21)

1904–13. *Stamps of Great Britain (King Edward VII) optd with T* **20**, *by D.L.R.*
66 **83** ½d. blue-green (3.06) 80 90
67 ½d. yellow-green (11.08) .. .. 2·00 3·50
68 1d. scarlet (4.05) (S. £50) .. .. 3·75 25
69 **86** 2½d. ultramarine (29.11.04) .. .. 3·50 5·00
a. Stop after "P" in "PROTECTORATE" £800
70 **93** 1s. green and scarlet (10.12) .. 24·00 50·00
71 1s. green and carmine (1913) (S. £60) 28·00 55·00
Nos. 70 and 71 are the Somerset House printings.

1912 (Sept). *T* **102** *of Great Britain (King George V, wmk Crown) optd with T* **20**.
72 **102** 1d. scarlet 55 60
a. No cross on crown .. .. .. — 70·00
b. Aniline scarlet .. .. .. £120 80·00

1913 (July)–**24**. *Stamps of Great Britain (King George V) optd.*
(a) With T **20** *(wmk Script Cypher, T* **100**)
73 **105** ½d. green (*shades*) .. .. .. 85 1·50
74 **104** 1d. scarlet (*shades*) (4.15) .. .. 2·50 40
75 **105** 1½d. red-brown (12.20) .. .. .. 1·75 3·00
76 **106** 2d. reddish orange (Die I) .. .. 2·50 3·50
a. Orange (Die I) (1921)
77 2d. orange (Die II) (1924) .. .. 22·00 5·00
78 **104** 2½d. ultramarine .. .. .. 2·50 12·00
a. Blue (1915) ..
79 **106** 3d. blue-violet .. .. 5·50 10·00
80 4d. slate-green .. .. 4·50 13·00
81 **107** 6d. reddish purple (*shades*), **C** .. 6·50 13·00
a. Purple, **C**
82 **108** 1s. bistre (S. £60) .. .. .. 7·00 16·00
a. Bistre-brown
73/82 .. .. *Set of* 9 30·00 70·00
(b) With T **21** *(wmk T* **110**)
(i) *Waterlow printings*. (1914–15)
83 **109** 2s. 6d. deep sepia-brown (1.15) £130 £170
a. Re-entry £650 £800
b. Opt double, one albino £200
84 5s. rose-carmine (1914) £180 £275
a. Opt double, one albino £275
83/84 Optd "Specimen" .. *Set of* 2 £250
(ii) *D.L.R. printings*. (1916–20)
85 **109** 2s. 6d. grey-brown (7.16) £130 £160
a. Re-entry £750
86 2s. 6d. deep brown (1920) £150 £180
a. Opt treble, two albino
87 5s. bright carmine (8.19) £250 £300
a. Opt double, one albino £350
(iii) *B.W. printings*. (1920–23)
88 **109** 2s. 6d. chocolate-brown (7.23) £130 £160
a. Major Re-entry £1500
b. Opt double, one albino
89 5s. rose-red (7.20) £160 £225
90 5s. deep carmine £180 £225
a. Opt treble, two albino £275

1925–27. *As 1913–24, but W* **111** *(block letters)*.
91 **105** ½d. green (1927) .. .. .. 70 1·75
92 **104** 1d. scarlet (8.25) 75 70
93 **106** 2d. orange (Die II) (7.25) .. .. 1·50 1·00
94 3d. violet (10.26) .. .. .. 4·50 11·00
a. Opt double, one albino
95 4d. grey-green (10.26) .. .. 4·50 16·00
96 **107** 6d. purple, **C** (12.25) .. .. 9·00 20·00
97 6d. purple, **O** (1926) .. .. 22·00 27·00
98 **108** 1s. bistre-brown (10.26) .. .. 8·50 24·00
91/98 .. .. *Set of* 8 45·00 90·00

22 King George V, Baobab Tree and Cattle drinking

23 King George VI, Baobab Tree and Cattle drinking

(Des from photo by Resident Commissioner, Ngamiland, Recess Waterlow)

1932 (12 Dec). *Wmk Mult Script CA. P* 12½.
99 **22** ½d. green 40 30
a. Imperf between (horiz pair) .. £7500
100 1d. scarlet 50 25
101 2d. brown 70 30
102 **22** 3d. ultramarine 90 50
103 4d. orange .. .. 1·00 3·00
104 6d. purple .. .. 2·50 1·50
105 1s. black and olive-green .. .. 5·00 7·00
106 2s. black and orange .. .. 18·00 32·00
107 2s.6d. black and scarlet .. .. 19·00 30·00
108 3s. black and purple .. .. 28·00 40·00
109 5s. black and ultramarine .. .. 38·00 45·00
110 10s. black and brown .. .. 90·00 £100
99/110 .. .. *Set of* 12 £180 £225
99/110 Perf "Specimen" .. .. *Set of* 12 £250

1935 (4 May). *Silver Jubilee. As Nos. 91/4 of Antigua but ptd by B.W. P* 11 × 12.
111 1d. deep blue and scarlet 25 60
a. Extra flagstaff .. .. 90·00
b. Short extra flagstaff .. .. .. 55·00
c. Lightning conductor .. .. .. 55·00
d. Flagstaff on right-hand turret .. .. 55·00
e. Double flagstaff .. .. 40·00
112 2d. ultramarine and grey-black 60 75
a. Extra flagstaff .. .. 70·00
b. Short extra flagstaff .. .. .. 50·00
c. Lightning conductor .. .. .. 50·00
113 3d. brown and deep blue .. .. .. 70 1·00
a. Extra flagstaff .. .. 90·00
b. Short extra flagstaff .. .. .. 60·00
c. Lightning conductor .. .. .. 60·00
114 6d. slate and purple .. .. .. 1·25 1·00
a. Extra flagstaff .. .. 80·00
b. Short extra flagstaff .. .. .. 60·00
c. Lightning conductor .. .. .. 55·00
111/14 .. .. *Set of* 4 3·00 3·00
111/14 Perf "Specimen" .. .. *Set of* 4 65·00
For illustrations of plate varieties see Omnibus section following Zululand.

1937 (12 May). *Coronation. As Nos. 13/15 of Aden. P* 14.
115 1d. scarlet 35 40
116 2d. yellow-brown 50 40
117 3d. bright blue 50 70
115/17 .. .. *Set of* 3 1·25 1·40
115/17 Perf "Specimen" .. .. *Set of* 3 50·00

(Recess Waterlow)

1938 (1 Apr)–**52**. *Wmk Mult Script CA. P* 12½.
118 **23** ½d. green .. .. 1·10 1·40
a. Light yellowish green (1941) .. 2·50 2·50
b. Yellowish green (4.43) .. .. 1·00 1·40
c. Deep green (4.49) .. .. .. 60 1·50
119 1d. scarlet 15 20
120 1½d. dull blue .. .. 2·75 1·25
a. Light blue (4.43) 30 40
121 2d. chocolate-brown 15 20
122 3d. deep ultramarine 15 60
123 4d. orange 25 80
124 6d. reddish purple .. .. .. 3·50 2·50
a. Purple (1944) .. .. .. 2·25 2·00
125 1s. black and brown-olive .. .. 90 1·25
a. Grey-black and olive-green (21.5.52) 4·00 6·00
126 2s.6d. black and scarlet .. .. 5·50 6·50
127 5s. black and deep ultramarine .. 13·00 6·50
a. Grey-black & dp ultramarine (10.46) 40·00 24·00
128 10s. black and red-brown .. .. 10·00 13·00
118/28 .. .. *Set of* 11 30·00 28·00
118/28 Perf "Specimen" .. .. *Set of* 11 £150

Bechuanaland
(24)

1945 (3 Dec). *Victory. Stamps of South Africa optd with T* **24**. *Inscr alternately in English and Afrikaans.*
Un. pair *Used pair*
129 **55** 1d. brown and carmine 20 25
130 **56** 2d. slate-blue and violet 20 35
131 **57** 3d. deep blue and blue 20 35
a. Opt omitted (in vert pair with normal) £4000
129/31 .. .. *Set of* 3 55 85

1947 (17 Feb). *Royal Visit. As Nos. 32/5 of Basutoland.*
132 1d. scarlet 10 10
133 2d. green 10 10
134 3d. ultramarine 10 10
135 1s. mauve 10 10
132/5 .. .. *Set of* 4 35 20
132/5 Perf "Specimen" .. .. *Set of* 4 80·00

1948 (1 Dec). *Royal Silver Wedding. As Nos. 30/1 of Aden.*
136 1½d. ultramarine 15 10
137 10s. black .. .. 16·00 24·00

1949 (10 Oct). *75th Anniv of Universal Postal Union. As Nos. 114/17 of Antigua.*
138 1½d. blue 25 15
139 3d. deep blue 55 50
140 6d. magenta 60 80
141 1s. olive 80 80
138/41 .. .. *Set of* 4 2·00 2·00

1953 (3 June). *Coronation. As No. 47 of Aden.*
142 2d. black and brown 10 25

OMNIBUS ISSUES

Details, together with prices for complete sets, of the various Omnibus issues from the 1935 Silver Jubilee series to date are included in a special section following Zululand at the end of the catalogue.

25 Queen Elizabeth II, Baobab Tree and Cattle drinking

26 Queen Victoria, Queen Elizabeth II and Landscape

(Des from photo by Resident Commissioner, Ngamiland. Recess Waterlow)

1955 (3 Jan)–**58**. *Wmk Mult Script CA. P* 13½ × 14.
143 **25** ½d. green 10 15
144 1d. rose-red 20 10
145 2d. red-brown 35 15
146 3d. ultramarine 60 15
a. Bright ultramarine (16.1.57) .. 70 20
146*b* 4d. red-orange (1.12.58) .. .. 3·75 4·00
147 4½d. blackish blue 60 25
148 6d. purple 45 30
149 1s. black and brown-olive 50 40
150 1s. 3d. black and lilac .. .. 3·75 5·00
151 2s. 6d. black and rose-red .. .. 4·75 5·00
152 5s. black and violet-blue .. .. 6·00 5·00
153 10s. black and red-brown .. .. 11·00 12·00
143/53 .. .. *Set of* 12 29·00 29·00

(Photo Harrison)

1960 (21 Jan). *75th Anniv of Bechuanaland Protectorate. W w* **12**. *P* 14½ × 14.
154 **26** 1d. sepia and black 10 10
155 3d. magenta and black 10 10
156 6d. bright blue and black 10 15
154/6 .. .. *Set of* 3 20 25

New Currency. 100 cents = 1 rand

1c (27) 1c (I) 1c (II) 2½c (I) 2½c (II)

3 (I) 3 (II) 3 (III) (3½ c. on 4d.) 5c (I) 5c (II) R1 (I) R1 (II)

2½c
Spaced "c" (R. 10/3)

1961 (14 Feb–June). *Nos.* 144/6*a and* 148/53 *surch as T* **27** *by South African Govt Printer, Pretoria.*
157 **25** 1 c. on 1d. rose-red (Type I) 10 10
a. Type II (6.6) 10 10
158 2 c. on 2d. red-brown 10 10
159 2½ c. on 2d. red-brown (Type I) .. 10 10
a. Type II 10 10
b. Pair, one without surch £650
160 2½ c. on 3d. bright ultramarine .. 1·25 1·50
a. Spaced "c" .. .. .. 20·00
161 3½ c. on 4d. red-orange (Type I) .. 40 20
a. Type II .. .. 75 1·00
b. Wide surch (I) .. .. .. 8·00 8·50
c. Wide surch (II) .. .. .. 27·00 28·00
d. Type III (6.6) 15 10
162 5 c. on 6d. purple (Type I) 50 30
a. Type II (12.5) 15 10
163 10 c. on 1s. black and brown-olive .. 15 10
a. Pair, one without surch £650
164 12½ c. on 1s. 3d. black and lilac 25 15
165 25 c. on 2s. 6d. black and rose-red .. 75 40
166 50 c. on 5s. black and violet-blue .. 1·25 65
167 1 r. on 10s. black & red-brown (Type I) £200 90·00
a. Type II (1st Ptg) (17.3) .. .. 5·00 3·00
b. Type II (2nd Ptg) .. .. 3·25 2·00
157/167b .. .. *Set of* 11 6·50 4·25
No. 161—3½ c. on 4d. Types I and II of "3" were mixed in the sheet of 60 stamps—38 of Type I, 22 of Type II. The "wide surcharge" measures 9½ mm overall (with "C" spaced 1½ mm from "½") and comes on 8 of the 10 stamps in the last vertical row (5 × Type I, 3 × Type II). The surcharge on the remainder of the sheet varies between 8½ and 9½ mm.
Type III was a later printing.

Nos. 167a/b—1 rand (Type II). The First Printing (No. 167a) had the surcharge at bottom left; in the Second Printing (No. 167b) it was placed towards the bottom of the stamp, either centrally or towards the right.
A later printing of the 12½ c. on 1s. 3d. was from a fresh setting of type, but is insufficiently different for separate listing. Later printings of the 10 c. and 25 c. were identical with the originals.

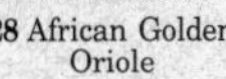

28 African Golden Oriole

39 Bechuana Ox

(Des P. Jones. Photo Harrison)

1961 (2 Oct). *T* **28**, **39** *and similar designs.* W w **12**. *P* 14½ × 14 (25, 50 *c.*) *or* 14 × 14½ (*others*).
168 1 c. yellow, red, black and lilac 25 25
169 2 c. orange, black and yellow-olive .. 25 35
170 2½ c. carmine, green, black and bistre .. 25 10
171 3½ c. yellow, black, sepia and pink 35 35
172 5 c. yellow, blue, black and buff 80 30
173 7½ c. brown, red, black and apple-green .. 60 60
174 10 c. red, yellow, sepia & turquoise-green .. 60 50
175 12½ c. buff, blue, red and grey-black .. .. 7·00 3·25
176 20 c. yellow-brown and drab 50 70
177 25 c. deep brown and lemon 50 75
178 35 c. deep blue and orange .. .. .. 80 1·40
179 50 c. sepia and olive .. .. .. 1·00 1·75
180 1 r. black and cinnamon .. .. .. 2·50 2·50
181 2 r. brown and turquoise-blue .. .. 13·00 6·50
168/81 .. .. *Set of* 14 25·00 17·00

Designs: *Vert*—2 c. Hoopoe; 2½ c. Scarlet-chested Sunbird; 3½ c. Yellow-rumped Bishop; 5 c. Swallow-tailed Bee Eater; 7½ c. African Grey Hornbill; 10 c. Red-headed Weaver; 12½ c. Brown-hooded Kingfisher; 20 c. Woman musician; 35 c. Woman grinding maize; 1 r. Lion; 2 r. Police camel patrol. *Horiz*—25 c. Baobab Tree.

1963 (4 June). *Freedom from Hunger. As No.* 76 *of Aden.*
182 12½ c. bluish green 25 15

1963 (2 Sept). *Red Cross Centenary. As Nos.* 147/8 *of Antigua.*
183 2½ c. red and black 20 10
184 12½ c. red and blue 40 35

1964 (23 April). 400*th Birth Anniv of William Shakespeare. As No.* 164 *of Antigua.*
185 12½c. light brown 15 15

C. BECHUANALAND

INTERNAL SELF-GOVERNMENT

42 Map and Gaberones Dam

(Des Mrs. M. Townsend, adapted V. Whiteley. Photo Harrison)

1965 (1 Mar). *New Constitution.* W w **12**. *P* 14½ × 14.
186 **42** 2½ c. red and gold 10 10
187 5 c. ultramarine and gold 10 10
188 12½ c. brown and gold 10 15
189 25 c. green and gold 15 30
186/9 .. .. *Set of* 4 25 45

1965 (17 May). *I.T.U. Centenary. As Nos.* 166/7 *of Antigua.*
190 2½ c. red and bistre-yellow 20 10
191 12½ c. mauve and brown 45 30

1965 (25 Oct). *International Co-operation Year. As Nos.* 168/9 *of Antigua.*
192 1 c. reddish purple and turquoise-green .. 10 10
193 12½ c. deep bluish green and lavender .. 60 55

1966 (24 Jan). *Churchill Commemoration. As Nos.* 170/3 *of Antigua.*
194 1 c. new blue 15 15
195 2½ c. deep green 25 10
196 12½ c. brown 65 20
197 20 c. bluish violet 70 25
194/7 .. .. *Set of* 4 1·50 65

43 Haslar Smoke Generator

(Des V. Whiteley. Photo Harrison)

1966 (1 June). *Bechuanaland Royal Pioneer Corps. T* **43** *and similar horiz designs.* W w **12**. *P* 14½.
198 2½ c. Prussian blue, red and light emerald .. 15 10
199 5 c. brown and light blue 15 10
200 15 c. Prussian blue, rosine and emerald .. 20 10
201 35 c. buff, blackish brown, red and green .. 30 60
198/201 .. .. *Set of* 4 70 70

Designs:—5 c. Bugler; 15 c. Gun-site; 35 c. Regimental cap badge.

POSTAGE DUE STAMPS

BECHUANALAND (D 1)

PROTECTORATE — BECHUANALAND PROTECTORATE (D 2)

1926 (Jan). *Type* D 1 *of Great Britain, optd with Types* D 1 *or* D 2 (2*d.*).
D1 ½d. emerald (No. D10) .. .. .. 3·25 40·00
D2 1d. carmine (No. D9) .. .. .. 3·25 35·00
D3 2d. agate (No. D13) .. .. .. 6·00 60·00
D1/3 .. .. *Set of* 3 11·00 £120

D 3

1c 1c

I (Small) II (Large)

(Typo D.L.R.)

1932 (12 Dec)–**58**. *Wmk Mult Script CA. P* 14.
D4 **D 3** ½d. sage-green .. .. 3·50 12·00
D5 1d. carmine, **O** .. .. 3·50 4·50
a. Chalky paper (27.11.58) .. .. 30 3·50
D6 2d. violet, **O** .. .. 4·50 13·00
a. Chalky paper (27.11.58) .. .. 60 6·00
D4/6a .. .. *Set of* 3 4·00 19·00
D4/6 Perf "Specimen" .. .. *Set of* 3 60·00

1961 (14 Feb). *Surch as T* **27**.
D7 **D 3** 1 c. on 1d., **C** (Type I) 25 50
a. Type II (chalky paper) 15 80
ab. Double surch (Type II) £100
b. Type II (ordinary paper) .. .. 16·00
D8 2 c. on 2d., **C** (Type I) 25 70
a. Type II (chalky paper) .. .. 15 1·00
b. Type II (ordinary paper) .. .. 65·00
D9 5 c. on ½d. 20 60
D7/9 .. .. *Set of* 3 45 1·60

1961 (15 Nov). *As Type* D **3** *but values in cents. Chalky paper. Wmk Mult Script CA. P* 14.
D10 1 c. carmine 15 40
D11 2 c. violet 15 60
D12 5 c. green .. .. 30 1·00
D10/12 .. .. *Set of* 3 55 1·75

POSTAL FISCAL STAMPS

The following stamps issued for fiscal purposes were each allowed to be used for postal purposes for a short time. No. F2 was used by the public because the word "POSTAGE" had not been obliterated and No. F3 because the overprint did not include the words "Revenue only" as did the contemporary fiscal overprints for Basutoland and Swaziland.

Bechuanaland Protectorate (F 1)

£5 (F 2)

Bechuanaland Protectorate. (F 3)

1910 (July). *No.* 266 *of Transvaal, optd with Type* F **1**.
F1 6d. black and orange, **C** (B.) £110 £180

1918. *No.* 15 *surch with Type* F **2** *at top.*
F2 **4** £5 on 1s. green and black £4750

1922. *No.* 4*b of South Africa optd with Type* F **3**, *in varying positions.*
F3 1d. scarlet .. .. 40·00 75·00
a. Opt double, one albino .. .. .. 90·00

The stamps of Bechuanaland were withdrawn on independence, 29 September 1966. For later issues see BOTSWANA.

Belize

(*formerly* British Honduras)

✲BELIZE✲

(81)

1973 (11 June*). *As Nos.* 277/*b*, 278, 256, 259, 262/6 *and* 338/40 *of British Honduras with T* **81** *in silver and black by D.L.R.* W w **12** (*upright*). *P* 13 × 12½.
347 ½ c. Crana 10 10
348 1 c. Jew Fish 10 10
349 2 c. White-lipped Peccary ("Waree") .. 10 10
350 3 c. Grouper 10 10
351 4 c. Collared Anteater 10 10
352 5 c. Bone Fish 10 10
353 10 c. Paca ("Gibnut") 15 15
a. Black (value etc. omitted) £200
354 15 c. Dolphin 20 20
355 25 c. Kinkajou ("Night Walker") 35 35
356 50 c. Mutton Snapper 55 55
357 $1 Tayra ("Bush Dog") .. .. .. 90 1·25
358 $2 Great Barracuda .. .. .. 1·75 2·00
359 $5 Puma .. .. 2·50 3·75
347/59 .. .. *Set of* 13 6·00 8·00

*This is the local date of issue: the Crown Agents released the stamps on 1 June.

1973 (14 Nov). *Royal Wedding. As Nos.* 165/6 *of Anguilla. Centre multicoloured.* W w **12** (*sideways*). *P* 13½.
360 26 c. light turquoise-blue 15 10
361 50 c. ochre 15 20

82 Crana

1974 (1 Jan). *Designs as Nos.* 256/67 *and* 277 *of British Honduras inscr.* "BELIZE" *as in T* **82**. W w **12**. *P* 13½.
362 ½ c. Type **82** 10 10
363 1 c. Jew Fish 10 10
364 2 c. White-lipped Peccary ("Waree") .. 10 10
365 3 c. Grouper 10 10
366 4 c. Collared Anteater 10 10
367 5 c. Bone Fish 10 10
368 10 c. Paca ("Gibnut") 15 15
369 15 c. Dolphin 20 20
370 25 c. Kinkajou ("Night Walker") 35 35
371 50 c. Mutton Snapper 60 70
372 $1 Tayra ("Bush Dog") .. .. .. 1·00 1·50
373 $2 Great Barracuda .. .. .. 1·50 2·00
374 $5 Puma .. .. 3·50 5·00
362/74 .. .. *Set of* 13 7·00 9·00

83 Deer

(Des Mrs. Hosek; adapted PAD Studio, Litho Questa)

1974 (1 May). *Mayan Artefacts* (1*st series*). *T* **83** *and similar horiz designs showing pottery motifs. Multicoloured.* W w **12**. *P* 14½.
375 3 c. Type **83** 10 10
376 6 c. Jaguar deity 10 10
377 16 c. Sea monster 10 10
378 26 c. Cormorant 15 10
379 50 c. Scarlet macaw 30 30
375/9 .. .. *Set of* 5 60 50

See also Nos. 398/402.

84 *Parides arcas*

(Des J. Cooter from the collection of P. T. Hill. Litho Harrison)

1974 (2 Sept)–**75**. *Butterflies. Horiz designs as T* **84**. *Multicoloured.* W w **12** (*sideways*). *P* 14 (½, 1, 2, 3, 4, 5, 10, 26 *c.*) *or* 14 × 14½ (*others*).
380 ½ c. Type **84** 20 20
381 1 c. *Thecla regalis* 25 15
382 2 c. *Colobura dirce* 20 15
383 3 c. *Catonephele numilia* 20 15
384 4 c. *Battus belus* 30 15
385 5 c. *Callicore patelina* 45 15
386 10 c. *Callicore astala* 50 15
387 15 c. *Nessaea aglaura* .. .. .. 1·25 75
388 16 c. *Prepona pseudojoiceyi* .. .. 1·25 80
389 25 c. *Papilio thoas* 80 35
390 26 c. *Hamadryas arethusa* .. .. 2·25 4·00
391 50 c. *Thecla bathildis* .. .. .. 1·25 50
392 $1 *Caligo uranus* .. .. .. 2·50 70
393 $2 *Heliconius sapho* .. .. .. 2·50 1·25
394 $5 *Eurytides philolaus* .. .. .. 3·75 4·00
395 $10 *Philaethria dido* (2.1.75) .. .. 10·00 4·00
380/95 .. .. *Set of* 16 25·00 16·00

See also Nos. 403/13 and 426/33.

85 Churchill when Prime Minister, and Coronation Scene

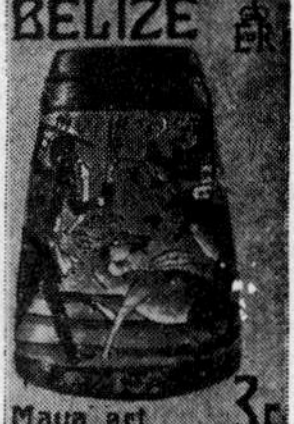

86 The Actun Balam Vase

(Des J.W. Litho Questa)

1974 (30 Nov). *Birth Centenary of Sir Winston Churchill. T* **85** *and similar horiz design. Multicoloured.* W w **14** (*sideways*). *P* 14.
396 50 c. Type **85** 20 20
397 $1 Churchill in stetson, and Williamsburg Liberty Bell 30 30

(Des Mrs. Hosek; adapted P. Powell. Litho Questa)

1975 (2 June). *Mayan Artefacts (2nd series). T* **86** *and similar vert designs showing decorated vessels. Multicoloured. W w* 14. *P* 14.

398 3 c. Type **86** 10 10
399 6 c. Seated figure 10 10
400 16 c. Costumed priest 10 10
401 26 c. Head with headdress 15 10
402 50 c. Layman and priest 20 20
398/402 .. .. *Set of* 5 45 40

1975–78. *As Nos.* 380, 382/7 *and* 389 *and new value* (35 c.), *but W w* **14** (*sideways on* ½, 2, 3, 4, 5, 10 *and* 35 *c.*). *P* 14 × 14½ (15, 25 *c.*) *or* 14 (*others*).

403 ½ c. Type **84** (11.6.75) 30 60
405 2 c. *Colobura dirce* (17.5.77) 25 20
406 3 c. *Catonephele numulia* (17.5.77) 45 10
407 4 c. *Battus belus* (7.3.77) 80 10
408 5 c. *Callicore patelina* (11.2.77) .. .. 1·00 15
409 10 c. *Callicore astala* (11.2.77) .. .. 1·00 15
410 15 c. *Nessaea aglaura* (17.5.77) 65 35
412 25 c. *Papilio thoas* (27.1.78) 85 40
413 35 c. Type **84** (25.7.77) .. .. 2·00 3·00
403/13 .. .. *Set of* 9 6·50 4·50

1975–77. *As Nos.* 387, 389, 391 *and* 394 *but W w* **12** *upright.*

426 15 c. *Nessaea aglaura* (20.10.75) 60 90
428 25 c. *Papilio thoas* (7.3.77) 75 75
429 50 c. *Thecla bathildis* (7.3.77) .. .. .. 2·00 1·40
433 $5 *Eurytides philolaus* (20.10.75) .. .. 5·50 6·50
426/33 .. .. *Set of* 4 8·00 8·50

87 Musicians

(Des PAD Studio. Litho Harrison)

1975 (17 Nov). *Christmas. T* **87** *and similar multicoloured designs. W w* **12** (*upright on* 6 *c.* 26 *c.*) *or sideways* (*others*). *P* 14 × 14½ (*horiz*) *or* 14½ × 14 (*vert*).

435 6 c. Type **87** 10 10
436 26 c. Children and "crib" 15 10
437 50 c. Dancer and drummers (*vert*) 20 10
a. Imperf (pair) £100
438 $1 Family and map (*vert*) 30 25
435/8 .. .. *Set of* 4 65 40

88 William Wrigley Jr. and Chicle Tapping

(Des PAD Studio. Litho Questa)

1976 (29 Mar). *Bicentenary of American Revolution. T* **88** *and similar horiz designs. Multicoloured. W w* **14** (*sideways*). *P* 14.

439 10 c. Type **88** 10 10
440 35 c. Charles Lindbergh and *Spirit of St. Louis* 25 40
441 $1 J. L. Stephens (archaeologist) .. .. 60 1·00
439/41 .. .. *Set of* 3 85 1·40

89 Cycling

(Des J.W. Litho Walsall)

1976 (17 July). *Olympic Games. Montreal. T* **89** *and similar horiz designs. Multicoloured. W w* **14** (*sideways*). *P* 14.

442 35 c. Type **89** 15 10
443 45 c. Running 20 15
444 $1 Shooting 35 50
442/4 .. .. *Set of* 3 65 65

(90) (91)

1976 (30 Aug). *No.* 390 *surch with T* **90** *by Harrison.*

445 20 c. on 26 c. *Hamadryas arethusa* 30 70

1976 (18 Oct). *West Indian Victory in World Cricket Cup. As Nos.* 559/60 *of Barbados.*

446 35 c. Map of the Caribbean 50 50
447 $1 The Prudential Cup .. .. .. 1·10 1·50

1976 (2 Dec). *No.* 426 *surch with T* **91** *by the Govt Printery, Belize.*

448 5 c. on 15 c. *Nessaea aglaura* .. .. .. 45 1·00

92 Queen and Bishops

(Des R. Granger Barrett. Litho Enschedé)

1977 (7 Feb). *Silver Jubilee. T* **92** *and similar horiz designs. Multicoloured. W w* **14** (*sideways*). *P* 13 × 13½.

449 10 c. Royal Visit, 1975 .. .. 10 10
450 35 c. Queen and Rose Window 30 20
451 $2 Type **92** .. .. 80 1·25
449/51 .. .. *Set of* 3 1·10 1·40

93 Red-capped Manakin **94** Laboratory Workers

(Des and litho J.W.)

1977 (3 Sept). *Birds* (*1st series*). *T* **93** *and similar vert designs. Multicoloured. W w* **14**. *P* 14.

452 8 c. Type **93** 40 15
453 10 c. Hooded Oriole 45 20
454 25 c. Blue-crowned Motmot 75 55
455 35 c. Slaty-breasted Tinamou 95 75
456 45 c. Ocellated Turkey .. .. .. 1·25 90
457 $1 White Hawk .. .. 2·00 2·00
452/7 .. .. *Set of* 6 5·25 4·00
MS458 110 × 133 mm. Nos. 452/7 .. .. .. 5·25 7·00

See also Nos. 467/73, 488/94 and 561/7.

(Des G. Hutchins. Litho J.W.)

1977 (2 Dec). *75th Anniv of Pan-American Health Organisation. T* **94** *and similar horiz design. Multicoloured. W w* **14** (*sideways*). *P* 13½.

459 35 c. Type **94** 20 20
460 $1 Mobile medical unit 40 65
MS461 126 × 95 mm. Nos. 459/60. P 13 .. .. 85 1·25

BELIZE DEFENCE FORCE
1ST JANUARY 1978

(95)

1978 (15 Feb). *Establishment of Belize Defence Force. Nos.* 409 *and* 413 *optd with T* **95** *in gold by Govt Printery, Belize.*

462 10 c. *Callicore astala* 15 15
463 35 c. *Parides arcas* 30 40

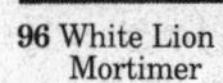

96 White Lion of Mortimer **97** *Russelia sarmentosa*

(Des. C. Abbott. Litho Questa)

1978 (21 Apr). *25th Anniv of Coronation* (1st issue). *T* **96** *and similar vert designs. P* 15.

464 75 c. bistre, carmine and silver 25 30
a. Sheetlet. Nos. 464/6 × 2 .. .. .. 1·40
465 75 c. multicoloured 25 30
466 75 c. bistre, carmine and silver 25 30
464/6 .. .. *Set of* 3 65 80

Designs:—No. 464, Type **96**; No. 465, Queen Elizabeth II; No 466, Jaguar (Maya god of Day and Night).

Nos. 464/6 were printed together in small sheets of 6, containing two *se-tenant* strips of 3 with horizontal gutter margin between.

See also Nos. 495/503.

(Des. J.W. Litho Questa)

1978 (31 July). *Birds* (*2nd series*). *Vert designs as T* **93**. *Multicoloured. W w* **14**. *P* 14½.

467 10 c. White-capped Parrot 25 20
468 25 c. Crimson-collared Tanager 65 45
469 35 c. Citreoline Trogon 80 55
470 45 c. American Finfoot .. .. .. 1·00 1·00
471 50 c. Muscovy Duck .. .. .. 1·10 1·10
472 $1 King Vulture .. .. 1·60 2·40
467/72 .. .. *Set of* 6 5·00 5·25
MS473 111 × 133 mm. Nos. 467/72 .. .. 5·00 6·50

(Des J. Cooter. Litho Questa)

1978 (16 Oct). *Christmas. Wild Flowers and Ferns. T* **97** *and similar vert designs. Multicoloured. W w* **14**. *P* 14 × 13½.

474 10 c. Type **97** 10 10
475 15 c. *Lygodium polymorphum* 15 10
476 35 c. *Heliconia aurantiaca* 20 15
477 45 c. *Adiantum tetraphyllum* 25 25
478 50 c. *Angelonia ciliaris* 25 25
479 $1 *Thelypteris obliterata* 45 50
474/79 .. .. *Set of* 6 1·25 1·10

98 Internal Airmail Service, 1937

(Des D. Bowen. Litho Questa)

1979 (15 Jan). *Centenary of U.P.U. Membership. T* **98** *and similar horiz designs. Multicoloured. W w* **14** (*sideways*). *P* 13½ × 14.

480 5 c. Type **98** 10 10
481 10 c. M.V. *Heron H* on mail service, 1949 .. 10 10
482 35 c. Internal mail service, 1920 (canoe) .. 20 20
483 45 c. Stann Creek Railway mail, 1910 .. 45 45
484 50 c. Mounted mail courier, 1882 .. .. 30 30
485 $2 R.M.S. *Eagle*, 1856 .. .. .. 1·00 1·25
480/5 .. .. *Set of* 6 1·90 2·10

15¢

(99) (100)

1979. *No.* 413 *surch.* (*a*) *By typography, locally, with T* **99**.

486 15 c. on 35 c. Type **84** (March) .. .. .. 28·00

(*b*) *By lithography, in Great Britain, with T* **100**

487 15 c. on 35 c. Type **84** (June) 25 50

(Des J.W. Litho Questa)

1979 (16 Apr). *Birds* (*3rd series*). *Vert designs as T* **93**. *Multicoloured. P* 14.

488 10 c. Boat-billed Heron 30 10
489 25 c. Grey-necked Wood Rail 55 20
490 35 c. Lineated Woodpecker 65 30
491 45 c. Blue-grey Tanager 70 40
492 50 c. Laughing Falcon 70 70
493 $1 Long-tailed Hermit .. .. .. 1·10 1·40
488/93 .. .. *Set of* 6 3·50 2·75
MS494 113 × 136 mm. Nos. 488/93 .. .. 3·50 3·75

PRINTER. The following issues to No. 734 were printed in lithography by Lito Nacional, Porto, Portugal.

AVAILABILITY. Certain values of some issues to No. 734 were only available in restricted quantities in Belize.

101 Paslow Building, Belize G.P.O.

(Des A. Medina)

1979 (31 May). *25th Anniv of Coronation* (*2nd issue*). *T* **101** *and similar multicoloured designs. P* 14.

495 25 c. Type **101** 20 10
496 50 c. Houses of Parliament 35 10
497 75 c. Coronation State Coach 55 10
498 $1 Queen on horseback (*vert*) 70 10
499 $2 Prince of Wales (*vert*) .. .. .. 1·40 15
500 $3 Queen and Duke of Edinburgh (*vert*) .. 2·10 20
501 $4 Portrait of Queen (*vert*) .. .. .. 2·75 25
502 $5 St. Edward's Crown (*vert*) .. .. 3·50 30
495/502 .. .. *Set of* 8 10·00 1·00
MS503 Two sheets, both 126 × 95 mm: (a) $5 Princess Anne on horseback at Montreal Olympics (*vert*), $10 Queen at Montreal Olympics (*vert*); (b) $15 As Type **101** .. .. .. *Set of* 2 *sheets* 18·00

Nos. 495/502 also exist imperforate from a restricted printing (*price for set of* 8 £40 *mint*).

ALTERED CATALOGUE NUMBERS

Any Catalogue numbers altered from the last edition are shown as a list in the introductory pages.

102 Safety Aeroplane (1909)

(Des A. Medina)

1979 (30 July). *Death Centenary of Sir Rowland Hill and 75th Anniv of I.C.A.O. (International Civil Aviation Organization). T* **102** *and similar horiz designs. Multicoloured. P* 14.

504 4 c. Type **102** 10 10
505 25 c. Boeing "707-720" 20 10
506 50 c. "Concorde" 30 10
507 75 c. Handley Page "W8b" (1922) 45 10
508 $1 Avro "F" (1912) 60 10
509 $1.50, Cody (1910) 95 15
510 $2 Triplane II (1909) .. .. 1·25 25
511 $3 Santos Dumont's aeroplane (1906) .. 1·90 35
512 $4 First motorized flight, Wright brothers (1903) .. .. 2·50 50
504/12 .. .. *Set of* 9 7·00 1·25
MS513 Two sheets: (a) 115 × 95 mm. $5 Dunne "D5" (1910), $5 G.B. 1969 "Concorde" stamp; (b) 130 × 95 mm. $10 Boeing "707–720" (*different*). *Set of* 2 *sheets* 18·00

Nos. 504/12 also exist imperforate from a restricted printing (*price for set of* 9 £55 *mint*).

103 Handball **104** Olympic torch

(Des A. Medina)

1979 (10 Oct). *Olympic Games. Moscow* (1980). *T* **103** *and similar vert designs. Multicoloured. P* 14.

514 25 c. Type **103** 20 10
515 50 c. Weightlifting 35 10
516 75 c. Athletics 55 10
517 $1 Football 70 10
518 $2 Yachting .. .. 1·40 15
519 $3 Swimming .. .. 1·75 20
520 $4 Boxing .. .. 2·00 25
521 $5 Cycling .. .. 2·50 30
514/21 .. .. *Set of* 8 8·50 1·00
MS522 Two sheets: (a) 126 × 92 mm. $5 Athletics (*different*), $10 Boxing (*different*); (b) 92 × 126 mm. $15 As $5 .. .. *Set of* 2 *sheets* 16·00

Nos. 514/21 also exist imperforate from a restricted printing (*price for set of* 8 £55 *mint*).

(Des A. Medina)

1979 (4 Dec). *Winter Olympic Games. Lake Placid* (1980). *T* **104** *and similar vert designs. Multicoloured. P* 14.

523 25 c. Type **104** 20 10
524 50 c. Giant slalom 35 10
525 75 c. Figure-skating 55 10
526 $1 Slalom skiing 70 10
527 $2 Speed-skating .. .. 1·40 15
528 $3 Cross-country skiing .. .. .. 2·10 20
529 $4 Shooting .. .. 2·75 25
530 $5 Gold, Silver and Bronze medals .. 3·50 30
523/30 .. .. *Set of* 8 10·00 1·00
MS531 Two sheets: (a) 127 × 90 mm. $5 Lighting the Olympic Flame, $10 Gold, Silver and Bronze medals (*different*); (b) 90 × 127 mm. $15 Olympic Torch (*different*) .. .. *Set of* 2 *sheets* 20·00

Nos. 523/30 also exist imperforate from a restricted printing (*price for set of* 8 £55 *mint*).

105 *Cypraea zebra* **106** Girl and Flower Arrangement

(Des C. Abbott)

1980 (7 Jan). *Shells. Multicoloured designs as T* **105**. *P* 14.

532 1 c. Type **105** 10 10
533 2 c. *Macrocallista maculata* 10 10
534 3 c. *Arca zebra* (*vert*) 10 10
535 4 c. *Chama macerophylla* (*vert*) 15 10
536 5 c. *Latirus cariniferus* 15 10
537 10 c. *Conus spurius* (*vert*) 20 10
538 15 c. *Murex cabritii* (*vert*) 25 10
539 20 c. *Atrina rigida* 30 10
540 25 c. *Chlamys imbricata* (*vert*) 30 10
541 35 c. *Conus granulatus* 40 10
542 45 c. *Tellina radiata* (*vert*) 50 10
543 50 c. *Leucozonia nassa leucozonalis* 55 10
544 85 c. *Tripterotyphis triangularis* 80 10
545 $1 *Strombus gigas* (*vert*) 95 10
546 $2 *Strombus gallus* (*vert*) .. .. .. 2·00 30
547 $5 *Fasciolaria tulipa* .. .. .. 3·75 75
548 $10 *Arene cruentata* .. .. .. 6·50 1·25
532/548 .. .. .. *Set of* 17 15·00 2·50
MS549 Two sheets, each 125 × 90 mm: (a) Nos. 544 and 547; (b) Nos. 546 and 548 .. .. 11·00 13·00

Some of the above exist with a different date in the imprint at the foot of each stamp.

(Des A. Medina ($5), C. Mullin (others))

1980 (15 Mar). *International Year of the Child. T* **106** *and similar vert designs. Multicoloured. P* 14.

550 25 c. Type **106** 20 10
551 50 c. Boy holding football 30 10
552 75 c. Boy with butterfly 45 10
553 $1 Girl holding doll 60 10
554 $1.50, Boy carrying basket of fruit 95 15
555 $2 Boy holding shell .. .. .. 1·25 20
556 $3 Girl holding posy .. .. .. 1·90 25
557 $4 Boy and girl wrapped in blanket .. 2·50 30
550/7 .. .. *Set of* 8 7·00 1·00
MS558 130 × 95 mm. $5 Three children of different races, $5 "Madonna with Cat" (A. Dürer) (*each* 35 × 53 *mm*). P 13 .. .. 6·00
MS559 111 × 151 mm. $10 Children and Christmas tree (73 × 110 *mm*). P 13 .. .. 6·00

Nos. 550/7 also exist imperforate from a restricted printing (*price for set of* 8 £35 *mint*).

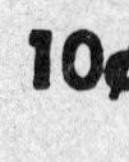

(**107**) **108** Jabiru

1980 (March). *No.* 412 *surch with T* **107**.

560 10 c. on 25 c. *Papilio thoas* 15 25
a. Surch inverted .. .. 60·00

(Des J.W. Litho Questa)

1980 (16 June). *Birds* (4*th series*). *T* **108** *and similar vert designs. Multicoloured. P* 13.

561 10 c. Type **108** .. .. 1·50 1·25
a. Sheetlet. Nos. 561/6 .. .. .. 12·00
562 25 c. Barred Antshrike .. .. .. 1·75 1·50
563 35 c. Northern Royal Flycatcher .. .. 2·00 1·75
564 45 c. White-necked Puffbird .. .. 2·25 2·00
565 50 c. Ornate Hawk-eagle .. .. .. 2·50 2·25
566 $1 Golden-masked Tanager .. .. 3·25 2·75
561/6 .. .. *Set of* 6 12·00 10·50
MS567 85 × 90 mm. $2 Type **108**, $3 As $1 .. 10·00 9·00

Nos. 561/6 were printed together, *se-tenant* in sheetlets of 6 or in "double" sheetlets of 12. Stamps from the "double" sheetlets have a red frame and red imprint at foot.

40c

109 Speed Skating (**110**)

1980 (20 Aug). *Medal Winners, Winter Olympic Games, Lake Placid. T* **109** *and similar vert designs. Multicoloured. P* 14.

568 25 c. Type **109** 20 10
569 50 c. Ice hockey 30 10
570 75 c. Figure-skating 45 10
571 $1 Alpine skiing 60 10
572 $1.50, Giant slalom (women) 95 15
573 $2 Speed-skating (women) .. .. .. 1·25 20
574 $3 Cross-country skiing .. .. .. 1·90 25
575 $5 Giant slalom .. .. 3·00 30
568/75 .. .. *Set of* 8 7·50 1·00
MS576 Two sheets: (a) 126 × 91 mm. $5 Type **109**; $10 Type **109**; (b) 91 × 126 mm. $10 As 75 c. *Set of* 2 *sheets* 15·00

Nos. 568/75 also exist imperforate from a restricted printing (*price for set of* 8 £55 *mint*)

1980 (3 Oct). *"ESPAMER" International Stamp Exhibition, Madrid. Nos.* 560/5 *optd* (*Nos.* 577/9) *or surch as T* **110**.

577 10 c. Type **107** 60 60
a. Sheetlet. Nos. 577/82 .. .. .. 6·00
578 25 c. Barred Antshrike 75 75
579 35 c. Northern Royal Flycatcher .. .. 1·10 1·10
580 40 c. on 45 c. White-necked Puffbird .. .. 1·40 1·40
581 40 c. on 50 c. Ornate Hawk-eagle .. .. 1·40 1·40
582 40 c. on $1 Golden-masked Tanager .. .. 1·40 1·40
577/82 .. .. *Set of* 6 6·00 6·00

111 Witch in Sky **112** Queen Elizabeth The Queen Mother

(Des C. Mullin)

1980 (24 Nov). *Fairy Tales. Sleeping Beauty. T* **111** *and similar vert designs illustrating the story. P* 14.

583 35 c. multicoloured 25 10
584 40 c. multicoloured 35 10
585 50 c. multicoloured 45 10
586 75 c. multicoloured 60 10
587 $1 multicoloured 70 15
588 $1.50, multicoloured .. .. 1·10 20
589 $3 multicoloured .. .. 2·10 25
590 $4 multicoloured .. .. 2·75 30
583/90 .. .. *Set of* 8 7·50 1·00
MS591 Two sheets: (a) 82 × 110 mm. $8 "Paumgartner Altar-piece" (Dürer); (b) 110 × 82 mm. $5 Marriage ceremony, $5 Sleeping Beauty and Prince on horseback .. .. *Set of* 2 *sheets* 12·50

Nos. 583/90 also exist imperforate from a restricted printing (*price for set of* 8 £55 *mint*).

(Des C. Mullen)

1980 (12 Dec). 80*th Birthday of Queen Elizabeth the Queen Mother. P* 13.

592 **112** $1 multicoloured 85 30
MS593 82 × 110 mm, $5 As Type **112** (41 × 32 *mm*) 4·00 4·00

No. 592 exists imperforate from a restricted printing (*price* £4.50 *mint*).

$1

113 The Annunciation (**114**)

(Des C. Mullin)

1980 (30 Dec). *Christmas. T* **113** *and similar vert designs. Multicoloured. P* 14.

594 25 c. Type **113** 20 10
595 50 c. Bethlehem 35 10
596 75 c. The Holy Family 55 10
597 $1 The Nativity 70 10
598 $1.50, The flight into Egypt 90 15
599 $2 Shepherds following the Star .. .. 1·10 20
600 $3 Virgin, Child and Angel .. .. .. 1·60 25
601 $4 Adoration of the Kings .. .. .. 1·90 30
594/601 .. .. *Set of* 8 6·50 1·00
MS602 Two sheets, each 82 × 111 mm: (a) $5 As $1; (b) $10 As $3 .. .. .. *Set of* 2 *sheets* 10·50

1981 (22 May). *"WIPA" International Stamp Exhibition. Vienna. Nos.* 598 *and* 601/2b *surch with T* **114**.

603 $1 on $1.50, The flight into Egypt 60 65
604 $2 on $4 Adoration of the Kings .. .. 1·25 1·40
MS605 82 × 111 mm. $2 on $10 Virgin, Child and Angel .. .. 1·25 1·50

OMNIBUS ISSUES

Details, together with prices for complete sets, of the various Omnibus issues from the 1935 Silver Jubilee series to date are included in a special section following Zululand at the end of the catalogue.

115 Paul Harris (founder) **116** Prince of Wales Coat of Arms

1981 (26 May). *75th Anniv of Rotary International. T* **115** *and similar multicoloured designs. P* 14.

606	25 c. Type **115** . .	20	25
607	50 c. Emblems of Rotary activities . .	35	35
608	$1 75th Anniversary emblem . .	70	65
609	$1·50, Educational scholarship programme (*horiz*) . .	1·10	1·00
610	$2 "Project Hippocrates" . .	1·40	1·40
611	$3 Emblems (*horiz*) . .	2·10	2·00
612	$5 Emblem and handshake (*horiz*) . .	3·50	3·25
606/12	. . *Set of* 7	8·50	8·00
MS613	Two sheets: (a) 95 × 130 mm. $10 As 50 c.; (b) 130 × 95 mm, $5 As $1, $10 As $2 *Set of 2 sheets*	17·50	

*Nos. 606/13, together with a 75 c. value showing a map, were originally issued on 30 March 1981, but were withdrawn from sale after two hours as there were objections to the colours used on the map. The stamps, without the offending 75 c., were reissued on 26 May. First Day covers carry the later date and there are no reports of examples used before 26 May.

(Des C. Mullin)

1981 (16 July). *Royal Wedding. T* **116** *and similar vert designs. Multicoloured.* (a) *Size* 22 × 38 *mm* (*from sheets of* 27). *P* 13½ × 14.

614	50 c. Type **116** . .	35	40
	a. Horiz pair. Nos. 614/15 . .	1·10	
615	$1 Prince Charles in military uniform . .	70	75
	a. Horiz pair. Nos. 615/16 . .	1·90	
616	$1.50, Royal couple . .	1·10	1·25

(*b*) *Size* 25 × 42 *mm with gold borders* (*sheets of* 6 *stamps and* 3 *labels*). *P* 13.

617	50 c. Type **116** . .	35	15
618	$1 As No. 615 . .	70	35
619	$1.50, As No. 616 . .	1·10	45
614/19	. . *Set of* 6	3·75	3·00
MS620	145 × 85 mm. $3 × 3 As Nos 614/16, but 30 × 47 mm. P 14 . .	5·00	6·50

Nos. 614/16 were each printed in blocks of 9 (3 × 3), the blocks *se-tenant* within the sheet.

Nos. 614/16 also exist imperforate from a restricted printing (*price for set of* 3 £9 *mint*).

10c

(**117**)

1981 (22 Aug). *No.* 538 *surch with T* **117**.

621	10 c. on 15 c. *Murex cabritii* . .	35	45
	a. Surch double . .	†	—

For a similar surcharge, but with rectangular obliterating panel see No. 728.

118 Athletics

(Des C. Mullin)

1981 (14 Sept). *History of the Olympic Games. T* **118** *and similar vert designs. Multicoloured. P* 14.

622	85 c. Type **118** . .	60	10
623	$1 Cycling . .	70	10
624	$1.50, Boxing . .	1·10	10
625	$2 1984 Games–Los Angeles and Sarajevo	1·40	20
626	$3 Baron Pierre de Coubertin . .	2·10	30
627	$5 Olympic Flame . .	3·50	40
622/7	. . *Set of* 6	8·50	1·00
MS628	Two sheets, each 175 × 123 mm: (a) $5 As $3, $10 As $5 (*each* 35 × 53 *mm*). P 13½; (b) $15 As $2 (45 × 67 *mm*). P 14½. . . *Set of 2 sheets*	21·00	

The two miniature sheets of No. **MS**628 also exist with the stamps and borders printed in gold from a restricted printing.

NEW INFORMATION

The editor is always interested to correspond with people who have new information that will improve or correct the Catalogue.

INDEPENDENCE

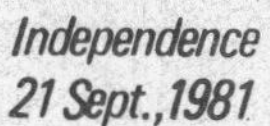

$1

(**119**) (**120**)

1981 (21 Sept). *Independence Commemoration* (*1st issue*). *Optd as T* **119** *by Benex Press, Belize City.* (*a*) *On Nos.* 532/44 *and* 546/9.

629	1 c. Type **119** . .	10	10
630	2 c. *Macrocallista maculata* . .	10	10
631	3 c. *Arca zebra* (*vert*) . .	10	10
632	4 c. *Chama macerophylla* (*vert*) . .	10	10
	a. Opt inverted . .	†	
633	5 c. *Latirus cariniferus* . .	10	10
634	10 c. *Conus spurius* (*vert*) . .	10	10
635	15 c. *Murex cabritii* (*vert*) . .	10	10
636	20 c. *Atrina rigida* . .	10	15
637	25 c. *Chlamys imbricata* (*vert*) . .	20	25
638	35 c. *Conus granulatus* . .	25	30
639	45 c. *Tellina radiata* (*vert*) . .	30	35
640	50 c. *Leucozonia nassa leucozonalis* . .	30	35
641	85 c. *Tripterotyphis triangularis* . .	55	60
642	$2 *Strombus gallus* (*vert*) . .	1·25	1·40
643	$5 *Fasciolaria tulipa* . .	3·00	3·25
	a. Opt inverted . .	†	—
644	$10 *Arene cruentata* . .	6·00	6·50
629/44	. . *Set of* 16	11·00	12·00
MS645	Two sheets, each 126 × 91 mm: (a) Nos. 641 and 643; (b) Nos. 642 and 644 . . *Set of 2 sheets*	11·00	

On the vertical designs and the miniature sheets the overprint is in roman type.

The 10c. exists with different imprint dates.

Examples of the miniature sheets have been seen showing forged overprints apparently applied by rubber handstamp.

(*b*) *On Nos.* 606/13

646	25 c. Type **115** (Gold) . .	20	25
647	50 c. Emblems of Rotary activities . .	35	35
648	$1 75th Anniversary emblem . .	70	65
649	$1.50, Educational scholarship programme . .	1·10	1·00
650	$2 "Project Hippocrates" (Gold) . .	1·40	1·40
651	$3 Emblems . .	2·10	2·00
652	$5 Emblems and handshake . .	3·50	3·25
646/52	. . *Set of* 7	10·50	8·00
MS653	Two sheets: (a) 95 × 130 mm. $10 As 50 c.; (b) 130 × 95 mm. $5 As $1, $10 As $2 (Gold) *Set of 2 sheets*	17·50	

See also Nos. 657/63.

1981 (13 Nov). *"ESPAMER" International Stamp Exhibition, Buenos Aires. Nos.* 609 *and* **MS**613b *surch with T* **120**.

654	$1 on $1.50, Educational scholarship programme . .	1·00	1·00
MS655	95 × 130 mm. $1 on $5 75th anniversary emblem, $1 on $10 "Project Hippocrates" . .	3·50	3·75

(**121**)

1981 (14 Nov). *"Philatelia 81" International Stamp Exhibition, Frankfurt. No.* **MS**549 *surch with T* **121** *in red.*

MS656	Two sheets, each 125 × 90 mm: (a) $1 on 85 c. *Tripterotyphis triangularis*, $1 on $5 *Fasciolaria tulipa*; (b) $1 on $2 *Strombus gallus*. $1 on $10 *Arene cruentata* . . *Set of 2 sheets*	18·00	

122 Black Orchid **123** Uruguayan Footballer

(Des C. Mullin)

1981 (18 Dec)–**82**. *Independence Commemoration* (*2nd issue*) *T* **122** *and similar multicoloured designs. P* 14.

657	10 c. Belize Coat of Arms (*horiz*) (10.2.82) . .	15	10
658	35 c. Map of Belize (10.2.82) . .	35	30
659	50 c. Type **122** . .	60	35
660	85 c. Baird's Tapir (*horiz*) . .	80	60
661	$1 Mahogany Tree . .	85	65
662	$2 Keel-billed Toucan (*horiz*) . .	1·75	1·40
657/62	. . *Set of* 6	4·00	3·00
MS663	130 × 98 mm. $5 As 10 c. P 14½ (10.2.82)	4·00	3·50

(Des C. Mullin)

1981 (28 Dec). *World Cup Football Championship, Spain* (*1st issue*). *T* **123** *and similar vert designs. Multicoloured. P* 14.

664	10 c. Type **123** . .	10	10
665	25 c. Italian footballer . .	20	10
666	50 c. German footballer . .	30	10
667	$1 Brazilian footballer . .	60	15
668	$1.50, Argentinian footballer . .	95	25
669	$2 English footballer . .	1·25	35
664/9	. . *Set of* 6	3·00	80
MS670	Two sheets: (a) 145 × 115 mm. $2 "SPAIN '82" logo; (b) 155 × 115 mm. $3 Footballer (46 × 76 *mm*) . . *Set of 2 sheets*	3·00	3·25

124 British 19th-century Warship

(Des C. Mullin)

1982 (15 Mar). *Sailing Ships. T* **124** *and similar horiz designs. Multicoloured. P* 14.

671	10 c. Type **124** . .	25	10
672	25 c. *Madagascar* (1837) . .	50	15
673	35 c. Brig *Whitby* (1838) . .	65	15
674	50 c. *China* (1838) . .	80	20
675	85 c. *Swiftsure* (1850) . .	1·25	30
676	$2 *Windsor Castle* (1857) . .	2·00	50
671/6	. . *Set of* 6	5·00	1·10
MS677	110 × 87 mm. $5 Ships in battle . .	4·50	3·50

(**125**) **126** Princess Diana

1982 (28 Apr). *"ESSEN '82" International Stamp Exhibition, West Germany. Nos.* 662 *and* 669 *surch with T* **125**.

678	$1 on $2 Keel-billed Toucan . .	1·25	75
679	$1 on $2 English footballer . .	1·25	75

(Des C. Mullin)

1982 (20 May). *21st Birthday of Princess of Wales. T* **126** *and similar vert designs showing portrait of Princess of Wales with different backgrounds.* (*a*) *Size* 22 × 38 *mm* (*from sheets of* 25). *P* 13½ × 14.

680	50 c. multicoloured . .	35	35
	a. *Tête-bêche* (pair) . .	70	
681	$1 multicoloured . .	70	65
	a. *Tête-bêche* (pair) . .	1·40	
682	$1.50, multicoloured . .	1·10	1·00
	a. *Tête-bêche* (pair) . .	2·25	

(*b*) *Size* 25 × 43 *mm* (*from sheets of* 6 *stamps and* 3 *labels*). *P* 13

683	50 c. multicoloured . .	35	10
684	$1 multicoloured . .	70	20
685	$1.50, multicoloured . .	1·10	30
680/5	. . *Set of* 6	3·50	2·25
MS686	145 × 85 mm. $3 × 3 As Nos. 680/2, but 30 × 47 mm. P 14 . .	6·25	6·00

Stamps as Nos. 680/2, size 30 × 47 mm. and perforated 14, exist from a limited printing. These have gold backgrounds to the central ovals and gold frames. In addition the Queen's head and the centre oval are embossed (*Price per set of* 3 £25 *mint*).

127 Lighting Camp-fire

(Des C. Mullin)

1982 (31 Aug). *125th Birth Anniv of Lord Baden-Powell. T* **127** *and similar horiz designs. Multicoloured. P* 14.

687	10 c. Type **127** . .	15	10
688	25 c. Bird watching . .	30	25
689	35 c. Three scouts, one playing guitar . .	40	30
690	50 c. Hiking . .	50	35
691	85 c. Scouts with flag . .	80	60
692	$2 Saluting . .	1·75	1·40
687/92	. . *Set of* 6	3·50	2·50
MS693	Two sheets: each 85 × 115 mm: (a) $2 Scout with flag; (b) $3 Portrait of Lord Baden-Powell . . *Set of 2 sheets*	4·75	

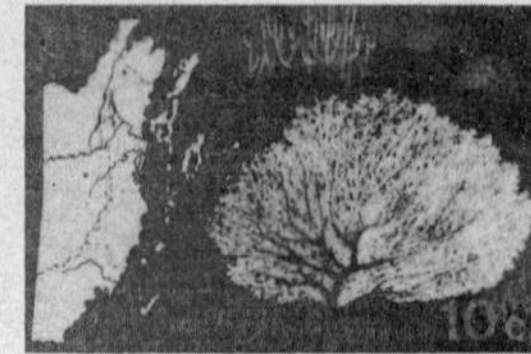

128 *Gorgonia ventalina*

(Des C. Mullin)

1982 (20 Sept). *First Anniv of Independence. Marine Life. T* **128** *and similar horiz designs. P* 14.
694 10 c. Type **128** 20 10
695 35 c. *Carpiuis corallinus* 40 10
696 50 c. *Plexaura flexuasa* 50 10
697 85 c. *Candylactis gigantea* 80 15
698 $1 *Stenopus hispidus* 90 20
699 $2 *Abudefduf saxatilis* . . . . 1·50 35
694/9 . . . . *Set of* 6 3·75 80
MS700 130 × 98 mm. $5 *Schyllarides aequinocialis*. P 14½ . . . . 3·50 3·50

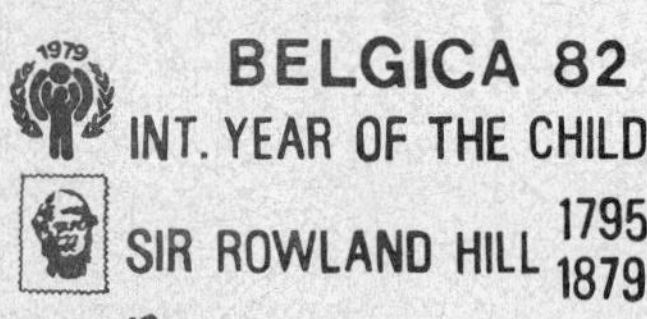

(129)

1982 (1 Oct). *"BELGICA 82" International Stamp Exhibition, Brussels. Nos* 687/92 *optd as T* **129** *in gold.*
701 10 c. Type **127** 50 30
702 25 c. Bird watching . . . . 1·40 75
703 35 c. Three scouts, one playing guitar . . 1·75 1·00
704 50 c. Hiking . . . . 2·25 1·50
705 85 c. Scouts with flag . . . . 3·75 2·50
706 $2 Saluting . . . . 9·00 6·50
701/6 . . . . *Set of* 6 17·00 11·50

BIRTH OF H.R.H.

PRINCE
WILLIAM ARTHUR
PHILIP LOUIS
21ST JUNE 1982

(130)

131 Scotland v New Zealand

1982 (21 Oct). *Birth of Prince William of Wales (1st issue). Nos.* 680/6 *optd as T* **130** *in silver. (a) Size* 22 × 38 *mm.*
707 50 c. multicoloured 35 35
a. *Tête-bêche* (pair) 70
b. Opt double . . . . 75·00
708 $1 multicoloured 70 65
a. *Tête-bêche* (pair) . . . . 1·40
709 $1.50, multicoloured . . . . 1·10 1·00
a. *Tête-beche* (pair) . . . . 2·25

(*b*) *Size* 25 × 43 *mm*

710 50 c. multicoloured 35 35
a. Opt double . . . .
711 $1 multicoloured 70 65
712 $1.50, multicoloured . . . . 1·10 1·00
707/12 . . . . *Set of* 6 3·50 3·50
MS713 145 × 85 mm. $3 × 3 As Nos. 707/9, but 30 × 47 mm. . . . . 6·25 6·00

A similar overprint exists on the stamps from the limited printing described beneath No. **MS**686 (*Price per set of* 3 £25 *mint*).

1982 (25 Oct). *Birth of Prince William of Wales (2nd issue). Nos* 614/20 *optd as T* **130** *in gold (a) Size* 22 × 38 *mm.*
714 50 c. Type **116** . . . . 2·50 1·00
a. Horiz pair. Nos. 714/15 . . . . 7·50
715 $1 Prince Charles in military uniform . . 5·00 2·00
a. Horiz pair. Nos. 715/16 . . . . 12·50
716 $1.50, Royal couple . . . . 7·50 3·00

(*b*) *Size* 25 × 42 *mm*

717 50 c. Type **116** 35 35
718 $1 As No. 715 . . . . 70 70
719 $1.50, As No. 716 . . . . 1·10 1·10
714/9 . . . . *Set of* 6 15·50 7·25
MS720 145 × 85 mm. $3 × 3 As Nos. 714/16 but 30 × 47 mm . . . . 6·25 6·50

No. **MS**720 occurs with two different sizes of overprint. On the normal version the top line of the overprint, "BIRTH OF H.R.H." measures 19½ mm in length. On examples with the larger overprint this measures 22 mm. (*Price for miniature sheet with larger overprint £35 mint.*)

(Des Baumann)

1982 (10 Dec). *World Cup Football Championship, Spain (2nd issue). T* **131** *and similar horiz designs. Multicoloured. P* 14.
721 20 c. + 10 c. Type **131** 20 15
722 30 c. + 15 c. Scotland v New Zealand (*different*) 30 15
723 40 c. + 20 c. Kuwait v France 40 15
724 60 c. + 30 c. Italy v Brazil 60 20
725 $1 + 50 c. France v Northern Ireland . . 1·10 35
726 $1.50 + 75 c. Austria v Chile . . . . 1·50 45
721/6 . . . . *Set of* 6 3·50 1·25
MS727 Two sheets: (a) 91 × 137 mm. $1 + 50 c. Germany v Italy (50 × 70 *mm*); (b) 122 × 116 mm. $2 + $1 England v France (50 × 70 *mm*) *Set of* 2 *sheets* 3·00 3·25

10c

(132)

133 Belize Cathedral

1983 (28 Jan). *No.* 538 *surch with T* **132**.
728 10 c. on 15 c. *Murex cabritii* . . . .

No. 728 differs from the previous provisional, No. 621, in the size of the obliterating panel over the original face value. On No. 621 this measures 4½ × 4½ mm, but No. 728 shows it larger, 7 × 5½ mm.

1983 (7 March). *Visit of Pope John Paul II. P* 13½.
729 **133** 50 c. multicoloured 70 35
MS730 135 × 110 mm. $2.50, Pope John Paul II (30 × 47 *mm*). P 14 . . . . 3·00 2·75

134 Map of Belize

10c

(135)

1983 (14 Mar). *Commonwealth Day. T* **134** *and similar multicoloured designs. P* 13.
731 35 c. Type **134** 25 30
732 50 c. "Maya Stella" from Lamanai Indian church (*horiz*) 35 35
733 85 c. Supreme Court Building (*horiz*) . . 60 60
734 $2 University Centre, Belize (*horiz*) . . 1·40 1·40
731/4 . . . . *Set of* 4 2·40 2·40

1983 (15 Apr). *No.* 658 *surch with T* **135**.
735 10 c. on 35 c. Map of Belize . . . .

136 Lana's "Flying boat" 1670

(Des C. Mullin)

1983 (16 May). *Bicentenary of Manned Flight. T* **136** *and similar horiz designs. Multicoloured. P* 14.
736 10 c. Type **136** 10 10
737 25 c. Barthelemy Lourenco's flying machine, 1709 . . . . 20 25
738 50 c. Guyton de Morveau's airship . . 30 35
739 85 c. Early dirigible 55 60
740 $1 The *Clement Bayard* 60 65
741 $1.50, *R-34* airship . . . . 95 1·00
736/41 . . . . *Set of* 6 2·25 2·50
MS742 Two sheets: (a) 125 × 84 mm. $3 Night scene from the *Nassau* balloon; (b) 115 × 128 mm. $3 Montgolfier balloon (*vert*) . . *Set of* 2 *sheets* 3·50 3·75

$1.25

$1.25

(137) (138)

1983 (9 June). *Nos.* 662 *and* 699 *surch with T* **137/8**.
743 $1.25 on $2 Keel-billed Toucan (surch T 137) 2·50 2·50
a. Surch double . . . . † —
744 $1.25 on $2 *Abudefduf saxatilis* (surch T 138) 3·50 3·00

10C 10C

(139) (140)

1983 (28 Sept). *No.* 541 *surch with T* **139/40**.
745 10 c. on 35 c. *Conus granulatus* (surch T **139**)
a. Surch inverted . . . .
b. Vert pair, lower stamp without "10 c"
c. Surch double . . . .
746 10 c. on 35 c. *Conus granulatus* (surch T **140**) 20·00
a. Surch triple . . . .

141 Altun Ha

(Des G. Vasarhelyi. Litho Format)

1983 (14 Nov). *Maya Monuments. T* **141** *and similar horiz designs. Multicoloured. P* 13½ × 14.
747 10 c. Type **141** 10 10
748 15 c. Xunantunich 10 10
749 75 c. Cerros 55 60
750 $2 Lamanai . . . . 1·40 1·50
747/50 . . . . *Set of* 4 1·90 2·10
MS751 102 × 72 mm. $3 Xunantunich (*different*) 2·10 2·25

142 Belmopan Earth Station

(Des G. Vasarhelyi. Litho Format)

1983 (28 Nov). *World Communications Year. T* **142** *and similar horiz designs. Multicoloured. P* 14.
752 10 c. Type **142** 10 10
753 15 c. *Telstar* 2 . . . . 10 10
754 75 c. U.P.U. logo 55 60
755 $2 M.V. *Heron H* mail service . . 1·40 1·50
752/5 . . . . *Set of* 4 1·90 2·10

143 Jaguar Cub

(Des G. Vasarhelyi. Litho Format)

1983 (9 Dec). *The Jaguar. T* **143** *and similar horiz designs. Multicoloured. P* 14.
756 5 c. Type **143** 10 10
757 10 c. Adult Jaguar 15 10
758 85 c. Jaguar in river 95 65
759 $1 Jaguar on rock . . . . 1·10 75
756/9 . . . . *Set of* 4 2·10 1·40
MS760 102 × 72 mm. $3 Jaguar in tree (44 × 28 *mm*). P 13½ × 14 . . . . 2·25 2·25

144 Pope John Paul II

(Des G. Vasarhelyi. Litho Format)

1983 (22 Dec). *Christmas. T* **144** *and similar designs showing Pope John Paul II at Papal Mass on 11 March 1983 in Belize. P* 13½ × 14.
761 10 c. multicoloured 20 10
762 15 c. multicoloured 25 10
763 75 c. multicoloured 90 60
764 $2 multicoloured . . . . 2·00 1·50
761/4 . . . . *Set of* 4 3·00 2·10
MS765 102 × 72 mm. $3 multicoloured . . 3·25 2·75

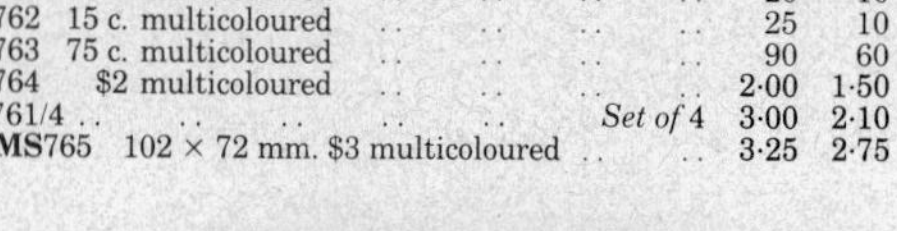

145 Foureye Butterflyfish

(Des G. Drummond. Litho Format)

1984 (27 Feb)–**88**. *Marine Life from the Belize Coral Reef. T* **145** *and similar horiz designs. Multicoloured.* A. *P* 15. B. *P* 13½ (7.88).

		A		B	
766	1 c. Type **145**	10	10	†	
767	2 c. Cushion Star	10	10	†	
768	3 c. Flower Coral	10	10	†	
769	4 c. Fairy Basslet	10	10	†	
770	5 c. Spanish Hogfish	10	10	†	
771	6 c. Star-eyed Hermit Crab	10	10	†	
772	10 c. Sea Fans and Fire Sponge	10	10	10	10
773	15 c. Blueheads	10	10	10	10
774	25 c. Blue-striped Grunt	15	15	15	20
775	50 c. Coral Crab	35	30	25	30
776	60 c. Tube Sponge	40	35	30	35
777	75 c. Brain Coral	40	45	†	
778	$1 Yellow-tail Snapper	70	60	55	60
779	$2 Common Lettuce Slug	1·10	1·25	†	
780	$5 Yellow Damselfish	2·50	2·75	†	
781	$10 Rock Beauty	5·25	5·50	†	
766/81	*Set of* 16	10·00	11·00	†	

VISIT OF THE LORD
ARCHBISHOP OF CANTERBURY
8th-11th MARCH 1984

(146)

1984 (8 Mar). *Visit of the Archbishop of Canterbury. Nos.* 772 *and* 775 *optd with T* **146**.

782	10 c. Sea Fans and Fire Sponge	10	10
783	50 c. Coral Crab	35	40

147 Shooting

(Des G. Vasarhelyi. Litho Format)

1984 (30 Apr). *Olympic Games, Los Angeles. (a) Sheet stamps. T* **147** *and similar horiz designs. Multicoloured. P* 13½ × 14.

784	25 c. Type **147**	20	25
785	75 c. Boxing	55	60
786	$1 Marathon	70	80
787	$2 Cycling	1·40	1·60
784/7	*Set of* 4	2·50	3·00
MS788	101 × 72 mm. $3 Statue of Discus-thrower	2·10	2·50

(b) Booklet stamps. Similar designs to T **147** *but Royal cypher replaced by Queen's head. P* 14½.

789	5 c. 1896 Marathon	10	10
	a. Booklet pane. No. 789 × 4	30	
790	20 c. Sprinting	15	20
	a. Booklet pane. No. 790 × 4	60	
791	25 c. Shot-putting	20	25
	a. Booklet pane. No. 791 × 4	80	
792	$2 Olympic torch	1·40	1·75
	a. Booklet pane. No. 792 × 4	5·50	
789/92	*Set of* 4	1·75	2·00

148 British Honduras 1866 1s. Stamp

149 Prince Albert

(Des G. Vasarhelyi. Litho Format)

1984 (26 Sept). *"Ausipex" International Stamp Exhibition, Melbourne. T* **148** *and similar horiz designs. Multicoloured. P* 14 × 13½ ($2) *or* 15 (*others*).

793	15 c. Type **148**	10	15
794	30 c. Bath mail coach, 1784	20	25
795	65 c. Sir Rowland Hill and Penny Black	45	55
796	75 c. British Honduras railway locomotive, 1910	55	65
797	$2 Royal Exhibition Buildings, Melbourne (46 × 28 *mm*)	1·40	1·75
793/7	*Set of* 5	2·40	3·00
MS798	103 × 73 mm. $3 Australia 1932 Sydney Harbour Bridge 5s. and British Honduras 1866 1s. stamps (44 × 28 *mm*). P 13½ × 14	2·10	2·50

(Des G. Vasarhelyi. Litho Format)

1984 (15 Oct). *500th Anniv of British Royal House of Tudor* (1985). *T* **149** *and similar vert designs showing members of the Royal Family. Multicoloured. P* 14.

799	50 c. Type **149**	35	40
	a. Sheetlet. Nos. 799/800 × 2	1·40	
800	50 c. Queen Victoria	35	40
801	75 c. King George VI	55	60
	a. Sheetlet. Nos. 801/2 × 2	2·25	
802	75 c. Queen Elizabeth the Queen Mother	55	60
803	$1 Princess of Wales	70	80
	a. Sheetlet. Nos. 803/4 × 2	2·75	
804	$1 Prince of Wales	70	80
799/804	*Set of* 6	3·00	3·25
MS805	147 × 97 mm. $1.50, Prince Philip; $1.50, Queen Elizabeth II	2·10	2·50

Nos. 799/804 were only issued in sheetlets of four stamps of one value, two of each design, with an illustrated vertical gutter margin

150 White-fronted Amazon

151 Effigy Censer, 1450 (Santa Rita Site)

(Des. G. Vasarhelyi. Litho Format)

1984 (1 Nov). *Parrots. T* **150** *and similar multicoloured designs. P* 11.

806	$1 Type **150**	1·25	1·00
	a. Block of 4. Nos. 806/9	4·50	
807	$1 White-capped Parrot (*horiz*)	1·25	1·00
808	$1 Mealy Amazon (*horiz*)	1·25	1·00
809	$1 Red-lored Amazon	1·25	1·00
806/9	*Set of* 4	4·50	3·50
MS810	102 × 73 mm. $3 Scarlet Macaw. P 13½ × 14	3·25	3·00

Nos. 806/9 were issued together, *se-tenant*, in blocks of 4 throughout the sheet, each block forming a composite design.

(Des G. Vasarhelyi. Litho Format)

1984 (30 Nov). *Maya Artefacts. T* **151** *and similar vert designs. Multicoloured. P* 15.

811	25 c. Type **151**	20	25
812	75 c. Vase, 675 (Actun Chapat)	55	60
813	$1 Tripod Vase, 500 (Santa Rita site)	70	80
814	$2 Sun god Kinich Ahau, 600 (Altun Ha site)	1·40	1·75
811/14	*Set of* 4	2·50	3·00

152 Governor-General inspecting Girl Guides

153 White-tailed Kite

(Des R. Granger Barrett. Litho Format)

1985 (15 Mar). *International Youth Year and 75th Anniv of Girl Guide Movement. T* **152** *and similar horiz designs. Multicoloured. P* 15.

815	25 c. Type **152**	40	40
816	50 c. Girl Guides camping	60	60
817	90 c. Checking map on hike	95	95
818	$1.25, Students in laboratory	1·25	1·25
819	$2 Lady Baden-Powell (founder)	1·75	1·75
815/19	*Set of* 5	4·50	4·50

(Des G. Vasarhelyi. Litho Format ($1, $5) Questa (others))

1985 (30 May)–**88**. *Birth Bicentenary of John J. Audubon (ornithologist). T* **153** *and similar multicoloured designs showing original paintings. P* 15 ($1) *or* 14 (*others*).

820	10 c. Type **153**	20	10
821	15 c. Ruby-crowned Kinglet (*horiz*)	30	15
822	25 c. Painted Bunting	40	30
822*a*	60 c. As 25 c. (1988)	60	50
823	75 c. Belted Kingfisher	80	70
824	$1 Common Cardinal	95	85
825	$3 Long-billed Curlew (*horiz*)	2·25	2·50
820/5	*Set of* 7	5·00	4·50
MS826	139 × 99 mm. $5 "John James Audubon" (John Syme). P 13½ × 14	4·00	4·00

154 The Queen Mother with Princess Elizabeth, 1928

INAUGURATION OF
NEW GOVERNMENT –
21st. DECEMBER 1984

(155)

(Des G. Vasarhelyi. Litho Format)

1985 (20 June). *Life and Times of Queen Elizabeth the Queen Mother. T* **154** *and similar multicoloured designs. P* 13½ × 14.

827	10 c. Type **154**	10	10
828	15 c. The Queen Mother, 1980	10	10
829	75 c. Waving to the crowd, 1982	55	60
830	$5 Four generations of Royal Family at Prince William's Christening	3·50	3·75
827/30	*Set of* 4	3·75	4·00
MS831	Two sheets, each 138 × 98 mm. (a) $2 The Queen Mother with Prince Henry (from photo by Lord Snowdon) (38 × 50 *mm*); (b) $5 The Queen Mother, 1984 (38 × 50 *mm*) *Set of* 2 *sheets*	5·00	5·50

1985 (24 June). *Inauguration of New Government. Nos.* 772/3 *and* 775 *optd with T* **155**.

832	10 c. Sea Fans and Fire Sponge	20	10
833	15 c. Blueheads	25	15
834	50 c. Coral Crab	75	40
832/4	*Set of* 3	1·10	55

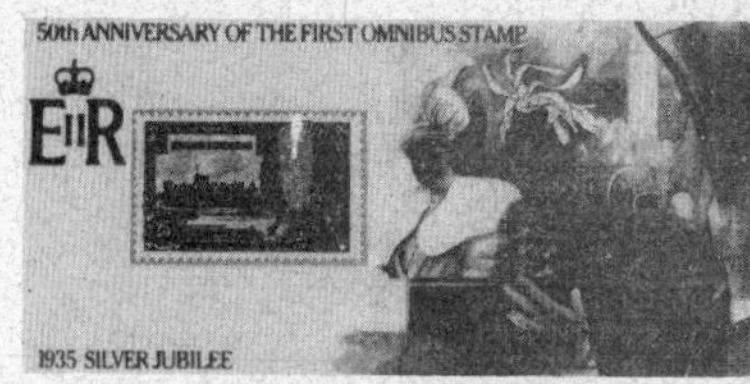

156 British Honduras 1935 Silver Jubilee 25 c. stamp and King George V with Queen Mary in Carriage

(Des Harrison. Litho Format)

1985 (25 July). *50th Anniv of First Commonwealth Omnibus Issue. T* **156** *and similar horiz designs showing British Honduras/Belize stamps. Multicoloured. P* 14.

835	50 c. Type **156**	35	40
	a. Sheetlet. Nos. 835/44	3·25	
836	50 c. 1937 Coronation 3 c., and King George VI and Queen Elizabeth in Coronation robes	35	40
837	50 c. 1946 Victory 3 c., and Victory celebrations	35	40
838	50 c. 1948 Royal Silver Wedding 4 c., and King George VI and Queen Elizabeth at Westminster Abbey service	35	40
839	50 c. 1953 Coronation 4 c., and Queen Elizabeth II in Coronation robes	35	40
840	50 c. 1966 Churchill 25 c., Sir Winston Churchill and fighter aircraft	35	40
841	50 c. 1972 Royal Silver Wedding 50 c., and 1948 Wedding photograph	35	40
842	50 c. 1973 Royal Wedding 50 c., and Princess Anne and Capt. Mark Phillips at their Wedding	35	40
843	50 c. 1977 Silver Jubilee $2, and Queen Elizabeth II during tour	35	40
844	50 c. 1978 25th anniv of Coronation 75 c. and Imperial Crown	35	40
835/44	*Set of* 10	3·25	3·50
MS845	138 × 98 mm. $5 Queen Elizabeth II in Coronation robes (38 × 50 *mm*). P 13½ × 14	3·50	3·75

Nos. 835/44 were printed together, *se-tenant*, in sheetlets of 10.

157 Mounted Postboy and Early Letter to Belize

COMMONWEALTH SUMMIT
CONFERENCE, BAHAMAS
16th-22nd OCTOBER 1985

(158)

(Des G. Drummond. Litho Format)

1985 (1 Aug). *350th Anniv of the British Post Office. T* **157** *and similar horiz designs. Multicoloured. P* 15.

846	10 c. Type **157**	20	10
847	15 c. Packet ship beating off privateer	30	15
848	25 c. P.O. packet *Duke of Marlborough*	40	25
849	75 c. P.O. packet *Diana*	80	60
850	$1 Falmouth P.O. packet ship	90	1·00
851	$3 S.S. *Conway*	2·50	3·00
846/51	*Set of* 6	4·50	4·50

1985 (5 Sept). *Commonwealth Heads of Government Meeting, Nassau, Bahamas. Nos.* 827/31 *optd with T* **158** *in silver*.

852	10 c. Type **154**	10	10
853	15 c. The Queen Mother, 1980	10	15
854	75 c. Waving to the crowd, 1980	55	60
855	$5 Four generations of Royal Family at Prince William's christening	3·50	3·75
852/5	*Set of* 4	3·75	4·00
MS856	Two sheets, each 138 × 98 mm. (a) $2 The Queen Mother with Prince Henry (from photo by Lord Snowdon) (38 × 50 *mm*); (b) $5 The Queen Mother, 1984 (38 × 50 *mm*) *Set of* 2 *sheets*	5·00	5·50

80TH ANNIVERSARY OF
ROTARY INTERNATIONAL

(159)

160 Royal Standard and Belize Flag

1985 (25 Sept). *80th Anniv of Rotary International. Nos.* 815/19 *optd with T* **159**.

857	25 c. Type **152**	25	25
858	50 c. Girl Guides camping	40	40
859	90 c. Checking map on hike	70	70
860	$1.25, Students in laboratory	95	95
861	$2 Lady Baden-Powell (founder)	1·50	1·50
857/61	*Set of* 5	3·50	3·50

(Des G. Vasarhelyi. Litho Format)

1985 (9 Oct). *Royal Visit. T* **160** *and similar multicoloured designs. P* 15×14½.
862 25 c. Type **160** 35 35
a. Horiz strip of 3. Nos. 862/4 3·50
863 75 c. Queen Elizabeth II 80 80
864 $4 Royal Yacht *Britannia* (81×39 *mm*) 2·75 3·00
862/4 *Set of* 3 3·50 3·50
MS865 138×98 mm. $5 Queen Elizabeth II (38×50 *mm*). P 13½×14 3·75 4·00
Nos. 862/4 were printed together, *se-tenant*, in horizontal strips of 3 within small sheets of 9 stamps.

161 Mountie in Canoe (Canada)

(Des Walt Disney Productions. Litho Format)

1985 (1 Nov). *Christmas. 30th Anniv of Disneyland, U.S.A. T* **161** *and similar vert designs showing dolls from "It's a Small World" exhibition. Multicoloured. P* 11.
866 1 c. Type **161** 10 10
867 2 c. Indian chief and squaw (U.S.A.) 10 10
868 3 c. Incas climbing Andes (South America) 10 10
869 4 c. Africans beating drums (Africa) 10 10
870 5 c. Snake-charmer and dancer (India and Far East) 10 10
871 6 c. Boy and girl with donkey (Belize) 10 10
872 50 c. Musician and dancer (Balkans) 50 50
873 $1.50, Boys with camel (Egypt and Saudi Arabia) 1·40 1·40
874 $3 Woman and girls playing with kite (Japan) 2·50 2·50
866/74 *Set of* 9 4·25 4·25
MS875 127×102 mm. $4 Beefeater and castle (Great Britain). P 13½×14 3·25 3·50

PRE"WORLD CUP FOOTBALL"
MEXICO 1986

(**162**)

163 Indian Costume

1985 (20 Dec). *World Cup Football Championship, Mexico* (1986) (*1st issue*). *Nos.* 835/45 *optd with T* **162**.
876 50 c. Type **156** 35 40
a. Sheetlet. Nos. 876/85 3·25
877 50 c. 1937 Coronation 3 c., and King George VI and Queen Elizabeth in Coronation robes 35 40
878 50 c. 1946 Victory 3 c., and Victory celebrations 35 40
879 50 c. 1948 Royal Silver Wedding 4 c., and King George VI and Queen Elizabeth at Westminster Abbey service 35 40
880 50 c. 1953 Coronation 4 c., and Queen Elizabeth II in Coronation robes 35 40
881 50 c. 1966 Churchill 25 c., Sir Winston Churchill and fighter aircraft 35 40
882 50 c. 1972 Royal Silver Wedding 50 c., and 1948 Wedding photograph 35 40
883 50 c. 1973 Royal Wedding 50 c., and Princess Anne and Capt. Mark Phillips at their Wedding 35 40
884 50 c. 1977 Silver Jubilee $2, and Queen Elizabeth II during tour 35 40
885 50 c. 1978 25th anniv of Coronation 75 c., and Imperial Crown 35 40
876/85 *Set of* 10 3·25 3·50
MS886 138×98 mm. $5 Queen Elizabeth II in Coronation robes 3·50 3·75
See also Nos. 936/40.

(Des Jane Clark. Litho Format)

1986 (15 Jan). *Costumes of Belize. T* **163** *and similar vert designs. Multicoloured. P* 15.
887 5 c. Type **163** 20 10
888 10 c. Maya 25 10
889 15 c. Garifuna 30 15
890 25 c. Creole 40 25
891 50 c. Chinese 65 45
892 75 c. Lebanese 80 70
893 $1 European *c* 1900 1·00 1·00
894 $2 Latin 1·75 1·75
887/94 *Set of* 8 4·75 4·00
MS895 139×98 mm. $5 Amerindian (38×50 *mm*). P 13½×14. 5·00 5·50

164 Pope Pius X

165 Princess Elizabeth aged Three

(Des G. Vasarhelyi. Litho Format)

1986 (15 Apr). *Easter. 20th-century Popes. T* **164** *and similar multicoloured designs. P* 11.
896 50 c. Type **164** 75 75
a. Sheetlet. Nos. 896/903 5·50
897 50 c. Benedict XV 75 75
898 50 c. Pius XI 75 75
899 50 c. Pius XII 75 75
900 50 c. John XXIII 75 75
901 50 c. Paul VI 75 75
902 50 c. John Paul I 75 75
903 50 c. John Paul II 75 75
896/903 *Set of* 8 5·50 5·50
MS904 147×92 mm. $4 Pope John Paul II preaching (*vert*). P 13½×14 4·75 5·00
Nos. 896/903 were printed together, *se-tenant*, in sheetlets of eight stamps and one stamp-size label.

(Des G. Vasarhelyi. Litho Format)

1986 (21 Apr). *60th Birthday of Queen Elizabeth II. T* **165** *and similar vert designs. Multicoloured. P* 14×13½.
905 25 c. Type **165** 15 20
a. Sheetlet. Nos. 905/8, each×2 6·25
906 50 c. Queen wearing Imperial State Crown 35 40
907 75 c. At Trooping the Colour 50 55
908 $3 Queen wearing diadem 2·10 2·25
905/8 *Set of* 4 2·75 3·00
MS909 147×93 mm. $4 Queen Elizabeth II (37×50 *mm*). P 13½×14 2·75 3·00
Nos. 905/8 were printed together, *se-tenant*, in sheetlets of eight stamps, two of each value, and one stamp-size label.

166 Halley's Comet and Japanese *Planet A* Spacecraft

(Des G. Vasarhelyi. Litho Format)

1986 (30 Apr). *Appearance of Halley's Comet. T* **166** *and similar multicoloured designs. P* 13½×14.
910 10 c. Type **166** 15 15
a. Sheetlet. Nos. 910/12, each×3 1·90
911 15 c. Halley's Comet, 1910 20 20
912 50 c. Comet and European *Giotto* spacecraft 35 40
913 75 c. Belize Weather Bureau 50 55
a. Sheetlet. Nos. 913/15, each×3 7·75
914 $1 Comet and U.S.A. space telescope 70 75
915 $2 Edmond Halley 1·40 1·50
910/15 *Set of* 6 3·00 3·25
MS916 147×93 mm. $4 Computer enhanced photograph of Comet (37×50 *mm*) 2·75 3·00
Nos. 910/12 and 913/15 were each printed together, *se-tenant*, in horizontal and vertical strips of 3, within the two sheetlets of nine.

167 George Washington

(Des G. Vasarhelyi. Litho Format)

1986 (5 May). *United States Presidents. T* **167** *and similar vert designs. Multicoloured. P* 11.
917 10 c. Type **167** 15 15
a. Sheetlet. Nos. 917/22 3·00
918 20 c. John Adams 20 20
919 30 c. Thomas Jefferson 20 25
920 50 c. James Madison 35 40
921 $1.50, James Monroe 1·00 1·10
922 $2 John Quincy Adams 1·40 1·50
917/22 *Set of* 6 3·00 3·25
MS923 147×93 mm. $4 George Washington (*different*). P 13½×14 2·75 3·00
Nos. 917/19 and 920/2 were printed together, *se-tenant*, in horizontal strips of 3, separated by three stamp-size labels, within the sheetlet of six stamps.

168 Auguste Bartholdi (sculptor) and Statue's Head

(Des G. Vasarhelyi. Litho Format)

1986 (15 May). *Centenary of Statue of Liberty. T* **168** *and similar multicoloured designs. P* 13½×14.
924 25 c. Type **168** 15 20
a. Sheetlet. Nos. 924/7, each×2 6·25
925 50 c. Statue's head at U.S. Centennial Celebration, Philadelphia, 1876 35 40
926 75 c. Unveiling Ceremony, 1886 50 55
927 $3 Statue of Liberty and flags of Belize and U.S.A. 2·10 2·25
924/7 *Set of* 4 2·75 3·00
MS928 147×92 mm. $4 Statue of Liberty and New York skyline (37×50 *mm*) 2·75 3·00
Nos. 924/7 were printed together, *se-tenant*, in sheetlets of eight stamps, two of each value, and one stamp-size label.

169 British Honduras 1866 1s. Stamp

(Des G. Vasarhelyi. Litho Format)

1986 (22 May). *"Ameripex" International Stamp Exhibition, Chicago. T* **169** *and similar multicoloured designs. P* 13½×14.
929 10 c. Type **169** 15 15
a. Sheetlet. Nos. 929/31, each×3 1·90
930 15 c. 1981 Royal Wedding $1.50 stamp 20 20
931 50 c. U.S.A. 1918 24 c. airmail inverted centre error 35 40
932 75 c. U.S.S. *Constitution* (frigate) 50 55
a. Sheetlet. Nos. 932/4, each×3 7·75
933 $1 Liberty Bell 70 75
934 $2 White House 1·40 1·50
929/34 *Set of* 6 3·00 3·25
MS935 147×93 mm. $4 Capitol, Washington (37×50 *mm*) 2·75 3·00
Nos. 929/31 and 932/4 were each printed together, *se-tenant*, in horizontal and vertical strips of 3, within the two sheetlets of nine.

170 English and Brazilian Players

(Des G. Vasarhelyi. Litho Format)

1986 (16 June). *World Cup Football Championship, Mexico* (*2nd issue*). *T* **170** *and similar multicoloured designs. P* 11.
936 25 c. Type **170** 20 20
a. Sheetlet. Nos. 936/9, each×2 6·25
937 50 c. Mexican player and Maya statues 40 40
938 75 c. Two Belizean players 55 55
939 $3 Aztec stone calendar 2·25 2·25
936/9 *Set of* 4 3·00 3·00
MS940 147×92 mm. $4 Flags of competing nations on two footballs (37×50 *mm*). P 13½×14 3·00 3·50
Nos. 936/9 were printed together, *se-tenant*, in sheetlets of eight stamps, two of each value, and one stamp-size label.

171 Miss Sarah Ferguson

ARGENTINA–
WINNERS 1986

(**172**)

(Des G. Vasarhelyi. Litho Format)

1986 (23 July). *Royal Wedding. T* **171** *and similar multicoloured designs. P* 14½.
941 25 c. Type **171** 15 20
a. Horiz strip of 3. Nos. 941/3 . . 2·50
942 75 c. Prince Andrew 50 55
943 $3 Prince Andrew and Miss Sarah Ferguson (92×41 *mm*) . . 2·10 2·25
941/3 . . *Set of* 3 2·50 2·75
MS944 155×106 mm. $1 Miss Sarah Ferguson (*different*), $3 Prince Andrew (*different*) . . 2·75 3·00
Nos. 941/3 were printed together, *se-tenant*, in horizontal strips of 3 within small sheets of nine stamps.

1986 (15 Aug). *World Cup Football Championship Winners, Mexico. Nos.* 936/40 *optd with T* **172**.
945 25 c. Type **170** 15 20
a. Sheetlet. Nos. 945/8, each×2 . . 6·25
946 50 c. Mexican player and Maya statues . . 35 40
947 75 c. Two Belizean players 50 55
948 $3 Aztec stone calendar . . . . 2·10 2·25
945/8 . . *Set of* 4 2·75 3·00
MS949 147×92 mm. $4 Flags of competing nations on two footballs (37×50 *mm*) . . 2·75 3·00

(173)

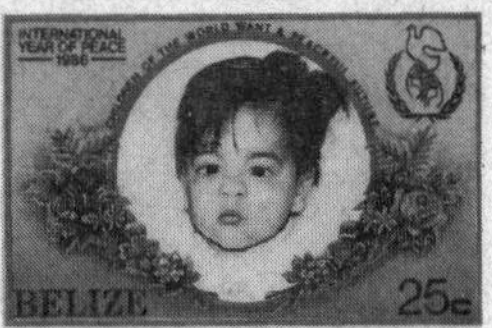

174 Amerindian Girl

1986 (28 Aug). *"Stockholmia '86" International Stamp Exhibition, Sweden. Nos.* 929/35 *optd with T* **173**.
950 10 c. Type **169** 15 15
a. Sheetlet. Nos. 950/2, each×3 . . 1·90
951 15 c. 1981 Royal Wedding $1.50 stamp . . 20 20
952 50 c. U.S.A. 1918 24 c. airmail inverted centre error . . 35 40
953 75 c. U.S.S. *Constitution* . . 50 55
a. Sheetlet. Nos. 953/5, each×3 . . 8·00
954 $1 Liberty Bell . . 70 75
955 $2 White House . . 1·40 1·50
950/5 . . *Set of* 6 3·00 3·25
MS956 147×93 mm. $4 Capitol, Washington (37×50 *mm*) . . 2·75 3·00

(Des G. Vasarhelyi. Litho Format)

1986 (3 Oct). *International Peace Year. T* **174** *and similar multicoloured designs. P* 13½×14.
957 25 c. Type **174** 15 20
a. Sheetlet. Nos. 957/60, each×2 . . 6·25
958 50 c. European boy and girl . . 35 40
959 75 c. Japanese girl . . 50 55
960 $3 Indian boy and European girl . . 2·10 2·25
957/60 . . *Set of* 4 2·75 3·00
MS961 132 × 106 mm. $4 As 25 c. but vert (35 × 47 *mm*) . . 2·75 3·00
Nos. 957/60 were printed together, *se-tenant*, in sheetlets of eight stamps, two of each value, and one stamp-size label.

175 *Amanita lilloi*

176 Jose Carioca

(Des G. Drummond. Litho Format)

1986 (30 Oct). *Fungi and Toucans. T* **175** *and similar vert designs. Multicoloured. P* 14×13½.
962 5 c. Type **175** 10 10
a. Sheetlet Nos. 962, 964, 966 and 969, each×2 . . 4·75
963 10 c. Keel-billed Toucan . . 15 15
a. Sheetlet. Nos. 963, 965 and 967/8, each ×2 . . 4·00
964 20 c. *Boletellus cubensis* . . 20 20
965 25 c. Collared Aracari . . 20 20
966 75 c. *Psilocybe caerulescens* . . 70 70
967 $1 Emerald Toucanet . . 80 80
968 $1.25, Crimson-rumped Toucanet . . 95 95
969 $2 *Russula puiggarii* . . 1·40 1·40
962/9 . . *Set of* 8 4·00 4·00
Nos. 962, 964, 966 and 969, and Nos. 963, 965 and 967/8, were each printed together, *se-tenant*, in sheetlets of eight stamps, two of each value, and one stamp-size label.

(Des Walt Disney Productions. Litho Format)

1986 (14 Nov). *Christmas. T* **176** *and similar vert designs showing Walt Disney cartoon characters in scenes from "Saludos Amigos". Multicoloured. P* 11.
970 2 c. Type **176** 10 10
971 3 c. Jose Carioca, Panchito and Donald Duck . . 10 10
972 4 c. Daisy Duck as Rio Carnival dancer . . 10 10
973 5 c. Mickey and Minnie Mouse as musician and dancer . . 10 10
974 6 c. Jose Carioca using umbrella as flute . . 10 10
975 50 c. Donald Duck and Panchito . . 55 55
976 65 c. Jose Carioca and Donald Duck playing hide and seek . . 70 70
977 $1.35, Donald Duck playing maracas . . 1·10 1·10
978 $2 Goofy as matador . . 1·60 1·60
970/8 . . *Set of* 9 3·50 3·50
MS979 131 × 111 mm. $4 Donald Duck. P 13½×14 . . 3·50 3·75

177 Princess Elizabeth in Wedding Dress, 1947

178 *America II*, 1983

(Des G. Vasarhelyi. Litho Format)

1987 (7 Oct). *Royal Ruby Wedding. T* **177** *and similar vert designs. Multicoloured. P* 15.
980 25 c. Type **177** 15 20
981 75 c. Queen and Duke of Edinburgh, 1972 . . 45 50
982 $1 Queen on her 60th birthday . . 60 65
983 $4 In Garter robes . . 2·40 2·50
980/3 . . *Set of* 4 3·25 3·50
MS984 171×112 mm. $6 Queen and Duke of Edinburgh (44×50 *mm*). P 13½×14 . . 3·50 3·75

(Des G. Vasarhelyi. Litho Format)

1987 (21 Oct). *America's Cup Yachting Championship. T* **178** *and similar multicoloured designs. P* 15.
985 25 c. Type **178** 15 20
986 75 c. *Stars and Stripes*, 1987 . . 45 50
987 $1 *Australia II*, 1983 . . 60 65
988 $4 *White Crusader* . . 2·40 2·50
985/8 . . *Set of* 4 3·25 3·50
MS989 171×112 mm. $6 Sails of *Australia II* (44×50 *mm*). P 13½×14 . . 3·50 3·75

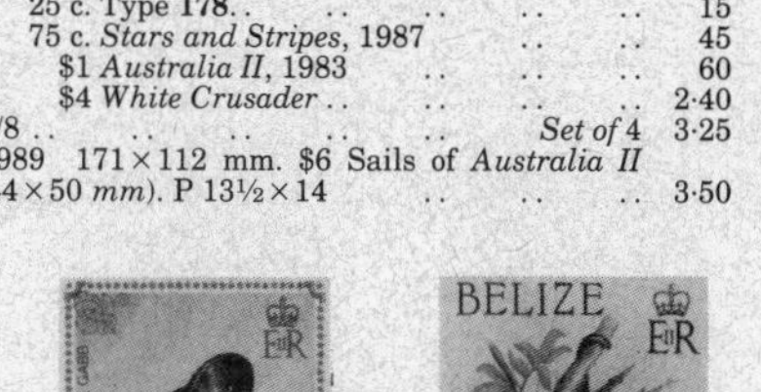

179 "Mother and Child"

180 Black-handed Spider Monkey

(Des G. Vasarhelyi. Litho Format)

1987 (4 Nov). *Wood Carvings by George Gabb. T* **179** *and similar vert designs. Multicoloured. P* 15.
990 25 c. Type **179** 15 20
991 75 c. "Standing Form" . . 45 50
992 $1 "Love-doves" . . 60 65
993 $4 "Depiction of Music" . . 2·40 2·50
990/3 . . *Set of* 4 3·25 3·50
MS994 173×114 mm. $6 "African Heritage" (44×50 *mm*). P 13½×14 . . 3·50 3·75

(Des G. Drummond. Litho Format)

1987 (11 Nov). *Primates. T* **180** *and similar vert designs. Multicoloured. P* 15.
995 25 c. Type **180** 15 20
996 75 c. Black Howler Monkey . . 45 50
997 $1 Spider Monkeys with baby . . 60 65
998 $4 Two Black Howler Monkeys . . 2·40 2·50
995/8 . . *Set of* 4 3·25 3·50
MS999 171×112 mm. $6 Young Spider Monkey (41×48 *mm*). P 13½×14 . . 3·50 3·75

181 Guides on Parade

(Des G. Vasarhelyi. Litho Format)

1987 (25 Nov). *50th Anniv of Girl Guide Movement in Belize. T* **181** *and similar multicoloured designs. P* 15.
1000 25 c. Type **181** 15 20
1001 75 c. Brownie camp . . 45 50
1002 $1 Guide camp . . 60 65
1003 $4 Olave, Lady Baden-Powell . . 2·40 2·50
1000/3 . . *Set of* 4 3·25 3·50
MS1004 173×114 mm. $6 As $4, but vert (44×50 *mm*). P 13½×14 . . 3·50 3·75

182 Indian Refugee Camp

183 *Laelia euspatha*

(Des G. Vasarhelyi. Litho Format)

1987 (3 Dec). *International Year of Shelter for the Homeless. T* **182** *and similar horiz designs. Multicoloured. P* 15.
1005 25 c. Type **182** 15 20
1006 75 c. Filipino family and slum . . 45 50
1007 $1 Family in Middle East shanty town . . 60 65
1008 $4 Building modern house in Belize . . 2·40 2·50
1005/8 . . *Set of* 4 3·25 3·50

(Des G. Drummond. Litho Format)

1987 (16 Dec). *Christmas. Orchids. T* **183** *and similar vert designs showing illustrations from Sanders'* Reichenbachia. *Multicoloured. P* 13½×14.
1009 1 c. Type **183** 10 10
a. Sheetlet. Nos. 1009/15, each × 2 . . 1·10
1010 2 c. *Cattleya citrina* . . 10 10
1011 3 c. *Masdevallia backhousiana* . . 10 10
1012 4 c. *Cypripedium tautzianum* . . 10 10
1013 5 c. *Trichopilia suavis alba* . . 10 10
1014 6 c. *Odontoglossum hebraicum* . . 10 10
1015 7 c. *Cattleya trianaei schroederiana* . . 10 10
1016 10 c. *Saccolabium giganteum* . . 10 10
a. Sheetlet. Nos. 1016/22, each × 2 . . 9·00
1017 30 c. *Cattleya warscewiczii* . . 25 25
1018 50 c. *Chysis bractescens* . . 35 35
1019 70 c. *Cattleya rochellensis* . . 45 45
1020 $1 *Laelia elegans schilleriana* . . 65 65
1021 $1.50, *Laelia anceps percivaliana* . . 95 95
1022 $3 *Laelia gouldiana* . . 1·90 1·90
1009/22 . . *Set of* 14 4·75 4·75
MS1023 171×112 mm. $5 *Cattleya dowiana aurea* (40×47 *mm*) . . 3·00 3·25
Nos. 1009/1015 and 1016/22 were each printed together, *se-tenant*, in sheetlets of fourteen stamps, containing two of each value and one stamp-size label.

184 Christ condemned to Death

185 Basketball

(Des G. Vasarhelyi. Litho Format)

1988 (21 Mar). *Easter. The Stations of the Cross. T* **184** *and similar vert designs. Multicoloured. P* 13½×14.
1024 40 c. Type **184** 25 30
a. Sheetlet. Nos. 1024/37 . . 3·25
1025 40 c. Christ carrying the Cross . . 25 30
1026 40 c. Falling for the first time . . 25 30
1027 40 c. Christ meets Mary . . 25 30
1028 40 c. Simon of Cyrene helping to carry the Cross . . 25 30
1029 40 c. Veronica wiping the face of Christ . . 25 30
1030 40 c. Christ falling a second time . . 25 30
1031 40 c. Consoling the women of Jerusalem . . 25 30
1032 40 c. Falling for the third time . . 25 30
1033 40 c. Christ being stripped . . 25 30
1034 40 c. Christ nailed to the Cross . . 25 30
1035 40 c. Dying on the Cross . . 25 30
1036 40 c. Christ taken down from the Cross . . 25 30
1037 40 c. Christ being laid in the sepulchre . . 25 30
1024/37 . . *Set of* 14 3·25 3·75
Nos. 1024/37 were printed together, *se-tenant*, in a sheetlet of 14 stamps and one stamp-size label which appears in the central position.

(Des J. McDaniel. Litho Questa)

1988 (15 Aug). *Olympic Games, Seoul. T* **185** *and similar vert designs. Multicoloured. P* 14.
1038 10 c. Type **185** 10 10
1039 25 c. Volleyball . . 15 20
1040 60 c. Table tennis . . 35 40
1041 75 c. Diving . . 45 50
1042 $1 Judo . . 60 65
1043 $2 Hockey . . 1·25 1·40
1038/43 . . *Set of* 6 2·50 3·00
MS1044 76×106 mm. $3 Gymnastics . . 1·75 1·90

186 Public Health Nurse, c. 1912

187 Collared Anteater ("Ants Bear")

(Des O. Fernandez. Litho Questa)

1988 (18 Nov). *125th Anniv of International Red Cross. T* **186** *and similar horiz designs. Multicoloured. P* 14.

1045	60 c. Type **186**	35	40
1046	75 c. Hospital ship and ambulance launch, 1937	45	50
1047	$1 Ambulance at hospital tent, 1956	60	65
1048	$2 Ambulance plane, 1940	1·25	1·40
1045/8	*Set of* 4	2·40	2·75

(Des J. Barberis. Litho Questa)

1989 (24 Feb–30 June). *Small Animals of Belize. T* **187** *and similar multicoloured designs.* W w **16** (10 c.), *no wmk (others). P* 14.

1049	10 c. Paca ("Gibnut") (30.6)	10	10
1050	25 c. Four-eyed Opossum (*vert*)	15	20
1051	50 c. Type **187**	30	35
1052	60 c. As 10 c.	35	40
1053	75 c. Red Brocket	45	50
1054	$2 Collared Peccary	1·25	1·40
1049/54	*Set of* 6	2·40	2·75

(Des A. Theobald ($5), D. Miller (others). Litho Questa)

1989 (20 July). *20th Anniv of First Manned Landing on Moon. Multicoloured designs as T* **126** *of Ascension.* W w **16** (*sideways on* 50, 75 *c.*). *P* 14×13½ (25 *c.*, $1) *or* 14 (*others*).

1055	25 c. Docking of "Apollo 9" modules	15	20
1056	50 c. "Apollo 9" command service module in space (30×30 *mm*)	30	35
1057	75 c. "Apollo 9" emblem (30×30 *mm*)	45	50
1058	$1 "Apollo 9" lunar module in space	60	65
1055/8	*Set of* 4	1·40	1·50
MS1059	83×100 mm. $5 "Apollo 11" command service module undergoing tests. P 14×13½.	3·00	3·25

WORLD STAMP EXPO '89
United States Postal Service
Nov. 17 — 20 and
Nov. 24 — Dec. 3 1989
Washington Convention Center
Washington, DC

(188)

189 Wesley Church

1989 (17 Nov). *"World Stamp Expo '89" International Stamp Exhibition, Washington. No.* **MS**1059 *optd with T* **188**.

MS1060	83×100 mm. $5 "Apollo 11" command service module undergoing tests	3·00	3·25

(Des Jennifer Toombs. Litho B.D.T.)

1989 (13 Dec). *Christmas. Belize Churches. T* **189** *and similar vert designs. W* w **16**. *P* 13½.

1061	10 c. black, rose-pink and cinnamon	10	10
1062	25 c. black, reddish lilac and rose-lilac	15	20
1063	60 c. black, pale turquoise-blue and cobalt	35	40
1064	75 c. black, pale blue-green and sage-green	45	50
1065	$1 blk, pale greenish yell & chrome-yell	60	65
1061/5	*Set of* 5	1·50	1·60

Designs:—25 c. Baptist Church; 60 c. St. John's Anglican Cathedral; 75 c. St. Andrew's Presbyterian Church; $1 Holy Redeemer Roman Catholic Cathedral.

POSTAGE DUE STAMPS

D 2

(Des P. Powell. Litho Questa)

1976 (1 July). *Type* D **2** *and similar vert designs, but with different frames.* W w **14** (*sideways*). *P* 13½ x 14.

D 6	D 2	1 c. red and dull green	10	25
D 7	–	2 c. light magenta and bluish violet	10	25
D 8	–	5 c. dull green and orange-brown	10	35
D 9	–	15 c. apple-green and dull vermilion	15	60
D10	–	25 c. orange and olive-green	20	85
D6/10		*Set of* 5	50	2·10

CAYES OF BELIZE

A chain of several hundred islands, coral atolls, reefs and sand-banks stretching along the eastern seaboard of Belize.

Appendix

The following issues for the Cayes of Belize fall outside the criteria for full listing as detailed on page xi.

1984

Marine Life, Map and Views. 1, 2, 5, 10, 15, 25, 75 *c.*, $3, $5
250th Anniv of Lloyd's List (*newspaper*). 25, 75 *c.*, $1, $2.
Olympic Games, Los Angeles. 10, 15, 75 *c.*, $2
90th Anniv of "Caye Service" Local Stamps. 10, 15, 75 *c.*, $2

1985

Birth Bicentenary of John J. Audubon (*ornithologist*). 25, 75 c., $1, $3
Shipwrecks. $1 × 4

Bermuda

The first internal postal system for Bermuda was organised by the proprietor of the *Bermuda Gazette* in 1784. This service later competed with that of the Bermuda Post Office, set up in 1812.

The British G.P.O. retained control of the overseas posts, however, until this service passed to the Bermuda authorities in 1859.

For illustrations of the handstamp types see BRITISH POST OFFICES ABROAD notes, following GREAT BRITAIN.

CROWNED-CIRCLE HANDSTAMPS

CC1 CC1 ST. GEORGES BERMUDA (R.) (1.8.1845)
. . . . *Price on cover* £5500

CC2 IRELAND ISLE BERMUDA (R.) (1.8.1845)
. . . . *Price on cover* £3750

CC3 HAMILTON BERMUDA (R.) (13.11.1846)
. . . . *Price on cover* £3000

For Nos. CC1 and CC3 used as adhesive Postmasters' Stamps see Nos. O7 and O6.

PRICES FOR STAMPS ON COVER TO 1945

Nos. 1/11	*from* × 5
Nos. 12/17	*from* × 10
Nos. 19/29*a*	*from* × 8
Nos. 30/*a*	*from* × 10
Nos. 31/4	*from* × 4
Nos. 34*a*/55	*from* × 3
Nos. 56/8	*from* × 10
Nos. 59/76	*from* × 4
Nos. 76*a*/93	*from* × 3
Nos. 94/7	*from* × 4
Nos. 98/106	*from* × 3
Nos. 107/15	*from* × 4
Nos. 116/21	*from* × 5
No. 122	*from* × 20

COLONY

O 1

O 2

1848–61. *Postmasters' Stamps. Adhesives prepared and issued by the postmasters at Hamilton and St. Georges. Dated as given in brackets.*

(*a*) *By W. B. Perot at Hamilton*

O1	O 1	1d. black/*bluish grey* (1848) . .	. . —	£70000
O2		1d. black/*bluish grey* (1849) . .	. . —	£100000
O3		1d. red/*thick white* (1853) . .	. . —	£70000
O4		1d. red/*bluish wove* (1854) . .	. . —	£100000
O5		1d. red/*bluish wove* (1856) . .	. . —	£120000
O6	O 2	(1d.) carmine-red/*bluish laid* (1861)	. . —	£70000

(*b*) *By J. H. Thies at St. Georges*
As Type O **2** *but inscr* "ST. GEORGES"

O7	–	(1d.) carmine-red/*buff* (1860) . .	. . —	£60000

Stamps of Type O **1** bear manuscript value and signature, the dates being those shown on the eleven known examples. The stamps are distributed between the dates as follows: 1848 three examples, 1849 two examples, 1853 three examples, 1854 two examples, 1856 one example.

It is believed that the franking value of Nos. O6/7 was 1d., although this is not shown on the actual stamps. Four examples are known of this type used from Hamilton from March 1861 (and one unused), and five used from St. Georges between July 1860 and January 1863.

Prices shown reflect our estimation of value based on known copies. For instance of the two copies known of No. O4, one is in the Royal collection and the other is on entire.

1

2

3

4

5

(Typo D.L.R.)

1865–1903. *Wmk Crown CC.* (*a*) *P* 14.

1	1	1d. rose-red (25.9.65) . .	60·00	1·25
2		1d. pale rose . .	75·00	5·00
3	2	2d. dull blue (14.3.66) . .	95·00	15·00
4		2d. bright blue . .	£110	9·00
5	3	3d. yellow-buff (10.3.73)	£425	60·00
5*a*		3d. orange . .	£525	55·00
6	4	6d. dull purple (25.9.65)	£750	75·00
7		6d. dull mauve . .	22·00	12·00
8	5	1s. green (25.9.65) . .	£140	30·00

(*b*) *Imperf*

9	1	1d. rose-red . .	£11000	£8000

(*c*) *P* 14 × 12½

10	3	3d. yellow-buff (1882) . .	£140	45·00
10*a*	4	6d. bright mauve (1903)	13·00	22·00
11	5	1s. green (1894) . .	11·00	£100
		a. Vert strip of 3, two stamps imperf horiz . .	£9000	

Though manufactured early in 1880, stamps *P* 14 × 12½ were not issued until the dates given above.

THREE PENCE THREE PENCE
(6) (6*a*)

THREE PENCE One Penny.
(7) (8)

1874 (12 Mar–19 May). *Nos.* 1 *and* 8 *surch diagonally.*

(*a*) *With T* **6** ("P" *and* "R" *different type*)

12	1	3d. on 1d. rose-red . .	£7000	£8000
13	5	3d. on 1s. green . .	£1500	£850

(*b*) *With T* **6***a* ("P" *same type as* "R")

13*b*	5	3d. on 1s. green . .	£2000	£800

(*c*) *With T* **7** (19 May)

14	5	3d. on 1s. green . .	£1100	£650

The 3d. on 1d. was a trial surcharge which was not regularly issued, though a few specimens were postally used before 1879. Nos. 13, 13*b* and 14, being handstamped, are found with double or partial double surcharges.

(Surch by Queen's Printer, Donald McPhee Lee)

1875 (March–May). *Surch with T* **8**.

15	2	1d. on 2d. (No. 4) (23 Apr)	£700	£300
		a. No stop after "Penny" . .	£7500	£5000
16	3	1d. on 3d. (No. 5) (8 May)	£450	£350
17	5	1d. on 1s. (No. 8) (11 Mar)	£500	£250
		a. Surch inverted . .	—	£8500
		b. No stop after "Penny" . .	—	£6500

It is emphasised that the prices quoted for Nos. 12/17 are for fine examples. The many stamps from these provisional issues which are in inferior condition are worth much less.

9

10

11

(Typo D.L.R.)

1880 (23 Mar). *Wmk Crown CC. P* 14.

19	**9**	½d. stone	1·25	3·50
20	**10**	4d. orange-red	9·00	1·50

(Typo D.L.R.)

1883–98. *Wmk Crown CA. P* 14.

21	**9**	½d. dull green (Oct, 1892)	1·90	1·90
21*a*		½d. deep grey-green (1893)	1·90	70
22	**1**	1d. dull rose (Dec. 1883)	90·00	3·00
23		1d. rose-red	55·00	2·25
24		1d. carmine-rose (1886)	25·00	70
24*a*		1d. aniline carmine (1889)	3·00	20
25	**2**	2d. blue (Dec. 1886)	26·00	3·00
26		2d. aniline purple (July, 1893)	8·50	3·75
26*a*		2d. brown-purple (1898)	2·50	1·25
27	**11**	2½d. deep ultramarine (10.11.84)	8·00	1·00
27*a*		2½d. pale ultramarine	4·00	40
28	**3**	3d. grey (Jan, 1886)	18·00	5·50
29	**5**	1s. yellow-brown (1893)	15·00	13·00
29*a*		1s. olive-brown	13·00	11·00
21/9*a*		*Set of* 7	60·00	20·00
21, 26 & 29 Optd "Specimen"		*Set of* 3	£375	

1893 PROVISIONAL POSTCARD. During a shortage of 1d. stamps a limited supply of September 1880 postcard, franked with Nos. 19 and 22, was surcharged "One Penny" across the two stamps. This surcharge was applied by the *Royal Gazette* press. It is generally believed that an individual in the Post Office acquired all the examples, but provisional postcards are known used to Europe and, one example only, locally. *Price from* £550 *unused,* £1400 *used.*

(12)

13 Dry Dock

1901. *As Nos.* 29/*a but colour changed, surch with T* **12** *by D.L.R.*

30	**5**	¼d. on 1s. dull grey (11.1.01) (Optd S. £75)	20	25
30*a*		¼d. on 1s. bluish grey (18.3.01)	20	30
		ab. "F" in "FARTHING" inserted by handstamp	£3500	

Three examples of No. 30ab are known, one being in the Royal Collection. It would appear that the "F" in position one of an unspecified horizontal row was either weak or missing and an additional impression of the letter was then inserted by a separate handstamp.

(Typo D.L.R.)

1902 (Nov)–**04.** *Wmk Crown CA. P* 14.

31	**13**	½d. black and green (12.03)	6·00	1·25
32		1d. brown and carmine	6·00	10
33		3d. magenta and sage-green (9.03)	1·75	1·75
34	**10**	4d. orange-brown (18.1.04)	22·00	32·00
31/4		*Set of* 4	32·00	32·00
31/3 Optd "Specimen"		*Set of* 3	£120	

1906–09. *Wmk Mult Crown CA. P* 14.

34*a*	**13**	¼d. brown and violet (9.08)	50	2·00
35		½d. black and green (12.06)	7·00	65
36		1d. brown and carmine (4.06)	9·50	20
37		2d. grey and orange (10.07)	7·50	10·00
38		2½d. brown and ultramarine (12.06)	8·50	12·00
39		4d. blue and chocolate (11.09)	3·00	11·00
34*a*/39		*Set of* 6	32·00	32·00
34*a*, 37/39 Optd "Specimen"		*Set of* 4	£190	

1908–10. *Wmk Mult Crown CA. P* 14.

41	**13**	½d. green (3.09)	3·25	2·50
42		1d. red (5.08)	12·00	10
43		2½d. blue (14.2.10)	12·00	5·75
41/3		*Set of* 3	25·00	7·50
41/3 Optd "Specimen"		*Set of* 3	£170	

14

15

HIGH VALUE KEY TYPES. The reign of King Edward VII saw the appearance of the first in a new series of "key type" designs, initially on the issues of Malaya — Straits Settlements and Nyasaland, to be used for high value denominations where a smaller design was felt to be inappropriate. The system was extended during the reign of King George V, using the portrait as Bermuda Type **15**, to cover Bermuda, Ceylon, Leeward Islands, Malaya — Straits Settlements, Malta and Nyasaland. A number of these territories continued to use the key type concept for high value King George VI stamps and one, Leeward Islands, for stamps of Queen Elizabeth II.

In each instance the King George V issues were printed in sheets of 60 (12×5) on various coloured papers. The system utilised a common "head" plate used with individual "duty" plates which printed the territory name and face value.

Two major plate flaws occur on the King George V head plate: the break in scroll on R.1/12 and the broken crown and scroll on R.2/12. Both of these occur in different states, having been repaired and then damaged once again, perhaps on several occasions. The prices quoted in the listings are for examples approximately as illustrated.

Break in scroll (R. 1/12)

Broken crown and scroll (R. 2/12)

(Recess (**14**), Typo (**15**) D.L.R.)

1910–25. *Wmk Mult Crown CA. P* 14.

44	**14**	¼d. brown (26.3.12)	1·50	2·25
		a. Pale brown	40	1·50
45		½d. green (4.6.10)	1·10	25
		a. Deep green	3·50	90
46		1d. red (I) (15.10.10)	6·50	25
		a. Rose-red	12·00	25
		b. Carmine (12.19)	28·00	4·50

47 14 2d. grey (1.13) .. .. 2·75 4·75
48 2½d. blue (27.3.12) .. .. .. 3·25 60
49 3d. purple/*yellow* (1.13) .. .. .. 1·75 5·00
49*a* 4d. red/*yellow* (1.9.19) .. .. .. 4·25 6·00
50 6d. purple (26.3.12) .. .. .. 11·00 16·00
a. Pale claret (2.6.24) .. .. .. 10·00 8·00
51 1s. black/*green* (26.3.12) .. .. .. 2·00 3·75
a. Jet-black/olive (1925) .. .. .. 3·50 9·00
51*b* 15 2s. purple and blue/*blue*, **C** (19.6.20) .. 10·00 28·00
ba. Break in scroll .. .. .. 90·00
bb. Broken crown and scroll .. .. 90·00
52 2s. 6d. black and red/*blue*, **C** (1.4.18) .. 17·00 45·00
a. Break in scroll £110
52*b* 4s. black and carmine, **C** (19.6.20) .. 60·00 70·00
ba. Break in scroll £190
bb. Broken crown and scroll £190
53 5s. deep green and deep red/*yellow*, **C** (1.4.18) .. .. 48·00 70·00
a. Break in scroll £160
b. Broken crown and scroll £160
c. Green and carmine-red/pale yellow, **C** (1920) .. .. 32·00 48·00
ca. Break in scroll £130
cb. Broken crown and scroll £130
54 10s. green and carmine/*pale bluish green*, **C** (1.4.18) £150 £200
a. Break in scroll £350
b. Broken crown and scroll £350
c. Green and red/pale bluish green, **C** (1922) £120 £160
ca. Break in scroll £300
cb. Broken crown and scroll £300
55 £1 purple and black/*red*, **C** (1.4.18) .. £400 £600
a. Break in scroll £750
b. Broken crown and scroll £850
44/55 .. .. *Set of* 15 £600 £900
44/55 Optd "Specimen" .. .. *Set of* 15 £1000

Nos. 44 to 51*a* are comb-perforated 13.8 × 14 or 14. No. 45 exists also line-perforated 14, probably from the printing dispatched to Bermuda on 13 March 1911.

Beware of cleaned copies of the 10s. with faked postmarks.

See also Nos. 76*b*/93

WAR TAX (16) **WAR TAX** (17)

1918 (4 May). *Nos. 46 and 46a optd locally with T* **16**.
56 14 1d. red 25 40
a. Rose-red 25 65

1920 (5 Feb). *No. 46b optd with T* **17**.
58 14 1d. carmine 20 80

The War Tax stamps represented a compulsory levy in addition to normal postal fees until 31 Dec 1920. Subsequently they were valid for ordinary postage.

18

19

(Des by the Governor (Gen. Sir James Willcocks). Typo D.L.R.)

1920 (11 Nov)–**21**. *Tercentenary of Representative Institutions* (1*st issue*). *P* 14. (*a*) *Wmk Mult Crown CA* (*sideways*) (19.1.21).
59 18 ¼d. brown, **O** .. .. 50 4·50
a. "C" missing from wmk .. .. 85·00
b. "A" missing from wmk .. ..
60 ½d. green, **O** .. .. 1·10 7·00
61 2d. grey, **O** .. .. 6·50 18·00
a. "C" missing from wmk £160
62 3d. dull and deep purple/*pale yellow*, **C** 6·00 16·00
63 4d. black and red/*pale yellow*, **C** .. 6·50 15·00
64 1s. black/*blue-green*, **C** .. .. 12·00 30·00
(*b*) *Wmk Mult Script CA* (*sideways*)
65 18 1d. carmine, **O** .. .. 1·00 30
66 2½d. bright blue, **O** .. .. .. 5·00 8·00
67 6d. dull and bright purple, **C** (19.1.21) 12·00 30·00
59/67 .. .. *Set of* 9 45·00 £120
59/67 Optd "Specimen" .. .. *Set of* 9 £250

(Des. H. J. Dale. Recess D.L.R.)

1921 (12 May). *Tercentenary of Representative Institutions* (2*nd issue*). *P* 14. (*a*) *Wmk Crown CA* (*sideways*).
68 19 2d. slate-grey .. .. 4·50 14·00
69 2½d. bright ultramarine .. .. .. 5·50 3·00
a. "C" missing from wmk £160
b. "A" missing from wmk £160
70 3d. purple/*pale yellow* .. .. .. 4·00 12·00
71 4d. red/*pale yellow* .. .. .. 10·00 16·00
72 6d. purple .. .. 8·00 24·00
a. "C" missing from wmk £200
73 1s. black/green .. .. 16·00 27·00
(*b*) *Wmk Mult Script CA* (*sideways*)
74 19 ¼d. brown .. .. 35 2·75
75 ½d. green .. .. 2·75 6·00
76 1d. deep carmine .. .. .. 2·00 35
a. "C" missing from wmk .. ..
68/76 .. .. *Set of* 9 45·00 95·00
68/76 Optd "Specimen" .. .. *Set of* 9 £250

MINIMUM PRICE

The minimum price quote is 10p which represents a handling charge rather than a basis for valuing common stamps. For further notes about prices see introductory pages.

I II III

Three Types of the 1d.

I. Scroll at top left very weak and figure "1" has pointed serifs.

II. Scroll weak. "1" has square serifs and "1d" is heavy.

III. Redrawn. Scroll is completed by a strong line and "1" is thinner with long square serifs.

I II

Two Types of the 2½*d.*

I. Short, thick figures, especially of the "1", small "d".

II. Figures taller and thinner, "d" larger.

1922–34. *Wmk Mult Script CA. P* 14.
76*b* 14 ¼d. brown (7.28) .. .. .. 40 1·25
77 ½d. green (11.22) 30 15
78 1d. scarlet (I) (11.22) .. .. .. 5·00 60
a. Carmine (6.24) .. .. .. 10·00 60
78*b* 1d. carmine (II) (12.25) .. .. .. 11·00 1·50
c. Scarlet (8.27) .. .. .. 7·00 80
79 1d. scarlet (III) (10.28) .. .. .. 4·00 30
a. Carmine-lake (1934) .. .. .. 7·00 60
79*b* 1½d. red-brown (27.3.34) .. .. .. 3·50 35
80 2d. grey (12.23) .. .. 90 1·50
81 2½d. pale sage-green (12.22) .. .. 2·00 1·50
a. Deep sage-green (1924) .. .. 1·00 1·50
82 2½d. ultramarine (I) (1.12.26) .. .. 2·00 35
82*a* 2½d. ultramarine (II) (3.32) .. .. 1·75 35
83 3d. ultramarine (12.24) .. .. .. 14·00 25·00
84 3d. purple/*yellow* (10.26) .. .. 80 1·00
85 4d. red/*yellow* (8.24) .. .. .. 1·00 1·25
86 6d. purple (8.24) 80 80
87 1s. black/*emerald* (10.27) .. .. 4·50 6·00
a. Brownish black/yellow-green (1934) 30·00 45·00
88 15 2s. purple and bright blue/*pale blue*, **C** (1.9.27) .. .. 35·00 55·00
a. Break in scroll £110
b. Broken crown and scroll £110
c. Purple and blue/grey-blue **C** (1931) 35·00 55·00
ca. Break in scroll £110
cb. Broken crown and scroll £110
89 2s. 6d. black and carmine/*pale blue*, **C** (4.27) .. .. 48·00 70·00
a. Break in scroll £140
b. Broken crown and scroll £140
c. Black and red/blue to deep blue, **C** (6.29) .. .. 48·00 70·00
ca. Break in scroll £140
cb. Broken crown and scroll £140
d. Grey-black and pale orange-vermilion/grey-blue, **C** (3.30) .. £2500 £2500
da. Break in scroll £3500
db. Broken crown and scroll £3500
e. Black and vermilion/deep blue, **C** (9.31) .. .. 48·00 70·00
ea. Break in scroll £140
eb. Broken crown and scroll £140
f. Black and bright orange-vermilion/deep blue, **C** (8.32) £2750 £2500
fb. Broken crown and scroll £3750
92 10s. green and red/*pale emerald*, **C** (12.24) £120 £180
b. Broken crown and scroll £300
c. Green and red/deep emerald, **C** (1931) £120 £170
cb. Broken crown and scroll £300
93 12s. 6d. grey and orange, **CO** (8.32) .. £300 £350
a. Break in scroll £525
b. Broken crown and scroll £525
76*b*/93 .. .. *Set of* 16 £475 £600
76*b*/93 Optd/Perf "Specimen" .. *Set of* 16 £800

Nos. 76*b* to 87 exist both line-perf 13.75 or 13.75 × 14 and comb-perf 13.8 × 14 except Nos. 76*b*, 79*b*, 82*a* and 87*a* which are line-perf only.

The true No. 89*d* is the only stamp on grey-blue paper; other deeper orange-vermilion shades exist on different papers.

No. 93 on ordinary paper would seem to be an error. Our prices are for the chalky paper.

Beware of fiscally used 2s. 6d. 10s. and 12s. 6d. stamps cleaned and bearing faked postmarks. Large quantities were used for a "head tax" levied on travellers leaving the country.

For 12s. 6d. design inscribed "Revenue" at both sides see No. F1 under POSTAL FISCAL.

(Recess Waterlow)

1935 (6 May). *Silver Jubilee. As T* **13** *of Antigua. Wmk Mult Script CA. P* 11 × 12.
94 1d. deep blue and scarlet 45 55
95 1½d. ultramarine and grey 70 75
96 2½d. brown and deep blue .. .. .. 1·40 90
97 1s. slate and purple .. .. .. 9·00 13·50
j. Kite and vertical log .. .. .. 70·00
k. Kite and horizontal log .. .. .. 70·00
94/7 .. .. *Set of* 4 10·50 14·00
94/7 Perf "Specimen" .. .. *Set of* 4 £120

For illustrations of plate varieties see Omnibus section following Zululand.

20 Hamilton Harbour

21 South shore near Spanish Rock

22 *Lucie* (yacht)

23 Grape Bay, Paget Parish

24 Point House, Warwick Parish

25 House at Par-la-Ville, Hamilton

(Recess B.W.)

1936 (14 Apr)–**47**. *Wmk Mult Script CA* (*sideways on horiz designs*). *P* 12.
98 20 ½d. bright green 10 10
99 21 1d. black and scarlet 15 15
100 1½d. black and chocolate 75 15
101 22 2d. black and pale blue .. .. .. 4·00 2·00
102 23 2½d. light and deep blue 70 25
103 24 3d. black and scarlet .. .. .. 2·25 90
104 25 6d. carmine-lake and violet 45 10
a. Claret and dull violet (6.47) 65 25
105 23 1s. green .. .. 3·25 4·75
106 20 1s. 6d. brown 30 10
98/106 .. .. *Set of* 9 10·50 7·50
98/106 Perf "Specimen" .. .. *Set of* 9 £200

All are line-perf 11.9, except printings of the 6d. from July 1951 onwards, which are comb-perf 11.9 × 11.75.

1937 (14 May). *Coronation Issue. As T* **2** *of Aden. P* 14.
107 1d. scarlet 50 40
108 1½d. yellow-brown 60 30
109 2½d. bright blue .. .. 1·10 1·50
107/9 .. .. *Set of* 3 2·00 2·00
107/9 Perf "Specimen" .. .. *Set of* 3 70·00

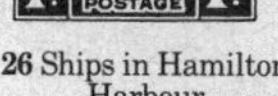

26 Ships in Hamilton Harbour

27 St. David's Lighthouse

28 White-tailed Tropic Bird, Arms of Bermuda and Native Flower

(Des Miss Higginbotham (T **28**). Recess B.W.)

1938 (20 Jan)–**1952**. *T* **22**, *T* **23** (*but with portrait of King George VI*) *and T* **26** *to* **28**. *Wmk Mult Script CA. P* 12.
110 26 1d. black and red (*a*) (*b*) 40 20
111 1½d. deep blue and purple-brown (*a*) (*b*) 1·50 70
a. Blue and brown (*a*) (3.43) .. .. 1·75 1·25
b. Lt blue & purple-brn (*a*) (*b*) (9.45) 70 35
112 22 2d. light blue and sepia (*a*) .. .. 27·00 5·00
112*a* 2d. ultramarine and scarlet (*a*) (*b*) (12.11.40) .. .. 1·50 80
113 23 2½d. light and deep blue (*a*) .. .. 8·50 90
113*a* 2½d. lt blue & sepia-black (*a*) (18.12.41) 1·25 80
b. Pale blue & sepia-black (*a*) (3.43) 1·50 1·10
c. Bright blue and deep sepia-black (*b*) (23.9.52) 85 70
114 27 3d. black and rose-red (*a*) .. .. 11·00 70
114*a* 3d. black & deep blue (*a*) (*b*) (16.7.41) 90 40
114*b* 28 7½d. black, blue & brt grn (*a*) (18.12.41) 3·25 1·50
c. Black, blue & yellow-grn (*a*) (3.43) 2·75 2·25
115 23 1s. green (*a*) (*b*) 80 50
a. Bluish green (*b*) (20.6.52) .. .. 3·25 2·75

Perforations. Two different perforating machines were used on the various printings of these stamps: (*a*) the original 11.9 line perforation; (*b*) 11.9 × 11.75 comb perforation, introduced in July 1950. These perforations occur as indicated above.

29 King George VI

Shading omitted from top right scroll (R. 1/1. March 1943 ptgs of 2s. and £1)

Lower right scroll with broken tail (R. 2/10. Line perforated printings only)

Broken top right scroll (R. 5/11. Line perforated ptgs only. A retouched state of the flaw is visible in later ptgs up to March 1943)

Broken lower right scroll (R. 5/12. Occurs on printings made between May 1941 and March 1943)

Gash in chin (R. 2/5. Occurs on ptgs made between May 1941 and March 1943)

(Typo D.L.R.)

1938 (20 Jan)–**53**. *T* **29**. *P* 14 (*comb*). *Wmk Mult Script CA*.

116 2s. dp purple & ultramarine/*grey-blue*, **C** 75·00 10·00
a. Perf 14¼, line. *Deep purple and ultramarine/grey-blue*, **C** (14.11.41)* £175 70·00
ac. Lower right scroll with broken tail £300 £150
ad. Broken top right scroll £425 £225
ae. Broken lower right scroll £425 £225
af. Gash in chin £300 £150
b. Purple and blue/deep blue, **O** (7.6.42) 7·00 1·50
be. Broken lower right scroll £100 40·00
bf. Gash in chin 60·00 25·00
c. Purple & deep blue/pale blue, **O** (5.3.43) 7·50 1·50
cb. Shading omitted from top right scroll £225 £125
ce. Broken lower right scroll £225 £125
cf. Gash in chin £150 80·00
d. Perf 13. *Dull purple and blue/pale blue*, **O** (15.2.50) 15·00 10·00
e. Perf 13. *Reddish purple and blue/pale blue*, **O** (10.10.50) 7·50 5·00

117 2s. 6d. black and red/*grey-blue*, **C** 45·00 6·00
a. Perf 14¼, line. *Black and red/grey-blue*, **C** (30.3.42)* £300 £100
ac. Lower right scroll with broken tail £450 £200
ad. Broken top right scroll £650 £300
ae. Broken lower right scroll £650 £300
af. Gash in chin £450 £200
b. Black and red/pale blue, **O** (5.3.43) 12·00 6·50
be. Broken lower right scroll £180
bf. Gash in chin £110
c. Perf 13. *Black and orange-red/pale blue*, **O** (10.10.50) 12·00 7·00
d. Perf 13. *Black and red/pale blue*, **O** (18.6.52) 11·00 9·00

118 5s. green and red/*yellow*, **C** 75·00 18·00
a. Pale green and red/yellow, **C** (14.3.39)* £140 40·00
b. Perf 14¼, line. *Green and red/yellow*, **C** (5.1.43)* £140 25·00
bc. Lower right scroll with broken tail £225 75·00
bd. Broken top right scroll £325 £125
be. Broken lower right scroll £325 £125
bf. Gash in chin £225 75·00
c. Pale bluish green and carmine-red/pale yellow, **O** (5.3.43) £140 70·00
ce. Broken lower right scroll £325
cf. Gash in chin £250
d. Green and red/pale yellow, **O** (11.45)* 28·00 11·00
e. Perf 13. *Yellow-green and red/pale yellow (shades)*, **OC** (15.2.50) 11·00 11·00

119 10s. green and deep lake/*pale emerald*, **C** £300 £225
a. Bluish green & deep red/green, (8.39)* £180 £130
b. Perf 14¼, line. *Yellowish green and deep red/green*, **O** (1942)* £250 £200
bc. Lower right scroll with broken tail £425
bd. Broken top right scroll £600
be. Broken lower right scroll £600
bf. Gash in chin £425
c. Yellowish green and deep carmine-red/green, **O** (5.3.43) 65·00 50·00
ce. Broken lower right scroll £450
cf. Gash in chin £300
d. Deep green and dull red/green (emerald back), **O** (11.12.46) 85·00 55·00
e. Perf 13. *Green and vermilion/green*, **O** (19.9.51) 24·00 25·00
f. Perf 13. *Green and dull red/green*, **O** (16.4.53) 19·00 28·00

120 12s. 6d. deep grey and brownish orange (*shades*), **C** £450 £400
a. Grey and pale orange, **CO** (9.11.40)* 65·00 40·00
ae. Broken lower right scroll (1943 ptg only) £550
af. Gash in chin £375
b. Grey and yellow†, **O** (7.9.47)* £500 £475
c. Perf 13. *Grey and pale orange*, **C** (10.10.50) 70·00 50·00

(*b*) *Wmk Mult Crown CA*

121 £1 purple and black/*red*, **C** £200 £110
a. Pale purple & blk/pale red, **C** (13.3.43)* 60·00 50·00
ab. Shading omitted from top right scroll £400
ae. Broken lower right scroll £400
af. Gash in chin £275
b. Deep reddish purple and black/pale red, **C** (29.3.45)* 55·00 45·00
be. Broken lower right scroll £500
bf. Gash in chin £350
c. Perf 13. *Violet and black/scarlet*, **C** (7.12.51) 42·00 45·00
d. Perf 13. *Bright violet & black/scarlet*, **C** (10.12.52) £150 £110

110*a*/21c *Set of* 16 £170 £130
110/21 Perf "Specimen" *Set of* 16 £1100

Following extensive damage to their printing works on 29 December 1940 much of De La Rue's work was transferred to other firms operating under their supervision. It is understood that Williams Lea & Co produced those new printings ordered for the Bermuda high value stamps during 1941. The first batch of these printings showed the emergency use, by Williams Lea, of a 14¼ line perforating machine (exact gauge 14.15) instead of the comb perforation (exact gauge 13.9 × 13.8).

Dates marked * are those of earliest known use.

In No. 116*b* the coloured surfacing of the paper is mottled with white specks sometimes accompanied by very close horizontal lines.

In Nos. 116*c*, 117*b* and 118*a* the surfacing is the same colour as the back, sometimes applied in widely spaced horizontal lines giving the appearance of laid paper.

No. 120 can be easily identified from the chalk-surfaced printings of No. 120*a* by the deep centre shade and by the paper, which is very stout for the 1938 printings.

†No. 120*b* is the so-called "lemon" shade.

HALF
PENNY

X **X**

(30)

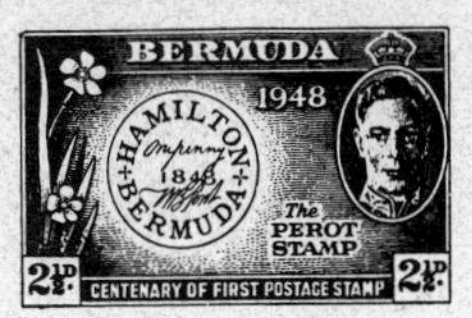

31 Postmaster Perot's Stamp

1940 (20 Dec). *No. 110 surch with T* **30**.
122 **26** ½d. on 1d. black and red (*shades*) 15 45

The spacing between "PENNY" and "X" varies from 12½ mm to 14 mm.

1946 (6 Nov). *Victory. As Nos. 28/9 of Aden.*
123 1½d. brown 15 15
124 3d. blue 15 15
123/4 Perf "Specimen" *Set of* 2 65·00

1948 (1 Dec). *Royal Silver Wedding. As Nos. 30/1 of Aden.*
125 1½d. red-brown 30 50
126 £1 carmine 48·00 48·00

(Recess B.W.)

1949 (11 Apr). *Centenary of Postmaster Perot's Stamp. Wmk Mult Script CA. P* 13½.
127 **31** 2½d. blue and brown 15 15
128 3d. black and blue 15 15
129 6d. violet and green 15 15
127/9 *Set of* 3 40 40

1949 (10 Oct). *75th Anniv of Universal Postal Union. As Nos. 114/17 of Antigua.*
130 2½d. blue-black 75 65
131 3d. deep blue 90 75
132 6d. purple 1·00 75
133 1s. blue-green 1·00 75
130/3 *Set of* 4 3·25 2·50

1953 (4 June). *Coronation. As No. 47 of Aden, but ptd by B.W.*
134 1½d. black and blue 20 15

32 Easter Lilies

34 Easter Lily

37 Map of Bermuda

Die I "Sandy's"

Die II "Sandys"

(Des C. Deakins (½d., 3d., 1s. 3d., 5s.), J. Berry (1d., 1½d., 2½d., 4d., 1s.). B. Brown (2d., 6d., 8d.), D. Haig (4½d., 9d.), Pamela Braley-Smith (2s. 6d.) and E. C. Leslie (10s.) Recess (except £1, centre typo), B.W.)

1953 (9 Nov)–**62**. *T* **32, 34, 37,** *and similar designs. Wmk Mult Script CA. P* 13½.
135 **32** ½d. olive-green 10 20
a. Yellow-olive (19.5.54) 10 15
136 – 1d. black and red 20 15
a. Black and deep red (19.5.54) 15 10
137 **34** 1½d. green 20 10
138 – 2d. ultramarine and brown-red 40 15
139 – 2½d. rose-red 90 50
140 **37** 3d. deep purple (I) 25 10
140*a* 3d. deep purple (II) (2.1.57) 50 10
141 – 4d. black and bright blue 20 20
142 – 4½d. emerald 45 80
143 – 6d. black and deep turquoise 2·50 40
143*a* – 8d. black and red (16.5.55) 1·60 20
143*b* – 9d. violet (6.1.58) 5·50 1·50
144 – 1s. orange 40 15
145 **37** 1s. 3d. blue (I) 1·00 20
a. Greenish blue (21.9.54) 1·50 60
145*b* 1s. 3d. blue (II) (2.1.57) 3·50 30
bc. Bright blue (14.8.62) 3·50 60
146 – 2s. brown 1·75 85
147 – 2s. 6d. scarlet 1·25 45
148 – 5s. carmine 7·50 85
149 – 10s. deep ultramarine 8·50 4·25
a. Ultramarine (13.2.57) 14·00 8·00
150 – £1 brown, blue, red, grn & bronze-grn 20·00 18·00
135/150 *Set of* 18 48·00 27·00

Designs: *Horiz*—1d., 4d. Postmaster Perot's stamps; 2d. *Victory II* (racing dinghy); 2½d. Sir George Somers and *Sea Venture*; 4½d., 9d. *Sea Venture*, inter-island boat, coin and Perot stamp; 6d., 8d. White-tailed Tropic Bird; 1s. Early Bermudian coinage; 2s. Arms of St. Georges; 5s. Hog coin; 10s. Obverse and reverse of hog coin; £1 Arms of Bermuda. *Vert*.—2s. 6d. Warwick Fort.

Nos. 136, 138 and 143 exist in coils, constructed from normal sheets.

1953 (26 Nov). *Royal Visit. As No. 143 but inscr* "ROYAL VISIT 1953" *in top left corner.*
151 6d. black and deep turquoise 20 20

Three Power Talks
December, 1953.
(46)

Three Power Talks
December, 1953.
(46*a*)

First setting (Type **46**). First line 24½ mm long.
Second setting (Type **46***a*). First line 25¼ mm long.

1953 (8 Dec). *Three Power Talks. Nos.* 140 *and* 145 *optd with T* **46**.
152 **37** 3d. deep purple (Type **46**) (B.) 10 10
a. Optd with Type **46***a* 20 15
153 1s. 3d. blue (Type **46**) (R.) 10 10
a. Optd with Type **46***a* 75 90

50TH ANNIVERSARY
U S – BERMUDA
OCEAN RACE 1956
(47)

48 Perot's Post Office

1956 (22 June). *50th Anniv of United States–Bermuda Yacht Race. Nos. 143a and 145a optd with T 47 by the Bermuda Press.*
154 8d. black and red (Bk.) 15 15
155 1s. 3d. greenish blue (R.) 15 25

(Des W. Harrington. Recess B.W.)

1959 (1 Jan.) *Wmk Mult Script CA. P* 13½.
156 **48** 6d. black and deep mauve 20 15

49 Arms of King James I and Queen Elizabeth II

(Des W. Harrington. Recess; arms litho D.L.R.)

1959 (29 July). *350th Anniv of First Settlement. Arms, red, yellow and blue; frame colours below.* W w **12**. *P* 13.
157 **49** 1½d. grey-blue 15 10
158 3d. drab-grey 15 20
159 4d. reddish purple 20 25
160 8d. slate-violet 25 15
161 9d. olive-green 25 70
162 1s. 3d. brown 25 25
157/162 .. .. *Set of* 6 1·10 1·50

50 The Old Rectory, St. George's, *circa* 1730 **67** *Tsotsi in the Bundu* (Finn class yacht)

(Des W. Harrington. Photo Harrison)

1962 (26 Oct)–**68**. *Horiz designs as T* **50**. *W w* **12** *(upright). P* 12½.
163 1d. reddish purple, black and orange .. 10 20
164 2d. lilac, indigo, yellow and green .. 10 15
a. Lilac omitted £600 £250
b. Green omitted .. .. .. † —
c. Imperf (pair) £600
d. Pale lilac, indigo, yellow and green (22.10.68) 15 15
165 3d. yellow-brown and light blue 10 10
a. Yellow-brown omitted £1500
166 4d. red-brown and magenta 20 25
167 5d. grey-blue and rose .. .. .. 50 1·25
168 6d. grey-blue, emerald and light blue .. 20 10
169 8d. bright blue, bright green and orange 30 10
170 9d. light blue and brown 25 25
170*a* 10d. violet and ochre (8.2.65) .. .. 3·25 1·00
171 1s. black, emerald, bright blue & orange 20 10
172 1s. 3d. lake, grey and bistre 50 15
173 1s. 6d. violet and ochre .. .. .. 1·25 2·50
174 2s. red-brown and orange .. .. 2·00 1·00
175 2s. 3d. bistre-brown and yellow-green .. 2·00 4·50
176 2s. 6d. bistre-brn, bluish grn & olive-yell 55 35
177 5s. brown-purple and blue-green .. 1·25 1·25
178 10s. magenta, deep bluish green and buff 4·00 5·00
179 £1 black, yellow-olive and yellow-orange 11·00 12·00
163/79 .. .. *Set of* 18 24·00 26·00

Designs:—2d. Church of St. Peter, St. Georges; 3d. Government House, 1892; 4d. The Cathedral, Hamilton, 1894; 5d. H.M. Dockyard, 1811; 6d. Perot's Post Office, 1848; 8d. G.P.O. Hamilton, 1869; 9d. Library, Par-la-Ville; 10d., 1s. 6d. Bermuda cottage, *circa* 1705; 1s. Christ Church, Warwick, 1719; 1s. 3d. City Hall, Hamilton, 1960; 2s. Town of St. George; 2s. 3d. Bermuda house, *circa* 1710; 2s. 6d. Bermuda house, early 18th-century; 5s. Colonial Secretariat, 1833; 10s. Old Post Office, Somerset, 1890; £1 The House of Assembly, 1815.

A single copy of No. 164b is known, used on piece.

See also Nos. 195/200 and 246a.

1963 (4 June). *Freedom from Hunger. As No. 76 of Aden.*
180 1s. 3d. sepia 80 35

1963 (2 Sept). *Red Cross Centenary. As Nos. 147/8 of Antigua.*
181 3d. red and black 75 25
182 1s. 3d. red and blue .. .. 2·00 1·50

(Des V. Whiteley. Photo D.L.R.)

1964 (28 Sept). *Olympic Games, Tokyo. W w* **12**. *P* 14 × 13½.
183 **67** 3d. red, violet and blue.. .. .. 10 10

1965 (17 May). *I.T.U. Centenary. As Nos. 166/7 of Antigua.*
184 3d. light blue and emerald 75 25
185 2s. yellow and ultramarine .. .. .. 1·50 1·25

68 Scout Badge and St. Edward's Crown

(Des W. Harrington. Photo Harrison)

1965 (24 July). *50th Anniv of Bermuda Boy Scouts Association. W w* **12**. *P* 12½.
186 **68** 2s. multicoloured 30 20

1965 (25 Oct). *International Co-operation Year. As Nos. 168/9 of Antigua.*
187 4d. reddish purple and turquoise-green .. 50 20
188 2s. 6d. deep bluish green and lavender .. 1·50 80

1966 (24 Jan). *Churchill Commemoration. As Nos. 170/3 of Antigua.*
189 3d. new blue 50 20
190 6d. deep green .. .. 1·00 45
191 10d. brown .. .. 1·25 75
192 1s. 3d. bluish violet .. .. 1·50 1·40
189/92 .. .. *Set of* 4 4·75 2·50

1966 (1 July). *World Cup Football Championships. As Nos. 176/7 of Antigua.*
193 10d. violet, yellow-green, lake & yellow-brn .. 50 15
194 2s. 6d. chocolate, blue-grn, lake & yell-brn .. 75 65

1966 (25 Oct)–**69**. *Designs as Nos.* 164, 167 (1s. 6d.), 169, 170*a*/1 *and* 174 *but W w* **12** *(sideways).*
195 2d. lilac, indigo, yellow and green (20.5.69).. 1·40 1·75
196 8d. bright blue, bright green and orange (14.2.67) 50 50
197 10d. violet and ochre (1.11.66) 75 60
198 1s. black, emerald, bright blue and orange (14.2.67) 50 35
199 1s. 6d. grey-blue and rose (1.11.66) .. .. 3·00 1·75
200 2s. red-brown and orange .. .. .. 3·00 3·25
195/200 .. .. *Set of* 6 8·00 7·50

The 2d. value exists with PVA gum only, and the 8d. exists with PVA gum as well as gum arabic.

1966 (1 Dec). *20th Anniv of U.N.E.S.C.O. As Nos. 196/8 of Antigua.*
201 4d. slate-violet, red, yellow and orange .. 60 15
202 1s. 3d. orange-yellow, violet and deep olive 1·25 65
203 2s. black, bright purple and orange.. .. 2·00 1·25
201/3 .. .. *Set of* 3 3·50 1·90

69 G.P.O. Building

(Des G. Vasarhelyi. Photo Harrison)

1967 (23 June). *Opening of New General Post Office. Hamilton.* W w **12**. *P* 14½.
204 **69** 3d. multicoloured 10 10
205 1s. multicoloured 10 10
206 1s. 6d. multicoloured 10 10
207 2s. 6d. multicoloured 15 10
204/7 .. .. *Set of* 4 35 20

70 *Mercury* (cable ship) and Chain Links

(Des V. Whiteley. Photo Harrison)

1967 (14 Sept). *Inauguration of Bermuda–Tortola Telephone Service. T* **70** *and similar horiz designs. Multicoloured. W w* **12**. *P* 14½ × 14.
208 3d. Type **70** 10 10
209 1s. Map, telephone and microphone.. .. 10 10
210 1s. 6d. Telecommunications media 15 10
211 2s. 6d. *Mercury* (cable ship) and marine fauna 20 15
208/11 .. .. *Set of* 4 40 25

74 Human Rights Emblem and Doves

(Des M. Farrar Bell. Litho Harrison)

1968 (1 Feb). *Human Rights Year. W w* **12**. *P* 14 × 14½.
212 **74** 3d. indigo, blue and dull green.. .. 10 10
213 1s. yellow-brown, blue and light blue .. 10 10
214 1s. 6d. black, blue and rose 10 10
215 2s. 6d. grey-green, blue and yellow .. 15 20
212/15 .. .. *Set of* 4 30 20

REPRESENTATIVE GOVERNMENT

75 Mace and Queen's Profile

(Des R. Granger Barrett. Photo Harrison)

1968 (1 July). *New Constitution. T* **75** *and similar horiz design. W w* **12**. *P* 14.
216 **75** 3d. multicoloured 10 10
217 1s. multicoloured 10 10
218 – 1s. 6d. greenish yellow, black & turq-bl 10 10
219 – 2s. 6d. lilac, black and orange-yellow .. 15 10
216/19 .. .. *Set of* 4 30 20

Design:—1s. 6d., 2s. 6d. Houses of Parliament and House of Assembly, Bermuda.

77 Football, Athletics and Yachting

(Des V. Whiteley. Photo Harrison)

1968 (24 Sept). *Olympic Games, Mexico. W w* **12**. *P* 12½.
220 **77** 3d. multicoloured 10 10
a. Red-brown ("BERMUDA" and value) omitted £1500
221 1s. multicoloured 10 10
222 1s. 6d. multicoloured 15 10
223 2s. 6d. multicoloured 20 10
220/3 .. .. *Set of* 4 45 20

78 Brownie and Guide

79 Guides and Badge

(Des Harrison. Litho Format)

1969 (17 Feb). *50th Anniv of Bermuda Girl Guides. P* 14.
224 **78** 3d. multicoloured 10 10
225 1s. multicoloured 15 10
226 **79** 1s. 6d. multicoloured 20 10
227 2s. 6d. multicoloured 35 15
224/7 .. .. *Set of* 4 70 25

1c

80 Emerald-studded Gold Cross and Seaweed **(82)**

(Des K. Giles adapted by V. Whiteley. Photo Harrison)

1969 (29 Sept). *Underwater Treasure. T* **80** *and similar vert design. Multicoloured. W w* **12** *(sideways). P* 14½ × 14.
228 4d. Type **80** 20 10
229 1s. 3d. Emerald-studded gold cross and seabed 35 15
230 2s. Type **80** 45 35
231 2s. 6d. As 1s. 3d. 45 50
228/31 .. .. *Set of* 4 1·25 95

(New Currency. 100 cents = 1 dollar)

1970 (6 Feb). *Decimal Currency. As Nos.* 163, 165/6, 168, 170, 172, 175/9 *and* 195/200 *surch as T* **82**. *W w* **12** *(sideways on* 2, 5, 10, 12, 15, 18, 24, 30, 60 *c.,* $1.20 *and* $2.40).
232 1 c. on 1d. reddish purple, black and orange 10 15
233 2 c. on 2d. lilac, indigo, yellow and green .. 10 10
a. Lilac omitted £550
b. Pair, one without surch .. ..
c. Wmk upright (No. 164) 60 90
d. Surch on No. 164*d* .. .. .. 70 1·00
234 3 c. on 3d. yellow-brown and light blue .. 10 10
235 4 c. on 4d. red-brown and magenta (Br.) .. 10 10
236 5 c. on 8d. bright blue, brt green & orange 15 15
237 6 c. on 6d. grey-blue, emerald & light blue 15 15
a. Horiz pair, one with albino surch, the other with albino bar .. ..
238 9 c. on 9d. light blue and brown (Br.) .. 25 35
239 10 c. on 10d. violet and ochre 25 25
240 12 c. on 1s. black, emerald, brt blue & orange 25 15
241 15 c. on 1s. 3d. lake, grey and bistre .. .. 1·25 1·00
242 18 c. on 1s. 6d. grey-blue and rose 80 65
243 24 c. on 2s. red-brown and orange 85 75

244 30 c. on 2s. 6d. bistre-brown, bluish green and olive-yellow 80 90
245 36 c. on 2s. 3d. bistre-brown and yellow-green 1·50 2·00
246 60 c. on 5s. brown-purple and blue-green .. 2·25 2·75
a. Surch omitted† £400
247 $1.20, on 10s. mag., dp bluish grn & buff .. 4·00 7·50
248 $2.40, on £1 black, yellow-olive & yell-orge 7·00 12·00
232/48 .. .. Set of 17 18·00 26·00

†No. 246a differs from the normal No. 177 by its watermark, which is sideways, and its gum, which is PVA.

83 Spathiphyllum

(Des W. Harrington. Photo D.L.R.)

1970 (6 July)–**75**. *Flowers. Multicoloured designs as T* **83**. *W* w **12** (*sideways on horiz designs*). *P* 14.

249 1 c. Type **83** 10 15
250 2 c. Bottlebrush 20 25
251 3 c. Oleander (*vert*) 10 10
252 4 c. Bermudiana 10 10
253 5 c. Poinsettia 30 20
254 6 c. Hibiscus 30 30
255 9 c. Cereus 20 20
256 10 c. Bougainvillea (*vert*) 20 15
257 12 c. Jacaranda 80 60
258 15 c. Passion-Flower .. .. 90 1·40
258*a* 17 c. As 15 c. (2.6.75) .. .. .. 1·50 1·50
259 18 c. Coralita .. .. 1·50 2·25
259*a* 20 c. As 18 c. (2.6.75) .. .. .. 1·50 1·50
260 24 c. Morning Glory .. .. 1·50 2·75
260*a* 25 c. As 24 c. (2.6.75) .. .. .. 1·50 1·75
261 30 c. Tecoma .. .. 1·00 1·25
262 36 c. Angel's Trumpet .. .. 1·25 2·25
262*a* 40 c. As 36 c. (2.6.75) .. .. .. 1·50 2·00
263 60 c. Plumbago .. .. 1·75 2·75
263*a* $1 As 60 c. (2.6.75) .. .. .. 2·50 2·75
264 $1.20, Bird of Paradise flower .. .. 2·75 3·50
264*a* $2 As $1.20 (2.6.75) .. .. .. 4·25 5·00
265 $2.40, Chalice Cup.. .. .. .. 5·50 9·00
265*a* $3 As $2.40 (2.6.75) .. .. .. 7·50 10·00
249/65*a* .. .. Set of 24 35·00 45·00

See also Nos. 303/6 and 340/1.

84 The State House, St. George's

(Des G. Drummond. Litho Questa)

1970 (12 Oct). *350th Anniv of Bermuda Parliament. T* **84** *and similar horiz designs. Multicoloured. W* w **12** (*sideways*). *P* 14.

266 4 c. Type **84** 10 10
267 15 c. The Sessions House, Hamilton 20 15
268 18 c. St. Peter's Church, St George's 20 20
269 24 c. Town Hall, Hamilton 35 35
266/9 .. .. Set of 4 75 65
MS270 131 × 95 mm. Nos. 266/9 .. .. .. 1·75 3·50

85 Street Scene, St. George's

(Des G. Drummond. Litho Questa)

1971 (8 Feb). *"Keep Bermuda Beautiful". T* **85** *and similar horiz designs. Multicoloured. W* w **12** (*sideways*). *P* 14.

271 4 c. Type **85** 20 10
272 15 c. Horseshoe Bay 45 40
273 18 c. Gibb's Hill Lighthouse .. .. .. 90 1·00
274 24 c. Hamilton Harbour .. .. .. 1·00 1·50
271/4 .. .. Set of 4 2·25 2·75

86 Building of the *Deliverance*

(Des E. Amos. Adapted C. Abbott. Litho Questa)

1971 (10 May). *Voyage of the "Deliverance". T* **86** *and similar multicoloured designs. W* w **12** (*sideways on* 4 *c. and* 24 *c.*). *P* 14.

275 4 c. Type **86** 50 20
276 15 c. *Deliverance* and *Patience* at Jamestown 1·50 1·75
277 18 c. Wreck of the *Sea Venture* .. .. 1·75 2·25
278 24 c. *Deliverance* and *Patience* on the high seas 1·90 2·50
275/8 .. .. Set of 4 5·00 6·00

The 15 c. and 18 c. are vert designs.

87 Green overlooking Ocean View

(Des G. Drummond. Litho D.L.R.)

1971 (1 Nov). *Golfing in Bermuda. T* **87** *and similar horiz designs. Multicoloured. W* w **12** (*sideways*). *P* 13.

279 4 c. Type **87** 25 10
280 15 c. Golfers at Port Royal 45 60
281 18 c. Castle Harbour 50 60
282 24 c. Belmont 60 85
279/82 .. .. Set of 4 1·60 2·00

HEATH - NIXON
DECEMBER 1971

(88)

1971 (20 Dec). *Anglo-American Talks. Nos.* 252, 258, 259 *and* 260 *optd with T* **88** *by Format.*

283 4 c. Bermudiana 10 10
284 15 c. Passion Glory 10 15
285 18 c. Coralita 15 40
286 24 c. Morning Glory 20 50
283/6 .. .. Set of 4 50 1·10

89 Bonefish

(Des Maynard Reece. Litho B.W.)

1972 (21 Aug). *World Fishing Records. T* **89** *and similar horiz designs. Multicoloured. W* w **12**. *P* 13½ × 14.

287 4 c. Type **89** 20 10
288 15 c. Wahoo 25 25
289 18 c. Yellowfin Tuna 30 40
290 24 c. Greater Amberjack 35 60
287/90 .. .. Set of 4 1·00 1·10

90 "Admiralty Oar" and Mace

(Des (from photograph by D. Groves) and photo Harrison)

1972 (20 Nov). *Royal Silver Wedding. Multicoloured; background colour given. W* w **12**. *P* 14 × 14½.

291 **90** 4 c. bright bluish violet 10 10
292 15 c. rose-carmine 15 20

91 Palmetto

92 Bernard Park, Pembroke, 1973

(Des Jennifer Toombs. Litho J.W.)

1973 (3 Sept). *Tree Planting Year. T* **91** *and similar vert designs. Multicoloured. W* w **12** (*sideways*). *P* 14.

293 4 c. Type **91** 25 10
294 15 c. Olivewood Bark 80 75
a. Brown (Queen's head and value) omitted £700
295 18 c. Bermuda Cedar .. .. 90 1·00
296 24 c. Mahogany .. .. 1·00 1·40
293/6 .. .. Set of 4 2·75 3·00

1973 (21 Nov*). *Royal Wedding. As Nos.* 165/6 *of Anguilla. Centre multicoloured. W* w **12** (*sideways*). *P* 13½.

297 15 c. bright mauve 10 10
298 18 c. steel blue 10 15

*This is the local date of issue. The Crown Agents released the stamps on the 14 November.

(Des J.W. Litho Questa)

1973 (17 Dec). *Lawn Tennis Centenary. T* **92** *and similar horiz designs. Multicoloured. W* w **12**. *P* 14.

299 4 c. Type **92** 30 10
300 15 c. Clermont Court, 1873 .. .. .. 60 50
301 18 c. Leamington Spa Court, 1872 .. .. 70 1·00
302 24 c. Staten Island Courts, 1874 .. .. 85 1·25
299/302 .. .. Set of 4 2·25 2·50

1974 (13 June)–**76**. *As Nos.* 253/4, 257 *and* 261, *but wmk upright.*

303 5 c. Poinsettia .. .. 90 1·75
304 6 c. Hibiscus .. .. 4·00 4·00
305 12 c. Jacaranda .. .. 1·75 2·75
306 30 c. Tecoma (11.6.76) .. .. 3·00 4·00
303/6 .. .. Set of 4 8·50 11·50

Nos. 307/19 vacant.

93 Weather Vane, City Hall

94 Jack of Clubs and "good bridge hand"

(Des G. Drummond. Litho Questa)

1974 (24 June). *50th Anniv of Rotary in Bermuda. T* **93** *and similar horiz designs. Multicoloured. W* w **12** (*sideways*). *P* 14.

320 5 c. Type **93** 15 10
321 17 c. St. Peter's Church, St George's 45 35
322 20 c. Somerset Bridge 50 80
323 25 c. Map of Bermuda, 1626 .. .. .. 60 1·25
320/3 .. .. Set of 4 1·50 2·25

(Des J.W. Litho Format)

1975 (27 Jan). *World Bridge Championships, Bermuda. T* **94** *and similar vert designs. Multicoloured. W* w **12**. *P* 14.

324 5 c. Type **94** 25 10
325 17 c. Queen of Diamonds and Bermuda Bowl 65 50
326 20 c. King of Hearts and Bermuda Bowl .. 70 1·25
327 25 c. Ace of Spades and Bermuda Bowl .. 80 1·40
324/7 .. .. Set of 4 2·25 3·00

95 Queen Elizabeth II and the Duke of Edinburgh

(Des and photo Harrison)

1975 (17 Feb). *Royal Visit. W* w **14**. *P* 14 × 14½.

328 **95** 17 c. multicoloured 60 65
329 20 c. multicoloured .. .. .. 65 1·10

96 "Cavalier" Flying-boat, 1937

(Des R. Granger Barrett. Litho Questa)

1975 (28 Apr). *50th Anniv of Air-mail Service to Bermuda. T* **96** *and similar horiz designs. Multicoloured. W* w **14** (*sideways*). *P* 14.

330 5 c. Type **96** 40 10
331 17 c. Airship *Los Angeles*, 1925 .. .. 1·25 75
332 20 c. Lockheed "Constellation", 1946 .. .. 1·40 1·75
333 25 c. Boeing "747", 1970 .. .. .. 1·50 2·25
330/3 .. .. Set of 4 4·00 4·25
MS334 128 × 85 mm. Nos. 330/3 .. .. .. 6·50 8·50

97 Supporters of American Army raiding Royal Magazine

98 Launching *Ready* (bathysphere)

(Des J. Cooter. Litho J.W.)

1975 (27 Oct). *Bicentenary of Gunpowder Plot, St. George's. T* **97** *and similar horiz designs. Multicoloured. W* w **14** (*sideways*). *P* 13 × 13½.

335 5 c. Type **97** 20 10
336 17 c. Setting off for raid 40 25
337 20 c. Loading gunpowder aboard American ship 45 60
338 25 c. Gunpowder on beach 50 70
335/8 .. .. Set of 4 1·40 1·50
MS339 165 × 138 mm. Nos. 335/8. P 14 (*sold for* 75 *c.*) .. .. 2·50 4·50

1975 (8 Dec)–**76**. *As Nos.* 250 *and* 254 *but* W w **14** (*sideways*).

No.	Description		
340	2 c. Bottlebrush	70	80
341	6 c. Hibiscus (11.6.76)	1·90	1·90

Nos. 342/56 vacant.

(Des G. Drummond. Litho Questa)

1976 (29 Mar). *50th Anniv of Bermuda Biological Station. T* **98** *and similar multicoloured designs.* W w **14** (*sideways on* 17 *and* 20 *c.*). *P* 14.

No.	Description		
357	5 c. Type **98**	35	10
358	17 c. View from the sea (*horiz*)	70	60
359	20 c. H.M.S. *Challenger*, 1873 (*horiz*)	75	1·50
360	25 c. Beebe's bathysphere descent, 1934	1·00	1·60
357/60	*Set of* 4	2·50	3·50

99 *Christian Radich*

(Des R. Granger Barrett. Litho J.W.)

1976 (15 June). *Tall Ships Race,* 1976. *T* **99** *and similar horiz designs. Multicoloured.* W w **12** (*sideways*). *P* 13.

No.	Description		
361	5 c. Type **99**	45	15
362	12 c. *Juan Sebastian de Elcano*	80	95
363	17 c. U.S.C.G. *Eagle*	95	95
364	20 c. *Winston S. Churchill*	1·10	1·75
365	40 c. *Kruzenshtern*	1·50	2·25
366	$1 *Cutty Sark* trophy	2·50	4·50
361/6	*Set of* 6	6·50	9·50

100 Silver Trophy and Club Flags

(Des C. Abbott. Litho Questa)

1976 (16 Aug). *75th Anniv of the St. George's v. Somerset Cricket Cup Match. T* **100** *and similar horiz designs. Multicoloured.* W w **14** (*sideways*). *P* 14½ × 14.

No.	Description		
367	5 c. Type **100**	35	10
368	17 c. Badge and Pavilion, St. George's Club	75	55
369	20 c. Badge and Pavilion Somerset Club	1·00	2·00
370	25 c. Somerset playing field	1·50	3·00
367/70	*Set of* 4	3·25	5·00

101 Royal Visit, 1975 **102** Stockdale House, St. George's 1784–1812

(Des Harrison. Litho Walsall)

1977 (7 Feb). *Silver Jubilee. T* **101** *and similar vert designs. Multicoloured.* W w **14**. *P* 13½.

No.	Description		
371	5 c. Type **101**	15	10
372	20 c. St. Edward's Crown	25	15
373	$1 Queen in Chair of Estate	80	1·10
371/3	*Set of* 3	1·10	1·25

(Des G. Drummond. Litho J.W.)

1977 (20 June). *Centenary of U.P.U. Membership. T* **102** *and similar horiz designs. Multicoloured.* W w **14** (*sideways*). *P* 13.

No.	Description		
374	5 c. Type **102**	15	10
375	15 c. Perot Post Office and stamp	35	50
376	17 c. St. George's P.O. *circa* 1860	35	50
377	20 c. Old G.P.O., Hamilton, *circa* 1935	45	60
378	40 c. New G.P.O., Hamilton, 1967	75	1·10
374/8	*Set of* 5	1·90	2·50

103 17th-Century Ship approaching Castle Island **104** Great Seal of Queen Elizabeth I

(Des R. Granger Barrett. Litho Questa)

1977 (26 Sept). *Piloting. T* **103** *and similar horiz designs. Multicoloured.* W w **14** (*sideways*). *P* 13½.

No.	Description		
379	5 c. Type **103**	20	10
380	15 c. Pilot leaving ship, 1795	45	45
381	17 c. Pilots rowing out to paddle-steamer	50	50
382	20 c. Pilot gigs and brig *Harvest Queen*	65	1·25
383	40 c. Modern pilot cutter and R.M.S. *Queen Elizabeth 2*	1·25	2·00
379/83	*Set of* 5	2·75	3·75

(Des BG Studio. Litho Questa)

1978 (28 Aug). *25th Anniv of Coronation. T* **104** *and similar vert designs. Multicoloured.* W w **14**. *P* 14 × 13½.

No.	Description		
384	8 c. Type **104**	10	10
385	50 c. Great Seal of Queen Elizabeth II	30	30
386	$1 Queen Elizabeth II	60	75
384/6	*Set of* 3	80	1·00

105 White-tailed Tropic Bird

(Des G. Drummond. Photo Harrison)

1978 (15 Nov)–**83**. *Wildlife. Horiz designs as T* **105**. *Multicoloured.* W w **14** (*sideways on* 8, 15, 20, 40 *c. and* $1). *P* 14 × 14½ (4, 5 *c.*, $2, 3, 5) *or* 14 (*others*).

No.	Description		
387	3 c. Type **105**	30	15
	a. Perf 14 × 14½ (3.8.83)*	40	20
388	4 c. White-eyed Vireo	40	15
389	5 c. Eastern Bluebird	40	15
390	7 c. Whistling Frog (19.2.79)	40	15
391	8 c. Common Cardinal	40	15
392	10 c. Spiny Lobster (19.2.79)	15	10
393	12 c. Land Crab (19.2.79)	25	25
394	15 c. Lizard (Skink) (19.2.79)	20	15
395	20 c. Foureye Butterfly Fish (12.3.79)	20	25
396	25 c. Red Hind (12.3.79)	30	20
	a. Greenish blue omitted		
397	30 c. Monarch Butterfly (19.2.79)	1·50	80
398	40 c. Rock Beauty (12.3.79)	45	70
399	50 c. Banded Butterfly Fish (12.3.79)	55	60
400	$1 Blue Angelfish (12.3.79)	95	1·25
401	$2 Humpback Whale (12.3.79)	2·00	2·50
402	$3 Green Turtle (19.2.79)	2·75	3·00
403	$5 Cahow	6·50	6·00
387/403	*Set of* 17	16·00	15·00

*Earliest known postmark date.

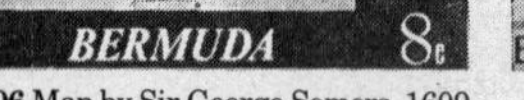

106 Map by Sir George Somers, 1609 **107** Policeman and Policewoman

(Des J. Cooter. Litho Questa)

1979 (14 May). *Antique Maps. T* **106** *and similar multicoloured designs.* W w **14** (*sideways on* 8, 15, 25 *and* 50 *c.*) *P* 14 × 13½ (20 *c.*) *or* 13½ × 14 (*others*).

No.	Description		
404	8 c. Type **106**	10	10
405	15 c. Map by John Seller, 1685	15	15
406	20 c. Map by H. Moll, 1729–40 (*vert*)	20	25
407	25 c. Map by Desbruslins, 1740	25	30
408	50 c. Map by Speed, 1626	45	70
404/8	*Set of* 5	1·00	1·25

(Des L. Curtis. Litho Questa)

1979 (26 Nov). *Centenary of Police Force. T* **107** *and similar multicoloured designs.* W w **14** (*sideways on* 20 *and* 25 *c.*). *P* 14.

No.	Description		
409	8 c. Type **107**	15	10
410	20 c. Policeman directing traffic (*horiz*)	40	45
411	25 c. Police patrol launch (*horiz*)	45	50
412	50 c. Police car and motorcycle	80	1·00
409/12	*Set of* 4	1·60	1·90

108 1848 1d. "Perot" and Penny Black Stamps

(Des J.W. Litho Enschedé)

1980 (25 Feb). *Death Centenary of Sir Rowland Hill* (1979). *T* **108** *and similar horiz designs. Multicoloured.* W w **14** (*sideways*). *P* 13 × 13½.

No.	Description		
413	8 c. Type **108**	10	10
414	20 c. 1848 1d. "Perot" stamp and Sir Rowland Hill	15	20
415	25 c. 1848 1d. "Perot" stamp and early letter	15	25
416	50 c. 1848 1d. "Perot" stamp and "Paid 1" cancellation	25	50
413/16	*Set of* 4	60	90

109 British Airways "Tristar 500" Airliner approaching Bermuda **110** Gina Swainson with Rose

(Des R. Granger Barrett. Litho Harrison)

1980 (6 May). *"London 1980" International Stamp Exhibition. Mail-carrying Transport. T* **109** *and similar horiz designs. Multicoloured.* W w **14** (*sideways*). *P* 13 × 13½.

No.	Description		
417	25 c. Type **109**	25	15
418	50 c. S.S. *Orduna* in Grassy Bay	40	35
419	$1 *Delta* at St. George's Harbour	70	80
420	$2 *Lord Sidmouth* in Old Ship Channel, St. George's	1·25	1·50
417/20	*Set of* 4	2·40	2·50

(Des Walsall. Litho Questa)

1980 (8 May). *"Miss World 1979–80" (Gina Swainson) Commemoration. T* **110** *and similar vert designs. Multicoloured.* W w **14**. *P* 14 × 13½.

No.	Description		
421	8 c. Type **110**	15	10
422	20 c. After crowning ceremony	20	20
423	50 c. On Peacock Throne at "Welcome Home" party	35	35
424	$1 In Bermuda carriage	70	90
421/4	*Set of* 4	1·25	1·40

111 Queen Elizabeth the Queen Mother

(Des and litho Harrison)

1980 (4 Aug). *80th Birthday of Queen Elizabeth the Queen Mother.* W w **14** (*sideways*). *P* 14.

No.	Description		
425 **111**	25 c. multicoloured	30	40

112 Bermuda from Satellite **113** Kitchen, 18th-century

(Des. L. Curtis. Litho Questa)

1980 (24 Sept). *Commonwealth Finance Ministers Meeting. T* **112** *and similar horiz designs. Multicoloured.* W w **14** (*sideways*). *P* 14.

No.	Description		
426	8 c. Type **112**	10	10
427	20 c. "Camden"	20	30
428	25 c. Princess Hotel, Hamilton	20	30
429	50 c. Government House	35	70
426/9	*Set of* 4	75	1·25

(Des J.W. Litho Questa)

1981 (21 May). *Heritage Week. T* **113** *and similar horiz designs. Multicoloured.* W w **14** (*sideways*). *P* 14.

No.	Description		
430	8 c. Type **113**	15	10
431	25 c. Gathering Easter lilies, 20th-century	40	40
432	30 c. Fishing, 20th-century	50	50
433	40 c. Stone cutting, 19th-century	55	55
434	50 c. Onion shipping, 19th-century	65	65
435	$1 Privateering, 17th-century	1·50	2·00
430/5	*Set of* 6	3·25	3·75

114 Wedding Bouquet from Bermuda **115** "Service", Hamilton

(Des J.W. Litho Questa)

1981 (22 July). *Royal Wedding. T* **114** *and similar vert designs. Multicoloured.* W w **14**. *P* 14.

No.	Description		
436	30 c. Type **114**	30	30
437	50 c. Prince Charles as Royal Navy Commander	50	55
438	$1 Prince Charles and Lady Diana Spencer	90	1·25
436/8	*Set of* 3	1·50	1·90

(Des L. Curtis. Litho Questa)

1981 (28 Sept). *25th Anniv of Duke of Edinburgh Award Scheme. T* **115** *and similar vert designs. Multicoloured.* W w **14**. *P* 14.

439 10 c. Type **115** 15 10
440 25 c. "Outward Bound", Paget Island 25 20
441 30 c. "Expedition", St. David's Island 25 30
442 $1 Duke of Edinburgh .. .. .. 80 1·25
439/42 .. .. *Set of 4* 1·25 1·75

116 *Conus species*

(Des Walsall. Litho Questa)

1982 (22 Apr). *Sea-shells. T* **116** *and similar horiz designs. Multicoloured.* W w **14** (*sideways*). *P* 14.

443 10 c. Type **116** 20 10
444 25 c. *Bursa finlayi* 50 50
445 30 c. *Sconsia striata* 55 65
446 $1 *Murex pterynotus lightbourni* .. .. 1·60 2·25
443/6 .. .. *Set of 4* 2·50 3·25

117 Regimental Colours and Colour Party   **118** Charles Fort

(Des G. Drummond. Litho Questa)

1982 (17 June). *Bermuda Regiment. T* **117** *and similar horiz designs. Multicoloured.* W w **14** (*sideways*). *P* 14.

447 10 c. Type **117** 20 10
448 25 c. Queen's Birthday Parade 50 40
449 30 c. Governor inspecting Guard of Honour .. 60 60
450 40 c. Beating the Retreat 65 70
451 50 c. Ceremonial gunners 75 90
452 $1 Guard of Honour, Royal visit, 1975 .. 1·50 2·50
447/52 .. .. *Set of 6* 3·75 4·75

(Des L. Curtis. Litho Questa)

1982 (18 Nov) *Historic Bermuda Forts. T* **118** *and similar multi-coloured designs.* W w **14** (*sideways on* 30 c. *and* $1). *P* 14.

453 10 c. Type **118** 20 15
454 25 c. Pembroks Fort 50 55
455 30 c. Southampton Fort (*horiz*) 60 80
456 $1 Smiths Fort and Pagets Fort (*horiz*) .. 1·75 3·00
453/6 .. .. *Set of 4* 2·75 4·00

119 Arms of Sir Edwin Sandys   **120** Early Fitted Dinghy

(Des Harrison. Litho J.W.)

1983 (14 Apr). *Coats of Arms* (1st *series*). *T* **119** *and similar vert designs. Multicoloured.* W w **14**. *P* 13.

457 10 c. Type **119** 30 15
458 25 c. Arms of the Bermuda Company 80 60
459 50 c. Arms of William Herbert, Earl of Pembroke .. .. 1·50 1·75
460 $1 Arms of Sir George Somers .. .. 2·25 3·00
457/60 .. .. *Set of 4* 4·25 5·00

See also Nos. 482/5 and 499/502.

(Des L. Curtis. Litho Harrison)

1983 (23 June). *Fitted Dinghies. T* **120** *and similar vert designs. Multicoloured.* W w **14** (*sideways*). *P* 14.

461 12 c. Type **120** 20 10
462 30 c. Modern dinghy inshore 45 45
463 40 c. Early dinghy (*different*) 60 60
464 $1 Modern dinghy with red and white spinnaker .. .. 1·50 2·25
461/4 .. .. *Set of 4* 2·50 3·00

121 Curtiss "Jenny" Seaplane (First Flight over Bermuda)   **122** Joseph Stockdale

(Des A. Theobald. Litho Walsall)

1983 (13 Oct). *Bicentenary of Manned Flight. T* **121** *and similar horiz designs. Multicoloured.* W w **14** (*sideways*). *P* 14.

465 12 c. Type **121** 20 15
466 30 c. *Pilot Radio*, Stinson seaplane (First completed flight between U.S.A. and Bermuda) 45 50
467 40 c. Short "Empire" flying boat *Cavalier* (First scheduled passenger flight) .. 60 80
468 $1 U.S.S. *Los Angeles* (airship) moored to U.S.S. *Patoka* .. .. 1·50 2·25
465/8 .. .. *Set of 4* 2·50 3·25

(Des L. Curtis. Litho Harrison)

1984 (26 Jan). *Bicentenary of Bermuda's First Newspaper and Postal Service. T* **122** *and similar multicoloured designs.* W w **14** (*sideways on* 40 c. *and* $1). *P* 14.

469 12 c. Type **122** 20 15
470 30 c. *The Bermuda Gazette* 50 60
471 40 c. Stockdale's postal service (*horiz*) .. 70 80
472 $1 *Lady Hammond* (mail boat) (*horiz*) .. 2·00 2·75
469/72 .. .. *Set of 4* 3·00 4·00

123 Sir Thomas Gates and Sir George Somers   **124** Swimming

(Des R. Granger Barrett. Litho Walsall)

1984 (3 May). *375th Anniv of First Settlement. T* **123** *and similar horiz designs. Multicoloured.* W w **14** (*sideways*). *P* 14.

473 12 c. Type **123** 20 15
474 30 c. Jamestown, Virginia 50 55
475 40 c. Wreck of *Sea Venture* 90 75
476 $1 Fleet leaving Plymouth, Devon .. .. 2·00 2·50
473/6 .. .. *Set of 4* 3·25 3·50
MS477 130 × 73 mm. Nos. 474 and 476 .. .. 2·50 3·25

(Des C. Collins. Litho J.W.)

1984 (19 July). *Olympic Games, Los Angeles. T* **124** *and similar multicoloured designs.* W w **14** (*sideways on* 30 c., $1). *P* 14.

478 12 c. Type **124** 20 15
479 30 c. Track and field events (*horiz*) 50 55
480 40 c. Equestrian competition 70 75
481 $1 Sailing (*horiz*) .. .. 2·00 2·25
478/81 .. .. *Set of 4* 3·00 3·25

(Des Harrison. Litho J.W.)

1984 (27 Sept). *Coats of Arms* (2nd *series*). *Vert designs as T* **119**. *Multicoloured.* W w **14**. *P* 13.

482 12 c. Arms of Henry Wriothesley, Earl of Southampton 25 15
483 30 c. Arms of Sir Thomas Smith 60 60
484 40 c. Arms of William Cavendish, Earl of Devonshire 80 80
485 $1 Town arms of St. George .. .. 2·00 2·50
482/5 .. .. *Set of 4* 3·25 3·50

125 Buttery   **126** Osprey

(Des D. Miller. Litho Walsall)

1985 (24 Jan). *Bermuda Architecture. T* **125** *and similar multi-coloured designs.* W w **14** (*inverted on* 12 c., $1.50, *sideways on* 30 c., 40 c.). *P* 13½ × 13 (12 c., $1.50) *or* 13 × 13½ (30 c., 40 c.).

486 12 c. Type **125** 25 15
487 30 c. Limestone rooftops (*horiz*) 50 50
488 40 c. Chimneys (*horiz*) 65 70
489 $1.50, Entrance archway .. .. .. 2·25 2·50
486/9 .. .. *Set of 4* 3·25 3·50

(Des D. Miller. Litho Walsall)

1985 (28 Mar). *Birth Bicentenary of John J. Audubon (ornithologist). T* **126** *and similar multicoloured designs showing original drawings.* W w **14** (*sideways on* 40 c.). *P* 14.

490 12 c. Type **126** 70 25
491 30 c. Yellow-crowned Night Heron .. .. 1·00 65
492 40 c. Great Egret (*horiz*) .. .. .. 1·25 85
493 $1.50, Eastern Bluebird .. .. .. 3·00 3·25
490/3 .. .. *Set of 4* 5·50 4·50

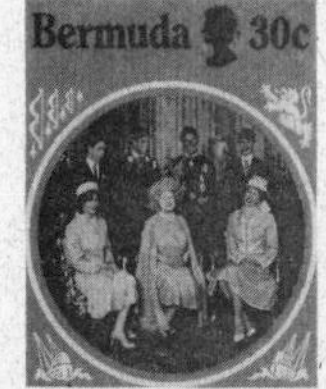

127 The Queen Mother with Grandchildren, 1980   **128** Halley's Comet and Bermuda Archipelago

(Des A. Theobald ($1), C. Abbott (others). Litho Questa)

1985 (7 June). *Life and Times of Queen Elizabeth the Queen Mother. T* **127** *and similar vert designs. Multicoloured.* W w **16**. *P* 14½ × 14.

494 12 c. Queen Consort, 1937 .. .. .. 25 15
495 30 c. Type **127** 50 50
496 40 c. At Clarence House on 83rd birthday .. 60 60
497 $1.50, With Prince Henry at his christening (from photo by Lord Snowdon) .. 2·25 2·75
494/7 .. .. *Set of 4* 3·25 3·50
MS498 91 × 73 mm. $1 With Prince Charles at 80th Birthday celebrations. Wmk sideways .. 1·50 2·00

(Des Harrison. Litho J.W.)

1985 (19 Sept). *Coats of Arms* (3rd *series*). *Vert designs as T* **119**. *Multicoloured.* W w **14**. *P* 13 × 13½.

499 12 c. Hamilton 50 15
500 30 c. Paget 80 70
501 40 c. Warwick 95 95
502 $1.50, City of Hamilton .. .. .. 3·00 3·50
499/502 .. .. *Set of 4* 4·75 4·75

(Des Jennifer Toombs. Litho Walsall)

1985 (21 Nov). *Appearance of Halley's Comet. T* **128** *and similar horiz designs. Multicoloured.* W w **16** (*sideways*). *P* 14 × 14½.

503 15 c. Type **128** 55 25
504 40 c. Halley's Comet, A.D. 684 (from Nuremberg Chronicles, 1493) .. .. .. 1·10 85
505 50 c. "Halley's Comet, 1531" (from Peter Apian woodcut, 1532) .. .. .. 1·25 95
506 $1.50, "Halley's Comet, 1759" (Samuel Scott) .. .. 2·75 3·00
503/6 .. .. *Set of 4* 5·00 4·50

129 *Constellation* (1943)

(Des L. Curtis. Litho Questa)

1986 (16 Jan)—**89**. *Ships Wrecked on Bermuda. T* **129** *and similar horiz designs. Multicoloured.* W w **16** (*sideways*). *P* 14. A. *Without imprint date at foot.* B. *With imprint date* "1989" (7.89).

No.	Description	A		B	
507	3 c. Type **129**	10	10	†	
508	5 c. *Early Riser* (1876)	10	10	†	
509	7 c. *Madiana* (1903) (20.3.86)	10	10	†	
510	10 c. *Curlew* (1856)	10	10	†	
511	12 c. *Warwick* (1619)	10	15	†	
512	15 c. H.M.S. *Vixen* (1890) (18.9.86)	15	20	†	
512*c*	18 c. As 7 c. (22.9.88)	20	25	†	
513	20 c. *San Pedro* (1594) (20.3.86)	20	25	†	
514	25 c. *Alert* (1877) (18.9.86)	25	30	†	
515	40 c. *North Carolina* (1880) (18.9.86)	40	45	†	
516	50 c. *Mark Antonie* (1777) (18.9.86)	50	55	†	
517	60 c. *Mary Celestia* (1864) (20.3.86)	60	65	†	
517*c*	70 c. *Caesar* (1818) (27.10.88)	75	80	†	
518	$1 *L'Herminie* (1839) (18.9.86)	1·50	1·25	1·00	1·10
519	$1.50, As 70 c. (20.3.86)	1·90	2·00	†	
520	$2 *Lord Amherst* (1778) (20.3.86)	2·50	2·75	2·10	2·25
521	$3 *Minerva* (1849) (20.3.86)	3·50	3·75	3·00	3·25
522	$5 *Caraquet* (1923) (18.9.86)	5·25	5·50	†	
523	$8 H.M.S. *Pallas* (1788)	8·25	8·50	†	
507/23	*Set of 19*	22·00	24·00		

NEW INFORMATION

The editor is always interested to correspond with people who have new information that will improve or correct the Catalogue.

(Des A. Theobald. Litho Harrison)

1986 (21 Apr). *60th Birthday of Queen Elizabeth II. Vert designs as T* **110** *of Ascension. Multicoloured.* W w **16**. *P* 14½×14.

524	15 c. Princess Elizabeth aged three, 1929	30	30
525	40 c. With Earl of Rosebery at Oaks May Meeting, Epsom, 1954	60	60
526	50 c. With Duke of Edinburgh, Bermuda, 1975	75	75
527	60 c. At British Embassy, Paris, 1972	90	90
528	$1.50, At Crown Agents Head Office, London, 1983	2·25	2·50
524/8	*Set of* 5	4·25	4·50

(Des G. Drummond. Litho Walsall)

1986 (22 May). *"Ameripex '86" International Stamp Exhibition, Chicago. Horiz designs as T* **164** *of Bahamas, showing Bermuda stamps (Nos. 529/32). Multicoloured.* W w **16** *(sideways). P* 14.

529	15 c. 1984 375th Anniv of Settlement miniature sheet	45	30
530	40 c. 1973 Lawn Tennis Centenary 24 c.	75	60
531	50 c. 1983 Bicentenary of Manned Flight 12 c.	85	75
532	$1 1976 Tall Ships Race 17 c.	1·75	2·00
529/32	*Set of* 4	3·50	3·25
MS533	80×80 mm. $1.50, Statue of Liberty and S.S. *Queen of Bermuda*	2·50	3·00

No. **MS**533 also commemorates the Centenary of the Statue of Liberty.

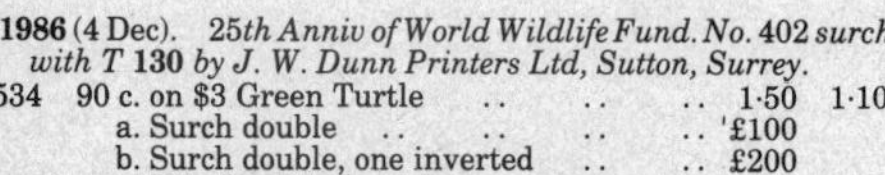

(130)

1986 (4 Dec). *25th Anniv of World Wildlife Fund. No. 402 surch with T* **130** *by J. W. Dunn Printers Ltd, Sutton, Surrey.*

534	90 c. on $3 Green Turtle	1·50	1·10
	a. Surch double	£100	
	b. Surch double, one inverted	£200	
	c. "90 c" omitted		

131 Train in Front Street, Hamilton, 1940

(Des A. Theobald. Litho Walsall)

1987 (22 Jan). *Transport (1st series). Bermuda Railway. T* **131** *and similar horiz designs. Multicoloured.* W w **16** *(sideways). P* 14.

535	15 c. Type **131**	55	25
536	40 c. Train crossing Springfield Trestle	1·00	75
537	50 c. "St. George Special" at Bailey's Bay Station	1·25	1·25
538	$1 50, Boat train at St. George	2·50	3·25
535/8	*Set of* 4	4·75	5·00

See also Nos. 535/8 and 574/7.

132 "Bermuda Settlers", 1901

(Des L. Curtis. Litho Walsall)

1987 (30 Apr). *Paintings by Winslow Homer. T* **132** *and similar horiz designs. Multicoloured.* W w **16** *(sideways). P* 14×14½.

(a) Sheet stamps (No. 541 with a buff frame).

539	15 c. Type **132**	25	25
540	30 c. "Bermuda", 1900	45	45
541	40 c. "Bermuda Landscape", 1901	55	55
542	50 c. "Inland Water", 1901	70	70
543	$1.50, "Salt Kettle", 1899	2·25	2·50
539/43	*Set of* 5	3·75	4·00

(b) Booklet stamps, each with grey frame

544	40 c. Type **132**	60	60
	a. Booklet pane. Nos. 544/8, each × 2	5·50	
545	40 c. As No. 540	60	60
546	40 c. As No. 541	60	60
547	40 c. As No. 542	60	60
548	40 c. As No. 543	60	60
544/8	*Set of* 5	2·75	2·75

133 PanAm Sikorsky "S-42B" *Bermuda Clipper* Flying Boat at Mooring

(Des A. Theobald. Litho Walsall)

1987 (18 June). *50th Anniv of Inauguration of Bermuda – U.S.A. Air Service. T* **133** *and similar horiz designs. Multicoloured.* W w **16** *(sideways). P* 14.

549	15 c. Type **133**	35	15
550	40 c. Imperial Airways Short "S-23" *Cavalier* flying boat at mooring	70	60
551	50 c. *Bermuda Clipper* in flight over signpost	80	70
552	$1.50, *Cavalier* on apron and *Bermuda Clipper* in flight	2·50	2·75
549/52	*Set of* 4	4·00	3·75

134 19th-century Wagon carrying Telephone Poles

135 Mail Wagon, *c.* 1869

(Des L. Curtis. Litho B.D.T.)

1987 (1 Oct). *Centenary of Bermuda Telephone Company. T* **134** *and similar horiz designs. Multicoloured.* W w **16** *(sideways). P* 14×13½.

553	15 c. Type **134**	25	15
554	40 c. Early telephone exchange	60	60
555	50 c. Early and modern telephones	70	70
556	$1.50, Communications satellite orbiting Earth	2·25	2·50
553/6	*Set of* 4	3·50	3·50

(Des O. Bell. Litho Questa)

1988 (3 Mar). *Transport (2nd series). Horse-drawn Carts and Wagons. T* **135** *and similar horiz designs. Multicoloured.* W w **16** *(sideways). P* 14.

557	15 c. Type **135**	25	15
558	40 c. Open cart, *c.* 1823	55	55
559	50 c. Closed cart, *c.* 1823	65	65
560	$1.50, Two-wheeled wagon, *c.* 1930	2·00	2·50
557/60	*Set of* 4	3·00	3·50

136 "Old Blush"

137 Devonshire Parish Militia, 1812

(Des R. Gorringe. Litho B.D.T.)

1988 (21 Apr). *Old Garden Roses (1st series). T* **136** *and similar multicoloured designs.* W w **14** *(sideways on horiz designs). P* 14×13½ *(vert) or* 13½×14 *(horiz).*

561	15 c. Type **136**	25	25
562	30 c. "Anna Olivier"	40	40
563	40 c. *Rosa chinensis semperflorens (vert)*	55	55
564	50 c. "Archduke Charles"	65	65
565	$1.50, *Rosa chinensis viridiflora (vert)*	1·75	1·90
561/5	*Set of* 5	3·25	3·50

See also Nos. 584/8 and, for these designs with the royal cypher instead of the Queen's head, Nos. 589/98.

(Des D. Miller (18 c.), E. Nisbet and D. Miller (others). Litho Questa)

1988 (13 Oct). *300th Anniv of Lloyd's of London. Multicoloured designs as T* **123** *of Ascension.* W w **16** *(sideways on* 50, 60 *c.). P* 14.

566	18 c. Loss of H.M.S. *Lutine*, 1799	25	25
567	50 c. *Sentinel* (cable ship) *(horiz)*	70	65
568	60 c. *Bermuda*, Hamilton, 1931 *(horiz)*	80	75
569	$2 Loss of H.M.S. *Valerian* in hurricane, 1926	2·75	3·00
566/9	*Set of* 4	4·00	4·25

(Des A. Barbosa. Litho Harrison)

1988 (10 Nov). *Military Uniforms. T* **137** *and similar vert designs. Multicoloured.* W w **14**. *P* 14½.

570	18 c. Type **137**	25	25
571	50 c. 71st (Highland) Regiment, 1831-34	65	65
572	60 c. Cameron Highlanders, 1942	75	75
573	$2 Troop of horse, 1774	2·50	2·75
570/3	*Set of* 4	3·75	4·00

138 *Corona*

139 Morgan's Island

(Des C. Abbott, adapted L. Curtis. Litho Questa)

1989 (16 Feb). *Transport (3rd series). Ferry Services. T* **138** *and similar horiz designs. Multicoloured.* W w **16** *(sideways). P* 14.

574	18 c. Type **138**	25	25
575	50 c. Rowing boat ferry	65	65
576	60 c. St. George's barge ferry	75	75
577	$2 *Laconia*	2·50	2·75
574/7	*Set of* 4	3·75	4·00

(Des A. Theobald. Litho Questa)

1989 (11 May). *150 Years of Photography. T* **139** *and similar horiz designs. Multicoloured.* W w **14** *(sideways). P* 14×14½.

578	18 c. Type **139**	20	25
579	30 c. Front Street, Hamilton	35	40
580	50 c. Waterfront, Front Street, Hamilton	60	65
581	60 c. Crow Lane from Hamilton Harbour	70	75
582	70 c. Shipbuilding, Hamilton Harbour	85	90
583	$1 Dockyard	1·25	1·40
578/83	*Set of* 6	3·50	4·00

(Des R. Gorringe. Litho B.D.T.)

1989 (13 July). *Old Garden Roses (2nd series). Multicoloured designs as T* **136**. W w **14** *(sideways on* 50, 60 *c. and* $1.50). *P* 14×13½ (18, 30 *c.) or* 13½×14 *(others).*

584	18 c. "Agrippina" *(vert)*	20	25
585	30 c. "Smith's Parish" *(vert)*	35	40
586	50 c. "Champney's Pink Cluster"	60	65
587	60 c. "Rosette Delizy"	70	75
588	$1.50, *Rosa bracteata*	1·75	1·90
584/8	*Set of* 5	3·25	3·50

For these designs with the royal cypher instead of the Queen's head, see Nos. 589/98.

1989 (13 July). *Booklet stamps. Old Garden Roses designs as Nos.* 561/5 *and* 584/8, *but with royal cypher at top left instead of Queen's head. Multicoloured.* W w **14** *(sideways on horiz, inverted on vert designs). P* 13½.

589	50 c. As No. 565 *(vert)*	60	65
	a. Booklet pane. Nos. 589/98	5·50	
590	50 c. As No. 563 *(vert)*	60	65
591	50 c. Type **136**	60	65
592	50 c. As No. 562	60	65
593	50 c. As No. 564	60	65
594	50 c. As No. 585 *(vert)*	60	65
595	50 c. As No. 584 *(vert)*	60	65
596	50 c. As No. 586	60	65
597	50 c. As No. 587	60	65
598	50 c. As No. 588	60	65
589/98	*Set of* 10	5·50	5·75

Booklet pane No. 589a has margins on three sides.

140 Main Library, Hamilton

141 1865 1d. Rose

(Des O. Bell. Litho B.D.T.)

1989 (5 Oct). *150th Anniv of Bermuda Library. T* **140** *and similar horiz designs. Multicoloured.* W w **14** *(sideways). P* 13½×14.

599	18 c. Type **140**	20	25
600	50 c. The Old Rectory, St. George's	60	65
601	60 c. Somerset Library, Springfield	70	75
602	$2 Cabinet Building, Hamilton	2·40	2·50
599/602	*Set of* 4	3·50	3·75

(Des D. Miller. Litho Questa)

1989 (3 Nov). *Commonwealth Postal Conference. T* **141** *and similar vert designs. Multicoloured.* W w **16**. *P* 14.

603	18 c. brownish grey, brown-rose & brt scar	20	25
604	50 c. brownish grey, slate-bl & pale grey-bl	60	65
605	60 c. brownish grey, dull purple and purple	70	75
606	$2 brownish grey, dull green & brt emer	2·40	2·50
603/6	*Set of* 4	3·50	3·75

Designs:—50 c. 1866 2d. blue; 60 c. 1865 6d purple; $2 1865 1s. green.

POSTAL FISCAL

1937 (1 Feb). *As T* **15**, *but inscr* "REVENUE" *at each side. Wmk Mult Script CA. P* 14.

F1	12s. 6d. grey and orange, **C**	£900	£900
	a. Break in scroll (R. 1/12)	£1900	
	b. Broken crown and scroll (R. 2/12)	£1900	

No. F1 was issued for fiscal purposes during 1936. Its use as a postage stamp was authorised from 1 February to April 1937. The used price quoted above is for examples postmarked during this period. Later in the same year postmarks with other dates were obtained by favour.

For illustration of No. F1a/b see above No. 44.

Botswana
(*formerly* Bechuanaland)

INDEPENDENCE

47 National Assembly Building

(Des R. Granger Barrett. Photo Harrison)

1966 (30 Sept). *Independence. T* **47** *and similar horiz designs. Multicoloured. P* 14½.

No.	Description	Unused	Used
202	2½ c. Type **47**	10	10
	a. Imperf (pair)	£225	
203	5 c. Abattoir, Lobatsi	10	10
204	15 c. National Airways "Dakota"	20	10
205	35 c. State House, Gaberones	25	20
202/5	*Set of* 4	50	30

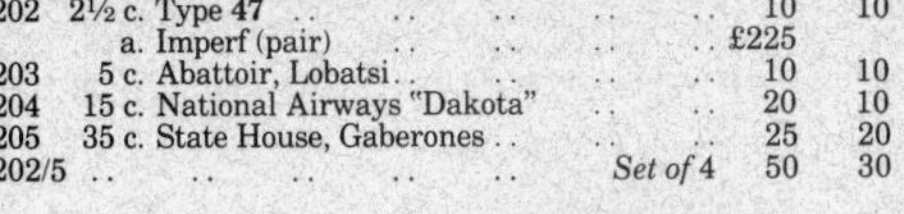

(51)

52 Golden Oriole

1966 (30 Sept). *Nos.* 168/81 *of Bechuanaland optd as T* **51**.

No.	Description	Unused	Used
206	1 c. yellow, red, black and lilac	15	10
207	2 c. orange, black and yellow-olive	20	10
208	2½ c. carmine, green, black and bistre	25	10
209	3½ c. yellow, black, sepia and pink	40	15
	a. Yellow, black, sepia and flesh	60	25
210	5 c. yellow, blue, black and buff	40	20
211	7½ c. brown, red, black and apple-green	40	30
	a. Blue-green omitted		
212	10 c. red, yellow, sepia & turquoise-green	60	20
213	12½ c. buff, blue, red and grey-black	1·75	75
214	20 c. yellow-brown and drab	40	45
215	25 c. deep brown and lemon	40	50
216	35 c. deep blue and orange	50	65
217	50 c. sepia and olive	50	70
218	1 r. black and cinnamon	75	1·25
219	2 r. brown and turquoise-blue	1·00	2·50
206/19	*Set of* 14	6·50	7·00

No. 209*a* was a special printing produced to make up quantities. It does not exist without the overprint.

No. 211a shows the background in yellow instead of apple-green, the blue-green overlay being omitted.

(Des D. M. Reid-Henry. Photo Harrison)

1967 (3 Jan). *Birds. Vert designs as T* **52**. *Multicoloured. P* 14 × 14½.

No.	Description	Unused	Used
220	1 c. Type **52**	20	15
	a. Error. Wmk **105** of Malta	†	£700
221	2 c. Hoopoe	40	10
222	3 c. Groundscraper Thrush	55	10
223	4 c. Cordon-bleu	55	10
224	5 c. Secretary Bird	55	10
225	7 c. Yellow-billed Hornbill	60	40
226	10 c. Burchell's Gonolek	60	15
227	15 c. Malachite Kingfisher	3·50	45
228	20 c. African Fish Eagle	3·25	65
229	25 c. Go-away Bird	2·00	60
230	35 c. Scimitar-bill	4·25	70
231	50 c. Comb Duck	3·25	1·50
232	1 r. Levaillant's Barbet	4·75	3·25
233	2 r. Didric Cuckoo	9·50	11·00
220/33	*Set of* 14	30·00	17·00

A used copy of the 20 c. has been seen with the pale brown colour missing, resulting in the value (normally shown in white) being omitted.

The 1, 2, 4, 7 and 10 c. values exist with PVA gum as well as gum arabic.

66 Students and University

(Des V. Whiteley. Photo Harrison)

1967 (7 Apr). *First Conferment of University Degrees. P* 14 × 14½.

No.	Description	Unused	Used
234 **66**	3 c. sepia, ultramarine & lt orange-yell	10	10
235	7 c. sepia, ultram & lt greenish bl	10	10
236	15 c. sepia, ultramarine and rose	10	10
237	35 c. sepia, ultramarine and light violet	20	20
234/7	*Set of* 4	30	30

67 Bushbuck

(Des G. Vasarhelyi. Photo Harrison)

1967 (2 Oct). *Chobe Game Reserve. T* **67** *and similar horiz designs. Multicoloured. P* 14.

No.	Description	Unused	Used
238	3 c. Type **67**	10	10
239	7 c. Sable Antelope	15	15
240	35 c. Fishing on Chobe River	70	45
238/40	*Set of* 3	80	60

70 Arms of Botswana and Human Rights Emblem

(Litho D.L.R.)

1968 (8 Apr). *Human Rights Year. T* **70** *and similar horiz designs showing Arms of Botswana and Human Rights emblem arranged differently. P* 13½ × 13.

No.	Description	Unused	Used
241	3 c. multicoloured	10	10
242	15 c. multicoloured	10	10
243	25 c. multicoloured	15	20
241/3	*Set of* 3	25	30

73 Eland and Giraffe Rock Paintings, Tsodilo Hills

75 "Baobab Trees" (Thomas Baines)

76 National Museum and Art Gallery

(Litho D.L.R.)

1968 (30 Sept). *Opening of National Museum and Art Gallery. T* **73/6** *and similar multicoloured design. P* 12½ (7 c.), 12½ × 13½ (15 c.), *or* 13 × 13½ (*others*).

No.	Description	Unused	Used
244	3 c. Type **73**	10	10
245	7 c. Girl wearing ceremonial beads (30 × 48 *mm*)	20	15
246	10 c. Type **75**	30	25
247	15 c. Type **76**	40	35
244/7	*Set of* 4	85	70
MS248	132 × 82 mm. Nos. 244/7. P 13	1·10	2·00

77 African Family, and Star over Village

(Des Mrs M. E. Townsend, adapted J. Cooter. Litho Enschedé)

1968 (11 Nov). *Christmas. P* 13 × 14.

No.	Description	Unused	Used
249 **77**	1 c. multicoloured	10	10
250	2 c. multicoloured	10	10
251	5 c. multicoloured	10	10
252	25 c. multicoloured	15	25
249/52	*Set of* 4	20	30

78 Scout, Lion and Badge in Frame

(Des D.L.R. Litho Format)

1969 (21 Aug). *22nd World Scout Conference, Helsinki. T* **78** *and similar multicoloured designs. P* 13½.

No.	Description	Unused	Used
253	3 c. Type **78**	25	10
254	15 c. Scouts cooking over open fire (*vert*)	75	50
255	25 c. Scouts around camp fire	75	70
253/5	*Set of* 3	1·50	1·10

81 Woman, Child and Christmas Star

82 Diamond Treatment Plant, Orapa

(Des A. Vale, adapted V. Whiteley. Litho Harrison)

1969 (6 Nov). *Christmas. P* 14½ × 14.

No.	Description	Unused	Used
256 **81**	1 c. pale blue and chocolate	10	10
257	2 c. pale yellow-olive and chocolate	10	10
258	4 c. yellow and chocolate	10	10
259	35 c. chocolate and bluish violet	20	20
256/9	*Set of* 4	30	30
MS260	86 × 128 mm. Nos. 256/9. P 14½ (*shades*)	70	1·10

(Des J.W. Litho Harrison)

1970 (23 Mar). *Developing Botswana. T* **82** *and similar designs. Multicoloured. P* 14½ × 14 (3 *c.*, 7 *c.*) *or* 14 × 14½ (*others*).

No.	Description	Unused	Used
261	3 c. Type **82**	20	10
262	7 c. Copper-nickel mining	35	15
263	10 c. Copper-nickel mine, Selebi-Pikwe (*horiz*)	45	20
264	35 c. Orapa diamond mine, and diamonds (*horiz*)	1·25	65
261/4	*Set of* 4	2·00	95

83 Mr. Micawber (*David Copperfield*)

(Des V. Whiteley. Litho Walsall)

1970 (6 July). *Death Centenary of Charles Dickens. T* **83** *and similar horiz designs. Multicoloured. P* 11.

No.	Description	Unused	Used
265	3 c. Type **83**	10	10
266	7 c. Scrooge (*A Christmas Carol*)	15	10
267	15 c. Fagin (*Oliver Twist*)	30	30
268	25 c. Bill Sykes (*Oliver Twist*)	55	55
265/8	*Set of* 4	90	80
MS269	114 × 81 mm. Nos. 265/8	2·00	3·25

84 U.N. Building and Emblem

(Des J. Cooter. Litho Walsall)

1970 (24 Oct). *25th Anniv of United Nations. P* 11.

No.	Description	Unused	Used
270 **84**	15 c. bright blue, chestnut and silver	15	20

85 Crocodile

(Des A. Vale. Litho Questa)

1970 (3 Nov). *Christmas. T* **85** *and similar horiz designs. Multicoloured. P* 14.

No.	Description	Unused	Used
271	1 c. Type **85**	10	10
272	2 c. Giraffe	10	10
273	7 c. Elephant	10	10
274	25 c. Rhinoceros	15	25
271/4	*Set of* 4	25	30
MS275	128 × 90 mm. Nos. 271/4	1·25	2·00

86 Sorghum

(Des J.W. Litho Questa)

1971 (6 April). *Important Crops. T* **86** *and similar horiz designs. Multicoloured. P* 14.

No.	Description	Unused	Used
276	3 c. Type **86**	10	10
277	7 c. Millet	10	10
278	10 c. Maize	10	10
279	35 c. Groundnuts	20	35
276/9	*Set of* 4	25	40

87 Map and Head of Cow

88 King bringing Gift of Gold

(Des A. Vale, adapted L. Curtis. Litho Harrison)

1971 (30 Sept). *Fifth Anniv of Independence. T* **87** *and similar vert designs inscr* "PULA" (local greeting). *P* 14½ × 14.

280 3 c. black, brown and apple-green 10 10
281 4 c. black, new blue and pale blue 10 10
282 7 c. black and red-orange 20 10
283 10 c. multicoloured 20 15
284 20 c. multicoloured 60 80
280/4 .. .. *Set of* 5 1·00 1·10

Designs:—4 c. Map and cogs; 7 c. Map and zebra; 10 c. Map and sorghum stalk crossed by tusk; 20 c. Arms and map of Botswana.

(Des A. Vale. Litho Questa)

1971 (11 Nov). *Christmas. T* **88** *and similar vert designs. Multicoloured. P* 14.

285 2 c. Type **88** 10 10
286 3 c. King bearing frankincense 10 10
287 7 c. King bearing myrrh 10 10
288 20 c. Three Kings behold the star 35 50
285/8 .. .. *Set of* 4 40 55
MS289 85 × 128 mm. Nos. 285/8 .. .. .. 1·00 2·00

89 Orion

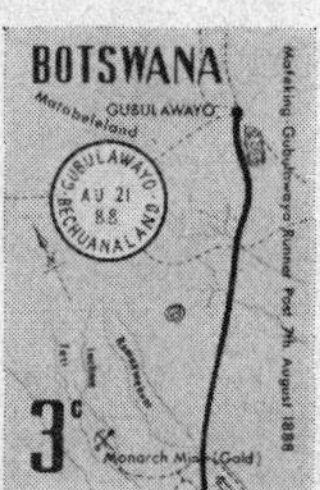

90 Postmark and Map

(Des R. Granger Barrett. Litho Questa)

1972 (24 Apr). *"Night Sky". T* **89** *and similar vert designs. P* 14.

290 3 c. turquoise-blue, black and red 20 10
291 7 c. dull blue, black and yellow 45 60
292 10 c. dull green, black and orange 55 75
293 20 c. deep violet-blue, black and blue-green .. 1·00 1·25
290/3 .. .. *Set of* 4 2·00 2·40

Constellations:—7 c. The Scorpion; 10 c. The Centaur; 20 c. The Cross.

(Des M. Bryan. Litho A. & M.)

1972 (21 Aug). *Mafeking-Gubulawayo Runner Post. T* **90** *and similar vert designs. Multicoloured. P* 13½ × 13.

294 3 c. Type **90** 20 10
295 4 c. Bechuanaland stamp and map 25 35
296 7 c. Runners and map 40 50
297 20 c. Mafeking postmark and map .. .. 1·00 1·25
294/7 .. .. *Set of* 4 1·75 2·00
MS298 84 × 216 mm. Nos. 294/7 vertically *se-tenant*, forming a composite map design .. .. 5·50 8·00

For these designs redrawn smaller with changed inscriptions see Nos. 652/6.

91 Cross, Map and Bells

92 Thor

(Des M. Bryan. Litho Questa)

1972 (6 Nov). *Christmas. Vert designs each with Cross and Map as T* **91**. *Multicoloured. P* 14.

299 2 c. Type **91** 10 10
300 3 c. Cross, map and candle 10 10
301 7 c. Cross, map and Christmas tree 15 20
302 20 c. Cross, map, star and holly 40 55
299/302 .. .. *Set of* 4 60 75
MS303 96 × 119 mm. Nos. 299/302 .. .. 1·25 2·50

(Des Edna Elphick. Litho Questa)

1973 (23 Mar). *I.M.O./W.M.O. Centenary. T* **92** *and similar designs showing Norse myths. Multicoloured. P* 14.

304 3 c. Type **92** 10 10
305 4 c. Sun God's chariot (*horiz*) 15 15
306 7 c. Ymir, the frost giant 20 15
307 20 c. Odin and Sleipnir (*horiz*) 50 60
304/7 .. .. *Set of* 4 85 85

93 Livingstone and River Scene

(Des G. Vasarhelyi. Litho Walsall Security Printers, Ltd)

1973 (10 Sept). *Death Centenary of Dr. Livingstone. T* **93** *and similar horiz design. Multicoloured. P* 13½.

308 3 c. Type **93** 10 10
309 20 c. Livingstone meeting Stanley 50 60

94 Donkey and Foal at Village Trough

95 Gaborone Campus

(Des M. Bryan. Litho Questa)

1973 (3 Dec). *Christmas. T* **94** *and similar multicoloured designs. P* 14.

310 3 c. Type **94** 10 10
311 4 c. Shepherd and flock (*horiz*) 10 10
312 7 c. Mother and child 10 10
313 20 c. Kgotla meeting (*horiz*) 40 60
310/13 .. .. *Set of* 4 55 70

(Des. M. Bryan, adapted P. Powell. Litho Questa)

1974 (8 May). *Tenth Anniv of University of Botswana, Lesotho and Swaziland. T* **95** *and similar horiz designs. Multicoloured. P* 14.

314 3 c. Type **95** 10 10
315 7 c. Kwaluseni Campus 10 10
316 20 c. Roma Campus 15 20
317 35 c. Map and flags of the three countries .. 20 35
314/17 .. .. *Set of* 4 35 55

96 Methods of Mail Transport

(Des. M. Bryan. Litho J.W.)

1974 (29 May). *Centenary of Universal Postal Union. T* **96** *and similar horiz designs. Multicoloured. P* 14.

318 2 c. Type **96** 45 35
319 3 c. Post Office, Palapye, *circa* 1889 .. .. 45 35
320 7 c. Bechuanaland Police Camel Post, *circa* 1900 .. .. 70 70
321 20 c. Mail-planes of 1920 and 1974 .. .. 2·50 2·50
318/21 .. .. *Set of* 4 3·50 3·50

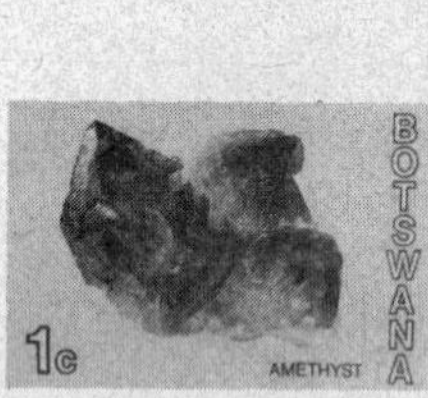

97 Amethyst

98 *Stapelia variegata*

(Des M. Baylis, adapted PAD Studio. Photo Enschedé)

1974 (1 July). *Botswana Minerals. T* **97** *and similar horiz designs. Multicoloured. P* 14 × 13.

322 1 c. Type **97** 40 20
323 2 c. Agate—"Botswana Pink" 45 20
324 3 c. Quartz 55 20
325 4 c. Copper nickel 60 30
326 5 c. Moss agate 60 30
327 7 c. Agate 70 30
328 10 c. Stilbite 80 40
329 15 c. Moshaneng Banded Marble .. .. 1·50 75
330 20 c. Gem diamonds .. .. 2·50 80
331 25 c. Chrysotile .. .. 2·50 70
332 35 c. Jasper .. .. 3·50 1·50
333 50 c. Moss quartz .. .. 3·75 2·25
334 1 r. Citrine .. .. 7·50 6·00
335 2 r. Chalcopyrite .. .. 14·00 12·00
322/35 .. .. *Set of* 14 35·00 23·00

(Des M. Bryan. Litho Questa)

1974 (4 Nov). *Christmas. T* **98** *and similar vert designs showing flowers. Multicoloured. P* 14.

336 2 c. Type **98** 20 10
337 7 c. *Hibiscus lunarifolius* 50 20
338 15 c. *Ceratotheca triloba* .. .. .. 1·10 50
339 20 c. *Nerine laticoma* .. .. 1·25 60
336/9 .. .. *Set of* 4 2·75 1·25
MS340 85 × 130 mm. Nos. 336/9 .. .. .. 2·75 3·25

99 President Sir Seretse Khama

100 Ostrich

(Des M. Bryan, adapted G. Vasarhelyi. Photo Enschedé)

1975 (24 Mar). *Tenth Anniv of Self-Government. P* 13½ × 13.

341 **99** 4 c. multicoloured 10 10
342 10 c. multicoloured 15 10
343 20 c. multicoloured 25 15
344 35 c. multicoloured 45 35
341/4 .. .. *Set of* 4 85 55
MS345 93 × 130 mm. Nos. 341/4 .. .. .. 1·00 1·50

(Des M. Bryan. Litho Questa)

1975 (23 June). *Rock Paintings, Tsodilo Hills. T* **100** *and similar horiz designs. Multicoloured. P* 14.

346 4 c. Type **100** 25 10
347 10 c. White Rhinoceros 70 10
348 25 c. Spotted Hyena .. .. 1·75 45
349 35 c. Scorpion .. .. 2·00 90
346/9 .. .. *Set of* 4 4·25 1·40
MS350 150 × 150 mm. Nos. 346/9 .. .. 7·00 7·00

101 Map of British Bechuanaland, 1885

102 *Aloe marlothii*

(Des M. Bryan, adapted G. Vasarhelyi. Litho Harrison)

1975 (13 Oct). *Anniversaries. T* **101** *and similar multicoloured designs. P* 14 × 14½ (25 *c.*) *or* 14½ × 14 (*others*).

351 6 c. Type **101** 30 15
352 10 c. Chief Khama, 1875 .. .. .. 40 15
353 25 c. Chiefs Sebele, Bathoen and Khama, 1895 (*horiz*) 80 65
351/3 .. .. *Set of* 3 1·40 85

Events:—6 c. 90th Anniv of Protectorate; 10 c. Centenary of Khama's Accession; 25 c. 80th Anniv of Chiefs' visit to London.

(Des M. Bryan. Litho Questa)

1975 (3 Nov). *Christmas. T* **102** *and similar vert designs showing aloes. Multicoloured. P* 14½.

354 3 c. Type **102** 20 10
355 10 c. *Aloe lutescens* 55 35
356 15 c. *Aloe zebrina* 90 85
357 25 c. *Aloe littoralis* .. .. 1·25 1·25
354/7 .. .. *Set of* 4 2·50 2·25

103 Drum

(Des M. Bryan. Litho Questa)

1976 (1 Mar). *Traditional Musical Instruments. T* **103** *and similar horiz designs. Multicoloured. P* 14.

358 4 c. Type **103** 15 10
359 10 c. Hand Piano 25 10
360 15 c. Segankuru (violin) 30 20
361 25 c. Kudu Signal Horn 40 40
358/61 .. .. *Set of* 4 1·00 65

104 One Pula Note

(Des M. Bryan from banknotes by D.L.R. Litho Questa)

1976 (28 June). *First National Currency. T* **104** *and similar horiz designs. Multicoloured. P* 14.

362	4 c. Type **104**	15	10
363	10 c. Two pula note	20	10
364	15 c. Five pula note	35	20
365	25 c. Ten pula note	45	45
362/5	*Set of* 4	1·00	70
MS366	163 × 107 mm. Nos. 362/5	1·50	2·00

(New Currency. 100 thebe = 1 pula)

1t	1t	2t	2t
(105) (Type I)	(105) (Type II)	(I)	(II)
4t	4t	5t	5t
(I)	(II)	(I)	(II)
15t	15t	20t	20t
(I)	(II)	(I)	(II)

(Surch in letterpress by Govt Printer, Pretoria (Type I), or in lithography by Enschedé (Type II))

1976 (23 Aug)–77. *Nos.* 322/35 *surch as T* **105.**

367	1 t. on 1 c. Type **97** (I)	25	10
	a. Type II Surch (15.7.77)	30	15
368	2 t. on 2 c. Agate—"Botswana Pink" (I)	30	10
	a. Type II Surch (15.7.77)	35	20
369	3 t. on 3 c. Quartz (surch at top right) (Gold)	30	10
	a. Surch at bottom right (17.10.77)		
370	4 t. on 4 c. Copper nickel (I)	40	10
	a. Type II Surch (15.7.77)	60	30
371	5 t. on 5 c. Moss agate (I)	40	10
	a. Type II Surch (15.7.77)	60	30
372	7 t. on 7 c. Agate (surch at top right)	55	20
	a. Surch at bottom right (17.10.77)		
373	10 t. on 10 c. Stilbite	65	25
374	15 t. on 15 c. Moshaneng Banded Marble (I) (Gold)	90	55
	a. Type II Surch (15.7.77)	1·25	90
375	20 t. on 20 c. Gem diamonds (I)	1·50	55
	a. Type II Surch (15.7.77)	1·75	1·00
376	25 t. on 25 c. Chrysotile	1·50	70
377	35 t. on 35 c. Jasper	1·75	1·00
378	50 t. on 50 c. Moss quartz (surch at top right)	2·00	1·50
	a. Surch at bottom right (17.10.77)		
379	1 p. on 1 r. Citrine (surch at top right)	3·50	3·25
	a. Surch at bottom left (17.10.77)		
380	2 p. on 2 r. Chalcopyrite (Gold)	6·00	7·00
367/80	*Set of* 14	18·00	14·00
367a/75a	*Set of* 6	4·25	2·50

Nos. 369a, 372a, 378a and 379a come from a second Pretoria printing, using the same type, on a small stock returned from the Crown Agents.

106 Botswanan Cattle

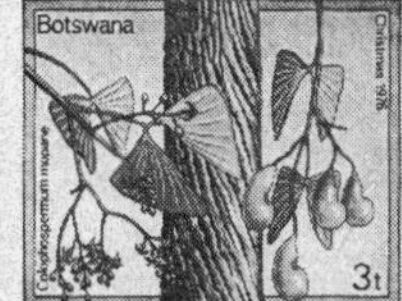

107 *Colophospermum mopane*

(Des M. Bryan. Litho Questa)

1976 (30 Sept). *Tenth Anniv of Independence. T* **106** *and similar multicoloured designs. P* 14.

381	4 t. Type **106**	15	10
382	10 t. Deer, Okavango Delta (*vert*)	30	10
383	15 t. Schools and pupils	40	20
384	25 t. Rural weaving (*vert*)	55	30
385	35 t. Miner (*vert*)	70	50
381/5	*Set of* 5	1·90	1·10

Nos. 381/5 were printed on sand-grained paper which has an uneven surface.

(Des M. Bryan. Litho J.W.)

1976 (1 Nov). *Christmas. T* **107** *and similar horiz designs showing trees. Multicoloured. P* 13.

386	3 t. Type **107**	15	10
387	4 t. *Baikiaea plurijuga*	15	10
388	10 t. *Sterculia rogersii*	40	15
389	25 t. *Acacia nilotica*	80	50
390	40 t. *Kigelia africana*	1·25	90
386/90	*Set of* 5	2·50	1·50

108 Coronation Coach

(Des M. Bryan, adapted G. Vasarhelyi. Litho Cartor S.A., France)

1977 (7 Feb). *Silver Jubilee. T* **108** *and similar horiz designs. Multicoloured. P* 12.

391	4 t. Queen and Sir Seretse Khama	10	10
392	25 t. Type **108**	20	15
393	40 t. The Recognition	35	35
391/3	*Set of* 3	60	50

109 African Clawless Otter

110 Cwihaba Caves

(Des M. Bryan. Litho Questa)

1977 (6 June). *Diminishing Species. T* **109** *and similar horiz designs. Multicoloured. P* 14.

394	3 t. Type **109**	35	20
395	4 t. Serval	35	20
396	10 t. Bat-eared Fox	90	40
397	25 t. Temminck's Ground Pangolin	2·00	1·10
398	40 t. Brown Hyena	3·00	1·90
394/8	*Set of* 5	6·00	3·50

(Des M. Bryan. Litho J.W.)

1977 (12 Aug). *Historical Monuments. T* **110** *and similar horiz designs. Multicoloured. P* 14.

399	4 t. Type **110**	15	10
400	5 t. Khama Memorial	15	10
401	15 t. Green's Tree	40	40
402	20 t. Mmajojo Ruins	40	45
403	25 t. Ancient morabaraba board	45	50
404	35 t. Matsieng's footprint	55	60
399/404	*Set of* 6	1·90	2·00
MS405	154 × 105 mm. Nos. 399/404	2·10	2·40

111 *Hypoxis nitida*

112 Little Black Bustard

(Des M. Bryan. Litho Questa)

1977 (7 Nov*). *Christmas. T* **111** *and similar vert designs showing lilies. Multicoloured. P* 14.

406	3 t. Type **111**	15	10
407	5 t. *Haemanthus magnificus*	15	10
408	10 t. *Boophane disticha*	35	10
409	25 t. *Vellozia retinervis*	75	35
410	40 t. *Ammocharis coranica*	1·00	75
406/10	*Set of* 5	2·25	1·10

*This is the local release date. The Crown Agents released the stamps on 31 October.

(Des M. Bryan. Photo Harrison)

1978 (3 July). *Birds. Vert designs as T* **112**. *Multicoloured. P* 14 × 14½ (1 *to* 20 *t.*) *or* 14 (25*t to* 5 *p.*).

411	1 t. Type **112**	25	25
412	2 t. Marabou Stork	25	25
413	3 t. Green Wood Hoopoe	25	25
414	4 t. Carmine Bee Eater	30	20
415	5 t. African Jacana	30	20
416	7 t. African Paradise Flycatcher	40	20
417	10 t. Bennett's Woodpecker	50	20
418	15 t. Red Bishop	60	45
419	20 t. Crowned Plover	60	60
420	25 t. Giant Kingfisher	60	60
421	30 t. White-faced Whistling Duck	60	50
422	35 t. Green Heron	60	50
423	45 t. Black-headed Heron	65	65
424	50 t. Spotted Eagle Owl	1·00	65
425	1 p. Gabar Goshawk	1·00	1·25
426	2 p. Martial Eagle	2·00	3·50
427	5 p. Saddle-bill Stork	7·50	8·50
411/27	*Set of* 17	16·00	17·00

113 Tawana making Karos

(Des M. Bryan. Litho Questa)

1978 (11 Sept). *Okavango Delta. T* **113** *and similar horiz designs. Multicoloured. P* 14.

428	4 t. Type **113**	10	10
429	5 t. Tribe localities	10	10
430	15 t. Bushmen collecting roots	30	30
431	20 t. Herero woman milking	35	35
432	25 t. Yei poling "mokoro" (canoe)	40	40
433	35 t. Mbukushu fishing	55	55
428/33	*Set of* 6	1·60	1·60
MS434	150 × 98 mm. Nos. 428/33	1·75	2·00

Nos. 428/34 were printed on sand-grained paper which has an uneven surface.

ALTERED CATALOGUE NUMBERS

Any Catalogue numbers altered from the last edition are shown as a list in the introductory pages.

114 *Caralluma lutea*

115 Sip Well

(Des M. Bryan. Litho J.W.)

1978 (6 Nov). *Christmas. Flowers. T* **114** *and similar vert designs. Multicoloured. P* 14.

435	5 t. Type **114**	15	10
436	10 t. *Hoodia lugardii*	25	15
437	15 t. *Ipomoea transvaalensis*	50	40
438	25 t. *Ansellia gigantea*	70	55
435/8	*Set of* 4	1·40	1·10

(Des M. Bryan. Litho Questa)

1979 (12 Feb). *Water Development. T* **115** *and similar vert designs. Multicoloured. P* 14.

439	3 t. Type **115**	10	10
440	5 t. Watering pit	15	10
441	10 t. Hand dug well	15	10
442	25 t. Windmill	30	30
443	40 t. Modern drilling rig	55	55
439/43	*Set of* 5	1·10	1·00

116 Pottery

117 1885 British Bechuanaland 1d. Stamp and Sir Rowland Hill

(Des M. Bryan. Litho Questa)

1979 (11 June). *Handicrafts. T* **116** *and similar vert designs. Multicoloured. P* 14½ × 14.

444	5 t. Type **116**	10	10
445	10 t. Clay modelling	15	10
446	25 t. Basketry	30	25
447	40 t. Beadwork	50	50
444/7	*Set of* 4	95	80
MS448	123 × 96 mm. Nos. 444/7	95	1·25

(Des M. Bryan. Litho Secura, Singapore)

1979 (27 Aug). *Death Centenary of Sir Rowland Hill. T* **117** *and similar horiz designs showing stamps and Sir Rowland Hill. Multicoloured. P* 13½.

449	5 t. Type **117**	10	10
450	25 t. 1932 Bechuanaland Protectorate 2d	35	40
451	45 t. 1967 2 c. definitive	45	55
449/51	*Set of* 3	80	95

118 Children Playing

119 *Ximenia caffra*

(Des K. Mosinyi (5 t.), M. Bryan (10 t.). Litho Questa)

1979 (24 Sept). *International Year of the Child. T* **118** *and similar multicoloured design. P* 14.

452	5 t. Type **118**	10	10
453	10 t. Child playing with doll (*vert*)	20	20

(Des M. Bryan. Litho Questa)

1979 (12 Nov). *Christmas. Fruit. T* **119** *and similar vert designs. Multicoloured. P* 14.

454	5 t. Type **119**	10	10
455	10 t. *Sclerocarya caffra*	20	20
456	15 t. *Hexalobus monopetalus*	35	35
457	25 t. *Ficus soldanella*	45	45
454/7	*Set of* 4	1·00	1·00

120 Flap-necked Chameleon

121 Rock Breaking

(Des M. Bryan. Litho Security Printers (M), Malaysia)

1980 (3 Mar). *Reptiles. T* **120** *and similar horiz designs. Multicoloured. P* 13½.

458	5 t. Type **120** ..	10	10
459	10 t. Leopard Tortoise ..	15	15
460	25 t. Puff Adder ..	40	40
461	40 t. White-throated Monitor ..	60	60
458/61	.. *Set of* 4	1·10	1·10

(Des M. Bryan. Litho Secura, Singapore)

1980 (7 July). *Early Mining. T* **121** *and similar horiz designs. Multicoloured. P* 13½.

462	5 t. Type **121** ..	10	10
463	10 t. Ore hoisting ..	15	15
464	15 t. Ore transport ..	30	30
465	20 t. Ore crushing ..	35	35
466	25 t. Smelting ..	40	40
467	35 t. Tools and products ..	55	55
462/7	.. *Set of* 6	1·60	1·60

122 "Chiwele and the Giant"

(Des W. Battiss. Litho Questa)

1980 (8 Sept). *Folktales. T* **122** *and similar multicoloured designs. P* 14 (5 *t.*), 14 × 13½ (45 *t.*) *or* 14½ × 14 (*others*).

468	5 t. Type **122** (35 × 22 *mm*) ..	10	10
469	10 t. "Kgori is not deceived" (28 × 37 *mm*) ..	15	10
470	30 t. "Nyambi's wife and Crocodile" (28 × 37 *mm*) ..	45	45
471	45 t. "Clever Hare" (44 × 27 *mm*) ..	60	60
468/71	.. *Set of* 4	1·10	1·10

123 Game watching. Makgadikgadi Pans

(Des M. Bryan. Litho Govt Printer, Pretoria)

1980 (6 Oct). *World Tourism Conference, Manila. P* 14.

472 **123**	5 t. multicoloured ..	10	10

124 *Acacia gerrardii*

125 Heinrich von Stephan with Bechuanaland 1949 3d. and Botswana 1974 3 c. U.P.U. Anniversary Commemoratives

(Des M. Bryan. Litho Govt Printer, Pretoria)

1980 (3 Nov). *Christmas. Flora. T* **124** *and similar vert designs. Multicoloured. P* 14 × 13½.

473	5 t. Type **124** ..	10	10
474	10 t. *Acacia nilotica* ..	20	10
475	25 t. *Acacia erubescens* ..	45	30
476	40 t. *Dichrostachys cinerea* ..	70	70
473/6	.. *Set of* 4	1·25	1·00

(Des M. Bryan. Litho Govt Printer, Pretoria)

1981 (7 Jan). *150th Birth Anniv of Heinrich von Stephan (founder of U.P.U.). T* **125** *and similar horiz design showing Von Stephan and U.P.U. anniversary commemoratives. Multicoloured. P* 14.

477	6 t. Type **125** ..	10	10
478	20 t. Bechuanaland 1949 6d. and Botswana 1974 7 c. ..	35	35

126 Emperor Dragonfly

127 Camphill Community Ramkoromane, Otse

(Des M. Bryan. Litho Govt Printer, Pretoria)

1981 (23 Feb). *Insects. T* **126** *and similar vert designs. Multicoloured. P* 14.

479	6 t. Type **126** ..	15	10
480	7 t. Praying Mantis ..	15	15
481	10 t. Elegant Grasshopper ..	20	15
482	20 t. Dung Beetle ..	35	35
483	30 t. Citrus Swallowtail Butterfly ..	70	50
484	45 t. Mopane Worm ..	80	65
479/84	.. *Set of* 6	2·10	1·75
MS485	180 × 89 mm. Nos. 479/84 ..	2·10	2·50

(Des M. Bryan. Litho Govt Printer, Pretoria)

1981 (6 Apr). *International Year for Disabled Persons. T* **127** *and similar horiz designs. Multicoloured. P* 14.

486	6 t. Type **127** ..	10	10
487	20 t. Resource Centre for the Blind, Mochudi	35	35
488	30 t. Tlamelong Rehabilitation Centre, Tlokweng ..	45	45
486/8	.. *Set of* 3	80	80

128 Woman reading Letter

129 Sir Seretse Khama and Building

(Des Petra Rouendaal. Litho Govt Printer, Pretoria)

1981 (8 June). *Literacy Programme. T* **128** *and similar vert designs. Multicoloured. P* 14.

489	6 t. Type **128** ..	10	10
490	7 t. Man filling in form ..	15	15
491	20 t. Boy reading newspaper ..	35	35
492	30 t. Child being taught to read ..	45	45
489/92	.. *Set of* 4	90	90

(Des G. Vasarhelyi. Litho Format)

1981 (13 July). *First Death Anniv of President Sir Seretse Khama. T* **129** *and similar horiz designs. Multicoloured. P* 14.

493	6 t. Type **129** ..	10	10
494	10 t. Seretse Khama and building (*different*)	15	15
495	30 t. Seretse Khama and Botswana flag ..	45	45
496	45 t. Seretse Khama and building (*different*)	70	70
493/6	.. *Set of* 4	1·25	1·25

25t

(130)

131 Traditional Ploughing

1981 (1 Sept). *Nos.* 417 *and* 422 *surch as T* **130**.

497	25 t. on 35 t. Green Heron ..	65	65
498	30 t. on 10 t. Bennett's Woodpecker ..	65	65

(Des K. Mosinyi. Litho Format)

1981 (21 Sept). *Cattle Industry. T* **131** *and similar horiz designs. Multicoloured. P* 14½.

499	6 t. Type **131** ..	10	10
500	20 t. Agricultural show ..	35	35
501	30 t. Botswana Meat Commission ..	45	45
502	45 t. Vaccine Institute, Botswana ..	70	70
499/502	.. *Set of* 4	1·40	1·40

132 *Nymphaea caerulea*

133 "Cattle Post Scene" (Boitumelo Golaakwena)

(Des M. Bryan. Litho Govt Printer, Pretoria)

1981 (11 Nov). *Christmas. Flowers. T* **132** *and similar vert designs. Multicoloured. P* 14.

503	6 t. Type **132** ..	20	10
504	10 t. *Nymphoides indica* ..	30	10
505	25 t. *Nymphaea lotus* ..	70	50
506	40 t. *Ottelia kunenensis* ..	1·00	90
503/6	.. *Set of* 4	2·00	1·40

(Litho Govt Printer, Pretoria)

1982 (15 Feb). *Children's Art. T* **133** *and similar horiz designs. Multicoloured. P* 14.

507	6 t. Type **133** ..	30	10
508	10 t. "Kgotla Meeting" (Reginald Klinck) ..	40	15
509	30 t. "Village Water Supply" (Keromemang Matswiri) ..	90	45
510	45 t. "With the Crops" (Kennedy Balemoge) ..	1·10	70
507/10	.. *Set of* 4	2·40	1·25

134 Common Type

135 African Masked Weaver

(Des K. Mosinyi and V. Moremi. Litho Govt Printer, Pretoria)

1982 (3 May). *Traditional Houses. T* **134** *and similar horiz designs. Multicoloured. P* 14.

511	6 t. Type **134** ..	30	10
512	10 t. Kgatleng type ..	40	15
513	30 t. North Eastern type ..	90	55
514	45 t. Sarwa type ..	1·10	1·00
511/14	.. *Set of* 4	2·40	1·60

(Des M. Bryan. Photo Harrison)

1982 (2 Aug). *Birds. T* **135** *and similar multicoloured designs. P* 14×14½ (1 *t. to* 10 *t.*) *or* 14½×14 (*others*).

515	1 t. Type **135** ..	15	15
516	2 t. Lesser Double-collared Sunbird ..	20	15
517	3 t. Red-throated Bee Eater ..	20	15
518	4 t. Ostrich ..	20	15
519	5 t. Grey-headed Gull ..	25	15
520	6 t. African Pygmy Goose ..	25	15
521	7 t. Cattle Egret ..	25	10
522	8 t. Lanner Falcon ..	35	15
523	10 t. Yellow-billed Stork ..	35	10
524	15 t. Red-billed Pintail (*horiz*) ..	40	10
525	20 t. Barn Owl (*horiz*) ..	75	30
526	25 t. Hammerkop (*horiz*) ..	60	25
527	30 t. South African Stilt (*horiz*) ..	65	25
528	35 t. Blacksmith Plover (*horiz*) ..	70	30
529	45 t. Senegal Wattled Plover (*horiz*) ..	80	35
530	50 t. Helmet Guineafowl (*horiz*) ..	90	60
531	1 p. Cape Vulture (*horiz*) ..	1·50	1·50
532	2 p. Augur Buzzard (*horiz*) ..	2·50	2·50
515/32	.. *Set of* 18	10·00	6·50

136 *Coprinus comatus*

137 President Quett Masire

(Des G. Condy. Litho Mardon Printers Ltd, Zimbabwe)

1982 (2 Nov). *Christmas. Fungi. T* **136** *and similar vert designs. Multicoloured. P* 14½.

533	7 t. Type **136** ..	40	10
534	15 t. *Lactarius delicosus* ..	75	15
535	35 t. *Amanita pantherina* ..	1·50	55
536	50 t. *Boletus edulis* ..	2·00	1·00
533/6	.. *Set of* 4	4·25	1·60

(Des G. Vasarhelyi. Litho Questa)

1983 (14 Mar). *Commonwealth Day. T* **137** *and similar horiz designs. Multicoloured. P* 14.

537	7 t. Type **137** ..	10	10
538	15 t. Native dancers ..	15	20
539	35 t. Melbourne conference centre ..	45	50
540	45 t. Meeting of Heads of State, Melbourne ..	55	60
537/40	.. *Set of* 4	1·00	1·25

138 Wattled Crane

139 Wooden Spoons

(Des Petra Rouendaal (50 t.), G. Condy (others). Litho Mardon Printers Ltd, Zimbabwe)

1983 (19 Apr). *Endangered Species. T* **138** *and similar vert designs. Multicoloured. P* 14 × 14½.
541 7 t. Type **138** 45 15
542 15 t. *Aloe lutescens* 60 35
543 35 t. Roan Antelope 85 85
544 50 t. Ivory Palm (*Hyphaene ventricosa*) .. 1·00 1·25
541/4 .. .. *Set of* 4 2·50 2·40

(Des M. Bryan. Litho Mardon Printers Ltd, Zimbabwe)

1983 (20 July). *Traditional Artifacts. T* **139** *and similar vert designs. Multicoloured. P* 14½.
545 7 t. Type **139** 10 10
546 15 t. Personal ornaments 15 20
547 35 t. Ox-hide milk bag 45 50
548 50 t. Decorated knives 55 60
545/8 .. .. *Set of* 4 1·10 1·25
MS549 115 × 102 mm. Nos. 545/8 .. .. .. 1·25 1·50

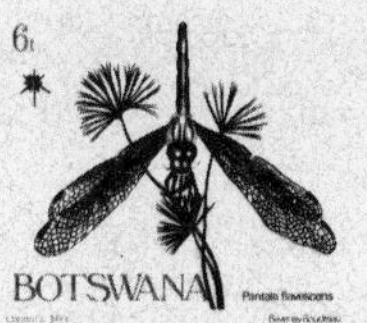

140 *Pantala flavescens*

141 Sorting Diamonds

(Des Beverley Boudreau. Litho Mardon Printers Ltd, Zimbabwe)

1983 (7 Nov). *Christmas. Dragonflies. T* **140** *and similar horiz designs. Multicoloured. P* 14½ × 14.
550 6 t. Type **140** 15 10
551 15 t. *Anex imperator* 25 20
552 25 t. *Trithemis arteriosa* 35 35
553 45 t. *Chlorolestes elegans* 60 70
550/3 .. .. *Set of* 4 1·25 1·25

(Des M. Kahn. Litho Mardon Printers Ltd, Zimbabwe)

1984 (19 Mar). *Mining Industry. T* **141** *and similar multicoloured designs. P* 14½.
554 7 t. Type **141** 25 10
555 15 t. Lime kiln 40 20
556 35 t. Copper-nickel smelter plant (*vert*) .. 60 40
557 50 t. Stockpiled coal (*vert*) 75 65
554/7 .. .. *Set of* 4 1·75 1·25

142 Riding Cattle

143 Avro "504" Aircraft

(Des S. Mogotsi. Litho Mardon Printers Ltd, Zimbabwe)

1984 (18 June). *Traditional Transport. T* **142** *and similar horiz designs. Multicoloured. P* 14½ × 14.
558 7 t. Type **142** 10 10
559 25 t. Sledge 25 30
560 35 t. Wagon 35 40
561 50 t. Two wheeled donkey cart 50 55
558/61 .. .. *Set of* 4 1·10 1·25

(Des V. Larsson. Litho Mardon Printers Ltd, Zimbabwe)

1984 (8 Oct). *40th Anniv of International Civil Aviation Organization. T* **143** *and similar horiz designs, each with I.C.A.O. emblem. Multicoloured. P* 14½ × 14.
562 7 t. Type **143** 25 10
563 10 t. Westland "Wessex" 35 15
564 15 t. Junkers "Ju 52/3M" 50 25
565 25 t. De Havilland "Dragon Six" 60 35
566 35 t. Douglas "DC3 Dakota" 70 50
567 50 t. Fokker "F27 Friendship" 85 90
562/7 .. .. *Set of* 6 3·00 2·00

144 *Papilio demodocus*

145 Seswaa (meat dish)

(Des M. Kahn. Litho Mardon Printers Ltd, Zimbabwe)

1984 (5 Nov). *Christmas. Butterflies. T* **144** *and similar horiz designs. Multicoloured. P* 14½ × 14.
568 7 t. Type **144** 45 15
569 25 t. *Byblia acheloia* 75 50
570 35 t. *Hypolimnas missipus* 90 70
571 50 t. *Graphium taboranus* .. .. 1·25 1·25
568/71 .. .. *Set of* 4 3·00 2·40

(Des K. Mosinyi. Litho Mardon Printers Ltd, Zimbabwe)

1985 (18 Mar). *5th Anniv of Southern African Development Co-ordination Conference. Traditional Foods. T* **145** *and similar vert designs. Multicoloured. P* 14½.
572 7 t. Type **145** 10 10
573 15 t. Bogobe (cereal porridge) 10 15
574 25 t. Madila (soured coagulated cows milk) 15 20
575 50 t. Phane (caterpillars) 35 40
572/5 .. .. *Set of* 4 60 75
MS576 117 × 103 mm. Nos. 572/5 .. .. .. 65 80

146 1885 British Bechuanaland Overprint on Cape of Good Hope ½d.

147 Bechuanaland Border Police, 1885–95

(Des D. Finlay and J. Hodgson. Litho Mardon Printers Ltd, Zimbabwe)

1985 (24 June). *Centenary of First Bechuanaland Stamps. T* **146** *and similar designs. P* 14½.
577 7 t. black, grey-black and orange-vermilion 20 10
578 15 t. black, deep brown and greenish yellow 30 15
579 25 t. black and bright scarlet 40 25
580 35 t. black, ultramarine and gold 50 35
581 50 t. multicoloured 60 65
577/81 .. .. *Set of* 5 1·75 1·25

Designs: *Vert*—15 t. 1897 Bechuanaland Protectorate overprint on G.B. 3d.; 25 t. Bechuanaland Protectorate 1932 1d. definitive. *Horiz*—35 t. Bechuanaland 1965 Internal Self-Government 5 c.; 50 t. Botswana 1966 Independence 2½ c.

(Des V. Larsson. Litho Mardon Printers Ltd, Zimbabwe)

1985 (5 Aug). *Centenary of Botswana Police. T* **147** *and similar horiz designs. Multicoloured. P* 14½ × 14.
582 7 t. Type **147** 35 10
583 10 t. Bechuanaland Mounted Police, 1895–1902 .. .. 45 15
584 25 t. Bechuanaland Protectorate Police, 1903–66 .. .. 70 40
585 50 t. Botswana Police, from 1966 .. .. 1·00 80
582/5 .. .. *Set of* 4 2·25 1·25

148 *Cucumis metuliferus*

149 Mr. Shippard and Chief Gaseitsiwe of the Bangwaketse

(Des Audrey Renew. Litho Mardon Printers Ltd, Zimbabwe)

1985 (4 Nov). *Christmas. Edible Wild Cucumbers. T* **148** *and similar horiz designs. Multicoloured. P* 14½ × 14.
586 7 t. Type **148** 15 10
587 15 t. *Acanthosicyos naudinianus* 20 15
588 25 t. *Coccinia sessifolia* 35 25
589 50 t. *Momordica balsamina* 55 45
586/9 .. .. *Set of* 4 1·10 80

(Des A. Campbell. Litho Mardon Printers Ltd, Zimbabwe)

1985 (30 Dec). *Centenary of Declaration of Bechuanaland Protectorate. T* **149** *and similar vert designs. Multicoloured. P* 14 × 14½.
590 7 t. Type **149** 10 10
591 15 t. Sir Charles Warren and Chief Sechele of the Bakwena 15 15
592 25 t. Revd. Mackenzie and Chief Khama of the Bamangwato 25 25
593 50 t. Map showing Protectorate 45 45
590/3 .. .. *Set of* 4 80 80
MS594 130 × 133 mm. Nos. 590/3 .. .. .. 90 1·25

150 Halley's Comet over Serowe

151 Milk Bag

(Des L. Hutchings. Litho Mardon Printers Ltd, Zimbabwe)

1986 (24 Mar). *Appearance of Halley's Comet. T* **150** *and similar horiz designs. Multicoloured. P* 14½ × 14.
595 7 t. Type **150** 20 10
596 15 t. Comet over Bobonong at sunset 30 15
597 35 t. Comet over Gomare at dawn 55 35
598 50 t. Comet over Thamaga and Letlhakeng 65 45
595/8 .. .. *Set of* 4 1·50 95

(Des B. Mazebedi. Litho Mardon Printers Ltd, Zimbabwe)

1986 (23 June). *Traditional Milk Containers. T* **151** *and similar vert designs. Multicoloured. P* 14½.
599 8 t. Type **151** 10 10
600 15 t. Clay pot and calabashes 15 15
601 35 t. Wooden milk bucket 35 35
602 50 t. Milk churn 45 45
599/602 .. .. *Set of* 4 95 95

152 Map showing National Parks and Reserves

153 *Ludwigia stogonifera*

(Des K. Bogatsu, A. Campbell, I. Marshall and K. Mosinyi. Litho Govt Printer, Pretoria)

1986 (30 Sept). *20th Anniv of Independence. Sheet* 100 × 120 *mm, containing T* **152** *and similar vert designs. Multicoloured. P* 14.
MS603 20 t. Type **152**; 20 t. Morupule Power Station; 20 t. Cattle breeding in Kgalagadi; 20 t. National Assembly Building .. .. 75 1·00

(Des Julia Cairns. Litho Mardon Printers Ltd, Zimbabwe)

1986 (3 Nov). *Christmas. Flowers of Okavango. T* **153** *and similar vert designs. Multicoloured. P* 14 × 14½.
604 8 t. Type **153** 30 10
605 15 t. *Sopubia mannii* 50 20
606 35 t. *Commelina diffusa* 75 50
607 50 t. *Hibiscus diversifolius* .. .. .. 1·00 1·00
604/7 .. .. *Set of* 4 2·25 1·50

154 Divining

(155)

157 Cape Fox

156 Oral Rehydration Therapy

(Des K. Mosinyi. Litho Mardon Printers Ltd, Zimbabwe)

1987 (2 Mar). *Traditional Medicine. T* **154** *and similar horiz designs. Multicoloured. P* 14½ × 14.
608 8 t. Type **154** 15 10
609 15 t. Lightning prevention 20 15
610 35 t. Rain making 40 30
611 50 t. Blood letting 55 60
608/11 .. .. *Set of* 4 1·10 1·00

1987 (1 Apr). *Nos.* 520, 523 *and* 530 *surch as T* **155**.
612 3 t. on 6 t. African Pygmy Goose 10 10
613 5 t. on 10 t. Yellow-billed Stork 10 10
614 20 t. on 50 t. Helmet Guineafowl (*horiz*) .. 20 15
612/14 .. .. *Set of* 3 35 30

(Des A. Nunoo. Litho Govt Printer, Pretoria)

1987 (1 June). *U.N.I.C.E.F. Child Survival Campaign. T* **156** *and similar vert designs. Multicoloured. P* 14.
615 8 t. Type **156** 10 10
616 15 t. Growth monitoring 15 15
617 35 t. Immunization 35 40
618 50 t. Breast feeding 45 60
615/18 .. .. *Set of* 4 95 1·10

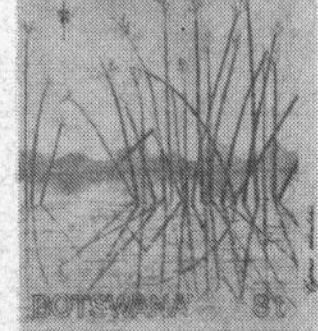

158 *Cyperus articulatus*

(Des P. Huebsch. Photo Harrison)

1987 (3 Aug). *Animals of Botswana. T* **157** *and similar horiz designs. Multicoloured. P* 14.
619 1 t. Type **157** 10 10
620 2 t. Lechwe 10 10
621 3 t. Zebra 10 10
622 4 t. Duiker 10 10
623 5 t. Banded Mongoose 10 10
624 6 t. Rusty-spotted Genet 10 10

625	8 t. Hedgehog	10	10
626	10 t. Scrub Hare	10	10
627	12 t. Hippopotamus	10	10
628	15 t. Suricate	10	10
629	20 t. Caracal	10	10
630	25 t. Steenbok	10	15
631	30 t. Gemsbok	15	20
632	35 t. Square-lipped Rhinoceros	20	25
633	40 t. Mountain Reedbuck	20	25
634	50 t. Rock Dassie	25	30
635	1 p. Giraffe	55	60
636	2 p. Tsessebe	1·10	1·25
637	3 p. Side-striped Jackal	1·60	1·75
638	5 p. Hartebeest	2·75	3·00
619/38	*Set of* 20	7·25	8·00

(Des Julia Cairns. Litho National Printing & Packaging, Zimbabwe)

1987 (26 Oct). *Christmas. Grasses and Sedges of Okavango. T* **158** *and similar vert designs. Multicoloured. P* 14×14½.

639	8 t. Type **158**	10	10
640	15 t. Broomgrass	15	15
641	30 t. *Cyperus alopurcides*	35	30
642	1 p. Bulrush Sedge	85	80
639/42	*Set of* 4	1·25	1·10
MS643	88×99 mm. Nos. 639/42	1·25	1·50
	a. 30 t. value imperf vert	40·00	

159 Planting Seeds with Digging Stick

160 Red Lechwe at Water-hole

(Des K. Mosinyi. Litho National Printing & Packaging, Zimbabwe)

1988 (14 Mar). *Early Cultivation. T* **159** *and similar horiz designs. Multicoloured. P* 14½×14.

644	8 t. Type **159**	10	10
645	15 t. Using iron hoe	15	15
646	35 t. Wooden ox-drawn plough	30	30
647	50 t. Villagers using lesotlas	40	45
644/7	*Set of* 4	85	85

(Des P. Augustinus. Litho National Printing & Packaging, Zimbabwe)

1988 (6 June). *Red Lechwe. T* **160** *and similar horiz designs. Multicoloured. P* 14½×14.

648	10 t. Type **160**	15	10
649	15 t. Red Lechwe and early morning sun	20	15
650	35 t. Female and calf	30	30
651	75 t. Herd on the move	60	60
648/51	*Set of* 4	1·10	1·00

161 Gubulawayo Postmark and Route Southwards to Tati

162 Pope John Paul II and Outline Map of Botswana

(Des M. Bryan, adapted Lucy Phalayagae. Litho National Printing & Packaging, Zimbabwe)

1988 (22 Aug). *Centenary of Mafeking-Gubalawayo Runner Post. Designs as Nos.* 294/8, *but redrawn smaller with changed inscription as in T* **161**. *Multicoloured. P* 14½.

652	10 t. Type **161**	15	10
653	15 t. Bechuanaland 1888 6d. on 6d. stamp and route from Tati southwards	20	15
654	30 t. Runners and twin routes south from Shoshong	30	35
655	60 t. Mafeking postmark and routes to Bechuanaland and Transvaal	45	50
652/5	*Set of* 4	1·00	1·00
MS656	81×151 mm. Nos. 652/5 vertically *se-tenant*, forming a composite map design	1·00	1·25

(Des P. Lodoen. Litho National Printing & Packaging, Zimbabwe)

1988 (13 Sept). *Visit of Pope John Paul II. T* **162** *and similar vert designs. Multicoloured. P* 14×14½.

657	10 t. Type **162**	15	10
658	15 t. Pope John Paul II	20	15
659	30 t. Pope giving blessing and outline map	30	35
660	80 t. Pope John Paul II *(different)*	65	70
657/60	*Set of* 4	1·10	1·10

163 National Museum and Art Gallery

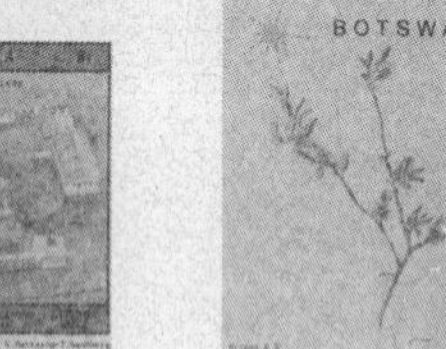

164 *Grewia flava*

(Des G. Mattsson and T. Sandberg (8 t.), A. Campbell (15 t.), K. Bogatsu (30 t.), T. Sandberg (60 t.). Litho National Printing & Packaging, Zimbabwe)

1988 (30 Sept). *20th Anniv of National Museum and Art Gallery, Gaborone. T* **163** *and similar vert designs. Multicoloured. P* 14½.

661	8 t. Type **163**	10	10
662	15 t. Pottery	15	15
663	30 t. Blacksmith's buffalo bellows	25	25
664	60 t. Children and mobile museum van	45	50
661/4	*Set of* 4	85	90

(Des Verena Blomberg-Ermatinger. Litho National Printing & Packaging, Zimbabwe)

1988 (31 Oct). *Flowering Plants of South-eastern Botswana. T* **164** *and similar vert designs. Multicoloured. P* 14×14½.

665	8 t. Type **164**	10	10
666	15 t. *Cienfuegosia digitata*	15	15
667	40 t. *Solanum seaforthianum*	35	35
668	75 t. *Carissa bispinosa*	60	60
665/8	*Set of* 4	1·10	1·10

165 Basket Granary

166 Female Slaty Egret with Eggs

(Des K. Mosinyi. Litho National Printing & Packaging, Zimbabwe)

1989 (13 Mar). *Traditional Grain Storage. T* **165** *and similar vert designs. Multicoloured. P* 14 × 14½.

669	8 t. Type **165**	10	10
670	15 t. Large letlole granary	10	10
671	30 t. Pot granary	20	25
672	60 t. Two types of serala	35	40
669/72	*Set of* 4	65	75

The use of different paper stocks led to a wide range of shades in this issue.

(Des P. Augustinus. Litho Harrison)

1989 (5 July). *Slaty Egret. T* **166** *and similar horiz designs. Multicoloured. P* 15×14.

673	8 t. Type **166**	10	10
674	15 t. Chicks in nest	10	10
675	30 t. Slaty Egret in flight	20	25
676	60 t. Pair building nest	35	40
673/6	*Set of* 4	70	75
MS677	119×89 mm. Nos. 673/6	75	85

167 "My Work at Home" (Ephraim Seeletso)

168 *Eulophia angolensis*

(Litho Govt Printer, Pretoria)

1989 (4 Sept). *Children's Paintings. T* **167** *and similar multicoloured designs. P* 14.

678	10 t. Type **167**	10	10
679	15 t. "My Favourite Game" (hopscotch) (Neelma Bhatia) *(vert)*	10	10
680	30 t. "My Favourite Toy" (clay animals) (Thabo Habana)	20	25
681	1 p. "My School Day" (Thabo Olesitse)	60	65
678/81	*Set of* 4	85	90

(Des Julia Cairns. Litho Govt Printer, Pretoria)

1989 (30 Oct). *Christmas. Orchids. T* **168** *and similar vert designs. Multicoloured. P* 14.

682	8 t. Type **168**	10	10
683	15 t. *Eulophia hereroensis*	10	10
684	30 t. *Eulophia speciosa*	20	25
685	60 t. *Eulophia petersii*	35	40
682/5	*Set of* 4	70	75

POSTAGE DUE STAMPS

REPUBLIC OF

BOTSWANA

(D 4)

D 5 African Elephant

D 6 Common Zebra

1967 (1 Mar). *Nos. D10/12 of Bechuanaland optd with Type* D **4**.

D13	1 c. carmine	15	1·00
D14	2 c. violet	15	1·25
D15	5 c. green	20	1·25
D13/15	*Set of* 3	45	3·25

(Des and litho B.W.)

1971 (9 June). *P* 13½.

D16	D **5**	1 c. carmine	45	1·00
D17		2 c. bluish violet	55	1·10
D18		6 c. sepia	90	1·75
D19		14 c. blue-green	1·40	2·25
D16/19		*Set of* 4	3·00	5·50

(Des M. Bryan. Litho Govt Printer, Pretoria)

1977 (18 Apr)–**84**. *P* 12½.

D20	D **6**	1 t. black and vermilion (1978)	10	30
		a. Black and bright orange (1980)	20	35
		b. Perf 14 (1982?)	10	20
D21		2 t. black and emerald	15	40
		a. Perf 14 (23.11.82*)	15	30
D22		4 t. black and red	15	40
		a. Perf 14 (14.2.82*)	15	30
D23		10 t. black and deep ultramarine	15	40
		a. Perf 14 (7.3.84)	15	30
D24		16 t. black and chestnut	35	1·00
		a. Perf 14 (7.3.84)	25	60
D20/24		*Set of* 5	80	2·25
D20b/24a		*Set of* 5	70	1·50

* First supplies of Nos. D20b, D21a and D22a were sent to Botswana in June 1981. The dates quoted for the 2 t. and 4 t. are earliest known dates of use. Early use of the 1 t. has yet to be identified.

Nos. D20b/4a are on white paper.

(Litho National Printing & Packaging, Zimbabwe)

1989 (1 Apr). *P* 14½.

D25	D **6**	1 t. black and reddish orange	10	10
D26		2 t. black and emerald	10	10
D27		4 t. black and bright scarlet	10	10
D28		10 t. black and deep ultramarine	10	10
D29		16 t. black and reddish brown	10	10
D25/9		*Set of* 5	45	45

Details on the zebra and of the grass stems are less distinct on Nos. D25/9 than on previous versions of Type D **6**.

British Antarctic Territory

1 M.V. *Kista Dan*

(Des B.W. (No. 15*a*), M. Goaman (others). Recess B.W.)

1963 (1 Feb)–**69**. *Horiz designs as T* **1**, *W w* **12**. *P* 11 × 11½.

1 ½d. deep blue 35 45
2 1d. brown 35 25
3 1½d. orange-red and brown-purple 35 25
4 2d. purple 35 25
5 2½d. myrtle-green 40 25
6 3d. deep blue 85 25
7 4d. sepia 60 30
8 6d. olive and deep ultramarine .. .. 1·25 30
9 9d. olive-green .. .. 1·25 35
10 1s. deep turquoise-blue .. .. 1·25 30
11 2s. deep violet and orange-sepia .. .. 12·00 5·00
12 2s. 6d. blue .. .. 12·00 5·00
13 5s. red-orange and rose-red .. .. .. 18·00 8·00
14 10s. deep ultramarine and emerald .. .. 40·00 20·00
15 £1 black and light blue .. .. .. 85·00 45·00
15*a* £1 red and brownish black (1.12.69) .. £150 £120
1/15*a* .. .. *Set of* 16 £300 £180

Designs:—1d. Manhauling; 1½d. Muskeg (tractor); 2d. Skiing; 2½d. Beaver (aircraft); 3d. R.R.S. *John Biscoe II*, 4d. Camp scene; 6d. H.M.S. *Protector*; 9d. Sledging; 1s. Otter (aircraft); 2s. Huskies; 2s. 6d. Helicopter; 5s. Snocat (tractor); 10s. R.R.S. *Shackleton*; £1 (No. 15) Antarctic Map; £1 (No. 15*a*) H.M.S. *Endurance*.

1966 (24 Jan). *Churchill Commemoration. As Nos.* 170/3 *of Antigua.*

16 ½d. new blue 80 35
17 1d. deep green .. .. 3·00 65
18 1s. brown .. .. 21·00 3·00
19 2s. bluish violet .. .. 24·00 3·75
16/19 .. .. *Set of* 4 45·00 7·00

BRITISH ANTARCTIC TERRITORY

17 Lemaire Channel and Icebergs

(Des R. Granger Barrett. Litho Format)

1969 (6 Feb). *25th Anniv of Continuous Scientific Work. T* **17** *and similar horiz designs. W w* **12** (*sideways*). *P* 14.

20 3½d. black, pale blue and ultramarine .. 3·25 1·50
21 6d. multicoloured .. .. 3·25 1·50
22 1s. black, pale blue and vermilion .. .. 3·25 1·50
23 2s. black, orange and turquoise-blue .. 4·25 1·75
20/3 .. .. *Set of* 4 12·50 5·50

Designs:—6d. Radio Sonde balloon; 1s. Muskeg pulling tent equipment; 2s. Surveyors with theodolite.

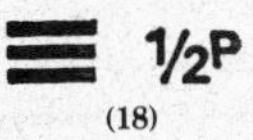

(18)

Antarctic Treaty 1961-1971

British Antarctic Territory

19 Setting up Camp

1971 (15 Feb). *Decimal Currency. As Nos.* 1/14, *but glazed paper, colours changed and surch as T* **18**.

24 ½p. on ½d. blue 60 70
25 1p. on 1d pale brown 90 30
26 1½p. on 1½d. red and pale brown-purple .. 90 30
27 2p. on 2d. bright purple 95 25
28 2½p. on 2½d. green .. .. 1·25 40
29 3p. on 3d. blue .. .. 2·00 55
30 4p. on 4d. bistre-brown .. .. .. 2·00 55
31 5p. on 6d. olive and ultramarine .. .. 3·25 1·75
32 6p. on 9d. dull green .. .. 8·50 3·75
33 7½p. on 1s. turquoise-blue .. .. .. 8·50 4·00
34 10p. on 2s. violet and orange-sepia .. .. 14·00 9·00
35 15p. on 2s. 6d. pale blue .. .. .. 14·00 9·00
36 25p. on 5s. orange and pale rose-red .. .. 20·00 12·00
37 50p. on 10s. ultramarine and emerald .. 60·00 35·00
24/37 .. .. *Set of* 14 £120 70·00

(Des M. Goaman. Recess and litho Enschedé)

1971 (23 June). *10th Anniv of Antarctic Treaty. Vert designs each including Antarctic Map and Queen Elizabeth, as T* **19**. *Multicoloured. W w* **12** (*sideways*). *P* 14 × 13.

38 1½p. Type **19** .. .. 5·00 2·50
39 4p. Snow Petrels .. .. 7·50 3·50
40 5p. Weddell Seals .. .. 7·50 3·75
41 10p. Adelie Penguins .. .. 9·50 5·00
38/41 .. .. *Set of* 4 27·00 13·50

20 Kerguelen Fur Seals and Emperor Penguins

21 James Cook and H.M.S. *Resolution*

(Des (from photograph by D. Groves) and photo Harrison)

1972 (13 Dec*). *Royal Silver Wedding. Multicoloured; background colour given. W w* **12**. *P* 14 × 14½.

42 **20** 5p. red-brown .. .. 3·25 1·50
43 10p. brown-olive .. .. 3·25 1·50

*This is the local release date; they were issued by the Crown Agents on 20 November.

(Des J.W. Litho Questa)

1973 (14 Feb). *T* **21** *and similar vert designs. Multicoloured. W w* **12** (*sideways*). *P* 14 × 14½.

44 ½p. Type **21** (*shades*) .. .. 1·25 2·00
45 1p. Thaddeus Von Bellingshausen and *Vostok* 2·50 2·75
46 1½p. James Weddell and *Jane* .. .. 8·00 3·75
47 2p. John Biscoe and *Tula* 90 90
48 2½p. J. S. C. Dumont d'Urville and *L'Astrolabe* 90 90
49 3p. James Clark Ross and H.M.S. *Erebus* .. 95 95
50 4p. C. A. Larsen and *Jason* 95 95
51 5p. Adrien de Gerlache and *Belgica* .. 1·00 1·00
52 6p. Otto Nordenskjöld and *Antarctic* .. 1·00 1·00
53 7½p. W. S. Bruce and *Scotia* .. .. .. 1·50 1·50
54 10p. Jean-Baptiste Charcot and *Pourquoi Pas?* .. .. 1·75 1·75
55 15p. Ernest Shackleton and *Endurance* .. 3·00 3·00
56 25p. Hubert Wilkins and *San Francisco* .. 3·00 3·25
57 50p. Lincoln Ellsworth and *Polar Star* .. 3·00 5·50
58 £1 John Rymill and *Penola* .. .. 6·00 12·00
44/58 .. .. *Set of* 15 32·00 35·00

The 25 and 50p. show aircraft; the rest show ships.

See also Nos. 64/78.

1973 (23 Dec*). *Royal Wedding. As Nos.* 165/6 *of Anguilla. Centre multicoloured. W w* **12** (*sideways*). *P* 13½.

59 5p. ochre 40 20
60 15p. light turquoise-blue 70 30

*This is the local date of issue: the Crown Agents released the stamps on 14 November.

22 Churchill and Churchill Peninsula, B.A.T.

(Des G. Vasarhelyi. Litho Format)

1974 (10 Dec*). *Birth Centenary of Sir Winston Churchill. T* **22** *and similar horiz design. Multicoloured. W w* **12** (*sideways on* 5p). *P* 14.

61 5p. Type **22** .. .. 1·75 1·50
62 15p. Churchill and *Trepassey* ("Operation Tabarin", 1943) .. .. 2·25 2·00
MS63 114 × 88 mm. Nos. 61/2. Wmk upright .. 7·50 7·50

*This is the local date of issue: the Crown Agents released the stamps on 30 November.

1975 (11 June)–**81**. *As Nos.* 44/58 *but W w* **14**. *Ordinary paper* (½, 2, 2½, 3, 5, 10, 15, 25, 50*p*.) *or chalk-surfaced paper* (1, 1½, 4, 6, 7½*p*., £1). *P* 12 (4, 6, 7½*p*.) *or* 14 × 14½ (*others*).

64 ½p. Type **21** .. .. 90 1·10
a. Chalk-surfaced paper (14.3.78) 30 45
65 1p. Thaddeus Von Bellingshausen and *Vostok* (14.3.78) 25 45
a. Ordinary paper (11.12.79) 30 60
66 1½p. James Weddell and *Jane* (14.3.78) .. 25 45
a. Ordinary paper (11.12.79) 30 60
67 2p. John Biscoe and *Tula* (11.12.79) 90 55
68 2½p. J. S. C. Dumont d'Urville and *L'Astrolabe* (11.12.79) 50 50
69 3p. James Clark Ross and H.M.S. *Erebus* (11.12.79) .. .. 1·00 75
70 4p. C. A. Larsen and *Jason* (5.12.80) .. 35 1·00
71 5p. Adrien de Gerlache and *Belgica* (11.12.79) 2·00 1·25
72 6p. Otto Nordenskjöld and *Antarctic* (5.12.80) 60 1·40
73 7½p. W. S. Bruce and *Scotia* (5.12.80) .. 90 1·50
74 10p. Jean-Baptiste Charcot and *Pourquoi Pas?* (11.12.79) .. .. 1·00 1·10
a. Perf 12. Chalk-surfaced paper (25.11.81) 1·00 1·75
75 15p. Ernest Shackleton and *Endurance* (11.12.79) .. .. 1·00 1·25
a. Perf 12. Chalk-surfaced paper (25.11.81) 1·00 1·75
76 25p. Hubert Wilkins and *San Francisco* (11.12.79) .. .. 1·25 1·50
a. Perf 12. Chalk-surfaced paper (25.11.81) 1·25 2·00
77 50p. Lincoln Ellsworth and *Polar Star* (11.12.79) .. .. 2·00 2·25
a. Perf 12. Chalk-surfaced paper (5.12.80) 1·10 1·60
78 £1 John Rymill and *Penola* (14.3.78) .. 4·00 2·00
a. Perf 12 (5.12.80) .. .. 2·00 2·75
64a/78a .. .. *Set of* 15 12·00 15·00

23 Sperm Whale

(Des J. Cooter. Litho Questa)

1977 (4 Jan). *Whale Conservation. T* **23** *and similar horiz designs. W w* **14** (*sideways*). *P* 13½.

79 2p. brownish black, slate and bright blue .. 2·75 1·25
80 8p. grey, brownish black and rosine .. .. 3·75 1·75
81 11p. multicoloured .. .. 4·00 1·75
82 25p. grey-blue, brownish blk & lt blue-green 5·00 2·00
79/82 .. .. *Set of* 4 14·00 6·00

Designs:—8p. Fin Whale; 11p. Humpback Whale; 25p. Blue Whale.

24 The Queen before Taking the Oath

25 Emperor Penguin

(Des J.W. Litho Questa)

1977 (7 Feb). *Silver Jubilee. T* **24** *and similar horiz designs. Multicoloured. W w* **14** (*sideways*). *P* 13½.

83 6p. Prince Philip's visit, 1956/7 .. .. 95 20
84 11p. Coronation Oath .. .. 1·25 30
85 33p. Type **24** .. .. 1·50 45
83/5 .. .. *Set of* 3 3·25 85

(Des C. Abbott. Litho Questa)

1978 (2 June). *25th Anniv of Coronation. T* **25** *and similar vert designs. P* 15.

86 25p. green, deep bluish green and silver .. 1·00 65
a. Sheetlet Nos. 86/8 × 2 .. .. .. 5·50
87 25p. multicoloured .. .. 1·00 65
88 25p. green, deep bluish green and silver .. 1·00 65
86/8 .. .. *Set of* 3 2·75 1·75

Designs:— No. 86. Black Bull of Clarence; No. 87, Queen Elizabeth II; No. 88, Type **25**.

Nos. 86/8 were printed together in small sheets of 6, containing two *se-tenant* strips of 3 with a horizontal gutter margin between.

26 Macaroni Penguins

(Des G. Drummond. Litho Walsall)

1979 (14 Jan). *Penguins. T* **26** *and similar horiz designs. Multicoloured. W w* **14** (*sideways*). *P* 13½.

89 3p. Type **26** .. .. 6·50 2·75
90 8p. Gentoo penguins .. .. 2·50 1·00
91 11p. Adelie penguins .. .. 2·75 1·25
92 25p. Emperor penguins .. .. 4·00 1·75
89/92 .. .. *Set of* 4 14·00 6·00

27 Sir John Barrow and *Tula*

(Des A. Theobald. Litho Secura, Singapore)

1980 (14 Dec†). *150th Anniv of Royal Geographical Society. Former Presidents. T* **27** *and similar horiz designs. Multicoloured. W w* **14** (*sideways*). *P* 13½.

93 3p. Type **27** 15 10
94 7p. Sir Clement Markham and *Discovery* .. 20 25
95 11p. Lord Curzon and launch *James Caird* 25 30
96 15p. Sir William Goodenough 30 35
97 22p. Sir James Wordie 45 55
98 30p. Sir Raymond Priestley 55 65
93/8 .. .. *Set of* 6 1·75 2·00

†This is the local date of issue; the Crown Agents released the stamps on 1 December.

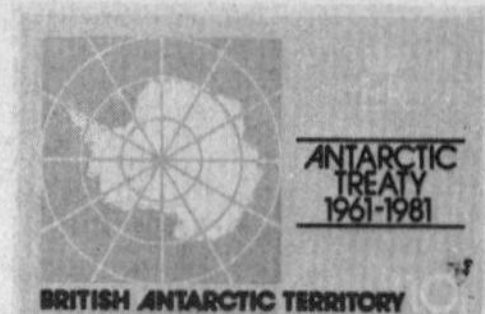

28 Map of Antarctic

(Des Walsall. Litho Questa)

1981 (1 Dec). *20th Anniv of Antarctic Treaty. T* **28** *and similar horiz designs. W w* **14** *(sideways). P* 13½ × 14.

99	10p. black, new blue and azure	30	50
100	13p. black, new blue and apple green	35	55
101	25p. black, new blue and mauve	50	70
102	26p. black, brown-ochre and rose-red	50	70
99/102	*Set of* 4	1·50	2·25

Designs:—13p. Conservation research ("scientific co-operation"); 25p. Satellite image mapping ("technical co-operation"); 26p. Global geophysics ("scientific co-operation").

29 Map of Gondwana showing position of Continents 280 million years ago, and Contemporary Landscape Scene

30 British Antarctic Territory Coat of Arms

(Des C. Abbott. Litho Walsall)

1982 (8 Mar). *Gondwana—Continental Drift and Climatic Change. T* **29** *and similar horiz designs depicting maps of Gondwana showing position of continents, and contemporary landscape scenes. Multicoloured. W w* **14** *(sideways). P* 13½ × 14.

103	3p. Type **29**	15	25
104	6p. 260 million years ago	20	35
105	10p. 230 million years ago	25	40
106	13p. 175 million years ago	30	45
107	25p. 50 million years ago	50	65
108	26p. Present day	50	65
	a. Gold (royal cypher) omitted		
103/8	*Set of* 6	1·75	2·50

(Des Jennifer Toombs. Litho Questa)

1982 (1 July). *21st Birthday of Princess of Wales. T* **30** *and similar vert designs. Multicoloured. W w* **14**. *P* 14½ × 14.

109	5p. Type **30**	15	20
110	17p. Princess of Wales (detail of painting by Bryan Organ)	35	50
111	37p. Wedding ceremony	75	1·00
112	50p. Formal portrait	95	1·40
109/12	*Set of* 4	2·00	2·75

31 Leopard Seal

(Des R. Granger Barrett. Litho Walsall)

1983 (3 Jan). *10th Anniv (1982) of Antarctic Seal Conservation Convention. T* **31** *and similar horiz designs. Multicoloured. W w* **14** *(sideways). P* 11.

113	5p. Type **31**	20	20
114	10p. Weddell Seals	30	30
115	13p. Southern Elephant Seals	35	35
116	17p. Kerguelen Fur Seals	45	45
117	25p. Ross Seal	55	55
118	34p. Crabeater Seals	70	70
113/18	*Set of* 6	2·25	2·25

32 De Havilland "Twin Otter"

(Des Harrison. Litho Questa)

1983 (20 Dec). *Bicentenary of Manned Flight. T* **32** *and similar horiz designs. Multicoloured. W w* **14** *(sideways). P* 14.

119	5p. Type **32**	25	20
120	13p. De Havilland "Single Otter"	40	35
121	17p. Consolidated "Canso"	55	45
122	50p. Lockheed "Vega"	1·10	1·10
119/22	*Set of* 4	2·10	1·90

33 *Corethron criophilum*

(Des I. Loe. Litho Walsall)

1984 (15 Mar). *Marine Life. T* **33** *and similar horiz designs. Multicoloured. W w* **14** *(sideways). P* 14.

123	1p. Type **33**	10	10
124	2p. *Desmonena gaudichaudi*	10	10
125	3p. *Tomopteris carpenteri*	10	10
126	4p. *Pareuchaeta antarctica*	10	10
127	5p. *Antarctomysis maxima*	10	10
128	6p. *Antarcturus signiensis*	10	10
129	7p. *Serolis cornuta*	10	15
130	8p. *Parathemisto gaudichaudii*	15	20
131	9p. *Bovallia gigantea*	15	20
132	10p. *Euphausia superba*	20	25
133	15p. *Colossendeis australis*	25	30
134	20p. *Todarodes sagittatus*	35	40
135	25p. *Notothenia neglecta*	45	50
136	50p. *Chaenocephalus aceratus*	90	95
137	£1 Crabeater Seal	1·75	1·90
138	£3 Antarctic marine food chain	5·00	5·25
123/38	*Set of* 16	9·00	9·50

34 M.Y. *Penola* in Stella Creek

35 Robert McCormick and McCormick's Skua

(Des A. Theobald. Litho Questa)

1985 (23 Mar). *50th Anniv of British Graham Land Expedition. T* **34** *and similar horiz designs. Multicoloured. W w* **14** *(sideways). P* 14½.

139	7p. Type **34**	25	20
140	22p. Northern Base, Winter Island	60	50
141	27p. D. H. Fox "Moth" at Southern Base, Barry Island	70	60
142	54p. Dog team near Ablation Point, George VI Sound	1·25	1·25
139/42	*Set of* 4	2·50	2·25

(Des I. Strange. Litho Questa)

1985 (4 Nov). *Early Naturalists. T* **35** *and similar vert designs. Multicoloured. W w* **14**. *P* 14½ × 14.

143	7p. Type **35**	35	20
144	22p. Sir Joseph Dalton Hooker and *Deschampsia antarctica*	70	50
145	27p. Jean René C. Quoy and Hourglass Dolphin	80	60
146	54p. James Weddell and Weddell Seal	1·25	1·25
143/6	*Set of* 4	2·75	2·25

36 Dr. Edmond Halley

37 Snow Crystal

(Des A. Theobald. Litho Questa)

1986 (6 Jan). *Appearance of Halley's Comet. T* **36** *and similar vert designs. Multicoloured. W w* **14**. *P* 14.

147	7p. Type **36**	35	20
148	22p. Halley Station, Antarctica	70	50
149	27p. "Halley's Comet, 1531" (from Peter Apian woodcut, 1532)	80	60
150	54p. *Giotto* spacecraft	1·25	1·25
147/50	*Set of* 4	2·75	2·25

(Des C. Abbott. Litho Questa)

1986 (6 Dec). *50th Anniv of International Glaciological Society. T* **37** *and similar vert designs showing snow crystals. W w* **16**. *P* 14½.

151	10p. cobalt and deep ultramarine	30	30
152	24p. pale turquoise-green & dp bluish green	60	60
153	29p. mauve and deep mauve	70	70
154	58p. violet-blue and bright violet	1·25	1·50
151/4	*Set of* 4	2·50	2·75

NEW INFORMATION

The editor is always interested to correspond with people who have new information that will improve or correct the Catalogue.

38 Captain Scott, 1904

39 I.G.Y. Logo

(Des A. Theobald. Litho Questa)

1987 (19 Mar). *75th Anniv of Captain Scott's Arrival at South Pole. T* **38** *and similar horiz designs. Multicoloured. W w* **16** *(sideways). P* 14 × 14½.

155	10p. Type **38**	35	25
156	24p. Hut Point and *Discovery*, Ross Island, 1902–4	70	55
157	29p. Cape Evans Hut, 1911–13	80	65
158	58p. Scott's Expedition at South Pole, 1912	1·40	1·40
155/8	*Set of* 4	3·00	2·50

(Des L. Curtis. Litho Questa)

1987 (25 Dec). *30th Anniv of International Geophysical Year. T* **39** *and similar vert designs. W w* **16**. *P* 14½ × 14.

159	10p. black and pale green	25	35
160	24p. multicoloured	55	65
161	29p. multicoloured	65	75
162	58p. multicoloured	1·25	1·50
159/62	*Set of* 4	2·40	3·00

Designs:—25p. Port Lockroy; 29p. Argentine Islands; 58p. Halley Bay.

40 Aurora over South Ice Plateau Station

41 *Xanthoria elegans*

(Des D. Hartley. Litho Questa)

1988 (19 Mar). *30th Anniv of Commonwealth Trans-Antarctic Expedition. T* **40** *and similar vert designs. Multicoloured. W w* **16**. *P* 14.

163	10p. Type **40**	25	25
164	24p. "Otter" aircraft at Theron Mountains	55	55
165	29p. Seismic ice-depth sounding	60	65
166	58p. "Sno-cat" over crevasse	1·10	1·25
163/6	*Set of* 4	2·25	2·40

(Des I. Loe. Litho Walsall)

1989 (25 Mar). *Lichens. T* **41** *and similar horiz designs. Multicoloured. W w* **14** *(sideways). P* 14.

167	10p Type **41**	20	25
168	24p *Usnea aurantiaco-atra*	50	55
169	29p *Cladonia chlorophaea*	55	60
170	58p *Umbilicaria antarctica*	1·10	1·25
167/70	*Set of* 4	2·10	2·40

British Central Africa *see* Nyasaland Protectorate

British Columbia & Vancouver Island

PRICES FOR STAMPS ON COVER

No. 1	—
Nos. 2/3	*from* × 6
Nos. 11/12	—
Nos. 13/14	*from* × 6
Nos. 21/2	*from* × 10
Nos. 23/7	*from* × 6
Nos. 28/33	*from* × 10

1

(Typo D.L.R.)

1860. *No Wmk. Imperf.*
1 1 2½d. pale dull red £2250

1860. *No wmk. P* 14.
2 1 2½d. deep reddish rose £275 £180
3 2½d. pale reddish rose £275 £180

From 20 June 1864 to 1 November 1865, the 2½d. was sold for 3d., and did duty as a 3d. provisional. No 1 was never actually issued.

VANCOUVER ISLAND

2 3

(Typo D.L.R.)

1865 (19 Sept). *Wmk Crown CC. (a) Imperf.*
11 2 5c. rose £20000 £8000
12 3 10 c. blue £1800 £1300

(b) P 14
13 2 5 c. rose £200 £130
14 3 10 c. blue £200 £140

Medium or poor copies of Nos. 11 and 12 can be supplied at much lower prices, when in stock.

BRITISH COLUMBIA

4

(Typo D.L.R.)

1865 (1 Nov)–**67**. *Wmk Crown CC. P* 14.
21 4 3d. deep blue .. .. 70·00 60·00
22 3d. pale blue (1867) .. .. .. 70·00 60·00

On 19 November 1866, British Columbia and Vancouver Island were consolidated as one territory called British Columbia, after which date the current stamps of each colony were distributed and used throughout the combined territory.

Though bearing the names of both colonies the 2½d. of 1860 was mainly used for inland postage in British Columbia.

TWO CENTS (5) 5.CENTS.5 (6)

1868–71. *T* 4 *in various colours. Wmk Crown CC. Surch as T* 5 *or* 6.

(a) P 12½ (3.69)
23 5 c. red (Bk.) £500 £500
24 10 c. lake (B.) £400 £400
25 25 c. yellow (V.) £350 £350
26 50 c. mauve (R.) £400 £350
27 $1 green (G.) £600 £700

(b) P 14
28 2 c. brown (Bk.) (1.68) .. .. .. 70·00 70·00
29 5 c. pale red (Bk.) (5.69) .. .. .. 85·00 85·00
30 10 c. lake (B.) £700
31 25 c. yellow (V.) (7.69) £100 £100
32 50 c. mauve (R.) (2.71) £400 £600
33 $1 green (G.) £600

Nos. 30 and 33 were not issued.

The stamps of British Columbia were withdrawn from use on 20 July 1871, when the Colony joined the Dominion of Canada.

British East Africa

The area which became British East Africa had been part of the domain of the Zanzibari Sultans since 1794. In 1887 the administration of the province was granted to the British East Africa Association, incorporated as the Imperial British East Africa Company the following year.

Company post offices were established at Lamu and Mombasa in May 1890, British mails having been previously sent via the Indian post office on Zanzibar, opened in 1875.

A German postal agency opened at Lamu on 22 November 1888 and continued to operate until 31 March 1891, using German stamps. These can be identified by the "LAMU/OSTAFRIKA" cancellations and are listed under German East Africa in our *Part* 7 (*Germany*) catalogue.

PRICES FOR STAMPS ON COVER

Nos. 1/3	*from* × 6
Nos. 4/19	*from* × 20
Nos. 20/6	*from* × 3
Nos. 27/8	*from* × 6
Nos. 29/30	*from* × 10
Nos. 31/2	*from* × 4
Nos. 33/47	*from* × 10
No. 48	*from* × 10
Nos. 49/63	*from* × 6
No. 64	*from* × 5
Nos. 65/79	*from* × 10
Nos. 80/91	*from* × 5
Nos. 92/9	*from* × 10

BRITISH EAST AFRICA COMPANY ADMINISTRATION

BRITISH EAST AFRICA COMPANY HALF ANNA (1)

BRITISH EAST AFRICA COMPANY 1 ANNA (2)

(Surch D.L.R.)

1890 (May). *Stamps of Great Britain (Queen Victoria) surch as T* 1 *or* 2 (1 *a. and* 4 *a.*).
1 57 ½ a. on 1d. deep purple £350 £200
2 73 1 a. on 2d. green and carmine £425 £250
3 78 4 a. on 5d. dull purple and blue £475 £275

A copy of the ½ a. with the short crossbar of "F" in "HALF" omitted exists in the Royal Collection but is the only known example.

Stamps of INDIA were used in British East Africa during August and September 1890 being postmarked "MOMBASA" or "LAMU".

3

4

5 ANNAS. (5)

(Litho B.W.)

1890 (Oct)–**1894**. *P* 14.
4 3 ½ a. dull brown .. .. 1·75 1·75
a. Imperf (pair) £450 £350
b. Deep brown (9.93) .. .. .. 70 1·50
ba. Imperf (pair) £400 £300
bb. Imperf between (horiz pair) .. £1400 £750
bc. Imperf between (vert pair) .. £475 £450
c. Pale brown (12.94) .. .. .. 1·00 1·75
5 1 a. blue-green .. .. 3·00 3·00
aa. "ANL" (broken "D") (R.6/3) .. £160 £200
a. Imperf (pair) £500 £350
ab. "ANL" (broken "D") (R.6/3) .. £4500
b. Deep blue-green (12.94) 75
ba. Imperf (pair) £500 £350
6 2 a. vermilion .. .. 2·75 3·25
a. Imperf (pair) £850 £400
7 2½ a. black/*yellow-buff* (7.91) .. .. 35·00 13·00
a. Black/pale buff (7.92) .. .. 32·00 3·25
b. Black/bright yellow (9.93) .. .. 3·75 3·00
bb. Imperf (pair) £500 £400
bc. Imperf between (horiz pair) .. £450 £400
bd. Imperf between (vert pair) .. £750 £400
8 3 3 a. black/*dull red* (2.91) .. .. 6·00 9·00
a. Black/bright red (9.93) .. .. 1·25 2·00
ab. Imperf (pair) £500 £350
ac. Imperf between (horiz pair) .. £475 £350
ad. Imperf between (vert pair) .. £400 £325
9 4 a. yellow-brown .. .. .. 2·50 4·50
a. Imperf (pair) £850 £400
10 4 a. grey (*imperf*) £1200 £1400
11 4½ a. dull violet (2.91) .. .. .. 22·00 13·00
a. Brown-purple (9.93) .. .. 2·50 12·00
ab. Imperf (pair) £700 £350
ac. Imperf between (horiz pair) .. £1200 £1100
ad. Imperf between (vert pair) .. £500 £400
12 8 a. blue .. .. 5·50 6·50
a. Imperf (pair) £1100 £400
13 8 a. grey £275 £250
14 1 r. carmine .. .. 6·00 9·00
a. Imperf (pair) £2000 £500
15 1 r. grey £250 £250
16 4 2 r. brick-red .. .. 11·00 14·00
17 3 r. slate-purple .. .. 8·00 17·00
18 4 r. ultramarine .. .. 12·00 23·00
19 5 r. grey-green .. .. 30·00 45·00
4/19 .. .. *Set of* 15 (*perf*) £525 £550

For the 5 a. and 7½ a. see Nos. 29/30.

The paper of Nos. 7, 7*a*, 7*b*, 8 and 8*a* is coloured on the surface only.

Printings of 1890/92 are on thin paper having the outer margins of the sheets imperf and bearing sheet watermark "PURE LINEN WOVE BANK" and "W. C. S. & Co." in a monogram, the trademark of the makers, Messrs. William Collins, Sons & Co.

1893/94 printings are on thicker coarser paper with outer margins perforated through the selvedge and without watermark. Single specimens cannot always be distinguished by lack of watermark alone. Exceptions are the 1893 printings of the 2½ a. and 3 a. which were on Wiggins Teape paper showing a sheet watermark of "1011" in figures 1 centimetre high.

Nos. 7 (coloured through) and 16/19 on thick unwatermarked paper are from a special printing made for presentation purposes.

The printings of the 4 a., 8 a. and 1 r. values in grey were intended for fiscal purposes, but in the event, were made available for postal use.

Forgeries of the 4 a., 8 a., 1 r., grey and 2 to 5 r. exist. The latter are common and can be distinguished by the scroll above "LIGHT" where there are five vertical lines of shading in the forgeries and seven in the genuine stamps. Forged cancellations exist on the commoner stamps. Beware of "imperf" stamps made by trimming margins of stamps from marginal rows.

1891. *Mombasa Provisionals. (a) New value handstamped in dull violet, and manuscript initials in black.*
20 3 "½ Anna" on 2 a. vermilion ("A.D.") (January) £1900 £700
a. "½ Anna" double .. .. .. — £2000
21 "1 Anna" on 4 a. brown ("A.B.") (February) £3250 £1200

(b) Manuscript value and initials in black
22 3 "½ Anna" on 2 a. vermilion ("A.D.") (January) .. .. .. — £600
a. Error. "½ Annas" ("A.D.") .. .. — £1500
23 "½ Anna" on 2 a. vermilion ("A.B.") (February) £2000 £500
a. Error. "½ Annas" ("A.B.") .. .. — £750
24 "½ Anna" on 3 a. black/*dull red* ("A.B.") (May) £2500 £800
25 "1 Anna" on 3 a. black/*dull red* ("V.H.M.") (June) £2500 £850
26 "1 Anna" on 4 a. brown ("A.B.") (March) £1700 £700

A.D. = Andrew Dick, Chief Accountant.
A.B. = Archibald Brown, Cashier of the Company.
V.H.M. = Victor H. Mackenzie, Bank Manager.

(Surch B.W.)

1894 (1 Nov). *Surch as T* 5.
27 3 5 a. on 8 a. blue .. .. .. 50·00 70·00
28 7½ a. on 1 r. carmine .. .. .. 50·00 70·00
27/28 Handstamped "Specimen" .. *Set of* 2 90·00

Forgeries exist.

1894 (Dec). *No wmk. P* 14.
29 3 5 a. black/*grey-blue* .. .. .. 1·25 9·50
30 7½ a. black .. .. 1·25 9·50
29/30 Handstamped "Specimen" .. *Set of* 2 75·00

These two stamps have "LD" after "COMPANY" in the inscription.

The paper of No. 29 is coloured on the surface only.

1895 (Feb.). *Surch with manuscript value and initials* ("T.E.C.R.").
31 3 "½ anna" on 3 a. black/*dull red* (19.2) £160 45·00
32 "1 anna" on 3 a. black/*dull red* (22.2) £1700 £950

T.E.C.R. = T. E. C. Remington, Postmaster at Mombasa.

The Company experienced considerable financial problems during 1894 with the result that the British Government agreed to assume the administration of the territory, as a protectorate, on 1 July 1895.

IMPERIAL ADMINISTRATION

BRITISH EAST AFRICA (6)

2½ (7)

(Handstamped at Mombasa)

1895 (1 July). *Handstamped with T* 6.
33 3 ½ a. deep brown .. .. .. 48·00 18·00
a. Pale brown .. .. .. 50·00 24·00
b. Double £200 £200
34 1 a. blue-green .. .. .. 50·00 50·00
a. Double £200 £200
35 2 a. vermilion .. .. .. 95·00 80·00
a. Double £250 £250
36 2½ a. black/*bright yellow* .. .. 80·00 48·00
a. Double £250 £250
37 3 a. black/*dull red* .. .. .. 38·00 32·00

38 3 4 a. yellow-brown .. 35·00 35·00
a. Double .. £250 £250
39 4½ a. dull violet .. 90·00 80·00
a. Double .. £350 £350
b. *Brown-purple* .. £550 £475
ba. Double .. £1100 £950
40 5 a. black/*grey-blue* .. £120 90·00
a. Double .. £500 £500
b. Inverted .. † £2000
41 7½ a. black .. 70·00 70·00
a. Double .. £325 £325
42 8 a. blue .. 70·00 65·00
a. Double .. £350 £350
b. Inverted .. £1800
43 1 r. carmine .. 40·00 42·00
a. Double .. £275 £300
44 4 2 r. brick-red .. £160 £160
45 3 r. slate-purple .. 85·00 90·00
a. Double .. £550 £550
b. Inverted
46 4 r. ultramarine .. £100 95·00
a. Double .. £550 £550
47 5 r. grey-green .. £250 £225
a. Double .. £850 £850
33/47 .. *Set of* 15 £1100 £1000

Forgeries exist.

1895 (1 Oct). *No. 39 surch locally with T* **7**.
48 3 2½ a. on 4½ a. dull violet (R.) .. 65·00 60·00
a. Opt (T **6**) double .. £500 £450

British East Africa (8) — British East Africa (9)

SETTING OF TYPE 8. This consisted of 120 impressions in 10 horizontal rows of 12 stamps. This matched the size of the pane for all the Indian issues to 1 r. with the exception of the 6 a. The sheets of this value contained four panes, each 8 × 10, which meant that the outer vertical margins also received the overprint.

The setting of Type **9** is not known.

Although only the one setting was used for the low values it is known that some of the overprint errors occurred, or were corrected, during the course of the various printings.

(Overprinted at the offices of *The Zanzibar Gazette*)

1895 (11 Nov)–**96**. *Stamps of India* (*Queen Victoria*) *optd with T* **8** *or* **9** (2 *r. to* 5 *r.*).
49 **23** ½ a. deep green .. 3·00 2·75
a. "Britlsh" for "British" .. £1600 £1200
b. "Br1tish" for "British" (R. 10/12) .. £175
c. "Afr1ca" for "Africa" (R. 1/11) .. £175
d. Opt double, one albino .. £500
50 **25** 1 a. plum .. 2·75 3·25
a. "Britlsh" for "British" .. £1750 £1100
b. "Br1tish" for "British" (R. 10/12) .. £175
c. "Afr1ca" for "Africa" (R. 1/11) .. £175
51 **26** 1½ a. sepia (23.11.95) .. 3·75 3·00
a. "Br1tish" for "British" (R. 10/12) .. £200
b. "Afr1ca" for "Africa" (R. 1/11) .. £200
52 **27** 2 a. ultramarine .. 2·75 2·50
a. "Britlsh" for "British" .. £1300
b. "Br1tish" for "British" (R. 10/12) .. £175
c. "Afr1ca" for "Africa" (R. 1/11) .. £175 £175
53 **36** 2½ a. green .. 5·00 2·50
a. "Biitish" for "British" .. £2750
b. "Bpitish" for "British" .. £2750
c. "Britlsh" for "British" .. † £1100
d. "Eas" for "East" (R. 2/12) .. £600 £800
e. "Br1tish" for "British" (R. 10/12) .. £225 £200
f. "Afr1ca" for "Africa" (R. 1/11) .. £225
54 **28** 3 a. brown-orange (18.12.95) .. 7·50 8·00
a. "Br1tish" for "British" (R. 10/12) .. £250 £250
b. "Afr1ca" for "Africa" (R. 1/11) .. £250
55 **29** 4 a. olive-green (18.12.95) .. 18·00 13·00
a. *Slate-green* .. 16·00 13·00
b. "Br1tish" for "British" (R. 10/12) .. £300 £300
c. "Afr1ca" for "Africa" (R. 1/11) .. £300
56 **21** 6 a. pale brown (18.12.95) .. 22·00 27·00
a. "Br1tish" for "British" (R. 10/8) .. £375
b. "Afr1ca" for "Africa" (R. 1/7) .. £375
c. Opt double, one albino .. £750
57 **31** 8 a. dull mauve (18.12.95) .. 45·00 48·00
a. "Br1tish" for "British" (R. 10/12) .. £425
b. "Afr1ca" for "Africa" (R. 1/11) .. £425
c. *Magenta* (1896) .. 28·00 35·00
ca. Inverted "a" for "t" of "East" (R. 2/12) .. † £2000
58 **32** 12 a. purple/*red* (18.12.95) .. 19·00 26·00
a. "Br1tish" for "British" (R. 10/12) .. £375 £375
b. "Afr1ca" for "Africa" (R. 1/11) .. £375
59 **33** 1 r. slate (18.12.95) .. 45·00 48·00
a. "Br1tish" for "British" (R. 10/12) .. £550
b. "Afr1ca" for "Africa" (R. 1/11) .. £550
60 **37** 1 r. green and carmine (1896) .. 23·00 32·00
a. Inverted "a" for "t" of "East" (R. 2/12) .. £1800
b. "Br1tish" for "British" (R. 10/12) .. £375
c. "Afr1ca" for "Africa" (R. 1/11) .. £375
d. Opt double, one sideways .. £275 £400
61 **38** 2 r. carmine and yellow-brown (18.12.95) 48·00 70·00
62 3 r. brown and green (18.12.95) .. 60·00 80·00
63 5 r. ultramarine and violet (18.12.95) .. 75·00 90·00
a. Opt double .. £1800
49/63 .. *Set of* 15 £300 £350

The 2½ a. is known on cover used on 31 October but was probably from a trial printing released in error.

The relative horizontal positions of the three lines of the overprint vary considerably but the distance vertically between the lines of the overprint is constant.

There are other varieties, such as inverted "s" in "British", wide and narrow "B", and inverted "V" for "A" in "Africa" (R.1/1 and R.6/7).

The 2, 3, and 5 r., normally overprinted in larger type than the lower values, are also known with a smaller overprint, for use as specimen stamps for the U.P.U. These were not issued for postal purposes (*price* £250 *un per set*). The lower values were reprinted at the same time using similar type to the original overprint.

Forgeries exist.

2½ (10)

11

1895 (Dec). *No.* 51 *surch locally with T* **10**, *in bright red*.
64 **26** 2½ on 1½ a. sepia .. 38·00 32·00
a. Inverted "1" in fraction (R.5/7, R.10/7) .. £375 £375

The setting of Type **10** was in 5 horizontal rows of 12 stamps, repeated twice for each pane.

No. 51 also exists surcharged with T **12**, **13** and **14** in *brown-red*. These stamps were sent to the Postal Union authorities at Berne, but were never issued to the public (*Price unused*: T **12** £40, T **13** £70, T **14** £60).

(Recess D.L.R.)

1896 (19 May)–**1901**. *Wmk Crown CA*. *P* 14.
65 **11** ½ a. yellow-green .. 85 45
66 1 a. carmine-rose .. 1·25 30
a. Bright rose-red .. 1·25 25
b. Rosine (1901) .. 15·00 2·25
67 2 a. chocolate .. 1·50 2·75
68 2½ a. deep blue .. 4·50 1·10
a. Violet-blue .. 5·00 1·40
69 3 a. grey .. 2·50 4·75
70 4 a. deep green .. 5·50 2·50
71 4½ a. orange-yellow .. 3·75 6·00
72 5 a. yellow-bistre .. 7·50 4·00
73 7½ a. mauve .. 5·00 15·00
74 8 a. grey-olive .. 2·50 4·50
75 1 r. pale dull blue .. 20·00 17·00
a. Ultramarine .. 20·00 17·00
76 2 r. orange .. 50·00 24·00
77 3 r. deep violet .. 50·00 27·00
78 4 r. carmine-lake .. 50·00 40·00
79 5 r. sepia .. 50·00 40·00
a. Thin "U" in "RUPEES" (R.3/2) .. £950 £950
65/79 .. *Set of* 15 £225 £150
65/79 Optd "Specimen" .. *Set of* 15 £275

(Overprinted at the offices of *The Zanzibar Gazette*)

1897 (Jan). *Stamps of Zanzibar* (1896 *issue*) *optd with T* **8**. *Wmk Single Rosette*.
80 **13** ½ a. green and red .. 32·00 32·00
81 1 a. indigo and red .. 60·00 60·00
82 2 a. red-brown and red .. 25·00 20·00
83 4½ a. orange and red .. 30·00 25·00
84 5 a. bistre and red .. 32·00 28·00
85 7½ a. mauve and red .. 38·00 35·00
80/85 .. *Set of* 6 £180 £180

The above six stamps exist with an overprint similar to T **8** but normally showing a stop after "Africa". These overprints (in red on the 1 a.) were made officially to supply the U.P.U. However, the stop does not always show. Pieces are known showing overprints with and without stop *se-tenant* (including the red overprint on the 1 a.).

Stamps of Zanzibar, wmk. "Multiple Rosettes" and overprinted with T **8** are forgeries.

2½ (12) — 2½ (13) — 2½ (14)

SETTING OF TYPES 12/14. The panes of 120 were surcharged by two applications of a setting of 60 (6 × 10). This contained 26 examples of Type **12**, 10 of Type **13** and 24 of Type **14**.

1897 (Jan). *Nos.* 157 *and* 162 *of Zanzibar optd with T* **8** *and further surch locally, in red*.
86 **12** 2½ on 1 a. indigo and red .. 60·00 48·00
b. Opt Type **8** double .. £4000
87 **13** 2½ on 1 a. indigo and red .. £100 80·00
88 **14** 2½ on 1 a. indigo and red .. 60·00 48·00
a. Opt Type **8** double .. £4500
89 **12** 2½ on 3 a. grey and red .. 60·00 48·00
90 **13** 2½ on 3 a. grey and red .. £100 80·00
91 **14** 2½ on 3 a. grey and red .. 60·00 48·00
86/91 .. *Set of* 6 £400 £300

Both the notes after No. 85 also apply here.

A special printing for U.P.U. requirements was made with the 2½ surcharge on the 1 a. and 3 a. stamps overprinted as T **8** but *with stop* after "Africa". It also included a "2" over "1" error in T **14**.

15

(Recess D.L.R.)

1897 (Nov)–**1903**. *Wmk Crown CC*. *P* 14.
92 **15** 1 r. grey-blue .. 24·00 23·00
a. Dull blue (1901) .. 20·00 13·00
b. Bright ultramarine (1903) .. 85·00 65·00
93 2 r. orange .. 45·00 48·00
94 3 r. deep violet .. 45·00 55·00
95 4 r. carmine .. 85·00 £110
96 5 r. deep sepia .. 95·00 £140
97 10 r. yellow-bistre (S. £60) .. £150 £225
98 20 r. pale green (S. £125) .. £700 £900
99 50 r. mauve (S. £250) .. £2250 £2750
92/96 Optd "Specimen" .. *Set of* 5 £175

In 1903 stamps of British East Africa were superseded by those of East Africa and Uganda Protectorate (*See* KENYA, UGANDA and TANGANYIKA).

British Forces in Egypt *see* Egypt

British Guiana

The postal service from what was to become British Guiana dates from the last years of the 18th-century, being placed on a more regular basis after the final British occupation.

An inland postal system was organised in 1850, using the adhesive stamps of British Guiana, but, until 1 May 1860, overseas mails continued to be the province of the British G.P.O. The stamps of Great Britain being supplied for use on such letters from 11 May 1858.

For illustration of the handstamp and postmark type see BRITISH POST OFFICES ABROAD notes, following GREAT BRITAIN.

CROWNED-CIRCLED HANDSTAMPS

The provision of a handstamp, probably as Type CC **1**, inscribed "DEMERARA", is recorded in the G.P.O. proof book under 1 March 1856. No examples have been reported. A further handstamp, as Type CC **6**, recorded in the proof book on 17 February 1866, is known used as a cancellation in at least two instances, *circa* 1868.

GEORGETOWN (DEMERARA)

Stamps of GREAT BRITAIN *cancelled* "A 03" *as Type* **2**.

1858 *to* **1860**.
Z1 1d. rose-red (1857), *perf* 14 .. £120
Z2 4d. rose (1857) .. £110
Z3 6d. lilac (1856) .. £100
a. Azure paper
Z4 1s. green (1856) .. £900

NEW AMSTERDAM (BERBICE)

Stamps of GREAT BRITAIN *cancelled* "A 04" *as Type* **2**.

1858 *to* **1860**.
Z5 1d. rose-red (1857), *perf* 14
Z6 2d. blue (1858) (Plate Nos. 7, 8) .. £350
Z7 4d. rose (1857) .. £250
Z8 6d. lilac (1856) .. £175
Z9 1s. green (1856) .. £1000

PRICES FOR STAMPS ON COVER TO 1945

Nos. 1/21	*from* × 3
No. 23	†
Nos. 24/7	*from* × 3
Nos. 29/115	*from* × 4
Nos. 116/24	*from* × 6
Nos. 126/36	*from* × 5
Nos. 137/59	*from* × 6
Nos. 162/5	*from* × 8
Nos. 170/4	*from* × 5
Nos. 175/89	*from* × 6
No. 192	*from* × 20
Nos. 193/210	*from* × 4
Nos. 213/15	*from* × 5
Nos. 216/21	*from* × 3
Nos. 222/4	*from* × 8
Nos. 233/50	*from* × 3
No. 251	—
Nos. 252/7	*from* × 3
Nos. 259/82	*from* × 4
Nos. 283/7	*from* × 5
Nos. 288/300	*from* × 4
Nos. 301/4	*from* × 5
Nos. 305/7	*from* × 6
Nos. 308/19	*from* × 5
Nos. D1/4	*from* × 12
Nos. O1/12	*from* × 12

CROWN COLONY

1

2

(Set up and printed at the office of the *Royal Gazette*, Georgetown, British Guiana)

1850 (1 July)–**51**. *Type-set. Black impression.* (*a*) *Medium wove paper. Prices are for*—I. *Cut square.* II. *Cut round.*

I *Used* II *Used*
1 1 2 c. *rose* (1.3.51) .. — £55000
2 4 c. *orange* .. £15000 £2500
3 4 c. *lemon-yellow* .. £20000 £3000
4 8 c. *green* .. £8500 £2000

5 1 12 c. *blue* .. £4000 £1700
6 12 c. *indigo* .. £8500 £1700
7 12 c. *pale blue* .. £8000 £2250
a. "2" of "12" with straight foot .. — £3500
b. "1" of "12" omitted .. † £24000

(*b*) *Pelure paper*

8 1 4 c. *pale yellow* .. £30000 £3000

These stamps were initialled by the postmaster, or the Post Office clerks, before they were issued. The initials are—E. T. E. D(alton), E. D. W(ight), J. B. S(mith), H. A. K(illikelley), and W. H. L(ortimer). There are several types of each value and it has been suggested that the setting contained one horizontal row of four slightly different impressions.

Only ten examples of No. 1 have been recorded.

(Litho Waterlow)

1852 (1 Jan). *Surface-coloured paper. Imperf.*

			Un	*Used*
9	2	1 c. black/*magenta*	£8500	£4250
10		4 c. black/*deep blue*	£10000	£4250

There are two types of each value.

Reprints, on thicker paper and perf $12^1/_2$, were made in 1865 (*Price £10 either value*).

Such reprints with the perforations removed are sometimes offered as genuine originals.

CONDITION. Prices for Nos. 9 to 21 are for fine copies. Poor to medium specimens can be supplied when in stock at much lower rates.

3

4

5

(Dies eng and stamps litho Waterlow)

1853–59. *Imperf.* (*a*) *Original printing.*

11 3 1 c. vermilion .. £3000 £1000

This 1 c. in *reddish brown* is probably a proof (*Price* £650).

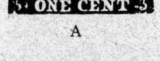

A

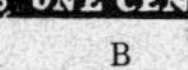
B

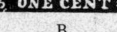

C

D

A. "O" large and 1 mm from left corner.
B. "O" small and ¾ mm from left corner.
C. "O" small and ¾ mm from left corner. "NT" widely spaced.
D. "ONE" close together, "O" 1¼ mm from left corner.

(*b*) *Fresh lithographic transfers from the* 4 c. *with varying labels of value. White line above value* (1858–59).

12 3 1 c. dull red (A) .. £1800 £700
13 1 c. brownish red (A) .. £4000 £700
14 1 c. dull red (B) .. £2250 £750
15 1 c. brownish red (B) .. £4000 £750
16 1 c. dull red (C) .. £2250 £750
17 1 c. dull red (D) .. £3500 £2250

1853–59. *Imperf.*

18 4 4 c. deep blue .. £900 £400
a. Retouched .. £1900 £800
19 4 c. blue (1855) .. £750 £400
20 4 c. pale blue (1859) .. £650 £300
a. Retouched .. £1500 £550

The 4 c. value was produced from transfers from the original 1 c., with the bottom inscription removed, teamed with a new face value. The join often shows as a white line or traces of it above the label of value and lower corner figures. In some stamps on the sheet this line is missing, owing to having been retouched, and in these cases a line of colour usually appears in its place.

The 1 c. and 4 c. stamps were reprinted in 1865 from fresh transfers of five varieties. These are on thin paper and perf $12^1/_2$ (*Price £8 each unused*).

1860 (May). *Figures in corners framed. Imperf.*

21 5 4 c. blue .. £2500 £425

6

(Type-set and printed at the *Official Gazette* by Baum and Dallas, Georgetown).

1856. (*a*) *Surface-coloured paper.*

23 6 1 c. black/*magenta*
24 4 c. black/*magenta* (Feb) .. — £5500
25 4 c. black/*rose-carmine* (Sept) .. — £7500
26 4 c. black/*blue* (Oct) .. — £30000

(*b*) *Paper coloured through*

27 6 4 c. black/*deep blue* (Aug) .. — £40000

Since only one example of No. 23 is known, no market price can be given. This celebrated stamp frequently termed "the world's rarest", was last on the market in 1980.

These stamps, like those of the first issue, were initialled before being issued; the initials are—E.T.E.D., E.D.W., C.A. W(atson), and W.H.L.

The 4 c. is known in four types, differing in the position of the inscriptions.

PAPERMAKERS' WATERMARKS. Seven different papermakers' watermarks were used in the period 1860 to 1875 and stamps bearing portions of these are worth a premium.

7

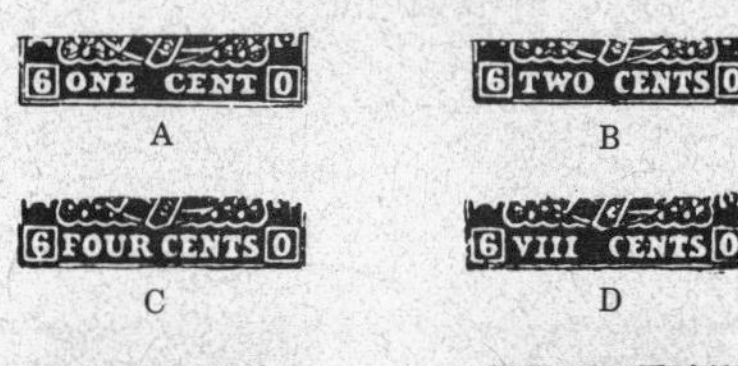
A B C D E F

(Dies eng and litho Waterlow)

1860 (July)–**63**. *Tablets of value as illustrated. Thick paper. P* 12.

29 7 1 c. pale rose .. £800 £150
30 2 c. deep orange (8.60) .. £100 30·00
31 2 c. pale orange .. £100 30·00
32 4 c. deep blue (8.60) .. £250 42·00
33 4 c. blue .. £200 40·00
34 8 c. brownish rose .. £275 45·00
35 8 c. pink .. £225 42·00
36 12 c. lilac (11.61) .. £350 32·00
37 12 c. grey-lilac .. £300 32·00
38 24 c. deep green (6.63) .. £750 60·00
39 24 c. green .. £750 60·00

The 1 c. was reprinted in 1865 on *thin* paper, P $12^1/_2$—13, and in a different shade. *Price* £5.

The 12 c. in both shades is frequently found surcharged with a large "5d" in *red*; this is to denote the proportion of postage repayable by the colony to Great Britain for overseas letters.

1861 (1 Nov). *Colour changed. Thick paper P* 12.

40 7 1 c. reddish brown .. £200 70·00

1862–66. (*a*) *Thin paper. P* 12.

41 7 1 c. brown .. £300 £140
42 1 c. black (1863) .. 60·00 30·00
43 2 c. orange .. 65·00 24·00
44 4 c. blue .. 70·00 23·00
45 4 c. pale blue .. 65·00 17·00
46 8 c. pink (1863) .. 85·00 32·00
47 12 c. dull purple (1863) .. 85·00 16·00
48 12 c. purple .. 85·00 17·00
49 12 c. lilac .. 90·00 25·00
50 24 c. green .. £450 55·00

(*b*) *Thin paper. P* $12^1/_2$–13 (1863)

51 7 1 c. black .. 40·00 13·00
52 2 c. orange .. 60·00 13·00
53 4 c. blue .. 65·00 17·00
54 8 c. pink .. £120 50·00
55 12 c. brownish lilac .. £325 70·00
56 24 c. green .. £450 50·00

Copies are found on *pelure* paper.

(*c*) *Medium paper. P* $12^1/_2$–13

57 7 1 c. black (1864) .. 35·00 18·00
58 2 c. deep orange (1864) .. 50·00 15·00
59 2 c. orange .. 55·00 11·00
60 4 c. greyish blue (1864) .. 60·00 11·00
61 4 c. blue .. 60·00 18·00
62 8 c. pink (1864) .. £100 32·00
63 12 c. brownish lilac (1865) .. £225 48·00
64 24 c. green (1864) .. £110 48·00
65 24 c. deep green .. £225 48·00

(*d*) *Medium paper. P* 10 (March 1866)

65*a* 7 12 c. grey-lilac .. £225 48·00

8

9

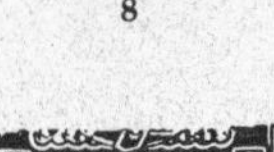
G

H

I

K

New transfers for the 1 c., 2 c., 8 c., and 12 c. with the spaces between values and the word "CENTS" about 1 mm.

1863–75. *Medium paper* (*a*) *P* $12^1/_2$–13 (1863–68).

66 8 1 c. black (1866) .. 18·00 13·00
67 2 c. orange-red (1865) .. 28·00 3·25
68 2 c. orange .. 25·00 3·25
69 9 6 c. blue (1865) .. 75·00 35·00
70 6 c. greenish blue .. 75·00 38·00
71 6 c. deep blue .. 75·00 35·00
72 6 c. milky blue .. 80·00 35·00
73 8 8 c. pink (1868) .. 85·00 10·00
74 8 c. carmine .. 85·00 10·00
75 8 12 c. grey-lilac (1867) .. £275 16·00
76 12 c. brownish purple .. £325 18·00
77 9 24 c. green (*perf* 12) .. £175 17·00
78 24 c. yellow-green (*perf* 12) .. 80·00 8·00
79 24 c. yellow-green (*perf* $12^1/_2$–13) .. 90·00 7·50
80 24 c. green (*perf* $12^1/_2$–13) (1864) .. 90·00 9·00
81 24 c. blue-green (*perf* $12^1/_2$–13) .. £120 17·00
82 48 c. pale red .. £110 42·00
83 48 c. deep red .. £110 42·00
84 48 c. carmine-rose .. £200 42·00

The 4 c. corresponding to this issue can only be distinguished from that of the previous issue by minor plating flaws.

There is a variety of the 6 c. with stop before "VICISSIM".

Varieties of most of the values of issues of 1863–64 and 1866 are to be found on both very thin and thick papers.

(*b*) *P* 10 (1866–74)

85 8 1 c. black (1869) .. 7·50 2·00
86 1 c. grey-black .. 8·50 4·00
87 2 c. orange (1868) .. 9·00 1·25
88 2 c. reddish orange .. 18·00 2·50
89 4 c. slate-blue .. 50·00 9·00
90 4 c. blue .. 55·00 5·00
a. Bisected (on cover) .. † £3250
b. Ditto Imperf (on cover) .. † —
91 4 c. pale blue .. 60·00 7·50
92 9 6 c. milky blue (1867) .. 80·00 19·00
93 6 c. ultramarine .. 80·00 30·00
94 6 c. dull blue .. 80·00 27·00
95 8 8 c. pink (1874) .. 80·00 11·00
96 8 c. brownish pink .. 80·00 11·00
96*a* 8 c. carmine .. 80·00 13·00
97 12 c. pale lilac (1867) .. £160 12·00
98 12 c. grey-lilac .. 85·00 12·00
99 12 c. brownish grey .. 85·00 14·00
100 12 c. lilac .. 85·00 14·00
101 9 24 c. deep green .. £160 9·00
102 24 c. bluish green .. — 8·00
103 24 c. yellow-green .. £110 7·50
104 48 c. crimson (1867) .. £250 24·00
105 48 c. red .. £250 22·00
104 Handstamped "Specimen" .. £150
104 Perf "Specimen" .. £100

(*c*) *P* 15 (1875–76)

106 8 1 c. black .. 22·00 7·50
107 2 c. orange-red .. £100 8·50
108 2 c. orange .. £100 8·50
109 4 c. bright blue .. £175 65·00
111 9 6 c. ultramarine .. £225 55·00
112 8 8 c. deep rose (1876) .. £125 48·00
113 12 c. lilac .. £325 42·00
114 9 24 c. yellow-green .. £450 35·00
115 24 c. deep green .. £450 35·00

There is a variety of the 48 c. with stop after "P" in "PETIMUSQUE".

Imperforate stamps of this and of the previous issue are considered to be proofs.

PRICES for stamps of the 1862 issue are for good average copies. Copies with roulettes on all sides very seldom occur and do not exist in marginal positions.

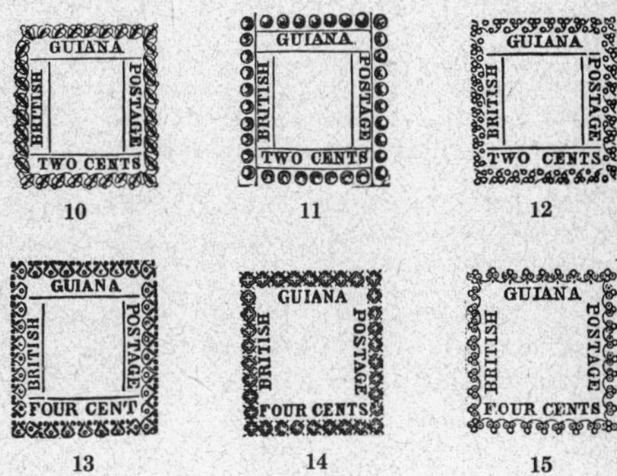
10 11 12 13 14 15

(Type-set and printed at the Office of the *Royal Gazette*, Georgetown)

1862 (Sept). *Black on coloured paper. Roul* 6.

116 10 1 c. *rose* .. £1100 £200
a. Unsigned .. £130
b. Wrong ornament (as T **13**) at left (R. 1/1) .. — £325
c. "1" for "I" in "BRITISH" (R. 1/5) .. — £325
117 11 1 c. *rose* .. £1200 £250
a. Unsigned .. £140
b. Narrow "T" in "CENTS" (R. 3/1) .. — £325
c. Wrong ornament (as T **15**) at top (R. 3/3) .. — £325
d. "1" for "I" in "BRITISH" and italic "S" in "POSTAGE" (R. 3/5) .. — £325
118 12 1 c. *rose* .. £2000 £325
a. Unsigned .. £300
b. "1" for "I" in "GUIANA" (R. 4/4) .. — £325
c. Wrong ornament (as T **15**) at left (R. 4/5) .. — £325
d. "C" for "O" in "POSTAGE" (R. 4/6) .. — £325
119 10 2 c. *yellow* .. £1100 £180
a. Unsigned .. £130
b. Wrong ornament (as T **13**) at left (R. 1/1) .. — £325
c. "1" for "I" in "BRITISH" (R. 1/5) .. — £325
120 11 2 c. *yellow* .. £1400 £250
a. Unsigned .. £140
b. "C" for "O" in "TWO" and narrow "T" in "CENTS" (R. 3/1) .. — £325
c. Wrong ornament (as T **15**) at top (R. 3/3) .. — £325
d. "1" for "I" in "BRITISH" and italic "S" in "POSTAGE" (R. 3/5) .. — £325
e. Italic "T" in "TWO" (R. 3/6) .. — £325

121 12 2 c. *yellow* £2200 £325
a. Unsigned £300
b. "1" for "I" in "GUIANA" (R. 4/4) .. — £325
c. Wrong ornament (as T 15) at left (R. 4/5) .. .. — £325
d. "C" for "O" in "POSTAGE" (R. 4/6) — £325
122 13 4 c. *blue* £1100 £200
a. Unsigned £225
b. Wrong ornament (as T 15) at left (R. 1/6) .. .. — £350
c. Wrong ornament (as T 15) at top and italic "S" in "CENTS" (R. 2/2) .. — £350
d. Ornament omitted at right (R. 2/4) — £350
123 14 4 c. *blue* £1200 £300
a. Unsigned £225
b. With inner frame lines (as in T 10/13) (R. 2/5–6) £2500 £1200
ba. "1" for "I" in "BRITISH" (R. 2/5) .. £2500 £1200
c. "1" for "I" in "BRITISH" and "GUIANA" (R. 4/1) .. .. .. — £350
124 15 4 c. *blue* £1300 £300
a. Unsigned £225
b. Wrong ornament (as T 12) at foot (R. 3/1) .. .. — £350
c. Italic "S" in "CENTS" (R. 3/2) .. — £350
d. Italic "S" in "BRITISH" (R. 3/3) .. — £350

Stamps were initialled across the centre before use by the Acting Receiver-General, Robert Mather. Black was used on the 1 c., red for the 2 c. and an ink which appears white for the 4 c.

The three values of this provisional were each printed in sheets of 24 (6 × 4). The 1 c. and 2 c. were produced from the same setting of the border ornaments which contained 12 examples as Type **10** (Rows 1 and 2), 8 as Type **11** (R. 3/1 to R. 4/2) and 4 as Type **12** (R. 4/3–6).

The setting of the 4 c. contained 10 examples as Type **13** (R. 1/1 to R. 2/4), 8 as Type **14** (R. 2/5–6 and Row 4) and 6 as Type **15** (Row 3).

16 (17)

(Typo D.L.R.)

1876 (1 July)–**79**. *Wmk Crown CC.* (*a*) *P* 14.
126 16 1 c. slate .. .. 2·75 1·40
127 2 c. orange .. .. 28·00 1·00
128 4 c. blue .. .. 80·00 6·50
129 6 c. brown .. .. 60·00 5·50
130 8 c. rose .. .. 85·00 75
131 12 c. pale violet .. .. .. 50·00 1·25
132 24 c. emerald-green .. .. .. 50·00 3·00
133 48 c. red-brown .. .. .. 90·00 11·00
134 96 c. olive-bistre £400 £250
126/134 .. .. *Set of* 9 £750 £250
126/132, 134 Handstamped/Perf "Specimen" *Set of* 8 £500

(*b*) *P* 12½ (1877)
135 16 4 c. blue £1200 £200

(*c*) *Perf compound of* 14 × 12½ (1879)
136 16 1 c. slate .. .. — £200

1878. *Provisionals. Various stamps with old values ruled through with thick bars, in black ink, the bars varying in depth of colour.*

(*a*) *With two horiz bars* (17 Apr)
137 16 (1 c.) on 6 c. brown .. .. .. 35·00 55·00

(*b*) *Official stamps with horiz bars across* "OFFICIAL" (end Aug)
138 8 1 c. black .. .. £100 60·00
139 16 1 c. slate .. .. 95·00 45·00
140 2 c. orange .. .. £100 60·00

(*c*) *With horiz and vert bars as T* **17** (6 Nov)
141 9 (1 c.) on 6 c. ultramarine (93) .. .. £110 65·00
142 16 (1 c.) on 6 c. brown .. .. .. £140 65·00

(*d*) *Official stamps with bars across* "OFFICIAL" (23 Nov)

(i) *With two horiz bars and one vert*
144 16 (1 c.) on 4 c. blue .. .. .. 95·00 60·00
145 (1 c.) on 6 c. brown .. .. .. £110 60·00
146 8 (2 c.) on 8 c. rose .. .. .. £180 70·00

(ii) *With one horiz bar and one vert*
147 16 (1 c.) on 4 c. blue .. .. .. — £1000
148 8 (2 c.) on 8 c. rose .. .. .. £160 70·00

1 2 2
(18) (19) (20)

1881 (21 Dec). *No. 134 with old value ruled through with bar in black ink and surch.*
149 18 1 on 96 c. olive-bistre .. .. 3·50 4·75
a. Bar in red .. .. ..
b. Bar omitted .. .. ..
150 19 2 on 96 c. olive-bistre .. .. 4·00 8·00
a. Bar in red .. .. ..
b. Bar omitted .. .. ..
151 20 2 on 96 c. olive-bistre .. .. 29·00 29·00

In the setting of 60 Type **19** occurs on the first five vertical rows and Type **20** on the sixth.

1 2 2
(21) (23) (24)

1881 (28 Dec). *Various stamps with old value ruled with bar and surch.* (*a*) *On No.* 105.
152 21 1 on 48 c. red .. .. .. 26·00 5·00
a. Bar omitted .. ..

On Official stamps (including unissued 48 *c. optd with Type* **O 2**)
153 21 1 on 12 c. brownish purple (O4) .. 85·00 48·00
154 1 on 48 c. red-brown .. .. 95·00 70·00
155 23 2 on 12 c. pale violet (O11) .. .. 60·00 20·00
a. Surch double £500 £350
b. Do. T **23** and **24** .. .. ..
c. Extra bar through "OFFICIAL" ..
156 24 2 on 12 c. pale violet (O11) .. .. £160 80·00
157 23 2 on 24 c. emerald-green (O12) .. .. 65·00 26·00
a. Surch double £600
158 24 2 on 24 c. emerald-green (O12) £250 £250
159 19 2 on 24 c. green (O5) .. .. .. £170 90·00

On Nos. 149/59 the bar is found in various thicknesses ranging from 1 to 4 mm.

26 27

(Type-set, Baldwin & Co. Georgetown)

1882 (9 Jan). *Black impression. P* 12. *Perforated with the word* "SPECIMEN" *diagonally.*
162 26 1 c. *magenta* .. .. .. 35·00 28·00
a. Imperf between (*pair*) .. ..
b. Without "SPECIMEN" £120 £110
c. "1" with foot .. .. .. 65·00 55·00
163 2 c. *yellow* .. .. 48·00 40·00
a. Without "SPECIMEN" £120 £110
b. Small "2" .. .. .. 48·00 40·00
164 27 1 c. *magenta* .. .. .. 35·00 28·00
a. Without "SPECIMEN" £120 £110
b. "1" with foot .. .. .. 65·00 55·00
165 2 c. *yellow* .. .. 45·00 35·00
a. Bisected diagonally (1 c.) .. ..
b. Without "SPECIMEN" £120 £110
c. Small "2" .. .. 75·00 65·00

These stamps were perforated "SPECIMEN" as a precaution against fraud. Stamps are known with "SPECIMEN" double.

The 1 c. and 2 c. stamps were printed in separate sheets; but utilising the same clichés, these being altered according to the face value required. Two settings were used, common to both values:—

1st setting. Four rows of three, T **26** being Nos. 5, 6, 7, 8, 11 and 12, and T **27** the remainder.

From this setting there were two printings of the 2 c., but only one of the 1 c.

2nd setting. Six rows of two, T **26** being Nos. 3, 7, 8, 9, 11 and 12, and T **27** the remainder.

There were two printings of each value from this setting.

Se-tenant pairs are worth about 20% more.

The "1" with foot occurs on T **27** on No. 9 in the first setting and on T **26** on No. 7 in the first printing only of the second setting.

The small "2" appears on T **26** in the first setting on Nos. 6, 7, 8 and 12 in the first printing and on Nos. 7, 8 and 12 only in the second printing: in the second setting it comes on Nos. 3, 9 and 12 in the first printing and on Nos. 9, 11 and 12 in the second printing. On T **27** the variety occurs in the first setting on No. 9 of the second printing only and in the second setting on No. 10 in both printings.

(Typo D.L.R.)

1882. *Wmk Crown C.A. P* 14.
170 16 1 c. slate (27 Jan) .. .. .. 6·00 20
171 2 c. orange (27 Jan) .. .. .. 17·00 15
a. Value doubly printed .. ..
172 4 c. blue .. .. 60·00 5·00
173 6 c. brown .. .. 5·00 6·50
174 8 c. rose .. .. 65·00 40
170/4 .. .. *Set of* 5 £140 11·00
170/4 Perf "Specimen" .. .. *Set of* 5 £250

INLAND 4 CENTS 4 CENTS
(*a*) (*b*)
Two types of "4"

2 CENTS
REVENUE
(28)

6 6
(*c*) (*d*)
Two types of "6"

1888–89. *T* **16** (*without value in lower label*) *optd.* "INLAND REVENUE", *and surch with value as T* **28**, *by D.L.R. Wmk Crown CA. P* 14.
175 1 c. dull purple (8.89) 50 20
176 2 c. dull purple (25.5.89) 95 25
177 3 c. dull purple 50 20
178 4 c. dull purple (*a*) .. .. .. 2·00 30
a. Larger figure "4" (*b*) .. .. 22·00 9·00
179 6 c. dull purple (*c*) .. .. .. 2·25 1·40
a. Figure 6 with straight top (*d*) .. 15·00 3·25
180 8 c. dull purple (8.89) .. .. .. 1·50 25
181 10 c. dull purple .. .. .. 5·50 2·50
182 20 c. dull purple .. .. .. 15·00 9·00
183 40 c. dull purple .. .. .. 17·00 15·00
184 72 c. dull purple (1.10.88) .. .. 24·00 22·00
185 $1 green (1.10.88) £400 £275
186 $2 green (1.10.88) £180 £140
187 $3 green (1.10.88) .. .. .. £110 80·00
188 $4 green (*a*) (1.10.88) £325 £275
a. Larger figure "4" (*b*) £850 £850
189 $5 green (1.10.88) £200 £140
175/189 .. .. *Set of* 15 £1200 £850

Nos. 175/89 were surcharged in settings of 60 (6×10). No. 178a occurs on all stamps in the third vertical row, No. 179a in the fourth and sixth vertical rows and No. 188a in the second vertical row.

2
(29)

30

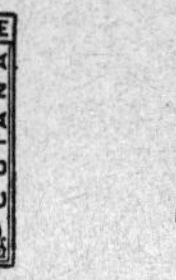

(31)

1889 (6 June). *No.* 176 *surch with T* **29** *in red by* Official Gazette.
192 "2" on 2 c. dull purple 55 15

The varieties with figure "2" *inverted* or *double* were made privately by a postal employee in Demerara.

1889 (Sept). *Wmk Crown CA. P* 14.
193 30 1 c. dull purple and slate-grey 90 90
194 2 c. dull purple and orange 80 10
195 4 c. dull purple and ultramarine .. 3·75 1·50
196 4 c. dull purple and cobalt .. .. 9·00 2·25
197 6 c. dull purple and brown .. .. 16·00 6·50
198 6 c. dull purple and maroon .. .. 6·00 3·50
199 8 c. dull purple and rose .. .. 5·50 60
200 12 c. dull purple and bright purple .. 12·00 1·00
200*a* 12 c. dull purple and mauve .. .. 8·00 2·00
201 24 c. dull purple and green .. .. 7·50 2·50
202 48 c. dull purple and orange-red .. .. 13·00 8·50
203 72 c. dull purple and red-brown .. .. 19·00 22·00
204 72 c. dull purple and yellow-brown .. 50·00 60·00
205 96 c. dull purple and carmine .. .. 48·00 55·00
206 96 c. dull purple and rosine .. .. 60·00 65·00
193/205 .. .. *Set of* 10 £100 85·00
193/205 Optd "Specimen" .. .. *Set of* 10 £180

1890 (15 July). *Stamps of* 1888–89 *surch locally* "One Cent", *in red, as in T* **31**.
207 1 c. on $1 (No. 185) 80 35
a. Surch double .. .. — 75·00
208 1 c. on $2 (No. 186) 50 60
a. Surch double .. .. 75·00
209 1 c. on $3 (No. 187) .. .. .. 1·40 1·25
a. Surch double .. .. 60·00
210 1 c. on $4 (No. 188) .. .. .. 2·00 4·50
a. Surch double .. .. 65·00
b. Larger figure "4" (*b*) .. .. 10·00 18·00
207/10 .. .. *Set of* 4 4·25 6·00

1890–91. *Colours changed. Wmk Crown CA. P* 14
213 30 1 c. sea-green (12.90) 30 10
214 5 c. ultramarine (1.91) .. .. .. 2·50 10
215 8 c. dull purple and greenish black (10.90) .. .. 2·50 2·75
213/15 .. .. *Set of* 3 4·75 2·75
213/15 Optd "Specimen" .. .. *Set of* 3 60·00

32 Mount Roraima

33 Kaieteur Falls

(Recess D.L.R.)

1898 (18 July). *Queen Victoria's Jubilee. Wmk Crown CC (sideways on T* **32**). *P* 14.
216 32 1 c. blue-black and carmine .. .. 2·50 25
217 33 2 c. brown and indigo .. .. .. 4·75 90
a. Imperf between (horiz pair) .. £2750
218 2 c. brown and blue .. .. .. 11·00 90
219 32 5 c. green and sepia .. .. .. 15·00 2·00
a. Imperf between (horiz pair) ..
220 33 10 c. blue-black and orange-red .. .. 15·00 20·00
221 32 15 c. red-brown and blue .. .. .. 15·00 16·00
216/21 .. .. *Set of* 5 45·00 35·00
216/21 Optd "Specimen" .. .. *Set of* 5 90·00

A second plate was later used for the 1 c. on which the lines of shading on the mountains in the background are strengthened, and those along the ridge show distinct from each other, whereas, in the original, they are more or less blurred. In the second plate the shading of the sky is less pronounced.

TWO CENTS.
(34)

35

(Surch at Printing Office of the *Daily Chronicle*, Georgetown)

1899 (22 Feb). *Surch with T* **34**
222 32 2 c. on 5 c. (No. 219) .. .. .. 1·40 1·10
a. No stop after "CENTS" .. .. 35·00 38·00
223 33 2 c. on 10 c. (No. 220) .. .. .. 60 1·25
a. No stop after "CENTS" .. .. 20·00 35·00
c. "GENTS" for "CENTS" (R. 5/7) .. 50·00 55·00
d. Surch inverted £275 £300
224 32 2 c. on 15 c. (No. 221) .. .. .. 1·25 1·25
a. No stop after "CENTS" .. .. 50·00 55·00
b. Surch double £425 £475
c. Surch double, one without stop
d. Surch inverted £300 £325
222/4 .. .. *Set of* 3 3·00 3·25

The "no stop" variety occurs on R. 9/5 in sheets of No. 222 and of the first setting of No. 223 and on R. 2/9 in the second setting of No. 223.

Of No. 224c. only one specimen exists.

1900–7. *T* **30**. *Wmk Crown CA. P* 14
233 1 c. grey-green (1907) .. 3·50 1·75
234 2 c. dull purple and carmine .. 2·75 25
235 2 c. dull purple and black/*red* (1901) .. 80 10
236 6 c. grey-black and ultramarine (1902) .. 6·50 11·00
237 48 c. grey and purple-brown (1901) .. 35·00 32·00
a. Brownish grey and brown (1907) .. 22·00 28·00
238 60 c. green and rosine (1903) .. 48·00 £100
233/8 .. *Set of* 6 80·00 £130
233/8 Optd "Specimen" .. *Set of* 6 90·00
No. 233 is a reissue of No. 213 in non-fugitive ink.

1905–7. *T* **30**. *Wmk Multiple Crown CA. P* 14.
240 1 c. grey-green, **OC** .. 90 30
241 2 c. purple and black/*red*, **OC** .. 2·25 10
242 4 c. dull purple and ultramarine, **OC** .. 6·00 6·50
243 5 c. dull purple and blue/*blue*, **OC** (1.5.05) (Optd S. £20) .. 3·50 3·50
244 6 c. grey-black and ultramarine, **OC** .. 14·00 22·00
245 12 c. dull and bright purple, **OC** .. 22·00 28·00
246 24 c. dull purple and green, **OC** (1906) .. 3·75 4·50
247 48 c. grey and purple-brown, **OC** .. 13·00 20·00
248 60 c. green and rosine, **OC** .. 13·00 45·00
249 72 c. purple and orange-brown, **C** (1907) .. 24·00 45·00
250 96 c. black & vermilion/*yellow*, **C** (20.11.05) (Optd S. £30) .. 32·00 45·00
240/50 .. *Set of* 11 £120 £200

1905. *Optd* "POSTAGE AND REVENUE". *Wmk Multiple Crown CA. P* 14.
251 **35** $2.40 green and violet, **C** (S. £75) .. £160 £225

1907–10. *Colours changed. Wmk Mult Crown CA. P* 14
252 **30** 1 c. blue-green, **O** .. 2·75 2·25
253 2 c. rose-red, **O** .. 4·25 10
a. Redrawn (1910) .. 4·75 10
254 4 c. brown and purple, **O** .. 2·25 60
255 5 c. ultramarine, **O** .. 2·50 70
256 6 c. grey and black, **O** .. 13·00 7·00
257 12 c. orange and mauve, **O** .. 4·00 4·00
252/7 .. *Set of* 6 25·00 13·00
253/7 Optd "Specimen" .. *Set of* 5 75·00

In No. 253a the flag at the main truck is close to the mast, whereas in the original type it appears to be flying loose from halyards. There are two background lines above the value "2 CENTS" instead of three and the "S" is further away from the end of the tablet.

37

War
Tax
(38)

(Typo D.L.R.)

1913–21. *Wmk Mult Crown CA. P* 14.
259 **37** 1 c. yellow-green, **O** .. 90 70
a. Blue-green, **O** (1917) .. 90 25
260 2 c. carmine, **O** .. 50 10
a. Scarlet, **O** (1916) .. 80 10
b. Wmk sideways
261 4 c. brown and bright purple, **C** (1914) .. 1·50 25
a. Deep brown and purple, **C** .. 2·00 25
262 5 c. bright blue, **O** .. 60 85
263 6 c. grey and black, **O** .. 75 85
264 12 c. orange and violet, **C** .. 70 90
265 24 c. dull purple and green, **O** (1915) .. 2·00 4·00
266 48 c. grey and purple-brown, **C** (1914) .. 7·50 9·00
267 60 c. green and rosine, **C** (1915) .. 11·00 30·00
268 72 c. purple and orange-brown, **C** (1915) 30·00 48·00
269 96 c. black and vermilion/*yellow*, **C** (1915) 25·00 40·00
a. White back (1913) .. 14·00 27·00
b. On lemon (1916) (Optd S. £20) .. 16·00 30·00
c. On pale yellow (1921) (Optd S. £20) 18·00 45·00
259/69*a* .. *Set of* 11 60·00 £110
259/69*a* Optd "Specimen" .. *Set of* 11 £130

1918 (4 Jan). *No. 260a optd with T* **38**, *by D.L.R.*
271 **37** 2 c. scarlet .. 15 15
The relative position of the words "WAR" and "TAX" vary considerably in the sheet.

1921–27. *Wmk Mult Script CA. P* 14
272 **37** 1 c. green, **O** (1922) .. 90 25
273 2 c. rose-carmine, **O** .. 50 20
274 2 c. bright violet, **O** (1923) .. 30 10
275 4 c. brown and bright purple, **O** (1922) .. 90 10
276 6 c. bright blue, **O** (1922) .. 1·25 25
277 12 c. orange and violet, **O**(1922) .. 1·25 1·50
278 24 c. dull purple and green, **C** .. 1·50 4·50
279 48 c. black and purple, **C** (1926) .. 8·00 3·50
280 60 c. green and rosine, **C** (1926) .. 6·50 20·00
281 72 c. dull purple & orange-brn, **C** (1923) 7·00 24·00
282 96 c. black and red/*yellow*, **C** (1927) .. 12·00 28·00
272/82 .. *Set of* 11 35·00 75·00
272/82 Optd "Specimen" .. *Set of* 11 £150

39 Ploughing a Rice Field

40 Indian shooting Fish

(Recess Waterlow)

1931 (21 July). *Centenary of County Union T* **39/40** *and similar designs. Wmk Mult Script CA. P* 12½.
283 1 c. emerald-green .. 60 75
284 2 c. brown .. 60 10
285 4 c. carmine .. 1·75 35
286 6 c. blue .. 1·25 2·50
287 $1 violet .. 17·00 35·00
283/7 .. *Set of* 5 19·00 35·00
283/7 Perf "Specimen" .. *Set of* 5 75·00
Designs: *Vert*—4 c., $1 Kaieteur Falls. *Horiz*—6 c. Public buildings, Georgetown.

43 Ploughing a Rice Field

44 Gold Mining

(Recess Waterlow)

1934 (1 Oct)–**51**. *T* **40** *(without dates at top of frame),* **43/4** *and similar designs. Wmk Mult Script CA (sideways on horiz designs). P* 12½.
288 **43** 1 c. green .. 35 30
289 **40** 2 c. red-brown .. 65 15
290 **44** 3 c. scarlet .. 10 10
aa. Wmk error. Crown missing
a. Perf 12½×13½ (30.12.43) .. 10 10
b. Perf 13×14 (28.4.49) .. 15 10
291 – 4 c. slate-violet .. 1·25 35
a. Imperf between (vert pair) .. † £7500
b. Imperf horiz (vert pair) .. £4750
292 – 6 c. deep ultramarine .. 2·50 1·50
293 – 12 c. red-orange .. 10 10
a. Perf 14×13 (16.4.51) .. 10 30
294 – 24 c. purple .. 1·75 2·50
295 – 48 c. black .. 5·50 6·00
296 – 50 c. green .. 9·00 13·00
297 – 60 c. red-brown .. 25·00 25·00
298 – 72 c. purple .. 1·25 55
299 – 96 c. black .. 20·00 26·00
300 – $1 bright violet .. 32·00 24·00
288/300 .. *Set of* 13 90·00 90·00
288/300 Perf "Specimen" .. *Set of* 13 £130
Designs: *Vert*—4 c., 50 c. Kaieteur Falls (as No. 285, but with dates omitted); 96 c. Sir Walter Raleigh and his son. *Horiz*—6 c. Shooting logs over falls; 12 c. Stabroek Market 24 c. Sugar cane in punts; 48 c. Forest road; 60 c. Victoria Regia Lilies; 72 c. Mount Roraima; $1 Botanical Gardens.

1935 (6 May). *Silver Jubilee. As T* **13** *of Antigua.*
301 2 c. ultramarine and grey .. 15 10
f. Diagonal line by turret .. 10·00
h. Dot by flagstaff .. 10·00
302 6 c. brown and deep blue .. 80 30
f. Diagonal line by turret .. 25·00
g. Dot to left of chapel .. 25·00
303 12 c. green and indigo .. 1·25 2·75
f. Diagonal line by turret .. 30·00
h. Dot by flagstaff .. 30·00
304 24 c. slate and purple .. 3·00 4·50
h. Dot by flagstaff .. 50·00
301/4 .. *Set of* 4 4·75 7·00
301/4 Perf "Specimen" .. *Set of* 4 60·00
For illustrations of plate varieties see Omnibus section following Zululand.

1937 (12 May). *Coronation. As T* **2** *of Aden.*
305 2 c. yellow-brown .. 15 10
306 4 c. grey-black .. 40 15
307 6 c. bright blue .. 65 50
305/7 .. *Set of* 3 1·10 65
305/7 Perf "Specimen" .. *Set of* 3 45·00

53 South America

54 Victoria Regia Lilies

(Recess Waterlow)

1938 (1 Feb)–**1952**. *As earlier types but with portrait of King George VI as in T* **53/4**. *Wmk Mult Script CA. P* 12½
308 **43** 1 c. yellow-green .. 3·00 35
aa. Green (1944) .. 10 10
a. Perf 14×13 (1949) .. 10 20
309 – 2 c. slate-violet .. 20 10
a. Perf 13×14 (28.4.49) .. 20 10
310 **53** 4 c. scarlet and black .. 30 10
a. Imperf horiz (vert pair) .. £4500 £3500
b. Perf 13×14 (1952) .. 35 10
311 **40** 6 c. deep ultramarine .. 25 10
a. Perf 13×14 (24.10.49) .. 25 25
312 – 24 c. blue-green .. 10·00 6·00
a. Wmk sideways .. 1·00 10
313 – 36 c. bright violet (7.3.38) .. 1·00 10
a. Perf 13×14 (13.12.51) .. 1·50 30
314 – 48 c. orange .. 50 25
a. Perf 14×13 (14.6.51) .. 90 1·00
315 – 60 c. red-brown .. 3·00 1·75
316 – 96 c. purple .. 2·00 2·00
a. Perf 12½×13½ (1944) .. 1·25 3·00
b. Perf 13×14 (8.2.51) .. 2·25 3·25
317 – $1 bright violet .. 3·50 35
a. Perf 14×13(1951) .. £180 £225
318 – $2 purple (11.6.45) .. 4·00 8·00
a. Perf 14×13 (9.8.50) .. 4·50 7·50
319 **54** $3 red-brown (2.7.45) .. 20·00 18·00
a. Bright red-brown (12.46) .. 25·00 27·00
b. Perf 14×13. *Red-brown* (29.10.52) .. 17·00 32·00
308a/19 .. *Set of* 12 29·00 27·00
308/19 Perf "Specimen" .. *Set of* 12 £180
Designs: *Vert*—2 c., 36 c. Kaieteur Falls; 96 c. Sir Walter Raleigh and his son. *Horiz*—24 c. Sugar cane in punts; 48 c. Forest road; 60 c. Shooting logs over falls; $1 Botanical Gardens; $2 Mount Roraima.

1946 (21 Oct). *Victory. As Nos. 28/9 of Aden.*
320 3 c. carmine .. 10 10
321 6 c. blue .. 10 10
320/1 Perf "Specimen" .. *Set of* 2 45·00

1948 (20 Dec). *Royal Silver Wedding. As Nos. 30/1 of Aden; (recess $3).*
322 3 c. scarlet .. 10 15
323 $3 red-brown .. 9·00 12·00

1949 (10 Oct). *75th Anniv of Universal Postal Union. As Nos. 114/17 of Antigua.*
324 4 c. carmine .. 20 15
325 6 c. deep blue .. 25 25
326 12 c. orange .. 25 25
327 24 c. blue-green .. 25 45
324/7 .. *Set of* 4 85 1·00

1951 (16 Feb). *University College of B.W.I. As Nos. 118/19 of Antigua.*
328 3 c. black and carmine .. 15 10
329 6 c. black and blue .. 25 10

1953 (2 June). *Coronation. As No. 47 of Aden.*
330 4 c. black and scarlet .. 10 10

55 G.P.O. Georgetown

62 Felling Greenheart.

(Centre litho, frame recess ($1); recess (others). Waterlow (until 1961), then D.L.R.)

1954 (1 Dec)–**63**. *T* **55, 62** *and similar designs. Wmk Mult Script CA. P* 12½×13* *(horiz) or* 13 *(vert).*
331 1 c. black .. 10 10
332 2 c. myrtle-green .. 10 10
333 3 c. brown-olive and red-brown .. 80 10
334 4 c. violet .. 10 10
a. D.L.R. ptg (5.12.61) .. 2·50 90
ab. Deep violet (3.1.63) .. 1·75 40
335 5 c. scarlet and black .. 10 10
336 6 c. yellow-green .. 10 10
a. D.L.R. ptg. *Green* (22.5.62) .. 25 20
337 8 c. ultramarine .. 10 10
a. D.L.R. ptg. *Blue* (19.9.61) .. 1·25 20
338 12 c. black and reddish brown .. 25 10
a. Black and light brown (13.6.56) .. 15 10
b. D.L.R. ptg. *Black and brown* (11.7.61) 1·75 40
339 24 c. black and brownish orange .. 1·25 10
a. Black and orange (13.6.56) .. 1·25 10
340 36 c. rose-carmine and black .. 55 20
341 48 c. ultramarine and brown-lake .. 45 45
a. Brt ultram & pale brn-lake (13.6.56) 40 40
ab. D.L.R. ptg (19.9.61) .. 12·00 8·00
342 72 c. carmine and emerald .. 4·50 2·75
a. D.L.R. ptg (17.7.62) .. 10·00 12·00
343 $1 pink, yellow, green and black .. 7·00 90
344 $2 deep mauve .. 5·00 1·25
a. D.L.R. ptg. *Reddish mauve* (11.7.61) 12·00 2·25
345 $5 ultramarine and black .. 11·00 7·00
a. D.L.R. ptg (19.9.61) .. 22·00 13·00
331/45 .. *Set of* 15 27·00 11·50
Designs: *Horiz*—2 c. Botanical Gardens; 3 c. Victoria Regia Lilies; 5 c. Map of Caribbean; 6 c. Rice combine-harvester; 8 c. Sugar cane entering factory; 24 c. Mining for bauxite; 36 c. Mount Roraima; $1 Channel-billed Toucan; $2 Dredging gold. *Vert*—4 c. Amerindian shooting fish; 48 c. Kaieteur Falls; 72 c. Arapaima; $5 Arms of British Guiana.
The separately listed De La Rue printings are identifiable as singles by the single wide-tooth perfs at each side at the bottom of the stamps. In the Waterlow these wide teeth are at the top.
*All the Waterlow printing and early De La Rue printings of the horizontal designs measure 12.3 × 12.8, but De La Rue printings of 22 May 1962 and all later printings (including those on the Block CA watermark) measure 12.3 × 12.6.
See also Nos. 354/65.

SELF-GOVERNMENT

70

(Photo Harrison)

1961 (23 Oct). *History and Culture Week.* W w **12** P 14½ × 14.

346 **70** 5 c. sepia and orange-red 10 10
347 6 c. sepia and blue-green 10 10
348 30 c. sepia and yellow-orange 20 15
346/8 .. *Set of* 3 25 20

1963 (14 July). *Freedom from Hunger. As No.* 76 *of Aden.*

349 20 c. reddish violet .. 25 10

1963 (2 Sept). *Red Cross Centenary. As Nos.* 147/8 *of Antigua.*

350 5 c. red and black .. 10 10
351 20 c. red and blue .. 35 20

1963–65. *As Nos.* 333/44, *but wmk* w **12**.

354 3 c. brown-olive and red-brown (12.65) .. 2·00 2·25
356 5 c. scarlet and black (28.5.64) .. 15 10
359 12 c. black and yellowish brown (6.10.64) .. 15 10
360 24 c. black and bright orange (10.12.63) .. 90 10
361 36 c. rose-carmine and black (10.12.63) .. 60 20
362 48 c. bright ultramarine and Venetian red (25.11.63) .. 1·25 1·50
363 72 c. carmine and emerald (25.11.63) .. 4·00 10·00
364 $1 pink, yellow, green and black (10.12.63) 4·50 90
365 $2 reddish mauve (10.12.63) .. 5·00 14·00
354/65 .. *Set of* 9 17·00 26·00

There was no London release of No. 354.
For 1 c. value, see No. 393aA of Guyana.

71 Weightlifting

(Photo D.L.R.)

1964 (1 Oct). *Olympic Games, Tokyo.* W w **12**. P 13 × 13½.

367 **71** 5 c. orange .. 10 10
368 8 c. blue .. 10 10
369 25 c. magenta .. 10 10
367/9 .. *Set of* 3 15 15

1965 (17 May). *I.T.U. Centenary. As Nos.* 166/7 *of Antigua.*

370 5 c. emerald and yellow-olive .. 10 10
371 25 c. light blue and magenta .. 20 15

1965 (25 Oct). *International Co-operation Year. As Nos.* 168/9 *of Antigua.*

372 5 c. reddish purple and turquoise-green .. 10 10
373 25 c. deep bluish green and lavender .. 25 20

72 St. George's Cathedral, Georgetown

(Des Jennifer Toombs, Photo Harrison)

1966 (24 Jan). *Churchill Commemoration.* W w **12**. P 14 × 14½.

374 **72** 5 c. black, crimson and gold .. 25 10
375 25 c. black, blue and gold .. 85 40

1966 (3 Feb). *Royal Visit. As Nos.* 174/5 *of Antigua.*

376 3 c. black and ultramarine .. 50 15
377 25 c. black and magenta .. 1·50 60

POSTAGE DUE STAMPS

D 1

(Typo D.L.R.)

1940 (Mar)–**55**. *Wmk Mult Script CA.* P 14.

D 1 D 1 1 c. green, **O** .. 1·00 2·75
a. Deep green, **C** (30.4.52) .. 40 2·50
b. W9*a* (Crown missing), **C** .. 75·00
c. W9*b* (St. Edward's Crown), **C** .. 40·00
D 2 2 c. black, **O** .. 3·25 2·50
aa. Chalky paper (30.4.52) .. 40 2·50
a. W9*a* (Crown missing), **C** .. 65·00
b. W9*b* (St. Edward's Crown), **C** .. 35·00
D 3 4 c. bright blue, **C** (1.5.52) .. 30 2·75
a. W9*a* (Crown missing), **C** .. 60·00
b. W9*b* (St. Edward's Crown), **C** .. 35·00
D 4 12 c. scarlet, **O** .. 5·50 7·00
a. Chalky paper (19.7.55) .. 4·00 11·00
D1*a*/4a .. *Set of* 4 4·50 13·50
D1, D2 and D4 Perf "Specimen" .. *Set of* 3 50·00

OFFICIAL STAMPS

OFFICIAL (O 1) **OFFICIAL** (O 2)

1875. *Optd with Type* O **1** (1 c), *or* O **2** (*others*) *P*.10.

O1 **8** 1 c. black (R.) .. 25·00 10·00
a. Imperf between (pair) .. — £2000
O2 2 c. orange .. £100 14·00
O3 8 c. rose .. £225 85·00
O4 **7** 12 c. brownish purple .. £900 £375
O5 **9** 24 c. green .. £600 £170

Two types of the word "OFFICIAL" are found on each value. On the 1 c., the word is either 16 or 17 mm long. On the other values the chief difference is in the shape and position of the letter "o" in "OFFICIAL". In one case the "o" is upright, in the other it slants to the left.

1877. *Optd with Type* O **2**. *Wmk Crown CC. P* 14.

O 6 **16** 1 c. slate .. £140 50·00
a. Imperf between (vert pair) .. — £4000
O 7 2 c. orange .. 70·00 11·00
O 8 4 c. blue .. 75·00 20·00
O 9 6 c. brown .. £1500 £325
O10 8 c. rose .. £1500 £275

Prepared for use, but not issued

O11 **16** 12 c. pale violet .. £750
O12 24 c. green .. £900

The "OFFICIAL" overprints have been extensively forged.
The use of Official stamps was discontinued in June 1878.

British Guiana attained independence on 25 May 1966. For later issues see GUYANA.

British Honduras

It is recorded that the first local post office was established by the inhabitants in 1809, but Belize did not become a regular packet port of call until 1829. A branch office of the British G.P.O. was established in 1857 and the stamps of Great Britain were supplied for use on overseas mail from 1858.

The colonial authorities took over the postal service on 1 April, 1860, the Great Britain stamps being withdrawn the following month. There was no inland postal service until 1862.

For illustrations of the handstamp and postmark types see BRITISH POST OFFICES ABROAD notes, following GREAT BRITAIN.

BELIZE

CROWNED-CIRCLE HANDSTAMPS

CC1 CC 1*b* BELIZE (R.)(13.11.1841) .. *Price on cover* £4000

Stamps of GREAT BRITAIN *cancelled* "A 06" *as Type* **2**.

1858 *to* **1860.**

Z1 1d. rose-red (1857), *perf* 14 .. £850
Z2 4d. rose (1857) .. £350
Z3 6d. lilac (1856) .. £350
Z4 1s. green (1856) .. £900

PRICES FOR STAMPS ON COVER TO 1945

Nos. 1/4	*from* × 20
Nos. 5/16	*from* × 25
Nos. 17/22	*from* × 20
Nos. 23/6	*from* × 10
Nos. 27/30	*from* × 15
Nos. 35/42	*from* × 20
Nos. 43/4	*from* × 30
Nos. 49/50	*from* × 25
Nos. 51/69	*from* × 15
Nos. 80/100	*from* × 6
Nos. 101/10	*from* × 5
Nos. 111/20	*from* × 15
Nos. 121/2	*from* × 8
No. 123	*from* × 10
Nos. 124/37	*from* × 6
Nos. 138/42	*from* × 10
Nos. 143/9	*from* × 8
Nos. 150/61	*from* × 5
Nos. D1/3	*from* × 30

CROWN COLONY

1

(Typo D.L.R.)

1865 (1 Dec). *No wmk.* P 14.

1 **1** 1d. pale blue .. 50·00 45·00
a. Imperf between (pair) ..
2 1d. blue .. 50·00 45·00
3 6d. rose .. £170 90·00
4 1s. green .. £200 85·00
a. In horiz pair with 6d. .. £15000
b. In vert pair with 1d. .. £22000

In the first printing all three values were printed in the same sheet separated by horizontal and vertical gutter margins. The sheet comprised two panes of 60 of the 1d. at the top with a pane of 60 of the 1s. at bottom left and another of 6d. at bottom right. Copies of 1d. *se-tenant* with the 6d. are not known. There were two later printings of the 1d. but they were in sheets without the 6d. and 1s.

1872–79. *Wmk Crown CC.* (a) P 12½.

5 **1** 1d. pale blue .. 55·00 16·00
6 1d. deep blue (1874) .. 50·00 16·00
7 3d. red-brown .. 95·00 65·00
8 3d. chocolate (1874) .. £110 80·00
9 6d. rose .. £150 27·00
9*a* 6d. bright rose-carmine (1874) .. £250 38·00
10 1s. green .. £250 28·00
10*a* 1s. deep green (1874) .. £200 20·00
b. Imperf between (horiz pair) .. — £13000

(*b*) P 14 (1877–79)

11 **1** 1d. pale blue (1878) .. 48·00 15·00
12 1d. blue .. 40·00 10·00
a. Imperf between (horiz pair) .. £3500
13 3d. chestnut .. 80·00 14·00
14 4d. mauve (1879) .. £110 6·50
15 6d. rose (1878) .. £250 £150
16 1s. green .. £150 11·00
a. Imperf between (pair) ..

1882–87. *Wmk Crown CA.* P 14.

17 **1** 1d. blue (4.84) .. 35·00 13·00
18 1d. rose (1884) .. 15·00 11·00
a. Bisected (½d.) (on cover) ..
19 1d. carmine (1887) .. 30·00 13·00
20 4d. mauve (7.82) .. 65·00 3·00
21 6d. yellow (1885) .. £200 £140
22 1s. grey (1.87) .. £225 £120
18,22 Optd "Specimen" .. *Set of* 2 £200

2 CENTS (2) **TWO** (3) **2 CENTS** (4)

1888 (1 Jan). *Stamps of* 1872–79 (*wmk Crown CC*), *surch locally as T* **2**. (*a*) P 12½.

23 **1** 2 c. on 6d. rose .. £100 90·00
24 3 c. on 3d. chocolate .. £9000 £4000

(*b*) P 14

25 **1** 2 c. on 6d. rose .. 65·00 65·00
a. Surch double .. £1000
b. Bisected (1 c.) (on cover) .. † £140
c. Slanting "2" with curved foot .. £600
26 3 c. on 3d. chestnut .. 55·00 55·00

There are very dangerous forgeries of these surcharges.

1888. *Stamps of* 1882–87 (*wmk Crown CA*), *surch locally as T* **2**, P 14.

27 **1** 2 c. on 1d. rose .. 6·50 15·00
a. Surch inverted .. £1000 £900
b. Surch double .. £900 £850
c. Bisected (1 c.) (on cover) .. † £180
28 10 c. on 4d. mauve .. 28·00 15·00
29 20 c. on 6d. yellow .. 26·00 30·00
30 50 c. on 1s. grey .. £325 £450
a. Error. "5" for "50" .. £6000

Various settings were used for the surcharges on Nos. 23/30, the most common of which was of 36 (6 × 6) impressions. For No. 29 this setting was so applied that an albino surcharge occurs in the margin above each stamp in the first horizontal row.

The same setting was subsequently amended, by altering the "2" to "1", to surcharge the 4d. value. As this was in sheets of 30 it was only necessary to alter the values on the bottom five rows of the setting. Albino surcharges once again occur in the top margin of the sheet, but, as the type in the first horizontal row remained unaltered, these read "20 CENTS" rather than the "10 CENTS" on the actual stamps.

1888 (Mar). *No.* 30 *further surch locally with T* **3**.

35 **1** "TWO" on 50c. on 1s. grey (R.) .. 32·00 55·00
a. Bisected (1 c.) (on cover) .. † £200
b. Surch in black .. £9000 £7500
c. Surch double (R. + Blk.) .. £7000 £6500

1888 (July)–**91**. *Surch in London as T* **4**. *Wmk Crown CA.* P 14.

36 **1** 1 c. on 1d. dull green (?12.91) .. 25 85
37 2 c. on 1d. carmine .. 20 1·25
a. Bisected (1 c.) (on cover) .. † 90·00
38 3 c. on 3d. red-brown .. 55 1·25
39 6 c. on 3d. ultramarine (?4.91) .. 85 7·00
40 10 c. on 4d. mauve .. 1·25 40
a. Surch double .. £1000
41 20 c. on 6d. yellow (2.89) .. 6·00 14·00
42 50 c. on 1s. grey (11.88) .. 16·00 40·00
36/42 .. *Set of* 7 23·00 60·00
36/42 Optd "Specimen" .. *Set of* 7 £350

(5)

FIVE (6)

15 (7)

1891. *Stamps of* 1888–9 *surch locally. (a) With T* **5** (May).

No.	Type	Description		
43	1	6 c. on 10 c. on 4d. mauve (R.)	40	1·50
		a. "6" and bar inverted	£375	£375
		b. "6" only inverted	—	£2250
44		6 c. on 10 c. on 4d. mauve (Blk.)	40	1·50
		a. "6" and bar inverted	£2250	£650
		b. "6" only inverted	—	£2250

Of variety (b) only six copies of each can exist, as one of each of these errors came in the first six sheets, and the mistake was then corrected. Of variety (a) more copies exist.

Essays are known with "SIX" in place of "6", both with and without bars (*price* £70 *and* £375 *respectively*). Although not issued, we mention them, as two contemporary covers franked with them are known.

(*b*) *With T* **6/7** (23 Oct)

No.	Type	Description		
49	1	5 c. on 3 c. on 3d. red-brown	40	1·40
		a. Wide space between "I" and "V"	38·00	48·00
		b. "FIVE" and bar double	£175	
50		15 c. on 6 c. on 3d. ultramarine (R.)	5·00	14·00
		a. Surch double		

8

9

10

11

(Typo D.L.R.)

1891 (July)–**1901**. *Wmk Crown CA. P* 14.

No.	Type	Description		
51	8	1 c. dull green (4.95)	60	30
52		2 c. carmine-rose	60	10
53		3 c. brown	2·00	1·25
54		5 c. ultramarine (4.95)	12·00	25
55	11	5 c. grey-black & ultram/*blue* (10.00)	3·75	65
56	8	6 c. ultramarine	2·50	45
57	9	10 c. mauve and green (4.95)	8·50	7·50
58	10	10 c. dull purple and green (1901)	4·00	7·00
59	9	12 c. pale mauve and green	23·00	5·50
		a. Violet and green	2·50	2·00
60		24 c. yellow and blue	5·50	14·00
		a. Orange and blue	22·00	42·00
61		25 c. red-brown and green (4.95)	23·00	45·00
62	10	50 c. green and carmine (3.98)	15·00	28·00
63	11	$1 green and carmine (12.99)	27·00	48·00
64		$2 green and ultramarine (12.99)	42·00	65·00
65		$5 green and black (12.99)	£180	£225
51/65		*Set of* 15	£275	£400
51/65 Optd "Specimen"		*Set of* 15	£300	

1899 (1 July). *Optd* "REVENUE" A. *Opt* 12 *mm long*. B. *Opt* 11 *mm long*.

No.	Description	A		B	
66	5 c. (No. 54)	2·75	2·00	6·00	6·50
	a. "BEVENUE"	48·00	55·00	†	
67	10 c. (No. 57)	3·00	11·00	15·00	27·00
	a. "BEVENUE"	£160	—	†	
	b. "REVENU"	—	—	£325	£350
68	25 c. (No. 61)	2·75	16·00	4·00	22·00
	a. "BEVENUE"	75·00	£120	†	
	b. "REVE UE"	—	—	†	
69	50 c. No. 42)	£120	£180	£160	£250
	a. "BEVENUE"	£2500	—	†	

Two minor varieties, a small "U" and a tall, narrow "U" are found in the word "REVENUE".

The overprint setting of 60 (6 × 10) contained 43 examples of the 12 mm size and 17 of the 11 mm. The smaller size overprints occur on R.8/1, R8/3 to 6 and on all positions in Rows 9 and 10.

The "BEVENUE" error appears on R.6/4 and, it is believed, "REVE UE" comes from R.6/6. Both occur on parts of the printing only. The missing "E" developed during the overprinting and damage to this letter can be observed on at least eight positions in the setting. Examples of No. 67b are now known to exist on both sizes of the overprint.

14

15

(Typo D.L.R.)

1902 (10 Oct)–**04**. *Wmk Crown CA. P* 14.

No.	Type	Description		
80	14	1 c. grey-green and green (28.4.04)	1·75	11·00
81		2 c. purple and black/*red* (18.3.03)	60	25
82		5 c. grey-black and blue/*blue*	2·25	30
83	15	20 c. dull and bright purple (28.4.04)	3·00	14·00
80/3		*Set of* 4	7·00	23·00
80/3 Optd "Specimen"		*Set of* 4	70·00	

1904–07. *Wmk Mult Crown CA. P* 14.

No.	Type	Description		
84	14	1 c. grey-green and green, **OC**	50	90
85		2 c. purple and black/*red*, **OC**	50	10
86		5 c. grey-black and blue/*blue*, **C**	1·75	20
87	15	10 c. dull purple and emerald-green, **C**	4·00	8·50
89		25 c. dull purple and orange, **C**	6·00	25·00
90		50 c. grey-green and carmine, **C**	10·00	35·00
91	14	$1 grey-green and carmine, **C**	26·00	45·00
92		$2 grey-green and blue, **C**	55·00	85·00
93		$5 grey-green and black, **C**	£170	£225
84/93		*Set of* 9	£250	£375
87/93 Optd "Specimen"		*Set of* 6	£225	

Dates of issue:—1 c. 8.05; 2 c. 12.04; 5 c. 5.2.06; others 20.9.07

1908 (7 Dec)–**11**. *Colours changed. Wmk Mult Crown CA. P* 14.

No.	Type	Description		
95	14	1 c. blue-green, **O** (1.7.10)	2·00	20
96		2 c. carmine, **O**	1·50	10
97		5 c. ultramarine, **O** (1.6.09)	1·75	10
100	15	25 c. black/*green*, **C** (14.10.11)	2·75	27·00
95/100		*Set of* 4	7·00	27·00
96/100 Optd "Specimen"		*Set of* 3	70·00	

16

17

(18)

(Typo D.L.R.)

1913–21. *Wmk Mult Crown CA. P* 14.

No.	Type	Description		
101	16	1 c. blue-green, **O**	25	15
		a. Yellow-green (13.3.17)	1·00	75
102		2 c. red, **O**	70	75
		a. Bright scarlet (1915)	75	25
		b. Dull scarlet (8.17)	2·00	1·25
		c. Red/bluish	5·00	4·50
103		3 c. orange, **O** (16.4.17)	20	15
104		5 c. bright blue, **O**	1·25	30
105	17	10 c. dull purple and yellow-green, **C**	2·50	6·50
		a. Dull purple and bright green (1917)	4·75	11·00
106		25 c. black/*green*, **C**	1·25	7·50
		a. On blue-green, olive back (8.17)	2·00	7·00
		b. On emerald back (1921)	1·75	15·00
107		50 c. purple and blue/*blue*, **C**	4·00	9·00
108	16	$1 black and carmine, **C**	5·00	15·00
109		$2 purple and green, **C**	40·00	45·00
110		$5 purple and black/*red*, **C**	£160	£180
101/10		*Set of* 10	£190	£225
101/10 Optd "Specimen"		*Set of* 10	£250	

1915–16. *Optd with T* **18**, *in violet.*

No.	Type	Description		
111	16	1 c. green (30.12.15)	60	5·50
		a. Yellow-green (6.6.16)	15	4·50
112		2 c. scarlet (3.11.15)	40	50
113		5 c. bright blue (29.7.15)	15	2·50
111/13 Optd "Specimen"		*Set of* 3	£100	

These stamps were shipped early in the 1914–18 war, and were thus overprinted, so that if seized by the enemy, they could be distinguished and rendered invalid.

WAR (19)

WAR (20)

21

1916 (23 Aug). *No.* 111 *optd locally with T* **19.**

No.	Type	Description		
114	16	1 c. green	10	25
		a. Opt inverted	£175	£200

1917. *Nos.* 101 *and* 103 *optd with T* **19.**

No.	Type	Description		
116	16	1 c. blue-green	20	1·25
		a. Yellow-green	20	1·25
118		3 c. orange	20	1·50
		a. Overprint double	£300	

1918. *Nos.* 101 *and* 103 *optd with T* **20**.

No.	Type	Description		
119	16	1 c. blue-green	10	25
		a. Yellow-green	1·40	2·50
120		3 c. orange	10	75
119/20 Optd "Specimen"		*Set of* 2	£100	

(Recess D.L.R.)

1921 (28 Apr). *Peace Commemoration. Wmk Mult Crown CA* (*sideways*). *P* 14.

No.	Type	Description		
121	21	2 c. rose-red (Optd S. £45)	70	25

1921 (26 Nov). *Wmk Mult Script CA. P* 14.

No.	Type	Description		
122	16	1 c. green, **O** (Optd S. £40)	90	4·50

1922 (4 Jan). *As T* **21** *but with words* "PEACE" *omitted. Wmk Mult Script CA* (*sideways*). *P* 14.

No.	Description		
123	4 c. slate (Optd S. £45)	1·75	25

22

BELIZE
RELIEF FUND
PLUS
3 CENTS
(23)

(Typo D.L.R.)

1922 (1 Aug)–**33**. *Ordinary paper* (1 *c. to* 5 *c.*) *or chalk-surfaced paper* (*others*). *P* 14 (*a*) *Wmk Mult Crown CA.*

No.	Type	Description		
124	22	25 c. black/*emerald*	3·50	20·00
125		$5 purple and black/*red* (1.10.24)	£160	£180

(*b*) *Wmk Mult Script CA*

No.	Type	Description		
126	22	1 c. green (2.1.29)	55	1·75
127		2 c. brown (1.3.23)	20	15
128		2 c. rose-carmine (10.12.26)	35	10
129		3 c. orange (1933)	3·00	2·50
130		4 c. grey (1.10.29)	90	20
131		5 c. ultramarine	90	55
		a. Milky blue (1923)	2·25	3·00
132		10 c. dull purple and sage-green (1.12.22)	60	25
133		25 c. black/*emerald* (1.10.24)	80	3·50
134		50 c. purple and blue/*blue* (1.11.23)	2·50	8·50
136		$1 black and scarlet (2.1.25)	4·00	13·00
137		$2 yellow-green and bright purple	25·00	48·00
124/37		*Set of* 13	£180	£250
124/37 Opted/Perf "Specimen"		*Set of* 13	£250	

1932 (2 May). *Belize Relief Fund. Surch as T* **23.** *Wmk Mult Script CA. P* 14.

No.	Type	Description		
138	22	1 c. + 1 c. green	70	4·50
139		2 c. + 2 c. rose-carmine	75	4·50
140		3 c. + 3 c. orange	85	5·50
141		4 c. + 4 c. grey (R.)	1·50	8·50
142		5 c. + 5 c. ultramarine	4·00	13·00
138/42		*Set of* 5	7·00	32·00
138/42 Perf "Specimen"		*Set of* 5	£110	

1935 (6 May). *Silver Jubilee. As Nos.* 91/4 *of Antigua, but ptd by B. W. & Co. P* 11 × 12.

No.	Description		
143	3 c. ultramarine and grey-black	35	45
	a. Extra flagstaff	50·00	
	b. Short extra flagstaff	30·00	
	c. Lightning conductor	25·00	
	d. Flagstaff on right-hand turret	35·00	
144	4 c. green and indigo	60	50
	a. Extra flagstaff	£180	
	c. Lightning conductor	65·00	
	d. Flagstaff on right-hand turret	65·00	
	e. Double flagstaff	60·00	
145	5 c. brown and deep blue	1·25	60
146	25 c. slate and purple	1·25	1·75
	a. Extra flagstaff	£250	
	b. Short extra flagstaff	£120	
	c. Lightning conductor	£100	
	d. Flagstaff on right-hand turret	£100	
	e. Double flagstaff	85·00	
143/6	*Set of* 4	3·00	3·00
143/6 Perf "Specimen"	*Set of* 4	65·00	

For illustrations of plate varieties see Omnibus section following Zululand.

1937 (12 May). *Coronation. As Nos.* 13/15 *of Aden.*

No.	Description		
147	3 c. orange	30	25
148	4 c. grey-black	40	25
149	5 c. bright blue	40	40
147/9	*Set of* 3	1·00	80
147/9 Perf "Specimen"	*Set of* 3	50·00	

24 Maya Figures

25 Chicle Tapping

(Recess B.W.)

1938 (10 Jan)–**47**. *T* **24/5** *and similar designs. Wmk Mult Script CA* (*sideways on horizontal stamps*). *P* 11½ × 11 (*horiz designs*) *or* 11 × 11½ (*vert designs*).

No.	Description		
150	1 c. bright magenta and green (14.2.38)	10	25
151	2 c. black and scarlet (14.2.38)	10	20
	a. Perf 12 (1947)	75	30
152	3 c. purple and brown	10	10
153	4 c. black and green	10	10
154	5 c. mauve and dull blue	10	10
155	10 c. green and reddish brown (14.2.38)	35	15
156	15 c. brown and light blue (14.2.38)	35	10
157	25 c. blue and green (14.2.38)	90	35
158	50 c. black and purple (14.2.38)	2·75	1·40
159	$1 scarlet and olive (28.2.38)	9·00	3·25
160	$2 deep blue and maroon (28.2.38)	9·00	9·00
161	$5 scarlet and brown (28.2.38)	15·00	18·00
150/61	*Set of* 12	35·00	29·00
150/61 Perf "Specimen"	*Set of* 12	£140	

Designs: *Vert*—3 c. Cohune palm; $1 Court House, Belize. $2 Mahogany felling; $5 Arms of Colony. *Horiz*—4 c. Local products; 5 c. Grapefruit; 10 c. Mahogany logs in river; 15 c. Sergeant's Cay; 25 c. Dorey; 50 c. Chicle industry.

1946 (9 Sept). *Victory. As Nos.* 28/9 *of Aden.*

No.	Description		
162	3 c. brown	10	10
163	5 c. blue	10	10
162/3 Perf "Specimen"	*Set of* 2	40·00	

1948 (1 Oct). *Royal Silver Wedding. As Nos.* 30/1 *of Aden.*

No.	Description		
164	4 c. green	15	10
165	$5 brown	13·00	28·00

36 Island of St George's Cay

37 H.M.S. *Merlin*

(Recess Waterlow)

1949 (10 Jan). *150th Anniv of Battle of St. George's Cay. Wmk Mult Script CA. P* 12½.

166 **36** 1 c. ultramarine and green 10 10
167 3 c. blue and yellow-brown 10 15
168 4 c. olive and violet 10 20
169 **37** 5 c. brown and deep blue 20 10
170 10 c. green and red-brown 20 10
171 15 c. emerald and ultramarine 20 10
166/71 .. .. *Set of* 6 65 65

1949 (10 Oct). *75th Anniv of U.P.U. As Nos.* 114/17 *of Antigua.*

172 4 c. blue-green 15 15
173 5 c. deep blue 30 15
174 10 c. red-brown 35 35
175 25 c. blue 40 40
172/5 .. .. *Set of* 4 1·10 95

1951 (16 Feb). *Inauguration of B.W.I. University College. As Nos.* 118/19 *of Antigua.*

176 3 c. reddish violet and brown 25 15
177 10 c. green and brown 35 15

1953 (2 June). *Coronation. As No.* 47 *of Aden.*

178 4 c. black and green 15 30

38 Arms of British Honduras

46 Maya Indian

(Recess Waterlow (until 20.6.1961), then D.L.R.)

1953 (2 Sept)–**62**. *T* **38**, **46** *and similar designs. Wmk Mult Script CA. P* 13½.

179 1 c. green and black 10 15
a. Perf 13½×13 (3.10.61) 10 15
180 2 c. yellow-brown and black 10 45
a. Perf 14 (18.9.57) 10 10
b. Perf 13½×13 (20.6.61) 10 20
181 3 c. reddish violet and bright purple .. 10 10
a. Perf 14 (18.9.57) 10 10
b. Perf 13½×13 (20.6.61) .. .. 1·50 2·00
ba. *Reddish lilac and pale magenta* (19.1.62) 45 70
182 4 c. brown and green 10 15
183 5 c. deep olive-green and scarlet 10 10
a. Perf 14 (15.5.57) 10 10
ab. D.L.R. ptg (3.10.61) .. .. 90 1·00
184 10 c. slate and bright blue 10 10
a. Perf 13½×13 (19.1.62) 10 10
185 15 c. green and violet 15 10
186 25 c. bright blue and yellow-brown .. 3·25 70
187 50 c. yellow-brown and reddish purple .. 1·00 1·25
a. *Pale yellow-brown & pale pur* (22.3.60) 2·75 1·50
188 $1 slate-blue and red-brown .. .. 3·50 2·50
189 $2 scarlet and grey .. .. .. 5·50 4·00
190 $5 purple and slate .. .. .. 18·00 12·00
179/90 .. .. *Set of* 12 28·00 19·00

Designs: *Horiz*—2 c. Baird's Tapir ("Mountain Cow"); 3 c. Mace and Legislative Council Chamber, 4 c. Pine industry; 5 c. Spiny Lobster; 10 c. Stanley Field Airport; 15 c. Maya frieze; 25 c. Blue Butterfly; $1 Nine-banded Armadillo; $2 Hawkesworth Bridge. *Vert*—$5 Mountain Orchid.

Nos. 179/90 were released a day earlier by the Crown Agents in London.

Stamps from the Waterlow printings perforated 13½ × 13 or 14 have a very fine perforation tooth at the *top* of each vertical side. On the De La Rue printings this tooth is at the *bottom*.

50 "Belize from Fort George, 1842" (C. J. Hullmandel)

51 Public Seals, 1860 and 1960.

52 Tamarind Tree, Newtown Barracks.

(Recess B.W.)

1960 (1 July). *Post Office Centenary. W w* **12**. *P* 11½ × 11.

191 **50** 2 c. green 10 10
192 **51** 10 c. deep carmine 10 10
193 **52** 15 c. blue 10 15
191/3 .. .. *Set of* 3 25 25

NEW CONSTITUTION
1960
(53)

HURRICANE
HATTIE
(54)

1961 (1 Mar). *New Constitution. Nos.* 180a, 181a *and* 184/5 *optd with T* **53** *by Waterlow.*

194 2 c. yellow-brown and black 10 10
195 3 c. reddish violet and bright purple .. 10 10
196 10 c. slate and bright blue 10 10
197 15 c. green and violet 10 10
194/7 .. .. *Set of* 4 20 15

1962 (15 Jan). *Hurricane Hattie Relief Fund. Nos.* 179a, 184a, 186 *and* 187 *optd with T* **54** *by D.L.R.*

198 1 c. green and black 10 10
199 10 c. slate and bright blue 10 10
200 25 c. bright blue and yellow-brown .. 25 10
201 50 c. yellow-brown and reddish purple .. 15 15
198/201 .. .. *Set of* 4 40 30

55 Great Curassow

(Des D. R. Eckelberry. Photo Harrison)

1962 (2 Apr). *Horiz designs on T* **55**. *Multicoloured. W w* **12** *(upright). P* 14 × 14½.

202 1 c. Type **55** 35 15
a. Orange-yellow (knob) omitted .. ..
203 2 c. Red-legged Honey-creeper 50 10
a. Turquoise-blue (bird's head) omitted .. £110
204 3 c. Northern Jacana 50 15
a. Blue-green (legs) omitted £170
205 4 c. Great Kiskadee 60 15
206 5 c. Scarlet-rumped Tanager 75 10
207 10 c. Scarlet Macaw 75 10
a. Blue omitted £160
208 15 c. Slaty-tailed Trogon 65 10
209 25 c. Red-footed Booby .. .. .. 1·50 30
210 50 c. Keel-billed Toucan .. .. .. 2·25 35
a. Pale blue (claw and beak) omitted ..
211 $1 Magnificent Frigate Bird .. .. 4·00 75
212 $2 Rufous-tailed Jacamar .. .. 7·50 3·00
a. *Shade** .. .. 15·00 10·00
213 $5 Montezuma Oropendola .. .. 15·00 13·00
202/13 .. .. *Set of* 12 30·00 16·00

On No. 212*a*, the bird is myrtle-green and red-brown instead of yellow-green and orange-brown.

See also Nos. 239/45.

1963 (4 June). *Freedom from Hunger. As No.* 76 *of Aden.*

214 22 c. bluish green 30 15

1963 (2 Sept). *Red Cross Centenary. As Nos.* 147/8 *of Antigua.*

215 4 c. red and black 10 10
216 22 c. red and blue 30 35

SELF-GOVERNMENT

SELF GOVERNMENT
1964
(56)

DEDICATION OF SITE
NEW CAPITAL
9th OCTOBER 1965
(57)

1964. *New Constitution. Nos.* 202, 204/5, 207 *and* 209 *optd with T* **56**.

217 1 c. Type **55** (20.4) 10 10
a. Opt inverted £100
b. Orange-yellow (knob) omitted .. .. 55·00
218 3 c. Northern Jacana (20.4) 10 10
219 4 c. Great Kiskadee (3.2) 10 10
220 10 c. Scarlet Macaw (20.4) 10 10
221 25 c. Red-footed Booby (3.2) 15 20
217/21 .. .. *Set of* 5 20 25

1965 (17 May). *I.T.U. Centenary. As Nos.* 166/7 *of Antigua.*

222 2 c. orange-red and light green 10 10
223 50 c. yellow and light purple 35 25

1965 (25 Oct). *International Co-operation Year. As Nos.* 168/9 *of Antigua.*

224 1 c. reddish purple and turquoise-green .. 10 10
225 22 c. deep bluish green and lavender .. 15 10

1966 (24 Jan). *Churchill Commemoration. As Nos.* 170/3 *of Antigua.*

226 1 c. new blue 10 10
227 4 c. deep green 10 10
228 22 c. brown 25 10
229 25 c. bluish violet 30 25
226/9 .. .. *Set of* 4 60 35

1966 (1 July). *Dedication of new Capital Site. As Nos.* 202, 204/5, 207 *and* 209 *but wmk sideways, optd with T* **57** *by Harrison.*

230 1 c. Type **55** 10 10
a. Orange-yellow (knob) omitted .. .. 55·00
231 3 c. Northern Jacana 10 10
232 4 c. Great Kiskadee 10 10
233 10 c. Scarlet Macaw 10 10
234 25 c. Red-footed Booby 15 20
230/4 .. .. *Set of* 5 25 25

58 Citrus Grove

(Des V. Whiteley. Photo Harrison)

1966 (1 Oct). *Stamp Centenary. T* **58** *and similar horiz designs. Multicoloured. W w* **12**. *P* 14 × 14½.

235 5 c. Type **58** 10 10
236 10 c. Half Moon Cay 10 10
237 22 c. Hidden Valley Falls 10 10
238 25 c. Maya Ruins, Xunantunich 15 10
235/8 .. .. *Set of* 4 25 15

1967. *As Nos.* 202, *etc, but wmk sideways.*

239 1 c. Type **55** (16.2) 10 10
240 2 c. Red-legged Honey-creeper (28.11) .. 15 15
241 4 c. Great Kiskadee (16.2) 20 15
242 5 c. Scarlet-rumped Tanager (16.2) .. 30 10
243 10 c. Scarlet Macaw (28.11) 50 10
244 15 c. Slaty-tailed Trogon (28.11) 60 10
245 50 c. Keel-billed Toucan (16.2) .. .. 2·75 2·50
239/45 .. .. *Set of* 7 4·00 3·00

The 15 c. value exists with PVA gum as well as gum arabic.

59 Sailfish

60 *Schomburgkia tibicinis*

(Des R. Granger Barrett. Photo Harrison)

1967 (1 Dec). *International Tourist Year. T* **59** *and similar horiz designs. W w* **12**. *P* 12½.

246 5 c. deep violet-blue, black and light yellow 10 10
247 10 c. brown, black and orange-red .. 10 10
248 22 c. yellow-orange, black and bright green .. 15 10
249 25 c. lt greenish blue, black & greenish yellow 15 15
246/9 .. .. *Set of* 4 30 20

Designs:—10 c. Red Brocket; 22 c. Jaguar; 25 c. Tarpon.

(Des Sylvia Goaman, Photo Harrison)

1968 (16 Apr). *20th Anniv of Economic Commission for Latin America. T* **60** *and similar vert designs. Multicoloured. W w* **12** *(sideways). P* 14½ × 14.

250 5 c. Type **60** 10 10
251 10 c. *Maxillaria tenuifolia* 15 10
252 22 c. *Bletia purpurea* 25 10
253 25 c. *Sobralia macrantha* 30 20
250/3 .. .. *Set of* 4 70 25

61 Monument to Belizean Patriots

62 Monument at Site of New Capital

(Des G. Vasarhelyi. Litho B.W.)

1968 (15 July). *Human Rights Year. W w* **12**. *P* 13½.

254 **61** 22 c. multicoloured 10 10
255 **62** 50 c. multicoloured 10 10

63 Jew Fish

(Des J. W. Litho D.L.R.)

1968 (15 Oct). *Wildlife. Horiz designs as T* **63**. *Multicoloured. No wmk. P* 13 × 12½.

256 1 c. Type **63** 10 10
257 2 c. White-lipped Peccary ("Warree") .. 10 10
258 3 c. Grouper 10 10
259 4 c. Collared Anteater 10 15
260 5 c. Bonefish 10 15
261 10 c. Paca ("Gibnut") 15 10
262 15 c. Dolphin 30 20
263 25 c. Kinkajou ("Night Walker") 30 20
264 50 c. Mutton Snapper 70 70
265 $1 Tayra ("Bush Dog") .. .. 2·00 1·25
266 $2 Great Barracuda .. .. .. 2·50 2·00
267 $5 Puma .. .. 7·00 6·50
256/67 .. .. *Set of* 12 12·00 10·00

See also Nos. 276/8 and 338/40

64 *Rhyncholaelia digbyana*

65 Ziricote Tree

(Des Sylvia Goaman. Photo Harrison)

1969 (9 Apr). *Orchids of Belize* (1st series). *T* **64** *and similar vert designs. Multicoloured. W* w **12** (*sideways*). *P* 14½ × 14.

268 5 c. Type **64** .. 20 10
269 10 c. *Cattleya bowringiana* .. 25 10
270 22 c. *Lycaste cochleatum* .. 45 10
271 25 c. *Coryanthes speciosum* .. 60 25
268/71 .. *Set of* 4 1·40 40

See also Nos. 287/90.

(Des V. Whiteley. Litho D.L.R.)

1969 (1 Sept). *Indigenous Hardwoods* (1st series). *T* **65** *and similar vert designs. Multicoloured. W* w **12**. *P* 14.

272 5 c. Type **65** .. 10 10
273 10 c. Rosewood .. 10 10
274 22 c. Mayflower .. 10 10
275 25 c. Mahogany .. 10 15
272/5 .. *Set of* 4 20 20

See also Nos. 291/4, 315/18 and 333/7.

1969–72. *As Nos.* 257/8, 261, 267 *and new value and design* (½ *c.*), *but W* w **12** (*sideways*).

276 ½ c. Crana Fish (ultramarine background) (1.9.69) .. 10 10
277 ½ c. Crana Fish (yellow-olive background) (1.2.71) .. 15 10
a. Black (inscr and value) omitted .. £140
277*c* 2 c. White-lipped Peccary (5.5.72) .. 1·50 1·50
277*d* 3 c. Grouper (5.5.72) .. 1·50 1·50
277*e* 10 c. Paca (5.5.72) .. 2·25 2·00
278 $5 Puma (12.5.70) .. 8·00 12·00
276/8 .. *Set of* 6 12·50 15·00

66 "The Virgin and Child" (Bellini

POPULATION
CENSUS 1970

(68

(Des adapted by G. Drummond. Litho Format)

1969 (1 Nov). *Christmas. Paintings. T* **66** *and similar vert design. Multicoloured. W* w **12**. *P* 14× 14½.

279 5 c. Type **66** .. 10 10
280 15 c. Type **66** .. 10 10
281 22 c. "The Adoration of the Kings" (Veronese) 10 10
282 25 c. As 22 c. .. 10 10
279/82 .. *Set of* 4 25 15

Although released by the Crown Agents on 1 October this issue was not put on sale locally until 1 November.

1970 (2 Feb). *Population Census. As Nos.* 260 *and* 262/3 *but* W w **12** (*sideways*) *and No.* 277*e optd with T* **68**.

283 5 c. Bonefish .. 10 10
284 10 c. Paca .. 10 10
285 15 c. Dolphin .. 10 10
286 25 c. Kinkajou .. 10 10
283/6 .. *Set of* 4 15 20

(Des G. Drummond. Litho Format)

1970 (2 Apr). *Orchids of Belize* (2nd series). *As T* **64**. *Multicoloured. W* w **12**. *P* 14.

287 5 c. Black Orchid .. 20 10
288 15 c. White Butterfly Orchid .. 30 10
289 22 c. Swan Orchid .. 40 10
290 25 c. Butterfly Orchid .. 45 25
287/90 .. *Set of* 4 1·25 40

69 Santa Maria

70 "The Nativity" (A. Hughes).

(Des Jennifer Toombs, Litho Questa)

1970 (7 Sept). *Indigenous Hardwoods* (2nd series). *T* **69** *and similar vert designs. Multicoloured. W* w **12** (*sideways*). *P* 14 × 14½.

291 5 c. Type **69** .. 10 10
292 15 c. Nargusta .. 10 10
293 22 c. Cedar .. 15 10
294 25 c. Sapodilla .. 20 25
291/4 .. *Set of* 4 45 45

(Des J. Cooter Litho J.W.)

1970 (7 Nov*). *Christmas. T* **70** *and similar vert design. Multicoloured. W* w **12**. *P* 14.

295 ½ c. Type **70** .. 10 10
296 5 c. "The Mystic Nativity" (Botticelli) .. 10 10
297 10 c. Type **70** .. 10 10
298 15 c. As 5 c .. 10 10
299 22 c. Type **70** .. 10 10
300 50 c. As 5 c. .. 20 30
295/300 .. *Set of* 6 35 40

*These stamps were released by the Crown Agents in London on 2 November.

71 Legislative Assembly House

(Des. G. Drummond. Litho Enschedé)

1971 (30 Jan). *Establishment of New Capital, Belmopan. T* **71** *and similar horiz designs. Multicoloured. W* w **12** *upright* (5 *c.*, 10 *c.*) *or sideways* (*others*). *P* 13 × 13½.

301 5 c. Old Capital, Belize .. 10 10
302 10 c. Government Plaza .. 10 10
303 15 c. Type **71** .. 10 10
304 22 c. Magistrates' Court .. 15 10
305 25 c. Police H.Q. .. 15 15
306 50 c. New G.P.O. .. 25 40
301/6 .. *Set of* 6 70 75

The 5 c. and 10 c. are larger, 60 × 22 mm.

72 *Tabebuia chrysantha*

(Des Sylvia Goaman. Litho Questa)

1971 (27 Mar). *Easter. T* **72** *and similar horiz designs showing flowers. Multicoloured. W* w **12** (*sideways*). *P* 14.

307 ½ c. Type **72** .. 10 10
308 5 c. *Hymenocallis littorallis* .. 10 10
309 10 c. *Hippeastrum equestre* .. 10 10
310 15 c. Type **72** .. 10 10
311 22 c. As 5 c. .. 10 10
312 25 c. As 10 c. .. 15 20
307/12 .. *Set of* 6 35 40

RACIAL EQUALITY
YEAR-1971

(73)

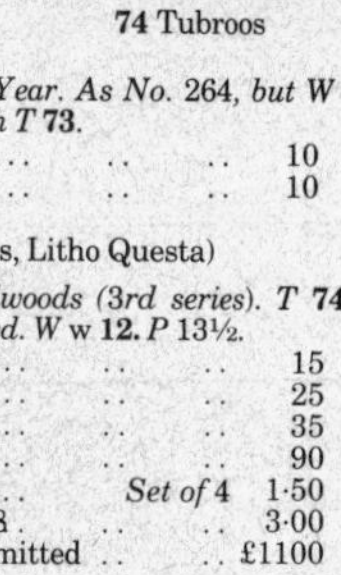

74 Tubroos

1971 (14 June). *Racial Equality Year. As No.* 264, *but W* w **12** (*sideways*) *and No.* 277*e optd with T* **73**.

313 10 c. Paca .. 10 10
314 50 c. Mutton Snapper .. 10 15

(Des Jennifer Toombs, Litho Questa)

1971 (16 Aug). *Indigenous Hardwoods* (3rd series). *T* **74** *and similar vert designs. Multicoloured. W* w **12**. *P* 13½.

315 5 c. Type **74** .. 15 10
316 15 c. Yemeri .. 25 30
317 26 c. Billywebb .. 35 35
318 50 c. Logwood .. 90 1·25
315/18 .. *Set of* 4 1·50 1·75
MS319 96 × 171 mm. Nos. 315/18 .. 3·00 5·50
a. Silver (Queen's head) omitted .. £1100

OMNIBUS ISSUES

Details, together with prices for complete sets, of the various Omnibus issues from the 1935 Silver Jubilee series to date are included in a special section following Zululand at the end of the catalogue.

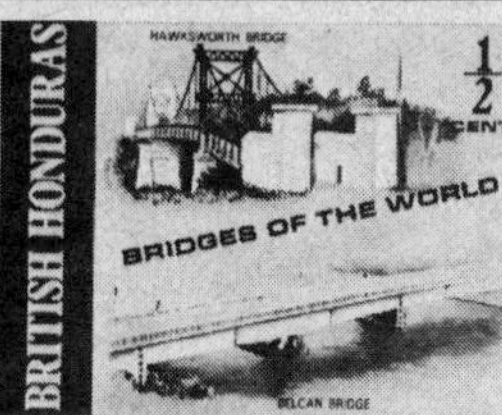

75 Hawksworth and Belcan Bridges

(Des and litho J.W.)

1971 (23 Sept). *Bridges of the World. T* **75** *and similar horiz designs. Multicoloured. W* w **12** (*sideways*). *P* 13½.

320 ½ c. Type **75** .. 10 10
321 5 c. Narrows Bridge, N.Y. and Quebec Bridge 10 10
322 26 c. London Bridge (1871) and reconstructed, Arizona (1971) .. 15 10
323 50 c. Belize Mexican Bridge and Swing Bridge 20 35
320/3 .. *Set of* 4 30 40

76 *Petrae volubis*

77 Seated Figure

(Des G. Drummond. Litho Format)

1972 (28 Feb). *Easter. T* **76** *and similar vert designs showing wild flowers. Multicoloured. W* w **12**. *P* 14½.

324 6 c. Type **76** .. 10 10
325 15 c. Yemeri .. 30 30
326 26 c. Mayflower .. 45 45
327 50 c. Tiger's Claw .. 70 70
324/7 .. *Set of* 4 1·40 1·40

(Des Jennifer Toombs. Litho Questa)

1972 (22 May). *Mayan Artefacts. T* **77** *and similar multicoloured designs. W* w **12** (*sideways except* 16 *c.*). *P* 13½ × 13 (16 *c.*) *or* 13 × 13½ (*others*).

328 3 c. Type **77** .. 10 10
329 6 c. Priest in "dancing" pose .. 10 10
330 16 c. Sun God's head (*horiz*) .. 15 15
331 26 c. Priest and Sun God .. 25 20
332 50 c. Full-front figure .. 50 75
328/32 .. *Set of* 5 90 1·10

Nos. 328/32 are inscribed on the reverse with information about the artefacts depicted.

78 Banak

79 Orchids of Belize

(Des Jennifer Toombs. Litho Questa)

1972 (21 Aug). *Indigenous Hardwoods* (4th series). *T* **78** *and similar vert designs. Multicoloured. W* w **12** (*sideways*). *P* 14½.

333 3 c. Type **78** .. 10 10
334 5 c. Quamwood .. 10 10
335 16 c. Waika Chewstick .. 15 10
336 26 c. Mamee-Apple .. 25 20
337 50 c. My Lady .. 55 70
333/7 .. *Set of* 5 95 1·00

1972 (17 Nov). *As Nos.* 258 *and* 260/1, *but W* w **12** (*upright*).

338 3 c. Grouper .. 45 60
339 5 c. Bonefish .. 50 65
340 10 c. Paca .. 70 1·10
338/40 .. *Set of* 3 1·50 2·10

(Des (from photograph by D. Groves) and photo Harrison)

1972 (20 Nov). *Royal Silver Wedding. Multicoloured; background colour given. W* w **12**. *P* 14 × 14½.

341 **79** 26 c. deep myrtle-green .. 25 10
342 50 c. bright bluish violet .. 40 40

80 Baron Bliss Day

(Des J.W. Litho Questa)

1973 (9 Mar). *Festivals of Belize. T* **80** *and similar horiz designs. Multicoloured.* W w **12**. *P* 14½ × 14.

343 3 c. Type **80** 10 10
344 10 c. Labour Day 15 10
345 26 c. Carib Settlement Day 20 15
346 50 c. Pan American Day 35 60
343/6 .. .. *Set of* 4 65 75

POSTAGE DUE STAMPS

D 1

(Typo D.L.R.)

1923–64. *Wmk Mult Script CA. P* 14.

D1 **D 1** 1 c. black, **O** .. .. 45 4·50
a. Chalky paper (25.9.56) .. .. 50 6·00
b. White uncoated paper (9.4.64) .. 12·00 18·00
D2 2 c. black, **O** .. .. 60 3·50
a. Chalky paper (25.9.56) .. .. 50 6·00
D3 4 c. black, **O** .. .. 1·25 6·00
a. Chalky paper (25.9.56) .. .. 90 8·00
D1/3 .. .. *Set of* 3 2·10 12·50
D1a/3a .. .. *Set of* 3 1·75 18·00
D1/3 Optd "Specimen" .. *Set of* 3 42·00

The early ordinary paper printings were yellowish and quite distinct from No. D1b.

1965 (3 Aug)–**72.** *As Nos.* D2a *and* D3a, *but Wmk* w **12** (*sideways on* 2 c.). *P* 13½ × 13 (2 c.) *or* 13½ × 14 (4 c.).

D4 **D 1** 2 c. black (10.1.72) .. .. 75 2·25
D5 4 c. black .. .. 50 2·50

On 1 June 1973, British Honduras was renamed BELIZE.

British Indian Ocean Territory

This Crown Colony was created on 8 November 1965 and comprised the Chagos Archipelago, previously administered by Mauritius, together with the islands of Aldabra, Farquhar and Desroches, previously administered by Seychelles.

(Currency. 100 cents=1 rupee)

B.I.O.T.

(1)

1968 (17 Jan). *As Nos.* 196/200, 202/4 *and* 206/12 *of Seychelles, optd with T* **1**. W w **12** (*sideways on* 5, 10, 15, 20, 25, 50, 75 *c. and* 10 *r.*).

1 5 c. multicoloured 10 10
a. No stop after "I" .. .. 3·00 4·00
b. No stop after "O" .. .. 2·00 3·00
2 10 c. multicoloured 10 10
a. No stop after "I" .. .. 3·00 4·00
b. No stop after "O" .. .. 2·00 3·00
3 15 c. multicoloured 10 15
a. No stop after "I" .. .. 3·00 4·00
b. No stop after "O" .. .. 2·00 3·00
4 20 c. multicoloured 15 15
a. No stop after "I" .. .. 3·00 4·00
b. No stop after "O" .. .. 2·00 3·00
5 25 c. multicoloured 15 15
a. No stop after "I" .. .. 3·25 4·50
b. No stop after "O" .. .. 2·25 3·50
6 40 c. multicoloured 15 20
a. No stop after "I" .. .. 6·50 7·50
b. No stop after "O" .. .. 4·00 5·00
7 45 c. multicoloured 20 30
a. No stop after "I" .. .. 6·50 7·50
b. No stop after "B" .. .. 6·50 7·50
c. No stop after "O" .. .. 4·00 5·00
8 50 c. multicoloured 20 30
a. No stop after "I" .. .. 6·50 7·50
b. No stop after "O" .. .. 4·00 5·00
9 75 c. multicoloured 20 35
10 1 r. multicoloured 30 35
a. No stop after "I" .. .. 7·00 8·00
b. No stop after "O" .. .. 4·50 5·50
11 1 r. 50, multicoloured .. .. 1·75 1·50
a. No stop after "I" .. .. 10·00 12·00
b. No stop after "O" .. .. 7·00 9·00
12 2 r. 25, multicoloured .. .. 3·75 3·75
a. No stop after "I" .. .. 16·00 20·00
b. No stop after "O" .. .. 10·00 13·00
13 3 r. 50, multicoloured .. .. 4·00 4·50
a. No stop after "I" .. .. 20·00 25·00
b. No stop after "O" .. .. 14·00 17·00
14 5 r. multicoloured .. .. 5·50 7·00
a. No stop after "I" .. .. 27·00 30·00
b. No stop after "O" .. .. 19·00 23·00
15 10 r. multicoloured .. .. 11·00 14·00
a. No stop after "B" .. .. 48·00 55·00
b. No stop after "I" .. .. 48·00 55·00
c. No stop after "O" .. .. 40·00 45·00
1/15 .. .. *Set of* 15 25·00 29·00

These were issued by the Crown Agents on 15 January but owing to shipping delays they were not put on sale locally until 17 January.

The positions of the "no stop" varieties are as follows:

After "I": R. 2/4 on horiz stamps except 45 c. where it occurs on R. 3/3, and R. 8/5 on vert stamps except 10 r. where it occurs on R. 4/3.

After "O": R. 3/2 and 5/1 on vert stamps, R. 2/1 and 4/4 on horiz stamps (only occurs on R. 2/1 for 45 c.), and R. 2/7 and 5/9 on 10 r. value.

After "B": R. 10/4 (45 c.) or R. 1/8 (10 r.).

We have seen a sheet of the 5 c. and of the 10 c. with all stops in place so either the no stop varieties developed during printing or they were discovered and inserted during the printing.

2 Lascar

(Des G. Drummond, based on drawings by Mrs. W. Veevers-Carter. Litho D.L.R.)

1968 (23 Oct)–**70.** *Marine Life. Multicoloured designs as T* **2**. *White paper (Nos. 20a, 23a, 24a) or cream paper (others).* W w **12** (*sideways on horiz, inverted on vert designs*). *P* 14.

16 5 c. Type **2** 30 30
17 10 c. Hammerhead Shark (*vert*) 30 30
18 15 c. Tiger Shark 30 30
19 20 c. Bat Ray 30 30
20 25 c. Butterfly Fish (*vert*) .. .. 80 1·00
20*a* 30 c. Robber Crab (7.12.70) .. .. 1·50 2·25
21 40 c. Caranx 40 40
22 45 c. Garfish (*vert*) .. .. 2·00 2·50
23 50 c. Barracuda 45 25
23*a* 60 c. Spotted Pebble Crab (7.12.70) .. .. 1·75 3·00
24 75 c. Parrot Fish .. .. 2·50 2·75
24*a* 85 c. Dorade (*Elegatis bipinnulatus*) (7.12.70) 2·50 3·00
25 1 r. Giant Hermit Crab 75 35
26 1 r. 50, Humphead .. .. 2·50 2·50
27 2 r. 25, Rock Cod .. .. 7·00 8·50
28 3 r. 50, Black Marlin .. .. 3·50 3·75
29 5 r. black, blue-green and greenish blue (Whale Shark) (*vert*) .. .. 4·50 5·00
30 10 r. Lion Fish .. .. 7·50 8·00
a. Imperf (pair) £225
16/30 .. .. *Set of* 18 35·00 40·00

See also No. 52.

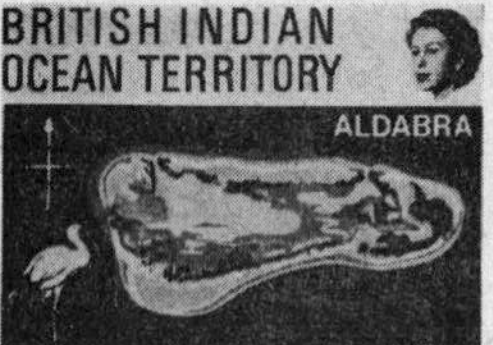

3 Sacred Ibis and Aldabra Coral Atoll

(Des and litho D.L.R.)

1969 (10 July). *Coral Atolls.* W w **12** (*sideways*). *P* 13½ × 13.

31 **3** 2 r. 25, multicoloured 70 35

4 Outrigger Canoe

(Des Mrs. M. Hayward adapted by V. Whiteley. Litho D.L.R.)

1969 (15 Dec.) *Ships of the Islands. T* **4** *and similar horiz designs. Multicoloured.* W w **12** (*sideways*). *P* 13½ × 14.

32 45 c. Type **4** 65 75
33 75 c. Pirogue 65 80
34 1 r. M. V. *Nordvaer* 70 90
35 1 r. 50, *Isle of Farquhar* .. .. 80 1·00
32/5 .. .. *Set of* 4 2·50 3·00

5 Giant Land Tortoise

(Des G. Drummond. Litho Format)

1971 (1 Feb). *Aldabra Nature Reserve. T* **5** *and similar horiz designs. Multicoloured.* W w **12** (*sideways*). *P* 13½.

36 45 c. Type **5** .. .. 2·50 2·00
37 75 c. Aldabra Lily .. .. 3·00 2·50
38 1 r. Aldabra Snail .. .. 3·25 2·75
39 1 r. 50, Western Reef Herons .. .. 6·00 5·00
36/9 .. .. *Set of* 4 13·50 11·00

6 Arms of Royal Society and White-throated Rail

(Des V. Whiteley. Litho J.W.)

1971 (30 June). *Opening of Royal Society Research Station on Aldabra.* W w **12** (*sideways*). *P* 13½.

40 **6** 3 r. 50, multicoloured .. .. 8·00 8·00

7 Staghorn Coral

(Des V. Whiteley. Litho A. & M.)

1972 (1 Mar). *Coral. T* **7** *and similar horiz designs. Multicoloured.* W w **12** (*sideways*). *P* 13½.

41 40 c. Type **7** .. .. 2·50 2·00
42 60 c. Brain coral .. .. 3·00 2·50
43 1 r. Mushroom coral .. .. 3·00 3·00
44 1 r. 75, Organ Pipe coral .. .. 4·00 4·00
41/4 .. .. *Set of* 4 11·00 10·00

On some sheets of No. 43 the inks have been applied in a different order, resulting in an almost total absence of blue.

8 White-throated Rail and Sacred Ibis

9 "Christ on the Cross"

(Des (from photograph by D. Groves) and photo Harrison)

1972 (20 Nov). *Royal Silver Wedding. Multicoloured; background colour given.* W w **12**. *P* 14 × 14½.

45 **8** 95 c. deep dull green 60 40
a. Silver (frame and inscr) ptd double .. £450
b. Slate-green .. .. 1·40 1·75
46 1 r. 50, bright bluish violet 60 40

(Des Jennifer Toombs. Litho Questa)

1973 (9 Apr). *Easter. T* **9** *and similar vert design showing illustrations from 17th-century Ethiopian manuscript. Multicoloured.* W w **12** (*sideways*). *P* 14.

47 45 c. Type **9** 20 40
48 75 c. Joseph and Nicodemus burying Jesus .. 30 55
49 1 r. Type **9** 30 60
50 1 r. 50. As 75 c. 35 70
47/50 .. .. *Set of* 4 1·00 2·00
MS51 126 × 110 mm. Nos. 47/50 .. .. 1·10 4·00

1973 (2 Oct). *As No.* 16 *but white paper and wmk upright.*

52 5 c. Type **2** .. .. 25 1·40

No. 52 differs in shade from No. 16 because of the change of paper.

10 Upsidedown Jellyfish

11 M.V. *Nordvaer*

(Des G. Drummond. Litho Walsall)

1973 (12 Nov). *Wildlife (1st series). T* **10** *and similar vert designs. Multicoloured.* W w **12** (*sideways*). *P* 14.

53 50 c. Type **10** .. .. 2·25 2·75
54 1 r. Butterflies .. .. 2·25 2·75
55 1 r. 50, Spider .. .. 2·50 2·75
53/5 .. .. *Set of* 3 6·00 7·50

See also Nos. 58/61, 77/80 and 86/9.

(Des C. Abbott. Litho Walsall)

1974 (14 July). *Fifth Anniv of "Nordvaer" Travelling Post Office. T* **11** *and similar vert design. Multicoloured. W w* **12** *(sideways). P* 14.

56 85 c. Type **11** 40 50
57 2 r. 50, *Nordvaer* off shore . . . . . . 60 1·10

12 Auger Shells

(Des PAD Studio. Litho J.W.)

1974 (12 Nov). *Wildlife (2nd series). T* **12** *and similar horiz designs showing shells. Multicoloured. W w* **12**. *P* 13½ × 14.

58 45 c. Type **12** . . . . . . 1·00 1·00
59 75 c. Green Turban . . . . . . 1·10 1·25
60 1 r. Drupe Snail . . . . . . 1·40 1·50
61 1 r. 50, Helmet Shell . . . . . . 1·50 1·75
58/61 . . . . . . *Set of* 4 4·50 5·00

13 Aldabra Drongo 14 *Grewia salicifolia*

(Des R. Granger Barrett. Litho Questa)

1975 (28 Feb). *Birds. Multicoloured designs as T* **13**. *W w* **12** *(sideways on horiz designs). P* 14.

62 5 c. Type **13** . . . . . . 55 1·00
63 10 c. Black Coucal . . . . . . 55 1·00
64 20 c. Mascarene Fody . . . . . . 60 1·00
65 25 c. White Tern . . . . . . 60 1·25
66 30 c. Crested Tern . . . . . . 60 1·25
67 40 c. Brown Booby . . . . . . 60 1·25
68 50 c. Common Noddy (*horiz*) . . . . 65 1·40
69 60 c. Grey Heron . . . . . . 80 1·60
70 65 c. Blue-faced Booby (*horiz*) . . . . 80 1·60
71 95 c. Madagascar White Eye (*horiz*) . . 1·00 1·75
72 1 r. Green Heron (*horiz*) . . . . 1·25 1·75
73 1 r. 75, Lesser Frigate Bird (*horiz*) . . 1·75 3·00
74 3 r. 50, White-tailed Tropic Bird (*horiz*) . . 2·75 3·75
75 5 r. Souimanga Sunbird (*horiz*) . . 4·00 5·00
76 10 r. Madagascar Turtle Dove (*horiz*) . . 7·50 9·00
62/76 . . . . . . *Set of* 15 21·00 32·00

(Des Sylvia Goaman. Litho Questa)

1975 (10 July). *Wildlife (3rd series). T* **14** *and similar vert designs showing seashore plants. Multicoloured. W w* **12** *(sideways). P* 14.

77 50 c. Type **14** 35 50
78 65 c. *Cassia aldabrensis* 40 60
79 1 r. *Hypoestes aldabrensis* 55 80
80 1 r. 60, *Euphorbia pyrifolia* 65 90
77/80 . . . . . . *Set of* 4 1·75 2·50

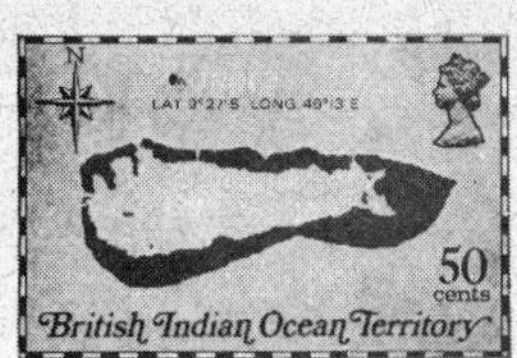

15 Map of Aldabra

(Des L. Curtis. Litho Questa)

1975 (8 Nov). *10th Anniv of Territory. Maps. T* **15** *and similar horiz designs. Multicoloured. W w* **12**. *P* 13½.

81 50 c. Type **15** 50 65
82 1 r. Desroches 65 85
83 1 r. 50, Farquhar . . . . . . 80 1·00
84 2 r. Diego Garcia . . . . . . 90 1·25
81/4 . . . . . . *Set of* 4 2·50 3·25
MS85 147 × 147 mm. Nos. 81/4 (wmk sideways) 4·25 6·50

16 Crimson Speckled Moth

(Des PAD Studio. Litho Questa)

1976 (22 Mar). *Wildlife (4th series). T* **16** *and similar horiz designs. Multicoloured. W w* **12** *(sideways). P* 13½.

86 65 c. Type **16** 50 90
87 1 r. 20, *Dysdercus fasciatus* (weevil) . . . . 65 1·10
88 1 r. 50, *Sphex torridus* (wasp) . . . . 70 1·25
89 2 r. *Oryctes rhinoceros* (beetle) . . . . 75 1·25
86/9 . . . . . . *Set of* 4 2·40 4·00

When the Seychelles achieved independence on 29 June 1976 the islands of Aldabra, Farquhar and Desroches reverted to its administration. The British Indian Ocean Territory at the present time thus consists only of the Chagos Archipelago, an island group, the largest of whose five main atolls is Diego Garcia. There is no indigenous population and the Commissioner for the Territory resides in London. The last definitive issue was withdrawn in August 1979.

British Levant

The term "British Levant" is used by stamp collectors to describe the issues made by various British Post Offices within the former Turkish Empire.

Arrangements for the first such service were included amongst the terms of a commercial treaty between the two countries in 1832, but the system did not start operations until September 1857 when a post office for civilian use was opened in Constantinople, replacing the Army Post Office which had existed there since June 1854.

Eventually the number of British Post Offices grew to five:

Beyrout (Beirut, Lebanon). Opened 1873, closed 30 September 1914.

Constantinople (Istanbul). Opened 1 September 1857, closed 30 September 1914, re-opened 4 February 1919, finally closed 27 September 1923.

Salonica (Thessalonika, Greece). Opened 1 May 1900, closed October 1914. The city was captured by Greek troops on 7 November 1912 and incorporated into Greece by the Treaty of London (July 1913).

Smyrna (Izmir). Opened 1872, closed 30 September 1914, re-opened 1 March 1919, finally closed September 1922. Between 15 May 1919 and 8 September 1922 the city was under Greek occupation.

Stamboul (a sub-office of Constantinople). Opened 1 April 1884, closed 25 August 1896, re-opened 10 February 1908, finally closed 30 September 1914.

Stamps from the two British Post Offices in Egypt, still technically part of the Turkish Empire, are listed under EGYPT.

A. BRITISH POST OFFICES IN TURKISH EMPIRE, 1857–1914

For illustrations of the postmark types see BRITISH POST OFFICES ABROAD notes, following GREAT BRITAIN.

After 15 August 1905 the post offices were supplied with Great Britain stamps overprinted "LEVANT". Subsequent examples of unoverprinted stamps with Levant postmarks did not originate from the post offices and are now omitted from the listing. The use of such stamps during 1919–22 at Constantinople and Smyrna is, however, covered by a later note.

BEYROUT (BEIRUT)

Stamps of GREAT BRITAIN *cancelled "G 06" or circular postmark as in Types* **8**, **18** *or* **20**.

1873.

Z 1 ½d. rose-red (1870–90) . . . . . . *From* 25·00
Plate Nos. 12, 13, 14, 19, 20.
Z 2 1d. rose-red (1864–79) . . . . . . *From* 8·00
Plate Nos. 107, 118, 130, 140, 145, 148, 155, 157, 162, 167, 177, 179, 180, 184, 185, 186, 187, 195, 198, 200, 203, 204, 211, 213, 215, 218, 220, 222.
Z 3 1½d. lake-red (1870–74) (Plate 3) £200
Z 4 2d. blue (1858–69) . . . . . . *From* 14·00
Plate Nos. 13, 14, 15.
Z 5 2½d. rosy mauve (1875) (*blued paper*) . . . . 70·00
Plate No. 1.
Z 6 2½d. rosy mauve (1875–76) . . . . *From* 30·00
Plate Nos. 1, 2, 3.
Z 7 2½d. rosy mauve (1876–79) . . . . *From* 25·00
Plate Nos. 3, 4, 5, 6, 7, 8, 9, 10, 11, 12, 13, 14, 15, 16, 17.
Z 8 2½d. blue (1880) . . . . . . *From* 15·00
Plate Nos. 17, 18, 19, 20.
Z 9 2½d. blue (1881) . . . . . . *From* 8·00
Plate Nos. 21, 22, 23.
Z10 3d. rose (1867–73) (Plate No. 10) . . . .
Z11 3d. rose (1873–76) . . . . . .
Plate Nos. 12, 15, 16, 18, 19, 20.
Z12 3d. rose (1881) (Plate Nos. 20, 21) . . . .
Z13 4d. vermilion (1865–73) . . . . *From* 32·00
Plate Nos. 11, 12, 13, 14.
Z14 4d. vermilion (1876) (Plate No. 15) £160
Z15 4d. sage-green (1877) . . . . . .
Plate Nos. 15, 16.
Z16 4d. grey-brown (1880) *wmk* Large Garter (Plate No. 17) . . . . . .
Z17 4d. grey-brown (1880) *wmk* Crown . . . .
Plate Nos. 17, 18.
Z18 6d. mauve (1870) (Plate Nos. 8, 9) . . . .
Z19 6d. buff (1872–73) . . . . . . *From* 75·00
Plate Nos. 11, 12.
Z20 6d. chestnut (1872) (Plate No. 11) . . . . 32·00
Z21 6d. grey (1873) (Plate No. 12) . . . .
Z22 6d. grey (1874–80) . . . . . . *From* 25·00
Plate Nos. 13, 14, 15, 16, 17.
Z23 8d. orange (1876) . . . . . .
Z24 10d. red-brown (1867) £160
Z25 1s. green (1867–73) . . . . . . 17·00
Plate Nos. 6, 7.
Z26 1s. green (1873–77) . . . . . . *From* 32·00
Plate Nos. 8, 9, 10, 12, 13.
Z27 1s. orange-brown (1880) (Plate No. 13) . .
Z28 1s. orange-brown (1881) . . . . . . 40·00
Plate Nos. 13, 14.
Z29 2s. blue (1867) £125
Z30 5s. rose (1867) (Plate Nos. 1, 2) . . *From* £600

1880.

Z31 ½d. deep green . . . . . . 4·00
Z32 ½d. pale green . . . . . . 3·75
Z33 1d. Venetian red . . . . . . 6·25
Z34 1½d. Venetian red £125
Z35 2d. pale rose . . . . . . 27·00
Z36 2d. deep rose . . . . . . 27·00
Z37 5d. indigo . . . . . . 55·00

1881.

Z38 1d. lilac (14 *dots*) . . . . . .
Z39 1d. lilac (16 *dots*) . . . . . .

1884.

Z40–46 ½d., 1½d., 2d., 2½d., 4d., 5d., 1s. . . *From* 3·25

1887.

Z47–55 ½d., 1½d., 2d., 2½d., 3d., 4½d., 5d., 6d., 1s. . . . . . . *From* 2·75

1900.

Z56–57 ½d., 1s. . . . . . . *From* 2·75

1902–04. *De La Rue ptgs.*

Z58–64 ½d. blue-green, ½d. yellow-green, 1d., 2½d., 5d., 10d., 1s. . . . . *From* 1·50

POSTAL FISCALS

Z65 1d. purple (*wmk* Anchor) . . . . . .
Z66 1d. purple (*wmk* Orb) . . . . . .

CONSTANTINOPLE

Stamps of GREAT BRITAIN *cancelled "C" or circular postmark as in Types* **1**, **10** *or* **19**.

1857.

Z 68 ½d. rose-red (1870–79) . . . . . . *From* 20·00
Plate Nos. 5, 6, 10, 11, 12, 13, 14, 15, 20.
Z 69 1d. red-brown (1854), Die I, *wmk* Small Crown, *perf* 16 . . . . . .
Z 70 1d. red-brown (1855), Die II, *wmk* Small Crown, *perf* 14 . . . . . .
Z 71 1d. red-brown, (1855), Die II, *wmk* Large Crown, *perf* 14 . . . . . . 16·00
Z 72 1d. rose-red (1857) . . . . . . 6·00
Z 73 1d. rose-red (1861) Alphabet IV . . . .
Z 74 1d. rose-red (1864–79) . . . . *From* 3·75
Plate Nos. 71, 72, 73, 74, 76, 78, 79, 80, 81, 83, 85, 87, 89, 90, 92, 93, 94, 95, 96, 97, 99, 101, 102, 105, 106, 108, 109, 110, 113, 116, 118, 119, 120, 121, 122, 123, 124, 125, 127, 129, 130, 131, 134, 135, 136, 137, 138, 140, 141, 143, 144, 145, 146, 147, 148, 149, 150, 151, 152, 155, 156, 157, 158, 159, 160, 161, 162, 163, 164, 166, 167, 170, 171, 172, 173, 174, 175, 176, 177, 178, 179, 180, 181, 183, 184, 186, 187, 188, 189, 190, 191, 192, 193, 194, 195, 196, 197, 198, 200, 201, 203, 204, 205, 206, 207, 208, 210, 212, 214, 215, 216, 220, 222, 224.
Z 75 1½d. rose-red (1870) (Plate 1) £180
Z 76 2d. blue (1855), *wmk* Large Crown, *perf* 14. (Plate Nos. 5, 6) . . . . . .
Z 77 2d. blue (1858–69) . . . . *From* 7·50
Plate Nos. 8, 9, 12, 13, 14, 15.
Z 78 2½d. rosy mauve (1875–76) (*blued paper*) (Plate Nos. 1, 2) . . . . *From* 50·00
Z 79 2½d. rosy mauve (1875–76) . . . . *From* 25·00
Plate Nos. 1, 2, 3.
Z 80 2½d. rosy mauve (*Error of Lettering*) . . . .
Z 81 2½d. rosy mauve (1876–79) . . . . *From* 23·00
Plate Nos. 3 to 17.
Z 82 2½d. blue (1880–81) . . . . *From* 11·00
Plate Nos. 17, 18, 19, 20.
Z 83 2½d. blue (1881) (Plate Nos. 21, 22, 23) . . 6·00
Z 84 3d. carmine-rose (1862) (Plate No. 2) . . £110
Z 85 3d. rose (1865) (Plate No. 4) . . . . 65·00
Z 86 3d. rose (1867–73) (Plate Nos. 4 to 10) . . 65·00
Z 87 3d. rose (1873–76) . . . . . . 20·00
Plates, 11, 12, 15, 16, 17, 18, 19.
Z 88 3d. rose (1881) (Plate No. 21) . . . .
Z 89 3d. on 3d. lilac (1883) (Plate No. 21) . .
Z 90 4d. rose (1857) . . . . . . 40·00
a. *Rose-carmine* . . . . . .
Z 91 4d. red (1862) (Plate Nos. 3, 4) . . *From* 35·00
Z 92 4d. vermilion (1865–73) . . . . *From* 26·00
Plate Nos. 7 to 14.
Z 93 4d. vermilion (1876) (Plate No. 15) . . £140
Z 94 4d. sage-green (1877) . . . . . . 75·00
Plate Nos. 15, 16.
Z 95 4d. grey-brown (1880) *wmk* Large Garter (Plate No. 17) . . . . . .
Z 96 4d. grey-brown (1880) *wmk* Crown (Plate Nos. 17, 18) . . . . . . *From* 17·00
Z 97 6d. lilac (1856) . . . . . . 50·00
Z 98 6d. lilac (1862) (Plate Nos. 3, 4) . . *From* 35·00
Z 99 6d. lilac (1865–67) . . . . . . 32·00
Plate Nos. 5, 6.
Z100 6d. lilac (1867) (Plate No. 6) . . . . 40·00
Z101 6d. violet (1867–70) . . . . *From* 32·00
Plate Nos. 6, 8, 9.
Z102 6d. buff (1872–73) . . . . . . 48·00
Plate Nos. 11, 12.
Z103 6d. chestnut (1872) (Plate No. 11) . . 26·00
Z104 6d. grey (1873) (Plate No. 12) . . . . 50·00
Z105 6d. grey (1874–76) . . . . *From* 20·00
Plate Nos. 13, 14, 15, 16.
Z106 6d. grey (1881–82) (Plate Nos. 17, 18) . . 15·00
Z107 6d. on 6d. lilac (1883) . . . . . . 65·00
a. Dots slanting (Letters MI or SJ) . . £110
Z108 8d. orange (1876) £275
Z109 10d. red-brown (1867), *wmk* Emblems . . £10000
Z110 10d. red-brown (1867) £160
Z111 1s. green (1856) . . . . . . 70·00

Z112 1s. green (1862) . . . . 60·00
Z113 1s. green (1862) ("K" *variety*) . . . .
Z114 1s. green (1862) (*thick paper*) . . . .
Z115 1s. green (1865) (Plate No. 4) . . . . . 35·00
Z116 1s. green (1867–73) . . . . . *From* 10·00
Plate Nos. 4, 5, 6, 7.
Z117 1s. green (1873–77) . . . . . *From* 26·00
Plate Nos. 8, 9, 10, 11, 12, 13.
Z118 1s. orange-brown (1880) (Plate No. 13) . . £175
Z119 1s. orange-brown (1881) . . . . *From* 32·00
Plate Nos. 13, 14.
Z120 2s. blue (1867) . . . . 85·00
Z121 5s. rose (1867–74) . . . . . *From* £200
Plate Nos. 1, 2.
Z122 5s. rose (1882) (*white paper*) £850
Z123 5s. rose (1882) (*blued paper*) £1000

1880.
Z124 ½d. deep green . . . . 3·50
Z125 ½d. pale green . . . . 4·25
Z126 1d. Venetian red . . . . 2·50
Z127 2d. pale rose . . . . 26·00
Z128 2d. deep rose . . . . 32·00
Z129 5d. indigo . . . .

1881.
Z130 1d. lilac (14 *dots*) . . . .
Z131 1d. lilac (16 *dots*) . . . . 2·25

1883 *to* **1884.**
Z132 ½d. slate 3.75
Z133–136 1½d., 2d., 2½d., 3d. . . . *From* 6·00
Z137–141 4d., 5d., 6d., 9d., 1s. . . . . *From* 65·00
Z142 2s. 6d. lilac (*blued paper*) . . . . .
Z143 2s. 6d. lilac (*white paper*) . . . . . 80·00
Z144 5s. rose (*blued paper*) . . . . .
Z145 5s. rose (*white paper*) . . . . .

1887.
Z146–157 ½d., 1½d., 2d., 2½d., 3d., 4d., 4½d., 5d., 6d., 9d., 10d., 1s. . . . . *From* 2·25

1900.
Z158–159 ½d., 1s. . . . . . . *From* 2·25

1902–04. *De La Rue ptgs.*
Z160–174 ½d. blue-green, ½d. yellow-green, 1d., 1½d., 2d., 2½d., 3d., 4d. brown and green, 5d., 6d., 9d., 10d., 1s., 2s. 6d., 5s. . *From* 2·25

POSTAL FISCAL

Z175 1d. purple (No. F19) (1868) . . . . .

SALONICA

Stamps of GREAT BRITAIN *cancelled with circular postmark as in Type* **18** *or double-circle datestamp.*

1900.
Z202 ½d. vermilion (1887) . . . . 8·50
Z203 ½d. green (1900) . . . . 10·00
Z204 1d. lilac (1881) . . . . 12·00
Z205 6d. purple/*red* (1887) . . . . . . 14·00
Z206 1s. green and carmine (1900) . . . . . 70·00
Z207 5s. rose (*white paper*) (1883) £600

1902.
Z208 ½d. blue-green . . . . 14·00
Z209 ½d. yellow-green . . . . 8·50
Z209*a* 1d. scarlet . . . . 8·50
Z209*b* 2½d. blue . . . . 12·00
Z209*c* 1s. green and carmine . . . . . . 25·00

SMYRNA (IZMIR)

Stamps of GREAT BRITAIN *cancelled* "F 87" *or circular postmark as in Type* **8**, **16** *or* **18**.

1872.
Z210 ½d. rose-red (1870–79) . . . . *From* 14·00
Plates 11, 12, 13, 14, 15.
Z211 1d. rose-red (1864–79) . . . . *From* 6·00
Plate Nos. 120, 124, 134, 137, 138, 139, 140, 142, 143, 145, 146, 148, 149, 150, 151, 152, 153, 155, 156, 157, 158, 159, 160, 161, 162, 163, 164, 166, 167, 168, 169, 170, 171, 172, 173, 174, 175, 176, 177, 178, 183, 184, 185, 186, 187, 188, 191, 193, 195, 196, 198, 200, 201, 204, 210, 215, 217, 218.
Z212 1½d. lake-red (1870–74) (Plate Nos. 1, 3) *From* £200
Z213 2d. blue (1858) *wmk* Large Crown, *perf* 16
Z214 2d. blue (1858–69) . . . . *From* 11·00
Plate Nos. 13, 14, 15.
Z215 2½d. rosy mauve (1875) (*blued paper*) . . 55·00
Plate No. 1.
Z216 2½d. rosy mauve (1875–76) . . . *From* 26·00
Plate Nos. 1, 2, 3.
Z217 2½d. rosy mauve (*Error of lettering*) . .
Z218 2½d. rosy mauve (1876–79) . . . *From* 22·00
Plate Nos. 3, 4, 5, 6, 7, 8, 9, 10, 11, 12, 13, 14, 15, 16, 17.
Z219 2½d. blue (1880) . . . . . *From* 8·50
Plate Nos. 17, 18, 19, 20.
Z220 2½d. blue (1881) . . . . 7·00
Plate Nos. 21, 22, 23.
Z221 3d. rose (1867–73) . . . . . . 25·00
Plate Nos. 5, 7, 9, 10.
Z222 3d. rose (1873–76) (Plate No. 14) . . .
Z223 4d. vermilion (1865–73) . . . . . 26·00
Plate Nos. 12, 13, 14.
Z224 4d. vermilion (1876) (Plate No. 15) . . £130
Z225 4d. sage-green (1877) . . . . . . 85·00
Plate Nos. 15, 16.
Z226 4d. grey-brown (1880) *wmk* Large Garter (Plate No. 17) . . . .
Z227 4d. grey-brown (1880) *wmk* Crown (Plate Nos. 17, 18) . . . . . *From* 15·00
Z228 6d. buff (1872–73) . . . . *From* 70·00
Plate Nos. 11, 12.
Z229 6d. chestnut (1872) (Plate No. 11) . .
Z230 6d. grey (1873) (Plate No. 12) . . . . 65·00
Z231 6d. grey (1874–80) . . . . *From* 22·00
Plate Nos. 13, 14, 15, 16, 17.
Z232 6d. grey (1881–82) (Plate Nos. 17, 18) . . . 50·00
Z233 6d. on 6d. lilac (1883) . . . . . . 70·00
Z234 8d. orange (1876) . . . .
Z235 9d. straw (1867) £175
Z236 10d. red-brown (1867) £130
Z237 1s. green (1867–73) (Plate Nos. 6, 7) . .
Z238 1s. green (1873–77) . . . . *From* 27·00
Plate Nos. 8, 9, 10, 11, 12, 13.
Z239 1s. orange-brown (1880) (Plate No. 13) . . £160
Z240 1s. orange-brown (1881) (Plate Nos. 13, 14) . . 40·00
Z241 5s. rose (1867–74) (Plate No. 2) . . .

1880.
Z242 ½d. deep green . . . . 4·00
Z243 ½d. pale green . . . . 3·75
Z244 1d. Venetian red . . . . 6·50
Z245 1½d. Venetian red . . . . 70·00
Z246 2d. pale rose . . . . 24·00
Z247 2d. deep rose . . . . 26·00
Z248 5d. indigo . . . . 48·00

1881.
Z249 1d. lilac (16 *dots*) . . . . 3·75

1884.
Z250 ½d. slate-blue . . . . 6·00
Z251–252 2d., 2½d. . . . . . *From* 6·00
Z253–255 4d., 5d., 1s. . . . . . *From* 70·00

1887.
Z256–264 ½d., 1½d., 2d., 2½d., 3d., 4d., 5d., 6d., 1s. . . . . *From* 2·75

1900.
Z265–266 ½d., 1s. . . . . . . *From* 3·00

1902–04. *De La Rue ptgs.*
Z267–281 ½d. blue-green, ½d. yellow-green, 1d., 1½d., 2d., 2½d., 3d., 4d. brown and green, 5d., 6d., 9d., 10d., 1s., 2s. 6d., 5s. . *From* 3·75

STAMBOUL (CONSTANTINOPLE)

Stamps of GREAT BRITAIN *cancelled* "S" *as Type* **10**, *or circular postmarks inscribed either* "BRITISH POST OFFICE CONSTANTINOPLE S" *or* "BRITISH POST OFFICE STAMBOUL" *as Type* **18**.

1884.
Z296 ½d. slate . . . . 15·00
Z297 1d. lilac . . . . 7·00
Z298 2d. lilac . . . .
Z299 2½d. lilac . . . . 9·00
Z300 5d. green . . . . 70·00

1887.
Z306–317 ½d., 1½d., 2d., 2½d., 3d., 4d., 4½d., 5d., 6d., 9d., 10d., 1s. . . . . . *From* 3·00

The "S" cancellation was in use from 1885 to 1891 and the "Stamboul" mark from 1892 to 1896, when the office was closed, and from its reopening in 1908 to 1914. The "CONSTANTINOPLE S" handstamp was normally used as a back stamp, but can be found cancelling stamps in the period 1885 to 1892.

PRICES FOR STAMPS ON COVER	
Nos. 1/3a	*from* × 8
Nos. 4/6*a*	*from* × 5
Nos. 7/40	*from* × 3
Nos. L1/10	*from* × 6
Nos. L11/17	*from* × 3

I. TURKISH CURRENCY

Following the depreciation of the Turkish piastre against sterling in 1884 it was decided to issue stamps surcharged in Turkish currency to avoid speculation. During the early period unsurcharged stamps of Great Britain remained on sale from the British Post Offices at the current rate of exchange until replaced by "LEVANT" overprints.

80 PARAS (1) **4 PIASTRES** (2) **12 PIASTRES** (3)

***Stamps of Great Britain (Queen Victoria) surch as T* 1 *to* 3**

PRINTERS. Nos. 1/24 were surcharged or overprinted by De La Rue, *unless otherwise stated.*

1885 (1 Apr).
1 **64** 40 pa. on 2½d. lilac . . . . . 55·00 75
2 **62** 80 pa. on 5d. green . . . . . £175 9·50
3 **58** 12 pi. on 2s. 6d. lilac/*bluish* . . . £250 £125
a. On white paper . . . . . 38·00 22·00

1887 (June)–**96**.
4 **74** 40 pa. on 2½d. purple/*blue* . . . 1·75 10
a. Surch double £1800 £2500
5 **78** 80 pa. on 5d. purple and blue (6.90) . 9·00 25
a. Small "0" in "80" . . . . . £120 70·00
6 **81** 4 pi. on 10d. dull purple and carmine (11.96) . . . . . 28·00 10·00
a. Dull purple and deep bright carmine . . . . . 27·00 9·50
b. Large, wide "4" . . . . . 75·00 45·00

No. 5a occurs twice on each sheet in positions R.4/2 and R.4/8 of both the upper and the lower pane.

1893 (25 Feb). *Roughly handstamped at Constantinople, as T* **1**.
7 **71** 40 pa. on ½d. vermilion £375 £100

This provisional was in use for five days only at the Constantinople and Stamboul offices. As fraudulent copies were made with the original handstamp, and can be found "used" on piece cancelled by fraudulent use of the usual canceller, this stamp should only be purchased from undoubted sources. It is also known with genuine handstamp inverted.

1902–5. *Stamps of King Edward VII surch as T* **1** *to* **3**.
8 **86** 40 pa. on 2½d. ultramarine, **O** (3.02) . . 4·25 10
a. Pale ultramarine . . . . . 4·25 10
ab. Surch double . . . . . † £1750
9 **89** 80 pa. on 5d. purple and ultramarine, **O** (5.6.02) . . . . . 2·75 85
a. Small "0" in "80" £175 £190
10 **92** 4 pi. on 10d. dull purple and carmine, **O** (6.9.02) . . . . . 8·50 4·00
a. No cross on crown . . . . . 90·00 90·00
b. Chalky paper . . . . . 6·00 8·50
ba. Chalky. No cross on crown . . 85·00 £100
11 **94** 12 pi. on 2s. 6d. lilac, **O** (29.8.03) . . 25·00 32·00
a. Pale dull purple, **C** . . . . 55·00 65·00
b. Dull purple, **C** . . . . . 28·00 32·00
12 **95** 24 pi. on 5s. carmine, **O** (15.8.05) . . 30·00 48·00
8/12 . . . . . . *Set of* 5 60·00 80·00
9/11 Optd "Specimen" . . . *Set of* 3 £150

No. 9a only occurs on the first printing of 80 pa. on 5d.

1 PIASTRE
(4)

1905–08. *Surch in* "PIASTRES" *instead of* "PARAS" *as T* **4** *and* **2**.
13 **86** 1 pi. on 2½d. ultramarine, **O** (17.4.06) . . 3·00 10
14 **89** 2 pi. on 5d. dull purple and ultramarine, **O** (11.11.05) . . . . . 10·00 2·00
a. Chalky paper (1.08) . . . . 10·00 1·50
b. Slate-purple and ultramarine, **C** . . 17·00 6·00

1 Piastre (5) **1 PIASTRE 10 PARAS** (6)

1906 (2 July). *Issued at Beyrout. No. L4 surch with T* **5** *by American Press, Beyrout.*
15 **85** 1 pi. on 2d. grey-green and carmine, **O** £1350 £600

1909 (16 Nov–Dec). *Stamps of King Edward VII surch as T* **1** (30 *pa.*), **6**, *and* **2** (5 *pi.*).
16 **84** 30 pa. on 1½d. pale dull purple and green, **C** . . . . . 3·75 1·25
a. Surch double, one albino . .
17 **87** 1 pi. 10 pa. on 3d. dull purple/*orange-yellow*, **C** . . . . . 7·00 16·00
18 **88** 1 pi. 30 pa. on 4d. green and chocolate-brown, **C** . . . . . 6·00 14·00
19 1 pi. 30 pa. on 4d. pale orange, **O** (16.12.09) . . . . . 8·50 16·00
20 **83** 2 pi. 20 pa. on 6d. dull purple, **C** . . 15·00 35·00
21 **93** 5 pi. on 1s. dull green and carmine, **C** (Optd S. £60) . . . . . 3·75 6·00
16/21 . . . . . . *Set of* 6 40·00 80·00

1¾ PIASTRE (7) **4** Normal "4" **4** Pointed "4"

1910 (24 Jan). *Stamps of King Edward VII surch as T* **7**.
22 **87** 1¼ pi. on 3d. dull purple/*orange-yellow*, **C** 40 1·00
23 **88** 1¾ pi. on 4d. pale orange, **O** . . 40 60
a. Orange-red, **O** . . . . . 1·75 3·00
b. Thin, pointed "4" in fraction . . 10·00 35·00
24 **83** 2½ pi. on 6d. dull purple, **C** . . . 90 65
22/4 . . . . . . *Set of* 3 1·50 2·00

No. 23b occurs in the first and seventh vertical rows of the sheet. The variety also occurs on No. 38, but not on No. 38b.

1 PIASTRE (8) **1 PIASTRE** (9)

TYPE DIFFERENCES. In T **4** the letters are tall and narrow and the space enclosed by the upper part of the "A" is small.

In T **8** the opening of the "A" is similar but the letters are shorter and broader, the "P" and the "E" being particularly noticeable.

In T **9** the letters are short and broad, but the "A" is thin and open.

1911–13. *Stamps of King Edward VII, Harrison or Somerset House ptgs, surch at Somerset House.*

(*a*) *Surch with T* **4** (20 *July*)
25 **86** 1 pi. on 2½d. bright blue (*perf* 14) . . 3·25 3·00
26 1 pi. on 2½d. bright blue (*perf* 15 × 14) (14.10.11) . . . . . 6·00 1·75
a. Dull blue . . . . . 6·00 1·25
b. Surch double, one albino . . . £175

(*b*) *Surch with T* **8**
27 **86** 1 pi. on 2½d. brt blue (*perf* 15 × 14) (3.12) . . . . . 10·00 2·00
a. Dull blue . . . . . 12·00 3·00

(*c*) *Surch with T* **9** (7.12)
28 **86** 1 pi. on 2½d. bright blue (*perf* 15 × 14) 24·00 45
a. Dull blue . . . . . 24·00 45

(*d*) *Surch as T* **1** *to* **3** (1911–13)
29 **84** 30 pa. on 1½d. reddish purple and bright green (22.8.11) . . . . . 4·25 55
a. Slate-purple and green . . . 4·75 2·25
b. Surch double, one albino . . 50·00
30 **89** 2 pi. on 5d. dull reddish purple and bright blue (13.5.12) . . . . 3·25 1·50
a. Deep dull reddish purple and bright blue . . . . . 3·75 2·00
31 **92** 4 pi. on 10d. dull purple and scarlet (26.6.12) . . . . . 11·00 8·00
a. Dull reddish purple and aniline pink
b. Dull reddish purple and carmine 9·00 11·00
c. No cross on crown . . . .

32 **93** 5 pi. on 1s. green and carmine (1913) .. 11·00 5·00
33 **94** 12 pi. on 2s. 6d. dull reddish purple (3.2.12) .. .. 90·00 £110
a. *Dull greyish purple* .. .. 29·00 30·00
b. *Pale dull reddish purple* .. .. 29·00 30·00
34 **95** 24 pi. on 5s. carmine (1913) .. .. 48·00 60·00
a. Surch double, one albino ..
29/34 .. .. *Set of* 6 90·00 95·00

1913 (Apr)–**14**. *Stamps of King George V, wmk Royal Cypher, surch as T* **1** (*30 pa.*), **9** (*1 pi.*), **7** *or* **2** (*4 and 5 pi.*).
35 **105** 30 pa. on 1½d. red-brown (4.13) .. 3·00 4·75
a. Surch double, one albino ..
36 **104** 1 pi. on 2½d. cobalt-blue (6.13) .. 70 10
a. *Bright blue* 70 15
37 **106** 1¼ pi. on 3d. dull reddish violet (9.13) .. 1·50 4·25
a. *Violet* .. .. .. 1·50 4·25
38 1¾ pi. on 4d. deep grey-green (7.13) .. 3·00 5·50
a. Thin, pointed "4" in fraction .. 55·00 80·00
b. *Grey-green* .. .. .. 2·50 5·00
39 **108** 4 pi. on 10d. turquoise-blue (12.13) .. 5·00 12·00
40 5 pi. on 1s. bistre-brown (1.14) .. .. 17·00 40·00
35/40 .. .. *Set of* 6 27·00 60·00

II. BRITISH CURRENCY

Stamps overprinted "LEVANT", were for use on parcels, newspapers and printed matter. The face values were left in sterling to simplify accounting with the steamship and railway companies involved in the transmission of these classes of mail. They replaced those unoverprinted Great Britain stamps which had remained on sale from the Levant Post Offices after the introduction of the Turkish currency surcharges.

LEVANT

(L 1)

1905 (15 Aug)–**12**. *Stamps of King Edward VII optd with Type* **L 1**.

(*a*) *De La Rue ptgs*
L 1 **83** ½d. pale yellowish green, **O** .. .. 1·50 15
a. *Yellowish green*, **O** .. .. 1·50 15
L 2 1d. scarlet, **O** .. .. 1·25 15
a. *Bright scarlet*, **O** .. .. .. 2·00 90
L 3 **84** 1½d. dull purple and green, **O** .. .. 4·50 1·50
a. Chalky paper .. .. .. 11·00 2·00
L 4 **85** 2d. grey-green and carmine, **O** .. 3·00 9·00
a. Chalky paper .. .. .. 2·00 6·00
b. *Pale blue-green and carmine*, **C** .. 3·00 7·00
L 5 **86** 2½d. ultramarine, **O** .. .. .. 7·50 17·00
L 6 **87** 3d. purple/*orange-yellow*, **O** .. .. 5·50 13·00
L 7 **88** 4d. grey-green and brown, **O** .. .. 7·00 14·00
a. *Green and chocolate-brown*, **O** .. 8·00 14·00
L 8 **89** 5d. dull purple and ultramarine, **O** .. 14·00 25·00
L 9 **83** 6d. pale dull purple, **O** .. .. 11·00 25·00
L10 **93** 1s. dull green and carmine, **O** .. 25·00 30·00
a. Chalky paper .. .. .. 25·00 30·00
L1/10 .. .. *Set of* 10 70·00 £120

(*b*) *Harrison ptgs optd at Somerset House*
L11 **83** ½d. dull yellow-green (*p*. 14) (2.12) .. 5·50 10·00
a. *Dull green* .. .. 5·50 10·00
b. *Deep dull green* .. .. .. 5·50 10·00

On 28 December 1909 all values, except for the ½d., 1d. and 2d. stamps, were withdrawn from sale. Subsequent dated cancellations on the withdrawn values are philatelic, being worth only a fraction of the used prices quoted.

1911–13. *Stamps of King George V optd with Type* **L 1** *at Somerset House*. (*a*) *Die A. Wmk Crown*.
L12 **98** ½d. green (No. 322) (12.9.11) 40 90
L13 **99** 1d. carmine-red (No. 327) (1.1.12) .. 40 3·75
a. No cross on crown .. .. ..
b. Opt double, one albino .. .. 70·00

(*b*) *Redrawn types. Wmk Crown*
L14 **101** ½d. green (No. 339) (21.3.12) 25 10
a. *Yellow-green* 50 15
L15 **102** 1d. bright scarlet (No. 341) (24.2.12) .. 25 15
a. *Scarlet* (No. 342) 50 15
b. Opt triple, two albino .. ..

(*c*) *New types. Wmk Royal Cypher* (7.13)
L16 **105** ½d. green (No. 351) 15 25
a. *Yellow-green* 20 50
L17 **104** 1d. scarlet (No. 357) .. .. .. 15 1·25
a. *Vermilion* .. .. 90 2·00

Similar overprints were issued when the British Post Offices reopened in 1919, and are listed below.

B. BRITISH POST OFFICES IN CONSTANTINOPLE AND SMYRNA, 1919–1923

CONSTANTINOPLE

Following the occupation of Constantinople by Allied forces a British Military Post Office was opened for civilian use on 4 February 1919. During the period of its existence stamps of Great Britain with face values to 10s. were available and such use can be identified by the following cancellations:
"FIELD POST OFFICE H12" (4 February 1919 to March 1919)
"ARMY POST OFFICE Y" (March 1919 to July 1919)
"ARMY POST OFFICE S.X.3" (April 1919 to July 1919)
"BRITISH A.P.O. CONSTANTINOPLE" (July 1919 to Sept 1920).

Of these four marks the first two types were also used for military mail.

The office reverted to civilian control in July 1920, Nos. 41/50 and L18/24 being intended for its use.

NEW INFORMATION

The editor is always interested to correspond with people who have new information that will improve or correct the Catalogue.

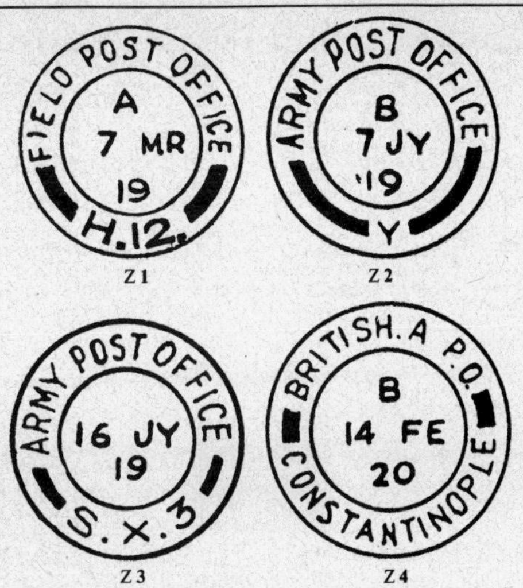

Z 1 Z 2 Z 3 Z 4

1919–20. *Used at the Army Post Office. Stamps of* GREAT BRITAIN *cancelled with Types* **Z 1**, **Z 2**, **Z 3**, **Z 4**.
Z176–187 ½d., 1d., 1½d., 2d. Die I, 2½d., 4d., 6d., 9d. agate, 1s., 2s. 6d., 5s., 10s. .. *From* 3·00

1920–21. *Used at the Civilian Post Office. Stamps of* GREAT BRITAIN *cancelled with Type* **18** *or double-circle datestamp*.
Z188–201 ½d., 1d., 1½d., 2d. Die I, 2½d., 3d., 4d., 5d., 6d., 10d., 1s, 2s. 6d., 5s., 10s .. *From* 2·50

SMYRNA

When the office re-opened on 1 March 1919 existing stocks of surcharged or overprinted issues were utilised until they were exhausted in mid-1920. During this period examples of Nos. 24, 29*a*, 30*a*, 33*b*/7, 39/40, L4*b*, L14/17 are known with commercial postmarks. These stamps were supplemented and finally replaced in mid-1920 by ordinary stamps of Great Britain.

Stamps of GREAT BRITAIN *cancelled with circular postmark as Type* **18** *or with* "REGISTERED" *oval*.
Z282–293 ½d., 1d., 1½d., 2d. Die I, 2d. Die II, 2½d. blue, 2½d. Prussian blue, 4d., 6d., 10d., 1s., 2s. 6d., 5s. .. .. .. *From* 4·50

PRICES FOR STAMPS ON COVER
Nos. 41/50 *from* × 2
Nos. L18/24 *from* × 5

Stamps of Great Britain surch at Somerset House

I. TURKISH CURRENCY

1½ PIASTRES (10) **15 PIASTRES** (11)

1921 (Aug). *Stamps of King George V, wmk Royal Cypher, surch as T* **1** (*30 pa.*), **10** *and* **11** (*15 and 18¾ pi.*).
41 **105** 30 pa. on ½d. green .. .. .. 20 3·00
a. *Yellow-green* .. .. .. 30 4·50
42 **104** 1½ pi. on 1d. bright scarlet 20 10
a. *Vermilion* 60 75
b. *Scarlet-vermilion* 30 60
43 3¾ pi. on 2½d. blue 50 25
a. *Dull Prussian blue* .. .. 7·50 2·00
44 **106** 4½ pi. on 3d. violet .. .. .. 80 2·75
a. *Bluish violet* .. .. .. 1·00 2·50
45 **107** 7½ pi. on 5d. brown 30 10
a. *Yellow-brown* 40 20
46 **108** 15 pi. on 10d. turquoise-blue 45 15
47 18¾ pi. on 1s. bistre-brown .. .. 3·50 3·50
a. *Olive-bistre* .. .. .. 3·50 4·50

45 PIASTRES

(12)

1921. *Stamps of King George V* (*Bradbury, Wilkinson printing*) *surch as T* **12**.
48 **109** 45 pi. on 2s. 6d. chocolate-brown .. 27·00 40·00
a. *Olive-brown* .. .. .. 42·00 55·00
49 90 pi. on 5s. rose-red .. .. 32·00 30·00
50 180 pi. on 10s. dull grey-blue .. .. 55·00 40·00
a. Opt double, one albino ..
41/50 .. .. *Set of* 10 £110 £110
47/50 Optd "Specimen" .. .. *Set of* 4 £300

II. BRITISH CURRENCY

1921. *Stamps of King George V optd as Type* **L 1**.
L18 **106** 2d. reddish orange (Die I) .. .. 1·25 15·00
a. *Bright orange* .. .. .. 2·00 15·00
L19 3d. bluish violet .. .. .. 7·50 10·00
L20 4d. grey-green .. .. .. 4·25 13·00
L21 **107** 5d. yellow-brown .. .. .. 9·00 17·00
L22 6d. dull purple, **C** .. .. .. 14·00 20·00
a. *Reddish purple*, **C** .. .. .. 12·00 8·00
L23 **108** 1s. bistre-brown (Optd S. £75) .. 10·00 6·50
a. *Olive-bistre* .. .. .. 10·00 6·50
L24 **109** 2s. 6d. chocolate-brown (Optd S. 150) 42·00 65·00
a. *Olive-brown* .. .. .. 65·00 95·00
L18/24 .. .. *Set of* 7 75·00 £120

On No. L24 the letters of the overprint are shorter, being only 3 mm high.

Nos. 41/50 and L18/24 were used at the Constantinople office only.

C. BRITISH FIELD OFFICE IN SALONICA

These overprints were originally prepared for use by a civilian post office to be set up on Mt Athos, Northern Greece. When the project was abandoned they were placed on sale at the Army Field Office in Salonica.

PRICES FOR STAMPS ON COVER
Nos. S1/8 *from* × 10

Levant

(S 1)

1916 (end Feb–9 Mar). *Stamps of Gt. Britain, optd with Type* **S 1** *by Army Printing Office, Salonica*.
S 1 **105** ½d. green .. .. 18·00 40·00
a. Opt double £1700 £1800
b. Vert pair, one without opt £800 £900
S 2 **104** 1d. scarlet .. .. 18·00 40·00
a. Opt double £950 £1000
S 3 **106** 2d. reddish orange (Die I) .. .. 75·00 £120
S 4 3d. bluish violet .. .. .. 65·00 £110
a. Opt double .. ..
S 5 4d. grey-green .. .. 75·00 £120
S 6 **107** 6d. reddish purple, **C** .. .. 48·00 95·00
a. Vert pair, one without opt £900 £1000
S 7 **108** 9d. agate £200 £350
a. Opt double £6000 £6000
S 8 1s. bistre-brown £170 £300
S 1/8 .. .. *Set of* 8 £600 £1100

There are numerous forgeries of this overprint.

All values can be found with an additional albino overprint, inverted on the gummed side.

British New Guinea
see Papua

British Occupation of Iraq
see Iraq

British Occupation of Italian Colonies

PRICES FOR STAMPS ON COVER TO 1945
Nos. M1/21 *from* × 4
Nos. MD1/5 *from* × 10
Nos. S1/9 *from* × 4
The above prices refer to covers from the territories concerned, not examples used in Great Britain.

MIDDLE EAST FORCES

For use in territory occupied by British Forces in Eritrea (1942), Italian Somaliland (1942), Cyrenaica (1943), Tripolitania (1943), and some of the Dodecanese Islands (1945).

PRICES. Our prices for used stamps with "M.E.F." overprints are for specimens with identifiable postmarks of the territories in which they were issued. These stamps were also used in the United Kingdom with official sanction, from the summer of 1950 onwards, and with U.K. postmarks are worth about 25 per cent less.

PRINTERS. Considerable research has been undertaken to discover the origins of Nos. M1/10. It is now suggested that Nos. M1/5, previously assigned to Harrison and Sons, were produced by the Army Printing Services, Cairo, and that the smaller printing, Nos. M6/10, previously identified as the work of the Army Printing Services, Cairo, was from an unidentified printer within the Middle East Forces area.

M.E.F. (M 1)

Opt. 14 mm long. Regular lettering and upright oblong stops.

M.E.F. (M 2)

Opt. 13½ mm long. Regular lettering and square stops.

M.E.F. (M 2a)

Opt. 13½ mm long. Rough lettering and round stops.

(Illustrations twice actual size)

1942 (2 Mar). *Stamps of Great Britain optd. W* **127**. *P* 15 × 14.

(a) With Type M 1

No.	Type	Description	Unused	Used
M 1	**128**	1d. scarlet (No. 463)	15	40
M 2		2d. orange (No. 465)	15	60
M 3	**128**	2½d. ultramarine (No. 466)	15	15
M 4		3d. violet (No. 467)	15	10
		a. Opt double	—	£1200
M 5	**129**	5d. brown	15	15

(b) With Type M 2

No.	Type	Description	Unused	Used
M 6	**128**	1d. scarlet (No. 463)	18·00	6·50
		a. Optd. with Type M 2*a*	15·00	6·00
		b. Nos. M6/a *se-tenant* vert	50·00	40·00
M 7		2d. orange (No. 465)	32·00	27·00
		a. Optd with Type M 2*a*	26·00	22·00
		b. Nos. M7/a *se-tenant* vert	£100	80·00
M 8		2½d. ultramarine (No. 466)	15·00	6·50
		a. Optd with Type M 2*a*	12·00	5·00
		b. Nos. M8/a *se-tenant* vert	45·00	35·00
M 9		3d. violet (No. 467)	35·00	15·00
		a. Optd with Type M 2*a*	27·00	12·00
		b. Nos. M9/a *se-tenant* vert	£100	60·00
M10	**129**	5d. brown	£120	45·00
		a. Optd with Type M 2*a*	£110	40·00
		b. Nos. M10/a *se-tenant* vert	£350	£250

See note after No. M21.

Nos. M6/10 were issued in panes of 60 (6 × 10), rows 2, 3, and 7 being overprinted with Type M 2 and the other seven rows with Type M 2*a*.

M.E.F. (M 3)

Optd 13½ mm long. Regular lettering and upright oblong stops.

(Illustration twice actual size)

1943 (1 Jan)–**1947**. *Stamps of Great Britain optd with Type* M 3 *by Harrison & Sons. W* **127**, *P* 15 × 14 *(1d. to 1s.); W* **133**, *P* 14 *(others).*

No.	Type	Description	Unused	Used
M11	**128**	1d. pale scarlet (No. 486)	50	10
M12		2d. pale orange (No. 488)	50	10
M13		2½d. light ultramarine (No. 489)	30	10
M14		3d. pale violet (No. 490)	45	10
M15	**129**	5d. brown	60	10
M16		6d. purple	30	10
M17	**130**	9d. deep olive-green	65	10
M18		1s. bistre-brown	50	10
M19	**131**	2s. 6d. yellow-green	6·00	30
M20		5s. red (1947)	11·00	17·00
M21	**132**	10s. ultramarine (1947)	14·00	8·00
M11/21		*Set of* 11	30·00	23·00
M18/21 Optd "Specimen"		*Set of* 4	£600	

The overprint on No. M15 should not be confused with the other overprints on the 5d. value. It can be distinguished from No. M5 by the ½ mm difference in length; and from No. M10 by the more intense colour, thicker lettering and larger stops.

POSTAGE DUE STAMPS

M.E.F. (MD 1)

1942. *Postage Due Stamps of Great Britain optd with Type* MD 1, *in blue-black. W* **127** *(sideways). P* 14 × 15.

No.	Type	Description	Unused	Used
MD1	D 1	½d. emerald	25	1·75
MD2		1d. carmine	25	1·25
MD3		2d. agate	1·25	1·00
MD4		3d. violet	50	2·00
MD5		1s. deep blue (Optd S. £150)	2·50	5·00
MD1/5		*Set of* 5	4·25	10·00

CYRENAICA

In June 1949 the British authorities recognised the leader of the Senussi, Amir Mohammed Idris Al-Senussi, as Amir of Cyrenaica with autonomy in internal affairs.

(Currency. 1000 millièmes = 1 Egyptian pound)

24 Mounted Warrior 25

(Recess Waterlow)

1950 (16 Jan). *P* 12½.

No.	Type	Description	Unused	Used
136	**24**	1 m brown	10	15
137		2 m. carmine	10	15
138		3 m. orange-yellow	10	15
139		4 m. blue-green	90	1·40
140		5 m. grey-black	25	35
141		8 m. orange	30	35
142		10 m. violet	35	35
143		12 m. scarlet	35	35
144		20 m. blue	40	40
145	**25**	50 m. ultramarine and purple-brown	1·90	2·25
146		100 m. carmine and black	6·00	7·00
147		200 m. violet and deep blue	8·00	15·00
148		500 m. orange-yellow and green	30·00	48·00
136/148		*Set of* 13	45·00	70·00

POSTAGE DUE STAMPS

D 26

(Recess Waterlow)

1950 (16 Jan). *P* 12½

No.	Type	Description	Unused	Used
D149	**D 26**	2 m. brown	28·00	35·00
D150		4 m. blue-green	28·00	35·00
D151		8 m. scarlet	28·00	35·00
D152		10 m. orange	28·00	35·00
D153		20 m. orange-yellow	28·00	35·00
D154		40 m. blue	28·00	35·00
D155		100 m. grey-brown	28·00	35·00
D149/155		*Set of* 7	£180	£225

On 24 December 1951 Cyrenaica united with Tripolitania, Fezzan and Ghadames to form the independent Kingdom of Libya, whose issues are listed in Part 13 (*Africa since Independence F—M*) of this catalogue.

ERITREA

BRITISH MILITARY ADMINISTRATION

B. M. A. ERITREA 10 CENTS (E 1)

B. M. A. ERITREA 5 SHILLINGS (E 2)

SH. 50 (Normal) SH .50 (Misplaced Stop)

1948–9. *Stamps of Great Britain surch as Types* E 1 *or* E 2.

No.	Type	Description	Unused	Used
E 1	**128**	5 c. on ½d. pale green	30	65
E 2		10 c. on 1d. pale scarlet	40	1·75
E 3		20 c. on 2d. pale orange	45	2·25
E 4		25 c. on 2½d. light ultramarine	30	60
E 5		30 c. on 3d. pale violet	75	2·75
E 6	**129**	40 c. on 5d. brown	30	2·00
E 7		50 c. on 6d. purple	30	60
E 7*a*	**130**	65 c. on 8d. bright carmine (1.2.49)	3·00	2·00
E 8		75 c. on 9d. deep olive-green	50	75
E 9		1 s. on 1s. bistre-brown	50	50
E10	**131**	2 s. 50 c. on 2s. 6d. yellow-green	5·00	10·00
		a. Misplaced stop (R. 4/7)	35·00	
E11		5 s. on 5s. red	5·00	12·00
E12	**132**	10 s. on 10s. ultramarine	8·50	17·00
E1/12		*Set of* 13	22·00	45·00

BRITISH ADMINISTRATION

1950 (6 Feb). *As Nos.* E1/12, *but surch* "B.A. ERITREA" *and new values instead of* "B.M.A." *etc.*

No.	Type	Description	Unused	Used
E13	**128**	5 c. on ½d. pale green	25	2·25
E14		10 c. on 1d. pale scarlet	25	1·00
E15		20 c. on 2d. pale orange	25	70
E16		25 c. on 2½d. light ultramarine	25	60
E17		30 c. on 3d. pale violet	25	70
E18	**129**	40 c. on 5d. brown	40	80
E19		50 c. on 6d. purple	30	20
E20	**130**	65 c. on 8d. bright carmine	40	1·00
E21		75 c. on 9d. deep olive-green	25	25
E22		1 s. on 1s. bistre-brown	30	15
E23	**131**	2 s. 50 c. on 2s. 6d. yellow-green	3·25	4·50
E24		5 s. on 5s. red	5·50	9·00
E25	**132**	10 s. on 10s. ultramarine	24·00	30·00
E13/25		*Set of* 13	32·00	45·00

1951 (3 May). *Nos.* 503/4, 506/7 *and* 509/11 *of Great Britain surch* "B.A. ERITREA" *and new values.*

No.	Type	Description	Unused	Used
E26	**128**	5 c. on ½d. pale orange	25	50
E27		10 c. on 1d. light ultramarine	25	35
E28		20 c. on 2d. pale red-brown	25	25
E29		25 c. on 2½d. pale scarlet	25	25
E30	**147**	2 s. 50 c. on 2s. 6d. yellow-green	4·50	6·50
E31	**148**	5 s. on 5s. red	11·00	16·00
E32		10 s. on 10s. ultramarine	13·00	16·00
E26/32		*Set of* 7	26·00	35·00

POSTAGE DUE STAMPS

B. M. A. ERITREA 10 CENTS (ED 1)

1948. *Postage Due stamps of Great Britain surch as Type* ED 1.

No.	Type	Description	Unused	Used
ED1	D 1	5 c. on ½d. emerald	9·00	18·00
ED2		10 c. on 1d. carmine	7·50	16·00
		a. No stop after "B"	45·00	
ED3		20 c. on 2d. agate	7·00	12·00
		a. No stop after "A"	30·00	
		b. No stop after "B" (R. 1/9)	40·00	
ED4		30 c. on 3d. violet	8·00	11·00
ED5		1 s. on 1s. deep blue	15·00	18·00
ED1/5		*Set of* 5	42·00	65·00

1950 (6 Feb). *As Nos.* ED1/5, *but surch* "B.A. ERITREA" *and new values instead of* "B.M.A." *etc.*

No.	Type	Description	Unused	Used
ED6	D 1	5 c. on ½d. emerald	10·00	20·00
ED7		10 c. on 1d. carmine	8·00	14·00
		a. "C" of "CENTS" omitted	£850	
		ab. "C" omitted and vertical oblong for "E" of "CENTS"		
ED8		20 c. on 2d. agate	8·00	11·00
ED9		30 c. on 3d. violet	8·50	11·00
ED10		1 s. on 1s. deep blue	12·00	17·00
ED6/10		*Set of* 5	42·00	65·00

Stamps of Ethiopia were used in Eritrea after 15 September 1952 following federation with Ethiopia.

SOMALIA

BRITISH OCCUPATION

E.A.F.

(S 1. "East Africa Forces")

1943 (15 Jan)–**46**. *Stamps of Great Britain optd with Type* S 1, *in blue.*

No.	Type	Description	Unused	Used
S1	**128**	1d. pale scarlet	25	40
S2		2d. pale orange	25	80
S3		2½d. light ultramarine	25	1·50
S4		3d. pale violet	25	15
S5	**129**	5d. brown	25	40
S6		6d. purple	25	90
S7	**130**	9d. deep olive-green	60	2·00
S8		1s. bistre-brown	60	15
S9	**131**	2s. 6d. yellow-green (1946)	5·00	4·25
S1/9		*Set of* 9	7·00	9·50
S8/9 Optd "Specimen"		*Set of* 2	£250	

The note *re* used prices above Type M 1 of Middle East Forces also applies to the above issue.

BRITISH MILITARY ADMINISTRATION

1948 (27 May). *Stamps of Great Britain surch* "B.M.A./SOMALIA" *and new values, as Types* E 1 *and* E 2 *of Eritrea.*

No.	Type	Description	Unused	Used
S10	**128**	5 c. on ½d. pale green	20	1·25
S11		15 c. on 1½d. pale red-brown	55	6·00
S12		20 c. on 2d. pale orange	20	2·00
S13		25 c. on 2½d. light ultramarine	20	1·25
S14		30 c. on 3d. pale violet	1·40	9·00
S15	**129**	40 c. on 5d. brown	25	20
S16		50 c. on 6d. purple	30	2·00
S17	**130**	75 c. on 9d. deep olive-green	1·60	7·50
S18		1 s. on 1s. bistre-brown	1·00	20
S19	**131**	2 s. 50 c. on 2s. 6d. yellow-green	3·00	12·00
		a. Misplaced stop (R. 4/7)	45·00	
S20		5 s. on 5s. red	6·00	18·00
S10/20		*Set of* 11	13·00	50·00

For illustration of No. S19a, see previous column above No. E1 of Eritrea.

BRITISH ADMINISTRATION

1950 (2 Jan). *As Nos.* S10/20, *but surch* "B.A./SOMALIA" *and new values, instead of* "B.M.A." *etc.*

No.	Type	Description	Unused	Used
S21	**128**	5 c. on ½d. pale green	20	85
S22		15 c. on 1½d. pale red-brown	60	6·00
S23		20 c. on 2d. pale orange	60	2·50
S24		25 c. on 2½d. light ultramarine	40	1·75
S25		30 c. on 3d. pale violet	1·00	3·00
S26	**129**	40 c. on 5d. brown	55	85
S27		50 c. on 6d. purple	40	1·00
S28	**130**	75 c. on 9d. deep olive-green	1·00	4·50
S29		1 s. on 1s. bistre-brown	60	1·50
S30	**131**	2 s. 50 c. on 2s. 6d. yellow-green	4·00	12·00
S31		5 s. on 5s. red	7·50	13·00
S21/31		*Set of* 11	15·00	40·00

Somalia reverted to Italian Administration on 1 April 1950 later becoming independent. Later issues will be found listed in Part 8 (*Italy and Switzerland*) of this catalogue.

TRIPOLITANIA

BRITISH MILITARY ADMINISTRATION

1948 (1 July). *Stamps of Great Britain surch* "B.M.A./TRIPOLITANIA" *and new values, as Types* E 1 *and* E 2 *of Eritrea, but expressed in M(ilitary) A(dministration) L(ire).*

No.	Type	Description	Unused	Used
T 1	**128**	1 l. on ½d. pale green	25	80
T 2		2 l. on 1d. pale scarlet	20	25
T 3		3 l. on 1½d. pale red-brown	20	50
T 4		4 l. on 2d. pale orange	25	50
T 5		5 l. on 2½d. light ultramarine	25	20
T 6		6 l. on 3d. pale violet	20	40

T 7	129	10 l. on 5d. brown	20	25
T 8		12 l. on 6d. purple	25	20
T 9	130	18 l. on 9d. deep olive-green	50	65
T10		24 l. on 1s. bistre-brown	50	65
T11	131	60 l. on 2s. 6d. yellow-green	1·75	4·50
T12		120 l. on 5s. red	5·00	13·00
T13	132	240 l. on 10s. ultramarine	10·00	42·00
T1/13		*Set of* 13	18·00	60·00

BRITISH ADMINISTRATION

1950 (6 Feb). *As Nos.* T1/13, *but surch.* "B.A. TRIPOLITANIA" *and new values, instead of* "B.M.A." *etc.*

T14	128	1 l. on ½d. pale green	35	3·25
T15		2 l. on 1d. pale scarlet	30	40
T16		3 l. on 1½d. pale red-brown	35	2·75
T17		4 l. on 2d. pale orange	25	2·50
T18		5 l. on 2½d. light ultramarine	25	70
T19		6 l. on 3d. pale violet	25	1·25
T20	129	10 l. on 5d. brown	25	80
T21		12 l. on 6d. purple	25	50
T22	130	18 l. on 9d. deep olive-green	35	1·60
T23		24 l. on 1s. bistre-brown	45	2·50
T24	131	60 l. on 2s. 6d. yellow-green	3·75	9·50
T25		120 l. on 5s. red	9·00	18·00
T26	132	240 l. on 10s. ultramarine	12·00	25·00
T14/26		*Set of* 13	24·00	60·00

1951 (3 May). *Nos.* 503/7 *and* 509/11 *of Great Britain surch* "B.A. TRIPOLITANIA" *and new values.*

T27	128	1 l. on ½d. pale orange	20	1·75
T28		2 l. on 1d. light ultramarine	20	90
T29		3 l. on 1½d. pale green	25	1·75
T30		4 l. on 2d. pale red-brown	20	1·25
T31		5 l. on 2½d. pale scarlet	20	1·40
T32	147	60 l. on 2s. 6d. yellow-green	3·50	12·00
T33	148	120 l. on 5s. red	7·50	16·00
T34	149	240 l. on 10s. ultramarine	15·00	27·00
T27/34		*Set of* 8	24·00	55·00

POSTAGE DUE STAMPS

1948. *Postage Due stamps of Great Britain surch.* "B.M.A./ TRIPOLITANIA" *and new values, as Type* ED 1 *of Eritrea, but expressed in M(ilitary) A(dministration) L(ire).*

TD1	D 1	1 l. on ½d. emerald	3·50	15·00
		a. No stop after "A"	30·00	
TD2		2 l. on 1d. carmine	2·50	15·00
		a. No stop after "A"	22·00	
TD3		4 l. on 2d. agate	5·50	13·00
		a. No stop after "A"	35·00	
TD4		6 l. on 3d. violet	7·50	20·00
TD5		24 l. on 1s. deep blue	26·00	55·00
TD1/5		*Set of* 5	40·00	£110

1950 (6 Feb). *As Nos.* TD1/5, *but surch* "B.A. TRIPOLITANIA" *and new values, instead of* "B.M.A." *etc.*

TD 6	D 1	1 l. on ½d. emerald	6·00	24·00
		a. No stop after "B"	50·00	
TD 7		2 l. on 1d. carmine	2·50	14·00
		a. No stop after "B"	35·00	
TD 8		4 l. on 2d. agate	2·75	15·00
		a. No stop after "B"	35·00	
TD 9		6 l. on 3d. violet	13·00	38·00
		a. No stop after "B"	70·00	
TD10		24 l. on 1s. deep blue	29·00	60·00
		a. No stop after "A"	£110	
		b. No stop after "B"	£110	
TD7/10		*Set of* 5	48·00	£140

Tripolitania became part of the independent kingdom of Libya on 24 December 1951.

British P.Os in Crete

BRITISH ADMINISTRATION (CANDIA PROVINCE (NOW IRAKLION))

During the provisional Joint Administration by France, Great Britain, Italy, and Russia.

PRICES FOR STAMPS ON COVER

No. 1 *from* × 10
Nos. 2/5 —

1

2

1898 (25 Nov). *Handstruck locally. Imperf.*

1	1	20 pa. bright violet	£350	£225

1898 (3 Dec). *Litho by M. Grundmann, Athens. P* 11½.

2	2	10 pa. blue	8·00	12·00
		a. Imperf (pair)	£250	
3		20 pa. green	8·00	12·00
		a. Imperf (pair)	£250	

1899. *P* 11½.

4	2	10 pa. brown	8·00	14·00
		a. Imperf (pair)	£250	
5		20 pa. rose	14·00	15·00
		a. Imperf (pair)	£250	

The British postal service closed at the end of 1899.

British P.O. in Siam
(Bangkok)

PRICES FOR STAMPS ON COVER

The issues of the British Post Office in Siam are worth from × 40 the prices quoted for used stamps when on cover.

(1)

1882–85. *Stamps of Straits Settlements optd with T* 1.

(a) On issue of 1867

1	–	32 c. on 2 a. yellow (No. 9)	£6000	£7000

(b) On issues of 1867–82. *Wmk Crown CC*

2	5	2 c. brown	£500	£550
3		4 c. rose	£500	£400
		a. Opt double	—	£4500
4	18	5 c. purple-brown	55·00	55·00
5	5	6 c. lilac	40·00	40·00
6	6	8 c. orange	£850	55·00
7	19	10 c. slate	65·00	40·00
8	6	12 c. blue	£350	£130
9	7	24 c. green	£160	38·00
10	8	30 c. claret	£6500	£3500
11	9	96 c. grey	£1200	£900

(c) On issue of April 1883

12	9	2 c. on 32 c. pale red (*Wide* "E") (No. 59))	£500	£600
13		2 c. on 32 c. pale red (*Wide* "S") (No. 60))	£600	£700

(d) On issues of 1882–84. *Wmk Crown CA*

14	5	2 c. brown	40·00	40·00
15		2 c. rose	18·00	18·00
		a. Opt inverted	£7500	£2500
		b. Opt double	£2500	
16		4 c. rose	70·00	65·00
17		4 c. brown	26·00	26·00
		a. Opt double	£3000	
18	18	5 c. blue	65·00	40·00
19	5	6 c. lilac	40·00	30·00
20	6	8 c. orange	30·00	22·00
		a. Opt inverted	£5500	£3000
21	19	10 c. slate	40·00	30·00
22	6	12 c. dull purple	65·00	40·00
23	7	24 c. green	£1100	£800

The use of these stamps ceased on 1 July 1885.

British Postal Agencies in Eastern Arabia

Certain Arab States in Eastern Arabia, whilst remaining independent, had British postal administrations.

Bahrain and Kuwait (from 1948) and Qatar (from 1957) used British stamps overprinted and surcharged in local currency. Abu Dhabi (from 1964) and Trucial States (from 1961 and used only in Dubai) had definitive issues made under the auspices of the British Agencies.

In addition, British stamps were surcharged with value only for use in Muscat and certain other states. They were formerly listed under Muscat as they were first put on sale there, but in view of their more extended use, the list has been transferred here, retaining the same numbering.

The stamps were used in Muscat from 1 April 1948 to 29 April 1966; in Dubai from 1 April 1948 to 6 January 1961; in Qatar: Doha from August 1950, Umm Said from February 1956, to 31 March 1957; and in Abu Dhabi from 30 March 1963 (Das Island from December 1960) to 29 March 1964.

Certain of them were placed on sale in Kuwait Post Offices in 1951 and in 1953 due to shortages of stamps with "KUWAIT" overprint; and they can all be found commercially used from that state and from Bahrain.

Stamps of Great Britain surcharged

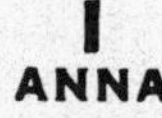
1 ANNA
(3)

2 RUPEES
(4)

1948 (1 Apr). *Surch with T* 3 (½ *a. to* 1 *r.*) *or* 4 (2 *r.*).

16	128	½ a. on ½d. pale green	50	65
17		1 a. on 1d. pale scarlet	50	20
18		1½ a. on 1½d. pale red-brown	50	20
19		2 a. on 2d. pale orange	50	45
20		2½ a. on 2½d. light ultramarine	50	1·10
21		3 a. on 3d. pale violet	55	10
22	129	6 a. on 6d. purple	60	10
23	130	1 r. on 1s. bistre-brown	2·75	50
24	131	2 r. on 2s. 6d. yellow-green	6·50	16·00
16/24		*Set of* 9	11·00	17·00

One example of No. 22 is known with the surcharge almost completely omitted from position R. 20/2 in the sheet.

2½ ANNAS
(5)

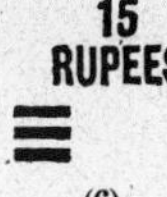
15 RUPEES
(6)

1948 (26 Apr). *Royal Silver Wedding. Nos.* 493/4 *surch with T* 5 *or* 6.

25	137	2½ a. on 2½d. ultramarine	40	40
26	138	15 r. on £1 blue	28·00	35·00

1948 (29 July). *Olympic Games. Nos.* 495/8 *surch with new values in* "ANNAS" *or* "1 RUPEE", *as T* 5/6, *but in one line on* 2½ *a. (vert) or* 6 *a. and* 1 *r. (horiz) and grills obliterating former values of all except* 2½ *a.*

27	139	2½ a. on 2½d. ultramarine	35	60
28	140	3 a. on 3d. violet	45	80
29	141	6 a. on 6d. bright purple	45	85
30	142	1 r. on 1s. brown	75	1·40
		a. Surch double	£500	
27/30		*Set of* 4	1·75	3·25

1949 (10 Oct). *75th Anniv of Universal Postal Union. Nos.* 499/502 *surch with new values in* "ANNAS" *or* "1 RUPEE" *as T* 3/4, *but all in one line, with grills obliterating former values.*

31	143	2½ a. on 2½d. ultramarine	50	1·00
32	144	3 a. on 3d. violet	50	1·25
33	145	6 a. on 6d. bright purple	60	1·10
34	146	1 r. on 1s. brown	1·25	1·25
31/4		*Set of* 4	3·00	4·25

2 RUPEES
(6*a*)

2 RUPEES
(6*b*)

Type **6***a*. "2" and "RUPEES" level and in line with lower of the two bars.

Type **6***b*. "2" raised in relation to "RUPEES" and whole surcharge below the lower bar.

1950 (2 Oct)–**55.** *Nos.* 503/8 *surch as T* 3 *and No.* 509 *with T* **6***a*.

35	128	½ a. on ½d. pale orange (3.5.51)	25	2·00
36		1 a. on 1d. light ultramarine (3.5.51)	25	1·25
37		1½ a. on 1½d. pale green (3.5.51)	1·50	5·50
38		2 a. on 2d. pale red-brown (3.5.51)	25	3·00
39		2½ a. on 2½d. pale scarlet (3.5.51)	30	5·50
40	129	4 a. on 4d. light ultramarine	25	1·75
41	147	2 r. on 2s. 6d. yellow-green (3.5.51)	20·00	4·00
		a. Surch with Type 6*b* (1955)	85·00	65·00
35/41		*Set of* 7	21·00	20·00

1952 (5 Dec)–**54.** *Stamps of Queen Elizabeth II wmk Tudor Crown, surch as T* 3 *(in one line on* 2½ *and* 6 *a.).*

42	154	½ a. on ½d. orange-red (31.8.53)	10	10
43		1 a. on 1d. ultramarine (31.8.53)	10	10
44		1½ a. on 1½d. green	10	10
45		2 a. on 2d. red-brown (31.8.53)	10	10
46	155	2½ a. on 2½d. carmine-red	10	10
47		3 a. on 3d. deep lilac (B.) (18.1.54)	20	10
48	156	4 a. on 4d. ultramarine (2.11.53)	55	60
49	157	6 a. on 6d. reddish purple (18.1.54)	35	10
50	160	12 a. on 1s. 3d. green (2.11.53)	2·00	30
51	159	1 r. on 1s. 6d. grey-blue (2.11.53)	2·00	10
42/51		*Set of* 10	5·00	1·00

1953 (10 June). *Coronation. Nos.* 532/5 *surch with new values.*

52	161	2½ a. on 2½d. carmine-red	1·75	80
53	162	4 a. on 4d. ultramarine	1·75	80
54	163	12 a. on 1s. 3d. deep yellow-green	3·25	85
55	164	1 r. on 1s. 6d. deep grey-blue	4·50	45
52/5		*Set of* 4	10·00	2·75

2 RUPEES I

2 RUPEES II

2 RUPEES III

(7)

5 RUPEES I

5 RUPEES II

(8)

Types of surcharges

2 rupees.

Type I. *On Waterlow ptg.* Top of "R" level with top of "2" and other letters of "RUPEES". Bars 7 mm long.

Type II. *On Waterlow ptg.* "R" dropped out of alignment with "2" and other letters of "RUPEES". Bars 6½ mm long.

Type III. *On De La Rue ptg.* Top of "R" below level of top of "2". Bars 7–7¼ mm long and with left sides aligned with "S".

5 rupees.

Type I. *On Waterlow ptg.* Ends of letters square and sharp. There were two printings made in March and May 1957.
Type II. *On De La Rue ptg.* Type is thicker and ends of letters are relatively rounded.

For differences between Waterlow and De La Rue printings of the basic stamps see notes in Great Britain after No. 539.

1955–60. *T* **166/7** *(Waterlow ptgs) (W* **165**, *St. Edward's Crown) surch with T* **7/8**.

56	**166**	2 r. on 2s. 6d. black-brown (Type I) (23.9.55)	3·25	70
		a. Type II (2.57)	4·00	2·00
		b. Type III (No. 536a D.L.R.) (6.60)	27·00	45·00
57	**167**	5 r. on 5s. rose-red (Type I) (1.3.57)	9·00	2·00
		a. Wide surcharge	£200	£180
		b. Type II (No. 537a D.L.R.) (27.1.60)	25·00	42·00

No. 57a ("5" and "R" spaced 2¼ mm instead of 1¼ mm) occurred on the last stamp of Row 8 of the first "Waterlow" issue.

1956–57. *Stamps of Queen Elizabeth II, W* **165**, *St. Edward's Crown, surch as T* **3** *(in one line on 2½ and 6 a.).*

58	**154**	1 a. on 1d. ultramarine (4.3.57)	35	50
58a		1½ a. on 1½d. green (1956)	—	£375
59		2 a. on 2d. red-brown (8.6.56)	70	90
60	**155**	2½ a. on 2½d. carmine-red (8.6.56)	80	1·25
61		3 a. on 3d. deep lilac (B.) (3.2.57)	1·00	2·50
62	**156**	4 a. on 4d. ultramarine (9.12.56)	4·75	9·00
63	**157**	6 a. on 6d. red-purple (10.2.57)	1·10	2·50
64	**159**	1 r. on 1s. 6d. grey-blue (2.8.56)	3·00	15
58/64 *(ex 58a)*		*Set of* 7	10·50	15·00

NP 1 NP (9) 3 NP NP (10) 75 NP (11)

1957 (1 Apr)–**59.** *Value in naye paise. Stamps of Queen Elizabeth II, W* **165**, *St. Edward's Crown, surch as T* **9** (1, 15, 25, 40, 50 *n.p.*), **11** (75 *n.p.*) *or* **10** *(others).*

65	**157**	1 n.p. on 5d. brown	10	20
66	**154**	3 n.p. on ½d. orange-red	20	25
67		6 n.p. on 1d. ultramarine	20	30
68		9 n.p. on 1½d. green	20	25
69		12 n.p. on 2d. light red-brown	30	35
70	**155**	15 n.p. on 2½d. carmine-red (Type I)	30	10
		a. Type II (4.59)	25	70
71		20 n.p. on 3d. deep lilac (B.)	20	10
72	**156**	25 n.p. on 4d. ultramarine	70	1·25
73	**157**	40 n.p. on 6d. reddish purple	30	10
		a. Deep claret (3.59)	35	10
74	**158**	50 n.p. on 9d. bronze-green	1·25	40
75	**160**	75 n.p. on 1s. 3d. green	2·00	35
65/75		*Set of* 11	5·00	2·75

15 NP

(12)

1957 (1 Aug). *World Scout Jubilee Jamboree. Nos. 557/9 surch in one line as T* **12** *(15 n.p.), or in two lines (others).*

76	15 n.p. on 2½d. carmine-red	25	60
77	25 n.p. on 4d. ultramarine	30	60
78	75 n.p. on 1s. 3d. green	35	65
76/8	*Set of* 3	80	1·75

1960 (26 Apr)–**61.** *Stamps of Queen Elizabeth II, W* **179**, *Mult Crown, surch as T* **9** (1, 15, 30, 40, 50 *n.p.*), **11** (75 *n.p.*), **3** (1 *r.*), **7** (2 *r.*, 5 *r.*) *or* **10** *(others).*

79	**157**	1 n.p. on 5d. brown (30.8.60)	10	20
80	**154**	3 n.p. on ½d. orange-red (21.6.60)	55	80
81		5 n.p. on 1d. ultramarine (8.4.61)	50	40
82		6 n.p. on 1d. ultramarine (21.6.60)	1·25	90
83		10 n.p. on 1½d. green (8.4.61)	50	40
84		12 n.p. on 2d. light red-brown (21.6.60)	2·50	2·50
85	**155**	15 n.p. on 2½d. carmine-red (Type II)	25	10
86		20 n.p. on 3d. deep lilac (B.) (28.9.60)	25	10
87	**156**	30 n.p. on 4½d. chestnut (8.4.61)	40	40
88	**157**	40 n.p. on 6d. deep claret (28.9.60)	45	10
89	**158**	50 n.p. on 9d. bronze-green (8.4.61)	80	80
90	**160**	75 n.p. on 1s. 3d. green (8.4.61)	1·00	90
91	**159**	1 r. on 1s. 6d. grey-blue (8.4.61)	4·50	1·75
92	**166**	2 r. on 2s. 6d. black-brown (No. 595) (8.4.61)	7·00	16·00
93	**167**	5 r. on 5s. rose-red (No. 596) (8.4.61)	16·00	30·00
79/93		*Set of* 15	32·00	48·00

British Solomon Islands *see* Solomon Islands

British Somaliland *see* Somaliland Protectorate

British South Africa Company *see* Rhodesia

British Virgin Islands

CROWN COLONY

Apart from the 1951 Legislative Council issue, the word "BRITISH" did not appear regularly on the stamps until 1968 when it was introduced to avoid confusion with the nearby Virgin Islands of the United States (the former Danish West Indies).

Most mail from the early years of the islands' history was sent via the Danish island of St. Thomas.

It is not known exactly when the first post office, or agency, was established on Tortola, but an entry in a G.P.O. account book suggests that it was operating by 1787. Correspondence is known from the postmaster in 1791. The stamps of Great Britain were used there from 1858 to May 1860, when the colonial authorities assumed responsibility for the overseas mails from the British G.P.O.

For illustrations of the handstamp and postmark types see BRITISH POST OFFICES ABROAD notes, following GREAT BRITAIN.

TORTOLA

CROWNED-CIRCLE HANDSTAMPS

CC1	CC **1**	TORTOLA (R.) (15.12.1842) *Price on cover*	£4000
CC2	CC **5**	TORTOLA (R.) (21.6.1854) *Price on cover*	—

No. CC2 is known used as an Official Paid mark during the years 1900 to 1918. *Price on cover* £900.

Stamps of GREAT BRITAIN *cancelled* "A 13" *as Type* **2**.

1858 *to* **1860.**

Z1	1d. rose-red (1857), *perf* 14	£3000
Z2	4d. rose (1857)	£2750
Z3	6d. lilac (1856)	£1100
Z4	1s. green (1856)	

PRICES FOR STAMPS ON COVER TO 1945

Nos. 1/7	*from* × 10
Nos. 8/22	*from* × 6
Nos. 24/31	*from* × 4
Nos. 32/41	*from* × 5
No. 42	*from* × 10
Nos. 43/50	*from* × 4
Nos. 54/77	*from* × 3
Nos. 78/81	*from* × 6
Nos. 82/101	*from* × 3
Nos. 103/6	*from* × 4
Nos. 107/9	*from* × 6
Nos. 110/21	*from* × 2

1 St. Ursula 2

(Litho Nissen & Parker from original dies by Waterlow)

1866. *No wmk. P* 12 *(a) White wove paper.*

1	**1**	1d. green	45·00	60·00
2		1d. deep green	45·00	60·00
3	**2**	6d. rose	90·00	£110
4		6d. deep rose	£130	£140
		a. Large "V" in "VIRGIN"	£450	£550
		(b) Toned paper		
5	**1**	1d. green	45·00	60·00
		a. Perf 15 × 12	£4250	£5500
6		1d. deep green	£100	£120
7	**2**	6d. rose-red	60·00	90·00
		a. Large "V" in "VIRGIN" (R. 2/1)	£350	£425

The above were printed in sheets of 25.

6d. stamps showing part of the papermaker's watermark ("A. Cowan & Sons Extra Superfine A. C. & S.") are worth 50% more.

Beware of fakes of No. 5a made from perf 12 stamps.

3 4

Normal Variety

1s. Long-tailed "S" in "ISLANDS" (R. 3/1)

(Litho Nissen and Parker from original dies by Waterlow)

1867–70. *No wmk. P* 15. *1s. with double-lined frame.*

		(a) White wove paper		
8	**1**	1d. blue-green (1870)	65·00	70·00
9		1d. yellow-green (1868)	80·00	80.00
10	**2**	6d. pale rose	£450	£450
11	**4**	1s. black and rose-carmine	£200	£275
		a. Long-tailed "S"	£525	£575
		(b) Toned paper		
12	**1**	1d. yellow-green (1868)	85·00	80·00
13	**2**	6d. dull rose (1868)	£225	£275
14	**4**	1s. black and rose-carmine *(blued)*	£200	£275
		aa. Long-tailed "S"	£525	£575
14a		1s. black and rose-carmine	£275	£300
		b. Long-tailed "S"	£550	£600
		(c) Pale rose paper		
15	**3**	4d. lake-red	50·00	70·00
		(d) Buff paper		
16	**3**	4d. lake-red	40·00	60·00
17		4d. lake-brown	40·00	60·00

The thin lines of the frame on the 1s. are close together and sometimes merge into one.

The 1d. was originally in sheets of 20, but from 1870 was in sheets of 12; the 4d. was in sheets of 25; the 6d. and 1s. were in sheets of 20.

In Type 4 the figure of the Virgin was printed by typography and the remainder of the design by lithography.

1867. *As T* **4**, *but with crimson frames superimposed with bands extending through margins. P* 15.

18	**4**	1s. black and rose-carmine *(white paper)*	45·00	55·00
		a. Long-tailed "S"	£110	£130
		b. Figure of Virgin omitted	£55000	
19		1s. black and rose-carmine *(toned paper)*	45·00	55·00
		a. Long-tailed "S"	£110	£130
20		1s. black and rose-carmine *(blued paper)*	£700	£850
		a. Long-tailed "S"	£1600	£1400

1868. *Nos. 11 and 14a with frame lines retouched so as to make them single lines. Margins remain white. P* 15.

21	**4**	1s. black and rose-carmine *(white paper)*	£130	£160
		aa. Long-tailed "S"	£300	£375
21a		1s. black and rose-carmine *(toned paper)*	£130	£160
		b. Long-tailed "S"	£300	£375

(Litho D.L.R.)

1878. *Wmk Crown CC (sideways). P* 14.

22	**1**	1d. green	70·00	80·00
		a. Yellow-green	£170	£120
		b. Wmk upright	90·00	£110

6 (Die I)

4D

(7)

(Typo D.L.R.)

1880. *Wmk Crown CC. P* 14.

24	**6**	1d. emerald-green (Sept)	45·00	65·00
25		2½d. red-brown (Mar)	65·00	85·00

1883 (June)–**84.** *Wmk Crown CA. P* 14.

26	**6**	½d. yellow-buff	65·00	75·00
27		½d. yellow-green (11.83)	3·25	8·00
		a. Dull bluish green	8·00	13·00
29		1d. pale rose (15.9.83)	18·00	22·00
		a. Deep rose	50·00	55·00
31		2½d. ultramarine (9.84)	2·50	8·00

Nos. 25, 27 and 31 exist imperf but it is not known whether they were issued *(Price* £1000 *in pairs, each).*

(Litho D.L.R.)

1887–89. *Wmk Crown CA. P* 14.

32	**1**	1d. red (6.89)	2·00	7·00
33		1d. rose-red	2·25	7·00
34		1d. rose	5·00	14·00
35	**3**	4d. chestnut	40·00	75·00
36		4d. pale chestnut	40·00	75·00
37		4d. brown-red	50·00	80·00
38	**2**	6d. dull violet	15·00	48·00
39		6d. deep violet	15·00	48·00
40	**4**	1s. sepia (2.89)	70·00	£110
41		1s. brown *to* deep brown	50·00	80·00
34/40 Optd "Specimen"		*Set of* 4	£300	

The De La Rue transfers of T 1 to 4 are new transfers and differ from those of Messrs. Nissen and Parker, particularly T 4

1888 (July). *No. 19 surch with T* **7**, *in violet.*

42	**4**	4d. on 1s. black and rose-carmine/*toned*	£110	£150
		a. Surch double	£6000	
		b. Surch inverted (in pair with normal)	£40000	
		c. Long-tailed "S"	£300	£400

The special issues for Virgin Islands were superseded on 31 October 1890, by the general issue for Leeward Islands. In 1899, however, a new special issue (given below) appeared; it did not supersede the general issue for Leeward Islands, but was used concurrently, as were all subsequent issues, until 1 July 1956, when the general Leeward Islands stamps were withdrawn.

8

9

10

(Recess D.L.R.)

1899 (Jan). *Wmk Crown CA. P 14.*
43 8 ½d. yellow-green . . 60 55
a. Error. "HALFPFNNY" (R. 10/1) . . 80·00 £100
b. Error. "HALΓPENNY" (R. 8/2) . . 80·00 £100
c. Imperf between (horiz pair) . . £6500
44 1d. brick-red . . 2·25 2·00
45 2½d. ultramarine . . 12·00 4·00
46 4d. brown . . 5·00 12·00
a. Error. "FOURPENCF" . . £1300 £1200
47 6d. dull violet . . 4·50 4·50
48 7d. deep green . . 7·00 8·00
49 1s. brown-yellow . . 16·00 27·00
50 5s. indigo . . 65·00 80·00
43/50 . . *Set of* 8 £100 £130
43/50 Optd "Specimen" . . *Set of* 8 £200

(Typo D.L.R.)

1904 (1 June). *Wmk Mult Crown CA. P 14.*
54 9 ½d. dull purple and green . . 50 40
55 1d. dull purple and scarlet . . 85 35
56 10 2d. dull purple and ochre . . 3·25 4·50
57 9 2½d. dull purple and ultramarine . . 1·75 2·00
58 10 3d. dull purple and black . . 2·75 3·00
59 9 6d. dull purple and brown . . 2·75 3·00
60 10 1s. green and scarlet . . 2·75 4·75
61 2s. 6d. green and black . . 18·00 38·00
62 9 5s. green and blue . . 38·00 55·00
54/62 . . *Set of* 9 60·00 £100
54/62 Optd "Specimen" . . *Set of* 9 £175

11

12

(Typo D.L.R.)

1913 (Feb)–**19**. *Wmk Mult Crown CA. P 14.*
63 11 ½d. green, O . . 75 1·60
64 ½d. yellow-green O (8.16) . . 1·25 2·75
65 ½d. blue-green and deep green, O (3.19) 85 2·50
66 1d. deep red, O . . 7·50 9·00
67 1d. deep red and carmine, O . . 2·25 8·00
68 1d. scarlet, O (10.17) . . 1·75 7·00
69 1d. carmine-red, O (3.19) . . 23·00 17·00
70 12 2d. grey, O . . 3·75 9·00
71 2d. slate-grey, O (1919) . . 4·00 13·00
72 11 2½d. bright blue, O . . 4·00 6·50
73 12 3d. purple/*yellow*, C . . 1·40 4·75
74 11 6d. dull and bright purple, C . . 2·75 3·75
75 12 1s. black/*green*, C . . 3·25 4·00
76 2s. 6d., black and red/*blue*, C . . 32·00 38·00
77 11 5s. green and red/*yellow*, C . . 32·00 60·00
63/77 . . *Set of* 9 75·00 £120
63/77 Optd "Specimen" . . *Set of* 9 £200

WAR STAMP
(13)

14

1916 (20 Oct)–**19**. *Optd with T* 13.
78 11 1d. carmine . . 90 10·00
a. Watermark sideways . . £650
b. Pale red/bluish . . 20 2·50
c. Scarlet . . 20 1·50
79 12 3d. purple/*yellow* . . 25 6·00
a. Purple/lemon . . 2·00 6·50
b. Purple/pale yellow (11.3.19) . . 85 10·00
78/9 Optd "Specimen" . . *Set of* 2 80·00

1921 (18 Nov). *As 1913–19, but wmk Mult Script CA.*
80 11 ½d. green, O . . 85 12·00
81 1d. scarlet and deep carmine, O . . 1·25 8·00
80/1 Optd "Specimen" . . *Set of* 2 70·00

(Typo D.L.R.)

1922 (15 June)–**29**. *T* 14. *P* 14. (*a*) *Wmk Mult Crown CA.*
82 3d. purple/*pale yellow*, C . . 40 4·25
83 1s. black/*emerald*, C . . 65 7·00
84 2s. 6d. black and red/*blue*, C . . 3·75 9·00
85 5s. green and red/*pale yellow*, C . . 26·00 55·00
82/5 . . *Set of* 4 28·00 65·00
82/5 Optd "Specimen" . . *Set of* 4 £100

(*b*) *Wmk Mult Script CA*
86 ½d. dull green, O . . 20 65
87 1d. rose-carmine, O . . 20 50
88 1d. bright violet, O (1927) . . 70 2·00
89 1d. scarlet, O (1929) . . 3·50 5·00
90 1½d. carmine-red, O (1927) . . 1·25 2·25
91 1½d. Venetian red, O (1928) . . 1·75 2·00
92 2d. grey, O . . 60 2·50
93 2½d. pale bright blue, O . . 1·50 7·00
94 2½d. dull orange, O (1.9.23) . . 1·25 1·25
95 2½d. bright blue, O (1927) . . 80 3·50
96 3d. purple/*pale yellow*, O (1928) . . 1·25 4·00
97 5d. dull purple and olive, C . . 5·00 20·00
98 6d. dull and bright purple, C . . 1·25 4·50
99 1s. black/*emerald*, C (1928) . . 1·25 6·00
100 2s. 6d. black and red/*blue*, C (1928) . . 15·00 22·00
101 5s. green and red/*yellow*, C (1.9.23) . . 16·00 35·00
86/101 . . *Set of* 16 45·00 £110
86/101 Optd/Perf "Specimen" . . *Set of* 16 £300

In the 1½d. stamps the value is in colour on a white ground.

1935 (6 May). *Silver Jubilee. As Nos. 91/4 of Antigua but printed by Waterlow. P* 11 × 12.
103 1d. deep blue and scarlet . . 45 75
j. Kite and vertical log . . 25·00
k. Kite and horizontal log . . 25·00
104 1½d. ultramarine and grey . . 45 75
j. Kite and vertical log . . 25·00
k. Kite and horizontal log . . 25·00
105 2½d. brown and deep blue . . 55 80
j. Kite and vertical log . . 30·00
k. Kite and horizontal log . . 30·00
106 1s. slate and purple . . 2·75 6·50
j. Kite and vertical log . . 50·00
k. Kite and horizontal log . . 50·00
103/6 . . *Set of* 4 3·75 8·00
103/6 Perf "Specimen" . . *Set of* 4 80·00

For illustrations of plate varieties see Omnibus section following Zululand.

1937 (12 May). *Coronation. As T* 2 *of Aden. Recess B.W. Wmk Mult Script CA. P* 11 × 11½.
107 1d. carmine . . 20 30
108 1½d. yellow-brown . . 40 60
109 2½d. blue . . 45 70
107/9 . . *Set of* 3 95 1·40
107/9 Perf "Specimen" . . *Set of* 3 55·00

15 King George VI and Badge of Colony

16 Map

(Photo Harrison)

1938 (1 Aug)–**47**. *Wmk Mult Script CA. P* 14.
110 15 ½d. green, CO . . 15 15
111 1d. scarlet, CO . . 15 15
112 1½d. red-brown, CO . . 15 15
113 2d. grey, CO . . 35 15
114 2½d. ultramarine, CO . . 40 20
115 3d. orange, CO . . 30 20
116 6d. mauve, CO . . 65 20
117 1s. olive-brown, CO . . 90 25
118 2s. 6d. sepia, CO . . 4·00 2·00
119 5s. carmine, CO . . 7·00 2·00
120 10s. blue C (1.12.47) . . 7·00 8·00
121 £1 black, C (1.12.47) . . 11·00 20·00
110/21 . . *Set of* 12 28·00 30·00
110/21 Perf "Specimen" . . *Set of* 12 £250

In substitution for the original chalky paper, the ordinary paper of Nos. 110/19 is thick, smooth and opaque and first appeared in August 1942 (1s. to 5s.) and in October 1943 (pence values).

1946 (1 Nov). *Victory. As Nos. 28/9 of Aden.*
122 1½d. lake-brown . . 10 10
123 3d. orange . . 10 10
122/3 Perf "Specimen" . . *Set of* 2 55·00

1949 (3 Jan). *Royal Silver Wedding. As Nos. 30/1 of Aden.*
124 2½d. ultramarine . . 10 10
125 £1 black . . 9·00 10·00

1949 (10 Oct). *75th Anniv of U.P.U. As Nos. 114/17 of Antigua.*
126 2½d. ultramarine . . 15 15
127 3d. orange . . 30 20
128 6d. magenta . . 35 15
129 1s. olive . . 35 35
126/9 . . *Set of* 4 1·00 75

(New Currency. 100 cents = 1 B.W.I. dollar)

1951. *Inauguration of B.W.I. University College. As Nos. 118/19 of Antigua.*
130 3 c. black and brown-red (10.4) . . 20 15
131 12 c. black and redish violet (16.2) . . 35 25

(Recess Waterlow)

1951 (2 Apr). *Restoration of Legislative Council. Wmk Mult Script CA. P* 14½ x 14.
132 16 6 c. orange . . 20 50
133 12 c. purple . . 20 50
134 24 c. olive . . 20 50
135 $1.20 carmine . . 45 75
132/5 . . *Set of* 4 95 2·00

ALTERED CATALOGUE NUMBERS

Any Catalogue numbers altered from the last edition are shown as a list in the introductory pages.

17 Sombrero Lighthouse

18 Map of Jost Van Dyke

(Recess D.L.R.)

1952 (15 Apr). *T* 17/18 *and similar designs. Wmk Mult Script CA. P* 12½ × 13 (*vert*) *or* 13 × 12½ (*horiz*).
136 1 c. black . . 25 40
137 2 c. deep green . . 35 30
138 3 c. black and brown . . 25 40
139 4 c. carmine-red . . 35 40
140 5 c. claret and black . . 45 50
141 8 c. bright blue . . 35 30
142 12 c. dull violet . . 35 30
143 24 c. deep brown . . 35 30
144 60 c. yellow-green and blue . . 2·75 6·50
145 $1.20, black and bright blue . . 3·00 5·50
146 $2.40, yellowish green and red-brown . . 7·00 6·00
147 $4.80, bright blue and carmine . . 8·00 8·00
136/47 . . *Set of* 12 20·00 26·00

Designs: *Horiz*—3 c. Sheep industry; 4 c. Map of Anegada; 5 c. Cattle industry; 8 c. Map of Virgin Gorda; 12 c. Map of Tortola; 60 c. Dead Man's Chest; $1.20, Sir Francis Drake Channel; $2.40, Road Town; $4.80, Map of Virgin Islands. *Vert*—24 c. Badge of the Presidency.

1953 (2 June). *Coronation. As No. 47 of Aden.*
148 2 c. black and green . . 15 45

29 Map of Tortola

30 Brown Pelican

(Recess D.L.R.)

1956 (1 Nov)–**62**. *Designs as T* 29/30. *Wmk Mult Script CA. P* 13×12½ (½ *c. to* $1.20) *or* 12×11½ ($2.40 *and* $4.80).
149 ½ c. black and reddish purple . . 10 10
a. Black and deep reddish purple (19.4.60) 20 20
150 1 c. turquoise-blue and slate . . 60 10
a. Turquoise and slate-violet (26.11.62) 1·50 70
151 2 c. vermilion and black . . 25 10
152 3 c. blue and deep olive . . 20 15
153 4 c. deep brown and turquoise-green . . 25 10
154 5 c. grey-black . . 35 10
155 8 c. yellow-orange and deep blue . . 25 40
156 12 c. ultramarine and rose-red . . 60 35
157 24 c. myrtle-green and brown-orange . . 45 20
158 60 c. indigo and yellow-orange . . 2·75 3·50
159 $1.20, deep yellow-green and carmine-red 1·25 3·25
160 $2.40, lemon and deep dull purple . . 16·00 10·00
161 $4.80, blackish brown and turquoise-blue 16·00 13·00
149/61 . . *Set of* 13 35·00 27·00

Designs: *Size as T* 29—1 c. Virgin Islands Sloop; 2 c. Nelthrop Red Poll Bull; 3 c. Road Harbour; 4 c. Mountain travel; 5 c. Badge of the Presidency; 8 c. Beach scene; 12 c. Boat launching; 24 c. White Cedar tree; 60 c. Bonito; $1.20, Treasury Square. *Size as T* 30—$4.80, Magnificent Frigate Bird.

(New Currency. 100 cents = 1 U.S. dollar)

(42)

1962 (10 Dec). *Nos. 149/53 and 155/61 surch in U.S. currency as T* 42 *by D.L.R. W w* 12.
162 1 c. on ½ c. black and deep reddish purple . . 20 10
163 2 c. on 1 c. turquoise and slate-violet . . 20 10
164 3 c. on 2 c. vermilion and black . . 20 10
165 4 c. on 3 c. black and deep olive . . 20 10
166 5 c. on 4 c. deep brown and turquoise-green 20 10
167 8 c. on 8 c. yellow-orange and deep blue . . 20 10
168 10 c. on 12 c. ultramarine and rose-red . . 20 10
169 12 c. on 24 c. myrtle-green and brown-orange 20 10
170 25 c. on 60 c. indigo and yellow-orange . . 65 45
171 70 c. on $1.20, dp yellow-green & carmine-red 35 45
a. Stop to right of C in surcharge instead of beneath it (in pair with normal) . . 3·75 6·50
172 $1.40 on $2.40, lemon and deep dull purple 4·75 3·00
173 $2.80 on $4.80, blackish brown and turquoise-blue . . 6·00 3·00
162/73 . . *Set of* 12 12·00 6·50

No. 171a occurs on the first stamp on Rows 1 to 10.

1963 (4 June). *Freedom from Hunger. As No. 76 of Aden.*
174 25 c. reddish violet . . 20 10

1963 (2 Sept). *Red Cross Centenary. As Nos. 147/8 of Antigua.*
175 2 c. red and black . . 10 10
176 25 c. red and blue . . 25 20

1964 (23 Apr). *400th Birth Anniv of William Shakespeare. As No. 164 of Antigua.*
177 10 c. bright blue . . 10 10

43 Bonito

44 Map of Tortola **45** Badge of the Colony

(Des and recess D.L.R.)

1964 (2 Nov)–**68**. *Designs as T* **43/5**. *W w* **12**. *P* 11½×12 ($2.80), 13×13½ (70 c., $1, $1.40), *or* 13×12½ (*others*).
178 1 c. blue and olive-green 10 15
179 2 c. yellow-olive and rose-red 10 10
180 3 c. sepia and turquoise-blue 80 20
181 4 c. black and carmine-red 20 15
182 5 c. black and deep bluish green 20 15
183 6 c. black and brown-orange 15 20
184 8 c. black and magenta 15 15
185 10 c. lake and deep lilac 40 10
a. *Bright lake and reddish lilac* (26.11.68) 1·25 40
186 12 c. deep bluish green and deep violet-blue 75 55
187 15 c. yellow-green and grey-black 35 70
188 25 c. green and purple .. .. .. 3·50 40
189 70 c. black and yellow-brown .. .. 2·00 1·50
190 $1 yellow-green and chestnut .. .. 2·50 1·50
191 $1.40, light blue and rose .. .. 7·00 5·50
192 $2.80, black and bright purple .. .. 9·50 8·00
178/92 .. .. *Set of* 15 25·00 17·00

Designs: *Horiz as T* **43**—2 c. Soper's Hole; 3 c. Brown Pelican; 4 c. Dead Man's Chest; 5 c. Road Harbour; 6 c. Fallen Jerusalem; 8 c. The Baths, Virgin Gorda; 10 c. Map of Virgin Islands; 12 c. *Youth of Tortola* (Tortola-St. Thomas ferry); 15 c. The Towers, Tortola; 25 c. Beef Island Airfield. *Vert as T* **44**—$1 Virgin Gorda; $1.40, Yachts at anchor.

1965 (17 May). *I.T.U. Centenary. As Nos.* 166/7 *of Antigua.*
193 4 c. yellow and turquoise 10 10
194 25 c. light blue and orange-buff 20 15

1965 (25 Oct). *International Co-operation Year. As Nos.* 168/9 *of Antigua.*
195 1 c. reddish purple and turquoise-green .. 10 10
196 25 c. deep bluish green and lavender 30 15

1966 (24 Jan). *Churchill Commemoration. As Nos.* 170/3 *of Antigua.*
197 1 c. new blue 10 10
198 2 c. deep green 10 10
199 10 c. brown 30 10
200 25 c. bluish violet 60 25
197/200 .. .. *Set of* 4 90 40

1966 (22 Feb). *Royal Visit. As Nos.* 174/5 *of Antigua.*
201 4 c. black and ultramarine 30 10
202 70 c. black and magenta .. .. .. 1·10 45

58 R.M.S. *Atrato*, 1866

(Des R. Granger Barrett. Litho B.W.)

1966 (25 Apr). *Stamp Centenary. T* **58** *and similar horiz designs. W w* **12** (*sideways*). *P* 13.
203 5 c. black, red, yellow and emerald 15 10
204 10 c. black, green and rose-red/*cream*.. .. 25 10
205 25 c. black, rose-red and blue/*pale green* .. 40 10
206 60 c. black, red and green/*pale blue* 75 40
203/6 .. .. *Set of* 4 1·40 65

Design:—10 c. 1d. and 6d. stamps of 1866; 25 c. Air mail transport, Beef Island, and 6d. stamp of 1866; 60 c. Landing mail at Roadtown, 1866 and 1d. stamp of 1866.

50c.

(62)

1966 (15 Sept). *As Nos.* 189 *and* 191/2 *but wmk sideways, surch as T* **62**.
207 50 c. on 70 c. black and yellow-brown.. .. 70 70
208 $1.50 on $1.40, light blue and rose .. .. 2·00 2·00
209 $3 on $2.80, black and bright purple .. 2·50 2·75
207/9 .. .. *Set of* 3 4·75 5·00

1966 (1 Dec). *20th Anniv of U.N.E.S.C.O. As Nos.* 196/8 *of Antigua.*
210 2 c. slate-violet, red, yellow and orange .. 10 10
211 12 c. orange-yellow, violet and deep olive .. 20 10
212 60 c. black, bright purple and orange.. .. 50 20
210/12 .. .. *Set of* 3 65 30

63 Map of Virgin Islands

(Des G. Vasarhelyi. Photo Harrison)

1967 (18 Apr). *New Constitution. W w* **12**. *P* 14½.
213 **63** 2 c. multicoloured 10 10
214 10 c. multicoloured 10 10
215 25 c. multicoloured 15 10
216 $1 multicoloured 50 25
213/16 .. .. *Set of* 4 65 30

64 *Mercury* (cable ship) and Bermuda-Tortola Link

(Des G. Drummond, Photo Harrison)

1967 (14 Sept). *Inauguration of Bermuda-Tortola Telephone Service. T* **64** *and similar horiz designs. Multicoloured. W w* **12**. *P* 14½.
217 4 c. Type **64** 10 10
218 10 c. Chalwell Telecommunications Station 10 10
219 50 c. *Mercury* (cable ship) 30 20
217/19 .. .. *Set of* 3 45 20

67 Blue Marlin

(Des V. Whiteley. Photo Enschedé)

1968 (2 Jan). *Game Fishing. T* **67** *and similar horiz designs. W w* **12** (*sideways*). *P* 12½ × 12.
220 2 c. multicoloured 10 10
221 10 c. multicoloured 20 10
222 25 c. black, blue and bright violet 40 10
223 40 c. multicoloured 75 25
220/3 .. .. *Set of* 4 1·25 30

Designs:—10 c. Cobia; 25 c. Wahoo; 50 c. Fishing launch and map.

1968
INTERNATIONAL
YEAR FOR
HUMAN RIGHTS

(71)

72 Dr. Martin Luther King, Bible, Sword and Armour Gauntlet

1968 (29 July). *Human Rights Year. Nos.* 185 *and* 188 *optd with T* **71**.
224 10 c. lake and deep lilac 10 10
225 25 c. green and purple.. .. .. .. 15 10

29 July was the date of issue in the islands. The Crown Agents supplies went on sale in London on 1 July, the local consignment being delayed in transit.

(Des V. Whiteley. Litho Format)

1968 (15 Oct). *Martin Luther King Commemoration. W w* **12** (*sideways*). *P* 14.
226 **72** 4 c. multicoloured 10 10
227 25 c. multicoloured 15 10

73 DHC-6 "Twin Otter"

(Des R. Granger Barrett. Litho Format)

1968 (16 Dec). *Opening of Beef Island Airport Extension. T* **73** *and similar horiz designs. Multicoloured. P* 14.
228 2 c. Type **73** 10 10
229 10 c. HS "748" Airliner 10 10
230 25 c. HS "Heron" 20 10
231 $1 Royal Engineers cap badge 60 45
228/31 .. .. *Set of* 4 90 65

77 Long John Silver and Jim Hawkins **78** Jim Hawkins escaping from the Pirates

(Des Jennifer Toombs. Photo Enschedé)

1969 (18 Mar). *75th Death Anniv of Robert Louis Stevenson. Scenes from "Treasure Island". T* **77/8** *and similar designs. W w* **12** (*sideways on* 10 c., $1). *P* 13½ × 13 (4 c., 40 c.) *or* 13 × 13½ (*others*).
232 4 c. indigo, pale yellow and carmine-red .. 25 10
233 10 c. multicoloured 30 10
234 40 c. brown, black and blue 50 20
235 $1 multicoloured 75 35
232/5 .. .. *Set of* 4 1·60 60

Designs: *Vert*—40 c. The fight with Israel Hands. *Horiz*—$1 Treasure trove.

82 Yachts in Road Harbour, Tortola

(Des J. Cooter, Litho P.B.)

1969 (20 Oct). *Tourism. T* **82** *and similar multicoloured designs. W w* **12** (*sideways on* 2 c., $1). *P* 12½.
236 2 c. Tourist and Rock Grouper (fish) (*vert*) .. 15 10
237 10 c. Type **82** 20 10
238 20 c. Sun-bathing at Virgin Gorda National Park 30 10
239 $1 Tourist and Pipe Organ Cactus, at Virgin Gorda (*vert*) 75 50
236/9 .. .. *Set of* 4 1·25 65

85 Carib Canoe

(Des and litho J.W.)

1970 (16 Feb)–**74**. *Horiz designs as T* **85**. *W w* **12** (*sideways*). *P* 14.
240 ½ c. buff, red-brown and sepia 10 25
241 1 c. new blue, apple-green and chalky blue .. 15 25
a. Perf 13½ (12.11.74) 55 70
242 2 c. yellow-orange, red-brown and slate .. 25 35
243 3 c. orange-red, cobalt and sepia 25 35
244 4 c. greenish blue, chalky blue & bistre-brn 25 35
245 5 c. emerald, pink and black 30 10
246 6 c. reddish violet, mauve and myrtle-green 40 40
247 8 c. apple-green, greenish yellow and sepia .. 50 65
248 10 c. greenish blue, yellow-brown & red-brown 50 15
a. Perf 13½ (12.11.74) .. .. .. 1·25 1·50
249 12 c. yellow, crimson and brown 65 45
a. Perf 13½ (12.11.74) .. .. .. 1·50 2·00
250 15 c. turquoise-green, orange & bistre-brown 1·50 75
a. Perf 13½ (12.11.74) .. .. .. 1·75 2·00
251 25 c. grey-green, steel-blue and plum.. .. 2·00 90
252 50 c. magenta, dull green and purple-brown .. 2·25 1·50
253 $1 salmon, olive-green and red-brown .. 2·75 3·25
254 $2 buff, slate and grey .. .. .. 4·50 6·00
255 $3 ochre, deep blue and sepia .. .. 5·00 6·50
256 $5 violet and grey .. .. 8·00 9·00
240/56 .. .. *Set of* 17 26·00 28·00

Designs:—1 c. *Santamariagallante* (Columbus' flagship). 2 c. *Elizabeth Bonaventure* (Drake's flagship); 3 c. Dutch Buccaneer, *circa* 1660; 4 c. *Thetis*, 1827 (after etching by E. W. Cooke); 5 c. Henry Morgan's ship (17th-century); 6 c. H.M.S. *Boreas* (Captain Nelson, 1784); 8 c. H.M.S. *Eclair*, 1804; 10 c. H.M.S. *Formidable*, 1782; 12 c. H.M.S. *Nymph*, 1778; 15 c. *Windsor Castle*, Post Office Packet, 1807; 25 c. H.M.S. *Astrea*, 1808; 50 c. Wreck of R.M.S. *Rhone*, 1860; $1 Tortola Sloop; $2 H.M.S. *Frobisher*; $3 Tanker *Booker Viking*, 1967; $5 Hydrofoil *Sun Arrow*.

See also Nos. 295/300.

102 *A Tale of Two Cities*

(Des W. G. Brown. Litho D.L.R.)

1970 (4 May). *Death Centenary of Charles Dickens. T* **102** *and similar horiz designs showing original book illustrations.* W w **12** (*sideways*). *P* 14.

257 5 c. black, light rose and grey 10 10
258 10 c. black, light blue and pale green.. .. 20 10
259 25 c. black, light green and pale yellow .. 30 15
257/9 .. .. *Set of* 3 55 20

Designs:—10 c. *Oliver Twist*; 25 c. *Great Expectations*.

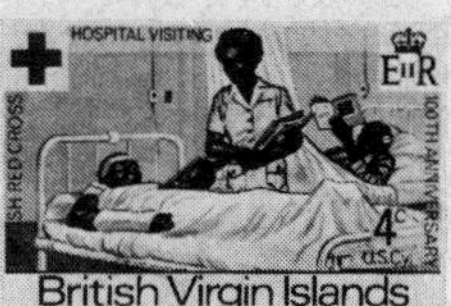

103 Hospital Visit

(Des R. Granger Barrett. Litho Questa)

1970 (10 Aug). *Centenary of British Red Cross. T* **103** *and similar horiz designs. Multicoloured.* W w **12** (*sideways*). *P* 14.

260 4 c. Type **103** 10 10
261 10 c. First Aid Class 15 10
262 25 c. Red Cross and Coat of Arms 25 15
260/2 .. .. *Set of* 3 40 20

104 Mary Read **105** Children and "UNICEF"

(Des and litho J.W.)

1970 (16 Nov). *Pirates. T* **104** *and similar vert designs. Multicoloured.* W w **12**. *P* 14 × 14½.

263 ½ c. Type **104** 10 10
264 10 c. George Lowther 35 10
265 30 c. Edward Teach (Blackbeard) 85 20
266 60 c. Henry Morgan .. .. 1·25 60
263/6 .. .. *Set of* 4 2·25 85

(Des L. Curtis. Litho Format)

1971 (13 Dec). *25th Anniv of UNICEF.* W w **12** (*sideways*). *P* 13½ × 14.

267 **106** 15 c. multicoloured 10 10
268 30 c. multicoloured 20 25

VISIT OF
H.R.H.
THE
PRINCESS MARGARET

1972 **1972**

(106)

1972 (7 Mar). *Royal Visit of Princess Margaret. Nos.* 244 *and* 251 *optd with T* **106**.

269 4 c. greenish blue, chalky blue & bistre-brn 10 10
270 25 c. grey-green, steel-blue and plum.. .. 20 30

107 Seaman of 1800 **108** Sailfish and the *Sir Winston Churchill* (cadet ship)

(Des J. W. Litho Questa)

1972 (17 Mar). *"Interpex" Stamp Exhibition, New York. T* **107** *and similar vert designs showing Naval Uniforms. Multicoloured.* W w **12** (*sideways*). *P* 13½.

271 ½ c. Type **107** 10 10
272 10 c. Boatswain, 1787–1807 .. .. .. 25 10
273 30 c. Captain, 1795–1812 .. .. .. 75 45
274 60 c. Admiral, 1787–95. .. .. .. 1·50 1·25
271/4 .. .. *Set of* 4 2·25 1·75

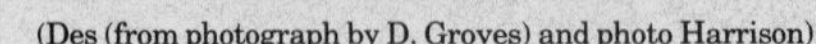

(Des (from photograph by D. Groves) and photo Harrison)

1972 (24 Nov). *Royal Silver Wedding. Multicoloured; background colour given.* W w **12**. *P* 14 × 14½.

275 **108** 15 c. bright blue 20 10
276 25 c. turquoise-blue 20 15
a. Blue omitted* £225

*The omission of the blue colour results in the Duke's suit appearing sepia instead of deep blue.

109 Blue Marlin

(Des G. Drummond. Litho Questa)

1972 (12 Dec). *Game Fish. T* **109** *and similar horiz designs. Multicoloured.* W w **12**. *P* 13½.

277 ½ c. Type **109** 10 15
a. Pair. Nos. 277/8 .. .. 10 30
278 ½ c. Wahoo 10 15
279 15 c. Allison Tuna 25 25
280 25 c. White Marlin 30 30
281 50 c. Sailfish 70 80
282 $1 Dolphin .. .. 1·40 1·75
277/82 .. .. *Set of* 6 2·50 3·00
MS283 194 × 158 mm. Nos. 277/82 .. .. 4·75 6·50

Nos. 277/8 were printed horizontally and vertically *se-tenant* within the sheet.

110 J. C. Lettsom **111** Green-throated Carib and Antillean Crested Hummingbird

(Des J. Cooter. Litho Questa)

1973 (9 Mar). *"Interpex 1973" (Quakers). T* **110** *and similar multicoloured designs.* W w **12** (*sideways on* ½ c. *and* 15 c.). *P* 13½.

284 ½ c. Type **110** 5 10
285 10 c. Lettsom House (*horiz*) 15 10
286 15 c. Dr. W. Thornton 20 10
287 30 c. Dr. Thornton and Capitol, Washington (*horiz*) 25 20
288 $1 William Penn (*horiz*) 70 85
284/8 .. .. *Set of* 5 1·25 1·10

(Des G. Drummond. Litho Questa)

1973 (30 June). *First Issue of Coinage. T* **111** *and similar horiz designs showing coins and local scenery. Multicoloured.* W w **12**. *P* 14.

289 1 c. Type **111** 10 10
290 5 c. Zenaida Dove 30 10
291 10 c. Ringed Kingfisher 40 10
292 25 c. Mangrove Cuckoo 55 15
293 50 c. Brown Pelican .. .. 75 1·00
294 $1 Magnificent Frigatebird.. .. .. 1·25 1·75
289/94 .. .. *Set of* 6 3·00 2·75

1973 (17 Oct). *As Nos.* 240, 243/5 *and* 248/9, *but wmk upright*.

295 ½ c. buff, red-brown and sepia 25 60
296 3 c. orange-red, cobalt and sepia .. .. 75 1·25
297 4 c. greenish blue, chalky blue & bistre-brn 75 1·25
298 5 c. emerald, pink and black.. .. .. 75 1·25
299 10 c. greenish blue, yellow-brown & red-brown 1·00 1·75
300 12 c. yellow, dull crimson and light brown .. 1·60 2·75
295/300 .. .. *Set of* 6 4·50 8·00

1973 (14 Nov). *Royal Wedding. As Nos.* 165/6 *of Anguilla. Centre multicoloured.* W w **12** (*sideways*). *P* 13½.

301 5 c. brown-ochre 10 10
302 50 c. light turquoise-blue 20 15

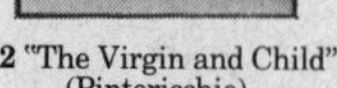

112 "The Virgin and Child" (Pintoricchio) **113** Crest of the *Canopus* (French)

(Des G. Drummond. Litho Questa)

1973 (7 Dec). *Christmas. T* **112** *and similar vert designs Multicoloured.* W w **12**. *P* 14.

303 ½ c. Type **112** 10 10
304 3 c. "Virgin and Child" (Lorenzo di Credi) .. 10 10
305 25 c. "Virgin and Child" (Crivelli) 15 10
306 50 c. "Virgin and Child with St. John" (Luini) 30 40
303/6 .. .. *Set of* 4 50 50

(Des J. Cooter. Litho Questa)

1974 (22 Mar). *"Interpex 1974" (Naval Crests). T* **113** *and similar vert designs. Multicoloured.* W w **12**. *P* 14.

307 5 c. Type **113** 10 10
308 18 c. U.S.S. *Saginaw* 25 25
309 25 c. H.M.S. *Rothesay* 30 30
310 50 c. H.M.C.S. *Ottawa* 45 60
307/10 .. .. *Set of* 4 1·00 1·10
MS311 196 × 128 mm. Nos. 307/10 .. .. 1·75 3·25

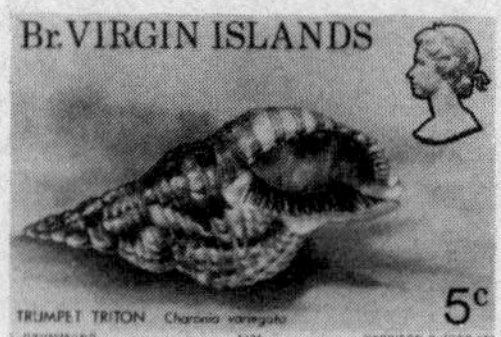

114 Christopher Columbus **115** Trumpet Triton

(Des J. W. Litho Format)

1974 (19 Aug). *Historical Figures. T* **114** *and similar vert designs.* W w **12**. *P* 14.

312 5 c. orange and black.. .. .. .. 20 10
313 10 c. greenish blue and black 35 10
314 25 c. reddish violet and black 50 25
315 40 c. yellow-brown and sepia 70 75
312/15 .. .. *Set of* 4 1·60 1·00
MS316 84 × 119 mm. Nos. 312/15 .. .. 1·60 2·00

Portraits:—10 c. Sir Walter Raleigh; 25 c. Sir Martin Frobisher; 40 c. Sir Francis Drake.

(Des G. Drummond. Litho Harrison)

1974 (30 Sept). *Seashells. T* **115** *and similar horiz designs. Multicoloured.* W w **12**. *P* 13 × 13½.

317 5 c. Type **115** 20 15
a. Wmk T **53** of Lesotho (sideways) .. £140
318 18 c. West Indian Murex 50 30
319 25 c. Bleeding Tooth 60 35
320 75 c. Virgin Islands Latirus .. .. .. 1·75 1·75
317/20 .. .. *Set of* 4 2·75 2·25
MS321 146 × 95 mm. Nos. 317/20 .. .. 3·00 5·00

116 Churchill and St. Mary, Aldermanbury, London **117** H.M.S. *Boreas*

(Des J. W. Litho Questa)

1974 (30 Nov). *Birth Centenary of Sir Winston Churchill. T* **116** *and similar horiz design. Multicoloured.* W w **14** (*sideways*). *P* 14.

322 10 c. Type **116** 15 10
323 50 c. St. Mary, Fulton, Missouri 35 50
MS324 141 × 108 mm. Nos. 322/3 .. .. 80 1·40

(Des J. Cooter. Litho J. W.)

1975 (14 Mar). *"Interpex 1975" Stamp Exhibition, New York. Ships' Figureheads. T* **117** *and similar vert designs. Multicoloured.* W w **12**. *P* 13.

325 5 c. Type **117** 15 10
326 18 c. *Golden Hind* 35 15
327 40 c. H.M.S. *Superb* 50 20
328 85 c. H.M.S. *Formidable* .. .. .. 1·10 1·00
325/8 .. .. *Set of* 4 1·90 1·25
MS329 192 × 127 mm. Nos. 325/8. (Wmk inverted). P 14 .. .. 3·00 4·50

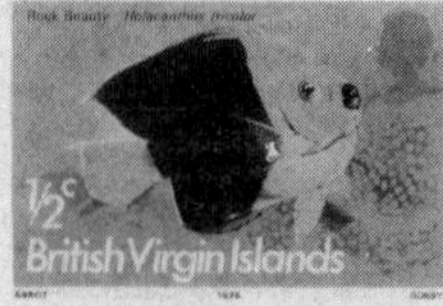

118 Rock Beauty

(Des C. Abbott. Litho Questa)

1975 (16 June–15 Aug). *Fishes. Horiz designs as T* **118**. *Multi-coloured. W w* **14** *(sideways). P* 14.

330 ½ c. Type **118** 10 20
331 1 c. Squirrelfish 15 25
332 3 c. Queen Triggerfish 15 25
333 5 c. Blue Angelfish 20 20
334 8 c. Stoplight Parrotfish 25 25
335 10 c. Queen Angelfish 25 25
336 12 c. Nassau Grouper 30 30
337 13 c. Blue Tang 30 30
338 15 c. Sergeant Major 35 35
339 18 c. Jewfish 45 60
340 20 c. Bluehead Wrasse 50 50
341 25 c. Grey Angelfish 50 60
342 60 c. Glasseye Snapper .. .. 1·00 1·25
343 $1 Blue Chromis .. .. 1·50 1·75
344 $2.50, French Angelfish .. .. 3·50 3·75
345 $3 Queen Parrotfish.. .. .. 4·25 4·75
346 $5 Four-eye Butterfly Fish (15.8) .. .. .. 7·50 7·50
330/46 .. .. *Set of* 17 19·00 20·00

The original imprint at foot has the date "1975". Some values were later reprinted with the date altered to "1977".

The imprints on all the stamps show the designer's name as "Abbot".

119 St. George's Parish School (First meeting-place, 1950)

(Des R. Granger Barrett. Litho Questa)

1975 (27 Nov). *25th Anniv of Restoration of Legislative Council. T* **119** *and similar horiz designs. Multicoloured. W w* **14** *(sideways). P* 14.

347 5 c. Type **119** 10 10
348 25 c. Legislative Council Building 25 10
349 40 c. Mace and gavel 35 15
350 75 c. Commemorative scroll 55 65
347/50 .. .. *Set of* 4 1·10 80

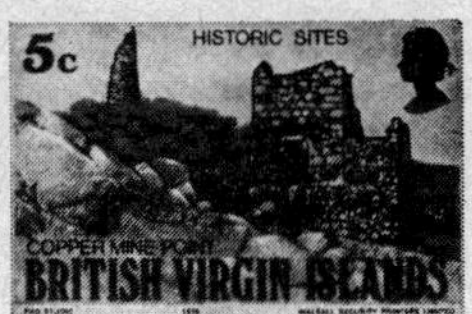

120 Copper Mine Point

(Des PAD Studio. Litho Walsall)

1976 (12 Mar). *Historic Sites. T* **120** *and similar horiz designs. Multicoloured. W w* **14** *(sideways). P* 14½.

351 5 c. Type **120** 10 10
352 18 c. Pleasant Valley 20 10
353 50 c. Callwood Distillery 40 30
354 75 c. The Dungeon 60 65
351/4 .. .. *Set of* 4 1·10 1·00

121 Massachusetts Brig *Hazard*

(Des J. W. Litho Questa)

1976 (29 May). *Bicentenary of American Revolution. T* **121** *and similar horiz designs. Multicoloured, W w* **14** *(sideways). P* 14.

355 8 c. Type **121** 40 15
356 22 c. American Privateer *Spy* 80 45
357 40 c. Continental Navy frigate *Raleigh* .. 1·50 1·00
358 75 c. Frigate *Alliance* and H.M.S. *Trepassy* .. 2·00 1·90
355/8 .. .. *Set of* 4 4·25 3·25
MS359 114 × 89 mm. Nos. 355/8 .. .. .. 6·50 8·50

122 Government House, Tortola **123** Royal Visit, 1966

(Des Walsall. Litho Questa)

1976 (29 Oct). *Fifth Anniv of Friendship Day with U.S. Virgin Is. T* **122** *and similar multicoloured designs. W w* **14** *(sideways on* 8 *and* 75 *c.). P* 14.

360 8 c. Type **122** 10 10
361 15 c. Government House, St. Croix *(vert)* .. 10 10
362 30 c. Flags *(vert)* 15 10
363 75 c. Government seals 30 40
360/3 .. .. *Set of* 4 50 55

(Des J. Cooter. Litho Walsall)

1977 (7 Feb). *Silver Jubilee. T* **123** *and similar vert designs (inscr "SILVER JUBILEE" at top). Multicoloured. W w* **14**. *P* 13½.

364 8 c. Type **123** 10 10
365 30 c. The Holy Bible 15 15
366 60 c. Presentation of Holy Bible 25 40
364/6 .. .. *Set of* 3 40 50

For stamps with different inscription, see Nos. 371/3.

The imprint at the stamp's foot gives the designer (wrongly) as "Waddington Studio".

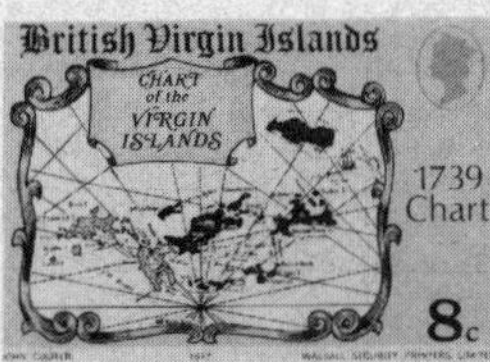

124 Chart of 1739

(Des J. Cooter. Litho Walsall)

1977 (13 June). *18th-Century Maps. T* **124** *and similar horiz designs. Multicoloured. W w* **14**. *P* 13½.

367 8 c. Type **124** 30 10
368 22 c. French Map, 1758 .. .. 55 30
369 30 c. Map from English and Danish surveys, 1775 .. .. 75 65
370 75 c. Map of 1779 .. .. 1·25 1·50
367/70 .. .. *Set of* 4 2·50 2·25

1977 (26 Oct). *Royal Visit. Designs as Nos.* 364/6 *but inscr.* "SILVER JUBILEE ROYAL VISIT" *at top, and face-values changed.*

371 5 c. Type **123** 10 10
372 25 c. The Holy Bible 15 10
373 50 c. Presentation of Holy Bible 30 25
371/3 .. .. *Set of* 3 45 35

The above also differ from Nos. 364/6 in having the silver frame removed and the silver lettering replaced by white. The imprint at foot now has the designer's name correctly given as "J. E. Cooter".

125 Divers checking Equipment **126** Fire Coral

(Des J. W. Litho Rosenbaum Bros, Vienna)

1978 (10 Feb). *Tourism. T* **125** *and similar vert designs. Multi-coloured. W w* **14**. *P* 13½.

374 ½ c. Type **125** 10 10
375 5 c. Cup coral on wreck of *Rhone* 15 10
376 8 c. Sponge formation on wreck of *Rhone* .. 20 10
377 22 c. Cup coral and sponges 50 15
378 30 c. Sponges inside cave 60 20
379 75 c. Marine life .. .. 1·10 85
374/9 .. .. *Set of* 6 2·25 1·25

(Des G. Drummond. Litho Harrison)

1978 (27 Feb). *Corals. T* **126** *and similar horiz designs. Multi-coloured. W w* **14** *(sideways). P* 14.

380 8 c. Type **126** 25 15
381 15 c. Staghorn coral 40 30
382 40 c. Brain coral 75 85
383 75 c. Elkhorn coral .. .. 1·50 1·60
380/3 .. .. *Set of* 4 2·50 2·50

127 Iguana **128** Lignum Vitae

(Des Jennifer Toombs. Litho Questa)

1978 (2 June). *25th Anniv of Coronation. T* **127** *and similar vert designs. P* 15.

384 50 c. brown-ochre, green and silver 25 40
a. Sheetlet. Nos. 384/6 × 2 .. .. .. 1·25
385 50 c. multicoloured 25 40
386 50 c. brown-ochre, green and silver 25 40
384/6 .. .. *Set of* 3 65 1·10

Designs:—No. 384, Plantagenet Falcon; No. 385, Queen Elizabeth II; No. 386, Type **127**.

(Des and litho J.W.)

1978 (4 Sept). *Flowering Trees. T* **128** *and similar horiz designs. Multicoloured. W w* **14** *(sideways). P* 13.

387 8 c. Type **128** 15 10
388 22 c. Ginger Thomas 25 15
389 40 c. Dog Almond 35 20
390 75 c. White Cedar 60 70
387/90 .. .. *Set of* 4 1·25 1·00
MS391 131 × 95 mm. Nos. 387/90. P 14 .. .. 1·75 2·40

129 *Eurema lisa*

(Des G. Hutchins. Litho Questa)

1978 (4 Dec). *Butterflies. T* **129** *and similar horiz designs. Multi-coloured. W w* **14** *(sideways). P* 14.

392 5 c. Type **129** 25 10
393 22 c. *Dione vanillae* 75 20
394 30 c. *Heliconius charitonius* 85 30
395 75 c. *Hemiargus hanno* .. .. 1·25 1·25
392/5 .. .. *Set of* 4 2·75 1·75
MS396 159 × 113 mm. No. 392 × 6 and 393 × 3 2·50 3·25

130 Spiny Lobster

(Des Picton Print. Litho Harrison)

1979 (10 Feb). *Wildlife Conservation. T* **130** *and similar multi-coloured designs. W w* **14** *(sideways on* 5 *and* 22 *c.). P* 14.

397 5 c. Type **130** 15 10
398 15 c. Large Iguana *(vert)* 30 10
399 22 c. Hawksbill Turtle 50 15
400 75 c. Black Coral *(vert)* .. .. 1·10 90
397/400 .. .. *Set of* 4 1·90 1·10
MS401 130 × 153 mm. Nos. 397/400 (wmk sideways) .. .. 2·25 3·00

131 Strawberry Cactus **132** West Indian Girl

(Des BG Studio. Litho Format)

1979 (7 May). *Cacti. T* **131** *and similar vert designs. Multi-coloured. W w* **14**. *P* 14.

402 ½ c. Type **131** 10 10
403 5 c. Snowy Cactus 15 10
404 13 c. Barrel Cactus 25 20
405 22 c. Tree Cactus 40 35
406 30 c. Prickly Pear 45 40
407 75 c. Dildo Cactus .. .. 80 1·00
402/7 .. .. *Set of* 6 1·90 1·90

(Des R. Granger Barrett. Litho Questa)

1979 (9 July). *International Year of the Child. T* **132** *and similar vert designs. Multicoloured. W w* **14** *(inverted). P* 14½ × 14.

408 5 c. Type **132** 10 10
409 10 c. African boy 10 10
410 13 c. Asian girl 10 10
411 $1 European boy 50 85
408/11 .. .. *Set of* 4 65 1·00
MS412 91 × 114 mm. Nos. 408/11 .. .. .. 70 1·50

133 1956 Road Harbour 3 c. Definitive Stamp **134** Pencil Urchin

(Des J. W. Photo Heraclio Fournier)

1979 (1 Oct). *Death Centenary of Sir Rowland Hill. T* **133** *and similar designs showing stamps. P* 13½.

413 5 c. deep blue, new blue and brown-olive .. 10 10
414 13 c. deep blue and claret 10 10
415 75 c. deep blue and bright purple 45 50
413/15 .. .. *Set of* 3 55 55
MS416 37 × 91 mm. $1 deep blue & carm-red. P 13 70 1·25

Designs: (39 × 27 *mm*)—13 c. 1889 2½d.; 75 c. Great Britain unissued 1910 2d. Tyrian plum. (40 × 28 *mm*)—$1. 1867 1s. "Missing Virgin" error.

(Des BG Studio. Litho Questa)

1979 (17 Dec)–**82**. *Marine Life. Vert designs as T* **134**. *Multicoloured. W* w **14**. *Ordinary paper. P* 14.

417	½ c. Calcified Algae (1.4.80)	10	20
418	1 c. Purple-tipped Sea Anemone (1.4.80)	10	20
419	3 c. Common Starfish (1.4.80)	10	20
420	5 c. Type **134**	20	10
	a. Chalk-surfaced paper (27.8.82)	15	10
421	8 c. Triton's Trumpet (shell)	35	20
	a. Chalk-surfaced paper (27.8.82)	35	20
422	10 c. Christmas Tree Worms	25	25
423	13 c. Flamingo Tongue Snail (1.4.80)	35	35
	a. Chalk-surfaced paper (27.8.82)	35	25
424	15 c. Spider Crab	30	25
	a. Chalk-surfaced paper (27.8.82)	30	25
425	18 c. Sea Squirts (1.4.80)	40	45
426	20 c. True Tulip (shell)	40	35
	a. Chalk-surfaced paper (27.8.82)	40	35
427	25 c. Rooster Tail Conch (shell)	70	60
428	30 c. Fighting Conch (shell) (1.4.80)	65	50
	a. Chalk-surfaced paper (27.8.82)	65	50
429	60 c. Mangrove Crab (1.4.80)	1·75	1·25
430	$1 Coral Polyps (1.4.80)	2·50	2·00
431	$2.50, Peppermint Shrimp	3·50	4·25
432	$3 West Indian Murex (shell)	4·00	4·75
433	$5 Carpet Anemone (1.4.80)	7·75	8·50
417/33	*Set of* 17	21·00	21·00

Nos. 420a/28a were printed with a changed imprint date, "1982".

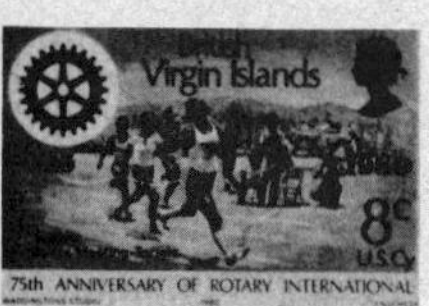

135 Rotary Athletics Meeting, Tortola

136 Brown Booby

(Des J. W. Litho Enschedé)

1980 (23 Feb). *75th Anniv of Rotary International. T* **135** *and similar horiz designs. Multicoloured. W* w **14** (*sideways*). *P* 13½ × 14.

434	8 c. Type **135**	10	10
435	22 c. Paul P. Harris (founder) and Rotary emblem	15	10
436	60 c. "Creation of a National Park", Mount Sage, Tortola	40	40
437	$1 Rotary anniversary emblem	70	75
434/7	*Set of* 4	1·25	1·25
MS438	149 × 148 mm. Nos. 434/7	1·75	2·50

(Des K. Penny. Litho Secura, Singapore)

1980 (6 May). *"London 1980" International Stamp Exhibition. Birds. T* **136** *and similar horiz designs. Multicoloured. W* w **14** (*sideways*). *P* 13½.

439	20 c. Type **136**	20	20
	a. Wmk upright	40	40
440	25 c. Magnificent Frigate Bird	25	25
	a. Wmk upright	1·75	1·75
441	50 c. White-tailed Tropic Bird	40	40
	a. Wmk upright	65	65
442	75 c. Brown Pelican	55	55
439/42	*Set of* 4	1·25	1·25
MS443	152 × 130 mm. Nos. 439/42	1·25	1·60

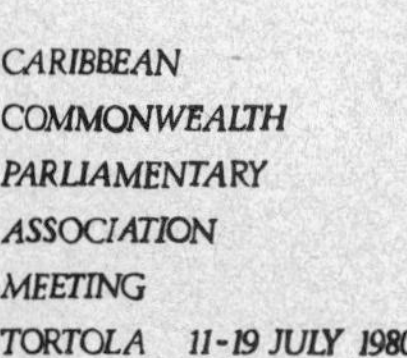

(137)

138 Sir Francis Drake

1980 (7 July). *Caribbean Commonwealth Parliamentary Association Meeting, Tortola. Nos.* 414/15 *optd with T* **137**.

444	13 c. deep blue and claret	15	10
445	75 c. deep blue and bright blue	40	40

(Des Franklin Mint. Litho Questa)

1980 (26 Sept). *Sir Francis Drake Commemoration. T* **138** *and similar vert designs. Multicoloured. W* w **14** (*inverted on* 75 *c.*). *P* 14 × 14½.

446	8 c. Type **138**	25	10
447	15 c. Queen Elizabeth I	35	15
448	30 c. Drake receiving knighthood	50	30
449	75 c. *Golden Hind* and coat of arms	1·10	80
446/9	*Set of* 4	2·00	1·25
MS450	171 × 121 mm. Nos. 446/9. Wmk inverted	2·00	2·25
	a. 75 c. value in miniature sheet imperf	£150	
	b. 30 c. value in miniature sheet imperf	£150	

139 Jost van Dyke

(Des Jennifer Toombs. Litho Rosenbaum Bros, Vienna)

1980 (1 Dec). *Island Profiles. T* **139** *and similar horiz designs. Multicoloured. W* w **14** (*sideways*). *P* 13½.

451	2 c. Type **139**	10	10
452	5 c. Peter Island	10	10
453	13 c. Virgin Gorda	15	10
454	22 c. Anegada	20	10
455	30 c. Norman Island	30	15
456	$1 Tortola	85	1·00
451/6	*Set of* 6	1·50	1·10
MS457	95 × 88 mm. No. 456 (wmk upright)	85	1·50
	a. Error. Imperf	£325	
	b. Gold and black omitted	£325	

140 Dancing Lady

141 Wedding Bouquet from British Virgin Islands

(Des C. Abbott. Litho Walsall)

1981 (3 Mar). *Flowers. T* **140** *and similar vert designs. Multicoloured. W* w **14** (*sideways*). *P* 11.

458	5 c. Type **140**	15	10
459	20 c. Love in the Mist	40	25
460	22 c. *Pitcairnia angustifolia*	40	25
461	75 c. Dutchman's Pipe	1·40	1·40
462	$1 Maiden Apple	1·60	1·60
458/62	*Set of* 5	3·50	3·25

(Des J. W. Litho Harrison)

1981 (22 July). *Royal Wedding. T* **141** *and similar vert designs. Multicoloured. W* w **14**. *P* 14.

463	10 c. Type **141**	10	10
464	35 c. Prince Charles and Queen Elizabeth the Queen Mother in Garter robes	30	15
465	$1.25, Prince Charles and Lady Diana Spencer	80	80
463/5	*Set of* 3	1·10	90

142 Stamp Collecting

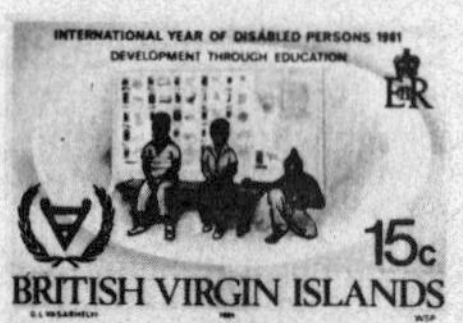

143 "Development through Education"

(Des BG Studio. Litho Questa)

1981 (10 Oct). *25th Anniv of Duke of Edinburgh Award Scheme. T* **142** *and similar vert designs. Multicoloured. W* w **14**. *P* 14.

466	10 c. Type **142**	10	10
467	15 c. Athletics	10	10
468	50 c. Camping	25	25
469	$1 Duke of Edinburgh	40	45
466/9	*Set of* 4	65	80

(Des G. Vasarhelyi. Litho Walsall)

1981 (19 Oct). *International Year for Disabled Persons. T* **143** *and similar horiz designs. Multicoloured. W* w **14** (*sideways*). *P* 14.

470	15 c. Type **143**	20	20
471	20 c. Fort Charlotte Children's Centre	30	30
472	30 c. "Developing cultural awareness"	40	40
473	$1 Fort Charlotte Children's Centre (*different*)	1·25	1·25
470/3	*Set of* 4	2·00	2·00

PRICES OF SETS

Set prices are given for many issues, generally those containing three stamps or more. Definitive sets include one of each value or major colour change, but do not cover different perforations, die types or minor shades. Where a choice is possible the set prices are based on the cheapest versions of the stamps included in the listings.

144 Detail from "The Adoration of the Shepherds" (Rubens)

145 Green-throated Caribs and Erythrina

(Des J. W. Litho Questa)

1981 (30 Nov). *Christmas. T* **144** *and similar designs showing details from "The Adoration of the Shepherds" by Rubens. W* w **14**. *P* 14.

474	5 c. multicoloured	10	10
475	15 c. multicoloured	20	10
476	30 c. multicoloured	40	15
477	$1 multicoloured	1·00	1·10
474/7	*Set of* 4	1·50	1·25
MS478	117 × 90 mm. 50 c. multicoloured (*horiz*) (wmk sideways)	75	85

(Des Walsall. Litho Format)

1982 (5 Apr). *Hummingbirds. T* **145** *and similar vert designs. Multicoloured. W* w **14**. *P* 14 × 14½.

479	15 c. Type **145**	40	15
480	30 c. Green-throated Carib and Bougainvillea	65	45
481	35 c. Antillean Crested Hummingbirds and *Granadilla passiflora*	75	55
482	$1.25, Antillean Crested Hummingbird and Hibiscus	2·50	2·75
479/82	*Set of* 4	4·00	3·50

146 "People caring for People"

147 Princess at Victoria and Albert Museum, November 1981

(Des Harrison. Litho Format)

1982 (3 May). *Tenth Anniv of Lions Club of Tortola. T* **146** *and similar horiz designs. Multicoloured. W* w **14** (*sideways*). *P* 13½ × 14.

483	10 c. Type **146**	15	15
484	20 c. Tortola Headquarters	30	20
485	30 c. "We Serve"	40	30
486	$1.50, "Lions" symbol	1·90	1·75
483/6	*Set of* 4	2·50	2·25
MS487	124 × 102 mm. Nos. 483/6	3·00	3·25

(Des C. Abbott. Litho Harrison)

1982 (2 July*). *21st Birthday of Princess of Wales. T* **147** *and similar vert designs. Multicoloured. W* w **14**. *P* 14½ × 14.

488	10 c. British Virgin Islands coat of arms	15	10
489	35 c. Type **147**	30	30
490	50 c. Bride and groom proceeding into Vestry	50	50
491	$1.50, Formal portrait	1·25	1·60
488/91	*Set of* 4	2·00	2·25

*This is the local release date. The Crown Agents released the stamps on 1 July.

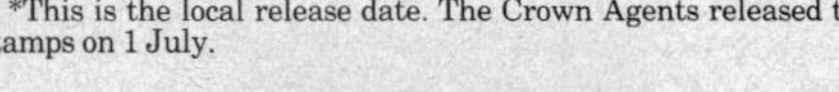

148 Douglas "DC-3"

(Des A. Theobald. Litho Questa)

1982 (10 Sept). *10th Anniv of Air BVI. T* **148** *and similar horiz designs. Multicoloured. W* w **14** (*sideways*). *P* 14.

492	10 c. Type **148**	20	15
493	15 c. Britten-Norman "Islander"	25	20
494	60 c. Hawker Siddeley "748"	90	75
495	75 c. Runway scene	1·10	90
492/5	*Set of* 4	2·25	1·75

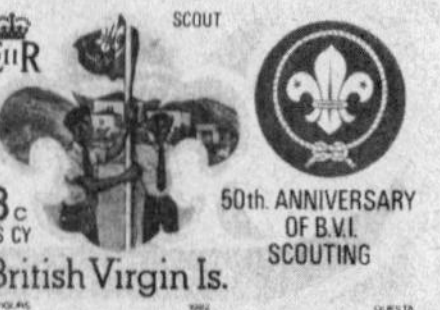

149 Scouts raising Flag

(Des R. Vigurs. Litho Questa)

1982 (18 Nov). *75th Anniv of Boy Scout Movement* ($1) *and 50th Anniv of Scouting in B.V.I.* (*others*). *T* **149** *and similar horiz designs. Multicoloured. W w* **14** (*sideways*). *P* 14.

496 8 c. Type **149** 20 10
497 20 c. Cub Scout 45 25
498 50 c. Sea Scout.. .. .. 85 55
499 $1 First camp, Brownsea Island, and portrait of Lord Baden-Powell .. .. .. 1·50 1·50
496/9 .. .. *Set of* 4 2·75 2·25

150 Legislature in Session

151 Florence Nightingale

(Des G. Vasarhelyi. Litho Enschedé)

1983 (10 Mar). *Commonwealth Day. T* **150** *and similar horiz designs. Multicoloured. W w* **14** (*sideways*). *P* 13 × 13½.

500 10 c. Type **150** 10 10
501 30 c. Tourism 25 20
502 35 c. Satellite view of Earth showing Virgin Islands 25 25
503 75 c. B.V.I. and Commonwealth flags .. 70 90
500/3 .. .. *Set of* 4 1·10 1·25

(Des L. Curtis. Litho Questa)

1983 (9 May). *Nursing Week. T* **151** *and similar multicoloured designs. W w* **14** (*sideways on* 60 *c. and* 75 *c.*). *P* 14.

504 10 c. Type **151** 30 15
505 30 c. Staff nurse and assistant nurse 60 45
506 60 c. Public Health nurses testing blood pressure (*horiz*) .. .. 1·10 95
507 75 c. Peebles Hospital (*horiz*) .. .. .. 1·40 1·25
504/7 .. .. *Set of* 4 3·00 2·50

152 Frame Construction

(Des R. Burnett. Litho Harrison)

1983 (25 July). *Traditional Boat-building. T* **152** *and similar horiz designs. Multicoloured. W w* **14** (*sideways*). *P* 14.

508 15 c. Type **152** 30 25
509 25 c. Planking 45 40
510 50 c. Launching 80 70
511 $1 Maiden voyage .. .. 1·50 1·40
508/11 .. .. *Set of* 4 2·75 2·50
MS512 127 × 101 mm. Nos. 508/11 .. .. 2·75 3·50

153 Grumman "Goose" Seaplane

154 "Madonna and Child with the Infant Baptist"

(Des Walsall. Litho Questa)

1983 (15 Sept). *Bicentenary of Manned Flight. T* **153** *and similar horiz designs. Multicoloured. W w* **14** (*sideways*). *P* 14.

513 10 c. Type **153** 20 15
514 30 c. De Havilland "Heron" 45 45
515 60 c. EMB "110P1 Bandeirante" 85 85
516 $1.25, British Aerospace "HS 748" .. .. 1·50 1·60
513/16 .. .. *Set of* 4 2·75 2·75

(Des M. Joyce. Litho Questa)

1983 (7 Nov). *Christmas. 500th Birth Anniv of Raphael. T* **154** *and similar vert designs showing details of different paintings. Multicoloured. W w* **14**. *P* 14½ × 14.

517 8 c. Type **154** 10 10
518 15 c. "La Belle Jardinière" 20 25
519 50 c. "Madonna Del Granduca" 65 70
520 $1 "The Terranuova Madonna" .. .. 1·25 1·40
517/20 .. .. *Set of* 4 2·00 2·25
MS521 108 × 101 mm. Nos. 517/20 .. .. 2·10 2·50

NEW INFORMATION

The editor is always interested to correspond with people who have new information that will improve or correct the Catalogue.

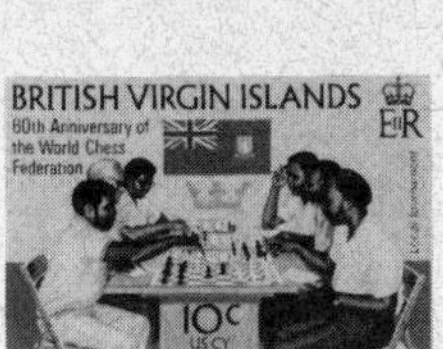

155 Local Tournament

156 Port Purcell

(Des L. Curtis. Litho Questa)

1984 (20 Feb). *60th Anniv of World Chess Federation. T* **155** *and similar multicoloured designs. W w* **14** (*sideways on* 10 *c. and* $1, *inverted on* 35 *c.*). *P* 14.

522 10 c. Type **155** 45 20
523 35 c. "Staunton" chess pieces (*vert*) 75 50
524 75 c. Winning position, 1980 Chess Olympiad (*vert*) .. .. 1·75 1·75
525 $1 B.V.I. Gold Medal from 1980 Chess Olympiad .. .. 2·00 2·25
522/5 .. .. *Set of* 4 4·50 4·25

(Des L. Curtis. Litho Questa)

1984 (16 Apr). *250th Anniv of "Lloyd's List" (newspaper). T* **156** *and similar vert designs. Multicoloured. W w* **14**. *P* 14½ × 14.

526 15 c. Type **156** 25 30
527 25 c. Boeing "747" 45 50
528 50 c. Loss of R.M.S. *Rhone* 90 95
529 $1 M.S. *Booker Viking* .. .. .. 1·50 1·60
526/9 .. .. *Set of* 4 2·75 3·00

157 Mail Ship *Boyne*, Aeroplane and U.P.U. Logo

(Des L. Curtis. Litho Walsall)

1984 (16 May). *Universal Postal Union Congress, Hamburg. Sheet* 90 × 69 *mm. W w* **14** (*sideways*). *P* 14.

MS530 **157** $1 pale blue and black .. .. 1·90 2·40

158 Running

159 Steel Band

(Des R. Granger Barrett. Litho Walsall)

1984 (3 July). *Olympic Games, Los Angeles. T* **158** *and similar horiz designs. Multicoloured. W w* **14** (*sideways*). *P* 14.

531 15 c. Type **158** 25 30
a. Pair. Nos. 531/2 .. .. 50 60
532 15 c. Runner 25 30
533 20 c. Wind-surfing 30 35
a. Pair. Nos. 533/4 .. .. 60 70
534 20 c. Surfer 30 35
535 30 c. Sailing 40 50
a. Pair. Nos. 535/6 .. .. 80 1·00
536 30 c. Yacht 40 50
531/6 .. .. *Set of* 6 1·75 2·10
MS537 97 × 69 mm. $1 Torch bearer. Wmk upright 1·50 1·90

Nos. 531/2, 533/4 and 535/6 were printed together, *se-tenant*, in horizontal and vertical pairs throughout the sheets.

(Des D. Miller. Litho Format)

1984 (14 Aug). *150th Anniv of Abolition of Slavery. T* **159** *and similar vert designs showing various aspects of Emancipation Festival. Multicoloured. W w* **14**. *P* 14.

538 10 c. Type **159** 20 25
a. Horiz strip of 5. Nos. 538/42 90
539 10 c. Dancing girls 20 25
540 10 c. Men in traditional costumes 20 25
541 10 c. Girl in traditional costume 20 25
542 10 c. Festival Queen 20 25
543 30 c. Green and yellow dinghies 40 45
a. Horiz strip of 5. Nos. 543/7 .. .. 1·75
544 30 c. Blue and red dinghies 40 45
545 30 c. White and blue dinghies 40 45
546 30 c. Red and yellow dinghies 40 45
547 30 c. Blue and white dinghies 40 45
538/47 .. .. *Set of* 10 2·50 3·00

Nos. 538/42 and 543/7 were each printed together, *se-tenant*, in horizontal strips of 5 throughout the sheet, forming composite designs. On Nos. 543/7 the sail colours of the dinghies are described to assist identification.

160 Sloop

(Des R. Burnett. Litho J.W.)

1984 (15 Nov). *Boats. T* **160** *and similar horiz designs. Multicoloured. W w* **14** (*sideways*). *P* 13 × 13½.

548 10 c. Type **160** 20 20
549 35 c. Fishing boat 65 65
550 60 c. Schooner .. .. 1·10 1·10
551 75 c. Cargo boat .. .. 1·40 1·40
548/51 .. .. *Set of* 4 3·00 3·00
MS552 125 × 90 mm. Nos. 548/51. P 14 .. .. 3·00 3·50

161 One Cent Coin and Aerial View

162 Red-billed Tropic Bird

(Litho Walsall)

1985 (15 Jan). *New Coinage. T* **161** *and similar horiz designs showing coins and local scenery. Multicoloured. W w* **14** (*sideways*). *P* 14½.

553 1 c. Type **161** 10 10
554 5 c. Five cent coin and boulders on beach .. 10 10
555 10 c. Ten cent coin and scuba diving 20 20
556 25 c. Twenty-five cent coin and yachts .. 45 45
557 50 c. Fifty cent coin and jetty .. .. .. 90 1·00
558 $1 One dollar coin and beach at night .. 1·75 2·00
553/8 .. .. *Set of* 6 3·00 3·50
MS559 103 × 156 mm. Nos. 553/8 .. .. 3·00 4·00

A set of stamps showing Michael Jackson the entertainer was prepared in 1985, but was never released for postal use. Samples of two $1.50 values were, however, distributed for publicity purposes before the issue was cancelled.

(Des N. Arlott. Litho Questa)

1985 (3 July). *Birds of the British Virgin Islands. T* **162** *and similar vert designs. Multicoloured. W w* **14**. *P* 14.

560 1 c. Type **162** 10 10
561 2 c. Yellow-crowned Night Heron 10 10
562 5 c. Mangrove Cuckoo 10 10
563 8 c. Northern Mockingbird 10 10
564 10 c. Grey Kingbird 30 10
565 12 c. Red-necked Pigeon 10 15
566 15 c. Least Bittern 40 20
567 18 c. Smooth-billed Ani 20 25
568 20 c. Clapper Rail 50 25
569 25 c. American Kestrel 60 30
570 30 c. Pearly-eyed Thrasher 30 35
571 35 c. Bridled Quail Dove 75 40
572 40 c. Green Heron 40 45
573 50 c. Scaly-breasted Ground Dove 50 55
574 60 c. Little Blue Heron 60 65
575 $1 Audubon's Shearwater .. .. .. 2·00 1·25
576 $2 Blue-faced Booby .. .. 2·10 2·25
577 $3 Cattle Egret .. .. 4·75 4·00
578 $5 Zenaida Dove .. .. 5·25 5·50
560/78 .. .. *Set of* 19 17·00 15·00

For these stamps watermarked w **16** see Nos. 647/60.

IMPERFORATES AND MISSING COLOURS. Various issues between Nos. 579 and 609 exist either imperforate or with colours omitted. Such items are not listed as there is no evidence that they fulfil the criteria outlined on page xi of this catalogue.

163 The Queen Mother at Festival of Remembrance

164 Seaside Sparrow

(Des Maxine Marsh. Litho Format)

1985 (26 Aug). *Life and Times of Queen Elizabeth the Queen Mother. Various vertical portraits as T* **163**. *Multicoloured. P* 12½. *A. W w* **15** (*sideways*). *B. No wmk.*

		A.		B.	
579	10 c. Type **163**	15	20	2·50	2·50
	a. Horiz pair. Nos. 579/80 ..	30	40	5·00	5·00
580	10 c. At Victoria Palace Theatre, 1984	15	20	2·50	2·50
581	25 c. At the engagement of the Prince of Wales, 1981 ..	35	40	2·50	2·50
	a. Horiz pair. Nos. 581/2 ..	70	80	5·00	5·00
582	25 c. Opening Celia Johnson Theatre, 1985	35	40	2·50	2·50
583	50 c. The Queen Mother on her 82nd birthday	70	75	3·00	3·00
	a. Horiz pair. Nos. 583/4 ..	1·40	1·50	6·00	6·00
584	50 c. At the Tate Gallery, 1983	70	75	3·00	3·00
585	75 c. At the Royal Smithfield Show, 1983	1·10	1·25	3·00	3·00
	a. Horiz pair. Nos. 585/6 ..	2·25	2·50	6·00	6·00

586 75 c. Unveiling Mountbatten statue, 1983 .. .. 1·10 1·25 3·00 3·00
579/86 .. .. *Set of* 8 4·25 4·50 20·00 20·00
MS587 85 × 114 mm. $1 At Columbia University; $1 At a Wedding, St. Margaret's Westminster, 1983 3·50 4·00 †

The two designs of each value were issued, *se-tenant*, in horizontal pairs within the sheets.

Each *se-tenant* pair shows a floral pattern across the bottom of the portraits which stops short of the left-hand edge on the left-hand stamp and of the right-hand edge on the right-hand stamp.

Designs as Nos. 583/4 and 585/6, but with face values of $1 × 2 and $2.50 × 2, also exist in additional miniature sheets from a restricted printing issued 18 December 1985.

(Des R. Vigurs. Litho Format)

1985 (17 Dec). *Birth Bicentenary of John J. Audubon (ornithologist).* T **164** *and similar vert designs, showing original paintings. Multicoloured.* P 15.
588 5 c. Type **164** 20 10
589 30 c. Passenger Pigeon 60 45
590 50 c. Yellow-breasted Chat .. .. .. 90 1·10
591 $1 American Kestrel .. .. .. 1·60 1·75
588/91 .. .. *Set of* 4 3·00 3·00

165 S.V. *Flying Cloud* (**166**)

(Des G. Drummond. Litho Format)

1986 (27 Jan). *Visiting Cruise Ships.* T **165** *and similar horiz designs. Multicoloured.* W w **15**. P 15.
592 35 c. Type **165** .. .. 1·00 70
593 50 c. M.V. *Newport Clipper* .. .. .. 1·25 90
594 75 c. M.V. *Cunard Countess* .. .. .. 1·75 1·50
595 $1 M.V. *Sea Goddess* .. .. .. 2·00 2·00
592/5 .. .. *Set of* 4 5·50 4·50

1986 (17 Apr). *Inaugural Flight of Miami–Beef Island Air Service. Nos.* 581/2 *and* 585/6 *optd with* T **166**. A. W w **15** *(sideways).* B. *No wmk.*

		A.		B.	
596	25 c. At the engagement of the Prince of Wales, 1981 ..	35	40	2·25	2·25
	a. Horiz pair. Nos. 596/7 ..	70	80	4·50	4·50
597	25 c. Opening Celia Johnson theatre, 1985	35	40	2·25	2·25
598	75 c. At the Royal Smithfield Show, 1983	1·10	1·25	2·25	2·25
	a. Horiz pair. Nos. 598/9 ..	2·25	2·50	4·50	4·50
599	75 c. Unveiling Mountbatten statue, 1983	1·10	1·25	2·25	2·25
596/9	.. .. .. *Set of* 4	2·50	3·00	8·00	8·00

167 Queen Elizabeth II in 1958

(Des Court House Studio. Litho Format)

1986 (21 Apr). *60th Birthday of Queen Elizabeth II.* T **167** *and similar multicoloured designs.* P 12½.
600 12 c. Type **167** 15 20
601 35 c. At a Maundy Service 40 45
a. Wmk w **15** (sideways) .. .. .. 6·00
602 $1.50, Queen Elizabeth .. .. .. 1·90 2·00
a. Wmk w **15** (sideways) .. .. .. 6·00
603 $2 During a visit to Canberra, 1982 (*vert*) .. .. 2·50 2·75
600/3 .. .. *Set of* 4 4·50 4·75
MS604 85 × 115 mm $3 Queen with bouquet .. 4·00 4·25

168 Miss Sarah Ferguson

169 Harvesting Sugar Cane

(Des Court House Studio. Litho Format)

1986 (23 July–15 Oct). *Royal Wedding.* T **168** *and similar multicoloured designs.* P 12½.
605 35 c. Type **168** 50 55
a. Pair. Nos. 605/6 .. .. 1·00 1·10
b. Wmk w **15** .. .. 4·00
ba. Pair. Nos. 605b/6b .. .. .. 8·00
606 35 c. Prince Andrew and Miss Sarah Ferguson 50 55
b. Wmk w **15** .. .. 4·00
607 $1 Prince Andrew in morning dress (*horiz*) 1·40 1·50
a. Pair. Nos. 607/8 .. .. 2·75 3·00
608 $1 Miss Sarah Ferguson (*different*) (*horiz*) 1·40 1·50
605/8 .. .. *Set of* 4 3·50 3·75
MS609 115 × 85 mm. $4 Duke and Duchess of York in carriage after wedding (*horiz*) (15.10.86) 5·00 5·25

Nos. 605/6 and 607/8 were each printed together, *se-tenant*, in horizontal and vertical pairs throughout the sheets.

Nos. 605/8 imperforate come from souvenir stamp booklets.

Nos. 605/8 overprinted "Congratulations to T.R.H. The Duke & Duchess of York" were not issued.

(Des Toni Lance. Litho Questa)

1986 (30 July). *History of Rum Making.* T **169** *and similar horiz designs. Multicoloured.* W w **15**. P 14.
610 12 c. Type **169** 45 25
611 40 c. Bringing sugar cane to mill 85 60
612 60 c. Rum distillery .. .. 1·25 1·25
613 $1 Delivering barrels of rum to ship .. 2·25 2·50
610/13 .. .. *Set of* 4 4·25 4·25
MS614 115 × 84 mm. $2 Royal Navy rum issue. Wmk sideways .. .. 4·00 4·50

170 C.S. *Sentinel*

171 Statue of Liberty at Sunset

(Des Court House Studio. Litho Format)

1986 (28 Oct). *20th Anniv of Cable and Wireless Caribbean Headquarters, Tortola.* T **170** *and similar horiz designs. Multicoloured.* W w **15**. P 12½.
615 35 c. Type **170** 55 65
a. Vert pair. Nos. 615/16 .. .. .. 1·10 1·25
616 35 c. C.S. *Retriever* (1961) 55 65
617 60 c. C.S. *Cable Enterprise* (1964) .. .. 1·00 1·25
a. Vert pair. Nos. 617/18 .. .. .. 2·00 2·50
618 60 c. C.S. *Mercury* (1962) .. .. .. 1·00 1·25
619 75 c. C.S. *Recorder* (1955) .. .. .. 1·25 1·40
a. Vert pair. Nos. 619/20 .. .. .. 2·50 2·75
620 75 c. C.S. *Pacific Guardian* (1984) .. .. 1·25 1·40
621 $1 S.S. *Great Eastern* (1860's) .. .. 1·50 1·75
a. Vert pair. Nos. 621/2 .. .. .. 3·00 3·50
622 $1 C.S. *Cable Venture* (1977) .. .. 1·50 1·75
615/22 .. .. *Set of* 8 7·75 9·00
MS623 Four sheets, each 102 × 131 mm. (a) 40 c. × 2 As 35 c. (b) 50 c. × 2 As 60 c. (c) 80 c. × 2 As 75 c. (d) $1.50 × 2 As $1 .. *Set of* 4 *sheets* 8·00 8·25

The two designs of each value were printed, *se-tenant*, in vertical pairs throughout the sheets.

(Des Court House Studio. Litho Format)

1986 (15 Dec). *Centenary of Statue of Liberty.* T **171** *and similar vert views of Statue in separate miniature sheets. Multicoloured.* P 14 × 13½.
MS624 Nine sheets, each 85 × 115 mm. 50 c.; 75 c.; 90 c.; $1; $1.25; $1.50; $1.75; $2; $2.50 *Set of* 9 *sheets* 15·00 15·00

172 18th-century Spanish Galleon

173 Outline Map and Flag of Montserrat

(Des J. Batchelor. Litho Questa)

1987 (15 Apr). *Shipwrecks.* T **172** *and similar horiz designs. Multicoloured.* W w **15**. P 14.
625 12 c. Type **172** 35 20
626 35 c. H.M.S. *Astrea*, 1808 .. .. .. 80 65
627 75 c. R.M.S. *Rhone*, 1867 .. .. .. 1·50 1·50
628 $1.50, S.S. *Rocus*, 1929 .. .. .. 2·75 3·00
625/8 .. .. *Set of* 4 5·00 4·75
MS629 86 × 65 mm. $2.50, *Volvart*, 1819 .. 4·50 5·00

(Des R. Burnett. Litho Walsall)

1987 (28 May). *11th Meeting of Organization of Eastern Caribbean States.* T **173** *and similar vert designs, each showing outline map and flag. Multicoloured.* W w **16**. P 14.
630 10 c. Type **173** 15 15
631 15 c. Grenada 20 25
632 20 c. Dominica 25 30
633 25 c. St. Kitts–Nevis 30 35
634 35 c. St. Vincent and Grenadines 45 50
635 50 c. British Virgin Islands 60 65
636 75 c. Antigua and Barbuda 90 95
637 $1 St. Lucia .. .. 1·25 1·40
630/7 .. .. *Set of* 8 3·75 4·00

174 Spider Lily

175 Early Mail Packet and 1867 1s. Stamp

(Des Jennifer Toombs. Litho Questa)

1987 (20 Aug). *Opening of Botanical Gardens.* T **174** *and similar vert designs. Multicoloured.* W w **16**. P 14.
638 12 c. Type **174** 40 20
639 35 c. Barrel Cactus 80 55
640 $1 Wild Plantain .. .. 1·75 2·00
641 $1.50, Little Butterfly Orchid .. .. 3·50 3·50
638/41 .. .. *Set of* 4 5·75 5·50
MS642 139 × 104 mm. $2.50, White Cedar .. 3·50 4·00

1987 (28 Oct). *As Nos.* 564, 566, 568/9, 571, 575 *and* 577 *but* W w **16**. P 14.
647 10 c. Grey Kingbird 10 10
649 15 c. Least Bittern 15 20
651 20 c. Clapper Rail 20 25
652 25 c. American Kestrel 25 30
654 35 c. Bridled Quail Dove 35 40
658 $1 Audubon's Shearwater .. .. .. 1·00 1·10
660 $3 Cattle Egret .. .. 3·00 3·25
647/60 .. .. *Set of* 7 4·50 5·00

(Des and litho Walsall)

1987 (17 Dec). *Bicentenary of Postal Services.* T **175** *and similar horiz designs, each including stamp and cancellation. Multicoloured.* W w **16** *(sideways).* P 14½.
662 10 c. Type **175** 20 15
663 20 c. Map and 1899 1d. 35 30
664 35 c. Post Office and Customs House, *c* 1913, and 1867 4d. 60 65
665 $1.50, Mail plane and 1964 25 c. definitive 2·50 2·75
662/5 .. .. *Set of* 4 3·25 3·50
MS666 70 × 60 mm. $2.50, Mail ship, 1880's, and 1880 1d. .. .. 3·00 3·25

(Litho Questa)

1988 (11 Aug). *500th Birth Anniv of Titian (artist). Vert designs as* T **238** *of Antigua. Multicoloured.* P 13½ × 14.
667 10 c. "Salome" 15 15
668 12 c. "Man with the Glove" 20 20
669 20 c. "Fabrizio Salvaresio" 30 30
670 25 c. "Daughter of Roberto Strozzi" 35 35
671 40 c. "Pope Julius II" 55 55
672 50 c. "Bishop Ludovico Beccadelli" 65 65
673 60 c. "King Philip II" 75 75
674 $1 "Empress Isabella of Portugal" .. .. 1·40 1·40
667/74 .. .. *Set of* 8 4·00 4·00
MS675 Two sheets, each 110 × 95 mm. (a) $2 "Emperor Charles V at Muhlberg" (detail). (b) $2 "Pope Paul III and his Grandsons" (detail) *Set of* 2 *sheets* 4·75 5·00

176 Aircraft over Sir Francis Drake Channel and Pawn

(Des B. Bundock. Litho Questa)

1988 (25 Aug). *First British Virgin Islands Open Chess Tournament.* T **176** *and similar horiz designs. Multicoloured.* P 14.
676 35 c. Type **176** 70 60
677 $1 Jose Capablanca (former World Champion) and king .. .. .. 1·90 1·90
MS678 109 × 81 mm. $2 Chess match .. .. 3·50 3·75

177 Hurdling

(Des L. Fried. Litho B.D.T.)

1988 (8 Sept). *Olympic Games, Seoul. T* **177** *and similar horiz designs. Multicoloured. P* 14.

679 12 c. Type **177** 20 20
680 20 c. Windsurfing 30 30
681 75 c. Basketball 95 95
682 $1 Tennis . . . . 1·40 1·40
679/82 . . . . . . *Set of* 4 2·50 2·50
MS683 71 × 102 mm. $2 Athletics . . . . 2·40 2·50

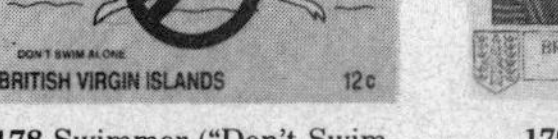

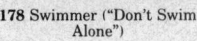

178 Swimmer ("Don't Swim Alone") **179** Princess Alexandra

(Des I. Arbell. Litho Questa)

1988 (26 Sept). *125th Anniv of International Red Cross. T* **178** *and similar designs. P* 14.

684 12 c. black, bright scarlet and cobalt . . 20 20
685 30 c. black, bright scarlet and cobalt . . 40 40
686 60 c. black, bright scarlet and cobalt . . 75 75
687 $1 black, bright scarlet and cobalt . . 1·40 1·40
684/7 . . . . . . *Set of* 4 2·50 2·50
MS688 68 × 96 mm. 50 c. × 4 black and bright scarlet . . . . 2·40 2·50

Designs: *Horiz*—30 c. Swimmers ("No swimming during electrical storms"); 60 c. Beach picnic ("Don't eat before swimming"); $1 Boat and equipment ("Proper equipment for boating"). *Vert*—50 c. × 4 Recovery position; clearing airway; mouth-to-mouth resuscitation; cardiac massage.

(Litho Questa)

1988 (9 Nov). *Visit of Princess Alexandra. T* **179** *and similar vert designs showing different portraits. P* 14.

689 40 c. multicoloured 70 55
690 $1.50, multicoloured . . . . . . 2·25 2·50
MS691 102 × 98 mm. $2 multicoloured . . 2·40 2·50

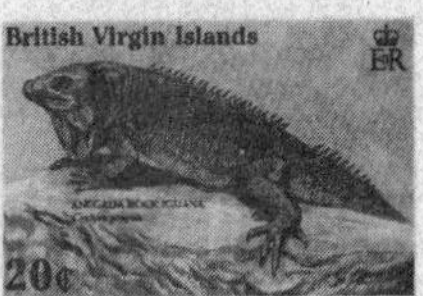

180 Brown Pelican in Flight **181** Anegada Rock Iguana

(Des S. Barlowe. Litho Questa)

1988 (30 Nov). *Wildlife (1st series). Aquatic Birds. T* **180** *and similar multicoloured designs. P* 14.

692 10 c. Type **180** 20 15
693 12 c. Brown Pelican perched on post . . 25 20
694 15 c. Brown Pelican 30 30
695 35 c. Brown Pelican swallowing fish . . 60 70
692/5 . . . . . . *Set of* 4 1·25 1·25
MS696 106 × 76 mm. $2 Northern Shoveler (*horiz*) . . . . 2·40 2·50

No. **MS**696 is without the WWF logo.

(Des S. Barlowe. Litho Questa)

1988 (15 Dec). *Wildlife (2nd series). Endangered Species. T* **181** *and similar multicoloured designs. P* 14.

697 20 c. Type **181** 25 30
698 40 c. Virgin Gorda Dwarf Gecko 50 55
699 60 c. Hawksbill Turtle 70 75
700 $1 Humpback Whale . . . . . . 1·25 1·40
697/700 . . . . . . *Set of* 4 2·40 2·75
MS701 106 × 77 mm. $2 Trunk Turtle (*vert*) . . 2·40 2·50

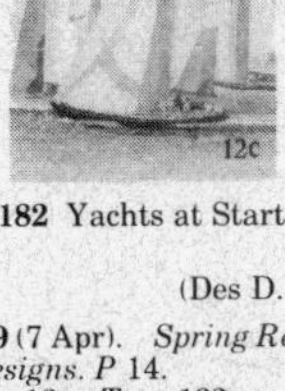

182 Yachts at Start 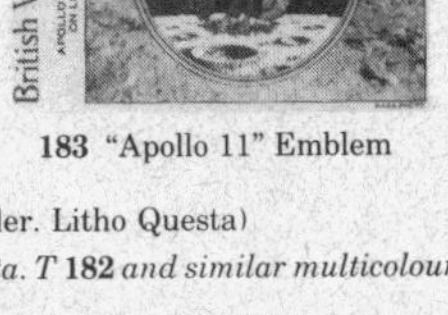 **183** "Apollo 11" Emblem

(Des D. Miller. Litho Questa)

1989 (7 Apr). *Spring Regatta. T* **182** *and similar multicoloured designs. P* 14.

702 12 c. Type **182** 15 20
703 40 c. Yacht tacking (*horiz*) 50 55
704 75 c. Yachts at sunset 90 95
705 $1 Yachts rounding buoy (*horiz*) . . 1·25 1·40
702/5 . . . . . . *Set of* 4 2·50 2·75
MS706 83×69 mm. $2 Yacht under full sail . . 2·40 2·50

(Des D. Miller. Litho Questa)

1989 (18 May). *500th Anniv of Discovery of America by Columbus (1992). Pre-Columbian Arawak Society. Multicoloured designs as T* **247** *of Antigua, but horiz. P* 14.

707 10 c. Arawak in hammock 10 15
708 20 c. Making fire 25 30
709 25 c. Making implements 30 35
710 $1.50, Arawak family . . . . . . 1·75 1·90
707/10 . . . . . . *Set of* 4 2·10 2·40
MS711 85×70 mm. $2 Religious ceremony . . 2·40 2·50

(Des W. Hanson. Litho Questa)

1989 (28 Sept). *20th Anniv of First Manned Landing on Moon. T* **183** *and similar multicoloured designs. P* 14.

712 15 c. Type **183** 20 25
713 30 c. Edwin Aldrin deploying scientific experiments 35 40
714 65 c. Aldrin and U.S. flag on Moon . . 75 80
715 $1 "Apollo 11" capsule after splashdown . . 1·25 1·40
712/15 . . . . . . *Set of* 4 2·25 2·50
MS716 102×77 mm. $2 Neil Armstrong (38×50 *mm*). P $13^1/_2$×14 . . . . . . 2·40 2·50

184 Black Harry and Nathaniel Gilbert preaching to Slaves **185** Player tackling

(Des R. Vigurs. Litho Questa)

1989 (24 Oct). *Bicentenary of Methodist Church in British Virgin Islands. T* **184** *and similar multicoloured designs. P* 14.

717 12 c. Type **184** 15 20
718 25 c. Methodist school exercise book . . 30 35
719 35 c. East End Methodist Church, 1810 . . 40 45
720 $1.25, Revd. John Wesley (founder of Methodism) and church youth choir . . 1·50 1·60
717/20 . . . . . . *Set of* 4 2·10 2·40
MS721 100×69 mm. $2 Dr. Thomas Coke . . 2·40 2·50

(Des R. Vigurs. Litho Questa)

1989 (6 Nov). *World Cup Football Championship, Italy, 1990. T* **185** *and similar vert designs. Multicoloured. P* 14.

722 5 c. Type **185** 10 10
723 10 c. Player dribbling ball 10 15
724 20 c. Two players chasing ball 25 30
725 $1.75, Goalkeeper diving for ball . . 2·10 2·25
722/5 . . . . . . *Set of* 4 2·25 2·50
MS726 100×70 mm. $2 British Virgin Islands team captain . . . . . . 2·40 2·50

OFFICIAL STAMPS

OFFICIAL

(O 1)

Two varieties of overprint:

Type I. Foot of "OFFICIAL" 15–16 mm from top of design. Light impression with little or no black outline to letters.

Type II. Foot of "OFFICIAL" 20 mm from top of design. Heavy impression with thick black outline to letters.

1985 (Feb). *Nos.* 418/19, 420*a*/1*a*, 423*a*/4*a*, 425, 426*a*, 427, 428*a and* 429/33 *optd as Type* O 1 *in silver by Questa.*

O 1 1 c. Purple-tipped Sea Anemone (I) . . 15 20
a. Opt Type II . . . . . . 13·00
O 2 3 c. Common Starfish (I) 20 20
a. Opt Type II . . . . . . 13·00
O 3 5 c. Type **134** (II) 20 15
O 4 8 c. Triton's Trumpet (shell) (I) . . 30 15
a. Opt Type II . . . .
O 5 13 c. Flamingo Tongue Snail (II) . . 40 35
O 6 15 c. Spider Crab (I) 45 45
O 7 18 c. Sea Squirts (I) 50 50
a. Opt Type II . . . .
O 8 20 c. True Tulip (shell) (I) 50 50
O 9 25 c. Rooster Tail Conch (shell) (I) . . 60 60
O10 30 c. Fighting Conch (shell) (I) . . 70 70
a. Optd on No. 428 . . . . 6·00
O11 60 c. Mangrove Crab (I) . . . . 1·50 1·50
O12 $1 Coral Polyps (I) . . . . 2·25 2·25
O13 $2.50, Peppermint Shrimp (I) . . 3·75 4·25
O14 $3 West Indian Murex (shell) (I) . . 4·75 5·50
O15 $5 Carpet Anemone (I) . . . . 7·50 9·00
O1/15 . . . . . . *Set of* 15 21·00 24·00

OFFICIAL

(O 2)

1986 (10 Feb–Sept). *Nos.* 560/78 *optd with Type* O 2 *by Questa.*

O16 1 c. Type **162** (9.86) 10 10
O17 2 c. Yellow-crowned Night Heron . . 15 10
O18 5 c. Mangrove Cuckoo (9.86) . . 10 10
O19 8 c. Northern Mockingbird 25 15
O20 10 c. Grey Kingbird (9.86) 20 15
O21 12 c. Red-necked Pigeon 30 30
O22 15 c. Least Bittern (9.86) 25 25
O23 18 c. Smooth-billed Ani 40 40
O24 20 c. Clapper Rail (9.86) 30 30
O25 25 c. American Kestrel (9.86) . . 35 35
O26 30 c. Pearly-eyed Thrasher (9.86) . . 40 40
O27 35 c. Bridled Quail Dove (9.86) . . 45 45
O28 40 c. Green Heron 75 75
O29 50 c. Scaly-breasted Ground Dove . . 1·00 1·00
O30 60 c. Little Blue Heron . . . . 1·25 1·25
O31 $1 Audubon's Shearwater . . . . 2·00 2·00
O32 $2 Blue-faced Booby . . . . 3·75 3·75
O33 $3 Cattle Egret . . . . . . 5·00 5·00
O34 $5 Zenaida Dove (9.86) . . . . 6·50 6·50
O16/34 . . . . . . *Set of* 19 21·00 21·00

Brunei

Sultan Hashim Jalil-ul-alam Akamudin, 1885–1906

For many years the status of the 1895 issue remained uncertain to such an extent that the 1906 provisionals on Labuan were taken to be the first issue of Brunei.

The 1895 "Star and Crescent" design stamps were, from their first appearance, considered bogus or, at best, as an issue made purely for philatelic purposes. Research into the background of the events surrounding the set led to the publication, in 1933, of the original agreement between Sultan Hashim and J. C. Robertson dated 20 August 1894 which made clear that the stamps fulfilled a genuine postal purpose. Although Robertson and his partners intended to exploit the philatelic sales for their own benefit the agreement testifies, as does other evidence, to the use of the stamps by the Sultan for his postal service. As Brunei did not, at that time, belong to any local or international postal union the stamps were only valid within the state or on mail to Labuan or Sarawak. Items for further afield required franking with Labuan stamps in addition. Although most covers surviving are addressed to Robertson's associates enough commercial covers and cards exist to show that there was, indeed, a postal service.

PRICES FOR STAMPS ON COVER TO 1945

Nos. 1/10 are rare used on cover.
Nos. 11/22 *from* × 30
Nos. 23/33 *from* × 25
Nos. 34/50 *from* × 10
Nos. 51/9 *from* × 12
Nos. 60/78 *from* × 8

The Sarawak Government maintained a post office at the coal mining centre of Brooketon, and the stamps of SARAWAK were used there from 1893 until the office was handed over to Brunei in February 1907.

1 Star and Local Scene

(Litho in Glasgow)

1895 (18 July). *P* 13–13½.

No.	Type	Description	Unused	Used
1	1	½ c. brown	75	7·50
2		1 c. brown-lake	75	7·50
3		2 c. grey-black	3·00	7·50
4		3 c. deep blue	3·00	7·50
5		5 c. deep blue-green	5·50	8·50
6		8 c. plum	7·50	10·00
7		10 c. orange-red	7·00	12·00
		a. Imperf (pair)	£450	
8		25 c. turquoise-green	13·00	18·00
9		50 c. yellow-green	18·00	35·00
10		$1 yellow-olive	20·00	55·00
1/10		*Set of* 10	65·00	£150

BRUNEI. (2) BRUNEI. TWO CENTS. (3) BRUNEI. 25 CENTS. (4)

(Optd by Govt Printer, Singapore)

1906 (1 Oct). *Stamps of Labuan, T* **18** *(Nos. 116c, etc.), optd with T* **2**, *or surch as T* **3** *or* **4** *(25 c.), in red. P* 13½ *or* 14 *(1 c.).*

No.	Description	Unused	Used
11	1 c. black and purple	15·00	24·00
	a. Error. Opt in black	£2000	£2500
12	2 c. on 3 c. black and sepia	1·50	4·50
	a. "BRUNEI" double	£3500	£2500
13	2 c. on 8 c. black and vermilion	20·00	45·00
	a. "TWO CENTS" double	£5500	
	b. "TWO CENTS" omitted in vert pair with normal	£7000	
14	3 c. black and sepia	20·00	45·00
15	4 c. on 12 c. black and yellow	1·25	4·25
16	5 c. on 16 c. green and brown	24·00	32·00
17	8 c. black and vermilion	8·50	17·00
18	10 c. on 16 c. green and brown	6·00	16·00
19	25 c. on 16 c. green and brown	90·00	£120
20	30 c. on 16 c. green and brown	80·00	£110
21	50 c. on 16 c. green and brown	80·00	£110
22	$1 on 8 c. black and vermilion	80·00	£110
11/22	*Set of* 12	£375	£550

Sultan Mohamed Jemal-ul-Alam, 1906–1924

PRINTERS. All Brunei stamps from Nos. 23 to 113 were recess-printed by De La Rue.

OMNIBUS ISSUES

Details, together with prices for complete sets, of the various Omnibus issues from the 1935 Silver Jubilee series to date are included in a special section following Zululand at the end of the catalogue.

5 View on Brunei River

1907–10. *Wmk Mult Crown CA. P* 14.

No.	Type	Description	Unused	Used
23	5	1 c. grey-black and pale green	2·25	6·50
24		2 c. grey-black and scarlet	2·50	4·50
25		3 c. grey-black and chocolate	9·00	18·00
26		4 c. grey-black and mauve	6·00	10·00
		a. Grey-black and reddish purple (1910)	45·00	60·00
27		5 c. grey-black and blue	30·00	55·00
28		8 c. grey-black and orange	5·50	23·00
29		10 c. grey-black and deep green	4·50	7·00
30		25 c. pale blue and ochre-brown	15·00	26·00
31		30 c. violet and black	13·00	22·00
32		50 c. green and deep brown	13·00	22·00
33		$1 red and grey	45·00	70·00
23/33		*Set of* 11	£130	£225
23/33 Optd "Specimen"		*Set of* 11	£275	

I

II

I Double plate. Lowest line of shading on water is dotted.
II Single plate. Dotted line of shading removed.

Stamps printed in two colours are as I.

1908 (12 June)–**20.** *Colours changed. Double or single plates. Wmk Mult Crown CA. P* 14.

No.	Type	Description	Unused	Used
34	5	1 c. green (I)	50	2·00
35		1 c. green (II) (1911)	25	75
36		2 c. black and brown (5.4.11)	80	1·25
37		3 c. scarlet (I)	1·40	75
38		3 c. scarlet (II) (1916)	18·00	26·00
39		4 c. claret (II)	75	75
40		5 c. black and orange	6·50	6·50
41		8 c. blue and indigo-blue (10.08)	6·00	9·50
42		10 c. purple/*yellow* (II) (1912)	1·25	85
		a. On pale yellow (Optd S. £25)	1·00	2·75
43		25 c. deep lilac (II) (30.5.12)	2·25	7·00
44		30 c. purple and orange-yellow (18.3.12)	8·50	12·00
45		50 c. black/*green* (II) (1912)	18·00	35·00
		a. On blue-green (1920)	6·50	14·00
46		$1 black and red/*blue* (18.3.12)	20·00	42·00
47		$5 carmine/*green* (I) (1910)	60·00	£120
48		$25 black/*red* (I) (1910)	£450	£800
34/47		*Set of* 12	£100	£190
34/48 Optd "Specimen"		*Set of* 13	£450	

The used price for No. 48 is for a cancelled-by-favour example, dated before December 1941; there being no actual postal rate for which this value could be used. Examples dated after 1945 are worth much less.

Retouch Normal

MALAYA-
BORNEO
EXHIBITION.
1922.
(6)

RETOUCHES. We list the very distinctive 5 c. Retouch (top left value tablet, 1st row, 8th stamp) but there are others of interest, notably in the clouds.

1916. *Colours changed. Single plates. Wmk Mult Crown CA. P* 14.

No.	Type	Description	Unused	Used
49	5	5 c. orange	4·50	7·00
		a. "5 c." retouch	£130	£160
50		8 c. ultramarine	4·50	12·00
49/50 Optd "Specimen"		*Set of* 2	£100	

MALAYA-BORNEO EXHIBITION OVERPRINTS. These were produced from a setting of 30 examples, applied twice to overprint the complete sheet of 60 stamps. Three prominent overprint flaws exist, each occurring on all the stamps in two vertical rows of the sheet.

HI — Short "I" (all stamps in 2nd and 8th vertical rows)
EX — Broken "E" (all stamps in 4th and 10th vertical rows)
NE — Broken "N" (all stamps in 6th and 12th vertical rows)

(Optd by Govt Printer, Singapore)

1922 (31 Mar). *Optd with T* **6**, *in black.*

No.	Type	Description	Unused	Used
51	5	1 c. green (II)	1·75	15·00
		a. Short "I"	5·50	
		b. Broken "E"	5·50	
		c. Broken "N"	5·50	
52		2 c. black and brown	3·75	17·00
		a. Short "I"	9·00	
		b. Broken "E"	9·00	
		c. Broken "N"	9·00	
53	5	3 c. scarlet (II)	5·00	27·00
		a. Short "I"	11·00	
		b. Broken "E"	11·00	
		c. Broken "N"	11·00	
54		4 c. claret (II)	4·00	35·00
		a. Short "I"	10·00	
		b. Broken "E"	10·00	
		c. Broken "N"	10·00	
55		5 c. orange (II)	7·50	45·00
		a. "5 c." retouch	£275	£500
		b. Short "I"	16·00	
		c. Broken "E"	16·00	
		d. Broken "N"	16·00	
56		10 c. purple/*yellow* (II)	6·50	48·00
		a. Short "I"	14·00	
		b. Broken "E"	14·00	
		c. Broken "N"	14·00	
57		25 c. purple (II)	14·00	75·00
		a. Short "I"	30·00	
		b. Broken "E"	30·00	
		c. Broken "N"	30·00	
58		50 c. black/*blue-green* (II)	45·00	£140
		a. Short "I"	80·00	
		b. Broken "E"	80·00	
		c. Broken "N"	80·00	
59		$1 black and red/*blue*	70·00	£175
		a. Short "I"	£120	
		b. Broken "E"	£120	
		c. Broken "N"	£120	
51/9		*Set of* 9	£140	£500

Sultan Ahmed Tajudin Akhazul Khairi Wadin, 1924–1950

7 Native houses, Water Village

1924 (Feb)–**37.** *Printed from single plates as Type* II, *except* 30 c. *and* $1 *as Type* I. *Wmk Mult Script CA. P* 14.

No.	Type	Description	Unused	Used
60	5	1 c. black (9.26)	25	35
61		2 c. brown (3.24)	90	3·00
62		2 c. green (3.33)	25	30
63		3 c. green (3.24)	80	4·25
64		4 c. maroon (3.24)	1·25	75
65		4 c. orange (1929)	65	50
66		5 c. orange-yellow* (3.24)	1·25	90
		a. "5 c." retouch	90·00	£110
67		5 c. grey (1931)	5·00	3·75
		a. "5 c." retouch	£200	£250
68		5 c. chocolate (1933)	75	15
		a. "5 c." retouch	50·00	50·00
69	7	6 c. intense black** (3.24)	6·50	8·50
70		6 c. scarlet (1931)	3·75	9·00
71	5	8 c. ultramarine (9.27)	4·25	5·00
72		8 c. grey-black (1933)	2·00	55
73		10 c. purple/*yellow* (3.37)	6·50	10·00
74	7	12 c. blue	4·50	8·00
		a. Pale greenish blue (1927)	£130	£200
75	5	25 c. slate-purple (1931)	5·00	7·00
76		30 c. purple and orange-yellow (1931)	4·50	9·50
77		50 c. black/*emerald* (1931)	7·00	12·00
78		$1 black and red/*blue* (1931)	24·00	48·00
60/78		*Set of* 19	70·00	£120
60/72, 74/8 Optd/Perf "Specimen"		*Set of* 18	£350	

*For 5 c. orange, see No. 82. No. 66 is a "Wet" printing and No. 82 a "Dry".

**For 6 c. black, see No. 83. Apart from the difference in shade there is a variation in size, No. 69 being 37¾ mm long and No. 83 39 mm.

The 2 c. orange in Type **5** and the 6 c. greenish black, 8 c. red and 15 c. ultramarine in Type **7** were not issued without the Japanese Occupation overprint, although unoverprinted copies exist.

During the life of this issue De La Rue changed the method of production from a "Wet" to a "Dry" process. Initially the stamps were printed on ungummed paper which was dampened before being put on the press. Once the paper had dried, and contracted in the process, the gum was then applied. "Dry" printings, introduced around 1934, were on pre-gummed paper. The contraction of the "Wet" printings was considerable and usually involves a difference of between 0.5 mm and 1 mm when compared with the larger "Dry" printings. The following stamps occur from both "Wet" and "Dry" versions: 1 c., 2 c. green, 4 c. orange, 5 c. chocolate, 6 c. scarlet, 8 c. grey-black, 10 c. and 25 c.

Stamps of this issue can be found either line or comb perforated.

After the cessation of hostilities with the Japanese postal services were re-introduced by the British Military Administration. Post offices under B.M.A. control were opened at Brunei Town and Kuala Belait on 17 December 1945 where B.M.A. overprints on the stamps of NORTH BORNEO and SARAWAK were used until the reappearance of Brunei issues on 2 January 1947.

Redrawn clouds (R. 1/1 of No. 80*ab* only)

1947 (2 Jan)–**51**. *Colours changed and new values. Wmk Mult Script CA. P* 14.

79 **5** 1 c. chocolate . . 30 45
a. "A" missing from wmk
80 2 c. grey . . 30 75
a. Perf 14½ × 13½ (25.9.50) . . 1·25 1·40
ab. Black (27.6.51) . . 1·00 1·75
ac. Redrawn clouds . . 25·00
81 **7** 3 c. green . . 75 1·75
82 **5** 5 c. orange* . . 50 70
a. "5 c." retouch . . 50·00 55·00
b. Perf 14½ × 13½ (25.9.50) . . 4·00 5·00
c. Ditto. "5 c." retouch . . 60·00 60·00
83 **7** 6 c. black* . . 90 2·00
84 **5** 8 c. scarlet . . 30 20
a. Perf 13 (25.1.51) . . 20 2·00
85 10 c. violet . . 20 10
a. Perf 14½ × 13½ (25.9.50) . . 1·50 2·25
86 15 c. ultramarine . . 30 15
87 25 c. purple . . 40 40
a. Perf 14½ × 13½ (25.1.51) . . 40 2·75
88 30 c. black and orange . . 35 45
a. Perf 14½ × 13½ (25.1.51) . . 45 3·25
89 50 c. black . . 40 20
a. Perf 13 (25.9.50) . . 1·00 8·00
90 $1 black and scarlet . . 1·25 60
91 $5 green and red-orange (2.2.48) . . 15·00 14·00
92 $10 black and purple (2.2.48) . . 22·00 32·00
79/92 . . *Set of* 14 40·00 48·00
79/92 Perf "Specimen" *Set of* 14 £180

*See also Nos. 66 and 69.

The 1, 2, 3, 5, 6 and 10 c. values utilised the plates of the pre-war issue and were line perforated until the introduction of the 14½ × 13½ comb machine for some values in 1950–51. The 8, 15, 50 c., $1, $2 and $5 were from new plates with the sheets comb perforated. The 30 c. was initially a pre-war plate, but it is believed that a new plate was introduced in 1951.

8 Sultan Ahmed Tajudin and Water Village

1949 (22 Sept). *Sultan's Silver Jubilee. Wmk Mult Script CA. P* 13.

93 **8** 8 c. black and carmine . . 55 60
94 25 c. purple and red-orange . . 55 50
95 50 c. black and blue . . 70 80
93/5 . . *Set of* 3 1·60 1·75

1949 (10 Oct). *75th Anniv of Universal Postal Union. As Nos.* 114/17 *of Antigua.*

96 8 c. carmine . . 65 80
97 15 c. deep blue . . 1·25 90
98 25 c. magenta . . 1·25 90
99 50 c. blue-black . . 1·50 90
96/9 . . *Set of* 4 4·25 3·25

Sutan Sir Omar Ali Saifuddin-Wasa'adul Khairi Wadin, 1950–1967

9 Sultan Omar Ali Saifuddin

10 Native houses, Water Village

1952 (1 Mar)–**58**. *Wmk Mult Script CA. P* 13.

100 **9** 1 c. black . . 10 15
101 2 c. black and orange . . 10 15
102 3 c. black and lake-brown . . 10 10
103 4 c. black and green . . 10 10
104 6 c. black and grey . . 10 10
105 8 c. black and crimson . . 20 10
a. Black and crimson-lake (15.2.56) . . 20 10
106 10 c. black and sepia . . 15 10
107 12 c. black and violet . . 45 10
108 15 c. black and pale blue . . 60 10
109 25 c. black and purple . . 60 10
a. Black and reddish purple (8.10.53) 1·25 20
110 50 c. black and ultramarine . . 50 10
a. Black and blue (22.6.55) . . 60 10
111 **10** $1 black and green . . 1·25 60
a. Black and bronze-green (23.7.58) . . 1·75 75
112 $2 black and scarlet . . 4·50 2·00
113 $5 black and maroon . . 9·50 3·50
a. Black and brown-purple (15.2.56) . . 8·50 3·00
100/13 . . *Set of* 14 15·00 5·50

No. 106 exists in coils constructed from normal sheets.
See also Nos. 118/31 and 202/9.

11 Brunei Mosque and Sultan Omar

(Recess B.W.)

1958 (24 Sept). *Opening of Brunei Mosque. W w* **12**. *P* 13½.

114 **11** 8 c. black and myrtle-green . . 10 45
115 15 c. black and carmine . . 10 15
116 35 c. black and deep lilac . . 20 70
114/16 . . *Set of* 3 35 1·10

12 "Protein Foods"

(Des M. Goaman. Photo Harrison)

1963 (4 June). *Freedom from Hunger. W w* **12**. *P* 14 × 14½.

117 **12** 12 c. sepia . . 2·00 90

1964–72. *As Nos.* 100/13, *but W w* **12**. *Glazed paper* ($2, 5) *or ordinary paper* (*others*).

118 **9** 1 c. black (17.3.64) . . 10 10
a. Glazed paper. *Grey* (28.11.69) . . 10 15
ab. Slate-grey (30.6.72) . . 10 15
119 2 c. black and orange (17.3.64) . . 25 10
a. Glazed paper (27.5.70) . . 15 10
120 3 c. black and lake-brown (10.11.64) . . 30 10
a. Glazed paper (27.5.70) . . 25 10
121 4 c. black and green (12.5.64) . . 10 10
a. Glazed paper (22.4.70) . . 15 10
ab. Black and emerald (19.11.71) . . 25 60
122 6 c. black and grey (12.5.64) . . 40 10
a. Black (28.11.69) . . 2·50 3·00
b. Glazed paper (28.11.69) . . 35 10
ba. Light grey (19.11.71) . . 25 60
123 8 c. black and crimson-lake (12.5.64) . . 20 10
a. Glazed paper (27.5.70) . . 40 15
ab. Black and brown-red (19.11.71) . . 35 60
124 10 c. black and sepia (12.5.64) . . 15 10
a. Glazed paper (31.3.70) . . 45 10
ab. Grey and pale brown (coil) (11.10.71) 40 60
125 12 c. black and violet (12.5.64) . . 45 10
a. Glazed paper (5.11.70) . . 75 20
126 15 c. black and pale blue (12.5.64) . . 25 10
a. Glazed paper (28.11.69) . . 25 10
127 25 c. black and purple (12.5.64) . . 55 10
a. Glazed paper (18.5.70) . . 2·00 90
ab. Glazed paper. *Black and reddish violet* (30.4.71) . . 2·25 35
128 50 c. black and ultramarine (10.11.64) . . 75 10
a. Black & brt ultramarine (17.3.69) . . 1·00 40
b. Glazed paper (5.11.70) . . 2·00 45
ba. Grey and indigo (21.12.71) . . 2·50 50
129 **10** $1 black and bronze-green (14.5.68) . . 1·50 1·75
a. Glazed paper (5.11.70) . . 2·25 2·50
130 $2 black and scarlet (5.11.70) . . 20·00 13·00
131 $5 black and maroon (5.11.70) . . 22·00 18·00
118/29 . . *Set of* 12 4·50 2·25
118a/29a, 130/1 . . *Set of* 14 45·00 32·00

Printings of the 6 and 15 c. issued on 28 November 1969 were on both ordinary and glazed paper, the 6 c. on ordinary producing a distinct shade.

No. 124a exists in coils constructed from normal sheets.

13 I.T.U. Emblem

(Des M. Goaman. Litho Enschedé)

1965 (17 May). *I.T.U. Centenary. W w* **12**. *P* 11 × 11½.

132 **13** 4 c. mauve and orange-brown . . 35 10
133 75 c. orange-yellow and light emerald . . 1·00 75

14 I.C.Y. Emblem

(Des V. Whiteley. Litho Harrison)

1965 (25 Oct). *International Co-operation Year. W w* **12**. *P* 14.

134 **14** 4 c. reddish purple and turquoise-green 20 10
135 15 c. deep bluish green and lavender . . 55 35

15 Sir Winston Churchill and St. Paul's Cathedral in Wartime

(Des Jennifer Toombs. Photo Harrison)

1966 (24 Jan). *Churchill Commemoration. W w* **12**. *P* 14.

136 **15** 3 c. black, cerise, gold and new blue . . 30 15
137 10 c. black, cerise, gold and deep green . . 1·25 20
138 15 c. black, cerise, gold and brown . . 1·50 35
139 75 c. black, cerise, gold and bluish violet 3·00 2·00
136/9 . . *Set of* 4 5·50 2·50

16 Footballer's Legs, Ball and Jules Rimet Cup

(Des V. Whiteley. Litho Harrison)

1966 (4 July). *World Cup Football Championships. W w* **12** (*sideways*). *P* 14.

140 **16** 4 c. violet, yellow-green, lake & yell-brn 20 15
141 75 c. chocolate, blue-grn, lake & yell-brn 75 60

17 W.H.O. Building

(Des M. Goaman. Litho Harrison)

1966 (20 Sept). *Inauguration of W.H.O. Headquarters, Geneva. W w* **12** (*sideways*). *P* 14.

142 **17** 12 c. black, yellow-green and light blue 35 20
143 25 c. black, light purple and yellow-brown 55 35

18 "Education"

19 "Science"

20 "Culture"

(Des Jennifer Toombs. Litho Harrison)

1966 (1 Dec). *20th Anniv of U.N.E.S.C.O. W w* **12** (*sideways*). *P* 14.

144 **18** 4 c. slate-violet, red, yellow and orange 35 10
145 **19** 15 c. orange-yellow, violet and deep olive 75 40
146 **20** 75 c. black, bright purple and orange . . 2·25 2·50
144/6 . . *Set of* 3 3·00 2·75

Sultan Sir Hassanal Bolkiah Mu'izzadin Waddaulah, 1967

21 Religious Headquarters Building

(Des and photo Harrison)

1967 (19 Dec). *1400th Anniv of Revelation of the Koran. W w* **12** (*sideways*). *P* 12½.

147 **21** 4 c. multicoloured . . 10 10
148 10 c. multicoloured . . 15 10
149 – 25 c. multicoloured . . 20 20
150 – 50 c. multicoloured . . 35 50
147/50 . . *Set of* 4 70 80

Nos. 149/50 are as T **21** but have sprigs of laurel flanking the main design (which has a smaller circle) in place of flagpoles.

COVER PRICES

Cover factors are quoted at the beginning of each country for most issues to 1945. An explanation of the system can be found on page x. The factors quoted do not, however, apply to philatelic covers.

22 Sultan of Brunei, Mosque and Flags

(Des V. Whiteley. Photo Enschedé)

1968 (9 July). *Installation of Y.T.M. Seri Paduka Duli Pengiran Temenggong. T* **22** *and similar multicoloured design. P* 14 × 13 (12 c.) *or* 13 × 14 (*others*).

151 4 c. Type **22** 15 20
152 12 c. Sultan of Brunei, Mosque and Flags (*horiz*) 40 55
153 25 c. Type **22** 50 90
151/3 .. .. *Set of* 3 95 1·50

23 Sultan of Brunei 24 Sultan of Brunei

(Des V. Whiteley. Litho D.L.R.)

1968 (15 July). *Sultan's Birthday. W w* **12** (*sideways*). *P* 12.

154 **23** 4 c. multicoloured 10 10
155 12 c. multicoloured 20 20
156 25 c. multicoloured 30 40
154/6 .. .. *Set of* 3 55 65

(Des V. Whiteley. Photo Harrison)

1968 (1 Aug). *Coronation of the Sultan of Brunei. W w* **12** (*sideways*). *P* 14½ × 14.

157 **24** 4 c. multicoloured 15 10
158 12 c. multicoloured 25 25
159 25 c. multicoloured 40 35
157/9 .. .. *Set of* 3 70 65

25 New Building and Sultan's Portrait

26 New Building and Sultan's Portrait

(Photo Enschedé)

1968 (29 Sept). *Opening of Language and Literature Bureau. W w* **12** (*sideways*). *P* 13½ (10 c.) *or* 12½ × 13½ (*others*).

160 **25** 10 c. multicoloured 10 20
a. Tête-bêche (pair) 20 40
161 **26** 15 c. multicoloured 20 20
162 30 c. multicoloured 40 45
160/2 .. .. *Set of* 3 65 75

The above were scheduled for release in 1967, and when finally issued had the year altered by overprinting.

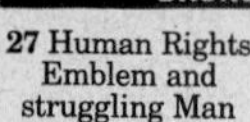

27 Human Rights Emblem and struggling Man

28 Sultan of Brunei and W.H.O. Emblem

(Des V. Whiteley. Litho Harrison)

1968 (16 Dec). *Human Rights Year. W w* **12**. *P* 14.

163 **27** 12 c. black, yellow and green 10 10
164 25 c. black, yellow and blue 15 15
165 75 c. black, yellow and dull purple 45 65
163/5 .. .. *Set of* 3 65 80

(Des V. Whiteley. Litho Format)

1968 (19 Dec). *20th Anniv of World Health Organization. P* 14.

166 **28** 4 c. yellow, black and cobalt 10 10
167 15 c. yellow, black and deep bluish violet 25 20
168 25 c. yellow, black and pale yellow-olive 35 40
166/8 .. .. *Set of* 3 60 65

29 Deep Sea Oil-Rig, Sultan of Brunei and inset portrait of Pengiran Di-Gadong

(Des adapted by V. Whiteley. Photo Enschedé)

1969 (10 July). *Installation* (9*th May*, 1968) *of Pengiran Shahbandar as Y.T.M. Seri Paduka Duli Pengiran Di-Gadong Sahibol Mal. W w* **12**. *P* 14 × 13.

169 **29** 12 c. multicoloured 35 20
170 40 c. multicoloured 70 55
171 50 c. multicoloured 80 65
169/71 .. .. *Set of* 3 1·75 1·25

30 Aerial View of Parliament Buildings

(Des Harrison. Litho D.L.R.)

1969 (23 Sept). *Opening of Royal Audience Hall and Legislative Council Chamber. P* 15.

172 **30** 12 c. multicoloured 15 15
173 25 c. multicoloured 25 30
174 – 50 c. rose-red and bluish violet 50 50
172/4 .. .. *Set of* 3 80 85

Design:—50 c. Elevation of new buildings.

32 Youth Centre and Sultan's Portrait

(Des V. Whiteley. Litho D.L.R.)

1969 (20 Dec). *Opening of the New Youth Centre. W w* **12**. *P* 15 × 14½.

175 **32** 6 c. flesh, slate-lilac and black 15 10
176 10 c. olive-yellow, grey-green and blackish brown 20 10
177 30 c. yellow-olive, yellow-brown & black 55 35
175/7 .. .. *Set of* 3 80 45

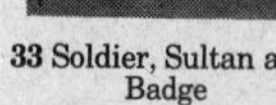

33 Soldier, Sultan and Badge

34 Badge, and Officer in Full-dress Uniform

(Des Maj. M. A. Bowman. Adapted V. Whiteley. Litho Questa)

1971 (3 May). *Tenth Anniv of Royal Brunei Malay Regiment. Multicoloured designs, each with Badge and Sultan's portrait as T* **33**. *W w* **12** (*sideways on* 15 *and* 75 *c.*). *P* 14½.

178 10 c. Type **33** 45 25
179 15 c. Helicopter (*horiz*) 55 45
180 75 c. *Pahlawan* (patrol boat) (*horiz*) .. 2·50 3·75
178/80 .. .. *Set of* 3 3·25 4·00

(Des Supt. T. Swan. Litho Format)

1971 (14 Aug). *50th Anniv of Royal Brunei Police Force. T* **34** *and similar vert designs. Multicoloured. W w* **12** (*sideways*). *P* 14½.

181 10 c. Type **34** 50 30
182 15 c. Badge and Patrol Constable 70 70
183 50 c. Badge and Traffic Constable .. .. 2·25 3·50
181/3 .. .. *Set of* 3 3·00 4·00

35 Perdana Wazir, Sultan of Brunei and view of Water Village

(Des and litho Harrison)

1971 (27 Aug). *Installation of the Yang Teramat Mulia as the Perdana Wazir* (1970). *T* **35** *and similar horiz designs showing different views of Brunei Town. W w* **12**. *P* 14.

184 **35** 15 c. multicoloured 40 40
185 – 25 c. multicoloured 70 80
186 – 50 c. multicoloured .. .. 1·40 2·25
184/6 .. .. *Set of* 3 2·25 3·00

36 Pottery

(Des C. Abbott. Litho Questa)

1972 (29 Feb). *Opening of Brunei Museum. T* **36** *and similar horiz designs. Multicoloured. W w* **12** (*sideways*). *P* 13½.

187 10 c. Type **36** 25 10
188 12 c. Straw-work 30 20
189 15 c. Leather-work 35 20
190 25 c. Gold-work .. .. 1·00 1·10
191 50 c. Museum Building (58 × 21 *mm*) .. 2·00 2·50
187/91 .. .. *Set of* 5 3·50 3·75

37 Brunei Museum, Queen Elizabeth and Sultan of Brunei

(Des locally. Photo Enschedé)

1972 (29 Feb). *Royal Visit. T* **37** *and similar horiz designs each with portraits of Queen and Sultan. Multicoloured. W w* **12** (*sideways*). *P* 13 × 13½.

192 10 c. Type **37** 20 20
193 15 c. Native houses 30 30
194 25 c. Mosque 75 90
195 50 c. Royal Assembly Hall .. .. .. 2·00 2·50
192/5 .. .. *Set of* 4 3·00 3·50

38 Secretariat Building

(Des Harrison. Litho J.W.)

1972 (4 Oct). *Renaming of Brunei Town as Bandar Seri Begawan. T* **38** *and similar horiz designs. W w* **12** (*sideways*). *P* 13½.

196 10 c. multicoloured 15 15
197 15 c. green, light yellow and black 20 15
198 25 c. ultramarine, lemon and black 30 40
199 50 c. rosine, pale turquoise-blue and black .. 70 90
196/9 .. .. *Set of* 4 1·25 1·40

Views:—15 c. Darul Hana Palace; 25 c. Old Brunei Town; 50 c. Town and Water Village.

39 Blackburn "Beverley" parachuting Supplies

(Des Trident Artists. Litho Questa)

1972 (15 Nov). *Opening of R.A.F. Museum, Hendon. T* **39** *and similar horiz design. Multicoloured. W w* **12** (*sideways on* 75 *c.*). *P* 14 × 13½ (25 *c.*) *or* 13½ × 14 (75 *c.*).

200 25 c. Type **39** .. .. 1·25 1·25
201 75 c. Blackburn "Beverley" landing .. .. 3·00 3·25

1972 (17 Nov)–**74**. *As Nos.* 119/26, *but W w* **12** (*sideways*). *Glazed paper.*

202	**9**	2 c. black and orange (9.5.73)	20	1·40
203		3 c. black and lake-brown	70	40
204		4 c. black and green	50	35
205		6 c. black and grey	90	25
206		8 c. black and brown-red (9.5.73)	50	1·25
207		10 c. black and sepia	70	25
		a. *Black and bistre-brown* (24.7.74)	80	1·00
208		12 c. black and violet	1·50	2·00
209		15 c. black and pale blue	1·25	2·00
202/9		*Set of* 8	5·50	7·00

40 Girl with Traditional Flower-pot, and Boy with Bowl and Pipe

(Des (from photograph by D. Groves) and photo Harrison)

1972 (20 Nov). *Royal Silver Wedding. Multicoloured; background colour given.* W w **12**. *P* 14 × 14½.

210	**40**	12 c. carmine-red	10	10
211		75 c. deep myrtle-green	20	50

41 Interpol H.Q., Paris

(Des Shamir Bros. Litho Harrison)

1973 (7 Sept). *50th Anniv of Interpol. T* **41** *and similar horiz design.* W w **12** (*inverted on* 50 *c.*). *P* 14 × 14½.

212	25 c. bright green, purple and dull blue-black	1·25	1·25
213	50 c. pale greenish blue, ultramarine & carm	1·25	1·25

The 50 c. shows a different view of the H.Q.

42 Sultan, Princess Anne and Capt. Phillips

(Des PAD Studio. Litho Format)

1973 (14 Nov). *Royal Wedding.* W w **12**. *P* 14.

214	**42**	25 c. multicoloured	10	10
215		50 c. multicoloured	15	25

43 Churchill Painting

44 Sultan Sir Hassanal Bolkiah Mu'izzaddin Waddaulah

(Des C. Abbott. Litho Questa)

1973 (31 Dec). *Opening of Churchill Memorial Building. T* **43** *and similar vert design. Multicoloured.* W w **12** (*sideways*). *P* 14 × 13½.

216	12 c. Type **43**	10	15
217	50 c. Churchill Statue	30	55

(Des Staff Artists, Dept of Language and Literature. Photo Harrison)

1974 (15 July*). *Multicoloured; background colour given.* W w **12** (*sideways*). *P* 13½ × 14½.

218	**44**	4 c. turquoise-green	10	10
219		5 c. pale blue	10	10
220		6 c. olive	20	10
221		10 c. lavender	15	10
222		15 c. light brown	20	10
223		20 c. stone	20	10
224		25 c. sage-green	25	15
225		30 c. bright blue	25	15
226	**44**	35 c. grey	35	20
227		40 c. bright purple	35	20
228		50 c. cinnamon	40	20
229		75 c. light yellow-green	60	80
230		$1 pale salmon	1·25	1·50
231		$2 greenish yellow	2·25	3·25
232		$5 silver	4·50	7·50
233		$10 gold	8·00	15·00
218/33		*Set of* 16	17·00	26·00

*This was the London release date. The stamps were not put on sale locally until 29 August 1974, but First Day Covers were cancelled with the 15 July date.

See also Nos. 244/59 and 260/2.

45 Aerial View of Airport

(Des Harrison. Litho B.W.)

1974 (18 July). *Inauguration of Brunei International Airport. T* **45** *and similar horiz design. Multicoloured.* W w **12** (*sideways on* 75 *c.*). *P* 14 × 14½ (50 *c.*) *or* 12½ × 13 (75 *c.*).

234	50 c. Type **45**	75	1·00
235	75 c. Sultan in Army uniform, and airport (48 × 36 *mm*)	1·25	1·50

46 U.P.U. Emblem and Sultan

(Des J.W. Litho Harrison)

1974 (28 Oct). *Centenary of Universal Postal Union.* W w **12** (*sideways*). *P* 14½.

236	**46**	12 c. multicoloured	20	20
237		50 c. multicoloured	40	75
238		75 c. multicoloured	50	1·00
236/8		*Set of* 3	1·00	1·75

47 Sir Winston Churchill

(Des C. Abbott. Litho Questa)

1974 (30 Nov). *Birth Centenary of Sir Winston Churchill. T* **47** *and similar horiz design. Multicoloured.* W w **14** (*sideways*). *P* 14.

239	12 c. Type **47**	20	20
240	75 c. Churchill smoking cigar (profile)	35	70

48 Boeing "737" and R.B.A. Crest

(Des PAD Studio. Litho Enschedé)

1975 (14 May). *Inauguration of Royal Brunei Airlines. T* **48** *and similar horiz designs. Multicoloured. No wmk. P* 12½ × 12.

241	12 c. Type **48**	30	25
242	35 c. "737" over Bandar Seri Begawan Mosque	80	1·00
243	75 c. "737" in flight	1·75	2·00
241/3	*Set of* 3	2·50	3·00

1975 (13 Aug)–**78**. *As Nos.* 218/33, *but W w* **14** (*sideways*).

244	**44**	4 c. turquoise-green	15	15
245		5 c. pale blue	15	15
246		6 c. olive	20	15
247		10 c. lavender	20	10
		a. Pale bluish violet (19.4.77)	15	10
248		15 c. light brown	30	15
249		20 c. stone	40	20
250		25 c. sage-green	60	30
		a. Grey-olive (25.5.78)	30	20
251		30 c. bright blue	35	30
252		35 c. grey	40	40
253		40 c. bright purple	55	40
254		50 c. cinnamon	70	35
		a. Blue omitted†	28·00	
255		75 c. light yellow-green	80	70
256		$1 pale salmon	80	90
257	**44**	$2 greenish yellow	2·00	2·50
258		$5 silver	4·50	6·00
259		$10 gold	10·00	14·00
244/59		*Set of* 16	20·00	24·00

†The blue colour on the 50 c. value is only evident in the bluish green stripes of the sash and on several of the medal ribbons.

1976 (12 Apr). *As Nos.* 221 *and* 223/4 *but W* w **12** (*upright*).

260	**44**	10 c. lavender	40	15
261		20 c. stone	70	45
262		25 c. sage-green	85	50
260/2		*Set of* 3	1·75	1·00

(**49**) **50** Royal Coat of Arms

(Surchd by Govt Printer, Brunei)

1976 (16 Aug). *No.* 246 *surch with T* **49** *in silver.*

263	**44**	10 c. on 6 c. olive	65	50
		a. Surch on No. 220		

(Des C. Abbott. Litho D.L.R.)

1977 (7 June). *Silver Jubilee. T* **50** *and similar vert designs. Multicoloured.* W w **14**. *P* 13½ × 14.

264	10 c. Type **50**	15	20
265	20 c. Imperial State Crown	20	35
	a. Silver omitted	£300	
266	75 c. Queen Elizabeth (portrait by Annigoni)	45	75
264/6	*Set of* 3	70	1·10

51 The Moment of Crowning **52** Royal Crest

(Des J. Cooter. Litho Enschedé)

1978 (2 June). *25th Anniv of Coronation. T* **51** *and similar vert designs. Multicoloured.* W w **14**. *P* 13½ × 13.

267	10 c. Type **51**	10	10
268	20 c. Queen in Coronation regalia	15	20
269	75 c. Queen's departure from Abbey	50	80
267/9	*Set of* 3	65	1·00

(Des local artist; adapted BG Studio. Litho Cartor S.A., France)

1978 (1 Aug). *10th Anniv of Sultan's Coronation. T* **52** *and similar vert designs.* W w **14** (*inverted*). *P* 12.

270	10 c. black, scarlet and greenish yellow	10	10
271	20 c. multicoloured	15	20
272	75 c. multicoloured	50	75
270/2	*Set of* 3	65	95
MS273	182 × 77 mm. Nos. 270/2	3·25	4·50

Designs:—20 c. Coronation ceremony; 75 c. Royal Crown.

53 Human Rights Emblem and struggling Man

54 Smiling Children

(Des V. Whiteley; adapted L. McCombie. Litho Questa)

1978 (10 Dec). *Human Rights Year.* W w **14**. *P* 14½.

274	**53**	10 c. black, yellow and scarlet	10	10
275		20 c. black, yellow and violet	20	20
276		75 c. black, yellow and bistre	50	75
274/6		*Set of* 3	70	90

Type **53** is similar to the design used for the 1968 Human Rights Year issue.

(Des L. Curtis. Litho Harrison)

1979 (30 June). *International Year of the Child. T* **54** *and similar horiz design.* W w **14** *(sideways). P* 14.

277 10 c. multicoloured 10 10
278 $1 black and dull green . . . . 65 1·00
Design:—$1 I.Y.C. emblem.

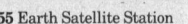

55 Earth Satellite Station

56 Hegira Symbol

(Des A. Theobald. Litho Questa)

1979 (23 Sept). *Telisai Earth Satellite Station. T* **55** *and similar horiz designs. Multicoloured.* W w **14** *(sideways). P* 14.

279 10 c. Type **55** 10 10
280 20 c. Satellite and antenna 15 15
281 75 c. Television camera, telex machine and telephone 40 75
279/81 . . . . *Set of* 3 60 90

(Litho Secura, Singapore)

1979 (21 Nov). *Moslem Year 1400 AH Commemoration.* W w **14**. *P* 13 × 13½.

282 **56** 10 c. black, yellow and emerald 10 15
283 20 c. black, yellow and light blue 15 20
284 75 c. black, yellow and violet . . . . 45 1·00
282/4 . . . . *Set of* 3 60 1·25
MS285 178 × 200 mm. Nos. 282/4 . . . . 1·00 1·50

57 Installation Ceremony

58 Royal Umbrella and Sash

(Des BG Studio. Litho Questa)

1980 (8 Nov). *1st Anniv of Prince Sufri Bolkiah's Installation as First Wazir. T* **57** *and similar vert design. Multicoloured.* W w **14**. *P* 13½.

286 10 c. Type **57** 10 10
287 75 c. Prince Sufri 35 50
Nos. 286/7 have blue borders.

(Des BG Studio. Litho Secura, Singapore)

1980 (6 Dec). *1st Anniv of Prince Jefri Bolkiah's Installation as Second Wazir. Vert designs as T* **57**. *Multicoloured.* W w **14**. *P* 13½.

288 10 c. Installation ceremony 15 10
289 75 c. Prince Jefri 45 60
Nos. 288/9 have green borders.

(Des BG Studio. Litho Security Printers (M), Malaysia)

1981 (18 Jan*). *Royal Regalia (1st series). T* **58** *and similar multicoloured designs. P* 13½ × 13 *(50 c.) or* 12 × 11½ *(others).*

290 10 c. Type **58** 15 15
291 15 c. Sword and Shield 20 20
292 20 c. Lance and Sheath 25 35
293 30 c. Betel-leaf Container 35 55
294 50 c. Coronation Crown (23 × 40 *mm*) . . 60 1·50
290/4 . . . . *Set of* 5 1·40 2·50
MS295 98 × 142 mm. Nos. 290/4 . . . . 1·75 2·50

*This is the local release date. The Crown Agents released the stamps on 19 January.

See also Nos. 298/303, 314/19 and 320/5.

59 I.T.U. and W.H.O. Emblems

60 Shield and Broadsword

(Litho Security Printers (M), Malaysia)

1981 (17 May). *World Telecommunications and Health Day. P* 13 × 13½.

296 **59** 10 c. black and bright crimson 15 10
297 75 c. black, chalky blue & pale violet-bl 75 1·40

(Des BG Studio. Litho Security Printers (M), Malaysia)

1981 (15 July). *Royal Regalia (2nd series). T* **60** *and similar multicoloured designs. P* 12.

298 10 c. Type **60** 10 10
299 15 c. Blunderbuss and Pouch 15 15
300 20 c. Crossed Lances and Sash 20 20
301 30 c. Sword, Shield and Sash 30 35
302 50 c. Forked Lance 50 75
303 75 c. Royal Drum (29 × 45 *mm*) . . . . 70 1·25
298/303 . . . . *Set of* 6 1·60 2·50

61 Prince Charles as Colonel of the Welsh Guards

62 Fishing

(Des J.W. Litho Format)

1981 (29 July). *Royal Wedding. T* **61** *and similar vert designs. Multicoloured.* W w **14**. *P* 14.

304 10 c. Wedding bouquet from Brunei 20 15
305 $1 Type **61** 75 75
306 $2 Prince Charles and Lady Diana Spencer 1·40 1·75
304/6 . . . . *Set of* 3 2·10 2·40

(Des local artist. Litho Secura, Singapore)

1981 (16 Oct). *World Food Day. T* **62** *and similar vert design. Multicoloured. P* 12 × 11½.

307 10 c. Type **62** 15 10
308 $1 Farm produce and machinery . . . . 1·25 1·75

63 Blind Man and Braille Alphabet

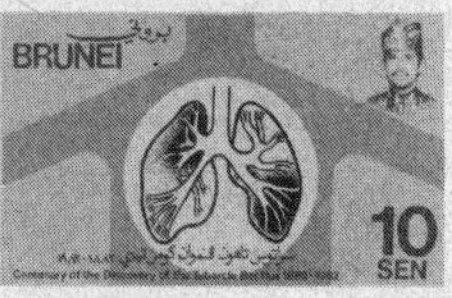

64 Drawing of Infected Lungs

(Des local artist. Litho Security Printers (M), Malaysia)

1981 (16 Dec). *International Year for Disabled Persons. T* **63** *and similar vert designs. Multicoloured.* W w **14**. *P* 12.

309 10 c. Type **63** 20 10
310 20 c. Deaf people and sign language 50 25
a. Wmk sideways 60 40
311 75 c. Disabled person and wheelchairs . . 1·25 1·75
309/11 . . . . *Set of* 3 1·75 1·90

(Des local artist. Litho Security Printers (M), Malaysia)

1982 (24 May). *Centenary of Robert Koch's Discovery of Tubercle Bacillus. T* **64** *and similar horiz design. Multicoloured.* W w **14**. *P* 12 *(10 c.) or* 13½ *(75 c.).*

312 10 c. Type **64** 15 10
313 75 c. Magnified tubercle bacillus and microscope . . . . 75 1·40

(Des PAD Studio. Litho Security Printers (M), Malaysia)

1982 (31 May). *Royal Regalia (3rd series). Multicoloured designs as T* **60**. W w **14** *(sideways). P* 13½ *(75 c.) or* 12 × 11½ *(others).*

314 10 c. Ceremonial Ornament 10 10
315 15 c. Silver Betel Caddy 15 15
316 20 c. Traditional Flower-pot 20 20
317 30 c. Solitary Candle 30 30
318 50 c. Golden Pipe 50 80
319 75 c. Royal Chin Support (28 × 45 *mm*) . . 70 1·40
314/19 . . . . *Set of* 6 1·75 2·75

(Des BG Studio. Litho Security Printers (M), Malaysia)

1982 (15 July). *Royal Regalia (4th series). Multicoloured designs as T* **60**. W w **14** *(sideways). P* 12 *(75 c.) or* 12 × 11½ *(others).*

320 10 c. Royal Mace 15 10
321 15 c. Ceremonial Shield and Spears 25 15
322 20 c. Embroidered Ornament 30 20
323 30 c. Golden-tasselled Cushion 45 45
324 50 c. Ceremonial Dagger and Sheath . . 70 1·25
325 75 c. Religious Mace (28 × 45 *mm*) . . . . 90 1·75
320/5 . . . . *Set of* 6 2·50 3·50

65 Brunei Flag

(Des Siti Zaleha Haji Kaprawi. Litho Secura, Singapore)

1983 (14 Mar). *Commonwealth Day. T* **65** *and similar horiz designs. P* 13 × 13½.

326 10 c. multicoloured 15 15
a. Horiz strip of 4. Nos. 326/9 . . . . 1·75
327 20 c. bright blue, black and buff 20 20
328 75 c. bright blue, black and bright green . . 45 55
329 $2 bright blue, black and lemon . . . . 1·10 1·75
326/9 . . . . *Set of* 4 1·75 2·40

Designs:—20 c. Brunei Mosque; 75 c. Machinery; $2 Sultan of Brunei.

Nos. 326/9 were printed together, *se-tenant*, in horizontal strips of four throughout the sheet.

66 "Postal Service"

67 Football

(Litho Secura, Singapore)

1983 (15 Aug). *World Communications Year. T* **66** *and similar horiz designs. P* 13½.

330 10 c. multicoloured 10 10
331 75 c. yellow, orange-brown and black . . 50 50
332 $2 multicoloured . . . . 1·40 1·75
330/2 . . . . *Set of* 3 1·75 2·10

Designs:—75 c. "Telephone Service"; $2 "Communications".

(Litho Security Printers (M), Malaysia)

1983 (23 Sept). *Official Opening of the Negara Hassanal Bolkiah Stadium. T* **67** *and similar multicoloured designs. P* 12.

333 10 c. Type **67** 15 10
334 75 c. Athletics 75 85
335 $1 View of stadium (44 × 27 *mm*) . . 95 1·40
333/5 . . . . *Set of* 3 1·75 2·10

68 Fishermen and Crustacea

(Litho Secura, Singapore)

1983 (23 Sept). *Fishery Resources. T* **68** *and similar horiz designs. Multicoloured. P* 13½ × 14.

336 10 c. Type **68** 10 10
337 50 c. Fishermen with net 40 45
338 75 c. Fishing trawler 60 75
339 $1 Fishing with hook and tackle . . . . 80 1·10
336/9 . . . . *Set of* 4 1·75 2·25

INDEPENDENCE

From No. 349 onwards issues are inscribed "BRUNEI DARUSSALAM".

69 Royal Assembly Hall

(Des Haji Salleh Bin Haji Ibrahim (No. 346) Pengiran Haji Muhammed Bin Pengiran Duraman (No. **MS**348) or Siti Zaleha Haji Kaprawi (others). Litho Cartor, France)

1984 (1 Jan). *Independence. T* **69** *and similar designs. P* 13.

340 10 c. pale stone and bright orange 8 10
341 20 c. flesh and brown-red 15 20
342 35 c. rose-pink and plum 30 35
343 50 c. pale blue and new blue 40 45
344 75 c. bright yellow-green and emerald . . 55 60
345 $1 light brownish grey and light brown . . 75 80
346 $3 multicoloured . . . . 2·25 3·00
340/6 . . . . *Set of* 7 4·00 5·00
MS347 150 × 120 mm. Nos. 340/6 . . . . 4·50 5·50
MS348 Two sheets each 150 × 120 mm. containing 4 stamps (34 × 69 *mm.*). (a) 25 c. × 4 grey-black and new blue (Signing of the Brunei Constitution). (b) 25 c. × 4 multicoloured (Signing of Brunei-U.K. Friendship Agreement) . . *Set of* 2 *sheets* 1·60 2·00

Designs:—34 × 25 *mm.* 20 c. Government Secretariat Building; 35 c. New Supreme Court; 50 c. Natural gas well; 75 c. Omar Ali Saifuddin Mosque; $1 Sultan's Palace; 68 × 29 *mm.* $3 Brunei flag and map of South-East Asia.

70 Natural Forests and Enrichment Planting

(Des Awang Nor Ariffin bin Md. Yassin. Litho Secura, Singapore)

1984 (21 Apr). *Forestry Resources. T* **70** *and similar horiz designs. Multicoloured. P* 13½ × 14.

349 10 c. Type **70** 20 10
350 50 c. Forests and water resources 60 60
351 75 c. Recreation forests .. .. .. 90 1·25
352 $1 Forests and wildlife .. .. .. 1·40 1·60
349/52 .. .. *Set of* 4 2·75 3·25

71 Sultan Omar Saifuddin 50 c. Stamp of 1952

(Recess and litho D.L.R.)

1984 (22 Oct). *"Philakorea" International Stamp Exhibition, Seoul. T* **71** *and similar vert designs. Multicoloured. P* 13.

353 10 c. Type **71** 10 10
354 75 c. Brunei River view 10 c. stamp of 1907 .. 55 70
355 $2 Star and view ½ c. stamp of 1895 .. 1·50 2·00
353/5 .. .. *Set of* 3 1·90 2·50
MS356 Three sheets, 117 × 100 mm, each containing one stamp as Nos. 353/5 *Set of 3 sheets* 2·25 2·75
a. Line perf 14 at left *Set of 3 sheets* 4·50 5·50

The stamps within the miniature sheets were perforated by means of a three-sided comb gauging 13 and completed by a line perforation at left. Normally this line perforation is also 13, but on **MS**356a it measures 14.

72 United Nations Emblem

73 Young People and Brunei Flag

(Des Awang Nor Ariffin bin Md. Yassin (Nos. 357, 359), Haji Salleh bin Haji Ibrahim (358) or Siti Zaleha Haji Kaprawi (360). Litho Cartor, France)

1985 (23 Sept). *Admission of Brunei to World Organizations (1st issue). T* **72** *and similar horiz designs. W w* **17** *(sideways). P* 13.

357 50 c. black, gold and pale greenish blue .. 40 50
358 50 c. multicoloured 40 50
359 50 c. multicoloured 40 50
360 50 c. multicoloured 40 50
357/60 .. .. *Set of* 4 1·40 1·75
MS361 110 × 151 mm. Nos. 357/60 .. .. 1·50 2·25

Designs:—No. 357, Type **72**; No. 358, Organization of Islamic Countries logo; 359, Commonwealth logo; 360, A.S.E.A.N. emblem.

See also Nos. 383/7.

(Des Siti Zaleha Haji Kaprawi. Litho Security Printers (M), Malaysia)

1985 (17 Oct). *International Youth Year. T* **73** *and similar horiz designs. Multicoloured. P* 12.

362 10 c. Type **73** 15 10
363 75 c. Young people at work .. .. .. 90 1·25
364 $1 Young people serving the community .. .. 1·00 1·75
362/4 .. .. *Set of* 3 1·90 2·75

74 Palestinian Emblem

75 Early and Modern Scout Uniforms

(Des Haji Salleh bin Haji Ibrahim. Litho Secura, Singapore)

1985 (29 Nov). *International Palestinian Solidarity Day. P* 12 × 12½.

365 **74** 10 c. multicoloured 20 10
366 50 c. multicoloured 65 65
367 $1 multicoloured .. .. 1·10 1·40
365/7 .. .. *Set of* 3 1·75 2·00

(Des Awang Nor Ariffin bin Md. Yassin. Litho Secura, Singapore)

1985 (14 Dec). *National Scout Jamboree. T* **75** *and similar vert designs. Multicoloured. P* 13½.

368 10 c. Type **75** 20 10
369 20 c. Scout on tower signalling with flag .. 30 30
370 $2 Jamboree emblem .. .. .. 1·75 2·50
368/70 .. .. *Set of* 3 2·00 2·50

76 Sultan Sir Hassanal Bolkiah Mu'izzaddin Waddaulah

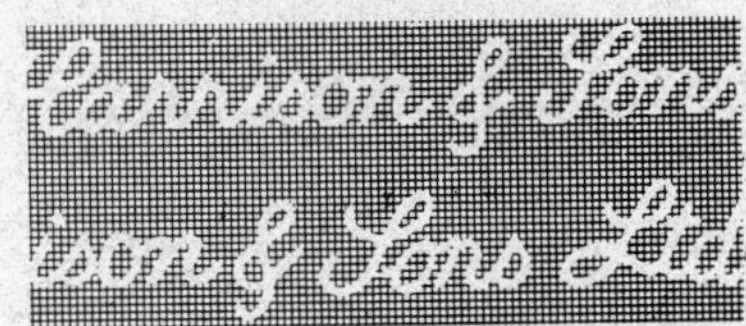

77

(Des Awang Nor Ariffin bin Md. Yassin. Photo Harrison)

1985 (23 Dec)–**86**. *W* **77**. *P* 13½ × 14½ (10 *to* 75 *c.*) *or* 14 ($1 *to* $10).

371 **76** 10 c. multicoloured 10 10
372 15 c. multicoloured 10 10
373 20 c. multicoloured 10 10
374 25 c. multicoloured 15 20
375 35 c. multicoloured (15.1.86) 20 25
376 40 c. multicoloured (15.1.86) 20 25
377 50 c. multicoloured (15.1.86) 30 35
378 75 c. multicoloured (15.1.86) 40 45
379 $1 multicoloured (23.2.86) 55 60
380 $2 multicoloured (23.2.86) .. .. 1·10 1·25
381 $5 multicoloured (23.2.86) .. .. 2·75 3·00
382 $10 multicoloured (29.3.86) .. .. 5·75 6·00
371/82 .. .. *Set of* 12 10·50 11·50

Nos. 379/82 are larger, size 32 × 39 mm.

(Des Awang Nor Ariffin bin Md. Yassin. Litho Cartor, France)

1986 (30 Apr). *Admission of Brunei to World Organizations (2nd issue). Horiz designs as T* **72**. *W w* **17** *(sideways). P* 13.

383 50 c. black, gold and bright yellow-green .. 40 55
384 50 c. black, gold and bright pinkish mauve .. 40 55
385 50 c. black, gold and orange-red 40 55
386 50 c. black, gold and dull ultramarine .. 40 55
383/6 .. .. *Set of* 4 1·40 2·00
MS387 105 × 155 mm. Nos. 383/6. Wmk upright 1·50 2·25

Designs:—No. 383, World Meteorological Organization emblem; 384, International Telecommunication Union emblem; 385, Universal Postal Union emblem; 386, International Civil Aviation Organization emblem.

78 Soldiers on Assault Course and Helicopter

79 Tunggul Charok Buritan, Alam Bernaga (Alam Besar), Pisang-Pisang and Sandaran

(Des Awang Nor Ariffin bin Md. Yassin. Litho Secura, Singapore)

1986 (31 May). *25th Anniv of Brunei Armed Forces. T* **78** *and similar horiz designs. Multicoloured. P* 13½.

388 10 c. Type **78** 35 40
a. Horiz strip of 4. Nos. 388/91 .. .. 2·00
389 20 c. Operating computer 45 55
390 50 c. Anti-aircraft missile, helicopter and missile boat 70 80
391 75 c. Army commanders and parade .. 75 90
388/91 .. .. *Set of* 4 2·00 2·40

Nos. 388/91 were printed together, *se-tenant*, in horizontal strips of 4 throughout the sheet, forming a composite design.

(Des Awang Nor Ariffin bin Md. Yassin. Litho Secura, Singapore)

1986 (15 July). *Royal Ensigns (1st series). T* **79** *and similar vert designs. P* **12**.

392 10 c. black, greenish yellow and red .. 20 10
393 75 c. multicoloured 80 80
394 $2 black, greenish yellow and green .. 1·75 2·25
392/4 .. .. *Set of* 3 2·50 2·75

Designs:—75 c. Ula-Ula Besar, Sumbu Layang and Payong Haram; $2 Panji-Panji, Chogan Istiadat (Chogan Di-Raja) and Chogan Ugama.

(Des Awang Nor Ariffin bin Md. Yassin. Litho Secura, Singapore)

1986 (30 Sept). *Royal Ensigns (2nd series). Vert designs as T* **79**. *P* 12.

395 10 c. multicoloured 20 10
396 75 c. black, red and greenish yellow .. 80 80
397 $2 multicoloured .. .. 1·75 2·25
395/7 .. .. *Set of* 3 2·50 2·75

Designs:—10 c. Dadap, Tunggul Kawan, Ambal, Payong Ubor-Ubor, Sapu-Sapu Ayeng and Rawai Lidah; 75 c. Payong Tinggi and Payong Ubor-Ubor Tiga Ringkat; $2 Lambang Duli Yang Maha Mulia and Mahligai.

80 Stylised Peace Doves

81 Drug Addict in Cage and Syringe (poster by Othman bin Ramboh)

(Des Zainal Abidin Haji Ibrahim. Litho Security Printers (M), Malaysia)

1986 (24 Oct). *International Peace Year. T* **80** *and similar horiz designs. Multicoloured. P* 12.

398 50 c. Type **80** 65 65
399 75 c. Stylised hands and "1986" 80 80
400 $1 International Peace Year emblem and arms of Brunei .. .. 1·00 1·00
398/400 .. .. *Set of* 3 2·25 2·25

(Litho Security Printers (M), Malaysia)

1987 (15 Mar). *National Anti-drug Campaign. Children's Posters. T* **81** *and similar vert designs. Multicoloured. P* 12.

401 10 c. Type **81** 25 10
402 75 c. Drug addict and noose (Arman bin Mohd. Zaman) 80 90
403 $1 Blindfolded drug addict and noose (Abidin bin Hj. Rashid) .. .. .. 1·00 1·25
401/3 .. .. *Set of* 3 1·90 2·00

82 Cannon ("badil") 83 Map showing Member Countries

(Des Haji Salleh bin Haji Ibrahim. Litho Security Printers (M), Malaysia)

1987 (15 July). *Brassware (1st series). T* **82** *and similar vert designs. Multicoloured. P* 12.

404 50 c. Type **82** 40 40
405 50 c. Lamp ("pelita") 40 40
406 50 c. Betel container ("langguai") 40 40
407 50 c. Water jug ("kiri") 40 40
404/7 .. .. *Set of* 4 1·40 1·40

See also Nos. 434/7.

(Des Zainal Abidin bin Haji Ibrahim. Litho Security Printers (M), Malaysia)

1987 (8 Aug). *20th Anniv of Association of South East Asian Nations. T* **83** *and similar horiz designs. Multicoloured. P* 14 × 13½.

408 20 c. Type **83** 15 15
409 50 c. Dates and figures "20" 30 35
410 $1 Flags of member states 60 65
408/10 .. .. *Set of* 3 95 1·00

84 Brunei Citizens

(Des Pengiran Haji Muhammad bin Pengiran Duraman. Litho Secura, Singapore)

1987 (29 Sept). *25th Anniv of Language and Literature Bureau* (1986). *T* **84** *and similar horiz designs. Multicoloured. P* 13×12½.

No.	Description	Mint	Used
411	10 c. Type **84**	15	15
	a. Horiz strip of 3. Nos. 411/13	1·50	
412	50 c. Flame emblem and hands holding open book	30	35
413	$2 Scenes of village life	1·25	1·40
411/13	*Set of* 3	1·50	1·75

Nos. 411/13 were printed together, *se-tenant*, in horizontal strips of three throughout the sheet, each strip forming a composite design taken from a mural.

85 *Artocarpus odoratissima*

(Litho Security Printers (M), Malaysia)

1987 (31 Oct). *Local Fruits (1st series). T* **85** *and similar horiz designs. Multicoloured. P* 12.

No.	Description	Mint	Used
414	50 c. Type **85**	30	35
	a. Horiz strip of 4. Nos. 414/17	1·10	
415	50 c. *Canarium odontophyllum mig.*	30	35
416	50 c. *Litsea garciae*	30	35
417	50 c. *Mangifera foetida lour*	30	35
414/17	*Set of* 4	1·10	1·25

Nos. 414/17 were printed together, *se-tenant*, in horizontal strips of 4 throughout the sheet.

See also Nos. 421/4.

86 Modern House　　**87** Wooden Lathe

(Litho Security Printers (M), Malaysia)

1987 (28 Nov). *International Year of Shelter for the Homeless. T* **86** *and similar horiz designs, each showing modern Brunei housing. P* 13×12½.

No.	Description	Mint	Used
418	50 c. multicoloured	30	35
419	75 c. multicoloured	45	50
420	$1 multicoloured	60	65
418/20	*Set of* 3	1·25	1·40

(Des Awang Nor Ariffin bin Md. Yassin. Litho Security Printers (M), Malaysia)

1988 (30 Jan). *Local Fruits (2nd series). Horiz designs as T* **85**. *Multicoloured. P* 12.

No.	Description	Mint	Used
421	50 c. *Durio spp*	30	35
	a. Horiz strip of 4. Nos. 421/4	1·10	
422	50 c. *Durio oxleyanus*	30	35
423	50 c. *Durio graveolens* (blue background)	30	35
424	50 c. *Durio graveolens* (white background)	30	35
421/4	*Set of* 4	1·10	1·25

Nos. 421/4 were printed together, *se-tenant*, in horizontal strips of four throughout the sheet.

(Des Awang Padzil bin Haji Ahmad. Litho Security Printers (M), Malaysia)

1988 (29 Feb). *Opening of Malay Technology Museum. T* **87** *and similar vert designs. Multicoloured. P* 12.

No.	Description	Mint	Used
425	10 c. Type **87**	10	10
426	75 c. Crushing sugar cane	45	50
427	$1 Bird scarer	60	65
425/7	*Set of* 3	1·00	1·10

88 Beragi Bunga Sakah-Sakah dan Bunga Cengkih Cloth　　**89** Sultan reading Proclamation

(Des Awang Nor Ariffin bin Md. Yassin. Litho Security Printers (M), Malaysia)

1988 (30 Apr). *Handwoven Material (1st series). T* **88** *and similar horiz designs showing different patterns. Multicoloured. P* 12.

No.	Description	Mint	Used
428	10 c. Type **88**	10	10
429	20 c. Jong Sarat cloth	10	10
430	25 c. Si Pugut cloth	15	20
431	40 c. Si Pugut Bunga Berlapis cloth	25	30
432	75 c. Si Lobang Bangsi Bunga Belitang Kipas cloth	45	50
428/32	*Set of* 5	90	1·10
MS433	150×204 mm. Nos. 428/32	1·00	1·25

See also Nos. 442/7.

(Des Haji Salleh bin Haji Ibrahim. Litho Security Printers (M), Malaysia)

1988 (30 June). *Brassware (2nd series). Vert designs as T* **82**. *Multicoloured. P* 12.

No.	Description	Mint	Used
434	50 c. Lidded two-handled pot ("periok")	30	35
435	50 c. Candlestick ("lampong")	30	35
436	50 c. Shallow circular dish with stand ("gangsa")	30	35
437	50 c. Repousse box with lid ("celapa")	30	35
434/7	*Set of* 4	1·10	1·25

(Des Awang Nor Ariffin bin Md. Yassin. Litho Security Printers (M), Malaysia)

1988 (1 Aug). *20th Anniv of Sultan's Coronation. T* **89** *and similar vert designs. Multicoloured. P* 14 (20, 75 *c.) or* 12½× 13 ($2).

No.	Description	Mint	Used
438	20 c. Type **89**	10	10
439	75 c. Sultan reading from Koran	45	50
440	$2 In Coronation robes (26×63 *mm*)	1·25	1·40
438/40	*Set of* 3	1·60	1·75
MS441	164×125 mm. Nos. 438/40	1·75	2·00

In No. **MS**441 the perforations of the stamps are as Nos. 438/40 except for the 75 c. which is perforated 13 at right.

(Des Awang Nor Ariffin bin Md. Yassin. Litho Security Printers (M), Malaysia)

1988 (29 Sept). *Handwoven Material (2nd series). Horiz designs as T* **88**. *Multicoloured. P* 12.

No.	Description	Mint	Used
442	10 c. Beragi cloth	10	10
443	20 c. Bertabur cloth	10	10
444	25 c. Sukma Indra cloth	15	20
445	40 c. Si Pugut Bunga cloth	25	30
446	75 c. Beragi Si Lobang Bangsi Bunga Cendera Kesuma cloth	45	50
442/6	*Set of* 5	90	1·10
MS447	150×204 mm. Nos. 442/6	1·00	1·25

90 Malaria-carrying Mosquito

(Litho Cartor, France)

1988 (17 Dec). *40th Anniv of World Health Organization. T* **90** *and similar horiz designs. Multicoloured. P* 14×13½.

No.	Description	Mint	Used
448	25 c. Type **90**	20	20
449	35 c. Man with insecticide spray and sample on slide	25	25
450	$2 Microscope and magnified malaria cells	1·40	1·40
448/50	*Set of* 3	1·60	1·60

91 Sultan and Council of Ministers　　**92** Dove escaping from Cage

(Des Norariffin bin Md Yassin. Litho Security Printers (M), Malaysia)

1989 (23 Feb). *5th Anniv of National Day. T* **91** *and similar multicoloured designs. P* 12.

No.	Description	Mint	Used
451	20 c. Type **91**	15	15
452	30 c. Guard of honour	25	25
453	60 c. Firework display (27 × 55 *mm*)	40	40
454	$2 Congregation in mosque	1·40	1·40
451/4	*Set of* 4	2·00	2·00
MS455	164 × 124 mm. Nos. 451/4	2·25	2·50

(Des Haji Salleh bin Haji Ibrahim. Litho Secura, Singapore)

1989 (1 Apr). *"Freedom of Palestine". T* **92** *and similar horiz designs. Multicoloured. P* 13½.

No.	Description	Mint	Used
456	20 c. Type **92**	15	15
457	75 c. Map and Palestinian flag	65	65
458	$1 Dome of the Rock, Jerusalem	80	80
456/8	*Set of* 3	1·40	1·40

MINIMUM PRICE

The minimum price quote is 10p which represents a handling charge rather than a basis for valuing common stamps. For further notes about prices see introductory pages.

JAPANESE OCCUPATION OF BRUNEI

Japanese forces landed in Northern Borneo on 16 December 1941 and the whole of Brunei had been occupied by 6 January 1942.

Brunei, North Borneo, Sarawak and, after a short period, Labuan, were administered as a single territory by the Japanese. Until September–October 1942, previous stamp issues, without overprint, continued to be used in conjunction with existing postmarks. From the Autumn of 1942 onwards unoverprinted stamps of Japan were made available and examples can be found used from the area for much of the remainder of the War. Japanese Occupation issues for Brunei, North Borneo and Sarawak were equally valid throughout the combined territory but not, in practice, equally available.

PRICES FOR STAMPS ON COVER

Nos. J1/16	*from* × 5
Nos. J17/20	—

本日大

府政國帝本日大　　便郵國帝

(1)　　(2)

("Imperial Japanese Government")　　("Imperial Japanese Postal Service $3")

1942 (Oct)–**44.** *Stamps of Brunei handstamped with T* **1** *in violet to blue. Wmk Mult Script CA* (*except Nos.* J18/19, *Mult Crown CA*). *P* 14.

No.	Type	Description	Mint	Used
J 1	**5**	1 c. black	5·00	10·00
J 2		2 c. green	25·00	80·00
J 3		2 c. orange (9.44)	2·50	5·00
J 4		3 c. green	20·00	60·00
J 5		4 c. orange	3·00	7·50
J 6		5 c. chocolate	3·00	7·50
		a. "5 c." retouch	£150	£300
J 7	**7**	6 c. greenish grey (*p* 14 × 11½) (9.44)	50·00	£100
J 8		6 c. scarlet	£450	£550
J 9	**5**	8 c. grey-black	£550	£800
J10	**7**	8 c. red	3·00	7·00
J11	**5**	10 c. purple/*yellow* (9.44)	7·00	13·00
J12	**7**	12 c. blue (9.44)	7·00	13·00
J13		15 c. ultramarine (9.44)	7·00	13·00
J14	**5**	25 c. slate-purple (9.44)	16·00	25·00
J15		30 c. purple and orange-yellow	90·00	£180
J16		50 c. black/*emerald* (9.44)	29·00	38·00
J17		$1 black and red/*blue* (9.44)	45·00	55·00
J18		$5 carmine/*green* (9.44)	£800	
J19		$25 black/*red* (9.44)	£850	

The overprint varies in shade from violet to blue, and, being handstamped, exists double and treble.

Nos. J3, J7, J10 and J13 were not issued without the overprint.

1944 (May). *No. 60 of Brunei surch with T* **2** *in orange-red.*

No.	Type	Description	Mint	Used
J20	**5**	$3 on 1 c. black	£2500	£2000

Burma

Stamps of India were used in Burma from 1854 and, after 1856, individual examples can be identified by the use of the concentric octagonal postmarks of the Bengal Postal Circle of which the following were supplied to Burmese post offices:

Type A
No. B 156
(Rangoon)

Type B
No. B 5
(Akyab)

B5	Akyab	B146	Pegu
B12*	Bassein	B150	Prome
B22	Nga Thine Khyoung	B156*	Rangoon
B56	Amherst	B159	Sandoway
B108	Kyouk Phyoo	B165	Sarawah (*to* 1860)
B111	Meeaday	B165	Henzada (*from* 1861)
B112	Mengyee	B171	Shoay Gyeen
B127	Moulmein	B173	Sittang
B128	Mergui	B179	Thayetmyo
B129	Tavoy	B181	Toungoo
B133	Myanoung	B227	Port Blair
B136	Namayan		

*Exists in black or blue. Remainder in black only.

Akyab, Moulmein and Rangoon used postmarks as both Type A and Type B, Port Blair as Type B only and the remainder as Type A only.

From 1860 various types of duplex cancellations were introduced and Burmese examples can be identified when sufficient of the left-hand portion is visible on the stamp. Such marks were issued for the following offices:

Akyab	Rangoon
Bassein	Rangoon C.R.H.
Mandalay	(Cantonment Receiving House)
Moulmein	Thayetmyo
Port Blair	Toungoo
Prome	

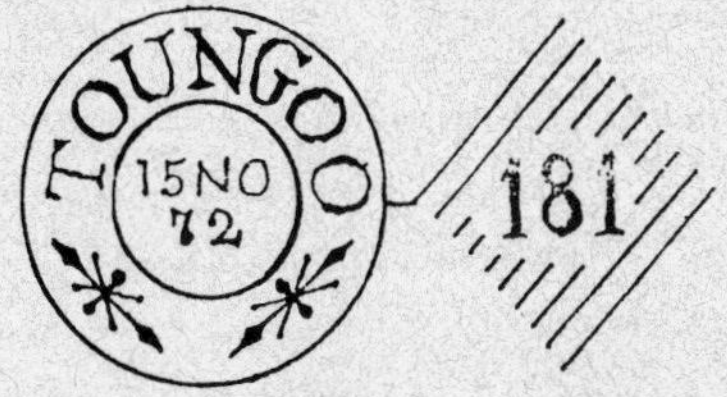

1862 Duplex from
Toungoo

1865 Duplex from
Akyab

During 1875, a further series of duplex marks was introduced in which the right-hand portion of the cancellation included the office code number, prefixed by the letter "R" for Rangoon:

R–1	Rangoon	1/R–8	Amherst
R–1/1	Rangoon Cantonment	R–9	Myanoung
R–2	Akyab	R–10	Port Blair
R–3	Bassein	R–11	Prome
R–4	Henzada	R–12	Sandoway
R–5	Kyouk Phyoo	R–13	Shwegyeen
R–6	Mandalay	R–14	Tavoy
R–7	Mergui	R–15	Thayetmyo
R–8	Moulmein	R–16	Tounghoo

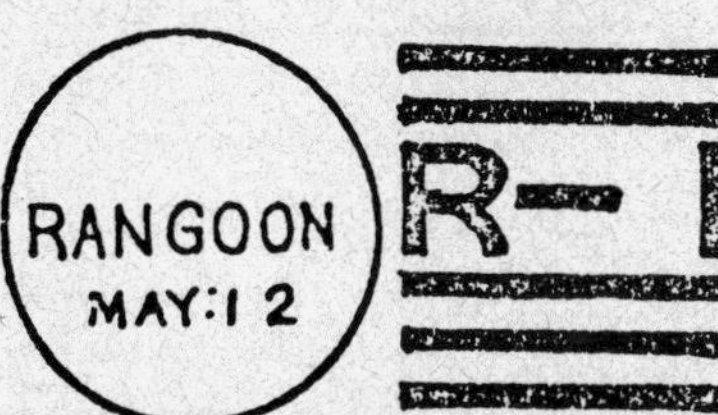

1875 type from
Rangoon

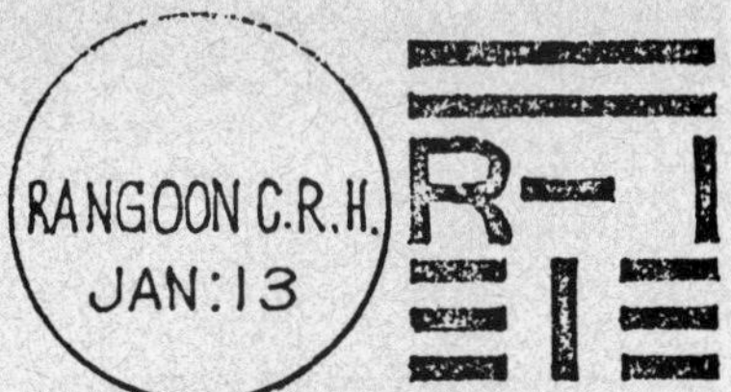

1875 type from Rangoon
Cantonment Receiving House

From 1886 the whole of Burma was united under the Crown and the post offices were supplied with circular date stamps giving the name of the town.

Most Indian stamps, both postage and official, issued during the period were supplied to post offices in Burma. None of the imperforates printed by De La Rue have been seen however, and from the later issues the following have not been recorded with Burma postmarks:

Nos. 39a, 66a, 68, 85a, 92a, 110a/b, 148a, 155a, 165, 192a/c, 195a/b, O15, O38, O40b, O50a/b, O76a, O101a, O102, O103/a, O104/5 and O142.

The value of most India stamps used in Burma coincides proportionately with the used prices quoted for India, but some, especially the provisional surcharges, are extremely rare with Burmese postmarks. Stamps of the face value of 2 r. and above from the reigns of Victoria and Edward VII are more common with telegraph cancellations than with those of the postal service.

PRICES FOR STAMPS ON COVER TO 1945	
Nos. 1/18	*from* × 6
Nos. 18a/33	*from* × 4
No. 34	*from* × 5
Nos. 35/50	*from* × 8
Nos. O1/27	*from* × 15

BRITISH ADMINISTRATION

From 1 January 1886 Burma was a province of the Indian Empire but was separated from India and came under direct British administration on 1 April 1937.

BURMA (1) BURMA (1a)

1937 (1 April). *Stamps of India (King George V inscr* "INDIA POSTAGE"*) optd with T* **1** *or* **1a** *(rupee values).* W **69**. *P* 14.

No.	Description	Unused	Used
1	3 p. slate	25	10
2	½ a. green	25	10
3	9 p. deep green	30	10
4	1 a. chocolate	30	10
5	2 a. vermilion (*small die*)	30	10
6	2½ a. orange	30	10
7	3 a. carmine	65	30
8	3½ a. deep blue	65	10
	a. Dull blue	4·00	4·00
9	4 a. sage-green	70	10
10	6 a. bistre	60	35
11	8 a. reddish purple	1·50	10
12	12 a. claret	1·75	85
13	1 r. chocolate and green	4·00	50
14	2 r. carmine and orange	7·00	5·00
15	5 r. ultramarine and purple	15·00	9·00
16	10 r. green and scarlet	38·00	20·00
17	15 r. blue and olive	£110	70·00
18	25 r. orange and blue	£200	£140
1/18	*Set of* 18	£325	£225

The opt is at top on all values except the 3 a.

2 King George VI and "Chinthes"

3 King George VI and "Nagas"

4 Royal Barge

8 King George VI and Peacock

10 Elephants' Heads

(Des Maung Kyi (2 a. 6 p.), Maung Hline (3 a.), Maung Ohn Pe (3 a. 6 p.) and N. K. D. Naigamwalla (8 a.). Litho Security Ptg Press, Nasik)

1938 (15 Nov)–**40**. *T* **2/4**, **8** *and similar designs.* W **10**. *P* 14 (*vert*) *or* 13½ × 13 (*horiz*).

No.	Type	Description	Unused	Used
18a	2	1 p. red-orange (1.8.40)	1·00	60
19		3 p. bright violet	10	20
20		6 p. bright blue	10	10
21		9 p. yellow-green	1·00	80
22	3	1 a. purple-brown	10	10
23		1½ a. turquoise-green	20	35
24		2 a. carmine	45	10
25	4	2 a. 6 p. claret	75	20
26	–	3 a. dull violet	2·25	60
27	–	3 a. 6 p. light blue and blue	1·25	3·00
28	3	4 a. greenish blue	35	10
29	–	8 a. myrtle-green	1·75	30
30	8	1 r. purple and blue	3·75	20
31		2 r. brown and purple	5·00	75
32	–	5 r. violet and scarlet	23·00	8·50
33	–	10 r. brown and myrtle	42·00	32·00
18a/33		*Set of* 16	75·00	42·00

Designs: *Horiz (as T* **4**)—3 a. Burma teak; 3 a. 6 p. Burma rice; 8 a. River Irrawaddy. *Vert (as T* **8**)—5 r., 10 r. King George VI and "Nats".

The 1 a. exists lithographed and typographed, the latter having a "Jubilee" line in the sheet margin.

COMMEMORATION
POSTAGE STAMP
6th MAY 1840

(11)

1940 (6 May). *Centenary of First Adhesive Postage Stamps. No.* 25 *surch with T* **11**.

No.	Type	Description	Unused	Used
34	4	1 a. on 2 a. 6 p. claret	1·50	35

For stamps issued in 1942–45 see under Japanese Occupation.

CHIN HILLS DISTRICT. This area, in the far north-west of the country, remained in British hands when the Japanese overran Burma in May 1942.

During the period July to December 1942 the local officials were authorised to produce provisional stamps and the letters "OHMS" are known overprinted by typewriter on Nos. 3, 20, 22, 23, 24, 28 and 31 of Burma or handstamped, in violet, on Nos. 25, 27 and 29. The two types can also occur together or in combination with a handstamped "Service".

From early in 1943 ordinary postage stamps of India were used from the Chin Hills post offices of Falam, Haka, Fort White and Tiddim, this expedient continuing until the fall of Falam to the Japanese on 7 November 1943.

The provisional stamps should only be collected on Official cover where dates and the sender's handwriting can be authenticated.

BRITISH MILITARY ADMINISTRATION

MILY ADMN (12) MILY ADMN (13)

1945 (from 16 June). *Nos.* 18a *to* 33, *optd with T* **12** (*small stamps*) *or* **13** (*others*).

No.	Type	Description	Unused	Used
35	2	1 p. red-orange	10	10
		a. Opt omitted (in pair with normal)		
36		3 p. bright violet	10	25
37		6 p. bright blue	10	20
38		9 p. yellow-green	10	20
39	3	1 a. purple-brown (16.6)	10	10
40		1½ a. turquoise-green (16.6)	10	15
41		2 a. carmine	10	15
42	4	2 a. 6 p. claret	15	50
43	–	3 a. dull violet	40	20
44	–	3 a. 6 p. light blue and blue	10	55
45	3	4 a. greenish blue	10	25
46	–	8 a. myrtle-green	10	30
47	8	1 r. purple and blue	15	45
48		2 r. brown and purple	20	80
49	–	5 r. violet and scarlet	20	80
50	–	10 r. brown and myrtle	50	80
35/50		*Set of* 16	2·00	4·75

BRITISH CIVIL ADMINISTRATION

1946 (1 Jan). *As Nos.* 19/33, *but colours changed.*

No.	Type	Description	Unused	Used
51	2	3 p. brown	10	40
52		6 p. deep violet	10	10
53		9 p. green	10	60
54	3	1 a. blue	10	10
55		1½ a. orange	10	10
56		2 a. claret	10	30
57	4	2 a. 6 p. greenish blue	10	40
57a	–	3 a. blue-violet	85	40
57b	–	3 a. 6 p. black and ultramarine	10	40
58	3	4 a. purple	10	30
59	–	8 a. maroon	1·00	40
60	8	1 r. violet and maroon	30	15
61		2 r. brown and orange	1·75	1·25
62	–	5 r. green and brown	1·75	2·75
63	–	10 r. claret and violet	1·75	4·50
51/63		*Set of* 15	7·00	11·00

MINIMUM PRICE

The minimum price quote is 10p which represents a handling charge rather than a basis for valuing common stamps. For further notes about prices see introductory pages.

14 Burman

(Des A. G. I. McGeogh. Litho Nasik)

1946 (2 May). *Victory. T* **14** *and similar vert designs. W* **10** *(sideways). P* 13.

64 9 p. turquoise-green 10 10
65 1½ a. violet 10 10
66 2 a. carmine 15 10
67 3 a. 6 p. ultramarine 15 10
64/7 .. .. *Set of* 4 40 30

Designs:—1½ a. Burmese woman; 2 a. Chinthe; 3 a. 6 p. Elephant.

INTERIM BURMESE GOVERNMENT

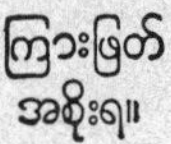

(**18** *Trans.* "Interim Government")

1947 (1 Oct). *Stamps of* 1946 *optd with T* **18** *(small stamps) or larger opt (others).*

68 **2** 3 p. brown 40 20
69 6 p. deep violet 10 25
70 9 p. green 10 25
a. Opt inverted .. .. 12·00 12·00
71 **3** 1 a. blue 10 25
72 1½ a. orange 45 10
73 2 a. claret 10 15
74 **4** 2 a. 6 p. greenish blue 60 35
75 – 3 a. blue-violet 35 25
76 – 3 a. 6 p. black and ultramarine 10 30
77 **3** 4 a. purple 40 30
78 – 8 a. maroon 75 30
79 **8** 1 r. violet and maroon 80 30
80 2 r. brown and orange .. .. 1·00 1·00
81 – 5 r. green and brown .. .. 1·50 1·90
82 – 10 r. claret and violet .. .. 1·60 1·90
68/82 .. .. *Set of* 15 7·00 7·00

The 3 p., 6 p., 2 a., 2 a. 6 p., 3 a. 6 p. and 1 r. are also known with overprint inverted.

OFFICIAL STAMPS

BURMA **BURMA**

SERVICE **SERVICE**

(O 1) (O 1*a*)

1937 (Apr–June). *Stamps of India (King George V inscr* "INDIA POSTAGE"*) optd with Type* O 1 *or* O 1a *(rupee values). W* **69**. *P* 14.

O 1 3 p. slate 10 10
O 2 ½ a. green 35 10
O 3 9 p. deep green 30 30
O 4 1 a. chocolate 30 10
O 5 2 a. vermilion (*small die*) 30 35
O 6 2½ a. orange 85 55
O 7 4 a. sage-green 60 10
O 8 6 a. bistre .. .. 1·25 2·50
O 9 8 a. reddish purple (1.4.37) 70 30
O10 12 a. claret (1.4.37) .. .. 1·00 1·50
O11 1 r. chocolate and green (1.4.37) .. .. 4·25 1·25
O12 2 r. carmine and orange .. .. 9·00 9·50
O13 5 r. ultramarine and purple .. .. 32·00 20·00
O14 10 r. green and scarlet .. .. 70·00 60·00
O1/14 .. .. *Set of* 14 £110 85·00

For the above issue the stamps were either overprinted "BURMA" and "SERVICE" at one operation or had the two words applied separately. Research has yet to establish if all values exist with both forms of overprinting.

SERVICE **SERVICE**

(O 2) (O 3)

1939. *Nos.* 19/24 *and* 28 *optd with Type* O **2** *(typo) and Nos.* 25 *and* 29/33 *optd with Type* O **3** *(litho).*

O15 **2** 3 p. bright violet 10 20
O16 6 p. bright blue 10 20
O17 9 p. yellow-green .. .. 2·00 40
O18 **3** 1 a. purple-brown 10 15
O19 1½ a. turquoise-green .. .. 2·00 40
O20 2 a. carmine 35 20
O21 **4** 2 a. 6 p. claret .. .. 3·50 2·50
O22 **3** 4 a. greenish blue .. .. 3·75 45
O23 – 8 a. myrtle-green .. .. 7·00 2·00
O24 **8** 1 r. purple and blue .. .. 7·00 2·00
O25 2 r. brown and purple .. .. 11·00 3·50
O26 – 5 r. violet and scarlet .. .. 38·00 16·00
O27 – 10 r. brown and myrtle .. .. 60·00 25·00
O15/27 .. .. *Set of* 13 £120 48·00

1946. *British Civil Administration. Nos.* 51/6 *and* 58 *optd with Type* O **2** *(typo) and Nos.* 57 *and* 59/63 *optd with Type* O **3** *(litho).*

O28 **2** 3 p. brown 25 70
O29 6 p. deep violet 35 55
O30 9 p. green 10 80
O31 **3** 1 a. blue 10 80
O32 1½ a. orange 10 15
O33 2 a. claret 10 70
O34 **4** 2 a. 6 p. greenish blue 25 90
O35 **3** 4 a. purple 10 60
O36 – 8 a. maroon 15 80
O37 **8** 1 r. violet and maroon .. .. 50 1·25
O38 2 r. brown and orange .. .. 3·50 5·00
O39 – 5 r. green and brown .. .. 7·00 13·00
O40 – 10 r. claret and violet .. .. 8·50 17·00
O28/40 .. .. *Set of* 13 19·00 38·00

1947. *Interim Burmese Government. Nos.* O28/40 *optd with T* **18** *(small stamps) or larger opt (others).*

O41 **2** 3 p. brown 10 40
O42 6 p. deep violet 20 10
O43 9 p. green 20 65
O44 **3** 1 a. blue .. .. 1·00 55
O45 1½ a. orange .. .. 1·50 20
O46 2 a. claret .. .. 1·25 15
O47 **4** 2 a. 6 p. greenish blue .. .. 2·00 1·50
O48 **3** 4 a. purple .. .. 1·50 35
O49 – 8 a. maroon .. .. 2·00 80
O50 **8** 1 r. violet and maroon .. .. 4·00 1·00
O51 2 r. brown and orange .. .. 7·50 8·00
O52 – 5 r. green and brown .. .. 9·00 12·00
O53 – 10 r. claret and violet .. .. 13·00 20·00
O41/53 .. .. *Set of* 13 40·00 40·00

Later stamp issues will be found listed in Part 21 (*South-East Asia*) of this catalogue.

JAPANESE OCCUPATION OF BURMA

PRICES FOR STAMPS ON COVER

Nos. J1/44	—
Nos. J45/71	*from* × 5
No. J72	*from* × 6
Nos. J73/94	*from* × 12
Nos. J95/101	—
Nos. J102/8	*from* × 15

BURMA INDEPENDENCE ARMY ADMINISTRATION

The Burma Independence Army, formed by Aung San in 1941, took control of the Delta area of the Irrawaddy in May 1942. They reopened a postal service in the area and were authorised by the Japanese to overprint local stocks of stamps with the Burmese emblem of a peacock.

Postage and Official stamps with the peacock overprints or handstamps were used for ordinary postal purposes with the probable exception of No. J44.

DISTINGUISHING FEATURES. Type **1**. Body and head of Peacock always clearly outlined by broad uncoloured band. There are four slightly different sub-types of overprint Type **1**.

Type **2**. Peacock with slender neck and more delicately detailed tail. Clear spur on leg at right. Heavy fist-shaped blob of ink below and parallel to beak and neck.

Type **4**. No basic curve. Each feather separately outlined. Straight, short legs.

Type **5**. Much fine detail in wings and tail in clearly printed overprints. Thin, long legs ending in claws which, with the basic arc, enclose clear white spaces in well-printed copies. Blob of colour below beak shows shaded detail and never has the heavy fist-like appearance of this portion in Type **2**.

Two sub-types may be distinguished in Type **5**, the basic arc of one having a chord of 14–15 mm and the other 12½–13 mm.

Type **6**. Similar to Type **5**, but with arc deeply curved and reaching nearly to the top of the wings. Single diagonal line parallel to neck below beak.

Collectors are warned against forgeries of these overprints, often in the wrong colours or on the wrong values.

(1)

(2)

(3)

1942 (May). *Stamps of Burma overprinted with the national device of a Peacock.*

I. *Overprinted at Myaungmya*

A. *With Type* **1** *in black*

On Postage Stamps of King George V

J 1 9 p. deep green (No. 3) .. .. 50·00
J 2 3½ a. deep blue (No. 8) .. .. 30·00

On Official Stamp of King George V

J 3 6 a. bistre (No. O8) .. .. 50·00

On Postage Stamps of King George VI

J 4 **2** 9 p. yellow-green £110
J 5 **3** 1 a. purple-brown £250
J 6 4 a. greenish blue (opt black on red) .. £120
a. Triple opt, black on double red .. £350

On Official Stamps of King George VI

J 7 **2** 3 p. bright violet .. .. 10·00 25·00
J 8 6 p. bright blue .. .. 7·00 18·00
J 9 **3** 1 a. purple-brown .. .. 6·50 12·00
J 9*a* 1½ a. turquoise-green £500
J10 2 a. carmine .. .. 11·00 25·00
J11 4 a. greenish blue .. .. 10·00 22·00

The overprint on No. J6 was apparently first done in red in error, and then corrected in black. Some stamps have the black overprint so accurately superimposed that the red hardly shows. These are rare.

Nos. J5 and J9 exist with the Peacock overprint on both the typographed and the litho printings of the original stamps.

B. *With Types* **2** *or* **3** *(rupee values), in black*

On Postage Stamps of King George VI

J12 **2** 3 p. bright violet .. .. 8·00 24·00
J13 6 p. bright blue .. .. 22·00 30·00
J14 9 p. yellow-green .. .. 8·50 20·00
J15 **3** 1 a. purple-brown .. .. 7·00 17·00
J16 2 a. carmine .. .. 7·50 18·00
J17 4 a. greenish blue .. .. 17·00 28·00
a. Opt double .. ..
b. Opt inverted £375
c. Opt double, one inverted £300
d. Opt double, both inverted £350
J18 1 r. purple and blue £190
J19 2 r. brown and purple £120

The Myaungmya overprints (including No. J44) are usually clearly printed.

(4)

(5)

(6)

Type **5** generally shows the details of the peacock much less clearly and, due to heavy inking, or careless impression, sometimes appears as almost solid colour.

Type **6** was officially applied only to postal stationery. However, the handstamp remained in the possession of a postal official who used it on postage stamps after the war. These stamps are no longer listed.

II. *Handstamped (at Pyapon?) with T* **4**, *in black (so-called experimental type)*

On Postage Stamps of King George VI

J19*a* **3** 1 a. purple-brown .. .. 85·00
J20 2 a. carmine .. .. 45·00
J21 4 a. greenish blue £250

Unused specimens of these stamps are usually in poor condition.

III. *Overprinted at Henzada with T* **5** *in blue, or blue-black*

On Postage Stamps of King George V

J22 3 p. slate (No. 1) .. .. 2·75 8·00
a. Opt double .. .. 9·00 22·00
J23 9 p. deep green (No. 3) .. .. 15·00 30·00
a. Opt double .. .. 48·00
J24 2 a. vermilion (No. 5) .. .. 50·00 85·00

On Postage Stamps of King George VI

J25 **2** 1 p. red-orange .. .. 75·00 £100
J26 3 p. bright violet .. .. 16·00 32·00
J27 6 p. bright blue .. .. 14·00 27·00
a. Opt double .. .. 70·00
b. Clear opt, on back and front .. £130
J28 9 p. yellow-green £240
J29 **3** 1 a. purple-brown .. .. 6·00 13·00
a. Opt inverted £120
J30 1½ a. turquoise-green .. .. 9·50 20·00
a. Opt omitted (in pair with normal) ..
J31 2 a. carmine .. .. 9·50 20·00
J32 4 a. greenish blue .. .. 27·00 40·00
a. Opt double .. .. 75·00
b. Opt inverted £450

On Official Stamps of King George VI

J33 **2** 3 p. bright violet .. .. 60·00 90·00
J34 6 p. bright blue .. .. 55·00 85·00
J35 **3** 1½ a. turquoise-green .. .. 65·00 £100
J35*a* 2 a. carmine £180 £180
J36 4 a. greenish blue £400

(6*a*)

("Yon Thon" = "Office use")

V. *Official Stamp of King George VI optd at Myaungmya with Type* 6*a in black*

J44 **7** 8 a. myrtle-green .. .. 50·00

No. J44 was probably for official use.

There are two types of T 6*a*, one with base of peacock 8 mm long and the other with base about 5 mm long. The neck and other details also vary. The two types are found *se-tenant* in the sheet.

Stocks of the peacock types were withdrawn when the Japanese Directorate-General took control of the postal services in the Delta in August 1942.

JAPANESE ARMY ADMINISTRATION

7

8 Farmer

1942 (1 June). *Impressed by hand. Thick yellowish paper. P 12 × 11. No gum.*
J45 **7** (1 a.) red .. .. 30·00 45·00

This device was the personal seal of Yano Sitza, the Japanese official in charge of the Posts and Telegraphs department of the Japanese Army Administration. It was impressed on paper already perforated by a line machine. Some stamps show part of the papermaker's watermark, either "ABSORBO DUPLICATOR" or "ELEPHANT BRAND", each with an elephant.

Other impressions of this seal on different papers, and showing signs of wear, were not valid for postal purposes.

(Des T. Kato. Typo *Rangoon Gazette* Press)

1942 (15 June). *Value in annas. P 11 or 11 × 11½. Laid bâtonné paper. No gum.*
J46 **8** 1 a. scarlet .. .. 13·00 14·00

Some stamps show part of the papermaker's watermark, either "ELEPHANT BRAND" or "TITAGHUR SUPERFINE", each with an elephant.

½A. (9) 1R. (10)

1942 (22 Sept). *(a) Contemporary Japanese definitive stamps (Cat. Nos. in brackets) surch as T* **9/10**.
J47 **9** ¼ a. on 1 s. chestnut (317) .. .. 13·00 17·00
a. Surch inverted .. .. .. 65·00 65·00
b. Surch double, one inverted.. .. 80·00
J48 ½ a. on 2 s. scarlet (318) .. .. .. 13·00 17·00
a. Surch inverted .. .. .. 50·00
b. Surch double, one inverted.. .. 70·00
J49 ¾ a. on 3 s. green (319) .. .. .. 29·00 32·00
a. Surch inverted .. .. .. 70·00 70·00
b. Surch double, one inverted.. .. — 95·00
J50 1 a. on 5 s. claret (396) .. .. .. 22·00 26·00
a. Surch inverted .. .. .. 70·00 70·00
b. Surch double, one inverted.. .. 90·00 90·00
c. Surch omitted (in pair with normal) — £110
J51 3 a. on 7 s. green (323) .. .. .. 38·00 42·00
a. Surch inverted .. .. .. 80·00
J52 4 a. on 4 s. green (320) .. .. .. 26·00 30·00
a. Surch inverted .. .. .. 80·00
J53 8 a. on 8 s. violet (324) £120 £130
a. Surch inverted £140 £150
b. Surch double, one inverted.. .. £250
c. Surch in red £225 £250
d. Red surch inverted £300
e. Surch double (black and red) .. £275
J54 **10** 1 r. on 10 s. lake (325) .. .. 14·00 18·00
a. Surch inverted .. .. .. 80·00 80·00
b. Surch double .. .. .. 80·00
c. Surch double (black and red) .. £150
d. Surch omitted (in pair with normal) £100 £100
e. Surch omitted (in pair with inverted surch) £140
J55 2 r. on 20 s. ultramarine (328) .. .. 35·00 35·00
a. Surch inverted .. .. .. 90·00 £100
b. Surch double, one inverted.. .. 90·00
c. Surch omitted (in pair with normal black surch) £110 £110
d. Surch in red .. .. .. 35·00 35·00
e. Red surch inverted .. .. .. 90·00 90·00
f. Red surch double £100 £100
g. Surch omitted (in pair with normal red surch) .. .. — £140
h. Surch double (black and red) .. £140
J56 **9** 5 r. on 30 s. blue-green (330) .. .. 11·00 15·00
a. Surch inverted £130
b. Surch double £100
c. Surch double, one inverted.. .. £150
d. Surch omitted (in pair with normal surch) £120 £120
e. Surch omitted (in pair with inverted black surch) £190
f. Surch in red .. .. .. 21·00 24·00
fa. Red surch inverted .. .. .. 70·00 70·00
fb. J56a and J56fa *se-tenant* .. £250 £250
fc. Surch omitted (in pair with normal red surch) £110 £110

(b) Japanese stamp commemorating the fall of Singapore similarly surch
J56*g* **9** 4 a. on 4 + 2 s. green and red (386) .. 85·00 95·00
h. Surch omitted (in pair with normal) £450
ha. Surch omitted (in pair with inverted surch) £450
i. Surch inverted £300

(New Currency. 100 cents = 1 rupee)

(11) (12) (13)

1942 (15 Oct). *Previous issues, with "anna" surcharges obliterated, and handstamped with new value in cents, as T* **11** *and* **12** *(No. J57 handstamped with new value only). (a) T* **8** *(Farmer).*
J57 5 c. on 1 a. scarlet .. .. 8·00 11·00

(b) Contemporary Japanese issues
J58 1 c. on ¼ a. on 1 s. (J47) .. .. .. 27·00 27·00
a. "1 c." omitted in pair with normal ..
J59 2 c. on ½ a. on 2 s. (J48) .. .. .. 27·00 27·00
J60 3 c. on ¾ a. on 3 s. (J49) .. .. .. 30·00 30·00
a. Surch in blue .. .. 85·00
J61 5 c. on 1 a. on 5 s. (J50) .. .. .. 40·00 45·00
J62 10 c. on 3 a. on 7 s. (J51) .. .. .. 55·00 60·00
J63 15 c. on 4 a. on 4 s. (J52) .. .. .. 23·00 23·00
J64 20 c. on 8 a. on 8 s. (J53) £130 £130
a. 20 c. on 8 a. (R.) on 8 s. (J53c) .. .. — £120

The "anna" surcharges were obliterated by any means available, in some cases by a bar or bars, and in others by the butt of a pencil dipped in ink. In the case of the fractional surcharges, the letter "A" and one figure of the fraction, were sometimes barred out, leaving the remainder of the fraction to represent the new value, e.g. the "1" of "½" deleted to create the 2 c. surcharge or the "4" of "¾" to create the 3 c. surcharge.

1942. *Contemporary stamps of Japan (Cat. Nos. in brackets) surcharged in cents only, as T* **13**.
J65 1 c. on 1 s. chestnut (317) .. .. .. 11·00 13·00
a. Surch inverted .. .. .. 55·00 55·00
J66 2 c. on 2 s. scarlet (318) .. .. .. 24·00 24·00
J67 3 c. on 3 s. green (319) .. .. .. 22·00 24·00
a. Pair, with and without surch .. — £100
b. Surch inverted .. .. .. 75·00
c. Surch in blue .. .. .. 70·00 80·00
d. Surch in blue inverted £140 £150
J68 5 c. on 5 s. claret (396) .. .. .. 28·00 28·00
a. Surch in violet £100
b. Surch in violet inverted .. .. — £120
J69 10 c. on 7 s. green (323) .. .. .. 26·00 30·00
J70 15 c. on 4 s. green (320) .. .. .. 11·00 13·00
a. Surch inverted .. .. .. 70·00 75·00
b. Pair, with and without surch .. — 95·00
J71 20 c. on 8 s. violet (324) .. .. .. 70·00 65·00

Nos. J67c and J68a were issued for use in the Shan States.

BURMESE GOVERNMENT

On 1 November 1942 the Japanese Army Administration handed over the control of the postal department to the Burmese Government. On 1 August 1943 Burma was declared by the Japanese to be independent.

14 Burma State Crest

15 Farmer

(Des U Tun Tin and Maung Tin from drawing by U Ba Than. Typo Rangoon)

1943 (15 Feb). *P 11. No gum.*
J72 **14** 5 c. scarlet .. .. 9·00 11·00
a. Imperf .. .. 10·00 12·00
ab. Printed on both sides .. .. 80·00

No. J72 was usually sold affixed to envelopes, particularly those with the embossed 1 a. King George VI stamp, which it covered. Unused specimens off cover are not often seen and blocks are rare.

1943. *P 11½. Typo. No gum.*
J73 **15** 1 c. orange (22 March) 60 85
a. Brown-orange .. .. .. 70 1·00
J74 2 c. yellow-green (24 March) 60 90
a. Blue-green .. .. .. 3·00
J75 3 c. light blue (25 March) 60 75
a. On laid paper .. .. .. 8·00 9·50
J76 5 c. carmine (small "c") (17 March) 4·25 3·75
J77 5 c. carmine (large "C") 60 60
a. Imperf (pair) £200
b. "G" for "C" (R.2/6) £150
J78 10 c. grey-brown (25 March) .. .. 1·25 1·25
a. Imperf (pair) £200
J79 15 c. magenta (26 March) 20 70
a. On laid paper .. .. .. 6·00 9·50
b. Inverted "C" in value .. .. 65·00
J80 20 c. grey-lilac (29 March) 20 65
J81 30 c. deep blue-green (29 March) .. 20 70

The 1 c., 2 c. and 3 c. have large "C" in value as illustrated. The 10 c. and higher values have small "c". Nos. J73/81 had the face values inserted individually into the plate used for No. J46 with the original face value removed. There were a number of printings for each value, often showing differences such as missing stops, various founts of figures or "c", etc., in the value tablets.

There are marked varieties of shade in this issue.

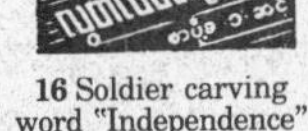
16 Soldier carving word "Independence"

17 Rejoicing Peasant

18 Boy with National Flag

(Des Maung Ba Thit (**16**), Naung Ohn Maung (**17**), and Maung Soi Yi (**18**). Typo State Press, Rangoon)

1943 (1 Aug). *Independence Day. (a) P 11.*
J82 **16** 1 c. orange .. .. 3·75 4·50
J83 **17** 3 c. light blue .. .. 4·00 4·75
J84 **18** 5 c. carmine .. .. 4·00 4·50

(b) Rouletted
J82*a* **16** 1 c. orange .. .. 75 1·25
b. Perf × roul .. .. .. 38·00
c. Imperf (pair) .. .. .. 38·00 45·00
J83*a* **17** 3 c. light blue .. .. 75 1·25
b. Perf × roul .. .. .. 38·00
c. Imperf (pair) .. .. .. 38·00 45·00
J84*a* **18** 5 c. carmine .. .. 75 1·25
aa. Horiz roulette omitted (vert pair)
b. Perf × roul .. .. .. 28·00 32·00
c. Imperf (pair) .. .. .. 38·00 45·00

The stamps perf × rouletted may have one, two, or three sides perforated.

The rouletted stamps often appear to be roughly perforated owing to failure to make clean cuts. These apparent perforations are very small and quite unlike the large, clean holes of the stamps perforated 11.

A few imperforate sets, mounted on a special card folder and cancelled with the commemorative postmark were presented to officials. These are rare.

19 Burmese Woman

20 Elephant carrying Log

21 Watch Tower, Mandalay

(Typo G. Kolff & Co, Batavia)

1943 (1 Oct). *P 12½.*
J85 **19** 1 c. red-orange .. .. 3·00 4·50
J86 2 c. yellow-green 30 60
J87 3 c. deep violet 50 60
a. Bright violet 60 60
J88 **20** 5 c. carmine 35 50
J89 10 c. blue 30 50
J90 15 c. red-orange 35 55
J91 20 c. yellow-green 20 75
J92 30 c. olive-brown 20 75
J93 **21** 1 r. red-orange 20 75
J94 2 r. bright violet .. .. 25 1·40

22 Bullock Cart

23 Shan Woman

(24 "Burma State" and value)

(Typo G. Kolff & Co, Batavia)

1943. *Issue for Shan States. P 12½.*
J 95 **22** 1 c. olive-brown .. .. 10·00 10·00
J 96 2 c. yellow-green .. .. 10·00 10·00
J 97 3 c. bright violet .. .. 2·50 3·00
J 98 5 c. ultramarine .. .. 2·00 3·00
J 99 **23** 10 c. blue .. .. 8·00 9·00
J100 20 c. carmine .. .. 9·00 9·00
J101 30 c. olive-brown .. .. 10·00 10·00

The Shan States, except for the frontier area around Keng Tung which was ceded to Thailand, were placed under the administration of the Burmese Government on 24 December 1943, and these stamps were later overprinted as T **24** for use throughout Burma.

1944 (1 Nov). *Optd as T* **24** *(the lower characters differ for each value).*
J102 **22** 1 c. olive-brown .. .. 1·10 2·00
J103 2 c. yellow-green 25 75
a. Opt inverted £170
J104 3 c. bright violet .. .. 1·00 2·00
J105 5 c. ultramarine 65 75
J106 **23** 10 c. blue .. .. 1·00 1·60
J107 20 c. carmine 25 95
J108 30 c. olive-brown 25 95

The British 14th Army recaptured Mandalay on 20 March 1945 and Rangoon on 6 May.

STAMPS AUCTION NEWS
2 Jan. 1989

Record Prices Set for Canada Pence in Charles Firby Auction

The famed 12 penny pair of Canada realized $165,000 ($203,000 Canadian) when sold by Charles G. Firby Auctions on Oct. 29. The mint pair of black stamps was issued in 1851.

The pair was offered as part of the 450-lot auction of a Canadian first-issue collection formed by Sam C. Nickle of Calgary, Alberta. This was the highest price ever paid for a Canadian philatelic item sold at public auction.

The bidding began at $135,000 and increased by $5,000 increments. Five bids later, the piece was knocked down at

Acting as agent for a Toronto commission brought the total price. "I was pleased," Jamie "This piece is ... He would ... by any me... The ... believes

Philatelic Literature Review 37:1/7

Year's Major U.S. Auction Had Something for Everyone

by Steven J. Rod

The major American philatelic literature auction of the past year seems to have been the October 31, 1987, Charles G. Firby "Rarities of Philatelic Literature Sale" held at Southfield, Michigan. This sale truly seems to have had something for every... with prices realized ranging from $2.50 to $4,200. Well, okay, if you take away one expensive lot, the prices ranged from $2.50 to $1,150. Take away those ... figure lots and there were eight lots at $400 to $725 and nineteen lots ...

Philatelic Literature Review 37:4/179

Prices 'Out of Sight' at Firby's 2nd 'Rarities' Sale

by William Hagan

Chuck Firby's second "Rarities" sale featured Roger Koerber's Philatelic li... "also a portion of his retail stock." Of the four sessions (three on Mond... 29, and one on Tuesday, August 30), I was able to attend only the secon... and I spent only about thirty minutes examining material.

Probably the most exciting lot was No. 803, Roger's P... titles . . . masters and templates . . . buyer ac... quires rights to Postilion name . . . 650 imprint... binders . . ." A tremendous number of potent... buyers (more than twenty) refused to be scar... by the $5,000 estimate. The lot was ... $14,000 and, after the sale, the word...

Canadian Stamp News
May 20, 1986

Record prices set at Firby a...

Collectors and agents alike witnessed record prices at the Charles G. Firby March 18 public auction held near the Detroit Metropolitan Airport.

All prices quoted are in United States dollars and include the buyers premium.

The auction began with Ray Simrak Gold Medal Canadian Airmail Collection.

The very first lot set the tone of the sale. An orange ABN ... proof

international route cover on the North American Continent is listed by AAMC at cv $1,000 and was estimated at $1,250 plus. After some healthy floor bidding it was finally knocked down at $6,700 plus 10 per cent, a total realization of $7,370 — almost 600 per cent of estimate.

Another item is the Grand Ar... cover, ... survivin... titive ...

sold fo... 125, ... Haileybu... cv $25... $412.50

The SCADTA covers also standing p... Lot 228, on... estimated plus, close... Lot 229

This 12 Pence Pair realized $165,000.00 in our OCTOBER 29, 1989 AUCTION. Highest price ever paid for a Canadian Stamp at auction.

Before You Sell Your Stamps Talk To Us.

We understand what it takes to Establish Records. We've done it Again & Again & Again & Again...

You spent much time & money forming your collection & we feel that it is important to present your material in the same way: professionally & with great care.

Our lotting, presentation & international buyers assure you of the highest possible realization. The kind of realization that makes headlines.

After all, when the experts review our sales & prices realized it becomes obvious that we know how to sell your stamps.

No collection is too small to receive our individual attention. We encourage you to call Collect to learn more about how best to offer your collection or to request our "Auction Consignment Information" brochure which describes the auction process.

That way you may very well come up with some records of your own.

If an outright sale is more to your liking, you can count on us for a prompt response & "instant" payment. Just Ask.

Charles G. Firby
AUCTIONS

APS

LICENSED and BONDED

6695 Highland Road, Pontiac, MI 48054
Phone 313-666-3946 FAX 313-666-2992

Bushire

BRITISH OCCUPATION

PRICES FOR STAMPS ON COVER
Nos. 1/14 *from* × 10
Nos. 15/29 *from* × 5

BUSHIRE
Under British
Occupation.
(1)

Stamps of Iran (Persia) overprinted with T 1

1915 (15 Aug). *Nos.* 361, *etc.* (*Ahmed Mirza*).

No.	Description	Unused	Used
1	1 ch. orange and green	17·00	22·00
	a. No stop	55·00	60·00
2	2 ch. sepia and carmine	19·00	18·00
	a. No stop	55·00	55·00
3	3 ch. green and grey	20·00	27·00
	a. No stop	65·00	85·00
4	5 ch. carmine and brown	£200	£200
5	6 ch. brown-lake and green	17·00	16·00
	a. No stop	50·00	48·00
6	9 ch. indigo-lilac and brown	21·00	23·00
	a. No stop	65·00	70·00
	b. Opt double		
7	10 ch. brown and carmine	23·00	23·00
	a. No stop	70·00	70·00
8	12 ch. blue and green	30·00	35·00
	a. No stop	90·00	£100
9	24 ch. green and purple	42·00	32·00
	a. No stop	£120	95·00
10	1 kr. carmine and blue	42·00	25·00
	a. Double overprint	£4500	
	b. No stop	£120	80·00
11	2 kr. claret and green	£100	90·00
	a. No stop	£275	£275
12	3 kr. black and lilac	£140	£150
	a. No stop	£300	£300
13	5 kr. blue and red	65·00	60·00
	a. No stop	£225	£225
14	10 kr. rose and bistre-brown	55·00	55·00
	a. No stop	£200	£200

Nos. 1/14 were overprinted in strips of 10, five different settings having been identified. The "No stop" variety occurs on the second setting stamp 10 (where the gap between "Under" and "British" measures 2 mm) and stamp 9 of the third, fourth and fifth settings (on which position the gap is 3 mm).

1915 (Sept). *Nos.* 426, *etc.* (*Coronation of Shah Ahmed*) *optd in strips of* 5.

No.	Description	Unused	Used
15	1 ch. deep blue and carmine	£300	£300
16	2 ch. carmine and deep blue	£5000	£5500
17	3 ch. deep green	£375	£400
18	5 ch. vermilion	£3750	£4000
19	6 ch. carmine and green	£3000	£3250
20	9 ch. deep violet and brown	£475	£500
21	10 ch. brown and deep green	£750	£800
22	12 ch. ultramarine	£850	£950
23	24 ch. sepia and brown	£375	£400
24	1 kr. black, brown and silver	£350	£375
25	2 kr. carmine, slate and silver	£300	£325
26	3 kr. sepia, dull lilac and silver	£425	£450
27	5 kr. slate, sepia and silver	£400	£425
	a. Opt inverted	—	£7500
28	1 t. black, violet and gold	£350	£400
29	3 t. red, crimson and gold	£1600	£1700

Examples of overprint Type 1 on Iran No. 414, 1 ch. on 5 ch. (previously No. 30), are now believed to be forged.

Bushire, a seaport town of Persia, was occupied by the British on 8 August 1915. The Persian postal authorities resumed control on 16 October 1915.

Cameroons

BRITISH OCCUPATION

Allied operations against the German protectorate of Kamerun commenced in August 1914 and were completed by February 1916. The territory was divided, under an Anglo-French agreement, on 1 April 1916 with the British administering areas in the north and in the west along the Nigerian border.

Supplies of Kamerun stamps were found on the German steamer *Professor Woermann* captured at Freetown and these were surcharged, probably in Sierra Leone, and issued by the Cameroons Expeditionary Force at Duala in June 1915. It is believed that further stocks of German stamps found in the post office were used, unsurcharged, during 1916.

PRICES FOR STAMPS ON COVER
The stamps of British Occupation of Cameroons are rare used on cover.

A

B

C. E. F.
1d.
(1)

C. E. F.
1s.
(2)

SETTINGS. Nos. 1/3 were surcharged from a setting of 100 (10 × 10) with the face value changed for the 1d.

Nos. 4 and 6/9 were surcharged from a common setting of 50 (5 × 10) with the face value amended.

No. 5 was surcharged from a setting of 10 in a vertical strip repeated across the sheet.

Nos. 10/13 were surcharged from a common setting of 20 (4 × 5) with the face value amended.

Different fount "d" (R. 1/10, 6/9, 10/10)
"1" with thin serifs (R. 5/1)
Large "3" (R. 3/5, 3/10)
Short "4" (R. 10/2, 10/7)
"s" inverted (R. 3/4)

1915 (June). *Stamps of German Kamerun, Types* A *and* B, *surch as T* 1 (*Nos.* 1/9) *or* 2 (*Nos.* 10/13) *in black or blue.*

No.	Type	Description	Unused	Used
1	A	½d. on 3 pf. (No. K7) (B.)	4·00	9·00
		a. Different fount "d"	25·00	50·00
2		½d. on 5 pf. (No. K21 *wmk lozenges*) (B.)	1·25	4·50
		a. Different fount "d"	8·00	22·00
		b. Surch double	—	£350
		ba. Surch double, one albino	85·00	
3		1d. on 10 pf. (No. K22 *wmk lozenges*) (B.)	1·25	3·50
		a. "1" with thin serifs	10·00	27·00
		b. Surch double	£125	
		ba. Surch double, one albino	55·00	
		c. "1d." only double	£1200	
		d. Surch triple, two albino	£140	
		e. Surch in black	12·00	24·00
		ea. "1" with thin serifs	85·00	
		eb. "C.E.F." omitted	£1750	
4		2d. on 20 pf. (No. K23 *wmk lozenges*)	3·25	9·00
		a. Surch double, one albino	£140	
5		2½d. on 25 pf. (No. K11)	8·50	19·00
		a. Surch double	£4000	
		ab. Surch double, one albino		
6		3d. on 30 pf. (No. K12)	8·50	19·00
		a. Large "3"	£325	
		b. Surch triple, two albino	£140	
7		4d. on 40 pf. (No. K13)	8·50	19·00
		a. Short "4"	£325	
		b. Surch triple, two albino	£140	
		c. Surch quadruple, three albino		
8		6d. on 50 pf. (No. K14)	8·50	19·00
		a. Surch double, one albino	£140	
9		8d. on 80 pf. (No. K15)	8·50	19·00
10	B	1s. on 1 m. (No. K16)	£110	£250
		a. "s" inverted	£425	£850
11		2s. on 2 m. (No. K17)	£110	£250
		a. "s" inverted	£425	£850
		b. Surch double, one albino	£550	
12		3s. on 3 m. (No. K18)	£110	£250
		a. "s" inverted	£425	£850
		b. Surch double	£3500	
		ba. Surch double, one albino	£550	
13		5s. on 5 m. (No. K25a *wmk lozenges*)	£140	£275
		a. "s" inverted	£475	£900
1/13		*Set of* 13	£450	£1000

The stamps of Nigeria were subsequently used in British Cameroons and the area was administered as part of Nigeria from February 1924.

For stamps optd "CAMEROONS U.K.T.T.", see under SOUTHERN CAMEROONS.

Canada

CANADIAN PROVINCES. The following Provinces issued their own stamps before joining the Confederation of Canada, whilst the former Dominion of Newfoundland became part of Canada in 1949. Their issues are listed in alphabetical order in this Catalogue:

BRITISH COLUMBIA and VANCOUVER ISLAND
NEW BRUNSWICK
NEWFOUNDLAND
NOVA SCOTIA
PRINCE EDWARD ISLAND

NEW CARLISLE, GASPÉ

POSTMASTER'S PROVISIONAL ENVELOPE

1

1851 (7 April).
1 1 3d. black

Only one example is known, with the impression cancelled by the signature of the postmaster, R. W. Kelly.

COLONY OF CANADA

The first British post offices in what was to become the colony of Canada were opened at Quebec, Montreal and Trois Rivières during 1763. These, and subsequent, offices remained part of the British G.P.O. system until 6 April 1851.

For illustration of the handstamp types see BRITISH POST OFFICES ABROAD notes, following GREAT BRITAIN.

QUEBEC

CROWNED-CIRCLE HANDSTAMPS

CC1 CC 1*b* QUEBEC L.C. (R.) (13.1.1842) *Price on cover* £150

PRICES FOR STAMPS ON COVER TO 1945

Nos. 1/23	*from* × 2
Nos. 25/8	*from* × 3
Nos. 29/43*a*	*from* × 3
Nos. 44/5	*from* × 8
Nos. 46/61	*from* × 2
Nos. 62/7*b*	*from* × 3
Nos. 68/75*b*	*from* × 2
Nos. 76/*c*	*from* × 10
Nos. 77/*a*	*from* × 5
Nos. 78/83	*from* × 3
Nos. 115/20	*from* × 6
Nos. 121/49	*from* × 3
Nos. 150/65	*from* × 2
Nos. 166/72	*from* × 3
Nos. 173/87	*from* × 5
Nos. 188/95	*from* × 2
Nos. 196/215	*from* × 3
Nos. 219/224*b*	*from* × 4
Nos. 225/45	*from* × 2
Nos. 246/55	*from* × 8
Nos. 256/310	*from* × 2
No. 312	*from* × 20
No. 313	*from* × 10
Nos. 315/18	*from* × 2
Nos. 319/28	*from* × 3
Nos. 329/40	*from* × 2
Nos. 341/400	*from* × 1
Nos. R1/11	*from* × 5
Nos. S1/3	*from* × 8
No. S4	*from* × 6
No. S5	*from* × 5
Nos. S6/11	*from* × 3
Nos. S12/14	*from* × 5
Nos. D1/8	*from* × 4
Nos. D9/13	*from* × 5
Nos. D14/24	*from* × 4

1 American Beaver (Designed by Sir Sandford Fleming)

2 Prince Albert

3

Major re-entry: Line though "EE PEN"

(T **1/6**. Eng and recess Rawdon, Wright, Hatch and Edson, New York)

1851. *Imperf. Laid paper.*

No.	Type	Description	Unused	Used
1	1	3d. red (23 April)	£7000	£600
1*a*		3d. orange-vermilion	£7000	£600
		b. Major re-entry	—	£1600
2	2	6d. slate-violet (15 May)	£7500	£900
3		6d. brown-purple	£8000	£1200
		a. Bisected (3d.) on cover	†	£20000
4	3	12d. black (14 June)	£55000	£38000

There are several re-entries on the plate of the 3d. in addition to the major re-entry listed. All re-entries occur in this stamp on all papers.

Forgeries of the 3d. are known without the full stop after "PENCE".

4

5

6 Jacques Cartier

1852–57. *Imperf.*

A. *Handmade wove paper, varying in thickness* (1852–56)

No.	Type	Description	Unused	Used
5	1	3d. red	£850	£160
		a. Bisected (1½d.) on cover	†	£22000
6		3d. deep red	£1000	£160
7		3d. scarlet-vermilion	£1400	£170
8		3d. brown-red	£1000	£160
		a. Bisected (1½d.) on cover	†	—
		b. Major re-entry (*all shades*) *from*	—	£650

9 2 6d. slate-violet £7500 £900
a. Bisected (3d.) on cover .. .. † £12000
10 6d. greenish grey £7500 £950
11 6d. brownish grey £8000 £1000
12 5 7½d. yellow-green (*shades*) (2.6.57) .. £7000 £1500
13 6 10d. bright blue (1.55) £7000 £1200
14 10d. dull blue £6500 £1100
15 10d. blue *to* deep blue £7000 £1200
a. Major re-entry (*all shades*) *from* — £2000
16 3 12d. black .. .. — £38000

B. *Machine-made medium to thick wove paper of a more even hard texture with more visible mesh. Clearer impressions* (1857)
17 4 ½d. deep rose (1.8.57) £500 £350
18 1 3d. red £1300 £450
a. Bisected (1½d.) on cover .. .. † £15000
b. Major re-entry .. .. ..
19 2 6d. grey-lilac £12000 £2000
20 6 10d. blue *to* deep blue £6500 £1200
a. Major re-entry .. .. .. — £2500

C. *Thin soft horizontally ribbed paper* (1857)
21 4 ½d. deep rose £2750 £1600
a. Vertically ribbed paper £4500 £2000
22 1 3d. red £2500 £400
a. Major re-entry .. ..

D. *Very thick soft wove paper* (1857)
23 2 6d. reddish purple £11000 £2500
a. Bisected (3d.) on cover .. .. † £18000

Bisected examples of the 3d. value were used to make up the 7½d. Canadian Packet rate to England from May 1856 until the introduction of the 7½d. value on 2 June 1857.

The 7½d. and 10d. values can be found in wide and narrow versions. These differences are due to shrinkage of the paper, which was wetted before printing and then contracted unevenly during drying. The width of these stamps varies between 17 and 18 mm.

The listed major re-entry on the 10d. occurs on R.3/5 and shows strong doubling of the top frame line and the left-hand "8d. stg." with a line through the lower parts of "ANAD" and "ENCE". Smaller re-entries occur on all values.

Examples of the 12d. come from a proof sheet used for postal purposes by the postal authorities.

The 3d. is known perforated 14 and also *percé en scie* 13. Both are contemporary, but were unofficial.

1858–59. *P* 11¾. A. *Machine-made medium to thick wove paper with a more even hard texture.*
25 4 ½d. deep rose (12.58) £1100 £450
a. Lilac-rose £1400 £550
26 1 3d. red (1.59) £2250 £300
27 2 6d. brownish grey (1.59) £5000 £1800
a. Slate-violet £5000 £1600

B. *Thin soft horizontally ribbed paper*
27*b* 4 ½d. deep rose-red .. .. — £3000
28 1 3d. red .. .. — £1200

(New Currency. 100 cents = 1 dollar)

7

8 American Beaver

9 Prince Albert

10

11 Jacques Cartier

(Recess A.B.N. Co)

(On 1 May 1858, Messrs. Rawdon, Wright, Hatch and Edson joined with eight other firms to form "The American Bank Note Co" and the "imprint" on sheets of the following stamps has the new title of the firm with "New York" added.)

1859 (1 July). *P* 12.
29 7 1 c. pale rose (to rose-red) .. .. £150 22·00
30 1 c. deep rose (to carmine-rose) .. £170 40·00
a. Imperf (pair) £3000
b. Imperf × perf .. .. ..
31 8 5 c. pale red .. .. £140 10·00
32 5 c. deep red .. .. £140 10·00
a. Re-entry* (R.3/8) .. .. .. — £500
b. Imperf (pair) £7000
c. Bisected (2½ c.) with 10 c. on cover † £3500
33 9 10 c. black-brown £5000 £1300
a. Bisected (5 c.), on cover .. † £5000
33*b* 10 c. deep red-purple £2250 £500
ba. Bisected (5 c.), on cover .. † £3500
34 10 c. purple (*shades*) .. .. .. £600 35·50
a. Bisected (5 c.), on cover .. † £3500
35 10 c. brownish purple .. .. .. £550 35·00
36 10 c. brown (to pale) .. .. .. £550 35·00
a. Bisected (5 c.), on cover .. † £4250
37 10 c. dull violet .. .. £500 35·00
38 10 c. bright red-purple .. .. .. £500 35·00
a. Imperf (pair) £5500
39 10 12½ c. deep yellow-green .. .. £400 35·00
40 12½ c. pale yellow-green .. .. £350 35·00
41 12½ c. blue-green .. .. .. £350 35·00
a. Imperf (pair) £2500
b. Imperf between (vert pair) .. ..

42 11 17 c. deep blue .. .. £600 60·00
a. Imperf (pair) £3000
43 17 c. slate-blue .. .. £650 80·00
43*a* 17 c. indigo .. .. £600 60·00
b. Imperf (pair) £3000

*The price of No. 32a is for the very marked re-entry showing oval frame line doubled above "CANADA". Slighter re-entries are worth from £30 upwards in used condition.

As there were numerous P.O. Dept. orders for the 10 c., 12½ c. and 17 c. and some of these were executed by more than one separate printing, with no special care to ensure uniformity of colour, there is a wide range of shade, especially in the 10 c., and some shades recur at intervals after periods during which other shades predominated. The colour-names given in the above list therefore represent groups only.

It has been proved by leading Canadian specialists that the perforations may be an aid to the approximate dating of a particular stamp, the gauge used measuring 11¾ × 11¾ from mid-July, 1859 to mid 1863, 12 × 11¾ from March 1863 to mid 1865 and 12 × 12 from April 1865 to 1868. Exceptionally in the 5 c. value many sheets were perforated 12 × 12 between May and October, 1862, whilst the last printings of the 12½ c. and 17 c. perf 11¾ × 11¾ were in July 1863, the perf 12 × 11¾ starting towards the end of 1863.

12

(Recess A.B.N. Co)

1864 (1 Aug). *P* 12.
44 12 2 c. rose-red £350 £100
45 2 c. bright rose £350 £100
a. Imperf (pair) £1700

DOMINION OF CANADA

On 1 July 1867, Canada, Nova Scotia, and New Brunswick were united, the combined territory being termed "The Dominion of Canada". Under the Act of Union provision was made for the admission of Newfoundland, Prince Edward Island, British Columbia, Rupert's Land, and Northwest Territory.

13

14

Large types

PRINTERS. Nos. 46/120 were recess-printed by the British American Bank Note Co at Ottawa or Montreal.

1868 (Mar)–**71.** *As T* 13 *and* 14 (*various frames*). *Ottawa printings. P* 12.

(*a*) *Thin rather transparent crisp paper*
46 13 ½ c. black .. .. 50·00 40·00
47 14 1 c. red-brown .. .. .. £250 40·00
48 2 c. grass-green .. .. .. £300 30·00
49 3 c. red-brown .. .. .. £550 20·00
50 6 c. blackish brown £600 £250
51 12½ c. bright blue £450 £150
52 15 c. deep reddish purple £700 £190

In these first printings the impression is generally blurred and the lines of the background are less clearly defined than in later printings.

(*b*) *Medium to stout wove paper* (1868–71)
53 13 ½ c. black .. .. 35·00 30·00
54 ½ c. grey-black .. .. .. 35·00 30·00
a. Imperf between (pair) .. ..
b. Watermarked £8750 £5500
55 14 1 c. red-brown .. .. .. £275 35·00
a. Laid paper £6500 £1600
b. Watermarked (1868) £1800 £225
56 1 c. deep orange (Jan, 1869) .. £650 60·00
56*a* 1 c. orange-yellow (May (?), 1869) .. £650 60·00
56*b* 1 c. pale orange-yellow .. .. £750 70·00
ba. Imperf .. .. ..
57 2 c. deep green .. .. .. £300 22·00
57*a* 2 c. pale emerald-green (1871) .. £350 28·00
ab. Bisected (1 c. with 2 c. to make 3 c. rate) on cover .. .. † £4000
ac. Laid paper .. .. .. — £48000
57*d* 2 c. bluish green .. .. .. £300 22·00
da. Watermarked (1868) £1400 £200
58 3 c. brown-red .. .. .. £650 15·00
a. Laid paper £6000 £300
b. Watermarked (1868) £2250 £160
59 6 c. blackish brown (*to* chocolate) .. £600 28·00
a. Watermarked (1868) £2000 £550
59*b* 6 c. yellow-brown (1870) .. .. £550 32·00
ba. Bisected (3 c.), on cover .. † £2000
60 12½ c. bright blue .. .. .. £350 32·00
a. Imperf horiz (vert pair) .. † —
b. Watermarked (1868) £1400 £180
60*c* 12½ c. pale dull blue (milky) .. £350 32·00
61 15 c. deep reddish purple .. .. £450 60·00
61*a* 15 c. pale reddish purple .. .. £400 60·00
ab. Watermarked (1868) .. .. — £1500
61*b* 15 c. dull violet-grey .. .. £200 28·00
ba. Watermarked (1868) .. .. — £700
61*c* 15 c. dull grey-purple .. .. .. £300 28·00

The watermark on the stout paper stamps consists of the words "E & G BOTHWELL CLUTHA MILLS," in large double-lined capitals. Portions of one or two letters only may be found on these stamps, which occur in the early printings of 1868.

The papers may, in most cases, be easily divided if the stamps are laid face downwards and carefully compared. The thin hard paper is more or less transparent and shows the design through the stamp; the thicker paper is softer to the feel and more opaque.

The paper of this issue may be still further subdivided in several values into sets on—(a) *Medium to stout wove.* (b) *Thin, soft, very white*: and (c) *Thinner and poorer quality, sometimes greyish or yellowish* (*from* 1878 *to end of issue*).

Of the 2 c. laid paper No. 57ac two examples only are known.

21

Small type

1870–89. *As T* 21 (*various frames*). *Ottawa* (1870–73) *and Montreal printings. P* 12 (*or slightly under*).
Papers (*a*) 1870–80. *Medium to stout wove.*
(*b*) 1870–72. *Thin, soft, very white.*
(*c*) 1878–97. *Thinner and poorer quality.*

62 21 1 c. bright orange (*a, b*) (1870–73) .. £110 20·00
a. Thick soft paper (1871) .. ..
62*b* 1 c. orange-yellow (*a*) (1876–79) .. 30·00 85
62*c* 1 c. pale dull yellow (*a*) (1877–79) .. 20·00 30
62*d* 1 c. bright yellow (*a, c*) (1878–97) .. 14·00 15
da. Imperf (pair) (*c*) £300
db. Bisected (½ c.) (on *Railway News*) .. † £3000
dc. Printed both sides £1400
62*e* 1 c. lemon-yellow (*c*) (1880) .. ..
63 2 c. deep green (*a, b*) (1872–73 & 1876–78) 70·00 50
63*a* 2 c. grass-green (*c*) (1878–88) .. 35·00 20
ab. Imperf (pair) (1891–93?) .. £325
ac. Bisected (1 c.) on cover .. † £1300
64 3 c. Indian red (*a*) (1.70) .. .. £800 70·00
a. Perf 12½ (2.70) £3500 £500
64*b* 3 c. pale rose-red (*a*) (9.70) .. £275 8·00
64*c* 3 c. deep rose-red (*a, b*) (1870–73) .. £300 8·50
ca. Thick soft paper (Jan, 1871) .. — £300
64*d* 3 c. dull red (*a, c*) (1876–88) .. 50·00 70
64*e* 3 c. orange-red (*a, c*) (1876–88) (*shades*) .. 40·00 55
64*f* 3 c. rose-carmine (*c*) (Oct 1888–April 1889) £350 11·00
65 5 c. olive-grey (*a, c*) (February, 1876–88) £130 3·75
66 6 c. yellowish brown (*a, b, c*) (1872–73 and 1876–90) .. .. £120 9·00
a. Bisected (3 c.) on cover .. † £1600
67 10 c. pale lilac-magenta (*a*) (1876–?) .. £450 45·00
67*a* 10 c. deep lilac-magenta (*a, c*) (March, 1876–88) .. .. .. £400 45·00
67*b* 10 c. lilac-pink (March, 1888) .. £130 90·00

Nos. 62*d* and 63*a* were printed in the same shades during the second Ottawa period.

No. 64a was issued in New Brunswick and Nova Scotia.

One used copy of the 10 c. perf 12½ has been reported.

22

1873–79. *As T* 13, 14, 21 *and* 22. *Montreal printings. Medium to stout wove paper. P* 11½ × 12 *or* 11¾ × 12.
68 13 ½ c. black .. .. 35·00 32·00
69 21 1 c. bright orange .. .. .. £150 16·00
69*a* 1 c. orange-yellow (1873–79) .. £140 8·00
69*b* 1 c. pale dull yellow (1877–79) .. £130 13·00
69*c* 1 c. lemon-yellow (1879) .. ..
70 2 c. deep green (1873–78) .. .. £170 11·00
71 3 c. dull red (1875–79) .. .. £190 9·00
71*a* 3 c. orange-red (1873–79) .. .. £190 9·00
72 22 5 c. olive-green (1 Oct, 1875) .. £850 80·00
a. Perf 12 .. .. £3500 £800
72*b* 21 5 c. olive-grey (1876–79) .. .. £300 20·00
73 6 c. yellowish brown (1876–79) .. £300 20·00
74 10 c. very pale lilac-magenta (1874) .. £800 £250
74*a* 10 c. deep lilac-magenta (1876–79) .. £500 £170
75 14 15 c. dull grey-purple (1874) .. £600 £225
75*a* 15 c. lilac-grey (Mar, 1877) £800 £225
ab. Script Wmk* £9000 £2250
ac. "BOTHWELL" watermark† .. .. † —
75*b* 15 c. slate £800 £450

*The watermark on No. 75ab is part of the words "Alexr. Pirie & Sons" in script lettering, a very small quantity of paper thus watermarked having been used for printing this stamp.

†For description of this watermark see below No. 61c.

Several used examples of the 12½ c. have been reported in these perforations.

1879–88. *Montreal printings. Medium to stout wove paper. P* 12.
76 14 15 c. clear deep violet £2250 £500
76*a* 15 c. deep slate (1881) .. .. .. £130 25·00
76*b* 15 c. slaty blue (1887) .. .. .. £130 25·00
76*c* 15 c. slate-purple (*shades*) (July, 1888–92) 60·00 16·00

The last printing of No. 76c took place at Ottawa.

27

1882–97. *Montreal (to March 1889) and Ottawa printings. Thinnish paper of poor quality. P* 12.

77 **27** ½ c. black (July, 1882–97) 4·50 3·75
77*a* ½ c. grey-black 4·50 3·75
ab. Imperf (pair) (1891–93?) £400
ac. Imperf between (pair) £700

1889–97. *As T* **14** *and* **21** *(various frames). Ottawa printings. Thinnish paper of poor quality, often toned grey or yellowish. P* 12.

78 **21** 2 c. dull sea-green 32·00 20
78*a* 2 c. blue-green (July, 1889–91) 26·00 30
79 3 c. bright vermilion (April, 1889–97) 18·00 10
a. Imperf (pair) (1891–93?) £350
80 5 c. brownish grey (May, 1889) 38·00 30
a. Imperf (pair) (1891–93) £375
81 6 c. deep chestnut (Oct, 1890) 28·00 7·00
a. "5 c." re-entry* £2000 £1300
81*b* 6 c. pale chestnut 28·00 7·00
ba. Imperf (pair) (1891–93?) £450
82 10 c. salmon-pink £200 £110
82*a* 10 c. carmine-pink (April, 1890) £130 14·00
ab. Imperf (pair) (1891–93?) £325
82*b* 10 c. brownish red (1894?) £110 14·00
ba. Imperf (pair) £300
83 **14** 15 c. slate-violet (*shades*) (May, 1890) 60·00 16·00
a. Imperf (brown-purple) (pair) £800

*No. 81a shows traces of the 5 c. value 2½ mm lower than the 6 c. design.

The 1 c. showed no change in the Ottawa printings, so is not included. The 2 c. reverted to its previous grass-green shade in 1891. The 15 c. stamps are generally found with yellowish streaky gum; about 1895 remainders of this value were used concurrently with the 1888 and 1890 shades. They vary from grey and slate to a nearly true blue.

28

29

(Recess B.A.B.N.)

1893 (17 Feb). *P* 12.

115 **28** 20 c. vermilion £200 40·00
a. Imperf (pair) £1400
116 50 c. blue £275 24·00
a. Imperf (Prussian blue) (pair) £1400

1893 (1 Aug). *P* 12.

117 **29** 8 c. pale bluish grey 55·00 3·00
a. Imperf (pair) £450
118 8 c. bluish slate 55·00 3·00
119 8 c. slate-purple 55·00 3·00
120 8 c. blackish purple 55·00 3·00

PRINTERS. The following stamps to No. 287 were recess-printed by the American Bank Note Co, Ottawa, which in 1923 became the Canadian Bank Note Co.

30

(Des L. Pereira and F. Brownell)

1897 (19 June). *Jubilee issue. P* 12.

121 **30** ½ c. black 42·00 45·00
122 1 c. orange 6·00 1·50
123 1 c. orange-yellow 6·00 1·50
a. Bisected (½ c.) on cover
124 2 c. green 9·00 3·75
125 2 c. deep green 10·00 3·75
126 3 c. carmine 5·00 80
127 5 c. slate-blue 23·00 12·00
128 5 c. deep blue 20·00 9·00
129 6 c. brown 75·00 75·00
130 8 c. slate-violet 32·00 25·00
131 10 c. purple 50·00 35·00
132 15 c. slate 80·00 80·00
133 20 c. vermilion 80·00 80·00
134 50 c. pale ultramarine £120 95·00
135 50 c. bright ultramarine £120 95·00
136 $1 lake £400 £400
137 $2 deep violet £700 £250
138 $3 bistre £800 £600
139 $4 violet £800 £600
140 $5 olive-green £800 £600
121/40 *Set of* 16 £3750 £2700
133/40 Handstamped "Specimen" *Set of* 7 £1750

No 123a was used on issues of the *Railway News* of 5, 6 and 8 November 1897 and must be on a large part of the original news paper with New Glasgow postmark.

31

32

(From photograph by W. & D. Downey, London)

1897–98. *P* 12.

141 **31** ½ c. grey-black (9.11.97) 3·75 3·00
142 ½ c. black 6·00 4·00
a. Imperf (pair) £375
143 1 c. blue-green (12.97) 13·00 30
a. Imperf (pair) £375
144 2 c. violet (12.97) 14·00 60
a. Imperf (pair) £375
145 3 c. carmine (1.98) 18·00 20
a. Imperf (pair) £700
146 5 c. deep blue/*bluish* (12.97) 55·00 70
a. Imperf (pair) £375
147 6 c. brown (12.97) 55·00 16·00
a. Imperf (pair) £700
148 8 c. orange (12.97) 70·00 5·00
a. Imperf (pair) £375
149 10 c. brownish purple (1.98) £120 50·00
a. Imperf (pair) £375
141/9 *Set of* 8 £300 70·00

IMPERF SIDES. Stamps with one side, or two adjacent sides imperf come from booklet panes.

Two types of the 2 c.

Die Ia. Frame consists of four fine lines.
Die Ib. Frame has one thick line between two fine lines.

The die was retouched in 1900 for Plates 11 and 12 producing weak vertical frame lines and then retouched again in 1902 for Plates 15 to 20 resulting in much thicker frame lines. No. 155*b* covers both states of the retouching.

1898–1902. *P* 12.

150 **32** ½ c. black (9.98) 1·25 85
a. Imperf (pair) £375
151 1 c. blue-green (6.98) 18·00 15
152 1 c. deep green/*toned paper* 18·00 15
a. Imperf (pair) £700
153 2 c. dull purple (Die Ia) (9.98) 20·00 25
a. Thick paper (6.99) 90·00 10·00
154 2 c. violet (Die Ia) 20·00 10
154*a* 2 c. reddish purple (Die Ia) 38·00 75
155 2 c. rose-carmine (Die Ia) (20.8.99) 22·00 10
a. Imperf (pair) £300
155*b* 2 c. rose-carmine (Die Ib) (1900) 27·00 25
c. Booklet pane of 6 (11.6.00) £750
156 3 c. rose-carmine (6.98) 28·00 20
157 5 c. slate-blue/*bluish* 70·00 70
a. Imperf (pair) £750
158 5 c. Prussian blue/*bluish* 70·00 70
159 6 c. brown (9.98) 65·00 27·00
a. Imperf (pair) £650
160 7 c. greenish yellow (23.12.02) 45·00 10·00
161 8 c. orange-yellow (10.98) 70·00 16·00
162 8 c. brownish orange 70·00 16·00
a. Imperf (pair) £650
163 10 c. pale brownish purple (11.98) £150 11·00
164 10 c. deep brownish purple £150 11·00
a. Imperf (pair) £650
165 20 c. olive-green (29.12.00) £300 45·00
150/65 *Set of* 11 £700 £100

The 7 c. and 20 c. also exist imperf but unlike the values listed in this condition, they have no gum. (*Price,* 7 c. £275, 20 c. £1400 *pair, un.*)

33

(Des Postmaster-General Mulock; frame, recess; colours, typo)

1898 (7 Dec). *Imperial Penny Postage. Design in black. British possessions in red. Oceans in colours given. P* 12.

166 **33** 2 c. lavender 24·00 3·75
167 2 c. greenish blue 17·00 3·50
168 2 c. blue 17·00 3·00
a. Imperf (pair) £350

1899 (5 Jan). *Provisionals used at Port Hood. No.* 156 *divided vertically and handstamped.*

169 **32** "1" in blue, on ⅓ of 3 c. — £3500
170 "2" in violet, on ⅔ of 3 c. — £3000

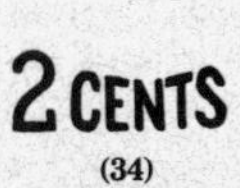

(34)

35 King Edward VII

1899. *Surch with T* **34**, *by Public Printing Office.*

171 **31** 2 c. on 3 c. carmine (8 Aug) 10·00 3·75
a. Surch inverted £250
172 **32** 2 c. on 3 c. rose-carmine (28 July) 12·00 2·50
a. Surch inverted £250

(Des King George V when Prince of Wales and J. A. Tilleard)

1903 (1 July)–**12.** *P* 12.

173 **35** 1 c. pale green 15·00 10
174 1 c. deep green 13·00 10
175 1 c. green 13·00 10
176 2 c. rose-carmine 11·00 10
a. Booklet pane of 6 £750
177 2 c. pale rose-carmine 13·00 10
a. Imperf (pair) (18.7.09) 26·00 26·00
178 5 c. blue/*bluish* 55·00 90
179 5 c. indigo/*bluish* 55·00 1·25
180 **35** 7 c. yellow-olive 50·00 1·00
181 7 c. greenish bistre 60·00 1·50
181*a* 7 c. straw (1.12) 90·00 35·00
182 10 c. brown-lilac 80·00 4·00
183 10 c. pale dull purple 80·00 4·00
184 10 c. dull purple 80·00 4·00
185 20 c. pale olive-green (27.9.04) £200 14·00
186 20 c. deep olive-green (H/S S. £70) £225 14·00
187 50 c. deep violet (19.11.08) £300 48·00
173/87 *Set of* 7 £600 60·00

The 1 c., 5 c., 7 c. and 10 c. exist imperforate but are believed to be proofs.

IMPERFORATE AND PART-PERFORATED SHEETS. Prior to 1946 many Canadian issues exist imperforate, or with other perforation varieties, in the colours of the issued stamps and, usually, with gum. In the years before 1927 such examples are believed to come from imprimatur sheets, removed from the Canadian Post Office archives. From 1927 until 1946 it is known that the printers involved in the production of the various issues submitted several imperforate plate proof sheets of each stamp to the Post Office authorities for approval. Some of these sheets or part sheets were retained for record purposes, but the remainder found their way onto the philatelic market.

Part-perforated sheets also occur from 1927–29 issues.

From 1908 until 1946 we now only list and price such varieties of this type which are known to be genuine errors, sold from post offices. Where other imperforate or similar varieties are known they are recorded in footnotes.

It is possible, and in some cases probable, that some imperforate varieties listed before 1908 may have also been removed from the archives as mentioned above, but it is far harder to be explicit over the status of this earlier material.

36 King George V and Queen Mary when Prince and Princess of Wales

37 Jacques Cartier and Samuel Champlain

(Des Machado)

1908 (16 July). *Quebec Tercentenary T* **36/7** *and similar horiz designs. P* 12.

188 ½ c. sepia 3·25 2·00
189 1 c. blue-green 6·50 1·25
190 2 c. carmine 9·00 60
191 5 c. indigo 35·00 9·50
192 7 c. olive-green 45·00 28·00
193 10 c. violet 55·00 40·00
194 15 c. brown-orange 75·00 48·00
195 20 c. dull brown £100 55·00
188/95 *Set of* 8 £300 £170

Designs:—2 c. King Edward VII and Queen Alexandra; 5 c. Champlain's House in Quebec; 7 c. Generals Montcalm and Wolfe; 10 c. Quebec in 1700; 15 c. Champlain's departure for the West; 20 c. Cartier's arrival before Quebec.

Some values exist on both *toned* and *white* papers.

Nos. 188/95 exist imperforate.

WET AND DRY PRINTINGS. Until the end of December 1922 all Canadian stamps were produced by the "wet" method of recess-printing in which the paper was dampened before printing, dried and then gummed.

In late December 1922 the Canadian Bank Note Co. began to use the "dry" process in which the paper was gummed before printing. Late printings of the 3 c. brown were the first stamps to be produced by this method, but the changeover was not completed until January 1926.

"Dry" printings have a sharper appearance and can often be found with a degree of embossing showing on the reverse. Stamps from "wet" printings shrink during drying and are narrower than "dry" examples. In many cases the difference can be as great as 0.5 mm. On some early booklet panes the difference is in the vertical, rather than the horizontal, measurement.

On Nos. 196/215 all values only exist from "wet" printings except the 3 c., 20 c. and 50 c. which come from both types of printing.

44

1911–22. *P* 12.

196 **44** 1 c. yellow-green (22.12.11) 4·50 10
a. With fine horiz lines across stamp 25·00 6·00
197 1 c. bluish green 4·50 10
a. Booklet pane of 6 (1.5.13) 28·00
198 1 c. deep bluish green 5·50 10
199 1 c. deep yellow-green 4·50 10
a. Booklet pane of 6 28·00
200 2 c. rose-red (22.12.11) 4·00 10
201 2 c. deep rose-red 4·25 10
a. Booklet pane of 6 (1.12) 28·00
202 2 c. pale rose-red 4·00 10
a. With fine horiz lines across stamp 20·00 4·00
203 2 c. carmine 4·50 10
204 3 c. brown (6.8.18) 6·00 10
205 3 c. deep brown 4·50 10
a. Booklet pane of 4 + 2 labels (2.22) 45·00
205*b* 5 c. deep blue (17.1.12) 55·00 50
206 5 c. indigo 55·00 60
206*a* 5 c. grey-blue 55·00 50
206*b* 7 c. straw (12.1.12) 60·00 9·00
207 7 c. pale sage-green (1914) £180 22·00
208 7 c. olive-yellow (1915) 20·00 1·25
209 7 c. yellow-ochre (1916) 17·00 1·25
210 10 c. brownish purple (12.1.12) 75·00 95

MISSING OUT? PUT AN...

UNBEATABLE TEAM TO WORK FOR YOU!

Each year at Eastern Auctions we offer over twenty-five thousand lots of USA, Commonwealth, foreign, and especially, CANADA and NEWFOUNDLAND.

CONSIDER THE ADVANTAGES

★1. Building a collection? There's no better place to find those elusive items you've been looking for than pages of our monthly auction catalogues. British North American stamps are our speciality! We hold four public and eight mail auctions annually.

★2. Thinking of selling? We've helped hundreds of collectors over the years. Our terms are competitive and our catalogues expertly produced. Your choice of public auction or outright purchase can be arranged. Contact Gary Lyon for further details!

★3. Having trouble with that want list? Well send it along to us. We'll get to work right away. We maintain an excellent stock of Canada, Newfoundland and provinces.

★4. We get results! Whether buying or selling, our international contacts and mailing list can work for you.

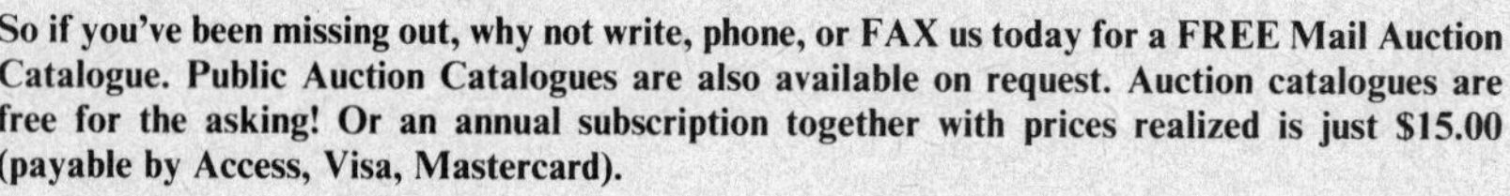

So if you've been missing out, why not write, phone, or FAX us today for a FREE Mail Auction Catalogue. Public Auction Catalogues are also available on request. Auction catalogues are free for the asking! Or an annual subscription together with prices realized is just $15.00 (payable by Access, Visa, Mastercard).

Eastern Auctions Ltd.

P.O. Box 250G, Bathurst, N.B., Canada E2A 3Z4 PH: (506) 548–8986. FAX (506) 546–6627

IAN KIMMERLY STAMPS

240 Catherine Street – *Suite 100,*
Ottawa, Canada
K2P 2G8

☎ (613) 235–9119
FAX (613) 235–9504

PUBLIC AUCTIONS
Each of our regular public auctions has a strong selection of Canadian and worldwide stamps. Lots are always designed and described with collectors in mind.

MAIL ORDER
Write to our efficient mail order department and we will do our very best to obtain the stamps you need.

RETAIL
We have a friendly store in the heart of Canada's attractive capital. *Finding top quality stamps for all collectors is our specialty.*

R. MARESCH & SON

DEALERS IN FINE STAMPS SINCE 1924

CANADA'S PREMIER AUCTION HOUSE

- **PUBLIC AUCTIONS**
  – We will gladly send you a sample catalogue with prices realized, or our current auction sale catalogue, free upon request.
- **CANADA AND PROVINCES**
  – Our speciality. Also a wide range of Commonwealth and Foreign.
- **CONSIGNMENTS**
  – Ten percent commission rate with no other charges. Liberal advances to any amount.

330 BAY ST., SUITE 703,
TORONTO, ONTARIO, CANADA M5H 2S8
Telephone (416) 363–7777 Fax (416) 363–6511

211 44 10 c. reddish purple .. .. .. 75·00 95
212 20 c. olive-green (23.1.12) .. .. .. 28·00 85
213 20 c. olive .. .. 28·00 85
214 50 c. grey-black (26.1.12) .. .. .. £100 6·00
215 50 c. sepia .. .. 38·00 2·00
196/215 .. .. .. *Set of* 8 £200 6·00
The 20 c. and 50 c. values exist imperforate.

1912 (Nov)–**1921**. *For use in coil-machines. (a) P 12 × imperf.*
216 44 1 c. yellow-green (1914) .. .. 3·50 6·00
217 1 c. blue-green .. .. .. 10·00 15·00
a. Two large holes at top and bottom (pair) (7.18) .. .. .. 50·00 50·00
218 2 c. deep rose-red (1914) .. .. 20·00 12·00
218*a* 3 c. brown (1921) .. .. .. 3·00 4·00
No. 217a has two large holes about 3½ mm in diameter in the top and bottom margins. They were for experimental use in a vending machine at Toronto in July 1918 and were only in use for two days.
The 1 c. and 2 c. also exist with two small "V" shaped holes about 9.5 mm apart at top which are gripper marks due to modifications made in vending machines in 1917.

(*b*) *Imperf × perf* 8
219 44 1 c. yellow-green (9.12) .. .. .. 7·00 50
220 1 c. blue-green .. .. .. 9·00 50
a. With fine horiz lines across stamp 45·00
221 2 c. carmine (9.12) .. .. .. 11·00 25
222 2 c. rose-red .. .. 12·00 40
223 2 c. scarlet .. .. 20·00 3·50
224 3 c. brown (8.18) .. .. .. 3·50 20

(*c*) *P* 8 × *imperf*
224*a* 44 1 c. blue-green (15.2.13) .. .. 48·00 40·00
224*b* 2 c. carmine (15.2.13) .. .. 48·00 40·00
The stamps imperf × perf 8 were sold in coils over the counter; those perf 8 × imperf were on sale in automatic machines. Varieties showing perf 12 on 2 or 3 adjacent sides and 1 or 2 sides imperf are from booklets, or the margins of sheets.

(45)

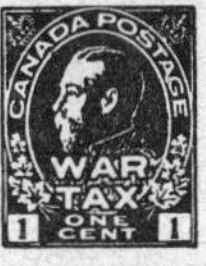
46

47

1915 (12 Feb). *Optd with T* **45**.
225 44 5 c. blue £100 £150
226 20 c. olive-green .. .. .. 50·00 65·00
227 50 c. sepia (R.) .. .. .. 70·00 90·00
225/7 .. .. *Set of* 3 £170 £250
These stamps were intended for tax purposes, but owing to ambiguity in an official circular dated 16 April 1915, it was for a time believed that their use for postal purposes was authorised. The position was clarified by a further circular on 20 May 1916 which made clear that Nos. 225/7 were for fiscal use only.

1915. *P* 12.
228 46 1 c. green (15.4.15) .. .. .. 2·50 10
229 2 c. carmine-red (16.4.15) .. .. 2·75 20
230 2 c. rose-carmine .. .. .. 4·00 2·00

Die I

Die II

In Die I there is a long horizontal coloured line under the foot of the "T", and a solid bar of colour runs upwards from the "1" to the "T".
In Die II this solid bar of colour is absent, and there is a short horizontal line under the left side of the "T", with two short vertical dashes and a number of dots under the right-hand side.

1916 (1 Jan). *P* 12.
231 47 2 c. + 1 c. rose-red (Die I) .. .. 7·50 55
232 2 c. + 1 c. bright carmine (Die I) .. 7·50 55
233 2 c. + 1 c. scarlet (Die I) .. .. 7·50 55

1916 (Feb). *Imperf × perf* 8 (*coils*).
234 47 2 c. + 1 c. rose-red (Die I) .. .. 45·00 3·75

1916 (July). *P* 12 × 8.
235 47 2 c. + 1 c. carmine-red (Die I) .. .. 12·00 25·00
236 2 c. + 1 c. bright rose-red (Die I) .. 12·00 25·00

1916 (Aug). *P* 12.
237 47 2 c. + 1 c. carmine-red (Die II) .. .. 70·00 11·00

1916 (Aug). *Colour changed. (a) P* 12.
238 47 2 c. + 1 c. brown (Die I) .. .. .. £100 11·00
239 2 c. + 1 c. yellow-brown (Die II) .. 2·00 10
a. Imperf (pair) .. .. ..
240 2 c. + 1 c. deep brown (Die II) .. .. 8·50 10

(*b*) *Imperf × perf* 8
241 47 2 c. + 1 c. brown (Die I) .. .. .. 55·00 3·00
a. Pair, 241 and 243 .. ..
243 2 c. + 1 c. deep brown (Die II) .. .. 18·00 60
This value also exists p 12 × imperf or imperf × p 12, but was not issued with these perforations.

48 Quebec Conference, 1864, from painting "The Fathers of Confederation", by Robert Harris

1917 (15 Sept). *50th Anniv of Confederation. P* 12.
244 48 3 c. bistre-brown .. .. .. 16·00 55
245 3 c. deep brown .. .. 18·00 75
No. 244 exists imperforate.

Die I. Space between top of "N" and oval frame line and space between "CENT" and lower frame line.
Die II. "ONE CENT" appears larger so that "N" touches oval and "CENT" almost touches frame line. There are other differences but this is the most obvious one.

Die I. The lowest of the three horizontal lines of shading below the medals does not touch the three heavy diagonal lines; three complete white spaces over both "E's" of "THREE"; long centre bar to figures "3". Vertical spandrel lines fine.
Die II. The lowest horizontal line of shading touches the first of the three diagonal lines; two and a half spaces over first "E" and spaces over second "E" partly filled by stem of maple leaf; short centre bar to figures "3". Vertical spandrel lines thick. There are numerous other minor differences.

WET AND DRY PRINTINGS. See notes above No. 196.
On Nos. 246/63 all listed items occur from both "wet" and "dry" printings except Nos. 246aa/ab, 248aa, 256, 259, 260 and 262 which come "wet" only, and Nos. 246a, 248/a, 252/4*a*, 256b and 263 which are "dry" only.

1922–31. *As T* **44**. (*a*) *P* 12.
246 44 1 c. chrome-yellow (Die I) (7.6.22) .. 2·50 15
aa. Booklet pane of 4 + 2 labels (7.22) 35·00
ab. Booklet pane of 6 (12.22) .. .. 20·00
a. Die II (1925) .. .. .. 4·25 10
247 2 c. deep green (6.6.22) .. .. .. 2·25 10
aa. Booklet pane of 4 + 2 labels (7.22) 25·00
ab. Booklet pane of 6 (12.22) £250
b. Thin paper (9.24) .. .. .. 2·25 2·00
248 3 c. carmine (Die I) (18.12.23) .. .. 2·25 10
aa. Booklet pane of 4 + 2 labels (12.23) 25·00
a. Die II (11.24) .. .. .. 8·00 10
249 4 c. olive-yellow (7.7.22) .. .. 7·00 90
a. Yellow-ochre .. .. .. 7·00 90
250 5 c. violet (2.2.22) .. .. .. 5·00 40
a. Thin paper (9.24) .. .. .. 5·00 8·00
b. Reddish violet (1925) .. .. 5·00 40
251 7 c. red-brown (12.12.24) .. .. 10·00 6·00
a. Thin paper .. .. £100 20·00
252 8 c. blue (1.9.25) .. .. .. 17·00 7·00
253 10 c. blue (20.2.22) .. .. .. 18·00 50
254 10 c. bistre-brown (1.8.25) .. .. 17·00 50
a. Yellow-brown .. .. .. 18·00 90
255 $1 brown-orange (22.7.23) .. .. 50·00 3·75
246/55 .. .. *Set of* 10 £110 18·00
The $1 differs from T **44** in that the value tablets are oval.
Nos. 249/55 exist imperforate.

(*b*) *Imperf × perf* 8
256 44 1 c. chrome-yellow (Die I) (1922) .. 3·75 3·00
a. Imperf horiz (vert pair) (1924) .. £300
b. Die II (1925) .. .. .. 4·50 4·25
c. Do. Imperf horiz (vert pair) (1927) 9·00
257 2 c. deep green (26.7.22) .. .. 6·00 50
b. Imperf horiz (vert pair) (1927) .. 9·00
258 3 c. carmine (Die I) (9.4.24) .. .. 35·00 4·00
a. Imperf horiz (vert pair) (1924) .. £350
b. Die II (1925) .. .. .. 55·00 14·00
256/8 .. .. *Set of* 3 40·00 6·75
Nos. 256a, 256c, 257b and 258a come from coil printings sold in sheet form. Those issued in 1924 were from "wet" printings and those in 1927 from "dry". A "wet" printing of No. 257b, issued in 1924, also exists (*Price* £300 *mint*), but cannot be identified from that issued in 1927 except by the differences between "wet" and "dry" stamps.

(*c*) *Imperf* (*pairs*)
259 44 1 c. chrome-yellow (Die I) (6.10.24) .. 65·00 65·00
260 2 c. deep green (6.10.24) .. .. 65·00 65·00
261 3 c. carmine (Die I) (31.12.23)† .. .. 35·00 40·00

(*d*) *P* 12 × *imperf*
262 44 2 c. deep green (9.24) .. .. .. 65·00 80·00

(*e*) *P* 12 × 8
263 44 3 c. carmine (Die II) (24.6.31) .. .. 2·00 1·75
Nos. 259 to 261 were on sale only at the Philatelic Branch P.O. Dept, Ottawa.
†Earliest known postmark.

2 CENTS
(49)

2
CENTS
(50)

1926. *No.* 248 *surch.*
(*a*) *With T* **49**, *by the Govt Printing Bureau*
264 44 2 c. on 3 c. carmine (12.10.26) .. .. 27·00 45·00
a. Pair, one without surch £250
b. On Die II £450
(*b*) *With T* **50**, *by the Canadian Bank Note Co*
265 44 2 c. on 3 c. carmine (4.11.26) .. .. 10·00 14·00
a. Surch double (partly treble) .. £200

51 Sir J. A. Macdonald
52 "The Fathers of Confederation"

53 Parliament Buildings, Ottawa

54 Sir W. Laurier

55 Canada, Map 1867–1927

1927 (29 June). *60th Anniv of Confederation. P* 12. I. *Commemorative Issue. Inscr* "1867–1927 CANADA CONFEDERATION".
266 51 1 c. orange .. .. 1·75 65
267 52 2 c. green .. .. 1·25 10
268 53 3 c. carmine .. .. 3·00 2·50
269 54 5 c. violet .. .. 2·00 1·75
270 55 12 c. blue .. .. 10·00 1·75
266/70 .. .. *Set of* 5 16·00 6·00
Nos. 266/70 exist imperforate, imperf × perf or perf × imperf.

56 Darcy McGee

57 Sir W. Laurier and Sir J. A. Macdonald

58 R. Baldwin and L. H. Lafontaine

II. *Historical Issue*
271 56 5 c. violet .. .. 2·75 90
272 57 12 c. green .. .. 7·50 3·00
273 58 20 c. carmine .. .. 9·50 5·00
271/3 .. .. *Set of* 3 18·00 8·00
Nos. 271/3 exist imperforate, imperf × perf or perf × imperf.

59
(Des H. Schwartz)

1928 (21 Sept). *Air. P* 12.
274 59 5 c. olive-brown .. .. 2·50 1·00
No. 274 exists imperforate, imperf × perf or perf × imperf.

60 King George V

61 Mt Hurd and Indian Totem Poles

62 Quebec Bridge

63 Harvesting with Horses

64 *Bluenose* (fishing schooner)

65 Parliament Buildings, Ottawa

1928–29. (*a*) *P* 12.
275 **60** 1 c. orange (25.10.28) .. .. .. 1·60 10
a. Booklet pane of 6 .. .. .. 16·00
276 2 c. green (16.10.28) 65 10
a. Booklet pane of 6 .. .. .. 16·00
277 3 c. lake (12.12.28) .. .. .. 13·00 7·00
278 4 c. olive-bistre (16.8.29) .. .. 13·00 3·25
279 5 c. violet (12.12.28) .. .. .. 3·75 1·50
a. Booklet pane of 6 (6.1.29) .. .. 75·00
280 8 c. blue (21.12.28) .. .. .. 7·50 1·50
281 **61** 10 c. green (5.11.28) .. .. .. 6·00 40
282 **62** 12 c. grey-black (6.1.29) .. .. 12·00 2·75
283 **63** 20 c. lake (6.1.29) .. .. .. 20·00 3·50
284 **64** 50 c. blue (6.1.29) .. .. .. 80·00 24·00
285 **65** $1 olive-green (6.1.29) .. .. £100 30·00
a. Brown-olive £250 £100
275/85 .. .. .. *Set of* 11 £200 60·00

(*b*) *Imperf* × *perf* 8 (5.11.28)
286 **60** 1 c. orange .. .. .. 7·00 13·00
287 2 c. green .. .. .. 6·00 1·00

Slight differences in the size of many Canadian stamps, due to paper shrinkage, are to be found.

Nos. 275/85 exist imperforate, imperf × perf or perf × imperf. *Tête-bêche* horizontal pairs of the 1 c., 2 c. and 5 c. are also known from uncut booklet sheets.

PRINTERS. The following stamps to No. 334 were recess-printed by the British American Bank Note Co, Ottawa.

66

67 Parliamentary Library, Ottawa

68 The Old Citadel, Quebec

69 Harvesting with Tractor

70 Acadian Memorial Church and Statue of "Evangeline", Grand Pre, Nova Scotia

71 Mt Edith Cavell, Canadian Rockies

Die I 1 c. Die II

Die I 2 c. Die II

1 c. Die I. Three thick coloured lines and one thin between "P" and ornament, at right. Curved line in ball-ornament short.
Die II. Four thick lines. Curved line longer.

2 c. Die I. Three thick coloured lines between "P" and ornament, at left. Short line in ball.
Die II. Four thick lines. Curved line longer.

1930–31. (*a*) *P* 11.
288 **66** 1 c. orange (I) (17.7.30) 35 25
289 2 c. green (I) (6.7.30) 50 10
a. Booklet pane of 6 (17.6.30) .. .. 25·00
290 4 c. yellow-bistre (5.11.30) .. .. 5·50 1·50
291 5 c. violet (18.6.30) .. .. .. 2·50 1·25
292 8 c. blue (13.8.30) .. .. .. 5·50 6·50
293 **67** 10 c. olive-green (15.9.30) .. .. 5·00 30
a. Imperf (pair) £900
294 **68** 12 c. grey-black (4.12.30) .. .. 7·50 1·75
295 **69** 20 c. red (4.12.30) .. .. .. 13·00 20
296 **70** 50 c. blue (4.12.30) .. .. .. 80·00 8·00
297 **71** $1 olive-green (4.12.30) .. .. 90·00 12·00
288/97 .. .. .. *Set of* 10 £180 28·00
Nos. 294/7 exist imperforate.

(*b*) *Imperf* × *perf* 8½
298 **66** 1 c. orange (I) .. .. .. 8·00 6·00
299 2 c. green (I) .. .. .. 3·00 2·00

Colours changed and new value. (*a*) *P* 11
300 **66** 1 c. green (I) (6.12.30) 80 10
a. Imperf (pair) .. .. ..
b. Booklet pane of 6 (21.7.31) .. .. 35·00
c. Booklet pane of 4 + 2 labels (13.11.31) £110
d. Die II 75 10
301 2 c. scarlet (I) (17.11.30) 70 10
a. Booklet pane of 6 (17.11.30) .. .. 18·00
b. Die II 90 10
302 2 c. deep brown (I) (4.7.31) .. .. 1·00 2·00
a. Booklet pane of 6 (23.7.31) .. .. 32·00
b. Die II 70 10
ba. Booklet pane of 4 + 2 labels (13.11.31) £120
303 3 c. scarlet (13.7.31) 90 10
a. Booklet pane of 4 + 2 labels .. .. 25·00
304 5 c. deep slate-blue (13.11.30) .. .. 4·50 10
a. Dull blue .. .. .. 9·00 10
305 8 c. red-orange (5.11.30) .. .. 5·00 1·50
300/5 .. .. .. *Set of* 6 11·50 1·50

(*b*) *Imperf* × *perf* 8½
306 **66** 1 c. green (I) .. .. .. 3·50 3·50
307 2 c. scarlet (I) .. .. .. 4·00 1·40
308 2 c. deep brown (I) (4.7.31) .. .. 7·00 45
309 3 c. scarlet (13.7.31) .. .. .. 11·00 20
306/9 .. .. .. *Set of* 4 23·00 5·00

Some low values in the above and subsequent issues have been printed by both Rotary and "Flat plate" processes. The former can be distinguished by the gum, which has a striped appearance.

For 13 c. bright violet, T **68**, see No. 325.

72 Mercury and Western Hemisphere

73 Sir Georges Etienne Cartier

(Des H. Schwartz)

1930 (4 Dec). *Air. P* 11.
310 **72** 5 c. deep brown .. .. .. 12·00 8·50

1931 (30 Sept). *P* 11.
312 **73** 10 c. olive-green .. .. .. 2·50 10
No. 312 exists imperforate.

(74)

(75)

1932 (22 Feb). *Air. No.* 274 *surch with T* **74**.
313 **59** 6 c. on 5 c. olive-brown .. .. .. 1·50 1·25

Examples of this stamp with surcharge inverted, surcharge double, surcharge triple or surcharge omitted in pair with normal are not now believed to have been regularly issued. Such "errors" have also been forged and collectors are warned against forged examples, some of which bear unauthorized markings which purport to be the guarantee of Stanley Gibbons Ltd.

1932 (21 June). *Nos.* 301/*b surch with T* **75**.
314 **66** 3 c. on 2 c. scarlet (I) .. .. .. 1·40 1·40
314*a* 3 c. on 2 c. scarlet (II) 60 10

76 King George V

77 Duke of Windsor when Prince of Wales

78 Allegory of British Empire

6 6
OTTAWA CONFERENCE
1932
(79)

1932 (12 July). *Ottawa Conference. P* 11. (*a*) *Postage stamps.*
315 **76** 3 c. scarlet 60 35
316 **77** 5 c. blue .. .. .. 5·00 2·00
317 **78** 13 c. green .. .. .. 6·00 4·50

(*b*) *Air. No.* 310 *surch with T* **79**
318 **72** 6 c. on 5 c. deep brown (B.) .. .. 10·00 8·00
315/18 .. .. .. *Set of* 4 19·00 13·50

80 King George V

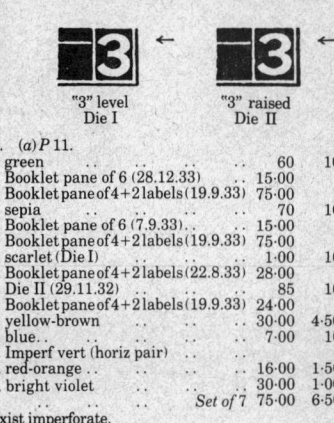

"3" level Die I

"3" raised Die II

1932 (1 Dec)–**33.** (*a*) *P* 11.
319 **80** 1 c. green 60 10
a. Booklet pane of 6 (28.12.33) .. 15·00
b. Booklet pane of 4+2 labels (19.9.33) 75·00
320 2 c. sepia 70 10
a. Booklet pane of 6 (7.9.33) .. 15·00
b. Booklet pane of 4+2 labels (19.9.33) 75·00
321 3 c. scarlet (Die I) .. .. .. 1·00 10
a. Booklet pane of 4+2 labels (22.8.33) 28·00
b. Die II (29.11.32) 85 10
ba. Booklet pane of 4+2 labels (19.9.33) 24·00
322 4 c. yellow-brown .. .. .. 30·00 4·50
323 5 c. blue .. .. .. 7·00 10
a. Imperf vert (horiz pair) ..
324 8 c. red-orange .. .. .. 16·00 1·50
325 **68** 13 c. bright violet .. .. .. 30·00 1·00
319/25 .. .. .. *Set of* 7 75·00 6·50
Nos. 319/25 exist imperforate.

(*b*) *Imperf* × *perf* 8½ (1933)
326 **80** 1 c. green .. .. .. 12·00 1·50
327 2 c. sepia .. .. .. 13·00 45
328 3 c. scarlet (Die II) .. .. .. 8·50 25
326/8 .. .. .. *Set of* 3 30·00 2·00

81 Parliament Buildings, Ottawa

1933 (18 May). *U.P.U. Congress Preliminary Meeting. P* 11.
329 **81** 5 c. blue .. .. .. 3·50 1·25
No. 329 exists imperforate.

WORLD'S
GRAIN EXHIBITION &
CONFERENCE

REGINA 1933
(82)

1933 (24 July). *World's Grain Exhibition and Conference, Regina. Optd with T* **82**. *P* 11.
330 **69** 20 c. red (B.) .. .. .. 20·00 4·50
No. 330 exists imperforate.

83 S.S. *Royal William* (after S. Skillett)

84 Jacques Cartier approaching Land

1933 (17 Aug). *Centenary of First Trans-Atlantic Steamboat Crossing. P* 11.
331 **83** 5 c. blue .. .. .. 6·00 1·00
No. 331 exists imperforate.

1934 (1 July). *Fourth Centenary of Discovery of Canada. P* 11.
332 **84** 3 c. blue .. .. .. 2·00 40
No. 332 exists imperforate.

85 U.E.L. Statue, Hamilton

86 Seal of New Brunswick

1934 (1 July). 150*th Anniv of Arrival of United Empire Loyalists. P* 11.
333 **85** 10 c. olive-green .. .. .. 9·50 2·50
No. 333 exists imperforate.

1934 (16 Aug). 150*th Anniv of Province of New Brunswick. P* 11.
334 **86** 2 c. red-brown 70 75
No. 334 exists imperforate.

PRINTERS. The following stamps were recess-printed (except where otherwise stated) by the Canadian Bank Note Co, Ottawa, until No. 616.

87 Queen Elizabeth II when Princess

89 King George V and Queen Mary

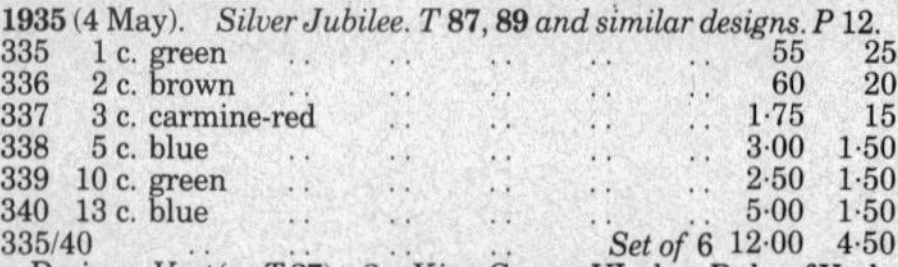

1935 (4 May). *Silver Jubilee. T* **87, 89** *and similar designs. P* 12.

335		1 c. green	55	25
336		2 c. brown	60	20
337		3 c. carmine-red	1·75	15
338		5 c. blue	3·00	1·50
339		10 c. green	2·50	1·50
340		13 c. blue	5·00	1·50
335/40		*Set of* 6	12·00	4·50

Designs: *Vert* (*as T* **87**)—2 c. King George VI when Duke of York; 5 c. King Edward VIII when Prince of Wales. *Horiz* (*as T* **89**)—10 c. Windsor Castle; 13 c. Royal Yacht *Britannia*.

Nos. 335/40 exist imperforate.

93 King George V

94 Royal Canadian Mounted Policeman

99 Daedalus

1935 (1 June–5 Nov). *T* **93/4, 99** *and similar designs.* (*a*) *Postage.* (i) *P* 12.

341	**93**	1 c. green	25	10
		a. Booklet pane of 6 (19.8.35)	20·00	
		b. Booklet pane of 4+2 labels (22.7.35)	50·00	
342		2 c. brown	45	10
		a. Booklet pane of 6 (16.11.35)	22·00	
		b. Booklet pane of 4+2 labels (22.7.35)	50·00	
343		3 c. scarlet	60	10
		a. Booklet pane of 4 + 2 labels	24·00	
344		4 c. yellow	1·00	60
345		5 c. blue	1·00	10
		a. Imperf vert (horiz pair)	£250	
346		8 c. orange	1·00	1·40
347	**94**	10 c. carmine	2·75	10
348	–	13 c. purple	3·00	20
349	–	20 c. olive-green	9·00	30
350	–	50 c. deep violet	25·00	2·25
351	–	$1 bright blue	35·00	3·00
341/51		*Set of* 11	70·00	7·00

(ii) *Coil stamps. Imperf × perf* 8

352	**93**	1 c. green (5.11.35)	10·00	1·75
353		2 c. brown (14.10.35)	6·00	1·00
354		3 c. scarlet (20.7.35)	5·50	30
352/4		*Set of* 3	19·00	2·75

(*b*) *Air. P* 12

355	**99**	6 c. red-brown	1·25	35
		a. Imperf vert (horiz pair)		

Designs: *Horiz* (*as T* **94**)—13 c. Confederation Conference, Charlottetown, 1864; 20 c. Niagara Falls; 50 c. Parliament Buildings, Victoria, British Columbia; $1 Champlain Monument, Quebec.

Nos. 341/51 and 355 exist imperforate.

100 King George VI and Queen Elizabeth

1937 (10 May). *Coronation. P* 12.

356	**100**	3 c. carmine	60	10

No. 356 exists imperforate.

101 King George VI

102 Memorial Chamber Parliament Buildings, Ottawa

107 Seaplane over S.S. *Distributor* on River Mackenzie

(T **101**. Photograph by Bertram Park)

1937–38. *T* **101/2, 107** *and similar designs.* (*a*) *Postage.* (i) *P* 12.

357	**101**	1 c. green (1.4.37)	55	10
		a. Booklet pane of 6 (18.5.37)	3·50	
		b. Booklet pane of 4+2 labels (14.4.37)	17·00	
358		2 c. brown (1.4.37)	70	10
		a. Booklet pane of 6 (3.5.38)	10·00	
		b. Booklet pane of 4+2 labels (14.4.37)	24·00	
359		3 c. scarlet (1.4.37)	90	10
		a. Booklet pane of 4+2 labels (14.4.37)	4·25	
360		4 c. yellow (10.5.37)	2·50	75
361		5 c. blue (10.5.37)	2·50	10
362		8 c. orange (10.5.37)	2·50	80
363	**102**	10 c. rose-carmine (15.6.38)	6·00	10
		a. Red	6·00	10
364	–	13 c. blue (15.11.38)	12·00	25
365	–	20 c. red-brown (15.6.38)	18·00	20
366	–	50 c. green (15.6.38)	45·00	5·00
367	–	$1 violet (15.6.38)	70·00	5·50
		a. Imperf horiz (vert pair)	£1800	
357/67		*Set of* 11	£140	11·50

Nos. 357/67 exist imperforate.

(ii) *Coil stamps. Imperf × perf* 8

368	**101**	1 c. green (15.6.37)	2·50	90
369		2 c. brown (18.6.37)	2·50	1·25
370		3 c. scarlet (15.4.37)	7·50	40
368/70		*Set of* 3	11·50	2·25

(*b*) *Air. P* 12

371	**107**	6 c. blue (15.6.38)	3·50	20

Designs: *Horiz* (*as T* **107**)—13 c. Entrance to Halifax Harbour; 20 c. Fort Garry Gate, Winnipeg; 50 c. Entrance, Vancouver Harbour; $1 Chateau de Ramezay, Montreal.

108 Queen Elizabeth II when Princess and Princess Margaret

109 National War Memorial, Ottawa

110 King George VI and Queen Elizabeth

1939 (15 May). *Royal Visit. P* 12.

372	**108**	1 c. black and green	50	10
373	**109**	2 c. black and brown	50	15
374	**110**	3 c. black and carmine	40	10
372/4		*Set of* 3	1·25	20

Nos. 372/4 exist imperforate.

111 King George VI in Naval uniform

112 King George VI in Military uniform

113 King George VI in Air Force uniform

114 Grain Elevator

116 Parliament Buildings

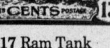

117 Ram Tank

121 Air Training Camp

1942 (1 July)–**1948.** *War Effort. T* **111/14, 116/17, 121** *and similar designs.* (*a*) *Postage.* (i) *P* 12.

375	**111**	1 c. green	65	10
		a. Booklet pane of 6 (24.11.42)	2·50	
		b. Booklet pane of 4+2 labels (12.9.42)	13·00	
376	**112**	2 c. brown	1·00	10
		a. Booklet pane of 6 (6.10.42)	12·00	
		b. Booklet pane of 4+2 labels (12.9.42)	13·00	
377	**113**	3 c. carmine-lake	85	10
		a. Booklet pane of 4+2 labels (20.8.42)	3·50	
378		3 c. purple (30.6.43)	60	10
		a. Booklet pane of 6 (1.12.47)	7·00	
		b. Booklet pane of 4+2 labels (28.8.43)	4·50	
379	**114**	4 c. slate	2·50	45
380	**112**	4 c. carmine-lake (9.4.43)	40	10
		a. Booklet pane of 6 (3.5.43)	3·50	
381	**111**	5 c. blue	2·00	10
382	–	8 c. red-brown	3·50	40
383	**116**	10 c. brown	4·00	10
384	**117**	13 c. dull green	3·00	4·00
385		14 c. dull green (16.4.43)	8·50	30
386	–	20 c. chocolate	6·50	15
387	–	50 c. violet	20·00	1·50
388	–	$1 blue	55·00	3·50
375/88		*Set of* 14	95·00	9·50

Nos. 375/88 exist imperforate.

(ii) *Coil stamps. Imperf × perf* 8

389	**111**	1 c. green (9.2.43)	60	1·00
390	**112**	2 c. brown (24.11.42)	1·50	1·00
391	**113**	3 c. carmine-lake (23.9.42)	1·50	2·75
392		3 c. purple (19.8.43)	3·50	2·00
393	**112**	4 c. carmine-lake (13.5.43)	3·25	1·00
389/93		*Set of* 5	9·00	7·00

(iii) *Booklet stamps. Imperf × perf* 12 (1.9.43)

394	**111**	1 c. green	1·50	40
		a. Booklet pane of 3	4·50	
395	**113**	3 c. purple	1·50	70
		a. Booklet pane of 3	4·50	
396	**112**	4 c. carmine-lake	1·50	1·00
		a. Booklet pane of 3	4·50	
394/6		*Set of* 3	4·00	1·90

Nos. 394/6 are from booklets in which the stamps are in strips of three, imperforate at top and bottom and right-hand end.

(iv) *Coil stamps. Imperf × perf* 9½

397	**111**	1 c. green (13.7.48)	3·50	4·00
397*a*	**112**	2 c. brown (1.10.48)	7·50	16·00
398	**113**	3 c. purple (2.7.48)	5·50	5·00
398*a*	**112**	4 c. carmine-lake (22.7.48)	5·50	3·50
397/8*a*		*Set of* 4	20·00	26·00

(*b*) *Air. P* 12

399	**121**	6 c. blue (1.7.42)	5·50	1·75
400		7 c. blue (16.4.43)	1·00	10

Designs: *Horiz* (*as T* **114**)—8 c. Farm scene. (*as T* **117**)—20 c. Launching of Corvette H.M.C.S. *La Malbaie*, Sorel; 50 c. Munitions factory; $1 H.M.S. *Cossack* (destroyer).

122 Ontario Farm Scene

129 Alexander Graham Bell and "Fame"

1946 (16 Sept—Dec). *Peace Re-conversion. T* **122** *and similar horiz designs. P* 12 (*a*). *Postage.*

401	8 c. brown	1·00	75
402	10 c. olive-green	1·25	10
403	14 c. sepia	3·00	15
404	20 c. slate	2·50	10
405	50 c. green	12·00	1·00
406	$1 purple	27·00	1·00

(*b*) *Air*

407	7 c. blue	2·25	10
	a. Booklet pane of 4 (1.12.47)	6·50	
401/7	*Set of* 7	45·00	2·75

Designs:—7 c. Canada Geese in flight; 10 c. Great Bear Lake; 14 c. St. Maurice River Power Station; 20 c. Combine Harvester; 50 c. Lumbering in British Columbia; $1 *Abegweit* (train ferry), Prince Edward Is.

1947 (3 Mar). *Birth Centenary of Bell* (*inventor of telephone*). *P* 12.

408	**129**	4 c. blue	10	10

130 "Canadian Citizenship".

131 Queen Elizabeth II when Princess

1947 (1 July). *Advent of Canadian Citizenship and Eightieth Anniv of Confederation. P* 12.

409	**130**	4 c. blue	10	10

(From photograph by Dorothy Wilding)

1948 (16 Feb). *Princess Elizabeth's Marriage. P* 12.

410	**131**	4 c. blue	10	10

132 Queen Victoria, Parliament Building, Ottawa, and King George VI 133 Cabot's Ship *Matthew*

1948 (1 Oct). *One Hundred Years of Responsible Government. P* 12.
411 **132** 4 c. grey 10 10

1949 (1 Apr). *Entry of Newfoundland into Canadian Confederation. P* 12.
412 **133** 4 c. green 10 10

134 "Founding of Halifax, 1749" (C. W. Jefferys)

1949 (21 June). *Bicentenary of Halifax, Nova Scotia. P* 12.
413 **134** 4 c. violet 10 10

135 136 137

138 King George VI 139

(From photographs by Dorothy Wilding)

1949 (15 Nov)–**51**. (i) *P* 12.
414 **135** 1 c. green 10 10
415 **136** 2 c. sepia 15 10
415*a* 2 c. olive-green (25.7.51) 30 10
416 **137** 3 c. purple 15 10
a. Booklet pane of 4+2 labels (12.4.50) 1·75
417 **138** 4 c. carmine-lake 15 10
a. Booklet pane of 6 (5.5.50) 20·00
417*b* 4 c. vermilion (2.6.51) 40 10
c. Booklet pane of 6 5·00
418 **139** 5 c. blue 60 10
414/18 *Set of* 7 1·60 25

(ii) *Imperf × perf* 9½ (*coil stamps*)
419 **135** 1 c. green (18.5.50) 70 1·00
420 **136** 2 c. sepia (18.5.50) 3·00 3·50
420*a* 2 c. olive-green (9.10.51) 1·00 1·00
421 **137** 3 c. purple (18.5.50) 1·50 2·00
422 **138** 4 c. carmine-lake (20.4.50) 8·50 6·00
422*a* 4 c. vermilion (27.11.51) 1·25 1·25
419/22*a* *Set of* 6 14·50 13·50

(iii) *Imperf × perf* 12 (*booklets*)
422*b* **135** 1 c. green (18.5.50) 25 60
ba. Booklet pane of 3 80
423 **137** 3 c. purple (18.5.50) 90 70
a. Booklet pane of 3 2·75
423*b* **138** 4 c. carmine-lake (18.5.50) 11·00 6·50
ba. Booklet pane of 3 32·00
423*c* 4 c. vermilion (25.10.51) 4·00 3·75
ca. Booklet pane of 3 12·00
422*b*/3*c* *Set of* 4 14·50 10·50

These booklet panes are imperforate at top, bottom and right-hand end.

140 King George VI 141 Oil Wells in Alberta

(From photograph by Dorothy Wilding)

1950 (19 Jan). *As T* 135/9 *but without* "POSTES POSTAGE", *as T* **140**. (i) *P* 12.
424 1 c. green 10 10
425 2 c. sepia 10 20
426 3 c. purple 10 30
427 4 c. carmine-lake 10 10
428 5 c. blue 25 80
424/8 *Set of* 5 50 1·40

(ii) *Imperf × perf* 9½ (*coil stamps*)
429 1 c. green 15 40
430 3 c. purple 55 1·00

1950 (1 Mar). *P* 12.
431 **141** 50 c. green 7·00 50

142 Drying Furs 143 Fisherman

1950 (2 Oct). *P* 12.
432 **142** 10 c. brown-purple 30 10

1951 (1 Feb). *P* 12.
433 **143** $1 ultramarine 40·00 3·50

144 Sir R. L. Borden 145 W. L. Mackenzie King

1951 (25 June). *Prime Ministers* (1*st issue*). *P* 12.
434 **144** 3 c. blue-green 10 15
435 **145** 4 c. rose-carmine 10 10
See also Nos. 444/5, 475/6 and 483/4.

146 Mail Trains, 1851 and 1951 147 SS. *City of Toronto* and SS. *Prince George*

148 Mail Coach and Aeroplane 149 Reproduction of 3d., 1851

1951 (24 Sept). *Canadian Stamp Centenary. P* 12.
436 **146** 4 c. black 35 10
437 **147** 5 c. violet 65 1·50
438 **148** 7 c. blue 35 45
439 **149** 15 c. scarlet 35 10
436/9 *Set of* 4 1·50 1·90

150 Queen Elizabeth II when Princess and Duke of Edinburgh 151 Forestry Products

1951 (26 Oct). *Royal Visit. P* 12.
440 **150** 4 c. violet 10 10

(Des A. L. Pollock)

1952 (1 Apr). *P* 12.
441 **151** 20 c. grey 65 10

152 Red Cross Emblem

1952 (26 July). *18th International Red Cross Conference, Toronto. Design recess; cross litho. P* 12.
442 **152** 4 c. scarlet and blue 10 10

153 Canada Goose 154 Pacific Coast Indian House and Totem Pole

(Des E. Hahn)

1952 (3 Nov). *P* 12.
443 **153** 7 c. blue 20 10

1952 (3 Nov). *Prime Ministers* (2*nd issue*). *Various portraits as T* **144**. *P* 12.
444 3 c. reddish purple 10 10
445 4 c. orange-red 10 10
Portraits:—3 c. Sir John J. C. Abbott; 4 c. A. Mackenzie.

(Des E. Hahn)

1953 (2 Feb). *P* 12.
446 **154** $1 black 7·50 20

155 Polar Bear 156 Elk 157 American Bighorn

(Des J. Crosby (2 c.), E. Hahn (others))

1953 (1 Apr). *National Wild Life Week. P* 12.
447 **155** 2 c. blue 10 10
448 **156** 3 c. sepia 10 10
449 **157** 4 c. slate 10 10
447/9 *Set of* 3 25 15

158 Queen Elizabeth II 159

(From photograph by Karsh, Ottawa)

1953 (1 May–3 Sept). (*a*) *Sheet stamps. P* 12.
450 **158** 1 c. purple-brown 10 10
451 2 c. green 10 10
452 3 c. carmine 10 10
a. Booklet pane of 4+2 labels (17.7) 1·25
453 4 c. violet 15 10
a. Booklet pane of 6 (6.7) 2·75
454 5 c. ultramarine 15 10
450/4 *Set of* 5 50 15

(*b*) *Coil stamps. Imperf × perf* 9½
455 **158** 2 c. green (30.7) 1·25 1·00
456 3 c. carmine (27.7) 1·50 1·00
457 4 c. violet (3.9) 1·50 1·00
455/7 *Set of* 3 3·75 2·75

(*c*) *Booklet stamps. Imperf × perf* 12 (12.8)
458 **158** 1 c. purple-brown 1·75 1·90
a. Booklet pane of 3 5·00
459 3 c. carmine (17.7) 1·75 1·90
a. Booklet pane of 3 5·00
460 4 c. violet (6.7) 1·75 1·90
a. Booklet pane of 3 5·00
458/60 *Set of* 3 5·00 5·25

These booklet stamps have top and bottom or top, bottom and right-hand sides imperforate.

(Des E. Hahn)

1953 (1 June). *Coronation. P* 12
461 **159** 4 c. violet 10 10

160 Textile Industry

161 Queen Elizabeth II

(Des A. L. Pollock)

1953 (2 Nov). *P* 12.
462 **160** 50 c. deep bluish green 1·00 10

(From photograph by Dorothy Wilding)

1954–62. (i) *P* 12.
463 **161** 1 c. purple-brown (10.6.54) 10 10
a. Booklet pane. Five stamps plus printed label (1.6.56) 60
p. Two phosphor bands (13.1.62) 70 1·25
464 2 c. green (10.6.54) 10 10
a. Pack. Two blocks of 25 (12.61) 5·00
p. Two phosphor bands (13.1.62) 70 1·25
465 3 c. carmine (10.6.54) 20 10
a. Imperf vert (horiz pair) £1200
p. Two phosphor bands (13.1.62) 70 1·50
466 4 c. violet (10.6.54) 15 10
a. Booklet pane. Five stamps plus printed label (1.6.56) 1·50
b. Booklet pane of 6 (7.7.55) 3·50
p. One phosphor band (13.1.62) 2·00 6·00
467 5 c. bright blue (1.4.54) 15 10
a. Booklet pane. Five stamps plus printed label (14.7.54) 1·50
b. Pack. One block of 20 (12.61) 4·50
p. Two phosphor bands (13.1.62) 2·00 6·00
468 6 c. red-orange (10.6.54) 45 30
463/8 *Set of* 6 1·00 45
463p/7p *Set of* 5 5·50 14·50

(ii) *Imperf × perf 9½ (coil stamps)*

469 161 2 c. green (9.9.54) 30 50
470 4 c. violet (23.8.54) 55 50
471 5 c. bright blue (6.7.54) 80 30
469/71 .. .. *Set of* 3 1·50 1·10

Nos. 464a and 467b are blocks with the outer edges imperf. These come from "One Dollar Plastic Packages" sold at post offices.

WINNIPEG PHOSPHOR BANDS. In 1962 facer-cancelling machines were introduced in Winnipeg which were activated by phosphor bands on the stamps. Under long or short wave ultra-violet light the phosphor glows and there is also a short after-glow when the lamp is turned off. This should not be confused with the fluorescent bands introduced in Ottawa in 1971.

162 Walrus **163** American Beaver **164** Northern Gannet

(Des E. Hahn)

1954 (1 Apr). *National Wild Life Week. P* 12.
472 **162** 4 c. slate-black 20 10
473 **163** 5 c. ultramarine 20 10
a. Booklet pane. Five stamps plus one printed label .. .. .. 1·40

(Des L. Hyde)

1954 (1 Apr). *P* 12.
474 **164** 15 c. black 40 10

1954 (1 Nov). *Prime Ministers* (3*rd issue*). *Various portraits as T* **144**. *P* 12.
475 4 c. violet 15 10
476 5 c. bright blue 15 10
Portraits:—4 c. Sir John Thompson; 5 c. Sir Mackenzie Bowell.

165 Eskimo Hunter

(Des H. Beament)

1955 (21 Feb). . *P* 12.
477 **165** 10 c. purple-brown 15 10

166 Musk Ox **167** Whooping Cranes

(Des E. Hahn (4 c.), Dr. W. Rowan (5 c.))

1955 (4 Apr). *National Wild Life Week. P* 12.
478 **166** 4 c. violet 10 10
479 **167** 5 c. ultramarine 35 10

168 Dove and Torch **169** Pioneer Settlers

(Des W. Lohse)

1955 (1 June). *Tenth Anniv of International Civil Aviation Organisation. P* 12.
480 **168** 5 c. ultramarine 10 10

(Des L. Hyde)

1955 (30 June). 50*th Anniv of Alberta and Saskatchewan Provinces. P* 12.
481 **169** 5 c. ultramarine 10 10

170 Scout Badge and Globe **173** Ice-hockey Players

(Des L. Hyde)

1955 (20 Aug). *Eighth World Scout Jamboree, Niagara-on-the-Lake. P* 12.
482 **170** 5 c. orange-brown and green 20 10

1955 (8 Nov). *Prime Ministers* (4*th issue*). *Various portraits as T* **144**. *P* 12.
483 4 c. violet 10 10
484 5 c. bright blue 10 10
Portraits:—4 c. R. B. Bennett; 5 c. Sir Charles Tupper.

(Des J. Simpkins)

1956 (23 Jan). *Ice-hockey Commemoration. P* 12.
485 **173** 5 c. ultramarine 15 10

174 Reindeer **175** Mountain Goat

(Des E. Hahn)

1956 (12 Apr). *National Wild Life Week. P* 12.
486 **174** 4 c. violet 15 10
487 **175** 5 c. bright blue 15 10

176 Pulp and Paper Industry **177** Chemical Industry

(Des A. J. Casson (20 c.), A. L. Pollock (25 c.))

1956 (7 June). *P* 12.
488 **176** 20 c. green 30 10
489 **177** 25 c. red 35 10

178

(Des A. Price)

1956 (9 Oct). *Fire Prevention Week. P* 12
490 **178** 5 c. red and black 15 10

179 Fishing **180** Swimming

(Des L. Hyde)

1957 (7 Mar). *Outdoor Recreation. T* **179/180** *and similar horiz designs. P* 12.
491 **179** 5 c. ultramarine 25 10
a. Block of 4. Nos. 491/4 .. .. 1·25
492 **180** 5 c. ultramarine 25 10
493 – 5 c. ultramarine 25 10
494 – 5 c. ultramarine 25 10
491/4 .. .. *Set of* 4 1·25 35

Designs:— No. 493, Hunting. No. 494, Skiing.

No. 491/4 are printed together in sheets of 50 (5 × 10). In the first, second, fourth and fifth vertical rows the four different designs are arranged in *se-tenant* blocks, whilst the central row is made up as follows (reading downwards):—Nos. 491/4, 491/2 (or 493/4), 491/4.

183 White-billed Diver **184** Thompson with Sextant, and North American Map

(Des L. Hyde)

1957 (10 Apr). *National Wild Life Week. P* 12.
495 **183** 5 c. black 15 10

(Des G. A. Gundersen)

1957 (5 June). *Death Centenary of David Thompson (explorer). P* 12.
496 **184** 5 c. ultramarine 15 10

185 Parliament Buildings, Ottawa **186** Globe within Posthorn

(Des Carl Mangold)

1957 (14 Aug). 14*th U.P.U. Congress, Ottawa. P* 12.
497 **185** 5 c. grey-blue 15 10
498 **186** 15 c. blackish blue 25 90

187 Miner **188** Queen Elizabeth II and Duke of Edinburgh

(Des A. J. Casson)

1957 (5 Sept). *Mining Industry. P* 12.
499 **187** 5 c. black 25 10

(From photographs by Karsh, Ottawa)

1957 (10 Oct). *Royal Visit. P* 12.
500 **188** 5 c. black 15 10

189 "A Free Press" **190** Microscope

(Des A. L. Pollock)

1958 (22 Jan). *The Canadian Press. P* 12.
501 **189** 5 c. black 10 15

(Des A. L. Pollock)

1958 (5 Mar). *International Geophysical Year. P* 12.
502 **190** 5 c. blue 15 10

191 Miner panning for Gold **192** La Verendrye (statue)

(Des J. Harman)

1958 (8 May). *Centenary of British Columbia. P* 12.
503 **191** 5 c. deep turquoise-green 15 10

(Des G. Trottier)

1958 (4 June). *La Verendrye (explorer) Commemoration. P* 12.
504 **192** 5 c. ultramarine 10 10

193 Samuel de Champlain and the Heights of Quebec **194** Nurse

(Des G. Trottier)

1958 (26 June). 350*th Anniv of Founding of Quebec. P* 12.
505 **193** 5 c. brown-ochre and deep green .. 15 10

(Des G. Trottier)

1958 (30 July). *National Health. P* 12.
506 **194** 5 c. reddish purple 15 10

195 "Petroleum 1858–1958" **196** Speaker's Chair and Mace

(Des A. L. Pollock)

1958 (10 Sept). *Centenary of Canadian Oil Industry*. P 12.
507 **195** 5 c. scarlet and olive 15 10

(Des G. Trottier and C. Dair)

1958 (2 Oct). *Bicentenary of First Elected Assembly*. P 12.
508 **196** 5 c. deep slate 10 10

197 The "Silver Dart" **198** Globe showing N.A.T.O. Countries

1959 (23 Feb). *50th Anniv of First Flight of the "Silver Dart" in Canada*. P 12.
509 **197** 5 c. black and ultramarine 10 10

(Des P. Weiss)

1959 (2 Apr). *Tenth Anniv of North Atlantic Treaty Organisation*. P 12.
510 **198** 5 c. ultramarine 20 10

199 **200** Queen Elizabeth II

(Des Helen Fitzgerald)

1959 (13 May). *"Associated Country Women of the World" Commemoration*. P 12.
511 **199** 5 c. black and yellow-olive 10 10

(Des after painting by Annigoni)

1959 (18 June). *Royal Visit*. P 12.
512 **200** 5 c. lake-red 20 10

201 Maple Leaf linked with American Eagle **202** Maple Leaves

(Des A. L. Pollock, G. Trottier (of Canada); W. H. Buckley, A. J. Copeland, E. Metzl (of the United States))

1959 (26 June). *Opening of St. Lawrence Seaway*. P 12.
513 **201** 5 c. ultramarine and red 15 10
a. Centre inverted £12000 £6000

It is believed that No. 513a occurred on two printer's sheets, each of 200 stamps. About 230 examples have been discovered.

(Des P. Weiss)

1959 (10 Sept). *Bicentenary of Battle of Plains of Abraham (Quebec)*. P 12.
514 **202** 5 c. deep green and red 15 10

203

204 Dollard des Ormeaux

(Des Helen Fitzgerald)

1960 (20 Apr). *Golden Jubilee of Canadian Girl Guides Movement*. P 12.
515 **203** 5 c. ultramarine and orange-brown .. 15 10

(Des P. Weiss)

1960 (19 May). *Tercentenary of Battle of the Long Sault*. P 12.
516 **204** 5 c. ultramarine and light brown .. 15 10

OMNIBUS ISSUES

Details, together with prices for complete sets, of the various Omnibus issues from the 1935 Silver Jubilee series to date are included in a special section following Zululand at the end of the catalogue.

205 Surveyor, Bulldozer and Compass Rose

206 E. Pauline Johnson

(Des B. J. Reddie)

1961 (8 Feb). *Northern Development*. P 12.
517 **205** 5 c. emerald and red 10 10

(Des B. J. Reddie)

1961 (10 Mar). *Birth Centenary of E. Pauline Johnson (Mohawk poetess)*. P 12.
518 **206** 5 c. green and red 10 10

207 Arthur Meighen (statesman)

208 Engineers and Dam

1961 (19 Apr). *Arthur Meighen Commemoration*. P 12.
519 **207** 5 c. ultramarine 10 10

(Des B. J. Reddie)

1961 (28 June). *Tenth Anniv of Colombo Plan*. P 12.
520 **208** 5 c. blue and brown 10 10

209 "Resources for Tomorrow"

210 "Education"

(Des A. L. Pollock)

1961 (12 Oct). *Natural Resources*. P 12.
521 **209** 5 c. blue-green and brown 10 10

(Des Helen Fitzgerald)

1962 (28 Feb). *Education Year*. P 12.
522 **210** 5 c. black and orange-brown 10 10

211 Lord Selkirk and Farmer

212 Talon bestowing Gifts on Married Couple

(Des Phillips-Gutkin Ltd)

1962 (3 May). *150th Anniv of Red River Settlement*. P 12.
523 **211** 5 c. chocolate and green 10 10

(Des P. Weiss)

1962 (13 June). *Jean Talon Commemoration*. P 12.
524 **212** 5 c. blue 10 10

213 Br Columbia & Vancouver Is 2½d. stamp of 1860, and Parliament Buildings, B.C.

214 Highway (map version) and Provincial Arms

(Des Helen Bacon)

1962 (22 Aug). *Centenary of Victoria, B.C.* P 12.
525 **213** 5 c. red and black 15 10

(Des A. L. Pollock)

1962 (31 Aug). *Opening of Trans-Canada Highway*. P 12.
526 **214** 5 c. black and orange-brown 10 10

215 Queen Elizabeth II and Wheat (agriculture) Symbol

216 Sir Casimir Gzowski

(From drawing by Ernst Roch)

1962–64. *Horiz designs as T* **215** *showing Queen Elizabeth II and industry symbols*. (i) *P* 12.
527 1 c. chocolate (4.2.63) 10 10
a. Booklet pane. Five stamps plus one printed label (15.5.63) .. .. 2·50
p. Two phosphor bands (15.5.63) 15 20
528 2 c. green (2.5.63) 10 10
a. Pack. Two blocks of 25 .. .. 6·00
p. Two phosphor bands (15.5.63) 20 20
529 3 c. reddish violet† (2.5.63) 15 10
p. Two phosphor bands (15.5.63) 30 25
530 4 c. carmine-red (4.2.63) 15 10
a. Booklet pane. Five stamps plus one printed label (15.5.63) .. .. 2·50
b. Pack. One block of 25 .. .. .. 3·75
p. One centre phosphor band (*narrow*)* (2.63) 40 70
pa. One centre phosphor band (*wide*) (8.64) 1·75 2·50
pb. One side phosphor band (12.64) 40 70
531 5 c. ultramarine (3.10.62) 15 10
a. Booklet pane. Five stamps plus one printed label (5.63) .. .. 2·50
b. Pack. One block of 20 .. .. .. 4·75
c. Imperf horiz (vert pair) .. .. .. — £800
p. Two phosphor bands (31.1.63?) 35 15
pa. Pack. One block of 20 .. .. .. 14·00
527/31 .. .. *Set of* 5 60 15

(ii) *P* 9½ × *imperf coil stamps*)
532 2 c. green (1963) .. .. 3·75 4·75
532*a* 3 c. reddish violet (1964) .. .. .. 3·75 2·50
533 4 c. carmine-red (15.5.63) .. .. .. 1·75 1·75
534 5 c. ultramarine (15.5.63) .. .. .. 1·75 40
532/4 .. .. *Set of* 4 10·00 8·50

Symbols:–1 c. Crystals (Mining); 2 c. Tree (Forestry); 3 c. Fish (Fisheries); 4 c. Electricity pylon (Industrial power).

Nos. 528a, 530b, 531b and 531pa are blocks with the outer edges imperf. These come from "One Dollar Plastic Packages" sold at post offices.

†This is a fugitive colour which tends to become reddish on drying. In successive printings the violet colour became more and more reddish as the printer tried to match the shade of each previous printing instead of referring back to the original shade. A deep reddish violet is also known from Plate 3. As there is such a range of shades it is not practical to list them.

*On No. 530p the band is 4 mm wide as against 8 mm on No. 530pa. No. 530pb exists with the band at either left or right side of the stamp, the bands being applied across alternate vertical perforations.

(Des P. Weiss)

1963 (5 Mar). *150th Birth Anniv of Sir Casimir Gzowski (engineer)*. P 12.
535 **216** 5 c. reddish purple 10 10

217 "Export Trade"

218 Frobisher and barque *Gabriel*

(Des A. L. Pollock)

1963 (14 June). P 12.
536 **217** $1 carmine .. .. 8·00 1·50

(Des P. Weiss)

1963 (21 Aug). *Sir Martin Frobisher Commemoration*. P 12.
537 **218** 5 c. ultramarine 20 10

219 Horseman and Map

220 Canada Geese

(Des B. J. Reddie)

1963 (25 Sept). *Bicentenary of Quebec–Trois-Rivieres–Montreal Postal Service*. P 12.
538 **219** 5 c. red-brown and deep green 15 10

(Des A. Short and P. Arthur)

1963 (30 Oct). *P* 12.
539 **220** 15 c. blue . . . . 1·25 10

221 Jet Airliner (composite) and Uplands Airport, Ottawa

222 "Peace on Earth"

1964. *P* 12.
540 **221** 7 c. blue (11 Mar) . . 30 50
540*a* 8 c. blue (18 Nov) . . 40 25

1964 (8 Apr). *"Peace". Litho and recess. P* 12.
541 **222** 5 c. ochre, blue and turquoise-blue . . 10 10

223 Maple Leaves

1964 (14 May). *"Canadian Unity". P* 12.
542 **223** 5 c. lake-red and light blue . . 10 10

224 White Trillium and Arms of Ontario

236 Maple Leaf and Arms of Canada

1964–66. *Provincial Emblems. T* **224, 236** *and similar horiz designs. Recess (No. 555) or litho and recess (others). P* 12.
543 5 c. green, brown and orange (30.6.64) . . 30 20
544 5 c. green, orange-brown and yellow (30.6.64) 30 20
545 5 c. carmine-red, green and bluish violet (3.2.65) . . 30 20
546 5 c. blue, red and green (3.2.65) . . 30 20
547 5 c. purple, green and yellow-brown (28.4.65) 30 20
548 5 c. red-brown, deep bluish green and mauve (28.4.65) . . 30 20
549 5 c. slate-lilac, green and light reddish purple (21.7.65) . . 30 20
550 5 c. green, yellow and rose-red (19.1.66) . . 30 20
551 5 c. sepia, orange and green (19.1.66) . . 30 20
552 5 c. black, green and red (23.2.66) . . 30 20
553 5 c. drab, green and yellow (23.3.66) . . 30 20
554 5 c. blue, green and rose-red (23.3.66) . . 30 20
555 5 c. red and blue (30.6.66) . . 30 20
543/55 *Set of* 13 3·50 2·40

Designs:—No. 543, Type **224;** No. 544, Madonna Lily and Arms of Quebec; No. 545, Purple Violet and Arms of New Brunswick; No. 546, Mayflower and Arms of Nova Scotia; No. 547, Dogwood and Arms of British Columbia; No. 548, Prairie Crocus and Arms of Manitoba; No. 549, Lady's Slipper and Arms of Prince Edward Island; No. 550, Wild Rose and Arms of Alberta; No. 551, Prairie Lily and Arms of Saskatchewan; No. 552, Pitcher Plant and Arms of Newfoundland; No. 553, Mountain Avens and Arms of Northwest Territories; No. 554, Fireweed and Arms of Yukon Territory; No. 555, Type **236**.

8 (237)

238 Fathers of the Confederation Memorial, Charlottetown

1964 (15 July). *No. 540 surch with T* **237**.
556 **221** 8 c. on 7 c. blue 15 15

(Des P. Weiss)

1964 (29 July). *Centenary of Charlottetown Conference. P* 12.
557 **238** 5 c. black 10 10

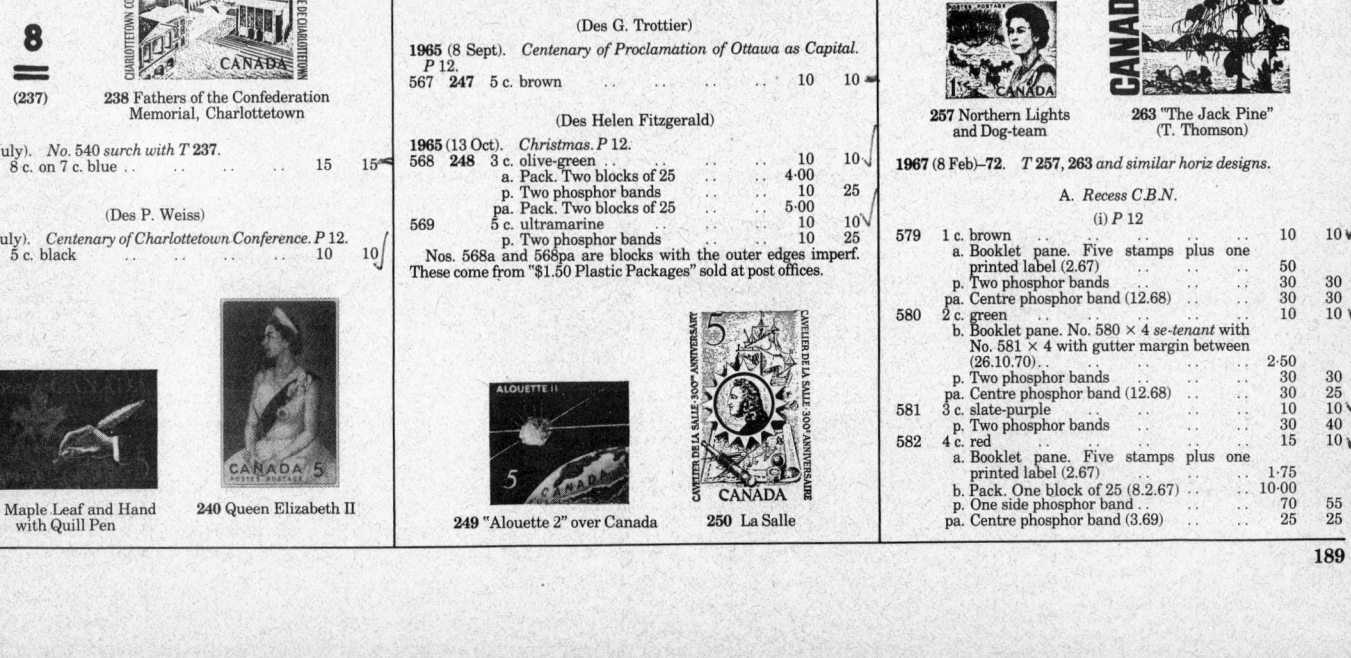

239 Maple Leaf and Hand with Quill Pen

240 Queen Elizabeth II

(Des P. Weiss)

1964 (9 Sept). *Centenary of Quebec Conference. P* 12.
558 **239** 5 c. light red and chocolate . . 10 10

(Portrait by Anthony Buckley)

1964 (5 Oct). *Royal Visit. P* 12.
559 **240** 5 c. reddish purple . . 15 10

241 "Canadian Family"

242 "Co-operation"

1964 (14 Oct). *Christmas. P* 12.
560 **241** 3 c. scarlet . . 10 10
a. Pack. Two blocks of 25 . . 5·00
p. Two phosphor bands . . 60 80
pa. Pack. Two blocks of 25 . . 9·50
561 5 c. ultramarine . . 10 10
p. Two phosphor bands . . 90 1·50

Nos. 560a and 560pa are blocks with the outer edges imperf. These come from "$1.50 Plastic Packages" sold at post offices.

1965 (3 Mar). *International Co-operation Year. P* 12.
562 **242** 5 c. grey-green . . 25 10

243 Sir W. Grenfell

244 National Flag

1965 (9 June). *Birth Centenary of Sir Wilfred Grenfell (missionary). P* 12.
563 **243** 5 c. deep bluish green . . 15 10

1965 (30 June). *Inauguration of National Flag. P* 12.
564 **244** 5 c. red and blue . . 10 10

245 Sir Winston Churchill

246 Peace Tower, Parliament Buildings, Ottawa

(Des P. Weiss from photo by Karsh. Litho)

1965 (12 Aug). *Churchill Commemoration. P* 12.
565 **245** 5 c. purple-brown . . 15 10

(Des Philips-Gutkin)

1965 (8 Sept). *Inter-Parliamentary Union Conference, Ottawa. P* 12.
566 **246** 5 c. deep green . . 10 10

247 Parliament Buildings, Ottawa 1865

248 "Gold, Frankincense and Myrrh"

(Des G. Trottier)

1965 (8 Sept). *Centenary of Proclamation of Ottawa as Capital. P* 12.
567 **247** 5 c. brown . . 10 10

(Des Helen Fitzgerald)

1965 (13 Oct). *Christmas. P* 12.
568 **248** 3 c. olive-green . . 10 10
a. Pack. Two blocks of 25 . . 4·00
p. Two phosphor bands . . 10 25
pa. Pack. Two blocks of 25 . . 5·00
569 5 c. ultramarine . . 10 10
p. Two phosphor bands . . 10 25

Nos. 568a and 568pa are blocks with the outer edges imperf. These come from "$1.50 Plastic Packages" sold at post offices.

249 "Alouette 2" over Canada

250 La Salle

1966 (5 Jan). *Launching of Canadian Satellite, "Alouette 2". P* 12.
570 **249** 5 c. ultramarine . . 15 10

(Des Brigdens Ltd., Toronto)

1966 (13 Apr). *300th Anniv of La Salle's Arrival in Canada. P* 12.
571 **250** 5 c. deep bluish green . . 15 10

251 Road Signs

252 Canadian Delegation and Houses of Parliament

(Des Helen Fitzgerald)

1966 (2 May). *Highway Safety. Invisible gum. P* 12.
572 **251** 5 c. yellow, blue and black . . 15 10

(Des P. Pederson (Brigdens Ltd))

1966 (26 May). *London Conference Centenary. P* 12.
573 **252** 5 c. red-brown . . 10 10

253 Douglas Point Nuclear Power Station

254 Parliamentary Library, Ottawa

(Des A. L. Pollock)

1966 (27 July). *Peaceful Uses of Atomic Energy. P* 12.
574 **253** 5 c. ultramarine . . 10 10

(Des Brigdens Ltd)

1966 (8 Sept). *Commonwealth Parliamentary Association Conference, Ottawa. P* 12.
575 **254** 5 c. purple . . 10 10

255 "Praying Hands", after Dürer

256 Flag and Canada on Globe

(Des G. Holloway)

1966 (12 Oct). *Christmas. P* 12.
576 **255** 3 c. carmine . . 10 10
a. Pack. Two blocks of 25 . . 3·00
p. Two phosphor bands . . 15 20
pa. Pack. Two blocks of 25 . . 5·00
577 5 c. orange . . 10 10
p. Two phosphor bands . . 15 50

Nos. 576a and 576pa are blocks with the outer edges imperf. These come from "$1.50 Plastic Packages" sold at post offices.

(Des Brigdens Ltd)

1967 (11 Jan). *Canadian Centennial. Invisible gum. P* 12.
578 **256** 5 c. scarlet and blue . . 10 10
p. Two phosphor bands . . 20 45

257 Northern Lights and Dog-team

263 "The Jack Pine" (T. Thomson)

1967 (8 Feb)–**72.** *T* **257, 263** *and similar horiz designs.*

A. *Recess C.B.N.*

(i) *P* 12

579 1 c. brown . . 10 10
a. Booklet pane. Five stamps plus one printed label (2.67) . . 50
p. Two phosphor bands . . 30 30
pa. Centre phosphor band (12.68) . . 30 30
580 2 c. green . . 10 10
b. Booklet pane. No. 580 × 4 *se-tenant* with No. 581 × 4 with gutter margin between (26.10.70) . . 2·50
p. Two phosphor bands . . 30 30
pa. Centre phosphor band (12.68) . . 30 25
581 3 c. slate-purple . . 10 10
p. Two phosphor bands . . 30 40
582 4 c. red . . 15 10
a. Booklet pane. Five stamps plus one printed label (2.67) . . 1·75
b. Pack. One block of 25 (8.2.67) . . 10·00
p. One side phosphor band . . 70 55
pa. Centre phosphor band (3.69) . . 25 25

583 5 c. blue 15 10
a. Booklet pane. Five stamps plus one printed label (3.67) .. .. 6·00
b. Pack. One block of 20 (2.67) .. .. 17·00
p. Two phosphor bands 45 25
pa. Pack. One block of 20 (8.2.67) .. .. 35·00
pb. Centre phosphor band (12.68) 25 20
583*c* 6 c. black (2.72) 90 20
cp. Centre phosphor band (2.72) .. .. 1·00 50
584 8 c. purple-brown 25 20
585 10 c. olive-green 25 10
p. Two phosphor bands (9.12.69) 75 40
586 15 c. dull purple 30 10
p. Two phosphor bands (9.12.69) 80 70
587 20 c. deep blue 65 10
p. Two phosphor bands (9.12.69) .. .. 1·25 90
588 25 c. myrtle-green 70 10
p. Two phosphor bands (9.12.69) .. .. 2·50 2·00
589 50 c. cinnamon .. .. 1·50 10
590 $1 scarlet .. .. 3·50 40
579/90 .. .. *Set of* 13 7·50 1·00
579pa/588p .. .. .. *Set of* 10 6·50 5·50

(ii) *Perf* 9½ × *imperf* (*coil stamps*)

591 3 c. slate-purple (3.67) .. .. .. 1·25 1·50
592 4 c. red (3.67) .. .. 1·25 1·50
593 5 c. blue (2.67) .. .. 1·25 75

(iii) *Perf* 10 × *imperf* (*coil stamps*)

594 6 c. orange-red (1.69) 40 35
a. Imperf (vert pair) £250
595 6 c. black (8.70) 35 30
a. Imperf (vert pair) £350
596 7 c. green (30.6.71) 40 30
a. Imperf (vert pair) £450
597 8 c. black (30.12.71) 30 20
a. Imperf (vert pair) £175

B. *Recess B.A.B.N.*

(i) *P* 10 (*sheets* (601/p) *or booklets*)

598 1 c. brown (9.68) 15 30
a. Booklet pane. No. 598 × 5 *se-tenant* with No. 599 × 5 (9.68) .. .. .. 2·25
b. Booklet pane. No. 601 × 4 *se-tenant* with No. 598 plus one printed label (10.68) .. 2·50
599 4 c. red (9.68) 25 40
a. Booklet pane. 25 stamps plus two printed labels .. .. 9·00
600 5 c. blue (9.68) 25 40
a. Booklet pane of 20 .. .. .. 6·50
601 6 c. orange-red (10.68) 45 10
a. Booklet pane. 25 stamps plus two printed labels (1.69) .. .. 12·00
p. Two phosphor bands (1.11.68) 40 45
602 6 c. black (1.70) 75 40
a. Booklet pane. 25 stamps plus two printed labels .. .. 14·00
603 6 c. black (*re-engraved die*) (8.70) .. .. 3·25 1·40
a. Booklet pane of 4 .. .. 12·00

(ii) *P* 12½ × 12 (*sheets* (606/10) *or booklets*)

604 1 c. brown (30.6.71) 35 60
a. Booklet pane. Nos. 604 × 4,605 × 4 and 609 × 12 *se-tenant* .. .. .. 10·00
b. Booklet pane. No. 604 × 3, No. 608 and No. 610 × 2 *se-tenant* (30.12.71) .. .. 2·25
c. Booklet pane. No. 604 × 6, No. 608 and No. 610 × 11 *se-tenant* (30.12.71) .. 6·50
d. Booklet pane. No. 604, No. 605 and No. 609 × 3 *se-tenant* plus one printed label 5·00
e. Booklet pane. No. 604 × 4, No. 608 and No. 610 × 5 *se-tenant* (8.72) .. .. 2·50
605 3 c. slate-purple (30.6.71) .. .. .. 1·25 2·00
606 6 c. orange-red (3.69) 45 10
p. Two phosphor bands 75 20
607 6 c. black (7.1.70) 25 10
a. Booklet pane. 25 stamps plus two printed labels (8.70) .. .. 16·00
p. Two phosphor bands 60 70
608 6 c. black (*re-engraved die*) (9.70) 35 10
a. Booklet pane of 4 (11.70) .. .. .. 5·00
p. One centre phosphor band (9.71) .. .. 1·00 60
609 7 c. myrtle-green (30.6.71) 30 10
p. Two phosphor bands 60 45
610 8 c. slate-black (30.12.71) 30 10
p. Two phosphor bands 60 35

Designs: (*as T* **257**)—2 c. Totem pole; 3 c. Combine-harvester and oil derrick; 4 c. Ship in lock; 5 c. Harbour scene; 6 c., 7 c. "Transport"; 8 c. (Nos. 597, 610) Library of Parliament. (*as T* **263**)—8 c. (No. 584) "Alaska Highway" (A. Y. Jackson); 15 c. "Bylot Island" (L. Harris); 20 c. "Quebec Ferry" (J. W. Morrice); 25 c. "The Solemn Land" (J. E. H. MacDonald); 50 c. "Summer's Stores" (grain elevators) (J. Ensor); $1 "Oilfield" (near Edmonton) (H. G. Glyde).

Nos. 582b, 583b and 583pa are blocks with the outer edges imperf. These come from "One Dollar Plastic Packages" sold at post offices.

No. 582p comes with the band to the left or right of the stamp, the phosphor having been applied across alternate vertical perforations.

Normal

Re-engraved

When the basic postal rate was changed to 6 c. the C.B.N. lent their die to B.A.B.N. who made a duplicate die from it by transfer. Parts of this proved to be weak, but it was used for Nos. 601/2 and 606/7. B.A.B.N. later re-engraved their die to make fresh plates which were used for Nos. 603 and 608. No. 608 first appeared on sheets from Plate 4.

There are no records of dates of issue of the booklets, packs and coils, but supplies of these were distributed to depots in the months indicated.

IMPERF BETWEEN PAIRS FROM COIL STAMPS. Nos. 595/6 (and possibly others) are known in blocks or horizontal pairs imperf between vertically. Coils are supplied to post offices in batches of ten coils held together by roulettes between every fourth stamp so that they can easily be split apart. If two or more unsplit coils are purchased it is possible to obtain blocks or pairs imperf between vertically.

Vertical coil stamps are also known imperf between horizontally or with some stamps apparently completely imperf. These can result from blind perforations identifiable by slight indentations.

WHITE FLUORESCENT PAPER. Different papers with varying degrees of whiteness have been used for Canadian stamps, but during 1968–70 a distinctive very white and highly fluorescent paper was used known as "hybrite"; this fluoresces on the back and front. This paper has also been employed for commemorative issues, some of which exist on more than one type of paper. The white fluorescent papers are recorded in the Stanley Gibbons *Elizabethan Catalogue*.

FLUORESCENT BANDS. During the second half of 1971 new sorting machines were installed in the Ottawa area which were activated by stamps bearing fluorescent bands. These differ from the Winnipeg phosphor bands in that there is no after-glow and they are hardly visible to the naked eye and so can only be distinguished by using an ultra-violet lamp. For this reason they are outside the scope of this catalogue but instead are recorded in footnotes. They are, however, fully listed in the Stanley Gibbons *Elizabethan Catalogue*.

In the 1967–72 definitive issue fluorescent bands occur on some printings of Nos. 579, 580, 581, 582, 583*c*, 585, 586, 597, 604, 608 and 610.

The experiments were successful and what was at first called "Ottawa tagging" has since come into more general use and the Winnipeg phosphor was phased out. However, the substance at first used (known as OP–4) was found to migrate to envelopes, documents, album pages, etc. as well as to adjoining stamps. Late in 1972 this fault was cured by using another substance (called OP–2). The migrating bands were used on early printings of Nos. 604, 608 and 610 as well as certain stamps referred to in a footnote after No. 692. It is most advisable to use plastic mounts for housing stamps with migrating bands or else clear acetate should be affixed to the album leaves.

269 Canadian Pavilion

270 Allegory of "Womanhood" on Ballot-box

(Des C.B.N.)

1967 (28 Apr). *World Fair, Montreal. P* 12.
611 **269** 5 c. blue and red 10 10

(Des Helen Fitzgerald. Litho)

1967 (24 May). *50th Anniv of Women's Franchise. P* 12.
612 **270** 5 c. reddish purple and black 10 10

271 Queen Elizabeth II and Centennial Emblem

272 Athlete

(Portrait from photo by Anthony Buckley)

1967 (30 June). *Royal Visit. P* 12.
613 **271** 5 c. plum and orange-brown 10 10

(Des Brigdens Ltd)

1967 (19 July). *Fifth Pan-American Games, Winnipeg. P* 12.
614 **272** 5 c. rose-red 10 10

273 "World News"

274 Governor-General Vanier

(Des W. McLauchlan)

1967 (31 Aug). *50th Anniv of the Canadian Press. P* 12.
615 **273** 5 c. blue 10 10

(Des from photo by Karsh)

1967 (15 Sept). *Vanier Commemoration. P* 12.
616 **274** 5 c. black 10 10

PRINTERS. The following were printed either by the Canadian Bank Note Co, Ottawa (C.B.N.) or the British American Bank Note Co, Ottawa (B.A.B.N.), *except where otherwise stated.*

275 People of 1867 and Toronto, 1967

276 Carol Singers

(Des and recess C.B.N.)

1967 (28 Sept). *Centenary of Toronto as Capital City of Ontario. P* 12.
617 **275** 5 c. myrtle-green and vermilion 10 10

(Des and recess B.A.B.N.)

1967 (11 Oct). *Christmas. P* 12.
618 **276** 3 c. scarlet 10 10
a. Pack. Two blocks of 25 .. .. 2·75
p. Two phosphor bands 10 20
pa. Pack. Two blocks of 25 .. .. 3·00
619 5 c. emerald-green 10 10
p. Two phosphor bands 10 25

Nos. 618a and 618pa are blocks with the outer edges imperf. These come from "$1.50 Plastic Packs" sold at post offices.

277 Grey Jays

278 Weather Map and Instruments

(Des M. G. Loates. Litho C.B.N.)

1968 (15 Feb). *Wild Life. P* 12.
620 **277** 5 c. multicoloured 25 10
See also Nos. 638/40.

(Des and litho B.A.B.N.)

1968 (13 Mar). *Bicentenary of First Meteorological Readings. P* 11.
621 **278** 5 c. multicoloured 10 10

279 Narwhal

280 Globe, Maple Leaf and Rain Gauge

(Des J. A. Crosby. Litho B.A.B.N.)

1968 (10 Apr). *Wildlife. P* 11.
622 **279** 5 c. multicoloured 10 10

No. 622 has a background of yellow-green and pale blue but copies are known with the yellow-green apparently missing. This "yellow-green" is produced by an overlay of yellow on the blue but we have not come across any copies where the yellow is completely missing and the wide range of colour variation is due to technical dificulties in maintaining an exact blend of the two colours.

(Des I. von Mosdossy. Litho B.A.B.N.)

1968 (8 May). *International Hydrological Decade. P* 11.
623 **280** 5 c. multicoloured 10 10

IMPERF EDGES. On Nos. 624/54, 657 and 659 (stamps printed by the B.A.B.N. Co.) the outer edges of the sheets were guillotined to remove the imprints for P.O. stock so that single stamps may, therefore, be found with either one, or two adjacent sides imperforate.

281 *Nonsuch*

282 Lacrosse Players

(Recess and photo B.A.B.N.)

1968 (5 June). *300th Anniv of Voyage of the "Nonsuch". P* 10.
624 **281** 5 c. multicoloured 15 10

(Des J. E. Aldridge. Recess and photo B.A.B.N.)

1968 (3 July). *Lacrosse. P* 10.
625 **282** 5 c. black, red and lemon 10 10

283 Front Page of *The Globe*, George Brown and Legislative Building   **284** H. Bourassa

(Des N. Sabolotny. Recess and photo B.A.B.N.)

1968 (21 Aug). *150th Birth Anniv of George Brown (politician and journalist)*. P 10.
626 **283** 5 c. multicoloured 10 10

(Des, recess and litho C.B.N.)

1968 (4 Sept). *Birth Centenary of Henri Bourassa (journalist and politician)*. P 12.
627 **284** 5 c. black, red and pale cream 10 10

285 John McCrae, Battlefield and First Lines of "In Flanders Fields"   **286** Armistice Monument, Vimy

(Des I. von Mosdossy. Litho C.B.N.)

1968 (15 Oct). *50th Death Anniv of John McCrae (soldier and poet)*. P 12.
628 **285** 5 c. multicoloured 10 10

(Des and recess C.B.N.)

1968 (15 Oct). *50th Anniversary of 1918 Armistice*. P 12.
629 **286** 15 c. slate-black 30 40

287 Eskimo Family (carving)   **288** "Mother and Child" (carving)

(Designs from Eskimo carvings by Munamee (6 c.) and unknown carver (5 c.). Photo C.B.N.)

1968. *Christmas*. P 12.
630 **287** 5 c. black and new blue (1.11.68) .. 10 10
a. Booklet pane of 10 (15.11.68) .. 2·25
p. One centre phosphor band 10 15
pa. Booklet pane of 10 (15.11.68) .. 2·50
631 **288** 6 c. black and ochre (15.11.68) 10 10
p. Two phosphor bands 15 25

289 Curling   **290** Vincent Massey

(Des D. Eales. Recess and photo B.A.B.N.)

1969 (15 Jan). *Curling*. P 10.
632 **289** 6 c. black, new blue and scarlet .. 10 10

(Des I. von Mosdossy. Recess and litho C.B.N.)

1969 (20 Feb). *Vincent Massey, First Canadian-born Governor-General*. P 12.
633 **290** 6 c. sepia and yellow-ochre 10 10

291 "Return from the Harvest Field" (Suzor-Côté)   **292** Globe and Tools

(Photo C.B.N.)

1969 (14 Mar). *Birth Centenary of Marc Aurèle de Foy Suzor-Côté (painter)*. P 12.
634 **291** 50 c. multicoloured .. .. .. 70 2·00

(Des J. Hébert. Recess B.A.B.N.)

1969 (21 May). *50th Anniv of International Labour Organisation*. P 12½ × 12.
635 **292** 6 c. bronze-green 10 10

293 Vickers "Vimy" Aircraft over Atlantic Ocean   **294** "Sir William Osler" (J. S. Sargent)

(Des R. W. Bradford. Recess and photo B.A.B.N.)

1969 (13 June). *50th Anniv of First Non-stop Transatlantic Flight*. P 12 × 12½.
636 **293** 15 c. chocolate, bright green & pale blue 35 55

(Des, recess and photo B.A.B.N.)

1969 (23 June). *50th Death Anniv of Sir William Osler (physician)*. P 12½ × 12.
637 **294** 6 c. deep blue, light blue and chestnut 10 10

295 White-throated Sparrows   **298** Flags of Winter and Summer Games

(Des M. G. Loates. Litho C.B.N.)

1969 (23 July). *Birds*. *T* **295** *and similar multicoloured designs*. P 12.
638 6 c. Type **295** 25 10
639 10 c. Savannah Sparrow (*horiz*) 65 80
640 25 c. Hermit Thrush (*horiz*) .. .. .. 1·90 2·50
638/40 .. .. *Set of* 3 2·50 3·00

(Des C. McDiarmid. Recess and litho C.B.N.)

1969 (15 Aug). *Canadian Games*. P 12.
641 **298** 6 c. emerald, scarlet and blue 10 10

299 Outline of Prince Edward Island showing Charlottetown   **300** Sir Isaac Brock and Memorial Column

(Des L. Fitzgerald. Recess and photo B.A.B.N.)

1969 (15 Aug). *Bicentenary of Charlottetown as Capital of Prince Edward Island*. P 12 × 12½.
642 **299** 6 c. yellow-brown, black and blue 10 10

(Des I. von Mosdossy. Recess and litho C.B.N.)

1969 (12 Sept). *Birth Bicentenary of Sir Isaac Brock*. P 12.
643 **300** 6 c. orange, bistre and bistre-brown 10 10

301 Children of the World in Prayer   **302** Stephen Butler Leacock, Mask and "Mariposa"

(Des Rapid Grip and Batten Ltd. Litho C.B.N.)

1969 (8 Oct). *Christmas*. P 12.
644 **301** 5 c. multicoloured 10 10
a. Booklet pane of 10 .. .. 1·75
p. One centre phosphor band 10 20
pa. Booklet pane of 10 .. .. 2·50
645 6 c. multicoloured 10 10
a. Black (inscr, value and frame omitted) £1100
p. Two phosphor bands 10 25

(Des, recess and photo B.A.B.N.)

1969 (12 Nov). *Birth Centenary of Stephen Butler Leacock (humorist)*. P 12 × 12½.
646 **302** 6 c. multicoloured 10 10

303 Symbolic Cross-roads   **304** "Enchanted Owl" (Kenojuak)

(Des K. C. Lochhead. Litho C.B.N.)

1970 (27 Jan). *Centenary of Manitoba*. P 12.
647 **303** 6 c. ultramarine, lemon and vermilion 10 10
p. Two phosphor bands 10 30

(Des N. E. Hallendy and Miss S. Van Raalte. Recess C.B.N.)

1970 (27 Jan). *Centenary of Northwest Territories*. P 12.
648 **304** 6 c. carmine-red and black 10 10

305 Microscopic View of Inside of Leaf   **306** Expo 67 Emblem and Stylized Cherry Blossom

(Des I. Charney. Recess and photo B.A.B.N.)

1970 (18 Feb). *International Biological Programme*. P 12 × 12½.
649 **305** 6 c. emerald, orange-yellow & ultram .. 10 10

(Des E. R. C. Bethune. Litho C.B.N.)

1970 (18 Mar). *World Fair, Osaka*. *T* **306** *and similar horiz designs*. *Multicoloured; colour of Cherry Blossom given*. P 12.
650 25 c. red .. .. 1·25 1·00
a. Block of 4. Nos. 650/3 .. .. .. 4·50
p. Two phosphor bands .. .. .. 1·50 2·00
pa. Block of 4. Nos. 650p/3p .. .. 5·50
651 25 c. violet .. .. 1·25 1·00
p. Two phosphor bands .. .. .. 1·50 2·00
652 25 c. green .. .. 1·25 1·00
p. Two phosphor bands .. .. .. 1·50 2·00
653 25 c. blue .. .. 1·25 1·00
p. Two phosphor bands .. .. .. 1·50 2·00
650/3 .. .. *Set of* 4 4·50 3·50

Designs:—No. 650, Type **306**; No. 651, Dogwood and stylized cherry blossom; No. 652, White Trillium and stylized cherry blossom; No. 653, White Garden Lily and stylized cherry blossom.

Nos. 650/3 and 650p/3p are printed together in sheets of 50 (5 × 10). In the first, second, fourth and fifth vertical rows the four different designs are arranged in *se-tenant* blocks, whilst the centre row is composed as follows (reading downwards:—650(p)/3(p), 650(p) × 2, 653(p), 651(p), 652(p) and 650(p).

310 Henry Kelsey   **311** "Towards Unification"

(Des D. Burton. Recess and photo B.A.B.N.)

1970 (15 Apr). *300th Birth Anniv of Henry Kelsey (explorer)*. P 12 × 12½.
654 **310** 6 c. multicoloured 10 10

(Des B. Fisher. Litho B.A.B.N.)

1970 (13 May). *25th Anniv of United Nations*. P 11.
655 **311** 10 c. blue 25 25
p. Two phosphor bands .. .. 40 1·00
656 15 c. magenta and bluish lilac 40 35
p. Two phosphor bands .. .. 40 1·25

312 Louis Riel (Métis leader)   **313** Mackenzie's Inscription, Dean Channel

(Des R. Derreth. Photo B.A.B.N.)

1970 (19 June). *Louis Riel Commemoration*. P 12½ × 12.
657 **312** 6 c. greenish blue and vermilion .. 10 10

(Design from Government Archives photo. Recess C.B.N.)

1970 (25 June). *Sir Alexander Mackenzie (explorer)*. P 12 × 11½.
658 **313** 6 c. bistre-brown 10 10

314 Sir Oliver Mowat (statesman) **315** "Isles of Spruce" (A. Lismer)

(Des E. Roch. Recess and photo B.A.B.N.)

1970 (12 Aug). *Sir Oliver Mowat Commemoration. P* 12.
659 **314** 6 c. vermilion and black 10 10

(Litho Ashton-Potter)

1970 (18 Sept). *50th Anniv of "Group of Seven" (artists). P* 11.
660 **315** 6 c. multicoloured 10 10

316 "Horse-drawn Sleigh" (D. Niskala) **317** "Christ in Manger" (C. Fortier)

(Des from children's drawings. Litho C.B.N.)

1970 (7 Oct). *Christmas. Horiz designs as T* **316/17**, *showing children's drawings. Multicoloured. P* 12.
661 5 c. Type **316** 20 10
a. Strip of 5. Nos. 661/5 .. .. .. 1·50
p. One centre phosphor band 25 15
pa. Strip of 5. Nos. 661p/5p .. .. .. 1·50
662 5 c. "Stable" and Star of Bethlehem" (L. Wilson) (26 × 21 *mm*) 20 10
p. One centre phosphor band 25 15
663 5 c. "Snowmen" (M. Lecompte) (26 × 21 *mm*) 20 10
p. One centre phosphor band 25 15
664 5 c. "Skiing" (D. Durham) (26 × 21 *mm*) .. 20 10
p. One centre phosphor band 25 15
665 5 c. "Santa Claus" (A. Martin) (26 × 21 *mm*) 20 10
p. One centre phosphor band 25 15
666 6 c. "Santa Claus" (E. Bhattacharya) (26 × 21 *mm*) 25 10
a. Strip of 5. Nos. 666/70 .. .. .. 1·75
p. Two phosphor bands 30 20
pa. Strip of 5. Nos. 666p/70p.. .. .. 2·00
667 6 c. "Christ in Manger" (J. McKinney) (26 × 21 *mm*) 25 10
p. Two phosphor bands 30 20
668 6 c. "Toy Shop" (N. Whateley) (26 × 21 *mm*) 25 10
p. Two phosphor bands 30 20
669 6 c. "Christmas Tree" (J. Pomperleau) (26 × 21 *mm*) 25 10
p. Two phosphor bands 30 20
670 6 c. "Church" (J. McMillan) (26 × 21 *mm*) .. 25 10
p. Two phosphor bands 30 20
671 10 c. Type **317** 30 25
p. Two phosphor bands 55 60
672 15 c. "Trees and Sledge" (J. Dojcak) (35 × 21 mm) 45 60
p. Two phosphor bands 70 75
661/72 .. .. *Set of* 12 3·25 1·25
661p/672p .. .. *Set of* 12 4·25 2.75

The designs of the 5 c. and 6 c. were each issued with the various designs *se-tenant* in a diamond shaped arrangement within the sheet. This generally results in *se-tenant* pairs both vert and horiz, but due to the sheet arrangement vert and horiz pairs of the same design exist from the two centre vert and horiz rows.

328 Sir Donald A. Smith **329** "Big Raven" (E. Carr)

(Des Dora de Pédery-Hunt. Litho C.B.N.)

1970 (4 Nov). *150th Birth Anniv of Sir Donald Alexander Smith. P* 12.
673 **328** 6 c. yellow, brown and bronze-green .. 10 10

(Litho C.B.N.)

1971 (12 Feb). *Birth Centenary of Emily Carr (painter). P* 12.
674 **329** 6 c. multicoloured 10 10

330 Laboratory Equipment **331** "The Atom"

(Des R. Webber. Litho B.A.B.N.)

1971 (3 Mar). *50th Anniv of Discovery of Insulin. P* 10½.
675 **330** 6 c. multicoloured 20 10

(Des R. Webber. Litho B.A.B.N.)

1971 (24 Mar). *Birth Centenary of Lord Rutherford (scientist). P* 11.
676 **331** 6 c. yellow, red and deep chocolate 20 10

332 Maple "Keys" **333** Louis Papineau

(Des Alma Duncan. Litho Ashton-Potter)

1971. *"The Maple Leaf in Four Seasons". T* **332** *and similar vert designs. Multicoloured. P* 11.
677 6 c. Type **332** (Spring) (14.4) 20 15
a. Imperf (pair) £650
678 6 c. Green leaves (Summer) (16.6) 20 15
679 7 c. Autumn leaves (3.9) 20 15
a. Grey (inscr and value) omitted £2000
680 7 c. Withered leaves and snow (Winter) (19.11) 20 15
677/80 .. .. *Set of* 4 70 55

(Des L. Marquart. Recess and photo B.A.B.N.)

1971 (7 May). *Death Centenary of Louis-Joseph Papineau (politician). P* 12½ × 12.
681 **333** 6 c. multicoloured 10 15

334 Chart of Coppermine River **335** "People" and Computer Tapes

(Des L. Marquart. Recess and photo B.A.B.N.)

1971 (7 May). *Bicentenary of Samuel Hearne's Expedition to Coppermine. P* 12 × 12½.
682 **334** 6 c. red, sepia and pale buff 15 15

(Des H. Kleefeld. Litho C.B.N.)

1971 (1 June). *Centenary of First Canadian Census. P* 11½.
683 **335** 6 c. blue, red and black 10 10

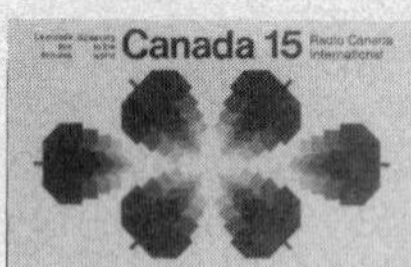

336 Maple Leaves

(Des B. Kramer. Litho C.B.N.)

1971 (1 June). *Radio Canada International. P* 12.
684 **336** 15 c. red, yellow and black .. .. 50 1·00
p. Two phosphor bands .. .. 1·25 2·50

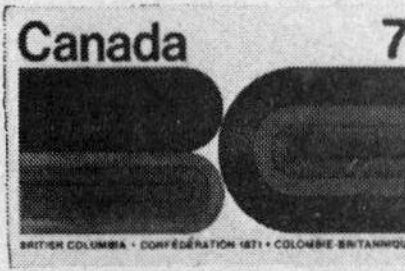

337 "BC"

(Des E. R. C. Bethune. Litho C.B.N.)

1971 (20 July). *Centenary of British Columbia's Entry into the Confederation. P* 12.
685 **337** 7 c. multicoloured 10 10

338 "Indian Encampment on Lake Huron" (Kane) **339** "Snowflake"

(Des and litho B.A.B.N.)

1971 (11 Aug). *Death Centenary of Paul Kane (painter). P* 12½.
686 **338** 7 c. multicoloured 15 10

(Des Lisl Levinsohn. Recess (6 c., 7 c.) or recess and litho (others) C.B.N.)

1971 (6 Oct). *Christmas. T* **379** *and similar design. P* 12.
687 **339** 6 c. deep blue 10 10
p. One centre phosphor band 15 20
688 7 c. deep emerald 15 10
p. Two phosphor bands 25 30
689 – 10 c. silver and cerise 40 70
p. Two phosphor bands .. .. .. 60 1·00
690 – 15 c. silver, brown-purple and lavender 55 80
p. Two phosphor bands .. .. .. 75 1·40
687/90 .. .. *Set of* 4 1·10 1·50
687p/90p .. .. *Set of* 4 1·60 2·75

Design:—10 c., 15 c. "Snowflake" design similar to T **339** but square (26 × 26 mm).

340 Pierre Laporte (Quebec Cabinet Minister) **341** Skaters

(Des G. Gundersen. Recess and litho B.A.B.N.)

1971 (20 Oct). *First Anniv of the Assassination of Pierre Laporte. P* 12½ × 12.
691 **340** 7 c. black/*pale buff* 10 10

(Des Design Workshop, Toronto. Litho C.B.N.)

1972 (1 Mar). *World Figure Skating Championships, Calgary. P* 11½ × 12.
692 **341** 8 c. purple 10 10

MIGRATING FLUORESCENT BANDS. These are referred to in the notes after No. 610. In the following issues they exist on Nos. 719/20 and 731/2 and on early printings only of Nos. 702/6.

342 J. A. MacDonald **343** Forest, Central Canada

344 Vancouver

Type I

Type II

Two types of 10 c. (No. 702):
Type I. Light impression of green recess colour. Cross-hatching around "Canada" clearly visible (plate 1).
Type II. Green recess colour much more deeply etched. Cross-hatching around "Canada" entirely obscured (plates 2 and 3).

Type I

Type II

Two types of 15 c.:
Type I. Trees on hillside, shown in blue, clearly detailed (plate 1).
Type II. Trees shown in solid colour (plate 2).

Two types of 25 c.:
Type I. Bears' shadows evenly shaded.
Type II. Shadows have a solid central area.

(Des D. Annesley (1 to 10 c. (701)), R. Derreth (others))

1972–77. *Various designs as T* **342/4**.

(*a*) *T* **342** *and similar vert portraits. Recess C.B.N.* (*1 to 6 c. and last ptgs of 7 and 8 c.* (*No.* 700), *B.A.B.N.* (*7, 8, 10 c. and booklet panes*). *Two fluorescent bands. P* 12 × 12½ (*1 to 8 c.*) *or* 13 (*10 c.*). (17.10.73)

693	1 c. orange	10	10
	a. Booklet pane. Nos. 693 × 3, 698 and 700 × 2 (10.4.74)	55	
	b. Booklet pane. Nos. 693 × 6, 698 and 700 × 11 (17.1.75)	1·90	
	c. Booklet pane Nos. 693 × 2, 694 × 4 and 701a × 4 (1.9.76)	1·10	
694	2 c. deep green	10	10
695	3 c. agate	10	10
696	4 c. black	10	10
697	5 c. deep magenta	10	10
698	6 c. Indian red	10	10
699	7 c. reddish brown (8.4.74)	10	10
700	8 c. dull ultramarine	15	10
	a. Perf 13 (12.76)	70	20
701	10 c. brown-lake (1.9.76)	20	10
	a. Perf 12 × 12½ (*booklets*)	30	30

(*b*) *T* **343** *and similar vert designs. Recess and photo B.A.B.N. Two fluorescent bands. P* 12½ × 12 (8.9.72)

702	10 c. dp green, blue-green & yellow-orge (I)	35	10
	a. Type II (7.74)	40	15
	b. Perf 13 (2.76)	20	10
	p. Two phosphor bands	90	90
703	15 c. dull ultramarine and orange-brown (I)	40	10
	a. Type II (1975)	90	50
	b. Perf 13 (2.76)	25	10
	p. Two phosphor bands	95	1·40
704	20 c. pale orange, reddish violet & ultram	40	10
	a. Perf 13 (2.76)	30	10
	p. Two phosphor bands	1·25	1·75
705	25 c. deep ultramarine and pale blue (I) ..	45	10
	a. Type II (1975)	3·00	80
	b. Perf 13 (2.76)	30	10
	p. Two phosphor bands	1·75	2·50
706	50 c. blue-green, royal blue and buff ..	45	10
	a. Blue-green, ultramarine and buff (8.74)	65	10
	b. Perf 13 (2.76)	40	10

(*c*) *T* **344** *and similar horiz design. Recess B.A.B.N. and litho Ashton-Potter. No fluorescent bands. P* 11 (17.3.72)

707	$1 multicoloured	5·00	3·00
708	$2 multicoloured	1·50	1·50

(*d*) *T* **344.** *Recess and photo B.A.B.N. Two fluorescent bands. P* 12½ × 12 (24.10.73)

709	$1 multicoloured	1·25	55
	a. Perf 13 (4.77)	70	30

(*e*) *As Nos.* 700/1. *Recess C.B.N. Imperf × perf* 10 (*coil stamps*)

710	8 c. dull ultramarine (10.4.74)	35	10
	a. Imperf (horiz pair)	70·00	
711	10 c. brown-lake (1.9.76)	20	15
	a. Imperf (horiz pair)	£110	

Designs (1 to 7c. show Canadian Prime Ministers):—2 c. W. Laurier; 3 c. R. Borden; 4 c. W. L. Mackenzie King; 5 c. R. B. Bennett; 6 c. L. B. Pearson; 7 c. Louis St. Laurent; 8 and 10 c. (Nos. 701/a, 711), Queen Elizabeth II; 15 c. American Bighorn sheep; 20 c. Prairie landscape from the air; 25 c. Polar Bears; 50 c. Seashore, Eastern Canada; $2 Quebec.

Stamps from booklets exist with one or two adjacent sides imperforate.

345 Heart

(Des Joyce Wieland. Recess B.A.B.N.)

1972 (7 Apr). *Heart Disease* (*World Health Day*). *P* 12 × 12½.

719	**345** 8 c. carmine	10	10

This stamp exists on two kinds of paper, with or without fluorescent bands.

346 Frontenac and Fort Saint-Louis, Quebec

(Des L. Marquart. Recess and photo B.A.B.N.)

1972 (17 May). *300th Anniv of Governor Frontenac's Appointment to New France. P* 12 × 12½.

720	**346** 8 c. brown-red, orange-brn & dp ultram	10	10

This exists with or without fluorescent bands.

347 Plains Indians' Artefacts **347*a*** Buffalo Chase

(Des G. Beaupré. Litho Ashton-Potter (721/2, 725/6 and 729/30), B.A.B.N. (723/4), C.B.N. (727/8))

1972–76. *Canadian Indians. P* 12 × 12½ (721/2, 725/6), 12 (723/4), 13 (727/30), 12½ × 12 (731/6) *or* 12½ (737/40).

(*a*) *Horiz designs issued in se-tenant pairs, the first showing Artefacts as T* **347**, *the second showing Scenes from Indian Life as T* **347*a***

721	8 c. multicoloured (6.7.72)	40	10
	a. Pair. Nos. 721/2	85	1·00
722	8 c. deep brown, yellow & grey-black (6.7.72)	40	10
723	8 c. multicoloured (21.2.73)	40	10
	a. Pair. Nos. 723/4	85	1·00
724	8 c. multicoloured (21.2.73)	40	10
725	8 c. multicoloured (16.1.74)	40	10
	a. Pair. Nos. 725/6	85	1·00
726	8 c. dp brown, yellow & grey-black (16.1.74)	40	10
727	8 c. multicoloured (4.4.75)	40	10
	a. Pair. Nos. 727/8	85	1·00
	ab. Imperf between (horiz pair)	£400	
728	8 c. multicoloured (4.4.75)	40	10
729	10 c. multicoloured (17.9.76)	40	20
	a. Pair. Nos. 729/30	85	1·00
730	10 c. light stone and black (17.9.76)	40	20

Designs show the following tribes: Nos. 721/2 (T **347**/*a*), Plains Indians; 723/4, Algonkians; 725/6, Pacific Coast Indians; 727/8, Subarctic Indians; 729/30, Iroquoians.

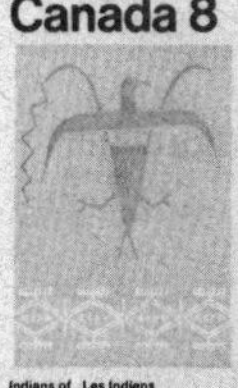

348 Thunderbird and Tribal Pattern **348*a*** Dancer in Ceremonial Costume

(Des G. Beaupré. Recess and photo B.A.B.N. (731/6). Litho and embossed Ashton-Potter (737, 739). Litho Ashton-Potter (738, 740))

(*b*) *Vert designs issued in se-tenant pairs, the first showing Thunderbird and pattern as T* **348**, *the second Costumes as T* **348*a***

731	8 c. light yellow-orange, rose-red and black (4.10.72)	40	15
	a. Pair. Nos. 731/2	85	1·00
732	8 c. multicoloured (4.10.72)	40	15
733	8 c. light rose-red, violet and black (28.11.73)	40	10
	a. Pair. Nos. 733/4	85	1·00
734	8 c. turquoise-green, lake-brown and black (28.11.73)	40	10
735	8 c. rose-red and black (22.2.74)	40	10
	a. Pair. Nos. 735/6	85	1·00
736	8 c. multicoloured (22.2.74)	40	10
737	8 c. myrtle-green, grey-brown and black (4.4.75)	40	10
	a. Pair. Nos. 737/8	85	1·00
738	8 c. multicoloured (4.4.75)	40	10
739	10 c. olive-bistre, reddish orange and black (17.9.76)	40	20
	a. Pair. Nos. 739/40	85	1·00
740	10 c. multicoloured (17.9.76)	40	20
721/40	.. .. *Set of* 20	7·50	2·10

Designs show the following tribes: Nos. 731/2 (T **348**/*a*), Plains Indians; 733/4, Algonkians; 735/6, Pacific Coast Indians; 737/8, Subarctic Indians; 739/40, Iroquoians.

Nos. 721/2 and 731/2 exist with or without fluorescent bands and the remainder only with fluorescent bands.

MINIMUM PRICE

The minimum price quote is 10p which represents a handling charge rather than a basis for valuing common stamps. For further notes about prices see introductory pages.

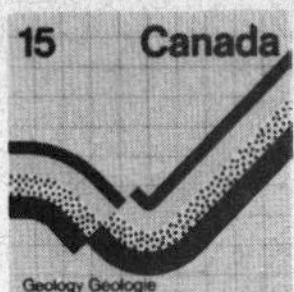

349 Earth's Crust **350** Candles

(Des Gottschalk and Ash Ltd. Litho Ashton-Potter)

1972 (2 Aug). *Earth Sciences. T* **349** *and similar square designs. P* 12.

741	15 c. multicoloured	1·00	1·40
	a. Block of 4. Nos. 741/4	3·50	
742	15 c. pale grey, dull ultramarine and black ..	1·00	1·40
743	15 c. multicoloured	1·00	1·40
744	15 c. light emerald, red-orange and black ..	1·00	1·40
741/4	.. .. *Set of* 4	3·50	5·00

Designs and Events:—No. 741, Photogrammetric surveying (12th Congress of International Society of Photogrammetry); No. 742, "Siegfried" lines (6th Conference of International Cartographic Association); No. 743, Type **349** (24th International Geological Congress); No. 744, Diagram of village at road-intersection (22nd International Geographical Congress).

Nos. 741/4 were issued in sheets of 64, made up of 4 panes of 16, each pane having a marginal commemorative inscription. Within a pane are 4 copies of each design, arranged in *se-tenant* blocks of 4.

This issue exists with or without fluorescent bands.

(Des R. Webber. Litho Ashton-Potter)

1972 (1 Nov). *Christmas. T* **350** *and similar designs. P* 12½ × 12 (*6 and 8 c.*) *or* 11 × 10½ (*others*).

745	**350** 6 c. multicoloured	15	10
	p. One centre phosphor band	25	20
746	8 c. multicoloured	20	10
	p. Two phosphor bands	30	35
747	– 10 c. multicoloured	40	25
	p. Two phosphor bands	70	1·00
748	– 15 c. multicoloured	50	40
	p. Two phosphor bands	80	1·40
745/8	.. .. *Set of* 4	1·10	65
745p/8p	.. .. *Set of* 4	1·90	2·75

Designs: *Horiz* (36 × 20 *mm*)—10 c. Candles with fruits and pine boughs; 15 c. Candles with prayer-book, caskets and vase.

This issue also exists with fluorescent bands.

351 "The Blacksmith's Shop" (Krieghoff) **352** François de Montmorency-Laval

(Des and litho B.A.B.N. and Saults & Pollard Ltd., Winnipeg)

1972 (29 Nov). *Death Centenary of Cornelius Krieghoff* (*painter*). *P* 12½.

749	**351** 8 c. multicoloured	20	10

This stamp exists with or without fluorescent bands.

FLUORESCENT BANDS. Stamps from No. 750 onwards were issued only with two fluorescent bands, *unless otherwise stated*. Examples are known with the bands omitted in error, but such varieties are outside the scope of the catalogue.

(Des M. Fog and G. Lorange. Litho Ashton-Potter)

1973 (31 Jan). *350th Birth Anniv of Monsignor de Laval* (*First Bishop of Quebec*). *P* 11.

750	**352** 8 c. ultramarine, gold and silver ..	15	15

353 Commissioner French and Route of the March West

(Des Dallaire Morin DeVito Inc. Litho Ashton-Potter)

1973 (9 Mar). *Centenary of Royal Canadian Mounted Police. T* **353** *and similar horiz designs. Multicoloured* (*except* 8 c.). *P* 11.

751	8 c. Type **353** (deep reddish brown, dull orange and orange-vermilion)	25	10
752	10 c. Spectrograph	80	1·25
753	15 c. Mounted policeman	1·10	1·40
751/3	.. .. *Set of* 3	2·00	2·50

354 Jeanne Mance

(Des R. Bellemare. Litho Ashton-Potter)

1973 (18 Apr). *300th Death Anniv of Jeanne Mance* (*nurse*). *P* 11.

754	**354** 8 c. multicoloured	15	15

355 Joseph Howe

356 "Mist Fantasy" (MacDonald)

(Des A. Fleming. Litho Ashton-Potter)

1973 (16 May). *Death Centenary of Joseph Howe (Nova Scotian politician). P* 11.
755 **355** 8 c. gold and black 15 15

(Des and litho Ashton-Potter)

1973 (8 June). *Birth Centenary of J. E. H. MacDonald (artist). P* 12½.
756 **356** 15 c. multicoloured 30 55

357 Oaks and Harbour

(Des A. Mann. Recess and photo B.A.B.N.)

1973 (22 June). *Centenary of Prince Edward Island's Entry into the Confederation. P* 12.
757 **357** 8 c. pale orange and brown-red . . 15 20

358 Scottish Settlers

359 Queen Elizabeth II

(Des P. Swan. Litho Ashton-Potter)

1973 (20 July). *Bicentennial of Arrival of Scottish Settlers at Pictou, Nova Scotia. P* 12 × 12½.
758 **358** 8 c. multicoloured 20 15

(Des A. Fleming from photograph by Anthony Buckley. Eng G. A. Gundersen. Recess and photo B.A.B.N.)

1973 (2 Aug). *Royal Visit and Commonwealth Heads of Government Meeting, Ottawa. P* 12 × 12½.
759 **359** 8 c. multicoloured 25 15
760 15 c. red, black and bright gold . . 1·00 1·50
a. Red, black and pale dull gold . . 1·10 1·50

360 Nellie McClung

361 Emblem of 1976 Olympics

(Des S. Mennie. Litho Ashton-Potter)

1973 (29 Aug). *Birth Centenary of Nellie McClung (feminist). P* 10½ × 11.
761 **360** 8 c. multicoloured 15 15

(Des Wallis and Matanovic. Litho Ashton-Potter)

1973 (20 Sept). *Olympic Games, Montreal (1976) (1st issue). P* 12 × 12½.
762 **361** 8 c. multicoloured 15 10
763 15 c. multicoloured 30 70
See also Nos. 768/71, 772/4, 786/9, 798/802, 809/11, 814/16, 829/31, 833/7 and 842/4.

362 Ice-skate

363 Diving

(Des A. Maggs. Litho Ashton-Potter)

1973 (7 Nov). *Christmas. T* **362** *and similar vert designs. Multicoloured. P* 12½ × 12 (6, 8 *c.) or* 11 (*others*).
764 6 c. Type **362** 10 10
765 8 c. Bird decoration 15 10
766 10 c. Santa Claus (20 × 36 *mm*) 60 90
767 15 c. Shepherd (20 × 36 *mm*) . . . . . . 70 1·00
764/7 . . . . *Set of* 4 1·40 1·90

(Des Hunter, Straker, Templeton Ltd. Recess C.B.N.)

1974 (22 Mar). *Olympic Games, Montreal (1976) (2nd issue). "Summer Activities". T* **363** *and similar vert designs. Each deep blue. P* 12.
768 8 c. Type **363** 15 10
a. Block of 4. Nos. 768/71 55
769 8 c. "Jogging" 15 10
770 8 c. Cycling 15 10
771 8 c. Hiking 15 10
768/71 . . . . *Set of* 4 55 35
Nos. 768/71 were printed in *se-tenant* blocks of four throughout the sheet. Each design has a second (latent) image—the Canadian Olympic Games symbol—which appears when the stamp is viewed obliquely to the light.
See also Nos. 786/9.

(Des Wallis and Matanovic. Litho Ashton-Potter)

1974 (17 Apr). *Olympic Games, Montreal (1976) (3rd issue). As T* **361** *but smaller* (20 × 36½ *mm*). *P* 12½.
772 **361** 8 c. + 2 c. multicoloured 15 25
773 10 c. + 5 c. multicoloured 25 60
774 15 c. + 5 c. multicoloured 30 80
772/4 . . . . *Set of* 3 65 1·50

364 Winnipeg Signpost, 1872

365 Postmaster and Customer

(Des J. R. MacDonald. Litho and embossed Ashton-Potter)

1974 (3 May). *Winnipeg Centennial. P* 12½ × 12.
775 **364** 8 c. multicoloured 15 10

(Des S. Mennie. Litho Ashton-Potter)

1974 (11 June). *Centenary of Canadian Letter Carrier Delivery Service. T* **365** *and similar horiz designs. Multicoloured. P* 13½.
776 8 c. Type **365** 40 25
a. Block of 6. Nos. 776/81 . . . . . . 2·25
777 8 c. Postman collecting mail 40 25
778 8 c. Mail handler 40 25
779 8 c. Mail sorters 40 25
780 8 c. Postman making delivery 40 25
781 8 c. Rural delivery by car 40 25
776/81 . . . . *Set of* 6 2·25 1·40
Nos. 776/81 were printed in *se-tenant* combinations throughout a sheet of 50, giving 6 blocks of 6 and 14 single stamps.

366 "Canada's Contribution to Agriculture"

367 Telephone Development

(Des M. Brett, P. Cowley-Brown, and A. McAllister. Litho Ashton-Potter)

1974 (12 July). *"Agricultural Education". Centenary of Ontario Agricultural College. P* 12½ × 12.
782 **366** 8 c. multicoloured 15 10

(Des R. Webber. Litho Ashton-Potter)

1974 (26 July). *Centenary of Invention of Telephone by Alexander Graham Bell. P* 12½.
783 **367** 8 c. multicoloured 15 10

COVER PRICES

Cover factors are quoted at the beginning of each country for most issues to 1945. An explanation of the system can be found on page x. The factors quoted do not, however, apply to philatelic covers.

368 Bicycle Wheel

(Des Burns and Cooper. Recess and photo B.A.B.N.)

1974 (7 Aug). *World Cycling Championships, Montreal. P* 12 × 12½.
784 **368** 8 c. black, rosine and silver 15 10

369 Mennonite Settlers

(Des W. Davies. Litho Ashton-Potter)

1974 (28 Aug). *Centenary of Arrival of Mennonites in Manitoba. P* 12½.
785 **369** 8 c. multicoloured 15 10

(Des Hunter, Straker, Templeton Ltd. Recess C.B.N.)

1974 (23 Sept). *Olympic Games, Montreal (1976) (4th issue). "Winter Activities". Horiz designs as T* **363**, *each rosine. P* 13½ × 13.
786 8 c. Snow-shoeing 30 15
a. Block of 4. Nos. 786/9 . . . . . . 1·10
787 8 c. Skiing 30 15
788 8 c. Skating 30 15
789 8 c. Curling 30 15
786/9 . . . . *Set of* 4 1·10 55

370 Mercury, Winged Horses and U.P.U. Emblem

(Des G. Gundersen. Recess and photo B.A.B.N.)

1974 (9 Oct). *Centenary of Universal Postal Union. P* 12 × 12½.
790 **370** 8 c. violet, red-orange and cobalt . . 15 10
791 15 c. red-orange, violet and cobalt . . 50 1·00

371 "The Nativity" (J. P. Lemieux)

372 Marconi and St. John's Harbour, Newfoundland

(Des Wallis and Matanovic. Litho Ashton-Potter)

1974 (1 Nov). *Christmas. T* **371** *and similar horiz designs showing paintings. Multicoloured. P* 13½.
792 6 c. Type **371** 10 10
793 8 c. "Skaters in Hull" (H. Masson) (34 × 31 *mm*) 10 10
794 10 c. "The Ice Cone, Montmorency Falls" (R. C. Todd) 20 45
795 15 c. "Village in the Laurentian Mountains" (C. A. Gagnon) 30 70
792/5 . . . . *Set of* 4 60 1·10

(Des J. Boyle. Litho Ashton-Potter)

1974 (15 Nov). *Birth Centenary of Guglielmo Marconi (radio pioneer). P* 13.
796 **372** 8 c. multicoloured 15 10

373 Merritt and Welland Canal

374 Swimming

(Des W. Rueter. Recess (B.A.B.N.) and litho (C.B.N.))

1974 (29 Nov). *William Merritt Commemoration. P* 13 × 13½.
797 **373** 8 c. multicoloured 15 15

(Des Wallis and Matanovic. Litho C.B.N.)

1975 (5 Feb). *Olympic Games, Montreal (1976) (5th issue). T* **374** *and similar horiz designs. Multicoloured.*
798 8 c. + 2 c. Type **374** 20 20
799 10 c. + 5 c. Rowing 25 65
800 15 c. + 5 c. Sailing 35 80
798/800 . . . . *Set of* 3 70 1·50

375 "The Sprinter"

376 "Anne of Green Gables" (Lucy Maud Montgomery)

(Des A. R. Fleming. Litho and embossed Ashton-Potter)

1975 (14 Mar). *Olympic Games, Montreal* (1976) (6*th issue*). *T* **375** *and similar multicoloured design showing sculpture by R. T. McKenzie. P* 12½ × 12 ($1) *or* 12 × 12½ ($2).

801 $1 Type **375** .. .. 2·00 2·75
802 $2 "The Diver" (*vert*) .. .. 2·75 4·50

(Des P. Swan (No. 803), C. Gagnon (No. 804). Litho Ashton-Potter)

1975 (15 May). *Canadian Writers* (1*st series*). *T* **376** *and similar vert design. Multicoloured. P* 13½.

803 8 c. Type **376** 20 10
a. Pair. Nos. 803/4 .. .. 40 70
804 8 c. "Maria Chapdelaine" (Louis Hémon) .. 20 10

Nos. 803/4 were printed horizontally and vertically *se-tenant* throughout the sheet.

See also Nos. 846/7, 940/1 and 1085/6.

377 Marguerite Bourgeoys (founder of the Order of Notre Dame)

378 S. D. Chown (founder of United Church of Canada)

(Des Design and Communication, Montreal. Litho Ashton-Potter (Nos. 805/6). Des W. Southern. Eng G. Gundersen. Recess and photo B.A.B.N. (Nos. 807/8))

1975 (30 May). *Canadian Celebrities. T* **377/8** *and similar vert designs.*

(*a*) *As T* **377.** *P* 12½ × 12

805 8 c. multicoloured 25 15
806 8 c. multicoloured 25 15

(*b*) *As T* **378.** *P* 12 × 12½

807 8 c. sepia, flesh and light yellow 25 10
a. Pair. Nos. 807/8 .. .. 45 70
808 8 c. sepia, flesh and light yellow 25 10
805/8 .. .. *Set of* 4 90 35

Designs:—No. 805, Type **377**; No. 806, Alphonse Desjardins (leader of Credit Union movement); No. 807, Type **378**; No. 808, Dr. J. Cook (first moderator of Presbyterian Church in Canada).

Nos. 807/8 were printed together in the sheet horizontally and vertically *se-tenant*.

379 Pole-vaulting

380 "Untamed" (photo by Walt Petrigo)

(Des P. Swan. Litho Ashton-Potter)

1975 (11 June). *Olympic Games, Montreal* (1976) (7*th issue*). *T* **379** *and similar vert designs. Multicoloured. P* 12 × 12½.

809 20 c. Type **379** 25 35
810 25 c. Marathon-running 40 65
811 50 c. Hurdling 50 90
809/11 .. .. *Set of* 3 1·00 1·75

(Des B. Reilander. Litho C.B.N.)

1975 (3 July). *Centenary of Calgary. P* 12 × 12½.

812 **380** 8 c. multicoloured 15 15

381 I.W.Y. Symbol

382 Fencing

(Des Susan McPhee. Recess and photo B.A.B.N.)

1975 (14 July). *International Women's Year. P* 13.

813 **381** 8 c. lt grey-brown, bistre-yellow & blk 10 10

(Des J. Hill. Litho C.B.N.)

1975 (6 Aug). *Olympic Games, Montreal* (1976) (8*th issue*). *T* **382** *and similar vert designs showing combat sports. Multicoloured. P* 13.

814 8 c. + 2 c. Type **382** 25 20
815 10 c. + 5 c. Boxing 30 80
816 15 c. + 5 c. Judo 35 85
814/16 .. .. *Set of* 3 80 1·75

383 "Justice-Justitia" (statue by W. S. Allward)

384 *William D. Lawrence*

(Des A. Fleming. Litho Ashton-Potter)

1975 (2 Sept). *Centenary of Canadian Supreme Court. P* 12½.

817 **383** 8 c. multicoloured 10 15

(Des T. Bjarnason. Recess and photo B.A.B.N.)

1975 (24 Sept). *Canadian Ships* (1*st series*). *T* **384** *and similar horiz designs showing coastal ships. P* 13.

818 8 c. yellow-brown and black 60 20
a. Block of 4. Nos. 818/21 .. .. .. 2·25
819 8 c. blue-green and black 60 20
820 8 c. yellow-green and black 60 20
821 8 c. yellow-brown and black 60 20
818/21 .. .. *Set of* 4 2·25 70

Designs:—No. 819, *Neptune*; No. 820, *Beaver*; No. 821, *Quadra.*

Nos. 818/21 were printed together, *se-tenant*, in different combinations throughout the sheet, giving ten blocks of 4 and ten single stamps.

See also Nos. 851/4, 902/5 and 931/4.

385 "Santa Claus" (G. Kelly)

386 Text, Badge and Bugle

(Des B. Reilander from children's paintings. Litho Ashton-Potter)

1975 (22 Oct). *Christmas. T* **385** *and similar multicoloured designs. P* 13.

822 6 c. Type **385** 10 10
a. Pair. Nos. 822/3 .. .. 20 30
823 6 c. "Skater" (Bill Cawsey) 10 10
824 8 c. "Child" (D. Hébert) 10 10
a. Pair. Nos. 824/5 .. .. 25 35
825 8 c. "Family" (L. Caldwell) 10 10
826 10 c. "Gift" (D. Lovely) 20 40
827 15 c. "Trees" (R. Kowalski) (*horiz*) 30 65
822/7 .. .. *Set of* 6 85 1·50

Nos. 822/3 and 824/5 were respectively issued together *se-tenant* in an alternate arrangement within the sheet.

(Des R. Kavach. Recess and photo B.A.B.N.)

1975 (10 Nov). 50*th Anniv of Royal Canadian Legion. P* 12½ × 13.

828 **386** 8 c. multicoloured 10 10

387 Basketball

(Des J. Hill. Litho Ashton-Potter)

1976 (7 Jan). *Olympic Games, Montreal* (9*th issue*). *T* **387** *and similar vert designs. Multicoloured. P* 13.

829 8 c. + 2 c. Type **387** 25 15
830 10 c. + 5 c. Gymnastics 30 70
831 20 c. + 5 c. Soccer 40 90
829/31 .. .. *Set of* 3 85 1·60

NEW INFORMATION

The editor is always interested to correspond with people who have new information that will improve or correct the Catalogue.

388 Games Symbol and Snow Crystal

389 "Communications Arts"

(Des R. Harder. Litho Ashton-Potter)

1976 (6 Feb). 12*th Winter Olympic Games. Innsbruck. P* 12½.

832 **388** 20 c. multicoloured 20 35

(Des R. Webber. Litho C.B.N.)

1976 (6 Feb). *Olympic Games, Montreal* (10*th issue*). *T* **389** *and similar vert designs. Multicoloured. P* 12 × 12½.

833 20 c. Type **389** 20 15
834 25 c. "Handicrafts" 30 55
835 50 c. "Performing Arts" 40 85
833/5 .. .. *Set of* 3 80 1·40

390 Place Ville Marie and Notre-Dame Church

(Des J. and P. Mercier. Recess and photo B.A.B.N.)

1976 (12 Mar). *Olympic Games, Montreal* (11*th issue*). *T* **390** *and similar horiz design. Multicoloured. P* 13.

836 $1 Type **390** .. .. 2·50 4·50
837 $2 Olympic Stadium and flags .. .. .. 3·00 5·50

391 Flower and Urban Sprawl

392 Benjamin Franklin and Map

(Des I. McLeod. Litho Ashton-Potter)

1976 (12 May). *U.N. Conference on Human Settlements* (*HABITAT*), *Vancouver. P* 12 × 12½.

838 **391** 20 c. multicoloured 15 25

(Des B. Reilander. Recess and photo B.A.B.N.)

1976 (1 June). *Bicentenary of American Revolution. P* 13.

839 **392** 10 c. multicoloured 15 20

393 Wing Parade before Mackenzie Building

394 Transfer of Olympic Flame by Satellite

(Des W. Davies. Litho C.B.N.)

1976 (1 June). *Royal Military College Centenary. T* **393** *and similar vert design. Multicoloured. P* 12 × 12½.

840 8 c. Colour party and Memorial Arch 15 10
a. Pair. Nos. 840/1 .. .. 30 60
ab. Printed double (pair) .. ..
841 8 c. Type **393** 15 10

Nos. 840/1 were printed horizontally and vertically *se-tenant* throughout the sheet.

(Des P. Swan. Litho Ashton-Potter)

1976 (18 June). *Olympic Games, Montreal* (12*th issue*). *T* **394** *and similar horiz designs. Multicoloured. P* 13½.

842 8 c. Type **394** 10 10
843 20 c. Carrying the Olympic flag 15 30
844 25 c. Athletes with medals 25 50
842/4 .. .. *Set of* 3 45 80

395 Archer

(Des T. Bjarnason. Litho C.B.N.)

1976 (3 Aug). *Olympiad for the Physically Disabled. P* 12 × 12½.
845 **395** 20 c. multicoloured 15 25

396 "Sam McGee" (Robert W. Service) **397** "Nativity" (F. Mayer)

(Des D. Bierk (No. 846), A. Dumas (No. 847). Litho Ashton-Potter)

1976 (17 Aug). *Canadian Writers (2nd series). T* **396** *and similar vert design. Multicoloured. P* 13.
846 8 c. Type **396** 15 10
a. Pair. Nos. 846/7 .. .. 30 55
847 8 c. "Le Survenant" (Germaine Guèvremont) 15 10
Nos. 846/7 were printed horizontally and vertically *se-tenant* throughout the sheet.

(Des B. Reilander. Litho Ashton-Potter)

1976 (3 Nov). *Christmas. T* **397** *and similar vert designs showing stained-glass windows. Multicoloured. P* 13½.
848 8 c. Type **397** 10 10
849 10 c. "Nativity" (G. Maile & Son) 10 10
850 20 c. "Nativity" (Yvonne Williams) 20 50
848/50 .. .. *Set of* 3 30 50

398 *Northcote* **399** Queen Elizabeth II

(Des T. Bjarnason. Recess and litho C.B.N.)

1976 (19 Nov). *Canadian Ships (2nd series). T* **398** *and similar horiz designs showing inland vessels. P* 12 × 12½.
851 10 c. ochre, chestnut and black 25 20
a. Block of 4. Nos. 851/4 90
852 10 c. violet-blue and black 25 20
853 10 c. bright blue and black 25 20
854 10 c. apple-green, olive-green and black .. 25 20
851/4 .. .. *Set of* 4 90 55
Designs:—No. 851, Type **398**; No. 852, *Passport*; No. 853, *Chicora*; No. 854, *Athabasca*.
Nos. 851/4 were printed together, *se-tenant*, in different combinations throughout the sheet, giving ten blocks of 4 and ten single stamps.

(Des K. Rodmell from photograph by P. Grugeon. Litho ("25" die-stamped) Ashton-Potter)

1977 (4 Feb). *Silver Jubilee. P* 12½ × 12.
855 **399** 25 c. multicoloured 25 50

400 Bottle Gentian **401** Queen Elizabeth II (bas-relief by J. Huta) **402** Houses of Parliament

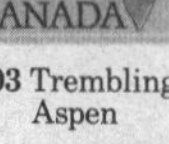

403 Trembling Aspen **404** Prairie Town Main Street

405 Fundy National Park

(Des R. Derreth (Nos. 870/4). T. Bjarnason (880/3*a*), R. Bolt (884), B. Laycock and W. Tibbles (884*b*), B. Laycock (884*c*), A. Collier (885), W. Tibbles and G. Weber (No. 885*a*), W. Terry and W. Tibbles (885*b*), L. Marois and W. Tibbles (885*c*), Heather Cooper (others). Eng Y. Baril (880/3*a*))

1977 (1 Mar)–**86**. (*a*) *Vert designs as T* **400** *showing flowers. Multicoloured.* (i) *Recess and litho C.B.N. Sheet stamps. P* 12 × 12½.
856 1 c. Type **400** (22.4.77) 10 10
857 2 c. Red Columbine (22.4.77) 10 10
858 3 c. Canada Lily (22.4.77) 10 10
859 4 c. Hepatica (22.4.77) 10 10
860 5 c. Shooting Star (22.4.77) 10 10
861 10 c. Franklin's Lady's Slipper Orchid (22.4.77) 15 10
a. Perf 13 × 13½ (8.78) 25 10

(ii) *Recess and photo B.A.B.N. Booklet stamps* (1, 2 c.) *or sheet stamps (others). P* 12 × 12½ (1, 2 c.) *or* 13 × 13½ *(others)*
862 1 c. Type **400** (10.77) .. .. .. 35 1·25
a. Booklet pane. Nos. 862 × 2 and 867a × 4 2·00
b. Perf 13 × 13½ (from sheets (16.8.79) .. 10 10
863 2 c. Red Columbine (17.5.78) 30 50
a. Booklet pane. Nos. 863 × 4 and 868a × 3 plus one printed label .. .. .. 2·25
b. Perf 13 × 13½ (from sheets) (2.8.79) .. 10 10
864 3 c. Canada Lily (11.4.79) 10 10
864*a* 4 c. Hepatica (3.7.79) 10 10
865 5 c. Shooting Star (23.1.79) 10 10
865*a* 10 c. Franklin's Lady's Slipper Orchid (4.10.79) 20 10
866 12 c. Jewelweed (6.7.78) 15 15
866*a* 15 c. Canada Violet (16.8.79) 15 10

(*b*) *T* **401**. *Recess and photo B.A.B.N. P* 13 × 13½
867 12 c. black, grey and cobalt (1.3.77) .. 15 10
a. Perf 12×12½ (from booklets) (10.77) 40 50
868 14 c. black, grey and rose-red (7.3.78) .. 20 10
a. Perf 12×12½ (from booklets) (17.5.78) 45 50
ab. Booklet pane. No. 868a×25, plus two printed labels (13.11.78) .. .. 8·00
869 17 c. black, grey & yellowish green (8.3.79) 25 10
a. Perf 12×12½ (from booklets) (28.3.79) 25 10
ab. Booklet pane. No. 869a×25, plus two printed labels (3.7.79) .. .. 5·50
869*b* 30 c. maroon, grey & reddish pur (11.5.82) 50 30
ba. Maroon, grey and bright mauve (9.83) 60 40
869*c* 32 c. black, grey and light blue (24.5.83) .. 45 35

(*c*) *T* **402**. (i) *Recess C.B.N. (Nos. 872a, 873/4) or B.A.B.N. (others). Booklet stamps (Nos. 870/1) or sheet stamps (others). P* 12×12½ *(1, 5 c.) or* 13×13½ *(others)*
870 1 c. indigo (28.3.79) .. .. .. 90 1·75
a. Booklet pane. Nos. 869a × 2, 870 and 871 × 3 .. .. 2·00
871 5 c. deep rose-lilac (28.3.79) 25 10
872 12 c. blue (chalk-surfaced paper) (3.5.77) .. 20 10
a. New blue (ordinary paper) (4.78) .. 25 10
873 14 c. scarlet (7.3.78) 15 10
874 17 c. deep green (8.3.79) 20 10

(ii) *Recess C.B.N. Coil stamps. Imperf × perf* 10
874*b* 12 c. new blue (3.5.77) 20 25
ba. Imperf (horiz pair) .. .. .. 90·00
874*c* 14 c. scarlet (7.3.78) 30 30
ca. Imperf (horiz pair) .. .. .. 90·00
874*d* 17 c. deep green (8.3.79) 30 15
da. Imperf (horiz pair) £100

(*d*) *Vert designs as T* **403** *showing leaves. Multicoloured. Recess and photo B.A.B.N. P* 13½
875 15 c. Type **403** (8.8.77) 15 10
876 20 c. Douglas Fir (8.8.77) 15 10
877 25 c. Sugar Maple (8.8.77) 15 10
878 30 c. Red Oak (7.3.78) 20 10
879 35 c. White Pine (8.3.79) 25 10

(*e*) *Horiz designs at T* **404** *showing city streets. Multicoloured. P* 13½

(i) *Recess and photo B.A.B.N. No fluorescent bands* (75, 80 c.) (6.7.78)
880 50 c. Type **404** .. .. 1·25 70
881 75 c. Eastern city street 85 55
882 80 c. Maritimes street 85 45

(ii) *Recess and litho C.B.N.*
883 50 c. Type **404** (13.12.78) 85 25
883*a* 60 c. Ontario city street (11.5.82) 65 45

(*f*) *Horiz designs as T* **405** *showing national parks. Multicoloured. Recess and litho C.B.N. or B.A.B.N. (ptgs of Nos. 884b, 885a and 885c from 26 Sept 1986). No. 884 with or without fluorescent bands, others only exist without. P* 13½.
884 $1 Type **405** (24.1.79) 90 50
ab. Black (inscr and value) ptd albino ..
884*b* $1 Glacier (15.8.84) 85 45
884*c* $1.50, Waterton Lakes (18.6.82) .. .. 2·50 1·75
885 $2 Kluane (27.4.79) .. .. .. 1·50 45
885*a* $2 Banff (21.6.85) .. .. .. 2·00 90
885*b* $5 Point Pelee (10.1.83) .. .. .. 5·50 2·00
885*c* $5 La Mauricie (14.3.86) .. .. .. 4·75 2·50

The main differences between No. 861a and No. 865*a* are in the background. On No. 865*a* this is toned and has the blurred edges typical of photogravure. No. 861a has a background of solid appearance with the edges clean. The B.A.B.N. version also has stronger lines on the recess part of the design.

No. 883 can be identified from 880 in that the brown printing from the recess plate of the former is deeper and the detail more defined; the registration plate of the car in the foreground can clearly be seen under a glass as "1978". The "hidden date" (1977) occurs alongside the grain elevator door on No. 880. Also the colours from the lithographic plates of No. 883 are much bolder than those from the photogravure cylinders of 880. In addition the paper of No. 883 has a shiny appearance.

No. 884ab shows an uninked impression of the recess-printed part of the design.

Stamps with one or two adjacent sides imperforate come from booklets.

ALTERED CATALOGUE NUMBERS

Any Catalogue numbers altered from the last edition are shown as a list in the introductory pages.

406 Puma **407** "April in Algonquin Park"

(Des R. Bateman. Litho Ashton-Potter)

1977 (30 Mar). *Endangered Wildlife* (*1st series*). *P* 12½.
886 **406** 12 c. multicoloured 15 15
See also Nos. 906, 936/7, 976/7 and 1006/7.

(Litho Ashton-Potter)

1977 (26 May). *Birth Centenary of Tom Thomson (painter). T* **407** *and similar square design. Multicoloured. P* 12.
887 12 c. Type **407** 15 10
a. Pair. Nos. 887/8 .. .. .. 30 60
888 12 c. "Autumn Birches" 15 10
Nos. 887/8 were printed horizontally and vertically *se-tenant* throughout the sheet.

408 Crown and Lion **409** Peace Bridge, Niagara River

(Des A. Hobbs. Litho (No. 890 also embossed) Ashton-Potter)

1977 (30 June). *Anniversaries. T* **408** *and similar horiz design. Multicoloured. P* 12½.
889 12 c. Type **408** 15 15
890 12 c. Order of Canada 15 15
Events:—No. 889, 25th Anniv of first Canadian-born Governor-General; No. 890, Tenth Anniv of Order of Canada.

(Des R. Harder. Litho Ashton-Potter)

1977 (4 Aug). *50th Anniv of Opening of Peace Bridge. P* 12½.
891 **409** 12 c. multicoloured 15 15

410 Sir Sandford Fleming (engineer)

(Des W. Davies. Recess B.A.B.N.)

1977 (16 Sept). *Famous Canadians. T* **410** *and similar horiz design. P* 13.
892 12 c. grey-blue 15 10
a. Pair. Nos. 892/3 .. .. .. 30 55
893 12 c. reddish brown 15 10
Design:—No. 892, Joseph E. Bernier (explorer) and C. G. S. *Arctic*.
The above were printed together, horizontally and vertically *se-tenant* throughout the sheet.

411 Peace Tower, Parliament Buildings, Ottawa **412** Hunter Braves following Star

(Des S. Ash. Litho Ashton-Potter)

1977 (19 Sept). *23rd Commonwealth Parliamentary Conference. P* 12½.
894 **411** 25 c. multicoloured 20 25

(Des R. G. White. Litho C.B.N.)

1977 (26 Oct). *Christmas. T* **412** *and similar horiz designs depicting Canada's first Christmas carol "Jesous Ahatonhia". Multicoloured. P* 13½ × 13.
895 10 c. Type **412** 10 10
896 12 c. Angelic choir and the Northern Lights .. 10 10
a. Imperf (vert pair) £500
897 25 c. Christ Child and chiefs 20 45
895/7 .. .. *Set of* 3 35 45

413 Seal Hunter (soapstone sculpture) **414** Pinky (fishing boat)

(Des R. Derreth. Litho Ashton-Potter)

1977 (18 Nov). *Canadian Eskimos ("Inuits") (1st series). Hunting. T* **413** *and similar horiz designs. Multicoloured. P* 12 × 12½.

898 12 c. Type **413** 15 10
a. Pair. Nos. 898/9 .. .. 30 45
899 12 c. Fishing with spear 15 10
900 12 c. Disguised archer 15 10
a. Pair. Nos. 900/1 .. .. 30 45
901 12 c. Walrus hunting 15 10
898/901 .. .. *Set of* 4 60 25

Nos. 898/9 and 900/1 were each printed together, *se-tenant*, in horizontal and vertical pairs throughout the sheet.

See also Nos. 924/7, 958/61 and 989/92.

(Des T. Bjarnason. Recess and litho C.B.N.)

1977 (18 Nov). *Canadian Ships (3rd series). T* **414** *and similar horiz designs, showing sailing craft. Multicoloured. P* 12 × 12½.

902 12 c. Type **414** 12 10
a. Block of 4. Nos. 902/5 45
903 12 c. Five-masted schooner 12 10
904 12 c. Tern schooner 12 10
905 12 c. Mackinaw boat 12 10
902/5 .. .. *Set of* 4 45 35

Nos. 902/5 were printed together, *se-tenant*, in different combinations throughout the sheet, giving ten blocks of 4 and ten single stamps.

415 Peregrine Falcon

416 Pair of 1851 12d. Black Stamps

(Des R. Bateman. Litho Ashton-Potter)

1978 (18 Jan). *Endangered Wildlife (2nd series). P* 12½.

906 **415** 12 c. multicoloured 20 15

(Des C. Brett. Recess and photo B.A.B.N.)

1978 (18 Jan). *"CAPEX 78" International Stamp Exhibition, Toronto (1st issue). P* 13.

907 **416** 12 c. black and brownish grey 10 10

See also Nos. 914/17.

417 Games Emblem

418 "Captain Cook" (Nathaniel Dance)

(Des S. Ash. Litho Ashton-Potter)

1978 (31 Mar). *Commonwealth Games. Edmonton (1st issue). T* **417** *and similar horiz design. Multicoloured. P* 12½.

908 14 c. Type **417** 10 10
909 30 c. Badminton 20 40

A used example of No. 909 has been seen on which the red colour and the fluorescent bands were omitted.

See also No. 918/21.

(Des W. Rueter. Litho Ashton-Potter)

1978 (26 Apr). *Bicentenary of Cook's Third Voyage. T* **418** *and similar vert design. Multicoloured. P* 13½.

910 14 c. Type **418** 20 10
a. Pair. Nos. 910/11 .. .. .. 40 65
911 14 c. "Nootka Sound" (J. Webber) .. 20 10

Nos. 910/11 were printed together, *se-tenant*, in horizontal and vertical pairs throughout the sheet.

419 Hardrock Silver Mine, Cobalt, Ontario

420 Prince's Gate (Exhibition entrance)

(Des W. Davies. Litho Ashton-Potter)

1978 (19 May). *Resource Development. T* **419** *and similar horiz design. Multicoloured. P* 12½.

912 14 c. Type **419** 15 10
a. Pair. Nos. 912/13 .. .. .. 30 60
913 14 c. Giant excavators, Athabasca Tar Sands 15 10

Nos. 912/13 were printed together, *se-tenant*, in horizontal and vertical pairs throughout the sheet.

(Des C. Brett. Eng R. Couture. Recess and photo B.A.B.N.)

1978 (10 June). *"CAPEX 78" International Stamp Exhibition, Toronto (2nd issue). Horiz designs as T* **416**. *Two fluorescent bands (none on $1.25 from miniature sheet). P* 13.

914 14 c. Prussian blue, pale grey and brownish grey 15 10
915 30 c. deep rose, pale grey and brownish grey 20 35
916 $1.25, slate-violet, pale grey & brnish grey 80 1·10
914/16 .. .. *Set of* 3 1·00 1·40
MS917 101 × 76 mm. Nos. 914/16 .. .. 1·50 2·25

Designs:—14 c. Pair of 1855 10d. Cartier stamps; 30 c. Pair of 1857 ½d. deep rose stamps; $1.25, Pair of 1851 6d. Prince Albert stamps.

(Des S. Ash. Litho Ashton-Potter)

1978 (3 Aug). *Commonwealth Games, Edmonton (2nd issue). Horiz designs as T* **417**. *Multicoloured. P* 12½.

918 14 c. Games stadium 10 10
a. Pair. Nos. 918/19 .. .. .. 20 45
919 14 c. Running 10 10
920 30 c. Alberta Legislature building .. 25 20
a. Pair. Nos. 920/1 .. .. .. 50 1·10
921 30 c. Bowls 25 20
918/21 .. .. *Set of* 4 65 45

Nos. 918/19 and 920/1 were each printed together, *se-tenant*, in horizontal and vertical pairs throughout the sheet.

(Des T. Dimson, Litho Ashton-Potter)

1978 (16 Aug). *Centenary of National Exhibition. P* 12½.

922 **420** 14 c. multicoloured 15 20

421 Marguerite d'Youville

422 "Madonna of the Flowering Pea" (Cologne School)

(Des A. Dumas. Litho C.B.N.)

1978 (21 Sept). *Marguerite d'Youville (founder of Grey Nuns) Commemoration. P* 13.

923 **421** 14 c. multicoloured 15 15

(Des R. Derreth. Litho Ashton-Potter)

1978 (27 Sept). *Canadian Eskimos ("Inuits") (2nd series). Travel. Horiz designs as T* **413**. *Multicoloured. P* 13½.

924 14 c. Woman on foot (painting by Pitseolak) .. 15 10
a. Pair. Nos. 924/5 .. .. .. 30 45
925 14 c. "Migration" (soapstone sculpture of sailing umiak by Joe Talurinili) .. 15 10
926 14 c. Aeroplane (stonecut and stencil print by Pudlo) 15 10
a. Pair. Nos. 926/7 .. .. .. 30 45
927 14 c. Dogteam and dogsled (ivory sculpture by Abraham Kingmeatook) 15 10
924/7 .. .. *Set of* 4 60 25

Nos. 924/5 and 926/7 were each printed together, *se-tenant*, in horizontal and vertical pairs throughout the sheet.

(Des J. Morin. Litho Ashton-Potter)

1978 (20 Oct). *Christmas. Paintings. T* **422** *and similar vert designs. Multicoloured. P* 12½.

928 12 c. Type **422** 10 10
929 14 c. "The Virgin and Child with St. Anthony and Donor" (detail, Hans Memling) .. 10 10
930 30 c. "The Virgin and Child" (Jacopo di Cione) 25 50
928/30 .. .. *Set of* 3 35 55

423 *Chief Justice Robinson*

424 Carnival Revellers

(Des T. Bjarnason. Recess and litho C.B.N.)

1978 (15 Nov). *Canadian Ships (4th series). T* **423** *and similar horiz designs showing ice vessels. Multicoloured. P* 13.

931 14 c. Type **423** 20 20
a. Block of 4. Nos. 931/4 80
932 14 c. *St. Roch* 20 20
933 14 c. *Northern Light* 20 20
934 14 c. *Labrador* 20 20
931/4 .. .. *Set of* 4 80 70

Nos. 931/4 were printed together, *se-tenant*, in different combinations throughout the sheet, giving ten blocks of 4 and ten single stamps.

(Des A. Dumas. Litho Ashton-Potter)

1979 (1 Feb). *Quebec Carnival. P* 13.

935 **424** 14 c. multicoloured 15 15

425 Eastern Spiny Soft-shelled Turtle (*Trionyx spinifera*)

426 Knotted Ribbon round Woman's Finger

(Des G. Lowe (17 c.), R. Bateman (35 c.). Litho Ashton-Potter)

1979 (10 Apr). *Endangered Wildlife (3rd series). T* **425** *and similar horiz design. Multicoloured. P* 12½.

936 17 c. Type **425** 20 10
937 35 c. Bowhead Whale (*Balaena mysticetus*) .. 40 60

(Des D. Haws. Litho Ashton-Potter)

1979 (27 Apr). *Postal Code Publicity. T* **426** *and similar vert design. Multicoloured. P* 13.

938 17 c. Type **426** 15 10
a. Pair. Nos. 938/9 .. .. .. 30 50
939 17 c. Knotted string round man's finger .. 15 10

Nos. 938/9 were printed together, *se-tenant*, in horizontal and vertical pairs throughout the sheet.

427 Scene from "Fruits of the Earth" by Frederick Philip Grove

428 Charles-Michel de Salaberry (military hero)

(Des Rosemary Kilbourne (No. 940), Monique Charbonneau (941). Litho C.B.N.)

1979 (3 May). *Canadian Writers (3rd series). T* **427** *and similar horiz design. Multicoloured. P* 13.

940 17 c. Type **427** 15 10
a. Pair. Nos. 940/1 .. .. .. 30 60
941 17 c. Scene from "Le Vaisseau d'Or" by Émile Nelligan 15 10

Nos. 940/1 were printed together, *se-tenant*, in horizontal and vertical pairs throughout the sheet.

(Des T. Dimson. Litho and embossed Ashton-Potter)

1979 (11 May). *Famous Canadians. T* **428** *and similar vert design. Multicoloured. P* 13.

942 17 c. Type **428** 15 10
a. Pair. Nos. 942/3 .. .. .. 30 50
943 17 c. John By (engineer) 15 10

Nos. 942/3 were printed together, *se-tenant*, in horizontal and vertical pairs throughout the sheet.

429 Ontario

430 Paddling Kayak

(Des R. Bellemare. Litho Ashton-Potter)

1979 (15 June). *Canada Day. Flags. Sheet* 128 × 140 *mm containing T* **429** *and similar horiz designs. Multicoloured. P* 13.

MS944 17 c. × 12; Type **429**; Quebec; Nova Scotia; New Brunswick; Manitoba; British Columbia; Prince Edward Island; Saskatchewan; Alberta; Newfoundland; Northwest Territories; Yukon Territory .. .. 2·75 3·25

(Des J. Eby. Litho Ashton-Potter)

1979 (3 July). *Canoe-Kayak Championships. P* 12½.

956 **430** 17 c. multicoloured 15 15

431 Hockey Players

432 Toy Train

(Des J. Eby. Litho Ashton-Potter)

1979 (16 Aug). *Women's Field Hockey Championships, Vancouver. P* 12½.

957 **431** 17 c. black, yellow and emerald 15 15

(Des R. Derreth. Litho Ashton-Potter)

1979 (13 Sept). *Canadian Eskimos ("Inuits") (3rd series). "Shelter" (Nos. 958/9) and "Community" (Nos. 960/1). Horiz designs as T* **413**. *Multicoloured. P* 13.

958 17 c. "Summer Tent" (print by Kiakshuk) .. 15 10
a. Pair. Nos. 958/9 .. .. .. 30 55
959 17 c. "Five Eskimos building an Igloo" (soapstone sculpture by Abraham) 15 10
960 17 c. "The Dance" (print by Kalvak) 15 10
a. Pair. Nos. 960/1 .. .. .. 30 55
961 17 c. "Inuit drum dance" (soapstone sculptures by Madeleine Isserkut and Jean Mapsalak) 15 10
958/61 .. .. *Set of* 4 60 25

Nos. 958/9 and 960/1 were each printed together, *se-tenant*, in horizontal and vertical pairs throughout the sheet.

(Des A. Maggs. Litho C.B.N.)

1979 (17 Oct). *Christmas. T* **432** *and similar multicoloured designs showing toys. Fluorescent frame* (35 c.) *or two fluorescent bands* (*others*). *P* 13.

962	15 c. Type **432**	10	10
963	17 c. Hobby-horse	10	10
964	35 c. Rag-doll (*vert*)	25	50
962/4	*Set of* 3	35	50

433 "Child watering Tree of Life" (painting by Marie-Annick Viatour)

434 Canadair "CL-215"

(Des J. Morin. Litho Ashton-Potter)

1979 (24 Oct). *International Year of the Child. P* 13.

965	**433**	17 c. multicoloured	15	15

(Des R. Bradford and J. Charette. Litho Ashton-Potter)

1979 (15 Nov). *Canadian Aircraft* (1*st series*). *Flying Boats. T* **434** *and similar horiz designs. Multicoloured. P* 12½.

966	17 c. Type **434**	15	10
	a. Pair. Nos. 966/7	30	60
967	17 c. Curtiss "HS-2L"	15	10
968	35 c. Vickers "Vedette"	30	15
	a. Pair. Nos. 968/9	60	1·00
969	35 c. Consolidated "Canso"	30	15
966/9	*Set of* 4	90	45

Nos. 966/7 and 968/9 were each printed together, *se-tenant*, in horizontal and vertical pairs throughout the sheet.

See also Nos. 996/9, 1026/9 and 1050/3.

435 Map of Arctic Islands

436 Skiing

(Des Gottschalk and Ash Ltd. Litho Ashton-Potter)

1980 (23 Jan). *Centenary of Arctic Islands Acquisition. P* 13.

970	**435**	17 c. multicoloured	15	20

(Des C. Malenfant. Litho C.B.N.)

1980 (23 Jan). *Winter Olympic Games, Lake Placid, U.S.A. P* 13.

971	**436**	35 c. multicoloured	25	50

437 "A Meeting of the School Trustees" (painting by Robert Harris)

438 Atlantic Whitefish (*Coregonus canadensis*)

(Des J. Morin. Litho Ashton-Potter)

1980 (6 Mar). *Centenary of Royal Canadian Academy of Arts. T* **437** *and similar horiz designs. Multicoloured. P* 13.

972	17 c. Type **437**	15	10
	a. Pair. Nos. 972/3	30	30
973	17 c. "Inspiration" (sculpture by Philippe Hébert)	15	10
974	35 c. "Sunrise on the Saguenay" (painting by Lucius O'Brien)	25	15
	a. Pair. Nos. 974/5	50	90
975	35 c. Sketch of design for original Parliament Buildings by Thomas Fuller	25	15
972/5	*Set of* 4	70	35

Nos. 972/3 and 974/5 were each printed together, *se-tenant*, in horizontal and vertical pairs throughout the sheet.

(Des M. Dumas (No. 976), R. Bateman (No. 977). Litho Ashton-Potter)

1980 (6 May). *Endangered Wildlife* (4*th series*). *T* **438** *and similar horiz design. Multicoloured. P* 12½.

976	17 c. Type **438**	15	15
977	17 c. Prairie Chicken (*Tympanuchus cupido pinnatus*)	15	15

439 Garden Flowers

440 "Helping Hand"

(Des Heather Cooper. Litho Ashton-Potter)

1980 (29 May). *International Flower Show, Montreal. P* 13.

978	**439**	17 c. multicoloured	15	15

(Des R. Harder. Litho and embossed Ashton-Potter)

1980 (29 May). *Rehabilitation. P* 12½.

979	**440**	17 c. gold and ultramarine	15	15

441 Opening Bars of "O Canada"

442 John G. Diefenbaker

(Des F. Peter. Litho Ashton-Potter)

1980 (6 June). *Centenary of "O Canada"* (*national song*). *T* **441** *and similar horiz design. Multicoloured. P* 12½.

980	17 c. Type **441**	15	10
	a. Pair. Nos. 980/1	30	40
981	17 c. Galixa Lavallee (composer), Adolphe-Basile Routhier (original writer) and Robert Stanley Wier (writer of English version)	15	10

Nos. 980/1 were printed together, *se-tenant*, in horizontal and vertical pairs throughout.

(Des B. Reilander. Eng Y. Baril. Recess C.B.N.)

1980 (20 June). *John G. Diefenbaker* (*former Prime Minister*) *Commemoration. P* 13½ × 13.

982	**442**	17 c. deep ultramarine	15	15

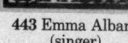

443 Emma Albani (singer)

444 Alberta

(Des C. Webster (No. 985), H. Brown (others). Litho Ashton-Potter)

1980 (4 July). *Famous Canadians. T* **443** *and similar multicoloured designs. P* 13.

983	17 c. Type **443**	15	10
	a. Pair. Nos. 983/4	30	40
984	17 c. Healey Willan (composer)	15	10
985	17 c. Ned Hanlan (oarsman) (*horiz*)	15	10
983/5	*Set of* 3	40	15

Nos. 983/4 were printed together, *se-tenant*, in horizontal and vertical pairs throughout the sheet.

(Des G. Hunter and C. Yaneff. Litho Ashton-Potter)

1980 (27 Aug). *75th Anniv of Alberta and Saskatchewan Provinces. T* **444** *and similar horiz design. Multicoloured. P* 13.

986	17 c. Type **444**	15	15
987	17 c. Saskatchewan	15	15

445 Uraninite Molecular Structure

446 "Christmas Morning" (J. S. Hallam)

(Des J. Charette. Litho C.B.N.)

1980 (3 Sept). *Uranium Resources. P* 13.

988	**445**	35 c. multicoloured	30	30

(Des R. Derreth. Litho C.B.N.)

1980 (25 Sept). *Canadian Eskimos* ("*Inuits*") (4*th series*). *Spirits. Horiz designs as T* **413**. *Multicoloured. P* 13½.

989	17 c. "Return of the Sun" (print by Kenojouak)	15	10
	a. Pair. Nos. 989/90	30	40
990	17 c. "Sedna" (sculpture by Ashoona Kiawak)	15	10
991	35 c. "Shaman" (print by Simon Tookoome)	25	10
	a. Pair. Nos. 991/2	50	70
992	35 c. "Bird Spirit" (sculpture by Doris Hagiolok)	25	10
989/92	*Set of* 4	70	25

Nos. 989/90 and 991/2 were each printed together, *se-tenant*, in horizontal and vertical pairs throughout the sheet.

(Des Yvon Laroche. Litho Ashton-Potter)

1980 (22 Oct). *Christmas. Paintings. T* **446** *and similar vert designs. Multicoloured. P* 12½ × 12.

993	15 c. Type **446**	10	10
994	17 c. "Sleigh Ride" (Frank Hennessy)	15	10
995	35 c. "McGill Cab Stand" (Kathleen Morris)	30	45
993/5	*Set of* 3	50	45

447 Avro Canada "CF-100"

(Des R. Bradford and J. Charette. Litho C.B.N.)

1980 (10 Nov). *Canadian Aircraft* (2*nd series*). *T* **447** *and similar horiz designs. Multicoloured. P* 13.

996	17 c. Type **447**	15	10
	a. Pair. Nos. 996/7	30	50
997	17 c. Avro "Lancaster"	15	10
998	35 c. Curtiss "JN-4 (Canuck)"	30	15
	a. Pair. Nos. 998/9	60	90
999	35 c. Hawker "Hurricane"	30	15
996/9	*Set of* 4	80	35

Nos. 996/7 and 998/9 were each printed together, *se-tenant*, in horizontal and vertical pairs throughout the sheet.

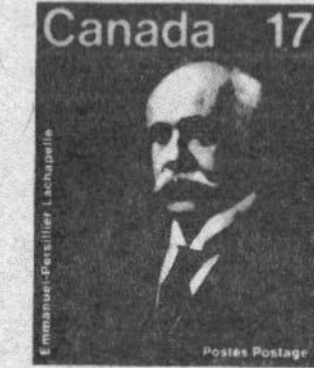

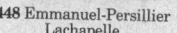

448 Emmanuel-Persillier Lachapelle

449 Mandora Instrument (18th-century)

(Des J. Morin. Litho Ashton-Potter)

1980 (5 Dec). *Dr. Emmanuel-Persillier Lachapelle* (*founder of Notre-Dame Hospital, Montreal*) *Commemoration. P* 13½.

1000	**448**	17 c. cobalt, chocolate and brown	15	15

(Des C. Webster. Litho Ashton-Potter)

1981 (19 Jan). *"The Look of Music" Exhibition, Vancouver. P* 12½.

1001	**449**	17 c. multicoloured	15	15

450 Henrietta Edwards

451 Vancouver Marmot (*Marmota vancouverensis*)

(Des Muriel Wood and D. Goddard. Litho C.B.N.)

1981 (4 Mar). *Feminists. T* **450** *and similar horiz designs. Multicoloured. P* 13.

1002	17 c. Type **450**	15	15
	a. Block of 4. Nos. 1002/5	55	
1003	17 c. Louise McKinney	15	15
1004	17 c. Idola Saint-Jean	15	15
1005	17 c. Emily Stowe	15	15
1002/5	*Set of* 4	55	55

Nos. 1002/5 were printed together, *se-tenant*, in different combinations throughout the sheet, giving ten blocks of 4 and ten single stamps.

(Des M. Dumas (17 c.), R. Bateman (35 c.). Litho C.B.N.)

1981 (6 Apr). *Endangered Wildlife* (5*th series*). *T* **451** *and similar horiz design. Multicoloured. P* 13.

1006	17 c. Type **451**	15	10
1007	35 c. American Bison (*Bison bison athabascae*)	35	30

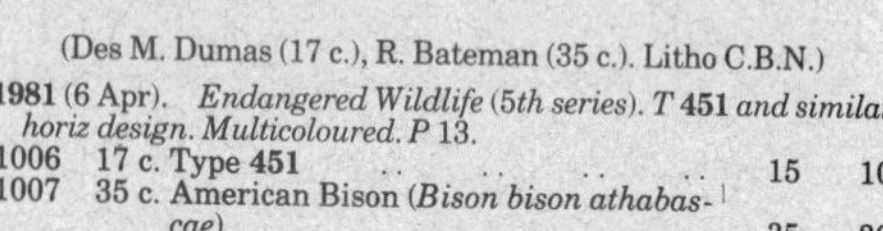

452 Kateri Tekakwitha

453 "Self Portrait" (Frederick H. Varley)

(Des L. Marquart. Litho Ashton-Potter)

1981 (24 Apr). *17th-century Canadian Catholic Women. Statues by Emile Brunet. T* **452** *and similar vert design. P* 12½.
1008 17 c. red-brown and pale grey-olive 15 10
a. Pair. Nos. 1008/9 .. .. 30 40
1009 17 c. steel blue and new blue 15 10
Designs:—No. 1008, Type **452**; No. 1009, Marie de l'Incarnation.
Nos. 1008/9 were printed together, *se-tenant*, in horizontal and vertical pairs throughout the sheet.

(Des P. Fontaine. Litho Ashton-Potter (17 c. (*both*)), B.A.B.N. (35 c.))

1981 (22 May). *Canadian Paintings. T* **453** *and similar multi-coloured designs. P* 12½ (17 c. (*both*)) *or* 13 × 13½ (35 c.).
1010 17 c. Type **453** 15 10
1011 17 c. "At Baie Saint-Paul" (Marc-Aurele Fortin) (*horiz*) 15 10
1012 35 c. "Untitled No. 6" (Paul-Emile Borduas) .. 30 30
1010/12 .. .. *Set of* 3 55 45

454 Canada in 1867 **455** Frère Marie-Victorin

(Des R. Bellemare. Litho B.A.B.N.)

1981 (30 June). *Canada Day. Maps showing evolution of Canada from Confederation to present day. T* **454** *and similar horiz designs. Multicoloured. P* 13½.
1013 17 c. Type **454** 15 15
a. Horiz strip of 4. Nos. 1013/16 55
1014 17 c. Canada in 1873 .. .. 15 15
1015 17 c. Canada in 1905 .. .. 15 15
1016 17 c. Canada since 1949 .. .. .. 15 15
1013/16 .. .. *Set of* 4 55 55
Nos. 1013/16 were printed together, *se-tenant*, in horizontal strips of 4 throughout the sheet.

(Des R. Hill. Litho and embossed Ashton-Potter)

1981 (22 July). *Canadian Botanists. T* **455** *and similar vert design. Multicoloured. P* 12½ × 12.
1017 17 c. Type **455** 15 10
a. Pair. Nos. 1017/18 .. .. .. 30 40
1018 17 c. John Macoun 15 10
Nos. 1017/18 were printed together, *se-tenant*, in horizontal and vertical pairs throughout the sheet.

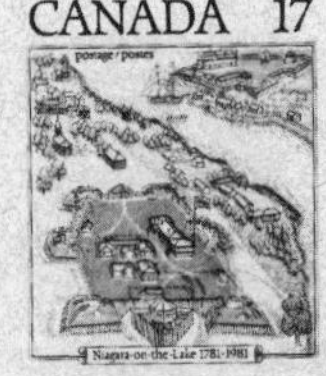

456 The Montreal Rose **457** Drawing of Niagara-on-the-Lake

(Des J.-P. Beaudin, J. Morin and T. Yakobina. Litho C.B.N.)

1981 (22 July). *Montreal Flower Show. P* 13½.
1019 **456** 17 c. multicoloured 15 15

(Des J. Mardon. Recess and litho B.A.B.N.)

1981 (31 July). *Bicentenary of Niagara-on-the-Lake* (*town*). *P* 13 × 13½.
1020 **457** 17 c. multicoloured 15 15

458 Acadian Community **459** Aaron R. Mosher

(Des N. DeGrâce. Litho Ashton-Potter)

1981 (14 Aug). *Centenary of first Acadia* (*community*) *Convention. P* 13½.
1021 **458** 17 c. multicoloured 15 15

(Des R. Hill. Litho Ashton-Potter)

1981 (8 Sept). *Birth Centenary of Aaron R. Mosher* (*founder of Canadian Labour Congress*). *P* 13½.
1022 **459** 17 c. multicoloured 15 15

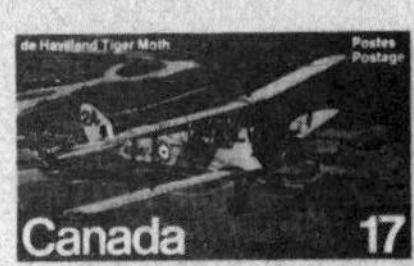

460 Christmas Tree, 1781 **461** De Havilland "Tiger Moth"

(Des Anita Kunz and W. Tibbles. Litho Ashton-Potter)

1981 (16 Nov). *Christmas. Bicentenary of First Illuminated Christmas Tree in Canada. T* **460** *and similar vert designs. Multi-coloured. P* 13½.
1023 15 c. Type **460** 15 10
1024 15 c. Christmas Tree, 1881 .. .. .. 15 10
1025 15 c. Christmas Tree, 1981 .. .. .. 15 10
1023/5 .. .. *Set of* 3 40 15

(Des R. Bradford and J. Charette. Litho Ashton-Potter)

1981 (24 Nov). *Canadian Aircraft* (*3rd series*). *T* **461** *and similar horiz designs. Multicoloured. P* 12½.
1026 17 c. Type **461** 20 10
a. Pair. Nos. 1026/7 .. .. 40 40
1027 17 c. Canadair "CL-41 (Tutor)" 20 10
1028 35 c. Avro "Canada" jetliner 35 20
a. Pair. Nos. 1028/9 .. .. 70 70
1029 35 c. De Havilland Canada "Dash 7" 35 20
1026/9 .. .. *Set of* 4 1·10 45
The two designs of each value were printed together, *se-tenant*, in horizontal and vertical pairs throughout the sheet.

462 Canadian Maple Leaf Emblem **463** 1851 3d. Stamp

(Des R. Bellemare. Recess B.A.B.N. (No. 1030*a*), C.B.N. (others))

1981 (29 Dec). *Ordinary paper.* (*a*) *Sheet stamp. P* 13 × 13½.
1030 **462** A (30 c.), bright scarlet 20 25
a. Carmine-red, chalk-surfaced paper 20 25

(*b*) *Coil stamp. Imperf* × *perf* 10
1031 **462** A (30 c.), bright scarlet 25 35
a. Imperf (pair) £300
Nos. 1030/1 were printed before a new first class domestic letter rate had been agreed, "A" representing the face value of the stamp later decided at 30 c. Because of U.P.U. regulations these stamps were only intended for use within Canada.

(Recess, or recess and photo (Nos. 1032/*b*), B.A.B.N. (Nos. 1032/5*b*) or C.B.N. (Nos. 1036/(*a*))

1982 (1 Mar)–**83**. *Designs as Nos.* 1030/1 *but including face values.*

(*a*) *Sheet stamps* (*Nos.* 1032, 1032*b*) *or from booklets* (*Nos.* 1032a, 1032ba). *P* 13 × 13½
1032 **462** 30 c. verm, slate-blue & azure (11.5.82) 30 25
a. Perf 12 × 12½ (from booklets) (30.6.82) 30 50
ab. Booklet pane. No. 1032a × 20 plus one printed label .. .. .. 5·00
1032*b* 32 c. verm, orge-brn & stone (10.2.83) 35 40
ba. Perf 12 × 12½ (from booklets) (8.4.83) 35 50
bb. Booklet pane. No. 1032ba × 25 plus two printed labels .. .. .. 9·50

(*b*) *Booklet stamps. Ordinary paper. P* 12 × 12½*
1033 **462** 5 c. maroon 10 10
a. Booklet pane. Nos. 1033 × 2, 1034 and 1035 plus two printed labels in bottom row 45
ab. Ditto. Printed labels in top row (10.82) 75
b. Chalk-surfaced paper (8.82) .. 15 10
ba. Booklet pane. Nos. 1033b × 2, 1034a and 1035a plus two printed labels in bottom row 70
bb. Ditto. Printed labels in top row (10.82) 70
c. Booklet pane. Nos. 1033 × 2, 1033*d* and 1035*b* plus two printed labels (15.2.83) 60
1033*d* 8 c. indigo (15.2.83) 55 10
1034 10 c. bottle green 40 15
a. Chalk-surfaced paper 65 15
1035 30 c. carmine-red 60 30
a. Chalk-surfaced paper 75 30
1035*b* 32 c. Indian red (15.2.83) 75 40

(*c*) *Coil stamps. Imperf* × *perf* 10
1036 **462** 30 c. bright scarlet (20.5.82)† 35 25
1036*a* 32 c. Indian red (10.2.83) 75 75
ab. Imperf (pair) £140
*The 30 c. and 32 c. values are perforated on two sides, the other values on three.
†The 30 c. coil stamp was originally intended for release on 11 May, but, due to production difficulties, it was not placed on sale until 20 May; F.D.C.s, however, carry the 11 May postmark.

(Des Gottschalk and Ash Ltd. Litho C.B.N.)

1982 (11 Mar–20 May). *"Canada 82" International Philatelic Youth Exhibition, Toronto. Stamps on Stamps. T* **463** *and similar horiz designs. Multicoloured. P* 13½.
1037 30 c. Type **463** 25 25
1038 30 c. 1908 Centenary of Quebec 15 c. commemorative (20.5.82) 25 25
1039 35 c. 1935 10 c. 25 30
1040 35 c. 1928 10 c. (20.5.82) 25 30
1041 60 c. 1929 50 c. (20.5.82) 50 75
1037/41 .. .. *Set of* 5 1·40 1·75
MS1042 159 × 108 mm. Nos. 1037/41 (20.5.82) .. 1·75 2·00

464 Jules Léger **465** Stylised Drawing of Terry Fox

(Des P. Fontaine from photograph by M. Bedford. Litho Ashton-Potter)

1982 (2 Apr). *Jules Léger* (*politician*) *Commemoration. P* 13½.
1043 **464** 30 c. multicoloured 20 15

(Des F. Peter. Litho Ashton-Potter)

1982 (13 Apr). *Cancer-victim Terry Fox's "Marathon of Hope"* (*Trans-Canada fund-raising run*) *Commemoration. P* 12½.
1044 **465** 30 c. multicoloured 20 15

466 Stylised Open Book

(Des F. Peter. Litho Ashton-Potter)

1982 (16 Apr). *Patriation of Constitution. P* 12 × 12½.
1045 **466** 30 c. multicoloured 20 15

467 1880's Male and Female Salvationists with Street Scene **468** "The Highway near Kluane Lake" (Yukon Territory) (Jackson)

(Des T. Dimson. Litho C.B.N.)

1982 (25 June). *Centenary of the Salvation Army in Canada. P* 13½.
1046 **467** 30 c. multicoloured 20 20

(Des J. Morin and P. Sasseville. Litho Ashton-Potter)

1982 (30 June). *Canada Day. Paintings of Canadian Landscapes. Sheet, 139 × 139 mm, containing T* **468** *and similar horiz designs. Multicoloured. P* 12½ × 12.
MS1047 30 c. × 12, Type **468**; "Street Scene, Montreal" (Quebec) (Hébert); "Breakwater" (Newfoundland) (Pratt); "Along Great Slave Lake" (Northwest Territories) (Richard); "Till Hill" (Prince Edward Island) (Lamb); "Family and Rainstorm" (Nova Scotia) (Colville); "Brown Shadows" (Saskatchewan) (Knowles); "The Red Brick House" (Ontario) (Milne); "Campus Gates" (New Brunswick) (Bobak); "Prairie Town—Early Morning" (Alberta) (Kerr); "Totems at Ninstints" (British Columbia) (Plaskett); "Doc Snider's House" (Manitoba) (FitzGerald) .. .. 3·25 3·75

469 Regina Legislature Building **470** Finish of Race

(Des Kim Martin and R. Russell. Litho Ashton-Potter)

1982 (3 Aug). *Regina Centenary. P* 13½ × 13.
1048 **469** 30 c. multicoloured 20 15

(Des B. Reilander. Litho Ashton-Potter)

1982 (4 Aug). *Centenary of Royal Canadian Henley Regatta. P* 12½.
1049 **470** 30 c. multicoloured 20 20

471 Fairchild "FC-2W1"

472 Decoy

(Des R. Bradford. Litho Ashton-Potter)

1982 (5 Oct). *Canadian Aircraft (4th series). Bush Aircraft. T* **471** *and similar horiz designs. Multicoloured. P* 12½.

1050 30 c. Type **471** 35 15
a. Pair. Nos. 1050/1 .. .. 70 60
1051 30 c. De Havilland Canada "Beaver" 35 15
1052 60 c. Fokker "Super Universal" 65 60
a. Pair. Nos. 1052/3 .. .. 1·25 1·25
1053 60 c. Noorduyn "Norseman" 65 60
1050/3 .. .. *Set of* 4 1·90 1·40

Nos. 1050/1 and 1052/3 were each printed together, *se-tenant*, in horiz and vert pairs throughout the sheet.

(Des J. P. Beaudin and J. Morin. Litho C.B.N. (Nos. 1054a, 1055a, 1056a, 1057a, 1058a) or Ashton-Potter (others))

1982 (19 Oct)–**87**. *Heritage Artifacts. T* **472** *and similar designs. No fluorescent bands (1 c. to 5 c.). P* 12 × 12½ *(37 c. to 72 c.) or* 14 × 13½ *(others).*

1054 1 c. black, grey-brown and brown .. 10 10
a. Perf 13 × 13½ (10.1.85) 15 10
1055 2 c. black, pale turquoise-blue & dp bl-grn 10 10
a. Perf 13 × 13½ (10.2.84) 15 10
ab. Imperf (horiz pair) £475
1056 3 c. black, dull violet-blue and chalky blue 10 10
a. Perf 13 × 13½ (10.1.85) 15 10
1057 5 c. black, flesh and chestnut 10 10
a. Perf 13 × 13½ (6.7.84) 10 10
1058 10 c. black, light blue & deep turquoise-blue 10 10
a. Perf 13 × 13½ (15.3.85) 20 10
1059 20 c. black, brownish grey and sepia .. 20 10
1060 25 c. multicoloured (6.5.87) 20 10
1061 37 c. grey-black, deep yellow-green and sage-green (8.4.83) 50 40
1062 39 c. brownish black, violet-grey and slate-violet (1.8.85) 50 30
1063 42 c. multicoloured (6.5.87) 45 25
1064 48 c. blackish brown, red-brown and pale pink (8.4.83) 70 55
1065 50 c. black, dull turquoise-blue & turq. blue (1.8.85) 75 20
1066 55 c. multicoloured (6.5.87) 55 40
1067 64 c. grey-black, black & pale grey (8.4.83) 80 65
1068 68 c. black, pale brn & reddish brn (1.8.85) 75 55
1069 72 c. multicoloured (6.5.87) 75 65
1054/69 .. .. *Set of* 16 5·75 4·00

Designs: *Vert (as T* **472**)—2 c. Fishing spear; 3 c. Stable lantern; 5 c. Bucket; 10 c. Weathercock; 20 c. Skates; 25 c. Butter stamp. *Horiz* (26 × 20 *mm*)—37 c. Plough; 39 c. Settle-bed; 42 c. Linen chest; 48 c. Cradle; 50 c. Sleigh; 55 c. Iron kettle; 64 c. Kitchen stove; 68 c. Spinning wheel; 72 c. Hand-drawn cart.

No. 1058a has a fluorescent frame instead of bands.

475 Mary, Joseph and Baby Jesus

476 Globes forming Symbolic Designs

(Des J. Eby. Litho C.B.N.)

1982 (3 Nov). *Christmas. Nativity Scenes. T* **475** *and similar vert designs. Multicoloured. P* 13.

1080 30 c. Type **475** 20 10
1081 35 c. The Shepherds 25 35
1082 60 c. The Three Wise Men 45 70
1080/2 .. .. *Set of* 3 80 1·00

(Des R. Bellemare. Litho Ashton-Potter)

1983 (10 Mar). *World Communications Year. Fluorescent frame. P* 12 × 12½.

1083 **476** 32 c. multicoloured 25 25

477 Map of World showing Canada

(Des R. Harder. Litho Ashton-Potter)

1983 (14 Mar). *Commonwealth Day. Without fluorescent bands. P* 12½.

1084 **477** $2 multicoloured .. .. 1·75 2·25

478 Scene from Novel "Angéline de Montbrun" by Laure Conan (Félicité Angers)

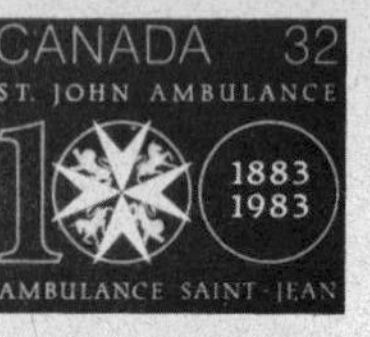

479 St. John Ambulance Badge and "100"

(Des R. Milot (No. 1085), Claire Pratt (No. 1086), adapted W. Tibbles. Litho C.B.N.)

1983 (22 Apr). *Canadian Writers (4th series). T* **478** *and similar horiz design. Multicoloured. P* 13.

1085 32 c. Type **478** 25 15
a. Pair. Nos. 1085/6 .. .. 50 70
1086 32 c. Woodcut illustrating "Sea-gulls" (poem by E. J. Pratt) 25 15

Nos. 1085/6 were printed together, *se-tenant*, in horizontal and vertical pairs throughout the sheet.

(Des L. Fishauf. Litho Ashton-Potter)

1983 (3 June). *Centenary of St. John Ambulance in Canada. P* 13.

1087 **479** 32 c. brt rose-red, gold & dp chocolate 25 20

480 Victory Pictogram

481 Fort William, Ontario

(Des Krista Huebner, D. Kilvert and P.-Y. Pelletier. Litho C.B.N.)

1983 (28 June). *"Universiade 83" World University Games, Edmonton. P* 13.

1088 **480** 32 c. multicoloured 25 15
1089 64 c. multicoloured 50 70

(Des R. Harder. Litho Ashton-Potter)

1983 (30 June). *Canada Day. Forts (1st series). T* **481** *and similar horiz designs. Multicoloured. P* 12½ × 13.

1090 32 c. Fort Henry, Ontario (44 × 22 *mm*) .. 35 35
a. Booklet pane. Nos. 1090/9 .. .. 3·25
1091 32 c. Type **481** 35 35
1092 32 c. Fort Rodd Hill, British Columbia .. 35 35
1093 32 c. Fort Wellington, Ontario (28 × 22 *mm*) .. 35 35
1094 32 c. Fort Prince of Wales, Manitoba (28 × 22 *mm*) 35 35
1095 32 c. Halifax Citadel, Nova Scotia (44 × 22 *mm*) 35 35
1096 32 c. Fort Chambly, Quebec 35 35
1097 32 c. Fort No. 1, Point Levis, Quebec 35 35
1098 32 c. Coteau-du-Lac Fort, Quebec (28 × 22 *mm*) 35 35
1099 32 c. Fort Beauséjour, New Brunswick (28 × 22 *mm*) 35 35
1090/9 .. .. *Set of* 10 3·25 3·25

Nos. 1090/9 were only available from $3.20 stamp booklets containing the *se-tenant* pane, No. 1090a.

See also Nos. 1163/72.

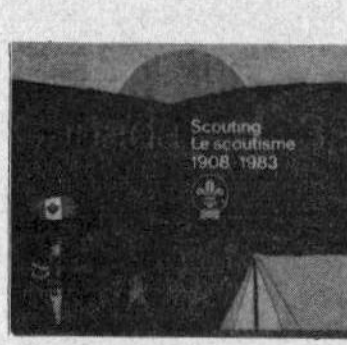

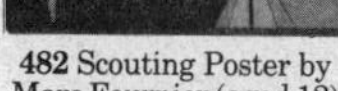

482 Scouting Poster by Marc Fournier (aged 12)

483 Cross Symbol

(Des F. Dallaire. Litho Ashton-Potter)

1983 (6 July). *75th Anniv of Scouting in Canada and 15th World Scout Jamboree, Alberta. P* 13.

1100 **482** 32 c. multicoloured 30 25

(Des G. Tsetsekas. Recess and photo B.A.B.N.)

1983 (22 July). *6th Assembly of the World Council of Churches, Vancouver. P* 13.

1101 **483** 32 c. blue-green and grey-lilac 25 20

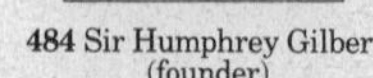

484 Sir Humphrey Gilbert (founder)

485 "NICKEL" Deposits

(Des R. Hill. Litho C.B.N.)

1983 (3 Aug). *400th Anniv of Newfoundland. P* 13.

1102 **484** 32 c. multicoloured 25 20

(Des J. Capon. Litho ("NICKEL" die-stamped) C.B.N.)

1983 (12 Aug). *Centenary of Discovery of Sudbury Nickel Deposits. P* 13.

1103 **485** 32 c. multicoloured 25 20

486 Josiah Henson and Escaping Slaves

487 Type 0-4-0, *Dorchester* Locomotive

(Des T. Kew and J. Hamel. Litho B.A.B.N.)

1983 (16 Sept). *Nineteenth-century Social Reformers. T* **486** *and similar horiz design. Multicoloured. P* 13 × 13½ *(No.* 1104) *or* 13 *(No.* 1105).

1104 32 c. Type **486** 25 25
1105 32 c. Father Antoine Labelle and rural village (32 × 26 *mm*) 25 25

(Des E. Roch. Litho Ashton-Potter)

1983 (3 Oct). *Railway Locomotives. (1st series). T* **487** *and similar horiz designs. Multicoloured. P* 12½ × 13.

1106 32 c. Type **487** 40 15
a. Pair. Nos. 1106/7 .. .. 80 70
1107 32 c. Type 4-4-0, *Toronto* 40 15
1108 37 c. Type 0-6-0, *Samson* 45 40
1109 64 c. Type 4-4-0, *Adam Brown* 85 70
1106/9 .. .. *Set of* 4 1·90 1·25

Nos. 1106/7 were printed together, *se-tenant*, in horizontal and vertical pairs throughout the sheet.

See also Nos. 1132/6, 1185/8 and 1223/6.

488 School Coat of Arms

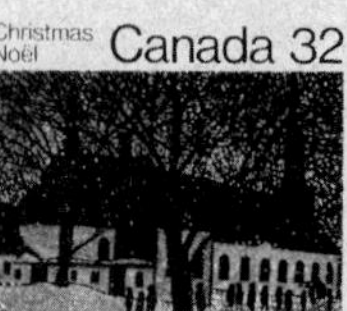

489 City Church

(Des Denise Saulnier. Litho C.B.N.)

1983 (28 Oct). *Centenary of Dalhousie Law School. P* 13.

1110 **488** 32 c. multicoloured 25 25

(Des C. Simard. Litho Ashton-Potter)

1983 (3 Nov). *Christmas. Churches. T* **489** *and similar horiz designs. Multicoloured. P* 13.

1111 32 c. Type **489** 30 10
1112 37 c. Family walking to church 40 30
1113 64 c. Country chapel .. .. 65 1·00
1111/13 .. .. *Set of* 3 1·25 1·25

490 Royal Canadian Regiment and British Columbia Regiment

(Des W. Southern and R. Tibbles. Litho C.B.N.)

1983 (10 Nov). *Canadian Army Regiments. T* **490** *and similar vert design. Multicoloured. P* 13.

1114 32 c. Type **490** 30 15
a. Pair. Nos. 1114/15 .. .. .. 60 70
1115 32 c. Royal Winnipeg Rifles and Royal Canadian Dragoons 30 15

Nos. 1114/15 were printed together, *se-tenant*, in horizontal and vertical pairs throughout the sheet.

PRICES OF SETS

Set prices are given for many issues, generally those containing three stamps or more. Definitive sets include one of each value or major colour change, but do not cover different perforations, die types or minor shades. Where a choice is possible the set prices are based on the cheapest versions of the stamps included in the listings.

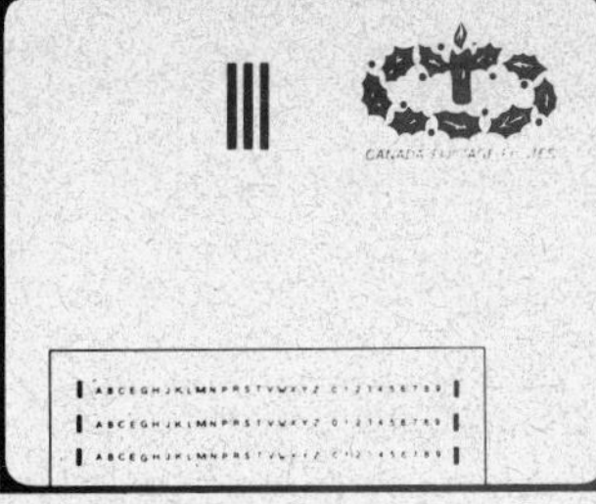

(*Illustration reduced: actual size* 112 × 88 mm)

"STICK 'N TICK" POSTAGE LABELS. Prepaid labels in the above design, printed in a combination of red, green and black, were tested by the Canadian Post Office in Winnipeg, Manitoba, between 21 November and 17 December 1983. These self-adhesive labels were sold to the public in kits of 12 or 25, at a saving of 35 c. or $1.11 on the normal postage. They were primarily intended for use on Christmas cards and were only valid on mail posted to Canadian addresses.

The label was affixed to normally addressed envelopes, but the user was then required to mark the postal code on the three lines at the foot. It was hoped that this incentive would increase the use of the postal codes and so speed automatic mail sorting.

The system was extended to seven other cities in 1984. The second version had separate postage paid and Postal Code labels, being available from 5 November until 17 December 1984.

491 Gold Mine in Prospecting Pan

492 Montreal Symphony Orchestra

(Des K. Hughes. Litho Ashton-Potter)

1984 (15 Mar). 50*th Anniv of Yellowknife. P* 13½.
1116 **491** 32 c. multicoloured 30 20

(Des J. Delisle and P. Kohler. Litho Ashton-Potter)

1984 (24 Mar). 50*th Anniv of Montreal Symphony Orchestra. P* 12½.
1117 **492** 32 c. multicoloured 35 20

493 Jacques Cartier

494 *Eagle* (U.S. Coastguard cadet ship)

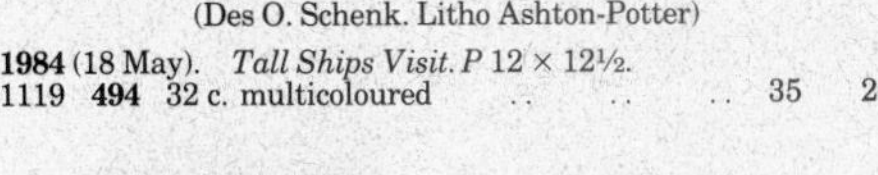

(Des Y. Paquin, Engraved C. Haley. Recess French Govt Ptg Wks, Perigueux)

1984 (20 Apr). 450*th Anniv of Jacques Cartier's Voyage to Canada. P* 13.
1118 **493** 32 c. multicoloured 35 20

(Des O. Schenk. Litho Ashton-Potter)

1984 (18 May). *Tall Ships Visit. P* 12 × 12½.
1119 **494** 32 c. multicoloured 35 20

495 Service Medal

496 Oared Galleys

(Des W. Tibbles and C. Webster. Litho Ashton-Potter)

1984 (28 May). 75*th Anniv of Canadian Red Cross Society. P* 13½.
1120 **495** 32 c. multicoloured 35 20

(Des P. Dorn. Photo and recess B.A.B.N.)

1984 (18 June). *Bicentenary of New Brunswick. P* 13½.
1121 **496** 32 c. multicoloured 35 20

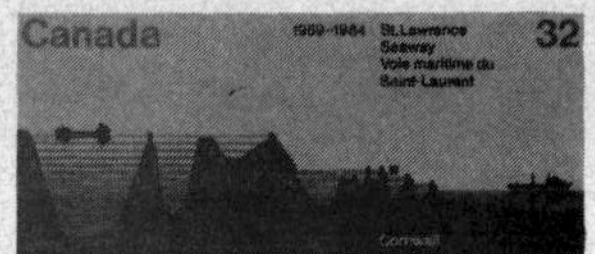

497 St. Lawrence Seaway

(Des E. Barenscher. Litho C.B.N.)

1984 (26 June). 25*th Anniv of St. Lawrence Seaway. P* 13.
1122 **497** 32 c. multicoloured 35 20

498 New Brunswick

499 Loyalists of 1784

(Des J. Morin and T. Yakobina. Litho C.B.N.)

1984 (29 June). *Canada Day. Paintings by Jean Paul Lemieux. Sheet,* 138 × 122 *mm, containing T* **498** *and similar multi-coloured designs. P* 13.
MS1123 32 c. × 12, Type **498**; British Columbia; Northwest Territories; Quebec; Manitoba; Alberta; Prince Edward Island; Saskatchewan; Nova Scotia (*vert*); Yukon Territory, Newfoundland; Ontario (*vert*) .. .. 5·00 5·00

The captions on the Northwest Territories and Yukon Territory paintings were transposed at the design stage.

(Des W. Davies. Litho B.A.B.N.)

1984 (3 July). *Bicentenary of Arrival of United Empire Loyalists. P* 13 × 13½.
1124 **499** 32 c. multicoloured 30 20

500 St. John's Basilica

501 Coat of Arms of Pope John Paul II

(Des J. Morin and R. Ethier. Litho C.B.N.)

1984 (17 Aug). *Bicentenary of Roman Catholic Church in Newfoundland. P* 13½.
1125 **500** 32 c. multicoloured 30 20

(Des L. Rivard. Litho Ashton-Potter)

1984 (31 Aug). *Papal Visit. P* 12½.
1126 **501** 32 c. multicoloured 40 20
1127 64 c. multicoloured .. .. .. 85 1·10

502 Louisbourg Lighthouse, 1734

(Des D. Noble and K. Rodmell. Litho Ashton-Potter)

1984 (21 Sept). *Canadian Lighthouses* (1*st series*). *T* **502** *and similar horiz designs. Multicoloured. P* 12½.
1128 32 c. Type **502** 55 55
a. Block of 4. Nos. 1128/31 .. .. .. 2·00
1129 32 c. Fisgard Lighthouse, 1860 .. .. 55 55
1130 32 c. Ile Verte Lighthouse, 1809 .. .. 55 55
1131 32 c. Gibraltar Point Lighthouse, 1808 .. 55 55
1128/31 .. .. *Set of* 4 2·00 2·00

Nos. 1128/31 were printed together, *se-tenant*, in different combinations throughout the sheet, giving ten blocks of 4 and ten single stamps.

See also Nos. 1176/80.

503 Type 0-6-0, *Scotia* Locomotive

(Des E. Roch. Litho Ashton-Potter)

1984 (25 Oct). *Railway Locomotives* (2*nd series*). *T* **503** *and similar horiz designs. Multicoloured. P* 12½ × 13.
1132 32 c. Type **503** 65 20
a. Pair. Nos. 1132/3 .. .. .. 1·25 90
1133 32 c. Type 4-4-0, *Countess of Dufferin* .. 65 20
1134 37 c. Type 2-6-0, GT Class E3 .. .. 70 55
1135 64 c. Type 4-6-0, CP Class D10a .. .. 1·10 90
1132/5 .. .. *Set of* 4 2·75 1·75
MS1136 153 × 104 mm. As Nos. 1132/5, but with background colour changed from pale green to pale grey-blue .. .. 2·75 3·00

Nos. 1132/3 were issued together, *se-tenant*, in horizontal and vertical pairs throughout the sheet.

No. **MS**1136 commemorates "CANADA 84" National Stamp Exhibition, Montreal.

See also Nos. 1185/8 and 1223/6.

504 "The Annunciation" (Jean Dallaire)

505 Pilots of 1914–18, 1939–45 and 1984

(Des J. Morin and T. Yakobina. Litho Ashton-Potter)

1984 (2 Nov). *Christmas. Religious Paintings. T* **504** *and similar horiz designs. Multicoloured. P* 13½.
1137 32 c. Type **504** 30 10
1138 37 c. "The Three Kings" (Simone Bouchard) .. 35 35
1139 64 c. "Snow in Bethlehem" (David Milne) .. 60 80
1137/9 .. .. *Set of* 3 1·10 1·10

(Des W. Southern and R. Tibbles. Litho Ashton-Potter)

1984 (9 Nov). 60*th Anniv of Royal Canadian Air Force. P* 12 × 12½.
1140 505 32 c. multicoloured 35 20

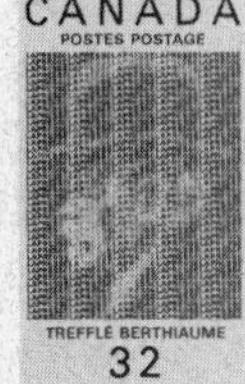

506 Treffle Berthiaume (editor)

507 Heart and Arrow

(Des P.-Y. Pelletier. Litho Ashton-Potter)

1984 (16 Nov.) *Centenary of La Presse (newspaper). P* 13 × 13½.
1141 **506** 32 c. agate, vermilion and pale grey-brown 35 20

(Des F. Dallaire. Litho Ashton-Potter)

1985 (8 Feb). *International Youth Year. P* 12½.
1142 **507** 32 c. multicoloured 30 20

508 Astronaut in Space, and Planet Earth

509 Emily Murphy

(Des L. Holloway. Litho Ashton-Potter)

1985 (15 Mar). *Canadian Space Programme. P* 13½.
1143 **508** 32 c. multicoloured 40 20

(Des Muriel Wood and R. Tibbles. Litho Ashton-Potter)

1985 (17 Apr). *Women's Rights Activists. T* **509** *and similar horiz design. Multicoloured. P* 13½.
1144 32 c. Type **509** 40 40
a. Horiz pair. Nos. 1144/5 .. .. 80 80
1145 32 c. Therese Casgrain 40 40

Nos. 1144/5 were printed together, *se-tenant*, in horizontal pairs throughout the sheet.

510 Gabriel Dumont (Métis leader) and Battle of Batoche, 1885

(Des R. Derreth. Litho Ashton-Potter)

1985 (6 May). *Centenary of the North-West Rebellion. P* 14 × 13½.
1146 **510** 32 c. blue, carmine and grey .. 30 20

511 Rear View, Parliament Building, Ottawa

512 Queen Elizabeth II

512*a* Queen Elizabeth II in 1984 (from photo by Karsh)

(Des R. Bellemare. Eng R. Couture (Nos. 1161/2). Des T. Yakobina and C. Candlish (Nos. 1162*a*/*b*), R. Harder (others))

1985 (21 June)–**89**. *No fluorescent bands* (1 *c. to* 6 *c.*) *or fluorescent frame* (34 *c.*, 36 *c.*, 37 *c.*, 38 *c.*).

(*a*) *T* **511** *and similar horiz designs*

(i) *Booklet stamps. Recess B.A.B.N. Chalk-surfaced paper* (37 *c.*) *or ordinary paper* (*others*). *P* 12½×12.

1147 – 1 c. grey-olive (30.3.87) 20 30
a. Booklet pane. Nos. 1147×2, 1150×2, 1152 and label .. 1·60
b. Chalk-surfaced paper (1.10.87) 20 30
ba. Booklet pane. Nos. 1147b×2, 1150a×2, 1152a and label .. 1·60
bb. Booklet pane. Nos. 1147b, 1150a×2, 1153 and two labels (3.2.88) .. .. .. 1·40
1148 – 2 c. bottle green 10 10
a. Booklet pane. Nos. 1148×3, 1149×2 and 1151 .. .. 1·60
b. Booklet pane. Nos. 1148×3, 1150*b*, 1154 and label (18.1.89) 45
1149 – 5 c. sepia 20 10
1150 – 6 c. chestnut (30.3.87) 25 10
a. Chalk-surfaced paper (1.10.87) 25 10
1150*b* – 6 c. blackish purple (18.1.89) .. 10 10
1151 **511** 34 c. blue-black 85 60
1152 36 c. reddish purple (30.3.87) .. 75 65
a. Chalk-surfaced paper (1.10.87) 75 65
1153 37 c. dull ultramarine (3.2.88) .. 55 40
1154 38 c. deep blue (18.1.89) 35 40

(ii) *Litho C.B.N.* (*Nos.* 1155 (*from sheets*), 1156/7*c*), *B.A.B.N.* (*No.* 1155 (*from booklets*)) *or Ashton-Potter* (*Nos.* 1155b, 1156a, 1157a/ba, 1157ca/cb). *Chalk-surfaced paper* (*Nos.* 1155b/ba, 1156, 1156b/bb *and* 1157c/cb). *P* 13×13½ (*No.* 1157*c*) *or* 13½×13 (*others*).

1155 **511** 34 c. multicoloured 50 10
a. Booklet pane. No. 1155×25 (1.8.85) .. .. .. 11·50
b. Perf 13½×14 (4.7.86) .. 65 40
ba. Booklet pane. No. 1155b×25 .. 11·50
1156 36 c. multicoloured (30.3.87) .. 30 35
a. Ordinary paper 30 35
b. Perf 13½×14 .. .. .. 45 35
ba. Booklet pane. No. 1156a×10 .. 3·00
bb. Booklet pane. No. 1156a×25 (19.5.87) .. .. .. 7·25
1157 – 37 c. multicoloured (30.12.87) .. 45 35
a. Perf 13½×14 (5.1.88) .. 50 45
ab. Booklet pane. No. 1157a×10 .. 5·00
ac. Booklet pane. No. 1157a×25 (2.5.88) .. .. .. 12·00
ad. Chalk-surfaced paper (5.1.88) 60 50
ae. Booklet pane. No. 1157ad×25 .. 15·00
1157*c* – 38 c. multicoloured (29.12.88) .. 35 40
ca. Booklet pane. No. 1157c×10 and two labels .. .. 3·50
cb. Booklet pane. No. 1157c×25 and two labels .. .. 9·00

(iii) *Coil stamps. Recess C.B.N. P* 10×*imperf*

1158 **511** 34 c. purple-brown (1.8.85) .. 80 80
a. Imperf (pair) .. .. ..
1159 36 c. carmine-vermilion (19.5.87) .. 55 55
1160 36 c. deep ultramarine (22.2.88) .. 40 40
a. Imperf (pair) £160
1160*b* 38 c. bottle green (1.2.89) 35 40

(*b*) *Recess and photo B.A.B.N. P* 13×13½

1161 **512** 34 c. black and cobalt (12.7.85) .. 45 25
1162 36 c. black & reddish pur (1.10.87) 75 60

(*c*) *Litho B.A.B.N.* (*Nos.* 1162*a*/*b*) *or Ashton-Potter* (*No.* 1162ba). *P* 13½×13 (*No.* 1162*a*) *or* 13×12½ (*No.* 1162*b*)

1162*a* **512***a* 37 c. multicoloured (30.12.87) .. 50 30
1162*b* 38 c. multicoloured (29.12.88) .. 35 40
ba. Perf 13×13½. Chalk-surfaced paper 35 40
bb. Booklet pane. No. 1162ba×10 and two labels .. .. 3·50

Designs:—1 c., 5 c., 6 c. (No. 1150*b*) East Block, Parliament Building; 2 c., 6 c. (No. 1150) West Block, Parliament Building; 37 c. (No. 1157) Front view, Parliament Building; 38 c. (No. 1157c) Side view, Parliament Building.

Stamps from booklet panes Nos. 1147a, 1147ba/bb and 1148a/b have one or two adjacent sides imperforate. Stamps from the first and last vertical columns of booklet panes Nos. 1155a, 1155ba, 1156ba/bb, 1157ab/ac, 1157ae, 1157ca/cb and 1162bb are imperforate at left or right. Those from the bottom row of No. 1157ac are also imperforate at foot.

Nos. 1157c and 1162*b* have a slightly larger design image, 22×17 mm.

(Des R. Harder. Litho Ashton-Potter)

1985 (28 June). *Canada Day. Forts* (2*nd series*). *Horiz designs as T* **481**. *Multicoloured. P* 12½×13.

1163 34 c. Lower Fort Garry, Manitoba (44×22 *mm*) 40 40
a. Booklet pane. Nos. 1163/62 .. .. 3·50
1164 34 c. Fort Anne, Nova Scotia 40 40
1165 34 c. Fort York, Ontario 40 40
1166 34 c. Castle Hill, Newfoundland (28×22 *mm*) 40 40
1167 34 c. Fort Whoop Up, Alberta (28×22 *mm*) 40 40
1168 34 c. Fort Erie, Ontario (44×22 *mm*) .. 40 40
1169 34 c. Fort Walsh, Saskatchewan 40 40
1170 34 c. Fort Lennox, Quebec 40 40
1171 34 c. York Redoubt, Nova Scotia (28×22 *mm*) 40 40
1172 34 c. Fort Frederick, Ontario (28×22 *mm*) 40 40
1163/72 .. .. .. *Set of* 10 3·50 3·50

Nos. 1163/72 were only available from $3.40 stamp booklets containing the *se-tenant* pane, No. 1163a.

MINIMUM PRICE

The minimum price quote is 10p which represents a handling charge rather than a basis for valuing common stamps. For further notes about prices see introductory pages.

513 Louis Hébert (apothecary)

514 Parliament Buildings and Map of World

515 Guide and Brownie Saluting

(Des C. Malenfant. Litho Ashton-Potter)

1985 (30 Aug). *45th International Pharmaceutical Sciences Congress of Pharmaceutical Federation, Montreal. Fluorescent frame. P* 12½.

1173 **513** 34 c. multicoloured 45 30

(Des E. Barenscher. Litho Ashton-Potter)

1985 (3 Sept). *74th Conference of Inter-Parliamentary Union, Ottawa. P* 13½.

1174 **514** 34 c. multicoloured 45 30

(Des Barbara Griffin. Recess and photo B.A.B.N.)

1985 (12 Sept). *75th Anniv of Girl Guide Movement. Fluorescent frame. P* 13½×13.

1175 **515** 34 c. multicoloured 45 30

516 Sisters Islets Lighthouse

517 Santa Claus in Reindeer-drawn Sleigh

(Des B. Reilander (No. **MS**1180), L. Rivard (others). Litho Ashton-Potter)

1985 (3 Oct). *Canadian Lighthouses* (2*nd series*). *T* **516** *and similar horiz designs. Multicoloured. P* 13½.

1176 34 c. Type **516** 60 75
a. Block of 4. Nos. 1176/9 .. .. 2·25
1177 34 c. Pelee Passage Lighthouse 60 75
1178 34 c. Haut-fond Prince Lighthouse 60 75
1179 34 c. Rose Blanche Lighthouse, Cains Island 60 75
1176/9 .. .. .. *Set of* 4 2·25 2·75
MS1180 109×90 mm. Nos. 1176/9 .. .. 2·25 2·75

Nos. 1176/9 were printed together, *se-tenant*, in different combinations throughout the sheet, giving ten blocks of 4 and ten single stamps.

No. **MS**1180 Publicises "Capex 87" International Stamp Exhibition, Toronto.

(Des Barbara Carroll and C. Yaneff. Litho Ashton-Potter)

1985 (23 Oct). *Christmas. Santa Claus Parade. T* **517** *and similar horiz designs. Multicoloured. P* 13½.

1181 32 c. Canada Post's parade float 35 10
a. Booklet pane. No. 1181×10 .. 3·25
1182 34 c. Type **517** 40 10
1183 39 c. Acrobats and horse-drawn carriage .. 45 60
1184 68 c. Christmas tree, pudding and goose on float 75 85
1181/4 .. .. .. *Set of* 4 1·75 1·50

No. 1181 was only available from $3.20 stamp booklets, which had the upper and lower edges of the pane imperforate. This value was intended for use on greeting cards posted on or before 31 January 1986, and represented a 2 c. saving of postage. After this date these stamps could be used for any postal purpose in conjunction with other values.

(Des E. Roch. Litho Ashton-Potter)

1985 (7 Nov). *Railway Locomotives* (3*rd series*). *Horiz designs as T* **503**. *Multicoloured. P* 12½×13.

1185 34 c. Class "K2" 35 20
a. Pair. Nos. 1185/6 .. .. 70 80
1186 34 c. Class "P2a" 35 20
1187 39 c. Class "O10a" 40 45
1188 68 c. Class "H4D" 65 70
1185/8 .. .. .. *Set of* 4 1·60 1·40

Nos. 1185/6 were printed together, *se-tenant*, in horizontal and vertical pairs throughout the sheet.

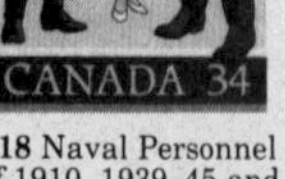

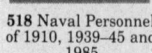

518 Naval Personnel of 1910, 1939–45 and 1985

519 "The Old Holton House, Montreal" (James Wilson Morrice)

(Des W. Southern and R. Tibbles. Litho C.B.N.)

1985 (8 Nov). *75th Anniv of Royal Canadian Navy. Fluorescent frame. P* 13½×13.

1189 **518** 34 c. multicoloured 45 30

(Des L. Parent and J. Morin. Litho C.B.N.)

1985 (15 Nov). *125th Anniv of Montreal Museum of Fine Arts. P* 13½.

1190 **519** 34 c. multicoloured 40 30

520 Map of Alberta showing Olympic Sites

(Des P.-Y. Pelletier. Litho Ashton-Potter)

1986 (13 Feb). *Winter Olympic Games, Calgary* (1988) (1*st issue*). *Fluorescent frame. P* 12½×13.

1191 **520** 34 c. multicoloured 40 40

See also Nos. 1216/17, 1236/7, 1258/9 and 1281/4.

521 Canada Pavilion

522 Molly Brant

(Des Debbie Adams. Recess and photo B.A.B.N.)

1986 (7 Mar). *"Expo '86" World Fair, Vancouver* (1*st issue*). *T* **521** *and similar horiz design. Multicoloured. Fluorescent frame. P* 13×13½.

1192 34 c. Type **521** 35 40
1193 39 c. Early telephone, dish aerial and satellite 40 60

See also Nos. 1196/7.

(Des Sara Tyson. Litho Ashton-Potter)

1986 (14 Apr). *250th Birth Anniv of Molly Brant* (*Iroquois leader*). *P* 13½.

1194 **522** 34 c. multicoloured 40 40

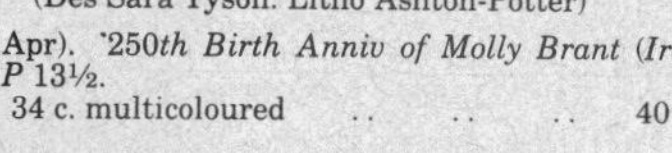

523 Philippe Aubert de Gaspé and Scene from *Les Anciens Canadiens*

524 Canadian Field Post Office and Cancellation, 1944

(Des Y. Paquin and P. Fontaine. Litho Ashton-Potter)

1986 (14 Apr). *Birth Bicentenary of Philippe Aubert de Gaspé* (*author*). *Fluorescent frame. P* 12½.

1195 **523** 34 c. multicoloured 40 40

(Des Debbie Adams. Recess and photo B.A.B.N.)

1986 (28 Apr). *"Expo '86" World Fair, Vancouver* (2*nd issue*). *Multicoloured designs as T* **521**. *Fluorescent frame. P* 13½×13 (34 *c.*) *or* 13×13½ (68 *c.*).

1196 34 c. Expo Centre, Vancouver (*vert*) .. 35 40
1197 68 c. Early and modern trains 70 75

(Des J. DesRosiers. Litho Ashton-Potter)

1986 (9 May). *75th Anniv of Canadian Forces Postal Service. P* 13½.

1198 **524** 34 c. multicoloured 40 40

525 Great Blue Heron

526 Railway Rotary Snowplough

(Des J.-L. Grondin and P. Fontaine. Litho Ashton-Potter)

1986 (22 May). *Birds of Canada. T* **525** *and similar horiz designs. Multicoloured. P* 13½.

1199 34 c. Type **525** 60 75
a. Block of 4. Nos. 1199/1202 .. .. 2·25
1200 34 c. Snow Goose 60 75
1201 34 c. Great Horned Owl 60 75
1202 34 c. Spruce Grouse 60 75
1199/1202 .. .. .. *Set of* 4 2·25 2·75

Nos. 1199/1202 were printed together, *se-tenant*, in different combinations throughout the sheet, giving ten blocks of 4 and ten single stamps.

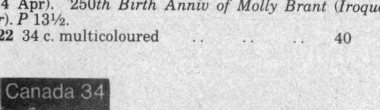

(Des R. Hill. Litho C.B.N.)

1986 (27 June). *Canada Day. Science and Technology. Canadian Inventions* (1st series). *T* **526** *and similar vert designs. Multicoloured. P* 13½.

1203 34 c. Type **526** 50 60

a. Block of 4. Nos. 1203/6 .. .. 1·75

1204 34 c. Space shuttle *Challenger* launching satellite with Canadarm 50 60

1205 34 c. Pilot wearing anti-gravity flight suit and "Spitfire" 50 60

1206 34 c. Variable-pitch propeller and Avro "504K" airplane 50 60

1203/6 .. .. *Set of* 4 1·75 2·25

Nos. 1203/6 were printed together, *se-tenant*, in blocks of 4 throughout the sheet.

See also Nos. 1241/4 and 1292/5.

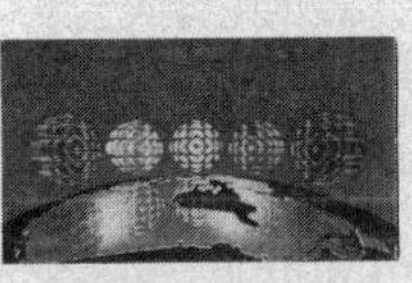

527 C.B.C. Logos over Map of Canada

528 Ice Age Artefacts, Tools and Settlement

(Des R. Mah and G. Tsetsekas. Litho Ashton-Potter)

1986 (23 July). *50th Anniv of Canadian Broadcasting Corporation. P* 12½.

1207 **527** 34 c. multicoloured 35 40

(Des F. Hagan. Litho Ashton-Potter)

1986 (29 Aug–1 Oct). *Exploration of Canada* (1st series). *Discoverers. T* **528** *and similar horiz designs. Multicoloured. P* 12½ × 13.

1208 34 c. Type **528** 35 50

a. Block of 4. Nos. 1208/11 .. .. 1·25

1209 34 c. Viking ships 35 50

1210 34 c. John Cabot's *Matthew*, 1497, compass and fish 35 50

1211 34 c. Henry Hudson cast adrift, 1611 .. 35 50

1208/11 .. .. *Set of* 4 1·25 1·75

MS1212 119 × 84 mm. Nos. 1208/11 .. .. 1·40 1·90

Nos. 1208/11 were printed together, *se-tenant*, in different combinations throughout the sheet, giving ten blocks of 4 and ten single stamps.

No. **MS**1212 publicises "Capex '87" International Stamp Exhibition, Toronto.

See also Nos. 1232/5, 1285/8 and 1319/22.

529 Crowfoot (Blackfoot Chief) and Indian Village

530 Peace Dove and Globe

(Des Wanda Lewicka and J. Morin. Litho C.B.N.)

1986 (5 Sept). *Founders of the Canadian West. T* **529** *and similar horiz design. Multicoloured. P* 13 × 13½.

1213 34 c. Type **529** 35 55

a. Pair. Nos. 1213/14 .. .. .. 70 1·10

1214 34 c. James Macleod of the North West Mounted Police and Fort Macleod .. 35 55

Nos. 1213/4 were printed together, *se-tenant*, in horizontal and vertical pairs throughout the sheet.

(Des Carole Jeghers. Litho and embossed Ashton-Potter)

1986 (16 Sept). *International Peace Year. P* 13½.

1215 **530** 34 c. multicoloured 35 40

531 Ice Hockey

532 Angel with Crown

(Des P.-Y. Pelletier. Litho C.B.N.)

1986 (15 Oct). *Winter Olympic Games, Calgary* (1988) (2nd issue). *T* **531** *and similar vert design. Multicoloured. P* 13½ × 13.

1216 34 c. Type **531** 45 70

a. Pair. Nos. 1216/17 .. .. .. 90 1·40

1217 34 c. Biathlon 45 70

Nos. 1216/17 were printed together, *se-tenant*, in horizontal and vertical pairs throughout the sheet.

See also Nos. 1236/7, 1258/9 and 1281/4.

(Des T. Dimson. Litho Ashton-Potter)

1986 (29 Oct). *Christmas. T* **532** *and similar multicoloured designs. Fluorescent frame* (34 *to* 68 *c.*). *P* 13½ × *imperf* (29 *c.*) *or* 12½ (*others*).

1218 29 c. Angel singing carol (36 × 22 *mm*) .. 30 15

a. Booklet pane. No. 1218 × 10 .. .. 3·00

1219 34 c. Type **532** 35 25

1220 39 c. Angel playing lute 40 45

1221 68 c. Angel with ribbon .. .. 70 1·00

1218/21 .. .. *Set of* 4 1·60 1·75

No. 1218 was only available from $2.90 stamp booklets, which had the sides of the pane imperforate. In addition to the design each stamp in the pane included an integral horizontal label showing a bar code. This value was intended for use on greeting cards posted on or before 31 January 1987, and represented a 5 c. saving when used in conjunction with special postcoded envelopes. These stamps were valid for normal postal purposes after 31 January when used with other values.

533 John Molson with Theatre Royal, Montreal, *Accommodation* (paddle-steamer) and Railway Train

534 Toronto's First Post Office

(Des C. Malenfant. Litho Ashton-Potter)

1986 (4 Nov). *150th Death Anniv of John Molson* (*businessman*). *P* 12½.

1222 **533** 34 c. multicoloured 35 40

(Des E. Roch. Litho Ashton-Potter)

1986 (21 Nov). *Railway Locomotives* (4*th series*). *Horiz designs as T* **503**, *but size* 60 × 22 *mm. Multicoloured. P* 12½ × 13.

1223 34 c. Class "V-1-a" 55 55

a. Pair. Nos. 1223/4 .. .. .. 1·10 1·10

1224 34 c. Class "T1a" 55 55

1225 39 c. Class "U-2-a" 65 65

1226 68 c. Class "H1c" 95 95

1223/6 .. .. *Set of* 4 2·40 2·40

Nos. 1223/6 were issued together, *se-tenant*, in horizontal and vertical pairs throughout the sheet.

(Des J. Mardon (stamps) and B. Reilander (sheet). Recess and litho B.A.B.N.)

1987 (16 Feb–12 June). *"Capex '87" International Stamp Exhibition, Toronto. T* **534** *and similar horiz designs showing Post Offices. Fluorescent frame. P* 13 × 13½.

1227 34 c. Type **534** 35 20

1228 36 c. Nelson-Miramichi, New Brunswick (12.6) 40 35

1229 42 c. Saint-Ours, Quebec (12.6) 45 45

1230 72 c. Battleford, Saskatchewan (12.6) .. 75 85

1227/30 .. .. *Set of* 4 1·75 1·60

MS1231 155 × 92 mm. 36 c. As No. 1227 and Nos. 1228/30 (12.6) .. .. 1·75 2·25

535 Étienne Brûlé exploring Lake Superior

(Des F. Hagan and J. Britton. Litho Ashton-Potter)

1987 (13 Mar). *Exploration of Canada* (2*nd series*). *Pioneers of New France. T* **535** *and similar horiz designs. Multicoloured. P* 12½ × 13.

1232 34 c. Type **535** 45 45

a. Block of 4. Nos. 1232/5 .. .. 1·60

1233 34 c. Radisson and des Groseilliers with British and French flags 45 45

1234 34 c. Jolliet and Father Marquette on the Mississippi 45 45

1235 34 c. Jesuit missionary preaching to Indians 45 45

1232/5 .. .. *Set of* 4 1·60 1·60

Nos. 1232/5 were printed together, *se-tenant*, in different combinations throughout the sheet, giving ten blocks of 4 and ten single stamps.

(Des P.-Y. Pelletier. Litho C.B.N.)

1987 (3 Apr). *Winter Olympic Games, Calgary* (1988) (3*rd issue*). *Vert designs as T* **531**. *Multicoloured. P* 13½ × 13.

1236 36 c. Speed skating 30 35

1237 42 c. Bobsleighing 40 45

536 Volunteer Activities

537 Canadian Coat of Arms

(Des W. Davies. Litho Ashton-Potter)

1987 (13 Apr). *National Volunteer Week. P* 12½ × 13.

1238 **536** 36 c. multicoloured 30 35

(Des R. Tibbles. Litho Ashton-Potter)

1987 (15 Apr). *5th Anniv of Canadian Charter of Rights and Freedoms. Fluorescent frame. P* 14 × 13½.

1239 **537** 36 c. multicoloured 30 35

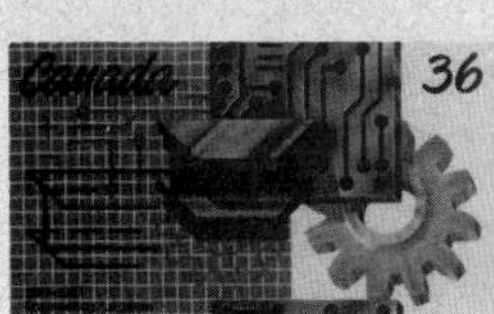

538 Steel Girder, Gear Wheel and Microchip

539 R. A. Fessenden (AM Radio)

(Des L. Holloway, R. Kerr and Nita Wallace. Litho Ashton-Potter)

1987 (19 May). *Centenary of Engineering Institute of Canada. P* 12½ × 13.

1240 **538** 36 c. multicoloured 30 35

(Des R. Hill. Litho C.B.N.)

1987 (25 June). *Canada Day. Science and Technology. Canadian Inventors* (2*nd series*). *T* **539** *and similar vert designs. Multicoloured. P* 13½.

1241 36 c. Type **539** 30 35

a. Block of four. Nos. 1241/4 .. .. 1·10

1242 36 c. C. Fenerty (newsprint pulp) 30 35

1243 36 c. G.-E. Desbarats and W. Leggo (half-tone engraving) 30 35

1244 36 c. F. N. Gisborne (first North American undersea telegraph) 30 35

1241/4 .. .. *Set of* 4 1·10 1·25

Nos. 1241/4 were printed together, *se-tenant*, in blocks of four throughout the sheet.

540 *Segwun*

541 Figurehead from *Hamilton*, 1813

(Des D. Champion. Litho C.B.N.)

1987 (20 July). *Canadian Steamships. T* **540** *and similar multicoloured design. P* 13.

1245 36 c. Type **540** 40 50

a. Horiz pair. Nos. 1245/6 .. .. 80 1·00

1246 36 c. *Princess Marguerite* (52 × 22 *mm*) .. 40 50

Nos. 1245/6 were printed together horizontally, *se-tenant*, throughout the sheet of 25, with No. 1245 occurring in columns 1, 3 and 5 and No. 1246 in columns 2 and 4.

(Des L.-A. Rivard. Litho Ashton-Potter)

1987 (7 Aug). *Historic Shipwrecks. T* **541** *and similar horiz designs. Multicoloured. P* 13½ × 13.

1247 36 c. Type **541** 30 35

a. Block of four. Nos. 1247/50 .. .. 1·10

1248 36 c. Hull of *San Juan*, 1565 .. .. .. 30 35

1249 36 c. Wheel from *Breadalbane*, 1853 .. 30 35

1250 36 c. Bell from *Ericsson*, 1892 .. .. 30 35

1247/50 .. .. *Set of* 4 1·10 1·25

Nos. 1247/50 were printed together, *se-tenant*, in different combinations throughout the sheet, giving ten blocks of 4 and ten single stamps.

542 Air Canada Boeing "767" and Globe

543 Summit Symbol

(Des D. Carter and Debbie Adams. Litho C.B.N.)

1987 (1 Sept). *50th Anniv of Air Canada. P* 13½.

1251 **542** 36 c. multicoloured 30 35

(Des C. Gaudreau. Litho Ashton-Potter)

1987 (2 Sept). *2nd International Francophone Summit, Quebec. Fluorescent frame. P* 13 × 12½.

1252 **543** 36 c. multicoloured 30 35

544 Commonwealth Symbol

545 Poinsettia

(Des G. Tsetsekas. Litho Ashton-Potter)

1987 (13 Oct). *Commonwealth Heads of Government Meeting, Vancouver. Fluorescent frame. P* 13 × 12½.
1253 **544** 36 c. multicoloured 35 40

(Des C. Simard. Litho Ashton-Potter)

1987 (2 Nov). *Christmas. Christmas Plants. T* **545** *and similar multicoloured designs. Fluorescent frame. P* 12½ × 13 (31 c.) *or* 13½ (*others*).
1254 31 c. Decorated Christmas tree and presents (36 × 20 *mm*) 30 35
a. Booklet pane. No. 1254 × 10 .. .. 3·00
1255 36 c. Type **545** 35 40
1256 42 c. Holly wreath 40 45
1257 72 c. Mistletoe and decorated tree 65 70
1254/7 .. .. *Set of* 4 1·50 1·75
On No. 1254 the left-hand third of the design area is taken up by a bar code which has fluorescent bands between the bars. This value was only available from $3.10 stamp booklets which had the sides of the pane imperforate. This value was intended for use on greeting cards posted on or before 31 January 1988 and represented a 5 c. saving when used in conjunction with special postcoded envelopes.

(Des P.-Y. Pelletier. Litho C.B.N.)

1987 (13 Nov). *Winter Olympic Games, Calgary* (1988) (*4th issue*). *Vert designs as T* **531**. *Multicoloured. Fluorescent frame. P* 13½ × 13.
1258 36 c. Cross-country skiing 35 40
a. Pair. Nos. 1258/9 .. .. .. 70 80
1259 36 c. Ski-jumping 35 40
Nos. 1258/9 were printed together, *se-tenant*, in horizontal and vertical pairs throughout the sheet.

546 Football, Grey Cup and Spectators

(Des L. Holloway. Litho Ashton-Potter)

1987 (20 Nov). *75th Grey Cup Final (Canadian football championship), Vancouver. Fluorescent frame. P* 12½.
1260 **546** 36 c. multicoloured 35 40

547 Flying Squirrel **548** Lynx

548a Runnymede Library, Toronto

(Des Gottschalk & Ash International (1 c. to 25 c.), B. Tsang (43 c. to 76 c.), R. Bellemare ($1, $2). Litho Ashton-Potter (1 c. to 76 c.). Recess and litho B.A.B.N. ($1, $2))

1988 (18 Jan)–**89**. *Canadian Mammals and Architecture. Multicoloured. Fluorescent frame* (10 c. *to* 76 c.) *or no fluorescent frame* (*others*).

(*a*) *Horiz designs as T* **547**. *Chalk-surfaced paper. P* 13×13½
1261 1 c. Type **547** (3.10.88) 10 10
1262 2 c. Porcupine (3.10.88) 10 10
1263 3 c. Muskrat (3.10.88) 10 10
1264 5 c. Varying Hare (3.10.88) 10 10
1265 6 c. Red Fox (3.10.88) 10 10
1266 10 c. Striped Skunk (3.10.88) 10 10
1267 25 c. American Beaver (3.10.88) 25 30

(*b*) *Horiz designs as T* **548**. *Chalk-surfaced paper* (57 c.) *or ordinary paper* (*others*). *P* 12×12½ (43, 57, 74 c.) *or* 14½×14 (*others*)
1268 43 c. Type **548** 50 50
1269 44 c. Walrus (18.1.89) 40 45
a. Chalk-surfaced paper (9.6.89) .. 40 45
b. Perf 12½×13. Chalk-surfaced paper 40 45
ba. Booklet pane. No. 1269b×5 and label with margins all round .. .. 2·10
1270 57 c. Killer Whale 70 70
a. Ordinary paper (26.9.88) 70 70
1271 59 c. Musk Ox (18.1.89) 55 60
1272 74 c. Wapiti 85 85
1273 76 c. Brown Bear (18.1.89) 70 75
a. Chalk-surfaced paper (25.8.89) .. 70 75
b. Perf 12½×13. Chalk-surfaced paper 70 75
ba. Booklet pane. No. 1273b×5 and label with margins all round .. .. 3·50

(*c*) *Horiz designs as T* **548a**. *Ordinary paper. P* 13½
1275 $1 Type **548a** (5.5.89) .. .. ..
1276 $2 McAdam Railway Station, New Brunswick (5.5.89) .. .. 1·90 2·00
1261/76 .. .. *Set of* 15 6·25 6·50
The 44, 59 and 76 c. values are slightly larger than the original three, measuring 27×21 mm.
Nos. 1269b and 1273b were only issued in stamp booklets.

(Des P.-Y. Pelletier. Litho Ashton-Potter)

1988 (12 Feb). *Winter Olympic Games, Calgary* (*5th issue*). *Vert designs as T* **531**. *Multicoloured. Fluorescent frame. P* 12×12½ (37 *c.*) *or* 12½ (*others*).
1281 37 c. Slalom skiing 40 40
a. Pair. Nos. 1281/2 .. .. .. 80 80
1282 37 c. Curling 40 40
1283 43 c. Figure skating 45 45
1284 74 c. Luge 70 70
1281/4 .. .. *Set of* 4 1·75 1·75
Nos. 1281/2 were printed together, *se-tenant*, in horizontal and vertical pairs throughout the sheet.

549 Trade Goods, Blackfoot Encampment and Page from Anthony Henday's Journal

(Des F. Hagan. Litho Ashton-Potter)

1988 (17 Mar). *Exploration of Canada* (*3rd series*). *Explorers of the West. T* **549** *and similar horiz designs. Multicoloured. Fluorescent frame. P* 12½×13.
1285 37 c. Type **549** 35 40
a. Block of 4. Nos. 1285/8 .. .. 1·25
1286 37 c. *Discovery* and map of George Vancouver's voyage 35 40
1287 37 c. Simon Fraser's expedition portaging canoes 35 40
1288 37 c. John Palliser's surveying equipment and view of prairie 35 40
1285/8 .. .. *Set of* 4 1·25 1·40
Nos. 1285/8 were printed together, *se-tenant*, in different combinations throughout the sheet, giving ten blocks of 4 and ten single stamps.

550 "The Young Reader" (Ozias Leduc) **551** Duck landing on Marsh

(Des P.-Y. Pelletier. Eng G. Prosser. Recess and photo B.A.B.N.)

1988 (20 May). *Canadian Art* (1*st series*). *No fluorescent bands. P* 13×13½.
1289 **550** 50 c. multicoloured 50 70
No. 1289 was issued in sheets of 16 with descriptive texts on the margins.
See also No. 1327.

(Des T. Telmet and J. Gault. Litho C.B.N.)

1988 (1 June). *Wildlife and Habitat Conservation. T* **551** *and similar horiz design. Multicoloured. Fluorescent frame. P* 13 × 13½.
1290 37 c. Type **551** 35 40
a. Pair. Nos. 1290/1 .. .. .. 70 80
1291 37 c. Moose feeding in marsh 35 40
Nos. 1290/1 were printed together, *se-tenant*, in horizontal and vertical pairs throughout the sheet.

552 Kerosene Lamp and Diagram of Distillation Plant **553** Short-tailed Swallowtail

(Des R. Hill. Litho Ashton-Potter)

1988 (17 June). *Canada Day. Science and Technology. Canadian Inventions* (*3rd series*). *T* **552** *and similar vert designs. Multicoloured. Fluorescent frame. P* 12½×13.
1292 37 c. Type **552** 35 40
a. Block of 4. Nos. 1292/5 .. .. 1·25
1293 37 c. Ears of Marquis wheat 35 40
1294 37 c. Electron microscope and magnified image 35 40
1295 37 c. Patient under "Cobalt 60" cancer therapy 35 40
1292/5 .. .. *Set of* 4 1·25 1·40
Nos. 1292/5 were printed together, *se-tenant*, in blocks of four throughout the sheet.

(Des Heather Cooper. Litho Ashton-Potter)

1988 (4 July). *Canadian Butterflies. T* **553** *and similar vert designs. Multicoloured. Fluorescent frame. P* 12×12½.
1296 37 c. Type **553** 35 40
a. Block of four. Nos. 1296/9 .. .. 1·25
1297 37 c. Northern Blue 35 40
1298 37 c. Macoun's Arctic 35 40
1299 37 c. Canadian Tiger Swallowtail 35 40
1296/9 .. .. *Set of* 4 1·25 1·40
Nos. 1296/9 were printed together, *se-tenant*, in different combinations throughout the sheet, giving ten blocks of 4 and ten single stamps.

554 St. John's Harbour Entrance and Skyline **555** Club Members working on Forestry Project and Rural Scene

(Des L.-A. Rivard. Litho Ashton-Potter)

1988 (22 July). *Centenary of Incorporation of St. John's, Newfoundland. Fluorescent frame. P* 13½×13.
1300 **554** 37 c. multicoloured 35 40

(Des Debbie Adams. Litho Ashton-Potter)

1988 (5 Aug). *75th Anniv of 4-H Clubs. Fluorescent frame. P* 13½×13.
1301 **555** 37 c. multicoloured 35 40

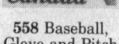

556 Saint-Maurice Ironworks **557** Tahltan Bear Dog

(Des Hélène Racicot and Michèle Cayer. Eng Y. Baril. Recess and litho C.B.N.)

1988 (19 Aug). *250th Anniv of Saint-Maurice Ironworks, Québec. Fluorescent frame. P* 13½.
1302 **556** 37 c. black, pale orange and cinnamon 35 40

(Des Mia Lane and D. Nethercott. Litho Ashton-Potter)

1988 (26 Aug). *Canadian Dogs. T* **557** *and similar horiz designs. Multicoloured. Fluorescent frame. P* 12½×12.
1303 37 c. Type **557** 35 40
a. Block of 4. Nos. 1303/6 .. .. 1·25
1304 37 c. Nova Scotia Duck Tolling Retriever .. 35 40
1305 37 c. Canadian Eskimo Dog 35 40
1306 37 c. Newfoundland 35 40
1303/6 .. .. *Set of* 4 1·25 1·40
Nos. 1303/6 were printed together, *se-tenant*, in different combinations throughout the sheet, giving ten blocks of 4 and ten single stamps.

558 Baseball, Glove and Pitch **559** Virgin with Inset of Holy Child

(Des L. Holloway. Litho C.B.N.)

1988 (14 Sept). *150th Anniv of Baseball in Canada. Fluorescent frame. P* 13½ × 13.
1307 **558** 37 c. multicoloured 35 40

(Des E. Roch and T. Yakobina. Litho Ashton-Potter)

1988 (27 Oct). *Christmas. Icons. T* **559** *and similar multicoloured designs. Fluorescent frame. P* 12½×13 (32 *c.*) *or* 13½ (*others*).
1308 32 c. Holy Family (36×21 *mm*) 30 35
a. Booklet pane. No. 1308×10 .. .. 3·00
1309 37 c. Type **559** 35 40
1310 43 c. Virgin and Child 40 45
1311 74 c. Virgin and Child (*different*) .. 70 75
1308/11 .. .. *Set of* 4 1·60 1·75
On No. 1308 the left-hand third of the design area is taken up by a bar code which has fluorescent bands between the bars. This value was only available from $3.20 stamp booklets which had the sides and bottom of the pane imperforate. It was intended for use on greeting cards posted on or before 31 January 1989.
No. 1309 also commemorates the Millenium of Ukrainian Christianity.

560 Bishop Inglis and Nova Scotia Church

561 Frances Ann Hopkins and "Canoe Manned by Voyageurs"

(Des S. Slipp and K. Sollows. Litho Ashton-Potter)

1988 (1 Nov). *Bicentenary of Consecration of Charles Inglis (first Canadian Anglican bishop) (1987). Fluorescent frame. P* 12½ × 12.

1312 **560** 37 c. multicoloured 35 40

(Des D. Nethercott. Litho Ashton-Potter)

1988 (18 Nov). *150th Birth Anniv of Frances Ann Hopkins (artist). Fluorescent frame. P* 13½ × 13.

1313 **561** 37 c. multicoloured 35 40

562 Angus Walters and *Bluenose* (schooner)

563 Chipewyan Canoe

(Des R. Hill. Litho Ashton-Potter)

1988 (18 Nov). *20th Death Anniv of Angus Walters (yachtsman). Fluorescent frame. P* 13½.

1314 **562** 37 c. multicoloured 35 40

(Des L.-A. Rivard and B. Leduc. Litho Ashton-Potter)

1989 (1 Feb). *Small Craft of Canada (1st series). Native Canoes. T* **563** *and similar horiz designs. Multicoloured. Fluorescent frame. P* 13½ × 13.

1315 38 c. Type **563** 35 40
a. Block of 4. Nos. 1315/18 . . . . 1·25
1316 38 c. Haida canoe 35 40
1317 38 c. Inuit kayak 35 40
1318 38 c. Micmac canoe 35 40
1315/18 . . . . . . *Set of* 4 1·25 1·40

Nos. 1315/18 were printed together, *se-tenant*, throughout the sheet, giving ten blocks of 4 and ten single stamps.

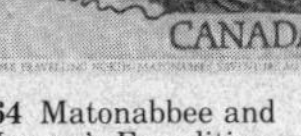

564 Matonabbee and Hearne's Expedition

565 Construction of Victoria Bridge, Montreal and William Notman

(Des F. Hagan. Litho Ashton-Potter)

1989 (22 Mar). *Exploration of Canada (4th series). Explorers of the North. T* **564** *and similar horiz designs. Multicoloured. Fluorescent frame. P* 12½×13.

1319 38 c. Type **564** 40 45
a. Block of 4. Nos. 1319/22 . . . . 1·40
1320 38 c. Relics of Franklin's expedition and White Ensign 40 45
1321 38 c. Joseph Tyrrell's compass, hammer and fossil 40 45
1322 38 c. Vilhjalmur Stefansson, camera on tripod and sledge dog team 40 45
1319/22 . . . . . . *Set of* 4 1·40 1·60

Nos. 1319/22 were printed together, *se-tenant*, in different combinations throughout the sheet, giving ten blocks of 4 and ten single stamps.

(Des J. Morin and T. Yakobina. Litho Ashton-Potter)

1989 (23 June). *Canada Day. "150 Years of Canadian Photography". T* **565** *and similar horiz designs, each showing early photograph and photographer. Multicoloured. P* 12½×12.

1323 38 c. Type **565** 40 45
a. Block of 4. Nos. 1323/6 . . . . 1·40
1324 38 c. Plains Indian village and W. Hanson Boorne 40 45
1325 38 c. Horse-drawn sleigh and Alexander Henderson 40 45
1326 38 c. Quebec street scene and Jules-Ernest Livernois 40 45
1323/6 . . . . . . *Set of* 4 1·40 1·60

Nos. 1323/6 were printed together, *se-tenant*, in blocks of 4 throughout the sheet.

NEW INFORMATION

The editor is always interested to correspond with people who have new information that will improve or correct the Catalogue.

566 Tsimshian Ceremonial Frontlet, *c* 1900

567 Canadian Flag and Forest

(Des P.-Y. Pelletier. Litho and die-stamped Ashton-Potter)

1989 (29 June). *Canadian Art (2nd series). No fluorescent bands. P* 12½×13.

1327 **566** 50 c. multicoloured 55 60

No. 1327 was issued in a similar sheet format to No. 1289

(Des Gottschalk & Ash International. Litho Ashton-Potter)

1989 (30 June). *Self-adhesive booklet stamp. Fluorescent frame. Die-cut.*

1328 **567** 38 c. multicoloured 40 45
a. Booklet pane. No. 1328×12 . . 4·75

No. 1328 was only available from $5 self-adhesive booklets in which the backing card forms the booklet cover.

568 Archibald Lampman

569 Spindle Coral

(Des R. Milot. Litho Ashton-Potter)

1989 (7 July). *Canadian Poets. T* **568** *and similar horiz design. Multicoloured. Fluorescent frame. P* 13½.

1329 38 c. Type **568** 40 45
a. Pair. Nos. 1329/30 . . . . 80 90
1330 38 c. Louis-Honoré Fréchette 40 45

Nos. 1329/30 were printed together, *se-tenant*, in horizontal and vertical pairs throughout the sheet.

(Des E. Roch. Litho Ashton-Potter)

1989 (4 Aug). *Mushrooms. T* **569** *and similar vert designs. Multicoloured. Fluorescent frame. P* 13½.

1331 38 c. Type **569** 40 45
a. Block of 4. Nos. 1331/4 . . . . 1·40
1332 38 c. Admirable Boletus 40 45
1333 38 c. Cinnabar Chantarelle 40 45
1334 38 c. Common Morel 40 45
1331/4 . . . . . . *Set of* 4 1·40 1·60

Nos. 1331/4 were printed together, *se-tenant*, in different combinations throughout the sheet, giving ten blocks of 4 and ten single stamps.

570 Night Patrol, Korea

571 Globe in Box

(Des T. Telmet, N. Fontaine and J. Gault. Eng Y. Baril. Recess and litho C.B.N.)

1989 (8 Sept). *75th Annivs of Canadian Regiments. T* **570** *and similar horiz design. Multicoloured. Fluorescent frame. P* 13.

1335 38 c. Type **570** (Princess Patricia's Canadian Light Infantry) 40 45
a. Vert pair. Nos. 1335/6 . . . . 80 90
1336 38 c. Trench raid, France, 1914-18 (Royal 22e Régiment) 40 45

Nos. 1335/6 were printed together, *se-tenant*, in vertical pairs throughout the sheet.

(Des L. Holloway and Nita Wallace. Litho Ashton-Potter)

1989 (2 Oct). *Canada Export Trade Month. Fluorescent frame. P* 13½×13.

1337 **571** 38 c. multicoloured 40 45

572 Film Director

573 "Snow II" (Lawren S. Harris)

(Des W. Tibbles from paper sculptures by J. Milne. Litho Ashton-Potter)

1989 (4 Oct). *Arts and Entertainment. T* **572** *and similar vert designs. Fluorescent frame. P* 13×13½.

1338 38 c. grey-brown, blackish brown and bright reddish violet 40 45
a. Block of 4. Nos. 1338/41 . . . . 1·50
1339 38 c. grey-brown, blackish brown & brt grn 40 45
1340 38 c. grey-brn, blackish brn & brt magenta 40 45
1341 38 c. grey-brown, blackish brown & new bl 40 45
1338/41 . . . . . . *Set of* 4 1·50 1·60

Designs:—No. 1339, Actors; No. 1340, Dancers; No. 1341, Musicians.

Nos. 1338/41 were printed together, *se-tenant*, in different combinations throughout the sheet, giving ten blocks of 4 and ten single stamps.

(Des D. Nethercott and Viviane Warburton. Litho Ashton-Potter)

1989 (26 Oct). *Christmas. Paintings of Winter Landscapes. T* **573** *and similar multicoloured designs. Fluorescent frame. P* 12½×13 (33 *c.*), 13×13½ (38 *c.*) *or* 13½ (*others*).

1342 33 c. "Champ-de-Mars, Winter" (William Brymner) (35×21 *mm*) 35 40
a. Booklet pane. No. 1342×10 . . . . 3·50
1343 38 c. "Bend in the Gosselin River" (Marc-Aurèle Suzor-Coté) (21×35 *mm*) . . 40 45
a. Perf 13×12½ 40 45
ab. Booklet pane. No. 1343a×10 . . 4·00
1344 44 c. Type **573** 45 50
a. Booklet pane. No. 1344×5 plus one printed label . . . . 2·25
1345 76 c. "Ste. Agnès" (A. H. Robinson) . . 80 85
a. Booklet pane. No. 1345×5 plus one printed label . . . . 4·00
1342/5 . . . . . . *Set of* 4 1·75 2·00

On No. 1342 the left-hand third of the design area is taken up by a bar code which has fluorescent bands between the bars. This value was only available from $3.30 stamp booklets which had the sides and bottom of the pane imperforate. It was intended for use on greeting cards posted on or before 31 January 1990.

No. 1343a was only issued in $3.80 stamp booklets.

Booklet pane No. 1343ab has the outer edges of the pane imperforate while Nos. 1344a and 1345a have the vertical edges imperforate.

574 Canadians listening to Declaration of War, 1939

(Des J.-P. Armanville and P.-Y. Pelletier. Litho C.B.N.)

1989 (10 Nov). *50th Anniv of Outbreak of Second World War. T* **574** *and similar horiz designs. Fluorescent frame. P* 13½.

1346 38 c. black, silver and slate-purple . . 40 45
a. Block of 4. Nos. 1346/9 . . . . 1·50
1347 38 c. black, silver and olive-grey . . 40 45
1348 38 c. black, silver and grey-green . . 40 45
1349 38 c. black, silver and azure . . 40 45
1346/9 . . . . . . *Set of* 4 1·50 1·60

Designs:—No. 1347, Army mobilization; No. 1348, British Commonwealth air crew training; No. 1349, North Atlantic convoy.

Nos. 1346/9 were printed together, *se-tenant*, in different combinations throughout the sheet, giving four blocks of 4.

Index to Canada Stamp Designs from 1942

The following index is intended to facilitate the identification of Canadian issues from 1942. Portrait stamps are usually listed under surnames only, views under the name of the town or city and other issues under the main subject or a prominent word and date chosen from the inscription. Simple abbreviations have occasionally been resorted to and when the same design or subject appears on more than one stamp, only the first of each series is indicated.

Index to Canada Stamp Designs from 1942—*Continued*

REGISTRATION STAMPS

R 1

(Eng and recess – printed British-American Bank Note Co, Montreal and Ottawa)

1875 (15 Nov)–**92.** *White wove paper.* (*a*) *P* 12 (*or slightly under*).

R 1	R 1	2 c. orange	55·00	1·00
R 2		2 c. orange-red (1889)	60·00	6·00
R 3		2 c. vermilion	70·00	7·00
		a. Imperf (pair)		
R 4		2 c. rose-carmine (1888)	£110	32·00
R 5		5 c. yellow-green (1878)	70·00	1·00
R 6		5 c. deep green	60·00	1·00
		a. Imperf (pair)	£600	
R 7		5 c. blue-green (1888)	75·00	1·25
R 7*a*		5 c. dull sea-green (1892)	85·00	3·25
R 8		8 c. bright blue	£325	£225
R 9		8 c. dull blue	£325	£225
		(*b*) *P* 12 × 11½ *or* 12 × 11¾		
R10	R 1	2 c. orange	£180	50·00
R11		5 c. green (*shades*)	£325	£120

SPECIAL DELIVERY STAMPS

PRINTERS. The following Special Delivery and Postage Due Stamps were recess-printed by the American Bank Note Co (to 1928), the British American Bank Note Co (to 1934), and the Canadian Bank Note Co (1935 onwards).

S 1

1898–1920. *P* 12.

S1	S 1	10 c. blue-green (28.6.98)	60·00	6·00
S2		10 c. deep green (12.13)	35·00	4·50
S3		10 c. yellowish green (8.20)	35·00	3·75

The differences between Types I and II (figures "10" with and without shading) formerly illustrated were due to wear of the plate. There was only one die.

S 2

S 3 Mail-carrying, 1867 and 1927

1922 (21 Aug). *P* 12.

S4	S 2	20 c. carmine-red	30·00	2·50

No. S4 exists in two slightly different sizes due to the use of "wet" or "dry" printing processes. See note below No. 195.

1927 (29 June). *60th Anniversary of Confederation. P* 12.

S5	S 3	20 c. orange	8·00	6·50

No. S5 exists imperforate, imperf × perf or perf × imperf.

S 4

1930 (2 Sept). *P* 11.

S6	S 4	20 c. brown-red	35·00	4·00

1932 (24 Dec). *Type as* S 4, *but inscr* "CENTS" *in place of* "TWENTY CENTS". *P* 11.

S7	20 c. brown-red	38·00	11·00

S 5 Allegory of Progress

(Des A. Foringer)

1935 (1 June). *P* 12.

S8	S 5	20 c. scarlet	3·50	1·25

No. S8 exists imperforate.

S 6 Canadian Coat of Arms

1938–39. *P* 12.

S 9	S 6	10 c. green (1.4.39)	7·00	55
S10		20 c. scarlet (15.6.38)	26·00	22·00

Nos. S9/10 exist imperforate.

≡10 10≡

(S 7)

1939 (1 Mar). *Surch with Type* **S 7.**

S11	S 6	10 c. on 20 c. scarlet	5·50	6·50

S 8 Coat of Arms and Flags

S 9 Trans-Canada Plane

1942 (1 July)–**1943.** *War Effort. P* 12. (*a*) *Postage.*

S12	S 8	10 c. green	1·75	20
		(*b*) *Air*		
S13	S 9	16 c. ultramarine	1·75	20
S14		17 c. ultramarine (1.4.43)	1·75	30

Nos. S12/14 exist imperforate.

S 10 Arms of Canada and Peace Symbols

S 11 Transatlantic Plane over Quebec

1946 (16 Sept)–**1947.** *P* 12. (*a*) *Postage.*

S15	S 10	10 c. green	1·25	20
		(*b*) *Air.* (i) *Circumflex accent in* "EXPRÊS"		
S16	S 11	17 c. ultramarine	3·00	2·50
		(ii) *Grave accent in* "EXPRÈS"		
S17	S 11	17 c. ultramarine (1947)	3·00	2·50

POSTAGE DUE STAMPS

PRINTERS. See note under "Special Delivery Stamps".

D 1

D 2

1906 (1 July)–**28.** *P* 12.

D1	D 1	1 c. dull violet	6·00	2·50
D2		1 c. red violet (1916)	8·00	2·75
		a. Thin paper (10.24)	13·00	13·00
D3		2 c. dull violet	9·00	70
D4		2 c. red-violet (1917)	8·00	80
		a. Thin paper (10.24)	17·00	10·00
D5		4 c. violet (3.7.28)	45·00	40·00
D6		5 c. dull violet	10·00	1·25
D7		5 c. red-violet (1917)	10·00	1·25
		a. Thin paper (10.24)	15·00	10·00
D8		10 c. violet (3.7.28)	28·00	12·00
D1/8		*Set of* 5	85·00	50·00

The 1 c., 2 c. and 5 c. values exist imperforate.

Printings up to October 1924 used the "wet" method, those from mid 1925 onwards the "dry". For details of the differences between these two methods, see above No. 196.

1930–2. *P* 11.

D 9	D 2	1 c. bright violet (14.7.30)	8·00	9·00
D10		2 c. bright violet (21.8.30)	6·50	85
D11		4 c. bright violet (14.10.30)	15·00	8·00
D12		5 c. bright violet (12.12.31)	11·00	12·00
D13		10 c. bright violet (24.8.32)	65·00	23·00
D9/13		*Set of* 5	95·00	48·00

Nos. D9/11 and D13 exist imperforate.

D 3

D 4

D 5

1933–4. *P* 11.

D14	D 3	1 c. violet (5.5.34)	7·00	10·00
D15		2 c. violet (20.12.33)	4·75	3·00
D16		4 c. violet (12.12.33)	10·00	7·50
D17		10 c. violet (20.12.33)	15·00	13·00
D14/17		*Set of* 4	32·00	30·00

No. D14 exists imperforate.

1935–65. *P* 12.

D18	D 4	1 c. violet (14.10.35)	40	10
D19		2 c. violet (9.9.35)	40	10
D20		3 c. violet (4.65)	2·50	7·00
D21		4 c. violet (2.7.35)	80	10
D22		5 c. violet (12.48)	65	25
D23		6 c. violet (1957)	1·50	4·50
D24		10 c. violet (16.9.35)	60	10
D18/24		*Set of* 7	6·00	11·00

The 1 c., 2 c., 4 c. and 10 c., exist imperforate.

1967–78. *Litho. P* 12½ × 12 (20 c., 24 c., 50 c.) *or* 12 (*others*).

		(*a*) *Size* 20 × 17½ *mm*		
D25	D 5	1 c. scarlet (3.67)	1·00	1·75
D26		2 c. scarlet (3.67)	1·00	60
D27		3 c. scarlet (3.67)	1·00	2·00
D28		4 c. scarlet (2.67)	2·25	1·25
D29		5 c. scarlet (3.67)	3·50	3·25
D30		6 c. scarlet (2.67)	1·60	3·00
D31		10 c. scarlet (1.67)	2·00	2·50
D25/31		*Set of* 7	11·00	13·00
		(*b*) *Size* 19½ × 16 *mm*		
D32	D 5	1 c. scarlet (12.70)	30	30
		a. Perf 12½ × 12 (11.77)	15	60
D33		2 c. scarlet (1972)	25	1·25
D34		3 c. scarlet (1.74)	60	1·50
D35		4 c. scarlet (4.69)	85	75
		a. Perf 12½ × 12 (11.77)	45	1·25
D36		5 c. scarlet (2.69)	20·00	32·00
		a. Perf 12½ × 12 (11.77)	50	1·50
D37		6 c. scarlet (1972)	1·50	2·75
D38		8 c. scarlet (1.69)	75	60
		a. Perf 12½ × 12 (28.6.78)	1·00	1·60
D39		10 c. scarlet (4.69)	1·25	60
		a. Perf 12½ × 12 (9.77)	60	80
D40		12 c. scarlet (1.69)	1·25	65
		a. Perf 12½ × 12 (9.77)	1·50	2·00
D41		16 c. scarlet (1.74)	70	2·00
D42		20 c. scarlet (10.77)	60	1·50
D43		24 c. scarlet (10.77)	60	1·75
D44		50 c. scarlet (10.77)	1·00	2·25
D32a/44		*Set of* 13	8·00	16·00

There are no records of dates of issue of the above but supplies were distributed to depots in the months indicated.

Both white and ordinary papers have been used for Nos. D32/41. These are listed in Stanley Gibbons *Two Reigns Catalogue.*

OFFICIAL STAMPS

We do not list stamps perforated "O.H.M.S."

O.H.M.S.

(O 1)

1949. *Nos.* 375/6, 378, 380 *and* 402/7 *optd as Type* O 1.

(a) Postage

O1 **111** 1 c. green .. 1·00 1·75
a. Missing stop after "S" .. £110 40·00
O2 **112** 2 c. brown .. 8·00 10·00
a. Missing stop after "S" .. £120 80·00
O3 **113** 3 c. purple .. 1·00 1·10
O4 **112** 4 c. carmine-lake .. 1·25 30
O5 – 10 c. olive-green .. 2·50 15
a. Missing stop after "S" .. 60·00 26·00
O6 – 14 c. sepia .. 4·00 80
a. Missing stop after "S" .. 75·00 40·00
O7 – 20 c. slate .. 8·50 60
a. Missing stop after "S" .. £110 40·00
O8 – 50 c. green .. £160 £100
a. Missing stop after "S" .. £500 £300
O9 – $1 purple .. 45·00 40·00
a. Missing stop after "S" .. £750 £650

(b) Air

O10 – 7 c. blue .. 12·00 2·50
a. Missing stop after "S" .. £110 60·00
O1/10 .. *Set of* 10 £225 £140

MISSING STOP VARIETIES. These occur on R.6/2 of the lower left pane (Nos. O1a, O2a and O15a) or R.10/2 of the lower left pane (Nos. O5a, O6a, O7a, O8a, O9a and O10a).

1949–50. *Nos.* 414/15, 416/17, 418 *and* 431 *optd as Type* O 1.

O11 **135** 1 c. green .. 20 20
O12 **136** 2 c. sepia .. 35 45
O13 **137** 3 c. purple .. 40 25
O14 **138** 4 c. carmine-lake .. 55 10
O15 **139** 5 c. blue (1949) .. 1·00 65
a. Missing stop after "S" .. 65·00 32·00
O16 **141** 50 c. green (1950) .. 26·00 20·00
O11/16 .. *Set of* 6 26·00 20·00

G (O 2) **G** (O 3) **G** (O 4)

Type O **4** differs from Type O **3** in having a thinner appearance and an upward sloping left serif to the lower arm. It results from a new plate introduced in 1961/62. Variations in thickness are known in Type O **2** but these are due to wear and subsequent cleaning of the plate.

1950 (2 Oct)–**52.** *Nos.* 402/4, 406/7, 414/18 *and* 431 *optd with Type* O **2** (*1 to 5 c.*) *or* O **3** (*7 c. to $1*). *(a) Postage.*

O17 **135** 1 c. green .. 10 10
O18 **136** 2 c. sepia .. 50 30
O19 2 c. olive-green (11.51) .. 55 10
O20 **137** 3 c. purple .. 50 10
O21 **138** 4 c. carmine-lake .. 70 10
O22 4 c. vermilion (1.5.52) .. 75 10
O23 **139** 5 c. blue .. 1·50 30
O24 – 10 c. olive-green .. 1·50 10
O25 – 14 c. sepia .. 4·50 1·25
O26 – 20 c. slate .. 9·00 20
O27 **141** 50 c. green .. 6·50 6·50
O28 – $1 purple .. 48·00 40·00

(b) Air

O29 – 7 c. blue .. 11·00 6·00
O17/29 .. *Set of* 13 75·00 50·00

1950–51. *Nos.* 432/3 *optd with Type* O **3**.

O30 **142** 10 c. brown-purple .. 80 10
a. Opt omitted in pair with normal .. £350 £350
O31 **143** $1 ultramarine (1.2.51) .. 55·00 55·00

1952–53. *Nos.* 441, 443 *and* 446 *optd with Type* O **3**.

O32 **153** 7 c. blue (3.11.52) .. 80 75
O33 **151** 20 c. grey (1.4.52) .. 80 10
O34 **154** $1 black (2.2.53) .. 7·00 7·00
O32/4 .. *Set of* 3 8·00 7·00

1953 (1 Sept)–**61.** *Nos.* 450/4 *and* 462 *optd with Type* O **2** (*1 to 5 c.*) *or* O **3** (*50 c.*).

O35 **158** 1 c. purple-brown .. 15 10
O36 2 c. green .. 20 10
O37 3 c. carmine .. 20 10
O38 4 c. violet .. 25 10
O39 5 c. ultramarine .. 25 10
O40 **160** 50 c. deep bluish green (2.11.53) .. 2·00 50
a. Opt Type O 4 (24.4.61*) .. 2·00 1·75
O35/40 .. *Set of* 6 2·50 60
* Earliest recorded date.

1955–56. *Nos.* 463/4 *and* 466/7 *optd with Type* O **2**.

O41 **161** 1 c. purple-brown (12.11.56) .. 15 15
O42 2 c. green (19.1.56) .. 15 10
O43 4 c. violet (23.7.56) .. 30 10
O44 5 c. bright blue (11.1.55) .. 15 10
O41/4 .. *Set of* 4 65 25

1955–62. *Nos.* 477 *and* 488 *optd with Type* O **3**.

O45 **165** 10 c. purple-brown (21.2.55) .. 25 10
a. Opt Type O 4 (28.3.62*) .. 25 30
O46 **176** 20 c. green (4.12.56) .. 40 10
a. Opt Type O 4 (10.4.62*) .. 4·00 30
* Earliest recorded date.

1963 (15 May). *Nos.* 527/8 *and* 530/1 *optd as Type* O **2**.

O47 1 c. chocolate .. 30 2·00
O48 2 c. green .. 30 2·00
a. Type O **2** omitted (vert pair with normal) £550
O49 4 c. carmine-red .. 30 1·75
O50 5 c. ultramarine .. 30 55
O47/50 .. *Set of* 4 1·10 5·75

No. O48a comes from the top row of an upper pane on which the overprint was misplaced downwards by one row. Owing to the margin between the panes the top row of the bottom pane had the overprint at the top of the stamp.

The use of official stamps was discontinued on 31 December 1963.

OFFICIAL SPECIAL DELIVERY STAMPS

1950. *No.* S15 *optd as Type* O **1**, *but larger.*

OS1 S **10** 10 c. green .. 12·00 12·00

1950 (2 Oct). *No.* S15 *optd as Type* O **2**, *but larger.*

OS2 S **10** 10 c. green .. 16·00 18·00

Cape of Good Hope

PRICES FOR STAMPS ON COVER

Nos. 1/4	*from* × 4
Nos. 5/14	*from* × 3
Nos. 18/21	*from* × 5
No. 22	—
Nos. 23/6	*from* × 5
Nos. 27/31	*from* × 8
Nos. 32/3	*from* × 10
No. 34	*from* × 25
No. 35	*from* × 20
No. 36	*from* × 10
Nos. 37/8	*from* × 25
Nos. 39/40	*from* × 10
Nos. 41/2	*from* × 12
Nos. 43/54	*from* × 10
Nos. 55/6	*from* × 25
No. 57	*from* × 50
Nos. 58/69	*from* × 10
Nos. 70/8	*from* × 6

PRICES. Our prices for early Cape of Good Hope are for stamps in very fine condition. Exceptional copies are worth more, poorer copies considerably less.

1 Hope

2

(Des Charles Bell, Surveyor-General. Eng W. Humphrys. Recess P.B.)

1853 (1 Sept). *W* **2**. *Imperf. (a) Paper deeply blued.*

1 **1** 1d. pale brick-red .. £3500 £275
a. Deep brick-red .. £5000 £300
2 4d. deep blue .. £2000 £160

Plate proofs of the 4d. in a shade similar to the issued stamp exist on ungummed watermarked paper. The blueing on the reverse of these proofs is uneven giving a blotchy appearance.

(b) Paper slightly blued (blueing not so pronounced at back)

3 **1** 1d. brick-red .. £3000 £200
a. Brown-red .. £3250 £225
4 4d. deep blue .. £1300 £110
a. Blue .. £1400 £150

Both values are known with wmk sideways.

1855–8. *W* **2**. *(a) Imperf.*

5 **1** 1d. brick-red/*cream toned paper* (1857) .. £5000 £900
a. Rose (1858) .. £450 £200
b. Deep rose-red .. £600 £225
6 4d. deep blue/*white paper* (1855) .. £475 45·00
a. Blue .. £275 45·00
7 **1** 6d. slate-lilac/*blued paper* (18.2.58) .. £4250 £450
b. Pale rose-lilac/white paper .. £700 £200
c. Deep rose-lilac/white paper .. £1700 £300
d. Slate-purple/blued paper .. £3500 £1000
8 1s. bright yellow-green/*white paper* (18.2.58) £2500 £180
a. Deep dark green .. £225 £500

The method adopted for producing the plate of the 4d., 6d., and 1s. stamps involved the use of two dies, so that there are two types of each of these values, differing slightly in detail, but produced in equal numbers.

All values of this issue are known with watermark sideways.

The 1d. value in dull rose on ungummed watermarked paper with watermark sideways is a plate proof. The 6d. is known bisected and used with 1d. for 4d. rate.

The paper of No. 5 is similar to that of Nos. 1/4, but is without the blueing. It is much thicker than the white paper used for later printings of the 1d. The evolution of the paper on these Cape of Good Hope stamps is similar to that on the line-engraved issues of Great Britain. Examples of the 6d. slate-lilac apparently on white paper have had the blueing washed out.

The 4d. value is known printed in black on white watermarked paper. Eleven authenticated copies have been recorded, the majority of which show cancellations or, at least, some indication that they have been used.

It was, at one time, believed that these stamps came from a small supply printed in black to mark the death of the Prince Consort, but references to examples can be found in the philatelic press before news of this event reached Cape Town.

It is now thought that these stamps represent proof sheets, possibly pressed into service during a shortage of stamps in 1861.

There is, however, no official confirmation of this theory. (*Price £30000 un, £25000 with obliteration*).

(b) Unofficially rouletted

9 **1** 1d. brick-red .. — £2750
10 4d. blue .. — £2250
11 6d. rose-lilac .. — £1500
12 1s. bright yellow-green .. — £2750
a. Deep dark green .. — £3000

These rouletted stamps are best collected on cover.

3 Hope

(Local provisional (so-called "wood-block") issue. Engraved on steel by C. J. Roberts. Printed from stereotyped plates by Saul Solomon & Co, Cape Town)

1861 (Feb–April). *Laid paper. Imperf.*

13 **3** 1d. vermilion (27 February) .. £13000 £2000
a. Carmine (7 March) .. £22000 £3000
b. Brick-red (10 April) .. £30000 £4250
c. Error. Pale milky blue .. — £28000
ca. Pale bright blue .. — £30000
14 4d. pale milky blue (23 February) £9000 £1500
aa. Retouch or repair to rt-hand corner — £5500
a. Pale grey-blue (March?) .. £10000 £1500
b. Pale bright blue (March?) .. £10000 £1900
ba. Retouch or repair to rt-hand corner — £5500
c. Deep bright blue (12 April) .. £75000 £4500
d. Blue .. £12000 £3000
e. Error. Vermilion .. £85000 £40000
ea. Carmine .. — £80000

Both values were officially reprinted in March, 1883, on wove paper. The 1d. is in deep red, and the 4d. in a deeper blue than that of the deepest shade of the issued stamp.

Specimens of the reprints have done postal duty, but their use thus was not intended. There are no reprints of the errors or of the retouched 4d.

Further reprints were made privately but with official permission, in 1940/41, in colours much deeper than those of any of the original printings, and on thick carton paper.

Examples of the 4d. are known unofficially rouletted.

Early in 1863, Perkins Bacon Ltd handed over the four plates used for printing the triangular Cape of Good Hope stamps to De La Rue & Co, Ltd, who made all the subsequent printings.

(Printed from the P.B. plates by D.L.R.)

1863–4. *Imperf. (a) W* **2**.

18 **1** 1d. deep carmine-red .. £100 £225
a. Deep brown-red .. £350 £225
b. Brownish red .. £350 £225
19 4d. deep blue .. £100 42·00
a. Blue .. £120 60·00
b. Slate-blue .. £2000 £500
c. Steel-blue .. £2000 £300
20 6d. bright mauve .. £150 £450
21 1s. bright emerald-green .. £350 £450
a. Pale emerald-green .. £1100

(b) Wmk Crown CC (sideways)

22 **1** 1d. deep carmine-red .. £15000

No. 22 was a trial printing, and is only known unused.

Our prices for the 4d. blue are for stamps which are blue by comparison with the other listed shades. An exceptionally pale shade is recognised by specialists and is rare.

All values of this issue are known with watermark lying sideways.

With the exception of the 4d., these stamps may be easily distinguished from those printed by Perkins Bacon by their colours, which are quite distinct.

The De La Rue stamps of all values are less clearly printed, the figure of Hope and the lettering of the inscriptions standing out less boldly, while the fine lines of the background appear blurred and broken when examined under a glass. The background as a whole often shows irregularity in the apparent depth of colour, due to wear of the plates.

For note regarding the two dies of the 4d., 6d., and 1s. values, see after No. 8.

All the triangular stamps were demonetised as from 1 October 1900.

Four Pence.

4 "Hope" seated, with vine and ram. (With outer frame-line)

(5)

(Des Charles Bell; die engraved on steel and stamps typo by D.L.R.)

1864–77. *With outer frame-line surrounding the design. Wmk Crown CC. P* 14.

No.	Type	Description	Unused	Used
23	4	1d. carmine-red (5.65)	65·00	7·00
		a. Rose-red	65·00	7·50
24		4d. pale blue (8.65)	80·00	2·00
		a. Blue	90·00	2·00
		b. Ultramarine	£200	50·00
		c. Deep blue (1872)	£110	2·00
25		6d. pale lilac (before 21.3.64)	85·00	12·00
		a. Deep lilac	£170	6·50
		b. Violet (to bright) (1877)	90·00	1·50
26		1s. deep green (1.64)	£400	11·00
		a. Green	80·00	2·00
		b. Blue-green	85·00	3·00

The 1d. rose-red, 6d. lilac, and 1s. blue-green are known imperf, probably from proof sheets.

The 1d. and 4d. stamps of this issue may be found with side and/or top outer frame-lines missing, due to wear of the plates.

(Surch by Saul Solomon & Co, Cape Town)

1868 (17 Nov). *No. 25a surch with T* 5.

No.	Type	Description	Unused	Used
27	4	4d. on 6d. deep lilac (R.)	85·00	10·00
		a. "Peuce" for "Pence"	£1800	£700
		b. "Fonr" for "Four"	—	£700

Specimens may also be found with bars omitted or at the top of the stamp, due to misplacement of the sheet.

The space between the words and bars varies from 12½ to 16 mm, stamps with spacing 15½ and 16 mm being rare. There were two printings, one of 120,000 in November 1868 and another of 1,000,000 in December. Stamps showing widest spacings are probably from the earlier printing.

6 (No outer frame-line)

(Die re-engraved. Typo D.L.R.)

1871–6. *Outer frame-line removed. Wmk Crown CC. P* 14.

No.	Type	Description	Unused	Used
28	6	½d. pale grey-black (12.75)	3·25	2·25
		a. Deep grey-black	3·00	2·00
29		1d. pale carmine-red (2.72)	14·00	35
		a. Deep carmine-red	15·00	35
30		4d. dull blue (12.76)	70·00	50
		a. Deep blue	70·00	80
		b. Ultramarine	£160	28·00
31		5s. yellow-orange (25.8.71)	£100	8·00

The ½d., 1d. and 5s. are known imperf, probably from proof sheets.

For the 3d. of this issue see Nos. 36 and 39.

ONE PENNY (7) THREE PENCE (8)

(Surch by Saul Solomon & Co, Cape Town)

1874–6. *Nos. 25a and 26a surch with T* 7.

No.	Type	Description	Unused	Used
32	4	1d. on 6d. deep lilac (R.) (1.9.74)	£225	35·00
		a. "E" of "PENNY" omitted	—	£500
33		1d. on 1s. green (11.76)	27·00	20·00

These provisionals are found with the bar only, either across the centre of the stamp or at top, with value only; or with value and bar close together, either at top or foot. Such varieties are due to misplacement of sheets during surcharging.

1879 (1 Nov). *No. 30 surch with T* 8.

No.	Type	Description	Unused	Used
34	6	3d. on 4d. blue (R.)	55·00	90
		a. "PENCB" for "PENCE"	£1200	£275
		b. "THE.EE" for "THREE"	£1500	£350
		c. Surch double	£6000	£2750
		d. Variety b. double		

The double surcharge must also have existed showing variety a. but only variety b. is known.

There are numerous minor varieties, including letters broken or out of alignment, due to defective printing and use of poor type.

The spacing between the bar and the words varies from 16½ to 18 mm.

THREEPENCE (9) 3 (10) 3 (11)

(Surch by D.L.R.)

1880 (Feb). *Special printing of the 4d. in new colour, surch, with T* 9. *Wmk Crown CC.*

No.	Type	Description	Unused	Used
35	6	3d. on 4d. pale dull rose	32·00	1·50

A minor constant variety exists with foot of "P" in "PENCE" broken off, making the letter appear shorter.

1880 (1 July). *Wmk Crown CC. P* 14.

No.	Type	Description	Unused	Used
36	6	3d. pale dull rose	85·00	8·00

(Surch by Saul Solomon & Co, Cape Town)

1880 (Aug). *No. 36 surch.*

No.	Type	Description	Unused	Used
37	10	"3" on 3d. pale dull rose	22·00	75
		a. Surch inverted	£550	40·00
		b. Vert pair. Nos. 37/8	£300	£200
38	11	"3" on 3d. pale dull rose	60·00	2·25
		a. Surch inverted	£6000	£900

The "3" (T 10) is sometimes found broken. Vertical pairs are known showing the two types of surcharge *se-tenant*, and vertical strips of three exist, the top stamp having surcharge T 10, the middle stamp being without surcharge, and the lower stamp having surcharge T 11 (*price for strip of 3 un.* £3000).

1881 (Jan). *Wmk Crown CC. P* 14.

No.	Type	Description	Unused	Used
39	6	3d. pale claret	40·00	1·75
		a. Deep claret	45·00	1·50

This was a definite colour change made at the request of the Postmaster-General owing to the similarity between the colours of the 1d. stamp and the 3d. in pale dull rose. Imperf copies are probably from proof sheets.

Proofs of this value were printed in brown, on unwatermarked wove paper and imperf, but the colour was rejected as unsuitable.

1882 (July). *Wmk Crown CA. P* 14.

No.	Type	Description	Unused	Used
40	6	3d. pale claret	5·50	90
		a. Deep claret	6·00	75

One Half-penny. (12)

13 "Cabled Anchor"

(Surch by Saul Solomon & Co, Cape Town)

1882 (July). *Nos. 39a and 40a surch with T* 12.

No.	Type	Description	Unused	Used
41	6	½d. on 3d. deep claret (Wmk CC)	£1500	£110
		a. Hyphen omitted	—	£3000
42		½d. on 3d. deep claret (Wmk CA)	3·50	2·00
		a. "p" in "penny" omitted	£2000	£700
		b. "y" in "penny" omitted	£1000	
		c. Hyphen omitted	£450	£350

Varieties also exist with broken and defective letters, and with the obliterating bar omitted or at the top of the stamp.

1882–83. *Wmk Crown CA. P* 14.

No.	Type	Description	Unused	Used
43	6	½d. black (1.9.82)	6·00	20
		a. Grey-black	3·50	15
44		1d. rose-red (7.82)	20·00	15
		a. Deep rose-red	17·00	15
45		2d. pale bistre (1.9.82)	42·00	15
		a. Deep bistre	48·00	10
46	4	6d. mauve (to bright) (8.82)	45·00	70
47	6	5s. orange (8.83)	£700	£200

Imperf pairs of the ½d., 1d., and 2d. are known, probably from proof sheets.

For the 3d. stamp with this watermark see No. 40.

1884–90. *W* 13. *P* 14.

No.	Type	Description	Unused	Used
48	6	½d. black (1.86)	80	10
		a. Grey-black	80	10
49		1d. rose-red (12.85)	90	10
		a. Carmine-red	90	10
50		2d. pale bistre (12.84)	4·50	10
		a. Deep bistre	1·75	10
51		4d. blue (6.90)	2·50	15
		a. Deep blue	2·75	15
52	4	6d. reddish purple (12.84)	35·00	1·60
		a. Purple (shades)	2·75	15
		b. Bright mauve	9·00	40
53		1s. yellow-green (12.85)	55·00	2·25
		a. Blue-green (1889)	14·00	30
54	6	5s. orange (7.87)	38·00	3·00
48/54		*Set of* 7	55·00	3·50

All the above stamps are known in imperf pairs, probably from proof sheets.

For later shade and colour changes, etc., see Nos. 59, etc.

2½d (14)

15

ONE PENNY. (16)

(Surch by D.L.R.)

1891 (Mar). *Special printing of the 3d. in new colour, surch with T* 14.

No.	Type	Description	Unused	Used
55	6	2½d. on 3d. pale magenta	2·75	70
		a. Deep magenta	90	20
		b. "1" with horiz serif	35·00	30·00

No. 55b occurs on two stamps (Nos. 8 and 49) of the pane of 60.

Two types of "d" are found in the surcharge, one with square end to serif at top, and the other with pointed serif.

1892 (June). *W* 13. *P* 14.

No.	Type	Description	Unused	Used
56	15	2½d. sage-green	85	10
		a. Olive-green	3·50	55

(Surch by W. A. Richards & Sons, Cape Town)

1893 (Mar). *Nos. 50/a surch with T* 16.

No.	Type	Description	Unused	Used
57	6	1d. on 2d. pale bistre	1·40	10
		a. Deep bistre	70	10
		b. No stop after "PENNY"	26·00	11·00
		c. Surch double	—	£400

No. 57b occurs on stamp No. 42 of the upper left-hand pane, and on No. 6 of the lower right-hand pane.

Minor varieties exist showing broken letters and letters out of alignment or widely spaced. Also with obliterating bar omitted, due to misplacement of the sheet during surcharging.

17 "Hope" standing. Table Bay in background

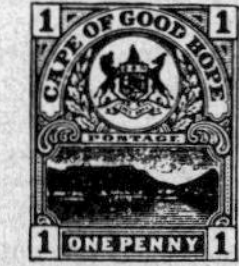

18 Table Mountain and Bay with Arms of the Colony

(Des Mr. Mountford. Typo D.L.R.)

1893 (Oct). *W* 13. *P* 14.

No.	Type	Description	Unused	Used
58	17	1d. rose-red	20	10
		a. Carmine	20	10

The above stamp is known in imperf pairs, probably from proof sheets.

1893–98. *New colours, etc. W* 13. *P* 14.

No.	Type	Description	Unused	Used
59	6	½d. pale yellow-green (12.96)	45	10
		a. Green	2·00	20
60		2d. chocolate-brown (3.97)	1·25	10
61	15	2½d. pale ultramarine (3.96)	1·00	15
		a. Ultramarine	85	10
62	6	3d. bright magenta (9.98)	2·00	40
63		4d. sage-green (3.97)	3·25	45
64		1s. blue-green (12.93)	13·00	45
		a. Deep blue-green	30·00	4·00
65		1s. yellow-ochre (5.96)	4·25	35
66		5s. brown-orange (6.96)	28·00	3·50
59/66		*Set of* 8	48·00	5·00

1898–1902. *W* 13. *P* 14.

No.	Type	Description	Unused	Used
67	17	½d. green (9.98)	20	10
68		3d. magenta (3.02)	2·00	50

(Des E. Sturman. Typo D.L.R.)

1900 (Jan). *W* 13. *P* 14.

No.	Type	Description	Unused	Used
69	18	1d. carmine	25	10

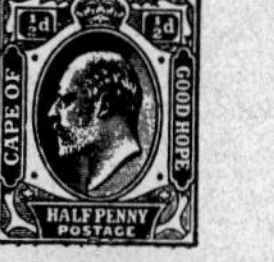

19

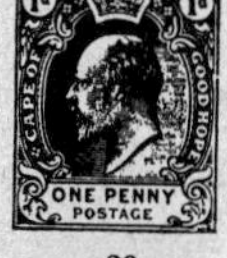

20

21

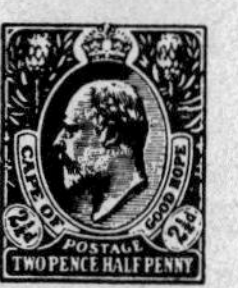

22

23

24

25

26

27

(Typo D.L.R.)

1902 (Dec)–**04.** *W* 13. *P* 14.

No.	Type	Description	Unused	Used
70	19	½d. green	40	10
71	20	1d. carmine	40	10
72	21	2d. brown (10.04)	1·50	55
73	22	2½d. ultramarine (3.04)	2·50	4·00
74	23	3d. magenta (4.03)	1·50	20
75	24	4d. olive-green (2.03)	3·00	55
76	25	6d. bright mauve (3.03)	3·00	25
77	26	1s. yellow-ochre	4·75	40
78	27	5s. brown-orange (2.03)	25·00	6·50
70/8		*Set of* 9	38·00	11·50

All values exist in imperf pairs, from proof sheets.

When the Union of South Africa came into being in 1910 the stamps of the Cape of Good Hope (except the already demonetised triangulars) became available for postal use throughout the Union, until 31 December 1937, from which date the stamps of the four provinces of the Union were demonetised. For Union issues see under SOUTH AFRICA.

MINIMUM PRICE

The minimum price quote is 10p which represents a handling charge rather than a basis for valuing common stamps. For further notes about prices see introductory pages.

NEW INFORMATION

The editor is always interested to correspond with people who have new information that will improve or correct the Catalogue.

BRITISH KAFFRARIA

The history of the Cape eastern frontier was punctuated by a series of armed conflicts with the native population, known as the Kaffir Wars. After a particularly violent outbreak in 1846 the Governor, Sir Harry Smith, advanced the line of the Cape frontier to the Keikama and Tyumie Rivers. In the area between the new frontier and the Kei River a buffer state, British Kaffraria, was established on 17 December 1847. This area was not annexed to the Cape, but was administered as a separate Crown dependency by the Governor of Cape Colony in his capacity as High Commissioner for South Africa.

The territory, with its administration based on King William's Town, used the stamps of the Cape of Good Hope from 1853 onwards, the mail being sent via Port Elizabeth or overland from the Cape. Covers from British Kaffraria franked with the triangular issues are rare.

The first postal marking known from British Kaffraria is the 1849 type octagonal numeral No. 47 from Port Beaufort. Oval postmarks of the 1853 type were used at Alice, Aliwal North, Bedford, Fort Beaufort, King William's Town and Queenstown. In 1864 numeral cancellations were issued to all post offices within the Cape system and it is known that the following numbers were initially assigned to post towns in Kaffraria: 4 (King William's Town), 7 (Bedford), 11 (Queenstown), 29 (East London), 32 (Fort Beaufort), 38 (Aliwal North) and 104 (Cathcart).

It is believed that post offices may have also existed at Adelaide, Barkly East, Sterkstoom and Stutterheim, but, to date, no examples of handstamps or cancellations are known from them during the British Kaffraria period.

Following the decimation by famine of the Xhosa tribes in 1857 British Kaffraria was annexed to Cape Colony in 1865. The area eventually formed the basis of the Ciskei independent "homeland".

MAFEKING SIEGE STAMPS

PRICES FOR STAMPS ON COVER
Nos. 1/16 — *from* × 7
Nos. 17/22 — *from* × 8

23 MARCH to 17 MAY 1900

There are numerous forgeries of the Mafeking overprints, many of which were brought home by soldiers returning from the Boer War.

MAFEKING,
3d.
BESIEGED.
(1)

MAFEKING
3d.
BESIEGED.
(2)

(Surcharged by Townsend & Co, Mafeking)

1900 (23 Mar–25 Apr). *Various stamps surch as T* 1 *and* 2.

(A) *Cape of Good Hope stamps surch as T* 1 (23 Mar)

1 **6** 1d. on ½d. green .. £150 48·00
2 **17** 1d. on ½d. green (24.3) .. £175 55·00
3 3d. on 1d. carmine .. £150 48·00
4 **6** 6d. on 3d. magenta (24.3) .. £4500 £250
5 1s. on 4d. sage-green (24.3) .. £3250 £325

A variety in the setting of each value exists without comma after "MAFEKING".

(B) *Nos.* 59 *and* 61/3 *of Bechuanaland Protectorate surch as T* 1

6 1d. on ½d. vermilion (28.3) .. £150 48·00
a. Surch inverted .. — £3750
b. Vert pair, surch tête-bêche .. — £6500
7 3d. on 1d. lilac (4.4) .. £850 65·00
a. Surch double .. — £5000
8 6d. on 2d. green and carmine (6.4) .. £1000 65·00
9 6d. on 3d. purple/*yellow* (30.3) .. £2500 £250
a. Surch inverted .. — £9000
b. Surch double

(C) *Nos.* 12 *and* 35 *of British Bechuanaland surch as T* 1

10 6d. on 3d. lilac and black (27.3) .. £400 60·00
11 1s. on 4d. green and purple-brown (29.3) £1200 65·00
a. Surch double .. — £6000
b. Surch treble .. — £7000
c. Surch double, one inverted .. — £7000

(D) *Nos.* 61/2 *and* 65 *of Bechuanaland Protectorate surch as T* 2 (25 Apr)

12 3d. on 1d. lilac .. £900 55·00
a. Surch double .. — £6000
13 6d. on 2d. green and carmine .. £1100 60·00
14 1s. on 6d. purple/*rose-red* .. £2500 80·00

(E) *Nos.* 36/7 *of British Bechuanaland surch as T* 2

15 1s. on 6d. purple/*rose-red* (3.5) .. £5500 £600
16 2s. on 1s. green (25.3) .. £5500 £300

No. 11a has both surcharges T 1. Copies exist with normal surcharge T 1 and the second surcharge T 2 but are believed to be trials (*Price* £3500, *unused or used*).

In the stamps overprinted "BECHUANALAND PROTECTORATE" and "BRITISH BECHUANALAND" the local surcharge is so adjusted as not to overlap the original overprint.

3 Cadet Sergt.-major Goodyear

4 General Baden-Powell

(Des Dr. W. A. Hayes (T 3), Capt. H. Greener (T 4))

1900 (7–11 Apr). *Produced photographically by Dr. D. Taylor. Horiz laid paper with sheet wmk* "OCEANA FINE". *P* 12.

(*a*) 18½ *mm wide*. (*b*) 21 *mm wide*

17 **3** 1d. pale blue/*blue* .. £800 £250
18 1d. deep blue/*blue* .. £800 £275
19 **4** 3d. pale blue/*blue* (*a*) .. £1100 £400
a. Reversed design .. £20000 £15000
20 3d. deep blue/*blue* (*a*) .. £1200 £325
a. Imperf between (horiz pair) .. — £15000
b. Double print .. — £9500
21 3d. pale blue/*blue* (*b*) (11.4) .. £5500 £700
22 3d. deep blue/*blue* (*b*) (11.4) .. £6000 £950

These stamps vary a great deal in colour from deep blue to pale grey.

No. 18 in an imperforate pair is now believed to be a proof. The only known example is untrimmed and without gum.

VRYBURG

PRICES FOR STAMPS ON COVER
Nos. 1/4 — *from* × 5
Nos. 11/12 — *from* × 2

TEMPORARY BOER OCCUPATION

½ PENCE
Z.A.R.
(1)

1899 (Nov). *Cape stamps surch as T* 1. A. *Surch* 10 *mm high*. B. *Surch* 12 *mm high*.

			A.		B.	
1	**6**	½ PENCE, green	£200	90·00	£1500	£650
2	**17**	1 PENCE, rose	£250	£110	£1700	£750
3	**4**	2 PENCE on 6d. mauve	†		£3000	£500
4	**15**	2½ pence, blue	£2250	£425	£10000	£4000

Nos. 1A, 2A, 4A and 3B are known with italic "Z" in the surcharge. *Prices from* 6 *times normal*.

BRITISH REOCCUPATION

V. R.
SPECIAL
POST
(2)

1900 (May). *Provisionals issued by the Military Authorities. Stamps of Transvaal optd with T* 2.

11 **30** ½d. green .. — £1500
12 1d. carmine and green .. £6000 £2500
13 2d. deep brown and green
14 2½d. blue and green

Cayman Islands

The first post office was opened at Georgetown in April 1889. The stamps of Jamaica with the following cancellations were used until 19 February 1901.

PRICES OF NOS. Z1/27. These are for a single stamp showing a clear impression of the postmark. Nos. Z1, 2, 6/8, 11/13, 18, 22 and Z25 are known used on cover and these are worth considerably more.

GEORGETOWN, GRAND CAYMAN

Z 1

Z 2

Z 3

Stamps of JAMAICA *cancelled with Type* Z 1.

1889 *to* **1894**.

Z1 ½d. yellow-green (No. 16) .. £375
Z2 1d. purple and mauve (No. 27) .. £375
Z3 2d. green (No. 28) .. £750
Z4 2½d. dull purple and blue (No. 29) .. £850
Z5 4d. red-orange (No. 22) .. £1600

Stamps of JAMAICA *cancelled with Type* Z 2.

1895 *to* **1898**.

Z6 ½d. yellow-green (No. 16) .. £450
Z7 1d. purple and mauve (No. 27) .. £375
Z8 2½d. dull purple and blue (No. 29) .. £600
Z9 3d. sage-green (No. 21) .. £2000

Stamps of JAMAICA *cancelled with Type* Z 3.

1898 *to* **1901**.

Z10 ½d. yellow-green (No. 16) .. £350
a. Green (No. 16*a*) .. £350
Z11 1d. purple and mauve (No. 27) .. £350
Z12 1d. red (No. 31) (1900) .. £350
Z13 2½d. dull purple and blue (No. 29) .. £500

OFFICIAL STAMPS

Stamps of JAMAICA *cancelled with Type* Z 1.

1890 *to* **1894.**

Z14 ½d. green (No. O1) .. £700
Z15 ½d. green (No. O3) (1893) .. £1100
Z16 1d. rose (No. O4) .. £1000
Z17 2d. grey (No. O5) .. £1600

Stamps of JAMAICA *cancelled with Type* Z 2.

1895 *to* **1898**.

Z18 ½d. green (No. O3) .. £1300
Z19 1d. rose (No. O4) .. £2000
Z20 2d. grey (No. O5) .. £2000

STAKE BAY, CAYMAN BRAC

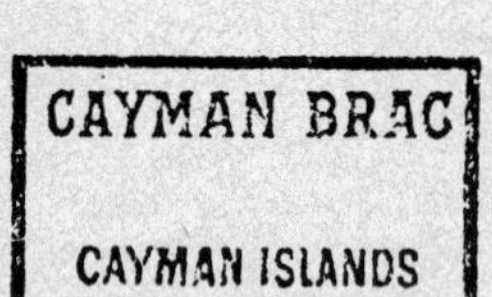

Z 4

Z 5

Stamps of JAMAICA *cancelled with Type* Z 4.

1898 *to* **1900**.

Z21 ½d. yellow-green (No. 16) .. £1500
Z22 1d. purple and mauve (No. 27) .. £1600
Z23 2d. green (No. 28) .. £2000
Z24 2½d. dull purple and blue (No. 29) .. £1500

Stamps of JAMAICA *cancelled with Type* Z 5.

1900 *to* **1901**.

Z25 1d. purple and mauve (No. 27) .. £1600
Z26 1d. red (No. 31) .. £1900
Z27 2½d. dull purple and blue (No. 29) .. £1600

PRICES FOR STAMPS ON COVER TO 1945
Nos. 1/2 — *from* × 25
Nos. 3/12 — *from* × 5
Nos. 13/19 — *from* × 4
Nos. 25/34 — *from* × 5
Nos. 38/52*b* — *from* × 4
Nos. 53/67 — *from* × 5
Nos. 69/83 — *from* × 4
Nos. 84/95 — *from* × 6
Nos. 96/9 — *from* × 5
Nos. 100/11 — *from* × 4
Nos. 112/14 — *from* × 6
Nos. 115/26 — *from* × 2

DEPENDENCY OF JAMAICA

1

2

3

(T 1/9 and 12/13 typo D.L.R.)

1900 (Nov). *Wmk Crown CA. P* 14.

1 **1** ½d. deep green .. 3·75 6·50
a. Pale green .. 1·50 5·00
2 1d. rose-carmine .. 2·25 75
a. Pale carmine .. 6·00 6·00
1/2 Optd "Specimen" .. *Set of* 2 £100

1902 (Jan)–**03**. *Wmk Crown CA. P* 14.
3 **2** ½d. green (15.9.02) .. .. 3·50 13·00
4 1d. carmine (6.3.03) .. .. 5·00 6·50
5 2½d. bright blue .. .. 5·50 10·00
6 6d. brown .. .. 17·00 30·00
7 **3** 1s. orange .. .. 48·00 60·00
3/7 .. .. *Set of* 5 70·00 £110
3/7 Optd "Specimen" .. .. *Set of* 5 £200

1905 (Mar–18 Oct). *Wmk Mult Crown CA. P* 14.
8 **2** ½d. green .. .. 1·50 3·25
9 1d. carmine (18.10) .. .. 10·00 16·00
10 2½d. bright blue .. .. 3·50 2·75
11 6d. brown .. .. 16·00 32·00
12 **3** 1s. orange .. .. 30·00 45·00
8/12 .. .. *Set of* 5 55·00 90·00

1907 (13 Mar). *Wmk Mult Crown CA. P* 14.
13 **3** 4d. brown and blue .. .. 16·00 25·00
14 **2** 6d. olive and rose .. .. 16·00 35·00
15 **3** 1s. violet and green .. .. 27·00 42·00
16 5s. salmon and green £160 £225
13/16 .. .. *Set of* 4 £200 £275
13/16 Optd "Specimen" .. .. *Set of* 4 £225

One Halfpenny. (4) ½D (5) 1D (6)

1907 (30 Aug). *No. 9 surch at Govt Printing Office, Kingston, with T* 4.
17 **2** ½d. on 1d. carmine .. .. .. 27·00 45·00

1907 (Nov). *No. 16 handstamped at Georgetown P.O. with T* 5 *or* 6.
18 **3** ½d. on 5s. salmon and green (26.11) .. £225 £300
a. Surch inverted £12000
b. Surch double £8000 £9000
c. Surch double, one inverted ..
d. Surch omitted (in pair with normal) £20000
19 1d. on 5s. salmon and green (23.11) .. £225 £300
a. Surch double £11000

The ½d. on 5s. may be found with the figures "1" or "2" omitted, owing to defective handstamping.

8

9

2½D (10)

1907 (27 Dec)–**09**. *Ordinary paper* (½*d. to* 2½*d.*) *or chalk-surfaced papers* (*others*). *P* 14. (*a*) *Wmk Mult Crown CA*.
25 **8** ½d. green .. .. 60 1·50
26 1d. carmine 60 55
27 2½d. ultramarine (30.3.08) .. .. 2·75 3·50
28 **9** 3d. purple/*yellow* (30.3.08) .. .. 2·75 6·50
29 4d. black and red/*yellow* (30.3.08) .. 42·00 48·00
30 **8** 6d. dull and bright purple (2.10.08) .. 4·50 18·00
a. Dull purple and violet-purple .. 15·00 28·00
31 **9** 1s. black/*green* (5.4.09) .. .. 4·00 13·00
32 5s. green and red/*yellow* (30.3.08) .. 35·00 48·00

(*b*) *Wmk Crown CA* (30.3.08)
33 **9** 1s. black/*green* .. .. .. 27·00 55·00
34 **8** 10s. green and red/*green* £200 £300
25/34 .. .. *Set of* 10 £275 £450
25/34 (*except* 31) Optd "Specimen" .. *Set of* 9 £350

1908 (12 Feb). *No. 13 handstamped locally with T* 10.
35 2½d. on 4d. brown and blue £1600 £2250
a. Surch double £20000 £15000

No. 35 should only be purchased when accompanied by an expert committee's certificate or similar form of guarantee.

The 1d. on 4d. (No. 29) was intended as a revenue stamp and was never authorised for postal use (*price* £225 *un.*). Used examples were either cancelled by favour or passed through the post in error. Exists with surcharge inverted (*price* £2500 *un.*) or surcharge double.

MANUSCRIPT PROVISIONALS. During May and June 1908 supplies of ½d. and 1d. stamps became exhausted, and the payment of postage was indicated by a manuscript endorsement. Such endorsements were in use from 12 May to 1 June.

Price on cover
MP1 "Postage Paid G.A.P." (12 May to 1 June) .. £1750
MP1*a* "½ Postage Paid G.A.P." (23 May) £2250

In October of the same year there was a further shortage of ¼d. stamps and the manuscript endorsements were again introduced.
MP2 "Pd ¼d. W. G. McC." (4 to 27 October) £225
MP3 "Paid" (7 October) £3500
MP4 "Pd ¼d" (8 October) £2750
MP5 "Paid ¼GAP. asst." (15 October) £2750

No. MP2 exists in different inks and formats.

Manuscript endorsement for the 2½d. rate is also known, but this is thought to have been done by oversight.

11

12

13

1908 (30 June)–**09**. *Wmk Mult Crown CA. Litho. P* 14.
38 **11** ¼d. brown, **O** (Optd S. £65) 25 20
a. Grey-brown (2.09) 70 75

1912 (24 Apr)–**20**. *Wmk Mult Crown CA. Ordinary paper* (¼*d. to* 2½*d.*) *or chalk-surfaced paper* (*others*). *P* 14.
40 **13** ¼d. brown (10.2.13) 20 25
41 **12** ½d. green .. .. 30 2·00
42 1d. red (25.2.13) .. .. .. 1·00 75
43 **13** 2d. pale grey .. .. 50 2·50
44 **12** 2½d. bright blue (26.8.14) .. .. 6·50 7·50
a. Deep bright blue (9.11.17) .. .. 8·00 13·00
45 **13** 3d. purple/*yellow* (26.11.14) .. .. 9·00 17·00
a. White back (19.11.13) .. .. 1·75 4·50
b. On lemon (12.3.18) (Optd S. £50) .. 1·50 10·00
c. On orange-buff (1920) .. .. 5·00 16·00
d. On pale yellow (1920) .. .. 2·50 15·00
46 4d. black and red/*yellow* (25.2.13) .. 75 3·25
47 **12** 6d. dull and bright purple (25.2.13) .. 2·25 5·00
48 **13** 1s. black/*green* (15.5.16) (Optd S. £50) .. 3·50 13·00
a. White back (19.11.13) .. .. 1·75 2·75
49 2s. purple and bright blue/*blue* .. 7·50 22·00
50 3s. green and violet .. .. .. 16·00 32·00
51 5s. green and red/*yellow* (26.8.14) .. 50·00 75·00
52 **12** 10s. deep green and red/*green* (26.11.14) (Optd S. £80) .. .. .. 80·00 £120
a. White back (19.11.13) .. .. 80·00 £120
b. On blue-green, olive back (5.10.18) .. 70·00 £140
40/52*b* .. .. *Set of* 13 £130 £250
40/4, 45*a*, 46/7, 48*a*, 49/51, 52*a* Optd "Specimen" *Set of* 13 £375

WAR STAMP. 1½d (14) WAR STAMP. 1½d (15) 1½d Straight serif (Left-hand pane R. 10/2)

1917 (26 Feb). *T* 12, *surch with T* 14 *or* 15.
53 **14** 1½d. on 2½d. deep blue .. .. .. 1·75 6·00
a. No fraction bar .. .. .. 40·00 60·00
b. Missing stop after "STAMP" (R.1/4) £170
54 **15** 1½d. on 2½d. deep blue .. .. .. 30 2·50
a. No fraction bar .. .. .. 27·00 55·00
b. Straight serif .. .. .. 27·00 55·00

In No. 53 the spacing between the word "STAMP" and the top of the figure "1" varies between 1½ mm and 5 mm.

WAR STAMP 1½d (16) WAR STAMP 1½d (17) WAR STAMP 1½d. (18)

1917 (4 Sept). *T* 12 *surch with T* 16 *or* 17.
55 **16** 1½d. on 2½d. deep blue £800 £1200
56 **17** 1½d. on 2½d. deep blue (Optd S.£100) .. 20 40

1919–20. *T* 12 *and* 13 (2½*d. special printing*), *optd only, or surch in addition*.
57 **16** ½d. green (4.2.19) 20 90
58 **18** 1½d. on 2d. grey (10.3.20) .. .. 90 3·75
59 **17** 1½d. on 2½d. orange (4.2.19) 25 80
57, 59 Optd "Specimen" .. .. *Set of* 2 90·00

In T 16 the "R" of "WAR" has a curved foot and the other letters vary slightly from T 17. "1½d." is in thin type. In T 17 the "R" has a straight foot, and the "1½d." differs.

The ½d. stamps on *buff* paper, and later consignments of the 2d. T 13 on *pinkish*, derived their colour from the paper in which they were packed for despatch from England.

19

20 King William IV and King George V

(Recess D.L.R.)

1921 (4 Apr)–**26**. *P* 14. (*a*) *Wmk Mult Crown CA*.
60 **19** 3d. purple/*orange-buff* .. .. .. 1·25 7·00
a. Purple/pale yellow .. .. .. 45·00 60·00
62 4d. red/*yellow* (1.4.22) .. .. .. 80 3·75
63 1s. black/*green* .. .. .. 1·25 6·00
64 5s. yellow-green/*pale yellow* .. .. 16·00 40·00
a. Deep green/pale yellow .. .. 35·00 55·00
b. Blue-green/pale yellow .. .. 40·00 65·00
c. Deep green/orange-buff (19.11.21) .. 55·00 80·00
67 10s. carmine/*green* (19.11.21) .. .. 55·00 80·00
60/7 .. .. *Set of* 5 70·00 £120
60/7 Optd "Specimen" .. .. *Set of* 5 £225

(*b*) *Wmk Mult Script CA*
69 **19** ¼d. yellow-brown (1.4.22) 15 50
70 ½d. pale grey-green (1.4.22) 30 25
71 1d. deep carmine-red (1.4.22) 50 85
72 1½d. orange-brown 90 20
73 2d. slate-grey (1.4.22) .. .. .. 1·25 3·25
74 2½d. bright blue (1.4.22) 50 45
75 3d. purple/*yellow* (29.6.23) 50 75
76 4½d. sage-green (29.6.23) .. .. .. 90 3·00
77 6d. claret (1.4.22) .. .. .. 5·50 15·00
a. Deep claret .. .. .. 13·00 22·00
79 1s. black/*green* (15.5.25) .. .. 1·75 11·00
80 2s. violet/*blue* (1.4.22) .. .. 7·00 11·00
81 3s. violet (1.4.22) .. .. .. 15·00 15·00
82 5s. green/*yellow* (15.2.25) .. .. 22·00 35·00
83 10s. carmine/*green* (5.9.26) .. .. 48·00 65·00
69/83 .. .. *Set of* 14 90·00 £150
69/83 Optd "Specimen" .. .. *Set of* 14 £400

"A.S.R." PROVISIONAL. On the night of 9/10 November 1932 the Cayman Brac Post Office at Stake Bay, and its contents, was destroyed by a hurricane. Pending the arrival of replacement stamp stocks and cancellation the Postmaster, Mr. A. S. Rutty, initialled covers to indicate that postage had been paid. Those destined for overseas addresses additionally received a "Postage Paid" handstamp when they passed through Kingston, Jamaica.

Price on cover
MP6 Endorsed "A.S.R." in manuscript £2750
MP7 Endorsed "A.S.R." in manuscript and hand-stamped "Postage Paid" £3250

These emergency arrangements lasted until 19 December.

(Recess Waterlow)

1932 (5 Dec). *Centenary of the "Assembly of Justices and Vestry". Wmk Mult Script CA. P* 12½.
84 **20** ¼d. brown 40 90
85 ½d. green .. .. 1·50 3·75
86 1d. scarlet .. .. 1·50 2·75
87 1½d. red-orange .. .. 1·50 1·00
88 2d. grey .. .. 1·50 1·75
89 2½d. ultramarine .. .. 1·50 1·00
90 3d. olive-green .. .. 1·75 2·75
91 6d. purple .. .. 6·00 11·00
92 1s. black and brown .. .. .. 13·00 20·00
93 2s. black and ultramarine .. .. 38·00 48·00
94 5s. black and green .. .. .. 80·00 £100
95 10s. black and scarlet £250 £350
84/95 .. .. *Set of* 12 £350 £475
84/95 Perf "Specimen" .. .. *Set of* 12 £500

1935 (6 May). *Silver Jubilee. As Nos.* 91/4 *of Antigua.*
96 ½d. black and green 15 20
f. Diagonal line by turret .. .. .. 15·00
97 2½d. brown and deep blue .. .. .. 60 1·00
98 6d. light blue and olive-green .. .. 1·00 1·25
h. Dot by flagstaff .. .. 35·00
99 1s. slate and purple .. .. 2·50 3·75
h. Dot by flagstaff .. .. 50·00
96/9 .. .. *Set of* 4 3·75 5·50
96/9 Perf "Specimen" .. .. *Set of* 4 75·00

For illustrations of plate varieties see Omnibus section following Zululand.

21 Cayman Islands

24 Conch Shells and Coconut Palms

(Recess Waterlow)

1935 (1 May)–**36**. *T* 21, 24 *and similar designs. Wmk Mult Script CA. P* 12½.
100 **21** ¼d. black and brown 15 15
101 – ½d. ultramarine & yellow-green (1.1.36) 40 15
102 – 1d. ultramarine and scarlet .. .. 2·25 50
103 **24** 1½d. black and orange 90 65
104 – 2d. ultramarine and purple 85 80
105 – 2½d. blue and black (1.1.36) .. .. 3·00 60
106 **21** 3d. black and olive-green .. .. 2·00 65
107 – 6d. bright purple and black (1.1.36) .. 8·50 3·00
108 – 1s. ultramarine and orange (1.1.36) .. 4·00 4·50
109 – 2s. ultramarine and black .. .. 30·00 30·00
110 – 5s. green and black .. .. .. 35·00 45·00
111 **24** 10s. black and scarlet .. .. .. 55·00 70·00
100/11 .. .. *Set of* 12 £120 £140
100/11 Perf "Specimen" .. .. *Set of* 12 £250

Designs: *Horiz*—½d., 2d., 1s. Cat boat; 1d., 2s. Red-footed Booby; 2½d., 6d. 5s. Hawksbill Turtles.

1937 (13 May). *Coronation Issue. As Nos.* 13/15 *of Aden but ptd by B.W. P* 11 × 11½.
112 ½d. green 30 15
113 1d. carmine 50 15
114 2½d. blue 75 35
112/14 .. .. *Set of* 3 1·40 60
112/14 Perf "Specimen" .. .. *Set of* 3 60·00

26 Beach View

27 Dolphin fish (*Coryphaena hippurus*)

(Recess D.L.R. (½d., 2d., 6d., 1s., 10s.), Waterlow (others))

1938 (5 May)–**48**. *T* 26/7 *and similar designs. Wmk Mult Script CA* (*sideways on* ¼*d.,* 1*d.,* 1½*d.,* 2½*d.,* 3*d.,* 2*s.,* 5*s.*). *Various perfs.*
115 **26** ¼d. red-orange (*p* 12½) 10 30
a. Perf 13½ × 12½ (16.7.43) 10 45
116 **27** ½d. green (*p* 13 × 11½) 35 20
a. Perf 14 (16.7.43) 45 75
117 – 1d. scarlet (*p* 12½) 12 20
118 **26** 1½d. black (*p* 12½) 10 10
119 – 2d. violet (*p* 11½ × 13) 60 25
a. Perf 14 (16.7.43) 25 30
120 – 2½d. bright blue (*p* 12½) 15 20
120*a* – 2½d. orange (*p* 12½) (25.8.47) .. .. 1·25 25
121 – 3d. orange (*p* 12½) 15 15

121*a* – 3d. bright blue (*p* 12½) (25.8.47) .. 70 25
122 – 6d. olive-green (*p* 11½ × 13) .. .. 4·00 2·25
a. Perf 14 (16.7.43) 75 35
b. Brownish olive (*p* 11½ × 13) (8.7.47) .. .. 75 1·25
123 **27** 1s. red-brown (*p* 13 × 11½) .. .. 1·75 1·50
a. Perf 14 (16.7.43) .. .. .. 1·25 50
124 **26** 2s. yellow-green (*shades*) (*p* 12½) .. 24·00 14·00
a. Deep green (16.7.43) .. .. 12·00 6·00
125 – 5s. carmine-lake (*p* 12½) .. .. 12·00 9·00
a. Crimson (1948) .. .. .. 18·00 16·00
126 – 10s. chocolate (*p* 11½ × 13) .. .. 15·00 8·00
a. Perf 14 (16.7.43) .. .. 15·00 8·00
115/26*a* .. .. .. *Set of* 14 38·00 23·00
115/26 Perf "Specimen" .. .. *Set of* 14 £250

Designs: *Horiz* (*as T* **26**)—1d., 3d. Cayman Islands map; 2½d., 5s. *Rembro* (schooner). *Vert* (*as T* **27**)—2d., 6d., 10s. Hawksbill Turtles.

1946 (26 Aug). *Victory. As Nos.* 28/9 *of Aden.*
127 1½d. black 10 10
128 3d. orange-yellow 10 10
127/8 Perf "Specimen" .. .. *Set of* 2 55·00

1948 (29 Nov). *Royal Silver Wedding. As Nos.* 30/1 *of Aden.*
129 ½d. green 10 10
130 10s. violet-blue .. .. 10·00 6·50

1949 (10 Oct). *75th Anniv of Universal Postal Union. As Nos.* 114/17 *of Antigua.*
131 2½d. orange 20 15
132 3d. deep blue 50 20
133 6d. olive 55 30
134 1s. red-brown 55 30
131/4 .. .. *Set of* 4 1·60 85

31 Cat Boat

32 Coconut Grove, Cayman Brac

(Recess B.W.)

1950 (2 Oct). *T* **31/2** *and similar horiz designs. Wmk Mult Script CA. P* 11½ × 11.
135 ¼d. bright blue and pale scarlet 15 60
136 ½d. reddish violet and emerald-green .. 10 60
137 1d. olive-green and deep blue 60 75
138 1½d. green and brown 30 75
139 2d. reddish violet and rose-carmine .. 60 1·50
140 2½d. turquoise and black 40 60
141 3d. bright green and light blue .. .. 1·40 90
142 6d. red-brown and blue .. .. .. 80 1·25
143 9d. scarlet and grey-green .. .. .. 2·00 2·00
144 1s. brown and orange .. .. .. 2·50 2·50
145 2s. violet and reddish purple .. .. 6·50 5·00
146 5s. olive-green and violet .. .. .. 8·00 6·00
147 10s. black and scarlet .. .. .. 8·50 7·50
135/47 .. .. *Set of* 13 28·00 26·00

Designs:—1d. Green Turtle; 1½d. Thatch rope industry; 2d. Cayman seamen; 2½d. Map of Cayman Islands; 3d. Parrot Fish; 6d. Bluff, Cayman Brac; 9d. Georgetown harbour; 1s. Turtle in "crawl"; 2s. *Ziroma* (schooner); 5s. Boat-building; 10s. Government Offices, Grand Cayman.

44 South Sound Lighthouse, Grand Cayman

45 Queen Elizabeth II

1953 (2 Mar)–**62**. *Designs previously used for King George VI issue but with portrait of Queen Elizabeth II as in T* **44/5**. *Wmk Mult Script CA. P* 11½×11 *or* 11×11½ (4d., £1).
148 ¼d. deep bright blue & rose-red (21.2.55) 25 10
a. Bright blue and bright rose-red (5.12.56) 20 10
149 ½d. purple and bluish green (7.7.54) .. 10 15
150 1d. brown-olive and indigo (7.7.54) .. 50 10
151 1½d. deep green and red-brown (7.7.54) .. 15 10
152 2d. reddish violet and cerise (2.6.54) .. 1·00 25
153 2½d. turquoise-blue and black (2.6.54) .. 1·25 20
154 3d. bright green and blue (21.2.55) .. 2·75 25
155 4d. black and deep blue .. .. .. 1·25 10
a. Black and greenish blue (13.10.54) .. 3·50 3·00
b. Black and deep bright blue (10.7.62) 2·50 2·00
156 6d. lake-brown and deep blue (7.7.54) .. 85 10
157 9d. scarlet and bluish green (2.6.54) .. 1·50 10
158 1s. brown and red-orange (21.2.55) .. 2·25 10
159 2s. slate-violet & reddish purple (21.2.55) 6·50 4·00
160 5s. olive-green and slate-violet (21.2.55) 7·00 3·50
161 10s. black and rose-red (21.2.55) .. .. 10·00 7·00
161*a* £1 blue (6.1.59) .. .. 20·00 8·50
148/61*a* .. .. *Set of* 15 48·00 22·00

Designs: *Horiz*—¼d. Cat boat; ½d. Coconut grove, Cayman Brac; 1d. Green Turtle; 1½d. Thatch rope industry; 2d. Cayman seamen; 2½d. Map of Cayman Islands; 3d. Parrot Fish; 6d. Bluff, Cayman Brac; 9d. Georgetown harbour; 1s. Turtle in "crawl"; 2s. *Ziroma* (schooner); 5s. Boat-building; 10s. Government Offices, Grand Cayman.

1953 (2 June). *Coronation. As No.* 47 *of Aden but ptd by B.W.*
162 1d. black and emerald 10 25

46 Arms of the Cayman Islands

(Photo D.L.R.)

1959 (4 July). *New Constitution. Wmk Mult Script CA. P* 12.
163 **46** 2½d. black and light blue 10 15
164 1s. black and orange 15 10

CROWN COLONY

47 Cuban Amazon

48 Cat Boat

(Recess B.W.)

1962 (28 Nov)–**64**. *T* **47/8** *and similar designs. W w* **12**. *P* 11×11½ (*vert*) *or* 11½×11 (*horiz*).
165 ¼d. emerald and red 15 20
a. Emerald and rose (18.2.64) 20 25
166 1d. black and yellow-olive 20 10
167 1½d. yellow and purple 55 15
168 2d. blue and deep brown 15 15
169 2½d. violet and bluish green 15 15
170 3d. bright blue and carmine 15 10
171 4d. deep green and purple 70 25
172 6d. bluish green and sepia .. .. .. 1·25 20
173 9d. ultramarine and purple 50 20
174 1s. sepia and rose-red 40 10
175 1s. 3d. bluish green and orange-brown .. 1·25 1·50
176 1s. 9d. deep turquoise and violet .. .. 3·50 70
177 5s. plum and deep green .. .. .. 3·00 1·75
178 10s. olive and blue .. .. 7·00 6·00
179 £1 carmine and black .. .. .. 12·00 11·00
165/79 .. .. *Set of* 15 26·00 20·00

Designs: *Horiz*—1½d. *Schomburgkia thomsoniana* (orchid); 2d. Map of Cayman Islands; 2½d. Fisherman casting net; 3d. West Bay Beach; 4d. Green Turtle; 6d. *Lydia E. Wilson* (schooner); 1s. Iguana; 1s. 3d. Swimming Pool, Cayman Brac; 1s. 9d. Water sports; 5s. Fort George. *Vert*—9d. Angler with Kingfish; 10s. Coat of Arms; £1 Queen Elizabeth II.

1963 (4 June). *Freedom from Hunger. As No.* 76 *of Aden.*
180 1s. 9d. carmine 30 10

1963 (2 Sept). *Red Cross Centenary. As Nos.* 147/8 *of Antigua.*
181 1d. red and black 15 10
182 1s. 9d. red and blue 70 40

1964 (23 April). *400th Birth Anniv of William Shakespeare. As No.* 164 *of Antigua.*
183 6d. magenta 10 10

1965 (17 May). *I.T.U. Centenary. As Nos.* 166/7 *of Antigua.*
184 1d. blue and light purple 15 10
185 1s. 3d. bright purple and green 40 25

1965 (25 Oct). *International Co-operation Year. As Nos.* 168/9 *of Antigua.*
186 1d. reddish purple and turquoise-green .. 10 10
187 1s. deep bluish green and lavender 30 15

1966 (24 Jan). *Churchill Commemoration. As Nos.* 170/3 *of Antigua.*
188 ¼d. new blue 10 10
189 1d. deep green 15 10
190 1s. brown 30 10
191 1s. 9d. bluish violet 40 35
188/91 .. .. *Set of* 4 75 50

1966 (4 Feb). *Royal Visit. As Nos.* 174/5 *of Antigua.*
192 1d. black and ultramarine 25 10
193 1s. 9d. black and magenta .. .. .. 1·00 30

1966 (1 July). *World Cup Football Championships. As Nos.* 176/7 *of Antigua.*
194 1½d. violet, yellow-green, lake & yellow-brn 10 10
195 1s. 9d. chocolate, blue-grn, lake & yell-brn 25 15

1966 (20 Sept). *Inauguration of W.H.O. Headquarters, Geneva. As Nos.* 178/9 *of Antigua.*
196 2d. black, yellow-green and light blue .. 15 10
197 1s. 3d. black, light purple and yellow-brown 40 30

62 Telephone and Map

(Des V. Whiteley. Litho Harrison)

1966 (5 Dec). *International Telephone Links. W w* **12**. *P* 14½ × 14.
198 **62** 4d. red, black, greenish blue & ol-grn 10 10
199 9d. violet-blue, black, brown-red & lt grn 10 10

1966 (12 Dec*). *20th Anniv of U.N.E.S.C.O. As Nos.* 196/8 *of Antigua.*
200 1d. slate-violet, red, yellow and orange .. 15 10
201 1s. 9d. orange-yellow, violet and deep olive 45 10
202 5s. black, bright purple and orange .. 1·25 55
200/2 .. .. *Set of* 3 1·75 65

*This is the local date of issue; the Crown Agents released the stamps on 1 December.

63 BAC 1-11 Airliner over Cayman Schooner

(Des V. Whiteley. Photo Harrison)

1966 (17 Dec). *Opening of Cayman Jet Service. W w* **12**. *P* 14½.
203 **63** 1s. black, new blue and olive-green .. 10 10
204 1s. 9d. deep purple-brown, ultramarine and emerald 15 10

64 Water-skiing

(Des G. Vasarhelyi. Photo Harrison)

1967 (1 Dec). *International Tourist Year. T* **64** *and similar horiz designs. Multicoloured. W w* **12**. *P* 14½ × 14.
205 4d. Type **64** 10 10
a. Gold omitted £110
206 6d. Skin diving 10 10
207 1s. Sport fishing 10 10
208 1s. 9d. Sailing 15 10
205/8 .. .. *Set of* 4 30 15

A used copy of No. 207 is known with yellow omitted.

68 Former Slaves and Emblem

(Des and photo Harrison)

1968 (3 June). *Human Rights Year. W w* **12**. *P* 14½ × 14.
209 **68** 3d. deep bluish green, black and gold .. 10 10
210 9d. brown, gold and myrtle-green .. 10 10
211 5s. ultramarine, gold and myrtle-green 30 25
209/11 .. .. *Set of* 3 40 25

69 Long-jumping

(Des R. Granger Barrett. Litho P.B.)

1968 (1 Oct). *Olympic Games, Mexico. T* **69** *and similar multi-coloured designs. W w* **12**. *P* 13½.
212 1s. Type **69** 10 10
213 1s. 3d. High jumping 10 10
214 2s. Pole vaulting (*vert*) 15 15
212/14 .. .. *Set of* 3 25 20

72 "The Adoration of the Shepherds" (Fabritius)

(Des and photo Harrison)

1968–69. *Christmas. T* **72** *and similar horiz design. Centres multicoloured; country name and frames in gold; value and background in colours given. P* 14 × 14½.

(*a*) *W w* **12**. (18.11.68)
215 **72** ¼d. brown 10 10
a. Gold omitted £180
216 – 1d. bluish violet 10 10
217 **72** 6d. bright blue 10 10
218 – 8d. cerise 10 10
219 **72** 1s. 3d. bright green 10 10
220 – 2s. grey 15 10

(*b*) *No wmk* (8.1.69)
221 **72** ¼d. bright purple 10 10
215/21 .. .. *Set of* 7 30 25

Design:—1d., 8d., 2s. "The Adoration of the Shepherds" (Rembrandt).

74 Grand Cayman Thrush

76 Arms of the Cayman Islands

(Des G. Vasarhelyi. Litho Format)

1969 (5 June). *Designs as T* **74** *and T* **76** *in black, ochre and red (£1) or multicoloured (others). No wmk. P* 14.

222	¼d. Type **74**	10	10
223	1d. Brahmin Cattle (*horiz*)	10	10
224	2d. Blowholes on the coast (*horiz*)	10	10
225	2½d. Map of Grand Cayman (*horiz*)	15	10
226	3d. Georgetown scene (*horiz*)	15	10
227	4d. Royal Poinciana (*horiz*)	30	10
228	6d. Cayman Brac and Little Cayman on Chart (*horiz*)	30	10
229	8d. Motor vessels at berth (*horiz*)	30	10
230	1s. Basket-making (*horiz*)	20	10
231	1s. 3d. Beach scene (*horiz*)	35	70
232	1s. 6d. Straw-rope making (*horiz*)	40	80
233	2s. Barracuda (*horiz*)	1·00	80
234	4s. Government House (*horiz*)	35	80
235	10s. Type **76**	1·00	1·75
236	£1 Queen Elizabeth II (*vert*)	2·00	2·50
222/36	*Set of* 15	6·00	7·00

1969 (11 Aug). *As No.* 222, *but wmk* w **12** (*sideways*).

237	**74**	¼d. multicoloured	10	15

(New Currency. 100 cents = 1 dollar.)

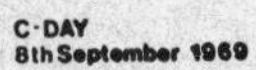

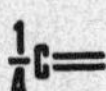

(89)

1969 (8 Sept). *Decimal Currency. No.* 237, *and as Nos.* 223/36, *but wmk* w **12** (*sideways on horiz designs*), *surch as T* **89**.

238	¼ c. on ¼d. Type **74**	10	20
239	1 c. on 1d. Brahmin Cattle	10	10
240	2 c. on 2d. Blowholes on the coast	10	10
241	3 c. on 4d. Royal Poinciana	10	10
242	4 c. on 2½d. Map of Grand Cayman	10	10
243	5 c. on 6d. Cayman Brac and Little Cayman on Chart	10	10
244	7 c. on 8d. Motor vessels at berth	10	10
245	8 c. on 3d. Georgetown scene	15	10
246	10 c. on 1s. Basket-making	25	10
247	12 c. on 1s. 3d. Beach scene	35	40
248	15 c. on 1s. 6d. Straw-rope making	45	50
249	20 c. on 2s. Barracuda	1·25	1·50
250	40 c. on 4s. Government House	45	80
251	$1 on 10s. Type **76**	1·50	1·60
252	$2 on £1 Queen Elizabeth II	2·00	3·25
238/52	*Set of* 15	6·00	8·00

90 "Virgin and Child" (Vivarini)

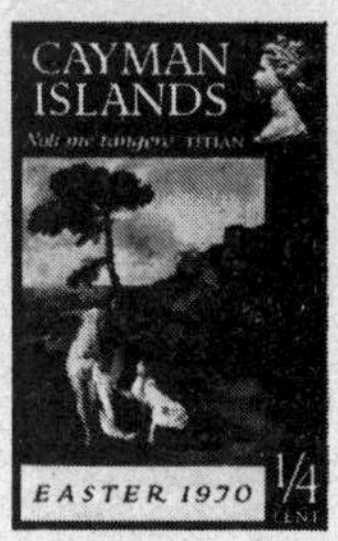

92 "Noli me tangere" (Titian)

(Des adapted by G. Drummond. Photo Harrison)

1969 (14 Nov*). *Christmas. Multicoloured; background colours given.* W w **12** (*sideways on* 1, 7 *and* 20 c.). *P* 14½.

253	**90**	¼ c. orange-red	10	10
254		¼ c. magenta	10	10
255		¼ c. emerald	10	10
		a. Gold frame omitted	£140	
256		¼ c. new blue	10	10
257	–	1 c. ultramarine	10	10
258	**90**	5 c. orange-red	10	10
259	–	7 c. myrtle-green	10	10
260	**90**	12 c. emerald	15	10
261	–	20 c. brown-purple	20	20
253/61		*Set of* 9	45	30

Design:—1, 7, 20 c. "The Adoration of the Kings" (Gossaert).

*This is the local release date. The Crown Agents released the stamps on 4 November.

(Des L. Curtis. Litho D.L.R.)

1970 (23 Mar). *Easter. Paintings multicoloured; frame colours given. P* 14.

262	**92**	¼ c. carmine-red	10	10
263		¼ c. deep green	10	10
264		¼ c. yellow-brown	10	10
265		¼ c. pale violet	10	10
266		10 c. chalky blue	10	10
267		12 c. chestnut	10	10
268		40 c. plum	25	25
262/8		*Set of* 7	45	30

93 Barnaby (*Barnaby Rudge*)

97 Cayman Red-legged Thrush

(Des Jennifer Toombs. Photo Harrison)

1970 (17 June). *Death Centenary of Charles Dickens. T* **93** *and similar vert designs.* W w **12** (*sideways*). *P* 14½ × 14.

269	1 c. black, olive-green and greenish yellow	10	10
270	12 c. black, lake-brown and red	10	10
271	20 c. black, ochre-brown and gold	15	10
272	40 c. black, bright ultramarine and new blue	20	25
269/72	*Set of* 4	40	35

Designs:—12 c. Sairey Gamp (*Martin Chuzzlewit*); 20 c. Mr. Micawber and David (*David Copperfield*); 40 c. The "Marchioness" (*The Old Curiosity Shop*).

1970 (8 Sept). *Decimal Currency. Designs as Nos.* 223/37, *but with values inscr in decimal currency as T* **97**. W w **12** (*sideways on cent values*). *P* 14.

273	¼ c. Type **97**	10	10
274	1 c. Brahmin Cattle	10	10
275	2 c. Blowholes on the coast	10	10
276	3 c. Royal Poinciana	20	10
277	4 c. Map of Grand Cayman	20	10
278	5 c. Cayman Brac and Little Cayman on Chart	35	10
279	7 c. Motor vessels at berth	30	10
280	8 c. Georgetown scene	30	10
281	10 c. Basket-making	30	10
282	12 c. Beach scene	90	45
283	15 c. Straw-rope making	1·25	1·00
284	20 c. Barracuda	2·50	1·25
285	40 c. Government House	85	75
286	$1 Type **76**	1·75	2·50
287	$2 Queen Elizabeth II	2·75	4·00
273/87	*Set of* 15	10·50	9·50

98 The Three Wise Men

(Des G. Drummond. Litho Format)

1970 (8 Oct). *Christmas. T* **98** *and similar horiz design.* W w **12** (*sideways*). *P* 14.

288	**98**	¼ c. apple-green, grey and emerald	10	10
289	–	1 c. black, lemon and turquoise-green	10	10
290	**98**	5 c. grey, red-orange and crimson	10	10
291	–	10 c. black, lemon and orange-red	10	10
292	**98**	12 c. grey, pale turquoise & ultram	10	10
293	–	20 c. black, lemon and green	15	15
288/93		*Set of* 6	40	30

Design:—1, 10, 20 c. Nativity scene and Globe.

100 Grand Cayman Terrapin

(Des V. Whiteley. Photo Harrison)

1971 (28 Jan). *Turtles. T* **100** *and similar diamond-shaped designs.* W w **12** (*sideways, reading from inscr to* "ISLANDS"). *P* 14½ × 14.

294	5 c. Type **100**	30	25
295	7 c. Green Turtle	35	25
296	12 c. Hawksbill Turtle	55	30
297	20 c. Turtle Farm	1·00	1·40
294/7	*Set of* 4	2·00	2·00

101 *Dendrophylax fawcettii*

102 "Adoration of the Kings" (French, 15th Cent)

(Des Sylvia Goaman. Litho Questa)

1971 (7 Apr). *Orchids. T* **101** *and similar vert designs. Multicoloured.* W w **12**. *P* 14.

298	¼ c. Type **101**	10	10
299	2 c. *Schomburgkia thomsoniana*	40	30
300	10 c. *Vanilla claviculata*	90	90
301	40 c. *Oncidium variegatum*	2·75	3·50
298/301	*Set of* 4	3·75	4·25

(Des Jennifer Toombs. Litho Questa)

1971 (15 Oct*). *Christmas. T* **102** *and similar vert designs. Multicoloured.* W w **12**. *P* 14.

302	¼ c. Type **102**	10	10
303	1 c. "The Nativity" (Parisian, 14th Cent.)	10	10
304	5 c. "Adoration of the Magi" (Burgundian, 15th Cent.)	10	10
305	12 c. Type **102**	10	10
306	15 c. As 1 c.	15	20
307	20 c. As 5 c.	20	30
302/7	*Set of* 6	50	65
MS308	113 × 115 mm. Nos. 302/7	1·25	2·25

*This is the local date of issue. The Crown Agents released the stamps on 27 September.

103 Turtle and Telephone Cable

(Des Anglo Arts Associates. Litho Walsall)

1972 (10 Jan). *Co-Axial Telephone Cable.* W w **12** (*sideways*). *P* 14.

309	**103**	2 c. multicoloured	10	10
310		10 c. multicoloured	10	10
311		40 c. multicoloured	25	40
309/11		*Set of* 3	25	45

104 Court House Building

(Des C. Abbott. Litho Questa)

1972 (15 Aug). *New Government Buildings. T* **104** *and similar horiz design. Multicoloured.* W w **12**. *P* 13½.

312	5 c. Type **104**	10	10
313	15 c. Legislative Assembly Building	10	10
314	25 c. Type **104**	15	15
315	40 c. As 15 c.	20	30
312/15	*Set of* 4	35	45
MS316	121 × 108 mm. Nos. 312/15	70	2·00

105 Hawksbill Turtle and Conch Shell

(Des (from photograph by D. Groves) and photo Harrison)

1972 (20 Nov). *Royal Silver Wedding. Multicoloured; background colour given.* W w **12**. *P* 14 × 14½.

317	**105**	12 c. deep slate-violet	10	10
318		30 c. yellow-olive	15	15
		a. Blue omitted*	£275	

*The omission of the blue colour results in the Duke's suit appearing sepia instead of deep blue.

106 $1 Coin and Note **107** "The Way of Sorrow"

(Des and photo D.L.R.)

1973 (15 Jan). *First Issue of Currency. T* **106** *and similar horiz designs. Multicoloured. W* w **12** *(sideways). P* 13.

319 3 c. Type **106** 10 10
320 6 c. $5 Coin and note 10 10
321 15 c. $10 Coin and note 20 15
322 25 c. $25 Coin and note 30 30
319/22 .. .. *Set of* 4 60 45
MS323 128 × 107 mm. Nos. 319/22 .. .. 2·00 2·50

(Des G. Drummond. Litho Questa)

1973 (11 Apr*). *Easter. T* **107** *and similar multicoloured designs showing stained-glass windows. W* w **12** *(sideways on* 10 *and* 12 c.). *P* 14½.

324 10 c. Type **107** 10 10
325 12 c. "Christ Resurrected" 10 10
326 20 c. "The Last Supper" (*horiz*) 15 15
327 30 c. "Christ on the Cross" (*horiz*) 20 25
324/7 .. .. *Set of* 4 45 45
MS328 122 × 105 mm. Nos. 324/7. Imperf .. 70 1·60

*This is the local date of issue; the Crown Agents released the stamps on 15 March.

108 "The Nativity" (Sforza Book of Hours) **109** White-winged Dove

(Des J. Cooter. Litho Questa)

1973 (2 Oct). *Christmas. T* **108** *and similar vert design. W* w **12** *(sideways). P* 14.

329 **108** 3 c. multicoloured 10 10
330 – 5 c. multicoloured 10 10
331 **108** 9 c. multicoloured 10 10
332 – 12 c. multicoloured 10 10
333 **108** 15 c. multicoloured 15 10
334 – 25 c. multicoloured 20 20
329/34 .. .. *Set of* 6 50 40

Design:—5, 12, 25 c. "The Adoration of the Magi" (Breviary of Queen Isabella).

1973 (14 Nov). *Royal Wedding. As Nos.* 165/6 *of Anguilla. Centre multicoloured. W* w **12** *(sideways). P* 13½.

335 10 c. sage-green 10 10
336 30 c. bright mauve 15 10

(Des M. Goaman. Litho Walsall)

1974 (2 Jan). *Birds* (1*st series*). *T* **109** *and similar vert designs. Multicoloured. W* w **12** *(sideways). P* 14.

337 3 c. Type **109** 95 20
338 10 c. Vitelline Warbler .. .. 1·75 20
339 12 c. Antillean Grackle .. .. 1·75 25
340 20 c. West Indian Red-bellied Woodpecker .. 2·75 60
341 30 c. Stripe-headed Tanager .. .. 4·00 1·50
342 50 c. Yucatan Vireo .. .. 5·50 2·75
337/42 .. .. *Set of* 6 15·00 5·00

See also Nos. 383/8.

110 Old School Building

(Des PAD Studio. Litho Questa)

1974 (1 May). *25th Anniv of University of West Indies. T* **110** *and similar horiz designs. Multicoloured. W* w **12** *(sideways). P* 14.

343 12 c. Type **110** 10 10
344 20 c. New Comprehensive School 10 10
345 30 c. Creative Arts Centre, Mona 15 25
343/5 .. .. *Set of* 3 25 30

111 Hermit Crab and Staghorn Coral

(Des J.W. Litho Kynoch Press)

1974 (1 Aug). *Multicoloured designs as T* **111** *(size* 41½ × 27 *mm). W* w **12** *(sideways on* $1 *and* $2). *P* 14.

346 1 c. Type **111** .. .. 1·25 35
347 3 c. Treasure-chest and Lion's Paw .. .. 1·50 50
348 4 c. Treasure and Spotted Scorpion-fish .. 50 50
349 5 c. Flintlock pistol and Brain Coral .. 1·50 50
350 6 c. Blackbeard and Green Turtle 35 60
351 9 c. Jewelled pomander and Pork-fish .. 2·75 3·50
352 10 c. Spiny Lobster and treasure .. .. 2·00 50
353 12 c. Jewelled sword and dagger, and Sea-fan 35 45
354 15 c. Cabrit's Murex and treasure 40 60
355 20 c. Queen Conch and treasure .. .. 4·50 1·75
356 25 c. Hogfish and treasure 45 70
357 40 c. Gold chalice and sea-whip .. .. 1·50 1·00
358 $1 Coat of arms (*vert*) .. .. .. 2·75 3·25
359 $2 Queen Elizabeth II (*vert*) .. .. .. 4·00 6·50
346/59 .. .. *Set of* 14 21·00 19·00

See also Nos. 364/6, 412/19 and 445/52.

112 Sea Captain and Ship (Shipbuilding)

(Des G. Vasarhelyi. Litho D.L.R.)

1974 (7 Oct). *Local Industries. T* **112** *and similar horiz designs. Multicoloured. W* w **12** *(inverted on* 8 c. *and* 12 c.). *P* 14 × 13½.

360 8 c. Type **112** 10 10
361 12 c. Thatcher and cottages 10 10
362 20 c. Farmer and plantation 20 20
360/2 .. .. *Set of* 3 35 35
MS363 92 × 132 mm. Nos. 360/2 .. .. .. 80 1·50

1974–75. *As Nos.* 346/7 *and design of* 351, *but wmk sideways.*

364 1 c. Type **111** (29.9.75) .. .. .. 1·25 1·50
365 3 c. Treasure-chest and Lions-paw (12.11.74) 2·25 2·00
366 8 c. Jewelled pomander and Pork-fish (16.12.74) .. .. 2·50 5·50
364/6 .. .. *Set of* 3 5·50 8·00

Nos. 367/79 vacant.

113 Arms of Cinque Ports and Lord Warden's Flag **114** "The Crucifixion"

(Des P. Powell. Litho D.L.R.)

1974 (30 Nov). *Birth Centenary of Sir Winston Churchill. T* **113** *and similar vert design. Multicoloured. W* w **12** *(sideways). P* 13½ × 14.

380 12 c. Type **113** 15 10
381 50 c. Churchill's coat of arms 45 70
MS382 98 × 86 mm. Nos. 380/1 .. .. .. 85 1·60

(Des M. Goaman. Litho Questa)

1975 (1 Jan). *Birds* (2*nd series*). *Multicoloured designs as T* **109**. *W* w **12** *(sideways). P* 14.

383 3 c. Common Flicker 45 20
384 10 c. Black-billed Whistling Duck 70 45
385 12 c. Yellow Warbler 80 55
386 20 c. White-bellied Dove .. .. .. 1·40 1·25
387 30 c. Magnificent Frigate Bird .. .. 2·25 2·00
388 50 c. Cuban Amazon .. .. 2·75 2·75
a. Error. Wmk Lesotho T **53** (inverted) .. £500
383/8 .. .. *Set of* 6 7·50 6·50

(Des PAD Studio. Litho D.L.R.)

1975 (24 Mar). *Easter. French Pastoral Staffs. T* **114** *and similar vert design showing "The Crucifixion" (different). Multicoloured. W* w **12** *(sideways). P* 13½ × 14.

389 **114** 15 c. multicoloured 10 15
390 – 35 c. multicoloured 20 30
MS391 128 × 98 mm. Nos. 389/90. W w **12** (*upright*) 55 1·25
a. Error. Imperf .. .. ..

See also Nos. 396/**MS**398.

115 Israel Hands

(Des J.W. Litho Harrison)

1975 (25 July). *Pirates. T* **115** *and similar horiz designs. Multicoloured. W* w **12** *(sideways). P* 14.

392 10 c. Type **115** 20 10
393 12 c. John Fenn 20 10
394 20 c. Thomas Anstis 40 35
395 30 c. Edward Low 55 55
392/5 .. .. *Set of* 4 1·25 1·00

(Des PAD Studio. Litho Questa)

1975 (31 Oct). *Christmas. Vert designs as T* **114** *showing "Virgin and Child with Angels" (both different). W* w **14**. *P* 14.

396 12 c. multicoloured 10 10
397 50 c. multicoloured 30 30
MS398 113 × 85 mm. Nos. 396/7 .. .. .. 1·00 1·60

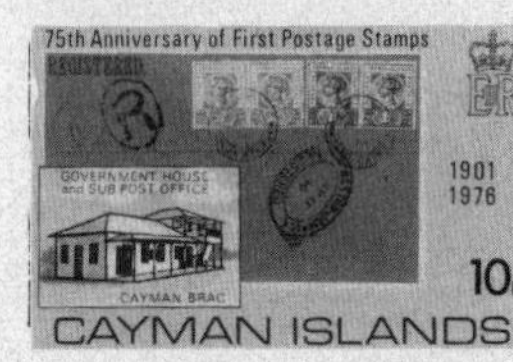

116 Registered Cover, Government House and Sub-Post Office

(Des J. Cooter. Litho Questa)

1976 (12 Mar). *75th Anniv of First Cayman Is. Postage Stamp. T* **116** *and similar horiz designs. Multicoloured. W* w **14** *(sideways). P* 13½.

399 10 c. Type **116** 10 10
400 20 c. ½d. stamp and 1890–94 postmark .. 15 15
401 30 c. 1d. stamp and 1908 surcharge 25 25
402 50 c. ½d. and 1d. stamps 40 50
399/402 .. .. *Set of* 4 85 85
MS403 117 × 147 mm. Nos. 399/402 .. .. 1·75 3·00

117 Seals of Georgia, Delaware and New Hampshire

(Des P. Powell. Litho J.W.)

1976 (29 May). *Bicentenary of American Revolution. T* **117** *and similar horiz designs showing seals of the States given. Multicoloured. W* w **14** *(sideways). P* 13½ × 14.

404 10 c. Type **117** 30 15
405 15 c. S. Carolina, New Jersey and Maryland 50 20
406 20 c. Virginia, Rhode Is. and Massachusetts .. 60 25
407 25 c. New York, Connecticut and N. Carolina 60 35
408 30 c. Pennsylvania seal, Liberty Bell and U.S. Great Seal 70 40
404/8 .. .. *Set of* 5 2·40 1·25
MS409 166 × 124 mm. Nos. 404/8. P 14 .. .. 5·00 6·50

118 Racing Dinghies **119** Queen Elizabeth II and Westminster Abbey

(Des C. Abbott. Litho D.L.R.)

1976 (16 Aug). *Olympic Games, Montreal. T* **118** *and similar vert design. Multicoloured. W* w **14**. *P* 14.

410 20 c. Type **118** 15 10
411 50 c. Racing dinghy 45 50

1976 (3 Sept)–**78**. *As Nos.* 347/9, 352, 355, 358/9 *and* 366, *but* W w **14** *(upright on* $1, *inverted on* $2, *sideways on others). Chalk-surfaced paper* (4, 5 c. *and* $1) *or ordinary paper (others).*

412 3 c. Treasure-chest and Lion's Paw 85 70
a. Chalk-surfaced paper (19.10.77) .. .. 1·50 1·75
413 4 c. Treasure and Spotted Scorpion-fish (19.10.77) .. .. 1·10 55

414 5 c. Flintlock pistol and Brain Coral (19.10.77).. .. .. 1·50 65
415 8 c. Jewelled pomander and Pork-fish .. .. 2·25 75
a. Chalk-surfaced paper (19.10.77).. .. 2·25 2·50
416 10 c. Spiny Lobster and treasure .. .. 1·25 1·25
a. Chalk-surfaced paper (27.1.78) .. .. 1·75 2·00
417 20 c. Queen Conch and treasure .. .. 3·25 3·00
a. Chalk-surfaced paper (27.1.78) .. .. 3·50 3·00
418 $1 Coat of arms (19.10.77) .. .. .. 6·50 5·50
419 $2 Queen Elizabeth II .. .. .. 7·50 6·50
a. Chalk-surfaced paper (19.10.77).. .. 11·00 15·00
412/19 .. .. *Set of* 8 22·00 17·00
Nos. 420/6 vacant.

(Des BG Studio. Litho Questa)

1977 (7 Feb). *Silver Jubilee. T* **119** *and similar multicoloured designs. W* w **14** *(sideways on* 50 *c.). P* 13½.
427 8 c. Prince of Wales' visit, 1973 .. .. 10 20
428 30 c. Type **119** 15 40
429 50 c. Preparation for the Anointing (*horiz*) .. 30 75
427/9 .. .. *Set of* 3 50 1·25

120 Scuba Diving

(Des Jennifer Toombs. Litho J.W.)

1977 (25 July). *Tourism. T* **120** *and similar horiz designs. Multicoloured. W* w **14** *(sideways). P* 13½.
430 5 c. Type **120** 10 10
431 10 c. Exploring a wreck 15 10
432 20 c. Fairy Basslet (fish) 45 20
433 25 c. Sergeant majors (fish) 55 35
430/3 .. .. *Set of* 4 1·10 60
MS434 146 × 89 mm. Nos. 430/3. P 14½.. .. 2·00 2·75

121 *Composia fidelissima*

(Des J. Cooter. Litho Enschedé)

1977 (2 Dec). *Butterflies. T* **121** *and similar horiz designs. Multicoloured. W* w **14** *(sideways). P* 14 × 13.
435 5 c. Type **121** 25 10
436 8 c. Passion-flower Butterfly.. .. .. 35 15
437 10 c. Monarch Butterfly 35 15
438 15 c. *Agraulis vanillae* 60 30
439 20 c. Nymphalid Butterfly 75 35
440 30 c. *Anartia jatrophae* 95 50
435/40 .. .. *Set of* 6 3·00 1·40

122 Cruise Liner *Southward* **123** "The Crucifixion" (Dürer)

(Des G. Hutchins. Litho Questa)

1978 (23 Jan). *New Harbour and Cruise Ships. T* **122** *and similar multicoloured designs. W* w **14** *(sideways on* 3, 5 *c.). P* 14 × 14½ *(*3, 5 *c.) or* 14½ × 14 *(others).*
441 3 c. Type **122**.. .. .. .. 15 10
442 5 c. Cruise liner *Renaissance* 20 10
443 30 c. New harbour (*vert*) 70 25
444 50 c. Cruise liner *Daphne* (*vert*) 90 55
441/4 .. .. *Set of* 4 1·75 85

(Litho Walsall)

1978 (16 Mar)–**80**. *Designs as Nos.* 346/7, 349, 352, 355 *and* 357/9 *but smaller,* 40 × 26 *or* 26 × 40 *mm. W* w **14** *(sideways on* 1 *to* 40 *c.). Chalk-surfaced paper.*
445 1 c. Type **111** 75 60
446 3 c. Treasure-chest and Lion's Paw 80 45
447 5 c. Flintlock pistol and Brain Coral (11.12.79).. .. .. 1·25 1·25
448 10 c. Spiny Lobster and treasure (25.5.78) .. 1·60 55
449 20 c. Queen Conch and treasure (25.5.78) .. 3·25 1·25
450 40 c. Gold chalice and sea-whip (1979*) .. 10·00 11·00
451 $1 Coat of arms (30.7.80) .. .. 7·00 7·50
452 $2 Queen Elizabeth II (3.4.80) .. .. 7·00 13·00
445/52 .. .. *Set of* 8 28·00 32·00
*Supplies of No. 450 were sent to Cayman Islands on 7 May 1979. It is not known when these stamps were first placed on sale.
Nos. 453/8 vacant.

(Des Jennifer Toombs. Litho Cartor S.A., France)

1978 (20 Mar). *Easter and 450th Death Anniv of Dürer. T* **123** *and similar vert designs. W* w **14** *(inverted on* 20 *c.). P* 12.
459 10 c. magenta and black 15 10
460 15 c. yellow and black.. .. .. .. 25 15
461 20 c. turquoise-green and black 30 20
462 30 c. lilac and black 45 35
459/62 .. .. *Set of* 4 1·00 70
MS463 120 × 108 mm. Nos. 459/62 .. .. 1·50 2·25
Designs:—15 c. "Christ at Emmaus"; 20 c. "The Entry into Jerusalem"; 30 c. "Christ washing Peter's Feet".

124 "Explorers" Singing Game **125** Yale of Beaufort

(Des Walsall. Litho Questa)

1978 (25 Apr). *3rd International Council Meeting of Girls' Brigade. T* **124** *and similar vert designs. Multicoloured. W* w **14**. *P* 14.
464 3 c. Type **124** 15 10
465 10 c. Colour party 25 10
466 20 c. Girls and Duke of Edinburgh Award interests 50 20
467 50 c. Girls using domestic skills .. .. 1·00 80
464/7 .. .. *Set of* 4 1·75 1·10

(Des C. Abbott. Litho Questa)

1978 (2 June). *25th Anniv of Coronation. T* **125** *and similar vert designs. P* 15.
468 30 c. apple-green, deep magenta and silver .. 15 25
a. Sheetlet. Nos. 468/70 × 2 90
469 30 c. multicoloured 15 25
470 30 c. apple-green, deep magenta and silver .. 15 25
468/70 .. .. *Set of* 3 40 65
Designs:—No. 468, Type **125**; No. 469, Queen Elizabeth II; No. 470, Screech Owl.
Nos. 468/70 were printed together in small sheets of 6, containing two *se-tenant* strips of 3, with horizontal gutter margin between.

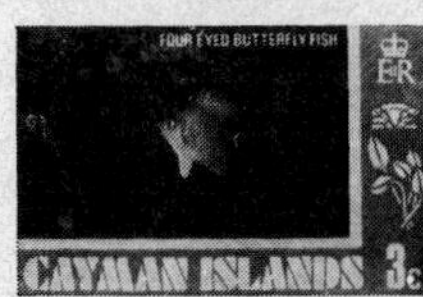

126 Four Eyed Butterfly Fish

(Des G. Hutchins. Litho Walsall)

1978 (29 Aug). *Fish (1st series). T* **126** *and similar horiz designs. Multicoloured. W* w **14** *(sideways). P* 14.
471 3 c. Type **126** 15 10
472 5 c. Grey Angel Fish 20 10
473 10 c. Squirrel Fish 35 10
474 15 c. Parrot Fish 45 30
475 20 c. Spanish Hogfish 50 35
476 30 c. Queen Angel Fish 60 50
471/6 .. .. *Set of* 6 2·00 1·25
Examples of the 15 c. value inscribed "SERGEANT MAJOR FISH" and 20 c. inscribed "PARROT FISH" were prepared, but not issued for postal purposes.
See also Nos. 483/8.

127 Lockheed "Lodestar"

(Des A. Theobald. Litho Format)

1979 (5 Feb). *25th Anniv of Owen Roberts Airfield. T* **127** *and similar horiz designs. Multicoloured. W* w **14** *(sideways). P* 14½ × 14.
477 3 c. Type **127** 15 10
478 5 c. Consolidated "PBY" 15 10
479 10 c. Vickers "Viking".. .. .. .. 20 10
480 15 c. B.A.C. "1-11" on tarmac.. .. .. 30 20
481 20 c. Piper "Cheyenne", H.S. "125" and Bell "47" (helicopter) 40 30
482 30 c. B.A.C. "1-11" over airfield 60 45
477/82 .. .. *Set of* 6 1·60 1·10

128 Trumpetfish

(Des R. Granger Barrett. Litho Questa)

1979 (20 Apr). *Fish (2nd series). T* **128** *and similar horiz designs. Multicoloured. W* w **14** *(sideways). P* 14.
483 1 c. Type **128** 10 10
484 3 c. Nassau Grouper 15 10
485 5 c. French Angelfish 15 10
486 10 c. Schoolmaster Snappers 20 10
487 20 c. Banded Butterflyfish 35 25
488 50 c. Blackbar Soldierfish 70 70
483/8 .. .. *Set of* 6 1·40 1·25

129 1900 1d. Stamp

(Des J.W. Litho Walsall)

1979 (15 Aug). *Death Centenary of Sir Rowland Hill. T* **129** *and similar horiz designs showing stamps and Sir Rowland Hill. W* w **14** *(sideways). P* 13½.
489 5 c. black, rose-carmine and grey-blue .. 10 10
490 10 c. multicoloured 10 10
491 20 c. multicoloured 20 20
489/91 .. .. *Set of* 3 25 25
MS492 138 × 90 mm. 50 c. multicoloured 45 65
Designs:—10 c. Great Britain 1902 3d.; 20 c. 1955 £1 definitive; 50 c. 1908 2½d.

130 Holy Family and Angels

(Des G. Vasarhelyi. Litho Secura, Singapore)

1979 (20 Nov). *Christmas. T* **130** *and similar horiz designs. Multicoloured. W* w **14** *(sideways). P* 13½ × 13.
493 10 c. Type **130** 15 10
494 20 c. Angels appearing before shepherds .. 20 10
495 30 c. Nativity scene 30 20
496 40 c. Wise men following star.. .. .. 40 30
493/6 .. .. *Set of* 4 95 60

131 Local Rotary Project

(Des Walsall. Litho Secura, Singapore)

1980 (14 Feb). *75th Anniv of Rotary International. T* **131** *and similar designs in black, bistre-yellow and deep ultramarine. W* w **14** *(sideways on* 20 *c.). P* 13½ × 13 *(*20 *c.) or* 13 × 13½ *(others).*
497 20 c. Type **131** 20 15
498 30 c. Paul P. Harris (founder) (*vert*) 25 20
499 50 c. Rotary anniversary emblem (*vert*) .. 35 30
497/9 .. .. *Set of* 3 70 60

132 Walking Mail Carrier (late 19th-century)

(Des J.W. Litho Walsall)

1980 (6 May). *"London 1980" International Stamp Exhibition. T* **132** *and similar horiz designs. Multicoloured. W* w **14** *(sideways). P* 14.
500 5 c. Type **132** 10 10
501 10 c. Delivering mail by cat boat (late 19th-century) 15 10
502 15 c. Mounted mail carrier (early 20th-century) 20 10
503 30 c. Horse-drawn waggonette (early 20th-century) 30 15
504 40 c. Postman on bicycle (mid 20th-century) .. 30 15
505 $1 Motor transport (late 20th-century) .. 65 55
500/5 .. .. *Set of* 6 1·50 1·00

NEW INFORMATION

The editor is always interested to correspond with people who have new information that will improve or correct the Catalogue.

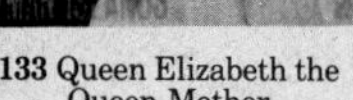

133 Queen Elizabeth the Queen Mother **134** Atlantic Spiny Oyster

(Des and litho Harrison)

1980 (4 Aug). *80th Birthday of Queen Elizabeth the Queen Mother. W* w **14** (*sideways*). *P* 14.
506 **133** 20 c. multicoloured 20 25

(Des J.W. Litho Walsall)

1980 (12 Aug). *Shells* (1*st series*). *T* **134** *and similar horiz designs. Multicoloured. W* w **14** (*sideways*). *P* 14½ × 14.
507 5 c. Type **134** 15 10
508 10 c. West Indian Murex 20 10
509 30 c. Triton 45 35
510 50 c. Murex-line vase shell 60 65
507/10 .. .. *Set of* 4 1·25 1·10
See also Nos. 565/8 and 582/5.

135 Lantana **136** Juvenile Tarpon and Fire Sponge

(Des G. Hutchins. Litho Rosenbaum Bros, Vienna)

1980 (21 Oct). *Flowers* (1*st series*). *T* **135** *and similar horiz designs. Multicoloured. W* w **14** (*sideways*). *P* 13½.
511 5 c. Type **135** 10 10
512 15 c. Bauhinia 25 10
513 30 c. Hibiscus Rosa 35 10
514 $1 Milk and Wine Lily .. .. 1·00 75
511/14 .. .. *Set of* 4 1·50 85
See also Nos. 541/4.

(Des G. Drummond. Litho J.W.)

1980 (9 Dec)–**82**. *Flora and Fauna of the Mangrove Swamp. Vert designs as T* **136**. *Multicoloured. W* w **14**. *P* 13½ × 13.
A. *Without imprint date.*
B. *Printed with imprint date at foot of designs* (14.6.82).

		A		B	
515	3 c. Type **136**	25	20	40	30
516	5 c. Mangrove Root Oyster ..	25	15	40	25
517	10 c. Mangrove Crab	25	20	40	25
518	15 c. Lizard and Crescent Spot Butterfly	40	30	70	60
519	20 c. Louisiana Heron	1·25	70	1·75	90
520	30 c. Red Mangrove Flower ..	70	60	80	75
521	40 c. Red Mangrove Seeds ..	75	80	90	85
522	50 c. Waterhouse's Leaf-nosed Bat..	1·25	1·50	1·75	1·75
523	$1 Black-crowned Night Heron	3·50	3·50	3·50	3·50
524	$2 Cayman Islands coat of arms	3·00	3·75	3·75	4·50
525	$4 Queen Elizabeth II ..	5·00	6·50	8·00	9·00
515/25	.. .. *Set of* 11	15·00	16·00	20·00	20·00

Nos. 516B/24B exist with different imprint dates.
For stamps in these designs, but watermark w **16**, see Nos. 626 and 631/2.

137 Eucharist **138** Wood Slave

(Des Jennifer Toombs. Litho Questa)

1981 (17 Mar). *Easter. T* **137** *and similar vert designs. Multicoloured. W* w **14**. *P* 14.
526 3 c. Type **137** 10 10
527 10 c. Crown of thorns 10 10
528 20 c. Crucifix 20 10
529 $1 Lord Jesus Christ 70 80
526/9 .. .. *Set of* 4 90 90

(Des R. Granger Barrett. Litho Rosenbaum Bros, Vienna)

1981 (16 June). *Reptiles and Amphibians. T* **138** *and similar horiz designs. Multicoloured. W* w **14** (*sideways*). *P* 13½.
530 20 c. Type **138** 30 20
531 30 c. Cayman Iguana 45 35
532 40 c. Lion Lizard 55 45
533 50 c. Terrapin ("Hickatee") 65 55
530/3 .. .. *Set of* 4 1·75 1·40

139 Prince Charles **140** Disabled Scuba Divers

(Des J.W. Litho Walsall)

1981 (22 July). *Royal Wedding. T* **139** *and similar vert designs. Multicoloured. W* w **14**. *P* 14.
534 20 c. Wedding bouquet from Cayman Islands 25 10
535 30 c. Type **139** 40 10
536 $1 Prince Charles and Lady Diana Spencer 1·00 1·00
534/6 .. .. *Set of* 3 1·50 1·10

(Des J.W. Litho Walsall)

1981 (29 Sept). *International Year for Disabled Persons. T* **140** *and similar horiz designs. Multicoloured. W* w **14** (*sideways*). *P* 14.
537 5 c. Type **140** 10 10
538 15 c. Old School for the Handicapped.. .. 30 20
539 20 c. New School for the Handicapped .. 35 25
540 $1 Disabled people in wheelchairs, by the sea 1·60 1·25
537/40 .. .. *Set of* 4 2·10 1·60

(Des G. Hutchins. Litho Questa)

1981 (20 Oct). *Flowers* (2*nd series*). *Horiz designs as T* **135**. *Multicoloured. W* w **14** (*sideways*). *P* 13½.
541 3 c. Bougainvillea 10 10
542 10 c. Morning Glory 20 10
543 20 c. Wild Amaryllis 45 25
544 $1 Cordia .. .. 1·75 1·75
541/4 .. .. *Set of* 4 2·25 2·00

141 Dr. Robert Koch and Microscope **142** Bride and Groom walking down Aisle

(Des and litho Walsall)

1982 (24 Mar). *Centenary of Robert Koch's Discovery of Tubercle Bacillus. T* **141** *and similar multicoloured designs. W* w **14** (*sideways on* 15 *c., inverted on* 30 *c.*). *P* 14½.
545 15 c. Type **141** 25 25
546 30 c. Koch looking through microscope (*vert*) 45 45
547 40 c. Microscope (*vert*) 70 70
548 50 c. Dr. Robert Koch (*vert*) 80 80
545/8 .. .. *Set of* 4 2·00 2·00

(Des Jennifer Toombs. Litho J.W.)

1982 (1 July). *21st Birthday of Princess of Wales. T* **142** *and similar vert designs. Multicoloured. W* w **14**. *P* 13.
549 20 c. Cayman Islands coat of arms 35 35
550 30 c. Lady Diana Spencer in London, June 1981 .. .. 45 45
551 40 c. Type **142** 55 55
552 50 c. Formal portrait 65 70
549/52 .. .. *Set of* 4 1·75 1·90

143 Pitching Tent **144** "Madonna and Child with the Infant Baptist"

(Des L. Walker. Litho Questa)

1982 (24 Aug). *75th Anniv of Boy Scout Movement. T* **143** *and similar horiz designs. Multicoloured. W* w **14** (*sideways*). *P* 14.
553 3 c. Type **143** 10 10
554 20 c. Scouts camping 40 40
555 30 c. Cub Scouts and Leaders 55 55
556 50 c. Boating skills 85 85
553/6 .. .. *Set of* 4 1·75 1·75

(Des PAD Studio. Litho Questa)

1982 (26 Oct). *Christmas. Raphael Paintings. T* **144** *and similar vert designs. Multicoloured. W* w **14**. *P* 14½ × 14.
557 3 c. Type **144** 10 10
558 10 c. "Madonna of the Tower" 20 20
559 20 c. "Ansidei Madonna" 35 35
560 30 c. "Madonna and Child" 50 50
557/60 .. .. *Set of* 4 1·00 1·00

145 Mace

(Des and litho Walsall)

1982 (9 Nov). *150th Anniv of Representative Government. T* **145** *and similar horiz designs. Multicoloured. W* w **14** (*sideways*). *P* 14½ × 14.
561 3 c. Type **145** 10 10
562 10 c. Old Courthouse 20 20
563 20 c. Commonwealth Parliamentary Association coat of arms 35 35
564 30 c. Legislative Assembly building 50 60
561/4 .. .. *Set of* 4 1·00 1·10

(Des J.W. Litho Format)

1983 (11 Jan). *Shells* (2*nd series*). *Horiz designs as T* **134**. *Multicoloured. W* w **14** (*sideways*). *P* 13½ × 13.
565 5 c. *Natica canrena* 15 10
566 10 c. *Cassis tuberosa* 25 20
567 20 c. *Strombus gallus* 45 40
568 $1 *Cypraecassis testiculus* .. .. .. 1·75 1·75
565/8 .. .. *Set of* 4 2·40 2·25

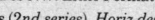

146 Legislative Building, Cayman Brac

(Des C. Abbott. Litho Questa)

1983 (15 Feb). *Royal Visit. T* **146** *and similar multicoloured designs. W* w **14** (*sideways on* 20 *c.*, 30 *c.*). *P* 14.
569 20 c. Type **146** 45 35
570 30 c. Legislative Building, Grand Cayman .. 60 50
571 50 c. Duke of Edinburgh (*vert*) .. .. .. 1·25 90
572 $1 Queen Elizabeth II (*vert*) .. .. .. 2·00 2·00
569/72 .. .. *Set of* 4 4·00 3·25
MS573 113 × 94 mm. Nos. 569/72 (wmk sideways) 4·00 4·25

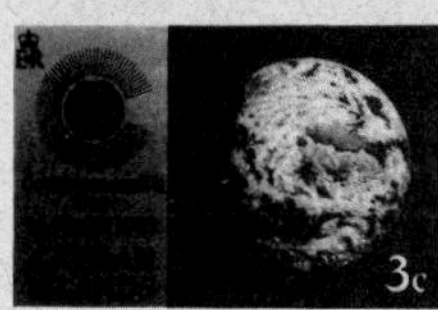

147 Satellite View of Earth

(Des J.W. Litho Questa)

1983 (14 Mar). *Commonwealth Day. T* **147** *and similar horiz designs. Multicoloured. W* w **14** (*sideways*). *P* 14.
574 3 c. Type **147** 10 10
575 15 c. Cayman Islands and Commonwealth flags 25 30
576 20 c. Fishing 30 35
577 40 c. Portrait of Queen Elizabeth II 60 65
574/7 .. .. *Set of* 4 1·10 1·25

148 MRCU "Cessna" Aircraft **149** *Song of Norway* (cruise liner)

(Des Harrison. Litho Questa)

1983 (10 Oct). *Bicentenary of Manned Flight. T* **148** *and similar horiz designs. Multicoloured. W* w **14** (*sideways*). *P* 14.
578 3 c. Type **148** 10 10
579 10 c. Consolidated "PBY Catalina" 25 20
580 20 c. Boeing "727-200" 40 40
581 40 c. Hawker-Siddeley "HS 748" 70 75
578/81 .. .. *Set of* 4 1·25 1·25

(Des J.W. Litho Questa)

1984 (18 Jan). *Shells* (3*rd series*). *Horiz designs as T* **134**. *Multicoloured. W* w **14** (*sideways*). *P* 14 × 14½.
582 3 c. *Natica floridana* 20 10
583 10 c. *Conus austini* 35 25
584 30 c. *Colubraria obscura* 80 70
585 50 c. *Turbo cailletii* .. .. 1·10 1·40
582/5 .. .. *Set of* 4 2·25 2·25

(Des G. Vasarhelyi and L. Curtis. Litho Questa)

1984 (18 June). *250th Anniv of "Lloyd's List" (newspaper). T* **149** *and similar vert designs. Multicoloured. W* w **14**. *P* 14½ × 14.
586 5 c. Type **149** 15 10
587 10 c. View of old harbour 25 25
588 25 c. Wreck of R.M.S. *Ridgefield* 50 55
589 50 c. Schooner *Goldfield* .. .. 1·00 1·10
586/9 .. .. *Set of* 4 1·75 1·75
MS590 105 × 75 mm. $1 Schooner *Goldfield* (*different*) .. .. 2·10 2·25

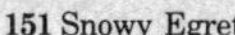

(150) 151 Snowy Egret

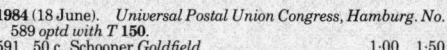

1984 (18 June). *Universal Postal Union Congress, Hamburg. No. 589 optd with T* **150**.
591 50 c. Schooner *Goldfield* . . . . . . 1·00 1·50

(Des Josephine Martin. Litho Questa)

1984 (15 Aug). *Birds of the Cayman Islands (1st series). T* **151** *and similar horiz designs. Multicoloured. W w* **14** *(sideways). P* 14×14½.
592 5 c. Type **151** 45 15
593 10 c. Bananaquit 55 25
594 35 c. Belted Kingfisher . . . . 1·75 1·25
595 $1 Brown Booby . . . . 4·00 4·25
592/5 . . . . *Set of* 4 6·00 5·50
See also Nos. 627/30.

152 Couple on Beach at Sunset

153 *Schomburgkia thomsoniana (var. minor)*

(Des G. Wilby. Litho Questa)

1984 (17 Oct). *Christmas. Local Festivities. T* **152** *and similar vert designs. Multicoloured. W w* **14** *(sideways). P* 14.
596 5 c. Type **152** 15 15
a. Horiz strip of 4. Nos. 596/9 . . 55
597 5 c. Family and schooner . . 15 15
598 5 c. Carol singers . . 15 15
599 5 c. East End bonfire . . 15 15
600 25 c. Yachts . . 55 55
a. Horiz strip of 4. Nos. 600/3 . . 2·00
601 25 c. Father Christmas in power-boat . . 55 55
602 25 c. Children on beach . . 55 55
603 25 c. Beach party . . 55 55
596/603 . . *Set of* 8 2·40 2·40
MS604 59×79 mm. $1 As No. 599, but larger, 27×41 mm . . 2·10 2·25
Nos. 597/600 and 601/4 were each printed together, *se-tenant*, in horizontal strips of 4 throughout the sheets, the four designs of each value forming a composite picture of a beach scene at night (5 c.) or in the daytime (25 c.).

(Des Liza Horstman. Litho J.W.)

1985 (13 Mar). *Orchids. T* **153** *and similar vert designs. Multicoloured. W w* **14**. *P* 14×13½.
605 5 c. Type **153** 35 10
606 10 c. *Schomburgkia thomsoniana* . . 50 20
607 25 c. *Encyclia plicata* . . 1·25 70
608 50 c. *Dendrophylax fawcettii* . . 1·50 2·00
605/8 . . *Set of* 4 3·25 2·75

154 Freighter Aground

155 Athletics

(Des Walsall. Litho J.W.)

1985 (22 May). *Shipwrecks. T* **154** *and similar horiz designs. Multicoloured. W w* **14** *(sideways). P* 14.
609 5 c. Type **154** 30 10
610 25 c. Submerged sailing ship . . 80 50
611 35 c. Wrecked trawler . . 95 95
612 40 c. Submerged wreck on its side . . 1·25 1·40
609/12 . . *Set of* 4 3·00 2·75

(Des Harrison. Litho Walsall)

1985 (14 Aug). *International Youth Year. T* **155** *and similar multicoloured designs. W w* **14** *(sideways on 5 c., 15 c.). P* 14×14½ *(5, 15 c.) or* 14½×14 *(others)*.
613 5 c. Type **155** 10 10
614 15 c. Students in library . . 25 30
615 25 c. Football *(vert)* . . 45 50
616 50 c. Netball *(vert)* . . 85 90
613/16 . . *Set of* 4 1·50 1·60

156 Morse Key (1935) 157 Magnificent Frigate Bird

(Des G. Vasarhelyi. Litho Walsall)

1985 (25 Oct). *50th Anniv of Telecommunications System. T* **156** *and similar vert designs. Multicoloured. W w* **16**. *P* 14.
617 5 c. Type **156** 10 10
618 10 c. Hand cranked telephone . . 20 20
619 25 c. Tropospheric scatter dish (1966) . . 45 45
620 50 c. Earth station dish aerial (1979) . . 85 85
617/20 . . *Set of* 4 1·40 1·40

(Des A. Theobald. Litho Format)

1986 (21 Apr). *60th Birthday of Queen Elizabeth II. Vert designs as T* **110** *of Ascension. Multicoloured. W w* **16**. *P* 14×14½.
621 5 c. Princess Elizabeth at wedding of Lady May Cambridge, 1931 . . 10 10
622 10 c. In Norway, 1955 . . 15 20
623 25 c. Queen inspecting Royal Cayman Islands Police, 1983 . . 45 50
624 50 c. During Gulf tour, 1979 . . 85 90
625 $1 At Crown Agents Head Office, London, 1983 . . 1·75 1·90
621/5 . . *Set of* 5 3·00 3·25

(Litho J.W.)

1986 (Apr). *As No.* 516B, *but W w* **16**. *P* 13½×13.
626 5 c. Mangrove Root Oyster . . 75 75

(Des Harrison. Litho Questa)

1986 (21 May). *Birds of the Cayman Islands (2nd series). T* **157** *and similar multicoloured designs. W w* **16** *(sideways on 10, 40 c.). P* 14.
627 10 c. Type **157** 40 20
628 25 c. Black-billed Whistling Duck *(vert)* . . 75 65
629 35 c. La Sagra's Flycatcher *(vert)* . . 85 85
630 40 c. Yellow-faced Grassquit . . 1·00 1·25
627/30 . . *Set of* 4 2·75 2·75

(Litho Questa)

1986 (June). *As Nos.* 516B/17B, *but different printer and W w* **16**. *P* 14.
631 5 c. Mangrove Root Oyster . . 75 60
632 10 c. Mangrove Crab . . 1·25 90

(Des D. Miller. Litho Walsall)

1986 (23 July) *Royal Wedding. Square designs as T* **112** *of Ascension. Multicoloured. W w* **16**. *P* 14½×14.
633 5 c. Prince Andrew and Miss Sarah Ferguson . . 20 10
634 50 c. Prince Andrew aboard H.M.S. *Brazen* . . 1·10 1·00

158 Red Coral Shrimp 159 Golf

(Des D. Miller. Litho Walsall)

1986 (15 Sept). *Marine Life. T* **158** *and similar vert designs. Multicoloured. W w* **14**. *P* 13½×13.
635 5 c. Type **158** 10 10
636 10 c. Yellow Crinoid . . 15 20
637 15 c. *Calcinus tibicen* (hermit crab) . . 20 25
638 20 c. Tube dwelling Anemone . . 25 30
639 25 c. Christmas Tree Worm . . 35 40
640 35 c. Spiny Puffer Fish . . 45 50
641 50 c. Orangeball Anemone . . 65 70
642 60 c. *Astrophyton muricatum* (basket starfish) . . 80 85
643 75 c. Flamingo Tongue Snail . . 1·00 1·10
644 $1 *Condylactis gigantea* (sea anemone) . . 1·40 1·50
645 $2 Diamond Blenny . . 2·75 3·00
646 $4 Flaming Scallop . . 5·50 5·75
635/46 . . *Set of* 12 12·00 13·00
No. 644 is incorrectly inscribed "Conolylactis gigantea".
The 5, 10, 15, 20 c., $1, $2 and $4 values exist with different imprint dates at foot.

(Des L. Curtis. Litho Walsall)

1987 (26 Jan). *Tourism. T* **159** *and similar horiz designs. Multicoloured. W w* **16** *(sideways). P* 13×13½.
647 10 c. Type **159** 25 20
648 15 c. Sailing . . 40 30
649 25 c. Snorkelling . . 55 45
650 35 c. Paragliding . . 70 70
651 $1 Game fishing . . 1·75 2·25
647/51 . . *Set of* 5 3·25 3·50

160 Ackee 161 Lion Lizard

(Des Jennifer Toombs. Litho Questa)

1987 (20 May). *Cayman Islands Fruits. T* **160** *and similar vert designs. Multicoloured. W w* **16**. *P* 14½×14.
652 5 c. Type **160** 10 10
653 25 c. Breadfruit . . 45 45
654 35 c. Pawpaw . . 60 60
655 $1 Soursop . . 1·60 2·25
652/5 . . *Set of* 4 2·50 3·00

(Des I. Loe. Litho Questa)

1987 (26 Aug). *Lizards. T* **161** *and similar horiz designs. Multicoloured. W w* **16** *(sideways). P* 13½×14.
656 10 c. Type **161** 25 20
657 50 c. Iguana . . 90 90
658 $1 Anole . . 1·75 1·75
656/8 . . *Set of* 3 2·75 2·50

162 Poinsettia

163 *Hemiargus ammon erembis* and *Strymon martialis*

(Des Annette Robinson. Litho Walsall)

1987 (18 Nov). *Flowers. T* **162** *and similar square designs. Multicoloured. W w* **16**. *P* 14½×14.
659 5 c. Type **162** 20 10
660 25 c. Periwinkle . . 70 50
661 35 c. Yellow Allamanda . . 80 70
662 75 c. Blood Lily . . 1·50 2·00
659/62 . . *Set of* 4 3·00 3·00

(Des Jane Thatcher. Litho Questa)

1988 (29 Mar). *Butterflies. T* **163** *and similar horiz designs. Multicoloured. W w* **16** *(sideways). P* 14.
663 5 c. Type **163** 20 10
664 25 c. *Phocides pigmalion batabano* . . 60 50
665 50 c. *Anaea troglodyta cubana* . . 1·00 1·00
666 $1 *Papilio andraemon andraemon* . . 1·75 2·00
663/6 . . *Set of* 4 3·25 3·25

164 Green Heron 165 Cycling

(Des Jane Thatcher. Litho Walsall)

1988 (27 July). *Herons. T* **164** *and similar vert designs. Multicoloured. W w* **16**. *P* 14.
667 5 c. Type **164** 20 10
668 25 c. Louisiana Heron . . 60 40
669 50 c. Yellow-crowned Night Heron . . 1·00 1·00
670 $1 Little Blue Heron . . 1·75 1·75
667/70 . . *Set of* 4 3·25 3·00

(Des L. Curtis. Litho Walsall)

1988 (21 Sept). *Olympic Games, Seoul. T* **165** *and similar horiz designs. Multicoloured. W w* **16** *(sideways). P* 14×14½.
671 10 c. Type **165** 15 20
672 50 c. Cayman Airways airliner and national team . . 70 75
673 $1 Sailing . . 1·40 1·50
671/3 . . *Set of* 3 2·00 2·25
MS674 53×60 mm. $1 Tennis. W w 14 (sideways) 1·40 1·50

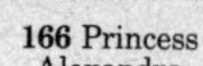

166 Princess Alexandra

167 Georgetown Post Office and Cayman Postmark on Jamaica 1d., 1889

(Des N. Harvey. Litho B.D.T.)

1988 (1 Nov). *Visit of Princess Alexandra. T* **166** *and similar vert design. Multicoloured. W* w **14**. *P* 15×14.

675 5 c. Type **166** 10 10
676 $1 Princess Alexandra in evening dress .. 1·50 1·50

(Des L. Curtis. Litho Questa)

1989 (12 Apr). *Centenary of Cayman Islands Postal Service. T* **167** *and similar horiz designs. Multicoloured. W* w **16** *(sideways). P* 14×14½.

677 5 c. multicoloured 15 15
678 25 c. yellowish green, black and new blue .. 55 55
679 35 c. multicoloured 70 70
680 $1 multicoloured .. .. 1·75 1·75
677/80 .. .. *Set of* 4 2·75 2·75

Designs:—25 c. *Orinoco* (mail steamer) and 1900 ½d. stamp; 35 c. G.P.O., Grand Cayman and "London 1980" $1 stamp; $1 Cayman Airways plane and 1966 1s. Jet Service stamp.

168 Captain Bligh ashore in West Indies

169 Panton House

(Des Jane Hartley. Litho B.D.T.)

1989 (24 May). *Captain Bligh's Second Breadfruit Voyage, 1791-93. T* **168** *and similar vert designs. Multicoloured. W* w **16**. *P* 14.

681 50 c. Type **168** .. .. 1·25 1·25
a. Horiz strip of 5. Nos. 681/5 .. .. 5·75
682 50 c. H.M.S. *Providence* (sloop) at anchor .. 1·25 1·25
683 50 c. Breadfruit in tubs and H.M.S. *Assistant* (transport) .. .. .. 1·25 1·25
684 50 c. Sailors moving tubs of breadfruit .. 1·25 1·25
685 50 c. Midshipman and stores .. .. 1·25 1·25
681/5 .. .. *Set of* 5 5·75 5·75

Nos. 681/5 were printed together, *se-tenant* as a composite design, in horizontal strips of five throughout the sheet.

(Des S. Conlin. Litho Walsall)

1989 (18 Oct). *Architecture. T* **169** *and similar square designs showing George Town buildings. Multicoloured. W* w **14**. *P* 14½×14.

686 5 c. Type **169** 10 15
687 10 c. Town Hall and Clock Tower 15 20
688 25 c. Old Court House 40 45
689 35 c. Elmslie Memorial Church 55 60
690 $1 Post Office .. .. 1·50 1·60
686/90 .. .. *Set of* 5 2·50 2·75

170 Map of Grand Cayman, 1773, and Surveying Instruments

(Des N. Shewring. Litho Walsall)

1989 (15 Nov). *Island Maps and Survey Ships. T* **170** *and similar horiz designs. Multicoloured. W* w **16** *(sideways). P* 14×14½.

691 5 c. Type **170** 10 15
692 25 c. Map of Cayman Islands, 1956, and surveying instruments 40 45
693 50 c. H.M.S. *Mutine*, 1914 .. .. .. 75 80
694 $1 H.M.S. *Vidal*, 1956 .. .. .. 1·50 1·60
691/4 .. .. *Set of* 4 2·50 2·75

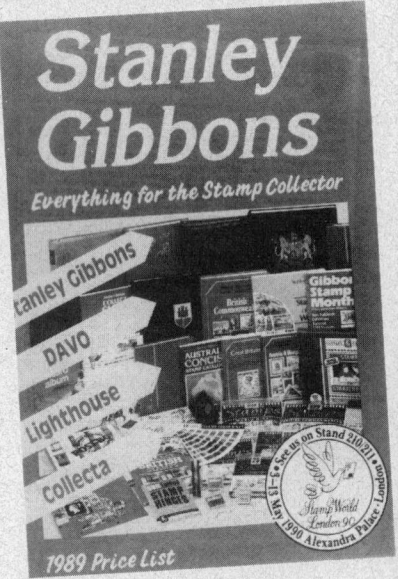

Ceylon

PRICES FOR STAMPS ON COVER TO 1945

Nos. 1/4	*from* × 5
Nos. 5/19	*from* × 4
Nos. 23/117	*from* × 8
Nos. 118/20	*from* × 15
Nos. 121/38	*from* × 6
Nos. 139/41	†
Nos. 142/3	*from* × 10
Nos. 146/51	*from* × 6
Nos. 151*a*/2	†
Nos. 153/93	*from* × 8
Nos. 194/201	*from* × 12
Nos. 202/43	*from* × 6
Nos. 245/9	*from* × 4
Nos. 250/5	*from* × 5
Nos. 256/64	*from* × 4
Nos. 265/76	*from* × 3
Nos. 277/88	*from* × 4
Nos. 289/300	*from* × 8
Nos. 301/25	*from* × 2
Nos. 326/9*a*	—
Nos. 330/7*a*	*from* × 4
Nos. 338/52	*from* × 2
Nos. 353/4	—
Nos. 355/9	*from* × 2
No. 360	—
Nos. 360*a*/*g*	*from* × 2
Nos. 361/2	*from* × 5
Nos. 363/71	*from* × 3
Nos. 372/82	*from* × 2
Nos. 383/5	*from* × 3
Nos. 386/97	*from* × 2
Nos. 398/9	*from* × 8
Nos. O1/17	*from* × 30

CROWN COLONY

PRICES. The prices of the imperf stamps of Ceylon vary greatly according to condition. The following prices are for fine copies with four margins.

Poor to medium specimens can be supplied at much lower prices.

1

2

(Recess P.B.)

1857 (1 April). *Blued paper. Wmk Star W* w **1.** *Imperf.*

1	**1**	6d. purple-brown	£7500	£450

Collectors should beware of proofs with faked watermark, often offered as originals.

(Typo D.L.R.)

1857 (Oct)–**58.** *No wmk. Imperf.* (*a*) *Blue glazed paper.*

3	**2**	½d. lilac	£3000	£450
		(*b*) *White glazed paper*		
4	**2**	½d. lilac (1858)	£150	£120

3

4

NOTE. Beware of stamps of Type **3** which are often offered with corners added.

(Recess P.B.)

1857–9. *White paper. Wmk Star, W* w **1.** (*a*) *Imperf.*

5	**1**	1d. blue (24.8.57)	£550	18·00
6		1d. deep blue	£650	25·00
		a. Blued paper	—	£150
7		2d. deep green (24.8.57)	£150	50·00
8		2d. yellow-green	£500	90·00
9	**3**	4d. dull rose (23.4.59)	£50000	£4500
10	**1**	5d. chestnut (2.7.57)	£1500	£150
11		6d. purple-brown	£1800	£125
12		6d. brown	£5000	£400
12*a*		6d. deep brown	£6000	£1000
13	**3**	8d. brown (23.4.59)	£17000	£1500
14		9d. purple-brown (23.4.59)	£26000	£900
15	**4**	10d. orange-vermilion (2.7.57)	£800	£250
16		1s. dull violet (2.7.57)	£4000	£200
17	**3**	1s. 9d. green (23.4.59)	£700	£800
18		1s. 9d. pale yellow-green	£2500	£1800
19		2s. blue (23.4.59)	£5000	£1100
		(*b*) *"Unofficial" P* 7½ (*No.* 22*a*) *or rouletted* (*Nos.* 20/2)		
20	**2**	½d. lilac (*No wmk*)	£5000	
21	**1**	1d. blue (*Wmk Star*)	£5000	
22		2d. deep green (*Wmk Star*)	£1800	£1000
22*a*		1s. 9d. green (*Wmk Star*)	£4000	

These stamps are believed to have been made by a Ceylon firm, or firms, for their own convenience.

(Recess P.B.)

1861. *Wmk Star, W* w **1.** (*a*) *Clean-cut perf* 14 *to* 15½.

23	**1**	1d. deep blue	85·00	12·00
24		1d. pale blue	£200	35·00
25		2d. green	£175	35·00
27		5d. chestnut	75·00	8·00
29	**4**	1s. dull violet	75·00	22·00
30	**3**	2s. blue	£1800	£375
		(*b*) *Intermediate perf* 14 *to* 15½		
31	**1**	1d. deep blue	65·00	12·00
32		1d. blue	65·00	15·00
33		2d. green	65·00	24·00
		a. Imperf between (vert pair) ..	†	—
34	**3**	4d. dull rose	£1800	£250
34*a*	**1**	5d. chestnut	£325	£125
35		6d. brown	£1300	70·00
36		6d. yellowish brown	—	£110
36*a*		6d. olive-brown	—	80·00
37	**3**	8d. brown	£1200	£300
38		9d. dull purple-brown	£3500	£250
40	**4**	1s. bright violet	90·00	22·00
41		1s. dull violet	65·00	13·00
		(*c*) *Rough perf* 14 *to* 15½		
42	**1**	1d. blue	55·00	6·00
43		1d. blue (*bleuté paper*)	£275	20·00
44	**3**	4d. rose-red	£130	35·00
45		4d. deep rose-red	£130	38·00
47	**1**	6d. yellowish brown	£1200	95·00
48		6d. blackish brown	£400	55·00
48*a*		6d. olive-brown	45·00	£450
49	**3**	8d. brown	£1100	£275
50		8d. yellow-brown	£1000	£225
51		9d. olive-brown	£350	25·00
52		9d. yellowish brown	£450	48·00
53		9d. deep brown	55·00	22·00
53*a*	**4**	10d. orange-vermilion	£175	20·00
		b. Imperf vert (horiz pair)	†	—
54		1s. dull violet	£225	15·00
55	**3**	2s. blue	£500	80·00
56		2s. deep blue	£600	95·00
		(*d*) *Rough perf* 14 *to* 15½. *Prepared for use, but not issued*		
57	**3**	1s. 9d. green	£475	

No. 34 is distinguished from Nos. 44/5 with fraudulently altered perfs by its colour.

(Recess or typo (T **2**). D.L.R.)

1862–64. *No wmk.* (*a*) *Smooth paper. P* 13.

58	**1**	1d. blue	60·00	6·00
59		5d. deep red-brown	£850	£150
60		6d. reddish brown	70·00	20·00
61		6d. deep brown	80·00	20·00
62	**3**	9d. brown	£800	50·00
63	**4**	1s. cold violet	£1500	75·00
		(*b*) *Smooth paper. P* 11½, 12		
64	**1**	1d. blue	£550	80·00
		a. Imperf between (horiz pair)	†	£4000
		(*c*) *Glazed paper. P* 12½ (1864)		
65	**2**	½d. pale lilac	£150	90·00

The 1s. is known imperf, but not used. The "no wmk" stamps were printed on paper having the papermaker's name and date, "T H SAUNDERS 1862" across the sheets, and one or more of these letters or figures are often found on the stamps.

(Recess P.B., perforated by D.L.R.)

1864 (Sept). *Wmk Star, W* w **1.** *P* 12½.

66	**4**	10d. vermilion	£225	15·00
67		10d. orange-red	£225	15·00

5

6

T **5.** 23 mm high. "CC" oval.
T **6.** 21½ mm high. "CC" round and smaller.

(Recess or typo (T **2**) D.L.R.)

1863–6. *Paper medium thin and slightly soft.* W **5.** *Wmks arranged in four panes, each of* 60, *with the words* "CROWN COLONIES" *between the panes. Portions of these letters often appear on the stamps.*

		(*a*) *P* 11½, 12		
68	**1**	1d. blue	£1400	£140
		(*b*) *P* 13		
69	**1**	6d. brown	£1200	70·00
70	**3**	9d. brown	£2250	£325
		(*c*) *P* 12½		
71	**2**	½d. mauve	16·00	15·00
72		½d. lilac	20·00	12·00
73		½d. deep lilac	28·00	18·00
74	**1**	1d. dark blue	42·00	3·00
75		1d. blue	42·00	3·00
76		2d. yellow-green	£5500	£300
77		2d. deep bottle-green	—	£3250
78		2d. grey-green	30·00	6·00
79		2d. emerald-green	80·00	55·00
80		2d. maize	£225	£190
81	**3**	4d. lake-rose	£300	50·00
82	**3**	4d. rose	£140	27·00
83	**1**	5d. reddish brown	85·00	32·00
84		5d. deep sage-green	£1100	£190
84*a*		5d. pale sage-green	£650	£125
85		6d. brown	50·00	8·00
86		6d. reddish brown	60·00	9·00
87		6d. deep brown	50·00	4·00
88	**3**	8d. light carmine-brown	50·00	24·00
89		8d. dark carmine-brown	35·00	14·00
90		9d. brown	£170	18·00
91	**4**	10d. vermilion	£800	25·00
91*a*		10d. orange	£800	85·00
92	**3**	2s. dark blue	£160	25·00

The ½d. lilac; 1d. blue; 2d. grey-green; 2d. maize; and 5d. deep sage-green and pale sage-green, are known imperf.

1867. *Paper hand-made. Prepared and used only for these Ceylon stamps.* W **6.** *Wmks arranged in one pane of* 240 *in* 20 *rows of* 12, *with the words* "CROWN COLONIES" *twice in each side margin. P* 12½.

93	**1**	1d. pale blue	45·00	5·00
94		1d. Prussian blue	40·00	4·00
95		2d. maize	40·00	5·00
96		2d. olive-yellow	24·00	6·00
97		2d. greenish yellow	£125	42·00
98		2d. orange-yellow	22·00	5·00
99	**3**	4d. pale rose	80·00	28·00
100		4d. rose	24·00	7·50
101	**1**	5d. pale sage-green	27·00	6·00
102		5d. deep olive-green	55·00	7·00
103		5d. deep myrtle-green	16·00	22·00
104		6d. deep brown	27·00	5·00
105		6d. blackish brown	38·00	6·00
106		6d. red-brown	18·00	18·00
107	**3**	8d. pale carmine-brown	60·00	38·00
108		8d. deep carmine-brown	27·00	30·00
109		9d. bistre-brown	£190	25·00
110		9d. deep brown	18·00	6·00
111	**4**	10d. vermilion	£850	£140
111*a*		10d. red-orange	24·00	5·00
112		10d. orange	40·00	7·50
113		1s. lilac	£325	32·00
114		1s. violet	60·00	5·50
115	**3**	2s. pale blue	£150	38·00
116		2s. blue	75·00	14·00
117		2s. Prussian blue	60·00	11·00

The 1d. pale blue, 1d. Prussian blue, 6d. deep brown, 9d. deep brown and 10d. orange are known imperf but only unused.

PRINTERS. All stamps from No. 118 to 367 were typographed by De La Rue & Co, Ltd, London.

7

8

1866. *Wmk Crown CC. P* 12½.

118	**7**	3d. rose	£140	45·00

1867–8. *Wmk Crown CC. P* 14.

119	**8**	1d. blue	8·50	4·50
120	**7**	3d. pale rose (1867)	35·00	17·00
		a. Deep rose	42·00	20·00

(New Currency. 100 cents = 1 rupee)

9

10

11

12

13

14

15

16

17

18

19

1872–80. *Wmk Crown CC. (a) P* 14.
121 **9** 2 c. pale brown (*shades*) .. .. 4·00 1·00
122 **10** 4 c. grey .. .. 20·00 80
123 4 c. rosy-mauve (1880) .. .. .. 35·00 1·50
124 **11** 8 c. orange-yellow .. .. .. 26·00 4·00
a. Yellow .. .. 18·00 4·25
126 **12** 16 c. pale violet .. .. .. 40·00 2·75
127 **13** 24 c. green .. .. .. 25·00 2·00
128 **14** 32 c. slate (1877) .. .. .. 65·00 9·50
129 **15** 36 c. blue .. .. 55·00 11·00
130 **16** 48 c. rose .. .. 50·00 5·00
131 **17** 64 c. red-brown (1877) .. .. £130 40·00
132 **18** 96 c. drab .. .. £110 21·00
121/132 .. .. .. *Set of* 11 £475 85·00

(b) P 14 × 12½
133 **9** 2 c. brown .. .. £300 30·00
134 **10** 4 c. grey .. .. £300 15·00
135 **11** 8 c. orange-yellow .. .. .. £250 23·00

(c) P 12½
136 **9** 2 c. brown .. .. £1100 60·00
137 **10** 4 c. grey £550 £120

(d) P 12½ × 14
138 **19** 2 r. 50 c. dull-rose (1879) £350 £250

(e) Prepared for use and sent out to Ceylon, but not issued unsurcharged
139 **14** 32 c. slate (*p* 14 × 12½) £600
140 **17** 64 c. red-brown (*p* 14 × 12½) £800
141 **19** 2 r. 50, dull rose (*p* 12½) £800

FORGERIES.—Beware of forged overprint and surcharge varieties on Victorian issues.

SIXTEEN

16

CENTS
(20)

1882 (Oct). *Nos.* 127 *and* 131 *surch as T* **20** *by Govt Printer.*
142 **13** 16 c. on 24 c. green .. .. .. 13·00 6·50
a. Surch inverted .. .. ..
143 **17** 20 c. on 64 c. red-brown .. .. .. 8·00 3·00
a. Surch double .. .. .. — £1000

1883–98. *Wmk Crown CA. (a) P* 14.
146 **9** 2 c. pale brown .. .. .. 25·00 1·50
147 2 c. dull green (1884) (Optd S. £110) 1·25 15
148 **10** 4 c. rosy mauve .. .. .. 1·25 25
149 4 c. rose (1884) (Optd S. £110) .. 2·75 7·50
150 **11** 8 c. orange .. .. 2·75 4·75
a. Yellow (1898) .. .. .. 2·75 4·75
151 **12** 16 c. pale violet £700 £120

(b) Trial perforation. P 12
151*a* **9** 2 c. dull green £1300
151*b* **10** 4 c. rose £1400
151*c* **13** 24 c. brown-purple £1500

(c) Prepared for use and sent out to Ceylon, but not issued unsurcharged. P 14
152 **13** 24 c. brown-purple (Optd S. £225) .. £650

Postage &

FIVE
CENTS

Revenue
(21)

TEN
CENTS
(22)

Twenty
Cents
(23)

One Rupee
Twelve
Cents
(24)

1885. *T* **10/19** *surch locally as T* **21/24**.

I. *Wmk Crown CC. (a) P* 14
153 **21** 5 c. on 16 c. pale violet .. .. ..
154 5 c. on 24 c. green .. .. .. £800 65·00
155 5 c. on 32 c. slate .. .. .. 35·00 12·00
a. Surch inverted .. .. .. — £550
b. Dark grey .. .. .. 40·00 15·00
156 5 c. on 36 c. blue .. .. .. 55·00 7·00
a. Surch inverted .. .. .. — £700
157 5 c. on 48 c. rose .. .. .. £325 20·00
158 5 c. on 64 c. red-brown .. .. 35·00 4·00
a. Surch double .. .. .. — £500
159 5 c. on 96 c. drab .. .. .. £180 35·00
161 **22** 10 c. on 16 c. pale violet .. ..
162 10 c. on 24 c. green .. .. .. £225 55·00
163 10 c. on 36 c. blue £250 £120
164 10 c. on 64 c. red-brown .. .. £125 40·00
165 20 c. on 24 c. green .. .. .. 26·00 9·50
166 **23** 20 c. on 32 c. slate .. .. .. 18·00 12·00
a. Dark grey .. .. .. 23·00 14·00
167 25 c. on 32 c. slate .. .. .. 9·50 4·25
a. Dark grey .. .. .. 10·50 5·50
168 28 c. on 48 c. rose .. .. .. 20·00 4·50
a. Surch double .. .. .. — £600
169 **22** 30 c. on 36 c. blue .. .. .. 7·50 6·50
a. Surch inverted .. .. .. £140 75·00
170 56 c. on 96 c. drab .. .. .. 12·00 8·00

(b) P 14 × 12½
172 **21** 5 c. on 32 c. slate .. .. .. £100 22·00
173 5 c. on 64 c. red-brown .. .. .. £110 18·00
174 **22** 10 c. on 64 c. red-brown .. .. 28·00 38·00
a. Imperf between (vert pair) £1500
175 **24** 1 r. 12 c. on 2 r. 50 c. dull rose (*p* 12½) £170 48·00
176 1 r. 12 c. on 2 r. 50 c. dull rose (*p* 12½ × 14) .. .. .. 40·00 25·00

II. *Wmk Crown CA. P* 14
177 **21** 5 c. on 4 c. rosy mauve .. .. ..
178 5 c. on 4 c. rose .. .. .. 7·50 1·75
a. Surch inverted .. .. .. — £200
179 5 c. on 8 c. orange-yellow .. .. 22·00 4·50
a. Surch double .. .. .. — £450
b. Surch inverted .. .. .. — £550
180 5 c. on 16 c. pale violet .. .. 30·00 8·00
a. Surch inverted .. .. .. — £120
182 5 c. on 24 c. brown-purple .. .. — £475
184 **22** 10 c. on 16 c. pale violet £1900 £425
185 10 c. on 24 c. brown-purple .. .. 7·50 5·00
186 15 c. on 16 c. pale violet .. .. 7·00 5·50

The 5 c. on 24 c. green watermarked Crown CA previously catalogued is now regarded as a forgery.

REVENUE AND POSTAGE

5 CENTS
(25)

10 CENTS
(26)

1 R. 12 C.
(27)

1885. *T* **11/15**, **18** *and* **19** *surch with T* **25/7** *by D.L.R. P* 14.

(a) Wmk Crown CA
187 **25** 5 c. on 8 c. lilac .. .. .. 4·50 70
188 **26** 10 c. on 24 c. brown-purple .. .. 8·50 4·50
189 15 c. on 16 c. orange-yellow .. .. 24·00 5·00
190 28 c. on 32 c. slate .. .. .. 9·50 2·50
191 30 c. on 36 c. olive-green .. .. 18·00 12·00
192 56 c. on 96 c. drab .. .. .. 24·00 7·00

(b) Wmk Crown CC (sideways)
193 **27** 1 r. 12 c. on 2 r. 50, dull rose .. .. 26·00 40·00
187/93 .. .. .. *Set of* 7 £100 65·00
187/93 Optd "Specimen" .. .. *Set of* 7 £450

28

29

1886. *Wmk Crown CA. P* 14.
195 **28** 5 c. dull purple 75 10
196 **29** 15 c. sage-green .. .. .. 1·90 75
197 15 c. olive-green .. .. .. 2·00 45
198 25 c. yellow-brown .. .. .. 1·10 1·00
a. Value in yellow .. .. .. 75·00 50·00
199 28 c. slate .. .. 6·00 1·40
195, 197/9 Optd "Specimen" .. *Set of* 4 £120

Six plates were used for the 5 c., No. 195, between 1885 and 1901, each being replaced by its successor as it became worn. Examples from the worn plates show thicker lines in the background and masses of solid colour under the chin, in front of the throat, at the back of the neck and at the base.

30

1887. *Wmk Crown CC (sideways). White or blued paper. P* 14.
201 **30** 1 r. 12, dull rose (Optd S. £80) .. 12·00 12·00
a. Wmk upright .. .. .. 18·00 25·00

TWO CENTS
(31)

TWO
(32)

2 Cents
(33)

Two Cents
(34)

2 Cents
(35)

1888–90. *Nos.* 148/9 *surch with T* **31/5**.
202 **31** 2 c. on 4 c. rosy mauve 45 20
a. Surch inverted .. .. .. 7·00 8·00
b. Surch double, one inverted .. .. — 50·00
203 2 c. on 4 c. rose 45 30
a. Surch inverted .. .. .. 8·00 9·00
b. Surch double .. .. .. — 60·00
204 **32** 2 (c.) on 4 c. rosy mauve 60 20
a. Surch inverted .. .. .. 12·00 13·00
b. Surch double .. .. .. 22·00 22·00
c. Surch double, one inverted .. .. 15·00 13·00
205 **32** 2 (c.) on 4 c. rose .. .. .. 1·00 20
a. Surch inverted .. .. .. 60·00
b. Surch double .. .. .. 20·00 24·00
c. Surch double, one inverted .. .. 24·00 28·00
206 **33** 2 c. on 4 c. rosy mauve .. .. 22·00 16·00
a. Surch inverted .. .. .. — 23·00
b. Surch double, one inverted .. .. 32·00
207 2 c. on 4 c. rose .. .. .. 1·00 75
a. Surch inverted .. .. .. 7·00 7·00
b. Surch double .. .. .. 65·00 65·00
c. Surch double, one inverted .. .. 5·50 5·50
208 **34** 2 c. on 4 c. rosy mauve .. .. 24·00 14·00
a. Surch inverted .. .. .. 40·00 20·00
209 2 c. on 4 c. rose .. .. .. 1·00 45
a. Surch inverted .. .. .. 6·50 5·00
b. Surch double .. .. .. 20·00 24·00
c. Surch double, one inverted .. .. 6·50 4·75
210 **35** 2 c. on 4 c. rosy mauve .. .. 20·00 14·00
a. Surch inverted .. .. .. 32·00 28·00
b. Surch double, one inverted .. .. 32·00 35·00
c. Surch double .. .. .. — 60·00
d. "s" of "Cents" inverted .. .. — £140
e. As d. Whole surch inverted ..
211 2 c. on 4 c. rose .. .. .. 2·25 50
a. Surch inverted .. .. .. 6·50 3·50
b. Surch double .. .. .. 30·00 25·00
c. Surch double, one inverted .. .. 7·50 6·50
d. "s" of "Cents" inverted .. .. — 60·00
209, 211 Optd "Specimen" .. .. *Set of* 2 60·00

The 4 c. rose and the 4 c. rosy mauve are found surcharged "Postal Commission 3 (or "Three") Cents". They denote the extra commission charged by the Post Office on postal orders which had not been cashed within three months of the date of issue. For a short time the Post Office did not object to the use of these stamps on letters.

POSTAGE

Five Cents

REVENUE
(36)

FIFTEEN
CENTS
(37)

1890. *No.* 197 *surch with T* **36**.
233 5 c. on 15 c. olive-green (Optd S. £30) .. 60 75
a. Surch inverted .. .. .. 12·00 12·00
b. Surch double .. .. .. 75·00 75·00
c. "Flve" for "Five" .. .. .. 65·00 55·00
d. Variety as c, inverted .. .. — £600
e. "REVENUE" omitted .. .. 65·00 55·00
f. Inverted "s" in "Cents" .. .. 13·00 16·00
g. Variety as f, and whole surch inverted £550
h. "REVENUE" omitted and inverted "s" in "Cents" £225
i. "POSTAGE" spaced between "T" and "A" 26·00 32·00

1891. *Nos.* 198/9 *surch with T* **37**.
239 **29** 15 c. on 25 c. yellow-brown .. .. 5·50 6·00
240 15 c. on 28 c. slate .. .. .. 5·50 7·50

3 Cents
(38)

39

1892. *Nos.* 148/9 *and* 199 *surch with T* **38**.
241 **10** 3 c. on 4 c. rosy mauve .. .. 45 1·25
242 3 c. on 4 c. rose (Optd S. £30) .. 70 3·50
243 **29** 3 c. on 28 c. slate .. .. .. 80 1·25
a. Surch double .. .. .. 42·00
241/3 .. .. *Set of* 3 1·75 5·50

1893–99. *Wmk Crown CA. P* 14.
245 **39** 3 c. terracotta and blue-green 85 45
246 **10** 4 c. carmine-rose (1898) .. .. 5·00 5·00
247 **29** 30 c. bright mauve and chestnut .. 3·75 1·40
a. Bright violet and chestnut .. 2·50 1·40
249 **19** 2 r. 50, purple/*red* (1899) .. .. 16·00 30·00
245/9 .. .. *Set of* 4 21·00 32·00
245, 247/9 Optd "Specimen" .. .. *Set of* 3 60·00

Six Cents
(40)

2 R. 25 C.
(41)

1899. *(a) No.* 196 *surch with T* **40**.
250 **29** 6 c. on 15 c. sage-green 45 45

(b) As No. 138 *but colour changed and perf* 14, *surch as T* **41**.
254 **19** 1 r. 50 c. on 2 r. 50, slate .. .. 19·00 30·00
255 2 r. 25 c. on 2 r. 50, yellow .. .. 24·00 45·00
250/5 Optd "Specimen" .. .. *Set of* 3 70·00

43

1899–1900. *Wmk Crown CA* (1 *r.* 50, 2 *r.* 25 *wmk Crown CC*). *P* 14.
256 **9** 2 c. pale orange-brown 90 30
257 **39** 3 c. deep green 70 45
258 **10** 4 c. yellow .. .. .. 70 2·00
259 **29** 6 c. rose and black 70 45

260 39 12 c. sage-green and rose 2·00 4·00
261 29 15 c. blue 3·25 1·25
262 39 75 c. black and red-brown 4·00 4·00
263 43 1 r. 50, rose 15·00 30·00
264 2 r. 25, dull blue 28·00 32·00
256/64 *Set of* 9 50·00 70·00
256/64 Optd "Specimen" *Set of* 9 £125

44 45 46

47 48

1903 (29 May)–**05**. *Wmk Crown CA. P* 14.
265 44 2 c. red-brown (21.7.03) 70 20
266 45 3 c. green (11.6.03) 80 70
267 4 c. orange-yellow and blue 1·25 2·25
268 46 5 c. dull purple (2.7.03) 1·50 30
269 47 6 c. carmine (5.11.03) 3·25 1·25
270 45 12 c. sage-green and rosine (13.8.03) 3·75 4·75
271 48 15 c. blue (2.7.03) 6·50 1·75
272 25 c. bistre (11.8.03) 4·00 7·00
273 30 c. dull violet and green 3·25 4·00
274 45 75 c. dull blue and orange (31.3.05) 2·75 14·00
275 48 1 r. 50, greyish slate (7.4.04) 45·00 42·00
276 2 r. 25, brown and green (12.4.04) 35·00 30·00
265/76 *Set of* 12 95·00 95·00
265/76 Optd "Specimen" *Set of* 12 £140

1904 (13 Sept)–**05**. *Wmk Mult Crown CA. P* 14.
277 44 2 c. red-brown, O (17.11.04) 55 10
278 45 3 c. green, O (17.11.04) 75 15
279 4 c. orange and ultramarine, O 35 50
280 46 5 c. dull purple, OC (29.11.04) 1·75 70
281 47 6 c. carmine, O (11.10.04) 1·10 15
282 45 12 c. sage-green and rosine, O (29.9.04) 1·50 1·75
283 48 15 c. blue, O (1.12.04) 90 50
284 25 c. bistre, O (5.1.05) 6·00 3·75
285 30 c. violet and green, O (7.9.05) 2·50 1·50
286 45 75 c. dull blue and orange, O (25.5.05) 5·25 8·00
287 48 1 r. 50, grey, O (5.1.05) 15·00 10·00
288 2 r. 25, brown and green, O (22.12.04) 15·00 27·00
277/88 *Set of* 12 45·00 48·00

50

51

1908. *Wmk Mult Crown CA. P* 14.
289 50 5 c. deep purple, O (26 May) 85 10
290 5 c. dull purple, O 1·50 30
291 51 6 c. carmine, O (6 June) 70 10
289, 291 Optd "Specimen" *Set of* 2 48·00

1910 (1 Aug)–**11**. *Wmk Mult Crown CA. P* 14.
292 44 2 c. brown-orange, O (20.5.11) 1·50 1·00
293 48 3 c. green, O (5.7.11) 85 70
294 10 c. sage-green and maroon, O 1·50 70
295 25 c. grey, O 2·50 70
296 50 c. chocolate, O 4·00 6·50
297 1 r. purple/*yellow*, O 7·50 10·00
298 2 r. red/*yellow*, O 15·00 25·00
299 5 r. black/*green*, O 35·00 55·00
300 10 r. black/*red*, O 60·00 £110
292/300 *Set of* 9 £110 £190
292/300 Optd "Specimen" *Set of* 9 £180

52

53

(A)

(B)

Most values in Type 52 were produced by two printing operations, using "Key" and "Duty" plates. Differences in the two Dies of the Key plate are described in the introduction to this catalogue.

In the Ceylon series, however, the 1 c. and 5 c. values, together with later printings of the 3 c. and 6 c., were printed from special plates at one operation. These plates can be identified by the large "C" in the value tablet (see illustration A). Examples of these values from Key and Duty plates printing have value tablet as illustration B. The 3 c. and 5 c. stamps from the single plates *resemble* Die I, and the 1 c. and 6 c. Die II, although in the latter case the inner top corners of the side panels are square and not curved.

1912–25. *T* **52** *and* **53** (*50 r. to 1000 r.*). *Wmk Mult Crown CA. P* 14.

(*a*) *Printed from single plates. Value tablet as* A
301 1 c. brown, O 30 10
302 3 c. blue-green, O 1·60 45
303 5 c. purple, O 3·00 1·25
304 5 c. bright magenta, O 50 30
a. Wmk sideways 35·00
305 6 c. pale scarlet, O 5·00 85
306 6 c. carmine, O 5·50 1·25
a. Wmk sideways 13·00 20·00

(*b*) *Printed from Key and Duty plates at two operations. Die I.* 3 c. *and* 6 c. *have value tablet as* B
307 2 c. brown-orange, O 40 20
308 2 c. deep orange-brown, O 30 20
309 3 c. yellow-green, O 3·50 1·75
310 3 c. deep green, O 2·00 80
311 6 c. scarlet, O 1·10 50
312 6 c. bright scarlet, O 1·40 70
313 10 c. sage-green, O 2·75 1·40
314 10 c. deep sage-green, O 3·50 1·75
315 15 c. ultramarine, O 1·50 1·25
316 15 c. deep bright blue, O 2·25 1·75
317 25 c. yellow and blue, O 1·75 1·50
318 25 c. orange and blue, O 4·50 3·50
319 30 c. blue-green and violet, C 3·25 2·00
320 30 c. yellow-green and violet, C 4·50 2·75
a. Wmk sideways 3·75
321 50 c. black and scarlet, C 1·25 1·75
322 1 r. purple/*yellow*, C 1·75 2·75
a. White back (1914) (Optd S. £32) 1·25 2·50
b. On lemon (1916) (Optd S. £32) 4·00 5·50
c. On orange-buff 15·00 20·00
d. On pale yellow (Optd S. £32) 4·00 7·50
323 2 r. black and red/*yellow*, C 3·25 8·00
a. White back (Optd S. £32) 2·00 7·50
b. On lemon (Optd S. £32) 15·00 20·00
c. On orange-buff 24·00 26·00
d. On pale yellow 24·00 26·00
324 5 r. black/*green*, C 14·00 18·00
a. White back (Optd S. £35) 10·00 22·00
b. On blue-green, olive back (1921) (Optd S. £40) 11·00 22·00
c. On emerald back (Die II) (Optd S. £50) 42·00 65·00
325 10 r. purple and black/*red*, C 35·00 40·00
a. Die II 40·00 55·00
326 20 r. black and red/*blue*, C 70·00 60·00
327 50 r. dull purple, C (S. £100) £300
a. Break in scroll £500
b. Broken crown and scroll £500
328 100 r. grey-black, C (S. £250) £1300
a. Break in scroll £1800
b. Broken crown and scroll £1800
329 500 r. dull green, C (S. £350) £3750
a. Break in scroll £5500
b. Broken crown and scroll £5500
329*c* 1000 r. purple/*red*, C (1925) (S. £600) £13000
ca. Break in scroll £17000
cb. Broken crown and scroll £17000
301/25 *Set of* 14 55·00 70·00
301/26 Optd "Specimen" *Set of* 15 £200

For illustrations of the varieties on Nos. 327/9*c* see above No. 44 of Bermuda.

WAR
STAMP
(54)

WAR
STAMP
ONE CENT
(55)

1918 (18 Nov). (*a*) *Optd with T* **54**.
330 52 2 c. brown-orange 15 40
a. Opt inverted 24·00 26·00
b. Opt double 24·00 26·00
c. Opt omitted in pair with opt inverted
331 3 c. blue-green (No. 302) 10 20
332 3 c. yellow-green (No. 309) 65 2·00
a. Opt double 40·00 42·00
333 5 c. purple 15 30
a. Opt double 24·00 26·00
334 5 c. bright magenta 55 1·00
a. Opt inverted 24·00 26·00
b. Opt double 24·00 26·00

(*b*) *Surch with T* **55**
335 52 1 c. on 5 c. purple 10 25
336 1 c. on 5 c. bright magenta 20 20
330/1, 333, 335 Optd "Specimen" *Set of* 4 85·00

Collectors are warned against forgeries of the errors in the "WAR STAMP" overprints.

1918. *Surch as T* **55**, *but without* "WAR STAMP".
337 52 1 c. on 5 c. purple (Optd S. £30) 15 25
337*a* 1 c. on 5 c. bright magenta 35 80
ab. Opt double

1921–34. *Wmk Mult Script CA. P* 14.

A. **1921–27.** *The original issue.*

(*a*) *Printed from single plates. Value tablet as* A
338 52 1 c. brown, O (1927) 15 35
339 3 c. green, O (5.5.22) 45 1·00
340 5 c. bright magenta, O (1927) 10 15
341 6 c. carmine-red, O (3.8.21) 35 75

(*b*) *Printed from Key and Duty plates at two operations. Die I* (10 c. *to* 30 c. *and* 1 r.) *or Die II* (2c., 50 c., 2 r. *to* 20 r.)
342 52 2 c. brown-orange, O (1927) 30 25
343 10 c. sage-green, O (16.9.21) 60 40
344 15 c. ultramarine, O (30.5.22) 2·50 5·00
345 20 c. bright blue, O (1922) 2·50 3·00
346 25 c. yellow and blue, O (17.10.21) 80 1·25
347 30 c. yellow-green and violet, C (15.3.22) 1·40 2·50
348 50 c. black and scarlet, C (1922) 1·00 80
349 1 r. purple/*pale yellow*, C (1923) 10·00 14·00
350 2 r. black and red/*pale yellow*, C (1923) 3·50 6·50
351 52 5 r. black/*emerald*, C (1925) 15·00 27·00
352 20 r. black and red/*blue*, C (1924) 60·00 60·00
353 53 50 r. dull purple, C (1924) (S. £100) £325
a. Break in scroll £550
b. Broken crown and scroll £550
354 100 r. grey-black, C (1924) (S. £250) £1300
a. Break in scroll £1800
b. Broken crown and scroll £1800
338/51 *Set of* 14 35·00 55·00
338/52 Optd "Specimen" *Set of* 15 £180

B. **1922–27.** *New values and colour changed.*

(*a*) *Printed from single plates. Value tablet as* A
355 52 3 c. slate-grey, O (1923) 10 20
a. Wmk sideways
356 6 c. bright violet, O 15 15

(*b*) *Printed from Key and Duty plates at two operations. Die I* (*12 c., 15 c.*) *or Die II* (*9 c.*)
357 52 9 c. red/*yellow*, O (1926) 30 25
358 12 c. rose-scarlet, O (1924) 2·25 3·50
359 15 c. green/*pale yellow*, O 1·25 1·25
360 53 100 r. dull purple and blue, C (24.10.27) (S. £250) £1200
a. Break in scroll £1700
b. Broken crown and scroll £1700
355/9 Optd "Specimen" *Set of* 5 £120

C. **1924–25.** *Key and Duty plates. Change to Die II.*
360*c* 52 10 c. sage green, O 45 60
360*d* 12 c. rose-scarlet, O (1924) 80 1·50
360*e* 15 c. green/*pale yellow*, O 1·25 1·50
360*f* 20 c. bright blue, O 55 45
360*g* 25 c. yellow and blue, O 1·60 1·50
360*h* 30 c. yellow-green and violet, C 1·40 1·25
360*i* 1 r. purple/*pale yellow*, C 6·00 11·00
360*c*/*i* *Set of* 7 11·00 17·00

D. **1934.** *Key and Duty plates. Reappearance of Die I (Key Plate 23).*
360*j* 52 50 c. black and scarlet, C 35·00 55·00

For illustrations of the varieties on Nos. 353/4 and 360 see above No. 44 of Bermuda.

2 Cents.
(56)

57

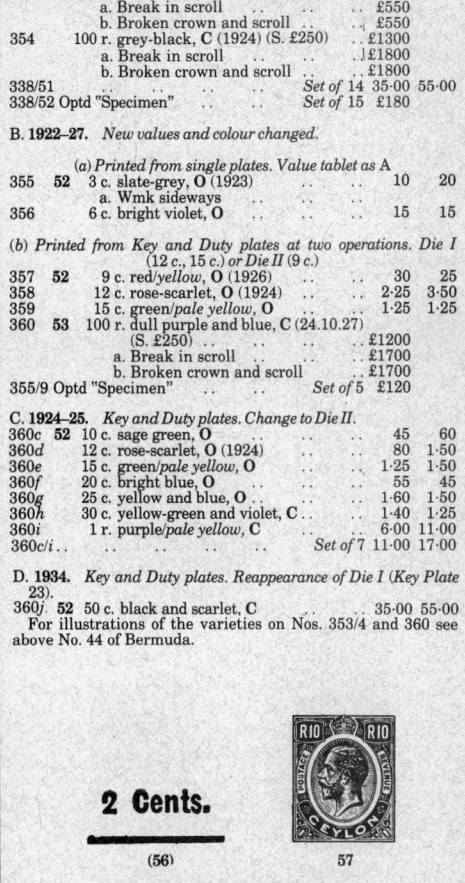

(Surch at Ceylon Govt Printing Works)

1926 (27 Nov). *Surch as T* **56**.
361 52 2 c. on 3 c. slate-grey 50 1·00
a. Surch double 48·00
b. Bar omitted 40·00
362 5 c. on 6 c. bright violet 50 40
361/2 Optd "Specimen" *Set of* 2 50·00

1927 (27 Nov)–**29**. *Wmk Mult Script CA. P* 14.
363 57 1 r. dull and bright purple, C (1928) 1·75 1·25
364 2 r. green and carmine, C (1929) 3·75 2·75
365 5 r. green and dull purple, C (1928) 12·00 17·00
366 10 r. green and brown-orange, C 28·00 55·00
367 20 r. dull purple and blue, C 60·00 £110
363/7 *Set of* 5 95·00 £160
363/7 Optd "Specimen" *Set of* 5 £125

No. 364. Collectors are warned against faked 2 r. stamps, showing what purports to be a double centre.

58 Tapping Rubber

60 Adam's Peak

(Recess D.L.R. (2, 3, 20, 50 c.), B.W. (others))

1935 (1 May)–**36.** *T* **58**, **60** *and similar designs. Wmk Mult Script CA* (*sideways on* 10, 15, 25, 30 *c. and* 1 *r.*). *Various perfs.*
368 2 c. black and carmine (*p* 12 × 13) 25 25
a. Perf 14 4·75 40
369 3 c. blk & ol-green (*p* 13 × 12) (1.10.35) 35 25
a. Perf 14 15·00 30
370 6 c. black & blue (*p* 11 × 11½) (1.1.36) 30 25
371 9 c. green & orange (*p* 11 × 11½) (1.1.36) 50 30
372 10 c. black & purple (*p* 11½ × 11) (1.6.35) 80 70
373 15 c. red-brown and green (*p* 11½ × 11) 1·00 50
374 20 c. black & grey-blue (*p* 12 × 13) (1.1.36) 1·75 1·25
375 25 c. deep blue & chocolate (*p* 11½ × 11) 1·25 60
376 30 c. carm & green (*p* 11½ × 11) (1.8.35) 3·00 1·25
377 50 c. black and mauve (*p* 14) (1.1.36) 3·75 50
378 1 r. vio-bl & chocolate (*p* 11½ × 11) (1.7.35) 5·50 5·00
368/78 *Set of* 11 16·00 9·75
368/78 Perf "Specimen" *Set of* 11 £120

Designs: *Vert*—6 c. Colombo Harbour; 9 c. Plucking tea; 20 c. Coconut Palms. *Horiz*—10 c. Hill paddy (rice); 15 c. River scene; 25 c. Temple of the Tooth, Kandy; 30 c. Ancient irrigation tank; 50 c. Wild elephants; 1 r. Trincomalee.

1935 (6 May). *Silver Jubilee. As Nos. 91/4 of Antigua.*
379 6 c. ultramarine and grey 30 30
g. Dot to left of chapel .. .. .. 15·00
h. Dot by flagstaff .. .. 15·00
i. Dash by turret .. .. 20·00
380 9 c. green and indigo 70 50
g. Dot to left of chapel .. .. .. 25·00
h. Dot by flagstaff .. .. 25·00
381 20 c. brown and deep blue .. .. .. 3·00 1·25
f. Horiz line from turret .. .. .. 50·00
g. Dot to left of chapel .. .. .. 50·00
382 50 c. slate and purple .. .. 5·00 3·50
h. Dot by flagstaff .. .. 70·00
379/82 .. .. *Set of* 4 8·00 5·00
379/82 Perf "Specimen" .. .. *Set of* 4 75·00

For illustrations of plate varieties, see Omnibus section following Zululand.

1937 (12 May). *Coronation. As Nos. 13/15 of Aden but ptd by B.W. & Co. P* 11 × 11½.
383 6 c. carmine 55 10
384 9 c. green .. .. 1·00 1·00
385 20 c. blue .. .. 2·00 1·75
383/5 .. .. *Set of* 3 3·25 2·50
383/5 Perf "Specimen" .. .. *Set of* 3 50·00

69 Tapping Rubber

70 Sigiriya (Lion Rock)

71 Ancient Guard-stone, Anuradhapura

72 King George VI

Apostrophe flaw (Centre Pl 1 R. 6/6) (ptg of 1 Jan 1943 only)

(Recess B.W. (stamps perf 11 × 11½ or 11½ × 11), D.L.R. (all others) T **72** typo D.L.R.)

1938–49. *T* **69/72** *and designs as 1935–36, but with portrait of King George VI instead of King George V and* "POSTAGE & REVENUE" *omitted. Wmk Mult Script CA (sideways on* 10, 15, 25, 30 *c. and* 1 *r.). Various perfs.*
386 **69** 2 c. blk & carm (*p* 11½×13) (25.4.38) 3·75 60
a. Perf 13½×13 (1938) .. .. .. 45·00 95
b. Perf 13½ (25.4.38) 25 10
c. Perf 11×11½ (17.2.44) 15 20
d. Perf 12 (22.4.49) .. .. 25 1·00
387 **60** 3 c. black & dp blue-green (*p* 13×11½) (21.3.38) .. .. 8·00 30
a. Perf 13×13½ (1938) .. .. .. £150 4·00
b. Perf 13½ (21.3.38) 75 10
c. Perf 14 (7.41) .. .. 55·00 75
d. Perf 11½×11 (14.5.42) 20 10
e. Perf 12 (14.1.46) 15 10
387*f* – 5 c. sage-grn & orge (*p* 13½) (1.1.43) 20 10
fa. Apostrophe flaw .. .. 18·00
g. Perf 12 (1947) 25 20
388 – 6 c. black and blue (*p* 11×11½) (1.1.38) 10 10
389 **70** 10 c. blk & light bl (*p* 11½×11) (1.2.38) 35 10
a. Wmk upright (1.6.44) 35 15
390 – 15 c. grn & red-brn (*p* 11½×11) (1.1.38) 40 10
a. Wmk upright (23.7.45) 40 15
391 – 20 c. blk & grey-bl (*p* 11×11½) (15.1.38) 85 10
392 – 25 c. dp bl & choc (*p* 11½×11) (15.1.38) 1·50 30
a. Wmk upright (1944) 25 10
393 – 30 c. carm & grn (*p* 11½×11) (1.2.38) 4·25 75
a. Wmk upright (16.4.45) .. .. .. 3·75 1·75
394 – 50 c. blk & mve (*p* 13×11½) (25.4.38) .. 90·00 40·00
a. Perf 13×13½ (1938) .. .. .. £180 2·25
b. Perf 13½ (25.4.38) .. .. .. 4·00 20
c. Perf 14 (4.42) .. .. 60·00 16·00
d. Perf 11½×11 (14.5.42) .. .. .. 1·50 20
e. Perf 12 (14.1.46) 90 15
395 – 1 r. blue-violet & chocolate (*p* 11½×11) (1.2.38) .. .. 4·25 35
a. Wmk upright (1944) .. .. .. 4·50 80
396 **71** 2 r. blk and carm (*p* 11×11½) (1.2.38) 3·75 90
396*a* 2 r. blk & vio (*p* 11×11½) (15.3.47) .. 1·00 65
397 **72** 5 r. green & purple, C (*p* 14) (10.10.38) 13·00 1·50
a. Green and pale purple, O (19.2.43) 8·50 1·00
386/97*a* (*cheapest*) .. .. *Set of* 14 22·00 4·00
386/97 Perf "Specimen" .. .. *Set of* 14 £225

Designs: *Vert*—5 c. Coconut Palms; 6 c. Colombo Harbour; 20 c. Plucking tea. *Horiz*—15 c. River scene; 25 c. Temple of the Tooth, Kandy; 30 c. Ancient irrigation tank; 50 c. Wild elephants; 1 r. Trincomalee.

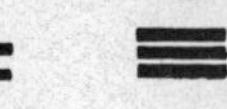

3 CENTS

(73) (74)

1940–41. *Nos.* 388 *and* 391 *surch.*
398 **73** 3 c. on 6 c. (10.5.41) 10 10
399 **74** 3 c. on 20 c. (5.11.40) 40 15

1946 (10 Dec). *Victory. As Nos.* 28/9 *of Aden.*
400 6 c. blue 10 10
401 15 c. brown 10 15
400/1 Perf "Specimen" .. .. *Set of* 2 45·00

75 Parliament Building

76 Adam's Peak

(Des R. Tenison and M. S. V. Rodrigo. Recess B.W.)

1947 (25 Nov). *Inauguration of New Constitution. T* **75/6** *and similar designs. Wmk Mult Script CA. P* 11 × 12 (*horiz*) *or* 12 × 11 (*vert*).
402 6 c. black and blue 10 15
403 10 c. black, orange and carmine 10 20
404 15 c. green and purple 10 15
405 25 c. ochre and emerald-green 10 15
402/5 .. .. *Set of* 4 35 60
402/5 Perf "Specimen" .. .. *Set of* 4 80·00

Designs: *Horiz*—15 c. Temple of the Tooth. *Vert*—25 c. Anuradhapura.

DOMINION

79 Lion Flag of Dominion

80 D. S. Senanayake

81 Lotus Flowers and Sinhalese Letters "Sri"

(Recess (flag typo) B.W.)

1949 (4 Feb–Apr). *First Anniv of Independence.* (*a*) *Wmk Mult Script CA (sideways on* 4 *c.). P* 12½ × 12 (4 *c.*) *or* 12 × 12½ (5 *c.*).
406 **79** 4 c. yellow, carmine and brown .. 10 10
407 **80** 5 c. brown and green 10 10

(*b*) *W* **81** (*sideways on* 15 *c.*). *P* 13 × 12½ (15 *c.*) *or* 12 × 12½ (25 *c.*) (5 April)
408 **79** 15 c. yellow, carmine and vermilion .. 25 15
409 **80** 25 c. brown and blue 15 15
406/9 .. .. *Set of* 4 40 40

The 15 c. is larger, measuring 28 × 12 mm.

82 Globe and Forms of Transport

83

84

(Recess D.L.R.)

1949 (10 Oct). *75th Anniv of Universal Postal Union. W* **81**. *P* 13 (25 *c.*) *or* 12 (*others*).
410 **82** 5 c. brown and bluish green 35 10
411 **83** 15 c. black and carmine .. .. .. 1·10 60
412 **84** 25 c. black and ultramarine .. .. 1·25 25
410/12 .. .. *Set of* 3 2·40 80

85 Kandyan Dancer

88 Sigiriya (Lion Rock)

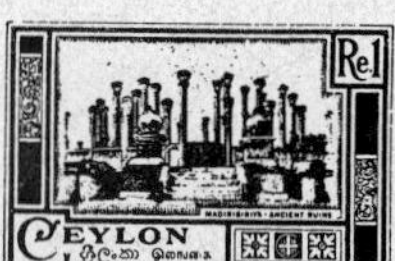

89 Octagon Library, Temple of the Tooth

90 Ruins at Madirigiriya

(Recess B.W.)

1950 (4 Feb). *T* **85, 88/90** *and similar designs. W* **81**. *P* 11 × 11½ (75 *c.*), 11½ × 11 (1 *r.*), 12 × 12½ (*others*).
413 4 c. purple and scarlet 10 10
414 5 c. green 10 10
415 15 c. blue-green and violet 75 10
416 30 c. carmine and yellow 25 15
417 75 c. ultramarine and orange 65 10
418 1 r. deep blue and brown 95 10
413/18 .. .. *Set of* 6 2·50 30

Designs: *Vert* (*as T* **88**)—5 c. Kiri Vehera, Polonnaruwa; 15 c. Vesak Orchid.

For these values with redrawn inscriptions see Nos. 450/1, 454, 456, 460 and 462.

91 Sambars, Ruhuna National Park

92 Ancient Guard-stone, Anuradhapura

96 Star Orchid

97 Rubber Plantation

99 Tea Plantation

I. No. 424 II. No. 424a (Dot added)

(Photo Courvoisier)

1951 (1 Aug)–**54.** *T* **91/2, 96/7, 99** *and similar designs. No wmk. P* 11½.
419 2 c. brown and blue-green (15.5.54) 10 10
420 3 c. black and slate-violet (15.5.54) 10 15
421 6 c. brown-black & yellow-green (15.5.54) .. 10 10
422 10 c. green and blue-grey 75 15
423 25 c. orange-brown & bright blue (15.3.54) .. 10 10
424 35 c. red and deep green (I) (1.2.52) 50 20
a. Type II (1954) 90 10
425 40 c. deep brown (15.5.54) 45 25
426 50 c. indigo and slate-grey (15.3.54) 30 10
427 85 c. black and deep blue-green (15.5.54) .. 50 10
428 2 r. blue and deep brown (15.5.54) .. .. 4·00 20
429 5 r. brown and orange (15.3.54) .. .. 4·75 50
430 10 r. red-brown and buff (15.3.54) .. .. 12·00 3·25
419/30 .. .. *Set of* 12 21·00 4·50

Designs: *Vert* (*as T* **91**)—6 c. Harvesting rice; 10 c. Coconut trees; 25 c. Sigiriya fresco. (*As T* **99**)—5 r. Bas-relief, Anuradhapura; 10 r. Harvesting rice. *Horiz* (*as T* **97**)—50 c. Outrigger canoe; (*as T* **99**)—2 r. River Gal Dam.

For these values with redrawn inscriptions see Nos. 448, etc.

103 Ceylon Mace and Symbols of Progress

(Photo Harrison)

1952 (23 Feb). *Colombo Plan Exhibition. Chalk-surfaced paper. W* **81** *(sideways). P* 14½ × 14.
431 **103** 5 c. green 10 10
432 15 c. ultramarine 20 15

104 Queen Elizabeth II **105** Ceremonial Procession

(Recess B.W.)

1953 (2 June). *Coronation. W* **81**. *P* 12 × 13.
433 **104** 5 c. green 40 10

(Recess D.L.R.)

1954 (10 Apr). *Royal Visit. W* **81** *(sideways). P* 13 × 12½.
434 **105** 10 c. deep blue 15 10

106 King Coconuts **107** Farm Produce

(Photo Courvoisier)

1954 (1 Dec). *No wmk. P* 11½.
435 **106** 10 c. orange, bistre-brown and buff .. 10 10
For this design with redrawn inscription see No. 453.

(Photo Harrison)

1955 (10 Dec). *Royal Agricultural and Food Exhibition. W* **81** *(sideways). P* 14 × 14½.
436 **107** 10 c. brown and orange 10 10

108 Sir John Kotelawala and House of Representatives

(Photo Courvoisier)

1956 (26 Mar). *Prime Minister's 25 Years of Public Service. P* 11½.
437 **108** 10 c. deep bluish green 10 10

109 Arrival of Vijaya in Ceylon **110** Lampstand and Dharmachakra

111 Hand of Peace and Dharmachakra **112** Dharmachakra encircling the Globe

(Photo Courvoisier)

1956. *Buddha Jayanti. P* 11½.
438 **109** 3 c. blue and brownish grey (23 May) .. 15 10
439 **110** 4 c. + 2 c. grnish yell & dp bl (10 May) 15 30
440 **111** 10 c. + 5 c. carm, yellow & grey (10 May) 15 25
441 **112** 15 c. bright blue (23 May) 15 10
438/41 .. .. *Set of* 4 55 55

113 Mail Transport **114** Stamp of 1857

(Photo Enschedé (4 c., 10 c.), Courvoisier (others))

1957 (1 Apr). *Centenary of First Ceylon Postage Stamp. P* 12½ × 13 *(4 c., 10 c.) or* 11½ *(others).*
442 **113** 4 c. orange-red and deep bluish green 25 10
443 10 c. vermilion and blue 30 10
444 **114** 35 c. brown, yellow and blue 30 20
445 85 c. brown, yellow and grey-green .. 50 75
442/5 .. .. *Set of* 4 1·10 95

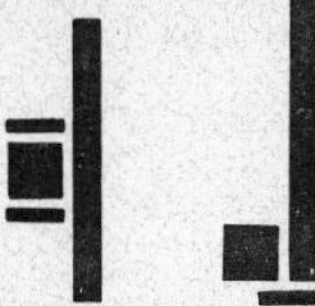

(115) **(116)** **117** Kandyan Dancer

1958 (15 Jan). *Nos.* 439/40 *with premium obliterated as T* **115** *(4 c.) or T* **116** *(10 c.).*
446 **110** 4 c. greenish yellow and deep blue .. 10 10
a. Opt inverted .. .. .. 8·00
b. Opt double .. .. 10·00
447 **111** 10 c. carmine, yellow and grey .. 10 10
a. Opt inverted .. .. .. 13·00
The 4 c. exists with opt misplaced to right so that some stamps show the vertical bar on the left *(Price £18 un.)*.

(Recess B.W. (4 c., 5 c., 15 c., 30 c., 75 c., 1 r.). Photo Courvoisier (others))

1958 (14 May)–**62**. *As earlier types, but inscriptions redrawn as in T* **117**. *W* **81** *(4, 5, 15, 30, 75 c., 1 r.) or no wmk (others). P* 11×11½ *(75 c.),* 11½×11 *(1 r.),* 12×12½ *(4, 5, 15, 30 c.), or* 11½ *(others).*
448 **91** 2 c. brown and blue-green 10 10
449 **92** 3 c. black and slate-violet 10 15
450 **117** 4 c. purple and scarlet 10 10
451 – 5 c. green (1.10.58) 10 10
a. Yellow-green (13.6.61) 40 10
b. Deep green (19.6.62) 15 10
452 – 6 c. brown-black and yellow-green .. 10 15
453 **106** 10 c. orge, bistre-brown & buff (1.10.58) 10 10
454 – 15 c. blue-green and violet (1.10.58) .. 80 10
455 – 25 c. orange-brown and bright blue .. 10 10
456 **88** 30 c. carmine and yellow (1.5.59) .. 15 20
457 **96** 35 c. red and deep green (II) (15.7.58) 90 10
459 – 50 c. indigo and slate-grey (15.7.58) .. 30 10
460 **89** 75 c. ultramarine and orange (1.5.59) 25 20
a. Ultramarine & brown-orge (3.4.62) 25 15
461 **99** 85 c. black and deep blue-green (1.5.59) 3·50 1·50
462 **90** 1 r. deep blue and brown (1.10.58) .. 40 10
463 – 2 r. blue and deep brown 75 10
464 – 5 r. brown and orange .. .. 1·25 10
465 – 10 r. red-brown and buff .. .. 2·50 70
448/65 .. .. *Set of* 17 10·00 3·25
Designs: *Vert (as T* **117**)—5 c. Kiri Vehera Polonnaruwa; 6 c. Harvesting rice; 15 c. Vesak Orchid; 25 c. Sigiriya fresco. *(as T* **99**)—5 r. Bas-relief, Anuradhapura; 10 r. Harvesting rice. *Horiz (as T* **97**)—50 c. Outrigger canoe. *(as T* **99**)—2 r. River Gal Dam.

118 "Human Rights" **119** Portraits of Founders and University Buildings

(Photo Enschedé)

1958 (10 Dec). *Tenth Anniv of Declaration of Human Rights. P* 13 × 12½.
466 **118** 10 c. vermilion and dull purple 10 10
467 85 c. vermilion and deep blue-green .. 25 45

(Photo Enschedé)

1959 (31 Dec). *Institution of Pirivena Universities. P* 13 × 12½.
468 **119** 10 c. red-orange and ultramarine .. 10 10

120 Uprooted Tree **121** S.W.R.D. Bandaranaike

(Des W. A. Ariyasena. Photo Courvoisier)

1960 (7 Apr). *World Refugee Year. P* 11½.
469 **120** 4 c. red-brown and gold.. .. .. 10 10
470 25 c. blackish violet and gold 10 15

(Photo Courvoisier)

1961 (8 Jan–15 June). *Prime Minister Bandaranaike Commemoration. P* 11½.
471 **121** 10 c. deep blue and greenish blue .. 10 10
a. Portrait redrawn (15.6.61)* .. 10 10
*Earliest known postmark date.
No. 471a can be identified by Mr. Bandaranaike's dark hair at temples.

122 Ceylon Scout Badge  **123** Campaign Emblem

(Des W. A. Ariyasena. Photo Courvoisier)

1962 (26 Feb). *Golden Jubilee of Ceylon Boy Scouts Association. P* 11½.
472 **122** 35 c. buff and blue 15 10

(Photo Harrison)

1962 (7 Apr). *Malaria Eradication. W* **81**. *P* 14½ × 14.
473 **123** 25 c. red-orange and sepia 10 10

124 "DH85 Leopard-Moth" and "Comet" Airliner **125** "Produce" and Campaign Emblem

(Photo Courvoisier)

1963 (28 Feb). *25th Anniv of Airmail. P* 11½.
474 **124** 50 c. black and light blue 15 25

(Photo Courvoisier)

1963 (21 Mar). *Freedom from Hunger. P* 11½.
475 **125** 5 c. vermilion and blue 20 25
476 25 c. brown and yellow-olive 65 25

(126) **127** "Rural Life"

1963 (1 June). *No.* 450 *surch with T* **126**.
477 **117** 2 c. on 4 c. purple and scarlet 10 10
a. Surch inverted .. .. .. 16·00
b. Surch double .. .. .. 13·00

(Photo Harrison)

1963 (5 July). *Golden Jubilee of Ceylon Co-operative Movement* (1962). *W* **81**. *P* 14 × 14½.
478 **127** 60 c. rose-red and black 15 20

128 S. W. R. D. Bandaranaike **129** Terrain, Elephant and Tree

(Recess Courvoisier)

1963 (26 Sept). *P* 11½.
479 **128** 10 c. light blue 10 10

(Photo Harrison)

1963 (9 Dec). *National Conservation Week. W* **81** *(sideways). P* 14×14½.
480 **129** 5 c. sepia and blue 10 10

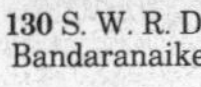

130 S. W. R. D. Bandaranaike **131** Anagarika Dharmapala (Buddhist missionary)

(T **130/1.** Photo Courvoisier)

1964 (1 July). *P* 11½.
481 **130** 10 c. deep violet-blue and greenish grey 10 10

1964 (16 Sept). *Birth Centenary of Anagarika Dharmapala (founder of Maha Bodhi Society). P* 11½.
482 **131** 25 c. sepia and olive-yellow 10 10

134 Southern Grackle

138 Ruins at Madirigiriya

135 D. S. Senanayake **136**

146 Tea Plantation

149 Map of Ceylon

(Des A. Dharmasiri (5 r.); P. A. Miththapala (10 r.). Photo Courvoisier (10 c. (486), 20 c.), Harrison (10 c. (487), 60 c., 1 r., 5 r., 10 r.), D.L.R. (others incl sheet))

1964 (1 Oct)–**72.** *T* **134/6, 138, 146, 149** *and similar designs. No wmk (Nos.* 486, 489), *W* **81** *(others; sideways on Nos.* 487, 494, 499). *P* 11½ *(Nos.* 486, 489), 14½ × 14 *(No.* 494) *or* 14 *(others).*
485 **134** 5 c. multicoloured (5.2.66) 25 20
486 **135** 10 c. myrtle-green (22.3.66) 10 10
487 **136** 10 c. myrtle-green (23.9.68) 10 10
a. Imperf (pair) .. .. .. 38·00
488 – 15 c. multicoloured (5.2.66) 90 10
489 **138** 20 c. brown-purple and buff 10 10
494 – 60 c. multicoloured (5.2.66) 90 25
a. Red omitted .. .. .. 30·00
b. Blue and green omitted* .. .. 30·00
495 – 75 c. multicoloured (5.2.66) 90 30
a. No wmk (8.6.72) .. .. .. 3·25 2·00
497 **146** 1 r. brown and bluish green 80 10
a. Brown omitted .. .. .. 85·00
b. Bluish green omitted £130
499 – 5 r. multicoloured (15.8.69) .. .. 1·50 1·50
500 **149** 10 r. multicoloured (1.10.69) .. .. 6·50 1·75
485/500 .. .. *Set of* 10 11·00 3·75
MS500*a* 148 × 174 mm. As Nos. 485, 488, 494 and 495. Imperf. .. .. 4·00 4·00

Designs: *Horiz (as T* **134**)—15 c. Common Peafowl; 60 c. Ceylon Junglefowl; 75 c. Asian Black-headed Oriole. *(as T* **138**)—5 r. Girls transplanting rice.

The 5 c., 75 c. and 1 r. exist with PVA gum as well as gum arabic.

In the miniature sheet the inscriptions on the 60 c. have been rearranged to conform with the style of the other values.

*Actually only the blue printing is omitted on this sheet, but where this was printed over the yellow to form the leaves it appeared as green.

150 Exhibition Buildings and Cogwheels

151 Trains of 1864 and 1964

(Photo State Printing Works, Budapest)

1964 (1 Dec). *Industrial Exhibition. T* **150** *and similar horiz design. No wmk. P* 11.
501 – 5 c. multicoloured 10 25
a. Pair. Nos. 501/2 .. .. .. 10 1·25
502 **150** 5 c. multicoloured 10 25

No. 501 is inscribed "INDUSTRIAL EXHIBITION" in Sinhala and Tamil, No. 502 in Sinhala and English. The stamps were issued together *se-tenant* in alternate vertical rows, producing horizontal pairs.

(Photo Harrison)

1964 (21 Dec). *Centenary of Ceylon Railways. T* **151** *and similar horiz design. W* **81** *(sideways). P* 14 × 14½.
503 – 60 c. blue, reddish purple & yellow-grn 1·25 20
a. Pair. Nos. 503/4 .. .. .. 2·50 1·25
504 **151** 60 c. blue, reddish purple & yellow-grn 1·25 20

No. 503 is inscribed "RAILWAY CENTENARY" in Sinhala and Tamil, No. 504 in Sinhala and English. The stamps were issued together *se-tenant* in alternate horizontal rows, producing vertical pairs.

152 I.T.U. Emblem and Symbols

153 I.C.Y. Emblem

(Photo Harrison)

1965 (17 May). *I.T.U. Centenary. W* **81** *(sideways). P* 14½.
505 **152** 2 c. bright blue and red 15 45
506 30 c. brown and red .. .. 1·25 45
a. Value omitted £100

No. 506a was caused by the misplacement of the red.

(Photo Courvoisier)

1965 (26 June). *International Co-operation Year. T* **153** *and similar horiz design. P* 11½.
507 3 c. deep blue and rose-carmine 15 40
508 50 c. black, rose-carmine and gold 80 50

No. 508 is similar to T **153** but has the multilingual inscription "CEYLON" rearranged.

154 Town Hall, Colombo

(**155**)

(Photo Courvoisier)

1965 (29 Oct). *Centenary of Colombo Municipal Council. P* 11 × 11½.
509 **154** 25 c. myrtle-green and sepia 10 10

1965 (18 Dec). *No.* 481 *surch with T* **155.**
510 **130** 5 c. on 10 c. dp vio-bl & greenish grey 10 10

157 Kandy and Council Crest

158 W.H.O. Building

(Photo Harrison)

1966 (15 June). *Kandy Municipal Council Centenary. W* **81.** *P* 14 × 13½.
512 **157** 25 c. multicoloured 10 10

(Litho D.L.R.)

1966 (8 Oct). *Inauguration of W.H.O. Headquarters, Geneva. P* 14.
513 **158** 4 c. multicoloured 30 75
514 1 r. multicoloured .. .. .. 2·25 1·50

159 Rice Paddy and Map of Ceylon

160 Rice Paddy and Globe

(Photo Courvoisier)

1966 (25 Oct). *International Rice Year. P* 11½.
515 **159** 6 c. multicoloured 10 30
516 **160** 30 c. multicoloured 20 15

161 U.N.E.S.C.O. Emblem

162 Water-resources Map

(Litho State Ptg Wks, Vienna)

1966 (3 Nov). *20th Anniv of U.N.E.S.C.O. P* 12.
517 **161** 3 c. multicoloured 40 30
518 50 c. multicoloured .. .. .. 2·00 30

(Litho D.L.R.)

1966 (1 Dec). *International Hydrological Decade. P* 14.
519 **162** 2 c. orange-brown, greenish yellow & bl 10 40
520 2 r. orge-brn, grnish yell, bl & yell-grn 60 1·00

163 Devotees at Buddhist Temple

167 Galle Fort and Clock Tower

(Photo State Ptg Wks, Vienna)

1967 (2 Jan). *Poya Holiday System. T* **163** *and similar horiz designs. Multicoloured. P* 12.
521 5 c. Type **163** 10 10
522 20 c. Mihintale 10 10
523 35 c. Sacred Bo-tree, Anuradhapura 10 10
524 60 c. Adam's Peak 10 10
521/4 .. .. *Set of* 4 20 20

(Litho Rosenbaum Brothers, Vienna)

1967 (5 Jan). *Centenary of Galle Municipal Council. P* 13½.
525 **167** 25 c. multicoloured 10 10

168 Field Research

(Litho Rosenbaum Bros, Vienna)

1967 (1 Aug). *Centenary of Ceylon Tea Industry. T* **168** *and similar horiz designs. Multicoloured. P* 13½.
526 4 c. Type **168** 10 20
527 40 c. Tea-tasting equipment 30 20
528 50 c. Leaves and bud 30 10
529 1 r. Shipping tea 65 10
526/9 .. .. *Set of* 4 1·25 50

172 Elephant Ride

173 Ranger, Jubilee Emblem and Flag

(Litho Rosenbaum Bros, Vienna)

1967 (15 Aug). *International Tourist Year. P* 13½.
530 **172** 45 c. multicoloured 70 20

1967 (15 Sept). *1st National Stamp Exhibition. No.* **MS**500*a optd* "FIRST NATIONAL STAMP EXHIBITION 1967".
MS531 148 × 174 mm. Nos. 485, 488, 494/5. Imperf 3·50 4·50

(Litho D.L.R.)

1967 (19 Sept). *Golden Jubilee of Ceylon Girl Guides Association. P* 12½ × 13.
532 **173** 3 c. multicoloured 10 10
533 25 c. multicoloured 25 10

174 Col. Olcott and Buddhist Flag

(Litho Rosenbaum Bros, Vienna)

1967 (8 Dec). *60th Death Anniv of Colonel H. S. Olcott (theosophist). P* 13½.
534 **174** 15 c. multicoloured 10 10

175 Independence Hall

176 Lion Flag and Sceptre

(Photo Harrison)

1968 (2 Feb). *20th Anniv of Independence. W* **81** *(sideways). P* 14.
535 **175** 5 c. multicoloured 10 15
536 **176** 1 r. multicoloured 20 10

177 Sir D. B. Jayatilleke **178** Institute of Hygiene

(Litho D.L.R.)

1968 (14 Feb). *Birth Centenary of Sir Baron Jayatilleke (scholar and statesman). P* 14.
537 **177** 25 c. yellow-brown and sepia 10 10

(Litho B.W.)

1968 (7 Apr). *20th Anniv of World Health Organization.* W **81.** *P* 12.
538 **178** 50 c. multicoloured 10 10

179 Aircraft over Terminal Building **181** Open Koran and "1400"

(Des and litho B.W.)

1968 (5 Aug). *Opening of Colombo Airport.* W **81.** *P* 13½.
539 **179** 60 c. grey-blue, chestnut, red and yellow 10 10

(Des M. I. M. Mohideen. Photo Harrison)

1968 (14 Oct). *1400th Anniv of the Holy Koran.* W **81.** *P* 14.
541 **181** 25 c. multicoloured 10 10

182 Human Rights Emblem **183** All Ceylon Buddhist Congress Headquarters

(Photo Pakistan Security Printing Corp)

1968 (10 Dec). *Human Rights Year. P* 12½ × 13½.
542 **182** 2 c. multicoloured 10 10
543 20 c. multicoloured 10 10
544 40 c. multicoloured 10 10
545 2 r. multicoloured .. .. .. 45 1·75
542/5 .. .. *Set of* 4 55 1·75

(Des A. Dharmasiri. Litho Rosenbaum Bros, Vienna)

1968 (19 Dec). *Golden Jubilee of All Ceylon Buddhist Congress. P* 13½.
546 **183** 5 c. multicoloured 10 15

A 50 c. value showing a footprint was prepared but its release was stopped the day before it was due for issue. However, some are known to have been released in error at rural offices (*Price £12 mint*).

184 E. W. Perera (patriot) **185** Symbols of Strength in Savings

(Photo Harrison)

1969 (17 Feb). *E. W. Perera Commemoration.* W **81.** *P* 14 × 13½.
547 **184** 60 c. brown 10 10

(Des A. Dharmasiri. Photo Harrison)

1969 (20 Mar). *Silver Jubilee of National Savings Movement.* W **81.** *P* 14.
548 **185** 3 c. multicoloured 10 10

186 Seat of Enlightenment under Sacred Bodhi Tree **187** Buduresmala (Six fold Buddha-Rays)

(Des L. T. P. Manjusree. Litho D.L.R.)

1969 (10 Apr). *Vesak Day (inscr "Wesak").* W **81** (*sideways*). *P* 15.
549 **186** 4 c. multicoloured 10 10
550 **187** 6 c. multicoloured 10 10
551 **186** 35 c. multicoloured 10 10
549/51 .. .. *Set of* 3 15 15

No. 549 exists with the gold apparently omitted. Normally the gold appears (without a separate plate number) over an underlay of olive-green on carmine. In one sheet we have seen, the gold only shows as tiny specks under a strong magnifying glass and as there may be intermediate stages of faint printing we do not list this.

188 A. E. Goonesinghe **189** I.L.O. Emblem

(Des and photo Harrison)

1969 (29 Apr). *Commemoration of Goonesinghe (founder of Labour Movement in Ceylon).* W **81.** *P* 14.
552 **188** 15 c. multicoloured 10 10

(Photo Harrison)

1969 (4 May). *50th Anniv of International Labour Organisation.* W **81** (*sideways*). *P* 14.
553 **189** 5 c. black and turquoise-blue 10 10
554 25 c. black and carmine-red 10 10

190 Convocation Hall, University of Ceylon **192** Uranium Atom

(Des Ahangama Edward (35 c.); L. D. P. Jayawardena (50 c.); A. Dharmasiri (60 c.); 4 c. from photograph. Litho Rosenbaum Bros, Vienna)

1969 (1 Aug). *Educational Centenary.* T **190, 192** *and similar multicoloured designs. P* 13½.
555 4 c. Type **190** 10 10
556 35 c. Lamp of Learning, Globe and flags (*horiz*) 10 10
557 50 c. Type **192** 15 10
558 60 c. Symbols of Scientific education 15 10
555/8 .. .. *Set of* 4 40 20

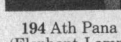

194 Ath Pana (Elephant Lamp) **195** Rock Fortress of Sigiriya

(Des from photographs. Litho Rosenbaum Bros, Vienna)

1969 (1 Aug). *Archaeological Centenary. P* 13½.
559 **194** 6 c. multicoloured 10 20
560 **195** 1 r. multicoloured 25 10

196 Leopard **197** Emblem and Symbols

(Litho Rosenbaum Bros, Vienna)

1970 (11 May). *Wildlife Conservation.* T **196** *and similar horiz designs. Multicoloured. P* 13½.
561 5 c. Water Buffalo 10 25
562 15 c. Slender Loris 25 20
a. Brown-black and orange-brown colours omitted .. .. 35·00
563 50 c. Spotted Deer .. .. 60 1·00
a. Imperf (in vert pair with stamp perf 3 sides) .. .. 75·00
564 1 r. Type **196** .. .. 90 1·75
561/4 .. .. *Set of* 4 1·60 3·00

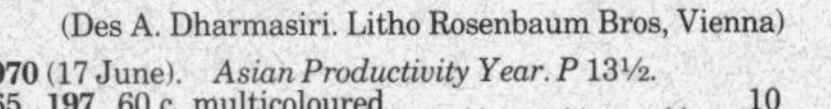

In No. 562a the sky is blue instead of violet and the animal is in green and yellow only.

(Des A. Dharmasiri. Litho Rosenbaum Bros, Vienna)

1970 (17 June). *Asian Productivity Year. P* 13½.
565 **197** 60 c. multicoloured 10 10

198 New U.P.U. H.Q. Building **199** Oil Lamp and Caduceus

(Litho Rosenbaum Bros, Vienna)

1970 (14 Aug). *New U.P.U. Headquarters Building. P* 13½.
566 **198** 50 c. yellow-orange, black and new blue 10 10
a. New blue (Building) omitted .. 60·00
567 1 r. 10, vermilion, black and new blue 35 30

(Des A. Dharmasiri. Litho Rosenbaum Bros, Vienna)

1970 (1 Sept). *Centenary of Colombo Medical School. P* 13½.
568 **199** 5 c. multicoloured 10 20
a. Vert pair, bottom stamp imperf .. £120
569 45 c. multicoloured 25 35

200 Victory March and S. W. R. D. Bandaranaike **201** U.N. Emblem and Dove of Peace

(Des A. Dharmasiri. Litho D.L.R.)

1970 (25 Sept). *Definitive issue marking establishment of United Front Government. P* 13½.
570 **200** 10 c. multicoloured 10 10

(Des A. Dharmasiri. Photo Pakistan Security Printing Corp)

1970 (24 Oct). *25th Anniv of United Nations. P* 12½ × 13½.
571 **201** 2 r. multicoloured 55 80

202 Keppetipola Dissawa **203** Ola Leaf Manuscript

(Des A. Dharmasiri. Litho Harrison)

1970 (26 Nov). *152nd Death Anniv of Keppetipola Dissawa (Kandyan patriot). P* 14 × 14½.
572 **202** 25 c. multicoloured 10 10

(Des A. Dharmasiri. Photo Pakistan Security Printing Corp)

1970 (21 Dec). *International Education Year. P* 13.
573 **203** 15 c. multicoloured 25 25

204 C. H. de Soysa **205** D. E. H. Pedris (patriot) **206** Lenin

(Des L. D. P. Jayawardena. Litho Pakistan Security Printing Corp)

1971 (3 Mar). *135th Birth Anniv of C. H. de Soysa (philanthropist). P* 13½.
574 **204** 20 c. multicoloured 10 15

(Des L. D. P. Jayawardena. Litho Harrison)

1971 (8 July). *D. E. H. Pedris Commemoration. P* 14 × 14½.
575 **205** 25 c. multicoloured 10 25

(Des L. D. P. Jayawardena. Litho Harrison)

1971 (31 Aug). *Lenin Commemoration. P* 14½.
576 **206** 40 c. multicoloured 15 25

207 Ananda Rajakaruna (**208**)

(Des A. Dharmasiri (Nos. 577 and 579), P. A. Miththapala (Nos. 578 and 580), L. D. P. Jayawardena (No. 581). Litho Harrison)

1971 (29 Oct). *Poets and Philosophers. T* **207** *and similar vert designs. P* 14 × 13½.
577 5 c. royal blue 10 15
578 5 c. lake-brown 10 15
579 5 c. red-orange 10 15
580 5 c. deep slate-blue 10 15
581 5 c. brown 10 15
577/81 .. .. *Set of* 5 30 70
Portraits: No. 577, Type **207**; No. 578, Arumuga Navalar; No. 579, Rev. S. Mahinda; No. 580, Ananda Coomaraswamy; No. 581, Cumaratunga Munidasa.

1971 (26 Nov–2 Dec). *Nos.* 549/50, 555, 559 *and* 570 *surch as T* **208** *(obliterating shape differs).*
582 **186** 5 c. on 4 c. multicoloured 50 70
a. Surch inverted .. .. .. 5·50
b. Pair, one with "X" omitted .. 75·00
c. Surch double, one inverted
d. Ditto. Pair, one with "X" omitted 32·00
583 **190** 5 c. on 4 c. multicoloured 10 30
a. Surch inverted .. .. .. 4·25
b. Surch double, one inverted .. 7·00
584 **200** 15 c. on 10 c. multicoloured (2 Dec) .. 10 10
a. Surch inverted .. .. .. 4·00
b. Surch double .. .. .. 5·50
c. Surch and dot transposed ..
d. Surch at right, dot omitted ..
585 **187** 25 c. on 6 c. multicoloured 15 40
a. Surch double, one inverted .. 15·00
b. Surch inverted .. .. .. 12·00
586 **194** 25 c. on 6 c. multicoloured 15 40
a. Surch inverted .. .. .. 4·00
582/6 .. .. *Set of* 5 90 1·75
Nos. 584c/d were caused by a misplacement of the surcharge on one sheet.

209 Colombo Plan Emblem and Ceylon **210** Globe and CARE Package

(Des P. A. Miththapala. Litho Harrison)

1971 (28 Dec). *20th Anniv of Colombo Plan. P* 14 × 14½.
587 **209** 20 c. multicoloured 15 20

(Des A. Dharmasiri. Litho Harrison)

1971 (28 Dec). *20th Anniv of CARE (Co-operative for American Relief Everywhere). P* 14 × 13½.
588 **210** 50 c. new blue, lilac and violet 35 20

211 W.H.O. Emblem and Heart **212** Map of Asia and U.N. Emblem

(Des A. Miththapala. Litho D.L.R.)

1972 (2 May). *World Health Day. P* 13 × 13½.
589 **211** 25 c. multicoloured 25 30

(Des L. D. P. Jayawardena. Litho B.W.)

1972 (2 May). *25th Anniv of ECAFE (Economic Commission for Asia and the Far East). P* 13.
590 **212** 85 c. multicoloured .. .. .. 85 1·10

OFFICIAL STAMPS

1869. *Issues of* 1867–68 *overprinted* "SERVICE" *in block letters.*
Although these stamps were prepared for use and sent out to the colony, they were never issued.

Prices:

Narrow "SERVICE"		Wide "SERVICE"	
No. 98. 2d.	48·00	No. 119. 1d.	45·00
104. 6d.	55·00	120. 3d.	65·00
108. 8d.	65·00		
113. 1s.	75·00		
116. 2s.	85·00		
116. 2s. *imp.*	£500		

On

Service

(O 3)

Contemporary issues overprinted with Type O 3

1895–96.
O1 **9** 2 c. green .. .. 5·00 20
O2 **39** 3 c. terracotta and blue-green .. .. 6·50 40
O3 **28** 5 c. dull purple .. .. 1·25 20
O4 **29** 15 c. sage-green .. .. 7·00 30
O5 25 c. yellow-brown .. .. 8·00 80
O6 30 c. bright mauve and brown .. .. 8·00 25
O7 **30** 1 r. 12, dull rose (*wmk sideways*) .. 45·00 42·00
a. Wmk upright .. .. ..
O1/7 .. .. *Set of* 7 70·00 42·00

1899–1900.
O 8 **9** 2 c. pale orange-brown .. .. .. 1·50 50
O 9 **39** 3 c. deep green .. .. 6·00 60
O10 **29** 15 c. blue .. .. 8·00 60
O11 **39** 75 c. black and red-brown (R.) (1899) .. 5·50 4·00
O8/11 .. .. *Set of* 4 19·00 5·25

1903. *King Edward VII.*
O12 **44** 2 c. orange-brown .. .. .. 4·50 70
O13 **45** 3 c. green .. .. 2·75 2·00
O14 **46** 5 c. dull purple .. .. 5·50 70
O15 **48** 15 c. blue .. .. 14·00 2·50
O16 25 c. bistre .. .. 17·00 15·00
O17 30 c. dull violet and green .. .. .. 6·50 1·50
O12/17 .. .. *Set of* 6 45·00 20·00
About half a dozen sheets of the 15 c. were overprinted with a space of 3 mm instead of 4 mm between the words "On" and "Service".

POSTAL FISCAL

1952 (1 Dec). *As T* **72** *but inscr* "REVENUE" *at sides.*
F1 10 r. dull green and yellow-orange, C .. 45·00 28·00
This revenue stamp was on sale for postal use from 1 December 1952, until 14 March 1954.

On 22 May 1972, Ceylon became the Republic of SRI LANKA.

Channel Islands

These issues are now listed under GREAT BRITAIN after the Postal Fiscal Issues.

China—British Post Offices
see after Hong Kong

China—British Post Offices see after Hong Kong

Christmas Island

Formerly a part of the Straits Settlements and then of the Colony of Singapore, Christmas Island became an Australian territory on 15 October 1958.

Stamps of the STRAITS SETTLEMENTS and later SINGAPORE were used on Christmas Island from 1901 until 1942 and subsequently from 1946 to 1958.

(Currency. 100 cents = 1 dollar (Malayan))

1 Queen Elizabeth II

(Des G. Lissenden. Recess with name and value typo in black. Note Printing Branch, Commonwealth Bank, Melbourne)

1958 (15 Oct). *No wmk. P* 14½.
1 **1** 2 c. yellow-orange 55 15
2 4 c. brown 60 15
3 5 c. deep mauve 60 15
4 6 c. grey-blue .. .. 1·50 20
5 8 c. black-brown .. .. 2·50 50
6 10 c. violet .. .. 2·50 25
7 12 c. carmine .. .. 3·00 1·25
8 20 c. blue .. .. 3·00 1·50
9 50 c. yellow-green .. .. 4·50 1·50
10 $1 deep bluish green .. .. .. 5·00 1·50
1/10 .. .. *Set of* 10 21·00 6·50

PRINTERS. Nos. 11/32 were printed by the Note Printing Branch, Reserve Bank of Australia, Melbourne. Nos. 33/82 were printed in photogravure by Harrison and Sons, Ltd, London.

2 Map

11 White-tailed Tropic Bird

(Des G. Lissenden (2, 8c.), P. Morriss (4, 5, 10, 20 c.), B. Stewart (others). Recess)

1963 (28 Aug). *T* 2 *and similar designs and T* **11**. *P* 14½ × 14 ($1) *or* 14½ *(others).*
11 2 c. orange 40 15
12 4 c. red-brown 50 15
13 5 c. purple 50 15
14 6 c. indigo 40 15
15 8 c. black .. .. 1·60 35
16 10 c. violet 40 15
17 12 c. brown-red 40 20
18 20 c. blue .. .. 1·00 25
19 50 c. green .. .. 2·00 30
20 $1 yellow .. .. 4·75 60
11/20 .. .. *Set of* 10 10·00 2·25
Designs: *Vert*—4 c. Moonflower; 5 c. Robber Crab; 8 c. Phosphate train; 10 c. Raising phosphate. *Horiz*—6 c. Island scene; 12 c. Flying Fish Cove; 20 c. Loading cantilever; 50 c. Christmas Island Frigate Bird.

I Thick lettering

II Thinner lettering

1965. *50th Anniv of Gallipoli Landing. As T* **184** *of Australia, but slightly larger* (22 × 34½ *mm*) *and colour changed. Photo.*
21 10 c. sepia, black and emerald (I) (14.4) .. 20 25
a. *Black-brown, black and light emerald* (II) (24.4) .. .. 1·50 1·25

(New Currency. 100 cents = 1 dollar (Australian))

12 Golden Striped Grouper 13 "Angel" (mosaic)

(Des G. Hamori. Photo)

1968 (6 May)–**70.** *Fishes. T* **12** *and similar horiz designs. Multicoloured. P* 13½.
22 1 c. Type **12** 45 15
23 2 c. Moorish Idol 60 20
24 3 c. Forceps Fish 60 20
25 4 c. Queen Triggerfish 60 20
a. Deep blue (face value) omitted £475
26 5 c. Regal Angelfish 75 20
27 9 c. Surgeon Fish .. .. 2·00 40
28 10 c. Scorpion Fish .. .. 1·50 20
28*a* 15 c. Saddleback Butterfly (fish) (14.12.70) .. 10·00 7·00
29 20 c. Clown Butterfly (fish) .. .. .. 4·00 55
29*a* 30 c. Ghost Pipefish (14.12.70) .. .. 10·00 7·00
30 50 c. Blue Lined Surgeon .. .. .. 10·00 2·50
31 $1 Meyers Butterfly (fish) .. .. .. 15·00 5·00
22/31 .. .. *Set of* 12 48·00 21·00

(Des G. Hamori. Photo)

1969 (10 Nov). *Christmas. P* 13½.
32 **13** 5 c. red, deep blue and gold 10 10

14 "The Ansidei Madonna" (Raphael) 15 "The Adoration of the Shepherds" (ascr to the School of Seville)

(Des Harrison)

1970 (26 Oct). *Christmas. Paintings. T* **14** *and similar vert design. Multicoloured. P* 14 × 14½.
33 3 c. Type **14** 10 10
34 5 c. "The Virgin and Child, St. John the Baptist and an Angel" (Morando) .. 10 10

(Des Harrison)

1971 (4 Oct). *Christmas. T* **15** *and similar vert design. Multi-coloured. W w* **12**. *P* 14.
35 6 c. Type **15** 50 50
36 20 c. "The Adoration of the Shepherds" (Reni) 1·00 1·00

16 H.M.S. *Flying Fish*, 1887 **17** Angel of Peace

(Des V. Whiteley)

1972 (7 Feb)–**73**. *Ships. Horiz designs as T* **16**. *Multicoloured. P* 14 × 13½.
37 1 c. *Eagle*, 1714 (5.6.72) 20 15
38 2 c. H.M.S. *Redpole*, 1890 (5.6.72) 25 20
39 3 c. M.V. *Hoi Houw*, 1959 (5.6.72) 25 20
40 4 c. *Pigot*, 1771 (6.2.73) 25 20
41 5 c. S.S. *Valetta*, 1968 (6.2.73) 25 20
42 6 c. Type **16** 30 25
43 7 c. *Asia*, 1805 .. .. 30 25
44 8 c. T.S.S. *Islander*, 1929–60.. .. .. 35 35
45 9 c. H.M.S. *Imperieuse**, 1888 (6.2.73) .. 55 40
46 10 c. H.M.S. *Egeria*, 1887 (4.6.73) 55 40
47 20 c. *Thomas*, 1615 .. .. 85 70
48 25 c. H.M.S. *Gordon*, 1864 (4.6.73) .. .. 1·00 75
49 30 c. *Cygnet*, 1688 (4.6.73) .. .. .. 1·25 85
50 35 c. S.S. *Triadic*, 1958 (4.6.73) .. .. 1·40 90
51 50 c. H.M.S. *Amethyst*, 1857 (6.2.73).. .. 2·00 1·75
52 $1 *Royal Mary*, 1643 (5.6.72) .. .. 3·00 2·25
37/52 .. .. *Set of* 16 11·00 9·00
*The design is wrongly inscribed "H.M.S. *Imperious*".

(Des Jennifer Toombs)

1972 (2 Oct). *Christmas. T* **17** *and similar vert design. Multi-coloured. P* 14.
53 3 c. Type **17** 50 50
a. Pair. Nos. 53/4 .. .. 1·00 1·00
54 3 c. Angel of Joy 50 50
55 7 c. Type **17** 65 65
a. Pair. Nos. 55/6 .. .. 1·25 1·25
56 7 c. As No. 54.. .. .. 65 65
53/6 .. .. *Set of* 4 2·25 2·25
Nos. 53/4 and 55/6 have the two designs printed horizontally *se-tenant* within the sheet.

18 Virgin and Child, and Map **19** Mary and Holy Child within Christmas Star

(Des P. L. S. Cheong)

1973 (2 Oct). *Christmas. P* 14 × 13.
57 **18** 7 c. multicoloured 75 35
58 25 c. multicoloured .. .. 2·75 1·25

(Des Jennifer Toombs)

1974 (2 Oct). *Christmas. P* 13 × 14½.
59 **19** 7 c. mauve and grey-black 60 60
60 30 c. light orange, bright yell & grey-blk 1·75 2·25

20 "The Flight into Egypt" **21** Dove of Peace and Star of Bethlehem

(Des Jennifer Toombs)

1975 (2 Oct). *Christmas. P* 14 × 13.
61 **20** 10 c. light greenish yellow, agate and gold 35 25
62 35 c. bright rose, deep blue and gold .. 1·25 1·25

(Des R. Bates)

1976 (2 Oct). *Christmas. P* 13½.
63 **21** 10 c. cerise, lemon and bright mauve .. 40 40
a. Pair. Nos. 63/4 .. .. .. 80 80
64 – 10 c. cerise, lemon and bright mauve .. 40 40
65 **21** 35 c. reddish violet, light greenish blue and light yellow-green 65 65
a. Pair. Nos. 65/6 .. .. .. 1·25 1·25
66 – 35 c. reddish violet, light greenish blue and light yellow-green 65 65
63/6 .. .. *Set of* 4 2·00 2·00
Nos. 64 and 66 are "mirror-images" of T **21**, the two designs of each value being printed horizontally *se-tenant* throughout the sheet.

22 William Dampier (explorer) **23** Australian Coat of Arms on Map of Christmas Island

(Des V. Whiteley Studio)

1977 (30 Apr)–**78**. *Famous Visitors. Horiz designs as T* **22** *in black, vermilion and greenish yellow* (45 *c.*) *or multicoloured* (*others*). *P* 14 × 13.
67 1 c. Type **22** 10 10
68 2 c. Capt. de Vlamingh (explorer) (22.2.78) .. 15 10
69 3 c. Vice-Admiral MacLear (22.2.78) .. 15 10
70 4 c. Sir John Murray (oceanographer) (22.2.78) 15 15
71 5 c. Admiral Aldrich (31.5.78) 15 10
72 6 c. Andrew Clunies-Ross (first settler) .. 15 15
73 7 c. J. J. Lister (naturalist) (31.5.78).. .. 20 10
74 8 c. Admiral of the Fleet Sir William May (1.9.78) 20 15
75 9 c. Henry Ridley (botanist) 20 15
76 10 c. George Clunies-Ross (phosphate miner) (1.9.78) 20 15
77 20 c. Capt. Joshua Slocum (yachtsman) (1.9.78) 40 35
78 45 c. Charles Andrews (naturalist) (31.5.78) .. 85 45
79 50 c. Richard Hanitsch (biologist) (31.5.78) .. 95 60
80 75 c. Victor Purcell (scholar) (1.9.78).. .. 85 85
81 $1 Fam Choo Beng (educator) .. .. 1·25 1·25
82 $2 Sir Harold Spencer-Jones (astronomer) (22.2.78) .. .. 2·50 2·25
67/82 .. .. *Set of* 16 7·50 6·50

(Des Mrs S. Muir. Litho Harrison)

1977 (2 June). *Silver Jubilee. P* 14½ × 13½.
83 **23** 45 c. multicoloured 60 70

24 "A Partridge in a Pear Tree" **25** Abbott's Booby

(Des Jennifer Toombs. Litho Questa)

1977 (20 Oct)–**78**. *Christmas. T* **24** *and similar vert designs depicting the carol "The Twelve Days of Christmas". Multi-coloured. P* 14.

A. *No wmk*. B. *W w* **14** (27.1.78)

		A.		B.	
84	10 c. Type **24**	15	20	25	20
	a. Sheetlet. Nos. 84/95	1·60	—	2·75	—
85	10 c. "Two turtle doves" ..	15	20	25	20
86	10 c. "Three French hens" ..	15	20	25	20
87	10 c. "Four calling birds" ..	15	20	25	20
88	10 c. "Five gold rings" ..	15	20	25	20
89	10 c. "Six geese a-laying" ..	15	20	25	20
90	10 c. "Seven swans a-swimming"	15	20	25	20
91	10 c. "Eight maids a-milking" ..	15	20	25	20
92	10 c. "Nine ladies dancing" ..	15	20	25	20
93	10 c. "Ten lords a-leaping" ..	15	20	25	20
94	10 c. "Eleven pipers piping" ..	15	20	25	20
95	10 c. "Twelve drummers drumming" ..	15	20	25	20
84/95	.. .. *Set of* 12	1·60	2·10	2·75	2·10

Nos. 84/95 were printed as a *se-tenant* block within a sheetlet 142 × 170 mm.

(Des Jennifer Toombs. Litho Questa)

1978 (21 Apr). *25th Anniv of Coronation. T* **25** *and similar vert designs. P* 15.
96 45 c. black and bright ultramarine 60 85
a. Sheetlet. Nos. 96/8 × 2 .. .. .. 3·25
97 45 c. multicoloured 60 85
98 45 c. black and bright ultramarine 60 85
96/8 .. .. *Set of* 3 1·60 2·25
Designs:—No. 96, White Swan of Bohun; No. 97, Queen Elizabeth II; No. 98, Type **25**.
Nos. 96/8 were printed together in small sheets of 6, containing two *se-tenant* strips of 3 with horizontal gutter margin between.

MINIMUM PRICE

The minimum price quote is 10p which represents a handling charge rather than a basis for valuing common stamps. For further notes about prices see introductory pages.

26 "Christ Child" **27** Chinese Children

(Des Jennifer Toombs. Litho J.W.)

1978 (2 Oct). *Christmas. Scenes from "The Song of Christmas". T* **26** *and similar horiz designs. Multicoloured. P* 14.
99 10 c. Type **26** 15 15
a. Sheetlet. Nos. 99/107 .. .. .. 1·25
100 10 c. "Herald Angels" 15 15
101 10 c. "Redeemer" 15 15
102 10 c. "Israel" 15 15
103 10 c. "Star" 15 15
104 10 c. "Three Wise Men" 15 15
105 10 c. "Manger".. .. .. 15 15
106 10 c. "All He Stands For" 15 15
107 10 c. "Shepherds Came" 15 15
99/107 .. .. *Set of* 9 1·25 1·25
Nos. 99/107 were printed together, *se-tenant*, in a small sheet of 9.

(Des Jennifer Toombs. Litho Questa)

1979 (20 Apr). *International Year of the Child. T* **27** *and similar vert designs showing children of different races. Multicoloured, colour of inscr given. P* 14.
108 20 c. apple-green (Type **27**) 40 40
a. Horiz strip of 5. Nos. 108/12 .. .. 1·75
109 20 c. turquoise-green (Malay children) .. 40 40
110 20 c. lilac (Indian children) 40 40
111 20 c. rose (European children) 40 40
112 20 c. orange-yellow ("Oranges and Lemons").. 40 40
108/12 .. .. *Set of* 5 1·75 1·75
Nos. 108/12 were printed together, *se-tenant*, in horizontal strips of 5 throughout the sheet, forming a composite design.

28 1958 2 c. Definitive **29** Wise Men following Star

(Des J.W. Litho Questa)

1979 (27 Aug). *Death Centenary of Sir Rowland Hill. T* **28** *and similar horiz designs showing stamps and Sir Rowland Hill. Multicoloured. P* 13½.
113 20 c. Type **28** 25 30
a. Horiz strip of 5. Nos. 113/17 .. .. 1·10
114 20 c. 1963 2 c. Map definitive 25 30
115 20 c. 1965 50th anniversary of Gallipoli Landing 10 c. commemorative 25 30
116 20 c. 1968 4 c. Queen Triggerfish definitive .. 25 30
117 20 c. 1969 5 c. Christmas issue 25 30
113/17 .. .. *Set of* 5 1·10 1·40
Nos. 113/17 were printed together, *se-tenant*, in horizontal strips of 5 throughout the sheet.

(Des L. Curtis. Litho Walsall)

1979 (22 Oct). *Christmas. T* **29** *and similar horiz design. Multi-coloured. P* 14 × 14½.
118 20 c. Type **29** 20 25
119 55 c. Virgin and Child.. .. .. .. 45 60

30 9th Green **31** Surveying

(Des R. Granger Barrett. Litho Format)

1980 (12 Feb). *25th Anniv of Christmas Island Golf Club. T* **30** *and similar horiz design. Multicoloured. P* 14½ × 14.
120 20 c. Type **30** 40 25
121 55 c. Clubhouse 70 50

(Des L. Curtis. Litho Walsall)

1980 (6 May). *Phosphate Industry* (1*st issue*). *T* **31** *and similar horiz designs. Multicoloured. P* 14.
122 15 c. Type **31** 15 15
123 22 c. Drilling for samples 20 20
124 40 c. Sample analysis 30 30
125 55 c. Mine planning 40 40
122/5 .. .. *Set of* 4 95 95
See also Nos. 126/9, 136/9 and 140/3.

(Des L. Curtis. Litho Walsall)

1980 (14 July). *Phosphate Industry* (2*nd issue*). *Horiz designs as T* **31**. *Multicoloured. P* 14.
126 15 c. Jungle clearing 15 15
127 22 c. Overburden removal 20 20
128 40 c. Open cut mining 30 25
129 55 c. Restoration 35 30
126/9 .. .. *Set of* 4 90 80

32 Angel with Harp

33 *Cryptoblepharus egeriae*

(Des Jennifer Toombs. Litho Walsall)

1980 (6 Oct). *Christmas. T* **32** *and similar vert designs. Multicoloured. P* 13½ × 13.
130 15 c. Type **32** 15 15
a. Sheetlet. Nos. 130/5 1·40
131 15 c. Angel with wounded soldier 15 15
132 22 c. Virgin and Child 20 20
133 22 c. Kneeling couple 20 20
134 60 c. Angel with harp (*different*) 45 45
135 60 c. Angel with children 45 45
130/5 *Set of* 6 1·40 1·40
Nos. 130/5 were printed together in small sheets of 6, containing two *se-tenant* strips of 3 (Nos. 130, 132, 134 and 131, 133, 135) with horizontal gutter margin between.

(Des L. Curtis. Litho Walsall)

1981 (9 Feb). *Phosphate Industry* (3rd issue). *Horiz designs as T* **31.** *Multicoloured. P* 14.
136 22 c. Screening and stockpiling 20 20
137 28 c. Train loading 25 25
138 40 c. Railing 40 40
139 60 c. Drying 55 55
136/9 *Set of* 4 1·25 1·25

(Des L. Curtis. Litho Walsall)

1981 (4 May). *Phosphate Industry* (4th issue). *Horiz designs as T* **31.** *Multicoloured. P* 14.
140 22 c. Crushing 25 20
141 28 c. Conveying 30 25
142 40 c. Bulk storage 45 40
143 60 c. Ship loading 55 55
140/3 *Set of* 4 1·50 1·25

(Des L. Curtis. Litho Walsall)

1981 (10 Aug). *Reptiles. T* **33** *and similar horiz designs. Multicoloured. P* 13.
144 24 c. Type **33** 25 25
145 30 c. *Emoia nativitata* 30 30
146 40 c. *Lepidodactylus listeri* 45 45
147 60 c. *Cyrtodactylus sp. nov.* 65 65
144/7 *Set of* 4 1·50 1·50

34 Scene from Carol "Away in a Manger"

35 Eastern Reef Heron

(Des Jennifer Toombs. Litho Questa)

1981 (19 Oct). *Christmas. T* **34** *and similar horiz designs showing scenes from carol "Away in a Manger". P* 14½ × 14.
148 18 c. silver, deep blue and turquoise-blue 40 40
a. Sheetlet. Nos. 148/51 1·75
149 24 c. multicoloured 45 45
150 40 c. multicoloured 50 50
151 60 c. multicoloured 60 60
148/51 *Set of* 4 1·75 1·75
Nos. 148/51 were printed together, *se-tenant*, in sheetlets of 4.

(Des N. Arlott. Litho Questa)

1982 (8 Mar)–**83**. *Birds. Multicoloured designs as T* **35.** *P* 14.
152 1 c. Type **35** 15 10
153 2 c. Common Noddy 20 10
154 3 c. White-bellied Swiftlet (14.6.82) 20 20
155 4 c. Christmas Island Imperial Pigeon (14.6.82) 20 20
156 5 c. Christmas Island White Eye (21.2.83) 20 15
157 10 c. Island Thrush (14.6.82) 20 20
158 25 c. Red-tailed Tropic Bird 45 25
159 30 c. Emerald Dove (21.2.83) 45 30
160 40 c. Brown Booby (23.8.82) 60 35
161 50 c. Red-footed Booby (23.8.82) 55 45
162 65 c. Christmas Island Frigate Bird (23.8.82) 55 55
163 75 c. White-tailed Tropic Bird (23.8.82) 65 65
164 80 c. Australian Kestrel (*vert*) (21.2.83) 80 65
165 $1 Indonesian Hawk Owl (*vert*) (21.2.83) 1·00 90
166 $2 Australian Goshawk (*vert*) (14.6.82) 1·50 2·75
167 $4 Abbott's Booby (*vert*) 3·00 3·25
152/67 *Set of* 16 9·50 10·00

36 Joseph

37 "Mirror" Dinghy and Club House

(Des Jennifer Toombs. Litho and embossed Walsall)

1982 (18 Oct). *Christmas. Origami Paper Sculptures. T* **36** *and similar vert designs. Multicoloured. P* 14½ × 14.
168 27 c. Type **36** 30 30
a. Horiz strip of 3. Nos. 168/70 1·25
169 50 c. Angel 45 45
170 75 c. Mary and baby Jesus 65 65
168/70 *Set of* 3 1·25 1·25
Nos. 168/70 were printed together, *se-tenant*, in horiz strips of 3 throughout the sheet.

(Des L. McCombie. Litho Format)

1983 (2 May). *25th Anniv of Christmas Island Boat Club. T* **37** *and similar multicoloured designs. P* 14 × 14½ (27, 35 *c.*) *or* 14½ × 14 (*others*).
171 27 c. Type **37** 35 35
172 35 c. Ocean-going yachts 40 40
173 50 c. Fishing launch and cargo ship (*horiz*) 50 50
174 75 c. Dinghy-racing and cantilever (*horiz*) 70 70
171/4 *Set of* 4 1·75 1·75

38 Maps of Christmas Island and Australia, Eastern Grey Kangaroo and White-tailed Tropic Bird

39 Candle and Holly

(Des A. Theobald. Litho Questa)

1983 (1 Oct). *25th Anniv of Christmas Island as an Australian Territory. T* **38** *and similar horiz designs. Multicoloured. P* 14.
175 24 c. Type **38** 20 20
176 30 c. Christmas Island and Australian flag 25 25
177 85 c. Maps of Christmas Island and Australia, with Boeing "727" 70 70
175/7 *Set of* 3 1·10 1·10

(Des J.W. Litho Walsall)

1983 (31 Oct). *Christmas. Candles. T* **39** *and similar vert designs. Multicoloured. P* 13.
178 24 c. Type **39** 20 20
179 30 c. Six gold candles 25 25
180 85 c. Candles 70 70
178/80 *Set of* 3 1·10 1·10

40 Feeding on Leaf

41 *Leucocoprinus fragilissimus*

(Des L. Curtis. Litho Questa)

1984 (20 Feb). *Red Land Crab. T* **40** *and similar horiz designs showing various aspects of crab's life. Multicoloured. P* 14 × 14½.
181 30 c. Type **40** 30 30
182 40 c. Migration 40 40
183 55 c. Development stages 50 50
184 85 c. Adult female and young 70 70
181/4 *Set of* 4 1·75 1·75

(Des I. Loe. Litho Format)

1984 (30 Apr). *Fungi. T* **41** *and similar vert designs. Multicoloured. P* 14 × 14½.
185 30 c. Type **41** 45 30
186 40 c. *Microporus xanthopus* 55 40
187 45 c. *Trogia anthidepas* 65 45
188 55 c. *Haddowia longipes* 75 60
189 85 c. *Phillipsia domingensis* 90 75
185/9 *Set of* 5 3·00 2·25

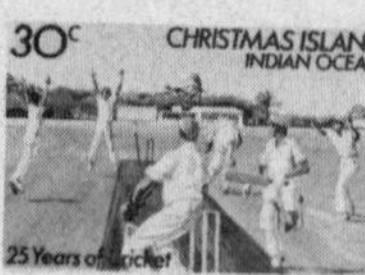

42 Run-out

43 Arrival of Father Christmas

(Des A. Theobald. Litho J.W.)

1984 (23 July). *25th Anniversary of Cricket on Christmas Island. T* **42** *and similar horiz designs. Multicoloured. P* 14.
190 30 c. Type **42** 60 35
191 40 c. Bowled-out 70 45
192 55 c. Batsman in action 90 65
193 85 c. Fielder diving for catch 1·10 1·00
190/3 *Set of* 4 3·00 2·25

(Des D. Slater. Litho B.D.T.)

1984 (21 Sept). *Christmas and "Ausipex" International Stamp Exhibition, Melbourne. Sheet* 100 × 100 *mm containing T* **43** *and similar horiz designs. Multicoloured. P* 13½.
MS194 30 c. Type **43**; 55 c. Distribution of presents; 85 c. Departure of Father Christmas 2·00 2·25
No. **MS**194 also contains three labels horizontally *se-tenant* with the stamps and forming composite designs with them.

44 Robber Crab

45 "Once in Royal David's City"

(Des L. Curtis. Litho Walsall)

1985 (30 Jan). *Crabs* (1*st series*). *T* **44** *and similar horiz designs. Multicoloured. P* 13 × 13½.
195 30 c. Type **44** 55 40
196 40 c. Horn-eyed Ghost Crab 65 50
197 55 c. Purple Hermit Crab 80 65
198 85 c. Little Nipper 1·10 1·00
195/8 *Set of* 4 2·75 2·25
See also Nos. 199/202 and 203/6.

(Des L. Curtis. Litho Walsall)

1985 (29 Apr). *Crabs* (2*nd series*). *Horiz designs as T* **44.** *Multicoloured. P* 13 × 13½.
199 33 c. Blue Crab 60 40
200 45 c. Tawny Hermit Crab 70 50
201 60 c. Red Nipper 85 65
202 90 c. Smooth-handed Ghost Crab 1·25 95
199/202 *Set of* 4 3·00 2·25

(Des L. Curtis. Litho Walsall)

1985 (22 July). *Crabs* (3*rd series*). *Horiz designs as T* **44.** *Multicoloured. P* 13 × 13½.
203 33 c. Red Crab 60 55
204 45 c. Mottled Crab 70 65
205 60 c. Rock Hopper Crab 90 85
206 90 c. Yellow Nipper 1·25 1·50
203/6 *Set of* 4 3·00 3·25

(Des Jennifer Toombs. Litho Harrison)

1985 (28 Oct). *Christmas. Carols. T* **45** *and similar vert designs. Multicoloured. P* 14 × 14½.
207 27 c. Type **45** 45 45
a. Horiz strip of 5. Nos. 207/11 3·00
208 33 c. "While Shepherds Watched Their Flocks by Night" 55 55
209 45 c. "Away in a Manger" 65 65
210 60 c. "We Three Kings of Orient Are" 75 75
211 90 c. "Hark the Herald Angels Sing" 1·00 1·00
207/11 *Set of* 5 3·00 3·00
Nos. 207/11 were printed together, *se-tenant* in horizontal strips of 5 throughout the sheet.

46 Halley's Comet over Christmas Island

47 Ridley's Orchid

(Des L. Curtis. Litho Format)

1986 (30 Apr). *Appearance of Halley's Comet. T* **46** *and similar horiz designs. Multicoloured. P* 14.
212 33 c. Type **46** 55 55
213 45 c. Edmond Halley 70 70
214 60 c. Comet and ship loading phosphate 85 85
215 90 c. Comet over Flying Fish Cove 1·25 1·25
212/15 *Set of* 4 3·00 3·00

(Des I. Loe. Litho Format)

1986 (30 June). *Native Flowers. T* **47** *and similar vert designs. Multicoloured. P* 14.
216 33 c. Type **47** 50 50
217 45 c. Hanging Flower 65 65
218 60 c. Hoya 75 75
219 90 c. Sea Hibiscus 1·10 1·10
216/19 *Set of* 4 2·75 2·75

(Des D. Miller. Litho Walsall)

1986 (23 July). *Royal Wedding. Square designs as T* **112** *of Ascension. Multicoloured. P* 14½ × 14.
220 33 c. Prince Andrew and Miss Sarah Ferguson 45 35
221 90 c. Prince Andrew piloting helicopter, Digby, Canada, 1985 95 1·10

48 Father Christmas and Reindeer in Speed Boat

(Des G. Vasarhelyi. Litho Walsall)

1986 (30 Sept). *Christmas. T* **48** *and similar horiz designs. Multicoloured. P* 13×13½.

222	30 c. Type **48**	40	40
223	36 c. Father Christmas and reindeer on beach	50	50
224	55 c. Father Christmas fishing	70	70
225	70 c. Playing golf	90	90
226	$1 Sleeping in hammock	1·10	1·10
222/6	*Set of* 5	3·25	3·25

49 H.M.S. *Flying Fish* and Outline Map of Christmas Island

(Des L. Curtis. Litho Format)

1987 (21 Jan). *Centenary of Visits by H.M.S. "Flying Fish" and H.M.S. "Egeria". T* **49** *and similar horiz design. Multicoloured. P* 14½.

227	36 c. Type **49**	55	55
228	90 c. H.M.S. *Egeria* and outline map	1·40	1·40

50 Blind Snake

51 Children watching Father Christmas in Sleigh

(Des G. Drummond. Litho Questa)

1987 (25 Mar)–**89**. *Wildlife. T* **50** *and similar horiz designs. Multicoloured. P* 14.

229	1 c. Type **50**	10	10
	a. Sheetlet of 16. Nos. 229/44 (1.3.88)	10·50	
230	2 c. Blue-tailed Skink	10	10
231	3 c. Insectivorous Bat (24.6.87)	10	10
232	5 c. Green Cricket (1.3.88)	10	10
233	10 c. Christmas Island Fruit Bat (24.6.87)	10	10
234	25 c. Gecko	20	25
235	30 c. Praying Mantis (1.3.88)	25	30
236	36 c. Indonesian Hawk Owl (24.6.87)	30	35
237	40 c. Bull Mouth Helmet Shell (26.8.87)	35	40
237*a*	41 c. Nudibranch (*Phidiana* sp) (1.9.89)	35	40
238	50 c. Textile Cone Shell (26.8.87)	40	45
239	65 c. Brittle Stars (26.8.87)	55	60
240	75 c. Royal Angelfish (26.8.87)	60	65
241	90 c. Christmas Island White (butterfly) (1.3.88)	75	80
242	$1 Mimic (butterfly) (1.3.88)	85	90
243	$2 Shrew (*Crocidura attenuata trichura*) (24.6.87)	1·60	1·75
244	$5 Green Turtle	4·25	4·50
229/44	*Set of* 17	9·75	10·50

No. 229a was originally only available from a presentation pack, but was, subsequently, sold separately by the Christmas Island Post Office. Stamps from it show "1988" imprint date. Examples from the ordinary sheets are without imprint date.

(Des D. Miller. Litho CPE Australia Ltd, Melbourne)

1987 (7 Oct). *Christmas. Sheet,* 165×65 *mm, containing T* **51** *and similar multicoloured designs. P* 13½.

MS245 30 c. Type **51**; 37 c. Father Christmas distributing gifts (48×22 *mm*); 90 c. Children with presents (48×22 *mm*); $1 Singing carols .. 2·50 2·75

The stamps within No. **MS**245 form a composite design of a beach scene.

(Des Sue Passmore. Litho CPE Australia Ltd, Melbourne)

1988 (26 Jan). *Bicentenary of Australian Settlement. Arrival of First Fleet. Square designs as Nos.* 1105/9 *of Australia, but each inscribed* "CHRISTMAS ISLAND Indian Ocean" *and* "AUSTRALIA BICENTENARY".

246	37 c. Aborigines watching arrival of Fleet, Botany Bay	60	60
	a. Horiz strip of 5. Nos. 246/50	2·75	
247	37 c. Aboriginal family and anchored ships	60	60
248	37 c. Fleet arriving at Sydney Cove	60	60
249	37 c. Ship's boat	60	60
250	37 c. Raising the flag, Sydney Cove, 26 January 1788	60	60
246/50	*Set of* 5	2·75	2·75

Nos. 246/50 were printed together, *se-tenant*, in horizontal strips of five throughout the sheet, forming a composite design.

52 Captain William May

53 Pony and Trap, 1910

(Des Josephine Martin. Litho Questa)

1988 (8 June). *Centenary of British Annexation. T* **52** *and similar vert designs. Multicoloured. P* 14½×14.

251	37 c. Type **52**	35	40
252	53 c. Annexation ceremony	50	55
253	95 c. H.M.S. *Imperieuse* firing salute	90	95
254	$1.50, Building commemorative cairn	1·40	1·50
251/4	*Set of* 4	2·75	3·00

(Des L. Curtis. Litho Walsall)

1988 (24 Aug). *Centenary of Permanent Settlement. T* **53** *and similar horiz designs. Multicoloured. P* 14×14½.

255	37 c. Type **53**	45	40
256	55 c. Phosphate mining, 1910	60	55
257	70 c. Steam locomotive, 1914	85	70
258	$1 Arrival of first aircraft, 1957	1·25	1·00
255/8	*Set of* 4	2·75	2·40

54 Beach Toys

55 Food on Table ("Good Harvesting")

(Des N. Shewring. Litho Format)

1988 (15 Nov). *Christmas. Toys and Gifts. T* **54** *and similar vert designs. Multicoloured. P* 14.

259	32 c. Type **54**	40	35
260	39 c. Flippers, snorkel and mask	50	40
261	90 c. Model soldier, doll and soft toys	1·10	90
262	$1 Models of racing car, lorry and jet aircraft	1·25	1·00
259/62	*Set of* 4	3·00	2·40

(Des D. Miller. Litho Questa)

1989 (31 Jan). *Chinese New Year. T* **55** *and similar horiz designs. Multicoloured. P* 14 × 14½.

263	39 c. Type **55**	45	40
264	70 c. Decorations ("Prosperity")	80	70
265	90 c. Chinese girls ("Good Fortune")	1·10	90
266	$1 Lion dance ("Progress Every Year")	1·25	1·00
263/6	*Set of* 4	3·25	2·75

56 Sir John Murray

57 Four Children

(Des S. Noon. Litho Walsall)

1989 (16 Mar). *75th Death Anniv of Sir John Murray (oceanographer). T* **56** *and similar horiz designs. Multicoloured. P* 14 × 14½.

267	39 c. Type **56**	50	50
268	80 c. Map of Christmas Island showing Murray Hill	95	95
269	$1 Oceanographic equipment	1·25	1·25
270	$1.10, H.M.S. *Challenger* (survey ship)	1·50	1·50
267/70	*Set of* 4	3·75	3·75

(Des C. Burke. Litho Questa)

1989 (31 May). *Malay Hari Raya Festival. T* **57** *and similar vert designs. Multicoloured. P* 14.

271	39 c. Type **57**	50	50
272	55 c. Man playing tambourine	70	70
273	80 c. Girl in festival costume	1·00	1·00
274	$1.10, Christmas Island Mosque	1·40	1·40
271/4	*Set of* 4	3·25	3·25

58 *Huperzia phlegmaria*

59 Virgin Mary and Star

(Des Kerrie Rockett. Litho Walsall)

1989 (16 Aug). *Ferns. T* **58** *and similar vert designs. Multicoloured. P* 14.

275	41 c. Type **58**	60	60
276	65 c. *Asplenium polydon*	85	85
277	80 c. Common Bracken	1·00	1·00
278	$1.10, Birds-nest Fern	1·40	1·40
275/8	*Set of* 4	3·50	3·50

(Des G. Maynard. Litho Leigh-Mardon Ltd, Melbourne)

1989 (4 Oct). *Christmas. T* **59** *and similar vert designs. Multicoloured. P* 14½.

279	36 c. Type **59**	35	40
280	41 c. Christ Child in manger	40	45
281	80 c. Shepherds and Star	75	80
282	$1.10, Three Wise Men following Star	1·00	1·10
279/82	*Set of* 4	2·25	2·50

(60)

1989 (18 Oct). *"Melbourne Stampshow '89". No.* 237*a and as No.* 242, *but with imprint date, optd with T* **60**.

283	41 c. Nudibranch (*Phidiana* sp)	40	45
284	$1 Mimic (butterfly)	95	1·00

Cocos (Keeling) Is.

Formerly incorporated with Singapore: an Australian territory since 23 November 1955.

The stamps of the STRAITS SETTLEMENTS were used by a postal agency operating on Cocos (Keeling) Islands from 1 April 1933 until 1 March 1937. The postal agency reopened on 2 September 1952 and used the stamps of SINGAPORE until the islands were transferred to Australia in 1955. From 1955 until 1963 stamps of AUSTRALIA were in use.

PRINTERS. All the following stamps to No. 31 were printed by the Note Printing Branch, Reserve Bank of Australia, Melbourne.

1 Copra Industry

2 "Super Constellation"

1963 (11 June). *T 1/2 and similar designs. Recess. P 14½ × 14 (5d., 2s. 3d.) or 14½ (others).*

1	3d. chocolate	1·75	1·25
2	5d. ultramarine	1·50	65
3	8d. scarlet	4·50	1·75
4	1s. green	3·00	55
5	2s. deep purple	9·00	3·00
6	2s. 3d. deep green	35·00	3·25
1/6	*Set of* 6	48·00	9·50

Designs: *Vert (as T 1)*—8d. Map of islands; 2s. Jukong (sailboat). *Horiz (as T 1)*—1s. Palms. *(as T 2)*—2s. 3d. White Tern.

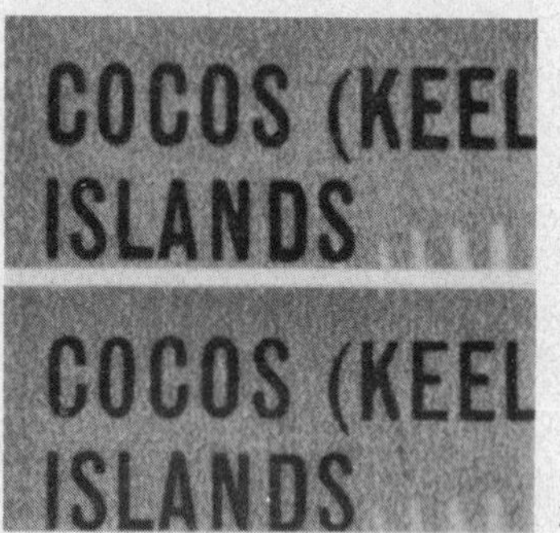

I Thick lettering

II Thinner lettering

1965. *50th Anniv of Gallipoli Landing. As T 184 of Australia, but slightly larger (22 × 34½ mm) and colour changed. Photo.*

7	5d. sepia, black and emerald (I) (14.4)	60	45
	a. Black-brown, black and light emerald (II) (24.4)	2·00	1·25

With the introduction of decimal currency on 14 February 1966, Australian stamps were used in Cocos Islands, until the appearance of the new definitives on 9 July 1969.

7 Reef Clam

8 Great Frigate Bird

(Des L. Annois (1 c. to 6 c.); P. Jones (10 c. to $1). Photo)

1969 (9 July). *Decimal Currency. T 8 or designs as T 7. Multicoloured. P 13½.*

8	1 c. Turban Shell (*vert*)	30	20
9	2 c. Burrowing clam (*vert*)	1·00	45
10	3 c. Type **7**	30	15
11	4 c. Blenny (fish)	30	15
	a. Salmon-pink omitted	£650	
12	5 c. Coral	35	15
13	6 c. Flying Fish	75	20
14	10 c. Banded Rail	1·50	50
15	15 c. Java Sparrow	1·00	20
16	20 c. Red-tailed Tropic Bird	1·00	20
17	30 c. Sooty Tern	1·25	25
18	50 c. Eastern Reef Heron (*vert*)	2·00	30
19	$1 Type **8**	3·50	1·00
8/19	*Set of* 12	12·00	3·25

9 *Dragon,* 1609

10 Map of Cocos (Keeling) Islands Union Flag, Stars and Trees

(Des R. Honisett. Photo)

1976 (29 Mar). *Ships. Multicoloured designs as T 9. P 13½.*

20	1 c. Type **9**	25	20
21	2 c. H.M.S. *Juno*, 1857	20	20
22	5 c. H.M.S. *Beagle*, 1836	30	20
23	10 c. H.M.A.S. *Sydney*, 1914	35	25
24	15 c. S.M.S. *Emden*, 1914	80	40
25	20 c. *Ayesha*, 1907	85	50
26	25 c. T.S.S. *Islander*, 1927	90	75
27	30 c. M.V. *Cheshire*, 1951	1·00	75
28	35 c. Jukong (sailboat)	1·00	80
29	40 c. C.S. *Scotia*, 1900	1·00	80
30	50 c. R.M.S. *Orontes*, 1929	1·40	90
31	$1 Royal Yacht *Gothic*, 1954	1·75	1·40
20/31	*Set of* 12	8·75	6·50

The 2 c. to 20 c., 35 c. and 40 c. are horizontal designs.

(Des Marg Towt. Litho Asher and Co, Melbourne)

1979 (3 Sept). *Inauguration of Independent Postal Service (20 c.) and Establishment of First Statutory Council (50 c.). T 10 and similar horiz design. Multicoloured. P 15½ × 15.*

32	20 c. Type **10**	25	30
33	50 c. Council seal and jukong (sailboat)	35	50

11 Bright Yellow Long-nosed Butterfly Fish

12 "Peace on Earth"

(Des Marg Towt. Litho Asher and Co, Melbourne)

1979 (3 Sept)–**80.** *Fishes. Horiz designs as T 11. Multicoloured. P 13½ × 13 (22 c., 28 c., 60 c.) or 15½ × 15 (others).*

34	1 c. Type **11**	10	25
35	2 c. Clown Butterfly Fish (19.11.79)	20	15
36	5 c. *Anthias sp.*	20	35
37	10 c. Meyer's Butterfly Fish (18.2.80)	25	25
38	15 c. Wrasse (19.11.79)	30	25
39	20 c. Charles' Clown Fish (19.11.79)	45	30
39*a*	22 c. Yellow-striped Emerald Triggerfish (1.7.80)	30	30
40	25 c. *Cheilinus fasciatus* (18.2.80)	45	35
40*a*	28 c. *Macropharyngodon meleagris* (1.7.80)	35	35
41	30 c. *Chaetodon madagascariensis* (19.11.79)	65	45
42	35 c. Angel Fish	45	70
43	40 c. Hog Fish (19.11.79)	70	60
44	50 c. Wrasse (*different*) (19.11.79)	85	75
45	55 c. *Anampses meleagrides* (18.2.80)	75	75
45*a*	60 c. Grouper (1.7.80)	75	75
46	$1 Surgeon Fish	1·25	2·00
47	$2 Three-banded Butterfly Fish (18.2.80)	2·00	2·50
34/47	*Set of* 17	9·00	9·50

(Des D. Pitt. Litho Asher & Co, Melbourne)

1979 (22 Oct). *Christmas. T 12 and similar multicoloured design. P 15 × 15½ (25 c.) or 15½ × 15 (55 c.).*

48	25 c. Type **12**	25	35
49	55 c. "Goodwill Toward Men" (*horiz*)	40	55

13 Star, Map of Cocos (Keeling) Islands and Island Landscape

14 "Administered by the British Government, 1857"

(Des P. Arnold. Litho Asher and Co, Melbourne)

1980 (22 Oct). *Christmas. T 13 and similar horiz designs. Multicoloured. P 13.*

50	15 c. Type **13**	10	10
51	28 c. Map and Wise Men following star	15	15
52	60 c. Map and Nativity scene	40	40
50/2	*Set of* 3	60	60

(Des Sue Wilson. Litho Asher and Co, Melbourne)

1980 (24 Nov). *25th Anniv of Cocos (Keeling) Islands as an Australian Territory. T 14 and similar horiz designs. Multicoloured. P 13½ × 13.*

53	22 c. Type **14**	15	15
	a. Horiz strip of 5. Nos. 53/7	70	
54	22 c. "Administered by the Government of Ceylon, 1878, 1942–6"	15	15
55	22 c. "Administered by the Straits Settlements, 1886"	15	15
56	22 c. "Administered by the Colony of Singapore, 1946"	15	15
57	22 c. "Administered by the Australian Government, 1955"	15	15
53/7	*Set of* 5	70	70

Nos. 53/7 were printed together, *se-tenant*, in horizontal strips of 5 throughout the sheet, forming a composite design.

15 *Eye of the Wind* and Map of Cocos (Keeling) Islands

16 Aerial View of Animal Quarantine Station

(Des Sue Wilson. Litho Asher and Co, Melbourne)

1980 (18 Dec). *"Operation Drake" (round the world expedition) and 400th Anniv of Sir Francis Drake's Circumnavigation of the World. T 15 and similar multicoloured designs. P 13.*

58	22 c. Type **15**	20	15
59	28 c. Map of the World showing voyage routes (*horiz*)	20	15
60	35 c. Sir Francis Drake and *Golden Hind*	20	15
61	60 c. Prince Charles and *Eye of the Wind*	35	30
58/61	*Set of* 4	85	65

(Des Cato Hibberd Design. Litho Leigh-Mardon Ltd, Melbourne)

1981 (12 May). *Opening of Animal Quarantine Station. T 16 and similar horiz designs. Multicoloured. P 13½ × 13.*

62	22 c. Type **16**	15	15
63	45 c. Unloading livestock	30	30
64	60 c. Livestock in pen	35	35
62/4	*Set of* 3	70	70

17 Consolidated "Catalina" *Guba II* Flying Boat

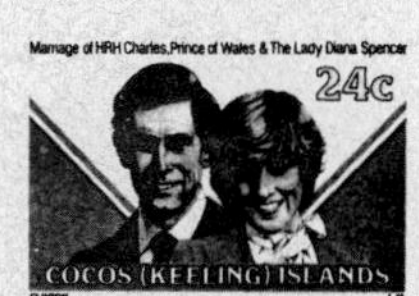

18 Prince Charles and Lady Diana Spencer

(Des R. Honisett. Litho Leigh-Mardon Ltd, Melbourne)

1981 (23 June). *Aircraft. T 17 and similar horiz designs. Multicoloured. P 13½ × 13.*

65	22 c. Type **17**	25	25
	a. Horiz strip of 5. Nos. 65/9	1·10	
66	22 c. Consolidated "Liberator" and Avro "Lancastrian"	25	25
67	22 c. Douglas "DC4 (Skymaster)" and Lockheed "Constellation"	25	25
68	22 c. Lockheed "Electra"	25	25
69	22 c. Boeing "727" airliners	25	25
65/9	*Set of* 5	1·10	1·10

Nos. 65/9 were printed together, *se-tenant*, in horizontal strips of 5 throughout the sheet.

(Des B. Clinton. Litho Leigh-Mardon Ltd, Melbourne)

1981 (29 July). *Royal Wedding. P 13½ × 13.*

70	**18**	24 c. multicoloured	40	20
71		60 c. multicoloured	85	60

19 "Angels we have heard on High"

20 *Pachyseris speciosa* and *Heliofungia actiniformis* (corals)

(Des B. Weatherhead. Litho Leigh-Mardon Ltd, Melbourne)

1981 (22 Oct). *Christmas. Scenes and Lines from Carol "Angels we have heard on High". T 19 and similar horiz designs. Multicoloured. P 13½ × 13.*

72	18 c. Type **19**	10	10
73	30 c. "Shepherds why this Jubilee?"	20	20
74	60 c. "Come to Bethlehem and see Him"	35	35
72/4	*Set of* 3	60	60

(Des B. Weatherhead. Litho Leigh-Mardon Ltd, Melbourne)

1981 (28 Dec). *150th Anniv of Charles Darwin's Voyage. T 20 and similar horiz designs. Multicoloured. P 13½ × 13.*

75	24 c. Type **20**	35	15
76	45 c. Charles Darwin in 1853 and *Pavona cactus* (coral)	55	30
77	60 c. H.M.S. *Beagle*, 1832, and *Lobophyllia hemprichii* (coral)	70	35
75/7	*Set of* 3	1·40	70
MS78	130 × 95 mm. 24 c. Cross-section of West Island; 24 c. Cross-section of Home Island	75	85

21 Queen Victoria **22** Lord Baden-Powell

(Des B. Weatherhead. Litho Cambec Press, Melbourne)

1982 (31 Mar). *125th Anniv of Annexation of Cocos (Keeling) Islands to British Empire. T* **21** *and similar horiz designs. Multicoloured. P* 13½ × 14.

79	24 c. Type **21**	20	15
80	45 c. Union flag	35	25
81	60 c. Capt. S. Fremantle (annexation visit, 1857)	40	35
79/81	*Set of* 3	85	65

(Des B. Clinton. Litho Cambec Press, Melbourne)

1982 (21 July). *75th Anniv of Boy Scout Movement. T* **22** *and similar multicoloured design. P* 13½ × 14 (27 *c.*) *or* 14 × 13½ (75 *c.*).

82	27 c. Type **22**	30	15
83	75 c. "75" and map of Cocos (Keeling) Islands (*vert*)	1·10	60

23 *Precis villida* **24** "Call His Name Immanuel"

(Des B. Hargreaves. Litho Harrison)

1982 (6 Sept)–**83**. *Butterflies and Moths. T* **23** *and similar multicoloured designs. P* 14.

84	1 c. Type **23**	25	15
85	2 c. *Cephonodes picus* (*horiz*) (6.1.83)	25	15
86	5 c. *Macroglossum corythus* (*horiz*)	35	15
87	10 c. *Chasmina candida* (6.1.83)	30	15
88	20 c. *Nagia linteola* (*horiz*) (6.4.83)	30	25
89	25 c. *Eublemma rivula* (1.7.83)	30	35
90	30 c. *Eurrhyparodes tricoloralis* (6.4.83)	35	40
91	35 c. *Hippotion boerhaviae* (*horiz*)	60	50
92	40 c. *Euploea core corinna* (6.4.83)	40	50
93	45 c. *Psara hipponalis* (*horiz*) (6.4.83)	50	60
94	50 c. *Danaus chrysippus* (*horiz*) (1.7.83)	55	70
95	55 c. *Hypolimas misippus* (6.1.83)	60	60
96	60 c. *Spodoptera litura* (1.7.83)	65	70
97	$1 *Achaea janata*	1·50	1·25
98	$2 *Hippotion velox* (*horiz*) (1.7.83)	2·00	2·25
99	$3 *Utetheisa pulchelloides* (*horiz*) (6.1.83)	2·75	2·75
84/99	*Set of* 16	10·50	10·50

(Des G. Hamori. Litho Cambec Press, Melbourne)

1982 (25 Oct). *Christmas. T* **24** *and similar horiz designs. Multicoloured. P* 13½ × 14.

100	21 c. Type **24**	20	20
101	35 c. "I bring you good tidings"	35	35
102	75 c. "Arise and flee into Egypt"	80	80
100/2	*Set of* 3	1·25	1·25

25 "God will look after us" (*Matt.* 1:20) **26** Hari Raya Celebrations

(Des R. Roberts. Litho Cambec Press, Melbourne)

1983 (25 Oct). *Christmas. Extracts from the New Testament. T* **25** *and similar vert designs. Multicoloured. P* 14 × 13½.

103	24 c. Type **25**	25	30
	a. Horiz strip of 5. Nos. 103/7	1·25	
104	24 c. "Our baby King, Jesus" (*Matthew* 2:2)	25	30
105	24 c. "Your Saviour is born" (*Luke* 2:11)	25	30
106	24 c. "Wise men followed the Star" (*Matthew* 2:9–10)	25	30
107	24 c. "And worship the Lord" (*Matthew* 2:11)	25	30
103/7	*Set of* 5	1·25	1·40

Nos. 103/7 were printed together, *se-tenant*, in horizontal strips of 5 throughout the sheet.

(Des Marg Towt. Litho Cambec Press, Melbourne)

1984 (24 Jan). *Cocos-Malay Culture.* (*1st series*). *Festivals. T* **26** *and similar vert designs. Multicoloured. P* 13½ × 13.

108	45 c. Type **26**	45	35
109	75 c. Melenggok dancing	65	50
110	85 c. Cocos-Malay wedding	75	55
108/10	*Set of* 3	1·75	1·25

See also Nos. 126/8.

27 Unpacking Barrel **28** Captain William Keeling

(Des R. Honisett. Litho Cambec Press, Melbourne)

1984 (20 Apr). *75th Anniv of Cocos Barrel Mail. T* **27** *and similar horiz designs. Multicoloured. P* 13½ × 14.

111	35 c. Type **27**	35	25
112	55 c. Jukong awaiting mail ship	60	50
113	70 c. P. & O. mail ship *Morea*	70	55
111/13	*Set of* 3	1·50	1·10
MS114	125 × 95 mm. $1 Retrieving barrel	90	1·25

(Des B. Clinton. Litho Cambec Press, Melbourne)

1984 (10 July). *375th Anniv of Discovery of Cocos (Keeling) Islands. T* **28** *and similar vert designs. Multicoloured. P* 14.

115	30 c. Type **28**	60	40
116	65 c. Keeling's ship *Hector*	1·25	90
117	95 c. Mariner's astrolabe	1·50	1·25
118	$1. 10, Map *circa* 1666	1·60	1·50
115/18	*Set of* 4	4·50	3·50

29 Malay Settlement, Home Island **30** "Rainbow" Fish

(Des E. Roberts. Litho Cambec Press, Melbourne)

1984 (21 Sept). *"Ausipex" International Stamp Exhibition, Melbourne. T* **29** *and similar horiz designs. Multicoloured. P* 13½ × 14.

119	45 c. Type **29**	65	50
120	55 c. Airstrip, West Island	75	60
MS121	130 × 95 mm. $2 Jukongs (native craft) racing	2·25	2·50

(Des R. Roberts. Litho Cambec Press, Melbourne)

1984 (31 Oct). *Christmas. T* **30** *and similar horiz designs. Multicoloured. P* 13½ × 14.

122	24 c. Type **30**	40	25
123	35 c. "Rainbow" butterfly	70	35
124	55 c. "Rainbow" bird	85	55
122/4	*Set of* 3	1·75	1·10

31 Cocos Islanders **32** Jukong building

(Des B. Weatherhead. Litho Cambec Press, Melbourne)

1984 (30 Nov). *Integration of Cocos (Keeling) Islands with Australia. Sheet* 90 × 52 *mm. containing T* **31** *and similar horiz design. Multicoloured. P* 13½ × 14.

MS125 30 c. Type **31**: 30 c. Australian flag on island 85 1·00

(Des Marg Towt. Litho Cambec Press, Melbourne)

1985 (30 Jan). *Cocos-Malay Culture* (*2nd series*). *Handicrafts. T* **32** *and similar vert designs. Multicoloured. P* 14 × 13½.

126	30 c. Type **32**	50	25
127	45 c. Blacksmithing	75	40
128	55 c. Woodcarving	85	50
126/8	*Set of* 3	1·90	1·10

33 C.S. *Scotia* **34** Red-footed Booby

(Des B. Clinton. Litho Cambec Press, Melbourne)

1985 (24 Apr). *Cable-laying Ships. T* **33** *and similar horiz designs. Multicoloured. P* 13½ × 14.

129	33 c. Type **33**	60	35
130	65 c. C.S. *Anglia*	1·40	70
131	80 c. C.S. *Patrol*	1·50	90
129/31	*Set of* 3	3·25	1·75

(Des Marg Towt. Litho Cambec Press, Melbourne)

1985 (17 July). *Birds of Cocos (Keeling) Islands. T* **34** *and similar multicoloured designs. P* 13½.

132	33 c. Type **34**	1·25	85
	a. Block of 3. Nos. 132/4	3·00	
	ab. Imperf vert (block of 3)	£500	
133	60 c. Rufous Night Heron (juvenile) (*horiz*)	1·50	1·10
134	$1 Banded Rail (*horiz*)	2·00	1·50
132/4	*Set of* 3	4·25	3·00

Nos. 132/4 were printed together, *se-tenant*, in blocks of 3 throughout the sheet, each block forming a composite design.

35 *Trochus maculatus* **36** Night Sky and Palm Trees

(Des G. Ryan. Litho Cambec Press, Melbourne)

1985 (18 Sept)–**86**. *Shells and Molluscs. T* **35** *and similar horiz designs. Multicoloured. P* 13½ × 14.

135	1 c. Type **35**	10	10
136	2 c. *Smaragdia rangiana* (29.1.86)	10	10
137	3 c. *Chama sp.* (29.1.86)	15	15
138	4 c. *Cypraea moneta* (30.7.86)	15	15
139	5 c. *Drupa morum*	15	15
140	10 c. *Conus miles* (29.1.86)	20	20
141	15 c. *Terebra maculata* (30.4.86)	25	25
142	20 c. *Fragum fragum* (30.4.86)	30	30
143	30 c. *Turbo lajonkaini* (30.4.86)	40	40
144	33 c. *Mitra fissurata*	40	40
145	40 c. *Lambis lambis* (30.4.86)	50	50
146	50 c. *Tridacna squamosa* (30.7.86)	60	60
147	60 c. *Cypraea histrio* (30.7.86)	70	70
148	$1 *Phillidia varicosa*	1·25	1·25
149	$2 *Halgerda tessellata* (30.7.86)	2·00	2·00
150	$3 *Harminoea cymbalum* (29.1.86)	3·50	3·50
135/50	*Set of* 16	9·50	9·50

(Des D. Goodwin. Litho Cambec Press, Melbourne)

1985 (30 Oct). *Christmas. Sheet* 121 × 88 *mm, containing T* **36** *and similar horiz designs. P* 13½ × 14.

MS151 27 c. × 4 multicoloured 1·75 2·00

The stamps within **MS**151 show a composite design of the night sky seen through a grove of palm trees. The position of the face value on the four stamps varies. Type **36** shows the top left design. The top right stamp shows the face value at bottom right, the bottom left at top left and the bottom right at top right.

37 Charles Darwin, *c* 1840 **38** Coconut Palm and Holly Sprigs

(Des B. Clinton. Litho Cambec Press, Melbourne)

1986 (1 Apr). *150th Anniv of Charles Darwin's Visit. T* **37** *and similar vert designs. Multicoloured. P* 14 × 13½.

152	33 c. Type **37**	60	40
153	60 c. Map of H.M.S. *Beagle*'s route Australia to Cocos Islands	1·00	80
154	$1 H.M.S. *Beagle*	1·50	1·25
152/4	*Set of* 3	2·75	2·25

(Des S. Hartshorne. Litho Cambec Press, Melbourne)

1986 (29 Oct). *Christmas. T* **38** *and similar horiz designs. Multicoloured. P* 13½ × 14.

155	30 c. Type **38**	45	30
156	90 c. Sea shell and Christmas tree bauble	1·25	1·25
157	$1 Tropical fish and bell	1·50	1·50
155/7	*Set of* 3	3·00	2·75

39 Jukong **40** Beach, Direction Island

(Des J. Earl. Litho Cambec Press, Melbourne)

1987 (28 Jan). *Sailing Craft. T* **39** *and similar horiz designs. Multicoloured. P* 13½×14.

158	36 c. Type **39**		65	65
	a. Horiz strip of 4. Nos. 158/61 ..		2·40	
159	36 c. Ocean racing yachts		65	65
160	36 c. *Sarimanok* (replica outrigger) ..		65	65
161	36 c. *Ayesha* (schooner)		65	65
158/61	.. ..	*Set of* 4	2·40	2·40

Nos. 158/61 were printed together, *se-tenant*, in horizontal strips of 5 throughout the sheet, each strip forming a composite background design.

(Des H. Missingham and R. Fletcher. Litho CPE Australia Ltd, Melbourne)

1987 (8 Apr). *Cocos Islands Scenes. T* **40** *and similar horiz designs. Multicoloured. P* 13½×14.

162	70 c. Type **40**		90	75
163	90 c. Palm forest, West Island		1·25	1·00
164	$1 Golf course		1·60	1·25
162/4	.. ..	*Set of* 3	3·50	2·75

41 Radio Transmitter and Palm Trees at Sunset　　**42** Batik Printing

(Des R. Fletcher. Litho CPE Australia Ltd, Melbourne)

1987 (29 July). *Communications. T* **41** *and similar horiz designs. Multicoloured. P* 13½×14.

165	70 c. Type **41**		90	90
166	75 c. Air liner at terminal		95	95
167	90 c. "Intelsat 5" satellite		1·25	1·25
168	$1 Airmail letter and globe		1·50	1·50
165/8	.. ..	*Set of* 4	4·25	4·25

(Des B. Clinton. Litho CPE Australia Ltd, Melbourne)

1987 (16 Sept). *Cocos (Keeling) Islands Malay Industries. T* **42** *and similar horiz designs. Multicoloured. P* 13½×14.

169	45 c. Type **42**		65	65
170	65 c. Jukong building		85	85
171	75 c. Copra production		1·00	1·00
169/71	.. ..	*Set of* 3	2·25	2·25

43 Hands releasing Peace Dove and Map of Islands　　**44** Coconut Flower

(Des Marg Towt. Litho CPE Australia Ltd, Melbourne)

1987 (28 Oct). *Christmas. T* **43** *and similar vert designs. Multicoloured. P* 14×13½.

172	30 c. Type **43**		40	30
173	90 c. Local children at Christmas party ..		1·25	85
174	$1 Island family and Christmas star ..		1·50	95
172/4	.. ..	*Set of* 3	2·75	1·90

(Des Sue Passmore. Litho CPE Australia Ltd, Melbourne)

1988 (26 Jan). *Bicentenary of Australian Settlement. Arrival of First Fleet. Square designs as Nos.* 1105/9 *of Australia but each inscribed* "COCOS (KEELING) ISLANDS" *and* "AUSTRALIA BICENTENARY".

175	37 c. Aborigines watching arrival of Fleet, Botany Bay		60	60
	a. Horiz strip of 5. Nos. 175/9		2·75	
176	37 c. Aboriginal family and anchored ships		60	60
177	37 c. Fleet arriving at Sydney Cove		60	60
178	37 c. Ship's boat		60	60
179	37 c. Raising the flag, Sydney Cove, 26 January 1788		60	60
175/9	.. ..	*Set of* 5	2·75	2·75

Nos. 175/9 were printed together, *se-tenant*, in horizontal strips of five throughout the sheet, forming a composite design.

(Des Celia Rosser. Litho CPE Australia Ltd, Melbourne)

1988 (13 Apr). *Life Cycle of the Coconut. T* **44** *and similar vert designs. Multicoloured. P* 14×13½.

180	37 c. Type **44**		50	40
181	65 c. Immature nuts		75	65
182	90 c. Coconut palm and mature nuts ..		1·10	90
183	$1 Seedlings		1·25	1·00
180/3	.. ..	*Set of* 4	3·25	2·75
MS184	102×91 mm. Nos. 180/3		3·25	3·50

MINIMUM PRICE

The minimum price quote is 10p which represents a handling charge rather than a basis for valuing common stamps. For further notes about prices see introductory pages.

45 Copra 3d. Stamp of 1963　　**46** *Pisonia grandis*

(Des R. Fletcher. Recess and litho Note Printing Branch, Reserve Bank of Australia, Melbourne)

1988 (15 June). *25th Anniv of First Cocos (Keeling) Islands Stamps. T* **45** *and similar vert designs, each showing stamp from 1963 definitive set. P* 15×14.

185	37 c. chocolate, black and azure		50	50
186	55 c. green, black and pale drab		70	70
187	65 c. ultramarine, black and pale grey-lilac		80	80
188	70 c. scarlet, black and bluish grey ..		85	85
189	90 c. deep purple, black and greenish grey ..		1·25	1·25
190	$1 deep green, black and light brown ..		1·40	1·40
185/90	.. ..	*Set of* 6	5·00	5·00

Designs:—55 c. Palms 1s.; 65 c. "Super Constellation" 5d.; 70 c. Map 8d.; 90 c. Jukong (sailboat) 2s.; $1 White Tern 2s. 3d.

(Des R. Fletcher. Litho CPE Australia Ltd, Melbourne)

1988 (29 July)–**89**. *Flora. T* **46** *and similar vert designs. Multicoloured. P* 14×13½.

191	1 c. Type **46**		10	10
192	2 c. *Cocos nucifera* (18.1.89)		10	10
193	5 c. *Morinda citrifolia*		10	10
194	10 c. *Cordia subcordata* (18.1.89)		10	10
195	30 c. *Argusia argentea* (18.1.89)		25	30
196	37 c. *Calophyllum inophyllum*		30	35
197	40 c. *Barringtonia asiatica* (19.4.89) ..		35	40
198	50 c. *Caesalpinia bonduc* (19.4.89)		40	45
199	90 c. *Terminalia catappa* (19.4.89) ..		75	80
200	$1 *Pemphis acidula* (19.4.89)		85	90
201	$2 *Scaevola sericea* (18.1.89)		1·60	1·75
202	$3 *Hibiscus tiliaceus*		2·50	2·75
191/202	.. ..	*Set of* 12	6·75	7·25

(Des R. Fletcher. Litho CPE Australia Ltd, Melbourne)

1988 (30 July). *"Sydpex '88" National Stamp Exhibition, Sydney. Sheet* 70×85 *mm. Multicoloured. P* 14×13½.

MS203	$3 As No. 202	2·75	3·00

47 Beach at Sunset　　**48** Capt. P. G. Taylor

(Des T. Bland. Litho CPE Australia Ltd, Melbourne)

1988 (12 Oct). *Christmas. P* 13½×14.

204	**47**	32 c. multicoloured		40	35
205		90 c. multicoloured		1·10	90
206		$1 multicoloured		1·25	1·00
204/6		.. ..	*Set of* 3	2·50	2·00

(Des B. Clinton. Litho CPE Australia Ltd, Melbourne)

1989 (19 July). *50th Anniv of First Indian Ocean Aerial Survey. T* **48** *and similar vert designs. P* 14×13½.

207	40 c. multicoloured		60	60
208	70 c. multicoloured		85	85
209	$1 multicoloured		1·25	1·25
210	$1.10, deep ultramarine, pale lilac & black		1·40	1·40
207/10	.. ..	*Set of* 4	3·75	3·75

Designs:—70 c. Consolidated Catalina "PBY2" *Guba II* and crew; $1 *Guba II* over Direction Island; $1.10, Unissued Australia 5s. stamp commemorating flight.

49 Jukong and Star　　**50** H.M.A.S. *Sydney* (cruiser)

(Des T. Bland. Litho Leigh-Mardon Ltd, Melbourne)

1989 (18 Oct). *Christmas. P* 14×13½.

211	**49**	35 c. multicoloured		35	40
212		80 c. multicoloured		75	80
213		$1.10, multicoloured		1·00	1·10
211/13		.. ..	*Set of* 3	1·90	2·10

(Des PCS Studios. Litho Leigh-Mardon Ltd, Melbourne)

1989 (9 Nov). *75th Anniv of Destruction of German Cruiser* Emden. *T* **50** *and similar horiz designs. Multicoloured. P* 13½×14.

214	40 c. Type **50**		40	45
	a. Horiz strip of 4, Nos. 214/17, with central label		2·75	
215	70 c. *Emden* (German cruiser)		65	70
216	$1 *Emden*'s steam launch		95	1·00
217	$1.10, H.M.A.S. *Sydney* and crest ..		1·00	1·10
214/17	.. ..	*Set of* 4	2·75	3·00
MS218	145×90 mm. Nos. 214/17		3·00	3·25

Nos. 214/17 were printed together, *se-tenant*, in horizontal strips of four stamps and one label throughout the sheet.

Cook Islands

(Rarotonga)

These are also known as the Hervey Islands. The islands of Manikiki, Rakahanga, and Pukapuka were annexed to the group in October 1890, and use the same stamps.

PRICES FOR STAMPS ON COVER TO 1945

Nos. 1/4	*from* × 5
Nos. 5/74	*from* × 4
Nos. 75/145	*from* × 3

BRITISH PROTECTORATE

1

2 Queen Makea Takau

3 White Tern or Torea

(Des F. Moss. Typo Govt Printing Office, Wellington)

1892 (19 Apr). *No wmk. P* 12½.

A. *Toned paper.* B. *White paper.*

			A.		B.	
1	**1**	1d. black	26·00	30·00	26·00	30·00
		a. Imperf between (vert pair)	£8500	—	†	
2		1½d. mauve	38·00	38·00	38·00	38·00
		a. Imperf (pair)	†		£12000	—
3		2½d. blue	38·00	38·00	38·00	38·00
4		10d. carmine	£140	£130	£160	£130
1/4		.. .. .. *Set of* 4	£200	£200	£225	£200

Nos. 1/4 were printed in sheets of 60 (6×10) from plates constructed from a matrix of 6 slightly different types.

(Eng A. E. Cousins. Typo Govt Printing Office, Wellington)

1893 (28 July)–**1900.** *W* **12***b of New Zealand* (N Z *and Star wide apart*) (*sideways on T* **3**). (*a*) *P* 12 × 11½.

5	**2**	1d. brown	24·00	30·00
6		1d. blue (3.4.94)	6·00	1·50
		a. Perf 12 × 11½ and 12½ mixed ..	†	£800
7		1½d. mauve	6·00	6·00
8		2½d. rose	23·00	23·00
		a. Rose-carmine	55·00	55·00
		ab. Perf 12 × 11½ and 12½ mixed ..	£1400	
9		5d. olive-black	12·00	13·00
10		10d. green	48·00	48·00
5/10		.. .. *Set of* 6	£110	£110

(*b*) *P* 11 (July 1896–1900)

11	**3**	½d. steel blue (1st setting) (11.99) ..	15·00	20·00
		a. Upper right "d" omitted	£1000	
		b. Second setting	7·00	9·00
		ba. Deep blue (1900)	3·50	4·75
12	**2**	1d. blue	3·00	4·50
13		1d. deep brown/*cream* (4.99)	6·50	12·00
		a. Wmk sideways		
		b. Bistre-brown (1900)		
14		1½d. deep lilac	4·75	6·00
		a. Deep mauve (1900)	4·75	6·00
15	**3**	2d. brown/*thin toned* (7.98)	6·00	6·50
		a. Deep brown (1900)	4·50	6·50
16	**2**	2½d. pale rose	32·00	38·00
		a. Deep rose (1900)	9·00	9·00
17		5d. olive-black	16·00	17·00
18	**3**	6d. purple/*thin toned* (7.98)	20·00	28·00
		a. Bright purple (1900)	14·00	19·00
19	**2**	10d. green	13·00	20·00
20	**3**	1s. red/*thin toned* (7.98)	50·00	70·00
		a. Deep carmine (1900)	38·00	48·00
11/20*a*		.. .. *Set of* 10	£100	£130

Examples of the 1d., 1½d., 2½d. and 5d. perforated 11 and on laid paper are perforation trials.

On the 1st setting of the ½d. the face values are misplaced in each corner. As corrected in the second setting the face values are correctly positioned in each corner.

ONE
HALF
PENNY

(4)

(5)

1899 (24 Apr). *No.* 12 *surch with T* **4** *by Govt Printer, Rarotonga.*

21	**2**	½d. on 1d. blue	32·00	42·00
		a. Surch inverted	£800	£850
		b. Surch double	£900	£750

NEW ZEALAND TERRITORY

1901 (8 Oct). *No.* 13 *optd with T* **5** *by Govt Printer, Rarotonga.*

22	**2**	1d. brown	£130	£125
		a. Crown inverted	£1500	£1300
		c. Optd with crown twice	£1400	£1500

1902. *No wmk. P* 11.

(*a*) *Medium white Cowan paper* (Feb)

23	**3**	½d. blue-green	5·50	6·50
24	**2**	1d. dull rose	8·00	10·00

(*b*) *Thick white Pirie paper* (May)

25	**3**	½d. yellow-green	3·25	3·50
		a. Imperf horiz (vert pair)	£1100	
26	**2**	1d. rose-red	8·00	10·00
		a. Rose-lake	7·50	6·50
27		2½d. dull blue	7·00	18·00

1902 (Sept). *W* **43** *of New Zealand* (*single-lined* NZ *and Star, close together; sideways on T* **2**). *P* 11.

28	**3**	½d. yellow-green	1·40	3·25
		a. Grey-green	14·00	22·00
29	**2**	1d. rose-pink	1·75	3·00
30		1½d. deep mauve	2·50	7·00
31	**3**	2d. deep brown	3·75	9·50
		a. No figures of value	£1600	£2000
		b. Perf 11 × 14	£600	
32	**2**	2½d. deep blue	3·75	6·50
33		5d. olive-black	30·00	35·00
34	**3**	6d. purple	24·00	27·00
35	**2**	10d. green	48·00	70·00
36	**3**	1s. carmine	48·00	60·00
		a. Perf 11 × 14	£600	
28/36		.. .. *Set of* 9	£150	£200

1909–11. *W* **43** *of New Zealand.*

37	**3**	½d. green (*p* 14½×14) (1911)	4·50	6·00
38	**2**	1d. deep red (*p* 14)	14·00	20·00
		a. Wmk sideways (24.12.09)	7·50	9·00

1913–19. *W* **43** *of New Zealand* (*sideways on T* **3**). *Chalk-surfaced paper.*

39	**3**	½d. deep green (*p* 14) (1915)	1·25	7·00
		a. Wmk upright	1·50	7·00
40	**2**	1d. red (*p* 14) (7.13)	2·00	3·75
41		1d. red (*p* 14 × 14½) (1914)	4·00	4·75
42		1½d. deep mauve (*p* 14) (1915)	55·00	40·00
43		1½d. deep mauve (*p* 14 × 15) (1916) ..	4·00	3·25
44	**3**	2d. deep brown (*p* 15 × 14) (1919) ..	5·00	24·00
45	**2**	10d. green (*p* 14 × 15) (1918)	13·00	42·00
46	**3**	1s. carmine (*p* 15 × 14) (1919)	20·00	45·00
39/46		.. .. *Set of* 6	40·00	£110

RAROTONGA

APA PENE

(8)

1919 (Apr–July). *Contemporary stamps of New Zealand surch as T* **8**.

(*a*) *Typographed. P* 14 × 15

50	**61**	½d. green (R.) (June)	20	45
51	**52**	1d. carmine (B.) (June)	20	40
52	**61**	1½d. orange-brown (R.) (June)	25	75
53		2d. yellow (R.)	30	70
54		3d. chocolate (B.) (July)	1·25	2·50

(*b*) *Recess.* (*a*) *P* 14 × 14½. (*b*) *P* 14 × 13½

55	**60**	2½d. blue (R.) (*a*) (June)	95	2·00
		a. Vert pair. Nos. 55/6	20·00	32·00
56		2½d. blue (R.) (*b*)	1·60	5·00
57		3d. chocolate (B.) (*a*)	70	1·50
		a. Vert pair. Nos. 57/8	20·00	38·00
58		3d. chocolate (B.) (*b*)	1·00	4·50
59		4d. violet (B.) (*a*)	1·00	3·75
		a. Vert pair. Nos. 59/60	22·00	45·00
60		4d. violet (B.) (*b*)	1·50	5·50
61		4½d. deep green (B.) (*a*)	1·10	5·00
		a. Vert pair. Nos. 61/2	25·00	48·00
62		4½d. deep green (B.) (*b*)	2·00	5·50
63		6d. carmine (B.) (*a*) (June)	1·50	5·00
		a. Vert pair. Nos. 63/4	40·00	65·00
64		6d. carmine (B.) (*b*)	2·50	6·50
65		7½d. red-brown (B.) (*b*)	1·25	5·50
66		9d. sage-green (R.) (*a*)	1·75	6·50
		a. Vert pair. Nos. 66/7	50·00	80·00
67		9d. sage-green (R.) (*b*)	3·25	6·50
68		1s. vermilion (B.) (*a*) (June)	2·75	11·00
		a. Vert pair. Nos. 68/9	65·00	95·00
69		1s. vermilion (B.) (*b*)	7·00	16·00
50/68 (*cheapest*)		.. .. .. *Set of* 12	11·00	38·00

9 Capt. Cook landing

10 Wharf at Avarua

11 "Capt. Cook" (Dance)

12 Palm Tree

13 Huts at Arorangi

14 Avarua Harbour

(Des, eng and recess Perkins, Bacon & Co)

1920 (23 Aug). *No wmk. P* 14.

70	**9**	½d. black and green	2·50	6·00
71	**10**	1d. black and carmine-red	1·60	4·00
72	**11**	1½d. black and dull blue	6·50	8·50
73	**12**	3d. black and chocolate	2·00	5·50
74	**13**	6d. brown and yellow-orange	1·75	8·00
75	**14**	1s. black and violet	5·00	17·00
70/5		.. .. *Set of* 6	17·00	45·00

Examples of the 1d. and 1s. with centre inverted were not supplied to the Post Office.

RAROTONGA

(15)

RAROTONGA

Trimmed overprint (R. 1/6 and R. 3/7)

1921 (Oct)–**23**. *Postal Fiscal stamps as Type* F **4** *of New Zealand optd with T* **15**. *W* **43** (*sideways*). *Chalk-surfaced "De La Rue" paper. P* 14½×14.

76	2s. deep blue (R.)	26·00	38·00
	a. Trimmed opt	45·00	
	b. Carmine opt (1923)	£140	£150
	ba. Trimmed opt	£250	
77	2s. 6d. grey-brown (B.)	18·00	35·00
	a. Trimmed opt	30·00	
78	5s. yellow-green (R.)	26·00	42·00
	a. Trimmed opt	45·00	
79	10s. maroon (B.)	45·00	50·00
	a. Trimmed opt	70·00	
80	£1 rose-carmine (B.)	75·00	90·00
	a. Trimmed opt	£110	
76/80	.. .. *Set of* 5	£170	£225

See also Nos. 85/9.

16 Te Po, Rarotongan Chief

17 Harbour, Rarotonga and Mt Ikurangi

(2½d. from a print; 4d. des A. H. Messenger. Plates by P.B. Recess Govt Ptg Office, Wellington)

1924–27. *W* **43** *of New Zealand. P* 14.

81	**9**	½d. black and green (13.5.26)	3·00	3·50
82	**10**	1d. black and deep carmine (10.11.24)	3·25	1·50
83	**16**	2½d. red-brown and steel blue (15.10.27)	2·25	11·00
84	**17**	4d. green and violet (15.10.27) ..	2·75	11·00
81/4		.. .. *Set of* 4	10·00	24·00

1926 (Feb–May). *As Nos.* 76/80, *but thick, opaque white chalk-surfaced "Cowan" paper.*

85	2s. blue (C.)	£100	£120
	a. Trimmed opt	£160	
86	2s. 6d. deep grey-brown (B.)	50·00	60·00
87	5s. yellow-green (R.) (May)	35·00	50·00
	a. Trimmed opt	60·00	
88	10s. brown-red (B.) (May)	48·00	65·00
89	£1 rose-pink (B.) (May)	75·00	85·00
85/9	.. .. *Set of* 5	£275	£350

1926–28. *T* **72** (*"Admiral" Type*) *of New Zealand, overprinted with T* **15**. (*a*) *"Jones" chalk-surfaced paper.*

90	2s. deep blue (R.) (10.26)	10·00	38·00

(*b*) *"Cowan" thick chalk-surfaced paper*

91	2s. light blue (R.) (18.6.27)	15·00	38·00
92	3s. bright mauve (R.) (30.1.28)	16·00	40·00
90/2	.. .. *Set of* 3	38·00	£100

TWO PENCE (18)

COOK ISLANDS. (19)

1931 (Mar). *Surch with T* **18**. *P* 14. (*a*) *No wmk.*

93	**11**	2d. on 1½d. black and blue (R.) ..	3·50	2·25

(*b*) *W* **43** *of New Zealand*

94	**11**	2d. on 1½d. black and blue (R.) ..	1·00	3·25

1931 (12 Nov)–**32.** *Postal Fiscal stamps as Type* F **6** *of New Zealand. W* **43**. *Thick, opaque, white chalk-faced "Cowan" paper. P* 14.

(*a*) *Optd with T* **15**

95	2s. 6d. deep brown (B.)	7·50	17·00
96	5s. green (R.)	16·00	38·00
97	10s. carmine-lake (B.)	30·00	55·00
98	£1 pink (B.)	55·00	80·00

(*b*) *Optd with T* **19** (3.32)

98*a*	£3 green (R.)	80·00	£140
98*b*	£5 blue (R.)	£170	£225

The £3 and £5 values were mainly used for fiscal purposes.

20 Capt. Cook landing

21 Capt. Cook

22 Double Maori Canoe

23 Natives working Cargo

24 Port of Avarua

25 R.M.S. *Monowai*

26 King George V

(Des L. C. Mitchell. Recess P.B.)

1932 (15 Mar–2 May). *No wmk. P* 13.

No.	Type	Description		
99	**20**	½d. black and deep green	2·25	6·50
		a. Perf 14	28·00	55·00
100	**21**	1d. black and lake	2·25	2·75
		a. Centre inverted	£2000	£2000
		b. Perf 13 and 14 mixed	£160	£180
		c. Perf 14	15·00	16·00
101	**22**	2d. black and brown	2·00	3·75
		a. Perf 14	8·00	11·00
102	**23**	2½d. black and deep blue	5·00	22·00
		a. Perf 14	11·00	22·00
103	**24**	4d. black and bright blue	15·00	25·00
		a. Perf 14	7·00	25·00
		b. Perf 14×13	48·00	75·00
		c. Perf comp of 14 and 13	60·00	
104	**25**	6d. black and orange	24·00	38·00
		a. Perf 14	2·75	9·00
105	**26**	1s. black and violet (*p* 14) (2 May)	4·25	15·00
99/105		*Set of* 7	23·00	75·00

No. 100b comes from the first vertical column of one sheet which was reperforated 14 at left.

(Recess from P.B. plates at Govt Printing Office, Wellington)

1933–36. *W* **43** *of New Zealand* (*Single* N Z *and Star*). *P* 14.

No.	Type	Description		
106	**20**	½d. black and deep green	40	70
107	**21**	1d. black and scarlet (1935)	45	70
108	**22**	2d. black and brown (1936)	35	20
109	**23**	2½d. black and deep blue	25	80
110	**24**	4d. black and bright blue	25	35
111	**25**	6d. black and orange-yellow (1936)	25	80
112	**26**	1s. black and violet (1936)	13·50	17·00
106/12		*Set of* 7	14·00	20·00

SILVER JUBILEE
OF
KING GEORGE V.
1910 - 1935.
(27)

Normal letters
B K E N
B K E N
Narrow letters

1935 (7 May). *Silver Jubilee. Optd with T* **27** (*wider vertical spacing on* 6d.). *Colours changed. W* **43** *of New Zealand. P* 14.

No.	Type	Description		
113	**21**	1d. red-brown and lake	50	70
		a. Narrow "K" in "KING"	2·75	
		b. Narrow "B" in "JUBILEE"	3·75	
114	**23**	2½d. dull and deep blue (R.)	75	1·00
		a. Narrow first "E" in "GEORGE"	3·50	5·00
115	**25**	6d. green and orange	2·75	4·50
		a. Narrow "N" in "KING"	16·00	
113/15		*Set of* 3	3·50	5·50

1936 (15 July)–**44.** *Stamps of New Zealand optd with T* **19**. *W* **43**.

(*a*) *Thick, white, opaque chalk-surfaced "Cowan" paper. P* 14

(i) *As T* **72** (*"Admiral" type*)

No.	Description		
116	2s. blue	12·00	32·00
117	3s. mauve	13·00	38·00

(ii) *As Type* F **6** (*"Arms" type*)

No.	Description		
118	2s. 6d. deep brown	15·00	32·00
119	5s. green (R.)	16·00	35·00
120	10s. carmine-lake	32·00	55·00
121	£1 pink	50·00	80·00
118/21	*Set of* 4	£100	£180

(*b*) *Thin, hard, chalk-surfaced "Wiggins, Teape" paper*

No.	Description		
122	2s. 6d. dull brown (12.40)	70·00	65·00
123	5s. green (R.) (10.40)	£200	£200
123*a*	10s. pale carmine-lake (11.44)	£120	£120
123*b*	£3 green (R.) (date?)	£300	£400
122/3*b*	*Set of* 4	£600	£700

COOK
IS'DS.
(28)

IS'DS.
Small second "S"
(R. 1/2)

1937 (1 June). *Coronation. Nos.* 599/601 *of New Zealand optd with T* **28**.

No.	Type	Description		
124	**106**	1d. carmine	30	10
		a. Small second "S"	3·50	
125		2½d. Prussian blue	50	20
		a. Small second "S"	4·50	
126		6d. red-orange	50	20
		a. Small second "S"	4·50	
124/6		*Set of* 3	1·10	45

29 King George VI

30 Native Village

31 Native Canoe

32 Tropical Landscape

(Des J. Berry (2s., 3s., and frame of 1s.). Eng B.W. Recess Govt Ptg. Office, Wellington)

1938 (2 May). *W* **43** *of New Zealand. P* 14.

No.	Type	Description		
127	**29**	1s. black and violet	2·75	2·25
128	**30**	2s. black and red-brown	5·50	4·50
129	**31**	3s. light blue and emerald-green	12·00	8·00
127/9		*Set of* 3	18·00	13·50

(Recess B.W.)

1940 (2 Sept). *Surch as in T* **32**. *W* **98** *of New Zealand. P* 13½ × 14.

No.	Type	Description		
130	**32**	3d. on 1½d. black and purple	10	15

Type **32** was not issued without surcharge.

1943–50. *Postal Fiscal stamps as Type* F **6** *of New Zealand optd with T* **19**. *W* **98**. *"Wiggins, Teape" chalk-surfaced paper. P* 14.

No.	Description		
131	2s. 6d. dull brown (3.46)	5·50	9·00
132	5s. green (R.) (11.43)	5·50	12·00
133	10s. carmine-lake (10.48)	28·00	38·00
134	£1 pink (11.47)	29·00	38·00
135	£3 green (R.) (1946?)	50·00	£130
136	£5 blue (R.) (25.10.50)	£200	£250
131/6	*Set of* 6	£275	£425

The £3 and £5 were mainly used for fiscal purposes.

For technical printing reasons all values also exist with watermark inverted. The prices quoted are for the cheapest form.

(Recess Govt Ptg Office, Wellington)

1944–46. *W* **98** *of New Zealand (sideways on* ½d. 1d., 1s., *and* 2s.). *P* 14.

No.	Type	Description		
137	**20**	½d. black and deep green (11.44)	85	1·50
138	**21**	1d. black and scarlet (3.45)	2·00	35
139	**22**	2d. black and brown (2.46)	1·25	1·25
140	**23**	2½d. black and deep blue (5.45)	65	80
141	**24**	4d. black and blue (4.44)	1·25	1·75
142	**25**	6d. black and orange (6.44)	90	60
143	**29**	1s. black and violet (9.44)	90	90
144	**30**	2s. black and red-brown (8.45)	8·00	8·50
145	**31**	3s. light blue and emerald-green (6.45)	12·00	15·00
137/45		*Set of* 9	25·00	28·00

COOK
ISLANDS
(33)

1946 (1 June). *Peace. Nos.* 668, 670, 674/5 *of New Zealand optd with T* **33** (*reading up and down at sides on* 2d.).

No.	Description		
146	1d. green	10	10
147	2d. purple (B.)	10	15
148	6d. chocolate and vermilion	15	15
149	8d. black and carmine (B.)	15	15
146/9	*Set of* 4	45	45

34 Ngatangiia Channel, Rarotonga

41 Map and Statue of Capt. Cook

(Des J. Berry. Recess Waterlow)

1949 (1 Aug)–**61.** *T* **34, 41** *and similar designs. W* **98** *of New Zealand (sideways on shilling values). P* 13½ × 13 (*horiz*) *or* 13 × 13½ (*vert*).

No.	Description		
150	½d. violet and brown	10	45
151	1d. chestnut and green	1·25	85
152	2d. reddish brown and scarlet	60	80
153	3d. green and ultramarine	35	1·00
	a. Wmk sideways (white opaque paper) (22.5.61)	2·00	2·50
154	5d. emerald-green and violet	70	90
155	6d. black and carmine	1·00	1·25
156	8d. olive-green and orange	40	2·25
157	1s. light blue and chocolate	3·75	2·75
158	2s. yellow-brown and carmine	3·00	6·00
159	3s. light blue and bluish green	4·75	8·00
150/9	*Set of* 10	14·00	22·00

Designs: *Horiz*—1d. Capt. Cook and map of Hervey Islands; 2d. Rarotonga and Revd. John Williams; 3d. Aitutaki and Palm trees; 5d. Rarotonga airfield; 6d. Penrhyn village; 8d. Native hut. *Vert*—2s. Native hut and palms; 3s. M.V. *Matua*.

See note on white opaque paper below No. 736 of New Zealand.

1953 (25 May). *Coronation. As Nos.* 715 *and* 717 *of New Zealand, but inscr* "COOK ISLANDS".

No.	Description		
160	3d. brown	80	45
161	6d. slate-grey	1·10	80

1/6
(44)

1960 (1 Apr). *No.* 154 *surch with T* **44**.

No.	Description		
162	1s. 6d. on 5d. emerald-green and violet	15	30

45 Tiare Maori

48 White Tern

52 Queen Elizabeth II

53 Island Scene

(Des J. Berry. Recess (1s. 6d.), litho (others) B.W.)

1963 (4 June). *T* **45, 48, 52/3** *and similar designs. Wmk T* **98** *of New Zealand (sideways). P* 13½ × 13 (1*d.*, 2*d.*, 8*d.*), 13 × 13½ (3*d.*, 5*d.*, 6*d.*, 1*s.*) *or* 13½ (*others*).

No.	Description		
163	1d. emerald-green and yellow	20	10
164	2d. brown-red and yellow	8	10
165	3d. yellow, yellow-green & reddish violet	25	10
166	5d. blue and black	2·25	30
167	6d. red, yellow and green	75	20
168	8d. black and blue	85	45
169	1s. orange-yellow and yellow-green	40	20
170	1s. 6d. bluish violet	2·75	2·00
171	2s. bistre-brown and grey-blue	75	75
172	3s. black and yellow-green	1·25	1·00
173	5s. bistre-brown and blue	8·50	3·25
163/73	*Set of* 11	16·00	7·50

Designs: *Vert* (*as T* **45**)—2d. Fishing god; 8d. Skipjack Tuna. *Horiz* (*as T* **48**)—3d. Frangipani; 6d. Hibiscus; 1s. Oranges. (*As T* **53**)—3s. Administration Centre, Mangaia; 5s. Rarotonga.

56 Eclipse and Palm

57 N.Z. Ensign and Map

(Des L. C. Mitchell. Litho B.W.)

1965 (31 May). *Solar Eclipse Observation, Manuae Island. W* **98** *of New Zealand. P* 13½.

No.	Type	Description		
174	**56**	6d. black, yellow and light blue	10	10

SELF-GOVERNMENT

(Des R. M. Conly (4d.), L. C. Mitchell (10d., 1s.), J. Berry (1s. 9d.). Litho B.W.)

1965 (16 Sept). *Internal Self-Government. T* **57** *and similar horiz designs. W* **98** *of New Zealand (sideways). P* 13½.

No.	Description		
175	4d. red and blue	10	10
176	10d. multicoloured	10	10
177	1s. multicoloured	10	10
178	1s. 9d. multicoloured	15	40
175/8	*Set of* 4	40	60

Designs:—10d. London Missionary Society Church; 1s. Proclamation of Cession, 1900; 1s. 9d. Nikao School.

In Memoriam
SIR WINSTON CHURCHILL
1874 - 1965
(61)

Airmail
(62)

1966 (24 Jan). *Churchill Commemoration. Nos.* 171/3 *and* 175/7 *optd with T* **61**, *in red.*

179 4d. red and blue 75 30
a. "l" for "1" in "1874" .. .. .. 3·00
180 10d. multicoloured .. .. .. 1·50 45
a. Opt inverted £200
b. "l" for "1" in "1874" .. .. .. 5·00
181 1s. multicoloured .. .. .. 1·50 65
a. Opt inverted £130
b. "l" for "1" in "1874" .. .. .. 5·00
182 2s. bistre-brown and grey-blue .. .. 1·50 1·25
a. "l" for "1" in "1874" .. .. .. 5·00
183 3s. black and yellow-green .. .. 1·50 1·25
a. "l" for "1" in "1874" .. .. .. 5·00
184 5s. bistre-brown and blue .. .. 2·00 1·75
a. "l" for "1" in "1874" .. .. .. 10·00
179/84 .. .. *Set of* 6 8·00 5·00

The lower case "l" for "1" in "1874" occurred on R. 6/5 for all values and additionally on R. 12/5 for the 2s., 3s. and 5s.

1966 (22 Apr). *Air. Various stamps optd with T* **62** *or surch also.*

185 6d. red, yellow and green (No. 167) .. .. 1·25 20
186 7d. on 8d. black and blue (No. 168) .. .. 1·25 25
187 10d. on 3d. yellow, yellow-green and reddish violet (No. 165) .. .. 1·00 15
188 1s. orange-yellow and yellow-green (No. 169) 1·00 15
189 1s. 6d. bluish violet (No. 170) .. .. 1·25 1·25
190 2s. 3d. on 3s. black and yellow-green (No. 172) 1·00 65
191 5s. bistre-brown and blue (No. 173) .. .. 1·50 1·50
192 10s. on 2s. bistre-brown and grey-blue (No. 171) .. .. 1·75 6·00
193 £1 pink (No. 134) .. .. 9·00 15·00
a. Aeroplane omitted .. .. .. 25·00 35·00
185/93 .. .. *Set of* 9 17·00 23·00

No. 193a occurred in all stamps of the last vertical row as insufficient aeroplane symbols were available. There are also numerous other varieties on all values, notably aeroplanes of different sizes and broken first "i" with dot missing owing to damaged type.

PRINTERS. The following stamps were printed in photogravure by Heraclio Fournier, Spain *except where otherwise stated.*

63 "Adoration of the Magi" (Fra Angelico)

1966 (28 Nov). *Christmas. T* **63** *and similar multicoloured designs.*
A. *P* 13 × 12 (*horiz*) *or* 12 × 13 (*vert*).
B. *P* 13 × 14½ (*horiz*) *or* 14½ × 13 (*vert*).

		A		B	
194	1d. Type **63**	25	20	10	10
195	2d. "The Nativity" (Memling) (*vert*)	11·00	6·00	10	10
196	4d. "Adoration of the Magi" (Velazquez) (*horiz*) ..	60	50	10	10
197	10d. "Adoration of the Magi" (Bosch) (*horiz*) ..	2·00	1·50	10	10
198	1s. 6d. "Adoration of the Shepherds" (J. de Ribera) (*vert*)	5·50	3·00	20	15
194/8	.. .. .. *Set of* 5	17·00	10·00	40	30

68 Tennis, and Queen Elizabeth II

(Des V. Whiteley)

1967 (12 Jan). *2nd South Pacific Games, Nouméa. T* **68** *and similar horiz designs in orange-brown, black and new blue* (1d.) *or multicoloured* (*others*). *P* 13½. (*a*) *Postage.*

199 ½d. Type **68** 10 10
200 1d. Netball and Games emblem 10 10
201 4d. Boxing and Cook Islands' team badge .. 10 10
202 7d. Football and Queen Elizabeth II 10 10

(*b*) *Air*

203 10d. Running and Games emblem 10 10
204 2s. 3d. Running and Cook Islands' team badge 15 10
199/204 .. .. *Set of* 6 35 20

(New Currency, 100 cents = 1 dollar)

1c (74) 2½c (I) 2½c (II)

These occur on alternative vertical rows within the sheet.

1967 (3 Apr–6 June). *Decimal Currency. Nos.* 134/6, 163/70 *and* 172/5 *surch as T* **74** *by the Government Printer. Sterling values unobliterated except No.* 218.

205 1 c. on 1d. emerald-green & yellow (4.5) .. 45 1·10
206 2 c. on 2d. brown-red & yellow 10 10
207 2½ c. on 3d. yellow, yellow-green and reddish violet (I) 20 10
208 2½ c. on 3d. yellow, yellow-green and reddish violet (II) 20 10
209 3 c. on 4d. red and blue 15 10
210 4 c. on 5d. blue and black (4.5) 80 20
211 5 c. on 6d. red, yellow and green 15 10
212 5 c. on 6d. black, yellow and light blue .. 2·00 40
213 7 c. on 8d. black and blue 15 10
214 10 c. on 1s. orange-yellow & yellow-green .. 15 10
215 15 c. on 1s. 6d. bluish violet (R.) (4.5.67) .. 2·00 1·00
216 30 c. on 3s. black and yellow-green (R.) (4.5.67) 12·00 4·50
217 50 c. on 5s. bistre-brown and blue (R.) (4.5.67) 3·50 1·25
218 $1 and 10s. on 10d. multicoloured (R.) (4.5.67) .. .. 12·00 6·50
219 $2 on £1 pink (R.) (6.6.67) £120 £120
220 $6 on £3 green (R.) (6.6.67) £170 £170
221 $10 on £5 blue (R.) (6.6.67) £250 £250
205/18 .. .. *Set of* 14 28·00 13·00

The surcharge on No. 218 is $1 and its equivalent of 10s. in the old currency. The "10d." is obliterated by three bars.

A large number of minor varieties exist in these surcharges, such as wrong fount letter "C" and figures.

75 Village Scene. Cook Islands 1d. Stamp of 1892 and Queen Victoria (from "Penny Black")

(Des V. Whiteley)

1967 (3 July). *75th Anniv of First Cook Islands Stamps. T* **75** *and similar horiz designs. Multicoloured. P* 13½.

222 1 c. (1d.) Type **75** 10 10
223 3 c. (4d.) Post Office, Avarua, Rarotonga and Queen Elizabeth II 15 10
224 8 c. (10d.) Avarua, Rarotonga and Cook Islands 10d. stamp of 1892 .. .. 30 10
225 18 c. (1s. 9d.) S.S. *Moana Roa*, "DC-3" aircraft, map and Captain Cook .. .. 1·00 20
222/5 .. .. *Set of* 4 1·40 30
MS226 134 × 109 mm. Nos. 222/5 .. .. 2·00 2·50

The face values are expressed in decimal currency and in the sterling equivalent.

Each value was issued in sheets of 8 stamps and 1 label.

79 Hibiscus **80** Queen Elizabeth II

81 Queen Elizabeth and Flowers

Two types of $4

I. Value 32½ mm long. Coarse screen.
II. Value 33½ mm long. Finer screen.

(Floral designs from paintings by Mrs. Kay W. Billings)

1967–71. *Multicoloured designs as T* **79/81**. *P* 14 × 13½. A. *Without fluorescent security markings.* B. *With fluorescent security markings.*

		A		B	
227	½ c. Type **79**	10	10	15	10
228	1 c. *Hibiscus syriacus* (27 × 37 *mm*)	10	10	15	10
229	2 c. Frangipani (27 × 37 *mm*)	10	10	15	10
230	2½ c. *Clitoria ternatea* (27 × 37 *mm*)	15	10	15	10
231	3 c. "Suva Queen" (27 × 37 *mm*)	25	10	25	10
232	4 c. Water Lily ("WALTER LILY") (27 × 37 *mm*) ..	45	60	†	
233	4 c. Water Lily (27 × 37 *mm*)	60	40	60	10
234	5 c. *Bauhinia bipinnata rosea* (27 × 37 *mm*)	15	10	15	10
235	6 c. Hibiscus (27 × 37 *mm*) ..	20	10	20	10
236	8 c. *Allamanda cathartica* (27 × 37 *mm*)	25	10	25	10
237	9 c. Stephanotis (27 × 37 *mm*)	25	10	25	10
238	10 c. *Poinciana regia flamboyant* (27 × 37 *mm*)	25	10	25	10
239	15 c. Frangipani (27 × 37 *mm*)	40	10	40	10
240	20 c. Thunbergia (27 × 37 *mm*)	1·00	40	1·00	25
241	25 c. Canna Lily (27 × 37 *mm*)	80	25	80	15
242	30 c. *Euphorbia pulcherrima poinsettia* (27 × 37 *mm*) ..	65	50	1·00	40
243	50 c. *Gardinia taitensis* (27 × 37 *mm*)	90	55	1·00	40
244	$1 Type **80**	2·00	80	1·75	80
245	$2 Type **80**	4·00	1·50	3·50	1·50
246	$4 Type **81** (I)	3·00	3·50	45·00	48·00
246c	$4 Type **81** (II)	†		11·00	8·50
247	$6 Type **81**	3·50	5·00	12·00	6·00
247c	$8 Type **81**	8·00	12·00	17·00	10·00
248	$10 Type **81**	8·00	12·00	19·00	12·00
227A/243A	.. .. *Set of* 17	5·75	2·75		
227B/243B	.. .. *Set of* 16			6·00	1·75

Dates of issue:—Nos. 227/238A, 31.7.67; Nos. 239/243A, 11.8.67; Nos. 244/245A, 31.8.67; Nos. 246/247A, 30.4.68; No. 248A, 12.7.68; No. 247cA, 21.4.69; Nos. 227/243B, 9.2.70; Nos. 244/245B, 12.10.70; No. 246cB, 14.7.71; No. 246B, 11.11.70; No. 247B, 12.2.71; No. 247cB, 3.5.71; No. 248B, 14.6.71.

The "WALTER" spelling error occurred on all stamps in one of the four post office sheets which went to make up the printing sheet and this was corrected in later supplies.

FLUORESCENT PAPER. This is on paper treated with fluorescent security markings, in the form of faint multiple coats of arms. Stamps exist with these markings inverted. In addition an invisible synthetic gum has been used which prevents curling and is suitable for use in the tropics without interleaving the sheets.

Some of the above are known with these markings omitted and can be distinguished when in unused condition from the original printings without markings by their synthetic invisible gum.

97 "Ia Orana Maria"

1967 (24 Oct). *Gauguin's Polynesian Paintings. T* **97** *and similar designs. Multicoloured. P* 13.

249 1 c. Type **97** 10 10
250 3 c. "Riders on the Beach" 10 10
251 5 c. "Still Life with Flowers" 10 10
252 8 c. "Whispered Words" 15 10
253 15 c. "Maternity" 25 10
254 22 c. "Why are you angry?" 30 15
249/54 .. .. *Set of* 6 75 35
MS255 156 × 132 mm. Nos. 249/54 .. .. 85 1·25

The 5 c. includes an inset portrait of Queen Elizabeth.

98 "The Holy Family" (Rubens)

HURRICANE
RELIEF
PLUS 5c
(99)

1967 (4 Dec). *Christmas. Renaissance Paintings. T* **98** *and similar designs. Multicoloured. P* 12 × 13.

256 1 c. Type **98** 10 10
257 3 c. "Adoration of the Magi" (Dürer) 10 10
258 4 c. "The Lucca Madonna" (J. van Eyck) .. 10 10
259 8 c. "The Adoration of the Shepherds" (J. da Bassano) 15 10
260 15 c. "Adoration of the Shepherds" (El Greco) 25 10
261 25 c. "Madonna and Child" (Correggio) .. 30 10
256/61 .. .. *Set of* 6 80 25

1968 (12 Feb). *Hurricane Relief. Nos.* 231A, 233A, 251, 238A, 241A *and* 243/4A *surch as T* **99** *by Govt Printer, Rarotonga.*

262 3 c. + 1 c. "Suva Queen" 15 10
263 4 c. + 1 c. Water Lily 15 10
264 5 c. + 2 c. "Still Life with Flowers" 15 10
a. Black surch albino .. .. ..
265 10 c. + 2 c. *Poinciana regia flamboyant* .. 15 10
266 25 c. + 5 c. Canna Lily 25 10
267 50 c. + 10 c. *Gardinia taitensis* 35 15
268 $1 + 10 c. Type **80** 60 30
262/8 .. .. *Set of* 7 1·60 75

The surcharge on No. 268 is as T **99**, but with seriffed letters. On No. 264 silver blocking obliterates the design area around the lettering.

PRICES OF SETS

Set prices are given for many issues, generally those containing three stamps or more. Definitive sets include one of each value or major colour change, but do not cover different perforations, die types or minor shades. Where a choice is possible the set prices are based on the cheapest versions of the stamps included in the listings.

100 "Matavai Bay, Tahiti" (J. Barralet)

101 *"Resolution* and *Discovery"* (J. Webber)

(Des J. Berry)

1968 (12 Sept). *Bicentenary of Captain Cook's First Voyage of Discovery. Multicoloured. Invisible gum. P* 13.

(*a*) *Postage. Vert designs as T* **100**

269	½ c. Type **100**	10	10
270	1 c. "Island of Huaheine" (John Cleveley)	15	10
271	2 c. "Town of St. Peter and St. Paul, Kamchatka" (J. Webber)	40	35
272	4 c. "The Ice Islands" (Antarctica: W. Hodges)	40	35

(*b*) *Air. Horiz designs as T* **101**

273	6 c. Type **101**	90	65
274	10 c. "The Island of Tahiti" (W. Hodges)	1·25	75
275	15 c. "Karakakooa, Hawaii" (J. Webber)	1·50	90
276	25 c. "The Landing at Middleburg" (J. Sherwin)	1·75	1·25
269/76	*Set of* 8	6·00	4·00

Each value was issued in sheets of 10 stamps and 2 labels.

FLUORESCENT PAPER. From No. 277, *unless otherwise stated*, all issues are printed on paper treated with fluorescent security markings with invisible synthetic gum. These markings may be inverted or omitted in error.

102 Sailing

103 "Madonna and Child" (Titian)

1968 (21 Oct). *Olympic Games, Mexico. T* **102** *and similar horiz designs. Multicoloured. P* 13.

277	1 c. Type **102**	10	10
278	5 c. Gymnastics	10	10
279	15 c. High-jumping	15	10
280	20 c. High-diving	15	10
281	30 c. Cycling	15	10
282	50 c. Hurdling	20	15
277/82	*Set of* 6	70	30

Each value was issued in sheets of 10 stamps and 2 labels.

1968 (2 Dec). *Christmas. Paintings. T* **103** *and similar vert designs. Multicoloured. P* 13½.

283	1 c. Type **103**	10	10
284	4 c. "The Holy Family with Lamb" (Raphael)	10	10
285	10 c. "The Virgin of the Rosary" (Murillo)	15	10
286	20 c. "Adoration of the Kings" (Memling)	20	10
287	30 c. "Adoration of the Magi" (Ghirlandaio)	25	10
283/7	*Set of* 5	70	20
MS288	114 × 177 mm. Nos. 283/7 plus label	1·25	1·50

104 Camp-fire Cooking

1969 (6 Feb). *Diamond Jubilee of New Zealand Scout Movement and Fifth National (New Zealand) Jamboree. T* **104** *and similar square designs. Multicoloured. P* 13½.

289	½ c. Type **104**	10	10
290	1 c. Descent by rope	10	10
291	5 c. Semaphore	10	10
292	10 c. Tree-planting	15	10
293	20 c. Constructing a shelter	25	10
294	30 c. Lord Baden-Powell and island scene	40	15
289/94	*Set of* 6	90	35

Each value was issued in sheets of 10 stamps and 2 labels.

105 High Jumping

1969 (7 July). *Third South Pacific Games, Port Moresby. T* **105** *and similar triangular designs. Multicoloured. Without fluorescent security markings. P* 13 × 13½.

295	½ c. Type **105**	10	10
296	½ c. Footballer	10	10
297	1 c. Basketball	10	10
298	1 c. Weightlifter	10	10
299	4 c. Tennis-player	10	10
300	4 c. Hurdler	10	10
301	10 c. Javelin-thrower	30	20
302	10 c. Runner	30	20
303	15 c. Golfer	45	25
304	15 c. Boxer	45	25
295/304	*Set of* 10	1·50	1·00
MS305	174 × 129 mm. Nos. 295/304 plus two labels	1·75	1·75

Each value was issued in sheets containing 5 *se-tenant* pairs of both designs and 2 labels.

106 Flowers, Map and Captain Cook

1969 (8 Oct). *South Pacific Conference, Nouméa. T* **106** *and similar horiz designs. Multicoloured. Without fluorescent security markings. P* 13.

306	5 c. Flowers, map and Premier Albert Henry	40	10
307	10 c. Type **106**	80	40
308	25 c. Flowers, map and N.Z. arms	85	60
309	30 c. Queen Elizabeth II, map and flowers	95	65
306/9	*Set of* 4	2·75	1·60

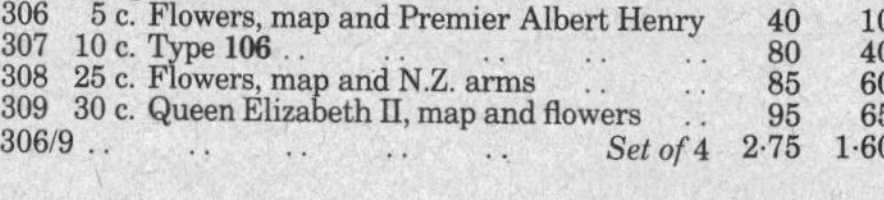

107 "Virgin and Child with Saints Jerome and Dominic" (Lippi)

108 "The Resurrection of Christ" (Raphael)

1969 (21 Nov). *Christmas. Paintings. T* **107** *and similar designs. Multicoloured. Without fluorescent security markings. P* 13.

310	1 c. Type **107**	10	10
311	4 c. "The Holy Family" (Fra Bartolomeo)	10	10
312	10 c. "The Adoration of the Shepherds" (A. Mengs)	15	10
313	20 c. "Madonna and Child with Saints" (R. Campin)	20	10
314	30 c. "The Madonna of the Basket" (Correggio)	20	15
310/14	*Set of* 5	60	30
MS315	132 × 97 mm. Nos. 310/14	85	1·40

Each value was issued in sheets of 9 stamps and 1 label.

1970 (12 Mar). *Easter. Paintings. T* **108** *and similar vert designs showing "The Resurrection of Christ" by the artists named. Multicoloured. P* 13.

316	4 c. Type **108**	10	10
317	8 c. Dirk Bouts	10	10
318	20 c. Altdorfer	15	10
319	25 c. Murillo	20	10
316/19	*Set of* 4	50	20
MS320	132 × 162 mm. Nos. 316/19	80	1·25

Each value was issued in sheets of 8 stamps and 1 label.

KIA ORANA
APOLLO 13
ASTRONAUTS
Te Atua to
Tatou Irinakianga

(**109**)

1970 (17–30 Apr). *Apollo* 13. *Nos.* 233, 236, 239/40, 242 *and* 245/6 *optd with T* **109** (4 *c. to* $2) *or with first three lines only in larger type* ($4), *by Govt Printer.* A. *Without fluorescent security markings.* B. *With fluorescent security markings.*

		A		B	
321	4 c. Water Lily	10	10		†
	a. Opt albino	42·00	—		†
322	8 c. *Allamanda cathartica*	10	10		†
323	15 c. Frangipani	10	10		†
324	20 c. Thunbergia	15	15		†
325	30 c. *Euphorbia pulcherrima poinsettia*	20	20		†
326	$2 Type **80**	60	90		†
327	$4 Type **81** (30.4)	65·00	65·00	1·25	2·75
321/6A, 327B	*Set of* 7	2·00	3·75		

110 The Royal Family

(Des V. Whiteley (5 c.), J. Berry ($1))

1970 (12 June). *Royal Visit to New Zealand. T* **110** *and similar horiz designs. Multicoloured. P* 13.

328	5 c. Type **110**	65	30
329	30 c. Captain Cook and H.M.S. *Endeavour*	2·75	1·75
330	$1 Royal Visit commemorative coin	4·00	3·00
328/30	*Set of* 3	6·75	4·50
MS331	145 × 97 mm. Nos. 328/30	8·00	9·00

Each value was issued in sheets of 8 stamps and 1 label.

FIFTH ANNIVERSARY
SELF-GOVERNMENT
AUGUST 1970

(**113**)

FOUR
DOLLARS
$4.00

(**114**)

1970 (27 Aug). *5th Anniv of Self-Government Nos.* 328/30 *optd with T* **113** (30 *c. and* $1), *or in single line in silver around frame of stamp* (5 *c.*).

332	5 c. Type **110**	40	15
333	30 c. Captain Cook and H.M.S. *Endeavour*	1·25	35
334	$1 Royal Visit commemorative coin	2·00	90
332/4	*Set of* 3	3·25	1·25

1970 (11 Nov). *Nos.* 247*c and* 248 *surch with T* **114** *by Govt Printer, Rarotonga.* A. *Without fluorescent security markings.* B. *With fluorescent security markings.*

			A		B	
335	**81**	$4 on $8 multicoloured	30·00	30·00	4·50	3·00
336		$4 on $10 multicoloured	48·00	48·00	1·50	1·75

There are variations in the setting of this surcharge and also in the rule.

115 Mary, Joseph and Christ in Manger

PLUS 20c
UNITED
KINGDOM
SPECIAL
MAIL SERVICE

(**116**)

(Des from De Lisle Psalter)

1970 (30 Nov). *Christmas. T* **115** *and similar square designs. Multicoloured. P* 13.

337	1 c. Type **115**	10	10
338	4 c. Shepherds and Apparition of the Angel	10	10
339	10 c. Mary showing Child to Joseph	15	10
340	20 c. The Wise Men bearing Gifts	20	10
341	30 c. Parents wrapping Child in swaddling clothes	25	15
337/41	*Set of* 5	65	35
MS342	100 × 139 mm. Nos. 337/41 plus label	90	1·50

Each value was issued in sheets of 5 stamps and 1 label. Stamps from the miniature sheet are smaller, since they do not have the buff parchment border as on the stamps from the sheets.

1971. *Nos.* 242B *and* 243B *surch as T* **116**.

343	30 c. + 20 c. *Euphorbia pulcherrima poinsettia* (25.2)	40	50
344	50 c. + 20 c. *Gardinia taitensis* (8.3)	1·50	1·75

The premium of 20 c. was to prepay a private delivery service fee in Great Britain during the postal strike. The mail was sent by air to a forwarding address in the Netherlands. No. 343 was intended for ordinary airmail ½ oz letters, and No. 344 included registration fee.

The postal strike ended on 8 March and both stamps were withdrawn on 12 March.

117 Wedding of Princess Elizabeth and Prince Philip

(Des from photographs. Litho Format)

1971 (11 Mar). *Royal Visit of H.R.H. The Duke of Edinburgh. T* **117** *and similar horiz designs. Multicoloured. P* 13½.

345 1 c. Type **117** 30 50
346 4 c. Queen Elizabeth, Prince Philip, Princess Anne and Prince Charles at Windsor .. 75 1·10
347 10 c. Prince Philip sailing .. .. .. 1·00 1·25
348 15 c. Prince Philip in polo gear .. .. 1·00 1·25
349 25 c. Prince Philip in naval uniform, and the Royal Yacht *Britannia* .. .. .. 1·50 2·00
345/9 .. .. *Set of* 5 4·00 5·50
MS350 168 × 122 mm. Nos 345/9 plus printed labels in positions 1, 3, 4, and 6 .. .. 4·50 7·00

Each value was issued in sheets of 7 stamps and 2 labels.

(118) (119)

1971 (8 Sept). *Fourth South Pacific Games, Tahiti. Nos.* 238B, 241B *and* 242B *optd with T* **118** *in black, or surch as T* **119** *in blue.*

351 10 c. *Poinciana regia flamboyant* 10 10
352 10 c. + 1 c. *Poinciana regia flamboyant* .. 10 10
353 10 c. + 3 c. *Poinciana regia flamboyant* .. 10 10
354 25 c. Canna Lily 15 10
355 25 c. + 1 c. Canna Lily 15 10
356 25 c. + 3 c. Canna Lily 15 10
357 30 c. *Euphorbia pulcherrima poinsettia* .. 15 10
358 30 c. + 1 c. *Euphorbia pulcherrima poinsettia* 15 10
359 30 c. + 3 c. *Euphorbia pulcherrima poinsettia* 15 10
351/9 .. .. *Set of* 9 1·10 50

The stamps additionally surcharged 1 c. or 3 c. helped to finance the Cook Islands' team at the games.

10c ≡

(120)

121 "Virgin and Child" (Bellini)

1971 (20 Oct). *Nos.* 230B, 233B, 236B/7B *and* 239B *surch with T* **120**.

360 10 c. on 2½ c. *Clitoria ternatea* 15 25
361 10 c. on 4 c. Water Lily 15 25
362 10 c. on 8 c. *Allamanda cathartica* 15 25
a. Surch inverted £140
363 10 c. on 9 c. Stephanotis 15 25
364 10 c. on 15 c. Frangipani 15 25
a. Surch double .. .. .. 95·00
360/4 .. .. *Set of* 5 65 1·10

1971 (30 Nov). *Christmas. T* **121** *and similar vert designs showing different paintings of the "Virgin and Child", by Bellini. P* 13.

365 1 c. multicoloured 10 10
366 4 c. multicoloured 10 10
367 10 c. multicoloured 25 10
368 20 c. multicoloured 50 10
369 30 c. multicoloured 50 20
365/9 .. .. *Set of* 5 1·25 35
MS370 135 × 147 mm. Nos. 365/9 .. .. 1·50 2·25
MS371 92 × 98 mm. 50 c. + 5 c. "The Holy Family in a Garland of Flowers (Jan Brueghel and Pieter van Avont) (41 × 41 *mm*) .. .. .. 60 1·40

Each value was issued in sheets of 8 stamps and 1 label.

SOUTH PACIFIC COMMISSION FEB. 1947 - 1972

(122)

123 St. John

1972 (17 Feb). *25th Anniv of South Pacific Commission. No.* 244B *optd with T* 122.

372 **80** $1 multicoloured 40 75

(Des from De Lisle Psalter)

1972 (6 Mar). *Easter. T* **123** *and similar vert designs. Multicoloured. P* 13.

373 5 c. Type **123** 10 10
374 10 c. Christ on the Cross 10 10
375 30 c. Mary, Mother of Jesus 25 25
373/5 .. .. *Set of* 3 35 35
MS376 79 × 112 mm. Nos. 373/5 forming triptych of "The Crucifixion" .. .. .. 80 2·25

Stamps from the miniature sheet do not have a border around the perforations, and are therefore smaller than stamps from sheets.

HURRICANE RELIEF PLUS 2c

(124)

Hurricane Relief Plus 5c

(125)

1972 (30 Mar). *Hurricane Relief. Nos.* 373/5 *surch as T* **124**, *and Nos.* 239B, 241B *and* 243B *surch as T* **125**, *by Govt Printer, Rarotonga.*

377 5 c. + 2 c. Type **123** (R.) 10 10
a. Albino surch .. .. .. 45·00
378 10 c. + 2 c. Christ on the Cross (R.) 15 15
379 15 c. + 5 c. Frangipani 20 20
380 25 c. + 5 c. Canna Lily 20 20
381 30 c. + 5 c. Mary, Mother of Jesus 20 20
a. Albino surch
382 50 c. + 10 c. *Gardinia taitensis* 25 25
377/82 .. .. *Set of* 6 90 90

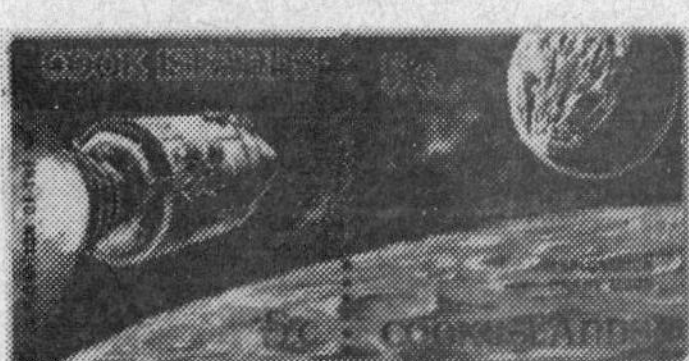

126 Rocket heading for Moon 127

1972 (17 Apr). *Apollo Moon Exploration Flights. T* **126/7** *and similar horiz designs. Multicoloured. P* 13.

383 5 c. Type **126** 15 10
384 5 c. Type **127** 15 10
385 10 c. } Astronauts on Moon 20 10
386 10 c. } .. 20 10
387 25 c. } Moon Rover and astronauts working .. 25 15
388 25 c. } .. 25 15
389 30 c. } Splashdown and helicopter 25 15
390 30 c. } .. 25 15
383/90 .. .. *Set of* 8 1·50 70
MS391 83 × 205 mm. Nos. 383/90 .. .. 3·00 4·50

These were issued in horizontal *se-tenant* pairs of each value, forming one composite design.

HURRICANE RELIEF Plus 2c

(128)

129 High-jumping

1972 (24 May). *Hurricane Relief. Nos.* 383/91 *surch as T* **128**.

392 5 c. + 2 c. Type **126** 10 10
393 5 c. + 2 c. Type **127** 10 10
394 10 c. + 2 c. } Astronauts on Moon 10 10
395 10 c. + 2 c. } .. 10 10
396 25 c. + 2 c. } Moon Rover and astronauts .. 15 15
397 25 c. + 2 c. } .. 15 15
398 30 c. + 2 c. } Splashdown and astronauts .. 15 15
399 30 c. + 2 c. } .. 15 15
392/9 .. .. *Set of* 8 75 75
MS400 83 × 205 mm. **MS**391 surch 3 c. on each stamp .. .. 2·50 3·50

1972 (26 June). *Olympic Games, Munich. T* **129** *and similar vert designs. Multicoloured. P* 13½.

401 10 c. Type **129** 15 10
402 25 c. Running 30 15
403 30 c. Boxing 30 20
401/3 .. .. *Set of* 3 70 40
MS404 88 × 78 mm. 50 c. + 5 c. Pierre de Coubertin 1·00 2·00
MS405 84 × 133 mm. Nos. 401/3 plus *se-tenant* label 1·25 2·00

Each value was issued in sheets of 8 stamps and 1 label.

130 "The Rest on the Flight into Egypt" (Caravaggio)

131 Marriage Ceremony

1972 (11 Oct). *Christmas T* **130** *and similar vert designs. Multicoloured. P* 13.

406 1 c. Type **130** 10 10
407 5 c. "Madonna of the Swallow" (Guercino) 15 10
408 10 c. "Madonna of the Green Cushion" (Solario) 20 10
409 20 c. "Madonna and Child" (di Credi) .. 35 15
410 30 c. "Madonna and Child" (Bellini) 60 25
406/10 .. .. *Set of* 5 1·25 45
MS411 141 × 152 mm. Nos. 406/10 plus *se-tenant* label in position 1 .. .. 1·75 2·25
MS412 101 × 82 mm. 50 c + 5 c. "The Holy Night" (Correggio) (31 × 43 *mm*) .. .. .. 60 1·50

Each value was issued in sheets of 9 stamps and 1 label.

1972 (20 Nov). *Royal Silver Wedding. T* **131** *and similar black and silver designs. P* 13.

413 5 c. Type **131** 25 15
414 10 c. Leaving Westminster Abbey 60 40
415 15 c. Bride and Bridegroom (40 × 41 *mm*) .. 75 50
416 30 c. Family Group (67 × 40 *mm*) .. .. 1·10 80
413/16 .. .. *Set of* 4 2·50 1·60

The 5, 10 and 15 c. values were each issued in sheets of 8 stamps and 1 label.

132 Taro Leaf

133 "Noli me Tangere" (Titian)

1973 (15 Mar). *Silver Wedding Coinage. T* **132** *and similar designs showing coins. P* 13.

417 1 c. black, rosy carmine and gold 10 10
418 2 c. black, bright blue and gold 10 10
419 5 c. black, green and silver 10 10
420 10 c. black, royal blue and silver 25 10
421 20 c. black, deep blue-green and silver .. 35 10
422 50 c. black, carmine and silver 65 15
423 $1 black, bright blue and silver .. .. 1·10 30
417/23 .. .. *Set of* 7 2·25 50

Designs: *As T* **132**—2 c. Pineapple; 5 c. Hibiscus. 46 × 30 *mm*—10 c. Oranges; 20 c. White Tern; 50 c. Skipjack Tuna. 32 × 55 *mm*—$1 Tangaroa.

Each value was issued in sheets of 20 stamps and 1 label.

1973 (9 Apr). *Easter. T* **133** *and similar vert designs. Multicoloured. P* 13.

424 5 c. Type **133** 10 10
425 10 c. "The Descent from the Cross" (Rubens) .. 15 10
426 30 c. "The Lamentation of Christ" (Dürer) .. 20 10
424/6 .. .. *Set of* 3 40 15
MS427 132 × 67 mm. Nos. 424/6 .. .. .. 50 1·25

Each value was issued in sheets of 15 stamps and 1 label.

1973 (30 Apr). *Easter. Children's Charity. Designs as Nos.* 424/6 *in separate Miniature Sheets* 67 × 87 *mm, each with a face value of* 50 c. + 5 c. *P* 13 × 14.

MS428 As Nos. 424/6 .. .. *Set of 3 sheets* 1·60 2·75

134 Queen Elizabeth II in Coronation Regalia

TENTH ANNIVERSARY
CESSATION OF
NUCLEAR TESTING
TREATY

(135)

1973 (1 June). *20th Anniv of Queen Elizabeth's Coronation. P 14 × 13½.*
429 **134** 10 c. multicoloured .. .. .. 65 1·25
MS430 64 × 89 mm. 50 c. as 10 c. P 13 × 14 .. 3·00 3·25
The perforated portion of **MS**430 is similar to No. 429, but has no borders.
No. 429 was issued in sheets of 5 stamps and 1 label.

1973 (25 July). *Tenth Anniv of Treaty Banning Nuclear Testing. Nos. 234B, 236B, 238B, and 240B/242B optd with T* **135**.
431 5 c. *Bauhinia bi-pinnata rosea* 10 10
432 8 c. *Allamanda cathartica* 10 10
433 10 c. *Poinciana regia flamboyant* 10 10
434 20 c. Thunbergia 15 15
435 25 c. Canna Lily 20 15
436 30 c. *Euphorbia pulcherrima poinsettia* .. 20 15
431/6 .. .. *Set of* 6 70 65

136 Tipairua

1973 (17 Sept). *Maori Exploration of the Pacific. T* **136** *and similar horiz designs showing sailing craft. Multicoloured. P* 13.
437 ½ c. Type **136** 10 10
438 1 c. Wa'a Kaulua 10 10
439 1½ c. Tainui 15 10
440 5 c. War canoe 40 10
441 10 c. Pahi 60 15
442 15 c. Amastasi 85 30
443 25 c. Vaka .. .. 1·10 50
437/443 .. .. *Set of* 7 3·00 1·10

137 The Annunciation

138 Princess Anne

1973 (30 Oct). *Christmas. T* **137** *and similar vert designs showing scenes from a 15th-century Flemish "Book of Hours". Multicoloured. P* 13.
444 1 c. Type **137** 10 10
445 5 c. The Visitation 10 10
446 10 c. Annunciation to the Shepherds 10 10
447 20 c. Epiphany 15 10
448 30 c. The Slaughter of the Innocents 20 15
444/8 .. .. *Set of* 5 40 30
MS449 121 × 128 mm. Nos. 444/8 plus *se-tenant* label .. .. 55 1·40
Each value was issued in sheets of 14 stamps and 1 label.
See also No. **MS**454.

1973 (14 Nov). *Royal Wedding. T* **138** *and similar vert designs. Multicoloured. P* 14 × 13½.
450 25 c. Type **138** 20 10
451 30 c. Capt. Mark Phillips 25 10
452 50 c. Princess Anne and Capt. Phillips .. 30 15
450/2 .. .. *Set of* 3 65 30
MS453 119 × 100 mm. No. 450/2 plus *se-tenant* label. P 13.. .. .. 75 45
Each value was issued in sheets of 8 stamps and 1 label.

1973 (3 Dec). *Christmas. Children's Charity. Designs as Nos. 444/8 in separate Miniature Sheets 50 × 70 mm, each with a face value of 50 c. + 5 c.*
MS454 As Nos. 444/8 .. .. *Set of 5 sheets* 75 80

NEW INFORMATION

The editor is always interested to correspond with people who have new information that will improve or correct the Catalogue.

139 Running

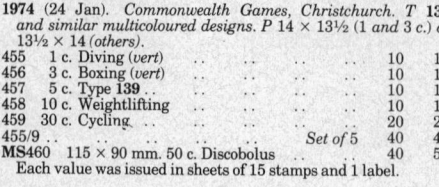

140 "Jesus carrying the Cross" (Raphael)

1974 (24 Jan). *Commonwealth Games, Christchurch. T* **139** *and similar multicoloured designs. P* 14 × 13½ (1 *and* 3 c.) *or* 13½ × 14 (*others*).
455 1 c. Diving (*vert*) 10 10
456 3 c. Boxing (*vert*) 10 10
457 5 c. Type **139** 10 10
458 10 c. Weightlifting 10 10
459 30 c. Cycling 20 25
455/9 .. .. *Set of* 5 40 40
MS460 115 × 90 mm. 50 c. Discobolus 40 55
Each value was issued in sheets of 15 stamps and 1 label.

1974 (25 Mar). *Easter. T* **140** *and similar vert designs. Multicoloured. P* 13½.
461 5 c. Type **140** 10 10
462 10 c. "The Holy Trinity" (El Greco) 10 10
463 30 c. "The Deposition of Christ" (Caravaggio) 25 15
461/3 .. .. *Set of* 3 30 20
MS464 130 × 70 mm. Nos. 461/3 .. .. .. 60 50
Each value was issued in sheets of 20 stamps and 1 label.

1974 (22 Apr). *Easter. Children's Charity. Designs as Nos. 461/3 in separate Miniature Sheets 59 × 87 mm, each with a face value of 50 c. + 5 c.*
MS465 As Nos. 461/3 .. .. *Set of 3 sheets* 70 1·40

141 Helmet Shell

142 Queen Elizabeth II

1974 (17 May)–**75**. *Sea-shells. Horiz designs as T* **141** (½ *to* 60 c.), *T* **142** *or larger horiz design* ($4 *to* $10). *Multicoloured. P* 14 × 13½ ($4 *to* $10) *or* 13½ (*others*).
466 ½ c. Type **141** 15 10
467 1 c. Vase shell 15 10
468 1½ c. Cockle shell 25 10
469 2 c. *Terebellum terebellum* 25 10
470 3 c. Bat volutes 40 10
471 4 c. Conch shell 40 10
472 5 c. Triton shell 40 10
473 6 c. Snake-head cowries 45 20
474 8 c. Helmet shell (*different*) 50 10
475 10 c. Auger shell 50 10
476 15 c. Metre shell 70 15
477 20 c. Naticacid shell 90 15
478 25 c. Scallop shell 90 25
479 30 c. Soldier Cone shell 90 20
480 50 c. Cloth of Gold Cone shell (26.8.74) .. 3·75 2·00
481 60 c. Olive shell (26.8.74) .. .. .. 3·75 2·00
482 $1 Type **142** (26.8.74) .. .. .. 2·50 2·75
483 $2 Type **142** (27.1.75) .. .. .. 2·50 2·10
484 $4 Queen Elizabeth II and seashells (17.3.75) .. .. 3·50 4·50
485 $6 As $4 (29.4.75) .. .. .. 10·00 7·00
486 $8 As $4 (30.5.75) .. .. .. 10·00 8·00
487 $10 As $4 (30.6.75) .. .. .. 10·00 9·00
466/82 .. .. *Set of* 17 15·00 7·50
Nos. 484/7 are larger, 60 × 39 mm.

143 Footballer and Australasian Map

144 Obverse and Reverse of Commemorative $2·50 Silver Coin

1974 (5 July). *World Cup Football Championships, West Germany. T* **143** *and similar horiz designs. Multicoloured. P* 13.
488 25 c. Type **143** 15 10
489 50 c. Map and Munich Stadium 30 25
490 $1 Footballer, stadium and World Cup .. 50 45
488/90 .. .. *Set of* 3 85 70
MS491 89 × 100 mm. Nos. 488/90 .. .. .. 1·25 2·75
Each value was issued in sheets of 8 stamps and 1 label.

1974 (22 July). *Bicentenary of Capt. Cook's Second Voyage of Discovery. T* **144** *and similar vert design. P* 14.
492 $2.50, silver, black and violet .. .. 13·00 7·00
493 $7.50, silver, black and deep turquoise-green 25·00 13·00
MS494 73 × 73 mm. Nos. 492/3 .. .. 45·00 48·00
Design:—$7.50. As T **144** but showing $7.50 coin.
Each value was issued in sheets of 5 stamps and 1 label.

145 Early Stamps of Cook Islands

146 "Madonna of the Goldfinch" (Raphael)

1974 (16 Sept). *Centenary of Universal Postal Union. T* **145** *and similar horiz designs. Multicoloured. P* 13½ × 14.
495 10 c. Type **145** 15 15
496 25 c. Old landing strip, Rarotonga, and stamp of 1898 .. .. 30 30
497 30 c. Post Office, Rarotonga, and stamp of 1920 30 30
498 50 c. U.P.U. emblem and stamps 40 40
495/8 .. .. *Set of* 4 1·00 1·00
MS499 118 × 79 mm. Nos. 495/8. P 13 .. .. 1·00 1·75
Each value was issued in sheets of 8 stamps and 1 label.

1974 (15 Oct). *Christmas. T* **146** *and similar vert designs. Multicoloured. P* 13.
500 1 c. Type **146** 10 10
501 5 c. "The Sacred Family" (Andrea del Sarto) 10 10
502 10 c. "The Virgin adoring the Child" (Correggio) 10 10
503 20 c. "The Holy Family" (Rembrandt) .. 20 20
504 30 c. "The Virgin and Child" (Rogier Van Der Weyden) 30 30
500/504 .. .. *Set of* 5 65 60
MS505 114 × 133 mm. Nos. 500/4 plus *se-tenant* label .. .. 75 1·25
Each value was issued in sheets of 15 stamps and 1 label.
See also No. **MS**512.

147 Churchill and Blenheim Palace

1974 (20 Nov). *Birth Centenary of Sir Winston Churchill. T* **147** *and similar horiz designs. Multicoloured. P* 13 × 14.
506 5 c. Type **147** 25 15
507 10 c. Churchill and Houses of Parliament .. 40 15
508 25 c. Churchill and Chartwell 80 30
509 30 c. Churchill and Buckingham Palace .. 90 35
510 50 c. Churchill and St. Paul's Cathedral .. 1·25 65
506/10 .. .. *Set of* 5 3·25 1·40
MS511 108 × 114 mm. Nos. 506/10 plus *se-tenant* label .. .. 4·00 2·25
Each value was issued in sheets of 5 stamps and 1 label.

1974 (9 Dec). *Christmas. Children's Charity. Designs as Nos. 500/504 in separate miniature sheets 53 × 69 mm, each with a face value of 50 c. + 5 c.*
MS512 As Nos. 500/4 .. .. *Set of 5 sheets* 90 1·60

148 Vasco Nuñez de Balboa and Discovery of Pacific Ocean (1513).

1975 (3 Feb). *Pacific Explorers. T* **148** *and similar horiz designs. Multicoloured. P* 13.
513 1 c. Type **148** 10 10
514 5 c. Fernando de Magellanes and map (1520) 35 20
515 10 c. Juan Sebastian de Elcano and *Vitoria* (1520) 60 20
516 25 c. Friar de Urdaneta and ship (1564–67) .. 1·50 75
517 30 c. Miguel Lopez de Legazpi and ship (1564–67) .. .. 1·60 80
513/17 .. .. *Set of* 5 3·75 1·90

149 "Apollo" Capsule

1975 (15 July). *"Apollo-Soyuz" Space Project. T* **149** *and similar horiz designs. Multicoloured. P* 13½.

518 25 c. Type **149** 30 15
519 25 c. "Soyuz" capsule 30 15
520 30 c. "Soyuz" crew 35 15
521 30 c. "Apollo" crew 35 15
522 50 c. Cosmonaut within "Soyuz" . . 40 25
523 50 c. Astronauts within "Apollo" . . 40 25
518/23 . . . . *Set of* 6 1·90 1·00
MS524 119 × 119 mm. Nos. 518/23. P 13 × 14 . . 2·00 2·50

Each value was issued in sheets containing 9 horizontal *se-tenant* pairs of the two designs, together with 2 labels.

150 $100 Commemorative Gold Coin

1975 (8 Aug). *Bicentenary of Captain Cook's Second Voyage. P* 13.

525 **150** $2 brown, gold and bluish violet . . 6·50 2·75

No. 525 was issued in sheets of 5 stamps and 1 label.

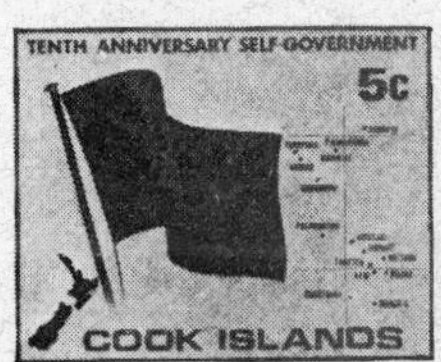

151 Cook Islands' Flag and Map

1975 (8 Aug). *Tenth Anniv of Self-Government. T* **151** *and similar multicoloured designs. P* 13.

526 5 c. Type **151** 20 10
527 10 c. Premier Sir Albert Henry and flag (*vert*) 30 10
528 25 c. Rarotonga and flag 70 30
526/8 . . . . *Set of* 3 1·10 45

152 "Madonna by the Fireside" (R. Campin)

153 "Entombment of Christ" (Raphael)

1975 (1 Dec). *Christmas. T* **152** *and similar vert designs. Multicoloured. P* 13½.

529 6 c. Type **152** 10 10
530 10 c. "Madonna in the Meadow" (Raphael) . . 10 10
531 15 c. "Madonna of the Oak" (attrib Raphael) . . 15 10
532 20 c. "Adoration of the Shepherds" (J. B. Maino) . . 20 15
533 35 c. "The Annunciation" (Murillo) . . 30 20
529/33 . . . . *Set of* 5 75 45
MS534 110 × 124 mm. Nos. 529/33 . . 75 85

1975 (15 Dec). *Christmas. Children's Charity. Designs as Nos.* 529/33 *in separate miniature sheets* 53 × 71 *mm, each with a face value of* 75 *c.* + 5 *c.*

MS535 As Nos. 529/33 . . *Set of 5 sheets* 1·50 1·75
a. Error. Miniature sheet as No. 531 imperf £250

1976 (29 Mar). *Easter. T* **153** *and similar square designs. Multicoloured. P* 13.

536 7 c. Type **153** 15 10
537 15 c. "Pietà" (Veronese) 25 15
538 35 c. "Pietà" (El Greco) 40 25
536/8 . . . . *Set of* 3 70 40
MS539 144 × 57 mm. Nos. 536/8 . . 70 85

Each value was issued in sheets of 20 stamps and 1 label.

1976 (3 May). *Easter. Children's Charity. Designs as Nos.* 536/8 *in separate miniature sheets* 69 × 69 *mm. each with a face value of* 60 *c.* + 5 *c.*

MS540 As Nos. 536/8 . . *Set of 3 sheets* 1·40 1·60

NEW INFORMATION

The editor is always interested to correspond with people who have new information that will improve or correct the Catalogue.

154 Benjamin Franklin and H.M.S. *Resolution*

1976 (29 May). *Bicentenary of American Revolution. T* **154** *and similar horiz designs. Multicoloured. P* 13.

541 $1 Type **154** . . . . 6·00 1·50
542 $2 Captain Cook and H.M.S. *Resolution* . . 8·00 2·50
MS543 118 × 58 mm. $3 Cook, Franklin and H.M.S. *Resolution* (74 × 31 *mm*) . . 14·00 8·00

Each value was issued in sheets of 5 stamps and 1 label.

Royal Visit July 1976

(155)

1976 (9 July). *Visit of Queen Elizabeth to the U.S.A. Nos.* 541/3 *optd with T* **155**.

544 $1 Type **154** . . . . 3·50 1·50
545 $2 Captain Cook and H.M.S. *Resolution* . . 5·50 2·50
MS546 $3 Cook, Franklin and H.M.S. *Resolution* 10·00 7·50

156 Hurdling

157 "The Visitation"

1976 (22 July). *Olympic Games, Montreal. T* **156** *and similar square designs. Multicoloured. P* 13.

547 7 c. } Type **156** . . 10 10
548 7 c. } . . 10 10
549 15 c. } Hockey . . 15 15
550 15 c. } . . 15 15
551 30 c. } Fencing . . 25 15
552 30 c. } . . 25 15
553 35 c. } Football . . 30 20
554 35 c. } . . 30 20
547/54 . . . . *Set of* 8 1·40 1·10
MS555 104 × 146 mm. Nos. 547/54 . . 1·40 2·00

Each value was issued in sheets containing 5 horizontal *se-tenant* pairs and 2 labels. In each pair the first stamp has the face-value on the right, the second has it on the left. Illustrated is the left-hand stamp of the 7 c. design.

1976 (12 Oct). *Christmas. T* **157** *and similar vert designs showing Renaissance sculptures. Multicoloured. P* 14 × 13½.

556 6 c. Type **157** 10 10
557 10 c. "Adoration of the Shepherds" . . 10 10
558 15 c. "Adoration of the Shepherds" (*different*) 15 10
559 20 c. "The Epiphany" 20 20
560 35 c. "The Holy Family" 25 25
556/60 . . . . *Set of* 5 70 60
MS561 116 × 110 mm. Nos. 556/60. P 13 . . 85 1·75

Each value was issued in sheets of 20 stamps and 1 label.

1976 (2 Nov.) *Christmas. Children's Charity. Designs as Nos.* 556/60 *in separate miniature sheets* 66 × 80 *mm, each with a face value of* 75 *c.* + 5 *c.*

MS562 As Nos. 556/60 . . *Set of 5 sheets* 2·00 2·00

158 Obverse and Reverse of $5 Mangaia Kingfisher Coin

1976 (15 Nov). *National Wildlife and Conservation Day. P* 13.

563 **158** $1 multicoloured . . . . 3·25 1·25

No. 563 was issued in sheets of 5 stamps and 1 label.

159 Imperial State Crown

160 "Christ on the Cross"

1977 (7 Feb). *Silver Jubilee. T* **159** *and similar vert designs. Multicoloured. P* 13.

564 25 c. Type **159** 90 75
565 25 c. Queen with regalia 90 75
566 50 c. Westminster Abbey . . . . 1·50 1·50
567 50 c. Coronation Coach . . . . 1·50 1·50
568 $1 Queen and Prince Philip . . 3·50 3·25
569 $1 Royal Visit, 1974 . . . . 3·50 3·25
564/9 . . . . *Set of* 6 10·50 10·00
MS570 130 × 136 mm. As Nos. 564/9 (borders and "COOK ISLANDS" in a different colour) . . 7·50 7·50

The two designs of each value are printed horizontally *se-tenant* throughout the sheet, and stamps from **MS**570 have borders and "COOK ISLANDS" in a different colour.

1977 (28 Mar). *Easter and 400th Birth Anniv of Rubens. T* **160** *and similar vert designs. Multicoloured. P* 14 × 13½.

571 7 c. Type **160** 25 10
572 15 c. "Christ on the Cross" 40 15
573 35 c. "The Deposition of Christ" . . 80 30
571/3 . . . . *Set of* 3 1·25 50
MS574 118 × 65 mm. Nos. 571/3. P 13 . . 1·25 1·10

Each value was issued in sheets of 24 stamps and 1 label.

1977 (18 Apr). *Easter. Children's Charity. Designs as Nos.* 571/3 *in separate miniature sheets* 60 × 79 *mm, each with a face value of* 60 *c.* + 5 *c. P* 13 × 14.

MS575 As Nos. 571/3 . . *Set of 3 sheets* 1·00 1·00

161 "Virgin and Child" (Memling)

162 Obverse and Reverse of $5 Cook Islands Swiftlet Coin

1977 (3 Oct). *Christmas. T* **161** *and similar vert designs. Multicoloured. P* 14.

576 6 c. Type **161** 10 10
577 10 c. "Madonna and Child with Saints and Donors" (Memling) . . 10 10
578 15 c. "Adoration of the Kings" (Geertgen) . . 20 10
579 20 c. "Virgin and Child with Saints" (Crivelli) 25 15
580 35 c. "Adoration of the Magi" (16th-cent Flemish School) . . 30 20
576/80 . . . . *Set of* 5 85 50
MS581 118 × 111 mm. Nos. 576/80. P 13½ . . 85 1·50

Each value was issued in sheets of 24 stamps and 1 label.

1977 (31 Oct). *Christmas. Children's Charity. Designs as Nos.* 576/80 *in separate miniature sheets* 69 × 69 *mm, each with a face value of* 75 *c.* + 5 *c.*

MS582 As Nos. 576/80 . . *Set of 5 sheets* 1·40 1·50

1977 (15 Nov). *National Wildlife and Conservation Day. P* 13.

583 **162** $1 multicoloured . . . . 3·50 1·75

No. 583 was issued in sheets containing 10 stamps and 2 labels.

163 Captain Cook and H.M.S. *Resolution* (from paintings by N. Dance and H. Roberts)

1978 (20 Jan). *Bicentenary of Discovery of Hawaii. T* **163** *and similar horiz designs. Multicoloured. P* 13½.

584 50 c. Type **163** . . . . 1·50 60
585 $1 Earl of Sandwich, and Cook landing at Owhyhee (from paintings by Thomas Gainsborough and J. Cleveley) . . 2·00 1·00
586 $2 Obverse and reverse of $200 coin and Cook monument, Hawaii . . 3·25 1·75
584/6 . . . . *Set of* 3 6·00 3·00
MS587 118 × 95 mm. Nos. 584/86 . . 7·00 7·50

Each value was issued in sheets of 5 stamps and 1 label.

164 "Pieta" (Van der Weyden)

165 Queen Elizabeth II

1978 (20 Mar). *Easter. Paintings from National Gallery, London. T* **164** *and similar horiz designs. Multicoloured. P* 13.

588	15 c. Type **164**	20	15
589	35 c. "The Entombment" (Michelangelo)	35	30
590	75 c. "The Supper at Emmaus" (Caravaggio)	65	55
588/90	*Set of* 3	1·10	90
MS591	114 × 96 mm. Nos. 588/90	1·10	1·50

Each value was issued in sheets of 5 stamps and 1 label.

1978 (10 Apr). *Easter. Children's Charity. Designs as Nos.* 588/90 *in separate miniature sheets, 85 × 72 mm, each with a face value of* 60 *c.* + 5 *c. P* 13½.

MS592	As Nos. 588/90 .. *Set of 3 sheets*	1·10	1·10

1978 (6 June). *25th Anniv of Coronation. T* **165** *and similar vert designs. Multicoloured. P* 13.

593	50 c. Type **165**	40	40
594	50 c. The Lion of England	40	40
595	50 c. Imperial State Crown	40	40
596	50 c. Statue of Tangaroa (god)	40	40
597	70 c. Type **165**	45	45
598	70 c. Sceptre with Cross	45	45
599	70 c. St. Edward's Crown	45	45
600	70 c. Rarotongan staff god	45	45
593/600	*Set of* 8	3·00	3·00
MS601	103 × 142 mm. Nos. 593/600*	2·50	3·25

Each value was issued in sheets containing the 4 designs and 2 labels.

* In No **MS**601 the designs of Nos. 595 and 599 are transposed.

5c 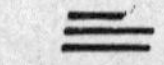

(166)

1978 (10 Nov). *Nos.* 466, 468, 473/4 *and* 478/81 *surch as T* **166**.

602	5 c. on 1½ c. Cockle shell (Silver)	25	10
603	7 c. on ½ c. Type **141**	30	15
604	10 c. on 6 c. Snake-head cowries (Gold)	35	15
605	10 c. on 8 c. Helmet shell (Gold)	35	15
606	15 c. on ½ c. Type **141**	40	20
607	15 c. on 25 c. Scallop shell (Silver)	40	20
608	15 c. on 30 c. Soldier Cone shell	40	20
609	15 c. on 50 c. Cloth of Gold Cone shell (Silver)	40	20
610	15 c. on 60 c. Olive shell (Gold)	40	20
611	17 c. on ½ c. Type **141**	45	25
612	17 c. on 50 c. Cloth of Gold Cone shell (Silver)	45	25
602/12	*Set of* 11	3·75	1·75

1728 · 250th ANNIVERSARY OF COOK'S BIRTH · 1978

(167)

1978 (13 Nov). *250th Birth Anniv of Captain Cook. Nos.* 584/7 *optd with T* **167** *on silver.*

613	50 c. Type **163**	1·50	75
614	$1 Earl of Sandwich, and Cook landing at Owhyhee (from paintings by Thomas Gainsborough and J. Cleveley)	2·00	1·00
615	$2 Obverse and reverse of $200 coin and Cook monument, Hawaii	3·00	2·00
613/15	*Set of* 3	6·00	3·25
MS616	Nos. 613/15	11·00	11·00

168 Obverse and Reverse of $5 Pitcairn Warblers Coin

1978 (15 Nov). *National Wildlife and Conservation Day. P* 13.

617	**168** $1 multicoloured	1·75	1·00

169 "The Virgin and Child" (Van der Weyden)

170 Virgin with Body of Christ

1978 (8 Dec). *Christmas. Paintings. T* **169** *and similar vert designs. Multicoloured. P* 13.

618	15 c. Type **169**	20	10
619	17 c. "The Virgin and Child" (Crivelli)	25	15
620	35 c. "The Virgin and Child" (Murillo)	40	30
618/20	*Set of* 3	75	50
MS621	107 x 70 mm. Nos. 618/20	90	1·25

MINIMUM PRICE

The minimum price quote is 10p which represents a handling charge rather than a basis for valuing common stamps. For further notes about prices see introductory pages.

1979 (12 Jan). *Christmas. Children's Charity. Designs as Nos.* 618/20 *in separate miniature sheets 57 x 87 mm. each with a face value of* 75 *c.* + 5 *c. P* 13½

MS622	As Nos. 618/20 .. *Set of 3 sheets*	1·00	1·00

1979 (5 Apr). *Easter. Details of Painting "Descent" by Gaspar de Crayar. T* **170** *and similar vert designs. Multicoloured. P* 13.

623	10 c. Type **170**	10	10
624	12 c. St. John	15	15
625	15 c. Mary Magdalene	20	20
626	20 c. Weeping angels	20	20
623/6	*Set of* 4	60	60
MS627	83 × 100 mm. As Nos. 623/6, but each with charity premium of 2 c.	65	75

Stamps from No. **MS**627 are slightly smaller, 32 × 40 mm, and are without borders.

171 "Captain Cook" (James Weber)

172 Post-Rider

1979 (23 July). *Death Bicentenary of Captain Cook. T* **171** *and similar vert designs. Multicoloured. P* 14 × 13.

628	20 c. Type **171**	30	20
629	30 c. H.M.S. *Resolution*	50	35
630	35 c. H.M.S. *Endeavour*	60	45
631	50 c. "Death of Captain Cook" (George Carter)	70	60
628/31	*Set of* 4	1·90	1·40
MS632	78 × 112 mm. Nos. 628/31	1·90	2·00

Stamps from No. **MS**632 have black borders.

1979 (10 Sept). *Death Centenary of Sir Rowland Hill. History of Mail Transport. T* **172** *and similar square designs. Multicoloured. P* 14.

633	30 c. Type **172**	35	25
634	30 c. Mail coach	35	25
635	30 c. Automobile	35	25
636	30 c. Railway train	35	25
637	35 c. *Cap-Horniers* (sailing ship)	40	25
638	35 c. River steamer	40	25
639	35 c. *Deutschland* (liner)	40	25
640	35 c. *United States* (liner)	40	25
641	50 c. Balloon *Neptune*	50	30
642	50 c. Junkers "F13" (aeroplane)	50	30
643	50 c. *Graf Zeppelin*	50	30
644	50 c. "Concorde"	50	30
633/44	*Set of* 12	4·50	3·00
MS645	132 × 104 mm. Nos. 633/44	4·50	5·00

Nos. 633/6, 637/40 and 641/4 were each printed together, *se-tenant*, in blocks of 4 throughout the sheets.

(173)

1979 (12 Sept). *Nos.* 466, 468 *and* 481 *surch as T* **173**.

646	6 c. on ½ c. Type **141** (Gold)	15	15
647	10 c. on 1½ c. Cockle shell (Silver)	20	20
648	15 c. on 60 c. Olive shell (Gold)	30	30
646/8	*Set of* 3	60	60

174 Brother and Sister

175 "Apollo 11" Emblem

1979 (10 Oct). *International Year of the Child. T* **174** *and similar horiz designs. Multicoloured. P* 13.

649	30 c. Type **174**	25	25
650	50 c. Boy with tree drum	40	40
651	65 c. Children dancing	50	50
649/51	*Set of* 3	1·00	1·00
MS652	102 × 75 mm. As Nos. 649/51, but each with charity premium of 5 c. P 13½ × 13	1·00	1·50

Designs for stamps from No. **MS**652 are as Nos. 649/51 but have I.Y.C. emblem in red.

1979 (7 Nov). *10th Anniv of Moon Landing. T* **175** *and similar vert designs. Multicoloured. P* 14.

653	30 c. Type **175**	30	35
654	50 c. Crew of "Apollo 11"	40	50
655	60 c. Astronaut on Moon	50	60
656	65 c. Command module after splashdown	55	65
653/6	*Set of* 4	1·60	1·90
MS657	119 × 105 mm. Nos. 653/6. P 13½	1·75	2·00

176 Obverse and Reverse of $5 Rarotongan Fruit Dove Coin

177 Glass Christmas Tree Ornaments

1979 (15 Nov). *National Wildlife and Conservation Day. P* 13 × 14.

658	**176** $1 multicoloured	2·25	1·90

1979 (14 Dec). *Christmas. T* **177** *and similar vert designs. Multicoloured. P* 13½. (a) *Postage.*

659	6 c. Type **177**	10	10
660	10 c. Hibiscus flower and star	10	10
661	12 c. Poinsettia flower, bells and candle	10	10
662	15 c. Poinsettia leaves and Tiki (god)	15	15
	(*b*) *Air*		
663	20 c. Type **177**	15	15
664	25 c. As 10 c.	20	20
665	30 c. As 12 c.	25	25
666	35 c. As 15 c.	30	30
659/66	*Set of* 8	1·10	1·10

1980 (15 Jan). *Christmas. Children's Charity. Designs as Nos.* 659/66 *with additional premiums.* (a) *Postage.*

667	6 c. + 2 c. Type **177**	10	10
668	10 c. + 2 c. Hibiscus flower and star	15	15
669	12 c. + 2 c. Poinsettia flower, bells and candle	15	20
670	15 c. + 2 c. Poinsettia leaves and Tiki (god)	15	20
	(*b*) *Air*		
671	20 c. + 4 c. Type **177**	15	25
672	25 c. + 4 c. As 10 c.	15	25
673	30 c. + 4 c. As 12 c.	20	30
674	35 c. + 4 c. As 15 c.	25	35
667/74	*Set of* 8	1·00	1·60

178 "Flagellation"

179 Dove with Olive Twig

1980 (31 Mar). *Easter. Illustrations by Gustave Doré. T* **178** *and similar vert designs in sepia and gold. P* 13.

675	20 c. Type **178**	15	20
676	20 c. "Crown of Thorns"	15	20
677	30 c. "Jesus Insulted"	25	30
678	30 c. "Jesus Falls"	25	30
679	35 c. "The Crucifixion"	25	30
680	35 c. "The Descent from the Cross"	25	30
675/80	*Set of* 6	1·10	1·40
MS681	120 × 110 mm. As Nos. 675/80, but each with charity premium of 2 c.	1·10	1·50

Nos. 675/6, 677/8 and 679/80 were each printed together, *se-tenant*, in vertical pairs throughout the sheet.

1980 (23 Apr). *Easter. Children's Charity. Designs as Nos.* 675/80 *in separate miniature sheets 60 × 71 mm, each with a face value of* 75 *c.* + 5 *c. P* 13.

MS682	As Nos. 675/80 .. *Set of 6 sheets*	90	1·50

1980 (27 May). *75th Anniv of Rotary International. T* **179** *and similar horiz designs. Multicoloured. P* 14.

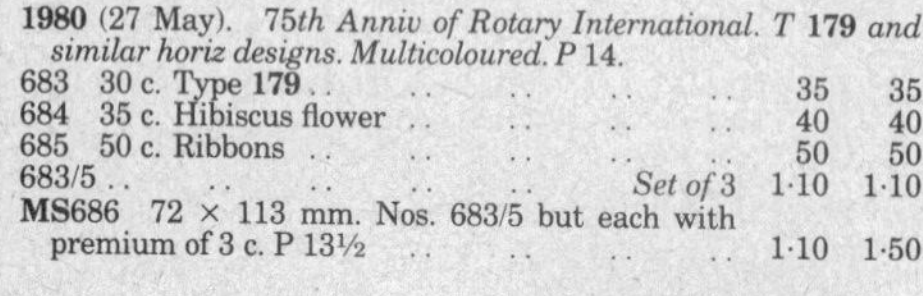

683	30 c. Type **179**	35	35
684	35 c. Hibiscus flower	40	40
685	50 c. Ribbons	50	50
683/5	*Set of* 3	1·10	1·10
MS686	72 × 113 mm. Nos. 683/5 but each with premium of 3 c. P 13½	1·10	1·50

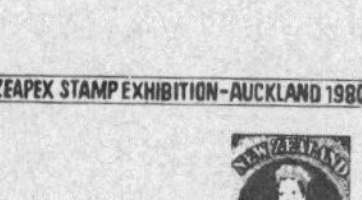

(180)

181 Queen Elizabeth the Queen Mother

1980 (22 Aug). *"Zeapex 80" International Stamp Exhibition, Auckland. Nos.* 633/45 *optd with T* **180** *in black on silver background.*

687	30 c. Type **172**	30	30
688	30 c. Mail coach	30	30
689	30 c. Automobile	30	30
690	30 c. Railway train	30	30
691	35 c. *Cap-Horniers* (sailing ship)	35	35
692	35 c. River steamer	35	35

693 35 c. *Deutschland* (liner) 35 35
694 35 c. *United States* (liner) 35 35
695 50 c. Balloon *Neptune* 65 45
696 50 c. Junkers "F13" (aeroplane) 65 45
697 50 c. *Graf Zeppelin* 65 45
698 50 c. "Concorde" 65 45
687/98 *Set of* 12 4·75 4·00
MS699 132 × 104 mm. Nos. 687/98 5·00 5·00

1980 (22 Aug). *"Zeapex 80" International Stamp Exhibition, Auckland. As No.* **MS**681 *but containing stamps without charity premium of* 2 c. *optd* "Zeapex '80 Auckland + 10 c" *in black on gold background.*
MS700 120 × 110 mm. Nos. 675/80 (*sold at* $1.80) 80 1·60
Stamps from No. **MS**700 are unaffected by the overprint which appears on the sheet margin.

1980 (23 Sept). *80th Birthday of Queen Elizabeth the Queen Mother. P* 13.
701 **181** 50 c. multicoloured 1·40 90
MS702 64 × 78 mm. **181** $2 multicoloured 2·00 2·25

182 Satellites orbiting Moon

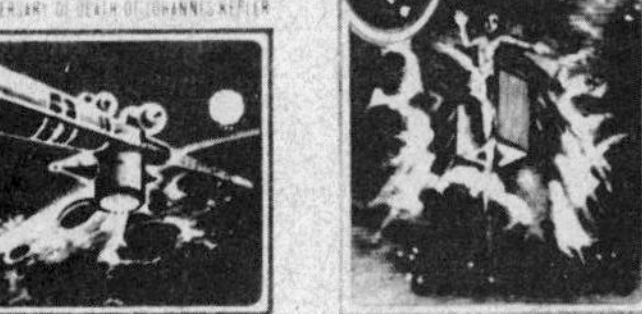
183 Scene from novel *From the Earth to the Moon*

1980 (7 Nov). *350th Death Anniv of Johannes Kepler (astronomer). T* **182** *and similar horiz designs. Multicoloured. P* 13.
703 12 c. Type **182** 45 35
704 12 c. Space-craft orbiting Moon 45 35
705 50 c. Space-craft orbiting Moon (*different*) 90 80
706 50 c. Astronaut and Moon vehicle 90 80
703/6 *Set of* 4 2·40 2·10
MS707 122 × 122 mm. Nos. 703/6 2·40 2·40
Nos. 703/4 and 705/6 were each printed together, *se-tenant*, in horizontal pairs throughout the sheet.

1980 (7 Nov). *75th Death Anniv of Jules Verne (author). T* **183** *and similar vert designs showing scenes from the novel "From the Earth to the Moon". P* 13.
708 20 c. multicoloured (green background) 35 35
709 20 c. multicoloured (brown background) 35 35
710 30 c. multicoloured (mauve background) 45 45
711 30 c. multicoloured (blue background) 45 45
708/11 *Set of* 4 1·40 1·40
MS712 121 × 122 mm. Nos. 708/11 1·50 1·75
Nos. 708/9 and 710/11 were each printed together, *se-tenant*, in horizontal pairs throughout the sheet.

184 *Siphonogorgia*

185 Annunciation

1980 (21 Nov)–**82**. *Corals (1st series). Multicoloured designs as T* **184**. *P* 13 (1 *c. to* $1) *or* 14 × 13½ ($2 *to* $10).
713 1 c. Type **184** 10 10
714 1 c. *Pavona praetorta* 10 10
715 1 c. *Stylaster echinatus* 10 10
716 1 c. *Tubastraea* 10 10
717 3 c. *Millepora alcicornis* 15 10
718 3 c. *Junceella gemmacea* 15 10
719 3 c. *Fungia fungites* 15 10
720 3 c. *Heliofungia actiniformis* 15 10
721 4 c. *Distichopora violacea* 15 10
722 4 c. *Stylaster* 15 10
723 4 c. *Gonipora* 15 10
724 4 c. *Caulastraea echinulata* 15 10
725 5 c. *Ptilosarcus gurneyi* 20 10
726 5 c. *Stylophora pistillata* 20 10
727 5 c. *Melithaea squamata* 20 10
728 5 c. *Porites andrewsi* 20 10
729 6 c. *Lobophyllia bemprichii* 20 10
730 6 c. *Palauastrea ramosa* 20 10
731 6 c. *Bellonella indica* 20 10
732 6 c. *Pectinia alcicornis* 20 10
733 8 c. *Sarcophyton digitatum* 20 10
734 8 c. *Melithaea albitincta* 20 10
735 8 c. *Plerogyra sinuosa* 20 10
736 8 c. *Dendrophyllia gracilis* 20 10
737 10 c. Type **184** (19.12.80) 25 15
738 10 c. As No. 714 (19.12.80) 25 15
739 10 c. As No. 715 (19.12.80) 25 15
740 10 c. As No. 716 (19.12.80) 25 15
741 12 c. As No. 717 (19.12.80) 25 15
742 12 c. As No. 718 (19.12.80) 25 15
743 12 c. As No. 719 (19.12.80) 25 15
744 12 c. As No. 720 (19.12.80) 25 15
745 15 c. As No. 721 (19.12.80) 30 20
746 15 c. As No. 722 (19.12.80) 30 20
747 15 c. As No. 723 (19.12.80) 30 20
748 15 c. As No. 724 (19.12.80) 30 20
749 20 c. As No. 725 (19.12.80) 35 25
750 20 c. As No. 726 (19.12.80) 35 25
751 20 c. As No. 727 (19.12.80) 35 25
752 20 c. As No. 728 (19.12.80) 35 25
753 25 c. As No. 729 (19.12.80) 35 25
754 25 c. As No. 730 (19.12.80) 35 25
755 25 c. As No. 731 (19.12.80) 35 25
756 25 c. As No. 732 (19.12.80) 35 25
757 30 c. As No. 733 (19.12.80) 40 30
758 30 c. As No. 734 (19.12.80) 40 30
759 30 c. As No. 735 (19.12.80) 40 30
760 30 c. As No. 736 (19.12.80) 40 30
761 35 c. Type **184** (16.3.81) 45 35
762 35 c. As No. 714 (16.3.81) 45 35
763 35 c. As No. 715 (16.3.81) 45 35
764 35 c. As No. 716 (16.3.81) 45 35
765 50 c. As No. 717 (16.3.81) 65 55
766 50 c. As No. 718 (16.3.81) 65 55
767 50 c. As No. 719 (16.3.81) 65 55
768 50 c. As No. 720 (16.3.81) 65 55
769 60 c. As No. 721 (16.3.81) 75 65
770 60 c. As No. 722 (16.3.81) 75 65
771 60 c. As No. 723 (16.3.81) 75 65
772 60 c. As No. 724 (16.3.81) 75 65
773 70 c. As No. 725 (13.4.81) 1·00 75
774 70 c. As No. 726 (13.4.81) 1·00 75
775 70 c. As No. 727 (13.4.81) 1·00 75
776 70 c. As No. 728 (13.4.81) 1·00 75
777 80 c. As No. 729 (13.4.81) 1·25 80
778 80 c. As No. 730 (13.4.81) 1·25 80
779 80 c. As No. 731 (13.4.81) 1·25 80
780 80 c. As No. 732 (13.4.81) 1·25 80
781 $1 As No. 733 (20.5.81) 1·75 1·00
782 $1 As No. 734 (20.5.81) 1·75 1·00
783 $1 As No. 735 (20.5.81) 1·75 1·00
784 $1 As No. 736 (20,5.81) 1·75 1·00
785 $2 As No. 723 (27.11.81) 4·50 2·25
786 $3 As No. 720 (27.11.81) 6·00 3·25
787 $4 As No. 726 (11.1.82) 4·00 4·50
788 $6 As No. 715 (11.1.82) 5·50 6·50
789 $10 As No. 734 (5.3.82) 12·00 13·00
713/89 *Set of* 77 60·00 45·00
Nos. 761/84 are 30 × 40 mm and Nos. 785/9, which include a portrait of Queen Elizabeth II in each design, are 55 × 35 mm in size.
The four designs of each value to the $1 were printed together, *se-tenant*, in horizontal strips of 4 (Nos. 713/60) or in blocks of 4 (Nos. 761/84) throughout the sheet.
For similar designs with redrawn frames and inscriptions see Nos. 966/92.

1980 (1 Dec). *Christmas. Illustrations from 13th-century French Prayer Book. T* **185** *and similar vert designs. Multicoloured. P* 14 × 13½.
801 15 c. Type **185** 15 15
802 30 c. Visitation 25 25
803 40 c. Nativity 30 30
804 50 c. Epiphany 40 40
801/4 *Set of* 4 1·00 1·00
MS805 89 × 114 mm. Nos. 801/4. P 13½ 1·25 1·50

1981 (9 Jan). *Christmas. Children's Charity. Designs as Nos. 801/4 in separate miniature sheets 55 × 68 mm, each with a face value of* 75 c. + 5 c. *Imperf.*
MS806 As Nos. 801/4 *Set of 4 sheets* 2·75 3·00

186 "The Crucifixion" (from book of Saint-Amand)

187 Prince Charles

1981 (10 Apr). *Easter. Illustrations from 12th-century French Prayer Books. T* **186** *and similar horiz designs. Multicoloured. P* 13½ × 14.
807 15 c. Type **186** 20 20
808 25 c. "Placing in Tomb" (from book of Ingeburge) 30 30
809 40 c. "Mourning at the Sepulchre" (from book of Ingeburge) 40 40
807/9 *Set of* 3 80 80
MS810 72 × 116 mm. As Nos. 807/9 but each with charity premium of 2 c. P 13½ 90 90

1981 (28 Apr). *Easter. Children's Charity. Designs as Nos. 807/9 in separate miniature sheets 64 × 53 mm, each with a face value of* 75 c. +5 c. *Imperf.*
MS811 As Nos. 807/9 *Set of 3 sheets* 1·50 1·50

1981 (29 July). *Royal Wedding. T* **187** *and similar vert design. Multicoloured. P* 14.
812 $1 Type **187** 1·50 1·50
813 $2 Prince Charles and Lady Diana Spencer 2·75 2·75
MS814 106 × 59 mm. Nos. 812/13. P 13½ 5·00 5·00
Nos. 812/13 were each printed in small sheets of 4.

188 Footballers

+
5
c
(189)

1981 (20 Oct). *World Cup Football Championship, Spain (1982). T* **188** *and similar horiz designs showing footballers. Multicoloured. P* 13½ × 14.
815 20 c. Type **188** 20 20
816 20 c. Figures to right of stamp 20 20
817 30 c. Figures to left 30 30
818 30 c. Figures to right 30 30
819 35 c. Figures to left 35 35
820 35 c. Figures to right 35 35
821 50 c. Figures to left 45 45
822 50 c. Figures to right 45 45
815/22 *Set of* 8 2·40 2·40
MS823 180 × 94 mm. As Nos. 815/22, but each stamp with a charity premium of 3 c. P 13½ 2·75 3·50
The two designs of each value were printed together, *se-tenant*, in horizontal pairs throughout the sheet, forming composite designs.

1981 (10 Nov). *International Year for Disabled Persons. Nos. 812/14 surch as T* **189**.
824 $1 + 5 c. Type **187** 2·50 2·50
825 $2 + 5 c. Prince Charles and Lady Diana Spencer 4·50 5·00
MS826 106 × 59 mm. $1 + 10 c., $2 + 10 c. As Nos. 824/5 7·00 9·00
Nos. 824/6 have commemorative inscriptions overprinted on the sheet margins.

190 "Holy Virgin with Child"

191 Princess of Wales (inscr "21st Birthday")

1981 (14 Dec). *Christmas. Details from Paintings by Rubens. T* **190** *and similar vert designs. Multicoloured. P* 14 × 13½.
827 8 c. Type **190** 20 10
828 15 c. "Coronation of St. Catherine" 25 15
829 40 c. "Adoration of the Shepherds" 45 35
830 50 c. "Adoration of the Magi" 55 40
827/30 *Set of* 4 1·25 90
MS831 86 × 110 mm. As Nos. 827/30, but each with a charity premium of 3 c. P 13½ 1·50 1·75

1982 (18 Jan). *Christmas. Children's Charity. Designs as Nos. 827/30 in separate miniature sheets 62 × 78 mm, each with a face value of* 75 c. + 5 c.
MS832 As Nos. 827/30 *Set of 4 sheets* 3·00 3·25

1982 (21 June). *21st Birthday of Princess of Wales. T* **191** *and similar horiz designs. Multicoloured. P* 14.
833 $1.25, Type **191** 1·25 1·25
a. Pair. Nos. 833/4 2·50 2·50
834 $1.25, As Type **191**, but inscr "1 July 1982" 1·25 1·25
835 $2.50, Princess (*different*) (inscr "21st Birthday") 1·75 1·75
a. Pair. Nos. 835/6 3·50 3·50
836 $2·50, As No. 835, but inscr "1 July 1982" 1·75 1·75
833/6 *Set of* 4 5·50 5·50
MS837 92 × 72 mm. $1.25, Type **191**; $2.50, As No. 835. Both inscribed "21st Birthday 1 July 1982". P 13½ 2·75 2·75
The two designs for each value were printed together, *se-tenant*, in small sheets of 4.

ROYAL BIRTH · 21 JUNE 1982
(192)

1982 (12 July). *Birth of Prince William of Wales (1st issue). Nos. 812/14 optd as T* **192**.
838 $1 Type **187** (optd with T **192**) 3·50 2·25
a. Pair. Nos. 838/9 7·00 4·50
839 $1 Type **187** (optd "PRINCE WILLIAM OF WALES") 3·50 2·25
840 $2 Prince Charles and Lady Diana Spencer (optd with T **192**) 6·00 5·00
a. Pair. Nos. 840/1 12·00 10·00
841 $2 Prince Charles and Lady Diana Spencer (optd. "PRINCE WILLIAM OF WALES") 6·00 5·00
838/41 *Set of* 4 17·00 13·00
MS842 106 × 59mm. Nos. 812/13 optd "21 JUNE 1982. ROYAL BIRTH" 9·00 7·00

1982 (3 Aug). *Birth of Prince William of Wales (2nd issue). Designs as Nos. 833/7 but with changed inscriptions. Multicoloured. P*14.
843 $1.25, As Type **191** (inscr "Royal Birth") 1·25 1·25
a. Pair. Nos. 843/4 2·50 2·50
844 $1.25, As Type **191** (inscr "21 June 1982") 1·25 1·25
845 $2.50, As No. 835 (inscr "Royal Birth") 1·75 1·75
a. Pair. Nos. 845/6 3·50 3·50
846 $2.50, As No. 835 (inscr "21 June 1982") 1·75 1·75
843/6 *Set of* 4 5·50 5·50
MS847 92 × 73 mm. $1.25, As Type **191**; $2.50, As No. 835. Both inscribed "Royal Birth 21 June 1982". P 13½ 2·75 2·75

193 "Serenade" **194** Franklin D. Roosevelt

(Litho Format)

1982 (10 Sept). *Norman Rockwell (painter) Commemoration. T* **193** *and similar vert designs. Multicoloured. P* 13½ × 14.
848 5 c. Type **193** .. 15 10
849 10 c. "The Hikers" .. 15 15
850 20 c. "The Doctor and the Doll" .. 30 25
851 30 c. "Home from Camp" .. 35 30
848/51 .. *Set of* 4 85 70

1982 (30 Sept). *Air. American Anniversaries. T* **194** *and similar vert designs. Multicoloured. P* 14.
852 60 c. Type **194** .. 90 70
853 80 c. Benjamin Franklin .. 1·00 80
854 $1.40, George Washington .. 1·50 1·25
852/4 .. *Set of* 3 3·00 2·50
MS855 116 × 60 mm. Nos. 852/4. P 13½ .. 3·00 3·00
Anniversaries:—60 c. Roosevelt birth centenary; 80 c. "Articles of Peace" negotiations bicentenary; $1.40, Washington 250th birth anniv.

195 "Virgin with Garlands" (detail) (Rubens) and Princess Diana with Prince William **196** Princess Diana and Prince William

1982 (30 Nov). *Christmas. T* **195** *and similar horiz designs depicting different details from Rubens' painting "Virgin with Garlands". P* 13½ × 14.
856 35 c. multicoloured .. 55 35
857 48 c. multicoloured .. 70 50
858 60 c. multicoloured .. 85 60
859 $1.70, multicoloured .. 1·50 1·40
856/9 .. *Set of* 4 3·25 2·50
MS860 104 × 83 mm. 60 c × 4. Designs, each 27 × 32 mm, forming complete painting "Virgin with Garlands". P 13 × 13½ .. 2·50 3·00

1982 (30 Nov). *Christmas. Birth of Prince William of Wales. Children's Charity. Sheet* 73 × 59 *mm. P* 13.
MS861 **196** 75 c. + 5 c. multicoloured .. 1·10 1·40
No. **MS**861 comes with 4 different background designs showing details from painting "Virgin with Garlands" (Rubens).

197 Statue of Tangaroa **198** Scouts using Map and Compass

1983 (14 Mar). *Commonwealth Day. T* **197** *and similar vert designs. Multicoloured. P* 14 × 13½.
862 60 c. Type **197** .. 55 60
863 60 c. Rarotonga oranges .. 55 60
864 60 c. Rarotonga airport .. 55 60
865 60 c. Prime Minister Sir Thomas Davis .. 55 60
862/5 .. *Set of* 4 2·00 2·10
Nos. 862/5 were issued together, *se-tenant*, in blocks of four throughout the sheet.

1983 (5 Apr). *75th Anniv of Boy Scout Movement and 125th Birth Anniv of Lord Baden-Powell. T* **198** *and similar vert designs. Multicoloured. P* 13.
866 12 c. Type **198** .. 40 20
867 12 c. Hiking .. 40 20
868 36 c. Campfire cooking .. 60 40
869 36 c. Erecting tent .. 60 40
870 48 c. Hauling on rope .. 75 55
871 48 c. Using bos'n's chair .. 75 55
872 60 c. Digging hole for sapling .. 90 70
873 60 c. Planting sapling .. 90 70
866/73 .. *Set of* 8 4·75 3·25
MS874 161 × 132 mm. As Nos. 866/73, but each with a premium of 2 c. .. 4·75 4·75
The two designs of each value were printed together, *se-tenant*, in horizontal pairs throughout the sheets.

XV WORLD JAMBOREE

(199)

1983 (4 July). *15th World Scout Jamboree, Alberta, Canada. Nos.* 866/74 *optd with T* **199** *(Nos.* 875, 877, 879, 881) *or with* "ALBERTA, CANADA 1983" *(others).*
875 12 c. Type **198** .. 20 20
876 12 c. Hiking .. 20 20
877 36 c. Campfire cooking .. 40 40
878 36 c. Erecting tent .. 40 40
879 48 c. Hauling on rope .. 55 55
880 48 c. Using bos'n's chair .. 55 55
881 60 c. Digging hole for sapling .. 70 70
882 60 c. Planting sapling .. 70 70
875/82 .. *Set of* 8 3·25 3·25
MS883 161 × 132 mm. As Nos. 875/82, but each with a premium of 2 c. .. 3·25 3·75
The two designs of each value were printed together, *se-tenant*, in horizontal pairs throughout the sheet. In each such pair the left-hand design is overprinted with Type **199** and the right-hand with "ALBERTA, CANADA 1983".

18c $5.60

(200) (201)

1983 (12–30 Aug). *Various stamps surch. (a) Nos.* 733/6, 745/8,753/ 64 *and* 773/6 *as T* **200.**
884 18 c. on 8 c. multicoloured (No. 733) .. 30 30
885 18 c. on 8 c. multicoloured (No. 734) .. 30 30
886 18 c. on 8 c. multicoloured (No. 735) .. 30 30
887 18 c. on 8 c. multicoloured (No. 736) .. 30 30
888 36 c. on 15 c. multicoloured (No. 745) .. 55 55
889 36 c. on 15 c. multicoloured (No. 746) .. 55 55
890 36 c. on 15 c. multicoloured (No. 747) .. 55 55
891 36 c. on 15 c. multicoloured (No. 748) .. 55 55
892 36 c. on 30 c. multicoloured (No. 757) .. 55 55
893 36 c. on 30 c. multicoloured (No. 758) .. 55 55
894 36 c. on 30 c. multicoloured (No. 759) .. 55 55
895 36 c. on 30 c. multicoloured (No. 760) .. 55 55
896 36 c. on 35 c. multicoloured (No. 761) (30.8.83) .. 55 55
897 36 c. on 35 c. multicoloured (No. 762) (30.8.83) .. 55 55
898 36 c. on 35 c. multicoloured (No. 763) (30.8.83) .. 55 55
899 36 c. on 35 c. multicoloured (No. 764) (30.8.83) .. 55 55
900 48 c. on 25 c. multicoloured (No. 753) .. 70 70
901 48 c. on 25 c. multicoloured (No. 754) .. 70 70
902 48 c. on 25 c. multicoloured (No. 755) .. 70 70
903 48 c. on 25 c. multicoloured (No. 756) .. 70 70
904 72 c. on 70 c. multicoloured (No. 773) .. 1·00 1·00
905 72 c. on 70 c. multicoloured (No. 774) .. 1·00 1·00
906 72 c. on 70 c. multicoloured (No. 775) .. 1·00 1·00
907 72 c. on 70 c. multicoloured (No. 776) .. 1·00 1·00

(b) Nos. 788/9, 813, 835/6 *and* 854, *as T* **201** *in gold*
908 96 c. on $1.40, George Washington .. 1·50 1·50
909 96 c. on $2 Prince Charles and Lady Diana Spencer .. 8·50 5·50
a. Surch double .. £125
b. Error. Surch on No. 840 .. 16·00
ba. Pair, Nos. 909 b/c .. 32·00
c. Error. Surch on No. 841 .. 16·00
910 96 c. on $2·50 Princess Diana (inscr "21st Birthday") (30.8.83) .. 3·00 3·00
911 96 c. on $2.50. As No. 910 but inscr "1 July 1982" (30.8.83) .. 3·00 3·00
912 $5.60 on $6 *Stylaster echinatus* .. 9·50 8·50
913 $5.60 on $10 *Melithaea albitincta* (30.8.83) .. 8·50 8·50
884/913 .. *Set of* 30 42·00 40·00
The surcharge on No. 908 is printed in gold, on a black background, over the old value.

202 Union Flag **203** Dish Aerial, Satellite Earth Station

1983 (9 Sept). *Cook Islands Flags and Ensigns. T* **202** *and similar horiz designs. Multicoloured. P* 13½ × 14. *(a) Postage. Gold frames.*
914 6 c. Type **202** .. 10 10
915 6 c. Group Federal flag .. 10 10
916 12 c. Raratonga ensign .. 10 10
917 12 c. Flag of New Zealand .. 10 10
918 15 c. Cook Islands' flag (1973–79) .. 15 15
919 15 c. Cook Islands' National flag .. 15 15

(b) Air. Silver frames and backgrounds changed
920 20 c. Type **202** .. 20 25
921 20 c. Group Federal flag .. 20 25
922 30 c. Raratonga ensign .. 25 30
923 30 c. Flag of New Zealand .. 25 30
924 35 c. Cook Islands' flag (1973–79) .. 30 35
925 35 c. Cook Islands' National flag .. 30 35
914/25 .. *Set of* 12 1·75 2·00
MS926 Two sheets, each 132 × 120 mm. (a) Nos. 914/19; (b) Nos. 920/5. P 13 .. 1·90 2·75
The two designs of each value were issued as *se-tenant* horizontal pairs within the sheets.

1983 (10 Oct). *World Communications Year. T* **203** *and similar vert designs showing satellites. P* 13.
927 36 c. multicoloured .. 30 35
928 48 c. multicoloured .. 45 45
929 60 c. multicoloured .. 55 60
930 96 c. multicoloured .. 85 90
927/30 .. *Set of* 4 1·90 2·10
MS931 90 × 65 mm. $2 multicoloured .. 1·75 2·00

204 "La Belle Jardinière" **205** Montgolfier Balloon 1783

1983 (14 Nov). *Christmas. 500th Birth Anniv of Raphael. T* **204** *and similar vert designs. Multicoloured. P* 14 × 13½.
932 12 c. Type **204** .. 10 10
933 18 c. "Madonna and Child with Five Saints" .. 25 25
934 36 c. "Madonna and Child with St. John" .. 35 35
935 48 c. "Madonna of the Fish" .. 45 45
936 60 c. "The Madonna of the Baldacchino" .. 60 60
932/6 .. *Set of* 5 1·60 1·60
MS937 139 × 113 mm. As Nos. 932/6 but each with a premium of 3 c. .. 1·60 1·75
Nos. 932/6 were each printed in small sheets of 5 stamps and 1 label.

1983 (9 Dec). *Christmas. 500th Birth Anniv of Raphael. Children's Charity. Designs as Nos. 932/6 in separate miniature sheets* 66 × 82 *mm., each with a face value of* 85 c. + 5 c. *P* 13.
MS938 As Nos. 932/6 .. *Set of 5 sheets* 4·00 4·25

1984 (16 Jan). *Bicentenary of Manned Flight* (1983). *T* **205** *and similar vert designs. Multicoloured. P* 13.
939 36 c. Type **205** .. 30 35
940 48 c. Adorne's ascent, Strasbourg, 1784 .. 40 45
941 60 c. Balloon driven by sails, 1785 .. 55 60
942 72 c. Ascent of man on horse, 1798 .. 70 75
943 96 c. Godard's aerial acrobatics, 1850 .. 85 90
939/43 .. *Set of* 5 2·50 2·75
MS944 104 × 85 mm. $2.50, Blanchard and Jeffries crossing Channel, 1785 .. 2·25 2·75
MS945 122 × 132 mm. As Nos. 939/43 but each with a premium of 5 c. .. 2·50 3·00
Nos. 939/43 were each printed in small sheets of 5 stamps and 1 label.

206 Cuvier's Beaked Whale **207** Athens, 1896

1984 (10 Feb). *Save the Whales. T* **206** *and similar horiz designs. Multicoloured. P* 13.
946 10 c. Type **206** .. 25 15
947 18 c. Risso's Dolphin .. 45 30
948 20 c. True's Beaked Whale .. 45 30
949 24 c. Long-finned Pilot Whale .. 55 30
950 30 c. Narwhal .. 60 40
951 36 c. White Whale (Beluga) .. 70 55
952 42 c. Common Dolphin .. 80 60
953 48 c. Commerson's Dolphin .. 85 70
954 60 c. Bottle-nosed Dolphin .. 1·10 80
955 72 c. Sowerby's Beaked Whale .. 1·25 1·00
956 96 c. Common Porpoise .. 1·40 1·25
957 $2 Boutu .. 2·25 2·25
946/57 .. *Set of* 12 9·50 7·75

1984 (8 Mar). *Olympic Games, Los Angeles. T* **207** *and similar vert designs showing official posters of earlier Games. Multicoloured. P* 13½.
958 18 c. Type **207** .. 15 20
959 24 c. Paris, 1900 .. 20 25
960 36 c. St. Louis, 1904 .. 30 35
961 48 c. London, 1948 .. 40 45
962 60 c. Tokyo, 1964 .. 45 50
963 72 c. Berlin, 1936 .. 55 60
964 96 c. Rome, 1960 .. 75 80
965 $1.20 Los Angeles, 1930 .. 90 95
958/65 .. *Set of* 8 3·50 3·75

208 *Siphonogorgia*

$3.60

(209)

1984 (23 Mar–10 Aug). *Corals (2nd series). (a) Designs as No. 713 etc, but with redrawn frames and inscriptions as in T* **208**. *Multicoloured. P* 13.

966	1 c. Type **208**	10	10
967	2 c. *Millepora alcicornis*	10	10
968	3 c. *Distichopora violacea*	10	10
969	5 c. *Ptilosarcus gurneyi*	10	10
970	10 c. *Lobophyllia bemprichii*	10	10
971	12 c. *Sarcophyton digitatum*	10	10
972	14 c. *Pavona praetorta*	10	10
973	18 c. *Junceella gemmacea*	15	15
974	20 c. *Stylaster*	15	15
975	24 c. *Stylophora pistillata*	15	20
976	30 c. *Palauastrea ramosa*	20	25
977	36 c. *Melithaea albitincta*	25	30
978	40 c. *Stylaster echinatus*	25	30
979	42 c. *Fungia fungites*	30	35
980	48 c. *Gonipora*	30	35
981	50 c. *Melithaea squamata* (15 May)	30	35
982	52 c. *Bellonella indica* (15 May)	35	40
983	55 c. *Plerogyra sinuosa* (15 May)	35	40
984	60 c. *Tubastraea* (15 May)	40	45
985	70 c. *Heliofungia actiniformis* (15 May)	45	50
986	85 c. *Caulastraea echinulata* (15 May)	55	60
987	96 c. *Porites andrewsi* (15 May)	65	70
988	$1.10, *Pectinia alcicornis* (15 May)	75	80
989	$1.20, *Dendrophyllia gracilis* (15 May)	80	85

(b) Nos. 785/9 surch as T **209** *in gold on black*

990	$3.60 on $2 *Gonipora* (28 June)	2·40	2·50
991	$4.20 on $3 *Heliofungia actiniformis* (28 June)	2·75	3·00
992	$5 on $4 *Stylophora pistillata* (28 June)	3·25	3·50
993	$7.20 on $6 *Stylaster echinatus* (20 July)	5·00	5·25
994	$9.60 on $10 *Melithaea albitincta* (10 Aug)	6·25	6·50
966/94	*Set of* 29	24·00	26·00

Equestrian
Team Dressage
Germany

(210)

1984 (24 Aug). *Olympic Gold Medal Winners. Nos. 963/5 optd as T* **210**.

995	72 c. Berlin, 1936 (optd T 210)	60	65
996	96 c. Rome, 1960 (optd "Decathlon Daley Thompson Great Britain")	80	85
997	$1.20 Los Angeles, 1930 (optd "Four Gold Medals Carl Lewis U.S.A."	1·00	1·10
995/7	*Set of* 3	2·25	2·40

211 Capt. Cook's Cottage, Melbourne

1984 (20 Sept). *"Ausipex" International Stamp Exhibition, Melbourne. T* **211** *and similar horiz designs. Multicoloured. P* 13.

998	36 c. Type **211**	65	65
999	48 c. "H.M.S. *Endeavour* careened for Repairs" (Sydney Parkinson)	1·00	1·00
1000	60 c. "Cook's landing at Botany Bay" (E. Phillips Fox)	1·25	1·25
1001	$2 "Capt. James Cook" (John Webber)	2·75	2·75
998/1001	*Set of* 4	5·00	5·00
MS1002	140 × 100 mm. As Nos. 998/1001, but each stamp with a face value of 90 c.	5·50	6·00

Commemorating-
15 Sept. 1984

(212)

213 "Virgin on Throne with Child" (Giovanni Bellini)

1984 (15 Oct). *Birth of Prince Henry. Nos. 812 and 833/6 optd or surch (No. 1007) as T* **212**.

1003	$1.25, Type **191** (optd with T **212**) (Gold)	1·75	1·10
	a. Pair. Nos. 1003/4	3·50	2·25
1004	$1.25, As Type **191**, but inscr "1 July 1982" (optd "Birth H.R.H. Prince Henry") (Gold)	1·75	1·10
1005	$2.50, Princess Diana (inscr "21st Birthday") (optd with T **212**) (Gold)	3·00	2·00
	a. Pair. Nos. 1005/6	6·00	4·00
1006	$2.50, As No. 835, but inscr "1 July 1982" (optd "Birth H.R.H. Prince Henry") (Gold)	3·00	2·00
1007	$3 on $1 Type **187** (surch "Royal Birth Prince Henry 15 Sept. 1984") (Sil.)	6·00	4·00
1003/7	*Set of* 5	13·50	9·25

1984 (21 Nov). *Christmas. T* **213** *and similar vert designs. Multicoloured. P* 14.

1008	36 c. Type **213**	30	35
1009	48 c. "Virgin and Child" (anonymous, 15th century)	40	45
1010	60 c. "Virgin and Child with Saints" (Alvise Vivarini)	45	50
1011	96 c. "Virgin and Child with Angels" (H. Memling)	75	80
1012	$1.20, "Adoration of Magi" (G. Tiepolo)	90	95
1008/12	*Set of* 5	2·50	2·75
MS1013	120 × 113 mm. As Nos. 1008/12, but each with a premium of 5 c. P 13½.	2·75	3·00

1984 (10 Dec). *Christmas. Designs as Nos. 1008/12 in separate miniature sheets, 62 × 76 mm, each with a face value of 95 c. + 5 c. P* 13½.

MS1014	As Nos. 1008/12	*Set of 5 sheets* 3·75	4·00

214 Downy Woodpecker

1985 (23 Apr). *Birth Bicentenary of John J. Audubon (ornithologist). T* **214** *and similar vert designs showing original paintings. Multicoloured. P* 13 × 13½.

1015	30 c. Type **214**	65	40
1016	55 c. Black-throated Blue Warbler	90	70
1017	65 c. Yellow-throated Warbler	1·00	80
1018	75 c. Chestnut-sided Warbler	1·10	1·00
1019	95 c. Dickcissel	1·40	1·10
1020	$1.15, White-crowned Sparrow	1·60	1·25
1015/20	*Set of* 6	6·00	4·75
MS1021	Three sheets, each 76 × 75 mm. (a) $1.30, Red-cockaded Woodpecker. (b) $2.80, Seaside Sparrow. (c) $5.30, Zenaida Dove *Set of* 3 *sheets*	8·50	8·50

215 "The Kingston Flyer" (New Zealand)

(Des and litho Format)

1985 (14 May). *Famous Trains. T* **215** *and similar horiz designs. Multicoloured. Ordinary paper. P* 14 × 13½.

1022	20 c. Type **215**	55	20
1023	55 c. Class "640" (Italy)	85	50
1024	65 c. "Gotthard" type (Switzerland)	1·00	55
1025	75 c. Union Pacific No. 6900 (U.S.A.)	1·25	65
1026	95 c. "Super Continental" type (Canada)	1·50	80
1027	$1.15, "TGV" type (France)	1·75	95
1028	$2.20, "The Flying Scotsman" (Great Britain)	2·50	1·75
1029	$3.40, "The Orient Express"	2·75	2·75
1022/9	*Set of* 8	11·00	7·00

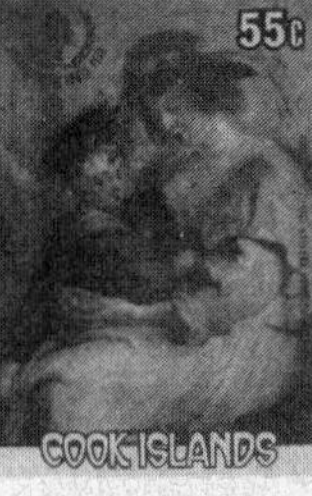

216 "Helena Fourment" (Peter Paul Rubens)

217 "Lady Elizabeth, 1908" (Mabel Hankey)

1985 (6 June). *International Youth Year. T* **216** *and similar vert designs. Multicoloured. P* 13.

1030	55 c. Type **216**	65	50
1031	65 c. "Vigee-Lebrun and Daughter" (E. Vigee-Lebrun)	75	55
1032	75 c. "On the Terrace" (P. Renoir)	85	65
1033	$1.30, "Young Mother Sewing" (M. Cassatt)	1·25	1·40
1030/3	*Set of* 4	3·25	2·75
MS1034	103 × 106 mm. As Nos. 1030/3, but each with a premium of 10 c.	3·25	3·50

1985 (28 June). *Life and Times of Queen Elizabeth the Queen Mother. T* **217** *and similar vert designs showing paintings. Multicoloured. P* 13.

1035	65 c. Type **217**	50	55
1036	75 c. "Duchess of York, 1923" (Savely Sorine)	60	65
1037	$1.15, "Duchess of York, 1925" (Philip de Laszlo)	90	95
1038	$2.80, "Queen Elizabeth, 1938" (Sir Gerald Kelly)	2·10	2·25
1035/8	*Set of* 4	3·75	4·00
MS1039	69 × 81 mm. $5.30, As $2.80	4·00	4·25

Nos. 1035/8 were each printed in small sheets of 4 stamps.

For these designs in a miniature sheet, each with a face value of 55 c., see No. **MS**1079.

218 Albert Henry (Prime Minister, 1965–78)

219 Golf

1985 (29 July). *20th Anniv of Self-Government. T* **218** *and similar vert designs. Multicoloured. P* 13.

1040	30 c. Type **218**	25	30
1041	50 c. Sir Thomas Davis (Prime Minister, 1978–Apr 1983 and from Nov 1983)	40	45
1042	65 c. Geoffrey Henry (Prime Minister, Apr–Nov 1983)	50	55
1040/2	*Set of* 3	1·00	1·10
MS1043	134 × 70 mm. As Nos. 1040/2, but each stamp with a face value of 55 c.	1·25	1·40

1985 (29 July). *South Pacific Mini Games, Rarotonga. T* **219** *and similar vert designs. Multicoloured. P* 14.

1044	55 c. Type **219**	1·00	1·00
1045	65 c. Rugby	1·10	1·10
1046	75 c. Tennis	1·25	1·25
1044/6	*Set of* 3	3·00	3·00
MS1047	126 × 70 mm. Nos. 1044/6, but each with a premium of 10 c. P 13½.	3·25	3·50

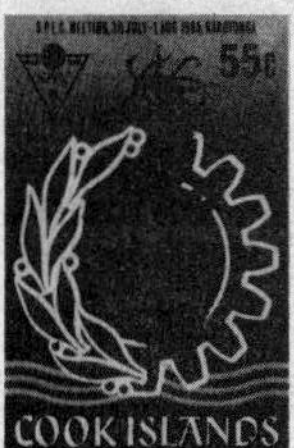

220 Sea Horse, Gearwheel and Leaves

221 "Madonna of the Magnificat"

1985 (29 July). *Pacific Conferences, Rarotonga. P* 13.

1048	**220**	55 c. black, gold and rosine	45	50
1049		65 c. black, gold and violet	50	55
1050		75 c. black, gold and blue-green	60	65
1048/50		*Set of* 3	1·40	1·50
MS1051		126 × 81 mm. As Nos. 1048/50, but each stamp with a face value of 50 c.	1·25	1·40

No. 1048 shows the South Pacific Bureau for Economic Co-operation logo and is inscribed "S.P.E.C. Meeting, 30 July–1 Aug 1985, Rarotonga". No. 1049 also shows the S.P.E.C. logo, but is inscribed "South Pacific Forum, 4–6 Aug 1985, Rarotonga". No. 1050 shows the Pacific Islands Conference logo and the inscription "Pacific Islands Conference, 7–10 Aug 1985, Rarotonga".

1985 (18 Nov). *Christmas. Virgin and Child Paintings by Botticelli. T* **221** *and similar vert designs. Multicoloured. P* 14.

1052	55 c. Type **221**	60	50
1053	65 c. "Madonna with Pomegranate"	65	55
1054	75 c. "Madonna and Child with Six Angels"	75	65
1055	95 c. "Madonna and Child with St. John"	95	80
1052/5	*Set of* 4	2·75	2·25
MS1056	90 × 104 mm. As Nos. 1052/5, but each stamp with a face value of 50 c. P 13½	1·75	2·00

1985 (9 Dec). *Christmas. Virgin and Child Paintings by Botticelli. Square designs* (46 × 46 *mm*) *as Nos.* 1052/5 *in separate miniature sheets,* 50 × 51 *mm, with face values of* $1.20, $1.45, $2.20 *and* $2.75. *Imperf.*

MS1057	As Nos. 1052/5	*Set of 4 sheets* 7·00	7·50

222 "The Eve of the Deluge" (John Martin)

223 Queen Elizabeth II

1986 (13 Mar). *Appearance of Halley's Comet. Paintings. T* **222** *and similar vert designs. Multicoloured. P* 14.
1058 55 c. Type **222** 70 60
1059 65 c. "Lot and his Daughters" (Lucas van Leyden) 80 70
1060 75 c. "Auspicious Comet" (from treatise *c* 1587) 90 80
1061 $1.25, "Events following Charles I" (Herman Saftleven) .. .. .. 1·50 1·25
1062 $2 "Ossian receiving Napoleonic Officers" (Anne Louis Girodet-Trioson) .. 2·25 2·00
1058/62 .. .. *Set of* 5 5·50 4·75
MS1063 130×100 mm. As Nos. 1058/62, but each with a face value of 70 c. P 13½ .. .. 3·00 3·50
MS1064 84×63 mm. $4 "Halley's Comet of 1759 over the Thames" (Samuel Scott). P 13½ .. 3·25 3·75

1986 (21 Apr). *60th Birthday of Queen Elizabeth II. T* **223** *and similar vert designs showing formal portraits. P* 13×13½.
1065 95 c. multicoloured .. .. 1·25 1·25
1066 $1.25, multicoloured .. .. 1·50 1·50
1067 $1.50, multicoloured .. .. 1·75 1·75
1065/7 .. .. *Set of* 3 4·00 4·00
MS1068 Three sheets, each 44×75 mm. As Nos. 1065/7, but with face values of $1.10, $1.95 and $2.45 .. .. .. *Set of* 3 *sheets* 6·50 7·50

224 U.S.A. 1847 Franklin 5 c. Stamp and H.M.S. *Resolution* at Rarotonga

225 Head of Statue of Liberty

1986 (21 May). *"Ameripex '86" International Stamp Exhibition, Chicago. T* **224** *and similar horiz designs. Multicoloured. P* 14.
1069 $1 Type **224** .. .. 1·50 1·50
1070 $1.50, Chicago .. .. 2·00 2·00
1071 $2 1975 definitive $2, Benjamin Franklin and H.M.S. *Resolution* .. .. .. 2·50 2·50
1069/71 .. .. *Set of* 3 5·50 5·50

1986 (4 July). *Centenary of Statue of Liberty. T* **225** *and similar vert designs. Multicoloured. P* 14.
1072 $1 Type **225** 75 75
1073 $1.25, Hand and torch of Statue 90 90
1074 $2.75, Statue of Liberty .. .. .. 2·00 2·00
1072/4 .. .. *Set of* 3 3·25 3·25

226 Miss Sarah Ferguson

(227)

1986 (23 July). *Royal Wedding. T* **226** *and similar multicoloured designs. P* 14 ($1, $2) *or* 13½×13 ($3).
1075 $1 Type **226** .. .. 1·00 1·00
1076 $2 Prince Andrew .. .. 1·75 1·75
1077 $3 Prince Andrew and Miss Sarah Ferguson (57×31 *mm*) .. .. 2·50 2·50
1075/7 .. .. *Set of* 3 4·75 4·75
Nos. 1075/7 were each printed in small sheets of 4 stamps.

1986 (4 Aug). *"Stampex '86" Stamp Exhibition, Adelaide. No.* **MS**1002 *optd with T* **227** *in gold (circle) and black (inscr) only on design as No.* 1001.
MS1078 90 c.×4 multicoloured .. .. 4·00 4·50
The "Stampex '86" exhibition emblem is also overprinted on the sheet margin.

1986 (4 Aug). *86th Birthday of Queen Elizabeth the Queen Mother. Designs as Nos.* 1035/8 *in miniature sheet,* 91×116 *mm, each stamp with a face value of* 55 *c. Multicoloured. P* 13×13½.
MS1079 55 c.×4. As Nos. 1035/8 .. .. .. 2·50 3·00

228 "The Holy Family with St. John the Baptist and St. Elizabeth"

+10c

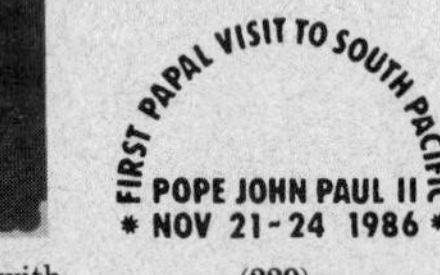

(229)

1986 (17 Nov). *Christmas. Paintings by Rubens. T* **228** *and similar vert designs. Multicoloured. P* 13½.
1080 55 c. Type **228** 40 45
1081 $1.30, "Virgin with the Garland" 90 95
1082 $2.75, "The Adoration of the Magi" (detail) .. .. 1·90 2·00
1080/2 .. .. *Set of* 3 3·00 3·00
MS1083 140×100 mm. As Nos. 1080/2, but each size 36×46 mm with a face value of $2.40 .. 6·00 7·50
MS1084 80×70 mm. $6.40, As No. 1081 but size 32×50 mm .. .. 6·00 7·50

1986 (21 Nov). *Visit of Pope John Paul II to South Pacific. Nos.* 1080/4 *surch as T* **229** *in silver.*
1085 55 c. + 10 c. Type **228** 60 60
1086 $1.30 + 10 c. "Virgin with the Garland" 1·25 1·25
1087 $2.75 + 10 c. "The Adoration of the Magi" (detail) .. .. 2·50 2·50
1085/7 .. .. *Set of* 3 4·00 4·00
MS1088 140×100 mm. As Nos. 1085/7, but each size 36×46 mm with a face value of $2.40 + 10 c. 6·50 8·00
MS1089 80×70 mm. $6.40 + 50 c. As No. 1086 but size 32×50 mm .. .. 6·50 8·00

HURRICANE RELIEF
10c (230)
+50c (231)

1987 (10–12 Feb). *Various stamps surch as T* **230** *by N.Z. Govt Printer.*

(*a*) *On Nos.* 741/56, 761/76 *and* 787/8
1090 10 c. on 15 c. *Distichopora violacea* (11.2) .. 10 10
1091 10 c. on 15 c. *Stylaster* (11.2) 10 10
1092 10 c. on 15 c. *Gonipora* (11.2) 10 10
1093 10 c. on 15 c. *Caulastraea echinulata* (11.2) 10 10
1094 10 c. on 25 c. *Lobophyllia bemprichii* (11.2) 10 10
1095 10 c. on 25 c. *Palauastrea ramosa* (11.2) .. 10 10
1096 10 c. on 25 c. *Bellonella indica* (11.2) .. 10 10
1097 10 c. on 25 c. *Pectinia alcicornis* (11.2) .. 10 10
1098 18 c. on 12 c. *Millepora alcicornis* (11.2) .. 15 15
1099 18 c. on 12 c. *Junceella gemmacea* (11.2) . 15 15
1100 18 c. on 12 c. *Fungia fungites* (11.2) .. 15 15
1101 18 c. on 12 c. *Heliofungia actiniformis* (11.2) 15 15
1102 18 c. on 20 c. *Ptilosarcus gurneyi* (11.2) .. 15 15
1103 18 c. on 20 c. *Stylophora pistillata* (11.2) .. 15 15
1104 18 c. on 20 c. *Melithaea squamata* (11.2) .. 15 15
1105 18 c. on 20 c. *Porites andrewsi* (11.2) .. 15 15
1106 55 c. on 35 c. Type **184** (11.2) 40 45
1107 55 c. on 35 c. *Pavona praetorta* (11.2) .. 40 45
1108 55 c. on 35 c. *Stylaster echinatus* (11.2) .. 40 45
1109 55 c. on 35 c. *Tubastraea* (11.2) 40 45
1110 65 c. on 50 c. As No. 1098 (11.2) 45 50
1111 65 c. on 50 c. As No. 1099 (11.2) 45 50
1112 65 c. on 50 c. As No. 1100 (11.2) 45 50
1113 65 c. on 50 c. As No. 1101 (11.2) 45 50
1114 65 c. on 60 c. As No. 1090 (11.2) 45 50
1115 65 c. on 60 c. As No. 1091 (11.2) 45 50
1116 65 c. on 60 c. As No. 1092 (11.2) 45 50
1117 65 c. on 60 c. As No. 1093 (11.2) 45 50
1118 75 c. on 70 c. As No. 1102 (11.2) 55 60
1119 75 c. on 70 c. As No. 1103 (11.2) 55 60
1120 75 c. on 70 c. As No. 1104 (11.2) 55 60
1121 75 c. on 70 c. As No. 1105 (11.2) 55 60
1122 $6.40 on $4 *Stylophora pistillata* .. 4·50 4·75
1123 $7.20 on $6 *Stylaster echinatus* .. 5·00 5·25

(*b*) *On Nos.* 812/13 *in gold* (12 Feb)
1124 $9.40 on $1 Type **187** .. .. .. 15·00 16·00
1125 $9.40 on $2 Prince Charles and Lady Diana Spencer .. .. 15·00 16·00

(*c*) *On Nos.* 835/6 *in gold* (12 Feb)
1126 $9.40 on $2.50 Princess of Wales (inscr "21st Birthday") .. .. .. 15·00 16·00
1127 $9.40 on $2.50 As No. 1126, but inscr "1 July 1982" .. .. 15·00 16·00

(*d*) *On Nos.* 966/8, 971/2, 975, 979/80, 982 *and* 987/9
1128 5 c. on 1 c. Type **208** 10 10
1129 5 c. on 2 c. *Millepora alcicornis* 10 10
1130 5 c. on 3 c. *Distichopora violacea* 10 10
1131 5 c. on 12 c. *Sarcophyton digitatum* .. 10 10
1132 5 c. on 14 c. *Pavona praetorta* 10 10
1133 18 c. on 24 c. *Stylophora pistillata* 15 15
1134 55 c. on 52 c. *Bellonella indica* 40 45
1135 65 c. on 42 c. *Fungia fungites* 45 50
1136 75 c. on 48 c. *Gonipora* 55 60
1137 95 c. on 96 c. *Porites andrewsi* 70 75
1138 95 c. on $1.10 *Pectinia alcicornis* 70 75
1139 95 c. on $1.20 *Dendrophyllia gracilis* .. 70 75

(*e*) *On Nos.* 998/1001 *in gold* (*No.* 1143) *or gold* (*value*) *and black* (*bars*) (*others*) (12 Feb)
1140 $1.30 on 36 c. Type **211** .. .. .. 1·40 1·50
1141 $1.30 on 48 c. "The *Endeavour* careened for Repairs" (Sydney Parkinson) .. 1·40 1·50
1142 $1.30 on 60 c. "Cook's landing at Botany Bay" (E. Phillips Fox) .. .. .. 1·40 1·50
1143 $1.30 on $2 "Capt. James Cook" (John Webber) .. .. 1·40 1·50

(*f*) *On Nos.* 1065/7 *in gold* (12 Feb)
1144 **223** $2.80 on 95 c. multicoloured .. .. 7·00 7·50
1145 – $2.80 on $1.25 multicoloured .. .. 7·00 7·50
1146 – $2.80 on $1.50 multicoloured .. .. 7·00 7·50

(*g*) *On Nos.* 1075/7 *in gold* (*value*) *and black* (*bars*) (12 Feb)
1147 $2.80 on $1 Type **226** .. .. .. 6·00 6·50
1148 $2.80 on $2 Prince Andrew .. .. 6·00 6·50
1149 $2.80 on $3 Prince Andrew and Miss Sarah Ferguson (57 × 31 *mm*) .. 6·00 6·50
1090/149 .. .. *Set of* 60 £100 £120

1987 (17 June). *Various stamps surch as T* **230**.

(*a*) *On Nos.* 785/6 *and* 789
1150 $2.80 on $2 *Gonipora* .. .. .. 2·10 2·25
1151 $5 on $3 *Heliofungia actiniformis* .. .. 4·00 4·25
1152 $9.40 on $10 *Melithaea albitincta* .. .. 7·50 7·75

(*b*) *On Nos.* 838/42 (*in gold on Nos.* 1153/6)
1153 $9.40 on $1 Type **187** (No. 838) .. 7·50 7·75
a. Pair. Nos. 1153/4 .. .. .. 15·00 15·50
1154 $9.40 on $1 Type **187** (No. 839) .. .. 7·50 7·75
1155 $9.40 on $2 Prince Charles and Lady Diana Spencer (No. 840) .. .. 7·50 7·75
a. Pair. Nos. 1155/6 .. .. .. 15·00 15·50
1156 $9.40 on $2 Prince Charles and Lady Diana Spencer (No. 841) .. .. 7·50 7·75
1150/6 .. .. *Set of* 7 40·00 40·00
MS1157 106×59 mm. $9.20 on $1 Type **187**; $9.20 on $2 Prince Charles and Lady Diana Spencer .. .. 14·50 16·00

1987 (30 June–31 July). *Hurricane Relief Fund. Various stamps surch as T* **231**.

(*a*) *On Nos.* 1035/9 *in silver*
1158 65 c. + 50 c. Type **217** 80 85
1159 75 c. + 50 c. "Duchess of York, 1923" (Savely Sorine) 85 90
1160 $1.15 + 50 c. "Duchess of York, 1925" (Philip de Laszlo) .. .. .. 1·10 1·25
1161 $2.80 + 50 c. "Queen Elizabeth, 1938" (Sir Gerald Kelly) .. .. .. 2·25 2·40
MS1162 69×81 mm. $5.30 + 50 c. As $2.80 + 50 c. .. .. 4·00 4·50

(*b*) *On Nos.* 1058/62 (*in silver on Nos.* 1164/6)
1163 55 c. + 50 c. Type **222** 75 80
1164 65 c. + 50 c. "Lot and his Daughters" (Lucas van Leyden) 80 85
1165 75 c. + 50 c. "Auspicious Comet" (from treatise *c* 1587) 85 90
1166 $1.25 + 50 c. "Events following Charles I" (Herman Saftleven) .. .. 1·25 1·40
1167 $2 + 50 c. "Ossian receiving Napoleonic Officers" (Anne Louis Girodet-Trioson) .. .. 1·75 2·00

(*c*) *On Nos.* 1065/8 (*in silver on No.* 1169) (31 July)
1168 **223** 95 c. + 50 c. multicoloured .. .. 1·00 1·10
1169 – $1.25 + 50 c. multicoloured .. .. 1·25 1·40
1170 – $1.50 + 50 c. multicoloured .. .. 1·40 1·50
MS1171 Three sheets, each 44×75 mm. As Nos. 1168/70, but with face values of $1.10 + 50 c., $1.95 + 50 c., $2.45 + 50 c. *Set of* 3 *sheets* 5·00 6·00

(*d*) *On Nos.* 1069/71 (*in silver on No.* 1172)
1172 $1 + 50 c. Type **224** .. .. 1·00 1·10
1173 $1.50 + 50 c. Chicago .. .. .. 1·40 1·50
1174 $2 + 50 c. 1975 definitive $2, Benjamin Franklin and H.M.S. *Resolution* .. 1·75 1·90

(*e*) *On Nos.* 1072/4 (*in silver on Nos.* 1175 *and* 1177)
1175 $1 + 50 c. Type **225** .. .. 1·00 1·10
1176 $1.25 + 50 c. Hand and torch of Statue .. 1·25 1·40
1177 $2.75 + 50 c. Statue of Liberty .. .. 2·25 2·40

(*f*) *On Nos.* 1075/7 *in silver* (31 July)
1178 $1 + 50 c. Type **226** .. .. 1·00 1·25
1179 $2 + 50 c. Prince Andrew .. .. .. 1·75 1·90
1180 $3 + 50 c. Prince Andrew and Miss Sarah Ferguson (57×31 *mm*) .. .. 2·40 2·50

(*g*) *On Nos.* 1080/4 *in silver*
1181 55 c. + 50 c. Type **228** 75 80
1182 $1.30 + 50 c. "Virgin with the Garland" .. 1·25 1·40
1183 $2.75 + 50 c. "The Adoration of the Magi" (detail) .. .. 2·25 2·40
MS1184 140×100 mm. As No. 1181/3, but each size 36×46 mm with a face value of $2.40 + 50 c. 6·00 7·00
MS1185 80×70 mm. $6.40 + 50 c. As No. 1182, but size 32×50 mm. .. .. 4·75 5·50

(*h*) *On Nos.* 1122, 1134/7 *and* 1150/1
1186 55 c. + 25 c. on 52 c. *Bellonella indica* .. 55 60
1187 65 c. + 25 c. on 42 c. *Fungia fungites* .. 65 70
1188 75 c. + 25 c. on 48 c. *Gonipora* 70 75
1189 95 c. + 25 c. on 96 c. *Porites andrewsi* .. 85 90
1190 $2.80 + 50 c. on $2 *Gonipora* .. .. 2·25 2·40
1191 $5 + 50 c. on $3 *Heliofungia actiniformis* 3·75 4·00
1192 $6.40 + 50 c. on $4 *Stylophora pistillata* .. 4·75 5·00
1158/92 .. .. *Set of* 31 40·00 45·00

ROYAL
WEDDING
FORTIETH
ANNIVERSARY
(232)

1987 (20 Nov). *Royal Ruby Wedding. Nos.* 484 *and* 787 *optd with T* **232** *in black on gold.*
1193 $4 Queen Elizabeth II and seashells .. 2·75 3·25
1194 $4 Queen Elizabeth II and *Stylophora pistillata* .. .. 2·75 3·25

233 "The Holy Family" (Rembrandt)

1987 (7 Dec). *Christmas. T* **233** *and similar horiz designs showing different paintings of the Holy Family by Rembrandt. P* 13½.
1195 $1.25, multicoloured .. .. 1·00 1·00
1196 $1.50, multicoloured .. .. 1·25 1·25
1197 $1.95, multicoloured .. .. 1·60 1·60
1195/7 .. .. *Set of* 3 3·50 3·50
MS1198 100 × 140 mm. As Nos. 1195/7, but each size 47 × 36 mm with a face value of $1.15 .. 2·40 2·75
MS1199 70 × 80 mm. $6 As No. 1196, but size 40 × 31 mm. P 13 × 13½ .. .. 4·25 4·75

234 Olympic Commemorative $50 Coin

(Des G. Vasarhelyi)

1988 (26 Apr). *Olympic Games, Seoul. T* **234** *and similar vert designs. Multicoloured. P* 13½×14.
1200 $1.50, Type **234** .. .. 1·10 1·25
a. Horiz strip of 3. Nos. 1200/2 .. .. 3·00
1201 $1.50, Olympic torch and Seoul Olympic Park .. .. 1·10 1·25
1202 $1.50, Steffi Graf playing tennis and Olympic medal .. .. .. 1·10 1·25
1200/2 .. .. *Set of* 3 3·00 3·50
MS1203 131×81 mm. $10 Combined design as Nos. 1200/2, but measuring 114×47 mm. P 13½ 8·50 9·00
Nos. 1200/2 were printed together, *se-tenant*, in horizontal strips of 3 throughout the sheet, each strip forming a composite design.

MILOSLAV MECIR
CZECHOSLOVAKIA
GOLD MEDAL WINNER
MEN'S TENNIS

(235)

1988 (12 Oct). *Olympic Tennis Medal Winners, Seoul. Nos.* 1200/3 *optd as T* **235**.
1204 $1.50, Type **234** (optd with T **235**) .. 1·10 1·25
a. Horiz strip of 3. Nos. 1204/6 .. .. 3·00
1205 $1.50, Olympic torch and Seoul Olympic Park (optd "TIM MAYOTTE UNITED STATES GABRIELA SABATINI ARGENTINA SILVER MEDAL WINNERS") .. .. .. 1·10 1·25
1206 $1.50, Steffi Graf playing tennis and Olympic medal (optd "GOLD MEDAL WINNER STEFFI GRAF WEST GERMANY") .. .. .. 1·10 1·25
1204/6 .. .. *Set of* 3 3·00 3·50
MS1207 131×81 mm. $10 Combined design as Nos. 1200/2, but measuring 114×47 mm. (optd "GOLD MEDAL WINNER SEOUL OLYMPIC GAMES STEFFI GRAF-WEST GERMANY") .. 7·00 7·50

236 "Virgin and Child" **237** "Apollo II" leaving Earth

1988 (11 Nov). *Christmas. T* **236** *and similar vert designs showing paintings of "The Nativity"* ($6.40) *or different versions of "Virgin and Child" by Dürer. P* 13½.
1208 70 c. multicoloured 70 70
1209 85 c. multicoloured 80 80
1210 95 c. multicoloured 90 90
1211 $1.25, multicoloured .. .. 1·10 1·10
1208/11 .. .. *Set of* 4 3·25 3·25
MS1212 80 × 100 mm. $6.40, multicoloured (45 × 60 *mm*) .. .. 4·50 4·75

(Des G. Vasarhelyi)

1989 (14 July). *20th Anniv of First Manned Landing on Moon. T* **237** *and similar horiz designs. Multicoloured. P* 13.
1213 40 c. Type **237** 30 35
a. Horiz pair. Nos. 1213/14 .. .. 60 70
1214 40 c. Lunar module over Moon 30 35
1215 55 c. Armstrong stepping onto Moon .. 40 45
a. Horiz pair. Nos. 1215/16 .. .. 80 90
1216 55 c. Astronaut on Moon 40 45
1217 65 c. Working on lunar surface 50 55
a. Horiz pair. Nos. 1217/18 .. .. 1·00 1·10
1218 65 c. Conducting experiment 50 55
1219 75 c. "Apollo 11" leaving Moon 55 60
a. Horiz pair. Nos. 1219/20 .. .. 1·10 1·25
1220 75 c. Splashdown in South Pacific .. 55 60
1213/20 .. .. *Set of* 8 3·25 3·50
MS1221 108×91 mm. $4.20, Astronauts on Moon .. .. 3·25 3·50
Nos. 1213/14, 1215/16, 1217/18 and 1219/20 were each printed together, horizontally *se-tenant*, in sheets of 12.

238 Raratonga Flycatcher

(Des G. Drummond)

1989 (4 Oct). *Endangered Birds of the Cook Islands. T* **238** *and similar horiz designs. Multicoloured. (a) Postage. P* 13½×13
1222 15 c. Type **238** 10 15
1223 20 c. Pair of Raratonga Flycatchers .. 15 20
1224 65 c. Pair of Rarotongan Fruit Doves .. 50 55
1225 70 c. Rarotongan Fruit Dove 50 55
1222/5 .. .. *Set of* 4 1·10 1·25

(b) Air. P 13½
MS1226 Four sheets, each 70×53 mm. As Nos. 1222/5, but with face values of $1, $1.25, $1.50, $1.75 and each size 50×32 mm. .. *Set of* 4 *sheets* 4·00 4·25

239 Villagers

1989 (24 Nov). *Christmas. T* **239** *and similar multicoloured designs showing details from "Adoration of the Magi" by Rubens. P* 13.
1227 70 c. Type **239** 50 55
1228 85 c. Virgin Mary 65 70
1229 95 c. Christ Child 70 75
1230 $1.50, Boy with gift .. .. .. 1·10 1·25
1227/30 .. .. *Set of* 4 2·75 3·00
MS1231 85×120 mm. $6.40, "Adoration of the Magi" (45×60 mm). P 13½ .. .. .. 4·75 5·00

OFFICIAL STAMPS

O.H.M.S. (O 1) O.H.M.S. (O 2)

1975 (17 Mar–19 May). *Nos.* 228/31, 233, 235/7, 239/40, 243/5 *and* 246c/7 *optd with Type* O 1 (5, 10, 18, 25 *and* 30 *c. surch also), in black and silver*
O 1 1 c. *Hibiscus syriacus* .. .. ..
O 2 2 c. Frangipani .. ..
O 3 3 c. "Suva Queen" .. ..
O 4 4 c. Water Lily .. ..
O 5 5 c. on 2½ c. *Clitoria ternatea* .. ..
O 6 8 c. *Allamanda cathartica* .. .. ..
O 7 10 c. on 6 c. Hibiscus .. ..
O 8 18 c. on 20 c. Thunbergia .. .. ..
O 9 25 c. on 9 c. Stephanotis .. .. ..
O10 30 c. on 15 c. Frangipani .. .. ..
O11 50 c. *Gardinia taitensis* .. .. ..
O12 $1 Type **80** .. ..
O13 $2 Type **80** .. ..
O14 $4 Type **81** (19 May) .. .. ..
O15 $6 Type **81** (19 May) .. .. ..
O1/15 .. .. *Set of* 15 † 30·00
These stamps were only sold to the public cancelled-to-order and not in unused condition.

1978 (19 Oct)–**79**. *Nos.* 466/7, 474, 478/81, 484/5, 542 *and* 568/9 *optd or surch* (2, 5, 10, 15, 18 *and* 35 *c.*) *as Type* O **2**.
O16 1 c. Vase shell (Silver) 15 10
O17 2 c. on ½ c. Type **141** 15 10
O18 5 c. on ½ c. Type **141** 20 10
O19 10 c. on 8 c. Helmet shell (Silver) 25 10
O20 15 c. on 50 c. Cloth of Gold Cone shell (Silver) 35 10
O21 18 c. on 60 c. Olive shell (Silver) 35 15
O22 25 c. Scallop shell 45 20
O23 30 c. Soldier Cone shell (Silver) 45 25
O24 35 c. on 60 c. Olive shell (Silver) 55 30
O25 50 c. Cloth of Gold Cone shell (Silver) .. 80 35
O26 60 c. Olive shell (Silver) 90 45
O27 $1 Queen and Prince Philip (Silver) .. 3·25 1·25
O28 $1 Royal Visit, 1974 (Silver) .. .. 3·25 1·25
O29 $2 Captain Cook and H.M.S. *Resolution* .. 4·50 3·00
O30 $4 Queen Elizabeth II and seashells (15.2.79) .. .. 5·50 3·25
O31 $6 As $4 (15.2.79) .. .. 7·50 6·00
O16/31 .. .. *Set of* 16 26·00 15·00
These stamps were originally only sold to the public cancelled-to-order and not in unused condition. They were made available to overseas collectors in mint condition during 1980.

O.H.M.S. (O 3) 75c O.H.M.S. (O 4)

O.H.M.S. (O 5)

1985 (10 July)–**86**. *(a) Nos.* 969/74, 976, 978, 981, 984/6 *and* 988/9 *optd or surch as Type* O **3** *by silver foil embossing*
O32 5 c. *Ptilosarcus gurneyi* 10 10
O33 10 c. *Lobophyllia bemprichii* 10 10
a. Opt double, one albino .. .. 50·00
O34 12 c. *Sarcophyton digitatum* (5.5.86) .. 10 10
O35 14 c. *Pavona praetorta* (5.5.86) 10 10
O36 18 c. *Junceella gemmacea* (5.5.86) 15 15
O37 20 c. *Stylaster* 15 15
O38 30 c. *Palauastrea ramosa* 20 25
O39 40 c. *Stylaster echinatus* 25 30
O40 50 c. *Melithaea squamata* (5.5.86) 30 35
O41 55 c. on 85 c. *Caulastraea echinulata* .. 35 40
a. "O.H.M.S." albino .. .. .. † —
O42 60 c. *Tubastraea* 40 45
O43 70 c. *Heliofungia actiniformis* (5.5.86) .. 45 50
O44 $1.10, *Pectinia alcicornis* 75 80
O45 $2 on $1.20, *Dendrophyllia gracilis* .. 1·40 1·50

(b) Nos. 862/5 *surch with Type* O **4** *by gold foil embossing*
O46 75 c. on 60 c. Type **197** (5.5.86) 50 55
O47 75 c. on 60 c. Rarotonga oranges (5.5.86) .. 50 55
O48 75 c. on 60 c. Rarotonga airport (5.5.86) .. 50 55
O49 75 c. on 60 c. Prime Minister Sir Thomas Davis (5.5.86) 50 55

(c) Nos. 786/8 *surch as T* **209** *in silver and black further optd with Type* O **5** *by silver foil embossing.*
O50 $5 on $3 *Heliofungia actiniformis* (5.5.86) 3·25 3·50
O51 $9 on $4 *Stylophora pistillata* (30.5.89) .. 6·00 6·25
O52 $14 on $6 *Stylaster echinatus* (12.7.89) .. 9·00 9·25
O32/52 .. .. *Set of* 21 22·00 24·00

AITUTAKI

Stamps of COOK ISLANDS were used in Aitutaki from 1892 until 1903.

PRICES FOR STAMPS ON COVER TO 1945

Nos. 1/8	*from* × 4
Nos. 9/14	*from* × 3
Nos. 15/29	*from* × 4
Nos. 30/2	*from* × 6

A. NEW ZEALAND DEPENDENCY

The island of Aitutaki, previously under British protection, was annexed by New Zealand on 11 June 1901.

Stamps of New Zealand overprinted or surcharged.

AITUTAKI. (1)
Ava Pene. (2) ½d.
Tai Pene. (3) 1d.
Rua Pene Ma Te Ava. (4) 2½d.
Toru Pene. (5) 3d.
Ono Pene. (6) 6d.
Tai Tiringi. (7) 1s.

1903 (29 June)–**11**. 1902 *issue surch with T* 1 *at top, and T* **2** *to* **7** *at foot. W* **43**. *(a) P* 14.
1 **23** ½d. green (R.) .. .. 3·25 6·50
2 **42** 1d. carmine (B.) .. .. 4·00 5·50
3 **27** 2½d. deep blue (R.) (9.11) .. .. 6·50 16·00
a. "Ava" without stop £130 £170
1/3 .. .. *Set of* 3 12·50 25·00

(b) P 11
4 **27** 2½d. blue (R.) .. .. 7·00 11·00
5 **28** 3d. yellow-brown (B.) .. .. .. 6·50 15·00
6 **31** 6d. rose-red (B.) .. .. 17·00 25·00
7 **34** 1s. bright red (B.) .. .. .. 55·00 75·00
a. "Tiringi" without stop (R. 7/12) .. £375 £475
8 1s. orange-red (B.) .. .. .. 65·00 85·00
a. "Tiringi" without stop (R. 7/12) .. £500 £600
b. Orange-brown £140 £160
c. Do. "Tiringi" without stop (R. 7/12) .. £950 £1100
4/7 .. .. *Set of* 4 75·00 £110

Nos. 1/2 and 4/7 were placed on sale in Auckland on 12 June 1903.

There were four states of the overprint used for No. 3. On the first the "no stop" variety (No. 3a) occurs on R. 6/8, on the second it appears on R. 1/4, 2/4 and 6/8, on the third on R. 5/8 and 6/8, and on the fourth all stops are present.

AITUTAKI.

Ono Pene.

(8)

1911–16. *½d. and* 1*d. surch as on Nos.* 1/2, 6*d. and* 1*s. as T* **8**.
9 **50** ½d. green (R.) (9.11) .. .. .. 55 2·50
10 **52** 1d. carmine (B.) (2.13) .. .. .. 2·25 7·00
11 **51** 6d. carmine (B.) (*p* 14 × 14½)(23.5.16) 35·00 60·00
12 1s. vermilion (B.) (*p* 14 × 14½) (9.14) 55·00 £100
9/12 .. .. *Set of* 4 80·00 £150

1916–17. *King George V stamps surch as T* **8**. *P* 14 × 14½.
13 **60** 6d. carmine (B.) (6.6.16) .. .. .. 7·50 18·00
a. Perf 14 × 13½ .. .. .. 14·00 35·00
b. Vert pair. Nos. 13/13a .. .. 48·00 90·00
14 1s. vermilion (B.) (3.17) .. .. .. 30·00 60·00
a. Perf 14 × 13½ .. .. .. 28·00 60·00
b. Vert pair. Nos. 14/14a £140 £250
c. "Tai" without dot £200 £325
d. "Tiringi" no dot on second "i" .. £250 £350
e. "Tiringi" no dot on third "i" .. £300 £400

1917–18. *King George V stamps optd* "AITUTAKI", *only, as in T* **8**. *W* **43**. *P* 14 × 14½.
15 **60** 2½d. deep blue (R.) (12.18) .. .. 1·40 8·50
a. Perf 14 × 13½ .. .. .. 2·00 8·50
b. Vert pair. Nos. 15/15a .. .. 70·00 £110
16 3d. chocolate (B.)(1.18) .. .. .. 1·25 9·00
a. Perf 14 × 13½ .. .. .. 1·75 10·00
b. Vert pair. Nos. 16/16a .. .. 65·00 £110
17 6d. carmine (B.)(11.17) .. .. .. 4·50 9·00
a. Perf 14 × 13½ .. .. .. 7·00 17·00
b. Vert pair. Nos. 17/17a .. .. 70·00 £110
18 1s. vermilion (B.)(11.17) .. .. .. 10·00 18·00
a. Perf 14 × 13½ .. .. .. 14·00 25·00
b. Vert pair. Nos. 18/18a .. .. 80·00 £130
15/18 .. .. *Set of* 4 15·00 38·00

1917–20. *Optd* "AITUTAKI", *as in T* **8**. *Typo. W* **43**. *P* 14 × 15.
19 **61** ½d. green (R.) (2.20) .. .. .. 1·00 3·50
20 **52** 1d. carmine (B.)(5.20) .. .. .. 1·75 6·00
21 **61** 1½d. slate (R.)(11.17) .. .. .. 3·25 14·00
22 1½d. orange-brown (R.) (2.19) .. .. 80 5·50
23 3d. chocolate (B.)(6.19) .. .. .. 3·50 10·00
19/23 .. .. *Set of* 5 9·25 35·00

(Des and recess Perkins, Bacon & Co)

1920 (23 Aug). *As Types of Cook Islands, but inscr* "AITUTAKI". *No wmk. P* 14.
24 **9** ½d. black and green .. .. .. 2·75 10·00
25 **10** 1d. black and dull carmine .. .. 2·25 5·00
26 **11** 1½d. black and sepia .. .. .. 5·50 9·00
27 **12** 3d. black and deep blue .. .. 1·75 9·00
28 **13** 6d. red-brown and slate .. .. 5·00 14·00
29 **14** 1s. black and purple .. .. .. 7·50 16·00
24/29 .. .. *Set of* 6 22·00 55·00

(Recess Govt Printing Office, Wellington)

1924–27. *As Types of Cook Islands, but inscr* "AITUTAKI". *W* **43** *of New Zealand. P* 14.
30 **9** ½d. black and green (5.27) .. .. 2·00 7·50
31 **10** 1d. black and deep carmine (10.24) .. 2·50 6·50
32 **16** 2½d. black and dull blue (10.27) .. .. 6·00 27·00
30/2 .. .. *Set of* 3 9·50 38·00

Cook Islands stamps superseded those of Aitutaki on 15 March 1932. Separate issues were resumed in 1972.

B. PART OF COOK ISLANDS

On 9 August 1972, Aitutaki became a Port of Entry into the Cook Islands, and at the close of business on the previous day, Cook Islands stamps were withdrawn from sale there. Whilst remaining part of the Cook Islands, Aitutaki has a separate postal service.

PRINTERS. Stamps of Aitutaki were printed in photogravure by Heraclio Fournier, Spain, *unless otherwise stated*. All issues are on paper treated with fluorescent security markings, and with synthetic gum. The fluorescent markings can be found inverted or omitted.

(9)

Aitutaki (10)

(Optd by Govt Printer, Wellington)

1972 (9 Aug). *Nos.* 227B *etc. of Cook Is. optd with T* **9** *(applied horizontally on* $1), *by New Zealand Govt Printer.*
33 ½ c. Type **79** 30 80
34 1 c. *Hibiscus syriacus* .. .. .. 70 1·40
35 2½ c. *Clitoria ternatea* .. .. .. 3·50 8·00
36 4 c. Water Lily (No. 233B) 70 85
37 5 c. *Bauhinia bi-pinnata rosea* .. .. 4·50 8·50
38 10 c. *Poinciana regia flamboyant* .. .. 4·50 6·50
39 20 c. Thunbergia .. .. 70 1·00
40 25 c. Canna Lily .. .. 70 1·00
41 50 c. *Gardinia taitensis* .. .. .. 3·75 3·25
42 $1 Type **80** .. .. 6·50 6·50
*a. Shade** .. ..
33/42 .. .. *Set of* 10 23·00 35·00

* No. 42*a* has the border flowers predominantly in a carmine colour instead of scarlet, and may be due to a missing yellow colour.

1972 (27 Oct). *Christmas. Nos.* 406/8 *of Cook. Is. optd in silver with T* **10**.
43 **130** 1 c. multicoloured 10 10
44 – 5 c. multicoloured 10 15
45 – 10 c. multicoloured 10 25
43/5 .. .. *Set of* 3 20 40

1972 (20 Nov). *Royal Silver Wedding. As Nos.* 413 *and* 415 *of Cook Is., but inscr* "COOK ISLANDS Aitutaki".
46 **131** 5 c. black and silver .. .. .. 4·75 2·75
47 – 15 c. black and silver .. .. .. 2·75 1·50

AITUTAKI (11)
AITUTAKI (12)

1972 (24 Nov). *No.* 245B *of Cook Is. optd with T* **11** *by Govt Printer, Rarotonga.*
48 **80** $2 multicoloured .. .. 60 1·00
a. Optd "AJTUTAKI" for "AITUTAKI" (R. 2/4) .. .. 25·00
b. On No. 245A (gum arabic printing) .. 50·00
ba. Optd "AJTUTAKI" for "AITUTAKI" (R. 2/4) .. ..

1972 (11 Dec). *Nos.* 227B *etc of Cook Is. optd with T* **12**, *by Heraclio Fournier.*
49 ½ c. Type **79** 10 10
50 1 c. *Hibiscus syriacus* 10 10
51 2½ c. *Clitoria ternatea* 10 10
52 4 c. Water Lily (No. 233B) 15 15
53 5 c. *Bauhinia bi-pinnata rosea* 15 15
54 10 c. *Poinciana regia flamboyant* 25 25
55 20 c. Thunbergia 45 50
56 25 c. Canna Lily 50 55
57 50 c. *Gardinia taitensis* 80 90
58 $1 Type **80** .. .. 1·50 1·75
49/58 .. .. *Set of* 10 3·50 4·00

MINIMUM PRICE

The minimum price quote is 10p which represents a handling charge rather than a basis for valuing common stamps. For further notes about prices see introductory pages.

13 "Christ Mocked" (Grünewald)

AITUTAKI (14)

1973 (6 Apr). *Easter. T* **13** *and similar vert designs. Multicoloured. P* 13.
59 1 c. Type **13** 10 10
60 1 c. "St. Veronica" (Van der Weyden) .. 10 10
61 1 c. "The Crucified Christ with Virgin Mary, Saints and Angels" (Raphael) .. 10 10
62 1 c. "Resurrection" (Piero della Francesca) .. 10 10
63 5 c. "The Last Supper" (Master of Amiens) .. 15 15
64 5 c. "Condemnation" (Holbein) 15 15
65 5 c. "Christ on the Cross" (Rubens) 15 15
66 5 c. "Resurrection" (El Greco) 15 15
67 10 c. "Disrobing of Christ" (El Greco) 15 15
68 10 c. "St. Veronica" (Van Oostsanen) 15 15
69 10 c. "Christ on the Cross" (Rubens) 15 15
70 10 c. "Resurrection" (Bouts) 15 15
59/70 .. .. *Set of* 12 1·25 1·25

Nos. 59/62, 63/6 and 67/70 were each printed together, *se-tenant*, in blocks of 4 throughout the sheet.

1973 (14 May). *Silver Wedding Coinage. Nos.* 417/23 *of Cook Is. optd in silver and black as T* **14**.
71 1 c. black, rosy carmine and gold 10 10
72 2 c. black, bright blue and gold 10 10
73 5 c. black, green and silver 10 10
74 10 c. black, royal blue and silver 15 10
75 20 c. black, deep blue-green and silver .. 20 15
76 50 c. black, carmine and silver 40 30
77 $1 black, bright blue and silver 65 45
71/7 .. .. *Set of* 7 1·40 1·00

TENTH ANNIVERSARY CESSATION OF NUCLEAR TESTING TREATY (15)

16 Red Hibiscus and Princess Anne

1973 (13 Aug). *Tenth Anniv of Treaty Banning Nuclear Testing. Nos.* 236B, 238B, 240B *and* 243B *of Cook Is. optd with T* **15** *and T* **12** *together.*
78 8 c. *Allamanda cathartica* 15 15
79 10 c. *Poinciana regia flamboyant* 15 15
80 20 c. Thunbergia 30 20
81 50 c. *Gardinia taitensis* 70 50
78/81 .. .. *Set of* 4 1·10 90

1973 (14 Nov). *Royal Wedding. T* **16** *and similar horiz design. Multicoloured. P* 13½ × 14.
82 25 c. Type **16** 25 10
83 30 c. Capt. Phillips and Blue Hibiscus .. 25 10
MS84 114 × 65 mm. Nos. 82/3. P 13 .. .. 50 40

17 "Virgin and Child" (Montagna)

18 *Murex ramosus*

1973 (10 Dec). *Christmas. T* **17** *and similar vert designs showing "The Virgin and Child" by the artists listed. Multicoloured. P* 13½.
85 1 c. Type **17** 10 10
86 1 c. Crivelli 10 10
87 1 c. Van Dyck 10 10
88 1 c. Perugino 10 10
89 5 c. Veronese (child at shoulder) 10 10
90 5 c. Veronese (child on lap) 10 10
91 5 c. Cima 10 10
92 5 c. Memling 10 10
93 10 c. Memling 10 10
94 10 c. Del Colle 10 10
95 10 c. Raphael 10 10
96 10 c. Lotto 10 10
85/96 .. .. *Set of* 12 80 80

Nos. 85/8, 89/92 and 93/6 were each printed together, *se-tenant*, in blocks of 4 throughout the sheet.

1974 (31 Jan)–**75**. *T* **18** *and similar horiz designs showing sea-shells. Multicoloured. P* 13.
97 ½ c. Type **18** 15 15
98 1 c. *Nautilus macromphallus* 15 15

99 2 c. *Harpa major* 20 20
100 3 c. *Phalium strigatum* 20 20
101 4 c. *Cypraea talpa* 20 20
102 5 c. *Mitra stictica* 20 20
103 8 c. *Charonia tritonis* 25 20
104 10 c. *Murex triremis* 25 20
105 20 c. *Oliva sericea* 60 25
106 25 c. *Tritonalia rubeta* 70 25
107 60 c. *Strombus latissimus* .. .. .. 1·40 70
108 $1 *Biplex perca* .. .. 1·75 1·10
109 $2 Queen Elizabeth II and *Terebra maculata* (20.1.75) .. .. 5·50 5·50
110 $5 Queen Elizabeth II and *Cypraea hesitata* (28.2.75) .. .. 14·00 9·50
97/110 .. .. *Set of* 14 23·00 17·00
Nos. 109/110 are larger, 53 × 25 mm.

19 Bligh and H.M.S. *Bounty*

(Des G. Vasarhelyi)

1974 (11 Apr). *William Bligh's Discovery of Aitutaki. T* **19** *and similar horiz designs. Multicoloured. P* 13½.
114 1 c. Type **19** 20 10
115 1 c. H.M.S. *Bounty* 20 10
116 5 c. Bligh, and H.M.S. *Bounty* at Aitutaki .. 40 15
117 5 c. Aitutaki chart of 1856 .. .. .. 40 15
118 8 c. Capt. Cook and H.M.S. *Resolution* .. 50 15
119 8 c. Map of Aitutaki and inset location map .. 50 15
114/119 .. .. *Set of* 6 2·00 70
Nos. 114/15, 116/17 and 118/19 were each printed together, *se-tenant*, in horizontal and vertical pairs throughout the sheet.
See also Nos. 123/8.

20 Aitutaki Stamps of 1903, and Map

21 "Virgin and Child" (Hugo van der Goes)

1974 (15 July). *Centenary of Universal Postal Union. T* **20** *and similar horiz design. Multicoloured. P* 13½ × 14.
120 25 c. Type **20** 40 40
121 50 c. Stamps of 1903 and 1920, and map .. 60 60
MS122 66 × 75 mm. Nos. 120/1. P 13 .. 1·00 2·00
Each value was issued in sheets of 5 stamps and 1 label.

1974 (9 Sept). *Air. As Nos. 114/119, but larger (46 × 26 mm), denominations changed, and inscr "AIR MAIL".*
123 10 c. Type **19** 50 15
124 10 c. H.M.S. *Bounty* 50 15
125 25 c. Bligh, and H.M.S. *Bounty* at Aitutaki 65 25
126 25 c. Aitutaki chart of 1856 .. .. .. 65 25
127 30 c. Capt. Cook and H.M.S. *Resolution* .. 65 25
128 30 c. Map of Aitutaki and inset location map 65 25
123/8 .. .. *Set of* 6 3·25 1·10
Nos. 123/4, 125/6 and 127/8 were each printed together, *se-tenant*, in horizontal and vertical pairs throughout the sheet.

1974 (11 Oct). *Christmas. T* **21** *and similar vert designs showing "Virgin and Child" by the artists listed. Multicoloured. P* 13.
129 1 c. Type **21** 10 10
130 5 c. Bellini 10 10
131 8 c. Gerard David 10 10
132 10 c. Antonello da Messina 10 10
133 25 c. Joos van Cleve 20 20
134 30 c. Master of the Life of St. Catherine .. 20 20
129/34 .. .. *Set of* 6 65 65
MS135 127 × 134 mm. Nos. 129/34 .. .. 1·25 1·60
Each value was issued in sheets of 15 stamps and 1 label.

22 Churchill as Schoolboy

+1c

(**23**)

1974 (29 Nov). *Birth Centenary of Sir Winston Churchill. T* **22** *and similar vert designs. Multicoloured. P* 13½.
136 10 c. Type **22** 30 25
137 25 c. Churchill as young man 60 50
138 30 c. Churchill with troops 75 60
139 50 c. Churchill painting .. .. .. 1·10 80
140 $1 Giving "V" sign .. .. 2·00 1·50
136/40 .. .. *Set of* 5 4·25 3·25
MS141 115 × 108 mm. Nos. 136/40 plus *se-tenant* label. P 13 .. .. 5·00 4·00
Each value was issued in sheets of 5 stamps and 1 label.

1974 (2 Dec). *Children's Christmas Fund. Nos. 129/34 surch with T* **23**.
142 1 c. + 1 c. multicoloured 10 10
143 5 c. + 1 c. multicoloured 10 10
144 8 c. + 1 c. multicoloured 10 10
145 10 c. + 1 c. multicoloured 10 10
146 25 c. + 1 c. multicoloured 20 20
147 30 c. + 1 c. multicoloured 20 20
142/7 .. .. *Set of* 6 55 55

24 Soviet and U.S. Flags

25 "Madonna and Child with Saints Francis and John" (Lorenzetti)

1975 (24 July). *"Apollo-Soyuz" Space Project. T* **24** *and similar horiz design. Multicoloured. P* 13 × 14.
148 25 c. Type **24** 30 20
149 50 c. Daedalus and space capsule 40 30
MS150 123 × 61 mm. Nos. 148/9 .. .. 1·00 1·10
Each value was issued in sheets of 8 stamps and 1 label.

1975 (24 Nov). *Christmas. T* **25** *and similar vert designs. Multicoloured. P* 13½.
151 6 c. } Type **25** 10 10
152 6 c. } .. 10 10
153 6 c. } .. 10 10
154 7 c. } "Adoration of the Kings" (Van der Weyden) .. 10 10
155 7 c. } .. 10 10
156 7 c. } .. 10 10
157 15 c. } "Madonna and Child Enthroneth with Saints Onufrius and John the Baptist" (Montagna) .. 15 15
158 15 c. } .. 15 15
159 15 c. } .. 15 15
160 20 c. } "Adoration of the Shepherds" (Reni) .. 20 15
161 20 c. } .. 20 15
162 20 c. } .. 20 15
151/62 .. .. *Set of* 12 1·50 1·40
MS163 104 × 201 mm. Nos. 151/62. P 13 .. .. 2·25 2·50
Nos. 151/3, 154/6, 157/9 and 160/2 were each printed together, *se-tenant*, in horizontal strips of 3 throughout the sheet, forming composite designs. Type **25** shows the left-hand stamp of the 6 c. design.

1975 (19 Dec). *Children's Christmas Fund. Nos. 151/62 surch as T* **23**, *in silver.*
164 6 c. + 1 c. } Type **25** 15 10
165 6 c. + 1 c. } .. 15 10
166 6 c. + 1 c. } .. 15 10
167 7 c. + 1 c. } "Adoration of the Kings" (Van der Weyden) .. 15 10
168 7 c. + 1 c. } .. 15 10
169 7 c. + 1 c. } .. 15 10
170 15 c. + 1 c. } "Madonna and Child" (Montagna) .. 20 15
171 15 c. + 1 c. } .. 20 15
172 15 c. + 1 c. } .. 20 15
173 20 c. + 1 c. } "Adoration of the Shepherds" (Reni) .. 25 20
174 20 c. + 1 c. } .. 25 20
175 20 c. + 1 c. } .. 25 20
164/75 .. .. *Set of* 12 2·00 1·50

26 "The Descent" (detail, 15th-cent Flemish School)

27 "The Declaration of Independence" (detail)

1976 (5 Apr). *Easter. Various vert designs showing portions of "The Descent" as in T* **26**. *P* 13.
176 **26** 15 c. multicoloured 15 10
177 – 30 c. multicoloured 20 15
178 – 35 c. multicoloured 25 20
176/8 .. .. *Set of* 3 55 40
MS179 87 × 67 mm. Nos. 176/8 forming a complete picture of "The Descent". P 12½ × 13 .. .. 1·00 1·25
Stamps from No. **MS**179 have no borders and are therefore smaller than stamps from the sheets.
Each value was issued in sheets of 8 stamps and 1 label.

1976 (1 June). *Bicentenary of American Revolution. T* **27** *and similar vert designs showing paintings by John Trumbull. Multicoloured. P* 13.
180 30 c. } Type **27** 60 30
181 30 c. } .. 60 30
182 30 c. } .. 60 30
183 35 c. } "The Surrender of Lord Cornwallis at Yorktown" .. 70 40
184 35 c. } .. 70 40
185 35 c. } .. 70 40
186 50 c. } "The Resignation of General Washington" .. 80 45
187 50 c. } .. 80 45
188 50 c. } .. 80 45
180/8 .. .. *Set of* 9 5·75 3·00
MS189 132 × 120 mm. Nos. 180/8. P 13 .. .. 5·00 4·25
Nos. 180/2, 183/5 and 186/8 were each printed together, *se-tenant*, in horizontal strips of 3 throughout the sheet, forming composite designs. Each sheet includes 3 stamp-size labels. Type **27** shows the left-hand stamp of the 30 c. design.
Stamps from No. **MS**189 have their borders in a different colour and come with a different inscription.

28 Cycling

1976 (15 July). *Olympic Games, Montreal. T* **28** *and similar horiz designs. Multicoloured. P* 13 × 14.
190 15 c. Type **28** 20 15
191 35 c. Sailing 40 20
192 60 c. Hockey 55 25
193 70 c. Sprinting 60 30
190/3 .. .. *Set of* 4 1·60 80
MS194 107 × 97 mm. Nos. 190/3 .. .. 1·60 1·60
Stamps from No. **MS**194 have borders of a different colour.
Each value was issued in sheets of 5 stamps and 1 label.

ROYAL VISIT JULY 1976

(**29**)

30 "The Visitation"

1976 (30 July). *Visit of Queen Elizabeth to the U.S.A. Nos.* 190/**MS**194 *optd with T* **29**.
195 15 c. Type **28** 25 15
196 35 c. Sailing 40 25
197 60 c. Hockey 60 40
198 70 c. Sprinting 70 45
195/8 .. .. *Set of* 4 1·75 1·10
MS199 107 × 97 mm. Nos. 195/8 .. .. 1·75 2·50

1976 (18 Oct). *Christmas. T* **30** *and similar vert designs. Figures in gold; background colours given. P* 13.
200 6 c. } deep bluish green 10 10
201 6 c. } .. 10 10
202 7 c. } dull brown-purple 10 10
203 7 c. } .. 10 10
204 15 c. } deep blue 10 10
205 15 c. } .. 10 10
206 20 c. } reddish violet 15 15
207 20 c. } .. 15 15
200/207 .. .. *Set of* 8 60 60
MS208 128 × 96 mm. As Nos. 200/207 but with borders on three sides .. .. 1·00 1·40
Designs:—No. 201, Angel: No. 202, Angel; No. 203, Shepherds; No. 204, Joseph; No. 205, Mary and the Child; No. 206, Wise Man; No. 207, Two Wise Men.
Nos. 200/1, 202/3, 204/5 and 206/7 were each printed together, *se-tenant*, in horizontal pairs throughout the sheet, forming composite designs. Type **30** shows the left-hand stamp of the 6 c. design.

+1c

(**31**)

32 Alexander Graham Bell and First Telephone

1976 (19 Nov). *Children's Christmas Fund. Nos.* 200/**MS**208 *surch in silver as T* **31**.
209 6 c. + 1 c. } "The Visitation" 10 10
210 6 c. + 1 c. } .. 10 10
211 7 c. + 1 c. } "Angel and Shepherds" 10 10
212 7 c. + 1 c. } .. 10 10
213 15 c. + 1 c. } "The Holy Family" 15 15
214 15 c. + 1 c. } .. 15 15
215 20 c. + 1 c. } "The Magi" 15 15
216 20 c. + 1 c. } .. 15 15
209/16 .. .. *Set of* 8 70 70
MS217 128 × 96 mm. As Nos. 209/216 but with a premium of "+ 2 c." and borders on three sides .. 80 1·40

1977 (3 Mar). *Telephone Centenary* (1976). *T* **32** *and similar horiz design. P* 13.
218 25 c. black, gold and dull scarlet 20 15
219 70 c. black, gold and lilac 40 40
MS220 116 × 59 mm. As Nos. 218/19 but with different colours .. .. 70 1·00
Design:—70 c. Earth Station and satellite.

33 "Christ on the Cross" (detail)

1977 (31 Mar). *Easter and 400th Birth Anniv of Rubens. T* **33** *and similar horiz designs. Multicoloured. P* 13½ × 14.

221	15 c. Type **33**	30	15
222	20 c. "Lamentation for Christ"	35	20
223	35 c. "Christ with Straw"	45	25
221/3	*Set of* 3	1·00	55
MS224	115 × 57 mm. Nos. 221/3. P 13 × 12½	1·00	1·25

Each value was issued in sheets of 8 stamps and 1 label.

34 Capt. Bligh, George III and H.M.S. *Bounty*

1977 (21 Apr). *Silver Jubilee. T* **34** *and similar horiz designs. Multicoloured. P* 13.

225	25 c. Type **34**	50	45
226	35 c. Rev. Williams, George IV and Aitutaki Church	60	50
227	50 c. Union Jack, Queen Victoria and island map	75	75
228	$1 Balcony scene, 1953	1·25	1·25
225/8	*Set of* 4	2·75	2·75
MS229	130 × 87 mm. Nos. 225/8 but with gold borders. P 13½ × 13	2·75	2·75

Each value was issued in sheets of 5 stamps and 1 label.

35 The Shepherds

+1c
(36)

1977 (14 Oct). *Christmas. T* **35** *and similar vert designs. Multicoloured. P* 13½ × 14.

230	6 c. Type **35**	10	10
231	6 c. Angel	10	10
232	7 c. Mary, Jesus and ox	10	10
233	7 c. Joseph and donkey	10	10
234	15 c. Three Kings	10	10
235	15 c. Virgin and Child	10	10
236	20 c. Joseph	10	10
237	20 c. Mary and Jesus on donkey	10	10
230/7	*Set of* 8	55	55
MS238	130×95 mm. Nos. 230/7	70	1·25

Each design covers two stamps; Type **35** shows the left-hand stamp of the 6 c. design.

1977 (15 Nov). *Children's Christmas Fund. Nos. 230/7 surch with T* **36**.

239	6 c. + 1 c.	Type 35	10	10
240	6 c. + 1 c.		10	10
241	7 c. + 1 c.	The Holy Family	10	10
242	7 c. + 1 c.		10	10
243	15 c. + 1 c.	The Three Kings with Virgin and Child	10	10
244	15 c. + 1 c.		10	10
245	20 c. + 1 c.	Flight into Egypt	10	10
246	20 c. + 1 c.		10	10
239/46		*Set of* 8	55	55
MS247	130 × 95 mm. As Nos. 239/46 but each with premium of "+ 2 c."		70	85

37 Hawaiian Goddess

38 "Christ on the Way to Calvary" (Martini)

1978 (19 Jan). *Bicentenary of Discovery of Hawaii. T* **37** *and similar multicoloured designs. P* 13½.

248	35 c. Type **37**	45	25
249	50 c. Figurehead of H.M.S. *Resolution* (*horiz*)	75	40
250	$1 Hawaiian temple figure	1·00	70
248/50	*Set of* 3	2·00	1·25
MS251	168 × 75 mm. Nos. 248/50	2·00	2·75

1978 (17 Mar). *Easter. Details of Paintings from Louvre, Paris. T* **38** *and similar horiz designs. Multicoloured. P* 13½ × 14.

252	15 c. Type **38**	10	10
253	20 c. "Piéta of Avignon" (E. Quarton)	15	10
254	35 c. "Pilgrims at Emmaus" (Rembrandt)	20	15
252/4	*Set of* 3	40	30
MS255	108 × 83 mm. Nos. 252/4	45	70

Each value was printed in two panes of 9 within the sheet, both panes including one *se-tenant* stamp-size label.

1978 (17 Mar). *Easter. Children's Charity. Designs as Nos. 252/4, but smaller (34 × 26 mm) and without margins, in separate miniature sheets 75 × 58 mm, each with a face value of 50 c. + 5 c. P* 14.

MS256	As Nos. 252/4 *Set of 3 sheets*	1·00	1·00

39 Yale of Beaufort

40 "Adoration of the Infant Jesus"

1978 (15 June). *25th Anniv of Coronation. T* **39** *and similar vert designs. Multicoloured. P* 13½ × 13.

257	$1 Type **39**	55	65
258	$1 Queen Elizabeth II	55	65
259	$1 Aitutaki ancestral statue	55	65
257/9	*Set of* 3	1·50	1·75
MS260	98 × 127 mm. Nos. 257/9 × 2	1·75	1·75

Stamps from No. **MS**260 have coloured borders, the upper row in lavender and the lower in apple-green.

Nos. 257/9 were printed together, *se-tenant*, in small sheets of 6, containing two horizontal strips of 3.

1978 (4 Dec). *Christmas. 450th Death Anniv of Dürer. T* **40** *and similar vert designs. Multicoloured. P* 13 × 14.

261	15 c. Type **40**	25	15
262	17 c. "The Madonna with Child"	30	15
263	30 c. "The Madonna with the Iris"	40	20
264	35 c. "The Madonna of the Siskin"	45	25
261/4	*Set of* 4	1·25	65
MS265	101 × 109 mm. As Nos. 261/4 but each with premium of "+ 2 c."	90	1·00

Nos. 261/4 were each printed in small sheets of 6, including 1 *se-tenant* stamp-size label.

41 "Captain Cook" (Nathaniel Dance)

42 Girl with Flowers

1979 (20 July). *Death Bicentenary of Captain Cook. Paintings. T* **41** *and similar vert designs. Multicoloured. P* 14 × 13½.

266	50 c. Type **41**	1·00	80
267	75 c. "H.M.S. *Resolution* and *Adventure* at Matavai Bay" (William Hodges)	1·25	95
MS268	94×58 mm. Nos. 266/7. P 13½	2·25	3·00

1979 (1 Oct). *International Year of the Child. T* **42** *and similar vert designs. Multicoloured. P* 14 × 13½.

269	30 c. Type **42**	15	15
270	35 c. Boy playing guitar	20	20
271	65 c. Children in canoe	30	30
269/71	*Set of* 3	60	60
MS272	104 × 80 mm. As Nos. 269/71, but each with a premium of "+ 3 c."	70	1·00

43 "Man writing a Letter" (painting by G. Metsu)

44 "The Burial of Christ" (detail, Quentin Metsys)

1979 (14 Nov). *Death Centenary of Sir Rowland Hill. T* **43** *and similar horiz designs. Multicoloured. P* 13.

273	50 c. Type **43**	70	70
274	50 c. Sir Rowland Hill with Penny Black, 1903 ½d. and 1911 1d. stamps	70	70
275	50 c. "Girl in Blue reading a Letter" (painting by J. Vermeer)	70	70
276	65 c. "Woman writing a Letter" (painting by G. Terborch)	75	75
277	65 c. Sir Rowland Hill with Penny Black, 1903 3d. and 1920 ½d. stamps	75	75
278	65 c. "Lady reading a Letter" (painting by J. Vermeer)	75	75
273/8	*Set of* 6	4·00	4·00
MS279	151 × 85 mm. 30 c. × 6. As Nos. 273/8	2·50	3·00

Nos. 273/5 and 276/8 were printed together, *se-tenant*, in horizontal strips of 3, the sheet having two panes separated by margin, one containing 273/5 × 3, the other containing 276/8 × 3.

1980 (3 Apr). *Easter. T* **44** *and similar vert designs showing different details of painting "The Burial of Christ" by Quentin Metsys. P* 13.

280	20 c. multicoloured	20	15
281	30 c. multicoloured	30	25
282	35 c. multicoloured	35	30
280/2	*Set of* 3	75	60
MS283	93 × 71 mm. As Nos. 280/2, but each with premium of "+ 2 c."	75	75

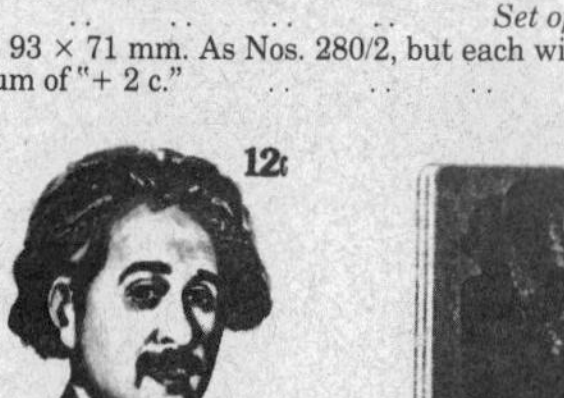

45 Einstein as Young Man

46 Ancestor Figure, Aitutaki

1980 (21 July). *25th Death Anniv of Albert Einstein (physicist). T* **45** *and similar vert designs. Multicoloured. P* 14 × 13½.

284	12 c. Type **45**	20	20
285	12 c. Atom and "E=mc²" equation	20	20
286	15 c. Einstein as middle-aged man	25	25
287	15 c. Cross over nuclear explosion (Nuclear Test Ban Treaty, 1963)	25	25
288	20 c. Einstein as old man	30	30
289	20 c. Hand over bomb explosion (Nuclear Test Ban Treaty, 1963)	30	30
284/9	*Set of* 6	1·40	1·40
MS290	113 × 118 mm. Nos. 284/9. P 13½	1·40	1·60

Nos. 284/5, 286/7 and 288/9 were each printed together, *se-tenant*, in horizontal pairs throughout the sheet.

1980 (26 Sept). *South Pacific Festival of Arts. T* **46** *and similar vert designs. Multicoloured. P* 13½.

291	6 c. Type **46**	10	10
292	6 c. Staff god image, Rarotonga	10	10
293	6 c. Trade adze, Mangaia	10	10
294	6 c. Carved image of Tangaroa, Rarotonga	10	10
295	12 c. Wooden image, Aitutaki	10	10
296	12 c. Hand club, Rarotonga	10	10
297	12 c. Carved mace "god", Mangaia	10	10
298	12 c. Fisherman's god, Rarotonga	10	10
299	15 c. Ti'i image, Aitutaki	15	15
300	15 c. Fisherman's god, Rarotonga (*different*)	15	15
301	15 c. Carved mace "god", Cook Islands	15	15
302	15 c. Carved image of Tangaroa, Rarotonga (*different*)	15	15
303	20 c. Chief's headdress, Aitutaki	15	15
304	20 c. Carved "mace" god, Cook Islands (*different*)	15	15
305	20 c. Staff god image, Rarotonga (*different*)	15	15
306	20 c. Carved image of Tangaroa, Rarotonga (*different*)	15	15
291/306	*Set of* 16	1·60	1·60
MS307	134 × 194 mm. Nos. 291/306	1·60	1·75

The four designs of each value were printed together, *se-tenant*, in blocks of 4 throughout the sheet.

47 Virgin and Child (13th-century)

48 "Mourning Virgin"

1980 (21 Nov). *Christmas. Sculptures. T* **47** *and similar vert designs showing various Virgin and Child works from the periods given. Multicoloured. P* 13.

308	15 c. Type **47**	15	15
309	20 c. 14th-century	15	15
310	25 c. 15th-century	15	15
311	35 c. 15th-century (*different*)	20	20
308/11	*Set of* 4	60	60
MS312	82 × 120 mm. As Nos. 306/11 but each with premium of 2 c.	70	80

1981 (31 Mar). *Easter. Details of Sculpture "Burial of Christ" by Pedro Roldan. T* **48** *and similar vert designs. P* 14.

313	30 c. gold and myrtle-green	25	25
314	40 c. gold and deep reddish lilac	30	30
315	50 c. gold and Prussian blue	30	30
313/15	*Set of* 3	75	75
MS316	107 × 60 mm. As Nos. 313/15 but each with premium of 2 c.	75	85

Designs:—40 c. "Christ"; 50 c. "Saint John".

49 Gouldian Finch (*Poephila gouldiae*) **50** Prince Charles

1981 (6 Apr)–**82**. *Birds (1st series). Multicoloured designs as T* **49**. *P* 14 × 13½ (*1 to 10 c.*), 13½ × 14 (*15 to 70 c.*) *or* 13 (*$1 to $4*).

317 1 c. Type **49** 15 10
318 1 c. Common Starling (*Sturnus vulgaris*) .. 15 10
319 2 c. Golden Whistler (*Pachycephala pectoralis*) 15 10
320 2 c. Scarlet Robin (*Petroica multicolor*) .. 15 10
321 3 c. Rufous Fantail (*Rhipidura rufifrons*) .. 20 10
322 3 c. Peregrine Falcon (*Falco peregrinus*) .. 20 10
323 4 c. Java Sparrow (*Padda oryzivora*) .. 20 10
324 4 c. Barn Owl (*Tyto alba*) 20 10
325 5 c. Tahitian Lory (*Vini peruviana*) 20 10
326 5 c. White-breasted Wood Swallow (*Artamus leucorhynchus*) 20 10
327 6 c. Purple Swamphen (*Porphyrio porphyrio*) 25 10
328 6 c. Rock Dove (*Columba livia*) 25 10
329 10 c. Chestnut-breasted Mannikin (*Lonchura castaneothorax*) 40 10
330 10 c. Zebra Dove (*Geopelia striata*) 40 10
331 12 c. Eastern Reef Heron (*Egretta sacra*) .. 40 15
332 12 c. Common Mynah (*Acridotheres tristis*) .. 40 15
333 15 c. Whimbrel (*Numenius phaeopus*) (*horiz*) (8.5.81) 50 15
334 15 c. Black-browed Albatross (*Diomeda melanophris*) (*horiz*) (8.5.81) 50 15
335 20 c. American Golden Plover (*Pluvialis dominica*) (*horiz*) (8.5.81) 60 20
336 20 c. White Tern (*Gygis alba*) (*horiz*) (8.5.81) 60 20
337 25 c. Spotbill Duck (*Anas superciliosa*) (*horiz*) (8.5.81) 70 25
338 25 c. Brown Booby (*Sula leucogaster*) (*horiz*) (8.5.81) 70 25
339 30 c. Great Frigate Bird (*Fregata minor*) (*horiz*) (8.5.81) 90 30
340 30 c. Pintail (*Anas acuta*) (*horiz*) (8.5.81) .. 90 30
341 35 c. Long-billed Reed Warbler (*Conopoderas caffra caffra*) (14.1.82) .. .. 1·00 35
342 35 c. Pomarine Skua (*Stercorarius pomarinus*) (14.1.82) .. .. 1·00 35
343 40 c. Banded Rail (*Gallirallus philippensis goodsoni*) (14.1.82) .. .. .. 1·25 40
344 40 c. Spotted Triller (*Lalage maculosa pumila*) (14.1.82) .. .. 1·25 40
345 50 c. Royal Albatross (*Diomedea epomophora*) (14.1.82) .. .. 1·40 60
346 50 c. Stephen's Lory (*Vini stepheni*) (14.1.82) 1·40 60
347 70 c. Red-headed Parrot Finch (*Erythrura cyaneovirens*) (14.1.82) .. .. 2·00 1·50
348 70 c. Orange Dove (*Ptilinopus victor victor*) (14.1.82) .. .. 2·00 1·50
349 $1 Blue-headed Flycatcher (*Myiagra azureocapilla whitneyi*) (15.2.82) .. 2·50 2·00
350 $2 Red-bellied Flycatcher (*Myiagra vanikorensis rufiventris*) (15.5.82) .. 5·50 4·00
351 $4 Red Munia (*Amandava amandava*) (19.3.82) .. .. 8·00 7·00
352 $5 Flat-billed Kingfisher (*Halcyon recurvirostris*) (19.3.82) .. .. .. 10·00 9·00
317/52 .. .. *Set of* 36 42·00 27·00

The two designs of each value (1 c. to 70 c.) were printed together, *se-tenant*, in horizontal and vertical pairs throughout the sheet.

Nos. 341/8 are 35 × 27 mm and Nos. 349/52, which include a portrait of Queen Elizabeth II, 35 × 48 mm in size.

See also Nos. 475/94 for redrawn designs as Type **65**.

Nos. 353/90 are vacant.

1981 (10 June). *Royal Wedding. T* **50** *and similar multicoloured designs. P* 14 (*$1.40*) *or* 13 × 13½ (*others*).

391 60 c. Type **50** 50 50
392 80 c. Lady Diana Spencer 60 60
393 $1.40, Prince Charles and Lady Diana (87 × 70 *mm*) .. .. .. 1·00 1·00
391/3 .. .. *Set of* 3 1·90 1·90

+5c

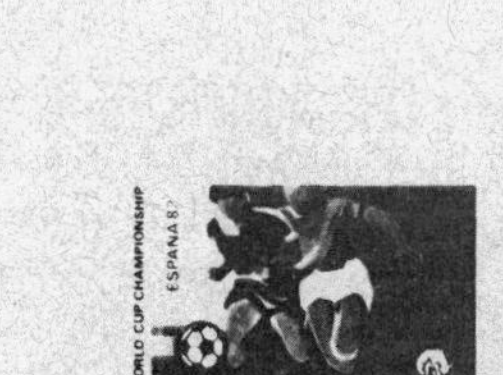

(**51**) **52** Footballers **53** "The Holy Family"

1981 (23 Nov). *International Year for Disabled Persons. Nos. 391/3 surch with T* **51** *on gold background.*

394 60 c. + 5 c. Type **50** .. .. .. 1·25 1·25
395 80 c. + 5 c. Lady Diana Spencer .. .. 1·75 1·75
396 $1. 40 + 5 c.Prince Charles and Lady Diana .. .. 3·25 3·25
394/6 .. .. *Set of* 3 5·50 5·50

Nos. 394/6 have commemorative inscriptions overprinted on the sheet margins.

1981 (30 Nov). *World Cup Football Championship, Spain* (1982). *T* **52** *and similar horiz designs showing footballers. Multicoloured. P* 14.

397 12 c. Ball to left of stamp 15 15
398 12 c. Ball to right 15 15
399 15 c. Ball to right 20 20
400 15 c. Ball to left 20 20
401 20 c. Ball to left 25 25
402 20 c. Ball to right 25 25
403 25 c. Type **52** 30 30
404 25 c. "ESPANA 82" inscr on printed background 30 30
397/404 .. .. .. *Set of* 8 1·60 1·60
MS405 100 × 137 mm. 12 c. + 2 c., 15 c. + 2 c., 20 c. + 2 c., 25 c. + 2 c., each × 2. As Nos. 397/404 1·75 2·00

The two designs of each value were printed together, *se-tenant*, in horizontal pairs throughout the sheet.

1981 (10 Dec). *Christmas. Details from Etchings by Rembrandt. T* **53** *and similar designs in purple-brown and gold. P* 14.

406 15 c. Type **53** 20 15
407 30 c. "Virgin with Child" 35 30
408 40 c. "Adoration of the Shepherds" (*horiz*) .. 50 45
409 50 c. "The Holy Family" (*horiz*) 60 50
406/9 .. .. *Set of* 4 1·50 1·25
MS410 Designs as Nos. 406/9 in separate miniature sheets, 65 × 82 mm or 82 × 65 mm, each with a face value of 80 c. + 5 c. P 14 × 13½ .. .. *Set of 4 sheets* 2·75 3·00

54 Princess of Wales (**55**)

1982 (24 June). *21st Birthday of Princess of Wales. T* **54** *and similar vert designs. Multicoloured. P* 14.

411 70 c. Type **54** 70 70
412 $1 Prince and Princess of Wales 85 85
413 $2 Princess Diana (*different*) .. .. 1·60 1·75
411/13 .. .. *Set of* 3 2·75 3·00
MS414 82 × 91 mm. Nos. 411/13 .. .. .. 2·75 2·75

Nos. 411/13 were each printed in small sheets of 6 including two *se-tenant* stamp-size labels. The silver markings in the margins of the individual stamps differ for each position in the sheetlet.

1982 (13 July). *Birth of Prince William of Wales (1st issue). Nos. 391/3 optd as T* **55**.

415 60 c. Type **50** (optd with **T 55**) .. .. 2·00 1·50
a. Pair. Nos. 415/16 .. .. .. 4·00 3·00
416 60 c. Type **50** (optd "COMMEMORATING THE ROYAL BIRTH") .. .. 2·00 1·50
417 80 c. Lady Diana Spencer (optd with **T 55**) .. 2·50 1·75
a. Pair. Nos. 417/18 .. .. .. 5·00 3·50
418 80 c. Lady Diana Spencer (optd "COMMEMORATING THE ROYAL BIRTH") .. 2·50 1·75
419 $1.40, Prince Charles and Lady Diana (87 × 70 *mm*) (optd as **T 55**) .. 4·50 3·00
a. Pair. Nos. 419/20 .. .. .. 9·00 6·00
420 $1.40, Prince Charles and Lady Diana (87 × 70 *mm*) (optd "COMMEMORATING THE ROYAL BIRTH") .. .. 4·50 3·00
415/20 .. .. *Set of* 6 16·00 11·00

Nos. 415/16, 417/18 and 419/20 were each printed together in *se-tenant* pairs, horiz and vert, throughout the sheets.

1982 (5 Aug). *Birth of Prince William of Wales (2nd issue). As Nos. 411/14, but inscr* "ROYAL BIRTH 21 JUNE 1982 PRINCE WILLIAM OF WALES". *Multicoloured. P* 14.

421 70 c. Type **54** 70 70
422 $1 Prince and Princess of Wales 85 85
423 $2 Princess Diana (*different*) .. .. 1·60 1·60
421/3 .. .. *Set of* 3 2·75 2·75
MS424 81 × 91 mm. Nos. 421/3 .. .. .. 2·75 3·00

56 "Virgin and Child" (12th-century sculpture) **57** Aitutaki Bananas

1982 (10 Dec). *Christmas. Religious Sculptures. T* **56** *and similar vert designs. Multicoloured. P* 13.

425 18 c. Type **56** 25 25
426 36 c. "Virgin and Child" (12th-century) .. 35 35
427 48 c. "Virgin and Child" (13th-century) .. 55 55
428 60 c. "Virgin and Child" (15th-century) .. 65 65
425/8 .. .. *Set of* 4 1·60 1·60
MS429 99 × 115 mm. As Nos. 425/8 but each with 2 c. charity premium .. .. .. 1·60 2·00

Nos. 425/8 were each printed in small sheets of 6 including one *se-tenant*, stamp size, label, depicting the Prince and Princess of Wales with Prince William.

1983 (14 Mar). *Commonwealth Day. T* **57** *and similar horiz designs. Multicoloured. P* 13.

430 48 c. Type **57** 75 50
431 48 c. Ancient Ti'i image 75 50
432 48 c. Tourist canoeing 75 50
433 48 c. Captain William Bligh and chart .. 75 50
430/3 .. .. *Set of* 4 2·75 1·75

Nos. 430/3 were issued together, *se-tenant*, in blocks of four throughout the sheet.

15th WORLD SCOUT JAMBOREE

58 Scouts around Campfire (**59**)

1983 (18 Apr). *75th Anniv of Boy Scout Movement, T* **58** *and similar horiz designs. Multicoloured. P* 13½ × 14.

434 36 c. Type **58** 75 45
435 48 c. Scout saluting 90 55
436 60 c. Scouts hiking .. .. .. 1·10 75
434/6 .. .. *Set of* 3 2·50 1·60
MS437 78 × 107 mm. As Nos. 434/6 but each with premium of 3 c. P 13 .. .. .. 2·50 2·75

1983 (11 July). *15th World Scout Jamboree, Alberta, Canada. Nos. 434/7 optd with T* **59**.

438 36 c. Type **58** 75 45
439 48 c. Scout saluting 90 55
440 60 c. Scouts hiking .. .. .. 1·10 75
438/40 .. .. *Set of* 3 2·50 1·60
MS441 78 × 107 mm. As Nos. 438/40 but each with a premium of 3 c. .. .. .. 2·50 2·75

18c $1.20

60 Modern Sport Balloon (**61**) (**62**)

1983 (22 July). *Bicentenary of Manned Flight. T* **60** *and similar vert designs showing different modern sport balloons. P* 14 × 13.

442 18 c. multicoloured 15 15
443 36 c. multicoloured 35 30
444 48 c. multicoloured 40 35
445 60 c. multicoloured 55 45
442/5 .. .. *Set of* 4 1·25 1·10
MS446 64 × 80 mm. $2.50, multicoloured (48½ × 28½ *mm*) .. .. 1·90 2·50

Nos. 442/5 were each issued in small sheets of 4 stamps.

1983 (22 Sept). *Various stamps surch.*

(*a*) *Nos.* 335/48 *and* 352 *as T* **61**

447 18 c. on 20 c. American Golden Plover (*Pluvialis dominica*) 30 15
448 18 c. on 20 c. White Tern (*Gygis alba*) .. 30 15
449 36 c. on 25 c. Spotbill Duck (*Anas superciliosa*) 50 30
450 36 c. on 25 c. Brown Booby (*Sula leucogaster*) 50 30
451 36 c. on 30 c. Great Frigate Bird (*Fregata minor*) 50 30
452 36 c. on 30 c. Pintail (*Anas acuta*) 50 30
453 36 c. on 35 c. Long-billed Reed Warbler (*Conopoderas caffra caffra*) 50 30
454 36 c. on 35 c. Pomarine Skua (*Stercorarius pomarinus*) 50 30
455 48 c. on 40 c. Banded Rail (*Gallirallus philippensis goodsoni*) 70 40
456 48 c. on 40 c. Spotted Triller (*Lalage maculosa pumila*) 70 40
457 48 c. on 50 c. Royal Albatross (*Diomedea epomophora*) 70 40
458 48 c. on 50 c. Stephen's Lory (*Vini stepheni*) 70 40
459 72 c. on 70 c. Red-headed Parrot Finch (*Erythrura cyaneovirens*) .. .. 1·25 60
460 72 c. on 70 c. Orange Dove (*Ptilinopus victor victor*) .. .. 1·25 60
461 $5.60 on $5 Flat-billed Kingfisher (*Halcyon recurvirostris*) .. .. .. 8·00 4·75

(*b*) *Nos.* 392/3 *and* 412/13 *as T* **62**

462 96 c. on 80 c. Lady Diana Spencer (Gold) .. 4·50 2·50
a. Error. Surch on No. 417 .. .. 12·00
ab. Pair. Nos. 462/a/b .. .. .. 25·00
b. Error. Surch on No. 418 .. .. 12·00
463 96 c. on $1 Prince and Princess of Wales .. 4·00 2·00
464 $1.20 on $1.40, Prince Charles and Lady Diana (Gold) .. .. .. 4·50 2·50
a. Error. Surch on No. 419 .. .. 12·00
ab. Pair. Nos. 464a/b .. .. .. 25·00
b. Error. Surch on No. 420 .. .. 12·00
465 $1.20 on $2, Princess Diana .. .. 4·00 2·00
447/65 .. .. .. *Set of* 19 30·00 17·00

On Nos. 462 and 464 the gold surcharge is printed on a black obliterating panel over the original face value.

63 International Mail **64** "Madonna of the Chair"

1983 (29 Sept). *World Communications Year. T* **63** *and similar vert designs. Multicoloured. P* 14 × 13½.
466 48 c. Type **63** 55 45
467 60 c. Telecommunications 75 60
468 96 c. Space satellites .. .. 1·10 90
466/8 .. .. *Set of* 3 2·25 1·75
MS469 126 × 53 mm. Nos. 466/8. P 13 .. .. 2·25 2·50

1983 (21 Nov). *Christmas. 500th Birth Anniv of Raphael. T* **64** *and similar horiz designs. Multicoloured. P* 13½ × 14.
470 36 c. Type **64** 25 30
471 48 c. "The Alba Madonna" 35 40
472 60 c. "Conestabile Madonna" 50 55
470/2 .. .. *Set of* 3 1·00 1·10
MS473 95 × 116 mm. As Nos. 470/2, but each with a premium of 3 c. P 13 .. .. 1·25 1·40

1983 (15 Dec). *Christmas. 500th Birth Anniv of Raphael. Children's Charity. Designs as Nos. 470/2 in separate miniature sheets 46 × 47 mm, but each with different frames and a face value of 85 c. + 5 c. Imperf.*
MS474 As Nos. 470/2 .. .. *Set of 3 sheets* 2·75 2·75

65 Gouldian Finch **66** Javelin-throwing

1984 (13 Feb–2 July). *Birds (2nd series). Designs as Nos. 317 etc. but with redrawn frames and inscriptions as in T* **65**. *Multicoloured. P* 13 × 13½ ($3 *to* $9.60) *or* 14 (*others*).
475 2 c. Type **65** 10 10
476 3 c. Common Starling 10 10
477 5 c. Scarlet Robin 10 10
478 10 c. Golden Whistler 10 10
479 12 c. Rufous Fantail 10 10
480 18 c. Peregrine Falcon 10 10
481 24 c. Barn Owl 15 20
482 30 c. Java Sparrow 20 25
483 36 c. White-breasted Wood Swallow 25 30
484 48 c. Tahitian Lory 30 35
485 50 c. Rock Dove (26 Mar) 30 35
486 60 c. Purple Swamphen (26 Mar) 40 45
487 72 c. Zebra Dove (26 Mar) 50 55
488 96 c. Chestnut-breasted Mannikin (26 Mar) .. 65 70
489 $1.20, Common Mynah (26 Mar) 80 85
490 $2.10, Eastern Reef Heron (30 Apr) .. 1·40 1·50
491 $3 Blue-headed Flycatcher (30 × 42 *mm*) (30 Apr) .. .. 2·00 2·10
492 $4.20, Red-bellied Flycatcher (30 × 42 *mm*) (5 June) .. .. 2·75 3·00
493 $5.60, Red Munia (30 × 42 *mm*) (5 June) 3·75 4·00
494 $9.60, Flat-billed Kingfisher (30 × 42 *mm*) (2 July) .. .. 6·25 6·50
475/94 .. .. *Set of* 20 18·00 19·00

1984 (24 July). *Olympic Games, Los Angeles. T* **66** *and similar vert designs showing Memorial Coliseum and various events. Multicoloured. P* 13 × 13½.
495 36 c. Type **66** 30 35
496 48 c. Shot-putting 40 45
497 60 c. Hurdling 45 55
498 $2 Basketball .. .. 1·10 1·50
495/8 .. .. *Set of* 4 2·00 2·50
MS499 88 × 117 mm. As Nos. 495/8, but each with a charity premium of 5 c. .. .. .. 2·00 3·00

1984 (21 Aug). *Olympic Gold Medal Winners. Nos. 495/8 optd as T* **209** *of Cook Islands in gold on black background.*
500 36 c. Type **66** (optd "Javelin Throw Tessa Sanderson Great Britain") 30 35
501 48 c. Shot-putting (optd "Shot Put Claudia Losch Germany") 40 45
502 60 c. Hurdling (optd "Heptathlon Glynis Nunn Australia") 45 55
503 $2 Basketball (optd "Team Basketball United States") .. .. 1·10 1·50
500/3 .. .. *Set of* 4 2·00 2·50

ALTERED CATALOGUE NUMBERS

Any Catalogue numbers altered from the last edition are shown as a list in the introductory pages.

15.9.84 Birth
Prince Henry
$3

67 Capt. William Bligh and Chart (**68**)

1984 (14 Sept). *"Ausipex" International Stamp Exhibition, Melbourne. T* **67** *and similar horiz designs. Multicoloured. P* 14.
504 60 c. Type **67** 65 65
505 96 c. H.M.S. *Bounty* and map .. .. .. 1·00 1·00
506 $1.40, Aitutaki stamps of 1974, 1979 and 1981 with map .. .. 1·40 1·40
504/6 .. .. *Set of* 3 2·75 2·75
MS507 85 × 113 mm. As Nos. 504/6, but each with a premium of 5 c. P 13½ .. .. 3·00 3·25

1984 (10 Oct). *Birth of Prince Henry (1st issue). No. 391 surch with T* **68** *in gold.*
508 $3 on 60 c. Type **50** .. .. 4·00 3·00
On No. 508 the gold surcharge is printed on a black obliterating panel over the original face value.

69 The Annunciation **70** Princess Diana with Prince Henry

1984 (16 Nov). *Christmas. Details from Altarpiece, St. Paul's Church, Palencia, Spain. T* **69** *and similar vert designs. Multicoloured. P* 13½ × 13.
509 36 c. Type **69** 30 35
510 48 c. The Nativity 40 45
511 60 c. The Epiphany 45 50
512 96 c. The Flight into Egypt 75 80
509/12 .. .. *Set of* 4 1·75 1·90
MS513 Designs as Nos. 509/12 in separate miniature sheets, each 45 × 53 mm and with a face value of 90 c. + 7 c. Imperf. .. .. *Set of 4 sheets* 3·00 3·25

1984 (10 Dec). *Birth of Prince Henry (2nd issue). T* **70** *and similar vert designs. Multicoloured. P* 14.
514 48 c. Type **70** 45 45
515 60 c. Prince William with Prince Henry .. 50 50
516 $2.10, Prince and Princess of Wales with children .. .. 1·60 1·60
514/16 .. .. *Set of* 3 2·25 2·25
MS517 113 × 65 mm. As Nos. 514/16, but each with a face value of 96 c. + 7 c. P13½ .. .. .. 2·25 2·40

71 Grey Kingbird **72** The Queen Mother, aged Seven

1985 (22 Mar). *Birth Bicentenary of John J. Audubon (ornithologist). T* **71** *and similar vert designs showing original paintings. Multicoloured. P* 13.
518 55 c. Type **71** 60 60
519 65 c. Bohemian Waxwing 65 65
520 75 c. Summer Tanager 75 75
521 95 c. Common Cardinal 90 90
522 $1.15, White-winged Crossbill .. .. 1·10 1·10
518/22 .. .. *Set of* 5 3·50 3·50

1985 (14 June). *Life and Times of Queen Elizabeth the Queen Mother. T* **72** *and similar horiz designs. Multicoloured. P* 13.
523 55 c. Type **72** 45 50
524 65 c. Engagement photograph, 1922 .. .. 50 55
525 75 c. With young Princess Elizabeth 60 65
526 $1.30, With baby Prince Charles .. .. 1·00 1·10
523/6 .. .. *Set of* 4 2·25 2·50
MS527 75 × 49 mm. $3 Queen Mother on her 63rd birthday .. .. 2·25 2·40
Nos. 523/6 were each printed in sheetlets of 4.
For these stamps in a miniature sheet see No. **MS**550.

73 "The Calmady Children" (T. Lawrence)

1985 (16 Sept). *International Youth Year. T* **73** *and similar horiz designs. Multicoloured. P* 13.
528 75 c. Type **73** 50 55
529 90 c. "Madame Charpentier's Children" (Renoir) 60 65
530 $1.40, "Young Girls at Piano" (Renoir) .. 95 1·00
528/30 .. .. *Set of* 3 1·90 2·00
MS531 103 × 104 mm. As Nos. 528/30, but each with a premium of 10 c. .. .. 2·25 2·50

74 "Adoration of the Magi" (Giotto) and *Giotto* Spacecraft

1985 (15 Nov). *Christmas. Appearance of Halley's Comet (1st issue). T* **74** *and similar multicoloured designs. P* 13.
532 95 c. Type **74** 75 80
533 95 c. As Type **74** but showing *Planet A* spacecraft 75 80
534 $1.15, Type **74** 90 95
535 $1.15, As No. 533 .. .. 90 95
532/5 .. .. *Set of* 4 3·00 3·25
MS536 52 × 55 mm. $6.40, As Type **74** but without spacecraft (30 × 31 *mm*). Imperf .. .. 6·50 7·00
Nos. 532/3 and 534/5 were each printed together, *se-tenant*, in horizontal pairs throughout the sheets.

75 Halley's Comet, A.D. 684 (from "Nuremberg Chronicle") **76** Queen Elizabeth II on Coronation Day (from photo by Cecil Beaton)

1986 (25 Feb). *Appearance of Halley's Comet (2nd issue). T* **75** *and similar multicoloured designs. P* 13½ × 13.
537 90 c. Type **75** 65 70
538 $1.25, Halley's Comet, 1066 (from Bayeux Tapestry) 85 90
539 $1.75, Halley's Comet, 1456 (from "Lucerne Chronicles") .. .. 1·25 1·40
537/9 .. .. *Set of* 3 2·50 2·75
MS540 107 × 82 mm. As Nos. 537/9, but each with a face value of 95 c. .. .. 1·90 2·50
MS541 65 × 80 mm. $4.20, "Melencolia I" (Albrecht Dürer woodcut) (61 × 76 *mm*). Imperf .. 2·75 3·25

1986 (21 Apr). *60th Birthday of Queen Elizabeth II. T* **76** *and similar vert design. Multicoloured. P* 14.
542 95 c. Type **76** 85 85
MS543 58 × 68 mm. $4.20, As T **76**, but showing more of the portrait without oval frame. P 13½ 3·50 4·00
No. 542 was printed in sheetlets of five stamps and one stamp-size label at top left.

77 Head of Statue of Liberty **78** Prince Andrew and Miss Sarah Ferguson

1986 (27 June). *Centenary of Statue of Liberty. T* **77** *and similar horiz design. Multicoloured. P* 14.
544 $1 Type **77** 70 75
545 $2.75, Statue of Liberty at sunset .. .. 1·90 2·00
MS546 91 × 79 mm. As Nos. 544/5, but each with a face value of $1.25. P 13½ .. .. .. 1·90 2·25

1986 (23 July). *Royal Wedding. P* 14.
547 **78** $2 multicoloured .. .. 2·00 2·00
MS548 85×70 mm. **78** $5 mult. P 13½ .. .. 4·25 4·50
No. 547 was printed in sheetlets of 5 stamps and one stamp-size label at top left.

1986 (4 Aug). *"Stampex '86" Stamp Exhibition, Adelaide. No.* **MS**507 *with "Ausipex" emblems obliterated in gold.*
MS549 As Nos. 504/6, but each with a premium of 5 c. .. .. 3·00 3·50
The "Stampex '86" exhibition emblem is overprinted on the sheet margin.

1986 (4 Aug). *86th Birthday of Queen Elizabeth the Queen Mother. Nos.* 523/6 *in miniature sheet,* 132×82 *mm. P* 13½×13.
MS550 Nos. 523/6 .. .. 3·25 3·50

+10c

79 "St. Anne with Virgin and Child" (**80**)

1986 (21 Nov). *Christmas. Paintings by Dürer. T* **79** *and similar vert designs. Multicoloured. P* 13½.
551 75 c. Type **79** 60 60
552 $1.35, "Virgin and Child" 95 95
553 $1.95, "The Adoration of the Magi" .. 1·60 1·60
554 $2.75, "Madonna of the Rosary" .. .. 2·00 2·00
551/4 .. .. *Set of* 4 4·75 4·75
MS555 88×125 mm. As Nos. 551/4, but each stamp with a face value of $1.65 .. .. 5·00 6·00

1986 (25 Nov). *Visit of Pope John Paul II to South Pacific. Nos.* 551/5 *surch with T* **80** *in silver.*
556 75 c. + 10 c. Type **79** .. .. .. 1·00 1·00
557 $1.35 + 10 c. "Virgin and Child" .. .. 1·50 1·50
558 $1.95 + 10 c. "The Adoration of the Magi" 2·00 2·00
559 $2.75 + 10 c. "Madonna of the Rosary" .. 2·75 2·75
556/9 .. .. *Set of* 4 6·50 6·50
MS560 88 × 125 mm. As Nos. 556/9, but each stamp with a face value of $1.65 + 10 c. .. 7·00 7·50

2.50

Royal Wedding 40th Anniv

(**81**) (**82**)

1987 (29 Apr). *Hurricane Relief Fund. Nos.* 544/5, 547, 551/4 *and* 556/9 *surch with T* **81** *in black (Nos.* 563, 569*) or silver (others).*
561 75 c. + 50 c. Type **79** .. .. .. 1·10 1·10
562 75 c. + 10 c. + 50 c. Type **79** .. .. 1·25 1·25
563 $1 + 50 c. Type **77** .. .. 1·40 1·40
564 $1.35 + 50 c. "Virgin and Child" (Dürer) .. 1·60 1·60
565 $1.35 + 10 c. + 50 c. "Virgin and Child" (Dürer) .. .. 1·75 1·75
566 $1.95 + 50 c. "The Adoration of the Magi" (Dürer) .. .. 2·10 2·10
567 $1.95 + 10 c. + 50 c. "The Adoration of the Magi" (Dürer) .. .. 2·10 2·10
568 $2 + 50 c. Type **78** .. .. 2·10 2·10
569 $2.75 + 50 c. Statue of Liberty at sunset .. 2·75 2·75
570 $2.75 + 50 c. "Madonna of the Rosary" (Dürer) .. .. 2·75 2·75
571 $2.75 + 10 c. + 50 c. "Madonna of the Rosary" (Dürer) .. .. 3·00 3·00
561/71 .. .. *Set of* 11 20·00 20·00

1987 (20 Nov). *Royal Ruby Wedding. Nos.* 391/3 *surch as T* **82**.
572 $2.50 on 60 c. Type **50** .. .. .. 2·25 2·25
573 $2.50 on 80 c. Lady Diana Spencer .. .. 2·25 2·25
574 $2.50 on $1.40, Prince Charles and Lady Diana (87×70 *mm*) .. .. .. 2·25 2·25
572/4 .. .. *Set of* 3 6·00 6·00
On Nos. 572/4 the original values are obliterated in gold.

83 "Angels" (detail from "Virgin with Garland")

1987 (10 Dec). *Christmas. T* **83** *and similar designs showing different details of angels from "Virgin with Garland" by Rubens. P* 13×13½.
575 70 c. multicoloured 50 55
576 85 c. multicoloured 60 65
577 $1.50, multicoloured .. .. .. 1·00 1·10
578 $1.85, multicoloured .. .. .. 1·25 1·40
575/8 .. .. *Set of* 4 3·00 3·25
MS579 92×120 mm. As Nos. 575/8, but each with a face value of 95 c. .. .. .. 3·50 4·00
MS580 96×85 mm. $6 "Virgin with Garland" (*diamond,* 56×56 *mm*). P 13 .. .. 5·50 6·00

84 Chariot Racing and Athletics

(Des G. Vasarhelyi. Litho Questa)

1988 (22 Aug). *Olympic Games, Seoul. T* **84** *and similar horiz designs showing ancient and modern Olympic sports. Multicoloured. P* 14½.
581 70 c. Type **84** 50 55
582 85 c. Greek runners and football 60 65
583 95 c. Greek wrestling and handball .. 65 70
584 $1.40, Greek hoplites and tennis .. .. 1·00 1·10
581/4 .. .. *Set of* 4 2·50 2·75
MS585 103×101 mm. As Nos. 581 and 584, but each with face value of $2 .. .. .. 2·75 3·00

1988 (10 Oct). *Olympic Medal Winners, Los Angeles. Nos.* 581/4 *optd as T* **235** *of Cook Islands.*
586 70 c. Type **84** (optd "FLORENCE GRIFFTH JOYNER UNITED STATES 100 M AND 200 M") 50 55
587 85 c. Greek runners and football (optd "GELINDO BORDIN ITALY MARATHON") 60 65
588 95 c. Greek wrestling and handball (optd "HITOSHI SAITO JAPAN JUDO") .. 65 70
589 $1.40, Greek hoplites and tennis (optd "STEFFI GRAF WEST GERMANY WOMEN'S TENNIS") .. .. 1·00 1·10
586/9 .. .. *Set of* 4 2·50 2·75

85 "Adoration of the Shepherds" (detail)

1988 (2 Nov). *Christmas. T* **85** *and similar multicoloured designs showing paintings by Rembrandt. P* 13½.
590 55 c. Type **85** 40 45
591 70 c. "The Holy Family" 50 55
592 85 c. "Presentation in the Temple" 60 65
593 95 c. "The Holy Family" (*different*) 65 70
594 $1.15, "Presentation in the Temple" (*different*) 80 85
590/4 .. .. *Set of* 5 2·75 3·00
MS595 85 × 101 mm. $4.50, As Type **85** but 52 × 34 mm. P 14 .. .. .. 3·25 3·50

86 H.M.S. *Bounty* leaving Spithead and King George III

(Des Jennifer Toombs)

1989 (3 July). *Bicentenary of Discovery of Aitutaki by Capt. Bligh. T* **86** *and similar horiz designs. Multicoloured. P* 13½×13.
596 55 c. Type **86** 40 45
597 65 c. Breadfruit plants 50 55
598 75 c. Old chart showing Aitutaki and Capt. Bligh 55 60
599 95 c. Native outrigger and H.M.S. *Bounty* off Aitutaki 70 75
600 $1.65, Fletcher Christian confronting Bligh .. .. 1·25 1·40
596/600 .. .. .. *Set of* 5 3·00 3·25
MS601 94×72 mm. $4.20, "Mutineers casting Bligh adrift" (Robert Dodd) (60×45 *mm*). P 13½ 3·25 3·50

87 "Apollo 11" Astronaut on Moon

1989 (28 July). *20th Anniv of First Manned Landing on Moon. T* **87** *and similar horiz designs. Multicoloured. P* 13½×13.
602 75 c. Type **87** 55 60
603 $1.15, Conducting experiment on Moon .. 85 90
604 $1.80, Astronaut on Moon carrying equipment .. .. 1·40 1·50
602/4 .. .. *Set of* 3 2·50 2·75
MS605 105×86 mm. $6.40, Astronaut on Moon with U.S. flag (40×27 *mm*). P 13½ .. .. 4·75 5·00

OFFICIAL STAMPS

O H.M.S.

(O 1)

1978 (3 Nov)–**79**. *Nos.* 98/105, 107/10 *and* 227/8 *optd or surch (Nos.* O8/9 *and* O15*) as Type* O **1**.
O 1 1 c. *Nautilus macromphallus* 35 10
O 2 2 c. *Harpa major* 45 10
O 3 3 c. *Phalium strigatum* 45 10
O 4 4 c. *Cypraea talpa* (Gold) 45 10
O 5 5 c. *Mitra stictica* 45 10
O 6 8 c. *Charonia tritonis* 55 10
O 7 10 c. *Murex triremis* 65 15
O 8 15 c. on 60 c. *Strombus latissimus* .. .. 1·00 20
O 9 18 c. on 60 c. *Strombus latissimus* .. .. 1·00 20
O10 20 c. *Oliva sericea* (Gold) .. .. .. 1·00 20
O11 50 c. Union Jack, Queen Victoria and island map .. .. 2·00 55
O12 60 c. *Strombus latissimus* .. .. .. 2·50 70
O13 $1 *Biplex perca* .. .. 3·25 1·00
O14 $2 Queen Elizabeth II and *Terebra maculata* (20.2.79) .. .. 4·50 1·50
O15 $4 on $1 Balcony scene, 1953 (Sil.) (20.2.79) 7·00 2·50
O16 $5 Queen Elizabeth II and *Cypraea hesitata* (20.2.79) .. .. 7·50 3·50
O1/16 .. .. *Set of* 16 30·00 9·50
These stamps were originally only sold to the public cancelled-to-order and not in unused condition.
They were made available to overseas collectors in mint condition during 1980.

75c

O.H.M.S. O.H.M.S.

(O 2) (O 3)

1985 (9 Aug)–**88**. *(a) Nos.* 351, 475, 477/88 *and* 489/94 *optd or surch as Type* O **2** *by foil embossing in blue ($14) or emerald (others).*
O17 2 c. Type **65** 10 10
O18 5 c. Scarlet Robin 10 10
O19 10 c. Golden Whistler 10 10
O20 12 c. Rufous Fantail 10 10
O21 18 c. Peregrine Falcon 10 10
O22 20 c. on 24 c. Barn Owl 10 15
O23 30 c. Java Sparrow 20 25
O24 40 c. on 36 c. White-breasted Wood Swallow 25 30
O25 50 c. Rock Dove 30 35
O26 55 c. on 48 c. Tahitian Lory 35 40
O27 60 c. Purple Swamphen 40 45
O28 65 c. on 72 c. Zebra Dove 45 50
O29 80 c. on 96 c. Chestnut-breasted Mannikin 55 60
O30 $1.20, Common Mynah (15.6.88) .. 80 85
O31 $2.10, Eastern Reef Heron (15.6.88) .. 1·40 1·50
O32 $3 Blue-headed Flycatcher (30×42 *mm*) (1.10.86) .. .. 2·00 2·10
O33 $4.20, Red-bellied Flycatcher (30×42 *mm*) (1.10.86) .. .. .. 2·75 3·00
O34 $5.60, Red Munia (30×42 *mm*) (1.10.86) 3·75 4·00
O35 $9.60, Flat-billed Kingfisher (30×42 *mm*) (1.10.86) .. .. 6·25 6·50
O36 $14 on $4 Red Munia (35×48 *mm*) (15.6.88) .. .. 9·00 9·25

(b) Nos. 430/3 *surch as Type* O **3** *by gold foil embossing*
O37 75 c. on 48 c. Type **57** 50 55
O38 75 c. on 48 c. Ancient Ti'i image 50 55
O39 75 c. on 48 c. Tourist canoeing 50 55
O40 75 c. on 48 c. Captain William Bligh and chart 50 55
O17/40 .. .. *Set of* 24 28·00 29·00

PENRHYN ISLAND

Stamps of COOK ISLANDS were used on Penrhyn Island from late 1901 until the issue of the surcharged stamps in May 1902.

PRICES FOR STAMPS ON COVER TO 1945	
Nos. 1/8	*from* × 4
Nos. 9/10	*from* × 50
Nos. 11/13	—
Nos. 14/18	*from* × 3
Nos. 19/23	*from* × 2
Nos. 24/37	*from* × 3
Nos. 38/40	*from* × 5

A. NEW ZEALAND DEPENDENCY

The island of Penrhyn, previously under British protection, was annexed by New Zealand on 11 June 1901.

Stamps of New Zealand overprinted or surcharged

PENRHYN ISLAND.
½ PENI.
(1)

PENRHYN ISLAND.
TAI PENI.
(2) 1d.

PENRHYN ISLAND.
2½ PENI.
(3)

1902 (5 May). *1902 issue surch with T* **1, 2** *and* **3**.

(*a*) *Thick, white Pirie paper. No wmk. P* 11
1 **27** 2½d. blue (R.) .. .. 1·25 3·50
a. "½" and "P" spaced (all stamps in 8th vert row) .. .. 12·00 22·00

(*b*) *Thin, hard Basted Mills paper. W* **38** *of New Zealand.*

(i) *P* 11
3 **42** 1d. carmine (Br.) £375 £375

(ii) *P* 14
4 **23** ½d. green (R.) .. .. 80 3·25
a. No stop after "ISLAND" .. .. 85·00 90·00
5 **42** 1d. carmine (Br.) .. .. 3·00 6·50
a. Pale carmine .. .. 3·00 6·50

(iii) *P* 11×14
7 **42** 1d. carmine (Br.) £375 £375

(iv) *Mixed perfs*
8 **42** 1d. carmine (Br.) £250

(*c*) *Thin, hard Cowan paper. W* **38** *of New Zealand.* (i) *P* 14
9 **23** ½d. green (R.) .. .. 90 3·50
a. No stop after "ISLAND" (R. 10/6) .. 90·00 £110
10 **42** 1d. carmine (B.) .. .. 90 2·75
a. No stop after "ISLAND" (R. 10/6) .. 40·00 55·00

(ii) *P* 11×14
11 **42** 1d. carmine (B.) .. ..

(iii) *Mixed perfs*
12 **23** ½d. green (R.) £400 £450
13 **42** 1d. carmine (B.) £100 £120

PENRHYN ISLAND.
(4)

Toru Pene.
(5) 3d.

Ono Pene.
(6) 6d.

Tahi Silingi.
(7) 1s.

1903 (28 Feb). *1902 issue surch with name at top, T* **4**, *and values at foot, T* **5/7**. *W* **43** *of New Zealand. P* 11.
14 **28** 3d. yellow-brown (B.) .. .. .. 9·00 14·00
15 **31** 6d. rose-red (B.) .. .. .. 15·00 25·00
16 **34** 1s. brown-red (B.) .. .. .. 38·00 48·00
17 1s. bright red (B.) .. .. .. 38·00 48·00
18 1s. orange-red (B.) .. .. .. 45·00 45·00
14/16 .. .. *Set of* 3 55·00 75·00

1914–15. *Surch with T* **1** (½d.) *or optd with T* **4** *at top and surch with T* **6/7** *at foot.*
19 **50** ½d. yellow-green (C.) (5.14) .. .. 90 3·50
a. No stop after "ISLAND" .. .. 32·00 55·00
b. No stop after "PENI" (R. 3/17) .. 70·00 £100
20 ½d. yellow-green (Verm.) (1.15) .. .. 65 3·50
a. No stop after "ISLAND" .. .. 15·00 28·00
b. No stop after "PENI" (R. 3/5, 3/17) .. 35·00 60·00
22 **51** 6d. carmine (B.) (8.14) .. .. 27·00 48·00
23 1s. vermilion (B.) (8.14) .. .. 45·00 70·00
19/23 .. .. *Set of* 4 65·00 £110

The "no stop after ISLAND" variety occurs on R. 1/4, 1/10, 1/16, 1/22, 6/4, 6/10, 6/16 and 6/22 of the carmine surcharge, No. 19, and on these positions plus R. 1/12, 1/24, 6/12 and 6/24 for the vermilion, No. 20.

1917–20. *King George V stamps optd with name only. T* **4**. *W* **43** *of New Zealand. P* 14×14½.
24 **60** 2½d. blue (R.) (10.20) .. .. .. 1·25 3·75
a. No stop after "ISLAND" (R. 10/8) .. 80·00 £120
b. Perf 14×13½ .. .. .. 3·00 7·00
c. Vert pair. Nos. 24/4b .. .. 50·00 70·00
25 3d. chocolate (B.) (6.18) .. .. 9·00 25·00
a. Perf 14×13½ .. .. .. 9·50 27·00
b. Vert pair. Nos. 25/5a .. .. 70·00 £100
26 6d. carmine (B.) (1.18) .. .. 5·00 12·00
a. No stop after "ISLAND" (R. 10/8) .. £140 £200
b. Perf 14×13½ .. .. .. 7·00 16·00
c. Vert pair. Nos. 26/6b .. .. 55·00 90·00
27 1s. vermilion (B.) (12.17) .. .. 12·00 25·00
a. No stop after "ISLAND" (R. 10/8) .. £200 £300
b. Perf 14×13½ .. .. .. 15·00 30·00
c. Vert pair. Nos. 27/7b £110 £160
24/7 .. .. *Set of* 4 24·00 60·00

1917–20. *Optd as T* **4**. *Typo. W* **43** *of New Zealand. P* 14×15.
28 **61** ½d. green (R.) (2.20) .. .. .. 65 1·25
a. No stop after "ISLAND" (R. 2/24) .. 45·00 60·00
b. Narrow spacing .. .. .. 5·00 7·50
29 1½d. slate (R.) (11.17) .. .. .. 4·00 7·50
a. Narrow spacing .. .. .. 17·00 28·00
30 1½d. orange-brown (R.) (2.19) .. .. 60 5·50
a. Narrow spacing .. .. .. 5·00 17·00
31 3d. chocolate (B.) (6.19) .. .. 3·00 8·00
a. Narrow spacing .. .. .. 14·00 28·00
28/31 .. .. *Set of* 4 7·50 20·00

The narrow spacing variety occurs on R. 1/5–8, 4/21–4, 7/5–8 and 9/21–4.

(Recess P.B.)

1920 (23 Aug). *As Types of Cook Islands but inscr* "PENRHYN". *No wmk. P* 14.
32 **9** ½d. black and emerald .. .. .. 90 4·00
a. Part imperf block of 4 .. .. £1200
33 **10** 1d. black and deep red .. .. .. 1·25 4·00
34 **11** 1½d. black and deep violet .. .. 6·50 9·00
35 **12** 3d. black and red .. .. .. 2·00 5·00
36 **13** 6d. red-brown and sepia .. .. 3·25 13·00
37 **14** 1s. black and slate-blue .. .. 9·00 17·00
32/7 .. .. *Set of* 6 20·00 45·00

No. 32a comes from sheets on which two rows were imperforate between horizontally and the second row additionally imperforate vertically.

Examples of the ½d. and 1d. with centre inverted were not supplied to the Post Office.

(Recess Govt Printing Office, Wellington)

1927–29. *As Types of Cook Islands, but inscr* "PENRHYN". *W* **43**. *P* 14.
38 **9** ½d. black and green (5.29) .. .. 2·00 7·50
39 **10** 1d. black and deep carmine (14.3.28) .. 2·00 6·50
40 **16** 2½d. red-brown and dull blue (10.27) .. 1·75 10·00
38/40 .. .. *Set of* 3 5·25 22·00

Cook Islands stamps superseded those of Penrhyn Islands on 15 March 1932. Separate issues were resumed in 1973.

B. PART OF COOK ISLANDS

The following issues are for use in all the islands of the Northern Cook Islands group.

PRINTERS. The note above No. 33 of Aitutaki concerning printers and gum also applies here. All issues, except Nos. 41A/52A and **MS**412, are on paper treated with fluorescent security markings. The markings can be found inverted or omitted.

PENRHYN

PENRHYN
NORTHERN
(8)

PENRHYN
NORTHERN
(9)

1973 (24 Oct–14 Nov). *Nos.* 228/45 *of Cook Is optd with T* **8** (*without* "NORTHERN" *on* $1, $2).
A. *Without fluorescent security markings. Gum arabic*
B. *With fluorescent security markings. PVA gum*

		A.		B.	
41	1 c. multicoloured	80	—	10	10
42	2 c. multicoloured	1·25	—	10	10
43	3 c. multicoloured	1·75	—	10	10
44	4 c. multicoloured (No. 233) ..	2·00	—	10	10
	a. Optd on Cook Is No. 232 ..	60·00	—	†	
45	5 c. multicoloured	2·50	—	10	10
46	6 c. multicoloured	2·50	—	20	30
47	8 c. multicoloured	2·75	—	30	40
48	15 c. multicoloured	4·25	—	45	50
49	20 c. multicoloured	†		75	80
50	50 c. multicoloured	16·00	—	1·75	1·75
51	$1 multicoloured	28·00	—	2·25	2·25
52	$2 multicoloured (14.11) ..	48·00	—	2·50	2·50
41A/52A	.. .. *Set of* 11	£100	—	†	
41B/52B	.. .. *Set of* 12	†		7·50	7·50

1973 (14 Nov). *Royal Wedding. Nos.* 450/2 *of Cook Is optd as T* **9**, *in silver.*
53 **138** 25 c. multicoloured 85 20
54 – 30 c. multicoloured 85 20
55 – 50 c. multicoloured 85 20
53/5 .. .. *Set of* 3 2·25 55

10 *Ostracion sp*

11 Penrhyn Stamps of 1902

1974 (15 Aug)–**75**. *Fishes. T* **10** *and similar horiz designs. Multicoloured. P* 13½ (½ c. *to* $1) *or* 13 × 12½ ($2, $5).
56 ½ c. Type **10** 20 15
57 1 c. *Monodactylus argenteus* 40 15
58 2 c. *Pomacanthus imperator* 50 15
59 3 c. *Chelmon rostratus* 50 15
60 4 c. *Chaetodon ornatissimus* 50 15
61 5 c. *Chaetodon melanotus* 50 15
62 8 c. *Chaetodon raffessi* 50 15
63 10 c. *Chaetodon ephippium* 55 15
64 20 c. *Pygoplites diacanthus* .. .. 1·25 25
65 25 c. *Heniochus acuminatus* .. .. 1·25 25
66 60 c. *Plectorhynchus chaetodonoides* .. 2·50 90
67 $1 *Balistipus undulatus* .. .. 2·75 1·25
68 $2 Birds-eye view of Penrhyn (12.2.75) .. 5·50 5·50
69 $5 Satellite view of Australasia (12.3.75) .. 6·50 5·50
56/69 .. .. *Set of* 14 21·00 13·50

Nos. 68/9 are larger, 63 × 25 mm.

1974 (27 Sept). *Centenary of Universal Postal Union. T* **11** *and similar vert design. Multicoloured. P* 13.
70 25 c. Type **11** 20 20
71 50 c. Stamps of 1920 .. .. 35 35
Each value was issued in sheets of 8 stamps and 1 label.

12 "Adoration of the Kings" (Memling)

1974 (30 Oct). *Christmas. T* **12** *and similar horiz designs. Multicoloured. P* 13.
72 5 c. Type **12** 15 10
73 10 c. "Adoration of the Shepherds" (Hugo van der Goes) 20 10
74 25 c. "Adoration of the Magi" (Rubens) .. 35 15
75 30 c. "The Holy Family" (Borgianni) 45 25
72/5 .. .. *Set of* 4 1·00 50

13 Churchill giving "V" Sign

(14)

1974 (30 Nov.) *Birth Centenary of Sir Winston Churchill. T* **13** *and similar vert design. P* 13.
76 30 c. agate and gold 90 70
77 50 c. myrtle-green and gold .. .. .. 1·10 80
Design:—50 c. Full-face portrait.

1975 (24 July). *"Apollo-Soyuz" Space Project. No. 69 optd with T* **14**.
78 $5 Satellite view of Australasia .. .. 3·50 4·50

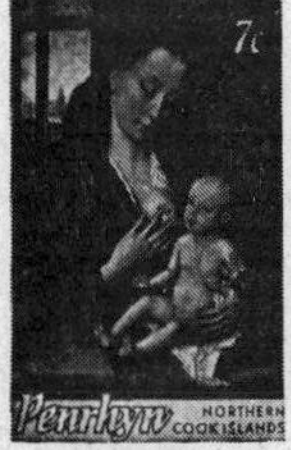

15 "Virgin and Child" (Bouts)

16 "Pietà"

1975 (21 Nov). *Christmas. T* **15** *and similar vert designs showing the "Virgin and Child". Multicoloured. P* 14 × 13.
79 7 c. Type **15** 25 10
80 15 c. Leonardo da Vinci 50 20
81 35 c. Raphael 85 35
79/81 .. .. *Set of* 3 1·50 60

1976 (19 Mar). *Easter and 500th Birth Anniv of Michelangelo. T* **16** *and similar vert designs. P* 14 × 13.
82 15 c. sepia and gold 25 15
83 20 c. blackish purple and gold 30 15
84 35 c. myrtle-green and gold 40 20
82/4 .. .. *Set of* 3 85 45
MS85 112 × 72 mm. Nos. 82/4 .. .. .. 85 1·25
Each value was issued in sheets of 8 stamps and 1 label.

17 "Washington crossing the Delaware" (E. Leutze)

18 Running

1976 (20 May). *Bicentenary of American Revolution. T* **17** *and similar vert designs. Multicoloured. P* 13.
86 30 c. } Type **17**.. .. .. 50 15
87 30 c. } .. 50 15
88 30 c. } .. 50 15
89 50 c. } "The Spirit of '76" (A. M. Willard) .. 60 20
90 50 c. } .. 60 20
91 50 c. } .. 60 20
86/91 .. .. *Set of* 6 3·00 95
MS92 103 × 103 mm. Nos. 86/91. P 13 .. .. 3·00 3·50
Nos. 86/8 and 89/91 were each printed together, *se-tenant*, in horizontal strips of 3 throughout the sheet, forming composite designs. Each sheet includes 3 stamp-size labels. Type **17** shows the left-hand stamp of the 30 c. design.

1976 (9 July). *Olympic Games, Montreal. T* **18** *and similar horiz designs. Multicoloured. P* 14.
93 25 c. Type **18** 25 15
94 30 c. Long Jumping 30 15
95 75 c. Throwing the Javelin 55 25
93/5 .. .. *Set of* 3 1·00 50
MS96 86 × 128 mm. Nos. 93/5. P 14 × 13 .. 1·00 1·75

19 "The Flight into Egypt"

20 The Queen in Coronation Robes

1976 (20 Oct). *Christmas. Dürer Engravings. T* **19** *and similar horiz designs. P* 13.
97 7 c. black and silver 10 10
98 15 c. steel blue and silver 20 15
99 35 c. violet and silver 30 25
97/9 .. .. *Set of* 3 55 45
Designs:—15 c. "Adoration of the Magi"; 35 c. "The Nativity".

1977 (24 Mar). *Silver Jubilee. T* **20** *and similar vert designs. Multicoloured. P* 13.
100 50 c. Type **20** 60 70
101 $1 Queen and Prince Philip.. .. .. 70 75
102 $2 Queen Elizabeth II .. .. .. 1·00 1·00
100/2 .. .. *Set of* 3 2·10 2·25
MS103 128 × 87 mm. Nos. 100/2. P 13 .. .. 2·75 2·75
Stamps from the miniature sheet have silver borders.

21 "The Annunciation"

22 Iiwi

1977 (23 Sept). *Christmas. T* **21** *and similar designs showing illustrations by J. S. von Carolsfeld. P* 13.
104 7 c. light stone, purple-brown and gold .. 25 15
105 15 c. pale rose, deep maroon and gold .. 40 15
106 35 c. blackish green, pale green and gold .. 70 30
104/6 .. .. *Set of* 3 1·25 55
Designs:—15 c. "The Announcement to the Shepherds"; 35 c. "The Nativity".

1978 (19 Jan). *Bicentenary of Discovery of Hawaii. T* **22** *and similar vert designs showing extinct Hawaiian birds or artefacts. Multicoloured. P* 13.
107 20 c. Type **22** 50 30
108 20 c. Elgin cloak 50 30
109 30 c. Apapane 60 40
110 30 c. Feather image of a god 60 40
111 35 c. Moorhen 70 45
112 35 c. Feather cape, helmet and staff 70 45
113 75 c. Hawaii O-o .. .. 1·25 80
114 75 c. Feather image and cloak .. .. .. 1·25 80
107/14 .. .. *Set of* 8 5·50 3·50
MS115 Two sheets each 78 × 119 mm containing (a) Nos. 107, 109, 111, 113; (b) Nos. 108, 110, 112, 114.. .. .. 6·50 7·50
Nos. 107/8, 109/10, 111/12 and 113/14 were each printed together, *se-tenant*, in horizontal and vertical pairs throughout the sheet.

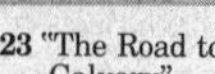

23 "The Road to Calvary"

24 Royal Coat of Arms

1978 (10 Mar). *Easter and 400th Birth Anniv of Rubens. T* **23** *and similar vert designs. Multicoloured. P* 13.
116 10 c. Type **23** 10 10
117 15 c. "Christ on the Cross" 15 15
118 35 c. "Christ with Straw" 25 25
116/18 .. .. *Set of* 3 45 45
MS119 87 × 138 mm. Nos. 116/18 .. .. 60 1·25
Stamps from No. **MS**119 are slightly larger (28 × 36 mm.)

1978 (17 Apr). *Easter. Children's Charity. Designs as Nos. 116/18 in separate miniature sheets. 49 × 68 mm, each with a face value of 60 c. + 5 c. P* 12½–13.
MS120 As Nos. 116/18 .. .. *Set of 3 sheets* 1·25 2·25

1978 (24 May). *25th Anniv of Coronation. T* **24** *and similar vert designs. P* 13.
121 90 c. black, gold and deep lilac 55 75
122 90 c. multicoloured 55 75
123 90 c. black, gold and deep bluish green .. 55 75
121/3 .. .. *Set of* 3 1·50 2·00
MS124 75 × 122 mm. Nos. 121/3 .. .. .. 1·50 2·25
Designs:—No. 122, Queen Elizabeth II; No. 123, New Zealand coat of arms.
Nos. 121/3 were printed together in small sheets of 6, containing two *se-tenant* strips of 3, with horizontal gutter margin between.

25 "Madonna of the Pear"

26 Sir Rowland Hill and G.B. Penny Black Stamp

1978 (29 Nov). *Christmas. 450th Death Anniv of Dürer. T* **25** *and similar vert design. Multicoloured. P* 14.
125 30 c. Type **25** 35 25
126 35 c. "The Virgin and Child with St. Anne" .. 35 25
MS127 101 × 60 mm. Nos. 125/6. P 13½.. .. 70 1·25
Nos. 125/6 were each printed in small sheets of 6.

1979 (26 Sept). *Death Centenary of Sir Rowland Hill. T* **26** *and similar vert designs. Multicoloured. P* 13½ × 14.
128 75 c. Type **26** 75 65
129 75 c. 1974 Centenary of Universal Postal Union 25 c. and 50 c. commemoratives .. 75 65
130 90 c. Sir Rowland Hill.. .. .. .. 90 80
131 90 c. 1978 25th anniv of Coronation 90 c. (Queen Elizabeth II) commemorative .. 90 80
128/31 .. .. *Set of* 4 3·00 2·75
MS132 116 × 58 mm. Nos. 128/31 .. .. 3·00 3·50
Stamps from No. **MS**132 have cream backgrounds.
Nos. 128/9 and 130/1 were each printed together, *se-tenant*, in horizontal and vertical pairs throughout small sheets of 8.

27 Max and Moritz

28 "Christ carrying Cross" (Book of Ferdinand II)

1979 (20 Nov). *International Year of the Child. Illustrations from Max and Moritz stories by Wilhelm Busch. T* **27** *and similar horiz designs. Multicoloured. P* 13.
133 12 c. Type **27** 20 10
134 12 c. Max and Moritz looking down chimney .. 20 10
135 12 c. Max and Moritz making off with food .. 20 10
136 12 c. Cook about to beat dog 20 10
137 15 c. Max sawing through bridge 25 10
138 15 c. Pursuer approaching bridge 25 10
139 15 c. Bridge collapsing under pursuer .. 25 10
140 15 c. Pursuer in river 25 10
141 20 c. Baker locking shop 30 20
142 20 c. Max and Moritz coming out of hiding .. 30 20
143 20 c. Max and Moritz falling in dough .. 30 20
144 20 c. Max and Moritz after being rolled into buns by baker 30 20
133/44 .. .. *Set of* 12 2·75 1·50
Nos. 133/6, 137/40 and 141/4 were each printed together, *se-tenant*, in sheets of 4, either with or without labels containing extracts from the books on the top and bottom selvedge.

1980 (28 Mar). *Easter. Scenes from 15th-century Prayer Books. T* **28** *and similar vert designs. Multicoloured. P* 13.
145 12 c. Type **28** 10 10
146 20 c. "The Crucifixion" (William Vrelant, Book of Duke of Burgundy) 15 15
147 35 c. "Descent from the Cross" (Book of Ferdinand II) 25 25
145/7 .. .. *Set of* 4 45 45
MS148 111 × 65 mm. Nos. 145/7 .. .. .. 45 70
Stamps from No. **MS**148 have cream borders.

1980 (28 Mar). *Easter. Children's Charity. Designs as Nos. 145/7 in separate miniature sheets 54 × 85 mm, each with a face value of 70 c. + 5 c.*
MS149 As Nos. 145/7 .. .. *Set of 3 sheets* 75 1·50

PRICES OF SETS

Set prices are given for many issues, generally those containing three stamps or more. Definitive sets include one of each value or major colour change, but do not cover different perforations, die types or minor shades. Where a choice is possible the set prices are based on the cheapest versions of the stamps included in the listings.

29 Queen Elizabeth the Queen Mother in 1937

30 Falk Hoffman, D.D.R. (platform diving) (gold)

1980 (17 Sept). *80th Birthday of Queen Elizabeth the Queen Mother. P* 13.
150 **29** $1 multicoloured .. .. .. 2·00 1·50
MS151 55 × 84 mm. **29** $2.50 multicoloured .. 3·00 2·75

1980 (14 Nov). *Olympic Games, Moscow. Medal Winners. T* **30** *and similar vert designs. Multicoloured. P* 13½.
152 10 c. Type **30** 10 10
153 10 c. Martina Jaschke, D.D.R. (platform diving) (gold) 10 10
154 20 c. Tomi Polkolainen, Finland (archery) (gold) 15 15
155 20 c. Kete Losaberidse, U.S.S.R. (archery) (gold) 15 15
156 30 c. Czechoslovakia (football) (gold) 20 20
157 30 c. D.D.R. (football) (silver) 20 20
158 50 c. Barbel Wockel, D.D.R. (200-metre dash) (gold) 30 30
159 50 c. Pietro Mennea, Italy (200-metre dash) (gold) 30 30
152/9 .. .. *Set of* 8 1·40 1·40
MS160 150 × 106 mm. Nos. 152/9. P 13 .. .. 1·40 1·75
Stamps from No. **MS**160 have gold borders.
Nos. 152/3, 154/5, 156/7 and 158/9 were each printed together, *se-tenant*, in horizontal pairs throughout the sheet.

31 "The Virgin of Counsellors" (Luis Dalmau)

32 Amatasi

1980 (5 Dec). *Christmas. Paintings. T* **31** *and similar vert designs. Multicoloured. P* 13.
161 20 c. Type **31** 15 15
162 35 c. "Virgin and Child" (Serra brothers) .. 20 20
163 50 c. "The Virgin of Albocacer" (Master of the Porciuncula) 30 30
161/3 .. .. *Set of* 3 60 60
MS164 135 × 75 mm. Nos. 161/3 .. .. 90 1·25

1980 (5 Dec). *Christmas. Children's Charity. Designs as Nos.* 161/3 *in separate miniature sheets,* 54 × 77 *mm, each with a face value of* 70 *c.* + 5 *c.*
MS165 As Nos. 161/3 .. .. *Set of* 3 *sheets* 2·50 2·75

1981 (16 Feb–21 Sept). *Sailing Craft and Ships (1st series). Multicoloured designs as T* **32**. *P* 14 *(Nos.* 166/85*),* 13 × 14½ *(Nos.* 186/205*) or* 13½ *(Nos.* 206/8*).*
166 1 c. Type **32** 10 10
167 1 c. Ndrua 10 10
168 1 c. Waka 10 10
169 1 c. Tongiaki 10 10
170 3 c. Va'a Teu'ua 20 10
171 3 c. *Victoria*, 1500 .. .. 20 10
172 3 c. *Golden Hind*, 1560 .. .. 20 10
173 3 c. *Boudeuse*, 1760 .. .. 20 10
174 4 c. H.M.S. *Bounty*, 1787 .. .. .. 20 10
175 4 c. *L'Astrolabe*, 1811 .. .. 20 10
176 4 c. *Star of India*, 1861 .. .. 20 10
177 4 c. *Great Republic*, 1853 .. .. 20 10
178 6 c. *Balcutha*, 1886 .. .. 25 10
179 6 c. *Coonatto*, 1863 .. .. 25 10
180 6 c. *Antiope*, 1866 .. .. 25 10
181 6 c. *Teaping*, 1863 .. .. 25 10
182 10 c. *Preussen*, 1902 .. .. 25 10
183 10 c. *Pamir*, 1921 .. .. 25 10
184 10 c. *Cap Hornier*, 1910 .. .. 25 10
185 10 c. *Patriarch*, 1869 .. .. 25 10
186 15 c. As Type **32** (16 Mar) 30 30
187 15 c. As No. 167 (16 Mar) 30 30
188 15 c. As No. 168 (16 Mar) 30 30
189 15 c. As No. 169 (16 Mar) 30 30
190 20 c. As No. 170 (16 Mar) 30 30
191 20 c. As No. 171 (16 Mar) 30 30
192 20 c. As No. 172 (16 Mar) 30 30
193 20 c. As No. 173 (16 Mar) 30 30
194 30 c. As No. 174 (16 Mar) 45 45
195 30 c. As No. 175 (16 Mar) 45 45
196 30 c. As No. 176 (16 Mar) 45 45
197 30 c. As No. 177 (16 Mar) 45 45
198 50 c. As No. 178 (16 Mar) 75 75
199 50 c. As No. 179 (16 Mar) 75 75
200 50 c. As No. 180 (16 Mar) 75 75
201 50 c. As No. 181 (16 Mar) 75 75
202 $1 As No. 182 (15 May) .. .. .. 1·25 95
203 $1 As No. 183 (15 May) .. .. .. 1·25 95
204 $1 As No. 184 (15 May) .. .. .. 1·25 95
205 $1 As No. 185 (15 May) .. .. .. 1·25 95
206 $2 *Cutty Sark*, 1869 (26 June) .. .. 3·00 2·25
207 $4 *Mermerus*, 1872 (26 June) .. .. 6·00 4·00
208 $6 H.M.S. *Resolution* and *Discovery*, 1776–80 (21 Sept) .. .. .. 8·00 5·50
166/208 .. .. *Set of* 43 30·00 23·00
Nos. 186/205 are 41 × 25 mm and Nos. 206/8 47 × 33 mm in size.
On Nos. 166/205 the four designs of each value were printed together, *se-tenant*, in blocks of 4 throughout the sheet.
For redrawn versions of these designs in other face values see Nos. 337/55.

33 "Jesus at the Grove" (Veronese)

34 Prince Charles as Young Child

1981 (5 Apr). *Easter. Paintings. T* **33** *and similar vert designs. Multicoloured. P* 14.
218 30 c. Type **33** 25 20
219 40 c. "Christ with Crown of Thorns" (Titian) .. 30 25
220 50 c. "Pietá" (Van Dyck) 40 30
218/20 .. .. *Set of* 3 85 65
MS221 110 × 68 mm. Nos. 218/20. P 13½ .. 1·00 1·50

1981 (5 Apr). *Easter. Children's Charity. Designs as Nos.* 218/20 *in separate miniature sheets* 70 × 86 *mm., each with a face value of* 70 *c.* + 5 *c. P* 13½.
MS222 As Nos. 218/20 .. .. *Set of* 3 *sheets* 2·00 2·50

1981 (10 July). *Royal Wedding. T* **34** *and similar vert designs. Multicoloured. P* 14.
223 40 c. Type **34** 35 40
224 50 c. Prince Charles as schoolboy 40 45
225 60 c. Prince Charles as young man 45 50
226 70 c. Prince Charles in ceremonial Naval uniform 50 55
227 80 c. Prince Charles as Colonel-in-Chief, Royal Regiment of Wales 55 60
223/7 .. .. *Set of* 5 2·00 2·25
MS228 99 × 89 mm. Nos. 223/7 .. .. 2·00 2·50
Nos. 223/7 were each printed in small sheets of 6 including one *se-tenant* stamp-size label.

1981 (30 Nov). *International Year for Disabled Persons. Nos.* 223/8 *surch as T* **51** *of Aitutaki.*
229 40 c. + 5 c. Type **34** 50 75
230 50 c. + 5 c. Prince Charles as schoolboy .. 60 85
231 60 c. + 5 c. Prince Charles as young man .. 70 95
232 70 c. + 5 c. Prince Charles in ceremonial Naval uniform 75 85
233 80 c. + 5 c. Prince Charles as Colonel-in-Chief, Royal Regiment of Wales.. .. .. 75 1·10
229/33 .. .. *Set of* 5 3·00 4·00
MS234 99 × 89 mm. As Nos. 229/33, but 10 c. premium on each stamp .. .. 3·50 5·00
Nos. 229/34 have commemorative inscriptions overprinted on the sheet margins.

35 Footballer

36 "The Virgin on a Crescent"

1981 (7 Dec). *World Cup Football Championship, Spain* (1982). *T* **35** *and similar vert designs showing footballers. Multicoloured. P* 13.
235 15 c. Type **35** 15 15
236 15 c. Footballer wearing orange jersey with black and mauve stripes.. .. .. .. 15 15
237 15 c. Player in blue jersey 15 15
238 35 c. Player in blue jersey 25 25
239 35 c. Player in red jersey 25 25
240 35 c. Player in yellow jersey with green stripes 25 25
241 50 c. Player in orange jersey 35 35
242 50 c. Player in mauve jersey 35 35
243 50 c. Player in black jersey 35 35
235/43 .. .. *Set of* 9 2·00 2·00
MS244 113 × 151 mm. As Nos. 235/43, but each stamp with a premium of 3 c. .. .. .. 3·00 2·75
The three designs of each value were printed together, *se-tenant*, in horizontal strips of 3 throughout the sheet.

1981 (15 Dec). *Christmas. Details from Engravings by Dürer. T* **36** *and similar vert designs in violet, deep reddish purple and stone. P* 13 × 13½.
245 30 c. Type **36** 45 35
246 40 c. "The Virgin at the Fence" 55 45
247 50 c. "The Holy Virgin and Child" 65 55
245/7 .. .. *Set of* 3 1·50 1·25
MS248 134 × 75 mm. As Nos. 245/7, but each stamp with a premium of 2 c. .. .. .. 1·50 1·50
MS249 Designs as Nos. 245/7 in separate miniature sheets, 58 × 85 mm, each with a face value of 70 c. + 5 c. P 14 × 13½ .. *Set of* 3 *sheets* 2·25 2·25

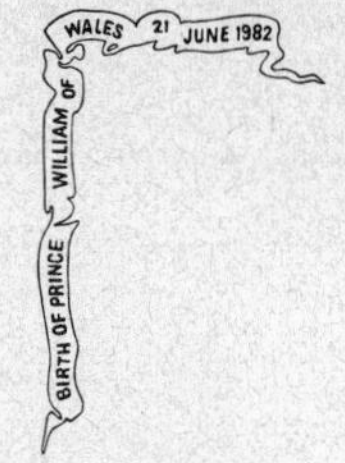

37 Lady Diana Spencer as Baby

(38)

1982 (1 July). *21st Birthday of Princess of Wales. T* **37** *and similar vert designs. Multicoloured. P* 14.
250 30 c. Type **37** 30 30
251 50 c. As young child 45 45
252 70 c. As schoolgirl 60 60
253 80 c. As teenager 80 80
254 $1.40, As young lady.. .. .. .. 1·25 1·25
250/4 .. .. *Set of* 5 3·00 3·00
MS255 87 × 110 mm. Nos. 250/4 .. .. .. 3·00 3·25

1982 (30 July). *Birth of Prince William of Wales. Nos.* 223/8 *optd with T* **38**.
256 40 c. Type **34** 90 80
257 50 c. Prince Charles as schoolboy .. .. 1·25 90
258 60 c. Prince Charles as young man .. .. 1·40 1·00
259 70 c. Prince Charles in ceremonial Naval uniform .. .. 1·60 1·25
260 80 c. Prince Charles as Colonel-in-Chief, Royal Regiment of Wales .. .. .. 2·00 1·60
256/60 .. .. *Set of* 5 6·50 5·00
MS261 99 × 89 mm. Nos. 256/60 .. .. .. 8·50 7·00

1982 (6 Sept). *Birth of Prince William of Wales. As Nos.* 250/5 *but with changed inscriptions. Multicoloured. P* 13½ × 14.
262 30 c. As Type **37** (inscr "21 JUNE 1982. BIRTH OF PRINCE WILLIAM OF WALES") .. 25 30
263 30 c. As Type **37** (inscr "COMMEMORATING THE BIRTH OF PRINCE WILLIAM OF WALES") 25 30
264 50 c. As No. 251 (inscr. "21 JUNE 1982. BIRTH OF PRINCE WILLIAM OF WALES") .. 40 45
265 50 c. As No. 251 (inscr "COMMEMORATING THE BIRTH OF PRINCE WILLIAM OF WALES") 40 45
266 70 c. As No. 252 (inscr "21 JUNE 1982. BIRTH OF PRINCE WILLIAM OF WALES") .. 60 65
267 70 c. As No. 252 (inscr "COMMEMORATING THE BIRTH OF PRINCE WILLIAM OF WALES") 60 65
268 80 c. As No. 253 (inscr "21 JUNE 1982. BIRTH OF PRINCE WILLIAM OF WALES") .. 60 65
269 80 c. As No. 253 (inscr "COMMEMORATING THE BIRTH OF PRINCE WILLIAM OF WALES") 60 65
270 $1.40, As No. 254 (inscr "21 JUNE 1982. BIRTH OF PRINCE WILLIAM OF WALES") .. 1·10 1·25
271 $1.40, As No. 254 (inscr "COMMEMORATING THE BIRTH OF PRINCE WILLIAM OF WALES") .. .. 1·10 1·25
262/71 .. .. *Set of* 10 5·50 6·00
MS272 88 × 109 mm. As **MS**255 (stamps inscr "21 JUNE 1982. ROYAL BIRTH PRINCE WILLIAM OF WALES" .. .. 2·75 2·75
Nos. 262/3, 264/5, 266/7, 268/9 and 270/1 were printed together, *se-tenant*, in sheets of 5 stamps and 1 label, there being three examples of the "21 JUNE 1982 . . ." and two of the "COMMEMORATING . . ." in each sheet.

39 "Virgin and Child" (detail, Joos Van Cleve)

40 Red Coral

1982 (10 Dec). *Christmas. Details from Renaissance Paintings of "Virgin and Child". T* **39** *and similar vert designs. Multicoloured. P* 14 × 13½.
273 35 c. Type **39** 30 30
274 48 c. "Virgin and Child" (Filippino Lippi) .. 45 45
275 60 c. "Virgin and Child" (Cima da Conegliano) 60 60
273/5 .. .. *Set of* 3 1·25 1·25
MS276 134 × 73 mm. As Nos. 273/5 but each with 2 c. charity premium. P 13 .. .. .. 1·60 2·00
Nos. 273/5 were each printed in small sheets of 6 including one *se-tenant*, stamp size, label, depicting the Prince and Princess of Wales with Prince William.

1982 (10 Dec). *Christmas. Children's Charity. Designs as Nos.* 273/5*, but without frames, in separate miniature sheets,* 60 × 85 *mm, each with a face value of* 70 *c.* + 5 *c. P* 13.
MS277 As Nos. 273/5 .. .. *Set of* 3 *sheets* 1·75 1·90

1983 (14 Mar). *Commonwealth Day. T* **40** *and similar vert designs. Multicoloured. P* 13.
278 60 c. Type **40** 50 60
279 60 c. Aerial view of Penrhyn atoll 50 60
280 60 c. Eleanor Roosevelt on Penrhyn during Second World War 50 60
281 60 c. Map of South Pacific 50 60
278/81 .. .. *Set of* 4 1·75 2·10
Nos. 278/81 were issued together, *se-tenant*, in blocks of four throughout the sheet.

41 Scout Emblem and Blue Tropical Flower

XV
WORLD
JAMBOREE
CANADA
1983

(42)

1983 (5 Apr). *75th Anniv of Boy Scout Movement. T* **41** *and similar horiz designs. Multicoloured. P* 13 × 14.
282 36 c. Type **41** 65 45
283 48 c. Emblem and pink flower 80 55
284 60 c. Emblem and orange flower 95 75
282/4 .. .. *Set of* 3 2·25 1·60
MS285 86 × 46 mm. $2 As 48 c., but with elements of design reversed .. .. 2·40 2·75

1983 (8 July). *15th World Scout Jamboree, Alberta, Canada. Nos.* 282/5 *optd with T* **42**.
286 36 c. Type **41** 65 45
287 48 c. Emblem and pink flower 80 55
288 60 c. Emblem and orange flower 95 75
286/8 .. .. *Set of* 3 2·25 1·60
MS289 86 × 46 mm. $2 As 48 c., but with elements of design reversed .. .. 2·40 2·75

43 School of Sperm Whales

44 *Mercury* (cableship)

1983 (29 July). *Whale Conservation. T* **43** *and similar vert designs. Multicoloured. P* 13.
290 8 c. Type **43** 35 15
291 15 c. Harpooner preparing to strike 55 25
292 35 c. Whale attacking boat 95 55
293 60 c. Dead whales marked with flags .. .. 1·60 85
294 $1 Dead whales on slipway .. .. .. 1·90 1·25
290/4 .. .. *Set of* 5 4·75 2·75

1983 (23 Sept). *World Communications Year. T* **44** *and similar horiz designs. Multicoloured. P* 13.
295 36 c. Type **44** 40 35
296 48 c. Men watching cable being laid 50 45
297 60 c. *Mercury* (*different*) 70 60
295/7 .. .. *Set of* 3 1·40 1·25
MS298 115 × 90 mm. As Nos. 295/7 but each with charity premium of 3 c. .. .. 1·50 1·60
On No. **MS**298 the values are printed in black and have been transposed with the World Communications Year logo.

1983 (26 Sept). *Various stamps surch as T* **200** *of Cook Islands.*

(a) Nos. 182/5, 190/7 *and* 206
299 18 c. on 10 c. *Preussen*, 1902 .. .. .. 20 20
300 18 c. on 10 c. *Pamir*, 1921 .. .. .. 20 20
301 18 c. on 10 c. *Cap Hornier*, 1910 .. .. 20 20
302 18 c. on 10 c. *Patriarch*, 1869 .. .. .. 20 20
303 36 c. on 20 c. Va'a Teu'ua 35 35
304 36 c. on 20 c. *Victoria*, 1500 .. .. .. 35 35
305 36 c. on 20 c. *Golden Hind*, 1560 .. .. 35 35
306 36 c. on 20 c. *Boudeuse*, 1760 .. .. .. 35 35
307 36 c. on 30 c. H.M.S. *Bounty*, 1787 .. .. 35 35
308 36 c. on 30 c. *L'Astrolabe*, 1811 .. .. 35 35
309 36 c. on 30 c. *Star of India*, 1861 .. .. 35 35
310 36 c. on 30 c. *Great Republic*, 1853 .. .. 35 35
311 $1.20 on $2 *Cutty Sark*, 1869 .. .. .. 1·40 1·40

(b) Nos. 252/3
312 72 c. on 70 c. Princess Diana as schoolgirl .. 2·00 1·50
313 96 c. on 80 c. Princess Diana as teenager .. 2·25 1·75
299/313 .. .. *Set of* 15 8·50 7·00

1983 (28 Oct). *Nos.* 208, 225/6, 254 *and* 268/9 *surch as T* **200** *of Cook Islands.*
314 48 c. on 60 c. Prince Charles as young man (Gold) .. .. 3·00 1·50
a. Error. Surch on No. 258 .. .. 5·00 4·50
315 72 c. on 70 c. Prince Charles in ceremonial Naval uniform .. .. 3·50 1·75
a. Error. Surch on No. 259 .. .. 5·50 4·50
316 96 c. on 80 c. As No. 253 (inscr "21 JUNE 1982 . . .") .. .. 2·50 1·00
a. Error. Surch on No. 260 .. .. 6·50 5·00
317 96 c. on 80 c. As No. 253 (inscr "COMMEMORATING. . .") .. .. 1·50 1·00
318 $1.20 on $1.40, Princess Diana as young lady 3·00 1·50
319 $5.60 on $6, H.M.S. *Resolution* and *Discovery*, 1776–80 .. .. 7·00 4·50
314/19 .. .. *Set of* 6 18·00 10·00

45 George Cayley's Airship Design, 1837

1983 (31 Oct). *Bicentenary of Manned Flight. T* **45** *and similar horiz designs. Multicoloured. P* 13. *A. Inscr* "NORTHERN COOK ISLANDS". *B. Corrected spelling optd in black on silver over original inscription.*

		A		B	
320	36 c. Type **45**	75	60	30	35
321	48 c. Dupuy De Lome's man-powered airship, 1872 ..	1·00	70	40	45
322	60 c. Santos Dumont's sixth airship, 1901	1·25	1·00	45	50
323	96 c. Lebaudy's practical airship, 1902	2·00	1·50	75	80
324	$1.32 LZ 127 *Graf Zeppelin*, 1929	3·00	2·00	1·00	1·10
320/4	.. .. .. *Set of* 5	7·25	5·50	2·75	3·00
MS325	113 × 138 mm. Nos. 320/4	8·00	10·00	2·75	4·00

46 "Madonna in the Meadow"

47 Waka

1983 (30 Nov). *Christmas. 500th Birth Anniv of Raphael. T* **46** *and similar vert designs. Multicoloured. P* 13.
326 36 c. Type **46** 35 40
327 42 c. "Tempi Madonna" 35 40
328 48 c. "The Smaller Cowper Madonna" 45 50
329 60 c. "Madonna della Tenda" 55 60
326/9 .. .. *Set of* 4 1·60 1·75
MS330 87 × 115 mm. As Nos. 326/9 but each with a charity premium of 3 c. .. .. 1·75 2·00

1983 (1 Dec). *Nos.* 266/7, 227 *and* 270/1 *surch as T* **200** *of Cook Islands.*
331 72 c. on 70 c. As No. 252 (inscr "21 JUNE 1982. . .") .. .. 2·00 1·25
332 72 c. on 70 c. As No. 252 (inscr "COMMEMORATING. . .") .. .. 1·25 90
333 96 c. on 80 c. Prince Charles as Colonel-in-Chief, Royal Regiment of Wales .. .. 2·00 1·00
334 $1.20 on $1.40, As No. 254 (inscr "21 JUNE 1982. . .") .. .. 2·25 1·25
335 $1.20 on $1.40, As No. 254 (inscr "COMMEMORATING. . .") .. .. 1·75 1·00
331/5 .. .. *Set of* 5 8·50 5·00

1983 (28 Dec). *Christmas. 500th Birth Anniv of Raphael. Children's Charity. Designs as Nos.* 326/9 *in separate miniature sheets,* 65 × 84 *mm, each with a face value of* 75 c. + 5 c. *P* 13.
MS336 As Nos. 326/9 .. .. *Set of* 4 *sheets* 3·00 3·50

1984 (8 Feb–15 June). *Sailing Craft and Ships (2nd series). Designs as Nos.* 166, *etc. but with redrawn frames, inscriptions and compass rose at top right as in T* **47**. *Multicoloured. P* 13 × 13½ ($9.60), 13 ($3, $5) *or* 11 (*others*).
337 2 c. Type **47** 10 10
338 4 c. Amatasi 10 10
339 5 c. Ndrua 10 10
340 8 c. Tongiaki 10 10
341 10 c. *Victoria* 10 10
342 18 c. *Golden Hind* 10 10
343 20 c. *Boudeuse* 10 15
344 30 c. H.M.S. *Bounty* 20 25
345 36 c. *L'Astrolabe* 25 30
346 48 c. *Great Republic* 30 35
347 50 c. *Star of India* (21 Mar) 30 35
348 60 c. *Coonatto* (21 Mar) 40 45
349 72 c. *Antiope* (21 Mar) 50 55
350 80 c. *Balcutha* (21 Mar) 55 60
351 96 c. *Cap Hornier* (21 Mar) 65 70
352 $1.20, *Pamir* (21 Mar) 80 85
353 $3 *Mermerus* (41 × 31 *mm*) (4 May) .. 2·00 2·10
354 $5 *Cutty Sark* (41 × 31 *mm*) (4 May) .. 3·25 3·50
355 $9.60, H.M.S. *Resolution* and *Discovery* (41 × 31 *mm*) (15 June) .. .. 6·25 6·50
337/55 .. .. *Set of* 19 14·50 15·00

48 Olympic Flag

1984 (20 July). *Olympic Games, Los Angeles. T* **48** *and similar horiz designs. Multicoloured. P* 13½ × 13.
356 35 c. Type **48** 30 35
357 60 c. Olympic torch and flags 50 55
358 $1.80, Ancient athletes and Coliseum .. 1·50 1·60
356/8 .. .. *Set of* 3 2·10 2·25
MS359 103 × 86 mm. As Nos. 356/8 but each with a charity premium of 5 c. .. .. 2·40 2·50

NEW INFORMATION

The editor is always interested to correspond with people who have new information that will improve or correct the Catalogue.

49 Penrhyn Stamps of 1978, 1979 and 1981

1984 (20 Sept). *"Ausipex" International Stamp Exhibition, Melbourne. T* **49** *and similar horiz design. Multicoloured. P* 13½ × 13.
360 60 c. Type **49** 50 55
361 $1.20, Location map of Penrhyn .. .. 1·00 1·10
MS362 90 × 90 mm. As Nos. 360/1, but each with a face value of 96 c. .. .. 1·75 2·00

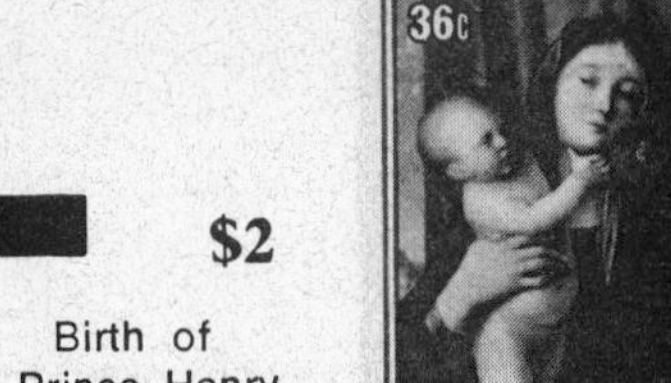

$2
Birth of
Prince Henry
15 Sept. 1984

(50)

51 "Virgin and Child" (Giovanni Bellini)

1984 (18 Oct). *Birth of Prince Henry. Nos.* 223/4 *and* 250/1 *surch as T* **50**.
363 $2 on 30 c. Type **37** .. .. 2·25 1·50
364 $2 on 40 c. Type **34** .. .. 2·75 1·75
365 $2 on 50 c. Prince Charles as schoolboy .. 2·75 1·75
366 $2 on 50 c. Lady Diana as young child (Gold) 2·25 1·50
363/6 .. .. *Set of* 4 9·00 6·00

1984 (15 Nov). *Christmas. Paintings of the Virgin and Child by different artists. T* **51** *and similar vert designs. Multicoloured. P* 13 × 13½.
367 36 c. Type **51** 30 35
368 48 c. Lorenzo di Credi 40 45
369 60 c. Palma the Older 45 50
370 96 c. Raphael 75 80
367/70 .. .. *Set of* 4 1·75 1·90
MS371 93 × 118 mm. As Nos. 367/70, but each with a charity premium of 5 c. .. .. 2·00 2·50

1984 (10 Dec). *Christmas. Children's Charity. Designs as Nos.* 367/70, *but without frames, in separate miniature sheets* 67 × 81 *mm, each with a face value of* 96 c. + 10 c. *P* 13½.
MS372 As Nos. 367/70 .. .. *Set of* 4 *sheets* 3·00 3·25

52 Harlequin Duck

1985 (9 Apr). *Birth Bicentenary of John J. Audubon (ornithologist). T* **52** *and similar horiz designs showing original paintings. Multicoloured. P* 13.
373 20 c. Type **52** 40 25
374 55 c. Sage Grouse 80 60
375 65 c. Solitary Sandpiper 95 65
376 75 c. Dunlin .. .. 1·25 75
373/6 .. .. *Set of* 4 3·00 2·00
MS377 Four sheets, each 70 × 53 mm. As Nos. 373/6, but each with a face value of 95 c. .. 3·50 4·50

53 Lady Elizabeth Bowes-Lyon, 1921

54 "The House in the Wood"

1985 (24 June). *Life and Times of Queen Elizabeth the Queen Mother. T* **53** *and similar vert designs, each deep bluish violet, silver and yellow. P* 13.
378 75 c. Type **53** 60 65
379 95 c. With baby Princess Elizabeth, 1926 .. 75 80
380 $1.20, Coronation Day, 1937 .. .. .. 95 1·00
381 $2.80, On her 70th birthday .. .. .. 2·10 2·25
378/81 .. .. *Set of* 4 4·00 4·25
MS382 66 × 90 mm. $5 The Queen Mother .. 3·75 4·00
Nos. 378/81 were each printed in small sheets of 4 stamps.
For these stamps in a miniature sheet see No. **MS**403.

1985 (10 Sept). *International Youth Year and Birth Centenary of Jacob Grimm (folklorist). T* **54** *and similar vert designs. Multicoloured. P* 13 × 13½.

383 75 c. Type **54** 70 60
384 95 c. "Snow-White and Rose-Red" 85 75
385 $1.15, "The Goose Girl" .. .. .. 1·10 95
383/5 .. .. *Set of* 3 2·40 2·10

55 "The Annunciation"

1985 (25 Nov). *Christmas. Paintings by Murillo. T* **55** *and similar horiz designs. Multicoloured. P* 14.

386 75 c. Type **55** 60 65
387 $1.15, "Adoration of the Shepherds" .. 85 90
388 $1.80, "The Holy Family" .. .. .. 1·40 1·50
386/8 .. .. *Set of* 3 2·50 2·75
MS389 66 × 131 mm. As Nos. 386/8, but each with a face value of 95 c. P 13½ .. .. 2·25 2·50
MS390 Three sheets, each 66 × 72 mm. As Nos. 386/8, but with face values of $1.20, $1.45 and $2.75. P 13½ .. .. .. *Set of 3 sheets* 4·00 4·25

56 Halley's Comet

1986 (4 Feb). *Appearance of Halley's Comet. T* **56** *and similar horiz design showing details of the painting "Fire and Ice" by Camille Rendal. Multicoloured. P* 13½ × 13.

391 $1.50, Type **56** .. .. 1·10 1·25
392 $1.50, Stylised *Giotto* spacecraft .. .. 1·10 1·25
MS393 108 × 43 mm. $3 As Nos. 391/2 (104 × 39 *mm*). Imperf .. .. 2·25 2·50

Nos. 391/2 were printed together, *se-tenant*, in horizontal pairs throughout the sheet, forming a composite design of the complete painting.

57 Princess Elizabeth aged Three, 1929, and Bouquet

58 Statue of Liberty under Construction, Paris

1986 (21 Apr). *60th Birthday of Queen Elizabeth II. T* **57** *and similar horiz designs. Multicoloured. P* 13½ × 13 ($2.50) *or* 14 (*others*).

394 95 c. Type **57** 80 80
395 $1.45, Profile of Queen Elizabeth and St. Edward's Crown .. .. 1·25 1·25
396 $2.50, Queen Elizabeth aged three and in profile with Imperial State Crown (56 × 30 *mm*) .. .. 2·00 2·00
394/6 .. .. *Set of* 3 3·50 3·50

1986 (27 June). *Centenary of Statue of Liberty* (1*st issue*). *T* **58** *and similar vert designs, each black, gold and yellow-green. P* 13 × 13½.

397 95 c. Type **58** 65 70
398 $1.75, Erection of Statue, New York .. 1·10 1·25
399 $3 Artist's impression of Statue, 1876 .. 2·10 2·25
397/9 .. .. *Set of* 3 3·50 3·75

See also No. **MS**412.

59 Prince Andrew and Miss Sarah Ferguson

$2.00

(**60**)

1986 (23 July). *Royal Wedding. T* **59** *and similar vert design. Multicoloured. P* 13.

400 $2.50, Type **59** .. .. 2·00 2·25
401 $3.50, Profiles of Prince Andrew and Miss Sarah Ferguson .. .. 2·75 3·00

Nos. 400/1 were each printed in sheetlets of 4 stamps and 2 stamp-size labels.

1986 (4 Aug). *"Stampex '86" Stamp Exhibition, Adelaide. No.* **MS**362 *surch with T* **60** *in black on gold.*

MS402 $2 on 96 c. × 2 .. .. 3·75 4·25

The "Stampex '86" exhibition emblem is overprinted on the sheet margin.

1986 (4 Aug). *86th Birthday of Queen Elizabeth the Queen Mother. Nos.* 378/81 *in miniature sheet,* 90 × 120 *mm. P* 13 × 13½.

MS403 Nos. 378/81 .. .. 5·00 5·50

61 "The Adoration of the Shepherds"

SOUTH PACIFIC PAPAL VISIT
21 TO 24 NOVEMBER 1986
+10c

(**62**)

1986 (20 Nov). *Christmas. Engravings by Rembrandt. T* **61** *and similar vert designs, each red-brown, yellow-ochre and gold. P* 13.

404 65 c. Type **61** 50 50
405 $1.75 "Virgin and Child" .. .. .. 1·40 1·40
406 $2.50 "The Holy Family" .. .. .. 2·00 2·00
404/6 .. .. *Set of* 3 3·50 3·50
MS407 120 × 87 mm. As Nos. 404/6, but each size 31 × 39 mm with a face value of $1.50. P 13½ × 13 .. .. 4·00 4·50

1986 (24 Nov). *Visit of Pope John Paul II to South Pacific. Nos.* 404/7 *surch as T* **62** *in greenish blue.*

408 65 c. + 10 c. Type **61** 85 85
409 $1.75 + 10 c. "Virgin and Child" .. .. 2·00 2·00
410 $2.50 + 10 c. "The Holy Family" .. .. 2·50 2·50
408/10 .. .. *Set of* 3 4·75 4·75
MS411 120 × 87 mm. As Nos. 408/10, but each size 31 × 39 mm with a face value of $1.50 + 10 c. .. 4·75 5·50

63 Head and Torch of Statue of Liberty

1987 (15 Apr). *Centenary of Statue of Liberty* (1986) (2*nd issue*). *Two sheets, each* 122 × 122 *mm, containing T* **63** *and similar multicoloured designs. Litho. P* 14 × 13½ (*vert*) *or* 13½ × 14 (*horiz*).

MS412 Two sheets (a) 65 c. Type **63**; 65 c. Torch at sunset; 65 c. Restoration workers with flag; 65 c. Statue and Manhattan skyline; 65 c. Workers and scaffolding. (b) 65 c. Workers on Statue crown (*horiz*); 65 c. Aerial view of Ellis Island (*horiz*); 65 c. Ellis Island Immigration Centre (*horiz*); 65 c. View from Statue to Ellis Island and Manhattan (*horiz*); 65 c. Restoration workers (*horiz*) .. .. .. *Set of 2 sheets* 7·00 8·00

Fortieth Royal Wedding
Anniversary 1947–87

(**64**)

1987 (20 Nov). *Royal Ruby Wedding. Nos.* 68/9 *optd with T* **64** *in magenta.*

413 $2 Birds-eye view of Penrhyn .. .. 1·40 1·50
414 $5 Satellite view of Australasia .. .. 3·50 3·75

65 "The Garvagh Madonna"

66 Athletics

1987 (11 Dec). *Christmas. Religious Paintings by Raphael. T* **65** *and similar vert designs. Multicoloured. P* 13½.

415 95 c. Type **65** 70 70
416 $1.60, "The Alba Madonna" .. .. 1·25 1·25
417 $2.25, "The Madonna of the Fish" .. 1·75 1·75
415/17 .. .. *Set of* 3 3·25 3·25
MS418 91 × 126 mm. As Nos. 415/17, but each with a face value of $1.15 .. .. .. 3·75 4·25
MS419 70 × 86 mm. $4.80, As No. 417, but size 36 × 39 mm .. .. 5·50 6·00

1988 (29 July). *Olympic Games, Seoul. T* **66** *and similar horiz designs. Multicoloured. P* 13½ × 13 (*horiz*) *or* 13 × 13½ (*vert*).

420 55 c. Type **66** 45 45
421 95 c. Pole vaulting (*vert*) 70 70
422 $1.25, Shotputting 95 95
423 $1.50, Lawn Tennis (*vert*) .. .. 1·25 1·25
421/3 .. .. *Set of* 4 3·00 3·00
MS424 110 × 70 mm. As Nos. 421 and 423, but each with a face value of $2.50 .. .. .. 3·75 4·25

1988 (14 Oct). *Olympic Gold Medal Winners, Seoul. Nos.* 420/4 *optd as T* **235** *of Cook Islands.*

425 55 c. Type **66** (optd "CARL LEWIS UNITED STATES 100 METERS") 40 45
426 95 c. Pole vaulting (optd "LOUISE RITTER UNITED STATES HIGH JUMP") .. 65 70
427 $1.25, Shot putting (optd "ULF TIMMERMANN EAST GERMANY SHOT-PUT") 90 95
428 $1.50, Lawn Tennis (optd "STEFFI GRAF WEST GERMANY WOMEN'S TENNIS") .. .. 1·10 1·25
425/8 .. .. *Set of* 4 2·75 3·00
MS429 110 × 70 mm. $2.50, As No. 421 (optd "JACKIE JOYNER-KERSEE United States Heptathlon"); $2.50, As No. 423 (optd "STEFFI GRAF West Germany Women's Tennis MILOSLAV MECIR Czechoslovakia Men's Tennis") .. .. 3·75 4·50

67 "Virgin and Child"

68 Neil Armstrong stepping onto Moon

1988 (9 Nov). *Christmas. T* **67** *and similar designs showing different "Virgin and Child" paintings by Titian. P* 13 × 13½.

430 70 c. multicoloured 50 55
431 85 c. multicoloured 60 65
432 95 c. multicoloured 65 70
433 $1.25, multicoloured 90 95
430/3 .. .. *Set of* 4 2·40 2·50
MS434 100 × 80 mm. $6.40, As Type **67**, but diamond-shaped (57 × 57 *mm*). P 13 .. .. 4·50 4·75

(Des G. Vasarhelyi)

1989 (24 July). *20th Anniv of First Manned Landing on Moon. T* **68** *and similar horiz designs. Multicoloured. P* 14.

435 55 c. Type **68** 40 45
436 75 c. Astronaut on Moon carrying equipment 55 60
437 95 c. Conducting experiment on Moon .. 70 75
438 $1.25, Crew of "Apollo 11" .. .. .. 95 1·00
439 $1.75, Crew inside "Apollo 11" .. .. 1·40 1·50
435/9 .. .. *Set of* 5 3·50 3·75

69 Virgin Mary

1989 (17 Nov). *Christmas. T* **69** *and similar multicoloured designs showing details from "The Nativity" by Dürer. P* 13.

440 55 c. Type **69** 40 45
441 70 c. Christ Child and cherubs 50 55
442 85 c. Joseph 65 70
443 $1.25, Three women .. .. 95 1·00
440/3 .. .. *Set of* 4 2·25 2·40
MS444 88 × 95 mm. $6.40, "The Nativity" (31 × 50 *mm*) .. .. 4·75 5·00

MINIMUM PRICE

The minimum price quote is 10p which represents a handling charge rather than a basis for valuing common stamps. For further notes about prices see introductory pages.

OFFICIAL STAMPS

O.H.M.S.

(O 1)

1978 (14 Nov). *Nos.* 57/66, 89/91 *and* 101/2 *optd or surch (Nos.* O8/9 *and* O12) *as Type* O 1.

O 1	1 c. *Mondactylus argenteus*	15	10
O 2	2 c. *Pomacanthus imperator*	15	10
O 3	3 c. *Chelmon rostratus*	25	10
O 4	4 c. *Chaetodon ornatissimus*	25	10
O 5	5 c. *Chaetodon melanotus*	30	10
O 6	8 c. *Chaetodon raffessi*	35	15
O 7	10 c. *Chaetodon ephippium*	40	15
O 8	15 c. on 60 c. *Plectorhynchus chaetodonoides*	45	25
O 9	18 c. on 60 c. *Plectorhynchus chaetodonoides*	50	25
O10	20 c. *Pygoplites diacanthus*	50	25
O11	25 c. *Heniochus acuminatus* (Silver)	55	30
O12	30 c. on 60 c. *Plectorhynchus chaetodonoides*	55	35
O13	50 c. } "The Spirit of '76" (A. M. Willard) (Gold)	70	55
O14	50 c. }	70	55
O15	50 c. }	70	55
O16	$1 Queen and Prince Philip (Silver) ..	2·25	1·40
O17	$2 Queen Elizabeth II (Gold)	4·50	2·75
O1/17	.. .. *Set of* 17	12·00	7·00

These stamps were originally only sold to the public cancelled-to-order and not in unused condition. They were made available to overseas collectors in mint condition during 1980.

65c

O.H.M.S.

O.H.M.S.

(O 2) (O 3)

1985 (15 Aug)–**87**. (*a*) *Nos.* 206/8, 337/47 *and* 349/55 *optd or surch as Type* O 2 *by foil embossing in red* ($2, $4, $6) *or silver (others)*

O18	2 c. Type **47**	10	10
O19	4 c. Amatasi	10	10
O20	5 c. Ndrua	10	10
O21	8 c. Tongiaki	10	10
O22	10 c. *Victoria*	10	10
O23	18 c. *Golden Hind*	15	15
O24	20 c. *Boudeuse*	15	15
O25	30 c. H.M.S. *Bounty*	20	25
O26	40 c. on 36 c. *L'Astrolabe*	25	30
O27	50 c. *Star of India*	30	35
O28	55 c. on 48 c. *Great Republic*	35	40
O29	75 c. on 72 c. *Antiope* (29.4.86)	50	55
O30	75 c. on 96 c. *Cap Hornier* (29.4.86) ..	50	55
O31	80 c. *Balcutha* (29.4.86)	55	60
O32	$1.20, *Pamir* (29.4.86)	80	85
O33	$2 *Cutty Sark* (29.4.86)	1·40	1·50
O34	$3 *Mermerus* (29.4.86)	2·00	2·10
O35	$4 *Mermerus* (29.4.86)	2·75	3·00
O36	$5 *Cutty Sark* (2.11.87)	3·25	3·50
O37	$6 H.M.S. *Resolution* and *Discovery* (2.11.87)	4·00	4·25
O38	$9.60, H.M.S. *Resolution* and *Discovery* (2.11.87)	6·25	6·50

(*b*) *Nos.* 278/81 *surch as Type* O 3 *by silver foil embossing*

O39	65 c. on 60 c. Type **40**	45	50
O40	65 c. on 60 c. Aerial view of Penrhyn atoll ..	45	50
O41	65 c. on 60 c. Eleanor Roosevelt on Penrhyn during Second World War	45	50
O42	65 c. on 60 c. Map of South Pacific	45	50
O18/42	.. .. *Set of* 25	23·00	25·00

Cyprus

Cyprus was part of the Turkish Ottoman Empire from 1571.

The first records of an organised postal service date from 1871 when a post office was opened at Nicosia (Lefkosa) under the jurisdiction of the Damascus Head Post Office. Various stamps of Turkey from the 1868 issue onwards are known used from this office, cancelled "KIBRIS", in Arabic, within a double-lined oblong. Manuscript cancellations have also been reported. The records report the opening of a further office at Larnaca (Tuzla) in 1873, but no cancellation for this office has been identified.

To provide an overseas postal service the Austrian Empire opened a post office in Larnaca during 1845. Stamps of the Austrian Post Offices in the Turkish Empire were placed on sale there from 1 June 1864 and were cancelled with an unframed straight-line mark or circular date stamp. This Austrian post office closed on 6 August 1878.

BRITISH ADMINISTRATION

Following the convention with Turkey, Great Britain assumed the administration of Cyprus on 11 July 1878 and the first post office, as part of the British G.P.O. system, was opened at Larnaca on 27 July 1878. Further offices at Famagusta, Kyrenia, Limassol, Nicosia and Paphos followed in September 1878. In addition two Camp post offices, mainly for the use of the administration, were established at Nicosia (Headquarters Camp) and Polymedia (Polemidhia) (near Limassol). These were supplied with numeral postmarks in January 1881, which can be found cancelling Great Britain stamps for a short period after that date.

The stamps of Great Britain were supplied to the various offices as they opened and continued to be used until the Cyprus Administration assumed responsibility for the postal service on 1 April 1880, although scattered examples are known dating from 1881.

For illustrations of the postmark types see BRITISH POST OFFICES ABROAD notes, following GREAT BRITAIN.

FAMAGUSTA

Stamps of GREAT BRITAIN *cancelled* "982" *as Type* **9**

1878 *to* **1880–81.**
Z1 ½d. rose-red (1870–79) (Plate Nos. 11, 13) £450
Z2 1d. rose-red (1864–70) .. ..
Plate Nos. 145, 174, 181, 193, 202, 206, 215.
Z3 2d. blue (1858–69) (Plate Nos. 13, 14, 15) £900
Z4 2½d. rosy mauve (1876) (Plate Nos. 13, 16) £800
Z5 6d. grey (1874–80) (Plate No. 15) .. .. ..
Z6 1s. green (1873–77) (Plate No. 12) £1400
Z7 1s. orange-brown (1881) (Plate No. 14) £2000

KYRENIA

Stamps of GREAT BRITAIN *cancelled* "974" *as Type* **9**

1878 *to* **1880.**
Z 8 ½d. rose-red (1870–79) (Plate No. 1) .. ..
Z 9 1d. rose-red (1864–79) .. .. .. *From* £225
Plate Nos. 168, 171, 193, 196, 206, 207, 209, 220.
Z10 2d. blue (1858–69) (Plate Nos. 13, 15) .. *From* £550
Z11 2½d. rosy mauve (1876–79) .. .. .. *From* £150
Plate Nos. 12, 13, 14, 15.
Z12 4d. sage-green (1877) (Plate No. 16) .. ..
Z13 6d. grey (1874–80) (Plate No. 16) .. .. ..

LARNACA

Stamps of GREAT BRITAIN *cancelled* "942" *as Type* **9**

1878 *to* **1880–81.**
Z14 ½d. rose-red (1870–79) .. .. .. *From* £250
Plate Nos. 11, 12, 13, 14, 15, 19, 20.
Z15 1d. rose-red (1864–79) .. .. .. *From* £100
Plate Nos. 129, 131, 146, 154, 170, 171, 174, 175, 176, 177, 178, 179, 181, 182, 183, 184, 187, 188, 190, 191, 192, 193, 194, 195, 196, 197, 198, 199, 200, 201, 202, 203, 204, 205, 206, 207, 208, 209, 210, 212, 213, 214, 215, 216, 217, 218, 220, 221, 222, 225.
Z16 1½d. lake-red (1870) (Plate No. 3) £1200
Z17 2d. blue (1858–69 (Plate Nos. 9, 13, 14, 15) .. 60·00
Z18 2½d. rosy mauve (1876–79) .. .. .. *From* 25·00
Plate Nos. 4, 5, 6, 8, 10, 11, 12, 13, 14, 15, 16, 17.
Z19 2½d. blue (1880–81) (Plate Nos. 17, 18, 19, 20) .. £400
Z20 2½d. blue (1881) (Plate No. 21) £400
Z21 4d. sage-green (1877) (Plate Nos. 15, 16) £500
Z22 6d. grey (1874–76) (Plate Nos. 15, 16, 17) £275
Z23 6d. pale buff (1872–73) (Plate No. 11) £1100
Z24 8d. orange (1876) £3000
Z25 1s. green (1873–77) (Plate Nos. 12, 13) £375
Z26 1s. orange-brown (1881) (Plate No. 14) £1500
Z27 5s. rose (1874) (Plate No. 2) £3250

LIMASSOL

Stamps of GREAT BRITAIN *cancelled* "975" *as Type* **9**

1878 *to* **1880.**
Z28 ½d. rose-red (1870–79) (Plate Nos. 11, 13, 15, 19) £225
Z29 1d. rose-red (1864–79) .. .. .. *From* 75·00
Plate Nos. 160, 171, 173, 174, 177, 179, 184, 187, 190, 193, 195, 196, 197, 198, 200, 202, 206, 207, 208, 209, 210, 213, 215, 216, 218, 220, 221, 222, 225.
Z30 1½d. lake-red (1870–74) (Plate No. 3) £1500
Z31 2d. blue (1858–69) (Plate Nos. 14, 15) .. *From* £110
Z32 2½d. rosy-mauve (1876–80) .. .. .. *From* 70·00
Plate Nos. 11, 12, 13, 14, 15, 16.
Z33 2½d. blue (1880) (Plate Nos. 17, 19, 20) .. *From* £1200
Z34 4d. sage-green (Plate No. 16) £300

NICOSIA

Stamps of GREAT BRITAIN *cancelled* "969" *as Type* **9**

1878 *to* **1880–81.**
Z35 ½d. rose-red (1870–79) £250
Plate Nos. 12, 13, 14, 15, 20.
Z36 1d. rose-red (1864–79) .. .. .. *From* 75·00
Plate Nos. 170, 171, 174, 189, 190, 192, 193, 195, 196, 198, 200, 202, 203, 205, 206, 207, 210, 212, 214, 215, 218, 221, 222, 225.
Z37 2d. blue (1858–69) (Plate Nos. 14 and 15) .. ..
Z38 2½d. rosy mauve (1876–79) .. .. .. *From* 95·00
Plate Nos. 10, 11, 12, 13, 14, 15, 16.
Z39 2½d. blue (1880) (Plate No. 20) .. .. ..
Z40 2½d. blue (1881) (Plate No. 21) .. .. ..
Z41 4d. vermilion (1876) (Plate No. 15) .. ..
Z42 4d. sage-green (1877) (Plate No. 16) £500
Z43 6d. grey (1873) (Plate No. 16) £500

PAPHOS

Stamps of GREAT BRITAIN *cancelled* "981" *as Type* **9**

1878 *to* **1880.**
Z44 ½d. rose-red (1870–79) (Plate No. 13, 15) .. ..
Z45 1d. rose-red (1864–79) .. .. .. *From* £250
Plate Nos. 196, 201, 202, 204, 206, 213, 217.
Z46 2d. blue (1858–69) (Plate No. 15) £600
Z47 2½d. rosy mauve (1876–79) .. .. .. *From* £300
Plate Nos. 13, 14, 15.

HEADQUARTER CAMP, NICOSIA

Stamps of GREAT BRITAIN *cancelled* "D 48" *as Type* **8**

1881.
Z48 ½d. rose-red (1870–79) (Plate Nos. 13, 20) £1200
Z49 1d. rose-red (1864–79) .. .. .. *From* £550
Plate Nos. 123, 171, 174, 177, 201, 204, 205, 214, 218.
Z50 2d. blue (1858–69) (Plate No. 15) £1200

POLYMEDIA (POLEMIDHIA) CAMP, LIMASSOL

Stamps of GREAT BRITAIN *cancelled* "D 47" *as Type* **8**

1881.
Z51 ½d. rose-red (1870–79) (Plate No. 11) £1300
Z52 1d. rose-red (1864–79) .. .. .. *From* £550
Plate Nos. 78, 99, 110, 132, 175, 192, 197, 205, 206, 207, 208, 209.
Z53 2d. blue (1858–69) (Plate No. 15) £1100

"D 48" differs from Type **8** in that the "D" is taller and narrower and the "4" has pronounced serifs. Stamps with "D 47" and "D 48" having four bars instead of three were used in Great Britain before the altered postmarks were sent to Cyprus.

PRICES FOR STAMPS ON COVER TO 1945	
Nos. 1/10	*from* × 7
Nos. 11/49	*from* × 4
Nos. 50/122	*from* × 3
Nos. 123/43	*from* × 4
Nos. 144/50	*from* × 3
Nos. 151/63	*from* × 5

PERFORATION. Nos. 1/122 are perf 14.

Stamps of Great Britain overprinted

CYPRUS (1) **CYPRUS** (2)

(Optd by D.L.R.)

1880 (1 Apr).
1 **1** ½d. rose .. .. 90·00 90·00
a. Opt double (Plate 15) .. .. — £6000

Plate No.	*Un.*	*Used.*	*Plate No.*	*Un.*	*Used*
12.	£125	£190	19.	£2750	£650
15.	90·00	90·00			

2 **2** 1d. red .. .. 7·50 26·00
a. Opt double (Plate 208) £7000
aa. Opt double (Plate 218) £3000
b. Vert pair, top stamp without opt (Plate 208) £8000

174.	£900	£950	208.	70·00	35·00
181.	£170	£125	215.	9·00	26·00
184.	£6000	£1800	216.	12·00	27·00
193.	£525	†	217.	9·00	27·00
196.	£525	†	218.	11·00	27·00
201.	7·50	26·00	220.	£500	£400
205.	18·00	26·00			

3 **2** 2½d. rosy mauve .. .. 1·75 5·00
a. Large thin "C" (Plate 14) (BK, JK) .. 20·00 45·00
b. Large thin "C" (Plate 15) (BK, JK) .. 24·00 75·00

14.	1·75	5·00	15.	2·50	13·00

4 **2** 4d. sage-green (Plate 16) £120 £150
5 6d. grey (Plate 16) £500 £600
6 1s. green (Plate 13) £600 £450

No. 3 has been reported from Plate 9.

HALF-PENNY (3) 18 mm **HALF-PENNY** (4) 16 or 16½ mm

HALF-PENNY (5) 13 mm **30 PARAS** (6)

(Optd by Govt Ptg Office, Nicosia)

1881 (Feb–June). *No. 2 surch.*
7 **3** ½d. on 1d. red (Feb) .. .. .. 55·00 60·00
a. "HALFPENN" (BG, LG) (*all plates*) .. .. *From* £750 £750

Plate No.	*Un.*	*Used.*	*Plate No.*	*Un.*	*Used.*
174.	95·00	£170	215.	£350	£450
181.	75·00	£100	216.	55·00	60·00
201.	55·00	60·00	217.	£450	£350
205.	60·00	60·00	218.	£325	£350
208.	£140	£180	220.	£140	£160

8 **4** ½d. on 1d. red (Apr) £100 £110
a. Surch double (Plates 201 and 216) £2000

201.	£100	£110	218.	—	—
216.	£250	£325			

9 **5** ½d. on 1d. red (June) .. .. .. 40·00 50·00
a. Surch double (Plate 201) .. ..
aa. Surch double (Plate 205) £550
ab. Surch double (Plate 215) £425 £425
b. Surch treble (Plate 205) £1800
ba. Surch treble (Plate 215) £500
bb. Surch treble (Plate 217) .. ..
bc. Surch treble (Plate 218) £750
c. Surch quadruple (Plate 205) .. £1600
ca. Surch quadruple (Plate 215) .. £1500
d. "CYPRUS" double (Plate 218) ..

201.	—	—	217.	60·00	50·00
205.	£110	—	218.	60·00	65·00
215.	40·00	55·00			

10 **6** 30 paras on 1d. red (June) .. .. 75·00 75·00
a. Surch double, one invtd (Plate 216) £1900
aa. Surch double, one invtd (Plate 220) £900 £950

201.	75·00	75·00	217.	£110	£110
216.	75·00	80·00	220.	£120	£120

(New Currency: 40 paras = 1 piastre. 180 piastres = £1)

7 **½** (8) **½** (8) **30 PARAS** (9)

(Typo D.L.R.)

1881 (1 July). *Die I. Wmk Crown CC.*
11 **7** ½ pi. emerald-green .. .. .. £175 40·00
12 1 pi. rose .. .. £325 30·00
13 2 pi. blue .. .. £425 30·00
14 4 pi. pale olive-green £800 £225
15 6 pi. olive-grey £1250 £375

Stamps of Queen Victoria initialled "J.A.B." or overprinted "POSTAL SURCHARGE" with or without the same initials were employed for accounting purposes between the Chief Post Office and sub-offices, the initials are those of the then Postmaster, Mr. J. A. Bulmer.

1882 (Mar)–**86**. *Die I*. Wmk Crown CA.*
16 **7** ½pi. emerald-green (5.82) £4000 £325
a. Dull green (4.83) .. .. .. 6·50 30
17 30 pa. pale mauve (7.6.82) .. .. 50·00 16·00
18 1 pi. rose (3.82) .. .. 55·00 70
19 2 pi. blue (4.83) .. .. 85·00 90
20 4 pi. deep olive-green (1883) .. .. £375 26·00
a. Pale olive-green .. .. .. £325 20·00
21 6 pi. olive-grey (1.83) .. .. .. 32·00 15·00
22 12 pi. orange-brown (1886) (Optd S. £400) £160 32·00
16*a*/22 .. .. *Set of* 7 £625 80·00

* For description and illustrations of Dies I and II see Introduction.

See also Nos. 31/7.

(Surch by Govt Ptg Office, Nicosia)

1882. *Surch with T* **8/9**. (*a*) *Wmk Crown CC.*
23 **7** ½ on ½ pi. emerald-green (6.82) .. .. £300 50·00
24 30 pa. on 1 pi. rose (22.5.82) £1250 £100

(*b*) *Wmk Crown CA*
25 **7** ½ on ½ pi. emerald-green (5.82) .. 85·00 6·50
a. Surch double .. .. .. — £2250

½ **½** (10)

Two varieties of T **10**:
(*a*) Fractions approx 6 mm apart
(*b*) Fractions approx 8 mm apart

11

1886 (Apr). *Surch with T* **10** (*a*) *by De La Rue.*

(*a*) *Wmk Crown CC*
26 **7** ½ on ½ pi. emerald-green £5000

(*b*) *Wmk Crown CA*
27 **7** ½ on ½ pi. emerald-green .. .. £180 60·00

The status of No. 26 remains in doubt as it is not known used.

1886 (May–June). *Surch with T* **10**(*b*) *by De La Rue.*

(*a*) *Wmk Crown CC*
28 **7** ½ on ½ pi. emerald-green £5000 £375
a. Large "1" at left .. .. .. — £1200
b. Small "1" at right £7500 £1900

(*b*) *Wmk Crown CA*
29 **7** ½ on ½ pi. emerald-green (June) .. £150 7·00
a. Large "1" at left £900 £175
b. Small "1" at right £1400 £250

A third type of this surcharge is known with the fraction spaced approximately 10 mm apart on CA paper with postmarks from August 1886. This may be due to the shifting of type.

1892–94. *Die II. Wmk Crown CA.*
31 **7** ½ pi. dull green .. .. 2·50 30
32 30 pa. mauve .. .. 2·25 2·00
33 1 pi. carmine .. .. 7·00 80
34 2 pi. ultramarine .. .. 10·00 80
35 4 pi. olive-green .. .. 45·00 14·00
a. Pale olive-green .. .. .. 16·00 10·00
36 6 pi. olive-grey (1894) £120 £225
37 12 pi. orange-brown (1893) £110 £150
31/37 .. .. *Set of* 7 £240 £350

1894 (14 Aug)–**96**. *Colours changed and new values. Die II. Wmk Crown CA.*
40 **7** ½ pi. green and carmine (1896) .. .. 3·75 35
41 30 pa. bright mauve and green (1896) .. 2·00 55
42 1 pi. carmine and blue (1896) .. .. 4·00 35
43 2 pi. blue and purple (1896) .. .. 4·50 40
44 4 pi. sage-green and purple (1896) .. 9·00 2·75
45 6 pi. sepia and green (1896) .. .. 6·50 6·50
46 9 pi. brown and carmine.. .. .. 14·00 7·50
47 12 pi. orange-brown and black (1896) .. 12·00 38·00
48 18 pi. greyish slate and brown .. .. 45·00 35·00
49 45 pi. grey-purple and blue £110 £110
40/49 .. .. *Set of* 10 £180 £170
40/49 Optd "Specimen" .. .. *Set of* 10 £300

(Typo D.L.R.)

1902–04. *Wmk Crown CA.*
50 **11** ½ pi. green and carmine (12.02) .. 2·50 30
51 30 pa. violet and green (2.03) .. .. 3·25 80
a. Mauve and green .. .. .. 4·50 2·50
52 1 pi. carmine and blue (9.03) .. .. 9·00 1·75
53 2 pi. blue and purple (2.03) .. .. 18·00 6·50
54 4 pi. olive-green and purple (9.03) .. 22·00 9·50
55 6 pi. sepia and green (9.03) .. .. 35·00 48·00
56 9 pi. brown and carmine (5.04) .. 75·00 £120
57 12 pi. chestnut and black (4.03) .. 12·00 22·00
58 18 pi. black and brown (5.04) .. .. 50·00 80·00
59 45 pi. dull purple and ultramarine (10.03) £200 £275
50/59 .. .. *Set of* 10 £375 £475
50/59 Optd "Specimen" .. .. *Set of* 10 £450

1904–10. *Wmk Mult Crown CA.*
60 **11** 5 pa. bistre and black (14.1.08) .. 25 20
61 10 pa. orange and green (12.06) .. 1·25 25
a. Yellow and green.. .. .. 25·00 5·50
62 ½ pi. green and carmine (1.7.04) .. 1·75 15
63 30 pa. purple and green (1.7.04) .. 5·00 75
a. Violet and green (1910) .. .. 7·50 1·50
64 1 pi. carmine and blue (11.04) .. 1·50 25
65 2 pi. blue and purple (11.04) .. .. 3·00 60
66 4 pi. olive-green and purple (2.05) .. 9·00 6·00
67 6 pi. sepia and green (17.7.04) .. 8·50 5·50
68 9 pi. brown and carmine (30.5.04) .. 12·00 6·50
a. Yellow-brown and carmine .. 13·00 14·00
69 12 pi. chestnut and black (4.06) .. 20·00 14·00
70 18 pi. black and brown (16.6.04) .. 25·00 8·00
71 45 pi. dull purple and ultram (15.6.04) 50·00 75·00
60/71 .. .. *Set of* 12 £120 £110
60/61 Optd "Specimen" .. .. *Set of* 2 £120

12  **13**

(Typo D.L.R.)

1912 (July)–**15**. *Wmk Mult Crown CA.*
74 **12** 10 pa. orange and green (11.12) .. 2·25 80
a. Wmk sideways .. .. .. — £1800
b. Orange-yellow and bright green (8.15) .. .. 2·25 40
75 ½ pi. green and carmine .. .. 1·25 20
a. Yellow-green and carmine .. 3·75 80
76 30 pa. violet and green (3.13) .. .. 1·50 20
77 1 pi. rose-red and blue (9.12) .. .. 3·75 1·25
a. Carmine and blue (8.15?) .. 12·00 4·00
78 2 pi. blue and purple (7.13) .. .. 4·50 90
79 4 pi. olive-green and purple .. .. 2·75 2·40
80 6 pi. sepia and green .. .. .. 2·75 4·75
81 9 pi. brown and carmine (3.15) .. 18·00 12·00
a. Yellow-brown and carmine .. 18·00 18·00
82 12 pi. chestnut and black (7.13) .. 7·50 12·00
83 18 pi. black and brown (3.15) .. .. 20·00 18·00
84 45 pi. dull purple and ultramarine (3.15) 50·00 80·00
74/84 .. .. *Set of* 11 95·00 £120
74/84 Optd "Specimen" .. .. *Set of* 11 £300

1921–23. *(a) Wmk Mult Script CA.*
85 **12** 10 pa. orange and green .. .. 2·00 2·25
86 10 pa. grey and yellow (1923) .. .. 8·00 9·00
87 30 pa. violet and green .. .. .. 2·50 40
88 30 pa. green (1923) .. .. .. 4·25 40
89 1 pi. carmine and blue .. .. 6·00 15·00
90 1 pi. violet and red (1922) .. .. 3·00 2·75
91 1½ pi. yellow and black (1922) .. .. 3·25 3·75
92 2 pi. blue and purple .. .. .. 9·50 8·00
93 2 pi. carmine and blue (1922).. .. 9·00 18·00
94 2¾ pi. blue and purple (1922) .. .. 8·50 14·00
95 4 pi. olive-green and purple .. .. 5·50 12·00
96 6 pi. sepia and green (1923) .. .. 7·50 25·00
97 9 pi. brown and carmine (1922) .. 22·00 32·00
a. Yellow-brown and carmine .. 30·00 45·00
98 18 pi. black and brown (1923) .. .. 50·00 85·00
99 45 pi. dull purple and ultramarine (1923) £130 £180
85/99 .. .. *Set of* 15 £250 £375
85/99 Optd "Specimen" .. .. *Set of* 15 £450

(b) Wmk Mult Crown CA (1923)
100 **12** 10s. green and red/*pale yellow* .. £350 £475
101 £1 purple and black/*red* £950 £1100
100/101 Optd "Specimen" .. .. *Set of* 2 £500

1924–28. *Chalk-surfaced paper.* (a) *Wmk Mult Crown CA.*
102 **13** £1 purple and black/*red* **£325 £400**

(b) Wmk Mult Script CA
103 **13** ¼ pi. grey and chestnut 30 15
104 ½ pi. black .. .. 1·00 3·50
105 ¾ pi. green .. .. 1·00 45
106 1 pi. purple and chestnut 65 20
107 1½ pi. orange and black.. .. .. 90 3·00
108 2 pi. carmine and green .. .. 1·50 4·50
109 2¾ pi. bright blue and purple .. .. 1·60 1·75
110 4 pi. sage-green and purple .. .. 2·00 1·50
111 4½ pi. black and orange/*emerald* .. 2·00 3·00
112 6 pi. olive-brown and green .. .. 2·25 3·50
113 **13** 9 pi. brown and purple .. .. 2·75 2·75
114 12 pi. chestnut and black .. .. 5·00 22·00
115 18 pi. black and orange.. .. .. 16·00 4·00
116 45 pi. purple and blue .. .. .. 25·00 28·00
117 90 pi. green and red/*yellow* .. .. 50·00 75·00
117*a* £5 black/*yellow* (1928) (Optd S. £900) £3500 £4750

CROWN COLONY

1925. *Wmk Mult Script CA.*
118 **13** ½ pi. green, **C** .. .. 1·75 1·25
119 ¾ pi. brownish black, **C** .. .. 1·75 10
120 1½ pi. scarlet, **O**.. .. .. .. 2·25 25
121 2 pi. yellow and black, **C** .. .. 4·00 3·25
122 2½ pi. bright blue, **O** .. .. .. 1·75 25
102/122 .. .. .. *Set of* 21 *to* £1 £400 £500
102/22 Optd "Specimen" .. .. *Set of* 21 £600

In the above set the fraction bar in the value is horizontal. In Nos. 91, 94, 107 and 109 it is diagonal.

14 Silver Coin of Amathus, 6th-cent B.C.

16 Map of Cyprus

(Recess B.W.)

1928 (1 Feb). 50*th Anniv of British Rule. T* **14**, **16** *and similar designs. Wmk Mult Script CA. P* 12.
123 ¾ pi. deep dull purple.. .. .. .. 1·25 40
124 1 pi. black and greenish blue .. .. 1·25 65
125 1½ pi. scarlet .. .. 2·50 2·00
126 2½ pi. light blue .. .. 1·75 2·00
127 4 pi. deep brown .. .. 5·00 7·00
128 6 pi. blue .. .. 5·00 14·00
129 9 pi. maroon .. .. 5·00 9·50
130 18 pi. black and brown .. .. .. 16·00 17·00
131 45 pi. violet and blue .. .. .. 32·00 45·00
132 £1 blue and bistre-brown £250 £300
123/132 .. .. *Set of* 10 £275 £350
123/32 Optd "Specimen" .. .. *Set of* 10 £500

Designs: *Vert*—1 pi. Zeno (philosopher); 2½ pi. Discovery of body of St Barnabas; 4 pi. Cloister, Abbey of Bella Paise; 9 pi. Tekke of Umm Haram; 18 pi. Statue of Richard I, Westminster; 45 pi. Ayia Sofiya Mosque, Famagusta; £1 King George V. *Horiz*—6 pi. Badge of Cyprus.

24 Ruins of Vouni Palace

25 Small Marble Forum, Salamis

30 Ayia Sofiya Mosque, Nicosia

31 Bayraktar Mosque, Nicosia

(Recess Waterlow)

1934 (1 Dec). T **24/5**, **30/31** *and similar designs. Wmk Mult Script CA (sideways on ½ pi., 1½ pi, 2½ pi., 4½ pi., 6 pi., 9 pi., and 18 pi.), P* 12½.
133 ¼ pi. ultramarine and orange-brown .. 25 50
a. Imperf between (vert pair) .. £10000 £10000
134 ½ pi. green 45 40
a. Imperf between (vert pair) .. £7500 £8000
135 ¾ pi. black and violet 70 10
a. Imperf between (vert pair) .. £10000
136 1 pi. black and red-brown 70 80
a. Imperf between (vert pair) .. £8000 £8000
b. Imperf between (horiz pair) .. £6500
137 1½ pi. carmine 70 45
138 2½ pi. ultramarine .. .. .. 1·25 80
139 4½ pi. black and crimson .. .. 3·00 2·25
140 6 pi. black and blue .. .. .. 6·00 11·00
141 9 pi. sepia and violet .. .. .. 3·00 3·00
142 18 pi. black and olive-green .. .. 32·00 24·00
143 45 pi. green and black .. .. .. 45·00 35·00
133/43 .. .. *Set of* 11 80·00 70·00
133/43 Perf "Specimen" .. .. *Set of* 11 £275

Designs: *Horiz.*—¾ pi. Church of St. Barnabas and St. Hilarion, Peristerona; 1 pi. Roman theatre, Soli; 1½ pi. Kyrenia Harbour; 2½ pi. Kolossi Castle; 45 pi. Forest scene, Troodos. *Vert*—9 pi. Queen's Window, St. Hilarion Castle; 18 pi. Buyuk Khan, Nicosia.

1935 (6 May). *Silver Jubilee. As Nos.* 91/4 *of Antigua, but ptd by Waterlow & Sons. P* 11 × 12.
144 ¾ pi. ultramarine and grey 40 15
145 1½ pi. deep blue and scarlet.. .. .. 2·25 2·25
k. Kite and horizontal log .. .. 40·00
146 2½ pi. brown and deep blue .. .. .. 3·75 1·50
147 9 pi. slate and purple .. .. .. 8·00 4·50
144/7 .. .. *Set of* 4 13·00 7·50
144/7 Perf "Specimen" .. .. *Set of* 4 80·00

For illustration of plate variety see Omnibus section following Zululand.

1937 (12 May). *Coronation. As Nos.* 13/15 *of Aden, but ptd by B.W. & Co. P* 11 × 11½.
148 ¾ pi. grey 55 20
149 1½ pi. carmine 95 60
150 2½ pi. blue .. .. 2·00 1·75
148/50 .. .. *Set of* 3 3·25 2·25
148/50 Perf "Specimen" .. .. *Set of* 3 65·00

35 Vouni Palace

36 Map of Cyprus

37 Othello's Tower, Famagusta

38 King George VI

(Recess Waterlow)

1938 (12 May)–**1951**. *T* **35** *to* **38** *and other designs as* 1934, *but with portrait of King George VI. Wmk Mult Script CA. P* 12½.
151 **35** ¼ pi. ultramarine and orange-brown .. 10 10
152 **25** ½ pi. green 15 10
152*a* – ½ pi. violet (2.7.51) .. .. .. 1·25 20
153 – ¾ pi. black and violet .. .. .. 3·75 15
154 – 1 pi. orange 20 10
a. Perf 13½ × 12½ (1944) .. .. £250 23·00
155 – 1½ pi. carmine .. .. 3·50 1·50
155*a* – 1½ pi. violet (15.3.43) 20 20
155*ab* – 1½ pi. green (2.7.51) .. .. .. 1·50 15
155*b* – 2 pi. black and carmine (2.2.42) .. 20 10
c. Perf 12½ × 13½ (10.44) .. .. 1·50 3·00
156 – 2½ pi. ultramarine .. .. .. 9·00 4·00
156*a* – 3 pi. ultramarine (2.2.42) 20 15
156*b* – 4 pi. ultramarine (2.7.51) .. .. 2·75 30
157 **36** 4½ pi. grey 20 10
158 **31** 6 pi. black and blue 45 60
159 **37** 9 pi. black and purple 35 15
160 – 18 pi. black and olive-green .. .. 2·00 85
a. Black and sage-green (19.8.47) .. 4·00 1·50
161 – 45 pi. green and black .. .. .. 11·00 2·00
162 **38** 90 pi. mauve and black.. .. .. 23·00 3·50
163 £1 scarlet and indigo .. .. .. 32·00 17·00
151/63 .. .. *Set of* 19 80·00 28·00
151/63 Perf "Specimen" .. .. *Set of* 16 £325

Designs: *Horiz*—¾ pi., 2 pi. Peristerona Church; 1 pi. Soli Theatre; 1½ pi. Kyrenia Harbour; 2½ pi., 3 pi., 4 pi. Kolossi Castle; 45 pi. Forest scene. *Vert*—18 pi. Buyuk Khan, Nicosia.

1946 (21 Oct). *Victory. As Nos.* 28/9 *of Aden.*
164 1½ pi. deep violet 15 10
165 3 pi. blue 15 15
164/5 Perf "Specimen" .. .. *Set of* 2 60·00

1948 (20 Dec). *Royal Silver Wedding. As Nos.* 30/1 *of Aden.*
166 1½ pi. violet 25 20
167 £1 indigo .. .. 42·00 35·00

1949 (10 Oct). 75*th Anniv of Universal Postal Union. As Nos.* 114/17 *of Antigua but inscr* "CYPRUS" *(recess).*
168 1½ pi. violet 50 55
169 2 pi. carmine-red 70 80
170 3 pi. deep blue 80 90
171 9 pi. purple .. .. 1·00 1·00
168/71 .. .. *Set of* 4 2·75 3·00

1953 (2 June). *Coronation. As No.* 47 *of Aden, but ptd by B.W.*
172 1½ pi. black and emerald 25 10

(New Currency. 1000 mils. = £1)

39 Carobs

42 Copper Pyrites Mine

49 St. Hilarion Castle

52 Coins of Salamis, Paphos, Citium and Idalium

(Recess B.W.)

1955 (1 Aug)–**60**. *T* **39**, **42**, **49**, **52** *and similar designs. Wmk Mult Script CA. P* 13½ *(Nos.* 183/5*) or* 11½ *(others).*
173 2 m. blackish brown 10 40
174 3 m. blue-violet 10 15
175 5 m. brown-orange 10 10
a. Orange-brown (17.9.58) 20 10

176 10 m. deep brown and deep green 25 10
177 15 m. olive-green and indigo 90 20
aa. *Yellow-olive and indigo* (17.9.58) .. 4·00 1·25
a. *Bistre and indigo* (14.6.60) .. .. 6·00 2·25
178 20 m. brown and deep bright blue 25 15
179 25 m. deep turquoise-blue 50 30
a. *Greenish blue* (17.9.58) .. .. 2·75 1·25
180 30 m. black and carmine-lake 35 10
181 35 m. orange-brown & deep turquoise-blue 30 35
182 40 m. deep green and sepia 40 55
183 50 m. turquoise-blue and reddish brown .. 30 25
184 100 m. mauve and bluish green .. .. 4·50 40
185 250 m. deep grey-blue and brown .. .. 7·00 3·75
186 500 m. slate and purple .. .. 24·00 9·50
187 £1 brown-lake and slate .. .. 24·00 20·00
173/87 .. .. *Set of* 15 55·00 32·00

Designs: *Vert* (*as* T **40**)—3 m. Grapes; 5 m. Oranges. (*as* T **52**)—£1 Arms of Byzantium, Lusignan, Ottoman Empire and Venice. *Horiz* (as T **42**)—15 m. Troodos Forest; 20 m. Beach of Aphrodite; 25 m. Ancient coin of Paphos; 30 m. Kyrenia; 35 m. Harvest in Mesaoria; 40 m. Famagusta Harbour. (*as* T **50**)—100 m. Hala Sultan Tekke; 250 m. Kanakaria Church.

ΚΥΠΡΙΑΚΗ ΔΗΜΟΚΡΑΤΙΑ KIBRIS CUMHURIYETI

(**54** "Cyprus Republic") **55** Map of Cyprus

1960 (16 Aug)–**61**. *Nos.* 173/87 *optd as* T **54**, *in blue by B.W. Opt larger on Nos.* 191/7 *and in two lines on Nos.* 198/202.
188 2 m. blackish brown 20 20
189 3 m. blue-violet 20 15
190 5 m. brown-orange 25 10
a. *Orange-brown* (15.8.61) 25 10
191 10 m. deep brown and deep green 30 10
192 15 m. yellow-bistre and indigo 75 10
a. *Olive-green and indigo* .. .. 85·00 15·00
b. *Brownish bis & dp indigo* (10.10.61) 2·50 70
193 20 m. brown and deep bright blue .. 40 25
a. Opt double .. .. .. † £4750
194 25 m. deep turquoise-blue 80 45
a. *Greenish blue* .. .. 4·25 2·50
195 30 m. black and carmine-lake .. .. 1·25 10
a. Opt double .. .. .. † £6500
196 35 m. orange-brown & dp turquoise-blue 1·50 20
197 40 m. deep green and sepia .. .. 2·00 65
198 50 m. turquoise-blue and reddish brown .. 2·00 40
199 100 m. mauve and bluish green .. .. 8·50 40
200 250 m. deep grey-blue and brown .. .. 25·00 2·00
201 500 m. slate and purple .. .. 40·00 15·00
202 £1 brown-lake and slate .. .. 60·00 42·00
188/202 .. .. *Set of* 15 £130 55·00

Only a single used example of No. 195a is known.

(Recess B.W.)

1960 (16 Aug). *Constitution of Republic. W w* **12**. *P* 11½.
203 **55** 10 m. sepia and deep green 30 10
204 30 m. ultramarine and deep brown .. 40 10
205 100 m. purple and deep slate .. .. 1·00 65
203/5 .. .. *Set of* 3 1·50 75

PRINTERS. All the following were lithographed by Aspioti-Elka, Athens, *unless otherwise stated.*

56 Doves

(Des T. Kurpershoek)

1962 (19 Mar). *Europa. P* 14 × 13.
206 **56** 10 m. purple and mauve 10 10
207 40 m. ultramarine and cobalt 10 10
208 100 m. emerald and pale green 15 15
206/8 .. .. *Set of* 3 30 30

57 Campaign Emblem

1962 (14 May). *Malaria Eradication. P* 14 × 13½.
209 **57** 10 m. black and olive-green 10 10
210 30 m. black and brown 15 10

58 Mult K C K Δ and Map

WATERMARK VARIETIES. The issues printed by Aspioti-Elka with W **58** are known with the vertical stamps having the watermark normal or inverted and the horizontal stamps with the watermark reading upwards or downwards.

62 Selimiye Mosque, Nicosia

63 St. Barnabas's Church

1962 (17 Sept). *T* **62/3** *and similar designs. W* **58** (*sideways on* 25, 30, 40, 50, 250 *m.*, £1). *P* 13½ × 14 (*vert*) *or* 14 × 13½ (*horiz*).
211 3 m. deep brown and orange-brown 10 15
212 5 m. purple and grey-green 10 10
213 10 m. black and yellow-green 15 10
214 15 m. black and reddish purple 20 15
215 25 m. deep brown and chestnut 25 20
216 30 m. deep blue and light blue 20 10
217 35 m. light green and blue 35 10
218 40 m. black and violet-blue .. .. 1·00 90
219 50 m. bronze-green and bistre 50 10
220 100 m. deep brown and yellow-brown .. 3·50 30
221 250 m. black and cinnamon .. .. 8·00 2·00
222 500 m. deep brown and light green .. 17·00 9·00
223 £1 bronze-green and grey .. .. 22·00 23·00
211/23 .. .. *Set of* 13 48·00 32·00

Designs: *Vert*—3 m. Iron Age jug; 5 m. Grapes; 10 m. Bronze head of Apollo; 35 m. Head of Aphrodite; 100 m. Hala Sultan Tekke; 500 m. Mouflon. *Horiz*—30 m. Temple of Apollo Hylates; 40 m. Skiing, Troodos; 50 m. Salamis Gymnasium; 250 m. Bella Paise Abbey; £1 St. Hilarion Castle.

72 Europa "Tree"

(Des Lex Weyer)

1963 (28 Jan). *Europa. W* **58** (*sideways*). *P* 14 × 13½.
224 **72** 10 m. bright blue and black 50 15
225 40 m. carmine-red and black .. .. 1·75 1·25
226 150 m. emerald-green and black .. 4·00 2·75
224/6 .. .. *Set of* 3 5·50 3·75

73 Harvester

75 Wolf Cub in Camp

1963 (21 Mar). *Freedom from Hunger. T* **73** *and similar vert design. W* **58**. *P* 13½ × 14.
227 25 m. ochre, sepia and bright blue .. 50 25
228 75 m. grey, black and lake .. .. 2·75 1·00

Design:— 75 m. Demeter, Goddess of Corn.

1963 (21 Aug). *50th Anniv of Cyprus Scout Movement and Third Commonwealth Scout Conference, Platres. T* **75** *and similar vert designs. Multicoloured. W* **58**. *P* 13½ × 14.
229 3 m. Type **75** 10 15
230 20 m. Sea Scout 35 10
231 150 m. Scout with Mouflon .. .. 1·00 1·25
229/31 .. .. *Set of* 3 1·25 1·40
MS231*a* 110×90 mm. Nos. 229/31 (*sold at* 250 *m.*). Imperf £160 £190

78 Nurse tending Child

79 Children's Centre, Kyrenia

1963 (9 Sept). *Centenary of Red Cross. W* **58** (*sideways on* 100 *m.*). *P* 13½ × 14 (10 *m.*) *or* 14 × 13½ (100 *m.*).
232 **78** 10 m. red, blue, grey-bl, chestnut & blk 50 15
233 **79** 100 m. red, green, black and blue .. 3·50 3·50

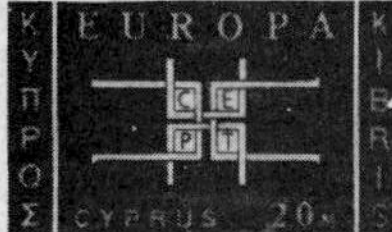

80 "Co-operation" (emblem) (**81**)

(Des A. Holm)

1963 (4 Nov). *Europa. W* **58** (*sideways*). *P* 14 × 13½.
234 **80** 20 m. buff, blue and violet 90 40
235 30 m. grey, yellow and blue .. .. 1·00 40
236 150 m. buff, blue and orange-brown .. 4·75 5·50
234/6 .. .. *Set of* 3 6·00 5·75

1964 (5 May). *U.N. Security Council's Cyprus Resolutions, March,* 1964, *Nos.* 213, 216, 218/20, *optd with T* **81** *in blue by Govt Printing Office, Nicosia.*
237 10 m. black and yellow-green 10 10
238 30 m. deep blue and light blue 10 10
239 40 m. black and violet-blue 15 15
240 50 m. bronze-green and bistre 15 10
241 100 m. deep brown and yellow-brown .. 20 40
237/41 .. .. *Set of* 5 60 70

82 Soli Theatre

1964 (15 June). *400th Birth Anniv of Shakespeare. T* **82** *and similar horiz designs. Multicoloured. W* **58**. *P* 13½ × 13.
242 15 m. Type **82** 15 10
243 35 m. Curium Theatre 15 10
244 50 m. Salamis Theatre 15 10
245 100 m. Othello Tower and scene from *Othello* .. 50 35
242/5 .. .. *Set of* 4 85 40

86 Running **89** Europa "Flower"

1964 (6 July). *Olympic Games, Tokyo. T* **86** *and similar designs. W* **58** (*sideways,* 25 *m.* 75 *m.*). *P* 13½ × 14 (10 *m.*) *or* 14 × 13½ (*others*)
246 10 m. brown, black and yellow 10 10
247 25 m. brown, blue and blue-grey 10 10
248 75 m. brown, black and orange-red .. 20 35
246/8 .. .. *Set of* 3 30 40
MS248*a* 110 × 90 mm. Nos. 246/8 (*sold at* 250 *m.*). Imperf .. .. .. 4·00 10·00

Designs: *Horiz*—25 m. Boxing; 75 m. Charioteers.

(Des G. Bétemps)

1964 (14 Sept). *Europa. W* **58**. *P* 13½ × 14.
249 **89** 20 m. chestnut and light ochre 25 10
250 30 m. ultramarine and light blue .. 35 10
251 150 m. olive and light blue-green .. 2·50 2·00
249/51 .. .. *Set of* 3 2·75 2·00

90 Dionysus and Acme **91** Silenus (satyr)

1964 (26 Oct). *Cyprus Wines. T* **90/1** *and similar multicoloured designs. W* **58** (*sideways,* 10 *m., or* 100 *m.*). *P* 14 × 13½ (*horiz*) 13½ × 14 (*vert*).
252 10 m. Type **90** 20 10
253 40 m. Type **91** 35 20
254 50 m. Commandaria Wine (*vert*) 45 10
255 100 m. Wine factory (*horiz*) .. .. 1·25 75
252/5 .. .. *Set of* 4 2·00 95

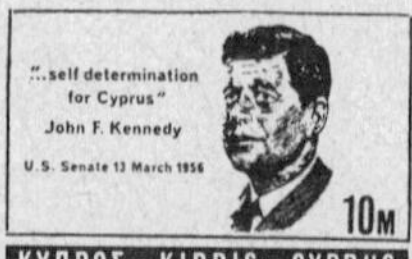

94 President Kennedy

1965 (15 Feb). *President Kennedy Commemoration. W* **58** *(sideways). P* 14 × 13½.
256 **94** 10 m. ultramarine 10 10
257 40 m. green 10 10
258 100 m. carmine-lake 15 15
256/8 .. .. *Set of* 3 25 25
MS258*a* 110 × 90 mm. Nos. 256/8 *(sold at* 250 *m.)*. Imperf .. .. 1·50 4·00

95 "Old Age"

96 "Maternity"

1965 (12 Apr). *Social Insurance Law. T* **95/6** *and similar design. W* **58**. *P* 13½ × 12 *(75 m.) or* 13½ × 14 *(others)*.
259 30 m. drab and dull green 15 10
260 45 m. light grey-green, blue & dp ultramarine 15 10
261 75 m. red-brown and flesh 65 75
259/61 .. .. *Set of* 3 85 75
Design: *Vert as T* **95**—45 m. "Accident".

98 I.T.U. Emblem and Symbols

1965 (17 May). *I.T.U. Centenary, W* **58** *(sideways). P* 14 × 13½.
262 **98** 15 m. black, brown and yellow 50 20
263 60 m. black, green and light green .. 2·75 1·50
264 75 m. black, indigo and light blue .. 3·00 1·75
262/4 .. .. *Set of* 3 5·50 3·00

99 I.C.Y. Emblem

1965 (17 May). *International Co-operation Year. W* **58** *(sideways). P* 14 × 13½.
265 **99** 50 m. brown, dp green & lt yellow-brown 1·00 10
266 100 m. purple, dp green & lt purple .. 1·50 30

100 Europa "Sprig"

U. N.
Resolution
on Cyprus
18 Dec. 1965
(101)

(Des. H. Karlsson)

1965 (27 Sept). *Europa. W* **58** *(sideways). P* 14 × 13½.
267 **100** 5 m. black, orange-brown and orange .. 15 10
268 40 m. black, orange-brown & lt emerald 75 75
269 150 m. black, orange-brown & lt grey .. 1·75 1·75
267/9 .. .. *Set of* 3 2·40 2·25

1966 (31 Jan). *U.N. General Assembly's Cyprus Resolution*, 18 *December* 1965. *Nos.* 211, 213, 216 *and* 221 *optd with T* **101**, *in blue by Govt Printing Office, Nicosia.*
270 3 m. deep brown and orange-brown .. 10 25
271 10 m. black and yellow-green 10 10
272 30 m. deep blue and light blue 15 15
273 250 m. black and cinnamon .. .. .. 35 1·75
270/3 .. .. *Set of* 4 65 2·00

102 Discovery of St. Barnabas's Body

104 St. Barnabas (icon)

103 St. Barnabas's Chapel

105 "Privileges of Cyprus Church"
(Actual size 102 × 82 *mm)*

1966 (25 Apr). 1900*th Death Anniv of St. Barnabas. W* **58** *(sideways on* 15 *m.,* 100 *m.,* 250 *m.). P* 14 × 13 *(25 m). or* 13 × 14 *(others).*
274 **102** 15 m. multicoloured 10 10
275 **103** 25 m. drab, black and blue 10 10
276 **104** 100 m. multicoloured 15 70
274/6 .. .. *Set of* 3 25 80
MS277 110 × 91 mm. **105** 250 m. mult. Imperf .. 2·75 10·00

(106)

107 General K. S. Thimayya and U. N. Emblem

1966 (30 May). *No.* 211 *surch with T* **106** *by Govt Printing Office, Nicosia.*
278 5 m. on 3 m. deep brown & orange-brown 10 10

1966 (6 June) *General Thimayya Commemoration. W* **58** *(sideways). P* 14 × 13.
279 **107** 50 m. black and light orange-brown .. 10 10

108 Europa "Ship"

(Des G. and J. Bender)

1966 (26 Sept). *Europa. W* 58. *P* 13½ × 14.
280 **108** 20 m. green and blue 15 10
281 30 m. bright purple and blue 15 10
282 150 m. bistre and blue 50 90
280/2 .. .. *Set of* 3 70 1·00

110 Church of St. James, Trikomo

119 Vase of 7th Century B.C.

120 Bronze Ingot-stand

1966 (21 Nov)–**69**. *T* **110**, **119/20** *and similar designs. W* **58** *(sideways on* 3, 15, 25, 50, 250, 500 *m.,* £1). *P* 12×13 *(3 m.),* 13×12 *(5, 10 m.),* 14×13½ *(15, 25, 50 m.),* 13½×14 *(20, 30, 35, 40, 100 m.) or* 13×14 *(others).*
283 3 m. grey-green, buff, black & light blue 15 20
284 5 m. bistre, black and steel-blue 10 10
a. Brownish bistre, black and steel-blue (18.4.69) 10 10
285 10 m. black and bistre 10 10
286 15 m. black, chestnut & light orange-brown 15 10
287 20 m. black, slate and brown 50 30
288 25 m. black, drab and lake-brown 30 10
289 30 m. black, yellow-ochre and turquoise .. 40 20
290 35 m. yellow, black and carmine-red .. 50 30
291 40 m. black, grey and new blue 70 20
a. Grey (background) omitted
292 50 m. black, slate and brown 90 10
293 100 m. black, red, pale buff and grey .. 2·00 15
294 250 m. olive-green, black & lt yellow-ochre 1·75 20
295 500 m. multicoloured .. .. 2·50 70
296 £1 black, drab and slate .. .. 5·00 4·50
283/96 .. .. *Set of* 14 13·00 6·50
Designs: *Horiz (as T* **110**)—3 m. Stavrovouni Monastery. *(As T* **119**)—15 m. Ancient ship (painting); 25 m. Sleeping Eros (marble statue); 50 m. Silver coin of Alexander the Great. *Vert (as T* **110**)—10 m. Zeno of Cibium (marble bust). *(As T* **119**)—20 m. Silver coin of Evagoras I; 30 m. St. Nicholas Cathedral, Famagusta; 35 m. Gold sceptre from Curium; 40 m. Silver dish from 7th century. *(As T* **120**)—500 m. "The Rape of Ganymede" (mosaic); £1 Aphrodite (marble statue).

123 Power Station, Limassol

124 Cogwheels

1967 (10 Apr). *First Development Programme. T* **123** *and similar designs but horiz. Multicoloured. W* **58** *(sideways on* 15 *to* 100 *m.). P* 13½ × 14 *(10 m.) or* 14 × 13½ *(others).*
297 10 m. Type **123** 10 10
298 15 m. Arghaka-Maghounda Dam 10 10
299 35 m. Troodos Highway 10 10
300 50 m. Hilton Hotel, Nicosia 10 10
301 100 m. Famagusta Harbour 15 25
297/301 .. .. *Set of* 5 35 40

(Des O. Bonnevalle)

1967 (2 May). *Europa. W* **58**. *P* 13½ × 14.
302 **124** 20 m. olive-green, green & pale yell-grn 20 10
303 30 m. reddish violet, lilac and pale lilac 20 10
304 150 m. brown, light reddish brown and pale yellow-brown 35 60
302/4 .. .. *Set of* 3 65 70

125 Throwing the Javelin

126 Running (amphora) and Map of Eastern Mediterranean
(Actual size 97 × 77 *mm)*

1967 (4 Sept). *Athletic Games, Nicosia. T* **125** *and similar designs and T* **126**. *Multicoloured. W* **58**. *P* 13½ × 13.

No.	Type	Description	Unused	Used
305		15 m. Type **125**	10	10
306		35 m. Running	10	15
307		100 m. High-jumping	10	15
305/7		*Set of* 3	15	30
MS308		110 × 90 mm. 250 m. Type **126** (wmk sideways). Imperf	85	2·50

127 Ancient Monuments

128 St. Andrew Mosaic

1967 (16 Oct). *International Tourist Year. T* **127** *and similar horiz designs. Multicoloured. W* **58**. *P* 13 × 13½.

No.	Type	Description	Unused	Used
309		10 m. Type **127**	10	10
310		40 m. Famagusta Beach	10	35
311		50 m. "Comet" at Nicosia Airport	10	10
312		100 m. Skier and youth hostel	15	40
309/12		*Set of* 4	30	75

1967 (8 Nov). *Centenary of St. Andrew's Monastery. W* **58** *(sideways). P* 13 × 13½.

No.	Type	Description	Unused	Used
313	**128**	25 m. multicoloured	10	10

129 "The Crucifixion" (icon)

130 The Three Magi

(Photo French Govt Ptg Wks, Paris)

1967 (8 Nov). *Cyprus Art Exhibition, Paris. P* 12½ × 13½.

No.	Type	Description	Unused	Used
314	**129**	50 m. multicoloured	10	10

1967 (8 Nov). *20th Anniv of U.N.E.S.C.O. W* **58** *(sideways). P* 13 × 13½.

No.	Type	Description	Unused	Used
315	**130**	75 m. multicoloured	15	20

131 Human Rights Emblem over Stars

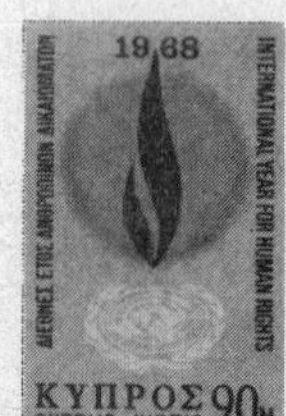

132 Human Rights and U.N. Emblems

133 Scroll of Declaration

(Actual size 95 × 75½ mm)

1968 (18 Mar). *Human Rights Year. W* **58**. *P* 13 × 14.

No.	Type	Description	Unused	Used
316	**131**	50 m. multicoloured	10	10
317	**132**	90 m. multicoloured	30	30
MS318		95 × 75½ mm. **133** 250 m. multicoloured. W **58** (sideways). Imperf.	50	2·00

134 Europa "Key"

(Des H. Schwarzenbach)

1968 (29 Apr). *Europa. W* **58** *(sideways). P* 14 × 13.

No.	Type	Description	Unused	Used
319	**134**	20 m. multicoloured	10	10
320		30 m. multicoloured	10	10
321		150 m. multicoloured	30	60
319/21		*Set of* 3	40	70

135 U.N. Children's Fund Symbol and Boy drinking Milk

136 Aesculapius

(Des A. Tassos)

1968 (2 Sept). *21st Anniv of U.N.I.C.E.F. W* **58** *(sideways). P* 14 × 13.

No.	Type	Description	Unused	Used
322	**135**	35 m. yellow-brown, carmine-red & blk	10	10

(Des A. Tassos)

1968 (2 Sept). *20th Anniv of W.H.O. W* **58**. *P* 13 × 14.

No.	Type	Description	Unused	Used
323	**136**	50 m. black, green and light olive	10	10

137 Throwing the Discus

138 I.L.O. Emblem

1968 (24 Oct). *Olympic Games, Mexico. T* **137** *and similar designs. Multicoloured. W* **58** *(sideways on 100 m.). P* 14 × 13 *(100 m.) or* 13 × 14 *(others).*

No.	Type	Description	Unused	Used
324		10 m. Type **137**	10	10
325		25 m. Sprint finish	10	10
326		100 m. Olympic Stadium (*horiz*)	10	30
324/6		*Set of* 3	15	40

(Des A. Tassos)

1969 (3 Mar). *50th Anniv of International Labour Organization. W* **58**. *P* 12 × 13½.

No.	Type	Description	Unused	Used
327	**138**	50 m. yellow-brown, blue and light blue	10	10
328		90 m. yellow-brown, black and pale grey	10	20

139 Mercator's Map of Cyprus, 1554

140 Blaeu's Map of Cyprus, 1635

1969 (7 Apr). *First International Congress of Cypriot Studies. W* **58** *(sideways). P* 14 × 14½.

No.	Type	Description	Unused	Used
329	**139**	35 m. multicoloured	10	20
330	**140**	50 m. multicoloured	10	10
		a. Wmk upright	—	2·00
		ab. Grey (shading on boats and cartouche) omitted	£160	

141 Europa Emblem

142 Common Roller

(Des L. Gasbarra and G. Belli)

1969 (28 Apr). *Europa. W* **58** *(sideways). P* 14 × 13½.

No.	Type	Description	Unused	Used
331	**141**	20 m. multicoloured	10	10
332		30 m. multicoloured	10	10
333		150 m. multicoloured	30	75
331/3		*Set of* 3	45	80

1969 (7 July). *Birds of Cyprus. T* **142** *and similar designs. Multicoloured. W* **58** *(sideways on horiz designs). P* 13½ × 12 *(horiz designs) or* 12 × 13½ *(vert designs).*

No.	Type	Description	Unused	Used
334		5 m. Type **142**	15	10
335		15 m. Audouin's Gull	20	10
336		20 m. Cyprus Warbler	25	10
337		30 m. Jay (*vert*)	30	10
338		40 m. Hoopoe (*vert*)	40	20
339		90 m. Eleanora's Falcon (*vert*)	1·50	3·00
334/9		*Set of* 6	2·50	3·25

The above were printed on glazed Samuel Jones paper with very faint watermark.

143 "The Nativity" (12th-century Wall Painting)

145 "Virgin and Child between Archangels Michael and Gabriel" (6th–7th-century Mosaic)

(Actual size 102 × 81 mm)

1969 (24 Nov). *Christmas. T* **143** *and similar horiz design, and T* **145**. *Multicoloured. W* **58** *(sideways). P* 13½ × 13.

No.	Type	Description	Unused	Used
340		20 m. Type **143**	10	10
341		45 m. "The Nativity" (14th-century wall painting)	10	15
MS342		110 × 90 mm. 250 m. Type **145**. Imperf	3·50	6·00
		a. Grey and light brown omitted		

146 Mahatma Gandhi

1970 (26 Jan). *Birth Centenary of Mahatma Gandhi. W* **58** *(sideways). P* 14 × 13½.

No.	Type	Description	Unused	Used
343	**146**	25 m. ultramarine, drab and black	15	10
344		75 m. yellow-brown, drab and black	20	35

147 "Flaming Sun"

148 Gladioli

(Des L. le Brocquy)

1970 (4 May). *Europa. W* **58** *(sideways). P* 14 × 13.

No.	Type	Description	Unused	Used
345	**147**	20 m. brown, greenish yellow & orange	10	10
346		30 m. new blue, greenish yellow & orge	10	10
347		150 m. bright purple, greenish yell & orge	35	90
345/7		*Set of* 3	50	1·00

1970 (3 Aug). *European Conservation Year. T* **148** *and similar vert designs. Multicoloured. W* **58**. *P* 13 × 13½.

No.	Type	Description	Unused	Used
348		10 m. Type **148**	10	10
349		50 m. Poppies	15	10
350		90 m. Giant fennel	35	1·00
348/50		*Set of* 3	55	1·00

149 I.E.Y. Emblem

150 Mosaic

151 Globe, Dove and U.N. Emblem

(Des G. Simonis (75 m.))

1970 (7 Sept). *International Events. W* **58** *(sideways on horiz designs). P* 13 × 14 (5 *m.*), *or* 14 × 13 *(others).*

351 **149** 5 m. black, red-brown & lt yellow-brn .. 10 10
352 **150** 15 m. multicoloured 10 10
353 **151** 75 m. multicoloured 10 20
351/3 .. .. *Set of* 3 15 25

Events:—5 m. International Education Year; 15 m. 50th General Assembly of International Vine and Wine Office; 75 m. 25th Anniv of United Nations.

152 Virgin and Child

153 Cotton Napkin

(Photo Harrison)

1970 (23 Nov). *Christmas. Wall-painting from Church of Panayia Podhythou, Galata. T* **152** *and similar multicoloured designs. P* 14 × 14½.

354 25 m. Archangel (facing right) 10 10
a. Horiz strip of 3. Nos. 354/6 30
355 25 m. Type **152** 10 10
356 25 m. Archangel (facing left) 10 10
357 75 m. Virgin and Child between Archangels 15 25
354/7 .. .. *Set of* 4 40 30

The 75 m. is horiz, size 42 × 30 mm, and the 25 m. values are vert, size as T **152**.

Nos. 354/6 were issued in *se-tenant* strips of three, throughout the sheet. The triptych thus formed is depicted in its entirety on the 75 m. value.

1971 (22 Feb). *Multicoloured designs as T* **153**. *W* **58** *(sideways on horiz designs). (a) Vert designs* 23 × 33 *mm. P* 12 × 13½.

358 3 m. Type **153** 10 20
359 5 m. St. George and Dragon (19th-cent bas-relief) 10 10

(*b*) *Vert* (10, 20, 25, 40, 50, 75 *m.*) *or horiz* (15, 30, 90 *m.*) *designs, each* 24 × 37 *or* 37 × 24 *mm. P* 13 × 14 (15, 30, 90 *m*) *or* 14 × 13 (*others*)

360 10 m. Woman in festival costume 15 10
361 15 m. Archaic Bichrome Kylix (cup) .. 20 10
a. Vert laid paper 60
362 20 m. A pair of donors (St. Mamas Church) 25 10
363 25 m. "The Creation" (6th-cent mosaic) .. 25 10
364 30 m. Athena and horse-drawn chariot (4th-cent B.C. terracotta) 30 10
365 40 m. Shepherd playing pipe (14th-cent fresco) 70 40
366 50 m. Hellenistic head (3rd cent B.C.) .. 60 10
367 75 m. "Angel" (mosaic detail), Kanakaria Church .. .. 1·75 50
368 90 m. Mycenaean silver bowl .. .. 1·75 75

(*c*) *Horiz* (250, 500 *m.*) *or vert* (£1) *designs, each* 41 × 28 *or* 28 × 41 *mm. P* 13½ × 13 (250, 500 *m.*) *or* 13 × 13½ (£1)

369 250 m. Moufflon (detail of 3rd-cent mosaic) (*shades*) .. .. 2·75 40
370 500 m. Ladies and sacred tree (detail, 6th-cent amphora) .. .. 1·25 70
371 £1 Horned god from Enkomi (12th-cent bronze statue) .. .. 1·75 75
358/71 .. .. *Set of* 14 10·50 3·25

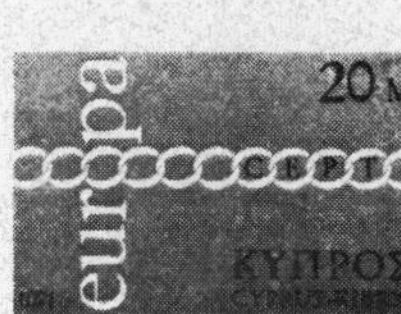

154 Europa Chain

155 Archbishop Kyprianos

(Des H. Haflidason)

1971 (3 May). *Europa. W* **58** *(sideways). P* 14 × 13

372 **154** 20 m. pale blue, ultramarine and black 10 10
373 30 m. apple green, myrtle-green & blk 10 10
374 150 m. lemon, bright green and black .. 25 80
372/4 .. .. *Set of* 3 40 90

The above were printed on glazed paper with very faint watermark.

1971 (9 July). *150th Anniv. of Greek War of Independence. T* **155** *and similar multicoloured designs. W* **58** *(sideways on* 30 *m.). P* 13½ × 12½ (30 *m.*) *or* 12½ × 13½ (*others*).

375 15 m. Type **155** 10 10
376 30 m. "Taking the Oath" (*horiz*) 10 10
377 30 m. Bishop Germanos, flag and freedom-fighters 20 40
375/7 .. .. *Set of* 3 30 45

156 Kyrenia Castle

157 Madonna and Child in Stable

1971 (20 Sept). *Tourism. T* **156** *and similar multicoloured designs. W* **58** *(sideways on* 15 *and* 100 *m.). P* 13½ × 13 (15 *m.,* 100 *m.*) *or* 13 × 13½ (*others*).

378 15 m. Type **156** 10 10
379 25 m. Gourd on sunny beach (*vert*) .. 10 10
380 60 m. Mountain scenery (*vert*) 15 30
381 100 m. Church of St. Evlalios, Lambousa .. 15 35
378/81 .. .. *Set of* 4 30 65

(Des A. Tassos)

1971 (22 Nov). *Christmas. T* **157** *and similar vert designs. Multicoloured. W* **58**. *P* 13 × 14.

382 10 m. Type **157** 10 10
a. Horiz strip of 3. Nos. 382/4 35
383 50 m. The Three Wise Men 15 15
384 100 m. The Shepherds 20 20
382/4 .. .. *Set of* 3 35 35

The 10 m. was issued in sheets of 100, and all three values were printed horizontally *se-tenant* in sheets of 36, the order being 50, 10 and 100 m.

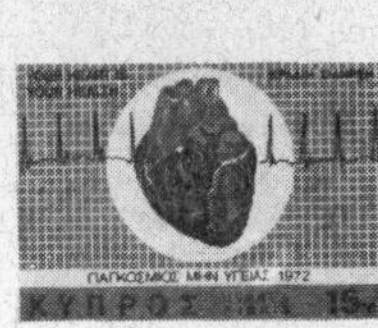

158 Heart

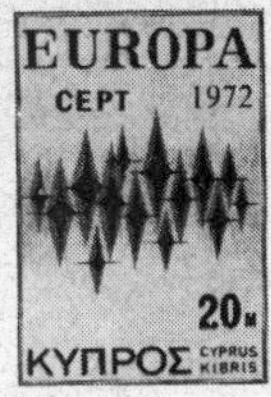

159 "Communications"

1972 (11 Apr). *World Health Month. W* **58** *(sideways). P* 13½ × 12.

385 **158** 15 m. multicoloured 10 10
386 50 m. multicoloured 15 25

(Des P. Huovinen)

1972 (22 May). *Europa. W* **58**. *P* 12½ × 13½.

387 **159** 20 m. yellow-orge, sepia & pale grey-brn 20 15
388 30 m. yell-orge, brt dp ultram & cobalt 20 15
389 150 m. yellow-orange, myrtle-green and pale-turquoise-green .. .. 1·25 2·00
387/9 .. .. *Set of* 3 1·50 2·10

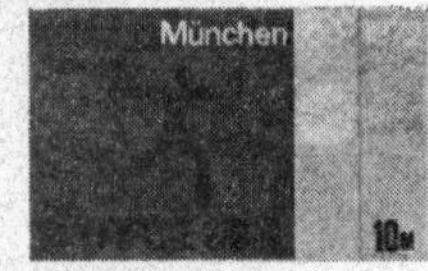

160 Archery

1972 (24 July). *Olympic Games. T* **160** *and similar horiz designs. Multicoloured. W* **58** *(sideways). P* 14 × 13.

390 10 m. Type **160** 10 10
391 40 m. Wrestling 15 10
392 100 m. Football 35 55
390/2 .. .. *Set of* 3 50 65

161 Stater of Marion

162 Bathing the Child Jesus

1972 (25 Sept). *Ancient Coins of Cyprus (1st series), T* **161** *and similar horiz designs. W* **58** *(sideways), P* 14 × 13.

393 20 m. pale turquoise-blue, black and silver .. 15 10
394 30 m. pale violet-blue, black and silver .. 20 10
395 40 m. brownish stone, black and silver .. 25 20
396 100 m. light salmon-pink, black and silver .. 80 1·00
393/6 .. .. *Set of* 4 1·25 1·25

Coins:—30 m. Stater of Paphos; 40 m. Stater of Lapithos, 100 m. Stater of Idalion.

See also Nos. 486/9.

(Des A. Tassos)

1972 (20 Nov). *Christmas. T* **162** *and similar vert designs showing portions of a mural in the Church of the Holy Cross of Agiasmati. Multicoloured. W* **58** *(sideways on* **MS**400). *P* 13 × 14.

397 10 m. Type **162** 10 10
398 20 m. The Magi 10 10
399 100 m. The Nativity 15 30
397/9 .. .. *Set of* 3 25 35
MS400 100 × 90 mm. 250 m. Showing the mural in full. Imperf .. .. 70 2·00

163 Mount Olympus, Troodos

1973 (13 Mar). *29th Internation Ski Federation Congress. T* **163** *and similar horiz design. Multicoloured. W* **58** *(sideways). P* 14 × 13.

401 20 m. Type **163** 10 10
402 100 m. Congress emblem 25 35

164 Europa "Posthorn"

(Des I. F. Anisdahl)

1973 (7 May). *Europa. W* **58** *(sideways). P* 14 × 13.

403 **164** 20 m. multicoloured 20 10
404 30 m. multicoloured 20 10
405 150 m. multicoloured .. .. .. 60 1·50
403/5 .. .. *Set of* 3 90 1·50

165 Archbishop's Palace, Nicosia

20M

(166)

1973 (23 July). *Traditional Architecture. T* **165** *and similar multicoloured designs. W* **58** *(sideways on* 20 *and* 100 *m.). P* 14 × 13 (20 *and* 100 *m.*) *or* 13 × 14 (*others*).

406 20 m. Type **165** 10 10
407 30 m. House of Hajigeorgajis Cornessios, Nicosia (*vert*) 10 10
408 50 m. House at Gourri, 1850 (*vert*) 15 10
409 100 n. House at Rizokarpaso, 1772 .. .. 40 75
406/9 .. .. *Set of* 4 65 90

1973 (24 Sept). *No.* 361 *surch with T* **166**.

410 20 m. on 15 m. Archaic Bichrome Kylix (cup) 15 15
a. Vert laid paper 50

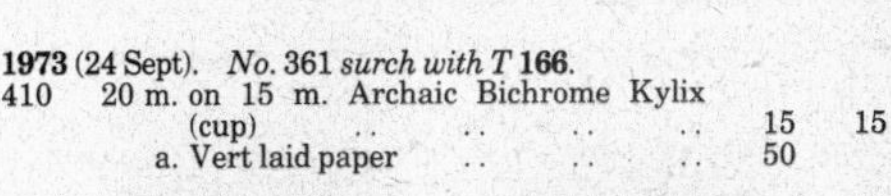

167 Scout Emblem

168 Archangel Gabriel

1973 (24 Sept). *Anniversaries. T* **167** *and similar designs.* W **58** *(sideways on 25 and 35 m.). P* 13 × 14 (10, 50 *and* 100 *m.) or* 14 × 13 *(others).*

No.	Description		
411	10 m. yellow-olive and deep brown	10	10
412	25 m. deep blue, and slate-lilac	10	10
413	35 m. light brown-olive, stone and sage-green	20	25
414	50 m. dull blue and indigo	20	10
415	100 m. brown and sepia	40	65
411/15	*Set of* 5	85	90

Designs and Events: *Vert*—10 m. Type **167** (60th Anniv of Cyprus Boy Scouts); 50 m. Airline emblem (25th Anniv of Cyprus Airways); 100 m. Interpol emblem (50th Anniv of Interpol). *Horiz*—25 m. Outline of Cyprus and E.E.C. nations (Association of Cyprus with the E.E.C.); 35 m. F.A.O. emblem (Tenth Anniv of F.A.O.).

1973 (26 Nov). *Christmas. Murals from Araka Church. T* **168** *and similar multicoloured designs.* W **58** *(sideways on* 100 *m.). P* 14 × 13 (100 *m.) or* 13 × 14 *(others).*

No.	Description		
416	10 m. Type **168**	10	10
417	20 m. Madonna and Child	10	10
418	100 m. Araka Church *(horiz)*	40	65
416/18	*Set of* 3	45	65

169 Grapes

170 "The Rape of Europa" (Silver Stater of Marion)

1974 (18 Mar). *Products of Cyprus. T* **169** *and similar vert designs. Multicoloured.* W **58**. *P* 13 × 14.

No.	Description		
419	25 m. Type **169**	10	15
420	50 m. Grapefruit	15	35
	a. Horiz strip of 3, Nos. 420/2	40	
421	50 m. Oranges	15	35
422	50 m. Lemons	15	35
419/22	*Set of* 4	50	1·10

Nos. 420/2 were printed together, horizontally *se-tenant* throughout the sheet.

1974 (29 Apr). *Europa.* W **58**. *P* 13½ × 14.

No.	Description		
423 **170**	10 m. multicoloured	10	10
424	40 m. multicoloured	15	15
425	150 m. multicoloured	60	1·50
423/5	*Set of* 3	75	1·50

171 Title Page of A. Kyprianos' "History of Cyprus" (1788)

REFUGEE
FUND
TAMEION
ΠΡΟΣΦΥΓΩΝ
GÖÇMENLER
FONU
10M

(172)

1974 (22 July*). *Second International Congress of Cypriot Studies. T* **171** *and similar multicoloured designs.* W **58** *(sideways on 25 m. and* **MS**429). *P* 14 × 13½ (25 *m.) or* 13½ × 14 *(others).*

No.	Description		
426	10 m. Type **171**	10	10
427	25 m. Solon (philosopher) in mosaic *(horiz)*	10	10
428	100 m. "St. Neophytos" (wall painting)	30	75
426/8	*Set of* 3	40	80
MS429	111 × 90 mm. 250 m. Ortelius' map of Cyprus and Greek Islands, 1584. Imperf	1·00	3·00

*Although this is the date appearing on first day covers the stamps were not put on sale until the 24th.

1974 (1 Oct). *Obligatory Tax. Refugee Fund No.* 359 *surch with T* **172**.

No.	Description		
430	10 m. on 5 m. St. George and Dragon	10	10

SECURITY
COUNCIL
RESOLUTION
353
20 JULY 1974

(173)

174 "Refugees"

1974 (14 Oct). *U.N. Security Council Resolution* 353. *Nos.* 360, 365, 366 *and* 369 *optd as T* **173**.

No.	Description		
431	10 m. Woman in festival costume	10	10
432	40 m. Shepherd playing pipe	20	35
433	50 m. Hellenistic head	20	10
434	250 m. Moufflon *(shades)*	60	2·00
431/4	*Set of* 4	1·00	2·25

1974 (2 Dec). *Obligatory Tax. Refugee Fund.* W **58** *(sideways). P* 12 × 12½.

No.	Description		
435 **174**	10 m. black and light grey	10	10

175 "Virgin and Child between Two Angels", Stavros Church

1974 (2 Dec). *Christmas. T* **175** *and similar multicoloured designs showing wall-paintings.* W **58** *(sideways on* 10 *m. and* 100 *m.). P* 13 × 14 (50 *m.) or* 14 × 13 *(others).*

No.	Description		
436	10 m. Type **175**	10	10
437	50 m. "Adoration of the Magi", Ayios Neophytos Monastery *(vert)*	20	10
438	100 m. "Flight into Egypt", Ayios Neophytos Monastery	25	45
436/8	*Set of* 3	45	50

176 Larnaca–Nicosia Mail-coach, 1878

177 "The Distaff" (M. Kashalos)

(Photo Harrison)

1975 (17 Feb). *International Events. T* **176** *and similar designs. No wmk. P* 14.

No.	Description		
439 **176**	20 m. multicoloured	20	10
440 –	30 m. ultramarine, slate-blk & dull orge	25	45
441 **176**	50 m. multicoloured	25	15
442 –	100 m. multicoloured	30	85
439/42	*Set of* 4	90	1·40

Designs and Events:—20 m., 50 m. Centenary of Universal Postal Union. *Vert.*—30 m. "Disabled Persons" (Eighth European Meeting of International Society for the Rehabilitation of Disabled Persons); 100 m. Council flag (25th Anniv of Council of Europe).

(Photo Harrison)

1975 (28 Apr). *Europa. T* **177** *and similar vert designs. Multicoloured. P* 13½ × 14½.

No.	Description		
443	20 m. Type **177**	20	25
	a. Horiz strip of 3. Nos. 443/5	75	
444	30 m. "Nature Morte" (C. Savva)	25	35
445	150 m. "Virgin and Child of Liopetri" (G. P. Georghiou)	40	85
443/5	*Set of* 3	75	1·25

Nos. 443/5 were printed horizontally *se-tenant* throughout the sheet.

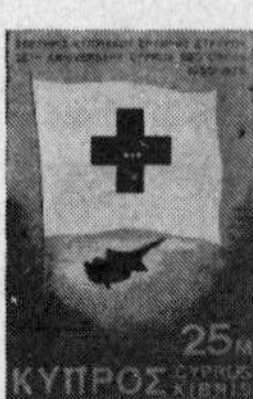

178 Red Cross Flag over Map

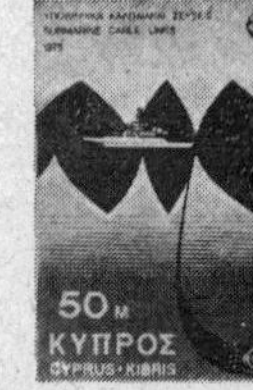

179 Submarine Cable Links

1975 (4 Aug). *International Events. T* **178** *and similar horiz designs. P* 12½ × 13½ (25 *m.) or* 13½ × 12½ *(others).*

No.	Description		
446	25 m. multicoloured	10	10
447	30 m. turquoise-green and greenish blue	10	10
448	75 m. red-brown, orge-brn & pale blue-grey	20	50
446/8	*Set of* 3	35	60

Designs and events: *Vert*—25 m. Type **178** (25th Anniversary of Cyprus Red Cross). *Horiz*—30 m. Nurse and lamp (International Nurses' Day); 75 m. Woman's Steatite Idol (International Women's Year).

1975 (13 Oct). *Telecommunications Achievements. T* **179** *and similar design.* W **58** *(sideways on* 100 *m.). P* 12 × 13½ (50 *m.) or* 13½ × 12 (100 *m.).*

No.	Description		
449	50 m. multicoloured	20	10
450	100 m. orange-yellow, dull violet and lilac	30	55

Design: *Horiz*—100 m. International subscriber dialling.

10M

(180)

181 Human-figured Vessel, 19th-Century

1976 (5 Jan). *No.* 358 *surch with T* **180**.

No.	Description		
451	10 m. on 3 m. Cotton napkin	10	10

1976 (3 May). *Europa. T* **181** *and similar vert designs. Multicoloured.* W **58**. *P* 13 × 14.

No.	Description		
452	20 m. Type **181**	10	10
453	60 m. Composite vessel, 2100–2000 B.C.	30	35
454	100 m. Byzantine goblet	40	65
452/4	*Set of* 3	70	90

182 Self-help Housing

183 Terracotta Statue of Youth

1976 (3 May). *Economic Reactivation. T* **182** *and similar horiz designs. Multicoloured.* W **58** *(sideways). P* 14 × 13.

No.	Description		
455	10 m. Type **182**	10	10
456	25 m. Handicrafts	15	15
457	30 m. Reafforestation	15	15
458	60 m. Air Communications	20	30
455/8	*Set of* 4	45	60

(Des A. Tassos)

1976 (7 June). *Cypriot Treasures. T* **183** *and similar designs.* W **58** *(sideways on horiz designs, upright on vert designs). Ordinary cream paper. P* 12 × 13½ (5, 10 *m.),* 13 × 14 (20, 25, 30 *m.),* 14 × 13 (40, 50, 60 *m.),* 13½ × 12 (100 *m.) or* 13 × 13½ (250 *m. to* £1).

No.	Description		
459	5 m. multicoloured	10	15
460	10 m. multicoloured	10	15
461	20 m. red, yellow and black	20	15
462	25 m. multicoloured	20	10
463	30 m. multicoloured	25	10
464	40 m. grey-green, light olive-bistre and black	30	15
465	50 m. buff, brown and black	35	10
466	60 m. multicoloured	45	10
467	100 m. multicoloured	50	20
468	250 m. deep dull blue, grey and black	70	70
469	500 m. black, stone and deep blue-green	80	1·75
470	£1 multicoloured	1·25	2·25
459/70	*Set of* 12	4·50	5·00

Sizes:—23 × 34 *mm*, 5 m., 10 m.; 34 × 23 *mm*, 100 m.; 24 × 37 *mm*, 20, 25, 30 m.; 37 × 24 *mm*, 40, 50, 60 m.; 28 × 41 *mm*, others.

Designs:—10 m. Limestone head; 20 m. Gold necklace from Lambousa; 25 m. Terracotta warrior; 30 m. Statue of a priest of Aphrodite; 40 m. Bronze tablet; 50 m. Mycenaean crater; 60 m. Limestone sarcophagus; 100 m. Gold bracelet from Lambousa; 250 m. Silver dish from Lambousa; 500 m. Bronze stand; £1 Statue of Artemis.

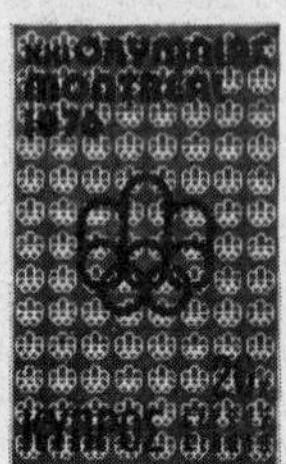

184 Olympic Symbol

185 "George Washington" (G. Stuart)

(Litho Harrison)

1976 (5 July). *Olympic Games, Montreal. T* **184** *and similar designs. P* 14.

No.	Description		
471	20 m. carmine-red, black and yellow	10	10
472	60 m. multicoloured	15	20
473	100 m. multicoloured	20	35
471/3	*Set of* 3	40	55

Designs: *Horiz*—60, 100 m. Olympic symbols *(different).*

1976 (5 July). *Bicentenary of American Revolution.* W **58**. *P* 13 × 13½.

No.	Description		
474 **185**	100 m. multicoloured	40	30

186 Children in Library

187 Archangel Michael

1976 (27 Sept). *International Events. T* **186** *and similar vert designs.* W **58**. *P* 13½ × 12½ (50 *m.) or* 13½ *(others).*

No.	Description		
475	40 m. multicoloured	15	15
476	50 m. yellow-brown and black	15	10
477	80 m. multicoloured	35	50
475/7	*Set of* 3	60	65

Designs and Events:—40 m. Type **186** (Promotion of Children's Books); 50 m. Low-cost housing (HABITAT Conference, Vancouver); 80 m. Eye protected by hands (World Health Day).

(Litho Harrison)

1976 (15 Nov). *Christmas. T* **187** *and similar vert designs, showing icons from Ayios Neophytis Monastery. Multicoloured. P* 12½.

478 10 m. Type **187** 15 10
479 15 m. Archangel Gabriel 15 10
480 150 m. The Nativity 60 80
478/80 .. .. *Set of* 3 80 80

188 "Cyprus 74" (wood-engraving by A. Tassos)

189 "View of Prodhromos" (A. Diamantis)

1977 (10 Jan)–82. *Obligatory Tax. Refugee Fund. W* **58**. *Ordinary cream paper. P* 13×12½.

481 **188** 10 m. grey-black 10 10
a. Chalk-surfaced cream paper (3.5.82)* .. ..

*Earliest known date of use.

For 1 c. value, see Nos. 634/b, 729 and 747.

1977 (2 May). *Europa. T* **189** *and similar horiz designs. Multicoloured. No wmk. P* 13½ × 13.

482 20 m. Type **189** 10 10
483 60 m. "Springtime at Monagroulli" (T. Kanthos) 25 55
484 120 m. "Old Port, Limassol" (V. Ioannides) .. 40 70
482/4 .. .. *Set of* 3 65 1·25

190 Overprinted 500 m. Stamp of 1960

191 Bronze Coin of Emperor Trajan

1977 (13 June). *Silver Jubilee. W* **58**. *P* 13 × 13½.

485 **190** 120 m. multicoloured 30 30

(Litho Harrison)

1977 (13 June). *Ancient Coins of Cyprus* (2nd *series*). *T* **191** *and similar horiz designs. P* 14.

486 10 m. brownish black, gold and ultramarine .. 10 10
487 40 m. brownish black, silver and pale blue .. 20 20
488 60 m. brownish black, silver and dull orange .. 25 25
489 100 m. brownish black, gold and blue-green .. 35 60
486/9 .. .. *Set of* 4 80 1·00

Designs:—40 m. Silver tetradrachm of Demetrios Poliorcetes; 60 m. Silver tetradrachm of Ptolemy VIII; 100 m. Gold Octadrachm of Arsinoe II.

192 Archbishop Makarios in Ceremonial Robes

193 Embroidery, Pottery and Weaving

1977 (10 Sept). *Death of Archbishop Makarios. T* **192** *and similar vert designs. Multicoloured. P* 13 × 13½.

490 20 m. Type **192** 15 10
491 60 m. Archbishop and doorway 20 10
492 250 m. Head and shoulders portrait .. .. 50 1·10
490/2 .. .. *Set of* 3 75 1·10

1977 (17 Oct). *Anniversaries and Events. T* **193** *and similar horiz designs. Multicoloured. W* 58 (*sideways*). *P* 13½ × 13.

493 20 m. Type **193** 10 10
494 40 m. Map of Mediterranean 15 15
495 60 m. Gold medals 20 15
496 80 m. "Sputnik" 20 50
493/6 .. .. *Set of* 4 60 80

Designs commemorate: 20 m. Revitalisation of handicrafts; 40 m. "Man and the Biosphere" Programme in the Mediterranean region; 60 m. Gold medals won by Cypriot students in the Orleans Gymnasiade; 80 m. 60th Anniv of Russian October Revolution.

194 "Nativity"

(Litho Harrison)

1977 (21 Nov). *Christmas. T* **194** *and similar horiz designs showing children's paintings. Multicoloured. P* 14 × 13½.

497 10 m. Type **194** 10 10
498 40 m. "The Three Kings" 10 10
499 150 m. "Flight into Egypt" 25 55
497/9 .. .. *Set of* 3 35 65

195 Demetrios Libertis

196 Chrysorrhogiatissa Monastery Courtyard

(Des A. Ioannides)

1978 (6 Mar). *Cypriot Poets. T* **195** *and similar horiz design. W* **58** (*sideways*). *P* 14 × 13.

500 40 m. dull brown and olive-bistre 10 10
501 150 m. grey, grey-black and light red 30 55

Design:—150 m. Vasilis Michaelides.

(Litho Harrison)

1978 (24 Apr). *Europa. Architecture. T* **196** *and similar horiz designs. Multicoloured. P* 14 × 13½.

502 25 m. Type **196** 10 10
503 75 m. Kolossi Castle 25 15
504 125 m. Municipal Library, Paphos 40 60
502/4 .. .. *Set of* 3 65 75

197 Archbishop of Cyprus, 1950–77

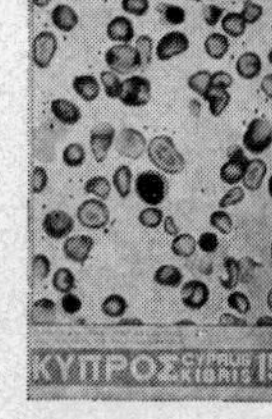

198 Affected Blood Corpuscles (Prevention of Thalassaemia)

(Des A. Ioannides (300 m.). Photo Harrison)

1978 (3 Aug). *Archbishop Makarios Commemoration. T* **197** *and similar vert designs. Multicoloured. P* 14 × 15.

505 15 m. Type **197** 15 20
a. Silver (inscr and emblem) omitted .. † —
b. Horiz strip of 5. Nos. 505/9 95
ba. Imperf (horiz strip of 5) .. ..
bb. Silver omitted (horiz strip of 5) ..
506 25 m. Exiled in Seychelles, 9 March 1956–28 March 1957 .. .. .. 15 20
507 50 m. President of the Republic, 1960–77 .. 20 25
508 75 m. "Soldier of Christ" 20 30
509 100 m. "Fighter for Freedom" 25 35
a. Silver (inscr and emblem) omitted ..
505/9 .. .. *Set of* 5 85 1·10
MS510 110 × 80 mm. 300 m. "The Great Leader". Imperf .. .. 1·40 3·00

Nos. 505/9 were printed together, *se-tenant*, in horizontal strips of 5 throughout the sheet.

Sheets of this issue are known with the silver omitted completely or only from the first or last vertical rows.

1978 (23 Oct). *Anniversaries and Events. T* **198** *and similar designs. P* 13½ × 14 (15, 35 *m.*) *or* 14 × 13½ (*others*).

511 15 m. multicoloured 10 10
512 35 m. multicoloured 10 10
513 75 m. black and grey 15 15
514 125 m. multicoloured 25 55
511/14 .. .. *Set of* 4 50 75

Designs and commemorations: *Vert*—35 m. Aristotle (sculpture) (2300th death anniversary). *Horiz*—75 m. "Heads" (Human Rights); 125 m. Wright brothers and *Flyer* (75th anniversary of powered flight).

199 Icon Stand

200 Aphrodite (statue from Soli)

(Litho Harrison)

1978 (4 Dec). *Christmas. T* **199** *and similar vert designs showing icon stands. P* 14 × 14½.

515 15 m. multicoloured 10 10
516 35 m. multicoloured 15 10
517 150 m. multicoloured 40 60
515/17 .. .. *Set of* 3 60 65

(Litho Harrison)

1979 (12 Mar). *Aphrodite* (*Greek goddess of love and beauty*) *Commemoration* (1*st issue*). *T* **200** *and similar horiz design showing Aphrodite emerging from the sea at Paphos* (*legendary birthplace*). *Multicoloured. P* 14 × 13½.

518 75 m. Type **200** 15 10
519 125 m. Aphrodite on a shell (detail from "Birth of Venus" by Botticelli) .. 25 25

See also Nos. 584/5.

201 Van, Larnaca–Nicosia Mail-coach and Envelope

202 Peacock Wrasse (*thalassoma pavo*)

(Des G. Simonis)

1979 (30 Apr). *Europa. Communications. T* **201** *and similar horiz designs. Multicoloured. W* **58** (*sideways*). *P* 14 × 13.

520 25 m. Type **201** 10 10
521 75 m. Radar, satellite and early telephone .. 15 10
522 125 m. Aircraft, ship and envelopes 25 35
520/2 .. .. *Set of* 3 45 45

(Des A. Tassos)

1979 (25 June). *Flora and Fauna. T* **202** *and similar multicoloured designs. W* **58** (*sideways on* 25 *and* 125 *m.*). *P* 13½ × 12 (25, 125 *m.*) *or* 12 × 13½ (*others*).

523 25 m. Type **202** 10 10
524 50 m. Black Partridge (*Francolinus francolinus*) (*vert*) 35 15
525 75 m. Cedar (*Cedar brevifolia*) (*vert*) 35 15
526 125 m. Mule (*Equus mulus*) 40 45
523/6 .. .. *Set of* 4 1·10 70

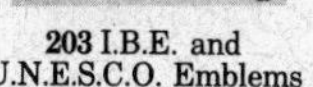

203 I.B.E. and U.N.E.S.C.O. Emblems

204 "Jesus" (from Church of the Virgin Mary of Arakas, Lagoudhera)

(Des Mrs. A. Kalathia (25 m.), A. Ioannides (others). Litho Harrison)

1979 (1 Oct). *Anniversaries and Events. T* **203** *and similar designs in black, yellow-brown and yellow-ochre* (50 *m.*) *or multicoloured* (*others*). *P* 12½.

527 15 m. Type **203** 10 10
528 25 m. Graphic design of dove and stamp album (*horiz*) 10 10
529 50 m. Lord Kitchener and map of Cyprus (*horiz*) 15 15
530 75 m. Child's face (*horiz*) 20 10
531 100 m. Graphic design of footballers (*horiz*) .. 20 20
532 125 m. Rotary International emblem and "75" 25 40
527/32 .. .. *Set of* 6 85 85

Commemorations:—15 m. 50th anniversary of International Bureau of Education; 25 m. 20th anniversary of Cyprus Philatelic Society; 50 m. Centenary of Cyprus Survey; 75 m. International Year of the Child; 100 m. 25th anniv of U.E.F.A. (European Football Association); 125 m. 75th anniv of Rotary International.

1979 (5 Nov). *Christmas. Icons. T* **204** *and similar vert designs. Multicoloured. W* **58**. *P* 13 × 13½ (35 *m.*) *or* 13½ × 14 (*others*).

533 15 m. Type **204** 10 10
534 35 m. "Nativity" (from the Iconostasis of the Church of St. Nicholas, Famagusta District) (29 × 41 *mm*) 10 10
535 150 m. "Holy Mary" (from Church of the Virgin Mary of Arakas, Lagoudhera) 25 30
533/5 .. .. *Set of* 3 35 40

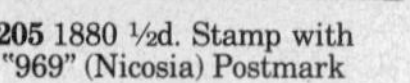

205 1880 ½d. Stamp with "969" (Nicosia) Postmark

206 St. Barnabas (Patron Saint of Cyprus)

(Des A. Tassos)

1980 (17 Mar). *Cyprus Stamp Centenary. T* **205** *and similar horiz designs. Multicoloured. W* **58** *(sideways). P* 13½ × 13.

536 40 m. Type **205** 10 10
537 125 m. 1880 2½d. stamp with "974" (Kyrenia) postmark 15 15
538 175 m. 1880 1s. stamp with "942" (Larnaca) postmark 15 20
536/8 .. .. *Set of* 3 30 35
MS539 105 × 85 mm. 500 m. 1880 1d., ½d., 2½d., 4d., 6d. and 1s. stamps (90 × 75 *mm*). Imperf .. 70 1·25

(Photo Harrison)

1980 (28 Apr). *Europa. Personalities. T* **206** *and similar vert design. Multicoloured. P* 12½.

540 40 m. Type **206** 10 10
541 125 m. Zeno of Citium (founder of the Stoic philosophy) 15 20
a. Pale Venetian red omitted £100

The pale Venetian red colour on No. 541 appears as an overlay on the bust. On No. 541a the bust is pure grey.

207 Sailing

208 Gold Necklace, Arsos (7th-century BC)

(Des A. Ioannides)

1980 (23 June). *Olympic Games, Moscow. T* **207** *and similar horiz designs. Multicoloured. W* **58** *(sideways). P* 13½ × 13.

542 40 m. Type **207** 10 10
543 125 m. Swimming 20 20
544 200 m. Gymnastics 25 25
542/4 .. .. *Set of* 3 50 50

1980 (15 Sept). *Archaeological Treasures. Multicoloured designs as T* **208**. *W* **58** *(sideways on* 15, 40, 150 *and* 500 *m.). Chalk-surfaced cream paper. P* 14 × 13 *(*15, 40, 150 *and* 500 *m.) or* 13 × 14 *(others).*

545 10 m. Type **208** 15 15
546 15 m. Bronze cow, Vouni Palace (5th-century B.C.) (*horiz*) 20 15
547 25 m. Amphora, Salamis (6th-century B.C.) .. 25 10
548 40 m. Gold finger-ring, Enkomi (13th-century B.C.) (*horiz*) 30 15
549 50 m. Bronze cauldron, Salamis (8th-century B.C.) 30 10
550 75 m. Funerary stele, Marion (5th-century B.C.) 45 10
551 100 m. Jug (15–14th-century B.C.) 50 15
552 125 m. Warrior (Terracotta) (6–5th-century B.C.) 50 15
553 150 m. Lions attacking bull (bronze relief), Vouni Palace (5th-century B.C.) (*horiz*) 65 15
554 175 m. Faience rhyton, Kition (13th-century B.C.) 70 20
555 200 m. Bronze statue of Ingot God, Enkomi (12th-century B.C.) 75 20
556 500 m. Stone bowl, Khirokitia (6th-millennium B.C.) (*horiz*) .. .. .. 1·50 70
557 £1 Ivory plaque, Salamis (7th-century B.C.) 2·00 1·25
558 £2 "Leda and the Swan" (mosaic), Kouklia (3rd-century A.D.) .. .. .. 3·25 2·00
545/58 .. .. *Set of* 14 10·00 4·50

209 Cyprus Flag

210 Peace Dove and Head Silhouettes

1980 (1 Oct). *20th Anniv of Republic. T* **209** *and similar multicoloured designs. P* 13½ × 13 *(*125 *m.) or* 13 × 14 *(others).*

559 40 m. Type **209** 10 10
560 125 m. Signing Treaty of Establishment (41 × 29 *mm*) 15 15
561 175 m. Archbishop Makarios 30 25
559/61 .. .. *Set of* 3 50 45

1980 (29 Nov). *International Palestinian Solidarity Day. T* **210** *and similar horiz design showing Peace Dove and head silhouettes. W* **58** *(sideways). P* 13½ × 13.

562 40 m. grey and black 20 20
a. Horiz pair. Nos. 562/3 .. .. .. 55 55
563 125 m. grey and black 35 35

Nos. 562/3 were printed together, *se-tenant*, in horizontal pairs throughout the sheet.

211 Pulpit, Tripiotis Church, Nicosia

212 Folk-dancing

1980 (29 Nov). *Christmas. T* **211** *and similar vert designs. Multicoloured. W* **58**. *P* 13 × 14.

564 25 m. Type **211** 10 10
565 100 m. Holy Doors, Panayia Church, Paralimni (24 × 37 *mm*) 15 15
566 125 m. Pulpit, Ayios Lazaros Church, Larnaca 15 15
564/6 .. .. *Set of* 3 30 30

(Litho Harrison)

1981 (4 May). *Europa. Folklore. T* **212** *and similar vert design showing folk-dancing from paintings by T. Photiades. P* 14.

567 40 m. multicoloured 20 10
568 175 m. multicoloured 65 50

213 Self-portrait

214 *Ophrys kotschyi*

1981 (15 June). *500th Anniv of Leonardo da Vinci's Visit. T* **213** *and similar multicoloured designs. W* **58** *(sideways on* 125 *m.). P* 12 × 14 *(*125 *m.) or* 13½ × 14 *(others).*

569 50 m. Type **213** 20 10
570 125 m. "The Last Supper" (50 × 25 *mm*) .. 50 30
571 175 m. Cyprus lace and Milan Cathedral .. 70 50
569/71 .. .. *Set of* 3 1·25 80

(Des A. Tassos)

1981 (6 July). *Cypriot Wild Orchids. T* **214** *and similar vert designs. Multicoloured. W* **58**. *P* 13½ × 14.

572 25 m. Type **214** 35 25
a. Block of 4. Nos. 572/5 .. .. .. 1·60
573 50 m. *Orchis punctulata* 40 30
574 75 m. *Orphrys argolica elegans* 45 35
575 150 m. *Epipactis veratrifolia* 55 50
572/5 .. .. *Set of* 4 1·60 1·25

Nos. 572/5 were printed together, *se-tenant*, in blocks of 4 throughout the sheet.

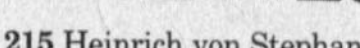

215 Heinrich von Stephan

216 "The Lady of the Angels" (from Church of the Transfiguration of Christ, Palekhori)

(Des A. Tassos (200 m.), A. Ioannides (others))

1981 (28 Sept). *Commemorations. T* **215** *and similar horiz designs. W* **58** *(sideways). P* 13½ × 13.

576 25 m. brown-olive, dp yellow-green & brt bl .. 10 10
577 40 m. multicoloured 15 10
578 125 m. black, vermilion and deep yellow-green 35 25
579 150 m. multicoloured 40 30
580 200 m. multicoloured 50 35
576/80 .. .. *Set of* 5 1·40 95

Designs and commemorations:—25 m. Type **215** (150th birth anniversary of Henrich von Stephan (founder of U.P.U.)); 40 m. Stylised man holding dish of food (World Food Day); 125 m. Stylised hands (International Year for Disabled Persons); 150 m. Stylised building and flower (European Campaign for Urban Renaissance); 200 m. Prince Charles, Lady Diana Spencer and St. Paul's Cathedral (Royal Wedding).

(Des A. Tassos)

1981 (16 Nov). *Christmas. Murals from Nicosia District Churches. T* **216** *and similar multicoloured designs. W* **58** *(sideways on* 25 *and* 125 *m.). P* 12½.

581 25 m. Type **216** 10 10
582 100 m. "Christ Pantokrator" (from Church of Madonna of Arakas, Lagoudera) (*vert*) 35 20
583 125 m. "Baptism of Christ" (from Church of Our Lady of Assinou, Nikitari) .. 45 30
581/3 .. .. *Set of* 3 80 50

217 "Louomene" (statue of Aphrodite bathing, 250 B.C.)

218 Naval Battle with Greek Fire

1982 (12 Apr). *Aphrodite (Greek goddess of love and beauty) Commemoration (2nd issue). T* **217** *and similar vert design. Multicoloured. W* **58**. *P* 13½ × 14.

584 125 m. Type **217** 50 30
585 175 m. "Anadyomene" (Aphrodite emerging from the waters) (Titian) 60 40

(Photo Harrison)

1982 (3 May). *Europa. Historic Events. T* **218** *and similar horiz design. Multicoloured. P* 12½.

586 40 m. Type **218** 20 10
587 175 m. Conversion of Roman Proconsul Sergius Paulus to Christianity, Paphos, 45 A.D. 65 75

100 =

219 Monogram of Christ (mosaic)

(220)

1982 (5 July). *World Cultural Heritage. T* **219** *and similar multicoloured designs. W* **58** *(sideways on* 50 *and* 225 *m.). P* 13½ × 14 *(*125 *m.) or* 12½ *(others).*

588 50 m. Type **219** 20 10
589 125 m. Head of priest-king of Paphos (sculpture) (24 × 37 *mm*) 40 30
590 225 m. Theseus (Greek god) (mosaic) .. 70 60
588/90 .. .. *Set of* 3 1·10 90

1982 (6 Sept). *No. 550 surch with T* **220** *by Govt Ptg Office, Nicosia.*

591 100 m. on 75 m. Funerary stele, Marion (5th-century B.C.) 30 20

221 Cyprus and Stylised "75"

222 Holy Communion—The Bread

(Des A. Tassos)

1982 (8 Nov). *75th Anniv of Boy Scout Movement. T* **221** *and similar multicoloured designs. W* **58** *(sideways on* 100 *m. and* 175 *m.). P* 12½ × 13½ *(*125 *m.) or* 13½ × 12½ *(others).*

592 100 m. Type **221** 40 20
593 125 m. Lord Baden-Powell (*vert*) 45 30
594 175 m. Camp-site 55 55
592/4 .. .. *Set of* 3 1·25 95

1982 (6 Dec). *Christmas. T* **222** *and similar designs. W* **58** *(sideways on* 25 *and* 250 *m.). P* 12½ × 12 *(*25 *and* 250 *m.) or* 13½ × 14 *(*100 *m.).*

595 25 m. multicoloured 10 10
596 100 m. gold and black 30 15
597 250 m. multicoloured 70 75
595/7 .. .. *Set of* 3 1·00 85

Designs: *Vert*—100 m. Holy Chalice. *Horiz*—250 m. Holy Communion—The Wine.

PRICES OF SETS

Set prices are given for many issues, generally those containing three stamps or more. Definitive sets include one of each value or major colour change, but do not cover different perforations, die types or minor shades. Where a choice is possible the set prices are based on the cheapest versions of the stamps included in the listings.

223 Cyprus Forest Industries' Sawmill

(Des A. Tassos)

1983 (14 Mar). *Commonwealth Day. T* **223** *and similar horiz designs. Multicoloured.* W **58** (*sideways*). *P* 14 × 13½.

598 50 m. Type **223** 10 10
599 125 m. "Ikarios and the Discovery of Wine" (3rd-cent mosaic) 25 25
600 150 m. Folk-dancers, Commonwealth Film and Television Festival, 1980 .. .. 30 35
601 175 m. Royal Exhibition Building, Melbourne (Commonwealth Heads of Government Meeting, 1981) 35 40
598/601 .. .. *Set of* 4 90 1·00

224 Cyprosyllabic Inscription (6th-cent B.C.)

225 Speckled Wood Argus

(Des G. Simonis. Photo Harrison)

1983 (3 May). *Europa. T* **224** *and similar horiz design. Multicoloured. P* 14½ × 14.

602 50 m. Type **224** 20 10
603 200 m. Copper ore, ingot (Enkomi 1400-1250 B.C.) and bronze jug (2nd-cent A.D.) .. 60 75

(Des A. Tassos)

1983 (28 June). *Butterflies. T* **225** *and similar horiz designs. Multicoloured.* W w **58**. *P* 12½.

604 60 m. Type **225** 20 20
605 130 m. Brown Argus 35 35
606 250 m. Azure Spirit of Paphos 85 85
604/6 .. .. *Set of* 3 1·25 1·25

(New Currency: 100 cents = £1 (Cyprus))

1c

=

(226)

227 View of Power Station

1983 (3 Oct). *Nos.* 545/56 *surch as T* **226** *by Govt Printing Office, Nicosia.*

607 1 c. on 10 m. Type **208** 15 15
608 2 c. on 15 m. Bronze cow, Vouni Palace (5th-century B.C.) 15 15
609 3 c. on 25 m. Amphora, Salamis (6th-century B.C.) 15 15
610 4 c. on 40 m. Gold finger-ring, Enkomi (13th-century B.C.) 20 15
611 5 c. on 50 m. Bronze cauldron, Salamis (8th-century B.C.) 20 20
612 6 c. on 75 m. Funerary stele, Marion (5th-century B.C.) 20 15
613 10 c. on 100 m. Jug (15–14th-century B.C.) .. 30 25
614 13 c. on 125 m. Warrior (Terracotta) (6–5th-century B.C.) 40 35
615 15 c. on 150 m. Lions attacking bull (bronze relief), Vouni Palace (5th-century B.C.) 50 40
616 20 c. on 200 m. Bronze statue of Ingot God, Enkomi (12th-century B.C.) 55 50
617 25 c. on 175 m. Faience rhyton, Kition (13th-century B.C.) 65 70
618 50 c. on 500 m. Stone bowl, Khirokitia (6th-millennium B.C.) .. .. 1·25 1·25
607/18 .. .. *Set of* 12 4·25 4·00

(Des A. Tassos)

1983 (27 Oct). *Anniversaries and Events. T* **227** *and similar vert designs. Multicoloured.* W **58**. *P* 13 × 14.

619 3 c. Type **227** 10 10
620 6 c. W.C.Y. logo 20 15
621 13 c. *Sol Olympia* (liner) and *Polys* (tanker) 40 30
622 15 c. Human Rights emblem and map of Europe 45 35
623 20 c. Nicos Kazantzakis (poet) 55 45
624 25 c. Archbishop Makarios in church 65 65
619/24 .. .. *Set of* 6 2·10 1·75

Commemorations:—3 c. 30th anniv of the Cyprus Electricity Authority; 6 c. World Communications Year; 13 c. 25th anniv of International Maritime Organization; 15 c. 35th anniv of Universal Declaration of Human Rights; 20 c. Birth centenary; 25 c. 70th birth anniv.

228 St. Lazaros Church, Larnaca

229 Waterside Cafe, Larnaca

(Des A. Tassos)

1983 (12 Dec). *Christmas. T* **228** *and similar vert designs. Multicoloured.* W **58**. *P* 12 × 13½.

625 4 c. Type **228** 10 10
626 13 c. St. Varvara Church, Kaimakli, Nicosia 30 35
627 20 c. St. Ioannis Church, Larnaca 50 60
625/7 .. .. *Set of* 3 80 90

(Litho Harrison)

1984 (6 Mar). *Old Engravings. T* **229** *and similar horiz designs. Each pale stone and black. P* 14½ × 14 (6 *c.*) *or* 14 (*others*).

628 6 c. Type **229** 15 10
629 20 c. Bazaar at Larnaca (30 × 25 *mm*) .. 50 55
630 30 c. Famagusta Gate, Nicosia (30 × 25 *mm*) 80 1·00
628/30 .. .. *Set of* 3 1·40 1·50
MS631 110 × 85 mm. 75 c. "The Confession" (St. Lazarus Church, Larnaca) .. .. .. 1·90 2·00

230 C.E.P.T. 25th Anniversary Logo

(Des J. Larrivière. Litho Harrison)

1984 (30 Apr). *Europa.* W **58**. *P* 12½.

632 **230** 6 c. apple-green, deep bl-green & blk .. 15 10
633 15 c. light blue, dull ultram & blk .. 40 55

A. Waddington ptgs (Nos. 634/*a*)

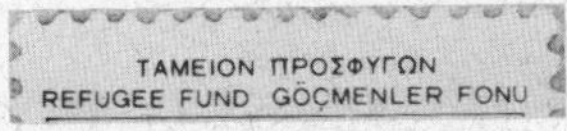

B. Aspioti-Elka ptg (No. 634*b*)

(Des A. Tassos)

1984 (18 June)–**88**. *Obligatory Tax. Refugee Fund. Design as T* **188** *but new value and* "1984" *date. P* 13 × 12½.

(*a*) *Litho J.W.* W **58**. *Chalk-surfaced cream paper*
634 1 c. grey-black (A) 10 10

(*b*) *Litho J.W. No wmk. Ordinary white paper*
634*a* 1 c. grey-black (A) (21.2.87)* 20 20

(*c*) *Litho Aspioti-Elka.* W **50**. *Chalk-surfaced cream paper*
634*b* 1 c. grey-black (B) (9.5.88)* 15 15

*Earliest known date of use.

In addition to the redrawn inscriptions there are other minor differences between the work of the two printers.

For a further version of this design, showing "1974" at top right, see Nos. 729 and 747.

231 Running

(Des. K. Haine. Litho Harrison)

1984 (18 June). *Olympic Games. Los Angeles. T* **231** *and similar horiz designs. Multicoloured.* W **58** (*sideways*). *P* 14.

635 3 c. Type **231** 10 10
636 4 c. Olympic column 10 10
637 13 c. Swimming 35 40
638 20 c. Gymnastics 50 60
635/8 .. .. *Set of* 4 90 1·00

232 Prisoners-of-War

233 Open Stamp Album (25th Anniv of Cyprus Philatelic Society)

(Des A. Tassos)

1984 (20 July). 10*th Anniv of Turkish Landings in Cyprus. T* **232** *and similar horiz design. Multicoloured. P* 14 × 13½.

639 15 c. Type **232** 40 45
640 20 c. Map and burning buildings 50 55

(Litho Harrison)

1984 (15 Oct). *Anniversaries and Events. T* **233** *and similar multicoloured designs.* W **58** (*sideways on horiz designs*). *P* 12½.

641 6 c. Type **233** 25 10
642 10 c. Football in motion (*horiz*) (50th anniv of Cyprus Football Association) 35 30
643 15 c. "Dr. George Papanicolaou" (medical scientist – birth cent) 55 55
644 25 c. Antique map of Cyprus and ikon (*horiz*) (International Symposia on Cartography and Medieval Paleography) .. .. 85 1·00
641/4 .. .. *Set of* 4 1·75 1·75

234 St. Mark (miniature from 11th-century Gospel)

235 Autumn at Platania, Troodos Mountains

(Litho Harrison)

1984 (26 Nov). *Christmas. Illuminated Gospels. T* **234** *and similar vert designs. Multicoloured.* W **58**. *P* 12½.

645 4 c. Type **234** 20 10
646 13 c. Beginning of St. Mark's Gospel 65 55
647 20 c. St. Luke (miniature from 11th-century Gospel) .. .. 1·00 1·10
645/7 .. .. *Set of* 3 1·75 1·60

(Litho Harrison)

1985 (18 Mar.) *Cyprus Scenes and Landscapes. T* **235** *and similar multicoloured designs. Ordinary white paper. P* 14 × 15 (6 *c.*, 20 *c.*, 25 *c.*, £1, £5) *or* 15 × 14 (*others*).

648 1 c. Type **235** 10 10
649 2 c. Ayia Napa Monastery 10 10
650 3 c. Phini Village—panoramic view 10 10
651 4 c. Kykko Monastery 10 10
652 5 c. Beach at Makronissos, Ayia Napa .. 10 15
653 6 c. Village street, Omodhos (*vert*) 15 20
654 10 c. Panoramic sea view 20 25
655 13 c. Windsurfing 30 35
656 15 c. Beach at Protaras 35 40
657 20 c. Forestry for development (*vert*) .. 45 50
658 25 c. Sunrise at Protaras (*vert*) 55 60
659 30 c. Village house, Pera 65 70
660 50 c. Apollo Hylates Sanctuary, Curium .. 1·10 1·25
661 £1 Snow on Troodos Mountains (*vert*) .. 2·25 2·40
662 £5 Personification of Autumn, House of Dionyssos, Paphos (*vert*) .. .. 11·00 11·50
648/62 .. .. *Set of* 15 16·00 17·00

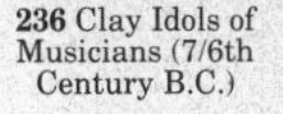

236 Clay Idols of Musicians (7/6th Century B.C.)

237 Cyprus Coat of Arms (25th Anniv of Republic)

(Litho Harrison)

1985 (6 May). *Europa. European Music Year. T* **236** *and similar horiz design. Multicoloured.* W **58** (*sideways*). *P* 12½.

663 6 c. Type **236** 55 10
664 15 c. Violin, lute, flute and score from the "Cyprus Suite" 95 70

(Des G. Simonis (4 c., 13 c.), Harrison (others). Litho Harrison)

1985 (23 Sept). *Anniversaries and Events. T* **237** *and similar designs. P* 14½ (4, 20 *c.*) *or* 14 × 13½ (*others*).

665 4 c. multicoloured 25 10
666 6 c. multicoloured 30 10
667 13 c. multicoloured 60 50
668 15 c. black, olive-black and yellow-orange .. 80 75
669 20 c. multicoloured .. .. 85 1·00
665/9 .. .. *Set of* 5 2·50 2·25

Designs: *Horiz* (43 × 30 *mm*)—6 c. "Barn of Liopetri" (detail) (Pol. Georghiou) (30th anniv of EOKA Campaign); 13 c. Three profiles (International Youth Year); 15 c. Solon Michaelides (composer and conductor) (European Music Year). *Vert* (*as T* **237**)—20 c. U.N. Building, New York, and flags (40th anniv of United Nations Organization).

238 "The Visit of the Madonna to Elizabeth" (Lambadistis Monastery, Kalopanayiotis)

239 Figure from Hellenistic Spoon Handle

(Litho Harrison)

1985 (18 Nov). *Christmas. Frescoes from Cypriot Churches. T* **238** *and similar vert designs. Multicoloured. P* 12½.

670 4 c. Type **238** 20 10
671 13 c. "The Nativity" (Lambadistis Monastery, Kalopanayiotis) 85 45
672 20 c. "Candlemas-day" (Asinou Church) .. 1·10 80
670/2 .. .. *Set of* 3 2·00 1·25

(Des A. Ioannides. Litho Harrison)

1986 (17 Feb). *New Archaeological Museum Fund. T* **239** *and similar horiz designs. Multicoloured. P* 15 × 14.

673 15 c. Type **239**.. .. .. 70 45
674 20 c. Pattern from early Ionian helmet and foot from statue.. .. .. .. 90 70
675 25 c. Roman statue of Eros and Psyche .. 1·00 85
676 30 c. Head of statue .. .. 1·25 95
673/6 .. .. *Set of* 4 3·50 2·75
MS677 111 × 90 mm. Nos. 673/6 (*sold at* £1) .. 3·75 4·25

Two-thirds of the amount received from sales of Nos. 673/7 was devoted to the construction of a new Archaeological Museum, Nicosia.

No. 676 also commemorates the 50th anniversary of the Department of Antiquities.

240 Cyprus Moufflon and Cedars

(Des G. Simonis)

1986 (28 Apr). *Europa. Protection of Nature and the Environment. T* **240** *and similar horiz design. Multicoloured. W* **58** *(sideways). P* 14 × 13.

678 7 c. Type **240**.. .. .. 60 15
679 17 c. Greater Flamingos at Larnaca Salt Lake .. .. 1·50 1·25

241 *Chlamys pesfelis*

7c

(242)

(Des T. Katsoulides)

1986 (1 July). *Sea Shells. T* **241** *and similar horiz designs. Multicoloured. W* **58** *(sideways). P* 14 × 13½.

680 5 c. Type **241**.. .. .. 20 10
681 7 c. *Charonia variegata* 25 10
682 18 c. *Murex brandaris* 60 60
683 25 c. *Cypraea spurca* 85 85
680/3 .. .. *Set of* 4 1·75 1·50

1986 (13 Oct). *Nos.* 653 *and* 655 *surch as T* **242**.

684 7 c. on 6 c. Village street, Omodhos (*vert*) .. 25 20
685 18 c. on 13 c. Windsurfing 55 45

For 15 c. on 4 c. see No. 730.

243 Globe, Outline Map of Cyprus and Swallows (Overseas Cypriots' Year)

(Des T. Katsoulides)

1986 (13 Oct). *Anniversaries and Events. T* **243** *and similar horiz designs. Multicoloured. W* **58** *(sideways). P* 13½ × 13.

686 15 c. Type **243**.. .. .. 75 45
687 18 c. Halley's Comet over Cyprus beach (40 × 23 *mm*) .. .. 1·00 1·00
a. Horiz pair. Nos. 687/8 .. .. .. 2·00 2·00
688 18 c. Comet's tail over sea and Edmond Halley (40 × 23 *mm*) .. .. 1·00 1·00
686/8 .. .. *Set of* 3 2·50 2·25

Nos. 687/8 were printed together, *se-tenant*, in horizontal pairs throughout the sheet, each pair forming a composite design.

244 Pedestrian Crossing

245 "The Nativity" (Church of Panayia tou Araka)

(Des A. Ioannides)

1986 (10 Nov). *Road Safety Campaign. T* **244** *and similar horiz designs. Multicoloured. W* **58** *(sideways). P* 14 × 13.

689 5 c. Type **244**.. .. .. 55 20
690 7 c. Motor cycle crash helmet 55 20
691 18 c. Hands fastening car seat belt .. .. 1·40 1·40
689/91 .. .. *Set of* 3 2·25 1·60

(Des G. Simonis)

1986 (24 Nov). *Christmas. International Peace Year. T* **245** *and similar vert designs showing details of Nativity frescoes from Cypriot churches. Multicoloured. W* **58** *(inverted). P* 13½ × 14.

692 5 c. Type **245**.. .. .. 25 15
693 15 c. Church of Panayia tou Moutoulla .. 75 70
694 17 c. Church of St. Nicholas tis Steyis .. 90 80
692/4 .. .. *Set of* 3 1·75 1·50

246 Church of Virgin Mary, Asinou

(Photo Harrison)

1987 (22 Apr). *Troodos Churches on the World Heritage List. T* **246** *and similar horiz designs. Multicoloured. P* 12½.
695 15 c. Type **246** 65 65
a. Sheetlet. Nos. 695/703 . . . . . . 5·50
696 15 c. Fresco of Virgin Mary, Moutoulla's Church 65 65
697 15 c. Church of Virgin Mary, Podithou . . 65 65
698 15 c. Fresco of Three Apostles, St. Ioannis Lampadistis Monastery 65 65
699 15 c. Annunciation fresco, Church of the Holy Cross, Pelentriou 65 65
700 15 c. Fresco of Saints, Church of the Cross, Ayiasmati 65 65
701 15 c. Fresco of Archangel Michael and Donor, Pedoula's Church of St. Michael 65 65
702 15 c. Church of St. Nicolaos, Steyis 65 65
703 15 c. Fresco of Prophets, Church of Virgin Mary, Araka 65 65
695/703 . . . . *Set of* 9 5·50 5·50
Nos. 695/703 were printed together, *se-tenant*, in sheetlets of nine.

247 Proposed Central Bank of Cyprus Building

(Des G. Simonis)

1987 (11 May). *Europa. Modern Architecture. T* **247** *and similar horiz design. W* **58** *(sideways). P* 14×13½.
704 7 c. multicoloured 40 10
705 18 c. black, brownish grey and sage-green . . 85 80
Design:—18 c. Headquarters complex, Cyprus Telecommunications Authority.

248 Remains of Ancient Ship and Kyrenia Castle

(Des Y. Pantzopoulow)

1987 (3 Oct). *Voyage of "Kyrenia II" (replica of ancient ship). T* **248** *and similar horiz designs. Multicoloured. W* **58** *(sideways). P* 14×13½.
706 2 c. Type **248** 15 15
707 3 c. *Kyrenia II* under construction, 1982–5 15 15
708 5 c. *Kyrenia II* at Paphos, 1986 . . . . 25 20
709 17 c. *Kyrenia II* at New York, 1986 . . . . 60 65
706/9 . . . . *Set of* 4 1·00 1·00

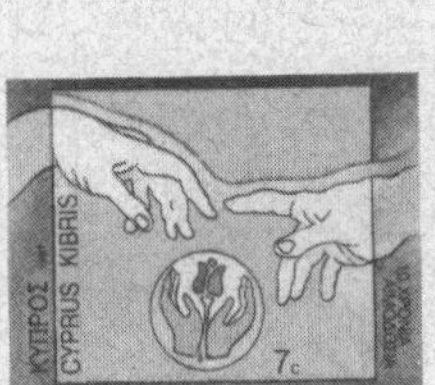

249 Hands (from Michelangelo's *Creation*) and Emblem (10th anniv of Blood Donation Co-ordinating Committee)

250 Nativity Crib

(Des A. Ioannides)

1987 (2 Nov). *Anniversaries and Events. T* **249** *and similar horiz designs. Multicoloured. W* **58** *(sideways). P* 14×13½.
710 7 c. Type **249** 35 25
711 15 c. Snail with flowered shell and countryside (European Countryside Campaign) 70 60
712 20 c. Symbols of ocean bed and Earth's crust ("Troodos '87" Ophiolites and Oceanic Lithosphere Symposium) 90 70
710/12 . . . . *Set of* 3 1·75 1·40

(Des A. Ioannides)

1987 (30 Nov). *Christmas. Traditional Customs. T* **250** *and similar square designs. Multicoloured. W* **58** *(sideways). P* 14.
713 5 c. Type **250** 15 15
714 15 c. Door knocker decorated with foliage . . 50 60
715 17 c. Bowl of fruit and nuts 55 75
713/15 . . . . *Set of* 3 1·10 1·40

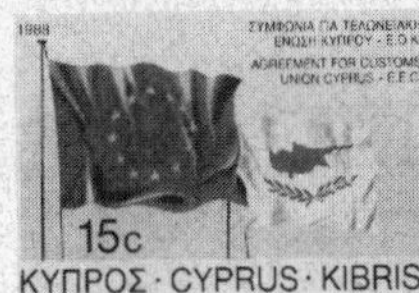

251 Flags of Cyprus and E.E.C.

(Des G. Simonis. Litho Alexandros Matsoukis, Athens)

1988 (11 Jan). *Cypriot–E.E.C. Customs Union. T* **251** *and similar horiz design. Multicoloured. W* **58**. *P* 13×13½.
716 15 c. Type **251** 40 50
717 18 c. Outline maps of Cyprus and E.E.C. countries 50 60

252 Intelpost Telefax Terminal

(Des A. Ioannides. Litho Alexandros Matsoukis, Athens)

1988 (9 May). *Europa. Transport and Communications. T* **252** *and similar horiz designs. Multicoloured. W* **58**. *P* 14×14½.
718 7 c. Type **252** 30 30
a. Horiz pair. Nos. 718/19 . . . . 60 60
719 7 c. Car driver using mobile telephone . . 30 30
720 18 c. Nose of Cyprus Airways airliner and flamingos 65 65
a. Horiz pair. Nos. 720/1 . . . . 1·25 1·25
721 18 c. Airliner in flight and flamingos . . 65 65
718/21 . . . . *Set of* 4 1·75 1·75
The two designs of each value were printed together, *se-tenant*, in horizontal pairs throughout the sheets of ten.

253 Sailing

254 Conference Emblem

(Des A. Ioannides. Photo Courvoisier)

1988 (27 June). *Olympic Games, Seoul. T* **253** *and similar vert designs. Multicoloured. Granite paper. P* 12.
722 5 c. Type **253** 15 15
723 7 c. Athletes at start 20 30
724 10 c. Shooting 25 35
725 20 c. Judo 50 70
722/5 . . . . *Set of* 4 1·00 1·40

(Des A. Ioannides. Litho M. A. Moatsos, Athens)

1988 (5 Sept). *Non-Aligned Foreign Ministers' Conference, Nicosia. T* **254** *and similar horiz designs. W* **58** *(sideways). P* 14×13½.
726 1 c. black, pale blue and emerald 10 10
727 10 c. multicoloured 25 30
728 50 c. multicoloured . . . . . . 1·25 1·75
726/8 . . . . *Set of* 3 1·40 2·00
Designs:— 10 c. Emblem of Republic of Cyprus; 50 c. Nehru, Tito, Nasser and Makarios.

255 "Cyprus 74" (wood-engraving by A. Tassos)

256 "Presentation of Christ at the Temple" (Church of Holy Cross tou Agiasmati)

(Litho M. A. Moatsos, Athens)

1988 (12 Sept). *Obligatory Tax. Refugee Fund. Design as Nos. 634/b, but with upper and lower inscriptions redrawn and "1974" added as in T* **255**. *W* **58**. *Chalk-surfaced paper. P* 13×12½.
729 **255** 1 c. brownish black and brownish grey . . 15 15
For this design printed in photogravure and perforated 11½, see No. 747.

1988 (3 Oct). *No. 651 surch as T* **242**.
730 15 c. on 4 c. Kykko Monastery 35 40

(Adapted G. Simonis. Litho M. A. Moatsos, Athens)

1988 (28 Nov). *Christmas. T* **256** *and similar vert designs showing frescoes from Cypriot churches. Multicoloured. W* **58**. *P* 13½ × 14.
731 5 c. Type **256** 20 15
732 15 c. "Virgin and Child" (St. John Lampadistis Monastery) 50 50
733 17 c. "Adoration of the Magi" (St. John Lampadistis Monastery) 60 60
731/3 . . . . *Set of* 3 1·10 1·10

257 Human Rights Logo

258 Basketball

(Des G. Simonis. Litho M. A. Moatsos, Athens)

1988 (10 Dec). *40th Anniv of Universal Declaration of Human Rights. W* **58** *(inverted). P* 13½ × 14.
734 **257** 25 c. azure, dull violet-blue and cobalt . . 60 70

(Des A. Ioannides. Litho Alexandros Matsoukis, Athens)

1989 (10 Apr). *Third Small European States' Games, Nicosia. T* **258** *and similar horiz designs. Multicoloured. P* 13½.
735 1 c. Type **258** 10 15
736 5 c. Javelin 15 20
737 15 c. Wrestling 35 40
738 18 c. Athletics 45 50
735/8 . . . . *Set of* 4 95 1·10
MS739 109×80 mm. £1 Angel and laurel wreath (99×73 *mm*). Imperf . . . . . . 2·50 2·75

259 Lingri Stick Game

(Des S. Michael. Litho Alexandros Matsoukis, Athens)

1989 (8 May). *Europa. Children's Games. T* **259** *and similar horiz designs. Multicoloured. P* 13×13½.
740 7 c. Type **259** 20 25
a. Horiz pair. Nos. 740/1 . . . . 40 50
741 7 c. Ziziros 20 25
742 18 c. Sitsia 45 50
a. Horiz pair. Nos. 742/3 . . . . 90 1·00
743 18 c. Leapfrog 45 50
740/3 . . . . *Set of* 4 1·10 1·40
Nos. 740/1 and 742/3 were each printed together, *se-tenant*, in horizontal pairs throughout the sheets.

A

MACHINE LABELS. From 29 May 1989 gummed labels in the above design, ranging in value from 1 c. to £99.99, were available from machines at Eleftheria Square P.O., Nicosia ("001") and District P.O., Limassol ("002").

260 "Universal Man"

261 Stylized Human Figures

(Des A. Ioannides. Photo Courvoisier)

1989 (7 July). *Bicentenary of the French Revolution. Granite paper. P* 11½.
744 **260** 18 c. multicoloured 45 50

(Des A. Ioannides. Litho Alexandros Matsoukis, Athens)

1989 (4 Sept). *Centenary of Interparliamentary Union* (15 c.) *and 9th Non-Aligned Summit Conference, Belgrade* (30 c.). *T* **261** *and similar vert design. Multicoloured. P* 13½.
745 15 c. Type **261** 35 40
746 30 c. Conference logo 75 80

(Photo Courvoisier)

1989 (4 Sept). *Obligatory Tax. Refugee Fund. As T* **255**, *but inscr "1989". Granite paper. P* 11½.
747 **255** 1 c. brownish black and brownish grey . . 10 10

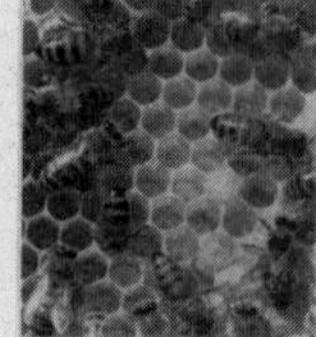
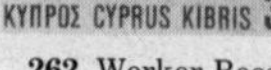

262 Worker Bees tending Larvae

263 Outstretched Hand and Profile (aid for Armenian earthquake victims)

(Litho Alexandros Matsoukis, Athens)

1989 (16 Oct). *Bee-keeping. T* **262** *and similar vert designs. Multicoloured. P* 13½×14.

748	3 c. Type **262**	.. ..	10	10
749	10 c. Bee on Rock-rose flower	.. ..	25	30
750	15 c. Bee on Lemon flower ..	.. ..	35	40
751	18 c. Queen and worker bees	.. ..	45	50
748/51	.. ..	*Set of* 4	1·00	1·10

(Des A. Ioannides. Litho Alexandros Matsoukis, Athens)

1989 (13 Nov). *Anniversaries and Events. T* **263** *and similar vert designs. Multicoloured. P* 13½×14.

752	3 c. Type **263**	.. ..	10	10
753	5 c. Airmail envelope (Cyprus Philatelic Society F.I.P. membership)	.. ..	15	20
754	7 c. Crab symbol and daisy (European Cancer Year) ..	.. .. ..	20	25
755	17 c. Vegetables and fish (World Food Day)		40	45
752/5	.. ..	*Set of* 4	80	90

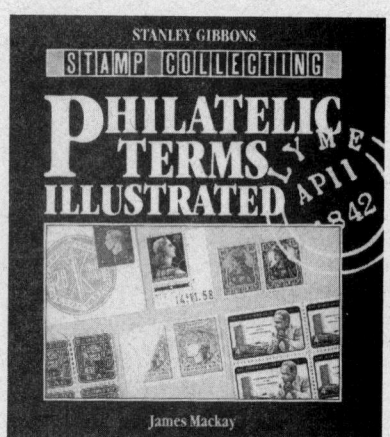

TURKISH CYPRIOT POSTS

After the inter-communal clashes during December 1963, a separate postal service was established on 6 January 1964 between some of the Turkish Cypriot areas, using handstamps inscribed "KIBRIS TURK POSTALARI". During 1964, however, an agreement was reached between representatives of the two communities for the restoration of postal services. This agreement, to which the United Nations representatives were a party, was ratified in November 1966 by the Republic's Council of Ministers. Under the scheme postal services were provided for the Turkish Cypriot communities in Famagusta, Larnaca, Limassol, Lefka, Nicosia and Paphos staffed by Turkish Cypriot employees of the Cypriot Department of Posts.

On 8 April 1970 5 m. and 15 m. locally-produced labels, originally designated "Social Aid Stamps", were issued by the Turkish Cypriot community and these can be found on commercial covers. These local stamps are outside the scope of this catalogue.

On 29 October 1973 Nos. 1/7 were placed on sale, but were used only on mail between the Turkish Cypriot areas.

Following the intervention by the Republic of Turkey on 20 July 1974 these stamps replaced issues of the Republic of Cyprus in that part of the island, north and east of the Attila Line, controlled by the Autonomous Turkish Cypriot Administration.

30M

1 50th Anniversary Emblem (2)

(Des F. Direkoglu Miss E. Ata and G. Pir. Litho Darbhane, Istanbul)

1974 (27 July*). *50th Anniv of Republic of Turkey. T 1 and similar designs in vermilion and black (15 m.) or multicoloured (others). P 12 × 11½ (vert) or 11½ × 12 (horiz).*

1 3 m. Woman sentry *(vert)* .. .. .. 30·00 30·00
2 5 m. Military Parade, Nicosia 60 40
3 10 m. Man and woman with Turkish flags *(vert)* 50 20
4 15 m. Type 1 .. .. 2·50 1·50
5 20 m. Atatürk statue, Kyrenia Gate, Nicosia *(vert)* 70 20
6 50 m. "The Fallen" *(vert)* .. .. .. 2·00 1·50
7 70 m. Turkish flag and map of Cyprus .. 16·00 16·00
1/7 .. .. *Set of* 7 48·00 48·00

*This is the date on which Nos. 1/7 became valid for international mail.

On 13 February 1975 a Turkish Cypriot Federated State was proclaimed in that part of Cyprus under Turkish occupation and later 9,000 Turkish Cypriots were transferred from the South to the North of the island.

1975 (3 Mar). *Proclamation of the Turkish Federated State of Cyprus. Nos. 3 and 5 surch as T 2.*

8 30 m. on 20 m. Atatürk statue, Kyrenia Gate, Nicosia .. .. 75 1·00
9 100 m. on 10 m. Man and woman with Turkish flags .. .. 1·50 2·25

On No. 9 the surcharge appears at the top of the stamp and the inscription at the bottom.

3 Namik Kemal's Bust, Famagusta

4 Map of Cyprus

(Des I. Özişik. Litho Güzel Sanatlar Matbaasi, Ankara)

1975 (21 Apr). *Multicoloured designs as T 3. Imprint at foot with date "1975". P 13.*

10 3 m. Type 3 .. .. 15 20
11 10 m. Atatürk Statue, Nicosia 15 10
12 15 m. St. Hilarion Castle 25 20
13 20 m. Atatürk Square, Nicosia 35 20
14 25 m. Famagusta Beach 35 25
15 30 m. Kyrenia Harbour 45 10
16 50 m. Lala Mustafa Pasha Mosque, Famagusta *(vert)* 60 10
17 100 m. Interior, Kyrenia Castle .. .. 1·25 75
18 250 m. Castle walls, Kyrenia .. .. 2·25 2·25
19 500 m. Othello Tower, Famagusta *(vert)* .. 4·50 4·00
10/19 .. .. *Set of* 10 9·50 7·00

See also Nos. 37/8.

(Des B. Erkmen (30 m.), S. Tuga (50 m.), N. Cüneş (150 m). Litho Ajans-Türk Matbassi, Ankara)

1975 (20 July). *"Peace in Cyprus". T 4 and similar multicoloured designs. P 13.*

20 30 m. Type 4 .. .. 50 15
21 50 m. Map, laurel and broken chain 65 20
22 150 m. Map and laurel-sprig on globe *(vert)* .. 1·90 1·00
20/2 .. .. *Set of* 3 2·75 1·25

5 "Pomegranates" (I. V. Guney)

(Litho Güzel Sanatlar Matbaasi, Ankara)

1975 (29 Dec). *Europa. Paintings. T 5 and similar horiz design. Multicoloured. P 13.*

23 90 m. Type 5 .. .. 80 60
24 100 m. "Harvest Time" (F. Direkoglu) 80 60

10 M ——

(6)

7 "Expectation"

1976 (28 Apr). *Nos. 16/17 surch as T 6 at Govt Printing House, Nicosia in horizontal clichés of 10.*

25 10 m. on 50 m. Lala Mustafa Pasha Mosque, Famagusta 50 70
26 30 m. on 100 m. Interior, Kyrenia Castle .. 50 80

(Litho Ajans-Türk Matbassi, Ankara)

1976 (3 May). *Europa. T 7 and similar vert design showing ceramic statuette. Multicoloured. P 13.*

27 60 m. Type 7 .. .. 30 40
28 120 m. "Man in Meditation" 40 50

8 Carob

9 Olympic Symbol "Flower"

(Des S. Atlihan. Litho Güzel Sanatlar Matbaasi, Ankara)

1976 (28 June). *Export Products—Fruits. T 8 and similar horiz designs. Multicoloured. P 13.*

29 10 m. Type 8 .. .. 15 10
30 25 m. Mandarin 25 10
31 40 m. Strawberry 30 10
32 60 m. Orange 40 15
33 80 m. Lemon 50 70
29/33 .. .. *Set of* 5 1·40 95

(Des C. Mutver (60 m.), A. B. Kocamanoglu (100 m.). Litho Güzel Sanatlar Matbaasi, Ankara)

1976 (17 July). *Olympic Games. Montreal. T 9 and similar horiz design. Multicoloured. P 13.*

34 60 m. Type 9 .. .. 25 20
35 100 m. Olympic symbol and doves 35 25

10 Kyrenia Harbour

11 Liberation Monument, Karaeglanoglu (Ay. Georghios)

(Des I. Özişik. Litho Ajans-Türk Matbassi, Ankara)

1976 (2 Aug). *New design (5 m.) or as Nos. 12/13 but redrawn with lettering altered and new imprint at foot with date "1976". P 13.*

36 5 m. Type 10 .. .. 30 10
37 15 m. St. Hilarion Castle 30 10
38 20 m. Atatürk Square, Nicosia 30 10
36/8 .. .. *Set of* 3 80 25

Nos. 39/46 vacant.

(Des D. Erimez and C. Gizer. Litho Ajans-Türk Matbassi, Ankara)

1976 (1 Nov). *Liberation Monument. T 11 and similar vert design. P 13.*

47 11 30 m. lt turquoise-blue, lt flesh & black 15 20
48 – 150 m. light verm, light flesh & blk 35 45

No. 48 shows a different view of the Monument.

12 Hotel, Salamis Bay

(Litho Türk Tarih Kurumu Basimevi, Ankara)

1977 (2 May). *Europa. T 12 and similar horiz design. Multicoloured. P 13.*

49 80 m. Type 12 .. .. 30 65
50 100 m. Kyrenia Port 35 65

13 Pottery

14 Arap Ahmet Pasha Mosque, Nicosia

(Litho Güzel Sanatlar Matbaasi, Ankara)

1977 (27 June). *Handicrafts. T 13 and similar designs. Multicoloured. P 13.*

51 15 m. Type 13 .. .. 10 10
52 30 m. Decorated gourds *(vert)* 10 10
53 125 m. Basketware 30 50
51/3 .. .. *Set of* 3 40 65

(Litho APA Ofset Basimevi, Istanbul)

1977 (2 Dec). *Turkish Buildings in Cyprus. T 14 and similar horiz designs. Multicoloured. P 13.*

54 20 m. Type 14 .. .. 10 10
55 40 m. Paphos Castle 10 10
56 70 m. Bekir Pasha aqueduct 15 20
57 80 m. Sultan Mahmut library 15 25
54/7 .. .. *Set of* 4 45 60

15 Namik Kemal (bust) and House, Famagusta

16 Old Man and Woman

(Des B. Ozak. Litho Ticaret Matbaacilik TAS, Izmir)

1977 (21 Dec). *Namik Kemal (patriotic poet). T 15 and similar multicoloured design. P 12½ × 13 (30 m.) or 13 × 12½ (140 m.)*

58 30 m. Type 15 .. .. 15 15
59 140 m. Namik Kemal (portrait) *(vert)* 35 50

(New Currency. 100 kurus = 1 lira)

(Des G. Pir. Litho Ajans-Türk Matbassi, Ankara)

1978 (17 Apr). *Social Security. T 16 and similar vert designs. P 13 × 13½.*

60 150 k. black, yellow and blue 10 10
61 275 k. black, red-orange and green 15 15
62 375 k. black, blue and red-orange 25 20
60/2 .. .. *Set of* 3 45 40

Designs:—275 k. Injured man with crutch; 375 k. Woman with family.

17 Oratory in Büyük Han, Nicosia

18 Motorway Junction

(Des I. Özisik. Litho APA Ofset Basimevi, Istanbul)

1978 (2 May). *Europa. T 17 and similar horiz design. Multicoloured. P 13.*

63 225 k. Type 17 .. .. 30 20
64 450 k. Cistern in Selimiye Mosque, Nicosia .. 45 35

(Litho APA Ofset Basimevi, Istanbul)

1978 (10 July). *Communications. T 18 and similar horiz designs. Multicoloured. P 13.*

65 75 k. Type 18 .. .. 10 10
66 100 k. Hydrofoil 10 10
67 650 k. Boeing "720" at Ercan Airport 25 25
65/7 .. .. *Set of* 3 35 35

19 Dove with Laurel Branch

20 Kemal Atatürk

(Des E. Kaya (725 k.), C. Kirkbesoglu (others). Litho APA Ofset Basimevi, Istanbul)

1978 (13 Sept). *National Oath. T* **19** *and similar designs. P* 13.
68 150 k. orange-yellow, violet and black 10 10
69 225 k. black, Indian red and orange-yellow .. 10 10
70 725 k. black, cobalt and orange-yellow .. 20 20
68/70 .. .. *Set of* 3 35 35
Designs: *Vert*—225 k. "Taking the Oath". *Horiz*—725 k. Symbolic dove.

(Des C. Mutver. Litho Türk Tarih Kurumu Basimevi, Ankara)

1978 (10 Nov). *Kemal Atatürk Commemoration. P* 13.
71 **20** 75 k. pale turquoise-grn & turq-grn .. 10 10
72 450 k. pale flesh and light brown .. 15 15
73 650 k. pale blue and light blue 20 25
71/3 .. .. *Set of* 3 40 40

50 Krs.
xxxxx

(21)

22 Gun Barrel with Olive Branch and Map of Cyprus

1979 (4 June). *Nos.* 30/3 *surch as T* **21**, *by Govt Printing Office, Lefkosa*
74 50 k. on 25 m. Mandarin 10 10
75 1 l. on 40 m. Strawberry 10 10
76 3 l. on 60 m. Orange 10 10
77 5 l. on 80 m. Lemon 20 15
74/7 .. .. *Set of* 4 35 25

(Des N. Dündar. Litho Ajans-Türk Matbassi, Ankara)

1979 (20 July). *5th Anniv of Turkish Peace Operation in Cyprus. Sheet* 72 × 52 *mm. Imperf.*
MS78 **22** 15 l. black, deep turquoise-blue and pale green .. .. 1·00 1·25

23 Postage Stamp and Map of Cyprus

24 Symbolised Microwave Antenna

(Des S. Mumcu. Litho Ajans-Türk Matbassi, Ankara)

1979 (20 Aug). *Europa. Communications. T* **23** *and similar horiz designs. Multicoloured. P* 13.
79 2 l. Type **23** 10 10
80 3 l. Postage stamps, building and map .. 10 10
81 8 l. Telephones, Earth and satellite 20 30
79/81 .. .. *Set of* 3 35 45

(Litho Ticaret Matbaacilik TAS, Izmir)

1979 (24 Sept). *50th Anniv of International Consultative Radio Committee. P* 13 × 12½.
82 **24** 2 l. multicoloured 15 10
83 5 l. multicoloured 15 10
84 6 l. multicoloured 20 15
82/4 .. .. *Set of* 3 45 30

25 School Children

26 Lala Mustafa Pasha Mosque, Magusa

(Des H. Hastürk (1½ l.), G. Akansel (4½ l.), P. Yalyali (6 l.). Litho APA Ofset Basimevi, Istanbul)

1979 (29 Oct). *International Year of the Child. Children's Drawings. T* **25** *and similar multicoloured designs. P* 13.
85 1½ l. Type **25** 15 15
86 4½ l. Children and globe (*horiz*) 25 20
87 6 l. College children 30 20
85/7 .. .. *Set of* 3 65 50

(Des S. Mumcu (20 l.), I. Ozisik (others). Litho Ajans-Türk Matbassi, Ankara)

1980 (23 Mar). *Islamic Commemorations. T* **26** *and similar vert designs. Multicoloured. P* 13.
88 2½ l. Type **26** 10 10
89 10 l. Arap Ahmet Pasha Mosque, Lefkosa .. 25 15
90 20 l. Mecca and Medina 35 20
88/90 .. .. *Set of* 3 65 40
Commemorations:—2½ l. 1st Islamic Conference in Turkish Cyprus; 10 l. General Assembly of World Islam Congress; 20 l. Moslem Year 1400AH.

27 Ebu-Su'ud Efendi (philosopher)

28 Omer's Shrine, Kyrenia

(Litho Ajans-Türk Matbassi, Ankara)

1980 (23 May). *Europa. Personalities. T* **27** *and similar vert. design. Multicoloured. P* 13.
91 5 l. Type **27** 15 10
92 30 l. Sultan Selim II 60 40

(Litho Guzel Sanatlar Matbaasi, Ankara)

1980 (25 June). *Ancient Monuments, T* **28** *and similar horiz designs. P* 13.
93 2½ l. new blue and stone 10 10
94 3½ l. grey-green and pale rose-pink 10 10
95 5 l. lake and pale blue-green 10 10
96 10 l. deep mauve and pale green 20 10
97 20 l. dull ultramarine & pale greenish yellow 35 25
93/7 .. .. *Set of* 5 65 45
Designs:—3½ l. Entrance gate, Famagusta; 5 l. Funerary monuments (16th-century), Famagusta; 10 l. Bella Paise Abbey, Kyrenia; 20 l. Selimiye Mosque, Nicosia.

29 Cyprus 1880 6d.

30 Dome of the Rock

31 Extract from World Muslim Congress Statement in Turkish

(Des S. Mumcu. Litho Ajans-Türk Matbassi, Ankara)

1980 (16 Aug). *Cyprus Stamp Centenary. T* **29** *and similar designs showing stamps. P* 14.
98 7½ l. black, drab and grey-olive 10 10
99 15 l. brown, grey-blue and blue 15 15
100 50 l. black, rose and grey 50 55
98/100 .. .. *Set of* 3 65 70
Designs: *Horiz*:—15 l. Cyprus 1960 Constitution of the Republic 30 m. commemorative. *Vert*—50 l. Social Aid local, 1970.

(Litho Guzel Sanatlar Matbaasi, Ankara)

1980 (16 Oct). *Palestinian Solidarity. T* **30** *and similar multicoloured design. P* 13.
101 15 l. Type **30** 25 15
102 35 l. Dome of the Rock (*horiz*) 65 30

(Des S. Mumcu. Litho Turk Tarih Kurumu Basimevi, Ankara)

1981 (24 Mar). *Solidarity with Islamic Countries Day. T* **31** *and similar vert design showing extract from World Muslim Congress statement. P* 13.
103 1 l. rosine, stone and olive-sepia 15 15
104 35 l. black, pale blue-green and myrtle-green 55 40
Design:—35 l. Extract in English

32 "Atatürk" (F. Duran)

33 Folk-dancing

(Litho Ajans-Türk Matbassi, Ankara)

1981 (19 May). *Atatürk Stamp Exhibition, Lefkosa. P* 13.
105 **32** 20 l. multicoloured 25 35
No. 105 was printed in sheets of 100, including 50 *se-tenant* stamp-size labels.

(Litho Ticaret Matbaacilik TAS, Izmir)

1981 (29 June). *Europa, Folklore. T* **33** *and similar horiz design showing folk-dancing. P* 12½ × 13.
106 10 l. multicoloured 35 15
107 30 l. multicoloured 60 35

MINIMUM PRICE

The minimum price quote is 10p which represents a handling charge rather than a basis for valuing common stamps. For further notes about prices see introductory pages.

34 "Kemal Atatürk" (I. Calli)

35 Wild Convolvulus

(Litho Basim Ofset, Ankara)

1981 (23 July). *Birth Centenary of Kemal Atatürk. Sheet* 70 × 95 *mm. Imperf.*
MS108 **34** 150 l. multicoloured .. .. 1·10 1·25

(Litho Turk Tarih Kurumu Basimevi, Ankara)

1981 (28 Sept)–**82**. *Flowers, Multicoloured designs as T* **35**. *P* 13.
109 1 l. Type **35** 10 10
110 5 l. Persian Cyclamen (*horiz*) (22.1.82) .. 10 10
111 10 l. Spring Mandrake (*horiz*) 10 10
112 25 l. Corn Poppy 10 10
113 30 l. Wild Arum (22.1.82) 15 10
114 50 l. Sage-leaved Rock Rose (*horiz*) (22.1.82) 30 15
115 100 l. *Cistus salviaefolius L.* (22.1.82) .. 60 20
116 150 l. Giant Fennel (*horiz*) .. .. .. 1·10 70
109/16 .. .. *Set of* 8 2·25 1·25

36 Stylized Disabled Person in Wheelchair

37 Turkish and Palestinian Flags

(Des H. Ulucam (7½ l.), N. Kozal (others). Litho Türk Tarih Kurumu Basimevi, Ankara)

1981 (16 Oct). *Commemorations. T* **36** *and similar multicoloured designs. P* 13.
117 7½ l. Type **36** 20 20
118 10 l. Heads of people of different races, peace dove and barbed wire (*vert*) 30 35
119 20 l. People of different races reaching out from globe, with dishes (*vert*) 40 50
117/19 .. .. *Set of* 3 80 95
Commemorations:—7½ l. International Year for Disabled Persons; 10 l. Anti-apartheid Publicity; 20 l. World Food Day.

(Des H. Ulucam. Litho Türk Tarih Kurumu Basimevi, Ankara)

1981 (29 Nov). *Palestinian Solidarity. P* 13.
120 **37** 10 l. multicoloured 25 20

38 Prince Charles and Lady Diana Spencer

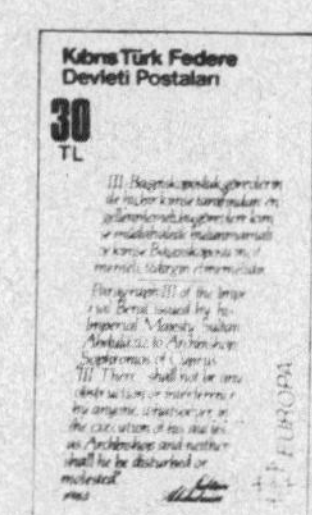

39 Charter issued by Sultan Abdul Aziz to Archbishop Sophronios

(Des H. Ulucam. Litho Türk Tarih Kurumu Basimevi, Ankara)

1981 (30 Nov). *Royal Wedding. P* 13
121 **38** 50 l. multicoloured .. .. 1·00 65

(Des H. Ulucam, Litho Tezel Ofset, Lefkosa)

1982 (30 July). *Europa (CEPT). Sheet* 83 × 124 *mm containing T* **39** *and similar vert design. Multicoloured. P* 12½ × 13.
MS122 30 l. × 2. Type **39**; 70 l. × 2, Turkish forces landing at Tuzla, 1571 .. .. 2·25 1·75

40 Buffavento Castle

41 "Wedding" (A. Örek)

(Des H. Ulucam (Nos. 123/5). Litho Tezel Ofset, Lefkosa)

1982 (20 Aug). *Tourism. T* **40** *and similar multicoloured designs. P* 12.

123 5 l. Type **40** 10 10
124 10 l. Windsurfing (*horiz*) 10 10
125 15 l. Kantara Castle (*horiz*) 15 10
126 30 l. Shipwreck (300 B.C.) (*horiz*) 30 30
123/6 .. .. *Set of* 4 55 50

(Litho Ajans-Türk Matbassi, Ankara)

1982 (3 Dec). *Paintings* (1*st series*). *T* 41 *and similar multi-coloured design. P* 13.

127 30 l. Type **41** 15 25
128 50 l. "Carob Pickers" (O. Naxim Selenge) (*vert*) 30 40

See also Nos. 132/3, 157/8, 176/7, 185/6, 208/9, 225/7 and 248/50.

42 Cross of Lorraine, Koch and Bacillus (Cent of Koch's Discovery of Tubercle Bacillus)

43 "Calloused Hands" (Salih Oral)

(Des H. Ulucam. Litho Tezel Ofset, Lefkosa)

1982 (15 Dec.) *Anniversaries and Events. T* **42** *and similar multi-coloured designs. P* 12.

129 10 l. Type **42** 10 10
130 30 l. Spectrum on football pitch (World Cup Football Championships, Spain) .. 25 30
131 70 l. "75" and Lord Baden-Powell (75th anniv of Boy Scout movement and 125th birth anniv) (*vert*) 65 80
129/31 .. .. *Set of* 3 90 1·10

(Litho Ajans-Türk Matbassi, Ankara)

1983 (16 May). *Paintings* (2*nd series*). *T* 43 *and similar vert design. Multicoloured. P* 13.

132 30 l. Type **43** 40 40
133 35 l. "Malya—Limassol Bus" (Emin Cizenel) 40 40

44 Old Map of Cyprus by Piri Reis

45 First Turkish Cypriot 10 m. Stamp

(Litho Türk Tarih Kurumu Basimevi, Ankara)

1983 (30 June). *Europa. Sheet* 82 × 78 *mm, containing T* **44** *and similar horiz design. Multicoloured. P* 13.

MS134 100 l. Type **44**; 100 l. Cyprus as seen from "Skylab" .. .. 1·10 1·25

(Des E. Ata (15 l.), A. Hasan (20 l.), G. Pir (25 l.), H. Ulucam (others). Litho Ajans-Türk Matbassi, Ankara)

1983 (1 Aug). *Anniversaries and Events. T* **45** *and similar multi-coloured designs commemorating World Communications Year* (30, 50 *l*). *or* 25*th Anniv. of T.M.T.* (*Turkish Cypriot Resistance Organization*). *P* 13.

135 15 l. Type **45** 15 15
136 20 l. "Turkish Achievements in Cyprus" (*horiz*)) 20 20
137 25 l. "Liberation Fighters" 25 25
138 30 l. Dish aerial and telegraph pole (*horiz*) .. 30 30
139 50 l. Dove and envelopes (*horiz*) 55 55
135/9 .. .. *Set of* 5 1·25 1·25

46 European Bee Eater

Kuzey Kıbrıs
Türk Cumhuriyeti
15.11.1983

15

(47)

(Des E. Cizenel. Litho Ajans-Türks Matbassi, Ankara)

1983 (10 Oct). *Birds of Cyprus. T* **46** *and similar horiz designs. Multicoloured. P* 13.

140 10 l. Type **46** 30 30
a. Block of 4. Nos. 140/3 .. .. .. 1·90
141 15 l. Goldfinch 35 35
142 50 l. European Robin 70 70
143 65 l. Golden Oriole 75 75
140/3 .. .. *Set of* 4 1·90 1·90

Nos. 140/3 were printed together, *se-tenant*, in blocks of 4 throughout the sheet.

1983 (7 Dec). *Establishment of the Republic. Nos.* 109, 111/12 *and* 116 *surch as T* **47** (*No.* 145) *or optd only.*

144 10 l. *Mandragara officinarum* 10 10
145 15 l. on 1 l. Type **35** 10 10
a. Surch inverted .. .. 75·00
146 25 l. *Papaver rhoeas L* 15 20
147 150 l. *Ferula communis L* .. .. .. 75 1·25
144/7 .. .. *Set of* 4 90 1·40

48 C.E.P.T. 25th Anniversary Logo.

49 Olympic Flame

(Des J. Larrivière. Litho Tezel Ofset, Lefkosa)

1984 (30 May). *Europa. P* 12×12½.

148 **48** 50 l. lemon, chestnut and black .. 75 75
a. Pair. Nos. 148/9 .. .. .. 1·50 1·50
149 100 l. pale blue, bright blue and black 75 75

Nos. 148/9 were printed together, *se-tenant*, in horizontal and vertical pairs throughout the sheet.

(Des H. Ulucam. Litho Tezel Ofset, Lefkosa)

1984 (19 June). *Olympic Games, Los Angeles. T* **49** *and similar multicoloured designs. P* 12½ × 12 (10 *l.*) *or* 12 × 12½ (*others*).

150 10 l. Type **49** 10 10
151 20 l. Olympic events within rings (*horiz*) .. 10 10
152 70 l. Martial arts event (*horiz*) 25 40
150/2 .. .. *Set of* 3 35 55

50 Atatürk Cultural Centre

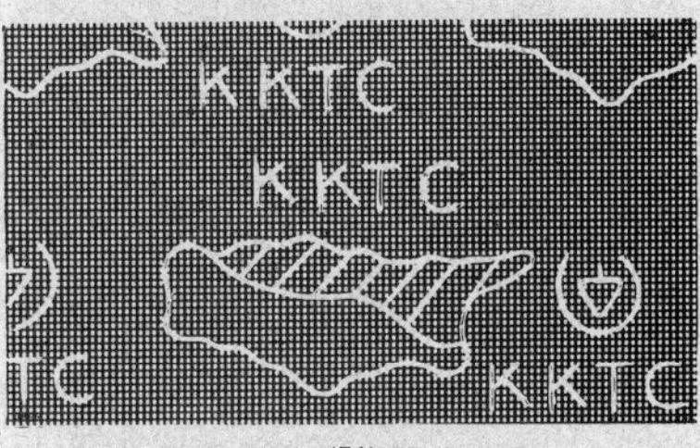

(51)

(Des H. Ulucam. Litho Tezel Ofset, Lefkosa)

1984 (20 July). *Opening of Atatürk Cultural Centre, Lefkosa. W* **51**. *P* 12 × 12½.

153 **50** 120 l. stone, black and chestnut .. 60 70

52 Turkish Cypriot Flag and Map

(Des C. Guzeloglu (20 l.), M. Gozbebek (70 l.). Litho Tezel Ofset Lefkosa)

1984 (20 July). 10*th Anniv of Turkish Landings in Cyprus. T* **52** *and similar horiz design. W* **51**. *Multicoloured. P* 12 × 12½.

154 20 l. Type **52** 20 15
155 70 l. Turkish Cypriot flag within book .. 50 60

53 Burnt and Replanted Forests

(Des H. Ulucam. Litho Tezel Ofset, Lefkosa)

1984 (20 Aug). *World Forestry Resources. W* **51**. *P* 12 × 12½.

156 **53** 90 l. multicoloured 70 75

ALTERED CATALOGUE NUMBERS

Any Catalogue numbers altered from the last edition are shown as a list in the introductory pages.

54 "Old Turkish Houses, Nicosia" (Cevdet Cagdas)

55 Kemal Atatürk, Flag and Crown

(Litho Tezel Ofset, Lefkosa)

1984 (21 Sept). *Paintings* (3*rd series*). *T* **54** *and similar horiz design. Multicoloured. W* **51**. *P* 13 × 12½.

157 20 l. Type **54** 15 15
158 70 l. "Scenery" (Olga Rauf) 35 50

See also Nos. 176/7, 185/6, 208/9, 225/7 and 248/50.

(Des H. Ulucam (20 l.), F. Isiman (70 l.). Litho Tezel Ofset, Lefkosa)

1984 (15 Nov). 1*st Anniv of Turkish Republic of Northern Cyprus. T* **55** *and similar multicoloured design. W* **51** (*sideways on* 20 *l., inverted on* 70 *l.*). *P* 12½.

159 20 l. Type **55** 10 10
160 70 l. Legislative Assembly voting for Republic (*horiz*) 25 40

56 Taekwondo Bout

57 "Le Regard" (Saulo Mercader)

(Des H. Ulucam. Litho Tezel Ofset, Lefkosa)

1984 (10 Dec). *International Taekwondo Championship, Girne. T* **56** *and similar horiz design. W* **51** (*sideways on* 10 *l.*). *P* 12½.

161 10 l. black, pale cinnamon and grey-black .. 15 10
162 70 l. multicoloured 55 60

Design:—70 l. Emblem and flags of competing nations.

(Litho Tezel Ofset, Lefkosa)

1984 (10 Dec). *Exhibition by Saulo Mercader* (*artist*). *T* **57** *and similar multicoloured design. W* **51** (*sideways on* 20 *l.*). *P* 12½ × 13 (20 *l.*) *or* 13 × 12½ (70 *l.*).

163 20 l. Type **57** 15 15
164 70 l. "L'equilibre de L'esprit (*horiz*) 50 60

58 Musical Instruments and Music

59 Dr. Fazil Kucuk (politician)

(Des H. Ulucam. Litho Tezel Ofset, Lefkosa)

1984 (10 Dec). *Visit of Nurnberg Chamber Orchestra. W* **51** (*sideways*). *P* 12½.

165 **58** 70 l. multicoloured 65 65

(Des Y. Calli (20 l.), E. Cizenel (70 l.). Litho Tezel Ofset, Lefkosa)

1985 (15 Jan). 1*st Death Anniv of Dr. Fazil Kucuk* (*politician*). *T* **59** *and similar vert design. Multicoloured. W* **51** (*inverted on* 70 *l.*).*P* 12½ × 12.

166 20 l. Type **59** 15 15
167 70 l. Dr. Fazil Kucuk reading newspaper .. 45 55

60 Goat

61 George Frederick Handel

(Des E. Cizenel. Litho Tezel Ofset, Lefkosa)

1985 (29 May). *Domestic Animals. T* **60** *and similar horiz designs. Multicoloured. W* **51**. *P* 12×12½.

168	100 l. Type **60**	35	20
169	200 l. Cow and calf	60	60
170	300 l. Ram	90	90
171	500 l. Donkey	1·50	1·75
168/71	*Set of* 4	3·00	3·00

(Litho Tezel Ofset, Lefkosa)

1985 (26 June). *Europa. Composers. T* **61** *and similar vert designs. W* **51** *(sideways). P* 12½×12.

172	20 l. brown-purple, myrtle-green & pale grn	55	55
	a. Block of 4. Nos. 172/5	2·75	
173	20 l. brown-purple, lake-brown & pale pink	55	55
174	100 l. brown-purple, steel blue & pale grey-bl	1·00	1·00
175	100 l. brown-purple, bistre-brown & pale cinn	1·00	1·00
172/5	*Set of* 4	2·75	2·75

Designs:—No. 172, Type **61**; 173, Guiseppe Domenico Scarlatti; 174, Johann Sebastian Bach; 175, Buhurizade Mustafa Itri Efendi.

Nos. 172/5 were printed together, *se-tenant*, in blocks of four throughout the sheet.

(Litho Tezel Ofset, Lefkosa)

1985 (15 Aug). *Paintings (4th series). Vert designs as T* **54**. *Multicoloured. W* **51**. *P* 12½×13.

176	20 l. "Village Life" (Ali Atakan)	20	15
177	50 l. "Woman carrying Water" (Ismet V. Güney)	55	65

62 Heads of Three Youths

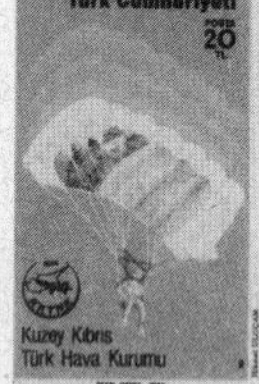

63 Parachutist (Aviation League)

(Des H. Uluçam. Litho Tezel Ofset, Lefkosa)

1985 (29 Oct). *International Youth Year. T* **62** *and similar horiz design. Multicoloured. W* **51** *(sideways). P* 12×12½.

178	20 l. Type **62**	20	15
179	100 l. Dove and globe	75	80

(Des H. Uluçam. Litho Tezel Ofset, Lefkosa)

1985 (29 Nov). *Anniversaries and Events. T* **63** *and similar designs. W* **51** *(inverted on Nos. 181/2, sideways on Nos. 183/4). P* 12×12½ *(Nos. 183/4) or* 12½×12 *(others).*

180	20 l. multicoloured	20	15
181	50 l. grey-black, light brown and dull ultramarine	45	40
182	100 l. light brown	80	80
183	100 l. multicoloured	80	80
184	100 l. multicoloured	80	80
180/4	*Set of* 5	2·75	2·75

Designs: *Vert*—No. 181, Louis Pasteur (Centenary of Discovery of Rabies vaccine); 182, İsmet İnönü (Turkish statesman) (birth centenary (1984)). *Horiz*—183, "40" in figures and symbolic flower (40th anniv of United Nations Organization); 184, Patient receiving blood transfusion (Prevention of Thalassaemia).

(Litho Tezel Ofset, Lefkosa)

1986 (20 June). *Paintings (5th series). Horiz designs as T* **54**. *Multicoloured. W* **51** *(sideways). P* 13×12½.

185	20 l. "House with Arches" (Gönen Atakol)	20	10
186	100 l. "Atatürk Square" (Yalkin Muhtaroğlu)	70	50

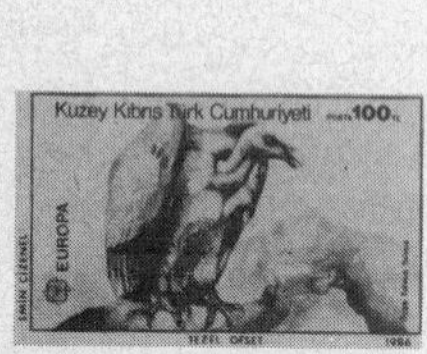

64 Griffon Vulture

65 Karagöz Show Puppets

(Des E. Çizenel (100 l.), H. Uluçam (200 l.). Litho Tezel Ofset, Lefkosa)

1986 (20 June). *Europa. Protection of Nature and the Environment. Sheet* 82×76 *mm. containing T* **64** *and similar horiz design. Multicoloured. W* **51** *(sideways). P* 12×12½.

MS187	100 l. Type **64**: 200 l. Litter on Cyprus landscape	1·25	1·40

(Des Y. Yazgin. Litho Tezel Ofset, Lefkosa)

1986 (25 July). *Karagöz Folk Puppets. W* **51** *(inverted). P* 12½×13.

188 **65**	100 l. multicoloured	75	40

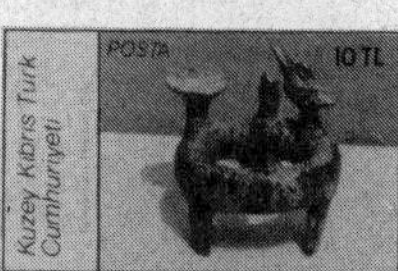

66 Old Bronze Age Composite Pottery

67 Soldiers, Defence Force Badge and Atatürk (10th anniv of Defence Forces)

(Litho Tezel Ofset, Lefkosa)

1986 (15 Sept). *Archaeological Artifacts. Cultural Links with Anatolia. T* **66** *and similar multicoloured designs. W* **51** *(sideways on* 10, 50 *l., inverted on* 20, 100 *l.). P* 12×12½ (10, 50 *l.*) *or* 12½×12 (20, 100 *l.*).

189	10 l. Type **66**	15	10
190	20 l. Late Bronze Age bird jug (*vert*)	20	10
191	50 l. Neolithic earthenware pot	35	20
192	100 l. Roman statue of Artemis (*vert*)	60	45
189/92	*Set of* 4	1·10	75

(Des. H. Uluçam (No. 196). Litho Tezel Ofset, Lefkosa)

1986 (13 Oct). *Anniversaries and Events. T* **67** *and similar multicoloured designs. W* **51** *(inverted on* 20, 50 *l., sideways on others). P* 12½×12 *(vert) or* 12×12½ *(horiz).*

193	20 l. Type **67**	20	10
194	50 l. Woman and two children (40th anniv of Food and Agriculture Organization)	35	25
195	100 l. Football and world map (World Cup Football Championship, Mexico) (*horiz*)	70	45
196	100 l. Orbit of Halley's Comet and *Giotto* spacecraft (*horiz*)	70	45
193/6	*Set of* 4	1·75	1·10

68 Güzelyurt Dam and Power Station

69 Prince Andrew and Miss Sarah Ferguson

(Litho Tezel Ofset, Lefkosa)

1986 (17 Nov). *Modern Development (1st series). T* **68** *and similar horiz designs. Multicoloured. W* **51** *(sideways). P* 12×12½.

197	20 l. Type **68**	25	15
198	50 l. Low cost housing project, Lefkosa	40	25
199	100 l. Kyrenia Airport	75	50
197/9	*Set of* 3	1·25	80

See also Nos. 223/4 and 258/63.

(Litho Tezel Ofset, Lefkosa)

1986 (20 Nov). *60th Birthday of Queen Elizabeth II and Royal Wedding. T* **69** *and similar vert design. Multicoloured. W* **51** *(inverted). P* 12½×13.

200	100 l. Type **69**	45	30
	a. Pair. Nos. 200/1	90	60
201	100 l. Queen Elizabeth II	45	30

Nos. 200/1 were printed together, *se-tenant*, in horizontal and vertical pairs throughout the sheet.

70 Locomotive No. 11 and Trakhoni Station

(Des H. Uluçam (50 l.). Litho Tezel Ofset, Lefkosa)

1986 (31 Dec). *Cyprus Railway. T* **70** *and similar horiz design. Multicoloured. W* **51** *(sideways). P* 12×12½.

202	50 l. Type **70**	50	35
203	100 l. Locomotive No. 1	90	90

Kuzey Kıbrıs Türk Cumhuriyeti

(71)

1987 (18 May). *Nos.* 94, 96/7 *and* 113 *optd as T* **71** *or surch also.*

204	10 l. deep mauve and pale green	10	10
205	15 l. on 3½ l. grey-green and pale rose-pink	10	10
206	20 l. dull ultramarine & pale greenish yellow	10	10
207	30 l. multicoloured	10	10
204/7	*Set of* 4	20	20

(Litho Tezel Ofset, Lefkosa)

1987 (27 May). *Paintings (6th issue). Vert designs as T* **54**. *Multicoloured. W* 51 *(inverted). P* 12½×13.

208	50 l. "Shepherd" (Feridun Işiman)	25	20
209	125 l. "Pear Woman" (Mehmet Uluhan)	50	45

72 Modern House (architect A. Vural Behaeddin)

73 Kneeling Folk Dancer

(Des H. Uluçam (50 l.). Litho Tezel Ofset, Lefkosa)

1987 (30 June). *Europa. Modern Architecture. T* **72** *and similar horiz design. Multicoloured. W* **51** *(sideways). P* 12×12½.

210	50 l. Type **72**	15	15
	a. Perf 12×imperf	15	15
	ab. Booklet pane. Nos. 210a/11a, each × 2	1·50	
211	200 l. Modern house (architect Necdet Turgay)	60	60
	a. Perf 12 × imperf	60	60

Nos. 210a and 211a come from 500 l. stamp booklets containing *se-tenant* pane No. 210ab.

(Des B. Ruhi. Litho Tezel Ofset, Lefkosa)

1987 (20 Aug). *Folk Dancers. T* **73** *and similar vert designs. Multicoloured. W* **51** *(inverted). P* 12½×12.

212	20 l. Type **73**	10	10
213	50 l. Standing male dancer	10	10
214	200 l. Standing female dancer	40	45
215	1000 l. Woman's headdress	2·00	2·10
212/15	*Set of* 4	2·40	2·50

74 Regimental Colour (1st Anniv of Infantry Regiment)

75 Ahmet Beliğ Pasha (Egyptian judge)

(Des H. Uluçam. Litho Tezel Ofset, Lefkosa)

1987 (30 Sept–2 Nov). *Anniversaries and Events. T* **74** *and similar multicoloured designs. W* **51** *(inverted on vert designs, sideways on horiz). P* 12½×12 *(vert) or* 12×12½ *(horiz).*

216	50 l. Type **74**	15	15
217	50 l. Pres. Denktash and Turgut Özal (1st anniv. of Turkish Prime Minister's visit) (*horiz*) (2.11)	15	15
218	200 l. Emblem and Crescent (5th Islamic Summit Conference, Kuwait)	55	55
219	200 l. Emblem and laurel leaves (Membership of Pharmaceutical Federation) (*horiz*)	55	55
216/19	*Set of* 4	1·25	1·25

(Des H. Uluçam. Litho Tezel Ofset, Lefkosa)

1987 (22 Oct). *Turkish Cypriot Personalities. T* **75** *and similar vert designs. W* **51** *(inverted). P* 12½×12.

220 **75**	50 l. brown and greenish yellow	15	15
221 –	50 l. multicoloured	15	15
222 –	125 l. multicoloured	35	35
220/2	*Set of* 3	60	60

Designs:—50 l. (No. 221) Mehmet Emin Pasha (Ottoman Grand Vizier); 125 l. Mehmet Kâmil Pasha (Ottoman Grand Vizier).

76 Tourist Hotel, Girne

77 *Piyale Pasha* (tug)

(Des A. Erduran. Litho Tezel Ofset, Lefkosa)

1987 (20 Nov). *Modern Development (2nd series). T* **76** *and similar horiz designs. Multicoloured. W* **51** *(sideways). P* 12×12½.

223	150 l. Type **76**	45	35
224	200 l. Dogu Akdeniz University	55	45

(Litho Tezel Ofset, Lefkosa)

1988 (2 May). *Paintings (7th issue). Multicoloured designs as* **T 54**. *W* **51** *(inverted on 20, 150 l, sideways on 50 l.). P* 12½×13 *(20, 150 l.) or* 13×12½ *(50 l.).*
225 20 l. "Woman making Pastry" (Ayhan Mentes) *(vert)* 10 10
226 50 l. "Chair Weaver" (Osman Güvenir) .. 10 10
227 150 l. "Woman weaving a Rug" (Zekâi Yesiladali) *(vert)* 20 25
225/7 .. .. *Set of* 3 35 35

(Des H. Uluçam. Litho Tezel Ofset, Lefkosa)

1988 (31 May). *Europa. Transport and Communications.* **T 77** *and similar multicoloured design. W* **51** *(sideways on 200 l., inverted on 500 l.). P* 12×12½ *(200 l.) or* 12½×12 *(500 l.).*
228 200 l. Type **77** 30 25
229 500 l. Dish aerial and antenna tower, Selvilitepe *(vert)* 70 60
No. 229 also commemorates the 25th anniversary of Bayrak Radio and Television Corporation.

78 Lefkosa

79 Bülent Ecevit

(Litho Tezel Ofset, Lefkosa)

1988 (17 June). *Tourism.* **T 78** *and similar horiz designs. Multicoloured. W* **51** *(sideways). P* 12×12½.
230 150 l. Type **78** 15 20
231 200 l. Gazi-Magusa 20 25
232 300 l. Girne 30 35
230/2 .. .. *Set of* 3 60 70

(Litho. Tezel Ofset, Lefkosa)

1988 (20 July). *Turkish Prime Ministers.* **T 79** *and similar vert designs. Multicoloured. W* **51**. *P* 12½×12.
233 50 l. Type **79** 10 10
234 50 l. Bülent Ulusu 10 10
235 50 l. Turgut Ozal 10 10
233/5 .. .. *Set of* 3 15 15

80 Red Crescent Members on Exercise

81 Hodori the Tiger (Games mascot) and Fireworks

(Des N. Kozal. Litho Tezel Ofset, Lefkosa)

1988 (8 Aug). *Civil Defence. W* **51** *(sideways). P* 12×12½.
236 **80** 150 l. multicoloured 15 20

(Des E. Cizenel (200 l.), N. Kozal (250 l.), H. Uluçam (400 l.). Litho Tezel Ofset, Lefkosa)

1988 (17 Sept). *Olympic Games, Seoul.* **T 81** *and similar horiz designs. Multicoloured. W* **51** *(sideways). P* 12×12½.
237 200 l. Type **81** 20 25
a. Imperf (pair) .. .. 70·00
238 250 l. Athletics 25 30
239 400 l. Shot and running track with letters spelling "SEOUL" 40 45
237/9 .. .. *Set of* 3 75 90

82 Sedat Simavi (journalist)

83 "Kemal Atatürk" (I. Calli)

(Des H. Uluçam (Nos. 241/3). Litho Tezel Ofset, Lefkosa)

1988 (17 Oct). *Anniversaries and Events.* **T 82** *and similar designs. W* **51** *(inverted on Nos. 240, 243 and 245, sideways on Nos. 241 and 244). P* 12½×12 *(vert) or* 12×12½ *(horiz).*
240 50 l. olive-green 10 10
241 100 l. multicoloured 10 10
242 300 l. multicoloured 30 35
243 400 l. multicoloured 40 45
244 400 l. multicoloured 40 45
245 600 l. multicoloured 65 70
240/5 .. .. *Set of* 6 1·75 1·90
Designs: *Horiz*—No. 241, Stylised figures around table and flags of participating countries (International Girne Conferences); 244, Presidents Gorbachev and Reagan signing treaty (Summit Meeting). *Vert*—No. 242, Cogwheels as flowers (North Cyprus Industrial Fair); 243, Globe (125th anniv of International Red Cross); 245, "Medical Services" (40th anniv of W.H.O.).

(Litho Tezel Ofset, Lefkosa)

1988 (10 Nov). *50th Death Anniv of Kemal Atatürk. Sheet* 72 × 102 *mm containing* **T 83** *and similar vert designs. Multicoloured. W* **51** *(inverted). P* 12½ × 12.
MS246 250 l. Type **83**; 250 l. "Kemal Atatürk" (N. Ismail); 250 l. In army uniform; 250 l. In profile .. .. 1·00 1·10

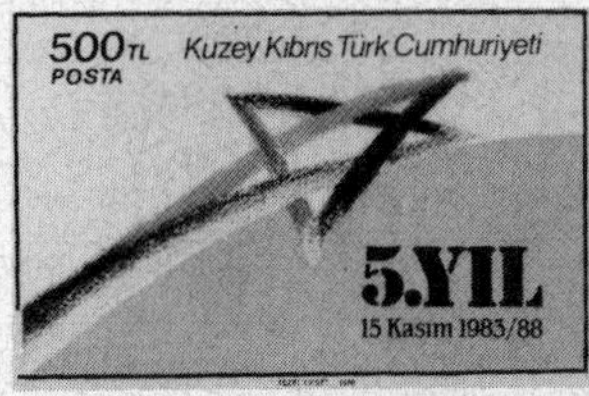

84 Abstract Design

(Des E. Cizenel. Litho Tezel Ofset, Lefkosa)

1988 (15 Nov). *5th Anniv of Turkish Republic of Northern Cyprus. Sheet* 98 × 76 *mm. W* **51** *(sideways). Imperf.*
MS247 **84** 500 l. multicoloured 55 60

(Litho Tezel Ofset, Lefkosa)

1989 (28 Apr). *Paintings (7th series). Multicoloured designs as* **T 54**. *W* **51** *(sideways on 150, 400 l., inverted on 600 l.). P* 12½×13 *(600 l.) or* 13×12½ *(others).*
248 150 l. "Dervis Pasa Mansion, Lefkosa" (Inci Kansu) 15 20
249 400 l. "Gamblers' Inn, Lefkosa" (Osman Güvenir) 40 45
250 600 l. "Mosque, Paphos" (Hikmet Ulucam) *(vert)* 65 70
248/50 .. .. *Set of* 3 1·10 1·25

85 Girl with Doll

86 Meeting of Presidents Vassiliou and Denktash

(Des N. Kozal. Litho Tezel Ofset, Lefkosa)

1989 (31 May). *Europa. Children's Games.* **T 85** *and similar vert design. Multicoloured. W* **51**. *P* 12½×12.
251 600 l. Type **85** 65 70
a. Imperf × p 12 .. .. 65 70
ab. Booklet pane. Nos. 251a/2a, each ×2 3·50
252 1000 l. Boy with kite .. .. 1·10 1·25
a. Imperf × p 12 .. .. 1·10 1·25
Nos. 251a and 252a come from 3200 l. stamp booklets containing *se-tenant* pane No. 251ab.

(Litho Tezel Ofset, Lefkosa)

1989 (30 June). *Cyprus Peace Summit, Geneva,* 1988. *W* **51** *(sideways). P* 12×12½.
253 **86** 500 l. deep rose-red and black 55 60

87 Chukar Partridge

88 Road Construction

(Des E. Cizenel. Litho Tezel Ofset, Lefkosa)

1989 (31 July). *Wildlife.* **T 87** *and similar horiz designs. Multicoloured. W* **51** *(sideways). P* 12×12½.
254 100 l. Type **87** 10 10
255 200 l. Cyprus Hare 20 25
256 700 l. Black Partridge 75 80
257 2000 l. Red Fox .. .. 2·10 2·25
254/7 .. .. *Set of* 4 2·75 3·00

(Litho Tezel Ofset, Lefkosa)

1989 (29 Sept). *Modern Development (3rd series).* **T 88** *and similar multicoloured designs. W* **51** *(sideways on 100, 700 l.). P* 12×12½ *(100, 700 l.) or* 12½×12 *(others).*
258 100 l. Type **88** 10 10
259 150 l. Laying water pipeline *(vert)* 15 20
260 200 l. Seedling trees *(vert)* 20 25
261 450 l. Modern telephone exchange *(vert)* .. 50 55
262 650 l. Steam turbine power station *(vert)* .. 70 75
263 700 l. Irrigation reservoir 75 80
258/63 .. .. *Set of* 6 2·25 2·40

MINIMUM PRICE

The minimum price quote is 10p which represents a handling charge rather than a basis for valuing common stamps. For further notes about prices see introductory pages.

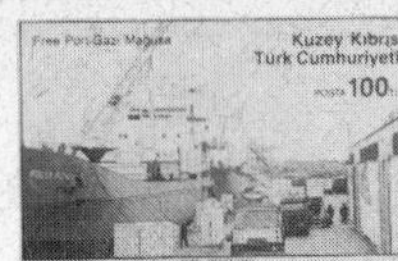

89 Unloading Freighter at Quayside (15th anniv of Gazi Magusa Free Port)

(Des E. Çizenel (450, 600 l.), Ö. Özünalp (500 l.), S. Oral (1000 l.). Litho Tezel Ofset, Lefkosa)

1989 (17 Nov). *Anniversaries.* **T 89** *and similar designs. W* **51** *(inverted on 450 l., sideways on others). P* 12½×13 *(450 l.) or* 12×12½ *(others).*
264 100 l. multicoloured 10 15
265 450 l. black, dull ultramarine & scar- verm 50 55
266 500 l. black, yellow-ochre and olive-grey .. 55 60
267 600 l. black, vermilion and new blue .. 65 70
268 1000 l. multicoloured .. .. 1·10 1·25
264/8 .. .. *Set of* 5 2·50 3·00
Designs: *Vert* (26×47 *mm*)—450 l. Airmail letter and stylized bird (25th anniv of Turkish Cypriot postal service). *Horiz (as* **T 89**)—500 l. Newspaper and printing press (centenary of *Saded* newspaper); 600 l. Statue of Aphrodite, lifebelt and seabird (30th anniv of International Maritime Organization); 1000 l. Soldiers (25th anniv of Turkish Cypriot resistance).

Cyrenaica
see British Occupation of Italian Colonies

Dominica

CROWN COLONY

A branch office of the British G.P.O. was opened at Roseau by 1845, using the crowned-circle handstamp supplied in that year. The stamps of Great Britain were used between May 1858 and March 1860, after which the colonial authorities assumed responsibility for the postal service. Until the introduction of Nos. 1/3 in 1874 No. CC1 and later handstamps were utilized.

For illustrations of handstamp and postmark types see BRITISH POST OFFICES ABROAD notes, following GREAT BRITAIN.

ROSEAU

CROWNED/CIRCLE HANDSTAMPS

CC1 CC 1 DOMINICA (R.) (17.5.1845) *Price on cover* £500
No. CC1 is also known struck in black on various adhesive stamps.

Stamps of GREAT BRITAIN *cancelled* "A 07" *as Type* **2**.

1858 *to* **1860**
Z1 1d. rose-red (1857), *perf* 14 .. £175
Z2 2d. blue (1858) (Plate No. 7) ..
Z3 4d. rose (1857) .. £275
Z4 6d. lilac (1856) .. £275
Z5 1s. green .. £1000

PRICES FOR STAMPS ON COVER TO 1945	
Nos. 1/3	*from* × 8
Nos. 4/26	*from* × 6
Nos. 27/95	*from* × 5
Nos. 96/8	*from* × 4
Nos. 99/109	*from* × 3
Nos. R1/6	*from* × 5

ONE PENNY
1

½
(2)

1
—
2
(3)

HALF PENNY
(4)

(Typo D.L.R.)

1874 (4 May). *Wmk Crown CC. P* 12½.
1 1 1d. lilac .. £175 38·00
2 6d. green .. £450 85·00
3 1s. dull magenta .. £300 65·00

NCE — Normal
NCE — Malformed "CE"

1877–79. *Wmk Crown CC. P* 14.
4 1 ½d. olive-yellow (1879) .. 7·00 25·00
5 1d. lilac .. 4·00 1·50
a. Bisected vert or diag (½d.) (on cover or card) .. † £1600
6 2½d. red-brown (1879) .. £200 24·00
7 4d. blue (1879) .. 95·00 2·50
a. Malformed "CE" in "PENCE" .. £2000 £300
8 6d. green .. £140 20·00
9 1s. magenta .. £120 35·00

1882 (25 Nov)–**83**. *No. 5 bisected and surch.*
10 2 ½(d.), in *black*, on half 1d. .. £140 26·00
a. Surch inverted .. £800 £800
b. Surcharges *tête-bêche* (pair) .. £1400
11 3 ½(d.), in *red*, on half 1d. .. 28·00 12·00
a. Surch inverted .. £800 £300
c. Surch double .. £1600
14 4 ½d. in *black*, on half 1d. (3.83) .. 35·00 20·00
a. Unsevered pair .. £120 £130
b. Surch double .. £800
Type 4 is found reading up or down.

1883–84. *Wmk Crown CA. P* 14.
15 1 ½d. olive-yellow .. 1·00 3·75
16 2½d. red-brown (1884) .. £130 2·00

Half Penny
(5)

One Penny
(6)

1886 (Mar). *Nos. 8 and 9 surch.*
17 5 ½d. on 6d. green .. 4·00 3·50
18 6 1d. on 6d. green .. £15000 £11000
a. Thick bar (approx 1 mm) .. — £14000
19 1d. on 1s. magenta .. 11·00 13·00
a. Surch double .. £4750 £2750
There are variations in the spacing of the letters of "One Penny" in the surcharge of No. 19

1886–88. *Wmk Crown CA. P* 14.
20 1 ½d. dull green .. 50 3·00
21 1d. lilac .. 15·00 5·00
a. Bisected (½d.) (on cover) .. † £1800
22 1d. rose (1887) .. 6·50 7·00
a. Deep carmine .. 2·00 2·75
b. Bisected (½d.) (on cover) .. † £1800
23 2½d. ultramarine (1888) .. 3·75 3·00
24 4d. grey .. 2·00 2·75
a. Malformed "CE" in "PENCE" .. £150 £175
25 6d. orange (1888) .. 5·50 17·00
26 1s. dull magenta (1888) .. £170 £225
20/26 .. *Set of* 7 £180 £225
20, 22/25 Optd "Speciment" .. *Set of* 5 £300

The stamps of Dominica were superseded by the general issue for Leeward Islands on 31 October 1890, but the sets following were in concurrent use with the stamps inscribed "LEEWARD ISLANDS" until 31 December 1939, when the island came under the administration of the Windward Islands.

WATERMARKS. Nos. 27/91 all have the watermark *sideways* except Nos. 36, 46 and 54.

9 View of Roseau from the Sea

10

(T 9 to 11 typo D.L.R.)

1903. *T* **9** *and* **10** *(5s.). Wmk Crown CC. P* 14.
27 ½d. green and grey-green, **OC** .. 1·75 2·25
28 1d. grey and red, **OC** .. 4·00 40
29 2d. green and brown, **OC** .. 2·50 4·00
30 2½d. grey and bright blue, **OC** .. 4·00 3·50
31 3d. dull purple and grey-black, **OC** .. 8·00 2·75
32 6d. grey and chestnut, **O** .. 4·25 13·00
33 1s. magenta and grey-green, **OC** .. 14·00 18·00
34 2s. grey-black and purple, **O** .. 17·00 25·00
35 2s. 6d. grey-green and maize, **O** .. 17·00 48·00
36 5s. black and brown, **O** .. 80·00 £130
27/36 .. *Set of* 10 £130 £225
27/36 Optd "Specimen" .. *Set of* 10 £160

1907–8. *T* **9** *and* **10** *(5s.). Wmk Multiple Crown CA. P* 14
37 ½d. green, **OC** .. 1·00 2·00
38 1d. grey and red, **C** .. 2·00 25
39 2d. green and brown, **C** .. 5·00 12·00
40 2½d. grey and bright blue, **C** .. 4·50 16·00
41 3d. dull purple and grey-black, **C** .. 5·00 13·00
42 6d. black and chestnut, **C** (1908) .. 48·00 60·00
43 1s. magenta and grey-green, **C** .. 3·75 22·00
44 2s. grey-black and purple, **C** (1908) .. 20·00 32·00
45 2s. 6d. grey-green and maize, **C** (1908) .. 20·00 40·00
46 5s. black and brown, **C** (1908) .. 55·00 70·00
37/46 .. *Set of* 10 £150 £225

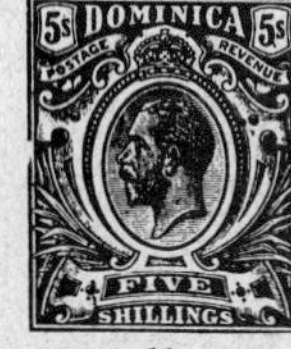

11

WAR TAX
ONE HALFPENNY
(12)

1908–21. *T* **9** *and* **11** *(5s.). Wmk Mult Crown CA. P* 14.
47 9 ½d. blue-green, **O** .. 1·75 1·40
a. Deep green, **O** (1918) .. 1·75 1·75
48 1d. carmine-red, **O** .. 2·00 25
a. Scarlet, **O** .. 1·00 40
49 2d. grey, **O** (1909) .. 3·00 11·00
a. Slate, **O** .. 3·50 11·00
50 2½d. blue, **O** .. 7·50 6·00
a. Bright blue, **O** .. 4·75 8·50
51 3d. purple *yellow*, **OC** (1909) .. 1·75 3·50
a. On pale yellow .. 8·50 10·00
52 6d. dull and bright purple, **C** (1909) .. 10·00 15·00
a. Dull purple, **O** .. 3·50 12·00
53 1s. black/*green*, **OC** (1910) .. 1·40 2·75
53*a* 2s. purple and deep blue/*blue*, **C** (1919) 18·00 38·00
53*b* 2s. 6d. black and red/*blue*, **C** (1921) .. 22·00 45·00
54 11 5s. red and green/*yellow*, **C** (1914) .. 42·00 55·00
47/54 .. *Set of* 10 80·00 £150
48/54 Optd "Specimen" .. *Set of* 9 £200
53 Optd "Specimen" in black instead of red .. 60·00

1916. *No. 47 surch with T* **12**
55 9 ½d. on ½d. blue-green (R.) .. 10 75
a. Small "O" in "ONE" .. 6·50 15·00

1918 (18 Mar). *No. 47 optd locally with T* **12** *but with* "ONE HALFPENNY" *blanked out.*
56 9 ½d. blue-green (Blk.) .. 50 4·00
The blanking out of the surcharge was not completely successful so that it almost always appears as an albino to a greater or lesser extent.

WAR TAX
(14)

1918 (June). *Nos. 47 and 51 optd in London with T* 14.
57 9 ½d. blue-green .. 10 30
58 3d. purple/*yellow* (R.) .. 20 2·00

WAR TAX
=1½D.=
(15)

1 ½D.
Short Fraction Bar (R.6/4)

1919. *Special printing of T* **9**, *surch with T* **15**.
59 9 1½d. on 2½d. orange (R.) .. 10 55
a. Short fraction bar .. 7·00 20·00
b. "C" and "A" missing from wmk ..
No. 59b shows the "C" omitted from one impression with the "A" missing from the next one to the right (as seen from the front of the stamp). The "C" is badly distorted in the second watermark.

1920. *As No. 59, but without* "WAR TAX".
60 9 1½d. on 2½d. orange (Blk.) .. 1·25 3·75
a. Short fraction bar .. 45·00 60·00
55/60 Optd "Specimen" .. *Set of* 6 £275

1921. *Wmk Mult Script CA. P* 14
62 9 ½d. blue-green .. 1·25 4·25
63 1d. carmine-red .. 1·10 2·50
64 1½d. orange .. 3·50 8·50
65 2d. grey .. 2·75 3·25
66 2½d. bright blue .. 1·25 8·00
67 6d. purple, **C** .. 2·50 22·00
69 2s. purple and blue/*blue* .. 23·00 48·00
70 2s. 6d. black and red/*blue* .. 23·00 48·00
62/70 .. *Set of* 8 48·00 £130
62/70 Optd "Specimen" .. *Set of* 8 £160
The 1½d. has figures of value, in the lower corner and no ornamentation below words of value.

16

(Typo D.L.R.)

1923 (Feb)–**33**. *Chalk-surfaced paper. P* 14.

(a) Wmk Multi Script CA
71 16 ½d. black and green .. 65 30
72 1d. black and bright violet .. 1·25 40
73 1d. black and scarlet (1933) .. 4·50 80
74 1½d. black and scarlet .. 90 30
75 1½d. black and red-brown (1933) .. 4·50 50
76 2d. black and grey .. 75 40
77 2½d. black and orange-yellow .. 70 5·00
78 2½d. black and ultramarine (1927) .. 2·00 1·00
79 3d. black and ultramarine .. 70 6·50
80 3d. black and red/*yellow* (1927) .. 1·00 1·00
81 4d. black and brown .. 75 4·00
82 6d. black and bright magenta .. 1·75 3·50
83 1s. black/*emerald* .. 1·40 2·25
84 2s. black and blue/*blue* .. 3·50 11·00
85 2s. 6d. black and red/*blue* .. 8·50 13·00
86 3s. black and purple/*yellow* (1927) .. 2·50 8·00
87 4s. black and red/*emerald* .. 5·00 11·00
88 5s. black and green/*yellow* (1927) .. 13·00 25·00

(b) Wmk Mult Crown CA
89 16 3s. black and purple/*yellow* .. 4·00 32·00
90 5s. black and green/*yellow* .. 7·50 30·00
91 £1 black and purple/*red* .. £250 £300
71/91 .. *Set of* 21 £275 £400
71/91 Optd/Perf "Specimen" .. *Set of* 21 £400

1935 (6 May). *Silver Jubilee. As Nos. 91/4 of Antigua.*
92 1d. deep blue and carmine .. 75 20
f. Diagonal line by turret .. 15·00
h. Dot by flagstaff .. 15·00
93 1½d. ultramarine and grey .. 1·00 40
f. Diagonal line by turret .. 20·00
h. Dot by flagstaff .. 20·00
94 2½d. brown and deep blue .. 1·40 75
95 1s. slate and purple .. 1·50 3·25
h. Dot by flagstaff .. 40·00
92/5 .. *Set of* 4 4·25 4·25
92/5 Perf "Specimen" .. *Set of* 4 60·00
For illustrations of plate varieties see Omnibus section following Zululand.

1937 (12 May). *Coronation. As Nos. 13/15 of Aden, but printed by B.W. P* 11 × 11½.
96 1d. carmine .. 30 10
97 1½d. yellow-brown .. 30 10
98 2½d. blue .. 60 65
96/8 .. *Set of* 3 1·10 75
96/8 Perf "Specimen" .. *Set of* 3 50·00

17 Fresh Water Lake

18 Layou River

(Recess Waterlow)

1938 (15 Aug)–**47**. *T* **17/18** *and similar horiz designs. Wmk Mult Script CA. P* 12½.
99 17 ½d. brown and green .. 10 15
100 18 1d. grey and scarlet .. 15 20
101 – 1½d. green and purple .. 20 30
102 – 2d. carmine and grey-black .. 30 35
103 – 2½d. purple and bright blue .. 4·00 1·50
a. Purple & brt ultram (8.42) .. 20 45

104 18 3d. olive-green and brown 20 40
104a – 3½d. ultramarine and purple (15.10.47) 75 45
105 17 6d. emerald-green and violet 40 50
105a 7d. green and yellow-brown (15.10.47) 75 50
106 – 1s. violet and olive-green 60 50
106a 18 2s. slate and purple (15.10.47) .. 2·25 3·50
107 17 2s. 6d. black and vermilion .. .. 4·00 3·00
108 18 5s. light blue and sepia .. .. 4·50 3·00
108a – 10s. black and brown-orange (15.10.47) 7·00 9·00
99/108a .. .. Set of 14 19·00 20·00
Designs:–1½d., 2½d., 3½d. Picking limes; 2d., 1s., 10s. Boiling Lake.

21 King George VI

(Photo Harrison)

1940 (15 Apr). *Wmk Mult Script CA. P* 15 × 14.
109 21 ¼d. chocolate, **CO** 10 10
99/109 Perf "Specimen" .. .. *Set of* 15 £225

1946 (14 Oct). *Victory. As Nos.* 28/9 *of Aden.*
110 1d. carmine 10 10
111 3½d. blue 10 10
110/11 Perf "Specimen" .. .. *Set of* 2 45·00

1948 (1 Dec.) *Royal Silver Wedding. As Nos.* 30/1 *of Aden.*
112 1d. scarlet 15 10
113 10s. red-brown .. .. 6·00 10·00

(New Currency. 100 cents = 1 dollar)

1949 (10 Oct). *75th Anniv of Universal Postal Union. As Nos.* 114/17 *of Antigua.*
114 5 c. blue 15 15
115 6 c. brown 30 20
116 12 c. purple 30 30
117 24 c. olive 30 30
114/17 .. .. *Set of* 4 95 85

1951 (16 Feb). *Inauguration of B.W.I. University College. As Nos.* 118/19 *of Antigua.*
118 3 c. yellow-green and reddish violet 20 10
119 12 c. deep green and carmine 30 10

22 King George VI

23 Drying Cocoa

(Photo Harrison (½ c.). Recess B.W. (others))

1951 (1 July). *T* **22** *and designs as T* **23**. *Wmk Mult Script CA. P* 15 × 14 (½ c.), 13½ × 13 ($2.40), 13 × 13½ (*others*).
120 ½ c. chocolate 10 15
121 1 c. black and vermilion 10 10
122 2 c. red-brown and deep green 10 10
123 3 c. green and reddish violet 10 20
124 4 c. brown-orange and sepia 15 15
125 5 c. black and carmine 30 15
a. "C" of "CA" missing from wmk
126 6 c. olive and chestnut 35 15
127 8 c. blue-green and blue 30 25
128 12 c. black and bright green 25 60
129 14 c. blue and violet 35 50
130 24 c. reddish violet and rose-carmine .. 25 25
131 48 c. bright green and red-orange .. .. 1·00 2·75
132 60 c. carmine and black .. .. .. 1·00 1·75
133 $1.20, emerald and black .. .. .. 4·00 2·00
134 $2.40, orange and black .. .. .. 16·00 14·00
120/134 .. .. *Set of* 15 21·00 20·00
Designs: *Horiz*—2 c., 60 c. Making Carib baskets; 3 c., 48 c. Lime plantation; 4 c. Picking oranges; 5 c. Bananas; 6 c. Botanical Gardens; 8 c. Drying vanilla beans; 12 c., $1.20, Fresh Water Lake; 14 c. Layou River; 24 c. Boiling Lake. *Vert*—$2.40, Picking oranges.

NEW
CONSTITUTION
1951
(34)

1951 (15 Oct). *New Constitution. Nos.* 123, 125, 127 *and* 129 *optd with T* 34 *by B.W.*
135 3 c. green and reddish violet 10 20
136 5 c. black and carmine 10 15
137 8 c. blue-green and blue (R.) 15 10
138 14 c. blue and violet (R.) 15 10
135/8 .. .. *Set of* 4 45 50

1953 (2 June). *Coronation. As No.* 47 *of Aden.*
139 2 c. black and deep green 10 10

MINIMUM PRICE

The minimum price quote is 10p which represents a handling charge rather than a basis for valuing common stamps. For further notes about prices see introductory pages.

35 Queen Elizabeth II

36 Mat Making

37 Picking Oranges

38 Canoe Making

(Photo Harrison (½ c.). Recess B.W. (others))

1954 (1 Oct)–**62**. *Designs previously used for King George VI issue, but with portrait of Queen Elizabeth II as in T* **35**/**8**. *Wmk Mult Script CA. P* 15×14 (½ c.), 13½×13 ($2.40), 13×13½ (*others*).
140 35 ½ c. brown 10 10
141 – 1 c. black and vermilion 10 10
142 – 2 c. chocolate and myrtle-green 10 10
a. Chocolate and grey-green (13.3.62) 60 60
143 – 3 c. green and purple 20 10
144 36 3 c. black and carmine (15.10.57) .. 35 15
145 37 4 c. brown-orange and sepia 10 10
146 – 5 c. black and carmine-red 20 10
147 38 5 c. light blue & sepia-brown (15.10.57) 3·00 20
a. Blue and sepia (13.3.62) .. .. 4·50 40
148 – 6 c. bronze-green and red-brown 10 10
149 – 8 c. deep green and deep blue 10 10
150 – 10 c. green and brown (15.10.57) .. 40 15
a. Green and deep brown (17.7.62) .. 70 30
151 – 12 c. black and emerald 30 10
152 – 14 c. blue and purple 15 10
153 – 24 c. purple and carmine 20 10
154 – 48 c. green and red-orange .. .. 1·00 4·50
155 36 48 c. deep brown and violet (15.10.57) .. 1·00 80
156 – 60 c. rose-red and black 50 75
157 – $1.20, emerald and black .. .. 6·00 5·00
158 – $2.40, yellow-orange and black .. 7·50 10·00
140/58 .. .. *Set of* 19 19·00 20·00
Designs: *Horiz*—1 c. Drying cocoa; 2 c., 60 c. Making Carib baskets; 3 c. (No. 143), 48 c. (No. 154) Lime plantation; 5 c. (No. 146) Bananas; 6 c. Botanical Gardens; 8 c. Drying vanilla beans; 10 c. Bananas (*different*); 12 c., $1.20, Fresh Water Lake; 14 c. Layou River; 24 c. Boiling Lake. *Vert*—$2.40, Picking oranges.

1958 (22 Apr). *Inauguration of British Caribbean Federation. As Nos.* 135/7 *of Antigua.*
159 3 c. deep green 10 10
160 6 c. blue 10 10
161 12 c. scarlet 15 10
159/61 .. .. *Set of* 3 30 15

40 Seashore at Rosalie

48 Traditional Costume

Two types of 14 c.

I. Eyes of model looking straight ahead.
II. Eyes looking to her right.

(Des S. Scott. Photo Harrison)

1963 (16 May)–**65**. *T* **40**, **48** *and similar designs. W* w **12** (*upright*). *P* 14 × 14½ (*vert*) or 14½ × 14 (*horiz*).
162 1 c. green, blue and sepia 10 10
163 2 c. bright blue 15 10
164 3 c. blackish brown and blue 15 10
165 4 c. green, sepia and slate-violet 15 10
166 5 c. magenta 15 10
167 6 c. green, bistre and violet 10 10
168 8 c. green, sepia and black 10 10
169 10 c. sepia and pink 10 10
170 12 c. green, blue and blackish brown .. 10 10
171 14 c. multicoloured (I) 20 10
171a 14 c. multicoloured (II) (1.4.65) 30 20
172 15 c. yellow, green and brown 15 10
173 24 c. multicoloured .. .. 2·00 10
174 48 c. green, blue and black 60 25
175 60 c. orange, green and black 65 50
176 $1.20, multicoloured .. .. .. 3·50 70
177 $2.40, blue, turquoise and brown .. .. 3·00 2·00
178 $4.80, green, blue and brown .. .. 6·50 9·00
162/78 .. .. *Set of* 17 16·00 12·00
Designs: *Vert*—2 c., 5 c. Queen Elizabeth II; 24 c. Imperial Amazon; $2.40, Trafalgar Falls; $4.80, Coconut Palm. *Horiz*—3 c. Sailing canoe; 4 c. Sulphur springs; 6 c. Road making; 8 c. Dug-out canoe; 10 c. Crapaud (toad); 12 c. Scott's Head; 15 c. Bananas; 48 c. Goodwill; 60 c. Cocoa tree; $1.20, Coat of Arms.
See also Nos. 200/4.

1963 (4 June). *Freedom from Hunger. As No.* 76 *of Aden.*
179 15 c. reddish violet 15 10

1963 (2 Sept). *Red Cross Centenary. As Nos.* 147/8 *of Antigua.*
180 5 c. red and black 15 10
181 15 c. red and blue 30 30

1964 (23 April). *400th Birth Anniv of William Shakespeare. As No.* 164 *of Antigua.*
182 15 c. bright purple 10 10

1965 (17 May). *I.T.U. Centenary. As Nos.* 166/7 *of Antigua.*
183 2 c. light emerald and blue 10 10
184 48 c. turquoise-blue and grey 30 15

1965 (25 Oct). *International Co-operation Year. As Nos.* 168/9 *of Antigua.*
185 1 c. reddish purple and turquoise-green .. 10 10
186 15 c. deep bluish green and lavender 20 10

1966 (24 Jan). *Churchill Commemoration. As Nos.* 170/3 *of Antigua.*
187 1 c. new blue 10 10
a. Gold omitted £400
188 5 c. deep green 10 10
189 15 c. brown 20 10
190 24 c. bluish violet 30 20
187/90 .. .. *Set of* 4 55 30

1966 (4 Feb). *Royal Visit. As Nos.* 174/5 *of Antigua.*
191 5 c. black and ultramarine 50 10
192 15 c. black and magenta 75 20

1966 (1 July). *World Cup Football Championships. As Nos.* 176/7 *of Antigua.*
193 5 c. violet, yellow-green, lake & yellow-brown 10 10
194 24 c. chocolate, blue-green, lake & yell-brown 20 10

1966 (20 Sept). *Inauguration of W.H.O. Headquarters, Geneva. As Nos.* 178/9 *of Antigua.*
195 5 c. black, yellow-green and light blue .. 10 10
196 24 c. black, light purple and yellow-brown .. 15 15

1966 (1 Dec). *20th Anniv of U.N.E.S.C.O. As Nos.* 196/8 *of Antigua.*
197 5 c. slate-violet, red, yellow and orange .. 10 10
198 15 c. orange-yellow, violet and deep olive .. 25 10
199 24 c. black, bright purple and orange 25 15
197/9 .. .. *Set of* 3 55 25

1966 (30 Dec)–**67**. *As Nos.* 165, 167/9 *and* 172 *but wmk* w **12** *sideways.*
200 4 c. green, sepia and slate-violet (16.5.67) .. 20 10
201 6 c. green, bistre and violet 15 10
202 8 c. green, sepia and black 20 10
203 10 c. sepia and pink (16.5.67) 20 10
204 15 c. yellow, green and brown (16.5.67) .. 20 10
200/4 .. .. *Set of* 5 85 40

ASSOCIATED STATEHOOD

56 Children of Three Races

(Des and photo Harrison)

1967 (2 Nov). *National Day. T* **56** *and similar horiz designs. Multicoloured. W* w **12**. *P* 14½.
205 5 c. Type **56** 10 10
206 10 c. The *Santa Maria* and motto 10 10
207 15 c. Hands holding motto ribbon 10 10
208 24 c. Belaire dancing 10 10
205/8 .. .. *Set of* 4 25 15

57 John F. Kennedy

(Des G. Vasarhelyi. Litho D.L.R.)

1968 (20 Apr). *Human Rights Year. T* **57** *and similar horiz designs. Multicoloured. W* w **12** (*sideways*). *P* 14 × 13½.
209 1 c. Type **57** 10 10
210 10 c. Cecil A. E. Rawle 10 10
a. Imperf (pair) £180
211 12 c. Pope John XXIII 10 10
212 48 c. Florence Nightingale 20 15
213 60 c. Albert Schweitzer 20 15
209/13 .. .. *Set of* 5 45 30

ASSOCIATED
STATEHOOD
(58)

NATIONAL DAY
3 NOVEMBER 1968
(59)

1968 (8 July). *Associated Statehood. As Nos.* 162, 170 *and* 174, *but wmk sideways, or Nos.* 163/4, 166, 170, 171*a*, 173, 175/8 *and* 200/4 *optd with T* **58**.
214 1 c. green, blue and sepia (Sil.) 10 10
215 2 c. bright blue (Sil.) 10 10
216 3 c. blackish brown and blue (Sil.) 10 10
217 4 c. green, sepia and slate-violet (Sil.) .. 10 10
218 5 c. magenta (Sil.) 10 10
219 6 c. green, bistre and violet 10 10
220 8 c. green, sepia and black 10 10
221 10 c. sepia and pink (Sil.) 15 10
222 12 c. green, blue and blackish brown (Sil.) (wmk sideways) 10 10
a. Wmk upright 10 10
224 14 c. multicoloured (II) (Sil.) 10 10
225 15 c. yellow, green and brown (Sil.) 10 10

226 24 c. multicoloured (Sil.) 60 10
227 48 c. green, bl & blk (Sil.) (wmk sideways) .. 55 70
a. Wmk upright 40 75
228 60 c. orange, green and black 70 70
229 $1.20, multicoloured .. .. .. 1·00 1·75
230 $2.40, blue, turquoise and brown (Sil.) .. 1·75 2·25
231 $4.80, green, blue and brown (Sil.) .. 2·00 2·75
214/31 .. .. *Set of* 17 6·50 7·50

The 2, 5, 6, 8 and 10 c. values exist with PVA gum as well as gum arabic.

1968 (3 Nov). *National Day. Nos.* 162/4, 171 *and* 176 *optd with T* **59**.

232 1 c. green, blue and sepia 10 10
a. Opt inverted .. .. 45·00
233 2 c. bright blue 10 10
a. Opt double .. .. 30·00
234 3 c. blackish brown and blue 10 10
a. Opt inverted .. .. 30·00
235 14 c. multicoloured (I) 10 10
a. Opt double .. .. 70·00
236 $1.20, multicoloured 30 40
a. Opt double .. .. 30·00
b. Vert pair, one opt omitted, other opt double £150
232/6 .. .. *Set of* 5 30 40

The above set was put on sale by the New York Agency on 1 November but not sold locally until the 3 November.

60 Forward shooting at Goal

(Des M. Shamir (1 c., 60 c.), K. Plowitz (5 c., 48 c.). Litho B.W.)

1968 (25 Nov). *Olympic Games, Mexico. T* **60** *and similar horiz designs. Multicoloured. P* 11½ × 11.

237 1 c. Type **60** 10 10
a. Horiz pair. Nos. 237/8 .. .. .. 10 10
238 1 c. Goalkeeper trying to save goal 10 10
239 5 c. Swimmers about to dive 10 10
a. Horiz pair. Nos. 239/40 .. .. .. 10 10
240 5 c. Swimmers diving 10 10
241 48 c. Javelin-throwing 15 15
a. Horiz pair. Nos. 241/2 .. .. .. 30 30
242 48 c. Hurdling 15 15
243 60 c. Basketball 15 15
a. Horiz pair. Nos. 243/4 .. .. .. 30 30
244 60 c. Basketball players 15 15
237/44 .. .. *Set of* 8 70 70

Nos. 237/44 were issued in sheets of 40 containing two panes of *se-tenant* pairs.

61 "The Small Cowper Madonna" (Raphael)

62 "Venus and Adonis" (Rubens)

(Photo Delrieu, Paris)

1968 (23 Dec). *Christmas. P* 12½ × 12.

245 **61** 5 c. multicoloured 10 10

Three other values were issued: 12 c. "Madonna of the Chair" (Raphael); 24 c. "Madonna and Child" (Italo-Byzantine, XVI century); $1.20 "Madonna and Child" (Byzantine, XIII century). Sizes as T **61**.

These only come from miniature sheets, containing two *se-tenant* strips of each value.

(Litho D.L.R.)

1969 (30 Jan). *20th Anniv of World Health Organisation. Paintings. T* **62** *and similar vert designs. Multicoloured. W* w **12**. *P* 15.

246 5 c. Type **62** 10 10
247 15 c. "The Death of Socrates" (J.-L. David) .. 10 10
248 24 c. "Christ and the Pilgrims of Emmaus" (Velasquez) 10 10
249 50 c. "Pilate washing his Hands" (Rembrandt) 20 15
246/9 .. .. *Set of* 4 40 20

66 Picking Oranges

67 "Strength in Unity" Emblem and Fruit Trees

(Des K. Plowitz. Litho Harrison)

1969 (10 Mar). *Tourism. T* **66** *and similar horiz designs. Multicoloured. W* w **12**. *P* 14½.

250 10 c. Type **66** 10 10
a. Horiz pair. Nos. 250/1 .. .. .. 10 15
251 10 c. Woman, child and ocean scene 10 10
252 12 c. Fort Yeoung Hotel 10 10
a. Horiz pair. Nos. 252/3 .. .. .. 15 20
253 12 c. Red-necked Amazons 10 10
254 24 c. Calypso band 10 15
a. Horiz pair. Nos. 254/5 .. .. .. 20 30
255 24 c. Women dancing 10 15
256 48 c. Underwater life 20 25
a. Horiz pair. Nos. 256/7 .. .. .. 40 50
257 48 c. Skin-diver and turtle 20 25
250/7 .. .. *Set of* 8 75 1·00

Each denomination was printed *se-tenant* throughout the sheet. The 12 c. values are on cream coloured paper.

(Litho B.W.)

1969 (July). *First Anniv of CARIFTA (Caribbean Free Trade Area). T* **67** *and similar horiz designs. Multicoloured. P* 13½ × 13.

258 5 c. Type **67** 10 10
259 8 c. "HS 748" aircraft, emblem and island .. 10 10
260 12 c. Chart of Caribbean Sea and emblem .. 10 10
261 24 c. Steamship unloading, tug and emblem .. 15 10
258/61 .. .. *Set of* 4 30 15

71 "Spinning"

72 Mahatma Gandhi Weaving and Clock Tower, Westminster

(Litho B.W.)

1969 (10 July). *50th Anniv of International Labour Organisation. T* **71** *and similar vert designs showing paintings of people at work by J. Millet, bordered by flags of member-nations of the I.L.O. Multicoloured. No wmk. P* 13 × 13½.

262 15 c. Type **71** 10 10
263 30 c. "Threshing" 10 10
264 38 c. "Flax-pulling" 15 10
262/4 .. .. *Set of* 3 25 20

(Des G. Vasarhelyi. Litho Format)

1969 (20 Oct). *Birth Centenary of Mahatma Gandhi. T* **72** *and similar horiz designs. Multicoloured. P* 14½.

265 6 c. Type **72** 30 10
266 38 c. Gandhi, Nehru and Mausoleum 50 15
267 $1.20, Gandhi and Taj Mahal .. .. 1·40 40
265/7 .. .. *Set of* 3 2·00 50

Nos. 265/7 are incorrectly inscribed "Ghandi".

75 "Saint Joseph"

(Des G. Vasarhelyi. Litho Govt Printer, Jerusalem)

1969 (3 Nov). *National Day. Stained Glass Windows. T* **75** *and similar vert designs. Multicoloured. P* 14.

268 6 c. Type **75** 10 10
269 8 c. "Saint John" 10 10
270 12 c. "Saint Peter" 10 10
271 60 c. "Saint Paul" 30 50
268/71 .. .. *Set of* 4 40 60

Nos. 268/71 were printed in sheets of 16 (4 × 4) containing 12 stamps and four printed labels in the top row. The labels each contain two lines of a patriotic poem by W. O. M. Pond, the first letter from each line spelling "DOMINICA".

79 Queen Elizabeth II

80 Purple-throated Carib and Flower

81 Government Headquarters

82 Coat of Arms

(Photo D.L.R.)

1969–72. *T* **79/82** *and similar horiz designs. Multicoloured. W* **41** *of Singapore* (60 *c. to* $4.80) *or no wmk* (*others*). *P* 13½ × 14 (½ *c.*), 14 × 13½ (1 *to* 50 *c.*) *or* 14 (60 *c. to* $4.80).

A. *Chalk-surfaced paper* (26.11.69)
B. *Glazed paper* (1972)

		A		B	
272	½ c. Type **79**	10	20	15	15
273	1 c. Type **80**	15	20	60	20
274	2 c. Poinsettia	15	10	40	10
275	3 c. Red-necked Pigeon ..	40	30	70	20
276	4 c. Imperial Amazon	40	30	70	20
277	5 c. Swallowtail Butterfly ..	55	20	75	25
278	6 c. Julia Butterfly ..	55	35	60	25
279	8 c. Shipping Bananas ..	20	10	40	20
280	10 c. Portsmouth Harbour ..	20	10	35	20
281	12 c. Copra Processing Plant ..	20	10	35	20
282	15 c. Straw Workers	20	10	35	25
283	25 c. Timber Plant	25	10	40	25
284	30 c. Pumice Mine	1·25	70	1·25	70
285	38 c. Grammar School and Playing Field	3·50	1·75	5·00	5·00
286	50 c. Roseau Cathedral	50	45	80	90
287	60 c. Type **81**	55	80	†	
288	$1.20, Melville Hall Airport (40 × 27 *mm*)	1·00	1·75	†	
289	$2.40, Type **82**	1·75	3·00	†	
290	$4.80, Type **79** (26 × 39 *mm*)	3·00	6·00	†	
272A/90A	.. .. *Set of* 19	13·00	15·00		
272B/90B	.. .. *Set of* 15			11·00	8·00

99 "Virgin and Child with St. John" (Perugino)

101 Astronaut's First Step onto the Moon

(Des G. Vasarhelyi. Litho B.W.)

1969 (19 Dec). *Christmas. Paintings. T* **99** *and similar vert designs. Multicoloured. P* 14 × 14½.

291 6 c. "Virgin and Child with St. John" (Lippi) 10 10
292 10 c. "Holy Family with the Lamb" (Raphael) 10 10
293 15 c. Type **99** 10 10
294 $1.20, "Madonna of the Rose Hedge" (Botticelli) 35 40
291/4 .. .. *Set of* 4 35 40
MS295 89 × 76 mm. Nos. 293/4. Imperf 55 90

(Des G. Vasarhelyi. Photo Banknote Printing Office, Helsinki)

1970 (6 Feb*). *Moon Landing. T* **101** *and similar horiz designs. Multicoloured. P* 12½.

296 ½ c. Type **101** 10 10
297 5 c. Scientific Experiment on the Moon, and Flag 10 10
298 8 c. Astronauts collecting Rocks 10 10
299 30 c. Module over the Moon 20 15
300 50 c. Moon Plaque 30 25
301 60 c. Astronauts 30 30
296/301 .. .. *Set of* 6 90 80
MS302 116 × 112 mm. Nos. 298/301. Imperf .. 1·25 1·75

*This is the date of release in Dominica, but the above were released by the Philatelic Agency in the U.S.A. on 2 February.

107 Giant Green Turtle

(Des G. Drummond. Litho Kyodo Printing Co, Tokyo)

1970 (7 Sept). *Flora and Fauna.* *T* **107** *and similar horiz designs. Multicoloured. P* 13.

303	6 c. Type **107**	30	15
304	24 c. Flying fish	50	40
305	38 c. Anthurium lily	60	55
306	60 c. Imperial and Red-necked Amazons	1·75	1·50
303/6	*Set of* 4	2·75	2·40
MS307	160 × 111 mm. Nos. 303/6	3·75	5·50

108 18th-Century National Costume

109 Scrooge and Marley's Ghost

(Des G. Drummond from local designs. Litho Questa)

1970 (30 Oct). *National Day.* *T* **108** *and similar horiz designs. Multicoloured. P* 14.

308	5 c. Type **108**	10	10
309	8 c. Carib Basketry	10	10
310	$1 Flag and Chart of Dominica	30	40
308/10	*Set of* 3	30	40
MS311	150 × 85 mm. Nos. 308/10 plus three labels	40	90

(Des R. Granger Barrett. Litho Questa)

1970 (23 Nov). *Christmas and Charles Dickens' Death Centenary.* *T* **109** *and similar vert designs showing scenes from "A Christmas Carol". Multicoloured. P* 14 × 14½.

312	2 c. Type **109**	10	10
313	15 c. Fezziwig's Ball	10	10
314	24 c. Scrooge and his Nephew's Party	10	10
315	$1.20, Scrooge and the Ghost of Christmas Present	40	60
312/15	*Set of* 4	55	70
MS316	142 × 87 mm. Nos. 312/15	1·50	3·00

110 "The Doctor" (Sir Luke Fildes)

(Des G. Vasarhelyi. Litho Questa)

1970 (28 Dec). *Centenary of British Red Cross.* *T* **110** *and similar horiz designs. Multicoloured. P* 14½ × 14.

317	8 c. Type **110**	10	10
318	10 c. Hands and Red Cross	10	10
319	15 c. Flag of Dominica and Red Cross Emblem	10	10
320	50 c. "The Sick Child" (E. Munch)	20	35
317/20	*Set of* 4	35	40
MS321	108 × 76 mm. Nos. 317/20	1·25	2·00

111 Marigot School

(Des G. Vasarhelyi. Litho Questa)

1971 (1 Mar). *International Education Year* (1970). *T* **111** *and similar horiz designs. Multicoloured. P* 13½.

322	5 c. Type **111**	10	10
323	8 c. Goodwill Junior High School	10	10
324	14 c. University of West Indies (Jamaica)	10	10
325	$1 Trinity College, Cambridge	25	30
322/5	*Set of* 4	25	30
MS326	85 × 85 mm. Nos. 324/5	40	75

112 Waterfall

(Des O. Bonnevalle. Litho Questa)

1971 (22 Mar). *Tourism.* *T* **112** *and similar horiz designs. Multicoloured. P* 13½.

327	5 c. Type **112**	10	10
328	10 c. Boat-building	10	10
329	30 c. Sailing	15	10
330	50 c. Yacht and motor launch	30	30
327/30	*Set of* 4	50	45
MS331	130 × 86 mm. Nos. 327/30	50	75

113 UNICEF Symbol in "D"

114 German Boy Scout

(Des G. Drummond. Litho Questa)

1971 (14 June). *25th Anniv of UNICEF. P* 14.

332	**113**	5 c. bluish violet, black and gold	10	10
333		10 c. yellow, black and gold	10	10
334		38 c. green, black and gold	10	10
335		$1.20 orange, black and gold	30	45
332/5		*Set of* 4	40	55
MS336		84 × 79 mm. Nos. 333 and 335	40	85

(Litho Format)

1971 (18 Oct). *World Scout Jamboree, Asagiri, Japan.* *T* **114** *and similar vert designs showing Boy Scouts from the nations listed. Multicoloured. W w* **12**. *P* 11.

337	20 c. Type **114**	15	10
338	24 c. Great Britain	20	10
339	30 c. Japan	25	10
340	$1 Dominica	50	40
337/40	*Set of* 4	1·00	55
MS341	114 × 102 mm. Nos. 339/40	1·25	2·00

The above were printed on thick paper and the watermark is very faint.

"Dominica" on the scout's shirt pocket is omitted on the $1 value from the miniature sheet.

115 Groine at Portsmouth

(Des V. Whiteley. Litho Format)

1971 (15 Nov). *National Day.* *T* **115** *and similar multicoloured designs. P* 13½.

342	8 c. Type **115**	10	10
343	15 c. Carnival scene	10	10
344	20 c. Carifta Queen (*vert*)	10	10
345	50 c. Rock of Atkinson (*vert*)	20	25
342/5	*Set of* 4	30	30
MS346	63 × 89 mm. $1.20, As 20 c. P 15	45	70

116 Eight Reals Piece, 1761

(Des G. Drummond. Litho Questa)

1972 (7 Feb). *Coins.* *T* **116** *and similar designs. P* 14.

347	10 c. black, silver and violet	10	10
348	30 c. black, silver and yellowish green	15	15
349	35 c. black, silver and bright blue	20	20
350	50 c. black, silver and vermilion	40	60
347/50	*Set of* 4	75	90
MS351	86 × 90 mm. Nos. 349/50	1·00	1·25

Designs: *Horiz*—30 c. Eleven and three bitt pieces, 1798. *Vert*—35 c. Two reals and two bitt pieces, 1770; 50 c. Mocos, Pieces-of-eight and eight reals-eleven bitts piece, 1798.

117 Common Opossum

(Des R. Granger Barrett. Litho Questa)

1972 (3 June). *U.N. Conference on the Human Environment, Stockholm.* *T* **117** *and similar horiz designs. Multicoloured. W w* **12** (*sideways*). *P* 14.

352	½ c. Type **117**	10	10
353	35 c. Brazilian Agouti (rodent)	40	15
354	60 c. Orchid	1·50	50
355	$1.20, Hibiscus	1·75	1·60
352/5	*Set of* 4	3·25	2·00
MS356	139 × 94 mm. Nos. 352/5	4·75	6·50

118 Sprinter

(Des R. Granger Barrett. Litho Format)

1972 (16 Oct*). *Olympic Games, Munich.* *T* **118** *and similar multicoloured designs. P* 14.

357	30 c. Type **118**	10	10
358	35 c. Hurdler	15	15
359	58 c. Hammer-thrower (*vert*)	15	20
360	72 c. Long-jumper (*vert*)	25	40
357/60	*Set of* 4	60	75
MS361	98 × 96 mm. Nos. 359/60. P 15	60	90

*This is the local release date; the American philatelic agency released the stamps on 9 October.

119 General Post Office

(Des G. Vasarhelyi. Litho Format)

1972 (1 Nov). *National Day.* *T* **119** *and similar horiz designs. Multicoloured. P* 13½.

362	10 c. Type **119**	10	10
363	20 c. Morne Diablotin	10	10
364	30 c. Rodney's Rock	15	15
362/4	*Set of* 3	25	25
MS365	83 × 96 mm. Nos. 363/4. P 15	40	70

120 Bananas and Imperial Amazon

(Des (from photograph by D. Groves) and photo Harrison)

1972 (20 Nov). *Royal Silver Wedding. Multicoloured; background colour given. W w* **12**. *P* 14 × 14½.

366	**120**	5 c. yellow-olive	10	10
		a. Deep yellow-olive	25	25
367		$1 myrtle-green	40	40

121 "The Adoration of the Shepherds" (Caravaggio)

122 Launching of Weather Satellite

(Des G. Vasarhelyi. Litho Format)

1972 (4 Dec*). *Christmas.* *T* **121** *and similar vert designs. Multicoloured. P* 13½.

368	8 c. Type **121**	10	10
369	14 c. "The Myosotis Virgin" (Rubens)	10	10
370	30 c. "Madonna and Child with St. Francesca Romana" (Gentileschi)	15	10
371	$1 "Adoration of the Kings" (Mostaert)	40	60
368/71	*Set of* 4	60	70
MS372	102 × 79 mm. Nos. 370/1. Imperf.	65	80

* This is the date of release in Dominica; the stamps were put on sale by the Philatelic agency in the U.S.A. on 27 November.

No. 368 is wrongly attributed to Boccaccino in the design.

(Des G. Vasarhelyi. Litho Format)

1973 (16 July). *I.M.O./W.M.O. Centenary.* *T* **122** *and similar multicoloured designs. P* 14½.

373	½ c. Type **122**	10	10
374	1 c. Nimbus satellite	10	10
375	2 c. Radiosonde balloon	10	10
376	30 c. Radarscope (*horiz*)	15	15
377	35 c. Diagram of pressure zones (*horiz*)	20	20
378	50 c. Hurricane shown by satellite (*horiz*)	30	35
379	$1 Computer weather-map (*horiz*)	60	65
373/9	*Set of* 7	1·25	1·40
MS380	90 × 105 mm. Nos. 378/9	90	1·25

123 Going to Hospital   124 Cyrique Crab

(Des G. Vasarhelyi. Litho Format)

1973 (20 Aug). *25th Anniv of W.H.O. T* **123** *and similar horiz designs. Multicoloured. P* 14½.
381 ½ c. Type **123** .. 10 10
382 1 c. Maternity care .. 10 10
383 2 c. Smallpox inoculation .. 10 10
384 30 c. Emergency service .. 20 15
385 35 c. Waiting for the doctor .. 25 15
386 50 c. Medical examination .. 30 25
387 $1 Travelling doctor .. 45 60
381/7 .. *Set of* 7 1·10 1·10
MS388 112 × 110 mm. Nos. 386/7. P 14 × 14½ .. 75 1·25
a. Perf 14½ .. 65·00 45·00

(Des G. Drummond. Litho Format)

1973 (15 Oct). *Flora and Fauna. T* **124** *and similar vert designs. Multicoloured. P* 14½.
389 ½ c. Type **124** .. 10 10
390 22 c. Blue Land-crab .. 35 10
391 25 c. Bread Fruit .. 35 15
392 $1.20, Sunflower .. 1·50 2·00
389/92 .. *Set of* 4 2·00 2·00
MS393 91 × 127 mm. Nos. 389/92 .. 3·25 4·50

125 Princess Anne and Captain Mark Phillips

(Des G. Drummond. Litho Format)

1973 (14 Nov). *Royal Wedding. P* 13½.
394 **125** 25 c. multicoloured .. 10 10
395 – $2 multicoloured .. 30 30
MS396 79 × 100 mm. 75 c. as 25 c. and $1.20 as $2 40 30
No. 395 is as T **125**, but the portrait has a different frame.
Nos. 394/5 were each issued in small sheets of five stamps and one stamp-size label.

126 "Adoration of the Kings" (Brueghel)

(Des M. Shamir. Litho Format)

1973 (26 Nov). *Christmas. T* **126** *and similar horiz designs. Multicoloured. P* 14½.
397 ½ c. Type **126** .. 10 10
398 1 c. "Adoration of the Magi" (Botticelli) .. 10 10
399 2 c. "Adoration of the Magi" (Dürer) .. 10 10
400 12 c. "Mystic Nativity" (Botticelli) .. 10 10
401 22 c. "Adoration of the Magi" (Rubens) .. 10 10
402 35 c. "The Nativity" (Dürer) .. 15 10
403 $1 "Adoration of the Shepherds" (Giorgione) 40 55
397/403 .. *Set of* 7 70 80
MS404 122 × 98 mm. Nos. 402/3 .. 65 1·10

127 Carib Basket-weaving

(Des G. Drummond. Litho Format)

1973 (17 Dec). *National Day. T* **127** *and similar multicoloured designs. P* 13½.
405 5 c. Type **127** .. 10 10
406 10 c. Staircase of the Snake .. 10 10
407 50 c. Miss Caribbean Queen (*vert*) .. 15 15
408 50 c. Miss Carifta Queen (*vert*) .. 15 15
409 $1 Dance group .. 25 30
405/9 .. *Set of* 5 50 60
MS410 95 × 127 mm. Nos. 405/6 and 409 .. 40 65

128 University Centre, Dominica

(Des G. Drummond. Litho Format)

1974 (21 Jan). *25th Anniv of West Indies University. T* **128** *and similar horiz designs. Multicoloured. P* 14½.
411 12 c. Type **128** .. 10 10
412 30 c. Graduation ceremony .. 10 10
413 $1 University coat of arms .. 25 35
411/13 .. *Set of* 3 30 35
MS414 97 × 131 mm. Nos. 411/13 .. 30 55

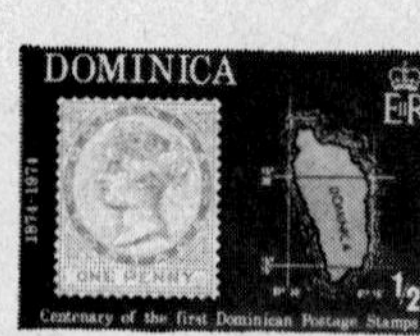

129 Dominicia 1d. Stamp of 1874 and Map   130 Footballer and Flag of Brazil

(Des G. Drummond. Litho Format)

1974 (27 May). *Stamp Centenary. T* **129** *and similar horiz designs. Multicoloured. P* 14½.
415 ½ c. Type **129** .. 10 10
416 1 c. 6d. stamp of 1874 and posthorn .. 10 10
417 2 c. 1s. stamp of 1874 and arms .. 10 10
418 10 c. Type **129** .. 15 10
419 50 c. As 1 c. .. 45 30
420 $1.20, As 2 c. .. 70 70
415/20 .. *Set of* 6 1·25 1·00
MS421 105 × 121 mm. Nos. 418/20 .. 25 1·50

(Des V. Whiteley. Litho Format)

1974 (12 Aug). *World Cup Football Championship, West Germany. T* **130** *and similar vert designs, showing footballers and flags of the countries given. Multicoloured. P* 14½.
422 ½ c. Type **130** .. 10 10
423 1 c. West Germany .. 10 10
424 2 c. Italy .. 10 10
425 30 c. Scotland .. 15 10
426 40 c. Sweden .. 15 10
427 50 c. Netherlands .. 20 15
428 $1 Yugoslavia .. 35 40
422/8 .. *Set of* 7 75 75
MS429 89 × 87 mm. Nos. 427/8 .. 50 70

131 Indian Hole

(Des G. Vasarhelyi. Litho Format)

1974 (1 Nov). *National Day. T* **131** *and similar horiz designs. Multicoloured. P* 13½.
430 10 c. Type **131** .. 10 10
431 40 c. Teachers' Training College .. 10 10
432 $1 Bay Oil distillery plant, Petite Savanne 30 45
430/2 .. *Set of* 3 40 45
MS433 96 × 143 mm. Nos. 430/2 .. 40 65

132 Churchill with "Colonist"

(Des G. Drummond. Litho Format)

1974 (25 Nov). *Birth Centenary of Sir Winston Churchill. T* **132** *and similar horiz designs. Multicoloured. P* 14½.
434 ½ c. Type **132** .. 10 10
435 1 c. Churchill and Eisenhower .. 10 10
436 2 c. Churchill and Roosevelt .. 10 10
437 20 c. Churchill and troops on assault-course .. 15 10
438 45 c. Painting at Marrakesh .. 25 10
439 $2 Giving the "V" sign .. 80 1·00
434/9 .. *Set of* 6 1·10 1·10
MS440 126 × 100 mm. Nos. 438/9. P 13 .. 1·10 1·75

133 Mailboats *Orinoco* (1851) and *Geesthaven* (1974)   134 "The Virgin and Child" (Tiso)

(Des G. Drummond. Litho Format)

1974 (4 Dec). *Centenary of Universal Postal Union. T* **133** *and similar horiz designs. Multicoloured. P* 13.
441 10 c. Type **133** .. 15 10
442 $2 De Havilland "4" (1918) and Boeing "747" (1974) .. 65 1·00
MS443 107 × 93 mm. $1.20 as 10 c. and $2.40 as $2 1·25 1·90
Nos. 442 and **MS**443 are inscr "De Haviland".

(Des M. Shamir. Litho Questa)

1974 (16 Dec). *Christmas. T* **134** *and similar vert designs. Multicoloured. P* 14.
444 ½ c. Type **134** .. 10 10
445 1 c. "Madonna and Child with Saints" (Costa) 10 10
446 2 c. "The Nativity" (School of Rimini, 14th-cent) .. 10 10
447 10 c. "The Rest on the Flight into Egypt" (Romanelli) .. 10 10
448 25 c. "Adoration of the Shepherds" (da Sermoneta) .. 10 10
449 45 c. "The Nativity" (Guido Reni) .. 15 10
450 $1 "The Adoration of the Magi" (Caselli) .. 30 40
444/50 .. *Set of* 7 60 60
MS451 114 × 78 mm. Nos. 449/50 .. 45 75

135 Trigger Fish

(Des G. Vasarhelyi. Litho Format)

1975 (2 June). *Fishes. T* **135** *and similar horiz designs. Multicoloured. P* 14.
452 ½ c. Type **135** .. 10 10
453 1 c. Cola .. 10 10
454 2 c. Sailfish .. 10 10
455 3 c. Vayway .. 10 10
456 20 c. Bechine .. 90 50
457 $2 Grouper .. 4·00 2·75
452/7 .. *Set of* 6 4·75 3·25
MS458 104 × 80 mm. No. 457. P 13 .. 4·00 4·25

136 *Myscelia antholia*

(Des J. W. Litho Format)

1975 (28 July). *Dominican Butterflies. T* **136** *and similar horiz designs. Multicoloured. P* 14½.
459 ½ c. Type **136** .. 10 10
460 1 c. *Lycorea ceres* .. 10 10
461 2 c. *Siderone nemesis* .. 10 10
462 6 c. *Battus polydamas* .. 25 10
463 30 c. *Anartia lytrea* .. 90 50
464 40 c. *Morpho peleides* .. 1·00 55
465 $2 *Dryas julia* .. 3·00 2·50
459/65 .. *Set of* 7 4·75 3·25
MS466 108 × 80 mm. No. 465. P 13 .. 3·00 3·25

137 R.M.S. *Yare*

(Des J. W. Litho Questa)

1975 (1 Sept). *"Ships Tied to Dominica's History". T* **137** *and similar horiz designs. Multicoloured. P* 14.
467 ½ c. Type **137** .. 10 10
468 1 c. R.M.S. *Thames* .. 10 10
469 2 c. S.S. *Lady Nelson* .. 10 10
470 20 c. S.S. *Lady Rodney* .. 45 35
471 45 c. M.V. *Statesman* .. 70 55
472 50 c. M.V. *Geestecape* .. 80 65
473 $2 M.V. *Geestestar* .. 4·50 3·25
467/73 .. *Set of* 7 6·00 4·50
MS474 78 × 103 mm. Nos. 472/3 .. 4·00 4·50

138 "Women in Agriculture"

139 Miss Caribbean Queen, 1975

(Litho Questa)

1975 (20 Oct). *International Women's Year. T* **138** *and similar horiz design. Multicoloured. P* 14.

No.	Description		
475	10 c. Type **138**	10	10
476	$2 "Women in Industry and Commerce"	40	60

(Litho Format)

1975 (6 Nov). *National Day. T* **139** *and similar multicoloured designs. P* 14 × 13½ *(vert) or* 13½ × 14 *(horiz).*

No.	Description		
477	5 c. Type **139**	10	10
478	10 c. Public Library *(horiz)*	10	10
479	30 c. Citrus Factory *(horiz)*	10	10
480	$1 National Day Trophy	25	50
477/80	*Set of* 4	35	60
MS481	130 × 98 mm. Nos. 478/80. Imperf	50	1·40

140 "Virgin and Child" (Mantegna)

141 Hibiscus

(Des M. Shamir. Litho Questa)

1975 (24 Nov). *Christmas. T* **140** *and similar vert designs showing "Virgin and Child". Multicoloured. P* 14.

No.	Description		
482	½ c. Type **140**	10	10
483	1 c. Fra Filippo Lippi	10	10
484	2 c. Bellini	10	10
485	10 c. Botticelli	10	10
486	25 c. Bellini	10	10
487	45 c. Correggio	15	10
488	$1 Dürer	30	50
482/88	*Set of* 7	65	70
MS489	139 × 85 mm. Nos. 487/88	80	1·50

(Des J.W. Litho Format)

1975 (8 Dec)–**78**. *T* **141** *and similar multicoloured designs.*

(a) Size as T **141**. *P* 14½

No.	Description		
490	½ c. Type **141**	10	10
491	1 c. African Tulip	15	10
492	2 c. Castor Oil Tree	15	10
493	3 c. White Cedar Flower	15	10
494	4 c. Egg Plant	15	10
495	5 c. Gare	20	10
496	6 c. Ochro	20	10
497	8 c. Zenaida Dove	40	10
498	10 c. Screw Pine	20	10
	a. Perf 13½ (1978)	25·00	
499	20 c. Mango Longue	25	15
500	25 c. Crayfish	35	15
501	30 c. Common Opossum ("Manicou")	40	20

(b) Size 28 × 44 *mm* ($10) *or* 44 × 28 *mm (others). P* 13½

No.	Description		
502	40 c. Bay Leaf Groves	45	25
503	50 c. Tomatoes	50	30
504	$1 Lime Factory	75	55
505	$2 Rum Distillery	1·75	2·00
506	$5 Bay Oil Distillery	4·25	4·50
507	$10 Queen Elizabeth II	10·00	13·00
490/507	*Set of* 18	18·00	19·00

142 American Infantry

143 Rowing

(Des J.W. Litho Format)

1976 (12 Apr). *Bicentenary of American Revolution. T* **142** *and similar vert designs. Multicoloured. P* 14½.

No.	Description		
508	½ c. Type **142**	10	10
509	1 c. British three-decker, 1782	10	10
510	2 c. George Washington	10	10
511	45 c. British sailors	75	30
512	75 c. British ensign	1·25	65
513	$2 Admiral Hood	3·00	2·00
508/13	*Set of* 6	4·50	2·75
MS514	105 × 92 mm. Nos. 512/13. P 13	5·00	5·50

(Des J.W. Litho Format)

1976 (24 May). *Olympic Games, Montreal. T* **143** *and similar vert designs. Multicoloured. P* 14½.

No.	Description		
515	½ c. Type **143**	10	10
516	1 c. Shot putting	10	10
517	2 c. Swimming	10	10
518	40 c. Relay	15	10
519	45 c. Gymnastics	15	10
520	60 c. Sailing	20	20
521	$2 Archery	55	80
515/21	*Set of* 7	1·10	1·10
MS522	90 × 104 mm. Nos. 520/1. P 13	1·25	1·75

144 Ringed Kingfisher

145 Viking Spacecraft System

(Des G. Drummond. Litho Format)

1976 (28 June). *Wild Birds. T* **144** *and similar multicoloured designs. P* 14½.

No.	Description		
523	½ c. Type **144**	10	10
524	1 c. Mourning Dove	10	10
525	2 c. Green Heron	15	10
526	15 c. Broad-winged Hawk	70	45
527	30 c. Blue-headed Hummingbird	1·25	70
528	45 c. Bananaquit	1·90	1·00
529	$2 Imperial Amazon	8·50	7·00
523/9	*Set of* 7	11·00	8·50
MS530	133 × 101 mm. Nos. 527/9. P 13	11·00	12·00

1976 (26 July). *West Indian Victory in World Cricket Cup. As Nos. 559/60 of Barbados.*

No.	Description		
531	15 c. Map of the Caribbean	75	75
532	25 c. Prudential Cup	1·00	1·00

(Des PAD Studio. Litho Format)

1976 (20 Sept). *Viking Space Mission. T* **145** *and similar multicoloured designs. P* 14½.

No.	Description		
533	½ c. Type **145**	10	10
534	1 c. Launching pad *(horiz)*	10	10
535	2 c. Titan IIID and Centaur DII	10	10
536	3 c. Orbiter and lander capsule	10	10
537	45 c. Capsule, parachute unopened	20	15
538	75 c. Capsule, parachute opened	30	25
539	$1 Lander descending *(horiz)*	40	35
540	$2 Space vehicle on Mars *(horiz)*	70	60
533/40	*Set of* 8	1·75	1·40
MS541	104 × 78 mm. Nos. 539/40. P 13	1·50	2·25

146 "Virgin and Child with Saints Anthony of Padua and Roch" (Giorgione)

147 Island Craft Co-operative

(Des M. Shamir. Litho Questa)

1976 (1 Nov). *Christmas. T* **146** *and similar vert designs showing "Virgin and Child" by the artists named. Multicoloured. P* 14.

No.	Description		
542	½ c. Type **146**	10	10
543	1 c. Bellini	10	10
544	2 c. Mantegna	10	10
545	6 c. Mantegna *(different)*	10	10
546	25 c. Memling	10	10
547	45 c. Correggio	15	10
548	$3 Raphael	70	1·00
542/8	*Set of* 7	85	1·10
MS549	140 × 85 mm. 50 c. as No. 547 and $1 as No. 548	65	1·10

(Des G. Drummond. Litho Questa)

1976 (22 Nov). *National Day. T* **147** *and similar horiz designs. Multicoloured. P* 13½.

No.	Description		
550	10 c. Type **147**	10	10
551	50 c. Harvesting bananas	15	10
552	$1 Boxing plant	30	35
550/2	*Set of* 3	45	45
MS553	96 × 122 mm. Nos. 550/2	50	90

148 Common Sundial

149 The Queen Crowned and Enthroned

(Des J.W. Litho Questa)

1976 (20 Dec). *Shells. T* **148** *and similar vert designs. Multicoloured. P* 14.

No.	Description		
554	½ c. Type **148**	10	10
555	1 c. Flame Helmet	10	10
556	2 c. Mouse Cone	10	10
557	20 c. Caribbean vase	45	10
558	40 c. West Indian Fighting Conch	70	25
559	50 c. Short Coral Shell	70	25
560	$3 Apple Murex	3·50	2·75
554/60	*Set of* 7	5·00	3·00
MS561	101 × 55 mm. $2 Long-spined Star Shell	2·50	3·00

(Des J.W. Litho Questa)

1977 (7 Feb). *Silver Jubilee. T* **149** *and similar horiz designs. Multicoloured. P* 14 × 13½.

No.	Description		
562	½ c. Type **149**	10	10
563	1 c. Imperial State Crown	10	10
564	45 c. Queen Elizabeth and Princess Anne	15	10
565	$2 Coronation Ring	25	30
566	$2.50, Ampulla and Spoon	30	40
562/6	*Set of* 5	60	70
MS567	104 × 79 mm. $5 Queen Elizabeth and Prince Philip	1·00	1·75

Nos. 562/6 also exist perf 12×11½ *(Price for set of* 5 £1 *mint or used)* from additional sheetlets of 5 stamps and one label. Stamps perforated 14×13½ are from normal sheets of 40. Stamps from the sheets of 5 have the arch at left in a different colour.

150 Joseph Haydn

151 Hiking

(Des J.W. Litho Questa)

1977 (25 Apr). *150th Death Anniv of Ludwig van Beethoven. T* **150** *and similar vert designs. Multicoloured. P* 14.

No.	Description		
568	½ c. Type **150**	10	10
569	1 c. Scene from "Fidelio"	10	10
570	2 c. Maria Casentini (dancer)	10	10
571	15 c. Beethoven and pastoral scene	15	10
572	30 c. "Wellington's Victory"	25	10
573	40 c. Henriette Sontag (singer)	35	10
574	$2 The young Beethoven	1·50	1·25
568/74	*Set of* 7	2·00	1·50
MS575	138 × 93 mm. Nos. 572/4	2·75	3·00

(Des J.W. Litho Questa)

1977 (8 Aug). *Caribbean Scout Jamboree, Jamaica. T* **151** *and similar horiz designs. Multicoloured. P* 14.

No.	Description		
576	½ c. Type **151**	10	10
577	1 c. First-aid	10	10
578	2 c. Camping	10	10
579	45 c. Rock climbing	35	15
580	50 c. Canoeing	40	20
581	$3 Sailing	2·00	1·75
576/81	*Set of* 6	2·50	2·00
MS582	111 × 113 mm. 75 c. Map reading and $2 Campfire singsong	1·60	1·75

152 Holy Family

ROYAL VISIT
W.I. 1977
(153)

(Des G. Vasarhelyi. Litho Questa)

1977 (17 Nov). *Christmas. T* **152** *and similar horiz designs showing book miniatures from Foix Book of Hours* ($3) *or De Lisle Psalter (others). Multicoloured. P* 14.

No.	Description		
583	½ c. Type **152**	10	10
584	1 c. Angel and Shepherds	10	10
585	2 c. Holy Baptism	10	10
586	6 c. Flight into Egypt	10	10
587	15 c. Three Kings with gifts	10	10
588	45 c. Holy Family in the Temple	15	10
589	$3 Flight into Egypt *(different)*	50	70
583/9	*Set of* 7	75	80
MS590	113 × 85 mm. 50 c. Virgin and Child; $2 Flight into Egypt *(different)*	60	75

1977 (28 Nov). *Royal Visit. Nos.* 562/7 *optd with T* **153**. A. *In top left-hand corner**. *P* 14 × 13½. B. *Above "JUBILEE". P* 12 × 11½.

		A.		B.	
591	½ c. Type **149**	†		10	10
592	1 c. Imperial State Crown	†		10	10
593	45 c. Queen Elizabeth and Princess Anne	15	10	15	10
594	$2 Coronation Ring	30	30	40	40
595	$2.50, Ampulla and Spoon	35	35	50	50
591/5	*Set of* 5	†		1·10	1·10
MS596	104 × 79 mm. $5 Queen Elizabeth and Prince Philip	1·00	1·50	†	
	a. Optd "W.I. 1977" only on stamp	7·50	7·50	†	

*Stamp from No. **MS**596 has the overprint to left of face-value.

No. **MS**596a is overprinted "W.I. 1977" beneath "ROYAL VISIT" inscription to left of stamp design. Overprint as T **153**, but in one line, appears at top left of *miniature sheet*.

154 "Sousouelle Souris"

(Des L. Honychurch and J.W. Litho Questa)

1978 (9 Jan). *"History of Carnival". T* **154** *and similar horiz designs. Multicoloured. P* 14.

597	½ c. Type **154**	10	10
598	1 c. Sensay costume	10	10
599	2 c. Street musicians	10	10
600	45 c. Douiette band	15	10
601	50 c. Pappy Show wedding	15	10
602	$2 Masquerade band	45	60
597/602	*Set of* 6	75	75
MS603	104 × 88 mm. $2.50 as No. 602	60	85

155 Col. Charles Lindbergh and *Spirit of St. Louis*

156 Queen receiving Homage

(Des G. Drummond. Litho Format)

1978 (13 Mar). *Aviation Anniversaries. T* **155** *and similar horiz designs. Multicoloured. P* 14½.

604	6 c. Type **155**	10	10
605	10 c. *Spirit of St. Louis*, New York, 20 May 1927	10	10
606	15 c. Lindbergh and map of Atlantic	15	10
607	20 c. Lindbergh reaches Paris, 21 May 1927	20	10
608	40 c. *LZ*1, Lake Constance, 1900	25	20
609	60 c. Count F. von Zeppelin and *LZ*2, 1906	35	30
610	$3 *LZ*127 (*Graf Zeppelin*), 1928	75	1·10
604/10	*Set of* 7	1·60	1·75
MS611	139 × 108 mm. 50 c. *Spirit of St. Louis* in mid-Atlantic; $2 *Graf Zeppelin*, 1928	80	1·10

The 6, 10, 15, 20 and 50 c. values commemorate the 50th anniversary of first solo transatlantic flight by Col. Charles Lindbergh; the other values commemorate anniversaries of various Zeppelin airships.

(Des J.W. Litho Questa)

1978 (2 June). *25th Anniv of Coronation. T* **156** *and similar vert designs. Multicoloured. P* 14.

612	45 c. Type**156**	15	10
613	$2 Balcony scene	30	30
614	$2.50, Queen and Prince Philip	40	40
612/14	*Set of* 3	75	65
MS615	76 × 107 mm. $5 Queen Elizabeth II	1·10	1·10

Nos. 612/14 also exist perf 12 (*Price for set of* 3 £1 *mint or used*) from additional sheetlets of 3 stamps and 1 label. Stamps perforated 14 come from sheets of 50. The stamps from sheetlets have changed background or inscription colours.

157 Wilbur Wright's Aeroplane

158 "Two Apostles" (Rubens)

(Des G. Vasarhelyi. Litho Format)

1978 (10 July). *75th Anniv of Powered Flight. T* **157** *and similar horiz designs. Multicoloured. P* 14½.

616	30 c. Type **157**	15	15
617	40 c. *Flyer*, 1908	20	20
618	60 c. *Flyer* I	25	25
619	$2 *Flyer* I (*different*)	85	85
616/19	*Set of* 4	1·25	1·25
MS620	116 × 89 mm. $3 Wilbur and Orville Wright	90	1·00

(Des BG Studio. Litho Questa)

1978 (16 Oct). *Christmas. Paintings. T* **158** *and similar vert designs. Multicoloured. P* 14.

621	20 c. Type **158**	10	10
622	45 c. "The Descent from the Cross" (Rubens)	15	10
623	50 c. "St Ildefonso receiving the Chasuble" (Rubens)	15	10
624	$3 "The Assumption of the Virgin" (Rubens)	55	80
621/4	*Set of* 4	75	90
MS625	113 × 83 mm. $2 "The Holy Family" (Sebastiano del Piombo*)	65	75

*This painting was incorrectly attributed to Rubens on the stamp.

INDEPENDENT

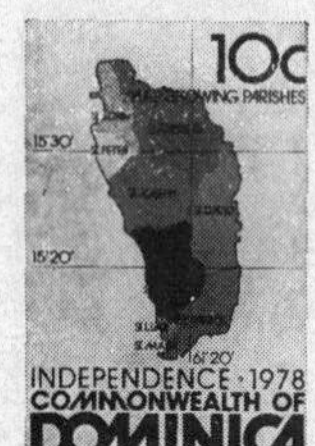

159 Map showing Parishes

INDEPENDENCE
3rd NOVEMBER
1978

(160)

(Des J.W. Litho Questa)

1978 (3 Nov). *Independence. T* **159** *and similar vert designs. Multicoloured. P* 14.

626	10 c. Type **159**	10	10
627	25 c. *Sabinea carinalis* (National flower)	15	10
628	45 c. New National flag	25	15
629	50 c. Coat of arms	25	15
630	$2 Patrick John (Prime Minister)	70	70
626/30	*Set of* 5	1·25	90
MS631	113 × 90 mm. $2.50, Type **159**	2·00	2·25

1978 (3 Nov)–**79**. *Independence. Nos.* 490/507 (10 *c. now perf* 13½) *optd as T* **160** *by typography*.

632	½ c. Type **141**	10	10
633	1 c. African Tulip	15	10
634	2 c. Castor Oil Tree	15	10
635	3 c. White Cedar Flower	20	15
636	4 c. Egg Plant	20	15
637	5 c. Gare	20	15
638	6 c. Ochro	20	15
639	8 c. Zenaida Dove	45	20
640	10 c. Screw Pine	20	15
	a. Perf 14½. Litho opt (7.79)	20	15
641	20 c. Mango Longue	25	15
642	25 c. Crayfish	35	20
643	30 c. Common Opossum	35	20
644	40 c. Bay Leaf Groves	30	25
	a. Litho opt (7.79)	30	25
645	50 c. Tomatoes	40	30
646	$1 Lime Factory	70	65
647	$2 Rum Distillery	1·25	1·00
648	$5 Bay Oil Distillery	2·50	2·25
649	$10 Queen Elizabeth II	5·50	4·50
	a. Litho opt (7.79)	5·50	4·50
632/49	*Set of* 18	12·00	10·00

For History of Aviation gold foil stamps see Appendix at the end of the Dominica listing.

161 Sir Rowland Hill

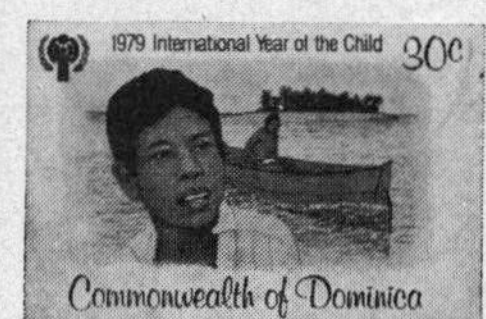

162 Children and Canoe

(Des BG Studio. Litho Questa)

1979 (19 Mar). *Death Centenary of Sir Rowland Hill. T* **161** *and similar vert designs. P* 14.

650	25 c. multicoloured	10	10
651	45 c. multicoloured	15	10
652	50 c. black, reddish violet and magenta	15	10
653	$2 black, magenta and yellow	50	65
650/3	*Set of* 4	75	80
MS654	186 × 96 mm. $5 black and vermilion	1·25	1·75

Designs:—45 c. Great Britain 1840 2d. blue; 50 c. 1874 1d. stamp; $2 Maltese Cross cancellations; $5 Penny Black.

Nos. 650/3 also exist perf 12 (*Price for set of* 4 80*p mint or used*) from additional sheetlets of 5 stamps and 1 label. Shades of these stamps differ from those perforated 14 which come from sheets of 40.

(Des BG Studio. Litho Questa)

1979 (23 Apr). *International Year of the Child. T* **162** *and similar horiz designs. Multicoloured. P* 14.

655	30 c. Type **162**	25	15
656	40 c. Children with bananas	35	25
657	50 c. Children playing cricket	50	40
658	$3 Child feeding rabbits	1·50	1·50
655/8	*Set of* 4	2·40	2·10
MS659	117 × 85 mm. $5 Child with catch of fish	1·50	1·75

163 Grouper

(Des G. Drummond. Litho Questa)

1979 (21 May). *Marine Wildlife. T* **163** *and similar horiz designs. Multicoloured. P* 14.

660	10 c. Type **163**	15	10
661	30 c. Striped Dolphin	35	15
662	50 c. White-tailed Tropic Bird	80	25
663	60 c. Brown Pelican	90	30
664	$1 Long-finned Pilot Whale	1·25	45
665	$2 Brown Booby	1·90	80
660/5	*Set of* 6	4·75	1·75
MS666	120 × 94 mm. $3 Elkhorn Coral	1·60	1·75

164 H.M.S. *Endeavour*

(Des J.W. Litho Questa)

1979 (16 July). *Death Bicentenary of Captain Cook. T* **164** *and similar horiz designs. Multicoloured. P* 14.

667	10 c. Type **164**	20	10
668	50 c. H.M.S. *Resolution*	45	45
669	60 c. H.M.S. *Discovery*	55	55
670	$2 Detail of Cook's chart of New Zealand, 1770	1·10	1·10
667/70	*Set of* 4	2·10	2·00
MS671	97 × 90 mm. $5 Captain Cook and signature	2·00	2·50

165 Cooking at Camp-fire

166 Colvillea

(Des M. Diamond. Litho Questa)

1979 (30 July). *50th Anniv of Girl Guide Movement in Dominica. T* **165** *and similar horiz designs. Multicoloured. P* 14.

672	10 c. Type **165**	15	10
673	20 c. Pitching emergency rain tent	20	10
674	50 c. Raising Dominican flag	25	10
675	$2.50, Singing and dancing to accordion	80	80
672/5	*Set of* 4	1·25	85
MS676	110 × 86 mm. $3 Guides of different age-groups	75	1·25

(Des J.W. Litho Questa)

1979 (3 Sept). *Flowering Trees. T* **166** *and similar vert designs. Multicoloured. P* 14.

677	20 c. Type **166**	15	10
678	40 c. Lignum Vitae	25	15
679	60 c. Dwarf Poinciana	35	25
680	$2 Fern Tree	90	90
677/80	*Set of* 4	1·50	1·25
MS681	114 × 89 mm. $3 Perfume Tree	75	1·10

167 Cathedral of the Assumption, Roseau

(Des W. Grout. Litho Questa)

1979 (11 Oct). *Christmas. Cathedrals. T* **167** *and similar multi-coloured designs. P* 14.

682	6 c. Type **167**	10	10
683	45 c. St. Paul's, London (*vert*)	15	10
684	60 c. St. Peter's, Rome	15	10
685	$3 Notre Dame, Paris (*vert*)	55	60
682/5	*Set of* 4	75	70
MS686	113 × 85 mm. 40 c. St. Patrick's, New York; $2 Cologne Cathedral (*both vert*)	50	80

HURRICANE RELIEF

(168)

169 Mickey Mouse and Octopus playing Xylophone

1979 (29 Oct). *Hurricane Relief. Nos. 495, 502 and 506/7 optd as T* **168**.

687	5 c. Gare	10	10
688	40 c. Bay Leaf Groves	10	10
689	$5 Bay Oil Distillery	1·25	1·50
690	$10 Queen Elizabeth II	2·00	2·25
687/90	*Set of* 4	3·00	3·75

(Litho Format)

1979 (2 Nov). *International Year of the Child. Walt Disney Cartoon Characters. T* **169** *and similar vert designs showing characters playing musical instruments. Multicoloured. P* 11.

691	½ c. Type **169**	10	10
692	1 c. Goofy playing guitar on rocking-horse	10	10
693	2 c. Mickey Mouse playing violin and Goofy playing bagpipes	10	10
694	3 c. Donald Duck playing drum with pneumatic drill	10	10
695	4 c. Minnie Mouse playing saxophone on roller-skates	10	10
696	5 c. Goofy as one-man-band	10	10
697	10 c. Dale being blown from French horn by Horace Horsecollar	10	10
698	$2 Huey, Dewey and Louie playing bass	2·25	1·25
699	$2.50, Donald Duck playing piano and Huey playing trumpet	2·50	1·50
691/9	*Set of* 9	4·50	2·75
MS700	127 × 102 mm. $3 Mickey Mouse playing piano. P 13½	2·00	2·00

170 Hospital Ward

(Des BG Studio. Litho Questa)

1980 (31 Mar). *75th Anniv of Rotary International. T* **170** *and similar horiz designs. Multicoloured. P* 14.

701	10 c. Type **170**	10	10
702	20 c. Electric-cardiogram	15	10
703	40 c. Site for mental hospital	20	15
704	$2.50, Paul P. Harris (founder)	55	70
701/4	*Set of* 4	80	85
MS705	128 × 113 mm. $3 Interlocking cogs of Rotary emblem and globe	60	80

1980 (6 May). *"London 1980" International Stamp Exhibition. As Nos. 650/3 optd with T* **262** *of Grenada. P* 12.

706	25 c. multicoloured	15	10
707	45 c. multicoloured	20	15
708	50 c. olive-brown, blue and rose-red	20	15
709	$2 olive-brown, vermilion and yellow	60	60
706/9	*Set of* 4	1·00	80

171 Shot Putting

(Des J.W. Litho Questa)

1980 (27 May). *Olympic Games, Moscow. T* **171** *and similar horiz designs. Multicoloured. P* 14.

710	30 c. Type **171**	10	10
711	40 c. Basketball	15	15
712	60 c. Swimming	20	20
713	$2 Gymnastics	55	65
710/13	*Set of* 4	80	90
MS714	114 × 86 mm. $3 The Marathon	70	90

172 "Supper at Emmaus" (Caravaggio)

(Des J.W. Litho Questa)

1980 (22 July). *Famous Paintings. T* **172** *and similar multicoloured designs. P* 13½.

715	20 c. Type **172**	10	10
716	25 c. "Portrait of Charles I Hunting" (Van Dyck) (*vert*)	10	10
717	30 c. "The Maids of Honour" (Velasquez) (*vert*)	15	10
718	45 c. "The Rape of the Sabine Women" (Poussin)	15	10
719	$1 "Embarkation for Cythera" (Watteau)	35	35
720	$5 "Girl before a Mirror" (Picasso) (*vert*)	1·50	1·50
715/20	*Set of* 6	2·00	2·00
MS721	114 × 111 mm. $3 "The Holy Family" (Rembrandt) (*vert*)	60	80

173 Scene from "Peter Pan"

(Litho Walsall)

1980 (1 Oct). *Christmas. Scenes from Walt Disney's Cartoon Film "Peter Pan". T* **173** *and similar horiz designs. P* 11.

722	½ c. multicoloured	10	10
723	1 c. multicoloured	10	10
724	2 c. multicoloured	10	10
725	3 c. multicoloured	10	10
726	4 c. multicoloured	10	10
727	5 c. multicoloured	10	10
728	10 c. multicoloured	10	10
729	$2 multicoloured	90	80
730	$2.50, multicoloured	1·00	95
722/30	*Set of* 9	2·00	1·90
MS731	124 × 98 mm. $4 multicoloured (*vert*)	2·00	2·25

174 Queen Elizabeth the Queen Mother in Doorway

(Litho Questa)

1980 (20 Oct). *80th Birthday of Queen Elizabeth the Queen Mother. P* 12.

732 **174**	40 c. multicoloured	40	40
733	$2.50, multicoloured	1·50	1·50
MS734	85 × 66 mm. **174** $3 multicoloured	2·00	2·00

Nos. 732/3 also exist perforated 14 (*price for pair £1.90 mint or used*) from additional sheetlets of 9. Stamps perforated 12 are from normal sheets of 50.

175 Douglas Bay

(Des G. Drummond. Litho Questa)

1981 (12 Feb). *Dominica Safari. T* **175** *and similar multicoloured designs. P* 14.

735	20 c. Type **175**	10	10
736	30 c. Valley of Desolation	15	15
737	40 c. Emerald Pool (*vert*)	20	20
738	$3 Indian River (*vert*)	1·40	1·60
735/8	*Set of* 4	1·75	1·90
MS739	84 × 104 mm. $4 Trafalgar Falls (*vert*)	1·75	2·25

(Litho Format)

1981 (30 Apr). *50th Anniv of Walt Disney's Cartoon Character, Pluto. Vert designs as T* **169**. *Multicoloured. P* 13½ × 14.

740	$2 Pluto and Fifi	1·25	1·25
MS741	128 × 102 mm. $4 Pluto in scene from film *Pluto's Blue Note*	2·40	2·50

176 Forest Thrush

177 Windsor Castle

(Des P. Barrett. Litho Questa)

1981 (30 Apr). *Birds. T* **176** *and similar horiz designs. Multicoloured. P* 14.

742	20 c. Type **176**	40	10
743	30 c. Wied's Crested Flycatcher	50	15
744	40 c. Blue-hooded Euphonia	60	20
745	$5 Lesser Antillean Pewee	3·25	3·25
742/5	*Set of* 4	4·25	3·25
MS746	121 × 95 mm. $3 Imperial Amazon	2·00	1·75

(Des J.W. Litho Questa)

1981 (23 June). *Royal Wedding. T* **177** *and similar vert designs. Multicoloured. A. P* 14. *B. P* 12.

		A		B	
747	45 c. Prince Charles and Lady Diana Spencer	20	10	2·25	2·25
748	60 c. Type **177**	25	15	2·25	2·25
749	$4 Prince Charles as helicopter pilot	1·00	1·00	2·25	2·25
747/9	*Set of* 3	1·25	1·10	6·00	6·00
MS750	96 × 82 mm. $5 Helicopter of Queen's Flight	1·25	1·25	†	

Nos. 747B/9B also exist from additional sheetlets of five stamps and one label with changed background colours.

178 Lady Diana Spencer

179 Ixora

(Manufactured by Walsall)

1981 (23 June). *Royal Wedding. Booklet stamps. T* **178** *and similar vert designs. Multicoloured. Roul 5 × imperf*. Self-adhesive.*

751	25 c. Type **178**	20	25
	a. Booklet pane. Nos. 751/2, each × 3	2·50	
752	$2 Prince Charles	70	90
753	$5 Prince Charles and Lady Diana Spencer	1·75	2·25
	a. Booklet pane of 1	1·75	
751/3	*Set of* 3	2·40	3·00

*The 25 c. and $2 values were separated by various combinations of rotary knife (giving a straight edge) and roulette. The $5 value exists only with straight edges.

(Litho Questa)

1981 (2 Nov). *Christmas. Horiz designs as T* **169** *showing scenes from Walt Disney's cartoon film "Santa's Workshop". P* 13½.

754	½ c. multicoloured	10	10
755	1 c. multicoloured	10	10
756	2 c. multicoloured	10	10
757	3 c. multicoloured	10	10
758	4 c. multicoloured	10	10
759	5 c. multicoloured	10	10
760	10 c. multicoloured	10	10
761	45 c. multicoloured	50	30
762	$5 multicoloured	3·00	2·50
754/62	*Set of* 9	3·25	2·75
MS763	129 × 103 mm. $4 multicoloured	2·25	2·50

(Des P. Barrett. Litho Questa)

1981 (1 Dec)–**85**. *Plant Life. Horiz designs as T* **179**. *Multicoloured. A. Without imprint date. P* 14

764A	1 c. Type **179**	10	15
765A	2 c. Flamboyant	10	15
766A	4 c. Poinsettia	10	10
767A	5 c. Bois Caribe (national flower of Dominica)	10	10
768A	8 c. Annatto or Roucou	10	10
769A	10 c. Passion Fruit	20	10
770A	15 c. Breadfruit or Yampain	25	10
771A	20 c. Allamanda or Buttercup	20	10
772A	25 c. Cashew Nut	20	10
773A	35 c. Soursop or Couassol	25	20
774A	40 c. Bougainvillea	25	20
775A	45 c. Anthurium	30	25
776A	60 c. Cacao or Cocoa	60	40
777A	90 c. Pawpaw Tree or Papay	60	45
778A	$1 Coconut Palm	85	60
779A	$2 Coffee Tree or Café	1·00	1·50
780A	$5 Heliconia or Lobster Claw	4·25	6·00
781A	$10 Banana/Fig	7·00	10·00
764A/81A	*Set of* 18	15·00	18·00

B. *With imprint date at foot of design. P* 14 (15, 60 *c.*) *or* 12 (*others*)

769B	10 c. Passion Fruit (1984)	35	10
	a. Perf 14 (7.85)	35	10
770B	15 c. Breadfruit or Yampain (7.85)	35	10
776B	60 c. Cacao or Cocoa (7.85)	70	30
778B	$1 Coconut Palm (1984)	1·00	60
780B	$5 Heliconia or Lobster Claw (1984)	3·25	3·50
781B	$10 Banana Fig (1984)	5·00	6·50
769B/81B	*Set of* 6	9·50	10·00

180 Curb slope for Wheelchairs

181 "Olga Picasso in an Armchair"

(Des BG Studio. Litho Format)

1981 (22 Dec). *International Year for Disabled Persons. T* **180** *and similar vert designs. Multicoloured. P* 14½.
782 45 c. Type **180** 50 25
783 60 c. Bus with invalid step 60 35
784 75 c. Motor car controls adapted for handicapped 70 40
785 $4 Bus with wheelchair ramp .. .. .. 2·50 2·50
782/5 .. .. *Set of* 4 4·00 3·25
MS786 82 × 96 mm. $5 Specially designed elevator control panel .. .. 3·00 3·00

(Des J.W. Litho Format)

1981 (30 Dec). *Birth Centenary of Picasso. T* **181** *and similar vert designs. Multicoloured. P* 14½.
787 45 c. Type **181** 45 25
788 60 c. "Bathers" 55 35
789 75 c. "Woman in Spanish Costume" 70 40
790 $4 "Detail of Dog and Cock" .. .. .. 2·50 2·50
787/90 .. .. *Set of* 4 3·75 3·25
MS791 140 × 115 mm. $5 "Sleeping Peasants" (detail) .. .. 2·75 2·75

(Litho Questa)

1982 (29 Jan). *World Cup Football Championship, Spain. Walt Disney Cartoon Characters. Horiz designs as T* **169**. *Multicoloured. P* 14 × 13½.
792 ½ c. Goofy chasing ball with butterfly net .. 10 10
793 1 c. Donald Duck with ball in beak 10 10
794 2 c. Goofy as goalkeeper 10 10
795 3 c. Goofy looking for ball 10 10
796 4 c. Goofy as park attendant puncturing ball with litter spike 10 10
797 5 c. Pete and Donald Duck playing 10 10
798 10 c. Donald Duck after kicking rock instead of ball 10 10
799 60 c. Donald Duck feeling effects of a hard game and Daisy Duck dusting ball .. 55 55
800 $5 Goofy hiding ball under his jersey from Mickey Mouse .. .. 2·75 2·75
792/800 .. .. *Set of* 9 3·25 3·25
MS801 132 × 105 mm. $4 Dale making off with ball 2·25 2·25

182 "Golden Days"

183 Elma Napier (first woman elected to B.W.I. Legislative Council)

(Des M.B.I. Studios. Litho Questa)

1982 (10 Mar). *Norman Rockwell (painter) Commemoration. T* **182** *and similar vert designs. Multicoloured. P* 14 × 13½.
802 10 c. Type **182** 10 10
803 25 c. "The Morning News" 15 10
804 45 c. "The Marbles Champ" 30 30
805 $1 "Speeding Along" 55 55
802/5 .. .. *Set of* 4 95 95

(Des BG Studio. Litho Questa)

1982 (15 Apr). *Decade for Women. T* **183** *and similar horiz designs. Multicoloured. P* 14.
806 10 c. Type **183** 10 10
807 45 c. Margaret Mead (anthropologist) 30 30
808 $1 Mabel ("Cissy") Caudeiron (folk song composer and historian) 55 55
809 $4 Eleanor Roosevelt .. .. 2·25 2·25
806/9 .. .. *Set of* 4 2·75 2·75
MS810 92 × 63 mm. $3 Florence Nightingale .. 1·75 2·25

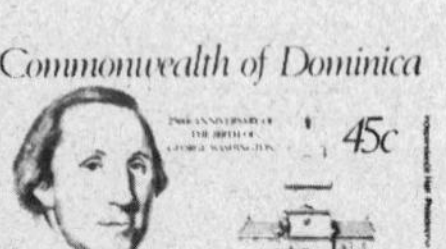
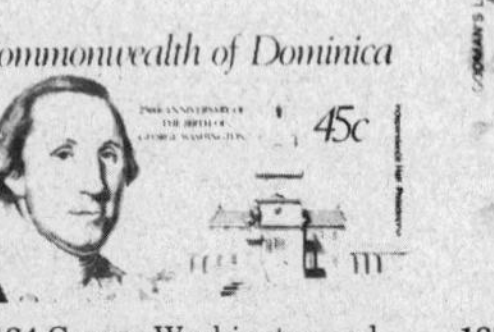

184 George Washington and Independence Hall, Philadelphia

185 Godman's Leaf Butterfly

(Des J.W. Litho Format)

1982 (1 May). *250th Birth Anniv of George Washington* (45, 90 c.) *and Birth Centenary of Franklin D. Roosevelt* (60 c., $2). *T* **184** *and similar horiz designs. Multicoloured. P* 14½.
811 45 c. Type **184** 40 25
812 60 c. Franklin D. Roosevelt and Capitol, Washington D.C. 50 35
813 90 c. Washington at Yorktown (detail, "The Surrender of Cornwallis" by Trumbull) 70 55
814 $2 Construction of dam (from W. Gropper's mural commemorating Roosevelt's "New Deal") .. .. 1·50 1·60
811/14 .. .. *Set of* 4 2·75 2·50
MS815 115 × 90 mm. $5 Washington and Roosevelt with U.S.A. flags of 1777 and 1933 .. .. 2·50 2·75

(Des P. Barrett. Litho Questa)

1982 (1 June). *Butterflies. T* **185** *and similar vert designs. Multicoloured. P* 14.
816 15 c. Type **185** 65 15
817 45 c. Zebra .. .. 1·10 35
818 60 c. Mimic .. .. 1·40 45
819 $3 Red Rim .. .. 3·25 3·25
816/19 .. .. *Set of* 4 5·75 3·75
MS820 77 × 105 mm. $5 Southern Dagger Tail .. 4·00 4·50

186 Prince and Princess of Wales

187 Scouts around Campfire

(Des PAD Studio. Litho Questa)

1982 (1 July). *21st Birthday of Princess of Wales. T* **186** *and similar vert designs. Multicoloured. P* 14½ × 14.
821 45 c. Buckingham Palace 30 30
822 $2 Type **186** 90 90
823 $4 Princess of Wales .. .. 1·60 1·60
821/3 .. .. *Set of* 3 2·50 2·50
MS824 103 × 75 mm. $5 Princess Diana (*different*) 2·00 2·25
Nos. 821/3 also exist in sheetlets of 5 stamps and 1 label.

(Des R. Sauber. Litho Questa)

1982 (3 Aug). *75th Anniv of Boy Scout Movement. T* **187** *and similar multicoloured designs. P* 14.
825 45 c. Type **187** 75 25
826 60 c. Temperature study, Valley of Desolation 1·00 50
827 75 c. Learning about native birds .. .. 1·25 65
828 $3 Canoe trip along Indian River .. .. 3·00 3·50
825/8 .. .. *Set of* 4 5·50 4·50
MS829 99 × 70 mm. $5 Dominican scouts saluting the flag (*vert*) .. .. 2·75 3·25

1982 (30 Aug). *Birth of Prince William of Wales. Nos.* 821/4 *optd with T* **171** *of Antigua.*
830 45 c. Buckingham Palace 30 30
831 $2 Type **186** .. .. 1·10 1·10
832 $4 Princess of Wales .. .. 1·90 1·90
830/2 .. .. *Set of* 3 3·00 3·00
MS833 103 × 75 mm. $5 Princess Diana (*different*) 2·25 2·50
Nos. 830/2 also exist in sheetlets of 5 stamps and 1 label.

188 "Holy Family of Francis I"

189 Cuvier's Beaked Whale

(Des Design Images. Litho Questa)

1982 (3 Nov). *Christmas. Raphael Paintings. T* **188** *and similar vert designs. Multicoloured. P* 13½ × 14.
834 25 c. Type **188** 15 10
835 30 c. "Holy Family of the Pearl" 20 15
836 90 c. "Canigiani Holy Family" 55 55
837 $4 "Holy Family of the Oak Tree" .. .. 1·90 1·90
834/7 .. .. *Set of* 4 2·50 2·40
MS838 95 × 125 mm. $5 "Holy Family of the Lamb" .. .. 2·40 2·50

(Des J. Cooter. Litho Questa)

1983 (15 Feb). *Save the Whales. T* **189** *and similar horiz designs. Multicoloured. P* 14.
839 45 c. Type **189** 60 35
840 60 c. Humpback Whale 75 45
841 75 c. Black Right Whale 85 55
842 $3 Melon-headed Whale .. .. 2·50 3·00
839/42 .. .. *Set of* 4 4·25 4·00
MS843 99 × 72 mm. $5 Pygmy Sperm Whale .. 3·50 3·75

190 Banana Export

(Des R. Vigurs. Litho Questa)

1983 (14 Mar). *Commonwealth Day. T* **190** *and similar horiz designs. Multicoloured. P* 14.
844 25 c. Type **190** 15 15
845 30 c. Road building 15 20
846 90 c. Community nursing 40 45
847 $3 Tourism—handicrafts .. .. 1·25 1·50
844/7 .. .. *Set of* 4 1·75 2·10

191 Map and Satellite Picture of Hurricane

(Des G. Vasarhelyi. Litho Questa)

1983 (18 Apr). *World Communications Year. T* **191** *and similar horiz designs. Multicoloured. P* 14.
848 45 c. Type **191** 20 25
849 60 c. Aircraft-to-ship transmission 30 35
850 90 c. Satellite communications 40 45
851 $2 Shortwave radio .. .. 95 1·00
848/51 .. .. *Set of* 4 1·75 1·90
MS852 110 × 85 mm. $5 Communications satellite 2·50 2·75

192 *Mayo-Mercury* Composite

(Des W. Wright. Litho Format)

1983 (19 July). *Bicentenary of Manned Flight. T* **192** *and similar horiz designs. Multicoloured. P* 14½.
853 45 c. Type **192** 20 25
854 60 c. Macchi "M.39" seaplane 30 35
855 90 c. Fairey "Swordfish" biplane 40 45
856 $4 Zeppelin "LZ3" .. .. 1·90 2·00
853/6 .. .. *Set of* 4 2·50 2·75
MS857 105 × 79 mm. $5 *Double Eagle II* (balloon) 2·50 2·75

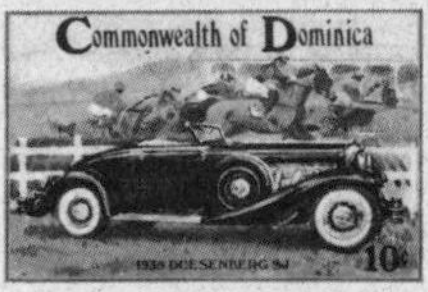

193 Duesenberg "SJ", 1935

(Des R. Sauber. Litho Questa)

1983 (1 Sept). *Classic Motor Cars. T* **193** *and similar horiz designs. Multicoloured. P* 14.
858 10 c. Type **193** 10 10
859 45 c. Studebaker "Avanti", 1962 .. .. .. 25 25
860 60 c. Cord "812", 1936 .. .. 35 35
861 75 c. MG "TC", 1945 .. .. 40 40
862 90 c. Camaro "350 SS", 1967 .. .. .. 45 45
863 $3 Porsch "356", 1948 .. .. 1·40 1·50
858/63 .. .. *Set of* 6 2·50 2·50
MS864 110 × 75 mm. $5 Ferrari "312 T", 1975 .. 2·50 2·60

194 "Charity"

(Des Design Images. Litho Format)

1983 (4 Oct). *Christmas. 500th Birth Anniv of Raphael. T* **194** *and similar horiz designs. Multicoloured. P* 13½.
865 45 c. Type **194** 30 25
866 60 c. "Hope" 40 35
867 90 c. "Faith" 55 45
868 $4 "The Cardinal Virtues" .. .. 2·00 2·00
865/8 .. .. *Set of* 4 3·00 2·75
MS869 101 × 127 mm. $5 "Justice" .. .. .. 2·50 2·75

195 Plumbeous Warbler **196** Donald Duck

(Des Jennifer Toombs. Litho Questa)

1984 (24 Apr). *Birds. T* **195** *and similar horiz designs. Multicoloured. P* 14.
870 5 c. Type **195** 30 10
871 45 c. Imperial Amazon 80 35
872 60 c. Blue-headed Hummingbird .. .. 1·00 60
873 90 c. Red-necked Amazon .. .. .. 1·40 1·10
870/3 .. .. *Set of* 4 3·25 1·75
MS874 72×72 mm. $5 Greater Flamingos .. 3·75 4·25

(Litho Format)

1984 (1 May). *Easter. T* **196** *and similar vert designs showing Disney cartoon characters and eggs. Multicoloured. P* 11.
875 ½ c. Type **196** 10 10
876 1 c. Mickey Mouse 10 10
877 2 c. Tortoise and Hare 10 10
878 3 c. Brer Rabbit and Brer Bear 10 10
879 4 c. Donald Duck (*different*) 10 10
880 5 c. White Rabbit 10 10
881 10 c. Thumper 10 10
882 $2 Pluto .. .. 1·50 1·40
883 $4 Pluto (*different*) .. .. .. 2·75 2·75
875/83 .. .. *Set of* 9 4·00 4·00
MS884 126 × 100 mm. $5 Chip and Dale. P 13½ × 14 .. .. 3·25 3·50

197 Gymnastics **198** *Atlantic Star*

(Des R. Sauber. Litho Questa)

1984 (14 May). *Olympic Games, Los Angeles. T* **197** *and similar vert designs. Multicoloured. P* 14.
885 30 c. Type **197** 20 25
886 45 c. Javelin-throwing 30 35
887 60 c. High diving 40 45
888 $4 Fencing .. .. 2·00 2·50
885/8 .. .. *Set of* 4 2·50 3·25
MS889 104 × 85 mm. $5 Equestrian event .. 2·75 3·25

(Des W. Wright. Litho Questa)

1984 (14 June). *Shipping. T* **198** *and similar horiz designs. Multicoloured. P* 14.
890 45 c. Type **198** 75 40
891 60 c. *Atlantic* (liner) .. .. 1·00 65
892 90 c. Carib fishing boat .. .. .. 1·40 85
893 $4 *Norway* (liner) .. .. 3·25 4·00
890/3 .. .. *Set of* 4 5·75 5·50
MS894 106×79 mm. $5 *Santa Maria*, 1492 .. 4·50 5·00

19th UPU
CONGRESS HAMBURG

(199)

200 *Guzmania lingulata*

1984 (19 June). *Universal Postal Union Congress, Hamburg. Nos.* 769A *and* 780A *optd with T* **199**.
895 10 c. Passion Fruit 10 10
896 $5 Heliconia or Lobster Claw .. .. 3·25 3·50

(Des P. Barrett. Litho Questa)

1984 (13 Aug). *"Ausipex" International Stamp Exhibition, Melbourne. Bromilaids. T* **200** *and similar vert designs. Multicoloured. P* 14.
897 45 c. Type **200** 30 35
898 60 c. *Pitcairnia angustifolia* 40 45
899 75 c. *Tillandsia fasciculata* 50 55
900 $3 *Aechmea smithiorum* .. .. 2·00 2·50
897/900 .. .. *Set of* 4 2·75 3·50
MS901 75 × 105 mm. $5 *Tillandsia utriculata* .. 3·25 3·50

201 "The Virgin and Child with Young St John" (Correggio) **202** "Before the Start" (Edgar Degas)

(Litho Format)

1984 (30 Oct). *450th Death Anniv of Correggio (painter). T* **201** *and similar vert designs. Multicoloured. P* 15.
902 25 c. Type **201** 25 20
903 60 c. "Christ bids Farewell to the Virgin Mary" 50 40
904 90 c. "Do not Touch Me" 75 60
905 $4 "The Mystical Marriage of St Catherine" 2·75 2·75
902/5 .. .. *Set of* 4 3·75 3·50
MS906 89 × 60 mm. $5 "The Adoration of the Magi" .. .. 3·00 3·50

(Litho Format)

1984 (30 Oct). *150th Birth Anniv of Edgar Degas (painter). T* **202** *and similar multicoloured designs. P* 15.
907 30 c. Type **202** 30 25
908 45 c. "Race on the Racecourse" 45 35
909 $1 "Jockeys at the Flagpole" 80 65
910 $3 "Racehorses at Longchamp" .. .. 2·00 2·25
907/10 .. .. *Set of* 4 3·25 3·25
MS911 89 × 60 mm. $5 "Self-portrait" (*vert*) .. 3·00 3·50

203 Tabby **204** Avro "748"

(Des. I. MacLaury. Litho Format)

1984 (12 Nov). *Cats. T* **203** *and similar horiz designs. Multicoloured. P* 15.
912 10 c. Type **203** 10 10
913 15 c. Calico Shorthair 10 10
914 20 c. Siamese 15 15
915 25 c. Manx 20 20
916 45 c. Abyssinian 35 30
917 60 c. Tortoise-shell Longhair 50 40
918 $1 Rex 80 65
919 $2 Persian .. .. 1·50 1·60
920 $3 Himalayan .. .. 2·25 2·50
921 $5 Burmese .. .. 3·50 4·00
912/21 .. .. *Set of* 10 8·50 9·00
MS922 105 × 75 mm. $5 Grey Burmese, Persian and American Shorthair .. .. 3·00 3·50

(Des Bonny Redecker. Litho Questa)

1984 (26 Nov). *40th Anniv of International Civil Aviation Organisation. T* **204** *and similar vert designs. Multicoloured. P* 14.
923 30 c. Type **204** 35 20
924 60 c. Twin "Otter" 65 40
925 $1 "Islander" .. .. 1·00 80
926 $3 "Casa" .. .. 2·25 2·75
923/6 .. .. *Set of* 4 3·75 3·75
MS927 102 × 75 mm. $5 Boeing "747" .. .. 3·00 3·50

205 Donald Duck, Mickey Mouse and Goofy with Father Christmas **206** Mrs. M. Bascom presenting Trefoil to Chief Guide Lady Baden-Powell

(Litho Questa)

1984 (30 Nov). *Christmas. Walt Disney Cartoon Characters. T* **205** *and similar vert designs. Multicoloured. P* 12 ($2) *or* 13½ × 14 (*others*).
928 45 c. Type **205** 70 30
929 60 c. Donald Duck as Father Christmas with toy train 85 50
930 90 c. Donald Duck as Father Christmas in sleigh .. .. 1·25 75
931 $2 Donald Duck and nephews in sledge .. 2·00 1·75
932 $4 Donald Duck in snow with Christmas tree 2·75 2·75
928/32 .. .. *Set of* 5 6·75 5·50
MS933 127 × 102 mm. $5 Donald Duck and nephews opening present .. .. 3·25 3·50
No. 931 was printed in sheetlets of 8 stamps.

(Des Marlise Najaka. Litho Questa)

1985 (28 Feb). *75th Anniv of Girl Guide Movement. T* **206** *and similar multicoloured designs. P* 14.
934 35 c. Type **206** 50 30
935 45 c. Lady Baden-Powell inspecting Dominican Brownies 70 35
936 60 c. Lady Baden-Powell with Mrs. M. Bascom and Mrs. A. Robinson (Guide leaders) .. 85 55
937 $3 Lord and Lady Baden-Powell (*vert*) .. 2·25 2·75
934/7 .. .. *Set of* 4 4·00 3·50
MS938 77 × 105 mm. $5 Flags of Dominica and Girl Guide Movement .. .. 3·25 3·75

(Litho Questa)

1985 (4 Apr). *Birth Bicentenary of John J. Audubon (ornithologist) (1st issue). Multicoloured designs as T* **198** *of Antigua showing original paintings. P* 14.
939 45 c. Clapper Rail 65 30
940 $1 Black and White Warbler (*vert*) .. 1·25 80
941 $2 Broad-winged Hawk (*vert*) .. .. 1·75 2·00
942 $3 Ring-necked Duck .. .. .. 2·25 2·50
939/42 .. .. *Set of* 4 5·50 5·00
MS943 101×73 mm. $5 Reddish Egret .. .. 3·25 3·50
Nos. 939/42 were each printed in sheetlets of five stamps and one stamp-size label which appears in the centre of the bottom row.
See also Nos. 1013/17.

207 Student with Computer **208** The Queen Mother visiting Sadlers Wells Opera

(Des BG Studio. Litho Questa)

1985 (30 Apr). *Duke of Edinburgh's Award Scheme. T* **207** *and similar vert designs. Multicoloured. P* 14.
944 45 c. Type **207** 35 30
945 60 c. Assisting doctor in hospital 55 40
946 90 c. Two youths hiking 75 65
947 $4 Family jogging .. .. 2·75 3·25
944/7 .. .. *Set of* 4 4·00 4·25
MS948 100×98 mm. $5 Duke of Edinburgh .. 2·75 3·00

(Des J.W. Litho Questa)

1985 (15 July). *Life and Times of Queen Elizabeth the Queen Mother. T* **208** *and similar vert designs. Multicoloured. P* 14.
949 60 c. Type **208** 50 40
950 $1 Fishing in Scotland 70 60
951 $3 On her 84th birthday .. .. .. 1·90 2·00
949/51 .. .. *Set of* 3 2·75 2·75
MS952 56×85 mm. $5 Attending Garter ceremony, Windsor Castle .. .. 3·00 3·00

209 Cricket Match ("Sports") **210** Two Players competing for Ball

(Des S. Heinmann. Litho Questa)

1985 (22 July). *International Youth Year. T* **209** *and similar horiz designs. Multicoloured. P* 14.
953 45 c. Type **209** .. .. 1·00 40
954 60 c. Bird-watching ("Environmental Study") 1·25 60
955 $1 Stamp collecting ("Education") .. 1·40 1·00
956 $3 Boating ("Leisure") .. .. .. 2·50 3·25
953/6 .. .. *Set of* 4 5·50 4·75
MS957 96×65 mm. $5 Young people linking hands .. .. 3·75 4·50

(Des Susan David. Litho Questa)

1985 (2 Sept). *300th Birth Anniv of Johann Sebastian Bach (composer). Vert designs as T* **206** *of Antigua showing antique musical instruments. P* 14.
958 45 c. multicoloured 75 40
959 60 c. multicoloured .. .. 1·00 60
960 $1 multicoloured .. .. 1·40 1·00
961 $3 multicoloured .. .. 3·00 3·50
958/61 .. .. *Set of* 4 5·50 5·00
MS962 109×75 mm. $5 black .. .. .. 4·00 4·50
Designs:—45 c. Cornett; 60 c. Coiled trumpet; $1 Piccolo; $3 Violoncello piccolo; $5 Johann Sebastian Bach.

(Litho Format)

1985 (25 Oct). *Royal Visit. Multicoloured designs as T* **207** *of Antigua. P* 14½.
963 60 c. Flags of Great Britain and Dominica .. 70 45
964 $1 Queen Elizabeth II (*vert*) .. .. 1·25 1·00
965 $4 Royal Yacht *Britannia* .. .. .. 3·50 4·00
963/5 .. .. *Set of* 3 5·00 5·00
MS966 111×83 mm. $5 Map of Dominica .. 3·50 4·00

(Litho Questa)

1985 (11 Nov). *150th Birth Anniv of Mark Twain (author). Horiz designs as T* **118** *of Anguilla showing Walt Disney cartoon characters in scenes from "Tom Sawyer". Multicoloured. P* 14×13½.

967 20 c. "The glorious whitewasher" 15 15
968 60 c. "Aunt Polly's home dentistry" .. 40 40
969 $1 "Aunt Polly's pain killer" 60 60
970 $1.50, Mickey Mouse balancing on fence .. 85 85
971 $2 "Lost in the cave with Becky" .. 1·25 1·25
967/71 .. .. *Set of* 5 3·00 3·00
MS972 126×101 mm. $5 Mickey Mouse as pirate .. .. 3·25 3·50

(Des Walt Disney Productions. Litho Questa)

1985 (11 Nov). *Birth Bicentenaries of Grimm Brothers (folklorists). Horiz designs as T* **119** *of Anguilla showing Walt Disney cartoon characters in scenes from "Little Red Cap". Multicoloured. P* 14×13½.

973 10 c. Little Red Cap (Daisy Duck) meeting the Wolf 10 10
974 45 c. The Wolf at the door 25 30
975 90 c. The Wolf in Grandmother's bed .. 55 60
976 $1 The Wolf lunging at Little Red Cap .. 60 65
977 $3 The Woodsman (Donald Duck) chasing the Wolf .. .. 1·75 1·90
973/7 .. .. *Set of* 5 3·00 3·25
MS978 126×101 mm. $5 The Wolf falling into cooking pot .. .. 3·00 3·25

(Litho Format)

1985 (27 Nov). *40th Anniv of United Nations Organization. Horiz designs as T* **208** *of Antigua showing United Nations (New York) stamps. Multicoloured. P* 14½.

979 45 c. Lord Baden-Powell and 1984 International Youth Year 35 c. 50 30
980 $2 Maimonides (physician) and 1966 W.H.O Building 11 c. .. .. .. 2·00 2·00
981 $3 Sir Rowland Hill (postal reformer) and 1976 25th anniv of U.N. Postal Administration 13 c. .. .. .. 2·25 2·25
979/81 .. .. *Set of* 3 4·25 4·00
MS982 110×85 mm. $5 "Apollo" spacecraft .. 3·50 3·75

(Des J. Iskowitz. Litho Questa)

1986 (26 Mar). *World Cup Football Championship, Mexico. T* **210** *and similar vert designs. Multicoloured. P* 14.

983 45 c. Type **210** 50 30
984 60 c. Player heading ball 60 45
985 $1 Two players competing for ball (*different*) 80 70
986 $3 Player with ball .. .. 2·25 2·50
983/6 .. .. *Set of* 4 3·75 3·50
MS987 114×84 mm. $5 Three players .. .. 3·75 4·25

211 Police in Rowing Boat pursuing River Pirates, 1890

(Des J. Iskowitz. Litho Questa)

1986 (27 Mar). *Centenary of Statue of Liberty. T* **211** *and similar multicoloured designs. P* 14.

988 15 c. Type **211** 35 20
989 25 c. Police patrol launch, 1986 .. .. 50 25
990 45 c. Hoboken Ferry Terminal, *c* 1890 .. 65 30
991 $4 Holland Tunnel entrance and staff, 1986 .. .. 2·75 3·50
988/91 .. .. *Set of* 4 3·75 3·75
MS992 104×76 mm. $5 Statue of Liberty (*vert*) .. 3·50 4·00

(Des W. Hanson. Litho Questa)

1986 (17 Apr). *Appearance of Halley's Comet. Horiz designs as T* **123** *of Anguilla. Multicoloured. P* 14.

993 5 c. Nasir al Din al Tusi (Persian astronomer) and Jantal Mantar Observatory, Delhi 10 10
994 10 c. Bell "X-1" Rocket Plane breaking sound barrier for first time, 1947 .. 10 10
995 45 c. Halley's Comet of 1531 (from "Astronomicum Caesareum", 1540) 35 30
996 $4 Mark Twain and quotation, 1910 .. 2·25 2·50
993/6 .. .. *Set of* 4 2·50 2·50
MS997 104×71 mm. $5 Halley's Comet over Dominica .. .. 2·75 3·25

(Des and litho Questa)

1986 (5 May). *60th Birthday of Queen Elizabeth II. Vert designs as T* **125** *of Anguilla. P* 14.

998 2 c. multicoloured 10 15
999 $1 multicoloured 70 70
1000 $4 multicoloured .. .. 2·25 2·40
998/1000 .. .. *Set of* 3 2·75 3·00
MS1001 120×85mm. $5 black and grey-brown .. 2·75 3·00

Designs:—2 c. Wedding photograph, 1947; $1 Queen meeting Pope John Paul II, 1982; $4 Queen on royal visit, 1971; $5 Princess Elizabeth with corgis, 1936.

212 Mickey Mouse and Pluto mounting Stamps in Album **213** William I

(Des Walt Disney Productions. Litho Format)

1986 (22 May). *"Ameripex" International Stamp Exhibition, Chicago. T* **212** *and similar horiz designs showing Walt Disney cartoon characters. Multicoloured. P* 11.

1002 25 c. Type **212** 35 35
1003 45 c. Donald Duck examining stamp under magnifying glass 55 55
1004 60 c. Chip n'Dale soaking and drying stamps 70 70
1005 $4 Donald Duck as scoutmaster awarding merit badges to Nephews .. .. 2·75 2·75
1002/5 .. .. *Set of* 4 4·00 4·00
MS1006 127×101 mm. $5 Uncle Scrooge conducting stamp auction. P 14×13½ .. 3·50 3·75

(Des Mary Walters. Litho Questa)

1986 (9 June). *500th Anniv of Succession of House of Tudor to English Throne* (1985). *T* **213** *and similar vert designs. Multicoloured. P* 14.

1007 10 c. Type **213** 15 15
1008 40 c. Richard II 35 35
1009 50 c. Henry VIII 40 40
1010 $1 Charles II 75 75
1011 $2 Queen Anne .. .. 1·50 1·50
1012 $4 Queen Victoria .. .. 2·50 2·50
1007/12 .. .. *Set of* 6 5·00 5·00

Nos. 1007/12 were each issued in sheetlets of five stamps and one stamp-size label showing the monarch's consort.

(Litho Questa)

1986 (18 June). *Birth Bicentenary of John J. Audubon (ornithologist) (1985) (2nd issue). Multicoloured designs as T* **198** *of Antigua showing original paintings. P* 12½×12 (25 *c.*, $4) *or* 12×12½ (*others*).

1013 25 c. Black-throated Diver 45 25
1014 60 c. Great Blue Heron (*vert*) 85 60
1015 90 c. Yellow-crowned Night Heron (*vert*) 1·10 85
1016 $4 Common Shoveler .. .. .. 3·00 3·50
1013/16 .. .. *Set of* 4 5·00 4·75
MS1017 73×103 mm. $5 Canada Goose. P 14 .. 4·00 4·50

Nos. 1013/16 were each issued in sheetlets of five stamps and one stamp-size label, which appears in the centre of the bottom row.

(Litho Questa)

1986 (1 July). *Royal Wedding. Vert designs as T* **213** *of Antigua. Multicoloured. P* 14.

1018 45 c. Prince Andrew and Miss Sarah Ferguson 35 30
1019 60 c. Prince Andrew 45 35
1020 $4 Prince Andrew climbing aboard aircraft .. .. 2·25 2·50
1018/20 .. .. *Set of* 3 2·75 2·75
MS1021 88×88 mm. $5 Prince Andrew and Miss Sarah Ferguson (*different*) .. .. .. 2·50 2·75

1986 (15 Sept). *World Cup Football Championship Winners, Mexico. Nos. 983/7 optd with T* **216** *of Antigua in gold.*

1022 45 c. Type **210** 50 30
1023 60 c. Player heading ball 60 45
1024 $1 Two players competing for ball .. 85 1·00
1025 $3 Player with ball .. .. .. 2·00 2·75
1022/5 .. .. *Set of* 4 3·50 4·00
MS1026 114×84 mm. $5 Three players .. .. 3·50 4·00

214 "The Virgin at Prayer" **215** Broad-winged Hawk

(Litho Questa)

1986 (2 Dec). *Christmas. Paintings by Dürer. T* **214** *and similar vert designs. Multicoloured. P* 14.

1027 45 c. Type **214** 35 30
1028 60 c. "Madonna and Child" 50 40
1029 $1 "The Madonna with the Pear" .. 75 75
1030 $3 "Madonna and Child with St. Anne" .. 2·00 2·50
1027/30 .. .. *Set of* 4 3·25 3·50
MS1031 76×102 mm. $5 "The Nativity" .. 3·50 3·75

1986 (16 Dec). *Appearance of Halley's Comet (2nd issue). Nos. 993/7 optd as T* **218** *of Antigua (in silver on $5).*

1032 5 c. Nasir al Din al Tusi (Persian astronomer) and Jantal Mantar Observatory, Delhi 10 10
1033 10 c. Bell "X-1" Rocket Plane breaking sound barrier for first time, 1947 .. 10 10
1034 45 c. Halley's Comet of 1531 (from "Astronomicum Caesareum", 1540) 20 25
1035 $4 Mark Twain and quotation, 1910 .. 1·75 1·90
1032/5 .. .. *Set of* 4 1·90 2·10
MS1036 104×71 mm. $5 Halley's Comet over Dominica .. .. 2·25 2·40

(Des S. Heinmann. Litho Format)

1987 (20 Jan). *Birds of Dominica. T* **215** *and similar vert designs. Multicoloured. Without imprint date. P* 15.

1037 1 c. Type **215** 10 10
1038 2 c. Ruddy Quail Dove 10 10
1039 5 c. Red-necked Pigeon 10 10
1040 10 c. Green Heron 10 10
1041 15 c. Moorhen 10 10
1042 20 c. Ringed Kingfisher 10 10
1043 25 c. Brown Pelican 10 10
1044 35 c. White-tailed Tropic Bird 15 20
1045 45 c. Red-legged Thrush 20 25
1046 60 c. Purple-throated Carib 25 30
1047 90 c. Magnificent Frigate Bird 35 40
1048 $1 Brown Trembler 40 45
1049 $2 Black-capped Petrel 80 85
1050 $5 Barn Owl .. .. 2·10 2·25
1051 $10 Imperial Parrot .. .. .. 4·00 4·25
1037/51 .. .. *Set of* 15 8·00 8·50

For similar stamps, with imprint date and perforated 14, see Nos. 1241/54.

(Des J. Iskowitz. Litho Format)

1987 (16 Feb). *America's Cup Yachting Championship. Multicoloured designs as T* **222** *of Antigua. P* 15.

1052 45 c. *Reliance*, 1903 .. .. 30 25
1053 60 c. *Freedom*, 1980 .. .. 35 30
1054 $1 *Mischief*, 1881 .. .. 55 55
1055 $3 *Australia*, 1977 .. .. 1·50 1·75
1052/5 .. .. *Set of* 4 2·40 2·50
MS1056 113×83 mm. $5 *Courageous*, 1977 (*horiz*) .. .. 2·75 3·25

(Litho Questa)

1987 (24 Mar). *Birth Centenary of Marc Chagall (artist). Multicoloured designs as T* **225** *of Antigua. P* 13½×14.

1057 25 c. "Artist and His Model" 15 15
1058 35 c. "Midsummer Night's Dream" .. 15 20
1059 45 c. "Joseph the Shepherd" 20 25
1060 60 c. "The Cellist" 25 30
1061 90 c. "Woman with Pigs" 40 45
1062 $1 "The Blue Circus" 45 50
1063 $3 "For Vava" .. .. 1·40 1·50
1064 $4 "The Rider" .. .. 1·75 1·90
1057/64 .. .. *Set of* 8 4·25 4·75
MS1065 Two sheets, each 110×95 mm. (a) $5 "Purim" (104×89 *mm*). (b) $5 "Firebird" (stage design) (104×89 *mm*) .. *Set of* 2 *sheets* 4·50 4·75

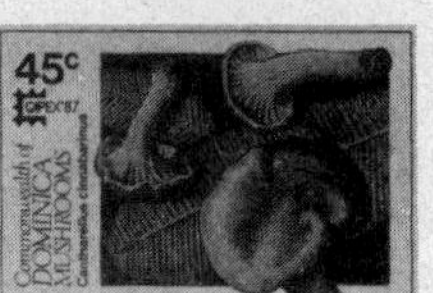

216 Morch Poulsen's Triton **217** *Cantharellus cinnabarinus*

(Des L. Birmingham. Litho Format)

1987 (11 May). *Sea Shells. T* **216** *and similar designs. P* 15.

1066 35 c. multicoloured 20 20
1067 45 c. bluish violet, black and bright rose .. 25 25
1068 60 c. multicoloured 30 30
1069 $5 multicoloured .. .. 2·40 2·40
1066/9 .. .. *Set of* 4 2·75 2·75
MS1070 109×75 mm. $5 multicoloured .. .. 2·50 3·00

Designs: *Vert*—45 c. Swainson Globe Purple Sea Snail; 60 c. Banded Tulip; $5 (No. 1069) Lamarck Deltoid Rock Shell. *Horiz*—$5 (No. **MS**1070) *Junonia volute*.

No. 1066 is inscribed "TIRITON" in error.

(Des BG Studio. Litho Questa)

1987 (15 June). *"Capex '87" International Stamp Exhibition, Toronto. Mushrooms of Dominica. T* **217** *and similar horiz designs. Multicoloured. P* 14.

1071 45 c. Type **217** 20 25
1072 60 c. *Boletellus cubensis* 25 30
1073 $2 *Eccilia cystiophorus* 90 95
1074 $3 *Xerocomus guadelupae* .. .. .. 1·40 1·50
1071/4 .. .. *Set of* 4 2·50 2·75
MS1075 85×85 mm. $5 *Gymnopilus chrysopellus* 2·25 2·40

218 Discovery of Dominica, 1493 **219** "Virgin and Child with St. Anne" (Dürer)

(Des I. MacLaury. Litho Format)

1987 (27 July). *500th Anniv of Discovery of America* (1992) (*1st issue*). *T* **218** *and similar horiz designs. Multicoloured. P* 15.

1076 10 c. Type **218** 15 15
1077 15 c. Caribs greeting Columbus's fleet .. 15 15
1078 45 c. Claiming the New World for Spain .. 25 25
1079 60 c. Wreck of *Santa Maria* 30 30
1080 90 c. Fleet leaving Spain 45 45
1081 $1 Sighting the New World 50 50

1082 $3 Trading with Indians .. 1·50 1·50
1083 $5 Building settlement .. 2·40 2·40
1076/83 .. *Set of* 8 5·00 5·00
MS1084 Two sheets, each 109×79 mm. (a) $5 Fleet off Dominica, 1493. (b) $5 Map showing Columbus's route, 1493 .. *Set of* 2 *sheets* 5·00 5·50
See also Nos. 1221/5.

(Des G. Welker. Litho Questa)

1987 (28 Sept). *Milestones of Transportation. Multicoloured designs as T* **226** *of Antigua. P* 14.
1085 10 c. H.M.S. *Warrior* (first ironclad warship), 1860 .. 15 15
1086 15 c. MAGLEV-MLU 001 (fastest passenger train), 1979 .. 15 15
1087 25 c. *Flying Cloud* (fastest clipper passage New York–San Francisco) (*vert*) .. 15 15
1088 35 c. First elevated railway, New York, 1868 (*vert*) .. 20 20
1089 45 c. *Tom Thumb* (first U.S. passenger locomotive), 1830 .. 25 25
1090 60 c. *Spray* (Slocum's solo circumnavigation), 1895–8 (*vert*) .. 30 30
1091 90 c. *Sea-Land Commerce* (fastest Pacific passage), 1973 (*vert*) .. 45 45
1092 $1 First cable cars, San Francisco, 1873 .. 50 50
1093 $3 "Orient Express", 1883 .. 1·50 1·50
1094 $4 *Clermont* (first commercial steamboat), 1807 .. 1·90 1·90
1085/94 .. *Set of* 10 4·75 4·75

(Litho Questa)

1987 (16 Nov). *Christmas. Religious Paintings. T* **219** *and similar vert designs. Multicoloured. P* 14.
1095 20 c. Type **219** .. 15 15
1096 25 c. "Virgin and Child" (Murillo) .. 15 15
1097 $2 "Madonna and Child" (Foppa) .. 90 1·10
1098 $4 "Madonna and Child" (Da Verona) .. 1·75 2·25
1095/8 .. *Set of* 4 2·75 3·25
MS1099 100×78 mm. $5 "Angel of the Annunciation" (anon, Renaissance period) .. 2·25 2·40

220 Three Little Pigs in People Mover, Walt Disney World

221 Kayak Canoeing

(Des Walt Disney Company. Litho Questa)

1987 (22 Dec). *60th Anniv of Mickey Mouse (Walt Disney cartoon character). T* **220** *and similar multicoloured designs showing cartoon characters in trains. P* 13½×14.
1100 20 c. Type **220** .. 15 15
1101 25 c. Goofy driving horse tram, Disneyland 15 15
1102 45 c. Donald Duck in *Roger E. Broggie*, Walt Disney World .. 25 25
1103 60 c. Goofy, Mickey Mouse, Donald Duck and Chip n'Dale aboard Big Thunder Mountain train, Disneyland .. 30 30
1104 90 c. Mickey Mouse in *Walter E. Disney*, Disneyland .. 45 45
1105 $1 Mickey and Minnie Mouse, Goofy, Donald and Daisy Duck in monorail, Walt Disney World .. 50 50
1106 $3 Dumbo flying over *Casey Jr* .. 1·50 1·50
1107 $4 Daisy Duck and Minnie Mouse in *Lilly Belle*, Walt Disney World .. 1·90 1·90
1100/7 .. *Set of* 8 4·50 4·50
MS1108 Two sheets, each 127×101 mm. (a) $5 Seven Dwarfs in Rainbow Caverns Mine train, Disneyland (*horiz*). (b) $5 Donald Duck and Chip n'Dale on toy train (from film *Out of Scale*) (*horiz*). P 14×13½ .. *Set of* 2 *sheets* 4·50 5·00

(Des and litho Questa)

1988 (15 Feb). *Royal Ruby Wedding. Vert designs as T* **234** *of Antigua. P* 14.
1109 45 c. multicoloured .. 35 25
1110 60 c. deep brown, black and light green .. 40 35
1111 $1 multicoloured .. 65 65
1112 $3 multicoloured .. 1·75 2·00
1109/12 .. *Set of* 4 2·75 3·00
MS1113 102×76 mm. $5 multicoloured .. 2·25 2·40
Designs:—45 c. Wedding portrait with attendants, 1947; 60 c. Princess Elizabeth with Prince Charles, *c.* 1950; $1 Princess Elizabeth and Prince Philip with Prince Charles and Princess Anne, 1950; $3 Queen Elizabeth; $5 Princess Elizabeth in wedding dress, 1947.

(Des D. Miller. Litho Questa)

1988 (14 Mar). *Olympic Games, Seoul. T* **221** *and similar vert designs. Multicoloured. P* 14.
1114 45 c. Type **221** .. 30 25
1115 60 c. Taekwon-do .. 35 30
1116 $1 High diving .. 60 60
1117 $3 Gymnastics on bars .. 1·50 1·75
1114/17 .. *Set of* 4 2·50 2·50
MS1118 81×110 mm. $5 Football .. 2·25 2·40

222 Carib Indian

223 White-tailed Tropic Bird

(Des K. Gromoll. Litho Format)

1988 (13 Apr). *"Reunion '88" Tourism Programme. T* **222** *and similar multicoloured designs. P* 15.
1119 10 c. Type **222** .. 10 10
1120 25 c. Mountainous interior (*horiz*) .. 15 15
1121 35 c. Indian River .. 15 20
1122 60 c. Belaire dancer and tourists .. 25 30
1123 90 c. Boiling Lake .. 40 45
1124 $3 Coral reef (*horiz*) .. 1·40 1·50
1119/24 .. *Set of* 6 2·10 2·40
MS1125 112×82 mm. $5 Belaire dancer .. 2·25 2·40

1988 (1 June). *Stamp Exhibitions. Nos.* **MS**1084 *and* 1092/3 *optd as T* **241** *of Antigua showing various emblems.*
1126 $1 First cable cars, San Francisco, 1873 (optd "FINLANDIA 88", Helsinki) .. 45 50
1127 $3 "Orient Express", 1883 (optd "INDEPENDENCE 40", Israel) .. 1·25 1·40
a. Opt albino ..
MS1128 Two sheets, each 109 × 79 mm. (a) $5 Fleet off Dominica, 1493 (optd "OLYMPHILEX '88", Seoul). (b) $5 Map showing Columbus's route, 1493 (optd "Praga '88", Prague) *Set of* 2 *sheets* 4·25 4·50

(Des S. Barlow. Litho Questa)

1988 (25 July). *Dominica Rain Forest Flora and Fauna. T* **223** *and similar vert designs. Multicoloured. P* 14½×14.
1129 45 c. Type **223** .. 30 30
a. Sheetlet. Nos. 1129/48 .. 5·50
1130 45 c. Blue-throated Euphonia .. 30 30
1131 45 c. Smooth-billed Ani .. 30 30
1132 45 c. Scaly-breasted Thrasher .. 30 30
1133 45 c. Purple-throated Carib .. 30 30
1134 45 c. Southern Daggertail and Clench's Hairstreak (butterflies) .. 30 30
1135 45 c. Trembler .. 30 30
1136 45 c. Imperial Parrot .. 30 30
1137 45 c. Mangrove Cuckoo .. 30 30
1138 45 c. Hercules Beetle .. 30 30
1139 45 c. Orion (butterfly) .. 30 30
1140 45 c. Red-necked Parrot .. 30 30
1141 45 c. Tillandsia (plant) .. 30 30
1142 45 c. Bananaquit and *polystacha luteola* (plant) .. 30 30
1143 45 c. False Chameleon .. 30 30
1144 45 c. Iguana .. 30 30
1145 45 c. Hypolimnas (butterfly) .. 30 30
1146 45 c. Green-throated Carib .. 30 30
1147 45 c. Heliconia (plant) .. 30 30
1148 45 c. Agouti .. 30 30
1129/48 .. *Set of* 20 5·50 5·50
Nos. 1129/48 were printed together, *se-tenant*, in a sheetlet of 20 forming a composite design.

224 Battery Hens

225 Gary Cooper

(Des J. Martin. Litho Questa)

1988 (5 Sept). *10th Anniv of International Fund for Agricultural Development. T* **224** *and similar multicoloured designs. P* 14.
1149 45 c. Type **224** .. 20 25
1150 60 c. Pig .. 25 30
1151 90 c. Cattle .. 40 45
1152 $3 Black Belly Sheep .. 1·25 1·40
1149/52 .. *Set of* 4 1·90 2·10
MS1153 95×68 mm. $5 Tropical fruits (*vert*) .. 2·10 2·25

(Des Lynda Bruscheni. Litho Questa)

1988 (8 Sept). *Entertainers. T* **225** *and similar vert designs. Multicoloured. P* 14.
1154 10 c. Type **225** .. 10 10
1155 35 c. Josephine Baker .. 15 20
1156 45 c. Maurice Chevalier .. 20 25
1157 60 c. James Cagney .. 25 30
1158 $1 Clark Gable .. 45 50
1159 $2 Louis Armstrong .. 80 85
1160 $3 Liberace .. 1·25 1·40
1161 $4 Spencer Tracy .. 1·60 1·75
1154/61 .. *Set of* 8 4·25 4·75
MS1162 Two sheets, each 105×75 mm. (a) $5 Humphrey Bogart. (b) $5 Elvis Presley. *Set of* 2 *sheets* 4·25 4·50

(Des Mary Walters. Litho Questa)

1988 (29 Sept). *Flowering Trees. Horiz designs as T* **242** *of Antigua. Multicoloured. P* 14.
1163 15 c. Sapodilla .. 10 10
1164 20 c. Tangerine .. 10 10
1165 25 c. Avocado Pear .. 10 10
1166 45 c. Amherstia .. 20 25
1167 90 c. Lipstick Tree .. 40 45
1168 $1 Cannonball Tree .. 45 50
1169 $3 Saman .. 1·25 1·40
1170 $4 Pineapple .. 1·60 1·75
1163/70 .. *Set of* 8 3·75 4·25
MS1171 Two sheets, each 96 × 66 mm. (a) $5 Lignum Vitae. (b) $5 Sea Grape *Set of* 2 *sheets* 4·25 4·50

(Litho Questa)

1988 (10 Oct). *500th Birth Anniv of Titian (artist). Vert designs as T* **238** *of Antigua. Multicoloured. P* 13½ × 14.
1172 25 c. "Jacopo Strada" .. 10 15
1173 35 c. "Titian's Daughter Lavinia" .. 15 20
1174 45 c. "Andrea Navagero" .. 20 25
1175 60 c. "Judith with Head of Holoferenes" .. 25 30
1176 $1 "Emilia di Spilimbergo" .. 45 50
1177 $2 "Martyrdom of St. Lawrence" .. 80 85
1178 $3 "Salome" .. 1·25 1·40
1179 $4 "St. John the Baptist" .. 1·60 1·75
1172/9 .. *Set of* 8 4·25 4·75
MS1180 Two sheets, each 110 × 95 mm. (a) $5 "Self Portrait". (b) $5 "Sisyphus" *Set of* 2 *sheets* 4·25 4·50

226 Imperial Parrot

227 President and Mrs. Kennedy

(Des K. Gromell. Litho Questa)

1988 (31 Oct). *10th Anniv of Independence. T* **226** *and similar multicoloured designs. P* 14.
1181 20 c. Type **226** .. 20 15
1182 45 c. Dominica 1874 1d. stamp and landscape (*horiz*) .. 30 25
1183 $2 1978 Independence 10 c. stamp and landscape (*horiz*) .. 1·00 1·25
1184 $3 Carib Wood (national flower) .. 1·50 1·75
1181/4 .. *Set of* 4 2·75 3·00
MS1185 116 × 85 mm. $5 Government Band (*horiz*) .. 2·10 2·25

(Des J. Martin. Litho Questa)

1988 (22 Nov). *25th Death Anniv of John F. Kennedy (American statesman). T* **227** *and similar multicoloured designs. P* 14.
1186 20 c. Type **227** .. 10 10
1187 25 c. Kennedy sailing .. 10 10
1188 $2 Outside Hyannis Port house .. 80 85
1189 $4 Speaking in Berlin (*vert*) .. 1·60 1·75
1186/9 .. *Set of* 4 2·40 2·50
MS1190 100 × 71 mm. $5 President Kennedy (*vert*) .. 2·10 2·25

228 Donald Duck's Nephews decorating Christmas Tree

229 Raoul Wallenberg (diplomat) and Swedish Flag

(Des Walt Disney Co. Litho Questa)

1988 (1 Dec). *Christmas. "Mickey's Christmas Mall". T* **228** *and similar vert designs showing Walt Disney cartoon characters. Multicoloured. P* 13½ × 14.
1191 60 c. Type **228** .. 35 35
a. Sheetlet. Nos. 1191/8 .. 2·50
1192 60 c. Daisy Duck outside clothes shop .. 35 35
1193 60 c. Winnie the Pooh in shop window .. 35 35
1194 60 c. Goofy with parcels .. 35 35
1195 60 c. Donald Duck as Father Christmas .. 35 35
1196 60 c. Mickey Mouse contributing to collection .. 35 35
1197 60 c. Minnie Mouse .. 35 35
1198 60 c. Chip n' Dale with peanut .. 35 35
1191/8 .. *Set of* 8 2·50 2·50
MS1199 Two sheets, each 127 × 102 mm. (a) $6 Mordie Mouse with Father Christmas. (b) $6 Mickey Mouse at West Indian market *Set of* 2 *sheets* 5·00 5·50
Nos. 1191/8 were printed together, *se-tenant* as a composite design, in sheetlets of eight.

(Des J. Genzo. Litho B.D.T.)

1988 (9 Dec). *40th Anniv of Universal Declaration of Human Rights. T* **229** *and similar multicoloured design. P* 14.
1200 $3 Type **229** .. .. 1·25 1·40
MS1201 92 × 62 mm. $5 Human Rights Day logo (*vert*) .. .. 2·10 2·25

230 Greater Amberjack

(Des J. Iskowitz. Litho Questa)

1988 (22 Dec). *Game Fishes. T* **230** *and similar horiz designs. Multicoloured. P* 14.
1202 10 c. Type **230** 15 10
1203 15 c. Blue Marlin 15 10
1204 35 c. Cobia 25 20
1205 45 c. Dolphin Fish 35 25
1206 60 c. Cero 45 40
1207 90 c. Mahogany Snapper 65 55
1208 $3 Yellowfin Tuna .. .. 2·00 2·25
1209 $4 Rainbow Parrotfish .. .. 2·50 2·75
1202/9 .. .. *Set of* 8 6·00 6·00
MS1210 Two sheets, each 104×74 mm. (a) $5 Manta Ray. (b) $5 Tarpon .. *Set of* 2 *sheets* 6·00 7·00

231 Leatherback Turtle

Men's c-1, 500m
O. Heukrodt DDR

(**232**)

(Des W. Wright. Litho Questa)

1988 (29 Dec). *Insects and Reptiles. T* **231** *and similar horiz designs. Multicoloured. P* 14.
1211 10 c. Type **231** 15 10
1212 25 c. Monarch (butterfly) 20 15
1213 60 c. Green Anole (lizard) 45 35
1214 $3 Praying Mantis .. .. 2·00 2·25
1211/14 .. .. *Set of* 4 2·50 2·50
MS1215 119×90 mm. $5 Hercules Beetle .. 3·00 3·50

1989 (20 Mar). *Olympic Medal Winners, Seoul. Nos.* 1114/18 *optd as T* **232** (*horizontally on No.* **MS**1220).
1216 45 c. Type **221** (optd with T **232**) 20 25
1217 60 c. Taekwon-do (optd "Women's Fly-weight N. Y. Choo S. Korea") 30 35
1218 $1 High diving (optd "Women's Platform Y. Xu China") 45 50
1219 $3 Gymnastics on bars (optd "V. Artemov USSR") .. .. 1·50 1·60
1216/19 .. .. *Set of* 4 2·25 2·40
MS1220 81×110 mm. $5 Football (optd "USSR defeated Brazil 3-2 on penalty kicks after a 1-1 tie") .. .. 2·40 2·50

(Des D. Miller. Litho Questa)

1989 (8 May). *500th Anniv of Discovery of America by Columbus* (1992) (*2nd issue*). *Pre-Columbian Carib Society. Designs as T* **247** *of Antigua, but horiz. Multicoloured. P* 14.
1221 20 c. Carib canoe 15 10
1222 35 c. Hunting with bows and arrows 25 20
1223 $1 Dugout canoe making 65 55
1224 $3 Shield contest .. .. 2·00 2·25
1221/4 .. .. *Set of* 4 2·75 2·75
MS1225 87×71 mm. $6 Ceremonial dance .. 3·25 3·75

233 Map of Dominica, 1766

234 Homerus Swallowtail

(Des U. Purins. Litho B.D.T.)

1989 (17 July). *"Philexfrance 89" International Stamp Exhibition, Paris. T* **233** *and similar multicoloured designs. P* 14.
1226 10 c. Type **233** 10 10
1227 35 c. French coin of 1653 (*horiz*) 15 20
1228 $1 French warship, 1720 (*horiz*) 45 50
1229 $4 Coffee plant (*horiz*) .. .. .. 1·90 2·00
1226/9 .. .. *Set of* 4 2·25 2·50
MS1230 98×98 mm. $5 Exhibition inscription (*horiz*) (black, grey and greenish yellow) .. 2·40 2·50

(Litho Questa)

1989 (31 Aug). *Japanese Art. Paintings by Taikan. Designs as T* **250** *of Antigua, but vert. Multicoloured. P* 13½×14.
1231 10 c. "Lao-tzu" (detail) 10 10
1232 20 c. "Red Maple Leaves" (panels 1 and 2) 10 10
1233 45 c. "King Wen Hui learns a Lesson from his Cook" (detail) 20 25
1234 60 c. "Red Maple Leaves" (panels 3 and 4) 30 35
1235 $1 "Wild Flowers" (detail) 45 50
1236 $2 "Red Maple Leaves" (panels 5 and 6) 95 1·00
1237 $3 "Red Maple Leaves" (panels 7 and 8) 1·50 1·60
1238 $4 "Indian Ceremony of Floating Lamps on the River" (detail) .. .. 1·90 2·00
1231/8 .. .. *Set of* 8 4·75 5·00
MS1239 Two sheets (a) 78×102 mm. $5 "Innocence" (detail). (b) 101×77 mm. $5 "Red Maple Leaves" (detail) .. .. *Set of* 2 *sheets* 4·75 5·00

Nos. 1231/8 were each printed in sheetlets of 10 containing two vertical strips of 5 stamps separated by printed labels commemorating Emperor Hirohito.

(Litho Questa)

1989 (31 Aug). *As Nos.* 1038/46 *and* 1048/51 *but with imprint date* ("1989"). *P* 14.
1241 2 c. Ruddy Quail Dove 10 10
1242 5 c. Red-necked Pigeon 10 10
1243 10 c. Green Heron 10 10
1244 15 c. Moorhen 10 10
1245 20 c. Ringed Kingfisher 10 10
1246 25 c. Brown Pelican 10 10
1247 35 c. White-tailed Tropic Bird 15 20
1248 45 c. Red-legged Thrush 20 25
1249 60 c. Purple-throated Carib 25 30
1251 $1 Brown Trembler 40 45
1252 $2 Black-capped Petrel 80 85
1253 $5 Barn Owl .. .. 2·10 2·25
1254 $10 Imperial Parrot .. .. .. 4·00 4·25
1241/54 .. .. *Set of* 13 7·25 7·75

(Des W. Wright. Litho Questa)

1989 (11 Sept). *Butterflies. T* **234** *and similar horiz designs. Multicoloured. P* 14.
1255 10 c. Type **234** 10 10
1256 15 c. *Morpho peleides* 10 10
1257 25 c. Julia 10 15
1258 35 c. Gundlach's Swallowtail 15 20
1259 60 c. Monarch 30 35
1260 $1 Gulf Fritillary 45 50
1261 $3 Red-splashed Sulphur .. .. .. 1·50 1·60
1262 $5 *Papilio andraemon* .. .. .. 2·40 2·50
1255/62 .. .. *Set of* 8 4·50 4·75
MS1263 Two sheets. (a) 105×74 mm. $6 *Adelpha cytherea*. (b) 105×79 mm. $6 *Adelpha iphicla* *Set of* 2 *sheets* 5·75 6·00

235 *Oncidium pusillum*

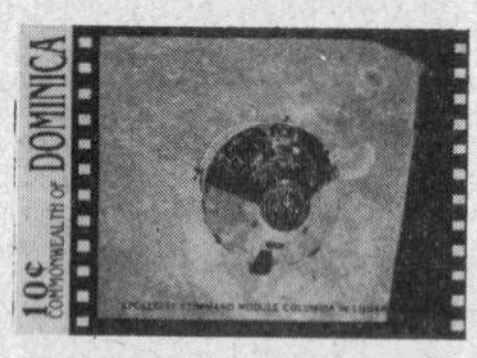

236 "Apollo 11" Command Module in Lunar Orbit

(Des William Hanson Studio. Litho Questa)

1989 (28 Sept). *Orchids. T* **235** *and similar vert designs. Multicoloured. P* 14.
1264 10 c. Type **235** 10 10
1265 35 c. *Epidendrum cochleata* 15 20
1266 45 c. *Epidendrum ciliare* 20 25
1267 60 c. *Cyrtopodium andersonii* 30 35
1268 $1 *Habenaria pauciflora* 45 50
1269 $2 *Maxillaria alba* .. .. .. 95 1·00
1270 $3 *Selenipedium palmifolium* .. .. 1·50 1·60
1271 $4 *Brassavola cucullata* .. .. .. 1·90 2·00
1264/71 .. .. *Set of* 8 5·00 5·25
MS1272 Two sheets, each 108×77 mm. (a) $5 *Oncidium lanceanum*. (b) $5 *Comparettia falcata* *Set of* 2 *sheets* 4·75 5·00

(Litho Questa)

1989 (31 Oct). *20th Anniv of First Manned Landing on Moon. T* **236** *and similar multicoloured designs. P* 14.
1273 10 c. Type **236** 10 10
1274 60 c. Neil Armstrong leaving lunar module 30 35
1275 $2 Edwin Aldrin at Sea of Tranquility .. 95 1·00
1276 $3 Astronauts Armstrong and Aldrin with U.S. flag .. .. .. 1·50 1·60
1273/6 .. .. *Set of* 4 2·50 2·75
MS1277 62×77 mm. $6 Launch of "Apollo 11" (*vert*) .. .. 2·75 3·00

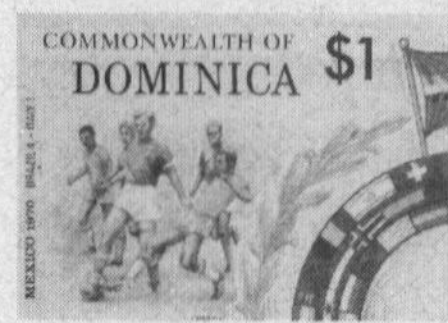

237 Brazil v Italy Final, 1970

(Des G. Vasarhelyi. Litho Questa)

1989 (8 Nov). *World Cup Football Championship, Italy. T* **237** *and similar horiz designs. Multicoloured. P* 14.
1278 $1 Type **237** 45 50
a. Sheetlet. Nos. 1278/81 .. .. 1·60
1279 $1 England v. West Germany, 1966 .. 45 50
1280 $1 West Germany v. Holland, 1974 .. 45 50
1281 $1 Italy v. West Germany, 1982 .. 45 50
1278/81 .. .. *Set of* 4 1·60 1·75
MS1282 106×86 mm. $6 Two players competing for ball .. .. 2·75 3·00

Nos. 1278/81 were printed together, *se-tenant*, in a sheetlet of 4 stamps, forming a composite central design of a football surrounded by flags of competing nations.

POSTAL FISCALS

REVENUE (R 1) Revenue (R 2)

1879–86. *Optd with Type* R **1**. (*a*) *Wmk Crown CC*.
R1 1 1d. lilac .. .. 42·00 7·50
a. Bisected vert (½d.) on cover ..
R2 6d. green .. .. 3·00 11·00
R3 1s. magenta .. .. 9·00 15·00
R1/3 .. .. *Set of* 3 50·00 30·00

(*b*) *Wmk Crown CA*
R4 1 1d. lilac (1886) .. .. 1·00 1·75

1888. *Optd with Type* R **2**. *Wmk Crown CA*.
R6 1 1d. carmine .. .. 50·00 42·00

Appendix

The following stamps have either been issued in excess of postal needs, or have not been made available to the public in reasonable quantities at face value. Miniature sheets, imperforate stamps etc., are excluded from this section.

1978–79

History of Aviation. $16 × 30, each embossed on gold foil.

East Africa

For the issues of the combined East African Postal Administration from 1933 until 1976 *see* KENYA, UGANDA AND TANZANIA.

East Africa and Uganda Protectorates *see* Kenya, Uganda and Tanganyika

East Africa (G.E.A.) *see* Tanzania

Egypt

TURKISH SUZERAINTY

In 1517 Sultan Selim I added Egypt to the Ottoman Empire, and it stayed more or less under Turkish rule until 1805, when Mohammed Ali became governor. He established a dynasty of governors owing nominal allegiance to the Sultan of Turkey until 1914.

Khedive Ismail

18 January 1863–26 June 1879

He obtained the honorific title of Khedive (viceroy) from the Sultan in 1867.

The operations of British Consular Post Offices in Egypt date from 1839 when the first office, at Alexandria, was opened. Further offices at Suez (1847) and Cairo (1859) followed.

Great Britain stamps were issued to Alexandria and Suez offices in 1860 and continued to be used there until the three offices closed in 1882, following the British Military Occupation.

Stamps issued after 1877 can be found with the Egyptian cancellation "Port Said", but these are on letters posted from British ships.

For cancellations used during the 1882 campaign see ARMY FIELD OFFICES at the end of the BRITISH POST OFFICES ABROAD section, following GREAT BRITAIN.

For illustrations of the handstamp and postmark types see BRITISH POST OFFICES ABROAD NOTES, following GREAT BRITAIN.

ALEXANDRIA

CROWNED-CIRCLE HANDSTAMPS

CC1 CC1b ALEXANDRIA (R. *or* Black) (5.1843) *Price on cover* £1250

Stamps of **GREAT BRITAIN** *cancelled* "B 01" *as in Types* **2**, **8**, **12** *or* **15**.

1860 *to* **1879.**

Z 1 ½d. rose-red (1870–79) .. .. *From* 15·00
Plate Nos. 5, 6, 8, 10, 13, 14, 15, 19, 20.
Z 2 1d. rose-red (1857) .. .. 6·00
Z 3 1d. rose-red (1861) (Alph IV)
Z 4 1d. rose-red (1864–79) .. .. .. *From* 6·00
Plate Nos. 71, 72, 73, 74, 76, 78, 79, 80, 81, 82, 83, 84, 85, 86, 87, 88, 89, 90, 91, 92, 93, 94, 95, 96, 97, 98, 99, 101, 102, 103, 104, 106, 107, 108, 109, 110, 111, 112, 113, 114, 115, 117, 118, 119, 120, 121, 122, 123, 124, 125, 127, 129, 130, 131, 133, 134, 136, 137, 138, 139, 140, 142, 143, 144, 145, 146, 147, 148, 149, 150, 152, 154, 156, 157, 158, 159, 160, 162, 163, 165, 168, 169, 170, 171, 172, 174, 175, 177, 179, 180, 181, 182, 183, 185, 188, 190, 198, 200, 203, 206, 210, 220.
Z 5 2d. blue (1858–69) .. .. *From* 6·00
Plate Nos. 7, 8, 9, 13, 14, 15.
Z 6 2½d. rosy mauve (1875) (blued *paper*) .. *From* 60·00
Plate Nos. 1, 2.
Z 7 2½d. rosy mauve (1875–6) (Plate Nos. 1, 2, 3) .. 27·00
Z 8 2½d. rosy mauve (*Error of Lettering*) £1250
Z 9 2½d. rosy mauve (1876–79) .. .. .. *From* 21·00
Plate Nos. 3, 4, 5, 6, 7, 8, 9.
Z10 3d. carmine-rose (1862) £110
Z11 3d. rose (1865) (Plate No. 4) .. .. .. 55·00
Z12 3d. rose (1867–73) (Plate Nos. 4, 5, 6, 7, 8, 9) *From* 21·00
Z13 3d. rose (1873–76) .. .. *From* 21·00
Plate Nos. 11, 12, 14, 15, 16, 18, 19.
Z14 3d. rose (1881) (Plate No. 20) .. .. ..
Z15 4d. rose (1857) .. .. 40·00
Z16 4d. red (1862) (Plate Nos. 3, 4) .. .. *From* 40·00
Z17 4d. vermilion (1865–73) .. .. 23·00
Plate Nos. 7, 8, 9, 10, 11, 12, 13, 14.
Z18 4d. vermilion (1876) (Plate No. 15) £120
Z19 4d. sage-green (1877) (Plate No. 15) .. .. 75·00
Z20 6d. lilac (1856) .. .. 45·00
Z21 6d. lilac (1862) (Plate Nos. 3, 4) .. .. *From* 40·00
Z22 6d. lilac (1865–67) (Plate Nos. 5, 6) .. *From* 30·00
Z23 6d. lilac (1867) (Plate No. 6) .. .. .. 42·00
Z24 6d. violet (1867–70) (Plate Nos. 6, 8, 9) .. *From* 30·00
a. Imperf (Plate No. 8) £1200
Z25 6d. buff (1872–73) (Plate Nos. 11, 12) .. *From* 55·00
Z26 6d. chestnut (1872) (Plate No. 11) .. .. .. 27·00
Z27 6d. grey (1873) (Plate No. 12) .. .. .. 45·00
Z28 6d. grey (1874–76) (Plate Nos. 13, 14, 15) .. *From* 21·00
Z29 9d. straw (1862) £120
Z30 9d. bistre (1862) .. ..
Z31 9d. straw (1865) .. ..
Z32 9d. straw (1867) .. ..
Z33 10d. red-brown (1867) £120
Z34 1s. green (1856) .. .. 60·00
Z35 1s. green (1862) .. .. 50·00
Z36 1s. green (1862) ("K" *variety*) .. .. ..
Z37 1s. green (1865) (Plate No. 4) .. .. .. 30·00
Z38 1s. green (1867–73) (Plate Nos. 4, 5, 6, 7) .. *From* 10·00
Z39 1s. green (1873–77) .. .. .. *From* 25·00
Plate Nos. 8, 9, 10, 11, 12, 13.
Z40 2s. blue (1867) .. .. 95·00
Z41 5s. rose (1867–74) (Plate Nos. 1, 2) .. *From* £225

CAIRO

CROWNED-CIRCLE HANDSTAMPS

CC2 CC6 CAIRO (R.) (23.3.1859) .. .. *Price on cover* £1750

SUEZ

CROWNED-CIRCLE HANDSTAMPS

CC3 CC1 SUEZ (R., B. *or* Black) (16.7.1847) *Price on cover* £2100

Stamps of GREAT BRITAIN *cancelled* "B 02" *as in Types* **2** *and* **8**, *or with circular date stamp as Type* **5**.

1860 *to* **1879.**

Z42 ½d. rose-red (1870–79) .. .. 23·00
Plate Nos. 6, 10, 11, 12, 13, 14.
Z43 1d. rose-red (1857) .. .. 7·50
Z44 1d. rose-red (1864–79) .. .. .. *From* 7·00
Plate Nos. 73, 74, 78, 79, 80, 81, 83, 84, 86, 87, 90, 91, 93, 94, 96, 97, 100, 101, 106, 107, 108, 110, 113, 118, 119, 120, 121, 122, 123, 124, 125, 129, 130, 131, 134, 137, 138, 140, 142, 143, 144, 145, 147, 148, 149, 150, 151, 152, 153, 154, 156, 158, 159, 160, 161, 162, 163, 164, 165, 166, 167, 168, 170, 174, 176, 177, 178, 179, 180, 181, 182, 184, 185, 186, 187, 189, 190, 205.
Z45 2d. blue (1858–69) .. .. *From* 12·00
Plate Nos. 8, 9, 13, 14, 15.
Z46 2½d. rosy mauve (1875) (blued *paper*) .. *From* 55·00
Plate Nos. 1, 2, 3.
Z47 2½d. rosy mauve (1875–76) (Plate Nos. 1, 2, 3) *From* 30·00
Z48 2½d. rosy mauve (*Error of Lettering*) £1250
Z49 2½d. rosy mauve (1876–79) .. .. .. *From* 24·00
Plate Nos. 3, 4, 5, 6, 7, 8, 9, 10.
Z50 3d. carmine-rose (1862) £120
Z51 3d. rose (1865) (Plate No. 4) .. .. .. 60·00
Z52 3d. rose (1867–73) (Plate Nos. 5, 6, 7, 8, 10) ..
Z53 3d. rose (1873–76) (Plate Nos. 12, 16) .. *From* 24·00
Z54 4d. rose (1857) .. .. 50·00
Z55 4d. red (1862) (Plate Nos. 3, 4) .. .. *From* 42·00
Z56 4d. vermilion (1865–73) .. .. .. *From* 27·00
Plate Nos. 7, 8, 9, 10, 11, 12, 13, 14.
Z57 4d. vermilion (1876) (Plate No. 15) .. ..
Z58 4d. sage-green (1877) (Plate No. 15) .. .. 75·00
Z59 6d. lilac (1856) .. .. 45·00
Z60 6d. lilac (1862) (Plate Nos. 3, 4) .. .. *From* 40·00
Z61 6d. lilac (1865–67) (Plate Nos. 5, 6) .. *From* 32·00
Z62 6d. lilac (1867) (Plate No. 6) .. .. .. 42·00
Z63 6d. violet (1867–70) (Plate Nos. 6, 8, 9) .. *From* 32·00
Z64 6d. buff (1872–73) (Plate Nos. 11, 12) .. *From* 60·00
Z65 6d. pale chestnut (Plate No. 12) (1872) £2250
Z66 6d. chestnut (1872) (Plate No. 11) .. .. .. 27·00
Z67 6d. grey (1873) (Plate No. 12) .. .. .. 50·00
Z68 6d. grey (1874–76) (Plate Nos. 13, 14, 15, 16) *From* 23·00
Z69 8d. orange (1876) .. ..
Z70 9d. straw (1862) £150
a. Thick paper .. ..
Z71 9d. bistre (1862) .. ..
Z72 9d. straw (1867) .. ..
Z73 10d. red-brown (1867) £150
Z74 1s. green (1856) .. .. 65·00
Z75 1s. green (1862) .. .. 55·00
Z76 1s. green (1862) ("K" *variety*) .. .. ..
Z77 1s. green (1865) (Plate No. 4) .. .. .. 40·00
Z78 1s. green (1867–73) (Plate Nos. 4, 5, 6, 7) .. *From* 11·00
Z79 1s. green (1873–77) .. .. .. *From* 27·00
Plate Nos. 8, 9, 10, 11, 12.
Z80 2s. blue (1867) £150
Z81 5s. rose (1867–74) (Plate Nos. 1, 2) .. *From* £250

PRICES FOR STAMPS ON COVER	
Nos. 1/41	*from* × 8
Nos. 42/3	*from* × 30
Nos. 44/83	*from* × 5
Nos. 84/97	*from* × 2
Nos. D57/70	*from* × 12
Nos. D71/86	*from* × 5
Nos. D84/103	*from* × 2
Nos. O64/87	*from* × 5
Nos. O88/101	*from* × 2

(Currency: 40 paras = 1 piastre)

1

2

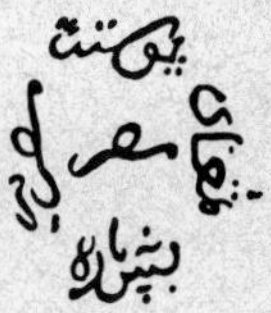
(3)

(Printed by Pellas Bros, Genoa. Litho, except for 1 pi. (typo). Black inscription (T **3**) litho, except on 1 pi. and 2 pi. (typo))

1866 (1 Jan). *Various designs as T* **1** *with black inscription as T* **3**. *The lowest group of characters indicates the value.* 1 *pi. no wmk, others W* **2** (*usually inverted*). *P* 12½.

1 5 pa. grey .. .. 24·00 20·00
a. Greenish grey .. .. 24·00 20·00
b. Imperf (pair) £150
c. Imperf between (pair) £250
d. Perf 12½×13 and compound .. .. 35·00 35·00
e. Perf 13 .. .. £200 £250
2 10 pa. brown .. .. 40·00 22·00
a. Imperf (pair) £110
b. Imperf between (pair) £300
c. Perf 12½×13 and compound .. .. 60·00 35·00
d. Perf 12½×15 .. .. £225 £250
e. Perf 13 .. .. £150 £170
3 20 pa. pale blue .. .. 60·00 22·00
a. Greenish blue .. .. 60·00 22·00
b. Imperf (pair) £200
c. Imperf between (pair) £350
d. Perf 12½×13 and compound .. .. 80·00 70·00
e. Perf 13 .. .. £350 £200
4 1 pi. claret .. .. 42·00 4·00
a. Imperf (pair) £100
b. Imperf between (pair) £300
c. Perf 12½×13 and compound .. .. 80·00 20·00
d. Perf 13 .. .. £250 £180
5 2 pi. yellow .. .. 70·00 32·00
a. Orange-yellow .. .. 70·00 32·00
b. Imperf (pair) .. ..
c. Imperf between (pair) £300 £300
d. Bisected diag (1 pi.) (on cover) .. † £1850
e. Perf 12½×13 and compound .. .. £110 40·00
f. Perf 12½×15 .. .. £120
6 5 pi. rose £200 £150
a. Imperf (pair) .. ..
b. Imperf between (pair) £800
c. Perf 12½×13 and compound £225
d. Error. Inscr 10 pi., perf 12½×15 .. £750 £650
e. Do. but imperf £440
7 10 pi. slate £225 £225
a. Imperf (pair) .. ..
b. Imperf between (pair) £1500
c. Perf 12½×13 and compound £350 £350
d. Perf 13 .. .. £1200

The 2 pi. bisected was authorised for use between 16 and 31 July 1867.

Stamps perforated 13 all round occurred only in the corner of a sheet and so are very rare; of the 10 pi. only 1 copy has been recorded unused. Compound perforations occur in many combinations.

The two halves of each background differ in minor details of the ornamentation. All values can be found with either half at the top.

Proofs of all values exist in smooth paper, without watermark. Beware of forgeries.

4

5

6

(Des F. Hoff, Hirschberg, Silesia. Litho V. Penasson, Alexandria)

1867 (1 Aug)–**69**. *W* **6**. *P* 15 × 12½.

11 4 5 pa. orange-yellow .. .. 15·00 7·00
a. Imperf (pair) .. ..
b. Imperf between (horiz pair) £150
12 10 pa. dull lilac .. .. 45·00 8·00
b. Bright mauve (7.69) .. .. .. 32·00 8·00
ba. Bisected diag (5 pa.) (on piece) (12.71) † £750
13 20 pa. deep blue-green .. .. .. 60·00 12·00
a. Pale blue-green .. .. 60·00 12·00
b. Yellowish green (7.69) .. .. .. 70·00 12·00

14 5 1 pi. dull rose-red *to* rose .. .. .. 9·00 90
a. Lake .. .. 75·00 22·00
b. Imperf (pair) .. .. ..
c. Imperf between (horiz pair) £150
d. Bisected diag (20 pa.) (on piece) .. † £750
e. Rouletted .. .. 50·00
15 2 pi. bright blue .. .. 70·00 12·00
a. Pale blue .. .. 70·00 12·00
b. Imperf (pair) .. .. ..
c. Imperf between (pair) £350
d. Bisected diag (1 pi.) (on cover) .. † —
e. Perf 12½ £200
16 5 pi. brown £300 £175

Each value was engraved four times, the resulting blocks being used to form sheets of 200. There are therefore four types showing minor variations for each value.

No. 12ba was used on newspapers.

Stamps printed both sides, both imperf and perf, come from printers' waste. The 1 pi. rose without watermark is a proof.

7

8 (Side panels transposed and inverted)

8*a* (I)

8*a* (II)

WATERMARK 8*a*. There are two types of this watermark which, as they are not always easy to distinguish, we do not list separately. Type II is slightly wider and less deep and the crescent is flatter than in Type I. The width measurement for Type I is generally about 14 mm and for Type II about 15 mm, but there is some variation within the sheets for both types.

Nos. 26/43, 45/7*a*, 49/*a*, 50/1 and 57 come with Type I only. Nos. 44*a*, 48/*a*, 52, 54*b*, 73/7 and 78 exist with both types of watermark (but No. 83 and official overprints on these stamps still require research); our prices are generally for Type II. Other watermarked issues between 1888 and 1907 have Type II watermarks only.

1872 (1 Jan)–**75**. *T* **7** (*the so-called "Penasson" printing**). *Thick opaque paper. W* **8***a*. I. *P* 12½×13½. II. *P* 13½.

A. LITHOGRAPHED

I II
26 7 20 pa. blue (*shades*) .. .. 85·00 25·00 £150 50·00
a. Imperf (pair) .. .. — — †
b. Imperf between (pair) — £1500 †
27 1 pi. red (*shades*) .. .. £175 4·50 £350 9·00

B. TYPOGRAPHED

I II
28 7 5 pa. brown (*shades*) .. 7·00 4·00 16·00 7·00
29 10 pa. mauve .. .. 6·00 3·00 6·00 2·50
30 20 pa. blue (*shades*) .. 26·00 3·50 40·00 12·00
31 1 pi. rose-red .. .. 20·00 75 40·00 3·00
a. Bisected (20 pa.) (on piece with No. 31) (7.75) † £375 †
32 2 pi. chrome-yellow .. 45·00 3·50 15·00 3·00
a. Bisected (1 pi.) (on piece) .. .. † £525 †
33 2½ pi. violet .. .. 45·00 8·50 £600 £170
34 5 pi. yellow-green .. .. £180 35·00 £250 50·00
a. Tête-bêche (pair) .. — — †

*The lithographed stamps are now believed to have been printed by Penasson, but the typographed by the Government Printing Works at Bûlâq, Cairo.

The lithographed and typographed stamps each show the characteristic differences between these two processes:—

The typographed stamps show the coloured lines of the design impressed into the paper and an accumulation of ink along the margins of the lines.

The lithographed stamps are essentially flat in appearance, without the heaping of the ink. Many of the 20 pa. show evidence of retouching, particularly of the outer frame lines.

The 2 pi. vertically bisected was used at Gallipoli.

See also the footnote below No. 41.

1874 (Oct)–**75**. *Typo from new stereos at Bûlâq, on thinner paper. W* **8***a*. I. *P* 12½. II. *P* 13½ × 12½.

I II
35 8 5 pa. brown (4.75) .. 5·50 2·50 3·25 2·50
a. Tête-bêche (vert pair) 35·00 35·00 60·00 60·00
ab. Tête-bêche (horiz pair) £250 £250 £300 £300
b. Imperf (pair) .. — — †
c. Imperf between) (pair) £100 £120 †
36 7 10 pa. grey-lilac (*shades*) .. 5·00 3·00 7·00 2·25
a. Tête-bêche (pair) £120 £120 £120 £120
b. Imperf (pair) .. — †
37 20 pa. grey-blue (*shades*) .. 45·00 3·00 4·50 2·50
a. Imperf between (pair) † £250 —
b. Bisected diag (10 pa.) (on cover) .. † — †
38 1 pi. red (*shades*) .. 3·00 65 22·00 1·25
a. Tête-bêche (vert pair) 75·00 75·00 £300 £300
ab. Tête-bêche (horiz pair) £250 £250 — —
b. Imperf (pair) .. — — †
c. Imperf between (pair) — 60·00 †
39 7 2 pi. yellow .. .. 38·00 3·00 5·00 3·75
a. Tête-bêche (pair) .. £350 £350 £350 £350
aa. Bisected diag (1 pi.) (on cover) .. .. † † £2000
b. Perf 12½×13½ .. † 32·00 7·00
ba. Tête-bêche (pair) .. † £750 —
40 2½ pi. violet .. .. 8·50 5·00 †
a. Tête-bêche (pair) .. £275 — †
b. Perf 12½×13½ .. † 32·00 14·00
ba. Tête-bêche (pair) .. † £850 £750
41 5 pi. green .. .. 48·00 16·00 †
a. Perf 12½×13½ .. † £300 £275
b. Imperf (pair) .. — — †

The 1872 printings have a thick line of colour in the top margin of the sheet and the other margins are all plain, an exception being the 5 pa., which on the majority of the sheets has the line at the righthand side of the sheet. The 1874–75 printings have a wide fancy border all round every sheet.

The 1872 printings are on thick opaque paper, with the impressions sharp and clear. The 1874–75 printings are on thinner paper, often semi-transparent and oily in appearance, and having the impressions very blurred and badly printed. These are only general distinctions and there are a number of exceptions.

The majority of the 1874–75 stamps have blind or defective perforations, while the 1872 stamps have clean-cut perfs.

There seem to be many different compositions of the sheets, containing the *tête-bêche* varieties, settings being known with 1, 3, 9 and 10 inverted stamps in various sheets. Sheets of the 5 pa. are known with 9 of the 20 horizontal rows inverted, giving vertical *tête-bêche* pairs; four stamps were inverted within their row giving four horizontal *tête-bêche* pairs.

(9)

1879 (1 Jan). *Stamps of* 1874 *surch as T* **9**, *at Bûlâq*.

I. *P* 12½. II. *P* 12½ × 13½

I II
42 7 5 pa. on 2½ pi. violet .. 6·00 6·00 6·50 6·50
a. Surch inverted .. 70·00 70·00 £140 £140
b. Tête-bêche (pair) .. £3000 — — —
c. Imperf (pair) .. — — †
43 10 pa. on 2½ pi. violet .. 10·00 10·00 15·00 15·00
a. Surch inverted .. 75·00 75·00 £110 £110
b. Tête-bêche (pair) .. £1300 — £1300 —
c. Imperf (pair) .. .. — — †

10

11

12

13

14

15

(Typo De La Rue)

1879 (1 Apr). *Ordinary paper. W* **8***a*. *P* 14.
44 10 5 pa. deep brown 20 15
a. Pale brown 30 15
45 11 10 pa. reddish lilac .. .. .. 30·00 3·00
46 12 20 pa. pale blue .. .. .. 50·00 1·50
47 13 1 pi. rose .. .. .. 15·00 10
a. Pale rose .. .. .. 14·00 10
48 14 2 pi. orange .. .. .. 18·00 40
a. Orange-yellow .. .. .. 16·00 50
49 15 5 pi. green .. .. .. 55·00 6·00
a. Blue-green .. .. .. 55·00 5·00

See also Nos. 50/6.

Khedive Tewfik

26 June 1879–7 January 1892

British troops were landed in Egypt in 1882 to secure the Suez Canal against a nationalist movement led by Arabi Pasha. Arabi was defeated at Tel-el-Kebir and British troops remained in Egypt until 1954. A British resident and consul-general advised the Khedive. Holders of this post were Sir Evelyn Baring (Lord Cromer), 1883–1907; Sir Eldon Gorst, 1907–11; and Lord Kitchener, 1911–14.

1881–1902. *Colours changed. Ordinary paper. W* **8***a*. *P* 14.
50 11 10 pa. claret (1.81) .. .. .. 40·00 4·00
51 10 pa. bluish grey (25.1.82) .. .. 5·50 80
52 10 pa. green (15.12.84) 20 10
53 12 20 pa. rose-carmine (15.12.84) .. .. 4·00 50
a. Bright rose .. .. .. 4·00 40
54 13 1 pi. blue (15.12.84) .. .. .. 1·50 10
a. Deep ultramarine .. .. .. 4·50 20
b. Pale ultramarine .. .. .. 1·50 10
c. Chalk-surfaced paper. *Ultramarine* (1902) .. .. .. 2·00 10
ca. Do. *Blue* .. .. .. 1·50 10
55 14 2 pi. orange-brown (1.8.93) .. .. 12·00 30
a. Chalk-surfaced paper (1902) .. 12·00 10
ab. Do. *Orange* .. .. .. 14·00 60
56 15 5 pi. pale grey (15.12.84) .. .. 12·00 50
a. Slate .. .. .. 11·00 40
b. Chalk-surfaced paper. *Slate-grey* (1902) .. .. .. 15·00 15

(17)

1884 (1 Feb). *Surch with T* **17** *at Bûlâq*.
57 15 20 pa. on 5 pi. green .. .. .. 6·50 1·25
a. Surch inverted .. .. .. 75·00 70·00

(New Currency: 1000 milliemes = 100 piastres = £1 Egyptian)

18

19

20

21

22

1888 (1 Jan)–**1906**. *Ordinary paper. W* **8***a*. *P* 14.
58 18 1 m. pale brown 25 10
a. Deep brown 30 10
b. Chalk-surfaced paper. *Pale brown* (1902) 15 10
ba. Do. *Deep brown* 15 10
59 19 2 m. blue-green 50 10
a. Green 50 10
ab. Chalk-surfaced paper (1902) .. 50 10
60 20 3 m. maroon (1.1.92) .. .. .. 2·00 1·00
61 3 m. yellow (1.8.93) .. .. .. 1·25 15
a. Orange-yellow .. .. .. 1·10 15
ab. Chalk-surfaced paper (1902) .. 1·25 10
62 21 4 m. vermilion (*chalk-surfaced paper*) (1906) 60 10
63 5 m. rose-carmine 90 10
a. Bright rose .. .. .. 1·10 10
b. Aniline rose .. .. .. 1·10 10
c. Chalk-surfaced paper. *Rose* (1902) .. 1·00 10
ca. Do. *Deep aniline rose* .. .. 1·25 10
64 22 10 p. mauve .. .. .. 15·00 80
a. Aniline mauve .. .. .. 17·00 80
b. Chalk-surfaced paper. *Mauve* (1902) 20·00 50

Khedive Abbas Hilmi

7 January 1892–19 December 1914

29 Nile Felucca

30 Cleopatra with Head-dress of Isis

31 Ras-el-Tin Palace, Alexandria

35 Pylon of Karnak Temple, Luxor

37 Rock Temples of Abu Simbel

(Typo De La Rue)

1914 (8 Jan). *W* **8***a*. *P* 14.
73 29 1 m. sepia 15 20
74 30 2 m. green 35 15
75 31 3 m. yellow-orange 40 25
a. Double impression
76 – 4 m. vermilion 80 65
77 – 5 m. lake 60 10
a. Wmk sideways (booklets) .. .. 10·00 15·00
78 – 10 m. dull blue .. .. 1·50 10
79 35 20 m. olive .. .. 3·75 10
80 – 50 m. purple .. .. 6·00 40
81 37 100 m. slate .. .. 10·00 60
82 – 200 m. maroon .. .. 23·00 1·50
73/82 .. .. *Set of* 10 42·00 3·50

Designs: *As T* **29**—4 m. Pyramids at Giza; 5 m. Sphinx; 10 m. Colossi of Thebes. *As T* **35**—50 m. Cairo Citadel; 200 m. Aswân Dam.

All the above exist imperforate, but imperforate stamps without watermark are proofs.

See also Nos. 84/95.

BRITISH PROTECTORATE

On 18 December 1914, after war with Turkey had begun, Egypt was declared to be a British protectorate. Abbas Hilmi was deposed, and his uncle, Hussein Kamil, was proclaimed Sultan of Egypt.

Sultan Hussein Kamil

19 December 1914–9 October 1917

(39)

1915 (15 Oct). *Surch with T* **39**, *at Bûlâq.*
83 **31** 2 m. on 3 m. yellow-orange 55 75
a. Surch inverted £200 £200
b. Surch double, one albino £120

Sultan Ahmed Fuad

9 October 1917–15 March 1922

40 (A) (B)

(Typo Harrison & Sons)

1921–22. W **40**. (*a*) *As Nos.* 73/82. (i) *P* 13½ × 14.
84 **29** 1 m. sepia (A) 15 25
a. Two dots omitted (B) .. .. 27·00 22·00
85 **30** 2 m. green .. .. .. 1·25 40
a. Imperf between (pair) .. ..
86 2 m. vermilion (1922) 30 30
87 **31** 3 m. yellow-orange (12.21) .. .. 1·00 35
88 – 4 m. green (1922) .. .. .. 1·50 1·50
89 – 5 m. lake (1.21) 60 10
a. Imperf between (pair) .. ..
90 – 5 m. pink (11.21) .. .. .. 1·00 10
91 – 10 m. dull blue .. .. .. 2·00 10
92 – 10 m. lake (9.22) .. .. .. 1·50 15

(ii) *P* 14
93 **35** 20 m. olive .. .. .. 5·00 10
94 – 50 m. purple .. .. .. 10·00 30
95 **37** 100 m. slate (1922) .. .. 38·00 3·50
84/95 .. .. .. *Set of* 12 55·00 6·25

41 Statue of Rameses II **42**

(*b*) *New design. P* 13½ × 14
96 **41** 15 m. indigo (3.22) .. .. .. 1·50 15
97 **42** 15 m. indigo .. .. .. 9·50 1·75

Type **42** was printed first; but because the inscription at right was erroneous the stamps were withheld and the corrected Type **41** printed and issued. Type **42** was released later.

POSTAGE DUE STAMPS

D 1 D 2 D 3

(Des L. Barkhausen. Litho V. Penasson, Alexandria)

1884 (1 Jan). *Impressed W* **6**. *P* 10½.
D57 **D 1** 10 pa. red .. .. .. 20·00 7·00
a. Imperf (pair) .. ..
b. Imperf between (pair) £100
D58 20 pa. red .. .. .. 50·00 12·00
D59 1 pi. red .. .. .. 70·00 25·00
D60 2 pi. red .. .. .. £100 10·00
D61 5 pi. red .. .. .. 12·00 18·00

1886 (1 Aug). *No wmk. P* 10½.
D62 **D 1** 10 pa. rose-red .. .. .. 18·00 3·00
a. Imperf between (pair) .. .. 75·00
D63 20 pa. rose-red .. .. .. £110 25·00
a. Imperf between (pair) .. ..
D64 1 pi. rose-red .. .. .. 13·00 3·00
a. Imperf between (pair) £100 £100
D65 2 pi. rose-red .. .. .. 13·00 3·00
a. Imperf between (pair) £100

Specialists distinguish four types of each value in both these issues.

(Litho V. Penasson, Alexandria)

1888 (1 Jan). *No wmk. P* 11½.
D66 **D 2** 2 m. green .. .. .. 6·50 7·00
a. Imperf between (pair) £150 £150
D67 5 m. rose-carmine .. .. .. 11·00 7·00
D68 1 p. blue .. .. .. 55·00 35·00
a. Imperf between (pair) £150
D69 2 p. orange .. .. .. 70·00 10·00
D70 5 p. grey £150 £125
a. With stop after left-hand "PIASTRES" £200 £150

Specialists distinguish four types of each value.
Beware of forgeries of the 5 p.

(Typo De La Rue)

1889 (Apr). *Ordinary or chalk-surfaced paper. W* **8a** (*upright*). *P* 14.
D71 **D 3** 2 m. green .. .. .. 5·00 50
a. Bisected (1 m.) (on cover with unbisected 2 m.) .. .. .. † £250
D72 4 m. maroon .. .. .. 1·50 50
D73 1 p. ultramarine .. .. .. 5·00 70
D74 2 p. orange .. .. .. 5·00 85
a. Bisected diagonally (1 p.) (on cover)

See also Nos. D84/6 for stamps with watermark sideways.

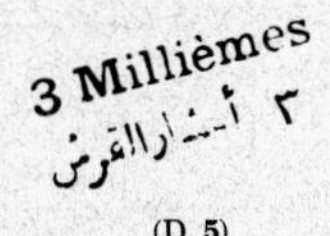

(D 4) (D 5)

Type D 4

The Arabic figure at right is less than 2 mm from the next character, which consists of a straight stroke only.

Type D 5

The distance is 3 mm and the straight character has a comma-like character above it. There are other minor differences.

1898 (Apr)–**1905**. *No.* D74 *surch, At Bûlâq.*

(*a*) *With Type* D **4**. *Ordinary paper*
D75 **D 3** 3 m. on 2 p. orange .. .. .. 45 1·25
a. Surch inverted .. .. 50·00 50·00
b. Pair, one without surch ..
c. Arabic "2" for "3" ..
d. Arabic "3" over "2" ..

No. D75c occurred in the first printing on positions 10, 20, 30, 40, 50 and 60 of the pane of 60 (the Arabic figure is the right-hand character of the second line–see illustration on page xvii). In the second printing the correct figure was printed on top to form No. D75d. The error was corrected in subsequent printings.

(*b*) *With Type* D **5**. *Ordinary or chalk-surfaced paper* (1905)
D76 **D 3** 3 m. on 2 p. orange .. .. .. 2·00 3·00
a. Surch inverted .. .. 50·00 50·00
b. Surch double £150

1918. *As Nos.* D71/3 *but wmk sideways.*
D84 **D 3** 2 m. bright green .. .. .. 6·00 3·00
D85 4 m. maroon .. .. .. 6·00 3·00
D86 1 p. dull ultramarine .. .. .. 11·00 8·00

D **6** D **7**

(Typo Harrison)

1921 (Oct)–**22**. *Chalk-surfaced paper. W* **40**. *P* 14 × 13½.
D 98 **D 6** 2 m. green .. .. .. 70 1·25
D 99 2 m. scarlet (1922) 70 50
D100 4 m. scarlet .. .. .. 4·00 3·00
D101 4 m. green .. .. .. 1·00 45
D102 **D 7** 10 m. deep slate-blue (11.21) .. .. 2·75 5·00
D103 10 m. lake (1922) .. .. .. 2·25 45
D98/103 .. .. .. *Set of* 6 10·00 9·50

OFFICIAL STAMPS

O 1 (O 2) (O 3)

(Typo De La Rue)

1893 (1 Jan). *Ordinary or chalk-surfaced paper. W* **8a**. *P* 14.
O64 **O 1** (–) chestnut 20 10
a. Wmk sideways .. .. 5·50 3·50

This stamp, with overprint 3 P.T. and Arabic equivalent, is a fiscal.

1907. *Nos.* 54ca, 55b, 58b, 59ab, 61ab *and* 63c *optd with Type* O **2**, *by De La Rue.*
O73 **18** 1 m. pale brown 30 10
O74 **19** 2 m. green 45 10
a. Opt double ..
O75 **20** 3 m. orange-yellow .. .. .. 1·00 25
O76 **21** 5 m. rose 90 10
O77 **13** 1 p. blue 75 10
O78 **15** 5 p. slate-grey .. .. .. 4·50 15
O73/8 .. .. .. *Set of* 6 7·00 40

1913 (Nov). *No.* 63c *optd at Bûlâq.*

(*a*) *With Type* O **3**
O79 **21** 5 m. rose .. .. .. — £200
a. Opt inverted .. ..

(*b*) *As Type* O **3** *but without inverted commas*
O80 **21** 5 m. rose .. .. .. 1·75 10
a. No stop after "S" (pos. 130) .. 15·00 15·00
b. Opt inverted .. .. £150 75·00

(O 4) (O 5) (O 6)

1914 (Dec)–**15**. *Stamps of* 1902–6 *and* 1914 *optd with Type* O 4 *at Bûlâq.*
O83 **29** 1 m. sepia (1.15) .. .. .. 1·00 1·50
a. No stop after "S" .. .. 10·00 15·00
O84 **19** 2 m. green (3.15) .. .. .. 1·25 1·50
a. No stop after "S" .. .. 10·00 15·00
b. Opt inverted .. .. 25·00 25·00
c. Opt double £300
O85 **31** 3 m. yellow-orange (3.15) .. .. 1·00 1·50
a. No stop after "S" .. .. 10·00 15·00
O86 **21** 4 m. vermilion (12.14) .. .. 2·00 1·25
a. Opt inverted £150 £125
b. Pair, one without opt
O87 – 5 m. lake (1.15) .. .. .. 2·25 50
a. No stop after "S" .. .. 10·00 15·00
O83/7 .. .. .. *Set of* 5 6·75 5·50

1915 (Oct). *Nos.* 59ab, 62 *and* 77 *optd lithographically with Type* O **5**, *at Bûlâq.*
O88 **19** 2 m. green 70 90
a. Opt inverted .. .. 15·00 15·00
b. Opt double .. .. 20·00
O89 **21** 4 m. vermilion .. .. .. 1·00 1·50
O90 – 5 m. lake .. .. .. 1·25 90
a. Pair, one without opt £225

1922. *Nos.* 84, *etc. optd lithographically with Type* O **6**, *at Bûlâq.*
O 98 **29** 1 m. sepia (A) (28.6) .. .. .. 2·00 3·00
a. Two dots omitted (B) £200
O 99 **30** 2 m. vermilion (16.6) .. .. 3·75 4·50
O100 **31** 3 m. yellow-orange (28.6) .. .. 65·00 70·00
O101 – 5 m. pink (13.3) .. .. .. 5·50 1·75

Egypt was declared to be an independent kingdom on 15 March 1922, and Sultan Ahmed Fuad became king.

Later stamp issues will be found listed in Part 19 (*Middle East*) of this catalogue.

EGYPTIAN POST OFFICES ABROAD

From 1865 Egypt operated various post offices in foreign countries. No special stamps were issued for these offices and use in them of unoverprinted Egyptian stamps can only be identified by the cancellation. Stamps with such cancellations are worth more than the used prices quoted in the Egypt listings.

Such offices operated in the following countries. An * indicates that details will be found under that heading elsewhere in the catalogue.

ETHIOPIA

A B

C D

MASSAWA. *Open Nov* 1867 *to Dec* 1885. *Postmark types* A (*also without* REGIE), B, C, D. *An Arabic seal type is also known on stampless covers.*

SENHIT (near Keren). *Open* 1878 *to* 1884? *Only one example, with hand-drawn cancellation, known.*

A post office is also recorded at Harar, but no postal marking has so far been reported.

SOMALILAND*

Unoverprinted stamps of Egypt used from 1876 until 1884.

SUDAN*

Unoverprinted stamps of Egypt used from 1867 until 1897.

TURKISH EMPIRE

E F

G H

I J

K L

M N

O

The offices are listed according to the spelling on the cancellation. The present-day name (if different) and country are given in brackets.

ALESSANDRETTA (Iskenderun, Turkey). *Open* 14 July 1870 *to* Feb 1872. *Postmark types* E, I.
BAIROUT (Beirut, Lebanon). *Open* 14 July 1870 *to* Feb 1872. *Postmark types* E, J.
CAVALA (Kavala, Greece). *Open* 14 July 1870 *to* Feb 1872. *Postmark type* E.
COSTANTINOPOLI (Istanbul, Turkey). *Open* 13 June 1865 *to* 30 June 1881. *Postmark types* E, F, O.
DARDANELLI (Canakkale, Turkey). *Open* 10 June 1868 *to* 30 June 1881. *Postmark types* H, K.
DJEDDAH, *see* GEDDA.
GALIPOLI (Gelibolu, Turkey). *Open* 10 June 1868 *to* 30 June 1881. *Postmark types* E, L.
GEDDA, DJEDDAH (Jeddah, Saudi Arabia). *Open* 8 June 1865 *to* 30 June 1881. *Postmark types* F, G (*also with year replacing solid half-circle*), O (*all spelt* GEDDA), D (*spelt* DJEDDAH).
IAFFA (Jaffa, Israel). *Open* 14 July 1870 *to* Feb 1872. *Postmark type* E.
LAGOS (Port Lago, Greece). *Open* 14 July 1870 *to* Feb 1872. *Postmark type* E.
LATAKIA (Syria). *Open* 14 July 1870 *to* Feb 1872. *Postmark type* E.
LEROS (Aegean Is.). *Open* July 1873 *to* Jan 1874 *and* May *to* Oct 1874. *Postmark type* E.
MERSINA (Mersin, Turkey). *Open* 14 July 1870 *to* Feb 1872. *Postmark type* E.
METELINO (Lesbos, Greece). *Open* 14 July 1870 *to* 30 June 1881. *Postmark types* E, M.
RODI (Rhodes, Greece). *Open* 13 Aug 1872 *to* 30 June 1881. *Postmark type* E.
SALONNICCHI (Thessaloniki, Greece). *Open* 14 July 1870 *to* Feb 1872. *Postmark type* E.
SCIO (Chios, Aegean Is.). *Open* 14 July 1870 *to* 30 June 1881. *Postmark types* E, N.
SMIRNE (Izmir, Turkey). *Open* 14 Nov 1865 *to* 30 June 1881. *Postmark types* E (*also without* "V. R."), F.
TENEDOS (Bozcaada, Turkey). *Open* 14 July 1870 *to* Mar 1871. *Postmark type* E.
TRIPOLI (Lebanon). *Open* 14 July 1870 *to* Feb 1872. *Postmark type* E.
VOLO (Volos, Greece). *Open* 14 July 1870 *to* Feb 1872. *Postmark type* E.

BRITISH FORCES IN EGYPT

From 1 November 1932, to 29 February 1936 members of the British Forces in Egypt and their families were allowed to send letters to the British Isles at reduced rates. Special seals which were on sale in booklets at N.A.A.F.I. Institutes and Canteens were used instead of Egyptian stamps, and were stuck on the back of the envelopes, letters bearing the seals being franked on the front with a hand-stamp inscribed "EGYPT POSTAGE PREPAID" in a double circle surmounted by a crown.

PRICES FOR STAMPS ON COVER	
Nos. A1/9	*from* × 5
No. A10	*from* × 2
No. A11	*from* × 5
No. A12	*from* × 100
No. A13	*from* × 20
No. A14	*from* × 200
No. A15	*from* × 20

A 1

A 2

(Des Lt.-Col. C. Fraser. Typo Hanbury, Tomsett & Co, London)

1932 (1 Nov)–**33.** *P* 11. (*a*) *Inscr* "POSTAL SEAL".
A1 A 1 1 p. deep blue and red . . . . . . 27·00 2·50
(*b*) *Inscr* "LETTER SEAL"
A2 A 1 1 p. deep blue and red (8.33) . . . . 14·00 55

(Des Sgt. W. F. Lait. Litho Walker & Co, Amalgamated Press, Cairo)

1932 (26 Nov)–**35.** *Christmas Seals. P* 11½.
A3 A 2 3 m. black/*azure* . . . . . . 26·00 50·00
A4 3 m. brown-lake (13.11.33) . . . . 6·00 20·00
A5 3 m. deep blue (17.11.34) . . . . 7·00 12·00
A6 3 m. vermilion (23.11.35) . . . . 1·25 8·00
a. Pale vermilion (19.12.35) . . . . 5·00 11·00

A 3

(Des Miss Waugh. Photo Harrison)

1934 (1 June)–**35.** (*a*) *P* 14½ × 14.
A7 A 3 1 p. carmine . . . . . . 24·00 50
A8 1 p. green (5.12.34) . . . . 3·00 2·75
(*b*) *P* 13½ × 14
A9 A 3 1 p. carmine (24.4.35) 90 85

JUBILEE
COMMEMORATION
1935

(A 4)

1935 (6 May). *Silver Jubilee. As No.* A9, *but colour changed and optd with Type* A 4, *in red.*
A10 A 3 1 p. ultramarine £200 £175

Xmas 1935
3 Milliemes

(A 5)

1935 (16 Dec). *Provisional Christmas Seal. No.* A9 *surch with Type* A 5.
A11 A 3 3 m. on 1 p. carmine . . . . 15·00 40·00

The seals and letter stamps were replaced by the following Army Post stamps issued by the Egyptian Postal Administration. No. A9 was accepted for postage until 15 March 1936.

A 6 King Fuad I

A 7 King Farouk

W 48 of Egypt

(Types A 6/A 7. Photo Survey Dept, Cairo)

1936. *W* **48** *of Egypt. P* 13½ × 14.
A12 A 6 3 m. green (9.11.36) 60 50
A13 10 m. carmine (1.3.36) . . . . . . 1·00 10

1939 (12 Dec). *W* **48** *of Egypt. P* 13 × 13½.
A14 A 7 3 m. green . . . . . . 50 2·00
A15 10 m. carmine 60 10

These stamps were withdrawn in April 1941 but the concession, without the use of special stamps, continued until October 1951 when the postal agreement was abrogated.

Falkland Islands

PRICES FOR STAMPS ON COVER TO 1945	
Nos. 1/4	*from* × 6
Nos. 5/12	*from* × 8
Nos. 13/14	*from* × 10
Nos. 15/38	*from* × 8
Nos. 41/2	*from* × 5
Nos. 43/59	*from* × 4
Nos. 60/80	*from* × 3
No. 115	*from* × 2
Nos. 116/26	*from* × 3
Nos. 127/38	*from* × 4
Nos. 139/42	*from* × 5
Nos. 143/5	*from* × 8
Nos. 146/63	*from* × 3

CROWN COLONY

(1) (2)

1869–76. *The Franks.*
FR1 1 In black, *on cover* £6500
FR2 2 In red, *on cover* (1876) £10000
On *piece*, No. FR1 on white or coloured papers £65; No. FR2 on white £90. The use of these franks ceased when the first stamps were issued.

3

½d.

(4)

In the ½d., 2d., 2½d. and 9d. the figures of value in the lower corners are replaced by small rosettes and the words of value are in colour.

NOTE. Nos. 1, 2, 3, 4, 8, 10, 11 and 12 exist with one or two sides imperf from the margin of the sheets.

(Recess B.W.)

1878–79. *No wmk. P* 14, 14½.
1 **3** 1d. claret (19.6.78) £550 £375
2 4d. grey-black (Sept 1879) £1000 £130
a. On wmkd paper £1800 £400
3 6d. blue-green (19.6.78) .. .. 45·00 45·00
4 1s. bistre-brown (1878) .. .. 45·00 45·00

No. 2a shows portions of the papermaker's watermark—"R. TURNER, CHAFFORD MILLS"—in ornate double-lined capitals.

1882 (22 Nov). *Wmk Crown CA (upright). P* 14, 14½.
5 **3** 1d. dull claret.. .. .. .. £300 85·00
a. Imperf between (horiz pair) .. £35000
6 4d. grey-black .. .. .. 60·00 55·00

1885 (23 Mar)–**87.** *Wmk Crown CA (sideways to left or right). P* 14, 14½.
7 **3** 1d. pale claret .. .. 50·00 32·00
8 1d. brownish claret (3.10.87) .. .. 60·00 30·00
a. Bisected (on cover) (1891)*.. .. † £2000
9 4d. pale grey-black .. .. .. £250 30·00
10 4d. grey-black (3.10.87) .. .. £250 30·00

*See note below No. 14.

1889 (26 Sept)–**91.** *Wmk Crown CA (upright). P* 14, 14½.
11 **3** 1d. red-brown (21.5.91).. .. . 65·00 50·00
a. Bisected (on cover)* .. † £2000
12 4d. olive grey-black .. .. 50·00 42·00

*See note below No. 14.

1891 (Jan). *Nos.* 8 *and* 11 *bisected diagonally and each half handstamped with T* **4**.
13 **3** ½d. on half of 1d. brownish claret (No. 8) £400 £275
a. Unsevered pair £1500 £1000
b. Unsevered pair *se-tenant* with unsurcharged whole stamp .. £7000
14 ½d. on half 1d. red-brown (No. 11) .. £325 £150
a. Unsevered pair .. .. — £600
b. Unsevered pair *se-tenant* with unsurcharged whole stamp ..

1891 PROVISIONALS. In 1891 the postage to the United Kingdom and Colonies was reduced from 4d. to 2½d. per half ounce. As no ½d. or 2½d. stamps were available the bisection of the 1d. was authorised from 1 January 1891. This authorisation was withdrawn on 11 January 1892, although bisects were accepted for postage until July of that year. The ½d. and 2½d. stamps were placed on sale from 10 September 1891.

Cork Cancel used in 1891

The Type **4** surcharge was not used regularly; unsurcharged bisects being employed far more frequently. Genuine bisects should be cancelled with the cork cancel illustrated above. The use of any other postmark, including a different cork cancel, requires date evidence linked to known mail ship sailings to prove authenticity.

Posthumous strikes of the surcharge on "souvenir" bisects usually show a broken "2" and/or a large full stop. These are known on bisected examples of No. 18 and on varieties such as surcharge inverted, double or sideways. Forgeries exist of all these provisionals.

1891 (May)–**1902.** *Wmk Crown CA (upright). P* 14, 14½.
15 **3** ½d. blue-green (May–Nov 1891) .. 14·00 20·00
16 ½d. green (20.5.92) .. .. .. 14·00 16·00
a. Deep dull green (15.4.96) .. 25·00 25·00
17 ½d. deep yellow-green (1894–95) .. 14·00 20·00
a. Yellow-green (19.6.99) .. .. 2·00 1·25
b. Dull yellowish green (13.1.1902) .. 3·00 1·25
18 1d. orange red-brown (14.10.91) .. 45·00 42·00
a. Brown (1891?) .. .. .. 35·00 40·00
19 1d. reddish chestnut (20.4.92) .. .. 35·00 40·00
20 1d. orange-brn (*Wmk reversed*) (18.1.94) 25·00 27·00
21 1d. claret (23.7.94) .. .. .. 30·00 30·00
22 1d. Venetian red (pale to deep) (1895–96) .. .. .. 7·50 6·00
a. Venetian claret (1898?) .. .. 11·00 8·00
23 1d. pale red (19.6.99) .. .. .. 5·00 1·00
24 1d. orange-red (13.1.1902) .. .. 6·00 2·00
25 2d. purple (pale to deep) (1895–98) .. 6·50 12·00
26 2d. reddish purple (15.4.96) .. .. 5·00 11·00
27 2½d. pale chalky ultram (May–Aug 1891) 75·00 35·00
28 2½d. dull blue (19.11.91).. .. .. 30·00 14·00
29 2½d. Prussian blue (18.1.94) £200 £180
30 2½d. ultramarine (1894–96) .. .. 12·00 6·50
a. Pale ultramarine (10.6.98).. .. 15·00 10·00
b. Deep ultramarine (18.9.1901) .. 15·00 20·00
31 4d. brownish black (wmk reversed (18.1.94) £350 £180
32 4d. olive-black (11.5.95) .. .. 14·00 20·00
33 6d. orange-yellow (19.11.91) .. .. 30·00 32·00
34 6d. yellow (15.4.96) .. .. .. 22·00 32·00
35 9d. pale reddish orange (15.11.95) .. 22·00 48·00
36 9d. salmon (15.4.96) .. .. .. 27·00 48·00
37 1s. grey-brown (15.11.95) .. .. 30·00 35·00
38 1s. yellow-brown (15.4.96) .. .. 27·00 35·00
15/38 .. .. *Set of* 8 90·00 £140
15, 26, 28, 33, 35 Optd "Specimen" .. *Set of* 5 £750

NOTES. The dates shown above are those on which the printer delivered the various printings to the Crown Agents. Several months could elapse before the stamps went on sale in the Colony, depending on the availability of shipping.

The plates used for these stamps did not fit the paper so that the watermark appears in all sorts of positions on the stamp. Well centred examples are scarce. Examples can also be found showing parts of the marginal watermarks, either CROWN AGENTS horizontally in letters 12 mm high or "CROWN AGENTS FOR THE COLONIES" vertically in 7 mm letters. Both are in double-lined capitals.

Many stamps between Nos. 5 and 38 can be found with the watermark reversed, inverted or both, in addition to those noted above where such variations are a constant feature.

The 2½d. ultramarine printing can sometimes be found in a violet shade, but the reason for this is unknown.

5

6

(Recess B.W.)

1898 (June). *Wmk Crown CC. P* 14, 14½.
41 **5** 2s. 6d. deep blue £200 £250
42 **6** 5s. red £180 £200
41/2 Optd "Specimen" .. .. *Set of* 2 £450

7

8

(Recess D.L.R.)

1904–12. *Wmk Mult Crown CA. P* 14.
43 **7** ½d. yellow-green .. .. .. 1·75 85
44 ½d. pale yellow-green on thick paper (1908) 4·75 7·50
45 ½d. deep yellow-green (1911) .. .. 3·25 3·00
46 1d. vermilion .. .. 4·00 1·25
47 1d. vermilion on thick paper (1908) .. 3·75 90
48 1d. dull coppery red on thick paper (1908) £160 35·00
49 1d. orange-vermilion (1911) .. .. 3·50 1·75
50 2d. purple .. .. 9·50 24·00
51 2d. reddish purple (1912) £250 £275
52 2½d. ultramarine (*shades*) .. .. 23·00 7·00
53 2½d. deep blue (1912) £250 £200
54 6d. orange .. .. 32·00 48·00
55 1s. brown .. .. 35·00 30·00
56 **8** 3s. green £130 £120
57 3s. deep green (1906) £120 £130
58 5s. red £140 £140
43/58 .. .. *Set of* 8 £325 £350
43/58 Optd "Specimen" .. .. *Set of* 8 £500

1906. *Wmk Mult Crown CA (sideways). P* 14.
59 **7** 1d. vermilion .. .. 75 1·75

SOUTH GEORGIA UNDERPRINT. The Post Office on South Georgia opened on 3 December 1909, a stock of Falkland Islands stamps with values from ½d. to 5s. being supplied, together with a straight-line handstamp inscribed "South Georgia". It was intended that this mark should be struck on covers, below the stamps, as an indication of the origin of the mail, the stamps themselves being cancelled with a Falkland Islands postmark. Examples are known on the Edward VII stamps and on some values of the Victorian issue. This underprint can, on occasion, be found struck across the stamps, rather than below them.

Its use continues after the introduction of the South Georgia cancellation in July 1910, but no example has been reported after June 1912. (*Price for example of underprint on cover* (a) *In conjunction with* "FALKLAND ISLANDS" *postmark* (December 1909 *to* June 1910) *from* £1800 (b) *In conjunction with* "SOUTH GEORGIA" *postmark* (July 1910 *to* June 1912) *from* £900).

SOUTH GEORGIA PROVISIONAL HANDSTAMPS. During October 1911 the arrival of the German South Polar Expedition at Grytviken, South Georgia, resulted in the local supply of stamps becoming exhausted. The Acting Magistrate, Mr. E. B. Binnie, who was also responsible for the postal facilities, produced a handstamp reading "Paid At SOUTH GEORGIA" which, together with a manuscript indication of the postage paid and his signature, was used on mail from 18 October 1911 to January 1912.
PH1 "Paid 1 At SOUTH GEORGIA EBB" *Price on cover* £4000
PH2 "Paid 2½ At SOUTH GEORGIA EBB" *Price on cover* £4750

9

10

(Recess D.L.R.)

1912–20. *Wmk Mult Crown CA. P* 13¾ × 14 *(comb)* (½*d. to* 1*s.*) *or* 14 *(line)* (3*s. to* £1).
60 **9** ½d. yellow-green .. .. 1·75 2·50
a. Perf 14 (line). *Dp yellow-green* (1914) 20·00 28·00
b. Perf 14 (line). *Deep olive* (1918) .. 16·00 10·00
c. Deep olive (1919) .. .. .. 2·75 5·00
ca. Printed both sides .. .. † £5000
d. Dull yellowish green (on thick greyish paper) (1920) .. .. .. 4·50 14·00
61 **9** 1d. orange-red .. .. 3·75 2·50
a. Perf 14 (line). *Orge-vermilion* (1914) 5·00 1·75
b. Perf 14 (line). *Vermilion* (1918) .. † £550
c. Orange-vermilion (1919) .. .. 3·00 2·75
d. Orange-vermilion (on thick greyish paper) (1920) .. .. .. 5·50 1·60
62 2d. maroon .. .. 8·50 14·00
a. Perf 14 (line). *Deep reddish purple* (1914) .. .. 30·00 30·00
b. Perf 14 (line). *Maroon* (1918) .. 35·00 38·00
c. Deep reddish purple (1919) .. .. 5·00 9·50
63 2½d. deep bright blue .. .. .. 10·00 15·00
a. Perf 14 (line). *Dp bright blue* (1914).. 12·00 15·00
b. Perf 14 (line). *Milky blue* (1916) .. £375 £450
c. Milky blue (1919) .. .. .. 5·00 13·00
64 6d. yellow-orange.. .. .. .. 10·00 17·00
a. Brown-orange (1919).. .. .. 9·00 14·00
65 1s. light bistre-brown .. .. .. 26·00 27·00
a. Pale bistre-brown (1919) .. .. 32·00 40·00
b. Deep brown (on thick greyish paper) (1920) .. .. 32·00 50·00
66 **10** 3s. slate-green .. .. 55·00 70·00
67 5s. deep rose-red .. .. 60·00 85·00
a. Reddish maroon (1914) £125 £140
b. Maroon (1916) .. .. .. 65·00 85·00
68 10s. red/*green* (1914) £140 £200
69 £1 black/*red* (1914) £400 £450
60/9 (*incl 67b*) .. .. .. *Set of* 11 £700 £850
60/9 (*incl 67a*) Optd "Specimen" .. *Set of* 11 £1400

The exact measurement of the comb perforation used for Type **9** is 13.7 × 13.9. The line perforation, used for the 1914, 1916 and 1918 printings and for all the high values in Type **10**, measured 14.1 × 14.1.

It was previously believed that all examples of the 1d. in vermilion with the line perforation were overprinted to form No. 90, but it has now been established that some unoverprinted sheets of No. 61b were used during 1919.

All 1919 printings show weak impressions of the background either side of the head caused by the poor paper quality.

SOUTH GEORGIA BISECTS. The 2½d. No. 63c and 6d. No. 64*a* were bisected and used as 1d. and 2½d. respectively in S. Georgia in March 1923. This procedure was not authorised from Port Stanley. (*Prices on cover:* 2½d. £4000, 6d. £10000.)

PORT FOSTER HANDSTAMP. Postal facilities at Port Foster, Deception Island, South Shetlands were first provided during the 1912–13 whaling season. Permission was given for stamps on cover to be cancelled with a straight-line "PORT FOSTER" handstamp as an indication of origin. The handstamp is known to have been applied to Edward VII 1d. and George V ½d. and 1d. Falkland Islands issues. It is sometimes used in conjunction with a "FALKLAND ISLANDS" circular postmark.

Unused stamps and higher values with this handstamp were, it is believed, subsequently "made to order".

WAR STAMP
(11)

2½D
(12)

1918 (7 Oct)–**20.** *Optd by Govt Printing Press, Stanley, with T* **11**.
70 **9** ½d. deep olive (line perf) (No. 60b) .. 1·00 6·50
a. Yellow-green (No. 60) (4.19) .. .. 7·50
ab. Albino opt £1000
b. Deep olive (comb perf) (No. 60c) (4.19) 50 6·50
c. Dull yellowish green (on thick greyish paper) (No. 60*d*) (5.20) .. .. 17·00 48·00
71 1d. vermilion (line perf) (No. 61b) .. 3·00 9·00
a. Opt double, one albino £400
b. Orange-vermilion (line perf) (No. 61a) (4.19) .. .. 6·50
c. Orange-vermilion (comb perf) (No. 61c) (4.19) .. .. 50 3·50
ca. Opt double £1500
d. Orange-vermilion (on thick greyish paper) (No. 61*d*) (5.20) .. .. 48·00 £110
72 1s. light bistre-brown (No. 65) .. .. 30·00 48·00
a. Pale bistre-brown (No. 65*a*) (4.19) .. 6·00 30·00
ab. Opt double, one albino £1100
ac. Opt omitted (in pair with normal) .. £5000
b. Deep brown (on thick greyish paper) (No. 65*b*) (5.20) .. .. .. 15·00 38·00
ba. Opt double, one albino £1100

There were five printings of the "WAR STAMP" overprint, but all, except that in May 1920, used the same setting. Composition of the five printings was as follows:
October 1918. Nos. 70, 71 and 72
January 1919. Nos. 70, 71 and 72
April 1919. Nos. 70*a*/*b*, 71*b*/*c* and 72*a*
October 1919. Nos. 70*b*, 71*c* and 72*a*
May 1920. Nos. 70*c*, 71*c*/*d* and 72*b*.

1921–28. *Wmk Mult Script CA. P* 14.
73 **9** ½d. yellowish green .. .. .. 2·25 2·75
a. Green (1925) .. .. 1·90 2·75
74 1d. dull vermilion (1924) .. .. 2·50 80
a. Orange-vermilion (shades) (1925) .. 3·75 80
75 2d. deep brown-purple (1923) .. .. 4·00 4·00
a. Purple-brown (1927) .. .. 3·75 3·75
b. Reddish maroon (1.28) .. .. 3·75 3·00
76 2½d. deep blue .. .. 17·00 15·00
a. Indigo (1927) .. .. .. 13·00 20·00
b. Deep steel-blue (1.28) .. .. 5·00 15·00
c. Prussian blue (10.28) £375 £550
77 2½d. deep purple/*pale yellow* (1923) .. 3·75 18·00
a. Pale purple/pale yellow (1925) .. 4·00 20·00
78 6d. yellow-orange (1925) .. .. 6·50 22·00
79 1s. deep ochre .. .. 18·00 35·00
80 **10** 3s. slate-green (1923) .. .. .. 90·00 £120
73/80 .. .. *Set of* 8 £110 £175
73/80 (*incl 76a*) Optd "Specimen" .. *Set of* 9 £650

Dates quoted above are those of despatch from Great Britain. No. 76c only occurred in part of the October 1928 printing. The remainder were in the deep steel-blue shade of the January 1928 despatch, No. 77*b*.

1928 (7 Feb). *No. 75a surch with T* 12.
115 9 2½d. on 2d. purple-brown £650 £700
a. Surch double £30000
No. 115 was produced on South Georgia during a shortage of 2½d. stamps. The provisional was withdrawn on 22 February 1928.

13 Fin Whale and Gentoo Penguins 14

(Recess P.B.)

1929 (2 Sept)–**36.** *P* 14. (*a*) *Wmk Mult Script CA.*
116 13 ½d. green 45 70
117 1d. scarlet 70 35
a. *Deep red* .. .. 6·00 12·00
118 2d. grey 70 60
119 2½d. blue 70 80
120 14 4d. orange (1931) .. .. .. 5·00 12·00
a. *Deep orange* .. .. 17·00 35·00
121 13 6d. purple .. .. 5·50 6·00
a. *Reddish purple* (1936) .. .. 22·00 25·00
122 1s. black/*emerald* .. .. .. 11·00 14·00
a. *On bright emerald* (1936) .. .. 20·00 25·00
123 2s. 6d. carmine/*blue* .. .. .. 19·00 25·00
124 5s. green/*yellow* .. .. .. 35·00 50·00
125 10s. carmine/*emerald* .. .. .. 60·00 85·00

(*b*) *Wmk Mult Crown CA*
126 13 £1 black/*red* £375 £475
116/126 .. .. .. *Set of* 11 £450 £600
116/26 Perf "Specimen" .. .. *Set of* 11 £1100
Two kinds of perforation exist:
A. Comb perf 13.9:—original values of 1929.
B. Line perf 13.9, 14.2 or compound:—4d. and 1936 printings of ½d., 1d., 6d. and 1s.

15 Romney Marsh Ram 26 King George V

(Des (except 6d.) by G. Roberts. Eng and recess B.W.)

1933 (2 Jan). *Centenary of British Administration. T* 15, 26 *and similar designs. Wmk Mult Script CA. P* 12.
127 ½d. black and green .. .. 1·50 3·75
128 1d. black and scarlet .. .. 2·50 1·25
129 1½d. black and blue .. .. 4·25 7·50
130 2d. black and brown .. .. 7·00 12·00
131 3d. black and violet .. .. 9·00 7·50
132 4d. black and orange .. .. 10·00 12·00
133 6d. black and slate .. .. 38·00 42·00
134 1s. black and olive-green .. .. .. 30·00 42·00
135 2s. 6d. black and violet £100 £130
136 5s. black and yellow £500 £650
a. *Black and yellow-orange* £1000 £1200
137 10s. black and chestnut £600 £750
138 £1 black and carmine £1750 £2250
127/138 .. .. .. *Set of* 12 £2750 £3500
127/38 Perf "Specimen" .. .. *Set of* 12 £2500
Designs: *Horiz*—1d. Iceberg; 1½d. Whale-catcher *Bransfield*; 2d. Port Louis; 3d. Map of Falkland Islands; 4d. South Georgia; 6d. Fin Whale; 1s. Government House, Stanley. *Vert*—2s. 6d. Battle Memorial; 5s. King Penguin; 10s. Coat of Arms.
Examples of all values are known with forged Port Stanley postmarks, dated 6 January 1933.

1935 (7 May). *Silver Jubilee. As Nos.* 91/4 *of Antigua, but printed by B.W. P* 11 × 12.
139 1d. deep blue and scarlet .. .. .. 1·25 40
b. Short extra flagstaff .. .. .. 85·00
d. Flagstaff on right-hand turret .. 75·00
e. Double flagstaff .. .. .. 60·00
140 2½d. brown and deep blue .. .. .. 3·75 1·25
b. Short extra flagstaff £125
d. Flagstaff on right-hand turret .. £125
e. Double flagstaff .. .. .. 85·00
l. Re-entry on value tablet (R. 8/1) .. £200 £100
141 4d. green and indigo .. .. .. 3·75 1·25
b. Short extra flagstaff £125
d. Flagstaff on right-hand turret .. £125
e. Double flagstaff .. .. .. 85·00
142 1s. slate and purple .. .. .. 4·00 1·25
a. Extra flagstaff £2500 £2500
b. Short extra flagstaff £150
c. Lightning conductor £150
d. Flagstaff on right-hand turret .. £150
e. Double flagstaff £100
139/42 .. .. .. *Set of* 4 11·50 3·75
139/42 Perf "Specimen" .. .. *Set of* 4 £200
For illustrations of plate varieties see Omnibus section following Zululand.

1937 (12 May). *Coronation. As Nos.* 13/15 *of Aden, but printed by B.W. P* 11 × 11½.
143 ½d. green 30 10
144 1d. carmine 40 15
145 2½d. blue 80 25
143/5 .. .. *Set of* 3 1·40 45
143/5 Perf "Specimen" .. .. *Set of* 3 £120

27 Whales' Jaw Bones

(Des G. Roberts (Nos. 146, 148/9, 158 and 160/3). Recess B.W.)

1938 (3 Jan)–**50.** *Horiz designs as T* 27. *Wmk Mult Script CA. P* 12.
146 ½d. black and green (*shades*) 15 20
147 1d. black and carmine .. .. 13·00 1·50
a. *Black and scarlet* .. .. 3·00 20
148 1d. black and violet (14.7.41) 90 35
a. *Black and purple-violet* (1.43) .. .. 1·50 70
149 2d. black and deep violet .. .. .. 1·00 40
150 2d. black and carmine-red (14.7.41) .. .. 75 2·25
a. *Black and red* (1.43) 75 30
151 2½d. black and bright blue 45 30
152 2½d. black and blue (15.6.49) .. .. .. 2·25 3·50
153 3d. black and blue (14.7.41) .. .. .. 1·75 90
a. *Black and deep blue* (1.43) .. .. 2·25 1·25
154 4d. black and purple .. .. 1·60 50
155 6d. black and brown .. .. 4·50 3·50
156 6d. black (15.6.49) .. .. 2·50 4·50
157 9d. black and grey-blue .. .. .. 3·00 50
158 1s. pale blue .. .. 45·00 18·00
a. *Deep blue* (1941) .. .. 7·50 2·50
159 1s. 3d. black and carmine-red (10.12.46) .. 1·25 1·10
160 2s. 6d. slate .. .. 40·00 6·50
161 5s. bright blue and pale brown .. .. 50·00 28·00
a. *Blue and buff-brown* (9.2.50) .. .. 50·00 28·00
b. *Indigo and yellow-brown* (1942) £350 £150
162 10s. black and orange .. .. 45·00 25·00
163 £1 black and violet .. .. 80·00 40·00
146/163 .. .. .. *Set of* 18 £225 £110
146/63 (*ex* 152, 156) Perf "Specimen" *Set of* 16 £800
Designs:—Nos. 147 and 150, Black-necked Swan; Nos. 148/9, Battle Memorial; Nos. 151 and 153, Flock of sheep; Nos. 152 and 154, Magellan Goose; No. 155/6, R.R.S. *Discovery II*; No. 157, R.R.S. *William Scoresby*; No. 158, Mount Sugar Top; No. 159; Turkey Vultures; No. 160, Gentoo Penguins; No. 161, Southern Sealion; No. 162, Deception Island; No. 163, Arms of Falkland Islands.

1946 (7 Oct). *Victory. As Nos.* 28/9 *of Aden.*
164 1d. dull violet 25 15
165 3d. blue 25 15
164/5 Perf "Specimen" .. .. *Set of* 2 £120

1948 (1 Nov). *Royal Silver Wedding. As Nos.* 30/1 *of Aden.*
166 2½d. ultramarine .. .. 2·00 70
167 £1 mauve .. .. 90·00 55·00

1949 (10 Oct). *75th Anniv of Universal Postal Union. As Nos.* 114/17 *of Antigua.*
168 1d. violet .. .. 1·50 75
169 3d. deep blue .. .. 4·50 1·25
170 1s. 3d. deep blue-green .. .. .. 5·50 2·25
171 2s. blue .. .. 5·50 4·75
168/71 .. .. *Set of* 4 15·00 8·00

39 Sheep 43 Arms of the Colony

(Recess Waterlow)

1952 (2 Jan). *T* 39, 43 *and similar designs. Wmk Mult Script CA. P* 13 × 13½ (*vert*) *or* 13½ × 13 (*horiz*).
172 ½d. green 70 70
173 1d. scarlet 80 40
174 2d. violet .. .. 2·75 1·50
175 2½d. black and light ultramarine 95 50
176 3d. deep ultramarine .. .. 1·00 65
177 4d. reddish purple .. .. 6·50 2·50
178 6d. bistre-brown .. .. 10·00 1·00
179 9d. orange-yellow .. .. 7·50 4·50
180 1s. black .. .. 9·00 80
181 1s. 3d. orange .. .. 3·25 11·00
182 2s. 6d. olive-green .. .. 11·00 10·00
183 5s. purple .. .. 6·00 6·50
184 10s. grey .. .. 14·00 30·00
185 £1 black .. .. 22·00 30·00
172/185 .. .. .. *Set of* 14 85·00 90·00
Designs: *Horiz*—1d. R.M.S. *Fitzroy*; 2d. Magellan Goose; 2½d. Map of Falkland Islands; 4d. Auster aircraft; 6d. M.S.S. *John Biscoe*; 9d. View of the Two Sisters; 1s. 3d. Kelp goose and gander; 10s. Southern Sealion and South American Fur Seal; £1 Hulk of *Great Britain*. *Vert*—1s. Gentoo Penguins; 2s. 6d. Sheep-shearing; 5s. Battle Memorial.

1953 (4 June). *Coronation. As No.* 47 *of Aden.*
186 1d. black and scarlet .. .. 1·00 1·25

53 M.S.S. *John Biscoe* 54 Austral Thrush

(Recess Waterlow)

1955–57. *Designs previously used for King George VI issue but with portrait of Queen Elizabeth II as in T* 53. *Wmk Mult Script CA. P* 13 × 13½ (*vert*) *or* 13½ × 13 (*horiz*).
187 ½d. green (2.9.57) .. .. 70 1·25
188 1d. scarlet (2.9.57) .. .. 1·25 50
189 2d. violet (3.9.56) .. .. 2·75 4·50
190 6d. deep yellow-brown (1.6.55) .. .. 3·50 60
191 9d. orange-yellow (2.9.57) .. .. .. 18·00 17·00
192 1s. black (15.7.55) .. .. 3·50 1·25
187/92 .. .. .. *Set of* 6 27·00 23·00
Designs: *Horiz*—½d. Sheep; 1d. R.M.S. *Fitzroy*; 2d. Magellan Goose; 9d. View of Two Sisters. *Vert*—1s. Gentoo Penguins.

(Recess Waterlow, then D.L.R. (from 9.1.62 onwards))

1960 (10 Feb)–**66.** *T* 54 *and similar horiz designs. W* w 12 (*upright*). *P* 13½.
193 ½d. black and myrtle-green .. .. .. 1·25 40
a. *Black and green* (DLR) (9.1.62) .. .. 3·50 1·50
194 1d. black and scarlet .. .. 1·25 20
a. *Black and carmine-red* (DLR) (15.7.63) 2·50 80
195 2d. black and blue .. .. 2·00 40
a. *Black and deep blue* (DLR) (25.10.66) 6·00 2·50
196 2½d. black and yellow-brown .. .. .. 1·25 20
197 3d. black and olive 70 15
198 4d. black and carmine .. .. 1·00 50
199 5½d. black and violet .. .. 1·25 90
200 6d. black and sepia .. .. 1·25 15
201 9d. black and orange-red .. .. .. 1·25 80
202 1s. black and maroon 80 15
203 1s. 3d. black and ultramarine .. .. .. 7·00 7·00
204 2s. black and brown-red .. .. .. 16·00 1·50
a. *Black and lake-brown* (DLR) (25.10.66) 38·00 12·00
205 5s. black and turquoise .. .. .. 17·00 7·50
206 10s. black and purple .. .. 30·00 10·00
207 £1 black and orange-yellow .. .. .. 48·00 25·00
193/207 .. .. .. *Set of* 15 £110 48·00
Designs:—1d. Southern Black-backed Gull; 2d. Gentoo Penguins; 2½d. Long-tailed Meadowlark; 3d. Magellan Geese; 4d. Falkland Islands Flightless Steamer Ducks; 5½d. Rockhopper Penguin; 6d. Black-browed Albatross; 9d. Silvery Grebe; 1s. Magellanic Oyster-catchers; 1s. 3d. Chilean Teal: 2s. Kelp Geese; 5s. King Cormorants; 10s. Common Caracara; £1 Black-necked Swan.

Waterlow De La Rue

The De La Rue printings of the ½d., 1d., 2d. and 2s. are all from Plate 2 and can be distinguished by the finer lines of shading on the Queen's face, neck and shoulders (appearing as a white face) and also the very faint cross hatching left of the face. Apart from this the shades differ in varying degrees. It is believed that the existing Waterlow plate may have been used by De La Rue to print supplies of the 6d. which have little to distinguish them from the original printing. A De La Rue Plate 2 for this value is known to exist which, although it shows the usual plate characteristics, does not differ in shade from the Waterlow printing.
See also No. 227.

69 Morse Key 70 One-valve Receiver

(Des M. Goaman. Photo Enschedé)

1962 (5 Oct). *50th Anniv of Establishment of Radio Communications. T* 69/70 *and similar vert design. W* w 12. *P* 11½ × 11.
208 69 6d. carmine-lake and orange .. .. 1·00 30
209 70 1s. deep bluish green and yellow-olive 1·25 35
210 – 2s. deep violet and ultramarine .. .. 1·25 40
208/10 .. .. .. *Set of* 3 3·25 95
Design:—2s. Rotary Spark Transmitter.

1963 (4 June). *Freedom from Hunger. As No.* 76 *of Aden.*
211 1s. ultramarine .. .. 13·00 85

1963 (2 Sept). *Red Cross Centenary. As Nos.* 147/8 *of Antigua.*
212 1d. red and black .. .. 4·00 50
213 1s. red and blue .. .. 17·00 4·50

1964 (23 April). *400th Birth Anniv of William Shakespeare. As No.* 164 *of Antigua.*
214 6d. black .. .. 1·00 30

FALKLAND ISLANDS
50th ANNIVERSARY
2½D
OF THE BATTLE OF THE FALKLAND ISLANDS

72 H.M.S. *Glasgow*

(Recess D.L.R.)

1964 (8 Dec) *50th Anniv of the Battle of the Falkland Islands.* **T 72** *and similar designs.* W w **12**. *P* 13 × 14 (2s.) *or* 13 (*others*).

215	2½d. black and red	6·00	2·25
216	6d. black and light blue	1·00	25
	a. Centre Type **72**	£16000	
217	1s. black and carmine-red	1·75	60
218	2s. black and blue	2·50	75
215/18	*Set of* 4	10·00	3·50

Designs: *Horiz*—6d. H.M.S. *Kent*; 1s. H.M.S. *Invincible*. *Vert*—2s. Battle Memorial.

It is believed that No. 216a came from a sheet which was first printed with the centre of the 2½d. and then accidently included among the supply of the 6d. value and thus received the wrong frame. There have been sixteen reports of stamps showing the error, although it is believed that some of these *may* refer to the same example.

1965 (26 May). *I.T.U. Centenary. As Nos.* 166/7 *of Antigua.*

219	1d. light blue and deep blue	85	20
220	2s. lilac and bistre-yellow	12·00	1·50

1965 (25 Oct). *International Co-operation Year. As Nos.* 168/9 *of Antigua.*

221	1d. reddish purple and turquoise-green	1·50	20
222	1s. deep bluish green and lavender	7·50	1·10

1966 (24 Jan). *Churchill Commemoration. As Nos.* 170/3 *of Antigua.*

223	½d. new blue	65	20
224	1d. deep green	2·25	15
225	1s. brown	6·50	80
226	2s. bluish violet	8·00	1·25
223/6	*Set of* 4	15·00	2·25

1966 (25 Oct). *As No.* 193 *but wmk* w **12** *sideways.*

227	**54**	½d. black and myrtle-green	15	20

76 Globe and Human Rights Emblem

77 Dusty Miller

(Des M. Farrar Bell. Photo Harrison)

1968 (4 July). *Human Rights Year.* W w **12**. *P* 14 × 14½.

228	**76**	2d. multicoloured	50	15
		a. Yellow omitted ("1968" white)	£750	
229		6d. muticoloured	55	15
230		1s. multicoloured	60	15
231		2s. multicoloured	70	30
228/31		*Set of* 4	2·10	65

(Des Sylvia Goaman. Photo Harrison)

1968 (9 Oct). *Flowers. Designs as* **T 77**. *Chalk-surfaced paper.* W w **12** (*sideways on vert designs*). *P* 14.

232	½d. multicoloured	10	15
233	1½d. multicoloured	20	15
234	2d. multicoloured	20	15
235	3d. multicoloured	30	15
236	3½d. multicoloured	30	15
237	4½d. multicoloured	35	30
238	5½d. olive-yellow, brown and yellow-green	40	40
239	6d. carmine, black and yellow-green	50	20
240	1s. multicoloured	60	45
241	1s. 6d. multicoloured	4·50	8·00
242	2s. multicoloured	5·50	6·50
243	3s. multicoloured	9·00	5·50
244	5s. multicoloured	20·00	11·00
245	£1 multicoloured	12·00	2·00
232/245	*Set of* 14	48·00	30·00

Designs: *Horiz*—1½d. Pig Vine; 3½d. Sea Cabbage; 5½d. Arrowleaf Marigold; 6d. Diddle Dee; 1s. Scurvy Grass; 5s. Felton's Flower. *Vert*—2d. Pale Maiden; 3d. Dog Orchid; 4½d. Vanilla Daisy; 1s. 6d. Prickly Burr; 2s. Fachine; 3s. Lavender; £1 Yellow Orchid.

For stamps inscribed in decimal currency see Nos. 276/88, 293/5 and 315.

91 DHC-2 Beaver Floatplane

(Des V. Whiteley. Litho Format)

1969 (8 Apr). *21st Anniv of Government Air Services.* **T 91** *and similar horiz designs. Multicoloured.* W w **12** *sideways*). *P* 14.

246	2d. Type **91**	35	20
247	6d. "Norseman"	40	25
248	1s. "Auster"	50	25
249	2s. Falkland Islands Arms	1·75	70
246/9	*Set of* 4	2·75	1·25

92 Holy Trinity Church, 1869

(Des G. Drummond. Litho Format)

1969 (30 Oct). *Centenary of Bishop Stirling's Consecration.* **T 92** *and similar horiz designs.* W w **12** (*sideways*). *P* 14.

250	2d. black, grey and apple-green	40	20
251	6d. black, grey and orange-red	50	25
252	1s. black, grey and lilac	55	30
253	2s. multicoloured	80	55
250/3	*Set of* 4	2·00	1·10

Designs:—6d. Christ Church Cathedral, 1969; 1s. Bishop Stirling; 2s. Bishop's Mitre.

96 Mounted Volunteer **97** S.S. *Great Britain* (1843)

(Des R. Granger Barrett. Litho B.W.)

1970 (30 Apr). *Golden Jubilee of Defence Force.* **T 96** *and similar designs. Multicoloured.* W w **12** (*sideways on 2d. and 1s.*). *P* 13.

254	2d. Type **96**	1·90	40
255	6d. Defence Post (*horiz*)	2·00	40
256	1s. Corporal in Number One Dress Uniform	2·25	40
257	2s. Defence Force Badge (*horiz*)	4·00	75
254/7	*Set of* 4	9·00	1·75

(Des V. Whiteley. Litho J.W.)

1970 (30 Oct). *Restoration of S.S. "Great Britain".* **T 97** *and views of the ship at different dates. Multicoloured.* W w **12** (*sideways*). *P* 14½ × 14.

258	2d. Type **97**	1·40	40
259	4d. In 1845	1·75	80
260	9d. In 1876	1·75	80
261	1s. In 1886	1·75	80
262	2s. In 1970	2·25	90
258/62	*Set of* 5	8·00	3·25

½p

(**98**)

99 Dusty Miller

1971 (15 Feb). *Decimal Currency. Nos.* 232/44 *surch as* **T 98**. W w **12** (*sideways on vert designs*). *P* 14.

263	½p. on ½d. multicoloured	20	20
264	1p. on 1½d. multicoloured	20	15
	a. Error. Surch 5p.	£325	
	b. Do. but surch at right	£700	
	c. Surch albino	£200	
	d. Surch albino in pair with normal	£1500	
265	1½p. on 2d. multicoloured	20	15
266	2p. on 3d. multicoloured	20	20
267	2½p. on 3½d. multicoloured	25	20
268	3p. on 4½d. multicoloured	25	20
269	4p. on 5½d. olive-yellow, brown & yell-grn	25	20
270	5p. on 6d. carmine, black and yellow-green	25	20
271	6p. on 1s. multicoloured	3·50	2·50
272	7½p. on 1s. 6d. multicoloured	6·00	3·25
273	10p. on 2s. multicoloured	6·00	3·00
274	15p. on 3s. multicoloured	6·00	2·75
275	25p. on 5s. multicoloured	6·50	3·25
263/75	*Set of* 13	27·00	15·00

1972 (1 June). *As Nos.* 232/44, *but Glazed, ordinary paper and with values inscr in decimal currency as* **T 99**. W w **12** (*sideways on* ½, 1½, 2, 3, 7½, 10 *and* 15*p.*). *P* 14.

276	½p. multicoloured	35	1·25
277	1p. multicoloured (as 1½d.)	30	30
278	1½p. multicoloured (as 2d.)	30	60
279	2p. multicoloured (as 3d.)	4·50	1·25
280	2½p. multicoloured (as 3½d.)	35	70
281	3p. multicoloured (as 4½d.)	35	70
282	4p. olive-yellow, brown & yell-grn (as 5½d.)	40	40
283	5p. carmine, black and yellow-green (as 6d.)	40	45
284	6p. multicoloured (as 1s.)	15·00	9·50
285	7½p. multicoloured (as 1s. 6d.)	1·50	4·00
286	10p. multicoloured (as 2s.)	5·00	4·50
287	15p. multicoloured (as 3s.)	3·75	5·00
288	25p. multicoloured (as 5s.)	4·50	6·00
276/88	*Set of* 13	32·00	32·00

See also Nos. 293/5 and 315.

100 Romney Marsh Sheep and Southern Sealions

(Des (from photograph by D. Groves) and photo Harrison)

1972 (20 Nov). *Royal Silver Wedding. Multicoloured; background colour given.* W w **12**. *P* 14 × 14½.

289	**100**	1p. grey-green	30	25
290		10p. bright blue	70	85

1973 (14 Nov). *Royal Wedding. As Nos.* 165/6 *of Anguilla. Centre multicoloured.* W w **12** (*sideways*). *P* 13½.

291	5p. bright mauve	25	10
292	15p. brown-ochre	40	20

1974 (25 Feb–18 Oct). *As Nos.* 276, 279 *and* 284, *but wmk upright on* ½*p. and* 2*p. and sideways on* 6*p.* *P* 14.

293	½p. multicoloured (18.10.74)	10·00	16·00
294	2p. multicoloured	5·50	2·75
295	6p. multicoloured (28.3.74)	2·00	2·25
293/5	*Set of* 3	16·00	19·00

101 South American Fur Seal **102** 19th-Century Mail-coach

(Des J. Cooter. Litho Walsall)

1974 (6 Mar). *Tourism.* **T 101** *and similar horiz designs. Multicoloured.* W w **12**. *P* 14.

296	2p. Type **101**	2·25	1·00
297	4p. Trout-fishing	3·00	1·25
298	5p. Rockhopper penguins	6·00	2·25
299	15p. Long-tailed Meadowlark	9·00	3·25
296/9	*Set of* 4	18·00	7·00

(Des PAD Studio. Litho Questa)

1974 (31 July). *Centenary of Universal Postal Union.* **T 102** *and similar vert designs. Multicoloured.* W w **12** (*sideways*). *P* 14.

300	2p. Type **102**	25	25
301	5p. Packet ship, 1841	35	45
302	8p. First U.K. aerial post, 1911	40	55
303	16p. Ship's catapult mail, 1920's	60	75
300/3	*Set of* 4	1·40	1·75

103 Churchill and Houses of Parliament

(Des G. Vasarhelyi. Litho Enschedé)

1974 (30 Nov). *Birth Centenary of Sir Winston Churchill.* **T 103** *and similar horiz design. Multicoloured.* W w **12**. *P* 13½.

304	16p. Type **103**	1·40	1·40
305	20p. Churchill and warships	1·90	1·60
MS306	108 × 83 mm. Nos. 304/5	6·50	7·00

104 H.M.S. *Exeter* **105** Seal and Flag Badge

(Des J.W. Litho Harrison)

1974 (13 Dec). *35th Anniv of the Battle of the River Plate.* **T 104** *and similar horiz designs. Multicoloured.* W w **12** (*sideways*). *P* 14.

307	2p. Type **104**	2·25	1·40
308	6p. H.M.N.Z. *Achilles*	3·50	2·75
309	8p. *Admiral Graf Spee*	4·00	3·75
310	16p. H.M.S. *Ajax*	7·00	8·50
307/10	*Set of* 4	15·00	15·00

(Des PAD Studio. Litho Walsall)

1975 (28 Oct). *50th Anniv of Heraldic Arms. T* **105** *and similar vert designs. Multicoloured.* W w **14** (*inverted*). *P* 14.

311	2p. Type **105**	35	35
312	7½p. Coat of arms, 1925	65	1·00
313	10p. Coat of arms, 1948	75	1·25
314	16p. Arms of the Dependencies, 1952	1·25	1·60
311/14	*Set of* 4	2·75	3·75

1975 (8 Dec). *As No.* 276 *but* W w 14 (*sideways*). *P* 14.

315 **99**	½p. multicoloured	1·00	1·75

106 ½p. Coin and Trout

(Des G. Drummond. Litho Questa)

1975 (31 Dec). *New Coinage. T* **106** *and similar horiz designs each showing coin as T* **106**. *Multicoloured.* W w **12** (*sideways*). *P* 14.

316	2p. Type **106**	70	45
317	5½p. Gentoo Penguin and 1p. coin	80	90
318	8p. Magellan Goose and 2p. coin	1·00	1·25
319	10p. Black-browed Albatross and 5p. coin	1·10	1·40
320	16p. Southern Sealion and 10p. coin	1·50	1·75
316/20	*Set of* 5	4·50	5·25

107 Gathering Sheep

(Des PAD Studio. Litho J.W.)

1976 (28 Apr). *Sheep Farming Industry. T* **107** *and similar horiz designs. Multicoloured.* W w **14** (*sideways*). *P* 13½.

321	2p. Type **107**	30	20
322	7½p. Shearing	70	60
323	10p. Dipping	90	80
324	20p. Shipping	1·50	1·50
321/4	*Set of* 4	3·00	2·75

108 The Queen awaiting Anointment

(Des M. and G. Shamir; adapted J.W. Litho Questa)

1977 (7 Feb–1 Nov). *Silver Jubilee. T* **108** *and similar horiz designs. Multicoloured. P* 13½. (*a*) W w **14** (*sideways*).

325	6p. Visit of Prince Philip, 1957	1·50	95
326	11p. Queen Elizabeth, ampulla and anointing spoon	80	75
	a. Booklet pane of 4 with blank margins (1.11.77)	3·25	
327	33p. Type **108**	1·00	1·25
	a. Booklet pane of 4 with blank margins (1.11.77)	4·00	
	(*b*) W w **12** (*sideways*) (*from booklets only*) (1.11.77)		
327*b*	6p. Visit of Prince Philip,1957	3·50	3·25
	ba. Booklet pane of 4 with blank margins	14·00	
325/7*b*	*Set of* 4	6·50	5·50

109 Map of Falkland Islands

(Des K. Penny. Litho Questa)

1977 (24 Oct). *Telecommunications. T* **109** *and similar horiz designs. Multicoloured.* W w **14** (*sideways*). *P* 14½.

328	3p. Type **109**	35	15
329	11p. Ship to shore communications	75	40
330	40p. Telex and telephone service	2·50	1·40
328/30	*Set of* 3	3·25	1·75

110 *A.E.S.*, 1957–74

(Des J. Smith; adapted R. Granger Barrett. Litho Questa)

1978 (25 Jan)–**82**. *Mail Ships. Horiz designs as T* **110**. *Multicoloured.* W w **14** (*sideways*). *P* 14. A. *Printed without imprint date.* B. *With imprint date* ("1982") *at foot of designs* (13.7.82*).

		A		B	
331	1p. Type **110**	10	15	30	50
332	2p. *Darwin*, 1957–73	15	15	40	50
333	3p. *Merak-N.*, 1951–2	15	15	50	50
334	4p. *Fitzroy*, 1936–57	25	20	55	55
335	5p. *Lafonia*, 1936–41	25	20	55	55
336	6p. *Fleurus*, 1924–33	30	20	55	55
337	7p. *Falkland*, 1914–34	30	30	55	70
338	8p. *Oravia*, 1900–12	35	35	60	90
339	9p. *Memphis*, 1890–97	35	35	60	90
340	10p. *Black Hawk*, 1873–80	35	35	60	90
341	20p. *Foam*, 1863–72	1·50	1·25	80	1·40
342	25p. *Fairy*, 1857–61	1·50	1·60	95	2·00
343	50p. *Amelia*, 1852–54	2·25	3·00	1·75	2·75
344	£1 *Nautilus*, 1846–48	4·00	6·00	2·50	4·50
345	£3 *Hebe*, 1842–46	11·00	16·00	5·50	9·50
331/45	*Set of* 15	20·00	27·00	15·00	24·00

*Nos. 331B/45B were not available locally until 1 December 1982.

111 Short "Hythe" at Stanley

(Des L. McCombie. Litho Walsall)

1978 (28 Apr). *26th Anniv of First Direct Flight, Southampton–Port Stanley. T* **111** *and similar horiz design. Multicoloured.* W w **14** (*sideways*). *P* 14.

346	11p. Type **111**	1·50	1·25
347	33p. Route map and Short "Hythe"	2·25	1·75

112 Red Dragon of Wales

113 First Fox Bay P.O. and 1d. Stamp of 1878

(Des C. Abbott. Litho Questa)

1978 (2 June). *25th Anniv of Coronation. T* **112** *and similar vert designs. P* 15.

348	25p. bistre, bright blue and silver	1·00	1·00
	a. Sheetlet. Nos. 348/50 × 2	6·00	
349	25p. multicoloured	1·00	1·00
350	25p. bistre, bright blue and silver	1·00	1·00
348/50	*Set of* 3	2·75	2·75

Designs:—No. 348, Type **112**; No. 349, Queen Elizabeth II; No. 350, Hornless Ram.

Nos. 348/50 were printed together in small sheets of 6, containing two *se-tenant* strips of 3, with horizontal gutter margin between.

(Des J. Cooter. Litho B.W.)

1978 (8 Aug). *Centenary of First Falkland Is Postage Stamps. T* **113** *and similar vert designs. Multicoloured.* W w **14**. *P* 13½ × 13.

351	3p. Type **113**	20	20
352	11p. Second Stanley P.O. and 4d. stamp of 1879	35	40
353	15p. New Island P.O. and 6d. stamp of 1878	40	50
354	22p. First Stanley P.O. and 1s. stamp of 1878	70	65
351/4	*Set of* 4	1·50	1·60

114 *Macrocystis pyrifera*

115 Britten-Norman "Islander" over Falkland Islands

(Des I. Strange. Litho Questa)

1979 (19 Feb). *Kelp and Seaweed. T* **114** *and similar multicoloured designs.* W w **14** (*sideways on* 11 *and* 15p.). *P* 14.

355	3p. Type **114**	20	15
356	7p. *Durvillea* sp	40	25
357	11p. *Lessonia* sp (*horiz*)	50	30
358	15p. *Callophyllis* sp (*horiz*)	70	35
359	25p. *Iradaea* sp	90	55
355/9	*Set of* 5	2·50	1·40

(Des G. Hutchins. Litho Rosenbaum Bros, Vienna)

1979 (1 May). *Opening of Stanley Airport. T* **115** *and similar horiz designs showing diagrammatic drawings. Multicoloured.* W w **14** (*sideways*). *P* 13½.

360	3p. Type **115**	30	20
361	11p. Fokker "F27" over South Atlantic	70	60
362	15p. Fokker "F28" over Airport	80	60
363	25p. Cessna "172 (Skyhawk)", Britten-Norman "Islander", Fokker "F27" and "F28" over runway	1·50	80
360/3	*Set of* 4	3·00	2·00

116 Sir Rowland Hill and 1953 Coronation 1d. Commemorative

(Des J.W. Litho Questa)

1979 (27 Aug). *Death Centenary of Sir Rowland Hill. T* **116** *and similar multicoloured designs showing stamps and portrait.* W w **14** (*sideways on* 3 *and* 25p.). *P* 14.

364	3p. Type **116**	25	25
365	11p. 1878 1d. stamp (*vert*)	50	70
366	25p. Penny Black	75	85
364/6	*Set of* 3	1·40	1·60
MS367	137 × 98 mm. 33p. 1916 5s. stamp (*vert*)	85	1·50

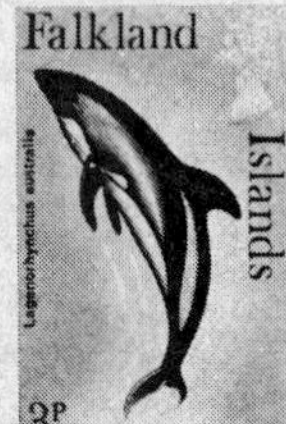

117 Mail Drop by "Beaver" Aircraft **118** Peale's Dolphin

(Des A. Peake; adapted J.W. Litho Questa)

1979 (26 Nov). *Centenary of U.P.U. Membership. T* **117** *and similar horiz designs. Multicoloured.* W w **14** (*sideways*). *P* 14.

368	3p. Type **117**	20	20
369	11p. Mail by horseback	45	55
370	25p. Mail by schooner *Gwendolin*	75	1·00
368/70	*Set of* 3	1·25	1·60

(Des I. Strange. Litho Harrison)

1980 (25 Feb). *Dolphins and Porpoises. T* **118** *and similar designs.* W w **14** (*sideways on* 6, 7, 15 *and* 25p.). *P* 14.

371	3p. black, chestnut and blue	25	25
372	6p. multicoloured	35	40
373	7p. multicoloured	35	40
374	11p. black, new blue and rose-red	60	65
375	15p. black, chestnut and greyish blue	75	75
376	25p. multicoloured	1·00	1·25
371/6	*Set of* 6	3·00	3·25

Designs: *Horiz*—6p. Commerson's Dolphin; 7p. Hourglass Dolphin; 15p. Dusky Dolphin; 25p. Killer Whale. *Vert*—11p. Spectacled Porpoise.

119 1878 Falkland Islands Postmark

(Des G. Hutchins. Litho Walsall)

1980 (6 May). *"London 1980" International Stamp Exhibition. T* **119** *and similar horiz designs showing postmarks.* W w **14** (*sideways*). *P* 14.

377	11p. black, gold and light blue	30	35
	a. Block of 6. Nos. 377/82	1·60	
378	11p. black, gold and greenish yellow	30	35
379	11p. black, gold and blue-green	30	35
380	11p. black, gold and pale violet	30	35
381	11p. black, gold and claret	30	35
382	11p. black, gold and flesh	30	35
377/82	*Set of* 6	1·60	1·90

Designs:—No. 377, Type **119**; No. 378, 1915 New Island; No. 379, 1901 Falkland Islands; No. 380, 1935 Port Stanley; No. 381, 1952 Port Stanley first overseas airmail; No. 382, 1934 Fox Bay.

Nos. 377/82 were printed together, *se-tenant*, as a sheetlet, containing one of each design.

120 Queen Elizabeth the Queen Mother

(Des Harrison. Litho Questa)

1980 (4 Aug). *80th Birthday of Queen Elizabeth the Queen Mother.* W w **14** (*sideways*). *P* 14.
383 **120** 11p. multicoloured 40 30

121 Forster's Caracara

(Des I. Strange. Litho Secura, Singapore)

1980 (11 Aug). *Birds of Prey. T* **121** *and similar horiz designs. Multicoloured.* W w **14** (*sideways*). *P* 13 × 13½.
384 3p. Type **121** 30 25
385 11p. Red-backed Buzzard 70 60
386 15p. Common Caracara 85 75
387 25p. Peregrine Falcon.. .. .. .. 1·25 1·00
384/7 .. .. *Set of* 4 2·75 2·40

122 Stanley

(Des C. Abbott. Litho Rosenbaum Bros, Vienna)

1981 (7 Jan). *Early Settlements. T* **122** *and similar horiz designs. Multicoloured.* W w **14** (*sideways*). *P* 14.
388 3p. Type **122** 20 15
389 11p. Port Egmont 40 35
390 25p. Port Louis 80 65
391 33p. Mission House, Keppel Island .. .. 1·10 80
388/91 .. .. *Set of* 4 2·25 1·75

123 Sheep

(Des P. Oxenham. Litho Questa)

1981 (9 Jan). *Farm Animals. T* **123** *and similar horiz designs. Multicoloured.* W w **14** (*sideways*). *P* 14.
392 3p. Type **123** 20 20
393 11p. Cattle 35 35
394 25p. Horse 70 75
395 33p. Dogs .. .. 1·00 1·00
392/5 .. .. *Set of* 4 2·00 2·10

124 Bowles and Carver, 1779

125 Wedding Bouquet from Falkland Islands

(Des I. Strange. Litho Walsall)

1981 (22 May). *Early Maps. T* **124** *and similar horiz designs in black, dull rose and stone* (26*p*.) *or multicoloured* (*others*). W w **14** (*sideways*). *P* 14.
396 3p. Type **124** 20 20
397 10p. J. Hawkesworth, 1773 .. .. .. 40 45
398 13p. Eman, Bowen, 1747 .. .. .. 55 60
399 15p. T. Boutflower, 1768 .. .. .. 55 65
400 25p. Philippe de Pretot, 1771.. .. .. 70 75
401 26p. Bellin *Petite Atlas Maritime*, Paris, 1764 70 75
396/401 .. .. *Set of* 6 2·75 3·00

(Des and litho J.W.)

1981 (22 July). *Royal Wedding. T* **125** *and similar vert designs. Multicoloured.* W w **14**. *P* 13½ × 13.
402 10p. Type **125** 45 40
403 13p. Prince Charles riding 55 50
404 52p. Prince Charles and Lady Diana Spencer 1·00 1·00
402/4 .. .. *Set of* 3 1·75 1·75

COVER PRICES

Cover factors are quoted at the beginning of each country for most issues to 1945. An explanation of the system can be found on page x. The factors quoted do not, however, apply to philatelic covers.

126 "Handicrafts"

127 "The Adoration of the Holy Child" (16th-century Dutch artist)

(Des BG Studio. Litho Questa)

1981 (14 Sept). *25th Anniv of Duke of Edinburgh Award Scheme. T* **126** *and similar vert designs. Multicoloured.* W w **14**. *P* 14.
405 10p. Type **126** 30 20
406 13p. "Camping" 50 30
407 15p. "Canoeing" 55 40
408 26p. Duke of Edinburgh 75 60
405/8 .. .. *Set of* 4 1·90 1·40

(Des BG Studio. Litho Walsall)

1981 (2 Nov). *Christmas. Paintings. T* **127** *and similar vert designs. Multicoloured.* W w **14**. *P* 14.
409 3p. Type **127** 20 20
410 13p. "The Holy Family in an Italian Landscape" (17th-century Genoan artist) .. 35 45
411 26p. "The Holy Virgin" (Reni) 55 75
409/11 .. .. *Set of* 3 1·00 1·25

128 Falkland Herring

(Des I. Strange. Litho Questa)

1981 (7 Dec). *Shelf Fishes. T* **128** *and similar multicoloured designs.* W w **14** (*sideways on* 5, 15 *and* 25*p*.). *P* 14 × 13½ (13, 26*p*.) *or* 13½ × 14 (*others*).
412 5p. Type **128** 15 15
413 13p. Rock Cod (*vert*) 30 30
414 15p. Patagonian Hake 35 35
415 25p. Southern Blue Whiting 60 65
416 26p. Grey-tailed Skate (*vert*) 60 65
412/16 .. .. *Set of* 5 1·75 1·90

129 *Lady Elizabeth*, 1913

(Des J. Smith. Litho Questa)

1982 (15 Feb). *Shipwrecks. T* **129** *and similar horiz designs. Multicoloured.* W w **14** (*sideways*). *P* 14½.
417 5p. Type **129** 25 30
418 13p. *Capricorn*, 1882 .. .. .. 40 50
419 15p. *Jhelum*, 1870 .. .. .. 45 60
420 25p. *Snowsquall*, 1864 .. .. .. 75 1·00
421 26p. *St. Mary*, 1890 .. .. .. 75 1·00
417/21 .. .. *Set of* 5 2·40 3·00

ARGENTINE OCCUPATION
2 April to 15 June 1982

Following incidents, involving the illegal presence of Argentine scrap-metal workers on the dependency of South Georgia during March 1982, Argentine forces attacked Port Stanley, the capital of the Falkland Islands early in the morning of 2 April. The small garrison of Royal Marines was overwhelmed and the Governor forced to agree to a cease-fire, before being deported.

South Georgia was occupied by the Argentines on the following day.

British forces, dispatched from the United Kingdom, recaptured South Georgia on 25 April, and, after landing at various points on East Falkland, forced the surrender of the Argentine troops throughout the islands on 15 June.

The last mail to be dispatched from the Falkland Islands prior to the invasion left on 31 March. The Port Stanley Post Office was closed on 2 April, when all current issues were withdrawn. From 5 April an Argentine post office operated in the town, initially accepting mail without stamps, which was then cancelled by a postmark inscribed "ISLAS MALVINAS". Any letters tendered franked with Falkland Islands issues had these cancelled by ball-point pen. A limited range of Argentine stamps was placed on sale from 8 April. The Argentine definitive overprinted "LAS MALVINAS SON ARGENTINAS" for use throughout the country, was also available.

Following the Argentine surrender a rudimentary mail service was operating by 17 June, but the Port Stanley Post Office did not re-open until 24 June.

The last mail from South Georgia before the invasion was sent out on 16 March, although items remaining in the post office there were evacuated by the Deputy Postmaster when he was deported to the United Kingdom by the Argentines. The first mail left after recapture by the British on 2 May.

BRITISH ADMINISTRATION RESTORED

130 Charles Darwin

131 Falkland Islands Coat of Arms

(Des L. Curtis. Litho Questa)

1982 (5 July*). *150th Anniv of Charles Darwin's Voyage. T* **130** *and similar horiz designs. Multicoloured.* W w **14** (*sideways*). *P* 14.
422 5p. Type **130** 20 20
423 17p. Darwin's microscope 50 55
424 25p. Falkland Islands Wolf ("Warrah") .. 65 75
425 34p. H.M.S. *Beagle* 85 95
a. Pale brown (background to side panels) omitted £600
422/5 .. .. *Set of* 4 2·00 2·25

*It was initially intended that these stamps were to be issued on 19 April. First Day covers were prepared, postmarked with this date, but, because of the Argentine invasion, the stamps were not actually released until 5 July. A postmark showing the actual date of issue was struck alongside the stamps on the First Day covers.

(Des C. Abbott. Litho J.W.)

1982 (16 Aug). *21st Birthday of Princess of Wales. T* **131** *and similar vert designs. Multicoloured.* W w **14**. *P* 13.
426 5p. Type **131** 15 15
427 17p. Princess at Royal Opera House, Covent Garden, November 1981.. .. .. 40 40
428 37p. Bride and groom in doorway of St Paul's 75 85
429 50p. Formal portrait .. .. .. 1·00 1·10
426/9 .. .. *Set of* 4 2·10 2·25

132 Map of Falkland Islands

(Des PAD Studio. Litho Format)

1982 (13 Sept). *Rebuilding Fund.* W w **14** (*sideways*). *P* 11.
430 **132** £1 + £1 multicoloured.. .. .. 3·50 4·75

1st PARTICIPATION
COMMONWEALTH GAMES 1982

(**133**)

134 Blackish Cinclodes

1982 (7 Oct). *Commonwealth Games, Brisbane. Nos.* 335B *and* 342B *optd with T* **133**.
431 5p. *Lafonia*, 1936–41 .. .. .. 15 25
432 25p. *Fairy*, 1857–61 .. .. .. 60 85

(Des I. Strange. Litho W. S. Cowells Ltd)

1982 (6 Dec). *Birds of the Passerine Family. T* **134** *and similar vert designs. Multicoloured.* W w **14** (*inverted on* 10*p*.). *P* 15 × 14½.
433 5p. Type **134** 15 15
434 10p. Black-chinned Siskin 25 25
435 13p. Short-billed Marsh Wren 30 30
436 17p. Black-throated Finch 35 35
437 25p. Correndera Pipit.. .. .. .. 50 50
438 34p. Dark-faced Ground Tyrant 65 65
433/8 .. .. *Set of* 6 2·00 2·00

135 Raising Flag, Port Louis, 1833

136 1933 British Administration Centenary 3d. Commemorative

(Des I. Strange and J. Sheridan. Litho Questa)

1983 (3 Jan). *150th Anniv of British Administration. T* **135** *and similar multicoloured designs. W* w **14** *(sideways on* 2, 10, 15, 25 *and* 50*p.). P* 14 × 13½ (1, 5, 20, 40*p*., £1, £2) *or* 13½ × 14 *(others).*

439 1p. Type **135** .. 10 10
440 2p. Chelsea pensioners and barracks, 1849 *(horiz)* .. 15 15
441 5p. Development of wool trade, 1874 .. 15 15
442 10p. Ship-repairing trade, 1850–1890 *(horiz)* 40 40
443 15p. Government House, early 20th century *(horiz)* .. 50 50
444 20p. Battle of Falkland Islands, 1914 .. 60 60
445 25p. Whalebone Arch, 1933 *(horiz)* .. 65 65
446 40p. Contribution to War effort, 1939–45 .. 1·10 1·25
447 50p. Duke of Edinburgh's visit, 1957 *(horiz)* .. 1·50 1·60
448 £1 Royal Marine uniforms .. 2·25 2·50
449 £2 Queen Elizabeth II .. 3·75 4·50
439/49 .. *Set of* 11 10·00 11·00

(Des L. Curtis. Litho Questa)

1983 (28 Mar*). *Commonwealth Day. T* **136** *and similar multicoloured designs. W* w **14** *(sideways on* 5p., 17p.). *P* 14.

450 5p. Type **136** .. 15 15
451 17p. 1933 British Administration Centenary ½d. commemorative .. 35 45
452 34p. 1933 British Administration Centenary 10s. commemorative *(vert)* .. 70 80
453 50p. 1983 British Administration 150th anniversary £2 commemorative *(vert)* .. 1·00 1·25
450/3 .. *Set of* 4 2·00 2·40

*This is the local date of issue: the Crown Agents released the stamps on 14 March.

137 British Army advancing across East Falkland

(Des A. Theobald. Litho Questa)

1983 (14 June). *First Anniv of Liberation. T* **137** *and similar horiz designs. Multicoloured. W* w **14** *(sideways). P* 14.

454 5p. Type **137** .. 15 20
455 13p. S.S. *Canberra* and M.V. *Norland* at San Carlos .. 30 35
456 17p. R.A.F. Hawker "Harrier" fighter .. 35 50
457 50p. H.M.S. *Hermes* (aircraft carrier) .. 1·00 1·10
454/7 .. *Set of* 4 1·60 1·90
MS458 169 × 130 mm. Nos. 454/7. P 12 .. 1·75 2·00

138 Diddle Dee

(Des A. Chater. Litho Questa)

1983 (10 Oct). *Native Fruits. T* **138** *and similar horiz designs. Multicoloured. W* w **14** *(sideways). P* 14.

459 5p. Type **138** .. 15 20
460 17p. Tea Berry .. 35 50
461 25p. Mountain Berry .. 50 65
462 34p. Native Strawberry .. 70 80
459/62 .. *Set of* 4 1·50 1·90

139 Britten-Norman "Islander"

(Des Harrison. Litho Questa)

1983 (14 Nov). *Bicentenary of Manned Flight. T* **139** *and similar horiz designs. Multicoloured. W* w **14** *(sideways). P* 14.

463 5p. Type **139** .. 15 20
464 13p. "DHC-2 Beaver" .. 35 45
465 17p. Noorduyn "Norseman" .. 40 50
466 50p. Auster .. 1·00 1·25
463/6 .. *Set of* 4 1·75 2·25

17 p

(140)

1984 (3 Jan). *Nos.* 443 *and* 445 *surch as T* **140** *by Govt Printer, Port Stanley.*

467 17p. on 15p. Government House, early 20th century .. 35 35
468 22p. on 25p. Whalebone Arch, 1933 .. 45 45

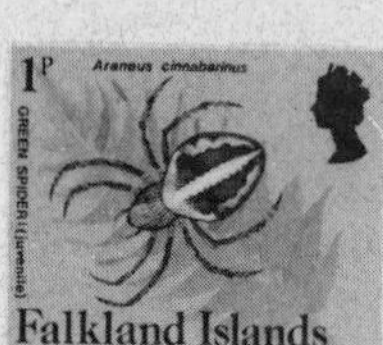

141 Green Spider (juvenile)

142 *Wavertree*

(Des I. Strange. Litho Questa)

1984 (3 Jan)–**86**. *Insects and Spiders. T* **141** *and similar horiz designs. Multicoloured. W* w **14** *(sideways). P* 14×14½.

A. Without imprint date.

469A 1p. Type **141** .. 15 15
470A 2p. Ichneumon Fly (*Alophophion occidentalis*) .. 25 15
471A 3p. Brocade Moth .. 15 15
472A 4p. Black Beetle .. 15 15
473A 5p. "The Queen of the Falklands" .. 15 15
474A 6p. Green Spider .. 15 20
475A 7p. Ichneumon Fly (*Trachysphyrus penai*) 15 20
476A 8p. Ochre Shoulder (moth) .. 15 20
477A 9p. Clocker Weevil .. 15 20
478A 10p. Hover Fly .. 20 25
479A 20p. Weevil .. 60 60
480A 25p. Metallic Beetle .. 75 75
481A 50p. Camel Cricket .. 1·00 1·25
482A £1 Beauchene Spider .. 1·75 2·25
483A £3 Southern Painted Lady .. 5·00 6·00
469A/83A .. *Set of* 15 9·75 11·50

B. With imprint date at foot of design

470B 2p. Ichneumon Fly (*Alophophion occidentalis*) (19.5.86) .. 20 20

(Des A. Theobald. Litho Questa)

1984 (7 May). *250th Anniv of "Lloyd's List" (newspaper). T* **142** *and similar vert designs. Multicoloured. W* w **14**. *P* 14½ × 14.

484 6p. Type **142** .. 30 25
485 17p. Port Stanley .. 60 50
486 22p. R.M.S. *Oravia* stranded .. 65 55
487 52p. *Cunard Countess* .. 1·25 1·25
484/7 .. *Set of* 4 2·50 2·25

143 Ship, Aircraft and U.P.U. Logo

144 Great Grebe

(Des E. Nisbet, adapted L. Curtis. Litho Questa)

1984 (25 June). *Universal Postal Union Congress, Hamburg. W* w **14** *(sideways). P* 14.

488 **143** 22p. multicoloured .. 45 50

(Des I. Strange. Litho Questa)

1984 (6 Aug). *Grebes. T* **144** *and similar vert designs. Multicoloured. W* w **14**. *P* 14½.

489 17p. Type **144** .. 65 45
490 22p. Silvery Grebe .. 80 60
491 52p. White-tufted Grebe .. 1·75 1·75
489/91 .. *Set of* 3 3·00 2·50

145 Black-browed Albatross

146 Technical Drawing of "Wren" Class Locomotive

(Des I. Strange. Litho Questa)

1984 (5 Nov). *Nature Conservation. T* **145** *and similar vert designs. Multicoloured. W* w **14**. *P* 14½ × 14.

492 6p. Type **145** .. 45 30
493 17p. Tussock grass .. 70 50
494 22p. Dusky Dolphin and Southern Sealion .. 85 70
495 52p. *Notothenia* (fish) and krill .. 1·25 1·50
492/5 .. *Set of* 4 3·00 2·75
MS496 130×90 mm. Nos. 492/5 .. 3·00 3·25

(Des C. Abbott. Litho Questa)

1985 (18 Feb). *70th Anniv of Camber Railway. T* **146** *and similar horiz designs, each black, deep brown and pale cinnamon. W* w **14** *(sideways). P* 14.

497 7p. Type **146** .. 20 25
498 22p. Sail-propelled trolley .. 50 55
499 27p. Locomotive at work .. 60 65
500 54p. "Falkland Islands Express" passenger train (75 × 25 *mm*). .. 1·10 1·25
497/500 .. *Set of* 4 2·25 2·40

147 Construction Workers' Camp

148 The Queen Mother on 84th Birthday

(Des N. Shewring. Litho Questa)

1985 (12 May). *Opening of Mount Pleasant Airport. T* **147** *and similar horiz designs. Multicoloured. W* w **16** *(sideways). P* 14½ × 14.

501 7p. Type **147** .. 40 30
502 22p. Building construction .. 80 60
503 27p. Completed airport .. 90 70
504 54p. Airliner over runway .. 1·50 1·25
501/4 .. *Set of* 4 3·25 2·50

(Des A. Theobald (£1), C. Abbott (others). Litho Questa)

1985 (7 June). *Life and Times of Queen Elizabeth the Queen Mother. T* **148** *and similar vert designs. Multicoloured. W* w **16**. *P* 14½ × 14.

505 7p. Attending reception at Lancaster House .. 15 20
506 22p. With Prince Charles, Mark Phillips and Princess Anne at Falklands Memorial Service .. 45 50
507 27p. Type **148** .. 55 60
508 54p. With Prince Henry at his christening (from photo by Lord Snowdon) .. 1·10 1·25
505/8 .. *Set of* 4 2·00 2·25
MS509 91 × 73 mm. £1 With Princess Diana at Trooping the Colour. Wmk sideways .. 2·00 2·25

149 Captain J. McBride and H.M.S. *Jason*, 1765

150 Painted Keyhole Limpet

(Des O. Bell. Litho Questa)

1985 (30 Sept). *Early Cartographers. T* **149** *and similar horiz designs. Multicoloured. W* w **14** *(sideways). P* 14 × 14½.

510 7p. Type **149** .. 35 25
511 22p. Commodore J. Byron and H.M.S. *Dolphin* and *Tamar*, 1765 .. 70 60
512 27p. Vice-Admiral R. FitzRoy and H.M.S. *Beagle*, 1831 .. 75 65
513 54p. Admiral Sir B. J. Sullivan and H.M.S. *Philomel*, 1842 .. 1·25 1·25
510/13 .. *Set of* 4 2·75 2·50

(Des I. Strange. Litho Questa)

1985 (4 Nov). *Early Naturalists. Vert designs as T* **35** *of British Antarctic Territory. Multicoloured. W* w **14**. *P* 14½ × 14.

514 7p. Philibert Commerson and Commerson's Dolphin .. 35 25
515 22p. René Primevère Lesson and *Lessonia sp.* (kelp) .. 70 55
516 27p. Joseph Paul Gaimard and Common Diving Petrel .. 85 65
517 54p. Charles Darwin and *Calceolaria darwinii* .. 1·60 1·40
514/17 .. *Set of* 4 3·25 2·50

(Des I. Strange. Litho Questa)

1986 (10 Feb). *Seashells. T* **150** *and similar horiz designs. Multicoloured. W* w **16** *(sideways). P* 14 × 14½.

518 7p. Type **150** .. 40 25
519 22p. Magellanic Volute .. 85 60
520 27p. Patagonian Scallop .. 95 70
521 54p. Rough Thorn Drupe .. 1·50 1·25
518/21 .. *Set of* 4 3·25 2·50

(Des A. Theobald. Litho Format)

1986 (21 Apr). *60th Birthday of Queen Elizabeth II. Vert designs as T* **110** *of Ascension. Multicoloured. W* w **16**. *P* 14 × 14½.

522 10p. With Princess Margaret at St. Paul's, Waldenbury, Welwyn, 1932 .. 25 25
523 24p. Queen making Christmas television broadcast, 1958 .. 55 55
524 29p. In robes of Order of the Thistle, St. Giles Cathedral, Edinburgh, 1962 .. 60 60
525 45p. Aboard Royal Yacht *Britannia*, U.S.A., 1976 .. 95 95
526 58p. At Crown Agents Head Office, London, 1983 .. 1·25 1·25
522/6 .. *Set of* 5 3·25 3·25

MINIMUM PRICE

The minimum price quote is 10p which represents a handling charge rather than a basis for valuing common stamps. For further notes about prices see introductory pages.

151 S.S. *Great Britain* crossing Atlantic, 1845

152 Head of Rockhopper Penguin

(Des O. Bell. Litho Format)

1986 (22 May). *"Ameripex '86" International Stamp Exhibition, Chicago. Centenary of Arrival of S.S. "Great Britain" in Falkland Islands. T* **151** *and similar horiz designs. Multicoloured. W w* **16** *(sideways). P* 14.

527	10p. Type **151**	40	30
528	24p. Beached at Sparrow Cove, 1937	75	65
529	29p. Refloated on pontoon, 1970	85	70
530	58p. Undergoing restoration, Bristol, 1986	1·40	1·25
527/30	*Set of* 4	3·00	2·50
MS531	109×109 mm. Nos. 527/30. Wmk upright	3·00	3·25

(Des I. Strange. Litho Questa)

1986 (25 Aug). *Rockhopper Penguins. T* **152** *and similar vert designs. Multicoloured. W w* **16**. *P* 14½×14.

532	10p. Type **152**	45	30
533	24p. Rockhopper Penguins at sea	80	60
534	29p. Courtship display	90	65
535	58p. Adult with chick	1·50	1·25
532/5	*Set of* 4	3·25	2·50

153 Prince Andrew and Miss Sarah Ferguson presenting Polo Trophy, Windsor

154 Survey Party, Sapper Hill

(Des D. Miller. Litho Questa)

1986 (10 Nov). *Royal Wedding. T* **153** *and similar vert designs. Multicoloured. W w* **16**. *P* 14½×14.

536	17p. Type **153**	55	40
537	22p. Prince Andrew and Duchess of York on wedding day	65	50
538	29p. Prince Andrew in battledress at opening of Fox Bay Mill	75	60
536/8	*Set of* 3	1·75	1·40

(Des L. Curtis. Litho Questa)

1987 (9 Feb). *Bicentenary of Royal Engineers' Royal Warrant. T* **154** *and similar horiz designs. Multicoloured. W w* **16** *(sideways). P* 14×14½.

539	10p. Type **154**	40	30
540	24p. Mine clearance by robot	75	60
541	29p. Boxer Bridge, Stanley	85	70
542	58p. Unloading mail, Mount Pleasant Airport	1·50	1·25
539/42	*Set of* 4	3·25	2·50

155 Southern Sea Lion

156 *Suillus luteus*

(Des I. Strange. Litho Questa)

1987 (27 Apr). *Seals. T* **155** *and similar horiz designs. Multicoloured. W w* **16** *(sideways). P* 14½.

543	10p. Type **155**	20	25
544	24p. Falkland Fur Seal	50	55
545	29p. Southern Elephant Seal	60	65
546	58p. Leopard Seal	1·10	1·25
543/6	*Set of* 4	2·10	2·40

(Des I. Strange. Litho Questa)

1987 (14 Sept). *Fungi. T* **156** *and similar vert designs. Multicoloured. W w* **16**. *P* 14½×14.

547	10p. Type **156**	40	40
548	24p. *Mycena sp.*	80	80
549	29p. *Camarophyllus adonis*	95	95
550	58p. *Gerronema schusteri*	1·60	1·60
547/50	*Set of* 4	3·25	3·25

OMNIBUS ISSUES

Details, together with prices for complete sets, of the various Omnibus issues from the 1935 Silver Jubilee series to date are included in a special section following Zululand at the end of the catalogue.

157 Victoria Cottage Home, c 1912

158 Morris Truck, Fitzroy, 1940

(Des D. Hartley. Litho Questa)

1987 (8 Dec). *Local Hospitals. T* **157** *and similar horiz designs. Multicoloured. W w* **16** *(sideways). P* 14.

551	10p. Type **157**	20	25
552	24p. King Edward VII Memorial Hospital, c 1914	50	55
553	29p. Churchill Wing, King Edward VII Memorial Hospital, c 1953	55	60
554	58p. Prince Andrew Wing, New Hospital, 1987	1·10	1·25
551/4	*Set of* 4	2·10	2·40

(Des D. Hartley. Litho Questa)

1988 (11 Apr). *Early Vehicles. T* **158** *and similar horiz designs. Multicoloured. W w* **16** *(sideways). P* 14.

555	10p. Type **158**	20	25
556	24p. Citroen "Kegresse" half-track, San Carlos, 1929	50	55
557	29p. Ford one ton truck, Port Stanley, 1933	55	60
558	58p. Ford "Model T" car, Darwin, 1935	1·10	1·25
555/8	*Set of* 4	2·10	2·40

159 Kelp Goose

(Des I. Strange. Litho Walsall)

1988 (25 July). *Falkland Islands Geese. T* **159** *and similar horiz designs. Multicoloured. W w* **16** *(sideways). P* 13½×14.

559	10p. Type **159**	20	25
560	24p. Magellan ("Upland") Goose	50	55
561	29p. Ruddy-headed Goose	55	60
562	58p. Ashy-headed Goose	1·10	1·25
559/62	*Set of* 4	2·10	2·40

(Des D. Miller (10, 24p.), E. Nesbit and D. Miller (29, 58p.). Litho Format)

1988 (14 Nov). *300th Anniv of Lloyd's of London. Multicoloured designs as T* **123** *of Ascension. W w* **14** *(sideways on 24, 29p.). P* 14.

563	10p. Silver from Lloyd's Nelson Collection	20	25
564	24p. Falkland Islands hydroponic market garden *(horiz)*	50	55
565	29p. *A.E.S.* (freighter) *(horiz)*	55	60
566	58p. *Charles Cooper* (full-rigged sailing ship), 1866	1·10	1·25
563/6	*Set of* 4	2·10	2·40

160 *Padua* (barque)

(Des A. Theobald. Litho Questa)

1989 (28 Feb)–**90**. *Cape Horn Sailing Ships. T* **160** *and similar multicoloured designs. W w* **14** *(sideways on horiz designs). P* 14.

567	1p. Type **160**	10	10
568	2p. *Priwall* (barque) *(vert)*	10	10
569	3p. *Passat* (barque)	10	10
570	4p. *Archibald Russell* (barque) *(vert)*	10	10
571	5p. *Pamir* (barque) *(vert)*	10	10
572	6p. *Mozart* (barquentine)	10	10
573	7p. *Pommern* (barque)	10	15
574	8p. *Preussen* (full-rigged ship)	15	20
575	9p. *Fennia* (barque)	15	20
576	10p. *Cassard* (barque)	20	25
577	20p. *Lawhill* (barque)	35	40
578	25p. *Garthpool* (barque)	45	50
579	50p. *Grace Harwar* (full-rigged ship)	90	95
580	£1 *Criccieth Castle* (full-rigged ship)	1·75	1·90
581	£3 *Cutty Sark* (full-rigged ship) *(vert)*	5·00	5·25
582	£5 *Flying Cloud* (full-rigged ship) (2.1.90)	9·00	9·25
567/82	*Set of* 16	16·00	17·00

161 Southern Right Whale

(Des I. Strange. Litho Questa)

1989 (15 May). *Baleen Whales. T* **161** *and similar horiz designs. Multicoloured. W w* **16** *(sideways). P* 13½×14.

583	10p. Type **161**	20	25
584	24p. Minke Whale	50	55
585	29p. Humpback Whale	55	60
586	58p. Blue Whale	1·10	1·25
583/6	*Set of* 4	2·10	2·40

162 "Gymkhana" (Sarah Gilding)

163 Vice-Admiral Sturdee and H.M.S. *Invincible* (battle cruiser)

(Adapted G. Vasarhelyi. Litho Walsall)

1989 (16 Sept). *Sports Associations' Activities. T* **162** *and similar horiz designs showing children's drawings. Multicoloured. W w* **16** *(sideways). P* 14.

587	5p. Type **162**	10	15
588	10p. "Steer Riding" (Karen Steen)	20	25
589	17p. "Sheep Shearing" (Colin Shepherd)	35	40
590	24p. "Sheepdog Trials" (Rebecca Edwards)	50	55
591	29p. "Horse Racing" (Dilys Blackley)	60	65
592	45p. "Sack Race" (Donna Newell)	90	1·00
587/92	*Set of* 6	2·40	2·75

(Des C. Collins. Litho B.D.T.)

1989 (8 Dec). *75th Anniv of Battle of the Falkland Islands and 50th Anniv of Battle of the River Plate. T* **163** *and similar vert designs. Multicoloured. W w* **16**. *P* 13½.

593	10p. Type **163**	20	25
594	24p. Vice-Admiral Graf von Spee and *Scharnhorst* (German cruiser)	50	55
595	29p. Commodore Harwood and H.M.S. *Ajax* (cruiser)	60	65
596	58p. Captain Langsdorff and *Admiral Graf Spee* (German pocket battleship)	1·10	1·25
593/6	*Set of* 4	2·25	2·40

FALKLAND ISLANDS DEPENDENCIES

The stamps of FALKLAND ISLANDS were used on South Georgia (Grytviken) from 3 December 1909 until 1944 and at Port Foster, Deception Island in the South Shetlands group from 1912 to 1931, both offices operating during the whaling season only.

PRICES FOR STAMPS ON COVER TO 1945
Nos. A1/D8 *from* × 10

A. GRAHAM LAND

For use at Port Lockroy (established February 1944) and Hope Bay bases.

GRAHAM LAND

DEPENDENCY OF

(A 1)

1944 (12 Feb)–**45**. *Falkland Islands Nos.* 146, 148, 150, 153/5, 157 *and* 158*a optd with Type* A 1, *in red, by B.W.*

A1	½d. black and green	20	85
	a. Blue-black and green	£200	
A2	1d. black and violet	20	85
A3	2d. black and carmine-red	30	85
A4	3d. black and blue	20	85
A5	4d. black and purple	1·40	1·00
A6	6d. black and brown	7·50	2·25
	a. Blue-black and brown (24.9.45)	20·00	
A7	9d. black and grey-blue	1·50	1·00
A8	1s. deep blue	1·50	1·00
A1/8 Perf "Specimen"	*Set of* 8	£300	

B. SOUTH GEORGIA

The stamps of Falkland Islands were used at Grytviken from 1909 until replaced by Nos. B1/8.

1944 (3 Apr)–**45**. *Falkland Islands Nos.* 146, 148, 150, 153/5, 157 *and* 158*a optd* "SOUTH GEORGIA/DEPENDENCY OF", *in red, as Type* A 1, *of Graham Land.*

B1	½d. black and green	20	85
B2	1d. black and violet	20	85
B3	2d. black and carmine-red	30	85
B4	3d. black and blue	20	85
B5	4d. black and purple	1·40	1·00
B6	6d. black and brown	7·50	2·25
	a. Blue-black and brown (24.9.45)	20·00	
B7	9d. black and grey-blue	1·50	1·00
B8	1s. deep blue	1·50	1·00
B1/8 Perf "Specimen"	*Set of* 8	£300	

For later issues, see after No. G44.

C. SOUTH ORKNEYS

For use at Louise Island base (established 1945).

1944 (21 Feb)–**45**. *Falkland Islands Nos.* 146, 148, 150, 153/5, 157 *and* 158*a optd* "SOUTH ORKNEYS/DEPENDENCY OF", *in red as Type* A 1 *of Graham Land.*

C1	½d. black and green	20	85
C2	1d. black and violet	20	85
C3	2d. black and carmine-red	30	85
C4	3d. black and blue	20	85
C5	4d. black and purple	1·40	1·00
C6	6d. black and brown	7·50	2·25
	a. Blue-black and brown (24.9.45)	20·00	
C7	9d. black and grey-blue	1·50	1·00
C8	1s. deep blue	1·50	1·00
C1/8 Perf "Specimen"	*Set of* 8	£300	

D. SOUTH SHETLANDS

For use at Deception Island base (established February 1944).

1944 (5 Feb)–**45**. *Falkland Islands Nos.* 146, 148, 150, 153/5, 157 *and* 158*a optd* "SOUTH SHETLANDS/DEPENDENCY OF", *in red, as Type* A 1 *of Graham Land.*

D1	½d. black and green	20	85
D2	1d. black and violet	20	85
D3	2d. black and carmine-red	30	85
D4	3d. black and blue	20	85
D5	4d. black and purple	1·40	1·00
D6	6d. black and brown	7·50	2·25
	a. Blue-black and brown (24.9.45)	20·00	
D7	9d. black and grey-blue	1·50	1·00
D8	1s. deep blue	1·50	1·00
D1/8 Perf "Specimen"	*Set of* 8	£300	
A1/D8	*Set of* 32	42·00	32·00

From 12 July 1946 to 16 July 1963, Graham Land, South Georgia, South Orkneys and South Shetlands used FALKLAND ISLANDS DEPENDENCIES stamps.

PRICES OF SETS

Set prices are given for many issues, generally those containing three stamps or more. Definitive sets include one of each value or major colour change, but do not cover different perforations, die types or minor shades. Where a choice is possible the set prices are based on the cheapest versions of the stamps included in the listings.

E. FALKLAND ISLANDS DEPENDENCIES

For use in all four dependencies.

G 1

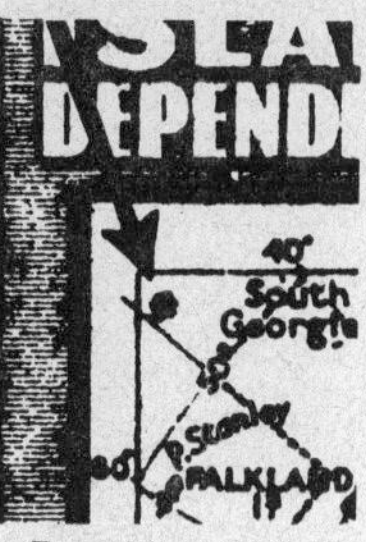

Extra island (Plate 1 R. 3/9)

Missing "I" in "S. Shetland Is." (Plate 1 R. 1/2)

(Map litho, frame recess D.L.R.)

1946 (11 Feb)–**49**. *Wmk Mult Script CA (sideways). P* 12.

(a) Map thick and coarse

G 1	G 1	½d. black and green	80	1·75
		a. Extra island	9·00	
		b. Missing "I"	9·00	
G 2		1d. black and violet	80	1·75
		a. Extra island	9·00	
		b. Missing "I"	9·00	
G 3		2d. black and carmine	1·00	2·00
		a. Extra island	10·00	
		b. Missing "I"	10·00	
G 4		3d. black and blue	1·00	3·00
		a. Extra island	10·00	
		b. Missing "I"	10·00	
G 5		4d. black and claret	2·00	4·25
G 6		6d. black and orange	4·00	4·50
		a. Extra island	28·00	
		b. Missing "I"	28·00	
		c. Black and ochre	45·00	90·00
		ca. Extra island	£100	
		cb. Missing "I"	£100	
G 7		9d. black and brown	1·50	2·75
G 8		1s. black and purple	1·75	4·00
G1/8		*Set of* 8	12·00	22·00
G1/8 Perf "Specimen"		*Set of* 8	£400	

(b) Map thin and clear (16.2.48)

G 9	G 1	½d. black and green	2·25	7·00
G10		1d. black and violet	1·50	9·00
G11		2d. black and carmine	4·50	11·00
G11*a*		2½d. black and deep blue (6.3.49)	9·00	7·00
G12		3d. black and blue	1·75	4·50
G13		4d. black and claret	7·00	12·00
G14		6d. black and orange	7·50	10·00
G15		9d. black and brown	7·50	10·00
G16		1s. black and purple	9·00	10·00
G9/16		*Set of* 9	45·00	70·00

In Nos. G1/8 a variety with a gap in the 80th parallel occurs six times in each sheet of all values in positions R. 1/4. 1/9, 3/4, 3/9, 5/4 and 5/9 (*Price for set of* 8 £60 *mint*).

In Nos. G9 to G16 the map is redrawn; the "o°" meridian does not touch the "S" of "COATS", the "n" of "Alexander" is not joined to the "L" of "Land" below, and the loops of letters "s" and "t" are generally more open.

A constant variety, dot on "T" of "SOUTH", occurs on R. 5/2, 5/4, 5/6, 5/8 and 5/10.

1946 (4 Oct). *Victory. As Nos.* 28/9 *of Aden.*

G17	1d. deep violet	50	15
G18	3d. blue	50	15
G17/18 Perf "Specimen"	*Set of* 2	£110	

1948 (6 Dec). *Royal Silver Wedding. As Nos.* 30/1 *of Aden but inscr* "FALKLAND ISLANDS DEPENDENCIES" (*recess* 1s.).

G19	2½d. ultramarine	1·00	75
G20	1s. violet-blue	5·50	1·75

1949 (10 Oct). *75th Anniv of U.P.U. As Nos.* 114/17 *of Antigua.*

G21	1d. violet	2·00	1·25
G22	2d. carmine-red	6·50	2·50
G23	3d. deep blue	8·00	1·25
G24	6d. red-orange	12·00	3·00
G21/4	*Set of* 4	26·00	7·00

1953 (4 June). *Coronation. As No.* 47 *of Aden.*

G25	1d. black and violet	1·50	1·25

G 2 *John Biscoe I*, 1947–52

G 3 *Trepassey*, 1945–47

(Recess Waterlow, then D.L.R. (from 27.3.62))

1954 (1 Feb)–**62**. *Types G* 2/3 *and similar designs showing ships. Wmk Mult Script CA. P* 12½.

G26	½d. black and bluish green	30	45
	a. Black and deep green (DLR) (17.4.62)	2·50	2·75
G27	1d. black and sepia-brown	75	40
	a. Black and sepia (DLR) (27.3.62)	9·00	3·50
G28	1½d. black and olive	35	40
	a. Black and yellow-olive (DLR) (21.9.62)	7·00	3·00
G29	2d. black and rose-red	70	20
G30	2½d. black and yellow-ochre	70	15
G31	3d. black and deep bright blue	70	15
G32	4d. black and bright reddish purple	2·00	30
G33	6d. black and deep lilac	2·00	35
G34	9d. black	2·00	40
G35	1s. black and brown	2·00	35
G36	2s. black and carmine	14·00	8·00
G37	2s. 6d. black and pale turquoise	14·00	6·00
G38	5s. black and violet	30·00	6·50
G39	10s. black and blue	48·00	18·00
G40	£1 black	£110	48·00
G26/40	*Set of* 15	£200	80·00

Designs: *Horiz*—1½d. *Wyatt Earp*, 1934–36; 2d. *Eagle*, 1944–45; 2½d. *Penola*, 1934–37; 3d. *Discovery II*, 1929–37; 4d. *William Scoresby*, 1926–46; 1s. *Deutschland*, 1910–12; 2s. *Pourquoi-pas?*, 1908–10; 10s. *Antarctic*, 1901–03. *Vert*—6d. *Discovery*, 1925–27; 9d. *Endurance*, 1914–16; 2s. 6d. *Français*, 1903–05; 5s. *Scotia*, 1902–04; £1 *Belgica*, 1897–99.

TRANS-ANTARCTIC EXPEDITION 1955-1958

(G 4)

1956 (30 Jan). *Trans-Antarctic Expedition. Nos.* G27, G30/1 *and* G33 *optd with Type* G 4.

G41	1d. black and sepia-brown	10	30
G42	2½d. black and yellow-ochre	40	30
G43	3d. black and deep bright blue	40	30
G44	6d. black and deep lilac	40	30
G41/4	*Set of* 4	1·25	1·10

The stamps of Falkland Islands Dependencies were withdrawn on 16 July 1963 after Graham Land, South Orkneys and South Shetlands had become a separate colony, BRITISH ANTARCTIC TERRITORY. From 17 July 1963 to 4 May 1980 South Georgia and South Sandwich Islands used SOUTH GEORGIA stamps.

F. SOUTH GEORGIA

1 Reindeer

2 South Sandwich Islands

(Des D.L.R. (No. 16), M. Goaman (others). Recess D.L.R.)

1963 (17 July)–**69**. *T* 1/2 *and similar designs. Ordinary or glazed paper* (*No.* 16). *W* w **12**. *P* 15.

1	½d. brown-red	50	30
	a. Perf 14 × 15 (13.2.67)	1·00	1·50
2	1d. violet-blue	70	15
3	2d. turquoise-blue	70	15
4	2½d. black	2·00	50
5	3d. bistre	1·25	15
6	4d. bronze-green	1·50	25
7	5½d. deep violet	1·25	15
8	6d. orange	75	15
9	9d. blue	2·00	25
10	1s. purple	75	15
11	2s. yellow-olive and light blue	11·00	4·00
12	2s. 6d. blue	12·00	4·00
13	5s. orange-brown	16·00	4·00
14	10s. magenta	38·00	10·00
15	£1 ultramarine	95·00	48·00
16	£1 grey-black (1.12.69)	10·00	16·00
1/16	*Set of* 16	£180	80·00

Designs: *Vert*—2d. Sperm Whale; 3d. South American Fur Seal; 6d. Light-mantled Sooty Albatross; 10s. Plankton and krill; £1 (No. 16) King Penguins. *Horiz*—2½d. Bearded and King Penguin; 4d. Fin Whale; 5½d. Southern Elephant-Seal; 9d. Whale-catcher; 1s. Leopard Seal; 2s. Shackleton's Cross; 2s. 6d. Wandering Albatross; 5s. Southern Elephant-Seal and South American Fur Seal; £1 (No. 15) Blue Whale.

1970 (22 Jan). *As No.* 1, *but wmk w* **12** *sideways and on glazed paper.*

17	½d. brown-red	1·60	2·00

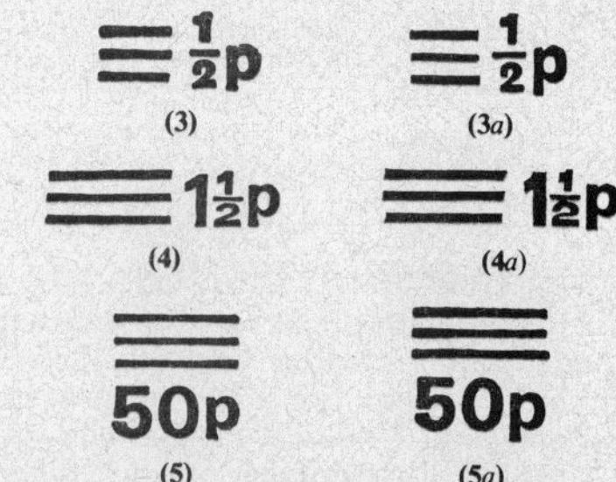

(3) (3*a*) (4) (4*a*) (5) (5*a*)

1971 (15 Feb)–**76.** *Decimal Currency. Nos.* 17 *and* 2/14 *surch as T* **3/4**. *Nos.* 18/a *wmk sideways, glazed paper. Others wmk upright, ordinary paper.*

18 ½p. on ½d. brown-red (T **3**) .. .. .. 95 1·60
a. Surch with T **3*a*** (16.6.72) .. .. 1·00 90
b. Do. Wmk upright (24.8.73) .. .. 1·75 3·50
19 1p. on 1d. violet-blue.. .. .. .. 1·50 55
a. Glazed paper (1.12.72) .. .. .. 3·00 1·75
b. Do. but wmk sideways (9.3.76) .. .. 1·50 4·00
20 1½p. on 5½d. deep violet (T **4**) .. .. 2·00 1·75
b. Surch with T **4*a***. Glazed paper (24.8.73) 4·50 4·00
21 2p. on 2d. turquoise-blue 70 40
22 2½p. on 2½d. black .. .. 1·00 40
23 3p. on 3d. bistre 80 50
24 4p. on 4d. bronze-green 90 50
25 5p. on 6d. orange 90 30
26 6p. on 9d. blue .. .. 1·50 70
27 7½p. on 1s. purple .. .. 1·50 70
28 10p. on 2s. yellow-olive and light blue .. 15·00 11·00
29 15p. on 2s. 6d. blue .. .. 15·00 11·00
30 25p. on 5s. orange-brown .. .. .. 13·00 9·00
31 50p. on 10s. magenta (Type **5**) .. .. 30·00 16·00
a. Surch with Type **5*a***. Glazed paper (1.12.72) .. .. 20·00 23·00
b. Do. but wmk sideways (9.3.76) .. .. 25·00 38·00
18/31a .. .. *Set of* 14 65·00 48·00

The surcharge on No. 19b shows a larger "p".
See also Nos. 53/66.

6 *Endurance* beset in Weddell Sea

(Des R. Granger Barrett. Litho A. & M.)

1972 (5 Jan). *50th Death Anniv of Sir Ernest Shackleton. T* **6** *and similar horiz designs. Multicoloured. W* w **12** (*sideways*). *P* 13½.

32 1½p. Type **6** 75 60
33 5p. Launching the longboat *James Caird* .. 1·25 85
34 10p. Route of the *James Caird* .. 1·50 1·00
35 20p. Sir Ernest Shackleton and the *Quest* .. 1·75 1·25
32/5 .. .. *Set of* 4 4·75 3·25

7 Southern Elephant-Seal and King Penguins

(Des (from photograph by D. Groves) and photo Harrison)

1972 (20 Nov). *Royal Silver Wedding. Multicoloured; background colour given. W* w **12**. *P* 14 × 14½.

36 **7** 5p. slate-green .. .. 1·00 35
37 10p. bluish violet .. .. 1·00 35

1973 (1 Dec*). *Royal Wedding. As Nos.* 165/6 *of Anguilla. Centre multicoloured. W* w **12** (*sideways*). *P* 13½.

38 5p. brown-ochre 25 10
39 15p. bright lilac 35 20

*This is the local date of issue: the Crown Agents released the stamps on 14 November.

8 Churchill and Westminster Skyline **9** Captain Cook

(Des L. Curtis. Litho Questa)

1974 (14 Dec*). *Birth Centenary of Sir Winston Churchill. T* **8** *and similar horiz design. Multicoloured. W* w **12** (*sideways*). *P* 14½.

40 15p. Type **8** .. .. 1·75 1·00
41 25p. Churchill and warship .. .. .. 1·75 1·00
MS42 122 × 98 mm. Nos. 40/1 .. .. 6·00 6·00

*This is the local date of issue: the Crown Agents released the stamps on 30 November.

(Des J. Cooter. Litho Questa)

1975 (26 Apr). *Bicentenary of Possession by Captain Cook. T* **9** *and similar horiz designs. Multicoloured. W* w **12** (*sideways on* 8 *and* 16*p.*). *P* 13.

43 2p. Type **9** .. .. 1·60 1·00
44 8p. H.M.S. *Resolution* .. .. .. 2·25 1·50
45 16p. Possession Bay .. .. 3·25 1·75
43/5 .. .. *Set of* 3 6·50 3·75

10 *Discovery* and Biological Laboratory **11** Queen and Retinue after Coronation

(Des J. W. Litho Format)

1976 (21 Dec). *50th Anniv of "Discovery" Investigations. T* **10** *and similar vert designs. Multicoloured. W* w **14**. *P* 14.

46 2p. Type **10** 85 35
47 8p. *William Scoresby* and water-sampling bottles .. .. 1·10 50
48 11p. *Discovery II* and plankton net .. .. 1·40 55
49 25p. Biological Station and krill .. .. 2·25 85
46/9 .. .. *Set of* 4 5·00 2·00

(Des G. Drummond. Litho Questa)

1977 (7 Feb). *Silver Jubilee. T* **11** *and similar horiz designs. Multicoloured. W* w **14** (*sideways*). *P* 13½.

50 6p. Visit by Prince Philip, 1957 .. .. 80 30
51 11p. Queen Elizabeth and Westminster Abbey 90 35
52 33p. Type **11** .. .. 1·25 50
50/2 .. .. *Set of* 3 2·75 1·00

1977 (17 May)–**78.** *As Nos.* 18a *etc., but W* w **14** (*inverted on* 1*p.; upright on* 3*p.,* 5*p. and* 50*p.; sideways on others*). *Glazed paper.*

53 ½p. on ½d. brown-red .. .. .. 1·00 1·75
54 1p. on 1d. violet-blue (16.8.77) .. .. 80 1·75
55 1½p. on 5½d. deep violet (16.8.77) .. .. 90 1·75
57 2½p. on 2½d. black (16.8.77) .. .. 6·00 3·50
58 3p. on 3d. bistre (16.8.77) .. .. 6·00 3·50
59 4p. on 4d. bronze-green (16.8.77) .. .. 16·00 14·00
60 5p. on 6d. orange .. .. 3·50 2·75
62 7½p. on 1s. purple (16.8.77) .. .. 4·00 8·00
63 10p. on 2s. yellow-olive and light blue (16.8.77) 4·00 8·00
64 15p. on 2s. 6d. blue (16.8.77) .. .. 4·00 8·00
65 25p. on 5s. orange-brown (16.8.77) .. .. 4·00 8·00
66 50p. on 10s. pale magenta (12.78) .. .. 2·50 8·50
53/66 .. .. *Set of* 12 45·00 60·00

Surcharges on the above differ from those on Nos. 18a/30 by having straight outlines and being slightly more slender. The change in paper also results in the colours appearing brighter.

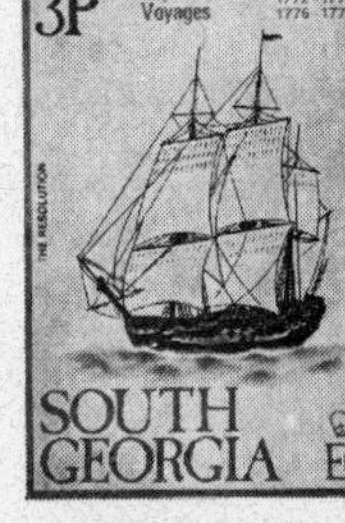

12 Fur Seal **13** H.M.S. *Resolution*

(Des C. Abbott. Litho Questa)

1978 (2 June). *25th Anniv of Coronation. T* **12** *and similar vert designs. P* 15.

67 25p. indigo, ultramarine and silver 75 95
a. Sheetlet. Nos. 67/9 × 2 .. .. 4·00
68 25p. multicoloured 75 95
69 25p. indigo, ultramarine and silver 75 95
67/9 .. .. *Set of* 3 2·00 2·50

Designs:—No. 67, Panther of Henry VI; No. 68, Queen Elizabeth II; No. 69, Type **12**.

Nos. 67/9 were printed together in small sheets of 6, containing two *se-tenant* strips of 3, with horizontal gutter margin between.

(Des and litho (25p. also embossed) Walsall)

1979 (14 Feb). *Bicentenary of Captain Cook's Voyages,* 1768–79. *T* **13** *and similar vert designs. Multicoloured. P* 11.

70 3p. Type **13** 80 75
71 6p. *Resolution* and map of South Georgia and S. Sandwich Isles showing route .. 70 55
72 11p. King Penguin (based on drawing by George Forster) .. .. 1·40 1·90
73 25p. Flaxman/Wedgwood medallion of Captain Cook.. .. .. 1·60 2·00
70/3 .. .. *Set of* 4 4·00 4·75

From 5 May 1980 South Georgia and South Sandwich Islands used stamps inscribed FALKLAND ISLANDS DEPENDENCIES.

G. FALKLAND ISLANDS DEPENDENCIES

For use in South Georgia and South Sandwich Islands.

14 Map of Falkland Islands Dependencies **15** Magellanic Clubmoss

(Des and litho J.W.)

1980 (5 May)–**84.** *Horiz designs as T* **14**. *Multicoloured. W* w **14** (*sideways*). *P* 13½. A. *Without imprint date.* B. *With imprint date* ("1984") *at foot of design* (3.5.84).

		A		B	
74	1p. Type **14**	20	25	15	20
75	2p. Shag Rocks	20	25	15	20
76	3p. Bird and Willis Islands ..	20	25	15	20
77	4p. Gulbrandsen Lake ..	20	30	15	20
78	5p. King Edward Point ..	20	30	25	25
79	6p. Sir Ernest Shackleton's Memorial Cross, Hope Point	25	30	25	25
80	7p. Sir Ernest Shackleton's Grave, Grytviken	30	40	20	25
81	8p. Grytviken Church ..	30	40	25	25
82	9p. Coaling Hulk *Louise* at Grytviken	30	45	30	35
83	10p. Clerke Rocks	30	45	50	35
84	20p. Candlemas Island	1·50	1·25	1·50	1·25
85	25p. Twitcher Rock and Cook Island, Southern Thule ..	1·50	1·50	1·50	1·25
86	50p. R.R.S. *John Biscoe II* in Cumberland Bay	1·50	2·00	1·75	1·75
87	£1 R.R.S. *Bransfield* in Cumberland Bay	2·00	2·75	†	
88	£3 H.M.S. *Endurance* in Cumberland Bay	5·00	6·50	†	
74/88	.. .. .. *Set of* 15	12·00	16·00		
74B/86B	.. .. *Set of* 13			6·50	6·00

For some of these designs watermarked W **16** (sideways) see Nos. 148/52.

(Des L. McCombie. Litho Rosenbaum Bros, Vienna)

1981 (5 Feb). *Plants. T* **15** *and similar vert designs. Multicoloured. W* w **14** (*inverted on* 25*p.*). *P* 14.

89 3p. Type **15** 25 25
90 6p. Alpine Cat's-tail 30 30
91 7p. Greater Burnet 30 30
92 11p. Antarctic Bedstraw 50 40
93 15p. Brown Rush 70 55
a. Light brown (Queen's head and territory inscr) omitted £1750
94 25p. Antarctic Hair Grass .. .. .. 1·00 80
89/94 .. .. *Set of* 6 2·75 2·40

16 Wedding Bouquet from Falkland Islands Dependencies **17** Introduced Reindeer during Calving, Spring

(Des J.W. Litho Format)

1981 (22 July). *Royal Wedding. T* **16** *and similar vert designs. Multicoloured. W* w **14**. *P* 14.

95 10p. Type **16** 30 40
96 13p. Prince Charles dressed for skiing .. 40 50
97 52p. Prince Charles and Lady Diana Spencer 1·00 1·00
95/7 .. .. *Set of* 3 1·50 1·75

(Des A. Theobald. Litho Format)

1982 (29 Jan). *Reindeer. T* **17** *and similar horiz designs. Multicoloured. W* w **14** (*sideways*). *P* 14.

98 5p. Type **17** 45 60
99 13p. Bull at rut, Autumn 65 80
100 25p. Reindeer and mountains, Winter .. 1·10 1·25
101 26p. Reindeer feeding on tussock grass, late Winter .. .. 1·10 1·25
98/101 .. .. *Set of* 4 3·00 3·50

18 Mite (*Gamasellus racovitzai*) **19** Lady Diana Spencer at Tidworth, Hampshire, July 1981

(Des I. Loe. Litho Questa)

1982 (16 Mar). *Insects. T* **18** *and similar vert designs. Multicoloured. W* w **14**. *P* 14.
102 5p. Type **18** 20 25
103 10p. Mite (*Alaskozetes antarcticus*) 30 35
104 13p. Ubiquitous Springtail (*Cryptopygus antarcticus*) 35 40
105 15p. Spider (*Notiomaso australis*) 40 45
106 25p. Beetle (*Hydromedion sparsutum*) .. 65 70
107 26p. Midge (*Parochlus steinenii*) 65 70
102/7 .. .. *Set of* 6 2·25 2·50

(Des C. Abbott. Litho Format)

1982 (7 Sept). *21st Birthday of Princess of Wales. T* **19** *and similar vert designs. Multicoloured. W* w **14**. *P* 13½ × 14.
108 5p. Falklands Islands Dependencies coat of arms 10 15
109 17p. Type **19** 30 35
a. Perf 13½ .. .. 8·50 8·50
110 37p. Bride and groom on steps of St Paul's .. 75 80
111 50p. Formal portrait .. .. 1·00 1·10
108/11 .. .. *Set of* 4 1·90 2·25

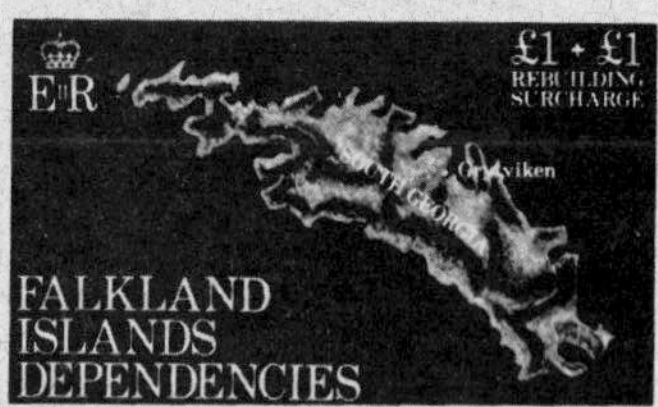

20 Map of South Georgia

(Des PAD Studio. Litho Format)

1982 (13 Sept). *Rebuilding Fund. W* w **14** (*sideways*). *P* 11.
112 **20** £1 + £1 multicoloured .. .. 3·50 4·50

21 Westland "Whirlwind"

22 *Euphausia superba*

(Des Harrison. Litho Questa)

1983 (23 Dec). *Bicentenary of Manned Flight. T* **21** *and similar horiz designs. Multicoloured. W* w **14** (*sideways*). *P* 14.
113 5p. Type **21** 20 20
114 13p. Westland "Wasp" 45 45
115 17p. Saunders-Roe "Walrus" 50 50
116 50p. Auster .. .. 1·25 1·25
113/16 .. .. *Set of* 4 2·25 2·25

(Des N. Weaver. Litho Questa)

1984 (23 Mar). *Crustacea. T* **22** *and similar vert designs. Multicoloured. W* w **14**. *P* 14½ × 14.
117 5p. Type **22** 15 20
118 17p. *Glyptonotus antarcticus* 40 50
119 25p. *Epimeria monodon* 50 60
120 34p. *Serolis pagenstecheri* 70 80
117/20 .. .. *Set of* 4 1·60 1·90

23 Zavodovski Island

(Des. J.W. Litho Questa)

1984 (8 Nov). *Volcanoes of South Sandwich Islands. T* **23** *and similar horiz designs. Multicoloured. W* w **14** (*sideways*). *P* 14 × 14½.
121 6p. Type **23** 35 25
122 17p. Mt Michael, Saunders Island 60 50
123 22p. Bellingshausen Island 70 60
124 52p. Bristol Island .. .. 1·10 1·10
121/4 .. .. *Set of* 4 2·50 2·25

24 Grey-headed Albatross

25 The Queen Mother

(Des I. Loe. Litho Questa)

1985 (5 May). *Albatrosses. T* **24** *and similar horiz designs. Multicoloured. W* w **14** (*sideways*). *P* 14½.
125 7p. Type **24** 30 25
126 22p. Black-browed Albatross 60 55
127 27p. Wandering Albatross 70 65
128 54p. Light-mantled Sooty Albatross .. .. 1·25 1·25
125/8 .. .. *Set of* 4 2·50 2·40

(Des A. Theobald (£1), C. Abbott (others). Litho Questa)

1985 (23 June). *Life and Times of Queen Elizabeth the Queen Mother. T* **25** *and similar vert designs. Multicoloured. W* w **16**. *P* 14½ × 14.
129 7p. At Windsor Castle on Princess Elizabeth's 14th Birthday, 1940 .. .. .. 20 20
130 22p. With Princess Anne, Lady Sarah Armstrong-Jones and Prince Edward at Trooping the Colour 50 50
131 27p. Type **25** 60 60
132 54p. With Prince Henry at his christening (from photo by Lord Snowdon) .. .. 1·25 1·25
129/32 .. .. *Set of* 4 2·25 2·25
MS133 91 × 73 mm. £1 Disembarking from Royal Yacht *Britannia*. Wmk sideways .. .. 2·25 2·75

(Des I. Strange. Litho Questa)

1985 (4 Nov). *Early Naturalists. Vert designs as T* **35** *of British Antarctic Territory. Multicoloured. W* w **14**. *P* 14½ × 14.
134 7p. Dumont d'Urville and *Durvillea antarctica* (kelp) 40 30
135 22p. Johann Reinhold Forster and King Penguin 80 70
136 27p. Johann Georg Adam Forster and Tussock Grass 90 80
137 54p. Sir Joseph Banks and Dove Prion .. 1·50 1·50
134/7 .. .. *Set of* 4 3·25 3·00

1985 (18 Nov). *As Nos. 84/8 but W* w **16** (*sideways*). *With imprint date* ("1985"). *P* 13½.
148 20p. Candlemas Island .. .. 1·50 1·75
149 25p. Twitcher Rock and Cook Island, Southern Thule .. .. 1·50 1·75
150 50p. R.R.S. *John Biscoe* in Cumberland Bay .. .. 2·00 2·25
151 £1 R.R.S. *Bransfield* in Cumberland Bay .. 2·75 3·00
152 £3 H.M.S. *Endurance* in Cumberland Bay .. .. 6·50 7·00
148/52 .. .. *Set of* 5 13·00 14·00

Under the new constitution, effective 3 October 1985, South Georgia and South Sandwich Islands ceased to be dependencies of the Falkland Islands. Issues inscribed for the separate territory are listed under SOUTH GEORGIA AND SOUTH SANDWICH ISLANDS.

Fiji

PRICES FOR STAMPS ON COVER TO 1945

Nos. 1/9	*from* × 6
Nos. 10/34	*from* × 5
Nos. 35/59	*from* × 8
Nos. 60/3	—
Nos. 64/9	*from* × 20
Nos. 70/5	*from* × 5
Nos. 76/103	*from* × 8
Nos. 104/14	*from* × 5
Nos. 115/24	*from* × 4
Nos. 125/37	*from* × 3
Nos. 138/241	*from* × 4
Nos. 242/5	*from* × 3
Nos. 246/8	*from* × 8
Nos. 249/66*b*	*from* × 2
No. 267	*from* × 8
Nos. D1/5*c*	*from* × 4
Nos. D6/10	*from* × 15
Nos. D11/18	*from* × 20

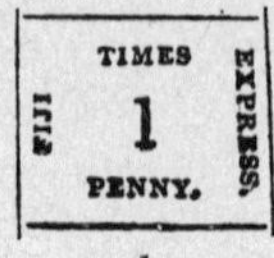

1

(Type-set and printed at the office of *The Fiji Times*, Levuka, Ovalau, Fiji)

1870 (1 Nov)–**71.** *Rouletted in the printing.* (*a*) *Quadrillé paper.*
1 1 1d. black/*rose* £2500 £2500
2 3d. black/*rose* £2250 £2500
3 6d. black/*rose* £2000 £2000
4 1s. black/*rose* £1500 £1800

(*b*) *Laid bâtonné paper* (1871)
5 1 1d. black/*rose* £750 £1400
6 3d. black/*rose* £1200 £1800
7 6d. black/*rose* £800 £1500
8 9d. black/*rose* £1300 £2000
9 1s. black/*rose* £800 £1000

Nos. 1/4 were printed *se-tenant* as a sheet of 24 (6 × 4) with the 6d. stamps in the first horizontal row, the 1s. in the second, the 1d. in the third and the 3d. in the fourth. Nos. 5/9 were produced from the same plate on which three of the 3d. impressions had been replaced with three 9d. values.

The issued stamps showed the vertical frame lines continuous from top to bottom of the sheet with the horizontal rules broken and not touching the verticals.

There are no reprints of these stamps, but the 1d., 3d., 6d. and 1s. are known in the correct type on *yellow wove* paper and are believed to be proofs.

There are also three different sets of imitations made by the proprietors of *The Fiji Times* to meet the demands of collectors:—

The first was produced in 1876 on *white wove* or *vertically laid* paper, rouletted on dotted lines and arranged in sheets of 40 (5 rows of 8) comprising 1d., 3d., 6d., 9d. and 1s.; the horizontal frame lines are continuous and the vertical ones broken.

The second was produced before 1888 on *thick rosy mauve wove* paper, rouletted on dotted lines and arranged in sheets of 30 (5 rows of 6) comprising 1s., 9d., 6d., 3d. and 1d.; the vertical frame lines are continuous and the horizontal ones broken.

The third only came to light in the 1960s and is rare, only one complete sheet being known. The sheet arrangement is the same as Nos. 1/4, which suggests that this was the first imitation to be produced. It is on *off-white wove* paper, rouletted on closely dotted or solid lines, with vertical frame lines continuous and the horizontal ones broken, as in the originals. These differ from the proofs mentioned above in that the lettering is slightly larger and the figures also differ.

The *Fiji Times* Express service ceased on 17 January 1872.

King Cakobau, June 1871–Oct 1874

2

3

Two

Cents

(4)

(Eng and electrotyped by A. L. Jackson. Typo Govt Printing Office, Sydney)

1871 (Oct). *Wove paper. Wmk* "FIJI POSTAGE" *in small sans-serif capitals across the middle row of stamps in the sheet. P* 12½.
10 **2** 1d. blue .. .. 80·00 £120
11 3d. pale yellow-green £150 £250
12 **3** 6d. rose £160 £275

The 3d. differs from T **2** in having a white circle containing square dots surrounding the centre.

All three values are known *imperf*, but were not issued in that condition.

See notes after No. 33b.

1872 (13 Jan). *Surch as T* **4**, *at Govt Ptg Office, Sydney.*
13 **2** 2 c. on 1d. pale blue .. .. 35·00 42·00
a. Deep blue .. .. 25·00 35·00
14 6 c. on 3d. yellow-green .. .. 50·00 50·00
15 **3** 12 c. on 6d. carmine-rose .. .. .. 70·00 70·00

CROWN COLONY

Ceded to Great Britain, 10 October 1874

V.R. (5) V.R. (6) 2d. (7)

Varieties:—

V.R. V.R.

(*Enlarged*)

Cross pattée stop Inverted "A"

Cross pattée stop after "R" (R. 3/6).
Round raised stop after "V" (R. 3/8).
Round raised stops after "V" and "R" (R. 3/9).
Inverted "A" for "V" (R. 3/10).
No stop after "R" (R. 2/3 on T **5**, R. 5/3 on T **6**).

(Optd at *Polynesian Gazette* Office, Levuka)

1874 (10 Oct). *Nos. 13/15 optd.* (*a*) *With T* **5**.
16 **2** 2 c. on 1d. blue £600 £170
a. No stop after "R" .. .. — £1000
b. Cross pattée stop after "R" .. .. .. — £1000
c. Round raised stop after "V" .. .. — £1000
d. Round raised stops after "V" and "R" — £1000
e. Inverted "A" for "V" .. .. .. — £1000
17 6 c. on 3d. green £900 £425
a. No stop after "R" .. ..
b. Cross pattée stop after "R" .. .. ..
c. Round raised stop after "V" .. ..
d. Round raised stops after "V" and "R"
e. Inverted "A" for "V" £2250
18 **3** 12 c. on 6d. rose £450 £160
a. No stop after "R" .. .. — £1000
b. Cross pattée stop after "R" .. .. .. — £1000
c. Round raised stop after "V" .. .. — £1000
d. Round raised stops after "V" and "R" — £1000
e. Inverted "A" for "V" .. .. .. — £1000
f. Opt inverted .. .. — £3250

(*b*) *With T* **6**
19 **2** 2 c. on 1d. blue £700 £180
a. No stop after "R" £1900 £1000
20 6 c. on 3d. green £1300 £625
a. No stop after "R" £2750
21 **3** 12 c. on 6d. rose £550 £170
a. No stop after "R" .. .. — £1000
b. Opt inverted £3750

Nos. 16/21 were produced in sheets of 50 (10 × 5) of which the top three rows were overprinted with Type **5** and the lower two with Type **6**.

1875. *Stamps of* 1874 *surch at* Polynesian Gazette *Office, Levuka, with T* 7.

(*a*) *In red* (May)

22 2 2d. on 6 c. on 3d. green (No. 17) £350 £120
a. No stop after "R" £1500 £650
b. Cross pattée stop after "R" £1500 £650
c. Round raised stop after "V" £1500 £650
d. Round raised stops after "V" and "R" £1500 £650
e. Inverted "A" for "V" £1500 £650
f. No stop after "2d" (R. 1/2) £1500 £650
23 2d. on 6 c. on 3d. green (No. 20) .. £450 £180
a. No stop after "R" £1500 £650
b. Stop between "2" and "d" (R. 5/7) £1500 £650

(*b*) *In black* (30 Sept)

24 2 2d. on 6 c. on 3d. green (No. 17) .. £850 £325
a. No stop after "R" £2500 £1200
b. Cross pattée stop after "R" .. £2500 £1200
c. Round raised stop after "V" .. £2500 £1200
d. Round raised stops after "V" and "R" £2500 £1200
e. Inverted "A" for "V" £2500 £1200
f. No stop after "2d" (R. 1/2) £2500 £1200
g. "V.R." double .. .. ..
25 2d. on 6 c. on 3d. green (No. 20) .. £1200 £450
a. No stop after "R" £2500 £1200
b. Stop between "2" and "d" (R. 5/7) .. £2500 £1200
c. "V.R." double .. .. .. — £3000

1875 (20 Nov). *No.* 15 *surch at* Polynesian Gazette *Office, Levuka, with T* 7 *and* "V.R." *at one operation.* (*a*) "V.R." *T* 5.

26 3 2d. on 12 c. on 6d. rose £850 £450
aa. Round raised stop after "R" .. ..
a. Inverted "A" for "V" (R. 1/3, 2/8, 4/4) £1100 £650
b. Do. and round raised stop after "V" (R. 3/3, 3/6, 3/8, 3/10) £1000 £600
c. As "a" and round raised stops after "R" and "V" (R. 3/2, 3/9) £1200 £700
d. Surch double .. .. .. — £2500

(*b*) "V.R." *T* 6

27 3 2d. on 12 c. on 6d. rose £850 £450
a. Surch double .. .. .. — £2750

The setting used for Nos. 26/7 was similar to that of Nos. 16/21, but the fourth stamp in the fourth row had a Type **5** "V.R." instead of a Type **6**.

The position of No. 26aa is not known.

Two Pence

(8) (9)

(Typo Govt Printing Office, Sydney, from plates of 1871)

1876–77. *On paper previously lithographed* "VR" *as T* 8, *the 3d. surch with T* 9. *P* 12½. (*a*) *Wove paper* (31.1.76).

28 2 1d. grey-blue .. .. 38·00 38·00
a. Dull blue .. .. 38·00 38·00
b. Doubly printed .. ..
c. Void corner .. .. ..
d. Imperf vert (horiz pair) ..
29 2d. on 3d. pale green .. .. .. 35·00 40·00
a. Deep green .. .. 35·00 40·00
30 3 6d. pale rose .. .. .. 60·00 55·00
a. Dull rose .. .. 48·00 45·00
b. Carmine-rose .. .. .. 55·00 45·00
c. Doubly printed .. .. ..

(*b*) *Laid paper* (5.1.77)

31 2 1d. blue .. .. 12·00 18·00
a. Deep blue .. .. 13·00 18·00
b. Void corner £225 £175
c. Imperf vert (horiz pair) .. £850
32 2d. on 3d. yellow-green .. .. 55·00 55·00
a. Deep yellow-green .. .. 55·00 55·00
b. Imperf between (pair) .. £850
c. Perf 10 .. .. .. £225
ca. Imperf vert (horiz pair) ..
d. Perf 11 .. .. .. £275
33 3 6d. rose .. .. 38·00 27·00
a. Carmine-rose .. .. .. 38·00 30·00
b. Imperf vert (horiz pair) .. £850

The 3d. *green* is known without the surcharge T **9** on wove paper and also without the surcharge and the monogram. In this latter condition it can only be distinguished from No. 11 by its colour, which is a fuller, deeper yellow-green.

Stamps on both wove and laid paper *imperf* are from printer's trial or waste sheets and were not issued.

All values are known on laid paper without the monogram "VR" and the 3d. stamp also without the surcharge but these are also believed to be from printer's trial sheets and were never issued. Being on laid paper they are easily distinguishable from Nos. 10/12.

1877 (12 Oct). *Optd with T* 8 *and surch as T* 9. *Laid paper. P* 12½.

34 2 4d. on 3d. mauve .. .. .. 55·00 30·00
a. Imperf vert (horiz pair) £850

10

11

A Four Pence
B Four Pence

Type A: Length 12½ mm
Type B: Length 14 mm
Note also the different shape of the two "e"s.

(Typo from new plates made from original dies of 1871 with "CR" altered to "VR" at Govt Printing Office, Sydney. 2d. and 4d. made from old 3d. die.)

1878–99. *Surcharges as T* 9 *or as Types* A *or* B *for 4d. value. Wove paper with paper-maker's name* "T. H. SAUNDERS" *or* "SANDERSON" *in double-lined capitals extending over seven stamps in each full sheet.* (*a*) *P* 12½ (1878–80).

35 10 1d. pale ultramarine (19.2.79) .. 3·50 4·00
a. Ultramarine .. .. .. 6·50 6·50
36 2d. on 3d. green (17.10.78) .. 4·00 7·00
37 2d. yellow-green (1.9.79) .. .. 9·50 8·00
a. Blue-green .. .. .. 13·00 11·00
b. Error. Ultramarine £18000
38 11 6d. rose (30.7.80) .. .. .. 75·00 12·00

(*b*) *P* 10 (1881–90)

39 10 1d. dull blue (11.5.82) .. .. .. 20·00 2·25
a. Ultramarine .. .. .. 6·00 2·00
b. Cambridge blue (12.7.83) .. .. 20·00 2·75
40 2d. yellow-green (20.10.81) .. .. 6·00 90
a. Blue-green .. .. .. 7·50 3·00
41 4d. on 1d. mauve (29.1.90) .. .. 15·00 9·00
42 4d. on 2d. pale mauve (A) (23.5.83) .. 45·00 9·00
a. Dull purple .. .. .. 45·00 9·00
43 4d. on 2d. dull purple (B) (7.11.88) .. — £110
44 4d. mauve (13.9.90) .. .. .. 40·00
a. Deep purple .. .. .. 40·00 45·00
45 11 6d. pale rose (11.3.85) .. .. .. 55·00 11·00
a. Bright rose .. .. .. 14·00 14·00

(*c*) *P* 10 × 12½ (1881–82)

46 10 1d. ultramarine (11.5.82) .. .. 50·00 24·00
47 2d. green (20.10.81) .. .. .. £150 35·00
48 11 6d. rose (20.10.81) .. .. .. £300 38·00

(*d*) *P* 12½ × 10 (1888–90)

49 10 1d. ultramarine (1890) .. .. ..
49*a* 2d. green (1888) .. .. ..

(*e*) *P* 10 × *nearly* 12 (3.9.86)

50 10 1d. ultramarine .. .. .. 48·00 6·50
51 2d. yellow-green .. .. .. 48·00 6·50

(*f*) *P nearly* 12 × 10 (1886–88)

51*a* 10 1d. dull blue (7.11.88) .. .. ..
51*b* 2d. yellow-green (3.9.86) .. ..
52 11 6d. rose (1887) .. ..

(*g*) *P* 11 × 10 (1892–93)

53 10 1d. ultramarine (18.8.92) .. .. 4·50 5·50
54 4d. pale mauve (18.8.92) .. .. 6·00 7·00
55 11 6d. pale rose (14.2.93) .. .. 6·50 9·50
a. Rose .. .. 9·50 11·00

(*h*) *P* 11 (1897–99)

56 10 4d. mauve (14.7.96) .. .. .. 7·00 6·00
57 11 6d. dull rose (14.7.96) .. .. 25·00 28·00
a. Printed both sides (12.99) .. £475 £425
b. Bright rose .. .. .. 32·00 14·00

(*i*) *P* 11 × *nearly* 12 (1896)*

58 10 4d. deep purple (14.7.96) .. .. 18·00
a. Bright purple .. .. .. 6·50 6·50
59 11 6d. rose (23.7.96) .. .. .. 28·00
a. Bright rose .. .. .. 6·00 4·50

(*j*) *Imperf* (1882–90)

60 10 1d. ultramarine .. .. ..
61 2d. yellow-green .. .. ..
62 4d. on 2d. pale mauve .. ..
63 11 6d. rose .. ..

*Under this heading are included stamps from several perforating machines with a gauge varying between 11·6 and 12.

Only four examples of No. 37b have been reported, one of which was subsequently destroyed.

In the absence of detailed information on dates of issue printing dates are quoted for Nos. 35/63 and 76/103.

12

13

(Typo Govt Printing Office, Sydney)

1881–99. *Paper-maker's name wmkd as previous issue.*

(*a*) *P* 10 (19.10.81)

64 12 1s. pale brown .. .. .. 35·00 11·00
a. Deep brown .. .. .. 35·00 13·00

(*b*) *P* 11 × 10 (1894)

65 12 1s. pale brown .. .. .. 35·00 28·00

(*c*) *P* 11 (1897)

66 12 1s. pale brown .. .. .. 27·00 14·00

(*d*) *P* 11 × *nearly* 12 (5.99)

67 12 1s. pale brown .. .. .. 23·00 8·50
a. Brown .. .. 23·00 8·50
b. Deep brown .. .. .. 30·00 35·00

(*e*) *P nearly* 12 × 11 (3.97)

68 12 1s. brown .. .. .. 35·00 30·00

Dates given of earliest known use.
Forgeries exist.

(Centre typo, frame litho Govt Printing Office, Sydney)

1882 (23 May). *Toned paper wmkd with paper-maker's name* "Cowan" *in old English outline type once in each sheet. P* 10.

69 13 5s. dull red and black .. .. 60·00 45·00

In July 1900, an electrotyped plate of a 5s. stamp was made and stamps were printed from it with pale orange-red centre and grey-black frame; these are known *perf* 10, *perf nearly* 12, and *imperf*. These stamps were sold as remainders with a special obliteration dated "15 Dec., 00," but were not issued for postal use. The design differs in many particulars from the issued stamp.

2½d. (14) 2½d. (15)

T 14. Fraction bar 1 mm from "2".
T 15. Fraction bar 2 mm from "2".

(Stamps typo in Sydney and surch at Govt Printing Office, Suva)

1891 (1 Jan). *T* 10 *surch. P* 10.

70 14 2½d. on 2d. green .. .. .. 48·00 48·00
71 15 2½d. on 2d. green £125 £125

½d. (16) 5d (17)

FIVE PENCE (18) 2 mm spacing
FIVE PENCE (19) 3 mm spacing

1892 (1 Mar)–**93.** *P* 10. (*a*) *Surch on T* 10.

72 16 ½d. on 1d. dull blue .. .. .. 42·00 55·00
a. Ultramarine .. .. .. 32·00 48·00
73 17 5d. on 4d. deep purple (25.7.92) .. 45·00 60·00
a. Dull purple .. .. .. 45·00 60·00

(*b*) *Surch on T* 11

74 18 5d. on 6d. brownish rose (30.11.92) .. 48·00 60·00
a. Bright rose .. .. .. 48·00 55·00
b. Perf 10 × 12½ .. .. ..
75 19 5d. on 6d. rose (4.1.93) .. .. 65·00
a. Deep rose .. .. .. 55·00
b. Brownish rose .. .. .. 55·00

20

21 Native Canoe

22

(Typo in Sydney)

1891–1902. *Wmk in sheet, either* "SANDERSON" *or* "NEW SOUTH WALES GOVERNMENT" *in outline capitals.*

(*a*) *P* 10 (1891–94)

76 20 ½d. slate-grey (26.4.92) .. .. 3·50 3·00
77 21 1d. black (19.9.94) .. .. .. 5·50 3·50
78 2d. pale green (19.9.94) .. .. 75·00 9·00
79 22 2½d. chocolate (8.6.91) .. .. 26·00 11·00
80 21 5d. ultramarine (14.2.93) .. .. 45·00 22·00

(*b*) *P* 11 × 10 (1892–93)

81 20 ½d. slate-grey (20.10.93) .. .. 4·00 10·00
82 21 1d. black (14.2.93) .. .. .. 4·75 2·50
83 2d. green (14.2.93) .. .. .. 6·00 3·25
84 22 2½d. chocolate (17.8.92) .. .. 18·00 13·00
a. Brown .. .. 7·00 6·50
b. Yellowish brown .. ..
85 21 5d. ultramarine (14.2.93) .. .. 7·00 7·50

(*c*) *P* 11 (1893–96)

86 20 ½d. slate-grey (2.6.96) .. .. 2·75 4·50
a. Greenish slate .. .. .. 2·50 5·50
87 21 1d. black (31.10.95) .. .. .. 2·50 2·50
88 1d. pale mauve (2.6.96) .. .. 3·00 1·00
a. Rosy mauve .. .. .. 3·00 1·00
89 2d. dull green (17.3.94) .. .. 4·75 80
a. Emerald-green .. .. .. 5·00 2·00
90 22 2½d. brown (31.10.95) .. .. 8·50 6·00
a. Yellowish brown .. .. .. 14·00 10·00
91 21 5d. ultramarine (14.2.93) £500

(*d*) *P* 10 × *nearly* 12 (1893–94)

93 21 1d. black (20.7.93) .. .. .. 9·00 4·75
94 2d. dull green (19.9.94) £400 £200

(*e*) *P nearly* 12 × 10 (19.9.94)

94*a* 20 ½d. pale grey .. .. ..

(*f*) *Perf nearly* 12 (1894–98)

95 20 ½d. greenish slate (19.9.94) .. .. 2·75 7·00
a. Grey .. .. 14·00
96 21 1d. black (19.9.94) .. .. .. £140 12·00
97 1d. rosy mauve (4.5.98) .. .. 4·50 3·75
98 2d. dull green (19.9.94) .. .. 60·00 23·00

(*g*) *P* 11 × *nearly* 12 (1895–97)

99 20 ½d. greenish slate (8.10.97) .. .. 1·00 2·50
100 21 1d. black (31.10.95) £200
101 1d. rosy mauve (14.7.96) .. .. 3·25 50
a. Pale rosy mauve .. .. .. 3·50 2·00
102 2d. dull green (26.7.97) .. .. 25·00 4·00
103 22 2½d. brown (26.7.97) .. .. 11·00 14·00
a. Yellow-brown .. .. .. 5·00 5·00

(*h*) *P nearly* 12 × 11 (1897–98)

103*b* 20 ½d. greenish slate (8.10.97) .. ..
103*c* 21 1d. rosy mauve (10.2.97) .. ..
103*d* 2d. dull green (4.5.98) .. ..

The 2½d. brown is known *doubly printed*, but only occurs in the remainders and with the special obliteration. It was never issued for postal use.

23

24

(Typo D.L.R.)

1903 (1 Feb). *Wmk Crown CA. P* 14.
104 **23** ½d. green and pale green .. .. 1·00 1·50
105 1d. dull purple and black/*red* .. .. 4·50 55
106 **24** 2d. dull purple and orange .. .. 1·00 1·25
107 **23** 2½d. dull purple and blue/*blue* .. .. 14·00 17·00
108 3d. dull purple and purple .. .. 1·25 4·00
109 **24** 4d. dull purple and black .. .. 1·25 2·50
110 **23** 5d. dull purple and green .. .. 1·25 5·00
111 **24** 6d. dull purple and carmine .. .. 1·50 2·50
112 **23** 1s. green and carmine .. .. 10·00 22·00
113 **24** 5s. green and black .. .. 23·00 48·00
114 **23** £1 grey-black and ultramarine .. £325 £350
104/14 .. .. *Set of* 11 £350 £375
104/14 Optd "Specimen" .. .. *Set of* 11 £375

1904–9. *Wmk Mult Crown CA. P* 14.
115 **23** ½d. green and pale green, **O** .. .. 4·75 1·50
116 1d. purple and black/*red*, **O** .. .. 7·50 10
117 1s. green and carmine, **C** (1909) .. 25·00 40·00
115/17 .. .. *Set of* 3 35·00 40·00

1906–12. *Colours changed. Wmk Mult Crown CA. P* 14.
118 **23** ½d. green, **O** (1908) .. .. .. 4·75 1·75
119 1d. red, **O** (1906) .. .. .. 1·75 10
120 2½d. bright blue, **O** (1910) .. .. 2·75 5·50
121 **24** 6d. dull purple, **C** (1910) .. .. 5·00 10·00
122 **23** 1s. black/*green*, **C** (1911) .. .. 4·00 10·00
123 **24** 5s. green and red/*yellow*, **C** (1911) .. 35·00 48·00
124 **23** £1 purple and black/*red*, **C** (1912) .. £325 £375
118/124 .. .. *Set of* 7 £350 £400
119/24 Optd "Specimen" .. .. *Set of* 6 £400

25 26 WAR STAMP (27)

(Typo D.L.R.)

1912 (Oct)–**23.** *Ordinary paper (¼d. to 4d.) or chalk-surfaced paper (others). Wmk Mult Crown CA. P* 14.
125 **26** ¼d. brown (1.4.16) 15 30
a. Deep brown 45 40
126 **25** ½d. green 40 50
a. Yellow-green (1915) .. .. 4·25 4·25
b. Blue-green (1917) .. .. .. 1·00 50
127 1d. carmine .. .. 1·90 10
a. Bright scarlet (1.16) .. .. 1·75 45
b. Deep rose (1919) .. .. .. 3·75 50
128 **26** 2d. greyish slate (5.14) 80 10
a. Wmk sideways .. .. ..
129 **25** 2½d. bright blue (5.14) .. .. 3·50 3·50
130 3d. purple/*yellow* (5.14) .. .. 2·75 3·50
a. Wmk sideways £550
b. On lemon (1915) .. .. .. 2·00 8·00
c. On pale yellow (Die I) .. .. 1·50 10·00
d. On pale yellow (Die II) (1923) .. 2·50 9·00
131 **26** 4d. black and red/*yellow* (5.14) .. 6·50 10·00
a. On lemon .. .. 5·00 13·00
b. On orange-buff (1.21) .. .. 35·00 55·00
c. On pale yellow (Die I) (1921) .. 7·50 14·00
d. On pale yellow (Die II) (1923) (Optd S. £35) .. .. .. 3·75 15·00
132 **25** 5d. dull purple and olive-green (5.14) 7·00 9·00
133 **26** 6d. dull and bright purple (5.14) .. 2·00 5·00
134 **25** 1s. black/*green* (10.13) .. .. 1·25 11·00
a. White back (4.14) .. .. .. 1·00 8·00
b. On blue-green, olive back (1917) .. 4·75 10·00
c. On emerald back (Die I) (1921) (Optd S. £35) .. .. .. 3·75 18·00
d. On emerald back (Die II) (1923) .. 3·50 14·00
135 **26** 2s. 6d. black and red/*blue* (29.1.16) .. 26·00 28·00
136 5s. green and red/*yellow* .. .. 26·00 40·00
137 **25** £1 purple and black/*red* (Die I) (5.14) £250 £275
a. Die II £250 £275
125/37a .. .. .. *Set of* 13 £275 £325
125/37 Optd "Specimen" .. *Set of* 13 £475

1915 (Dec)–**19.** *Optd locally with T* **27**.
138 **25** ½d. blue-green .. .. 20 1·50
a. Yellow-green .. .. 25 2·00
b. Opt inverted £500
c. Opt double .. ..
139 1d. carmine .. .. 15·00 20·00
a. Bright scarlet 60 75
ab. Horiz pair, one without opt .. £6500
c. Opt inverted £650
d. Deep rose (1919) .. .. .. 1·25 1·40
138/9 H/S "Specimen" .. .. *Set of* 2 £100

No. 139ab occurred on one pane of 120 only, the overprint being so misplaced that all the stamps of the last vertical row escaped it entirely.

Nos. 140/227 no longer used.

1922–27. *Wmk Mult Script CA. P* 14.
228 **26** ¼d. deep brown, **O** (1923) .. .. 1·75 9·00
229 **25** ½d. green, **O** (1923) .. .. .. 40 1·25
230 1d. carmine-red, **O** .. .. .. 2·50 2·00
231 1d. violet, **O** (1927) 90 10
232 **26** 1½d. scarlet, **O** (1927) .. .. .. 3·75 3·25
233 2d. grey, **O** 80 10
a. Face value omitted .. .. ..
234 **25** 3d. bright blue, **O** (1924) .. .. 90 1·25
235 **26** 4d. black and red/*lemon*, **O** (1924) .. 5·00 7·00
a. On orange-buff (1927) .. .. 12·00 18·00
236 **25** 5d. dull purple and sage-green, **O** .. 1·50 2·00
237 **26** 6d. dull and bright purple, **O** .. .. 1·75 1·25
238 **25** 1s. black/*emerald*, **C** (1924) .. .. 2·50 6·00
239 **26** 2s. purple and blue/*blue*, **C** (1927) .. 23·00 45·00
240 2s. 6d. black and red/*blue*, **C** (1925) .. 10·00 32·00
241 5s. green and red/*yellow*, **C** (1926) .. 25·00 48·00
228/241 .. .. *Set of* 14 70·00 £140
228/41 Optd "Specimen" .. *Set of* 14 £300

The 2d. imperforate with watermark Type **10** of Ireland came from a trial printing and was not issued.

Only one example of No. 233a is known. It was caused by an obstruction during the printing of the duty plate.

1935 (6 May). *Silver Jubilee. As Nos.* 91/4 *of Antigua.*
242 1½d. deep blue and carmine.. .. .. 45 1·75
a. Deep blue and aniline red .. .. 2·75 7·00
f. Diagonal line by turret .. .. 18·00
h. Dot by flagstaff.. .. .. .. 18·00
243 2d. ultramarine and grey 80 35
f. Diagonal line by turret .. .. 25·00
g. Dot to left of chapel .. .. .. 25·00
244 3d. brown and deep blue .. .. .. 2·25 2·50
245 1s. slate and purple .. .. .. 4·50 3·50
242/5 .. .. *Set of* 4 7·25 7·00
242/5 Perf "Specimen" .. .. *Set of* 4 75·00

For illustrations of plate varieties see Omnibus section following Zululand.

1937 (12 May). *Coronation. As Nos.* 13/15 *of Aden, but ptd by B.W. P* 11 × 11½.
246 1d. purple 70 45
247 2d. grey-black 80 45
248 3d. Prussian blue 80 45
246/8 .. .. *Set of* 3 2·10 1·25
246/8 Perf "Specimen" .. .. *Set of* 3 55·00

28 Native sailing Canoe

29 Native Village

30 Camakua (canoe)

31 Map of Fiji Islands

Two Dies of Type **30**:

Die I Empty Canoe — Die II Native in Canoe

Two Dies of Type **31**:

Die I Without "180°"

Die II With "180°"

Extra palm frond (R. 5/8)

Spur on arms medallion (Pl 2 R. 4/2) (ptg of 26 Nov 1945)

(Des V. E. Ousey (½d., 1s., 2s. 6d.), Miss C. D. Lovejoy (1d., 1½d., 5d.), Miss I. Stinson (3d., 5s.) and A. V. Guy (2d. (Nos. 253/4), 2½d., 6d., 2s.). Recess De La Rue (½d., 1½d., 2d., (Nos. 253/5a), 2½d., 6d., 8d., 1s. 5d., 1s. 6d.), Waterlow (others))

1938 (5 Apr)–**1955.** *T* **28/31** *and similar designs. Wmk Mult Script CA. Various perfs.*
249 **28** ½d. green (*p* 13½) 10 20
a. Perf 14 (10.41) .. .. .. 12·00 3·50
b. Perf 12 (8.48) 15 30
ba. Extra palm frond .. .. .. 4·00
250 **29** 1d. brown and blue (*p* 12½) 10 10
251 **30** 1½d. carmine (Die I) (*p* 13½) .. .. 7·50 35
252 1½d. carmine (Die II) (*p* 13½) (1.10.40) 40 65
a. Deep carmine (10.42) .. .. 4·00 3·25
b. Perf 14 (6.42) .. .. .. 8·50 16·00
c. Perf 12 (21.7.49) .. .. .. 90 1·25
253 **31** 2d. brown and green (Die I) (*p* 13½) 25·00 25
254 2d. brn & grn (Die II) (*p* 13½) (1.10.40) 11·00 14·00
255 – 2d. green & magenta (*p* 13½) (19.5.42) 40 25
a. Perf 12 (27.5.46) 55 20
256 **31** 2½d. brown & grn (Die II) (*p* 14) (6.1.42) 50 20
a. Perf 13½ (1.44) 40 20
b. Perf 12 (19.1.48) 70 50
257 – 3d. blue (*p* 12½) 45 15
a. Spur on arms medallion .. .. 50·00
258 – 5d. blue and scarlet (*p* 12½) .. .. 35·00 8·50
259 – 5d. yellow-grn & scar (*p* 12½) (1.10.40) 15 15
260 **31** 6d. black (Die I) (*p* 13×12) .. .. 60·00 9·00
261 6d. black (Die II) (*p* 13½) (1.10.40) .. 3·00 70
a. Violet-black (1.44) .. .. .. 25·00 20·00
b. Perf 12. *Black* (5.6.47) .. .. 1·25 40
261*c* – 8d. carmine (*p* 14) (15.11.48) 40 25
d. Perf 13 (7.6.50) .. .. .. 60 1·75
262 – 1s. black and yellow (*p* 12½) 30 20
263 – 1s. 5d. black & carmine (*p* 14) (13.6.40) 15 10
263*a* – 1s. 6d. ultramarine (*p* 14) (1.8.50) .. 1·75 80
b. Perf 13 (16.2.55) .. .. .. 1·25 14·00
264 – 2s. violet and orange (*p* 12½) 90 30
265 – 2s. 6d. green and brown (*p* 12½) .. 90 60
266 – 5s. green and purple (*p* 12½) .. .. 1·75 60
266*a* – 10s. orange & emer (*p* 12½) (13.3.50) 30·00 40·00
266*b* – £1 ultram & carm (*p* 12½) (13.3.50) 45·00 45·00
249/66*b* .. .. *Set of* 22 £200 £110
249/66 excl 261*c* and 263*a* Perf "Specimen" .. .. .. *Set of* 18 £450

Designs: *Horiz (as T* **30**)—2d. (Nos. 255/a) Government Offices. (*As T* **29**)—3d. Canoe and arms of Fiji; 8d., 1s. 5d., 1s. 6d. Arms of Fiji; 2s. Suva Harbour; 2s. 6d. River scene; 5s. Chief's hut. *Vert* (*as T* **29**)—5d. Sugar cane; 1s. Spearing fish by torchlight; 10s. Pawpaw Tree; £1 Police bugler.

2½d.

(42)

1941 (10 Feb). *No.* 254 *surch with T* **42** *by Govt Printer, Suva.*
267 **31** 2½d. on 2d. brown and green 25 10

1946 (17 Aug). *Victory. As Nos.* 28/9 *of Aden.*
268 2½d. green 10 10
a. Printed double, one albino £200
269 3d. blue 10 10
268/9 Perf "Specimen" .. .. *Set of* 2 60·00

1948 (17 Dec). *Royal Silver Wedding. As Nos.* 30/1 *of Aden.*
270 2½d. green 40 15
271 5s. violet-blue .. .. 14·00 5·00

1949 (10 Oct). *75th Anniv of U.P.U. As Nos.* 114/17 *of Antigua.*
272 2d. bright reddish purple 55 25
273 3d. deep blue 90 80
274 8d. carmine-red .. .. 90 1·00
275 1s. 6d. blue .. .. 1·10 1·00
272/5 .. .. *Set of* 4 3·00 2·75

43 Children Bathing

44 Rugby Football

(Recess B.W.)

1951 (17 Sept). *Health Stamps. Wmk Mult Script CA. P* 13½.
276 **43** 1d. + 1d. brown 10 20
277 **44** 2d. + 1d. green 10 20

1953 (2 June). *Coronation. As No.* 47 *of Aden.*
278 2½d. black and green 50 25

45 Arms of Fiji

(Recess D.L.R.)

1953 (16 Dec). *Royal Visit. Wmk Mult Script CA. P* 13.
279 **45** 8d. deep carmine-red 15 10

MINIMUM PRICE

The minimum price quote is 10p which represents a handling charge rather than a basis for valuing common stamps. For further notes about prices see introductory pages.

46 Queen Elizabeth II (after Annigoni) **47** Government Offices

48 Loading Copra **49** Sugar Cane Train

50 Preparing Bananas for Export **51** Gold Industry

(Des V. E. Ousey (½d., 1s., 2s. 6d.), A. V. Guy (6d.). Recess D.L.R. (½d., 2d., 6d., 8d.), Waterlow (1s., 2s. 6d., 10s., £1) B.W. (others))

1954 (1 Feb)–**59**. *T* **46/51** *and similar designs previously used for King George VI issue (but with portrait of Queen Elizabeth II as in T* **47**). *Wmk Mult Script CA. P* 12 (2*d.*), 13 (8*d.*), 12½ (6*d.*, 1*s.*, 2*s.* 6*d.*, 10*s.*, £1), 11½×11 (3*d.*, 1*s.* 6*d.*, 2*s.*, 5*s.*) *or* 11½ (½*d.*, 1*d.*, 1½*d.*, 2½*d.*).

280 – ½d. myrtle-green (1.7.54) 10 15
281 **46** 1d. turquoise-blue (1.6.56) 15 10
282 1½d. sepia (1.10.56) 25 10
283 **47** 2d. green and magenta .. .. 1·00 30
284 **46** 2½d. blue-violet (1.10.56) 70 10
285 **48** 3d. brown and reddish violet (1.10.56) 70 10
a. *Brown & dp reddish vio* (10.11.59) 1·75 10
287 – 6d. black (1.7.54) 75 15
288 – 8d. deep carmine-red (1.7.54) .. .. 1·00 65
a. *Carmine-lake* (6.3.58) .. .. 1·75 90
289 – 1s. black and yellow 70 10
290 **49** 1s. 6d. blue and myrtle-green (1.10.56) 14·00 90
291 **50** 2s. black and carmine (1.10.56) .. 5·50 20
292 – 2s. 6d. bluish green and brown .. 60 10
a. *Bluish green & red-brown* (14.9.54) 45 10
293 **51** 5s. ochre and blue (1.10.56) .. .. 20·00 80
294 – 10s. orange and emerald (1.7.54) .. 10·00 20·00
295 – £1 ultramarine and carmine (1.7.54) 42·00 17·00
280/95 .. .. *Set of* 15 85·00 38·00

Designs: *Vert* (22½ × 36 *mm*)—½d. Fijians sailing canoe. (25 × 31 *mm*)—1s. Spearing fish by torchlight; 10s. Paw-paw tree; £1 Police bugler. *Horiz* (36 × 22½ *mm*)—6d. Map of Fiji. (31 × 25 *mm*)—8d. Arms of Fiji; 2s. 6d. River scene.

52 River Scene

53 Cross of Lorraine

(Recess B.W.)

1954 (1 Apr). *Health Stamps. Wmk Mult Script CA. P* 11 × 11½.

296 **52** 1½d. + ½d. bistre-brown and green .. 10 15
297 **53** 2½d. + ½d. orange and black 10 10

54 Queen Elizabeth II (after Annigoni) **55** Fijian beating Lali

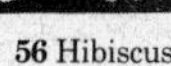

56 Hibiscus **60** Red Shining Parrot

(Des M. Goaman: Photo Harrison (8d., 4s.). Recess. B.W. (others))

1959–63. *T* **54/6**, **60** *and similar designs. Wmk Mult Script CA. P* 11½ (*T* **46** *and* **54**), 11½ × 11 (6*d.*, 10*d.*, 1*s.*, 2*s.* 6*d.*, 10*s.*, £1), 14½ × 14 (8*d.*) *or* 14 × 14½ (4*s*).

298 **46** ½d. emerald-green (14.11.61) 15 25
299 **54** 1d. deep ultramarine (3.12.62) 90 60
300 1½d. sepia (3.12.62) 90 25
301 **46** 2d. rose-red (14.11.61) 50 25
302 2½d. orange-brown (3.12.62) .. .. 1·25 1·50
303 **55** 6d. carmine and black (14.11.61) .. 1·00 10
304 **56** 8d. scarlet, yellow, green & blk (1.8.61) 40 25
305 – 10d. brown and carmine (1.4.63) .. 2·25 50
306 – 1s. light blue and blue (14.11.61) .. 1·50 10
307 – 2s. 6d. black and purple (14.11.61) .. 11·00 10
308 **60** 4s. red, green, blue & slate-grn (13.7.59) 1·75 1·75
309 – 10s. emerald and deep sepia (14.11.61) .. 7·50 3·50
310 – £1 black and orange (14.11.61) .. 25·00 7·00
298/310 .. .. *Set of* 13 48·00 14·00

Designs: *Horiz* (*as T* **55**)—10d. Yaqona ceremony; 1s. Location map; 2s. 6d. Nadi Airport; 10s. Cutting sugar-cane; £1 Arms of Fiji.

Nos. 299 and 311 have turtles either side of "Fiji" instead of shells.

63 Queen Elizabeth II **64** International Dateline

65 White Orchid **66** Orange Dove

(Des M. Goaman. Photo Harrison (3d., 9d. 1s. 6d., 2s., 4s., 5s.). Recess B.W. (others))

1962 (3 Dec)–**67**. *W w* **12** (*upright*). *P* 11½ (1*d.*, 2*d.*), 12½ (3*d.*), 11½×11 (6*d.*, 10*d.*, 2*s.* 6*d.*, 10*s.*, £1), 14½×14 (9*d.*, 2*s.*) *or* 14×14½ (1*s.* 6*d.*, 4*s.*, 5*s.*).

311 **54** 1d. deep ultramarine (14.1.64) 70 90
312 **46** 2d. rose-red (3.8.65) 45 15
313 **63** 3d. multicoloured 25 10
314 **55** 6d. carmine and black (9.6.64) .. 1·75 10
315 **56** 9d. scarlet, yellow, grn & ultram (1.4.63) 90 65
316 – 10d. brown and carmine (14.1.64) .. 60 40
317 – 1s. light blue and blue (24.1.66*) .. 2·00 30
318 **64** 1s. 6d. red, yellow, gold, black & blue .. 3·50 90
a. Error. Wmk sideways .. £550
319 **65** 2s. yellow-green, green & copper .. 12·00 1·75
a. *Apple-green, grn & copper* (16.5.67) 15·00 3·00
320 – 2s. 6d. black and purple (3.8.65) .. 75 25
a. *Black and deep purple* (8.67) .. 1·00 30
321 **60** 4s. red, yellow-green, bl & grn (1.4.64) 4·00 3·50
322 4s. red, green, blue & slate-grn (1.3.66) 2·25 4·00
323 **66** 5s. red, yellow and grey .. .. 12·00 35
324 – 10s. emerald and deep sepia (14.1.64) .. 7·00 6·00
325 – £1 black and orange (9.6.64) .. 16·00 11·00
311/25 .. .. .. *Set of* 15 55·00 27·00

Designs: *Horiz* (*as T* **55**)—10d. Yaqona Ceremony; 1s. Location map; 2s. 6d. Nadi Airport; 10s. Cutting sugar-cane; £1 Arms of Fiji.

*This is the earliest known used date in Fiji and it was not released by the Crown Agents until 1 November.

The 3d. value exists with PVA gum as well as gum arabic.

For 4s. with watermark sideways see No. 359.

ROYAL VISIT
1963
(67)

ROYAL VISIT 1963
(68)

1963 (1 Feb). *Royal Visit. Nos.* 313 *and* 306 *optd with T* **67/8**.

326 **67** 3d. multicoloured 10 10
327 **68** 1s. light blue and blue 10 10

1963 (4 June). *Freedom from Hunger. As No.* 76 *of Aden.*

328 2s. ultramarine .. .. 4·75 70

69 Running (**73** C.S. *Retriever*.)

(Des M. Goaman. Photo Harrison)

1963 (6 Aug). *First South Pacific Games, Suva. T* **69** *and similar designs. W w* **12**. *P* 14½.

329 3d. red-brown, yellow and black 20 10
330 9d. red-brown, violet and black 30 20
331 1s. red-brown, green and black 30 10
332 2s. 6d. red-brown, light blue and black .. 80 35
329/32 .. .. .. *Set of* 4 1·40 60

Designs: *Vert*—9d. Throwing the discus; 1s. Hockey. *Horiz*—2s. 6d. High-jumping.

1963 (2 Sept). *Red Cross Centenary. As Nos.* 147/8 *of Antigua.*

333 2d. red and black 50 10
334 2s. red and blue .. .. 2·50 60

1963 (3 Dec). *Opening of COMPAC (Trans-Pacific Telephone Cable). No.* 317 *optd with T* **73** *by B.W.*

335 1s. light blue and blue 25 10

74 Jamborette Emblem **75** Scouts of Three Races

(Des V. Whiteley assisted by Norman L. Joe, Asst. D.C., Fiji Scouts for Jamboree emblem. Photo Harrison)

1964 (4 Aug). 50*th Anniv of Fijian Scout Movement. W w* **12**. *P* 12½.

336 **74** 3d. multicoloured 10 10
337 **75** 1s. violet and yellow-brown 10 10

76 Flying-boat *Aotearoa* **78** *Aotearoa* and Map

(Des V. Whiteley. Photo Harrison)

1964 (24 Oct). 25*th Anniv of First Fiji-Tonga Airmail Service. T* **76**, **78** *and similar design. W w* **12**. *P* 14½ × 14 (1*s.*) *or* 12½ (*others*).

338 3d. black and vermilion 15 10
339 6d. vermilion and bright blue 25 10
340 1s. black and turquoise-blue 30 10
338/40 .. .. .. *Set of* 3 65 25

Design: *Vert* (*as T* **76**)—6d. Fiji Airways "Heron".

1965 (17 May). *I.T.U. Centenary. As Nos.* 166/7 *of Antigua.*

341 3d. blue and rose-carmine 50 10
342 2s. orange-yellow and bistre .. .. 1·25 25

1965 (25 Oct). *International Co-operation Year. As Nos.* 168/9 *of Antigua.*

343 2d. reddish purple and turquoise-green .. 30 10
344 2s. 6d. deep bluish green and lavender .. 70 25

1966 (24 Jan). *Churchill Commemoration. As Nos.* 170/3 *of Antigua.*

345 3d. new blue 70 10
346 9d. deep green 90 40
347 1s. brown 90 10
348 2s. 6d. bluish violet .. .. .. 1·00 50
345/8 .. .. *Set of* 4 3·25 1·00

1966 (1 July). *World Cup Football Championships. As Nos.* 176/7 *of Antigua.*

349 2d. violet, yellow-green, lake & yellow-brn .. 20 10
350 2s. chocolate, blue-green, lake & yellow-brn 50 15

79 H.M.S. *Pandora* approaching Split Island, Rotuma

(Des V. Whiteley. Photo Enschedé)

1966 (29 Aug). 175*th Anniv of Discovery of Rotuma. T* **79** *and similar horiz designs. Multicoloured. W w* **12** (*sideways*). *P* 14 × 13.

351 3d. Type **79** 15 10
352 10d. Rotuma Chiefs 15 10
353 1s. 6d. Rotumans welcoming H.M.S. *Pandora* 25 10
351/3 .. .. *Set of* 3 50 15

1966 (20 Sept). *Inauguration of W.H.O. Headquarters, Geneva. As Nos.* 178/9 *of Antigua.*

354 6d. black, yellow-green and light blue .. 1·00 20
355 2s. 6d. black, light purple and yellow-brown 2·50 55

LEGISLATIVE ASSEMBLY

82 Running

(Des V. Whiteley. Photo Harrison)

1966 (5 Dec*). *2nd South Pacific Games, Nouméa. T* **82** *and similar designs. W* w **12** *(sideways on 9d.). P* 14½ × 14 *(9d.) or* 14 × 14½ *(others).*

356 3d. black, chestnut and yellow-olive .. 10 10
357 9d. black, chestnut and greenish blue .. 10 10
358 1s. multicoloured 10 10
356/8 .. .. *Set of* 3 15 15

Designs: *Vert*—9d. Putting the shot. *Horiz*—1s. Diving.
*These were not released in London until 8.12.66.

1967 (16 Feb). *As No.* 321 *but wmk* w **12** *sideways.*
359 **60** 4s. red, yellow-green, blue and green .. 3·25 1·25

85 Military Forces Band

(Des G. Vasarhelyi. Photo Enschedé)

1967 (20 Oct). *International Tourist Year. T* **85** *and similar horiz designs. Multicoloured. W* w **12** *(sideways). P* 14 × 13.

360 3d. Type **85** 10 10
361 9d. Reef diving 10 10
362 1s. Beqa fire walkers 10 10
363 2s. *Oriana* (cruise liner) at Suva 40 10
360/3 .. .. *Set of* 4 60 20

89 Bligh (bust), H.M.S. *Providence* and Chart

91 Bligh's Tomb

90 "*Bounty*'s longboat being chased in Fiji waters"

(Des V. Whiteley. Photo Harrison)

1967 (11 Dec). *150th Death Anniv of Admiral Bligh. W* w **12** *(sideways on 1s.). P* 12½ × 13 *(1s.) or* 15 × 14 *(others).*

364 **89** 4d. multicoloured 10 10
365 **90** 1s. multicoloured 10 10
366 **91** 2s. 6d. multicoloured 15 10
364/6 .. .. *Set of* 3 30 15

92 Simmonds "Spartan" Seaplane

(Des V. Whiteley. Photo Harrison)

1968 (5 June). *40th Anniv of Kingsford Smith's Pacific Flight via Fiji. T* **92** *and similar horiz designs. W* w **12**. *P* 14 × 14½.

367 2d. black and green 10 10
368 6d. greenish blue, black and lake 10 10
369 1s. deep violet and turquoise-green 15 10
370 2s. orange-brown and blue 20 10
367/70 .. .. *Set of* 4 50 20

Designs—6d. H.S. "748" and airline insignias; 1s. *Southern Cross* and crew; 2s. Lockheed "Altair" monoplane.

96 Bure Huts

97 Eastern Reef Heron (after Belcher)

98 Sea Snake

99 Queen Elizabeth and Arms of Fiji

(Des G. Hamori (½d., 1d., 9d.), W. O. Cernohorsky (2d., 4s.) H. S. Robinson (4d., 10d.), D. W. Blair (6d., 5s.), P. D. Clarke (1s.), G. Vasarhelyi (2s. 6d.), W. O. Cernohorsky and E. Jones (3s.), E. Jones and G. Hamori (10s.), E. Jones (£1). Adapted V. Whiteley. Photo D.L.R.)

1968 (15 July). *T* **96/9** *and similar designs. W* w **12** *(sideways on all vert designs). P* 14 × 13½ *(2s., 2s. 6d., 5s., £1),* 13½ × 14 *(3d., 1s., 1s. 6d., 4s., 10s.) or* 13½ × 13 *(others).*

371 ½d. multicoloured 10 10
372 1d. deep greenish blue, red and yellow .. 10 10
373 2d. new blue, brown and ochre 10 10
374 3d. blackish green, blue and ochre 35 10
375 4d. multicoloured 70 10
376 6d. multicoloured 25 10
377 9d. multicoloured 15 15
378 10d. royal blue, orange and blackish brown .. 1·00 15
379 1s. Prussian blue and brown-red 20 10
380 1s. 6d. multicoloured .. .. .. 3·50 3·00
381 2s. turquoise, black and rosine .. .. 1·00 2·00
382 2s. 6d. multicoloured .. .. .. 1·00 75
383 3s. multicoloured .. .. 3·50 5·00
384 4s. yellow-ochre, black and olive .. .. 3·50 2·75
385 5s. multicoloured .. .. 3·50 2·50
386 10s. lake-brown, black and ochre .. .. 3·50 3·50
387 £1 multicoloured .. .. 3·50 7·50
371/87 .. .. *Set of* 17 20·00 25·00

Designs: *Horiz (as T* **96**)—1d. Passion Flowers; 2d. Pearly Nautilus; 4d. Hawk Moth; 6d. Angel Fish; 9d. Bamboo raft; 10d. Tiger Moth; 3s. Golden Cowrie Shell. *Vert (as T* **97**)—1s. Black Marlin; 1s. 6d. Orange-breasted Honeyeaters (after Belcher); 4s. Mining industry; 10s. Ceremonial Whale's Tooth. *Horiz as T* **98**—2s. 6d. Outrigger canoes; 5s. Bamboo Orchids.

113 Map of Fiji, W.H.O. Emblem and Nurses

(Des V. Whiteley. Litho D.L.R.)

1968 (9 Dec). *20th Anniv of World Health Organization. T* **113** *and similar horiz designs. Multicoloured. W* w **12** *(sideways). P* 14.

388 3d. Type **113** 10 10
389 9d. Transferring patient to Medical Ship *Vuniwai* 10 10
390 3s. Recreation 20 20
388/90 .. .. *Set of* 3 30 30

(New Currency. 100 cents = 1 dollar.)

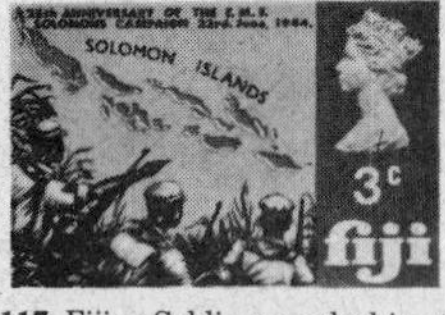

116 Passion Flowers

117 Fijian Soldiers overlooking the Solomon Islands

1969 (13 Jan)–**70**. *Decimal Currency. Designs as Nos.* 371/87, *but with values inscr in decimal currency as T* **116**. *W* w **12** *(sideways on vert designs) Chalk-surfaced paper. P* 14 × 13½ *(20, 25, 50 c. $2)* 13½ × 14 *(3, 10, 15, 40 c., $1) or* 13½ × 13 *(others).*

391 **116** 1 c. deep greenish blue, red and yellow .. 10 10
392 – 2 c. new blue, brown and ochre (as 2d.) .. 10 10
393 **97** 3 c. blackish green, blue and ochre .. 25 10
394 – 4 c. multicoloured (as 4d.) .. .. 1·25 10
395 – 5 c. multicoloured (as 6d.) 20 10
396 **96** 6 c. multicoloured 10 10
397 – 8 c. multicoloured (as 9d.) 10 10
398 – 9 c. royal blue, orange and blackish brown (as 10d.) .. .. .. 1·25 60
399 – 10 c. Prussian blue and brown-red (as 1s.) 20 10
400 – 15 c. multicoloured (as 1s. 6d.) .. .. 6·00 2·75
401 **98** 20 c. turquoise, black and rosine 75 80
402 – 25 c. multicoloured (as 2s. 6d.) 75 25
403 – 30 c. multicoloured (as 3s.) .. .. 6·00 2·25
404 – 40 c. yellow-ochre, black and olive (as 4s.) 4·00 3·25
405 – 50 c. multicoloured (as 5s.) .. .. 4·00 25
a. Glazed, ordinary paper (3.9.70) .. 5·50 1·50
406 – $1 lake-brown, black and ochre (as 10s.) 4·00 60
a. Glazed, ordinary paper (3.9.70) .. 5·50 3·50
407 **99** $2 multicoloured .. .. .. 4·00 5·00
391/407 .. .. *Set of* 17 24·00 14·00

(Des G. Drummond. Photo Harrison)

1969 (23 June). *25th Anniv of Fijian Military Forces' Solomons Campaign. T* **117** *and similar horiz designs. W* w **12**. *P* 14.

408 3 c. yellow-brown, black and bright emerald 15 10
409 10 c. multicoloured 20 10
410 25 c. multicoloured 30 20
408/10 .. .. *Set of* 3 60 30

Designs:—10 c. Regimental Flags and Soldiers in full dress and battledress; 25 c. Cpl. Sefanaia Sukanaivalu and Victoria Cross.

120 Javelin Thrower

123 Map of South Pacific and "Mortar-board"

(Des L. Curtis. Photo Harrison)

1969 (18 Aug). *3rd South Pacific Games, Port Moresby. T* **120** *and similar vert designs. W* w **12** *(sideways). P* 14½ × 14.

411 4 c. black, brown and vermilion 10 10
412 8 c. black, grey and new blue 10 10
413 20 c. multicoloured 15 10
411/13 .. .. *Set of* 3 25 10

Designs:—8 c. Yachting; 20 c. Games medal and winners' rostrum.

(Des G. Drummond. Photo Harrison)

1969 (10 Nov). *Inauguration of University of the South Pacific. T* **123** *and similar horiz designs. Multicoloured. W* w **12**. *P* 14 × 15.

414 2 c. Type **123** 10 10
415 8 c. R.N.Z.A.F. badge and "Sunderland" flying-boat over Laucala Bay (site of University) 15 10
416 25 c. Science students at work 25 10
414/16 .. .. *Set of* 3 45 15

ROYAL VISIT
1970

(126)

127 Chaulmugra Tree, Makogai

1970 (4 Mar). *Royal Visit. Nos.* 392, 399 *and* 402 *optd with T* **126**.

417 2 c. new blue, brown and ochre 10 15
418 10 c. Prussian blue and brown-red 10 10
419 25 c. multicoloured 20 10
417/19 .. .. *Set of* 3 35 25

(Des G. Drummond. Photo Harrison)

1970 (25 May). *Closing of Leprosy Hospital, Makogai. T* **127** *and similar designs. W* w **12** *(sideways on* 10 *c.). P* 14 × 14½.

420 2 c. multicoloured 10 10
421 10 c. pale turquoise-green and black 10 10
a. Pair. Nos. 421/2 .. .. 15 20
422 10 c. turquoise-blue, black and magenta .. 10 10
423 30 c. multicoloured 20 40
420/3 .. .. *Set of* 4 35 60

Designs: *Vert*—No. 421, "Cascade" (Semisi Maya); No. 422, "Sea Urchins" (Semisi Maya). *Horiz*—No. 423, Makogai Hospital.
Nos. 421/2 were printed together *se-tenant* throughout the sheet.

131 Abel Tasman and Log, 1643

(Des V. Whiteley. Litho D.L.R.)

1970 (18 Aug). *Explorers and Discoverers. T* **131** *and similar horiz designs. W* w **12** *(sideways). P* 13 × 12½.

424 2 c. black, brown and turquoise 40 25
425 3 c. multicoloured .. .. 1·00 25
426 8 c. multicoloured .. .. 1·00 15
427 25 c. multicoloured .. .. 1·00 15
424/7 .. .. *Set of* 4 3·00 70

Designs:—3 c. Captain Cook and H.M.S. *Endeavour*, 1774; 8 c. Captain Bligh and longboat, 1789; 25 c. Fijian and ocean-going canoe.

INDEPENDENT

135 King Cakobau and Cession Stone

139 1d. and 6d. Stamps of 1870

(Des J.W. Litho Format)

1970 (10 Oct). *Independence. T* **135** *and similar horiz designs. Multicoloured. W* w **12** *(sideways). P* 14.

428 2 c. Type **135** 10 10
429 3 c. Children of the World 10 10
430 10 c. Prime Minister and Fijian flag 10 10
431 25 c. Dancers in costume 20 20
428/31 .. .. *Set of* 4 30 25

The design for the 10 c. value does not incorporate the Queen's head profile.

(Des V. Whiteley. Photo Harrison)

1970 (2 Nov). *Stamp Centenary. T* **139** *and similar horiz designs. Multicoloured. W w* **12** *(sideways on 15 c.). P* 14½ × 14.
432 4 c. Type **139** 10 10
433 15 c. Fijian Stamps of all Reigns 15 15
434 20 c. *Fiji Times* Office and modern G.P.O. .. 15 15
432/4 .. .. *Set of* 3 35 35
The 15 c. is larger, 61 × 21 mm.

140 Grey-backed White Eye

141 Masked Shining Parrot

(Des G. Drummond. Litho Questa)

1971 (6 Aug)–**72**. *Birds and Flowers. Vert designs as T* **140/1**. *Multicoloured. W w* **12** *(upright).*

(a) Size as T **140**. *P* 13½ × 14
435 1 c. *Cirrhopetalum umbellatum* (4.1.72) .. 10 20
436 2 c. Cardinal Honeyeater (22.11.71) 10 10
437 3 c. *Calanthe furcata* (23.6.72) 25 20
438 4 c. *Bulbophyllum sp nov* (23.6.72) 25 20
439 5 c. Type **140** 25 10
440 6 c. *Phaius tancarvilliae* (23.6.72) .. .. 1·75 60
441 8 c. Blue-headed Flycatcher (22.11.71) .. 35 10
442 10 c. *Acanthephippium vitiense* (4.1.72) .. 40 10
443 15 c. *Dendrobium tokai* (23.6.72) .. .. 2·75 90
444 20 c. Slaty Flycatcher 90 30

(b) Size as T **141**. *P* 14
445 25 c. Yellow-faced Honeyeater (22.11.71) .. 1·00 20
446 30 c. *Dendrobium gordonii* (4.1.72) .. .. 4·50 90
447 40 c. Type **141** .. .. 2·75 50
448 50 c. White-throated Pigeon .. .. 2·75 50
449 $1 Collared Lory (22.11.71) .. .. 4·00 1·25
450 $2 *Dendrobium platygastrium* (4.1.72) .. 6·50 11·00
435/50 .. .. *Set of* 16 26·00 15·00
See also Nos. 459/73 and 505/20.

142 Women's Basketball

143 Community Education

(Des R. Granger Barrett. Litho Questa)

1971 (6 Sept). *Fourth South Pacific Games, Tahiti. T* **142** *and similar vert designs. W w* **12**. *P* 14.
451 8 c. multicoloured 10 10
452 10 c. cobalt, black and brown 10 10
453 25 c. pale turquoise-green, black and brown .. 30 25
451/3 .. .. *Set of* 3 45 30
Designs:—10c. Running; 25 c. Weightlifting.

(Des V. Whiteley. Litho Questa)

1972 (7 Feb). *25th Anniv of South Pacific Commission. T* **143** *and similar vert designs. Multicoloured. W w* **12**. *P* 14.
454 2 c. Type **143** 10 10
455 4 c. Public Health 10 10
456 50 c. Economic Growth 35 65
454/6 .. .. *Set of* 3 40 70

144 "Native Canoe"

145 Flowers, Conch and Ceremonial Whale's Tooth

(Des locally and adapted by A. B. New. Litho Questa)

1972 (10 Apr). *South Pacific Festival of Arts, Suva. W w* **12**. *P* 14.
457 **144** 10 c. black, orange and new blue .. 10 10

1972 (17 Nov)–**74**. *As Nos. 436/41, 443/5 and 447/50 but W w* **12** *sideways.*
459 2 c. Cardinal Honey-eater (12.12.73) .. 25 3·00
460 3 c. *Calanthe furcata* (8.3.73) 70 45
461 4 c. *Bulbophyllum sp nov* (11.4.73) .. .. 2·50 45
462 5 c. Type **140** (8.3.73) .. .. .. 1·50 50
463 6 c. *Phaius tancarvilliae* (11.4.73) .. .. 3·50 1·00
464 8 c. Blue-crested Broadbill (11.4.73) .. 2·00 75
466 15 c. *Dendrobium tokai* (11.4.73) .. .. 3·00 2·00
467 20 c. Slaty Flycatcher .. .. 4·00 2·00
468 25 c. Kandavu Honey-eater (11.4.73) .. .. 1·50 1·40
470 40 c. Type **141** (15.3.74) .. .. .. 2·75 3·00
471 50 c. White-throated Pigeon (15.3.74) .. 2·75 3·00
472 $1 Collared Lory .. .. 4·50 6·00
473 $2 *Dendrobium platygastrium* .. .. 9·00 11·00
459/73 .. .. *Set of* 13 35·00 32·00

(Des (from photograph by D. Groves) and photo Harrison)

1972 (20 Nov). *Royal Silver Wedding. Multicoloured; background colour given. W w* **12**. *P* 14 × 14½.
474 10 c. slate-green 20 10
475 25 c. bright purple 30 10
a. Blue printing omitted* £150
*The omission of the blue colour results in the Duke's suit appearing brown instead of deep blue.

HURRICANE RELIEF +10c

(146)

147 Line Out

1972 (4 Dec). *Hurricane Relief. Nos. 400 and 403 surch as T* **146**, *by the Reserve Bank of Australia.*
476 15 c. + 5 c. multicoloured 10 15
477 30 c. + 10 c. multicoloured 10 15

(Des J.W. Litho Questa)

1973 (9 Mar). *Diamond Jubilee of Fiji Rugby Union. T* **147** *and similar vert designs. Multicoloured. W w* **12** *(sideways). P* 14.
478 2 c. Type **147** 15 10
479 8 c. Body tackle 25 10
480 25 c. Conversion 65 30
478/80 .. .. *Set of* 3 95 40

148 Forestry Development

149 Christmas

(Des J.W. from local ideas. Litho Questa)

1973 (23 July). *Development Projects. T* **148** *and similar horiz designs. Multicoloured. W w* **12**. *P* 14.
481 5 c. Type **148** 10 10
482 8 c. Rice irrigation scheme 10 10
483 10 c. Low income housing 10 10
484 25 c. Highway construction 15 20
481/4 .. .. *Set of* 4 35 25

(Des L. Curtis. Litho Questa)

1973 (26 Oct). *Festivals of Joy. T* **149** *and similar vert designs. Multicoloured. W w* **12** *(sideways). P* 14.
485 3 c. Type **149** 10 10
486 10 c. Diwali 10 10
487 20 c. Id-ul-Fitar 15 10
488 25 c. Chinese New Year 15 10
485/8 .. .. *Set of* 4 35 25

150 Athletics

151 Bowler

(Des G. Drummond. Litho Questa)

1974 (7 Jan). *Commonwealth Games, Christchurch. T* **150** *and similar vert designs. W w* **12** *(sideways). P* 14.
489 3 c. Type **150** 15 10
490 8 c. Boxing 15 10
491 50 c. Bowling 50 65
489/91 .. .. *Set of* 3 70 70

(Des Hon. P. Snow. Adapted J.W. Litho Questa)

1974 (21 Feb). *Cricket Centenary. T* **151** *and similar multicoloured designs. W w* **12** *(sideways on 3 and 25 c.). P* 14.
492 3 c. Type **151** 50 25
493 25 c. Batsman and wicketkeeper .. .. 1·75 35
494 40 c. Fielder *(horiz)* .. .. .. 2·50 90
492/4 .. .. *Set of* 3 4·25 1·40

152 Fijian Postman

(Des L. Curtis. Litho Format)

1974 (22 May). *Centenary of the Universal Postal Union. T* **152** *and similar horiz designs. Multicoloured. W w* **12**. *P* 14.
495 3 c. Type **152** 10 10
496 8 c. Loading mail onto *Fijian Princess* .. 10 10
497 30 c. Fijian post office and mail bus 20 20
498 50 c. Modern aircraft 35 60
495/8 .. .. *Set of* 4 60 80

153 Cubs lighting Fire

154 Cakobau Club and Flag

(Des E. W. Roberts. Litho Questa)

1974 (30 Aug). *First National Scout Jamboree, Lautoka. T* **153** *and similar multicoloured designs. W w* **12** *(sideways on 40 c.). P* 14.
499 3 c. Type **153** 15 10
500 10 c. Scouts reading map 20 10
501 40 c. Scouts and Fijian flag *(vert)* .. .. 65 1·00
499/501 .. .. *Set of* 3 90 1·10

(Des J.W. Litho Enschedé)

1974 (9 Oct). *Centenary of Deed of Cession and Fourth Anniv of Independence. T* **154** *and similar horiz designs. Multicoloured. W w* **12** *(sideways on 8 and 50 c.). P* 13½ × 13 *(3 c.) or* 13 × 13½ *(others).*
502 3 c. Type **154** 10 10
503 8 c. King Cakobau and Queen Victoria .. 10 10
504 50 c. Raising the Royal Standard at Nasova Ovalau 30 55
502/4 .. .. *Set of* 3 40 60

1975 (9 Apr)–**77**. *As Nos. 435/44 and 446/50, but W w* **14** *(sideways on 1 and 10 c).*
505 1 c. *Cirrhopetalum umbellatum* 10 40
506 2 c. Cardinal Honey-eater 15 40
507 3 c. *Calanthe furcata* 20 40
508 4 c. *Bulbophyllum sp nov* (3.9.76) 25 10
509 5 c. Type **140** 20 30
510 6 c. *Phaius tancarvilliae* (3.9.76) 55 10
511 8 c. Blue-crested Broadbill (3.9.76) 35 10
512 10 c. *Acanthephippium vitiense* 40 30
513 15 c. *Dendrobium tokai* (3.9.76) .. .. 1·50 60
514 20 c. Slaty Flycatcher (15.7.77) .. .. 3·00 55
516 30 c. *Dendrobium gordonii* (3.9.76) .. .. 4·50 95
517 40 c. Type **141** (3.9.76) .. .. .. 3·00 60
518 50 c. White-throated pigeon (3.9.76) .. .. 3·25 65
519 $1 Collared Lory (3.9.76) .. .. .. 3·50 3·00
520 $2 *Dendrobium platygastrium* (3.9.76) .. 5·50 3·50
505/20 .. .. *Set of* 15 24·00 11·00

155 "Diwali" (Hindu Festival)

156 Steam Locomotive No. 21

(Des Jennifer Toombs. Litho Walsall)

1975 (31 Oct). *Festivals of Joy. T* **155** *and similar vert designs. Multicoloured. W w* **14** *(inverted). P* 14.
521 3 c. Type **155** 10 10
522 15 c. "Id-Ul-Fitar" (Muslim Festival) 10 10
523 25 c. Chinese New Year 15 15
524 30 c. Christmas 20 30
521/4 .. .. *Set of* 4 40 50
MS525 121 × 101 mm. Nos. 521/4. W w **14** (sideways) .. .. 1·75 4·50
a. Imperf between (vert) £1000

(Des R. Granger Barrett. Litho Questa)

1976 (26 Jan). *Sugar Trains. T* **156** *and similar horiz designs. Multicoloured. W w* **14** *(sideways). P* 14.
526 4 c. Type **156** 25 10
527 15 c. Diesel locomotive No. 8 .. .. .. 70 30
528 20 c. Diesel locomotive No. 1 .. .. .. 80 40
529 30 c. Free passenger train 95 70
526/9 .. .. *Set of* 4 2·50 1·25

157 Fiji Blind Society and Rotary Symbols

(Des V. Whiteley Studio. Litho J.W.)

1976 (26 Mar). *40th Anniv of Rotary in Fiji. T* **157** *and similar horiz design. W w* **14** *(sideways). P* 13.
530 10 c. ultramarine, pale sage-green and black .. 15 10
531 25 c. multicoloured 40 50
Design:—25 c. Ambulance and Rotary symbol.

158 D. H. "Drover"

(Des P. Powell. Litho Questa)

1976 (1 Sept). *25th Anniv of Air Services. T* **158** *and similar horiz designs. Multicoloured. W w* **14**. *P* 13½ × 14.
532 4 c. Type **158** 40 20
533 15 c. B.A.C. "1–11" .. .. 1·00 85
534 25 c. H.S. "748" .. .. 2·00 1·10
535 30 c. Britten-Norman "Trislander" .. .. 2·25 2·25
532/5 .. .. *Set of* 4 5·00 4·00

159 The Queen's Visit to Fiji, 1970

160 Map of the World

(Des L. Curtis. Litho Questa)

1977 (7 Feb). *Silver Jubilee. T* **159** *and similar vert designs. Multicoloured. W w* **14**. *P* 13½.
536 10 c. Type **159** 10 10
537 25 c. King Edward's Chair 15 10
538 30 c. Queen wearing cloth-of-gold supertunica 25 15
536/8 .. .. *Set of* 3 40 25

(Des J.W. Litho Walsall)

1977 (12 Apr). *E.E.C./A.C.P.* Council of Ministers Conference, Fiji. T* **160** *and similar horiz design. Multicoloured. W w* **14** *(sideways). P* 14.
539 4 c. Type **160** 10 10
540 30 c. Map of Fiji group.. .. .. .. 30 65
*A.C.P. = African, Caribbean, Pacific Group.

161 *Hibiscus rosa-sinensis*

(Des V. Whiteley Studio. Litho Walsall)

1977 (27 Aug). *21st Anniv of Fiji Hibiscus Festival. T* **161** *and similar horiz designs. W w* **14** *(sideways). P* 14.
541 **161** 4 c. multicoloured 10 10
542 – 15 c. multicoloured 15 10
543 – 30 c. multicoloured 25 15
544 – 35 c. multicoloured 40 35
541/4 .. .. *Set of* 4 80 60
Nos. 542/44 show different varieties of *H rosa-sinensis*.

162 Drua

163 White Hart of Richard II

(Des P. Powell. Litho Questa)

1977 (7 Nov). *Canoes. T* **162** *and similar horiz designs. Multicoloured. W w* **14** *(sideways). P* 14.
545 4 c. Type **162** 10 5
546 15 c. Tabilai 20 20
547 25 c. Takai 25 25
548 40 c. Camakua 35 70
545/8 .. .. *Set of* 4 80 1·10

(Des C. Abbott. Litho Questa)

1978 (21 Apr). *25th Anniv of Coronation. T* **163** *and similar vert designs. P* 15.
549 25 c. bistre, blue-green and silver 20 25
a. Sheetlet. Nos. 549/51 × 2 .. .. 1·10
550 25 c. multicoloured 20 25
551 25 c. bistre, blue-green and silver 20 25
549/51 .. .. *Set of* 3 55 65
Designs:—No. 549, Type **163**; No. 550, Queen Elizabeth II; No. 551, Banded Iguana.
Nos. 549/51 were printed together in small sheets of 6, containing two *se-tenant* strips of 3, with horizontal gutter margin between.

164 Defence Force surrounding Plane, Suva

(Des A. Theobald. Litho Harrison)

1978 (26 June). *Aviation Anniversaries. T* **164** *and similar horiz designs. Multicoloured. W w* **14** *(sideways). P* 14.
552 4 c. Type **164** 15 10
553 15 c. *Southern Cross* prior to leaving Naselai Beach 25 30
554 25 c. Wright *Flyer* 50 55
555 30 c. Bristol "F2B" 50 70
552/5 .. .. *Set of* 4 1·25 1·40
Anniversaries:—25 c. 75th of powered flight; 30 c. 60th of R.A.F.; others. 50th of first trans-Pacific flight by Kingsford-Smith.

165 Shallow Wooden Oil Dish in shape of Human Figure

166 Advent Crown with Candles (Christmas)

(Des J. Cooter. Litho Questa)

1978 (14 Aug). *Fijian Artifacts. T* **165** *and similar multicoloured designs. W w* **14** *(sideways on 15 and 25 c.). P* 14.
556 4 c. Type **165** 10 10
557 15 c. Necklace of cachalot teeth *(horiz)* .. 10 10
558 25 c. Double water bottle *(horiz)* 15 10
559 30 c. Finely carved Ula or throwing club .. 15 15
556/9 .. .. *Set of* 4 35 35

(Des Jennifer Toombs. Litho Harrison)

1978 (30 Oct). *Festivals. T* **166** *and similar horiz designs. Multicoloured. W w* **14** *(sideways). P* 14.
560 4 c. Type **166** 10 10
561 15 c. Lamps (Diwali) 10 10
562 25 c. Coffee pot, cups and fruit (Id-Ul-Fitr) .. 10 10
563 40 c. Lion (Chinese New Year) 25 40
560/3 .. .. *Set of* 4 35 60

167 Banded Iguana

(Des L. Curtis and G. Drummond. Litho Questa)

1979 (19 Mar). *Endangered Wildlife. T* **167** *and similar horiz designs. Multicoloured. W w* **14** *(sideways). P* 14.
564 4 c. Type **167** 10 10
565 15 c. Tree Frog 30 10
566 25 c. Long-legged Warbler 50 20
567 30 c. Pink-billed Parrot Finch 65 55
564/7 .. .. *Set of* 4 1·40 80

168 Women with Dholak

(Des J.W. Litho Questa)

1979 (11 May). *Centenary of Arrival of Indians. T* **168** *and similar horiz designs. Multicoloured. W w* **14** *(sideways). P* 14.
568 4 c. Type **168** 10 10
569 15 c. Men sitting round tanoa 10 10
570 30 c. Farmer and sugar cane plantation .. 15 10
571 40 c. Sailing ship *Leonidas* 40 25
568/71 .. .. *Set of* 4 60 45

169 Soccer

(Des BG Studio. Litho Questa)

1979 (2 July). *6th South Pacific Games. T* **169** *and similar horiz designs. Multicoloured. W w* **14** *(sideways). P* 14.
572 4 c. Type **169** 10 10
573 15 c. Rugby Union 25 10
574 30 c. Lawn tennis 45 35
575 40 c. Weightlifting 55 45
572/5 .. .. *Set of* 4 1·25 80

170 Indian Child and Map of Fiji

(Des D. Bowen. Litho Walsall)

1979 (17 Sept). *International Year of the Child. T* **170** *and similar horiz designs showing children and map of Fiji. Multicoloured. W w* **14** *(sideways). P* 14½ × 14.
576 4 c. + 1 c. Type **170** 10 10
577 15 c. + 2 c. European child 15 15
578 30 c. + 3 c. Chinese child 15 15
579 40 c. + 4 c. Fijian child 15 20
576/9 .. .. *Set of* 4 45 50

171 Old Town Hall, Suva

(Des J.W. Litho Questa (1, 2, 3, 10, 15, 20, 30 c., $5) or Harrison (others))

1979 (11 Nov)–**86**. *Architecture. Multicoloured designs as T* **171**. *W w* **14** *(sideways on horiz designs). P* 13½ × 13 ($1), 13 × 13½ ($2), 13½ × 14 ($5) *or* 14 *(others)*.

A. *Without imprint date at foot. Chalk-surfaced paper* (1, 2, 3, 10, 15, 20, 30 *c.*, $5). B. *With imprint date.*

No.	Description	A		B	
580	1 c. Type **171**	10	10	†	
	a. Ordinary paper	10	10	†	
581	2 c. Dudley Church, Suva ..	15	10	10	10
	a. Ordinary paper	10	10	10	10
582	3 c. Fiji International Telecommunications Building, Suva	25	20	†	
	a. Ordinary paper	10	15	†	
583	5 c. Lautoka Mosque	10	10	10	10
584	6 c. General Post Office, Suva ..	10	10	10	10
585	10 c. Fiji Visitors Bureau, Suva	20	10	†	
	a. Ordinary paper	10	10	†	
586	12 c. Public School, Levuka ..	10	10	†	
587	15 c. Colonial War Memorial Hospital, Suva	30	20	†	
	a. Ordinary paper	10	10	†	
588	18 c. Labasa Sugar Mill ..	15	20	†	
589	20 c. Rewa Bridge, Nausori ..	45	25	†	
	a. Ordinary paper	35	20	†	
590	30 c. Sacred Heart Cathedral, Suva *(vert)*	55	35	†	
	a. Ordinary paper	20	25	†	
591	35 c. Grand Pacific Hotel, Suva ..	25	30	†	
592	45 c. Shiva Temple, Suva ..	30	35	†	
593	50 c. Serua Island Village ..	35	40	†	
594	$1 Solo Lighthouse (30 × 46 *mm*)	70	75	†	
595	$2 Baker Memorial Hall, Nausori (46 × 30 *mm*) ..	1·40	1·50	†	
595*a*	$5 Government House (46 × 30 *mm*)	3·50	3·75	†	
580/95*a*	.. .. *Set of* 17	7·75	8·00	†	

Date of issue:—11.11.79 Nos. 580A/82A, 585A, 587A, 589A/90A, 595aA; 13.6.80 Nos. 580Aa, 581Aa, 582Aa, 585Aa, 587Aa, 589Aa, 590Aa; 22.12.80 Nos. 583A/84A, 586A, 588A, 591A/95A; 15.6.83 No. 584B; 1.84 No. 583B; 2.84 581Ba; 19.11.86 No. 581B.
For 2, 3, 4, 8 and 20 c. values watermarked w **16** see Nos. 720/30.

MINIMUM PRICE

The minimum price quote is 10p which represents a handling charge rather than a basis for valuing common stamps. For further notes about prices see introductory pages.

172 *Southern Cross*, 1873

(Des L. Dunn. Litho Secura, Singapore)

1980 (28 Apr). *"London 1980" International Stamp Exhibition. Mail-carrying Ships. T* **172** *and similar horiz designs. Multicoloured.* W w **14** *(sideways). P* 13½.

596 6 c. Type **172** 15 10
597 20 c. *Levuka*, 1910 .. .. 15 10
598 45 c. *Matua*, 1936 .. .. 30 35
599 50 c. *Oronsay*, 1951 .. .. 30 40
596/9 .. .. *Set of* 4 80 80

173 Sovi Bay

(Des BG Studio. Litho Questa)

1980 (18 Aug). *Tourism. T* **173** *and similar horiz designs. Multicoloured.* W w **14** *(sideways). P* 13½ × 14.

600 6 c. Type **173** 10 10
601 20 c. Evening scene, Yanuca Island 15 15
602 45 c. Dravuni Beach 20 40
603 50 c. Wakaya Island 20 45
600/3 .. .. *Set of* 4 50 95

174 Official Opening of Parliament, 1979

(Des J. Cooter. Litho J.W.)

1980 (6 Oct). *10th Anniv of Independence. T* **174** *and similar multicoloured designs.* W w **14** *(sideways on 6 and 45 c.). P* 13.

604 6 c. Type **174** 10 10
605 20 c. Fiji coat of arms *(vert)* 15 10
606 45 c. Fiji flag 20 20
607 50 c. Queen Elizabeth II *(vert)* 25 35
604/7 .. .. *Set of* 4 55 60

175 "Coastal Scene" (painting, Semisi Maya)

176 Prince Charles Sailing

(Des J.W. Litho Questa)

1981 (21 Apr). *International Year for Disabled Persons. T* **175** *and similar multicoloured designs.* W w **14** *(sideways on 6 and 35 c.). P* 14.

608 6 c. Type **175** 10 10
609 35 c. "Underwater Scene" (painting, Semisi Maya) 45 30
610 50 c. Semisi Maya (disabled artist) at work *(vert)* 55 40
611 60 c. "Peacock" (painting, Semisi Maya) *(vert)* 60 45
608/11 .. .. *Set of* 4 1·50 1·10

(Des J.W. Litho Questa)

1981 (22 July). *Royal Wedding. T* **176** *and similar vert designs. Multicoloured.* W w **14**. *P* 14.

612 6 c. Wedding bouquet from Fiji 10 10
613 45 c. Type **176** 45 15
614 $1 Prince Charles and Lady Diana Spencer 75 60
612/14 .. .. *Set of* 3 1·10 75

177 Operator Assistance Centre

178 "Eat Fiji Foods"

(Des A. Theobald. Litho Format)

1981 (17 Aug). *Telecommunications. T* **177** *and similar horiz designs. Multicoloured.* W w **14** *(sideways). P* 14.

615 6 c. Type **177** 10 10
616 35 c. Microwave station 55 50
617 50 c. Satellite earth station 75 75
618 60 c. Cable ship *Retriever* 90 90
615/18 .. .. *Set of* 4 2·10 2·00

(Des J.W. Litho Format)

1981 (21 Sept). *World Food Day.* W w **14**. *P* 14½ × 14.

619 **178** 20 c. multicoloured 25 15

179 Ratu Sir Lala Sukuna (first Speaker, Legislative Council)

(Des A. Theobald. Litho Format)

1981 (19 Oct). *Commonwealth Parliamentary Association Conference, Suva. T* **179** *and similar horiz designs.* W w **14** *(sideways). P* 14.

620 6 c. black, buff and orange-brown 10 10
621 35 c. multicoloured 30 30
622 50 c. multicoloured 45 45
620/2 .. .. *Set of* 3 75 75
MS623 73 × 53 mm. 60 c. multicoloured .. .. 70 1·00

Designs:—35 c. Mace of the House of Representatives; 50 c. Suva Civic Centre; 60 c. Flags of C.P.A. countries.

180 Bell "P-39 Airacobra"

(Des A. Theobald. Litho Walsall)

1981 (7 Dec). *World War II Aircraft. T* **180** *and similar horiz designs. Multicoloured.* W w **14** *(sideways). P* 14.

624 6 c. Type **180** 30 10
625 18 c. Consolidated "PBY-5 Catalina" 60 25
626 35 c. Curtiss "P-40 Warhawk" 70 40
627 60 c. Short "Singapore" .. .. 1·10 85
624/7 .. .. *Set of* 4 2·50 1·40

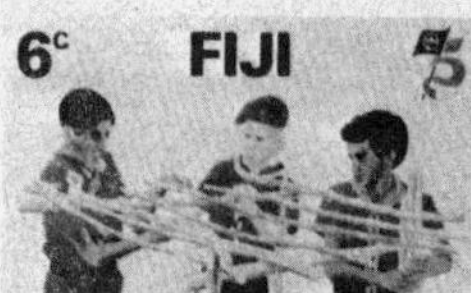

181 Scouts constructing Shelter

(Des B. Melton. Litho Questa)

1982 (22 Feb). *75th Anniv of Boy Scout Movement. T* **181** *and similar multicoloured designs.* W w **14** *(sideways on 6 and 45 c.). P* 14½.

628 6 c. Type **181** 15 10
629 20 c. Scouts sailing *(vert)* 50 30
630 45 c. Scouts by campfire 85 50
631 60 c. Lord Baden-Powell *(vert)* .. .. .. 1·00 1·00
628/31 .. .. *Set of* 4 2·25 1·75

182 Fiji Soldiers at U.N. Checkpoint

(Des J.W. Litho Format)

1982 (3 May). *Disciplined Forces. T* **182** *and similar horiz designs. Multicoloured.* W w **14** *(sideways). P* 14.

632 12 c. Type **182** 25 10
633 30 c. Soldiers engaged in rural development 50 45
634 40 c. Police patrol 70 60
635 70 c. *Kiro* (minesweeper) .. .. 1·00 1·10
632/5 .. .. *Set of* 4 2·25 2·00

183 Footballers and Fiji Football Association Logo

184 Bride and Groom leaving St. Paul's

(Des A. Theobald. Litho Walsall)

1982 (15 June). *World Cup Football Championship, Spain. T* **183** *and similar horiz designs.* W w **14** *(sideways). P* 14.

636 6 c. rosine, black and lemon 10 10
637 18 c. multicoloured 25 20
638 50 c. multicoloured 70 60
639 90 c. multicoloured .. .. 1·10 1·25
636/9 .. .. *Set of* 4 1·90 1·90

Designs:—18 c. Footballers and World Cup emblem; 50 c. Footballer and Bernabeu Stadium; 90 c. Footballers and Naranjito (mascot).

(Des C. Abbott. Litho Harrison)

1982 (1 July). *21st Birthday of Princess of Wales. T* **184** *and similar vert designs. Multicoloured.* W w **14**. *P* 14½ × 14.

640 20 c. Fiji coat of arms 25 25
641 35 c. Lady Diana Spencer at Broadlands, May 1981 .. .. 35 35
642 45 c. Type **184** 50 50
643 $1 Formal portrait .. .. 1·25 1·25
640/3 .. .. *Set of* 4 2·10 2·10

185 Prince Philip

186 Baby Jesus with Mary and Joseph

(Des C. Abbott. Litho Format)

1982 (1 Nov). *Royal Visit. T* **185** *and similar multicoloured designs.* W w **14**. *P* 14.

644 6 c. Type **185** 10 10
645 45 c. Queen Elizabeth II 65 90
MS646 128 × 88 mm. Nos. 644/5 and $1 Royal Yacht *Britannia (horiz)*. Wmk sideways .. .. 2·10 2·50

(Des G. Wilby. Litho Questa)

1982 (22 Nov). *Christmas. T* **186** *and similar horiz designs. Multicoloured.* W w **14** *(sideways). P* 14 × 14½.

647 6 c. Type **186** 10 10
648 20 c. Three Wise Men presenting gifts .. 30 20
649 35 c. Carol-singing 45 35
647/9 .. .. *Set of* 3 75 55
MS650 94 × 42 mm. $1 "Faith" (from the "Three Virtues" by Raphael) .. .. 1·25 1·50

187 Red-throated Lorikeet

188 Bure in Traditional Village

(Des N. Arlott. Litho Questa)

1983 (14 Feb). *Parrots. T* **187** *and similar vert designs. Multicoloured.* W w **14**. *P* 14.

651 20 c. Type **187** 65 15
652 40 c. Blue-crowned Lory 90 40
653 55 c. Masked Shining Parrot .. .. .. 1·00 70
654 70 c. Red Shining Parrot .. .. 1·25 1·00
651/4 .. .. *Set of* 4 3·50 2·00

(Des B. Melton. Litho Questa)

1983 (14 Mar). *Commonwealth Day. T* **188** *and similar horiz designs. Multicoloured.* W w **14** *(sideways). P* 14.

655 8 c. Type **188** 10 10
656 25 c. Barefoot firewalkers 20 15
657 50 c. Sugar industry 30 35
658 80 c. Kava "Yagona" ceremony 55 70
655/8 .. .. *Set of* 4 1·00 1·10

189 First Manned Balloon Flight, 1783

190 Nawanawa

(Des Harrison. Litho Questa)

1983 (18 July). *Bicentenary of Manned Flight. T* **189** *and similar horiz designs. Multicoloured.* W w **14** (*sideways*). *P* 14.

659 8 c. Type **189** 10 10
660 20 c. Wright brothers' *Flyer* 25 30
661 25 c. Douglas "Super DC3" 35 40
662 40 c. De Havilland "Comet" 55 60
663 50 c. Boeing "747" 65 70
664 58 c. Space Shuttle 75 80
659/64 .. .. *Set of* 6 2·40 2·50

(Des Harrison. Litho Format)

1983 (26 Sept). *Flowers* (1*st series*). *T* **190** *and similar vert designs. Multicoloured.* W w **14**. *P* 14 × 14½.

665 8 c. Type **190** 10 10
666 25 c. Rosawa 35 30
667 40 c. Warerega 55 50
668 $1 Saburo .. .. 1·25 1·40
665/8 .. .. *Set of* 4 2·00 2·00

See also Nos. 680/3.

191 Fijian beating Lali and Earth Satellite Station

192 *Dacryopinax spathularia*

(Des Garden Studio. Litho Questa)

1983 (7 Nov). *World Communications Year.* W w **14**. *P* 13½.

669 **191** 50 c. multicoloured 50 70

(Des Jennifer Toombs. Litho Enschedé)

1984 (9 Jan). *Fungi. T* **192** *and similar multicoloured designs.* W w **14** (*sideways on* 50 c. *and* $1). *P* 13½ × 13 (8 c. *to* 40 c.) *or* 13 × 13½ (*others*).

670 8 c. Type **192** 20 10
671 15 c. *Podoscypha involuta* 40 25
672 40 c. *Lentinus squarrosulus* 75 60
673 50 c. *Scleroderma flavidum* (*horiz*) 80 70
674 $1 *Phillipsia domingensis* (*horiz*) .. .. 1·40 1·40
670/4 .. .. *Set of* 5 3·25 2·75

193 *Tui Lau* on Reef

(Des L. Curtis. Litho Questa)

1984 (7 May). *250th Anniv of "Lloyd's List" (newspaper). T* **193** *and similar vert designs. Multicoloured.* W w **14**. *P* 14½ × 14.

675 8 c. Type **193** 20 10
676 40 c. S.S. *Tofua* 75 65
677 55 c. S.S. *Canberra* 90 85
678 60 c. Suva wharf 95 95
675/8 .. .. *Set of* 4 2·50 2·25

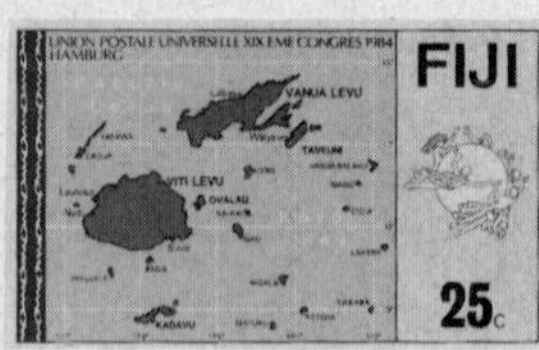

194 Map of Fijian Islands

(Des J. Cooter. Litho Questa)

1984 (14 June). *Universal Postal Union Congress, Hamburg. Sheet* 77 × 65 *mm.* W w **14** (*sideways*). *P* 14½.

MS679 **194** 25 c. multicoloured 35 50

(Des Harrison. Litho Format)

1984 (9 July). *Flowers* (2*nd series*). *Horiz designs as T* **190**. W w **14**. *P* 14 × 14½.

680 15 c. Drividrivi 25 25
681 20 c. Vesida 35 35
682 50 c. Vuga 80 80
683 70 c. Qaiqi .. .. 1·10 1·10
680/3 .. .. *Set of* 4 2·25 2·25

NEW INFORMATION

The editor is always interested to correspond with people who have new information that will improve or correct the Catalogue.

195 Prize Bull, Yalavou Cattle Scheme

(Des D. Hartley-Marjoram. Litho Walsall)

1984 (17 Sept). *"Ausipex" International Stamp Exhibition, Melbourne. T* **195** *and similar multicoloured designs.* W w **14** (*sideways on* 8, 40 c. *and* $1). *P* 14½ × 14 (25 c.) *or* 14 × 14½ (*others*).

684 8 c. Type **195** 15 10
685 25 c. Wailoa Power Station (*vert*) 40 40
686 40 c. Air Pacific Boeing "737" airliner 65 65
687 $1 Container ship *Fua Kavenga* .. .. 1·60 1·60
684/7 .. .. *Set of* 4 2·50 2·40

196 The Stable at Bethlehem

(Des G. Vasarhelyi. Litho Format)

1984 (5 Nov). *Christmas. Children's Paintings. T* **196** *and similar multicoloured designs.* W w **14** (*sideways on horiz designs*). *P* 14.

688 8 c. Type **196** 10 10
689 20 c. Outrigger canoe 30 20
690 25 c. Father Christmas and Christmas tree .. 35 25
691 40 c. Going to church 60 60
692 $1 Decorating Christmas tree (*vert*) .. 1·50 1·60
688/92 .. .. *Set of* 5 2·50 2·50

197 Monarch

198 Outrigger Canoe off Toberua Island

(Des Annette Robinson. Litho Questa)

1985 (4 Feb). *Butterflies. T* **197** *and similar multicoloured designs.* W w **14** (*sideways on* 8 c. *and* 25 c.). *P* 14.

693 8 c. Type **197** 40 10
694 25 c. Common Eggfly 75 40
695 40 c. Long-tailed Blue (*vert*) .. .. .. 1·00 60
696 $1 Meadow Argus (*vert*) .. .. .. 2·00 2·25
693/6 .. .. *Set of* 4 3·75 3·00

(Des D. Miller. Litho B.D.T.)

1985 (1 Apr). *"Expo '85" World Fair, Japan. T* **198** *and similar vert designs. Multicoloured.* W w **14**. *P* 14.

697 20 c. Type **198** 40 30
698 25 c. Wainivula Falls 60 40
699 50 c. Mana Island 75 70
700 $1 Sawa-I-Lau Caves .. .. 1·25 1·40
697/700 .. .. *Set of* 4 2·75 2·50

199 With Prince Charles at Garter Ceremony

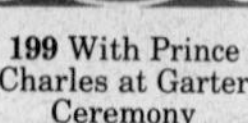

200 Horned Squirrel Fish

(Des A. Theobald ($1), C. Abbott (others). Litho Questa)

1985 (7 June). *Life and Times of Queen Elizabeth the Queen Mother. T* **199** *and similar vert designs. Multicoloured.* W w **16**. *P* 14½ × 14.

701 8 c. With Prince Andrew on her 60th Birthday 10 10
702 25 c. Type **199** 35 40
703 40 c. The Queen Mother at Epsom Races .. 50 60
704 50 c. With Prince Henry at his christening (from photo by Lord Snowdon) 65 80
701/4 .. .. *Set of* 4 1·40 1·75

MS705 91 × 73 mm. $1 With Prince Andrew at Royal Wedding, 1981. Wmk sideways .. .. 1·25 1·50

(Des M. Raj. Litho Questa)

1985 (23 Sept). *Shallow Water Marine Fishes. T* **200** *and similar horiz designs. Multicoloured.* W w **14** (*sideways*). *P* 14½.

706 40 c. Type **200** 65 55
707 50 c. Yellow-banded Goatfish 80 70
708 55 c. Fairy Cod 80 75
709 $1 Peacock Rock Cod .. .. 1·50 2·00
706/9 .. .. *Set of* 4 3·25 3·50

201 Collared Petrel

202 Children and "Peace for Fiji and the World" Slogan

(Des Doreen McGuinness. Litho Walsall)

1985 (4 Nov). *Seabirds. T* **201** *and similar vert designs. Multicoloured.* W w **14**. *P* 14 × 13½.

710 15 c. Type **201** 55 25
711 20 c. Lesser Frigate Bird 65 35
712 50 c. Brown Booby .. .. 1·25 1·25
713 $1 Crested Tern .. .. 2·25 2·50
710/13 .. .. *Set of* 4 4·25 4·00

(Des A. Theobald. Litho Format)

1986 (21 Apr). *60th Birthday of Queen Elizabeth II. Vert designs as T* **110** *of Ascension. Multicoloured.* W w **16**. *P* 14 × 14½.

714 20 c. With Duke of York at Royal Tournament, 1936 .. .. 30 30
715 25 c. Royal Family on Palace balcony after Princess Margaret's wedding, 1960 .. 35 35
716 40 c. Queen inspecting guard of honour, Suva, 1982 .. .. 55 55
717 50 c. In Luxembourg, 1976 .. .. 65 65
718 $1 At Crown Agents Head Office, London, 1983 .. .. 1·10 1·25
714/18 .. .. *Set of* 5 2·75 2·75

(Litho Questa)

1986 (Apr)–**88**. *As Nos.* 581/2, 589, *and new values.* W w **16** (*sideways*). *Chalk-surfaced paper* (2 c.). *With imprint date.* *P* 14.

720 2 c. Dudley Church, Suva 10 10
721 3 c. Fiji International Telecommunications Building, Suva (1.6.88) 10 10
722 4 c. Lautoka Mosque (as No. 583) (1.6.88) .. 10 10
724 8 c. Public School, Levuka (as No. 586) (1.12.86) 10 10
730 20 c. Rewa Bridge, Nausori (1.6.88) 15 20
720/30 .. .. *Set of* 5 30 35

No. 720 exists with different imprint dates below the design.

(Des G. Vasarhelyi. Litho Format)

1986 (23 June). *International Peace Year. T* **202** *and similar vert design. Multicoloured.* W w **16**. *P* 14½.

736 8 c. Type **202** 10 10
737 40 c. Peace dove and houses 50 60

203 Halley's Comet in Centaurus Constellation and Newton's Reflector

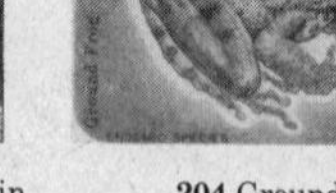

204 Ground Frog

(Des D. Hartley. Litho B.D.T.)

1986 (7 July). *Appearance of Halley's Comet. T* **203** *and similar vert designs. Multicoloured.* W w **16**. *P* 13½.

738 25 c. Type **203** 55 35
739 40 c. Halley's Comet over Lomaiviti 75 55
740 $1 *Giotto* spacecraft photographing Comet nucleus .. .. 1·25 1·75
738/40 .. .. *Set of* 3 2·25 2·40

(Litho Format)

1986 (1 Aug). *Reptiles and Amphibians. T* **204** *and similar horiz designs. Multicoloured.* W w **16** (*sideways*). *P* 14½.

741 8 c. Type **204** 30 10
742 20 c. Burrowing Snake 50 30
743 25 c. Spotted Gecko 60 35
744 40 c. Crested Iguana 80 55
745 50 c. Blotched Skink 90 90
746 $1 Speckled Skink .. .. 1·60 2·00
741/6 .. .. *Set of* 6 4·25 3·75

205 Gatawaka

206 Weasel Cone

(Des M. Raj. Litho Walsall)

1986 (10 Nov). *Ancient War Clubs. T* **205** *and similar vert designs. Multicoloured. W w* **16**. *P* 14.

747	25 c. Type **205**	50	35
748	40 c. Siriti	70	55
749	50 c. Bulibuli	85	85
750	$1 Culacula	1·60	2·00
747/50	*Set of* 4	3·25	3·25

(Des A. Riley. Litho Format)

1987 (26 Feb). *Cone Shells of Fiji. T* **206** *and similar vert designs. Multicoloured. W w* **16**. *P* 14×14½.

751	15 c. Type **206**	50	25
752	20 c. Pertusus Cone	60	30
753	25 c. Admiral Cone	65	35
754	40 c. Leaden Cone	85	60
755	50 c. Imperial Cone	95	95
756	$1 Geography Cone	1·60	2·00
751/6	*Set of* 6	4·50	4·00

207 Tagimoucia Flower

CAPEX'87
(208)

(Des M. Raj. Litho Format)

1987 (23 Apr). *Tagimoucia Flower. Sheet* 72×55 *mm. W w* **14** *(sideways). P* 14½.

MS757 **207**	$1 multicoloured	1·40	1·60

1987 (13 June). *"Capex '87" International Stamp Exhibition, Toronto. No.* **MS**757 *optd with T* **208**.

MS758	72×55 mm. $1 Type **207**	80	85

Stamps from Nos. **MS**757 and **MS**758 are identical as the overprint on **MS**758 appears on the margin of the sheet.

209 Traditional Fijian House

(Des National Focal Point, adapted L. Curtis. Litho Format)

1987 (20 July). *International Year of Shelter for the Homeless. T* **209** *and similar horiz design. Multicoloured. W w* **16** *(sideways). P* 14.

759	55 c. Type **209**	45	50
760	70 c. Modern bungalows	55	60

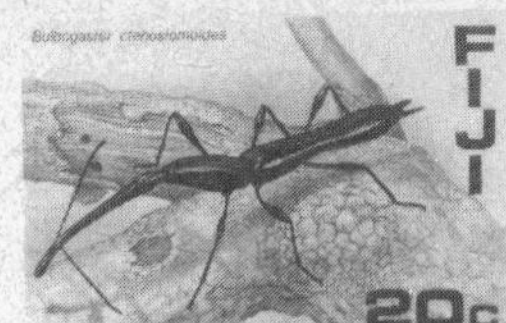

210 *Bulbogaster ctenostomoides*

(Des R. Lewington. Litho Walsall)

1987 (7 Sept). *Fijian Beetles. T* **210** *and similar horiz designs. Multicoloured. W w* **16** *(sideways). P* 13½×14.

761	20 c. Type **210**	20	20
762	25 c. *Paracupta flaviventris*	25	25
763	40 c. *Cerambyrhynchus schoenherri*	35	35
764	50 c. *Rhinoscapha lagopyga*	45	45
765	$1 *Xixuthrus heros*	80	85
761/5	*Set of* 5	1·90	1·90

PRICES OF SETS

Set prices are given for many issues, generally those containing three stamps or more. Definitive sets include one of each value or major colour change, but do not cover different perforations, die types or minor shades. Where a choice is possible the set prices are based on the cheapest versions of the stamps included in the listings.

REPUBLIC

Following a military coup on 25 September 1987 Fiji was declared a republic on 7 October. The Governor-General resigned on 15 October 1987 and Fiji's Commonwealth membership lapsed.

For the convenience of collectors we continue to list later issues in this volume.

211 The Nativity

212 Windsurfer and Beach

(Des G. Vasarhelyi. Litho Walsall)

1987 (19 Nov). *Christmas. T* **211** *and similar multicoloured designs. W w* **16** *(sideways on 40 c., 50 c.). P* 14×13½ *(vert) or* 13½×14 *(horiz).*

766	8 c. Type **211**	10	10
767	40 c. The Shepherds *(horiz)*	40	35
768	50 c. The Three Kings *(horiz)*	50	45
769	$1 The Three Kings presenting gifts	85	85
766/9	*Set of* 4	1·75	1·60

(Des Ahgrafik. Litho Questa)

1988 (27 Apr). *"Expo '88" World Fair, Brisbane. W w* **16** *(sideways). P* 14.

770 **212**	30 c. multicoloured	30	30

213 Woman using Fiji "Nouna" (stove)

214 Pottery Bowl

(Litho Questa)

1988 (14 June). *Centenary of International Council of Women. W w* **16** *(sideways). P* 14.

771 **213**	45 c. multicoloured	35	40

(Des N. Ahmed. Litho Questa)

1988 (29 Aug). *Ancient Fijian Pottery. T* **214** *and similar multicoloured designs. W w* **14** *(sideways) (69 c.) or w* **16** *(others, sideways on 75 c.). P* 14.

772	9 c. Type **214**	10	10
773	23 c. Cooking pot	20	25
774	58 c. Priest's drinking vessel	45	50
775	63 c. Drinking vessel	50	55
776	69 c. Earthenware oil lamp	55	60
777	75 c. Cooking pot with relief pattern *(vert)*	60	65
772/7	*Set of* 6	2·10	2·40

215 Fiji Tree Frog

216 *Dendrobium mohlianum*

(Des Doreen McGuinness. Litho Walsall)

1988 (3 Oct). *Fiji Tree Frog. T* **215** *and similar vert designs. Multicoloured. W w* **16**. *P* 14×13½.

778	18 c. Type **215**	25	20
779	23 c. Frog climbing grass stalks	30	25
780	30 c. On leaf	40	40
781	45 c. Moving from one leaf to another	55	55
778/81	*Set of* 4	1·40	1·25

(Des M. Raj. Litho Walsall)

1988 (21 Nov). *Native Flowers. T* **216** *and similar vert designs. Multicoloured. W w* **14**. *P* 14.

782	9 c. Type **216**	15	10
783	30 c. *Dendrobium cattilare*	35	35
784	45 c. *Degeneria vitiensis*	45	45
785	$1 *Degeneria roseiflora*	85	1·00
782/5	*Set of* 4	1·60	1·75

217 Battle of Solferino, 1859

(Des L. Curtis. Litho Questa)

1989 (6 Feb). *125th Anniv of International Red Cross. T* **217** *and similar designs. W w* **16** *(sideways on 58, 69 c.). P* 13½ × 14 *(horiz) or* 14 × 13½ *(vert).*

786	58 c. multicoloured	60	60
787	63 c. multicoloured	70	70
788	69 c. multicoloured	75	75
789	$1 black and bright scarlet	95	95
786/9	*Set of* 4	2·75	2·75

Designs: *Vert*—63 c. Henri Dunant (founder); $1 Anniversary logo. *Horiz*—69 c. Fijian Red Cross worker with blood donor.

218 Plan of *Bounty's* Launch

219 *Platygyra daedalea*

(Des Jennifer Toombs. Litho Questa)

1989 (28 Apr). *Bicentenary of Captain Bligh's Boat Voyage. T* **218** *and similar horiz designs. Multicoloured. W w* **16** *(sideways). P* 14×14½.

790	45 c. Type **218**	50	50
791	58 c. Cup, bowl and Bligh's journal	65	65
792	80 c. Bligh and extract from journal	90	90
793	$1 *Bounty's* launch and map of Fiji	1·10	1·10
790/3	*Set of* 4	2·75	2·75

(Des M. Raj. Litho Harrison)

1989 (21 Aug). *Corals. T* **219** *and similar multicoloured designs. W w* **14** *(sideways on 46, 60 c.). P* 14.

794	46 c. Type **219**	45	45
795	60 c. *Caulastrea furcata*	65	65
796	75 c. *Acropora echinata (vert)*	75	75
797	90 c. *Acropora humilis (vert)*	85	85
794/7	*Set of* 4	2·40	2·40

220 Goalkeeper

221 Congregation in Church

(Des S. Noon. Litho Questa)

1989 (25 Sept). *World Cup Football Championship, Italy (1990). T* **220** *and similar horiz designs. Multicoloured. W w* **16** *(sideways). P* 14×14½.

798	35 c. Type **220**	30	35
799	63 c. Goalkeeper catching ball	50	55
800	70 c. Player with ball	55	60
801	85 c. Tackling	70	75
798/801	*Set of* 4	1·90	2·00

(Des L. Curtis. Litho Questa)

1989 (1 Nov). *Christmas. T* **221** *and similar vert designs. Multicoloured. W w* **14**. *P* 14½×14.

802	9 c. Type **221**	10	10
803	45 c. *Delonix regia* (Christmas tree)	35	40
804	$1 The Nativity	80	85
805	$1.40, Fijian children under *Delonix regia* (tree)	1·10	1·25
802/5	*Set of* 4	2·00	2·25

POSTAGE DUE STAMPS

D 1

D 2

1917 (1 Jan). *Typo locally, on thick yellowish white laid paper. No gum. P* 11.

D1	D 1	½d. black	£600	£325
		a. *Se-tenant* strip of 8: 1d. (×3) + ½d. + 4d. + 3d. (×3)	£9000	
D2		1d. black	£250	65·00
D3		2d. black	£200	55·00
D4		3d. black	£250	70·00
D5		4d. black	£600	£325

No. D2a derives from sheets of 96 (8 × 12). The 2d. was printed separately in sheets of 84 (7 × 12). On all these sheets marginal copies were imperforate on the outer edge.

1917 (21 April)–**18**. *Narrower setting, value in ½d. as Type* D **2**.

D5*a*	½d. black	£550	£225
D5*b*	1d. black	£225	£100
D5*c*	2d. black (5.4.18)	£750	£500

1d. and 2d. stamps must have wide margins (3½ to 4 mm) on the vertical sides to be Nos. D2 or D3. Stamps with narrow margins of approximately the same width on all four sides are Nos. D5*b* or D5*c*.

Nos. D5*a/c* were printed in separate sheets of 84 (7 × 12). The marginal copies are perforated on all sides.

D 3

D 4

(Typo D.L.R.)

1918 (1 June). *Wmk Mult Crown CA. P* 14.

D 6	D 3	½d. black	2·25	11·00
D 7		1d. black	2·50	4·50
D 8		2d. black	2·50	7·50
D 9		3d. black	3·00	17·00
D10		4d. black	5·50	16·00
D6/10		*Set of* 5	14·00	50·00
D6/10 Optd "Specimen"		*Set of* 5	£150	

No postage due stamps were in use between 31 August 1931 and 3 July 1940.

(Typo Waterlow)

1940 (3 July). *Wmk Mult Script CA. P* 12½.

D11	D 4	1d. emerald-green	3·75	38·00
D12		2d. emerald-green	4·75	38·00
D13		3d. emerald-green	7·00	45·00
D14		4d. emerald-green	9·00	45·00
D15		5d. emerald-green	10·00	45·00
D16		6d. emerald-green	12·00	55·00
D17		1s. carmine-lake	16·00	60·00
D18		1s. 6d. carmine-lake	20·00	£100
D11/18		*Set of* 8	75·00	£350
D11/18 Perf "Specimen"		*Set of* 8	£180	

The use of postage due stamps was discontinued on 30 April 1946.

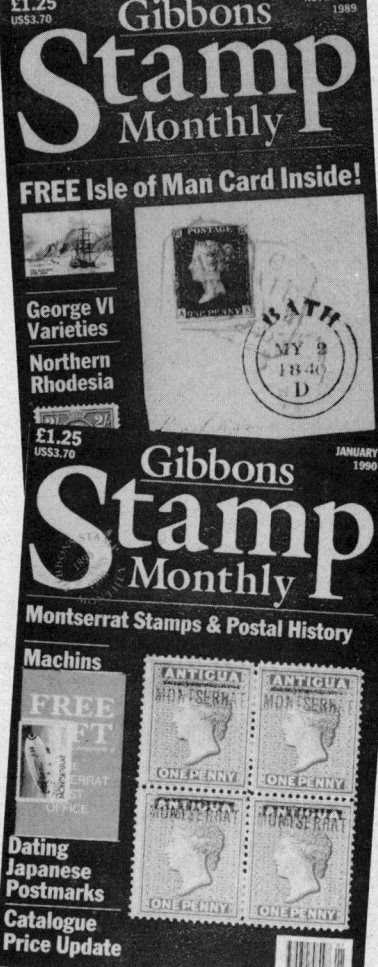

Gambia

PRICES FOR STAMPS ON COVER TO 1945

Nos. 1/20	*from* × 10
Nos. 21/36	*from* × 12
Nos. 37/44	*from* × 8
Nos. 45/142	*from* × 5
Nos. 143/6	*from* × 4
Nos. 147/9	*from* × 8
Nos. 150/61	*from* × 3

WEST AFRICAN SETTLEMENT

PRICES. The prices of Nos. 1 to 8 are for fine copies, with good margins and embossing. Brilliant or poor copies can be supplied at prices consistent with their condition.

DOUBLE EMBOSSING. The majority of the stamps of T 1 with so-called "double embossing" are merely specimens in which the printing and embossing do not register accurately and have no special value. We no longer list "twice embossed" or "twice embossed, once inverted" varieties as they are considered to be outside the scope of this catalogue.

1

(Typo and embossed by D.L.R.)

1869 (18 Mar)–**72.** *No wmk. Imperf.*

1	1	4d. brown	£475	£150
2		4d. pale brown (1871)	£400	£200
3		6d. deep blue (19.4.69)	£400	£175
3*a*		6d. blue (30.4.69)	£500	£150
4		6d. pale blue (17.2.72)	£2250	£1000

Our prices for the 6d., pale blue, No. 4, are for stamps which are pale by comparison with specimens of the "deep blue" and "blue" colour groups listed under Nos. 3 and 3*a*. An exceptionally pale shade is recognized by specialists and this is rare. The dates given are those of the earliest known postmarks.

1874 (Aug). *Wmk Crown CC. Imperf.*

5	1	4d. brown	£400	£200
6		4d. pale brown	£400	£200
7		6d. deep blue	£350	£225
8		6d. blue	£350	£200
		a. Sloping label		
		b. Wmk sideways		

SLOPING LABEL VARIETY. Traces of this flaw first occur in the 6d. imperforate on R.1/1 and R.1/5. In the perforated printings the variety on R.1/5 is much more pronounced and appears as illustrated above. Our listings are these examples from R.1/5, less noticeable varieties of this type from R.1/1, which slope from right to left, being worth less. These varieties continued to appear until the introduction of a new 6d. plate in 1893, used for No. 34.

1880–81. *Wmk Crown CC. P 14*. A. Wmk sideways. B. Wmk upright.*

			A		B	
10	1	½d. orange	£130	£110	3·50	8·00
11		½d. dull orange	†		3·50	8·00
12		1d. maroon	£225	£175	2·50	4·50
13		2d. rose	70·00	35·00	18·00	9·50
14		3d. bright ultramarine	£275	£200	42·00	25·00
14*b*		3d. pale dull ultramarine	†		35·00	20·00
15		4d. brown	£250	35·00	£140	14·00
16		4d. pale brown	£225	30·00	£130	15·00
17		6d. deep blue	£110	70·00	70·00	45·00
		a. Sloping label	£325	£225	£225	£150
18		6d. blue	£110	70·00	70·00	45·00
		a. Sloping label	£325	£225	£225	£150
19		1s. green	£350	£200	£175	£100
20		1s. deep green	£350	£200	£175	£100
10/20		*Set of* 7	£1200	£725	£400	£180

*There were three different printings of these stamps. The original supply, sent in June 1880 and covering all seven values, had watermark sideways and was perforated by a line machine. In October of the same year a further printing of the lowest five values had the watermark changed to upright, but was still with line perforation. The final printing, sent May 1881 and containing all values, also had watermark upright, but was perforated on a comb machine.

1886–93. *Wmk Crown CA, sideways. P 14.*

21	1	½d. myrtle-green (1887)	60	80
22		½d. grey-green	1·10	1·60
22*b*		1d. maroon	†	£15000
23		1d. crimson (1887)	3·25	3·50
23*a*		1d. aniline crimson	6·00	8·00
23*b*		1d. pale carmine	6·00	7·50
24		2d. orange (1887)	4·50	5·50
25		2d. deep orange	1·40	4·75
26		2½d. ultramarine (1887)	2·00	2·75
27		2½d. deep bright blue	1·75	1·50
28		3d. slate-grey (1886)	2·00	9·00
29		3d. grey	2·00	8·00
30		4d. brown (1887)	2·00	2·00
31		4d. deep brown	2·00	2·00
		a. Wmk upright		
32		6d. yellowish olive-green (1886)	40·00	30·00
		a. Sloping label	90·00	70·00
32*b*		6d. olive-green (1887)	48·00	35·00
		ba. Sloping label	£140	£110
33		6d. bronze-green (1889)	17·00	28·00
		a. Sloping label	50·00	58·00
33*b*		6d. deep bronze-green (1889)	17·00	28·00
		ba. Sloping label	50·00	58·00
34		6d. slate-green (1893)	10·00	22·00
35		1s. violet (1887)	2·75	14·00
36		1s. deep violet	2·75	16·00
36*b*		1s. aniline violet	£1100	
21/36		*Set of* 8	22·00	50·00
21/24, 32 Optd "Specimen"		*Set of* 4	£400	

The above were printed in panes of 15 on paper intended for larger panes. Hence the watermark is sometimes misplaced or omitted and letters from "CROWN AGENTS FOR THE COLONIES" from the margin may appear on the stamps.

The ½d., 2d., 3d., 4d., 6d. (No. 32) and 1s. with watermark Crown CA are known imperf (*price from* £1500).

The previously listed 3d. "pearl-grey" shade has been deleted as it is impossible to distinguish from other 3d. shades when it occurs on a single stamp. Sheets from this late printing can be identified by three coloured dots in the left sheet margin and one in the right, this being the reverse of the normal arrangement.

CROWN COLONY

2

3

4

(Typo D.L.R.)

1898 (2 May)–**1902.** *Wmk Crown CA. P 14.*

37	2	½d. dull green (*shades*)	1·50	1·75
38		1d. carmine (*shades*)	1·25	75
39		2d. orange and mauve	2·75	3·50
40		2½d. ultramarine	1·40	1·50
41		3d. reddish purple and blue	6·00	12·00
		a. Deep purple and ultramarine (1902)	85·00	£100
42		4d. brown and blue	4·75	15·00
43		6d. olive-green and carmine	8·00	15·00
44		1s. violet and green	12·00	30·00
37/44		*Set of* 8	35·00	70·00
37/44 Optd "Specimen"		*Set of* 8	£175	

1902 (13 Mar)–**05.** *Wmk Crown CA. P 14.*

45	3	½d. green (19.4.02)	60	2·00
46		1d. carmine	1·00	55
47		2d. orange and mauve (14.6.02)	3·25	2·00
48		2½d. ultramarine (14.6.02)	11·00	15·00
49		3d. purple and ultramarine (19.4.02)	9·00	3·25
50		4d. brown and ultramarine (14.6.02)	3·00	11·00
51		6d. pale sage-green & carmine (14.6.02)	3·25	9·50
52		1s. violet and green (14.6.02)	45·00	55·00
53	4	1s. 6d. green and carmine/*yellow* (6.4.05)	5·50	13·00
54		2s. deep slate and orange (14.6.02)	26·00	40·00
55		2s. 6d. purple and brown/*yellow* (6.4.05)	15·00	40·00
56		3s. carmine and green/*yellow* (6.4.05)	16·00	40·00
45/56		*Set of* 12	£110	£200
45/56 Optd "Specimen"		*Set of* 12	£225	

1904 (Aug)–**06.** *Wmk Mult Crown CA. P 14.*

57	3	½d. green (9.05)	1·00	25
58		1d. carmine	3·00	15
59		2d. orange and mauve (23.2.06)	8·50	2·25
60		2½d. bright blue (8.05)	2·00	3·00
		a. Bright blue and ultramarine	9·00	15·00
61		3d. purple and ultramarine (9.05)	4·50	2·00
62		4d. brown and ultramarine (23.2.06)	6·50	18·00
63	4	5d. grey and black (6.4.05)	7·50	12·00
64	3	6d. olive-green and carmine (23.2.06)	7·50	18·00
65	4	7½d. green and carmine (6.4.05)	5·00	15·00
66		10d. olive and carmine (6.4.05)	8·00	15·00
67	3	1s. violet and green (9.05)	15·00	35·00
68	4	2s. deep slate and orange (7.05)	38·00	48·00
57/68		*Set of* 12	90·00	£150
63, 65/6 Optd "Specimen"		*Set of* 3	70·00	

See also Nos. 72/85.

HALF PENNY

(5)

ONE PENNY

(6)

1906 (10 April). *Nos. 55 and 56 surch with T 5 or 6 by Govt Printer.*

69	½d. on 2s. 6d. purple and brown/*yellow*	32·00	55·00
70	1d. on 3s. carmine and green/*yellow*	45·00	40·00
	a. Surch double	£2250	£6000

No. 69 was surcharged in a setting of 30 (6 × 5), the spacing between the words and the bars being 5 mm on rows 1, 2 and 5; and 4 mm on rows 3 and 4. Constant varieties occur on R.2/1 (broken "E") and R.5/1 (dropped "Y") of the setting.

No. 70 was surcharged in a setting of 60 (6 × 10) and a similar dropped "Y" variety occurs on R.6/3 and R.8/5.

1909 (1 Oct). *Colours changed. Wmk Mult Crown CA. P 14.*

72	3	½d. blue-green	1·75	2·00
73		1d. red	1·75	15
74		2d. greyish slate	1·40	3·75
75		3d. purple/*yellow*	2·50	1·50
		a. Purple/lemon-yellow	5·50	2·00
76		4d. black and red/*yellow*	80	65
77	4	5d. orange and purple	1·00	1·25
78	3	6d. dull and bright purple	1·50	2·25
79	4	7½d. brown and blue	1·25	2·50
80		10d. pale sage-green and carmine	1·75	6·00
81	3	1s. black/*green*	1·50	5·50
82	4	1s. 6d. violet and green	6·50	18·00
83		2s. purple and bright blue/*blue*	4·25	13·00
84		2s. 6d. black and red/*blue*	20·00	18·00
85		3s. yellow and green	20·00	35·00
72/85		*Set of* 14	60·00	95·00
73/85 Optd "Specimen"		*Set of* 13	£275	

7

8

Split "A"

The split "A" variety occurs on No. 45 in the left-hand pane in printings to 1918 of all values up to 3s. (*Prices about six to ten times normal.*)

(Typo D.L.R.)

1912 (1 Sept)–**22.** *Wmk Mult Crown CA. P 14.*

86	7	½d. deep green, O	45	70
		a. Green	40	65
		b. Pale green (1916)	60	75
87		1d. red, O	35	20
		a. Rose-red	65	20
		b. Scarlet (1916)	90	50
88	8	1½d. olive-green and blue-green, O	30	30
89	7	2d. greyish slate, O	45	70
90		2½d. deep bright blue, O	4·00	2·50
		a. Bright blue	4·25	2·50
91		3d. purple/*yellow*, O	25	30
		a. On lemon (1917)	12·00	17·00
		b. On orange-buff (1920)	10·00	7·00
		c. On pale yellow	40	75
*92		4d. black and red/*yellow*, O	75	6·50
		a. On lemon (1917)	90	6·50
		b. On orange-buff (1920)	4·25	9·00
		c. On pale yellow	1·50	5·00
93	8	5d. orange and purple, O	50	1·25
94	7	6d. dull and bright purple, O	50	90
95	8	7½d. brown and blue, O	80	3·50
96		10d. pale sage-green and carmine, O	2·00	12·00
		a. Deep sage-green and carmine	1·50	10·00
97	7	1s. black/*green*, O	45	1·00
		a. On emerald back	50	6·00
98	8	1s. 6d. violet and green, O	4·00	8·50
99		2s. purple and blue/*blue*, O	2·25	6·00
100		2s. 6d. black and red/*blue*, O	2·50	11·00
101		3s. yellow and green, O	7·00	16·00
102		5s. green and red/*pale yellow*, C (1922)	30·00	45·00
86/102		*Set of* 17	50·00	£100
86/102 Optd "Specimen"		*Set of* 17	£375	

1921–22. *Wmk Mult Script CA. P 14.*

108	7	½d. dull green, O	30	4·00
109		1d. carmine-red, O	1·00	1·60
110	8	1½d. olive-green and blue-green, O	1·25	7·00
111	7	2d. grey, O	1·00	70
112		2½d. bright blue, O	50	3·50
113	8	5d. orange and purple, O	1·75	8·00
114	7	6d. dull and bright purple, O	1·75	6·00
115	8	7½d. brown and blue, O	2·00	13·00
116		10d. pale sage-green and carmine, O	5·00	13·00
117		4s. black and red, C (1922)	27·00	45·00
108/117		*Set of* 10	35·00	90·00
108/17 Optd "Specimen"		*Set of* 10	£200	

9

10

(Recess D.L.R.)

1922 (1 Sept)–**29.** *Portrait and shield in black. P 14*.*

(*a*) *Wmk Mult Crown CA*

118	9	4d. red/*yellow* (*a*)	90	1·50
119		7½d. purple/*yellow* (*a*)	1·50	6·50
120	10	1s. purple/*yellow* (*a*)	4·00	17·00
121		5s. green/*yellow* (*c*)	25·00	48·00
118/21		*Set of* 4	28·00	65·00
118/21 Optd/H/S "Specimen"		*Set of* 4	£180	

(*b*) *Wmk Mult Script CA*

122	9	½d. green (*abd*)	45	30
123		½d. deep green (*bd*) (1925)	80	50
124		1d. brown (*abd*)	60	10
125		1½d. bright rose-scarlet (*abd*)	70	10
126		2d. grey (*ab*)	70	75
127		2½d. orange-yellow (*b*)	70	4·25
128		3d. bright blue (*abd*)	75	10
129		4d. red/*yellow* (*bd*) (1.3.27)	2·00	5·50
130		5d. sage-green (*a*)	2·00	10·00
131		6d. claret (*ad*)	90	15
132		7½d. purple/*yellow* (*ab*) (1927)	4·50	17·00
133		10d. blue (*a*)	4·00	16·00

134 **10** 1s. purple/*yellow* (*aef*) (9.24) .. .. 2·25 25
a. Blackish purple/yellow-buff (*c*) (1929) 25·00 32·00
135 1s. 6d. blue (*af*) .. .. 6·50 12·00
136 2s. purple/*blue* (*ac*) .. .. .. 3·00 3·00
137 2s. 6d. deep green (*a*) .. .. .. 3·75 9·50
138 3s. bright aniline violet (*a*) .. .. 10·00 27·00
139 3s. slate-purple (*c*) (1928) £180 £350
140 4s. brown (*ace*) .. .. 3·75 14·00
141 5s. green/*yellow* (*acf*) (9.26) .. .. 8·00 22·00
142 10s. sage-green (*ce*) .. .. .. 45·00 60·00
122/42 .. .. *Set of* 19 90·00 £180
122/42 Optd "Specimen" .. .. *Set of* 19 £475

Perforations. A number of different perforating machines were used for the various printings of these stamps and the following varieties are known: (*a*) the original 14 line perforation; (*b*) 14 × 13.8 comb perforation used for Type **9**; (*c*) 13.8 × 13.7 comb perforation used for Type **10**; (*d*) 13.7 line perforation used for Type **9**; (*e*) 14 × 13.8 compound line perforation used for Type **10**; (*f*) 13.8 × 14 compound line perforation used for Type **10**. The occurrence of these perforations on the individual values is indicated by the letters shown after the colour descriptions above.

No. 139 has been faked, but note that this stamp is comb perf 13.8 × 13.7 whereas No. 138 is line perf 14 exactly. There are also shades of the slate-purple.

1935 (6 May). *Silver Jubilee. As T* **13** *of Antigua. Recess B.W. Wmk Mult Script CA. P* 11 × 12.
143 1½d. deep blue and scarlet 50 30
a. Extra flagstaff .. .. 60·00
b. Short extra flagstaff .. .. .. 50·00
c. Lightning conductor .. .. .. 45·00
d. Flagstaff on right-hand turret .. 45·00
e. Double flagstaff .. .. 35·00
144 3d. brown and deep blue 55 70
a. Extra flagstaff £130
b. Short extra flagstaff .. .. .. 80·00
c. Lightning conductor .. .. .. 70·00
145 6d. light blue and olive-green 90 90
a. Extra flagstaff £130
b. Short extra flagstaff .. .. .. 80·00
c. Lightning conductor .. .. .. 70·00
d. Flagstaff on right-hand turret .. 70·00
146 1s. slate and purple .. .. .. 1·25 90
a. Extra flagstaff £200
b. Short extra flagstaff £125
c. Lightning conductor £125
d. Flagstaff on right-hand turret .. £100
143/6 .. .. *Set of* 4 3·00 2·50
143/6 Perf "Specimen" .. .. *Set of* 4 80·00

For illustrations of plate varieties see Omnibus section following Zululand.

Examples of Nos 145a and 146a are known with the extra flagstaff erased from the stamp with a sharp point.

1937 (12 May). *Coronation. As T* **2** *of Aden. Recess B.W. Wmk Mult Script CA. P* 11 × 11½.
147 1d. yellow-brown 20 10
148 1½d. carmine 20 15
149 3d. blue 55 35
147/9 .. .. *Set of* 3 85 50
147/9 Perf "Specimen" .. .. *Set of* 3 50·00

11 Elephant (from Colony Badge)

(Recess B.W.)

1938 (1 Apr)–**46**. *Wmk Mult Script CA. P* 12.
150 **11** ½d. black and emerald-green 15 15
151 1d. purple and brown 20 10
152 1½d. lake and carmine .. .. .. 26·00 7·00
a. Lake and scarlet (1942) 20 25
152*b* 1½d. blue and black (2.1.45) 20 50
153 2d. blue and black .. .. .. 80 1·25
153*a* 2d. lake and scarlet (1.10.43) 20 40
154 3d. light blue and grey-blue 20 10
154*a* 5d. sage-green & purple-brn (13.3.41) .. 25 25
155 6d. olive-green and claret 20 15
156 1s. slate-blue and violet 50 10
156*a* 1s. 3d. chocolate & lt blue (28.11.46) .. 80 35
157 2s. carmine and blue .. .. .. 3·25 2·75
158 2s. 6d. sepia and dull green .. .. 4·75 1·75
159 4s. vermilion and purple .. .. 8·00 2·00
160 5s. blue and vermilion .. .. .. 7·50 3·25
161 10s. orange and black .. .. .. 9·50 5·50
150/161 .. .. *Set of* 16 32·00 17·00
150/61 Perf "Specimen" .. .. *Set of* 16 £180

1946 (6 Aug). *Victory. As Nos.* 28/9 *of Aden.*
162 1½d. black 10 10
163 3d. blue 10 10
162/3 Perf "Specimen" .. .. *Set of* 2 55·00

1948 (24 Dec). *Royal Silver Wedding. As Nos.* 30/1 *of Aden.*
164 1½d. black 25 10
165 £1 mauve .. .. 12·00 11·00

1949 (10 Oct). *75th Anniv of Universal Postal Union. As Nos.* **114/17** *of Antigua.*
166 1½d. blue-black 20 20
167 3d. deep blue 60 30
168 6d. magenta 60 25
169 1s. violet 65 20
166/9 .. .. *Set of* 4 1·90 85

1953 (2 June). *Coronation. As No.* 47 *of Aden, but ptd by B.W.*
170 1½d. black and deep bright blue 10 20

12 Tapping for Palm Wine

13 Cutter

(Des Mrs O. W. Meronti. Recess D.L.R.)

1953 (2 Nov)–**59**. *T* **12/13** *and similar horiz designs. Wmk Mult Script CA. P* 13½.
171 **12** ½d. carmine-red and bluish green .. 15 20
a. Carmine and bluish green (7.1.59) 20 25
172 **13** 1d. deep ultramarine and deep brown .. 40 10
a. Deep ultramarine & choc (22.8.56) 1·00 25
173 – 1½d. deep brown and grey-black .. 20 10
174 – 2½d. black and carmine-red 45 35
175 – 3d. deep blue and slate-lilac 35 10
176 – 4d. black and deep blue 60 80
177 **12** 6d. brown and reddish purple 35 10
178 – 1s. yellow-brown and yellow-green .. 45 10
179 **13** 1s. 3d. ultramarine and pale blue .. 4·00 15
a. Ultramarine and light blue (22.2.56) 4·50 25
180 – 2s. indigo and carmine .. .. 2·50 2·00
181 **13** 2s. 6d. deep bluish green and sepia .. 2·00 1·00
182 – 4s. grey-blue and Indian red .. .. 1·50 1·25
183 – 5s. chocolate and bright blue .. .. 1·50 1·50
184 – 10s. deep blue and myrtle-green .. 6·50 6·50
185 – £1 green and black .. .. .. 7·50 9·00
171/85 .. .. *Set of* 15 25·00 21·00

Designs:—1½d., 5s. Wollof woman; 2½d., 2s. Barra canoe; 3d., 10s. S.S. *Lady Wright*; 4d., 4s. James Island; 1s., 2s. 6d. Woman hoeing; £1 Elephant and palm (from Colony Badge).

20 Queen Elizabeth II and Palm

21 Queen Elizabeth II and West African Map

(Des J. R. F. Ithier (T **20**), A. W. Morley (T **21**). Recess B.W.)

1961 (2 Dec). *Royal Visit. W w* **12**. *P* 11½.
186 **20** 2d. green and purple 10 10
187 **21** 3d. turquoise-blue and sepia 10 10
188 6d. blue and cerise 10 10
189 **20** 1s. 3d. violet and myrtle-green .. 15 30
186/9 .. .. *Set of* 4 35 40

1963 (4 June). *Freedom from Hunger. As No.* 76 *of Aden.*
190 1s. 3d. carmine 40 15

1963 (2 Sept). *Red Cross Centenary. As Nos.* 147/8 *of Antigua.*
191 2d. red and black 15 10
192 1s. 3d. red and blue 40 25

SELF-GOVERNMENT

22 Beautiful Sunbird

SELF GOVERNMENT
1963

(**35**)

(Des V. Whiteley. Photo Harrison)

1963 (4 Nov). *Birds. Horiz designs as T* **22**. *Multicoloured. W w* **12**. *P* 12½ × 13.
193 ½d. Type **22** 15 15
194 1d. Yellow-mantled Whydah 20 10
195 1½d. Cattle Egret 55 60
196 2d. Senegal Parrot 50 15
197 3d. Rose-ringed Parakeet 50 15
198 4d. Violet Starling 50 40
199 6d. Village Weaver 80 10
200 1s. Rufous-crowned Roller 60 10
201 1s. 3d. Red-eyed Dove .. .. .. 6·00 1·40
202 2s. 6d. Double-spurred Francolin .. 5·50 2·25
203 5s. Palm-nut Vulture .. .. .. 5·00 2·75
204 10s. Orange-cheeked Waxbill .. .. 9·00 7·00
205 £1 African Emerald Cuckoo .. .. 20·00 14·00
193/205 .. .. *Set of* 13 45·00 26·00

1963 (7 Nov). *New Constitution. Nos.* 194, 197, 200/1 *optd with T* **35**.
206 1d. Yellow-mantled Whydah 10 10
207 3d. Rose-ringed Parakeet 10 10
208 1s. Rufous-crowned Roller 10 10
a. Opt double .. .. † —
209 1s. 3d. Red-eyed Dove 10 10
206/9 .. .. *Set of* 4 25 15

1964 (23 Apr). *400th Birth Anniv of William Shakespeare. As No.* 164 *of Antigua.*
210 6d. greenish blue 10 10

INDEPENDENT

36 Gambia Flag and River

37 Arms

(Des V. Whiteley. Photo Harrison)

1965 (18 Feb). *Independence. P* 14½.
211 **36** ½d. multicoloured 10 10
212 **37** 2d. multicoloured 10 10
213 **36** 7½d. multicoloured 10 10
214 **37** 1s. 6d. multicoloured 10 10
211/14 .. .. *Set of* 4 20 15

INDEPENDENCE
1965

(**38**)

39 I.T.U. Emblem and Symbols

1965 (18 Feb). *Nos.* 193/205 *optd with T* **38** *or with date centred* (1*d.*, 2*d.*, 3*d.*, 4*d.*, 1*s.*, 5*s.*).
215 ½d. Type **22** 15 15
216 1d. Yellow-mantled Whydah 15 10
217 1½d. Cattle Egret 20 25
218 2d. Senegal Parrot 20 15
219 3d. Rose-ringed Parakeet 25 15
220 4d. Violet Starling 25 30
221 6d. Village Weaver 25 10
222 1s. Rufous-crowned Roller 30 10
223 1s. 3d. Red-eyed Dove 50 10
224 2s. 6d. Double-spurred Francolin .. 50 15
225 5s. Palm-nut Vulture 50 40
226 10s. Orange-cheeked Waxbill .. .. 1·00 1·50
227 £1 African Emerald Cuckoo .. .. 3·00 6·00
215/27 .. .. *Set of* 13 6·50 8·50

(Des V. Whiteley. Photo Harrison)

1965 (17 May). *I.T.U. Centenary. P* 14½.
228 **39** 1d. silver and Prussian blue 15 10
229 1s. 6d. gold and bluish violet 45 15

THE GAMBIA. From this point onwards stamps are inscribed "The Gambia".

40 Sir Winston Churchill and Houses of Parliament

(Des Jennifer Toombs. Photo Harrison)

1966 (24 Jan). *Churchill Commemoration. P* 14 × 14½.
230 **40** 1d. multicoloured 10 10
231 6d. multicoloured 20 10
232 1s. 6d. multicoloured 40 30
230/2 .. .. *Set of* 3 65 35

41 Red-cheeked Cordon Bleu

42 Pin-tailed Whydah

(Des V. Whiteley. Photo Harrison)

1966 (18 Feb). *Birds. Horiz designs as T* **41**, *and T* **42**. *Multicoloured. P* 14 × 14½ (£1) *or* 12 × 13 (*others*).
233 ½d. Type **41** 20 15
234 1d. White-faced Whistling Duck 25 10
235 1½d. Red-throated Bee Eater 30 15
236 2d. Lesser Pied Kingfisher .. .. 1·50 20
237 3d. Golden Bishop 30 10
238 4d. African Fish Eagle 50 30
239 6d. Yellow-bellied Green Pigeon .. 40 10
240 1s. Blue-bellied Roller 40 10
241 1s. 6d. African Pygmy Kingfisher .. 85 30
242 2s. 6d. Spur-winged Goose 95 70

243	5s. Cardinal Woodpecker		1·00	75
244	10s. Violet Turaco		1·25	2·75
245	£1 Type 42		1·25	5·00
233/45		*Set of* 13	8·00	9·50

The ½d., 1d. and 2d. to 1s. values exist with PVA gum as well as gum arabic.

54 Arms, Early Settlement and Modern Buildings

(Photo, arms die-stamped Harrison)

1966 (24 June). *150th Anniv of Bathurst. P* 14½ × 14.

246 **54**	1d. silver, brown and yellow-orange		10	10
247	2d. silver, brown and light blue		10	10
248	6d. silver, brown and light emerald		10	10
249	1s. 6d. silver, brown and light magenta		10	10
246/9		*Set of* 4	15	15

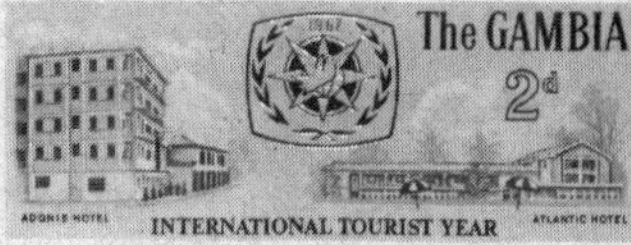

55 I.T.Y. Emblem and Hotels

(Des and photo (emblem die-stamped) Harrison)

1967 (20 Dec). *International Tourist Year. P* 14½ × 14.

250 **55**	2d. silver, brown and apple-green		10	10
251	1s. silver, brown and orange		10	10
252	1s. 6d. silver, brown and magenta		10	10
250/2		*Set of* 3	20	15

56 Handcuffs

(Des V. Whiteley. Photo Enschedé)

1968 (15 July). *Human Rights Year. T* **56** *and similar horiz designs. Multicoloured. P* 14 × 13.

253	1d. Type **56**		10	10
254	1s. Fort Bullen		10	10
255	5s. Methodist Church		30	25
253/5		*Set of* 3	35	25

59 Queen Victoria, Queen Elizabeth II and 4d. Stamp of 1869

(Des G. Drummond. Photo and embossing (cameo head) Harrison)

1969 (20 Jan). *Gambia Stamp Centenary. P* 14½ × 13½.

256 **59**	4d. sepia and yellow-ochre		10	10
257	6d. Prussian blue and deep yellow-green		10	10
258 –	2s. 6d. multicoloured		35	55
256/8		*Set of* 3	50	60

Design:—2s. 6d. Queen Elizabeth II with 4d. and 6d. stamps of 1869.

In the 6d. value the stamp illustrated is the 6d. of 1869.

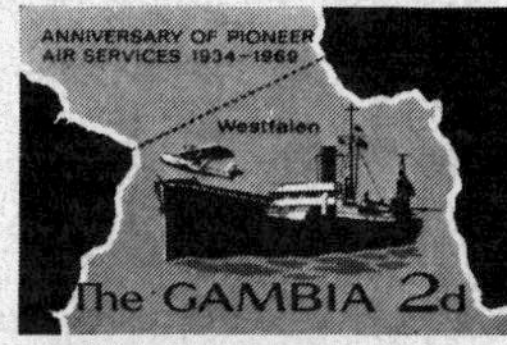

61 Catapult-Ship *Westfalen* launching Dornier "Wal"

(Des L. Curtis. Litho Format International)

1969 (15 Dec). *35th Anniv of Pioneer Air Services. T* **61** *and similar horiz designs showing various forms of transport, map of South Atlantic and Lufthansa emblem. Multicoloured. P* 13½ × 14.

259	2d. Type **61**		15	10
260	1s. Dornier "Wal" flying-boat		20	10
261	1s. 6d. *Graf Zeppelin* airship		30	50
259/61		*Set of* 3	60	60

REPUBLIC

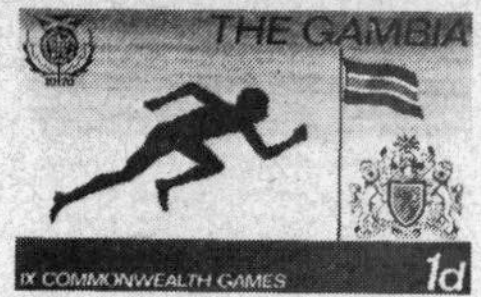

63 Athlete and Gambian Flag

(Des Jennifer Toombs. Litho Format)

1970 (16 July). *Ninth British Commonwealth Games, Edinburgh. P* 14.

262 **63**	1d. multicoloured		10	10
263	1s. multicoloured		10	10
264	5s. multicoloured		30	30
262/4		*Set of* 3	35	30

64 President Sir Dawda Kairaba Jawara and State House

(Des G. Vasarhelyi. Litho Questa)

1970 (2 Nov). *Republic Day. T* **64** *and similar multicoloured designs. P* 14.

265	2d. Type **64**		10	10
266	1s. President Sir Dawda Jawara		10	10
267	1s. 6d. President and flag of Gambia		10	10
265/7		*Set of* 3	15	15

The 1s. and 1s. 6d. are both vertical designs.

65 Methodist Church, Georgetown

(Des J. Cooter. Litho Questa)

1971 (16 Apr). *150th Anniv of Establishment of Methodist Mission. T* **65** *and similar multicoloured designs. P* 14.

268	2d. Type **65**		10	10
269	1s. Map of Africa and Gambian flag (*vert*)		10	10
270	1s. 6d. John Wesley and scroll (*horiz*)		10	15
268/70		*Set of* 3	15	20

(New Currency. 100 bututs = 1 dalasy)

66 Yellowfin Tunny

(Des J.W. Litho Format)

1971 (1 July). *New Currency. Fishes. Horiz designs as T* **66**. *Multicoloured. P* 14.

271	2 b. Type **66**		10	15
272	4 b. Peters' Mormyrid		10	15
273	6 b. Tropical Flying Fish		15	15
274	8 b. African Sleeper Goby		15	15
275	10 b. Yellowtail Snapper		20	15
276	13 b. Rock Hind		20	25
277	25 b. Gymnallabes		35	25
278	38 b. Tiger Shark		45	45
279	50 b. Electric Catfish		60	55
280	63 b. Black Synbranchus		70	90
281	1 d. 25, Smalltooth Sawfish		1·50	1·75
282	2 d. 50, Barracuda		3·75	4·00
283	5 d. Brown Bullhead		5·50	6·50
271/83		*Set of* 13	12·50	13·50

67 Mungo Park in Scotland

(Des J.W. from ideas by P. J. Westwood. Litho Questa)

1971 (10 Sept). *Birth Bicentenary of Mungo Park (explorer). T* **67** *and similar horiz designs. Multicoloured. W w* **12** *(sideways). P* 13½ × 13.

284	4 b. Type **67**		10	10
285	25 b. Dug-out canoe		20	10
286	37 b. Death of Mungo Park, Busa Rapids		30	25
284/6		*Set of* 3	55	30

68 Radio Gambia

(Des G. Drummond. Litho Questa)

1972 (1 July). *Tenth Anniv of Radio Gambia. T* **68** *and similar horiz design. P* 14.

287 **68**	4 b. orange-ochre and black		10	10
288 –	25 b. light new blue, red-orange and black		10	15
289 **68**	37 b. bright green and black		20	25
287/9		*Set of* 3	30	40

Design:—25 b. Broadcast-area map.

69 High-jumping

70 Manding Woman

(Des and litho D.L.R.)

1972 (31 Aug). *Olympic Games, Munich. P* 13.

290 **69**	4 b. multicoloured		10	10
291	25 b. multicoloured		10	10
292	37 b. multicoloured		15	20
290/2		*Set of* 3	20	20

(Des C. Abbott. Litho Questa)

1972 (16 Oct). *International Conference on Manding Studies, London. T* **70** *and similar vert designs. Multicoloured. P* 14 × 14½.

293	2 b. Type **70**		10	10
294	25 b. Musician playing the Kora		15	15
295	37 b. Map of Mali Empire		25	25
293/5		*Set of* 3	40	40

71 Children carrying Fanal

72 Groundnuts

(Des L. Curtis. Litho Enschedé)

1972 (1 Dec). *Fanals (Model Boats). T* **71** *and similar horiz design. Multicoloured. P* 13 × 13½.

296	2 b. Type **71**		10	10
297	1 d. 25, Fanal with lanterns		30	45

(Des locally; adapted G. Drummond. Litho Harrison)

1973 (31 Mar). *Freedom from Hunger Campaign. P* 14½ × 14.

298 **72**	2 b. multicoloured		10	10
299	25 b. multicoloured		15	10
300	37 b. multicoloured		25	20
298/300		*Set of* 3	40	30

73 Planting and Drying Rice

74 Oil Palm

(Des PAD Studio. Litho J.W.)

1973 (30 Apr). *Agriculture (1st series). T* **73** *and similar vert designs. Multicoloured. P* 14.

301	2 b. Type **73**		10	10
302	25 b. Guinea Corn		20	15
303	37 b. Rice		25	25
301/3		*Set of* 3	45	40

(Des PAD Studio. Litho Format)

1973 (16 July). *Agriculture (2nd series). T* **74** *and similar vert designs. Multicoloured. P* 12.

304	2 b. Type **74**	10	10
305	25 b. Limes	30	30
306	37 b. Oil palm (fruits)	40	40
304/6	*Set of* 3	65	65

75 Cassava

(Des PAD Studio. Litho Questa)

1973 (15 Oct). *Agriculture (3rd series). T* **75** *and similar horiz design. Multicoloured. P* 14.

307	2 b. Type **75**	10	10
308	50 b. Cotton	40	25

76 O.A.U. Emblem

(Des and litho D.L.R.)

1973 (1 Nov). *Tenth Anniv of O.A.U. P* 13½ × 13.

309	**76**	4 b. multicoloured	10	10
310		25 b. multicoloured	10	10
311		37 b. multicoloured	15	15
309/11		*Set of* 3	25	20

77 Red Cross — **78** Arms of Banjul

(Des J. Cooter. Litho Questa)

1973 (30 Nov). *25th Anniv of Gambian Red Cross. P* 14 × 14½.

312	**77**	4 b. dull orange-red, and black	10	10
313		25 b. dull orange-red, black and new blue	15	15
314		37 b. dull orange-red, black & lt yell-grn	20	20
312/14		*Set of* 3	35	35

(Des and litho D.L.R.)

1973 (17 Dec). *Change of Bathurst's Name to Banjul. P* 13½ × 13.

315	**78**	4 b. multicoloured	10	10
316		25 b. multicoloured	10	10
317		37 b. multicoloured	15	15
315/17		*Set of* 3	25	20

79 U.P.U. Emblem

(Des and litho D.L.R.)

1974 (24 Aug). *Centenary of Universal Postal Union. P* 13½.

318	**79**	4 b. multicoloured	10	10
319		37 b. multicoloured	20	30

80 Churchill as Harrow Schoolboy — **81** "Different Races"

(Des and litho J.W.)

1974 (30 Nov). *Birth Centenary of Sir Winston Churchill. T* **80** *and similar vert designs. Multicoloured. P* 13½.

320	4 b. Type **80**	10	10
321	37 b. Churchill as 4th Hussars officer	25	10
322	50 b. Churchill as Prime Minister	40	30
320/2	*Set of* 3	65	40

(Des G. Vasarhelyi. Litho Questa)

1974 (16 Dec). *World Population Year. T* **81** *and similar horiz designs. Multicoloured. P* 14.

323	4 b. Type **81**	10	10
324	37 b. "Multiplication and Division of Races"	15	15
325	50 b. "World Population"	20	25
323/5	*Set of* 3	35	40

82 Dr. Schweitzer and River Scene

(Des G. Vasarhelyi. Litho Walsall)

1975 (14 Jan). *Birth Centenary of Dr. Albert Schweitzer. T* **82** *and similar horiz designs. Multicoloured. P* 14.

326	10 b. Type **82**	15	10
327	50 b. Surgery scene	35	25
328	1 d. 25, River journey	75	55
326/8	*Set of* 3	1·10	75

83 Dove of Peace — **84** Development Graph

(Des and litho D.L.R.)

1975 (18 Feb). *Tenth Anniv of Independence. T* **83** *and similar horiz designs. Multicoloured. P* 13.

329	4 b. Type **83**	10	10
330	10 b. Gambian flag	10	10
331	50 b. Gambian arms	15	10
332	1 d. 25, Map of The Gambia	35	40
329/32	*Set of* 4	50	55

(Des PAD Studio. Litho Questa)

1975 (31 Mar). *Tenth Anniv of African Development Bank. T* **84** *and similar vert designs. Multicoloured. P* 14½.

333	10 b. Type **84**	10	10
334	50 b. Symbolic plant	20	15
335	1 d. 25, Bank emblem and symbols	55	60
333/5	*Set of* 3	70	75

85 "Statute of David" (Michelangelo) — **86** School Building

(Des C. Abbott. Litho Walsall)

1975 (14 Nov). *500th Birth Anniv of Michelangelo. T* **85** *and similar multicoloured designs. P* 14½ × 14 *(1 d. 25) or* 14 × 14½ *(others).*

336	10 b. Type **85**	10	10
337	50 b. "Madonna of the Steps"	15	10
338	1 d. 25, "Battle of the Centaurs" *(horiz)*	45	60
336/8	*Set of* 3	60	65

(Des G. Vasarhelyi. Litho Format)

1975 (17 Nov). *Centenary of Gambia High School. T* **86** *and similar horiz designs. Multicoloured. P* 14½.

339	10 b. Type **86**	10	10
340	50 b. Pupil with scientific apparatus	15	10
341	1 d. 50, School crest	35	35
339/41	*Set of* 3	50	40

NEW INFORMATION

The editor is always interested to correspond with people who have new information that will improve or correct the Catalogue.

87 "Teaching"

(Des A. B. Oliver; adapted by Jennifer Toombs. Litho Questa)

1975 (15 Dec). *International Women's Year. T* **87** *and similar horiz designs. Multicoloured. P* 14½.

342	4 b. Type **87**	10	10
343	10 b. "Planting rice"	10	10
344	50 b. "Nursing"	35	15
345	1 d. 50, "Directing traffic"	85	35
342/5	*Set of* 4	1·25	55

88 Woman playing Golf — **89** American Militiaman

(Des R. Granger Barrett. Litho J.W.)

1976 (18 Feb). *11th Anniv of Independence. T* **88** *and similar horiz designs. Multicoloured. P* 14½ × 14.

346	10 b. Type **88**	25	10
347	50 b. Man playing golf	90	20
348	1 d. 50, President playing golf	2·00	70
346/8	*Set of* 3	2·75	90

(Des C. Abbott. Litho Questa)

1976 (15 May). *Bicentenary of American Revolution. T* **89** *and similar vert designs. Multicoloured. P* 14 × 13½.

349	25 b. Type **89**	30	10
350	50 b. Soldier of the Continental Army	50	20
351	1 d. 25, Independence Declaration	80	60
349/51	*Set of* 3	1·40	80
MS352	110 × 80 mm. Nos. 349/51	2·50	3·75

90 Mother and Child — **91** Serval

(Des G. Vasarhelyi. Litho Questa)

1976 (28 Oct). *Christmas. P* 14.

353	**90**	10 b. multicoloured	10	10
354		50 b. multicoloured	15	10
355		1 d. 25, multicoloured	50	45
353/5		*Set of* 3	60	50

(Des G. Drummond. Litho Questa)

1976 (29 Nov). *Abuko Nature Reserve (1st series). T* **91** *and similar horiz designs. Multicoloured. P* 13½.

356	10 b. Type **91**	30	10
357	25 b. Bushbuck	70	20
358	50 b. Sitatunga	1·00	40
359	1 d. 25, Leopard	2·50	1·25
356/9	*Set of* 4	4·00	1·75
MS360	137 × 110 mm. Nos. 356/9	6·00	6·50

See also Nos. 400/3, 431/5 and 460/3.

92 Festival Emblem and Gambian Weaver

(Des E. N. Sillah; adapted C. Abbott. Litho Walsall)

1977 (12 Jan). *Second World Black and African Festival of Arts and Culture, Nigeria. P* 14.

361	**92**	25 b. multicoloured	15	10
362		50 b. multicoloured	20	15
363		1 d. 25, multicoloured	50	70
361/3		*Set of* 3	75	85
MS364		118 × 114 mm. Nos. 361/3	2·25	3·00

93 The Spurs and Jewelled Sword

(Des PAD Studio. Litho Questa)

1977 (7 Feb). *Silver Jubilee. T* **93** *and similar horiz designs. Multicoloured. P* 13½.

365	25 b. Queen's visit, 1961	1·00	60
366	50 b. Type **93**	50	40
367	1 d. 25, Oblation of the sword	1·00	75
365/7	*Set of* 3	2·25	1·60

94 Stone Circles, Kuntaur

(Des J.W. Litho Questa)

1977 (18 Feb). *Tourism. T* **94** *and similar horiz designs. Multicoloured. P* 14.

368	25 b. Type **94**	10	10
369	50 b. Ruined fort, James Island	20	20
370	1 d. 25, Mungo Park Monument	70	70
368/70	*Set of* 3	90	90

95 Widow of Last Year **96** Endangered Animals

(Des PAD Studio. Litho Questa)

1977 (1 July)–**79**. *Flowers and Shrubs. Multicoloured designs as T* **95**. *Chalk-surfaced paper (No. 376a) or ordinary paper (others). P* 14.

371	2 b. Type **95**	10	10
	a. Chalk-surfaced paper (23.11.79)	40	15
372	4 b. White Water-lily	10	20
	a. Chalk-surfaced paper (23.11.79)	40	20
373	6 b. Fireball Lily	10	20
	a. Chalk-surfaced paper (22.6.79)	40	20
374	8 b. Cocks-comb	10	15
	a. Chalk-surfaced paper (23.11.79)	30	15
375	10 b. Broad Leaved Ground Orchid	40	20
	a. Chalk-surfaced paper (23.11.79)	70	20
376	13 b. Fibre Plant (pale yellow background)	15	30
376a	13 b. Fibre Plant (pale olive-grey background) (*chalk-surfaced paper*) (25.7.79)	2·00	2·50
377	25 b. False Kapok	15	15
	a. Chalk-surfaced paper (16.3.78)	55	35
378	38 b. Baobab	25	45
	a. Chalk-surfaced paper (23.11.79)	60	35
379	50 b. Coral Tree	35	35
	a. Chalk-surfaced paper (16.3.78)	75	50
380	63 b. Gloriosa Lily	40	60
	a. Chalk-surfaced paper (23.11.79)	85	65
381	1 d. 25, Bell-flowered Mimosa	70	1·00
	a. Chalk-surfaced paper (23.11.79)	1·00	1·00
382	2 d. 50, Kindin Dolo	75	1·00
383	5 d. African Tulip Tree	1·25	2·00
371/83	*Set of* 14	6·00	8·00

The 6 to 38 b., 1 d. 25 and 2 d. 50 are vertical designs.

(Des N. Fortey (10, 50 b.), D. J. Thorp (25 b.), M. Langley (1 d. 25). Litho Questa)

1977 (15 Oct). *Banjul Declaration. T* **96** *and similar vert designs. P* 14.

384	10 b. black and light new blue	15	10
385	25 b. multicoloured	40	10
386	50 b. multicoloured	65	20
387	1 d. 25, black and light vermilion	1·40	75
384/7	*Set of* 4	2·40	1·00

Designs:—25 b. Extract from Declaration; 50 b. Declaration in full; 1 d. 25, Endangered insects and flowers.

ALTERED CATALOGUE NUMBERS

Any Catalogue numbers altered from the last edition are shown as a list in the introductory pages.

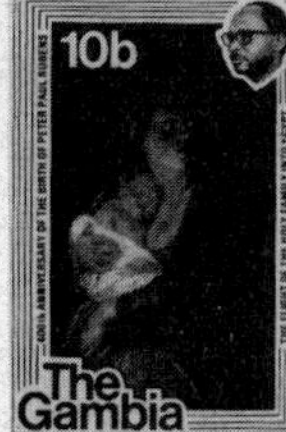

97 "Flight into Egypt" **98** Dome of the Rock, Jerusalem

(Des BG Studio and Enschedé. Litho Enschedé)

1977 (15 Dec). *400th Birth Anniv of Rubens. T* **97** *and similar vert designs. Multicoloured. P* 13½ × 14.

388	10 b. Type **97**	10	10
389	25 b. "The Education of the Virgin"	15	10
390	50 b. "Clara Serena Rubens"	35	20
391	1 d. "Madonna with Saints"	60	70
388/91	*Set of* 4	1·10	1·00

Nos. 388/91 were each printed in small sheets of 6 including 1 *se-tenant* stamp-size label.

(Des J. Cooter. Litho Questa)

1978 (3 Jan). *Palestinian Welfare. P* 14½ × 14.

392	**98**	8 b. multicoloured	50	15
393		25 b. multicoloured	2·00	85

99 Walking on a Greasy Pole **100** Lion

(Des J.W. Litho Harrison)

1978 (18 Feb). *13th Anniv of Independence. T* **99** *and similar vert designs showing scenes from the Independence Regatta. Multicoloured. P* 14.

394	10 b. Type **99**	10	10
395	50 b. Pillow fighting	15	10
396	1 d. 25, Long rowing boat	35	45
394/6	*Set of* 3	50	55

(Des Jennifer Toombs. Litho Questa)

1978 (15 Apr). *25th Anniv of Coronation. T* **100** *and similar vert designs. P* 15.

397	1 d. black, agate and orange-yellow	35	60
	a. Sheetlet. Nos. 397/9 × 2	1·90	
398	1 d. multicoloured	35	60
399	1 d. black, agate and orange-yellow	35	60
397/9	*Set of* 3	95	1·60

Designs:—No. 397, White Greyhound of Richmond; No. 398, Queen Elizabeth II; No. 399, Type **100**.

Nos. 397/9 were printed together in small sheets of 6, containing two *se-tenant* strips of 3, with horizontal gutter margin between.

101 Verreaux's Eagle Owl **102** M.V. *Lady Wright* (previous vessel)

(Des M. Bryan. Litho Questa)

1978 (28 Oct). *Abuko Nature Reserve (2nd series). T* **101** *and similar vert designs. Multicoloured. P* 14 × 13½.

400	20 b. Type **101**	1·00	25
401	25 b. Lizard Buzzard	1·10	30
402	50 b. African Harrier Hawk	1·75	80
403	1 d. 25, Long-crested Eagle	2·75	3·00
400/3	*Set of* 4	6·00	4·00

(Des A. Theobald. Litho Questa)

1978 (1 Dec). *New River Vessel "Lady Chilel Jawara" Commemoration. T* **102** *and similar horiz designs. Multicoloured. P* 14.

404	8 b. Type **102**	15	10
405	25 b. *Lady Chilel Jawara* (sectional view)	40	25
406	1 d. *Lady Chilel Jawara*	1·25	1·10
404/6	*Set of* 3	1·60	1·25

25b

103 Police Service (**104**)

(Des G. Vasarhelyi. Litho Questa)

1979 (18 Feb). *14th Anniv of Independence. T* **103** *and similar horiz designs. Multicoloured. P* 14.

407	10 b. Type **103**	25	10
408	50 b. Fire service	60	25
409	1 d. 25, Ambulance service	1·25	80
407/9	*Set of* 3	1·90	1·00

1979 (5–26 Mar). *Nos.* 376 *and* 380/1 *surch as T* **104**.

410	25 b. on 13 b. Fibre Plant	20	35
411	25 b. on 63 b. Gloriosa Lily (26.3.79)	15	20
412	25 b. on 1 d. 25, Bell-flowered Mimosa (26.3.79)	15	20
410/12	*Set of* 3	45	65

105 "Ramsgate Sands" (detail showing Children playing on Beach)

(Des C. Abbott. Litho Questa)

1979 (25 May). *International Year of the Child. T* **105** *and similar multicoloured designs showing the painting "Ramsgate Sands" by William Powell Frith. P* 14 × 13½ (25 *b.*) *or* 13½ × 14 (*others*).

413	10 b. Type **105**	10	10
414	25 b. Detail showing child paddling (*vert*)	20	10
415	1 d. Complete painting (60 × 23 *mm*)	60	60
413/15	*Set of* 3	80	65

106 1883 2½d. Stamp

(Des J.W. Litho Questa)

1979 (16 Aug). *Death Centenary of Sir Rowland Hill. T* **106** *and similar horiz designs showing stamps. Multicoloured. P* 14.

416	10 b. Type **106**	10	10
417	25 b. 1869 4d.	15	10
418	50 b. 1965 7½d. Independence commemorative	20	20
419	1 d. 25, 1935 1½d. Silver Jubilee commemorative	40	50
416/19	*Set of* 4	75	80
MS420	109 × 83 mm. No. 419	65	70

107 Satellite Earth Station under Construction **108** "Apollo 11" leaving Launch Pad

(Des A. Theobald. Litho Questa)

1979 (20 Sept). *Abuko Satellite Earth Station. T* **107** *and similar horiz designs. Multicoloured. P* 14.

421	25 b. Type **107**	20	10
422	50 b. Satellite Earth Station (completed)	30	20
423	1 d. "Intelsat" satellites	65	60
421/3	*Set of* 3	1·00	80

(Des and litho Walsall)

1979 (17 Oct). *10th Anniv of Moon Landing. T* **108** *and similar vert designs. Multicoloured.* (a) *Sheet stamps. P* 14.

424	25 b. Type **108**	20	10
425	38 b. "Apollo 11" in Moon orbit	25	20
426	50 b. Splashdown	30	40
424/6	*Set of* 3	65	60

(*b*) *Booklet stamps. Roul* 5 × *imperf.* Self-adhesive*

427	25 b. Type **108**	25	30
	a. Booklet pane. Nos. 427/9, each × 2	1·60	
428	38 b. As No. 425	30	35
429	50 b. As No. 426	30	40
430	2 d. Lunar module on Moon	1·50	1·75
	a. Booklet pane of 1	1·50	

*Nos. 427/9 are separated by various combinations of rotary-knife (giving a straight edge) and roulette. No. 430 exists only with straight edges.

109 Large Spotted Acraea

(Des J. Cooter. Litho Questa)

1980 (3 Jan). *Abuko Nature Reserve* (3*rd series*). *Butterflies. T* **109** *and similar horiz designs. Multicoloured. P* 13½.

431 25 b. Type **109** 25 20
432 50 b. Yellow Pansy 45 40
433 1 d. Veined Swallowtail 75 80
434 1 d. 25, Foxy Charaxes 80 85
431/4 .. .. *Set of* 4 2·00 2·00
MS435 145 × 122 mm. Nos. 431/4 .. .. .. 2·00 2·10

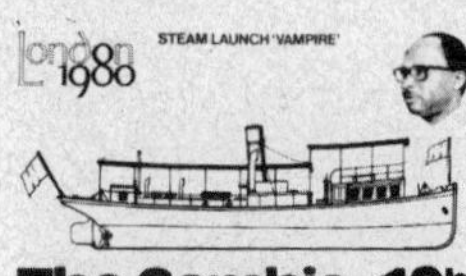

110 Steam Launch *Vampire*

(Des C. Abbott. Litho Harrison)

1980 (6 May). *"London 1980" International Stamp Exhibition. Mail Boats. T* **110** *and similar multicoloured designs. P* 14 (10, 25 *b.*) *or* 13 × 14 (*others*).

436 10 b. Type **110** 15 10
437 25 b. T.S.S. *Lady Denham* 20 10
438 50 b. T.S.C.M.Y. *Mansa Kila Ba* (49 × 26 *mm*) 30 20
439 1 d. 25, T.S.S. *Prince of Wales* (49 × 26 *mm*) .. 50 60
436/9 .. .. *Set of* 4 1·00 85

111 Queen Elizabeth the Queen Mother

(Des and litho Harrison)

1980 (4 Aug). *80th Birthday of Queen Elizabeth the Queen Mother. P* 14.

440 **111** 67 b. multicoloured 30 35

112 Phoenician Trading Vessel

113 "Madonna and Child" (Francesco de Mura)

(Des A. Theobald. Litho Walsall)

1980 (2 Oct). *Early Sailing Vessels. T* **112** *and similar horiz designs. Multicoloured. P* 14½ × 14.

441 8 b. Type **112** 10 10
442 67 b. Egyptian sea-going vessel 25 20
443 75 b. Portuguese caravel 30 30
444 1 d. Spanish galleon 50 50
441/4 .. .. *Set of* 4 1·00 1·00

(Des BG Studio. Litho Questa)

1980 (23 Dec). *Christmas. Paintings. T* **113** *and similar vert designs. Multicoloured. P* 14.

445 8 b. Type **113** 10 10
446 67 b. "Praying Madonna with Crown of Stars" (workshop of Correggio) 25 25
447 75 b. "La Zingarella" (workshop replica of Correggio painting) 25 30
445/7 .. .. *Set of* 3 50 60

114 New Atlantic Hotel

(Des BG Studio. Litho Format)

1981 (18 Feb). *World Tourism Conference, Manila. T* **114** *and similar horiz designs. Multicoloured. P* 14.

448 25 b. Type **114** 15 10
449 75 b. Ancient stone circle 40 40
450 85 b. Conference emblem 50 50
448/50 .. .. *Set of* 3 95 90

115 1979 Abuko Satellite Earth Station 50 b. Commemorative

116 Prince Charles in Naval Uniform

(Des BG Studio. Litho Questa)

1981 (17 May). *World Telecommunications Day. T* **115** *and similar horiz designs. P* 14.

451 50 b. multicoloured 55 30
452 50 b. multicoloured 55 30
453 85 b. black and brown-ochre 80 55
451/3 .. .. *Set of* 3 1·75 1·00

Designs:—No. 452, 1975 Birth Centenary of Dr. Albert Schweitzer 50 b. commemorative; No. 453, I.T.U. and W.H.O. emblems.

(Des and litho J.W.)

1981 (22 July). *Royal Wedding. T* **116** *and similar vert designs. Multicoloured. P* 13½ × 13.

454 75 b. Wedding bouquet from Gambia 30 20
455 1 d. Type **116** 35 30
456 1 d. 25, Prince Charles and Lady Diana Spencer 40 35
454/6 .. .. *Set of* 3 95 75

117 Planting-out Seedlings

(Des Jennifer Toombs. Litho Format)

1981 (4 Sept). *10th Anniv of West African Rice Development Association. T* **117** *and similar horiz designs. Multicoloured. P* 14.

457 10 b. Type **117** 10 10
458 50 b. Care of the crops 35 35
459 85 b. Winnowing and drying 55 55
457/9 .. .. *Set of* 3 85 85

118 Bosc's Monitor

(Des J. Cooter. Litho Format)

1981 (17 Nov). *Abuko Nature Reserve* (4*th series*). *Reptiles. T* **118** *and similar horiz designs. Multicoloured. P* 14.

460 40 b. Type **118** 35 20
461 60 b. Dwarf Crocodile 55 35
462 80 b. Royal Python 70 50
463 85 b. Chameleon 75 55
460/3 .. .. *Set of* 4 2·10 1·40

119 Examination Room

60B

(120)

(Des PAD Studio. Litho Walsall)

1982 (16 Mar). *30th Anniv of West African Examinations Council. T* **119** *and similar horiz designs. Multicoloured. P* 14.

464 60 b. Type **119** 50 30
465 85 b. First High School 65 45
466 1 d. 10, Council's office 85 55
464/6 .. .. *Set of* 3 1·75 1·10

1982 (19 Apr). *No.* 454 *surch with T* **120**.

467 60 b. on 75 b. Wedding bouquet from Gambia 2·50 2·50

121 Tree-planting ("Conservation")

(Des L. Curtis. Litho Harrison)

1982 (16 May). *75th Anniv of Boy Scout Movement. T* **121** *and similar horiz designs. Multicoloured. P* 14.

468 85 b. Type **121** 95 75
469 1 d. 25, Woodworking .. .. 1·40 1·25
470 1 d. 27, Lord Baden-Powell .. .. 1·40 1·50
468/70 .. .. *Set of* 3 3·25 3·25

122 Gambia Football Team

123 Gambia Coat of Arms

(Des A. Theobald. Litho Questa)

1982 (13 June). *World Cup Football Championship, Spain. T* **122** *and similar horiz designs. Multicoloured. P* 14.

471 10 b. Type **122** 10 10
472 1 d. 10, Gambian team practice 75 70
473 1 d. 25, Bernabéu Stadium, Madrid 80 75
474 1 d. 55, FIFA World Cup 85 80
471/4 .. .. *Set of* 4 2·25 2·10
MS475 114 × 85 mm. Nos. 471/4 .. .. .. 2·25 2·50

(Des C. Abbott. Litho Walsall)

1982 (1 July). *21st Birthday of Princess of Wales. T* **123** *and similar vert designs. Multicoloured. P* 14½ × 14.

476 10 b. Type **123** 10 10
477 85 b. Princess at Cardiff City Hall, October 1981 .. .. 40 30
478 1 d. 10, Bride and groom returning to Buckingham Palace 50 45
479 2 d. 50, Formal portrait .. .. 1·25 1·25
476/9 .. .. *Set of* 4 2·00 1·90

124 Vegetable Garden at Yundum Experimental Farm

(Des Harrison. Litho Questa)

1982 (5 Nov). *Economic Community of West African States Development. T* **124** *and similar horiz designs. Multicoloured. P* 14 × 14½.

480 10 b. Type **124** 15 10
481 60 b. Banjul/Kaolack microwave tower 75 65
482 90 b. Soap factory, Denton Bridge, Banjul .. 1·00 1·00
483 1 d. 25, Control tower, Yundum Airport .. 1·25 1·40
480/3 .. .. *Set of* 4 2·75 2·75

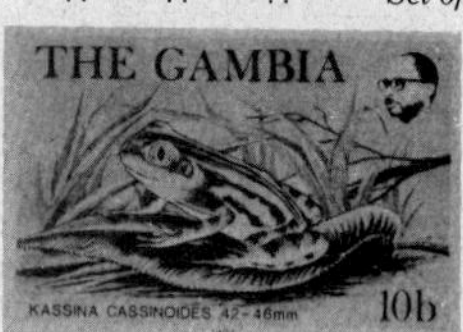

125 *Kassina cassinoides*

(Des PAD Studio. Litho Questa)

1982 (2 Dec). *Frogs. T* **125** *and similar horiz designs. Multicoloured. P* 14.

484 10 b. Type **125** 20 10
485 20 b. *Hylarana galamensis* 30 10
486 85 b. *Euphlyctis occipitalis* 70 60
487 2 d. *Kassina senegalensis* .. .. 1·60 2·00
484/7 .. .. *Set of* 4 2·50 2·50

126 Satellite View of Gambia

127 Blessed Anne Marie Javouhey (foundress of the Order)

(Des Walsall. Litho Questa)

1983 (14 Mar). *Commonwealth Day. T* **126** *and similar horiz designs. Multicoloured. P* 14.

No.	Description	Unused	Used
488	10 b. Type **126**	10	10
489	60 b. Batik cloth	30	45
490	1 d. 10, Bagging groundnuts	50	65
491	2 d. 10, Gambia flag	90	1·25
488/91	*Set of* 4	1·60	2·25

(Des G. Vasarhelyi. Litho Format)

1983 (8 Apr). *Centenary of Sisters of St. Joseph of Cluny's Work in Gambia. T* **127** *and similar multicoloured design. P* 13½.

No.	Description	Unused	Used
492	10 b. Type **127**	10	10
493	85 b. Bathurst Hospital, nun and school-children (*horiz*)	45	50

128 Canoes

(Des A. Theobald. Litho Walsall)

1983 (11 July). *River Craft. T* **128** *and similar horiz designs. Multicoloured. P* 14.

No.	Description	Unused	Used
494	1 b. Type **128**	10	10
495	2 b. Upstream ferry	10	10
496	3 b. **Dredger**	10	10
497	4 b. *Sir Dawda* (harbour launch)	10	10
498	5 b. Cargo liner	10	10
499	10 b. *Lady Dale* (60 ft launch)	10	10
500	20 b. **Container ship**	10	10
501	30 b. Large sailing canoe	10	10
502	40 b. *Lady Wright* (passenger and cargo ferry)	10	10
503	50 b. **Container ship** (*different*)	10	10
504	75 b. Fishing boats	10	10
505	1 d. Tug with groundnut barges	15	20
506	1 d. 25, Groundnut canoe	15	20
507	2 d. 50, *Banjul* (car ferry)	35	40
508	5 d. *Bintang Bolong* (ferry)	70	75
509	10 d. *Lady Chilel Jawara* (passenger and cargo ferry)	1·40	1·50
494/509	*Set of* 16	3·00	3·25

Nos. 494/509 come with a pattern of blue fluorescent security markings, resembling rosettes, printed on the reverse beneath the gum.

129 Osprey in Tree

(Des N. Arlott. Litho Questa)

1983 (12 Sept). *The Osprey. T* **129** *and similar horiz designs. Multicoloured. P* 14.

No.	Description	Unused	Used
510	10 b. Type **129**	40	15
511	60 b. Osprey	1·00	55
512	85 b. Osprey with catch	1·25	85
513	1 d. 10, In flight	1·60	1·50
510/13	*Set of* 4	3·75	2·75

130 Local Ferry

(Des L. Curtis. Litho Questa)

1983 (10 Oct). *World Communications Year. T* **130** *and similar horiz designs. Multicoloured. P* 14.

No.	Description	Unused	Used
514	10 b. Type **130**	10	10
515	85 b. Telex operator	45	50
516	90 b. Radio Gambia	45	50
517	1 d. 10, Loading mail onto aircraft	60	65
514/17	*Set of* 4	1·40	1·60

131 "St. Paul preaching at Athens" (detail) (Raphael)

(Des C. Abbott. Litho Questa)

1983 (1 Nov). *500th Birth Anniv of Raphael. T* **131** *and similar designs. P* 14.

No.	Description	Unused	Used
518	60 b. multicoloured	35	40
519	85 b. multicoloured	45	50
520	1 d. multicoloured	50	55
518/20	*Set of* 3	1·10	1·25
MS521	105 × 83 mm. 2 d. multicoloured	1·00	1·25

Nos. 519/21 show different details of "St. Paul preaching at Athens", the 85 b. and 1 d. being horizontal and the 2 d. vertical.

132 Early Balloon and Siege of Paris Cover

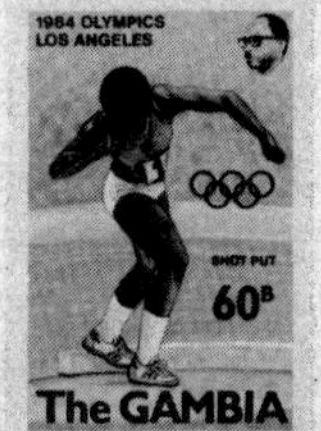

133 Shot-putting

(Des Harrison. Litho Questa)

1983 (12 Dec). *Bicentenary of Manned Flight. T* **132** *and similar horiz designs. Multicoloured. P* 14.

No.	Description	Unused	Used
522	60 b. Type **132**	35	40
	a. Booklet pane. Nos. 522/3, each × 2	1·60	
523	85 b. Lufthansa aircraft and flown cover	45	50
524	90 b. Junkers aircraft and Hans Bertram cover	45	50
	a. Booklet pane. Nos. 524/5, each × 2	2·25	
525	1 d. 25, Lunar module and H. E. Sieger's space cover	65	70
526	4 d. *Graf Zeppelin* (airship)	2·00	2·50
	a. Booklet pane of 1	2·00	
522/6	*Set of* 5	3·50	4·25

Nos. 522/6 come with a pattern of blue fluorescent security markings, resembling rosettes, printed on the reverse beneath the gum.

No. 526 only exists from booklets.

On 14 December 1983 four provisional surcharges, 1 d. 50 on 1 d. 25 (No. 439), 1 d. 50 on 1 d. 25 (No. 473), 2d. on 1 d. 25 (No. 456) and 2 d. on 1 d. 10 (No. 478), were issued in very limited quantities, there being, it is believed, no more than 600 complete sets (*Price for set of 4 £110 mint*).

(Des G. Vasarhelyi. Litho Questa)

1984 (30 Mar). *Olympic Games, Los Angeles (1st issue). T* **133** *and similar multicoloured designs. P* 11.

No.	Description	Unused	Used
527	60 b. Type **133**	25	30
528	85 b. High jumping (*horiz*)	35	40
529	90 b. Wrestling	35	40
530	1 d. Gymnastics	40	45
531	1 d. 25, Swimming (*horiz*)	50	55
532	2 d. Diving	80	85
527/32	*Set of* 6	2·40	2·75
MS533	100 × 80 mm. 5 d. Yachting. P 13½ × 14	2·00	2·25

See also Nos. 555/8.

134 Goofy

(Litho Format)

1984 (27 Apr). *Easter. T* **134** *and similar vert designs showing Walt Disney cartoon characters painting eggs. P* 11.

No.	Description	Unused	Used
534	1 b. Type **134**	10	10
535	2 b. Mickey Mouse	10	10
536	3 b. Huey, Dewey and Louie	10	10
537	4 b. Goofy (*different*)	10	10
538	5 b. Donald Duck	10	10
539	10 b. Chip 'n Dale	10	10
540	60 b. Pluto	35	35
541	90 b. Scrooge McDuck	50	50
542	5 d. Morty and Ferdie	2·25	2·40
534/42	*Set of* 9	3·00	3·25
MS543	125 × 100 mm. 5 d. Donald Duck (*different*). P 13½ × 14	2·25	2·50

135 Young Crocodiles Hatching

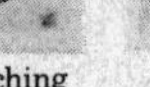

136 Port Banjul

(Des Doreen McGuinness. Litho Format)

1984 (23 May). *The Nile Crocodile. T* **135** *and similar horiz designs. Multicoloured. P* 14.

No.	Description	Unused	Used
544	4 b. Type **135**	10	10
545	6 b. Adult carrying young	10	10
546	90 b. Adult	70	80
547	1 d. 50, Crocodile at riverbank	1·25	1·75
544/7	*Set of* 4	1·90	2·50
MS548	126 × 94 mm. Nos. 544/7	1·90	2·50

Nos. 544/8 come with a pattern of blue fluorescent security markings, resembling rosettes, printed on the reverse beneath the gum.

(Des C. Collins. Litho Questa)

1984 (1 June). *250th Anniv of "Lloyd's List" (newspaper). T* **136** *and similar vert designs. Multicoloured. P* 14½ × 14.

No.	Description	Unused	Used
549	60 b. Type **136**	45	30
550	85 b. **Bulk carrier**	55	40
551	90 b. Sinking of the *Dagomba*	55	55
552	1 d. 25, 19th century frigate	85	85
549/52	*Set of* 4	2·25	1·90

Nos. 549/52 come with a pattern of blue fluorescent security markings, resembling rosettes, printed on the reverse beneath the gum.

19th UPU CONGRESS HAMBURG

(137)

138 Sprinting

1984 (19 June). *Universal Postal Union Congress, Hamburg. Nos.* 507/8 *optd with T* **137.**

No.	Description	Unused	Used
553	2 d. 50, *Banjul* (car ferry)	1·00	1·10
554	5 d. *Bintang Bolong* (ferry)	2·00	2·25

(Des G. Vasarhelyi. Litho Walsall)

1984 (27 July). *Olympic Games, Los Angeles (2nd issue). T* **138** *and similar horiz designs. Multicoloured. P* 14.

No.	Description	Unused	Used
555	60 b. Type **138**	25	30
556	85 b. Long jumping	35	40
557	90 b. Long-distance running	35	40
558	1 d. 25, Triple jumping	50	55
555/8	*Set of* 4	1·25	1·50

Nos. 555/8 come with a pattern of blue fluorescent security markings, resembling rosettes, printed on the reverse beneath the gum.

139 *Graf Zeppelin*

(Des D. Hartley-Marjoram. Litho Questa)

1984 (1 Nov). *50th Anniv of Gambia–South America Trans-atlantic Flights. T* **139** *and similar horiz designs. Multi-coloured. P* 14.

No.	Description	Unused	Used
559	60 b. Type **139**	55	35
560	85 b. Dornier "Wal" on S.S. *Westfalen*	75	50
561	90 b. Dornier "DO.18"	75	60
562	1 d. 25, Dornier "Wal"	85	1·00
559/62	*Set of* 4	2·75	2·25

Nos. 559/62 come with a pattern of blue fluorescent security markings, resembling rosettes, printed on the reverse beneath the gum.

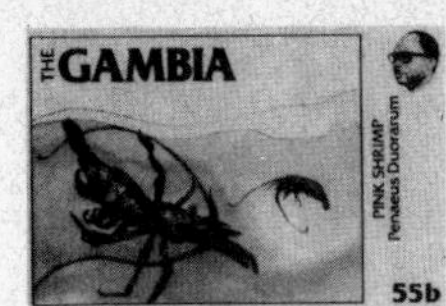

140 Pink Shrimp

(Des Pam Johnson. Litho Questa)

1984 (27 Nov). *Marine Life. T* **140** *and similar horiz designs. Multicoloured. P* 14.

No.	Description	Unused	Used
563	55 b. Type **140**	25	25
564	75 b. Atlantic Loggerhead Turtle	40	35
565	1 d. 50, Portuguese Man-of-War	70	70
566	2 d. 35, Fiddler Crab	95	1·25
563/6	*Set of* 4	2·10	2·25
MS567	105 × 70 mm. 5 d. Cowrie Snail	2·50	3·00

141 *Antanartia hippomene*

(Des Pam Johnson. Litho Questa)

1984 (27 Nov). *Butterflies. T* **141** *and similar horiz designs. Multicoloured. P* 14.

568 10 b. Type **141** 15 10
569 85 b. *Pseudacraea eurytus* 60 50
570 90 b. *Charaxes lactitinctus* 60 50
571 3 d. *Graphium pylades* .. .. .. 1·75 2·25
568/71 .. .. *Set of* 4 2·75 3·00
MS572 105×75 mm. 5 d. *Eurema hapale* .. 3·00 3·25

142 Oral Re-hydration Therapy

(Des L. Curtis. Litho Harrison)

1985 (27 Feb). *Campaign for Child Survival. T* **142** *and similar horiz designs. P* 14.

573 10 b. black, cobalt and deep cinnamon .. 10 10
574 85 b. multicoloured 35 40
575 1 d. 10, multicoloured 45 50
576 1 d. 50, multicoloured 60 65
573/6 .. .. *Set of* 4 1·25 1·40

Designs:—85 b. Growth monitoring; 1 d. 10, Health care worker with women and babies ("Promotion of breast feeding"); 1 d. 50, Universal immunisation.

Nos. 573/6 come with a pattern of blue fluorescent security markings, resembling rosettes, printed on the reverse beneath the gum.

143 Women at Market

144 Turkey Vulture

(Des G. Vasarhelyi. Litho Format)

1985 (11 Mar). *Women and Development. T* **143** *and similar horiz design. Multicoloured. P* 14.

577 60 b. Type **143** 25 30
578 85 b. Type **143** 35 40
579 1 d. Woman office worker 40 45
580 1 d. 25, As 1 d. 50 55
577/80 .. .. *Set of* 4 1·40 1·50

Nos. 577/80 come with a pattern of blue fluorescent security markings, resembling rosettes, printed on the reverse beneath the gum.

(Des and litho Questa)

1985 (15 July). *Birth Bicentenary of John J. Audubon (ornithologist). T* **144** *and similar multicoloured designs showing original paintings. P* 14.

581 60 b. Type **144** 60 20
582 85 b. American Anhinga 75 50
583 1 d. 50, Green Heron .. .. .. 1·00 1·00
584 5 d. Wood Duck .. .. 2·25 2·75
581/4 .. .. *Set of* 4 4·25 4·00
MS585 100×70 mm. 10 d. Great Northern Diver (inscr "Common Loon") (*horiz*) .. .. .. 3·50 4·00

145 The Queen Mother

GOLD MEDALLIST
CLAUDIA LOCH
WEST GERMANY

(146)

(Des J.W. Litho Questa)

1985 (29 July). *Life and Times of Queen Elizabeth the Queen Mother. T* **145** *and similar vert designs. Multicoloured. P* 14.

586 85 b. The Queen Mother and King George VI reviewing Home Guard 25 30
587 3 d. Type **145** 80 85
588 5 d. The Queen Mother with posy .. 1·40 1·50
586/8 .. .. *Set of* 3 2·25 2·40
MS589 56×85 mm. 10 d. The Queen Mother in Garter robes .. .. 2·75 3·00

(Des Walt Disney Studios. Litho Questa)

1985 (30 Oct). *150th Birth Anniv of Mark Twain (author). Horiz designs as T* **118** *of Anguilla showing Walt Disney cartoon characters in scenes from "Life on the Mississippi". Multicoloured. P* 14×13½.

590 1 d. 50, Mickey Mouse steering the *Calamity Jane* 40 45
591 2 d. Mickey and Minnie Mouse at antebellum mansion 55 60
592 2 d. 50, Donald Duck and Goofy heaving the lead 65 70
593 3 d. Poker game aboard the *Gold Dust* .. 80 85
590/3 .. .. *Set of* 4 2·25 2·40
MS594 126×101 mm. 10 d. Mickey Mouse and riverboat .. .. 2·75 3·00

(Des Walt Disney Productions. Litho Questa)

1985 (30 Oct). *Birth Bicentenaries of Grimm Brothers (folklorists). Designs as T* **119** *of Anguilla, but vert, showing Walt Disney cartoon characters in scenes from "Faithful John". Multicoloured. P* 13½×14.

595 60 b. The King (Mickey Mouse) and portrait of the Princess (Minnie Mouse) .. 20 25
596 85 b. The King showing the Princess his treasures 25 30
597 2 d. 35, Faithful John (Goofy) playing trumpet 70 75
598 5 d. Faithful John turned to stone .. .. 1·60 1·75
595/8 .. .. *Set of* 4 2·50 2·75
MS599 126×101 mm. 10 d. Faithful John after recovery .. .. 3·25 3·50

1985 (11 Nov). *Olympic Gold Medal Winners, Los Angeles. Nos. 527/33 optd as T* **146**.

600 60 b. Type **133** (optd with T **146**) 20 25
601 85 b. High jumping (optd "GOLD MEDALLIST ULRIKE MEYFARTH WEST GERMANY") 25 30
602 90 b. Wrestling (optd "GOLD MEDALLIST PASQUALE PASSARELLI WEST GERMANY") 25 30
603 1 d. Gymnastics (optd "GOLD MEDALLIST LI NING CHINA") 30 35
604 1 d. 25, Swimming (optd "GOLD MEDALLIST MICHAEL GROSS WEST GERMANY") 40 45
605 2 d. Diving (optd "GOLD MEDALLIST SYLVIE BERNIER CANADA") 60 65
600/5 .. .. *Set of* 6 1·75 2·10
MS606 100×80 mm. 5 d. Yachting (opt "GOLD MEDAL STAR CLASS U.S.A.") .. .. .. 1·75 1·90

147 Inspecting Maize

(Des J. Farleo. Litho Questa)

1985 (15 Nov). *United Nations Anniversaries. T* **147** *and similar horiz designs. Multicoloured. P* 14.

607 60 b. Type **147** 25 25
608 85 b. Football match, Independence Stadium, Banjul 30 30
609 1 d. 10, Rice fields 40 40
610 2 d. Central Bank of The Gambia 65 65
611 3 d. Cow and calf .. .. 1·10 1·10
612 4 d. Banjul harbour .. .. 1·50 1·50
613 5 d. Gambian fruits .. .. 1·75 2·00
614 6 d. Oyster Creek Bridge .. .. .. 2·25 2·50
607/14 .. .. *Set of* 8 7·50 8·00

Nos. 607, 609, 611 and 613 commemorate the 40th anniversary of the Food and Agriculture Organization and Nos. 608, 610, 612 and 614 the 40th anniversary of the United Nations Organization.

148 Fishermen in Fotoba, Guinea

149 "Virgin and Child" (Dieric Bouts)

(Des B. Bundock. Litho Questa)

1985 (24 Dec). *50th Anniv of Diocese of The Gambia and Guinea. T* **148** *and similar horiz designs. Multicoloured. P* 14.

615 60 b. Type **148** 20 25
616 85 b. St. Mary's Primary School, Banjul .. 25 30
617 1 d. 10, St. Mary's Cathedral, Banjul .. 35 50
618 1 d. 50, Mobile dispensary at Christy Kunda 45 60
615/18 .. .. *Set of* 4 1·10 1·50

(Des Mary Walters. Litho Format)

1985 (24 Dec). *Christmas. Religious Paintings. T* **149** *and similar vert designs. Multicoloured. P* 15.

619 60 b. Type **149** 20 25
620 85 b. "The Annunciation" (Robert Campin) .. 25 30
621 1 d. 50, "Adoration of the Shepherds" (Gerard David) 45 50
622 5 d. "The Nativity" (Gerard David) .. 1·60 1·75
619/22 .. .. *Set of* 4 2·25 2·50
MS623 106×84 mm. 10 d. "Adoration of the Magi" (Hieronymus Bosch) .. .. .. 3·25 3·50

150 Enrolment Card

(Des N. Waldman. Litho Questa)

1985 (27 Dec). *75th Anniv of Girl Guide Movement. T* **150** *and similar multicoloured designs. P* 14.

624 60 b. Type **150** 40 30
625 85 b. 2nd Bathurst Company centre .. 50 35
626 1 d. 50, Lady Baden-Powell (*vert*) 70 55
627 5 d. Miss Rosamond Fowlis (Gambian Guide Association leader) (*vert*) .. 2·00 2·50
624/7 .. .. *Set of* 4 3·25 3·25
MS628 97×67 mm. 10 d. Gambian Girl Guides (*vert*) .. .. 4·00 4·50

151 Girl and Village Scene

152 Two Players competing for Ball

(Des B. Bundock. Litho Questa)

1985 (31 Dec). *International Youth Year. T* **151** *and similar horiz designs. Multicoloured. P* 14.

629 60 b. Type **151** 25 25
630 85 b. Youth and wrestling bout 30 30
631 1 d. 10, Girl and Griot storyteller 40 55
632 1 d. 50, Youth and crocodile pool 50 65
629/32 .. .. *Set of* 4 1·25 1·60
MS633 106×76 mm. 5 d. Herdsman with cattle .. 2·00 2·50

(Des W. Hanson. Litho Questa)

1986 (18 Apr). *Appearance of Halley's Comet (1st issue). Horiz designs as T* **123** *of Anguilla. Multicoloured. P* 14.

634 10 b. Maria Mitchell (astronomer) and Kitt Peak National Observatory, Arizona .. 10 10
635 20 b. Neil Armstrong, first man on Moon, 1969 .. .. 15 10
636 75 b. "Skylab 4" and Comet Kohoutek, 1973 40 25
637 1 d. N.A.S.A.'s infra-red astronomical satellite and Halley's Comet 45 30
638 2 d. Comet of 1577 from Turkish painting .. 75 65
639 10 d. N.A.S.A.'s International Cometary Explorer .. .. 3·00 3·50
634/9 .. .. *Set of* 6 4·25 4·25
MS640 102×70 mm. 10 d. Halley's Comet .. 3·00 3·50

See also Nos. 679/84.

(Des and litho Questa)

1986 (21 Apr). *60th Birthday of Queen Elizabeth II. Vert designs as T* **125** *of Anguilla. P* 14.

641 1 d. black and yellow 25 30
642 2 d. 50, multicoloured 65 70
643 10 d. multicoloured .. .. 2·50 2·75
641/3 .. .. *Set of* 3 3·00 3·50
MS644 120×85 mm. 10 d. black and grey-brown 2·50 2·75

Designs:—No. 641, Duke of York and family, Royal Tournament, 1936; 642, Queen attending christening, 1983; 643, In West Germany, 1978; **MS**644, Duchess of York with her daughters, Balmoral, 1935.

(Des J. Birdsong. Litho Questa)

1986 (2 May). *World Cup Football Championship, Mexico. T* **152** *and similar vert designs. Multicoloured. P* 14.

645 75 b. Type **152** 25 25
646 1 d. Player kicking ball 30 30
647 2 d. 50, Player kicking ball (*different*) .. 75 75
648 10 d. Player heading ball .. .. .. 2·75 3·00
645/8 .. .. *Set of* 4 3·50 4·00
MS649 100×70 mm. 10 d. Goalkeeper saving goal .. .. 2·75 3·25

153 Mercedes "500" (1986)

(Des P. Rhymer. Litho Format)

1986 (31 May). *"Ameripex" International Stamp Exhibition, Chicago. Centenary of First Benz Motor Car* (1985). *T* **153** *and similar horiz designs. Multicoloured. P* 15.

650 25 b. Type **153** 10 15
651 75 b. Cord "810" (1935) 30 35
652 1 d. Borgward "Isabella Coupe" (1957) .. 40 45
653 1 d. 25, Lamborghini "Countach" (1985/6) 50 55
654 2 d. Ford "Thunderbird" (1955) 80 85

655 2 d. 25, Citroen "DS19" (1956) 90 95
656 5 d. Bugatti "Atlante" (1936) .. .. 2·00 2·10
657 10 d. Horch "853" (1936) .. .. .. 4·00 4·25
650/7 .. .. *Set of* 8 8·00 8·75
MS658 Two sheets, each 100×70 mm. (a) 12 d. Benz "8/20" (1913). (b) 12 d. Steiger "10/50" (1924) .. .. .. *Set of* 2 *sheets* 9·50 9·75

The 25 b. value is inscribed "MECEDES" and the 10 d. "LARL BENZ".

(Des J. Iskowitz. Litho Questa)

1986 (10 June). *Centenary of Statue of Liberty* (1*st issue*). *Multicoloured designs as T* **211** *of Dominica showing the Statue of Liberty and immigrants to the U.S.A. P* 14.

659 20 b. John Jacob Astor (financier) 10 10
660 1 d. Jacob Riis (journalist) 40 45
661 1 d. 25, Igor Sikorsky (aeronautics engineer) 50 55
662 5 d. Charles Boyer (actor) .. .. .. 2·00 2·10
659/62 .. .. *Set of* 4 2·75 3·00
MS663 114×80 mm. 10 d. Statue of Liberty (*vert*) .. .. 4·00 4·25

See also Nos. 705/9.

(Litho Questa)

1986 (1 July). *Royal Wedding. Vert designs as T* **213** *of Antigua. Multicoloured. P* 14.

664 1 d. Prince Andrew and Miss Sarah Ferguson 40 45
665 2 d. 50, Prince Andrew .. .. .. 1·00 1·10
666 4 d. Prince Andrew as helicopter pilot .. 1·60 1·75
664/6 .. .. *Set of* 3 2·75 3·00
MS667 88×88 mm. 7 d. Prince Andrew and Miss Sarah Ferguson (*different*) .. .. .. 3·00 3·25

1986 (16 Sept). *World Cup Football Championship Winners, Mexico. Nos.* 645/9 *optd with T* **216** *of Antigua in gold.*

668 75 b. Type **152** 30 30
669 1 d. Player kicking ball 40 40
670 2 d. 50, Player kicking ball (*different*) .. 1·00 1·00
671 10 d. Player heading ball .. .. .. 4·25 4·25
668/71 .. .. *Set of* 4 5·25 5·25
MS672 100×70 mm. 10 d. Goalkeeper saving goal .. .. 4·25 4·25

154 Minnie Mouse (Great Britain)

(Des Walt Disney Co. Litho Format)

1986 (4 Nov). *Christmas. T* **154** *and similar vert designs showing Walt Disney cartoon characters posting letters in various countries. Multicoloured. P* 11.

673 1 d. Type **154** 45 25
674 1 d. 25, Huey (U.S.A.) 50 30
675 2 d. Huey, Dewey and Louie (France) .. 70 45
676 2 d. 35, Kanga and Roo (Australia) 80 50
677 5 d. Goofy (Germany) .. .. .. 1·40 1·10
673/7 .. .. *Set of* 5 3·50 2·40
MS678 127×101 mm. 10 d. Goofy (Sweden). P 13½×14 .. .. 2·75 3·00

Nos. 673/8 also show the emblem of "Stockholmia '86" International Stamp Exhibition.

1986 (21 Dec). *Appearance of Halley's Comet* (2*nd issue*). *Nos.* 634/40 *optd with T* **218** *of Antigua in silver.*

679 10 b. Maria Mitchell (astronomer) and Kitt Peak National Observatory, Arizona .. 15 10
680 20 b. Neil Armstrong, first man on Moon, 1969 .. .. 20 10
681 75 b. "Skylab 4" and Comet Kohoutek, 1973 40 20
682 1 d. N.A.S.A.'s infra-red astronomical satellite and Halley's Comet 45 25
683 2 d. Comet of 1577 from Turkish painting 75 50
684 10 d. N.A.S.A.'s International Cometary Explorer .. .. 2·75 2·50
679/84 .. .. *Set of* 6 4·25 3·25
MS685 102×70 mm. 10 d. Halley's Comet .. 2·75 3·50

155 Bugarab and Tabala

156 "Snowing"

(Des B. Bundock. Litho Format)

1987 (21 Jan). *Manding Musical Instruments. T* **155** *and similar multicoloured designs. P* 15.

686 75 b. Type **155** 15 15
687 1 d. Balaphong and fiddle 15 20
688 1 d. 25, Bolongbato and konting (*vert*) .. 20 25
689 10 d. Antique and modern koras (*vert*) .. 1·60 1·75
686/9 .. .. *Set of* 4 1·90 2·10
MS690 100×70 mm. 12 d. Sabarr .. .. 1·90 2·00

(Litho Questa)

1987 (6 Feb). *Birth Centenary of Marc Chagall* (*artist*). *T* **156** *and similar multicoloured designs. P* 13½×14.

691 75 b. Type **156** 15 15
692 85 b. "The Boat" 15 20
693 1 d. "Maternity" 15 20
694 1 d. 25, "The Flute Player" 20 25
695 2 d. 35, "Lovers and the Beast" 40 45
696 4 d. "Fishers at Saint Jean" 65 70
697 5 d. "Entering the Ring" 80 85
698 10 d. "Three Acrobats" .. .. .. 1·60 1·75
691/8 .. .. *Set of* 8 3·75 4·00
MS699 Two sheets. (a) 110×68 mm. 12 d. "The Cattle Driver" (104×61 *mm*). (b) 109×95 mm. 12 d. "The Sabbath" (104×89 *mm*). Imperf. *Set of* 2 *sheets* 3·75 4·00

157 *America*, 1851

158 Arm of Statue of Liberty

(Des S. Heinmann. Litho Questa)

1987 (3 Apr). *America's Cup Yachting Championship. T* **157** *and similar horiz designs. Multicoloured. P* 14.

700 20 b. Type **157** 10 10
701 1 d. *Courageous*, 1974 .. .. .. 25 25
702 2 d. 50, *Volunteer*, 1887 .. .. .. 55 55
703 10 d. *Intrepid*, 1967 .. .. .. 1·90 1·90
700/3 .. .. *Set of* 4 2·50 2·50
MS704 114×89 mm. 12 d. *Australia II*, 1983 .. 2·25 2·40

(Des P. Kaplan. Litho Questa)

1987 (9 Apr). *Centenary of Statue of Liberty* (1986) (2*nd issue*). *T* **158** *and similar multicoloured designs. P* 14.

705 1 b. Type **158** 10 10
706 2 b. Launch passing Statue (*horiz*) 10 10
707 3 b. Schooner passing Statue (*horiz*) .. 10 10
708 5 b. Aircraft carrier and *Queen Elizabeth* 2 (*horiz*) 10 10
709 50 b. Checking Statue for damage 10 10
710 75 b. Cleaning in progress 15 15
711 1 d. Working on Statue 15 20
712 1 d. 25, Statue and fireworks 20 25
713 10 d. Statue illuminated .. .. .. 1·60 1·75
714 12 d. Statue and fireworks (*different*) .. 1·90 2·00
705/14 .. .. *Set of* 10 3·75 4·00

159 *Lantana camara*

160 Front of Mail Bus

(Des Dot Barlowe. Litho Questa)

1987 (25 May). *Flowers of Abuko Nature Reserve. T* **159** *and similar vert designs. Multicoloured. P* 14.

715 75 b. Type **159** 15 15
716 1 d. *Clerodendrum thomsoniae* 15 20
717 1 d. 50, *Haemanthus multiflorus* 25 30
718 1 d. 70, *Gloriosa simplex* 25 30
719 1 d. 75, *Combretum microphyllum* 30 35
720 2 d. 25, *Eulophia quineensis* 35 40
721 5 d. *Erythrina senegalensis* 80 85
722 15 d. *Dichrostachys glomerata* .. .. 2·40 2·50
715/22 .. .. *Set of* 8 4·25 4·50
MS723 Two sheets, each 100×70 mm. (a) 15 d. *Costus spectabilis*. (b) 15 d. *Strophanthus preussii* *Set of* 2 *sheets* 4·75 5·00

(Des BG Studio. Litho Questa)

1987 (15 June). *"Capex '87" International Stamp Exhibition, Toronto and 10th Anniv of Gambia Public Transport Corporation. Mail Buses. T* **160** *and similar multicoloured designs. P* 14.

724 20 b. Type **160** 10 10
725 75 b. Bus in Banjul (*horiz*) 15 15
726 1 d. Passengers queuing for bus (*horiz*) .. 15 20
727 10 d. Two buses on rural road .. .. 1·60 2·25
724/7 .. .. *Set of* 4 1·75 2·40
MS728 77×70 mm. 12 d. Parked bus fleet (*horiz*) 2·25 2·75

161 Basketball

162 "A Partridge in a Pear Tree"

(Litho Questa)

1987 (3 July). *Olympic Games, Seoul* (1988) (1*st issue*). *T* **161** *and similar vert designs. Multicoloured. P* 14.

729 50 b. Type **161** 10 10
730 1 d. Volleyball 15 20
731 3 d. Hockey (*horiz*) 50 55
732 10 d. Handball (*horiz*) .. .. .. 1·60 1·75
724/32 .. .. *Set of* 4 2·10 2·40
MS733 101×85 mm. 15 d. Football (*horiz*) .. 2·40 2·50

See also Nos. 779/83.

(Des Dot Barlowe. Litho Questa)

1987 (2 Nov). *Christmas. T* **162** *and similar multicoloured designs showing a Victorian couple in scenes from carol "The Twelve Days of Christmas". P* 14.

734 20 b. Type **162** 10 10
a. Sheetlet. Nos. 734/45 .. .. .. 5·25
735 40 b. "Two turtle doves" 10 10
736 60 b. "Three French hens" 10 10
737 75 b. "Four calling birds" 15 15
738 1 d. "Five golden rings" 15 20
739 1 d. 25, "Six geese a-laying" 20 25
740 1 d. 50, "Seven swans a-swimming" .. 25 30
741 2 d. "Eight maids a-milking" 30 35
742 3 d. "Nine ladies dancing" 50 55
743 5 d. "Ten lords a-leaping" 80 85
744 10 d. "Eleven pipers piping" .. .. 1·60 1·75
745 12 d. "Twelve drummers drumming" .. 1·90 2·00
734/45 .. .. *Set of* 12 5·25 5·75
MS746 100×70 mm. 15 d. Exchanging presents (*horiz*) .. .. 2·40 2·50

Nos. 734/45 were printed together, *se-tenant*, in sheetlets of twelve.

163 Campfire Singsong

(Litho Questa)

1987 (9 Nov). *World Scout Jamboree, Australia. T* **163** *and similar horiz designs. Multicoloured. P* 14.

747 75 b. Type **163** 20 15
748 1 d. Scouts examining African Katydid .. 25 20
749 1 d. 25, Scouts watching Red-tailed Tropic Bird 30 25
750 2 d. Scouts helping bus passenger .. .. 2·40 2·50
747/50 .. .. *Set of* 4 2·75 2·75
MS751 72×98 mm. 15 d. Scouts on field trip .. 3·00 3·25

(Des Walt Disney Company. Litho Questa)

1987 (9 Dec). *60th Anniv of Mickey Mouse* (*Walt Disney cartoon character*). *Multicoloured designs as T* **220** *of Dominica, but horiz. P* 14×13½.

752 60 b. Morty and Ferdie examining Trevithick's locomotive, 1804 .. .. 10 10
753 75 b. Clarabelle Cow in "Empire State Express", 1893 .. .. 15 15
754 1 d. Donald Duck inspecting Stephenson's *Rocket*, 1829 .. .. 15 20
755 1 d. 25, Piglet and Winnie the Pooh with Santa Fe Railway locomotive, 1920 .. 20 25
756 2 d. Donald and Daisy Duck with Class "GG-1", Pennsylvania Railway, 1933 .. 30 35
757 5 d. Mickey Mouse in *Stourbridge Lion*, 1829 80 85
758 10 d. Goofy in *Best Friend of Charleston*, 1830 1·60 1·75
759 12 d. Brer Bear and Brer Rabbit with Union Pacific No. M10001, 1934 .. .. 1·90 2·00
752/9 .. .. *Set of* 8 5·50 6·00
MS760 Two sheets, each 127×101 mm. (a) 15 d. Chip n'Dale in *The General*, 1855. (b) 15 d. Donald Duck and Mickey Mouse in modern French "TGV" train .. .. .. *Set of* 2 *sheets* 4·75 5·00

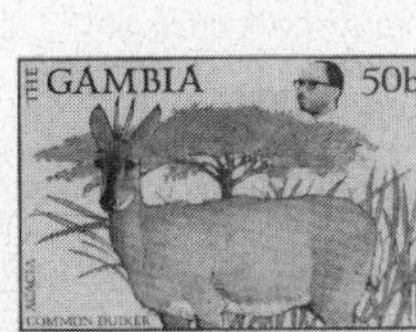

164 Common Duiker and Acacia

165 Wedding Portrait, 1947

(Des Mary Walters. Litho Format)

1988 (9 Feb). *Flora and Fauna. T* **164** *and similar multicoloured designs. P* 15.

761 50 b. Type **164** 10 10
762 75 b. Red-billed Hornbill and casuarina (*vert*) 15 15
763 90 b. West African Dwarf Crocodile and rice 15 20
764 1 d. Leopard and papyrus (*vert*) 15 20
765 1 d. 25, Crested Crane and millet 20 25
766 2 d. Waterbuck and baobab tree (*vert*) 30 35
767 3 d. Oribi and Senegal palm 50 55
768 5 d. Hippopotamus and papaya (*vert*) 80 85
761/8 *Set of* 8 2·10 2·40
MS769 98×69 mm. (a) 12 d. Red-throated Bee-eater and acacia (*vert*). (b) 12 d. Great White Pelican *Set of* 2 *sheets* 3·75 4·00

(Des and litho Questa)

1988 (15 Mar). *Royal Ruby Wedding. T* **165** *and similar vert designs. P* 14.

770 75 b. deep brown, black and brown-orange 15 15
771 1 d. deep brown, black and bright new blue 15 20
772 3 d. multicoloured 50 55
773 10 d. multicoloured 80 1·75
770/3 *Set of* 4 2·10 2·40
MS774 100×75 mm. 15 d. multicoloured 2·40 2·50

Designs:— 1 d. Engagement photograph; 3 d. Wedding portrait, 1947 (*different*); 10 d. Queen Elizabeth II and Prince Philip (photo by Karsh), 1986; 15 d. Wedding portrait with page, 1947.

1988 (19 Apr). *Stamp Exhibitions. Nos.* 689, 703, 722 *and* 726 *optd as T* **241** *of Antigua with various emblems.*

775 1 d. Passengers queuing for bus (optd "Independence 40", Israel) 15 20
776 10 d. Antique and modern koras (optd "FINLANDIA 88", Helsinki) 1·60 1·75
777 10 d. *Intrepid* (yacht), 1967 (optd "Praga '88", Prague) 1·60 1·75
778 15 d. *Dichrostachys glomerata* (optd "OLYMPHILEX '88", Seoul) 2·40 2·50
775/8 *Set of* 4 5·25 5·50

(Des A. DiLorenzo. Litho Questa)

1988 (3 May). *Olympic Games, Seoul (2nd issue). Multicoloured designs as T* **161**. *P* 14.

779 1 d. Archery 15 20
780 1 d. 25, Boxing 20 25
781 5 d. Gymnastics 80 85
782 10 d. Start of 100 metre race (*horiz*) 1·60 1·75
779/82 *Set of* 4 2·50 2·75
MS783 74×102 mm. 15 d. Medal winners on rostrum 2·40 2·50

166 Red Cross Flag (125th anniv)

(Des W. Wright. Litho Questa)

1988 (15 May). *Anniversaries and Events. T* **166** *and similar multicoloured designs. P* 14.

784 50 b. Type **166** 10 10
785 75 b. "Friendship" 7 spacecraft (25th anniv of first American manned Earth orbit) 15 15
786 1 d. British Airways "Concorde" (10th anniv of "Concorde" London–New York service) 15 20
787 1 d. 25, *Spirit of St. Louis* (60th anniv of first solo transatlantic flight) 20 25
788 2 d. "X-15" (20th anniv of fastest aircraft flight) 30 35
789 3 d. Bell "X-1" rocket plane (40th anniv of first supersonic flight) 50 55
790 10 d. English and Spanish galleons (400th anniv of Spanish Armada) 1·60 1·75
791 12 d. *Titanic* (75th anniv of sinking) 1·90 2·00
784/91 *Set of* 8 4·25 4·75
MS792 Two sheets. (a) 113×85 mm. 15 d. Kaiser Wilhelm Memorial Church, Berlin (*vert*) (750th anniv of Berlin). (b) 121×90 mm. 15 d. Kangaroo (Bicentenary of Australian Settlement) *Set of* 2 *sheets* 4·75 5·00

(Litho Questa)

1988 (7 July). *500th Birth Anniv of Titian (artist). Vert designs as T* **238** *of Antigua. Multicoloured. P* 13½×14.

793 25 b. "Emperor Charles V" 10 10
794 50 b. "St. Margaret and the Dragon" 10 10
795 60 b. "Ranuccio Farnese" 10 15
796 75 b. "Tarquin and Lucretia" 12 15
797 1 d. "The Knight of Malta" 15 20
798 5 d. "Spain succouring Faith" 80 85
799 10 d. "Doge Francesco Venier" 1·60 1·75
800 12 d. "Doge Grimani before the Faith" (detail) 1·90 2·00
793/800 *Set of* 8 4·25 4·75
MS801 110×95 mm. (a) 15 d. "Jealous Husband" (detail). (b) 15 d. "Venus blindfolding Cupid" *Set of* 2 *sheets* 4·75 5·00

167 John Kennedy sailing

(Des G. Hinlecky. Litho Questa)

1988 (1 Sept). *25th Death Anniv of President John F. Kennedy. T* **167** *and similar multicoloured designs. P* 14.

802 75 b. Type **167** 15 15
803 1 d. Kennedy signing Peace Corps legislation, 1962 15 20
804 1 d. 25, Speaking at U.N., New York (*vert*) 20 25
805 12 d. Grave and eternal flame, Arlington National Cemetery (*vert*) 1·90 2·00
802/5 *Set of* 4 2·10 2·40
MS806 99×72 mm. 15 d. John F. Kennedy (*vert*) 2·40 2·50

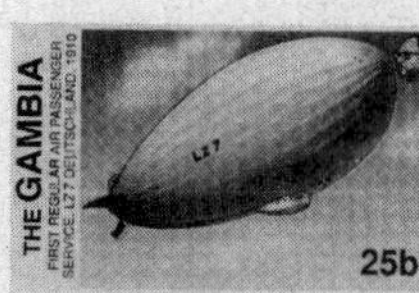

168 "LZ 7" *Deutschland* (first regular air passenger service), 1910

169 Emmett Kelley

(Des A. Fagbohun. Litho Questa)

1988 (1 Nov). *Milestones of Transportation. T* **168** *and similar multicoloured designs. P* 14.

807 25 b. Type **168** 10 10
808 50 b. Stephenson's *Locomotion* (first permanent public railway), 1825 10 10
809 75 b. G.M. *Sun Racer* (first world solar challenge), 1987 15 15
810 1 d. Sprague's *Premiere* (first operational electric tramway), 1888 15 20
811 1 d. 25, *Gold Rush* Bicycle (holder of man-powered land speed record), 1986 20 25
812 2 d. 50 Robert Goddard and rocket launcher (first liquid fuel rocket), 1925 40 45
813 10 d. *Orukter Amphibolos* (first steam traction engine), 1805 1·60 1·75
814 12 d. *Sovereign of the Seas* (largest cruise liner), 1988 1·90 2·00
807/14 *Set of* 8 4·00 4·50
MS815 Two sheets, each 71 × 92 mm. (a) 15 d. U.S.S. *Nautilus* (first nuclear-powered submarine), 1954 (*vert*). (b) 15 d. Fulton's *Nautilus* (first fish-shaped submarine), 1800's (*vert*) *Set of* 2 *sheets* 4·75 5·00

(Des J. Iskowitz. Litho Questa)

1988 (9 Nov). *Entertainers. T* **169** *and similar multicoloured designs. P* 14.

816 20 b. Type **169** 10 10
817 1 d. Gambia National Ensemble 20 20
818 1 d. 25, Jackie Gleason 25 25
819 1 d. 50, Laurel and Hardy 35 35
820 2 d. 50, Yul Brynner 55 55
821 3 d. Cary Grant 70 70
822 10 d. Danny Kaye 2·00 2·00
823 20 d. Charlie Chaplin 3·75 3·75
816/23 *Set of* 8 7·00 7·00
MS824 Two sheets. (a) 110 × 77 mm. 15 d. Marx Brothers (*horiz*). (b) 70 × 99 mm. 15 d. Fred Astaire and Rita Hayworth (*horiz*) *Set of* 2 *sheets* 5·50 6·00

170 Prince Henry the Navigator and Caravel

171 Projected Space Plane and Ernst Mach (physicist)

(Des A. Fagbohun. Litho Questa)

1988 (1 Dec). *Exploration of West Africa. T* **170** *and similar multicoloured designs. P* 14.

825 50 b. Type **170** 10 10
826 75 b. Jesse Ramsden's sextant, 1785 15 15
827 1 d. 15th-century hourglass 25 20
828 1 d. 25, Prince Henry the Navigator and Vasco da Gama 30 25
829 2 d. 50, Vasco da Gama and ship 55 45
830 5 d. Mungo Park and map of Gambia River (*horiz*) 1·00 85
831 10 d. Map of West Africa, 1563 (*horiz*) 2·00 2·00
832 12 d. Portuguese caravel (*horiz*) 2·25 2·50
825/32 *Set of* 8 6·00 6·00
MS833 Two sheets, each 65 × 100 mm. (a) 15 d. Ship from Columbus's fleet off Gambia. (b) 15 d. 15th-century ship moored off Gambia *Set of* 2 *sheets* 4·75 5·00

(Des G. Welker. Litho Questa)

1988 (12 Dec). *350th Anniv of Publication of Galileo's "Discourses". Space Achievements. T* **171** *and similar multicoloured designs. P* 14.

834 50 b. Type **171** 15 10
835 75 b. OAO III astronomical satellite and Niels Bohr (physicist) 20 15
836 1 d. Space shuttle, projected space station and Robert Goddard (physicist) (*horiz*) 25 20
837 1 d. 25, Jupiter probe, 1979, and Edward Barnard (astronomer) (*horiz*) 30 25
838 2 d. Hubble Space Telescope and George Hale (astronomer) 45 35
839 3 d. Earth-to-Moon laser measurement and Albert Michaelson (physicist) (*horiz*) 65 55
840 10 d. HEAO-2 *Einstein* orbital satellite and Albert Einstein (physicist) 1·75 2·00
841 20 d. *Voyager* (first non-stop round-the-world flight), 1987, and Wright Brothers (aviation pioneers) (*horiz*) 3·50 3·75
834/41 *Set of* 8 6·50 6·50
MS842 Two sheets. (a) 99 × 75 mm. 15 d. Great Red Spot on Jupiter (*horiz*). (b) 88 × 71 mm. 15 d. Neil Armstrong (first man on Moon), 1969 *Set of* 2 *sheets* 5·50 6·00

172 Passing Out Parade

(Des J. Genzo. Litho Questa)

1989 (10 Feb). *Army Day. T* **172** *and similar multicoloured designs. P* 14.

843 75 b. Type **172** 15 15
844 1 d. Standards of The Gambia Regiment 20 20
845 1 d. 25, Side drummer in ceremonial uniform (*vert*) 25 25
846 10 d. Marksman with Atlantic Shooting Cup (*vert*) 1·75 1·75
847 15 d. Soldiers on assault course (*vert*) 2·50 2·50
848 20 d. Gunner with 105 mm field gun 3·50 3·50
843/8 *Set of* 6 7·50 7·50

173 Mickey Mouse, 1928

174 "Le Coup de Lance" (detail)

(Des Walt Disney Company. Litho B.D.T.)

1989 (6 Apr). *60th Birthday of Mickey Mouse. T* **173** *and similar multicoloured designs. P* 13.

849 2 d. Type **173** 50 50
a. Sheetlet of 9. Nos. 849/57 4·00
850 2 d. Mickey Mouse, 1931 50 50
851 2 d. Mickey Mouse, 1936 50 50
852 2 d. Mickey Mouse, 1955 50 50
853 2 d. Mickey Mouse, 1947 50 50
854 2 d. Mickey Mouse as magician, 1940 50 50
855 2 d. Mickey Mouse with palette, 1960 50 50
856 2 d. Mickey Mouse as Uncle Sam, 1976 50 50
857 2 d. Mickey Mouse, 1988 50 50
849/57 *Set of* 9 4·00 4·00
MS858 138×109 mm. 15 d. Mickey Mouse at 60th birthday party (132×103 *mm*). Imperf 3·50 3·50

Nos. 849/57 were printed together, *se-tenant* as a composite design, in sheetlets of nine.

(Litho Questa)

1989 (14 Apr). *Easter. Religious Paintings by Rubens. T* **174** *and similar vert designs showing details. Multicoloured. P* 13½×14.

859 50 b. Type **174** 10 10
860 75 b. "Flagellation of Christ" 10 15
861 1 d. "Lamentation for Christ" 15 20
862 1 d. 25, "Descent from the Cross" 20 25
863 2 d. "Holy Trinity" 30 35
864 5 d. "Doubting Thomas" 80 85
865 10 d. "Lamentation over Christ" 1·60 1·75
866 12 d. "Lamentation with Virgin and St. John" 1·90 2·00
859/66 *Set of* 8 4·75 5·00
MS867 Two sheets each 96×110 mm. (a) 15 d. "The Last Supper". (b) 15 d. "Raising of the Cross" *Set of* 2 *sheets* 4·75 5·00

175 African Emerald Cuckoo

176 *Papilio antimachus*

(Des W. Wright. Litho Questa)

1989 (24 Apr). *West African Birds. T* **175** *and similar horiz designs. Multicoloured. P* 14.

868	20 b. Type **175**	15	10
869	60 b. Grey-headed Bush Shrike	20	15
870	75 b. Crowned Crane	20	20
871	1 d. Secretary Bird	30	25
872	2 d. Red-billed Hornbill	50	40
873	5 d. Superb Sunbird	1·25	1·00
874	10 d. Little Owl	2·25	2·00
875	12 d. Bateleur	2·50	2·50
868/75	*Set of* 8	6·50	6·00
MS876	Two sheets, each 115×86 mm. (a) 15 d. Ostrich. (b) 15 d. Red-billed Fire Finch *Set of* 2 *sheets*	6·50	7·00

(Des Mary Walters. Litho Questa)

1989 (15 May). *Butterflies of Gambia. T* **176** *and similar vert designs. Multicoloured. P* 14.

877	50 b. Type **176**	20	15
878	75 b. *Euphaedra neophron*	25	20
879	1 d. *Aterica rabena*	30	25
880	1 d. 25, *Salamis parhassus*	40	30
881	5 d. *Precis rhadama*	1·25	1·00
882	10 d. *Papilio demodocus*	2·00	2·00
883	12 d. *Charaxes etesippe*	2·25	2·25
884	15 d. *Danaus formosa*	2·75	2·75
877/84	*Set of* 8	8·50	8·00
MS885	Two sheets, each 99×68 mm. (a) 15 d. *Cymothoe pluto*. (b) 15 d. *Euphaedra ceres* *Set of* 2 *sheets*	6·00	6·50

177 Nigerian Steam Locomotive, 1959

PHILEXFRANCE '89

(178)

(Des A. Fagbohun. Litho Walsall)

1989 (15 June). *African Steam Locomotives. T* **177** *and similar multicoloured designs. P* 14.

886	50 b. Type **177**	10	10
887	75 b. Garratt Class "14A"	10	15
888	1 d. British-built locomotive, Sudan	15	20
889	1 d. 25, American-built locomotive, 1925	20	25
890	5 d. Scottish-built locomotive, 1955	80	85
891	7 d. Scottish-built locomotive, 1926	1·10	1·25
892	10 d. East African Railways British-built tank locomotive	1·60	1·75
893	12 d. American-built locomotive, Ghana	1·90	2·00
886/93	*Set of* 8	5·25	5·75
MS894	82×58 mm. (a) 15 d. British-built Class "25" from front (*vert*). (b) 15 d. British-built Class "25" from side (*vert*) *Set of* 2 *sheets*	4·75	5·00

1989 (23 June). *"Philexfrance '89" International Stamp Exhibition, Paris. Nos.* 686/90 *optd with T* **178**.

895	75 b. Type **155**	10	15
896	1 d. Balaphong and fiddle	15	20
897	1 d. 25, Bolongbato and konting (*vert*)	20	25
898	10 d. Antique and modern koras (*vert*)	1·60	1·75
895/8	*Set of* 4	1·75	2·10
MS899	100×70 mm. 12 d. Sabarr	1·90	2·00

(Litho Questa)

1989 (7 July). *Japanese Art. Multicoloured designs as T* **250** *of Antigua. P* 13½×14.

900	50 b. "Sparrow and Bamboo" (Hiroshige) (*vert*)	10	10
901	75 b. "Peonies and a Canary" (Hokusai) (*vert*)	10	15
902	1 d. "Crane and Marsh Grasses" (Hiroshige) (*vert*)	15	20
903	1 d. 25, "Crossbill and Thistle" (Hokusai) (*vert*)	20	25
904	2 d. "Cuckoo and Azalea" (Hokusai) (*vert*)	30	35
905	5 d. "Parrot on a Pine Branch" (Hiroshige) (*vert*)	80	85
906	10 d. "Mandarin Ducks in a Stream" (Hiroshige) (*vert*)	1·60	1·75
907	12 d. "Bullfinch and Drooping Cherry" (Hokusai) (*vert*)	1·90	2·00
900/7	*Set of* 8	4·50	5·00
MS908	Two sheets, each 102×77 mm. (a) 15 d. "Tit and Peony" (Hiroshige). (b) 15 d. "Peony and Butterfly" (Shigenobou). P 14×13½ *Set of* 2 *sheets*	4·75	5·00

Nos. 900/7 were each printed in sheets of 10 containing two vertical strips of 5 stamps separated by printed labels commemorating Emperor Hirohito.

Ghana
(*formerly* Gold Coast)

DOMINION

***CANCELLED REMAINDERS.** In 1961 remainders of some issues of 1957 to 1960 were put on the market cancelled-to-order in such a way as to be indistinguishable from genuine postally used copies for all practical purposes. Our used quotations which are indicated by an asterisk are the same for cancelled-to-order or postally used copies.

29 Dr. Kwame Nkrumah, Palm-nut Vulture and Map of Africa

GHANA
INDEPENDENCE
6TH MARCH,
1957.

(30)

(Photo Harrison)

1957 (6 Mar). *Independence. Wmk Mult Script CA. P* 14 × 14½.

No.	Type	Description	Unused	Used
166	29	2d. scarlet	10	10*
167		2½d. green	10	10*
168		4d. brown	10	10*
169		1s. 3d. deep blue	15	10*
166/9		*Set of* 4	40	15*

1957 (6 Mar)–**58**. *Nos.* 153/64 *of Gold Coast optd as T* **30**.

No.	Description	Unused	Used
170	½d. bistre-brown and scarlet	10	10*
	a. Olive-brown and scarlet	10	10*
171	1d. deep blue (R.)	10	10*
172	1½d. emerald-green	10	10*
173	2d. chocolate (26.5.58)	20	10
174	2½d. scarlet (26.5.58)	75	90
175	3d. magenta	10	10*
176	4d. blue (26.5.58)	2·00	2·50
177	6d. black and orange (R.)	10	10*
	a. Opt double	†	£190
178	1s. black and orange-red	10	10*
179	2s. brown-olive and carmine	20	10*
180	5s. purple and black	35	10*
181	10s. black and olive-green	60	10*
170/81	*Set of* 12	4·00	3·50*

Nos. 173/4 and 176 were officially issued on 26 May 1958 although, in error, small quantities were sold at certain post offices when the rest of the set appeared.

Nos. 170 and 171 exist in coils constructed from normal sheets.

31 Viking Ship

(Des W. Wind. Recess E. A. Wright Bank Note Co., Philadelphia)

1957 (27 Dec). *Inauguration of Black Star Shipping Line. T* **31** *and similar horiz designs. No wmk. P* 12.

No.	Description	Unused	Used
182	2½d. emerald-green	25	15
	a. Imperf between (vert pair)	£250	
	b. Imperf between (horiz pair)	£250	
183	1s. 3d. deep blue	45	70
	a. Imperf horiz (vert pair)	£250	
184	5s. bright purple	80	1·75
	a. Imperf vert (horiz pair)	£325	
182/4	*Set of* 3	1·40	2·40

Designs:—1s. 3d. Galleon; 5s. M.V. *Volta River*.

PRINTERS. Nos. 185/**MS**568 were printed in photogravure by Harrison & Sons *except where otherwise stated*.

34 Ambassador Hotel, Accra

35 Ghana Coat of Arms

1958 (6 Mar). *First Anniv of Independence. T* **34/5** *and similar designs. Wmk Mult Script CA. P* 14½ × 14 (2*s.*) *or* 14 × 14½ (*others*).

No.	Description	Unused	Used
185	½d. black, red, yellow, green and carmine	10	10
186	2½d. black, red, green and yellow	10	10
187	1s. 3d. black, red, yellow, green and blue	10	10
188	2s. red, yellow, blue, green, brown and black	15	25
185/8	*Set of* 4	30	30

Designs: *Horiz as T* 34—2½d. State Opening of Parliament; 1s. 3d. National Monument.

NEW INFORMATION

The editor is always interested to correspond with people who have new information that will improve or correct the Catalogue.

38 Map showing the Independent African States

39 Map of Africa and Flaming Torch

(Des R. Milton)

1958 (15 Apr). *First Conference of Independent African States, Accra. Wmk Mult Script CA. P* 13½ × 14½ (2½*d.,* 3*d*) *or* 14½ × 13½ (*others*).

No.	Type	Description	Unused	Used
189	38	2½d. black, bistre and bright carmine-red	10	10
190		3d. black, bistre, brown and bright green	10	10
191	39	1s. black, yellow, red and dull blue	10	10
192		2s. 6d. black, yellow, red and dull violet	15	20
189/92		*Set of* 4	25	25

40 Palm-nut Vulture over Globe

41 "Britannia" Airliner

(Des M. Goaman (2½d., 2s. 6d.), R. Milton (1s. 3d.), W. Wind (2s.))

1958 (15 July). *Inauguration of Ghana Airways. T* **40/1** *and similar designs. Wmk Mult Script CA. P* 15 × 14 (2*s.* 6*d.*) *or* 14 × 15 (*others*).

No.	Description	Unused	Used
193	2½d. black, yellow-bistre & rose-carmine	15	10
194	1s. 3d. multicoloured	25	15
195	2s. multicoloured	25	20
196	2s. 6d. black and bistre	35	30
193/6	*Set of* 4	90	60

Designs: *Horiz (as T* 41)—2s. "Stratocruiser" and Yellow-nosed Albatross. (*As T* 40)—2s. 6d. Palm-nut Vulture and jet aircraft.

PRIME
MINISTER'S
VISIT,
U.S.A. AND
CANADA

(44)

45

1958 (18 July). *Prime Minister's Visit to the United States and Canada. Nos.* 166/9 *optd with T* **44**.

No.	Type	Description	Unused	Used
197	29	2d. scarlet	10	10
198		2½d. green	10	10
199		4d. brown	10	10
200		1s. 3d. deep blue	10	10
197/200		*Set of* 4	20	15

(Des W. Wind)

1958 (24 Oct). *United Nations Day. Wmk Mult Script CA. P* 14 × 14½.

No.	Type	Description	Unused	Used
201	45	2½d. purple-brown, green and black	10	10
202		1s. 3d. purple-brown, blue and black	10	10
203		2s. 6d. purple-brown, violet and black	15	15
201/3		*Set of* 3	20	15

46 Dr. Nkrumah and Lincoln Statue, Washington

47

(Des M. Goaman)

1959 (12 Feb). *150th Birth Anniv of Abraham Lincoln. W* **47**. *P* 14 × 14½.

No.	Type	Description	Unused	Used
204	46	2½d. pink and deep purple	10	10
205		1s. 3d. light blue and blue	10	10
206		2s. 6d. orange-yellow & dp olive-green	15	10
204/6		*Set of* 3	20	15
MS206*a*		102 × 77 mm. Nos. 204/6. Imperf	55	1·40

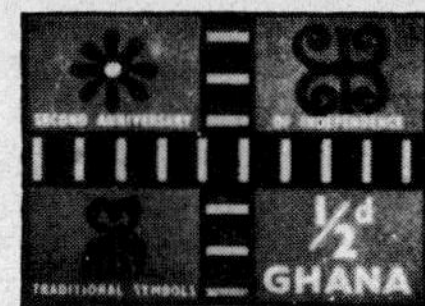

48 Kente Cloth and Traditional Symbols

(Des Mrs. T. Sutherland (½d.), M. Karoly (2½d.), K. Antubam (1s. 3d.), A. M. Medina (2s.))

1959 (6 Mar). *Second Anniv of Independence. T* **48** *and similar multicoloured designs. W* **47**. *P* 14½ × 14 (2*s.*) *or* 14 × 14½ (*others*).

No.	Description	Unused	Used
207	½d. Type **48**	10	10
208	2½d. Talking drums and elephant-horn blower	10	10
209	1s. 3d. "Symbol of Greeting" (*vert*)	10	10
210	2s. Map of Africa, Ghana flag and palms	25	40
207/10	*Set of* 4	40	50

52 Globe and Flags

(Des Mrs. H. Potter)

1959 (15 Apr). *Africa Freedom Day. W* **47** (*sideways*). *P* 14½ × 14.

No.	Type	Description	Unused	Used
211	52	2½d. multicoloured	10	10
212		8½d. multicoloured	10	10

53 "God's Omnipotence"

54 Nkrumah Statue, Accra

55 Ghana Timber

56 Volta River

65*a* Red-fronted Gazelle

Two Types of ½d. and 3d:

I. Inscr "GOD'S OMNIPOTENCE"
II. Inscr "GYE NYAMA"

(Des Mrs. T. Sutherland (½d., 3d.), Ghana Information Bureau (source of 1d. and 2d.), O. Haulkland (1½d.), A. Medina (2½d., 4d.), M. Goaman (6d., 1s. 3d., 2s. 6d.), W. Wind (11d., 1s., 2s., 5s.), W. H. Brown (10s.), M. Shamir (£1)).

1959 (5 Oct)–**61**. *T* **53/6**, **65***a*, *and similar multicoloured designs. W* **47** (*sideways on horiz designs*). *P* 11½ × 12 (½*d.*), 12 × 11½ (1*d.*), 14 × 14½ (1½*d.*, 11*d.*, 1*s.*, 2*s. and* 5*s.*), 14 × 15 (10*s.*) *or* 14½ × 14 (*others*). (*a*) *Postage.*

No.	Description	Unused	Used
213	½d. Type **53** (I)	10	10
	a. Type II (29.4.61)	20	10
214	1d. Type **54**	10	10
215	1½d. Type **55**	10	10
216	2d. Type **56**	10	10
217	2½d. Cocoa bean	10	10
218	3d. "God's Omnipotence" (I)	10	10
	a. Type II (29.4.61)	25	10
219	4d. Diamond and Mine	70	15
220	6d. Red-crowned Bishop	30	10
	a. Green (flag) omitted	30·00	
221	11d. Golden Spider Lily	25	10
222	1s. Shell Ginger	25	10
223	2s. 6d. Great Blue Turaco	1·75	15
224	5s. Tiger Orchid	4·50	50
225	10s. Tropical African Cichlid	2·75	70
225*a*	£1 Type **65***a* (29.4.61)	10·00	4·75
	(*b*) *Air*		
226	1s. 3d. Pennant-winged Nightjar	1·25	10
227	2s. Crowned Cranes	1·25	10
213/27	*Set of* 16	21·00	6·00

Nos. 217/224 and 226/7 are as Types **55/6**, the 11d., 1s., 5s. and 2s. (air) being vertical and the remainder horizontal. No. 225 is as Type **65***a*.

68 Gold Cup and West African Map

(Des K. Lehmann (½d., 3d.), M. & G. Shamir (1d.), W. Wind (8d.), and K. Antubam (2s. 6d.))

1959 (15 Oct). *West African Football Competition, 1959. T* **68** *and similar multicoloured designs. W* **47** *(sideways on horiz designs). P 14 × 14½ (1d., 2s. 6d) or 14½ × 14 (others).*

228	½d. Type **68**	10	10*
229	1d. Footballers (*vert*)	10	10*
230	3d. Goalkeeper saving ball	10	10*
231	8d. Forward attacking goal	20	10*
232	2s. 6d. "Kwame Nkrumah" Gold Cup (*vert*)	40	10*
228/32	. . . . *Set of* 5	65	20*

73 The Duke of Edinburgh and Arms of Ghana

(Des A. S. B. New)

1959 (24 Nov). *Visit of the Duke of Edinburgh to Ghana. W* **47** *(sideways). P 15 × 14.*

233 **73**	3d. black and magenta	10	10*

74 Ghana Flag and Talking Drums

75 Ghana Flag and U.N. Emblem

(Des K. Antubam (2s. 6d.), A. Medina (others))

1959 (10 Dec). *United Nations Trusteeship Council. T* **74/5** *and similar multicoloured designs. W* **47** *(sideways on 3d.). P 14½ × 14 (3d.) or 14 × 14½ (others).*

234	3d. Type **74**	10	10*
235	6d. Type **75**	10	10*
236	1s. 3d. Ghana flag and U.N. emblem (*vert*)	15	10*
237	2s. 6d. "Totem Pole" (*vert*)	15	15*
234/7	. . . . *Set of* 4	40	35*

78 Eagles in Flight

79 Fireworks

(Des A. Medina (½d.), M. Goaman (3d.), W. Wind (1s. 3d., 2s.))

1960 (6 Mar). *Third Anniv of Independence. T* **78/9** *and similar vert designs. Multicoloured. W* **47**. *P 14 × 14½.*

238	½d. Type **78**	10	10*
239	3d. Type **79**	10	10*
240	1s. 3d. "Third Anniversary"	15	10*
241	2s. "Ship of State"	15	15*
238/41	. . . . *Set of* 4	35	30*

82

(Des W. Wind)

1960 (15 Apr). *Africa Freedom Day. T* **82** *and similar horiz designs. Multicoloured. W* **47** *(sideways). P 14½ × 14.*

242	3d. Type **82**	10	10*
243	6d. Letter "f"	10	10*
244	1s. Letter "d"	10	10*
242/4	. . . . *Set of* 3	20	15*

REPUBLIC

85 President Nkrumah

(Des A. Medina (3d., 10s.), W. Wind (1s. 3d., 2s.))

1960 (1 July). *Republic Day. T* **85** *and similar multicoloured designs. W* **47**. *P 14½ × 14 (10s.) or 14 × 14½ (others).*

245	3d. Type **85**	10	10
246	1s. 3d. Ghana flag	10	10
247	2s. Torch of Freedom	15	10
248	10s. Arms of Ghana (*horiz*)	50	70
245/8	. . . . *Set of* 4	65	80
MS248*a*	102 × 77 mm. Nos. 245/8. Imperf . .	40	1·00

89 Olympic Torch

90 Athlete

(Des A. Medina (T **89**), W. Wind (T **90**))

1960 (15 Aug). *Olympic Games. W* **47** *(sideways on T* **90**). *P 14 × 14½ (T* **89**) *or 14½ × 14 (T* **90**).

249 **89**	3d. multicoloured	10	10
250	6d. multicoloured	10	10
251 **90**	1s. 3d. multicoloured	10	10
252	2s. 6d. multicoloured	15	15
249/52	. . . . *Set of* 4	30	25

91 President Nkrumah

94 U.N. Emblem and Ghana Flag

(Des M. Goaman (3d., 6d.), W. Wind (1s. 3d.))

1960 (21 Sept). *Founder's Day. T* **91** *and similar multicoloured designs. W* **47** *(sideways on 3d.). P 14½ × 14 (3d.) or 14 × 14½ (others).*

253	3d. Type **91**	10	10
254	6d. President Nkrumah (*vert*)	10	10
255	1s. 3d. Flag-draped column over map of African (*vert*)	10	10
253/5	. . . . *Set of* 3	15	15

(Des M. Goaman (3d., 1s. 3d.), W. Wind (6d.))

1960 (10 Dec). *Human Rights Day. T* **94** *and similar vert designs. W* **47**. *P 14 × 14½.*

256	3d. multicoloured	10	10
257	6d. yellow, black and blue	10	10
258	1s. 3d. multicoloured	15	10
256/8	. . . . *Set of* 3	25	15

Designs:—6d. U.N. emblem and Torch; 1s. 3d. U.N. emblem.

97 Talking Drums

100 Eagle on Column

(Des M. Goaman (3d.), A. S. B. New (6d.), W. Wind (2s.))

1961 (15 Apr). *Africa Freedom Day. T* **97** *and similar designs. W* **47** *(sideways on 2s.). P 14½ × 14 (2s.) or 14 × 14½ (others).*

259	3d. multicoloured	10	10
260	6d. red, black and green	10	10
261	2s. multicoloured	20	20
259/61	. . . . *Set of* 3	30	25

Designs: *Vert.*—6d. Map of Africa. *Horiz*—2s. Flags and map.

(Des A. S. B. New (3d.), M. Shamir (1s. 3d.), W. Wind (2s.))

1961 (1 July). *First Anniv of Republic. T* **100** *and similar vert designs. Multicoloured. W* **47**. *P 14 × 14½.*

262	3d. Type **100**	10	10
263	1s. 3d. "Flower"	10	10
264	2s. Ghana flags	20	25
262/4	. . . . *Set of* 3	30	30

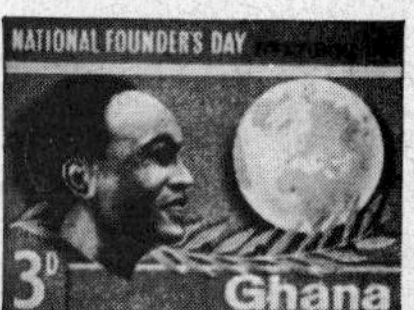

103 Dove with Olive Branch

106 Pres. Nkrumah and Globe

(Des V. Whiteley)

1961 (1 Sept). *Belgrade Conference. T* **103** *and similar designs. W* **47** *(sideways on 1s. 3d., 5s.). P 14 × 14½ (3d.) or 14½ × 14 (others).*

265	3d. yellow-green	10	10
266	1s. 3d. deep blue	10	10
267	5s. bright reddish purple	50	50
265/7	. . . . *Set of* 3	60	55

Designs: *Horiz.*—1s. 3d. World map, chain and olive branch; 5s. Rostrum, conference room.

(Des A. Medina (3d.), M. Goaman (1s. 3d.), Miriam Karoly (5s.))

1961 (21 Sept). *Founder's Day. T* **106** *and similar multicoloured designs. W* **47** *(sideways on 3d.). P 14½ × 14 (3d.) or 14 × 14½ (others).*

268	3d. Type **106**	10	10
269	1s. 3d. President and Kente Cloth (*vert*)	10	10
270	5s. President in national costume (*vert*)	60	70
268/70	. . . . *Set of* 3	70	70
MS270*a*	Three sheets 106 × 86 mm (3d.) or 86 × 106 mm (others) each with Nos. 268/70 in block of four. Imperf . . *Three sheets*	5·50	12·00

The 1s. 3d. Miniature Sheet is known with the brown colour omitted.

109 Queen Elizabeth II and African Map

(Des M. Goaman)

1961 (9 Nov). *Royal Visit. W* **47**. *P 14½ × 14.*

271 **109**	3d. multicoloured	10	10
272	1s. 3d. multicoloured	40	10
273	5s. multicoloured	1·25	1·00
271/3	. . . . *Set of* 3	1·60	1·10
MS273*a*	106 × 84 mm. No. 273 in block of four. Imperf	4·50	7·00

110 Ships in Tema Harbour

(Des C. Bottiau. Litho Enschedé & Sons)

1962 (10 Feb). *Opening of Tema Harbour. T* **110** *and similar horiz designs. Multicoloured. No wmk. P 14 × 13. (a) Postage.*

274	3d. Type **110**	10	10
	(*b*) *Air*		
275	1s. 3d. Aircraft and ships at Tema . .	20	10
276	2s. 6d. As 1s. 3d.	30	25
274/6	. . . . *Set of* 3	55	30

112 Africa and Peace Dove

113 Compass over Africa

(Des R. Hegeman. Litho Enschedé)

1962 (6 Mar). *First Anniv of Casablanca Conference. No wmk. P* 13 × 14. (*a*) *Postage.*
277 **112** 3d. multicoloured 10 10

(*b*) *Air*
278 **112** 1s. 3d. multicoloured 15 10
279 2s. 6d. multicoloured 25 30
277/9 .. .. *Set of* 3 40 35

(Des R. Hegeman)

1962 (24 Apr). *Africa Freedom Day. W* **47**. *P* 14 × 14½.
280 **113** 3d. sepia, blue-green and reddish purple 10 10
281 6d. sepia, blue-green and orange-brown 10 10
282 1s. 3d. sepia, blue-green and red .. 10 10
280/2 .. .. *Set of* 3 20 15

114 Ghana Star and "Five Continents"

115 Atomic Bomb-burst "Skull"

(Des M. Goaman (3d.), M. Shamir (6d.), W. Wind (1s. 3d.))

1962 (21 June). *Accra Assembly, T* **114/15** *and similar vert design. W* **47**. *P* 14 × 14½.
283 3d. black and lake-red 10 10
284 6d. black and scarlet 10 10
285 1s. 3d. turquoise 15 15
283/5 .. .. *Set of* 3 25 20
Design:—1s. 3d. Dove of Peace.

117 Patrice Lumumba

118 Star over Two Columns

(Des A. S. B. New)

1962 (30 June). *1st Death Anniv of Lumumba. W* **47**. *P* 14½ × 14.
286 **117** 3d. black and orange-yellow 10 10
287 6d. black, green and lake 10 10
288 1s. 3d. black, pink and black-green .. 15 15
286/8 .. .. *Set of* 3 20 15

(Des A. S. B. New (3d.), A. Medina (6d.), M. Goaman (1s. 3d.) Litho Enschedé)

1962 (1 July). *2nd Anniv of Republic. T* **118** *and similar multicoloured designs. P* 14 × 13½ (1s. 3d.) *or* 13½ × 14 (*others*).
289 3d. Type **118** 10 10
290 6d. Flaming torch 10 10
291 1s. 3d. Eagle trailing flag (*horiz*) 15 15
289/91 .. .. *Set of* 3 25 25

121 President Nkrumah

125 Campaign Emblem

(Litho Enschedé)

1962 (21 Sept). *Founder's Day. T* **121** *and similar vert designs. P* 13 × 14½.
292 1d. multicoloured 10 10
293 3d. multicoloured 10 10
294 1s. 3d. black and bright blue 15 10
295 2s. multicoloured 15 20
292/5 .. .. *Set of* 4 40 30
Designs:—3d. Nkrumah medallion; 1s. 3d. President Nkrumah and Ghana Star; 2s. Laying "Ghana" Brick.

1962 (3 Dec). *Malaria Eradication. W* **47**. *P* 14 × 14½.
296 **125** 1d. cerise 10 10
297 4d. yellow-green 10 10
298 6d. bistre 10 10
299 1s. 3d. bluish violet 15 15
296/9 .. .. *Set of* 4 25 20
MS299*a* 90 × 115 mm. Nos. 296/9. Imperf .. 65 85

126 Campaign Emblem

129 Map of Africa

1963 (21 Mar). *Freedom from Hunger. T* **126** *and similar designs. W* **47** (*sideways on* 4d., 1s. 3d.). *P* 14 × 14½ (1d.) *or* 14½ × 14 (*others*).
300 1d. multicoloured 15 10
301 4d. sepia, yellow and orange 50 15
302 1s. 3d. ochre, black and green .. .. 1·50 60
300/2 .. .. *Set of* 3 2·00 75
Designs: *Horiz*—4d. Emblem in hands; 1s. 3d. World map and emblem.

1963 (15 Apr). *Africa Freedom Day. T* **129** *and similar designs. W* **47** (*sideways on* 4d.). *P* 14½ × 14 (4d.) *or* 14 × 14½ (*others*).
303 1d. gold and red 10 10
304 4d. red, black and yellow 10 10
305 1s. 3d. multicoloured 10 10
306 2s. 6d. multicoloured 20 35
303/6 .. .. *Set of* 4 35 40
Designs: *Horiz*—4d. Carved stool. *Vert*—1s. 3d. Map and bowl of fire; 2s. 6d. Topi (antelope) and flag.

133 Red Cross

137 "3rd Anniversary"

(Des R. Hegeman (4d.), M. Shamir (others))

1963 (28 May). *Red Cross Centenary. T* **133** *and similar multicoloured designs. W* **47** (*sideways on* 1½d., 4d.). *P* 14½ × 14 (1d., 1s. 3d.) *or* 14 × 14½ (*others*).
307 1d. Type **133** 15 10
308 1½d. Centenary emblem (*horiz*) 25 30
309 4d. Nurses and child (*horiz*) 60 10
310 1s. 3d. Emblem, globe and laurel .. .. 1·40 1·10
307/10 .. .. *Set of* 4 2·25 1·40
MS310*a* 102 × 127 mm. Nos. 307/10. Imperf .. 2·00 4·00

(Des M. Goaman (1d., 4d.), R. Hegeman (others))

1963 (1 July). *3rd Anniv of Republic. T* **137** *and similar multicoloured designs. W* **47** (*sideways on* 1d., 4d.). *P* 14½ × 14 (*horiz*) *or* 14 × 14½ (*vert*).
311 1d. Type **137** 10 10
312 4d. Three Ghanaian flags 10 10
a. Black (stars on flag) omitted .. .. † –
313 1s. 3d. Map, flag and star (*vert*) 10 10
314 2s. 6d. Flag and torch (*vert*) 20 30
311/14 .. .. *Set of* 4 30 40

141 President Nkrumah and Ghana Flag

145 Rameses II, Abu Simbel

(Des R. Hegeman (1d., 4d.), M. Shamir (1s. 3d.), G. Rose (5s.))

1963 (21 Sept). *Founder's Day. T* **141** *and similar designs. W* **47** (*sideways on* 1s. 3d., 5s.). *P* 14 × 14½ (*vert*) *or* 14½ × 14 (*horiz*).
315 1d. multicoloured 10 10
316 4d. multicoloured 10 10
317 1s. 3d. multicoloured 10 10
a. Green omitted .. .. .. 55·00
318 5s. yellow and bright reddish purple .. 40 65
315/18 .. .. *Set of* 4 55 70
Designs: *Vert*—4d. Nkrumah and flag. *Horiz*—1s. 3d. Nkrumah and fireworks; 5s. Symbol of Wisdom.

(Des M. Farrar Bell and R. Hegeman. Litho (1½d., 2d.) or photo (others) Enschedé)

1963 (1 Nov). *Nubian Monuments Preservation. T* **145** *and similar multicoloured designs. No wmk. P* 11½ × 11 (*vert*) *or* 11 × 11½ (*horiz*).
319 1d. Type **145** 10 10
320 1½d. Rock paintings (*horiz*) 15 50
321 2d. Queen Nefertari (*horiz*) 15 10
322 4d. Sphinx, Sebua 25 15
323 1s. 3d. Rock Temple, Abu Simbel (*horiz*) .. 70 85
319/23 .. .. *Set of* 5 1·25 1·50

150 Steam and Diesel Locomotives

151 Eleanor Roosevelt and "Flame of Freedom"

(Des H. L. W. Stevens)

1963 (1 Dec). *60th Anniv of Ghana Railway. W* **47** (*sideways*). *P* 14½ × 14.
324 **150** 1d. multicoloured 10 10
325 6d. multicoloured 50 10
326 1s. 3d. multicoloured .. .. .. 1·00 60
327 2s. 6d. multicoloured .. .. .. 2·25 2·25
324/7 .. .. *Set of* 4 3·50 2·75

(Des R. Hegeman and F. H. Savage. Photo Enschedé)

1963 (10 Dec). *15th Anniv of Declaration of Human Rights. T* **151** *and similar multicoloured designs. No wmk. P* 11 × 11½ (1s. 3d.) *or* 11½ × 11 (*others*).
328 1d. Type **151** 10 10
329 4d. Type **151** 10 10
330 6d. Eleanor Roosevelt 10 10
331 1s. 3d. Eleanor Roosevelt and emblems (*horiz*) 10 10
328/31 .. .. *Set of* 4 15 15
No. 329 differs from No. 328 in the arrangement of the trailing "flame" and of the background within the circular emblem.

154 Sun and Globe Emblem

155 Harvesting Corn on State Farm

1964 (15 June). *International Quiet Sun Years. W* **47** (*sideways*). *Each blue, yellow, red and green; background colours given. P* 14½.
332 **154** 3d. pale brown 10 10
333 6d. pale grey 10 10
334 1s. 3d. mauve 10 10
332/4 .. .. *Set of* 3 15 10
MS334*a* 90 × 90 mm. No. 334 in block of four. Imperf .. .. 70 1·75
Nos. 332/4 each exist in a miniature sheet of 12 in different colours (i.e. 3d. in colours of 6d.; 6d. in colours of 1s. 3d.; 1s. 3d. in colours of 3d.) but these were not generally available to the public.

(Des M. Shamir. Photo Govt Printer, Israel)

1964 (1 July). *4th Anniv of Republic. T* **155** *and similar horiz designs. P* 13 × 14.
335 3d. olive, brown and yellow-olive 10 10
336 6d. bluish green, brown and turquoise-green 10 10
337 1s. 3d. brown-red, brown and salmon-red .. 10 10
338 5s. multicoloured 40 60
335/8 .. .. *Set of* 4 55 65
MS338*a* 126 × 100 mm. Nos. 335/8. Imperf .. 55 1·75
ab. Olive (central design and face value of 3d.) omitted
Designs:—6d. Oil refinery, Tema; 1s. 3d. "Communal Labour"; 5s. Procession headed by flag.

159 Globe and Dove

163 Pres. Nkrumah and Hibiscus Flowers

(Des M. Shamir. Litho Lewin-Epstein Ltd, Bat Yam, Israel)

1964 (15 July). *1st Anniv of African Unity Charter. T* **159** *and similar designs. P* 14.
339 3d. multicoloured 10 10
340 6d. deep bronze-green and red 10 10
341 1s. 3d. multicoloured 10 10
342 5s. multicoloured 40 60
339/42 .. .. *Set of* 4 55 65
Designs: *Vert*—6d. Map of Africa and quill pen; 5s. Planting flower. *Horiz*—1s. 3d. Hitched rope on map of Africa.

1964 (21 Sept). *Founder's Day. W* **47** (*sideways*). *P* 14 × 14½.
343 **163** 3d. sepia, red, deep green and light blue 10 10
344 6d. sepia, red, deep green and yellow .. 10 10
345 1s. 3d. sepia, red, deep green and grey .. 15 10
346 2s. 6d. sepia, red, dp grn & light emerald 20 25
343/6 .. .. *Set of* 4 40 30
MS346*a* 90 × 122 mm. No. 346 in block of four. Imperf .. .. 70 2·25

IMPERFORATE STAMPS. Many issues, including miniature sheets, from here onwards exist imperforate, but these were not sold at post offices.

164 Hurdling

(Des A. S. B. New (No. 352))

1964 (25 Oct). *Olympic Games, Tokyo. T* **164** *and similar multicoloured designs. W* **47** *(sideways on 1d., 2½d., 6d., 5s.). P 14½ × 14 (horiz) or 14 × 14½ (vert).*

347 1d. Type **164** 10 10
348 2½d. Running 10 15
349 3d. Boxing *(vert)* 10 10
350 4d. Long-jumping *(vert)* 10 10
351 6d. Football *(vert)* 10 10
352 1s. 3d. Athlete holding Olympic Torch *(vert)* 15 10
353 5s. Olympic Rings and flags .. .. .. 65 1·50
347/53 .. .. *Set of* 7 1·10 1·75
MS353*a* 128 × 102 mm. Nos. 351/3. Imperf .. 75 2·00

171 G. Washington Carver (botanist) and Plant **173** African Elephant

(Des M. Shamir)

1964 (7 Dec). *U.N.E.S.C.O. Week. W* **47**. *P 14½.*

354 **171** 6d. deep blue and green 10 10
355 – 1s. 3d. reddish purple and greenish blue 25 10
356 **171** 5s. sepia and orange-red .. .. 1·25 1·75
354/6 .. .. *Set of* 3 1·40 1·75
MS356*a* 127 × 77 mm. Nos. 354/6. Imperf .. 1·00 2·25

Design:—1s. 3d. Albert Einstein (scientist) and atomic symbol.

(Des A. S. B. New (No. 360). Photo Enschedé)

1964 (14 Dec). *Multicoloured designs as T* **173**. *P 11½ × 11 (vert) or 11 × 11½ (horiz).*

357 1d. Type **173** 20 10
358 1½d. Secretary Bird *(horiz)* 35 80
359 2½d. Purple Wreath (flower) 35 85
360 3d. Grey Parrot 45 30
361 4d. Blue-naped Mousebird *(horiz)* 60 50
362 6d. African Tulip Tree *(horiz)* 40 20
363 1s. 3d. Violet Starling *(horiz)* .. .. .. 1·25 1·25
364 2s. 6d. Hippopotamus *(horiz)* .. .. .. 1·50 4·00
357/64 .. .. *Set of* 8 4·50 7·00
MS364*a* (*a*) 150 × 86 mm. Nos. 357/9, (*b*) 150 × 110 mm. Nos. 360/4. Both Imperf .. *Two sheets* 5·50 11·00

181 I.C.Y. Emblem **182** I.T.U. Emblem and Symbols

(Litho Enschedé)

1965 (22 Feb). *International Co-operation Year. P 14 × 12½.*

365 **181** 1d. multicoloured 15 10
366 4d. multicoloured 45 25
367 6d. multicoloured 50 10
368 1s. 3d. multicoloured .. .. .. 1·00 1·50
365/8 .. .. *Set of* 4 1·90 1·75
MS368*a* 100 × 100 mm. No. 368 in block of four. Imperf .. .. 2·25 3·50

(Litho Enschedé)

1965 (12 Apr). *I.T.U. Centenary. P 13½.*

369 **182** 1d. multicoloured 10 10
370 6d. multicoloured 25 10
371 1s. 3d. multicoloured 50 20
372 5s. multicoloured .. .. 2·25 2·50
369/72 .. .. *Set of* 4 2·75 2·50
MS372*a* 132 × 115 mm. Nos. 369/72. Imperf .. 4·00 7·00

183 Lincoln's Home

(Des M. Farrar Bell (6d.), A. S. B. New (1s. 3d., 5s.), R. Hegeman (2s.))

1965 (17 May). *Death Centenary of Abraham Lincoln. T* **183** *and similar square-shaped designs. W* **47** *(sideways). P 12½.*

373 6d. multicoloured 15 10
374 1s. 3d. black, red and blue 30 15
375 2s. black, orange-brown and greenish yellow 40 30
376 5s. black and red .. .. 85 1·50
373/6 .. .. *Set of* 4 1·50 1·75
MS376*a* 115 × 115 mm. Nos. 373/6. Imperf .. 1·50 3·25
ab. Green (part of flag on 6d.) omitted ..

Designs:—1s. 3d. Lincoln's Inaugural Address; 2s. Abraham Lincoln; 5s. Adaptation of U.S. 90 c. Lincoln Stamp of 1869.

(New Currency. 100 pesewas = 1 cedi)

187 Obverse (Pres. Nkrumah) and Reverse of 5 p. Coin

(Photo Enschedé)

1965 (19 July). *Introduction of Decimal Currency. T* **187** *and similar horiz designs. Multicoloured. P* 11 × 13 *(5 p., 10 p.),* 13 × 12½ *(25 p.) or* 13½ × 14 *(50 p.).*

377 5 p. Type **187** 20 10
378 10 p. As Type **187** 25 10
379 25 p. Size 63 × 39 mm 70 80
380 50 p. Size 71 × 43½ mm .. .. .. 1·60 2·00
377/80 .. .. *Set of* 4 2·50 2·50

The coins in Nos. 378/80 are all circular and express the same denominations as on the stamps.

₵2·40
Ghana New Currency
19th July. 1965.

(188)

1965 (19 July). *Nos. 214, 216 and 218a/27 surch as T* **188** *diagonally upwards, (D) or horizontally, (H), by Govt Printer, Accra.*

(a) Postage

381 1 p. on 1d. multicoloured (R.) (D) 10 10
a. Surch inverted .. .. 15·00
b. Surch double .. ..
382 2 p. on 2d. multicoloured (Ultram.) (H) .. 10 10
a. Surch inverted .. .. ..
b. Surch double .. .. 10·00
c. Surch on back only .. .. ..
d. Surch on front and back .. ..
e. Red surch .. .. 26·00
f. Orange surch .. .. 26·00
g. Indigo surch .. ..
383 3 p. on 3d. multicoloured (II) (Br.) (H) .. 95 1·50
a. Surch inverted .. .. 18·00
b. Indigo surch .. ..
384 4 p. on 4d. multicoloured (B.) (H) 30 10
a. Surch inverted .. .. 14·00
b. Surch double .. ..
c. Red surch .. ..
385 6 p. on 6d. multicoloured (Blk.) (H) 15 10
a. Surch inverted .. .. 8·50
b. Surch double .. .. 15·00
c. Horiz pair, one without surch .. .. 40·00
d. Green (flag) omitted .. .. .. 50·00
386 11 p. on 11d. multicoloured (W.) (D) 25 10
a. Surch inverted .. .. 11·00
387 12 p. on 1s. multicoloured (B.) (D) 25 10
a. Surch double .. ..
b. Black surch .. .. 9·00
ba. Surch inverted .. .. 9·00
388 30 p. on 2s. 6d. multicoloured (B.) (H) .. 1·75 70
389 60 p. on 5s. multicoloured (B.) (D) .. .. 3·00 70
a. Surch double (G. + B.) .. .. .. 20·00
390 ₵1.20 on 10s. multicoloured (B.) (D) .. 1·75 2·25
a. Surch double (G. + B.) .. .. ..
391 ₵2.40 on £1 multicoloured (B.) (D) .. .. 2·00 5·50

(b) Air

392 15 p. on 1s. 3d. multicoloured (W.) (H) .. 1·25 15
a. Surch inverted .. ..
393 24 p. on 2s. multicoloured (G.) (D) .. .. 1·75 25
a. Surch on front and back .. .. 25·00
381/93 .. .. *Set of* 13 12·00 10·00

On the diagonal surcharges the values are horizontal.

The 30 p. was not released in Ghana until 30 July and the 3 p. sometime later.

Numerous minor varieties exist.

189 "OAU" and Flag

190 "OAU", Heads and Flag

191 "OAU" Emblem and Flag

192 African Map and Flag

1965 (21 Oct). *O.A.U. Summit Conference, Accra. T* **189/92** *and similar horiz designs. Multicoloured. W* **47** *(sideways, except on 6 p.). P 14 (T* **189/91**) *or 14½ × 14 (others).*

394 1 p. Type **189** 10 10
395 2 p. Type **190** 10 10
396 5 p. Type **191** 10 10
397 6 p. Type **192** 10 10
398 15 p. "Sunburst", map and flag 20 25
399 24 p. "O.A.U." on map, and flag 35 50
394/9 .. .. *Set of* 6 75 90

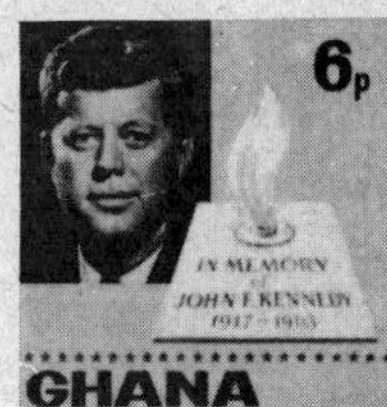

195 Goalkeeper saving Ball **198** Pres. Kennedy and Grave Memorial

(Photo Enschedé)

1965 (15 Nov). *African Soccer Cup Competition. T* **195** *and similar multicoloured designs. P* 13 × 14 *(15 p.) or* 14 × 13 *(others).*

400 6 p. Type **195** 10 10
401 15 p. Player with ball *(vert)* 20 20
402 24 p. Players, ball and soccer cup 35 40
400/2 .. .. *Set of* 3 60 60

(Des A. S. B. New (No. 405))

1965 (15 Dec)–**66**. *2nd Anniv of President Kennedy's Death. T* **198** *and similar square-shaped designs. W* **47** *(sideways). P 12½.*

403 6 p. multicoloured 15 10
404 15 p. violet, red and green 40 35
405 24 p. black and reddish violet 50 60
406 30 p. dull purple and black 60 75
403/6 .. .. *Set of* 4 1·50 1·60
MS407 114½ × 114 mm. Nos. 403/6. Imperf (21.3.66) .. .. 3·75 6·50

Designs:—15 p. Pres. Kennedy and Eternal Flame; 24 p. Pres. Kennedy and memorial inscription; 30 p. President Kennedy.

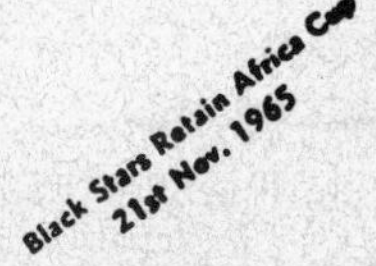

202 Section of Dam and Generators **(206)**

(Des A. S. B. New (No. 411). Photo Enschedé)

1966 (22 Jan). *Volta River Project. T* **202** *and similar horiz designs. P* 11 × 11½.
408 6 p. multicoloured 15 10
409 15 p. multicoloured 20 15
410 24 p. multicoloured 25 20
411 30 p. black and new blue 35 50
408/11 . . . . *Set of* 4 85 85
Designs:—15 p. Dam and Lake Volta; 24 p. Word "GHANA" as dam; 30 p. "Fertility".

1966 (7 Feb). *"Black Stars" Victory in African Soccer Cup Competition. Nos.* 400/2 *optd with T* **206**, *in black.*
412 6 p. Type **195** 10 10
a. Green opt. . . . . 20·00
b. Green opt double, one inverted . .
413 15 p. Player with ball 20 20
414 24 p. Players, ball and cup 35 35
a. Opt inverted* . . . . 26·00
ab. Vert pair, one without opt, the other with opt inverted . . . .
b. Error. Opt for 15 p. on 24 p. inverted.*
412/14 . . . . *Set of* 3 60 60
*In No. 414a the overprint reads downwards (top right to bottom left), but in No. 414b it reads upwards (bottom right to top left).

DATES OF ISSUE of miniature sheets are approximate as they are generally released some time after the related ordinary stamps, but it known that the G.P.O. sometimes apply first-day cancellations months after the dates shown on the cancellations.

207 W.H.O. Building and Ghana Flag

1966 (1 July). *Inauguration of W.H.O. Headquarters, Geneva. T* **207** *and similar horiz design. Multicoloured. W* **47**. *P* 14½ × 14.
415 6 p. Type **207** 30 10
416 15 p. Type **207** 60 40
417 24 p. W.H.O. Building and emblem 85 90
418 30 p. As 24 p. . . . . 1·00 1·40
415/18 . . . . *Set of* 4 2·50 2·50
MS419 120 × 101 mm. Nos. 415/18. Imperf (11.66) 8·50 11·00

209 Herring

214 African "Links" and Ghana Flag

(Des O. Hamann. Photo Enschedé)

1966 (10 Aug). *Freedom from Hunger. T* **209** *and similar horiz designs. Multicoloured. P* 14 × 13.
420 6 p. Type **209** 15 10
421 15 p. Flat Fish 35 15
422 24 p. Spade Fish 65 35
423 30 p. Red Snapper 80 75
424 60 p. Tuna . . . . 2·00 2·50
420/4 . . . . *Set of* 5 3·50 3·50
MS425 126 × 109 mm. No. 423 in block of four. Imperf (Nov) . . . . 7·50 10·00

(Photo Enschedé)

1966 (11 Oct). *Third Anniv of African Charter. T* **214** *and similar multicoloured designs. P* 13½.
426 6 p. Type **214** 10 10
427 15 p. Flags as "Quill", and diamond (*horiz*) . . 20 20
428 24 p. Ship's wheel, map and cocoa bean (*horiz*) 25 25
426/8 . . . . *Set of* 3 50 45

217 Player heading Ball, and Jules Rimet Cup

1966 (14 Nov). *World Cup Football Championships, England. T* **217** *and similar horiz designs. Multicoloured. W* **47**. *P* 14½ × 14.
429 5 p. Type **217** 15 10
430 15 p. Goalkeeper clearing ball 40 15
431 24 p. Player and Jules Rimet Cup (replica) . . 55 35
432 30 p. Players and Jules Rimet Cup (replica) . . 75 75
433 60 p. Players with ball . . . . . . 1·50 2·25
429/33 . . . . *Set of* 5 3·00 3·25
MS434 120 × 102 mm. 60 p. (block of four). Imperf 9·00 12·00

222 U.N.E.S.C.O. Emblem

1966 (23 Dec). *20th Anniv of U.N.E.S.C.O. W* **47** (*sideways*). *P* 14½.
435 **222** 5 p. multicoloured 20 10
436 15 p. multicoloured 45 35
437 24 p. multicoloured 70 70
438 30 p. multicoloured . . . . . . 1·25 1·50
439 60 p. multicoloured . . . . . . 2·25 3·25
435/9 . . . . *Set of* 5 4·25 5·50
MS440 140 × 115 mm. Nos. 435/9. Imperf . . 10·00 14·00

223 Fair Emblem and Crates

1967 (1 Feb). *Ghana Trade Fair, Accra. T* **223** *and similar multicoloured designs. W* **47** (*sideways on* 24 *p.*). *P* 14 × 14½ (24 *p.*) *or* 14½ × 14 (*others*).
441 5 p. Type **223** 10 10
442 15 p. Fair emblem and world map 15 10
443 24 p. Shipping and flags (*vert*) 25 20
444 36 p. Fair emblem and hand-held hoist . . 40 55
441/4 . . . . *Set of* 4 70 80

(New Currency. 100 new pesewas = 1 new cedi (1·2 old cedi))

1½Np (227)

N₵2.00 (228)

229 Ghana Eagle and Flag

1967 (23 Feb). *Nos.* 216, 219/23, 225/6 *and* 393 *surch as T* **227/8**.

(*a*) *Postage*
445 1½ n.p. on 2d. multicoloured (Blk.) . . . . 5·50 3·00
446 3½ n.p. on 4d. multicoloured (R.) 60 15
447 5 n.p. on 6d. multicoloured (R.) 35 10
448 9 n.p. on 11d. multicoloured (W.) 30 15
449 10 n.p. on 1s. multicoloured (W.) 30 15
450 25 n.p. on 2s. 6d. multicoloured (R.) . . 3·00 1·75
451 1 n.c. on 10s. multicoloured (R.) . . . . 6·50 11·00
452 2 n.c. on £1 multicoloured (R.) . . . . 12·00 20·00

(*b*) *Air*
453 12½ n.p. on 1s. 3d. multicoloured (W.) . . 1·75 70
454 20 n.p. on 24 p. on 2s. multicoloured (R.) . . 2·50 1·50
445/54 . . . . *Set of* 10 29·00 35·00
Inverted surcharges in a different type face on the 3½, 5 and 25 n.p. are fakes.

(Des M. Shamir)

1967 (24 Feb). *First Anniv of February 24 Revolution. W* **47** (*sideways*). *P* 14 × 14½.
455 **229** 1 n.p. multicoloured 10 10
456 4 n.p. multicoloured 10 10
457 12½ n.p. multicoloured 40 45
458 25 n.p. multicoloured . . . . . . 85 1·40
455/8 . . . . *Set of* 4 1·25 1·75
MS459 89 × 108 mm. Nos. 455/8. Perf or imperf . . 6·50 9·00

230 Maize

231 Forest Kingfisher

235 Rufous-crowned Roller

236 Akosombo Dam

1967 (1 June–4 Sept). *T* **230/1, 235/6** *and similar designs. W* **47** (1½, 2, 4, 50 *n.p. and* 1 *n.c.*) *or sideways* (*others*). *P* 11½ × 12 (1, 8 *n.p.*), 12 × 11½ (4 *n.p.*), 14 × 14½ (1½, 2, 2½, 20 *n.p.*, 2 *n.c.* 50) *or* 14½ × 14 (*others*).
460 1 n.p. multicoloured 10 10
a. Salmon omitted** . . . . . .
461 1½ n.p. multicoloured 60 10
a. Blue omitted* . . . . . . 70·00
b. Green printed double, once inverted†
c. Green omitted† . . . . . .
462 2 n.p. multicoloured (4.9) 10 10
a. Green (part of flag) omitted . .
b. Gold (frame) omitted . . . .
463 2½ n.p. multicoloured (4.9) 35 10
a. Wmk upright . . . . . . 30·00
ab. Face value omitted £160
464 3 n.p. multicoloured 15 15
a. Green (part of flag) omitted . .
465 4 n.p. multicoloured 90 10
a. Green (part of flag) omitted . .
b. Red (part of flag) omitted . . . .
c. Black (star, bird markings and shadow) omitted . . . . . . 50·00
466 6 n.p. multicoloured 15 10
467 8 n.p. multicoloured 15 10
468 9 n.p. multicoloured (4.9) 45 10
469 10 n.p. multicoloured 15 10
470 20 n.p. deep blue and new blue (4.9) 20 10
471 50 n.p. multicoloured . . . . . . 2·75 25
472 1 n.c. multicoloured (4.9) . . . . . . 1·50 75
473 2 n.c. multicoloured (4.9) . . . . . . 1·75 2·00
474 2 n.c. 50, multicoloured . . . . . . 2·50 3·00
460/74 . . . . *Set of* 15 11·00 5·75
Designs: *Vert* (*as T* **231**)—2 n.p. The Ghana Mace; 2½ n.p. Commelina; 20 n.p. Bush Hare; 2 n.c. Frangipani; 2 n.c. 50, Seat of State. *Horiz* (*as T* **236**)—3 n.p. Mud-fish; 9 n.p. Chameleon; 10 n.p. Tema Harbour; 50 n.p. Black-winged Stilt; 1 n.c. Wooden Stool. (*As T* **230**)—8 n.p. Adomi Bridge.
*In this stamp the blue not only affects the bird but is printed over the yellow background to give the value in green, so that its omission results in the value also being omitted.
**This affects the maize flowers, corn and foreground.
†This affects the feather-tips and the flag.
The 2 n.p. and 20 n.p. were officially issued on 4 September but small quanties of both were released in error on 1 June. The 2½ n.p. is also known to have been released in error in June.

245 Kumasi Fort

249 "Luna 10"

(Des O. Hamann)

1967 (1 July). *Castles and Forts. T* **245** *and similar designs. Multicoloured. W* **47** (*diagonal*). *P* 14½.
475 4 n.p. Type **245** 25 10
476 12½ n.p. Christiansborg Castle and British galleon . . . . 1·00 1·00
477 20 n.p. Elmina Castle and Portuguese galleon . . . . 1·40 1·75
478 25 n.p. Cape Coast Castle and Spanish galleon . . . . 1·75 2·25
475/8 . . . . *Set of* 4 4·00 4·50

(Des M. Shamir. Photo Enschedé)

1967 (16 Aug). *"Peaceful Use of Outer Space". T* **249** *and similar square designs. Multicoloured. P* 13½ × 14.
479 4 n.p. Type **249** 10 10
480 10 n.p. "Orbiter 1" 10 10
481 12½ n.p. Man in Space 20 25
479/81 . . . . *Set of* 3 35 35
MS482 140 × 90 mm. Nos. 479/81. Imperf . . . . 95 2·00

252 Scouts and Camp-fire

(Photo Enschedé)

1967 (18 Sept). *50th Anniv of Ghanaian Scout Movement. T* **252** *and similar horiz designs. Multicoloured. P* 14½ × 13.
483 4 n.p. Type **252** 20 10
484 10 n.p. Scout on march 50 15
485 12½ n.p. Lord Baden-Powell 70 55
483/5 . . . . *Set of* 3 1·25 65
MS486 167 × 95 mm. Nos. 483/5. Imperf . . . . 6·00 8·50

255 U.N. Headquarters Building

256 General View of U.N. H.Q., Manhattan

(Litho D.L.R.)

1967 (20 Nov). *United Nations Day (24 October). P* 13½.
487 **255** 4 n.p. multicoloured — 15 10
488 10 n.p. multicoloured — 20 15
489 **256** 50 n.p. multicoloured — 40 70
490 2 n.c. 50, multicoloured — 1·50 4·00
487/90 *Set of* 4 — 2·00 4·50
MS491 76 × 75 mm. No. 490. Imperf (4.12.67) — 4·50 8·00

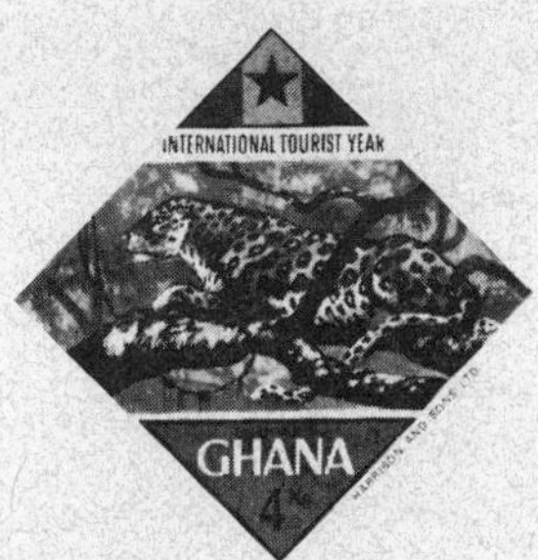

257 Leopard

1967 (28 Dec). *International Tourist Year. T* **257** *and similar diamond-shaped designs. Multicoloured. W* **47** *(diagonal). P* 12½.
492 4 n.p. Type **257** — 30 10
493 12½ n.p. Citrus Swallowtail Butterfly — 90 1·00
494 20 n.p. Carmine Bee Eater — 1·75 2·25
495 50 n.p. Waterbuck — 3·00 4·50
492/5 *Set of* 4 — 5·50 7·00
MS496 126 × 126 mm. Nos. 493/5. Imperf — 9·50 11·00

261 Revolutionaries entering Accra

(Litho D.L.R.)

1968 (24 Feb). *2nd Anniv of February Revolution. T* **261** *and similar horiz designs. Multicoloured. P* 14.
497 4 n.p. Type **261** — 10 10
498 12½ n.p. Marching troops — 20 20
499 20 n.p. Cheering people — 30 40
500 40 n.p. Victory celebrations — 50 1·25
497/500 *Set of* 4 — 1·00 1·75

265 Microscope and Cocoa Beans

1968 (18 Mar). *Cocoa Research. T* **265** *and similar horiz design. Multicoloured. W* **47** *(sideways). P* 14½ × 14.
501 2½ n.p. Type **265** — 5 10
502 4 n.p. Microscope and cocoa tree, beans and pods — 10 10
503 10 n.p. Type **265** — 15 15
504 25 n.p. As 4 n.p. — 60 80
501/4 *Set of* 4 — 80 90
MS505 102 × 102 mm. Nos. 501/4. Imperf — 2·00 3·00

267 Kotoka and Flowers

271 Tobacco

(Des A. S. B. New (No. 508) and F. Mate (others) Litho D.L.R.)

1968 (17 Apr). *1st Death Anniv of Lt.-Gen. E. K. Kotoka. T* **267** *and similar multicoloured designs. P* 14.
506 4 n.p. Type **267** — 10 10
507 12½ n.p. Kotoka and wreath — 20 20
508 20 n.p. Kotoka in civilian clothes — 35 65
509 40 n.p. Lt.-Gen. Kotoka *(vert)* — 50 1·00
506/9 *Set of* 4 — 1·00 1·75

(Des A. S. B. New (5 n.p.))

1968 (19 Aug). *T* **271** *and similar vert designs. Multicoloured. W* **47** *(sideways). P* 14 × 14½.
510 4 n.p. Type **271** — 15 10
511 5 n.p. North African Crested Porcupine — 15 10
512 12½ n.p. Rubber — 50 50
513 20 n.p. *Cymothoe sangaris* (butterfly) — 1·00 1·60
514 40 n.p. *Charaxes ameliae* (butterfly) — 1·75 3·25
510/14 *Set of* 5 — 3·25 5·00
MS515 88 × 114 mm. Nos. 410, 512/14. Imperf — 3·50 6·50

276 Surgeons, Flag and W.H.O. Emblem

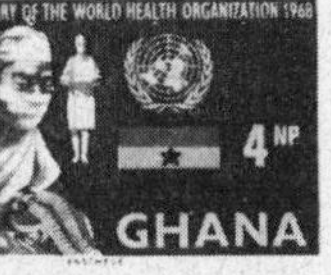

277 Hurdling

(Photo Enschedé)

1968 (11 Nov). *20th Anniv of World Health Organization. P* 14 × 13.
516 **276** 4 n.p. multicoloured — 15 10
517 12½ n.p. multicoloured — 30 35
518 20 n.p. multicoloured — 60 70
519 40 n.p. multicoloured — 1·00 1·50
516/19 *Set of* 4 — 1·75 2·40
MS520 132 × 110 mm. Nos. 516/19. Imperf — 3·00 5·00

1969 (10 Jan). *Olympic Games, Mexico (1968). T* **277** *and similar vert designs. Multicoloured. W* **47** *(sideways). P* 14 × 14½.
521 4 n.p. Type **277** — 10 10
522 12½ n.p. Boxing — 20 30
523 20 n.p. Torch, Olympic Rings and flags — 40 70
524 40 n.p. Football — 70 1·50
521/4 *Set of* 4 — 1·25 2·25
MS525 89 × 114 mm. Nos. 521/4. Imperf (17.1.69) — 3·50 4·50

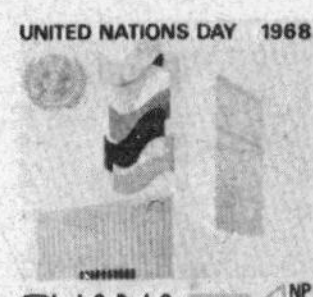

281 U.N. Building

285 Dr. J. B. Danquah

(Litho D.L.R.)

1969 (1 Feb). *United Nations Day (1968). T* **281** *and similar square-shaped designs. Multicoloured. P* 13½.
526 4 n.p. Type **281** — 10 10
527 12½ n.p. Native stool, staff and U.N. emblem — 15 20
528 20 n.p. U.N. building and emblem over Ghanaian flag — 25 35
529 40 n.p. U.N. emblem encircled by flags — 50 90
526/9 *Set of* 4 — 90 1·40
MS530 127 × 117 mm. No. 526/9. Imperf — 1·10 2·50

1969 (7 Mar). *Human Rights Year. T* **285** *and similar horiz design. Multicoloured. W* **47** *(sideways on* **MS**535*). P* 14½ × 14.
531 4 n.p. Type **285** — 10 10
532 12½ n.p. Dr. Martin Luther King — 15 25
533 20 n.p. As 12½ n.p. — 25 50
534 40 n.p. Type **285** — 45 1·00
531/4 *Set of* 4 — 80 1·60
MS535 116 × 50 mm. Nos. 531/4. Imperf (17.4.69) — 80 2·00

287 Constituent Assembly Building

1969 (10 Sept). *Third Anniv of the Revolution. T* **287** *and similar horiz design. W* **47** *(sideways on* **MS**540*). P* 14½ × 14.
536 4 n.p. Type **287** — 10 10
537 12½ n.p. Arms of Ghana — 10 10
538 20 n.p. Type **287** — 15 15
539 40 n.p. As 12½ n.p. — 20 35
536/9 *Set of* 4 — 40 60
MS540 114 × 89 mm. Nos. 536/9. Imperf — 70 1·75

NEW CONSTITUTION
1969
(289)

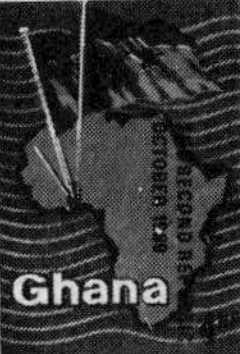

290 Map of Africa and Flags

1969 (1 Oct). *New Constitution. Nos. 460/74 optd with T* **289** *in various positions by Government Press, Accra.*
541 1 n.p. multicoloured (Horiz) — 10 20
542 1½ n.p. multicoloured (Vert down) — 25 30
a. Opt vert up — 6·00
b. Horiz opt — 25·00
ba. Opt omitted (in vert pair with normal) — £175
543 2 n.p. multicoloured (Vert up) — 10 20
a. Opt vert down — 5·00
b. Opt double — 12·00
544 2½ n.p. multicoloured (Vert up) — 10 20
a. Opt vert down — 18·00
545 3 n.p. multicoloured (Horiz) — 20 25
a. Opt inverted — 15·00
546 4 n.p. multicoloured (Y.) (Vert down) — 60 25
a. Black opt (vert down) — 6·00 1·00
b. Black opt (vert up) — 10·00
c. Red opt (vert down) — 18·00
d. Opt double (White vert down + yellow vert up) — 27·00
547 6 n.p. multicoloured (Horiz) — 15 30
548 8 n.p. multicoloured (Horiz) — 15 25
549 9 n.p. multicoloured (Horiz) — 15 30
550 10 n.p. multicoloured (Horiz) — 20 25
551 20 n.p. deep blue and new blue (Vert up) — 35 50
a. Opt vert down — 20·00
552 50 n.p. multicoloured (Horiz) — 3·25 3·50
a. Opt double
553 1 n.c. multicoloured (Horiz) — 2·25 3·50
554 2 n.c. multicoloured (R.) (Vert up) — 3·50 5·50
a. Opt double (vert up and down)
555 2 n.c. 50, multicoloured (Vert down) — 3·50 6·50
541/55 *Set of* 15 — 13·00 20·00

The 1 n.p. is known with the overprint inverted, "NEW CONSTITUTION" appearing between the stamps across the perforations.

(Litho D.L.R.)

1969 (4 Dec). *Inauguration of Second Republic. T* **290** *and similar vert designs. Multicoloured. P* 14.
556 4 n.p. Type **290** — 10 10
557 12½ n.p. Figure "2", branch and Ghanaian colours — 15 10
558 20 n.p. Hands receiving egg — 25 30
559 40 n.p. Type **290** — 50 70
556/9 *Set of* 4 — 90 1·00

293 I.L.O. Emblem and Cog-wheels

1970 (5 Jan). *50th Anniv of International Labour Organisation. W* **47** *(sideways). P* 14½ × 14.
560 **293** 4 n.p. multicoloured — 10 10
561 12½ n.p. multicoloured — 20 25
562 20 n.p. multicoloured — 30 45
560/2 *Set of* 3 — 55 70
MS563 117 × 89 mm. Nos. 560/2. Imperf — 70 1·90

294 Red Cross and Globe

298 General Kotoka, "VC-10" and Airport

1970 (2 Feb). *50th Anniv of League of Red Cross Societies. T* **294** *and similar multicoloured designs. W* **47** *(sideways on 4 n.p.). P* 14 × 14½ *(4 n.p.) or* 14½ × 14 *(others).*
564 4 n.p. Type **294** — 15 10
565 12½ n.p. Henri Dunant and Red Cross emblem *(horiz)* — 25 20
566 20 n.p. Patient receiving medicine *(horiz)* — 35 45
567 40 n.p. Patient having arm bandaged *(horiz)* — 70 1·10
564/7 *Set of* 4 — 1·25 1·60
MS568 114 × 89 mm. Nos. 564/7. Imperf — 2·50 5·50

(Des G. Vasarhelyi. Litho D.L.R.)

1970 (17 Apr). *Inauguration of Kotoka Airport. T* **298** *and similar horiz designs. Multicoloured. P* 13 × 13½.
569 4 n.p. Type **298** — 10 10
570 12½ n.p. Control tower and tail of "VC-10" — 20 15
571 20 n.p. Aerial view of airport — 30 30
572 40 n.p. Airport and flags — 60 80
569/72 *Set of* 4 — 1·10 1·25

302 Lunar Module landing on Moon

306 Adult Education

(Des A. Medina (4 n.p., 12½ n.p.), G. Vasarhelyi (others). Litho D.L.R.)

1970 (15 June). *Moon Landing. T* **302** *and similar multicoloured designs. P* 12½.

573 4 n.p. Type **302** .. 30 10
574 12½ n.p. Astronaut's first step onto the Moon .. 85 60
575 20 n.p. Astronaut with equipment on Moon (*horiz*) .. 1·40 1·40
576 40 n.p. Astronauts (*horiz*) .. 3·00 3·00
573/6 .. *Set of* 4 5·00 4·50
MS577 142 × 142 mm. Nos. 573/6. Imperf (with or without simulated perfs) .. 7·00 10·00

On 18 September 1970 Nos. 573/6 were issued overprinted "PHILYMPIA LONDON 1970" but it is understood that only 900 sets were made available for sale in Ghana and we do not consider that this is sufficient to constitute normal postal use. The miniature sheet was also overprinted but not issued in Ghana.

(Litho D.L.R.)

1970 (10 Aug). *International Education Year. T* **306** *and similar horiz designs. Multicoloured. P* 13.

578 4 n.p. Type **306** .. 10 10
579 12½ n.p. International education .. 20 20
580 20 n.p. "Ntesie" and I.E.Y. symbols .. 35 30
581 40 n.p. Nursery schools .. 60 85
578/81 .. *Set of* 4 1·10 1·25

310 Saluting March-Past

314 *Crinum ornatum*

(Litho D.L.R.)

1970 (1 Oct). *First Anniv of the Second Republic. T* **310** *and similar horiz designs. Multicoloured. P* 13 × 13½.

582 4 n.p. Type **310** .. 10 10
583 12½ n.p. Busia declaration .. 15 15
584 20 n.p. Doves symbol .. 25 30
585 40 n.p. Opening of Parliament .. 50 65
582/5 .. *Set of* 4 90 1·00

(Des G. Vasarhelyi. Photo Harrison)

1970 (2 Nov). *Flora and Fauna. T* **314** *and similar horiz designs. Multicoloured. W* **47** (*sideways*). *P* 14½ × 14.

586 4 n.p. Type **314** .. 65 10
587 12½ n.p. Lioness .. 90 35
588 20 n.p. *Anselia africana* (flower) .. 1·25 80
589 40 n.p. African Elephant .. 3·00 2·50
586/9 .. *Set of* 4 5·25 3·25

315 Kuduo Brass Casket

(Des G. Vasarhelyi. Photo Harrison)

1970 (7 Dec). *Monuments and Archaeological Sites in Ghana. T* **315** *and similar horiz designs. Multicoloured. W* **47**. *P* 14½ × 14.

590 4 n.p. Type **315** .. 15 10
591 12½ n.p. Akan Traditional House .. 30 20
592 20 n.p. Larabanga Mosque .. 50 50
593 40 n.p. Funerary Clay Head .. 80 1·10
590/3 .. *Set of* 4 1·60 1·75
MS594 89 × 71 mm. Nos. 590, 592 and 12½ n.p. Basilica of Pompeii; 40 n.p. Pistrinum of Pompeii. (wmk sideways). Imperf (2.71) .. 3·50 6·00

316 Trade Fair Building

(Des G. Drummond (4 n.p., 50 n.p.), A. Larkins (others). Photo Harrison)

1971 (5 Feb). *International Trade Fair, Accra. T* **316** *and similar multicoloured designs. W* **47** (*sideways, except* 50 *n.p.*). *P* 14 × 14½ (50 *n.p.*) *or* 14½ × 14 (*others*).

595 4 n.p. Type **316** .. 10 10
596 12½ n.p. Cosmetics and Pharmaceutical Goods 20 20
597 20 n.p. Vehicles .. 30 25
598 40 n.p. Construction Equipment .. 65 95
599 50 n.p. Transport and Packing Case (*vert*) .. 70 1·10
595/9 .. *Set of* 5 1·75 2·25

317 Christ on the Cross

318 Corn Cob

(Des from stained-glass windows. Litho D.L.R.)

1971 (19 May). *Easter. T* **317** *and similar square designs. Multicoloured. P* 13.

600 4 n.p. Type **317** .. 10 10
601 12½ n.p. Christ and Disciples .. 20 35
602 20 n.p. Christ blessing Disciples .. 35 75
600/2 .. *Set of* 3 60 1·00

(Photo Harrison)

1971 (15 June). *Freedom from Hunger Campaign. W* **47**. *P* 14 × 14½.

603 **318** 4 n.p. multicoloured .. 10 10
604 12½ n.p. multicoloured .. 35 60
605 20 n.p. multicoloured .. 65 1·10
603/5 .. *Set of* 3 1·00 1·60

Remainder stocks of the above were overprinted on the occasion of the death of Lord Boyd Orr and the 4 n.p. surcharged 60 n.p.

It is understood that 8,070 sets from the New York Agency were overprinted locally and returned to the Agency. Limited remainders of these stamps (only 330 of the 60 n.p.) were sold at the G.P.O. We do not list these as they were not freely on sale in Ghana.

319 Guides Emblem and Ghana Flag

320 Child-care Centre

(Des and litho Questa)

1971 (22 July). *Ghana Girl Guides Golden Jubilee. T* **319** *and similar horiz designs each with Guides Emblem. Multicoloured. P* 14.

606 4 n.p. Type **319** .. 20 10
607 12½ n.p. Mrs. E. Ofuatey-Kodjoe (founder) and guides with flags .. 60 50
608 20 n.p. Guides laying stones .. 90 90
609 40 n.p. Camp-fire and tent .. 1·50 1·75
610 50 n.p. Signallers .. 1·75 2·00
606/10 .. *Set of* 5 4·50 4·75
MS611 133 × 105 mm. Nos. 606/10. Imperf .. 7·50 10·00

(Des and litho D.L.R.)

1971 (7 Aug). *Y.W.C.A. World Council Meeting, Accra. T* **320** *and similar horiz designs. Multicoloured. P* 13.

612 4 n.p. Type **320** .. 10 10
613 12½ n.p. Council meeting .. 10 15
614 20 n.p. School typing-class .. 15 30
615 40 n.p. Building Fund Day .. 30 60
612/15 .. *Set of* 4 55 1·00
MS616 84 × 83 mm. Nos. 612/15. Imperf .. 70 1·75

321 Firework Display

322 Weighing Baby

(Photo Harrison)

1971 (22 Nov). *Christmas. T* **321** *and similar horiz designs. Multicoloured. W* **47** (*sideways on* 3 *and* 6 *n.p.*). *P* 14 × 14½ (1 *n.p.*) *or* 14½ × 14 (*others*).

617 1 n.p. Type **321** .. 10 10
618 3 n.p. African Nativity .. 10 20
619 6 n.p. The flight into Egypt .. 15 25
617/19 .. *Set of* 3 25 50

(Litho D.L.R.)

1971 (20 Dec). *25th Anniv of U.N.I.C.E.F. T* **322** *and similar multicoloured designs, each showing the U.N.I.C.E.F. symbol. No wmk* (**MS**624) *or W* **47** (*sideways on* 5 *and* 30 *n.p.*). *P* 13.

620 5 n.p. Type **322** .. 10 10
621 15 n.p. Mother and child (*horiz*) .. 30 30
622 30 n.p. Nurse .. 40 60
623 50 n.p. Young boy (*horiz*) .. 60 1·50
620/3 .. *Set of* 4 1·25 2·25
MS624 111 × 120 mm. Nos. 620/3. Imperf .. 3·50 5·50

323 Unity Symbol and Trade Fair Emblem

(Litho Questa)

1972 (23 Feb). *All-Africa Trade Fair. T* **323** *and similar horiz designs. Multicoloured. W* **47**. *P* 14.

625 5 n.p. Type **323** .. 10 10
626 15 n.p. Horn of Plenty .. 20 30
627 30 n.p. Fireworks on map of Africa .. 35 70
628 60 n.p. "Participating Nations" .. 50 1·50
629 1 n.c. As No. 628 .. 80 2·25
625/9 .. *Set of* 5 1·75 4·25

All designs include the Trade Fair Emblem as in T **323**.

On 24 June 1972, on the occasion of the Belgian International Philatelic Exhibition, Nos. 625/9 were issued overprinted "BELGICA 72" in red. Only very limited supplies were sent to Ghana (we understand not more than 900 sets), and for this reason we do not list them.

(New Currency. 100 pesewas = 1 cedi = 0.8 (1967) new cedi)

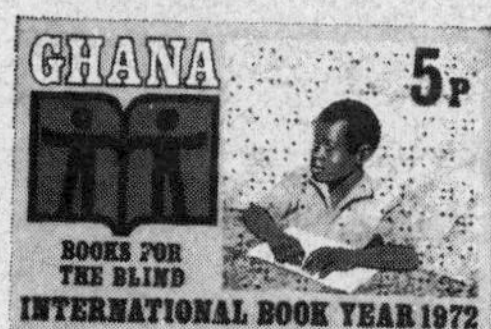

324 Books for the Blind

(Des and litho D.L.R.)

1972 (21 Apr). *International Book Year. T* **324** *and similar multicoloured designs. P* 13.

630 5 p. Type **324** .. 15 10
631 15 p. Children's books .. 35 40
632 30 p. Books for recreation .. 60 75
633 50 p. Books for students .. 1·00 1·60
634 1 c. Book and flame of knowledge (*vert*) .. 2·00 2·50
630/4 .. *Set of* 5 3·75 4·75
MS635 99 × 106 mm. Nos. 630/4. Imperf .. 7·50 10·00

325 *Hypoxis urceolata*

(Litho D.L.R.)

1972 (3 July). *Flora and Fauna. T* **325** *and similar horiz designs. Multicoloured. P* 13½.

636 5 p. Type **325** .. 30 10
637 15 p. Mona Monkey .. 65 65
638 30 p. *Crinum ornatum* .. 2·50 2·50
639 1 c. De Winton's Tree Squirrel .. 3·75 6·00
636/9 .. *Set of* 4 6·50 8·50

326 Football

(Litho D.L.R.)

1972 (5 Sept). *Olympic Games, Munich. T* **326** *and similar horiz designs. Multicoloured. P* 13.

640 5 p. Type **326** .. 10 10
641 15 p. Running .. 20 20
642 30 p. Boxing .. 40 55
643 50 p. Long-jumping .. 70 1·25
644 1 c. High-jumping .. 1·25 2·00
640/4 .. *Set of* 5 2·40 3·75
MS645 86 × 43 mm. 40 p. as No. 642 *se-tenant* with 60 p. as No. 640 .. 2·00 4·75

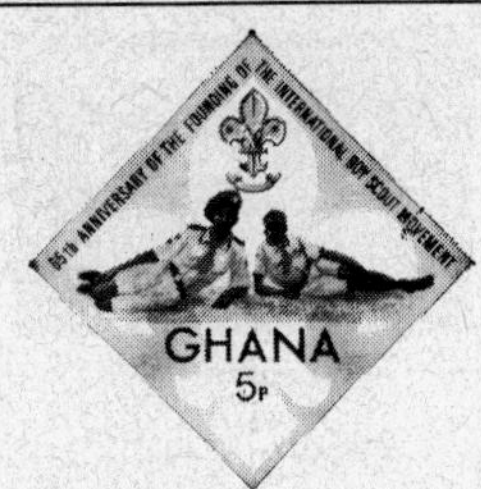

327 Senior Scout and Cub

(Litho Questa)

1972 (2 Oct). *65th Anniv of Boy Scouts. T* **327** *and similar diamond-shaped designs. Multicoloured. P* 13½.

No.	Description	Mint	Used
646	5 p. Type **327**	30	10
647	15 p. Scout and tent	65	45
648	30 p. Sea scouts	1·25	1·00
649	50 p. Leader with cubs	1·60	1·75
650	1 c. Training school	3·00	3·25
646/50	*Set of* 5	6·00	6·00
MS651	110 × 110 mm. 40 p. as 30 p.; 60 p. as 1 c.	2·75	4·50

328 "The Holy Night" (Correggio)

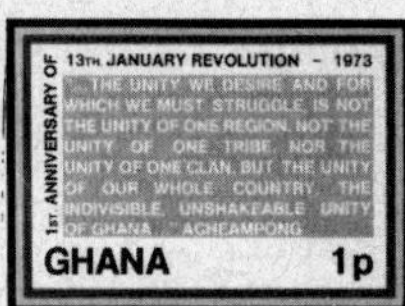

329 Extract from Speech

(Des G. Vasarhelyi and L. Apelt. Litho Questa)

1972 (1 Dec). *Christmas. T* **328** *and similar vert designs. Multicoloured. P* 13½.

No.	Description	Mint	Used
652	1 p. Type **328**	10	10
653	3 p. "Adoration of the Kings" (Holbein)	10	10
654	15 p. "Madonna of the Passion" (School of Ricco)	30	30
655	30 p. "King Melchior"	55	55
656	60 p. "King Gaspar, Mary and Jesus"	90	1·25
657	1 c. "King Balthasar"	1·50	2·00
652/7	*Set of* 6	3·00	3·75
MS658	139 × 90 mm. Nos. 655/7. Imperf.	6·00	8·00

Nos. 655/7 are from a 16th-cent. Norman stained-glass window.

(Des and litho D.L.R.)

1973 (10 Apr). *First Anniv of January 13 Revolution. T* **329** *and similar multicoloured designs. P* 13 × 14 (5, 15 *p.*) *or* 14 × 13 (*others*).

No.	Description	Mint	Used
659	1 p. Type **329**	10	10
660	3 p. Market scene	10	10
661	5 p. Selling bananas (*vert*)	10	10
662	15 p. Farmer with hoe and produce (*vert*)	20	25
663	30 p. Market traders	30	40
664	1 c. Farmer cutting palm-nuts	70	1·40
659/64	*Set of* 6	1·25	1·90
MS665	90 × 55 mm. 40 p. as 1 c. and 60 p. Miners	70	1·75

330 Under 5's Clinic

(Litho D.L.R.)

1973 (24 July). *25th Anniv of W.H.O. T* **330** *and similar square designs. Multicoloured. P* 13½.

No.	Description	Mint	Used
666	5 p. Type **330**	10	10
667	15 p. Radiography	25	25
668	30 p. Immunisation	35	50
669	50 p. Starving child	50	1·00
670	1 c. W.H.O. H.Q., Geneva	1·00	1·90
666/70	*Set of* 5	2·00	3·25

1st WORLD SCOUTING CONFERENCE IN AFRICA

(**331**)

1973 (14 Aug). *First World Scouting Conference, Nairobi/Addis Ababa. Nos. 646/51 optd with T* **331**.

No.	Description	Mint	Used
671	5 p. Type **327**	10	15
672	15 p. Scout and tent	35	55
673	30 p. Sea scouts	60	95
674	50 p. Leader with cubs	80	1·50
675	1 c. Training school	1·50	2·50
671/5	*Set of* 5	3·00	5·00
MS676	110 × 110 mm. 40 p. as 30 p.; 60 p. as 1 c.	2·00	5·50

332 Poultry Farming

(Litho Questa)

1973 (11 Sept). *Tenth Anniv of World Food Programme. T* **332** *and similar horiz designs. Multicoloured. P* 14.

No.	Description	Mint	Used
677	5 p. Type **332**	10	10
678	15 p. Mechanisation	15	15
679	50 p. Cocoa harvest	40	90
680	1 c. F.A.O. H.Q., Rome	60	1·90
677/80	*Set of* 4	1·00	2·75
MS681	92 × 104 mm. 40 p. as 15 p.; 60 p. as 1 c.	60	2·00

333 "Green Alert"

(Litho D.L.R.)

1973 (1 Oct). *50th Anniv of Interpol. T* **333** *and similar horiz designs. Multicoloured. P* 13.

No.	Description	Mint	Used
682	5 p. Type **333**	15	10
683	30 p. "Red Alert"	75	80
684	50 p. "Blue Alert"	1·50	1·75
685	1 c. "Black Alert"	3·00	4·00
682/5	*Set of* 4	4·75	6·00

334 Handshake

(Litho Format)

1973 (22 Oct). *Tenth Anniv of O.A.U. T* **334** *and similar horiz designs. Multicoloured. P* 14 × 14½.

No.	Description	Mint	Used
686	5 p. Type **334**	10	10
687	30 p. Africa Hall, Addis Ababa	15	30
688	50 p. O.A.U. emblem	30	70
689	1 c. "X" in colours of Ghana flag	45	1·25
686/9	*Set of* 4	90	2·10

335 Weather Balloon

336 Epiphany Scene

(Des G. Vasarhelyi. Litho Format)

1973 (16 Nov). *I.M.O./W.M.O. Centenary. T* **335** *and similar horiz designs. Multicoloured. P* 14 × 14½.

No.	Description	Mint	Used
690	5 p. Type **335**	10	10
691	15 p. Satellite "Tiros"	20	20
692	30 p. Computer weather map	40	65
693	1 c. Radar	80	2·25
690/3	*Set of* 4	1·25	2·75
MS694	120 × 95 mm. 40 p. as 15 p.; 60 p. as 30 p.	1·00	2·50

(Litho D.L.R.)

1973 (10 Dec). *Christmas. T* **336** *and similar vert designs. Multicoloured. P* 14.

No.	Description	Mint	Used
695	1 p. Type **336**	10	10
696	3 p. Madonna and Child	10	10
697	30 p. "Madonna and Child" (Murillo)	30	75
698	50 p. "Adoration of the Magi" (Tiepolo)	45	1·00
695/8	*Set of* 4	75	1·75
MS699	77 × 103 mm. Nos. 695/8. Imperf.	1·25	2·75

MINIMUM PRICE

The minimum price quote is 10p which represents a handling charge rather than a basis for valuing common stamps. For further notes about prices see introductory pages.

337 "Christ carrying the Cross" (Thomas de Kolozsvar)

338 Letters

(Des M. Shamir and A. Larkins. Litho D.L.R.)

1974 (17 Apr). *Easter. T* **337** *and similar vert designs. P* 14.

No.	Description	Mint	Used
700	5 p. multicoloured	10	10
701	30 p. bright blue, silver and sepia	20	35
702	50 p. light orange-vermilion, silver and sepia	30	60
703	1 c. dull yellow-green, silver and sepia	50	1·25
700/3	*Set of* 4	90	2·00
MS704	111 × 106 mm. 15 p. as No. 700, 20 p. as No. 701, 25 p. as No. 702. Imperf	80	1·50

Designs (from 15th-century English carved alabaster):—30 p. "The Betrayal"; 50 p. "The Deposition"; 1 c. "The Risen Christ and Mary Magdalene".

(Des A. Larkins. Litho Questa)

1974 (21 May). *Centenary of Universal Postal Union. T* **338** *and similar horiz designs. Multicoloured. P* 14½.

No.	Description	Mint	Used
705	5 p. Type **338**	10	10
706	9 p. U.P.U. Monument and H.Q.	15	15
707	50 p. Airmail letter	50	1·00
708	1 c. U.P.U. Monument and Ghana stamp	80	1·75
705/8	*Set of* 4	1·40	2·75
MS709	108 × 90 mm. 20 p. as No. 705, 30 p. as No. 706, 40 p. as No. 707, 60 p. as No. 708	75	1·60

1974 (7 June). *"Internaba 1974" Stamp Exhibition, Basle. Nos. 705/9 additionally inscribed* "INTERNABA 1974".

No.	Description	Mint	Used
710	5 p. Type **338**	10	10
711	9 p. U.P.U. Monument and H.Q.	15	15
712	50 p. Airmail letter	40	1·00
713	1 c. U.P.U. Monument and Ghana stamp	60	1·75
710/13	*Set of* 4	1·10	2·75
MS714	108 × 90 mm. 20 p. as No. 710; 30 p. as No. 711; 40 p. as No. 712; 60 p. as No. 713	1·50	3·00

339 Footballers

(Des G. Vasarhelyi. Litho Format)

1974 (17 June). *World Cup Football Championships, West Germany. T* **339** *and similar horiz designs showing footballers. P* 14½.

No.	Type	Description	Mint	Used
715	**339**	5 p. multicoloured	10	10
716	–	30 p. multicoloured	25	50
717	–	50 p. multicoloured	35	75
718	–	1 c. multicoloured	50	1·50
715/18		*Set of* 4	1·00	2·50
MS719		148 × 94 mm. 25, 40, 55 and 60 p. as Nos. 715/18	1·00	2·50

Nos. 715/18 also exist perf 13 (*Price for set of* 4 £2·25 *mint or used*) from additional sheetlets of 5 stamps and 1 label. Stamps perforated 14½ are from normal sheets of 25.

340 Roundabout

WEST GERMANY WINNERS

(**341**)

(Des and litho B.W.)

1974 (16 July). *Change to Driving on the Right. T* **340** *and similar designs. P* 13½ (5 *and* 15 *p.*) *or* 14½ × 14 (*others*).

No.	Description	Mint	Used
720	5 p. bright yellow-grn, rose-vermilion & blk	10	10
721	15 p. lavender, dull red and black	25	35
722	30 p. multicoloured	45	60
723	50 p. multicoloured	70	1·10
724	1 c. multicoloured	1·40	2·00
720/4	*Set of* 5	2·75	3·75

Designs: *Horiz*—15 p. Warning triangle sign. *Vert* (29 × 42 *mm*)—30 p. Highway arrow and slogan; 50 p. Warning hands; 1 c. Car on symbolic hands.

1974 (30 Aug). *West Germany's Victory in World Cup. Nos. 715/19 optd with T* **341**. *P* 14½.

No.	Type	Description	Mint	Used
725	**339**	5 p. multicoloured	10	10
726	–	30 p. multicoloured	35	40
727	–	50 p. multicoloured	50	55
728	–	1 c. multicoloured	90	1·25
725/8		*Set of* 4	1·75	2·10
MS729		148 × 94 mm. 25, 40, 55, 60 p. as Nos. 725/8	1·25	2·50

This overprint also exists on the stamps perforated 13 mentioned below No. **MS**719 (*Price for set of* 4 £2 *mint or used*).

342 "Planned Family"

(Des and litho D.L.R.)

1974 (12 Sept). *World Population Year. T* **342** *and similar horiz designs. Multicoloured. P* 12½.

730 5 p. Type **342** 10 10
731 30 p. Family planning clinic 25 35
732 50 p. Immunization 35 60
733 1 c. Population census enumeration .. .. 60 1·40
730/3 .. .. *Set of* 4 1·10 2·25

343 Angel

APOLLO
SOYUZ
JULY 15, 1975
(344)

(Des A. Medina (5 and 7 p.), A. Larkins (others). Litho D.L.R.)

1974 (19 Dec). *Christmas. T* **343** *and similar multicoloured designs. P* 13½.

734 5 p. Type **343** 10 10
735 7 p. The Magi (*diamond* 47 × 47 *mm*) .. 10 10
736 9 p. The Nativity 10 10
737 1 c. The Annunciation .. .. .. 60 1·40
734/7 .. .. *Set of* 4 80 1·50
MS738 128 × 128 mm. 15 p. Type **343**; 30 p. as 7 p.; 45 p. as 9 p.; 60 p. as 1 c. Imperf .. .. .. 80 2·25

1975 (15 Aug). *"Apollo–Soyuz" Space Link. Nos. 715/19 optd with T* **344**. *P* 14½.

739 5 p. multicoloured 10 10
740 30 p. multicoloured 25 25
741 50 p. multicoloured 45 55
742 1 c. multicoloured 70 80
739/42 .. .. *Set of* 4 1·25 1·50
MS743 148 × 94 mm. 25, 40, 55, 60 p. as Nos. 739/42 .. .. 1·50 2·00

This overprint also exists on the stamps perforated 13 mentioned below No. **MS**719 (*Price for set of* 4 *£*5·50 *mint or used*).

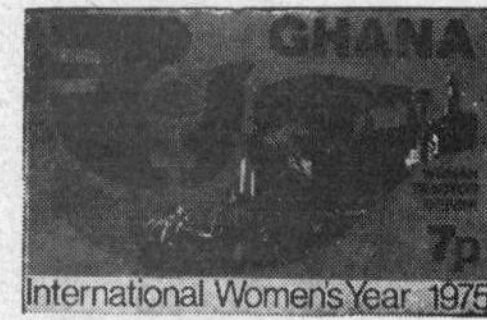

345 Tractor Driver

(Des and litho D.L.R.)

1975 (3 Sept). *International Women's Year. T* **345** *and similar horiz designs each showing I.W.Y. emblem. Multicoloured. P* 14 × 13½.

744 7 p. Type **345** 15 10
745 30 p. Motor mechanic 35 35
746 60 p. Factory workers 60 80
747 1 c. Cocoa research .. .. 90 1·40
744/7 .. .. *Set of* 4 1·75 2·40
MS748 136 × 110 mm. 15, 40, 65 and 80 p. as Nos. 744/7. Imperf .. .. 2·50 5·50

346 Angel

(Litho D.L.R.)

1975 (31 Dec). *Christmas. T* **346** *and similar horiz designs. P* 14 × 13½.

749 2 p. multicoloured 10 10
750 5 p. greenish yellow and light green 10 10
751 7 p. greenish yellow and light green 10 10
752 30 p. greenish yellow and light green 20 20
753 1 c. greenish yellow and light green .. .. 50 1·00
749/53 .. .. *Set of* 5 80 1·25
MS754 98 × 87 mm. 15, 40, 65 and 80 p. as Nos. 750/3. Imperf .. .. 90 2·50

Designs:—5 p. Angel with harp; 7 p. Angel with lute; 30 p. Angel with viol; 1 c. Angel with trumpet.

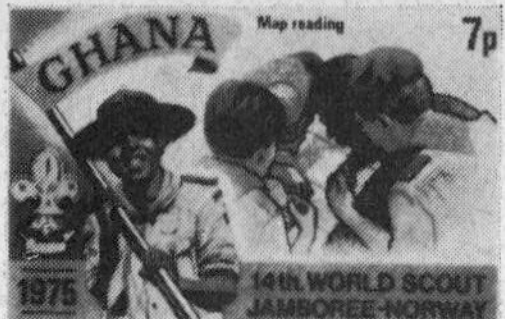

347 Map Reading

(Litho Format)

1976 (5 Jan). *14th World Scout Jamboree, Norway. T* **347** *and similar horiz designs. Multicoloured. P* 13½ × 14.

755 7 p. Type **347** 30 10
756 30 p. Sailing 85 75
757 60 p. Hiking .. .. 1·50 1·75
758 1 c. Life-saving .. .. 2·00 2·50
755/8 .. .. *Set of* 4 4·25 4·50
MS759 133 × 99 mm. 15, 40, 65 and 80 p. as Nos. 755/8 .. .. 3·50 5·00

348 Bottles (litre)

(Litho D.L.R.)

1976 (5 Jan). *Metrication Publicity. T* **348** *and similar horiz designs. Multicoloured. P* 14.

760 7 p. Type **348** 15 10
761 30 p. Scales (kilogramme) 40 40
762 60 p. Tape measure and bale of cloth (metre) 80 1·00
763 1 c. Ice, thermometer and kettle (temperature) .. .. 1·25 1·75
760/3 .. .. *Set of* 4 2·40 2·75

349 Fair Site

(Litho Format)

1976 (6 Apr). *International Trade Fair, Accra. T* **349** *and similar horiz designs. P* 13½.

764 **349** 7 p. multicoloured 10 10
765 – 30 p. multicoloured 20 20
766 – 60 p. multicoloured 50 60
767 – 1 c. multicoloured .. .. 70 1·00
764/7 .. .. *Set of* 4 1·40 1·60

Nos. 765/7 are as T **349** but show different views of the Fair.

'INTERPHIL' 76
BICENTENNIAL
EXHIBITION
(350)

351 Shot-put

1976 (28 May). *Interphil Stamp Exhibition, Philadelphia. Nos. 755/9 optd with T* **350** *in blue.*

768 7 p. Type **347** 15 15
769 30 p. Sailing 35 50
770 60 p. Hiking 55 75
771 1 c. Life-saving .. .. 80 1·25
768/71 .. .. *Set of* 4 1·75 2·40
MS772 133 × 99 mm. 15, 40, 65 and 80 p. as Nos. 768/71 .. .. 1·50 2·50

(Des PAD Studio. Litho Format)

1976 (9 Aug). *Olympic Games, Montreal. T* **351** *and similar vert designs. Multicoloured. P* 13½.

773 7 p. Type **351** 10 10
774 30 p. Football 20 25
775 60 p. Women's 1500 metres 35 50
776 1 c. Boxing 60 80
773/6 .. .. *Set of* 4 1·10 1·50
MS777 103 × 135 mm. 15, 40, 65 and 80 p. as Nos. 773/6 .. .. 1·75 2·00

Nos. 773/6 also exist perf 15 (*Price for set of* 4 *£*2.25 *mint or used*) from additional sheetlets of 5 stamps and 1 label. Stamps perforated 13½ are from normal sheets of 30.

352 Supreme Court

(Litho D.L.R.)

1976 (7 Sept). *Centenary of Supreme Court. T* **352** *and similar horiz designs. P* 14.

778 **352** 8 p. multicoloured 10 10
779 – 30 p. multicoloured 20 25
780 – 60 p. multicoloured 35 50
781 – 1 c. multicoloured .. .. 60 1·00
778/81 .. .. *Set of* 4 1·10 1·75

Nos. 779/81 show different views of the Court Building.

353 Examination for River Blindness

(Des and litho D.L.R.)

1976 (28 Oct). *Prevention of Blindness. T* **353** *and similar horiz designs. Multicoloured. P* 14 × 13½.

782 7 p. Type **353** 25 10
783 30 p. Entomologist 90 70
784 60 p. Normal vision .. .. 1·60 1·40
785 1 c. Blackfly eradication .. .. 2·50 2·25
782/5 .. .. *Set of* 4 4·75 4·00

354 Fireworks Party, Christmas Eve

(Des A. Adom & A. Larkins. Litho D.L.R.)

1976 (15 Dec). *Christmas. T* **354** *and similar horiz designs. Multicoloured. P* 13.

786 6 p. Type **354** 15 10
787 8 p. Children and gifts 20 15
788 30 p. Christmas feast 60 50
789 1 c. As 8 p. .. .. 1·50 2·00
786/9 .. .. *Set of* 4 2·25 2·50
MS790 122 × 98 mm. 15, 40, 65 and 80 p. as Nos. 786/9. Imperf .. .. 2·50 4·00

355 "Gallows Frame" Telephone and Alexander Graham Bell

EAST GERMANY
WINNERS
(356)

(Des A. Larkins. Litho Format)

1976 (17 Dec). *Telephone Centenary. T* **355** *and similar horiz designs showing telephones and Alexander Graham Bell. Multicoloured. P* 13.

791 8 p. Type **355** 20 15
792 30 p. 1895 telephone 45 45
793 60 p. 1929 telephone 90 90
794 1 c. 1976 telephone .. .. 1·40 1·40
791/4 .. .. *Set of* 4 2·75 2·75
MS795 125 × 92 mm. 15, 40, 65 and 80 p. as Nos. 791/4 .. .. 2·50 2·75

1977 (22 Feb). *Olympic Winners. Nos. 773/7 optd with the name of the country given, as T* **356**. *P* 13½.

796 7 p. East Germany 15 15
797 30 p. East Germany 40 40
798 60 p. U.S.S.R. 60 85
799 1 c. U.S.A. .. .. 80 1·50
796/9 .. .. *Set of* 4 1·75 2·50
MS800 103 × 135 mm. 15, 40, 65 and 80 p. as Nos. 796/9 .. .. 2·25 2·50

357 Dipo Dancers and Drum Ensemble

(Des A. Larkins. Litho Format)

1977 (24 Mar). *Second World Black and African Festival of Arts and Culture, Nigeria. T* **357** *and similar horiz designs. Multicoloured. P* 13½.

801 8 p. Type **357** 25 15
802 30 p. Arts and Crafts 70 70
803 60 p. Acon music and dancing priests .. .. 1·40 1·40
804 1 c. African huts .. .. 2·00 2·25
801/4 .. .. *Set of* 4 4·00 4·00
MS805 164 × 120 mm. 15, 40, 65 and 80 p. as Nos. 801/4 .. .. 4·00 4·25

PRINCE CHARLES
VISITS GHANA
17th TO 25th
MARCH, 1977

(358)

1977 (2 June). *Prince Charles's Visit to Ghana. Nos.* 791/5 *optd with T* **358**.

806 8 p. Type **355** 50 55
807 30 p. 1895 telephone .. .. 1·60 1·25
808 60 p. 1929 telephone .. .. 2·50 2·25
809 1 c. 1976 telephone .. .. 3·25 2·75
806/9 .. .. *Set of* 4 7·00 6·00
MS810 125 × 92 mm. 15, 40, 65 and 80 p. as Nos. 806/9 .. .. 7·00 7·00

359 Olive Colobus

360 "Le Chapeau de Paille" (Rubens—400th Birth Anniv)

(Des PAD Studio. Litho Format)

1977 (22 June). *Wildlife. T* **359** *and similar horiz designs. Multicoloured. P* 13½.

811 8 p. Type **359** 45 15
812 20 p. Temminck's Giant Squirrel .. .. .. 1·25 80
813 30 p. Hunting Dog .. .. 1·75 1·25
814 60 p. African Manatee .. .. 3·00 2·25
811/14 .. .. *Set of* 4 5·75 4·00
MS815 140 × 101 mm. 15, 40, 65 and 80 p. as Nos. 811/14 .. .. 5·50 5·50

(Des PAD Studio. Litho Format)

1977 (Sept). *Painters' Anniversaries. T* **360** *and similar vert designs. Multicoloured. P* 14 × 13½.

816 8 p. Type **360** 15 10
817 30 p. "Isabella of Portugal" (Titian—500th Birth Anniv) 40 40
818 60 p. "Duke and Duchess of Cumberland" (Gainsborough—250th Birth Anniv) .. 50 65
819 1 c. "Rubens and Isabella Brandt" .. .. 85 1·25
816/19 .. .. *Set of* 4 1·75 2·25
MS820 99 × 149 mm. 15, 40, 65 and 80 p. as Nos. 816/19 .. .. 1·75 2·25

361 The Magi, Madonna and Child

REFERENDUM 1978
VOTE EARLY

(362)

(Litho De La Rue, Colombia)

1977 (30 Dec). *Christmas. T* **361** *and similar multicoloured designs. P* 14 (1 *p.*, 8 *p.*) *or* 14 × 13½ (*others*).

821 1 p. Type **361** 10 10
822 2 p. Choir from Abossey Okai (45 × 27 *mm*) 10 10
823 6 p. Methodist Church, Wesley, Accra (45 × 27 *mm*) 10 10
824 8 p. Madonna and Child 15 10
825 30 p. Holy Spirit Cathedral, Accra (45 × 27 *mm*) 50 50
826 1 c. Ebeneezer Presbyterian Church, Accra (45 × 27 *mm*) .. .. 1·60 1·60
821/6 .. .. *Set of* 6 2·25 2·25
MS827 122 × 97 mm. 15, 40, 65 and 80 p. as Nos. 822/3 and 825/6. Imperf .. .. .. 2·00 3·75

Nos. 822/3 and 825/6 all have as a background the score to the carol "Hark the Herald Angels Sing".

1978 (Mar). 1978 *Referendum. Nos.* 821/7 *optd with T* **362** *by De La Rue, Colombia.*

828 1 p. Type **361** 10 10
829 2 p. Choir from Abossey Okai 10 10
830 6 p. Methodist Church, Wesley, Accra .. 10 10
831 8 p. Madonna and Child 15 10
832 30 p. Holy Spirit Cathedral, Accra 50 50
833 1 c. Ebeneezer Presbyterian Church, Accra 1·50 1·50
828/33 .. .. *Set of* 6 2·10 2·10
MS834 122 × 97 mm. 15, 40, 65, 80 p. as Nos. 829/30 and 832/3 .. .. 22·00 15·00

363 Cutting Bananas

(Litho De La Rue, Colombia)

1978 (15 May). *Operation "Feed Yourself". T* **363** *and similar horiz designs. Multicoloured. P* 14.

835 2 p. Type **363** 10 10
836 8 p. Home produce 10 10
837 30 p. Market 30 35
838 60 p. Fishing 55 60
839 1 c. Mechanisation .. .. 90 1·25
835/9 .. .. *Set of* 5 1·75 2·10

364 Wright Biplane

"CAPEX 78
JUNE 9-18 1978"

(365)

(Des J.W. Litho Format)

1978 (6 June). *75th Anniv of Powered Flight. T* **364** *and similar vert designs. P* 14 × 13½.

840 8 p. black, deep brown and brown-ochre .. 20 10
841 30 p. black, deep brown and blue-green .. 40 30
842 60 p. black, deep brown and rosine 60 60
843 1 c. black, deep brown and ultramarine .. 90 1·10
840/3 .. .. *Set of* 4 1·90 1·90
MS844 167 × 100 mm. 15, 40, 65, 80 p. as Nos. 840/3 .. .. 2·00 2·10

Designs:—30 p. "Heracles"; 60 p. D.H. "Comet"; 1 c. "Concorde".

1978 (9 June). *"CAPEX 1978" International Stamp Exhibition, Toronto. Nos.* 840/4 *optd with T* **365**.

845 8 p. black, deep brown and brown-ochre .. 15 15
846 30 p. black, deep brown and blue-green .. 25 25
847 60 p. black, deep brown and rosine 50 50
848 1 c. black, deep brown and ultramarine .. 80 80
845/8 .. .. *Set of* 4 1·50 1·50
MS849 167 × 100 mm. 15, 40, 65, 80 p. as Nos. 845/8 .. .. 1·60 2·25

366 Players and African Cup Emblem

(Litho Format)

1978 (1 July). *Football Championships. T* **366** *and similar horiz designs. Multicoloured. P* 13½ × 14.

850 8 p. Type **366** 20 15
851 30 p. Players and African Cup emblem (*different*) 30 30
852 60 p. Players and World Cup emblem 55 60
853 1 c. Goalkeeper and World Cup emblem .. 80 1·00
850/3 .. .. *Set of* 4 1·75 1·90
MS854 111 × 105 mm. 15, 40, 65, 80 p. as Nos. 850/3 .. .. 1·40 1·75

The 8 and 30 p. values commemorate the African Nations Cup; the other values the World Cup Football Championship, Argentina.

367 "The Betrayal"

"GHANA WINNERS"

(368)

(Litho Format)

1978 (15 July). *Easter. Details from drawings by Dürer. T* **367** *and similar vert designs. P* 14 × 13½.

855 11 p. black and bright reddish violet 10 10
856 39 p. black and flesh 25 30
857 60 p. black and orange-yellow 40 45
858 1 c. black and pale yellow-green 60 65
855/8 .. .. *Set of* 4 1·25 1·40

Designs:—39 p. "The Crucifixion"; 60 p. "The Deposition"; 1 c. "The Resurrection".

1978 (21 Aug). *Ghana—Winners of African Nations Football Cup and Argentina—Winners of World Cup Football Championship. Nos.* 850/1 *and* **MS**854 *optd with T* **368** *and Nos.* 852/3 *optd* "ARGENTINA WINS".

859 8 p. Type **366** 15 15
860 30 p. Players and African Cup emblem (*different*) 30 30
861 60 p. Players and World Cup emblem 45 45
862 1 c. Goalkeeper and World Cup emblem .. 75 75
859/62 .. .. *Set of* 4 1·50 1·50
MS863 111 × 105 mm. 15, 40, 65, 80 p. as Nos. 859/62 but all opt with T **368** .. .. .. 1·40 1·60

369 *Bauhinia purpurea*

(Litho Format)

1978 (20 Nov). *Flowers. T* **369** *and similar vert designs. Multicoloured. P* 14 × 13½.

864 11 p. Type **369** 20 10
865 39 p. *Cassia fistula* 65 55
866 60 p. *Plumeria acutifolia* 85 70
867 1 c. *Jacaranda mimosifolia* .. .. .. 1·25 1·00
864/7 .. .. *Set of* 4 2·50 2·10

370 Mail Van

(Litho Format)

1978 (4 Dec). *75th Anniv of Ghana Railways. T* **370** *and similar horiz designs. Multicoloured. P* 13½ × 14.

868 11 p. Type **370** 50 10
869 39 p. Pay and bank car .. .. 1·25 65
870 60 p. Steam locomotive, 1922 .. .. .. 1·75 1·00
871 1 c. Diesel locomotive 1960 .. .. .. 2·00 1·40
868/71 .. .. *Set of* 4 5·00 2·75

371 "Orbiter" Spacecraft

(Litho Format)

1979 (5 July). *"Pioneer" Venus Space Project. T* **371** *and similar horiz designs. Multicoloured. P* 14 × 13½.

872 11 p. Type **371** 15 10
873 39 p. "Multiprobe" spacecraft 35 30
874 60 p. "Orbiter" and "Multiprobe" spacecraft in Venus orbit 45 45
875 3 c. Radar chart of Venus .. .. .. 1·40 1·60
872/5 .. .. *Set of* 4 2·10 2·25
MS876 135 × 94 mm. 15, 40, 65 p., 2 c. as Nos. 872/5. Imperf .. .. 1·10 1·25

372 "O Come All Ye Faithful"

373 Dr. J. B. Danquah (lawyer and nationalist)

(Litho D.L.R.)

1979 (20 Dec). *Christmas. Opening Lines and Scenes from well known Carols. T* **372** *and similar horiz designs. Multicoloured. P* 14 × 14½.
877 8 p. Type **372** 10 10
878 10 p. "O Little Town of Bethlehem" 10 10
879 15 p. "We Three Kings of Orient Are" 10 10
880 20 p. "I Saw Three Ships come Sailing By" .. 10 15
881 2 c. "Away in a Manger" 65 80
882 4 c. "Ding Dong Merrily on High" .. .. 1·00 1·40
877/82 .. .. *Set of* 6 1·90 2·40
MS883 110 × 95 mm. 25, 65 p., 1, 2 c. as Nos. 877, 879 and 881/2 .. .. 75 1·00

(Litho D.L.R.)

1980 (21 Jan). *Great Ghanaians. T* **373** *and similar vert designs. Multicoloured. P* 14 × 13½.
884 20 p. Type **373** 15 10
885 65 p. John Mensah Sarbah (nationalist) .. 30 30
886 80 p. Dr. J. E. K. Aggrey (educationalist) .. 40 40
887 2 c. Dr. Kwame Nkrumah (nationalist) .. 65 65
888 4 c. G. E. (Paa) Grant (lawyer) .. .. 1·40 1·60
884/8 .. .. *Set of* 5 2·50 2·75

374 Tribesman ringing Clack Bells

375 Children in Classroom

(Des G. Vasarhelyi. Litho Format)

1980 (12 Mar). *Death Centenary of Sir Rowland Hill* (1979). *T* **374** *and similar horiz designs. Multicoloured.* (a) *P* 14½.
889 20 p. Type **374** 15 15
890 65 p. Chieftain with Golden Elephant staff .. 45 50
891 2 c. Tribesman banging drums .. .. 1·25 1·40
892 4 c. Chieftain with ivory and gold staff .. 2·50 2·75
889/92 .. .. *Set of* 4 3·75 4·25

(b) *P* 13½
893 25 p. Type **374** 15 20
894 50 p. As 65 p. 35 40
895 1 c. As 2 c. 70 75
896 5 c. As 4 c. .. .. 3·50 3·75
893/6 .. .. *Set of* 4 4·25 4·50
MS897 115 × 86 mm. Nos. 893/6. P 14½ .. .. 4·25 5·50
Nos. 893/6 were each printed in small sheets of 6 including one *se-tenant* stamp-size label.

(Des J.W. Litho Questa)

1980 (2 Apr). *International Year of the Child* (1979). *T* **375** *and similar vert designs. Multicoloured. P* 14½.
898 20 p. Type **375** 15 15
899 65 p. Children playing football 35 45
900 2 c. Children playing in boat .. .. .. 75 1·00
901 4 c. Mother and child .. .. 1·40 1·75
898/901 .. .. *Set of* 4 2·40 3·00
MS902 156 × 94 mm. 25, 50 p., 1, 3 c. as Nos. 898/901 .. .. 1·50 2·25

"LONDON 1980"
6th - 14th May 1980
(**376**)

"PAPAL VISIT"
8th - 9th May
1980
(**377**)

1980 (6 May). *"London 1980" International Stamp Exhibition. Nos.* 889/97 *optd with T* **376**. (a) *P* 14½.
903 20 p. Type **374** 15 15
904 65 p. Chieftain with Golden Elephant staff .. 45 50
905 2 c. Tribesman banging drums .. .. 1·10 1·40
906 4 c. Chieftain with ivory and gold staff .. 2·00 2·75
903/6 .. .. *Set of* 4 3·25 4·25

(b) *P* 13½
907 25 p. Type **374** 20 25
908 50 p. As 65 p. 45 50
909 1 c. As 2 c. .. .. 80 1·00
910 5 c. As 4 c. .. .. 2·75 3·50
907/10 .. .. *Set of* 4 3·75 4·75
MS911 115 × 86 mm. Nos. 907/10. P 14½ .. 3·75 5·50

1980 (8 May). *Papal Visit. Nos.* 898/902 *optd with T* **377**.
912 20 p. Type **375** 20 25
913 65 p. Children playing football 55 60
914 2 c. Children playing in boat .. .. 1·25 1·40
915 4 c. Mother and child .. .. 2·25 2·50
912/15 .. .. *Set of* 4 3·75 4·25
MS916 156 × 94 mm. 25, 50 p., 1, 3 c. as Nos. 912/15 .. .. 6·50 7·50

378 Parliament House

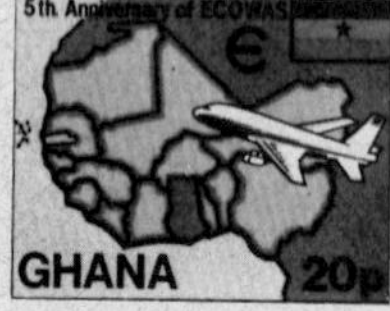

379 Airliner and Map of West Africa

(Litho Questa)

1980 (4 Aug). *Third Republic Commemoration. T* **378** *and similar horiz designs. Multicoloured. P* 14.
917 20 p. Type **378** 10 10
918 65 p. Supreme Court 20 25
919 2 c. The Castle 40 70
917/19 .. .. *Set of* 3 60 95
MS920 72 × 113 mm. 25 p., 1, 3 c. As Nos. 917/19 60 1·10

(Litho Questa)

1980 (5 Nov). *Fifth Anniv of E.C.O.W.A.S. (Economic Community of West African States). T* **379** *and similar horiz designs showing symbols named and map of West Africa. Multicoloured. P* 14.
921 20 p. Type **379** 10 10
922 65 p. Radio antenna 15 20
923 80 p. Cog-wheels 20 25
924 2 c. Corn ear 35 50
921/4 .. .. *Set of* 4 70 90

380 "O.A.U."

381 "The Adoration of the Magi"

(Litho Questa)

1980 (26 Nov). *Organisation of African Unity First Economic Summit, Nigeria. T* **380** *and similar vert designs. Multicoloured. P* 14½ × 14.
925 20 p. Type **380** 10 10
926 65 p. Banner with maps of Africa and Ghana 15 20
927 80 p. Map of Africa 20 25
928 2 c. Ghana flag, banner and map of Africa .. 35 65
925/8 .. .. *Set of* 4 70 1·00

(Litho Format)

1980 (10 Dec). *Christmas. Paintings by Fra Angelico. T* **381** *and similar vert designs. Multicoloured. P* 14.
929 15 p. Type **381** 10 10
930 20 p. "The Virgin and Child enthroned with four Angels" 10 10
931 2 c. "The Virgin and Child enthroned with eight Angels" 35 80
932 4 c. "The Annunciation" .. .. 60 1·60
929/32 .. .. *Set of* 4 1·00 2·25
MS933 77 × 112 mm. 25, 50 p., 1, 3 c. As Nos. 929/32 .. .. 75 1·25

382 "Health"

383 Narina Trogon

(Litho Format)

1980 (18 Dec). *75th Anniv of Rotary International. T* **382** *and similar horiz designs. Multicoloured. P* 14.
934 20 p. Type **382** 10 10
935 65 p. Rotary emblem and motto with maps of World and Ghana 15 30
936 2 c. Rotary emblem, globe and outstretched hands 35 85
937 4 c. "Eradication of Hunger" .. .. .. 60 1·50
934/7 .. .. *Set of* 4 1·10 2·50
MS938 121 × 93 mm. 25, 50 p., 1, 3 c. As Nos. 934/7 .. .. 1·10 2·00

(Des G. Drummond. Litho Harrison)

1981 (12 Jan). *Birds. T* **383** *and similar vert designs. Multicoloured. P* 14.
939 20 p. Type **383** 60 15
940 65 p. White-crowned Robin .. .. .. 1·25 50
941 2 c. Swallow-tailed Bee Eater .. .. 2·00 1·75
942 4 c. Rose-ringed Parakeet .. .. .. 3·25 3·25
939/42 .. .. *Set of* 4 6·50 5·00
MS943 89 × 121 mm. 25, 50 p., 1, 3 c. As Nos. 939/42. P 14½ .. .. 4·00 4·00

384 Pope John Paul II and Archbishop of Canterbury with President Limann during Papal Visit

385 Royal Yacht *Britannia*

(Litho Format)

1981 (3 Mar). *First Anniv of Papal Visit. P* 14 × 13½.
944 **384** 20 p. multicoloured 35 15
945 65 p. multicoloured 75 45
946 80 p. multicoloured 95 55
947 2 c. multicoloured .. .. 2·00 1·60
944/7 .. .. *Set of* 4 3·50 2·50

(Des J.W. Litho Questa)

1981 (8 July–16 Sept). *Royal Wedding. T* **385** *and similar vert designs. Multicoloured.* (i) *Sheet stamps* (8 July). (a) *P* 14.
948 20 p. Prince Charles and Lady Diana Spencer 15 10
949 80 p. Prince Charles on visit to Ghana .. 20 20
950 4 c. Type **385** .. .. 80 1·10
948/50 .. .. *Set of* 3 1·00 1·25
MS951 95 × 85 mm. 7 c. St. Paul's Cathedral .. 1·50 2·00

(b) *P* 12
952 65 p. As 20 p. 25 25
953 1 c. As 80 p. 45 45
954 3 c. Type **385** .. .. 1·00 1·40
952/4 .. .. *Set of* 3 1·50 1·90

(ii) *Booklet stamps. P* 14 (16 Sept)
955 2 c. Type **385** .. .. 1·25 1·25
a. Booklet pane. Nos. 955/6 each × 2 .. 7·50
956 5 c. As 20 p. .. .. 2·50 2·50
The 65 p., 1 and 3 c. values were each printed in small sheets of 6 including one *se-tenant* stamp-size label.
The above exist imperforate from a restricted printing (*Price for Nos.* 948/50 *set of* 3 £7, **MS**951 £9, *Nos.* 952/4 *set of* 3 £7·50 *and booklet pane No.* 955a £18, *all mint*).

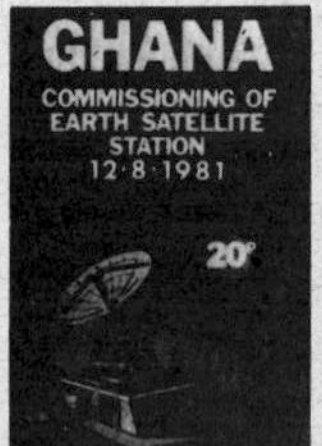

386 Earth Satellite Station

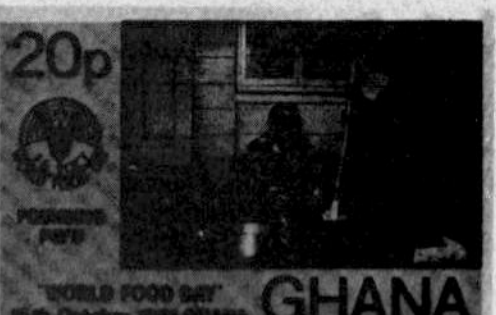

387 Pounding Fufu

(Litho Questa)

1981 (28 Sept). *Commissioning of Earth Satellite Station. T* **386** *and similar vert designs. Multicoloured. P* 14.
957 20 p. Type **386** 10 10
958 65 p. Satellites beaming signals to Earth .. 25 25
959 80 p. Satellite 30 30
960 4 c. Satellite orbiting Earth .. .. .. 1·75 1·75
957/60 .. .. *Set of* 4 2·10 2·10
MS961 112 × 100 mm. 25 p., 50 p., 1 c., 3 c. As Nos. 957/60 .. .. 1·50 2·00

(Des BG Studio. Litho Format)

1981 (16 Oct). *World Food Day. T* **387** *and similar horiz designs. Multicoloured. P* 13½ × 14.
962 20 p. Type **387** 10 10
963 65 p. Plucking Cocoa 25 25
964 80 p. Preparing Banku 35 35
965 2 c. Garri processing .. .. 1·00 1·75
962/5 .. .. *Set of* 4 1·50 2·25
MS966 131 × 99 mm. 25 p., 50 p., 1 c., 3 c. As Nos. 962/5 .. .. 1·50 2·25

388 "The Betrothal of St. Catherine of Alexandria" (Lucas Cranach)

389 Blind Person

(Des Clover Mill. Litho Format)

1981 (26 Nov). *Christmas. Details from Paintings. T* **388** *and similar vert designs. Multicoloured. P* 15.
967 15 p. Type **388** 10 10
968 20 p. "Angelic Musicians play for Mary and Child" (Aachener Altares) 10 10
969 65 p. "Child Jesus embracing his Mother" (Gabriel Metsu) 25 25

970 80 p. "Madonna and Child" (Fra Filippo Lippi) .. 30 30
971 2 c. "The Madonna with Infant Jesus" (Barnaba da Modena) 80 80
972 4 c. "The Immaculate Conception" (Murillo) 1·40 1·40
967/72 .. .. *Set of* 6 2·75 2·50
MS973 82 × 102 mm. 6 c. "Madonna and Child with Angels" (Hans Memling) .. .. 2·00 2·75

(Des G. Vasarhelyi. Litho Questa)

1982 (8 Feb). *International Year for Disabled Persons. T* **389** *and similar horiz designs. Multicoloured. P* 14.
974 20 p. Type **389** 10 10
975 65 p. Disabled person with crutches 35 35
976 80 p. Blind child reading braille 45 45
977 4 c. Disabled people helping one another .. 2·25 2·25
974/7 .. .. *Set of* 4 2·75 2·75
MS978 109 × 85 mm. 6 c. Group of disabled people 2·75 3·00

390 African Clawless Otter

391 Blue-spot Commodore

(Des G. Drummond. Litho Harrison)

1982 (22 Feb). *Flora and Fauna. T* **390** *and similar vert designs. Multicoloured. P* 14.
979 20 p. Type **390** 15 15
980 65 p. Bushbuck 40 40
981 80 p. Aardvark 50 50
982 1 c. Scarlet Bell Tree 60 60
983 2 c. Glory-Lilies .. .. 1·25 1·25
984 4 c. Blue-Pea .. .. 2·25 2·25
979/84 .. .. *Set of* 6 4·75 4·75
MS985 76 × 100 mm. 5 c. Chimpanzee .. .. 2·50 4·00

(Litho Harrison)

1982 (3 May). *Butterflies. T* **391** *and similar vert designs. Multicoloured. P* 14.
986 20 p. Type **391** 20 10
987 65 p. Emperor Swallowtail 50 35
988 2 c. Orange Admiral .. .. 1·25 1·50
989 4 c. Giant Charaxes .. .. 2·25 2·50
986/9 .. .. *Set of* 4 3·75 4·00
MS990 98 × 123 mm. 25 p., 50 p., 1 c., 3 c. As Nos. 986/9. P 14½ .. .. 6·50 7·50

392 Scouts planting Tree

(Des M. Diamond. Litho Format)

1982 (1 June). *75th Anniv of Boy Scout Movement. T* **392** *and similar multicoloured designs. P* 14½ × 15.
991 20 p. Type **392** 15 10
992 65 p. Scouts cooking on camp-fire 45 35
993 80 p. Sea Scouts sailing 65 45
994 3 c. Scouts observing elephant .. .. 1·75 2·00
991/4 .. .. *Set of* 4 2·75 2·50
MS995 101 × 71 mm. 5 c. Lord Baden-Powell (*vert*). P 15 × 14½ .. .. 3·75 5·00

393 Initial Stages of Construction

(Des C. Tetteh. Litho Questa)

1982 (28 June). *Kpong Hydro-Electric Project. T* **393** *and similar horiz designs. Multicoloured. P* 14.
996 20 p. Type **393** 20 10
997 65 p. Truck removing rubble 55 45
998 80 p. Hydro-electric turbines 80 65
999 2 c. Aerial view of completed plant .. .. 1·75 1·60
996/9 .. .. *Set of* 4 3·00 2·50

394 Footballers

(Des M. and S. Gerber Studio. Litho Format)

1982 (19 July). *World Cup Football Championship, Spain. T* **394** *and similar horiz designs showing footballers.* (a) *P* 14½.
1000 **394** 20 p. multicoloured 10 10
1001 – 65 p. multicoloured 35 35
1002 – 80 p. multicoloured 45 45
1003 – 4 c. multicoloured .. .. 2·00 2·00
1000/3 .. .. *Set of* 4 2·50 2·50
MS1004 110 × 90 mm. 6 c. multicoloured .. 2·75 2·75

(*b*) *P* 14 × 14½
1005 **394** 30 p. multicoloured 20 20
1006 – 80 p. multicoloured (as No. 1001) 45 45
1007 – 1 c. multicoloured (as No. 1002) 55 55
1008 – 3 c. multicoloured (as No. 1003) .. .. 1·60 1·60
1005/8 .. .. *Set of* 4 2·50 2·50
Nos. 1005/8 were each printed in small sheets including one *se-tenant*, stamp-size, label.

395 The Fight against Tuberculosis

396 The Shepherds worship Jesus

(Des M. Diamond. Litho Harrison)

1982 (9 Aug). *Centenary of Robert Koch's Discovery of Tubercle Bacillus. T* **395** *and similar horiz designs. Multicoloured. P* 14.
1009 20 p. Type **395** 25 10
1010 65 p. Robert Koch 70 45
1011 80 p. Robert Koch in Africa 80 60
1012 1 c. Centenary of discovery of Tuberculosis .. 95 95
1013 2 c. Robert Koch and Nobel Prize, 1905 .. 1·75 2·25
1009/13 .. .. *Set of* 5 4·00 4·00

(Des E. Oimensah. Litho Format)

1982 (22 Dec). *Christmas. T* **396** *and similar vert designs. Multicoloured. P* 14½.
1014 15 p. Type **396** 10 10
1015 20 p. Mary, Joseph and baby Jesus 10 10
1016 65 p. The Three Kings sight star 30 30
1017 4 c. Winged Angel .. .. 1·40 1·75
1014/17 .. .. *Set of* 4 1·75 2·00
MS1018 90 × 110 mm. 6 c. The Three Kings with Jesus .. .. 1·60 2·40

397 Ghana and Commonwealth Flags with Coat of Arms

WINNER ITALY
3–1
(**398**)

(Des J.W. Litho Format)

1983 (14 Mar). *Commonwealth Day. T* **397** *and similar vert designs. Multicoloured. P* 14½.
1019 20 p. Type **397** 15 10
1020 55 p. Satellite view of Ghana 35 30
1021 80 p. Minerals of Ghana 50 45
1022 3 c. African Fish Eagle .. .. 2·00 2·25
1019/22 .. .. *Set of* 4 2·75 2·75

1983 (30 May). *Italy's Victory in World Cup Football Championship* (1982). *Nos.* 1000/8 *optd with T* **398**, *in gold.* (a) *P* 14½.
1023 **394** 20 p. multicoloured 10 10
1024 – 65 p. multicoloured 25 30
1025 – 80 p. multicoloured 35 40
1026 – 4 c. multicoloured .. .. 1·75 1·90
1023/6 .. .. *Set of* 4 2·25 2·50
MS1027 110 × 90 mm. 6 c. multicoloured .. 1·75 2·00

(*b*) *P* 14 × 14½
1028 **394** 30 p. multicoloured 15 15
1029 – 80 p. multicoloured 35 45
1030 – 1 c. multicoloured 40 50
1031 – 3 c. multicoloured .. .. 1·25 1·50
1028/31 .. .. *Set of* 4 1·90 2·40
No. **MS**1027 has an additional overprint, "FINAL: ITALY V. W. GERMANY", on the sheet margin.

INFLATION HANDSTAMPS. During 1983 the value of the Ghanaian currency fell drastically and as a result, there was a considerable rise in postal rates.

To cope with this situation supplies of past commemorative issues were made available from the post offices, many being handstamped "NOT FOR PHILATELIC USE" in one line within a frame. These handstamps were usually applied in blue, haphazardly across the sheet with examples so far reported on Nos. 656/7, 664, 670, 680, 689, 703, 708, 718, 746/7, 753, 757, 762/3, 766, 775, 780/1, 791, 793, 799, 814, 817, 846, 850/1, 853, 856/7, 860, 865, 867, 869, 875 and 882.

 ₵1

(**398***a*)

399 Short-finned Pilot Whale

1983 (Oct). *No.* 470 *surch with T* **398***a*.
1031*a* 1 c. on 20 n.p. deep blue and new blue .. 15 15
ab. Surch triple .. ..

(Des J. Iskowitz. Litho Format)

1983 (15 Nov). *Coastal Marine Mammals. T* **399** *and similar horiz designs. Multicoloured. P* 14½.
1032 1 c. Type **399** 40 40
1033 1 c. 40, Risso's Dolphin 40 40
1034 2 c. 30, False Killer Whale 50 50
1035 3 c. Spinner Dolphin 70 70
1036 5 c. Atlantic Hump-backed Dolphin .. 1·00 1·00
1032/6 .. .. *Set of* 5 2·75 2·75
MS1037 117 × 76 mm. 6 c. As 5 c. .. .. 85 1·00

400 *Hemichramis fasciatus*

401 Communication Devices

(Des and litho De La Rue)

1983 (12 Dec). *T* **400** *and similar designs. P* 14.
1038 5 p. multicoloured 10 10
1039 10 p. multicoloured 10 10
1040 20 p. multicoloured 10 10
1041 50 p. deep grey-green, yellow-orange and black 10 10
1042 1 c. yellow-orange, violet-blue and black .. 10 10
1043 2 c. multicoloured 10 10
1044 3 c. multicoloured 10 10
1045 4 c. multicoloured 10 10
1046 5 c. multicoloured 10 10
1047 10 c. multicoloured 10 10
1038/47 .. .. *Set of* 10 45 45
Designs: *Horiz*—10 p. *Hemichramis fasciatus (different)*; 2 c. Jet airliner. *Vert*—20 p. *Haemanthus rupestris*; 50 p. Mounted warrior; 1 c. Scorpion; 3 c. White-collared Mangabey; 4 c. Demidoff's Galago; 5 c. *Kaemferia nigerica*; 10 c. Grey-backed Camaroptera.

(Des PAD Studio. Litho Questa)

1983 (13 Dec). *World Communications Year. T* **401** *and similar vert designs. Multicoloured. P* 14.
1048 1 c. Type **401** 10 10
1049 1 c. 40, Satellite dish aerial 10 10
1050 2 c. 30, Cable and cable-laying ship 20 15
1051 3 c. Switchboard operators 25 20
1052 5 c. Aircraft cockpit and air traffic controllers 30 35
1048/52 .. .. *Set of* 5 80 75
MS1053 95 × 70 mm. 6 c. Space satellite 25 40

402 Children receiving Presents

403 Soldiers with Rifles

(Des Designs Images. Litho Questa)

1983 (28 Dec). *Christmas. T* **402** *and similar multicoloured designs. P* 14 × 13½ (70 *p. and* 3 *c.*) *or* 14½ × 14 (*others*).
1054 70 p. Type **402** 10 10
1055 1 c. Nativity and Star of Bethlehem (28 × 36 *mm*) 10 10
1056 1 c. 40, Children celebrating (28 × 36 *mm*) .. 10 10
1057 2 c. 30, Family praying (28 × 36 *mm*) .. 10 15
1058 3 c. Dancing to bongo drum 15 20
1054/8 .. .. *Set of* 5 35 50
MS1059 70 × 90 mm. 6 c. As 2 c. 30 .. .. 25 45

(Des and litho B.D.T.)

1984 (26 Jan). *Namibia Day. T* **403** *and similar vert designs. P* 14.
1060 50 p. blue-green and black 10 10
1061 1 c. multicoloured 10 10
1062 1 c. 40, new blue, bright blue and black .. 10 10
1063 2 c. 30, multicoloured 10 15
1064 3 c. multicoloured 15 20
1060/4 .. .. *Set of* 5 40 55
Designs:—1 c. Soldiers supported by tank; 1 c. 40, Machete cutting chains; 2 c. 30, Peasant woman; 3 c. Soldiers and artillery support.

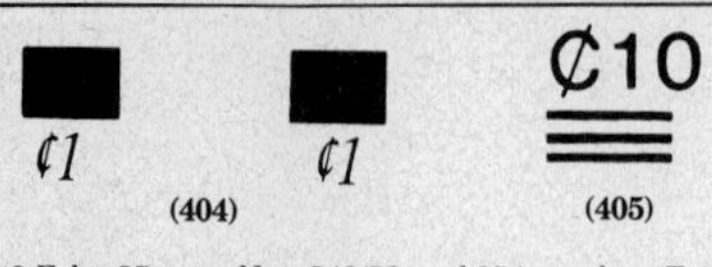

(404) (405)

1984 (8 Feb)–**85**. *(a) Nos. 948/52 and 954 surch as T* **404**
1065 1 c. on 20 p. Prince Charles and Lady Diana Spencer .. .. 4·00 3·00
1066 9 c. on 65 p. Prince Charles and Lady Diana Spencer (1985) .. .. .. 5·00 4·00
1067 9 c. on 80 p. Prince Charles on visit to Ghana .. .. 5·00 4·00
a. Imperf (pair) with surch inverted .. £275
1068 20 c. on 3 c. Type **385** (1985) .. .. 6·00 6·00
1069 20 c. on 4 c. Type **385** .. .. .. 6·00 6·00
MS1070 95×85 mm. 60 c. on 7 c. St. Paul's Cathedral .. .. 6·50 8·50

The above exist imperforate from a restricted printing *(Price for Nos. 1065, 1067, 1069 set of 3 £10, Nos. 1066 and 1068 set of 2* **£10** *and No.* **MS**1070 *£20, all mint).*

(b) Nos. 991/2 and 994/5 surch as T **405**
1071 10 c. on 20 p. Type **392** 40 45
1072 19 c. on 65 p. Scouts cooking on camp-fire .. 80 85
1073 30 c. on 3 c. Scouts observing elephant .. 1·25 1·40
MS1074 101×71 mm. 60 c. on 5 c. Lord Baden-Powell .. .. 2·00 3·50

(c) Nos. 1000/6 and 1008 surch as T **405**
1075 **394** 1 c. on 20 p. multicoloured 10 10
1076 – 9 c. on 65 p. multicoloured 40 45
1077 – 9 c. on 3 c. multicoloured 40 45
1078 **394** 10 c. on 30 p. multicoloured 40 45
1079 – 10 c. on 80 p. mult (No. 1002) .. 40 45
1080 – 20 c. on 4 c. mult (No. 1006) .. 85 90
1081 – 20 c. on 4 c. multicoloured 85 90
MS1082 110×90 mm. 60 c. on 6 c. multicoloured 2·00 2·25

(d) Nos. 1019/22 surch as T **405**
1083 1 c. on 20 p. Type **397** 10 10
1084 9 c. on 55 p. Satellite view of Ghana .. 40 45
1085 30 c. on 80 p. Minerals of Ghana .. .. 1·25 1·40
1086 50 c. on 3 c. African Fish Eagle .. .. 2·10 2·25

(e) Nos. 1023/9 and 1031 surch as T **405**
1087 **394** 1 c. on 20 p. multicoloured 10 10
1088 – 9 c. on 65 p. multicoloured 40 45
1089 – 9 c. on 3 c. multicoloured 40 45
1090 **394** 10 c. on 30 p. multicoloured 40 45
1091 – 10 c. on 80 p. mult (No. 1025) .. 40 45
1092 – 20 c. on 80 p. mult (No. 1029) .. 80 85
1093 – 20 c. on 4 c. multicoloured 80 85
MS1094 110×90 mm. 60 c. on 6 c. multicoloured 2·00 2·25
1065/9, 1071/3, 1075/81, 1083/93 .. *Set of* 26 35·00 32·00

c10

19TH U.P.U CONGRESS - HAMBURG

(406)

1984 (19 June). *Universal Postal Union Congress, Hamburg. Nos. 1035/7 surch as T* **406**.
1095 10 c. on 3 c. Spinner Dolphin 40 45
1096 50 c. on 5 c. Atlantic Hump-backed Dolphin .. .. 2·10 2·25
MS1097 117×76 mm. 60 c. on 6 c. As No. 1096 .. 2·50 3·50

407 Cross and Crown of Thorns **408** Women's 400 Metre Race

(Litho Format)

1984 (26 June). *Easter. T* **407** *and similar vert designs. Multicoloured. P* 15.
1098 1 c. Type **407** 10 10
1099 1 c. 40, Christ praying 10 15
1100 2 c. 30, The Resurrection 10 10
1101 3 c. Palm Sunday 10 15
1102 50 c. Christ on the road to Emmaus .. 1·90 2·25
1098/102 .. .. *Set of* 5 2·00 2·40
MS1103 102×86 mm. 60 c. Type **407** .. .. 2·00 3·00

(Des P. Cox and J. Iskowitz. Litho Format)

1984 (13 Aug). *Olympic Games, Los Angeles. T* **408** *and similar vert designs. Multicoloured. P* 15.
1104 1 c. Type **408** 10 10
1105 1 c. 40, Boxing 10 10
1106 2 c. 30, Hockey 15 15
1107 3 c. Men's 400 metre hurdles race .. 15 15
1108 50 c. Rhythmic gymnastics .. .. .. 2·10 2·25
1104/8 .. .. *Set of* 5 2·25 2·40
MS1109 103×78 mm. 70 c. Football .. .. 2·50 3·50

409 *Amorphophallus johnsonii* **410** Young Bongo

(Litho Harrison)

1984 (24 Aug). *Flowers. T* **409** *and similar vert designs. Multicoloured. P* 14.
1110 1 c. Type **409** 10 10
1111 1 c. 40, *Pancratium trianthum* 10 10
1112 2 c. 30, *Eulophia cucullata* 15 15
1113 3 c. *Amorphophallus abyssinicus* 15 15
1114 50 c. *Chlorophytum togoense* .. .. 3·25 3·75
1110/14 .. .. *Set of* 5 3·25 3·75
MS1115 70×96 mm. 60 c. Type **409** .. .. 3·00 4·00

(Des Susan David. Litho B.D.T.)

1984 (7 Sept). *Endangered Antelopes. T* **410** *and similar horiz designs. Multicoloured. P* 14.
1116 1 c. Type **410** 10 10
1117 2 c. 30, Bongo bucks fighting 20 15
1118 3 c. Bongo family 30 20
1119 20 c. Bongo herd in high grass .. .. 1·50 1·75
1116/19 .. .. *Set of* 4 1·90 2·00
MS1120 Two sheets, each 100×71 mm. (a) 70 c. Head of Kob; (b) 70 c. Head of Bush buck *Set of 2 sheets* 6·00 7·50

411 Dipo Girl **412** The Three Wise Men Bringing Gifts

(Des and litho B.D.T.)

1984 (3 Oct). *Ghanaian Culture. T* **411** *and similar vert designs. Multicoloured. P* 14.
1121 1 c. Type **411** 10 10
1122 1 c. 40, Adowa dancer 10 10
1123 2 c. 30, Agbadza dancer 10 10
1124 3 c. Damba dancer 10 15
1125 50 c. Dipo dancer .. .. 1·75 2·25
1121/5 .. .. *Set of* 5 1·90 2·40
MS1126 70×84 mm. 70 c. Mandolin player. P 14×15 .. .. 2·00 3·00

(Litho D.L.R.)

1984 (19 Nov). *Christmas. T* **412** *and similar vert designs. Multicoloured. P* 12×12½.
1127 70 p. Type **412** 10 10
1128 1 c. Choir of angels 10 10
1129 1 c. 40, Mary and shepherds at manger .. 10 10
1130 2 c. 30, The flight into Egypt 10 10
1131 3 c. Simeon blessing Jesus 10 15
1132 50 c. Holy Family and angels .. .. 1·75 2·25
1127/32 .. .. *Set of* 6 1·90 2·40
MS1133 70×90 mm. 70 c. Type **412** .. .. 2·50 2·75

VALERIE
BRISCO-HOOKS
U.S.A.

(413)

414 The Queen Mother attending Church Service

1984 (3 Dec). *Olympic Medal Winners, Los Angeles. Nos. 1104/9 optd as T* **413** *in gold.*
1134 1 c. Type **408** (optd with T **413**) 10 10
1135 1 c. 40, Boxing (optd "U.S. WINNERS") .. 10 15
1136 2 c. 30, Field hockey (optd "PAKISTAN (FIELD HOCKEY)") 10 10
1137 3 c. Men's 400 metre hurdles race (optd "EDWIN MOSES U.S.A.") 10 10
1138 50 c. Rhythmic gymnastics (optd "LAURI FUNG CANADA") .. .. 1·50 1·60
1134/8 .. .. *Set of* 5 1·60 1·75
MS1139 103×78 mm. 70 c. Football (optd "FRANCE") .. .. 1·75 2·50

Nos. 1135 and **MS**1139 have the overprint in one line and Nos. 1136/8 in two.

(Des J.W. Litho Questa)

1985 (24 July). *Life and Times of Queen Elizabeth the Queen Mother. T* **414** *and similar vert designs. Multicoloured. P* 14.
1140 5 c. Type **414** 15 20
1141 12 c. At Ascot Races 40 45
1142 100 c. At Clarence House on her 84th birthday .. .. 3·00 3·25
1140/2 .. .. *Set of* 3 3·25 3·50
MS1143 56×84 mm. 110 c. With Prince Charles at Garter ceremony .. .. 3·50 4·00

Stamps as Nos. 1140/2, but with face values of 8 c., 20 c. and 70 c., exist from additional sheetlets of 5 plus a label issued December 1985. These also have changed background colours and are perforated 12×12½ *(Price for set of 3 stamps £2.25 mint).*

415 Moslems going to Mosque **416** Youths clearing Refuse ("Make Ghana Clean")

(Des E. Mensah. Litho B.D.T.)

1985 (1 Aug.) *Islamic Festival of Id-el-Fitr. T* **415** *and similar vert designs. Multicoloured. P* 14.
1144 5 c. Type **415** 15 20
1145 8 c. Moslems at prayer 25 30
1146 12 c. Pilgrims visiting the Dome of the Rock 40 45
1147 18 c. Preaching the Koran 55 60
1148 50 c. Banda Nkwanta Mosque, Accra, and map of Ghana .. .. 1·50 1·60
1144/8 .. .. *Set of* 5 2·50 2·75

(Des E. Mensah. Litho Questa)

1985 (9 Aug). *International Youth Year. T* **416** *and similar vert designs. Multicoloured. P* 14×13½.
1149 5 c. Type **416** 10 10
1150 8 c. Planting sapling ("Make Ghana Green") 15 15
1151 12 c. Youth carrying bananas ("Feed Ghana") 20 25
1152 100 c. Open-air class ("Educate Ghana") .. 1·60 2·00
1149/52 .. .. *Set of* 4 1·75 2·25
MS1153 103×78 mm. 110 c. As 8 c. .. .. 1·75 3·00

417 Honda "Interceptor", 1984 **418** Fork-tailed Flycatcher

(Litho Questa)

1985 (9 Sept). *Centenary of the Motorcycle. T* **417** *and similar multicoloured designs. P* 14.
1154 5 c. Type **417** 25 20
1155 8 c. DKW, 1938 .. .. 35 30
1156 12 c. BMW "R 32", 1923 .. .. .. 50 45
1157 100 c. NSU, 1900 .. .. 3·50 3·75
1154/7 .. .. *Set of* 4 4·25 4·25
MS1158 78×108 mm. 110 c. Zündapp, 1973 *(vert)* .. .. 3·50 4·25

(Litho Questa)

1985 (16 Oct). *Birth Bicentenary of John J. Audubon (ornithologist). T* **418** *and similar vert designs showing original paintings. Multicoloured. P* 14.
1159 5 c. Type **418** 40 15
1160 8 c. Barred Owl 80 45
1161 12 c. Black-throated Mango 85 45
1162 100 c. White-crowned Pigeon .. .. .. 3·00 3·50
1159/62 .. .. *Set of* 4 4·50 4·00
MS1163 85×115 mm. 110 c. Downy Woodpecker 3·00 3·00

No. 1159 is inscribed "York-tailed Fly Catcher" in error.

419 United Nations Building, New York

(Des Mary Walters. Litho D.L.R.)

1985 (24 Oct). *40th Anniv of United Nations Organization. T* **419** *and similar horiz designs. Multicoloured. P* 14½ (18 c.) *or* 14½ × 14 (*others*).

1164 5 c. Type **419** 10 10
1165 8 c. Flags of member nations and U.N. Building 15 15
1166 12 c. Dove with olive branch 20 25
1167 18 c. General Assembly 30 35
1168 100 c. Flags of Ghana and United Nations .. .. 1·60 1·75
1164/8 .. .. *Set of* 5 2·10 2·40
MS1169 90 × 70 mm. 110 c. United Nations (New York) 1955 4 cent 10th anniv stamp .. .. 1·50 2·00

420 Coffee

(Des J. Iskowitz. Litho B.D.T.)

1985 (4 Nov). *20th Anniv of United Nations Conference on Trade and Development. T* **420** *and similar horiz designs showing export products. Multicoloured. P* 14.

1170 5 c. Type **420** 10 10
1171 8 c. Cocoa 15 15
1172 12 c. Timber 25 25
1173 18 c. Bauxite 45 40
1174 100 c. Gold .. .. 2·00 2·25
1170/4 .. .. *Set of* 5 2·75 2·75
MS1175 104 × 74 mm. 110 c. Agricultural produce and plate of food. P 15 × 14 .. .. .. 2·00 2·50

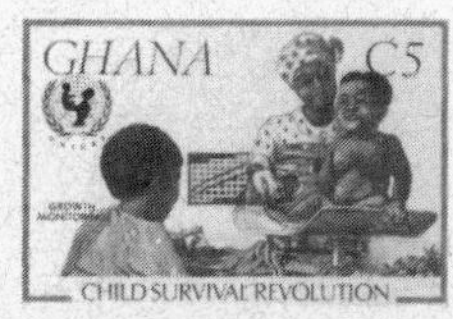

421 Growth Monitoring

(Des E. Mensah. Litho B.D.T.)

1985 (16 Dec). *U.N.I.C.E.F. Child Survival Campaign. T* **421** *and similar horiz designs. Multicoloured. P* 14.

1176 5 c. Type **421** 15 10
1177 8 c. Oral rehydration therapy 20 15
1178 12 c. Breast feeding 35 25
1179 100 c. Immunization .. .. 2·00 2·25
1176/9 .. .. *Set of* 4 2·40 2·50
MS1180 99 × 69 mm. 110 c. Campaign logo. P 15 × 14 .. .. 1·75 2·25

422 Airline Stewardess and Boys with Stamp Album

(Litho Questa)

1986 (27 Oct). *"Ameripex" International Stamp Exhibition, Chicago. T* **422** *and similar multicoloured designs. P* 14.

1181 5 c. Type **422** 10 10
1182 25 c. Globe and Ghana Airways aircraft .. 45 45
1183 100 c. Ghana Airways stewardess (*vert*) .. 1·75 2·00
1181/3 .. .. *Set of* 3 2·10 2·25
MS1184 90 × 70 mm. 150 c. Stamp collecting class .. .. 2·25 2·50

423 Kejetia Roundabout, Kumasi

424 Tackling

(Litho B.D.T.)

1986 (10 Nov). *"Inter-Tourism '86" Conference. T* **423** *and similar horiz designs. Multicoloured. P* 14.

1185 5 c. Type **423** 10 10
1186 15 c. Fort St. Jago, Elmina 30 30
1187 25 c. Tribal warriors 45 45
1188 100 c. Chief holding audience .. .. 1·75 2·25
1185/8 .. .. *Set of* 4 2·40 2·75
MS1189 110 × 70 mm. 150 c. African Elephants. P 15 × 14 .. .. 3·75 5·00

(Litho D.L.R.)

1987 (16 Jan). *World Cup Football Championship, Mexico* (1986). *T* **424** *and similar vert designs. Multicoloured. P* 14 × 14½.

1190 5 c. Type **424** 10 10
1191 15 c. Player taking control of ball .. 15 15
1192 25 c. Player kicking ball 30 25
1193 100 c. Player with ball .. .. 1·00 1·25
1190/3 .. .. *Set of* 4 1·40 1·50
MS1194 90 × 70 mm. 150 c. Player kicking ball (*different*) .. .. 1·50 2·00

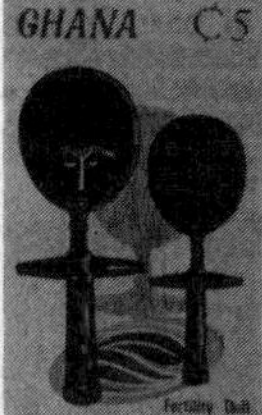

425 Fertility Doll

426 Children of Different Races, Peace Doves and Sun

(Litho D.L.R.)

1987 (22 Jan). *Ghanaian Fertility Dolls. T* **425** *and similar vert designs showing different dolls. P* 14 × 14½.

1195 **425** 5 c. multicoloured 10 10
1196 – 15 c. multicoloured 15 15
1197 – 25 c. multicoloured 30 25
1198 – 100 c. multicoloured .. .. .. 1·00 1·25
1195/8 .. .. *Set of* 4 1·40 1·50
MS1199 90 × 70 mm. **425** 150 c. multicoloured .. 1·50 2·00

(Litho D.L.R.)

1987 (2 Mar). *International Peace Year* (1986). *T* **426** *and similar multicoloured designs. P* 14 × 14½ (100 c.) *or* 14½ × 14 (*others*).

1200 5 c. Type **426** 10 10
1201 25 c. Plough, peace dove and rising sun .. 30 25
1202 100 c. Peace dove, olive branch and globe (*vert*) .. .. 1·00 1·25
1200/2 .. .. *Set of* 3 1·25 1·40
MS1203 90 × 70 mm. 150 c. Dove perched on plough (*vert*). P 14 × 14½ .. .. 1·50 2·00

427 Lumber and House under Construction

428 Demonstrator and Arms breaking Shackles

(Des and litho B.D.T.)

1987 (10 Mar). *"Gifex '87" International Forestry Exposition, Accra. T* **427** *and similar horiz designs. Multicoloured. P* 14.

1204 5 c. Type **427** 10 10
1205 15 c. Planks and furniture 15 15
1206 25 c. Felled trees 30 25
1207 200 c. Logs and wood carvings .. .. 1·90 2·00
1204/7 .. .. *Set of* 4 2·25 2·25

(Des W. Hanson. Litho D.L.R.)

1987 (8 Apr). *Appearance of Halley's Comet* (1986). *Horiz designs as T* **123** *of Anguilla. Multicoloured. P* 14½ × 14.

1208 5 c. Mikhail Lomonosov (scientist) and Chamber of Curiosities, St. Petersburg 10 10
1209 25 c. Lunar probe "Surveyor 3", 1966 .. 40 25
1210 200 c. Wedgwood plaques for Isaac Newton, 1790, and "Apollo 11" Moon landing, 1968 .. .. 2·25 2·10
1208/10 .. .. *Set of* 3 2·50 2·25
MS1211 100 × 70 mm. 250 c. Halley's Comet .. 2·25 2·75

(Litho D.L.R.)

1987 (18 May). *Solidarity with the People of Southern Africa. T* **428** *and similar vert designs. Multicoloured. P* 14 × 14½.

1212 5 c. Type **428** 10 10
1213 15 c. Miner and gold bars 15 15
1214 25 c. Xhosa warriors 30 25
1215 100 c. Nelson Mandela and shackles .. 1·00 1·25
1212/15 .. .. *Set of* 4 1·40 1·50
MS1216 70 × 90 mm. 150 c. Nelson Mandela .. 1·50 2·00

429 Aerophones

(Litho D.L.R.)

1987 (13 July). *Musical Instruments. T* **429** *and similar horiz designs. Multicoloured. P* 14½ × 14.

1217 5 c. Type **429** 10 10
1218 15 c. Xylophone 15 15
1219 25 c. Chordophones 30 25
1220 100 c. Membranophones .. .. .. 1·00 1·25
1217/20 .. .. *Set of* 4 1·40 1·50
MS1221 90 × 70 mm. 200 c. Idiophones .. .. 1·90 2·25

430 Woman filling Water Pot at Pump

431 Ga Women preparing Kpokpoi for Homowo Festival

(Litho B.D.T.)

1987 (21 Sept). *International Year of Shelter for the Homeless. T* **430** *and similar horiz designs. Multicoloured. P* 14.

1222 5 c. Type **430** 10 10
1223 15 c. Building house from breeze-blocks .. 10 15
1224 25 c. Modern village with stream 20 25
1225 100 c. Modern houses with verandahs .. 70 75
1222/5 .. .. *Set of* 4 95 1·00

(Litho Format)

1988 (6 Jan). *Ghana Festivals. T* **431** *and similar vert designs. Multicoloured. P* 15.

1226 5 c. Type **431** 10 10
1227 15 c. Efute hunters with deer, Aboakyir festival 10 15
1228 35 c. Fanti chief dancing at Odwira festival 20 25
1229 100 c. Chief in palanquin, Yam festival .. 70 75
1226/9 .. .. *Set of* 4 95 1·00

432 Port Installation

433 Nurse giving Injection

(Litho National Ptg Wks, Havana)

1988 (26 Jan). *5th Anniversary of 31 December Revolution (1987). T* **432** *and similar horiz designs. Multicoloured. P* 13.

1230 5 c. Type **432** 10 10
1231 15 c. Repairing railway line 10 10
1232 25 c. Planting cocoa 15 15
1233 100 c. Miners with ore truck 50 55
1230/3 .. .. *Set of* 4 70 75

(Litho Format)

1988 (1 Feb). *U.N.I.C.E.F. Global Immunization Campaign. T* **433** *and similar vert designs. Multicoloured. P* 15.

1234 5 c. Type **433** 10 10
1235 15 c. Girl receiving injection 10 15
1236 25 c. Schoolgirl crippled by polio 20 25
1237 100 c. Nurse giving oral vaccine to baby .. 70 75
1234/7 .. .. *Set of* 4 95 1·00

434 Akwadjan Men

¢100.00

(435)

(Litho Questa)

1988 (9 May). *Tribal Costumes. T* **434** *and similar vert designs. Multicoloured. P* 14.

1238 5 c. Type **434** 10 10
1239 25 c. Banaa man 15 15
1240 250 c. Agwasen women .. .. 1·25 1·40
1238/40 .. .. *Set of* 3 1·25 1·40

1988 (12 July)–**89**. *Nos.* 465/6, 469/70, 1038/42 *and* 1044 *surch as T* **435**.

1241 – 20 c. on 50 p. dp grey-green, yellow-orange and black (No. 1041) 10 10
a. Horiz pair, one without surch ..
1242 – 20 c. on 1 c. yellow-orange, violet-blue and black (No. 1042) (9.88) 10 10
a. Surch double ..
b. Surch double, one inverted .. † —
c. Surch inverted ..
d. Horiz pair, one without surch ..

1243 – 50 c. on 10 n.p. mult (No. 469) .. 20 20
a. Vert pair, one without surch ..
1244 – 50 c. on 10 p. mult (No. 1039) (9.88) 20 20
a. Surch inverted .. ..
b. Surch on front and back ..
ba. Surch on front and inverted surch on back .. ..
c. Pair, one without surch ..
1245 **235** 60 c. on 4 n.p. multicoloured .. 25 25
a. Surch double .. ..
b. Surch double, one inverted ..
c. Surch double, one albino ..
d. Surch inverted .. .. † —
1246 – 60 c. on 3 c. mult (No. 1044) (1989) 25 25
a. Decimal point omitted from surch (R. 4/5) .. .. ..
1247 **400** 80 c. on 5 p. multicoloured 35 35
a. Pair, one without surch ..
1248 – 100 c. on 20 n.p. deep blue and new blue (No. 470) 45 45
1249 – 100 c. on 20 p. mult (No. 1040) (9.88) 45 45
a. Surch double, one sideways ..
b. Horiz pair, one without surch ..
1250 **236** 200 c. on 6 n.p. multicoloured .. 85 85
1241/50 .. .. *Set of* 10 2·75 2·75

Other handstamped and manuscript surcharges can be found used during this period, but it is understood that only those listed above were authorised by the postal authorities.

436 Boxing

437 Nutrition Lecture

(Litho Questa)

1988 (10 Oct). *Olympic Games, Seoul. T* **436** *and similar horiz designs. Multicoloured. P* 14.
1251 20 c. Type **436** 10 10
1252 60 c. Athletics 30 35
1253 80 c. Discus-throwing 40 45
1254 100 c. Javelin-throwing 50 55
1255 350 c. Weightlifting .. .. 1·75 1·90
1251/5 .. .. *Set of* 5 2·75 3·00
MS1256 75×105 mm. 500 c. As 80 c. .. .. 2·75 3·00

(Litho B.D.T.)

1988 (14 Dec). *125th Anniv of International Red Cross. T* **437** *and similar vert designs. Multicoloured. P* 14.
1257 20 c. Type **437** 15 10
1258 50 c. Red Cross volunteer with blind woman 40 40
1259 60 c. Distributing flood relief supplies .. 50 50
1260 200 c. Giving first aid .. .. 1·50 1·50
1257/60 .. .. *Set of* 4 2·25 2·25

438 Tropical Forest

439 "African Solidarity"

(Litho B.D.T.)

1988 (19 Dec). *Christmas. T* **438** *and similar multicoloured designs. P* 14.
1261 20 c. Type **438** 15 10
1262 60 c. Christ Child (*vert*) 35 35
1263 80 c. Virgin and Child with Star (*vert*) .. 50 60
1264 100 c. Three Wise Men following Star .. 60 70
1265 350 c. Symbolic Crucifixion (*vert*) .. .. 2·00 2·50
1261/5 .. .. *Set of* 5 3·25 3·75
MS1266 100×70 mm. 500 c. Virgin and Child (*vert*) .. .. 2·50 2·75

(Litho B.D.T.)

1989 (3 Jan). *25th Anniv of Organization of African Unity* (1988). *T* **439** *and similar multicoloured designs. P* 14.
1267 20 c. Type **439** 15 15
1268 50 c. O.A.U. Headquarters, Addis Ababa 40 40
1269 60 c. Emperor Haile Selassie and Ethiopian flag (*horiz*) 55 55
1270 200 c. Kwame Nkrumah (former Ghanaian President) and flag (*horiz*) .. .. 1·50 1·50
1267/70 .. .. *Set of* 4 2·40 2·40

MINIMUM PRICE

The minimum price quote is 10p which represents a handling charge rather than a basis for valuing common stamps. For further notes about prices see introductory pages.

440 "Amor"

A. ZUELOW
DDR
60 KG
(441)

(Litho B.D.T.)

1989 (16 Jan). *500th Birth Anniversary of Titian (artist). T* **440** *and similar vert designs. Multicoloured. P* 14.
1271 20 c. Type **440** 15 10
1272 60 c. "The Appeal" 45 45
1273 80 c. "Bacchus and Ariadne" (detail) .. 60 60
1274 100 c. "Portrait of a Musician" 75 75
1275 350 c. "Philip II seated" .. .. .. 2·00 2·25
1271/5 .. .. *Set of* 5 3·50 3·75
MS1276 77×115 mm. 500 c. "Portrait of a Gentleman" .. .. 2·50 2·75

1989 (23 Jan). *Olympic Medal Winners, Seoul. Nos.* 1251/6 *optd as T* **441**.
1277 20 c. Type **436** (optd with T **441**) 15 15
1278 60 c. Athletics (optd "G. BORDIN ITALY MARATHON") 45 45
1279 80 c. Discus-throwing (optd "J. SCHULT DDR") 60 60
1280 100 c. Javelin-throwing (optd "T. KORJUS FINLAND") 75 75
1281 350 c. Weightlifting (optd "B. GUIDIKOV BULGARIA 75 KG") .. .. 2·25 2·25
1277/81 .. .. *Set of* 5 3·75 3·75
MS1282 75×105 mm. 500 c. As 80 c. (optd "GOLD J. SCHULT DDR SILVER R. OUBARTAS USSR BRONZE R. DANNEBERG W. GERMANY" on sheet margin) .. .. 2·50 2·75

POSTAGE DUE STAMPS

GHANA
(D 2)

D 3

1958 (25 June). *Postage Due stamps of Gold Coast. Chalk-surfaced paper. Optd with Type* D **2**, *in red.*
D 9 D 1 1d. black 10 20
D10 2d. black 10 25
D11 3d. black 10 30
D12 6d. black 15 45
D13 1s. black 20 80
D9/13 .. .. *Set of* 5 50 1·75

(Typo De La Rue)

1958 (1 Dec). *Chalk-surfaced paper. Wmk Mult Script CA. P* 14.
D14 D 3 1d. carmine 10 20
D15 2d. green 10 20
D16 3d. orange 10 30
D17 6d. bright ultramarine 10 50
D18 1s. reddish violet .. .. 15 1·50
D14/18 .. .. *Set of* 5 45 2·40

3p.
Ghana New Currency
19th July, 1965.
(D 4)

1½Np
(D 5)

1965 (19 July). *Nos.* D14/18 *surch as Type* D 4 *diagonally upwards* (D) *or horiz* (H), *by Govt Printer, Accra.*
D19 D 3 1 p. on 1d. (D) 10 25
a. Surch inverted .. .. 5·00
b. Surch double .. ..
D20 2 p. on 2d. (B.) (H) 10 30
a. Surch inverted .. .. .. 4·50
D21 3 p. on 3d. (Indigo) (H) 10 35
a. Surch inverted .. ..
b. Ultramarine surch .. .. ..
ba. Ditto. Surch inverted .. .. 6·50
bb. Ditto. Surch on back and face ..
c. Black surch .. ..
D22 6 p. on 6d. (R.) (H) 10 50
a. Surch inverted .. ..
b. Purple-brown surch .. .. ..
ba. Ditto. Surch double .. .. .. 19·00
c. Green surch .. .. .. 13·00
D23 12 p. on 1s. (B.) (D) 15 90
D19/23 .. .. *Set of* 5 45 2·00

On the diagonal surcharges the figures of value are horizontal.

1968 (Feb)–**70**. *Nos.* D20/2 *additionally surch as Type* D **5**, *in red* (1½ *n.p.*, 5 *n.p.*) *or black* (2½ *n.p.*).
D24 D 3 1½ n.p. on 2 p. on 2d. .. .. 4·25 3·75
a. Type D **5** double, one albino ..
b. Albino surch (Type D 4) .. ..
D25 2½ n.p. on 3 p. on 3d. (4.70?) .. 1·00 3·00
a. Type D **5** double, one albino .. 5·00
D26 5 n.p. on 6 p. on 6d. (1970) .. 1·00
D24/6 .. .. *Set of* 3 5·50

The above were three in a series of surcharges, the others being 1 n.p. on 1 p. and 10 n.p. on 12 p., which were prepared, but owing to confusion due to the two surcharges in similar currency it was decided by the authorities not to issue the stamps, however, Nos. D24/6 were issued in error.

(Litho D.L.R.)

1970. *Inscr in new currency. P* 14¼ × 14.
D27 D 3 1 n.p. carmine-red 20 75
D28 1½ n.p. green 20 80
D29 2½ n.p. yellow-orange .. .. .. 25 1·00
D30 5 n.p. ultramarine .. .. .. 30 1·25
D31 10 n.p. reddish violet .. .. .. 40 1·75
D27/31 .. .. *Set of* 5 1·25 5·00

(Litho D.L.R.)

1980–81. *Currency described as "p". P* 14½ × 14.
D32 D 3 2 p. reddish orange 10 20
D33 3 p. brown 10 20

Gibraltar

CROWN COLONY

Early details of postal arrangements in Gibraltar are hard to establish, although it is known that postal facilities were provided by the Civil Secretary's Office from the early 1750s. Gibraltar became a packet port in 1806, although the Civil Secretary's Office continued to be responsible for other mail. The two services were amalgamated on 1 January 1857 as a Branch Office of the British G.P.O., the control of the postal services not reverting to Gibraltar until 1 January 1886.

Spanish stamps could be used at Gibraltar from their introduction in 1850 and, indeed, such franking was required on letters weighing over ½ oz. sent to Spain after 1 July 1854. From 1 July 1856 until 31 December 1875 all mail to Spain required postage to be prepaid by Spanish stamps and these issues were supplied by the Gibraltar postal authorities, acting as a Spanish Postal Agent. The mail, forwarded under this system was cancelled at San Roque with a horizontal barred oval, later replaced by a cartwheel type mark showing numeral 63.

Stamps of Great Britain were issued for use in Gibraltar from 3 September 1857 to the end of 1885.

For illustrations of the postmark types see BRITISH POST OFFICES ABROAD notes, following GREAT BRITAIN.

Stamps of GREAT BRITAIN *cancelled* "G" *as Type* **1** (3 Sept 1857 *to* 19 Feb 1859).

Z 1 1d. red-brown (1854) Die I £300
Z 2 1d. red-brown (1855), Die II, *wmk* Small Crown, *perf* 16 .. .. £550
Z 3 1d. red-brown (1855), Die II, *wmk* Small Crown, *perf* 14 .. .. £250
Z 4 1d. red-brown (1855), Die II, *wmk* Large Crown, *perf* 14 .. .. 60·00
Z 5 1d. rose-red (1857), Die II, *wmk* Large Crown, *perf* 14 .. .. 20·00
Z 6 2d. blue (1855), *wmk* Small Crown, *perf* 14 .. £275
Z 7 2d. blue (1855–58), *wmk* Large Crown, *perf* 16 .. £275
Z 8 2d. blue (1855), *wmk* Large Crown, *perf* 14 *From* 55·00
Plate Nos. 5, 6.
Z 9 2d. blue (1858) (Plate No. 7) .. £200
Z10 4d. rose (1857) .. 42·00
a. Thick glazed paper
Z11 6d. lilac (1856) .. 40·00
Z12 6d. lilac (1856) (blued *paper*) .. £750
Z13 1s. green (1856) .. 75·00
a. Thick paper
Z14 1s. green (1856) (blued *paper*) .. £1300

Stamps of GREAT BRITAIN *cancelled* "A 26" *as in Types* **2, 5, 11** *or* **14** (20 Feb 1859 *to* 31 Dec 1885).

Z15 ½d. rose-red (1870–79) .. *From* 12·00
Plate Nos. 4, 5, 6, 8, 10, 11, 12, 13, 14, 15, 19, 20.
Z16 1d. red-brown (1841), *imperf* .. £850
Z17 1d. red-brown (1855), *wmk* Large Crown, *perf* 14 .. £150
Z18 1d. rose-red (1857), *wmk* Large Crown, *perf* 14 .. 12·00
Z19 1d. rose-red (1864–79) .. *From* 16·00
Plate Nos. 71, 72, 73, 74, 76, 78, 79, 80, 81, 82, 83, 84, 85, 86, 87, 88, 89, 90, 91, 92, 93, 94, 95, 96, 97, 98, 99, 100, 101, 102, 103, 104, 105, 106, 107, 108, 109, 110, 111, 112, 113, 114, 115, 116, 117, 118, 119, 120, 121, 122, 123, 124, 125, 127, 129, 130, 131, 132, 133, 134, 135, 136, 137, 138, 139, 140, 141, 142, 143, 144, 145, 146, 147, 148, 149, 150, 151, 152, 153, 154, 155, 156, 157, 158, 159, 160, 161, 162, 163, 164, 165, 166, 167, 168, 169, 170, 171, 172, 173, 174, 175, 176, 177, 178, 179, 180, 181, 182, 183, 184, 185, 186, 187, 188, 189, 190, 191, 192, 193, 194, 195, 196, 197, 198, 199, 200, 201, 202, 203, 204, 205, 206, 207, 208, 209, 210, 211, 212, 213, 214, 215, 216, 217, 218, 219, 220, 221, 222, 223, 224, 225.
Z20 1½d. lake-red (1870) (Plate No. 3) .. £250
Z21 2d. blue (1855), *wmk* Large Crown, *perf* 14 .. 95·00
Plate No. 6.
Z22 2d. blue (1858–69) .. *From* 16·00
Plate Nos. 7, 8, 9, 12, 13, 14, 15.
Z23 2½d. rosy mauve (1875) (blued *paper*) .. *From* £100
Plate Nos. 1, 2, 3.
Z24 2½d. rosy mauve (1875–76) (Plate Nos. 1, 2, 3) *From* 24·00
Z25 2½d. rosy mauve (*Error of Lettering*) .. £1600
Z26 2½d. rosy mauve (1876–79) .. *From* 20·00
Plate Nos. 3, 4, 5, 6, 7, 8, 9, 10, 11, 12, 13, 14, 15, 16, 17.
Z27 2½d. blue (1880–81) (Plate Nos. 17, 18, 19, 20) *From* 12·00
Z28 2½d. blue (1881) (Plate Nos. 21, 22, 23) .. *From* 10·00
Z29 3d. carmine-rose (1862) .. £150
Z30 3d. rose (1865) (Plate No. 4) .. 45·00
Z31 3d. rose (1867–73) .. *From* 18·00
Plate Nos. 4, 5, 6, 7, 8, 9, 10.
Z32 3d. rose (1873–76) .. *From* 22·00
Plate Nos. 11, 12, 14, 15, 16, 17, 18, 19, 20.
Z33 3d. rose (1881) (Plate Nos. 20, 21) ..
Z34 3d. lilac (1883) (3d. *on* 3d) .. 70·00
Z35 4d. rose (1857) .. 42·00
Z36 4d. red (1862) (Plate Nos. 3, 4) .. *From* 45·00
Z37 4d. vermilion (1865–73) .. *From* 30·00
Plate Nos. 7, 8, 9, 10, 11, 12, 13, 14.
Z38 4d. vermilion (1876) (Plate No. 15) .. £225
Z39 4d. sage-green (1877) (Plate Nos. 15, 16) .. 80·00
Z40 4d. grey-brown (1880) *wmk* Large Garter .. £130
Plate No. 17.
Z41 4d. grey-brown (1880) *wmk* Crown .. *From* 16·00
Plate Nos. 17, 18.
Z42 6d. lilac (1856) .. 42·00
Z43 6d. lilac (1862) (Plate Nos. 3, 4) .. *From* 38·00
Z44 6d. lilac (1865–67) (Plate Nos. 5, 6) .. *From* 32·00
Z45 6d. lilac (1867) (Plate No. 6) .. 42·00
Z46 6d. violet (1867–70) (Plate Nos. 6, 8, 9) .. *From* 32·00
Z47 6d. buff (1872–73) (Plate Nos. 11, 12) .. *From* £180
Z48 6d. chestnut (1872) (Plate No. 11) .. 28·00
Z49 6d. grey (1873) (Plate No. 12) .. 60·00
Z50 6d. grey (1874–80) .. *From* 24·00
Plate Nos. 13, 14, 15, 16, 17.
Z51 6d. grey (1881) (Plate Nos. 17, 18) .. £150
Z52 6d. lilac (1883) (6d. *on* 6d.) .. 80·00
Z53 8d. orange (1876) .. £170
Z54 9d. bistre (1862) .. £160
Z55 9d. straw (1862) .. £600
Z56 9d. straw (1865) .. £550
Z57 9d. straw (1867) .. £120
Z58 10d. red-brown (1867) .. £150
Z59 1s. green (1856) .. 70·00
Z60 1s. green (1862) .. 60·00
Z61 1s. green (1862) ("K" *variety*) .. £2000
Z62 1s. green (1865) (Plate No. 4) .. 35·00
Z63 1s. green (1867–73) (Plate Nos. 4, 5, 6, 7) .. *From* 12·00
Z64 1s. green (1873–77) .. *From* 36·00
Plate Nos. 8, 9, 10, 11, 12, 13.
Z65 1s. orange-brown (1880) (Plate No. 13) .. £180
Z66 1s. orange-brown (1881) (Plate Nos. 13, 14) *From* 38·00
Z67 2s. blue (1867) .. £120
Z68 5s. rose (1867) (Plate No. 1) .. £600

1880.

Z69 ½d. deep green .. 12·00
Z70 ½d. pale green .. 12·00
Z71 1d. Venetian red .. 12·00
Z72 1½d. Venetian red ..
Z73 2d. pale rose .. 60·00
Z74 2d. deep rose ..
Z75 5d. indigo ..

1881.

Z76 1d. lilac (14 *dots*) .. 17·00
Z77 1d. lilac (16 *dots*) .. 7·50

1884.

Z78–81 ½d. slate blue; 2d., 2½d., 3d. .. *From* 11·00
Z82–83 4d., 6d. .. *From* 70·00

POSTAL FISCAL

Z83*a* 1d. purple (Die 4) (1878) *wmk* Small Anchor £600
Z84 1d. purple (1881), *wmk* Orb .. £1100

PRICES FOR STAMPS ON COVER TO 1945

Nos. 1/7	*from* ×10
Nos. 8/33	*from* ×6
Nos. 39/45	*from* ×5
Nos. 46/109	*from* ×3
Nos. 110/13	*from* ×4
Nos. 114/17	*from* ×3
Nos. 118/20	*from* ×5
Nos. 121/31	*from* ×3

GIBRALTAR

(1)

1886 (1 Jan). *Contemporary types of Bermuda optd with T* **1** *by D.L.R. Wmk Crown CA. P* 14.

No.	Type			Unused	Used
1	**9**	½d. dull green	..	6·00	6·00
2	**1**	1d. rose-red	..	22·00	5·00
3	**2**	2d. purple-brown	..	70·00	70·00
4	**11**	2½d. ultramarine	..	85·00	2·75
		a. Optd in blue-black	..	£475	£150
5	**10**	4d. orange-brown	..	90·00	85·00
6	**4**	6d. deep lilac	..	£200	£180
7	**5**	1s. yellow-brown	..	£400	£350
1/7			*Set of* 7	£750	£625
1/3, 4a/7 Optd "Specimen"			*Set of* 7	£2000	

PRINTER. All Gibraltar stamps to No. 109 were typographed by De La Rue & Co, Ltd.

2

3

4

5

1886 (Nov)–**87**. *Wmk Crown CA. P* 14.

No.	Type			Unused	Used
8	**2**	½d. dull green (1.87)	..	3·25	2·75
9	**3**	1d. rose (12.86)	..	17·00	2·75
10	**4**	2d. brown-purple (12.86)	..	28·00	17·00
11	**5**	2½d. blue	..	40·00	2·25
12	**4**	4d. orange-brown (16.4.87)	..	55·00	55·00
13		6d. lilac (16.4.87)	..	80·00	80·00
14		1s. bistre (2.87)	..	£200	£200
8/14			*Set of* 7	£375	£325
8/14 Optd "Specimen"			*Set of* 7	£450	

See also Nos. 39 to 45.

5 CENTIMOS

(6)

7

1889 (1 Aug). *Surch as T* **6**.

No.	Type			Unused	Used
15	**2**	5 c. on ½d. green	..	8·00	12·00
16	**3**	10 c. on 1d. rose	..	7·00	6·50
17	**4**	25 c. on 2d. brown-purple	..	4·00	5·00
		a. Small "I" (R.6/2)	..	£110	£140
		b. Broken "N" (R.10/5)	..	£110	£140
18	**5**	25 c. on 2½d. bright blue	..	24·00	1·25
		a. Small "I" (R.6/2)	..	£250	£100
		b. Broken "N" (R.10/5)	..	£250	£100
19	**4**	40 c. on 4d. orange-brown	..	45·00	60·00
20		50 c. on 6d. bright lilac	..	45·00	50·00
21		75 c. on 1s. bistre	..	48·00	65·00
15/21			*Set of* 7	£160	£180
15/21 Optd "Specimen"			*Set of* 7	£300	

10 c., 40 c. and 50 c. values from this issue and that of 1889–96 are known bisected and used for half their value from various post offices in Morocco (*price on cover from* £750). These bisects were never authorised by the Gibraltar Post Office.

Two varieties of the figure "5" of the 5 c., 25 c., 50 c. and 75 c. may be found.

1889 (Nov)–**96**. *Issue in Spanish currency. Wmk Crown CA. P* 14.

No.	Type			Unused	Used
22	**7**	5 c. green	..	1·75	45
23		10 c. carmine	..	1·50	45
		b. Value omitted	..	£4500	
24		20 c. olive-green and brown (2.1.96)	..	14·00	10·00
25		20 c. olive-green (8.7.96)	..	7·00	16·00
26		25 c. ultramarine	..	12·00	70
		a. Deep ultramarine	..	16·00	80
27		40 c. orange-brown	..	2·50	2·25
28		50 c. bright lilac (1890)	..	2·00	1·50
29		75 c. olive-green (1890)	..	25·00	32·00
30		1 p. bistre (11.89)	..	60·00	20·00
31		1 p. bistre and ultramarine (6.95)	..	3·50	3·25
32		2 p. black and carmine (2.1.96)	..	7·00	24·00
33		5 p. slate-grey (12.89)	..	35·00	65·00
22/33			*Set of* 12	£150	£160
22/33 (excluding No. 25). Optd "Specimen"			*Set of* 11	£275	

1898 (1 Oct). *Reissue in Sterling currency. Wmk Crown CA. P* 14.

No.	Type			Unused	Used
39	**2**	½d. grey-green	..	90	1·25
40	**3**	1d. carmine	..	1·40	35
41	**4**	2d. brown-purple and ultramarine	..	4·75	1·50
42	**5**	2½d. bright ultramarine	..	7·50	40
43	**4**	4d. orange-brown and green	..	9·00	8·00
44		6d. violet and red	..	20·00	20·00
45		1s. bistre and carmine	..	20·00	16·00
39/45			*Set of* 7	55·00	42·00
39/45 Optd "Specimen"			*Set of* 7	£225	

No. 39 is greyer than No. 8, No. 40 brighter and deeper than No. 9 and No. 42 much brighter than No. 11.

8

9

½ Normal **½** Large "2"

2½d.

This occurs on R.10/1 in each pane of 60. The diagonal stroke is also longer.

1903 (1 May). *Wmk Crown CA. P* 14.

No.	Type			Unused	Used
46	**8**	½d. grey-green and green	..	4·00	4·75
47		1d. dull purple/*red*	..	14·00	60
48		2d. grey-green and carmine	..	11·00	13·00
49		2½d. dull purple and black/*blue*	..	1·25	60
		a. Large "2" in "½"	..	65·00	55·00
50		6d. dull purple and violet	..	10·00	17·00
51		1s. black and carmine	..	20·00	26·00
52	**9**	2s. green and blue	..	50·00	70·00
53		4s. dull purple and green	..	50·00	80·00
54		8s. dull purple and black/*blue*	..	70·00	90·00
55		£1 dull purple and black/*red*	..	£475	£525
46/55			*Set of* 10	£625	£750
46/55 Optd "Specimen"			*Set of* 10	£425	

1904–8. *Wmk Mult Crown CA. P* 14.

No.	Type			Unused	Used
56	**8**	½d. dull and bright green, **OC** (16.4.04*)	..	2·25	1·75
57		1d. dull purple/*red*, **OC** (6.9.04*)	..	1·50	40
		a. Bisected (½d.) (on card)	..	†	£1200
58		2d. grey-green and carmine, **OC** (9.1.05)		3·25	2·25
59		2½d. purple and black/*blue*, **C** (4.5.07)	..	20·00	55·00
		a. Large "2" in "½"	..	£170	£300
60		6d. dull purple and violet, **OC** (19.4.06)	..	5·00	7·00
61		1s. black and carmine, **OC** (13.10.05)	..	18·00	9·00
62	**9**	2s. green and blue, **OC** (2.2.05)	..	38·00	48·00
63		4s. deep purple and green, **C** (6.08)	..	£100	£130
64		£1 dp purple & black/*red*, **C** (15.3.08)	..	£500	£550
56/64			*Set of* 9	£600	£700

* Earliest known date of use.

1907–12. *Colours changed. Wmk Mult Crown CA. P* 14.

No.	Type			Unused	Used
66	**8**	½d. blue-green, **O** (1907)	..	1·50	80
67		1d. carmine, **O** (1.07)	..	85	45
		a. Wmk sideways	..	†	£2250
68		2d. greyish slate, **O** (5.10)	..	5·50	9·00
69		2½d. ultramarine, **O** (6.07)	..	3·00	1·25
		a. Large "2" in "½"	..	75·00	65·00
70		6d. dull and bright purple, **C** (3.12)	..	£100	£300
71		1s. black/*green*, **C** (1910)	..	17·00	18·00
72	**9**	2s. purple and bright blue/*blue*, **C** (4.10)		30·00	45·00
73		4s. black and carmine, **C** (4.10)	..	55·00	75·00
74		8s. purple and green, **C** (1911)	..	£180	£160
66/74			*Set of* 9	£350	£550
67/74 Optd "Specimen"			*Set of* 8	£425	

WAR TAX

10 11 (12)

1912 (17 July)–**24.** *Wmk Mult Crown CA. P* 14.
76 **10** ½d. blue-green, **O** 60 45
a. Yellow-green (4.17) .. .. .. 1·25 35
77 1d. carmine-red, **O** .. .. .. 1·75 55
a. Scarlet (6.16) .. .. .. 2·75 55
78 2d. greyish slate, **O** .. .. .. 2·50 1·25
79 2½d. deep bright blue, **O** .. .. .. 3·25 1·75
a. Large "2" in "½" .. .. .. 60·00 50·00
b. Pale ultramarine (1917) .. .. 6·00 2·00
ba. Large "2" in "½" .. .. .. 85·00 55·00
80 6d. dull purple and mauve, **C** .. .. 7·00 7·00
81 1s. black/*green*, **OC** .. .. .. 5·50 6·00
a. On blue-green, olive back (1919) .. 12·00 15·00
b. On emerald surface (12.23) (Optd S. £40) .. .. 16·00 32·00
c. On emerald back, **C** (3.24) .. .. 11·00 35·00
82 **11** 2s. dull purple and blue/*blue*, **C** .. 15·00 3·00
83 4s. black and carmine, **C** .. .. 25·00 42·00
84 8s. dull purple and green, **C** .. .. 45·00 55·00
85 £1 dull purple and black/*red*, **C** .. £160 £190
76/85 .. .. *Set of* 10 £225 £275
76/85 Optd "Specimen" .. .. *Set of* 10 £400

1918 (15 Apr). *Optd with T* **12** *by Beanland, Malin & Co, Gibraltar.*
86 **10** ½d. green 25 80
a. Opt double £500
Two printings of this overprint exist, the second being in slightly heavier type on a deeper shade of green.

3 PENCE THREE PENCE

(I) (II)

1921–27. *Wmk Mult Script CA. P* 14.
89 **10** ½d. green, **O** (25.4.27) 30 25
90 1d. carmine-red, **O** (2.21) .. .. 1·00 50
91 1½d. chestnut, **O** (1.12.22) 75 40
a. Pale chestnut (7.24) 75 30
93 2d. grey, **O** (17.2.21) .. .. .. 1·25 85
94 2½d. bright blue, **O** (2.21) .. .. 9·50 20·00
a. Large "2" in "½" £100 £140
95 3d. bright blue, **O** (I) (1.1.22) .. .. 2·50 4·25
a. Ultramarine .. .. 1·40 1·50
97 6d. dull purple and mauve, **C** (1.23) .. 5·50 3·75
a. Bright purple and magenta (22.7.26) 1·60 4·50
98 1s. black/*emerald*, **C** (20.6.24) .. .. 7·00 9·50
99 **11** 2s. grey-purple & blue/*blue*, **C** (20.6.24) 16·00 45·00
a. Reddish purple and blue/blue (1925) 4·75 25·00
100 4s. black and carmine, **C** (20.6.24) .. 38·00 55·00
101 8s. dull purple and green, **C** (20.6.24) .. £160 £250
89/101 .. .. *Set of* 11 £190 £300
89/101 Optd "Specimen" .. .. *Set of* 11 £400
The ½d. exists in coils constructed from normal sheets.

1925 (15 Oct)–**32.** *New values and colours changed. Wmk Mult Script CA. P* 14.
102 **10** 1s. sage-green and black, **C** (8.1.29) .. 9·00 11·00
a. Olive and black (1932) .. .. 9·00 11·00
103 **11** 2s. red-brown and black, **C** (8.1.29) .. 8·00 25·00
104 2s. 6d. green and black, **C** .. .. 7·00 15·00
105 5s. carmine and black, **C** .. .. 12·00 40·00
106 10s. deep ultramarine and black, **C** .. 32·00 48·00
107 £1 red-orange and black, **C** (16.11.27) .. £160 £180
108 £5 violet and black, **C** (Optd S. £700) £1800 £2750
102/7 .. .. *Set of* 6 £200 £275
102/7 Optd/Perf "Specimen" .. *Set of* 6 £375

1930 (12 Apr). *T* **10** *inscribed* "THREE PENCE". *Wmk Mult Script CA. P* 14.
109 3d. ultramarine (II) (Perf S. £70) .. .. 6·50 2·00

13 The Rock of Gibraltar

(Des Capt. H. St. C. Garrood. Recess D.L.R.)

1931–33. *T* **13.** *Wmk Mult Script CA.* A. *P* 14. B. *P* 13½ × 14.

		A		B	
110	1d. scarlet (1.7.31)	1·00	1·75	9·00	3·50
111	1½d. red-brown (1.7.31)	1·00	2·00	6·00	3·50
112	2d. pale grey (1.11.32)	2·75	1·00	10·00	2·25
113	3d. blue (1.6.33)	3·50	3·25	16·00	15·00
110/13	*Set of* 4	7·50	7·00	38·00	22·00
110/13 Perf "Specimen"	*Set of* 4	£150			

Figures of value take the place of both corner ornaments at the base of the 2d. and 3d.

1935 (6 May). *Silver Jubilee. As Nos.* 91/4 *of Antigua but ptd by B.W. P* 11 × 12.
114 2d. ultramarine and grey-black .. .. 1·60 2·50
a. Extra flagstaff .. .. .. 60·00
b. Short extra flagstaff .. .. .. 50·00
c. Lightning conductor .. .. .. 50·00
d. Flagstaff on right-hand turret .. .. 65·00
e. Double flagstaff .. .. .. 50·00
115 3d. brown and deep blue .. .. .. 3·25 3·50
a. Extra flagstaff £300
b. Short extra flagstaff £225
c. Lightning conductor £225
116 6d. green and indigo .. .. .. 7·00 7·00
a. Extra flagstaff £225
b. Short extra flagstaff £150
c. Lightning conductor £140
117 1s. slate and purple .. .. .. 7·00 8·50
a. Extra flagstaff £200
b. Short extra flagstaff £150
c. Lightning conductor £120
114/17 .. .. *Set of* 4 17·00 19·00
114/17 Perf "Specimen" .. *Set of* 4 £150
For illustrations of plate varieties see Omnibus section following Zululand.

1937 (12 May). *Coronation. As Nos.* 13/15 *of Aden, but ptd by B.W. P* 11 × 11½.
118 ½d. green 25 10
119 2d. grey-black 80 60
120 3d. blue .. .. 2·00 80
118/20 .. .. *Set of* 3 2·75 1·25
118/20 Perf "Specimen" .. .. *Set of* 3 70·00

14 King George VI

15 Rock of Gibraltar

16 The Rock (North Side)

(Des Captain H. St. C. Garrood. Recess D.L.R.)

1938 (25 Feb)–**51.** *Designs as T* **14/16.** *Wmk Mult Script CA.*
121 ½d. deep green (*p* 13½ × 14) 10 15
122 1d. yellow-brown (*p* 14) .. .. .. 8·00 2·25
a. Perf 13½ .. .. 8·50 2·00
ab. Perf 13½. Wmk sideways .. .. 1·75 6·00
b. Perf 13. Wmk sideways. *Red-brn* (1942) 40 55
c. Perf 13. Wmk sideways. *Deep brn* (1944) 20 3·00
d. Perf 13. *Red-brown* (1949) 35 95
123 1½d. carmine (*p* 14) .. .. .. 17·00 75
a. Perf 13½ .. .. £170 30·00
123*b* 1½d. slate-violet (*p* 13) (1.1.43) 20 60
124 2d. grey (*p* 14) .. .. .. 8·00 50
a. Perf 13½ 30 35
ab. Perf 13½. Wmk sideways .. .. £400 30·00
b. Perf 13. Wmk sideways (1943) 30 85
124*c* 2d. carmine (*p* 13) (*wmk sideways*) (15.7.44) 30 35
125 3d. light blue (*p* 13½) .. .. .. 9·00 40
a. Perf 14 .. .. 60·00 7·50
b. Perf 13 (1942) 25 30
ba. Greenish blue (2.51) .. .. .. 1·25 2·50
125*c* 5d. red-orange (*p* 13) (1.10.47) .. .. 70 1·25
126 6d. carmine and grey-violet (*p* 13½) (16.3.38) 16·00 3·00
a. Perf 14 .. .. £120 1·00
b. Perf 13 (1942) .. .. .. 1·75 1·25
c. Perf 13. *Scarlet and grey-violet* (1945) .. 3·75 2·10
127 1s. black and green (*p* 14) (16.3.38) .. 20·00 15·00
a. Perf 13½ .. .. 40·00 5·50
b. Perf 13 (1942) .. .. .. 2·50 2·00
128 2s. black and brown (*p* 14) (16.3.38) .. 50·00 25·00
a. Perf 13½ .. .. 85·00 30·00
b. Perf 13 (1942) .. .. .. 2·75 4·00
129 5s. black and carmine (*p* 14) (16.3.38) .. 65·00 90·00
a. Perf 13½ .. .. 24·00 17·00
b. Perf 13 (1944) .. .. .. 10·00 13·00
130 10s. black and blue (*p* 14) (16.3.38) .. 48·00 70·00
a. Perf 13 (1943) .. .. .. 35·00 25·00
131 £1 orange (*p* 13½ × 14) (16.3.38) .. 27·00 35·00
121/31 .. .. *Set of* 14 90·00 75·00
121/31 Perf "Specimen" .. *Set of* 14 £400
Designs:—½d., £1, Type **14.** *Horiz as T* **15/16**—1d., 1½d. (*both*), Type **15**; 2d. (*both*), Type **16**; 3d., 5d. Europa Point; 6d. Moorish Castle; 1s. Southport Gate; 2s. Eliott Memorial; 5s. Government House; 10s. Catalan Bay.
The ½d., 1d. and both colours of the 2d. exist in coils constructed from normal sheets. These were originally joined vertically, but, because of technical problems, the 1d. and 2d. grey were subsequently issued in horizontal coils. The 2d. carmine only exists in the horizontal version.

1946 (12 Oct). *Victory. As Nos.* 28/9 *of Aden.*
132 ½d. green 10 10
133 3d. ultramarine 15 20
132/3 Perf "Specimen" .. .. *Set of* 2 60·00

1948 (1 Dec). *Royal Silver Wedding. As Nos.* 30/1 *of Aden.*
134 ½d. green 50 20
135 £1 brown-orange .. .. .. 60·00 35·00

1949 (10 Oct). *75th Anniv of Universal Postal Union. As Nos.* 114/17 *of Antigua.*
136 2d. carmine .. .. 1·75 75
137 3d. deep blue .. .. 2·00 85
138 6d. purple .. .. 2·00 85
139 1s. blue-green .. .. 2·75 1·50
136/9 .. .. *Set of* 4 7·50 3·50

NEW
CONSTITUTION
1950
(23)

1950 (1 Aug). *Inauguration of Legislative Council. Nos.* 124*c*, 125*b*, 126*b and* 127*b optd as T* **23.**
140 **16** 2d. carmine 30 75
141 – 3d. light blue 30 75
142 – 6d. carmine and grey-violet 40 75
a. Opt double £425 £525
143 – 1s. black and green (R.) .. .. 40 1·25
140/3 .. .. *Set of* 4 1·25 3·25
On stamps from the lower part of the sheet of No. 142a the two impressions are almost coincident.

1953 (2 June). *Coronation. As No.* 47 *of Aden.*
144 ½d. black and bronze-green 20 15

24 Cargo and Passenger Wharves

25 Tower of Homage, Moorish Castle

26 Arms of Gibraltar

Major re-entry causing doubling of "ALTA" in "GIBRALTAR" (R. 4/6)

(Des N. Cummings. Recess (except £1, centre litho) De La Rue)

1953 (19 Oct)–**59.** *T* **24/26** *and similar designs. Wmk Mult Script CA. P* 13.
145 ½d. indigo and grey-green 15 25
146 1d. bluish green 60 25
a. Deep bluish green (31.12.57) 50 20
147 1½d. black 90 45
148 2d. deep olive-brown .. .. .. 1·00 15
a. Sepia (18.6.58) .. .. .. 1·75 35
149 2½d. carmine .. .. 1·50 25
a. Deep carmine (11.9.56) .. .. 1·50 10
150 3d. light blue .. .. 1·75 10
a. Deep greenish blue (8.6.55) .. .. 2·00 10
b. Greenish blue (18.6.58) .. .. 2·50 15
151 4d. ultramarine .. .. 1·75 90
a. Blue (17.6.59) .. .. .. 3·00 1·50
152 5d. maroon 35 50
a. Major re-entry .. .. .. 6·00
b. Deep maroon (31.12.57) .. .. 1·25 90
ba. Major re-entry .. .. .. 7·50
153 6d. black and pale blue 30 20
a. Black and blue (24.4.57) 70 30
b. Black and grey-blue (17.6.59) .. .. 1·00 60
154 1s. pale blue and red-brown 30 45
a. Pale blue and deep red-brown (27.3.56) 30 35
155 2s. orange and reddish violet .. .. 14·00 2·50
a. Orange and violet (17.6.59) .. .. 14·00 1·75
156 5s. deep brown .. .. 24·00 11·00
157 10s. reddish brown and ultramarine .. 70·00 35·00
158 £1 scarlet and orange-yellow .. .. 75·00 38·00
145/58 .. .. *Set of* 14 £160 80·00
Designs: *Horiz as T* **24**—1d. South View from Straits; 1½d. Tunney Fishing Industry; 2d. Southport Gate; 2½d. Sailing in the Bay 3d; *Saturnia* (liner); 4d. Coaling wharf; 5d. Airport; 6d. Europa Point; 1s. Straits from Buena Vista; 2s. Rosia Bay and Straits; 5s. Main Entrance, Government House.
Nos. 145/6, 148 and 150 exist in coils, constructed from normal sheets.

1954 (10 May). *Royal Visit. As No.* 150 *but inscr* "ROYAL VISIT 1954" *at top.*
159 3d. greenish blue 15 20

38 Gibraltar Candytuft

40 Rock and Badge of Gibraltar Regiment

39 Moorish Castle

(Des J. Celecia (½d., 2d., 2½d., 2s., 10s.), N. A. Langdon (1d., 3d., 6d., 7d., 9d., 1s.), M. Bonilla (4d.), L. V. Gomez (5s.), Sgt. T. A. Griffiths (£1). Recess (£1) or photo (others) D.L.R.)

1960 (29 Oct)–**62**. *Designs as T* **38/9**, *and T* **40**. *W* w **12** (*upright*). *P* 14 (£1) *or* 13 (*others*).
160 ½d. bright purple and emerald-green .. 15 30
161 1d. black and yellow-green 10 10
162 2d. indigo and orange-brown 15 10
163 2½d. black and blue 25 20
a. *Black and grey-blue* (16.10.62) .. 15 15
164 3d. deep blue and red-orange 25 10
165 4d. deep red-brown and turquoise .. 2·25 35
166 6d. sepia and emerald 70 20
167 7d. indigo and carmine-red 70 60
168 9d. grey-blue and greenish blue 50 40
169 1s. sepia and bluish green 90 25
170 2s. chocolate and ultramarine .. 8·50 1·75
171 5s. turquoise-blue and olive-brown .. 8·00 4·75
172 10s. yellow and blue .. .. 13·00 8·00
173 £1 black and brown-orange .. .. 20·00 14·00
160/73 .. .. *Set of* 14 48·00 28·00

Designs: *Horiz*—2d. St. George's Hall; 3d. The Rock by moonlight; 4d. Catalan Bay; 1s. Barbary Ape; 2s. Barbary Partridge; 5s. Blue Rock Thrush. *Vert*—2½d. The Keys; 6d. Map of Gibraltar; 7d. Air terminal; 9d. American War Memorial; 10s. Rock Lily (*Narcissus niveus*).

Nos. 160/2, 164 and 166 exist in coils, constructed from normal sheets.

See also No. 199.

1963 (4 June). *Freedom from Hunger. As No.* 76 *of Aden*.
174 9d. sepia .. .. 11·00 2·00

1963 (2 Sept). *Red Cross Centenary. As Nos.* 147/8 *of Antigua*.
175 1d. red and black 50 15
176 9d. red and blue .. .. 12·00 2·75

1964 (23 Apr). 400*th Birth Anniv of William Shakespeare. As No.* 164 *of Antigua*.
177 7d. bistre-brown 40 20

NEW CONSTITUTION 1964.

(52)

53 Bream

1964 (16 Oct). *New Constitution. Nos.* 164 *and* 166 *optd with T* **52**.
178 3d. deep blue and red-orange 15 10
179 6d. sepia and emerald 15 15
a. No stop after "1964" (R.2/5) .. .. 11·00 13·00

1965 (17 May). *I.T.U. Centenary. As Nos.* 166/7 *of Antigua*.
180 4d. light emerald and yellow .. .. 3·00 50
181 2s. apple-green and deep blue .. .. 9·00 2·50

1965 (25 Oct). *International Co-operation Year. As Nos.* 168/9 *of Antigua*.
182 ½d. deep bluish green and lavender 20 25
183 4d. reddish purple and turquoise-green .. 1·00 80

The value of the ½d. stamp is shown as "1/2".

1966 (24 Jan). *Churchill Commemoration. As Nos.* 170/3 *of Antigua*.
184 ½d. new blue 20 20
185 1d. deep green 30 10
186 4d. brown .. .. 1·50 10
187 9d. bluish violet .. .. 1·75 1·25
184/7 .. .. *Set of* 4 3·25 1·50

1966 (1 July). *World Cup Football Championships. As Nos.* 176/7 *of Antigua*.
188 2½d. violet, yellow-green, lake & yellow-brn 75 20
189 6d. chocolate, blue-green, lake & yellow-brn 1·00 50

PRINTERS. All stamps from here to No. 239 were printed in photogravure by Harrison and Sons Ltd, London.

(Des A. Ryman)

1966 (27 Aug). *European Sea Angling Championships, Gibraltar. T* **53** *and similar designs. W* w **12** (*sideways on* 1s.). *P* 13½ × 14 (1s.) *or* 14 × 13½ (*others*).
190 4d. rosine, bright blue and black 15 10
191 7d. rosine, deep olive-green and black .. 15 10
a. Black (value and inscr) omitted £550
192 1s. lake-brown, emerald and black 15 10
190/2 .. .. *Set of* 3 40 15

Designs: *Horiz*—7d. Scorpion Fish. *Vert*—1s. Stone Bass.

1966 (20 Sept). *Inauguration of W.H.O. Headquarters, Geneva. As Nos.* 178/9 *of Antigua*.
193 6d. black, yellow-green and light blue .. 2·25 1·50
194 9d. black, light purple and yellow-brown .. 2·75 1·50

56 "Our Lady of Europa"

57 H.M.S. *Victory*

(Des A. Ryman)

1966 (15 Nov). *Centenary of Re-enthronement of "Our Lady of Europa". W* w **12**. *P* 14 × 14½.
195 **56** 2s. bright blue and black 25 50

1966 (1 Dec). 20*th Anniv of U.N.E.S.C.O. As Nos.* 196/8 *of Antigua*.
196 2d. slate-violet, red, yellow and orange .. 25 10
197 7d. orange-yellow, violet and deep olive .. 60 10
198 5s. black, bright purple and orange.. .. 2·50 1·50
196/8 .. .. *Set of* 3 3·00 1·50

1966 (23 Dec). *As No.* 165 *but wmk* w **12** *sideways*.
199 4d. deep red-brown and turquoise 20 30

(Des A. Ryman)

1967 (3 Apr)–**69**. *Horiz designs as T* **57**. *Multicoloured. W* w **12**. *P* 14 × 14½.
200 ½d. Type **57** 10 15
a. Grey omitted £250
201 1d. S.S. *Arab* 10 10
202 2d. H.M.S. *Carmania* 15 10
a. Grey-blue (hull) omitted £1300
203 2½d. M.V. *Mons Calpe* 20 30
204 3d. S.S. *Canberra* 15 10
205 4d. H.M.S. *Hood* 25 10
205*a* 5d. Cable Ship *Mirror* (7.7.69) .. .. 2·25 45
206 6d. Xebec (sailing vessel) 25 20
207 7d. *Amerigo Vespucci* (training vessel) .. 25 30
208 9d. T.V. *Raffaello* 25 50
209 1s. *Royal Katherine* 25 35
210 2s. H.M.S. *Ark Royal* .. .. .. 2·25 1·50
211 5s. H.M.S. *Dreadnought* .. .. .. 3·50 4·00
212 10s. S.S. *Neuralia* .. .. 12·00 14·00
213 £1 *Mary Celeste* (sailing vessel) .. .. 12·00 16·00
200/13 .. .. *Set of* 15 30·00 35·00

The ½d., 1d., 2d., 3d., 6d., 2s., 5s. and £1 exist with PVA gum as well as gum arabic, but the 5d. exists with PVA gum only.

Nos. 201/2, 204/5 and 206 exist in coils constructed from normal sheets.

58 Aerial Ropeway

(Des A. Ryman)

1967 (15 June). *International Tourist Year. T* **58** *and similar designs but horiz. Multicoloured. W* w **12** (*sideways on* 7*d.*). *P* 14½ × 14 (7*d.*) *or* 14 × 14½ (*others*).
214 7d. Type **58** 10 10
215 9d. Shark fishing 10 10
216 1s. Skin-diving 10 10
214/16 .. .. *Set of* 3 25 15

59 Mary, Joseph and Child Jesus

60 Church Window

1967 (1 Nov). *Christmas. W* w **12** (*sideways on* 6*d.*). *P* 14.
217 **59** 2d. multicoloured 10 10
218 **60** 6d. multicoloured 10 10

61 Gen. Eliott and Route Map

62 Eliott directing Rescue Operations

(Des A. Ryman)

1967 (11 Dec). 250*th Birth Anniv of General Eliott. Multicoloured designs as T* **61** (4*d. to* 1*s.*) *or T* **62**. *W* w **12** (*sideways on horiz designs*). *P* 14 × 15 (1*s.*) *or* 15 × 14 (*others*).
219 4d. Type **61** 10 10
220 9d. Heathfield Tower and Monument, Sussex (38 × 22 *mm*) 10 10
221 1s. General Eliott (22 × 38 *mm*) 10 10
222 2s. Type **62** 30 15
219/22 .. .. *Set of* 4 45 25

65 Lord Baden-Powell

(Des A. Ryman)

1968 (27 Mar). 60*th Anniv of Gibraltar Scout Association. T* **65** *and similar horiz designs. W* w **12**. *P* 14 × 14½.
223 4d. buff and bluish violet 10 10
224 7d. ochre and blue-green 10 10
225 9d. bright blue, yellow-orange and black .. 15 10
226 1s. greenish yellow and emerald 15 10
223/6 .. .. *Set of* 4 45 25

Designs:—7d. Scout Flag over the Rock; 9d. Tent, scouts and salute; 1s. Scout badges.

66 Nurse and W.H.O. Emblem

68 King John signing Magna Carta

(Des A. Ryman)

1968 (1 July). 20*th Anniv of World Health Organization. T* **66** *and similar horiz design. W* w **12**. *P* 14 × 14½.
227 2d. ultramarine, black and yellow 10 10
228 4d. slate, black and pink 10 10

Design:—4d. Doctor and W.H.O. emblem.

(Des A. Ryman)

1968 (26 Aug). *Human Rights Year. T* **68** *and similar vert design. W* w **12** (*sideways*). *P* 13½ × 14.
229 1s. yellow-orange, brown and gold 10 10
230 2s. myrtle and gold 15 10

Design:—2s. "Freedom" and Rock of Gibraltar.

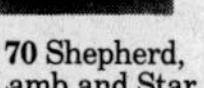

70 Shepherd, Lamb and Star

72 Parliament Houses

(Des A. Ryman)

1968 (1 Nov). *Christmas. T* **70** *and similar vert design. Multicoloured. W* w **12**. *P* 14½ × 13½.
231 4d. Type **70** 10 10
a. Gold (star) omitted .. .. ..
232 9d. Mary holding Holy Child 10 10

(Des A. Ryman)

1969 (26 May). *Commonwealth Parliamentary Association Conference. T* **72** *and similar designs. W* w **12** (*sideways on* 2*s.*). *P* 14 × 14½ (2*s.*) *or* 14½ × 14 (*others*).
233 4d. green and gold 10 10
234 9d. bluish violet and gold 10 10
235 2s. multicoloured 15 15
233/5 .. .. *Set of* 3 25 15

Designs: *Horiz*—9d. Parliamentary emblem and outline of "The Rock". *Vert*—2s. Clock Tower, Westminster (Big Ben) and arms of Gibraltar.

75 Silhouette of Rock, and Queen Elizabeth

77 Soldier and Cap Badge, Royal Anglian Regiment, 1969

(Des A. Ryman)

1969 (30 July). *New Constitution.* W w **12**. *P* 14 × 13½ (*in addition, the outline of the Rock is perforated*).

236 **75** ½d. gold and orange 10 10
237 5d. silver and bright green 10 10
a. Portrait and inscr in gold and silver*
238 7d. silver and bright purple 10 10
239 5s. gold and ultramarine 35 70
236/9 . . . . *Set of* 4 50 85

*No. 237a was first printed with the head and inscription in gold and then in silver but displaced slightly to lower left.

(Des A. Ryman. Photo D.L.R.)

1969 (6 Nov). *Military Uniforms* (1*st series*). *T* **77** *and similar vert designs. Multicoloured.* W w **12**. *P* 14.

240 1d. Royal Artillery officer, 1758 and modern cap badge 20 10
241 6d. Type **77** 55 20
242 9d. Royal Engineers' Artificer, 1786 and modern cap badge 75 30
243 2s. Private, Fox's Marines, 1704 and modern Royal Marines cap badge . . 4·00 1·60
240/3 . . . . *Set of* 4 5·00 2·00

Nos. 240/3 have a short history of the Regiment printed on the reverse side over the gum, therefore, once the gum is moistened the history disappears.

See also Nos. 248/51, 290/3, 300/3, 313/16, 331/4, 340/3 and 363/6.

80 "Madonna of the Chair" (detail, Raphael)

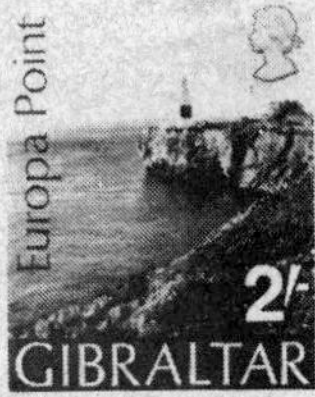

83 Europa Point

(Des A. Ryman. Photo Enschedé)

1969 (1 Dec). *Christmas. T* **80** *and similar vert designs. Multicoloured.* W w **12** (*sideways*). *P* 14 × *Roulette* 9.

244 5d. Type **80** 10 10
a. Strip of 3. Nos. 244/6 35
245 7d. "Virgin and Child" (detail, Morales) . . 15 15
246 1s. "The Virgin of the Rocks" (detail, Leonardo da Vinci) 15 20
244/6 . . . . *Set of* 3 35 40

Nos. 244/6 were issued together in *se-tenant* strips of three throughout the sheet.

(Des A. Ryman. Photo Enschedé)

1970 (8 June). *Europa Point.* W w **12**. *P* 13½.

247 **83** 2s. multicoloured 20 20

(Des A. Ryman. Photo D.L.R.)

1970 (28 Aug). *Military Uniforms* (2*nd series*). *Vert designs as T* **77**. *Multicoloured.* W w **12**. *P* 14.

248 2d. Royal Scots officer, 1839 and cap badge . . 40 10
249 5d. South Wales Borderers private, 1763 and cap badge 80 10
250 7d. Queen's Royal Regiment private, 1742 and cap badge 90 15
251 2s. Royal Irish Rangers piper, 1969 and cap badge . . . . 4·50 1·75
248/51 . . . . *Set of* 4 6·00 1·90

Nos. 248/51 have a short history of the Regiment printed on the reverse side under the gum.

88 No. 191a and Rock of Gibraltar

(Des A. Ryman. Litho D.L.R.)

1970 (18 Sept). *"Philympia 1970" Stamp Exhibition, London. T* **88** *and similar horiz design.* W w **12** (*sideways*). *P* 13.

252 1s. vermilion and bronze-green 10 10
253 2s. bright blue and magenta 15 15

Design:—2s. Victorian stamp (No. 23b) and Moorish Castle.

The stamps shown in the designs are well-known varieties with values omitted.

90 "The Virgin Mary" (stained-glass window by Gabriel Loire)

(Photo Enschedé)

1970 (1 Dec). *Christmas.* W w **12**. *P* 13 × 14.

254 **90** 2s. multicoloured 25 25

(New Currency: 100 pence = £1)

91 Saluting Battery, Rosia

92 Saluting Battery, Rosia, Modern View

(Des A. Ryman. Litho Questa)

1971 (15 Feb). *Decimal Currency. Designs as T* **91/2**. W w **12** (*sideways on horiz designs*). *P* 14.

255 ½p. multicoloured 10 10
a. Pair. Nos. 255/6 . . . . 20 20
256 ½p. multicoloured 10 10
257 1p. multicoloured 60 30
a. Pair. Nos. 257/8 . . . . 1·25 60
258 1p. multicoloured 60 30
259 1½p. multicoloured 20 15
a. Pair. Nos. 259/60 . . . . 40 30
260 1½p. multicoloured 20 15
261 2p. multicoloured . . . . . . 1·25 70
a. Pair. Nos. 261/2 . . . . 3·00 1·75
262 2p. multicoloured . . . . . . 1·25 70
263 2½p. multicoloured 20 15
a. Pair. Nos. 263/4 . . . . 40 30
264 2½p. multicoloured 20 15
265 3p. multicoloured 20 15
a. Pair. Nos. 265/6 . . . . 40 30
266 3p. multicoloured 20 15
267 4p. multicoloured . . . . . . 1·75 1·25
a. Pair. Nos. 267/8 . . . . 4·00 3·00
268 4p. multicoloured . . . . . . 1·75 1·25
269 5p. multicoloured 30 20
a. Pair. Nos. 269/70 . . . . 60 40
270 5p. multicoloured 30 20
271 7p. multicoloured 40 40
a. Pair. Nos. 271/2 . . . . 80 80
272 7p. multicoloured 40 40
273 8p. multicoloured 50 50
a. Pair. Nos. 273/4 . . . . 1·00 1·00
274 8p. multicoloured 50 50
275 9p. multicoloured 55 50
a. Pair. Nos. 275/6 . . . . 1·10 1·00
276 9p. multicoloured 55 50
277 10p. multicoloured 60 50
a. Pair. Nos. 277/8 . . . . 1·25 1·00
278 10p. multicoloured 60 50
279 12½p. multicoloured 70 75
a. Pair. Nos. 279/80 . . . . 1·40 1·50
280 12½p. multicoloured 70 75
281 25p. multicoloured . . . . . . 1·25 1·25
a. Pair. Nos. 281/2 . . . . 2·50 2·50
282 25p. multicoloured . . . . . . 1·25 1·25
283 50p. multicoloured . . . . . . 1·40 2·00
a. Pair. Nos. 283/4 . . . . 2·75 4·00
284 50p. multicoloured . . . . . . 1·40 2·00
285 £1 multicoloured . . . . . . 2·50 4·00
a. Pair. Nos. 285/6 . . . . 5·00 8·00
286 £1 multicoloured . . . . . . 2·50 4·00
255/86 . . . . *Set of* 32 23·00 24·00

Designs (the two versions of each value show the same Gibraltar view taken from an early 19th-century print (first design) or modern photograph (second design): *Horiz*—1p. Prince George of Cambridge Quarters and Trinity Church; 1½p. The Wellington Bust, Alameda Gardens; 2p. Gibraltar from the North Bastion; 2½p. Catalan Bay; 3p. Convent Garden; 4p. The Exchange and Spanish Chapel; 5p. Commercial Square and Library; 7p. South Barracks and Rosia Magazine; 8p. Moorish Mosque and Castle; 9p. Europa Pass Road; 10p. South Barracks from Rosia Bay; 12½p. Southport Gates; 25p. Trooping the Colour, The Alameda. *Vert*—50p. Europa Pass Gorge; £1 Prince Edward's Gate.

The two designs of each value were printed together, *se-tenant*, in horizontal and vertical pairs throughout.

See also Nos. 317/20 and 344/5.

93

94 Regimental Arms

(Des A. Ryman. Photo Harrison)

1971 (15 Feb). *Coil Stamps.* W w **12**. *P* 14½ × 14.

287 **93** ½p. red-orange 15 25
a. Coil strip (287 × 2, 288 × 2 and 289 *se-tenant*) . . . . . . 1·25
288 1p. blue 15 25
289 2p. bright green . . . . . . 65 1·10
287/9 . . . . *Set of* 3 90 1·50

(Des A. Ryman. Litho Questa)

1971 (6 Sept). *Military Uniforms* (3*rd series*). *Multicoloured designs as T* **77**, *showing uniform and cap-badge.* W w **12**. *P* 14.

290 1p. The Black Watch (1845) 45 20
291 2p. Royal Regt of Fusiliers (1971) 85 30
292 4p. King's Own Royal Border Regt (1704) . . 1·75 70
293 10p. Devonshire and Dorset Regt (1801) . . 5·00 2·50
290/3 . . . . *Set of* 4 7·50 3·25

Nos. 290/3 have a short history of the Regiment printed on the reverse side under the gum.

(Des A. Ryman. Litho Harrison)

1971 (25 Sept). *Presentation of Colours to the Gibraltar Regiment.* W w **12** (*sideways*). *P* 12½ × 12.

294 **94** 3p. black, gold and red 20 20

95 Nativity Scene

96 Soldier Artificer, 1773

(Des A. Ryman. Photo Enschedé)

1971 (1 Dec). *Christmas. T* **95** *and similar horiz design. Multicoloured.* W w **12**. *P* 13 × 13½.

295 3p. Type **95** 30 30
296 5p. Mary and Joseph going to Bethlehem . . 35 35

(Des A. Ryman. Litho Questa)

1972 (6 Mar). *Bicentenary of Royal Engineers in Gibraltar. T* **96** *and similar multicoloured designs.* W w **12** (*sideways on* 1 *and* 3*p.*). *P* 13½ × 14 (5*p.*) *or* 14 × 13½ (*others*).

297 1p. Type **96** 40 20
298 3p. Modern tunneller 60 50
299 5p. Old and new uniforms and badge (*horiz*) 75 65
297/9 . . . . *Set of* 3 1·60 1·25

(Des A. Ryman. Litho Questa)

1972 (19 July). *Military Uniforms* (4*th series*). *Multicoloured designs as T* **77**. W w **12** (*sideways*). *P* 14.

300 1p. Duke of Cornwall's Light Infantry, 1704 45 20
301 3p. King's Royal Rifle Corps, 1830 . . 1·50 50
302 7p. Officer, 37th North Hampshire, 1825 . . 2·50 1·25
303 10p. Royal Navy, 1972 . . . . . . 3·00 2·00
300/3 . . . . *Set of* 4 6·75 3·50

Nos. 300/303 have a short history of the Regiment printed on the reverse side under the gum.

97 "Our Lady of Europa"

98 Keys of Gibraltar and *Narcissus niveus*

(Des A. Ryman. Litho Harrison)

1972 (4 Oct). *Christmas.* W w **12** (*sideways*). *P* 14½ × 14.

304 **97** 3p. multicoloured 10 10
305 5p. multicoloured 10 20

These stamps have an inscription printed on the reverse side.

(Des (from photograph by D. Groves) and photo Harrison)

1972 (20 Nov). *Royal Silver Wedding. Multicoloured; background colour given.* W w **12**. *P* 14 × 14½.

306 **98** 5p. carmine-red 20 20
307 7p. deep grey-green 20 20

99 Flags of Member Nations and E.E.C. Symbol

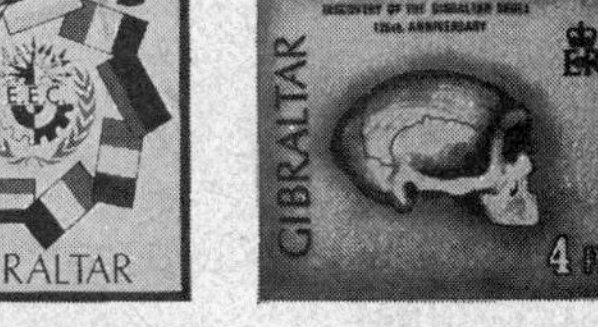

100 Skull

(Des A. Ryman. Litho Questa)

1973 (22 Feb). *Britain's Entry into E.E.C.* W w **12** (*sideways*). *P* 14½ × 14.

308 **99** 5p. multicoloured 30 30
309 10p. multicoloured 55 50

(Des A. Ryman. Litho B.W.)

1973 (22 May). *125th Anniv of Gibraltar Skull Discovery. T* **100** *and similar horiz designs. Multicoloured. W* w **12**. *P* 13 (10p.) *or* 13½ (*others*).

310	4p. Type **100**	80	50
311	6p. Prehistoric man	1·00	70
312	10p. Prehistoric family (40 × 26 *mm*)	1·50	1·25
310/12	*Set of* 3	3·00	2·25

(Des A. Ryman. Litho Questa)

1973 (22 Aug). *Military Uniforms* (5*th series*). *Multicoloured designs as T* **77**. *W* w **12** (*sideways*). *P* 14.

313	1p. King's Own Scottish Borderers, 1770	40	20
314	4p. Royal Welch Fusiliers, 1800	1·25	1·00
315	6p. Royal Northumberland Fusiliers, 1736	2·00	1·50
316	10p. Grenadier Guards, 1898	3·00	2·50
313/16	*Set of* 4	6·00	4·75

Nos. 313/16 have a short history of the Regiment printed on the reverse side under the gum.

1973 (12 Sept). *As Nos.* 261/2 *and* 267/8 *but W* w **12** *upright*.

317	2p. multicoloured	50	75
	a. Pair. Nos. 317/18	1·00	1·50
318	2p. multicoloured	50	75
319	4p. multicoloured	75	1·00
	a. Pair. Nos. 319/20	1·50	2·00
320	4p. multicoloured	75	1·00
317/20	*Set of* 4	2·50	3·25

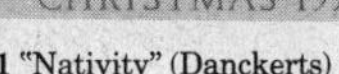

101 "Nativity" (Danckerts) **102** Victorian Pillar-box

(Des and litho Enschedé)

1973 (17 Oct). *Christmas. W* w **12**. *P* 12½ × 12.

321 **101**	4p. violet and Venetian red	20	15
322	6p. magenta and turquoise-blue	30	35

1973 (14 Nov). *Royal Wedding. As Nos.* 165/6 *of Anguilla. Centre multicoloured. W* w **12** (*sideways*). *P* 13½.

323	6p. turquoise	10	10
324	14p. yellow-green	20	20

(Des A. Ryman. Litho Walsall)

1974 (2 May). *Centenary of Universal Postal Union. T* **102** *and similar vert designs. Multicoloured.* (a) *W* w **12** (*sideways*). *P* 14½.

325	2p. Type **102**	15	20
326	6p. Pillar-box of George VI	25	30
327	14p. Pillar-box of Elizabeth II	40	65
325/7	*Set of* 3	70	1·00

(*b*) *No wmk. Imperf* × *roul* 5*. *Self-adhesive* (*from booklets*)

328	2p. Type **102**	25	70
	a. Booklet pane Nos. 328/30 *se-tenant*	4·50	
	b. Booklet pane Nos. 328 × 3 and 329 × 3	2·00	
329	6p. As No. 326	45	1·00
330	14p. As No. 327	4·25	6·00
328/30	*Set of* 3	4·50	7·00

*Nos. 328/30 were separated by various combinations of rotary-knife (giving a straight edge) and roulette.

(Des A. Ryman. Litho Questa)

1974 (21 Aug). *Military Uniforms* (6*th series*). *Multicoloured designs as T* **77**. *W* w **12** (*sideways*). *P* 14.

331	4p. East Lancashire Regt, 1742	50	50
332	6p. Somerset Light Infantry, 1833	70	70
333	10p. Royal Sussex Regt, 1790	1·00	1·25
334	16p. R.A.F. officer, 1974	2·25	2·50
331/4	*Set of* 4	4·00	4·50

Nos. 331/4 have a short history of the regiment printed on the reverse side under the gum.

103 "Madonna with the Green Cushion" (Solario) **104** Churchill and Houses of Parliament

(Des A. Ryman and M. Infante. Litho Questa)

1974 (5 Nov). *Christmas. T* **103** *and similar vert design. Multicoloured. W* w **14**. *P* 14.

335	4p. Type **103**	40	30
336	6p. "Madonna of the Meadow" (Bellini)	60	60

(Des L. Curtis. Litho Harrison)

1974 (30 Nov). *Birth Centenary of Sir Winston Churchill. T* **104** *and similar horiz design. W* w **12**. *P* 14 × 14½.

337	6p. black, reddish purple and light lavender	25	15
338	20p. brownish black, lake-brown and light orange-red	50	50
MS339	114 × 93 mm. Nos. 337/8. W w **12** (sideways). P 14	2·50	3·00

Design:—20p. Churchill and *King George V* (battleship).

(Des A. Ryman. Litho Questa)

1975 (14 Mar). *Military Uniforms* (7*th series*). *Multicoloured designs as T* **77**. *W* w **14**. *P* 14.

340	4p. East Surrey Regt, 1846	30	30
341	6p. Highland Light Infantry, 1777	50	50
342	10p. Coldstream Guards, 1704	70	80
343	20p. Gibraltar Regt, 1974	1·25	1·50
340/3	*Set of* 4	2·40	2·75

Nos. 340/3 have a short history of each regiment printed on the reverse side under the gum.

1975 (9 July). *As Nos.* 257/8 *but W* w **14** (*sideways*).

344	1p. multicoloured	65	80
	a. Pair. Nos. 344/5	1·25	1·40
345	1p. multicoloured	65	80

105 Girl Guides' Badge **106** Child at Prayer

(Des A. Ryman. Litho Harrison)

1975 (10 Oct). *50th Anniv of Gibraltar Girl Guides. W* w **12**. *P* 13 × 13½.

346 **105**	5p. gold, light blue and dull violet	30	40
347	7p. gold, sepia and light lake-brown	40	50
348 –	15p. silver, brownish black & yell-brn	65	85
	a. Silver omitted	†	—
346/8	*Set of* 3	1·25	1·60

No. 348 is a T **105** but shows a different badge.

(Des A. Ryman. Litho Walsall)

1975 (26 Nov). *Christmas. T* **106** *and similar vert designs. Multicoloured. W* w **14** (*sideways*). *P* 14.

349	6p. Type **106**	40	40
	a. Block of 6. Nos. 349/54	2·10	
350	6p. Angel with lute	40	40
351	6p. Child singing carols	40	40
352	6p. Three children	40	40
353	6p. Girl at prayer	40	40
354	6p. Boy and lamb	40	40
349/54	*Set of* 6	2·10	2·10

Nos. 349/54 were issued together *se-tenant* in small sheets of six (3 × 2) with the usual plate numbers and marginal inscriptions.

107 Bruges Madonna **108** Bicentennial Emblem and Arms of Gibraltar

(Des Jennifer Toombs. Litho Walsall)

1975 (17 Dec). *500th Birth Anniv of Michelangelo. T* **107** *and similar vert designs. Multicoloured.* (a) *W* w **14** (*sideways*). *P* 14.

355	6p. Type **107**	15	20
356	9p. Taddei Madonna	20	30
357	15p. Pietà	30	55
355/7	*Set of* 3	60	95

(*b*) *No wmk. Imperf* × *roul* 5*. *Self-adhesive* (*from booklets*)

358	6p. Type **107**	25	25
	a. Booklet pane Nos. 358/60 *se-tenant*	1·25	
	b. Booklet pane Nos. 358 × 2, 359 × 2 and 360 × 2	2·50	
359	9p. As No. 356	40	40
360	15p. As No. 357	70	70
358/60	*Set of* 3	1·25	1·25

*Nos. 358/60 were separated by various combinations of rotary knife (giving a straight edge) and roulette.

(Des A. Ryman. Litho Walsall)

1976 (28 May). *Bicentenary of American Revolution. W* w **14** (*inverted*). *P* 14.

361 **108**	25p. multicoloured	50	50
MS362	85 × 133 mm. No. 361 × 4	5·00	5·50

The edges of **MS**362 are rouletted.

(Des A. Ryman. Litho Walsall)

1976 (21 July). *Military Uniforms* (8*th series*). *Multicoloured designs as T* **77**. *W* w **14** (*inverted*). *P* 14.

363	1p. Suffolk Regt, 1795	15	15
364	6p. Northamptonshire Regt, 1779	30	30
365	12p. Lancashire Fusiliers, 1793	55	55
366	25p. Ordnance Corps, 1896	1·10	1·10
363/6	*Set of* 4	1·90	1·90

Nos. 363/6 have a short history of each regiment printed on the reverse side under the gum.

109 The Holy Family **110** Queen Elizabeth II, Royal Arms and Gibraltar Arms

(Des A. Ryman. Litho Questa)

1976 (3 Nov). *Christmas. T* **109** *and similar vert designs showing stained-glass windows in St. Joseph's Church, Gibraltar. Multicoloured. W* w **14**. *P* 14.

367	6p. Type **109**	20	15
368	9p. Madonna and Child	25	25
369	12p. St. Bernard	40	45
370	20p. Archangel Michael	60	80
367/70	*Set of* 4	1·25	1·50

(Des A. Ryman. Litho J.W.)

1977 (7 Feb). *Silver Jubilee. W* w **14**. *P* 13½.

371 **110**	6p. multicoloured	25	20
372	£1 multicoloured	1·75	2·25
MS373	124 × 115 mm. Nos. 371/2. P 13	2·40	3·00

The outer edges of the miniature sheet are either guillotined or rouletted.

111 Toothed Orchid (*Orchis tridentata*)

(Des A. Ryman. Litho Questa)

1977 (1 Apr)–**82**. *Multicoloured designs as T* **111**. *W* w **14** (*sideways on horiz designs; inverted on £5*). *Chalk-surfaced paper* (15*p*., £5). *P* 14.

374	½p. Type **111**	10	20
	a. Chalk-surfaced paper (22.2.82)	40	60
375	1p. Red Mullet (*Mullus surmuletus*) (*horiz*)	10	10
376	2p. Large Blue butterfly (*Maculinea arion*) (*horiz*)	30	25
377	2½p. Sardinian Warbler (*Sylvia melanocephala*)	40	25
378	3p. Giant Squill (*Scilla peruviana*)	20	10
379	4p. Grey Wrasse (*Crenilabrus cinereus*) (*horiz*)	25	10
	b. Chalk-surfaced paper (21.4.81)	55	20
380	5p. Red Admiral butterfly (*Vanessa atalanta*) (*horiz*)	45	35
381	6p. Black Kite (*Milvus migrans*)	45	20
382	9p. Shrubby Scorpion-vetch (*Coronilla valentina*)	90	70
383	10p. John Dory (fish) (*Zeus faber*) (*horiz*)	40	20
	a. Chalk-surfaced paper (21.4.81)	70	35
384	12p. Clouded Yellow butterfly (*Colias crocea*) (*horiz*)	1·00	25
	a. Chalk-surfaced paper (21.4.81)	2·00	75
384*b*	15p. Winged Asparagus Pea (*Tetragonolobus purpureus*) (12.11.80)	1·75	40
385	20p. Audouin's Gull (*Larus audouinii*)	1·25	75
386	25p. Barbary Nut (iris) (*Iris sisyrinchium*)	1·25	80
	a. Chalk-surfaced paper (21.4.81)	1·75	1·00
387	50p. Swordfish (*Xiphias gladius*) (*horiz*)	2·00	95
	a. Chalk-surfaced paper (21.4.81)	3·00	2·25
388	£1 Swallow-tail butterfly (*Papilio machaon*) (*horiz*)	4·75	3·25
389	£2 Hoopoe (*Upupa epops*)	7·50	8·50
389*a*	£5 Arms of Gibraltar (16.5.79)	10·00	10·00
374/89*a*	*Set of* 18	28·00	24·00

The ½p. to £2 values have a descriptive text printed on the reverse, beneath the gum.

The 9p. from the above issue exists with different dates in the imprint below the design.

112 "Our Lady of Europa" Stamp

(Des J. Cooter. Litho Questa)

1977 (27 May). *"Amphilex 77" Stamp Exhibition, Amsterdam.* T **112** *and similar vert designs. Multicoloured.* W w **14** (*sideways on* 6p.; *inverted on* 12p.). P 13½.

390	6p. Type 112	10	20
391	12p. "Europa Point" stamp	20	30
392	25p. "E.E.C. Entry" stamp	30	50
390/2	*Set of* 3	55	90

113 "The Annunciation" (Rubens)

114 Aerial View of Gibraltar

(Des A. Ryman. Litho Enschedé)

1977 (2 Nov). *Christmas and Rubens' 400th Birth Anniv.* T **113** *and similar multicoloured designs.* W w **14** (*sideways on* 12p.). P 13½.

393	3p. Type 113	10	10
394	9p. "The Adoration of the Magi"	20	20
395	12p. "The Adoration of the Magi" (*horiz*)	25	30
396	15p. "The Holy Family under the Apple Tree"	30	40
393/6	*Set of* 4	75	85
MS397	110 × 200 mm. Nos. 393/6 (wmk upright)	1·25	1·75

(Des A. Ryman. Litho Enschedé)

1978 (3 May). *Gibraltar from Space.* P 13½.

398 **114**	12p. multicoloured	25	40
	a. Horiz pair imperf 3 sides		
MS399	148×108 mm. 25p. multicoloured	60	80

Design:—25p. Aerial view of Straits of Gibraltar.

No. 398a occurs on the bottom pair from two sheets of 10 (2×5) and shows the stamps perforated at top only.

115 Holyroodhouse

(Des and litho Walsall)

1978 (12 June). *25th Anniv of Coronation.* T **115** *and similar horiz designs. Multicoloured.* (a) *From sheets.* P 13½ × 14.

400	6p. Type 115	20	15
401	9p. St. James's Palace	25	15
402	12p. Sandringham	30	25
403	18p. Balmoral	40	40
400/3	*Set of* 4	1·00	85
	(b) *From booklets. Imperf × roul 5*. Self-adhesive*		
404	12p. As No. 402	35	60
	a. Booklet pane. Nos. 404/5, each × 3	2·00	
405	18p. As No. 403	40	75
406	25p. Windsor Castle	70	1·10
	a. Booklet pane of 1	70	
404/6	*Set of* 3	1·25	2·25

*Nos. 404/5 were separated by various combinations of rotary-knife (giving a straight edge) and roulette. No. 406 exists only with straight edges.

116 "Sunderland", 1938–58

117 "Madonna with Animals"

(Des A. Theobald. Litho Harrison)

1978 (6 Sept). *60th Anniv of Royal Air Force.* T **116** *and similar horiz designs. Multicoloured.* W w **14** (*sideways*). P 14.

407	3p. Type 116	15	10
408	9p. "Caudron", 1918	35	35
409	12p. "Shackleton", 1953–66	40	40
410	16p. "Hunter", 1954–77	45	50
411	18p. "Nimrod", 1969–78	50	60
407/11	*Set of* 5	1·75	1·75

(Des A. Ryman. Litho Questa)

1978 (1 Nov). *Christmas. Paintings by Dürer.* T **117** *and similar vert designs. Multicoloured.* W w **14**. P 14.

412	5p. Type 117	10	10
413	9p. "The Nativity"	15	15
414	12p. "Madonna of the Goldfinch"	20	25
415	15p. "Adoration of the Magi"	30	40
412/15	*Set of* 4	65	80

118 Sir Rowland Hill and 1d. Stamp of 1886

(Des A. Ryman. Litho Format)

1979 (7 Feb). *Death Centenary of Sir Rowland Hill.* T **118** *and similar horiz designs.* W w **14** (*sideways*). P 13½ × 14.

416	3p. multicoloured	15	10
417	9p. multicoloured	30	15
418	12p. multicoloured	35	20
419	25p. black, dull claret and yellow	50	50
416/19	*Set of* 4	1·10	80

Designs:—9p. Sir Rowland Hill and 1p. coil stamp of 1971; 12p. Sir Rowland Hill and Post Office Regulations document, 1840; 25p. Sir Rowland Hill and "G" cancellation.

119 Posthorn, Dish Antenna and Early Telephone

120 African Child

(Des A. Ryman. Litho Format)

1979 (16 May). *Europa. Communications.* W w **14** (*sideways*). P 13½.

420	**119**	3p. green and pale green	15	10
421		9p. lake-brown and ochre	55	80
422		12p. ultramarine and dull violet-blue	70	1·00
420/2		*Set of* 3	1·25	1·75

(Des G. Hutchins. Litho Walsall)

1979 (14 Nov). *Christmas. International Year of the Child.* T **120** *and similar vert designs. Multicoloured.* W w **14** (*sideways*). P 14.

423	12p. Type 120	25	30
	a. Block of 6. Nos. 423/8	1·40	
424	12p. Asian child	25	30
425	12p. Polynesian child	25	30
426	12p. American Indian child	25	30
427	12p. Children of different races and Nativity scene	25	30
428	12p. European child	25	30
423/8	*Set of* 6	1·40	1·60

Nos. 423/8 were printed together, *se-tenant*, in blocks of 6, with margin separating the two blocks in each sheet.

121 Early Policemen

122 Peter Amigo (Archbishop)

(Des C. Abbott. Litho Questa)

1980 (5 Feb). *150th Anniv of Gibraltar Police Force.* T **121** *and similar horiz designs. Multicoloured.* W w **14** (*sideways*). P 14.

429	3p. Type 121	15	10
430	6p. Policemen of 1895, early 1900s and 1980	15	15
431	12p. Policeman and police ambulance	20	20
432	37p. Policewoman and police motor-cyclist	55	80
429/32	*Set of* 4	95	1·10

(Des A. Ryman. Litho Questa)

1980 (6 May). *Europa. Personalities.* T **122** *and similar vert designs. Multicoloured.* W w **14** (*inverted on No.* 434). P 14½ × 14.

433	12p. Type 122	20	25
434	12p. Gustavo Bacarisas (artist)	20	25
435	12p. John Mackintosh (philanthropist)	20	25
433/5	*Set of* 3	55	70

123 Queen Elizabeth the Queen Mother

124 "Horatio Nelson" (J. F. Rigaud)

(Des Harrison. Litho Questa)

1980 (4 Aug). *80th Birthday of Queen Elizabeth the Queen Mother.* W w **14** (*sideways*). P 14.

436	**123**	15p. multicoloured	25	25

(Des BG Studio. Litho Questa)

1980 (20 Aug). *175th Death Anniv of Nelson. Paintings.* T **124** *and similar multicoloured designs.* W w **14** (*sideways on* 9 *and* 40p.). P 14.

437	3p. Type 124	15	10
438	9p. "H.M.S. *Victory*" (*horiz*)	25	25
439	15p. "Horatio Nelson" (Sir William Beechey)	35	35
440	40p. "H.M.S. *Victory* being towed into Gibraltar" (Clarkson Stanfield) (*horiz*)	80	1·00
437/40	*Set of* 4	1·40	1·50
MS441	159 × 99 mm. No. 439	75	1·00

125 Three Kings

126 Hercules creating Mediterranean Sea

(Des A. Ryman. Litho Questa)

1980 (12 Nov). *Christmas.* T **125** *and similar horiz design, each in deep brown and orange-yellow.* W w **14** (*sideways*). P 14½.

442	15p. Type 125	25	35
	a. Horiz pair. Nos. 442/3	50	70
443	15p. Nativity scene	25	35

Nos. 442/3 were printed together, *se-tenant*, in horizontal pairs throughout the sheet.

(Des G. Vasarhelyi. Litho Enschedé)

1981 (24 Feb). *Europa. Folklore.* T **126** *and similar vert design. Multicoloured.* W w **14**. P 13½ × 13.

444	9p. Type 126	20	15
445	15p. Hercules and Pillars of Hercules (Straits of Gibraltar)	25	35

127 Dining-room

128 Prince Charles and Lady Diana Spencer

(Des A. Ryman. Litho Harrison)

1981 (22 May). *450th Anniv of The Convent (Governor's Residence).* T **127** *and similar square designs. Multicoloured.* W w **14** (*sideways*). P 14½ × 14.

446	4p. Type 127	10	10
447	14p. King's Chapel	20	20
448	15p. The Convent	20	20
449	55p. Cloister	85	1·10
446/9	*Set of* 4	1·10	1·40

(Des A. Ryman. Litho Questa)

1981 (27 July). *Royal Wedding.* W w **14** (*sideways*). P 14½.

450	**128**	£1 multicoloured	1·50	1·75

129

130 Paper Aeroplane

(Des A. Ryman. Litho Questa)

1981 (2 Sept). *Booklet stamps.* W w **14** (*sideways*). P 13½ × 14.

451	**129**	1p. black	10	10
		a. Booklet pane. Nos. 451/2 and 453 × 3 plus printed label	90	
		b. Booklet pane. Nos. 451/2 × 2 and 453 × 6 plus two printed labels	1·75	
452		4p. Prussian blue	10	10
453		15p. light green	25	30
451/3		*Set of* 3	35	45

(Des A. Ryman. Litho Walsall)

1981 (29 Sept*). *50th Anniv of Gibraltar Airmail Service.* T **130** *and similar horiz designs. Multicoloured.* W w **14** (*sideways*). P 14½ × 14.

454	14p. Type 130	20	20
455	15p. Airmail letters, post box and aircraft tail fin	20	20
456	55p. Aircraft circling globe	80	90
454/6	*Set of* 3	1·10	1·10

*This is the local release date. The Crown Agents released the stamps on 21 September.

131 Carol Singers **132** I.Y.D.P. Emblem and Stylised Faces

(Des Clive Torres (15p.); Peter Parody (55p.); adapted G. Vasarhelyi. Litho Questa)

1981 (19 Nov). *Christmas. Children's Drawings. T* **131** *and similar multicoloured design.* W w **14** (*sideways on 15p.*). *P* 14.
457 15p. Type 131 .. .. 30 15
458 55p. Postbox (*vert*) .. .. 1·00 85

(Des A. Ryman. Litho Questa)

1981 (19 Nov). *International Year For Disabled Persons.* W w **14** (*sideways*). *P* 14 × 14½.
459 **132** 14p. multicoloured 30 30

133 Douglas "DC 3" **134** Crest, H.M.S. *Opossum*

(Des A. Theobald. Litho J.W.)

1982 (10 Feb). *Aircraft. Horiz designs as T* **133**. *Multicoloured.* W w **14**. *P* 14.
460 1p. Type 133 .. .. 15 15
461 2p. Vickers "Viking" 15 15
462 3p. Airspeed "Ambassador" 20 15
463 4p. Vickers "Viscount" 30 10
464 5p. Boeing "727" 30 10
465 10p. Vickers "Vanguard" 45 25
466 14p. Short "Solent" 60 40
467 15p. Fokker "F.27 (Friendship)" 60 30
468 17p. Boeing "737" 75 35
469 20p. BAC "One-eleven" 60 40
470 25p. Lockheed "Constellation" 85 70
471 50p. De Havilland "Comet 4B" .. .. 1·75 1·25
472 £1 Saro "Windhover" .. .. .. 3·00 1·90
473 £2 Hawker Siddeley "Trident 2" .. .. 4·00 4·25
474 £5 D.H. "89A (Dragon Rapide)" .. .. 9·00 12·00
460/74 .. .. *Set of* 15 20·00 20·00

No. 469 exists with two different imprint dates.

For 2p. and 5p. values watermarked w **16** see Nos. 549 and 552.

(Des A. Ryman. Litho Questa)

1982 (14 Apr). *Naval Crests* (*1st series*). *T* **134** *and similar vert designs. Multicoloured.* W w **14**. *P* 14.
475 ½p. Type 134 .. .. 10 10
476 15½p. H.M.S. *Norfolk* 45 50
477 17p. H.M.S. *Fearless* 50 55
478 60p. H.M.S. *Rooke* .. .. .. 1·25 1·60
475/8 .. .. *Set of* 4 2·10 2·40

See also Nos. 493/6, 510/13, 522/5, 541/4, 565/8, 592/5 and 616/19.

135 "Spitfires" at Gibraltar **136** Gibraltar Chamber of Commerce Centenary

(Des A. Ryman. Litho Questa)

1982 (11 June). *Europa. Operation Torch. T* **135** *and similar horiz design. Multicoloured.* W w **14** (*sideways*). *P* 14.
479 14p. Type 135 .. .. 25 40
480 17p. General Giraud, General Eisenhower and Gibraltar 35 45

(Des A. Ryman. Litho Questa)

1982 (22 Sept). *Anniversaries. T* **136** *and similar vert designs. Multicoloured.* W w **14** (*sideways*). *P* 14½.
481 ½p. Type 136 .. .. 10 10
482 15½p. British Forces Postal Service centenary 30 25
483 60p. 75th anniv of Gibraltar Scout Association .. .. 1·10 1·25
481/3 .. .. *Set of* 3 1·25 1·40

NEW INFORMATION

The editor is always interested to correspond with people who have new information that will improve or correct the Catalogue.

137 Printed Circuit forming Map of World

(Des A. Ryman. Litho Harrison)

1982 (1 Oct). *International Direct Dialling.* W w **14** (*sideways*). *P* 14½.
484 **137** 17p. black, pale blue and bright orange 35 35

138 Gibraltar illuminated at Night and Holly

(Des A. Ryman. Litho Questa)

1982 (18 Nov). *Christmas. T* **138** *and similar horiz design. Multicoloured.* W w **14** (*sideways*). *P* 14 × 14½.
485 14p. Type 138 .. .. 30 30
486 17p. Gibraltar illuminated at night and Mistletoe 35 35

139 Yacht Marina

(Des Olympia Reyes. Litho Questa)

1983 (14 Mar). *Commonwealth Day. T* **139** *and similar multicoloured designs.* W w **14** (*sideways on* 4, 14p.). *P* 14.
487 4p. Type 139 .. .. 10 10
488 14p. Scouts and Guides Commonwealth Day Parade 30 35
489 17p. Flag of Gibraltar (*vert*) 35 40
490 60p. Queen Elizabeth II (from photo by Tim Graham) (*vert*) .. .. .. 1·25 1·40
487/90 .. .. *Set of* 4 1·75 2·00

140 St George's Hall Gallery

(Des A. Ryman. Litho Harrison)

1983 (21 May). *Europa. T* **140** *and similar horiz design.* W w **14** (*sideways*). *P* 13½ × 13.
491 16p. black and brown-ochre 30 35
492 19p. black and pale blue 40 40

Design:—19p. Water catchment slope.

(Des A. Ryman. Litho Questa)

1983 (1 July). *Naval Crests* (*2nd series*). *Vert designs as T* **134**. *Multicoloured.* W w **14**. *P* 14.
493 4p. H.M.S. *Faulknor* 10 10
494 14p. H.M.S. *Renown* 30 35
495 17p. H.M.S. *Ark Royal* 35 40
496 60p. H.M.S. *Sheffield* .. .. 1·25 1·50
493/6 .. .. *Set of* 4 1·75 2·10

141 Landport Gate, 1729

(Des Olympia Reyes. Litho Enschedé)

1983 (13 Sept). *Fortress Gibraltar in the 18th Century. T* **141** *and similar horiz designs. Multicoloured.* W w **14** (*sideways*). *P* 13 × 13½.
497 4p. Type 141 .. .. 10 10
498 17p. Koehler Gun, 1782 .. .. 35 45
499 77p. King's Bastion, 1779 .. .. .. 1·50 1·75
497/9 .. .. *Set of* 3 1·75 2·00
MS500 97 × 145 mm. Nos. 497/9 .. .. .. 1·90 2·25

142 "Adoration of the Magi" (Raphael) **143** 1932 2d. Stamp and Globe

(Des A. Ryman. Litho Questa)

1983 (17 Nov). *Christmas. 500th Birth Anniv of Raphael. T* **142** *and similar multicoloured designs.* W w **14** (*sideways on* 4p.). *P* 14.
501 4p. Type 142 .. .. 15 10
502 17p. "Madonna of Foligno" (*vert*) 45 35
503 60p. "Sistine Madonna" (*vert*) .. .. .. 1·40 1·40
501/3 .. .. *Set of* 3 1·75 1·60

(Des E. Field. Litho Walsall)

1984 (6 Mar). *Europa. Posts and Telecommunications. T* **143** *and similar vert design. Multicoloured.* W w **14**. *P* 14½ × 14.
504 17p. Type 143 .. .. 35 40
505 23p. Circuit board and globe 45 50

144 Hockey **145** Mississippi River Boat Float

(Des A. Ryman. Litho Walsall)

1984 (25 May). *Sports. T* **144** *and similar horiz designs. Multicoloured.* W w **14** (*sideways*). *P* 14 × 14½.
506 20p. Type 144 .. .. 40 45
507 21p. Basketball 40 45
508 26p. Rowing 55 60
509 29p. Football 60 65
506/9 .. .. *Set of* 4 1·75 2·00

(Des A. Ryman. Litho Walsall)

1984 (21 Sept). *Naval Crests* (*3rd series*). *Vert designs as T* **134**. *Multicoloured.* W w **14**. *P* 13½ × 13.
510 20p. H.M.S. *Active* 70 60
511 21p. H.M.S. *Foxhound* 70 60
512 26p. H.M.S. *Valiant* 85 80
513 29p. H.M.S. *Hood* .. .. 95 1·10
510/13 .. .. *Set of* 4 3·00 2·75

(Des A. Ryman. Litho Questa)

1984 (7 Nov). *Christmas. Epiphany Floats. T* **145** *and similar horiz design. Multicoloured.* W w **14** (*sideways*). *P* 14 × 14½.
514 20p. Type 145 .. .. 40 45
515 80p. Roman Temple float .. .. .. 1·60 1·75

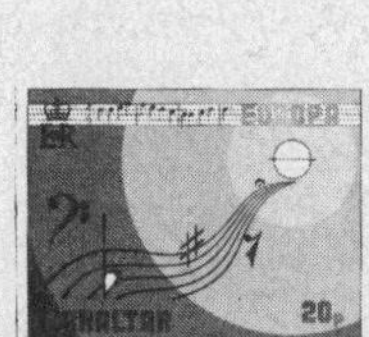

146 Musical Symbols, and Score from Beethoven's 9th (Choral) Symphony **147** Globe and Stop Polio Campaign Logo

(Des Olympia Reyes. Photo Courvoisier)

1985 (26 Feb). *Europa. European Music Year. T* **146** *and similar horiz design. Multicoloured. Granite paper. P* 12½.
516 **146** 20p. multicoloured 40 45
517 – 29p. multicoloured 60 65

The 29p. is as T **146** but shows different symbols.

(Des E. Field. Litho J.W.)

1985 (3 May). *Stop Polio Campaign. Vert designs as T* **147**. *Multicoloured.* W w **14** (*inverted*). *P* 13 × 13½.
518 26p. multicoloured (Type **147**) 50 55
a. Horiz strip of 4. Nos. 518/21 .. 1·75
519 26p. multicoloured ("ST" visible) 50 55
520 26p. multicoloured ("STO" visible) 50 55
521 26p. multicoloured ("STOP" visible) .. 50 55
518/21 .. .. *Set of* 4 1·75 2·00

Nos 518/21 were printed in horizontal *se-tenant* strips of four within the sheet. Each design differs in the position of the logo across the centre of the globe. On the left hand stamp in the strip only the letter "S" is visible, on the next "ST", on the next "STO" and on the last "STOP".

Other features of the design also differ, so that the word "Year" moves towards the top of the stamp and on No. 521 the upper logo is omitted.

(Des A. Ryman. Litho Questa)

1985 (3 July). *Naval Crests (4th series). Vert designs as* **T 134**. *Multicoloured.* W w **16**. *P* 14.

522 4p. H.M.S. *Duncan* 15 10
523 9p. H.M.S. *Fury* 25 25
524 21p. H.M.S. *Firedrake* 50 60
525 80p. H.M.S. *Malaya* .. .. 1·75 2·50
522/5 .. .. *Set of* 4 2·40 3·00

148 I.Y.Y. Logo **149** St. Joseph

(Des Olympia Reyes. Litho Walsall)

1985 (6 Sept). *International Youth Year.* **T 148** *and similar horiz designs. Multicoloured.* W w **14** (*sideways*). *P* 14×14½.

526 4p. Type **148** 15 10
527 20p. Hands passing diamond 50 50
528 80p. 75th anniv logo of Girl Guide Movement 1·75 2·00
526/8 .. .. *Set of* 3 2·25 2·40

(Des A. Ryman (4p.), Olympia Reyes (80p.). Litho Cartor, France)

1985 (25 Oct). *Christmas. Centenary of St. Joseph's Parish Church.* **T 149** *and similar vert designs. Multicoloured.* W w **16**. *P* 13½.

529 4p. Type **149** 20 20
a. Vert pair. Nos. 529/30 .. .. .. 40 40
530 4p. St. Joseph's Parish Church 20 20
531 80p. Nativity crib .. .. 1·75 2·00
529/31 .. .. *Set of* 3 2·00 2·25

Nos. 529/30 were printed together in panes of 25; No. 529 on rows, 1, 3 and 5, and No. 530 on rows 2 and 4. *Se-tenant* vertical pairs from rows 1/2 and 3/4, forming composite designs, have the stamps separated by a line of roulettes instead of perforations. Examples of No. 529 from row 5 have perforations on all four sides.

150 Swallowtail Butterfly and The Convent **151** 1887 Queen Victoria 6d. Stamp

(Des E. Field. Litho Walsall)

1986 (10 Feb). *Europa. Nature and the Environment.* **T 150** *and similar horiz design. Multicoloured.* W w **16** (*sideways*). *P* 13×13½.

532 22p. Type **150** 70 50
533 29p. Herring Gull and Europa Point .. 90 1·25

(Des A. Ryman. Litho Walsall)

1986 (26 Mar). *Centenary of First Gibraltar Postage Stamps.* **T 151** *and similar vert designs showing stamps. Multicoloured.* W w **16**. *P* 14×13½ (44*p.*) *or* 13½×13 (*others*).

534 4p. Type **151** 15 10
535 22p. 1903 Edward VII 2½d. 60 50
536 32p. 1912 George V 1d. 85 75
537 36p. 1938 George VI £1 .. .. .. 95 85
538 44p. 1953 Coronation ½d. (29×46 *mm*) .. 1·10 1·10
534/8 .. .. *Set of* 5 3·25 3·00
MS539 102×73 mm. 29p. 1886 "GIBRALTAR" overprint on Bermuda 1d. 60 70

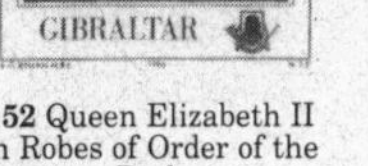

152 Queen Elizabeth II in Robes of Order of the Bath **153** Prince Andrew and Miss Sarah Ferguson

(Des A. Ryman. Litho Walsall)

1986 (22 May). *60th Birthday of Queen Elizabeth II.* W w **16**. *P* 14×13½.

540 **152** £1 multicoloured .. .. 2·00 2·40

(Des A. Ryman. Litho Questa)

1986 (28 Aug). *Naval Crests (5th series). Vert designs as* **T 134**. *Multicoloured.* W w **16**. *P* 14.

541 22p. H.M.S. *Lightning* 55 50
542 29p. H.M.S. *Hermione* 65 65
543 32p. H.M.S. *Laforey* 75 90
544 44p. H.M.S. *Nelson* .. .. 1·10 1·40
541/4 .. .. *Set of* 4 2·75 3·00

(Des A. Ryman. Litho Questa)

1986 (28 Aug). *Royal Wedding. Sheet* 115×85 *mm.* W w **16**. *P* 14½.

MS545 **153** 44p. multicoloured .. .. .. 95 1·10

154 Three Kings and Cathedral of St. Mary the Crowned **155** Neptune House

(Des M. Infante. Litho Walsall)

1986 (14 Oct). *Christmas. International Peace Year.* **T 154** *and similar vert design. Multicoloured.* W w **16**. *P* 14.

546 18p. Type **154** 55 40
547 32p. St. Andrew's Church 85 85

(Litho Questa)

1986 (12 Dec)–**87**. *As Nos.* 461 *and* 464, *but* W w **16** (*sideways*). *P* 14.

549 2p. Vickers "Viking" 40 40
552 5p. Boeing "727" (2.1.87) 70 70

(Des M. Infante. Litho Questa)

1987 (17 Feb). *Europa. Architecture.* **T 155** *and similar horiz design. Multicoloured.* W w **16**. *P* 14½.

563 22p. Type **155** 80 50
564 29p. Ocean Heights .. .. 1·40 80

(Des A. Ryman. Litho Walsall)

1987 (15 Apr). *Naval Crests (6th series). Vert designs as* **T 134**. *Multicoloured.* W w **16**. *P* 13½×13.

565 18p. H.M.S. *Wishart* (destroyer) 70 45
566 22p. H.M.S. *Charybdis* (cruiser) 85 55
567 32p. H.M.S. *Antelope* (destroyer) .. .. 1·25 1·25
568 44p. H.M.S. *Eagle* (aircraft carrier) .. .. 1·75 1·75
565/8 .. .. *Set of* 4 4·00 3·50

156 13-inch Mortar, 1783 **157** Victoria Stadium

(Des A. Ryman. Litho Format)

1987 (1 June). *Guns.* **T 156** *and similar horiz designs. Multicoloured.* W w **14**. *P* 12½.

569 1p. Type **156** 10 10
570 2p. 6-inch coastal gun, 1909 .. .. 10 10
571 3p. 8-inch howitzer, 1783 .. .. .. 10 10
572 4p. Bofors "L40/70" AA gun, 1951 .. 10 10
573 5p. 100 ton rifled muzzle-loader, 1882 .. 10 10
574 10p. 5.25-inch heavy AA gun, 1953 .. 20 25
575 18p. 25-pounder gun-how, 1943 .. .. 30 35
576 19p. 64-pounder rifled muzzle-loader, 1873 .. 35 40
577 22p. 12-pounder gun, 1758 .. .. .. 40 45
578 50p. 10-inch rifled muzzle-loader, 1870 .. 90 95
579 £1 Russian 24-pounder gun, 1854 .. .. 1·75 1·90
580 £3 9.2-inch "Mk.10" coastal gun, 1935 .. 5·00 5·25
581 £5 24-pounder gun, 1779 .. .. .. 9·00 9·25
569/81 .. .. *Set of* 13 16·00 17·00

(Des A. Ryman. Litho Walsall)

1987 (16 Sept). *Bicentenary of Royal Engineers' Royal Warrant.* **T 157** *and similar vert designs. Multicoloured.* W w **14**. *P* 14½.

582 18p. Type **157** 60 40
583 32p. Freedom of Gibraltar scroll and casket 90 80
584 44p. Royal Engineers' badge .. .. .. 1·25 1·25
582/4 .. .. *Set of* 3 2·50 2·25

158 The Three Kings

(Des Olympia Reyes. Litho Walsall)

1987 (12 Nov). *Christmas.* **T 158** *and similar horiz designs. Multicoloured.* W w **16** (*sideways*). *P* 14½.

585 4p. Type **158** 10 10
586 22p. The Holy Family 45 50
587 44p. The Shepherds .. .. 90 1·25
585/7 .. .. *Set of* 3 1·25 1·60

159 Liner passing Gibraltar **160** European Bee Eater

(Des Olympia Reyes. Litho Format)

1988 (16 Feb). *Europa. Transport and Communications.* **T 159** *and similar horiz designs. Multicoloured.* W w **14**. *P* 14½×14×*roul between se-tenant pairs.*

588 22p. Type **159** 70 70
a. Horiz pair. Nos. 588/9 .. .. .. 1·40 1·40
589 22p. Ferry, dish aerial and aircraft 70 70
590 32p. Horse-drawn carriage and modern coach 1·00 1·00
a. Horiz pair. Nos. 590/1 .. .. .. 2·00 2·00
591 32p. Car, telephone and Rock of Gibraltar .. 1·00 1·00
588/91 .. .. *Set of* 4 3·00 3·00

The two designs for each value were printed in sheets of ten, each containing five horizontal *se-tenant* pairs in which the stamps were rouletted between vertically.

(Des A. Ryman. Litho Walsall)

1988 (7 Apr). *Naval Crests (7th series). Vert designs as* **T 134**. W w **16**. *P* 13½×13.

592 18p. multicoloured 60 50
593 22p. black, brownish black and gold .. 75 60
594 32p. multicoloured .. .. 1·00 1·00
595 44p. multicoloured .. .. 1·50 1·75
592/5 .. .. *Set of* 4 3·50 3·50

Designs:—18p. H.M.S. *Clyde*; 22p. H.M.S. *Foresight*; 32p. H.M.S. *Severn*; 44p. H.M.S. *Rodney*.

(Des Olympia Reyes. Litho B.D.T.)

1988 (15 June). *Birds.* **T 160** *and similar horiz designs. Multicoloured.* W w **14** (*sideways*). *P* 13½.

596 4p. Type **160** 20 10
597 22p. Atlantic Puffin 70 50
598 32p. Honey Buzzard 85 85
599 44p. Blue Rock Thrush .. .. 1·25 1·50
596/9 .. .. *Set of* 4 2·75 2·75

161 *Zebu* (brigantine) **162** "Snowman" (Rebecca Falero)

(Des A. Ryman. Litho B.D.T.)

1988 (14 Sept). *Operation Raleigh.* **T 161** *and similar horiz designs. Multicoloured.* W w **14**. *P* 13.

600 19p. Type **161** 55 55
601 22p. Miniature of Sir Walter Raleigh and logo 60 60
602 32p. *Sir Walter Raleigh* (expedition ship) and world map 85 85
600/2 .. .. *Set of* 3 1·75 1·75
MS603 135×86 mm. 22p. As No. 601; 44p. *Sir Walter Raleigh* (expedition ship) passing Gibraltar .. .. 2·00 2·25

(Des A. Ryman. Litho Questa)

1988 (2 Nov). *Christmas. Children's Paintings.* **T 162** *and similar multicoloured designs.* W w **16** (*sideways*). *P* 14½ (44*p.*) *or* 14 (*others*).

604 4p. Type **162** 10 10
605 22p. "The Nativity" (Dennis Penalver) .. 45 50
606 44p. "Father Christmas" (Gavin Key) (23×31 *mm*) 90 95
604/6 .. .. *Set of* 3 1·25 1·40

163 Soft Toys and Toy Train **164** Port Sergeant with Keys

(Des Olympia Reyes. Litho Walsall)

1989 (15 Feb). *Europa. Children's Toys.* **T 163** *and similar horiz design. Multicoloured.* W w **16** (*sideways*). *P* 13×13½.

607 25p. Type **163** 55 60
608 32p. Soft toys, toy boat and doll's house .. 70 90

(Des A. Ryman. Litho Walsall)

1989 (28 Apr). *50th Anniv of Gibraltar Regiment. T* **164** *and similar vert designs. Multicoloured. W* w **14**. *P* 13½×13.

609	4p. Type **164**	15	10
610	22p. Regimental badge and colours	55	60
611	32p. Drum major	85	90
609/11	*Set of* 3	1·40	1·40
MS612	124×83 mm. 22p. As No. 610; 44p. Former Gibraltar Defence Force badge	1·50	1·60

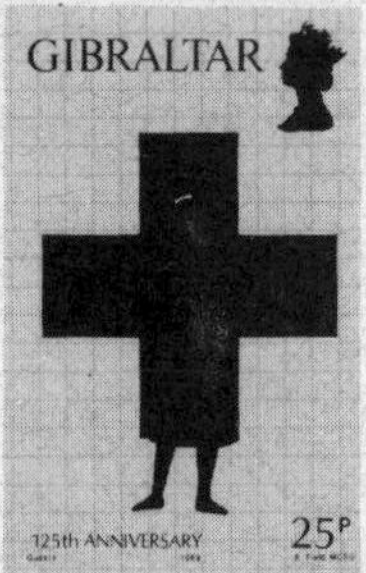

165 Nurse and Baby

166 One Penny Coin

(Des E. Field. Litho Questa)

1989 (7 July). *125th Anniv of International Red Cross. T* **165** *and similar vert designs. W* w **16**. *P* 15×14½.

613	25p. black, bright scarlet and grey-brown	50	55
614	32p. black, bright scarlet and grey-brown	65	70
615	44p. black, bright scarlet and grey-brown	90	95
613/15	*Set of* 3	1·90	2·00

Designs:—32p. Famine victims; 44p. Accident victims.

(Des A. Ryman. Litho B.D.T.)

1989 (7 Sept). *Naval Crests (8th series). Vert designs as T* **134**. *W* w **16**. *P* 14×13½.

616	22p. multicoloured	45	50
617	25p. black and gold	50	55
618	32p. gold, black and bright scarlet	65	70
619	44p. multicoloured	90	95
616/19	*Set of* 4	2·25	2·40

Designs:—22p. H.M.S. *Blankney;* 25p. H.M.S. *Deptford;* 32p. H.M.S. *Exmoor;* 44p. H.M.S. *Stork.*

(Des A. Ryman. Litho Questa)

1989 (11 Oct). *New Coinage. T* **166** *and similar vert designs in two miniature sheets. W* w **16** *(sideways). P* 14½.

MS620	72×94 mm. 4p. bronze, black & dull verm (Type **166**); 4p. bronze, blk & dp brn (two pence); 4p. silver, blk & greenish yellow (ten pence); 4p. silver, black and emerald (five pence)	30	35
MS621	100×95 mm. 22p. silver, black & reddish orge (fifty pence); 22p. gold, black & ultram (five pounds); 22p. gold, blk & orge-brn (two pounds); 22p. gold, blk & brt emer (one pound); 22p. gold, blk & brt reddish vio (obverse of coin series); 22p. silver, black and pale violet-blue (twenty pence)	1·60	1·75

167 Father Christmas in Sleigh

(Des M. Infante. Litho Questa)

1989 (11 Oct). *Christmas. T* **167** *and similar horiz designs. Multicoloured. W* w **16** *(sideways). P* 14½.

622	4p. Type **167**	10	10
623	22p. Shepherds and sheep	45	50
624	32p. The Nativity	65	70
625	44p. The Three Wise Men	90	95
622/5	*Set of* 4	1·90	2·00

POSTAGE DUE STAMPS

D 1

D 2

D 3 Gibraltar Coat of Arms

(Typo D.L.R.)

1956 (1 Dec). *Chalky paper. Wmk Mult Script CA. P* 14.

D1	D 1	1d. green	2·00	2·75
D2		2d. sepia	2·50	3·75
D3		4d. blue	3·00	4·75
D1/3		*Set of* 3	6·75	10·00

1971 (15 Feb). *As Nos.* D1/3 *but inscr in decimal currency.* W w **12**. *P* 17½ × 18.

D4	D 1	½p. green	45	80
D5		1p. sepia	40	70
D6		2p. blue	50	80
D4/6		*Set of* 3	1·25	2·10

(Des A. Ryman. Litho Questa)

1976 (13 Oct). *W* w **14**. *P* 14 × 13½.

D 7	D 2	1p. light red-orange	10	10
D 8		3p. bright blue	10	20
D 9		5p. orange-vermilion	15	25
D10		7p. reddish violet	20	30
D11		10p. greenish slate	30	40
D12		20p. green	55	65
D7/12		*Set of* 6	1·25	1·75

(Des A. Ryman. Litho Irish Security Stamp Ptg Ltd)

1984 (2 July). W w **14** *(sideways)*. *P* 15 × 14.

D13	D 3	1p. black	10	10
D14		3p. vermilion	10	10
D15		5p. ultramarine	10	10
D16		10p. new blue	20	25
D17		25p. deep mauve	45	50
D18		50p. reddish orange	90	95
D19		£1 blue-green	1·75	1·90
D13/19		*Set of* 7	3·25	3·50

Gilbert and Ellice Islands

The stamps of NEW ZEALAND, with face values up to 2s., were used at the New Zealand Postal Agencies on Fanning Island (27 November 1902 to 13 February 1939) and Washington Island (1 February 1921 to 30 March 1934).

PRICES FOR STAMPS ON COVER TO 1945	
Nos. 1/7	*from* × 5
Nos. 8/11	*from* × 8
Nos. 12/24	*from* × 4
Nos. 26/35	*from* × 5
Nos. 36/9	*from* × 3
Nos. 40/2	*from* × 8
Nos. 43/54	*from* × 4
Nos. D1/8	*from* × 4

BRITISH PROTECTORATE

GILBERT&ELLICE

PROTECTORATE

(1)

2 Pandanus Pine

1911 (1 Jan). *Stamps of Fiji optd with T* **1**. *Wmk Mult Crown CA.*

1	**23**	½d. green, **O**	4·50	27·00
2		1d. red, **O**	45·00	38·00
3	**24**	2d. grey, **O**	6·00	12·00
4	**23**	2½d. ultramarine, **O**	12·00	23·00
5		5d. purple and olive-green, **C**	27·00	42·00
6	**24**	6d. dull and bright purple, **C**	20·00	38·00
7	**23**	1s. black/*green*, **C** (R.)	17·00	32·00
1/7		*Set of* 7	£120	£180
1/7 Optd "Specimen"		*Set of* 7	£400	

The 2d. to 6d. are on special printings which were not issued without overprint.

(Recess D.L.R.)

1911. *Wmk Mult Crown CA. P* 14.

8	**2**	½d. green	2·75	9·00
9		1d. carmine	2·00	5·50
10		2d. grey	1·50	5·50
11		2½d. blue	1·50	7·50
8/11		*Set of* 4	7·00	25·00
8/11 Optd "Specimen"		*Set of* 4	£140	

3

WAR TAX

(5)

(Typo D.L.R.)

1912–24. *Wmk Mult Crown CA. P* 14.

12	**3**	½d. green, **O**	30	2·50
		a. Yellow-green (1914)	1·90	3·50
13		1d. carmine, **O**	65	2·25
		a. Scarlet (1916)	2·75	6·50
14		2d. greyish slate, **O** (1916)	8·00	16·00
15		2½d. bright blue, **O** (1916)	1·75	8·50
16		3d. purple/*yellow*, **C** (1919)	90	5·50
17		4d. black and red/*yellow*, **C**	60	3·50
18		5d. dull purple and sage-green, **C**	1·40	7·00
19		6d. dull and bright purple, **C**	1·25	7·50
20		1s. black/*green*, **C**	1·25	5·50
21		2s. purple and blue/*blue*, **C**	14·00	22·00
22		2s. 6d. black and red/*blue*, **C**	10·00	23·00
23		5s. green and red/*yellow*, **C**	22·00	40·00
24		£1 purple and black/*red*, **C** (Die II) (1924) (S. £350)	£800	£1400
12/24		*Set of* 13	£800	£1400
12/23 Optd "Specimen"		*Set of* 12	£375	

CROWN COLONY

1918 (June). *Optd with T* **5**.

26	**3**	1d. red (Optd S. £55)	20	2·75

1922–27. *Wmk Mult Script CA. P* 14.

27	**3**	½d. green, **O** (1923)	25	1·25
28		1d. violet, **O** (1927)	1·00	2·00
29		1½d. scarlet, **O** (1924)	75	1·00
30		2d. slate-grey, **O**	2·00	7·50
35		10s. green and red/*emerald*, **C** (1924)	£175	£225
27/35 Optd "Specimen"		*Set of* 5	£300	

1935 (6 May). *Silver Jubilee. As Nos.* 91/4 *of Antigua, but ptd by B.W. P* 11 × 12.

36	1d. ultramarine and grey-black	1·50	5·00
	d. Flagstaff on right-hand turret	45·00	
	e. Double flagstaff	45·00	
37	1½d. deep blue and scarlet	1·50	2·25
	d. Flagstaff on right-hand turret	45·00	
	e. Double flagstaff	45·00	
38	3d. brown and deep blue	5·00	6·50
	d. Flagstaff on right-hand turret	75·00	
	e. Double flagstaff	75·00	
39	1s. slate and purple	18·00	24·00
	d. Flagstaff on right-hand turret	£150	
	e. Double flagstaff	£150	
36/9	*Set of* 4	23·00	35·00
36/9 Perf "Specimen"	*Set of* 4	90·00	

For illustrations of plate varieties see Omnibus section following Zululand.

1937 (12 May). *Coronation. As Nos.* 13/15 *of Aden.*

40	1d. violet	25	15
41	1½d. scarlet	35	15
42	3d. bright blue	45	25
40/2	*Set of* 3	95	50
40/2 Perf "Specimen"	*Set of* 3	60·00	

6 Great Frigate Bird

7 Pandanus Pine

8 Canoe crossing Reef

(Recess B.W. (½d., 2d., 2s. 6d.), Waterlow (1d., 5d., 6d., 2s., 5s.), D.L.R. (1½d., 2½d., 3d., 1s.))

1939 (14 Jan)–**55.** *T* **6/8** *and similar horiz designs. Wmk Mult Script CA (sideways on ½d., 2d. and 2s. 6d.).*

43	½d. slate-blue & blue-green (*p* 11½ × 11)	15	25
44	1d. emerald-green and purple (*p* 12½)	15	50
45	1½d. black and carmine (*p* 13½)	25	75
46	2d. red-brown and black (*p* 11½ × 11)	15	80
47	2½d. black and olive-green (*p* 13½)	20	45
48	3d. black and ultramarine (*p* 13½)	15	80
	a. Perf 12. *Black and bright blue* (24.8.55)	40	1·50
49	5d. bright blue and sepia (*p* 12½)	1·75	70
50	6d. olive-green and violet (*p* 12½)	40	40
51	1s. black and turquoise-blue (*p* 13½)	2·00	90
	a. Perf 12 (8.5.51)	7·50	10·00
52	2s. bright blue and vermilion (*p* 12½)	8·00	6·50
53	2s. 6d. blue & emerald-green (*p* 11½ × 11)	10·00	8·50
54	5s. scarlet and bright blue (*p* 12½)	12·00	10·00
43/54	*Set of* 12	32·00	28·00
43/54 Perf "Specimen"	*Set of* 12	£225	

Designs: *As T* **6**—2d. Canoe and boat-house; 2s. 6d. Gilbert Islands canoe. *As T* **7**—5d. Ellice Islands canoe; 6d. Coconut palms; 2s. H.M.C.S. *Nimanoa*; 5s. Coat of arms. *As T* **8**—2½d. Native house; 3d. Seascape; 1s. Cantilever jetty, Ocean Island.

1946 (16 Dec). *Victory. As Nos.* 28/9 *of Aden.*

55	1d. purple	10	10
56	3d. blue	15	10
55/6 Perf "Specimen"	*Set of* 2	50·00	

1949 (29 Aug). *Royal Silver Wedding. As Nos.* 30/1 *of Aden.*

57	1d. violet	40	50
58	£1 scarlet	15·00	17·00

1949 (10 Oct). *75th Anniv of U.P.U. As Nos.* 114/17 *of Antigua.*

59	1d. purple	45	35
60	2d. grey-black	1·00	50
61	3d. deep blue	1·40	65
62	1s. blue	2·25	90
59/62	*Set of* 4	4·50	2·25

1953 (2 June). *Coronation. As No.* 47 *of Aden.*

63	2d. black and grey-black	45	1·00

18 Great Frigate Bird

19 Loading Phosphate from Cantilever

(Recess B.W. (½d., 2d., 2s. 6d.), Waterlow (1d., 5d., 6d., 2s., 5s.), D.L.R. (2½d., 3d., 1s., 10s.) and after 1962, 1d., 5d.)

1956 (1 Aug)–**62.** *Designs previously used for King George VI issue; but with portrait of Queen Elizabeth II as in T* **18**. *Wmk Mult Script CA. P* 11½×11 (½d., 2d., 2s. 6d.), 12½ (1d., 5d., 6d., 2s., 5s.) *or* 12 (2½d., 3d., 1s., 10s.).

64	½d. black and deep bright blue	30	40
65	1d. brown-olive and deep violet	40	15
66	2d. bluish green and deep purple	90	55
	a. Bluish green and purple (30.7.62)	3·00	2·50
67	2½d. black and myrtle-green	50	55
68	3d. black and carmine-red	50	45
69	5d. ultramarine and red-orange	4·25	1·25
	a. Ultramarine & brn-orge (DLR) (30.7.62)	7·50	6·00
70	6d. chestnut and black-brown	55	55
71	1s. black and bronze-green	55	50
72	2s. deep bright blue and sepia	7·00	3·25
73	2s. 6d. scarlet and deep blue	6·00	3·75
74	5s. greenish blue and bluish green	12·00	6·00
75	10s. black and turquoise	21·00	14·00
64/75	*Set of* 12	48·00	28·00

Designs: *Horiz* (30 × 22½ *mm*)—1d. Pandanus pine; 5d. Ellice Islands canoe; 6d. Coconut palms; 2s. H.M.C.S. *Nimanoa*; 5s. Coat of arms. (35½ × 22½ *mm*)—2d. Canoe and boat-house; 2½d. Native house; 3d. Seascape; 1s. Cantilever jetty, Ocean Island; 2s. 6d. Gilbert Islands canoe; 10s. Canoe crossing reef.

See also Nos. 85/6.

(Des R. Turrell (2d.), M. Thoma (2½d), M. A. W. Hook and A. Larkins (1s.). Photo D.L.R.)

1960 (1 May). *Diamond Jubilee of Phosphate Discovery at Ocean Island. T* **19** *and similar horiz designs. W w* **12**. *P* 12.

76	2d. green and carmine-rose	35	10
77	2½d. black and olive-green	35	10
78	1s. black and deep turquoise	40	20
76/8	*Set of* 3	1·00	35

Designs:—2½d. Phosphate rock; 1s. Phosphate mining.

1963 (1 Aug). *Freedom from Hunger. As No.* 76 *of Aden.*

79	10d. ultramarine	3·00	30

1963 (5 Oct). *Red Cross Centenary. As Nos.* 147/8 *of Antigua.*

80	2d. red and black	1·50	30
81	10d. red and blue	3·50	1·25

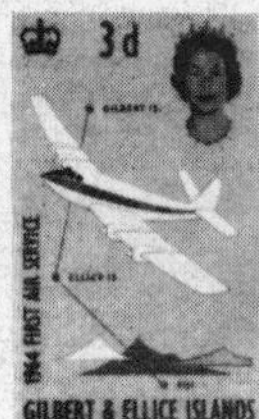

22 D.H. "Heron" Aircraft and Route Map

24 D.H. "Heron" Aircraft over Tarawa Lagoon

23 Eastern Reef Heron in Flight

(Des Margaret Barwick. Litho Enschedé)

1964 (20 July). *First Air Service. W w* **12** *(sideways, 3d., 3s. 7d.). P* 11 × 11½ *(1s.) or* 11½ × 11 *(others).*

82	**22**	3d. blue, black and light blue	30	10
83	**23**	1s. light blue, black and deep blue	40	10
84	**24**	3s. 7d. deep green, black and light emerald	70	25
82/4		*Set of* 3	1·25	40

(Recess B.W. (2d.), D.L.R. (6d.))

1964 (30 Oct)–**65.** *As Nos.* 66 *and* 70 *but wmk* w **12**.

85	2d. bluish green and purple	1·00	1·25
86	6d. chestnut and black-brown (26.4.65)*	1·50	2·25

*Earliest known postmark date.

1965 (4 June). *I.T.U. Centenary. As Nos.* 166/7 *of Antigua.*

87	3d. red-orange and deep bluish green	20	10
88	2s. 6d. turquoise-blue and light purple	80	20

25 Maneaba and Gilbertese Man blowing Bu Shell

26 Gilbertese Women's Dance

(Des V. Whiteley from drawings by Margaret Barwick. Litho B.W.)

1965 (16 Aug). *Vert designs as T* **25** *(½d. to 2s.) or horiz designs as T* **26** *(3s. 7d. to £1). Centres multicoloured. W w* **12**. *P* 12 × 11 *(½d. to 2s.) or* 11 × 12 *(3s. 7d. to £1).*

89	½d. turquoise-green	10	10
90	1d. deep violet-blue	10	10
91	2d. bistre	10	10
92	3d. rose-red	10	10
93	4d. purple	15	10
94	5d. cerise	20	10
95	6d. turquoise-blue	20	10
96	7d. bistre-brown	25	10
97	1s. bluish violet	35	10
98	1s. 6d. lemon	1·00	65
99	2s. yellow-olive	1·00	1·00
100	3s. 7d. new blue	2·00	65
101	5s. light yellow-olive	2·00	80
102	10s. dull green	3·50	1·25
103	£1 light turquoise-blue	4·00	2·50
89/103	*Set of* 15	13·00	6·25

Designs:—1d. Ellice Islanders reef fishing by flare; 2d. Gilbertese girl weaving head garland; 3d. Gilbertese woman performing Ruoia; 4d. Gilbertese man performing Kamei; 5d. Gilbertese girl drawing water; 6d. Ellice islander performing a Fatele; 7d. Ellice youths performing spear dance; 1s. Gilbertese girl tending Ikaroa Babai plant; 1s. 6d. Ellice islanders dancing a Fatele; 2s. Ellice islanders pounding Pulaka; 5s. Gilbertese boys playing stick game; 10s. Ellice youths beating the box for the Fatele; £1 Coat of arms.

1965 (25 Oct). *International Co-operation Year. As Nos.* 168/9 *of Antigua.*

104	½d. reddish purple and turquoise-green	10	10
105	3s. 7d. deep bluish green and lavender	60	15

1966 (24 Jan). *Churchill Commemoration. As Nos.* 170/3 *of Antigua.*
106 ½d. new blue 10 10
107 3d. deep green 30 10
108 3s. brown 65 25
109 3s. 7d. bluish violet 65 25
106/9 .. .. *Set of* 4 1·50 60

(New Currency. 100 cents = $1 Australian)

≡2c

(40)

41 H.M.S. *Royalist*

1966 (14 Feb). *Decimal currency. Nos.* 89/103 *surch as T* **40**.
110 1 c. on 1d. deep violet-blue 10 10
111 2 c. on 2d. bistre 10 10
112 3 c. on 3d. rose-red 10 10
113 4 c. on ½d. turquoise-green 10 10
114 5 c. on 6d. turquoise-blue 15 10
115 6 c. on 4d. purple 15 10
116 8 c. on 5d. cerise 15 10
117 10 c. on 1s. bluish violet 15 10
118 15 c. on 7d. bistre-brown 80 30
119 20 c. on 1s. 6d. lemon 45 25
120 25 c. on 2s. yellow-olive 45 20
121 35 c. on 3s. 7d. new blue .. .. 1·25 20
122 50 c. on 5s. light yellow-olive 75 35
123 $1 on 10s. dull green 75 40
124 $2 on £1 light turquoise-blue .. .. 1·50 1·25
110/24 .. .. *Set of* 15 6·00 3·00

1966 (1 July). *World Cup Football Championships. As Nos.* 176/7 *of Antigua.*
125 3 c. violet, yellow-green, lake & yellow-brn .. 15 10
126 35 c. chocolate, blue-green, lake & yell-brn .. 45 15

1966 (20 Sept). *Inauguration of W.H.O. Headquarters, Geneva. As Nos.* 178/9 *of Antigua.*
127 3 c. black, yellow-green and light blue .. 20 10
128 12 c. black, light purple and yellow-brown .. 55 40

1966 (1 Dec). *20th Anniv of U.N.E.S.C.O. As Nos.* 196/8 *of Antigua.*
129 5 c. slate-violet, red, yellow and orange .. 60 10
130 10 c. orange-yellow, violet and deep olive .. 80 10
131 20 c. black, bright purple and orange.. .. 1·75 45
129/31 .. .. *Set of* 3 2·75 55

(Des V. Whiteley. Photo Harrison)

1967 (1 Sept). *75th Anniv of the Protectorate. T* **41** *and similar horiz designs. W w* **12**. *P* 14½.
132 3 c. red, blue and myrtle-green 10 10
133 10 c. multicoloured 10 10
134 35 c. sepia, orange-yellow & dp bluish green .. 20 15
132/4 .. .. *Set of* 3 35 20
Designs:—10 c. Trading Post; 35 c. Island family.

44 Gilbertese Women's Dance

1968 (1 Jan). *Decimal Currency. Designs as Nos.* 89/103 *but with values inscr in decimal currency as T* **44**. *W w* **12** *(sideways on horiz designs). P* 12 × 11 *(vert) or* 11 × 12 *(horiz).*
135 1 c. deep violet-blue (as 1d.) 10 10
136 2 c. bistre (as 2d.) 10 10
137 3 c. rose-red (as 3d.) 10 10
138 4 c. turquoise-green (as ½d.) 10 10
139 5 c. turquoise-blue (as 6d.) 15 10
140 6 c. purple (as 4d.) 20 10
141 8 c. cerise (as 5d.) 20 10
142 10 c. bluish violet (as 1s.) 20 10
143 15 c. bistre-brown (as 7d.) 50 20
144 20 c. lemon (as 1s. 6d.).. .. .. 65 15
145 25 c. yellow-olive (as 2s.) .. .. 1·25 20
146 35 c. new blue .. .. 1·50 20
147 50 c. light yellow-olive (as 5s.) .. .. .. 1·50 1·25
148 $1 dull green (as 10s.) .. .. 1·50 1·75
149 $2 light turquoise-blue (as £1) .. .. .. 3·50 2·00
135/49 .. .. *Set of* 15 10·00 5·25

45 Map of Tarawa Atoll

(Des V. Whiteley. Photo D.L.R.)

1968 (21 Nov). *25th Anniv of the Battle of Tarawa. T* **45** *and similar designs. Multicoloured. W w* **12** *(sideways). P* 14.
150 3 c. Type **45** 10 10
151 10 c. Marines landing 10 10
152 15 c. Beach-head assault 15 10
153 35 c. Raising U.S. and British flags 20 15
150/3 .. .. *Set of* 4 50 40

46 Young Pupil against outline of Abemama Island

47 "Virgin and Child" in Pacific Setting

(Des J.W. (from original designs by Mrs V. J. Anderson and Miss A. Loveridge). Litho D.L.R.)

1969 (2 June). *End of Inaugural Year of South Pacific University. T* **46** *and similar horiz designs. W w* **12** *(sideways). P* 12½.
154 3 c. multicoloured 10 10
155 10 c. multicoloured 10 10
156 35 c. black, brown and grey-green 15 15
154/6 .. .. *Set of* 3 25 20
Designs:—10 c. Boy and girl students and Tarawa atoll; 35 c. University graduate and South Pacific islands.

(Des Jennifer Toombs. Litho B.W.)

1969 (20 Oct). *Christmas. W w* **12** *(sideways). P* 11½.
157 – 2 c. olive-grn & multicoloured *(shades)* 10 10
158 **47** 10 c. olive-grn & multicoloured *(shades)* 10 10
Design:—2 c. As T **47** but foreground has grass instead of sand.

48 "The Kiss of Life"

(Des Manate Tenang Manate. Litho J.W.)

1970 (9 Mar*). *Centenary of British Red Cross. W w* **12** *(sideways). P* 14.
159 **48** 10 c. multicoloured 15 10
160 – 15 c. multicoloured 20 10
161 – 35 c. multicoloured 45 20
159/61 .. .. *Set of* 3 70 30
Nos. 160/1 are as T **48**, but arranged differently.
*The above were released by the Crown Agents on 2 March, but not sold locally until the 9 March.

49 Foetus and Patients

(Des Jennifer Toombs. Litho Enschedé)

1970 (26 June). *25th Anniv of United Nations. T* **49** *and similar horiz designs. W w* **12** *(sideways). P* 12½ × 13.
162 5 c. multicoloured 15 10
163 10 c. black, grey and red 15 10
164 15 c. multicoloured 20 10
165 35 c. new blue, black and turquoise-green .. 30 15
162/5 .. .. *Set of* 4 70 35
Designs:—10 c. Nurse and surgical instruments; 15 c. X-ray plate and technician; 35 c. U.N. emblem and map.

53 Map of Gilbert Islands

57 "Child with Halo" (T. Collis)

(Des G. Vasarhelyi. Litho Harrison)

1970 (1 Sept). *Centenary of Landing in Gilbert Islands by London Missionary Society. T* **53** *and similar designs. W w* **12** *(sideways on vert designs). P* 14½ × 14 *(2 c., 35 c.) or* 14 × 14½ *(others).*
166 2 c. multicoloured 10 20
167 10 c. black and pale green 15 10
168 25 c. chestnut and cobalt 15 10
169 35 c. turquoise-blue, black and red 30 20
166/9 .. .. *Set of* 4 65 50
Designs: *Vert*—10 c. Sailing-ship *John Williams III*; 25 c. Rev. S. J. Whitmee. *Horiz*—35 c. M.V. *John Williams VII*.

(Des L. Curtis. Litho Format)

1970 (3 Oct). *Christmas. Sketches. T* **57** *and similar vert designs. Multicoloured. W w* **12**. *P* 14½.
170 2 c. Type **57** 10 10
171 10 c. "Sanctuary, Tarawa Cathedral" (Mrs. A. Burroughs) 10 10
172 35 c. "Three ships inside star" (Mrs. C. Barnett) 20 15
170/2 .. .. *Set of* 3 35 20

60 Casting Nets

(Des G. Drummond. Litho Walsall)

1971 (31 May). *Multicoloured designs as T* **60**. *W w* **12** *(sideways on* 2, 3, 4, 5, 20, 25 *and* 35 *c.). P* 14.
173 1 c. Cutting toddy *(vert)* 10 10
174 2 c. Lagoon fishing 15 10
175 3 c. Cleaning pandanus leaves 15 10
176 4 c. Type **60** 20 15
177 5 c. Gilbertese canoe 35 15
178 6 c. De-husking coconuts *(vert)* 30 25
179 8 c. Weaving pandanus fronds *(vert)*.. .. 35 15
180 10 c. Weaving a basket *(vert)* 40 15
181 15 c. Tiger shark and fishermen *(vert)* .. 2·75 1·25
182 20 c. Beating a rolled pandanus leaf .. .. 2·00 90
183 25 c. Loading copra .. .. 2·00 90
184 35 c. Fishing at night .. .. 2·00 50
185 50 c. Local handicrafts *(vert)* .. .. .. 1·75 1·25
186 $1 Weaving coconut screens *(vert)* .. .. 2·50 2·25
187 $2 Coat of Arms *(vert)* .. .. 9·50 10·00
173/87 .. .. *Set of* 15 22·00 16·00
See also Nos. 203/7.

61 House of Representatives

62 Pacific Nativity Scene

(Des V. Whiteley. Litho J.W.)

1971 (1 Aug). *New Constitution. T* **61** *and similar horiz design. Multicoloured. W w* **12** *(sideways). P* 14.
188 3 c. Type **61** 10 10
189 10 c. Maneaba Betio (Assembly hut) 20 10

(Des L. Curtis and T. Collis. Litho Questa)

1971 (1 Oct). *Christmas. T* **62** *and similar vert designs. W w* **12**. *P* 14 × 14½.
190 3 c. black, yellow and ultramarine 10 10
191 10 c. black, gold and turquoise-blue 10 10
192 35 c. black, gold and magenta.. .. .. 25 20
190/2 .. .. *Set of* 3 40 35
Designs:—10 c. Star and palm leaves; 35 c. Outrigger canoe and star.

63 Emblem and Young Boys

(Des G. Vasarhelyi. Litho Questa)

1971 (11 Dec). *25th Anniv of UNICEF. T* **63** *and similar horiz designs, showing UNICEF emblem and young boys. W w* **12** *(sideways). P* 14.
193 3 c. multicoloured 10 10
194 10 c. multicoloured 15 10
195 35 c. multicoloured 45 35
193/5 .. .. *Set of* 3 60 45

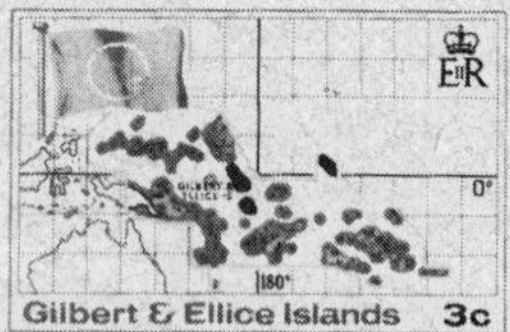

64 Flag and Map of South Pacific

(Des A. New. Litho Questa)

1972 (21 Feb). *25th Anniv of South Pacific Commission. T* **64** *and similar horiz designs. Multicoloured. W w* **12**. *P* 13½.
196 3 c. Type **64** 10 10
197 10 c. Flag and native boats 10 10
198 35 c. Flags of member nations 15 40
196/8 .. .. *Set of* 3 20 50

65 *Alveopora* 66 Star of Peace

(Des Sylvia Goaman after original designs by H. Wickison. Litho Questa)

1972 (26 May). *Coral. T* **65** *and similar horiz designs. Multicoloured. W* w **12** *(sideways). P* 14.
199 3 c. Type **65** 25 15
200 10 c. *Euphyllia* 35 10
201 15 c. *Melithea* 55 15
202 35 c. *Spongodes* .. .. 1·00 30
199/202 .. .. *Set of* 4 2·00 60

1972 (7 Sept)–**73.** *As Nos.* 174, 177/8 *and* 181/2 *but W* w **12** *upright on* 2, 5 *and* 20 *c.; sideways on* 6 *and* 15 *c.*
203 2 c. Lagoon fishing (13.6.73) .. .. .. 5·00 5·00
204 5 c. Gilbertese canoe .. .. 3·00 3·00
205 6 c. De-husking coconuts (13.6.73) .. .. 7·00 7·00
206 15 c. Tiger shark and fishermen .. .. 5·00 5·00
207 20 c. Beating a rolled pandanus leaf .. .. 5·00 5·00
203/7 .. .. *Set of* 5 22·00 22·00

(Des T. Matarena (35 c.), Father Bermond (others); adapted by Jennifer Toombs. Litho Questa)

1972 (15 Sept). *Christmas. T* **66** *and similar multicoloured designs. W* w **12** *(sideways on* 3 *and* 10 *c.). P* 13½.
208 3 c. Type **66** 10 10
209 10 c. "The Nativity" 10 10
210 35 c. Baby in "manger" (*horiz*) 15 15
208/10 .. .. *Set of* 3 20 20

67 Floral Head-dresses

(Des (from photograph by D. Groves) and photo Harrison)

1972 (20 Nov). *Royal Silver Wedding. Multicoloured; background colour given. W* w **12.** *P* 14 × 14½.
211 **67** 3 c. brown-olive 10 10
212 35 c. lake-brown 25 10

68 Funafuti ("The Land of Bananas") 69 Dancer

(Des H. Wickison; adapted J. Cooter. Litho Walsall)

1973 (5 Mar). *Legends of Island Names (1st series). T* **68** *and similar horiz designs. Multicoloured. W* w **12.** *P* 14½ × 14.
213 3 c. Type **68** 10 10
214 10 c. Butaritari ("The Smell of the Sea") .. 15 10
215 25 c. Tarawa ("The Centre of the World") .. 25 15
216 35 c. Abemama ("The Land of the Moon") .. 30 20
213/16 .. .. *Set of* 4 65 40
See also Nos. 252/5.

(Des Sister Juliette (3 c.), R. P. Turner (10 and 35 c.), C. Potts (50 c.); adapted Jennifer Toombs. Litho Questa)

1973 (24 Sept). *Christmas. T* **69** *and similar vert designs. Multicoloured. W* w **12** *(sideways). P* 14.
217 3 c. Type **69** 10 10
218 10 c. Canoe and lagoon 10 10
219 35 c. Lagoon at evening 20 10
220 50 c. Map of Christmas Island 30 35
217/20 .. .. *Set of* 4 60 50

1973 (14 Nov). *Royal Wedding. As Nos.* 165/6 *of Anguilla. Centre multicoloured. W* w **12** *(sideways). P* 13½.
221 3 c. pale green 10 10
222 35 c. Prussian blue 15 10

70 Meteorological Observation

(Des E. S. Cheek; adapted PAD Studio. Litho Questa)

1973 (26 Nov). *I.M.O./W.M.O. Centenary. T* **70** *and similar horiz designs. Multicoloured. W* w **12.** *P* 14.
223 3 c. Type **70** 80 30
224 10 c. Island observing-station 80 20
225 35 c. Wind-finding radar .. .. .. 1·50 40
226 50 c. World weather watch stations .. .. 2·00 1·50
223/6 .. .. *Set of* 4 4·50 2·25

71 Te Mataaua Crest

(Des J. Cooter. Litho Questa)

1974 (4 Mar). *Canoe Crests. T* **71** *and similar horiz designs showing sailing craft and the canoe crests given. Multicoloured. W* w **12.** *P* 13½.
227 3 c. Type **71** 10 10
228 10 c. Te Nimta-wawa 15 10
229 35 c. Tara-tara-venei-na 25 10
230 50 c. Te Bou-uoua 35 40
227/30 .. .. *Set of* 4 75 55
MS231 154 × 130 mm. Nos. 227/30 .. .. 2·50 5·00

72 £1 Stamp of 1924 and Te Koroba (canoe)

(Des E. S. Cheek; adapted J. Cooter. Litho Questa)

1974 (10 June). *Centenary of Universal Postal Union. T* **72** *and similar horiz designs. W* w **12.** *P* 14.
232 4 c. multicoloured 10 10
233 10 c. multicoloured 10 10
234 25 c. multicoloured 15 15
235 35 c. light vermilion and black 20 20
232/5 .. .. *Set of* 4 40 35
Designs:—10 c. 5s. stamp of 1939 and sailing vessel *Kiakia*; 25 c. $2 stamp of 1971 and B.A.C. "1-11"; 35 c. U.P.U. emblem.

73 Toy Canoe 74 North Front Entrance, Blenheim Palace

(Des H. Wickison and G. J. Hayward; adapted J. Cooter. Litho Questa)

1974 (5 Sept). *Christmas. T* **73** *and similar horiz designs. Multicoloured. W* w **12** *(sideways). P* 14.
236 4 c. Type **73** 10 10
237 10 c. Toy windmill 10 10
238 25 c. Coconut "ball" 15 15
239 35 c. Canoes and constellation Pleiades .. 20 15
236/9 .. .. *Set of* 4 45 35

(Des J. Cooter. Litho Questa)

1974 (30 Nov). *Birth Centenary of Sir Winston Churchill. T* **74** *and similar vert designs. Multicoloured. W* w **14.** *P* 14.
240 4 c. Type **74** 10 10
241 10 c. Churchill painting 10 10
242 35 c. Churchill's statue, London 25 10
240/2 .. .. *Set of* 3 40 25

75 Barometer Crab

(Des J. Cooter. Litho Questa)

1975 (27 Jan). *Crabs. T* **75** *and similar horiz designs. Multicoloured. W* w **12** *(sideways). P* 14.
243 4 c. Type **75** 25 15
244 10 c. *Ranina ranina* 35 10
245 25 c. Pelagic Swimming Crab 70 25
246 35 c. Ghost Crab 85 45
243/6 .. .. *Set of* 4 2·00 80

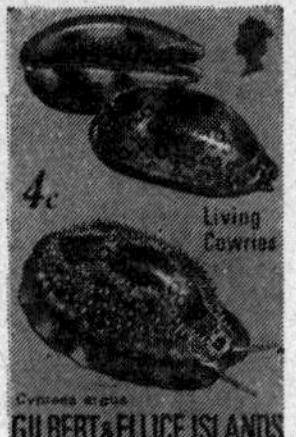

76 Eyed Cowrie 77 "Christ is Born"

(Des E. S. Cheek; adapted J. Cooter. Litho Questa)

1975 (26 May). *Cowrie Shells. T* **76** *and similar vert designs. Multicoloured. W* w **14.** *P* 14.
247 4 c. Type **76** 30 15
248 10 c. Sieve Cowrie 60 10
249 25 c. Mole Cowrie .. .. 1·25 45
250 35 c. Map Cowrie .. .. 1·75 65
247/50 .. .. *Set of* 4 3·50 1·25
MS251 146 × 137 mm. Nos. 247/50 .. .. 7·00 8·50

(Des J. Cooter. Litho Questa)

1975 (1 Aug). *Legends of Island Names (2nd series). Horiz designs as T* **68.** *Multicoloured. W* w **12** *(sideways). P* 14.
252 4 c. Beru ("The Bud") 10 10
253 10 c. Onotoa ("Six Giants") 10 10
254 25 c. Abaiang ("Land to the North") 20 15
255 35 c. Marakei ("Fish-trap floating on eaves") 30 20
252/5 .. .. *Set of* 4 60 40

(Des C. J. Barnett (4 and 25 c.), Philatelic Advisory Committee (10 c.), P. T. Burangke (35 c.); adapted J. Cooter. Litho Questa)

1975 (22 Sept). *Christmas. T* **77** *and similar vert designs. Multicoloured. W* w **14.** *P* 14.
256 4 c. Type **77** 10 10
257 10 c. Protestant Chapel, Tarawa 10 10
258 25 c. Catholic Church, Ocean Island 20 25
259 35 c. Fishermen and star 25 35
256/9 .. .. *Set of* 4 50 70

POSTAGE DUE STAMPS

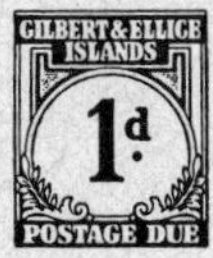

D 1

(Typo B.W.)

1940. *Wmk Mult Script CA. P* 12.
D1 D 1 1d. emerald-green .. .. 4·00 5·50
D2 2d. scarlet .. .. 5·00 6·50
D3 3d. brown .. .. 7·50 10·00
D4 4d. blue .. .. 10·00 15·00
D5 5d. grey-green .. .. 12·00 17·00
D6 6d. purple .. .. 13·00 19·00
D7 1s. violet .. .. 15·00 30·00
D8 1s. 6d. turquoise-green .. .. .. 30·00 60·00
D1/8 .. .. *Set of* 8 85·00 £150
D1/8 Perf "Specimen" .. .. *Set of* 8 £150

Stamps for the Gilbert and Ellice Islands were withdrawn on 31 December 1975 when the separate colonies of the GILBERT ISLANDS and TUVALU were created.

Gilbert Islands

On 1 January 1976, the Gilbert Islands and Tuvalu (Ellice Islands) became separate Crown Colonies.

1 Charts of Gilbert Islands and Tuvalu (formerly Ellice) Islands

THE GILBERT ISLANDS

(2)

(Des J. Cooter. Litho Questa)

1976 (2 Jan). *Separation of the Islands. T* **1** *and similar horiz design. Multicoloured. W* w **14** *(sideways). P* 14.
1 4 c. Type **1** 50 75
2 35 c. Maps of Tarawa and Funafuti .. .. 1·25 2·00

1976 (2 Jan). *Nos.* 173/86 *of Gilbert & Ellice Is optd as T* **2.**

(*a*) *W* w **12** *(sideways on Nos.* 5/7 *and* 9/10)
3 1 c. Cutting toddy (R.) 25 15
4 2 c. Lagoon fishing (R.) 50 40
5 2 c. Lagoon fishing (*wmk sideways*) (R.) .. 50 30
6 3 c. Cleaning pandanus leaves (R.) .. .. 15·00 17·00
7 4 c. Casting nets (R.) 30 35

8 20 c. Beating a pandanus leaf (R.) † £100
9 20 c. Beating a pandanus leaf (*wmk sideways*) (R.) 4·50 3·25
10 25 c. Loading copra 35·00 48·00
a. Opt double (Blk. + R.) £250
10*b* 50 c. Local handicrafts £700 £800

(*b*) W w **14** (*sideways on* 3, 5, 20, 25 *and* 35 c.; *inverted on others*)
11 1 c. Cutting toddy (R.) 20 20
12 3 c. Cleaning pandanus leaves (R.) 40 30
13 5 c. Gilbertese canoe (R.) 50 35
14 6 c. De-husking coconuts 50 40
15 8 c. Weaving pandanus fronds (R.) 50 45
16 10 c. Weaving a basket 50 45
17 15 c. Tiger Shark 1·50 1·00
18 20 c. Beating a pandanus leaf (R.) 1·50 80
19 25 c. Loading copra 2·00 1·00
20 35 c. Fishing at night (Gold) 2·00 1·75
21 50 c. Local handicrafts 2·50 2·75
22 $1 Weaving coconut screens (R.) 8·00 9·00
a. Opt double £275
3, 4, 7 *and* 12/22 *Set of* 14 19·00 17·00

3 M.V. *Teraaka*

(Des J. Cooter. Litho Questa)

1976 (1 July). *Horiz designs as T* **3**. *Multicoloured.* W w **14** (*sideways*). *P* 14.
23 1 c. Type **3** 15 15
24 3 c. M.V. *Tautunu* 20 20
25 4 c. Moorish Idol 20 20
26 5 c. Hibiscus 20 20
27 6 c. Eastern Reef Heron 35 25
28 7 c. Tarawa Cathedral 20 25
29 8 c. Frangipani 25 25
30 10 c. Maneaba building 20 30
31 12 c. Betio Harbour 45 45
32 15 c. Evening scene 55 45
33 20 c. Marakei Atoll 35 35
34 35 c. Tangintebu Chapel 35 40
35 40 c. Flamboyant tree 40 45
36 50 c. *Hypolimnas bolina elliciana* (butterfly) 2·25 1·75
37 $1 Ferry *Tabakea* 2·00 2·50
38 $2 National flag 2·25 2·75
23/38 *Set of* 16 9·00 9·50

4 Church

5 Porcupine Fish Helmet

(Des P. Powell. Litho Questa)

1976 (15 Sept). *Christmas. Children's Drawings. T* **4** *and similar multicoloured designs.* W w **14** (*sideways on* 5 *and* 35 c.). *P* 14.
39 5 c. Type **4** 35 15
40 15 c. Feasting (*vert*) 50 15
41 20 c. Maneaba (*vert*) 55 30
42 35 c. Dancing 70 45
39/42 *Set of* 4 1·90 95

(Des J. Cooter. Litho J.W.)

1976 (6 Dec). *Artefacts. T* **5** *and similar vert designs. Multicoloured.* W w **14**. *P* 13.
43 5 c. Type **5** 35 15
44 15 c. Shark's Teeth Dagger 50 35
45 20 c. Fighting Gauntlet 55 40
46 35 c. Coconut Body Armour 70 55
43/6 *Set of* 4 1·90 1·25
MS47 140 × 130 mm. Nos. 43/6. P 14 10·00 14·00

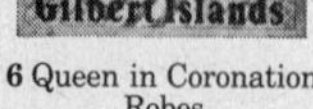

6 Queen in Coronation Robes

7 Commodore Byron and H.M.S. *Dolphin*

(Des J. Cooter. Litho Questa)

1977 (7 Feb). *Silver Jubilee. T* **6** *and similar vert designs. Multicoloured.* W w **14**. *P* 14.
48 8 c. Prince Charles' visit, 1970 15 10
49 20 c. Prince Philip's visit, 1959 20 15
50 40 c. Type **6** 30 35
48/50 *Set of* 3 60 55

(Des J. Cooter. Litho Questa)

1977 (1 June). *Explorers. T* **7** *and similar horiz designs. Multicoloured.* W w **14** (*sideways*). *P* 14.
51 5 c. Type **7** 1·00 1·50
52 15 c. Capt. Fanning and *Betsey* 1·50 2·75
53 20 c. Admiral Bellingshausen and *Vostok* 2·00 3·25
54 35 c. Capt. Wilkes and *Vincennes* 3·50 5·75
51/4 *Set of* 4 7·00 12·00

8 H.M.S. *Resolution* and H.M.S. *Discovery*

9 Emblem and Island Scene

(Des J. Cooter. Litho Questa)

1977 (12 Sept). *Christmas and Bicentenary of Capt. Cook's Discovery of Christmas Is. T* **8** *and similar multicoloured designs.* W w **14** (*sideways on* 15 *and* 40 c.). *P* 14.
55 8 c. Type **8** 55 10
56 15 c. Logbook entry (*horiz*) 70 15
57 20 c. Capt. Cook 85 20
58 40 c. Landing party (*horiz*) 1·75 60
55/8 *Set of* 4 3·50 95
MS59 140 × 140 mm. Nos. 55/8. Wmk sideways 10·00 12·00

(Des J. Cooter. Litho J.W.)

1977 (5 Dec). *50th Anniv of Scouting in the Gilbert Is. T* **9** *and similar multicoloured designs.* W w **14** (*sideways on* 15 *and* 20 c.). *P* 13.
60 8 c. Type **9** 20 10
61 15 c. Patrol meeting (*horiz*) 30 20
62 20 c. Mat making (*horiz*) 40 20
63 40 c. Canoeing 50 55
60/3 *Set of* 4 1·25 95

10 Taurus (The Bull)

11 Unicorn of Scotland

(Des J. Cooter. Litho Questa)

1978 (20 Feb). *Night Sky over the Gilbert Is. T* **10** *and similar vert designs.* W w **14**. *P* 14.
64 10 c. black and light new blue 20 15
65 20 c. black and light rose-red 30 30
66 25 c. black and sage-green 35 35
67 45 c. black and orange 50 60
64/7 *Set of* 4 1·25 1·25
Designs:—20 c. Canis Major (the Great Dog); 25 c. Scorpio (the Scorpion); 45 c. Orion (the Giant Warrior).

(Des C. Abbott. Litho Questa)

1978 (21 Apr). *25th Anniv of Coronation. T* **11** *and similar vert designs. P* 15.
68 45 c. green, bluish violet and silver 30 40
a. Sheetlet. Nos. 68/70 × 2 1·60
69 45 c. multicoloured 30 40
70 45 c. green, bluish violet and silver 30 40
68/70 *Set of* 3 80 1·10
Designs:—No. 68, Type **11**; No. 69, Queen Elizabeth II; No. 70, Great Frigate Bird.
Nos. 68/70 were printed together in small sheets of 6, containing two *se-tenant* strips of 3, with horizontal gutter margin between.

12 Birds in Flight to Tarawa

(Des local artists; adapted G. Hutchins. Litho Enschedé)

1978 (5 June). *25th Anniv of Return of King George V School to Tarawa. T* **12** *and similar horiz designs. Multicoloured.* W w **14** (*sideways*). *P* 14 × 13.
71 10 c. Type **12** 10 10
72 20 c. Tarawa, Abemama and school badge 20 20
73 25 c. Rejoicing islanders 20 20
74 45 c. King George V School on Tarawa and Abemama 35 35
71/4 *Set of* 4 75 75

13 "Te Kaue ni Maie"

14 H.M.S. *Endeavour*

(Des W. Walsh. Litho J.W.)

1978 (25 Sept). *Christmas. Kaue (traditional head decorations). T* **13** *and similar horiz designs. Multicoloured.* W w **14** (*sideways*). *P* 14.
75 10 c. Type **13** 15 10
76 20 c. "Te Itera" 20 15
77 25 c. "Te Bau" 25 20
78 45 c. "Te Tai" 35 30
75/8 *Set of* 4 85 65
MS79 149 × 99 mm. Nos. 75/8. P 13 × 13½ 1·75 4·50

(Des and litho (45 c. also embossed) Walsall)

1979 (22 Feb*). *Bicentenary of Captain Cook's Voyages, 1768–79. T* **14** *and similar vert designs. P* 11.
80 10 c. multicoloured 25 15
81 20 c. multicoloured 40 25
82 25 c. black, light green and pale lilac 50 35
83 45 c. multicoloured 75 70
80/3 *Set of* 4 1·75 1·25
Designs:—20 c. Green Turtle; 25 c. Quadrant; 45 c. Flaxman/Wedgwood medallion of Captain Cook.
*This was the local issue date; the stamps were released in London on 15 January.

The Gilbert Islands achieved independence on 12 July 1979 and were renamed KIRIBATI.

Gold Coast

CROWN COLONY

PRICES FOR STAMPS ON COVER TO 1945

Nos. 1/3	*from* × 10
Nos. 4/10	*from* × 8
Nos. 11/20	*from* × 10
Nos. 22/5	—
Nos. 26/34	*from* × 7
Nos. 35/6	*from* × 12
Nos. 38/69	*from* × 4
Nos. 70/98	*from* × 3
Nos. 100/2	—
Nos. 103/12	*from* × 5
Nos. 113/16	*from* × 3
Nos. 117/19	*from* × 4
Nos. 120/32	*from* × 3
Nos. D1/4	*from* × 8

1

ONE PENNY.
(2)

(Typo D.L.R.)

1875 (July). *Wmk Crown CC. P* 12½.
1 1 1d. blue £425 65·00
2 4d. magenta £400 75·00
3 6d. orange £600 55·00

1876–84. *Wmk Crown CC. P* 14.
4 1 ½d. olive-yellow (1879) 26·00 22·00
5 1d. blue 13·00 6·50
a. Bisected (½d.) (on cover) (1884) † £2250
6 2d. green (1879) 48·00 11·00
a. Bisected (1d.) (on cover) (1884) † £2000
b. Quartered (½d.) (on cover) (1884) † £2750
7 4d. magenta £150 6·00
a. Bisected (2d.) (on cover) (1884) † £3500
b. Quartered (1d.) (on cover) (1884) † £4500
8 6d. orange 90·00 18·00
a. Bisected (3d.) (on cover) (1884) † £4000
b. Sixth (1d.) (on cover) (1884) † £5000

During 1884 some values were in short supply and the use of bisects and other divided stamps is known as follows:
No. 5a. Used as part of 2½d. rate from Quittah
No. 6a. Used as 1d. rate from Cape Coast Castle, Quittah, Salt Pond, Secondee and Winnebah
No. 6b. Used as part of 2½d. rate from Cape Coast Castle
No. 7a. Used as 2d or as part of 2½d. rate from Quittah
No. 7b. Used as 1d. rate from Appam, Axim, Cape Coast Castle and Winnebah
No. 8a. Used as 3d. rate from Secondee
No. 8b. Used as 1d. rate from Winnebah

1883 (May)? *No. 7 surch locally.*
8c 1 "1d." on 4d. magenta

1883. *Wmk Crown CA. P 14.*
9 1 ½d. olive-yellow (January) £120 50·00
10 1d. blue (May) £850 60·00

1884 (Aug)–**91.** *Wmk Crown CA. P 14.*
11 1 ½d. green 65 35
a. Dull green 45 30
12 1d. rose-carmine 75 40
a. Carmine 75 30
b. Bisected (½d.) on cover † £2750
13 2d. grey 1·90 1·90
b. Slate 1·40 50
c. Bisected (1d.) (on cover)
d. Quartered (½d.) (on cover)
14 2½d. ultramarine and orange (13.3.91) 95 35
15 3d. olive-yellow (9.89) 5·00 4·00
a. Olive 3·75 4·00
16 4d. deep mauve (3.85) 2·00 80
a. Rosy mauve 3·00 2·50
17 6d. orange (1.89) 3·00 2·75
a. Orange-brown 4·50 2·75
b. Bisected (3d.) (on cover)
18 1s. violet (1888) 17·00 12·00
a. Bright mauve 3·50 1·00
19 2s. yellow-brown (1888) 65·00 26·00
a. Deep brown 22·00 15·00
11/19*a* *Set of* 9 35·00 25·00
14/15, 18/19 Optd "Specimen" *Set of* 4 £150

During 1886 and 1889 some values were in short supply and the use of bisects and other divided stamps is known as follows:
No. 12b. Used as part of 2½d. rate from Cape Coast Castle
No. 13c. Used as 1d. or as part of 2d. rate from Cape Coast Castle, Chamah and Dixcove
No. 13d. Used as part of 2½d. rate from Cape Coast Castle
No. 17b. Used as 3d. from Appam

1889 (Mar). *No. 17 surch with T 2.*
20 1 1d. on 6d. orange £100 48·00

In some sheets examples may be found with the bar and "PENNY" spaced 8 mm, the normal spacing being 7 mm.

USED HIGH VALUES. Until the introduction of airmail in 1929 there was no postal use for values over 10s. Post Offices did, however, apply postal cancellations to high value stamps required for telegram fees.

3 4

1889 (Sept)–**94.** *Wmk Crown CA. P 14.*
22 3 5s. dull mauve and blue 40·00 11·00
23 10s. dull mauve and red 60·00 15·00
a. Dull mauve and carmine £250 75·00
24 20s. green and red £3250
25 20s. dull mauve and black/*red* (1894) £150 35·00
22/5 Optd "Specimen" *Set of* 4 £500

1898–1902. *Wmk Crown CA. P 14.*
26 3 ½d. dull mauve and green 75 25
27 1d. dull mauve and rose 40 25
27a 4 2d. dull mauve and orange-red (1902) 20·00 35·00
28 3 2½d. dull mauve and ultramarine 3·75 3·00
29 4 3d. dull mauve and orange 4·50 1·00
30 6d. dull mauve and violet 5·50 1·00
31 3 1s. green and black 5·50 5·50
32 2s. green and carmine 9·00 14·00
33 5s. green and mauve (1900) 35·00 17·00
34 10s. green and brown (1900) 95·00 30·00
26/34 *Set of* 10 £160 95·00
26/34 Optd "Specimen" *Set of* 10 £250

1901 (6 Oct). *Nos. 28 and 30 surch with T 2.*
35 1d. on 2½d. dull mauve and ultramarine 1·25 3·00
36 1d. on 6d. dull mauve and violet 1·25 3·00
a. "ONE" omitted £400 £550

6 7 8

1902. *Wmk Crown CA. P 14.*
38 6 ½d. dull purple and green 40 40
39 1d. dull purple and carmine 75 15
40 7 2d. dull purple and orange-red 3·25 2·75
41 6 2½d. dull purple and ultramarine 4·00 6·00
42 7 3d. dull purple and orange 1·50 1·00
43 6d. dull purple and violet 1·50 1·00
44 6 1s. green and black 2·25 2·50
45 2s. green and carmine 10·00 8·50
46 5s. green and mauve 16·00 27·00
47 10s. green and brown 35·00 60·00
48 20s. purple and black/*red* £110 £120
38/48 *Set of* 11 £160 £200
38/48 Optd "Specimen" *Set of* 11 £250

1904–7. *Wmk Mult Crown CA. P 14.*
49 6 ½d. dull purple and green, **O** (3.06) 2·50 2·50
50 1d. dull purple and carmine, **OC** (10.04) 1·00 10
51 7 2d. dull purple and orange-red, **OC** (11.04) 3·50 30
52 6 2½d. dull purple & ultramarine, **O** (6.06) 25·00 16·00
53 7 3d. dull purple and orange, **OC** (8.05) 6·50 30
54 6d. dull purple and violet, **CO** (3.06) 17·00 1·25
57 2s. 6d. green & yell, **C** (3.06) (Optd S. £60) 26·00 48·00
49/57 *Set of* 7 70·00 60·00

1907–13. *Wmk Mult Crown CA. P 14.*
59 6 ½d. dull green, **O** (5.07) 1·25 30
a. Blue-green (1909) 1·75 90
60 1d. red, **O** (2.07) 80 10
61 7 2d. greyish slate, **O** (4.09) 2·00 30
62 6 2½d. blue, **O** (4.07) 3·50 1·75
63 7 3d. purple/*yellow*, **C** (16.4.09) 4·00 45
64 6d. dull and deep purple, **C** (12.08) 8·00 55
a. Dull and bright purple, **C** (1911) 3·50 2·50
65 6 1s. black/*green*, **C** (10.09) 4·50 40
66 2s. purple and blue/*blue*, **OC** (1910) 3·50 12·00
67 7 2s. 6d. blue and red/*blue*, **C** (1911) 17·00 28·00
68 6 5s. green and red/*yellow*, **C** (1913) 32·00 60·00
59/68 *Set of* 10 65·00 95·00
59/68 Optd "Specimen" *Set of* 10 £200

A 10s. green and red on green, and a 20s. purple and black on red, both Type **6**, were prepared for use but not issued. Both exist overprinted "Specimen" (*Price for 10s. in this condition* £375).

(Typo D.L.R.)

1908 (Nov). *Wmk Mult Crown CA. P 14.*
69 8 1d. red, **O** (Optd S. £45) 25 10

9 10 11

(Typo D.L.R.)

1913–21. *Ordinary paper (½d. to 2½d.) or chalk-surfaced paper (others). Wmk Mult Crown CA. P 14.*
70 9 ½d. green 65 50
a. Yellow-green (1916) 90 90
72 10 1d. red 20 10
a. Scarlet (1919) 65 30
74 11 2d. grey 1·50 2·00
a. Slate-grey 7·00 3·50
76 9 2½d. bright blue 75 30
77 11 3d. purple/*yellow* (8.15) (Optd S. £30) 80 40
a. White back (9.13) 30 40
b. On orange-buff (1919) 3·00 5·50
c. On pale yellow (Die II) (1919) 4·75 4·50
78 6d. dull and bright purple 2·00 1·75
79 9 1s. black/*green* 60 1·00
a. Wmk sideways
b. On blue green, olive back (1921) (Optd S. £30) 50 35
c. On emerald back (Die I) (1921) (Optd S. £30) 2·00 1·25
d. On emerald back (Die II) (1921) (Optd S. £35) 1·50 50
80 2s. purple and blue/*blue* (Die I) 5·00 1·10
a. Die II (1921) £120 65·00
81 11 2s. 6d. black and red/*blue* (Die I) 5·00 10·00
a. Die II (1921) 22·00 28·00
82 9 5s. green and red/*yellow* (1916) (Optd S. £40) 5·50 22·00
a. White back (10.13) 7·00 26·00
b. On orange-buff 25·00 42·00
c. On pale yellow (Die I) (1921) 42·00 60·00
d. Die II (1921) 27·00 85·00
83 10s. green and red/*green* 32·00 60·00
a. On blue-green, olive back (1919) 17·00 45·00
b. On emerald back (1921) 27·00 70·00
84 20s. purple and black /*red* (1916) 95·00 80·00
70/84 *Set of* 12 £120 £140
70/6, 77*a*, 78/81, 82*a*/4 Optd "Specimen" *Set of* 12 £250

WAR TAX

ONE PENNY

(12)

13 King George V and Christiansborg Castle

1918 (May). *Surch with T 12.*
85 10 1d. on 1d. red (Optd S. £50) 15 25

1921–24. *Ordinary paper (½d. to 3d.) or chalk-surfaced paper (others). Wmk Mult Script CA. P 14.*
86 9 ½d. green 25 30
87 10 1d. chocolate-brown (1922) 25 10
88 11 1½d. red (1922) 25 10
89 2d. grey 25 10
90 9 2½d. yellow-orange (1922) 25 4·50
91 11 3d. bright blue (1922) 25 30
94 6d. dull and bright purple 45 1·60
95 9 1s. black/*emerald* (1924) 95 2·25
96 2s. purple and blue/*blue* (1923) 2·00 3·25
97 11 2s. 6d. black and red/*blue* (1924) 4·00 9·00
98 9 5s. green and red/*pale yellow* (1924) 7·00 20·00
100 11 15s. dull purple and green (Die I) £110 £190
a. Die II (1924) (Optd S. £110) £100 £190
102 £2 green and orange (Die I) £400 £650
86/100a *Set of* 12 £110 £200
86/102 Optd "Specimen" *Set of* 13 £400

In Nos. 88, 100 and 102 the words "GOLD COAST" are in distinctly larger letters.

(Photo Harrison)

1928 (1 Aug). *Wmk Mult Script CA. P 13½ × 15.*
103 13 ½d. green 15 20
104 1d. red-brown 15 10
105 1½d. scarlet 35 1·50
106 2d. slate 15 10
107 2½d. orange-yellow 90 3·50
108 3d. blue 55 40
109 6d. black and purple 55 30
110 1s. black and vermilion 75 75
111 13 2s. black and violet 7·00 2·50
112 5s. carmine and olive-green 17·00 28·00
103/12 *Set of* 10 25·00 35·00
103/12 Optd "Specimen" *Set of* 10 £225

1935 (6 May). *Silver Jubilee. As Nos. 91/4 of Antigua, but printed by B.W. P 11 × 12.*
113 1d. ultramarine and grey-black 50 20
a. Extra flagstaff £120
b. Short extra flagstaff 65·00
c. Lightning conductor 75·00
d. Flagstaff on right-hand turret 50·00
114 3d. brown and deep blue 2·25 4·00
a. Extra flagstaff £120
c. Lightning conductor 75·00
115 6d. green and indigo 2·25 5·50
a. Extra flagstaff £120
b. Short extra flagstaff 75·00
c. Lightning conductor 75·00
d. Flagstaff on right-hand turret 75·00
116 1s. slate and purple 2·25 5·50
a. Extra flagstaff £120
b. Short extra flagstaff 75·00
c. Lightning conductor 75·00
113/16 *Set of* 4 6·50 14·00
113/16 Perf "Specimen" *Set of* 4 75·00

For illustrations of plate varieties see Omnibus section following Zululand.

1937 (12 May). *Coronation. As Nos. 13/15 of Aden, but printed by B.W. P 11 × 11½.*
117 1d. buff 45 30
118 2d. slate 55 60
119 3d. blue 80 95
117/19 *Set of* 3 1·60 1·75
117/19 Perf "Specimen" *Set of* 3 50·00

14

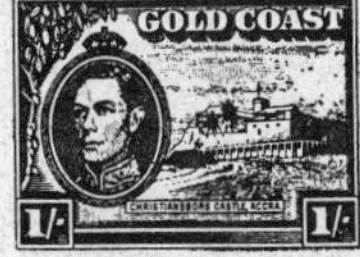

15 King George VI and Christiansborg Castle, Accra

(Recess B.W.)

1938 (1 Apr)–**41.** *Wmk Mult Script CA. P 12 × 11½ (T 14) or 11½ × 12 (T 15)*.*
120 14 ½d. green 20 10
121 1d. red-brown 25 10
122 1½d. scarlet 35 15
123 2d. slate 35 10
124 3d. blue 35 10
125 4d. magenta 50 50
126 6d. purple 50 10
127 9d. orange 50 40
128 15 1s. black and olive-green 55 10
129 1s. 3d. brown & turquoise-bl (12.4.41) 55 10
130 2s. blue and violet 2·25 2·75
131 5s. olive-green and carmine 2·75 5·00
132 10s. black and violet (7.40) 4·25 10·00
120/32 *Set of* 13 12·00 17·00
120/32 Perf "Specimen" *Set of* 13 £160

*Nos. 120 to 132, except 1s. 3d. and 10s., exist in two perforations: (*a*) Line-perf 12, from early printings; (*b*) Comb-perf 12 × 11.8 (vertical design) or 11.8 × 12 (horiz design) from later printings. The 1s. 3d. and 10s. exist only comb-perf 11.8 × 12.

1946 (14 Oct). *Victory. As Nos. 28/9 of Aden. P 13½ × 14.*
133 2d. slate-violet 3·50 2·00
a. Perf 13½ 10 10
134 4d. claret 2·00 2·50
a. Perf 13½ 25 65
133/4 Perf "Specimen" *Set of* 2 50·00

16 Northern Territories Mounted Constabulary

17 Christiansborg Castle

(Des B. A. Johnston (1½d.), M. Ziorkley and B. A. Abban (2d.), P.O. draughtsman (2½d.), C. Gomez (1s.), M. Ziorkley (10s.); others from photographs. Recess B.W.)

1948 (1 July). *T 16/17 and similar designs. Wmk Mult Script CA. P 12 × 11½ (vert) or 11½ × 12 (horiz).*
135 ½d. emerald-green 20 25
136 1d. blue 15 10
137 1½d. scarlet 75 70
138 2d. purple-brown 45 10
139 2½d. yellow-brown and scarlet 1·25 1·25
140 3d. light blue 1·50 15
141 4d. magenta 1·25 1·25
142 6d. black and orange 30 10
143 1s. black and vermilion 30 10
144 2s. sage-green and magenta 2·25 80
145 5s. purple and black 10·00 1·50
146 10s. black and sage-green 8·00 4·00
135/46 *Set of* 12 24·00 9·00
135/46 Perf "Specimen" *Set of* 12 £225

Designs: *Horiz*—1½d. Emblem of Joint Provincial Council; 2½d. Map showing position of Gold Coast; 3d. Manganese mine; 4d. Lake Bosumtwi; 1s. Breaking cocoa pods; 2s. Trooping the Colour; 5s. Surfboats. *Vert*—2d. Talking drums; 6d. Cocoa farmer; 10s. Forest.

1948 (20 Dec). *Royal Silver Wedding. As Nos. 30/1 of Aden.*
147 1½d. scarlet 20 15
148 10s. grey-olive .. .. 8·00 7·00

1949 (10 Oct). *75th Anniv of U.P.U. As Nos. 114/17 of Antigua.*
149 2d. red-brown 30 30
150 2½d. orange .. .. 1·00 1·50
151 3d. deep blue 75 70
152 1s. blue-green 75 50
149/52 .. .. *Set of* 4 2·50 2·75

28 Northern Territories Mounted Constabulary

(Recess B.W.)

1952 (19 Dec)–**54**. *Designs previously used for King George VI issue, but with portrait of Queen Elizabeth II, as in T* **28**. *Portrait faces left on* ½d., 4d., 6d., 1s. *and* 5s. *Wmk Mult Script CA. P* 12 × 11½ *(vert) or* 11½ × 12 *(horiz).*
153 ½d. yellow-brown and scarlet (1.4.53) .. 10 10
a. *Bistre-brown and scarlet* (7.4.54) .. 10 10
154 1d. deep blue (1.3.54) 15 10
155 1½d. emerald-green (1.4.53) 25 60
156 2d. chocolate (1.3.54) 30 10
157 2½d. scarlet 35 35
158 3d. magenta (1.4.53) 35 10
159 4d. blue (1.4.53) 30 10
160 6d. black and orange (1.3.54) 30 10
161 1s. black and orange-red (1.3.54) .. 30 10
162 2s. brown-olive and carmine (1.3.54) .. 4·50 30
163 5s. purple and black (1.3.54) .. .. 7·50 1·75
164 10s. black and olive-green (1.3.54) .. 7·50 7·50
153/64 .. .. *Set of* 12 20·00 9·50

Designs: *Horiz*—½d. Map showing position of Gold Coast; 1d. Christiansborg Castle; 1½d. Emblem of Joint Provincial Council; 3d. Manganese mine; 4d. Lake Bosumtwi; 1s. Breaking cocoa pods; 2s. Trooping the colour; 5s. Surfboats. *Vert*—2d. Talking drums; 6d. Cocoa farmer; 10s. Forest.

Nos. 153/4 exist in coils constructed from normal sheets.

1953 (2 June). *Coronation. As No. 47 of Aden, but ptd by B.W.*
165 2d. black and sepia 10 10

POSTAGE DUE STAMPS

D 1

(Typo D.L.R.)

1923. *Yellowish toned paper. Wmk Mult Script CA. P* 14.
D1 D 1 ½d. black .. .. 14·00 60·00
D2 1d. black .. .. 75 1·00
D3 2d. black .. .. 12·00 14·00
D4 3d. black .. .. 15·00 9·50
D1/4 .. .. .. *Set of* 4 38·00 75·00
D1/4 Optd "Specimen" .. *Set of* 4 70·00

1951–52. *Chalk-surfaced paper. Wmk Mult Script CA. P* 14.
D5 D 1 2d. black (13.12.51) .. .. 1·50 6·00
a. Error. Crown missing, W **9a** .. £180
b. Error. St. Edward's Crown, W **9b** .. £130
D6 3d. black (13.12.51) .. .. 1·50 6·00
a. Error. Crown missing, W **9a** .. £180
b. Error. St. Edward's Crown, W **9b** .. £130
D7 6d. black (1.10.52) .. .. 2·00 10·00
a. Error. Crown missing, W **9a** .. £225
b. Error. St. Edward's Crown, W **9b** .. £160
D8 1s. black (1.10.52) .. .. 2·25 20·00
b. Error. St. Edward's Crown, W **9b** .. £225
D5/8 .. .. *Set of* 4 6·50 38·00

On 6 March 1957 Gold Coast became the Dominion of GHANA.

Grenada

The earliest recorded postmark of the British administration of Grenada dates from 1784, and, although details of the early period are somewhat sparse, it would appear that the island's postal service was operated as a branch of the British G.P.O. In addition to a Packet Agency at St. George's, the capital, it is known that a further agency existed at Carriacou, in the Grenadines, for a few years after 1842.

Stamps of Great Britain were supplied to the St. George's office from 1858 until the colony assumed responsibility for the postal service in September 1860. Following the take-over the crowned-circle handstamp, No. CC2, was again used until the Grenada adhesives were issued in 1861.

There was no internal postal service before 1861.

For illustrations of the handstamp and postmark types see BRITISH POST OFFICE ABROAD notes, following GREAT BRITAIN.

CARRIACOU

CROWNED-CIRCLE HANDSTAMPS

CC1 CC 1 CARRIACOU (13.11.1846) .. .. .. †

Although recorded in the G.P.O. proof book no example of No. CC1 has been reported used from Grenada.

ST. GEORGE'S

CROWNED-CIRCLE HANDSTAMPS

CC2 CC 1 GRENADA (R.) (24.10.1850) *Price on cover* £750

Stamps of GREAT BRITAIN *cancelled* "A 15" *as Type* **2**

1858 *to* **1860**.
Z1 1d. rose-red (1857), *perf* 14 .. .. £325
Z2 2d. blue (1858) (Plate No. 7) £600
Z3 4d. rose (1857) £200
Z4 6d. lilac (1856) £120
Z5 1s. green (1856) £600

PRICES FOR STAMPS ON COVER TO 1945	
Nos. 1/3	*from* × 10
Nos. 4/13	*from* × 5
Nos. 14/19	*from* × 6
Nos. 20/3	*from* × 8
Nos. 24/7	*from* × 10
No. 28	—
No. 29	*from* × 5
Nos. 30/6	*from* × 8
Nos. 37/9	*from* × 4
No. 40	*from* × 20
Nos. 41/7	*from* × 4
Nos. 48/101	*from* × 3
Nos. 109/11	*from* × 5
Nos. 112/48	*from* × 3
Nos. 149/51	*from* × 6
Nos. 152/63	*from* × 2
Nos. D1/3	*from* × 25
Nos. D4/7	*from* × 12
Nos. D8/14	*from* × 20

CROWN COLONY

PRINTERS. Types **1** and **5** recess-printed by Perkins, Bacon and Co.

1

2 Small Star

(Eng C. H. Jeens)

1861 (June)–**62**. *No wmk. Wove paper. (a) Rough perf* 14 *to* 16.
1 1 1d. bluish green £3000 £275
2 1d. green (5.62) .. .. 50·00 38·00
a. Imperf between (horiz pair) ..
3 6d. rose (*shades*) .. .. .. £750 90·00

(*b*) *Perf* 11 *to* 12½
3a 1 6d. lake-red (5.62) £750

No. 3*a* is only known unused, and has also been seen on laid paper. (*Price* £1100).

SIDEWAYS WATERMARK. W **2/3** when sideways show two points of star downwards.

1863–71 W **2** (*Small Star*). *Rough perf* 14 *to* 16.
4 1 1d. green (3.64) .. .. 60·00 12·00
5 1d. yellowish green .. .. .. 95·00 22·00
6 6d. rose (*shades*) (5.63) .. .. £600 12·00
7 6d. orange-red (*shades*) (5.66) .. £600 12·00
8 6d. dull rose-red (wmk sideways) .. £3000 £225
9 6d. vermilion (5.71) .. .. .. £600 12·00
a. Double impression .. .. .. — £1750

The sideways wmk is an identifying aid to the rare shade, No. 8. Normally in this issue the wmk is upright, but it also exists sideways.

1873 (Jan). W **2** (*Small Star sideways*). *Clean-cut perf* 15.
10 1 1d. deep green .. .. 65·00 24·00
a. Bisected diag (on cover) .. .. † £6000
b. Imperf between (pair) .. .. — £3000

3 Large Star

4 Broad-pointed Star

1873 (Sept)–**74**. W **3** (*Large Star*). *Intermediate perf* 15.
11 1 1d. blue-green (wmk sideways) (2.74) .. 55·00 16·00
a. Double impression .. ..
12 6d. orange-vermilion (upright wmk) .. £600 25·00

POSTAGE

ONE SHILLING

5 (6)

NOTE. The early ½d., 2½d., 4d. and 1s. postage stamps were made by surcharging the undenominated Type **5** design.

The surcharges were from two founts of type—one about 1½ mm high, the other 2 mm high—so there are short and tall letters on the same stamp; also the spacing varies considerably, so that the length of the words varies.

Examples of Type **5** with surcharges, but without the "POSTAGE" inscription, are revenue stamps.

1875 (July). *Surch with T* **6**. *W* **3**. *P* 14.
13 5 1s. deep mauve (B.) .. .. .. £600 9·00
a. "SHLLIING" .. .. .. — £700
b. "NE SHILLING" .. .. .. — £2250
c. Inverted "S" in "POSTAGE" .. £3500 £500
d. "OSTAGE" .. ..

1875 (Dec.) W **3** (*Large Star, upright*).
14 1 1d. green *to* yellow-green (*p* 14) .. 50·00 5·00
a. Bisected diag (on cover) .. .. † £6000
15 1d. green (*p* 15) £7000 £2000

No. 14 was perforated at Somerset House. 40 sheets of No. 15 were perforated by Perkins, Bacon to replace spoilages and to complete the order.

1878 (Sept). W **2** (*Small Star, sideways*). *Intermediate perf* 15.
16 1 1d. green .. .. £225 25·00
17 6d. deep vermilion .. .. .. £750 25·00
a. Double impression .. .. .. — £1500

1879 (Dec). W **2** (*Small Star, upright*). *Rough perf* 15.
18 1 1d. pale green (*thin paper*) .. .. £300 16·00
a. Double impression .. .. ..

1881 (April). W **2** (*Small Star, sideways*). *Rough perf* 14½.
19 1 1d. green .. .. £110 5·50
a. Bisected diag (on cover) .. .. † £6000

POSTAGE POSTAGE POSTAGE

HALF-PENNY

FOUR PENCE

(7) (8) (9)

1881 (April). *Surch with T* **7/9**. *P* 14½. *(a) Wmk Large Star, T* **3**.
20 5 ½d. pale mauve .. .. 27·00 10·00
21 ½d. deep mauve .. .. 9·50 5·50
a. Imperf (pair) £275
ab. Ditto. "OSTAGE" (R.9/4.) £3000
b. Surch double £275
c. "OSTAGE" (R.9/4) £140 £130
d. No hyphen £130 £110
e. "ALF-PENNY" £2250
f. Wmk upright .. .. .. — £350
g. Ditto. "OSTAGE" (R.9/4) .. .. — £2000
22 2½d. rose-lake .. .. 35·00 5·50
a. Imperf (pair) £325
b. Imperf between (horiz pair) .. £1900
c. No stop .. .. .. £160 95·00
d. "PENCF" (R.8/12) £250 £180
23 4d. blue .. .. 90·00 8·00

The watermark is normally *sideways* on the ½d.

(*b*) *Wmk Broad-pointed Star, T* **4**
24 5 2½d. rose-lake .. .. £120 35·00
a. No stop £550 £200
b. "PENCF" (R.8/12) £600 £250
25 2½d. claret £375 £120
a. No stop £950 £475
b. "PENCF" (R.8/12) £1300 £600
25c 2½d. deep claret £600 £225
d. No stop £2250 £900
e. "PENCF" (R.8/12) £2750 £1100
26 4d. blue £200 £175

Examples of the "F" for "E" error on the 2½d. value should not be confused with a somewhat similar broken "E" variety. The latter is always without the stop and shows other damage to the "E". The authentic error always occurs with the full stop shown.

The "no stop" variety occurs on R.3/4, R.6/2, R.8/3 and R.9/7.

ONE PENNY POSTAGE. POSTAGE POSTAGE

(10) (11) (12)

1883 (Jan). *Revenue stamps (T* **5** *with green surcharge as in T* **10**) *optd for postage. W* **2** (*Small Star*). *P* 14½.

(*a*) *Optd horizontally with T* **11**.
27 5 1d. orange .. .. £200 45·00
a. "POSTAGE" inverted £1600 £1100
b. "POSTAGE" double £1200 £1100
c. Inverted "S" in "POSTAGE" .. £550 £500
d. Bisected diag (on cover) .. .. † £2750

(b) *Optd diagonally with T 11 twice on each stamp, the stamp being cut and each half used as ½d.*

28 5 Half of 1d. orange £550 £300
a. Unsevered pair £3500 £1300
b. "POSTAGE" inverted .. .. — £1100

(c) *Optd with T 12, the stamps divided diagonally and each half used as ½d.*

29 5 Half of 1d. orange £160 £120
a. Unsevered pair £1200 £600

Nos. 27/9 exist with wmk either upright or sideways.

1d. Revenue stamps are known with "POSTAGE" written by hand, in red or black. These were apparently used, but not officially authorised.

GRENADA POSTAGE ONE PENNY — 13; d. 1 POSTAGE. — (14); GRENADA POSTAGE & REVENUE ONE PENNY — 15

(Typo D.L.R.)

1883. *Wmk Crown CA. P 14.*
30 13 ½d. dull green (February) 90 60
a. *Tête-bêche* (pair) .. .. .. 4·00 13·00
31 1d. carmine (February) .. .. 42·00 3·25
a. *Tête-bêche* (pair) £160 £170
32 2½d. ultramarine (May) .. .. 6·50 50
a. *Tête-bêche* (pair) .. .. .. 20·00 40·00
33 4d. greyish slate (May) .. .. 4·50 1·75
a. *Tête-bêche* (pair) .. .. .. 16·00 32·00
34 6d. mauve (May) .. .. .. 3·50 3·75
a. *Tête-bêche* (pair) .. .. .. 18·00 45·00
35 8d. grey-brown (February) .. .. 8·00 12·00
a. *Tête-bêche* (pair) .. .. .. 32·00 70·00
36 1s. pale violet (April) .. .. 85·00 55·00
a. *Tête-bêche* (pair) £500
30/36 .. .. *Set of* 7 £130 65·00

Types 13 and 15 were printed in rows *tête-bêche* in the sheets.

1886. *Revenue stamps (T 5 with green surch as T 10), surch with T 14. P 14. (a) Wmk Large Star, T 3.*
37 5 1d. on 1½d. orange (October) .. .. 28·00 24·00
a. Surch inverted £225 £225
b. Surch double £225 £225
c. "THRFE" £225 £225
d. "PFNCE" £225 £225
e. "HALH" £225 £225
f. Bisected diag (on cover) .. .. † £1400
38 1d. on 1s. orange (December) .. .. 28·00 26·00
a. "POSTAGE" (no stop) £200
b. "SHILLNG" £400 £350
c. Wide space (3½ mm) between "ONE" and "SHILLING" £400 £350
d. Bisected diag (on cover) .. .. † £1400

(b) *Wmk Small Star, T 2*
39 5 1d. on 4d. orange (November) .. .. £110 80·00

1887 (Jan). *Wmk Crown CA. P 14.*
40 15 1d. carmine (Optd S. £50) 50 20
a. *Tête-bêche* (pair) .. .. .. 1·75 15·00

4d. POSTAGE — (16); HALF PENNY POSTAGE — (17)

1888 (31 Mar)–**91.** *Revenue stamps (T 5 with green surch as T 10) further surcharged. W 2. P 14½, and No. 35.*

I. *Surch with T 16.*
(a) *4 mm between value and "POSTAGE"*
41 5 4d. on 2s. orange .. .. .. 22·00 16·00
a. Upright "d" £275 £275
b. Wide space (2¼mm) between "TWO" and "SHILLINGS" £110 £110
c. First "S" in "SHILLINGS" inverted £300 £300
d. Imperf between (horiz pair)

(b) *5 mm between value and "POSTAGE"*
42 5 4d. on 2s. orange .. .. .. 35·00 28·00
a. Wide spacing (as 41b) £190 £225
b. "S" inverted (as 41c) £550 £550

II. *Surch as T 17* (December 1889)
43 5 ½d. on 2s. orange .. .. .. 12·00 17·00
a. Surch double £275 £300
b. Wide spacing (as 41b) £110 £120
c. "S" inverted (as 41c) £275 £275

POSTAGE d. AND 1 REVENUE — (18); POSTAGE AND REVENUE 1d. — (19); 2½d. — (20)

III. *Surch with T 18* (December 1890)
44 5 1d. on 2s. orange .. .. .. 70·00 70·00
a. Surcharge inverted £275
b. Wide spacing (as 41b) £190 £190
c. "S" inverted (as 41c) £400

IV. *Surch with T 19* (January 1891)
45 5 1d. on 2s. orange .. .. .. 35·00 35·00
a. No stop after "1d" £225
b. Wide spacing (as 41b) £190
c. "S" inverted (as 41c) £400

46 13 1d. on 8d. grey-brown .. .. .. 9·00 11·00
a. *Tête-bêche* (pair) .. .. .. 65·00
b. Surcharge inverted £275 £275
c. No stop after "1d" £225 £225

V. *Surch with T 20* (December 1891)
47 13 2½d. on 8d. grey-brown (Optd S. £65) .. 8·00 11·00
a. *Tête-bêche* (pair) .. .. .. 95·00
b. Inverted surcharge .. .. ..
c. Double surcharge £550 £750
d. Double surcharge, one inverted .. £400 £400
e. Treble surcharge .. .. .. — £850

There are two types of fraction; in one the "1" has horizontal serif and the "2" commences in a ball; in the other the "1" has sloping serif and the "2" is without ball.

Each type occurs 30 times in the pane of 60.

See also Nos. D4/7.

21; 22; 23 Flagship of Columbus. (Columbus named Grenada "La Concepcion")

(Type D.L.R.)

1895 (6 Sept)–**99.** *Wmk Crown CA. P 14.*
48 22 ½d. mauve and green (9.99) 90 50
49 21 1d. mauve and carmine (5.96) .. .. 2·00 20
50 2d. mauve and brown ((9.99) .. .. 25·00 32·00
51 2½d. mauve and ultramarine .. .. 5·00 60
52 22 3d. mauve and orange .. .. .. 6·50 14·00
53 21 6d. mauve and green .. .. .. 5·00 7·50
54 22 8d. mauve and black .. .. .. 12·00 23·00
55 1s. green and orange .. .. .. 13·00 20·00
48/55 .. .. *Set of* 8 60·00 90·00
48/55 Optd "Specimen" .. *Set of* 8 £140

(Recess D.L.R.)

1898 (15 Aug). *400th Anniv of Discovery of Grenada by Columbus. Wmk Crown CC. P 14*
56 23 2½d. ultramarine (Optd S. £85) .. .. 10·00 5·00
a. Bluish paper .. .. .. 30·00 40·00

24; 25

(Typo D.L.R.)

1902. *Wmk Crown CA. P 14.*
57 24 ½d. dull purple and green 80 25
58 25 1d. dull purple and carmine 90 20
59 2d. dull purple and brown .. .. 2·25 6·50
60 2½d. dull purple and ultramarine .. .. 2·50 1·25
61 24 3d. dull purple and orange .. .. 2·00 4·00
62 25 6d. dull purple and green .. .. 2·00 10·00
63 24 1s. green and orange .. .. .. 3·25 14·00
64 2s. green and ultramarine .. .. 14·00 32·00
65 25 5s. green and carmine .. .. .. 28·00 38·00
66 24 10s. green and purple .. .. .. 90·00 £140
57/66 .. .. *Set of* 10 £125 £220
57/66 Optd "Specimen" .. *Set of* 10 £200

1904–6. *Wmk Mult Crown CA. P 14.*
67 24 ½d. purple and green, O (1905) .. .. 12·00 15·00
68 25 1d. purple and carmine, O .. .. 6·50 2·50
69 2d. purple and brown, O (1905) .. .. 28·00 45·00
70 2½d. purple and ultramarine, O (1905) .. 28·00 45·00
71 24 3d. purple and orange, OC (1905) .. 1·75 3·50
72 25 6d. purple and green, OC (1906) .. 2·00 3·75
73 24 1s. green and orange, O (1905) .. .. 6·00 16·00
74 2s. green and ultramarine, OC (1906) 16·00 35·00
75 25 5s. green and carmine, O (1906) .. 38·00 48·00
76 24 10s. green and purple, O (1906) £120 £190
67/76 .. .. *Set of* 10 £225 £350

26 Badge of the Colony 27

(Recess D.L.R.)

1906. *Wmk Mult Crown CA. P14.*
77 26 ½d. green 45 20
78 1d. carmine 40 10
79 2d. orange .. .. 1·50 3·00
80 2½d. blue .. .. 3·00 1·25
a. Ultramarine .. .. .. 6·50 3·50

(Typo D.L.R.)

1908. *Wmk Crown CA. P 14.*
82 27 1s. black/*green*, C .. .. .. 13·00 22·00
83 10s. green and red/*green*, C .. .. 65·00 £110

1908–11. *Wmk Mult Crown CA. P 14.*
84 27 3d. dull purple/*yellow*, C .. .. 1·50 1·75
85 6d. dull purple and purple, C .. .. 12·00 23·00
86 1s. black/*green*, C (1911) .. .. 2·50 3·75
87 2s. blue and purple/*blue*, C .. .. 11·00 11·00
88 5s. green and red/*yellow*, C .. .. 35·00 48·00
77/88 .. .. .. *Set of* 11 £120 £200
77/80, 82/5, 87/8 Optd "Specimen" .. *Set of* 10 £200

28; WAR TAX — (29); WAR TAX — (30)

(Typo D.L.R.)

1913 (3 Jan)–**1922.** *Wmk Mult Crown CA. P 14.*
89 28 ½d. yellow-green, O 35 70
90 ½d. green, O 35 40
91 1d. red, O 45 15
92 1d. scarlet, O (1916) 55 30
93 2d. orange, O 40 25
94 2½d. bright blue, O .. .. .. 80 1·50
95 2½d. dull blue, O (1920) .. .. 2·50 3·75
96 3d. purple/*yellow*, C 30 85
a. White back (3.14) (Optd S. £30) .. 25 1·50
b. On lemon (1917) .. .. .. 1·75 5·00
c. On pale yellow (1921) .. .. 3·50 13·00
97 6d. dull and bright purple, C .. .. 80 5·00
98 1s. black/*green*, C .. .. .. 85 4·50
a. White back (3.14) (Optd S. £30) .. 70 4·50
b. On blue-green, olive back (1917) .. 35·00 48·00
c. On emerald surface .. .. 90 5·50
d. On emerald back (6.22) (Optd S. £30) .. .. .. 85 5·50
99 2s. purple and blue/*blue*, C .. .. 3·00 7·50
100 5s. green and red/*yellow*, C .. .. 10·00 30·00
a. On pale yellow (1921) (Optd S. £45) 18·00 40·00
101 10s. green and red/*green*, C .. .. 35·00 48·00
a. On emerald back (6.22) (Optd S. £55) .. .. .. 42·00 70·00
89/101*a* .. .. .. *Set of* 10 45·00 85·00
89/101 Optd "Specimen" .. *Set of* 10 £150
98 Optd in black instead of red .. .. 30·00

1916 (1 June). *Optd by Govt Press, St. George's. With T 29.*
109 28 1d. red (*shades*) (H/S S. £50) .. .. 2·00 2·00
a. Opt inverted £275
b. "T△X" .. .. .. 45·00 70·00

A small "A" in "WAR", 2 mm high is found on Nos. 29, 38 and 48 of the setting of 60 and a very small "A" in "TAX", 1½ mm high, on No. 11. Value about twice normal. The normal "A" is 2¼ mm high.

No. 109b is on No. 56 of the setting.

1916 (1 Sept)–**18.** *Optd with T 30 in London.*
111 28 1d. scarlet 15 20
a. Carmine-red/bluish (5.18) .. .. 2·25 2·25
111 Optd "Specimen" .. .. .. 40·00

1921–32. *T 28. Wmk Mult Script CA. P 14.*
112 ½d. green, O 30 15
113 1d. carmine-red, O 30 20
114 1d. brown, O (1923) 30 15
115 1½d. rose-red, O (6.22) 75 55
116 2d. orange, O 30 15
117 2d. grey, O (1926) .. .. .. 1·75 1·75
117*a* 2½d. dull blue 80 65
118 2½d. grey, O (6.22) .. .. .. 75 5·00
119 2½d. bright blue, O (1926) .. .. 80 2·25
120 2½d. ultramarine O (1931) .. .. 3·75 6·00
120*a* 2½d. chalky blue and blue, O (1932) .. 24·00 42·00
121 3d. bright blue, O (6.22) .. .. 1·00 5·00
122 3d. purple/*yellow*, C (1926) .. .. 50 3·50
123 4d. black and red/*yellow*, C (1926) .. 50 3·25
124 5d. dull purple and sage-green, C (27.12.22) 75 3·50
125 6d. dull and bright purple, C .. .. 1·10 8·50
126 6d. black and carmine, C (1926) .. 1·75 2·50
127 9d. dull purple and black, C (27.12.22) 2·00 5·50
128 1s. black/*emerald*, C (1923) .. .. 2·25 18·00
129 1s. chestnut, C (1926) .. .. .. 3·00 12·00
130 2s. purple and blue/*blue*, C (1922) .. 5·00 8·00
131 2s. 6d. black and carmine/*blue*, C (1929) 6·00 14·00
132 3s. green and violet, C (27.12.22) .. 6·00 20·00
133 5s. green and red/*pale yellow*, C (1923) 12·00 26·00
134 10s. green and red/*emerald*, C (1923) .. 45·00 85·00
112/19, 121/34 .. .. *Set of* 22 80·00 £200
112/34 Optd/Perf "Specimen" .. *Set of* 23 £375

31 Grand Anse Beach; 32 Badge of the Colony

33 Grand Etang

34 St. George's

(Recess Waterlow)

1934 (23 Oct)–**36.** *Wmk Mult Script CA (sideways on T* **32**). *P* 12½.
135 **31** ½d. green .. 15 40
a. Perf 12½ × 13½ (1936) .. 2·25 17·00
136 **32** 1d. black and sepia .. 70 1·00
a. Perf 13½ × 12½ (1936) .. 65 35
137 **33** 1½d. black and scarlet .. 1·75 1·00
a. Perf 12½ × 13½ (1936) .. 1·25 55
138 **32** 2d. black and orange .. 40 40
139 **34** 2½d. blue .. 25 30
140 **32** 3d. black and olive-green .. 35 80
141 6d. black and purple .. 70 1·10
142 1s. black and brown .. 80 2·50
143 2s. 6d. black and ultramarine .. 6·50 14·00
144 5s. black and violet .. 20·00 27·00
135/144 .. *Set of* 10 28·00 45·00
135/44 Perf "Specimen" .. *Set of* 10 £160

1935 (6 May). *Silver Jubilee. As T* **13** *of Antigua but ptd by Waterlow. P* 11 × 12.
145 ½d. black and green .. 20 20
j. Kite and vertical log .. 15·00
k. Kite and horizontal log .. 15·00
146 1d. ultramarine and grey .. 40 35
k. Kite and horizontal log .. 20·00
147 1½d. deep blue and scarlet .. 50 45
k. Kite and horizontal log .. 25·00
148 1s. slate and purple .. 3·50 7·50
k. Kite and horizontal log .. 45·00
145/8 .. *Set of* 4 4·25 8·00
145/8 Perf "Specimen" .. *Set of* 4 60·00

For illustrations of plate varieties see Omnibus section following Zululand.

1937 (12 May). *Coronation. As T* **2** *of Aden but ptd by B.W. P* 11 × 11½.
149 1d. violet .. 20 15
150 1½d. carmine .. 20 15
151 2½d. blue .. 50 30
149/51 .. *Set of* 3 80 55
149/51 Perf "Specimen" .. *Set of* 3 50·00

35 King George VI

(Photo Harrison)

1937 (12 July)–**45.** *Wmk Mult Script CA. P* 15 × 14.
152 **35** ¼d. brown, **CO** .. 10 10
a. Chocolate, **CO** (1.45) .. 10 10

The ordinary paper is thick, smooth and opaque.

36 Grand Anse Beach

40 Badge of the Colony

Colon flaw (R. 5/8. Corrected on ptg of Nov 1950)

(Recess D.L.R. (10s.), Waterlow (others))

1938 (16 Mar)–**50.** *As T* **31/4** *(but portrait of King George VI as in T* **36**) *and T* **40**. *Wmk Mult Script CA (sideways on T* **32**). *P* 12½ *or* 12 × 13 (10s.).
153 **36** ½d. yellow-green .. 2·25 45
a. Perf 12½ × 13½ (1938) .. 2·00 80
b. Perf 12½. *Blue-green* .. 10 25
ba. Perf 12½ × 13½. *Blue-green* .. 2·25 3·00
154 **32** 1d. black and sepia .. 15 10
a. Perf 13½ × 12½ (1938) .. 25 10
155 **33** 1½d. black and scarlet .. 40 10
a. Perf 12½ × 13½ (1938) .. 2·00 20
156 **32** 2d. black and orange .. 15 10
a. Perf 13½ × 12½ (1938) .. 50 10
157 **34** 2½d. bright blue .. 15 10
a. Perf 12½ × 13½ (?March 1950) .. £3000 £170
158 **32** 3d. black and olive-green .. 3·25 1·25
a. Perf 13½ × 12½ (16.3.38) .. 3·25 70
ab. Perf 13½ × 12½. *Black and brown-olive* (1942) .. 20 60
b. Perf 12½. *Black and brown-olive* (16.8.50) .. 20 70
ba. Colon flaw .. 12·00
159 6d. black and purple .. 35 15
a. Perf 13½ × 12½ (1942) .. 30 10
160 1s. black and brown .. 30 20
a. Perf 13½ × 12½ (1941) .. 60 40
161 **32** 2s. black and ultramarine .. 5·50 75
a. Perf 13½ × 12½ (1941) .. 6·50 65
162 5s. black and violet .. 2·00 1·50
a. Perf 13½ × 12½ (1947) .. 2·50 5·50
163 **40** 10s. steel blue and carmine *(narrow)* (*p* 12 × 13) .. 27·00 7·00
a. Perf 14. *Steel blue and bright carmine (narrow)* .. 65·00 42·00
b. Perf 14. *Slate-blue and bright carmine (narrow)* (1943) .. 75·00 60·00
c. Perf 12. *Slate-blue and bright carmine (narrow)* (1943) .. £275 £325
d. Perf 14. *Slate-blue and carmine-lake (wide)* (1944) .. 42·00 4·50
e. Perf 14. *Blue-black and carmine (narrow)* (1943) .. 10·00 7·00
f. Perf 14. *Blue-black and bright carmine (wide)* (1947) .. 15·00 20·00
152/163b .. *Set of* 12 17·00 7·50
152/63 Perf "Specimen" .. *Set of* 12 £200

In the earlier printings of the 10s. the paper was dampened before printing and the subsequent shrinkage produced narrow frames 23½ to 23¾ mm wide. Later printings were made on dry paper producing wide frames 24¼ mm wide.

No. 163a is one of the earlier printings line perf 13.8 × 14.1.

No. 163b is line-perf 14.1.

Nos. 163a and 163b may be found with gum more or less yellow due to local climatic conditions.

1946 (25 Sept). *Victory. As Nos.* 28/9 *of Aden.*
164 1½d. carmine .. 10 10
165 3½d. blue .. 10 10
164/5 Perf "Specimen" .. *Set of* 2 45·00

1948 (27 Oct). *Royal Silver Wedding. As Nos.* 30/1 *of Aden.*
166 1½d. scarlet .. 10 10
167 10s. slate-green .. 5·50 12·00

(New Currency. 100 cents = 1 West Indian dollar)

1949 (10 Oct). *75th Anniv of Universal Postal Union. As Nos.* 114/17 *of Antigua.*
168 5 c. ultramarine .. 15 10
169 6 c. olive .. 25 20
170 12 c. magenta .. 25 15
171 24 c. red-brown .. 25 20
168/71 .. *Set of* 4 80 60

41 King George VI

42 Badge of the Colony

43 Badge of the Colony

(Recess B.W. (T **41**), D.L.R. (others))

1951 (8 Jan). *Wmk Mult Script CA. P* 11½ (*T* **41**), 11½ × 12½ (*T* **42**), *and* 11½ × 13 (*T* **43**).
172 **41** ½ c. black and red-brown .. 15 70
173 1 c. black and emerald-green .. 15 25
174 2 c. black and brown .. 15 25
175 3 c. black and rose-carmine .. 15 10
176 4 c. black and orange .. 35 40
177 5 c. black and violet .. 20 10
178 6 c. black and olive .. 20 25
179 7 c. black and light blue .. 50 10
180 12 c. black and purple .. 1·25 30
181 **42** 25 c. black and sepia .. 2·25 50
182 50 c. black and blue .. 3·00 40
183 $1.50, black and yellow-orange .. 7·50 3·00
184 **43** $2.50, slate-blue and carmine .. 4·75 3·00
172/184 .. *Set of* 13 18·00 8·00

1951 (16 Feb). *Inauguration of B.W.I. University College. As Nos.* 118/19 *of Antigua.*
185 3 c. black and carmine .. 15 10
186 6 c. black and olive .. 15 10

NEW CONSTITUTION

1951

(44)

1951 (21 Sept). *New Constitution. Optd with T* **44** *by B.W.*
187 **41** 3 c. black and rose-carmine .. 5 10
188 4 c. black and orange .. 5 10
189 5 c. black and violet (R.) .. 10 10
190 12 c. black and purple .. 10 15
187/90 .. *Set of* 4 25 40

1953 (3 June). *Coronation. As No.* 47 *of Aden*
191 3 c. black and carmine-red .. 10 10

45 Queen Elizabeth II

46 Badge of the Colony

47 Badge of the Colony

(Recess B.W. (T **45**), D.L.R. (T **46/7**))

1953 (15 June)–**59.** *Wmk Mult Script CA. P* 11½ (*T* **45**), 11½ × 12½ (*T* **46**), *or* 11½ × 13 (*T* **47**).
192 **45** ½ c. black and brown (28.12.53) .. 10 10
193 1 c. black and deep emerald .. 10 10
194 2 c. black and sepia (15.9.53) .. 10 10
195 3 c. black and carmine-red (22.2.54) .. 10 10
196 4 c. black and brown-orange (22.2.54) .. 10 10
197 5 c. black and deep violet (22.2.54) .. 10 10
198 6 c. black and olive-green (28.12.53) .. 25 10
199 7 c. black and blue (6.6.55) .. 25 10
200 12 c. black and reddish purple .. 15 10
201 **46** 25 c. black and sepia (10.1.55) .. 55 20
202 50 c. black and deep blue (2.12.55) .. 1·75 40
203 $1.50, black & brown-orange (2.12.55) 4·50 2·75
204 **47** $2.50, slate-blue & carmine (16.11.59) 7·50 2·75
192/204 .. *Set of* 13 14·00 6·00

On 23 December 1965, No. 203 was issued surcharged "2" but this was intended for fiscal and revenue purposes and it was not authorised to be used postally, although some are known to have passed through the mail.

1958 (22 Apr). *Inauguration of British Caribbean Federation. As Nos.* 135/7 *of Antigua.*
205 3 c. deep green .. 10 10
206 6 c. blue .. 12 15
207 12 c. scarlet .. 15 10
205/7 .. *Set of* 3 35 20

48 Queen Victoria, Queen Elizabeth II, Mail Van and Post Office, St. George's

(Photo Harrison)

1961 (1 June). *Grenada Stamp Centenary. T* **48** *and similar horiz designs. W* w **12**. *P* 14½ × 14.
208 3 c. crimson and black .. 10 10
209 8 c. bright blue and orange .. 20 10
210 25 c. lake and blue .. 20 10
208/10 .. *Set of* 3 35 15

Designs:—8 c. Queen Victoria, Queen Elizabeth II and flagship of Columbus; 25 c. Queen Victoria, Queen Elizabeth II, R.M.S.P. *Solent* and "Dakota" aircraft.

1963 (4 June). *Freedom from Hunger. As No.* 76 *of Aden.*
211 8 c. bluish green .. 25 10

1963 (2 Sept). *Red Cross Centenary. As Nos.* 147/8 *of Antigua.*
212 3 c. red and black .. 10 10
213 25 c. red and blue .. 20 15

1964 (12 May)–**66.** *As Nos.* 194/8, 201/1, *but wmk* w **12**.
214 **45** 2 c. black and sepia .. 10 10
215 3 c. black and carmine-red .. 10 10
216 4 c. black and brown-orange .. 10 15
217 5 c. black and deep violet .. 10 10
218 6 c. black and olive-green (4.1.66) .. £160 55·00
219 12 c. black and reddish purple .. 15 10
220 **46** 25 c. black and sepia .. 45 15
214/20 .. *Set of* 7 £160 55·00

1965 (17 May). *I.T.U. Centenary. As Nos.* 166/7 *of Antigua.*
221 2 c. red-orange and yellow-olive .. 10 10
222 50 c. lemon and light red .. 25 15

1965 (25 Oct). *International Co-operation Year. As Nos.* 168/9 *of Antigua*
223 1 c. reddish purple and turquoise-green .. 10 10
224 25 c. deep bluish green and lavender .. 15 15

1966 (24 Jan). *Churchill Commemoration. As Nos.* 170/3 *of Antigua.*
225 1 c. new blue .. 10 10
226 3 c. deep green .. 10 10
227 25 c. brown .. 15 10
228 35 c. bluish violet .. 25 15
225/8 .. *Set of* 4 45 25

1966 (4 Feb). *Royal Visit. As Nos.* 174/5 *of Antigua.*
229 3 c. black and ultramarine .. 10 10
230 35 c. black and magenta .. 30 15

52 Hillsborough, Carriacou

53 Badge of the Colony

54 Queen Elizabeth II

55 Map of Grenada

(Des V. Whiteley. Photo Harrison)

1966 (1 Apr). *Horiz designs as T* **52**, *and T* **53/5**. *Multicoloured. W w* **12**. *P* 14½ ($1, $2, $3) *or* 14½ × 13½ (*others*).

231	1 c. Type **52**	10	10
232	2 c. Bougainvillea	10	10
233	3 c. Flamboyant plant	10	10
234	5 c. Levera beach	10	10
235	6 c. Carenage, St. George's	10	10
236	8 c. Annandale Falls	10	10
237	10 c. Cocoa pods	10	10
238	12 c. Inner Harbour	10	10
239	15 c. Nutmeg	15	10
240	25 c. St. George's	20	10
241	35 c. Grand Anse beach	30	10
242	50 c. Bananas	70	60
243	$1 Type **53**	1·75	1·00
244	$2 Type **54**	3·00	2·25
245	$3 Type **55**	3·25	4·00
231/45	*Set of* 15	9·00	7·50

1966 (1 July). *World Cup Football Championships. As Nos.* 176/7 *of Antigua.*

246	5 c. violet, yellow-green, lake & yellow-brn	10	10
247	50 c. chocolate, blue-green, lake & yelllow-brn	25	20

1966 (20 Sept). *Inauguration of W.H.O. Headquarters, Geneva. As Nos.* 178/9 *of Antigua.*

248	8 c. black, yellow-green and light blue	10	10
249	25 c. black, light purple and yellow-brown	15	15

1966 (1 Dec). *20th Anniv of U.N.E.S.C.O. As Nos.* 196/8 *of Antigua.*

250	2 c. slate-violet, red, yellow and orange	10	10
251	15 c. orange-yellow, violet and deep olive	15	10
252	50 c. black, bright purple and orange	30	25
250/2	*Set of* 3	45	30

ASSOCIATED STATEHOOD

(67)

(68)

1967 (3 Mar). *Statehood. Nos.* 232/3, 236 *and* 240 *optd with T* **67**, *in silver*

253	2 c. Bougainvillea	10	10
254	3 c. Flamboyant plant	10	10
255	8 c. Annandale Falls	10	10
256	25 c. St. George's	10	10
253/6	*Set of* 4	10	10

1967 (June). *World Fair, Montreal. Nos.* 232, 237, 239 *and* 243/4 *surch as T* **68** *or optd with "Expo" emblem only.*

257	1 c. on 15 c. Nutmeg	10	10
	a. Surch and opt albino	14·00	
258	2 c. Bougainvillea	10	10
259	3 c. on 10 c. Cocoa pods	10	10
260	$1 Type **53**	20	15
261	$2 Type **54**	35	20
257/61	*Set of* 5	50	35

ASSOCIATED STATEHOOD

(69)

70 Kennedy and Local Flower

1967 (Oct). *Statehood. Nos.* 231/45 *optd with T* **69**.

262	1 c. Type **52**	10	10
263	2 c. Bougainvillea	10	10
264	3 c. Flamboyant plant	10	10
265	5 c. Levera beach	10	10
266	6 c. Carenage, St. George's	10	10
267	8 c. Annandale Falls	10	10
268	10 c. Cocoa pods	10	10
269	12 c. Inner Harbour	10	10
270	15 c. Nutmeg	15	10
271	25 c. St. George's	20	10
272	35 c. Grand Anse beach	45	10
273	50 c. Bananas	60	20
274	$1 Type **53**	70	60
275	$2 Type **54**	1·25	2·00
276	$3 Type **55**	2·00	2·25
262/76	*Set of* 15	5·00	5·00

See also No. 295

(Des M. Shamir. Photo Harrison)

1968 (13 Jan). *50th Birth Anniv of President Kennedy. T* **70** *and similar horiz designs. Multicoloured. P* 14½ × 14.

277	1 c. Type **70**	10	10
?78	15 c. Type **70**	10	10
?79	25 c. Kennedy and strelitzia	10	10
280	35 c. Kennedy and roses	10	10
281	50 c. As 25 c.	15	15
282	$1 As 35 c.	25	25
?77/82	*Set of* 6	55	45

73 Scout Bugler

76 "Near Antibes"

(Des K. Plowitz. Photo Govt Printer, Israel)

1968 (17 Feb). *World Scout Jamboree, Idaho. T* **73** *and similar vert designs. Multicoloured. P* 13 × 13½.

283	1 c. Type **73**	10	10
284	2 c. Scouts camping	10	10
285	3 c. Lord Baden-Powell	10	10
286	35 c. Type **73**	20	10
287	50 c. As 2 c.	25	15
288	$1 As 3 c.	40	25
283/8	*Set of* 6	85	45

(Des G. Vasarhelyi. Photo Harrison)

1968 (23 Mar). *Paintings by Sir Winston Churchill. T* **76** *and similar horiz designs. Multicoloured. P* 14 × 14½.

289	10 c. Type **76**	10	10
290	12 c. "The Mediterranean"	10	10
291	15 c. "St. Jean Cap Ferratt"	15	10
292	25 c. Type **76**	15	10
293	35 c. As 15 c.	20	10
294	50 c. Sir Winston painting	30	25
289/94	*Set of* 6	85	45

$5

(80)

CHILDREN
NEED
MILK

2cts. + 3cts.

(81)

CHILDREN
NEED
MILK

1c. + 3cts.

(82)

1968 (18 May). *No.* 275 *surch with T* **80**

295	**54**	$5 on $2 multicoloured	1·50	2·25

1968 (22 July–19 Aug). *"Children Need Milk".*

(*a*) *Nos.* 244/5 *surch locally as T* **81** (22 July)

296	**54**	2 c. + 3 c. on $2 multicoloured	10	10
297	**55**	3 c. + 3 c. on $3 multicoloured	10	10
		a. Surch inverted	50·00	25·00
		b. Surch double	30·00	

(*b*) *Nos.* 243/4 *surch locally as T* **82** (19 Aug)

298	**53**	1 c. + 3 c. on $1 multicoloured	10	40
		a. Surch on No. 274	70·00	
		b. Surch double	50·00	
299	**54**	2 c. + 3 c. on $2 multicoloured	17·00	32·00
		a. Surch on No. 275	80·00	
296/9		*Set of* 4	17·00	32·00

83 Edith McGuire (U.S.A.)

86 Hibiscus

(Des M. Shamir. Photo Harrison)

1968 (24 Sept). *Olympic Games, Mexico. T* **83** *and similar square designs. P* 12½.

300	1 c. brown, black and blue	10	10
301	2 c. orange, brown, blue and lilac	10	10
	a. Orange (badge, etc.) omitted		
302	3 c. scarlet, brown and dull green	10	10
	a. Scarlet (rings, "MEXICO" etc.) omitted		
303	10 c. brown, black, blue and vermilion	10	10
304	50 c. orange, brown, blue and turquoise	15	20
305	60 c. scarlet, brown and red-orange	20	25
300/5	*Set of* 6	40	50

Designs:—2, 50 c. Arthur Wint (Jamaica); 3, 60 c. Ferreira da Silva (Brazil); 10 c. Type **83**.

Nos. 300/2 and 303/5 were issued in separate composite sheets containing three strips of three, with three *se-tenant* labels showing Greek athlete (Nos. 300/2) or Discobolos (Nos. 303/5). (*Price for two sheets £6 mint, £8 used.*)

(Des G. Vasarhelyi (No. 314*a*), V. Whiteley (75 c.), M. Shamir (others). Litho Format (Nos. 314*a* and 317*a*). Photo Harrison (others))

1968 (Oct)–**71**. *Multicoloured designs as T* **86**. *P* 13½ (*Nos.* 314*a and* 317*a*), 13½ × 14½ (*vert except No.* 314*a*) *or* 14½ × 13½ (*horiz except No.* 317*a*).

306	1 c. Type **86**	10	10
307	2 c. Strelitzia	10	10
308	3 c. Bougainvillea (1.7.69)	10	10
309	5 c. Rock Hind (*horiz*) (4.2.69)	10	10
310	6 c. Sailfish	10	10
311	8 c. Snapper (*horiz*) (1.7.69)	10	10
312	10 c. Marine Toad (*horiz*) (4.2.69)	10	10
313	12 c. Turtle	15	10
314	15 c. Tree Boa (*horiz*)	70	60
314*a*	15 c. Thunbergia (1970)	4·00	2·00
315	25 c. Greater Trinidadian Murine Opossum (4.2.69)	30	10
316	35 c. Nine-banded Armadillo (*horiz*) (1.7.69)	35	10
317	50 c. Mona Monkey	45	25
317*a*	75 c. Yacht in St. George's Harbour (*horiz*) (9.10.71)	7·50	4·50
318	$1 Bananaquit	1·50	1·50
319	$2 Brown Pelican (4.2.69)	2·50	4·25
320	$3 Magnificent Frigate Bird	3·50	4·50
321	$5 Bare-eyed Thrush (1.7.69)	3·75	8·50
306/21	*Set of* 18	23·00	24·00

Nos. 314*a*, 317*a* and the dollar values are larger—29 × 45½, 44 × 28½ and 25½ × 48 mm respectively.

102 Kidney Transplant

106 "The Adoration of the Kings" (Veronese)

(Des M. Shamir. Litho B.W.)

1968 (25 Nov). *20th Anniv of World Health Organization. T* **102** *and similar vert designs. Multicoloured. P* 13 × 13½.

322	5 c. Type **102**	10	10
323	25 c. Heart transplant	10	10
324	35 c. Lung transplant	15	10
325	50 c. Eye transplant	20	20
322/5	*Set of* 4	40	30

(Photo Harrison)

1968 (3 Dec). *Christmas. T* **106** *and similar square designs. P* 12½.

326	5 c. multicoloured	10	10
327	15 c. multicoloured	10	10
328	35 c. multicoloured	10	10
329	$1 multicoloured	30	40
326/9	*Set of* 4	40	45

Designs:—15 c. "Madonna and Child with Sts. John and Catherine" (Titian); 35 c. "Adoration of the Kings" (Botticelli); $1 "A Warrior Adoring" (Catena).

VISIT CARIFTA EXPO '69
April 5-30

(110)

1969 (Feb). *Caribbean Free Trade Area Exhibition. Nos.* 300/5 *surch in red as T* **110**.

330	5 c. on 1 c. brown, black and blue	10	10
	a. Surch double		
331	8 c. on 2 c. orange, brown, blue and lilac	10	10
	a. Surch double		
332	25 c. on 3 c. scarlet, brown and dull green	10	10
	a. Surch double		
333	35 c. on 10 c. brown, black, blue and vermilion	10	10
334	$1 on 50 c. orange, brown, blue & turquoise	20	25
335	$2 on 60 c. scarlet, brown and red-orange	35	40
	a. Scarlet (rings, "MEXICO" etc) omitted	†	—
330/5	*Set of* 6	65	70

The centre of the composite sheets is also overprinted with a commemorative inscription publicising CARIFTA EXPO 1969 (*Price for two sheets* £11 *mint or used*).

111 Dame Hylda Bynoe (Governor) and Island Scene

(Des and litho D.L.R.)

1969 (1 May). *Carifta Expo 1969. T* **111** *and similar horiz designs. Multicoloured. P* 13 × 13½.
336 5 c. Type **111** 10 10
337 15 c. Premier E. M. Gairy and Island scene .. 10 10
338 50 c. Type **111** 10 10
339 60 c. Emblems of 1958 and 1967 World's Fairs 10 10
336/9 .. .. *Set of* 4 25 20

114 Dame Hylda Bynoe **115** "Balshazzar's Feast" (Rembrandt)

(Photo Enschedé)

1969 (8 June). *Human Rights Year. T* **114/15** *and similar multi-coloured design. P* 12½ × 13 ($1) *or* 13 × 12½ *(others).*
340 5 c. Type **114** 10 10
341 25 c. Dr. Martin Luther King *(vert)* 10 10
342 35 c. Type **114** 10 10
343 $1 Type **115** 20 25
340/3 .. .. *Set of* 4 30 30

117 Batsman and Wicket-keeper

(Des M. Shamir and L. W. Denyer. Photo Harrison)

1969 (1 Aug). *Cricket. T* **117** *and similar horiz designs. P* 14 × 14½.
344 3 c. yellow, brown and ultramarine .. 25 15
a. Yellow (caps and wicket) omitted ..
345 10 c. multicoloured 30 15
346 25 c. brown, ochre and myrtle-green .. 60 30
347 35 c. multicoloured 80 45
344/7 .. .. *Set of* 4 1·75 95
Designs:—10 c. Batsman playing defensive stroke; 25 c. Batsman sweeping ball; 35 c. Batsman playing on-drive.
Nos. 344/7 were each issued in small sheets of 9 (3 × 3) with decorative borders.

129 Astronaut handling Moon Rock

(Des G. Vasarhelyi. Photo)

1969 (24 Sept). *First Man on the Moon. T* **129** *and similar multi-coloured designs. P* 13½ (½ *c.*) *or* 12½ *(others).*
348 ½ c. As Type **129** but larger (56 × 35 *mm*) .. 10 10
349 1 c. Moon rocket and moon 10 10
350 2 c. Module landing 10 10
351 3 c. Declaration left on moon 10 10
352 8 c. Module leaving rocket 10 10
353 25 c. Rocket lifting-off *(vert)* 15 10
354 35 c. Spacecraft in orbit *(vert)* 15 10
355 50 c. Capsule with parachutes *(vert)* .. 20 10
356 $1 Type **129** 35 30
348/56 .. .. *Set of* 9 85 55
MS357 115 × 90 mm. Nos. 351 and 356. Imperf 80 1·25

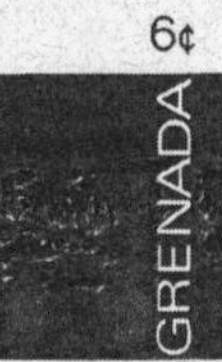

130 Gandhi

(Des A. Robledo. Litho B.W.)

1969 (8 Oct). *Birth Centenary of Mahatma Gandhi. T* **130** *and similar designs. P* 11½.
358 **130** 6 c. multicoloured 15 10
359 – 15 c. multicoloured 20 10
360 – 25 c. multicoloured 30 10
361 – $1 multicoloured .. .. 1·00 60
358/61 .. .. *Set of* 4 1·50 75
MS362 155 × 122 mm. Nos. 358/61. Imperf .. 2·50 3·50
Designs: *Vert*—15 c. Gandhi standing; 25 c. Gandhi walking. *Horiz*—$1 Head of Gandhi.

1969

2c

(**134**)

135 "Blackbeard" (Edward Teach)

1969 (23 Dec). *Christmas. Nos.* 326/9 *surch with T* **134** *in black (2 c.) or optd with new date only in silver (others).*
363 2 c. on 15 c. multicoloured 10 10
a. Surch inverted .. .. 50·00
364 5 c. multicoloured 10 10
365 35 c. multicoloured 10 10
a. Opt inverted .. .. 50·00
366 $1 multicoloured 25 50
a. Opt inverted .. .. 50·00
363/6 .. .. *Set of* 4 35 60

(Des K. Plowitz. Recess B.W.)

1970 (2 Feb). *Pirates. T* **135** *and similar vert designs. P* 13½.
367 15 c. black 35 10
368 25 c. dull green 50 10
369 50 c. lilac 90 20
370 $1 carmine .. .. 1·50 75
367/70 .. .. *Set of* 4 3·00 1·00
Designs:—25 c. Anne Bonney; 50 c. Jean Lafitte; $1 Mary Read.

(**139**) (**140**)

1970 (18 Mar). *No.* 348 *surch with T* **139**.
371 5 c. on ½ c. multicoloured 10 10
a. Surch double .. .. 55·00
b. Surch with T 140 .. .. 90 90

141 "The Last Supper" (detail, **142** Del Sarto)

(Des and litho B.W.)

1970 (13 Apr). *Easter. Paintings. T* **141/2** *and similar vert designs. Multicoloured. P* 11½.
372 5 c. } Type **141/2** 10 10
373 5 c. } .. 10 10
374 15 c. } "Christ crowned with Thorns" (detail, 10 10
375 15 c. } Van Dyck) 10 10
376 25 c. } "The Passion of Christ" (detail, 10 10
377 25 c. } Memling) 10 10
378 60 c. } "Christ in the Tomb" (detail, Rubens) .. 25 30
379 60 c. } .. 25 30
372/9 .. .. *Set of* 8 85 85
MS380 120 × 140 mm. Nos. 376/9 .. .. 85 1·25
Nos. 372/9 were issued with each design spread over two *se-tenant* stamps of the same denomination.

149 Girl with Kittens in Pram

(Des A. Robledo. Litho Questa)

1970 (27 May). *Birth Bicentenary of William Wordsworth (poet). "Children and Pets". T* **149** *and similar horiz designs. Multi-coloured. P* 11.
381 5 c. Type **149** 15 10
382 15 c. Girl with puppy and kitten 20 10
383 30 c. Boy with fishing rod and cat 35 15
384 60 c. Boys and girls with cats and dogs .. 55 30
381/4 .. .. *Set of* 4 1·10 60
MS385 Two sheets each 114 × 126 mm. Nos. 381, 383 and Nos. 382, 384. Imperf .. .. 1·60 2·00

153 Parliament of India

(Des G. Vasarhelyi. Litho Questa)

1970 (15 June). *Seventh Regional Conference of Commonwealth Parliamentary Association. T* **153** *and similar horiz designs. Multicoloured. P* 14
386 5 c. Type **153** 10 10
387 25 c. Parliament of Great Britain, Westminster 10 10
388 50 c. Parliament of Canada 15 15
389 60 c. Parliament of Grenada 15 15
386/9 .. .. *Set of* 4 40 35
MS390 126 × 90 mm. Nos. 386/9 .. .. .. 50 90

157 Tower of the Sun

(Litho Kyodo Printing Co, Tokyo)

1970 (8 Aug). *World Fair, Osaka. T* **157** *and similar multi-coloured designs. P* 13.
391 1 c. Type **157** 10 10
392 2 c. Livelihood and Industry Pavilion *(horiz)* 10 10
393 3 c. Flower painting, 1634 .. .. .. 10 10
394 10 c. "Adam and Eve" (Tintoretto) *(horiz)* .. 10 10
395 25 c. O.E.C.D. (Organisation for Economic Co-operation and Development) Pavilion *(horiz)* 10 10
396 50 c. San Francisco Pavilion 20 20
391/6 .. .. *Set of* 6 40 35
MS397 121 × 91 mm. $1 Japanese Pavilion (56 × 34 *mm*) 55 75

164 Roosevelt and "Raising U.S. Flag on Iwo Jima"

(Litho Questa)

1970 (3 Sept). *25th Anniv of Ending of World War II. T* **164** *and similar horiz designs. Multicoloured. P* 11.
398 ½ c. Type **164** 10 10
399 5 c. Zhukov and "Fall of Berlin" 30 15
400 15 c. Churchill and "Evacuation at Dunkirk" 60 25
401 25 c. De Gaulle and "Liberation of Paris" .. 90 45
402 50 c. Eisenhower and "D-Day Landing" .. 1·25 90
403 60 c. Montgomery and "Battle of Alamein" .. 1·50 1·75
398/403 .. .. *Set of* 6 4·25 3·25
MS404 163 × 113 mm. Nos. 398, 400, 402/3 .. 3·00 6·50
a. Brown (panel) on 60 c. value omitted ..

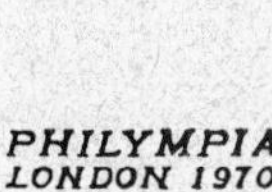

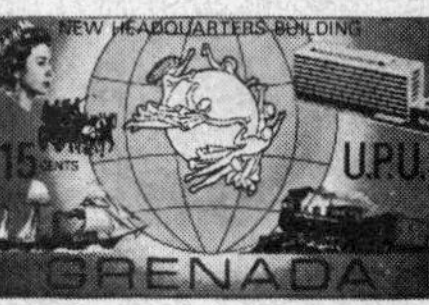

(**169**) **170** U.P.U. Emblem, Building and Transport

1970 (18 Sept). *"Philympia 1970" Stamp Exhibition, London. Nos.* 353/6 *optd with T* **169**
405 25 c. Rocket lifting-off 10 10
a. Albino opt .. .. 6·00
b. Opt inverted .. ..
406 35 c. Spacecraft in orbit 10 10
a. Opt inverted .. .. 40·00
407 50 c. Capsule with parachutes 15 15
a. Albino opt .. .. 1·50
408 $1 Type **129** (Sil.) (optd vert upwards) .. 20 30
a. Albino opt .. .. 10·00
405/8 .. .. *Set of* 4 40 50
The miniature sheet was also overprinted but we understand that only 300 of these were put on sale in Grenada.

(Litho Questa)

1970 (17 Oct). *New U.P.U. Headquarters Building. T* **170** *and similar multicoloured designs. P* 14.

409	15 c. Type **170**	15	10
410	25 c. As Type **170**, but modern transport	20	10
411	50 c. Sir Rowland Hill and U.P.U. Building	25	15
412	$1 Abraham Lincoln and U.P.U. Building	45	50
409/12	*Set of* 4	95	70
MS413	79 × 85 mm. Nos. 411/12	1·25	2·50

The 50 c. and $1 are both vertical designs.

171 "The Madonna of the Goldfinch" (Tiepolo)

172 19th-Century Nursing

(Des G. Vasarhelyi. Litho Questa)

1970 (5 Dec). *Christmas. T* **171** *and similar vert designs. Multicoloured. P* 13½.

414	½ c. Type **171**	10	10
415	½ c. "The Virgin and Child with St. Peter and St. Paul" (Bouts)	10	10
416	½ c. "The Virgin and Child" (Bellini)	10	10
417	2 c. "The Madonna of the Basket" (Correggio)	10	10
418	3 c. Type **171**	10	10
419	35 c. As No. 415	20	10
420	50 c. As 2 c.	30	15
421	$1 As No. 416	60	35
414/21	*Set of* 8	1·10	70
MS422	102 × 87 mm. Nos. 420/1	1·75	2·50

(Des G. Vasarhelyi. Litho Questa)

1970 (12 Dec). *Centenary of British Red Cross. T* **172** *and similar horiz designs. Multicoloured. P* 14½ × 14.

423	5 c. Type **172**	10	10
424	15 c. Military Ambulance, 1918	15	10
425	25 c. First-Aid Post, 1941	25	10
426	60 c. Red Cross Transport, 1970	60	60
423/6	*Set of* 4	1·00	70
MS427	113 × 82 mm. Nos. 423/6	1·25	1·60
	a. Error. Imperf	20·00	

173 John Dewey and Art Lesson

(Des G. Vasarhelyi. Litho Questa)

1971 (1 May). *International Education Year* (1970). *T* **173** *and similar horiz designs. Multicoloured. P* 13½.

428	5 c. Type **173**	10	10
429	10 c. Jean-Jacques Rousseau and "Alphabetisation"	15	10
430	50 c. Maimonides and laboratory	50	15
431	$1 Bertrand Russell and mathematics class	95	40
428/31	*Set of* 4	1·50	55
MS432	90 × 98 mm. Nos. 430/1	1·40	2·00

174 Jennifer Hosten and outline of Grenada

176 "Napolean reviewing the Guard" (E. Detaille)

175 French and Canadian Scouts

(Des local artist; adapted G. Drummond. Litho Format)

1971 (1 June). *Winner of "Miss World" Competition* (1970). *P* 13½.

433 **174**	5 c. multicoloured	10	10
434	10 c. multicoloured	15	10
435	15 c. multicoloured	15	10
436	25 c. multicoloured	15	10
437	35 c. multicoloured	20	10
438	50 c. multicoloured	45	55
433/8	*Set of* 6	1·10	75
MS439	92 × 89 mm. **174** 50 c. multicoloured. Printed on silk. Imperf	75	1·50

(Litho Format)

1971 (11 Sept). *13th World Scout Jamboree, Asagiri, Japan. T* **175** *and similar horiz designs. Multicoloured. P* 11.

440	5 c. Type **175**	10	10
441	35 c. German and American scouts	30	25
442	50 c. Australian and Japanese scouts	50	50
443	75 c. Grenada and British scouts	65	75
440/3	*Set of* 4	1·40	1·40
MS444	101 × 114 mm. Nos. 442/3	1·60	2·25

(Des G. Vasarhelyi. Litho Questa)

1971 (9 Oct). *150th Death Anniversary of Napolean Bonaparte. T* **176** *and similar vert designs showing paintings. Multicoloured. P* 13½.

445	5 c. Type **176**	15	15
446	15 c. "Napoleon before Madrid" (Vernet)	25	15
447	35 c. "Napoleon crossing Mt St. Bernard" (David)	30	15
448	$2 "Napoleon in his Study" (David)	1·25	1·75
445/8	*Set of* 4	1·75	2·00
MS449	101 × 76 mm. No. 447. Imperf	1·50	1·40

177 1d. Stamp of 1861 and Badge of Grenada

(Des R. Granger Barrett. Litho Questa)

1971 (6 Nov). *110th Anniv of the Postal Service. T* **177** *and similar horiz designs. Multicoloured. W w* **12** (*sideways**). *P* 11.

450	5 c. Type **177**	10	10
451	15 c. 6d. stamp of 1861 and Queen Elizabeth II	15	15
452	35 c. 1d. and 6d. stamps of 1861 and badge of Grenada	30	20
453	50 c. Scroll and 1d. stamp of 1861	45	50
450/3	*Set of* 4	90	80
MS454	96 × 114 mm. Nos. 452/3	75	1·00

* This issue is printed on thick paper and consequently the watermark is very faint.

178 Apollo Splashdown

(Des R. Granger Barrett. Litho Questa)

1971 (13 Nov). *Apollo Moon Exploration Series. T* **178** *and similar multicoloured designs. P* 11.

455	1 c. Type **178**	10	10
456	2 c. Recovery of Apollo 13	10	10
457	3 c. Separation of Lunar Module from Apollo 14	10	10
458	10 c. Shepard and Mitchell taking samples of moon rock	20	10
459	25 c. Moon Buggy	45	20
460	$1 Apollo 15 blast-off (*vert*)	1·40	1·25
455/60	*Set of* 6	2·00	1·50
MS461	77 × 108 mm. 50 c. as $1	1·10	1·50

179 67th Regiment of Foot, 1787

180 "The Adoration of the Kings" (Memling)

(Des G. Vasarhelyi. Litho Format)

1971 (11 Dec). *Military Uniforms. T* **179** *and similar vert designs. Multicoloured. P* 13½.

462	½ c. Type **179**	10	10
463	1 c. 45th Regiment of Foot, 1792	10	10
464	2 c. 29th Regiment of Foot, 1794	10	10
465	10 c. 9th Regiment of Foot, 1801	35	20
466	25 c. 2nd Regiment of Foot, 1815	70	35
467	$1 70th Regiment of Foot, 1764	2·25	2·00
462/7	*Set of* 6	3·00	2·25
MS468	108 × 99 mm. Nos. 466/7. P 15	3·50	3·75

(Des G. Vasarhelyi. Litho Questa)

1972 (15 Jan). *Christmas* (1971). *T* **180** *and similar vert designs. Multicoloured. P* 14 × 13½.

469	15 c. Type **180**	10	10
470	25 c. "Madonna and Child" (Michelangelo)	20	10
471	35 c. "Madonna and Child" (Murillo)	25	10
472	50 c. "The Virgin with the Apple" (Memling)	30	40
469/72	*Set of* 4	75	60
MS473	105 × 80 mm. $1 "The Adoration of the Kings" (Mostaert)	75	1·25

WINTER OLYMPICS
FEB. 3-13, 1972
SAPPORO, JAPAN

(181)

VOTE
FEB. 28 1972

(182)

1972 (3 Feb). *Winter Olympic Games, Sapporo, Japan. Nos.* 462/4 *and* **MS**468 *surch or optd only* (**MS**475).

(*a*) *Postage. As T* **181**

474	$2 on 2 c. multicoloured	60	90
MS475	108 × 99 mm. Nos. 466/7 (R.)	1·00	1·60

(*b*) *Air. As T* **181**, *but additionally surch* "AIR MAIL"

476	35 c. on ½ c. multicoloured	20	25
477	50 c. on 1 c. multicoloured	25	35

1972 (25 Feb). *General Election. Nos.* 307/8, 310 *and* 315 *optd with T* **182**.

478	2 c. multicoloured	10	10
479	3 c. multicoloured	10	10
	a. Opt inverted		
480	6 c. multicoloured	10	15
481	25 c. multicoloured	15	30
478/81	*Set of* 4	40	60

183 King Arthur

(Litho Questa)

1972 (4 Mar). *U.N.I.C.E.F. T* **183** *and similar multicoloured designs. P* 14.

482	½ c. Type **183**	10	10
483	1 c. Robin Hood	10	10
484	2 c. Robinson Crusoe (*vert*)	10	10
485	25 c. Type **183**	10	10
486	50 c. As No. 483	25	35
487	75 c. As No. 484	30	50
488	$1 Mary and her little lamb (*vert*)	45	70
482/8	*Set of* 7	1·10	1·60
MS489	65 × 98 mm. No. 488	55	80

INTERPEX
1972

(184)

12¢

(185)

AIR MAIL

(186)

1972 (17 Mar). *"Interpex" Stamp Exhibition, New York. Nos.* 433/9 *optd with T* **184**.

490 **174**	5 c. multicoloured	10	10
491	10 c. multicoloured	10	10
492	15 c. multicoloured	10	10
493	25 c. multicoloured	10	10
494	35 c. multicoloured	15	15
495	50 c. multicoloured	25	30
	a. Vert pair, top stamp with opt omitted	£100	
490/5	*Set of* 6	60	65
MS496	92 × 89 mm. **174** 50 c. multicoloured. Printed on silk. Imperf	7·50	12·00

1972 (20 Apr). *Nos.* 306/8 *surch with T* **185**, *and No.* 433 *surch similarly, but with obliterating bars under* "12c".

497	12 c. on 1 c. Type **88**	30	40
498	12 c. on 2 c. Strelitzia	30	40
499	12 c. on 3 c. Bougainvillea	30	40
500	12 c. on 5 c. Type **174**	30	40
497/500	*Set of* 4	1·10	1·40

1972. *Air. (a) Nos.* 306/12, 314*a*/17 *and* 318/21 *optd as T* **186** *or surch in addition* (2 May)

501 5 c. Rock Hind 10 10
a. Opt double
502 8 c. Snapper 10 10
a. Opt double
503 10 c. Marine Toad 10 10
a. Opt double 40·00
504 15 c. Thunbergia 25 10
505 25 c. Greater Trinidadian Murine Opossum 35 20
a. Horiz pair, one without opt £130
506 30 c. on 1 c. Type **86** 40 25
507 35 c. Nine-banded Armadillo 40 25
508 40 c. on 2 c. Strelitzia 50 25
509 45 c. on 3 c. Bougainvillea 55 35
510 50 c. Mona Monkey 55 35
a. Horiz pair, one without opt 90·00
b. Opt double £175
511 60 c. on 5 c. Rock Hind 60 40
512 70 c. on 6 c. Sailfish 70 50
513 $1 Bananaquit 2·25 60
514 $1.35 on 8 c. Snapper 2·25 95
515 $2 Brown Pelican 3·75 2·00
516 $3 Magnificent Frigate Bird 4·50 3·25
517 $5 Bare-eyed Thrush 5·50 6·00

(b) Nos. 440/3 *optd as T* **186** (5 June)

518 **175** 5 c. multicoloured 25 10
519 – 35 c. multicoloured 70 30
520 – 50 c. multicoloured 85 45
521 – 75 c. multicoloured 1·25 70
501/21 *Set of* 21 23·00 15·00

187 Yachting

(Litho Format)

1972 (8 Sept) *Olympic Games, Munich. T* **187** *and similar multi-coloured designs. P* 14. *(a) Postage.*

522 ½ c. Type **187** 10 10
523 1 c. Show-jumping 10 10
524 2 c. Running (*vert*) 10 10
525 35 c. As 2 c. 40 20
526 50 c. As 1 c. 55 40

(b) Air

527 25 c. Boxing 30 15
528 $1 As 25 c. 90 75
522/8 *Set of* 7 2·00 1·40
MS529 82 × 85 mm. 60 c. as 25 c. and 70 c. as 1 c. 1·00 1·40

188 Badge of Grenada and Nutmegs

(Des (from photographs by D. Groves) and photo Harrison)

1972 (20 Nov). *Royal Silver Wedding. Multicoloured; background colour given.* W w **12**. *P* 14 × 14½.

530 **188** 8 c. olive-brown 10 10
531 $1 ultramarine 45 55

189 Boy Scout Saluting

190 Madonna and Child

(Des R. Granger Barrett. Litho Questa)

1972 (2 Dec). *65th Anniv of Boy Scouts. T* **189** *and similar horiz designs. Multicoloured. P* 14. *(a) Postage.*

532 ½ c. Type **189** 10 10
533 1 c. Scouts knotting ropes 10 10
534 2 c. Scouts shaking hands 10 10
535 3 c. Lord Baden-Powell 10 10
536 75 c. As 2 c. 1·40 1·40
537 $1 As 3 c. 1·60 1·60

(b) Air

538 25 c. Type **189** 50 40
539 35 c. As 1 c. 70 50
532/9 *Set of* 8 4·00 3·50
MS540 87 × 88 mm. 60 c. as 3 c., and 70 c. as 2 c. 1·50 2·00

(Des V. Whiteley. Litho Format)

1972 (9 Dec). *Christmas. T* **190** *and similar vert designs. Multi-coloured. P* 13½.

541 1 c. Type **190** 10 10
542 3 c. The Three Kings 10 10
543 5 c. The Nativity 10 10
544 25 c. Type **190** 15 15
545 35 c. As 3 c. 20 20
546 $1 As 5 c. 60 60
541/6 *Set of* 6 1·00 1·00
MS547 102 × 76 mm. 60 c. Type **190** and 70 c. as 3 c. P 15 60 80

191 Greater Flamingoes

(Des M. and G. Shamir. Litho Questa)

1973 (26 Jan). *National Zoo. T* **191** *and similar horiz designs. Multicoloured. P* 14½.

548 25 c. Type **191** 70 35
549 35 c. Brazilian Tapir 80 45
550 60 c. Blue and Yellow Macaw, and Scarlet Macaw 1·40 1·00
551 70 c. Ocelot 1·50 1·25
548/51 *Set of* 4 3·75 2·75

192 Class II Racing Yacht

(Des V. Whiteley. Litho Format)

1973 (26 Feb). *Yachting. T* **192** *and similar horiz designs. Multi-coloured. P* 13½.

552 25 c. Type **192** 35 15
553 35 c. Harbour, St George's 40 15
554 60 c. Yacht *Bloodhound* 55 55
555 70 c. St. George's 70 75
552/5 *Set of* 4 1·75 1·40

193 Helios (Greek god) and Earth orbiting the Sun

(Des G. Vasarhelyi. Litho Format)

1973 (6 July). *I.M.O./W.M.O. Centenary. T* **193** *and similar horiz designs showing Greek Gods. Multicoloured. P* 13½.

556 ½ c. Type **193** 10 10
557 1 c. Poseidon and "Normad" storm detector 10 10
558 2 c. Zeus and radarscope 10 10
559 3 c. Iris and weather balloon 10 10
560 35 c. Hermes and "ATS-3" satellite 25 10
561 50 c. Zephyrus and diagram of pressure zones 40 25
562 75 c. Demeter and space photo 60 50
563 $1 Selene and rainfall diagram 65 80
556/63 *Set of* 8 1·75 1·50
MS564 123 × 92 mm. $2 Computer weather map (42 × 31 *mm*). P 13½. 90 1·25

194 Racing Class Yachts

195 Ignatius Semmelweis (obstetrician)

(Des G. Drummond. Litho Format)

1973 (3 Aug). *Carriacou Regatta. T* **194** *and similar horiz designs. Multicoloured. P* 13½.

565 ½ c. Type **194** 10 10
566 1 c. Cruising Class Yacht 10 10
567 2 c. Open-decked sloops 10 10
568 35 c. *Mermaid* (sloop) 35 20
569 50 c. St. George's Harbour 50 35
570 75 c. Map of Carriacou 70 60
571 $1 Boat-building 90 80
565/71 *Set of* 7 2·40 1·90
MS572 109 × 88 mm. $2 End of Race 1·25 1·75

(Des G. Vasarhelyi. Litho Format)

1973 (17 Sept). *25th Anniv of W.H.O. T* **195** *and similar vert designs. Multicoloured. P* 14½.

573 ½ c. Type **195** 10 10
574 1 c. Louis Pasteur 10 10
575 2 c. Edward Jenner 10 10
576 3 c. Sigmund Freud 10 10
577 25 c. Emil Von Behring (bacteriologist) 45 10
578 35 c. Carl Jung 55 20
579 50 c. Charles Calmette (bacteriologist) 80 30
580 $1 William Harvey 1·25 75
573/80 *Set of* 8 2·75 1·40
MS581 105 × 80 mm. $2 Marie Curie 2·00 2·00

196 Princess Anne and Capt. Mark Phillips

197 "Virgin and Child" (Maratti)

(Des G. Drummond. Litho Format)

1973 (14 Nov). *Royal Wedding. P* 13½.

582 **196** 25 c. multicoloured 10 10
583 $2 multicoloured 45 55
MS584 79 × 100 mm. 75 c. and $1 as Nos. 582/3 40 30

Nos. 582/3 were each issued in small sheets of five stamps and one stamp-size label.

(Litho Format)

1973 (10 Dec). *Christmas. T* **197** *and similar vert designs. Multi-coloured. P* 14½.

585 ½ c. Type **197** 10 10
586 1 c. "Madonna and Child" (Crivelli) 10 10
587 2 c. "Virgin and Child with Two Angels" (Verrocchio) 10 10
588 3 c. "Adoration of the Shepherds" (Roberti) 10 10
589 25 c. "The Holy Family with the Infant Baptist" (Baroccio) 15 10
590 35 c. "The Holy Family" (Bronzino) 20 10
591 75 c. "Mystic Nativity" (Botticelli) 30 20
592 $1 "Adoration of the Kings" (Geertgen) 40 30
585/92 *Set of* 8 1·00 60
MS593 89 × 89 mm. $2 "Adoration of the Kings" (Mostaert) (30 × 45 *mm*). P 13½ 1·00 1·10

INDEPENDENT

INDEPENDENCE
7TH FEB. 1974

(198)

199 Creative Arts Theatre, Jamaica Campus

1974 (7 Feb). *Independence. Nos.* 306/9, 311/13, 315/16 *and* 317*a*/21 *optd as T* **198**

594 1 c. Hibiscus 10 10
595 2 c. Strelitzia 10 10
596 3 c. Bougainvillea 10 10
597 5 c. Rock Hind 10 10
598 8 c. Snapper 15 10
599 10 c. Marine Toad 20 15
600 12 c. Turtle 20 15
601 25 c. Greater Trinidadian Murine Opossum 45 35
602 35 c. Nine-banded Armadillo 75 50
603 75 c. Yacht in St. George's Harbour 2·00 1·25
604 $1 Bananaquit 3·75 1·50
605 $2 Brown Pelican 6·00 3·50
606 $3 Magnificent Frigate Bird 10·00 5·00
607 $5 Bare-eyed Thrush 15·00 9·50
594/607 *Set of* 14 35·00 20·00

(Des G. Drummond. Litho Format)

1974 (10 Apr). *25th Anniv of University of West Indies. T* **199** *and similar multicoloured designs. P* 13½ × 14.

608 10 c. Type **199** 10 10
609 25 c. Marryshow House 10 10
610 50 c. Chapel, Jamaica Campus (*vert*) 20 10
611 $1 University arms (*vert*) 30 30
608/11 *Set of* 4 55 50
MS612 69 × 86 mm. $2 as No. 611 50 90

200 Nutmeg Pods and Scarlet Mace

201 Footballers (West Germany v Chile)

(Des G. Drummond. Litho Format)

1974 (19 Aug). *Independence*. T **200** *and similar vert designs. Multicoloured. P* 13½.

No.	Description	Unused	Used
613	3 c. Type **200**	10	10
614	8 c. Map of Grenada	10	10
615	25 c. Prime Minister Eric Gairy	15	10
616	35 c. Grand Anse Beach and flag	15	10
617	$1 Coat of arms	35	40
613/17	*Set of* 5	70	60
MS618	91 × 125 mm. $2 as $1	55	90

(Des G. Vasarhelyi. Litho Format)

1974 (3 Sept). *World Cup Football Championships, West Germany*. T **201** *and similar multicoloured designs showing footballers of the countries given. P* 14½.

No.	Description	Unused	Used
619	½ c. Type **201**	10	10
620	1 c. East Germany v Australia	10	10
621	2 c. Yugoslavia v Brazil	10	10
622	10 c. Scotland v Zaire	10	10
623	25 c. Netherlands v Uruguay	15	10
624	50 c. Sweden v Bulgaria	20	10
625	75 c. Italy v Haiti	35	15
626	$1 Poland v Argentina	50	25
619/26	*Set of* 8	1·25	60
MS627	114 × 76 mm. $2 Country flags. P 13	90	1·40

202 Early U.S. Mail-trains and "Concorde"

(Des G. Vasarhelyi. Litho Format)

1974 (8 Oct). *Centenary of Universal Postal Union*. T **202** *and similar horiz designs. Multicoloured. P* 14½.

No.	Description	Unused	Used
628	½ c. Type **202**	10	10
629	1 c. Mailboat *Caesar* (1839) and helicopter	10	10
630	2 c. Airmail transport	10	10
631	8 c. Pigeon post (1480) and telephone dial	15	10
632	15 c. 18th-century bellman and tracking antenna	20	10
633	25 c. Messenger (1450) and satellite	30	15
634	35 c. French pillar-box (1850) and mail-boat	50	25
635	$1 18th-century German postman and mail-train of the future	1·40	1·00
628/35	*Set of* 8	2·40	1·40
MS636	105 × 66 mm. $2 St. Gotthard mail-coach (1735). P 13	1·25	1·75

203 Sir Winston Churchill

204 "Madonna and Child of the Eucharist" (Botticelli)

(Des G. Vasarhelyi. Litho Format)

1974 (28 Oct). *Birth Centenary of Sir Winston Churchill*. T **203** *and similar portrait design. P* 13½.

No.	Description	Unused	Used
637 **203**	35 c. multicoloured	15	10
638 –	$2 multicoloured	45	50
MS639	129 × 96 mm. 75 c. as 35 c. and $1 as $2	50	75

(Des. M. Shamir. Litho Format)

1974 (18 Nov). *Christmas*. T **204** *and similar vert designs, showing "The Madonna and Child" by the artists given. Multicoloured. P* 14½.

No.	Description	Unused	Used
640	½ c. Type **204**	10	10
641	1 c. Niccolo di Pietro	10	10
642	2 c. Van der Weyden	10	10
643	3 c. Bastiani	10	10
644	10 c. Giovanni	10	10
645	25 c. Van der Weyden	15	10
646	50 c. Botticelli	25	20
647	$1 Mantegna	45	50
640/7	*Set of* 8	90	80
MS648	117 × 96 mm. $2 as 1 c. P 13	60	90

205 Yachts, Port Saline

(Des G. Drummond. Litho Format)

1975 (13 Jan)–**78**. *Multicoloured designs as* T **205**. A. *P* 14½ (½ *to* 50 *c.*) *or* 13½ (75 *c. to* $10). B. *P* 13.

No.	Description	A Unused	A Used	B Unused	B Used
649	½ c. Type **205** (*inscr* "POINT SALINE")	10	10	†	
	a. Inscr "POINT SALINES"	—	—	†	
650	1 c. Yacht club race	10	10	10	15
651	2 c. Carenage taxi	10	10	10	15
652	3 c. Large working boats	10	10	10	15
653	5 c. Deep-water dock	10	10	10	10
654	6 c. Cocoa beans in drying trays	10	10	10	10
655	8 c. Nutmegs	10	10	†	
656	10 c. Rum distillery, River Antoine Estate, *c* 1785	10	10	15	10
657	12 c. Cocoa tree	10	10	†	
658	15 c. Fishermen at Fontenoy	10	10	15	15
659	20 c. Parliament Building, St. George's	15	15	20	20
660	25 c. Fort George cannons	20	15	25	25
661	35 c. Pearls Airport	20	15	†	—
662	50 c. General Post Office	25	30	45	45
663	75 c. Carib's Leap, Sauteurs Bay (45 × 28 *mm*)	45	50	†	
664	$1 Carenage, St. George's (45 × 28 mm)	65	70	†	
665	$2 St. George's Harbour by night (45 × 28 mm)	1·00	1·50	†	
666	$3 Grand Anse Beach (45 × 28 *mm*)	1·25	2·00	†	
667	$5 Canoe Bay and Black Bay from Point Saline Lighthouse (45 × 28 *mm*)	1·75	2·75	†	
668	$10 Sugar-loaf Island from Levera Beach (45 × 28 *mm*)	4·50	6·50	†	
649/68	*Set of* 20	10·00	13·00	†	

No. 649a occurs on R. 6/1 and 7/1 from plate 1A and R. 10/5 from plate 1C.

Dates of issue:—13.1.75, Nos. 649A/62A; 22.1.75, 663A/7A; 26.3.75, No. 668A; 1978, Nos. 650B/4B, 656B, 658B/62B.

206 Sail-fish

(Des V. Whiteley. Litho Format)

1975 (3 Feb). *Big Game Fishing*. T **206** *and similar horiz designs. Multicoloured. P* 14½.

No.	Description	Unused	Used
669	½ c. Type **206**	10	10
670	1 c. Blue Marlin	10	10
671	2 c. White Marlin	10	10
672	10 c. Yellowfin Tuna	10	10
673	25 c. Wahoo	25	10
674	50 c. Dolphin	40	15
675	70 c. Grouper	60	20
676	$1 Great Barracuda	80	35
669/76	*Set of* 8	2·00	70
MS677	107 × 80 mm. $2 Blue Pointer or Mako Shark. P 13	1·00	1·25

207 Granadilla Barbadine

208 Dove, Grenada Flag and U.N. Emblem

(Des G. Vasarhelyi. Litho Format)

1975 (26 Feb). *Flowers*. T **207** *and similar horiz designs. Multicoloured. P* 14½.

No.	Description	Unused	Used
678	½ c. Type **207**	10	10
679	1 c. Bleeding Heart (Easter Lily)	10	10
680	2 c. Poinsettia	10	10
681	3 c. Cocoa flower	10	10
682	10 c. Gladioli	10	10
683	25 c. Redhead/Yellowhead	25	10
684	50 c. Plumbago	45	15
685	$1 Orange flower	70	25
678/85	*Set of* 8	1·40	55
MS686	102 × 82 mm. $2 Barbados Gooseberry. P 13	1·10	1·25

(Des G. Drummond. Litho Format)

1975 (19 Mar). *Grenada's Admission to the U.N.* (1974). T **208** *and similar vert designs. Multicoloured. P* 14½.

No.	Description	Unused	Used
687	½ c. Type **208**	10	10
688	1 c. Grenada and U.N. flags	10	10
689	2 c. Grenada coat of arms	10	10
690	35 c. U.N. emblem over map of Grenada	15	10
691	50 c. U.N. buildings and flags	20	15
692	$2 U.N. emblem and scroll	45	45
687/92	*Set of* 6	80	70
MS693	122 × 91 mm. 75 c. Type **208** and $1 as 2 c. P 13	65	90

CANCELLED REMAINDERS*. Some of the following issues have been remaindered, cancelled-to-order, at a fraction of their face-value. For all practical purposes these are indistinguishable from genuine postally used copies. Our used quotations which are indicated by an asterisk are the same for cancelled-to-order or postally used copies.

209 Paul Revere's Midnight Ride

210 "Blood of the Redeemer" (G. Bellini)

(Des J. Cornel (½ to 10 c.), PAD Studio (40 c. to $1), J.W. (**MS**704). Litho Format)

1975 (6 May). *Bicentenary of American Revolution* (1*st issue*). T **209** *and similar multicoloured designs. P* 14½.

(*a*) *Postage. Horiz designs*

No.	Description	Unused	Used
694	½ c. Type **209**	10	10*
695	1 c. Crispus Attucks	10	10*
696	2 c. Patrick Henry	10	10*
697	3 c. Franklin visits Washington	10	10*
698	5 c. Rebel troops	10	10*
699	10 c. John Paul Jones	10	10*

(*b*) *Air. Vert designs*

No.	Description	Unused	Used
700	40 c. "John Hancock" (Copley)	30	10*
701	50 c. "Benjamin Franklin" (Roslin)	45	15*
702	75 c. "John Adams" (Copley)	60	15*
703	$1 "Lafayette" (Casanova)	75	20*
694/703	*Set of* 10	2·00	60*
MS704	Two sheets 131 × 102 mm: $2 Grenada arms and U.S. seal; $2 Grenada and U.S. flags. P 13½	3·00	60*

Stamps from **MS**704 are horiz and larger: 47½ × 35mm.

Nos. 694/703 also exist perf 13 (*Price for set of* 10 £2 *mint or used*) from additional sheetlets of 5 stamps and 1 label. Stamps perforated 14½ are from normal sheets of 40.

See also Nos. 785/92.

(Des M. Shamir. Litho Format)

1975 (21 May). *Easter*. T **210** *and similar vert designs. Multicoloured. P* 14½.

No.	Description	Unused	Used
705	½ c. Type **210**	10	10*
706	1 c. "Pietà" (Bellini)	10	10*
707	2 c. "The Entombment" (Van der Weyden)	10	10*
708	3 c. "Pietà" (Bellini)	10	10*
709	35 c. "Pietà" (Bellini)	15	10*
710	75 c. "The Dead Christ" (Bellini)	30	10*
711	$1 "The Dead Christ supported by Angels" (Procaccini)	45	10*
705/11	*Set of* 7	90	30*
MS712	117 × 100 mm. $2 "Pietà" (Botticelli). P 13	1·00	30*

211 Wildlife Study

212 Leafy Jewel Box

(Des J.W. Litho Format)

1975 (2 July). *14th World Scout Jamboree, Norway*. T **211** *and similar horiz designs. Multicoloured. P* 14.

No.	Description	Unused	Used
713	½ c. Type **211**	10	10*
714	1 c. Sailing	10	10*
715	2 c. Map-reading	10	10*
716	35 c. First-aid	40	10*
717	40 c. Physical training	45	10*
718	75 c. Mountaineering	70	10*
719	$2 Sing-song	1·60	20*
713/19	*Set of* 7	3·00	40*
MS720	106 × 80 mm. $1 Boat-building	90	20*

(Des J.W. Litho Questa)

1975 (1 Aug). *Seashells*. T **212** *and similar vert designs. Multicoloured. P* 14.

No.	Description	Unused	Used
721	½ c. Type **212**	10	10*
722	1 c. Emerald Nerite	10	10*
723	2 c. Yellow Cockle	10	10*
724	25 c. Purple Sea Snail	30	10*
725	50 c. Turkey Wing	60	10*
726	75 c. West Indian Fighting Conch	95	10*
727	$1 Noble Wentletrap	1·25	15*
721/7	*Set of* 7	2·75	40*
MS728	102 × 76 mm. $2 Music Volute	1·60	30*

213 Lady or Large Tiger

214 Rowing

(Des J.W. Litho Format)

1975 (22 Sept). *Butterflies.* **T 213** *and similar vert designs. Multicoloured.* P 14.

729 ½ c. Type **213** .. 10 10*
730 1 c. Five Continent .. 10 10*
731 2 c. Large Striped Blue .. 10 10*
732 35 c. Gonatryx .. 40 10*
733 45 c. Spear-winged Cattleheart .. 45 10*
734 75 c. Rusty Nymula .. 75 15*
735 $2 Blue Night .. 1·75 20*
729/35 .. *Set of* 7 3·00 50*
MS736 108 × 83 mm. $1 *Papilio lycophron* .. 90 20*

(Des J.W. Litho Questa)

1975 (13 Oct). *Pan-American Games, Mexico City.* **T 214** *and similar vert designs. Multicoloured.* P 14.

737 ½ c. Type **214** .. 10 10*
738 1 c. Swimming .. 10 10*
739 2 c. Show-jumping .. 10 10*
740 35 c. Gymnastics .. 15 10*
741 45 c. Football .. 15 10*
742 75 c. Boxing .. 25 15*
743 $2 Cycling .. 65 20*
737/43 .. *Set of* 7 1·10 40*
MS744 106 × 81 mm. $1 Yachting .. 80 20*

215 "The Boy David" (Michelangelo)

216 "Madonna and Child" (Filippino Lippi)

(Des M. and G. Shamir. Litho J.W.)

1975 (3 Nov). *500th Birth Anniv of Michelangelo.* **T 215** *and similar vert designs. Multicoloured.* P 14.

745 ½ c. Type **215** .. 10 10*
746 1 c. "Young Man" (detail) .. 10 10*
747 2 c. "Moses" .. 10 10*
748 40 c. "Prophet Zachariah" .. 15 10*
749 50 c. "St John the Baptist" .. 15 10*
750 75 c. "Judith and Holofernes" .. 25 15*
751 $2 "Doni Madonna" (detail from "Holy Family") .. 60 20*
745/51 .. *Set of* 7 1·10 40*
MS752 104 × 89 mm. $1 "Madonna" (head from Pietà) .. 70 20*

The sculpture on No. 749 though ascribed to Michelangelo, shows a work by Francesco Sangallo.

(Des M. Shamir. Litho Questa)

1975 (8 Dec). *Christmas.* **T 216** *and similar vert designs showing "Virgin and Child". Multicoloured.* P 14.

753 ½ c. Type **216** .. 10 10*
754 1 c. Mantegna .. 10 10*
755 2 c. Luis de Morales .. 10 10*
756 35 c. G. M. Morandi .. 15 10*
757 50 c. Antonello da Messina .. 20 10*
758 75 c. Dürer .. 25 10*
759 $1 Velasquez .. 35 10*
753/9 .. *Set of* 7 90 35*
MS760 125 × 98 mm. $2 Bellini .. 75 30*

217 Bananaquit

218 Carnival Time

(Des G. Drummond. Litho Questa)

1976 (20 Jan). *Flora and Fauna.* **T 217** *and similar multicoloured designs.* P 14.

761 ½ c. Type **217** .. 10 10
762 1 c. Brazilian Agouti .. 10 10
763 2 c. Hawksbill Turtle (*horiz*) .. 10 10
764 5 c. Dwarf Poinciana .. 10 10
765 35 c. Albacore (*horiz*) .. 90 45
766 40 c. Cardinal's Guard .. 95 50
767 $2 Nine-banded Armadillo (*horiz*) .. 3·00 2·25
761/7 .. *Set of* 7 4·50 3·00
MS768 82 × 89 mm. $1 Belted Kingfisher .. 2·50 2·00

(Des G. Drummond. Litho Questa)

1976 (25 Feb). *Tourism.* **T 218** *and similar horiz designs. Multicoloured.* P 14.

769 ½ c. Type **218** .. 10 10
770 1 c. Scuba diving .. 10 10
771 2 c. Cruise Ship *Southward* at St. George's .. 10 10
772 35 c. Game fishing .. 40 20
773 50 c. St. George's Golf Course .. 75 35
774 75 c. Tennis .. 1·00 65
775 $1 Ancient rock carvings at Mount Rich .. 1·25 95
769/75 .. *Set of* 7 3·25 2·00
MS776 100 × 73 mm. $2 Small boat sailing .. 1·50 1·75

219 "Pietà" (Master of Okolicsno)

220 Sharpshooters

(Des M. and G. Shamir. Litho Questa)

1976 (29 Mar). *Easter.* **T 219** *and similar vert designs by the artists listed. Multicoloured.* P 14.

777 ½ c. Type **219** .. 10 10
778 1 c. Correggio .. 10 10
779 2 c. Van der Weyden .. 10 10
780 3 c. Dürer .. 10 10
781 35 c. Master of the Holy Spirit .. 15 10
782 75 c. Raphael .. 30 30
783 $1 Raphael .. 35 40
777/83 .. *Set of* 7 85 85
MS784 108 × 86 mm. $2 Crespi .. 70 1·00

(Des J.W. Litho Questa)

1976 (15 Apr). *Bicentenary of American Revolution (2nd issue).* **T 220** *and similar vert designs. Multicoloured.* P 14.

785 ½ c. Type **220** .. 10 10
786 1 c. Defending the Liberty Pole .. 10 10
787 2 c. Loading muskets .. 10 10
788 35 c. The fight for Liberty .. 30 15
789 50 c. Peace Treaty, 1783 .. 50 30
790 $1 Drummers .. 1·00 65
791 $3 Gunboat .. 2·50 2·00
785/91 .. *Set of* 7 4·00 2·75
MS792 93 × 79 mm. 75 c. as 35 c. and $2 as 50 c. .. 1·50 2·25

221 Nature Study

222 Volleyball

(Des G. Vasarhelyi. Litho Questa)

1976 (1 June). *50th Anniv of Girl Guides in Grenada.* **T 221** *and similar vert designs. Multicoloured.* P 14.

793 ½ c. Type **221** .. 10 10
794 1 c. Campfire cooking .. 10 10
795 2 c. First Aid .. 10 10
796 50 c. Camping .. 55 25
797 75 c. Home economics .. 85 40
798 $2 First Aid .. 2·50 1·50
793/8 .. *Set of* 6 3·50 2·00
MS799 111 × 85 mm. $1 Painting .. 1·25 1·75

(Des J.W. Litho Questa)

1976 (21 June). *Olympic Games, Montreal.* **T 222** *and similar vert designs. Multicoloured.* P 14.

800 ½ c. Type **222** .. 10 10
801 1 c. Cycling .. 10 10
802 2 c. Rowing .. 10 10
803 35 c. Judo .. 15 10
804 45 c. Hockey .. 20 20
805 75 c. Gymnastics .. 35 40
806 $1 High jump .. 50 65
800/6 .. *Set of* 7 1·10 1·40
MS807 106 × 81 mm. $3 Equestrian event .. 1·25 2·00

OMNIBUS ISSUES

Details, together with prices for complete sets, of the various Omnibus issues from the 1935 Silver Jubilee series to date are included in a special section following Zululand at the end of the catalogue.

223 "Cha-U-Kao at the Moulin Rouge"

224 Piper "Apache"

(Des M. Shamir. Litho Questa)

1976 (20 July). *75th Death Anniv of Toulouse Lautrec.* **T 223** *and similar vert designs. Multicoloured.* P 14.

808 ½ c. Type **223** .. 10 10
809 1 c. "Quadrille at the Moulin Rouge" .. 10 10
810 2 c. "Profile of a Woman" .. 10 10
811 3 c. "Salon in the Rue des Moulins" .. 10 10
812 40 c. "The Laundryman" .. 30 20
813 50 c. "Marcelle Lender dancing the Bolero" .. 35 25
814 $2 "Signor Boileau at the Cafe" .. 80 1·00
808/14 .. *Set of* 7 1·40 1·40
MS815 152 × 125 mm. $1 "Woman with Boa" .. 75 90

1976 (26 July). *West Indian Victory in World Cricket Cup. As Nos. 559/60 of Barbados.*

816 35 c. Map of the Caribbean .. 85 35
817 $1 The Prudential Cup .. 2·40 2·00

(Des J.W. Litho Questa)

1976 (18 Aug). *Aeroplanes.* **T 224** *and similar horiz designs. Multicoloured.* P 14.

818 ½ c. Type **224** .. 10 10
819 1 c. Beech "Twin Bonanza" .. 10 10
820 2 c. D.H. "Twin Otter" .. 10 10
821 40 c. Britten Norman "Islander" .. 55 35
822 50 c. D.H. "Heron" .. 65 45
823 $2 H.S. "748" .. 2·00 1·75
818/23 .. *Set of* 6 3·00 2·40
MS824 75 × 83 mm. $3 B.A.C. "1-11" .. 2·50 3·00

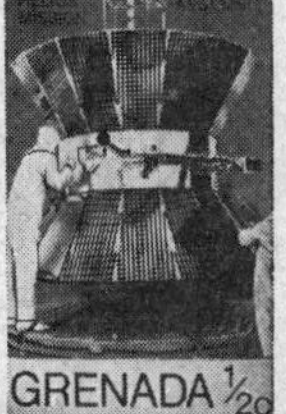

225 Satellite Assembly

226 S.S. *Geestland*

(Des PAD Studio. Litho Questa)

1976 (1 Sept). *Viking and Helios Space Missions.* **T 225** *and similar multicoloured designs.* P 14.

825 ½ c. Type **225** .. 10 10
826 1 c. Helios satellite .. 10 10
827 2 c. Helios encapsulation .. 10 10
828 15 c. Systems test .. 10 10
829 45 c. Viking lander (*horiz*) .. 20 20
830 75 c. Lander on Mars .. 35 35
831 $2 Viking encapsulation .. 90 90
825/31 .. *Set of* 7 1·40 1·40
MS832 110 × 85 mm. $3 Orbiter and lander .. 1·00 1·50

(Des J.W. Litho Format)

1976 (3 Nov). *Ships.* **T 226** *and similar horiz designs. Multicoloured.* P 14½.

833 ½ c. Type **226** .. 10 10
834 1 c. M. V. *Federal Palm* .. 10 10
835 2 c. H.M.S. *Blake* .. 10 10
836 25 c. M. V. *Vistafjord* .. 35 15
837 75 c. S.S. *Canberra* .. 90 70
838 $1 S.S. *Regina* .. 1·25 80
839 $5 S.S. *Arandora Star* .. 4·50 3·75
833/39 .. *Set of* 7 6·50 5·00
MS840 91 × 78 mm. $2 *Santa Maria* .. 2·00 2·50

227 "Altarpiece of San Barnaba" (Botticelli)

(Des PAD Studio. Litho Questa)

1976 (8 Dec). *Christmas.* **T 227** *and similar horiz designs. Multicoloured.* P 14.

841 ½ c. Type **227** .. 10 10
842 1 c. "Annunciation" (Botticelli) .. 10 10
843 2 c. "Madonna of Chancellor Rolin" (Jan van Eyck) .. 10 10
844 35 c. "Annunciation" (Fra Filippo Lippi) .. 15 10
845 50 c. "Madonna of the Magnificat" (Botticelli) 20 20
846 75 c. "Madonna of the Pomegranate" (Botticelli) .. 30 25
847 $3 "Madonna with St. Cosmas and Other Saints" (Botticelli) .. 1·00 1·00
841/7 .. *Set of* 7 1·50 1·40
MS848 71 × 57 mm. $2 "Gypsy Madonna" (Titian) 75 1·00

228 Alexander Graham Bell and Telephones   **229** Coronation Scene

(Des G. Vasarhelyi. Litho Questa)

1976 (17 Dec). *Telephone Centenary. T* **228** *and similar horiz designs. Multicoloured. P* 14.

849	½ c. Type **228**	10	10
850	1 c. Telephone-users within globe	10	10
851	2 c. Telephone satellite	10	10
852	18 c. Telephone viewer and console	15	10
853	40 c. Satellite and tracking stations	35	35
854	$1 Satellite transmitting to ships	65	65
855	$2 Dish aerial and modern telephone	1·10	1·10
849/55	*Set of* 7	2·00	2·00
MS856	107 × 80 mm. $5 Globe encircled by flags	2·25	3·25

(Des J.W. Litho Questa (Nos. 857/62), Walsall (863/6))

1977 (8 Feb). *Silver Jubilee. T* **229** *and similar vert designs. Multicoloured. (a) Sheet stamps. P* 13½ × 14.

857	½ c. Type **229**	10	10
858	1 c. Sceptre and orb	10	10
859	35 c. Queen on horseback	15	10
860	$2 Spoon and ampulla	60	60
861	$2.50 Queen and Prince Philip	65	60
857/61	*Set of* 5	1·25	1·10
MS862	103 × 79 mm. $5 Royal Visit to Grenada	1·00	2·00

Nos. 857/61 also exist perf 11½ × 12 (*Price for set of* 5 £1·25 *mint or used*) from additional sheetlets of 5 stamps and 1 label. They also have different frame colours to those perforated 13½ × 14, which come from normal sheets of 40.

(b) Booklet stamps. Roul 5 × *imperf**. *Self-adhesive*

863	35 c. As No. 861	25	25
	a. Booklet pane of 6	1·50	
864	50 c. As No. 860	55	70
	a. Booklet pane. Nos. 864/6	4·00	
865	$1 As No. 858	1·00	1·50
866	$3 As No. 859	2·75	3·75
863/6	*Set of* 4	4·00	5·75

*No. 863/6 are separated by various combinations of rotary knife (giving a straight edge) and roulette.

230 Water Skiing

(Des G. Drummond. Litho Questa)

1977 (Apr). *Easter Water Parade. T* **230** *and similar horiz designs. Multicoloured. P* 14.

867	½ c. Type **230**	10	10
868	1 c. Speedboat race	10	10
869	2 c. Row boat race	10	10
870	22 c. Swimming	15	10
871	35 c. Work boat race	25	20
872	75 c. Water polo	50	50
873	$2 Game fishing	1·40	1·40
867/73	*Set of* 7	2·25	2·10
MS874	115 × 85 mm. $3 Yacht race	1·50	2·25

231 Meeting Place, Grand Anse Beach

(Litho Questa)

1977 (14 June). *Seventh Meeting of Organization of American States. P* 14.

875 **231**	35 c. multicoloured	10	10
876	$1 multicoloured	25	40
877	$2 multicoloured	40	70
875/7	*Set of* 3	65	1·10

232 Rafting

(Des G. Drummond. Litho Questa)

1977 (6 Sept). *Caribbean Scout Jamboree, Jamaica. T* **232** *and similar horiz designs. Multicoloured. P* 14.

878	½ c. Type **232**	10	10
879	1 c. Tug-of-war	10	10
880	2 c. Sea Scouts regatta	10	10
881	18 c. Camp fire	25	10
882	40 c. Field kitchen	50	25
883	$1 Scouts and sea scouts	1·25	65
884	$2 Hiking and map reading	1·75	1·25
878/84	*Set of* 7	3·50	2·10
MS885	107 × 85 mm. $3 Semaphore	2·00	2·50

Royal Visit W. I. 1977

233 Angel and Shepherd   **(234)**

(Des G. Vasarhelyi. Litho Questa)

1977 (3 Nov). *Christmas. T* **233** *and similar horiz designs showing ceiling panels from the church of St. Martin in Zillis. Multicoloured. P* 14.

886	½ c. Type **233**	10	10
887	1 c. St. Joseph	10	10
888	2 c. Virgin and Child Fleeing to Egypt	10	10
889	22 c. Angel	10	10
890	35 c. A Magus on horseback	15	10
891	75 c. Three horses	20	20
892	$2 Virgin and Child	50	65
886/92	*Set of* 7	85	95
MS893	85 × 112 mm. $3 Magus offering gifts	1·00	1·40

1977 (10 Nov). *Royal Visit. Nos.* 857/62 *optd with T* **234**. *P* 13½ × 14 (35 *c.*, $2, $2.50) *or* 11½ × 12 (*others*).

894	½ c. Type **229**	10	10
895	1 c. Sceptre and orb	10	10
896	35 c. Queen on horseback	15	10
897	$2 Spoon and ampulla	40	40
898	$2.50, Queen and Prince Philip	45	45
894/8	*Set of* 5	1·00	85
MS899	103 × 79 mm. $5 Royal Visit to Grenada	1·00	1·50

Nos. 894/5 only exist perforated 11½ × 12, but the remaining three values come perforated 13½ × 14 or 11½ × 12 (*Nos.* 896/8 *perf* 11½ × 12. *Price for set of* 3 £1.50 *mint or used.*)

235 Christjaan Eijkman (Medicine)   **236** Count von Zeppelin and First Zeppelin Airship

(Des J.W. Litho Questa)

1978 (25 Jan). *Nobel Prize Winners. T* **235** *and similar vert designs. Multicoloured. P* 14.

900	½ c. Type **235**	10	10
901	1 c. Sir Winston Churchill (Literature)	10	10
902	2 c. Woodrow Wilson (Peace)	10	10
903	35 c. Frederic Passy (Peace)	15	10
904	$1 Albert Einstein (Physics)	55	40
905	$3 Carl Bosch (Chemistry)	1·75	1·25
900/5	*Set of* 6	2·25	1·75
MS906	114 × 99 mm. $2 Alfred Nobel	70	1·00

(Des G. Vasarhelyi. Litho Questa)

1978 (13 Feb). *75th Anniv of First Zeppelin Flight and 50th Anniv of Lindbergh's Transatlantic Flight. T* **236** *and similar horiz designs. Multicoloured. P* 14.

907	½ c. Type **236**	10	10
908	1 c. Lindbergh with *Spirit of St. Louis*	10	10
909	2 c. Airship *Deutschland*	10	10
910	22 c. Lindbergh's arrival in France	10	10
911	75 c. Lindbergh and *Spirit of St. Louis* in flight	30	30
912	$1 Zeppelin over Alps	40	40
913	$3 Zeppelin over White House	1·10	1·10
907/13	*Set of* 7	1·75	1·75
MS914	103 × 85 mm. 35 c. Lindbergh in cockpit; $2 Count von Zeppelin and airship	1·10	1·40

237 Rocket Launching   **238** Black-headed Gull

(Des J.W. Litho Questa)

1978 (28 Feb). *Space Shuttle. T* **237** *and similar vert designs. Multicoloured. P* 14.

915	½ c. Type **237**	10	10
916	1 c. Booster jettison	10	10
917	2 c. External tank jettison	10	10
918	18 c. Space shuttle in orbit	15	15
919	75 c. Satellite placement	35	35
920	$2 Landing approach	1·00	1·00
915/20	*Set of* 6	1·40	1·40
MS921	103 × 85 mm. $3 Shuttle after landing	1·10	1·25

(Des G. Drummond. Litho Questa)

1978 (9 Mar). *Wild Birds of Grenada. T* **238** *and similar vert designs. Multicoloured. P* 14.

922	½ c. Type **238**	10	10
923	1 c. Wilson's Petrel	10	10
924	2 c. Killdeer Plover	10	10
925	50 c. White-necked Jacobin	1·25	30
926	75 c. Blue-faced Booby	1·75	45
927	$1 Broad-winged Hawk	2·75	75
928	$2 Red-necked Pigeon	4·00	1·75
922/8	*Set of* 7	9·00	3·00
MS929	103 × 94 mm. $3 Scarlet Ibis	4·50	4·00

239 "The Landing of Marie de Medici at Marseilles"   **240** Ludwig van Beethoven

(Des PAD Studio. Litho Questa)

1978 (30 Mar). *400th Birth Anniv of Rubens. T* **239** *and similar vert designs showing paintings. Multicoloured. P* 13½ × 14.

930	5 c. Type **239**	10	10
931	15 c. "Rubens and Isabella Brandt"	10	10
932	18 c. "Marchesa Brigida Spindola-Doria"	10	10
933	25 c. "Ludovicus Nonninus"	10	10
934	45 c. "Helene Fourment and her Children"	15	15
935	75 c. "Clara Serena Rubens"	25	25
936	$3 "Le Chapeau de Paille"	60	80
930/6	*Set of* 7	1·10	1·40
MS937	65 × 100 mm. $5 "Self Portrait"	1·25	1·75

(Des PAD Studio. Litho Questa)

1978 (24 Apr). *150th Death Anniv of Beethoven. T* **240** *and similar multicoloured designs. P* 14.

938	5 c. Type **240**	10	10
939	15 c. Woman violinist (*horiz*	15	10
940	18 c. Musical instruments (*horiz*)	20	15
941	22 c. Piano (*horiz*)	20	15
942	50 c. Violins	40	30
943	75 c. Piano and sonata score	60	45
944	$3 Beethoven's portrait and home (*horiz*)	2·25	1·75
938/44	*Set of* 7	3·50	2·75
MS945	83 × 62 mm. $2 Beethoven and score	1·50	1·75

241 King Edward's Chair   **242** Queen Elizabeth II taking Salute at Trooping the Colour

(Des J.W. Litho Questa. (Nos. 946/9). Manufactured by Walsall. (Nos. 950/2))

1978 (2 May–14 June). *25th Anniv of Coronation. Multicoloured.*

(a) Sheet stamps. Vert designs as T **241**. *P* 14 (14 June)

946	35 c. Type **241**	15	10
947	$2 Queen with regalia	50	50
948	$2.50, St. Edward's Crown	60	50
946/8	*Set of* 3	1·10	1·00
MS949	102 × 76 mm. $5 Queen and Prince Philip	1·50	1·40

(b) Booklet stamps. Vert designs as T **242**. *Roul* 5 × *imperf**. *Self-adhesive* (2 May)

950	25 c. Type **242**	12	15
	a. Booklet pane. Nos. 950/1, each × 3	80	
951	35 c. Queen taking part in Maundy Thursday ceremony	15	25
952	$5 Queen and Prince Philip at Opening of Parliament	2·00	2·75
	a. Booklet pane of 1	2·00	
950/2	*Set of* 3	2·00	2·75

Nos. 946/8 also exist perf 12 (*Price for set of* 3 £1·10 *mint or used*) from additional sheetlets of 3 stamps and 1 label, issued 2 June. These have different frame colours from the stamps perforated 14, which come from normal sheets of 50.

*Nos. 950/1 are separated by various combinations of rotary-knife (giving a straight edge) and roulette. No. 952 exists only with straight edges.

243 Goalkeeper reaching for Ball **244** Aerial Phenomena, Germany, 1561 and U.S.A., 1952

(Des M. Rubin. Litho Format)

1978 (1 Aug). *World Cup Football Championship, Argentina. T* **243** *and similar vert designs showing goalkeeper reaching for ball. P* 14½.
953 40 c. multicoloured 10 10
954 60 c. multicoloured 15 20
955 90 c. multicoloured 25 30
956 $2 multicoloured 60 60
953/6 .. .. *Set of* 4 1·00 1·10
MS957 130 × 97 mm. $2.50, multicoloured .. 1·00 1·10

(Des G. Vasarhelyi. Litho Format)

1978 (17 Aug). *U.F.O. Research. T* **244** *and similar horiz designs. Multicoloured. P* 14½.
958 5 c. Type **244** 10 10
959 35 c. Various aerial phenomena, 1950 .. 25 25
960 $3 U.F.O.'s, 1965 .. .. 1·75 1·75
958/60 .. .. *Set of* 3 1·90 1·90
MS961 112 × 89 mm. $2 Sir Eric Gairy and U.F.O. research laboratory .. .. 1·25 1·25

245 Wright Glider, 1902

(Des G. Vasarhelyi. Litho Questa)

1978 (28 Aug). *75th Anniv of Powered Flight. T* **245** *and similar horiz designs. Multicoloured. P* 14.
962 5 c. Type **245** 10 10
963 15 c. *Flyer* 1, 1903 .. .. 10 10
964 18 c. *Flyer* 3 .. .. 10 10
965 22 c. *Flyer* 3 from above 15 10
966 50 c. Orville Wright and *Flyer* 25 20
967 75 c. *Flyer* 3 in Pau, France, 1908 .. 35 25
968 $3 Wilbur Wright and glider .. .. 1·10 70
962/8 .. .. *Set of* 7 1·90 1·25
MS969 114 × 85 mm. $2 Wright glider .. .. 1·25 1·25

246 Cook and Hawaiian Feast **247** "Paumgartner Altarpiece" (detail)

(Des G. Vasarhelyi. Litho Questa)

1978 (5 Dec). *Bicentenary of Discovery of Hawaii and 250th Birth Anniv of Captain Cook. T* **246** *and similar horiz designs. Multicoloured. P* 14.
970 18 c. Type **246** 45 15
971 35 c. Cook and Hawaiian warriors 65 25
972 75 c. Cook and Honolulu Harbour .. .. 1·00 60
973 $3 Cook (statue) and H.M.S. *Resolution* .. 2·50 2·00
970/3 .. .. *Set of* 4 4·25 2·75
MS974 116 × 88 mm. $4 Cook and death scene .. 3·00 3·25

(Des M. Rubin. Litho Questa)

1978 (20 Dec). *Christmas. Paintings by Dürer. T* **247** *and similar vert designs. Multicoloured. P* 14.
975 40 c. Type **247** 20 15
976 60 c. "The Adoration of the Magi" 25 20
977 90 c. "The Virgin and Child" 30 20
978 $2 "Virgin and Child with St. Anne" (detail) 65 55
975/8 .. .. *Set of* 4 1·25 1·00
MS979 113 × 83 mm. $4 "Madonna and Child" .. 1·10 1·50

MINIMUM PRICE

The minimum price quote is 10p which represents a handling charge rather than a basis for valuing common stamps. For further notes about prices see introductory pages.

248 National Convention and Cultural Centre (interior) **249** *Acalypha hispida*

(Des BG Studio. Litho Questa)

1979 (8 Feb). *5th Anniv of Independence. T* **248** *and similar vert designs. Multicoloured. P* 14.
980 5 c. Type **248** 10 10
981 18 c. National Convention and Cultural Centre (exterior) 10 10
982 22 c. Easter Water Parade, 1978 .. .. 10 10
983 35 c. Sir Eric M. Gairy (Prime Minister) .. 15 10
984 $3 The Cross, Fort Frederick 60 80
980/4 .. .. *Set of* 5 80 90

(Des J.W. Litho Questa)

1979 (26 Feb). *Flowers. T* **249** *and similar vert designs. Multicoloured. P* 14.
985 18 c. Type **249** 10 10
986 50 c. *Hibiscus rosa sinensis* 30 15
987 $1 *Thunbergia grandiflora* 55 25
988 $3 *Nerium oleander* .. .. 1·60 1·10
985/8 .. .. *Set of* 4 2·25 1·40
MS989 115 × 90 mm. $2 *Lagerstroemia speciosa* 1·00 1·10

250 Birds in Flight **251** Children playing Cricket

(Des M. Rubin. Litho Questa)

1979 (15 Mar). *30th Anniv of Declaration of Human Rights. T* **250** *and similar vert design. Multicoloured. P* 14.
990 15 c. Type **250** 10 10
991 $2 Bird in flight 55 65

(Des J.W. Litho Questa)

1979 (23 April). *International Year of the Child. T* **251** *and similar vert designs. Multicoloured. P* 14.
992 18 c. Type **251** 15 15
993 22 c. Children playing baseball 20 20
994 $5 Children playing in tree .. .. .. 3·50 3·00
992/4 .. .. *Set of* 3 3·50 3·00
MS995 114 × 92 mm. $4 Children with model spaceship .. .. 2·25 2·25

252 "Around the World in 80 Days"

(Des G. Vasarhelyi. Litho Questa)

1979 (4 May). *150th Birth Anniv of Jules Verne (author). T* **252** *and similar horiz designs showing scenes from his books and modern technological developments. Multicoloured. P* 14.
996 18 c. Type **252** 25 10
997 35 c. "20,000 Leagues under the Sea" 35 15
998 75 c. "From the Earth to the Moon" 50 25
999 $3 "Master of the World" .. .. .. 1·10 80
996/9 .. .. *Set of* 4 2·00 1·10
MS1000 110 × 85 mm. $4 "Clipper of the Clouds" 1·40 1·75

253 Mail Runner, Africa (early 19th-century) **254** "The Pistol of Peace" (vaccination gun), Map of Grenada and Children

(Des J.W. Litho Questa)

1979 (23 July). *Death Centenary of Sir Rowland Hill. T* **253** *and similar horiz designs. Multicoloured. P* 14.
1001 20 c. Type **253** 10 10
1002 40 c. Pony Express, America (mid 19th-century) 15 10
1003 $1 Pigeon post 35 25
1004 $3 Mail coach, Europe (18th-19th-century) 90 80
1001/4 .. .. *Set of* 4 1·25 1·10
MS1005 127 × 100 mm. $5 Sir Rowland Hill and 1891 1d. on 8d. *tête-bêche* block of 4 .. .. 1·25 1·75

Nos. 1001/4 also exist perf 12 (*Price for set of* 4 £1·25 *mint or used*) from additional sheetlets of 5 stamps and 1 label, issued 8 August. These have different background colours from the stamps perforated 14, which come from normal sheets of 40.

(Des G. Vasarhelyi. Litho Questa)

1979 (20 Aug). *International Year of the Child. "Grenada—First Nation 100% Immunized". P* 14.
1006 **254** 5 c. multicoloured 15 10
1007 $1 multicoloured 85 90

255 Reef Shark

(Des G. Drummond. Litho Questa)

1979 (22 Aug). *Marine Wildlife. T* **225** *and similar horiz designs. Mutlicoloured. P* 14.
1008 40 c. Type **255** 35 20
1009 45 c. Spotted Eagle Ray 35 20
1010 50 c. Manytooth Conger 40 25
1011 60 c. Golden Olive (shell) 50 30
1012 70 c. West Indian Murex (shell) 55 35
1013 75 c. Giant Tun (shell) 60 35
1014 90 c. Brown Booby 80 40
1015 $1 Magnificent Frigate Bird 90 45
1008/15 .. .. *Set of* 8 4·00 2·25
MS1016 109 × 78 mm. $2.50, Sooty Tern .. 1·75 1·75

256 The Flight into Egypt

(Des W. Grout. Litho Questa)

1979 (19 Oct). *Christmas. Religious Tapestries. T* **256** *and similar multicoloured designs. P* 14.
1017 6 c. Type **256** 10 10
1018 25 c. The Flight into Egypt (detail) 10 10
1019 30 c. Angel (*vert*) 15 10
1020 40 c. Doge Marino Grimani (detail) (*vert*) .. 15 15
1021 90 c. The Annunciation to the Shepherds (*vert*) 30 30
1022 $1 The Flight into Egypt (Rome) (*vert*) .. 35 35
1023 $2 The Virgin in Glory (*vert*) 60 60
1017/23 .. .. *Set of* 7 1·50 1·50
MS1024 111 × 148 mm. $4 Doge Marino Grimani (*vert*) .. .. 1·00 1·40

257 Mickey Mouse playing Baseball **258** Paul Harris (founder)

(Litho Format)

1979 (2 Nov). *International Year of the Child. Walt Disney Cartoon Characters. T* **257** *and similar vert designs showing characters playing sports. Multicoloured. P* 11.
1025 ½ c. Type **257** 10 10
1026 1 c. Donald Duck high-jumping 10 10
1027 2 c. Goofy playing basketball 10 10
1028 3 c. Goofy hurdling 10 10
1029 4 c. Donald Duck playing golf 10 10
1030 5 c. Mickey Mouse playing cricket 10 10
1031 10 c. Mickey Mouse playing football 10 10
1032 $2 Mickey Mouse playing tennis .. .. 1·90 1·50
1033 $2.50, Minnie Mouse riding horse .. .. 1·90 1·50
1025/33 .. .. *Set of* 9 3·75 3·00
MS1034 125 × 100 mm. $3 Goofy in riding gear. P 13½. .. .. 1·60 1·60

(Des J.W. Litho Questa)

1980 (25 Feb). *75th Anniv of Rotary International. T* **258** *and similar vert designs. Multicoloured. P* 14.

1035 6 c. Type **258** 10 10
1036 30 c. "Health" 15 15
1037 90 c. "Hunger" 30 30
1038 $2 "Humanity" 70 80
1035/8 .. .. *Set of* 4 1·00 1·10
MS1039 104 × 89 mm. $4 Rotary International emblem .. .. 1·00 1·60

PEOPLE'S REVOLUTION
13 MARCH 1979

(259)

1980 (28 Feb–8 Apr). *1st Anniv of Revolution (1st issue). Nos.* 651A/2A, 654A/7A, 659A, 660B *and* 662A/8A *optd with T* **259**.

1040 2 c. Carenage taxi 10 10
a. Optd on No. 651B .. .. 8·50
1041 3 c. Large working boats 10 10
a. Optd on No. 652B .. .. 8·50
1042 6 c. Cocoa beans in drying trays 10 10
1043 8 c. Nutmegs 10 10
1044 10 c. River Antoine Estate Rum Distillery, *c*. 1785 .. .. 10 10
1045 12 c. Cocoa Tree 10 10
1046 20 c. Parliament Building, St. George's .. 10 10
1047 25 c. Fort George cannons (8.4.80) 20 15
1048 50 c. General Post Office 30 25
1049 75 c. Caribs Leap, Sauteurs Bay 40 30
1050 $1 Carenage, St. George's 50 50
1051 $2 St. George's Harbour by night .. .. 95 1·40
1052 $3 Grand Anse Beach .. .. .. 1·75 2·50
1053 $5 Canoe Bay and Black Bay from Point Saline Lighthouse .. .. 2·75 3·75
1054 $10 Sugar Loaf Island from Levera Beach .. 4·50 6·00
1040/54 .. .. *Set of* 15 10·50 14·00
See also Nos. 1069/73.

260 Boxing

261 Tropical Kingbird

(Des Design Images Inc. Litho Questa)

1980 (24 Mar). *Olympic Games, Moscow. T* **260** *and similar horiz designs. Multicoloured. P* 14.

1055 25 c. Type **260** 10 10
1056 40 c. Cycling 15 10
1057 90 c. Show-jumping 20 20
1058 $2 Running 40 55
1055/8 .. .. *Set of* 4 75 80
MS1059 128 × 95 mm. $4 Sailing .. .. .. 80 1·40

(Des G. Drummond. Litho Questa)

1980 (8 Apr). *Wild Birds. T* **261** *and similar vert designs. Multicoloured. P* 14.

1060 20 c. Type **261** 45 10
1061 40 c. Rufous-breasted Hermit 55 20
1062 $1 Troupial .. .. 1·00 75
1063 $2 Ruddy Quail Dove .. .. .. 1·75 1·40
1060/3 .. .. *Set of* 4 3·25 2·25
MS1064 85 × 114 mm. $3 Prairie Warbler .. 2·25 2·50

LONDON 1980

(262)

263 Free Hot Lunch at Schools

1980 (6 May). *"London 1980" International Stamp Exhibition. Nos.* 1001/4 *optd with T* **262**. *P* 12.

1065 20 c. Type **253** 20 20
1066 40 c. Pony Express, America (mid 19th-century) 30 30
1067 $1 Pigeon Post 60 60
1068 $3 Mail coach, Europe (18th-19th-century) 1·75 1·75
1065/8 .. .. *Set of* 4 2·50 2·50

(Des M. Diamond. Litho Questa)

1980 (19 May). *1st Anniv of Revolution (2nd issue). T* **263** *and similar horiz designs. Multicoloured. P* 14.

1069 10 c. Type **263** 10 10
1070 40 c. "From tree to can" (agro-industry) .. 15 20
1071 $1 National Health care 40 45
1072 $2 New housing projects 75 90
1069/72 .. .. *Set of* 4 1·25 1·40
MS1073 110 × 85 mm. $5 Prime Minister Maurice Bishop (*vert*) .. .. 1·00 1·75

264 Jamb Statues, West Portal, Chartres Cathedral

(Des J.W. Litho Questa)

1980 (15 July). *Famous Works of Art. T* **264** *and similar horiz designs. Multicoloured. P* 13½.

1074 8 c. Type **264** 10 10
1075 10 c. "Les Demoiselles D'Avignon" (painting by Picasso) 10 10
1076 40 c. Winged Victory of Samothrace (statue) 15 20
1077 50 c. "The Night Watch" (painting by Rembrandt) 15 20
1078 $1 "Portrait of Edward VI as a Child" (painting by Holbein the Younger) .. 30 35
1079 $3 Portrait head of Queen Nefertiti (carving) .. .. 80 1·00
1074/9 .. .. *Set of* 6 1·25 1·75
MS1080 101 × 101 mm. $4 "Weier Haws" (detail of painting by Dürer) (*vert*) .. .. .. 75 1·00

265 Carib Canoes

(Des G. Drummond. Litho Questa)

1980 (9 Sept)–**84**. *Shipping. Horiz designs as T* **265**. *Multicoloured. A. Without imprint date. P* 14.

1081A ½ c. Type **265** 10 10
1082A 1 c. Boat building 10 10
1083A 2 c. Small working boat 10 10
1084A 4 c. Columbus' *Santa Maria* 20 10
1085A 5 c. West Indiaman barque, *circa* 1840 .. 20 10
1086A 6 c. R.M.S.P. *Orinoco, circa* 1851 .. 20 10
1087A 10 c. Working schooner 20 10
1088A 12 c. Trimaran at Grand Anse anchorage 20 10
1089A 15 c. Spice Island cruising yacht *Petite Amie* 20 10
1090A 20 c. Fishing pirogue 30 10
1091A 25 c. Harbour police launch 35 15
1092A 30 c. Grand Anse speed-boat 40 20
1093A 40 c. M.V. *Seimstrand* 45 25
1094A 50 c. Three-masted schooner *Ariadne* .. 60 35
1095A 90 c. M.V. *Geestide* 80 50
1096A $1 M.V. *Cunard Countess* .. .. 1·00 70
1097A $3 Rum-runner .. .. 2·75 2·75
1098A $5 S.S. *Statendam* off St. George's .. 4·75 5·00
1099A $10 Coast-guard patrol boat .. .. 8·50 10·00
1081A/99A .. .. *Set of* 19 19·00 19·00

B. *With imprint date at foot of design. P* 14 ($1) *or* 12 (*others*)

1081B ½ c. Type **265** (1982) 10 10
1085B 5 c. West Indiaman barque, *circa* 1840 (1982) 20 10
1087B 10 c. Working schooner (1982) 20 10
a. Perf 14 .. .. † —
1090B 20 c. Fishing pirogue (1982) 30 15
1091B 25 c. Harbour police launch (1982) .. 30 15
a. Perf 14 .. .. 1·50 75
1092B 30 c. Grand Anse speed-boat (1982) .. 35 20
a. Perf 14 .. .. 2·00 1·00
1093B 40 c. M.V. *Seimstrand* (1982) 45 25
1094B 50 c. Three-masted schooner *Ariadne* (1.84) 45 25
a. Perf 14 (1984) 45 25
1096B $1 M.V. *Cunard Countess* (1982) .. 8·00 3·50
1097B $3 Rum-runner (1982) .. .. .. 1·75 1·75
1098B $5 S.S. *Statendam* off St. George's (1982) .. .. 2·75 2·75
1099B $10 Coast-guard patrol boat (1.84) .. 8·00 8·00
1081B/99B .. .. *Set of* 12 20·00 15·00

(Litho Walsall)

1980 (25 Sept). *Christmas. Walt Disney Cartoon Scenes from "Snow White and the Seven Dwarfs". Horiz designs as T* **257**. *Multicoloured. P* 11.

1100 ½ c. Snow White at well 10 10
1101 1 c. The Wicked Queen 10 10
1102 2 c. Snow White singing to animals 10 10
1103 3 c. Snow White doing housework for Dwarfs 10 10
1104 4 c. The Seven Dwarfs 10 10
1105 5 c. Snow White with Dwarfs 10 10
1106 10 c. Witch offering Snow White apple .. 10 10
1107 $2.50, Snow White with Prince, and Dwarfs 2·25 1·25
1108 $3 Snow White and Prince .. .. .. 2·50 1·75
1100/8 .. .. *Set of* 9 4·75 3·00
MS1109 127 × 102 mm. $4 Snow White sleeping (*vert*) .. .. 2·00 1·90

(Litho Format)

1981 (19 Jan). *50th Anniv of Walt Disney's Cartoon Character, Pluto. Vert designs as T* **257**. *Multicoloured. P* 13½.

1110 $2 Pluto with birthday cake .. .. 1·25 1·00
MS1111 127 × 102 mm. $4 Pluto in scene from film *Pueblo Pluto* .. .. 2·10 2·25
No. 1110 was printed in small sheets of 8 stamps.

266 Revolution and Grenada Flags

1981 (13 Mar). *Festival of the Revolution. T* **266** *and similar triangular designs. Multicoloured. Litho. P* 12½.

1112 5 c. Type **266** 10 10
1113 10 c. Teacher, pupil, book and pencil ("education") 10 10
1114 15 c. Food processing plant ("industry") .. 10 10
1115 25 c. Selection of fruits and farm scene ("agriculture") 15 15
1116 40 c. Crawfish and boat ("fishing") 20 20
1117 90 c. *Cunard Countess* arriving at St. George's Harbour ("shipping") .. 50 50
1118 $1 Straw-work ("native handicrafts") .. 60 60
1119 $3 Map of Caribbean with expanded view of Grenada .. .. 1·75 1·75
1112/19 .. .. *Set of* 8 3·00 3·00

(Litho Format)

1981 (7 Apr). *Easter. Walt Disney Cartoon Characters. Vert designs as T* **257**. *Multicoloured. P* 11.

1120 35 c. Mickey Mouse and Goofy 25 25
1121 40 c. Donald Duck, Chip and Daisy Duck .. 25 25
1122 $2 Minnie Mouse .. .. 1·40 1·25
1123 $2.50, Pluto and Mickey Mouse .. .. 1·60 1·40
1120/3 .. .. *Set of* 4 3·25 2·75
MS1124 127 × 101 mm. $4 Goofy. P 13½ .. 2·75 2·50

267 "Woman-Flower"

268 Prince Charles playing Polo

(Des J.W. Litho Questa)

1981 (28 Apr). *Birth Centenary of Picasso. T* **267** *and similar vert designs. Multicoloured. P* 13½ × 14.

1125 25 c. Type **267** 15 15
1126 30 c. "Portrait of Madame" 20 15
1127 90 c. "Cavalier with Pipe" 45 45
1128 $4 "Large Heads" .. .. 2·00 1·75
1125/8 .. .. *Set of* 4 2·50 2·25
MS1129 128 × 103 mm. $5 "Woman on the Banks of the Seine" (after Courbet). Imperf .. .. 3·00 3·00

(Des J.W. Litho Format)

1981 (16 June). *Royal Wedding. T* **268** *and similar vert designs. Multicoloured.* (a) *P* 15.

1130 50 c. Prince Charles and Lady Diana Spencer 30 30
1131 $2 Holyrood House .. .. 1·00 1·00
1132 $4 Type **268** .. .. 1·75 2·25
a. Imperf (pair) £400
1130/2 .. .. *Set of* 3 2·75 3·25
MS1133 98 × 84 mm. $5 Glass Coach .. .. 2·40 2·50

(*b*) *P* 15 × 14½

1134 30 c. As 50 c. 20 20
1135 40 c. As $2 .. .. 30 30

The 30 and 40 c. values were each printed in small sheets of 6 including one *se-tenant* stamp-size label.

The $4 value, with changed background colour, also exists perforated 15 × 14½ (*price* £1.50 *mint or used*) from similar sheetlets in addition to the original version issued in sheets of 40.

269 Lady Diana Spencer

270 "The Bath" (Mary Cassatt)

(Manufactured by Walsall)

1981 (16 June). *Royal Wedding. Booklet stamps. T* **269** *and similar vert designs. Multicoloured. Roul* 5 × *imperf*. Self-adhesive.*

1136 $1 Type **269** 50 65
a. Booklet pane. Nos. 1136/7 each × 3 .. 3·50
1137 $2 Prince Charles .. .. 75 1·00
1138 $5 Prince Charles and Lady Diana Spencer 2·00 2·50
a. Booklet pane of 1 .. .. 2·00
1136/8 .. .. *Set of* 3 3·00 3·75

*The $1 and $2 values were each separated by various combinations of rotary knife (giving a straight edge) and roulette. The $5 value exists only with straight edges.

(Des BG Studio. Litho Questa)

1981 (Oct). *"Decade for Women". Paintings. T* **270** *and similar multicoloured designs. P* 14.
1139 15 c. Type **270** 10 10
1140 40 c. "Mademoiselle Charlotte du Val d'Ognes" (Constance Marie Charpentier) 25 20
1141 60 c. "Self-portrait" (Mary Beale) 40 30
1142 $3 "Woman in White Stockings" (Suzanne Valadon) .. .. 1·50 1·25
1139/42 .. .. *Set of* 4 2·00 1·75
MS1143 101 × 77 mm. $5 "The Artist hesitating between the Arts of Music and Painting" (Angelica Kauffman) (*horiz*) .. .. 2·75 2·75

(Litho Questa)

1981 (Nov). *Christmas. Horiz designs as T* **257** *showing scenes from Walt Disney's cartoon film "Cinderella". P* 13½.
1144 ½ c. multicoloured 10 10
1145 1 c. multicoloured 10 10
1146 2 c. multicoloured 10 10
1147 3 c. multicoloured 10 10
1148 4 c. multicoloured 10 10
1149 5 c. multicoloured 10 10
1150 10 c. multicoloured 10 10
1151 $2.50, multicoloured .. .. .. 2·25 1·50
1152 $3 multicoloured .. .. 2·25 1·75
1144/52 .. .. *Set of* 9 4·50 3·25
MS1153 127 × 103 mm. $5 multicoloured .. 3·25 2·75

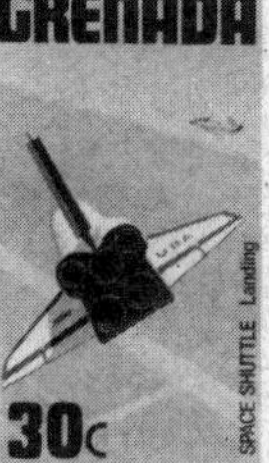

271 Landing

272 West German Footballer and Flag

(Des M. Brodie. Litho Format)

1981 (12 Nov). *Space Shuttle Project. T* **271** *and similar vert designs. Multicoloured. P* 14½.
1154 30 c. Type **271** 20 15
1155 60 c. Working in space 40 30
1156 70 c. Lift off 45 35
1157 $3 Separation .. .. 1·40 1·25
1154/7 .. .. *Set of* 4 2·25 1·75
MS1158 117 × 89 mm. $5 In orbit .. .. 2·50 2·50

(Des Clover Mill. Litho Format)

1981 (30 Nov.) *World Cup Football Championship, Spain* (1982). *T* **272** *and similar multicoloured designs. P* 14.
1159 25 c. + 10 c. Type **272** 30 30
1160 40 c. + 20 c. Argentinian footballer and flag .. 40 40
1161 50 c. + 25 c. Brazilian footballer and flag .. 55 50
1162 $1 + 50 c. English footballer and flag .. 1·00 95
1159/62 .. .. *Set of* 4 2·00 1·90
MS1163 141 × 128 mm. $5 + 50 c. Spanish orange mascot and Jules Rimet Trophy (*vert*) .. .. 2·75 3·00

Nos. 1159/62 were each printed in sheetlets of 12 on an overall background design showing a football.

273 General Post Office, St. George's

274 Artist without Hands

(Des J.W. Litho Format)

1981 (10 Dec). *Centenary of U.P.U. Membership. T* **273** *and similar horiz designs. Multicoloured. P* 15.
1164 25 c. Type **273** 15 15
1165 30 c. 1861 1d. stamp 20 20
1166 90 c. 1970 New U.P.U. Headquarters Building 25 c. commemorative 70 50
1167 $4 1961 Stamp Centenary 25 c. commemorative .. .. 2·00 2·00
1164/7 .. .. *Set of* 4 2·75 2·50
MS1168 113 × 87 mm. $5 1974 Centenary of U.P.U. ½ c. commemorative .. .. .. 2·40 2·50

(Litho Questa)

1982 (4 Feb). *International Year for the Disabled* (1981). *T* **274** *and similar vert designs. Multicoloured. P* 14.
1169 30 c. Type **274** 45 15
1170 40 c. Computer operator without hands .. 50 20
1171 70 c. Blind schoolteacher teaching braille .. 75 35
1172 $3 Midget playing drums .. .. .. 2·25 1·40
1169/72 .. .. *Set of* 4 3·50 1·90
MS1173 101 × 72 mm. $4 Auto mechanic confined to wheelchair .. .. 2·50 2·75

275 Tending Vegetable Patch

GRENADA

276 Flambeau

(Des Design Images. Litho Format)

1982 (19 Feb). *75th Anniv of Boy Scout Movement and 125th Birth Anniv of Lord Baden-Powell. T* **275** *and similar horiz designs. Multicoloured. P* 14½.
1174 70 c. Type **275** 50 45
1175 90 c. Map-reading 55 50
1176 $1 Bee-keeping 65 60
1177 $4 Hospital reading .. .. .. 2·25 2·25
1174/7 .. .. *Set of* 4 3·50 3·50
MS1178 100 × 71 mm. $5 Presentation of trophies 2·75 3·25

(Des G. Drummond. Litho Questa)

1982 (24 Mar). *Butterflies. T* **276** *and similar vert designs. Multicoloured. P* 14.
1179 10 c. Type **276** 55 15
1180 60 c. Large Orange Sulphur .. .. .. 1·50 40
1181 $1 Red Anartia .. .. 2·00 90
1182 $3 Polydamas Swallowtail .. .. .. 3·25 3·50
1179/82 .. .. *Set of* 4 6·50 4·50
MS1183 111 × 85 mm. $5 Caribbean Buckeye .. 3·25 3·75

277 "Saying Grace"

278 Kensington Palace

(Des M.B.I. Studio. Litho Questa)

1982 (14 Apr). *Norman Rockwell (painter) Commemoration. T* **277** *and similar vert designs. Multicoloured. P* 14 × 13½.
1184 15 c. Type **277** 25 10
1185 30 c. "Card Tricks" 45 15
1186 60 c. "Pharmacist" 70 25
1187 70 c. "Pals" 75 35
1184/7 .. .. *Set of* 4 1·90 75

(Des PAD Studio. Litho Questa)

1982 (1 July). *21st Birthday of Princess of Wales. T* **278** *and similar vert designs. Multicoloured. P* 14½ × 14.
1188 50 c. Type **278** 25 30
1189 60 c. Type **278** 40 35
1190 $1 Prince and Princess of Wales 50 55
1191 $2 As $1 .. .. 1·00 1·00
1192 $3 Princess of Wales .. .. .. 1·60 1·75
1193 $4 As $3 .. .. 2·00 1·90
1188/93 .. .. *Set of* 6 5·50 5·50
MS1194 103 × 75 mm. $5 Princess Diana (*different*) .. .. 2·40 2·50

Nos. 1188, 1190 and 1192 come from sheetlets of 5 stamps and 1 label.

279 Mary McLeod Bethune appointed Director of Negro Affairs, 1942

(Des Design Images. Litho Questa)

1982 (27 July). *Birth Centenary of Franklin D. Roosevelt. T* **279** *and similar horiz designs. Multicoloured. P* 14.
1195 10 c. Type **279** 10 10
1196 60 c. Huddie Ledbetter ("Leadbelly") in concert (Works Progress administration) 35 30
1197 $1.10, Signing bill No. 8802, 1941 (Fair Employment committee) 65 55
1198 $3 Farm Security administration .. .. 1·40 1·25
1195/8 .. .. *Set of* 4 2·25 1·90
MS1199 100 × 70 mm. $5 William Hastie, first Negro judicial appointee .. .. .. 2·40 2·50

1982 (30 Aug). *Birth of Prince William of Wales. Nos.* 1188/94 *optd with T* 171 *of Antigua.*
1200 50 c. Type **278** 25 30
1201 60 c. Type **278** 30 35
1202 $1 Prince and Princess of Wales 50 55
1203 $2 As $1 .. .. 95 1·00
1204 $3 Princess of Wales .. .. .. 1·60 1·75
1205 $4 As $3 .. .. 1·75 1·90
1200/5 .. .. *Set of* 6 4·75 5·50
MS1206 103 × 75 mm. $5 Princess Diana (*different*) .. .. 2·40 2·50

Nos. 1200, 1202 and 1204 come from sheetlets of 5 stamps and 1 label.

280 Apostle and Tormentor

(Des Clover Mill. Litho Format)

1982 (2 Sept). *Easter. Details from Painting "The Way to Calvary" by Raphael. T* **280** *and similar multicoloured designs. P* 14 × 14½ (40 c.) *or* 14½ × 14 (*others*).
1207 40 c. Type **280** 30 20
1208 70 c. Captain of the guards (*vert*) 55 35
1209 $1.10, Christ and apostle (*vert*) 75 45
1210 $4 Mourners (*vert*) .. .. 2·25 1·50
1207/10 .. .. *Set of* 4 3·50 2·25
MS1211 102 × 126 mm. $5 Christ falls beneath the cross (*vert*) .. .. 2·40 2·50

281 "Orient Express"

(Des Artists International. Litho Format)

1982 (4 Oct). *Famous Trains of the World. T* **281** *and similar horiz designs. Multicoloured. P* 15 × 14½.
1212 30 c. Type **281** 40 15
1213 60 c. "Trans-Siberian Express" 60 25
1214 70 c. "Golden Arrow" 75 35
1215 90 c. "Flying Scotsman" 90 40
1216 $1 German Federal Railways .. .. 1·25 75
1217 $3 German National Railways .. .. 2·50 2·25
1212/17 .. .. *Set of* 6 5·75 3·75
MS1218 109 × 81 mm. $5 "20th Century Limited" 3·00 3·50

282 Footballers

283 Killer Whale

(Des D. Miller. Litho Questa)

1982 (2 Dec). *World Cup Football Championship Winners. T* **282** *and similar horiz designs. P* 14 × 13½.
1219 60 c. multicoloured 35 35
1220 $4 multicoloured .. .. 2·00 2·00
MS1221 93 × 119 mm. $5 multicoloured .. 2·50 2·75

(Litho Questa)

1982 (14 Dec). *Christmas. Horiz designs as T* **257** *depicting scenes from Walt Disney's cartoon film "Robin Hood". P* 13½.
1222 ½ c. multicoloured 10 10
1223 1 c. multicoloured 10 10
1224 2 c. multicoloured 10 10
1225 3 c. multicoloured 10 10
1226 4 c. multicoloured 10 10
1227 5 c. multicoloured 10 10
1228 10 c. multicoloured 10 10
1229 $2.50, multicoloured .. .. .. 1·25 1·00
1230 $3 multicoloured .. .. 1·40 1·25
1222/30 .. .. *Set of* 9 2·50 2·25
MS1231 121 × 96 mm. $5 multicoloured .. .. 2·40 2·50

(Des Artists International. Litho Questa)

1983 (10 Jan). *Save the Whales. T* **283** *and similar vert designs. Multicoloured. P* 14.
1232 15 c. Type **283** 45 10
1233 40 c. Sperm Whale 85 25
1234 70 c. Blue Whale .. .. 1·25 65
1235 $3 Common Dolphin .. .. .. 2·50 2·50
1232/5 .. .. *Set of* 4 4·50 3·25
MS1236 84 × 74 mm. $5 Humpback Whale .. 3·50 4·00

284 "Construction of Ark"

(Des Design Images. Litho Format)

1983 (15 Feb). *500th Birth Anniv of Raphael. T* **284** *and similar horiz designs showing painting details. Multicoloured. P* 13½.

1237 25 c. Type **284** 15 15
1238 30 c. "Jacob's Vision" 15 20
1239 90 c. "Joseph interprets the Dreams to his Brothers" 40 45
1240 $4 "Joseph interprets Pharaoh's Dreams" 1·90 2·00
1237/40 .. .. *Set of* 4 2·25 2·50
MS1241 128 × 100 mm. $5 "Creation of the Animals" .. .. 2·50 2·75

285 Dentistry at Health Centre

(Des J.W. Litho Questa)

1983 (14 Mar). *Commonwealth Day. T* **285** *and similar horiz designs. Multicoloured. P* 14.

1242 10 c. Type **285** 10 10
1243 70 c. Airport runway construction 35 35
1244 $1.10, Tourism 55 55
1245 $3 Boat-building .. .. 1·40 1·40
1242/5 .. .. *Set of* 4 2·10 2·10

286 Maritime Communications via Satellite

(Des G. Vasarhelyi. Litho Questa)

1983 (29 Mar). *World Communications Year. T* **286** *and similar horiz designs. Multicoloured. P* 14.

1246 30 c. Type **286** 15 15
1247 40 c. Rural telephone installation 20 20
1248 $2.50, Satellite weather map .. .. 1·25 1·25
1249 $3 Airport control room .. .. .. 1·40 1·40
1246/9 .. .. *Set of* 4 2·75 2·75
MS1250 111 × 85 mm. $5 Communications satellite .. .. 2·50 3·00

287 Franklin Sport Sedan, 1928

(Des J. Mendola. Litho Format)

1983 (4 May). *75th Anniv of Model "T" Ford Car. T* **287** *and similar horiz designs showing cars of the 20th century. Multicoloured. P* 14½.

1251 6 c. Type **287** 10 10
1252 10 c. Delage "D8", 1933 .. .. .. 10 10
1253 40 c. Alvis, 1938 .. .. 20 25
1254 60 c. Invicta "S-type" tourer, 1931 .. .. 30 35
1255 70 c. Alfa-Romeo "1750 Gran Sport", 1930 .. 35 40
1256 90 c. Isotta Fraschini, 1930 .. .. .. 40 45
1257 $1 Bugatti "Royale Type 41" 45 50
1258 $2 BMW "328", 1938 .. .. .. 95 1·00
1259 $3 Marmon "V16", 1931 .. .. .. 1·40 1·50
1260 $4 Lincoln "K8" saloon, 1932 .. .. 1·90 2·00
1251/60 .. .. *Set of* 10 5·50 6·00
MS1261 114 × 90 mm. $5 Cougar "XR 7", 1972 .. 2·50 3·00

Nos. 1251/60 were each issued in sheets of eight stamps with a stamp-size label in the centre position.

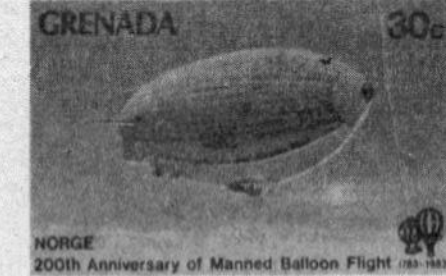

288 *Norge* (airship)

(Des W. Wright. Litho Questa)

1983 (18 July). *Bicentenary of Manned Flight. T* **288** *and similar multicoloured designs. P* 14.

1262 30 c. Type **288** 30 20
1263 60 c. Gloster "VI" seaplane 45 35
1264 $1.10, Curtiss "NC-4" flying boat 80 70
1265 $4 Dornier "Do 18" flying boat .. .. 2·50 2·25
1262/5 .. .. *Set of* 4 3·50 3·25
MS1266 114 × 85 mm. $5 Modern hot-air balloon (*vert*) .. .. 2·75 3·00

289 Morty

(Litho Format)

1983 (7 Nov). *Christmas. T* **289** *and similar vert designs showing Disney cartoon characters in scenes from "It's beginning to look a lot like Christmas" (song). Multicoloured. P* 11.

1267 ½ c. Type **289** 10 10
1268 1 c. Ludwig von Drake 10 10
1269 2 c. Gyro Gearloose 10 10
1270 3 c. Pluto and Figaro 10 10
1271 4 c. Morty and Ferdie 10 10
1272 5 c. Mickey Mouse and Goofy 10 10
1273 10 c. Chip'n Dale 10 10
1274 $2.50, Mickey and Minnie Mouse .. .. 1·75 1·40
1275 $3 Donald and Grandma Duck .. .. 2·00 1·75
1267/75 .. .. *Set of* 9 3·75 3·25
MS1276 127 × 102 mm. $5 Goofy with Christmas tree. P 13½ .. .. 3·00 3·25

290 Daisy Duck on Pommel Horse

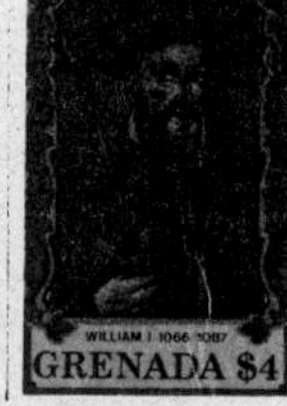

291 William I

(Litho Questa)

1984 (17 Jan–May). *Olympic Games, Los Angeles. T* **290** *and similar horiz designs showing Disney cartoon characters in Olympic events. Multicoloured. A. Inscr.* "1984 LOS ANGELES". *P* 14 × 13½. *B. Inscr.* "1984 OLYMPICS LOS ANGELES" *and Olympic emblem. P* 12 (May).

		A		B	
1277	½ c. Type **290**	10	10	10	10
1278	1 c. Mickey Mouse boxing	10	10	10	10
1279	2 c. Daisy Duck in archery event	10	10	10	10
1280	3 c. Clarabelle Cow on uneven bars	10	10	10	10
1281	4 c. Mickey and Minnie Mouse in hurdles race	10	10	10	10
1282	5 c. Donald Duck with Chip and Dale weightlifting	10	10	10	10
1283	$1 Little Hiawatha in single kayak	55	60	55	60
1284	$2 The Tortoise and the Hare in marathon	90	1·00	90	1·00
1285	$3 Mickey Mouse pole-vaulting	1·40	1·60	1·40	1·60
1277/85	.. .. *Set of* 9	2·75	3·00	2·75	3·00
MS1286	127 × 101 mm. $5 Donald Duck in medley relay (*vert*). P 13½ × 14	2·75	3·00	3·00	3·00

1984 (25 Jan). *British Monarchs. T* **291** *and similar vert designs. Multicoloured. Litho. P* 14.

1287 $4 Type **291** .. .. 2·50 2·75
a. Sheetlet. Nos. 1287/93 .. .. .. 17·50
1288 $4 William II .. .. 2·50 2·75
1289 $4 Henry I .. .. 2·50 2·75
1290 $4 Stephen .. .. 2·50 2·75
1291 $4 Henry II .. .. 2·50 2·75
1292 $4 Richard I .. .. 2·50 2·75
1293 $4 John .. .. 2·50 2·75
1294 $4 "Henry III" .. .. 2·50 2·75
a. Sheetlet. Nos. 1294/1300 .. .. .. 17·50
1295 $4 Edward I .. .. 2·50 2·75
1296 $4 Edward II .. .. 2·50 2·75
1297 $4 Edward III .. .. 2·50 2·75
1298 $4 Richard II .. .. 2·50 2·75
1299 $4 Henry IV .. .. 2·50 2·75
1300 $4 Henry V .. .. 2·50 2·75
1301 $4 Henry VI .. .. 2·50 2·75
a. Sheetlet. Nos. 1301/7 .. .. .. 17·50
1302 $4 Edward IV .. .. 2·50 2·75
1303 $4 Edward V .. .. 2·50 2·75
1304 $4 Richard III .. .. 2·50 2·75
1305 $4 Henry VII .. .. 2·50 2·75
1306 $4 Henry VIII .. .. 2·50 2·75
1307 $4 Edward VI .. .. 2·50 2·75
1308 $4 Lady Jane Grey .. .. .. 2·50 2·75
a. Sheetlet. Nos. 1308/14 .. .. .. 17·50
1309 $4 Mary I .. .. 2·50 2·75
1310 $4 Elizabeth I .. .. 2·50 2·75
1311 $4 James I .. .. 2·50 2·75
1312 $4 Charles I .. .. 2·50 2·75
1313 $4 Charles II .. .. 2·50 2·75
1314 $4 James II .. .. 2·50 2·75
1315 $4 William III .. .. 2·50 2·75
a. Sheetlet. Nos. 1315/21 .. .. .. 17·50
1316 $4 Mary II .. .. 2·50 2·75
1317 $$ Anne .. .. 2·50 2·75
1318 $4 George I .. .. 2·50 2·75
1319 $4 George II .. .. 2·50 2·75
1320 $4 George III .. .. 2·50 2·75
1321 $4 George IV .. .. 2·50 2·75
1322 $4 William IV .. .. 2·50 2·75
a. Sheetlet. Nos. 1322/8 .. .. .. 17·50
1323 $4 Victoria .. .. 2·50 2·75
1324 $4 Edward VII .. .. 2·50 2·75
1325 $4 George V .. .. 2·50 2·75
1326 $4 Edward VIII .. .. 2·50 2·75
1327 $4 George VI .. .. 2·50 2·75
1328 $4 Elizabeth II .. .. 2·50 2·75
1287/1328 .. .. *Set of* 42 95·00 £100

Nos. 1287/93, 1294/1300, 1301/7, 1308/14, 1315/21 and 1322/8 were printed together, in small sheets of 8 including one *se-tenant* stamp-size label.

Although inscribed "Henry III" the portrait on No. 1294 is actually of Edward I.

Although announced as all being issued on 25 January 1984 the different sheetlets were distributed at monthly intervals.

292 Lantana

(Des P.U.B. Graphics. Litho Format)

1984 (9 Apr). *Flowers. T* **292** *and similar horiz designs. Multicoloured. P* 15.

1329 25 c. Type **292** 20 15
1330 30 c. Plumbago 25 20
1331 90 c. Spider Lily 70 60
1332 $4 Giant Alocasia .. .. 2·50 2·50
1329/32 .. .. *Set of* 4 3·25 3·00
MS1333 108 × 90 mm. $5 Orange Trumpet Vine 3·50 3·75

19TH U.P.U CONGRESS - HAMBURG

293 Blue Parrot Fish (**294**)

(Litho Questa)

1984 (21 May). *Coral Reef Fishes. T* **293** *and similar horiz designs. Multicoloured. P* 14.

1334 10 c. Type **293** 45 10
1335 30 c. Flame-back Cherub Fish 65 30
1336 70 c. Painted Wrasse .. .. 1·25 1·00
1337 90 c. Straight-tailed Razor Fish .. .. 1·50 1·25
1334/7 .. .. *Set of* 4 3·50 2·40
MS1338 81 × 85 mm. $5 Spanish Hogfish .. 4·00 4·50

1984 (19 June). *Universal Postal Union Congress, Hamburg. Nos.* 1331/3 *optd with T* **294**.

1339 90 c. Spider Lily 60 65
1340 $4 Giant Alocasia .. .. 2·50 2·75
MS1341 108 × 90 mm. $5 Orange Trumpet Vine 3·25 3·50

295 Freighter

296 "The Night" (detail) (Correggio)

(Des Artists International. Litho Format)

1984 (16 July). *Ships. T* **295** *and similar horiz designs. Multicoloured. P* 15.

1342 40 c. Type **295** 75 30
1343 70 c. *Queen Elizabeth 2* .. .. .. 1·00 60
1344 90 c. Sailing boats .. .. 1·40 1·00
1345 $4 *Amerikanis* .. .. 4·00 4·00
1342/5 .. .. *Set of* 4 6·50 5·50
MS1346 107 × 80 mm. $5 Spanish galleon .. 5·50 6·00

(Litho Questa)

1984 (22 Aug). *450th Death Anniv of Correggio (painter). T* **296** *and similar vert designs showing paintings. Multicoloured. P* 14.

1347 10 c. Type **296** 25 10
1348 30 c. "The Virgin adoring the Child" 40 20
1349 90 c. "The Mystical Marriage of St. Catherine with St. Sebastian" .. .. 1·00 60
1350 $4 "The Madonna and the Fruit Basket" .. 3·00 3·00
1347/50 .. .. *Set of* 4 4·25 3·50
MS1351 54 × 73 mm. $5 "The Madonna at the Spring" .. .. 3·25 3·75

297 "L'Absinthe" (Degas) **298** Train on "Puffing Billy" Line, Victoria

(Litho Questa)

1984 (22 Aug). *150th Birth Anniv of Edgar Degas (painter). T* **297** *and similar multicoloured designs showing paintings. P* 14.

1352 25 c. Type **297** 30 15
1353 70 c. "Pouting" (*horiz*) 75 45
1354 $1.10, "The Millinery Shop" .. .. 1·25 85
1355 $3 "The Bellelli Family" (*horiz*) .. .. 2·50 2·50
1352/5 .. .. .. *Set of* 4 4·25 3·50
MS1356 84 × 54 mm. $5 "The Cotton Market" .. 3·25 3·75

(Des Bonny Redecker. Litho Questa)

1984 (21 Sept). *"Ausipex" International Stamp Exhibition, Melbourne. T* **298** *and similar vert designs. Multicoloured. P* 14.

1357 $1.10, Type **298** .. .. 1·25 1·00
1358 $4 Yacht *Australia II* (winner of America's Cup) .. .. 3·50 3·25
MS1359 107 × 76 mm. $5 Melbourne tram .. 3·75 4·50

299 *Locomotion* (1825)

OPENING OF
POINT SALINE
INT'L AIRPORT
(300)

(Des J.W. Litho Format)

1984 (3 Oct). *Railway Locomotives. T* **299** *and similar horiz designs. Multicoloured. P* 15.

1360 30 c. Type **299** 60 25
1361 40 c. *Novelty* (1829) 70 30
1362 60 c. *Washington Farmer* (1836) 80 45
1363 70 c. French Crampton type (1859) 90 50
1364 90 c. Dutch State Railways (1873) .. .. 1·00 80
1365 $1.10, *Champion* (1882) .. .. .. 1·25 1·25
1366 $2 Webb Compound type (1893) .. .. 1·75 2·00
1367 $4 Berlin "No. 74" (1900) .. .. .. 3·25 3·50
1360/7 .. .. .. *Set of* 8 9·00 8·00
MS1368 Two sheets, each 100 × 70 mm. (a) $5 Crampton *Phoenix* (1863); (b) $5 Mikado type (1897) .. .. 8·00 8·50

1984 (28 Oct). *Opening of Point Saline International Airport (1st issue). Nos.* 1247 *and* 1249/50 *optd as T* **300**.

1369 40 c. Rural telephone installation 25 30
1370 $3 Airport control room .. .. .. 1·75 1·90
MS1371 111×85 mm. $5 Communications satellite .. .. 3·00 3·25

On No. **MS**1371 the overprint, 54 × 8 mm., appears in two lines on the sheet margin only.

See also Nos. 1393/6.

301 Donald Duck as Father Christmas looking into Mirror

(Litho Questa)

1984 (26 Nov). *Christmas. Walt Disney Cartoon Characters. T* **301** *and similar vert designs. Multicoloured. P* 12 ($2) *or* 13½ × 14 (*others*).

1372 45 c. Type **301** 70 40
1373 60 c. Donald Duck filling stocking with presents 80 45
1374 90 c. As Father Christmas pulling a sleigh .. 1·00 75
1375 $2 As Father Christmas decorating Christmas tree .. .. 1·90 1·75
1376 $4 Donald Duck and nephews singing carols 2·75 2·75
1372/6 .. .. .. *Set of* 5 6·50 5·50
MS1377 127 × 102 mm. $5 As Father Christmas in sleigh .. .. 3·75 3·75

No. 1375 was printed in sheetlets of 8 stamps.

(Litho Questa)

1985 (11 Feb). *Birth Bicentenary of John J. Audubon (ornithologist) (1st issue). Multicoloured designs as T* **198** *of Antigua showing original paintings. P* 14.

1378 50 c. Clapper Rail (*vert*) 65 35
1379 70 c. Hooded Warbler (*vert*) 90 55
1380 90 c. Common Flicker (*vert*) .. .. .. 1·25 75
1381 $4 Bohemian Waxwing (*vert*) .. .. .. 3·25 3·75
1378/81 .. .. .. *Set of* 4 5·50 5·00
MS1382 82×112 mm. $5 Merlin ("Pigeon Hawk") .. .. 4·00 4·00

See also Nos. 1480/4.

302 Honda "XL500R"

(Des R. Sentnor. Litho Questa)

1985 (11 Mar). *Centenary of the Motor Cycle. T* **302** *and similar horiz designs. Multicoloured. P* 14.

1383 25 c. Type **302** 35 20
1384 50 c. Suzuki "GS1100ES" 50 35
1385 90 c. Kawasaki "KZ700" 80 60
1386 $4 BMW "K100" .. .. 2·75 3·00
1383/6 .. .. .. *Set of* 4 4·00 3·75
MS1387 109 × 81 mm. $5 Yamaha "500CC V Four" 3·00 3·50

303 "Explorer"

(Des Susan David. Litho Questa)

1985 (15 Apr). *75th Anniv of Girl Guide Movement. T* **303** *and similar horiz designs, showing work for Guide badges. Multicoloured. P* 14.

1388 25 c. Type **303** 15 20
1389 60 c. "Cook" 35 40
1390 90 c. "Musician" 50 55
1391 $3 "Home nurse" .. .. 1·60 1·75
1388/91 .. .. .. *Set of* 4 2·40 2·50
MS1392 97×70 mm. $5 Flags of Girl Guides and Grenada .. .. 2·75 3·00

304 Avro "748" on Inaugural Flight from Barbados

(Des Susan David. Litho Questa)

1985 (30 Apr). *Opening of Point Saline International Airport (1984) (2nd issue). T* **304** *and similar horiz designs. Multicoloured. P* 14.

1393 70 c. Type **304** 80 45
1394 $1 Pan Am "L1011" on inaugural flight from New York .. .. 1·25 80
1395 $4 "Tri-Star" on inaugural flight to Miami .. .. 3·00 3·50
1393/5 .. .. .. *Set of* 3 4·50 4·25
MS1396 101×72 mm. $5 Point Saline Airport terminal and Avro "748" on tarmac .. .. 3·25 3·75

305 McDonnell Douglas "DC-8"

(Des BG Studio. Litho Questa)

1985 (15 May). *40th Anniv of International Civil Aviation Organization. T* **305** *and similar horiz designs. Multicoloured. P* 14.

1397 10 c. Type **305** 10 10
1398 50 c. "Super Constellation" 25 30
1399 60 c. Vickers "Vanguard" 35 40
1400 $4 De Havilland "Twin Otter" .. .. 2·10 2·25
1397/400 .. .. .. *Set of* 4 2·50 2·75
MS1401 102×64 mm. $5 Avro "748" turboprop .. 2·75 3·00

ALTERED CATALOGUE NUMBERS

Any Catalogue numbers altered from the last edition are shown as a list in the introductory pages.

306 Model Boat Racing **307** Bird of Paradise (flower)

(Litho Format)

1985 (15 June). *Water Sports. T* **306** *and similar horiz designs. Multicoloured. P* 15.

1402 10 c. Type **306** 10 10
1403 50 c. Scuba diving, Carriacou 25 30
1404 $1.10, Windsurfers on Grand Anse Beach 60 65
1405 $4 Windsurfing .. .. 2·10 2·25
1402/5 .. .. .. *Set of* 4 2·75 3·00
MS1406 107×77 mm. $5 Beach scene .. .. 2·75 3·00

(Des Mary Walters. Litho Questa)

1985 (1 July)–88. *Native Flowers. T* **307** *and similar vert designs. Multicoloured. Chalk-surfaced paper.* A. *Without imprint date. P* 14. B. *Without imprint date. P* 12.

		A		B	
1407	½ c. Type **307**	10	10	10	10
1408	1 c. Passion Flower	10	10	10	10
1409	2 c. Oleander	10	10	10	10
1410	4 c. Bromeliad	10	10	10	10
1411	5 c. Anthurium	10	10	10	10
1412	6 c. Bougainvillea	10	10	10	10
1413	10 c. Hibiscus	15	10	10	10
1414	15 c. Ginger	20	10	10	10
1415	25 c. Poinsettia	25	15	10	10
1416	30 c. Mexican Creeper	35	20	10	15
1417	40 c. Angel's Trumpet	40	25	15	20
1418	50 c. Amaryllis	40	25	20	25
1419	60 c. Prickly Pear	50	35	25	30
1420	70 c. Chenille Plant	50	35	30	35
1420*c*	75 c. Cordia	30	35	†	
1421	$1 Periwinkle	75	55	40	45
1422	$1.10, Ixora	80	60	45	50
1423	$3 Shrimp Plant	1·60	1·50	1·25	1·40
1424	$5 Plumbago	2·50	2·50	2·00	2·10
1425	$10 *Lantana camara*	4·50	5·00	4·00	4·25
1425*c*	$20 Peregrina	8·50	9·50	†	
	cd. Ordinary paper	8·25	8·50	†	
1407A/25*c*A	*Set of* 21	20·00	20·00	†	
1407B/25B	*Set of* 19	†		9·00	9·75

C. *With imprint date. P* 14.

1413C 10 c. Hibiscus 10 10
1416C 30 c. Mexican Creeper 10 10
1418C 50 c. Amaryllis 20 25
1419C 60 c. Prickly Pear 25 30
1421C $1 Periwinkle 35 40
1413C/21C .. .. .. *Set of* 5 90 1·00

Dates of issue:—1.7.85, Nos. 1407A/24A; 11.11.85, No. 1425A; 3.86, Nos. 1407B/12B, 1414B/19B, 1421B/3B; 7.86, Nos. 1413B, 1420B, 1424B; 1.8.86, No. 1425*c*A; 12.86, No. 1425B; 5.8.87, No. 1425cdA; 1987, Nos. 1416C, 1418C/19C, 1421C; 7.88, No. 1413C; 1.12.88, No. 1420*c*A.

308 The Queen Mother at Royal Opera House, London **309** Youth Gardening (Horticulture)

(Des J.W. Litho Questa)

1985 (3 July). *Life and Times of Queen Elizabeth the Queen Mother. T* **308** *and similar multicoloured designs. P* 14.

1426 $1 Type **308** 55 60
1427 $1.50, The Queen Mother playing snooker at London Press Club (*horiz*) 80 85
1428 $2.50, At Epsom Races, 1960 .. .. 1·40 1·50
1426/8 .. .. .. *Set of* 3 2·50 2·75
MS1429 56×85 mm. $5 With Prince of Wales on 80th Birthday .. .. 2·75 3·00

Stamps as Nos. 1426/8, but with face values of 90 c., $1 and $3, exist from additional sheetlets of 5 plus a label issued December 1985. These also have changed background colours and are perforated 12½×12 ($1) or 12×12½ (others) (*Price for set of* 3 *stamps £2 mint*).

(Des Liane Fried. Litho Format)

1985 (21 Aug). *International Youth Year. T* **309** *and similar vert designs. Multicoloured. P* 15.

1430 25 c. Type **309** 15 20
1431 50 c. Young people on beach (Leisure) .. 25 30
1432 $1.10, Girls in classroom (Education) .. 60 65
1433 $3 Nurse and young patient (Health Care) .. .. 1·60 1·75
1430/3 .. .. .. *Set of* 4 2·40 2·50
MS1434 111×80 mm. $5 Children of different races .. .. 2·75 3·25

(Des Susan David. Litho Questa)

1985 (3 Sept). *300th Birth Anniv of Johann Sebastian Bach (composer). Vert designs as T* **206** *of Antigua. P* 14.
1435 25 c. multicoloured 35 20
1436 70 c. multicoloured 65 45
1437 $1 multicoloured 90 70
1438 $3 multicoloured .. .. 1·90 2·00
1435/8 .. .. *Set of* 4 3·50 3·00
MS1439 104×74 mm. $5 black, lavender-grey and cinnamon .. .. 3·25 3·75
Designs:—25 c. Crumhorn; 70 c. Oboe d'amore; $1 Violin; $3 Harpsichord; $5 Johann Sebastian Bach.

310 Cub Scouts Camping

(Des A. DiLorenzo. Litho Questa)

1985 (5 Sept). *4th Caribbean Cuboree. T* **310** *and similar multicoloured designs. P* 14.
1440 10 c. Type **310** 15 10
1441 50 c. Cub scouts swimming ("Physical Fitness") 35 30
1442 $1 Stamp collecting 70 60
1443 $4 Birdwatching .. .. 2·40 2·25
1440/3 .. .. *Set of* 4 3·25 3·00
MS1444 103×75 mm. $5 Cub scouts saluting leader (*vert*) .. .. 3·00 3·50

(Des Mary Walters. Litho Format)

1985 (4 Nov). *Royal Visit. Multicoloured designs as T* **207** *of Antigua. P* 14½.
1445 50 c. Flags of Great Britain and Grenada .. 50 30
1446 $1 Queen Elizabeth II (*vert*) 95 80
1447 $4 Royal Yacht *Britannia* .. .. .. 3·00 3·25
1445/7 .. .. *Set of* 3 4·00 4·00
MS1448 111×83 mm. $5 Map of Grenada .. 3·50 3·50

(Des Walt Disney Productions. Litho Questa)

1985 (4 Nov). *150th Birth Anniv of Mark Twain (author). Horiz designs as T* **118** *of Anguilla showing Walt Disney cartoon characters in scenes from "The Prince and the Pauper". Multicoloured. P* 14×13½.
1449 25 c. Mortie as Tom meeting the Prince (Ferdie) 15 20
1450 50 c. Tom and the Prince exchanging clothes 25 30
1451 $1.10, The Prince with John Cantry .. 60 65
1452 $1.50, The Prince knights Mike Hendon (Goofy) 80 85
1453 $2 Tom and the Whipping Boy .. .. 1·10 1·25
1449/53 .. .. *Set of* 5 2·50 3·00
MS1454 124×100 mm. $5 The Prince, Tom and Mike Hendon .. .. 2·75 3·00

(Des Walt Disney Productions. Litho Questa)

1985 (4 Nov). *Birth Bicentenaries of Grimm Brothers (folklorists). Horiz designs as T* **119** *of Anguilla, showing Walt Disney cartoon characters in scenes from "The Fisherman and his Wife". Multicoloured. P* 14×13½.
1455 30 c. The Fisherman (Goofy) catching enchanted fish 15 20
1456 60 c. The Fisherman scolded by his Wife (Clarabelle) 35 40
1457 70 c. The Fisherman's Wife with dream cottage 40 45
1458 $1 The Fisherman's Wife as King .. 60 65
1459 $3 The Fisherman and Wife in their original shack .. .. 1·75 1·90
1455/9 .. .. *Set of* 5 3·00 3·25
MS1460 126×100 mm. $5 The Fisherman in boat .. .. 3·00 3·25

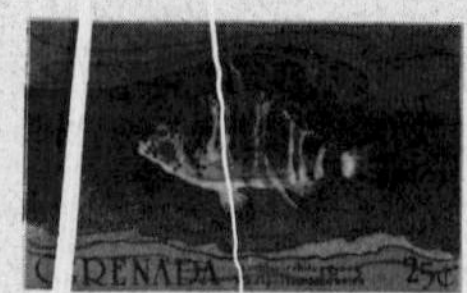

311 Redspotted Hawkfish

(Des R. Sauber. Litho Questa)

1985 (15 Nov). *Marine Life. T* **311** *and similar horiz designs. Multicoloured. P* 14.
1461 25 c. Type **311** 45 20
1462 50 c. Spotfin Butterflyfish 70 35
1463 $1.10, Fire Coral and Orange Sponges .. 1·25 1·25
1464 $3 Pillar Coral .. .. 2·50 2·75
1461/4 .. .. *Set of* 4 4·50 4·00
MS1465 127×100 mm. $5 Bigeye .. .. 3·50 4·00

(Litho Format)

1985 (22 Nov). *40th Anniv of United Nations Organization. Multicoloured designs as T* **208** *of Antigua showing United Nations (New York) stamps. P* 14½.
1466 50 c. Mary McLeod Bethune (educationist) and 1975 International Women's Year 10 c. 35 30
1467 $2 Maimonides (physician) and 1966 W.H.O. 5 c. .. .. 1·40 1·40
1468 $2.50, Alexander Graham Bell (telephone inventor) and 1956 I.T.U. 3 c. .. 1·60 1·75
1466/8 .. .. *Set of* 3 3·00 3·00
MS1469 110×85 mm. $5 Dag Hammarskjold (Secretary-General) (*vert*) .. .. .. 2·50 2·75

312 "The Adoration of the Shepherds" (Mantegna)

VISIT OF
PRES REAGAN
20 FEB. 1986
(**313**)

(Des Mary Walters. Litho Format)

1985 (23 Dec). *Christmas. Religious Paintings. T* **312** *and similar horiz designs. Multicoloured. P* 15.
1470 25 c. Type **312** 20 15
1471 60 c. "Journey of the Magi" (Sassetta) .. 40 35
1472 90 c. "Madonna and Child enthroned with Saints" (Raphael) 60 50
1473 $4 "Nativity" (Monaco) .. .. .. 2·50 2·75
1470/3 .. .. *Set of* 4 3·25 3·25
MS1474 107×81 mm. $5 "Madonna and Child enthroned with Saints" (Gaddi) .. .. .. 2·50 2·75

(Des J. Iskowitz. Litho Questa)

1986 (6 Jan). *Centenary of Statue of Liberty (1st issue). Multicoloured designs as T* **211** *of Dominica. P* 15.
1475 5 c. Columbus Monument, 1893 (*vert*) .. 10 10
1476 25 c. Columbus Monument, 1986 (*vert*) .. 20 15
1477 40 c. Mounted police, Central Park, 1895 .. 50 30
1478 $4 Mounted police, 1986 .. .. .. 2·75 3·00
1475/8 .. .. *Set of* 4 3·25 3·25
MS1479 104×76 mm. $5 Statue of Liberty (*vert*) 2·50 2·75
See also Nos. 1644/52.

(Litho Questa)

1986 (20 Jan). *Birth Bicentenary of John J. Audubon (ornithologist) (2nd issue). Multicoloured designs as T* **198** *of Antigua. P* 12×12½.
1480 50 c. Snowy Egret 45 30
1481 90 c. Greater Flamingo 70 60
1482 $1.10, Canada Goose 85 70
1483 $3 Smew .. .. 1·60 1·90
1480/3 .. .. *Set of* 4 3·25 3·25
MS1484 103×72 mm. $5 Brent Goose (*horiz*). P 14 .. .. 3·75 4·00
Nos. 1480/3 were each issued in sheetlets of five stamps and one stamp-size label, which appears in the centre of the bottom row.

1986 (20 Feb). *Visit of President Reagan. Nos.* 1418A *and* 1424A *optd with T* **313**.
1485 50 c. Amaryllis 25 30
1486 $5 Plumbago .. .. 2·50 2·75

314 Methodist Church, St. Georges

315 Player with Ball

(Litho Format)

1986 (24 Feb). *Bicentenary of Methodist Church in Grenada. T* **314** *and similar horiz design. Multicoloured. P* 15.
1487 60 c. Type **314** 30 35
MS1488 102×73 mm. $5 St. Georges .. .. 2·75 3·25

(Des N. Waldman. Litho Questa)

1986 (6 Mar). *World Cup Football Championship, Mexico. T* **315** *and similar vert designs. Multicoloured. P* 14.
1489 50 c. Type **315** 25 30
1490 70 c. Player heading ball 35 40
1491 90 c. Player controlling ball 45 50
1492 $4 Player controlling ball with right foot 2·00 2·10
1489/92 .. .. *Set of* 4 2·75 3·00
MS1493 101×71 mm. $5 Player tackling .. 2·75 3·25

(Des W. Hanson. Litho Questa)

1986 (20 Mar). *Appearance of Halley's Comet (1st issue). Horiz designs as T* **123** *of Anguilla. Multicoloured. P* 14.
1494 5 c. Clyde Tombaugh (astronomer) and Dudley Observatory, New York .. 10 10
1495 20 c. N.A.S.A. – U.S.A.F. "X-24B" Space Shuttle prototype, 1973 .. .. 10 15
1496 40 c. German comet medal, 1618 .. .. 20 25
1497 $4 Destruction of Sodom and Gomorrah, 1949 B.C. .. .. 2·00 2·10
1494/7 .. .. *Set of* 4 2·10 2·25
MS1498 102×70 mm. $5 Halley's Comet over Grenada .. .. 3·00 3·25
See also Nos. 1533/7 and 1980/4.

(Litho Questa)

1986 (21 Apr). *60th Birthday of Queen Elizabeth II. Vert designs as T* **125** *of Anguilla. P* 14.
1499 2 c. black and yellow 10 15
1500 $1.50, multicoloured 75 90
1501 $4 multicoloured .. .. 2·00 2·40
1499/1501 .. .. *Set of* 3 2·50 3·00
MS1502 120×85 mm. $5 black and grey-brown .. 3·00 3·25
Designs:—2 c. Princess Elizabeth in 1951; $1.50, Queen presenting trophy at polo match, Windsor, 1965; $4 At Epsom, Derby Day, 1977; $5 King George VI and family, 1939.

(Des Walt Disney Productions. Litho Format)

1986 (22 May). *"Ameripex" International Stamp Exhibition, Chicago. Horiz designs as T* **212** *of Dominica, showing Walt Disney cartoon characters playing baseball. Multicoloured. P* 11.
1503 1 c. Goofy as pitcher 10 10
1504 2 c. Goofy as catcher 10 10
1505 3 c. Mickey Mouse striking ball and Donald Duck as catcher 10 10
1506 4 c. Huey forcing out Dewey 10 10
1507 5 c. Chip n'Dale chasing flyball 10 10
1508 6 c. Mickey Mouse, Donald Duck and Clarabelle in argument 10 10
1509 $2 Minnie Mouse and Donald Duck reading baseball rules .. .. 1·40 1·10
1510 $3 Ludwig von Drake as umpire with Goofy and Pete colliding .. .. 1·75 1·60
1503/10 .. .. *Set of* 8 3·00 2·75
MS1511 Two sheets, each 126×101 mm. (a) $5 Donald Duck striking ball. (b) $5 Minnie and Mickey Mouse running between bases. P 14×13½ .. .. *Set of* 2 *sheets* 6·50 7·00

(Litho Questa)

1986 (1 July). *Royal Wedding. Vert designs as T* **213** *of Antigua. Multicoloured. P* 14.
1512 2 c. Prince Andrew and Miss Sarah Ferguson 10 15
1513 $1.10, Prince Andrew 70 70
1514 $4 Prince Andrew with H.M.S. *Brazen*'s helicopter .. .. 2·50 2·50
1512/14 .. .. *Set of* 3 3·00 3·00
MS1515 88×88 mm. $5 Prince Andrew and Miss Sarah Ferguson (*different*) .. .. .. 2·75 3·25

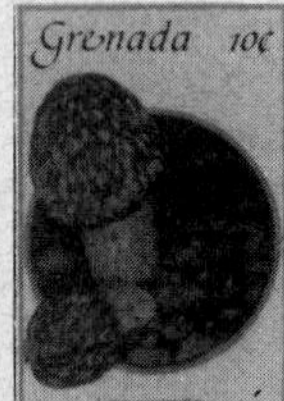

316 Brown-lined Latirus

317 *Lepiota roseolamellata*

(Des L. Birmingham. Litho Format)

1986 (15 July). *Sea Shells. T* **316** *and similar horiz designs. Multicoloured. P* 15.
1516 25 c. Type **316** 20 15
1517 60 c. Lamellose Wentletrap 40 35
1518 70 c. Turkey Wing 50 40
1519 $4 Rooster Tail Conch .. .. .. 2·00 2·10
1516/19 .. .. *Set of* 4 2·75 2·75
MS1520 110×75 mm. $5 Angular Triton .. 3·00 3·75

(Des R. Sauber. Litho Format)

1986 (1 Aug). *Mushrooms. T* **317** *and similar vert designs. Multicoloured. P* 15.
1521 10 c. Type **317** 25 15
1522 60 c. *Lentinus bertieri* 70 55
1523 $1 *Lentinus retinervis* .. .. .. 1·00 75
1524 $4 *Eccilia cystiophorus* .. .. .. 3·00 3·00
1521/4 .. .. *Set of* 4 4·50 4·00
MS1525 127×100 mm. $5 *Cystolepiota eriophora* 5·00 5·00

1986 (15 Sept). *World Cup Football Championship Winners, Mexico. Nos.* 1489/93 *optd with T* **216** *of Antigua in gold.*
1526 50 c. Type **315** 25 30
1527 70 c. Player heading ball 35 40
1528 90 c. Player controlling ball 45 50
1529 $4 Player controlling ball with right foot 2·00 2·10
1526/9 .. .. *Set of* 4 2·75 3·00
MS1530 101×71 mm. $5 Player tackling .. 2·75 3·25

318 Dove on Rifles and Mahatma Gandhi (Disarmament Week)

319 Cockerel and Hen

(Des Mary Walters. Litho Format)

1986 (15 Sept). *International Events. T* **318** *and similar multicoloured design. P* 15.
1531 60 c. Type **318** 30 35
1532 $4 Hands passing olive branch and Martin Luther King (International Peace Year) (*horiz*) .. .. 2·00 2·10

1986 (15 Oct). *Appearance of Halley's Comet (2nd issue). Nos.* 1494/8 *optd with T* **218** *of Antigua (in silver on $5).*
1533 5 c. Clyde Tombaugh (astronomer) and Dudley Observatory, New York .. 20 15
1534 20 c. N.A.S.A.—U.S.A.F. "X-24B" Space Shuttle prototype, 1973 .. .. 30 15
1535 40 c. German comet medal, 1618 .. .. 40 25
1536 $4 Destruction of Sodom and Gomorrah, 1949 B.C. .. .. 2·50 2·50
1533/6 .. .. *Set of* 4 3·00 2·75
MS1537 102×70 mm. $5 Halley's Comet over Grenada .. .. 2·50 2·75

(Des Walt Disney Co. Litho Format)

1986 (3 Nov). *Christmas. Multicoloured designs as T* **220** *of Antigua showing Walt Disney cartoon characters. P* 11.
1538 30 c. Mickey Mouse asleep in armchair (*vert*) 15 20
1539 45 c. Young Mickey Mouse with Father Christmas (*vert*) 25 30
1540 60 c. Donald Duck with toy telephone .. 30 35
1541 70 c. Pluto with pushcart 35 40
1542 $1.10, Daisy Duck with doll 55 60
1543 $2 Goofy as Father Christmas (*vert*) .. 1·00 1·10
1544 $2.50, Goofy singing carols at piano (*vert*) 1·25 1·40
1545 $3 Mickey Mouse, Donald Duck and nephew riding toy train .. .. 1·50 1·60
1538/45 .. .. *Set of* 8 4·75 5·25
MS1546 Two sheets, each 127×101 mm. (a) $5 Donald Duck, Goofy and Mickey Mouse delivering presents (*vert*). P 13½×14. (b) $5 Father Christmas playing toy piano. P 14×13½ *Set of* 2 *sheets* 5·00 5·50

(Litho Questa)

1986 (17 Nov). *Fauna and Flora. T* **319** *and similar horiz designs. Multicoloured. P* 14.
1547 10 c. Type **319** 15 10
1548 30 c. Fish-eating Bat 30 20
1549 60 c. Goat 50 35
1550 70 c. Cow 55 40
1551 $1 Anthurium .. .. 1·00 80
1552 $1.10, Royal Poinciana .. .. .. 1·00 90
1553 $2 Frangipani .. .. 1·75 1·75
1554 $4 Orchid .. .. 4·00 4·25
1547/54 .. .. *Set of* 8 8·50 8·00
MS1555 Two sheets, each 104×73 mm. (a) $5 Grenada landscape. (b) $5 Horse *Set of* 2 *sheets* 7·00 8·00

320 Maserati "Biturbo" (1984) **321** Pole Vaulting

(Des J. Martin. Litho Format)

1986 (20 Nov). *Centenary of Motoring. T* **320** *and similar horiz designs. Multicoloured. P* 15.
1556 10 c. Type **320** 10 10
1557 30 c. AC "Cobra" (1960) 15 20
1558 60 c. Corvette (1963) 30 35
1559 70 c. Dusenberg "SJ7" (1932) 35 40
1560 90 c. Porsche (1957) 45 50
1561 $1.10, Stoewer (1930) 55 60
1562 $2 Volkswagen "Beetle" (1957) .. .. 1·00 1·10
1563 $3 Mercedes "600 Limo" (1963) .. .. 1·50 1·60
1556/63 .. .. *Set of* 8 4·00 4·25
MS1564 Two sheets, each 106 × 77 mm. (a) $5 Stutz (1914). (b) $5 Packard (1941) *Set of* 2 *sheets* 5·00 5·25

(Des BG Studio. Litho Format)

1986 (1 Dec). *Olympic Games, Seoul, South Korea* (1988). *T* **321** *and similar vert designs. Multicoloured. P* 15.
1565 10 c. + 5 c. Type **321** 10 15
1566 50 c. + 20 c. Gymnastics 35 45
1567 70 c. + 30 c. Putting the shot 50 65
1568 $2 + $1 High jumping .. .. .. 1·50 1·75
1565/8 .. .. *Set of* 4 2·25 2·75
MS1569 80 × 100 mm. $3 + $1 Swimming .. 2·00 2·10
The premiums on Nos. 1565/9 were to support the participation of the Grenada team.

(Litho Questa)

1986 (19 Dec). *Birth Centenary of Marc Chagall (artist). Designs as T* **225** *of Antigua, showing various paintings. P* 13½×14 (*vert*) *or* 14×13½ (*horiz*).
1570/1609 $1×40 multicoloured .. *Set of* 40 16·00 18·00
MS1610 Ten sheets, each 110×95 mm. $5×10 multicoloured (*each* 104×89 *mm*). Imperf *Set of* 10 *sheets* 20·00 22·00
Although announced as all being released on 19 December 1986 the issue was distributed in ten parts, each of four stamps and one miniature sheet, at monthly intervals.

(Des J. Iskowitz. Litho Format)

1987 (5 Feb). *America's Cup Yachting Championship. Vert designs as T* **222** *of Antigua. Multicoloured. P* 15.
1611 10 c. *Columbia*, 1958 .. .. 10 10
1612 60 c. *Resolute*, 1920 .. .. 35 30
1613 $1.10, *Endeavor*, 1934 .. .. .. 70 65
1614 $4 *Rainbow*, 1934 .. .. 1·90 2·25
1611/14 .. .. *Set of* 4 2·75 3·00
MS1615 113×84 mm. $5 *Weatherly*, 1962 .. 2·25 2·40

322 Virgin Mary and Outline Map of Grenada **323** Black Grouper

(Des G. Hamilton (10, 30, 50 c.), Mary Walters (others). Litho Format)

1987 (27 Apr). *500th Anniv of Discovery of America by Columbus* (1992) (*1st issue*). *T* **322** *and similar multicoloured designs. P* 15.
1616 10 c. Type **322** 15 15
1617 30 c. *Santa Maria, Pinta* and *Nina* (*horiz*) .. 20 15
1618 50 c. Columbus and outline map of Grenada 25 30
1619 60 c. Christopher Columbus 25 30
1620 90 c. King Ferdinand and Queen Isabella of Spain (*horiz*) 40 45
1621 $1.10, Map of Antilles by Columbus .. 50 55
1622 $2 Caribs with sailing raft (*horiz*) .. 90 95
1623 $3 Columbus in the New World, 1493 (contemporary drawing) .. .. 1·40 1·50
1616/23 .. .. *Set of* 8 3·50 3·75
MS1624 Two sheets, each 104×72 mm. (a) $5 Route map and Columbus' signature. (b) $5 Columbus carrying Christ Child *Set of* 2 *sheets* 4·50 4·75
See also Nos. 2051/5.

(Des W. Wright. Litho Questa)

1987 (18 May). *Milestones of Transportation. Horiz designs as T* **226** *of Antigua. Multicoloured. P* 14.
1625 10 c. Cornu's first helicopter, 1907 .. 10 10
1626 15 c. *Monitor* and *Merrimack* (first battle between ironclad warships), 1862 .. 15 10
1627 30 c. "LZ1" (first Zeppelin), 1900 .. .. 20 15
1628 50 c. S.S. *Sirius* (first transatlantic steamship crossing), 1838 .. .. .. 25 30
1629 60 c. Steam locomotive on Trans-Siberian Railway (longest line) 25 30
1630 70 c. U.S.S. *Enterprise* (largest aircraft carrier), 1960 .. .. 30 35
1631 90 c. Blanchard's Balloon (first balloon across English Channel), 1785 .. 40 45
1632 $1.50, U.S.S. *Holland 1* (first steam-powered submarine), 1900 .. .. 70 75
1633 $2 S.S. *Oceanic* (first luxury liner), 1871 90 95
1634 $3 Lamborghini "Countach" (fastest commercial car), 1984 .. .. .. 1·40 1·50
1625/34 .. .. *Set of* 10 4·00 4·50

(Des J. Martin. Litho Format)

1987 (15 June). *"Capex '87" International Stamp Exhibition, Toronto. Game Fishes. T* **323** *and similar multicoloured designs. P* 15.
1635 10 c. Type **323** 15 15
1636 30 c. Blue Marlin (*horiz*) 20 15
1637 60 c. White Marlin 35 30
1638 70 c. Big Eye Thresher Shark (*horiz*) .. 45 35
1639 $1 Bonefish (*horiz*) 65 50
1640 $1.10, Wahoo (*horiz*) 70 60
1641 $2 Sailfish (*horiz*) .. .. 1·40 1·25
1642 $4 Albacore (*horiz*) .. .. .. 2·25 2·50
1635/42 .. .. *Set of* 8 5·50 5·25
MS1643 Two sheets, each 100×70 mm. (a) $5 Yellowfin Tuna. (b) $5 Barracuda (*horiz*) *Set of* 2 *sheets* 4·50 4·75

(Litho Questa)

1987 (5 Aug). *Centenary of Statue of Liberty* (1986) (*2nd issue*). *Multicoloured designs as T* **227** *of Antigua. P* 14.
1644 10 c. Computer projections of Statue and base (*horiz*) 10 10
1645 25 c. Statue and fireworks (*horiz*) 15 15
1646 50 c. Statue and fireworks (*different*) (*horiz*) 25 30
1647 60 c. Statue and boats 25 30
1648 70 c. Computer projections of top of Statue (*horiz*) 30 35
1649 $1 Rear view of Statue and fireworks .. 45 50
1650 $1.10, Aerial view of Statue 50 55
1651 $2 Statue and flotilla 90 95
1652 $4 *Queen Elizabeth 2* in New York Harbour .. .. 1·75 1·90
1644/52 .. .. *Set of* 9 4·00 4·50

324 Alice and the Rabbit Hole

(Des Walt Disney Co. Litho Questa)

1987 (9 Sept). *50th Anniv of First Full-Length Disney Cartoon Film. T* **324** *and similar designs. P* 14×13½.
1653/1706 30 c. × 54 multicoloured *Set of* 54 6·00 6·50
MS1707 Six sheets, each 127×102 mm. $5×6 multicoloured. P 13½×14 (*vert*) or 14×13½ (*horiz*) .. .. .. *Set of* 6 *sheets* 12·00 12·50
Nos. 1653/1706 (issued as six sheetlets each of nine different designs) and No. **MS**1707 depict scenes from *Alice in Wonderland, Cinderella, Peter Pan, Pinocchio, Sleeping Beauty* and *Snow White and the Seven Dwarfs.*

325 Isaac Newton holding Apple (Law of Gravity)

(Litho Questa)

1987 (9 Sept). *Great Scientific Discoveries. T* **325** *and similar horiz designs. Multicoloured. P* 14.
1708 50 c. Type **325** 35 30
1709 $1.10, John Jacob Berzelius and symbols of chemical elements 65 65
1710 $2 Robert Boyle (law of Pressure and Volume) .. .. 1·25 1·25
1711 $3 James Watt and drawing of steam engine .. .. 1·75 2·00
1708/11 .. .. *Set of* 4 3·50 3·75
MS1712 105×75 mm. $5 *Voyager* (experimental aircraft) and *Flyer 1* .. .. .. 2·25 2·40
No. 1711 is inscribed "RUDOLF DIESEL" in error.

326 Wade Boggs (Boston Red Sox) (**327**)

(Des W. Storozuk. Litho Questa)

1987 (2 Nov). *All-Star Baseball Game, Oakland, California. Sheet* 114×82 *mm, containing T* **326** *and similar horiz design. Multicoloured. P* 14×13½.
MS1713 $1 Type **326**; $1 Eric Davis (Cincinnati Reds) .. .. 90 1·00

1987 (2 Nov). *60th Anniv of International Social Security Association. Nos.* 1413A, 1418A *and* 1423A *optd with T* **327**.
1714 10 c. Hibiscus 10 10
1715 50 c. Amaryllis 25 30
1716 $3 Shrimp Plant .. .. 1·40 1·50
1714/16 .. .. *Set of* 3 1·50 1·60

(Litho Questa)

1987 (2 Nov). *Bicentenary of U.S. Constitution. Multicoloured designs as T* **232** *of Antigua. P* 14.
1717 15 c. Independence Hall, Philadelphia (*vert*) 10 10
1718 50 c. Benjamin Franklin (Pennsylvania delegate) (*vert*) 25 30
1719 60 c. State Seal, Massachusetts 25 30
1720 $4 Robert Morris (Pennsylvania delegate) (*vert*) .. .. 1·75 1·90
1717/20 .. .. *Set of* 4 2·10 2·25
MS1721 105×75 mm. $5 James Madison (Virginia delegate) (*vert*) .. .. .. 2·25 2·40
Nos. 1717/20 were each issued in sheetlets of five stamps and one stamp-size label, which appears in the centre of the bottom row.

328 Goofy in "The Shadow" **329** "The Annunciation" (Fra Angelico)

(Des Walt Disney Co. Litho Questa)

1987 (16 Nov). *"Hafnia '87" International Stamp Exhibition, Copenhagen. T* **328** *and similar vert designs showing Walt Disney cartoon characters in scenes from Hans Christian Andersen's fairy tales. Multicoloured. P* 13½×14.
1722 25 c. Type **328** 15 15
1723 30 c. Mother Stork and brood in "The Storks" 15 15
1724 50 c. King Richard, Robin Hood and Little John (from *Robin Hood*) in "The Emperor's New Clothes" 25 30
1725 60 c. Goofy and Pluto in "The Tinderbox" .. 25 30
1726 70 c. Daisy and Donald Duck in "The Shepherdess and the Chimney Sweep" .. 30 35
1727 $1.50, Mickey and Minnie Mouse in "The Little Mermaid" 70 75
1728 $3 Clarabelle and Goofy in "The Princess and the Pea" .. .. 1·40 1·50
1729 $4 Minnie Mouse and Pegleg Pete in "The Marsh King's Daughter" .. .. 1·75 1·90
1722/9 .. .. *Set of* 8 4·50 5·00
MS1730 Two sheets, each 127×102 mm. (a) $5 Goofy in "The Flying Trunk". (b) $5 Goofy as "The Sandman" .. .. *Set of* 2 *sheets* 4·50 4·75

(Litho Questa)

1987 (15 Dec). *Christmas. T* **329** *and similar vert designs showing religious paintings. Multicoloured. P* 14.
1731 15 c. Type **329** 15 10
1732 30 c. "The Annunciation" (attr. Hubert van Eyck) 25 15
1733 60 c. "The Adoration of the Magi" (Januarius Zick) 40 30
1734 $4 "The Flight into Egypt" (Gerard David) 2·00 2·50
1731/4 .. .. *Set of* 4 2·50 2·75
MS1735 99×75 mm. $5 "The Circumcision" (Giovanni Bellini studio) .. .. .. 2·50 3·00

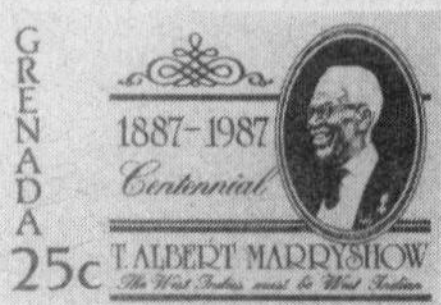

330 T. Albert Marryshow

(Litho Questa)

1988 (22 Jan). *Birth Centenary of T. Albert Marryshow (nationalist). P* 14.
1736 **330** 25 c. reddish brown, chestnut & brt crim .. 15 15

(Des and litho Questa)

1988 (15 Feb). *Royal Ruby Wedding. Vert designs as T* **234** *of Antigua. Multicoloured. P* 14.
1737 15 c. deep brown, black and bright new blue .. 10 10
1738 50 c. multicoloured 25 30
1739 $1 deep brown and black 45 50
1740 $4 multicoloured .. .. 1·75 1·90
1737/40 .. .. *Set of* 4 2·25 2·50
MS1741 76×100 mm. $5 multicoloured .. .. 2·25 2·50
Designs:—15 c. Wedding photograph, 1947; 50 c. Queen Elizabeth II with Prince Charles and Princess Anne, c. 1955; $1 Queen with Princess Anne, *c.* 1957; $4 Queen Elizabeth (from photo by Tim Graham), 1980; $5 Princess Elizabeth in wedding dress, 1947.

331 Goofy and Daisy Duck lighting Olympic Torch, Olympia

332 Scout fishing from Boat

(Des Walt Disney Company. Litho Questa)

1988 (13 Apr). *Olympic Games, Seoul. T* **331** *and similar vert designs showing Walt Disney cartoon characters. Multicoloured. P* 13½×14.
1742 1 c. Type **331** 10 10
1743 2 c. Donald and Daisy Duck carrying Olympic torch 10 10
1744 3 c. Donald Duck, Goofy and Mickey Mouse carrying flags of U.S., Korea and Spain 10 10
1745 4 c. Donald Duck releasing doves .. 10 10
1746 5 c. Mickey Mouse flying with rocket belt 10 10
1747 10 c. Morty and Ferdie carrying banner with Olympic motto 10 10
1748 $6 Donald Duck, Minnie Mouse and Hodori the Tiger (mascot of Seoul Games) .. .. 2·75 3·00
1749 $7 Pluto, Hodori and old post office, Seoul 3·25 3·50
1742/9 .. .. *Set of* 8 5·75 6·00
MS1750 Two sheets, each 127×101 mm. (a) $5 Mickey Mouse taking athlete's oath. (b) $5 Donald and Daisy Duck as athletes at Closing Ceremony .. .. .. *Set of* 2 *sheets* 4·50 4·75

1988 (19 Apr). *Stamp Exhibitions. Nos.* 1631/4 *optd as T* **241** *of Antigua with various emblems.*
1751 90 c. Blanchard's Balloon, 1785 (optd "OLYMPHILEX '88", Seoul) 40 45
1752 $1.50, U.S.S. *Holland 1*, 1900 (optd "INDEPENDENCE 40", Israel) .. 60 65
1753 $2 S.S. *Oceanic*, 1871 (optd "FINLANDIA 88", Helsinki) 80 85
1754 $3 Lamborghini "Countach", 1984 (optd "Praga 88", Prague) .. .. .. 1·25 1·40
1751/4 .. .. *Set of* 4 2·75 3·00

(Des J. Martin. Litho Questa)

1988 (3 May). *World Scout Jamboree, Australia. T* **332** *and similar multicoloured designs. P* 14.
1755 20 c. Type **332** 10 10
1756 70 c. Scouts hiking through forest (*horiz*) .. 40 40
1757 90 c. Practicing first aid (*horiz*) 50 50
1758 $3 Shooting rapids in inflatable canoe .. 1·50 2·00
1755/8 .. .. *Set of* 4 2·25 2·75
MS1759 114×80 mm. $5 Scout with Koala .. 2·10 2·25

PRICES OF SETS

Set prices are given for many issues, generally those containing three stamps or more. Definitive sets include one of each value or major colour change, but do not cover different perforations, die types or minor shades. Where a choice is possible the set prices are based on the cheapest versions of the stamps included in the listings.

333 *Santa Maria de Guia* (Columbus), 1498, and Map of Rotary District

334 Roseate Tern

(Des W. Hanson. Litho Questa)

1988 (5 May). *Rotary District* 405 *Conference, St. George's. T* **333** *and similar multicoloured design. P* 13½×14.
1760 $2 Type **333** 80 85
MS1761 133×90 mm. $10 Rotary emblem (*horiz*). P 14×13½ .. .. 4·25 4·50

(Des Mary Walters. Litho Questa)

1988 (31 May). *Birds. T* **334** *and similar vert designs. Multicoloured. P* 14.
1762 10 c. Type **334** 15 15
1763 25 c. Laughing Gull 20 20
1764 50 c. Osprey 40 35
1765 60 c. Rose-breasted Grosbeak 40 35
1766 90 c. Purple Gallinule 55 45
1767 $1.10, White-tailed Tropic Bird 60 60
1768 $3 Blue-faced Booby .. .. .. 1·40 1·60
1769 $4 Common Shoveler .. .. .. 1·75 2·00
1762/9 .. .. *Set of* 8 5·00 5·25
MS1770 Two sheets, each 100×71 mm. (a) $5 Belted Kingfisher. (b) $5 Brown-crested Flycatcher ("Rusty-tailed Flycatcher") *Set of* 2 *sheets* 4·25 4·50

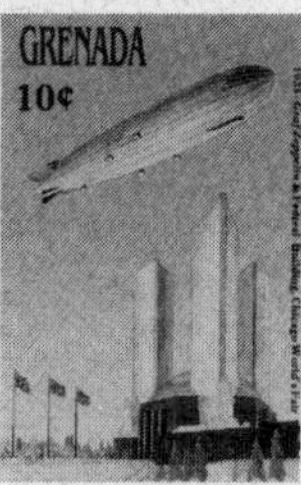

335 Vauxhall Type "OE 30/98", 1925

336 *Graf Zeppelin* over Chicago World's Fair, 1933

(Des W. Wright. Litho B.D.T.)

1988 (1 June). *Cars. T* **335** *and similar vert designs. Multicoloured. P* 13.
1771 $2 Type **335** 80 85
a. Sheetlet. Nos. 1771/80 .. .. 8·00
1772 $2 Wills "Sainte Claire", 1926 .. .. 80 85
1773 $2 Bucciali, 1928 .. .. .. 80 85
1774 $2 Irving Napier "Golden Arrow", 1929 80 85
1775 $2 Studebaker "President", 1930 .. 80 85
1776 $2 Thomas "Flyer", 1907 .. .. 80 85
1777 $2 Isotta-Fraschini "Tipo J", 1908 .. 80 85
1778 $2 Fiat 10/14HP, 1910 .. .. .. 80 85
1779 $2 Mercer "Type 35 Raceabout", 1911 .. 80 85
1780 $2 Marmon "Model 34 Cloverleaf", 1917 80 85
1781 $2 Tatra "Type 77", 1934 .. .. 80 85
a. Sheetlet. Nos. 1781/90 .. .. 8·00
1782 $2 Rolls-Royce "Phantom III", 1938 .. 80 85
1783 $2 Studebaker "Champion Starlight", 1947 .. .. 80 85
1784 $2 Porsche "Gmund", 1948 .. .. 80 85
1785 $2 Tucker, 1948 .. .. .. 80 85
1786 $2 Peerless "V-16", 1931 .. .. 80 85
1787 $2 Minerva "AL", 1931 .. .. .. 80 85
1788 $2 Reo "Royale", 1933 .. .. .. 80 85
1789 $2 Pierce Arrow "Silver Arrow", 1933 .. 80 85
1790 $2 Hupmobile "Aerodynamic", 1934 .. 80 85
1791 $2 Peugeot "404", 1965 .. .. .. 80 85
a. Sheetlet. Nos. 1791/1800 .. .. 8·00
1792 $2 Ford "Capri", 1969 .. .. .. 80 85
1793 $2 Ferrari "312T", 1975 .. .. 80 85
1794 $2 Lotus "T-79", 1978 .. .. .. 80 85
1795 $2 Williams-Cosworth "FW07", 1979 .. 80 85
1796 $2 H.R.G. "1500 Sports", 1948 .. .. 80 85
1797 $2 Crosley "Hotshot", 1949 .. .. 80 85
1798 $2 Volvo "PV444", 1955 .. .. 80 85
1799 $2 Maserati "Tipo 61", 1960 .. .. 80 85
1800 $2 Saab "96", 1963 .. .. .. 80 85
1771/1800 .. .. .. *Set of* 30 22·00 23·00
Nos. 1771/80, 1781/90 and 1791/1800 were each printed together, *se-tenant*, in sheetlets of 10.

(Litho Questa)

1988 (15 June). *500th Birth Anniv of Titian (artist). Multicoloured designs as T* **238** *of Antigua. P* 13½×14.
1801 10 c. "Lavinia Vecellio" 10 10
1802 20 c. "Portrait of a Man" 10 10
1803 25 c. "Andrea de Franceschi" 10 15
1804 90 c. "Head of a Soldier" 40 45
1805 $1 "Man with a Flute" 45 50
1806 $2 "Lucrezia and Tarquinius" 80 85
1807 $3 "Duke of Mantua with Dog" .. .. 1·25 1·40
1808 $4 "La Bella di Tiziano" .. .. .. 1·60 1·75
1801/8 .. .. *Set of* 8 4·25 4·75
MS1809 Two sheets, each 110×95 mm. (a) $5 "Allegory of Alfonso D'Avalos (detail). P 13½×14. (b) $5 "Fall of Man" (detail) (*horiz*). P 14×13½ .. .. .. *Set of* 2 *sheets* 4·25 4·50

(Des W. Hanson. Litho Questa)

1988 (1 July). *Airships. T* **336** *and similar multicoloured designs. P* 14.
1810 10 c. Type **336** 10 10
1811 15 c. *LZ-1* over Lake Constance, 1901 (*horiz*) 10 10
1812 25 c. *Washington* (balloon) and balloon barge, 1862 .. .. 10 15
1813 45 c. *Hindenberg* and Maybach "Zeppelin" car (*horiz*) 20 25
1814 50 c. Goodyear airship in Statue of Liberty Centenary Race, 1986 .. .. 20 25
1815 60 c. *Hindenberg* over Statue of Liberty, 1937 (*horiz*) 25 30
1816 90 c. Aircraft docking experiment with *Hindenberg* 1936 (*horiz*) 40 45
1817 $2 *Hindenberg* over Olympic Stadium, Berlin, 1936 .. .. 80 85
1818 $3 *Hindenberg* over Christ of the Andes Monument, 1937 .. .. .. 1·25 1·40
1819 $4 *Hindenberg* and *Bremen* (liner), 1936 (*horiz*) .. .. 1·60 1·75
1810/19 .. .. *Set of* 10 4·50 5·00
MS1820 (a) 75×95 mm. $5 *Graf Zeppelin*, 1930 (*horiz*). (b) 95×75 mm. $5 Zeppelin, 1935 (*horiz*) *Set of* 2 *sheets* 4·25 4·50

337 Tasmanian Wolf, Mickey Mouse and Pluto

338 Pineapple

(Des Walt Disney Co. Litho Questa)

1988 (1 Aug). *"Sydpex '88" National Stamp Exhibition, Sydney and 60th Birthday of Mickey Mouse. T* **337** *and similar horiz designs. Multicoloured. P* 14×13½.
1821 1 c. Type **337** 10 10
1822 2 c. Mickey Mouse feeding wallabies .. 10 10
1823 3 c. Mickey Mouse and Goofy with kangaroo 10 10
1824 4 c. Mickey and Minnie Mouse riding emus 10 10
1825 5 c. Mickey and Minnie Mouse with wombat 10 10
1826 10 c. Mickey Mouse and Donald Duck watching platypus 10 10
1827 $5 Mickey Mouse and Goofy photographing kookaburra .. .. 2·50 2·50
1828 $6 Mickey Mouse and Koala on map of Australia .. .. 2·75 2·75
1821/8 .. .. *Set of* 8 5·00 5·00
MS1829 Two sheets, each 127 × 102 mm. (a) $5 Mickey Mouse with birthday cake. (b) $5 Mickey and Minnie Mouse with parrots .. *Set of* 2 *sheets* 4·25 4·50

(Des J. Martin. Litho Questa)

1988 (11 Aug). *10th Anniv of International Fund for Agricultural Development. T* **338** *and similar multicoloured designs. P* 14.
1830 25 c. Type **338** 15 15
1831 75 c. Bananas 40 35
1832 $3 Mace and nutmeg (*horiz*) .. .. 1·50 1·75
1830/2 .. .. *Set of* 3 1·90 2·00

339 Lignum Vitae

(Des W. Wright. Litho Questa)

1988 (30 Sept). *Flowering Trees and Shrubs. T* **339** *and similar horiz designs. Multicoloured. P* 14.
1833 15 c. Type **339** 15 15
1834 25 c. Saman 20 15
1835 35 c. Red Frangipani 25 20
1836 45 c. Flowering Maple 30 25
1837 60 c. Yellow Poui 40 30
1838 $1 Wild Chestnut 60 50
1839 $3 Mountain Immortelle .. .. .. 1·50 1·75
1840 $4 Queen of Flowers .. .. .. 1·75 2·00
1833/40 .. .. *Set of* 8 4·50 4·75
MS1841 Two sheets, each 117 × 88 mm. (a) $5 Flamboyant. (b) $5 Orchid Tree .. *Set of* 2 *sheets* 4·25 4·50

340 Mickey Mantle (New York Yankees)

(Des Mary DeFiglio. Litho Questa)

1988 (28 Nov). *Major League Baseball Players (1st series). T* **340** *and similar horiz designs showing portraits or league emblems. P* 14 × 13½.
1842/1922 30 c. × 81 multicoloured .. *Set of* 81 8·75 9·00
Nos. 1842/1922 were issued as nine sheetlets, each of nine different designs.

(Des Walt Disney Co. Litho Questa)

1988 (1 Dec). *Christmas. "Mickey's Christmas Eve". Vert designs as T* **246** *of Antigua showing Walt Disney cartoon characters. Multicoloured. P* 13½ × 14.
1923 $1 Donald Duck's nephew on mantelpiece 45 50
a. Sheetlet. Nos. 1923/30 .. .. 3·25
1924 $1 Goofy with string of popcorn .. 45 50
1925 $1 Chip n' Dale decorating Christmas tree 45 50
1926 $1 Father Christmas in sleigh 45 50
1927 $1 Donald's nephew with stocking .. 45 50
1928 $1 Donald's nephew unpacking Xmas decorations 45 50
1929 $1 Donald Duck with present 45 50
1930 $1 Mickey Mouse with present 45 50
1923/30 .. .. *Set of* 8 3·25 3·50
MS1931 Two sheets, each 127 × 102 mm. (a) $5 Ferdie leaving drink for Father Christmas. (b) $5 Mordie and Ferdie asleep .. *Set of 2 sheets* 4·25 4·50

341 Tina Turner

342 Canada Atlantic Railway No. 2, 1889

(Litho Questa)

1988 (5 Dec). *Entertainers. T* **341** *and similar vert designs. Multicoloured. P* 14.
1932 10 c. Type **341** 15 15
1933 25 c. Lionel Ritchie 20 20
1934 45 c. Whitney Houston 30 30
1935 60 c. Joan Armatrading 45 45
1936 75 c. Madonna 55 55
1937 $1 Elton John 70 70
1938 $3 Bruce Springsteen .. .. 1·90 1·90
1939 $4 Bob Marley .. .. 2·50 2·50
1932/9 .. .. *Set of* 8 6·00 6·00
MS1940 115×155 mm. 55 c.×2 Yoko Minamino; $1×2 Yoko Minamino (*different*) .. .. 1·90 2·25
No. 1935 is incorrectly inscribed "JOAN AMMERTRADING".

(Des T. Hadley and W. Wright. Litho B.D.T.)

1989 (23 Jan). *North American Railway Locomotives. T* **342** *and similar vert designs. Multicoloured. P* 13.
1941 $2 Type **342** .. .. 95 1·00
a. Sheetlet. Nos. 1941/50 .. .. 9·50
1942 $2 Virginia & Truckee Railroad "J. W. Bowker" type, 1875 .. .. .. 95 1·00
1943 $2 Philadelphia & Reading Railway *Ariel*, 1872 .. .. 95 1·00
1944 $2 Chicago & Rock Island Railroad "America" type, 1867 .. .. 95 1·00
1945 $2 Lehigh Valley Railroad Consolidation No. 63, 1866 .. .. .. 95 1·00
1946 $2 Great Western Railway *Scotia*, 1860 95 1·00
1947 $2 Grand Trunk Railway "Birkenhead" Class, 1854 .. .. .. 95 1·00
1948 $2 Camden & Amboy Railroad *Monster*, 1837 .. .. 95 1·00
1949 $2 Baltimore & Ohio Railroad "Grasshopper" Class, 1834 .. .. 95 1·00
1950 $2 Baltimore & Ohio Railroad *Tom Thumb*, 1829 .. .. .. 95 1·00
1951 $2 United Railways of Yucatan *Yucatan*, 1925 .. .. 95 1·00
a. Sheetlet. Nos. 1951/60 .. .. 9·50
1952 $2 Canadian National Railways Class "T2", 1924 .. .. .. 95 1·00
1953 $2 St. Louis—San Francisco Railroad "Light Mikado" class, 1919 .. .. 95 1·00
1954 $2 Atlantic Coast Line Railroad "Light Pacific" class, 1919 .. .. .. 95 1·00
1955 $2 Edaville Railroad No. 7, 1913 .. 95 1·00
1956 $2 Denver & Rio Grande Western Railroad Class "K27", 1903 .. .. 95 1·00
1957 $2 Pennsylvania Railroad Class "E-2" No. 7002, 1902 .. .. .. 95 1·00
1958 $2 Pennsylvania Railroad Class "H6", 1899 .. .. 95 1·00
1959 $2 Mohawk & Hudson Railroad *De Witt Clinton*, 1831 .. .. 95 1·00
1960 $2 St. Clair Tunnel Company No. 598, 1891 .. .. 95 1·00
1961 $2 Chesapeake & Ohio Railroad Class "M-1" No. 500 steam turbine electric, 1947 .. .. 95 1·00
a. Sheetlet. Nos. 1961/70 .. .. 9·50
1962 $2 Rutland Railroad No. 93, 1946 .. 95 1·00
1963 $2 Pennsylvania Railroad Class "T1", 1942 .. .. 95 1·00
1964 $2 Chesapeake & Ohio Railroad Class "H-8", 1942 .. .. 95 1·00
1965 $2 Atchison, Topeka & Santa Fe Railway Model "FT" diesel, 1941 .. .. 95 1·00
1966 $2 Gulf, Mobile & Ohio Railroad Models "S-1" & "S-2" diesel, 1940 .. .. 95 1·00
1967 $2 New York, New Haven & Hartford Railroad Class "15", 1937 .. .. 95 1·00
1968 $2 Seaboard Air Line Railroad Class "R", 1936 .. .. 95 1·00
1969 $2 Newfoundland Railway Class "R-2", 1930 .. .. 95 1·00
1970 $2 Canadian National Railway diesel No. 9000, 1928 .. .. 95 1·00
1941/70 .. .. *Set of* 30 25·00 27·00
Nos. 1941/50, 1951/60 and 1961/70 were each printed together, *se-tenant*, in sheetlets of 10.

343 Women's Long Jump (Jackie Joyner-Kersee, U.S.A.)

344 Nebulae

(Des L. Fried. Litho B.D.T.)

1989 (6 Apr). *Olympic Gold Medal Winners, Seoul* (1988). *T* **343** *and similar vert designs. Multicoloured. P* 14.
1971 10 c. Type **343** 10 10
1972 25 c. Women's Singles Tennis (Steffi Graf, West Germany) 10 15
1973 45 c. Men's 1500 metres (Peter Rono, Kenya) 20 25
1974 75 c. Men's 1000 metres single kayak (Greg Barton, U.S.A.) 35 40
1975 $1 Women's team foil (Italy) 45 50
1976 $2 Women's 100 metres freestyle swimming (Kristin Otto, East Germany) .. .. 95 1·00
1977 $3 Men's still rings gymnastics (Holger Behrendt, East Germany) .. .. 1·50 1·60
1978 $4 Synchronized swimming pair (Japan) 1·90 2·00
1971/8 .. .. *Set of* 8 5·00 5·50
MS1979 Two sheets, each 76×100 mm. (a) $6 Olympic flame. (b) $6 Runner with Olympic torch .. .. .. *Set of 2 sheets* 5·75 6·00

(Litho Questa)

1989 (25 Apr). *Appearance of Halley's Comet* (1986) (*3rd issue*). *T* **344** *and similar horiz designs. P* 14.
1980 25 c. + 5 c. multicoloured 15 20
1981 75 c. + 5 c. black and turquoise-green .. 40 45
1982 90 c. + 5 c. multicoloured 45 50
1983 $2 + 5 c. multicoloured .. .. 1·00 1·10
1980/3 .. .. *Set of* 4 1·75 2·00
MS1984 111×78 mm. $5 + 5 c. multicoloured. Imperf .. .. 2·40 2·50
Designs: (*As T* **344**)—75 c. + 5 c. Marine astronomical experiments; 90 c. + 5 c. Moon's surface; $2 + 5 c. Edmond Halley, Sir Isaac Newton and his book *Principia*. (102×69 *mm*)—$5 + 5 c. 17th-century warships and astrological signs.

(Litho Questa)

1989 (15 May). *Japanese Art. Paintings by Hiroshige. Horiz designs as T* **250** *of Antigua. Multicoloured. P* 14×13½.
1985 10 c. "Shinagawa on Edo Bay" 10 10
1986 25 c. "Pine Trees on the Road to Totsuka" 10 15
1987 60 c. "Kanagawa on Edo Bay" 30 35
1988 75 c. "Crossing Banyu River to Hiratsuka" 35 40
1989 $1 "Windy Shore at Odawara" 45 50
1990 $2 "Snow-Covered Post Station of Mishima" .. .. 95 1·00
1991 $3 "Full Moon at Fuchu" .. .. 1·50 1·60
1992 $4 "Crossing the Stream at Okitsu" .. 1·90 2·00
1985/92 .. .. *Set of* 8 5·00 5·50
MS1993 Two sheets, each 102×76 mm. (a) $5 "Mountain Pass at Nissaka". (b) $5 "Mt Uzu at Okabe" .. .. .. *Set of 2 sheets* 4·75 5·00
Nos. 1985/92 were each printed in sheetlets of 10 containing two horizontal strips of 5 stamps separated by printed labels commemorating Emperor Hirohito.

345 Great Blue Heron

(Des D. Bruckner. Litho Questa)

1989 (6 June–13 Nov). *Birds. T* **345** *and similar multicoloured designs. P* 14.
1994 5 c. Type **345** 10 10
1995 10 c. Green Heron 10 10
1996 15 c. Turnstone 10 10
1997 25 c. Blue-winged Teal 10 10
1998 35 c. Ringed Plover (*vert*) 15 20
1999 45 c. Green-throated Carib ("Emerald-throated Hummingbird") (*vert*) .. 20 25
2000 50 c. Rufous-breasted Hermit (*vert*) .. 20 25
2001 60 c. Lesser Antillean Bullfinch (*vert*) .. 25 30
2002 75 c. Brown Pelican (*vert*) 30 35
2003 $1 Black-crowned Night Heron (*vert*) .. 40 45
2004 $3 American Kestrel ("Sparrow Hawk") (*vert*) .. .. 1·25 1·40
2005 $5 Barn Swallow (*vert*) .. .. 2·10 2·25
2006 $10 Red-billed Tropic Bird (*vert*) (13.11.89) 4·00 4·25
1994/2006 .. .. .. *Set of* 13 8·50 9·00

(Des D. Bruckner. Litho B.D.T.)

1989 (12 June). *World Cup Football Championship, Italy* (1990). *Vert designs as T* **252** *of Antigua. Multicoloured. P* 14.
2008 10 c. Scotland player 10 10
2009 25 c. England and Brazil players 10 15
2010 60 c. Paolo Rossi (Italy) 30 35
2011 75 c. Jairzinho (Brazil) 35 40
2012 $1 Sweden striker 45 50
2013 $2 Péle (Brazil) .. .. 95 1·00
2014 $3 Mario Kempes (Argentina) .. .. 1·50 1·60
2015 $4 Pat Jennings (Northern Ireland) .. 1·90 2·00
2008/15 .. .. *Set of* 8 5·00 5·50
MS2016 Two sheets. (a) 70×93 mm. $6 Players jumping for ball. (b) 82×71 mm. $6 Goalkeeper *Set of 2 sheets* 5·75 6·00

346 Xebec and Sugar Cane

(Des T. Agans. Litho B.D.T.)

1989 (7 July). *"Philexfrance 89" International Stamp Exhibition, Paris. T* **346** *and similar horiz designs showing French sailing vessels and plantation crops. Multicoloured. P* 14.
2017 25 c. Type **346** 10 15
2018 75 c. Lugger and cotton 35 40
2019 $1 Full-rigged ship and cocoa 45 50
2020 $4 Ketch and coffee .. .. .. 1·90 2·00
2017/20 .. .. *Set of* 4 2·50 2·75
MS2021 114×70 mm. $6 "View of Fort and Town of St. George, 1779" (105×63 *mm*). Imperf .. 2·75 3·00

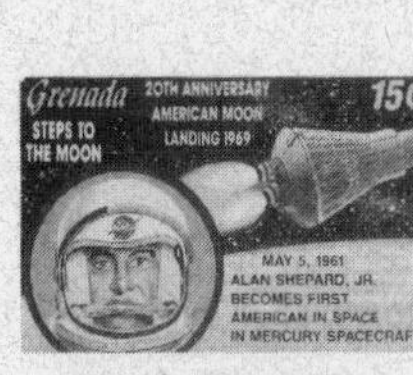

347 Alan Shepard and "Freedom 7" Spacecraft, 1961 (first American in Space)

348 *Hygrocybe occidentalis*

(Des L. Birmingham. Litho Questa)

1989 (20 July). *20th Anniv of First Manned Landing on Moon. T* **347** *and similar horiz designs. Multicoloured. P* 14.
2022 15 c. Type **347** 10 10
2023 35 c. "Friendship 7" spacecraft, 1962 (first manned earth orbit) 15 20
2024 45 c. "Apollo 8" orbiting Moon, 1968 (first manned lunar orbit) 20 25
2025 70 c. "Apollo 15" lunar rover, 1972 .. 35 40
2026 $1 "Apollo 11" emblem and lunar module *Eagle* on Moon, 1969 .. .. 45 50
2027 $2 "Gemini 8" and "Agena" rocket, 1966 (first space docking) .. .. .. 95 1·00
2028 $3 Edward White in space, 1965 (first U.S. space walk) .. .. .. 1·50 1·60
2029 $4 "Apollo 7" emblem .. .. .. 1·90 2·00
2022/9 .. .. *Set of* 8 5·00 5·50
MS2030 Two sheets, each 101×71 mm. (a) $5 Moon and track of "Apollo 11", 1969. (b) $5 Armstrong and Aldrin raising U.S. flag on Moon, 1969 .. .. .. *Set of 2 sheets* 4·75 5·00

(Des J. Cooter. Litho B.D.T.)

1989 (17 Aug). *Fungi. T* **348** *and similar vert designs. Multicoloured. P* 14.
2031 15 c. Type **348** 10 10
2032 40 c. *Marasmius haematocephalus* 20 25
2033 50 c. *Hygrocybe hypohaemacta* 25 30
2034 70 c. *Lepiota pseudoignicolor* 35 40
2035 90 c. *Cookeina tricholoma* 40 45
2036 $1.10, *Leucopaxillus gracillimus* 50 55
2037 $2.25, *Hygrocybe nigrescens* .. .. 1·10 1·25
2038 $4 *Clathrus crispus* .. .. .. 1·90 2·00
2031/8 .. .. *Set of* 8 4·25 4·50
MS2039 Two sheets, each 57×70 mm. (a) $6 *Mycena holoporphyra*. (b) $6 *Xeromphalina tenuipes* .. .. .. *Set of 2 sheets* 5·75 6·00

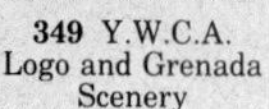

349 Y.W.C.A. Logo and Grenada Scenery   **350** Orion

(Litho Questa)

1989 (11 Sept). *Centenary of Young Women's Christian Association. T* **349** *and similar multicoloured design. P* 14.
2040 50 c. Type **349** 25 30
2041 75 c. Y.W.C.A. logo and town (*horiz*) .. 35 40

(Des Deborah Dudley Max. Litho B.D.T.)

1989 (2 Oct). *Butterflies. T* **350** *and similar horiz designs. Multicoloured. P* 14.
2042 6 c. Type **350** 10 10
2043 30 c. Southern Daggertail 15 20
2044 40 c. Soldier 20 25
2045 60 c. Silver Spot 30 35
2046 $1.10, Gulf Fritillary 50 55
2047 $1.25, Monarch 60 65
2048 $4 Polydamas Swallowtail .. .. 1·90 2·00
2049 $5 Flambeau .. .. 2·40 2·50
2042/9 .. .. *Set of* 8 5·50 5·75
MS2050 Two sheets, each 87×115 mm. (a) $6 White Peacock. (b) $6 St. Christopher Hairstreak .. .. .. *Set of 2 sheets* 5·75 6·00

351 Amerindian Hieroglyph   **352** Amos leaving Home

(Litho Questa)

1989 (16 Oct). *500th Anniv of Discovery of America by Columbus* (1992) (*2nd issue*). *T* **351** *and similar vert designs showing different hieroglyphs. P* 14.
2051 45 c. brownish black, black and new blue 20 25
2052 60 c. brownish black, black & bright green 30 35
2053 $1 brownish black, black & dp reddish vio 45 50
2054 $4 brownish black, black & orange-brn 1·90 2·00
2051/4 .. .. *Set of* 4 2·50 2·75
MS2055 74×86 mm. $6 brownish black, black and vermilion .. .. 2·75 3·00

(Des Walt Disney Co. Litho Questa)

1989 (20 Nov). *"World Stamp Expo '89" International Stamp Exhibition, Washington. T* **352** *and similar multicoloured designs showing Walt Disney cartoon characters in scenes from* Ben and Me. *P* 14×13½.
2056 1 c. Type **352** 10 10
2057 2 c. Meeting of Benjamin Franklin and Amos 10 10
2058 3 c. The Franklin stove 10 10
2059 4 c. Ben and Amos with bi-focals .. 10 10
2060 5 c. Amos on page of *Pennsylvania Gazette* 10 10
2061 6 c. Ben working printing press .. 10 10
2062 10 c. Conducting experiment with electricity 10 10
2063 $5 Ben disembarking in England .. 2·40 2·50
2064 $6 Ben with Document of Agreement .. 2·75 3·00
2056/64 .. .. *Set of* 9 5·00 5·25
MS2065 Two sheets, each 127×101 mm. (a) $6 Benjamin Franklin teaching (*vert*). P 13½×14. (b) $6 Signatories of Declaration of Independence. P 14×13½ .. .. *Set of 2 sheets* 5·50 5·75

POSTAGE DUE STAMPS

D 1

1d.
SURCHARGE
POSTAGE

(D 2)

(Typo D.L.R.)

1892 (18 Apr–Oct). (*a*) *Type* D 1. *Wmk Crown CA. P* 14.
D1 D 1 1d. blue-black .. .. 12·00 1·50
D2 2d. blue-black .. .. 60·00 1·50
D3 3d. blue-black .. .. 65·00 2·50
D1/3 .. .. *Set of* 3 £120 5·00

(*b*) *Nos.* 34 *and* 35 *surch locally as Type* D 2
D4 13 1d. on 6d. mauve (10.92) .. .. 35·00 1·25
a. *Tête-bêche* (pair) £200
b. Surch double .. .. — 85·00
D5 1d. on 8d. grey-brown (8.92) .. .. £200 3·25
a. *Tête-bêche* (pair) £900
D6 2d. on 6d. mauve (10.92) .. .. 65·00 2·50
a. *Tête-bêche* (pair) £375
D7 2d. on 8d. grey-brown (8.92) .. .. £400 9·00
a. *Tête-bêche* (pair) £1500

Nos. D4/7 were in use from August to November 1892. As supplies of Nos. D1/3 were available from April or May of that year it would not appear that they were intended for postage due purposes. There was a shortage of 1d. postage stamps in July and August, but this was alleviated by Nos. 44/5 which were still available. The provisionals *may* have been intended for postal purposes, but the vast majority appear to have been used philatelically.

1906 (July)–**11**. *Wmk Mult Crown CA. P* 14.
D 8 D 1 1d. blue-black (1911) .. .. .. 2·00 3·00
D 9 2d. blue-black .. .. 4·00 1·75
D10 3d. blue-black (9.06) .. .. .. 7·00 5·00
D8/10 .. .. *Set of* 3 11·50 9·00

1921 (Dec)–**22**. *As Type* D 1, *but inscr* "POSTAGE DUE". *Wmk Mult Script CA. P* 14.
D11 1d. black .. .. 90 1·00
D12 1½d. black (15.12.22) .. .. .. 4·00 6·50
D13 2d. black .. .. 2·00 1·75
D14 3d. black .. .. 2·00 3·50
D11/14 .. .. *Set of* 4 8·00 11·50
D11/14 Optd "Specimen" .. .. *Set of* 4 80·00

1952 (1 Mar). *As Type* D 1, *but inscr* "POSTAGE DUE". *Value in cents. Chalk-surfaced paper. Wmk Mult Script CA. P* 14.
D15 2 c. black .. .. 30 3·50
a. Error. Crown missing. W **9a** .. .. 45·00
b. Error. St. Edward Crown. W **9b** .. .. 25·00
D16 4 c. black .. .. 30 4·00
a. Error. Crown missing. W **9a** .. .. 45·00
b. Error. St. Edward Crown. W **9b** .. .. 25·00
D17 6 c. black .. .. 45 7·50
a. Error. Crown missing. W **9a** .. .. 55·00
b. Error. St. Edward Crown. W **9b** .. .. 38·00
D18 8 c. black .. .. 75 7·50
a. Error. Crown missing. W **9a** .. .. 90·00
b. Error. St. Edward Crown. W **9b** .. .. 60·00
D15/18 .. .. *Set of* 4 1·60 20·00

OFFICIAL STAMPS

P.R.G.

(O 1)

(= People's Revolutionary Government)

1982 (June). *Various stamps optd with Type* O 1.

(*a*) *Nos.* 1085A/97A *and* 1099A
O 1 5 c. West Indiaman barque, *circa* 1840 15 10
O 2 6 c. R.M.S.P. *Orinoco*, *circa* 1851 .. .. 15 10
O 3 10 c. Working Schooner 15 10
O 4 12 c. Trimaran at Grand Anse anchorage .. 15 10
O 5 15 c. Spice Island cruising yacht *Petite Amie* 20 10
O 6 20 c. Fishing pirogue 25 10
O 7 25 c. Harbour police launch 30 10
O 8 30 c. Grand Anse speedboat 30 15
O 9 40 c. M.V. *Seimstrand* 35 20
O10 50 c. Three-masted schooner *Ariadne* .. 40 25
O11 90 c. M.V. *Geestide* 70 45
O12 $1 M.V. *Cunard Countess* 70 45
O13 $3 Rum-runner .. .. 2·00 2·50
O14 $10 Coast-guard patrol boat .. .. 6·00 7·50

(*b*) *Nos.* 1130/2 *and* 1134/5
O15 30 c. Prince Charles and Lady Diana Spencer 1·75 2·00
O16 40 c. Holyrood House .. .. 2·25 2·50
O17 50 c. Prince Charles and Lady Diana Spencer 1·25 1·50
O18 $2 Holyrood House .. .. 2·75 3·00
O19 $4 Type **268** .. .. 6·50 7·50
O1/19 .. .. *Set of* 19 23·00 25·00

The $4 from sheetlets, perforated 14½ × 14 and with changed background colour, also exists with this overprint (*Price* £8.50 *mint*, £9 *used*).

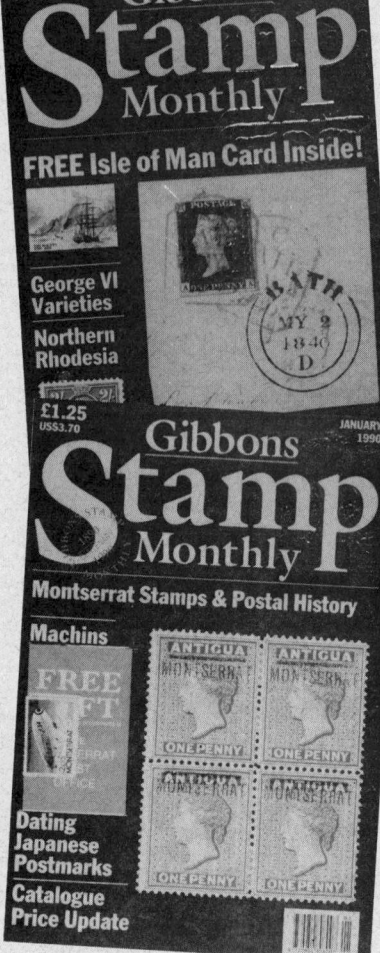

GRENADINES OF GRENADA

Part of a group of islands north of Grenada, the most important of which is Carriacou. The Grenadine islands further north are administered by St. Vincent, and their stamps are listed after that country.

(1)

GRENADINES

(2)

1973 (29 Dec). *Royal Wedding. Nos. 582/4 of Grenada optd with T* **1**.
1 **196** 25 c. multicoloured 20 10
2 $2 multicoloured 70 50
a. Albino opt .. ..
MS3 79 × 100 mm. 75 c. and $1 as Nos. 1/2 .. 1·25 50

1974 (29 May). *Nos. 306 etc of Grenada optd with T* **2**.
4 1 c. multicoloured 10 10
5 2 c. multicoloured 10 10
6 3 c. multicoloured 10 10
7 5 c. multicoloured 10 10
8 8 c. multicoloured 10 10
9 10 c. multicoloured 10 10
10 12 c. multicoloured 10 10
11 25 c. multicoloured 20 10
12 $1 multicoloured .. .. 1·25 45
13 $2 multicoloured .. .. 2·00 1·00
14 $3 multicoloured .. .. 2·25 1·50
15 $5 multicoloured .. .. 3·25 1·75
4/15 .. .. *Set of* 12 8·50 4·50

1974 (17 Sept). *World Cup Football Championships. As Nos. 619/27 of Grenada but additionally inscr* "GRENADINES".
16 ½ c. Type **201** 10 10
17 1 c. East Germany v Australia 10 10
18 2 c. Yugoslavia v Brazil 10 10
19 10 c. Scotland v Zaire 10 10
20 25 c. Netherlands v Uruguay 10 10
21 50 c. Sweden v Bulgaria 15 15
22 75 c. Italy v Haiti 20 20
23 $1 Poland v Argentina 25 25
16/23 .. .. *Set of* 8 70 70
MS24 114 × 76 mm. $2 Country flags 65 80

1974 (8 Oct). *Centenary of Universal Postal Union. Designs as Nos. 628 etc of Grenada, but additionally inscr* "GRENADINES".
25 8 c. Mailboat *Caesar* (1839) and helicopter .. 10 10
26 25 c. Messenger (1450) and satellite 15 10
27 35 c. Airmail transport 15 10
28 $1 Type **202** 40 40
25/8 .. .. *Set of* 4 70 60
MS29 172 × 109 mm. $1 Bellman and antenna; $2 18th-century postman and mail-train of the future. P 13 .. .. 80 1·00

1974 (11 Nov). *Birth Centenary of Sir Winston Churchill. As Nos. 637/9 of Grenada but additionally inscr* "GRENADINES".
30 **203** 35 c. multicoloured 15 10
31 – $2 multicoloured 40 45
MS32 129 × 96 mm. 75 c. as 35 c. and $1 as $2 .. 35 60

1974 (27 Nov). *Christmas. As Nos. 640/8 of Grenada but additionally inscr* "GRENADINES".
33 ½ c. Type **204** 10 10
34 1 c. Niccolo di Pietro 10 10
35 2 c. Van der Weyden 10 10
36 3 c. Bastiani 10 10
37 10 c. Giovanni 10 10
38 25 c. Van der Weyden 10 10
39 50 c. Botticelli 15 15
40 $1 Mantegna 30 25
33/40 .. .. *Set of* 8 65 60
MS41 117 × 96 mm. $2 as 1 c. 45 60

CANCELLED REMAINDERS*. Some of the following issues have been remaindered, cancelled-to-order, at a fraction of their face value. For all practical purposes these are indistinguishable from genuine postally used copies. Our used quotations, which are indicated by an asterisk, are the same for cancelled-to-order or postally used copies.

1975 (17 Feb). *Big Game Fishing. As Nos. 669 etc of Grenada, but additionally inscr* "GRENADINES" *and background colours changed.*
42 ½ c. Type **206** 10 10
43 1 c. Blue Marlin 10 10
44 2 c. White Marlin 10 10
45 10 c. Yellow Tuna 10 10
46 25 c. Wahoo 15 10
47 50 c. Dolphin 20 15
48 70 c. Grouper 25 20
49 $1 Great Barracuda 35 35
42/9 .. .. *Set of* 8 90 85
MS50 107 × 80 mm. $2 Blue Pointer or Mako Shark 60 90

1975 (11 Mar). *Flowers. As Nos. 678 etc of Grenada, but additionally inscr.* "GRENADINES".
51 ½ c. Type **207** 10 10
52 1 c. Bleeding Heart (Easter Lily) 10 10
53 2 c. Poinsettia 10 10
54 3 c. Cocoa flower 10 10
55 10 c. Gladioli 10 10
56 25 c. Redhead/Yellowhead 10 10
57 50 c. Plumbago 20 15
58 $1 Orange flower 30 20
51/8 .. .. *Set of* 8 65 50
MS59 102 × 82 mm. $2 Barbados Gooseberry .. 60 70

3 "Christ Crowned with Thorns" (Titian)

4 "Dawn" (detail from Medici Tomb)

(Des M. Shamir. Litho Format)

1975 (24 June). *Easter. T* **3** *and similar vert designs showing Crucifixion and Deposition scenes by the artists listed. Multicoloured. P* 14½.
60 ½ c. Type **3** 10 10*
61 1 c. Giotto 10 10*
62 2 c. Tintoretto 10 10*
63 3 c. Cranach 10 10*
64 35 c. Caravaggio 10 10*
65 75 c. Tiepolo 10 10*
66 $2 Velasquez 30 15*
60/6 .. .. *Set of* 7 55 30*
MS67 105 × 90 mm. $1 Titian. P 13 .. .. 40 25

(Des M. Shamir. Litho Format)

1975 (16 July). *500th Birth Anniv of Michelangelo. T* **4** *and similar vert designs. Multicoloured. P* 14½.
68 ½ c. Type **4** 10 10*
69 1 c. "Delphic Sibyl" 10 10*
70 2 c. "Giuliano de Medici" 10 10*
71 40 c. "The Creation" (detail) 15 10*
72 50 c. "Lorenzo de Medici" 15 10*
73 75 c. "Persian Sibyl" 15 10*
74 $2 "Head of Christ" 35 15*
68/74 .. .. *Set of* 7 80 35*
MS75 118 × 96 mm. $1 "The Prophet Jeremiah". P 13 .. .. 50 30

1975 (12 Aug). *Butterflies. Designs as Nos. 729 etc of Grenada, but additionally inscr* "GRENADINES". *P* 14½.
76 ½ c. Emperor 10 10
77 1 c. Queen 10 10
78 2 c. Tiger Pierid 10 10
79 35 c. Cracker 35 15
80 45 c. Scarce Bamboo Page 45 15
81 75 c. Apricot 70 25
82 $2 Purple King Shoemaker .. .. .. 1·40 70
76/82 .. .. *Set of* 7 2·75 1·25
MS83 104 × 77 mm. $1 Bamboo Page P. 13 .. 1·25 85

5 Progress "Standard" Badge

(Des J.W. Litho Format)

1975 (22 Aug). *14th World Scout Jamboree, Norway. T* **5** *and similar horiz designs. Multicoloured. P* 14½.
84 ½ c. Type **5** 10 10*
85 1 c. Boatman's badge 10 10*
86 2 c. Coxswain's badge 10 10*
87 35 c. Interpreter's badge 20 10*
88 45 c. Ambulance badge 20 10*
89 75 c. Chief Scout's award 30 10*
90 $2 Queen's Scout award 70 15*
84/90 .. .. *Set of* 7 1·25 35*
MS91 106 × 80 mm. $1 Venture award. P 13 .. 55 15*

6 The Surrender of Lord Cornwallis

(Des J.W. Litho Questa)

1975 (30 Sept)–**76**. *Bicentenary of American Revolution (1st issue). Multicoloured. (a) Horiz designs as T* **6**. *P* 14.
92 ½ c. Type **6** 10 10*
93 1 c. Minute-men 10 10*
94 2 c. Paul Revere's ride 10 10*
95 3 c. Battle of Bunker Hill 10 10*
96 5 c. Fifer and drummers 10 10*
97 45 c. Backwoodsman 50 10*
98 75 c. Boston Tea Party 65 10*
99 $2 Naval engagement .. .. .. 1·50 10*

(b) Larger designs. P 11 (16.1.76)
100 $2 George Washington (35 × 60 *mm*) .. 1·50 1·00
101 $2 White House and flags (60 × 35 *mm*) .. 1·50 1·00
92/101 .. .. *Set of* 10 5·00 2·25
MS102 Two sheets 113 × 128 mm containing No. 100, and 128 × 113 mm containing No. 101. Imperf .. .. 2·50 2·00
See also Nos. 176/**MS**183

7 Fencing

8 "Madonna and Child" (Dürer)

(Des J.W. Ltd. Litho Format)

1975 (27 Oct). *Pan-American Games, Mexico City. T* **7** *and similar horiz designs. Multicoloured. P* 14½.
103 ½ c. Type **7** 10 10*
104 1 c. Hurdling 10 10*
105 2 c. Pole-vaulting 10 10*
106 35 c. Weightlifting 15 10*
107 45 c. Throwing the javelin 15 10*
108 75 c. Throwing the discus 15 10*
109 $2 Diving 35 15*
103/109 .. .. *Set of* 7 75 35*
MS110 78 × 104 mm. $1 Sprinter. P 13 .. .. 40 15*

1975 (5 Nov)–**76**. *As Nos. 649A/68A of Grenada but additionally inscribed* "GRENADINES". *Multicoloured.*
111 ½ c. Yachts, Port Saline 10 10
112 1 c. Yacht Club race, St. George's 10 10
113 2 c. Carenage taxi 10 10
114 3 c. Large working boats 10 10
115 5 c. Deep-water dock, St. George's 10 10
116 6 c. Cocoa beans in drying trays 10 10
117 8 c. Nutmegs 10 10
118 10 c. Rum distillery, River Antoine Estate, *circa* 1785 .. .. 10 10
119 12 c. Cocoa tree 10 10
120 15 c. Fishermen landing catch at Fontenoy .. 10 10
121 20 c. Parliament Building, St. George's 10 10
122 25 c. Fort George cannons 10 10
123 35 c. Pearls Airport 15 15
124 50 c. General Post Office 20 20
125 75 c. Caribs Leap, Sauteurs Bay 40 40
126 $1 Carenage, St. George's 60 60
127 $2 St. George's Harbour by night .. .. 1·25 1·50
128 $3 Grand Anse beach .. .. .. 1·75 2·00
129 $5 Canoe Bay and Black Bay from Point Saline Lighthouse .. .. .. 3·00 3·75
130 $10 Sugar-loaf Island from Levera Beach (1.76) .. .. 5·00 5·50
111/30 .. .. *Set of* 20 12·00 13·00

(Des M. Shamir. Litho Questa)

1975 (17 Dec). *Christmas. T* **8** *and similar vert designs showing "Virgin and Child". Multicoloured. P* 14.
131 ½ c. Type **8** 10 10*
132 1 c. Dürer 10 10*
133 2 c. Correggio 10 10*
134 40 c. Botticelli 10 10*
135 50 c. Niccolo da Cremona 10 10*
136 75 c. Correggio 15 10*
137 $2 Correggio 30 15*
131/7 .. .. *Set of* 7 60 35*
MS138 114 × 102 mm. $1 Bellini 30 15*

9 Bleeding Tooth

(Des J.W. Litho Questa)

1976 (13 Jan). *Shells. T* **9** *and similar horiz designs. Multicoloured. P* 14.
139 ½ c. Type **9** 10 10*
140 1 c. Wedge Clam 10 10*
141 2 c. Hawk Wing Conch 10 10*
142 3 c. *Distorsio clathrata* 10 10*
143 25 c. Scotch Bonnet 20 10*
144 50 c. King Helmet 40 10*
145 75 c. Queen Conch 65 15*
139/45 .. .. *Set of* 7 1·25 30*
MS146 79 × 105 mm. $2 Atlantic Triton .. .. 1·00 30*

10 Cocoa Thrush

(Des J.W. Litho Questa)

1976 (4 Feb). *Flora and Fauna. T* **10** *and similar horiz designs. Multicoloured. P* 14.
147 ½ c. *Lignum vitae* 10 10
148 1 c. Type **10** 10 10
149 2 c. Tarantula 10 10
150 35 c. Hooded Tanager 65 30
151 50 c. *Nyctaginaceae* 80 35
152 75 c. Grenada Dove .. .. 1·50 1·00
153 $1 Marine Toad .. .. 2·00 1·25
147/53 .. .. *Set of* 7 4·50 2·75
MS154 108 × 84 mm. $2 Blue-hooded Euphonia 3·50 3·50

11 Hooked Sailfish

(Des G. Drummond. Litho Questa)

1976 (17 Feb). *Tourism. T* **11** *and similar horiz designs. Multicoloured. P* 14.

155 ½ c. Type **11** .. 10 10
156 1 c. Careened schooner, Carriacou .. 10 10
157 2 c. Carriacou Annual Regatta .. 10 10
158 18 c. Boat building on Carriacou .. 15 10
159 22 c. Workboat race, Carriacou Regatta .. 15 15
160 75 c. Cruising off Petit Martinique .. 30 30
161 $1 Water skiing .. 40 40
155/61 .. *Set of* 7 90 90
MS162 105 × 87 mm. $2 Yacht racing at Carriacou 70 1·25

12 Making a Camp Fire **13** "Christ Mocked" (Bosch)

(Des G. Vasarhelyi. Litho Questa)

1976 (17 Mar). *50th Anniv of Girl Guides in Grenada. T* **12** *and similar horiz designs. Multicoloured. P* 14.

163 ½ c. Type **12** .. 10 10
164 1 c. First aid .. 10 10
165 2 c. Nature study .. 10 10
166 50 c. Cookery .. 40 25
167 $1 Sketching .. 80 65
163/7 .. *Set of* 5 1·25 1·00
MS168 85 × 110 mm. $2 Guide playing guitar .. 1·00 1·75

(Des PAD Studio. Litho Questa)

1976 (28 Apr). *Easter. T* **13** *and similar vert designs. Multicoloured. P* 14.

169 ½ c. Type **13** .. 10 10
170 1 c. "Christ Crucified" (Antonello da Messina) 10 10
171 2 c. "Adoration of the Trinity" (Dürer) .. 10 10
172 3 c. "Lamentation of Christ" (Dürer) .. 10 10
173 35 c. "The Entombment" (Van der Weyden) .. 15 10
174 $3 "The Entombment" (Raphael) .. 50 60
169/74 .. *Set of* 6 60 70
MS175 57 × 72 mm. $2 "Blood of the Redeemer" (G. Bellini) .. 50 1·10

14 Frigate *South Carolina*

(Des J.W. Litho Questa)

1976 (18 May). *Bicentenary of American Revolution* (2nd issue). *T* **14** *and similar horiz designs. Multicoloured. P* 14.

176 ½ c. Type **14** .. 10 10
177 1 c. Schooner *Lee* .. 10 10
178 2 c. H.M.S. *Roebuck* .. 10 10
179 35 c. *Andrea Doria* .. 60 55
180 50 c. Sloop *The Providence* .. 80 70
181 $1 American frigate *Alfred* .. 2·00 1·75
182 $2 Frigate *Confederacy* .. 3·25 3·00
176/82 .. *Set of* 7 6·00 5·50
MS183 72 × 85 mm. $3 Cutter *Revenge* .. 2·50 4·00

15 Piper "Apache"

(Des J.W. Litho Format)

1976 (10 June). *Aeroplanes. T* **15** *and similar horiz designs. Multicoloured. P* 14.

184 ½ c. Type **15** .. 10 10
185 1 c. Beech "Twin Bonanza" .. 10 10
186 2 c. D.H. "Twin Otter" .. 10 10
187 40 c. Britten Norman "Islander" .. 25 20
188 50 c. D.H. "Heron" .. 30 25
189 $2 H.S. "748" .. 1·25 1·25
184/9 .. *Set of* 6 1·60 1·60
MS190 71 × 85 mm. $3 B.A.C. "1-11" .. 1·75 2·50

16 Cycling **17** "Virgin and Child" (Cima)

(Des J.W. Litho Format)

1976 (1 July). *Olympic Games, Montreal. T* **16** *and similar horiz designs. Multicoloured. P* 14.

191 ½ c. Type **16** .. 10 10
192 1 c. Pommel horse .. 10 10
193 2 c. Hurdling .. 10 10
194 35 c. Shot putting .. 10 10
195 45 c. Diving .. 15 10
196 75 c. Sprinting .. 15 15
197 $2 Rowing .. 35 35
191/7 .. *Set of* 7 70 70
MS198 101 × 76 mm. $3 Sailing .. 80 1·40

(Litho Format)

1976 (19 Oct). *Christmas. T* **17** *and similar multicoloured designs. P* 13½.

199 ½ c. Type **17** .. 10 10
200 1 c. "The Nativity" (Romanino) .. 10 10
201 2 c. "The Nativity" (Romanino) (*different*) .. 10 10
202 35 c. "Adoration of the Kings" (Bruegel) .. 10 10
203 50 c. "Madonna and Child" (Girolamo) .. 15 15
204 75 c. "Adoration of the Magi" (Giorgione) (*horiz*) .. 15 15
205 $2 "Adoration of the Kings" (School of Fra Angelico) (*horiz*) .. 30 40
199/205 .. *Set of* 7 70 70
MS206 120 × 100 mm. $3 "The Holy Family" (Garofalo) .. 60 1·25

18 Alexander Graham Bell and First Telephone

(Des G. Vasarhelyi. Litho Questa)

1977 (28 Jan). *Telephone Centenary* (1976). *T* **18** *and similar horiz designs showing Alexander Graham Bell and telephone. Multicoloured. P* 14.

207 ½ c. Type **18** .. 10 10
208 1 c. Telephone, 1895 .. 10 10
209 2 c. Telephone, 1900 .. 10 10
210 35 c. Telephone, 1915 .. 15 10
211 75 c. Telephone, 1920 .. 30 25
212 $1 Telephone, 1929 .. 50 50
213 $2 Telephone, 1963 .. 75 75
207/13 .. *Set of* 7 1·60 1·60
MS214 107 × 78 mm. $3 Telephone, 1976 .. 1·10 1·90

19 Coronation Coach **20** Royal Visit

(Des Jennifer Toombs. Litho and embossed Walsall. (Nos. 215/18). Des and litho Walsall (Nos. 219/22))

1977 (7 Feb). *Silver Jubilee. Multicoloured.*

(*a*) *Sheet stamps. Horiz designs as T* **19**. *P* 13½

215 35 c. Type **19** .. 10 10
216 $2 Queen entering Abbey .. 30 20
217 $4 Queen crowned .. 55 45
215/17 .. *Set of* 3 80 65
MS218 100 × 70 mm. $5 The Mall on Coronation Night .. 80 1·25

Nos. 215/17 also exist perf 11 (*Price for set of* 3 £1·50 *mint or used*) from additional sheetlets of 3 stamps and 1 label. These have different background colours from the stamps perforated 13½, which come from normal sheets of 25.

(*b*) *Booklet stamps. Vert designs as T* **20**. *Roul* 5 × *imperf.* Self-adhesive*

219 35 c. Type **20** .. 15 15
a. Booklet pane of 6 .. 1·00
220 50 c. Crown of St. Edward .. 40 60
a. Booklet pane. Nos. 220/2 .. 3·00
221 $2 The Queen and Prince Charles .. 1·50 1·40
222 $5 Royal Standard .. 1·60 1·50
219/22 .. *Set of* 4 3·25 3·25

*Nos. 219/22 are separated by various combinations of rotary knife (giving a straight edge) and roulette.

21 "Disrobing of Christ" (Fra Angelico) **22** "The Virgin adoring the Child" (Correggio)

(Des J.W. Litho Questa)

1977 (5 July). *Easter. Vert designs as T* **21** *showing paintings by the artists given. Multicoloured. P* 14.

223 ½ c. Type **21** .. 10 10
224 1 c. Fra Angelico .. 10 10
225 2 c. El Greco .. 10 10
226 18 c. El Greco .. 10 10
227 35 c. Fra Angelico .. 10 10
228 50 c. Giottino .. 15 15
229 $2 Antonello da Messina .. 40 40
223/9 .. *Set of* 7 65 65
MS230 121 × 94 mm. $3 Fra Angelico .. 60 1·40

(Des J.W. Litho Questa)

1977 (17 Nov). *Christmas. T* **22** *and similar vert designs. Multicoloured. P* 14.

231 ½ c. Type **22** .. 10 10
232 1 c. "Virgin and Child" (Giorgione) .. 10 10
233 2 c. "Virgin and Child" (Morales) .. 10 10
234 18 c. "Madonna della Tenda" (Raphael) .. 10 10
235 35 c. "Rest on the Flight into Egypt" (Van Dyck) .. 10 10
236 50 c. "Madonna and Child" (Lippi) .. 15 15
237 $2 "Virgin and Child" (Lippi) (*different*) .. 40 40
231/7 .. *Set of* 7 65 65
MS238 114 × 99 mm. $3 "Virgin and Child with Angels and Saints" (Ghirlandaio) .. 60 1·25

ROYAL VISIT W.I. 1977

(**23**)

1977 (23 Nov). *Royal Visit. Nos.* 215/18 *optd with T* **23**. *P* 13½.

239 35 c. Type **19** .. 15 10
240 $2 Queen entering Abbey .. 40 30
241 $4 Queen crowned .. 70 50
239/41 .. *Set of* 3 1·10 75
MS242 100 × 70 mm. $5 The Mall on Coronation Night .. 1·25 1·25

This overprint also exists on the stamps perforated 11, mentioned below No. **MS**218 (*price for set of* 3 £1·75 *mint or used*).

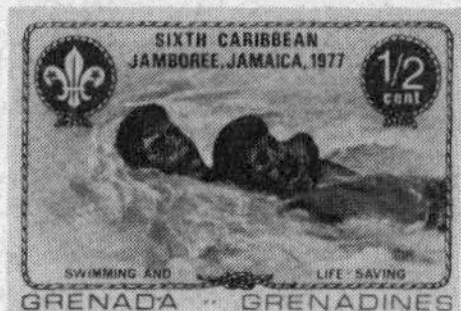

24 Life-saving

(Des G. Drummond. Litho Questa)

1977 (7 Dec). *Caribbean Scout Jamboree, Jamaica. T* **24** *and similar horiz designs. Multicoloured. P* 14.

243 ½ c. Type **24** .. 10 10
244 1 c. Overnight hike .. 10 10
245 2 c. Cubs tying knots .. 10 10
246 22 c. Erecting a tent .. 15 10
247 35 c. Gang show limbo dance .. 25 10
248 75 c. Campfire cooking .. 50 35
249 $3 Sea Scouts' yacht race .. 1·75 2·25
243/9 .. *Set of* 7 2·50 2·75
MS250 109 × 85 mm. $2 Pioneering project—Spring bridge .. 1·40 1·60

25 Blast-off

(Des J.W. Litho Questa)

1978 (3 Feb). *Space Shuttle. T* **25** *and similar horiz designs. Multicoloured. P* 14.

251 ½ c. Type **25** .. 10 10
252 1 c. Booster jettison .. 10 10
253 2 c. External tank jettison .. 10 10
254 22 c. Working in orbit .. 10 10
255 50 c. Shuttle re-entry .. 25 25
256 $3 Shuttle landing .. 1·00 1·00
251/6 .. *Set of* 6 1·25 1·25
MS257 85 × 103 mm. $2 Shuttle being towed .. 60 85

26 Alfred Nobel and Physiology/Medicine Medal

(Des J.W. Litho Questa)

1978 (22 Feb). *Nobel Prize Awards. T* **26** *and similar horiz designs. Multicoloured. P* 14.

258	½ c. Type **26**	10	10
259	1 c. Physics and Chemistry medal	10	10
260	2 c. Peace medal	10	10
261	22 c. Nobel Institute, Oslo	10	10
262	75 c. Peace Prize committee	35	35
263	$3 Literature medal	1·00	1·00
258/63	*Set of* 6	1·40	1·40
MS264	127 × 103 mm. $2 Peace medal and Nobel's will	50	60

27 German Zeppelin Stamp of 1930

(Des J.W. Litho Questa)

1978 (15 Mar). *75th Anniv of First Zeppelin Flight and 50th Anniv of Lindbergh's Trans-atlantic Flight. T* **27** *and similar horiz designs. Multicoloured. P* 14 × 13½.

265	5 c. Type **27**	10	10
266	15 c. French "Concorde" stamp, 1970	10	10
267	25 c. Liechtenstein Zeppelin stamp, 1931	15	10
268	35 c. Panama Lindbergh stamp, 1928	15	10
269	50 c. Russian airship stamp, 1931	20	20
270	$3 Spanish Lindbergh stamp, 1930	1·10	1·10
265/70	*Set of* 6	1·50	1·25
MS271	140 × 79 mm. 75 c. U.S.A. Lindbergh stamp, 1927; $2 German *Hindenburg* stamp, 1936	1·10	1·40

28 Coronation Ring

29 Drummer, Royal Regiment of Fusiliers.

(Des J.W. Litho Questa (Nos. 272/5). Manufactured by Walsall (Nos. 276/8))

1978 (12 Apr). *25th Anniv of Coronation. Multicoloured.*

(*a*) *Sheet stamps. Horiz designs as T* **28.** *P* 14

272	50 c. Type **28**	20	15
273	$2 Queen's Orb	50	40
274	$2.50, Imperial State Crown	55	45
272/4	*Set of* 3	1·10	90
MS275	97 × 67 mm. $5 Queen Elizabeth II	1·00	1·00

Nos. 272/4 also exist perf 12 (*Price for set of* 3 £1·50 *mint or used*) from additional sheetlets of 3 stamps and 1 label, issued 2 June. These have different background colours from the stamps perforated 14, which come from normal sheets of 50.

(*b*) *Booklet stamps. Vert designs as T* **29.** *Roul* 5 × *imperf.** *Self-adhesive*

276	18 c. Type **29**	25	35
	a. Booklet pane. Nos. 276/7 × 3	1·25	
277	50 c. Drummer, Royal Anglian Regiment	25	45
278	$5 Drum Major, Queen's Regiment	2·25	2·75
	a. Booklet pane of 1	2·25	
276/8	*Set of* 3	2·50	3·25

*Nos. 276/7 are separated by various combinations of rotary-knife (giving a straight edge) and roulette. No. 278 exists only with straight edges.

30 "Le Chapeau de Paille"

31 Wright *Flyer*

(Litho Questa)

1978 (18 May). *400th Birth Anniv of Rubens. T* **30** *and similar vert designs. Multicoloured. P* 14.

279	5 c. Type **30**	10	10
280	15 c. "Achilles slaying Hector"	10	10
281	18 c. "Helene Fourment and her Children"	10	10
282	22 c. "Rubens and Isabella Brandt"	15	10
283	35 c. "The Ildefonso Altarpiece"	15	10
284	$3 "Heads of Negroes" (detail)	80	80
279/84	*Set of* 6	1·00	1·00
MS285	85 × 127 mm. $2 "Self-portrait"	45	80

(Des BG Studio. Litho Questa)

1978 (10 Aug). *75th Anniv of Powered Flight. T* **31** *and similar designs. P* 14.

286	5 c. black, chestnut and pale blue	10	10
287	15 c. black, vermilion and yellow-ochre	10	10
288	18 c. black, vermilion and yellow-ochre	10	10
289	25 c. multicoloured	10	10
290	35 c. black, purple and magenta	15	10
291	75 c. multicoloured	25	25
292	$3 black, magenta and new blue	75	75
286/92	*Set of* 7	1·10	1·10
MS293	126 × 83 mm. $2 black, blue and bright blue-green	80	90

Designs: *Vert*—15 c. Orville Wright; 18 c. Wilbur Wright. *Horiz*—25, 75 c., $3, Wright *Flyer* (*all different*); 35 c. Wright glider; $2, Various Wright aircraft.

32 Audubon's Shearwater

33 Players with Ball

(Des Jennifer Toombs. Litho Questa)

1978 (28 Sept). *Birds. T* **32** *and similar multicoloured designs. P* 14.

294	5 c. Type **32**	25	10
295	10 c. Semipalmated Plover	35	10
296	18 c. Purple-throated Carib (*horiz*)	55	15
297	22 c. Red-billed Whistling Duck (*horiz*)	65	20
298	40 c. Caribbean Martin (*horiz*)	85	35
299	$1 White-tailed Tropic Bird	2·00	1·10
300	$2 Long-billed Curlew	3·00	1·50
294/300	*Set of* 7	7·00	3·00
MS301	78 × 78 mm. $5 Snowy Egret	4·50	4·50

(Des G. Vasarhelyi. Litho Questa)

1978 (2 Nov). *World Cup Football Championship, Argentina. T* **33** *and similar vert designs showing football scenes. P* 14.

302	15 c. multicoloured	10	10
303	35 c. multicoloured	20	10
304	50 c. multicoloured	25	20
305	$3 multicoloured	80	80
302/5	*Set of* 4	1·10	90
MS306	114 × 85 mm. $2 multicoloured	65	80

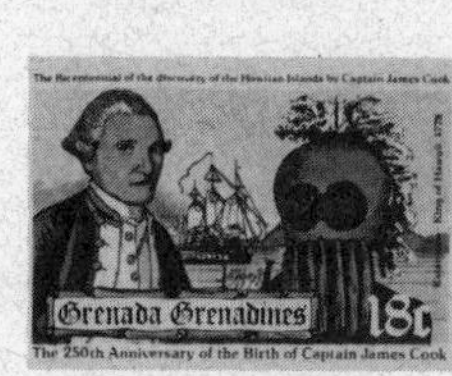

34 Captain Cook and Kalaniopu (king of Hawaii), 1778

35 "Virgin at Prayer"

(Des BG Studio. Litho Questa)

1978 (13 Dec). *250th Birth Anniv of Captain Cook and Bicentenary of Discovery of Hawaii. T* **34** *and similar horiz designs. Multicoloured. P* 14.

307	18 c. Type **34**	35	10
308	22 c. Captain Cook and native of Hawaii	40	15
309	50 c. Captain Cook and death scene, 14 February 1779	75	30
310	$3 Captain Cook and offering ceremony	2·25	1·75
307/10	*Set of* 4	3·25	2·00
MS311	171 × 113 mm. $4 H.M.S. *Resolution* (*vert*)	2·50	3·00

(Des M. Rubin. Litho Questa)

1978 (20 Dec). *Christmas. Paintings by Dürer. T* **35** *and similar vert designs. Multicoloured. P* 14.

312	40 c. Type **35**	15	10
313	60 c. "The Dresden Altarpiece"	15	15
314	90 c. "Madonna and Child with St. Anne"	20	15
315	$2 "Madonna and Child with Pear"	40	50
312/15	*Set of* 4	80	80
MS316	114 × 84 mm. $4 "Salvator Mundi"	80	1·40

36 *Strelitzia reginae*

37 Children with Pig

(Des J.W. Litho Questa)

1979 (15 Feb). *Flowers. T* **36** *and similar vert designs. Multicoloured. P* 14.

317	22 c. Type **36**	15	10
318	40 c. *Euphorbia pulcherrima*	25	15
319	$1 *Heliconia humilis*	55	30
320	$3 *Thunbergia alata*	1·25	80
317/20	*Set of* 4	2·00	1·10
MS321	114 × 90 mm. $2 *Bougainvillea glabra*	75	85

(Des G. Drummond. Litho Questa)

1979 (22 Mar). *International Year of the Child. T* **37** *and similar horiz designs. Multicoloured. P* 14.

322	18 c. Type **37**	10	10
323	50 c. Children with donkey	25	25
324	$1 Children with goats	30	35
325	$3 Children fishing	1·00	1·10
322/5	*Set of* 4	1·50	1·60
MS326	104 × 86 mm. $4 Child with coconuts	1·00	1·60

38 20,000 *Leagues Under the Sea*

(Des G. Vasarhelyi. Litho Questa)

1979 (20 Apr). *150th Birth Anniv of Jules Verne (author). T* **38** *and similar horiz designs showing scenes from his books and modern technological developments. Multicoloured. P* 14.

327	18 c. Type **38**	10	10
328	38 c. *From the Earth to the Moon*	20	20
329	75 c. *From the Earth to the Moon* (*different*)	35	35
330	$3 *Five Weeks in a Balloon*	1·00	1·00
327/30	*Set of* 4	1·50	1·50
MS331	111 × 86 mm. $4 *Around the World in 80 days*	1·00	1·60

39 Sir Rowland Hill and Mail Van

(Des BG Studio. Litho Questa)

1979 (30 July). *Death Centenary of Sir Rowland Hill. T* **39** *and similar horiz designs showing Sir Rowland Hill and mail transport. Multicoloured. P* 14.

332	15 c. Type **39**	10	10
333	$1 Cargo liner	45	35
334	$2 Diesel mail train	75	50
335	$3 "Concorde"	1·25	80
332/5	*Set of* 4	2·25	1·60
MS336	85 × 67 mm. $4 Sir Rowland Hill	1·00	1·25

Nos. 332/5 also exist perf 12 (*Price for set of* 4 £2·25 *mint or used*) from additional sheetlets of 5 stamps and 1 label issued 6 September. These have different background colours to the stamps perforated 14, which come from normal sheets of 40.

40 "Virgin and Child Enthroned" (11th-century Byzantine)

41 Great Hammerhead Shark

(Des G. Vasarhelyi. Litho Questa)

1979 (23 Oct). *Christmas. Sculptures. T* **40** *and similar vert designs. Multicoloured. P* 14.

337	6 c. Type **40**	10	10
338	25 c. "Presentation in the Temple" (Andre Beauneveu)	10	10
339	30 c. "Flight to Egypt", Utrecht, *circa* 1510	10	10
340	40 c. "Madonna and Child" (Jacopo della Quercia)	10	10
341	90 c. "Madonna della Mela" (Luca della Robbia)	15	15
342	$1 "Madonna and Child" (Antonio Rossellino)	20	20
343	$2 "Madonna", Antwerp, 1700	35	35
337/43	*Set of* 7	80	80
MS344	125 × 95 mm. $4 "Virgin", Krumau	65	1·10

(Des J.W. Litho Questa)

1979 (9 Nov). *Marine Life. T* **41** *and similar horiz designs. Multicoloured. P* 14 × 13½.

345	40 c. Type **41**	25	25
346	45 c. Banded Butterflyfish	25	25
347	50 c. Permit (fish)	30	30
348	60 c. Threaded Turban (shell)	35	35
349	70 c. Milk Conch (shell)	40	40
350	75 c. Great Blue Heron	40	40
351	90 c. Coloured Atlantic Natica (shell)	50	50

352 $1 Red-footed Booby 55 55
345/52 .. .. *Set of* 8 2·75 2·75
MS353 99 × 86 mm. $2.50 Collared Plover .. 1·25 1·25

42 Goofy as Doctor

43 Classroom

(Litho Format)

1979 (12 Dec). *International Year of the Child. Walt Disney Cartoon Characters. T* **42** *and similar multicoloured designs showing characters at various occupations. P* 11.
354 ½ c. Type **42** 10 10
355 1 c. Mickey Mouse as admiral 10 10
356 2 c. Goofy as fireman 10 10
357 3 c. Minnie Mouse as nurse 10 10
358 4 c. Mickey Mouse as drum major 10 10
359 5 c. Donald Duck as policeman 10 10
360 10 c. Donald Duck as pilot 10 10
361 $2 Goofy as postman (*horiz*) .. .. 1·25 80
362 $2.50, Donald Duck as train driver (*horiz*) .. 1·60 1·00
354/62 .. .. *Set of* 9 2·75 1·75
MS363 128 × 102 mm. $3 Mickey Mouse as fireman. P 13½ .. .. .. 1·50 1·75

1980 (10 Mar). *1st Anniv of Revolution. Nos.* 116 *and* 119/30 *optd with T* **258** *of Grenada.*
364 6 c. Cocoa beans in drying trays 10 10
365 12 c. Cocoa Tree 10 10
366 15 c. Fishermen landing catch at Fontenoy .. 10 10
367 20 c. Parliament Building, St. George's .. 10 10
368 25 c. Fort George cannons 15 10
369 35 c. Pearls Airport 20 10
370 50 c. General Post Office 35 15
371 75 c. Caribs Leap, Sauteurs Bay 40 20
372 $1 Carenage, St. George's 55 30
373 $2 St. George's Harbour by night 85 70
374 $3 Grand Anse Beach .. .. .. 1·60 1·60
375 $5 Canoe Bay and Black Bay from Point Saline Lighthouse .. .. .. 2·25 2·50
376 $10 Sugar Loaf Island from Levera Beach .. 3·75 4·25
364/76 .. .. *Set of* 13 9·50 9·00

(Des BG Studio. Litho Questa)

1980 (12 Mar). *75th Anniv of Rotary International. T* **43** *and similar horiz designs. Multicoloured. P* 14.
377 6 c. Type **43** 10 10
378 30 c. Rotary International emblem encircled by people of different races 15 10
379 60 c. Rotary International executive presenting doctor with cheque 30 20
380 $3 Nurses with young patients .. .. 1·00 75
377/80 .. .. *Set of* 4 1·40 1·00
MS381 85 × 72 mm. $4 Paul P. Harris (founder) 1·00 1·60

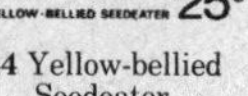

44 Yellow-bellied Seedeater

45 Running

(Des G. Drummond. Litho Questa)

1980 (14 Apr). *Wild Birds. T* **44** *and similar vert designs. Multicoloured. P* 14.
382 25 c. Type **44** 50 15
383 40 c. Blue-hooded Euphonia 55 20
384 90 c. Yellow Warbler .. .. .. 1·25 65
385 $2 Tropical Mockingbird .. .. 1·75 1·25
382/5 .. .. *Set of* 4 3·50 2·00
MS386 83 × 110 mm. $3 Barn Owl .. .. 2·50 2·50

(Des G. Vasarhelyi. Litho Questa)

1980 (21 Apr). *Olympic Games, Moscow. T* **45** *and similar horiz designs. Multicoloured. P* 14.
387 30 c. Type **45** 15 15
388 40 c. Football 15 20
389 90 c. Boxing 30 35
390 $2 Wrestling 60 75
387/90 .. .. *Set of* 4 1·00 1·25
MS391 104 × 75 mm. $4 Athletes in silhouette .. 75 1·10

LONDON 1980

(46)

47 Longspine Squirrelfish

1980 (6 May). *"London 1980" International Stamp Exhibition. Nos.* 332/5 *optd with T* **46**. *P* 12.
392 15 c. Type **39** 15 15
393 $1 Cargo liner 55 35
394 $2 Diesel mail train 90 65
395 $3 "Concorde" .. .. 1·40 1·10
392/5 .. .. *Set of* 4 2·75 2·00

(Des G. Drummond. Litho Questa)

1980 (6 Aug)–**84**. *Fishes. Horiz designs as T* **47**. *Multicoloured. P* 14. A. *Without imprint date.*
396 ½ c. Type **47** 10 10
397 1 c. Blue Chromis 10 10
398 2 c. Foureye Butterfly Fish 10 10
399 4 c. Sergeant Major 10 10
400 5 c. Yellowtail Snapper 10 10
401 6 c. Mutton Snapper 10 10
402 10 c. Cocoa Damselfish 10 10
403 12 c. Royal Gramma 10 10
404 15 c. Cherubfish 15 10
405 20 c. Blackbar Soldierfish 15 10
406 25 c. Comb Grouper 15 15
407 30 c. Longsnout Butterflyfish 20 20
408 40 c. Pudding Wife 25 25
409 50 c. Midnight Parrotfish 35 35
410 90 c. Redspotted Hawkfish 65 55
411 $1 Hogfish 70 60
412 $3 Beau Gregory .. .. .. 1·75 2·00
413 $5 Rock Beauty .. .. .. 2·75 3·00
414 $10 Barred Hamlet .. .. .. 6·00 7·00
396A/414A .. .. .. *Set of* 19 12·00 13·00

B. *With imprint date at foot of design.*
396B ½ c. Type **47** (*p* 12) (1982).. .. .. 7·00
402B 10 c. Cocoa Damselfish (1984) 20 20

(Litho Walsall)

1980 (7 Oct). *Christmas. Walt Disney Cartoon Scenes from "Bambi". Horiz designs as T* **42**. *Multicoloured. P* 11.
415 ½ c. Bambi with Mother 10 10
416 1 c. Bambi with quails 10 10
417 2 c. Bambi meets Thumper the rabbit .. 10 10
418 3 c. Bambi meets Flower the skunk 10 10
419 4 c. Bambi and Faline 10 10
420 5 c. Bambi with his father 10 10
421 10 c. Bambi on ice 10 10
422 $2.50, Faline with foals .. .. 1·00 85
423 $3 Bambi and Faline .. .. .. 1·25 1·00
415/23 .. .. *Set of* 9 2·25 1·90
MS424 127 × 102 mm. $4 Bambi as Prince of the Forest (*vert*) .. .. 1·00 1·10

48 "The Unicorn in Captivity" (15th-century unknown artist)

49 "Bust of a Woman"

(Litho Format)

1981 (25 Jan). *Paintings. T* **48** *and similar multicoloured designs. P* 13½.
425 6 c. Type **48** 10 10
426 10 c. "The Fighting *Temeraire*" (Turner) (*horiz*) 10 10
427 25 c. "Sunday Afternoon on the Ile de la Grande-Jatte" (Georges-Pierre Seurat) (*horiz*) 15 15
428 90 c. "Max Schmitt in a Single Scull" (Thomas Eakins) (*horiz*) 45 45
429 $2 "The Burial of the Count of Orgaz" (El Greco) 85 85
430 $3 "George Washington" (Gilbert Stuart) .. 1·10 1·10
425/30 .. .. *Set of* 6 2·40 2·40
MS431 66 × 101 mm. $5 "Kaiser Karl de Grosse" (detail, Dürer) .. .. 1·40 2·00

(Litho Format)

1981 (26 Jan). *50th Anniv of Walt Disney's Cartoon Character, Pluto. Vert designs as T* **42**. *Multicoloured. P* 13½.
432 $2 Mickey Mouse serving birthday cake to Pluto 90 80
MS433 127 × 101 mm. $4 Pluto in scene from film *Pluto's Dream House* .. .. .. 2·00 2·10
No. 432 was printed in small sheets of 8 stamps.

(Litho Format)

1981 (14 Apr). *Easter. Walt Disney Cartoon Characters. Vert designs as T* **42**. *Multicoloured. P* 11.
434 35 c. Chip 25 25
435 40 c. Dewey 25 25
436 $2 Huey 80 80
437 $2.50, Mickey Mouse .. .. .. 1·10 1·10
434/7 .. .. *Set of* 4 2·25 2·25
MS438 126 × 102 mm. $4 Jiminy Cricket. P 13½ 2·10 2·25

(Des J.W. Litho Questa)

1981 (5 May). *Birth Centenary of Picasso. T* **49** *and similar vert designs. Multicoloured. P* 14.
439 6 c. Type **49** 10 10
440 40 c. Woman (study for "Les Demoiselles d'Avignon") 20 15
441 90 c. "Nude with raised Arms (The Dancer of Avignon)" 40 30
442 $4 "The Dryad" .. .. 1·50 1·25
439/42 .. .. *Set of* 4 1·90 1·50
MS443 103 × 128 mm. $5 "Les Demoiselles d'Avignon". Imperf .. .. .. 2·25 2·00

50 Balmoral Castle

51 Lady Diana Spencer

(Des J.W. Litho Format)

1981 (16 June). *Royal Wedding. T* **50** *and similar vert designs. Multicoloured.* (a) *P* 15.
444 40 c. Prince Charles and Lady Diana Spencer 25 25
445 $2 Type **50** 75 75
446 $4 Prince Charles as parachutist .. .. 1·25 1·25
MS447 97 × 84 mm. $5 Royal Coach .. .. 1·50 1·50

(*b*) *P* 15 × 14½
448 30 c. As No. 444 .. .. 25 25
449 40 c. Type **50** 30 30
444/9 .. .. *Set of* 5 2·50 2·50
The 30 and 40 c. values were each printed in small sheets of 6 including one *se-tenant* stamp-size label.
The $4 value, with changed background colour, also exists perforated 15 × 14½ (*price* £1.50 *mint or used*) from similar sheetlets in addition to the original version from sheets of 40.

(Manufactured by Walsall)

1981 (16 June). *Royal Wedding. Booklet stamps. T* **51** *and similar multicoloured designs. Roul* 5 × *imperf**. *Self-adhesive.*
450 $1 Type **51** 45 55
a. Booklet pane. Nos. 450/1 each × 3 .. 3·00
451 $2 Prince Charles 70 90
452 $5 Prince Charles and Lady Diana Spencer (*horiz*) .. .. 2·00 2·50
a. Booklet pane of 1 .. .. .. 2·00
450/2 .. .. *Set of* 3 2·75 3·50
*The $1 and $2 values were each separated by various combinations of rotary knife (giving a straight edge) and roulette. The $5 value exists only with straight edges.

52 Amy Johnson (1st solo flight, Britain to Australia by Woman, May 1930)

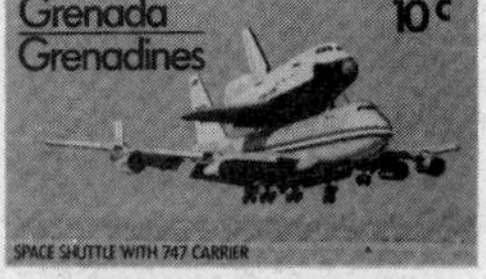

53 "747" Carrier

(Des BG Studio. Litho Questa)

1981 (13 Oct). *"Decade for Women". Famous Female Aviators. T* **52** *and similar vert designs. Multicoloured. P* 14.
453 30 c. Type **52** 15 15
454 70 c. Mme la Baronne de Laroche (1st qualified woman pilot, March 1910) 35 30
455 $1.10, Ruth Nichols (solo Atlantic flight attempt, June 1931) 50 40
456 $3 Amelia Earhart (1st North Atlantic solo flight by woman, May 1932) .. .. 1·40 1·10
453/6 .. .. *Set of* 4 2·25 1·75
MS457 90 × 85 mm. $5 Valentina Nikolayeva-Tereshkova (1st woman in space, June 1963) .. 2·00 2·00

(Litho Questa)

1981 (2 Nov). *Christmas. Horiz designs as T* **42** *showing scenes from Walt Disney's cartoon film "Lady and the Tramp". P* 13½.
458 ½ c. multicoloured 10 10
459 1 c. multicoloured 10 10
460 2 c. multicoloured 10 10
461 3 c. multicoloured 10 10
462 4 c. multicoloured 10 10
463 5 c. multicoloured 10 10
464 10 c. multicoloured 10 10
465 $2.50, multicoloured .. .. .. 1·25 1·00
466 $3 multicoloured .. .. 1·50 1·25
458/66 .. .. *Set of* 9 2·75 2·25
MS467 128 × 103 mm. $5 multicoloured .. .. 2·00 2·00

(Des M. Brodie. Litho Format)

1981 (2 Nov). *Space Shuttle Project. T* **53** *and similar horiz designs. Multicoloured. P* 14½.
468 10 c. Type **53** 20 10
469 40 c. Re-entry 30 15
470 $1.10, External tank separation 70 45
471 $3 Touchdown .. .. 1·60 1·00
468/71 .. .. *Set of* 4 2·50 1·50
MS472 117 × 89 mm. $5 Launch .. .. 2·75 2·75

OMNIBUS ISSUES

Details, together with prices for complete sets, of the various Omnibus issues from the 1935 Silver Jubilee series to date are included in a special section following Zululand at the end of the catalogue.

54 Footballer

55 Mail Van and Stage-Coach

(Des Clover Mill. Litho Questa)

1981 (30 Nov). *World Cup Football Championship, Spain* (1982). *T* **54** *and similar vert designs showing footballers. P* 14.

473 20 c. multicoloured 10 10
474 40 c. multicoloured 20 20
475 $1 multicoloured 45 45
476 $2 multicoloured 75 75
473/6 .. .. *Set of* 4 1·40 1·40
MS477 106 × 128 mm. $4 multicoloured .. .. 2·00 2·00

Nos. 473/6 were each printed in small sheets of 6 including one *se-tenant* stamp-size label.

(Des G. Vasarhelyi. Litho Format)

1982 (13 Jan). *Centenary of U.P.U. Membership. T* **55** *and similar horiz designs. Multicoloured. P* 14½.

478 30 c. Type **55** 25 15
479 40 c. U.P.U. emblem 30 20
480 $2.50, *Queen Elizabeth 2* (liner) and sailing ship .. .. 1·50 90
481 $4 Airliner and biplane .. .. 2·25 1·60
478/81 .. .. *Set of* 4 4·00 2·50
MS482 117 × 78 mm. $5 Streamlined diesel-electric, and steam trains .. .. 3·50 3·25

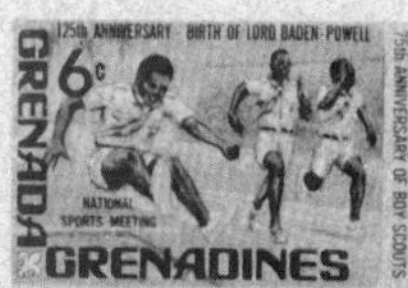

56 National Sports Meeting

(Des M. Diamond. Litho Format)

1982 (19 Feb). *75th Anniv of Boy Scout Movement and 125th Birth Anniv of Lord Baden-Powell. T* **56** *and similar horiz designs. Multicoloured. P* 14½.

483 6 c. Type **56** 15 10
484 90 c. Sea scouts sailing 65 30
485 $1.10, Handicraft 90 60
486 $3 Animal tending .. .. 1·90 1·40
483/6 .. .. *Set of* 4 3·25 2·10
MS487 100 × 71 mm. $5 Music around campfire .. 2·75 3·00

57 White Peacock

58 Prince and Princess of Wales

(Des J.W. Litho Questa)

1982 (24 Mar). *Butterflies. T* **57** *and similar horiz designs. Multicoloured. P* 14.

488 30 c. Type **57** 55 30
489 40 c. St. Vincent Long-tail Skipper 60 35
490 $1.10, Painted Lady .. .. 1·10 75
491 $3 Orion .. .. 2·00 1·60
488/91 .. .. *Set of* 4 3·75 2·75
MS492 103 × 77 mm. $5 Silver Spot .. .. 3·25 3·75

(Des PAD Studio. Litho Questa)

1982 (1 July). *21st Birthday of Princess of Wales. T* **58** *and similar vert designs. Multicoloured. P* 14½ × 14.

493 50 c. Blenheim Palace 30 30
494 60 c. As 50 c. 40 35
495 $1 Type **58** 50 50
496 $2 Type **58** .. .. 1·00 1·00
497 $3 Princess of Wales .. .. 1·60 1·40
498 $4 As $3 .. .. 2·00 1·75
493/8 .. .. *Set of* 6 5·50 4·75
MS499 103 × 75 mm. $5 Princess Diana (*different*) 2·40 2·25

Nos. 493, 495 and 497 come from sheetlets of 5 stamps and 1 label.

PRICES OF SETS

Set prices are given for many issues, generally those containing three stamps or more. Definitive sets include one of each value or major colour change, but do not cover different perforations, die types or minor shades. Where a choice is possible the set prices are based on the cheapest versions of the stamps included in the listings.

59 "New Deal"—Soil Conservation

60 "Presentation of Christ in the Temple"

(Des M. Diamond. Litho Questa)

1982 (27 July). *Birth Centenary of Franklin D. Roosevelt. T* **59** *and similar horiz designs. Multicoloured. P* 14.

500 30 c. Type **59** 15 15
501 40 c. Roosevelt and George Washington Carver (scientist) 20 15
502 70 c. Civilian conservation corps and reafforestation 45 35
503 $3 Roosevelt with Pres. Barclay of Liberia, Casablanca Conference, 1943 .. .. 1·60 1·25
500/3 .. .. *Set of* 4 2·25 1·90
MS504 100 × 72 mm. $5 Roosevelt delivering address at Howard University .. .. 2·00 2·10

1982 (30 Aug). *Birth of Prince William of Wales. Nos. 493/9 optd with T* **171** *of Antigua.*

505 50 c. Blenheim Palace 30 30
506 60 c. As 50 c. 35 35
507 $1 Type **58** 50 50
508 $2 Type **58** .. .. 1·00 1·00
509 $3 Princess of Wales .. .. 1·40 1·40
510 $4 As $3 .. .. 1·75 1·75
505/10 .. .. *Set of* 6 4·75 4·75
MS511 103 × 75 mm. $5 Princess Diana (*different*) 2·10 2·25

Nos. 505, 507 and 509 come from sheetlets of 5 stamps and 1 label.

(Des Clover Mill. Litho Format)

1982 (2 Sept). *Easter. T* **60** *and similar vert designs depicting Easter paintings by Rembrandt. Multicoloured. P* 14½.

512 30 c. Type **60** 20 15
513 60 c. "Descent from the Cross" 35 20
514 $2 "Raising of the Cross" .. .. .. 1·25 75
515 $4 "Resurrection of Christ" .. .. .. 2·25 1·75
512/15 .. .. *Set of* 4 3·50 2·50
MS516 101 × 126 mm. $5 "The Risen Christ" .. 2·50 2·40

61 "Santa Fe"

(Des Artists International. Litho Format)

1982 (4 Oct). *Famous Trains of the World. T* **61** *and similar vert designs. Multicoloured. P* 15.

517 10 c. Type **61** 35 15
518 40 c. "Mistral" 60 20
519 70 c. "Rheingold" 80 45
520 $1 "ET 403" 90 55
521 $1.10, Steam locomotive *Mallard* .. .. 1·25 70
522 $2 "Tokaido" .. .. 1·40 1·25
517/22 .. .. *Set of* 6 4·75 3·00
MS523 121 × 95 mm. $5 "Settebello" .. .. 2·75 3·00

62 Footballers

(Des D. Miller. Litho Questa)

1982 (2 Dec). *World Cup Football Championship Winners. T* **62** *and similar horiz designs. P* 14 × 13½.

524 60 c. multicoloured 35 35
525 $4 multicoloured .. .. 1·75 1·75
MS526 92 × 134 mm. $5 multicoloured .. .. 2·00 2·00

(Litho Questa)

1982 (14 Dec). *Christmas. Horiz designs as T* **42** *showing scenes from Walt Disney's cartoon film "The Rescuers". P* 13½.

527 ½ c. multicoloured 10 10
528 1 c. multicoloured 10 10
529 2 c. multicoloured 10 10
530 3 c. multicoloured 10 10
531 4 c. multicoloured 10 10
532 5 c. multicoloured 10 10
533 10 c. multicoloured 10 10
534 $2.50, multicoloured .. .. 1·00 1·00
535 $3 multicoloured .. .. 1·25 1·25
527/35 .. .. *Set of* 9 2·25 2·25
MS536 120 × 96 mm. $5 multicoloured .. .. 2·25 2·25

63 Short-finned Pilot Whale

(Des Artists International. Litho Questa)

1983 (10 Jan). *Save the Whales. T* **63** *and similar horiz designs. Multicoloured. P* 14.

537 10 c. Type **63** 55 20
538 60 c. Dall's Porpoise .. .. 1·25 70
539 $1.10, Humpback Whale .. .. 1·75 1·00
540 $3 Bowhead Whale .. .. 2·75 2·75
537/40 .. .. *Set of* 4 5·75 4·25
MS541 113 × 84 mm. $5 Spotted Dolphin .. 3·50 4·00

64 "David and Goliath"

(Des Design Images. Litho Format)

1983 (15 Feb). *500th Birth Anniv of Raphael. T* **64** *and similar horiz designs showing painting details. Multicoloured. P* 13½.

542 25 c. Type **64** 15 15
543 30 c. "David sees Bathsheba" 15 20
544 90 c. "Triumph of David" 40 45
545 $4 "Anointing of Solomon" .. .. .. 1·60 1·75
542/5 .. .. *Set of* 4 2·00 2·25
MS546 126 × 101 mm. $5 "Anointing of David" .. 1·75 2·00

65 Voice and Visual Communication

(Des Artists International. Litho Questa)

1983 (7 Apr). *World Communications Year. T* **65** *and similar horiz designs. Multicoloured. P* 14.

547 30 c. Type **65** 15 15
548 60 c. Ambulance 25 25
549 $1.10, Helicopters 45 45
550 $3 Satellite .. .. 1·25 1·25
547/50 .. .. *Set of* 4 1·90 1·90
MS551 127 × 85 mm. $5 Diver and Bottle-nosed Dolphin .. .. 2·25 2·50

66 Chrysler "Imperial Roadster", 1931

(Des R. Sauber. Litho Format)

1983 (4 May). *75th Anniv of Model "T" Ford Car. T* **66** *and similar horiz designs showing cars of the 20th century. Multicoloured. P* 14½.

552 10 c. Type **66** 10 10
553 30 c. Doble steam car, 1925 .. .. .. 15 20
554 40 c. Ford "Mustang", 1965 .. .. .. 20 25
555 60 c. Packard tourer, 1930 .. .. .. 30 35
556 70 c. Mercer "Raceabout" 1913 .. .. .. 35 40
557 90 c. Corvette "Stingray", 1963 .. .. .. 40 45
558 $1.10, Auburn "851 Supercharger Speedster", 1935 .. .. 50 55
559 $2.50, Pierce-Arrow "Silver Arrow", 1933 .. 90 1·00
560 $3 Duesenberg dual cowl phaeton, 1929 .. 1·25 1·40
561 $4 Mercedes-Benz "SSK", 1928 .. .. 1·60 1·75
552/61 .. .. *Set of* 10 5·00 5·75
MS562 119 × 90 mm. $5 McFarlan "Knickerbocker" cabriolet, 1923 .. .. 2·00 2·50

Nos. 552/61 were each issued in sheets of eight stamps with a stamp-size label in the centre position.

67 Short "Solent" Flying Boat

(Des W. Wright. Litho Questa)

1983 (18 July). *Bicentenary of Manned Flight. T* **67** *and similar horiz designs. Multicoloured. P* 14.
563 40 c. Type **67** 40 20
564 70 c. Curtiss "R3C-2" seaplane 55 35
565 90 c. Hawker "Nimrod" biplane 65 40
566 $4 Montgolfier balloon .. .. 2·25 2·25
563/6 .. .. *Set of* 4 3·50 3·00
MS567 112 × 85 mm. $5 *Viktoria Luise* (airship) .. 2·75 3·00

68 Goofy

69 Weightlifting

(Litho Walsall)

1983 (7 Nov). *Christmas. T* **68** *and similar vert designs showing Disney cartoon characters in scenes from "Jingle Bells" (Christmas carol). Multicoloured. P* 11.
568 ½ c. Type **68** 10 10
569 1 c. Clarabelle Cow 10 10
570 2 c. Donald Duck 10 10
571 3 c. Pluto 10 10
572 4 c. Morty and Ferdie 10 10
573 5 c. Huey, Dewey and Louie 10 10
574 10 c. Daisy and Chip 'n Dale 10 10
575 $2.50, Big Bad Wolf .. .. 1·90 1·90
576 $3 Mickey Mouse .. .. 2·40 2·40
568/76 .. .. *Set of* 9 4·00 4·00
MS577 102 × 124 mm. $5 Donald Duck in sleigh. P 13½ .. .. 3·25 3·25

(Des N. Waldman. Litho Questa)

1984 (9 Jan). *Olympic Games, Los Angeles. T* **69** *and similar vert designs. Multicoloured. P* 14.
578 30 c. Type **69** 15 15
579 60 c. Gymnastics 35 35
580 70 c. Archery 40 40
581 $4 Sailing .. .. 1·75 1·90
578/81 .. .. *Set of* 4 2·40 2·50
MS582 70 × 102 mm. $5 Basketball .. .. 1·75 2·25

70 Frangipani

71 Goofy

(Des J. Cooter. Litho Questa)

1984 (9 Apr). *Flowers. T* **70** *and similar vert designs. Multicoloured. P* 15.
583 15 c. Type **70** 15 10
584 40 c. Dwarf Poinciana 30 25
585 70 c. Walking Iris 55 45
586 $4 Lady's Slipper .. .. 2·25 2·50
583/6 .. .. *Set of* 4 3·00 3·00
MS587 66 × 57 mm. $5 Brazilian Glory Vine .. 2·75 3·00

(Litho Format)

1984 (1 May). *Easter. T* **71** *and similar vert designs showing Disney cartoon characters with Easter hats. Multicoloured. P* 11.
588 ½ c. Type **71** 10 10
589 1 c. Chip and Dale 10 10
590 2 c. Daisy Duck and Huey 10 10
591 3 c. Daisy Duck 10 10
592 4 c. Donald Duck 10 10
593 5 c. Merlin and Madam Mim 10 10
594 10 c. Flower 10 10
595 $2 Minnie and Mickey Mouse .. .. .. 1·25 1·40
596 $4 Minnie Mouse .. .. 2·00 2·25
588/96 .. .. *Set of* 9 3·25 3·50
MS597 126 × 100 mm. $5 Minnie Mouse (*different*). P 13½ × 14 .. .. 2·75 3·00

72 Bobolink

19th U.P.U CONGRESS
HAMBURG
(73)

(Litho Questa)

1984 (21 May). *Songbirds. T* **72** *and similar horiz designs. Multicoloured. P* 14.
598 40 c. Type **72** 70 50
599 50 c. Eastern Kingbird 80 60
600 60 c. Barn Swallow 90 70
601 70 c. Yellow Warbler 95 75
602 $1 Rose-breasted Grosbeak .. .. .. 1·25 1·00
603 $1.10, Yellowthroat .. .. 1·40 1·25
604 $2 Catbird .. .. 2·00 2·25
598/604 .. .. *Set of* 7 7·25 6·50
MS605 71 × 65 mm. $5 Fork-tailed Flycatcher .. 4·25 4·25

1984 (19 June). *Universal Postal Union Congress, Hamburg. Nos.* 585/7 *optd with T* **73**.
606 70 c. Walking Iris 60 50
607 $4 Lady's Slipper .. .. 2·50 2·50
MS608 66 × 57 mm. $5 Brazilian Glory Vine .. 2·75 3·00

74 *Geeststar*

(Litho Format)

1984 (16 July). *Ships. T* **74** *and similar horiz designs. Multicoloured. P* 15.
609 30 c. Type **74** 50 30
610 60 c. *Daphne* 80 60
611 $1.10, *Southwind* .. .. 1·25 1·25
612 $4 *Oceanic* .. .. 3·25 3·50
609/12 .. .. *Set of* 4 5·25 5·00
MS613 108 × 80 mm. $5 Pirate ship .. .. 3·50 4·00

(Litho Questa)

1984 (22 Aug). *450th Death Anniv of Correggio (painter). Multicoloured designs as T* **296** *of Grenada showing paintings. P* 14.
614 10 c. "The Hunt—Blowing the Horn" 10 10
615 30 c. "St. John the Evangelist" (*horiz*) .. 15 15
616 90 c. "The Hunt—The Deer's Head" 50 50
617 $4 "The Virgin crowned by Christ" (*horiz*) .. 2·00 2·00
614/17 .. .. *Set of* 4 2·50 2·50
MS618 73 × 63 mm. $5 "Martyrdom of the Four Saints" .. .. 2·40 3·00

(Litho Questa)

1984 (22 Aug). *150th Birth Anniv of Edgar Degas (painter). Vert designs as T* **297** *of Grenada showing paintings. Multicoloured. P* 14.
619 25 c. "The Song of the Dog" 15 15
620 70 c. "Cafe-concert" 35 35
621 $1.10, "The Orchestra of the Opera" .. 60 60
622 $3 "The Dance Lesson" .. .. .. 1·75 1·75
619/22 .. .. *Set of* 4 2·50 2·50
MS623 53 × 73 mm. $5 "Madame Camus at the Piano" .. .. 2·40 3·00

(Des Bonny Redecker. Litho Questa)

1984 (21 Sept). *"Ausipex" International Stamp Exhibition, Melbourne. Horiz designs as T* **298** *of Grenada. Multicoloured. P* 14.
624 $1.10, Queen Victoria Gardens, Melbourne 50 50
625 $4 Ayers Rock .. .. 2·00 2·00
MS626 107 × 76 mm. $5 River Yarra, Melbourne 2·50 3·00

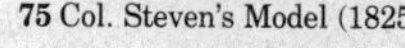

75 Col. Steven's Model (1825)

76 Kawasaki "750" (1972)

(Des Bonny Redecker. Litho Format)

1984 (3 Oct). *Railway Locomotives. T* **75** *and similar horiz designs. Multicoloured. P* 15.
627 20 c. Type **75** 40 25
628 50 c. *Royal George* (1827) 65 50
629 60 c. *Stourbridge Lion* (1829) 75 60
630 70 c. *Liverpool* (1830) 85 70
631 90 c. *South Carolina* (1832) .. .. .. 1·00 85
632 $1.10, *Monster* (1836) .. .. .. 1·25 1·00
633 $2 *Lafayette* (1837) .. .. 1·75 1·75
634 $4 *Lion* (1838) .. .. 3·25 3·25
627/34 .. .. *Set of* 8 9·00 8·00
MS635 Two sheets, each 100×70 mm. (a) $5 Sequin's locomotive (1829); (b) $5 *Der Adler* (1835) .. .. *Set of* 2 *sheets* 7·00 8·00

1984 (28 Oct). *Opening of Point Saline International Airport. Nos.* 547, 549 *and* **MS**551 *optd as T* **300** *of Grenada.*
636 30 c. Type **65** 20 25
637 $1.10, Helicopters 70 75
MS638 127 × 85 mm. $5 Diver and dolphin .. 3·00 3·50
The overprint on No. **MS**638 appears on the sheet margin as for No. **MS**1371 of Grenada.

(Litho Questa)

1984 (26 Nov). *Christmas. Walt Disney Cartoon Characters. Vert designs as T* **301** *of Grenada. Multicoloured. P* 12 ($2) *or* 13½ × 14 (*others*).
639 45 c. Donald Duck, and nephews knitting Christmas stockings 25 30
640 60 c. Donald Duck and nephews sitting on sofa 35 40
641 90 c. Donald Duck getting out of bed .. 50 55
642 $2 Donald Duck putting presents in wardrobe .. .. 1·10 1·25
643 $4 Nephews singing carols outside Donald Duck's window .. .. 2·10 2·25
639/43 .. .. *Set of* 5 3·75 4·25
MS644 126 × 102 mm. $5 Donald Duck filming nephews .. .. 3·00 3·00
No. 642 was printed in sheetlets of 8 stamps.

(Litho Questa)

1985 (11 Feb). *Birth Bicentenary of John J. Audubon (ornithologist) (1st issue). Multicoloured designs as T* **198** *of Antigua showing original paintings. P* 14.
645 50 c. Blue-winged Teal 55 30
646 90 c. White Ibis 90 60
647 $1.10, Swallow-tailed Kite .. .. .. 1·25 1·25
648 $3 Moorhen ("Common Gallinule") .. .. 2·25 2·50
645/8 .. .. *Set of* 4 4·50 4·25
MS649 82 × 111 mm. $5 Mangrove Cuckoo (*vert*) 3·25 3·75
See also Nos. 736/40.

(Des BG Studio. Litho Questa)

1985 (11 Mar). *Centenary of the Motor Cycle. T* **76** *and similar multicoloured designs. P* 14.
650 30 c. Type **76** 15 20
651 60 c. Honda "Goldwing GL1000" (1974) (*horiz*) 35 40
652 70 c. Kawasaki "Z650" (1976) (*horiz*) .. 40 45
653 $4 Honda "CBX" (1977) .. .. .. 2·10 2·25
650/3 .. .. *Set of* 4 2·75 3·00
MS654 113 × 76 mm. $5 BMW "R100RS" (1978) .. 2·75 3·00

77 Nursing Cadets folding Bandages (Health)

(Des Susan David. Litho Questa)

1985 (15 Apr). *International Youth Year. T* **77** *and similar horiz designs. Multicoloured. P* 14.
655 50 c. Type **77** 25 30
656 70 c. Scuba diver and turtle (Environment) .. 40 45
657 $1.10, Yachting (Leisure) 65 70
658 $3 Boys playing chess (Education) .. 1·60 1·75
655/8 .. .. *Set of* 4 2·50 3·00
MS659 98 × 70 mm. $5 Hands touching globe .. 2·75 3·00

(Des BG Studio. Litho Questa)

1985 (30 Apr). *40th Anniv of International Civil Aviation Organization. Horiz designs as T* **305** *of Grenada. Multicoloured. P* 14.
660 5 c. Lockheed "Lodestar" 10 10
661 70 c. Avro "748" Turboprop 55 45
662 $1.10, Boeing "727" 85 85
663 $3 Boeing "707" .. .. 2·00 2·25
660/3 .. .. *Set of* 4 3·25 3·25
MS664 87 × 68 mm. $4 Pilatus Britten-Norman "Islander" .. .. 2·75 3·00

78 Lady Baden-Powell (founder) and Grenadian Guide Leaders

(Des D. Francis. Litho Questa)

1985 (30 May). *75th Anniv of Girl Guide Movement. T* **78** *and similar multicoloured designs. P* 14.
665 30 c. Type **78** 25 20
666 50 c. Guide leader and guides on botany field trip 45 30
667 70 c. Guide leader and guides camping (*vert*) 70 45
668 $4 Guides sailing (*vert*) .. .. .. 2·50 2·25
665/8 .. .. *Set of* 4 3·50 3·00
MS669 100 × 73 mm. $5 Lord and Lady Baden-Powell (*vert*) .. .. 3·50 4·00

79 Grenadine Grizzled Skipper

80 The Queen Mother before Prince William's Christening

(Des I. MacLaury. Litho Questa)

1985 (17 June)–**86**. *Butterflies. T* **79** *and similar horiz designs. Multicoloured. A. P 14. B. P 12.*

		A		B	
670	½ c. Type **79**	10	10	10	10
671	1 c. Red Anartia	10	10	10	10
672	2 c. Lesser Antillean Giant Hairstreak	10	10	10	10
673	4 c. Santo Domingo Long-tail Skipper	15	10	10	10
674	5 c. Spotted Manuel's Skipper	15	10	10	10
675	6 c. Grenada's Polydamas Swallowtail	15	10	10	10
676	10 c. Palmira Sulphur	15	10	10	10
677	12 c. Pupillated Orange Sulphur	20	10	10	10
678	15 c. Migrant Sulphur	20	10	10	10
679	20 c. St. Christopher's Hairstreak	25	10	10	10
680	25 c. St. Lucia Mestra	25	15	10	10
681	30 c. Insular Gulf Fritillary	30	20	10	15
682	40 c. Michael's Caribbean Buckeye	40	25	15	20
683	60 c. Frampton's Flambeau	60	35	25	30
684	70 c. Bamboo Page	60	35	30	35
685	$1.10, Antillean Cracker	90	75	45	50
686	$2.50 Red Crescent Hairstreak	1·75	2·00	1·00	1·10
687	$5 Single-coloured Antillean White	3·00	3·50	2·10	2·25
688	$10 Lesser Whirlabout	5·50	6·00	4·00	4·25
688*c*	$20 Blue Night	8·00	8·25	8·25	8·50
670/88*c*	*Set of* 20	20·00	20·00	16·00	17·00

Dates of issue: 17.6.85, Nos. 670A/87A; 11.11.85, No. 688A; 1986, Nos. 670B/85B, 687B; 1.8.86, No. 688*c*A; 9.86, Nos. 686B, 688B; 5.89, No. 688*c*B.

(Des J.W. Litho Questa)

1985 (3 July). *Life and Times of Queen Elizabeth the Queen Mother. T* **80** *and similar multicoloured designs. P* 14.
689 $1 Type **80** .. 55 60
690 $1.50, In winner's enclosure at Ascot (*horiz*) 80 85
691 $2.50, With Prince Charles at Garter ceremony, Windsor Castle .. 1·25 1·50
689/91 *Set of* 3 2·40 2·75
MS692 56 × 85 mm. $5 At opening of Royal York Hospice, London .. 2·75 3·00

Stamps as Nos. 689/91, but with face values of 70 c., $1.10 and $3, exist from additional sheetlets of 5 plus a label issued 28 January 1986. These also have changed background colours and are perforated 12½ × 12 ($1.10) or 12 × 12½ (others) (*Price for set of* 3 *stamps* £2.10 *mint*).

81 Scuba Diving
82 Queen Conch

(Des Marlise Nakaja. Litho Format)

1985 (15 July). *Water Sports. T* **81** *and similar vert designs. Multicoloured. P* 15.
693 15 c. Type **81** .. 15 10
694 70 c. Boys playing in waterfall 45 45
695 90 c. Water skiing 55 55
696 $4 Swimming 2·10 2·25
693/6 *Set of* 4 3·00 3·00
MS697 103 × 78 mm. $5 Scuba diver 3·00 3·25

(Des Mary Walters. Litho Questa)

1985 (1 Aug). *Marine Life. T* **82** *and similar horiz designs. Multicoloured. P* 14.
698 60 c. Type **82** .. 40 40
699 90 c. Porcupine Fish and Fire Coral 55 55
700 $1.10, Ghost Crab .. 70 70
701 $4 West Indies Spiny Lobster 2·25 2·25
698/701 *Set of* 4 3·50 3·50
MS702 299 × 70 mm. $5 Long-spined Urchin 3·00 3·50

(Des Susan David. Litho Questa)

1985 (3 Sept). *300th Birth Anniv of Johann Sebastian Bach (composer). Vert designs as T* **206** *of Antigua. Multicoloured. P* 14.
703 15 c. Natural trumpet 25 10
704 60 c. Bass viol.. 50 40
705 $1.10, Flute.. 80 70
706 $3 Double flageolet 1·75 1·75
703/6 *Set of* 4 3·00 2·75
MS707 110 × 75 mm. $5 Johann Sebastian Bach 3·25 3·50

(Litho Format)

1985 (4 Nov). *Royal Visit. Multicoloured designs as T* **207** *of Antigua. P* 14½.
708 10 c. Arms of Great Britain and Grenada .. 10 10
709 $1 Queen Elizabeth II (*vert*) 70 70
710 $4 Royal Yacht *Britannia* .. 2·50 2·75
708/10 *Set of* 3 3·00 3·25
MS711 111 × 83 mm. $5 Map of Grenada Grenadines .. 3·00 3·00

(Litho Format)

1985 (22 Nov). *40th Anniv of United Nations Organization. Multicoloured designs as T* **208** *of Antigua showing United Nations (New York) stamps. P* 14½.
712 $1 Neil Armstrong (first man on Moon) and 1982 Peaceful Uses of Outer Space 20 c. .. 70 60
713 $2 Gandhi and 1971 Racial Equality Year 13 c. 1·40 1·25
714 $2.50, Maimonides (physician) and 1956 World Health Organization 3 c. .. 1·90 1·50
712/14 *Set of* 3 3·50 3·00
MS715 110 × 85 mm. $5 U.N. Under-Secretary Ralph Bunche (*vert*) 2·75 3·00

(Des Walt Disney Productions. Litho Questa)

1985 (27 Nov). *150th Birth Anniv of Mark Twain (author). Horiz designs as T* **118** *of Anguilla showing Walt Disney cartoon characters illustrating scenes from "Letters from Hawaii". Multicoloured. P* 14 × 13½.
716 25 c. Minnie Mouse dancing the hula 15 20
717 50 c. Donald Duck surfing 30 35
718 $1.50, Donald Duck roasting marshmallow in volcano 90 95
719 $3 Mickey Mouse and Chip'n'Dale canoeing 1·75 1·90
716/19 *Set of* 4 2·75 3·00
MS720 127 × 102 mm. $5 Mickey Mouse with cat 3·00 3·25

(Des Walt Disney Productions. Litho Questa)

1985 (27 Nov). *Birth Bicentenaries of Grimm Brothers (folklorists). Designs as T* **119** *of Anguilla, but vert, showing Walt Disney cartoon characters in scenes from "The Elves and the Shoemaker". Multicoloured. P* 13½ × 14.
721 30 c. Mickey Mouse as the unsuccessful Shoemaker 25 20
722 60 c. Two elves making shoes 40 35
723 70 c. The Shoemaker discovering the new shoes 45 40
724 $4 The Shoemaker's wife (Minnie Mouse) making clothes for the elves 2·25 2·10
721/4 *Set of* 4 3·00 2·75
MS725 126 × 101 mm. $5 The Shoemaker and his wife waving 2·75 3·00

83 "Madonna and Child" (Titian)

VISIT OF PRES. REAGAN

20 FEBRUARY 1986

(84)

(Des Mary Walters. Litho Format)

1985 (23 Dec). *Christmas. Religious Paintings. T* **83** *and similar vert designs. Multicoloured. P* 15.
726 50 c. Type **83** .. 25 30
727 70 c. "Madonna and Child with St. Mary and John the Baptist" (Bugiardini) 35 40
728 $1.10, "Adoration of the Magi" (Di Fredi) .. 55 60
729 $3 "Madonna and Child with Young St. John the Baptist" (Bartolomeo) 1·50 1·60
726/9 *Set of* 4 2·40 2·60
MS730 112 × 81 mm. $5 "The Annunciation" (Botticelli) .. 2·50 2·75

(Des J. Iskowitz. Litho Questa)

1986 (6 Jan). *Centenary of the Statue of Liberty. Multicoloured designs as T* **211** *of Dominica. P* 15.
731 5 c. Croton Reservoir, New York (1875) 10 10
732 10 c. New York Public Library (1986) 10 10
733 70 c. Old Boathouse, Central Park (1894) 35 40
734 $4 Boating in Central Park (1986) 2·00 2·10
731/4 *Set of* 4 2·25 2·40
MS735 103 × 76 mm. $5 Statue of Liberty (*vert*) 2·50 2·75

(Litho Questa)

1986 (28 Jan). *Birth Bicentenary of John J. Audubon (ornithologist) (2nd issue). Horiz designs as T* **198** *of Antigua. Multicoloured. P* 12½ × 12.
736 50 c. Louisiana Heron 70 40
737 70 c. Black-crowned Night Heron 85 50
738 90 c. American Bittern 95 65
739 $4 Glossy Ibis 2·25 2·75
736/9 *Set of* 4 4·25 4·00
MS740 103 × 74 mm. $5 King Eider. P 14 3·50 4·00

Nos. 736/9 were each issued in sheetlets of five stamps and one stamp-size label, which appears in the centre of the bottom row.

1986 (20 Feb). *Visit of President Reagan of U.S.A. Nos.* 684A *and* 687A *optd with T* **84**.
741 70 c. Bamboo Page 50 40
742 $5 Single-coloured Antillean White 3·00 3·25

85 Two Footballers
86 *Hygrocybe firma*

(Des BG Studio. Litho Questa)

1986 (18 Mar). *World Cup Football Championship, Mexico. Vert designs as T* **85** *showing footballers. P* 14.
743 10 c. multicoloured 10 10
744 70 c. multicoloured 50 40
745 $1 multicoloured 70 55
746 $4 multicoloured 2·50 2·50
743/6 *Set of* 4 3·50 3·25
MS747 86 × 104 mm. $5 multicoloured 2·50 2·75

(Des W. Hanson. Litho Questa)

1986 (26 Mar). *Appearance of Halley's Comet (1st issue). Horiz designs as T* **123** *of Anguilla. Multicoloured. P* 14.
748 5 c. Nicholas Copernicus (astronomer) and Earl of Rosse's six foot reflector telescope 10 10
749 20 c. "Sputnik I" (first satellite) orbiting Earth, 1957 15 15
750 40 c. Tycho Brahe's notes and sketch of 1577 Comet 25 25
751 $4 Edmond Halley and 1682 Comet 2·00 2·50
748/51 *Set of* 4 2·25 2·75
MS752 101 × 70 mm. $5 Halley's Comet 2·50 2·75

The captions of Nos. 750/1 are transposed.

(Litho Questa)

1986 (21 Apr). *60th Birthday of Queen Elizabeth II. Vert designs as T* **125** *of Anguilla. P* 14.
753 2 c. black and yellow .. 10 15
754 $1.50, multicoloured 1·00 1·00
755 $4 multicoloured 2·25 2·50
753/5 *Set of* 3 3·00 3·25
MS756 120 × 85 mm. $5 black and grey-brown .. 3·00 3·25

Designs:—2 c. Princesses Elizabeth and Margaret, Windsor Park, 1933; $1.50, Queen Elizabeth; $4 In Sydney, Australia, 1970; $5 The Royal Family, Coronation Day, 1937.

(Des Walt Disney Productions. Litho Format)

1986 (22 May). *"Ameripex '86" International Stamp Exhibition, Chicago. Horiz designs as T* **212** *of Dominica showing Walt Disney cartoon characters. Multicoloured. P* 11.
757 30 c. Donald Duck riding mule in Grand Canyon 25 25
758 60 c. Daisy Duck, Timothy Mouse and Dumbo on Golden Gate Bridge, San Francisco 45 45
759 $1 Mickey Mouse and Goofy in fire engine and Chicago Watertower 75 75
760 $3 Mickey Mouse as airmail pilot and White House 2·00 2·00
757/60 *Set of* 4 3·00 3·00
MS761 126 × 101 mm. $5 Donald Duck and Mickey Mouse watching Halley's Comet over Statue of Liberty. P 14 × 13½ 3·00 3·25

(Litho Questa)

1986 (1 July). *Royal Wedding. Vert designs as T* **213** *of Antigua. Multicoloured. P* 14.
762 60 c. Prince Andrew and Miss Sarah Ferguson 45 45
763 70 c. Prince Andrew in car 55 55
764 $4 Prince Andrew with naval helicopter .. 2·50 2·50
762/4 *Set of* 3 3·25 3·25
MS765 88 × 88 mm. $5 Prince Andrew and Miss Sarah Ferguson (*different*) 3·00 3·25

(Des BG Studio. Litho Format)

1986 (15 July). *Mushrooms of the Lesser Antilles. T* **86** *and similar vert designs. Multicoloured. P* 15.
766 15 c. Type **86** 30 15
767 50 c. *Xerocomus coccolobae* 70 40
768 $2 *Volvariella cubensis* 2·00 1·75
769 $3 *Lactarius putidus* 2·50 2·25
766/9 *Set of* 4 5·00 4·00
MS770 76 × 80 mm. $5 *Leptonia caeruleocapitata* 4·50 4·75

87 Giant Atlantic Pyram

88 Common Opossum

(Des L. Birmingham. Litho Format)

1986 (1 Aug). *Sea Shells. T* **87** *and similar multicoloured designs. P* 15.
771 15 c. Type **87** .. 30 15
772 50 c. Beau's Murex 70 40
773 $1.10, West Indian Fighting Conch 1·40 1·10
774 $4 Alphabet Coral shell 3·00 3·50
771/4 *Set of* 4 5·00 4·75
MS775 109 × 75 mm. $5 Brown-lined Paper Bubble (*horiz*) .. 4·00 4·75

1986 (15 Sept). *World Cup Football Championship Winners, Mexico. Nos.* 743/7 *optd with T* **216** *of Antigua in gold.*
776 **85** 10 c. multicoloured 15 15
777 – 70 c. multicoloured 55 45
778 – $1 multicoloured 75 65
779 – $4 multicoloured 2·50 2·75
776/9 *Set of* 4 3·50 3·50
MS780 86 × 104 mm. $5 multicoloured 3·50 3·75

(Des Dot and S. Barlowe. Litho Format)

1986 (15 Sept). *Wildlife. T* **88** *and similar multicoloured designs. P* 15.

781 10 c. Type **88** 15 15
782 30 c. Giant Toad 30 25
783 60 c. Land Tortoise (*Testudo denticulata*) .. 60 50
784 70 c. Murine Opossum (*vert*) 65 55
785 90 c. Burmese Mongoose (*vert*) 70 60
786 $1.10, Nine-banded Armadillo 85 85
787 $2 Agouti .. .. 1·40 1·50
788 $3 Humpback Whale .. .. 2·50 2·75
781/8 .. .. *Set of* 8 6·50 6·50
MS789 Two sheets, each 103×72 mm. (a) $5 Mona Monkey (*vert*) (b) $5 Iguana *Set of* 2 *sheets* 7·50 8·00

1986 (15 Oct). *Appearance of Halley's Comet (2nd issue). Nos.* 748/52 *optd with T* **218** *of Antigua (in silver on* 20 *c.,* $4 *and* $5).

790 5 c. Nicholas Copernicus (astronomer) and Earl of Rosse's six foot reflector telescope 15 15
791 20 c. "Sputnik I" (first satellite) orbiting Earth, 1957 .. .. 25 20
792 40 c. Tycho Brahe's notes and sketch of 1577 Comet 35 25
793 $4 Edmond Halley and 1682 Comet .. 2·50 2·75
790/3 .. .. *Set of* 4 3·00 3·00
MS794 102×70 mm. $5 Halley's Comet .. 3·00 3·25

(Des Walt Disney Co. Litho Format)

1986 (3 Nov). *Christmas. Multicoloured designs as T* **220** *of Antigua showing Walt Disney cartoon characters. P* 11.

795 25 c. Chip n'Dale with hummingbird .. 15 15
796 30 c. Robin delivering card to Mickey Mouse (*vert*) 15 20
797 50 c. Piglet, Pooh and Jose Carioca on beach 25 30
798 60 c. Grandma Duck feeding birds (*vert*) .. 30 35
799 70 c. Cinderella and birds with mistletoe (*vert*) 35 40
800 $1.50, Huey, Dewey and Louie windsurfing 75 80
801 $3 Mickey Mouse and Morty on beach with turtle .. .. 1·50 1·60
802 $4 Kittens playing on piano (*vert*) .. 2·00 2·10
795/802 .. .. *Set of* 8 5·00 5·25
MS803 Two sheets, each 127×102 mm. (a) $5 Mickey Mouse and Willie the Whale. P 14×13½. (b) $5 Bambi, Thumper and Blossom in snow (*vert*). P 13½×14 *Set of* 2 *sheets* 6·00 6·50

89 Cycling

90 Aston-Martin "Volanté" (1984)

(Des BG Studio. Litho Format)

1986 (18 Nov). *Olympic Games, Seoul, South Korea* (1988). *T* **89** *and similar vert designs. Multicoloured. P* 15.

804 10 c. + 5 c. Type **89** 10 15
805 50 c. + 20 c. Sailing 35 45
806 70 c. + 30 c. Gymnastics 50 65
807 $2 + $1 Horse trials .. .. 1·50 1·75
804/7 .. .. *Set of* 4 2·25 2·75
MS808 80×100 mm. $3 + $1 Marathon .. .. 2·00 2·10

The premiums on Nos. 804/8 were to support the participation of the Grenada team.

(Des W. Wright. Litho Format)

1986 (20 Nov). *Centenary of Motoring. T* **90** *and similar horiz designs. Multicoloured. P* 15.

809 10 c. Type **90** 10 15
810 30 c. Jaguar "Mk V" (1948) 15 20
811 60 c. Nash "Ambassador" (1956) 30 35
812 70 c. Toyota "Supra" (1984) 35 40
813 90 c. Ferrari "Testarossa" (1985) 45 50
814 $1 BMW "501B" (1955) 50 55
815 $2 Mercedes-Benz "280 SL" (1968) .. 1·00 1·10
816 $3 Austro-Daimler "ADR8" (1932) .. 1·50 1·60
809/16 .. .. *Set of* 8 4·00 4·25
MS817 Two sheets, each 116 × 85 mm. (a) $5 Morgan "+8" (1977). (b) $5 Checker taxi *Set of* 2 *sheets* 6·00 6·50

(Litho Questa)

1986 (19 Dec). *Birth Centenary of Marc Chagall (artist). Designs as T* **225** *of Antigua, showing various paintings. P* 13½×14 (*vert*) *or* 14×13½ (*horiz*).

818/57 $1.10×40 multicoloured .. *Set of* 40 18·00 19·00
MS858 Ten sheets, each 110×95 mm. $5×10 multicoloured (*each* 104×89 *mm*). Imperf *Set of* 10 *sheets* 20·00 22·00

Although announced as all being released on 19 December 1986 the issue was distributed in ten parts, each of four stamps and one miniature sheet, at monthly intervals.

(Des J. Iskowitz. Litho Format)

1987 (5 Feb). *America's Cup Yachting Championship. Multicoloured designs as T* **222** *of Antigua. P* 15.

859 25 c. *Defender*, 1895 .. .. 20 15
860 45 c. *Caletea*, 1886 .. .. 30 25
861 70 c. *Azzurra*, 1981 .. .. 45 45
862 $4 *Australia II*, 1983 .. .. .. 1·75 2·25
859/62 .. .. *Set of* 4 2·40 2·75
MS863 113×83 mm. $5 *Columbia* defeating *Shamrock*, 1899 (*horiz*) .. .. 2·75 3·00

(Des Mary Walters. Litho Format)

1987 (27 Apr). 500*th Anniv of Discovery of America by Columbus* (1992). *Vert designs as T* **322** *of Grenada. Multicoloured. P* 15.

864 15 c. Christopher Columbus 15 15
865 30 c. Queen Isabella of Castile 15 15
866 50 c. *Santa Maria* 25 30
867 60 c. Claiming the New World for Spain .. 25 30
868 90 c. Early Spanish map of Lesser Antilles .. 40 45
869 $1 King Ferdinand of Aragon 45 50
870 $2 Fort La Navidad (drawing by Columbus) 90 95
871 $3 Galley and Caribs, Hispaniola (drawing by Columbus) .. .. 1·40 1·50
864/71 .. .. *Set of* 8 3·50 3·75
MS872 Two sheets, 104×72 mm. (a) $5 Caribs pearl fishing. (b) $5 *Santa Maria* at anchor *Set of* 2 *sheets* 5·50 6·00

(Des W. Wright. Litho Questa)

1987 (18 May). *Milestones of Transportation. Horiz designs as T* **226** *of Antigua. Multicoloured. P* 14.

873 10 c. Saunders Roe "SR-N1" (first hovercraft), 1959 .. .. 10 10
874 15 c. Bugatti "Royale" (largest car), 1931 .. 10 10
875 30 c. Aleksei Leonov and "Voskhod II" (first spacewalk), 1965 .. .. 15 15
876 50 c. C.S.S. *Hunley* (first submarine to sink enemy ship), 1864 .. .. 25 30
877 60 c. Rolls Royce "Flying Bedstead" (first VTOL aircraft), 1954 .. .. .. 25 30
878 70 c. *Jenny Lind* (first mass produced locomotive class), 1847 .. .. 30 35
879 90 c. Duryea "Buggvaut" (first U.S. petrol-driven car), 1893 .. .. 40 45
880 $1.50, Steam locomotive, Metropolitan Railway, London (first underground line), 1863 .. .. 70 75
881 $2 S.S. *Great Britain* (first transatlantic crossing by screw-steamship), 1843 .. 90 95
882 $3 "Budweiser Rocket" (fastest car), 1979 1·40 1·50
873/82 .. .. *Set of* 10 4·00 4·50

(Des Susan Barrasi. Litho Format)

1987 (15 June). *"Capex '87" International Stamp Exhibition, Toronto. Game Fishes. Multicoloured designs as T* **323** *of Grenada, but horiz. P* 15.

883 6 c. Yellow Chub 10 10
884 30 c. Kingfish 15 15
885 50 c. Mako Shark 25 30
886 60 c. Dolphinfish 25 30
887 90 c. Bonito 40 45
888 $1.10, Cobia 50 55
889 $3 Great Tarpon .. .. 1·40 1·50
890 $4 Swordfish .. .. 1·75 1·90
883/90 .. .. *Set of* 8 4·25 4·50
MS891 100×70 mm. (a) $5 Jewfish. (b) $5 Amberjack .. .. .. *Set of* 2 *sheets* 5·50 6·00

(Litho Questa)

1987 (5 Aug). *Centenary of Statue of Liberty* (1986) (2nd issue). *Multicoloured designs as T* **227** *of Antigua. P* 14.

892 10 c. Cleaning face of Statue 10 10
893 15 c. Commemorative lapel badges 15 15
894 25 c. Band playing and Statue 20 20
895 30 c. Band on parade and Statue 20 20
896 45 c. Face of Statue 30 30
897 50 c. Cleaning head of Statue (*horiz*) .. 35 35
898 60 c. Models of Statue (*horiz*) 40 40
899 70 c. Small boat flotilla (*horiz*) 45 45
900 $1 Unveiling ceremony 60 60
901 $1.10, Statue and Manhattan skyline .. 65 65
902 $2 Parade of warships .. .. .. 1·10 1·10
903 $3 Making commemorative flags .. .. 1·60 1·60
892/903 .. .. *Set of* 12 5·50 5·50

(Litho Questa)

1987 (9 Sept). *Great Scientific Discoveries. Horiz designs as T* **325** *of Grenada. Multicoloured. P* 14.

904 60 c. Newton medal 35 30
905 $1 Louis Daguerre (inventor of daguerreotype) 60 50
906 $2 Antoine Lavoisier and apparatus .. 1·25 1·25
907 $3 Rudolf Diesel and diesel engine .. 2·00 2·00
904/7 .. .. *Set of* 4 3·75 3·50
MS908 105×75 mm. $5 Halley's comet .. .. 3·00 3·25

No. 907 is inscribed "JAMES WATT" in error.

(Litho Questa)

1987 (1 Nov). *Bicentenary of U.S. Constitution. Multicoloured designs as T* **232** *of Antigua. P* 14.

909 10 c. Washington addressing delegates, Constitutional Convention 10 15
910 50 c. Flag and State Seal, Georgia 35 35
911 60 c. Capitol, Washington (*vert*) 35 35
912 $4 Thomas Jefferson (statesman) (*vert*) .. 2·00 2·25
909/12 .. .. *Set of* 4 2·50 2·75
MS913 105×75 mm. $5 Alexander Hamilton (New York delegate) (*vert*) .. .. .. 2·50 3·00

Nos. 909/12 were each issued in sheetlets of five stamps and one stamp-size label, which appears in the centre of the bottom row.

(Des Walt Disney Co. Litho Questa)

1987 (16 Nov). *"Hafnia '87" International Stamp Exhibition, Copenhagen. Designs as T* **328** *of Grenada, but horiz, illustrating Hans Christian Andersen's fairy tales. Multicoloured. P* 14×13½.

914 25 c. Donald and Daisy Duck in "The Swineherd" 15 15
915 30 c. Mickey Mouse, Donald and Daisy Duck in "What the Good Man Does is Always Right" 15 15
916 50 c. Mickey and Minnie Mouse in "Little Tuk" 25 30
917 60 c. Minnie Mouse and Ferdie in "The World's Fairest Rose" 25 30
918 70 c. Mickey Mouse in "The Garden of Paradise" 30 35
919 $1.50, Goofy and Mickey Mouse in "The Naughty Boy" 70 75
920 $3 Goofy in "What the Moon Saw" .. 1·40 1·50
921 $4 Alice as "Thumbelina" .. .. .. 1·75 1·90
914/21 .. .. *Set of* 8 4·50 4·75
MS922 Two sheets, each 127×101 mm. (a) $5 Daisy Duck in "Hans Clodhopper". (b) $5 Aunt Matilda and Mickey Mouse in "Elder-Tree Mother" .. .. .. *Set of* 2 *sheets* 5·50 6·00

91 "The Virgin and Child with Saints Martin and Agnes"

92 Scout signalling with Semaphore Flags

(Litho Questa)

1987 (15 Dec). *Christmas. Religious Paintings by El Greco. T* **91** *and similar vert designs. Multicoloured. P* 14.

923 10 c. Type **91** 10 10
924 50 c. "St. Agnes" (detail from "The Virgin and Child with Saints Martin and Agnes") 35 30
925 60 c. "The Annunciation" 35 30
926 $4 "The Holy Family with St. Anne" .. 2·00 2·50
923/6 .. .. *Set of* 4 2·50 3·00
MS927 75×101 mm. $5 "The Adoration of the Shepherds" .. .. 3·00 3·25

(Des and litho Questa)

1988 (15 Feb). *Royal Ruby Wedding. Vert designs as T* **234** *of Antigua. Multicoloured. P* 14.

928 20 c. deep brown, black and light green .. 10 15
929 30 c. deep brown and black 15 15
930 $2 multicoloured 90 95
931 $3 multicoloured .. .. 1·40 1·50
928/31 .. .. *Set of* 4 2·25 2·50
MS932 76×100 mm. $5 multicoloured .. .. 2·50 2·75

Designs:—20 c. Queen Elizabeth II with Princess Anne, *c.* 1957; 30 c. Wedding photograph, 1947; $2 Queen with Prince Charles and Princess Anne, *c.* 1955; $3 Queen Elizabeth (from photo by Tim Graham), 1980; $5 Princess Elizabeth in wedding dress, 1947.

(Des Walt Disney Company. Litho Questa)

1988 (13 Apr). *Olympic Games, Seoul. Multicoloured designs as T* **331** *of Grenada, showing Walt Disney cartoon characters as Olympic competitors. P* 14×13½.

933 1 c. Minnie Mouse as rhythmic gymnast (*horiz*) 10 10
934 2 c. Pete and Goofy as pankration wrestlers (*horiz*) 10 10
935 3 c. Huey and Dewey as synchronized swimmers (*horiz*) 10 10
936 4 c. Huey, Dewey and Louey in hoplite race (*horiz*) 10 10
937 5 c. Clarabelle and Daisy Duck playing baseball (*horiz*) 10 10
938 10 c. Goofy and Donald Duck in horse race (*horiz*) 10 10
939 $6 Donald Duck and Uncle Scrooge McDuck windsurfing (*horiz*) .. .. 2·75 3·00
940 $7 Mickey Mouse in chariot race (*horiz*) .. 3·25 3·50
933/40 .. .. *Set of* 8 5·75 6·25
MS941 Two sheets, each 127×101 mm. (a) $5 Mickey Mouse throwing discus in pentathlon. (b) $5 Donald Duck playing tennis. P 13½×14 *Set of* 2 *sheets* 4·50 4·75

(Des J. Martin. Litho Questa)

1988 (3 May). *World Scout Jamboree, Australia. T* **92** *and similar multicoloured designs. P* 14.

942 50 c. Type **92** 25 30
943 70 c. Canoeing 30 35
944 $1 Cooking over campfire (*horiz*) 45 50
945 $3 Scouts around campfire (*horiz*) .. 1·40 1·50
942/5 .. .. *Set of* 4 2·10 2·40
MS946 110×77 mm. $5 Erecting tent (*horiz*) .. 2·25 2·40

(Des Mary Walters. Litho Questa)

1988 (31 May). *Birds. Designs as T* **334** *of Grenada, but horiz. Multicoloured. P* 14.

947 20 c. Yellow-crowned Night Heron 20 15
948 25 c. Brown Pelican 20 15
949 45 c. Audubon's Shearwater 30 25
950 60 c. Red-footed Booby 40 30
951 70 c. Bridled Tern 45 35
952 90 c. Red-billed Tropic Bird 60 45
953 $3 Blue-winged Teal .. .. .. 1·60 1·75
954 $4 Sora Rail .. .. 2·00 2·25
947/54 .. .. *Set of* 8 5·25 5·00
MS955 Two sheets, each 105×75 mm. (a) $5 Purple-throated Carib. (b) $5 Little Blue Heron *Set of* 2 *sheets* 4·50 5·50

(Litho Questa)

1988 (15 June). 500*th Birth Anniv of Titian (artist). Vert designs as T* **238** *of Antigua. Multicoloured. P* 13½×14.

956 15 c. "Man with Blue Eyes" 10 10
957 30 c. "The Three Ages of Man" (detail) .. 15 15
958 60 c. "Don Diego Mendoza" 25 30
959 75 c. "Emperor Charles V seated" 35 40
960 $1 "A Young Man in a Fur" 45 50
961 $2 "Tobias and the Angel" 90 95
962 $3 "Pietro Bembo" .. .. 1·40 1·50
963 $4 "Pier Luigi Farnese" .. .. .. 1·75 1·90
956/63 .. .. *Set of* 8 4·75 5·25
MS964 110×95 mm. (a) $5 "Sacred and Profane Love" (detail). (b) $5 "Venus and Adonis" (detail) *Set of* 2 *sheets* 5·00 5·50

(Des W. Hanson. Litho Questa)

1988 (1 July). *Airships. Multicoloured designs as T* **336** *of Grenada. P* 14.
965 10 c. *Hindenberg* over Sugarloaf Mountain, Rio de Janeiro, 1937 (*horiz*) 10 10
966 20 c. *Hindenberg* over New York, 1937 (*horiz*) 10 10
967 30 c. U.S. Navy airships on Atlantic escort duty, 1944 (*horiz*) 15 15
968 40 c. *Hindenberg* approaching Lakehurst, 1937 .. .. 20 25
969 60 c. *Graf Zeppelin* and *Hindenberg* over Germany, 1936 .. .. .. 25 30
970 70 c. *Hindenberg* and *Los Angeles* moored at Lakehurst, 1936 (*horiz*) 30 35
971 $1 *Graf Zeppelin II* over Dover, 1939 .. 45 50
972 $2 *Deutschland* on scheduled passenger flight, 1912 (*horiz*) 80 85
973 $3 *Graf Zeppelin* over Dome of the Rock, Jerusalem, 1931 (*horiz*) .. .. 1·25 1·40
974 $4 *Hindenberg* over Olympic stadium, Berlin, 1936 (*horiz*) .. .. 1·60 1·75
965/74 .. .. *Set of* 10 4·50 5·25
MS975 Two sheets (a) 76×95 mm. $5 *Graf Zeppelin*, 1933. (b) 95×76 mm. $5 *Graf Zeppelin*, 1931 (*horiz*) .. .. .. *Set of* 2 *sheets* 4·25 4·50

93 Bambi and his Mother

(Des Walt Disney Co. Litho Questa)

1988 (25 July). *Disney Animal Cartoon Films. T* **93** *and similar designs. P* 14×13½.
976/1029 30 c.×54 multicoloured .. *Set of* 54 5·75 7·25
MS1030 Six sheets, each 127×102 mm. $5×6 multicoloured. P 14×13½ (*horiz*) or 13½×14 (*vert*) .. .. .. *Set of* 6 *sheets* 11·50 12·00
Nos. 976/1029 (issued as six sheetlets each of nine different designs) and No. **MS**1030 depict scenes from *Bambi*, *Dumbo* ($5 vert), *Lady and The Tramp* ($5 vert), *The Aristocats*, *The Fox and the Hound* and *101 Dalmatians*.

(Des Walt Disney Co. Litho Questa)

1988 (1 Aug). *"Sydpex '88" National Stamp Exhibition, Sydney and 60th Birthday of Mickey Mouse. Horiz designs as T* **337** *of Grenada. Multicoloured. P* 14×13½.
1031 1 c. Mickey Mouse conducting at Sydney Opera House 10 10
1032 2 c. Mickey Mouse and Donald Duck at Ayers Rock 10 10
1033 3 c. Goofy and Mickey Mouse on sheep station 10 10
1034 4 c. Goofy and Mickey Mouse at Lone Pine Koala Sanctuary 10 10
1035 5 c. Mickey Mouse, Donald Duck and Goofy playing Australian football .. 10 10
1036 10 c. Mickey Mouse and Goofy camel racing 10 10
1037 $5 Donald Duck and his nephews bowling .. .. 2·40 2·40
1038 $6 Mickey Mouse with America's Cup trophy and *Australia II* (yacht) .. 2·75 2·75
1031/8 .. .. *Set of* 8 5·00 5·00
MS1039 Two sheets, each 127×102 mm. (a) $5 Goofy diving on Great Barrier Reef. (b) $5 Donald Duck, Mickey and Minnie Mouse at beach barbecue .. .. .. *Set of* 2 *sheets* 4·25 4·50

(Des W. Wright. Litho Questa)

1988 (30 Sept). *Flowering Trees and Shrubs. Multicoloured designs as T* **339** *of Grenada. P* 14.
1040 10 c. Potato Tree (*vert*) 15 15
1041 20 c. Wild Cotton 15 15
1042 30 c. Shower of Gold (*vert*) 20 15
1043 60 c. Napoleon's Button (*vert*) 35 30
1044 90 c. Geiger Tree 60 45
1045 $1 Fern Tree 70 50
1046 $2 French Cashew .. .. .. 1·25 1·25
1047 $4 Amherstia (*vert*) .. .. .. 2·00 2·25
1040/7 .. .. *Set of* 8 5·00 4·75
MS1048 Two sheets, each 117×88 mm. (a) $5 African Tulip Tree (*vert*). (b) $5 Swamp Immortelle .. .. .. *Set of* 2 *sheets* 4·25 4·50

(Des W. Wright. Litho B.D.T.)

1988 (7 Oct). *Cars. Vert designs as T* **335** *of Grenada. Multicoloured. P* 13.
1049 $2 Doble "Series E", 1925 .. .. 80 85
a. Sheetlet. Nos. 1049/58 .. .. 8·00
1050 $2 Alvis "12/50", 1926 .. .. .. 80 85
1051 $2 Sunbeam 3-litre, 1927 .. .. 80 85
1052 $2 Franklin "Airman", 1928 .. .. 80 85
1053 $2 Delage "D8S", 1929 .. .. .. 80 85
1054 $2 Mors, 1897 .. .. 80 85
1055 $2 Peerless "Green Dragon", 1904 .. 80 85
1056 $2 Pope-Hartford, 1909 .. .. .. 80 85
1057 $2 Daniels "Submarine Speedster", 1920 80 85
1058 $2 McFarlan 9.3 litre, 1922 .. .. 80 85
1059 $2 Frazer Nash "Lemans" replica, 1949 80 85
a. Sheetlet. Nos. 1059/68 .. .. 8·00
1060 $2 Pegaso "Z102", 1953 .. .. .. 80 85
1061 $2 Siata "Spyder V-8", 1953 .. .. 80 85
1062 $2 Kurtis-Offenhauser, 1953 .. .. 80 85
1063 $2 Kaiser-Darrin, 1954 .. .. .. 80 85
1064 $2 Tracta, 1930 .. .. 80 85
1065 $2 Maybach "Zeppelin", 1932 .. .. 80 85
1066 $2 Railton "Light Sports", 1934 .. .. 80 85
1067 $2 Hotchkiss, 1936 .. .. .. 80 85
1068 $2 Mercedes-Benz "W163", 1939 .. 80 85
1069 $2 Aston Martin "Vantage V8", 1982 .. 80 85
a. Sheetlet. Nos. 1069/78 .. .. 8·00
1070 $2 Porsche "956", 1982 .. .. .. 80 85
1071 $2 Lotus "Esprit Turbo", 1983 .. .. 80 85
1072 $2 McLaren "MP4/2", 1984 .. .. 80 85
1073 $2 Mercedes-Benz "190E 2.3-16", 1985 .. 80 85
1074 $2 Ferrari "250 GT Lusso", 1963 .. 80 85
1075 $2 Porsche "904", 1964 .. .. .. 80 85
1076 $2 Volvo "P1800", 1967 .. .. .. 80 85
1077 $2 McLaren-Chevrolet "M8D", 1970 .. 80 85
1078 $2 Jaguar "XJ6", 1981 .. .. .. 80 85
1049/78 .. .. *Set of* 30 22·00 23·00
Nos. 1049/58, 1059/68 and 1069/78 were each printed together, *se-tenant*, in sheetlets of 10.

(Des Walt Disney Co. Litho Questa)

1988 (1 Dec). *"Mickey's Christmas Parade". Multicoloured designs as T* **246** *of Antigua showing Walt Disney cartoon characters. P* 13½×14.
1079 $1 Dumbo 45 50
a. Sheetlet. Nos. 1079/86 .. .. 3·25
1080 $1 Goofy as Father Christmas 45 50
1081 $1 Minnie Mouse waving from window .. 45 50
1082 $1 Clarabelle, Mordie and Ferdie watching parade 45 50
1083 $1 Donald Duck's nephews 45 50
1084 $1 Donald Duck as drummer 45 50
1085 $1 Toy soldiers 45 50
1086 $1 Mickey Mouse on wooden horse .. 45 50
1079/86 .. .. *Set of* 8 3·25 3·50
MS1087 Two sheets, each 127 × 102 mm. (a) $7 Peter Pan and Captain Hook on float (*horiz*). (b) $7 Mickey Mouse as Father Christmas and Donald Duck in carnival train (*horiz*). P 14 × 13½ .. .. .. *Set of* 2 *sheets* 6·00 6·25

94 Middleweight Boxing (Gold, Henry Maske, East Germany)

95 Launch of "Apollo 11"

(Des L. Fried. Litho B.D.T.)

1989 (13 Apr). *Olympic Medal Winners, Seoul* (1988). *T* **94** *and similar horiz designs. Multicoloured. P* 14.
1088 15 c. Type **94** 10 10
1089 50 c. Freestyle wrestling (130 kg) (Bronze, Andreas Schroeder, East Germany) .. 25 30
1090 60 c. Women's team gymnastics (Bronze, East Germany) 30 35
1091 75 c. Platform diving (Gold, Greg Louganis, U.S.A.) 35 40
1092 $1 Freestyle wrestling (52 kg) (Gold, Mitsuru Sato, Japan) 45 50
1093 $2 Men's freestyle 4×200 metres relay swimming (Bronze, West Germany) .. 95 1·00
1094 $3 Men's 5000 metres (Silver, Dieter Baumann, West Germany) .. .. 1·50 1·60
1095 $4 Women's heptathlon (Gold, Jackie Joyner-Kersee, U.S.A.) .. .. 1·90 2·00
1088/95 .. .. *Set of* 8 5·25 5·75
MS1096 Two sheets, each 70×100 mm. (a) $6 Weightlifting (67.5 kg) (Gold, Joachim Kunz, East Germany). (b) $6 Team Three-Day Event (Gold, West Germany) .. .. *Set of* 2 *sheets* 5·50 5·75

(Litho Questa)

1989 (15 May). *Japanese Art. Paintings by Hiroshige. Horiz designs as T* **250** *of Antigua. Multicoloured. P* 14×13½.
1097 15 c. "Crossing the Oi at Shimada by Ferry" 10 10
1098 20 c. "Daimyo and Entourage at Arai" .. 10 10
1099 45 c. "Cargo Portage through Goyu" .. 20 25
1100 75 c. "Snowfall at Fujigawa" 35 40
1101 $1 "Horses for the Emperor at Chirifu" .. 45 50
1102 $2 "Rainfall at Tsuchiyama" .. .. 95 1·00
1103 $3 "An Inn at Ishibe" .. .. .. 1·50 1·60
1104 $4 "On the Shore of Lake Biwa at Otsu" 1·90 2·00
1097/104 .. .. *Set of* 8 5·00 5·25
MS1105 Two sheets, each 102×78 mm. (a) $5 "Fishing Village of Yokkaichi on the Mie". (b) $5 "Pilgrimage to Atsuta Shrine at Miya" *Set of* 2 *sheets* 4·75 5·00
Nos. 1097/104 were each printed in sheetlets of 10 containing two horizontal strips of 5 stamps separated by printed labels commemorating Emperor Hirohito.

(Des D. Bruckner. Litho B.D.T.)

1989 (12 June). *World Cup Football Championship, Italy* (1990). *Multicoloured designs as T* **252** *of Antigua. P* 14.
1106 15 c. World Cup trophy 10 10
1107 20 c. Flags of Argentina (winners 1986) and International Federation of Football Associations (F.I.F.A.) (*horiz*) 10 10
1108 45 c. Franz Beckenbauer (West Germany) with World Cup, 1974 .. .. 20 25
1109 75 c. Flags of Italy (winners 1982) and F.I.F.A. (*horiz*) 35 40
1110 $1 Péle (Brazil) with Jules Rimet trophy 45 50
1111 $2 Flags of West Germany (winners 1974) and F.I.F.A. (*horiz*) .. .. 95 1·00
1112 $3 Flags of Brazil (winners 1970) and F.I.F.A. (*horiz*) .. .. .. 1·50 1·60
1113 $4 Jules Rimet trophy and Brazil players 1·90 2·00
1106/13 .. .. *Set of* 8 5·00 5·25
MS1114 (a) 100×81 mm. $6 Goalkeeper (*horiz*). (b) 66×95 mm. $6 Péle with Jules Rimet trophy *Set of* 2 *sheets* 5·50 5·75

(Des W. Wright. Litho B.D.T.)

1989 (28 June). *North American Railway Locomotives. Vert designs as T* **342** *of Grenada. Multicoloured. P* 13.
1115 $2 Morris & Essex Railroad *Dover*, 1841 95 1·00
a. Sheetlet. Nos. 1115/24 .. .. 9·50
1116 $2 Baltimore & Ohio Railroad *Memmon* No. 57, 1848 .. .. .. 95 1·00
1117 $2 Camden & Amboy Railroad *John Stevens*, 1849 .. .. .. 95 1·00
1118 $2 Lawrence Machine Shop *Lawrence*, 1853 .. .. 95 1·00
1119 $2 South Carolina Railroad *James S. Corry*, 1859 .. .. .. 95 1·00
1120 $2 Mine Hill & Schuylkill Haven Railroad Flexible Beam No. 3 type, 1860 .. .. 95 1·00
1121 $2 Delaware, Lackawanna & Western Railroad *Montrose*, 1861 .. .. 95 1·00
1122 $2 Central Pacific Railroad *Pequop* No. 68, 1868 .. .. .. 95 1·00
1123 $2 Boston & Providence Railroad *Daniel Nason*, 1863 .. .. .. 95 1·00
1124 $2 Morris & Essex Railroad *Joe Scranton*, 1870 .. .. .. 95 1·00
1125 $2 Central Railroad of New Jersey No. 124, 1871 .. .. .. 95 1·00
a. Sheetlet. Nos. 1125/34 .. .. 9·50
1126 $2 Baldwin tramway steam locomotive, 1876 .. .. 95 1·00
1127 $2 Lackawanna & Bloomsburg Railroad *Luzerne*, 1878 .. .. .. 95 1·00
1128 $2 Central Mexicano Railroad No. 150, 1892 .. .. 95 1·00
1129 $2 Denver, South Park & Pacific Railroad *Breckenridge* No. 15, 1879 .. 95 1·00
1130 $4 Miles Planting & Manufacturing Company plantation locomotive *Daisy*, 1894 .. .. .. 95 1·00
1131 $2 Central of Georgia Railroad Baldwin "854" No. 1136, 1895 .. .. 95 1·00
1132 $2 Savannah, Florida & Western Railroad No. 111, 1900 .. .. 95 1·00
1133 $2 Douglas, Gilmore & Company contractors locomotive No. 3, 1902 .. 95 1·00
1134 $2 Lehigh Valley Coal Company compressed air locomotive No. 900, 1903 .. .. 95 1·00
1135 $2 Morgan's Louisiana & Texas Railroad McKeen diesel locomotive, 1908 .. 95 1·00
a. Sheetlet. Nos. 1135/44 .. .. 9·50
1136 $2 Clear Lake Lumber Company Type "B Climax" locomotive No. 6, 1910 .. 95 1·00
1137 $2 Blue Jay Lumber Company Heisler locomotive No. 10, 1912 .. .. 95 1·00
1138 $2 Stewartstown Railroad gasoline locomotive No. 6, 1920s .. .. 95 1·00
1139 $2 Bangor & Aroostook Railroad Class "G" No. 186, 1921 .. .. 95 1·00
1140 $2 Hammond Lumber Company No. 6, 1923 .. .. 95 1·00
1141 $2 Central Railroad of New Jersey diesel locomotive No. 1000, 1925 .. 95 1·00
1142 $2 Atchison, Topeka & Santa Fe Railroad "Super Chief" diesel express, 1935 .. 95 1·00
1143 $2 Norfolk & Western Railroad Class "Y-6", 1948 .. .. .. 95 1·00
1144 $2 Boston & Maine Railroad Budd diesel railcar, 1949 .. .. .. 95 1·00
1115/44 .. .. *Set of* 30 25·00 27·00
Nos. 1115/24, 1125/34 and 1135/44 were each printed together, *se-tenant*, in sheetlets of 10.

(Des Walt Disney Co. Litho Questa)

1989 (7 July). *"Philexfrance 89" International Stamp Exhibition, Paris. Multicoloured designs as T* **251** *of Antigua showing Walt Disney cartoon characters in Paris. P* 14×13½ (*horiz*) *or* 13½×14 (*vert*).
1145 1 c. Mickey Mouse and Donald Duck at Ecole Militaire inflating balloon .. 10 10
1146 2 c. Mickey and Minnie Mouse on river boat passing Conciergerie 10 10
1147 3 c. Mickey Mouse at Hotel de Ville (*vert*) 10 10
1148 4 c. Mickey Mouse at Genie of the Bastille monument (*vert*) 10 10
1149 5 c. Mickey and Minnie Mouse arriving at Opera House 10 10
1150 10 c. Mickey and Minnie Mouse on tandem in Luxembourg Gardens 10 10
1151 $5 Mickey Mouse in aeroplane over L'Arch de la Defense (*vert*) .. 2·40 2·50
1152 $6 Mickey Mouse at Place Vendome (*vert*) .. .. 2·75 3·00
1145/52 .. .. *Set of* 8 4·75 5·00
MS1153 Two sheets, each 127×102 mm. (a) $6 Mickey and Minnie Mouse on scooter in Place de la Concorde. (b) $6 Donald Duck, Mickey and Minnie Mouse in balloon over Versailles. P 14×13½ .. .. .. *Set of* 2 *sheets* 5·75 6·00

(Des L. Birmingham. Litho Questa)

1989 (20 July). *20th Anniv of First Manned Landing on Moon. T* **95** *and similar multicoloured designs. P* 14.
1154 25 c. Type **95** 10 15
1155 50 c. Splashdown (*horiz*) 25 30
1156 60 c. Modules in space 30 35
1157 75 c. Aldrin setting up experiment (*horiz*) 35 40
1158 $1 "Apollo 11" leaving Earth orbit (*horiz*) 45 50

1159 $2 Moving "Apollo 11" to launch site .. 95 1·00
1160 $3 Lunar module *Eagle* leaving Moon (*horiz*) .. .. 1·50 1·60
1161 $4 *Eagle* landing on Moon .. .. 1·90 2·00
1154/61 .. .. *Set of* 8 5·25 5·75
MS1162 (a) 71×100 mm. $5 Armstrong stepping onto Moon. (b) 101×72 mm. $5 Armstrong's footprint on Moon .. .. *Set of* 2 *sheets* 4·75 5·00

(Des J. Cooter. Litho B.D.T.)

1989 (17 Aug). *Fungi. Vert designs as T* **348** *of Grenada. Multicoloured. P* 14.
1163 6 c. *Collybia aurea* 10 10
1164 10 c. *Podaxis pistillaris* 10 10
1165 20 c. *Hygrocybe firma* 10 10
1166 30 c. *Agaricus rufoaurantiacus* 15 20
1167 75 c. *Leptonia howellii* 35 40
1168 $2 *Marasmiellus purpureus* .. .. 95 1·00
1169 $3 *Marasmius trinitatis* .. .. 1·50 1·60
1170 $4 *Hygrocybe martinicensis* .. .. 1·90 2·00
1163/70 .. .. *Set of* 8 4·50 4·75
MS1171 Two sheets, each 56×71 mm. (a) $6 *Agaricus purpurellus*. (b) $6 *Lentinus crinitus* *Set of* 2 *sheets* 5·50 5·75

(Des Deborah Dudley Max. Litho B.D.T.)

1989 (2 Oct). *Butterflies. Horiz designs as T* **350** *of Grenada. Multicoloured. P* 14.
1172 25 c. Androgeus Swallowtail 10 15
1173 35 c. Cloudless Sulphur 15 20
1174 45 c. Cracker 20 25
1175 50 c. Painted Lady 25 30
1176 75 c. Great Southern White 35 40
1177 90 c. Little Sulphur 40 45
1178 $2 Migrant Sulphur .. .. .. 95 1·00
1179 $3 Mimic .. .. 1·50 1·75
1172/9 .. .. *Set of* 8 3·50 4·00
MS1180 Two sheets, each 87×115 mm. (a) $6 Red Anartia. (b) $6 Giant Hairstreak *Set of* 2 *sheets* 5·50 5·75

96 Ethel Barrymore

97 Buddy Holly

(Des J. Genzo. Litho B.D.T.)

1989 (9 Oct). *425th Birth Anniv of Shakespeare. Shakespearean Actors. T* **96** *and similar horiz designs. Multicoloured. P* 14.
1181 15 c. Type **96** 10 10
1182 $1.10, Richard Burton 50 55
1183 $2 John Barrymore .. .. .. 95 1·00
1184 $3 Paul Robeson .. .. .. 1·50 1·60
1181/4 .. .. *Set of* 4 2·75 3·00
MS1185 103×77 mm. $6 Bando Tamasaburo and Nakamura Kanzaburo .. .. .. 2·75 3·00

(Des J. Genzo. Litho B.D.T.)

1989 (9 Oct). *Musicians. T* **97** *and similar vert designs. Multicoloured. P* 14.
1186 10 c. Type **97** 10 10
1187 25 c. Jimmy Hendrix 10 15
1188 75 c. Mighty Sparrow 35 40
1189 $4 Katsutoji Kineya .. .. .. 1·90 2·00
1186/9 .. .. *Set of* 4 2·10 2·40
MS1190 103×77 mm. $6 Kurt Weill .. .. 2·75 3·00

(Des D. Miller. Litho Questa)

1989 (16 Oct). *500th Anniv of Discovery of America by Columbus (1992) (2nd issue). Pre-Columbian Arawak Society. Vert designs as T* **247** *of Antigua. Multicoloured. P* 14.
1191 15 c. Arawaks canoeing 10 10
1192 75 c. Family and campfire 35 40
1193 90 c. Using stone tools 40 45
1194 $3 Eating and drinking .. .. 1·50 1·60
1191/4 .. .. *Set of* 4 2·10 2·25
MS1195 84×87 mm. $6 Making fire .. .. 2·75 3·00

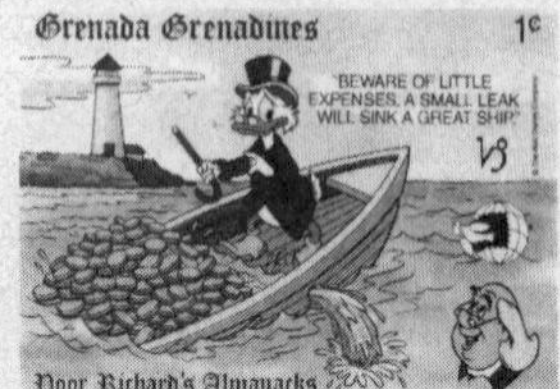

98 Uncle Scrooge McDuck with Gold Coins in Sinking Boat

(Des Walt Disney Co. Litho Questa)

1989 (17 Nov). *"World Stamp Expo '89" International Stamp Exhibition, Washington. T* **98** *and similar multicoloured designs of Walt Disney cartoon characters illustrating proverbs from* Poor Richard's Almanack. *P* 14×13½.
1196 1 c. Type **98** 10 10
1197 2 c. Robin Hood shooting apple off Friar Tuck 10 10
1198 3 c. Winnie the Pooh with honey .. 10 10
1199 4 c. Goofy, Minnie Mouse and Donald Duck exercising 10 10
1200 5 c. Pinnochio holding Jimminy Cricket 10 10
1201 6 c. Huey and Dewey putting up wallpaper 10 10
1202 8 c. Mickey Mouse asleep in storm .. 10 10
1203 10 c. Mickey Mouse as Benjamin Franklin selling *Pennsylvania Gazette* .. 10 10
1204 $5 Mickey Mouse with chicken, recipe book and egg .. .. 2·40 2·50
1205 $6 Mickey Mouse missing carriage .. 2·75 3·00
1196/1205 .. .. *Set of* 10 5·00 5·25
MS1206 Two sheets, each 127×102 mm. (a) $6 Mickey Mouse bowing. P 14×13½. (b) $6 Mickey Mouse delivering basket of food (*vert*). P 13½×14 .. .. .. *Set of* 2 *sheets* 5·50 5·75

OFFICIAL STAMPS

1982 (June). *Various stamps optd with Type* O 1 *of Grenada.*

(*a*) *Nos.* 400/12 *and* 414
O 1 5 c. Yellowtail Snapper 10 10
O 2 6 c. Mutton Snapper 10 10
O 3 10 c. Cocoa Damselfish 10 10
O 4 12 c. Royal Gramma 10 10
O 5 15 c. Cherubfish 10 10
O 6 20 c. Blackbar Soldierfish 10 10
O 7 25 c. Comb Grouper 10 10
O 8 30 c. Longsnout Butterflyfish 15 15
O 9 40 c. Pudding Wife 15 20
O10 50 c. Midnight Parrotfish 20 25
O11 90 c. Redspotted Hawkfish 40 35
O12 $1 Hogfish 40 40
O13 $3 Beau Gregory .. .. .. 1·25 1·25
O14 $10 Barred Hamlet .. .. .. 4·25 3·75

(*b*) *Nos.* 444/6 *and* 448/9
O15 30 c. Prince Charles and Lady Diana Spencer 1·50 1·75
O16 40 c. Prince Charles and Lady Diana Spencer 1·00 1·25
O17 40 c. Type **50** .. .. 2·00 2·25
O18 $2 Type **50** .. .. 2·50 2·75
O19 $4 Prince Charles as parachutist .. .. 6·50 7·00

The Royal Wedding $4 from sheetlets, perforated 14½ × 14 and with changed background colour, also exists with this overprint (*Price £8.50 mint, £9 used*).

(*c*) *Nos.* 473/6
O20 **54** 20 c. multicoloured 10 10
O21 – 40 c. multicoloured 15 20
O22 – $1 multicoloured 35 40
O23 – $2 multicoloured 70 75
O1/23 .. .. *Set of* 23 19·00 20·00

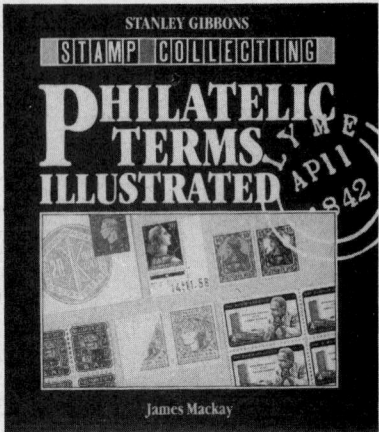

Griqualand West

Griqualand West was situated to the North of Cape Colony, bounded on the north by what became British Bechuanaland and on the east by the Orange Free State.

The area was settled in the early nineteenth century by the Griqua tribal group, although many members of the tribe, including the paramount chief, migrated to Griqualand East (between Basutoland and the east coast of South Africa) in 1861–63. There was little European involvement in Griqualand West before 1866, but in that year the diamond fields along the Vaal River were discovered. Sovereignty was subsequently claimed by the Griqua Chief, the Orange Free State and the South African Republic (Transvaal). In 1871 the British authorities arbitrated in favour of the Griqua Chief who promptly ceded his territory to Great Britain. Griqualand West became a separate Crown Colony in 1873.

During the initial stages of the prospecting boom mail was passed via the Orange Free State, but a post office connected to the Cape Colony postal system was opened at Klip Drift (subsequently Barkly) in late 1870. Further offices at De Beer's New Rush (subsequently Kimberley), Douglas and Du Toit's Pan (subsequently Beaconsfield) were open by September 1873.

Cape of Good Hope stamps were in use from October 1871, but those originating in Griqualand West can only be identified after the introduction of Barred Oval Diamond Numeral cancellations in 1873. Numbers known to have been issued in the territory are:

1 De Beers N.R. (New Rush) (subsequently Kimberley)
3 Junction R. & M. (Riet and Modder Rivers)
4 Barkly
6 or 9 Du Toit's Pan (subsequently Beaconsfield)
8 Langford (transferred to Douglas)
10 Thornhill

PRICES FOR STAMPS ON COVER

The stamps of Griqualand West are worth from ×10 the price quoted for used stamps, when on cover from the territory.

Stamps of the Cape of Good Hope, Crown CC, perf 14, overprinted.

1874 (Sept). *T* **4** *with manuscript surcharge.*

1		1d. in red on 4d. blue	£600	£900

G. W.

1877 (Mar). *T* **6** *optd.* "G.W." *as above. (a) In black.*

2		1d. carmine-red	£350	60·00
		a. Overprint double	†	£750
		(b) In red		
3		4d. blue	£250	50·00

G (1) G (2) G (3) G (4) G (5) G (6)
G (7) G (8) G (9) G (10) G (11)
G (12) G (13) G (14)

1877 (Apr)–**78**. *T* **4** *(4d. (Nos. 17/23), 6d. and 1s.) and T* **6** *(others) optd with large capital letter. (a) First printing. Optd in black on 1d. or red (others). Seven principal varieties of opt (T* **1, 2, 3, 4, 5, 6,** *and* **8**).

4	1	½d. grey-black	9·00	9·00
5	2	½d. grey-black	13·00	15·00
6	3	½d. grey-black	6·00	7·50
7	4	½d. grey-black	13·00	13·00
8	5	½d. grey-black	15·00	14·00
9	6	½d. grey-black	9·00	8·00
10	8	½d. grey-black		
11	1	1d. carmine-red	5·50	5·50
12	2	1d. carmine-red	16·00	14·00
13	3	1d. carmine-red	7·50	7·50
14	4	1d. carmine-red	11·00	11·00
15	5	1d. carmine-red	30·00	16·00
16	6	1d. carmine-red	7·50	7·00
17	1	4d. blue (T **4**)	60·00	9·00
18	2	4d. blue (T **4**)	£200	50·00
19	3	4d. blue (T **4**)	£160	20·00
20	4	4d. blue (T **4**)	£180	80·00
21	5	4d. blue (T **4**)	£180	90·00
22	6	4d. blue (T **4**)	90·00	22·00
23	8	4d. blue (T **4**)		
24	1	4d. blue (T **6**)	55·00	7·50
25	2	4d. blue (T **6**)	—	45·00
26	3	4d. blue (T **6**)	70·00	13·00
27	4	4d. blue (T **6**)	70·00	13·00
28	5	4d. blue (T **6**)	£130	50·00
29	6	4d. blue (T **6**)	48·00	12·00
30	8	4d. blue (T **6**)	£900	
31	1	6d. dull violet	35·00	14·00
32	2	6d. dull violet	90·00	32·00
33	3	6d. dull violet	50·00	11·00
34	4	6d. dull violet	95·00	45·00
35	5	6d. dull violet	90·00	45·00
36	6	6d. dull violet	50·00	11·00
37	8	6d. dull violet		
38	1	1s. green	48·00	10·00
		a. Opt inverted	—	£200
39	2	1s. green	85·00	23·00
		a. Opt inverted		
40	3	1s. green	24·00	7·50
41	4	1s. green	85·00	11·00
		a. Opt inverted		
42	5	1s. green	85·00	14·00
43	6	1s. green	45·00	10·00
		a. Opt inverted		
44	8	1s. green		
45	1	5s. orange	£225	9·00
46	2	5s. orange	—	25·00
47	3	5s. orange	£250	9·00
48	4	5s. orange	—	18·00
49	5	5s. orange	£400	15·00
50	6	5s. orange	£250	9·00
51	8	5s. orange	£1300	

The setting of the above was in two panes of 60. Sub-types of Types **1** and **2** are found. The 1d., Type **8**, of this setting can only be distinguished when *se-tenant* with Type **3**.

(b) Second printing, in black for all values. Nine principal varieties of opt (T **6** *to* **14**) (1878)

52	7	1d. carmine-red	7·00	7·00
53	8	1d. carmine-red	7·50	7·50
54	9	1d. carmine-red	13·00	22·00
55	10	1d. carmine-red	55·00	
56	11	1d. carmine-red	13·00	13·00
57	12	1d. carmine-red	55·00	55·00
58	13	1d. carmine-red	50·00	45·00
59	14	1d. carmine-red	£350	£300
60	6	4d. blue (T **6**)	£140	40·00
61	7	4d. blue (T **6**)	45·00	11·00
62	8	4d. blue (T **6**)	£140	28·00
63	9	4d. blue (T **6**)	55·00	13·00
64	10	4d. blue (T **6**)	£375	£100
65	11	4d. blue (T **6**)	£140	28·00
66	12	4d. blue (T **6**)	£190	50·00
67	13	4d. blue (T **6**)	£225	£130
68	14	4d. blue (T **6**)	—	£100
69	6	6d. dull violet	£225	55·00
70	7	6d. dull violet	90·00	45·00
		a. Opt double		
71	8	6d. dull violet	£225	50·00
72	9	6d. dull violet	£140	55·00
		a. Opt double	£425	
73	10	6d. dull violet	£225	
74	11	6d. dull violet	£650	£200
75	12	6d. dull violet	£225	90·00
76	13	6d. dull violet	£350	£140
77	14	6d. dull violet	£900	£250

The 1d., T **6**, of this printing can only be distinguished from the same variety of the first printing when it is *se-tenant* with another type.

The type without horizontal or vertical serifs, previously illustrated as T 10, is a broken "G" of the type now shown under that number.

Minor varieties may be found of T **7** and **12**.

Red overprints on the 4d., 1s. and 5s. Type **7** and 1s. and 5s. Type **8** exist but there is no evidence as to their status.

G (15) G (16) G (17)

1878 (July)–**79**. *T* **4** *(4d. (Nos. 86/7), 6d. and 1s.) and T* **6** *(others) optd with small capital letter. (a) First printing, in red or in black.*

		(i) Red overprint		
78	15	½d. grey-black	4·25	5·50
		a. Opt inverted	5·50	5·50
		b. Opt double	30·00	
		c. Opt double, both inverted	50·00	
79	16	½d. grey-black	5·50	5·50
		a. Opt inverted	5·50	7·00
		b. Opt double	50·00	50·00
		c. Opt double, both inverted		
80	15	4d. blue (T **6**)	£180	70·00
		a. Opt inverted	£600	50·00
81	16	4d. blue (T **6**)	—	55·00
		a. Opt inverted	£180	55·00
		(ii) Black overprint		
82	15	½d. grey-black	£130	70·00
		a. Opt inverted	£130	
		b. Black opt normal with additional red opt T **15** inverted	£250	
		c. Ditto, but red opt is T **16**	70·00	
83	16	½d. grey-black	23·00	23·00
		a. Opt inverted	23·00	23·00
		b. Black opt normal, with additional red opt T **15** inverted	90·00	
84	15	1d. carmine-red	5·50	4·00
		a. Opt inverted	5·50	5·50
		b. Ditto, with additional red opt T **15** inverted	19·00	20·00
		c. Ditto, with additional red opt T **16** inverted		
		d. Opt double	£120	30·00
		e. Opt double, both inverted	£120	45·00
85	16	1d. carmine-red	5·50	5·50
		a. Opt inverted	45·00	19·00
		b. Ditto with additional red opt T **16** inverted	45·00	45·00
		c. Opt double	—	55·00
		d. Opt double, both inverted	—	70·00
86	15	4d. blue (T **4**)	—	85·00
87	16	4d. blue (T **4**)	—	90·00
88	15	4d. blue (T **6**)	45·00	13·00
		a. Opt inverted	£130	55·00
		b. Opt double	—	£130
		c. Opt double, both inverted	—	£180
89	16	4d. blue (T **6**)	90·00	7·00
		a. Opt inverted	£140	19·00
		b. Opt double	—	£140
		c. Opt double, both inverted	—	£180
90	15	6d. dull violet	50·00	15·00
91	16	6d. dull violet	—	15·00
		(b) Second printing, in black only (1879)		
92	17	½d. grey-black	5·50	4·50
		a. Opt double	£200	£200
93		1d. carmine-red	5·50	3·25
		a. Opt inverted	—	70·00
		b. Opt double	—	£110
		c. Opt treble	—	£150
94	17	4d. blue (T **6**)	5·50	3·25
		b. Opt double	—	90·00
95		6d. mauve	50·00	5·50
		a. Opt inverted	—	22·00
		b. Opt double	£350	£130
96		1s. green	30·00	3·25
		a. Opt double	£170	75·00
97		5s. orange	£200	5·50
		a. Opt double	£275	55·00
		b. Opt treble	—	£225

Besides the type shown above, which is the normal, there are in this printing three or four minor varieties differing in the shape and size of the body of the letter. In this setting are also found at least two varieties very like the upright "antique" of the first printing in small capitals.

Beware of forged overprints.

Griqualand West was merged with Cape Colony in 1880 and the overprinted stamps became obsolete in October, 1880. The remaining stock was returned from Kimberley to Cape Town and redistributed among various post offices in Cape Colony, where they were used as ordinary Cape stamps.

Guyana

(*formerly* British Guiana)

GUYANA
INDEPENDENCE
1966
(73)

1966 (26 May)–**67**. *Various stamps as Nos. 331/45 of British Guiana, optd with T* **73**, *by De La Rue. (i) Wmk Mult Script CA.*

379	2 c. myrtle-green	10	10
380	3 c. brown-olive and red-brown	2·75	2·50
381	4 c. violet	10	10
383	6 c. yellow-green	10	10
384	8 c. ultramarine	10	10
385	12 c. black and reddish brown	10	10
392	$5 ultramarine and black	27·00	30·00
379/92	*Set of* 7	27·00	30·00

(ii) *Wmk w* **12**. A. *Upright*. B. *Sideways*

		A		B	
393	1 c.	10	10	10	10
	a. Opt omitted	80·00	—	†	
395	3 c.	10	10	†	
396	4 c.	10	10	10	10
397	5 c.	10	10	†	
398	6 c.	10	10	†	
399	8 c.	10	15	10	10
400	12 c.	10	10	10	10
401	24 c.	60	10	60	20
402	36 c.	25	25	20	20
403	48 c.	5·00	6·00	25	25
404	72 c.	30	50	55	70
405	$1	35	35	90	70
406	$2	50	75	75	1·00
407	$5	1·00	1·75	1·75	2·75
393A/407A	*Set of* 14	7·50	9·00		
393B/407B	*Set of* 11			4·50	5·50

Dates of issue: Of the above, the 1 c., 4 c., 6 c. (W w **12** upright) and the 12 c., 36 c., 72 c., $2 and $5 (W w **12** sideways) were issued on 28.2.67; the 8 c. upright wmk and the $1 sideways wmk, on 14.3.67; the rest on 26.5.66.

No. 393a is listed here as an error as there is no evidence of the 1 c. basic stamp having been issued as a printing with Block CA watermark.

See also Nos. 420/40.

74 Flag and Map

75 Arms of Guyana

(Des V. Whiteley. Photo Harrison)

1966 (26 May). *Independence. P* 14½.

408	**74**	5 c. multicoloured	10	10
409		15 c. multicoloured	10	10
410	**75**	25 c. multicoloured	10	10
411		$1 multicoloured	20	25
408/11		*Set of* 4	25	25

76 Bank Building

(Des R. Granger Barrett. Photo Enschedé)

1966 (11 Oct). *Opening of Bank of Guyana. P* 13½ × 14.

412	**76**	5 c. multicoloured	10	10
413		25 c. multicoloured	10	10

CANCELLED REMAINDERS.* In 1969 remainders of some issues were put on the market cancelled-to-order in such a way as to be indistinguishable from genuine postally used copies for all practical purposes. Our used quotations which are indicated by an asterisk are the same for cancelled-to-order or postally used copies.

77 British Guiana One Cent Stamp of 1856

(Des V. Whiteley. Litho D.L.R.)

1967 (23 Feb). *World's Rarest Stamp Commemoration. P* 12½.

414	**77**	5 c. black, magenta, silver & light ochre	10	10*
415		25 c. black, magenta, gold and light green	10	10*

78 Château Margot

GUYANA
INDEPENDENCE
1966

(82)

(Des R. Granger Barrett. Photo Harrison)

1967 (26 May). *First Anniv of Independence. T* **78** *and similar multicoloured designs. P* 14 (6 *c.*), 14½ × 14 (15 *c.*) *or* 14 × 14½ (*others*).

416	6 c. Type **78**	10	10*
417	15 c. Independence Arch	10	10*
418	25 c. Fort Island (*horiz*)	10	10*
419	$1 National Assembly (*horiz*)	20	15
416/19	*Set of* 4	20	15

1967–68. *Stamps as Nos.* 331/45 *of British Guiana optd with T* **82** *locally.*

(i) *Wmk Mult Script CA*

420	1 c. black (3.10.67)	10	10
	a. Opt inverted	28·00	
	b. Date misplaced 5 mm	8·00	
	c. Date misplaced 2 mm	8·00	
421	2 c. myrtle-green (3.10.67)	10	10
	a. "1966" for "GUYANA"	17·00	
	b. Date misplaced 5 mm	8·00	
	c. Date misplaced 2 mm	8·00	
422	3 c. brown-olive and red-brown (3.10.67)	25	10
	a. "1966" for "GUYANA"	12·00	
	b. Vert pair, one without opt	£300	
	c. Date misplaced 2 mm	8·00	
423	4 c. violet (10.67)	10	10
	a. Deep violet	15	15
	b. Opt inverted	35·00	
424	6 c. yellow-green (11.67)	10	10
	a. "1966" for "GUYANA"	18·00	
	b. Opt inverted	32·00	
	c. Opt double		
425	8 c. ultramarine (12.67)	10	10
426	12 c. black and brown (12.67)	10	10
426*a*	24 c. black and orange (date?)	£140	65·00
427	$2 reddish mauve (12.67)	80	1·40
428	$5 ultramarine and black (12.67)	1·50	2·25

(ii) *Wmk w* 12 (*upright*)

429	1 c. black (2.68)	10	10
430	2 c. myrtle-green (2.68)	10	10
431	3 c. brown-olive and red-brown (3.10.67)	20	10
	a. "1966" for "GUYANA"	75·00	
	b. Opt inverted	18·00	
432	4 c. violet (2.68)	10	10
433	5 c. scarlet and black (3.10.67)	2·00	80
	a. Deep scarlet and black	25	25
	c. Date misplaced 2 mm	8·00	
434	6 c. yellow-green (2.68)	10	10
	a. Opt double, one diagonal	45·00	
435	24 c. black and bright orange (11.12.67)	25	10
	a. Opt double, one diagonal (horiz pair)	£180	
436	36 c. rose-carmine and black (12.67)	15	10
437	48 c. bright ultramarine and Venetian red (12.67)	30	40
	a. Opt inverted	35·00	
438	72 c. carmine and emerald (12.67)	50	40
439	$1 pink, yellow, green and black (12.67)	1·50	50
440	$2 reddish mauve (12.67)	1·75	2·00
420/40 (*excl.* 426*a*)	*Set of* 21	7·00	7·00

The "1966" errors occurred on R. 7/10 and were later corrected. Nos. 425/8 and 436/40 were issued in mid-December, but some were cancelled-to-order with a November date in error.

On Nos. 420b and 421b the "1" of "1968" is below the second "D" of "INDEPENDENCE" (R. 6/3). On Nos. 420c, 421c, 423c and 433c it is below the second "E" (R. 6/1).

No. 433*a* is from a printing made specially for this overprint.

83 "Millie" (Blue and Yellow Macaw)

84 Wicket-keeping

(Des V. Whiteley. Photo Harrison)

1967–68. *Christmas. P* 14½ × 14. (*a*) *First issue* (6 Nov 1967).

441	**83**	5 c. yellow, new blue, blk & bronze-grn	10	10*
442		25 c. yellow, new blue, black and violet	15	10*

(*b*) *Second issue. Colours changed* (22 Jan 1968)

443	**83**	5 c. yellow, new blue, black and red	10	10*
444		25 c. yellow, new blue, blk & apple-grn	15	10*

(Des V. Whiteley. Photo Harrison)

1968 (8 Jan). *M.C.C.'s West Indies Tour. T* **84** *and similar vert designs. P* 14.

445	5 c. Type **84**	10	10*
	a. Strip of 3. Nos. 445/7	70	
446	6 c. Batting	10	10*
447	25 c. Bowling	30	10*
445/7	*Set of* 3	70	15*

Nos. 445/7 were issued in small sheets of 9 containing three *se-tenant* strips.

87 Sunfish

102 "Christ of St John of the Cross" (Salvador Dali)

(Des R. Granger Barrett. Photo Harrison)

1968 (4 Mar). *Multicoloured designs as T* **87**, *showing fish* (1 *to* 6 *c.*), *birds* (10 *to* 40 *c.*) *or animals* (*others*). *No wmk. P* 14 × 14½.

448	1 c. Type **87**	10	10
449	2 c. Pirai	10	10
450	3 c. Lukunani	10	10
451	5 c. Hassar	10	10
452	6 c. Patua	10	10
453	10 c. Spix's Guan (*vert*)	30	10
454	15 c. Harpy Eagle (*vert*)	40	10
455	20 c. Hoatzin (*vert*)	40	10
456	25 c. Guianan Cock of the Rock (*vert*)	45	10
457	40 c. Great Kiskadee (*vert*)	45	20
458	50 c. Brazilian Agouti ("Accouri")	70	40
459	60 c. White-lipped Peccary	80	10
460	$1 Paca ("Labba")	1·00	10
461	$2 Nine-banded Armadillo	1·50	2·00
462	$5 Ocelot	2·00	3·00
448/62	*Set of* 15	7·00	5·50

For Nos. 448/62 with W **106** see Nos. 485/99.

(Des and photo Harrison)

1968 (25 Mar). *Easter. P* 14.

463	**102**	5 c. multicoloured	10	10*
464		25 c. multicoloured	10	10*

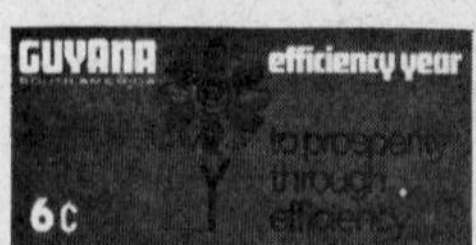

103 "Efficiency Year"

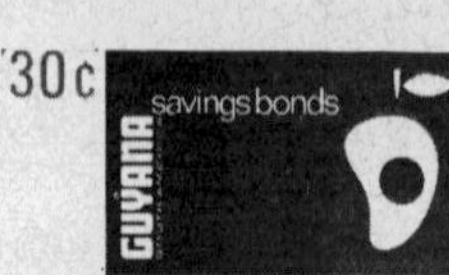

104 "Savings Bonds"

(Des W. Starzmann. Litho B.W.)

1968 (22 July). *"Savings Bonds and Efficiency". P* 14.

465	**103**	6 c. multicoloured	10	10*
466		25 c. multicoloured	10	10*
467	**104**	30 c. multicoloured	10	10*
468		40 c. multicoloured	10	10*
465/8		*Set of* 4	20	15*

105 Open Book, Star and Crescent

(Des R. Gates. Photo D.L.R.)

1968 (9 Oct). 1400*th Anniv of the Holy Quran. P* 14.

469	**105**	6 c. black, gold and flesh	10	10*
470		25 c. black, gold and lilac	10	10*
471		30 c. black, gold and light apple-green	10	10*
472		40 c. black, gold and cobalt	10	10*
469/72		*Set of* 4	20	15*

106 Lotus Blossoms

107 Broadcasting Greetings

(Des L. Pritchard; adapted G. Vasarhelyi. Litho D.L.R.)

1968 (11 Nov). *Christmas. T* **107** *and similar vert design. W* **106**. *P* 14.

473	6 c. brown, blue and green	10	10*
474	25 c. brown, reddish violet and green	10	10*
475	30 c. blue-green and turquoise-green	10	10*
476	40 c. red and turquoise-green	10	10*
473/6	*Set of* 4	20	15*

Designs:—25 c. Type **107**; 30, 40 c. Map showing radio link, Guyana–Trinidad.

109 Festival Ceremony

(Des J. Cooter. Litho P.B.)

1969 (26 Feb). *Hindu Festival of Phagwah. T* **109** *and similar horiz design. Multicoloured. W* **106** (*sideways*). *P* 13½.

477	6 c. Type **109**	10	10
478	25 c. Ladies spraying scent	10	10
479	30 c. Type **109**	10	10
480	40 c. As 25 c.	10	10
477/80	*Set of* 4	20	20

111 "Sacrament of the Last Supper" (Dali)

112 Map showing "CARIFTA" Countries

(Photo D.L.R.)

1969 (10 Mar). *Easter. W* **106** (*sideways*). *P* 13½ × 13.

481	**111**	6 c. multicoloured	10	10
482		25 c. multicoloured	10	10
483		30 c. multicoloured	10	10
484		40 c. multicoloured	10	10
481/4		*Set of* 4	20	15

1969–71. *As Nos.* 448/62, *but Wmk* **106** (*sideways on* 1 *to* 6 *c. and* 50 *c. to* $5). *Chalk-surfaced paper.*

485	1 c. Type **87**	10	10
486	2 c. Pirai	10	10
487	3 c. Lukunani	10	10
488	5 c. Hassar	10	10
489	6 c. Patua	10	10
490	10 c. Spix's Guan	15	10
	a. Glazed paper (21.12.71)	40	50
491	15 c. Harpy Eagle	20	10
	a. Glazed paper (21.12.71)	60	90
492	20 c. Hoatzin	20	15
493	25 c. Guianan Cock of the Rock	20	10
	a. Glazed paper (21.12.71)	75	1·00
494	40 c. Great Kiskadee	60	40
495	50 c. Brazilian Agouti ("Accouri")	35	15
496	60 c. White-lipped Peccary	35	55
497	$1 Paca ("Labba")	70	95
	a. Glazed paper (21.12.71)	2·50	3·75

498 $2 Nine-banded Armadillo .. .. 1·00 2·75
499 $5 Ocelot .. .. 1·50 5·50
485/99 .. .. .. *Set of* 15 5·00 9·50

These were put on sale by the Crown Agents on 25 March 1969 but although supplies were sent to Guyana in time they were not released there until needed as ample supplies remained of the stamps without watermark. It is understood that the 3 c. and 5 c. were put on sale in early May 1969 followed by the 25 c. but there are no records of when the remainder were released.

(Des J. Cooter. Litho P.B.)

1969 (30 Apr). *First Anniv of CARIFTA (Caribbean Free Trade Area). T* **112** *and similar design. W* **106** *(sideways on 25 c.). P* 13½.
500 6 c. rose-red, ultramarine and turquoise-blue 10 10
501 25 c. lemon, brown and rose-red 10 10
Design: *Horiz*—25 c. "Strength in Unity".

114 Building *Independence* (first aluminium ship) **116** Scouts raising Flag

(Des R. Gates. Litho B.W.)

1969 (30 Apr). *50th Anniv of International Labour Organization. T* **114** *and similar design. W* **106** *(sideways on* 40 c.). *P* 12 × 11 (30 c.) *or* 11 × 12 (40 c.).
502 30 c. turquoise-blue, black and silver 10 10
503 40 c. multicoloured 15 10
Design: *Horiz*—40 c. Bauxite processing plant.

(Des Jennifer Toombs. Litho B.W.)

1969 (13 Aug). *Third Caribbean Scout Jamboree and Diamond Jubilee of Scouting in Guyana. T* **116** *and similar horiz design. Multicoloured. W* **106** *(sideways). P* 13.
504 6 c. Type **116** 10 10
505 8 c. Camp-fire cooking 10 10
506 25 c. Type **116** 10 10
507 30 c. As 8 c. 10 10
508 50 c. Type **116** 15 15
504/8 .. .. *Set of* 5 30 30

118 Gandhi and Spinning-wheel **119** "Mother Sally Dance Troupe"

(Des G. Drummond. Litho Format)

1969 (1 Oct). *Birth Centenary of Mahatma Gandhi. W* **106** *(sideways). P* 14½.
509 **118** 6 c. black, brown and yellowish olive .. 15 10
510 15 c. black, brown and lilac 20 20

(Des V. Whiteley (5, 25 c.), J.W. (others). Litho B.W. (5, 25 c.), D.L.R. (others))

1969 (17 Nov). *Christmas. T* **119** *and similar vert design. Multicoloured. No wmk* (5, 25 c.) *or W* **106**. *P* 13½ (5, 25 c.) *or* 13 × 13½ *(others).*
511 5 c. Type **119** 10 10
a. Opt omitted .. .. 28·00
b. Opt double .. .. 25·00
512 6 c. City Hall, Georgetown (*horiz*) 10 10
a. Opt omitted .. .. 28·00
b. Opt inverted .. .. 30·00
513 25 c. Type **119** 10 10
a. Opt omitted .. .. 28·00
514 60 c. As 6 c. 20 25
511/14 .. .. *Set of* 4 25 30

Nos. 511/14 are previously unissued stamps optd as in T **119** by Guyana Lithographic Co, Ltd.

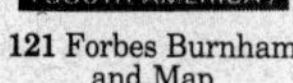

121 Forbes Burnham and Map **125** "The Descent from the Cross"

(Des L. Curtis. Litho D.L.R.)

1970 (23 Feb). *Republic Day. T* **121** *and similar designs. W* **106** *(sideways on* 15 *and* 25 c.). *P* 14.
515 5 c. sepia, ochre and pale blue 10 10
516 6 c. multicoloured 10 10
517 15 c. multicoloured 10 10
518 25 c. multicoloured 10 10
515/18 .. .. *Set of* 4 10 10

Designs: *Vert*—6 c. "Rural Self-help". *Horiz*—15 c. University of Guyana; 25 c. Guyana House.

(Des J. Cooter. Litho Questa)

1970 (24 Mar). *Easter. Paintings by Rubens. T* **125** *and similar vert design. Multicoloured. W* **106** *(inverted). P* 14 × 14½.
519 5 c. Type **125** 10 10
520 6 c. "Christ on the Cross" 10 10
521 15 c. Type **125** 10 10
522 25 c. As 6 c. 10 10
519/22 .. .. *Set of* 4 10 10

127 "Peace" and U.N. Emblem **128** "Mother and Child" (Philip Moore)

(Des and litho Harrison)

1970 (26 Oct). *25th Anniv of United Nations. T* **127** *and similar horiz design. Multicoloured. W* **106** *(inverted). P* 14.
523 5 c. Type **127** 10 10
524 6 c. U.N. Emblem, Gold-panning and Drilling 10 10
525 15 c. Type **127** 10 10
526 25 c. As 6 c. 10 10
523/6 .. .. *Set of* 4 10 10

(Des Harrison. Litho J.W.)

1970 (8 Dec). *Christmas. W* **106**. *P* 13½.
527 **128** 5 c. multicoloured 10 10
528 6 c. multicoloured 10 10
529 15 c. multicoloured 10 10
530 25 c. multicoloured 10 10
527/30 .. .. *Set of* 4 15 15

129 National Co-operative Bank **130** Racial Equality Symbol

(Des E. Samuels. Litho J.W.)

1971 (23 Feb). *Republic Day. W* **106** *(sideways). P* 14.
531 **129** 6 c. multicoloured 10 10
532 15 c. multicoloured 10 10
533 25 c. multicoloured 10 10
531/3 .. .. *Set of* 3 10 10

(Des E. Samuels. Litho Harrison)

1971 (22 Mar). *Racial Equality Year. W* **106** *(sideways). P* 14.
534 **130** 5 c. multicoloured 10 10
535 6 c. multicoloured 10 10
536 15 c. multicoloured 10 10
537 25 c. multicoloured 10 10
534/7 .. .. *Set of* 4 10 15

131 Young Volunteer felling Tree (from painting by J. Criswick). **132** Yellow Allamanda

(Des and litho Harrison)

1971 (19 July). *First Anniv of Self-help Road Project. W* **106**. *P* 14.
538 **131** 5 c. multicoloured 10 10
539 20 c. multicoloured 10 10
540 25 c. multicoloured 10 10
541 50 c. multicoloured 20 30
538/41 .. .. *Set of* 4 45 50

Two types of 25 c.:

I Flowers facing up. Value in centre.

II Flowers facing down. Value to right. Colours changed.

(Des V. Whiteley (1 to 40 c.), PAD Studio (others). Litho D.L.R. (1 to 6 c.), J.W. (10 c. to 40 c.), Format (50 c. to $5))

1971 (17 Sept)–**76**. *Flowering Plants. Vert designs as T* **132**. *Multicoloured. W* **106** *(sideways on* 1 c. *to* 40 c.). *P* 13 × 13½ (1 *to* 6 c.) *or* 13½ (10 c. *to* $5).
542 1 c. Pitcher Plant of Mt Roraima (15.1.72) 10 10
543 2 c. Type **132** 10 10
544 3 c. Hanging Heliconia 10 10
545 5 c. Annatto tree 10 10
546 6 c. Cannon-ball tree 10 10
547 10 c. Cattleya (18.9.72) 55 10
a. Perf 13 (28.1.76) 60 10
548 15 c. Christmas Orchid (18.9.72) 60 10
a. Perf 13 (3.9.76) 50 10
549 20 c. *Paphinia cristata* (18.9.72) 45 20
a. Perf 13 (28.1.76) 75 20
550 25 c. Marabunta (I) (18.9.72) .. .. 90 2·00
550*a* 25 c. Marabunta (II) (*wmk upright*) (20.8.73) 30 20
ab. Perf 13 (*wmk sideways*) (3.9.76) .. 45 10
551 40 c. Tiger Beard (18.9.72) 60 10
552 50 c. *Guzmania lingulata* (3.9.73) .. 40 30
553 60 c. Soldier's Cap (3.9.73) 40 30
554 $1 *Chelonanthus uliginoides* (3.9.73) .. 40 45
555 $2 *Norantea guianensis* (3.9.73) .. 60 1·50
556 $5 *Odontadenia grandiflora* (3.9.73) .. 1·00 1·50
542/56 .. .. *Set of* 16 6·00 6·00

The watermark is often indistinct, particularly on the early printings.

133 Child praying at Bedside **134** Obverse and Reverse of Guyana $1 Coin

(Des V. Bassoo (T **133**), M. Austin (25, 50 c.). Litho J.W.)

1971 (29 Nov). *Christmas. T* **133** *and similar vert design. Multicoloured. W* **106** *(sideways on* 5 c. *and* 20 c.). *P* 13½.
557 5 c. Type **133** 10 10
558 20 c. Type **133** 10 10
559 25 c. Carnival Masquerader 10 10
560 50 c. As 25 c. 20 30
557/60 .. .. *Set of* 4 35 50

(Des G. Drummond. Litho Questa)

1972 (23 Feb). *Republic Day. T* **134** *and similar vert design. W* **106** *(sideways). P* 14½ × 14.
561 **134** 5 c. silver, black and orange-red .. 10 10
562 – 20 c. silver, black and magenta 15 10
563 **134** 25 c. silver, black and ultramarine .. 15 15
564 – 50 c. silver, black and yellow-green .. 25 30
561/4 .. .. *Set of* 4 55 55

Design:—20, 50 c. Reverse and obverse of Guyana $1 coin.

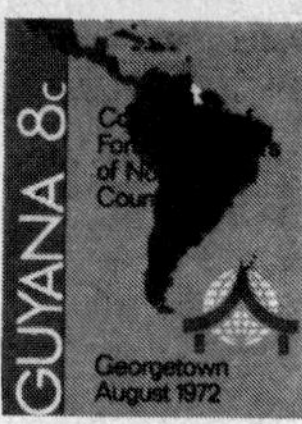

135 Hands and Irrigation Canal **136** Map and Emblem

(Des J. Criswick. Litho J.W.)

1972 (3 Apr). *Youman Nabi (Mohammed's Birthday). W* **106**. *P* 14.
565 **135** 5 c. multicoloured 10 10
566 25 c. multicoloured 10 10
567 30 c. multicoloured 10 10
568 60 c. multicoloured 20 20
565/8 .. .. *Set of* 4 35 35

(Des J. Criswick. Litho J.W.)

1972 (20 July). *Conference of Foreign Ministers of Non-aligned Countries. W* **106**. *P* 13½.
569 **136** 8 c. multicoloured 10 10
570 25 c. multicoloured 10 10
571 40 c. multicoloured 15 15
572 50 c. multicoloured 20 20
569/72 .. .. *Set of* 4 40 40

ALTERED CATALOGUE NUMBERS

Any Catalogue numbers altered from the last edition are shown as a list in the introductory pages.

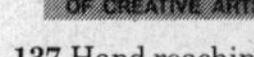

137 Hand reaching for Sun

138 Joseph, Mary, and the Infant Jesus

(Des G. Bowen. Litho J.W.)

1972 (25 Aug). *First Caribbean Festival of Arts.* *W* **106** *(inverted on* 40, 50 *c.). P* 13½.
573 **137** 8 c. multicoloured 10 10
574 25 c. multicoloured 10 10
575 40 c. multicoloured 15 20
576 50 c. multicoloured 20 25
573/6 .. .. *Set of* 4 45 55

(Des Megan Anderson. Litho B.W.)

1972 (18 Oct). *Christmas. W* **106**. *P* 13 × 13½.
577 **138** 8 c. multicoloured 10 10
578 25 c. multicoloured 10 10
579 40 c. multicoloured 15 25
580 50 c. multicoloured 15 25
577/80 .. .. *Set of* 4 40 60

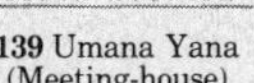

139 Umana Yana (Meeting-house)

140 Pomegranate

(Des J. Cooter. Litho Questa)

1973 (23 Feb). *Republic Day. T* **139** *and similar vert design. Multicoloured. W* **106** *(inverted on* 8 *c.). P* 14.
581 8 c. Type **139** 10 10
582 25 c. Bethel Chapel 10 10
583 40 c. As 25 c. 15 20
584 50 c. Type **139** 20 20
581/4 .. .. *Set of* 4 45 50

(Des E. Samuels. Litho Format)

1973 (19 Apr). *Easter. T* **140** *and similar multicoloured design. W* **106** *(sideways on* 25 *and* 40 *c.). P* 14½ (8, 50 *c.) or* 13½ *(others).*
585 8 c. Type **140** 10 10
586 25 c. Cross and map (34 × 47 *mm*) 10 10
587 40 c. As 25 c. 10 10
588 50 c. Type **140** 15 15
585/8 .. .. *Set of* 4 35 35

141 Stylized Blood Cell

142 Steel-Band Players

(Des S. Greaves. Litho Harrison)

1973 (1 Oct). *25th Anniv of Guyana Red Cross. W* **106**. *P* 14.
589 **141** 8 c. vermilion and black 10 10
590 25 c. vermilion and bright purple 15 15
591 40 c. vermilion and ultramarine 20 35
592 50 c. vermilion and blackish olive 30 50
589/92 .. .. *Set of* 4 60 95

(Des E. Samuels; adapted J. Cooter. Litho Questa)

1973 (20 Nov). *Christmas. T* **142** *and similar vert design. Multicoloured. W* **106**. *P* 14 (8, 25 *c.) or* 13½ *(others).*
593 8 c. Type **142** 10 10
594 25 c. Type **142** 10 10
595 40 c. "Virgin and Child" (stained-glass window) (34 × 47 *mm*) 20 25
596 50 c. As 40 c. 20 25
593/6 .. .. *Set of* 4 50 60

8c

=

143 Symbol of Progress (144)

(Des PAD Studio. Litho Questa)

1974 (23 Feb). *Republic Day. T* **143** *and similar vert design. Multicoloured. W* **106**. *P* 13½.
597 8 c. Type **143** 10 10
598 25 c. Wai-Wai Indian 10 10
599 40 c. Type **143** 15 20
600 50 c. As 25 c. 15 25
597/600 .. .. *Set of* 4 40 55

1974 (18 Mar). *No.* 546 *surch with T* **144**.
601 8 c. on 6 c. Cannon-ball tree 10 10
See also No. 620.

145 Kite with Crucifixion Motif

146 British Guiana 24 c. Stamp of 1874

(Des R. Savory; adapted J. Cooter. Litho Questa)

1974 (8 Apr). *Easter. T* **145** *and similar vert design. W* **106**. *P* 13½.
602 **145** 8 c. multicoloured 10 10
603 – 25 c. black and dull green 10 10
604 – 40 c. black and magenta 10 15
605 **145** 50 c. multicoloured 15 25
602/5 .. .. *Set of* 4 35 50
Design:—Nos. 603/4, "Crucifixion" in pre-Columbian style.

(Des R. Savory. Litho Harrison)

1974 (18 June). *Centenary of Universal Postal Union. T* **146** *and similar horiz design. W* **106** *(sideways on* 8 *and* 40 *c.). P* 13½ × 14 (8, 40 *c.) or* 14 *(others).*
606 **146** 8 c. multicoloured 10 10
607 – 25 c. bright yellow-green, deep slate-violet and black 15 10
608 **146** 40 c. multicoloured 15 20
609 – 50 c. bright yellow-green, reddish chestnut and black 20 25
606/9 .. .. *Set of* 4 50 55
Design (42 × 25 *mm*):—25 c., 50 c. U.P.U. emblem and Guyana postman.

147 Guides with Banner

148 Buck Toyeau

(Des M. Broodhagen; adapted J. Cooter. Litho Questa)

1974 (1 Aug). *Girl Guides' Golden Jubilee. T* **147** *and similar horiz design. Multicoloured. W* **106** *(sideways). P* 14½.
610 8 c. Type **147** 10 10
611 25 c. Guides in camp 20 15
612 40 c. As 25 c. 30 35
613 50 c. Type **147** 30 35
610/13 .. .. *Set of* 4 80 85
MS614 170 × 137 mm. Nos. 610/13 .. .. .. 1·40 1·40

(Des S. Greaves and R. Granger Barrett. Litho Enschedé)

1974 (18 Nov). *Christmas. T* **148** *and similar vert designs. Multicoloured. W* **106**. *P* 13½ × 13.
615 8 c. Type **148** 10 10
616 35 c. Five-fingers and awaras 10 10
617 50 c. Pawpaw and tangerine 15 10
618 $1 Pineapple and sapodilla 30 60
615/18 .. .. *Set of* 4 55 70
MS619 127 × 94 mm. Nos. 615/18 .. .. .. 90 1·40

1975 (20 Jan). *No.* 544 *surch as T* **144**.
620 8 c. on 3 c. Hanging Heliconia 10 10

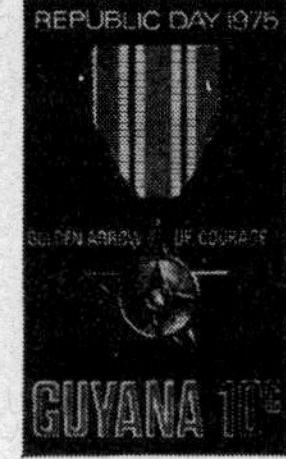

149 Golden Arrow of Courage

150 Old Sluice Gate

(Des L. Curtis. Litho D.L.R.)

1975 (23 Feb). *Republic Day. Guyana Orders and Decorations. T* **149** *and similar vert designs. W* **106**. *P* 13½.
621 10 c. Type **149** 10 10
622 35 c. Cacique's Crown of Honour 10 15
623 50 c. Cacique's Crown of Valour 15 20
624 $1 Order of Excellence 35 60
621/4 .. .. *Set of* 4 60 90

(Des E. Samuels; adapted PAD Studio. Litho Questa)

1975 (2 May). *Silver Jubilee of International Commission on Irrigation and Drainage. T* **150** *and similar horiz design. Multicoloured. W* **106** *(sideways on* 35 *c. and* $1). *P* 14.
625 10 c. Type **150** 10 10
626 35 c. Modern sluice gate 10 15
627 50 c. Type **150** 15 30
628 $1 As 35 c. 35 60
625/8 .. .. *Set of* 4 60 1·00
MS629 162 × 121 mm. Nos. 625/8. Wmk sideways 1·10 1·60

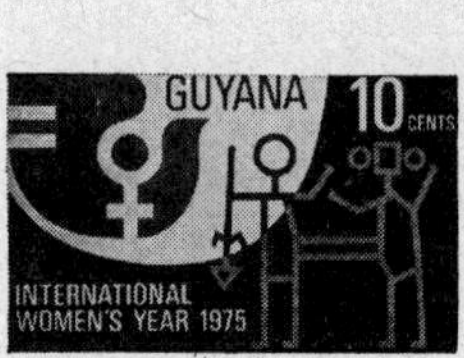

151 I.W.Y. Emblem and Rock Drawing

152 Freedom Monument

(Des C. Henriques; adapted PAD Studio. Litho Questa)

1975 (1 July). *International Women's Year. T* **151** *and similar horiz designs showing different rock drawings. W* **106** *(sideways). P* 14.
630 **151** 10 c. grey-green and yellow 10 10
631 – 35 c. reddish violet and greenish blue .. 20 10
632 – 50 c. royal blue and orange 25 15
633 – $1 brown and bright blue 45 45
630/3 .. .. *Set of* 4 85 65
MS634 178 × 89 mm. Nos. 630/3 .. .. .. 1·40 1·75

(Des PAD Studio. Litho Questa)

1975 (26 Aug). *Namibia Day. T* **152** *and similar vert design. Multicoloured. W* **106**. *P* 14.
635 10 c. Type **152** 10 10
636 35 c. Unveiling of Monument 15 10
637 50 c. Type **152** 25 15
638 $1 As 35 c. 35 35
635/8 .. .. *Set of* 4 70 60

153 G.N.S. Emblem

154 Court Building, 1875 and Forester's Badge

(Des C. Henriques; adapted PAD Studio. Litho Questa)

1975 (1 Oct*). *First Anniv of National Service. W* **106**. *P* 14.
639 **153** 10 c. greenish yellow, light green and light reddish violet 10 10
640 – 35 c. orange, lt green & reddish violet .. 10 10
641 – 50 c. light violet-blue, light green and light yellow-brown 15 15
642 – $1 light mauve, dull green & lt emerald 40 40
639/42 .. .. *Set of* 4 60 60
MS643 196 × 133 mm. Nos. 639/42. W **106** (inverted) .. .. 1·10 1·50
*This is the local date of issue; the Crown Agents released the stamps a day later.
Nos. 640/2 are as T **153** but have different symbols within the circle.

(Des R. Savory; adapted PAD Studio. Litho Questa)

1975 (14 Nov). *Centenary of Guyanese Ancient Order of Foresters. T* **154** *and similar horiz designs. Multicoloured.* W **106** *(sideways). P* 14.
644 10 c. Type **154** 10 10
645 35 c. Rock drawing of hunter and quarry .. 10 10
646 50 c. Crossed axes and bugle-horn 15 10
647 $1 Bow and arrow 40 40
644/7 .. .. *Set of* 4 60 50
MS648 129 × 97 mm. Nos. 644/7 .. .. .. 1·00 1·50

35c

(155)

156 Shoulder Flash

1976 (10 Feb). *No.* 553 *surch with T* **155**.
649 35 c. on 60 c. Soldier's Cap 20 25

(Des C. Henriques; adapted J.W. Litho Questa)

1976 (29 Mar). *50th Anniv of the St. John's Ambulance in Guyana. T* **156** *and similar vert designs.* W **106**. *P* 14.
650 **156** 8 c. silver, black and magenta 10 10
651 – 15 c. silver, black and orange 10 10
652 – 35 c. silver, black and green 20 20
653 – 40 c. silver, black and new blue 25 25
650/3 .. .. *Set of* 4 55 50
Nos. 651/3 are as T **156** but show different shoulder flashes.

157 Triumphal Arch

158 Flame in Archway

(Des C. Henriques. Litho J.W.)

1976 (25 May). *Tenth Anniv of Independence. T* **157** *and similar vert designs. Multicoloured.* W **106**. *P* 13½.
654 8 c. Type **157** 10 10
655 15 c. Stylised Victoria Regia lily 10 10
656 35 c. "Onward to Socialism" 15 15
657 40 c. Worker pointing the way 15 15
654/7 .. .. *Set of* 4 35 35
MS658 120×100 mm. Nos. 654/7. Wmk inverted. P 14½ 50 75

1976 (3 Aug). *West Indian Victory in World Cricket Cup. As Nos.* 559/60 *of Barbados.*
659 15 c. Map of the Caribbean .. .. .. 1·10 1·25
660 15 c. Prudential Cup .. .. 1·10 1·25

(Des G. Vasarhelyi. Litho J.W.)

1976 (21 Oct). *Deepavali Festival. T* **158** *and similar vert designs. Multicoloured.* W **106**. *P* 14.
661 8 c. Type **158** 10 10
662 15 c. Flame in hand 10 10
663 35 c. Flame in bowl 15 20
664 40 c. Goddess Latchmi 15 25
661/4 .. .. *Set of* 4 35 50
MS665 94 × 109 mm. Nos. 661/4 .. .. .. 50 75

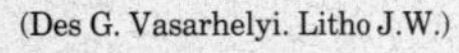

159 Festival Emblem and "Musical Instrument"

160 1 c. and 5 c. Coins

(Des C. Henriques. Litho Questa)

1977 (1 Feb). *Second World Black and African Festival of Arts and Culture, Nigeria.* W **106**. *P* 14.
666 **159** 10 c. dull red, black and gold 10 10
667 35 c. deep violet, black and gold 20 10
668 50 c. ultramarine, black and gold 25 25
669 $1 blue-green, black and gold 60 75
666/9 .. .. *Set of* 4 1·00 1·00
MS670 90 × 157 mm. Nos. 666/9 .. .. .. 1·50 2·25
The above were scheduled for release in 1975, and when finally issued had the original inscription obliterated and a new one applied by overprinting. Examples of Nos. 666/70 are known without overprint.

(Des J.W. Litho Questa)

1977 (26 May). *New Coinage. T* **160** *and similar horiz designs.* W **106**. *P* 14.
671 8 c. multicoloured 10 10
672 15 c. yellow-brown, grey and black 15 10
673 35 c. bright yellow-green, grey and black .. 30 30
674 40 c. carmine-red, grey and black 35 35
675 $1 multicoloured 70 80
676 $2 multicoloured .. .. 1·40 1·60
671/6 .. .. *Set of* 6 2·75 3·00
Designs:—15 c. 10 and 25 c. coins; 35 c. 50 c. and $1 coins; 40 c. $5 and $10 coins; $1 $50 and $100 coins; $2 Reverse of $1 coin.

161 Hand Pump, *circa* 1850

162 Cuffy Monument

(Des J. Porteous Wood. Litho Harrison)

1977 (15 Nov). *National Fire Prevention Week. T* **161** *and similar horiz designs. Multicoloured.* W **106**. *P* 14 × 14½.
677 8 c. Type **161** 10 10
678 15 c. Steam engine, *circa* 1860 .. .. 20 10
679 35 c. Fire engine, *circa* 1930 .. .. 35 30
680 40 c. Fire engine, 1977 .. .. .. 40 35
677/80 .. .. *Set of* 4 95 70

(Des BG Studio. Litho Questa)

1977 (7 Dec). *Cuffy Monument (commemorating 1763 Slave Revolt).* W **106**. *P* 14.
681 **162** 8 c. multicoloured 10 10
682 – 15 c. multicoloured 10 10
683 **162** 35 c. multicoloured 15 20
684 – 40 c. multicoloured 15 30
681/4 .. .. *Set of* 4 35 55
Nos. 682 and 684 show a different view of the monument.

163 American Manatee

(Des BG Studio. Litho Questa)

1978 (15 Feb). *Wildlife Conservation. T* **163** *and similar multicoloured designs.* W **106** *(sideways on* 8 *and* 15 *c.). P* 14.
685 8 c. Type **163** 20 10
686 15 c. Giant sea turtle 30 15
687 35 c. Harpy Eagle (*vert*) 80 75
688 40 c. Iguana (*vert*) 80 75
685/8 .. .. *Set of* 4 1·90 1·50

164 L. F. S. Burnham (Prime Minister) and Parliament Buildings, Georgetown

165 Dr. George Giglioli (scientist and physician)

1978 (27 Apr). *25th Anniv of Prime Minister's Entry into Parliament. T* **164** *and similar horiz designs.* W **106** *(sideways). P* 13½ × 14.
689 8 c. black, violet and bluish grey 10 10
690 15 c. black, light violet-blue and bluish grey .. 10 10
691 35 c. black, red and bluish grey 15 20
692 40 c. black, red-orange and bluish grey .. 15 20
689/92 .. .. *Set of* 4 40 45
MS693 176 × 118 mm. Nos. 689/92 .. .. 55 75
Designs:—15 c. Burnham, graduate and children ("Free Education"); 35 c. Burnham and industrial works (Nationalization of Bauxite industry); 40 c. Burnham and village scene ("The Co-operative Village").

(Des J.W. Litho Harrison)

1978 (4 Sept). *National Science Research Council. T* **165** *and similar multicoloured designs.* W **106** *(sideways on* 10 *and* 50 *c.). P* 13½ × 14 (10, 50 *c.) or* 14 × 13½ *(others).*
694 10 c. Type **165** 10 10
695 30 c. Institute of Applied Science and Technology (*horiz*) 15 15
696 50 c. Emblem of National Science Research Council 25 25
697 60 c. Emblem of Commonwealth Science Council (commemorating the 10th Meeting) (*horiz*) 25 25
694/7 .. .. *Set of* 4 60 60

166 *Prepona pheridamas*

167 *Agrias claudina*

(Des J. Cooter. Litho J.W.)

1978 (1 Oct)–**80**. *Butterflies. Horiz designs as T* **166** (5 *to* 60 *c.) or vert as T* **167** *($1 to $10). Multicoloured.* W **106**. *P* 14 × 13½ (5 *to* 60 *c.) or* 13 *($1 to $10).*
698 5 c. Type **166** 30 10
699 10 c. *Archonias bellona* 30 10
700 15 c. *Eryphanis polyxena* 40 10
701 20 c. *Helicopis cupido* 40 10
702 25 c. *Nessaea batesii* 45 10
702*a* 30 c. *Nymphidium mantus* (25.1.80) 45 25
703 35 c. *Siderone galanthis* 55 10
704 40 c. *Morpho rhetenor* (male) 55 10
705 50 c. *Hamadryas amphinome* 55 10
705*a* 60 c. *Papilio androgeus* (25.1.80) 55 30
706 $1 Type **167** .. .. 1·25 15
707 $2 *Morpho rhetenor* (female) .. .. .. 2·25 35
708 $5 *Morpho deidamia* .. .. 3·50 90
708*a* $10 *Elbella patrobas* (25.1.80) .. .. 4·75 3·50
698/708*a* .. .. *Set of* 14 14·50 5·00

168 Amerindian Stone-chip Grater in Preparation

169 Dish Aerial by Night

(Des L. Curtis. Litho Questa)

1978 (18 Dec). *National/International Heritage Year. T* **168** *and similar vert designs. Multicoloured.* W **106**. *P* 14.
709 10 c. Type **168** 10 10
710 30 c. Cassiri and decorated Amerindian jars .. 15 10
711 50 c. Fort Kyk-over-al 20 15
712 60 c. Fort Island 20 20
709/12 .. .. *Set of* 4 55 45

(Des L. Curtis. Litho Questa)

1979 (7 Feb). *Satellite Earth Station. T* **169** *and similar horiz designs. Multicoloured.* W **106** *(sideways). P* 14 × 14½.
713 10 c. Type **169** 10 10
714 30 c. Dish aerial by day 20 15
715 50 c. Satellite with solar veins 30 15
716 $3 Cylinder satellite .. .. 1·50 90
713/16 .. .. *Set of* 4 1·90 1·10

170 Sir Rowland Hill and British Guiana 1850 12 c. "Cottonreel" Stamp

171 "Me and my Sister"

(Des and litho J.W.)

1979 (11 June). *Death Centenary of Sir Rowland Hill. T* **170** *and similar multicoloured designs.* W **106** *(sideways on* 10 *and* 50 *c.). P* 14.
717 10 c. Type **170** 10 10
718 30 c. British Guiana 1856 1 c. black on magenta stamp (*vert*) 20 15
719 50 c. British Guiana 1898 1 c. stamp 30 25
720 $3 Printing press used for early British Guiana stamps (*vert*) .. .. 1·00 1·50
717/20 .. .. *Set of* 4 1·40 1·75

(Des J.W. Litho Questa)

1979 (20 Aug). *International Year of the Child. Paintings by local children. T* **171** *and similar multicoloured designs.* W **106** *(sideways on* 30, 50 *c. and* $3*). P* 13½.
721 10 c. Type **171** 10 10
722 30 c. "Fun with the Fowls" (*horiz*) 15 15
723 50 c. "Two Boys catching Ducks" (*horiz*) .. 20 20
724 $3 "Mango Season" (*horiz*) .. .. .. 65 1·25
721/4 .. .. *Set of* 4 90 1·50

172 "An 8 Hour Day"

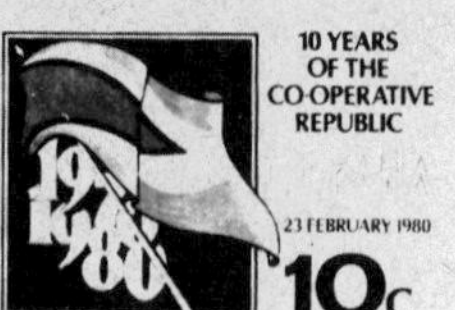

173 Guyana Flag

(Des C. Rodriguez. Litho Walsall)

1979 (27 Sept). *60th Anniv of Guyana Labour Union. T* **172** *and similar multicoloured designs. W* **106** *(sideways on 30 c.). P* 14 × 14½ (30 c.) *or* 14½ × 14 (*others*).

725 10 c. Type **172** 10 10
726 30 c. "Abolition of Night Baking" (*horiz*) .. 10 10
727 50 c. "Introduction of the Workmen's Compensation Ordinance" 15 15
728 $3 H. N. Critchlow (founder) 55 90
725/8 .. .. *Set of* 4 75 1·10

(Des BG Studio. Litho Questa)

1980 (23 Feb). *10th Anniv of Republic. T* **173** *and similar horiz designs. W* **106** (*sideways*). *P* 14.

729 10 c. multicoloured 10 10
730 35 c. black and red-orange 15 10
731 60 c. multicoloured 25 20
732 $3 multicoloured 70 90
729/32 .. .. *Set of* 4 1·00 1·10

Designs:—35 c. View of Demerara River Bridge; 60 c. Kaieteur Falls; $3 "Makanaima the Great Ancestral Spirit of the Amerindians".

174 Snoek

175 Children's Convalescent Home (Community Service)

(Des J.W. Litho Questa)

1980 (6 May). *"London 1980" International Stamp Exhibition. Fishes. T* **174** *and similar horiz designs. Multicoloured. W* **106** (*sideways*). *P* 14½.

733 35 c. Type **174** 20 25
a. Block of 12. Nos. 733/44 .. .. .. 2·10
734 35 c. Haimara 20 25
735 35 c. Electric Eel 20 25
736 35 c. Golden Rivulus 20 25
737 35 c. Pencil Fish 20 25
738 35 c. Four-eyed Fish 20 25
739 35 c. Pirai or Carib Fish 20 25
740 35 c. Smoking Hassar 20 25
741 35 c. Devil Ray 20 25
742 35 c. Flying Patwa 20 25
743 35 c. Arapaima Pirariucii 20 25
744 35 c. Lukanani 20 25
733/44 .. .. *Set of* 12 2·10 2·75

Nos. 733/44 were printed together, *se-tenant*, in a block of 12 within the sheetlet containing one of each design.

(Des local artist; adapted J.W. Litho Walsall)

1980 (23 June). *75th Anniv of Rotary International. T* **175** *and similar multicoloured designs. P* 14.

745 10 c. Type **175** 10 10
746 30 c. Rotary Club of Georgetown and Rotary emblems 10 10
747 50 c. District 404 emblem (*vert*) 20 20
748 $3 Rotary anniversary emblem (*vert*) .. 80 80
745/8 .. .. *Set of* 4 1·00 1·10

176 "C" encircling Globe, Caduceus Emblem and Sea

177 *Virola surinamensis*

(Des L. Curtis. Litho Enschedé)

1980 (23 Sept). *25th Anniv of Commonwealth Caribbean Medical Research Council. T* **176** *and similar horiz designs. Multicoloured. W* **106** (*sideways*). *P* 13.

749 10 c. Type **176** 10 10
750 60 c. Researcher with microscope, Caduceus emblem, stethoscope and beach scene .. 20 20
751 $3 Caduceus emblem, "C" encircling researcher and island silhouettes .. 85 1·00
749/51 .. .. *Set of* 3 1·00 1·10

(Des L. Curtis. Litho Format)

1980 (1 Dec). *Christmas. Trees and Foliage. T* **177** *and similar horiz designs. Multicoloured. W* **106** (*sideways*). *P* 13½.

752 10 c. Type **177** 10 10
753 30 c. *Hymenaea courbaril* 15 10
754 50 c. *Mora excelsa* 20 15
755 $3 *Peltogyne venosa* .. .. 1·00 1·10
752/5 .. .. *Set of* 4 1·25 1·25

GUYANA 30c
TREE PORCUPINE Coendou prehensilis

178 Brazilian Tree Porcupine

1981
CONFERENCE
$1·05 X

(179)

(Des G. Drummond. Litho Questa)

1981 (2 Mar). *Wildlife. T* **178** *and similar horiz designs. Multicoloured. W* **106** (*sideways*). *P* 14.

756 30 c. Type **178** 25 30
a. Sheetlet of 12. Nos. 756/67 .. .. 2·75
757 30 c. Red Howler 25 30
758 30 c. Common Squirrel-Monkey 25 30
759 30 c. Two-toed Sloth 25 30
760 30 c. Brazilian Tapir 25 30
761 30 c. Collared Peccary 25 30
762 30 c. Six-banded Armadillo 25 30
763 30 c. Tamandua ("Ant Eater") 25 30
764 30 c. Giant Anteater 25 30
765 30 c. Murine Opossum 25 30
766 30 c. Brown Four-eyed Opossum 25 30
767 30 c. Brazilian Agouti 25 30
756/67 .. .. *Set of* 12 2·75 3·25

Nos. 756/67 were printed together, *se-tenant*, within the sheet of 12.

See also No. 852.

1981 (4 May). *Liberation of Southern Africa Conference. No.* 635 *surch with T* **179** *by Govt Printer.*

768 $1.05 on 10 c. Type **152** 40 50

ROYAL
WEDDING
1981
$3·60
X

(180)

X

181 Map of Guyana

7·20

(182)

1981 (6 May). *Royal Wedding* (1*st issue*). *Nos.* 554 *and* 556 *surch as T* **180** *by Govt Printer. A. In blue. B. In black.*

		A		B	
769	$3.60 on $5 *Odontadenia grandiflora* ..	2·50	4·00	1·25	1·25
	a. Surch inverted	£100	—	†	
	b. Surch double	40·00	—	†	
770	$7.20 on $1 *Chelonanthus uliginoides* ..	2·00	2·50	3·00	3·00
	a. Surch on No. 556 ..	†		40·00	—
	b. Surch double	45·00	—	†	
	c. Surch triple				

See also Nos. 841/3 and 930/6.

(Surch by Govt Printer)

1981 (11 May). *W* **106** (*sideways*). *P* 13.

771 **181** 10 c. on 3 c. black, ind & Venetian red .. 40 10
772 30 c. on 2 c. black, ind & greenish grey .. 45 15
773 50 c. on 2 c. black, ind & greenish grey .. 55 25
774 60 c. on 2 c. black, ind & greenish grey .. 70 30
775 75 c. on 3 c. black, ind & Venetian red .. 70 45
a. Surch double .. .. 40·00
b. Surch triple .. .. 60·00
771/5 .. .. *Set of* 5 2·50 1·10

Nos. 771/5 are fiscal stamps surcharged for postal use.

See also Nos. 940/76, 988/9 and 1029.

1981 (11 May). *No.* 544 *surch with T* **182** *by Govt Printer.*

775c 720 c. on 3 c. Hanging Heliconia .. .. 50·00 15·00

1981

(183)

1981 (8 June). *Optd with T* **183** *by Bovell's Printery.*

776 **105** 25 c. black, gold and lilac (R.) 10 10
777 30 c. black, gold & lt apple-green (R.) .. 15 15
778 – 35 c. multicoloured (No. 645) (R.) .. 15 15
779 – $1 multicoloured (No. 554) .. .. 1·00 75
776/9 .. .. *Set of* 4 1·25 1·10

210
7
(184)

X
(185)

ESSEQUIBO
IS OURS
15
(186)

ESSEQUIBO
IS OURS
15
(186*a*)

1981 (8 June–1 July) *Nos.* 545 *and* 556 *surch with T* **184** (*No.* 780) *or as T* **185**, *all by Bovell's Printery.*

780 75 c. on 5 c. Annatto tree 50 30
781 210 c. on $5 *Odontadenia grandiflora* .. 80 70
781*a* 220 c. on 5 c. Annatto tree .. .. .. 50·00 8·00

1981 (8 June). *Nos.* D8/11 *surch in black* (15 c.) *or red* (*others*). A. *As T* **186**. B. *As T* **186***a*. *Both by Bovell's Printery.*

			A		B	
782	D 2	10 c. on 2 c. black	25	10	50	10
783		15 c. on 12 c. bright scarlet	25	15	60	25
784		20 c. on 1 c. olive	20	20	30	25
		a. "ESSEOUIBO" ..	†		25·00	—
785		45 c. on 2 c. black	75	25	1·25	65
786		55 c. on 4 c. dull ultram ..	30	30	3·00	3·00
787		60 c. on 4 c. dull ultram ..	†		50	25
		a. "ESSEOUIBO" ..	†		10·00	—
788		65 c. on 2 c. black	40	40	75	70
789		70 c. on 4 c. dull ultram ..	1·00	1·25	1·50	1·50
790		80 c. on 4 c. dull ultram ..	35	40	60	70
782A/90A		.. .. *Set of* 8	3·25	2·75		
782B/90B		.. .. *Set of* 9			8·00	6·50

With the exception of No. 787 these stamps were surcharged with a setting of eighteen (three horizontal rows) as Type **186** and twelve as Type **186***a*. The two types of surcharge can, therefore, be found as vertical *se-tenant* pairs.

No. 787 was produced from a setting of 12 containing Type **186***a* only. The same setting was also used for the bottom two rows of the 20 c. on 1 c. value. The "ESSEOUIBO" error occurs on the first stamp in the second horizontal row of this setting.

Examples of 15, 45 and 60 c. surcharges are also known on stamps with watermark w **12**.

1981
(187)

1981
(188)

1981
(189)

1981 (8 June–1 July). *Nos.* 491, 494 *and* 555 *optd with T* **187**, **188** *or* **189**, *all by Bovell's Printery.*

791 15 c. Harpy Eagle (R.) .. .. 2·50 10
a. Opt omitted (in vert pair with normal) .. † —
b. Opt in black .. .. 35·00 5·00
792 40 c. Great Kiskadee (1.7.81) .. .. 2·50 40
a. Opt double .. .. 28·00
793 $2 *Norantea guianensis* (1.7.81) .. .. 2·75 1·40
791/3 .. .. *Set of* 3 7·00 1·75

X
50c
(190)

120
(191)

150

(192)

(Surch by Bovell's Printery)

1981 (1 July). (*a*) *Postage.* (i) *No.* 545 *surch with T* **190**.

794 50 c. on 5 c. Annatto tree 25 20
a. Surch inverted .. .. 6·00

(ii) *No.* 554 *surch as T* **191**

795 120 c. on $1 *Chelonanthus uliginoides* .. 65 50
796 140 c. on $1 *Chelonanthus uliginoides* .. 60 50

(iii) *Nos.* F7 *and* F9 *surch as T* **192**

797 150 c. on $2 *Norantea guianensis* 50 50
798 360 c. on $2 *Norantea guianensis* .. .. 2·50 1·50
799 720 c. on 60 c. Soldier's Cap .. .. .. 2·50 2·75

(iv) *Nos.* 556 *and* 716 *surch as T* **185**

800 220 c. on $3 Cylinder satellite .. .. 1·50 75
801 250 c. on $5 *Odontadenia grandiflora* .. 1·00 80
802 280 c. on $5 *Odontadenia grandiflora* .. 1·25 1·25
803 375 c. on $5 *Odontadenia grandiflora* .. 1·40 1·40

(b) *Air. No.* 843 *with commemorative opt cancelled by three bars*

804 $1.10 on $2 *Norantea guianensis* .. .. 20·00 15·00

100
15
(193)

AIR
(194)

(Surch by Bovell's Printery)

1981 (1 July). *No.* 485 *surch.* (*a*) *Postage. With T* **193**.

805 15 c. on 1 c. Type **87** 10 10
a. Horiz strip of 3. Nos. 805/7 85

(*b*) *Air. As T* **194**

806 100 c. on 1 c. Type **87** 35 35
807 110 c. on 1 c. Type **87** 40 40

Nos. 805/7 were printed together, *se-tenant*, within the same sheet providing 36 examples of No. 805 and 32 each of the others. No. 805 appears in the six vertical columns of Rows 3 to 8 with horizontal pairs of Nos. 806/7 in vertical columns 1, 2, 9, 10 and vertical pairs in the central six vertical columns of Rows 1, 2, 9, 10.

ESSEQUIBO IS OURS (195) | ESSEQUIBO IS OURS (195a) | 1981 (196)

1981 (1 July). *No. 700 optd. A. With T* **195**. *B. With T* **195a**. *Both by Bovell's Printery.*

			A		B	
808	15 c. *Eryphanis polyxena*	..	30	10	40	15
	a. "I" of "IS" omitted	..	†		—	—

No. 808Ba is believed to occur on either R. 5/1 or R. 5/5.

1981 (7 July–15 Sept). *Various stamps optd with T* **196** *by Bovell's Printery.*

809	–	15 c. multicoloured (No. 548)	3·00	10
810	–	15 c. multicoloured (No. 659)	2·00	20
811	–	15 c. multicoloured (No. 660)	2·00	20
811*a*	–	40 c. multicoloured (No. F5)	—	£200
812	–	50 c. multicoloured (No. 623)	60	20
813	**150**	50 c. multicoloured	1·00	25
814	–	50 c. royal blue and orange (No. 632) ..	11·00	1·00
815	–	50 c. multicoloured (No. 646)	1·25	25
816	**159**	50 c. ultramarine, black and gold ..	5·00	1·00
817	–	50 c. multicoloured (No. F6)	1·50	30
818	–	60 c. multicoloured (No. 731) (15.9.81) ..	60	25
819	–	60 c. multicoloured (No. 750) (15.9.81) ..	60	25
820	–	$1 multicoloured (No. 624)	4·25	1·00
821	**159**	$1 blue-green, black and gold ..	2·75	50
822	–	$2 multicoloured (No. 555)	1·75	1·00
823	–	$3 multicoloured (No. 732)	2·00	95
824	–	$5 multicoloured (No. 556)	2·75	2·25

55 (197) | 55 (198)

110 (199)

440 (200) | 440 (201)

550 (202) | 550 (203)

240 (204)

(Surch by Bovell's Printery)

1981 (7 July–15 Sept). (*a*) *Various stamps surch as T* **197/203**.

825	**116**	55 c. on 6 c. multicoloured (surch T **197**) (15.9.81)	3·25	80
		a. Surch with T **198**	10·00	3·50
		b. Vert pair. Nos. 825/a	13·00	4·50
826	**111**	70 c. on 6 c. multicoloured (15.9.81) ..	45	30
827		100 c. on 6 c. multicoloured	50	35
		a. Surch inverted	3·50	1·25
828	–	100 c. on 8 c. multicoloured (No. 505) ..	2·50	40
829	**152**	100 c. on $1.05 on 10 c. mult (No. 768) (surch vert—reading upwards) ..	17·00	3·50
		a. Surch reading downwards		
830	**116**	110 c. on 6 c. multicoloured ..	2·50	40
831	**149**	110 c. on 10 c. multicoloured (surch vert—reading downwards)	1·50	40
832	**151**	110 c. on 10 c. grey-green and yellow ..	2·75	70
833	**154**	110 c. on 10 c. multicoloured ..	2·50	70
834	–	125 c. on $2 multicoloured (No. 555) ..	6·00	1·00
835	**116**	180 c. on 6 c. multicoloured (15.9.81) ..	3·00	65
836		400 c. on 6 c. multicoloured ..	3·00	1·75
837		440 c. on 6 c. multicoloured (surch T **200**)	10·00	5·00
		a. Surch with T **201**	2·75	1·75
		b. Vert pair. Nos. 837/a ..	13·00	7·00
838	–	550 c. on $10 multicoloured (No. O21) (surch T **202**) (15.9.81) ..	3·25	2·00
		a. Surch with T **203**	7·75	5·50
		b. Vert pair. Nos. 838/a ..	11·00	8·00
839	–	625 c. on 40 c. multicoloured (No. F5) ..	7·00	3·00
		(*b*) *No. 728 surch with T* **204**		
840	–	240 c. on $3 multicoloured (15.9.81) ..	7·00	1·50

Nos. 825/a, 837/a and 838/a were each printed together, *se-tenant*, in vertical pairs throughout sheets containing five of these pairs plus an additional fifteen examples of Nos. 825, 837a and 838.

75 Royal Wedding 1981 X 60 (205) | Royal Wedding 1981 X (206)

Air Mail X 1.10 Royal Wedding 1981 (207)

(Surch by Bovell's Printery)

1981 (22 July). *Royal Wedding* (2*nd issue*). (*a*) *Postage. Nos.* 544 *and* 556 *surch with T* **205/6**.

841	60 c. on 3 c. Hanging Heliconia	70	80
	a. Surch inverted	75·00	
	b. "Royal Wedding" diagonal (as T **206**) ..	75·00	
	c. Surch double (T **205** + T **206**) ..	45·00	
	d. Surch T **205** double	90·00	
842	75 c. on $5 *Odontadenia grandiflora* ..	80	90
	(*b*) *Air. No.* 555 *surch with T* **207**		
843	$1.10 on $2 *Norantea guianensis* ..	1·25	1·40
	a. Surch double	60·00	
	b. Surch inverted	£100	
841/3	.. .. *Set of* 3	2·50	2·75

It is believed No. 841b comes from trial sheets which were accidentally included in supplies of the normal No. 841.

Espana 82 (208) | 1831-1981 Von Stephan 330 (209)

1981 (22 July). *World Cup Football Championship, Spain* (1982) (1*st issue*). *No.* 781*a optd with T* **208** *by Bovell's Printery.*

844	220 c. on 5 c. Annatto tree	1·00	90

See also Nos. 937/9.

1981 (22 July). 150*th Birth Anniv of Heinrich von Stephan* (*founder of U.P.U.*). *No.* 720 *surch with T* **209**.

845	330 c. on $3 Printing press used for early British Guiana stamps.. ..	1·25	1·25

12 

(211)

1981 (24 Aug). *No.* 452 *surch as T* **211** *by Bovell's Printery.*

847	12 c. on 12 c. on 6 c. Patua	20	25
	a. Large surch omitted	17·00	
	b. Strip of 3. Nos. 847/9	50	
	c. Strip of 3. Nos. 847, 850/1 ..	50	
848	15 c. on 10 c. on 6 c. Patua	15	10
849	15 c. on 30 c. on 6 c. Patua	15	10
	a. Small surch omitted	25·00	
850	15 c. on 50 c. on 6 c. Patua	15	10
851	15 c. on 60 c. on 6 c. Patua	15	10

Nos. 847/51 are further surcharges on previously unissued stamps.

No. 847 exists with the smaller of the two 12 c. surcharges printed by either lithography or typography.

Nos. 847/9 and 847, 850/1 were each printed together, *se-tenant*, within the sheets providing 36 examples of No. 847 and 30 each of Nos. 848/9 or 850/1. Each sheet also contained four stamps cancelled with a black diagonal cross. In each instance No. 847 appeared in the six central vertical columns of Rows 3 to 8 with horizontal pairs of Nos. 848/9 or 850/1 in vertical columns 1, 2, 9, 10 and vertical pairs in R. 1/4–8, R. 2/4–8, R. 9/3–7 and R. 10/3–7.

1981 (1 Sept). *As No.* 762 *but perf* 12.

852	30 c. Six-banded Armadillo	35	15

No. 852 was printed in sheets of 50.

214 Coromantyn Free Negro Armed Ranger, *circa* 1772 and Cuffy Monument

215 Louis Braille

(Des G. Drummond. Litho Rosenbaum Bros, Vienna)

1981 (1 Oct). 16*th Anniv of Guyana Defence Force. T* **214** *and similar vert designs. Multicoloured. W* **106** (*inverted on* $1). *P* 13½.

853	15 c. on 10 c. Type **214**.. ..	25	10
854	50 c. Private, 27th Foot Regiment, *circa* 1825	30	30
855	$1 on 30 c. Private, Col. Fourgeoud's Marines, *circa* 1775 ..	50	50
856	$1.10 on $3 W.O. and N.C.O., Guyana Defence Force, 1966 ..	1·40	75
853/6	.. .. *Set of* 4	2·25	1·50

The 15 c., $1 and $1.10 values are surcharged on previously unissued stamps.

(Des G. Vasarhelyi. Litho Questa)

1981 (2 Nov). *International Year for Disabled Persons. Famous Disabled People. T* **215** *and similar horiz designs. Multicoloured. W* **106** (*sideways*). *P* 13½ × 14.

857	15 c. on 10 c. Type **215**.. ..	30	10
858	50 c. Helen Keller and Rajkumari Singh ..	70	55
859	$1 on 60 c. Beethoven and Sonny Thomas ..	60	60
860	$1.10 on $3 Renoir	85	70
857/60	.. .. *Set of* 4	2·25	1·75

The 15 c., $1 and $1.10 values are surcharged, by Bovell's Printery, on previously unissued stamps. Examples of Nos. 857 and 860 are known without surcharge.

12 (216) | X 50 AIR (217)

(Surch by Bovell's Printery)

1981 (10 Nov). *Nos.* 452 *and* 489 *surch.* (*a*) *Postage. With T* **216**.

		A. On No. 452		B. On No. 489	
861	12 c. on 6 c. Patua	15	10	15	10
	a. Strip of 3. Nos. 861/3 ..	1·25	—	1·10	—
	(*b*) *Air. As T* **217**				
862	50 c. on 6 c. Patua	25	15	20	15
863	$1 on 6 c. Patua	50	30	50	30

Nos. 861/3 were printed together, *se-tenant*, throughout the sheet. All sheets of Nos. 861B/3B and about half of Nos. 861A/3A contained 36 examples of the 12 c., 35 of the 50 c. and 29 of the $1. On the remainder of the unwatermarked sheets there were the same number of the 12 c., but 34 of the 50 c. and 30 of the $1. No. 861 appeared in the six central vertical columns of Rows 3 to 8 with horizontal pairs of Nos. 862/3 in vertical columns 1, 2, 9, 10 and vertical pairs in the six central vertical columns of Rows 1, 2, 9, 10. The additional $1 value on the second stage of the setting occurred on R. 9/1.

1981 (218)

1981 (14 Nov). *Nos.* 548 *and* 554/5 *optd with T* **218** *in red by Bovell's Printery.*

864	15 c. Christmas Orchid	2·00	10
	a. Optd on No. 548a.. ..	3·50	
865	$1 *Chelonanthus uliginoides*	40	35
866	$2 *Norantea guianensis*	90	95

110 (219) | 110 (220) | Nov 81 50c (221)

1981 (14 Nov). (*a*) *Nos.* 601, 620, 644, *and* O13 *surch with T* **219/20** *in blue by Bovell's Printery.*

867	110 c. on 10 c. Type **154** (surch T **219**) ..	1·50	45
868	110 c. on 110 c. on 8 c. on 3 c. Hanging Heliconia (surch T **219** + **220**)	2·00	60
	a. Type **220** albino	25·00	
869	110 c. on 110 c. on 8 c. on 6 c. Cannon-ball tree (surch T **219**+ **220**) ..	2·00	75
869*a*	110 c. on 10 c. on 25 c. Marabunta (surch T **219** vert)	2·00	75
	(*b*) *Nos.* 717, 720, 728, 749, 751 *and* 755 *surch with T* **220** *by Bovell's Printery*		
870	110 c. on 10 c. Type **170** (R.)	90	40
	a. Surch albino	15·00	
871	110 c. on 10 c. Type **176** (B.)	3·75	90
872	110 c. on $3 Printing press used for early British Guiana stamps (R.) (surch vert)	90	45
873	110 c. on $3 H.N. Critchlow (B.) (surch vert)	3·75	70

874 110 c. on $3 Caduceus emblem, "C" encircling researcher, and island silhouettes (B.) .. 1·00 45
a. Surch in red .. .. 2·75 1·25
875 110 c. on 43 *Peltogyne venosa* (B.) .. .. .. 2·50 80
a. Surch in red .. .. 48·00 6·00

(c) *No.* 698 *surch with T* **221** *by Herald Printing-Kitty*
876 50 c. on 5 c. Type **166** .. .. .. 1·50 20

X X
Human Rights
Day
1981
110 AIR

222 Yellow Allamanda (*Allamanda cathartica*)

(223)

1981 (14 Nov)–**82.** *Flowers. Coil stamps. Vert designs as T* **222**. *W* **106**. *P* 15 × 14.
877 15 c. on 2 c. grey-lilac, blue & turquoise-green 15 15
a. Vert pair. Nos. 877/8 .. 50 45
b. New blue surch (12.82) 20 10
ba. Vert pair. Nos. 877b/8b 65 50
878 15 c. on 8 c. grey-lilac, blue and mauve .. 15 15
b. New blue surch (12.82) 20 10
Design:—15 c. on 8 c. Mazaruni Pride (*Sipanea prolensis*).
Nos. 877/8 are surcharges on previously unissued stamps and were printed together, *se-tenant*, in vertical pairs throughout the coil.

1981 (14 Nov). *Air. Human Rights Day. No.* 748 *surch with T* **223** *in blue by Bovell's Printery.*
879 110 c. on $3 Rotary anniversary emblem .. 1·75 1·50

U.N.I.C.E.F.
1946 - 1981
125 XX

(224)

1981 (14 Nov). *35th Anniv of U.N.I.C.E.F. No.* 724 *surch with T* **224** *by Bovell's Printery.*
880 125 c. on $3 "Mango Season" .. .. .. 1·00 60

Cancun 81
50c

(224*a*)

1981 (14 Nov). *"Cancun 81" International Conference. No.* 698 *surch with T* **224*a*** *by Herald Printing-Kitty.*
880*a* 50 c. on 5 c. Type **166** .. .. .. 1·50 60

225 Tape Measure and Guyana Metrication Board Van

1982

(226)

(Des local artist; adapted A. Theobald. Litho Questa)

1982 (18 Jan). *Metrication. T* **225** *and similar vert designs. Multicoloured. W* **106**. *P* 14½ × 14.
881 15 c. Type **225** 15 15
a. Sheetlet of 6. Nos. 881/6 80
882 15 c. "Metric man" 15 15
883 15 c. "Postal service goes metric" 15 15
884 15 c. Weighing child on metric scales .. 15 15
885 15 c. Canje Bridge 15 15
886 15 c. Tap filling litre bucket 15 15
881/6 .. .. *Set of* 6 80 80
Nos. 881/6 were printed together, *se-tenant*, in a sheetlet of 6.

1982 (8 Feb). *Various stamps optd with T* **226** *in blue by Autoprint.*
887 – 20 c. multicoloured (No. 549) .. .. 1·50 20
a. Optd on No. 549a .. .. .. 4·00 1·50
888 **105** 25 c. black, gold and lilac 50 25
889 – 25 c. multicoloured (No. 550*a*) .. .. 2·00 35
a. Optd on No. 550 .. .. .. 10·00 3·00
b. Optd on No. 550ab .. .. .. 6·50 2·00
See also Nos. 914/17, 919/21, 923/4, 977, 992/8, 1001, 1004, 1006/8, 1015, 1017, 1059, 1117 and OP3/4.

20c

(227)

(228)

POSTAGE

(229)

1982 (8 Feb). *Nos.* 506, 546 *and* 601 *surch or optd as T* **227/9** *by Bovell's Printery (No.* 890) *or Autoprint (others).*
890 20 c. on 6 c. Cannon-ball tree (surch T **227**) (G.) 35 20
891 20 c. on 6 c. Cannon-ball tree (surch T **228**) (B.) 35 20
892 25 c. Type **116** (optd T **229**) (B.) .. .. 1·00 10
893 125 c. on 8 c. on 6 c. Cannon-ball tree (surch T **228**) (B.) 35 35

230 Guyana Soldier and Flag

1982 (8 Feb). *Savings Campaign. W* **106** *(sideways). P* 14 × 14½.
894 **230** $1 multicoloured 30 30
No. 894 is a fiscal stamp overprinted, by Bovell's Printery, for postal use.

110 X
BADEN POWELL
1857 - 1982

(231)

1982 (15–22 Feb). *125th Birth Anniv of Lord Baden-Powell and 75th Anniv of Boy Scout Movement. Nos.* 543, 545 *and* 601 *surch as T* **231** *by Bovell's Printery.*
895 15 c. on 2 c. Type **132** (surch T **231**) (22 Feb) 10 10
a. Sheetlet of 25. Nos. 895/6, each × 8, Nos. 897/8, each × 4 and No. 899 .. 8·00
896 15 c. on 2 c. Type **132** (surch "Scout Movement 1907–1982") (22 Feb) .. 10 10
897 15 c. on 2 c. Type **132** (surch "1907–1982") (22 Feb) 15 15
898 15 c. on 2 c. Type **132** (surch "1857–1982") (22 Feb) 15 15
899 15 c. on 2 c. Type **132** (surch "1982") (22 Feb) 10 10
900 110 c. on 5 c. Annatto tree (surch T **231**) .. 1·00 40
a. Sheetlet of 25. Nos. 900/1, each × 8, Nos. 902/3, each × 4, and No. 904 (22 Feb) 12·00
901 110 c. on 5 c. Annatto tree (surch "Scout Movement 1907–1982") 60 40
902 110 c. on 5 c. Annatto tree (surch "1907–1982") (22 Feb) .. .. 1·25 80
903 110 c. on 5 c. Annatto tree (surch "1857–1982") (22 Feb) .. .. 1·25 80
904 110 c. on 5 c. Annatto tree (surch "1982") (22 Feb) 60 40
a. "110" larger .. .. 95·00
905 125 c. on 8 c. on 6 c. Cannon-ball tree (surch T **231**) (G.) .. .. .. 1·00 50
a. Sheetlet of 25. Nos. 905/6, each × 8, Nos. 907/8, each × 4, and No. 909 (22 Feb) 16·00
906 125 c. on 8 c. on 6 c. Cannon-ball tree (surch "Scout Movement 1907–1982") (G.) .. 1·00 50
907 125 c. on 8 c. on 6 c. Cannon-ball tree (surch "1907–1982") (G.) (22 Feb) .. 1·50 90
908 125 c. on 8 c. on 6 c. Cannon-ball tree (surch "1857–1982") (G.) (22 Feb) .. 1·50 90
909 125 c. on 8 c. on 6 c. Cannon-ball tree (surch "1982") (G.) (22 Feb) 75 50
895/909 .. .. *Set of* 15 9·00 6·00
In addition to the sheetlets of 25, Nos. 895a, 900a and 905a, Nos. 899/901, 904/6 and 909 also come from sheets containing one type of surcharge only.
No. 904a occurs in the printing of sheets containing this surcharge only. The "110" is in the same size as the surcharge on Type **241**.

Geo Washington
1732 ... 1982
100

(232)

GEORGE
WASHINGTON
1732 — 1982

(233)

1982 (15 Feb). *250th Birth Anniv of George Washington. Nos.* 708, 718 *and* 720 *surch as T* **232** *by Herald Printing-Kitty or optd only with T* **233** *by Autoprint.*
910 100 c. on $3 Printing press used for early British Guiana stamps 45 50
911 400 c. on 30 c. British Guiana 1856 1 c. black on magenta stamp .. .. .. 1·60 1·90
a. Surch inverted .. .. .. 20·00
912 $5 *Morpho deidamia* (B.) .. .. .. 3·50 2·25
910/12 .. .. *Set of* 3 5·00 4·25

1982 (3 Mar). *Savings Campaign. Horiz design as T* **230**. *Multicoloured. W* **106**. *P* 14 × 14½.
913 110 c. on $5 Guyana male and female soldiers with flag 50 35
No. 913 is a fiscal stamp surcharged, by Bovell's Printery, for postal use.
See also No. 990.

45

(234)

(235)

210

(236)

1982 (15 Mar). *Easter. Nos.* 481/4 *optd with T* **226**, *in blue, or surch as T* **234**, *all by Autoprint.*
914 **111** 25 c. multicoloured 35 20
915 30 c. multicoloured 30 15
916 45 c. on 6 c. multicoloured (B.) 45 35
917 75 c. on 40 c. multicoloured (R.) 75 35
914/17 .. .. *Set of* 4 1·75 95
No. 917 exists with the surcharge either at the right or in the centre of the design.

1982 (15 Mar). *No.* 703 *surch with T* **235** *by Herald Printing-Kitty.*
918 20 c. on 35 c. *Siderone galanthis* 60 10

1982 (8 Apr). *No.* F5 *optd with T* **226** *and surch as T* **228** *in blue, both by Autoprint.*
919 180 c. on 40 c. Tiger Beard .. .. .. 2·50 60

1982 (23 Apr). *Nos.* 555/6 *optd with T* **226** *in blue by Autoprint.*
920 $2 *Norantea guianensis* 80 70
921 $5 *Odontadenia grandiflora* .. .. 1·40 1·60

1982 (23 Apr). *No.* 542 *surch as T* **228** *in blue by Autoprint.*
922 220 c. on 1 c. Pitcher Plant of Mt Roraima .. 1·00 60

1982 (27 Apr). *Nos.* 472 *and* 684 *optd with T* **226** *in blue by Autoprint.*
923 **105** 40 c. black, gold and cobalt 35 20
924 – 40 c. multicoloured 50 40

1982 (27 Apr). *Nos.* 469, 751, 842 *and* 843 *surch as T* **228**, *vertically (Nos.* 925/7), *or as T* **236** *(others), all in blue by Autoprint.*
925 **105** 80 c. on 6 c. black, gold and flesh .. 30 35
926 85 c. on 6 c. black, gold and flesh .. 50 35
927 – 160 c. on $1.10 on $2 multicoloured (No. 843) 75 55
928 – 210 c. on $3 multicoloured (No. 751) (surch reading up) .. .. 2·50 70
a. Surch reading down .. .. 12·00
929 – 235 c. on 75 c. on $5 multicoloured (No. 842) .. .. 9·00 2·00
The surcharge on No. 929 is as Type **236**, but horizontal.

85 130

(237) (238)

1 70

(239)

(Surch by Herald Printing-Kitty)

1982 (27 Apr–May). *Royal Wedding (3rd issue). Coil stamps. Nos.* 841/3 *surch as T* **237** *(No.* 930), **238** *(Nos.* 931/2, 934/5) *or* **239** *(others).*
930 85 c. on 60 c. on 3 c. Hanging Heliconia .. 1·25 35
931 130 c. on 60 c. on 3 c. Hanging Heliconia .. 1·50 55
a. Surch (as T **238**) inverted £100
932 160 c. on $1.10 on $2 *Norantea guianensis* (vert surch) .. .. .. 3·00 2·00
a. Surch (as T **238**) double .. .. 50·00
933 170 c. on $1.10 on $2 *Norantea guianensis* .. 9·00 4·00
934 210 c. on 75 c. on $5 *Odontadenia grandiflora* (B.) .. .. 1·50 90
a. Surch (as T **238**) inverted .. .. 45·00
935 235 c. on 75 c. on $5 *Odontadenia grandiflora* 2·00 1·50
a. Surch (T **206**) omitted .. ..
b. Surch (as T **238**) double .. ..
936 330 c. on $1.10 on $2 *Norantea guianensis* .. 6·00 1·50
930/6 .. .. *Set of* 7 22·00 9·75

ESPANA
1982

(240)

220 AIR
Princess
of Wales
1961 - 1982

(241)

1982 (15 May). *World Cup Football Championship, Spain (2nd issue). Nos.* 544, 546 *and* 554 *optd with T* **240** *or surch also as T* **228**, *both by Autoprint.*

937 $1 *Chelonanthus uliginoides* 75 60
938 110 c. on 3 c. Hanging Heliconia (B.) 75 40
939 250 c. on 6 c. Cannon-ball tree (B.) .. .. 1·00 90
937/9 .. .. *Set of* 3 2·25 1·75

See also No. 1218.

(Optd Govt Printer and surch by Autoprint)

1982 (17 May). *W* **106** *(sideways). P* 13.

940 **181** 15 c. on 2 c. black, ind & greenish grey 50 15
a. Opt ("ESSEQUIBO etc") omitted 18·00
941 20 c. on 2 c. black, ind & greenish grey 1·25 30
942 25 c. on 2 c. black, ind & greenish grey 2·00 20
943 30 c. on 2 c. black, ind & greenish grey 40 15
944 40 c. on 2 c. black, ind & greenish grey 1·25 30
a. Surch inverted .. .. .. 20·00
945 45 c. on 2 c. black, ind & greenish grey 1·50 45
946 50 c. on 2 c. black, ind & greenish grey 70 30
a. Opt ("ESSEQUIBO etc") omitted 18·00
947 60 c. on 2 c. black, ind & greenish grey 2·00 20
948 75 c. on 2 c. black, ind & greenish grey 1·50 25
949 80 c. on 2 c. black, ind & greenish grey 80 20
950 85 c. on 2 c. black, ind & greenish grey 75 25
951 100 c. on 3 c. black, ind and Venetian red 60 35
952 110 c. on 3 c. black, ind and Venetian red 80 30
953 120 c. on 3 c. black, ind and Venetian red 2·50 35
954 125 c. on 3 c. black, ind and Venetian red 1·25 35
955 130 c. on 3 c. black, ind and Venetian red 90 35
a. Surch inverted .. .. .. 17·00
b. Error. Nos. 952 and 955 *se-tenant*
c. Error. Nos. 955 and 956 *se-tenant*
956 150 c. on 3 c. black, ind and Venetian red 2·00 40
957 160 c. on 3 c. black, ind and Venetian red 1·50 40
958 170 c. on 3 c. black, ind and Venetian red 1·25 45
959 175 c. on 3 c. black, ind and Venetian red 1·75 45
960 180 c. on 3 c. black, ind and Venetian red 1·75 50
961 200 c. on 3 c. black, ind and Venetian red 2·00 45
962 210 c. on 3 c. black, ind and Venetian red 3·25 50
963 220 c. on 3 c. black, ind and Venetian red 3·75 60
964 235 c. on 3 c. black, ind and Venetian red 3·25 60
965 240 c. on 3 c. black, ind and Venetian red 3·00 60
966 250 c. on 3 c. black, ind and Venetian red 2·00 60
967 300 c. on 3 c. black, ind and Venetian red 3·50 75
968 330 c. on 3 c. black, ind and Venetian red 2·50 90
969 375 c. on 3 c. black, ind and Venetian red 3·00 1·00
970 400 c. on 3 c. black, ind and Venetian red 4·00 1·10
971 440 c. on 3 c. black, ind and Venetian red 3·50 1·10
972 500 c. on 3 c. black, ind and Venetian red 3·00 1·40
973 550 c. on 3 c. black, ind and Venetian red 3·00 1·75
974 625 c. on 3 c. black, ind and Venetian red 2·50 2·00
975 1500 c. on 2 c. black, ind & greenish grey 9·00 4·00
976 2000 c. on 2 c. black, ind & greenish grey 10·00 5·50
940/76 .. .. *Set of* 37 80·00 25·00

Nos. 940/76 are fiscal stamps, surcharged for postal use, as Type **181**, but with the overprinted inscription and face value redrawn. On the 15 to 85 c., the surcharged face value is in blue, on the 100 to 625 c. in black, and on the 1500 and 2000 c. in red.

Nos. 955b/c come from the first printing of the 130 c. which had one cliché of the 110 c. surcharge (R. 4/1) and three of the 150 c. (R. 2/8–10) included in error.

For 25 c. and 40 c. surcharges in black see Nos. 988/9 and for the 25 c. in red, No. 1029.

1982 (7 June). *No.* 548 *optd with T* **226** *in blue by Autoprint.*

977 15 c. Christmas Orchid .. .. .. 2·00 10
a. Optd on No. 548a .. .. .. 48·00 12·00

1982 (15 June). *No.* O26 *optd with T* **229** *in blue by Autoprint.*

978 100 c. on 6 c. Type **116** .. .. .. 2·50 35

1982 (25 June). *Air. 21st Birthday of Princess of Wales. Nos.* 542, 545 *and* 555 *surch as T* **241** *by Bovell's Printery.*

979 110 c. on 5 c. Annatto tree (R.) 75 50
a. Surch in black .. .. .. 60·00
980 220 c. on 1 c. Pitcher Plant of Mt Roraima .. 1·75 80
a. Surch double .. ..
981 330 c. on $2 *Norantea guianensis* (B.) .. 2·50 1·50
a. Surch in greenish blue .. ..
ab. Surch double .. .. ..
979/81 .. .. *Set of* 3 4·50 2·50

GUYANA
H.R.H.
Prince William
21st June 1982
000
000000000 $1.10

(242)

H.R.H.
Prince William
21st June 1982

$2.20

(243)

1982 (12 July). *Birth of Prince William of Wales. Surch as T* **242** *(50 c. and $1.10) or with T* **243** *(others), all in blue by Autoprint.*

(a) On stamps of British Guiana

982 50 c. on 2 c. myrtle-green (No. 332) 40 45
983 $1.10 on 3 c. brown-olive and red-brown (No. 354) .. .. 1·00 80
a. Surch inverted .. .. .. 35·00
b. Surch double .. .. ..
c. Surch on No. 333 .. .. .. 1·50 75
ca. Surch inverted .. .. .. 55·00
cb. Surch double .. .. .. 70·00
cc. Surch as T **243** (lines at foot) .. .. 40·00

(b) On stamps of Guyana previously optd "GUYANA INDEPENDENCE 1966"

984 50 c. on 2 c. myrtle-green (No. 430) .. .. 4·50 3·00
985 $1.10 on 3 c. brown-olive and red-brown (No. 431) .. .. 7·00 3·00
a. Surch on No. 422 .. .. .. 40·00 10·00
986 $1.25 on 6 c. yellow-green (No. 398A) .. 85 90
a. Surch inverted .. .. .. 50·00
b. Surch double .. .. .. 70·00
c. Surch on No. 434 .. .. .. 6·00 4·00
987 $2.20 on 24 c. black and brownish orange (No. 401B) .. .. 1·75 1·75
a. Surch inverted .. .. .. 70·00
b. Surch on No. 401A .. .. .. 12·00 10·00
c. Surch on No. 435 .. .. .. 38·00 25·00
982/7 .. .. *Set of* 6 14·00 4·00

Nos. 982, 983c and 985a have Mult Script CA watermark and the remainder watermark w **12** (sideways on No. 987).

1982 (13 July). *As Nos.* 942 *and* 944 *but with surcharged face values in black by Autoprint.*

988 **181** 25 c. on 2 c. black, ind & greenish grey .. 40 20
989 40 c. on 2 c. black, ind & greenish grey .. 15 15

1982 (13 July). *Savings Campaign. Coil stamp. As No.* 913 *but showing inverted comma before* "OURS" *in overprint.*

990 110 c. on $5 Guyana male and female soldiers with flag .. .. 4·50 50

ITALY
$2.35

(244)

50
C.A. & CARIB
GAMES
1982

(245)

1982 (15 July). *Italy's Victory in World Cup Football Championship. No.* F7 *optd as T* **240** *and surch with T* **244**, *both in blue by Autoprint.*

991 $2.35 on 180 c. on 60 c. Soldier's Cap .. 1·50 75

1982 (16 Aug). *Wildlife Protection. Nos.* 687 *and* 733/8 *optd with T* **226** *(vert on Nos.* 993/8*) in blue by Autoprint.*

992 35 c. Harpy Eagle .. .. .. 1·75 40
993 35 c. Type **174** .. .. .. 1·75 40
a. Block of 6. Nos. 993/8 .. .. 10·00
994 35 c. Haimara .. .. .. 1·75 40
995 35 c. Electric Eel .. .. .. 1·75 40
996 35 c. Golden Rivulus .. .. .. 1·75 40
997 35 c. Pencil Fish .. .. .. 1·75 40
998 35 c. Four-eyed Fish .. .. .. 1·75 40
992/8 .. .. *Set of* 7 11·00 2·50

1982 (16 Aug). *Central American and Caribbean Games, Havana. Nos.* 542/3 *surch as T* **245** *by Autoprint.*

999 50 c. on 2 c. Type **132** .. .. 1·00 45
a. Surch inverted .. .. .. † —
1000 60 c. on 1 c. Pitcher Plant of Mt Roraima .. 1·25 30

1982 (15 Sept). *No.* 730 *optd with T* **226** *vertically in blue by Autoprint.*

1001 35 c. black and red-orange 25 20

1982 (15 Sept). *Nos.* 841 *and* 979 *further surch as T* **228** *(No.* 1003 *has solid bar) in blue by Autoprint.*

1002 130 c. on 60 c. on 3 c. Hanging Heliconia .. 60 50
a. Surch as T **228** inverted £150
1003 170 c. on 110 c. on 5 c. Annatto tree .. .. 3·50 75
a. With six lines as in T **228** .. .. 90·00

1982 (15 Sept). *No.* 841 *optd with T* **226** *and surch as T* **228**, *both in blue by Autoprint.*

1004 440 c. on 60 c. on 3 c. Hanging Heliconia .. 2·75 1·50
a. T **226** and T **228** both inverted .. 65·00
b. Surch and optd on No. 841b .. .. 20·00
c. Without opt T **226** .. .. 18·00 2·00

No. 1004c also differs from No. 1004 by showing a "c" after the surcharge "60" on Type **205**.

Commonwealth
GAMES
AUSTRALIA
1982
1.25

(246)

INT.
FOOD DAY
1982

(247)

1982 (27 Sept). *Commonwealth Games, Brisbane, Australia. No.* 546 *surch with T* **246** *in blue by Autoprint.*

1005 $1.25 on 6 c. Cannon-ball tree .. .. 1·25 40

1982 (1 Oct). *Nos.* 552, 641 *and* 719 *optd with T* **226** *(vertically on Nos.* 1007/8*) in blue by Autoprint.*

1006 50 c. multicoloured (No. 552) .. .. .. 1·75 25
1007 50 c. light violet-blue, light green and light yellow-brown (No. 641) .. .. .. 1·25 25
1008 50 c. multicoloured (No. 719) 60 25

1982 (1 Oct). *Various Official stamps additionally optd for postal purposes as T* **229**, *but smaller (29 mm in length), all in blue by Autoprint.*

1009 15 c. Christmas Orchid (No. O23) (vert opt) 2·75 10
1010 50 c. *Guzmania lingulata* (No. O14) (vert opt) .. .. 1·25 25
1011 100 c. on $3 Cylinder satellite (No. O19) .. 1·75 50

1982 (15 Oct). *International Food Day. No.* 617 *optd with T* **247** *in blue by Autoprint.*

1012 50 c. Pawpaw and tangerine .. .. .. 12·00 1·25

INT. YEAR
OF THE
ELDERLY

(248)

Dr. R. KOCH
CENTENARY
TBC BACILLUS
DISCOVERY

(249)

F. D. ROOSEVELT
1882-1982

(250)

1982 (15 Oct). *International Year of the Elderly. No.* 747 *optd with T* **248** *in blue by Autoprint.*

1013 50 c. District 404 emblem .. .. .. 3·50 50

1982 (15 Oct). *Centenary of Robert Koch's Discovery of Tubercle Bacillus. No.* 750 *optd with T* **249** *in blue by Autoprint.*

1014 60 c. Researcher with microscope, Caduceus emblem, stethoscope and beach scene .. 1·50 30

1982 (15 Oct). *International Decade for Women. No.* 633 *optd with T* **226** *in blue by Autoprint.*

1015 $1 brown and bright blue .. .. .. 3·00 80
a. Opt inverted .. .. .. 20·00

1982 (15 Oct). *Birth Centenary of F. D. Roosevelt (American statesman). No.* 706 *optd with T* **250** *in blue by Autoprint.*

1016 $1 Type **167** .. .. 1·00 45

GAC Inaug. Flight
Georgetown—
Boa Vista, Brasil
200

(251)

50
CARICOM
Heads of Gov't
Conference
July 1982

(252)

1982 (15 Oct). *1st Anniv of G.A.C. Inaugural Flight Georgetown to Boa Vista, Brazil. No.* 842 *optd with T* **226** *and surch with T* **251**, *both in blue by Autoprint.*

1017 200 c. on 75 c. on $5 *Odontadenia grandiflora* 15·00 3·00

1982 (18 Nov). *CARICOM Heads of Government Conference, Kingston, Jamaica. Nos.* 881/6 *surch with T* **252** *by Herald Printing-Kitty.*

1018 50 c. on 15 c. Type **225** .. .. .. 1·00 30
a. Sheetlet of 6. Nos. 1018/23 .. .. 5·25
1019 50 c. on 15 c. "Metric man" .. .. 1·00 30
1020 50 c. on 15 c. "Postal service goes metric" .. 1·00 30
1021 50 c. on 15 c. Weighing child on metric scales 1·00 30
1022 50 c. on 15 c. Canje Bridge .. .. 1·00 30
1023 50 c. on 15 c. Tap filling litre bucket .. .. 1·00 30
1018/23 .. .. *Set of* 6 5·25 1·75

CHRISTMAS
1982

(253)

15

(254)

50

(255)

1982 (1 Dec). *Christmas. Nos.* 895/9 *optd with T* **253** *in red by Autoprint.*

1024 15 c. on 2 c. Type **132** (surch T **231**) 20 15
a. Sheetlet of 25. Nos. 1024/5, each × 8, Nos. 1026/7, each × 4 and No. 1028 .. 9·00
1025 15 c. on 2 c. Type **132** (surch "Scout Movement 1907–1982") 20 15
1026 15 c. on 2 c. Type **132** (surch "1907–1982") .. 30 25
1027 15 c. on 2 c. Type **132** (surch "1857–1982") .. 30 25
1028 15 c. on 2 c. Type **132** (surch "1982") .. .. 2·50 2·50
1024/8 .. .. *Set of* 5 3·25 3·00

Nos. 1024/8 were only issued in the *se-tenant* sheetlets of 25.

1982 (15 Dec). *As No. 942 but with surcharged face value in red by Autoprint.*
1029 **181** 25 c. on 2 c. black, indigo and greenish grey 50 10

1982 (15 Dec). *Nos. 543 and 546 surch as T* **254** *by Autoprint.*
1030 15 c. on 2 c. Type **132** (B.) 15 10
1031 20 c. on 6 c. Cannon-ball tree (Blk.) 25 10
For similar surcharges in different colours see Nos. 1034/5 and 1063; and for surcharges incorporating "c" Nos. 1085/7 and 1098/9.

1982 (15 Dec). *No. 489 surch as T* **255** *by Autoprint.*
1032 50 c. on 6 c. Patua 20 25
1033 100 c. on 6 c. Patua 40 45

1983 (5 Jan). *As Nos. 1030/1, but with colours of surcharge changed.*
1034 15 c. on 2 c. Type **132** (Blk.) 10 10
1035 20 c. on 6 c. Cannon-ball tree (G.) 10 10

1983
(256)

POSTAGE
(257)

258 Guyana Flag (inscr "60th BIRTHDAY ANNIVERSARY")

1983 (1 Feb). *Optd with T* **256** *by Autoprint.*
1036 – 15 c. multicoloured (No. 655) (opt vert) 5·00 2·00
1037 – 15 c. yellow-brown, grey and black (No. 672) 50 10
1038 – 15 c. multicoloured (No. 682) (opt vert) .. 40 10
1039 **214** 15 c. on 10 c. multicoloured (opt vert) .. 35 10
1040 **215** 15 c. on 10 c. multicoloured 15 10
1041 – 50 c. multicoloured (No. 646) .. .. 2·00 25
1042 – 50 c. multicoloured (No. 696) (opt vert) .. 2·50 25
1043 – 50 c. multicoloured (No. 719) .. .. 1·50 25
1036/43 .. .. *Set of* 8 11·00 3·00
See also Nos. 1060/1, 1069/70, 1072/9, 1096, 1101 and 1110/16.

1983 (1 Feb). *No. O17 optd for postal purposes with T* **257** *in red by Autoprint.*
1044 15 c. Harpy Eagle .. .. 2·25 10

1983 (8 Feb). *National Heritage. Nos. 710/12 and No. 778 surch as T* **234** *in black (No. 1045) or blue (others) by Autoprint.*
1045 90 c. on 30 c. Cassiri and decorated Amerindian jars .. .. 2·10 1·60
1046 90 c. on 35 c. Rock drawing of hunter and quarry 35 50
1047 90 c. on 50 c. Fork Kyk-over-al .. .. 2·10 1·60
1048 90 c. on 60 c. Fort Island .. .. .. 4·00 50
1045/8 .. .. *Set of* 4 7·00 3·75

(Des K. Everett (25 c.). Litho Format)

1983 (19 Feb). *President Burnham's 60th Birthday and 30 Years in Parliament. T* **258** *and similar multicoloured designs. W* **106** *(sideways) (25 c., $1.30). P* 13½ *($1.30) or* 14 *(others).*
1049 25 c. Type **258** 15 20
a. Horiz pair. Nos. 1049/50 .. .. .. 30 40
1050 25 c. As T **258**, but position of flag reversed and inscr "30th ANNIVERSARY IN PARLIAMENT" 15 20
1051 $1.30, Youth display (41 × 25 *mm*) 75 65
1052 $6 Presidential standard (43½ × 25 *mm*) .. 2·50 2·75
1049/52 .. .. *Set of* 4 3·25 3·50
Nos. 1049/50 were printed together, *se-tenant*, in horizontal pairs throughout the sheet.
For stamps as Nos. 1049/50, but without commemorative inscriptions, see Nos. 1108/9.

PRINTERS. Nos. 1053/1126 were surcharged or overprinted by Autoprint, Georgetown.

FIFTY CENTS
(259)

20 X
(260)

1983 (7 Mar). *Surch as T* **259**.
1053 **170** 50 c. on 10 c. mult (No. 717) (R.) .. 45 25
1054 – 50 c. on 400 c. on 30 c. multicoloured (No. 911) (surch vert) 65 25
1055 **152** $1 on 10 c. multicoloured (No. 635) (surch vert) .. .. 4·50 45
1056 $1 on $1.05 on 10 c. multicoloured (No. 768) (surch vert) .. .. .. 2·25 45
1056*a* – $1 on $1.10 on $2 multicoloured (No. 843) .. .. 1·50 1·25
1057 – $1 on 220 c. on 5 c. mult (No. 844) (B.) 6·00 1·00
1058 – $1 on 330 c. on $2 mult (No. 981) (B.) 50 45
1059 – $1 on $12 on $1.10 on $2 mult (similar to No. P3) (B.) .. .. .. 16·00 5·00
1053/9 .. .. *Set of* 8 29·00 9·00
Nos. 1057/9 have thin bars cancelling previous surcharges, and, in addition, No. 1059 is optd with T **226** in blue.
See also Nos. 1062 and 1080/4.

1983 (7 Mar). *No. 859 optd with T* **256**.
1060 $1 on 60 c. Beethoven and Sonny Thomas .. 1·25 45

1983 (11 Mar). *Conference of Foreign Ministers of Non-aligned Countries, New Delhi. No. 569 surch with T* **259** *and No. 570 optd with T* **256**.
1061 **136** 25 c. multicoloured (opt vert) .. .. 2·00 25
1062 50 c. on 8 c. mult (surch vert) (R.) .. 3·00 25

1983 (14 Mar). *As No. 1030, but colour of surcharge changed.*
1063 15 c. on 2 c. Type **132** (R.) 10 10

1983 (14 Mar). *No. 771 further surch with T* **260** *in blue.*
1064 **181** 20 c. on 10 c. on 3 c. black, indigo and Venetian red 25 10

Commonwealth Day 14 March 1983
(261)

$1.30

262

1983 (14 Mar). *Commonwealth Day. Nos. 398A and 401B surch as T* **261** *in black (25 c., $1.30) or blue (others).*
1065 25 c.on 6 c. yellow-green .. .. .. 1·50 20
1066 $1.20 on 6 c. yellow-green 80 50
1067 $1.30 on 24 c. black and bright orange .. 75 55
1068 $2.40 on 24 c. black and bright orange .. 1·40 1·25
1065/8 .. .. *Set of* 4 4·00 2·25

1983 (17 Mar). *Easter. Nos. 482/3 optd with T* **256**.
1069 **111** 25 c. multicoloured 10 10
1070 30 c. multicoloured 25 15

1983 (17 Mar). *25th Anniv of International Maritime Organization. British Guiana fiscal stamp optd in red as T* **262**. *Wmk Mult Crown CA. P* 14.
1071 $4.80, bright blue and deep dull green .. 4·50 4·50

1983 (1 Apr). *Optd with T* **256**.
1072 **152** 50 c. multicoloured (No. 637) (opt vert) .. 1·00 25
1073 **159** 50 c. ultramarine, black and gold (No. 668) (opt vert) .. .. .. 4·00 25
1073*a* – 50 c. multicoloured (No. 723) .. ..
1074 – 50 c. multicoloured (No. 854) (opt vert) .. 50 25
1075 – 50 c. multicoloured (No. 858) 30 25
1076 – $1 multicoloured (No. 628) .. .. 6·00 45
1077 – $1 multicoloured (No. 638) (vert opt) .. 4·50 45
1078 – $1 multicoloured (No. 675) .. .. 3·00 45
1079 – $1 on 30 c. mult (No. 855) (vert opt) .. 1·00 45
1079*a* – $3 multicoloured (No. 720) .. .. 5·00 45
1079*b* – $3 multicoloured (No. 724) .. ..
1079*c* – $3 multicoloured (No. 748) .. ..

1983 (1 Apr). *Surch with T* **259**, *vertically, in black (No. 1082) or blue (others).*
1080 **148** 50 c. on 8 c. multicoloured (No. 615) .. 1·25 25
1081 **162** 50 c. on 8 c. multicoloured (No. 681) .. 4·00 25
1082 **171** 50 c. on 10 c. multicoloured (No. 721) .. 2·00 25
1083 – 50 c. on 10 c. on 25 c. mult (No. O13) .. 2·00 25
1084 – 50 c. on 330 c. on $3 mult (No. 845) .. 1·75 25

1983 (2 May). *Surch as T* **254**, *but with "c" after new face value.*
1085 **105** 15 c. on 6 c. black, gold and flesh (No. 469) (B.) 10 10
1086 – 20 c. on 6 c. multicoloured (No. 546) .. 10 10
1087 **111** 50 c. on 6 c. multicoloured (No. 481) .. 25 30
For No. 1085 with black overprint, see No. 1098.

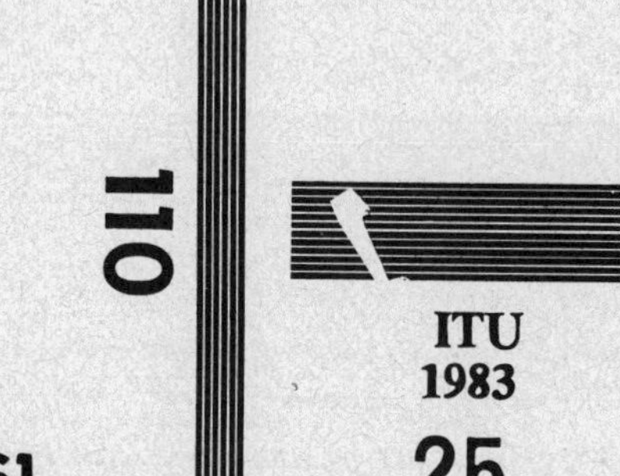

$1
(263)

(264)

25
(265)

1983 (2 May). *No. 489 surch with T* **263**.
1088 $1 on 6 c. Patua 45 50

1983 (2 May). *No. 639 surch with T* **264** *in blue.*
1089 **153** 110 c. on 10 c. greenish yellow, light green and light reddish violet .. 1·25 50
a. Error. Surch on 35 c (No. 640) 90·00

1983 (2 May). *Nos. 551 and 556 surch as T* **228** *in blue.*
1090 250 c. on 40 c. Tiger Beard .. .. .. 3·00 1·25
1091 400 c. on 25 c. *Odontadenia grandiflora* .. 3·00 1·90

1983 (17 May). *World Telecommunications and Health Day. Nos. 842 and 980 further surch as T* **265**.
1092 25 c. on 220 c. on 1 c. Pitcher Plant of Mt Roraima (surch T **265**) (R.) 25 20
a. Sheetlet of 25. Nos. 1092/3 each × 8 and No. 1094 × 9 .. .. 6·50
b. Six bars only at top .. ..
1093 25 c. on 220 c. on 1 c. Pitcher Plant of Mt Roraima (surch "WHO 1983 25") (R.) .. 25 20
b. Six bars only at top .. ..
1094 25 c. on 220 c. on 1 c. Pitcher Plant of Mt Roraima (surch "17 MAY '83 ITU/WHO 25") (R.) 25 20
b. Six bars only at top .. ..
1095 $4.50 on 75 c. on $5 *Odontadenia grandiflora* (surch "ITU/WHO 17 MAY 1983") (B.) .. .. 11·00 3·00
a. Surch on 235 c. on 75 c. on $5 (No. 929) .. 15·00 4·00
1092/5 .. .. *Set of* 4 11·00 3·25

1983 (18 May). *30th Anniv of President's Entry into Parliament. Nos. 690 and 692 surch as T* **259**, *the former additionally optd with T* **256**.
1096 $1 on 15 c. black, light violet-blue and bluish grey .. .. 4·50 50
1097 $1 on 40 c. black, red-orange and bluish grey 6·50 50
No. **MS**693 was also reissued with examples of Nos. 1096/7 affixed over the 8 c. and 35 c. values, and an example of No. 1050 added to the righthand sheet margin. These miniature sheets, revalued to $6, numbered on the reverse and cancelled with First Day of Issue postmarks, were for presentation purposes and were not available for postage.

1983 (23 May). *Surch as T* **254**, *but with "c" after new face value.*
1098 **105** 15 c. on 6 c. black, gold and flesh (No. 469) (Blk.) 10 10
1099 – 50 c. on 6 c. multicoloured (No. 489) (Blk.) 25 30

1983 (23 May). *No. 546 surch as T* **228**, *but with "c" after new face value.*
1100 20 c. on 6 c. Cannon-ball tree 10 10

1983 (23 May). *No. 611 optd with T* **256**.
1101 25 c. Guides in camp .. .. 25·00 1·25

$1.30 **120**

$1
(266)

(267)

(268)

1983 (23 May). *No. 489 surch with T* **266** *in red.*
1102 $1 on 6 c. Patua 45 50

1983 (15 June). *15th World Scout Jamboree, Alberta. Nos. 835/6 and O13 additionally surch or optd as T* **267**.
1103 – $1.30 on 100 c. on 8 c. multicoloured .. 2·25 80
1104 **116** 180 c. on 6 c. multicoloured .. .. 2·25 1·50
1105 $3.90 on 400 c. on 6 c. multicoloured .. 2·75 2·50
1103/5 .. .. *Set of* 3 6·50 4·25

1983 (22 June). *Nos. 659/60 surch as T* **254**.
1106 60 c. on 15 c. Map of the Caribbean .. .. 5·00 35
1107 $1.50 on 15 c. Prudential Cup .. .. 5·50 80

1983 (1 July). *As Nos. 1049/50, but without commemorative inscr above flag. W* **106** *(sideways). P* 14.
1108 25 c. As Type **258** 15 15
a. Horiz pair. Nos. 1108/9 .. .. 30 30
1109 25 c. As No. 1050 .. .. 15 15
Nos. 1108/9 were printed together, *se-tenant* in horizontal pairs throughout the sheet.

1983 (1 July). *Optd with T* **256**.
1110 **105** 30 c. black, gold and light apple-green (No. 471) 25 20
1111 – 30 c. multicoloured (No. 695) .. .. 7·00 30
1112 – 30 c. multicoloured (No. 718) (opt vert) .. 3·00 20
1113 – 30 c. multicoloured (No. 722) .. .. 4·50 20
1114 – 30 c. multicoloured (No. 746) .. .. 2·50 20
1115 – 60 c. multicoloured (No. 697) .. .. 2·75 20
1116 – 60 c. multicoloured (No. 731) .. .. 3·50 20
1110/16 .. .. *Set of* 7 21·00 1·25

1983 (1 July). *No. 553 optd with T* **226** *in blue.*
1117 60 c. Soldier's Cap .. .. 2·25 35

1983 (1 July). *Surch as T* **264** *in blue.*
1118 **157** 120 c. on 8 c. multicoloured (No. 654) .. 2·00 60
1119 **159** 120 c. on 10 c. dull red, black and gold (No. 666) .. .. 2·25 60
1120 – 120 c. on 35 c. multicoloured (No. 622) .. 2·25 60
1121 – 120 c. on 35 c. orange, light green and reddish violet (No. 640) .. 2·25 60

1983 (1 July). *Nos. 716 and 729 surch as T* **268**.
1122 120 c. on 10 c. Type **173** (R.) .. .. .. 2·25 60
1123 120 c. on 375 c. on $3 Cylinder satellite .. 2·00 60
No. 1123 also carries an otherwise unissued surcharge in red, reading "INTERNATIONAL SCIENCE YEAR 1982 375". As issued much of this is obliterated by two heavy bars.

CARICOM DAY 1983

120
GUYANA
(269)

60 **XXX**
(270)

1983 (1 July). *British Guiana No. D1a and Guyana No. D8 surch with T* **269** *in blue.*
1124 **D 1** 120 c. on 1 c. deep green .. .. 2·50 60
1125 **D 2** 120 c. on 1 c. olive .. .. .. 2·50 60

1983 (1 July). *CARICOM Day. No. 823 additionally surch with T* **270** *in red.*
1126 60 c. on $3 "Makanaima the Great Ancestral Spirit of the Amerindians" .. .. 1·50 35

271 *Kurupukari*

(Litho Format)

1983 (11 July*). *Riverboats. T* **271** *and similar horiz designs. W* **106**. *P* 14.
1127 30 c. black and vermilion 15 20
a. *Tête-bêche* (vert pair) 30
1128 60 c. black and bright reddish violet .. 30 35
a. *Tête-bêche* (vert pair) 60
1129 120 c. black and bright lemon .. .. 1·00 60
a. *Tête-bêche* (vert pair) .. .. .. 1·10
1130 130 c. black 60 65
a. *Tête-bêche* (vert pair) .. .. .. 1·25
1131 150 c. black and bright emerald 75 80
a. *Tête-bêche* (vert pair) .. .. .. 1·50
1127/31 .. .. *Set of* 5 2·50 2·40

Designs:—60 c. *Makouria*; 120 c. *Powis*; 130 c. *Pomeroon*; 150 c. *Lukanani*.

*Although not finally issued until 11 July First Day Covers of Nos. 1127/31 are postmarked with the intended release date of 1 July.

Nos. 1127/31 were each issued in sheets of 80 (10 × 8) with the bottom three rows inverted forming *tête-bêche* vertical pairs from Rows 5 and 6.

2.30

(272)

1983 (22 July). *Unissued Royal Wedding surcharge, similar to No.* 843, *surch as T* **272** *in blue by Autoprint.*
1132 $2.30 on $1.10 on $2 *Norantea guianensis* .. 1·50 1·50
1133 $3.20 on $1.10 on $2 *Norantea guianensis* .. 1·75 1·75

BW (273) **Mont Golfier 1783-1983** (274)

1983 (5 Sept). *Bicentenary of Manned Flight and 20th Anniv of Guyana Airways. Nos.* 701/2*a optd as T* **273/4**, *in red (Nos.* 1134/47) *or blue (Nos.* 1148/68) *by Autoprint.*
1134 20 c. multicoloured (optd T **273**) 10 10
a. Sheetlet of 25. Nos. 1134/8 each × 4 and 1139 × 5.. .. .. .. 2·50
1135 20 c. multicoloured (optd "LM") 10 10
1136 20 c. multicoloured (optd "GY 1963 1983") .. 10 10
1137 20 c. multicoloured (optd "JW") 10 10
1138 20 c. multicoloured (optd "CU") 10 10
1139 20 c. multicoloured (optd T **274**) 10 10
1140 25 c. multicoloured (optd "BGI") 50 25
a. Sheetlet of 25. Nos. 1140 × 2, 1141 × 8, 1142/44 each × 2, 1145 × 5 and 1146/7 each × 2.. .. .. .. 9·00
1141 25 c. multicoloured (optd "GEO") 15 10
1142 25 c. multicoloured (optd "MIA") 50 25
1143 25 c. multicoloured (optd "BVB") 50 25
1144 25 c. multicoloured (optd "PBM") 50 25
1145 25 c. multicoloured (optd T **274**) 20 12
1146 25 c. multicoloured (optd "POS") 50 25
1147 25 c. multicoloured (optd "JFK") 50 25
1148 30 c. multicoloured (optd "AHL") 25 15
a. Sheetlet of 25. Nos. 1148/54, 1155 × 5 and 1156/68 .. .. 7·00
1149 30 c. multicoloured (optd "BCG") 25 15
1150 30 c. multicoloured (optd "BMJ") 25 15
1151 30 c. multicoloured (optd "EKE") 25 15
1152 30 c. multicoloured (optd "GEO") 25 15
1153 30 c. multicoloured (optd "GFO") 25 15
1154 30 c. multicoloured (optd "IBM") 25 15
1155 30 c. multicoloured (optd T **274**) 25 15
1156 30 c. multicoloured (optd "KAI") 25 15
1157 30 c. multicoloured (optd "KAR") 25 15
1158 30 c. multicoloured (optd "KPG") 25 15
1159 30 c. multicoloured (optd "KRG") 25 15
1160 30 c. multicoloured (optd "KTO") 25 15
1161 30 c. multicoloured (optd "LTM") 25 15
1162 30 c. multicoloured (optd "MHA") 25 15
1163 30 c. multicoloured (optd "MWJ") 25 15
1164 30 c. multicoloured (optd "MYM") 25 15
1165 30 c. multicoloured (optd "NAI") 25 15
1166 30 c. multicoloured (optd "ORJ") 25 15
1167 30 c. multicoloured (optd "USI") 25 15
1168 30 c. multicoloured (optd "VEG") 25 15
1134/68 .. .. *Set of* 35 8·00 4·50

The overprints on the 20 c. value represent airlines, on the 25 c. international airports and on the 30 c. internal airports. Those on Nos. 1150 and 1154 were incorrect and examples of the former exist with the manuscript correction "PMT".

240 (275) **240** (275*a*)

1983 (14 Sept). *No.* 649 *surch with T* **275** *in blue by Autoprint.*
1169 240 c. on 35 c. on 60 c. Soldier's Cap .. .. 95 1·00
a. Surch with T **275*a*** .. .. .. 95 1·00
b. Pair. Nos. 1169/a .. .. .. 1·90

Types **275** and **275*a*** occur *se-tenant* within the sheet.

FAO 1983

30

(276)

277 G.B. 1857 1d. with Georgetown "AO3" Postmark

1983 (15 Sept). *F.A.O. Fisheries Project. Nos.* 485 *and* 487 *surch as T* **276** *in red by Autoprint.*
1170 30 c. on 1 c. Type **87** 15 15
1171 $2.60 on 3 c. Lukunani .. .. .. 1·25 1·25

(Des K. Everett. Litho Format)

1983 (1 Oct). *125th Anniv of Use of Great Britain Stamps in Guyana. T* **277** *and similar square designs. W* **106**. *P* 14½.

(*a*) *Inscriptions in black*
1172 **277** 25 c. lake-brown and black 10 10
a. *Tête-bêche* (pair) 20
1173 – 30 c. rose-red and black 10 15
a. *Tête-bêche* (pair) 20
1174 – 60 c. bright violet and black 25 30
a. *Tête-bêche* (pair) 50
1175 – 120 c. dull green and black 50 55
a. *Tête-bêche* (pair) .. .. .. 1·00

(*b*) *Inscriptions in bright blue*
1176 **277** 25 c. lake-brown and black 10 10
a. Block of 4. Nos. 1176/9 40
1177 – 25 c. rose-red and black 10 10
1178 – 25 c. bright violet and black 10 10
1179 – 25 c. dull green and black 10 10
1180 **277** 30 c. lake-brown and black 10 15
a. Block of 4. Nos. 1180/3 40
1181 – 30 c. rose-red and black 10 15
1182 – 30 c. bright violet and black 10 15
1183 – 30 c. dull green and black 10 15
1184 **277** 45 c. lake-brown and black 20 25
a. Block of 4. Nos. 1184/7 80
1185 – 45 c. rose-red and black 20 25
1186 – 45 c. bright violet and black 20 25
1187 – 45 c. dull green and black 20 25
1188 **277** 120 c. lake-brown and black 50 55
a. Block of 4. Nos. 1188/91 .. .. 2·50
1189 – 130 c. rose-red and black 55 60
1190 – 150 c. bright violet and black 65 70
1191 – 200 c. dull green and black 90 95
1172/91 .. .. *Set of* 20 4·50 5·00

Designs:—Nos. 1173, 1177, 1181, 1185, 1189, G.B. 1857 4d. rose; Nos. 1174, 1178, 1182, 1186, 1190, G.B. 1856 6d. lilac; Nos. 1175, 1179, 1183, 1187, 1191, G.B. 1856 1s. green.

Each design incorporates the "A03" postmark except Nos. 1189/91 which show mythical postmarks of the Crowned-circle type inscribed "DEMERARA", "BERBICE" or "ESSEQUIBO".

Nos. 1172/5 were each printed in sheets with the bottom row inverted, forming vertical *tête-bêche* pairs. Nos. 1176/87 were issued in sheets of 60, one for each value, with the four designs *se-tenant*. Nos. 1188/91 were issued in sheets of 20, containing five *se-tenant* blocks.

75

INT. COMMUNICATIONS YEAR 50

(278) (279)

1983 (15 Oct). *International Communications Year. No.* 716 *surch with T* **278** *by Autoprint.*
1192 50 c. on 375 c. on $3 Cylinder satellite .. 3·00 30

No. 1192 also carries an otherwise unissued "375" surcharge. As issued much of this surcharge is obliterated by two groups of six thin horizontal lines.

1983 (15 Oct). *St. John's Ambulance Commemoration. Nos.* 650 *and* 653 *surch as T* **279**, *vertically on No.* 1194 *by Autoprint.*
1193 **156** 75 c. on 8 c. silver, black and magenta .. 1·50 30
1194 – $1.20 on 40 c. silver, black and new blue 3·50 50

$1.20

Int. Food Day 1983

1918-1983

(280) (281)

1983 (15 Oct). *International Food Day. No.* 616 *surch with T* **280** *by Autoprint.*
1195 $1.20 on 35 c. Five-fingers and awaras .. 60 50

1983 (15 Oct). *65th Anniv of I.L.O. and 25th Death Anniv. of H. N. Critchlow (founder of Guyana Labour Union). No.* 840 *further optd with T* **281** *by Autoprint.*
1196 240 c. on $3 H. N. Critchlow .. .. .. 1·25 1·25

25c. (282) **Human Rights Day** (283)

1983 (1 Nov). *Deepavali Festival. Nos.* 661 *and* 663/4 *surch as T* **282** *by Autoprint.*
1197 25 c. on 8 c. Type **158** 15 10
1198 $1.50 on 35 c. Flame in bowl.. .. .. 1·00 60
1199 $1.50 on 40 c. Goddess Latchmi 70 60
1197/9 .. .. *Set of* 3 1·75 1·25

On Nos. 1198/9 the original face values are obliterated by "XX" and the surcharges are horizontal.

1983 (3 Nov). *No.* 732 *optd with T* **226** *and No.* 798 *further optd with T* **256**, *both vertically reading upwards by Autoprint.*
1200 $3 "Makanaima the Great Ancestral Spirit of the Amerindians" (B.) .. .. 1·25 1·00
a. Opt reading downwards .. .. 12·00
1201 360 c. on $2 *Norantea guianensis* .. .. 1·50 1·40

1983 (15 Nov). *Wildlife Protection. Nos.* 686 *and* 688 *surch as T* **234**, *and No.* 852 *optd with T* **256** *by Autoprint.*
1202 30 c. Six-banded Armadillo 20 15
1203 60 c. on 15 c. Giant sea turtle.. .. .. 35 30
1204 $1.20 on 40 c. Iguana.. .. .. .. 55 50
1202/4 .. .. *Set of* 3 1·00 85

1983 (1 Dec). *Human Rights Day. No.* 1079*c optd with T* **283** *by Autoprint.*
1205 $3 Rotary anniversary emblem .. .. 1·10 1·25

LOS ANGELES 1984

(284)

●●● 55

(284*a*)

1983 (6 Dec). *Olympic Games, Los Angeles* (1984). *Nos.* 733/44 *surch with T* **284** *by Herald Printing-Kitty or further surch with T* **284*a*** *by Autoprint.*
1206 55 c. on 125 c. on 35 c. Type **174** 25 25
a. Block of 12. Nos. 1206/17 .. .. 3·50
1207 55 c. on 125 c. on 35 c. Haimara 25 25
1208 55 c. on 125 c. on 35 c. Electric Eel.. .. 25 25
1209 55 c. on 125 c. on 35 c. Golden Rivulus .. 25 25
1210 55 c. on 125 c. on 35 c. Pencil Fish 25 25
1211 55 c. on 125 c. on 35 c. Four-eyed Fish .. 25 25
1212 55 c. on 125 c. on 35 c. Pirai or Carib Fish 25 25
1213 55 c. on 125 c. on 35 c. Smoking Hassar .. 25 25
1214 55 c. on 125 c. on 35 c. Devil Ray 25 25
1215 55 c. on 125 c. on 35 c. Flying Patwa .. 25 25
1216 55 c. on 125 c. on 35 c. Arapaima Pirariucii 25 25
1217 55 c. on 125 c. on 35 c. Lukanani 25 25
1217*a* 125 c. on 35 c. Type **174** .. .. .. 1·50
ab. Block of 12. Nos. 1217*a*/*l* .. .. 18·00
1217*b* 125 c. on 35 c. Haimara .. .. .. 1·50
1217*c* 125 c. on 35 c. Electric Eel .. .. .. 1·50
1217*d* 125 c. on 35 c. Golden Rivulus .. .. 1·50
1217*e* 125 c. on 35 c. Pencil Fish .. .. .. 1·50
1217*f* 125 c. on 35 c. Four-eyed Fish .. .. 1·50
1217*g* 125 c. on 35 c. Pirai or Carib Fish .. .. 1·50
1217*h* 125 c. on 35 c. Smoking Hassar .. .. 1·50
1217*i* 125 c. on 35 c. Devil Ray .. .. .. 1·50
1217*j* 125 c. on 35 c. Flying Patwa .. .. 1·50
1217*k* 125 c. on 35 c. Arapaima Pirariucii.. .. 1·50
1217*l* 125 c. on 35 c. Lukanani .. .. .. 1·50

1983 (14 Dec). *No.* F7 *with unissued "ESPANA 1982" surch, as Nos.* 938/9 *in blue, further optd with T* **256** *vertically by Autoprint.*
1218 180 c. on 60 c. Soldier's Cap 75 65
a. Opt (T **256**) omitted .. .. ..

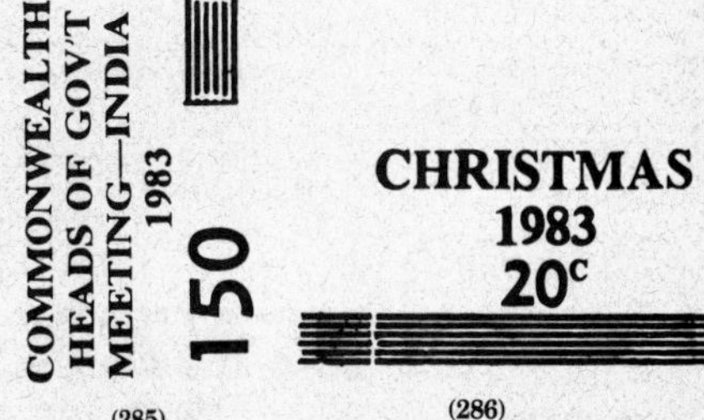

(285) (286)

1983 (14 Dec). *Commonwealth Heads of Government Meeting, New Delhi. No.* 542 *surch with T* **285** *by Autoprint.*
1219 150 c. on 1 c. Pitcher Plant of Mt Roraima .. 70 60

1983 (14 Dec). *Christmas. Nos.* 861A/B *further surch with T* **286** *by Autoprint.*

	A. *No wmk*		B. *Wmk* **106**	
1220 20 c. on 12 c. on 6 c. Patua ..	10	10	10	10

1984 (8 Jan). *Nos.* 838 *and* F9 *optd as T* **229**, *but smaller* 24 × 6 *mm, vertically in blue by Autoprint.*

1221 $2 *Norantea guianensis* .. .. 1·25 70
1221*a* 550 c. on $10 *Elbella patrobas* .. .. 3·50 3·25

17 ¢

(287)

1984 (Jan). *Flowers. Unissued coil stamps as T* **222** *handstamped with T* **287** *in blue.*

1222 17 c. on 2 c. grey-lilac, blue & turquoise-green 10 10
a. Vert pair. Nos. 1222/3 .. .. 25 25
1223 17 c. on 8 c. grey-lilac, blue and mauve .. 10 10

Nos. 1222/3 were intended for use on 8 c. postal stationery envelopes to uprate them to the new price of 25 c.

ALL
OUR HERITAGE
● 25

(288)

1984
● 25

(289)

1984
● 25

(290)

● 25

(291)

1984 (24 Feb). *Republic Day. No.* 703 *surch as T* **288/91** *in black and No.* 705*a optd as T* **288/9** *in blue by Autoprint.*

1224 25 c. on 35 c. multicoloured (surch T **288**) .. 10 10
a. Sheetlet of 25. No. 1224 × 6, Nos. 1225/7 each × 4, Nos. 1228/30 each × 2 and No. 1231 .. .. 2·50
1225 25 c. on 35 c. multicoloured (surch T **289**) .. 10 10
1226 25 c. on 35 c. multi (surch "REPUBLIC DAY") 10 10
1227 25 c. on 35 c. multicoloured (surch T **290**) .. 10 10
1228 25 c. on 35 c. multi (surch "BERBICE") .. 20 15
1229 25 c. on 35 c. multi (surch "DEMERARA") .. 20 15
1230 25 c. on 35 c. multi (surch "ESSEQUIBO") .. 20 15
1231 25 c. on 35 c. multicoloured (surch T **291**) .. 40 35
1232 60 c. multicoloured (opt T **288**) .. 25 30
a. Sheetlet of 25. Nos. 1232/3 each × 8 and No. 1234 × 9 .. .. 5·75
1233 60 c. multicoloured (opt "REPUBLIC DAY") 25 30
1234 60 c. multicoloured (opt T **289**) .. 25 30
1224/34 .. .. *Set of* 11 1·90 1·75

25 ¢ POSTAGE (+ 2·25) (SURTAX)
OLYMPIC
GAMES 84

(292)

1984 (1 Mar). *Guyana Olympic Committee Appeal. Nos.* 841/3 *handstamped with T* **292** *in blue.*

1235 25 c. +2.25 c. on 60 c. on 3 c. Hanging Heliconia 4·00 2·50
1236 25 c. +2.25 c. on 75 c. on $5 *Odontadenia grandiflora* .. .. 4·00 2·50
1237 25 c. +2.25 c. on $1.10 on $2 *Norantea guianensis* .. .. 4·00 2·50
1235/7 .. .. *Set of* 3 11·00 6·75

Nos. 1235/7 come from stamp booklets, the $2.25 charity premium on each stamp being donated to the local Olympic Committee Appeal Fund. All examples of these handstamps are inverted.

PRINTERS. Nos. 1238/97 and 1302/27 were overprinted or surcharged by Autoprint, Georgetown.

Protecting
Our Heritage

(293)

XXXXX
90

(294)

1984 (5 Mar). *Nature Protection. Various stamps optd with T* **293** *in black (except for No.* 1239 *in blue) with some additionally surch as T* **272** *(Nos.* 1238/40, 1250/1 *and* 1254/5) *or as T* **294** *(Nos.* 1242, 1247 *and* 1252/3) *all in blue.*

1238 20 c. on 15 c. multicoloured (No. 491) (opt + surch vert) .. .. 1·75 10
a. Opt T **293** in blue .. .. .. 12·00 50
1239 20 c. on 15 c. multicoloured (No. 791) (opt + surch vert) .. .. 1·75 10
a. Surch on No. 791a (pair) .. ..
1240 20 c. on 15 c. multicoloured (No. 1044) (opt + surch vert) .. .. 17·00 1·50
a. Opt T **293** in blue .. .. .. 4·00 1·00
1241 25 c. multicoloured (No. 550*a*) .. .. 3·00 10
a. On No. 550ab .. .. .. 32·00 3·00
1242 30 c. on 15 c. multicoloured (No. 548) .. 4·50 15
1243 40 c. multicoloured (No. 494) (opt vert) .. 2·00 20
1244 50 c. multicoloured (No. 552) 40 25
1245 50 c. multicoloured (No. F6) 40 25
a. Opt Type F 1 double .. .. 23·00
1246 60 c. multicoloured (No. 459) .. .. 4·25 30
a. On No. 496 .. .. .. 50·00 4·00
1247 90 c. on 40 c. multicoloured (No. 551) .. 2·75 40
a. On No. F5 .. .. .. 70·00 6·00
1248 180 c. on 40 c. multicoloured (No. 919) .. 2·75 70
1249 $2 multicoloured (No. 461) .. .. 23·00 1·25
1250 225 c. on 10 c. multicoloured (No. 490a) (opt + surch vert) .. .. 5·00 90
1251 260 c. on $1 multicoloured (No. 497a) .. 3·75 1·00
1252 320 c. on 40 c. multicoloured (No. 551) .. 2·75 1·25
1253 350 c. on 40 c. multicoloured (No. 551) .. 4·50 1·50
1254 390 c. on 50 c. multicoloured (No. 495) .. 2·75 1·75
a. On No. 458 .. .. .. 75·00 20·00
1255 450 c. on $5 multicoloured (No. 499) .. 3·00 1·90
1238/55 .. .. *Set of* 18 65·00 10·00

1984

(295)

(296)

1984 (17 Mar). *Easter. Nos.* 483 *and* 916/17 *optd with T* **295**, *and No.* 481 *surch as T* **272**, *but without decimal point, all in blue.*

1256 **111** 30 c. multicoloured 15 20
1257 45 c. on 6 c. multicoloured 20 25
1258 75 c. on 40 c. multicoloured 30 35
1259 130 c. on 6 c. multicoloured 55 60
1256/9 .. .. .. *Set of* 4 1·10 1·25

No. 1258 exists with the previous surcharge either at the right or in the centre of the design.

1984 (2 Apr). *Nos.* 937/9 *and* 991 *surch as T* **294**.

1260 75 c. on $1 *Chelonanthus uliginoides* .. 3·50 35
1261 75 c. on 110 c. on 3 c. Hanging Heliconia .. 4·50 35
1262 225 c. on 250 c. on 6 c. Cannon-ball tree .. 1·75 1·25
1263 230 c. on $2.35 on 180 c. on 60 c. Soldier's Cap 1·75 1·50

1984 (2 May). *Nos.* 899/901, 904/6 *and* 909 *surch as T* **294**.

1264 20 c. on 15 c. on 2 c. Type **132** (No. 899) 40 10
1265 75 c. on 110 c. on 5 c. Annatto tree (No. 904) 4·00 45
1266 90 c. on 110 c. on 5 c. Annatto tree (No. 900) (B.) .. .. 2·75 60
1267 90 c. on 110 c. on 5 c. Annatto tree (No. 901) (B.) .. .. 3·75 60
1268 120 c. on 125 c. on 8 c. on 6 c. Cannon-ball tree (No. 905) .. .. 3·75 75
1269 120 c. on 125 c. on 8 c. on 6 c. Cannon-ball tree (No. 906) .. .. 3·75 75
1270 120 c. on 125 c. on 8 c. on 6 c. Cannon-ball tree (No. 909) .. .. 2·00 75
1264/70 .. .. *Set of* 7 18·00 3·50

Nos. 1264/70 were surcharged on the sheets which contained one type of the previous surcharge only.

1984 (17 May). *World Telecommunications and Health Day. Nos.* 802 *and* 980 *surch as T* **296** *in blue.*

1271 25 c. on 220 c. on 1 c. Pitcher Plant of Mt Roraima (surch T **296**) 20 20
a. Sheetlet of 25. Nos. 1271/2 each × 8 and No. 1273 × 9 .. .. .. 4·50
1272 25 c. on 220 c. on 1 c. Pitcher Plant of Mt Roraima (surch "WHO DAY 1984") .. 20 20
1273 25 c. on 220 c. on 1 c. Pitcher Plant of Mt Roraima (surch "ITU/WHO DAY 1984") 20 20
1274 $4.50 on 280 c. on $5 *Odontadenis grandiflora* (surch "ITU/WHO DAY 1984") .. 1·75 1·75
1271/4 .. .. *Set of* 4 2·10 2·10

The surcharge is horizontal on No. 1274 and vertical on the others.

1984 (11 June). *No.* 1005 *surch vertically as T* **272**, *but without decimal point.*

1275 120 c. on $1.25 on 6 c. Cannon-ball tree .. 3·25 55

1984 (15 June). *World Forestry Conference. Nos.* 752/5 *surch as T* **272**, *but without decimal point, or optd with T* **295** *($3), and No.* 875 *surch as T* **294**.

1276 55 c. on 30 c. *Hymenaea courbaril* .. .. 1·50 30
1277 75 c. on 110 c. on $3 *Peltogyne venosa* (B.) .. 30 35
1278 160 c. on 50 c. *Mora excelsa* (B.) 65 70
1279 260 c. on 10 c. Type **177** (B.) .. .. 1·10 1·25
1280 $3 *Peltogyne venosa* (B.) .. .. 1·25 1·40
1276/80 .. .. *Set of* 5 4·25 3·50

1984 (18 June). *No.* 625 *surch vertically as T* **294**.

1281 55 c. on 110 c. on 10 c. Type **150** 25 30
1282 90 c. on 110 c. on 10 c. Type **150** (B.) 40 45

Nos. 1281/2 also carry an otherwise unissued 110 c. surcharge in blue as Type **264**.

UPU
Congress 1984
Hamburg

(297)

60

(298)

1984 (19 June). *U.P.U. Congress, Hamburg. Nos.* 1188/91 *optd with T* **297**.

1283 120 c. lake-brown and black 50 55
a. Block of 4. Nos. 1283/6 .. .. .. 2·50
1284 130 c. rose-red and black 55 60
1285 150 c. bright violet and black 60 65
1286 200 c. dull green and black 80 85
1283/6 .. .. *Set of* 4 2·25 2·40

1984 (21 June). *Nos.* 982/3 *and* 986/7 *surch with T* **298** *(60 c.) or as T* **272**, *but without the decimal point (others).*

1287 45 c. on 50 c. on 2 c. myrtle-green 20 25
1288 60 c. on $1.10 on 3 c. brown-olive and red-brown (B.) 75 30
a. Surch on No. 983c .. .. .. 1·50 30
1289 120 c. on $1.25 on 6 c. yellow-green 50 55
1290 200 c. on $2.20 on 24 c. black and brownish orange (B.) 80 85

1984 (30 June). *Nos.* 979/80 *and* 1003 *surch as T* **294**, *and No.* 981 *optd vertically with T* **295**.

1291 75 c. on 110 c. on 5 c. Annatto tree 30 35
1292 120 c. on 170 c. on 110 c. on 5 c. Annatto tree 50 55
1293 200 c. on 220 c. on 1 c. Pitcher Plant of Mt Roraima (B.) .. .. 3·00 85
1294 330 c. on $2 *Norantea guianensis* (B.) .. 1·40 1·50

CARICOM DAY 1984
60 XX

(299)

1984 (30 June). *CARICOM Day. No.* 1200 *additionally surch with T* **299**.

1295 60 c. on $3 "Makanaima the Great Ancestral Spirit of the Amerindians" 25 30

1984 (30 June). *No.* 544 *surch as T* **275** *in blue.*

1296 150 c. on 3 c. Hanging Heliconia 60 65

60
CARICOM
HEADS OF GOV'T
CONFERENCE
JULY 1984

(300)

301 Children and Thatched School

1984 (2 July). *CARICOM Heads of Government Conference. No.* 544 *surch with T* **300** *in blue.*

1297 60 c. on 3 c. Hanging Heliconia 25 30

(Litho Format)

1984 (16 July). *Centenary of Guyana Teachers' Association. T* **301** *and similar horiz designs. Multicoloured. W* **106** *(sideways). P* 14.

1298 25 c. Type **301** 10 15
a. Block of 4. Nos. 1298/301 35
1299 25 c. Torch and graduates 10 15
1300 25 c. Torch and target emblem 10 15
1301 25 c. Teachers of 1884 and 1984 in front of school 10 15
1298/301 .. .. .. *Set of* 4 35 55

Nos. 1298/301 were printed together, *se-tenant*, in blocks of 4 throughout the sheet.

INT.
CHESS
FED.
1924-1984
25 XX

(302)

25
TRACK
AND
FIELD

(303)

1984 (20 July). *50th Anniv of International Chess Federation. No.* 1048 *optd or surch as T* **302** *or optd with T* **295**, *all in blue.*

1302 25 c. on 90 c. on 60 c. Fort Island (surch T **302**) 15 15
a. Sheetlet of 25. No. 1302 × 16 and No. 1303 × 9 .. .. 5·00
1303 25 c. on 90 c. on 60 c. Fort Island (opt T **295**) .. 35 15
1304 75 c. on 90 c. on 60 c. Fort Island (surch T **302**) 40 35
a. Sheetlet of 25. No. 1304 × 16 and No. 1305 × 9 .. .. 9·00

1305 75 c. on 90 c. on 60 c. Fort Island (opt T **295**) .. 40 35
1306 90 c. on 60 c. Fort Island (opt T **302**) 50 45
a. Sheetlet of 25. No. 1306 × 16 and No. 1307 × 9 .. .. 11·00
1307 90 c. on 60 c. Fort Island (opt T **295**) 50 45
1302/7 .. .. *Set of* 6 2·10 1·60

Overprints as Type **295** occur in the central horizontal and vertical rows of each sheet.

1984 (28 July). *Olympic Games, Los Angeles. No.* 1051 *surch as T* **303** *in blue.*

1308 25 c. on $1.30, multicoloured (surch T **303**) .. 20 25
a. Booklet pane of 10. No. 1308 × 4 and Nos. 1309/10, each × 3 .. .. .. 2·00
b. Coil strip of 5. Nos. 1308 × 2, 1311 × 2 and 1312 .. .. 1·00
1309 25 c. on $1.30, mult (surch "BOXING") .. 20 25
1310 25 c. on $1.30, mult (surch "OLYMPIC GAMES 1984 LOS ANGELES") .. 20 25
1311 25 c. on $1.30, mult (surch "CYCLING") .. 40 25
1312 25 c. on $1.30, mult (surch "OLYMPIC GAMES 1984") .. .. .. 2·50 50
1313 $1.20 on $1.30, multicoloured (surch T **303**) 1·00 1·10
a. Booklet pane of 10. No. 1313 × 4 and Nos. 1314/15 each × 3 .. .. .. 10·00
b. Coil strip of 5. Nos. 1313 × 2, 1316 × 2 and 1317 .. .. 5·00
1314 $1.20 on $1.30, mult (surch "BOXING") .. 1·00 1·10
1315 $1.20 on $1.30, mult (surch "OLYMPIC GAMES 1984 LOS ANGELES") .. 1·00 1·10
1316 $1.20 on $1.30, mult (surch "CYCLING") .. 1·50 1·10
1317 $1.20 on $1.30, multicoloured (surch "OLYMPIC GAMES 1984") .. .. 3·00 1·50
1308/17 .. .. *Set of* 10 10·00 6·50

Nos. 1308 and 1313 come from booklets and coils, Nos. 1309/10 and 1314/15 from booklets only, and Nos. 1311/12 and 1316/17 from coils only.

The coils were constructed from normal sheets with coil joins on every fifth stamp.

(304)

1984 (15 Aug). *60th Anniv of Girl Guide Movement in Guyana. Nos.* 900/9 *surch with T* **304** *in blue.*

1318 25 c. on 110 c. on 5 c. Annatto tree (No. 900) 10 15
a. Sheetlet of 25. Nos. 1318/19, each × 8, Nos. 1320/1, each × 4 and No. 1322 .. 3·00
1319 25 c. on 110 c. on 5 c. Annatto tree (No. 901) .. 10 15
1320 25 c. on 110 c. on 5 c. Annatto tree (No. 902) .. 10 15
1321 25 c. on 110 c. on 5 c. Annatto tree (No. 903) .. 10 15
1322 25 c. on 110 c. on 5 c. Annatto tree (No. 904) .. 75 40
1323 25 c. on 125 c. on 8 c. on 6 c. Cannon-ball tree (No. 905) 10 15
a. Sheetlet of 25. Nos. 1323/4, each × 8, Nos. 1325/6, each × 4 and No. 1327 .. 3·00
1324 25 c. on 125 c. on 8 c. on 6 c. Cannon-ball tree (No. 906) 10 15
1325 25 c. on 125 c. on 8 c. on 6 c. Cannon-ball tree (No. 907) 10 15
1326 25 c. on 125 c. on 8 c. on 6 c. Cannon-ball tree (No. 908) 10 15
1327 25 c. on 125 c. on 8 c. on 6 c. Cannon-ball tree (No. 909) 75 40
1318/27 .. .. *Set of* 10 1·90 1·75

— 25 130 1984

(305) (306) (307)

1984 1984

(308) (309)

1984 (Sept–Nov). *Various stamps surch or optd.*

(a) As T **294** *or as T* **298** *(60 c.)*

1328 20 c. on 15 c. on 2 c. Type **132** (No. 1030) .. 15 10
1329 20 c. on 15 c. on 2 c. Type **132** (No. 1034) .. 45 10
1330 20 c. on 15 c. on 2 c. Type **132** (No. 1063) .. 30 10
1331 60 c. on 110 c. on 8 c. on 3 c. Hanging Heliconia (as No. 868, but without T **219**) (two vert obliterating panels) .. 24·00
a. One vert obliterating panel* .. 85·00
1332 120 c. on 125 c. on 8 c. on 6 c. Cannon-ball tree (No. 893) .. .. 1·50 50
1333 120 c. on 125 c. on $2 *Norantea guianensis* (No. 834) .. .. 22·00
1334 120 c. on 125 c. on $2 *Norantea guianensis* (No. O20) 90 50
1335 120 c. on 140 c. on $1 *Chelonanthus uliginoides* (No. 796) .. .. 2·50 50
1336 200 c. on 220 c. on 1 c. Pitcher Plant of Mt Roraima (No. 922) (B.) .. .. .. 1·50 85
1337 320 c. on $1.10 on $2 *Norantea guianensis* (No. 804) (B.) .. .. 2·50 2·00
1338 350 c. on 375 c. on $5 *Odontadenia grandiflora* (No. 803) (B.) .. .. 1·75 1·40
1339 390 c. on 400 c. on $5 *Odontadenia grandiflora* (No. 1091) (B.) .. .. 2·00 1·60
1340 450 c. on $5 *Odontadenia grandiflora* (No. O16) (B.) .. .. 2·25 1·90

*The small original printing of the 60 c. surcharge has the "8 c" and "110" values obliterated by a single vertical block of six lines. On the vast majority of the supply these features were covered by two vertical blocks of six lines each.

(b) As T **305** *(figures surch, bar in ballpoint pen)*

1341 25 c. on 10 c. Cattleya (No. 547) .. .. 9·00 2·00
a. Surch on No. 547a .. .. .. 35·00
1342 25 c. on 15 c. Christmas Orchid (No. 864a) .. 2·00 12
1342*a* 25 c. on 35 c. on 60 c. Soldier's Cap (No. 649) 70·00

(c) As T **306** *(on Nos.* 1343/8 *the original face value is obliterated by a fleur-de-lys*

1343 25 c. on 15 c. Christmas Orchid (No. 548) .. 90·00
1344 25 c. on 15 c. Christmas Orchid (No. 809) .. 42·00
1345 25 c. on 15 c. Christmas Orchid (No. 864) .. 6·00 1·75
1346 25 c. on 15 c. Christmas Orchid (No. 977) .. 1·75 10
a. Surch on No. 977a .. .. .. 90·00
1347 25 c. on 15 c. Christmas Orchid (No. 1009) .. 1·75 10
1348 25 c. on 15 c. Christmas Orchid (No. O23) .. 1·75 10
1349 130 c. on 110 c. on $2 *Norantea guianensis* (No. 804) .. .. 70·00
1350 130 c. on 110 c. on $2 *Norantea guianensis* (No. O22) .. .. 20·00 3·00
1351 600 c. on $7.20 on $1 *Chelonanthus uliginoides* (No. 770A) .. .. 25·00 5·00
a. With two fleur-de-lys over original opt 2·00 1·25
b. Surch on No. 770B .. .. .. 13·00 3·00
ba. With two fleur-de-lys over original opt 2·00

(d) With T **307** *(Nov)*

1352 20 c. *Paphinia cristata* (No. 549) .. .. 4·00 10
a. Optd on No. 549a .. .. .. 85·00
1353 $3.60 on $5 *Odontadenia grandiflora* (No. 769A) .. .. 7·50
a. Optd on No. 769B .. .. .. 18·00 2·00

(e) With T **308** *vertically in blue (Nov)*

1354 50 c. on 8 c. Type **136** (No. 1062) .. .. 4·00 25
1355 60 c. on 1 c. Pitcher Plant of Mt Roraima (No. 1000) 30 25
1356 $2 *Norantea guianensis* (No. O33) .. .. 1·25 1·00

(f) With T **309**

1357 20 c. *Paphinia cristata* (No. 549) .. .. 40·00
a. Optd on No. 549a .. .. .. 90·00
1357*b* 20 c. *Paphina cristata* (No. 887a) ("1984" omitted) .. ..
1358 25 c. Marabunta (No. 550) .. .. .. 65·00
1358*a* 25 c. Marabunta (No. 889) ("1984" omitted)
1358*b* 25 c. Marabunta (No. 889b) ("1984" omitted) .. ..
1359 25 c. Marabunta (No. F4) .. .. .. 2·25 50
a. Optd on No. F4a .. .. .. 1·50 10
1360 $3.60 on $5 *Odontadenia grandiflora* (No. 769A) .. .. 2·00 1·50
a. Optd on No. 769B .. .. .. 2·50

ICAO

(310)

(311)

1984 (6 Sept). *40th Anniv of International Civil Aviation Organization. Nos.* 981 *(with previously unissued surcharge),* 1017 *and* 1148/68 *optd as T* **310** *(30 c.) or T* **311** *(200 c.), all in blue by Autoprint.*

1361 30 c. multicoloured (No. 1148) 10 15
a. Sheetlet of 25. Nos. 1361/71, 1372 × 2 and 1373/84 .. .. 2·50
1362 30 c. multicoloured (No. 1149) 10 15
1363 30 c. multicoloured (No. 1150) 10 15
1364 30 c. multicoloured (No. 1151) 10 15
1365 30 c. multicoloured (No. 1152) 10 15
1366 30 c. multicoloured (No. 1153) 10 15
1367 30 c. mult (No. 1154) (optd "IMB/ICAO") 10 15
1368 30 c. mult (No. 1155) (optd "KCV/ICAO") 10 15
1369 30 c. mult (No. 1156) (optd "KAI/ICAO") 10 15
1370 30 c. multicoloured (No. 1157) 10 15
1371 30 c. multicoloured (No. 1158) 10 15
1372 30 c. mult (No. 1155) (optd "1984") .. 10 15
1373 30 c. mult (No. 1155) (optd "KPM/ICAO") 10 15
1374 30 c. multicoloured (No. 1159) 10 15
1375 30 c. multicoloured (No. 1160) 10 15
1376 30 c. multicoloured (No. 1161) 10 15
1377 30 c. mult (No. 1155) (optd "PMT/ICAO") 10 15
1378 30 c. multicoloured (No. 1162) 10 15
1379 30 c. multicoloured (No. 1163) 10 15
1380 30 c. multicoloured (No. 1164) 10 15
1381 30 c. multicoloured (No. 1165) 10 15
1382 30 c. multicoloured (No. 1166) 10 15
1383 30 c. multicoloured (No. 1167) 10 15
1384 30 c. multicoloured (No. 1168) 10 15
1385 200 c. on 330 c. on $2 mult (No. 981) .. 65 70
a. Opt T **311** omitted .. .. ..
1386 200 c. on 75 c. on $5 mult (No. 1017) .. 2·50 1·50
1361/86 .. .. *Set of* 26 5·00 5·25

No. 1385 also carries an otherwise unissued surcharge "G.A.C. Inaug. Flight Georgetown—Toronto 200" in black.

COVER PRICES

Cover factors are quoted at the beginning of each country for most issues to 1945. An explanation of the system can be found on page x. The factors quoted do not, however, apply to philatelic covers.

1984 $1.50 X

(312) (313) (314)

1984 (15 Sept). *Wildlife Protection. Nos.* 756/67 *optd with T* **312** *by Autoprint.*

1387 30 c. Type **178** 15 20
a. Sheetlet of 12. Nos. 1387/98 .. .. 1·60
1388 30 c. Red Howler 15 20
1389 30 c. Common Squirrel-Monkey 15 20
1390 30 c. Two-toed Sloth 15 20
1391 30 c. Brazilian Tapir 15 20
1392 30 c. Collared Peccary 15 20
1393 30 c. Six-banded Armadillo 15 20
1394 30 c. Tamandua ("Ant Eater") 15 20
1395 30 c. Giant Anteater 15 20
1396 30 c. Murine Opossum 15 20
1397 30 c. Brown Four-eyed Opossum 15 20
1398 30 c. Brazilian Agouti 15 20
1387/98 .. .. *Set of* 12 1·60 2·25

1984 (1 Oct). *Nos.* D6/7 *and* D10/11 *surch with T* **269** *in blue by Autoprint.*

1399 **D 2** 120 c. on 4 c. dp ultramarine (No. D6) 2·75 45
1400 120 c. on 4 c. dull ultram (No. D10) 10·00 75
1401 120 c. on 12 c. reddish scarlet (No. D7) 2·75 45
1402 120 c. on 12 c. bright scarlet (No. D11) 2·75 45
1399/402 .. .. *Set of* 4 16·00 1·90

1984 (15 Oct). *175th Birth Anniv of Louis Braille (inventor of alphabet for the blind). No.* 1040 *surch with T* **313** *in blue by Autoprint.*

1403 $1.50 on 15 c. on 10 c. Type **215** .. .. 2·50 55

1984 (15 Oct). *International Food Day. No.* 1012 *surch with T* **314** *by Tip Torres.*

1404 150 c. on 50 c. Pawpaw and tangerine .. 50 55

Type **314** places a "1" alongside the original face value and obliterates the "1982" date on the previous overprint.

1984 (15 Oct). *Birth Centenary of H. N. Critchlow (founder of Guyana Labour Union). No.* 873, *surch horizontally as T* **236**, *and No.* 1196, *both optd with T* **312** *by Autoprint.*

1405 240 c. on 110 c. on $3 H. N. Critchlow (No. 873) .. .. 1·00 85
1406 240 c. on $3 H. N. Critchlow (No. 1196) .. 5·00 85

1984 (22 Oct). *Nos.* 910/12 *surch as T* **272**, *but vertically and without the decimal point, and Nos.* 1184/7 *surch as T* **234** *by Autoprint.*

1407 **277** 25 c. on 45 c. lake-brown and black .. 15 15
a. Block of 4. Nos. 1407/10 .. 55
1408 – 25 c. on 45 c. rose-red and black (No. 1185) 15 15
1409 – 25 c. on 45 c. bright violet and black (No. 1186) 15 15
1410 – 25 c. on 45 c. dull green and black (No. 1187) 15 15
1411 – 120 c. on 100 c. on $3 multicoloured (No. 910) .. .. 2·75 45
1412 – 120 c. on 400 c. on 30 c. multicoloured (No. 911) 45 45
1413 – 320 c. on $5 mult (No. 912) (B.) .. 4·00 1·25
1407/13 .. .. *Set of* 7 7·00 2·50

25 X

MAHA SABHA 1934-1984

(315)

Philatelic Exhibition New York 1984

(316)

1984 (1 Nov). *Deepavali Festival. Nos.* 544/5 *surch as T* **315** *in blue by Autoprint.*

1414 25 c. on 5 c. Annatto tree 10 10
1415 $1.50 on 3 c. Hanging Heliconia 50 55

1984 (15 Nov). *A.S.D.A. Philatelic Exhibition, New York. Nos.* 1188/91 *optd with T* **316** *in red by Autoprint.*

1416 **277** 120 c. lake-brown and black 40 45
a. Block of 4. Nos. 1416/19 .. 1·90
1417 – 130 c. rose-red and black 45 50
1418 – 150 c. bright violet and black .. 50 55
1419 – 200 c. dull green and black 70 75
1416/19 .. .. *Set of* 4 1·90 2·00

(Litho Format)

1984 (16 Nov). *Olympic Games, Los Angeles (2nd issue). Design as No.* 1051, *but with Olympic rings and inscr* "OLYMPIC GAMES 1984 LOS ANGELES". *P* 13½.

1420 $1.20, Youth display (41 × 25 *mm*) .. .. 1·50 45

No. 1420 also exists from coils of 500 or 1,000 with numbers on the reverse of each stamp.

X 20

(317)

318 Pair of Swallow-tailed Kites on Tree

1984 (24 Nov). *Nos.* 847, 861B, 1099 *and* 1102 *surch as T* **317**.

1421 20 c. on 12 c. on 12 c. on 6 c. multicoloured (No. 847) 35 10
1422 20 c. on 12 c. on 6 c. mult (No. 861B) .. 60·00
1423 25 c. on 50 c. on 6 c. mult (No. 1099) .. 10 10
1424 60 c. on $1 on 6 c. mult (No. 1102).. .. 20 25

No. 1423 shows the previous surcharge obliterated by horizontal parallel lines.

(Litho Questa)

1984 (3 Dec). *Christmas. Swallow-tailed Kites. T* **318** *and similar horiz designs. Multicoloured. W* **106** *(sideways). P* 14×14½.

1425 60 c. Type **318** 60 60
a. Horiz strip of 5. Nos. 1425/9 .. .. 2·75
1426 60 c. Swallow-tailed Kite on branch .. 60 60
1427 60 c. Kite in flight with wings raised .. 60 60
1428 60 c. Kite in flight with wings lowered .. 60 60
1429 60 c. Kite gliding 60 60
1425/9 .. .. *Set of* 5 2·75 2·75

Nos. 1425/9 were printed together, *se-tenant*, in horizontal strips of 5 throughout the sheet with the backgrounds forming a composite design. Each stamp is inscribed "CHRISTMAS 1982"

319 St. George's Cathedral, Georgetown

(Litho Format)

1985 (8 Feb–Oct). *Georgetown Buildings. T* **319** *and similar horiz designs, each black and stone. W* **106** *(sideways). P* 14.

1430 25 c. Type **319** 10 10
1431 60 c. Demerara Mutual Life Assurance Building 20 25
1432 120 c. As No. 1431 .. .. 40 45
a. Horiz strip of 3. Nos. 1432/4 .. 1·25
b. No wmk (10.85) 40 45
ba. Horiz strip of 3. Nos. 1432b/4b .. 1·25
1433 120 c. Town Hall 40 45
b. No wmk (10.85) 40 45
1434 120 c. Victoria Law Courts.. .. .. 40 45
b. No wmk (10.85) 40 45
1435 200 c. As No. 1433 .. .. 70 75
1436 300 c. As No. 1434 .. .. 1·00 1·10
1430/6 .. .. *Set of* 7 3·00 3·25

Nos. 1432/4 were printed together, *se-tenant*, in horizontal strips of 3 within the sheet, forming a composite design.

International Youth Year 1985

(320)

Republic Day 1970-1985

(321)

1985 (15 Feb). *International Youth Year. As No.* 1420, *but W* **106** *(sideways), optd with T* **320** *by Tip Torres.*

1437 $1.20, Youth display .. .. .. 1·25 45

Examples used for this overprint all show the second line of the original inscription as "LOS ANGELLES".

1985 (22 Feb). *Republic Day. Nos* 1049/50 *and* 1052 *optd or surch as T* **321** *in red by Autoprint.*

1438 25 c. Type **238** 10 10
a. Horiz pair. Nos. 1438/9 .. .. 20 20
1439 25 c. Flag (inscr "30th ANNIVERSARY IN PARLIAMENT") 10 10
1440 120 c. on $6 Presidential standard.. .. 40 45
1441 130 c. on $6 Presidential standard.. .. 45 50
1438/41 .. .. *Set of* 4 1·00 1·00

322 Young Ocelot on Branch

International Youth Year 1985

(323)

(Des K. Everett. Litho Format)

1985 (11 Mar)–**87**. *Wildlife Protection. T* **322** *and similar multicoloured designs. W* **106** *inverted.* A. *P* 14½ (320 c., 330 c.) *or* 12½ *(others). Without imprint.* B. *P* 14. *With imprint date at foot* (18.2.87).

		A		B	
1442	25 c. Type **322** (grey-olive background)	1·00	10	†	
1443	60 c. Young Ocelot (*different*) (yell-brn background)..	20	25	†	
1444	120 c. As No. 1443	50	45	15	20
	a. Vert strip of 3. Nos. 1444/6 ..	1·50		40	
1445	120 c. Type **322**	50	45	15	20
1446	120 c. Young Ocelot (*diff*) (red-brown background) ..	50	45	15	20
1447	130 c. As No. 1446	45	50	†	
1448	320 c. Scarlet Macaw (28 × 46 *mm*)	2·00	1·25	†	
1449	330 c. Young Ocelot reaching for branch (28×46 *mm*)	1·10	1·25	†	
1442/9	.. .. .. *Set of* 8	5·75	4·25	†	

Nos. 1444/6 were printed together, *se-tenant*, in vertical strips of 3 throughout the sheet.

1985 (11 Mar–11 Apr). *No.* 940 *and Revenue stamp, as T* **181**, *surch as T* **305** *with fleur-de-lys over existing value, by Tip Torres, and Nos.* 912, 1016 *and* O 24 *surch as T* **272**, *but without the decimal point, by Autoprint.*

1450 30 c. on 50 c. multicoloured (No. O24) (B.) 15 10
1451 55 c. on 2 c. black, indigo & greenish grey 20 20
a. Opt "ESSEQUIBO etc" omitted .. 10·00
1452 55 c. on 15 c. on 2 c. black, indigo and greenish grey (No. 940) .. 20 20
1453 90 c. on $1 multicoloured (No. 1016) (B.) .. 1·00 30
1454 225 c. on $5 multicoloured (No. 912) (11.4) 1·50 70
1455 230 c. on $5 multicoloured (No. 912) (B.) .. 1·25 75
1456 260 c. on $5 multicoloured (No. 912) (B.) .. 1·25 80
1450/6 .. .. *Set of* 7 5·00 2·75

On Nos. 1454/6 the surcharges are sideways.

1985 (15 Apr). *International Youth Year Save the Children Fund Campaign. Nos.* 880, 1073*a*, 1079*b and* 1082 *optd or surch as T* **323** *in blue by Autoprint.*

1457 50 c. "Two Boys catching Ducks" (No. 1073*a*).. .. .. 1·50 20
1458 50 c. on 10 c. Type **171** (No. 1082) .. 3·00 20
1459 120 c. on 125 c. on $3 "Mango Season" (No. 880) .. .. 1·50 45
1460 $3 "Mango Season" (No. 1079*b*) .. 1·50 1·10
a. Opt Type **256** ("1983") omitted .. 12·00
1457/60 .. .. *Set of* 4 6·75 1·75

On Nos. 1457 and 1459/60 the overprints and surcharge as Type **323** are sideways.

Airy Hall

25

(324)

1985

(325)

1985 (2 May). *125th Anniv of British Guiana Post Office (1st issue). No.* 699 *surch as T* **324** *in blue by Autoprint.*

1461 25 c. on 10 c. multicoloured (surch T **324**) .. 15 10
a. Sheetlet of 25. Nos. 1461/85 .. 3·25
1462 25 c. on 10 c. multicoloured (surch "Belfield Arab. Coast") 15 10
1463 25 c. on 10 c. multicoloured (surch "Belfield E. C. Dem.") 15 10
1464 25 c. on 10 c. mult (surch "Belladrum") .. 15 10
1465 25 c. on 10 c. multicoloured (surch "Beterver-wagting") 15 10
1466 25 c. on 10 c. multicoloured (surch "Blairmont Ferry") 15 10
1467 25 c. on 10 c. mult (surch "Boeraserie") .. 15 10
1468 25 c. on 10 c. mult (surch "Brahm") .. 15 10
1469 25 c. on 10 c. mult (surch "Bushlot") .. 15 10
1470 25 c. on 10 c. mult (surch "De Kinderen") .. 15 10
1471 25 c. on 10 c. multicoloured (surch "Fort Wellington") 15 10
1472 25 c. on 10 c. mult (surch "Georgetown") .. 15 10
1473 25 c. on 10 c. mult (surch "Hague").. .. 15 10
1474 25 c. on 10 c. mult (surch "Leguan") .. 15 10
1475 25 c. on 10 c. mult (surch "Mahaica") .. 15 10
1476 25 c. on 10 c. mult (surch "Mahaicony") .. 15 10
1477 25 c. on 10 c. multicoloured (surch "New Amsterdam") 15 10
1478 25 c. on 10 c. mult (surch "Plaisance") .. 15 10
1479 25 c. on 10 c. multicoloured (surch "No. 6 Police Station") 15 10
1480 25 c. on 10 c. mult (surch "Queenstown") .. 15 10
1481 25 c. on 10 c. mult (surch "Vergenoegen") .. 15 10
1482 25 c. on 10 c. mult (surch "Vigilance") .. 15 10
1483 25 c. on 10 c. mult (surch "Vreed-en-Hoop") 15 10
1484 25 c. on 10 c. mult (surch "Wakenaam") .. 15 10
1485 25 c. on 10 c. mult (surch "Windsor Castle") 15 10
1461/85 .. .. .. *Set of* 25 3·25 2·25

The surcharged names are those of the post offices and postal agencies open in 1860.

See also Nos. 1694/717 and 2140/64.

1985 (17 May). *I.T.U./W.H.O. Day. Nos.* 1148/68 *optd with T* **325**, *or with single capital letter, in red by Autoprint.*

1486 30 c. multicoloured (No. 1148) 10 15
a. Sheetlet of 25. Nos. 1486/510.. .. 2·25
1487 30 c. multicoloured (No. 1149) 10 15
1488 30 c. multicoloured (No. 1150) 10 15
1489 30 c. multicoloured (No. 1151) 10 15
1490 30 c. multicoloured (No. 1152) 10 15
1491 30 c. multicoloured (No. 1153) 10 15
1492 30 c. multicoloured (No. 1154) (optd "I") .. 10 15
1493 30 c. multicoloured (No. 1155) (optd "T") .. 10 15
1494 30 c. multicoloured (No. 1156) (optd "U") .. 10 15
1495 30 c. multicoloured (No. 1157) 10 15
1496 30 c. multicoloured (No. 1158) 10 15
1497 30 c. multicoloured (No. 1155) (optd "W") .. 10 15
1498 30 c. multicoloured (No. 1155) (optd "H") .. 10 15
1499 30 c. multicoloured (No. 1155) (optd "O") .. 10 15
1500 30 c. multicoloured (No. 1159) 10 15
1501 30 c. multicoloured (No. 1160) 10 15
1502 30 c. multicoloured (No. 1161) (optd "D") .. 10 15
1503 30 c. multicoloured (No. 1155) (optd "A") .. 10 15
1504 30 c. multicoloured (No. 1162) (optd "Y") .. 10 15
1505 30 c. multicoloured (No. 1163) 10 15
1506 30 c. multicoloured (No. 1164) 10 15
1507 30 c. multicoloured (No. 1165) 10 15
1508 30 c. multicoloured (No. 1166) 10 15
1509 30 c. multicoloured (No. 1167) 10 15
1510 30 c. multicoloured (No. 1168) 10 15
1486/510 .. .. *Set of* 25 2·25 3·25

20

(326)

60

CARDI 1975-1985

(327)

1985 (21 May). *No.* 861B *surch with T* **326** *by Autoprint.*

1511 20 c. on 12 c. on 6 c. Patua 10 10
a. Surch on No. 861A (no wmk).. .. 6·00

For a similar surcharge, but with new face value at right see Nos. 1655/6.

1985 (29 May). *10th Anniv of Caribbean Agricultural Research Development Institute. No.* 544 *surch with T* **327** *in blue by Autoprint.*

1512 60 c. on 3 c. Hanging Heliconia 30 25

1985 (3 June). *No.* 839 *surch as Type* O **10** *by Autoprint, but with two blocks of obliterating bars over the previous surch.*

1513 600 c. on 625 c. on 40 c. Tiger Beard .. 3·25 2·25

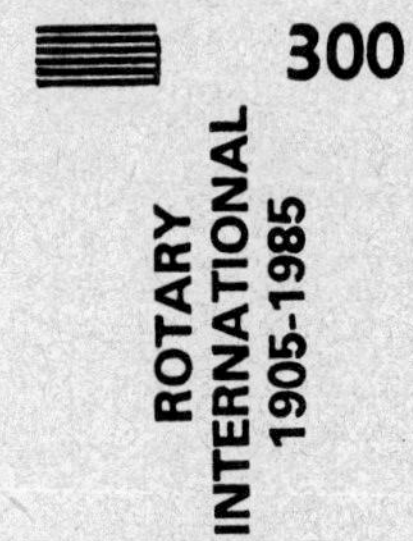

(328)

1985 (21 June). *80th Anniv of Rotary International. Nos.* 707 *and* 879 *surch as T* **328** *in red by Autoprint.*

1514 120 c. on 110 c. on $3 Rotary anniversary emblem .. .. 5·50 45
1515 300 c. on $2 *Morpho rhetenor* .. .. 1·75 1·10

No. 1205 exists with a similar 120 c. horizontal surcharge. A limited quantity was available mint, but examples are mainly found on First Day Covers (*Price £8 on First Day Cover*).

CARICOM DAY 1985

60 **XX**

(329)

1985 (28 June). *CARICOM Day. No.* 1200 *surch with T* **329** *in red.*

1516 60 c. on $3 "Makanaima the Great Ancestral Spirit of the Amerindians" .. 20 25

135th Anniversary Cotton Reel 1850-1985

120

(330)

1985 (28 June). *135th Anniv of First British Guiana Stamps. No.* 870 *surch with T* **330** *in red.*

1517 120 c. on 110 c. on 10 c. Type **170** 40 45

"REICHENBACHIA" ISSUES. Due to the proliferation of these designs the catalogue uses the book plate numbers as description for each design. The following index gives the species on each plate and the stamp numbers on which they occur.

Series 1

Plate No. 1 – *Odontoglossum crispum* – 1578, 2112
Plate No. 2 – *Cattleya percivaliana* – 1519, 2026, 2394
Plate No. 3 – *Cypripedium sanderianum* – 1525, 2084
Plate No. 4 – *Odontoglossum rossi* – 1533, **MS**1539, 2095, **MS**2105
Plate No. 5 – *Cattleya dowiana aurea* – 1667, 1942/3, 2030, 2464
Plate No. 6 – *Coelogyne cristata maxima* – 1526, **MS**1685, 1767, 2085, 2093, 2119, **MS**2234
Plate No. 7 – *Odontoglossum insleayi splendens* – 1520, 1967
Plate No. 8 – *Laelia euspatha* – 1571, 1933, 1950
Plate No. 9 – *Dendrobium wardianum* – 1552, 1776, 1979/80, 1996, 2002, 2005, 2017, 2022, 2138/9, 2387
Plate No. 10 – *Laelia autumnalis xanthotropis* – 1521, 1968, 2027
Plate No. 11 – *Phalaenopsis grandiflora aurea* – 1579, 2113
Plate No. 12 – *Cattleya lawrenceana* – 1518, 1935
Plate No. 13 – *Masdevallia shuttleworthii* and *M. xanthocorys* – 1527, 1684, 1768, 2092, 2107, 2110, 2120, 2233, 2448
Plate No. 14 – *Aeranthus sesquipedalis* – 1584, 2096, 2472
Plate No. 15 – *Cattleya mendelii* Duke of Marlborough – 1752, 2009, 2050, 2259
Plate No. 16 – *Zygopetalum intermedium* – 1559, 2090
Plate No. 17 – *Phaius humblotii* – 1732, 1885, 1965, 2062, 2393
Plate No. 18 – *Chysis bractescens* – 1528, 1536, 2087, 2133
Plate No. 19 – *Masdevallia backhousiana* – 1522, 1969, 2028
Plate No. 20 – *Cattleya citrina* – 1529, **MS**1570, 1770, 2086, 2094, **MS**2106, 2121, 2449
Plate No. 21 – *Oncidium jonesianum* and *Oncidium jonesianum phaeanthum* – 1585, 2097, 2129
Plate No. 22 – *Saccolabium giganteum* – 1553, **MS**1619, 1777, 1940/1, 1989, 1997, 2006, 2018, 2023, **MS**2232, 2388
Plate No. 23 – *Cypripedium io* – 1572, 1936
Plate No. 24 – *Odontoglossum blandum* – 1635, 1863, 1864/5, 1931, 1961, 2019, 2047, 2344
Plate No. 25 – *Maxillaria sanderiana* – 1530, 1771, 2108, 2111, 2122
Plate No. 26 – *Odontoglossum* Edward II – 1633, 2137, 2258, 2450
Plate No. 27 – *Vanda teres* – 1524, 2438
Plate No. 28 – *Odontoglossum hallii xanthoglossum* – 1580, 2114
Plate No. 29 – *Odontoglossum crispum hrubyanum* – 1531, 1537, 2088, 2134
Plate No. 30 – *Oncidium concolor* – 1532, 1538, 2089, 2135
Plate No. 31 – *Trichopilia suavis alba* – 1523, 1970, 2029
Plate No. 32 – *Cattleya superba splendens* – 1561
Plate No. 33 – *Odontoglossum luteo-purpureum* – 1634, 2098, 2342, 2479
Plate No. 34 – *Cypripedium niveum* – 1562
Plate No. 35 – *Stanhopea shuttleworthii* – 1563
Plate No. 36 – *Laelia anceps percivaliana* – 1558, 2439
Plate No. 37 – *Odontoglossum hebraicum* – 1627, 2115, 2440
Plate No. 38 – *Cypripedium oenanthum superbum* – 1560, 2445
Plate No. 39 – *Dendrobium superbiens* – 1737, 1985, 2063, 2104, 2414
Plate No. 40 – *Laelia harpophylla* – 1581, 1801, 2123, 2126
Plate No. 41 – *Lycaste skinneri* and *alba* – 1564
Plate No. 42 – *Phalaenopsis stuartiana* – 1582, 1657, 1802, 1993, 2125, 2127
Plate No. 43 – *Cattleya trianaei ernesti* – 1586, 1658, 1806, 2099, 2130/1
Plate No. 44 – *Sobralia xantholeuca* – 1556, 1971
Plate No. 45 – *Odontoglossum crispum kinlesideanum* – 1583, 1803, 2124, 2128
Plate No. 46 – *Cattleya trianaei schroederiana* – 1628, 2116, 2476
Plate No. 47 – *Epidendrum vitellinum* – 1557, 1972
Plate No. 48 – *Laelia anceps stella* and *barkeriana* – 1565
Plate No. 49 – *Odontoglossum harryanum* – 1554, 1778, 1912, 1964, 1966, 1994, 2003, 2007, 2015, 2024
Plate No. 50 – *Dendrobium leechianum* – 1672, 2031, 2403, 2496
Plate No. 51 – *Phalaenopsis speciosa* – 1573, 1934
Plate No. 52 – *Laelia elegans schilleriana* – 1551, 1949
Plate No. 53 – *Zygopetalum wendlandi* – 1621, 1849, 1930, 1954, 1962, 1983, 1986, 2020, 2048, 2361, 2364, E4
Plate No. 54 – *Cypripedium selligerum majus* – 1664, 2032, 2381, 2404
Plate No. 55 – *Angraecum articulatum* – 1597, 1625, 1853, 1927, 1990, 2046, 2265, 2463, 2465
Plate No. 56 – *Laelia anceps sanderiana* – 1629, 2117, 2441
Plate No. 57 – *Vanda coerulea* – 1622, 1973, 2395/6
Plate No. 58 – *Dendrobium nobile sanderianum* – 1630, 2118, 2442
Plate No. 59 – *Laelia gouldiana* – 1620, 2243, 2359
Plate No. 60 – *Odontoglossum grande* – 1682, 1944, 2038
Plate No. 61 – *Cypripedium rothschildianum* – 1574, 2356
Plate No. 62 – *Vanda sanderiana* – 1566
Plate No. 63 – *Dendrobium aureum* – 1575, 2357
Plate No. 64 – *Oncidium macranthum* – 1555, 1779, 1913, 1981/2, 1995, 2004, 2008, 2016, 2025
Plate No. 65 – *Cypripedium tautzianum* – 1598, 1626, 1854, 1963, 2021, 2049, 2221, 2434, 2437, E1
Plate No. 66 – *Cymbidium mastersi* – 1632, 2091, 2136, 2257, 2446
Plate No. 67 – *Angraecum caudatum* – 1631, 2132, 2256, 2443
Plate No. 68 – *Laelia albida* – 1734, 1884, 1937, 2056, 2378/9, 2435
Plate No. 69 – *Odontoglossum roezlii* – 1680, 2033, 2405, 2444
Plate No. 70 – *Oncidium ampliatum majus* – 1576, 2358
Plate No. 71 – *Renanthera lowii* – 1679, 1952, 1976, 2034, 2360
Plate No. 72 – *Cattleya warscewiczii* – 1577, 1951, 2429
Plate No. 73 – *Oncidium lanceanum* – 1623, 1974, 2397
Plate No. 74 – *Vanda hookeriana* – 1736, 1984, 2064, 2103, 2415, 2454
Plate No. 75 – *Cattleya labiata gaskelliana* – 1624, 1975, 2398/9
Plate No. 76 – *Epidendrum prismatocarpum* – 1751, 2058, 2453
Plate No. 77 – *Cattleya guttata leopoldi* – 1663, 1955, 1958, 2042, 2372/3
Plate No. 78 – *Oncidium splendidum* – 1669, 1959, 2043, 2451
Plate No. 79 – *Odontoglossum hebraicum aspersum* – 1670, 2035, 2100, 2343, 2406, 2473
Plate No. 80 – *Cattleya dowiana* var *chrysotoxa* – 1754, 2059
Plate No. 81 – *Cattleya trianae alba* – 1748, 1957, 2010, 2051, 2382
Plate No. 82 – *Odontoglossum humeanum* – 1753, 2011, 2052, 2260
Plate No. 83 – *Cypripedium argus* – 1671, 2039, 2466, 2480
Plate No. 84 – *Odontoglossum luteo-purpureum prionopetalum* – 1668, 2044, 2421
Plate No. 85 – *Cattleya rochellensis* – 1673, 1960, 2045, 2497
Plate No. 86 – *Odontoglossum triumphans* – 1731, 1847, 1868, 1953, 1956, 2055, 2055a, 2264, 2362, 2377, E2, E2a, E10, (Nos. 1847, 2055a, 2264, E2 and E10 are inscr "ONTOGLOSSUM" in error)
Plate No. 87 – *Phalaenopsis casta* – 1681, 1977, 2036, 2452, 2474, 2478
Plate No. 88 – *Oncidium tigrinum* – 1750, 2060, 2436
Plate No. 89 – *Cypripedium lemoinierianum* – 1749, 1978, 2012, 2053, 2422
Plate No. 90 – *Catasetum bungerothii* – 1738, 1932, 1938, 1947/8, 1988, 2014, 2057, 2380, 2433
Plate No. 91 – *Cattleya ballantiniana* – 1735, 1822, 1987, 2013, 2054, 2109, 2375/6, 2447
Plate No. 92 – *Dendrobium brymerianum* – 1665, 1939, 1945, 2040, 2384
Plate No. 93 – *Cattleya eldorado crocata* – 1733, 1991/2, 2065, 2401, 2416
Plate No. 94 – *Odontoglossum sanderianum* – 1683, 2037, 2345, 2407, 2484
Plate No. 95 – *Cattleya labiata warneri* – 1666, 2041, 2400, 2467
Plate No. 96 – *Odontoglossum schroderianum* – 1747, 2061, 2374

Series 2

Plate No. 1 – *Cypripedium morganiae burfordiense* – 2178
Plate No. 2 – *Cattleya bowringiana* – 1886, 1929, 2102, 2426
Plate No. 3 – *Dendrobium formosum* – 1919, 1998, 2389
Plate No. 4 – *Phaius tuberculosus* – 1813, 2428
Plate No. 5 – *Odontoglossum crispum mundyanum* – 1815, 2475
Plate No. 6 – *Laelia praestans* – 1881, 1999, 2390
Plate No. 7 – *Dendrobium phalaenopsis* var *statterianum* – 1917, 2365
Plate No. 8 – *Cypripedium boxalli atratum* – 1811, 2408
Plate No. 9 – *Odontoglossum wattianum* – 1816, 2101, 2409/10
Plate No. 10 – *Cypripedium lathamianum inversum* – 1869, 1880, 2423, 2482
Plate No. 11 – *Paphinia rugosa* and *Zygopetalum xanthinum* – E6
Plate No. 12 – *Dendrobium melanodiscus* – 1817, 2411/12
Plate No. 13 – *Laelia anceps schroderiana* – 1877, 1907, 2385, 2424
Plate No. 14 – *Phaius hybridus cooksonii* – 1920, 2366/7
Plate No. 15 – *Disa grandiflora* – 1918, 1926, 2386, 2419
Plate No. 16 – *Selenipedium hybridum grande* – 2314, 2331
Plate No. 17 – *Cattleya schroederae alba* – 1872, 2413
Plate No. 18 – *Lycaste skinnerii armeniaca* – 1923, 1928, 1946, 2420
Plate No. 19 – *Odontoglossum excellens* – 2175
Plate No. 20 – *Laelio-cattleya elegans* var *blenheimensis* – 1916, 2000, 2391
Plate No. 21 – *Odontoglossum coradinei* – 1810, 2383
Plate No. 22 – *Odontoglossum wilckeanum* var *rothschildianum* – 1922, 2368
Plate No. 23 – *Cypripedium lawrenceanum hyeanum* – O61
Plate No. 24 – *Cattleya intermedia punctatissima* – 1887, 1914, 2418
Plate No. 25 – *Laelia purpurata* – 2067
Plate No. 26 – *Masdevallia harryana splendens* – O57
Plate No. 27 – *Selenipedium hybridum nitidissimum* – 1874, 1915, 2402, 2425
Plate No. 28 – *Cattleya mendelii* var *measuresiana* – 1924, 2369/70
Plate No. 29 – *Odontoglossum vexillarium* (*miltonia vexillaria*) – 1818, 2485
Plate No. 30 – *Saccolabium coeleste* – 1809, 2363, 2430
Plate No. 31 – *Cypripedium hybridum youngianum* – 2324
Plate No. 32 – *Miltonia* (*hybrida*) *bleuana* – 1921, 2001, 2392
Plate No. 33 – *Laelia grandis* – 1873
Plate No. 34 – *Cattleya labiata* var *lueddemanniana* – 1819, 2431, 2481
Plate No. 35 – *Odontoglossum coronarium* – E8
Plate No. 36 – *Cattleya granulosa* var *schofieldiana* – 2316
Plate No. 37 – *Odontoglossum* (*hybridum*) *leroyanum* – 2174
Plate No. 38 – *Cypripedium* (*hybridum*) *laucheanum* and *eyermanianum* – 1814, 2477
Plate No. 39 – *Cychnoches chlorochilon* – 2172
Plate No. 40 – *Cattleya O'Brieniana* – 2276
Plate No. 41 – *Odontoglossum ramosissimum* – 2066
Plate No. 42 – *Dendrobium phalaenopsis* var – 1812, 2427
Plate No. 43 – *Cypripedium* (*hybridum*) *pollettianum* and *maynardii* – 2216, O55
Plate No. 44 – *Odontoglossum naevium* – 1878
Plate No. 45 – *Cypripedium* (*hybridium*) *castleanum* – 1876, 1925, 2371, 2417
Plate No. 46 – *Odontoglossum cervantesii decorum* – **MS**2275, **MS**2332
Plate No. 47 – *Cattleya amethystoglossa* – 2171
Plate No. 48 – *Cattleya* (*hybrida*) *arnoldiana* – 2217, O53
Plate No. 49 – *Cattleya labiata* – 2239
Plate No. 50 – *Dendrobium* (*hybridum*) *venus* and *cassiope* – 1879
Plate No. 51 – *Selenipedium* (*hybridum*) *weidlichianum* – 2177
Plate No. 52 – *Cattleya mossiae* var *reineckiana* – 2072
Plate No. 53 – *Cymbidium lowianum* – 2236
Plate No. 54 – *Oncidium loxense* – 2176
Plate No. 55 – *Cattleya* (*hybrida*) *hardyana* – **MS**2275, **MS**2332
Plate No. 56 – *Coelogyne sanderae* – 1875
Plate No. 57 – *Cypripedium leeanum* var *giganteum* – **MS**2275, **MS**2332
Plate No. 58 – *Coelogyne pandurata* – 2173
Plate No. 59 – *Schomburgkia sanderiana* – 2323
Plate No. 60 – *Oncidium superbiens* – 2227
Plate No. 61 – *Dendrobium johnsoniae* – 2235, O56
Plate No. 62 – *Laelia hybrida behrensiana* – 2322
Plate No. 63 – Hybrid *Calanthes Victoria Regina, Bella* and *Burfordiense* – E7
Plate No. 64 – *Cattleya mendelii* Quorndon House var – 2238
Plate No. 65 – *Arachnanthe clarkei* – 2073
Plate No. 66 – *Zygopetalum burtii* – 2240
Plate No. 67 – *Cattleya* (*hybrida*) *parthenia* – 2318
Plate No. 68 – *Phalaenopsis sanderiana* and *intermedia portei* – 2225, O58
Plate No. 69 – *Phaius blumei* var *assamicus* – 2317
Plate No. 70 – *Angraecum humblotii* – 2470, O63
Plate No. 71 – *Odontoglossum pescatorei* – 2471, O64
Plate No. 72 – *Cattleya rex* – 2193
Plate No. 73 – *Zygopetalum crinitum* – 2315, 2329,
Plate No. 74 – *Cattleya lueddemanniana alba* – 2219/20, 2222/3, 2328
Plate No. 75 – *Cymbidium* (*hybridum*) *winnianum* – O60
Plate No. 76 – Hybrid *Masdevallias courtauldiana, geleniana* and *measuresiana* – 2242
Plate No. 77 – *Cypripedium* (*hybridum*) *calypso* – 2191
Plate No. 78 – *Masdevallia chimaera* var *mooreana* – 2325
Plate No. 79 – *Miltonia phalaenopsis* – 2241
Plate No. 80 – *Lissochilus giganteus* – 2190
Plate No. 81 – *Aerides savageanum* – **MS**2275, **MS**2332
Plate No. 82 – *Thunia brymeriana* – 2069, 2483
Plate No. 83 – *Miltonia moreliana* – 2182
Plate No. 84 – *Oncidium kramerianum* – 2469, O65
Plate No. 85 – *Cattleya Victoria Regina* – 2068
Plate No. 86 – *Zygopetalum klabochorum* – 2180
Plate No. 87 – *Laelia autumnalis alba* – 2070, 2432
Plate No. 88 – *Spathoglottis kimballiana* – 2071
Plate No. 89 – *Laelio-cattleya* ("The Hon. Mrs. Astor") – 2181
Plate No. 90 – *Phaius hybridus amabilis* and *marthiae* – 2468, O59
Plate No. 91 – *Zygopetalum rostratum* – 2277
Plate No. 92 – *Coelogyne swaniana* – 2218, O54
Plate No. 94 – *Epidendrum atro-purpureum* var *randianum* – 2192
Plate No. 95 – *Dendrobium imperatrix* – 2226, O62
Plate No. 96 – *Vanda parishii* var *marriottiana* – 2237, 2330

PRICES OF SETS

Set prices are given for many issues, generally those containing three stamps or more. Definitive sets include one of each value or major colour change, but do not cover different perforations, die types or minor shades. Where a choice is possible the set prices are based on the cheapest versions of the stamps included in the listings.

CATTLEYA LAWRENCEANA
Plate No. 12 (Series 1)
25
Guyana

GUYANA

C 25 C

331 *Cattleya lawrenceana* (Plate No. 12 (Series 1)) **332** Arms of Guyana

(Litho Format)

1985 (9 July). *Centenary of Publication of Sanders'* Reichenbachia (*1st issue*). *T* **331** *and similar vert designs showing orchids. Multicoloured. No wmk. P* 13½×14.

1518 25 c. Type **331** 10 10
1519 60 c. Plate No. 2 (Series 1) 20 25
1520 60 c. Plate No. 7 (Series 1) 20 25
1521 60 c. Plate No. 10 (Series 1) 20 25
1522 60 c. Plate No. 19 (Series 1) 20 25
1523 60 c. Plate No. 31 (Series 1) 20 25
1524 120 c. Plate No. 27 (Series 1) 40 45
1525 130 c. Plate No. 3 (Series 1) 45 50
1526 130 c. Plate No. 6 (Series 1) 90 50
1527 130 c. Plate No. 13 (Series 1) 50 50
1528 130 c. Plate No. 18 (Series 1) .. .. 1·25 50
1529 130 c. Plate No. 20 (Series 1) 80 50
1530 130 c. Plate No. 25 (Series 1) 45 50
1531 130 c. Plate No. 29 (Series 1) .. .. 1·00 50
1532 130 c. Plate No. 30 (Series 1) .. .. 1·00 50
1533 200 c. Plate No. 4 (Series 1) 70 75
1518/33 .. .. *Set of* 16 7·00 6·00

Nos. 1518/33 were printed in four sheets each of 16 orchid stamps, arranged as blocks of four of each design, and 9 examples of Type **332** which appear on the vertical and horizontal gutters between the blocks.

For 130 c. stamps as Nos. 1526/7 and 1529/30, but with watermark **106** see Nos. 1767/71.

(Litho Format)

1985 (9 July–16 Sept). *Booklet and Coil Stamps. No wmk.*

1534 **332** 25 c. multicoloured (*imperf*×*p* 14) .. 10 10
1534*a* 25 c. multicoloured (*imperf* × *p* 13½) (16 Sept).. .. .. .. 10 10
1535 25 c. multicoloured (*p* 13½ × *imperf*) 10 10
1535*a* 25 c. multicoloured (*p* 14 × *imperf*) (16 Sept).. .. .. .. 10 10
1534/5*a* .. .. *Set of* 4 35 35

See note below No. 1533. Examples of Nos. 1534/5*a* were cut from the gutters of the orchid sheets and the white area surrounding the design varies considerably in size. Nos. 1534/5 occur from sheets with vertical orchid designs and Nos. 1534*a*/5*a* from those with horizontal designs.

See also Nos. 1807/8a (watermarked **106**), 1820/1*a* (additionally inscribed "1966–1986") and 2183/4 (within frame).

QUEEN MOTHER 1900 - 1985

(333)

25

International Youth Year 1985

(334)

1985 (9 July). *85th Birthday of Queen Elizabeth the Queen Mother* (*1st issue*). *Nos.* 1528 *and* 1531/3 *optd with T* **333** (*in two lines on No.* 1538) *or with similar opts* (*No.* **MS**1539), *all in blue by Format.*

1536 130 c. Plate No. 18 (Series 1) 45 50
1537 130 c. Plate No. 29 (Series 1) 45 50
1538 130 c. Plate No. 30 (Series 1) 45 50
1536/8 .. .. *Set of* 3 1·25 1·40
MS1539 100×126 mm. 200 c.×4 Plate No. 4 (Series 1) .. .. 7·50 8·00

The four stamps in No. **MS**1539 are overprinted "LADY BOWES-LYON 1900–1923", "DUCHESS OF YORK 1923–1937", "QUEEN ELIZABETH 1937–1952" or "QUEEN MOTHER 1952–1985", all reading upwards.

See also No. **MS**1570.

1985 (18 July). *International Youth Year. Nos.* 900/4 *surch with T* **334** *in red by Autoprint.*

1540 25 c. on 110 c. on 5 c. mult (No. 900) .. 10 10
a. Sheetlet of 25. Nos. 1540/1, each × 8, Nos. 1542/3, each × 4 and No. 1544 .. 4·00
1541 25 c. on 110 c. on 5 c. mult (No. 901) .. 10 10
1542 25 c. on 110 c. on 5 c. mult (No. 902) .. 25 10
1543 25 c. on 110 c. on 5 c. mult (No. 903) .. 25 10
1544 25 c. on 110 c. on 5 c. mult (No. 904) .. 80 15
1540/4 .. .. *Set of* 5 1·40 50

In addition to the sheetlet containing the five different original surcharges, Type **334** can also be found on the sheets of No. 900.

J. J. Audubon
1785-1985

240

225

1910 - 1985

(335)

(336)

1985 (26 July). *75th Anniv of Girl Guide Movement. No.* 612 *surch with T* **335** *by Tip Torres.*

1545 225 c. on 350 c. on 225 c. on 40 c. Guides in camp .. .. 3·50 90
a. Inverted "L"'s for 1's in surcharged dates .. ..

No. 1545a occurs on all stamps in the bottom row.

In addition to Type **335** No. 1545 also carries two otherwise unissued surcharges at top right.

Nos. 610 and 613 also exist surcharged with Type **335**. A limited quantity was available mint, but examples were mainly found on First Day Covers (*Price £25 per pair on First Day Cover*).

1985 (26 July). *Birth Bicentenary of John J. Audubon* (*ornithologist*). *No.* 992 *surch with T* **336** *by Tip Torres.*

1546 240 c. on 35 c. Harpy Eagle .. .. 4·00 1·75

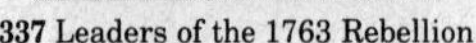

337 Leaders of the 1763 Rebellion

Guyana/Libya Friendship 1985 150

(338)

(Des K. Everett (150 c.). Litho Format)

1985 (29 July). *150th Anniv of Abolition of Slavery* (1984). *T* **337** *and similar horiz designs. P* 14.

1547 25 c. black and bluish grey 50 10
1548 60 c. black and mauve 25 25
1549 130 c. black and light greenish blue .. 50 50
1550 150 c. black and rose-lilac 60 55
1547/50 .. .. *Set of* 4 1·60 1·25

Designs:—60 c. Damon and Parliament Buildings, Georgetown; 130 c. Quamina and Demerara, 1823; 150 c. *Den Arendt* (slave ship), 1627.

Stamps in these designs, but with different background colours were prepared, but not issued.

(Litho Format)

1985 (1 Aug). *Centenary of Publication of Sanders'* Reichenbachia (*2nd issue*). *Vert designs as T* **331** *showing orchids. Multicoloured. No wmk. P* 13½×14.

1551 25 c. Plate No. 52 (Series 1) 10 10
1552 55 c. Plate No. 9 (Series 1) 20 25
1553 55 c. Plate No. 22 (Series 1) 20 25
1554 55 c. Plate No. 49 (Series 1) 20 25
1555 55 c. Plate No. 64 (Series 1) 20 25
1556 60 c. Plate No. 44 (Series 1) 20 25
1557 60 c. Plate No. 47 (Series 1) 20 25
1558 120 c. Plate No. 36 (Series 1) 40 45
1559 130 c. Plate No. 16 (Series 1) 45 50
1560 130 c. Plate No. 38 (Series 1) 45 50
1561 150 c. Plate No. 32 (Series 1) 50 55
1562 150 c. Plate No. 34 (Series 1) 50 55
1563 150 c. Plate No. 35 (Series 1) 50 55
1564 150 c. Plate No. 41 (Series 1) 50 55
1565 150 c. Plate No. 48 (Series 1) 50 55
1566 150 c. Plate No. 62 (Series 1) 50 55
1551/66 .. .. *Set of* 16 5·00 5·75

Nos. 1551/66 were printed in a similar sheet format to Nos. 1518/33.

For 55 c. stamps as Nos. 1552/5, but with watermark **106** see Nos. 1776/9.

For 50 c. stamps in designs of Nos 1554/5 see Nos. 1912/13.

1985 (16 Aug). *Signing of Guyana—Libya Friendship Treaty. No.* 621 *surch with T* **338** *by Autoprint.*

1567 150 c. on 10 c. Type **149** .. .. 6·50 2·75

ALTERED CATALOGUE NUMBERS

Any Catalogue numbers altered from the last edition are shown as a list in the introductory pages.

200

Mexico 1986

150 (339)

X (340) 275

(341)

1985 (16 Aug). *Namibia Day. No.* 636 *surch with T* **339** *in deep carmine by Tip Torres.*

1568 150 c. on 35 c. Unveiling of Monument .. 1·50 55

1985 (16 Aug). *World Cup Football Championship, Mexico* (1966) (*1st issue*). *No.* F2 *surch with T* **340** *by Autoprint.*

1569 275 c. on 3 c. Hanging Heliconia 90 95

See also No. 1727.

1985 (12 Sept). *85th Birthday of Queen Elizabeth the Queen Mother* (*2nd issue*). *Sheet* 120×129 *mm containing No.* 1529×4 *optd as No.* **MS**1539, *each stamp surch with T* **341** *by Tip Torres.*

MS1570 200 c. on 130 c. × 4 Plate No. 20 (Series 1) 8·00 6·00

(Litho Format)

1985 (16 Sept). *Centenary of Publication of Sanders'* Reichenbachia (*3rd issue*). *Multicoloured designs as T* **331** *showing orchids. No wmk. P* 13½×14 (*Nos.* 1571/7 *and* 1584) *or* 14×13½ (*others*).

1571 25 c. Plate No. 8 (Series 1) 10 10
1572 25 c. Plate No. 23 (Series 1) 10 10
1573 25 c. Plate No. 51 (Series 1) 10 10
1574 25 c. Plate No. 61 (Series 1) 10 10
1575 25 c. Plate No. 63 (Series 1) 10 10
1576 25 c. Plate No. 70 (Series 1) 10 10
1577 25 c. Plate No. 72 (Series 1) 10 10
1578 120 c. Plate No. 1 (Series 1) (*horiz*) .. 40 45
1579 120 c. Plate No. 11 (Series 1) (*horiz*) .. 40 45
1580 120 c. Plate No. 28 (Series 1) (*horiz*) .. 40 45
1581 150 c. Plate No. 40 (Series 1) (*horiz*) .. 50 55
1582 150 c. Plate No. 42 (Series 1) (*horiz*) .. 50 55
1583 150 c. Plate No. 45 (Series 1) (*horiz*) .. 50 55
1584 200 c. Plate No. 14 (Series 1) 65 70
1585 200 c. Plate No. 21 (Series 1) (*horiz*) .. 65 70
1586 200 c. Plate No. 43 (Series 1) (*horiz*) .. 65 70
1571/86 .. .. *Set of* 16 4·75 5·25

Nos. 1571/86 were printed in a similar sheet format to Nos. 1518/33.

For 150 c. and 200 c. stamps as Nos. 1581/3 and 1586, but with watermark **106** see Nos. 1801/6.

120

1955-1985

(342)

1965-1985 25

(343)

1985 (23 Sept). *30th Anniv of Commonwealth Caribbean Medical Research Council. Nos.* 819, 871, 874/*a*, 928*a and* 1014 *surch or optd* (*vertically reading upwards on Nos.* 1587/8) *as T* **342** *by Autoprint.*

1587 – 60 c. multicoloured (No. 819) 20 25
1588 – 60 c. multicoloured (No. 1014) .. 20 25
1589 **176** 120 c. on 110 c. on 10 c. multicoloured (No. 871) 40 45
1590 – 120 c. on 110 c. on $3 mult (No. 874) .. 40 45
1591 – 120 c. on 110 c. on $3 mult (No. 874a).. 40 45
1592 – 120 c. on 210 c. on $3 mult (No. 928a).. 40 45
1587/92 .. .. *Set of* 6 1·75 2·10

1985 (30 Sept). *20th Anniv of Guyana Defence Force. No.* 856 *surch as T* **343** *by Autoprint.*

1593 25 c. on $1.10 on $3 W.O. and N.C.O., Guyana Defence Force, 1966 .. 10 10
1594 225 c. on $1.10 on $3 W.O. and N.C.O., Guyana Defence Force, 1966 .. 70 75

1985 (5 Oct). *Fire Prevention. Nos.* 678 *and* 680 *optd with T* **325** *and surch as T* **255** *by Autoprint.*

1595 25 c. on 40 c. Fire engine, 1977 .. .. 1·75 10
1596 320 c. on 15 c. Steam engine, *circa* 1860 .. 4·75 1·50

(Litho Format)

1985 (7 Oct). *Centenary of Publication of Sanders'* Reichenbachia (*4th issue*). *Vert design as T* **331**. *Multicoloured. No wmk. P* 13½×14.

1597 60 c. Plate No. 55 (Series 1) 20 25

350

(344) (345)

1985 (12 Oct). *Columbus Day. Unissued value as T* **331** *surch with T* **344** *in red. Multicoloured. P* 13½ × 14.
1598 350 c. on 120 c. Plate No. 65 (Series 1) .. 1·75 1·60

1985 (15 Oct). *20th Death Anniv of Sir Winston Churchill. No.* 707 *optd with T* **345** *by Autoprint.*
1599 $2 *Morpho rhetenor* (female) .. .. 1·00 85

XX 1950-1985 200

United Nations 1945-1985

POSTAGE

(346) (347) (348)

1985 (15 Oct). *35th Anniv of International Commission on Irrigation and Drainage. No.* 625 *with unissued surcharge as T* **264** *in blue further surch as T* **346** *by Autoprint.*
1600 **150** 25 c. on 110 c. on 10 c. multicoloured .. 10 10
1601 200 c. on 110 c. on 10 c. multicoloured .. 65 70

1985 (24 Oct). *40th Anniv of United Nations Organization. Nos.* 714/16, 800 *and* O19 *optd with T* **347** *by Autoprint.*
1602 30 c. multicoloured (No. 714) .. .. 1·00 10
1603 50 c. multicoloured (No. 715) .. .. 1·00 20
1604 100 c. on $3 multicoloured (No. O19) .. 1·00 40
1605 225 c. on 220 c. on $3 multicoloured (No. 800) 4·00 75
1606 $3 multicoloured (No. 716) .. .. 2·00 1·10
1602/6 .. .. *Set of* 5 8·00 2·25

1985 (29 Oct). *Nos.* 551/3, O14/15, O18, O21, OP1/2 *and* F7 *optd as T* **348** *(horizontally* 22 × 4 *on Nos.* 1607 *and* 1615/16*) by Autoprint.*
1607 30 c. on $2 *Norantea guianensis* (No. O18) .. 10 10
1608 40 c. Tiger Beard (No. 551) .. .. .. 9·50 20
1609 50 c. *Guzmania lingulata* (No. 552) .. 20 20
1610 50 c. *Guzmania lingulata* (No. O14) .. 15 20
1611 60 c. Soldier's Cap (No. 553) 90 25
1612 60 c. Soldier's Cap (No. O15) 70 25
1613 60 c. Soldier's Cap (No. F7) 20 25
1614 $10 *Elbella patrobas* (No. O21) .. .. 5·00 4·00
1615 $15 on $1 *Chelonanthus uliginoides* (No. OP1) .. .. 7·00 6·00
1616 $20 on $1 *Chelonanthus uliginoides* (No. OP2) .. .. 8·00 7·50
1607/16 .. .. *Set of* 10 28·00 17·00

150 X

Deepavali 1985

Christmas 1985

(349) (350)

1985 (1 Nov). *Deepavali Festival. Nos.* 542/3 *surch as T* **349** *by Autoprint.*
1617 25 c. on 2 c. Type **132** 10 10
1618 150 c. on 1 c. Pitcher Plant of Mt Roraima .. 50 55

1985 (3 Nov). *Christmas. Sheet* 120 × 129 *mm containing No.* 1553 × 4 *optd as T* **350** *in red by Format.*
MS1619 55 c. × 4 Plate No. 22 (Series 1), each with a different overprint (Type **350**, "Happy New Year", "Merry Christmas" or "Happy Holidays") 80 85

(Litho Format)

1985 (4 Nov). *Centenary of Publication of Sanders'* Reichenbachia *(5th issue). Multicoloured designs as T* **331** *showing orchids. No wmk. P* 14 × 13½ (60, 200 *c.*) *or* 13½ × 14 *(others).*
1620 25 c. Plate No. 59 (Series 1) 10 10
1621 30 c. Plate No. 53 (Series 1) 10 10
1622 60 c. Plate No. 57 (Series 1) *(horiz)* .. 20 25
1623 60 c. Plate No. 73 (Series 1) *(horiz)* .. 20 25
1624 60 c. Plate No. 75 (Series 1) *(horiz)* .. 20 25
1625 75 c. Plate No. 55 (Series 1) 25 30
1626 100 c. Plate No. 65 (Series 1) 35 40
1627 120 c. Plate No. 37 (Series 1) 40 45
1628 120 c. Plate No. 46 (Series 1) 40 45
1629 120 c. Plate No. 56 (Series 1) 40 45
1630 120 c. Plate No. 58 (Series 1) 40 45
1631 120 c. Plate No. 67 (Series 1) 40 45
1632 130 c. Plate No. 66 (Series 1) 45 50
1633 150 c. Plate No. 26 (Series 1) 50 55
1634 200 c. Plate No. 33 (Series 1) *(horiz)* .. 65 70
1635 225 c. Plate No. 24 (Series 1) 70 75
1620/35 .. .. *Set of* 16 4·75 5·50

Nos. 1620/35 were printed in a similar sheet format to Nos. 1518/33.

The 30, 75, 100 and 225 c. values show face values and "Guyana" in blue. Examples of these four stamps with face values and "Guyana" in black were prepared, but not issued.

For stamps as Nos. 1621, 1625/6 and 1635, but with watermark **106** see Nos. 1849, 1853/4 and 1863.

For 50 c. in design of No. 1625 see No. 1927.

REICHENBACHIA 1886-1986

351 Clive Lloyd (cricketer) (**352**)

(Litho Format)

1985 (7 Nov). *Clive Lloyd's Testimonial Year. T* **351** *and similar vert designs. Multicoloured. W* **106** *(sideways on* $3.50*). P* 14½ × 14 (25 *c.*), 12½ ($3.50) *or* 14 *(others).*
1636 25 c. Type **351** 20 20
a. Horiz strip of 3. Nos. 1636/8 55
1637 25 c. Clive Lloyd, bat and wicket 20 20
1638 25 c. Cricket equipment 20 20
1639 60 c. As No. 1638 (25 × 33 *mm*) 40 30
1640 $1.30, As No. 1637 (25 × 33 *mm*) .. 75 60
1641 $2.25, Type **351** (25 × 33 *mm*) .. 1·25 90
1642 $3.50, Clive Lloyd with the Prudential Cup (36 × 56 *mm*) .. .. .. 1·75 1·50
1636/42 .. .. *Set of* 7 4·25 3·50

Nos. 1636/8 were printed together, *se-tenant*, in horizontal strips of 3 throughout the sheet.

1985 (15 Nov). *Wildlife Protection. Nos.* 756/67 *optd with T* **325** *vertically in red by Autoprint.*
1643 30 c. Type **178** 20 20
a. Sheetlet of 12. Nos. 1643/54 .. .. 2·25
1644 30 c. Red Howler 20 20
1645 30 c. Common Squirrel Monkey 20 20
1646 30 c. Two-toed Sloth 20 20
1647 30 c. Brazilian Tapir 20 20
1648 30 c. Collared Peccary 20 20
1649 30 c. Six-banded Armadillo 20 20
1650 30 c. Tamandua ("Ant Eater") 20 20
1651 30 c. Giant Anteater 20 20
1652 30 c. Murine Opossum 20 20
1653 30 c. Brown Four-eyed Opossum 20 20
1654 30 c. Brazilian Agouti 20 20
1643/54 .. .. *Set of* 12 2·25 2·25

1985 (23 Dec). *Nos.* 847 *and* 861B *surch as T* **326**, *but with face value of surch at right.*
1655 20 c. on 12 c. on 12 c. on 6 c. Patua (No. 847) 10 10
1656 20 c. on 12 c. on 6 c. Patua (No. 861B) .. 10 10

1986 (13 Jan). *Centenary of the Appearance of* Reichenbachia *Volume I. Nos.* 1582 *and* 1586 *optd with T* **352** *in reddish violet.*
1657 150 c. Plate No. 42 (Series 1) 50 55
1658 200 c. Plate No. 43 (Series 1) 65 70

Republic Day

1986 1986

(353) (354)

1986 (22 Feb). *Republic Day. Nos.* 1108/9 *and* 1052 *optd or surch as T* **353** *by Autoprint.*
1659 25 c. As Type **258** 10 10
a. Horiz pair. Nos. 1659/60 .. .. 15 20
1660 25 c. As No. 1050 .. .. .. 10 10
1661 120 c. on $6 Presidential standard (surch vert) 40 45
1662 225 c. on $6 Presidential standard (surch vert) 70 75
1659/62 .. .. *Set of* 4 1·10 1·25

(Litho Format)

1986 (26 Feb). *Centenary of Publication of Sanders'* Reichenbachia *(6th issue). Vert designs as T* **331**. *Multicoloured. No wmk. P* 13½ × 14.
1663 40 c. Plate No. 77 (Series 1) 15 15
1664 45 c. Plate No. 54 (Series 1) 15 20
1665 50 c. Plate No. 92 (Series 1) 15 20
1666 60 c. Plate No. 95 (Series 1) 20 25
1667 75 c. Plate No. 5 (Series 1) 25 30
1668 90 c. Plate No. 84 (Series 1) 30 35
1669 150 c. Plate No. 78 (Series 1) 50 55
1670 200 c. Plate No. 79 (Series 1) 65 70
1671 300 c. Plate No. 83 (Series 1) .. .. 1·00 1·10
1672 320 c. Plate No. 50 (Series 1) .. .. 1·10 1·25
1673 360 c. Plate No. 85 (Series 1) .. .. 1·25 1·40
1663/73 .. .. *Set of* 11 5·00 5·75

Nos. 1663/73 were printed in a similar sheet format to Nos. 1518/33.

1986 (24 Mar). *Easter. No.* 481 *optd with T* **354** *and surch as T* **317**, *but without the "X", both by Autoprint.*
1674 **111** 25 c. on 6 c. multicoloured 15 10
1675 50 c. on 6 c. multicoloured 25 20
1676 100 c. on 6 c. multicoloured 45 40
1677 200 c. on 6 c. multicoloured 80 70
1674/7 .. .. *Set of* 4 1·50 1·25

1926 1986 1926

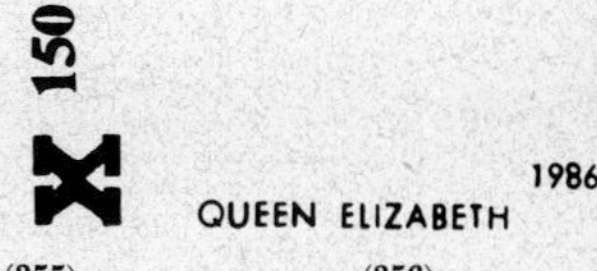

X 150

1986 QUEEN ELIZABETH

(355) (356)

1986 (27 Mar). *60th Anniv of St. John's Ambulance in Guyana. No.* 652 *surch with T* **355** *by Autoprint.*
1678 150 c. on 35 c. silver, black and green .. 75 55

(Litho Format)

1986 (4 Apr). *Centenary of Publication of Sanders'* Reichenbachia *(7th issue). Multicoloured designs as T* **331**. *No wmk. P* 13½ × 14 (225 *c.*) *or* 14 × 13½ *(others).*
1679 25 c. Plate No. 71 (Series 1) *(horiz)* .. 15 10
1680 120 c. Plate No. 69 (Series 1) *(horiz)* .. 60 45
1681 150 c. Plate No. 87 (Series 1) *(horiz)* .. 70 55
1682 225 c. Plate No. 60 (Series 1) 85 75
1683 350 c. Plate No. 94 (Series 1) *(horiz)* .. 1·50 1·25
1679/83 .. .. *Set of* 5 3·50 2·75

Nos. 1679/83 were printed in a similar sheet format to Nos. 1518/33.

1986 (21 Apr). *60th Birthday of Queen Elizabeth II. Nos.* 1526/7 *optd or surch as T* **356** *by Tip Torres.*
1684 130 c. Plate No. 13 (Series 1) 60 50
MS1685 100 × 126 mm. 130 c. on 130 c., 200 c. on 130 c., 260 c. on 130 c., 330 c. on 130 c., Plate No. 6 (Series 1) .. .. 3·00 3·25

The original face values on No. **MS** 1685 are obliterated by a floral pattern.

Protect the

60 ≡ 25

GUYANA INDEPENDENCE 1966-1986

(357) (358)

1986 (3 May). *Wildlife Protection. Nos.* 685, 739/44 *and* 993/8 *surch as T* **357** *by Tip Torres.*
1686 60 c. on 35 c. Type **174** 15 15
a. Block of 6. Nos. 1686/91 80
1687 60 c. on 35 c. Haimara 15 15
1688 60 c. on 35 c. Electric Eel 15 15
1689 60 c. on 35 c. Golden Rivulus 15 15
1690 60 c. on 35 c. Pencil Fish 15 15
1691 60 c. on 35 c. Four-eyed Fish 15 15
1691*a* 60 c. on 35 c. Pirai or Carib fish 15 15
ab. Block of 6. Nos. 1691*a/f* 80
1691*b* 60 c. on 35 c. Smoking Hassar 15 15
1691*c* 60 c. on 35 c. Devil Ray 15 15
1691*d* 60 c. on 35 c. Flying Patwa 15 15
1691*e* 60 c. on 35 c. Arapaima Pirariucii 15 15
1691*f* 60 c. on 35 c. Lukanani 15 15
1692 $6 on 8 c. Type **163** .. .. .. 1·25 1·25
1686/92 .. .. *Set of* 13 2·50 2·50

Nos. 1686/91 were previously overprinted with Type **226**.

On No. 1692 the previous value is covered by a fleur-de-lys.

1986 (5 May). *No.* 799 *surch as T* **326** *by Autoprint.*
1693 600 c. on 720 c. on 60 c. Soldier's Cap .. 1·00 75

1986 (15 May). *125th Anniv of British Guiana Post Office (2nd issue). No.* 702*a surch as T* **324** *by Autoprint.*
1694 25 c. on 30 c. multicoloured (surch "Abary") 10 10
a. Sheetlet of 25. Nos. 1694/1704, 1705 × 2, 1706/17 .. .. 1·75
1695 25 c. on 30 c. mult (surch "Anna Regina") 10 10
1696 25 c. on 30 c. mult (surch "Aurora") .. 10 10
1697 25 c. on 30 c. mult (surch "Bartica Grove") 10 10
1698 25 c. on 30 c. mult (surch "Bel Air") .. 10 10
1699 25 c. on 30 c. mult (surch "Belle Plaine") .. 10 10
1700 25 c. on 30 c. multicoloured (surch "Clonbrook") 10 10
1701 25 c. on 30 c. multicoloured (surch "T.P.O. Dem. Railway") 10 10
1702 25 c. on 30 c. mult (surch "Enmore") .. 10 10
1703 25 c. on 30 c. multicoloured (surch "Fredericksburg") 10 10
1704 25 c. on 30 c. mult (surch "Good Success") 10 10
1705 25 c. on 30 c. multicoloured (surch "1986") 10 10
1706 25 c. on 30 c. mult (surch "Mariabba") .. 10 10
1707 25 c. on 30 c. multicoloured (surch "Massaruni") 10 10
1708 25 c. on 30 c. multicoloured (surch "Nigg") 10 10
1709 25 c. on 30 c. multicoloured (surch "No. 50") 10 10

1710 25 c. on 30 c. mult (surch "No. 63 Benab") 10 10
1711 25 c. on 30 c. multicoloured (surch "Philadelphia") 10 10
1712 25 c. on 30 c. mult (surch "Sisters") .. 10 10
1713 25 c. on 30 c. mult (surch "Skeldon") .. 10 10
1714 25 c. on 30 c. mult (surch "Suddie") .. 10 10
1715 25 c. on 30 c. multicoloured (surch "Taymouth Manor") 10 10
1716 25 c. on 30 c. multicoloured (surch "Wales") 10 10
1717 25 c. on 30 c. multicoloured (surch "Whim") 10 10
1694/717 .. .. *Set of* 24 1·75 1·75

The surcharged names are those of postal agencies opened between 1860 and 1880.

1986 (26 May). *20th Anniv of Independence. (a) No.* 332 *of British Guiana, Nos* 398A, 401B *of Guyana surch as T* **358** *by Autoprint and No.* 656 *surch as T* **339** *by Tip Torres.*

1718 25 c. on 2 c. myrtle-green (No. 332) .. 10 10
1719 25 c. on 35 c. multicoloured (No. 656) .. 10 10
1720 60 c. on 2 c. myrtle-green (No. 332) .. 15 10
1721 120 c. on 6 c. yellow-green (No. 398A) .. 25 20
1722 130 c. on 24 c. black & brt orange (No. 401B) 25 20

(*b*) *Nos.* 1188/91 *surch as T* **358**, *but without* "GUYANA", *by Autoprint.*

1723 **277** 25 c. on 120 c. lake-brown, black and bright blue (No. 1188) 10 10
a. Block of 4. Nos. 1723/6 85
1724 – 25 c. on 130 c. rose-red, black and bright blue (No. 1189) 10 10
1725 – 25 c. on 150 c. bright violet, black and bright blue (No. 1190) 10 10
1726 – 225 c. on 200 c. dull green, black and bright blue (No. 1191) 50 50
1718/26 .. .. *Set of* 9 1·40 1·25

On Nos. 1721/2 "1986" has been added below the existing overprint.

Nos. 1718 and 1720 have Mult Script CA watermark, No. 1721 watermark w **12** upright and No. 1722 watermark w **12** sideways.

MEXICO
1986

225 (359)

CARICOM
DAY 1986
(360)

1986 (31 May). *World Cup Football Championship, Mexico (2nd issue). No.* 544 *surch with T* **359** *in blue by Autoprint.*

1727 225 c. on 3 c. Hanging Heliconia 45 35

1986 (28 June). *CARICOM Day. No.* 705a *optd with T* **360** *in blue by Autoprint.*

1728 60 c. *Papilio androgeus* 15 10

CARICOM
HEADS OF GOV'T
CONFERENCE
JULY 1986
60
(361)

INT. YEAR
OF PEACE
25
(362)

1986 (1 July). *CARICOM Heads of Government Conference, Georgetown. Nos.* 544 *and* 601 *surch as T* **361** *in blue by Autoprint.*

1729 25 c. on 8 c. on 6 c. Cannon-ball Tree .. 10 10
1730 60 c. on 3 c. Hanging Heliconia 20 15

(Litho Format)

1986 (10 July). *Centenary of Publication of Sanders'* Reichenbachia (*8th issue*). *Vert designs as T* **331**. *Multicoloured. No wmk. P* 13½×14.

1731 30 c. Plate No. 86 (Series 1) 10 10
1732 55 c. Plate No. 17 (Series 1) 15 10
1733 60 c. Plate No. 93 (Series 1) 15 10
1734 100 c. Plate No. 68 (Series 1) 20 15
1735 130 c. Plate No. 91 (Series 1) 25 20
1736 250 c. Plate No. 74 (Series 1) 50 40
1737 260 c. Plate No. 39 (Series 1) 50 40
1738 375 c. Plate No. 90 (Series 1) 70 55
1731/8 .. .. *Set of* 8 2·25 1·75

Nos. 1731/8 were printed in a similar sheet format to Nos. 1518/33.

For these designs with different face values see Nos. 1822, 1868 and 1884/5.

1986 (14 July). *International Peace Year. Nos.* 542 *and* 546 *surch as T* **362** *in blue (No.* 1739) *or black (others).*

1739 25 c. on 1 c. Pitcher Plant of Mt Roraima .. 10 10
a. Sheetlet of 25. No. 1739×24 and one label .. .. 1·25
1740 60 c. on 6 c. Cannon-ball Tree 10 10
a. Sheetlet of 25. Nos. 1740/3, each×4, and nine labels .. .. .. 2·25
1741 120 c. on 6 c. Cannon-ball Tree 15 20
1742 130 c. on 6 c. Cannon-ball Tree 15 20
1743 150 c. on 6 c. Cannon-ball Tree 20 25
1739/43 .. .. *Set of* 5 55 70

As surcharged the sheet of No. 1739 contained a stamp without face value, overprinted "1986", in the centre position.

Nos. 1740/3 were each surcharged in blocks of four from the corner positions of the same sheet. Stamps in the central horizontal and vertical rows were without value and were overprinted with one letter of "PEACE".

363 Halley's Comet and British Guiana 1907 2 c. Stamp

(Litho Format)

1986 (19 July). *Appearance of Halley's Comet. T* **363** *and similar vert design. P* 13½×14.

1744 **363** 320 c. rosine, black & deep reddish lilac 60 60
a. Horiz pair. Nos. 1744/5 .. .. 1·10 1·10
ab. Imperf between (horiz pair) ..
1745 – 320 c. multicoloured 60 60
MS1746 76×50 mm. Nos. 1744/5. Imperf .. 90 1·00

Design:—No. 1745, Guyana 1985 320 c. Macaw stamp.

(Litho Format)

1986 (24 July). *Centenary of Publication of Sanders'* Reichenbachia (*9th issue*). *Vert designs as T* **331**. *Multicoloured. No wmk. P* 13½×14.

1747 40 c. Plate No. 96 (Series 1) 10 10
1748 45 c. Plate No. 81 (Series 1) 10 10
1749 90 c. Plate No. 89 (Series 1) 20 15
1750 100 c. Plate No. 88 (Series 1) 20 15
1751 150 c. Plate No. 76 (Series 1) 30 25
1752 180 c. Plate No. 15 (Series 1) 40 30
1753 320 c. Plate No. 82 (Series 1) 55 45
1754 330 c. Plate No. 80 (Series 1) 65 50
1747/54 .. .. *Set of* 8 2·25 1·75

Nos. 1747/54 were printed in a similar sheet format to Nos. 1518/33.

1986 (28 July). *No.* 489 *surch as T* **317**, *but without the* "X".

1755 20 c. on 6 c. Patua 10 10

GUSIA
(364)

1936-1986
REGIONAL
PHARMACY
CONFERENCE
1986
130
(365)

1986 (15 Aug). *50th Anniv of Guyana United Sadr Islamic Association. Nos.* 469/70 *optd or surch as T* **364** *by Autoprint.*

1756 **105** 25 c. black, gold and lilac 10 10
1757 $1.50 on 6 c. black, gold and flesh .. 35 35

1986 (19 Aug). *Regional Pharmacy Conference. No.* 545 *surch with T* **365** *in blue.*

1758 130 c. on 5 c. Annatto Tree 30 20

(Litho Format)

1986 (21 Aug). *As previous* Reichenbachia *issues, but W* **106** *(sideways on horiz designs). P* 13½×14 *(vert) or* 14×13½ *(horiz).*

(*a*) *As Nos.* 1526/7 *and* 1529/30

1767 130 c. Plate No. 6 (Series 1) 25 20
1768 130 c. Plate No. 13 (Series 1) 25 20
1770 130 c. Plate No. 20 (Series 1) 25 20
1771 130 c. Plate No. 25 (Series 1) 25 20

(*b*) *As Nos.* 1552/5

1776 55 c. Plate No. 9 (Series 1) 15 10
1777 55 c. Plate No. 22 (Series 1) 15 10
1778 55 c. Plate No. 49 (Series 1) 15 10
1779 55 c. Plate No. 64 (Series 1) 15 10

(*c*) *As Nos.* 1581/3 *and* 1586

1801 150 c. Plate No. 40 (Series 1) (*horiz*) .. 25 20
1802 150 c. Plate No. 42 (Series 1) (*horiz*) .. 25 20
1803 150 c. Plate No. 45 (Series 1) (*horiz*) .. 25 20
1806 200 c. Plate No. 43 (Series 1) (*horiz*) .. 35 30
1767/1806 .. .. *Set of* 12 2·40 1·75

Nos. 1767/8, 1770/1, 1776/9, 1801/3 and 1806 were printed in a similar sheet format to Nos. 1518/33.

These stamps, together with unwatermarked values from the 1st to the 9th issues, also exist made up into two small books which reproduce the order of the plates in the original volumes.

1986 (21 Aug). *Booklet and Coil Stamps. As Nos.* 1534/5a, *but W* **106** *(sideways on Nos.* 1807*a*, 1808*a*).

1807 **332** 25 c. multicoloured (*imperf*×*p* 14) .. 10 10
1807*a* 25 c. multicoloured (*imperf*×*p* 13½) 10 10
1808 25 c. multicoloured (*p* 13½×*imperf*) 10 10
1808*a* 25 c. multicoloured (*p* 14×*imperf*) .. 10 10
1807/8*a* .. .. *Set of* 4 30 30

The note below Nos. 1534/5 also applies to Nos. 1807/8*a*.

(Litho Format)

1986 (23 Sept). *Centenary of Publication of Sanders'* Reichenbachia (*10th issue*). *Multicoloured designs as T* **331**. *No wmk. P* 14×13½ (*Nos.* 1810, 1812, 1815, 1818) *or* 13½×14 (*others*).

1809 30 c. Plate No. 30 (Series 2) 10 10
1810 45 c. Plate No. 21 (Series 2) (*horiz*) .. 10 10
1811 75 c. Plate No. 8 (Series 2) 15 10
1812 80 c. Plate No. 42 (Series 2) (*horiz*) .. 15 10
1813 90 c. Plate No. 4 (Series 2) 20 15
1814 130 c. Plate No. 38 (Series 2) 20 20
1815 160 c. Plate No. 5 (Series 2) (*horiz*) .. 30 25
1816 200 c. Plate No. 9 (Series 2) 35 30
1817 320 c. Plate No. 12 (Series 2) 60 50
1818 350 c. Plate No. 29 (Series 2) (*horiz*) .. 70 50
1819 360 c. Plate No. 34 (Series 2) 70 50
1809/19 .. .. *Set of* 11 3·00 2·40

Nos. 1809/19, together with Nos. 1820/1*a*, were printed in a similar sheet format to Nos. 1518/33.

(Litho Format)

1986 (23 Sept). *20th Anniv of Independence (2nd issue). Booklet and Coil Stamps. T* **332** *additionally inscr* "1966–1986" *at foot. No wmk.*

1820 25 c. multicoloured (*imperf*×*p* 14) .. 10 10
1820*a* 25 c. multicoloured (*imperf*×*p* 13½) .. 10 10
1821 25 c. multicoloured (*p* 13½×*imperf*) .. 10 10
1821*a* 25 c. multicoloured (*p* 14×*imperf*) .. 10 10
1820/1*a* .. .. *Set of* 4 30 30

Nos. 1820/1*a* together with Nos. 1809/19, were printed in the sheet format described beneath No. 1533.

(Litho Format)

1986 (26 Sept). *Centenary of Publication of Sanders'* Reichenbachia (*11th issue*). *Design as No.* 1735, *but with different face value. Multicoloured. No wmk. P* 13½×14.

1822 40 c. Plate No. 91 (Series 1) 15 10

120
(366)

650
12th World Orchid Conference
TOKYO JAPAN MARCH 1987
(367)

1986 (3 Oct). *Nos.* 1361/84 *surch with T* **366** *by Autoprint.*

1823 120 c. on 30 c. multicoloured (No. 1361) .. 20 20
a. Sheetlet of 25. Nos. 1823/33, 1834×2 and 1835/46 .. .. .. 4·25
1824 120 c. on 30 c. multicoloured (No. 1362) .. 20 20
1825 120 c. on 30 c. multicoloured (No. 1363) .. 20 20
1826 120 c. on 30 c. multicoloured (No. 1364) .. 20 20
1827 120 c. on 30 c. multicoloured (No. 1365) .. 20 20
1828 120 c. on 30 c. multicoloured (No. 1366) .. 20 20
1829 120 c. on 30 c. multicoloured (No. 1367) .. 20 20
1830 120 c. on 30 c. multicoloured (No. 1368) .. 20 20
1831 120 c. on 30 c. multicoloured (No. 1369) .. 20 20
1832 120 c. on 30 c. multicoloured (No. 1370) .. 20 20
1833 120 c. on 30 c. multicoloured (No. 1371) .. 20 20
1834 120 c. on 30 c. multicoloured (No. 1372) .. 20 20
1835 120 c. on 30 c. multicoloured (No. 1373) .. 20 20
1836 120 c. on 30 c. multicoloured (No. 1374) .. 20 20
1837 120 c. on 30 c. multicoloured (No. 1375) .. 20 20
1838 120 c. on 30 c. multicoloured (No. 1376) .. 20 20
1839 120 c. on 30 c. multicoloured (No. 1377) .. 20 20
1840 120 c. on 30 c. multicoloured (No. 1378) .. 20 20
1841 120 c. on 30 c. multicoloured (No. 1379) .. 20 20
1842 120 c. on 30 c. multicoloured (No. 1380) .. 20 20
1843 120 c. on 30 c. multicoloured (No. 1381) .. 20 20
1844 120 c. on 30 c. multicoloured (No. 1382) .. 20 20
1845 120 c. on 30 c. multicoloured (No. 1383) .. 20 20
1846 120 c. on 30 c. multicoloured (No. 1384) .. 20 20
1823/46 .. .. *Set of* 24 4·25 4·25

1986 (6 Oct). *12th World Orchid Conference, Tokyo (1st issue). Unissued design as No.* 1731, *but with different face value, surch with T* **367** *by Tip Torres.*

1847 650 c. on 40 c. Plate No. 86 (Series 1) .. 1·25 1·25

No. 1847 is inscribed "ONTOGLOSSUM TRIUMPHANS" in error.

See also Nos. 2138/9.

(Litho Format)

1986 (Oct)–**87**. *As previous* Reichenbachia *issues, Nos.* 1621, 1625/6, *and* 1635, *but W* **106**. *P* 13½×14.

1849 30 c. Plate No. 53 (Series 1) 10 10
1853 75 c. Plate No. 55 (Series 1) (1.87) .. 20 15
1854 100 c. Plate No. 65 (Series 1) (1.87) .. 25 15
1863 225 c. Plate No. 24 (Series 1) 35 35
1849/63 .. .. *Set of* 4 75 65

1492-1992 CHRISTOPHER COLUMBUS

320

(368)

1986 (10–30 Oct). *Columbus Day. Unissued design as No.* 1635, *but with different face value, surch with T* **368** *by Tip Torres.*

1864 320 c. on 150 c. Plate No. 24 (Series 1) (surch in black (figures and obliterating device) and red) 60 45
1865 320 c. on 150 c. Plate No. 24 (Series 1) (entire surch in red) (30 Oct) .. 60 45

1986 50

(369)

AIR UNICEF 1946-1986 120

(370)

1986 (15 Oct). *International Food Day. Nos.* 1170/1 *further surch as T* **369** *by Autoprint.*

1866 50 c. on 30 c. on 1 c. Type **87** 15 15
1867 225 c. on $2.60 on 3 c. Lukunani 45 45

(Litho Format)

1986 (23 Oct). *Centenary of Publication of Sanders'* Reichenbachia (12*th issue*). *Vert designs as T* **331**, *one as No.* 1731 *with different face value. Multicoloured. No wmk. P* 13½×14.

1868 40 c. Plate No. 86 (Series 1) 10 10
1869 90 c. Plate No. 10 (Series 2) 20 15

1986 (24 Oct). *Air.* 40*th Annivs of U.N.I.C.E.F. and U.N.E.S.C.O. No.* 706 *surch as T* **370** *by Autoprint.*

1870 120 c. on $1 Type **167** (surch T **370**) .. 25 25
a. Pair. Nos. 1870/1 .. .. .. 50 50
1871 120 c. on $1 Type **167** (surch "UNESCO 1946–1986") 25 25

Nos. 1870/1 were surcharged together, *se-tenant*, in horizontal and vertical pairs throughout the sheet.

(Litho Format)

1986 (30 Oct). *Centenary of Publication of Sanders'* Reichenbachia (13*th issue*). *Vert designs as T* **331**. *Multicoloured. No wmk. P* 13½×14.

1872 45 c. Plate No. 17 (Series 2) 10 10
1873 50 c. Plate No. 33 (Series 2) 10 10
1874 60 c. Plate No. 27 (Series 2) 10 10
1875 75 c. Plate No. 56 (Series 2) 15 15
1876 85 c. Plate No. 45 (Series 2) 15 15
1877 90 c. Plate No. 13 (Series 2) 20 15
1878 200 c. Plate No. 44 (Series 2) 35 30
1879 300 c. Plate No. 50 (Series 2) 60 45
1880 320 c. Plate No. 10 (Series 2) 60 45
1881 390 c. Plate No. 6 (Series 2) 70 55
1872/81 .. .. *Set of* 10 2·50 2·25

Nos. 1872/81 were printed in a similar sheet format to Nos. 1518/33.

For these designs with different face values see Nos. 1907, 1915 and 1925.

25 X Deepavali 1986

(371)

CHRISTMAS 1986 20

(372)

1986 (3 Nov). *Deepavali Festival. Nos.* 543 *and* 601 *surch as T* **371** *by Autoprint.*

1882 25 c. on 2 c. Type **132** 10 10
1883 200 c. on 8 c. on 6 c. Cannon-ball Tree .. 40 40

(Litho Format)

1986 (25 Nov). *Centenary of Publication of Sanders'* Reichenbachia (14*th issue*). *Vert designs as T* **331**, *two as Nos.* 1732 *and* 1734 *with different face values. Multicoloured. No wmk. P* 13½×14.

1884 40 c. Plate No. 68 (Series 1) 10 10
1885 80 c. Plate No. 17 (Series 1) 20 15
1886 200 c. Plate No. 2 (Series 2) 40 35
1887 225 c. Plate No. 24 (Series 2) 45 40
1884/7 .. .. *Set of* 4 1·00 90

Nos. 1884/7 were printed in a similar sheet format to Nos. 1518/33.

For these designs with different face values see Nos. 1914 and 1929.

1986 (26 Nov). *Christmas. No.* 452 *surch with T* **372** *and Nos.* 1425/9 *surch as T* **342**, *but without dates, all in red by Autoprint.*

1888 20 c. on 6 c. Patua 10 10
1889 120 c. on 60 c. Type **318** 30 30
a. Horiz strip of 5. Nos. 1889/93 .. 1·40
1890 120 c. on 60 c. Swallow-tailed Kite on branch 30 30
1891 120 c. on 60 c. Kite in flight with wings raised 30 30
1892 120 c. on 60 c. Kite in flight with wings lowered 30 30
1893 120 c. on 60 c. Kite gliding 30 30
1888/93 .. .. *Set of* 6 1·40 1·40

1986

(373)

$15

(374)

1986 (26 Nov). *Wildlife Protection. Nos.* 756/67 *optd with T* **373** *in blue by Autoprint.*

1894 30 c. Type **178** 10 10
a. Sheetlet of 12. Nos. 1894/905 .. .. 1·10
1895 30 c. Red Howler 10 10
1896 30 c. Common Squirrel-Monkey 10 10
1897 30 c. Two-toed Sloth 10 10
1898 30 c. Brazilian Tapir 10 10
1899 30 c. Collared Peccary 10 10
1900 30 c. Six-banded Armadillo 10 10
1901 30 c. Tamandua ("Ant Eater") 10 10
1902 30 c. Giant Anteater 10 10
1903 30 c. Murine Opossum 10 10
1904 30 c. Brown Four-eyed Opossum 10 10
1905 30 c. Brazilian Agouti 10 10
1894/905 .. .. .. *Set of* 12 1·10 1·10

1986 (1 Dec). *No.* 1642 *surch with T* **374** *in red by Autoprint.*

1906 $15 on $3.50, Clive Lloyd with the Prudential Cup .. .. 3·50 3·00

(Litho Format)

1986 (3 Dec). *Centenary of Publicction of Sanders'* Reichenbachia (15*th issue*). *Design as No.* 1877, *but with different face value. Multicoloured. No wmk. P* 13½×14.

1907 50 c. Plate No. 13 (Series 2) 15 10

GPOC

$10 1977 - 1987

375 Memorial (376)

(Litho Format)

1986 (13 Dec). *President Burnham Commemoration. T* **375** *and similar multicoloured designs. P* 12½.

1908 25 c. Type **375** 10 10
1909 120 c. Map of Guyana and flags 25 20
1910 130 c. Parliament Buildings and mace .. 25 20
1911 $6 L. F. Burnham and Georgetown mayoral chain (*vert*) .. .. .. 1·10 1·25
1908/11 .. .. *Set of* 4 1·50 1·60

(Litho Format)

1986 (15–22 Dec). *Centenary of Publication of Sanders'* Reichenbachia (16*th issue*). *Multicoloured designs as Nos.* 1554/5, 1874 *and* 1887 *with different face values. W* **106** *(Nos.* 1912/13*) or no wmk (others). P* 13½×14.

1912 50 c. Plate No. 49 (Series 1) (22.12) .. 10 10
1913 50 c. Plate No. 64 (Series 1) 10 10
1914 85 c. Plate No. 24 (Series 2) 15 15
1915 90 c. Plate No. 27 (Series 2) 15 15
1912/15 .. .. *Set of* 4 45 45

(Litho Format)

1986 (27 Dec). *Centenary of Publication of Sanders'* Reichenbachia (17*th issue*). *Vert designs as T* **331**. *Multicoloured. No wmk. P* 13½×14.

1916 25 c. Plate No. 20 (Series 2) 10 10
1917 40 c. Plate No. 7 (Series 2) 10 10
1918 85 c. Plate No. 15 (Series 2) 15 15
1919 90 c. Plate No. 3 (Series 2) 15 15
1920 120 c. Plate No. 14 (Series 2) 25 20
1921 130 c. Plate No. 32 (Series 2) 25 20
1922 150 c. Plate No. 22 (Series 2) 35 25
1923 320 c. Plate No. 18 (Series 2) 60 45
1924 330 c. Plate No. 28 (Series 2) 60 50
1916/24 .. .. *Set of* 9 2·25 1·75

Nos. 1916/24 were printed in a similar sheet format to Nos. 1518/33.

For these designs with different face values see Nos. 1926 and 1928.

(Litho Format)

1987 (5–16 Jan). *Centenary of Publication of Sanders'* Reichenbachia (18*th issue*). *Multicoloured designs as Nos.* 1625, 1876, 1886, 1918 *and* 1923 *with different face values. W* **106** *(No.* 1927*) or no wmk (others). P* 13½×14.

1925 35 c. Plate No. 45 (Series 2) 10 10
1926 50 c. Plate No. 15 (Series 2) 10 10
1927 50 c. Plate No. 55 (Series 1) (16.1) .. 10 10
1928 85 c. Plate No. 18 (Series 2) 20 15
1929 90 c. Plate No. 2 (Series 2) 20 15
1925/9 .. .. *Set of* 5 55 45

Nos. 1925/9 were printed in a similar sheet format to Nos. 1518/33.

1987 (19 Jan). 10*th Anniv of Guyana Post Office Corporation (1st issue). Unissued designs as Nos.* 1621 *and* 1635, *but with different face values, surch or optd as T* **376** *by Tip Torres.*

1930 $2.25, Plate No. 53 (Series 1) 40 35
1931 $10 on 150 c. Plate No. 24 (Series 1) .. 1·50 1·75

See also Nos. 2074/80.

200

200

(377)

(378)

200

TWO DOLLARS

(379) (380)

1987

15.00

(381)

225

(382)

120

(383)

120

(384)

1987 (9 Feb–Sept). *Various* Reichenbachia *issues surch as T* **377/84**.

(a) As T **377** *in red by Tip Torres (*9 Feb)
1932 200 c. on 40 c. Plate No. 90 (Series 1) .. 25 30

(b) As T **378** *by Tip Torres* (6 Mar)
1933 200 c. on 25 c. Plate No. 8 (Series 1) (No. 1571) 25 30
1934 200 c. on 25 c. Plate No. 51 (Series 1) (No. 1573) 25 30

(c) As T **379** *by Tip Torres (No.* 1935 *without ornament)* (6 Mar)
1935 $2 on 25 c. Plate No. 12 (Series 1) (No. 1518) 25 30
1936 $2 on 25 c. Plate No. 23 (Series 1) (No. 1572) 25 30

(d) As T **380** *by Tip Torres* (17 Mar)
1937 200 c. on 40 c. Plate No. 68 (Series 1) (No. 1884) (ornament inverted) .. 25 30
a. Ornament upright 25 30
1938 200 c. on 40 c. Plate No. 90 (Series 1) .. 25 30
1939 200 c. on 50 c. Plate No. 92 (Series 1) (No. 1665) 25 30
1940 200 c. on 50 c. Plate No. 22 (Series 1) (*wmkd*) 25 30
1941 200 c. on 55 c. Plate No. 22 (Series 1) (No. 1777) (*wmkd*) 25 30
1942 200 c. on 60 c. Plate No. 5 (Series 1) (ornament inverted) 25 30
1943 200 c. on 75 c. Plate No. 5 (Series 1) (No. 1667) (ornament inverted) .. 25 30
1944 200 c. on 75 c. Plate No. 60 (Series 1) .. 25 30
1945 200 c. on 75 c. Plate No. 92 (Series 1) .. 25 30
1946 200 c. on 85 c. Plate No. 18 (Series 2) (No. 1928) 25 30
1947 200 c. on 375 c. Plate No. 90 (Series 1) (No. 1738) 25 30
1948 200 c. on 375 c. Plate No. 90 (Series 1) (*wmkd*) 25 30
1937/48 .. .. *Set of* 12 2·75 3·25

(e) As T **377** *by Tip Torres* (March)
1949 200 c. on 25 c. Plate No. 52 (Series 1) (No. 1551) 25 30
1950 200 c. on 25 c. Plate No. 8 (Series 1) (No. 1571) 25 30
1951 200 c. on 25 c. Plate No. 72 (Series 1) (No. 1577) 25 30
1952 200 c. on 25 c. Plate No. 71 (Series 1) (No. 1679) (surch vert – reading downwards) 25 30
1953 200 c. on 30 c. Plate No. 86 (Series 1) (No. 1731) 25 30
1954 200 c. on 30 c. Plate No. 53 (Series 1) (No. 1849) (*wmkd*) 25 30
1955 200 c. on 40 c. Plate No. 77 (Series 1) (No. 1663) 25 30
1956 200 c. on 40 c. Plate No. 86 (Series 1) (No. 1868) 25 30
1957 200 c. on 45 c. Plate No. 81 (Series 1) (No. 1748) 25 30
1958 200 c. on 45 c. Plate No. 77 (Series 1) .. 25 30
1959 200 c. on 45 c. Plate No. 78 (Series 1) .. 25 30
1960 200 c. on 45 c. Plate No. 85 (Series 1) .. 25 30
1961 200 c. on 50 c. Plate No. 24 (Series 1) (*wmkd*) 25 30
1962 200 c. on 50 c. Plate No. 53 (Series 1) (*wmkd*) 25 30
1963 200 c. on 50 c. Plate No. 65 (Series 1) (*wmkd*) 25 30
1964 200 c. on 55 c. Plate No. 49 (Series 1) (No. 1554) 25 30
1965 200 c. on 55 c. Plate No. 17 (Series 1) (No. 1732) 25 30
1966 200 c. on 55 c. Plate No. 49 (Series 1) (No. 1778) (*wmkd*) 25 30
1967 200 c. on 60 c. Plate No. 7 (Series 1) (No. 1520) 25 30
1968 200 c. on 60 c. Plate No. 10 (Series 1) (No. 1521) 25 30
1969 200 c. on 60 c. Plate No. 19 (Series 1) (No. 1522) 25 30
1970 200 c. on 60 c. Plate No. 31 (Series 1) (No. 1523) 25 30
1971 200 c. on 60 c. Plate No. 44 (Series 1) (No. 1556) 25 30
1972 200 c. on 60 c. Plate No. 47 (Series 1) (No. 1557) 25 30
1973 200 c. on 60 c. Plate No. 57 (Series 1) (No. 1622) (surch vert – reading down) 25 30
1974 200 c. on 60 c. Plate No. 73 (Series 1) (No. 1623) (surch vert – reading up) .. 25 30
1975 200 c. on 60 c. Plate No. 75 (Series 1) (No. 1624) (surch vert – reading down) 25 30
1976 200 c. on 60 c. Plate No. 71 (Series 1) (surch vert – reading down) 25 30
1977 200 c. on 60 c. Plate No. 87 (Series 1) (surch vert – reading down) 25 30
1978 225 c. on 90 c. Plate No. 89 (Series 1) (No. 1749) 30 35
1949/78 .. .. *Set of* 30 6·75 8·00

(f) As T **381** *by Gardy Ptg* (March)
1979 120 c. on 50 c. Plate No. 9 (Series 1) (*wmkd*) 15 20
1980 120 c. on 55 c. Plate No. 9 (Series 1) (No. 1552) 15 20
1981 120 c. on 55 c. Plate No. 64 (Series 1) (No. 1555) 15 20
1982 120 c. on 55 c. Plate No. 64 (Series 1) (No. 1779) (*wmkd*) 15 20
1983 $10 on 25 c. Plate No. 53 (Series 1) .. 1·25 1·40
1984 $12 on 80 c. Plate No. 74 (Series 1) .. 1·60 1·75
1985 $15 on 80 c. Plate No. 39 (Series 1) .. 1·90 2·00
1986 $25 on 25 c. Plate No. 53 (Series 1) .. 3·25 3·50
1979/86 .. .. *Set of* 8 7·75 8·60

Nos. 1979/82 do not show a date as part of the surcharge. On No. 1986 the surcharge is achieved by a dollar sign in front of the original face value.

(g) With T **382** *by Gardy Ptg* (June)
1987 225 c. on 40 c. Plate No. 91 (Series 1) (No. 1822) 30 35
1988 225 c. on 40 c. Plate No. 90 (Series 1) .. 30 35
1989 225 c. on 50 c. Plate No. 22 (Series 1) (*wmkd*) 30 35
1990 225 c. on 60 c. Plate No. 55 (Series 1) (No. 1597) 30 35
1991 225 c. on 60 c. Plate No. 93 (Series 1) (No. 1733) 30 35
1992 225 c. on 80 c. Plate No. 93 (Series 1) .. 30 35
1993 225 c. on 150 c. Plate No. 42 (Series 1) (No. 1657) (surch vert – reading down) 30 35
1987/93 .. .. *Set of* 7 1·90 2·25

(h) As T **383** (July)
1994 120 c. on 50 c. Plate No. 49 (Series 1) (No. 1912) (*wmkd*) 15 20
1995 120 c. on 50 c. Plate No. 64 (Series 1) (No. 1913) (*wmkd*) 15 20
1996 120 c. on 50 c. Plate No. 9 (Series 1) (*wmkd*) 15 20
1997 120 c. on 50 c. Plate No. 22 (Series 1) (*wmkd*) 15 20
1998 120 c. on 50 c. Plate No. 3 (Series 2) .. 15 20
1999 120 c. on 50 c. Plate No. 6 (Series 2) .. 15 20
2000 120 c. on 50 c. Plate No. 20 (Series 2) .. 15 20
2001 120 c. on 50 c. Plate No. 32 (Series 2) .. 15 20
2002 120 c. on 55 c. Plate No. 9 (Series 1) (No. 1552) 15 20
2003 120 c. on 55 c. Plate No. 49 (Series 1) (No. 1554) 15 20
2004 120 c. on 55 c. Plate No. 64 (Series 1) (No. 1555) 15 20
2005 120 c. on 55 c. Plate No. 9 (Series 1) (No. 1776) (*wmkd*) 15 20
2006 120 c. on 55 c. Plate No. 22 (Series 1) (No. 1777) (*wmkd*) 15 20
2007 120 c. on 55 c. Plate No. 49 (Series 1) (No. 1778) (*wmkd*) 15 20
2008 120 c. on 55 c. Plate No. 64 (Series 1) (No. 1779) (*wmkd*) 15 20
2009 120 c. on 55 c. Plate No. 15 (Series 1) .. 15 20
2010 120 c. on 55 c. Plate No. 81 (Series 1) .. 15 20
2011 120 c. on 55 c. Plate No. 82 (Series 1) .. 15 20
2012 120 c. on 55 c. Plate No. 89 (Series 1) .. 15 20
1994/2012 .. .. *Set of* 19 2·50 3·50

(i) As T **384** *by Gardy Ptg* (Sept)
2013 120 c. on 40 c. Plate No. 91 (Series 1) (No. 1822) 15 20
2014 120 c. on 40 c. Plate No. 90 (Series 1) .. 15 20
2015 120 c. on 50 c. Plate No. 49 (Series 1) (No. 1912) (*wmkd*) 15 20
2016 120 c. on 50 c. Plate No. 64 (Series 1) (No. 1913) (*wmkd*) 15 20
2017 120 c. on 50 c. Plate No. 9 (Series 1) (*wmkd*) 15 20
2018 120 c. on 50 c. Plate No. 22 (Series 1) (*wmkd*) 15 20
2019 120 c. on 50 c. Plate No. 24 (Series 1) (*wmkd*) 15 20
2020 120 c. on 50 c. Plate No. 53 (Series 1) (*wmkd*) 15 20
2021 120 c. on 50 c. Plate No. 65 (Series 1) (*wmkd*) 15 20
2022 120 c. on 55 c. Plate No. 9 (Series 1) (No. 1776) (*wmkd*) 15 20
2023 120 c. on 55 c. Plate No. 22 (Series 1) (No. 1777) (*wmkd*) 15 20
2024 120 c. on 55 c. Plate No. 49 (Series 1) (No. 1778) (*wmkd*) 15 20
2025 120 c. on 55 c. Plate No. 64 (Series 1) (No. 1779) (*wmkd*) 15 20
2026 120 c. on 60 c. Plate No. 2 (Series 1) (No. 1519) 15 20
2027 120 c. on 60 c. Plate No. 10 (Series 1) (No. 1521) 15 20
2028 120 c. on 60 c. Plate No. 19 (Series 1) (No. 1522) 15 20
2029 120 c. on 60 c. Plate No. 31 (Series 1) (No. 1523) 15 20
2030 120 c. on 60 c. Plate No. 5 (Series 1) .. 15 20
2031 120 c. on 60 c. Plate No. 50 (Series 1) .. 15 20
2032 120 c. on 60 c. Plate No. 54 (Series 1) .. 15 20
2033 120 c. on 60 c. Plate No. 69 (Series 1) (surch vert – reading down) 15 20
2034 120 c. on 60 c. Plate No. 71 (Series 1) (surch vert – reading up) 15 20
a. Surch reading down 15 20
2035 120 c. on 60 c. Plate No. 79 (Series 1) .. 15 20
2036 120 c. on 60 c. Plate No. 87 (Series 1) (surch vert – reading up) 15 20
a. Surch reading down 15 20
2037 120 c. on 60 c. Plate No. 94 (Series 1) (surch vert – reading down) 15 20
2038 120 c. on 75 c. Plate No. 60 (Series 1) .. 15 20
2039 120 c. on 75 c. Plate No. 83 (Series 1) .. 15 20
2040 120 c. on 75 c. Plate No. 92 (Series 1) .. 15 20
2041 120 c. on 75 c. Plate No. 95 (Series 1) .. 15 20
2042 200 c. on 45 c. Plate No. 77 (Series 1) .. 15 20
2043 200 c. on 45 c. Plate No. 78 (Series 1) .. 15 20
2044 200 c. on 45 c. Plate No. 84 (Series 1) .. 15 20
2045 200 c. on 45 c. Plate No. 85 (Series 1) .. 15 20
2046 200 c. on 50 c. Plate No. 55 (Series 1) (No. 1927) (*wmkd*) 25 30
2047 200 c. on 50 c. Plate No. 24 (Series 1) (*wmkd*) 25 30
2048 200 c. on 50 c. Plate No. 53 (Series 1) (*wmkd*) 25 30
2049 200 c. on 50 c. Plate No. 65 (Series 1) (*wmkd*) 25 30
2050 200 c. on 55 c. Plate No. 15 (Series 1) .. 25 30
2051 200 c. on 55 c. Plate No. 81 (Series 1) .. 25 30
2052 200 c. on 55 c. Plate No. 82 (Series 1) .. 25 30
2053 200 c. on 55 c. Plate No. 89 (Series 1) .. 25 30
2054 225 c. on 40 c. Plate No. 91 (Series 1) (No. 1822) 30 35
2055 225 c. on 40 c. Plate No. 86 (Series 1) (No. 1868) 30 35
a. Inscr "ONTOGLOSSUM TRIUMPHANS" in error 30 35
2056 225 c. on 40 c. Plate No. 68 (Series 1) (No. 1884) 30 35
2057 225 c. on 40 c. Plate No. 90 (Series 1) .. 30 35
2058 225 c. on 65 c. Plate No. 76 (Series 1) .. 30 35
2059 225 c. on 65 c. Plate No. 80 (Series 1) .. 30 35
2060 225 c. on 65 c. Plate No. 88 (Series 1) .. 30 35
2061 225 c. on 65 c. Plate No. 96 (Series 1) .. 30 35
2062 600 c. on 80 c. Plate No. 17 (Series 1) (No. 1885) 80 85
2063 600 c. on 80 c. Plate No. 39 (Series 1) .. 80 85
2064 600 c. on 80 c. Plate No. 74 (Series 1) .. 80 85
2065 600 c. on 80 c. Plate No. 93 (Series 1) .. 80 85
2013/65 .. .. *Set of* 53 11·50 14·00

Initially some values were surcharged in sheets of sixteen orchid stamps together with nine examples of No. 2081. Subsequently, however, the surcharges appeared in the individual blocks of 4 with the arms design issued separately as Nos. 2082/3.

For 600 c. on 900 c. with surcharge as T **384** see No. 2219.

(Litho Format)

1987 (16 Feb). *Centenary of Publication of Sanders'* Reichenbachia *(19th issue). Vert designs as T* **331**. *Multicoloured. No wmk. P* 13½×14.
2066 180 c. Plate 41 (Series 2) 25 30
2067 230 c. Plate 25 (Series 2) 30 35
2068 300 c. Plate 85 (Series 2) 40 45
2069 330 c. Plate 82 (Series 2) 45 50
2070 425 c. Plate 87 (Series 2) 55 60
2071 440 c. Plate 88 (Series 2) 55 60
2072 590 c. Plate 52 (Series 2) 75 80
2073 650 c. Plate 65 (Series 2) 85 90
2066/73 .. .. *Set of* 8 3·75 4·00

Nos. 2066/73 were printed in a similar sheet format to Nos. 1518/33.

Post Office Corp.
1977-1987
25c
(385)

1987
200
(386)

1987 (17 Feb). *10th Anniv of Guyana Post Office Corporation (2nd issue). Nos.* 543, 545, 548a *and* 601 *surch as T* **385** *in blue by Autoprint.*
2074 25 c. on 2 c. Type **132** 10 10
2075 25 c. on 5 c. Annatto tree 10 10
2076 25 c. on 8 c on 6 c. Cannon-ball tree .. 10 10
2077 25 c. on 15 c. Christmas Orchid 10 10
2078 60 c. on 15 c. Christmas Orchid 10 10
2079 $1.20 on 2 c. Type **132** 15 20
2080 $1.30 on 15 c. Christmas Orchid 15 20
2074/80 .. .. *Set of* 7 55 65

1987 (6 Mar). *Nos.* 1534/5 *surch with T* **386** *by Tip Torres.*
2081 **332** 200 c. on 25 c. mult (*p* 13½ × 14) .. 25 30
2082 200 c. on 25 c. mult (*imperf* × *p* 14) .. 25 30
2083 200 c. on 25 c. mult (*p* 13½ × *imperf*) .. 25 30
2081/3 .. .. *Set of* 3 70 80

See note below No. 2065.

1987 **(387)** 1987 **(388)** 1987 **(389)** 1987 **(390)**

1987 (6 Mar–Dec). *Various* Reichenbachia *issues optd as T* **387/90**.

(a) With T **387** *by Tip Torres* (March)
2084 130 c. Plate No. 3 (Series 1) (No. 1525) .. 15 20
2085 130 c. Plate No. 6 (Series 1) (No. 1526) .. 15 20
2086 130 c. Plate No. 20 (Series 1) (No. 1529) .. 15 20
2087 130 c. Plate No. 18 (Series 1) (No. 1536) .. 15 20
2088 130 c. Plate No. 29 (Series 1) (No. 1537) .. 15 20
2089 130 c. Plate No. 30 (Series 1) (No. 1538) .. 15 20
2090 130 c. Plate No. 16 (Series 1) (No. 1559) .. 15 20
2091 130 c. Plate No. 66 (Series 1) (No. 1632) .. 15 20
2092 130 c. Plate No. 13 (Series 1) (No. 1684) .. 15 20
2093 130 c. Plate No. 6 (Series 1) (No. 1767) (*wmkd*) 15 20
2094 130 c. Plate No. 20 (Series 1) (No. 1770) (*wmkd*) 15 20
2095 200 c. Plate No. 4 (Series 1) (No. 1533) .. 25 30
2096 200 c. Plate No. 14 (Series 1) (No. 1584) .. 25 30
2097 200 c. Plate No. 21 (Series 1) (No. 1585) (opt vert – reading down) 25 30
2098 200 c. Plate No. 33 (Series 1) (No. 1634) (opt vert – reading down) 25 30
2099 200 c. Plate No. 43 (Series 1) (No. 1658) (opt vert – reading down) 25 30
2100 200 c. Plate No. 79 (Series 1) (No. 1670) .. 25 30
2101 200 c. Plate No. 9 (Series 2) (No. 1816) .. 25 30
2102 200 c. Plate No. 2 (Series 2) (No. 1886) .. 25 30
2103 250 c. Plate No. 74 (Series 1) (No. 1736) .. 35 40
2104 260 c. Plate No. 39 (Series 1) (No. 1737) .. 35 40
2084/2104 .. .. .. *Set of* 21 4·00 4·75
MS2105 100×129 mm. 200 c.×4 Plate 4 (Series 1) (No. **MS**1539) .. .. .. 1·00 1·10
MS2106 100×129 mm. 200 c. on 130 c.×4 Plate 20 (Series 1) (No. **MS**1570) .. .. 1·00 1·10

(b) With T **388** *by Gardy Ptg* (March)
2107 130 c. Plate No. 13 (Series 1) (No. 1527) .. 15 20
2108 130 c. Plate No. 25 (Series 1) (No. 1530) .. 15 20
2109 130 c. Plate No. 91 (Series 1) (No. 1735) .. 15 20
2110 130 c. Plate No. 13 (Series 1) (No. 1768) (*wmkd*) 15 20
2111 130 c. Plate No. 25 (Series 1) (No. 1771) (*wmkd*) 15 20
2107/11 .. .. *Set of* 5 70 90

(c) With T **389** *by Gardy Ptg* (July)
2112 120 c. Plate No. 1 (Series 1) (No. 1578) (opt vert – reading down) 15 20
2113 120 c. Plate No. 11 (Series 1) (No. 1579) (opt vert – reading down) 15 20
2114 120 c. Plate No. 28 (Series 1) (No. 1580) (opt vert – reading down) 15 20
2115 120 c. Plate No. 37 (Series 1) (No. 1627) .. 15 20
2116 120 c. Plate No. 46 (Series 1) (No. 1628) .. 15 20

2117 120 c. Plate No. 56 (Series 1) (No. 1629) .. 15 20
2118 120 c. Plate No. 58 (Series 1) (No. 1630) .. 15 20
2119 130 c. Plate No. 6 (Series 1) (No. 1767) (*wmkd*) 15 20
2120 130 c. Plate No. 13 (Series 1) (No. 1768) (*wmkd*) 15 20
2121 130 c. Plate No. 20 (Series 1) (No. 1770) (*wmkd*) 15 20
2122 130 c. Plate No. 25 (Series 1) (No. 1771) (*wmkd*) 15 20
2123 150 c. Plate No. 40 (Series 1) (No. 1581) (opt vert – reading down) 20 25
2124 150 c. Plate No. 45 (Series 1) (No. 1583) (opt vert – reading down) 20 25
2125 150 c. Plate No. 42 (Series 1) (No. 1657) (opt vert – reading down) 20 25
2126 150 c. Plate No. 40 (Series 1) (No. 1801) (*wmkd*) (opt vert – reading up) .. 20 25
2127 150 c. Plate No. 42 (Series 1) (No. 1802) (*wmkd*) (opt vert – reading up) .. 20 25
2128 150 c. Plate No. 45 (Series 1) (No. 1803) (*wmkd*) (opt vert – reading up) .. 20 25
2129 200 c. Plate No. 21 (Series 1) (No. 1585) (opt vert – reading down) 25 30
2130 200 c. Plate No. 43 (Series 1) (No. 1658) (opt vert – reading down) 25 30
2131 200 c. Plate No. 43 (Series 1) (No. 1806) (*wmkd*) (opt vert – reading up) .. 25 30
2112/31 .. .. *Set of* 20 3·25 4·25

(*d*) *With T* **390** *by Gardy Ptg* (Dec)

2132 120 c. Plate No. 67 (Series 1) (No. 1631) .. 15 20
2133 130 c. Plate No. 18 (Series 1) (No. 1536) .. 15 20
2134 130 c. Plate No. 29 (Series 1) (No. 1537) .. 15 20
2135 130 c. Plate No. 30 (Series 1) (No. 1538) .. 15 20
2136 130 c. Plate No. 66 (Series 1) (No. 1632) .. 15 20
2137 150 c. Plate No. 26 (Series 1) (No. 1633) .. 20 25
2132/7 .. .. *Set of* 6 85 1·10

650

12th World Orchid Conference

(391)

TOKYO JAPAN

28 MARCH 1927
PAA
GEO-POS

(392)

1987 (12 Mar). *12th World Orchid Conference, Tokyo (2nd issue). Nos.* 1552 *and* 1776 *surch with T* **391** *by Tip Torres.*

2138 650 c. on 55 c. Plate No. 9 (Series 1) (No. 1552) 85 90
2139 650 c. on 55 c. Plate No. 9 (Series 1) (No. 1776) 85 90

1987 (17 Mar). *125th Anniv of British Guiana Post Office (3rd issue). No.* 699 *surch as T* **324** *by Autoprint.*

2140 25 c. on 10 c. mult (surch "AGRICOLA") .. 10 10
a. Sheetlet of 25. Nos. 2140/64 .. 1·50
2141 25 c. on 10 c. mult (surch "BAGOTVILLE") 10 10
2142 25 c. on 10 c. mult (surch "BOURDA") .. 10 10
2143 25 c. on 10 c. mult (surch "BUXTON") .. 10 10
2144 25 c. on 10 c. mult (surch "CABACABURI") 10 10
2145 25 c. on 10 c. multicoloured (surch "CARMICHAEL STREET") 10 10
2146 25 c. on 10 c. multicoloured (surch "COTTON TREE") 10 10
2147 25 c. on 10 c. mult (surch "DUNOON") .. 10 10
2148 25 c. on 10 c. mult (surch "FELLOWSHIP") 10 10
2149 25 c. on 10 c. mult (surch "GROVE") .. 10 10
2150 25 c. on 10 c. mult (surch "HACKNEY") .. 10 10
2151 25 c. on 10 c. mult (surch "LEONORA") .. 10 10
2152 25 c. on 10 c. multicoloured (surch "1987") 10 10
2153 25 c. on 10 c. mult (surch "MALLALI") .. 10 10
2154 25 c. on 10 c. mult (surch "PROVIDENCE") 10 10
2155 25 c. on 10 c. mult (surch "RELIANCE") .. 10 10
2156 25 c. on 10 c. mult (surch "SPARTA") .. 10 10
2157 25 c. on 10 c. multicoloured (surch "STEWARTVILLE") 10 10
2158 25 c. on 10 c. mult (surch "TARLOGY") .. 10 10
2159 25 c. on 10 c. multicoloured (surch "T.P.O. BERBICE RIV.") 10 10
2160 25 c. on 10 c. multicoloured (surch "T.P.O. DEM. RIV.") 10 10
2161 25 c. on 10 c. multicoloured (surch "T.P.O. ESSEO. RIV.") 10 10
2162 25 c. on 10 c. multicoloured (surch "T.P.O. MASSARUNI RIV.") 10 10
2163 25 c. on 10 c. multicoloured (surch "TUSCHEN (De VRIENDEN)") 10 10
2164 25 c. on 10 c. multicoloured (surch "ZORG") 10 10
2140/64 .. .. *Set of* 25 1·50 1·50

The surcharged names are those of postal agencies opened by 1885.

1987 (28 Mar). *50th Anniv of First Georgetown to Port-of-Spain Flight by P.A.A. No.* 708a *optd with T* **392** *by Autoprint.*

2165 $10 *Elbella patrobas* .. .. 1·50 1·75

1987 (6 Apr). *No.* 704 *surch with figures only as T* **324** *by Autoprint.*

2166 25 c. on 40 c. *Morpho rhetenor* (male) .. 10 10

1987

(393)

120

(394)

1987

(395)

CAPEX '87

1987 (21 Apr). *Easter. Nos.* 481/2 *and* 484 *optd or surch as T* **393** *by Autoprint.*

2167 **111** 25 c. multicoloured 10 10
2168 120 c. on 6 c. multicoloured 15 20
2169 320 c. on 6 c. multicoloured 40 45
2170 500 c. on 40 c. multicoloured 65 70
2167/70 .. .. *Set of* 4 1·10 1·25

(Litho Format)

1987 (24 Apr). *Centenary of Publication of Sanders' Reichenbachia (20th issue). Multicoloured designs as T* **331**. *No wmk. P* 13½×14 (240, 260, 500, 560 *c.*) *or* 13½×14 (*others*).

2171 240 c. Plate No. 47 (Series 2) 30 35
2172 260 c. Plate No. 39 (Series 2) 35 40
2173 275 c. Plate No. 58 (Series 2) (*horiz*) .. 35 40
2174 390 c. Plate No. 37 (Series 2) (*horiz*) .. 45 50
2175 450 c. Plate No. 19 (Series 2) (*horiz*) .. 60 65
2176 460 c. Plate No. 54 (Series 2) (*horiz*) .. 60 65
2177 500 c. Plate No. 51 (Series 2) 65 70
2178 560 c. Plate No. 1 (Series 2) 75 80
2171/8 .. .. *Set of* 8 3·75 4·00

Nos. 2171/8 were printed in a similar sheet format to Nos. 1518/33.

1987 (Apr). *No.* 706 *optd with T* **394** *by Autoprint.*

2179 **167** $1 multicoloured 15 15

(Litho Format)

1987 (2 June). *Centenary of Publication of Sanders' Reichenbachia (21st issue). Vert designs as T* **331**. *Multicoloured. No wmk. P* 13½×14.

2180 500 c. Plate No. 86 (Series 2) 65 70
2181 520 c. Plate No. 89 (Series 2) 70 75
2182 $20 Plate No. 83 (Series 2) .. .. 2·50 2·75
2180/2 .. .. *Set of* 3 3·50 3·75

Nos. 2180/2 were printed in a similar sheet format to Nos. 1518/33, but included Nos. 2183/4 instead of Nos. 1534/5.

Two types of bird in coat of arms:

A B

(Litho Format)

1987 (2 June–29 Sept). *Booklet and Coil Stamps. As T* **332**, *but within frame. No wmk. A. Bird with short tail. B. Bird with crest and long tail.*

		A		B	
2183	25 c. mult (*imperf* × *p* 14) ..	10	10	10	10
2184	25 c. mult (*p* 13½ × *imperf*)	10	10	10	10

Nos. 2183/4 were cut from the gutters of the orchid stamps as detailed in the note below No. 1533.

1987 (10 June). *"Capex '87" International Stamp Exhibition, Toronto. Nos.* 1744/5 *optd with T* **395**.

2185 **363** 320 c. rosine, black and dp reddish lilac 40 45
a. Horiz pair. Nos. 2185/6 .. 80 90
ab. Imperf between (horiz pair) .. 80 90
2186 – 320 c. multicoloured 40 45

1987 (15 July). *Commonwealth Heads of Government Meeting, Vancouver. Nos.* 1066/8 *further optd with T* **394**.

2187 $1.20 on 6 c. yellow-green 15 20
2188 $1.30 on 24 c. black and bright orange .. 15 20
2189 $2.40 on 24 c. black and bright orange .. 30 35
2187/9 .. .. *Set of* 3 55 70

(Litho Format)

1987 (22 July). *Centenary of Publication of Sanders' Reichenbachia (22nd issue). Vert designs as T* **331**. *Multicoloured. No wmk. P* 13½×14.

2190 400 c. Plate No. 80 (Series 2) 50 55
2191 480 c. Plate No. 77 (Series 2) 60 65
2192 600 c. Plate No. 94 (Series 2) 80 85
2193 $25 Plate No. 72 (Series 2) .. .. 3·25 3·50
2190/3 .. .. *Set of* 4 4·75 5·00

Nos. 2190/3 were printed in a similar sheet format to Nos. 1518/33.

396 Steam Locomotive *Alexandra*

FAIREY NICHOLL
8 AUG 1927
GEO-MAZ

(397)

(Litho Format)

1987 (3 Aug–4 Dec). *Guyana Railways. T* **396** *and similar horiz designs. No wmk. P* 12½ ($10, $12) *or* 15 (*others*).

2194 **396** $1.20, bronze-green 25 25
a. Block of 4. Nos. 2194/7 90
2195 – $1.20, bronze-green 25 25
2196 – $1.20, bronze-green 25 25
2197 – $1.20, bronze-green 25 25
2198 **396** $1.20, maroon (4 Dec) 25 25
a. Block of 4. Nos. 2198/201 .. 90
2199 – $1.20, maroon (4 Dec) 25 25
2200 – $1.20, maroon (4 Dec) 25 25
2201 – $1.20, maroon (4 Dec) 25 25
2202 **396** $3.20, deep dull blue 60 60
a. Block of 5. Nos. 2202/6 .. .. 2·75
2203 – $3.20, deep dull blue 60 60
2204 – $3.20, deep dull blue 60 60
2205 – $3.20, deep dull blue 60 60
2206 – $3.20, deep dull blue 60 60
2207 – $3.30, brownish black (4 Dec) .. 60 60
a. Block of 5. Nos. 2207/11 .. .. 2·75
2208 **396** $3.30, brownish black (4 Dec) .. 60 60
2209 – $3.30, brownish black (4 Dec) .. 60 60
2210 – $3.30, brownish black (4 Dec) .. 60 60
2211 – $3.30, brownish black (4 Dec) .. 60 60
2212 – $10 multicoloured (4 Dec) .. 1·50 1·50
2213 – $12 multicoloured .. .. .. 1·75 1·75
2194/213 .. .. *Set of* 20 9·50 9·50

Designs: (*As T* **396**)—Nos. 2195, 2199, 2203, 2207, Front view of diesel locomotive; Nos. 2196, 2200, 2204, 2210, Steam locomotive with searchlight; Nos. 2197, 2201, 2205, 2209, Side view of diesel locomotive. (82×55 *mm*)—Nos. 2206, Molasses warehouses and early locomotive; No. 2211, Diesel locomotive and passenger train. (88×39 *mm*)—No. 2212, Cattle train; No. 2213, Molasses train.

Nos. 2194/7 and 2198/201 were each printed together, *se-tenant*, in blocks of 4, within the sheets of 40.

Nos. 2202/6 and 2207/11 were each printed together, *se-tenant*, in blocks of 5 within the sheets of 25. The order of the stamps as Type **396** differs in the $3.30 block.

1987 (7 Aug). *50th Anniv of First Flights from Georgetown to Massaruni and Mabaruma. No.* 706 *optd as T* **397** *by Autoprint.*

2214 **167** $1 multicoloured (optd T **397**) .. 15 15
a. Pair. Nos. 2214/15 .. .. 30 30
2215 $1 mult (optd "FAIREY NICHOLL 15 AUG 1927 GEO- MAB") .. 15 15

Nos. 2214/15 were overprinted together, *se-tenant*, in vertical or horizontal pairs within the sheet.

(Litho Format)

1987 (29 Sept). *Centenary of Publication of Sanders' Reichenbachia (23rd issue). Vert designs as T* **331**. *Multicoloured. No wmk. P* 13½×14.

2216 200 c. Plate No. 43 (Series 2) 25 30
2217 200 c. Plate No. 48 (Series 2) 25 30
2218 200 c. Plate No. 92 (Series 2) 25 30
2216/18 .. .. *Set of* 3 70 80

Nos. 2216/18 were printed in a similar sheet format to Nos. 1518/33.

(Litho Format)

1987 (9 Oct). *Centenary of Publication of Sanders' Reichenbachia (24th issue). Vert design as T* **331**, *optd as T* **384** *by Gardy Ptg* (600 *c.*). *Multicoloured. No wmk. P* 13½ × 14.

2219 600 c. on 900 c. Plate No. 74 (Series 2) .. 80 85
a. Pair. Nos. 2219/20 .. .. .. 1·90 2·10
2220 900 c. Plate No. 74 (Series 2) .. .. 1·10 1·25

Nos. 2219/20 were printed in a similar sheet format to Nos. 1518/33 with the surcharge on the first and last stamp of each block of four.

950

CRISTOVÃO COLOMBO
1492 — 1992

(398)

THE PASSING OF HALLEY'S COMET:
PROPHESY OF THE ARRIVAL OF
HERNAN CORTES 1519.
V CENTENARY OF THE LANDING OF
CHRISTOPHER COLUMBUS
IN THE AMERICAS
$ 20.00

(399)

1987 (9 Oct). *Columbus Day. No.* 1598 *further surch with T* **382**, *No.* 2220 *surch as T* **398** *and No.* **MS**1746 *surch with T* **399**.
2221 225 c. on 350 c. on 120 c. Plate No. 65 (Series 1) 30 35
2222 950 c. on 900 c. Plate No. 74 (Series 2) (surch with T **398**) .. .. .. 1·25 1·40
a. Horiz pair. Nos. 2222/3 .. .. 2·50 2·75
2223 950 c. on 900 c. Plate No. 74 (Series 2) (surch "950 CHRISTOPHE COLOMB 1492—1992") .. .. 1·25 1·40
2221/3 .. .. *Set of* 3 2·50 2·75
MS2224 76 × 50 mm. $20 on 320 c. × 2 Nos. 1744/5 .. .. 5·00 5·25
Nos. 2222/3 were surcharged together, *se-tenant*, in horizontal pairs in the sheetlet of 4.

(Litho Format)

1987 (26 Oct). *Centenary of Publication of Sanders'* Reichenbachia *(25th issue). Multicoloured designs as T* **331**. *No wmk. P* 13½ × 14 (575 *c.) or* 14 × 13½ *(others).*
2225 325 c. Plate No. 68 (Series 2) *(horiz)* .. 40 45
2226 420 c. Plate No. 95 (Series 2) *(horiz)* .. 55 60
2227 575 c. Plate No. 60 (Series 2) 75 80
2225/7 .. .. *Set of* 3 1·50 1·60
Nos. 2225/7, together with No. E7, were printed in a similar sheet format to Nos. 1518/33.

DEEPAVALI 1987 25

(400)

1987 (2 Nov). *Deepavali Festival. Nos.* 544/5 *surch as T* **400**.
2228 25 c. on 3 c. Hanging Heliconia 10 10
2229 $3 on 5 c. Annatto tree 40 45

CHRISTMAS 1987 20 (401)

120 1987 (402)

1987 (9 Nov). *Christmas. No.* 452 *surch with T* **401** *in red, previously unissued miniature sheet containing Nos.* 1425/9 *each surch with T* **402** *in blue and No.* **MS**1619 *with each stamp surch with T* **382**.
2230 20 c. on 6 c. Patua 10 10
MS2231 215 × 75 mm. 120 c. on 60 c. × 5 Nos. 1425/9 .. .. 80 85
MS2232 120 × 129 mm. 225 c. on 55 c. × 4 Plate No. 22 (Series 1), each with a different overprint (Type **350**, "Happy New Year", "Merry Christmas" or "Happy Holidays") .. .. 1·10 1·25

1987 (20 Nov). *Royal Ruby Wedding. Nos.* 1684/5 *optd with T* **390** (130 *c.) or surch as T* **384** *by Gardy Ptg.*
2233 130 c. Plate No. 13 (Series 1) 15 20
MS2234 600 c. on 130 c. on 130 c., 600 c. on 200 c. on 130 c., 600 c. on 260 c. on 130 c., 600 c. on 330 c. on 130 c., Plate No. 6 (Series 1) .. .. 3·00 3·25

(Litho Format)

1987 (23 Nov). *Centenary of Publication of Sanders'* Reichenbachia *(26th issue). Vert designs as T* **331**. *Multicoloured. No wmk. P* 13½ × 14.
2235 255 c. Plate No. 61 (Series 2) 35 40
2236 290 c. Plate No. 53 (Series 2) 40 45
2237 375 c. Plate No. 96 (Series 2) 50 55
2238 680 c. Plate No. 64 (Series 2) 90 95
2239 720 c. Plate No. 49 (Series 2) .. .. 95 1·00
2240 750 c. Plate No. 66 (Series 2) .. .. 95 1·00
2241 700 c. Plate No. 79 (Series 2) .. .. 1·00 1·10
a. Face value omitted .. .. ..
2242 850 c. Plate No. 76 (Series 2) .. .. 1·10 1·25
2235/42 .. .. *Set of* 8 5·50 6·00
Nos. 2235/42 were printed in a similar sheet format to Nos. 1518/33.

AIR

75

(403)

1987 (Nov). *Air. No.* 1620 *surch with T* **403** *by Gardy Ptg.*
2243 75 c. on 25 c. Plate No. 59 (Series 1) .. 10 10

Protect our Heritage '87 (404)

320 PROTECT OUR HERITAGE '87 (405)

1987 (9 Dec). *Wildlife Protection. Nos.* 756/67 *optd vertically with T* **394**, *Nos.* 1432b/4b *surch with T* **404** *in red and Nos.* 1631/3, 1752/3 *and* 1847 *optd with T* **405**.
2244 30 c. Type **178** 10 10
a. Sheetlet of 12. Nos. 2244/55 .. 1·00
2245 30 c. Red Howler 10 10
2246 30 c. Common Squirrel-Monkey 10 10
2247 30 c. Two-toed Sloth 10 10
2248 30 c. Brazilian Tapir 10 10
2249 30 c. Collared Peccary 10 10
2250 30 c. Six-banded Armadillo 10 10
2251 30 c. Tamandua ("Ant Eater") 10 10
2252 30 c. Giant Anteater 10 10
2253 30 c. Murine Opossum 10 10
2254 30 c. Brown Four-eyed Opossum 10 10
2255 30 c. Brazilian Agouti 10 10
2256 120 c. Plate No. 67 (Series 1) 20 20
2257 130 c. Plate No. 66 (Series 1) 20 20
2258 150 c. Plate No. 26 (Series 1) 25 25
2259 180 c. Plate No. 15 (Series 1) 30 30
2260 320 c. Plate No. 82 (Series 1) 45 45
2261 320 c. on 120 c. Demerara Mutual Life Assurance Building 45 45
a. Horiz strip of 3. Nos. 2261/3 .. 1·25
2262 320 c. on 120 c. Town Hall 45 45
2263 320 c. on 120 c. Victoria Law Courts .. 45 45
2264 650 c. on 40 c. Plate No. 86 (Series 1) .. 90 90
2244/64 .. .. *Set of* 21 4·00 4·00

AIR

(406)

1987 (Dec). *Air. No.* 1597 *optd with T* **406**.
2265 60 c. Plate No. 55 (Series 1) 10 10
No. 2265 was only issued in $15 stamp booklets.

★ AUSTRALIA ★ 1987 JAMBOREE 1988 (407)

* AUSTRALIA * $10 1987 Jamboree 1988 (408)

1988 (7 Jan). *World Scout Jamboree, Australia. Nos.* 830, 837/a *and* 1104 *handstamped with T* **407** *(No.* 2266*) or surch with T* **408** *by Tip Torres (others), all in red.*
2266 **116** 440 c. on 6 c. multicoloured (No. 837a) 20 25
2267 $10 on 110 c. on 6 c. mult (No. 830) .. 45 50
2268 $10 on 180 c. on 6 c. mult (No. 1104) 45 50
2269 $10 on 440 c. on 6 c. mult (No. 837) .. 45 50
a. On No. 837a 45 50
2266/9 .. .. *Set of* 4 1·40 1·60

IFAD For a World Without Hunger 25 (409)

Republic Day 1988 25 (410)

1988 (26 Jan). *10th Anniv of International Fund for Agricultural Development. Nos.* 485 *and* 487 *surch as T* **409** *by Autoprint.*
2270 25 c. on 1 c. Type **87** 10 10
2271 $5 on 3 c. Lukunani 20 25

1988 (23 Feb). *Republic Day. Nos.* 545, 548a *and* 555 *surch as T* **410** *in blue.*
2272 25 c. on 5 c. Annatto tree 10 10
2273 120 c. on 15 c. Christmas Orchid 10 10
2274 $10 on $2 *Noranthea guianensis* .. 45 50
2272/4 .. .. *Set of* 3 60 65

MINIMUM PRICE

The minimum price quote is 10p which represents a handling charge rather than a basis for valuing common stamps. For further notes about prices see introductory pages.

(Litho Format)

1988 (26 Feb). *Centenary of Publication of Sanders'* Reichenbachia *(27th issue). Four sheets, each* 102×127 *mm, containing vert designs as T* **331**. *Multicoloured. No wmk. P* 13½×14.
MS2275 (a) 320 c. Plate No. 46 (Series 2); 330 c. Plate No. 55 (Series 2); 350 c. Plate No. 57 (Series 2); 500 c. Plate No. 81 (Series 2). (b) 320 c. Plate No. 55 (Series 2); 330 c. Plate No. 46 (Series 2); 350 c. Plate No. 81 (Series 2); 500 c. Plate No. 57 (Series 2). (c) 320 c. Plate No. 57 (Series 2); 330 c. Plate No. 81 (Series 2); 350 c. Plate No. 46 (Series 2); 500 c. Plate No. 55 (Series 2). (d) 320 c. Plate No. 81 (Series 2); 330 c. Plate No. 57 (Series 2); 350 c. Plate No. 55 (Series 2); 500 c. Plate No. 46 (Series 2) *Set of* 4 *sheets* 2·50 2·75

(Litho Format)

1988 (24 Mar). *Centenary of Publication of Sanders'* Reichenbachia *(28th issue). Vert designs as T* **331**. *Multicoloured. No wmk. P* 13½×14.
2276 $10 Plate No. 40 (Series 2) 45 50
2277 $12 Plate No. 91 (Series 2) 50 55
Nos. 2276/7 were printed in a similar sheet format to Nos. 1518/33.

1988 (5 Apr). *125th Anniv of British Guiana Post Office (4th issue). No.* 702a *surch as T* **324** *by Autoprint.*
2278 25 c. on 30 c. mult (surch "Albouystown") .. 10 10
a. Sheetlet of 25. Nos. 2278/88, 2289×2, 2290/301 .. .. 2·10
2279 25 c. on 30 c. mult (surch "Anns Grove") .. 10 10
2280 25 c. on 30 c. mult (surch "Amacura") .. 10 10
2281 25 c. on 30 c. mult (surch "Arakaka") .. 10 10
2282 25 c. on 30 c. mult (surch "Baramanni") .. 10 10
2283 25 c. on 30 c. mult (surch "Cuyuni") .. 10 10
2284 25 c. on 30 c. mult (surch "Hope Placer") .. 10 10
2285 25 c. on 30 c. mult (surch "H M P S") .. 10 10
2286 25 c. on 30 c. multicoloured (surch "Kitty") 10 10
2287 25 c. on 30 c. mult (surch "M'M'Zorg") .. 10 10
2288 25 c. on 30 c. mult (surch "Maccaseema") .. 10 10
2289 25 c. on 30 c. multicoloured (surch "1988") 10 10
2290 25 c. on 30 c. mult (surch "Morawhanna") 10 10
2291 25 c. on 30 c. mult (surch "Naamryck") .. 10 10
2292 25 c. on 30 c. multicoloured (surch "Purini") 10 10
2293 25 c. on 30 c. mult (surch "Potaro Landing") 10 10
2294 25 c. on 30 c. mult (surch "Rockstone") .. 10 10
2295 25 c. on 30 c. mult (surch "Rosignol") .. 10 10
2296 25 c. on 30 c. mult (surch "Stanleytown") .. 10 10
2297 25 c. on 30 c. mult (surch "Santa Rosa") .. 10 10
2298 25 c. on 30 c. mult (surch "Tumatumari") .. 10 10
2299 25 c. on 30 c. mult (surch "Weldaad") .. 10 10
2300 25 c. on 30 c. mult (surch "Wismar") .. 10 10
2301 25 c. on 30 c. multicoloured (surch "TPO Berbice Railway") 10 10
2278/301 .. .. .. *Set of* 24 2·10 2·10
The surcharged names are those of postal agencies opened between 1886 and 1900.

120 Olympic Games 1988 (411)

Caricom Day 1988 25 (412)

1988 (3 May). *Olympic Games, Seoul. Nos.* 1206/17 *further surch with T* **411**.
2302 120 c. on 55 c. on 125 c. on 35 c. Type **174** 10 10
a. Block of 12. Nos. 2302/13 .. .. 1·10
2303 120 c. on 55 c. on 125 c. on 35 c. Haimara 10 10
2304 120 c. on 55 c. on 125 c. on 35 c. Electric Eel 10 10
2305 120 c. on 55 c. on 125 c. on 35 c. Golden Rivulus 10 10
2306 120 c. on 55 c. on 125 c. on 35 c. Pencil Fish 10 10
2307 120 c. on 55 c. on 125 c. on 35 c. Four-eyed Fish 10 10
2308 120 c. on 55 c. on 125 c. on 35 c. Pirai or Carib Fish 10 10
2309 120 c. on 55 c. on 125 c. on 35 c. Smoking Hassar 10 10
2310 120 c. on 55 c. on 125 c. on 35 c. Devil Ray 10 10
2311 120 c. on 55 c. on 125 c. on 35 c. Flying Patwa 10 10
2312 120 c. on 55 c. on 125 c. on 35 c. Arapaima Pirariucii 10 10
2313 120 c. on 55 c. on 125 c. on 35 c. Lukanani 10 10
2302/13 .. .. *Set of* 12 1·10 1·10

(Litho Format)

1988 (1 June). *Centenary of Publication of Sanders'* Reichenbachia *(29th issue). Vert designs as T* **331**. *Multicoloured. No wmk. P* 13½×14.
2314 320 c. Plate No. 16 (Series 2) 15 20
2315 475 c. Plate No. 73 (Series 2) 20 25
2316 525 c. Plate No. 36 (Series 2) 25 30
2317 530 c. Plate No. 69 (Series 2) 25 30
2318 $15 Plate No. 67 (Series 2) 65 70
2314/18 .. .. *Set of* 5 1·40 1·60
Nos. 2314/18 were printed in a similar sheet format to Nos. 1518/33.

1988 (15 June). *CARICOM Day. Nos.* 545/6 *and* 555 *surch as T* **412**.
2319 25 c. on 5 c. Annatto tree 10 10
2320 $1.20 on 6 c. Cannon-ball tree 10 10
2321 $10 on $2 *Norantea guianensis* 45 50
2319/21 .. .. *Set of* 3 60 65

(Litho Format)

1988 (15 June). *Centenary of Publication of Sanders' Reichenbachia (30th issue). Vert designs as T* **331**. *Multicoloured. No wmk. P* $13^1/_2$×14.

2322 700 c. Plate No. 62 (Series 2) 30 35
2323 775 c. Plate No. 59 (Series 2) 35 40
2324 875 c. Plate No. 31 (Series 2) 40 45
2325 950 c. Plate No. 78 (Series 2) 40 45
2322/5 .. .. *Set of* 4 1·25 1·50

Nos. 2322/5 were printed in a similar sheet format to Nos. 1518/33.

WHO 1948-1988 (413)

1988 (414)

1988 (17 June). *40th Anniv of World Health Day. No.* 705a *optd with T* **413** *or T* **414** *by Autoprint.*

2326 60 c. *Papilio androgeus* (T **413**) .. .. 2·00 2·00
a. Sheetlet of 25. Nos. 2326 and 2327×24 .. .. .. 2·50
2327 60 c. *Papilio androgeus* (T **414**) 10 10

Nos. 2326 and 2327 were overprinted together, *se-tenant*, in a sheetlet of 25 showing a single example of No. 2326 in the central position.

(Litho Format)

1988 (22 June). *Centenary of Publication of Sanders' Reichenbachia (31st issue). Vert design as T* **331**. *No wmk. P* $13^1/_2$×14.

2328 350 c. Plate No. 74 (Series 2) 15 20

No. 2328 was printed in a similar sheet format to Nos. 1518/33.

(Litho Format)

1988 (9 July). *Centenary of Publication of Sanders Reichenbachia (32nd issue). Vert designs as T* **331**, *with Nos. 2329/31 additional inscr* "1985 – 1988". *No wmk. P* $13^1/_2$×14.

2329 130 c. Plate No. 73 (Series 2) 10 10
2330 200 c. Plate No. 96 (Series 2) 10 10
2331 260 c. Plate No. 16 (Series 2) 10 10
2329/31 .. .. *Set of* 3 25 25

MS2332 Four sheets, each 102×127 mm. (a) 120 c. Plate No. 81 (Series 2); 120 c. Plate No. 57 (Series 2); 120 c. Plate No. 55 (Series 2); 120 c. Plate No. 46 (Series 2). (b) 150 c. Plate No. 57 (Series 2); 150 c. Plate No. 81 (Series 2); 150 c. Plate No. 46 (Series 2); 150 c. Plate No. 55 (Series 2). (c) 225 c. Plate No. 46 (Series 2); 225 c. Plate No. 55 (Series 2); 225 c. Plate No. 57 (Series 2); 225 c. Plate No. 81 (Series 2). (d) 305 c. Plate No. 55 (Series 2); 305 c. Plate No. 46 (Series 2); 305 c. Plate No. 81 (Series 2); 305 c. Plate No. 57 (Series 2) .. .. *Set of 4 sheets* 1·40 1·50

CONSERVE TREES (415)

CONSERVE WATER (416)

1988 (15 July). *Conservation of Resources.*

(*a*) *Nos.* 1444B/6B *optd as T* **415** *by Gardy Ptg*

2333 120 c. Young Ocelot (No. 1444B) (opt T **415**) 10 10
a. Block of 9. Nos. 2333/41 90
2334 120 c. Young Ocelot (No. 1444B) (opt "CONSERVE ELECTRICITY") .. 10 10
2335 120 c. Young Ocelot (No. 1444B) (opt "CONSERVE WATER") 10 10
2336 120 c. Type **322** (opt "CONSERVE ELECTRICITY") 10 10
2337 120 c. Type **322** (opt "CONSERVE WATER") 10 10
2338 120 c. Type **322** (opt T **415**) 10 10
2339 120 c. Young Ocelot (No. 1446B) (opt "CONSERVE WATER") 10 10
2340 120 c. Young Ocelot (No. 1446B) (opt T **415**) 10 10
2341 120 c. Young Ocelot (No. 1446B) (optd "CONSERVE ELECTRICITY") .. 10 10

(*b*) *Nos.* 1634, 1670, 1683 *and* 1863 *optd with T* **416** (*opt vert - reading upwards on Nos.* 2342, 2345) *by Tip Torres*

2342 200 c. Plate No. 33 (Series 1) 10 10
2343 200 c. Plate No. 79 (Series 1) 10 10
2344 225 c. Plate No. 24 (Series 1) 10 10
2345 350 c. Plate No. 94 (Series 1) 15 20
2333/45 .. .. *Set of* 13 1·25 1·25

The three different overprints as T **415** were applied, *se-tenant*, in strips of three, both horizontally and vertically, on blocks of nine.

BEWARE OF ANIMALS (417)

120 (418)

1988 (15 July). *Road Safety Campaign. Nos.* 2194/201 *optd as T* **417** *by Gardy Ptg.*

2346 **396** $1.20, bronze-green (opt T **417**) .. 10 10
a. Block of four. Nos. 2346/9 .. 40
2347 – $1.20, bronze-green (No. 2195) (opt "BEWARE OF CHILDREN") .. 10 10
2348 – $1.20, bronze-green (No. 2196) (opt "DRIVE SAFELY") 10 10
2349 – $1.20, bronze-green (No. 2197) (opt "DO NOT DRINK AND DRIVE") 10 10
2350 **396** $1.20, maroon (opt T **417**) 10 10
a. Block of four. Nos. 2350/3 .. 40
2351 – $1.20, maroon (No. 2199) (opt "BEWARE OF CHILDREN") .. 10 10
2352 – $1.20, maroon (No. 2200) (opt "DRIVE SAFELY") 10 10
2353 – $1.20, maroon (No. 2201) (opt "DO NOT DRINK AND DRIVE") .. 10 10
2346/53 .. .. *Set of* 8 70 70

1988 (July). *No.* 706 *optd with T* **414** *or surch with T* **418**, *both by Autoprint.*

2354 $1 Type **167** 10 10
2355 120 c. on $1 Type **167** 10 10

120

(419)

120 (420)

240 (421)

1988 (July–Oct). *Various* Reichenbachia *issues surch by Gardy Ptg.*

(*a*) *As T* **419**

2356 120 c. on 25 c. Plate No. 61 (Series 1) (No. 1574) 10 10
2357 120 c. on 25 c. Plate No. 63 (Series 1) (No. 1575) 10 10
2358 120 c. on 25 c. Plate No. 70 (Series 1) (No. 1576) 10 10
2359 120 c. on 25 c. Plate No. 59 (Series 1) (No. 1620) 10 10
2360 120 c. on 25 c. Plate No. 71 (Series 1) (No. 1679) (surch vert - reading down) 10 10
2361 120 c. on 30 c. Plate No. 53 (Series 1) (No. 1621) 10 10
2362 120 c. on 30 c. Plate No. 86 (Series 1) (No. 1731) 10 10
2363 120 c. on 30 c. Plate No. 30 (Series 2) (No. 1809) 10 10
2364 120 c. on 30 c. Plate No. 53 (Series 1) (No. 1849) (*wmkd*) 10 10
2365 120 c. on 30 c. Plate No. 7 (Series 2) .. 10 10
2366 120 c. on 30 c. Plate No. 14 (Series 2) ("120" at foot) 10 10
2367 120 c. on 30 c. Plate No. 14 (Series 2) ("120" at top below bars) 10 10
2368 120 c. on 30 c. Plate No. 22 (Series 2) .. 10 10
2369 120 c. on 30 c. Plate No. 28 (Series 2) ("120" at bottom right) 10 10
2370 120 c. on 30 c. Plate No. 28 (Series 2) ("120" at top left) 10 10
2371 120 c. on 35 c. Plate No. 45 (Series 2) (No. 1925) 10 10
2372 120 c. on 40 c. Plate No. 77 (Series 1) (No. 1663) ("120" at bottom right) .. 10 10
2373 120 c. on 40 c. Plate No. 77 (Series 1) (No. 1663) ("120" at top left) .. 10 10
2374 120 c. on 40 c. Plate No. 96 (Series 1) (No. 1747) 10 10
2375 120 c. on 40 c. Plate No. 91 (Series 1) (No. 1822) ("120" at bottom right) .. 10 10
2376 120 c. on 40 c. Plate No. 91 (Series 1) (No. 1822) ("120" at top left) .. 10 10
2377 120 c. on 40 c. Plate No. 86 (Series 1) (No. 1868) 10 10
2378 120 c. on 40 c. Plate No. 68 (Series 1) (No. 1884) ("120" at top left) .. 10 10
2379 120 c. on 40 c. Plate No. 68 (Series 1) (No. 1884) ("120" at bottom left) .. 10 10
2380 120 c. on 40 c. Plate No. 90 (Series 1) .. 10 10
2381 120 c. on 45 c. Plate No. 54 (Series 1) (No. 1664) 10 10
2382 120 c. on 45 c. Plate No. 81 (Series 1) (No. 1748) 10 10
2383 120 c. on 45 c. Plate No. 21 (Series 2) (No. 1810) 10 10
2384 120 c. on 50 c. Plate No. 92 (Series 1) (No. 1665) 10 10
2385 120 c. on 50 c. Plate No. 13 (Series 2) (No. 1907) 10 10
2386 120 c. on 50 c. Plate No. 15 (Series 2) (No. 1926) 10 10
2387 120 c. on 50 c. Plate No. 9 (Series 1) (*wmkd*) 10 10
2388 120 c. on 50 c. Plate No. 22 (Series 1) (*wmkd*) 10 10
2389 120 c. on 50 c. Plate No. 3 (Series 2) .. 10 10
2390 120 c. on 50 c. Plate No. 6 (Series 2) .. 10 10
2391 120 c. on 50 c. Plate No. 20 (Series 2) .. 10 10
2392 120 c. on 50 c. Plate No. 32 (Series 2) .. 10 10
2393 120 c. on 55 c. Plate No. 17 (Series 1) (No. 1732) 10 10
2394 120 c. on 60 c. Plate No. 2 (Series 1) (No. 1519) 10 10
2395 120 c. on 60 c. Plate No. 57 (Series 1) (No. 1622) (surch vert at top - reading down) 10 10
2396 120 c. on 60 c. Plate No. 57 (Series 1) (No. 1622) (surch vert at foot - reading down) 10 10
2397 120 c. on 60 c. Plate No. 73 (Series 1) (No. 1623) (surch vert - reading up) .. 10 10
2398 120 c. on 60 c. Plate No. 75 (Series 1) (No. 1624) (surch vert at top - reading down) 10 10
2399 120 c. on 60 c. Plate No. 75 (Series 1) (No. 1624) (surch vert at foot - reading down) 10 10
2400 120 c. on 60 c. Plate No. 95 (Series 1) (No. 1666) 10 10
2401 120 c. on 60 c. Plate No. 93 (Series 1) (No. 1733) 10 10
2402 120 c. on 60 c. Plate No. 27 (Series 2) (No. 1874) 10 10
2403 120 c. on 60 c. Plate No. 50 (Series 1) .. 10 10
2404 120 c. on 60 c. Plate No. 54 (Series 1) .. 10 10
2405 120 c. on 60 c. Plate No. 69 (Series 1) (surch vert - reading up) 10 10
2406 120 c. on 60 c. Plate No. 79 (Series 1) .. 10 10
2407 120 c. on 60 c. Plate No. 94 (Series 1) (surch vert - reading down) 10 10
2408 120 c. on 70 c. Plate No. 8 (Series 2) .. 10 10
2409 120 c. on 70 c. Plate No. 9 (Series 2) ("120" at foot above bars) 10 10
2410 120 c. on 70 c. Plate No. 9 (Series 2) ("120" at top right) 10 10
2411 120 c. on 70 c. Plate No. 12 (Series 2) ("120" at foot above bars) 10 10
2412 120 c. on 70 c. Plate No. 12 (Series 2) "120" at top left) 10 10
2413 120 c. on 70 c. Plate No. 17 (Series 2) .. 10 10
2414 120 c. on 80 c. Plate No. 39 (Series 1) .. 10 10
2415 120 c. on 80 c. Plate No. 74 (Series 1) .. 10 10
2416 120 c. on 80 c. Plate No. 93 (Series 1) .. 10 10
2417 120 c. on 85 c. Plate No. 45 (Series 2) (No. 1876) 10 10
2418 120 c. on 85 c. Plate No. 24 (Series 2) (No. 1914) 10 10
2419 120 c. on 85 c. Plate No. 15 (Series 2) (No. 1918) 10 10
2420 120 c. on 85 c. Plate No. 18 (Series 2) (No. 1928) 10 10
2421 120 c. on 90 c. Plate No. 84 (Series 1) (No. 1668) 10 10
2422 120 c. on 90 c. Plate No. 89 (Series 1) (No. 1749) 10 10
2423 120 c. on 90 c. Plate No. 10 (Series 2) (No. 1869) 10 10
2424 120 c. on 90 c. Plate No. 13 (Series 2) (No. 1877) 10 10
2425 120 c. on 90 c. Plate No. 27 (Series 2) (No. 1915) 10 10
2426 120 c. on 90 c. Plate No. 2 (Series 2) (No. 1929) 10 10
2427 200 c. on 80 c. Plate No. 42 (Series 2) (No. 1812) (surch vert - reading down) 10 10
2428 200 c. on 90 c. Plate No. 4 (Series 2) (No. 1813) 10 10

(*b*) *As T* **420** (Sept)

2429 120 c. on 25 c. Plate No. 72 (Series 1) (No. 1577) 10 10

(*c*) *As T* **421** (Oct)

2430 240 c. on 140 c. Plate No. 30 (Series 2) .. 10 10
2431 240 c. on 140 c. Plate No. 34 (Series 2) .. 10 10
2432 240 c. on 425 c. Plate No. 87 (Series 2) (No. 2070) 10 10
2433 260 c. on 375 c. Plate No. 90 (Series 1) (No. 1738) 10 10
2356/433 .. .. *Set of* 78 7·00 7·25

On No. 2433 there are no bars and the surcharge is placed over the original face value.

CONSERVE OUR RESOURCES (422)

+ (423)

AIR (424)

1988 (July). *Conservation of Resources. Various* Reichenbachia *issues optd with T* **422** *by Gardy Ptg.*

2434 100 c. Plate No. 65 (Series 1) (No. 1626) .. 10 10
2435 100 c. Plate No. 68 (Series 1) (No. 1734) .. 10 10
2436 100 c. Plate No. 88 (Series 1) (No. 1750) .. 10 10
2437 100 c. Plate No. 65 (Series 1) (No. 1854) (*wmkd*) 10 10
2438 120 c. Plate No. 27 (Series 1) (No. 1524) .. 10 10
2439 120 c. Plate No. 36 (Series 1) (No. 1558) .. 10 10
2440 120 c. Plate No. 37 (Series 1) (No. 1627) .. 10 10
2441 120 c. Plate No. 56 (Series 1) (No. 1629) .. 10 10
2442 120 c. Plate No. 58 (Series 1) (No. 1630) .. 10 10
2443 120 c. Plate No. 67 (Series 1) (No. 1631) .. 10 10
2444 120 c. Plate No. 69 (Series 1) (No. 1680) (opt vert - reading down) 10 10
2445 130 c. Plate No. 38 (Series 1) (No. 1560) .. 10 10
2446 130 c. Plate No. 66 (Series 1) (No. 1632) .. 10 10
2447 130 c. Plate No. 91 (Series 1) (No. 1735) .. 10 10
2448 130 c. Plate No. 13 (Series 1) (No. 1768) (*wmkd*) 10 10
a. Opt inverted 10 10
2449 130 c. Plate No. 20 (Series 1) (No. 1770) (*wmkd*) 10 10
2450 150 c. Plate No. 26 (Series 1) (No. 1633) .. 10 10
2451 150 c. Plate No. 78 (Series 1) (No. 1669) .. 10 10
2452 150 c. Plate No. 87 (Series 1) (No. 1681) (opt vert - reading down) 10 10
2453 150 c. Plate No. 76 (Series 1) (No. 1751) .. 10 10
2454 250 c. Plate No. 74 (Series 1) (No. 1736) .. 10 10
2434/54 .. .. *Set of* 21 1·90 2·00

The 130 c., No. 1768, exists in equal quantities with the overprint either upright or inverted.

NEW INFORMATION

The editor is always interested to correspond with people who have new information that will improve or correct the Catalogue.

1988 (3 Aug). *125th Anniv of International Red Cross. Nos. 2202/5 and 2207/10 optd with T* **423** *in red by Gardy Ptg.*

2455 **396** $3. 20, deep dull blue 15 20
a. Vert pair. Nos. 2455 and 2457 .. 30 40
2456 – $3. 20, deep dull blue (No. 2203) .. 15 20
a. Vert pair. Nos. 2456 and 2458 .. 30 40
2457 – $3. 20, deep dull blue (No. 2204) .. 15 20
2458 – $3. 20, deep dull blue (No. 2205) .. 15 20
2459 – $3. 30, brownish black (No. 2207) .. 15 20
a. Vert pair. Nos. 2459 and 2461 .. 30 40
2460 **396** $3. 30, brownish black .. 15 20
a. Vert pair. Nos. 2460 and 2462 .. 30 40
2461 – $3. 30, brownish black (No. 2209) .. 15 20
2462 – $3. 30, brownish black (No. 2210) .. 15 20
2455/62 .. .. *Set of* 8 1·10 1·40

Nos. 2455/62 were issued in vertical strips of ten, each strip containing two designs *se-tenant.*

1988 (Aug). *Air. Various* Reichenbachia *issues optd with T* **424** *by Gardy Ptg.*

2463 75 c. Plate No. 55 (Series 1) (No. 1625) .. 10 10
2464 75 c. Plate No. 5 (Series 1) (No. 1667) .. 10 10
2465 75 c. Plate No. 55 (Series 1) (No. 1853) (*wmkd*) 10 10
2466 75 c. Plate No. 83 (Series 1) 10 10
2467 75 c. Plate No. 95 (Series 1) 10 10
2463/7 .. .. *Set of* 5 25 25

(Litho Format)

1988 (15 Aug). *Centenary of Publication of Sanders'* Reichenbachia *(33rd issue). Multicoloured designs as T* **331**. *P* 13½×14 *(270 c., 360 c.) or* 14×13½ *(others).*

2468 270 c. Plate No. 90 (Series 2) 10 15
2469 360 c. Plate No. 84 (Series 2) 15 20
2470 550 c. Plate No. 70 (Series 2) (*horiz*) .. 25 30
2471 670 c. Plate No. 71 (Series 2) (*horiz*) .. 30 35
2468/71 .. .. *Set of* 4 70 90

Nos. 2468/71 were printed in a similar sheet format to Nos. 1518/33.

A further small book similar to those described under Nos. 1767/1806, containing stamps showing plate numbers 1 to 68 of the second series, was issued on 23 August 1988.

1928 — 1988
CRICKET
JUBILEE
(425)

1988 (5 Sept). *60th Anniv of Cricket in Guyana. Nos.* 1584, 1670, 1681 *and* 1815 *optd as T* **425** *or surch also by Gardy Ptg.*

2472 200 c. Plate No. 14 (Series 1) 10 10
2473 200 c. Plate No. 79 (Series 1) 10 10
2474 800 c. on 150 c. Plate No. 87 (Series 1) .. 35 40
2475 800 c. on 160 c. Plate No. 5 (Series 2) .. 35 40
2472/5 .. .. *Set of* 4 65 75

Nos. 2472 and 2474 were only issued in $20 stamp booklets.

OLYMPIC GAMES
1988
(426)

KOREA 1988

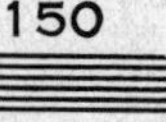

(427)

1988 (16 Sept). *Olympic Games, Seoul. (a) Nos.* 1628, 1634, 1671, 1681, 1683, 1814, 1818/19, 1880 *and* 2069 *optd as T* **426** *or surch also by Gardy Ptg.*

2476 120 c. Plate No. 46 (Series 1) 10 10
2477 130 c. Plate No. 38 (Series 2) 10 10
2478 150 c. Plate No. 87 (Series 1) 10 10
2479 200 c. Plate No. 33 (Series 1) 10 10
2480 300 c. Plate No. 83 (Series 1) 15 20
2481 300 c. on 360 c. Plate No. 34 (Series 2) .. 15 20
2482 320 c. Plate No. 10 (Series 2) 15 20
2483 330 c. Plate No. 82 (Series 2) 15 20
2484 350 c. Plate No. 94 (Series 1) (opt vert - reading up) 15 20
2485 350 c. Plate No. 29 (Series 2) 15 20

(b) Design as No. 1420, but incorrectly inscr "LOS ANGELLES", *optd or surch as T* **427**, *inscr* "OLYMPICS 1988" (A) *or* "KOREA 1988" (B), *by Gardy Ptg.*

2486 $1.20, multicoloured (A) 10 10
a. Horiz strip of 5. Nos. 2486, 2488, 2490, 2492 and 2494 40
b. Booklet pane of 10. Nos. 2486/95 .. 80
2487 $1.20, multicoloured (B) 10 10
2488 130 c. on $1.20, multicoloured (A) .. 10 10
2489 130 c. on $1.20, multicoloured (B) .. 10 10
2490 150 c. on $1.20, multicoloured (A) .. 10 10
2491 150 c. on $1.20, multicoloured (B) .. 10 10
2492 200 c. on $1.20, multicoloured (A) .. 10 10
2493 200 c. on $1.20, multicoloured (B) .. 10 10
2494 350 c. on $1.20, multicoloured (A) .. 15 20
2495 350 c. on $1.20, multicoloured (B) .. 15 20
2476/95 .. .. *Set of* 20 1·75 1·90

Nos. 2486/95 were issued in $20 stamp booklets which included pane No. 2486b. Nos. 2486, 2488, 2490, 2492 and 2494 were also available from sheets containing horizontal *se-tenant* strips of 5. All values later appeared in coils of 500 or 1,000.

V CENTENARY OF
THE LANDING OF
CHRISTOPHER COLUMBUS
IN THE AMERICAS
(428)

1988 (12 Oct). *Columbus Day. Nos.* 1672/3 *optd or surch as T* **428** *by Gardy Ptg.*

2496 320 c. Plate No. 50 (Series 1) 15 20
2497 $15 on 360 c. Plate No. 85 (Series 1) .. 65 70

EXPRESS LETTER STAMPS

$12.oo

EXPRESS

(E 1)

1986 (10 Nov). *Various stamps surch as Type* E 1 *by Tip Torres.*

E1 $12 on 350 c. on 120 c. mult (No. 1598) .. 1·50 1·60
E2 $15 on 40 c. multicoloured (as No. 1868, but inscr "ONTOGLOSSUM") .. .. 1·90 2·00
a. Surch on No. 1868 (inscr "ODONTOGLOSSUM") .. .. 1·90 2·00
E3 $20 on $6.40, multicoloured (No. **MS**1746) 2·50 2·75
E4 $25 on 25 c. multicoloured (as No. 1621, but value changed) .. .. 3·00 3·25
E1/4 .. .. *Set of* 4 8·00 8·50

The surcharges on Nos. E2/3 include a pattern of leaves over the original value. On No. E4 a dollar sign has been added in front of the original value and a small maltese cross overprinted above "EXPRESS" at bottom right.

1987 (3 Mar). *No.* E3 *additionally optd with small Maltese cross above surch.*

E5 $20 on $6.40, multicoloured .. .. 2·25 2·40
a. With additional "2" optd at bottom left .. 2·25 2·40

(Litho Format)

1987 (1 Sept–26 Oct). *Centenary of Publication of Sanders'* Reichenbachia. *Vert designs as T* **331** *additionally inscr* "EXPRESS". *Multicoloured. No wmk. P* 13½ × 14.

E6 $15 Plate No. 11 (Series 2) (29.9) .. .. 1·90 2·00
E7 $25 Plate No. 63 (Series 2) (26.10) .. .. 2·75 3·00
E8 $45 Plate No. 35 (Series 2) .. .. .. 5·00 5·25
E6/8 .. .. *Set of* 3 8·75 9·25

Nos. E6/8, in conjunction with postage issues, were printed in a similar sheet format to Nos. 1518/33.

EXPRESS

FORTY DOLLARS

(E 2) (*Illustration reduced. Actual size of surcharge* 64 × 36 *mm*)

1987 (Nov). *No.* 1744ab *surch with Type* E 2 *by Gardy Ptg.*

E9 $40 on $6.40, multicoloured .. .. 4·50 4·75

1987 (Dec). *No.* E 2 *additionally optd with T* **390** *by Gardy Ptg.*

E10 $15 on 40 c. multicoloured (inscr "ONTOGLOSSUM") .. .. .. 1·75 2·00

PARCEL POST STAMPS

PARCEL POST

X **X**

$15.00 **$15.00**

(P 1)

PARCEL POST

$12.00

(P 2)

1981 (8 June). *No.* 554 *surch as Type* P 1 *by Bovell's Printery.*

P1 $15 on $1 *Chelonanthus uliginoides* .. .. 7·50 5·50
P2 $20 on $1 *Chelonanthus uliginoides* .. .. 9·00 8·50

1983 (15 Jan). *No.* 843 *surch with Type* P 2 *in blue by Autoprint.*

P3 $12 on $1.10 on $2 *Norantea guianensis* .. 10·00 4·00

Parcel Post
$12.00

(P 3)

1983 (14 Sept). *Unissued Royal Wedding surch, similar to No.* 843, *further surch with Type* P 3 *in blue by Autoprint.*

P4 $12 on $1.10 on $2 *Norantea guianensis* .. 1·75 2·00

TWENTY FIVE DOLLARS
PARCEL POST 25.00

(P 4)

1985 (25 Apr). *No. 673 surch with Type* P 4 *in red by Tip. Torres.*
P5 $25 on 35 c. bright yellow-green, grey & black .. 9·00 8·00

POSTAGE DUE STAMPS

D 2

(Typo D.L.R.)

1967–68. *Chalky paper.* W w **12**. *P* 14.
D5 **D 2** 2 c. black (11.12.68) .. .. 40 3·75
D6 4 c. deep ultramarine .. .. 20 1·25
D7 12 c. reddish scarlet .. .. 30 2·25
D5/7 .. .. *Set of* 3 80 6·50

1973 (24 May). *Glazed, ordinary paper.* W **106**. *P* 14.
D 8 **D 2** 1 c. olive 15 90
D 9 2 c. black 15 90
D10 4 c. dull ultramarine 15 90
D11 12 c. bright scarlet .. .. 20 1·25
D8/11 .. .. *Set of* 4 60 3·50

OFFICIAL STAMPS

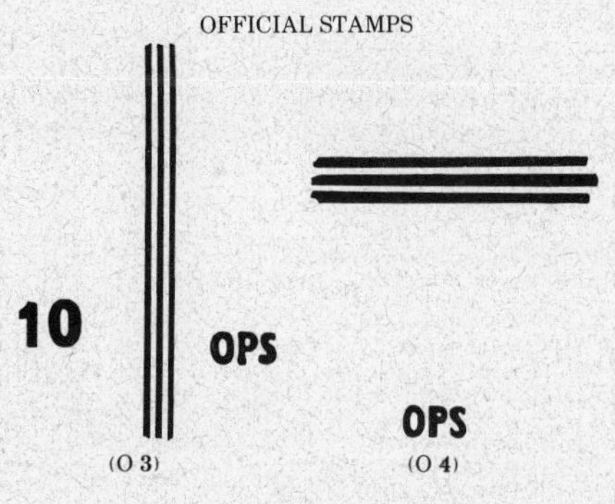

(O 3) (O 4)

OPS

(O 5)

1981 (8 June). *Nos.* 556, F4a *and* F6/7 *surch or optd with Types* O **3/5** *by Bovell's Printery.*
O13 10 c. on 25 c. Marabunta (Blk. + R.) .. .. 2·50 2·25
O14 50 c. *Guzmania lingulata* (R.) .. .. 1·25 50
O15 60 c. Soldier's Cap (R.) .. .. .. 1·00 30
O16 $5 *Odontadenia grandiflora* (opt Type O 5) (R.) .. .. 4·25 2·00
O13/16 .. .. *Set of* 4 8·00 4·50

(O 6) (O 7)

1981 (1 July). (a) *Postage. Nos.* 491, 708*a*, 716, 834 *and* F9 *optd or surch as Types* O **5/7** *or additionally surch as T* **227**.
O17 15 c. Harpy Eagle (opt Type O 6) .. .. 2·50 10
O18 30 c. on $2 *Norantea guianensis* (No. F9) (opt Type O 5) (Blk. + R.) 45 15
O19 100 c. on $3 Cylinder satellite (surch Type O 7) (Blk. + R.) .. .. .. 3·00 40
O20 125 c. on $2 *Norantea guianensis* (opt Type O 5) (R.) .. .. 3·00 45
O21 $10 *Elbella patrobas* (opt Type O 5) .. 4·00 4·00
(*b*) *Air. No.* 804 *optd with Type* O **5** *in red*
O22 $1.10 on $2 *Norantea guianensis* .. .. 3·00 3·00
a. Opt Type O **5** double £110
O17/22 .. .. *Set of* 6 14·00 7·00

1981 (7 July). *Nos.* 548, 719, 828 *and* 830 *optd with Type* O **5**.
O23 15 c. Christmas Orchid .. .. .. 3·00 75
O24 50 c. British Guiana 1898 1 c. stamp .. 1·25 25
O25 100 c. on 8 c. Camp-fire cooking .. .. 3·75 35
O26 110 c. on 6 c. Type **116** .. .. .. 4·50 60

OPS

OPS 250

(O 8) (O 9)

(Surch or optd by Autoprint)

1982 (17 May). (*a*) *Postage.* (i) *Various stamps optd with Type* O **8** *in blue*
O27 – 20 c. multicoloured (No. 701) 10 10
O28 **136** 40 c. multicoloured 75 25
O29 – 40 c. carmine-red, grey & blk (No. 674) 1·00 25
O30 – $2 multicoloured (No. 676) .. .. 6·00 1·00
O27/30 .. .. *Set of* 4 7·00 1·50
(ii) *No.* 911 *additionally surch with Type* O **9** *in blue*
O31 – 250 c. on 400 c. on 30 c. multicoloured .. 80 80
(*b*) *Air. No.* 980 *additionally optd with Type* O **8** *in blue*
O32 – 220 c. on 1 c. multicoloured .. .. 4·00 1·00

1982 (12 July). *No.* F9 *optd with Type* O **5** *in red by Bovell's Printery.*
O33 $2 *Norantea guianensis* .. .. .. 10·00 2·00

1982 (15 Sept). *Air. No.* 979 *optd with Type* O **8** *by Autoprint.*
O34 110 c. on 5 c. Annatto tree .. .. .. 3·00 1·00

1984 (2 Apr). *No.* 912 *surch as Type* O **9** *vertically, in blue (except for No.* O**37** *which has "OPS" in blue and "225" in black) by Autoprint.*
O35 150 c. on $5 multicoloured 55 60
O36 200 c. on $5 multicoloured 70 75
O37 225 c. on $5 multicoloured 80 85
O38 230 c. on $5 multicoloured 80 85
O39 260 c. on $5 multicoloured .. .. .. 95 1·00
O40 320 c. on $5 multicoloured .. .. .. 1·10 1·25
O41 350 c. on $5 multicoloured .. .. .. 1·25 1·40
O42 600 c. on $5 multicoloured .. .. .. 2·10 2·25
O35/42 .. .. *Set of* 8 7·50 8·00

25

(O 10)

(Surch or optd by Autoprint)

1984 (25 June). *Nos.* O32 *and* O34 *surch as Type* O **10** (25 *c.*, 60 *c.*) *or as T* **294** (*others*), *and No.* 981 *optd vertically with Type* O **8**.
O43 25 c. on 110 c. on 5 c. Annatto tree 10 10
O44 30 c. on 110 c. on 5 c. Annatto tree (B.) .. 15 15
O45 45 c. on 220 c. on 1 c. Pitcher Plant of Mt Roraima 15 20
O46 55 c. on 110 c. on 5 c. Annatto tree 20 25
O47 60 c. on 220 c. on 1 c. Pitcher Plant of Mt Roraima 20 25
O48 75 c. on 220 c. on 1 c. Pitcher Plant of Mt Roraima 25 30
O49 90 c. on 220 c. on 1 c. Pitcher Plant of Mt Roraima (B.) 35 40
O50 120 c. on 220 c. on 1 c. Pitcher Plant of Mt Roraima 45 50
O51 130 c. on 220 c. on 1 c. Pitcher Plant of Mt Roraima (B.) 50 55
O52 330 c. on $2 *Norantea guianensis* (B.) .. 1·10 1·25
O43/52 .. .. *Set of* 10 3·00 3·50

(Litho Format)

1987 (5 Oct). *Centenary of Publication of Sanders' Reichenbachia. Multicoloured designs as T* **331** *additionally inscr* "OFFICIAL". *No wmk. P* 14 × 13½ (230, 350, 600 *c.*, $12) *or* 13½ × 14 (*others*).
O53 120 c. Plate No. 48 (Series 2) 15 20
O54 130 c. Plate No. 92 (Series 2) 15 20
O55 150 c. Plate No. 43 (Series 2) 15 20
O56 200 c. Plate No. 61 (Series 2) 25 30
O57 225 c. Plate No. 26 (Series 2) 25 30
O58 230 c. Plate No. 68 (Series 2) (*horiz*) .. 25 30
O59 275 c. Plate No. 90 (Series 2) 30 35
O60 320 c. Plate No. 75 (Series 2) 35 40
O61 330 c. Plate No. 23 (Series 2) 40 45
O62 350 c. Plate No. 95 (Series 2) (*horiz*) .. 40 45
O63 600 c. Plate No. 70 (Series 2) (*horiz*) .. 70 75
O64 $12 Plate No. 71 (Series 2) (*horiz*) .. 1·40 1·50
O65 $15 Plate No. 84 (Series 2) .. .. 1·75 1·90
O53/65 .. .. *Set of* 13 5·75 6·50
Nos. O53/65 were printed in a similar sheet format to Nos. 1518/33.

OFFICIAL PARCEL POST STAMPS

1981 (8 June). *Nos.* P1/2 *optd with Type* O **5** *in red by Bovell's Printery.*
OP1 $15 on $1 *Chelonanthus uliginoides* .. .. 6·00 4·00
a. Opt in black .. .. .. 60·00 8·00
OP2 $20 on $1 *Chelonanthus uliginoides* .. .. 8·00 5·50

OPS

Parcel Post
$12.00

(OP 1)

1983 (15 Jan). *No.* 843 *surch with Type* OP **1**, *and optd with T* **226**, *both in blue by Autoprint.*
OP3 $12 on $1.10 on $2 *Norantea guianensis* .. 40·00 12·00
a. Surch Type OP1 omitted .. ..

1983 (22 Aug). *As No.* OP3, *but additionally optd with Type* O **8** *by Autoprint.*
OP4 $12 on $1.10 on $2 *Norantea guianensis* .. 15·00 6·50

1983 (3 Nov). *No.* P4 *additionally optd with Type* O **8** *in blue by Autoprint.*
OP5 $12 on $1.10 on $2 *Norantea guianensis* .. 8·00 5·00

POSTAL FISCAL STAMPS

REVENUE
ONLY
*

(F 1)

1975 (1 Nov). *Nos.* 543/5 *and* 550*a*/56 *optd with Type* F **1**.
F 1 2 c. Type **132** 30 20
F 2 3 c. Hanging Heliconia 30 20
F 3 5 c. Annatto tree 50 20
F 4 25 c. Marabunta (Type II) 60 20
a. Optd on No. 550 (Type I) .. .. 15·00 13·00
F 5 40 c. Tiger Beard 30 30
F 6 50 c. *Guzmania lingulata* 35 40
F 7 60 c. Soldier's Cap 50 50
F 8 $1 *Chelonanthus uliginoides* .. .. 85 1·00
F 9 $2 *Norantea guianensis* .. .. .. 1·75 2·25
F10 $5 *Odontadenia grandiflora* .. .. 5·50 6·00
F1/F10 .. .. *Set of* 10 10·00 10·00
Although intended for fiscal use Nos. F1/10 were allowed, by the postal authorities, as "an act of grace" to do duty as postage stamps until 30 June 1976.

Heligoland

Stamps of HAMBURG (see Part 7 (*Germany*) of this catalogue) were used in Heligoland until 16 April 1867. The Free City of Hamburg ran the Heligoland postal service between 1796 and 1 June 1866. Its stamps continued in use on the island until replaced by Heligoland issues.

PRICES FOR STAMPS ON COVER

Nos. 1/31	*from* × 3
Nos. 32/3	—

Collectors should be on their guard against reprints of Heligoland stamps, which are very numerous and of little value. Beware also of forgeries and forged cancellations on both originals and reprints.

PRINTERS. All the stamps of Heligoland were typographed at the Imperial Printing Works, Berlin.

1

2

3

(Des Wedding. Die eng E. Schilling)

1867. *Head embossed in colourless relief. Roul.*

1	1	½ sch. green and rose (Die I)	£275	£550
2		½ sch. green and rose (Die II)	£700	£1000
3		1 sch. rose and blue-green	£150	£150
4		2 sch. rose and grass-green	7·00	50·00
5		6 sch. green and rose	9·00	£250

In Nos. 1 to 9, the second colour is that of the spandrels in the ½ and 1 sch., and of the central background also in the 2 and 6 sch. In Die I the small curl below the chignon is solid and projects downwards, while in Die II it is in the shape of a hook opening to the left.

1869–72. *P* 13½ × 14½.

6	1	½ sch. yellow-green and rose	£150	£160
7		½ sch. blue-green and rose	£125	£140
8		1 sch. rose and pale blue-green	£100	£125
9		1 sch. rose and yellow-green	£100	£125

1873. *New values. P* 13½ × 14½.

10	1	¼ sch. rose and green	21·00	£1400
		a. Error. Green and rose	80·00	£2000
11		¼ sch. deep rose and pale green	80·00	£1400
12		¾ sch. green and rose	21·00	£1100
13		1½ sch. green and rose	50·00	£250

In Nos. 10, 10a, 11 and 13 the second colour is that of the central background.

In No. 12 the second colour is also that of the side labels and side marginal lines.

No. 10a results from a printing of the ¼ sch. in the colours of the 1½ sch.

(Des H. Gätke. Die eng E. Schilling)

1875. *Head embossed in colourless relief. P* 13½ × 14½.

15	2	1 pf. (¼d.) deep green and rose	6·00	£500
16		2 pf. (½d.) deep rose and green	6·00	£575
17		5 pf. (¾d.) deep yellow-green and rose	6·00	16·00
18		5 pf. (¾d.) deep green and rose	8·50	35·00
19		10 pf. (1½d.) deep rose and deep green	20·00	18·00
20		10 pf. (1½d.) scarlet and pale blue-green	6·00	18·00
21		10 pf. (1½d.) rose aniline & pale yellow-green	55·00	22·00
22		25 pf. (3d.) deep green and rose	8·00	24·00
23		50 pf. (6d.) rose and green	13·00	24·00

The first colour given above is that of the central background, the second that of the frame.

(Des H. Gätke. Die eng A. Schiffner)

1876. *P* 13½ × 14½.

24	3	3 pf. (⅝d.) green, red and yellow-orange	£125	£750
24*a*		3 pf. (⅝d.) pale green, red and yellow	£125	£750
25		20 pf. (2½d.) rose, green and yellow	90·00	55·00
26		20 pf. (2½d.) rose-carmine, deep green and orange	£100	50·00
27		20 pf. (2½d.) dull red, pale green and lemon	11·00	20·00
28		20 pf. (2½d.) vermilion aniline, bright green and lemon	11·00	20·00

Colours. 3 pf. (1) Frame and top band of shield. (2) Centre band of shield. (3) Border of shield.

20 pf. (1) Frame and centre band. (2) Upper band. (3) Border of shield.

4

5

(Des H. Gätke. Die eng A. Schiffner)

1879. (*a*) *P* 13½ × 14½.

29	4	1 m. (1s.) deep green, scarlet and black	80·00	£200
30		1 m. (1s.) deep green, rose aniline & blk.	90·00	£200
31	5	5 m. (5s.) deep green, rose aniline & blk.	£100	£950

(*b*) *P* 11½

32	4	1 m. (1s.) deep green, scarlet and black	£400	
33	5	5 m. (5s.) deep green, scarlet and black	£400	
		a. Imperf between (pair)	£2000	

The stamps perf 11½ are given above on the ground that specimens exist on the original envelopes and are known to have been genuinely postally used.

Numerous reprints of the ¼ sch. (including the *error*), ½ sch. (Die II), ¾ sch., 1 sch., 1½ sch., 2 sch., 6 sch., 1 pf., 2 pf. and 3 pf. were made between 1875 and 1895. It is impossible to describe them all here. Collectors should exercise caution in purchasing stamps of which reprints exist.

Heligoland was ceded to Germany on 9 Aug 1890.

Hong Kong

CROWN COLONY

The Hong Kong Post Office was established in February 1841, when much of the business previously transacted through the Macao postal agency was transferred to the island. The first cancellation is known from April 1842, but local control of the posts was shortlived as the Hong Kong Post Office became a branch of the British G.P.O. following the ratification of the Treaty of Nanking on 26 June 1843.

The colonial authorities resumed control of the postal service on 1 May 1860, although the previously established postal agencies in the Chinese Treaty Ports remained part of the British G.P.O. system until 1868.

For illustrations of the handstamp types see BRITISH POST OFFICES ABROAD notes, following GREAT BRITAIN.

CROWNED-CIRCLE HANDSTAMPS

CC1 CC1	HONG KONG (R.) (17.10.1843)	*Price on cover*	£550
CC2 CC1b	HONG KONG (R.) (21.8.1844)	*Price on cover*	£375
CC3 CC3	HONG KONG (R.) (16.6.1852)	*Price on cover*	£200

We no longer list the Great Britain stamps with obliteration "B 62" within oval. The Government notification dated 29 November 1862 stated that only the Hong Kong stamps to be issued on 8 December would be available for postage and the stamps formerly listed were all issued in Great Britain later than the date of the notice.

PRICES FOR STAMPS ON COVER TO 1945

Nos. 1/27	*from* × 6
Nos. 28/36	*from* × 4
Nos. 37/9	*from* × 5
Nos. 40/4	*from* × 4
Nos. 45/8	*from* × 10
Nos. 49/50	*from* × 4
No. 51	*from* × 15
Nos. 52/61	*from* × 5
Nos. 62/99	*from* × 4
Nos. 100/32	*from* × 3
Nos. 133/6	*from* × 2
Nos. 137/9	*from* × 4
Nos. 140/68	*from* × 2
Nos. D1/12	*from* × 8
Nos. F1/11	*from* × 4
No. F12	*from* × 3
Nos. P1/3	*from* × 2

PRINTERS. All definitive stamps up to 1960 were typographed by De La Rue & Co.

CONDITION. Mint or fine used specimens of the earlier Hong Kong stamps are rarely met with and are worth considerably more than our prices which are for stamps in average condition. Inferior specimens can be supplied at much lower prices.

1

2

3

1862 (8 Dec). *No wmk. P* 14.

1	1	2 c. brown	£170	45·00
		a. Deep brown	£275	50·00
2		8 c. yellow-buff	£300	30·00
3		12 c. pale greenish blue	£200	28·00
4	3	18 c. lilac	£225	25·00
5		24 c. green	£500	55·00
6		48 c. rose	£1400	£170
7		96 c. brownish grey	£1800	£180

1863–71. *Wmk Crown CC. P* 14.

8	1	2 c. deep brown (1865)	£100	14·00
		a. Brown	50·00	3·75
		b. Pale yellowish brown	60·00	5·50
9	2	4 c. grey (1863)	50·00	6·00
		a. Slate	50·00	3·00
		b. Deep slate	70·00	4·75
		c. Greenish grey	£120	20·00
		d. Bluish slate	£225	10·00
		e. Perf 12½ (1870)	£3000	£250
10		6 c. lilac (1863)	£180	4·50
		a. Mauve	£180	5·50
11	1	8 c. pale dull orange (1865)	£200	4·50
		a. Brownish orange	£170	4·50
		b. Bright orange	£190	4·00
12		12 c. pale greenish blue (1864?)	£400	17·00
		a. Pale blue	12·00	3·00
		b. Deep blue	90·00	5·50
13	3	18 c. lilac (1866)	£1500	£200
14		24 c. green (1865)	£190	5·00
		a. Pale green	£300	8·50
		b. Deep green	£375	14·00
15	2	30 c. vermilion (1863)	£350	7·50
		a. Orange-vermilion	£275	8·50
16		30 c. mauve (14.8.71)	85·00	2·25
17		48 c. pale rose (1865)	£400	20·00
		a. Rose-carmine	£425	11·00
		b. Bright claret	†	—
18		96 c. olive-bistre (1865)	£10000	£425
19		96 c. brownish grey (1866)	£425	18·00
		a. Brownish black	£550	15·00

There is a wide range of shades in this issue, of which we can only indicate the main groups.

No. 12 is the same shade as No. 3 without wmk, the impression having a waxy appearance.

Only one used copy of No. 17*b* is known.

See also Nos. 22 and 28/31.

16 cents.	*28 cents.*	**5 cents.**	**10 cents.**
(4)	(5)	(6)	(7)

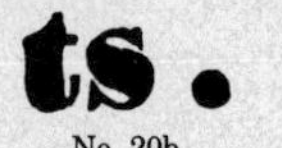

No. 20b

1876. *Nos.* 13 *and* 16 *surch with T* 4 *or* 5 *by Noronha and Sons, Hong Kong.*

20	3	16 c. on 18 c. lilac (June?)	£850	£110
		a. Space between "n" and "t"	£2500	£350
		b. Space between "s" and stop	£2500	£350
21	2	28 c. on 30 c. mauve (July?)	£500	40·00

1877 (Aug). *New value. Wmk Crown CC. P* 14.

22	3	16 c. yellow	£400	40·00

1880 (Mar–Sept). *Surch with T* 6 *or* 7.

23	1	5 c. on 8 c. bright orange (No. 11*b*) (Sept)	£250	45·00
		a. Surch inverted	—	£5500
		b. Surch double	—	£8500
24	3	5 c. on 18 c. lilac (No. 13)	£180	30·00
25	1	10 c. on 12 c. pale blue (No. 12*a*)	£225	40·00
		a. Blue	£325	45·00
26	3	10 c. on 16 c. yellow (No. 22) (August)	£950	70·00
		a. Surch inverted	—	£12000
27		10 c. on 24 c. green (No. 14) (June)	£375	50·00

1880. *Colours changed and new values. Wmk Crown CC. P* 14.

28	1	2 c. dull rose (July)	50·00	8·50
		a. Rose	60·00	9·50
29	2	5 c. blue (Nov)	£100	12·00
30		10 c. mauve (Nov)	£120	6·50
31	3	48 c. brown	£300	48·00

1882–83. *Wmk Crown CA. P* 14.

32	1	2 c. rose-lake	55·00	12·00
		a. Rose-pink	70·00	18·00
		b. Perf 12	£10000	
33		2 c. carmine (1883)	7·00	25
		a. Aniline carmine	8·00	25
34	2	5 c. pale blue	4·50	25
		a. Blue	4·50	25
35		10 c. dull mauve	£250	4·00
36		10 c. green (1883)	50·00	60
		a. Deep blue-green	£750	22·00

20 CENTS	**50 CENTS**	**1 DOLLAR**
(8)	(9)	(10)

1885 (June). *Surch with T* 8 *to* 10 *by De La Rue. Wmk Crown CA. P* 14.

37	2	20 c. on 30 c. orange-red	35·00	2·00
		a. Surch double		
38	3	50 c. on 48 c. yellowish brown	£120	9·00
39		$1 on 96 c. grey-olive	£200	20·00
37/9 Optd "Specimen"		*Set of* 3	£400	

1891–92. *Wmk Crown CA. P* 14. (*a*) *Colours changed* (1.1.91).

40	2	10 c. purple/*red*	4·25	15
41		30 c. yellowish green	65·00	22·00
		a. Grey-green	16·00	9·00
40, 41*a* Optd "Specimen"		*Set of* 2	£200	

(*b*) *Colours changed and surch with T* 8 *to* 10.

42	2	20 c. on 30 c. yellowish green (No. 41)	£100	60·00
		a. Grey-green (No. 41*a*)	50·00	45·00
43	3	50 c. on 48 c. dull purple (1892)	£180	£120
44		$1 on 96 c. purple/*red*	£300	£120
42*a*/44 Optd "Specimen"		*Set of* 3	£300	

Nos. 41/2, and 45, should not be confused with faded or washed copies of the grey-green, which turns to a very yellow-green shade when dampened.

弍 五十 壹員

(11) (20 c.) (12) (50 c.) (13) ($1)

1891. *Surch with T* **8/10** *as Nos. 42/4 but handstamped Chinese characters added at top of label at left* (*T* **11/13**).

No.	Type	Description	Unused	Used
45	**2**	20 c. on 30 c. yellowish green	28·00	3·00
		a. Grey-green	9·50	1·50
		b. "20 CENTS" double		
46	**3**	50 c. on 48 c. dull purple	28·00	2·50
47		$1 on 96 c. purple/*red*	£140	10·00

Type **11** consists of a single character for "2" intended to overstamp the "3" to convert the 30 c. to 20 c. Six different chops were made and three of the 50 c. Type **12**.

The errors of the Chinese surcharges previously listed on the above issue and also on Nos. 52 and 55 are now omitted as being outside the scope of the catalogue. While some without doubt possess philatelic merit, it is impossible to distinguish between the genuine errors and the clandestine copies made to order with the original chops. No. 55c is retained as this represents a distinctly different chop which was used for the last part of the printing.

1841 Hong Kong JUBILEE 1891 (14)

7 cents. (15)

14 cents. (16)

1891 (22 Jan). *50th Anniv of Colony. Optd with T* **14**.

No.	Type	Description	Unused	Used
48	**1**	2 c. carmine (No. 33)	£150	60·00
		a. Short "J" in "JUBILEE" ..	£250	90·00
		b. Short "U" in "JUBILEE" ..	£250	90·00
		c. Broken "1" in "1891" ..	£350	£130
		d. Tall narrow "K" in "KONG" ..	£500	£300
		e. Opt double	£7000	£5500
		f. Space between "O" and "N" of "HONG" ..	£1000	£450

This overprint was applied in a setting of 12 during a number of printings and other less marked varieties therefore exist.

1891 (1 Jan–Feb). *Surch with T* **15** *or* **16** *by Noronha and Sons, Hong Kong.*

No.	Type	Description	Unused	Used
49	**2**	7 c. on 10 c. green (No. 36) ..	38·00	5·50
		a. Antique "t" in "cents" (R.1/1) ..	£425	£140
		b. Surch double	£3500	£1000
50		14 c. on 30 c. mauve (No. 16) (Feb) ..	70·00	40·00
		a. Antique "t" in "cents" (R.1/1) ..	£1700	£850

The true antique "t" must not be confused with a small "t" with short foot, which is sometimes mistaken for it. In the antique "t" the cross-bar is accurately bisected by the vertical stroke, the latter being thick at the top. The lower curve bends towards the right and does not turn upwards so far as in the normal.

Dangerous forgeries of these two surcharges exist.

1896. *Wmk Crown CA. P* 14.

No.	Type	Description	Unused	Used
51	**2**	4 c. slate-grey	3·50	20

1898 (1 Apr). *Wmk Crown CA. P* 14.

(*a*) *Surch with T* **10**, *and handstamped Chinese characters as T* **13**.

No.	Type	Description	Unused	Used
52	**3**	$1 on 96 c. black	45·00	15·00
		a. Grey-black	45·00	15·00

(*b*) *Surch with T* **10** *only*

No.	Type	Description	Unused	Used
53	**3**	$1 on 96 c. black	£325	£500
		a. Grey-black (Optd S. £200) ..	£325	£500

10 CENTS (17) 拾 (18) 拾 (19)

1898 (April). (*a*) *Surch with T* **17**.

No.	Type	Description	Unused	Used
54	**2**	10 c. on 30 c. grey-green (No. 41*a*) ..	£200	£300
		a. Figures "10" widely spaced (1½ mm)		

Type **17** was applied in a setting of 12, No. 54a appearing on position 12.

(*b*) *As No.* 54, *but with Chinese character, T* **18**, *in addition*

No.	Type	Description	Unused	Used
55	**2**	10 c. on 30 c. grey-green (No. 41*a*) (H/S S. £100)	16·00	28·00
		a. Yellowish green (Optd S. £100) ..	60·00	
		b. Figures "10" widely spaced (1½ mm)	£175	£150
		c. Chinese character large (Type **19**) ..	£400	£250

1900 (Aug)–**01**. *Wmk Crown CA. P* 14.

No.	Type	Description	Unused	Used
56	**1**	2 c. dull green	4·50	20
57	**2**	4 c. carmine	2·75	20
58		5 c. yellow	5·50	2·75
59		10 c. ultramarine	8·00	55
60	**1**	12 c. blue (1901)	8·00	25·00
61	**2**	30 c. brown (12.01)	5·50	13·00
56/61		.. .. *Set of* 6	30·00	38·00
56/9, 61 Optd "Specimen"		.. *Set of* 5	£250	

20

21

22

23

1903. *Wmk Crown CA. P* 14.

No.	Type	Description	Unused	Used
62	**20**	1 c. dull purple and brown	60	15
63		2 c. dull green	1·75	60
64	**21**	4 c. purple/*red*	2·25	10
65		5 c. dull green and brown-orange ..	3·50	2·50
66		8 c. slate and violet	3·00	60
67	**20**	10 c. purple and blue/*blue*	8·50	30
68	**23**	12 c. green and purple/*yellow*	4·50	1·75
69		20 c. slate and chestnut	8·50	80
70	**22**	30 c. dull green and black	12·00	4·00
71	**23**	50 c. dull green and magenta	11·00	9·00
72	**20**	$1 purple and sage-green	30·00	9·50
73	**23**	$2 slate and scarlet	70·00	75·00
74	**22**	$3 slate and dull blue	70·00	90·00
75	**23**	$5 purple and blue-green	£120	£130
76	**22**	$10 slate and orange/*blue*	£375	£275
62/76		.. .. *Set of* 15	£650	£525
62/76 Optd "Specimen"		.. *Set of* 15	£600	

1904–7. *Wmk Mult Crown CA. P* 14.

No.	Type	Description	Unused	Used
77	**20**	2 c. dull green, **CO**	60	35
78	**21**	4 c. purple/*red*, **CO**	1·00	10
79		5 c. dull green and brown-orange, **CO** ..	2·75	80
80		8 c. slate and violet, **C** (1907) ..	3·50	1·25
81	**20**	10 c. purple and blue/*blue*, **O** ..	3·50	40
82	**23**	12 c. green and purple/*yellow*, **C** (1907) ..	4·00	4·25
83		20 c. slate and chestnut, **CO** ..	4·50	90
84	**22**	30 c. dull green and black, **CO** ..	8·00	3·75
85	**23**	50 c. green and magenta, **CO** ..	9·50	2·75
86	**20**	$1 purple and sage-green, **CO** ..	24·00	6·00
87	**23**	$2 slate and scarlet, **CO** ..	55·00	40·00
88	**22**	$3 slate and dull blue, **C** ..	60·00	75·00
89	**23**	$5 purple and blue-green, **C** ..	£110	£130
90	**22**	$10 slate and orange/*blue*, **CO** ..	£475	£325
77/90		.. .. *Set of* 14	£700	£525

1907–11. *Colours changed and new value. Wmk Mult Crown CA. P* 14.

No.	Type	Description	Unused	Used
91	**20**	1 c. brown, **O** (1910)	1·00	75
92		2 c. deep green, **O**	8·00	50
		a. Green	6·50	45
93	**21**	4 c. carmine-red, **O**	1·50	25
94	**22**	6 c. orange-vermilion and purple, **C** ..	7·00	2·50
95	**20**	10 c. bright ultramarine, **O**	5·00	30
96	**23**	20 c. purple and sage-green, **C** (1911) ..	25·00	16·00
97	**22**	30 c. purple and orange-yellow, **C** (1911)	26·00	11·00
98	**23**	50 c. black/*green*, **C** (1911) ..	17·00	6·00
99		$2 carmine-red and black, **C** (1910) ..	90·00	70·00
91/9		.. .. *Set of* 9	£160	95·00
91, 93/9 Optd "Specimen"		.. *Set of* 8	£325	

24

25

26

27

28

(A)

(B)

In Type A of the 25 c. the upper Chinese character in the left-hand label has a short vertical stroke crossing it at the foot. In Type B this stroke is absent.

1912 (Nov)–**21**. *Wmk Mult Crown CA. P* 14.

No.	Type	Description	Unused	Used
100	**24**	1 c. brown, **O**	75	30
		a. Black-brown	2·00	55
		b. Crown broken at right (R.9/2)	£130	£110
101		2 c. deep green, **O**	1·50	25
		a. Green	1·75	25
102	**25**	4 c. carmine-red, **O**	1·50	20
		a. Scarlet	5·00	50
103	**26**	6 c. yellow-orange, **O**	2·25	60
		a. Brown-orange	2·00	80
104	**25**	8 c. grey, **O** (1915)	12·00	3·25
		a. Slate	17·00	3·25
105	**24**	10 c. ultramarine, **O**	17·00	25
		a. Deep bright ultramarine	14·00	20
106	**27**	12 c. purple/*yellow*, **C**	1·00	3·25
		a. White back (Optd S. £50) (5.14)	3·50	7·00
107		20 c. purple and sage-green, **C**	1·75	60
108	**28**	25 c. purple and magenta, **C** (Type A) (1.14)	6·00	6·50
109		25 c. purple and magenta, **C** (Type B) (8.19)	32·00	32·00
110	**26**	30 c. purple and orange-yellow, **C**	17·00	3·50
		a. Purple and orange	9·00	3·00
111	**27**	50 c. black/*blue-green*, **C**	4·00	50
		a. White back (Optd S. £70) (5.14)	3·75	2·50
		b. On blue-green, olive back (1917)	£150	9·00
		c. On emerald surface (9.19)	8·00	10·00
		d. On emerald back (Optd S. £70) (7.12.21)	7·50	4·00
112	**24**	$1 purple and blue/*blue*, **C**	9·00	90
113	**27**	$2 carmine-red and grey-black, **C**	45·00	17·00
114	**26**	$3 green and purple, **C**	70·00	27·00
115	**27**	$5 green and red/*green*, **C**	£140	75·00
		a. White back (Optd S. £80) (5.14)	£140	70·00
		b. On blue-green, olive back (Optd S. £90) (1917)	£325	55·00
116	**26**	$10 purple and black/*red*, **C**	£150	45·00
100/16		*Set of* 17	£450	£170
100/16 Optd "Specimen"		*Set of* 17	£750	

1921 (Jan)–**37**. *Wmk Mult Script CA. P* 14.

No.	Type	Description	Unused	Used
117	**24**	1 c. brown, **O**	30	25
		b. Crown broken at right (R.9/2)		
118		2 c. blue-green, **O**	65	20
		a. Yellow-green	1·40	20
118*b*		2 c. grey, **O** (14.4.37)	4·00	3·00
119	**25**	3 c. grey, **O** (8.10.31)	1·00	35
120		4 c. carmine-rose, **O**	55	30
		a. Carmine-red	55	15
		b. Top of lower Chinese characters at right broken off	80·00	60·00
121		5 c. violet, **O** (16.10.31)	1·00	15
122		8 c. grey, **O**	4·50	20·00
123		8 c. orange, **O** (7.12.21)	80	70
124	**24**	10 c. bright ultramarine, **O**	60	10
124*a*	**27**	12 c. purple/*yellow*, **C** (3.4.33)	3·75	40
125		20 c. purple and sage-green, **C** (7.12.21)	1·50	10
126	**28**	25 c. purple & magenta, **C** (B) (7.12.21)	80	30
127	**26**	30 c. purple & chrome-yell, **C** (7.12.21)	1·50	1·25
		a. Purple and orange-yellow	8·00	2·25
128	**27**	50 c. black/*emerald*, **C** (1924)	3·25	10
129	**24**	$1 purple and blue/*blue*, **C** (7.12.21)	6·00	50
130	**27**	$2 carm-red & grey-blk, **C** (7.12.21)	32·00	1·75
131	**26**	$3 green and dull purple, **C** (1926)	75·00	15·00
132	**27**	$5 green and red/*emerald*, **C** (1925)	£110	18·00
117/32		*Set of* 18	£200	55·00
117/32 Optd/Perf "Specimen"		*Set of* 18	£600	

1935 (6 May). *Silver Jubilee. As Nos.* 91/4 *of Antigua, but ptd by B.W. P* 11 × 12.

No.	Description	Unused	Used
133	3 c. ultramarine and grey-black	1·75	1·75
	c. Lightning conductor	£100	
134	5 c. green and indigo	3·25	1·50
	a. Extra flagstaff	£180	£200
	b. Short extra flagstaff	£110	
	c. Lightning conductor	£110	
	d. Flagstaff on right-hand turret	£100	
135	10 c. brown and deep blue	4·00	80
136	20 c. slate and purple	13·00	4·00
	b. Short extra flagstaff	£160	
	d. Flagstaff on right-hand turret	£130	
133/6	*Set of* 4	20·00	7·00
133/6 Perf "Specimen"	*Set of* 4	90·00	

For illustrations of plate varieties see Omnibus section following Zululand.

1937 (12 May). *Coronation. As Nos.* 13/15 *of Aden, but ptd by B.W. P* 11 × 11½.

No.	Description	Unused	Used
137	4 c. green	1·25	85
138	15 c. carmine	2·75	1·50
139	25 c. blue	3·75	1·50
137/9	*Set of* 3	7·00	3·50
137/9 Perf "Specimen"	*Set of* 3	70·00	

29 King George VI

1938–52. *Wmk Mult Script CA. P* 14.

No.	Type	Description	Unused	Used
140	**29**	1 c. brown (24.5.38)	20	40
		a. Pale brown (27.2.52)	20	1·75
141		2 c. grey (5.4.38)	25	15
		a. Perf 14½ × 14 (1942)	65	2·75
142		4 c. orange (5.4.38)	60	40
		a. Perf 14½ × 14 (28.9.45)	1·75	2·00
143		5 c. green (24.5.38)	35	10
		a. Perf 14½ × 14 (12.41)	55	1·75
144		8 c. red-brown (1.11.41)	35	1·75
		a. Imperf (pair)	£12000	
145		10 c. bright violet (13.4.38)	10·00	60
		a. Dull reddish violet (9.4.46)	1·75	15
		b. Reddish lilac (9.4.47)	2·00	15
		c. Perf 14½ × 14. *Dull violet* (12.41)	1·25	10
146		15 c. scarlet (13.4.38)	20	15
147		20 c. black (1.2.46)	20	15
148		20 c. scarlet-vermilion (1.4.48)	90	20
		a. Rose-red (25.4.51)	2·25	1·25
149		25 c. bright blue (5.4.38)	3·00	45
150		25 c. pale yellow-olive (9.4.46)	70	1·25
151		30 c. yellow-olive (13.4.38)	75·00	85
		a. Perf 14½×14. *Yellowish olive* (12.41)	5·50	6·00
152		30 c. blue (9.4.46)	1·00	10
153		50 c. reddish purple, **O** (13.4.38)	4·50	25
		a. Bright purple, **C** (9.4.47)	1·25	10
		b. Perf 14½ × 14. *Deep magenta* (12.41)	2·00	50
154		80 c. carmine, **C** (2.2.48)	1·00	50
155		$1 dull lilac and blue, **C** (27.4.38)	3·50	1·50
		a. Pale reddish lilac and blue, **O** (11.41)	6·00	1·60
156		$1 red-orange and green, **OC** (9.4.46)	2·50	10
		a. Yellow-orange and green, **C** (6.11.52)	15·00	5·50
157		$2 red-orange and green, **C** (24.5.38)	48·00	9·00
158		$2 reddish violet and scarlet, **OC** (9.4.46)	2·50	25
159		$5 dull lilac and scarlet, **C** (2.6.38)	28·00	30·00
160		$5 green and violet, **O** (9.4.46)	18·00	2·50
		a. Yellowish green and violet, **OC** (9.4.46)	40·00	2·50
161		$10 green and violet, **C** (2.6.38)	£275	48·00
162		$10 bright lilac and blue, **O** (9.4.46)	45·00	14·00
		a. Reddish violet and blue, **C** (9.4.47)	70·00	18·00
140/62		*Set of* 23	£400	£100
140/62 Perf "Specimen"		*Set of* 23	£1200	

The varieties perf 14½ × 14 with the exception of the 4 c. were printed and perforated by Bradbury, Wilkinson & Co, Ltd, from De La Rue plates and are on rough-surfaced paper. The dates quoted for these are London release dates and it is believed that supplies did not reach Hong Kong before the Japanese occupation.

Nos. 142a and 144 were printed by Harrison & Sons in 1941 and issued in sheets of 120 (12 × 10) instead of two panes of 60 (6 × 10).

Also in 1941 Williams, Lea & Co printed the $1 and $2 perf 14 from De La Rue plates.

Nos. 160/*a* were separate printings released in Hong Kong on the same day.

No. 144a. One imperforate sheet was found and most of the stamps were sold singly to the public at a branch P.O. and used for postage.

30 Street Scene

31 *Empress of Japan* (liner) and Junk

(Des W. E. Jones. Recess B.W.)

1941 (26 Feb). *Centenary of British Occupation. T* **30/1** *and similar designs. Wmk Mult Script CA (sideways on horiz designs). P* 13½ × 13 (2 *c. and* 25 *c.*) *or* 13 × 13½ (*others*).

No.	Description	Unused	Used
163	2 c. orange and chocolate	80	90
164	4 c. bright purple and carmine	1·50	1·00
165	5 c. black and green	60	25
166	15 c. black and scarlet	2·75	60
167	25 c. chocolate and blue	3·00	1·00
168	$1 blue and orange	8·50	3·50
163/168	*Set of* 6	15·00	6·50
163/8 Perf "Specimen"	*Set of* 6	£160	

Designs: *Horiz*—5 c. The University; 15 c. The Harbour; $1 China Clipper and Seaplane. *Vert*—25 c. The Hong Kong Bank.

36 King George VI and Phoenix

37 Queen Elizabeth II

Extra character (R. 1/2)

(Des W. E. Jones. Recess D.L.R.)

1946 (29 Aug). *Victory. Wmk Mult Script CA. P* 13.

No.	Type	Description	Unused	Used
169	**36**	30 c. blue and red (*shades*)	1·00	30
		a. Extra character	16·00	
170		$1 brown and red	1·00	30
		a. Extra character	19·00	
169/70 Perf "Specimen"		*Set of* 2	£100	

1948 (22 Dec). *Royal Silver Wedding. As Nos.* 30/1 *of Aden.*

No.	Description	Unused	Used
171	10 c. violet	60	40
172	$10 carmine	65·00	25·00

1949 (10 Oct). *75th Anniv of Universal Postal Union. As Nos.* 114/17 *of Antigua.*

No.	Description	Unused	Used
173	10 c. violet	85	25
174	20 c. carmine-red	3·75	50
175	30 c. deep blue	3·50	75
176	80 c. bright reddish purple	5·50	1·75
173/6	*Set of* 4	12·00	3·00

1953 (2 June). *Coronation. As No.* 47 *of Aden.*

No.	Description	Unused	Used
177	10 c. black and slate-lilac	1·25	10

1954 (5 Jan)–**62**. *Ordinary paper* (5, 10, 15 *c.*) *or chalk-surfaced paper* (*others*). *Wmk Mult Script CA. P* 14.

No.	Type	Description	Unused	Used
178	**37**	5 c. orange	25	10
		a. Imperf (pair)	£800	
179		10 c. lilac	45	10
		a. Reddish violet (18.7.61)	1·00	10
180		15 c. green	1·25	20
		a. Pale green (6.12.55)	1·00	20
181		20 c. brown, **C**	1·00	15
182		25 c. scarlet, **C**	75	25
		a. Rose-red (26.2.58)	60	15
183		30 c. grey, **C**	1·50	10
		a. Pale grey (26.2.58)	1·50	10
184		40 c. bright blue, **C**	1·00	10
		a. Dull blue (10.1.61)	2·75	30
185		50 c. reddish purple, **C**	1·00	10
186		65 c. grey, **C** (20.6.60)	11·00	6·00
187		$1 orange and green, **C**	3·25	10
188		$1.30, blue and red, **C** (20.6.60)	16·00	90
		a. Bright blue and red (23.1.62)	23·00	1·50
189		$2 reddish violet and scarlet, **C**	6·00	30
		a. Lt reddish violet & scarlet (26.2.58)	6·00	30
190		$5 green and purple, **C**	27·00	1·00
		a. Yellowish green and purple (7.3.61)	40·00	1·50
191		$10 reddish violet and bright blue, **C**	27·00	2·50
		a. Lt reddish violet & brt blue (26.2.58)	30·00	2·50
178/91		*Set of* 14	80·00	11·00

No. 178a. One sheet was found: 90 stamps imperf, 10 perf three sides only.

38 University Arms

39 Statue of Queen Victoria

(Des and photo Harrison)

1961 (11 Sept). *Golden Jubilee of Hong Kong University. W w* **12**. *P* 11½ × 12.

No.	Type	Description	Unused	Used
192	**38**	$1 multicoloured	2·25	80
		a. Gold ptg omitted	£550	

(Des Cheung Yat-man. Photo Harrison)

1962 (4 May). *Stamp Centenary. W w* **12**. *P* 14½.

No.	Type	Description	Unused	Used
193	**39**	10 c. black and magenta	15	10
194		20 c. black and light blue	50	35
195		50 c. black and bistre	50	15
193/5		*Set of* 3	1·10	55

40 Queen Elizabeth II (after Annigoni) **41**

(Photo Harrison)

1962 (4 Oct)–**73**. *W w* **12** (*upright*). *Chalk-surfaced paper. P* 15 × 14 (5 *c. to* $1) *or* 14 × 14½ (*others*).

No.	Type	Description	Unused	Used
196	**40**	5 c. red-orange	10	10
197		10 c. bright reddish violet	35	10
		a. Reddish violet (19.11.71)	60	10
		ab. Glazed paper (14.4.72)	2·00	20
198		15 c. emerald	45	10

199 40 20 c. red-brown 40 10
a. *Brown* (13.12.71) 90 20
ab. Glazed paper (27.9.72) .. .. 2·25 60
200 25 c. cerise 60 35
201 30 c. deep grey-blue 45 10
a. *Chalky blue* (19.11.71) .. .. 1·00 10
ab. Glazed paper (27.9.72) .. .. 2·75 20
202 40 c. deep bluish green 35 15
203 50 c. scarlet 35 10
a. *Vermilion* (13.12.71) .. .. 1·25 20
ab. Glazed paper (27.9.72) .. .. 3·50 25
204 65 c. ultramarine .. .. .. 6·00 1·25
205 $1 sepia .. .. 7·00 10
206 41 $1.30, multicoloured .. .. .. 1·50 10
a. Pale yellow omitted† .. .. 14·00
b. Pale yellow inverted £1500
c. Ochre (sash) omitted .. .. 14·00
d. Glazed paper (3.2.71) .. .. 4·50 45
da. Ochre (sash) omitted .. ..
207 $2 multicoloured .. .. .. 3·25 15
a. Pale yellow omitted† .. .. 14·00
b. Ochre (sash) omitted .. .. 15·00
c. Pale yellow† and ochre (sash) omitted .. .. .. 65·00
d. Glazed paper (1973)* .. .. 60·00 2·50
208 $5 multicoloured .. .. .. 7·00 50
a. Ochre (sash) omitted .. .. 20·00
b. Glazed paper (3.2.71) .. .. 16·00 4·00
209 $10 multicoloured .. .. .. 16·00 1·50
a. Ochre (sash) omitted .. .. 60·00
b. Pale yellow† and ochre (sash) omitted £100
c. Glazed paper (1973)* .. .. £225 27·00
210 $20 multicoloured .. .. .. 26·00 7·00
196/210 .. .. .. *Set of* 15 65·00 10·00

*These are from printings which were sent to Hong Kong in March 1973 but not released in London.

†This results in the Queen's face appearing pinkish.

It is believed that No. 206b comes from the last two vertical rows of a sheet, the remainder of which had the pale yellow omitted.

The $1.30 to $20 exist with PVA gum as well as gum arabic. The glazed paper printings are with PVA gum only.

See also Nos. 222, etc.

1963 (4 June). *Freedom from Hunger. As No. 76 of Aden, but additionally inscr in Chinese characters.*
211 $1.30, bluish green .. .. 13·00 3·75

1963 (2 Sept). *Red Cross Centenary. As Nos. 147/8 of Antigua, but additionally inscr in Chinese characters at right.*
212 10 c. red and black .. .. 1·50 15
213 $1.30, red and blue .. .. 6·00 2·25

1965 (17 May). *I.T.U. Centenary. As Nos. 166/7 of Antigua.*
214 10 c. light purple and orange-yellow .. 1·00 15
215 $1.30, olive-yellow and deep bluish green .. 6·00 75

1965 (25 Oct). *International Co-operation Year. As Nos. 168/9 of Antigua.*
216 10 c. reddish purple and turquoise-green .. 1·00 10
217 $1.30, dp bluish green & lavender (*shades*) 5·00 65

1966 (24 Jan). *Churchill Commemoration. As Nos. 170/3 of Antigua but additionally inscr in Chinese characters.*
218 10 c. new blue .. .. 1·25 10
219 50 c. deep green .. .. 2·00 15
220 $1.30, brown.. .. .. .. 3·00 1·25
221 $2 bluish violet .. .. 4·00 3·00
218/21 .. .. .. *Set of* 4 9·00 4·00

1966 (Aug)–**72**. *As Nos. 196/208 and 210 but wmk W w* **12** *(sideways). Chalk-surfaced paper (5 c. to $1) or glazed, ordinary paper ($1.30 to $20).*
222 40 5 c. red-orange (5.12.66) 20 10
223 10 c. reddish violet (31.3.67)* 25 10
224 15 c. emerald (31.3.67)* 35 15
225 20 c. red-brown 40 15
a. Glazed, ordinary paper (14.4.72) .. 70 40
226 25 c. cerise (31.3.67)* 50 70
a. Glazed, ordinary paper (14.4.72) .. 2·00 1·50
227 30 c. deep grey-blue (31.3.70) .. 1·75 15
a. Glazed ordinary paper (14.4.72) .. 2·25 40
228 40 c. deep bluish green (1967) .. 60 15
a. Glazed, ordinary paper (14.4.72) .. 3·25 1·40
229 50 c. scarlet (31.3.67)* 60 10
230 65 c. ultramarine (29.3.67)* .. .. 2·50 3·00
a. *Bright blue* (16.7.68) .. .. 2·00 2·75
231 $1 sepia (29.3.67)* .. .. 6·00 40
232 41 $1.30, multicoloured (14.4.72) .. 4·00 60
233 $2 multicoloured (13.12.71) .. 7·00 1·00
a. Ochre (sash) omitted .. ..
234 $5 multicoloured (13.12.71) .. 32·00 4·50
236 $20 multicoloured (14.4.72) .. 70·00 35·00
222/36 .. .. .. *Set of* 14 £110 40·00

*Earliest known postmark dates.

The 5 c. to 25 c., 40 c. and 50 c. exist with PVA gum as well as gum arabic, but the 30 c., and all stamps on glazed paper exist with PVA gum only.

1966 (20 Sept). *Inauguration of W.H.O. Headquarters, Geneva. As Nos. 178/9 of Antigua, but additionally inscr in Chinese characters.*
237 10 c. black, yellow-green and light blue .. 90 10
238 50 c. black, light purple and yellow-brown .. 1·60 60

1966 (1 Dec). *20th Anniv of U.N.E.S.C.O. As Nos. 196/8 of Antigua, but additionally inscr in Chinese characters.*
239 10 c. slate-violet, red, yellow and orange .. 1·25 10
240 50 c. orange-yellow, violet and deep olive .. 4·00 40
241 $2 black, light purple and orange .. 17·00 6·50
239/41 .. .. .. *Set of* 3 20·00 6·50

MINIMUM PRICE

The minimum price quote is 10p which represents a handling charge rather than a basis for valuing common stamps. For further notes about prices see introductory pages.

42 Rams' Heads on Chinese Lanterns

(Des V. Whiteley. Photo Harrison)

1967 (17 Jan). *Chinese New Year ("Year of the Ram"). T* **42** *and similar horiz design. W w* **12** *(sideways). P* 14½.
242 10 c. rosine, olive-green and light yellow-olive 75 15
243 $1.30, emerald, rosine and light yellow-olive 4·00 3·00
Design:—$1.30, Three rams.

44 Cable Route Map

(Des V. Whiteley. Photo Harrison)

1967 (30 Mar). *Completion of Malaysia–Hong Kong Link of SEACOM Telephone Cable. W w* **12**. *P* 12½.
244 44 $1.30, new blue and red .. .. 1·75 1·25

45 Rhesus Macaques in Tree ("Year of the Monkey")

(Des R. Granger Barrett. Photo Harrison)

1968 (23 Jan). *Chinese New Year ("Year of the Monkey"). T* **45** *and similar horiz design. W w* **12** *(sideways). P* 14.
245 10 c. gold, black and scarlet .. .. 1·00 15
246 $1.30, gold, black and scarlet .. .. 3·50 3·75
Design:—$1.30, Family of Rhesus Macaques.

47 *Iberia* (liner) at Ocean Terminal

(Des and litho D.L.R.)

1968 (24 Apr). *Sea Craft. T* **47** *and similar horiz designs. P* 13.
247 10 c. multicoloured 60 10
a. Dull orange and new blue omitted .. £300
248 20 c. cobalt-blue, black and brown .. .. 1·00 35
249 40 c. orange, black and mauve .. .. 2·50 3·50
250 50 c. orange-red, black and green .. .. 2·75 50
a. Green omitted £300
251 $1 greenish yellow, black and red .. .. 4·75 2·00
252 $1.30, Prussian blue, black and pink .. 6·00 1·75
247/52 .. .. .. *Set of* 6 16·00 7·00
Designs:—20 c. Pleasure launch; 40 c. Car ferry; 50 c. Passenger ferry; $1, Sampan; $1.30, Junk.

53 *Bauhinia blakeana*

54 Arms of Hong Kong

(Des V. Whiteley. Photo Harrison)

1968 (25 Sept)–**73**. *W w* **12**. *P* 14 × 14½.
(*a*) *Upright wmk. Chalk-surfaced paper*
253 53 65 c. multicoloured .. .. .. 1·75 20
a. Glazed ordinary paper (3.73) .. 15·00 3·75
254 54 $1 multicoloured .. .. .. 1·75 30
(*b*) *Sideways wmk. Glazed, ordinary paper*
254*a* 53 65 c. multicoloured (27.9.72) .. .. 12·00 3·75
254*b* 54 $1 multicoloured (13.12.71) .. .. 2·00 1·00
Nos. 253/4 exist with PVA gum as well as gum arabic; Nos. 254*a*/*b* with PVA gum only.

55 "Aladdin's Lamp" and Human Rights Emblem

(Des R. Granger Barrett. Litho B.W.)

1968 (20 Nov). *Human Rights Year. W w* **12** *(sideways). P* 13½.
255 55 10 c. orange, black and myrtle-green .. 25 10
256 50 c. yellow, black & dp reddish purple .. 45 80

56 Cockerel

(Des R. Granger Barrett. Photo Enschedé)

1969 (11 Feb). *Chinese New Year ("Year of the Cock"). T* **56** *and similar multicoloured design. P* 13 × 13½ *(10 c.) or* 13½ × 13 *($1.30).*
257 10 c. Type **56** .. .. 1·00 15
a. Red omitted .. .. .. 60·00
258 $1.30, Cockerel (*vert*) .. .. .. 7·50 4·00

58 Arms of Chinese University

59 Earth Station and Satellite

(Des V. Whiteley. Photo Govt Ptg Bureau, Tokyo)

1969 (26 Aug). *Establishment of Chinese University of Hong Kong. P* 13½.
259 58 40 c. violet, gold and pale turquoise-blue 50 60

(Des V. Whiteley. Photo Harrison)

1969 (24 Sept). *Opening of Communications Satellite Tracking Station. W w* **12**. *P* 14 × 14½.
260 59 $1 multicoloured .. .. .. 1·75 1·50

60 Chow's Head

62 "Expo 70" Emblem

(Des R. Granger Barrett. Photo D.L.R.)

1970 (28 Jan). *Chinese New Year ("Year of the Dog"). T* **60** *and similar design. W w* **12** *(sideways on $1.30). P* 14.
261 10 c. lemon-yellow, orange-brown and black .. 1·60 25
262 $1.30, multicoloured .. .. .. 10·00 3·50
Design: *Horiz*—$1.30, Chow standing.

(Des and litho B.W.)

1970 (14 Mar). *World Fair, Osaka. T* **62** *and similar multicoloured design. W w* **12** *(sideways on 25 c.). P* 13½ × 13 *(15 c.) or* 13 × 13½ *(25 c.).*
263 15 c. Type **62** 10 20
264 25 c. Expo '70 Emblem and Junks (*horiz*) .. 15 40

64 Plaque in Tung Wah Hospital

65 Symbol

(Des M. F. Griffith. Photo Harrison)

1970 (9 Apr). *Centenary of Tung Wah Hospital. W w* **12** *(sideways). P* 14.
265 64 10 c. multicoloured 10 10
266 50 c. multicoloured 15 30

(Des J. Cooter. Litho B.W.)

1970 (5 Aug). *Asian Productivity Year. W w* **12**. *P* 14 × 13½.
267 65 10 c. multicoloured 15 10

66 Pig

(Des Kan Tai-Keung. Photo Govt Ptg Bureau, Tokyo)

1971 (20 Jan). *Chinese New Year ("Year of the Pig"). P* 13½.
268 66 10 c. multicoloured .. .. .. 1·25 20
269 $1.30, multicoloured .. .. .. 4·25 3·75

67 "60" and Scout Badge 68 Festival Emblem

(Des Kan Tai-Keung. Litho Harrison)

1971 (23 July). *Diamond Jubilee of Scouting in Hong Kong.* W w **12** (*sideways*). P 14 × 14½.

No.	Type	Description	Unused	Used
270	**67**	10 c. black, scarlet and yellow	15	10
271		50 c. black, green and blue	80	45
272		$2 black, magenta and bluish violet	3·00	5·50
270/2		*Set of* 3	3·50	5·50

(Des Kan Tai-Keung. Litho J.W.)

1971 (2 Nov). *Hong Kong Festival. T* **68** *and similar designs.* W w **12** (*sideways on* 10 c. *and* 50 c.). P 13½ × 14 (10 c.) *or* 14 (*others*).

No.	Type	Description	Unused	Used
273	**68**	10 c. orange and purple	30	10
274	–	50 c. multicoloured	50	35
275	–	$1 multicoloured	1·40	2·00
273/5		*Set of* 3	2·00	2·25

Designs: *Horiz* (39 × 23 *mm*)—50 c. Coloured streamers. *Vert* (23 × 39 *mm*)—$1 "Orchid".

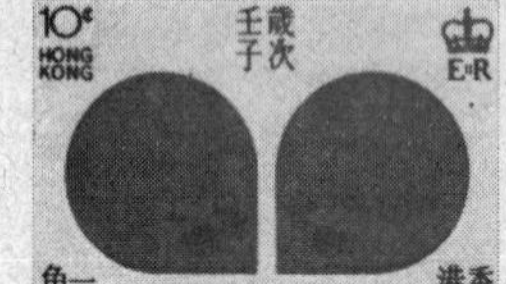

69 Stylised Rats

(Des Kan Tai-Keung. Photo D.L.R.)

1972 (8 Feb). *Chinese New Year ("Year of the Rat").* W w **12**. P 13½ × 13.

No.	Type	Description	Unused	Used
276	**69**	10 c. red, gold and black	30	10
277		$1.30, gold, red and black	3·50	3·25

70 Tunnel Entrance

(Des G. Drummond from painting by G. Baxter. Litho Harrison)

1972 (20 Oct). *Opening of Cross-Harbour Tunnel.* W w **12**. P 14 × 14½.

No.	Type	Description	Unused	Used
278	**70**	$1 multicoloured	1·75	1·50

71 Phoenix and Dragon 72 Ox

(Des (from photograph by D. Groves) and photo Harrison)

1972 (20 Nov). *Royal Silver Wedding.* W w **12**. P 14 × 14½.

No.	Type	Description	Unused	Used
279	**71**	10 c. multicoloured	10	10
		a. Gold omitted	£300	
280		50 c. multicoloured	45	40

(Des R. Granger Barrett. Photo Harrison)

1973 (25 Jan). *Chinese New Year ("Year of the Ox").* W w **12** (*sideways on* 10 c.). P 14.

No.	Type	Description	Unused	Used
281	**72**	10 c. reddish orange, brown and black	50	10
282	–	$1.30, lt yellow, yellow-orange & black	2·25	4·00

Design:—$1.30, similar to 10 c., but horiz.

73 Queen Elizabeth II 74

(Des from coinage. Photo ($10 and $20 also embossed) Harrison)

1973 (12 June). W w **12** (*sideways on* 15, 30, 40 *c.*, $1.30, 2, 5, 10, $20). P 14½ × 14 (*Nos.* 283/91) *or* 14 × 14½ (292/6).

No.	Type	Description	Unused	Used
283	**73**	10 c. bright orange	45	10
		a. Wmk sideways (from coils)	45	40
284		15 c. yellow-green	3·50	1·75
285		20 c. reddish violet	35	10
286		25 c. lake-brown	3·75	2·25
287		30 c. ultramarine	90	15
288		40 c. turquoise-blue	2·00	65
289		50 c. light orange-vermilion	90	15
290		65 c. greenish bistre	3·75	5·00
291		$1 bottle-green	2·00	25
292	**74**	$1.30, pale yellow and reddish violet	2·50	35
293		$2 pale green and reddish brown	3·25	50
294		$5 pink and royal blue	3·75	1·75
295		$10 pink and deep blackish olive	7·50	4·00
296		$20 pink and brownish black	14·00	15·00
283/96		*Set of* 14	42·00	29·00

Nos. 295/6 are known with embossing omitted, but it has been reported that such errors can be faked.

See also Nos. 311/24*c* and 340/53.

1973 (14 Nov). *Royal Wedding. As Nos.* 165/6 *of Anguilla, but additionally inscr in Chinese characters.*

No.	Type	Description	Unused	Used
297		50 c. ochre	25	15
298		$2 bright mauve	65	80

75 Festival Symbols forming Chinese Character

(Des Kan Tai-Keung. Litho B.W.)

1973 (23 Nov). *Hong Kong Festival. T* **75** *and similar horiz designs.* W w **12**. P 14.

No.	Type	Description	Unused	Used
299	**75**	10 c. brownish red and bright green	15	10
300	–	50 c. deep magenta and reddish orange	40	35
301	–	$1 bright green and deep mauve	90	1·60
299/301		*Set of* 3	1·25	1·75

Each value has the festival symbols arranged to form a Chinese character. "Hong" on the 10 c.; "Kong" on the 50 c.; "Festival" on the $1.

76 Tiger 77 Chinese Mask

(Des R. Granger Barrett. Litho Harrison)

1974 (8 Jan). *Chinese New Year ("Year of the Tiger").* W w **12** (*sideways on* $1.30). P 14.

No.	Type	Description	Unused	Used
302	**76**	10 c. multicoloured	1·00	10
303	–	$1.30, multicoloured	5·00	6·00

Design:—$1.30, Similar to T **76**, but vert.

(Des R. Hookham. Litho Enschedé)

1974 (1 Feb). *Arts Festival. Vert designs as T* **77** *showing Chinese opera masks.* W w **12** (*sideways*). P 12 × 12½.

No.	Type	Description	Unused	Used
304	**77**	10 c. multicoloured	40	10
305	–	$1 multicoloured	1·50	2·50
306	–	$2 multicoloured	1·75	3·00
304/6		*Set of* 3	3·25	5·00
MS307		159 × 94 mm. Nos. 304/6. Wmk upright. P 14 × 13	11·00	18·00

78 Pigeons with Letters

(Des Kan Tai-Keung. Litho Harrison)

1974 (9 Oct). *Centenary of Universal Postal Union. T* **78** *and similar horiz designs.* W w **12** (*sideways on* 10 *and* 50 *c.*). P 14.

No.	Type	Description	Unused	Used
308		10 c. light greenish blue, light yellow-green and slate-black	15	10
		a. No wmk	35·00	
309		50 c. deep mauve, orange and slate-black	30	25
310		$2 multicoloured	60	2·00
308/10		*Set of* 3	95	2·00

Designs:—50 c. Globe within letter; $2 Hands holding letters.

1975 (21 Jan)–**82**. *New values* (60, 70, 80 *and* 90 *c.*) *or as Nos.* 283/96 *but* W w **14** (*sideways on* 10, 20, 25, 50, 65 *c., and* $1).

No.	Type	Description	Unused	Used
311	**73**	10 c. bright orange (21.2.75)	35	10
		a. Wmk upright (from coils) (10.78)	50	70
312		15 c. yellow-green (21.1.75)	5·00	2·50
313	**73**	20 c. reddish violet (19.3.75)	15	10
		a. Deep reddish mauve (21.6.77)	30	10
		b. Deep reddish purple (22.6.79)	30	10
314		25 c. lake-brown (19.3.75)	5·00	3·00
315		30 c. ultramarine (9.4.75)	40	10
		a. Deep ultramarine (20.4.78)	60	15
316		40 c. turquoise-blue (19.3.75)	50	40
317		50 c. light orange-vermilion (19.3.75)	60	15
318		60 c. lavender (4.5.77)	65	40
319		65 c. greenish bistre (19.3.75)	6·00	5·50
320		70 c. yellow (4.5.77)	70	15
		a. Chrome-yellow (24.1.80)	80	25
321		80 c. bright magenta (4.5.77)	70	25
		a. Magenta (24.1.80)	90	30
321*b*		90 c. sepia (1.10.81)	3·25	80
322		$1 bottle-green (19.3.75)	1·75	30
		a. Blackish olive (24.1.80)	1·25	50
323	**74**	$1.30, pale yell & reddish vio (19.3.75)	1·40	30
324		$2 pale green & reddish brn (19.3.75)	1·50	60
		a. Pale green and brown (10.5.82)	1·75	60
324*b*		$5 pink and royal blue (20.4.78)	1·75	50
		ba. Pink & deep ultramarine (10.5.82)	2·75	90
324*c*		$10 pink & deep blackish olive (20.4.78)	2·00	2·00
324*d*		$20 pink and brownish black (20.4.78)	4·00	4·25
311/24*d*		*Set of* 18	30·00	19·00

Nos. 324*c*/*d* are known with the embossing omitted. See note after No. 296.

79 Stylized Hare

(Des Kan Tai-Keung. Litho Harrison)

1975 (5 Feb). *Chinese New Year ("Year of the Hare"). T* **79** *and similar horiz design.* P 14. (*a*) *No wmk.*

No.	Type	Description	Unused	Used
325	**79**	10 c. silver and light red	30	15
326	–	$1.30, gold and light green	3·00	4·00
		(*b*) W w **12**		
327	**79**	10 c. silver and light red	40	15
328	–	$1.30, gold and light green	3·00	4·00

Design:—$1.30, Pair of hares.

80 Queen Elizabeth II, the Duke of Edinburgh and Hong Kong Arms 81 Mid-Autumn Festival

(Des PAD Studio. Litho Questa)

1975 (30 Apr). *Royal Visit.* W w **14** (*sideways*). P 13½.

No.	Type	Description	Unused	Used
329	**80**	$1.30, multicoloured	1·25	1·75
330		$2 multicoloured	1·50	2·25

(Des Tao Ho. Litho De La Rue, Bogotá)

1975 (31 July). *Hong Kong Festivals of* 1975. *T* **81** *and similar vert designs. Multicoloured. No wmk.* P 13½ × 14.

No.	Type	Description	Unused	Used
331		50 c. Type **81**	50	20
332		$1 Dragon-boat Festival	1·25	2·00
333		$2 Tin Hau Festival	1·50	2·50
331/3		*Set of* 3	3·00	4·25
MS334		102 × 83 mm. Nos. 331/3	6·00	10·00

82 Hwamei 83 Dragon

(Des C. Kuan. Litho Harrison)

1975 (29 Oct). *Birds. T* **82** *and similar vert designs. Multicoloured.* W w **14**. P 14.

No.	Type	Description	Unused	Used
335		50 c. Type **82**	90	20
336		$1.30, Chinese Bulbul	3·25	3·50
337		$2 Black-capped Kingfisher	3·50	4·50
335/7		*Set of* 3	7·00	7·50

(Des Kan Tai-Keung. Litho Questa)

1976 (21 Jan). *Chinese New Year ("Year of the Dragon"). T* **83** *and similar horiz design.* W w **14** (*sideways*). P 14½.

No.	Type	Description	Unused	Used
338	**83**	20 c. mauve, dull lake and gold	35	10
339	–	$1.30, light yellow-green, lt red & gold	1·40	2·50

No. 339 is as T **83** but has the design reversed.

1976 (20 Feb–19 Mar). *As Nos.* 283, 285, 287 *and* 293/6 *but without wmk.*
340 **73** 10 c. bright orange (coil stamp) (19.3.76) 6·00 6·00
342 20 c. reddish violet .. .. 2·00 40
a. Imperf (pair) £275
344 30 c. ultramarine .. .. 2·75 70
350 **74** $2 pale green and reddish brown .. 5·00 2·75
351 $5 pink and royal blue.. .. .. 7·00 7·00
352 $10 pink and deep blackish olive (19.3.76) .. .. 23·00 18·00
353 $20 pink and brownish black (19.3.76) 48·00 32·00
340/53 .. .. *Set of* 7 80·00 60·00
No. 353 is known with the embossing omitted. See note after No. 296.

84 "60" and Girl Guides Badge

85 "Postal Services" in Chinese Characters

(Des P. Ma. Photo Harrison)

1976 (23 Apr). *Girl Guides Diamond Jubilee. T* **84** *and similar horiz design. Multicoloured. W w* **12.** *P* 14.
354 20 c. Type **84** 25 10
355 $1.30, Badge, stylised diamond and "60" .. 1·25 2·00

(Des Tao Ho. Litho Harrison)

1976 (11 Aug). *Opening of new G.P.O. T* **85** *and similar vert designs. W w* **14.** *P* 14.
356 20 c. yellow-green, lt greenish grey & black .. 15 10
357 $1.30, reddish orge, lt greenish grey & blk .. 60 1·00
358 $2 yellow, light greenish grey and black .. 80 1·75
356/8 .. .. *Set of* 3 1·40 2·50
Designs:—$1.30, Old G.P.O.; $2 New G.P.O.

86 Tree Snake on Branch

(Des Jennifer Wong. Litho J.W.)

1977 (6 Jan). *Chinese New Year ("Year of the Snake"). T* **86** *and similar horiz design. W w* **14** *(sideways). P* 13½.
359 **86** 20 c. multicoloured 35 10
360 – $1.30, multicoloured .. .. 2·25 3·50
The $1.30 shows a snake facing left.

87 Presentation of the Orb

88 Tram Cars

(Des Hong Kong Govt Services Dept; adapted J.W. Litho Harrison)

1977 (7 Feb). *Silver Jubilee. T* **87** *and similar multicoloured designs. W w* **14** *(sideways on $2). P* 14½ × 14 *($2) or* 14 × 14½ *(others).*
361 20 c. Type **78** 20 10
362 $1.30, Queen's visit, 1975 .. .. .. 70 1·10
363 $2 The Orb (*vert*) .. .. 80 1·10
361/3 .. .. *Set of* 3 1·50 2·00

(Des Tao Ho. Litho J.W.)

1977 (30 June). *Tourism. T* **88** *and similar vert designs. Multicoloured. W w* **14.** *P* 13½.
364 20 c. Type **88** 25 10
365 60 c. Star Ferryboat .. .. 70 1·00
366 $1.30, The Peak Railway .. .. .. 90 1·25
367 $2 Junk and sampan .. .. 1·10 1·50
364/7 .. .. *Set of* 4 2·75 3·50

89 Buttercup Orchid

90 Horse

(Des Beryl Walden. Litho Questa)

1977 (12 Oct). *Orchids. T* **89** *and similar vert designs. Multicoloured. W w* **14.** *P* 14.
368 20 c. Type **89** 45 10
369 $1.30, Lady's Slipper Orchid .. .. .. 1·25 1·50
370 $2 Susan Orchid .. .. 1·75 1·75
368/70 .. .. *Set of* 3 3·00 3·00

(Des Graphic Atelier Ltd, Hong Kong. Litho Harrison)

1978 (26 Jan). *Chinese New Year ("Year of the Horse"). W w* **14** *(sideways). P* 14½ × 14.
371 **90** 20 c. magenta, yellow-olive & brn-olive .. 20 10
372 $1.30, orange, yellow-brn & reddish brn 1·10 1·75

91 Queen Elizabeth II

92 Girl and Boy holding Hands

(Des G. Vasarhelyi. Litho Harrison)

1978 (2 June). *25th Anniv of Coronation. W w* **14.** *P* 14 × 14½.
373 **91** 20 c. magenta and ultramarine 15 10
374 $1.30, ultramarine and magenta .. 50 90

(Des Annette Walker. Litho Harrison)

1978 (8 Nov). *Centenary of Po Leung Kuk (child care organisation). T* **92** *and similar horiz design. Multicoloured. W w* **14** *(sideways). P* 14 × 14½.
375 20 c. Type **92** 10 10
376 $1.30, Ring of children 50 75

93 Electronics Industry

94 *Precis orithya orithya*

(Litho Harrison)

1979 (9 Jan). *Industries. T* **93** *and similar horiz designs. W w* **14** *(sideways). P* 14½.
377 20 c. orange-yellow, olive-yellow & yell-olive 10 10
378 $1.30, multicoloured 60 90
379 $2 multicoloured 60 95
377/9 .. .. *Set of* 3 1·25 1·75
Designs:—$1.30, Toy industry; $2, Garment industry.

(Des Jane Thatcher. Photo Harrison)

1979 (20 June). *Butterflies. T* **94** *and similar vert designs. Multicoloured. No wmk. P* 14.
380 20 c. Type **94** 30 10
381 $1 *Graphium sarpedon sarpedon* 60 70
382 $1.30, *Heliophorus epicles phoenicoparyphus* 75 1·00
383 $2 *Danus genutia genutia* .. .. .. 1·00 2·00
380/3 .. .. *Set of* 4 2·40 3·50

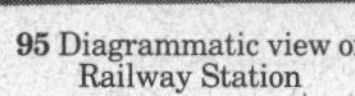

HONG KONG
香港
20¢

95 Diagrammatic view of Railway Station

96 Tsui Shing Lau Pagoda

(Des Tao Ho. Litho J.W.)

1979 (1 Oct). *Mass Transit Railway. T* **95** *and similar horiz designs. Multicoloured. W w* **14** *(sideways). P* 13½.
384 20 c. Type **95** 15 10
385 $1.30, Diagrammatic view of car 50 50
386 $2 Plan showing route of railway 60 70
384/6 .. .. *Set of* 3 1·10 1·10

(Des D. Leonard. Litho J.W.)

1980 (14 May). *Rural Architecture. T* **96** *and similar designs. W w* 14 *(sideways on $1.30 and $2). P* 13 × 13½ *(20 c.) or* 13½ × 13 *(others).*
387 20 c. black, magenta and yellow 10 10
388 $1.30, multicoloured 60 85
389 $2 multicoloured .. .. 75 1·40
387/9 .. .. *Set of* 3 1·25 2·00
Designs: *Horiz*—$1.30, Village House, Sai O; $2, Ching Chung Koon Temple.

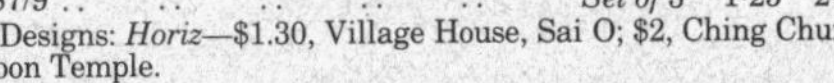

97 Queen Elizabeth the Queen Mother

98 Botanical Gardens

(Des Harrison. Litho Questa)

1980 (4 Aug). *80th Birthday of Queen Elizabeth the Queen Mother. W w* **14** *(sideways). P* 14.
390 **97** $1.30, multicoloured 55 70

(Des D. Chan. Litho J.W.)

1980 (12 Nov). *Parks. T* **98** *and similar vert designs. Multicoloured. W w* **14.** *P* 13½.
391 20 c. Type **98** 10 10
392 $1 Ocean Park 30 40
393 $1.30, Kowloon Park 40 65
394 $2 Country Parks .. .. 55 1·00
391/4 .. .. *Set of* 4 1·25 2·00

HONG KONG
香港
20c

99 *Epinephelus akaara*

100 Wedding Bouquet from Hong Kong

(Des Jane Thatcher. Litho J.W.)

1981 (28 Jan). *Fishes. T* **99** *and similar horiz designs. Multicoloured. W w* **14** *(sideways). P* 13½.
395 20 c. Type **99** 10 10
396 $1 *Nemipterus virgatus* 40 40
397 $1.30, *Choerodon azurio* 45 50
398 $2 *Scarus ghobban* 55 75
395/8 .. .. *Set of* 4 1·25 1·50

(Des J.W. Photo Harrison)

1981 (29 July). *Royal Wedding. T* **100** *and similar vert designs. Multicoloured. W w* **14** *(sideways). P* 14.
399 20 c. Type **100** 10 10
400 $1.30, Prince Charles in Hong Kong .. 35 35
401 $5 Prince Charles and Lady Diana Spencer 1·25 1·25
399/401 .. .. *Set of* 3 1·50 1·50

101 Suburban Development

102 "Victoria from the Harbour, *c* 1855"

(Des Tao Ho. Litho J.W.)

1981 (14 Oct). *Public Housing. T* **101** *and similar vert designs showing suburban development. W w* **14** *(inverted on No.* **MS**406*). P* 13½.
402 20 c. multicoloured 10 10
a. Red (jacket and trousers) omitted .. 70·00
403 $1 multicoloured 25 30
404 $1.30, multicoloured 35 40
405 $2 multicoloured 50 60
402/5 .. .. *Set of* 4 1·10 1·25
MS406 148 × 105 mm. Nos. 402/5 .. .. 1·50 2·25

(Des R. Solley. Litho Questa)

1982 (5 Jan). *Port of Hong Kong, Past and Present. T* **102** *and similar horiz designs. Multicoloured. W w* **14.** *P* 14½.
407 20 c. Type **102** 15 10
408 $1 "West Point, Hong Kong, 1847" 45 45
409 $1.30, Fleet of Junks 60 65
410 $2 Liner *Queen Elizabeth 2* at Hong Kong .. 80 1·25
407/10 .. .. *Set of* 4 1·75 2·25

NEW INFORMATION

The editor is always interested to correspond with people who have new information that will improve or correct the Catalogue.

103 Large Indian Civet

(Des Karen Phillipps. Litho Harrison)

1982 (4 May). *Wild Animals. T* **103** *and similar horiz designs. W* w **14** *(sideways). P* 14½.
411 20 c. black, salmon-pink and olive-bistre .. 15 10
412 $1 multicoloured 50 60
413 $1.30, black, emerald and yellow-orange .. 60 75
414 $5 black, orange-brown and greenish yellow 1·25 2·00
411/14 .. .. *Set of* 4 2·25 3·00
Designs:—$1 Chinese Pangolin; $1.30, Chinese Porcupine; $5 Indian Muntjac ("Barking Deer").

104 Queen Elizabeth II 105

(Des and photo ($5 to $50 also embossed) Harrison)

1982 (30 Aug). *W* w **14** *(sideways on Nos.* 427/30). *P* 14½ × 14 *(Nos.* 415/26) *or* 14 × 14½ *(others).*
415 **104** 10 c. bright carmine, carmine and lemon 30 10
416 20 c. bluish violet, violet and lavender .. 35 10
417 30 c. bluish violet, violet and salmon .. 40 10
418 40 c. vermilion and pale blue 50 10
419 50 c. chestnut, orange-brn & sage-green 60 10
420 60 c. bright purple and brownish grey .. 90 30
421 70 c. dp grey-grn, myrtle-grn & orge-yell 95 15
422 80 c. bistre-brown, lt brown & sage-grn 1·00 30
423 90 c. bottle-green, deep grey-green and pale turquoise-green .. .. 1·25 20
424 $1 reddish orge, red-orge & pale rose .. 1·25 20
425 $1.30, turquoise-blue and mauve .. 1·75 30
426 $2 ultramarine and flesh .. .. 2·00 50
427 **105** $5 dp magenta, brt purple & olive-yell 3·00 1·50
428 $10 sepia and grey-brown .. .. 3·50 3·00
429 $20 deep claret and pale blue .. .. 7·00 8·50
430 $50 deep claret and brownish grey .. 11·00 17·00
415/30 .. .. *Set of* 16 32·00 29·00
Nos. 415/30 come with a fluorescent security marking, "Hong Kong" in Chinese characters encircled by the same in English, printed over the central oval of the design.
Nos. 415 and 424 also exist from coils.
No. 428 is known with the embossing omitted. See note after No. 296.
For similar stamps without watermark see Nos. 471/87.

106 Table Tennis 107 Dancing

(Des A. Wong. Litho J.W.)

1982 (20 Oct). *Sport for the Disabled. T* **106** *and similar horiz designs. Multicoloured. W* w **14**. *P* 14 × 14½.
431 30 c. Type **106** 20 10
432 $1 Racing 35 40
433 $1.30, Basketball 45 60
434 $5 Archery .. .. 1·25 2·00
431/4 .. .. *Set of* 4 2·00 2·75

(Des Tao Ho. Litho J.W.)

1983 (26 Jan). *Performing Arts. T* **107** *and similar vert designs. W* w **14** *(sideways). P* 14.
435 30 c. cobalt and deep grey-blue 20 10
436 $1.30, rose and brown-purple 50 60
437 $5 bright green and deep green .. .. 1·40 2·25
435/7 .. .. *Set of* 3 1·90 2·75
Designs:—$1.30, "Theatre"; $5 "Music".

108 Aerial View of Hong Kong

(Des local artist. Litho Enschedé)

1983 (14 Mar). *Commonwealth Day. T* **108** *and similar horiz designs. Multicoloured. W* w **14** *(sideways). P* 14 × 13.
438 30 c. Type **108** 20 10
439 $1 *Liverpool Bay* (container ship) .. 45 60
440 $1.30, Hong Kong flag 55 70
441 $5 Queen Elizabeth II and Hong Kong .. 1·25 2·00
438/41 .. .. *Set of* 4 2·25 3·00

109 Victoria Harbour

(Des Tao Ho. Litho Harrison)

1983 (17 Aug). *Hong Kong by Night. T* **109** *and similar horiz designs. Multicoloured. W* w **14** *(sideways). P* 14.
442 30 c. Type **109** 20 10
443 $1 Space Museum, Tsim Sha Tsui Cultural Centre 55 70
444 $1.30, Fireworks display 65 80
a. Silver (value and inscr) omitted ..
445 $5 *Jumbo*, floating restaurant .. .. 1·75 2·50
a. Silver (value and inscr) omitted ..
442/5 .. .. *Set of* 4 2·75 3·75

110 Old and New Observatory Buildings

(Des C. Shun Wah. Litho Harrison)

1983 (23 Nov). *Centenary of Hong Kong Observatory. T* **110** *and similar horiz designs. W* w **14** *(sideways). P* 14½ × 14.
446 40 c. yellow-orange, bistre-brown and black .. 30 10
447 $1 reddish mauve, deep mauve and black .. 55 70
448 $1.30, new blue, steel-blue and black .. 65 80
449 $5 olive-yellow, brown-olive and black .. 1·75 2·50
446/9 .. .. *Set of* 4 3·00 3·75
Designs:—$1 Wind-measuring equipment; $1.30, Thermometer; $5 Ancient and modern seismometers.

111 "DH 86" *Dorado* (Hong Kong-Penang Service, 1936)

(Des M. Harris. Litho J.W.)

1984 (7 Mar). *Aviation in Hong Kong. T* **111** *and similar multi-coloured designs. W* w **14** *(sideways on* 40 c. *to* $1.30, *inverted on* $5). *P* 13½.
450 40 c. Type **111** 30 10
451 $1 Sikorsky "S-42B" (San Francisco-Hong Kong Service, 1937) 55 70
452 $1.30, Cathay-Pacific "Jumbo" jet leaving Kai Tak Airport 65 80
453 $5 Baldwin brothers' balloon, 1891 *(vert)* .. 1·75 2·75
450/3 .. .. *Set of* 4 3·00 4·00

112 Map by Capt E. Belcher, 1836

(Des R. Solley. Litho B.D.T.)

1984 (21 June). *Maps of Hong Kong. T* **112** *and similar horiz designs. Multicoloured. W* w **14** *(sideways). P* 14.
454 40 c. Type **112** 35 15
455 $1 Bartholomew map of 1929 .. .. 55 60
456 $1.30, Early map of Hong Kong waters .. 65 75
457 $5 Chinese-style map of 1819 .. .. 1·75 2·75
454/7 .. .. *Set of* 4 3·00 3·75

113 Cockerel

(Des J. Yim. Litho Cartor, France)

1984 (6 Sept). *Chinese Lanterns. T* **113** *and similar horiz designs showing stylised animals as lanterns. Multicoloured. W* w **14** *(sideways). P* 13½ × 13.
458 40 c. Type **113** 20 15
459 $1 Dog 35 50
460 $1.30, Butterfly 40 60
461 $5 Fish .. .. 1·40 2·50
458/61 .. .. *Set of* 4 2·10 3·25

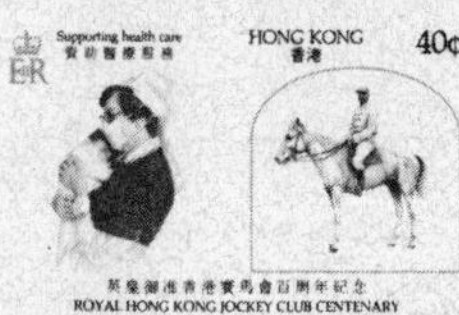

114 Jockey on Horse and Nurse with Baby ("Health Care")

(Des M. Harris. Litho Walsall)

1984 (21 Nov). *Centenary of Royal Hong Kong Jockey Club. T* **114** *and similar horiz designs showing aspects of Club's charity work. Multicoloured. W* w **14** *(sideways). P* 14½.
462 40 c. Type **114** 20 15
463 $1 Disabled man playing handball ("Support for Disabled") 40 55
464 $1.30, Ballerina ("The Arts") 45 65
465 $5 Humboldt Penguins ("Ocean Park") .. 1·75 2·50
462/5 .. .. *Set of* 4 2·50 3·50
MS466 178 × 98 mm. Nos. 462/5 .. .. 2·50 4·00

115 Hung Sing Temple

(Des M. Harris. Litho J.W.)

1985 (14 Mar). *Historic Buildings. T* **115** *and similar horiz designs. Multicoloured. P* 13½.
467 40 c. Type **115** 20 15
468 $1 St. John's Cathedral 40 55
469 $1.30, The Old Supreme Court Building .. 50 65
470 $5 Wan Chai Post Office .. .. .. 1·60 2·50
467/70 .. .. *Set of* 4 2·50 3·50

1985 (13 June)–**87**. *As Nos.* 415/16, 418/30 *and new value* ($1.70). *No wmk. P* 14½ × 14 (10 *c. to* $2) *or* 14 × 14½ *(others).*
471 **104** 10 c. brt carm, carm & lemon (23.10.85) 15 15
472 20 c. bluish violet, vio & lavender (6.87) 90 1·25
474 40 c. vermilion and pale blue (23.10.85).. 30 15
475 50 c. chestnut orange-brown and sage-green (23.10.85) 30 15
476 60 c. brt purple & brnish grey (23.10.85) 55 25
477 70 c. deep grey-green, myrtle-green and orange-yellow (23.10.85) 60 20
478 80 c. bistre-brown, light brown and sage-green (23.10.85) 65 35
479 90 c. bottle-green, deep grey-green and pale turquoise-green (23.10.85) .. 70 30
480 $1 reddish orange, red-orange and pale rose (23.10.85) 75 30
481 $1.30, turquoise-blue and mauve .. 90 35
482 $1.70, dull ultramarine, bright blue and bright green (2.9.85) .. .. 1·00 60
483 $2 ultramarine and flesh (23.10.85) .. 1·25 60
484 **105** $5 deep magenta, bright purple and olive-yellow (23.10.85) .. .. 2·00 1·50
485 $10 sepia and grey-brown (23.10.85) .. 2·50 2·50
486 $20 deep claret and pale blue (23.10.85) 3·00 4·00
487 $50 dp claret & brownish grey (23.10.85) 10·00 14·00
471/87 .. .. *Set of* 16 23·00 24·00

116 Prow of Dragon Boat

117 The Queen Mother with Prince Charles and Prince William, 1984

(Des R. Hookham. Litho Cartor S.A., France)

1985 (19 June). *10th International Dragon Boat Festival. T* **116** *and similar horiz designs showing different parts of dragon boat. Multicoloured. P* 13½ × 13.
488 40 c. Type **116** 20 15
489 $1 Drummer and rowers 30 45
490 $1.30, Rowers 35 55
491 $5 Stern of boat .. .. 1·25 2·00
488/91 .. .. *Set of* 4 1·90 2·75
MS492 190 × 100 mm. Nos. 488/91. P 13 × 12 .. 1·90 2·75

(Des C. Abbott. Litho Questa)

1985 (7 Aug). *Life and Times of Queen Elizabeth the Queen Mother. T* **117** *and similar vert designs. Multicoloured. P* 14½×14.

493 40 c. At Glamis Castle, aged 9 .. .. 25 10
494 $1 Type **117** 45 35
495 $1.30, The Queen Mother, 1970 (from photo by Cecil Beaton) 50 50
496 $5 With Prince Henry at his christening (from photo by Lord Snowdon) .. .. 1·10 1·50
493/6 .. .. *Set of* 4 2·10 2·25

118 Melastoma

(Des N. Jesse. Litho B.D.T.)

1985 (25 Sept). *Native Flowers. T* **118** *and similar horiz designs. Multicoloured. P* 13½.

497 40 c. Type **118** 40 15
498 50 c. Chinese Lily 40 20
499 60 c. Grantham's Camellia 40 25
500 $1.30, Narcissus 60 50
501 $1.70, Bauhinia 70 75
502 $5 Chinese New Year Flower .. .. 1·40 2·50
497/502 .. .. *Set of* 6 3·50 4·00

119 Hong Kong Academy for Performing Arts

(Des N. Jesse. Litho Format)

1985 (27 Nov). *New Buildings. T* **119** *and similar multi-coloured designs. P* 15.

503 50 c. Type **119** 30 15
504 $1.30, Exchange Square (*vert*) 55 35
505 $1.70, Hong Kong Bank Headquarters (*vert*) 75 65
506 $5 Hong Kong Coliseum .. .. .. 1·40 1·40
503/6 .. .. *Set of* 4 2·75 2·25

120 Halley's Comet in the Solar System

(Des A. Chan. Litho Cartor S.A., France)

1986 (26 Feb). *Appearance of Halley's Comet. T* **120** *and similar horiz designs. Multicoloured. P* 13½×13.

507 50 c. Type **120** 20 15
508 $1.30, Edmond Halley and Comet 35 45
509 $1.70, Comet over Hong Kong 40 60
510 $5 Comet passing the Earth .. .. 1·25 2·25
507/10 .. .. *Set of* 4 2·00 3·00
MS511 135×80 mm. Nos. 507/10 .. .. 2·00 3·25

(Des A. Theobald. Litho Harrison)

1986 (21 Apr). *60th Birthday of Queen Elizabeth II. Vert designs as T* **110** *of Ascension. Multicoloured. P* 14½×14.

512 50 c. At wedding of Miss Celia Bowes-Lyon, 1931 .. .. 20 10
513 $1 Queen in Garter procession, Windsor Castle, 1977 .. .. 30 25
514 $1.30, In Hong Kong, 1975 .. .. .. 35 30
515 $1.70, At Royal Lodge, Windsor, 1980 (from photo by Norman Parkinson) .. 35 35
516 $5 At Crown Agents Head Office, London, 1983 .. .. 85 1·10
512/16 .. .. *Set of* 5 1·90 1·90

121 Train, Airliner and Map of World

(Des Agay Ng Kee Chuen. Litho B.D.T.)

1986 (18 July). *"Expo '86" World Fair, Vancouver. T* **121** *and similar horiz designs. Multicoloured. P* 13½.

517 50 c. Type **121** 25 15
518 $1.30, Hong Kong Bank Headquarters and map of world 50 35
519 $1.70, Container ship and map of world .. 70 55
520 $5 Dish aerial and map of world .. .. 1·75 1·75
517/20 .. .. *Set of* 4 3·00 2·50

122 Hand-liner Sampan

123 "The Second Puan Khequa" (attr Spoilum)

(Des Graphic Communications Ltd. Litho B.D.T.)

1986 (24 Sept). *Fishing Vessels. T* **122** *and similar horiz designs, each showing fishing boat and outline of fish. Multicoloured. P* 13½.

521 50 c. Type **122** 20 10
522 $1.30, Stern trawler 50 35
523 $1.70, Long liner junk 70 60
524 $5 Junk trawler .. .. 1·75 1·75
521/4 .. .. *Set of* 4 2·75 2·50

(Des R. Solley. Litho B.D.T.)

1986 (9 Dec). *19th-century Hong Kong Portraits. T* **123** *and similar vert designs. Multicoloured. P* 14×13½.

525 50 c. Type **123** 20 10
526 $1.30, "Chinese Lady" (19th-century copy) 50 40
527 $1.70, "Lamqua" (self-portrait) 60 50
528 $5 "Wife of Wo Hing Qua" (attr G. Chinnery) .. .. 1·75 1·75
525/8 .. .. *Set of* 4 2·75 2·50

MACHINE LABELS. A single machine operated at the G.P.O. from 30 December 1986 issuing 10, 50 c., $1.30 and $1.70 labels, each inscribed "O1". The original design depicted a carp, but this was changed to a rabbit on 18 August 1987 when a second machine was installed at Tsim Sha Tsui post office which issues labels coded "O2".

It is the intention that the label design should change each year to reflect the Chinese calendar and labels showing a dragon were provided for both machines from 1 September 1988. For this third series the values were 10 c., 60 c., $1.40 and $1.80.

The same face values were used for the Year of the Snake labels, introduced on 24 February 1989. These showed an amended overall background pattern.

124 Rabbit

(Des Kan Tai-Keung. Litho B.D.T.)

1987 (21 Jan). *Chinese New Year ("Year of the Rabbit"). T* **124** *and similar horiz designs showing stylized rabbits. P* 13½.

529 50 c. multicoloured 20 10
530 $1.30, multicoloured 35 30
531 $1.70, multicoloured 40 35
532 $5 multicoloured .. .. 1·00 1·10
529/32 .. .. *Set of* 4 1·75 1·75
MS533 133×84 mm. Nos. 529/32 .. .. 1·75 2·50

Nos. 530/1 have the "0" omitted from their face values.

125 "Village Square, Hong Kong Island, 1838" (Auguste Borget)

126 Queen Elizabeth II and Central Victoria

(Des J. Yim. Litho B.D.T.)

1987 (23 Apr). *19th-century Hong Kong Scenes. T* **125** *and similar horiz designs. Multicoloured. P* 14.

534 50 c. Type **125** 25 10
535 $1.30, "Boat Dwellers, Kowloon Bay, 1838" (Auguste Borget) 45 25
536 $1.70, "Flagstaff House, 1846" (Murdoch Bruce) 55 35
537 $5 "Wellington Street, late 19th-century" (C. Andrasi) .. .. 1·00 1·25
534/7 .. .. *Set of* 4 2·00 1·75

Two types of Nos. 538/52.

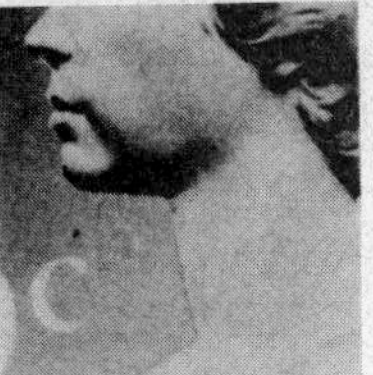

I. Heavy shading under mouth and cheek

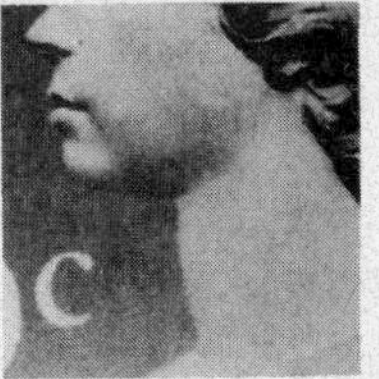

II. Lighter shading

(Des W. Hookham. Litho Leigh-Mardon Ltd, Melbourne)

1987 (13 July)–**88**. *T* **126** *and similar vert designs, each showing Queen Elizabeth II and Hong Kong skyline. P* 14½×14 (10 c. to $2) *or* 14 ($5 to $50). A. *Shading as Type* I. B. *Shading as Type* II (1.9.88).

No.	Type	Value	A		B	
538	126	10 c. multicoloured	15	15	15	15
539		40 c. multicoloured	25	15	25	15
540		50 c. multicoloured	25	15	25	15
541		60 c. multicoloured	25	20	25	15
542		70 c. multicoloured	30	20	30	20
543		80 c. multicoloured	30	20	30	20
544		90 c. multicoloured	40	25	40	25
545		$1 multicoloured	40	20	40	25
546		$1.30, multicoloured	50	30	50	25
546c		$1.40, multicoloured	†		55	35
547		$1.70, multicoloured	60	40	60	30
547c		$1.80, multicoloured	†		60	50
548		$2 multicoloured	60	40	60	30
549	–	$5 multicoloured	1·00	85	1·00	70
550	–	$10 multicoloured	1·75	1·75	1·75	1·50
551	–	$20 multicoloured	3·00	3·50	3·00	2·75
552	–	$50 multicoloured	7·50	9·00	7·50	8·00
538A/52A		*Set of* 15	16·00	16·00	†	
538B/52B		*Set of* 17	†		17·00	14·50

Designs (25×31 *mm*): $5 Kowloon; $10 Victoria Harbour; $20 Legislative Council Building; $50 Government House.

Nos. 538/52 carry the fluorescent security markings as described beneath Nos. 415/30 with the $5 to $50 values showing an additional vertical fluorescent bar at right.

For these stamps as Type II, but with imprint dates, see Nos. 600/15.

127 Hong Kong Flag

128 Alice Ho Miu Ling Nethersole Hospital, 1887

(Des R. Hookham. Photo Enschedé)

1987 (13 July)–**89**. *Coil Stamps. T* **127** *and similar vert design. P* 14½×14. A. *Without imprint date.* B. *With imprint date* "1989" (1.8.89).

No.	Value	A		B	
553	10 c. multicoloured	15	15	10	10
554	50 c. bistre, lake and black	30	30	10	10

Design:—50 c. Map of Hong Kong.

Nos. 553/4 carry the fluorescent security marking as described beneath Nos. 415/30.

The 1989 printing has every fifth stamp in the roll of 1,000 numbered on the reverse.

(Des A. Fung. Litho Walsall)

1987 (8 Sept). *Hong Kong Medical Centenaries. T* **128** *and similar horiz designs. Multicoloured. P* 14½.

555 50 c. Type **128** 15 10
556 $1.30, Matron and nurses, Nethersole Hospital, 1891 .. .. 25 25
557 $1.70, Scanning equipment, Faculty of Medicine 30 30
558 $5 Nurse and patient, Faculty of Medicine 80 1·00
555/8 .. .. *Set of* 4 1·40 1·50

129 Casual Dress with Fringed Hem, 220–589

(Des Sumiko Davies. Litho CPE Australia Ltd, Melbourne)

1987 (18 Nov). *Historical Chinese Costumes. T* **129** *and similar horiz designs. Multicoloured. P* 13½.

559 50 c. Type **129** 15 10
560 $1.30, Two-piece dress and wrap, 581–960 25 25
561 $1.70, Formal dress, Song Dynasty, 960–1279 .. .. 30 30
562 $5 Manchu empress costume, 1644–1911 .. 80 1·00
559/62 .. .. *Set of* 4 1·25 1·50

MINIMUM PRICE

The minimum price quote is 10p which represents a handling charge rather than a basis for valuing common stamps. For further notes about prices see introductory pages.

130 Dragon

131 White-breasted Kingfisher

(Des Kan Tai-Keung. Litho CPE Australia Ltd, Melbourne)

1988 (27 Jan). *Chinese New Year ("Year of the Dragon"). T* **130** *and similar horiz designs showing dragons. P* 13½.

563	50 c. multicoloured	15	10
564	$1.30, multicoloured	25	35
565	$1.70, multicoloured	30	45
566	$5 multicoloured	80	1·25
563/6	*Set of* 4	1·40	2·00
MS567	134×88 mm. Nos. 563/6	1·40	2·25

(Des Karen Phillipps. Litho CPE Australia Ltd, Melbourne)

1988 (20 Apr). *Hong Kong Birds. T* **131** *and similar vert designs. Multicoloured. P* 13½.

568	50 c. Type **131**	15	10
569	$1.30, Fukien Niltava	30	25
570	$1.70, Black Kite	35	30
571	$5 Pied Kingfisher	85	1·00
568/71	*Set of* 4	1·50	1·50

132 Chinese Banyan

133 Lower Terminal, Peak Tramway

(Des A. Chan. Litho B.D.T.)

1988 (16 June). *Trees of Hong Kong. T* **132** *and similar vert designs. Multicoloured. P* 13½.

572	50 c. Type **132**	15	10
573	$1.30, Hong Kong Orchid Tree	25	25
574	$1.70, Cotton Tree	30	30
575	$5 Schima	80	90
572/5	*Set of* 4	1·25	1·40
MS576	135×85 mm. Nos. 572/5	1·40	1·75

(Des Lilian Tang. Litho Leigh-Mardon Ltd, Melbourne)

1988 (4 Aug). *Centenary of The Peak Tramway. T* **133** *and similar vert designs. Multicoloured. P* 14½×15.

577	50 c. Type **133**	15	10
578	$1.30, Tram on incline	25	45
579	$1.70, Peak Tower Upper Terminal	30	45
580	$5 Tram	80	1·00
577/80	*Set of* 4	1·25	1·75
MS581	160×90 mm. Nos. 577/80	1·40	2·00

134 Hong Kong Catholic Cathedral

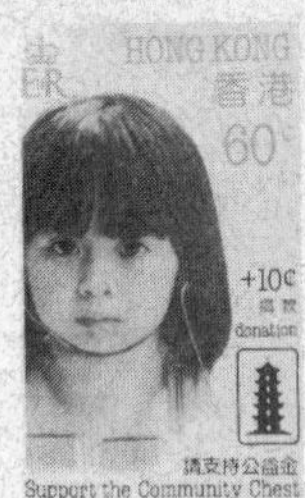

135 Deaf Girl

(Des C. Buendia. Litho CPE Australia Ltd, Melbourne)

1988 (30 Sept). *Centenary of Hong Kong Catholic Cathedral. P* 14.

582 **134**	60 c. multicoloured	15	15

(Des M. Tucker. Litho Harrison)

1988 (30 Nov). *Community Chest Charity. T* **135** *and similar vert designs. P* 14½.

583	60 c. + 10 c. brownish black, vermilion and greenish blue	15	15
584	$1.40 + 20 c. brownish black, vermilion and bright green	25	30
585	$1.80 + 30 c. brownish black, vermilion and bright orange	30	35
586	$5 + $1 brownish blk, verm and yell-brn	90	95
583/6	*Set of* 4	1·40	1·50

Designs:—$1.40, Elderly woman; $1.80, Blind boy using braille typewriter; $5 Mother and baby.

136 Snake

137 Girl and Doll

(Des Kan Tai-keung. Litho Enschedé)

1989 (18 Jan). *Chinese New Year ("Year of the Snake"). T* **136** *and similar horiz designs. Multicoloured. P* 13½ × 14.

587	60 c. Type **136**	10	15
	a. Booklet pane. Nos. 587 and 589, each ×5	1·75	
588	$1.40, Snake and fish	20	25
589	$1.80, Snake on branch	25	30
590	$5 Coiled snake	75	80
587/90	*Set of* 4	1·10	1·40
MS591	135×85 mm. Nos. 587/90	1·25	1·50

(Des M. Tucker. Litho B.D.T.)

1989 (4 May). *Cheung Chau Bun Festival. T* **137** *and similar vert designs. Multicoloured. P* 13½.

592	60 c. Type **137**	15	15
593	$1.40, Girl in festival costume	30	30
594	$1.80, Paper effigy of god Taai Si Wong	45	45
595	$5 Floral gateway	1·00	1·10
592/5	*Set of* 4	1·75	1·75

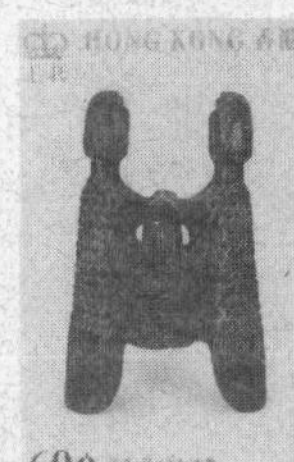

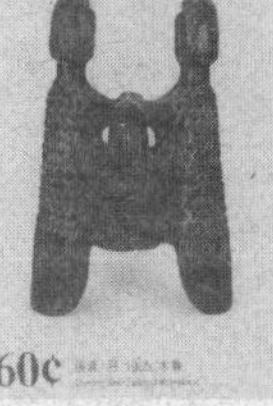

138 "Twins" (wood carving, Cheung Yee)

139 Lunar New Year Festivities

(Des Kan Tai-keung. Litho Enschedé)

1989 (19 July). *Modern Art. T* **138** *and similar vert designs. Multicoloured. P* 12×12½.

596	60 c. Type **138**	15	15
597	$1.40, "Figures" (acrylic on paper, Chan Luis)	30	30
598	$1.80, "Lotus" (copper sculpture, Van Lau)	45	45
599	$5 "Zen Painting" (ink and colour on paper, Lui Shou-kwan)	1·00	1·10
596/9	*Set of* 4	1·75	1·75

1989 (1 Aug). *As Nos.* 538B/46cB *and* 547cB/52B, *but with "1989" date added to designs. P* 14½×14 (10 *c. to* $2) *or* 14 ($5 *to* $50).

600	**126**	10 c. multicoloured	10	10
601		40 c. multicoloured	10	10
602		50 c. multicoloured	10	10
603		60 c. multicoloured	10	10
604		70 c. multicoloured	10	10
605		80 c. multicoloured	10	10
606		90 c. multicoloured	10	15
607		$1 multicoloured	15	20
608		$1.30, multicoloured	20	25
609		$1.40, multicoloured	20	25
610		$1.80, multicoloured	25	30
611		$2 multicoloured	30	35
612	–	$5 multicoloured	70	75
613	–	$10 multicoloured	1·40	1·50
614	–	$20 multicoloured	2·75	3·00
615	–	$50 multicoloured	7·25	7·50
600/15		*Set of* 16	12·50	13·50

(Des Sumiko Davies. Litho Enschedé)

1989 (6 Sept). *Hong Kong People. T* **139** *and similar vert designs. Multicoloured. P* 13×14½.

616	60 c. Type **139**	10	10
617	$1.40, Shadow boxing and horse racing	20	25
618	$1.80, Foreign-exchange dealer and traditional builder	30	35
619	$5 Multi-racial society	80	85
616/19	*Set of* 4	1·25	1·40

140 University of Science and Technology

(Des I. Leung. Litho CPE Australia Ltd, Melbourne)

1989 (5 Oct). *Building for the Future. T* **140** *and similar square designs. P* 13.

620	60 c. blue-black, orange-yellow & yellow-brn	10	10
621	70 c. black, pale rose and rose	10	15
622	$1.30, black, brt yellow-green & blue-grn	20	25
623	$1.40, black, azure and bright blue	20	25
624	$1.80, brownish black, pale turquoise-green and turquoise-blue	30	35
625	$5 agate, pale red-orange and orange-red	80	85
620/5	*Set of* 6	1·50	1·60

Designs:—70 c. Cultural Centre; $1.30, Eastern Harbour motorway interchange; $1.40, New Bank of China Building; $1.80, Convention and Exhibition Centre; $5 Light Rail Transit train.

141 Prince and Princess of Wales and Hong Kong Skyline

142

(Des Ng Kee-chuen. Litho Leigh-Mardon Ltd, Melbourne)

1989 (8 Nov). *Royal Visit. T* **141** *and similar vert designs, each showing portrait and different view. Multicoloured. W* **142** *(sideways). P* 14½.

626	60 c. Type **141**	10	10
627	$1.40, Princess of Wales	20	25
628	$1.80, Prince of Wales	30	35
629	$5 Prince and Princess of Wales in evening dress	80	85
626/9	*Set of* 4	1·25	1·40
MS630	128×75 mm. No. 629	80	85

143 Horse

(Des Kan Tai-Keung. Litho Enschedé)

1990 (23 Jan). *Chinese New Year ("Year of the Horse"). T* **143** *and similar horiz designs. P* 13½×12½.

631	60 c. multicoloured	10	10
	a. Booklet pane. Nos. 631 and 633, each×3	1·25	
632	$1.40, multicoloured	20	25
633	$1.80, multicoloured	30	35
634	$5 multicoloured	80	85
631/4	*Set of* 4	1·25	1·40
MS635	135×85 mm. Nos. 631/4	1·40	1·50

POSTAGE DUE STAMPS

PRINTERS. Nos. D1/23 were typographed by De La Rue & Co.

D 1 Post-office Scales

D 2

1923 (Dec)–**56.** *Wmk Mult Script CA. P* 14.

D1	D 1	1 c. brown, O	90	65
		a. Wmk sideways (1931)	90	1·25
		b. Chalk-surfaced paper, wmk sideways (21.3.56)	15	70
D2		2 c. green	8·00	4·50
		a. Wmk sideways (1928)	7·00	4·50
D3		4 c. scarlet	15·00	4·75
		a. Wmk sideways (1928)	15·00	6·00
D4		6 c. yellow	17·00	12·00
		a. Wmk sideways (1931)	17·00	17·00
D5		10 c. bright ultramarine	17·00	7·50
		a. Wmk sideways (1934)	30·00	9·50
D1/5		*Set of* 5	50·00	27·00
D1a/5a		*Set of* 5	65·00	35·00
D1/5 Optd "Specimen"		*Set of* 5	£160	

1938 (Feb)–**63.** *Wmk Mult Script CA (sideways). P* 14.

D 6	D 1	2 c. grey, O	5·00	4·00
		a. Chalky paper (21.3.56)	70	4·50
D 7		4 c. orange, O	9·00	4·25
		a. Chalky paper. *Orange-yellow* (23.5.61)	2·00	5·00
D 8		6 c. scarlet	8·00	6·00
D 9		8 c. chestnut (26.2.46)	4·50	20·00
D10		10 c. violet, O	11·00	45
		a. Chalky paper (17.9.63)	4·50	1·50
D11		20 c. black (26.2.46)	6·00	3·00
D12		50 c. blue (7.47)	19·00	14·00
D6a/12		*Set of* 7	40·00	48·00
D6/12 Perf "Specimen"		*Set of* 7	£240	

1965 (15 Apr)–**72.** *Chalk-surfaced paper. P* 14.

(a) Wmk w **12** *(sideways)*

D13	D 1	4 c. yellow-orange	3·50	10·00
D14		5 c. red (13.5.69)	2·00	3·00
		a. Glazed paper (17.11.72)	7·00	16·00
D15		10 c. violet (27.6.67)	1·50	2·50
D16		20 c. black (1965)	2·50	3·00
D17		50 c. deep blue (1965)	8·00	9·00
		a. Blue (13.5.69)	8·00	9·00
D13/17		*Set of* 5	16·00	25·00

(b) Wmk w **12** *(upright)*

D18	D 1	5 c. red (20.7.67)	1·00	3·00
D19		50 c. deep blue (26.8.70)	8·00	9·00

The 5 c. is smaller, 21 × 18 mm.

1972 (17 Nov)–**74.** *Glazed, ordinary paper. W* w **12** *(sideways).*

(a) P 14 × 14½

D20	D 1	10 c. bright reddish violet	2·50	3·00
D21		20 c. grey-black	3·00	4·50
D22		50 c. deep dull blue	3·00	8·00

(b) P 13½ × 14

D23	D 1	5 c. brown-red (1.5.74)	1·25	3·00
D20/3		*Set of* 4	9·00	17·00

(Typo Walsall)

1976 (19 Mar*)–**78.** *Smaller design* (21 × 17 *mm*) *with redrawn value-tablet. Glazed, ordinary paper. W* w **14**. *P* 14.

D25	D 1	10 c. bright reddish violet	20	1·50
		a. Chalk-surfaced paper (15.12.78)	15	60
D26		20 c. grey-black	35	1·75
		a. Chalk-surfaced paper (15.12.78)	15	75
D27		50 c. deep dull blue	50	2·50
		a. Chalk-surfaced paper (15.12.78)	40	1·25
D28		$1 yellow (1.4.76)	3·50	3·75
		a. Chalk-surfaced paper (15.12.78)	40	1·50
D25/8		*Set of* 4	4·00	8·50
D25a/8a		*Set of* 4	1·00	3·75

*This is the London release date. It is believed that the stamps were not released locally until 14 April.

(Typo Walsall)

1986 (11 Jan). *As Nos.* D27a/8a, *but without watermark. P* 14.

D29	D 1	50 c. slate-blue	60	1·50
D30		$1 lemon	80	2·25

(Des A. Chan. Litho B.D.T.)

1987 (25 Mar). *P* 14×15.

D31	D 2	10 c. light green	10	10
D32		20 c. red-brown	10	10
D33		50 c. bright violet	10	10
D34		$1 yellow-orange	15	20
D35		$5 dull ultramarine	70	75
D36		$10 bright rose-red	1·40	1·50
D31/6		*Set of* 6	2·25	2·50

MINIMUM PRICE

The minimum price quote is 10p which represents a handling charge rather than a basis for valuing common stamps. For further notes about prices see introductory pages.

POSTCARD STAMPS

Stamps specially surcharged for use on Postcards

3 CENTS (P 1)   THREE (P 2)

1879 (1 April). *Nos.* 22 *and* 13 *surch as Type* P **1**.

P1	**3**	3 c. on 16 c. yellow (No. 22)	£150	£200
P2		5 c. on 18 c. lilac (No. 13)	£120	£200

1879 (Nov). *No.* P2 *surch with Type* P **2**.

P3	**3**	3 c. on 5 c. on 18 c. lilac	£1800	£2750

POSTAL FISCAL STAMPS

I. Stamps inscribed "STAMP DUTY"

NOTE. The dated circular "Hong Kong" cancellation with "PAID ALL" in lower segment normally indicates fiscal, not postal, use, but a few instances are known where it was applied *in red*, for postal purposes.

F 1

F 2

F 3

1874–1902. *Wmk Crown CC. (a) P* 15½ × 15.

F1	F 1	$2 olive-green	£140	30·00
		a. Thin paper	£190	42·00
F2	F 2	$3 dull violet	£100	25·00
		a. Thin paper	£190	32·00
		b. Bluish paper		
F3	F 3	$10 rose-carmine	£2750	£325

(b) P 14

F4	F 1	$2 dull bluish green (12.90)	£130	80·00
F5	F 2	$3 dull mauve (3.02)	£140	£110
		a. Bluish paper	£900	
F6	F 3	$10 grey-green (1.92)	£1600	
F4/5 Optd "Specimen"		*Set of* 2	£250	

12 CENTS. (F 4)

F 5

1881 (Feb). *No.* F3 *surch with Type* F **4**.

F7	F 3	12 c. on $10 rose-carmine	£325	£110

1890 (24 Dec). *Wmk Crown CA. P* 14.

F8	F 5	2 c. dull purple	23·00	8·50

No. F8 was authorised for postal use between 24 and 30 December 1890.

(F 6)

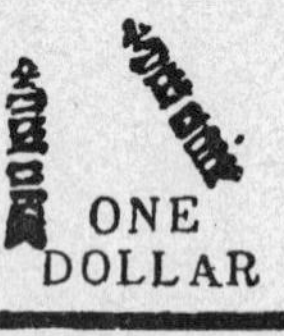

(F 7)

F 8

1891 (1 Jan). *Surch with Type* F **6**. *Wmk Crown CA. P* 14.

F9	F 3	$5 on $10 purple/*red* (Optd S. £100)	£120	60·00

1897 (Sept). *Surch with Type* F **7**.

F10	F 1	$1 on $2 olive-green (No. F1)	75·00	45·00
		a. Chinese surch wholly omitted	£750	£650
F11		$1 on $2 dull bluish green (No. F4) (H/S S. £90)	£110	75·00
		a. Chinese surch wholly omitted	£400	£300
		b. Diagonal portion of Chinese surch omitted	£5000	

1938 (11 Jan). *Wmk Mult Script CA. P* 14.

F12	F 8	5 c. green	35·00	5·50

Authorised for postal use on mail posted between 11 and 20 January 1938 (both dates inclusive).

II. Stamps overprinted "S.O." (Stamp Office), or "S.D." (Stamp Duty)

S. O. 印厘 (S 1)   S. D. 印厘 (S 2)

1891 (1 Jan). *Optd with Types* S **1** *or* S **2**.

S1	S 1	2 c. carmine (No. 33)	£300	£110
S2	S 2	2 c. carmine (No. 33)	£200	65·00
		a. Opt inverted	†	£1400
S3	S 1	10 c. purple/*red* (No. 40)	£400	£175

Examples of No. S1 exist with the "O" amended to "D" in manuscript.

Other fiscal stamps are found apparently postally used, but there is no evidence that this use was authorised.

JAPANESE OCCUPATION OF HONG KONG

Stamps of JAPAN from the 1937–40 and 1942–4 definitive issues were sold by Hong Kong post offices from 22 January 1942 until the Japanese surrender on 14 August 1945.

PRICES FOR STAMPS ON COVER
Nos. J1/3   *from* × 7

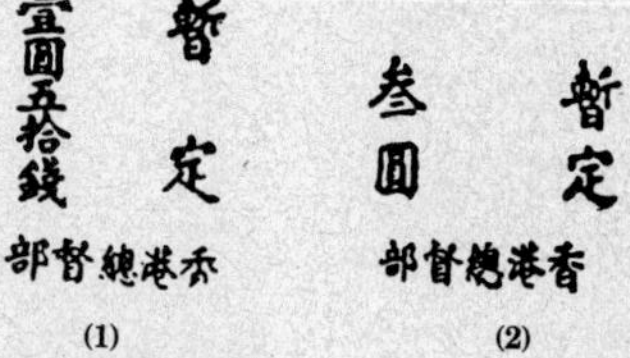

(1)   (2)

1945 (16 Apr). *Stamps of Japan surch with T* **1** *(No. J1) or as T* **2**.

J1	1.50 yen on 1 s. brown	15·00	12·00
J2	3 yen on 2 s. scarlet	9·00	9·50
J3	5 yen on 5 s. claret	£325	60·00

Designs (18½ × 22 *mm*):—1 s. Girl Worker; 2 s. Gen. Nogi; 5 s. Admiral Togo.

No. J3 has four characters of value similarly arranged but differing from T **2**.

BRITISH POST OFFICES IN CHINA

Under the terms of the 1842 Treaty of Nanking China granted Great Britain and its citizens commercial privileges in five Treaty Ports, Amoy, Canton, Foochow, Ningpo and Shanghai. British Consuls were appointed to each Port and their offices, as was usual during this period, collected and distributed mail for the British community. This system was formally recognised by a Hong Kong Government notice published on 16 April 1844. Mail from the consular offices was postmarked when it passed through Hong Kong.

The number of Chinese Treaty Ports was increased to sixteen by the ratification of the Treaty of Peking in 1860 with British postal facilities being eventually extended to the Ports of Chefoo, Hankow, Kiungchow (Hoihow), Swatow, Tainan (Anping) and Tientsin.

As postal business expanded the consular agencies were converted into packet agencies or post offices which passed under the direct control of the Hong Kong postal authorities on 1 January 1868.

In May 1898 the British Government leased the territory of Wei Hai Wei from China for use as a naval station to counter the Russian presence at Port Arthur.

The opening of the Trans-Siberia Railway and the extension of Imperial Penny Postage to the Treaty Port agencies resulted in them becoming a financial burden on the colonial post office. Control of the agencies reverted to the G.P.O., London, on 1 January 1911.

The pre-adhesive postal markings of the various agencies are a fascinating, but complex, subject. Full details can be found in *Hong Kong & the Treaty Ports of China & Japan* by F. W. Webb (Royal Philatelic Society, London—out of print) and in various publications of the Hong Kong Study Circle.

From 15 October 1864 the use of Hong Kong stamps on mail from the Treaty Ports became compulsory, although such stamps were, initially, not cancelled (with the exception of Amoy) until they reached Hong Kong where the "B62" killer was applied. Cancellation of mail at the actual Ports commenced during 1866 at Shanghai and Ningpo, spreading to all the agencies during the next ten years. Shanghai had previously used a c.d.s. on adhesives during 1863 and again in 1865–66.

The main types of cancellation used between 1866 and 1930 are illustrated below. The illustrations show the style of each postmark and no attempt has been made to cover differences in type letters or figures, arrangement, diameter or colour.

Until 1885 the vertical and horizontal killers were used to obliterate the actual stamps with an impression of one of the circular date stamps shown elsewhere on the cover. Many of the early postmarks were also used as backstamps or transit marks and, in the notes which follow, references to use are for the first appearance of the mark, not necessarily its first use as an obliterator.

Illustrations in this section are taken from *Hong Kong & the Treaty Ports of China & Japan* by F. W. Webb and are reproduced with the permission of the Royal Philatelic Society, London.

Postmark Types

Type A
Vertical killer

Type B
Horizontal killer

Type C
Name horizontal

Type D
Name curved

Type **E**
Double circle Name at top

Type **F**
Double circle Name at foot

Type G
Single circle Name at top

AMOY

One of the five original Treaty Ports, opened to British trade by the Treaty of Nanking in 1842. A consular postal agency was established in 1844 which later expanded into two separate offices, one on the off-shore island of Ku Lang Seu and the other in Amoy itself.

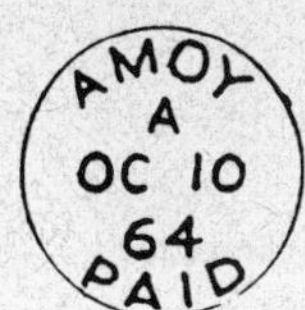

Amoy "PAID" (*supplied* 1858) *used* 1859–67
Type **A** ("A1") (*supplied* 1866) *used at Ku Lang Seu* 1869–82
Type **D** (*supplied* 1866) *used* 1867–1922
Type **B** ("D27") (*supplied* 1876) *used at Amoy* 1876–84
Type **C** *used* 1876–94
Type **F** (*supplied* 1913) *used* 1916–22

ANPING

Anping is the port for Tainan, on the island of Formosa, opened to British trade in 1860. A British Vice-consulate operated in the port and mail is known postmarked there between 1889 and 1895. Formosa passed under Japanese control in 1895 and British Treaty Port rights then lapsed.

Type **D** *used* 1889–95

CANTON

A British postal service was organised in Canton from 1834, but was closed when the foreign communities were evacuated in 1839. The city was one of the original Treaty Ports and a consular agency was opened there in 1844. The consulate closed during the riots of 1858, being replaced by a temporary postal agency at Whampoa, further down river. When British forces reached Canton a further temporary agency was set up in 1859, but both closed in 1863 when the consulate was re-established.

Type **A** ("C1") (*supplied* 1866) *used* 1875–83
Type **C** (*supplied* 1866) *used* 1866–1901
Type **D** *used* 1890–1922

CHEFOO

Chefoo was opened to British trade in 1860. Although a consulate was established in 1861 no organised postal agency was provided until 1903 when one was opened at the premises of Curtis Brothers, a commercial firm.

Type **E** (*supplied* 1902) *used* 1903–20
Type **D** (*supplied* 1907) *used* 1907–13
Type **F** *used* 1916–22

FOOCHOW

Foochow, originally known as Foochowfoo, was one of the original Treaty Ports opened to British trade in 1842. A British consulate and postal agency was established in June 1844.

Type **A** ("F1") (*supplied* 1866) *used* 1873–84
Type **D** (inscr "FOOCHOWFOO") (*supplied* 1866) *used* 1867–1905
Type **D** (inscr "FOOCHOW") (*supplied* 1894) *used* 1894–1917
Type **E** (inscr "B.P.O.") *used* 1906–10
Type **F** *used* 1915–22

HANKOW

Hankow, on the Yangtse River 600 miles from the sea, became a Treaty Port in 1860. A British consulate opened the following year, but no organised British postal agency was established until 1872.

Type **D** (*supplied* 1874) *used* 1874–1916
Type **B** ("D29") (*supplied* 1876) *used* 1878–83
Type **F** *used* 1916–22

KIUNGCHOW (HOIHOW)

Kiungchow, a city on the island of Hainan, and its port of Hoihow was added to the Treaty Port system in 1860. A consular postal agency was opened at Kiungchow in 1876, being transferred to Hoihow in 1878. A second agency was opened at Kiungchow in 1879.

Type **B** ("D28") (*supplied* 1876) *used* 1876–83
Type **D** (inscr "KIUNG-CHOW") (*supplied* 1876) *used* 1879–81

"REGISTERED KIUNG-CHOW" with "REGISTERED" removed (*originally supplied* 1876) *used* 1884–85
Type **D** (inscr "HOIHOW") *used* 1885–1922

NINGPO

Ningpo was one of the 1842 Treaty Ports and a consular postal agency was established there in 1844.

Type **A** ("N1") (*supplied* 1866) *used* 1870–82
Type **C** (*supplied* 1866) *used* 1870–99
Type **D** *used* 1895–1922

SHANGHAI

Shanghai was one of the original Treaty Ports of 1842 and a packet agency was opened at the British consulate in 1844. It moved to separate premises in 1861 and was upgraded to a Post Office in 1867.

British military post offices operated in Shanghai from 1927 until 1940.

Type **D** (inscr "SHANGHAE") (*supplied* 1861) *used* 1862–99

Sunburst *used* 1864–65
Type **A** ("S1") (*supplied* 1866) *used* 1867–85
Type **D** (inscr "SHANGHAI") (*supplied* 1885) *used* 1886–1906
Type **G** (inscr "B.P.O." at foot) (*supplied* 1904) *used* 1904–17
Type **G** (inscr "Br.P.O." at foot) (*supplied* 1907) *used* 1907–22
Type **E** (figures "I" to "VIII" at foot) *used* 1912–22

SWATOW

Swatow became a Treaty Port in 1860 and a consular packet agency was opened in the area made available for foreign firms during the same year. In 1867 the original agency was transferred to the Chinese city on the other side of the Han river, but a second agency was subsequently opened in the foreign concession during 1883.

Type **A** ("S2") (*supplied* 1866) *used* 1875–85
Type **C** (*supplied* 1866) *used* 1866–89
Type **D** (*supplied* 1883) *used* 1884–1922
Type **F** *used* 1916–22

TIENTSIN

Tientsin became a Treaty Port in 1860. A British consulate was established in 1861, but no formal postal agency was organised there until 1882. It was not, however, very successful and was closed during 1890. The British Post Office reopened on 1 October 1906 under the management of the Chinese Engineering and Mining Company.

British military post offices operated in Tientsin from 1927 until 1940.

Type **E** *used* 1906–13
Type **G** (supplied 1907) *used* 1907–22

WEI HAI WEI

The territory of Wei Hai Wei was leased from the Chinese by the British Government from 24 May 1898. At that time there were no organised postal services from the area, although a private local post did operate between the port and Chefoo from December 1898 until March 1899. A Chinese Imperial post office opened in March 1899 to be followed by a British postal agency on the offshore island of Liu Kung Tau on 1 September 1899. A second British agency opened at Port Edward on 1 April 1904.

Liu Kung Tau oval *used* 1899–1901
Type **D** (inscr "LIU KUNG TAU") (*supplied* 1899) *used* 1901–30

Port Edward rectangle *used* 1904–08
Type **D** (inscr "PORT EDWARD") (*supplied* 1907) *used* 1907–30

PRICES FOR STAMPS ON COVER

Nos. 1/14	*from* × 6
Nos. 15/17	—
Nos. 18/28	*from* × 8

CHINA

(1)

1917 (1 Jan)–**21.** *Stamps of Hong Kong*, 1912–21 (*wmk Mult Crown CA*), *optd with T* **1**, *at Somerset House.*

No.	Description		
1	1 c. brown, **O**	35	65
	a. Black-brown, **O**	55	1·00
	b. Crown broken at side	£120	£150
	c. Wmk sideways	†	£1750
2	2 c. green, **O**	25	15
3	4 c. carmine-red, **O**	50	10
4	6 c. orange, **O**	75	45
5	8 c. slate, **O**	1·25	60
6	10 c. ultramarine, **O**	75	10
7	12 c. purple/*yellow*, **C**	1·10	1·75
8	20 c. purple and sage-green, **C**	3·00	30
9	25 c. purple and magenta, **C** (A)	4·00	12·00
11	30 c. purple and orange-yellow, **C**	8·50	3·50
12	50 c. black/*blue-green* (*olive back*), **C**	13·00	75
	a. On emerald surface (1917?)	8·00	2·50
	b. On emerald back (1919)	6·00	1·75
	c. On white back (1920)	32·00	10·00
13	$1 reddish purple and bright blue/*blue*, **C** ..	22·00	1·75
	a. Grey-purple and blue/blue, **C** (1921) ..	20·00	3·25
14	$2 carmine-red and grey-black, **C**	60·00	35·00
15	$3 green and purple, **C**	85·00	70·00
16	$5 green and red/*blue-green* (*olive back*), **C**	£110	70·00
17	$10 purple and black/*red*, **C**	£375	£170
1/17	.. .. *Set of* 16	£600	£325
12/17	H/S "Specimen" .. .. *Set of* 6	£800	

1922 (Mar)–**27.** *As last, but wmk Mult Script CA.*

No.	Description		
18	1 c. brown, **O**	35	1·00
19	2 c. green, **O**	65	80
20	4 c. carmine-rose, **O**	1·25	75
	a. Lower Chinese character at right broken at top	70·00	55·00
21	6 c. orange-yellow, **O**	75	2·25
22	8 c. grey, **O**	90	7·50
23	10 c. bright ultramarine, **O**	75	1·00
24	20 c. purple and sage-green, **C**	2·50	2·75
25	25 c. purple and magenta, **C** (B)	5·50	24·00
26	50 c. black/*emerald*, **C** (1927) (H/S S. £200) ..	15·00	40·00
27	$1 purple and blue/*blue*, **C**	13·00	14·00
28	$2 carmine-red and grey-black, **C**	£110	90·00
18/28	.. .. *Set of* 11	£130	£160

The overprinted stamps Nos. 1/17 were introduced on 1 January 1917 for use in the then-existing agencies of Amoy,

Canton, Chefoo, Foochow, Hankow, Hoihow, Ningpo, Shanghai, Swatow and Tientsin. They were also supplied to the British naval base of Wei Hai Wei.

The British P.O.s in the Treaty Ports closed by agreement with the Chinese on 30 November 1922, but the above overprinted issues continued in use at the Wei Hai Wei offices until they in turn closed on 30 September 1930.

BRITISH POST OFFICES IN JAPAN

Under the terms of the Anglo-Japanese Treaty of Yedo, signed on 26 August 1858, five Japanese ports were opened to British trade. British consulates were established at Decima (Nagasaki), Kanagawa (Yokohama), Hiogo (Kobe) and Hakodadi (Hakodate). The postage stamps of Hong Kong became available at the Yokohama and Nagasaki consulates during October 1864 and at Hiogo in 1869, although cancellation of mail did not commence until 1866 at Yokohama and Nagasaki or 1876 at Hiogo. Japan became a member of the U.P.U. during 1877 and all of the British Postal Agencies were closed by the end of 1879.

For illustrations of postmark types see BRITISH POST OFFICES IN CHINA.

YOKOHAMA

The British Consulate opened in Kanagawa on 21 July 1859, but was relocated during 1860 to Yokohama where it provided postal services until a separate Post Office was established in 1867. The British Post Office in Yokohama closed on 31 December 1879.

Type **A** ("Y1") (*supplied* 1866) *used* 1868–79
Type **D** (*supplied* 1866) *used* 1866–79

NAGASAKI

The British Consulate opened in Nagasaki on 14 June 1859, but, with few British residents at the port, the consular staff found it inconvenient to carry out postal duties so that few Nagasaki c.d.s. or "N2" cancellations exist. The postal service was terminated on 30 September 1879.

Type **A** ("N2") (*supplied* 1866) *used* 1876–79
Type **D** (*supplied* 1866) *used* 1876–79

HIOGO

The Port of Hiogo (Kobe) was first opened to foreigners on 1 January 1868. The British Consular mail service at Hiogo commenced during 1869 to serve the foreigners at Hiogo, Kobe and Osaka. The cities of Hiogo and Kobe later merged to become the single city of Kobe. The consular office at Hiogo closed on 30 November 1879.

Type **B** ("D30") (*supplied* 1876) *used* 1876–79
Type **D** (*supplied* 1876) *used* 1876–79

HAKODATE

A British consular office existed at Hakodate, but it was never issued with a c.d.s., obliterator or Hong Kong stamps. No British covers are recorded from this consulate prior to opening of the Japanese Post Office.

India

PRICES FOR STAMPS ON COVER TO 1945

Nos. S1/3	*from* × 2
No. 1	†
Nos. 2/26	*from* × 3
Nos. 27/30	—
Nos. 31/4	*from* × 8
Nos. 35/49	*from* × 3
Nos. 50	†
Nos. 51/3	*from* × 4
Nos. 54/65	*from* × 2
Nos. 66/8	*from* × 5
Nos. 69/74	*from* × 3
Nos. 73/277	*from* × 2
Nos. O1/14	*from* × 6
Nos. O15/18	—
No. O19	*from* × 5
Nos. O20/30*a*	*from* × 10
No. O30*b*	†
Nos. O31/133	*from* × 6
Nos. O135/150	*from* × 2

(12 pies = 1 anna; 16 annas = 1 rupee)

ISSUE FOR SIND PROVINCE

1

1852 (1 July). "Scinde Dawk." *Embossed.*

S1	1	½ a. white	£4250	£800
S2		½ a. blue	£10000	£3250
S3		½ a. scarlet	—	£6500

These stamps were issued under the authority of Sir Bartle Frere, Commissioner in Sind. They were suppressed in October 1854.

No. S3 is on sealing wax (usually cracked). Perfect copies are very rare.

EAST INDIA COMPANY ADMINISTRATION

2 (*Much reduced*)

3

The ½ a., 1 a. and 4 a. were lithographed in Calcutta at the office of the Surveyor-General. The die was engraved by Mr Maniruddin (spelling uncertain). *Ungummed* paper watermarked as **T 2** (the "No. 4" paper) with the Arms of the East India Co in the sheet. The watermark is sideways on the ½ a. and 1 a., and upright on the 4 a. where the paper was trimmed so that only the central portion showing the oval and the arms was used. Imperforate.

1854 (April).

1	3	½ a. vermilion	£750
		a. Deep vermilion	£950

This stamp, with 9½ arches in the side border, was prepared for use and a supply was sent to Bombay, but was not officially issued.

The vermilion shade is normally found on toned paper and the deep vermilion on white.

ILLUSTRATIONS. Types 4/8 are shown twice actual size.

4

1854 (1 Oct). *Die I.*

2	4	½ a. blue	40·00	12·00
		a. Printed on both sides	—	£6000
3		½ a. pale blue	55·00	12·00
4		½ a. deep blue	48·00	16·00
5		½ a. indigo	£125	45·00

We give the official date of issue, but copies are known which were put on sale as much as a fortnight earlier.

These stamps were printed between 5 May and 29 July 1854 (Printing 30 millions).

4*a*

Die II

6	4*a*	½ a. blue	40·00	70·00
7		½ a. indigo	45·00	70·00

The bulk were printed between 1 and 12 August 1854, with some extra sheets on or before 2 November (Printing about 2 millions).

COVER PRICES

Cover factors are quoted at the beginning of each country for most issues to 1945. An explanation of the system can be found on page x. The factors quoted do not, however, apply to philatelic covers.

5

Die III

8	5	½ a. pale blue	£600	35·00
8*a*		½ a. blue	£600	35·00
9		½ a. greenish blue	£1000	£150
10		½ a. deep blue	£650	55·00

These stamps were printed between 3 July and 25 August 1855 (Printing about 4¾ millions).

THE THREE DIES OF THE ½ ANNA

DIE I. *Chignon shading* mostly solid blobs of colour. *Corner ornaments*, solid blue stars with long points, always conspicuous. *Band below diadem* always heavily shaded. *Diadem and jewels.* The middle and right-hand jewels usually show a clearly defined cross. *Outer frame lines.* Stamps with white or faintly shaded chignons and weak frame lines are usually Die I (worn state).

DIE II. *Chignon* normally shows much less shading. A strong line of colour separates hair and chignon. *Corner ornaments.* The right blue star is characteristic (see illustration) but tends to disappear. It never obliterates the white cross. *Band below diadem.* As Die I but heavier, sometimes solid. *Diadem and jewels.* As Die I but usually fainter. *Outer frame lines.* Always strong and conspicuous.

DIE III. *Chignon shading* shows numerous fine lines, often blurred. *Corner ornaments* have a small hollow blue star with short points, which tends to disappear as in Die II. *Band below diadem*, shows light shading or hardly any shading. *Diadem and jewels.* Jewels usually marked with a solid squat star. The ornaments between the stars appear in the shape of a characteristic white "w". *Frame lines* variable.

The above notes give the general characteristics of the three Dies, but there are a few exceptions due to retouching, etc.

6 (*See note below No. 14*)

Die I

11	6	1 a. deep red	£190	35·00
12		1 a. red	£160	32·00

Printing of these stamps commenced on 26 July 1854, and continued into August (Printing, see note below No. 14).

7

*Die II: With more lines in the chignon than in Die I, and with white curved line where chignon joins head**

13	7	1 a. deep red	90·00	40·00
14		1 a. dull red	35·00	35·00

*Very worn printings of Die II may be found with chignon nearly as white as in Die I.

In stamps of Die I, however, the small blob of red projecting from the hair into the chignon is always visible.

These stamps were printed in August and September 1854 (Total printing, Dies I and II together, about 7¾ millions).

8

Die III. With pointed bust

15 8 1 a. red £900 £125
16 1 a. dull red £900 £150

These stamps were printed between 7 July and 25 August 1855 (Printing, about 1½ millions).

9

NOTE. Our catalogue prices for Four Annas stamps are for cut-square specimens, with clear margins and in good condition. Cut-to-shape copies are worth from 3% to 20% of these prices according to condition.

Four Dies of the Head:—

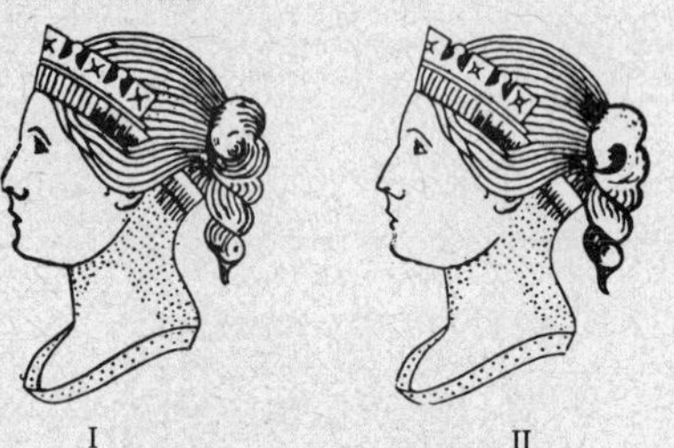

I II

DIE I. Band of diadem and chignon strongly shaded.

DIE II. Lines in band of diadem worn. Few lines in the upper part of the chignon, which, however, shows a strong drawn comma-like mark.

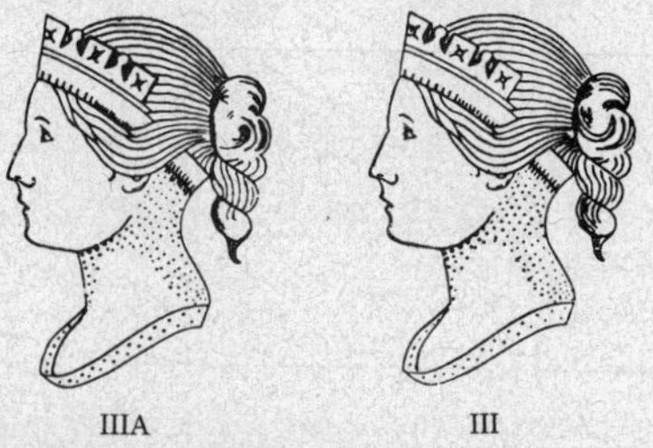

IIIA III

DIE IIIA. Upper part of chignon partly redrawn, showing two short, curved vertical lines in the NE corner. "Comma" has disappeared.

DIE III. Upper part of chignon completely redrawn, but band of diadem shows only a few short lines.

Two Dies of the Frame:—

Die I. Outer frame lines weak. Very small dots of colour, or none at all, in the "R" and "A's". The white lines to the right of "INDIA" are separated, by a line of colour, from the inner white circle.

Die II. Outer frame lines strengthened. Dots in the "R" and "A's" strong. White lines to right of "INDIA" break into inner white circle.

(Des Capt. H. Thuillier)

1854 (15 Oct). *W* **2** *upright, central portion only. Imperf.*
1st *Printing. Head Die I. Frame Die I. Stamps widely spaced and separated by blue wavy line.*

			Un	*Used*	*Us pr*
17	**9**	4 a. indigo and red	£2750	£425	£1400
18		4 a. blue and pale red	£2750	£425	£1400
		a. Head inverted	—	£22000/ £70000	—

This printing was made between 13 and 28 Oct 1854 (Printing, 206,040).

Twenty-seven confirmed examples of No. 18a are now known, only three of which are cut-square. The range of prices quoted reflects the difference in value between a sound cut-to-shape stamp and the finest example known.

2nd *Printing. Head Die II. Frame Die I. Stamps widely spaced and separated by blue wavy line.*

19	**9**	4 a. blue and red	£2750	£275	£900
20		4 a. indigo and deep red	£2750	£300	£1000

This printing was made between 1 and 13 Dec 1854 (Printing, 393,960).
This is known with head double.

3rd *Printing. Head Dies II, IIIA and III. Frame Dies I and II. Stamps widely spaced and separated by wavy line.*

21	**9**	4 a. bright blue and bright red (Head III, Frame I)	£6000	£1000	£3250
		a. Head II, Frame I	—	£1500	—
		b. Head IIIA, Frame I	—	£1500	£4500
		c. Head III, Frame II	—	—	£6500

This printing was made between 10 March and 2 April 1855 (Printing, 138,960).

4th *Printing. Head Die III. Frame Die II. Stamps closely spaced* 2 *to* 2½ *mm without separating line.*

22	**9**	4 a. deep blue and red	£1800	£250	£750
23		4 a. blue and red	£1700	£225	£700
24		4 a. pale blue and pale red ..	£1800	£250	£750

This printing was made between 3 April and 9 May 1855 (Printing, 540,960).
This is known with head double.

5th *Printing. Head Die III. Frame Die II. Stamps spaced* 4 *to* 6 *mm without separating line.*

25	**9**	4 a. blue and rose-red	£2750	£350	£1300
26		4 a. deep blue and red	£2750	£325	£1200

This printing was made between 4 Oct and 3 Nov 1855 (Printing, 380,064).

Serrated perf about 18, *or pin-perf*

27	½ a. blue (Die I)			
28	1 a. red (Die I)			
29	1 a. red (Die II)	—	£700	—
30	4 a. blue and red (Die II)	—	£3000	—

This is believed to be an unofficial perforation. Most of the known specimens bear Madras circle postmarks (C122 to C126), but some are known with Bombay postmarks. Beware of fakes.

BISECTS. The bisected stamps for issues between 1854 and 1860 were used exclusively in the Straits Settlements during shortages of certain values. Prices quoted are for those with Singapore "B 172" cancellations. Penang marks are considerably rarer.

10

11

(Plate made at Mint, Calcutta. Typo Stamp Office)

1854 (6 Oct). *Sheet wmk sideways, as W* **2** *but with* "No. 3" *at top left.* Imperf.*

31	**10**	2 a. green (*shade*)	85·00	22·00
		a. Bisected (1 a.) (1857) (on cover) ..	†	—
34		2 a. emerald-green	£850	

The 2 a. was also printed on paper with sheet wmk incorporating the words "STAMP OFFICE. One Anna", etc. (*Price* £250 *un or us*).
Apart from the rare emerald-green shade, there is a range of shades of No. 31 varying from bluish to yellowish green.
Many stamps show traces of lines external to the design shown in our illustration. Stamps with this frame on all four sides are scarce.
Many reprints of the ½, 1, 2, and 4 a. exist.

PRINTERS. All Indian stamps from No. 35 to 200 were typographed by De La Rue & Co.

1855 (Oct). *Blue glazed paper. No wmk. P* 14.

35	**11**	4 a. black	£190	11·00
		a. Imperf (pair)	£1300	£1300
		b. Bisected (2 a.) (1859) (on cover) ..	†	£4000
36		8 a. carmine (Die I)	£190	10·00
		a. Imperf (pair)	£1100	
		b. Bisected (4 a.) (1859) (on cover) ..	†	£16000

The first supply of the 4 a. was on white paper, but it is difficult to distinguish it from No. 45.
In the 8 a. the paper varies from deep blue to almost white.
For difference between Die I and Die II in the 8 a., see illustrations above No. 73.

1856–64. *No wmk. Paper yellowish to white. P* 14.

37	**11**	½ a. blue (Die I)	15·00	75
		a. Imperf (pair)	£275	£550
38		½ a. pale blue (Die I)	14·00	60
39		1 a. brown	8·00	90
		a. Imperf between (vert pair)		
		b. Imperf (pair)	£650	£800
		c. Bisected (½ a.) (1859) (on cover) ..	†	£15000
40		1 a. deep brown	14·00	1·25
41		2 a. dull pink	£110	12·00
		a. Imperf (pair)	£1100	
42		2 a. yellow-buff	48·00	9·00
		a. Imperf (pair)	£800	£1000
43		2 a. yellow	50·00	9·50
44		2 a. orange	60·00	10·00
		a. Imperf (pair)		
45		4 a. black	60·00	6·00
		a. Bisected diagonally (2 a.) (1859) (on cover)	†	£5500
		b. Imperf (pair)	£1100	£1300
46		4 a. grey-black	55·00	4·75
47		4 a. green (1864)	£250	18·00
48		8 a. carmine (Die I)	50·00	7·50
49		8 a. pale carmine (Die I)	50·00	7·50
		a. Bisected (4 a.) (1859) (on cover) ..	†	£16000

Prepared for use, but not officially issued

50	**11**	2 a. yellow-green	£450	£500
		a. Imperf (pair)	£1000	

This stamp is known with trial obliterations, and a few are known postally used. It also exists *imperf*, but is not known used thus.
For difference between Die I and Die II in the ½ a., see illustrations above No. 73.

CROWN COLONY

On the 1 November 1858, Her Majesty Queen Victoria assumed the government of the territories in India "heretofore administered in trust by the Honourable East India Company".

12

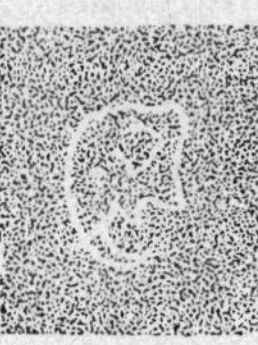

13

1860 (9 May). *No wmk. P* 14.

51	**12**	8 p. purple/*bluish*	£110	50·00
52		8 p. purple/*white*	13·00	4·50
		a. Bisected diagonally (4 p.) (1862) (on cover)	†	£16000
		b. Imperf (pair)	£1100	£1300
53		8 p. mauve	13·00	5·00

1865. *Paper yellowish to white. W* **13.** *P* 14.

54	**11**	½ a. blue (Die I)	2·00	30
		a. Imperf	—	£550
55		½ a. pale blue (Die I)	2·25	30
56	**12**	8 p. purple	6·50	5·00
57		8 p. mauve	5·50	5·00
58	**11**	1 a. pale brown	2·25	25
59		1 a. deep brown	2·00	25
60		1 a. chocolate	7·00	40
61		2 a. yellow	20·00	4·00
62		2 a. orange	21·00	1·10
		a. Imperf	—	£1100
63		2 a. brown-orange	14·00	2·75
64		4 a. green	£140	18·00
65		8 a. carmine (Die I)	£650	75·00

The 8 p. mauve, No. 57, is found variously surcharged "NINE" or "NINE PIE" by local postmasters, to indicate that it was being sold for 9 pies, as was the case during 1874. Such surcharges were made without Government sanction.
The stamps of India, wmk Elephant's Head, surcharged with a crown and value in "cents", were used in the Straits Settlements.

14

POSTAGE (15) POSTACE (16)

1866 (28 June). *Fiscal stamps as T* 14 *optd. Wmk Crown over* "INDIA". *P* 14 (*at sides only*). (*a*) *As T* **15**.

66		6 a. purple (G.)	£400	£110
		a. Overprint inverted	—	£7500

There are 20 different types of this overprint.

(*b*) *With T* **16**

68		6 a. purple (G.)	£650	£130

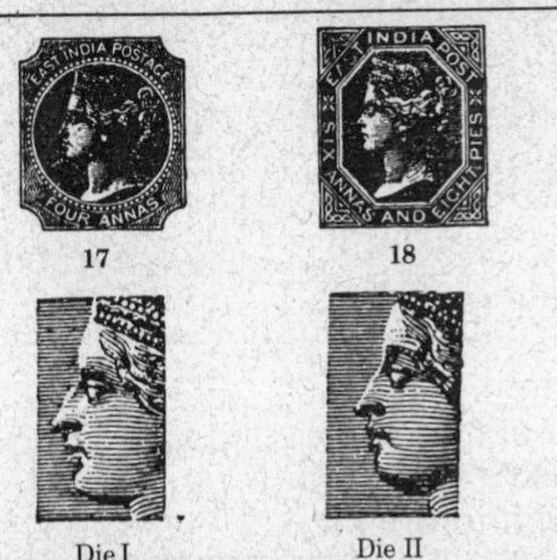

17 18

Die I Die II

Two Dies of 4 a:—

Die I.—Mouth closed, line from corner of mouth downwards only. Pointed chin.

Die II.—Mouth slightly open; lips, chin, and throat defined by line of colour. Rounded chin.

1866 (Sept)–**1878.** *W* **13.** *P* 14.

69	**17**	4 a. green (Die I)	22·00	60
70		4 a. deep green (Die I)	22·00	50
71		4 a. blue-green (Die II) (1878)	9·00	40
72	**18**	6 a. 8 p. slate (5.67)	22·00	18·00
		a. Imperf (pair)	£1200	

Die I (8 a.)

(Die I (½ a.)

Die II (8 a.)

Die II (½ a.)

1868 (1 Jan). *Die II. Profile redrawn and different diadem. W* **13.** *P* 14.

73	**11**	8 a. rose (Die II)	13·00	3·75
74		8 a. pale rose (Die II)	13·00	3·75

1873. *Die II. Features, especially the mouth, more firmly drawn. W* **13.** *P* 14.

75	**11**	½ a. deep blue (Die II)	1·10	25
76		½ a. blue (Die II)	1·25	25

19

20

1874 (18 July–1 Sept). *W* **13.** *P* 14.

77	**19**	9 p. bright mauve (18.7.74)	6·50	6·50
78		9 p. pale mauve	6·50	6·50
79	**20**	1 r. slate (1.9.74)	18·00	12·00

21

22

1876 (19 Aug). *W* **13.** *P* 14.

80	**21**	6 a. olive-bistre	4·75	1·75
81		6 a. pale brown	4·50	1·50
82	**22**	12 a. Venetian red	6·00	12·00

EMPIRE

Queen Victoria assumed the title of Empress of India in 1877, and the inscription on the stamps was altered from "EAST INDIA" to "INDIA".

23

24

25

26

27

28

29

30

31

32

33

34

1882 (1 Jan)–**88.** *W* **34.** *P* 14.

84	**23**	½ a. deep blue-green (1883)	1·75	10
85		½ a. blue-green	1·75	10
		a. Double impression	£200	
86	**24**	9 p. rose (1883)	50	1·25
87		9 p. aniline carmine	70	1·50
88	**25**	1 a. brown-purple (1883)	1·50	10
89		1 a. plum	1·50	10
90	**26**	1 a. 6 p. sepia	50	70
91	**27**	2 a. pale blue (1883)	2·50	15
92		2 a. blue	2·50	15
		a. Double impression	£375	£500
93	**28**	3 a. orange	9·00	3·25
94		3 a. brown-orange	4·50	35
95	**29**	4 a. olive-green (6.85)	7·00	15
96		4 a. slate-green	6·00	15
97	**30**	4 a. 6 p. yellow-green (1.5.86)	8·00	5·00
98	**31**	8 a. dull mauve (1883)	10·00	2·00
99		8 a. magenta	11·00	1·75
100	**32**	12 a. purple/*red* (1.4.88)	4·25	2·00
101	**33**	1 r. slate (1883)	9·50	3·00
84/101		*Set of* 11	45·00	13·00
97, 100		Handstamped "Specimen" *Set of* 2	75·00	

No. 92a is from a sheet of 2 a. stamps with a very marked double impression issued in Karachi in 1896–97. Most of the stamps were used on telegrams.

(35)

36

37

1891 (1 Jan). *No.* 97 *surch with T* **35** *by Govt Press, Calcutta.*

102	**30**	2½ a. on 4½ a. yellow-green	1·50	60

There are several varieties in this surcharge due to variations in the relative positions of the letters and figures.

1892 (Jan)–**97.** *W* **34.** *P* 14.

103	**36**	2½ a. yellow-green	1·00	40
104		2½ a. pale blue-green (1897)	1·75	60
105	**37**	1 r. green and rose	12·00	4·00
106		1 r. green and aniline carmine	5·50	2·00

38

(39)

40

USED HIGH VALUES. It is necessary to emphasise that used prices quoted for the following and all later high value stamps are for postally used copies.

(Head of Queen from portrait by von Angeli)

1895 (1 Sept). *W* **34.** *P* 14.

107	**38**	2 r. carmine and yellow-brown	30·00	10·00
107*a*		2 r. carmine and brown	35·00	12·00
108		3 r. brown and green	25·00	10·00
109		5 r. ultramarine and violet	28·00	22·00
107/9		*Set of* 3	75·00	38·00

1898 (1 Oct). *No.* 85 *surch with T* **39** *by Govt Press, Calcutta.*

110	**23**	¼ on ½ a. blue-green	10	20
		a. Surch double	70·00	
		b. Double impression of stamp	£160	

1899. *W* **34.** *P* 14.

111	**40**	3 p. aniline carmine	10	10

1900 (1 Oct)–**02.** *W* **34.** *P* 14.

112	**40**	3 p. grey	10	40
113	**23**	½ a. pale yellow-green	40	15
114		½ a. yellow-green	50	15
115	**25**	1 a. carmine	50	10
116	**27**	2 a. pale violet	2·50	45
117		2 a. mauve (1902)	3·50	90
118	**36**	2½ a. ultramarine	3·00	3·75
112/18		*Set of* 5	5·50	4·25

41

42

43

44

45

46

47

48

49

50

51

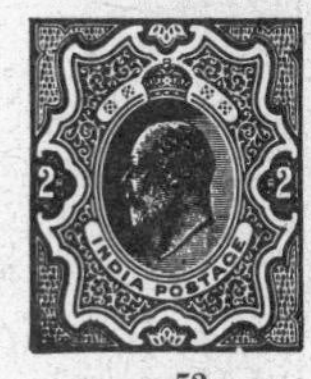

52

1902 (9 Aug)–**11.** *W* **34.** *P* 14.

119	**41**	3 p. grey	25	10
120		3 p. slate-grey (1904)	15	10
121	**42**	½ a. yellow-green	35	10
122		½ a. green	35	10
123	**43**	1 a. carmine	45	10
124	**44**	2 a. violet (13.5.03)	1·50	35
125		2 a. mauve	1·50	10
126	**45**	2½ a. ultramarine (1902)	3·25	15
127	**46**	3 a. orange-brown (1902)	3·25	15
128	**47**	4 a. olive (20.4.03)	3·00	25
129		4 a. pale olive	3·00	30
130		4 a. olive-brown	7·00	2·50
131	**48**	6 a. olive-bistre (6.8.03)	10·00	4·25
132		6 a. maize	10·00	4·25
133	**49**	8 a. mauve (8.5.03)	7·50	1·00
134		8 a. magenta (1910)	9·00	1·00
135	**50**	12 a. purple/*red* (1903)	7·50	2·00
136	**51**	1 r. green and carmine (1903)	6·00	70
137		1 r. green and scarlet (1911)	22·00	1·75
138	**52**	2 r. rose-red and yellow-brown (1903)	19·00	3·50
139		2 r. carmine and yellow-brown	19·00	3·25
140		3 r. brown and green (1904)	20·00	19·00
141		3 r. red-brown and green (1911)	26·00	19·00
142		5 r. ultramarine and violet (1904)	48·00	35·00
143		5 r. ultramarine and deep lilac (1911)	55·00	35·00
144		10 r. green and carmine (1909)	75·00	18·00
146		15 r. blue and olive-brown (1909)	£125	42·00
147		25 r. brownish orange and blue (1909)	£750	£800
119/147		*Set of* 17	£900	£800

No. 147 can often be found with telegraph cancellation; these can be supplied at one third of the price given above.

1905 (2 Feb). *No.* 122 *surch with T* **39.**

148	**42**	¼ on ½ a. green	15	10
		a. Surch inverted	—	£400

It is doubtful if No. 148a exists unused with genuine surcharge.

53

54

1906 (Dec)–**07.** *W* **34.** *P* 14.

149	**53**	½ a. green (12.06)	60	10
150	**54**	1 a. carmine (1.07)	50	10

55 56 57

58*

59

60

61 62 63

64 65 66

67

*T 58. Two types of the 1½ a.; (A) As illustrated. (B) Inscribed "1½ As". "ONE AND A HALF ANNAS".

1911 (Dec)–**22**. *W* 34. *P* 14.

No.	Type	Description		Unused	Used
151	**55**	3 p. pale grey (1912)		25	10
152		3 p. grey		15	10
153		3 p. slate-grey		15	10
154		3 p. blue-slate (1922)		85	25
155	**56**	½ a. yellow-green (1912)		30	10
		a. Double print		£125	
156		½ a. pale blue-green		30	10
159	**57**	1 a. rose-carmine		1·00	10
160		1 a. carmine		1·00	10
161		1 a. aniline carmine		1·00	10
162		1 a. pale rose-carmine, **C** (1918)		1·40	20
163	**58**	1½ a. chocolate (Type A) (1919)		1·50	15
164		1½ a. grey-brown (Type A)		3·50	1·00
165		1½ a. chocolate (Type B) (1921)		1·50	1·75
166	**59**	2 a. dull purple		1·00	10
167		2 a. mauve		1·00	15
168		2 a. violet		3·00	20
169		2 a. bright purple (Jan 1919)		3·00	20
170	**60**	2½ a. ultramarine (1912)		1·75	2·00
171	**61**	2½ a. ultramarine (1913)		1·00	15
172	**62**	3 a. dull orange		3·00	20
173		3 a. orange-brown		2·50	20
174	**63**	4 a. deep olive (1912)		3·25	20
175		4 a. olive-green		3·00	15
176	**64**	6 a. bistre (1912)		3·75	90
177		6 a. yellow-bistre		3·75	1·00
178		6 a. deep bistre-brown		8·00	1·50
179	**65**	8 a. purple (1912)		6·00	50
180		8 a. mauve		10·00	50
181		8 a. deep lilac		10·00	60
182		8 a. bright aniline mauve		12·00	1·25
183	**66**	12 a. dull claret (1912)		9·00	90
184		12 a. claret		7·00	90
185	**67**	1 r. brown and green (1913)		14·00	1·25
186		1 r. red-brown and blue-green		9·50	70
187		2 r. carmine and brown (1913)		13·00	90
188		5 r. ultramarine and violet (1913)		32·00	2·50
189		10 r. green and scarlet (1913)		50·00	8·00
190		15 r. blue and olive (1913)		90·00	13·00
191		25 r. orange and blue (1913)		£160	26·00
151/191			*Set of* 17	£350	48·00

A variety of the 3 pies exists with line joining "P" and "S" of the value at right, sometimes described as "3 Rs".

FORGERIES.—Collectors are warned against forgeries of all the later surcharges of India, and particularly the errors.

NINE

PIES

(68)

1921. *T* **57** *surch with T* **68**.

No.	Description	Unused	Used
192	9 p. on 1 a. rose-carmine	15	10
	a. Error. "NINE NINE"	38·00	55·00
	b. Error. "PIES PIES"	38·00	55·00
	c. Surch double	85·00	95·00
193	9 p. on 1 a. carmine-pink	50	20
194	9 p. on 1 a. aniline carmine	90	35

In the initial setting of the surcharge No. 192a occurred on R. 2/13–16 of the fourth pane and No. 192b on R. 4/13–16 of the third. For the second setting No. 192a was corrected. Examples of No. 192b still occur but on R. 2/13–16 of the third pane. Later printings showed this corrected also.

1922. *T* **56** *surch with T* **39**.

No.	Description	Unused	Used
195	¼ on ½ a. yellow-green	15	15
	a. Surch inverted	8·00	
	b. Surch omitted (in pair with normal)	£120	
196	¼ on ½ a. blue-green	20	20

1922–26. *W* **34**. *P* 14.

No.	Type	Description		Unused	Used
197	**57**	1 a. chocolate		30	10
198	**58**	1½ a. rose-carmine (Type B)		80	30
199	**61**	2½ a. orange		4·25	4·25
200	**62**	3 a. ultramarine		12·00	60
197/200			*Set of* 4	15·00	4·75

69 70 71

PRINTERS. The following issues of postage and contemporary official stamps were all printed by the Security Printing Press, Nasik, *unless otherwise stated.*

1926–33. *Typo. W* **69**. *P* 14.

No.	Type	Description		Unused	Used
201	**55**	3 p. slate		20	10
202	**56**	½ a. green		40	10
203	**57**	1 a. chocolate		40	10
		a. *Tête-bêche* (pair) (1932)		1·25	7·50
204	**58**	1½ a. rose-carmine (Type B) (1929)		1·25	10
205	**59**	2 a. bright purple		3·75	4·50
206	**70**	2 a. purple		90	10
		a. *Tête-bêche* (pair) (1933)		7·50	25·00
207	**61**	2½ a. orange (1929)		75	10
208	**62**	3 a. ultramarine		4·00	90
209		3 a. blue (1928)		4·00	10
210	**63**	4 a. pale sage-green		1·50	10
211	**71**	4 a. sage-green		4·50	10
212	**65**	8 a. reddish purple		4·00	10
213	**66**	12 a. claret		5·00	20
214	**67**	1 r. chocolate and green		5·00	15
		a. Chocolate (head) omitted		£1350	
215		2 r. carmine and orange		7·50	45
216		5 r. ultramarine and purple		17·00	1·25
217		10 r. green and scarlet (1927)		35·00	2·25
218		15 r. blue and olive (1928)		24·00	24·00
219		25 r. orange and blue (1928)		95·00	24·00
201/219			*Set of* 16	£180	50·00

72 D.H. "Hercules"

Missing tree-top (R. 11/6 of 8 a.)

(Des R. Grant. Litho)

1929 (22 Oct). *Air. W* **69** (*sideways*). *P* 14.

No.	Type	Description		Unused	Used
220	**72**	2 a. deep blue-green		1·00	50
221		3 a. blue		1·00	1·25
222		4 a. olive-green		2·25	65
223		6 a. bistre		2·25	90
224		8 a. purple		2·50	1·00
		a. Missing tree-top		40·00	30·00
225		12 a. rose-red		7·00	4·00
220/225			*Set of* 6	14·00	7·50

73 Purana Qila

(Des H. W. Barr. Litho)

1931 (9 Feb). *Inauguration of New Delhi. T* **73** *and similar horiz designs. W* **69** (*sideways*). *P* 13½ × 14.

No.	Description		Unused	Used
226	¼ a. olive-green and orange-brown		30	1·00
227	½ a. violet and green		35	40
228	1 a. mauve and chocolate		60	20
229	2 a. green and blue		1·00	90
230	3 a. chocolate and carmine		2·00	2·50
231	1 r. violet and green		5·00	11·00
226/231		*Set of* 6	8·00	14·00

Designs:—No. 227, War Memorial Arch; No. 228, Council House; No. 229, The Viceroy's House; No. 230, Government of India Secretariat; No. 231, Dominion Columns and the Secretariat.

79

80

81

82

83

(T **82/3** des T. I. Archer. 9 p. litho and typo; 1¼ a., 3½ a. litho; others typo)

1932–36. *W* **69**. *P* 14.

No.	Type	Description		Unused	Used
232	**79**	½ a. green (1934)		35	10
233	**80**	9 p. deep green (22.4.32)		25	10
234	**81**	1 a. chocolate (1934)		65	10
235	**82**	1¼ a. mauve (22.4.32)		25	10
236	**70**	2 a. vermilion		8·00	4·00
236*a*	**59**	2 a. vermilion (1934)		4·50	50
236*b*		2 a. vermilion (*small die*) (1936)		4·50	30
237	**62**	3 a. carmine		70	10
238	**83**	3½ a. ultramarine (22.4.32)		1·25	10
239	**64**	6 a. bistre (1935)		7·00	2·00
232/239			*Set of* 9	20·00	6·00

No. 236*a* measures 19 × 22.6 mm and No. 236*b* 18.4 × 21.8 mm.

84 Gateway of India, Bombay

1935 (6 May). *Silver Jubilee, T* **84** *and similar horiz designs. Litho W* **69** (*sideways*). *P* 13½ × 14.

No.	Description		Unused	Used
240	½ a. black and yellow-green		30	10
241	9 p. black and grey-green		30	10
242	1 a. black and brown		30	10
243	1¼ a. black and bright violet		30	10
244	2½ a. black and orange		45	30
245	3½ a. black and dull ultramarine		90	1·25
246	8 a. black and purple		2·00	1·50
240/246		*Set of* 7	4·00	2·75

Designs:—9 p. Victoria Memorial, Calcutta; 1 a. Rameswaram Temple, Madras; 1¼ a. Jain Temple, Calcutta; 2½ a. Taj Mahal, Agra; 3½ a. Golden Temple, Amritsar; 8 a. Pagoda in Mandalay.

91 King George VI

92 Dak Runner

93 King George VI

1937 (23 Aug–15 Dec). *Typo. W* **69**. *P* 13½ × 14 *or* 14 × 13½ (*T* **93**).

No.	Type	Description		Unused	Used
247	**91**	3 p. slate		40	10
248		½ a. red-brown		40	10
249		9 p. green (23.8.37)		1·50	10
250		1 a. carmine (23.8.37)		15	10
		a. *Tête-bêche* (vert pair)		30	1·25
251	**92**	2 a. vermilion		1·25	10
252	–	2½ a. bright violet		60	10
253	–	3 a. yellow-green		2·25	10
254	–	3½ a. bright blue		1·25	50
255	–	4 a. brown		8·00	10
256	–	6 a. turquoise-green		6·50	15
257	–	8 a. slate-violet		3·25	10
258	–	12 a. lake		14·00	30
259	**93**	1 r. grey and red-brown		1·00	10
260		2 r. purple and brown		3·75	10
261		5 r. green and blue		11·00	15
262		10 r. purple and claret		15·00	30
263		15 r. brown and green		55·00	55·00
264		25 r. slate-violet and purple		55·00	10·00
247/264			*Set of* 18	£150	60·00

Designs: *Horiz as T* **92**—2½ a. Dak bullock cart; 3 a. Dak tonga; 3½ a. Dak camel; 4 a. Mail train; 6 a. *Strathnaver* (liner); 8 a. Mail lorry; 12 a. Mail plane (small head).

100*a* King George VI

101 King George VI

102

103 Mail Plane (large head)

(*T* **100*a*/102** des T. I. Archer. Typo)

1940–43. *W* **69**. *P* 13½ × 14.

No.	Type	Description	Unused	Used
265	**100*a***	3 p. slate	25	10
266		½ a. purple (1.10.42)	40	10
267		9 p. green	40	10
268		1 a. carmine (1.4.43)	40	10
269	**101**	1 a. 3 p. yellow-brown	50	10
269*a*		1½ a. dull violet (9.42)	40	10
270		2 a. vermilion	45	10

271	101	3 a. bright violet (1942)	25	10
272		3½ a. bright blue	70	10
273	102	4 a. brown	45	10
274		6 a. turquoise-green	65	10
275		8 a. slate-violet	65	10
276		12 a. lake	2·50	10
277	103	14 a. purple (15.10.40)	1·75	15
265/277		*Set of* 14	9·00	60

The 1½ a. and 3 a. were at first printed by lithography and were of finer execution and without Jubilee lines in the sheet margins.

105 "Victory" and King George VI

= =
3 PIES

(106)

1946 (2 Jan). *Victory. Litho. W* **69**. *P* 13.

278	105	9 p. yellow-green (8.2.46)	25	10
279		1½ a. dull violet	25	10
280		3½ a. bright blue	65	50
281		12 a. claret (8.2.46)	1·10	55
278/81		*Set of* 4	2·00	1·10

1946 (8 Aug). *Surch with T* **106**.

282	101	3 p. on 1 a. 3 p. yellow-brown	10	10

DOMINION

301 Asokan Capital (Inscr reads "Long Live India")

302 Indian National Flag

303 Douglas DC4

(Des T. I. Archer. Litho)

1947 (21 Nov–15 Dec). *Independence. W* **69**. *P* 14 × 13½ (1½ *a.*) *or* 13½ × 14 (*others*).

301	301	1½ a. grey-green (15 Dec)	15	10
302	302	3½ a. orange-red, blue and green	25	20
303	303	12 a. ultramarine (15 Dec)	1·00	75
301/3		*Set of* 3	1·25	90

304 Lockheed "Constellation"

(Des T. I. Archer. Litho)

1948 (29 May). *Air. Inauguration of India-U.K. Air Service. W* **69**. *P* 13½ × 14.

304	304	12 a. black and ultramarine	90	90

305 Mahatma Gandhi **306**

(Photo Courvoisier)

1948 (15 Aug). *First Anniv of Independence. P* 11½.

305	305	1½ a. brown	80	20
306		3½ a. violet	2·50	1·00
307		12 a. grey-green	3·50	60
308	306	10 r. purple-brown and lake	60·00	40·00
305/8		*Set of* 4	60·00	40·00

307 Ajanta Panel

308 Konarak Horse

309 Trimurti

310 Bodhisattva

311 Nataraja

312 Sanchi Stupa, East Gate

313 Bodh Gaya Temple

314 Bhuvanesvara

315 Gol Gumbad, Bijapur

316 Kandarya Mahadeva Temple

317 Golden Temple, Amritsar

318 Victory Tower, Chittorgarh

319 Red Fort, Delhi

320 Taj Mahal, Agra

321 Qutb Minar, Delhi

322 Satrunjaya Temple, Palitana

(Des T. I. Archer and I. M. Das. Typo (low values), litho (rupee values))

1949 (15 Aug). *W* **69** (*sideways on Nos.* 310, 320 *and* 323*a*). *P* 14 (3 *p. to* 2 *a.*), 13½ (3 *a. to* 12 *a.*), 14 × 13½ (1 *r. and* 10 *r.*), 13½ × 14 (2 *r. and* 5 *r.*), 13 (15 *r.*).

309	307	3 p. slate-violet	15	10
310	308	6 p. purple-brown	25	10
311	309	9 p. yellow-green	40	10
312	310	1 a. turquoise	60	10
313	311	2 a. carmine	80	10
314	312	3 a. brown-orange	1·50	10
315	313	3½ a. bright blue	3·00	2·50
316	314	4 a. lake	5·00	10
317	315	6 a. violet	2·00	10
318	316	8 a. turquoise-green	2·00	10
319	317	12 a. dull blue	1·75	10
320	318	1 r. dull violet and green	9·00	10
321	319	2 r. claret and violet	6·50	15
322	320	5 r. blue-green and red-brown	16·00	45
323	321	10 r. purple-brown and deep blue	28·00	3·00
		a. Purple-brown and blue	45·00	3·25
324	322	15 r. brown and claret	12·00	11·00
309/324		*Set of* 16	75·00	16·00

For T **310** with statue reversed, see No. 333.

323 Globe and Asokan Capital

1949 (10 Oct). *75th Anniv of U.P.U. Litho. W* **69**. *P* 13.

325	323	9 p. green	75	75
326		2 a. rose	1·00	1·25
327		3½ a. bright blue	1·75	2·25
328		12 a. brown-purple	3·50	2·50
325/8		*Set of* 4	6·00	6·00

REPUBLIC

324 Rejoicing Crowds

328 As T **310**, but statue reversed

(Des D. J. Keymer & Co. Litho)

1950 (26 Jan). *Inauguration of Republic. T* **324** *and similar designs. W* **69** (*sideways on* 3½ *a.*). *P* 13.

329		2 a. scarlet	70	15
330		3½ a. ultramarine	1·50	2·75
331		4 a. violet	1·50	40
332		12 a. maroon	3·00	2·25
329/32		*Set of* 4	6·00	5·00

Designs: *Vert*—3½ a. Quill, ink-well and verse. *Horiz*—4 a. Ear of corn and plough; 12 a. Spinning-wheel and cloth.

1950 (15 July)–**51**. *Typo. W* **69**. *P* 14 (1 *a.*), 13½ (*others*).

333	328	1 a. turquoise	2·25	10
333*a*	313	2½ a. lake (30.4.51)	2·00	70
333*b*	314	4 a. bright blue (30.4.51)	5·00	10
333/*b*		*Set of* 3	8·50	70

329 *Stegodon ganesa*

330 Torch

1951 (13 Jan). *Centenary of Geological Survey of India. Litho. W* **69**. *P* 13.

334	329	2 a. black and claret	70	15

1951 (4 Mar). *First Asian Games, New Delhi. Litho. W* **69** (*sideways*). *P* 14.

335	330	2 a. reddish purple and brown-orange	75	20
336		12 a. chocolate and light blue	4·00	90

PROCESS. All the following issues were printed in photogravure, *except where otherwise stated.*

331 Kabir

332 Locomotives in 1853 and 1953

1952 (1 Oct). *Indian Saints and Poets. T* **331** *and similar vert designs. W* **69**. *P* 14.

337		9 p. bright emerald-green	30	10
338		1 a. carmine	30	10
339		2 a. orange-red	60	10
340		4 a. bright blue	1·25	10
341		4½ a. bright mauve	30	10
342		12 a. brown	1·50	60
337/42		*Set of* 6	3·75	90

Designs:—1 a. Tulsidas; 2 a. Meera; 4 a. Surdas; 4½ a. Ghalib; 12 a. Tagore.

1953 (16 Apr). *Railway Centenary. W* **69**. *P* 14½ × 14.

343	332	2 a. black	40	10

333 Mount Everest

1953 (2 Oct). *Conquest of Mount Everest.* W **69**. P 14½ × 14.

No.	Type	Description	Unused	Used
344	**333**	2 a. bright violet	40	10
345		14 a. brown	3·00	25

334 Telegraph Poles of 1851 and 1951

1953 (1 Nov). *Centenary of Indian Telegraphs.* W **69**. P 14½ × 14.

No.	Type	Description	Unused	Used
346	**334**	2 a. blue-green	30	10
347		12 a. blue	3·00	40

335 Postal Transport, 1854

1954 (1 Oct). *Stamp Centenary. T* **335** *and similar horiz designs.* W **69**. P 14½ × 14.

No.	Type	Description	Unused	Used
348		1 a. reddish purple	25	10
349		2 a. cerise	30	10
350		4 a. orange-brown	1·75	15
351		14 a. blue	1·50	40
348/51		*Set of* 4	3·50	60

Designs:—2, 14 a. "Airmail"; 4 a. Postal transport, 1954.

338 U.N. Emblem and Lotus

1954 (24 Oct). *United Nations Day.* W **69** (*sideways*). P 13.

No.	Type	Description	Unused	Used
352	**338**	2 a. turquoise-green	15	10

339 Forest Research Institute

1954 (11 Dec). *Fourth World Forestry Congress, Dehra Dun.* W **69**. P 14½ × 14.

No.	Type	Description	Unused	Used
353	**339**	2 a. ultramarine	10	10

340 Tractor

344 Woman Spinning

347 "Malaria Control" (Mosquito and Staff of Aesculapius)

1955 (26 Jan). *Five Year Plan. T* **340**, **344**, **347** *and similar designs.* W **69** (*sideways on small horiz designs*). P 14 × 14½ (*small horiz*) *or* 14½ × 14 (*others*).

No.	Type	Description	Unused	Used
354		3 p. bright purple	15	10
355		6 p. violet	15	10
356		9 p. orange-brown	15	10
357		1 a. blue-green	30	10
358		2 a. light blue	20	10
359		3 a. pale blue-green	40	10
360		4 a. rose-carmine	40	10
361		6 a. yellow-brown	40	10
362		8 a. blue	3·50	10
363		10 a. turquoise-green	60	60
364		12 a. bright blue	50	10
365		14 a. bright green	1·25	20
366		1 r. deep dull green	4·00	10
367		1 r. 2 a. grey	1·75	2·75
368		1 r. 8 a. reddish purple	4·50	3·00
369		2 r. cerise	4·00	10
370		5 r. brown	14·00	30
371		10 r. orange	14·00	1·25
354/71		*Set of* 18	45·00	7·50

Designs: *Horiz* (*as T* **340**)—6 p. Power loom; 9 p. Bullock-driven well; 1 a. Damodar Valley Dam; 4 a. Bullocks; 8 a. Chittaranjan Locomotive Works; 12 a. Hindustan Aircraft Factory, Bangalore; 1 r. Telephone engineer; 2 r. Rare Earth Factory, Alwaye; 5 r. Sindri Fertiliser Factory; 10 r. Steel plant. (*As T* **347**)—10 a. Marine Drive, Bombay; 14 a. Kashmir landscape; 1 r. 2 a. Cape Comorin; 1 r. 8 a. Mt Kangchenjunga. *Vert* (*as T* **344**)—3 a. Woman weaving with hand loom.

For stamps as Nos. 366, 369/71 but W **374** see Nos. 413/16.

358 Bodhi Tree

359 Round Parasol and Bodhi Tree

(Des C. Pakrashi (2 a.), R. D'Silva (14 a.))

1956 (24 May). *Buddha Jayanti.* W **69** (*sideways on 14 a.*). P 13 × 13½ (*2 a.*) *or* 13½ × 13 (*14 a.*).

No.	Type	Description	Unused	Used
372	**358**	2 a. sepia	15	10
373	**359**	14 a. vermilion	2·50	2·25

360 Lokmanya Bal Gangadhar Tilak

361 Map of India

1956 (23 July). *Birth Centenary of Tilak (journalist).* W **69**. P 13 × 13½.

No.	Type	Description	Unused	Used
374	**360**	2 a. chestnut	10	10

(New Currency 100 n(aye) p(aise) = 1 rupee.)

1957 (1 Apr)–**58.** W **69** (*sideways*). P 14 × 14½.

No.	Type	Description	Unused	Used
375	**361**	1 n.p. blue-green	10	10
376		2 n.p. light brown	10	10
377		3 n.p. deep brown	10	10
378		5 n.p. bright green	4·25	10
379		6 n.p. grey	10	10
379*a*		8 n.p. light blue-green (7.5.58)	1·25	80
380		10 n.p. deep dull green	4·25	10
381		13 n.p. bright carmine-red	25	10
381*a*		15 n.p. violet (16.1.58)	35	10
382		20 n.p. blue	25	10
383		25 n.p. ultramarine	25	10
384		50 n.p. orange	2·25	10
385		75 n.p. reddish purple	1·25	10
385*a*		90 n.p. bright purple (16.1.58)	70	40
375/85*a*		*Set of* 14	13·00	1·25

The 8, 15 and 90 n.p. have their value expressed as "nP".
For similar stamps but W **374** see Nos. 399/412.

362 The Rani of Jhansi

363 Shrine

1957 (15 Aug). *Indian Mutiny Centenary.* W **69**. P 14½ × 14 (*15 n.p.*) *or* 13 × 13½ (*90 n.p.*).

No.	Type	Description	Unused	Used
386	**362**	15 n.p. brown	15	10
387	**363**	90 n.p. reddish purple	1·50	40

364 Henri Dunant and Conference Emblem

365 "Nutrition"

1957 (28 Oct). *19th International Red Cross Conference, New Delhi.* W **69** (*sideways*). P 13½ × 13.

No.	Type	Description	Unused	Used
388	**364**	15 n.p. deep grey and carmine	10	10

1957 (14 Nov). *National Children's Day. T* **365** *and similar designs.* W **69** (*sideways on 90 n.p.*). P 14 × 13½ (*90 n.p.*) *or* 13½ × 14 (*others*).

No.	Type	Description	Unused	Used
389		8 n.p. reddish purple	10	10
390		15 n.p. turquoise-green	10	10
391		90 n.p. orange-brown	20	15
389/91		*Set of* 3	25	25

Designs: *Horiz*—15 n.p. "Education". *Vert*—90 n.p. "Recreation".

ALTERED CATALOGUE NUMBERS

Any Catalogue numbers altered from the last edition are shown as a list in the introductory pages.

368 Bombay University

369 Calcutta University

1957 (31 Dec). *Centenary of Indian Universities. T* **368/9** *and similar design.* W **69** (*sideways on T* **368**). P 14 × 14½ (*No.* 392) *or* 13½ × 14 (*others*).

No.	Type	Description	Unused	Used
392		10 n.p. violet	10	10
393		10 n.p. grey	10	10
394		10 n.p. light brown	10	10
392/4		*Set of* 3	20	20

Design: *Horiz as T* **369**—No. 394, Madras University.

371 J. N. Tata (founder) and Steel Plant

372 Dr. D. K. Karve

1958 (1 Mar). *50th Anniv of Steel Industry.* W **69**. P 14½ × 14.

No.	Type	Description	Unused	Used
395	**371**	15 n.p. orange-red	10	10

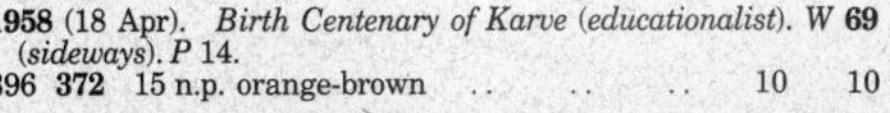

1958 (18 Apr). *Birth Centenary of Karve (educationalist).* W **69** (*sideways*). P 14.

No.	Type	Description	Unused	Used
396	**372**	15 n.p. orange-brown	10	10

373 "Wapiti" and "Hunter" Aircraft

374 Asokan Capital

1958 (30 Apr). *Silver Jubilee of Indian Air Force.* W **69**. P 14½ × 14.

No.	Type	Description	Unused	Used
397	**373**	15 n.p. blue	25	10
398		90 n.p. ultramarine	50	65

ASOKAN CAPITAL WATERMARK. When the watermark was originally introduced in 1958 the base of each individual capital was 10 mm wide. During 1985 a modified version, with the capital base measurement reduced to 8 mm, was introduced. Examples have been seen on Nos. 921a, 922a, 923a and 928a.

1958–63. *As Nos.* 366, 369/71 *and* 375/85*a but* W **374**.

No.	Type	Description	Unused	Used
399	**361**	1 n.p. blue-green (1960)	10	10
		a. Imperf (pair)	£100	
400		2 n.p. light brown (27.10.58)	10	10
401		3 n.p. deep brown (1958)	10	10
402		5 n.p. bright green (27.10.58)	10	10
403		6 n.p. grey (1963)	15	2·00
404		8 n.p. light blue-green (1958)	20	10
405		10 n.p. deep dull green (27.10.58)	15	10
		a. Imperf (pair)	†	—
406		13 n.p. bright carmine-red (1963)	15	1·75
407		15 n.p. violet (10.60)	15	10
408		20 n.p. blue (27.10.58)	25	10
409		25 n.p. ultramarine (27.10.58)	25	10
410		50 n.p. orange (1959)	30	10
411		75 n.p. reddish purple (1959)	40	10
412		90 n.p. bright purple (1960)	2·75	10
413	–	1 r. deep dull green (1959)	2·25	10
414	–	2 r. cerise (1959)	4·00	10
415	–	5 r. brown (1959)	9·00	30
416	–	10 r. orange (1959)	18·00	3·25
399/416		*Set of* 18	35·00	7·00

The 5, 10, 15, 20, 25 and 50 n.p. with serial numbers on the back are coil stamps prepared from sheets for experimenting with coil machines. In the event the machines were not purchased and the stamps were sold over the counter.

375 Bipin Chandra Pal

376 Nurse with Child Patient

1958 (7 Nov). *Birth Centenary of Pal (patriot).* W **374**. P 14 × 13½.

No.	Type	Description	Unused	Used
418	**375**	15 n.p. deep dull green	10	10

1958 (14 Nov). *National Children's Day.* W **374**. P 14 × 13½.

No.	Type	Description	Unused	Used
419	**376**	15 n.p. violet	10	10

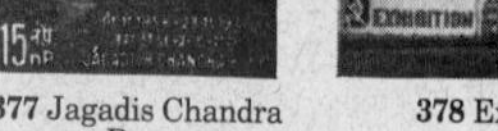

377 Jagadis Chandra Bose — **378** Exhibition Gate

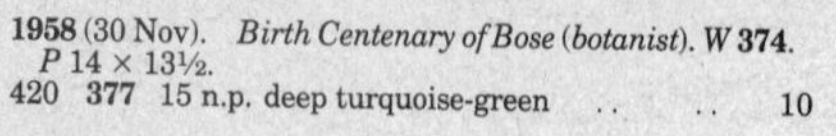

1958 (30 Nov). *Birth Centenary of Bose (botanist).* W **374**. *P* 14 × 13½.
420 **377** 15 n.p. deep turquoise-green 10 10

1958 (30 Dec). *India 1958 Exhibition, New Delhi.* W **374** *(sideways)*. *P* 14½ × 14.
421 **378** 15 n.p. reddish purple 10 10

379 Sir Jamsetjee Jejeebhoy — **380** "The Triumph of Labour" (after Chowdhury)

1959 (15 Apr). *Death Centenary of Jejeebhoy (philanthropist).* W **374**. *P* 14 × 13½.
422 **379** 15 n.p. brown 10 10

1959 (15 June). *40th Anniv of International Labour Organization.* W **374** *(sideways)*. *P* 14½ × 14.
423 **380** 15 n.p. dull green 10 10

381 Boys awaiting admission to Children's Home — **382** "Agriculture"

1959 (14 Nov). *National Children's Day.* W **374**. *P* 14 × 14½.
424 **381** 15 n.p. deep dull green 10 10
a. Imperf (pair) £550

1959 (30 Dec). *First World Agricultural Fair, New Delhi.* W **374**. *P* 13½ × 13.
425 **382** 15 n.p. grey 10 10

383 Thiruvalluvar (poet)

1960 (15 Feb). *Thiruvalluvar Commemoration.* W **374**. *P* 14 × 13½.
426 **383** 15 n.p. reddish purple 10 10

384 Yaksha pleading with the Cloud (from the "Meghaduta") — **385** Shakuntala writing a letter to Dushyanta (from the "Shakuntala")

1960 (22 June). *Kalidasa (poet) Commemoration.* W **374**. *P* 13.
427 **384** 15 n.p. grey 10 10
428 **385** 1 r. 3 n.p. pale yellow and brown .. 50 10

386 S. Bharati (poet) — **387** Dr. M. Visvesvaraya

1960 (11 Sept). *Subramania Bharati Commemoration.* W **374**. *P* 14 × 13½.
429 **386** 15 n.p. blue 10 10

1960 (15 Sept). *Birth Centenary of Dr. M. Visvesvaraya (engineer).* W **374**. *P* 13 × 13½.
430 **387** 15 n.p. brown and bright carmine .. 10 10

388 "Children's Health"

1960 (14 Nov). *Children's Day.* W **374**. *P* 13½ × 13.
431 **388** 15 n.p. deep dull green 10 10

389 Children greeting U.N. Emblem — **390** Tyagaraja (Indian Saint)

1960 (11 Dec). *U.N.I.C.E.F. Day.* W **374**. *P* 13½ × 13.
432 **389** 15 n.p. orange-brown and olive-brown 10 10

1961 (6 Jan). *Tyagaraja Commemoration.* W **374**. *P* 14 × 13½.
433 **390** 15 n.p. greenish blue 10 10

391 "First Aerial Post" cancellation

392 "Air India" Boeing 707 jetliner and Humber-Sommer plane

1961 (18 Feb). *50th Anniv of First Official Airmail Flight, Allahabad-Naini.* T **391/2** *and similar design.* W **374**. *P* 14 *(5 n.p.) or* 13 × 13½ *(others)*.
434 5 n.p. olive-drab 40 10
435 15 n.p. deep green and grey 90 30
436 1 r. purple and grey .. .. .. 3·75 1·00
434/6 .. .. *Set of* 3 4·50 1·25

Design: *Horiz as T* **392**—1 r. H. Pecquet flying Humber-Sommer plane and "Aerial Post" cancellation.

394 Shivaji on horseback — **395** Motilal Nehru (politician)

1961 (17 Apr). *Shivaji Commemoration.* W **374**. *P* 13 × 13½.
437 **394** 15 n.p. brown and green.. .. .. 15 10

1961 (6 May). *Birth Centenary of Pandit Motilal Nehru.* W **374**. *P* 14.
438 **395** 15 n.p. olive-brown and brown-orange .. 10 10

396 Tagore (poet) — **397** All India Radio Emblem and Transmitting Aerials

1961 (7 May). *Birth Centenary of Rabindranath Tagore.* W **374**. *P* 13 × 13½.
439 **396** 15 n.p. yellow-orange and blue-green .. 15 10

1961 (8 June). *Silver Jubilee of All India Radio.* W **374**. *P* 13½ × 13.
440 **397** 15 n.p. ultramarine 10 10

398 P. Chandra Ray — **399** V. N. Bhatkande

1961 (2 Aug). *Birth Centenary of Ray (scientist).* W **374**. *P* 14 × 13½.
441 **398** 15 n.p. grey 10 10

1961 (1 Sept). *Birth Centenary of Bhatkande (musician).* W **374**. *P* 13 × 13½.
442 **399** 15 n.p. olive-brown 10 10

400 Child at Lathe — **401** Fair Emblem and Main Gate

1961 (14 Nov). *Children's Day.* W **374**. *P* 14 × 13½.
443 **400** 15 n.p. brown 10 10

1961 (14 Nov). *Indian Industries Fair, New Delhi.* W **374**. *P* 14 × 14½.
444 **401** 15 n.p. blue and carmine 10 10

402 Indian Forest

1961 (21 Nov). *Centenary of Scientific Forestry.* W **374**. *P* 13 × 13½.
445 **402** 15 n.p. green and brown.. .. .. 10 10

403 Pitalkhora: Yaksha — **404** Kalibangan Seal

1961 (14 Dec). *Centenary of Indian Archaeological Survey.* W **374**. *P* 14 × 13½ *(15 n.p.) or* 13½ × 14 *(90 n.p.)*.
446 **403** 15 n.p. orange-brown 10 10
447 **404** 90 n.p. yellow-olive and light brown .. 20 10

MINIMUM PRICE

The minimum price quote is 10p which represents a handling charge rather than a basis for valuing common stamps. For further notes about prices see introductory pages.

405 M. M. Malaviya **406** Gauhati Refinery

1961 (24 Dec). *Birth Centenary of Malaviya (President of National Congress). W* **374**. *P* 14 × 13½.
448 **405** 15 n.p. deep slate 10 10

1962 (1 Jan). *Inauguration of Gauhati Oil Refinery. W* **374**. *P* 13 × 13½.
449 **406** 15 n.p. blue 15 10

407 Bhikaiji Cama **408** Panchayati at work and Parliament Building

1962 (26 Jan). *Birth Centenary of Bhikaiji Cama (revolutionary). W* **374**. *P* 14.
450 **407** 15 n.p. reddish purple 10 10

1962 (26 Jan). *Panchayati Raj Commemoration. W* **374**. *P* 13 × 13½.
451 **408** 15 n.p. bright purple 10 10

409 D. Saraswati (religious educator) **410** G. S. Vidhyarthi (patriot)

1962 (4 Mar). *Saraswati Commemoration. W* **374**. *P* 14.
452 **409** 15 n.p. orange-brown 10 10

1962 (25 Mar). *Vidhyarthi Commemoration. W* **374**. *P* 14 × 13½.
453 **410** 15 n.p. red-brown 10 10

411 Malaria Eradication Emblem **412** Dr. R. Prasad (former President of India)

1962 (7 Apr). *Malaria Eradication. W* **374**. *P* 13 × 13½.
454 **411** 15 n.p. yellow and claret 10 10

1962 (13 May). *Dr. Rajendra Prasad Commemoration. W* **374**. *P* 13.
455 **412** 15 n.p. bright purple (*shades*) 10 10

413 Calcutta High Court **416** Ramabai Ranade

1962. *Centenary of Indian High Courts. T* **413** *and similar horiz designs. W* **374**. *P* 14.
456 15 n.p. dull green (1 July) 10 10
457 15 n.p. red-brown (6 August) 10 10
458 15 n.p. slate (14 August) 10 10
456/8 .. .. *Set of* 3 25 20
Designs:—No. 457, Madras High Court; No. 458, Bombay High Court.

1962 (15 Aug). *Birth Centenary of Ramabai Ranade (social reformer). W* **374**. *P* 14 × 13½.
459 **416** 15 n.p. orange-brown 10 10

417 Indian Rhinoceros **418** "Passing the Flag to Youth"

1962 (1 Oct). *Wild Life Week. W* **374**. *P* 13½ × 14.
460 **417** 15 n.p. red-brown and deep turquoise .. 15 10

INSCRIPTIONS. From No. 461 onwards all designs are inscribed "BHARAT" in Devanagri, in addition to "INDIA" in English.

1962 (14 Nov). *Children's Day. W* **374**. *P* 13½ × 13.
461 **418** 15 n.p. orange-red and turquoise-green 10 10

419 Human Eye within Lotus Blossom **420** S. Ramanujan

1962 (3 Dec). *19th International Ophthalmology Congress, New Delhi. W* **374**. *P* 13½ × 13.
462 **419** 15 n.p. deep olive-brown 10 10

1962 (22 Dec). *75th Birth Anniv of Ramanujan (mathematician). W* **374**. *P* 13½ × 14.
463 **420** 15 n.p. deep olive-brown 10 10

Re.1

═══

421 S. Vivekananda (**422**)

1963 (17 Jan). *Birth Centenary of Vivekananda (philosopher). W* **374**. *P* 14 × 14½.
464 **421** 15 n.p. orange-brown and yellow-olive .. 10 10

1963 (2 Feb). *No. 428 surch with T* **422**.
465 **385** 1 r. on 1 r. 3 n.p. pale yellow & brn .. 30 10

423 Hands reaching for F.A.O. Emblem **424** Henri Dunant (founder) and Centenary Emblem

1963 (21 Mar). *Freedom from Hunger. W* **374**. *P* 13.
466 **423** 15 n.p. grey-blue 50 10

1963 (8 May). *Red Cross Centenary. W* **374**. *P* 13.
467 **424** 15 n.p. red and grey 60 10
a. Red (cross) omitted £2250

425 Artillery and Helicopter

1963 (15 Aug). *Defence Campaign. T* **425** *and similar horiz design. W* **374**. *P* 14.
468 15 n.p. grey-green 25 10
469 1 r. red-brown 55 40
Design:—1 r. Sentry and parachutists.

427 D. Naoroji (patriot) **428** Mrs. Annie Besant (patriot and theosophist, born 1847). (Stamp wrongly dated "1837")

1963 (4 Sept). *Dadabhoy Naoroji Commemoration. W* **374**. *P* 13.
470 **427** 15 n.p. grey 10 10

1963 (1 Oct). *Mrs. Annie Besant Commemoration. W* **374**. *P* 13½ × 14.
471 **428** 15 n.p. turquoise-green 10 10

429 Gaur **430** Lesser Panda

1963 (7 Oct). *Wild Life Preservation. T* **429/30** *and similar designs. W* **374**. *P* 13½ × 14 (10 *n.p.*) *or* 13 (*others*).
472 10 n.p. black and yellow-orange 60 80
473 15 n.p. orange-brown and green 70 30
474 30 n.p. slate and yellow-ochre .. .. 2·50 75
475 50 n.p. orange and deep grey-green .. .. 2·25 50
476 1 r. light brown and blue .. .. 2·25 50
472/6 .. .. *Set of* 5 7·50 2·50
Designs: *Vert*—30 n.p. Indian elephant. *Horiz* (*as T* **430**)—50 n.p. Tiger; 1 r. Lion.

434 "School Meals" **435** Eleanor Roosevelt at Spinning-wheel

1963 (14 Nov). *Children's Day. W* **374**. *P* 14 × 13½.
477 **434** 15 n.p. bistre-brown 10 10

1963 (10 Dec). *15th Anniv of Declaration of Human Rights. W* **374**. *P* 13½ × 13.
478 **435** 15 n.p. reddish purple 10 10

436 Dipalakshmi (bronze) **437** Gopabandhu Das (patriot and social reformer)

1964 (4 Jan). *26th International Orientalists Congress, New Delhi. W* **374**. *P* 13 × 13½.
479 **436** 15 n.p. deep ultramarine 10 10

1964 (4 Jan). *Gopabandhu Das Commemoration. W* **374**. *P* 13 × 13½.
480 **437** 15 n.p. deep dull purple 10 10

438 Purandaradasa

1964 (14 Jan). *400th Death Anniv of Purandaradasa (musician). W* **374**. *P* 13 × 13½.
481 **438** 15 n.p. light brown 10 10

439 S. C. Bose and I. N. A. Badge — **440** Bose and Indian National Army

1964 (23 Jan). *67th Birth Anniv of Subhas Chandra Bose (nationalist). W* **374**. *P* 13.
482 **439** 15 n.p. yellow-bistre 20 10
483 **440** 55 n.p. black, orange and orange-red .. 25 35

441 Sarojini Naidu — **442** Kasturba Gandhi

1964 (13 Feb). *85th Birth Anniv of Mrs. Sarojini Naidu (patriot). W* **374**. *P* 14.
484 **441** 15 n.p. deep grey-green and purple .. 10 10

1964 (22 Feb). *20th Death Anniv of Kasturba Gandhi. W* **374**. *P* 14 × 13½.
485 **442** 15 n.p. orange-brown 10 10

443 Dr. W. M. Haffkine (immunologist) — **444** Jawaharlal Nehru (statesman)

1964 (16 Mar). *Haffkine Commemoration. W* **374**. *P* 13.
486 **443** 15 n.p. deep purple-brown/*buff* 10 10

(Value expressed as paisa instead of naye paise.)

1964 (12 June). *Nehru Mourning Issue. No wmk. P* 13½ × 13.
487 **444** 15 p. deep slate 10 10

445 Sir A. Mookerjee — **446** Sri Aurobindo

1964 (29 June). *Birth Centenary of Sir Asutosh Mookerjee (education reformer). W* **374**. *P* 13½ × 13.
488 **445** 15 p. bistre-brown and yellow-olive .. 10 10

1964 (15 Aug). *92nd Birth Anniv of Sri Aurobindo (religious leader). W* **374**. *P* 13 × 13½.
489 **446** 15 p. dull purple 10 10

447 Raja R. Roy (social reformer) — **448** I.S.O. Emblem and Globe

1964 (27 Sept). *Raja Rammohun Roy Commemoration. W* **374**. *P* 13 × 13½.
490 **447** 15 n.p. brown 10 10

1964 (9 Nov). *Sixth International Organization for Standardization General Assembly, Bombay. No wmk. P* 13 × 13½.
491 **448** 15 p. carmine 10 10

449 Jawaharlal Nehru (from 1 r. commemorative coin) — **450** St. Thomas (after statue, Ortona Cathedral, Italy)

1964 (14 Nov). *Children's Day. No wmk. P* 14 × 13½.
492 **449** 15 p. slate 10 10

1964 (2 Dec). *St. Thomas Commemoration. No wmk. P* 14 × 13½.
493 **450** 15 p. reddish purple 10 20
No. 493 was issued on the occasion of Pope Paul's visit to India.

451 Globe — **452** J. Tata (industrialist)

1964 (14 Dec). *22nd International Geological Congress. W* **374**. *P* 14 × 13½.
494 **451** 15 p. blue-green 10 15

1965 (7 Jan). *Jamsetji Tata Commemoration. No wmk. P* 13½ × 13.
495 **452** 15 p. dull-purple and orange 10 15

453 Lala Lajpat Rai — **454** Globe and Congress Emblem

1965 (28 Jan). *Birth Centenary of Lala Lajpat Rai (patriot). No wmk. P* 13 × 13½.
496 **453** 15 p. light brown 10 10

1965 (8 Feb). *20th International Chamber of Commerce Congress, New Delhi. No wmk. P* 13½ × 13.
497 **454** 15 p. grey-green and carmine 10 15

455 Freighter *Jalausha* and Visakhapatnam — **456** Abraham Lincoln

1965 (5 Apr). *National Maritime Day. W* **374** (*sideways*). *P* 14½ × 14.
498 **455** 15 p. blue 15 15

1965 (15 Apr). *Death Centenary of Abraham Lincoln. W* **374**. *P* 13.
499 **456** 15 p. brown and yellow-ochre 10 10

457 I.T.U. Emblem and Symbols — **458** "Everlasting Flame"

1965 (17 May). *I.T.U. Centenary. W* **374** (*sideways*). *P* 14½ × 14.
500 **457** 15 p. reddish purple 50 25

1965 (27 May). *First Anniv of Nehru's Death. W* **374**. *P* 13.
501 **458** 15 p. carmine and blue 10 10

459 I.C.Y. Emblem — **460** Climbers on Summit

1965 (26 June). *International Co-operation Year. P* 13½ × 13.
502 **459** 15 p. deep olive and yellow-brown .. 30 25

1965 (15 Aug). *Indian Mount Everest Expedition. P* 13.
503 **460** 15 p. deep reddish purple 10 10

461 Bidri Vase — **462** Brass Lamp — **466** Electric Locomotive

474 Medieval Sculpture — **475** Dal Lake, Kashmir

1965–75. *T* **461/2, 466, 474/5** *and similar designs.*

(*a*) *W* **374** (*sideways on* 2, 3, 5, 6, 8, 30, 50, 60 *p.*, 2, 5, 10 *r.*). *P* 14 × 14½ (4, 10, 15, 20, 40, 70 *p.*, 1 *r.*) *or* 14½ × 14 (*others*)

504 2 p. red-brown (16.10.67) 10 20
505 3 p. brown-olive (16.10.67) 10 50
505*a* 4 p. lake-brown (15.5.68) 10 50
506 5 p. cerise (16.10.67) 10 10
a. Imperf (pair) £180
507 6 p. grey-black (1.7.66) 10 70
508 8 p. red-brown (15.3.67) .. .. .. 25 1·50
509 10 p. new blue (1.7.66) 25 10
510 15 p. bronze-green (15.8.65) 35 10
511 20 p. purple (16.10.67) 25 10
512 30 p. sepia (15.3.67) 15 10
513 40 p. maroon (2.10.68) 15 10
514 50 p. blue-green (15.3.67) 20 10
515 60 p. deep grey (16.10.67) 35 10
516 70 p. chalky blue (15.3.67) 60 10
517 1 r. red-brown and plum (1.7.66) .. 60 10
518 2 r. new blue & deep slate-violet (15.3.67) 2·00 10
519 5 r. deep slate-violet and brown (15.3.67) 2·50 25
520 10 r. black and bronze-green (14.11.65) .. 10·00 80
504/20 .. .. *Set of* 18 16·00 4·50

(*b*) *No wmk. P* 14½ × 14
520*a* 5 p. cerise (12.5.74*) 10 10

(*c*) *Wmk Large Star and* "INDIA GOVT"† *in sheet. P* 14½ × 14
521 2 p. red-brown (1.3.75) 10 30
521*a* 5 p. cerise (1.3.75) 10 10

Designs: *Horiz* (*as T* **466**)—4 p. Coffee berries; 15 p. Plucking tea; 20 p. Folland "Gnat" fighter aircraft; 40 p. Calcutta G.P.O.; 70 p. Hampi Chariot (sculpture). (*As T* **475**)—5 r. Bhakra Dam, Punjab; 10 r. Atomic Reactor, Trombay. *Vert* (*as T* **461/2**)—5 p. "Family Planning"; 6 p. Konarak Elephant; 8 p. Spotted Deer ("Chital"); 30 p. Indian dolls; 50 p. Mangoes; 60 p. Somnath Temple.

*Earliest known date of issue.

†The arrangement of this watermark in the sheet results in the words and the star appearing upright, inverted or sideways.

Two different postal forgeries exist of No. 511, both printed in lithography and without watermark. The cruder version is roughly perforated 15, but the more sophisticated is perforated 14 × 14½.

See also Nos. 721/38.

479 G. B. Pant (statesman) — **480** V. Patel

1965 (10 Sept). *Govind Ballabh Pant Commemoration. P* 13.
522 **479** 15 p. brown and deep green 10 10

1965 (31 Oct). *90th Birth Anniv of Vallabhbhai Patel (statesman). P 14×13½.*
523 **480** 15 p. blackish brown 10 15

481 C. Das

482 Vidyapati (poet)

1965 (5 Nov). *95th Birth Anniv of Chittaranjan Das (lawyer and patriot). P 13.*
524 **481** 15 p. yellow-brown 10 10

1965 (17 Nov). *Vidyapati Commemoration. P 14×14½.*
525 **482** 15 p. yellow-brown 10 10

483 Sikandra, Agra

484 Soldier, Fighters and Cruiser *Mysore*

1966 (24 Jan). *Pacific Area Travel Association Conference. New Delhi. P 13½×14.*
526 **483** 15 p. slate 10 10

1966 (26 Jan). *Indian Armed Forces. P 14*
527 **484** 15 p. violet 25 15

485 Lal Bahadur Shastri (statesman)

486 Kambar (poet)

1966 (26 Jan). *Shastri Mourning Issue. P 13×13½.*
528 **485** 15 p. black 10 10

1966 (5 Apr). *Kambar Commemoration. P 14 × 14½.*
529 **486** 15 p. grey-green 10 10

487 B. R. Ambedkar

488 Kunwar Singh (patriot)

1966 (14 Apr). *75th Birth Anniv of Dr. B. R. Ambedkar (lawyer and reformer). P 14 × 13½.*
530 **487** 15 p. purple-brown 10 10

1966 (23 Apr). *Kunwar Singh Commemoration. P 14 × 13½.*
531 **488** 15 p. chestnut 10 10

489 G. K. Gokhale

490 Acharya Dvivedi (writer)

1966 (9 May). *Birth Centenary of G. K. Gokhale (patriot). P 13 ½ × 13.*
532 **489** 15 p. brown-purple and pale yellow .. 10 10

1966 (15 May). *Dvivedi Commemoration. P 13½ × 14.*
533 **490** 15 p. drab 10 10

NEW INFORMATION

The editor is always interested to correspond with people who have new information that will improve or correct the Catalogue.

491 Maharaja Ranjit Singh (warrior)

492 Homi Bhabha (scientist) and Nuclear Reactor

1966 (28 June). *Maharaja Ranjit Singh Commemoration. P 14 × 13½.*
534 **491** 15 p. purple 10 10

1966 (4 Aug). *Homi Bhabha Commemoration. P 14½ × 14.*
535 **492** 15 p. dull purple 10 15

493 A. K. Azad (scholar)

494 Swami Tirtha

1966 (11 Nov). *Abul Kalam Azad Commemoration. P 13½ × 14.*
536 **493** 15 p. chalky blue 10 10

1966 (11 Nov). *60th Death Anniv of Swami Rama Tirtha (social reformer). P 13 × 13½.*
537 **494** 15 p. turquoise-blue 10 15

495 Infant and Dove Emblem

496 Allahabad High Court

(Des C. Pakrashi)

1966 (14 Nov). *Children's Day. P 13 × 13½.*
538 **495** 15 p. bright purple 10 10

1966 (25 Nov). *Centenary of Allahabad High Court. P 14½ × 14.*
539 **496** 15 p. dull purple 10 20

497 Indian Family

498 Hockey Game

1966 (12 Dec). *Family Planning. P 13.*
540 **497** 15 p. brown 10 10

1966 (31 Dec). *India's Hockey Victory in Fifth Asian Games. P 13.*
541 **498** 15 p. new blue 40 20

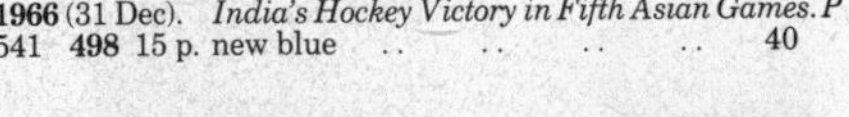

499 "Jai Kisan"

500 Voter and Polling Booth

1967 (11 Jan). *First Anniv of Shastri's Death. P 13½ × 14.*
542 **499** 15 p. yellow-green 10 10

1967 (13 Jan). *Indian General Election. P 13½ × 14.*
543 **500** 15 p. red-brown 10 10

501 Guru Dwara Shrine, Patna

502 Taj Mahal

1967 (17 Jan). *300th Birth Anniv (in 1966) of Guru Gobind Singh (National leader). P 14 × 13½.*
544 **501** 15 p. bluish violet 15 10

1967 (19 Mar). *International Tourist Year. P 14½ × 14.*
545 **502** 15 p. bistre-brown and orange 10 10

503 Nandalal Bose and "Garuda"

504 Survey Emblem and Activities

1967 (16 Apr). *First Death Anniv of Nandalal Bose (painter). P 14 × 13½.*
546 **503** 15 p. bistre-brown 10 10

1967 (1 May). *Survey of India Bicentenary. P 13½ × 13.*
547 **504** 15 p. reddish lilac 10 10

505 Basaveswara

506 Narsinha Mehta (poet)

1967 (11 May). *800th Death Anniv of Basaveswara (reformer and statesman). P 13½ × 14.*
548 **505** 15 p. orange-red 10 10

1967 (30 May). *Narsinha Mehta Commemoration. P 14 × 13½.*
549 **506** 15 p. blackish brown 10 10

507 Maharana Pratap (warrior)

508 Narayana Guru (reformer)

1967 (11 June). *Maharana Pratap Commemoration. P 14 × 14½.*
550 **507** 15 p. red-brown 10 10

1967 (21 Aug). *Narayana Guru Commemoration. P 14.*
551 **508** 15 p. brown 10 10

509 President Radhakrishnan

510 Martyrs' Memorial, Patna

1967 (5 Sept). *Radhakrishnan Commemoration. P 13.*
552 **509** 15 p. claret 10 10

1967 (1 Oct). *25th Anniv of "Quit India" Movement. P 14½ × 14.*
553 **510** 15 p. lake 10 10

511 Route Map

512 Wrestling

1967 (9 Nov). *Centenary of Indo-European Telegraph Service. P 13½ × 14.*
554 **511** 15 p. black and light blue 10 10

1967 (12 Nov). *World Wrestling Championships. P 13½ × 14.*
555 **512** 15 p. purple and light orange-brown .. 10 10

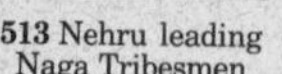

513 Nehru leading Naga Tribesmen

514 Rashbehari Basu (nationalist)

1967 (1 Dec). *"Nehru and Nagaland". P* 13 × 13½.
556 **513** 15 p. ultramarine 10 10

1967 (26 Dec). *Rashbehari Basu Commemoration. P* 14.
557 **514** 15 p. maroon 10 10

515 Bugle, Badge and Scout Salute

1967 (27 Dec). *Diamond Jubilee of Scout Movement. P* 14½ × 14.
558 **515** 15 p. chestnut 25 10

516 Men embracing Universe

517 Globe and Book of Tamil

1968 (1 Jan). *Human Rights Year. P* 13.
559 **516** 15 p. bronze-green 15 10

1968 (3 Jan). *International Conference-Seminar of Tamil Studies, Madras. P* 13.
560 **517** 15 p. reddish lilac 10 10

518 U.N. Emblem and Transport

519 Quill and Bow Symbol

1968 (1 Feb). *United Nations Conference on Trade and Development. P* 14½ × 14.
561 **518** 15 p. turquoise-blue 15 10

1968 (20 Feb). *Amrita Bazar Patrika (Newspaper) Centenary. P* 13½ × 14.
562 **519** 15 p. sepia and orange-yellow 10 10

520 Maxim Gorky

521 Emblem and Medal

1968 (28 Mar). *Birth Centenary of Maxim Gorky. P* 13½.
563 **520** 15 p. plum 10 10

1968 (31 Mar). *First Triennale, New Delhi. P* 13.
564 **521** 15 p. orange, royal blue and light blue . . 10 10
a. Orange omitted £475

522 Letter-box and "100,000"

523 Stalks of Wheat, Agricultural Institute and Production Graph

(Des C. Pakrashi)

1968 (1 July). *Opening of 100,000th Indian Post Office. P* 13.
565 **522** 20 p. red, blue and black 10 10

1968 (17 July). *Wheat Revolution. P* 13.
566 **523** 20 p. bluish green and orange-brown . . 10 10

524 "Self-portrait"

525 Lakshminath Bezbaruah

(Des from self-portrait)

1968 (17 Sept). *30th Death Anniv of Gaganendranath Tagore (painter). P* 13.
567 **524** 20 p. brown-purple and ochre 10 10

1968 (5 Oct). *Birth Centenary of Lakshminath Bezbaruah (writer). P* 13½ × 14.
568 **525** 20 p. blackish brown 10 10

526 Athlete's Legs and Olympic Rings

1968 (12 Oct). *Olympic Games, Mexico. P* 14½ × 14.
569 **526** 20 p. brown and grey 10 15
570 1 r. sepia and brown-olive 25 15

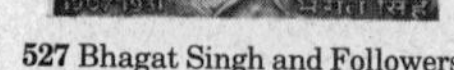

527 Bhagat Singh and Followers

528 Azad Hind Flag, Swords and Chandra Bose (founder)

1968 (19 Oct). *61st Birth Anniv of Bhagat Singh (revolutionary). P* 13.
571 **527** 20 p. yellow-brown 10 10

1968 (21 Oct). *25th Anniv of Azad Hind Government. P* 14 × 14½.
572 **528** 20 p. deep blue 10 10

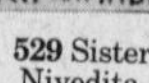

529 Sister Nivedita

530 Marie Curie and Radium Treatment

1968 (27 Oct). *Birth Centenary of Sister Nivedita. P* 14 × 14½.
573 **529** 20 p. deep bluish green 10 15

1968 (6 Nov). *Birth Centenary of Marie Curie. P* 14½ × 14.
574 **530** 20 p. slate-lilac 45 20

531 Map of the World

532 Cochin Synagogue

1968 (1 Dec). *21st International Geographical Congress. P* 13.
575 **531** 20 p. new blue 10 10

1968 (15 Dec). *400th Anniv of Cochin Synagogue. P* 13.
576 **532** 20 p. blue and carmine 20 10

533 I.N.S. *Nilgiri* (frigate)

534 Red-billed Blue Magpie

1968 (15 Dec). *Navy Day. P* 13.
577 **533** 20 p. grey-blue 35 15

1968 (31 Dec). *Birds. T* **534** *and similar designs. P* 14 × 14½ (1 r.) *or* 14½ × 14 (*others*).
578 20 p. multicoloured 40 15
579 50 p. scarlet, black and turquoise-green . . 95 35
580 1 r. deep blue, yellow-brown and pale blue . . 1·75 1·00
581 2 r. multicoloured . . . . 1·75 1·40
578/81 . . . . *Set of* 4 4·25 2·50

Designs: *Horiz*—50 p. Brown-fronted Pied Woodpecker; 2 r. Yellow-backed Slaty-headed Sunbird. *Vert*—1 r. Scimitar Babbler.

538 Bankim Chandra Chatterjee

539 Dr. Bhagavan Das

1969 (1 Jan). *130th Birth Anniv of Bankim Chandra Chatterjee (writer). P* 13½.
582 **538** 20 p. ultramarine 10 10

1969 (12 Jan). *Death Centenary of Dr. Bhagavan Das (philosopher). P* 13½.
583 **539** 20 p. pale chocolate 10 10

540 Dr. Martin Luther King

541 Mirza Ghalib and Letter Seal

1969 (25 Jan). *Martin Luther King Commemoration. P* 13½.
584 **540** 20 p. deep olive-brown 10 10

1969 (17 Feb). *Death Centenary of Mirza Ghalib (poet). P* 14½ × 14.
585 **541** 20 p. sepia, brown-red and flesh 10 10

542 Osmania University

1969 (15 Mar). *50th Anniv of Osmania University. P* 14½ × 14.
586 **542** 20 p. olive-green 10 10

543 Rafi Ahmed Kidwai

1969 (1 Apr). *20th Anniv of "ALL-UP" Air Mail Scheme. P* 13.
587 **543** 20 p. deep blue 15 10

544 I.L.O. Badge and Emblem

545 Memorial, and Hands dropping Flowers

1969 (11 Apr). *50th Anniv of International Labour Organisation. P* 14½ × 14.
588 **544** 20 p. chestnut 10 10

1969 (13 Apr). *50th Anniv of Jallianwala Bagh Massacre. P* 14 × 13½.
589 **545** 20 p. rose-carmine 10 10

546 Shri Nageswara Rao (patriot)   **547** Ardaseer Cursetjee Wadia, and Ships

1969 (1 May). *Kasinadhuni Nageswara Rao Pantulu Commemoration. P* 13½ × 14.
590 **546** 20 p. brown 10 10

1969 (27 May). *Ardaseer Cursetjee Wadia (ship building engineer). P* 14½ × 14.
591 **547** 20 p. turquoise-green 10 10

548 Serampore College   **549** Dr. Zakir Husain

1969 (7 June). *150th Anniv of Serampore College. P* 13½.
592 **548** 20 p. plum 10 10

1969 (11 June). *President Dr. Zakir Husain (patriot) Commemoration. P* 13.
593 **549** 20 p. sepia 10 10

550 Laxmanrao Kirloskar

1969 (20 June). *Birth Centenary of Laxmanrao Kirloskar (agriculturalist). P* 13.
594 **550** 20 p. grey-black 10 10

551 Gandhi and his Wife   **552** Gandhi's Head and Shoulders

553 Gandhi walking (woodcut)   **554** Gandhi with Charkha

(Des Suraj Sadan (20 p.), P. Chitnis (75 p.), Indian Security Press (1 r.) and C. Pakrashi (5 r.))

1969 (2 Oct). *Birth Centenary of Mahatma Gandhi. P* 13½ × 14 *(20 p.),* 14 × 14½ *(1 r.) or* 13 *(others).*
595 **551** 20 p. blackish brown 20 10
596 **552** 75 p. cinnamon and drab 85 40
597 **553** 1 r. blue .. .. 1·00 65
598 **554** 5 r. greyish brown and red-orange .. 4·00 5·00
595/8 .. .. *Set of* 4 5·50 5·50

555 *Ajanta* (tanker) and I.M.C.O. Emblem

1969 (14 Oct). *10th Anniv of Inter-Governmental Maritime Consultative Organization. P* 13.
599 **555** 20 p. violet-blue 20 10

556 Outline of Parliament Building and Globe   **557** Astronaut walking beside Space Module on Moon

1969 (30 Oct). *57th Inter-Parliamentary Conference, New Delhi. P* 14½ × 14.
600 **556** 20 p. new blue 10 10

1969 (19 Nov). *First Man on the Moon. P* 14 × 14½.
601 **557** 20 p. olive-brown 10 10

558 "Shri Nankana Sahib Gurudwara"   **559** Tiger's Head and Hands holding Globe

1969 (23 Nov). *500th Birth Anniv of Guru Nanak. P* 13½.
602 **558** 20 p. slate-violet 10 10

1969 (24 Nov). *International Union for the Conservation of Nature and Natural Resources Conference, New Delhi. P* 14½ × 14.
603 **559** 20 p. orange-brown and bronze-green .. 20 15

560 Sadhu Vaswani   **561** Thakkar Bapa

1969 (25 Nov). *90th Birth Anniv of Sadhu Vaswani (educationist). P* 14 × 14½.
604 **560** 20 p. grey 10 10

1969 (29 Nov). *Birth Centenary of Thakkar Bapa (humanitarian). P* 13½.
605 **561** 20 p. chocolate 10 10

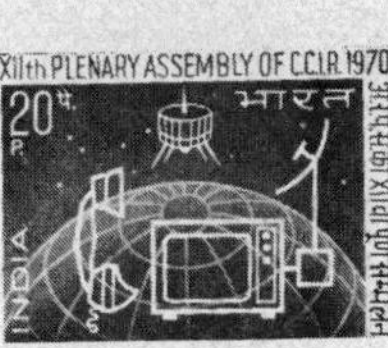

562 Satellite, Television, Telephone and Globe   **563** Thiru Annadurai

1970 (21 Jan). *12th Plenary Assembly of International Radio Consultative Committee. P* 13.
606 **562** 20 p. Prussian blue 10 10

1970 (3 Feb). *First Death Anniv of Thiru Annadurai (statesman). P* 13.
607 **563** 20 p. reddish purple and royal blue .. 10 10

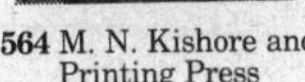

564 M. N. Kishore and Printing Press   **565** Nalanda College

1970 (19 Feb). *Munshi Newal Kishore (publisher) Commemoration. P* 13.
608 **564** 20 p. lake 10 10

1970 (27 Mar). *Centenary of Nalanda College. P* 14½ × 14.
609 **565** 20 p. brown 15 15

566 Swami Shraddhanand (social reformer)   **567** Lenin

1970 (30 Mar). *Swami Shraddhanand Commemoration. P* 14 × 13½.
610 **566** 20 p. yellow-brown 15 10

1970 (22 Apr). *Birth Centenary of Lenin. P* 13.
611 **567** 20 p. orange-brown and sepia 10 10

568 New U.P.U. H.Q. Building   **569** Sher Shah Suri (15th-century ruler)

1970 (20 May). *New U.P.U. Headquarters Building. P* 13.
612 **568** 20 p. emerald, grey and black 10 10

1970 (22 May). *Sher Shah Suri Commemoration. P* 13.
613 **569** 20 p. deep bluish green 10 10

570 V. D. Savarkar (patriot) and Cellular Jail   **571** "UN" and Globe

1970 (28 May). *V. D. Savarkar Commemoration. P* 13.
614 **570** 20 p. orange-brown 10 10

1970 (26 June). *25th Anniv of United Nations. P* 13.
615 **571** 20 p. light new blue 10 10

572 Symbol and Workers

1970 (18 Aug). *Asian Productivity Year. P* 14½ × 14.
616 **572** 20 p. violet 10 10

573 Dr. Montessori and I.E.Y. Emblem

1970 (31 Aug). *Birth Centenary of Dr. Maria Montessori (educationist). P* 13.
617 **573** 20 p. dull purple 10 10

574 J. N. Mukherjee (revolutionary) and Horse   **575** V. S. Srinivasa Sastri

1970 (9 Sept). *Jatindra Nath Mukherjee Commemoration. P* 14½ × 14.
618 **574** 20 p. chocolate 15 15

1970 (22 Sept). *Srinivasa Sastri (educationist). P* 13 × 13½.
619 **575** 20 p. yellow and brown-purple 15 10

576 I. C. Vidyasagar

577 Maharishi Valmiki

1970 (26 Sept). *50th Birth Anniv of I. C. Vidyasagar (educationist). P* 13.
620 **576** 20 p. brown and purple 10 10

1970 (14 Oct). *Maharishi Valmiki (holy poet). P* 13.
621 **577** 20 p. purple 10 10

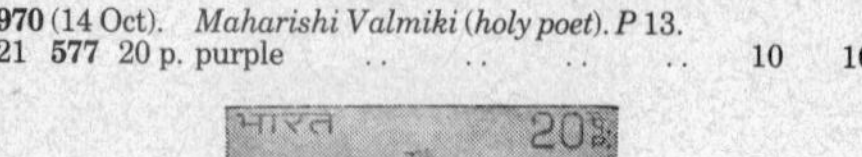

578 Calcutta Port

1970 (17 Oct). *Centenary of Calcutta Port Trust. P* 13½ × 13.
622 **578** 20 p. greenish blue 10 10

579 University Building

1970 (29 Oct). *50th Anniv of Jamia Millia Islamia University. P* 14½ × 14.
623 **579** 20 p. yellow-green 10 10

580 Jamnalal Bajaj

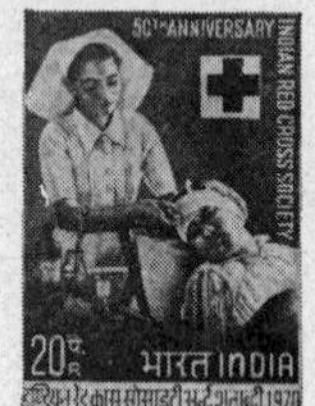

581 Nurse and Patient

1970 (4 Nov). *Jamnalal Bajaj (patriot). W* **374**. *P* 13½ × 13.
624 **580** 20 p. olive-grey 10 10

1970 (5 Nov). *50th Anniv of Indian Red Cross. W* **374** *(sideways). P* 13 × 13½.
625 **581** 20 p. red and greenish blue 10 10

582 Sant Namdeo

583 Beethoven

1970 (9 Nov). *700th Anniv of Sant (Saint) Namdeo. W* **374**. *P* 13.
626 **582** 20 p. orange 10 10

1970 (16 Dec). *Birth Bicentenary of Beethoven. P* 13.
627 **583** 20 p. orange and greyish black 40 15

584 Children examining Stamps

585 Girl Guide

1970 (23 Dec). *Indian National Philatelic Exhibition. T* **584** *and similar horiz design. P* 13.
628 20 p. orange and myrtle-green 10 10
629 1 r. orange-brown and pale yellow-brown .. 90 60
Design:—1 r. Gandhi commemorative through magnifier.

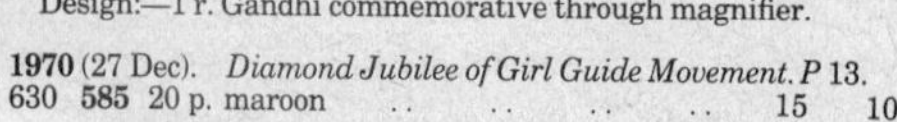

1970 (27 Dec). *Diamond Jubilee of Girl Guide Movement. P* 13.
630 **585** 20 p. maroon 15 10

586 Hands and Lamp (Emblem)

587 Vidyapith Building

1971 (11 Jan). *Indian Life Insurance. P* 13.
631 **586** 20 p. sepia and crimson 10 15

1971 (10 Feb). *Golden Jubilee of Kashi Vidyapith. P* 14½ × 14.
632 **587** 20 p. blackish brown 10 15

588 Saint Ravidas

589 C. F. Andrews

1971 (10 Feb). *Guru Ravidas (15th-cent Saint). P* 13.
633 **588** 20 p. lake 10 15

1971 (12 Feb). *Birth Centenary of Deenabandhu C. F. Andrews (philosopher). P* 13 × 13½.
634 **589** 20 p. chestnut 20 15

590 Acharya Narendra Deo (reformer)

591 Crowd and "100"

1971 (19 Feb). *15th Death Anniv of Acharya Narendra Deo. P* 13.
635 **590** 20 p. dull green 10 15

1971 (10 Mar). *Census Centenary. P* 13.
636 **591** 20 p. brown and blue 10 15

592 Sri Ramana Maharishi (mystic)

593 Raja Ravi Varma and "Damayanti and the Swan"

1971 (14 Apr). *21st Death Anniv of Ramana Maharishi. P* 13½.
637 **592** 20 p. orange and sepia 10 15

1971 (29 Apr). *65th Death Anniv of Ravi Varma (artist). P* 13.
638 **593** 20 p. green 10 15

594 Dadasaheb Phalke (cinematographer) and Camera

595 "Abhisarika" (Abanindranath Tagore)

1971 (30 Apr). *Birth Centenary of Dadasaheb Phalke. P* 13½ × 13.
639 **594** 20 p. deep maroon 15 15

1971 (7 Aug). *Abanindranath Tagore Commemoration. P* 14 × 14½.
640 **595** 20 p. grey, buff-yellow & blackish brown 15 15

596 Swami Virjanand (Vedic scholar)

597 Cyrus the Great and Procession

1971 (14 Sept). *Swami Virjanand Commemoration. P* 13½.
641 **596** 20 p. chestnut 10 15

1971 (12 Oct). *2500th Anniv of Charter of Cyrus the Great. P* 13.
642 **597** 20 p. blackish brown 25 15

598 Globe and Money Box

1971 (31 Oct). *World Thrift Day. P* 14½ × 14.
643 **598** 20 p. blue-grey 10 15

599 Ajanta Caves Painting

600 Women at Work

1971 (4 Nov). *25th Anniv of U.N.E.S.C.O. P* 13.
644 **599** 20 p. red-brown 20 20

(Des from painting by Geeta Gupta)

1971 (14 Nov). *Children's Day. P* 14 × 14½.
645 **600** 20 p. scarlet 10 15

शरणार्थी सहायता REFUGEE RELIEF
(601)

Refugee Relief
(602)

शरणार्थी सहायता REFUGEE RELIEF
(603)

REFUGEE RELIEF
(604)

REFUGEE RELIEF
(605)

Refugee Relief
(606)

Refugee relief
(606*a*)

शरणार्थी सहायता Refugee Relief
(606*b*)

607 Refugees

1971. *Obligatory Tax. Refugee Relief.*

(a) Provisional issues. No. 506 variously optd

(i) *For all India, optd at Nasik*
646 **601** 5 p. cerise (15 Nov) 10 10
a. Opt double .. .. 2·50

(ii) *For various areas*
647 **602** 5 p. Bangalore 60 15
a. Opt double, one inverted ..
648 **603** 5 p. Jaipur .. .. 1·75 20
649 **604** 5 p. Rajasthan 90 20
a. Error. "RELIEF REFUGEE" .. 12·00
b. Opt inverted
650 **605** 5 p. New Delhi .. .. 3·50 40
a. Opt inverted .. .. .. 5·50
650*b* **606** 5 p. Goa .. .. 3·00 75
650*c* **606*a*** 5 p. Jabalpur .. .. 1·75 40
650*d* **606*b*** 5 p. Alwar .. ..

(b) *Definitive issue. W* **374**. *P* 14 × 14½
651 **607** 5 p. carmine (1 Dec) 10 10

From 15 November 1971 and 31 March 1973, the Indian Government levied a 5 p. surcharge on all mail, except postcards and newspapers, for the relief of refugees from the former East Pakistan.

As supplies of the provisional overprint could not be sent to all Indian post offices in time, local postmasters were authorised to make their own overprints. Most of these were applied by rubber stamps and so we do not list them. Those listed have typographed overprints and No. 649 also has a rubber handstamp in native language. Some of the above overprints were also used in areas other than those where they were produced.

608 C. V. Raman (scientist) and Jewel

1971 (21 Nov). *Dr. C. V. Raman Commemoration. P 13.*
652 **608** 20 p. orange and deep brown 15 15

609 Visva Bharati Building and Rabindranath Tagore (pioneer)

1971 (24 Dec). *Golden Jubilee of Visva Bharati. P* 14½ × 14.
653 **609** 20 p. sepia and yellow-brown 10 15

610 Cricketers **611** Map and Satellite

1971 (30 Dec). *Indian Cricket Victories. P* 14½ × 14.
654 **610** 20 p. green, myrtle-green and sage-green 1·40 55

1972 (26 Feb). *Arvi Satellite Earth Station. P* 13½.
655 **611** 20 p. plum 10 15

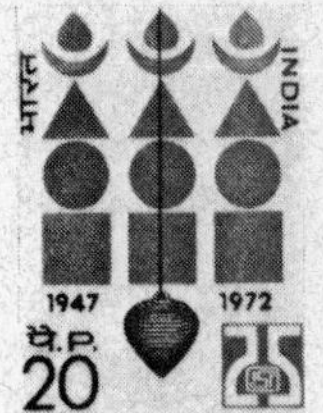

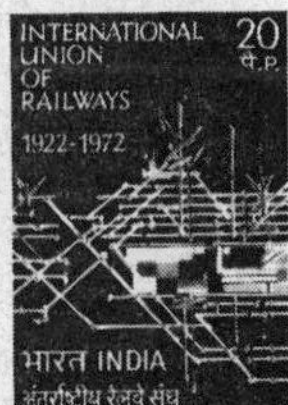

612 Elemental Symbols and Plumb-line **613** Signal-box Panel

1972 (29 May). *Silver Jubilee of Indian Standards Institution. P* 13.
656 **612** 20 p. turquoise-grey and black 10 15

1972 (30 June). *50th Anniv of International Railways Union. P* 13.
657 **613** 20 p. multicoloured 40 30
a. Blue omitted .. .. .. 45·00

614 Hockey-player **615** Symbol of Sri Aurobindo

1972 (10 Aug). *Olympic Games, Munich. T* **614** *and similar horiz design. P* 13.
658 20 p. deep bluish violet 15 10
659 1 r. 45, light turquoise-green & brown-lake 85 1·60
Design:—1 r. 45, Various sports.

1972 (15 Aug). *Birth Centenary of Sri Aurobindo. P* 13½.
660 **615** 20 p. yellow and new blue 15 15

616 Celebrating Independence Day in front of Parliament **617** Inter-Services Crest

1972 (15 Aug). *25th Anniversary of Independence* (*1st issue*). *P* 13.
661 **616** 20 p. multicoloured 15 15
See also Nos. 673/4.

1972 (15 Aug). *Defence Services Commemoration. P* 13.
662 **617** 20 p. multicoloured 25 15

618 V. O. Chidambaram Pillai (lawyer and politician) and Ship **619** Bhai Vir Singh

1972 (5 Sept). *Birth Centenary of V. O. Chidambaram Pillai. P* 13.
663 **618** 20 p. new blue and purple-brown .. 25 20

1972 (16 Oct). *Birth Centenary of Bhai Vir Singh* (*poet and saint*). *P* 13.
664 **619** 20 p. plum 15 15

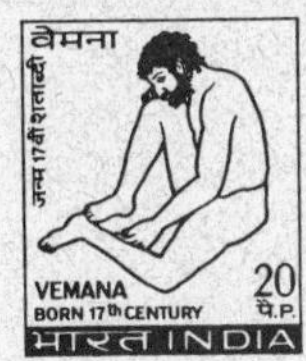

620 T. Prakasam **621** Vemana

1972 (16 Oct). *Birth Centenary of T. Prakasam* (*lawyer*). *P* 13.
665 **620** 20 p. brown 10 15

1972 (16 Oct). *300th Birth Anniv of Vemana* (*poet*). *W* **374**. *P* 13½ × 14.
666 **621** 20 p. black 10 15

622 Bertrand Russell **623** Symbol of "Asia 72"

1972 (16 Oct). *Birth Centenary of Bertrand Russell* (*philosopher*). *P* 13½ × 14.
667 **622** 1 r. 45, black .. .. 2·25 2·25

1972 (3 Nov). *"Asia '72" (Third Asian International Trade Fair). T* **623** *and similar vert design. W* **374**. *P* 13.
668 20 p. black and orange.. .. .. .. 10 15
669 1 r. 45, orange and slate-black .. .. 60 1·50
Design:—1 r. 45, Hand of Buddha.

624 V. A. Sarabhai and Rocket **625** Flag of U.S.S.R. and Kremlin Tower

1972 (30 Dec). *First Death Anniv of Vikram A. Sarabhai* (*scientist*). *P* 13.
670 **624** 20 p. brown and myrtle-green 15 15

1972 (30 Dec). *50th Anniv of U.S.S.R. P* 13.
671 **625** 20 p. light yellow and red 10 15

626 Exhibition Symbol **627** "Democracy"

1973 (8 Jan). *"Indipex '73" Stamp Exhibition* (*1st issue*). *P* 13.
672 **626** 1 r. 45, light mauve, gold and black .. 45 1·00
See also Nos. 701/**MS**704.

1973 (26 Jan). *25th Anniv of Independence* (*2nd issue*). *T* **627** *and similar multicoloured design. P* 13 (20 *p.*) *or* 14½ × 14 (1 *r.* 45).
673 20 p. Type **627** 15 15
674 1 r. 45, "Gnat" fighters over India Gate (38 × 20 *mm*) .. .. 85 1·60

628 Sri Ramakrishna Paramahamsa (religious leader) **629** Postal Corps Emblem

1973 (18 Feb). *Sri Ramakrishna Paramahamsa Commemoration. P* 13.
675 **628** 20 p. light brown 15 20

1973 (1 Mar). *First Anniv of Army Postal Service Corps. P* 13.
676 **629** 20 p. deep ultramarine and vermilion .. 40 20

630 Flag and Map of Bangladesh **631** Kumaran Asan

(Des C. Pakrashi)

1973 (10 Apr). *"Jai Bangla" (Inauguration of First Bangladesh Parliament). P* 13.
677 **630** 20 p. multicoloured 15 20

1973 (12 Apr). *Birth Centenary of Kumaran Asan* (*writer and poet*). *P* 13.
678 **631** 20 p. sepia 20 30

632 Flag and Flames **633** Dr. B. R. Ambedkar (social thinker and agitator)

(Des C. Pakrashi)

1973 (13 Apr). *Homage to Martyrs for Independence. P* 13.
679 **632** 20 p. multicoloured 15 20

(Des Charanjit Lal)

1973 (14 Apr). *Ambedkar Commemoration. P* 13.
680 **633** 20 p. bronze-green and deep purple .. 15 30

634 "Radha-Kishangarh" (Nihal Chand) **635** The Himalayas

1973 (5 May). *Indian Miniature Paintings. T* **634** *and similar vert designs. Multicoloured. P* 13.
681 20 p. Type **634** 30 30
682 50 p. "Dance Duet" (Aurangzeb's period) .. 60 90
683 1 r. "Lovers on a Camel" (Nasir-ud-din) .. 1·50 2·25
684 2 r. "Chained Elephant" (Zain-al-Abidin) .. 2·00 2·75
681/4 .. .. *Set of* 4 4·00 5·50

1973 (15 May). *15th Anniv of Indian Mountaineering Foundation. P* 13.
685 **635** 20 p. blue 25 35

636 Tail of Boeing "747"

637 Cross, Church of St. Thomas' Mount, Madras

(Des Air-India Art Studies from photograph by Jehangir Gazdar)

1973 (8 June). *25th Anniv of Air-India's International Services. P 13.*

686	**636**	1 r. 45, indigo and carmine-red ..	2·50	3·00

1973 (3 July). *19th Death Centenary of St. Thomas. P 13.*

687	**637**	20 p. blue-grey and agate	10	20

638 Michael Madhusudan Dutt (poet—Death Centenary)

639 A. O. Hume

1973 (21 July). *Centenaries. T* **638** *and similar horiz designs. P 13.*

688	20 p. sage-green and orange-brown	40	40
	a. Orange-brown omitted	£325	
689	30 p. red-brown	60	90
690	50 p. deep brown	75	1·40
691	1 r. dull violet and orange-vermilion ..	80	1·50
688/91	.. .. *Set of* 4	2·25	3·75

Designs:—30 p. V. D. Paluskar (musician—Birth Centenary); 50 p. Dr. Hansen (Centenary of discovery of leprosy bacillus); 1 r. Nicolaus Copernicus (astronomer—Fifth Birth Centenary).

1973 (31 July). *A. O. Hume Commemoration. P 13.*

692	**639**	20 p. grey	10	20

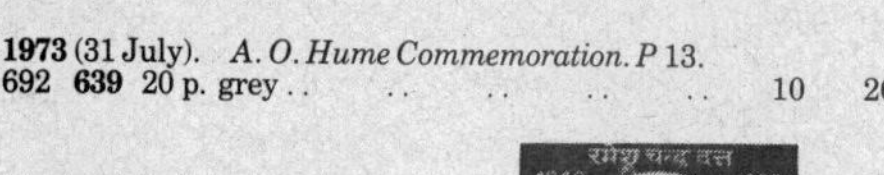

640 Gandhi and Nehru

641 R. C. Dutt

(Des C. Pakrashi from photograph)

1973 (15 Aug). *Gandhi and Nehru Commemoration. P 13.*

693	**640**	20 p. multicoloured	10	15

1973 (27 Sept). *R. C. Dutt Commemoration. P 13.*

694	**641**	20 p. brown	10	20

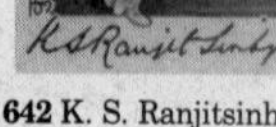

642 K. S. Ranjitsinhji

643 Vithalbhai Patel (nationalist)

1973 (27 Sept). *K. S. Ranjitsinhji Commemoration. P 13.*

695	**642**	30 p. myrtle-green	1·75	95

1973 (27 Sept). *Vithalbhai Patel Commemoration. P 13.*

696	**643**	50 p. light red-brown	10	20

644 President's Bodyguard

645 Interpol Emblem

1973 (30 Sept). *Bicentenary of President's Bodyguard. P 13.*

697	**644**	20 p. multicoloured	35	30

1973 (9 Oct). *50th Anniv of Interpol. P 13.*

698	**645**	20 p. brown	25	30

646 Syed Ahmad Khan (social reformer)

647 "Children at Play" (detail, Bela Raval)

1973 (17 Oct). *Syed Ahmad Khan Commemoration. P 13.*

699	**646**	20 p. sepia	10	20

1973 (14 Nov). *Children's Day. P 13.*

700	**647**	20 p. multicoloured	15	15

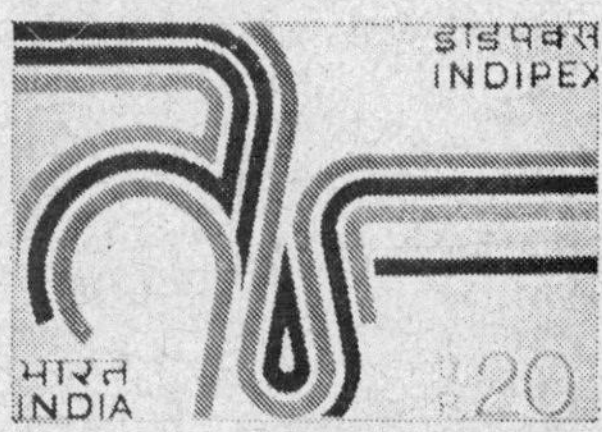

648 Indipex Emblem

1973 (14 Nov). *"Indipex '73" Philatelic Exhibition, New Delhi (2nd issue). T* **648** *and similar multicoloured designs. P 13½ × 13 (2 r.) or 13 × 13½ (others).*

701	20 p. Type **648**	20	30
702	1 r. Ceremonial elephant and 1½ a. stamp of 1947 (*vert*)	1·00	1·75
703	2 r. Common Peafowl (*vert*)	1·50	2·25
701/3	.. .. .. *Set of* 3	2·50	4·00
MS704	127 × 127 mm. Nos. 672 and 701/3. Imperf	4·75	8·00

649 Emblem of National Cadet Corps

650 Chakravarti Rajagopalachari (statesman)

1973 (25 Nov). *Silver Jubilee of National Cadet Corps. P 13.*

705	**649**	20 p. multicoloured	20	15

1973 (25 Dec). *C. Rajagopalachari Commemoration. P 13.*

706	**650**	20 p. olive-brown	10	20

651 "Sun" Mask

652 Chhatrapati

1974 (15 Apr). *Indian Masks. T* **651** *and similar multicoloured designs. P 13.*

707	20 p. Type **651**	15	15
708	50 p. "Moon" mask	30	45
709	1 r. "Narasimha"	80	1·25
710	2 r. "Ravana" (*horiz*)	1·25	2·00
707/10	.. .. .. *Set of* 4	2·25	3·50
MS711	109 × 135 mm. Nos. 707/10	3·75	6·00

1974 (2 June). *300th Anniv of Coronation of Chhatrapati Shri Shivaji Maharaj (patriot and ruler). P 13.*

712	**652**	25 p. multicoloured	25	20

653 Maithili Sharan Gupta (poet)

654 Kandukuri Veeresalingam (reformer)

1974 (3 July). *Indian Personalities (1st series). T* **653** *and similar vert designs. P 13.*

713	25 p. chestnut	15	25
714	25 p. deep brown	15	25
715	25 p. sepia	15	25
713/15	.. .. .. *Set of* 3	40	65

Portraits:—No. 714, Jainarain Vyas (politician and journalist); No. 715, Utkal Gourab Madhusudan Das (social reformer).

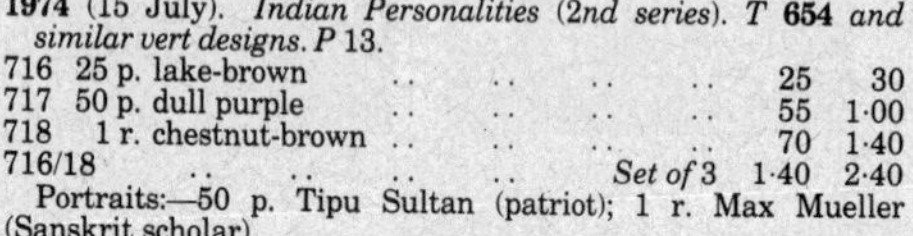

1974 (15 July). *Indian Personalities (2nd series). T* **654** *and similar vert designs. P 13.*

716	25 p. lake-brown	25	30
717	50 p. dull purple	55	1·00
718	1 r. chestnut-brown	70	1·40
716/18	.. .. .. *Set of* 3	1·40	2·40

Portraits:—50 p. Tipu Sultan (patriot); 1 r. Max Mueller (Sanskrit scholar).

655 Kamala Nehru

(Des Charanjit Lal)

1974 (1 Aug). *Kamala Nehru Commemoration. P 14½ × 14.*

719	**655**	25 p. multicoloured	25	30

656 W. P. Y. Emblem

1974 (14 Aug). *World Population Year. P 13½.*

720	**656**	25 p. maroon and buff	10	15

LARGE STAR AND INDIA GOVT WATERMARK. Two types exist of this sheet watermark. The initial arrangement resulted in the stars appearing upright, inverted and sideways, in either direction, within the same sheet.

Printings issued from the beginning of 1980 shows a second type on which the stars in each sheet all point in the same direction. All commemoratives with this watermark used the second type.

657 Spotted Deer

657*b* Bidri Vase

657*a* Vina

Two types of No. 732:

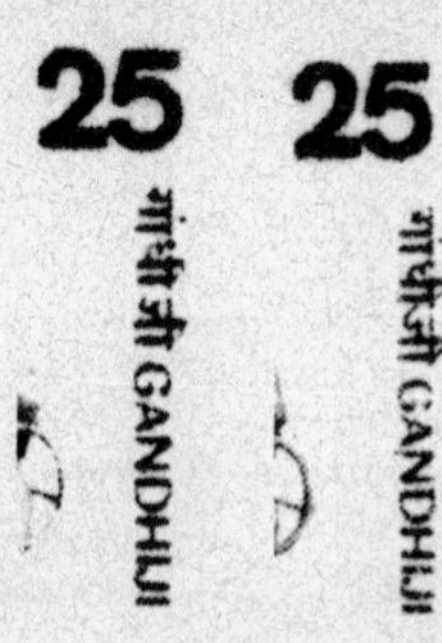

I II

Type I. Left shoulder cut square.
Top of Hindi inscription aligns with edge of shoulder.

Type II. Shoulder ends in point.
Top of English inscription aligns with edge of shoulder. Portrait redrawn slightly smaller.

Two types of No. 736:

I II

Type I. "INDIA" inscription falls below foot of main design. Distance between foot of "2" in face value and top of Hindi inscription 11 mm.

Type II. "INDIA" above foot of design. Distance between "2" and inscription 10½ mm. Inscription redrawn slightly smaller.

1974 (20 Aug)–**83.** *P* 14 × 14½ (10, 20, 50 *p.*) *or* 14½ × 14 (*others*).

(a) Various designs with values expressed with "p" *or* "Re" *as* *T* **657**/*a.* *W* **374** (*sideways*)

721 – 15 p. blackish brown (deep background) (1.10.74) .. .. 1·25 10
722 **657** 25 p. sepia (20.8.74) 75 15
a. Imperf (pair) £170
723 **657***a* 1 r. red-brown and black (1.10.74) .. 2·50 30
a. Black (face value and inscr) omitted £100

(b) Various designs with values expressed in numerals only as in *T* **657***b*

(i) *Wmk Large Star and* "INDIA GOVT" *in sheet**

724 **657***b* 2 p. red-brown (*photo*) (1.11.76) .. 15 30
724*a* 2 p. pale reddish brown (*litho*) (15.3.79) 15 30
725 – 5 p. cerise (as No. 506) (1.11.76) .. 10 10
727 **466** 10 p. new blue (5.7.79) 60 10

(ii) *W* **374** (*sideways on* 15, 25, 30, 60 *p.*, 1, 2, 5, 10 *r.*)

729 **466** 10 p. new blue (1.11.76) 15 10
a. Imperf (pair) .. .. ..
730 – 15 p. blackish brown (light background) (15.7.75) 80 10
731 – 20 p. deep dull green (15.7.75) 10 10
a. Imperf (horiz pair) £250
732 – 25 p. reddish brown (I) (1978) .. .. 1·00 20
a. Type II (5.79) .. .. .. 1·25 15
732*b* – 30 p. sepia (as No. 512) (1.5.79) 50 10
733 – 50 p. deep violet (15.7.75) .. .. 1·00 10
734 – 60 p. deep grey (as No. 515) (1.11.76) .. 30 20
735 **657***a* 1 r. red-brown and grey-black (15.7.75) 2·00 10
736 – 2 r. violet and blackish brown (I) (15.7.75) .. .. 5·00 25
a. Type II (1977) .. .. .. 5·00 25
737 – 5 r. deep slate-violet and brown (as No. 519) (1.11.76) .. .. .. 1·00 70
738 – 10 r. slate and bronze-green (as No. 520) (1.11.76) .. .. 1·25 1·25
b. Wmk upright .. .. ..
c. Perf 12½ × 13 (22.10.83) .. .. 1·10 1·10
ca. Wmk upright .. .. ..
721/38 .. .. .. *Set of* 18 17·00 3·25

Designs: *Vert as T* **657**, **657***b*:—15 p. Tiger; 25 p. Gandhi. *Horiz* (20 × 17 *mm*)—20 p. Handicrafts toy; 50 p. Demoiselle Crane in flight. *Horiz as T* **657***a*:—2 r. Himalayas.

*See note below No. 720. Nos. 724*a* and 727 exist on both types of watermark, Nos. 724 and 725 on the first type only.

No. 724*a* can be easily identified by the background of horizontal lines.

For stamps as No. 732, but with face value changed to 30 p., 35 p., 50 p. or 60 p. see Nos. 968, 979, 1073 and 1320.

The 2 r. value with the blackish brown omitted is a chemically produced fake.

658 President Giri

659 U.P.U. Emblem

(Des Charanjit Lal)

1974 (24 Aug). *Giri Commemoration. P* 13.
739 **658** 25 p. multicoloured 10 15

(Des C. Pakrashi (25 p.), A. Ramachandran (1 r.), Jyoti Bhatt (2 r.))

1974 (3 Oct). *Centenary of Universal Postal Union. T* **659** *and similar designs. P* 13.
740 25 p. violet-blue, royal blue and black .. 20 10
741 1 r. multicoloured .. .. 1·50 1·75
742 2 r. multicoloured .. .. 2·00 2·25
a. Red (inscr etc) omitted £225
740/2 .. .. *Set of* 3 3·25 3·50
MS743 108 × 108 mm. Nos. 740/2 .. .. .. 4·00 8·50

Designs: *Horiz*—1 r. Birds and nest, "Madhubani" style. *Vert*—2 r. Arrows around globe.

660 Woman Flute-player (sculpture)

661 Nicholas Roerich (medallion by H. Dropsy)

(Des Benoy Sarkar)

1974 (9 Oct). *Mathura Museum. T* **660** *and similar vert design. P* 13½.
744 25 p. chestnut and blackish brown 30 10
a. Horiz pair. Nos. 744/5 .. .. 60 80
745 25 p. chestnut and blackish brown 30 10

Design:—No. 745, Vidyadhara with garland.

Nos. 744/5 were printed together within the sheet, horizontally *se-tenant*.

1974 (9 Oct). *Birth Centenary of Professor Roerich. P* 13.
746 **661** 1 r. deep blue-green & greenish yellow 40 55

662 Pavapuri Temple

663 "Cat" (Rajesh Bhatia)

(Des Benoy Sarkar)

1974 (13 Nov). *2,500th Anniv of Bhagwan Mahavira's attainment of Nirvana. P* 13.
747 **662** 25 p. indigo 25 10

1974 (14 Nov). *Children's Day. P* 13.
748 **663** 25 p. multicoloured 40 20

664 Indian Dancers

665 Territorial Army Badge

(Des from painting by Amita Shah)

1974 (14 Nov). *25th Anniv of UNICEF in India. P* 14½ × 14.
749 **664** 25 p. multicoloured 35 20
a. Black (name and value) omitted £250

On No. 749a the background is in greenish black instead of the intense black of the normal.

(Des Benoy Sarkar)

1974 (16 Nov). *25th Anniv of Indian Territorial Army. P* 13.
750 **665** 25 p. black, bright yellow and emerald .. 50 30

666 Krishna as Gopal Bal with Cows (Rajasthan painting on cloth)

667 Symbols and Child's Face

1974 (2 Dec). *19th International Dairy Congress, New Delhi. P* 13½.
751 **666** 25 p. brown-purple and brown-ochre .. 25 15

(Des Benoy Sarkar)

1974 (8 Dec). *Help for Retarded Children. P* 13.
752 **667** 25 p. red-orange and black 10 15

668 Marconi

669 St. Francis Xavier's Shrine

1974 (12 Dec). *Birth Centenary of Guglielmo Marconi (radio pioneer). P* 13.
753 **668** 2 r. deep slate .. .. 1·25 1·25

1974 (24 Dec). *St Francis Xavier Celebration. P* 13.
754 **669** 25 p. multicoloured 10 15

670 Saraswati (Deity of Language and Learning)

671 Parliament House, New Delhi

1975 (10 Jan). *World Hindi Convention, Nagpur. P* 14 × 14½.
755 **670** 25 p. slate and carmine-red 25 20

For similar stamp see No. 761.

1975 (26 Jan). *25th Anniv of Republic. P* 13.
756 **671** 25 p. grey-black, silver and azure .. 20 20

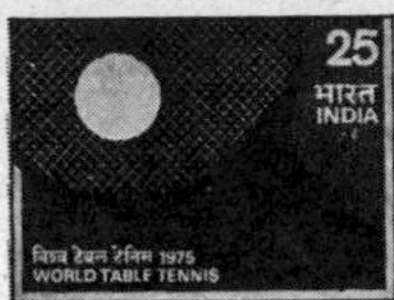

672 Table-tennis Bat

1975 (6 Feb). *World Table-tennis Championships, Calcutta. P* 13.
757 **672** 25 p. black, vermilion and yellow-olive 40 15

673 "Equality, Development and Peace"

674 Stylised Cannon

(Des Shyama Sarabhai)

1975 (16 Feb). *International Women's Year. P* 13.
758 **673** 25 p. multicoloured 75 40

(Des Benoy Sarkar)

1975 (8 Apr). *Bicentenary of Indian Army Ordnance Corps. P* 13.
759 **674** 25 p. multicoloured 45 25

675 Arya Samaj Emblem **676** Saraswati

1975 (11 Apr). *Centenary of Arya Samaj Movement. P* 13.
760 **675** 25 p. light red-orange & brownish black . . 30 30

1975 (12 Apr). *World Telugu Language Conference, Hyderabad. P* 14 × 14½.
761 **676** 25 p. black and deep bluish green . . 35 20

677 Satellite "Aryabhata"

1975 (20 Apr). *Launch of First Indian Satellite. P* 13.
762 **677** 25 p. lt blue, deep indigo & dull purple . . 35 35

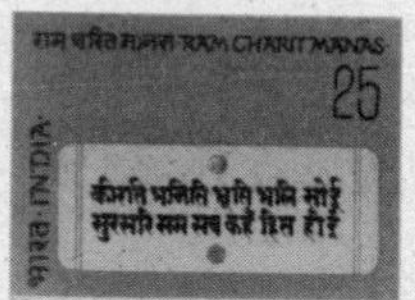

678 Blue-winged Pitta **679** "Ramcharitmanas" (poem by Goswami Tulsidas)

(Des J. P. Irani)

1975 (28 Apr). *Indian Birds. T* **678** *and similar multicoloured designs. P* 13.
763 25 p. Type **678** 45 15
764 50 p. Asian Black-headed Oriole 90 80
765 1 r. Western Tragopan (*vert*) . . . . 2·00 2·75
766 2 r. Himalayan Monal Pheasant (*vert*) . . 2·50 3·50
763/6 . . . . *Set of* 4 5·25 6·50

(Des R. K. Joshi)

1975 (24 May). *Ramcharitmanas Commemoration. P* 13.
767 **679** 25 p. black, orange-yellow & vermilion . . 35 15

680 Young Women within Y.W.C.A. Badge **681** "The Creation"

(Des Benoy Sarkar)

1975 (20 June). *Centenary of Indian Y.W.C.A. P* 13.
768 **680** 25 p. multicoloured 15 20

1975 (28 June). *500th Birth Anniv of Michelangelo. T* **681** *and similar designs showing "Creation" frescoes from Sistine Chapel. P* 14 × 13½.
769 50 p. multicoloured 50 60
a. Block of 4. Nos 769/72 . . . . . . 1·75
ab. Black (inscr & face value) omitted . . £300
770 50 p. multicoloured 50 60
771 50 p. multicoloured 50 60
772 50 p. multicoloured 50 60
769/72 . . . . *Set of* 4 1·75 2·25
T **681** illustrates No. 769. Nos. 770 and 772 are horizontal designs, size 49 × 34 mm.
Nos. 769/72 were printed in *se-tenant* blocks of four within the sheet, forming two composite designs in horizontal pairs.

682 Commission Emblem **683** Stylised Ground Antenna

1975 (28 July). *25th Anniv of International Commission on Irrigation and Drainage. P* 13½.
773 **682** 25 p. multicoloured 35 15

(Des Benoy Sarkar)

1975 (1 Aug). *Satellite Instructional Television Experiment. P* 13.
774 **683** 25 p. multicoloured 35 15

684 St. Arunagirinathar **685** Commemorative Text

1975 (14 Aug). *600th Birth Anniv of St. Arunagirinathar. P* 13½.
775 **684** 50 p. dull purple and slate-black . . 90 1·00

1975 (26 Aug). *Namibia Day. P* 13½.
776 **685** 25 p. grey-black and rose-red 40 40

686 Mir Anees (poet) **687** Memorial Temple to Ahilyabai Holkar (ruler)

1975 (4 Sept). *Indian Celebrities. P* 13½ (*No.* 777) *or* 13 (*No.* 778).
777 **686** 25 p. blackish green 20 30
778 **687** 25 p. chestnut 20 30

688 Bharata Natyam **689** Ameer Khusrau

1975 (20 Oct). *Indian Dances. T* **688** *and similar vert designs. Multicoloured. P* 13.
779 25 p. Type **668** 45 20
780 50 p. Orissi 75 65
a. Turquoise-green (dress) omitted . . 40·00
781 75 p. Kathak 80 70
782 1 r. Kathakali . . . . 1·10 1·25
783 1 r. 50, Kuchipudi . . . . . . 1·75 2·25
784 2 r. Manipuri . . . . 2·00 2·75
779/84 . . . . *Set of* 6 6·25 7·00

1975 (24 Oct). *650th Death of Anniv of Ameer Khusrau (poet). P* 13.
785 **689** 50 p. reddish brown and buff 55 70

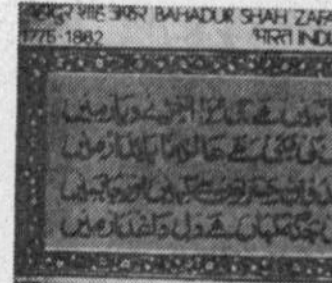

690 V. K. Krishna Menon **691** Text of Poem

1975 (24 Oct). *First Death Anniv of V. K. Krishna Menon (statesman). P* 13 × 13½.
786 **690** 25 p. olive 25 30

(Des R. K. Joshi)

1975 (24 Oct). *Birth Bicentenary of Bahadur Shah Zafar. P* 13½ × 13.
787 **691** 1 r. black, stone and yellow-brown . . 65 90

692 Sansadiya Soudha, New Delhi **693** V. Patel

1975 (28 Oct). *21st Commonwealth Parliamentary Conference, New Delhi. P* 14½ × 14.
788 **692** 2 r. olive . . . . 1·75 2·50

1975 (31 Oct). *Birth Centenary of Vallabhbhai Patel (statesman). P* 13 × 13½.
789 **693** 25 p. slate-green 15 25

694 N. C. Bardoloi **695** "Cow" (drawing by Sanjay Nathubhai Patel)

1975 (3 Nov). *Birth Centenary of Nabin Chandra Bardoloi (politician). P* 13 × 13½.
790 **694** 25 p. reddish brown 20 20

1975 (14 Nov). *Children's Day. P* 13½ × 13.
791 **695** 25 p. multicoloured 40 20

696 Printing Works, Nasik Road **697** Gurdwara Sisganj (site of martyrdom)

1975 (13 Dec). *50th Anniv of India Security Press. P* 13.
792 **696** 25 p. multicoloured 25 15

1975 (16 Dec). *Tercentenary of the Martyrdom of Guru Tegh Bahadur. P* 13.
793 **697** 25 p. multicoloured 30 15

698 Theosophical Society Emblem **699** Weather Cock

1975 (20 Dec). *Centenary of the Theosophical Society. P* 13.
794 **698** 25 p. multicoloured 35 20

(Des Benoy Sarkar)

1975 (24 Dec). *Centenary of the Indian Meteorological Department. P* 13 × 13½.
795 **699** 25 p. multicoloured 30 15

700 Early Mail Cart **701** L. N. Mishra (politician)

(Des Benoy Sarkar)

1975 (25 Dec). *"Inpex 75" National Philatelic Exhibition, Calcutta. T* **700** *and similar vert design. P* 13.
796 **700** 25 p. black and lake-brown 50 30
797 – 2 r. grey-brown, brown-purple & black 1·75 2·50
Design:—2 r. Indian Bishop Mark, 1775.

1976 (3 Jan). *1st Anniv of Mishra's Death. P* 13.
798 **701** 25 p. olive-sepia 25 25

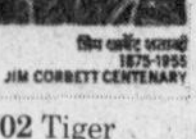

702 Tiger **703** Painted Storks

1976 (24 Jan). *Birth Centenary of Jim Corbett (naturalist). P* 13.
799 **702** 25 p. multicoloured 60 35

(Des Charanjit Lal)

1976 (10 Feb). *Keoladeo Ghana Bird Sanctuary, Bharatpur. P* 13.
800 **703** 25 p. multicoloured 70 35

704 Vijayanta Tank

705 Alexander Graham Bell

1976 (4 Mar). *Bicentenary of 16th Light Cavalry Regt. P* 13.
801 **704** 25 p. multicoloured 70 30

1976 (10 Mar). *Alexander Graham Bell Commemoration. P* 13.
802 **705** 25 p. grey-black and yellow-ochre 60 25

706 Muthuswami Dikshitar

707 Eye and Red Cross

1976 (18 Mar). *Birth Bicentenary of Dikshitar (composer). P* 13½.
803 **706** 25 p. purple 45 20

(Des Benoy Sarkar)

1976 (7 Apr). *World Health Day. Prevention of Blindness. P* 13.
804 **707** 25 p. reddish brown and dull vermilion .. 50 30

708 "Industries"

709 Diesel Locomotive, 1963

(Des Benoy Sarkar)

1976 (30 Apr). *Industrial Development. P* 13.
805 **708** 25 p. multicoloured 25 25

1976 (15 May). *Locomotives. T* **709** *and similar horiz designs. Multicoloured. P* 14½ × 14.
806 25 p. Type **709** 55 10
807 50 p. Steam locomotive, 1895 .. .. .. 1·25 55
808 1 r. Steam locomotive, 1963 .. .. .. 2·25 1·25
809 2 r. Steam locomotive, 1853 .. .. .. 3·00 2·50
806/9 .. .. *Set of* 4 6·50 4·00

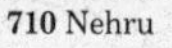

710 Nehru

711

712

Three types of Nehru portrait (*illustrated actual size*)
Type 710. Portrait measures 24 mm at base. First character above "NEHRU" has two prongs.
Type 711. Whole portrait is larger, measuring 25½ mm at base. Character above "NEHRU" has three prongs.
Type 712. Small portrait, 23 mm at base, with smaller inscription. Character above "NEHRU" has three prongs.

1976. *T* **710/12** *and similar vert design. W* **374**. *P* 13½.
810 **710** 25 p. dull violet (27.5.76) .. .. .. 2·00 40
810*a* **711** 25 p. dull violet (9.76) .. .. .. 2·00 40
810*b* **712** 25 p. dull violet (14.11.76) .. .. .. 2·00 40
811 – 25 p. red-brown (2.10.76) 75 30
a. Imperf (pair) .. .. ..
Design:—No. 811, Gandhi.
For these designs in a smaller size see Nos. 732, 968/9, 979/80 and 1073/4 and 1320.

713 "Spirit of 76" (Willard)

714 K. Kamaraj (politician)

1976 (29 May). *Bicentenary of American Revolution. P* 13.
812 **713** 2 r. 80, multicoloured .. .. .. 1·25 1·25

1976 (15 July). *Kamaraj Commemoration. P* 13.
813 **714** 25 p. sepia 10 10

715 "Shooting"

716 Subhadra Kumari Chauhan (poetess)

(Des Gopi Gajwani (25 p., 1 r.), Sukumar Shankar (1 r. 50), India Security Press (2 r. 80))

1976 (17 July). *Olympic Games, Montreal. T* **715** *and similar vert designs. P* 13.
814 25 p. deep violet and vermilion 25 10
815 1 r. multicoloured 90 90
816 1 r. 50, deep mauve and grey-black .. .. 1·10 1·60
817 2 r. 80, multicoloured .. .. .. 1·40 2·00
814/17 .. .. *Set of* 4 3·25 4·25
Designs:—1 r. Shot-put; 1 r. 50, Hockey; 2 r. 80, Sprinting.

1976 (6 Aug). *S. K. Chauhan Commemoration. P* 13.
818 **716** 25 p. grey-blue 10 20

717 Param Vir Chakra Medal

718 University Building, Bombay

(Des Benoy Sarkar)

1976 (15 Aug). *Param Vir Chakra Commemoration. P* 13.
819 **717** 25 p. multicoloured 10 15

1976 (3 Sept). *50th Anniv of Shreemati Nathibai Damodar Thackersey Women's University. P* 13½.
820 **718** 25 p. bluish violet 15 15

719 Bharatendu Harischandra (poet)

720 S. C. Chatterji (writer)

1976 (9 Sept). *Harischandra Commemoration. P* 13.
821 **719** 25 p. agate 10 15

1976 (15 Sept). *Birth Centenary of S. C. Chatterji. P* 13.
822 **720** 25 p. grey-black 10 15

NEW INFORMATION

The editor is always interested to correspond with people who have new information that will improve or correct the Catalogue.

721 Planned Family

722 Maharaja Agrasen and Coins

(Des A. K. Nagar)

1976 (22 Sept). *Family Planning. P* 14 × 14½.
823 **721** 25 p. multicoloured 10 15

1976 (24 Sept). *Maharaja Agrasen. P* 13.
824 **722** 25 p. red-brown 10 15

723 Swamp Deer

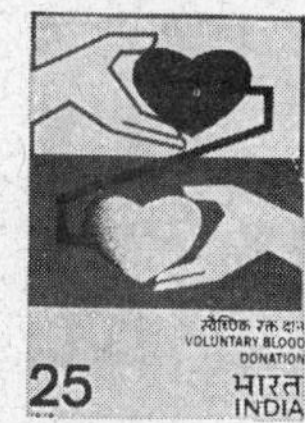

724 Hands holding Hearts

(Des from photos by Rajesh Bedi)

1976 (1 Oct). *Wildlife. T* **723** *and similar multicoloured designs. P* 14 × 14½ (25, 50 *p.*) *or* 14½ × 14 (*others*).
825 25 p. Type **723** 45 25
a. Black (name and year date) omitted ..
826 50 p. Lion .. .. 1·25 1·25
827 1 r. Leopard (*horiz*) .. .. 1·75 1·75
828 2 r. Caracal (*horiz*) .. .. 2·00 2·50
825/8 .. .. *Set of* 4 5·00 5·25

(Des B. G. Varma)

1976 (1 Oct). *Voluntary Blood Donation. P* 13.
829 **724** 25 p. yellow-ochre, scarlet and black .. 15 20

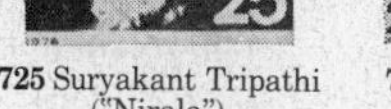

725 Suryakant Tripathi ("Nirala")

726 Painting of Folk-tale (H. D. Bhatia)

1976 (15 Oct). *80th Birth Anniv of "Nirala" (poet and novelist). P* 13.
830 **725** 25 p. deep blue 10 20

1976 (14 Nov). *Children's Day. P* 13½ × 14.
831 **726** 25 p. multicoloured 20 20

727 Hiralal Shastri (politician)

728 Dr. Hari Singh Gour (lawyer)

1976 (24 Nov). *Shastri Commemoration. P* 13.
832 **727** 25 p. sepia 15 20

1976 (26 Nov). *Dr. Gour Commemoration. P* 13.
833 **728** 25 p. deep reddish purple 15 20

729 A 300 B2 Airbus

730 Hybrid Coconut Palm

1976 (1 Dec). *Inauguration of Indian Airlines' Airbus. P* 14½ × 14.
834 **729** 2 r. multicoloured .. .. 2·00 2·00

1976 (27 Dec). *Diamond Jubilee of Coconut Research. P* 13.
835 **730** 25 p. multicoloured 15 20

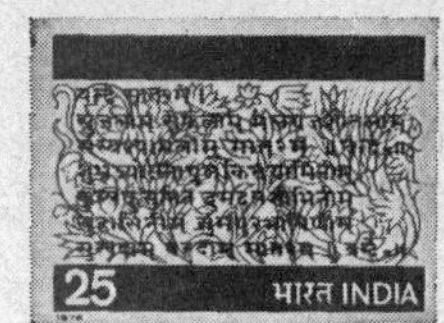

731 First Stanza of *Vande Mataram* (patriotic song by B. C. Chatterjee)

1976 (30 Dec). *"Vande Mataram" Commemoration. P* 13.
836 **731** 25 p. multicoloured 15 20

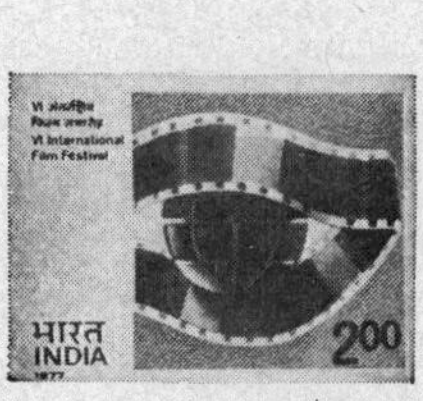

732 Globe and Film Strip **733** Seismograph and Crack in Earth's Crust

1977 (3 Jan). *Sixth International Film Festival of India, New Delhi. P* 13.
837 **732** 2 r. multicoloured .. .. .. 1·25 1·75

1977 (10 Jan). *Sixth World Conference on Earthquake Engineering, New Delhi. P* 13.
838 **733** 2 r. deep plum .. .. 1·25 1·75

734 Tarun Ram Phookun **735** Paramahansa Yogananda (religious leader)

1977 (22 Jan). *Birth Centenary of Tarun Ram Phookun (politician). P* 13.
839 **734** 25 p. blackish brown 10 20

1977 (7 Mar). *Yogananda Commemoration. P* 13.
840 **735** 25 p. reddish orange 15 20

736 Asian Regional Red Cross Emblem **737** Fahkruddin Ali Ahmed

1977 (9 Mar). *First Asian Regional Red Cross Conference, New Delhi. P* 13.
841 **736** 2 r. pink, deep blue and scarlet .. .. 1·50 2·25

1977 (22 Mar). *Death of President Ahmed. P* 13.
842 **737** 25 p. multicoloured 15 20

738 Emblem of Asian-Oceanic Postal Union

1977 (1 Apr). *15th Anniv of Asian-Oceanic Postal Union. P* 13.
843 **738** 2 r. multicoloured .. .. .. 1·50 2·00

739 Narottam Morarjee and *Loyalty* (liner) **740** Makhanlal Chaturvedi (writer and poet)

1977 (2 Apr). *Birth Centenary of Morarjee (industrialist). P* 13.
844 **739** 25 p. greenish blue 30 30

1977 (4 Apr). *Chaturvedi Commemoration. P* 13.
845 **740** 25 p. lake-brown 10 20

741 Mahaprabhu Vallabhacharya (philosopher) **742** Federation Emblem

1977 (14 Apr). *Vallabhacharya Commemoration. P* 13.
846 **741** 1 r. sepia 30 40

1977 (23 Apr). *50th Anniv of Federation of Indian Chambers of Commerce and Industry. P* 13.
847 **742** 25 p. dull purple, brown-ochre and buff .. 10 20

744 "Environment Protection" **745** Rajya Sabha Chamber

1977 (5 July). *World Environment Day. P* 13.
848 **744** 2 r. multicoloured .. .. .. 60 1·25

1977 (21 June). *25th Anniv of Rajya Sabha (Upper House of Parliament). P* 13.
849 **745** 25 p. multicoloured 10 15

746 Lotus

(Des from paintings by J. P. Irani)

1977 (1 July). *Indian Flowers. T* **746** *and similar multicoloured designs. P* 14½ × 14 (25 *p.*, 2 *r.*) *or* 14 × 14½ (*others*).
850 25 p. Type **746** 25 15
a. Black (inscription) omitted £250
851 50 p. Rhododendron (*vert*) 45 70
852 1 r. Kadamba (*vert*) .. .. .. 75 1·00
853 2 r. Gloriosa Lily .. .. .. 1·00 2·00
850/3 .. .. *Set of* 4 2·25 3·50

747 Berliner Gramophone **748** Coomaraswamy and Siva

(Des Benoy Sarkar)

1977 (20 July). *Centenary of Sound Recording. P* 13.
854 **747** 2 r. yellow-brown and black .. .. 1·00 1·75

1977 (22 Aug). *Birth Centenary of A. K. Coomaraswamy (art historian). P* 13.
855 **748** 25 p. multicoloured 20 25

749 Ganga Ram and Hospital **750** Dr. Samuel Hahnemann (founder of homeopathy)

1977 (4 Sept). *50th Death Anniv of Ganga Ram (social reformer). P* 14½ × 14.
856 **749** 25 p. maroon 15 20

1977 (6 Oct). *32nd International Homeopathic Congress, New Delhi. P* 13.
857 **750** 2 r. black and green .. .. .. 2·00 2·25

751 Ram Manohar Lohia (politician) **752** Early Punjabi Postman

1977 (12 Oct). *R. M. Lohia Commemoration. P* 13.
858 **751** 25 p. red-brown 25 25

1977 (12 Oct). *"Inpex-77" Philatelic Exhibition. Bangalore. T* **752** *and similar horiz design. P* 13 (25 *p.*) *or* 13½ × 14 (2 *r.*).
859 25 p. multicoloured 45 30
860 2 r. olive-grey/*flesh* .. .. .. 1·75 2·25
Design:—2 r. "Lion and Palm" essay, 1853.

753 Scarlet "Scinde Dawks" of 1852 **754** "Mother and Child" (Khajuraho sculpture)

1977 (19 Oct). *"Asiana 77" Philatelic Exhibition, Bangalore. T* **753** *and similar horiz design. P* 13.
861 1 r. orange, black and yellow .. .. 80 1·00
862 3 r. orange, black and light blue .. .. 1·60 2·50
Design:—3 r. Foreign mail arriving at Ballard Pier, Bombay, 1927.

1977 (23 Oct). *15th International Congress of Pediatrics, New Delhi. P* 13.
863 **754** 2 r. reddish brown and grey .. .. 1·75 2·50

755 Kittur Rani Channamma (warrior queen) **756** Symbolic Sun

1977 (23 Oct). *Kittur Rani Channamma Commemoration. P* 13.
864 **755** 25 p. grey-green 50 35

1977 (8 Nov). *Union Public Service Commission Commemoration. P* 13.
865 **756** 25 p. multicoloured 30 20

757 Ear of Corn **758** "Cats" (Nikur Dilipbhai)

(Des Benoy Sarkar)

1977 (13 Nov). *"Agriexpo 77" Agricultural Exhibition, Pragati Maidan. W* **374** *(sideways). P* 13.
866 **757** 25 p. blue-green 40 25

1977 (14 Nov). *Children's Day. T* **758** *and similar horiz design. Multicoloured. P* 13.
867 25 p. Type **758** 50 30
868 1 r. "Friends" (Bhavsar Ashish Ramanlal) .. 1·75 2·50

759 Jotirao Phooley (social reformer)

760 Diagram of Population Growth

1977 (28 Nov). *Indian Personalities. T* **759** *and similar vert design. W* **374** *(sideways). P* 13.
869 25 p. brown-olive 20 30
870 25 p. chestnut 20 30
Portrait:—No. 870, Senapti Bapat (revolutionary).

1977 (13 Dec). *41st Session of International Statistical Institute, New Delhi. P* 13.
871 **760** 2 r. blue-green and red .. .. .. 85 1·40

761 Kamta Prasad Guru and Vyakarna (Hindi Grammar)

762 Kremlin Tower and Soviet Flag

1977 (25 Dec). *Kamta Prasad Guru Commemoration. W* **374** *(sideways). P* 13½ × 14.
872 **761** 25 p. deep brown 10 20

1977 (30 Dec). *60th Anniv of October Revolution. P* 13.
873 **762** 1 r. multicoloured 45 75

763 Climber crossing a Crevice

764 "Shikara" on Lake Dal

1978 (15 Jan). *Conquest of Kanchenjunga (1977). T* **763** *and similar horiz design. Multicoloured. P* 13
874 25 p. Type **763** 10 10
875 1 r. Indian flag near summit.. .. .. .. 45 80

1978 (23 Jan). *27th Pacific Area Travel Association Conference, New Delhi. P* 13.
876 **764** 1 r. multicoloured 85 85

765 Children in Library

766 The Mother-Pondicherry (philosopher)

1978 (11 Feb). *Third World Book Fair, New Delhi. P* 13.
877 **765** 1 r. chestnut and slate 45 80

1978 (21 Feb). *Birth Centenary of the Mother-Pondicherry. P* 13.
878 **766** 25 p. brown and light grey 10 20

767 Wheat and Globe

768 Nanalal Dalpatram Kavi (poet)

1978 (23 Feb). *Fifth International Wheat Genetics Symposium, New Delhi. P* 13.
879 **767** 25 p. yellow and blue-green 10 20

1978 (16 Mar). *Nanalal Kavi Commemoration. W* **374** *(sideways). P* 13.
880 **768** 25 p. red-brown 10 20

769 Surjya Sen (revolutionary)

770 "Two Vaishnavas" (Jamini Roy)

1978 (22 Mar). *Surjya Sen Commemoration. W* **374** *(sideways). P* 13.
881 **769** 25 p. sepia and orange-red 10 20

1978 (23 Mar). *Modern Indian Paintings. T* **770** *and similar vert designs. Multicoloured. P* 14.
882 25 p. Type **770** 20 20
a. Black (face value and inscr) omitted .. £200
883 50 p. "The Mosque" (Sailoz Mookherjea) .. 40 70
884 1 r. "Head" (Rabindranath Tagore) .. .. 70 1·25
885 2 r. "Hill Women" (Amrita Sher Gil) .. 90 1·75
882/5 .. .. *Set of* 4 2·00 3·50

771 "Self-portrait" (Rubens)

772 Charlie Chaplin

1978 (4 Apr). *400th Birth Anniv of Rubens. P* 13.
886 **771** 2 r. multicoloured .. .. 1·75 2·50

1978 (16 Apr). *Charlie Chaplin Commemoration. P* 13.
887 **772** 25 p. Prussian blue and gold 45 25

773 Deendayal Upadhyaya (statesman)

774 Syama Prasad Mookerjee

1978 (5 May). *Deendayal Upadhyaya Commemoration. P* 13.
888 **773** 25 p. olive-brown and pale orange .. 10 20

1978 (6 July). *Syama Prasad Mookerjee (statesman) Commemoration. P* 13 × 13½.
889 **774** 25 p. brown-olive 15 20

775 Airavat (mythological) elephant), Jain Temple, Gujerat (Kachchh Museum)

776 Krishna and Arjuna in Battle Chariot

1978 (27 July). *Treasures from Indian Museums. T* **775** *and similar multicoloured designs. P* 13 × 13½ (25, 50 *p.*) *or* 13½ × 13 (*others*).
890 25 p. Type **775** 25 25
891 50 p. Kalpadruma (magical tree), Besnagar (Indian Museum) 55 80
892 1 r. Obverse and reverse of Kushan gold coin (National Museum) (*horiz*) .. .. 85 1·25
893 2 r. Dagger and knife of Emperor Jehangir, Mughal (Salar Jung Museum) (*horiz*) .. 1·10 1·75
890/3 .. .. *Set of* 4 2·50 3·50

1978 (25 Aug). *Bhagawadgeeta (Divine Song of India). P* 13.
894 **776** 25 p. gold and vermilion 10 20

777 Bethune College

778 E. V. Ramasami

1978 (4 Sept). *Centenary of Bethune College, Calcutta. P* 13.
895 **777** 25 p. deep brown and deep green .. 10 20

1978 (17 Sept). *E. V. Ramasami (reformer) Commemoration. P* 13.
896 **778** 25 p. black 10 10

779 Uday Shankar

780 Leo Tolstoy

1978 (26 Sept). *Uday Shankar (dancer) Commemoration. P* 13.
897 **779** 25 p. reddish brown and stone 10 20

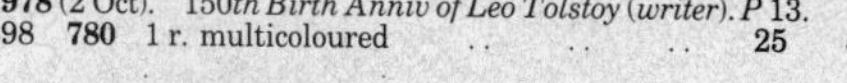

1978 (2 Oct). *150th Birth Anniv of Leo Tolstoy (writer). P* 13.
898 **780** 1 r. multicoloured 25 30

781 Vallathol Narayana Menon

782 "Two Friends" (Dinesh Sharma)

1978 (15 Oct). *Birth Centenary of Vallathol Narayana Menon (poet). P* 13.
899 **781** 25 p. bright purple and brown 10 20

1978 (14 Nov). *Children's Day. P* 13.
900 **782** 25 p. multicoloured 10 20

783 Machine Operator

784 Sowars (cavalrymen)

1978 (17 Nov). *National Small Industries Fair. P* 13½.
901 **783** 25 p. bronze-green 10 10

1978 (25 Nov). *175th Anniv of Skinner's Horse (cavalry regiment). P* 13.
902 **784** 25 p. multicoloured 40 40

785 Mohammad Ali Jauhar **786** Chakravarti Rajagopalachari

1978 (10 Dec). *Birth Centenary of Mohammad Ali Jauhar (patriot). P* 13.
903 **785** 25 p. olive-green 10 10

1978 (10 Dec). *Birth Centenary of Chakravarti Rajagopalachari (first post-independence Governor-General). P* 13.
904 **786** 25 p. lake-brown 10 10

787 Wright Brothers and *Flyer* **788** Ravenshaw College

1978 (23 Dec). *75th Anniv of Powered Flight. W* **374** *(sideways). P* 13 × 13½.
905 **787** 1 r. purple and yellow-ochre 25 20

1978 (24 Dec). *Centenary of Ravenshaw College. P* 14.
906 **788** 25 p. lake and deep green 10 20

789 Schubert **790** Uniforms of 1799, 1901 and 1979 with Badge

1978 (25 Dec). *150th Death Anniv of Franz Schubert (composer). P* 13.
907 **789** 1 r. multicoloured 40 55
a. Black (face value) omitted .. ..

Two black cylinders were used for the design of No. 907. No. 907a shows the black still present on the portrait.

(Des Charanjit Lal)

1979 (20 Feb). *Punjab Regiment. P* 13.
908 **790** 25 p. multicoloured 45 40

791 Bhai Parmanand **792** Gandhi with Young Boy

1979 (24 Feb). *Bhai Parmanand (historian) Commemoration. P* 13.
909 **791** 25 p. deep violet-blue 10 20

1979 (5 Mar). *International Year of the Child. T* **792** *and similar vert design. P* 13.
910 25 p. reddish brown and scarlet-vermilion .. 30 25
911 1 r. reddish brown and yellow-orange .. 70 1·25
Design:—1 r. Indian I.Y.C. emblem.

During October 1979 two stamps inscribed "HAPPY CHILD NATION'S PRIDE" with face values of 50 p. and 1 r. were issued to post offices. These were intended for sale as charity labels, without postal validity, the proceeds going to a Child Welfare fund. It would seem that the instructions issued were unclear, however, as some post offices sold these labels as postage stamps and accepted mail franked with them.

793 Albert Einstein **794** Rajarshi Shahu Chhatrapati

1979 (14 Mar). *Birth Centenary of Albert Einstein (physicist). P* 13.
912 **793** 1 r. blue-black 20 40

1979 (1 May). *Rajarshi Shahu Chhatrapati (ruler of Kolhapur State, 1874–1922, and precursor of social reform in India) Commemoration. P* 13.
913 **794** 25 p. deep dull purple 10 20

795 Exhibition Logo **796** Postcards under Magnifying Glass

1979 (2 July). *"India 80" International Stamp Exhibition (1st issue). P* 13.
914 **795** 30 p. deep green and orange 10 20
See also Nos. 942/5 and 955/8.

1979 (2 July). *Centenary of Indian Postcards. P* 13.
915 **796** 50 p. multicoloured 15 25

797 Raja Mahendra Pratap **798** Flounder, Herring and Prawn **799** Rubber Tapping

1979 (15 Aug). *Raja Mahendra Pratap (revolutionary and patriot) Commemoration. P* 13.
916 **797** 30 p. brown-olive 10 20

1979 (3 Sept)–**88**. *Designs as T* **798/9**. *P* 14½ × 14 (15, 20, 35 *p.*, 1, 2 *r.*), 13 (5*p.* (*No.* 938), 25*p.* (*No.* 925*b*), 3 *r.* 25, 10 *r.*) *or* 14 × 14½ (*others*).

(*a*) *Photo. Wmk Large Star and* "INDIA GOVT" *in sheet**

917	2 p.	slate-violet (31.3.80)	15	30
918	5 p.	new blue (26.11.79)	40	10
919	15 p.	deep bluish green (10.3.80)	60	10

(*b*) *Photo. W* **374**† (*sideways on* 15, 20, 35 *p.*, 1, 2 *r.*, 2 *r.* 25, 2 *r.* 80, 3 *r.* 25, *and* 10 *r.*)

920	2 p.	slate-violet (25.3.81)	10	10
921	5 p.	new blue (25.3.81)	10	10
	a.	Perf 13 (5.7.82)	25	10
	ab.	Wmk sideways (1988)	10	10
922	10 p.	deep green (25.1.82)	20	10
	a.	Perf 13 (5.7.82)	20	10
	ab.	Printed double		
	ac.	Wmk sideways (1988)	10	10
923	15 p.	deep bluish green (25.3.81)	10	10
	a.	Perf 13 (5.7.82)	10	10
924	20 p.	Indian red (25.3.81)	15	10
	a.	Perf 13 (5.7.82)	30	10
	ab.	Wmk upright (1988)	10	10
925	25 p.	red-brown (26.11.79)	45	10
	a.	Perf 13 (5.7.82)	15	10
925*b*	25 p.	deep blue-green (5.9.85)	25	10
	ba.	Wmk sideways (1988)	10	10
926	30 p.	yellowish green	35	10
	a.	Perf 13 (6.4.82)	25	10
	ab.	Wmk sideways (1987)	10	10
927	35 p.	cerise (15.9.80)	20	10
	a.	Perf 13 (5.7.82)	25	10
928	50 p.	deep violet (25.1.82)	40	10
	a.	Imperf (pair)	65·00	
	b.	Perf 13 (5.7.82)	40	10
	ba.	Wmk sideways (1988)	10	10
929	1 r.	bistre-brown (17.6.80)	20	10
	a.	Imperf (pair)		
	b.	Perf 13 (10.11.83)	10	10
	ba.	Wmk upright (1987)	10	10
932	2 r.	deep rose-lilac (7.12.80)	40	10
	a.	Perf 13 (10.11.83)	15	20
	ab.	Wmk upright (1987)		
933	2 r.	25, red and blue-green (25.3.81)	25	15
	a.	Wmk upright		
	ab.	Perf 13 (1983)	25	15
	b.	Perf 13 (*wmk sideways*) (1987)	15	20
934	2 r.	80, red and blue-green (25.3.81)	20	25
	a.	Wmk upright	20	25
934*b*	3 r.	25, reddish orange & bl-grn (28.12.82)	20	25
	ba.	Wmk upright	20	25

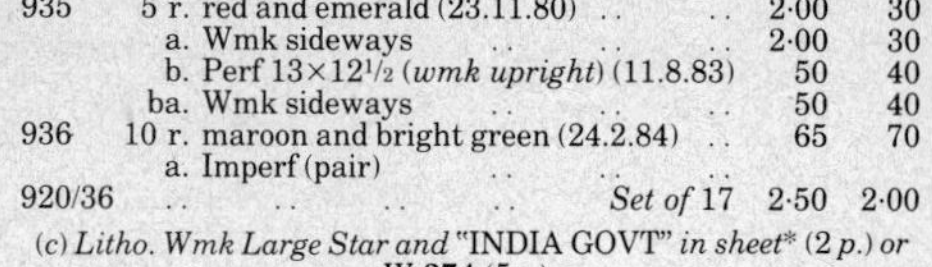

935	5 r.	red and emerald (23.11.80)	2·00	30
	a.	Wmk sideways	2·00	30
	b.	Perf 13×12½ (*wmk upright*) (11.8.83)	50	40
	ba.	Wmk sideways	50	40
936	10 r.	maroon and bright green (24.2.84)	65	70
	a.	Imperf (pair)		
920/36		*Set of* 17	2·50	2·00

(*c*) *Litho. Wmk Large Star and* "INDIA GOVT" *in sheet** (2 *p.*) *or* W **374** (5*p.*)

937	2 p.	slate-violet (2.2.81)	10	30
938	5 p.	new blue (29.11.82)	10	10

Designs: *Horiz as T* **798**—2 p. Adult education class; 10 p. Irrigation canal; 25 p. (No. 925) Chick hatching from egg; 25 p. (No. 925*b*) Village, wheat and tractor; 30 p. Harvesting maize; 50 p. Woman dairy farmer, cows and milk bottles. (36 × 19 *mm*)—10 r. Forest and hillside. *Vert as T* **798**—15 p. Farmer and agriculture symbols; 20 p. Mother feeding child; 35 p. "Family". (17 × 28 *mm*)—1 r. Cotton plant; 2 r. Weaving. *Vert as T* **799**—2 r. 25, Cashew; 2 r. 80, Apples; 3 r. 25, Oranges.

*See note concerning this watermark below No. 720. The 2 p. and 5 p. exist on both types of this watermark, the others on the second type only.

†For notes on the amended version of W **374** see above No. 399. The changes in watermark position from 1987 onwards show the reduced size base.

Nos. 920/1 and 923/4 were originally intended for issue on 9 March 1981 and First Day Covers showing this date are known from at least one post office.

At least one sheet of No. 924a exists without an impression from the ink cylinder on the first horizontal row.

No. 937 can be easily identified by the background of horizontal lines.

800 Jatindra Nath Das **801** De Havilland "Puss Moth" Aeroplane

1979 (13 Sept). *50th Death Anniv of Jatindra Nath Das (revolutionary). P* 13.
941 **800** 30 p. blackish brown 10 20

1979 (15 Oct). *Air. "India 80" International Stamp Exhibition (2nd issue). Mail-carrying Aircraft. T* **801** *and similar horiz designs. Multicoloured. P* 14½ × 14.
942 30 p. Type **801** 25 25
943 50 p. Indian Air Force "Chetak" helicopter .. 40 45
944 1 r. Indian Airlines Boeing "737" airliner .. 55 75
945 2 r. Air India Boeing "747" airliner .. 75 95
942/5 .. .. *Set of* 4 1·75 2·25

802 Early and Modern Lightbulbs **803** Gilgit Record

1979 (21 Oct). *Centenary of Electric Lightbulb. P* 13.
946 **802** 1 r. brown-purple 15 25

1979 (23 Oct). *National Archives. P* 14½ × 14.
947 **803** 30 p. yellow-ochre and sepia 10 15

804 Hirakud Dam **805** Fair Emblem

1979 (29 Oct). *50th Anniv, and 13th Congress, of International Commission on Large Dams. P* 13.
948 **804** 30 p. lake-brown and deep blue-green .. 10 15

1979 (10 Nov). *India International Trade Fair. P* 13.
949 **805** 1 r. grey-black and salmon 15 30

806 Child learning to Read

1979 (10 Nov). *International Children's Book Fair, New Delhi. P* 14½ × 14.
950 **806** 30 p. multicoloured 10 20

807 Dove with Olive Branch and I.A.E.A. Emblem

1979 (4 Dec). *23rd I.A.E.A. (International Atomic Energy Agency) Conference, New Delhi. P* 13.
951 **807** 1 r. multicloured 15 40

808 "Hindustan Pushpak" Aeroplane and "Rohini-1" Glider

809 Gurdwara Baoli Sahib Temple, Goindwal, Amritsar District

(Des R. N. Pasricha)

1979 (10 Dec). *Flying and Gliding. P* 13.
952 **808** 30 p. black, orange-brown and blue .. 30 30

1979 (21 Dec). *500th Birth Anniv of Guru Amar Das. P* 13.
953 **809** 30 p. multicoloured 10 25

810 Ring of People encircling U.N. Emblem and Cog-wheel

811 Army Post Office and Postmarks

1980 (21 Jan). *3rd U.N.I.D.O. (United Nations Industrial Development Organisation) General Conference, New Delhi. P* 13.
954 **810** 1 r. multicoloured 15 30

(Des Benoy Sarkar (30, 50 p.), India Security Press (others))

1980 (25 Jan). *"India 80" International Stamp Exhibition (3rd issue). T* **811** *and similar vert designs. No wmk (1 r.) or Large Star and "INDIA GOVT" in sheet* (others). P* 13.
955 30 p. grey-olive 20 20
956 50 p. bistre-brown and dull olive-bistre .. 40 60
957 1 r. Venetian red 45 70
958 2 r. olive-brown .. .. 60 1·10
955/8 .. .. *Set of* 4 1·50 2·40
Designs:—50 p. Money order; 1 r. Copper ticket; 2 r. Sir Rowland Hill and birthplace at Kidderminster.
*See note below No. 720.

812 Energy Symbols

813 Uniforms of 1780 and 1980, Crest and Ribbon

(Des C. Pakrashi)

1980 (17 Feb). *Institution of Engineers (India) Commemoration. Wmk Large Star and "INDIA GOVT" in sheet. P* 13.
959 **812** 30 p. gold and blue 10 20

1980 (26 Feb). *Bicentenary of Madras Sappers. P* 13.
960 **813** 30 p. multicoloured 20 25

814 Books

815 Bees and Honey-comb

(Des J. Gupta)

1980 (29 Feb). *4th World Book Fair, New Delhi. Wmk Large Star and "INDIA GOVT" in sheet. P* 13.
961 **814** 30 p. new blue 20 25

(Des M. Bardhan)

1980 (29 Feb). *2nd International Apiculture Conference, New Delhi. P* 13.
962 **815** 1 r. deep brown and olive-bistre .. 25 40

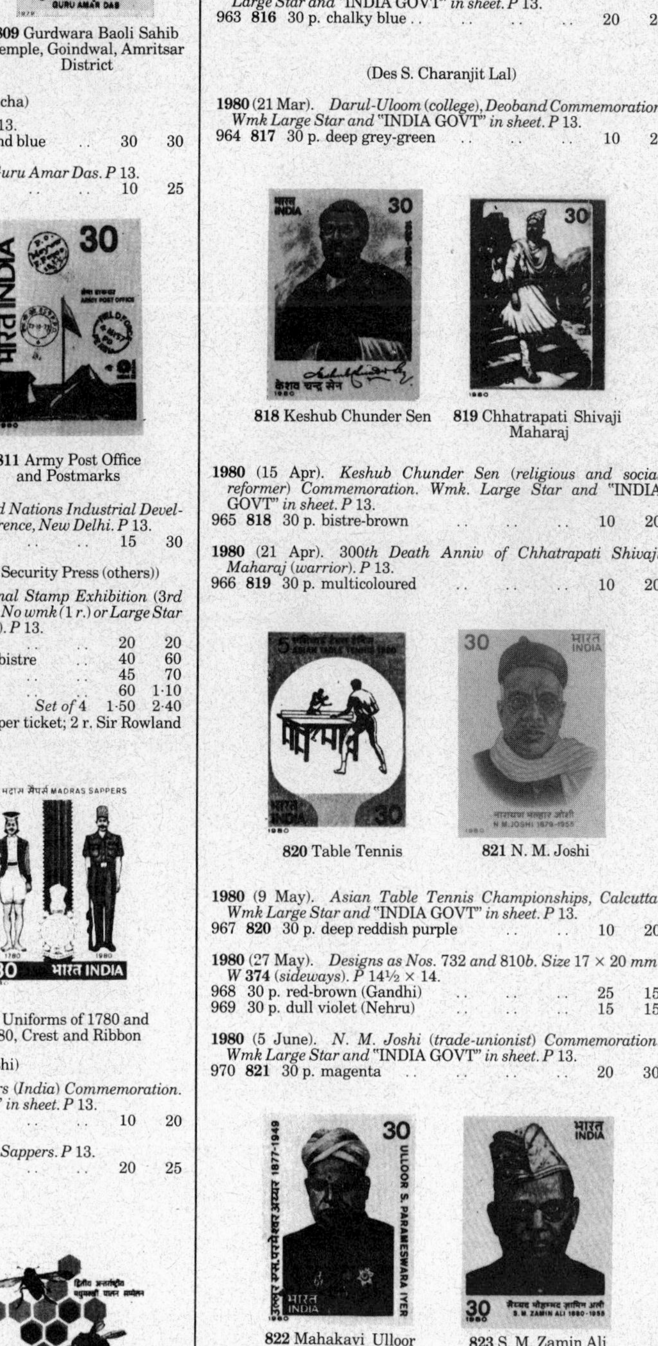

816 Welthy Fisher and Saksharta Nicketan (Literacy House), Lucknow

817 Darul-Uloom, Deoband

(Des M. Choudhury)

1980 (18 Mar). *Welthy Fisher (teacher) Commemoration. Wmk Large Star and "INDIA GOVT" in sheet. P* 13.
963 **816** 30 p. chalky blue 20 25

(Des S. Charanjit Lal)

1980 (21 Mar). *Darul-Uloom (college), Deoband Commemoration. Wmk Large Star and "INDIA GOVT" in sheet. P* 13.
964 **817** 30 p. deep grey-green 10 20

818 Keshub Chunder Sen

819 Chhatrapati Shivaji Maharaj

1980 (15 Apr). *Keshub Chunder Sen (religious and social reformer) Commemoration. Wmk. Large Star and "INDIA GOVT" in sheet. P* 13.
965 **818** 30 p. bistre-brown 10 20

1980 (21 Apr). *300th Death Anniv of Chhatrapati Shivaji Maharaj (warrior). P* 13.
966 **819** 30 p. multicoloured 10 20

820 Table Tennis

821 N. M. Joshi

1980 (9 May). *Asian Table Tennis Championships, Calcutta. Wmk Large Star and "INDIA GOVT" in sheet. P* 13.
967 **820** 30 p. deep reddish purple 10 20

1980 (27 May). *Designs as Nos. 732 and 810b. Size 17 × 20 mm. W* **374** *(sideways). P* 14½ × 14.
968 30 p. red-brown (Gandhi) 25 15
969 30 p. dull violet (Nehru) 15 15

1980 (5 June). *N. M. Joshi (trade-unionist) Commemoration. Wmk Large Star and "INDIA GOVT" in sheet. P* 13.
970 **821** 30 p. magenta 20 30

822 Mahakavi Ulloor

823 S. M. Zamin Ali

1980 (6 June). *Mahakavi Ulloor (poet) Commemoration. Wmk Large Star and "INDIA GOVT" in sheet. P* 13.
971 **822** 30 p. maroon 30 25

1980 (25 June). *S. M. Zamin Ali (educationalist and poet) Commemoration. Wmk Large Star and "INDIA GOVT" in sheet. P* 13.
972 **823** 30 p. bronze-green 10 20

824 Helen Keller

825 High-jumping

1980 (27 June). *Birth Centenary of Helen Keller (campaigner for the handicapped). P* 13.
973 **824** 30 p. black and dull orange 20 20

1980 (19 July). *Olympic Games, Moscow. T* **825** *and similar vert design. Multicoloured. P* 13½ × 14.
974 1 r. Type **825** 30 40
975 2 r. 80, Horse-riding 60 85

826 Prem Chand

827 Mother Teresa and Nobel Peace Prize Medallion

1980 (31 July). *Birth Centenary of Prem Chand (writer). Wmk Large Star and "INDIA GOVT" in sheet. P* 13.
976 **826** 30 p. red-brown 10 20

1980 (27 Aug). *Mother Teresa (Nobel Peace Prizewinner, 1979) Commemoration. Wmk Large Star and "INDIA GOVT" in sheet. P* 13.
977 **827** 30 p. bluish violet 15 25

828 Lord Mountbatten

829 Scottish Church College, Calcutta

1980 (28 Aug). *Lord Mountbatten Commemoration. P* 13.
978 **828** 2 r. 80, multicoloured .. .. .. 1·25 1·75

1980 (1 Sept)–**82**. *As Nos. 968/9, but new face value.*
979 35 p. red-brown (Gandhi) (16.9.80) 25 15
a. Perf 13 (5.7.82) 25 15
980 35 p. dull violet (Nehru) 15 15
a. Perf 13 (5.7.82) 15 15

(Des C. Pakrashi)

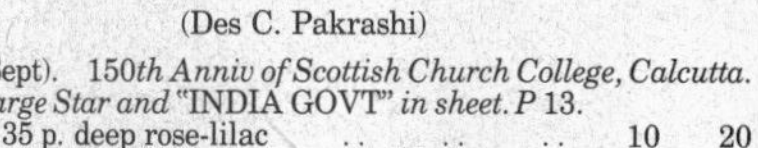

1980 (27 Sept). *150th Anniv of Scottish Church College, Calcutta. Wmk Large Star and "INDIA GOVT" in sheet. P* 13.
981 **829** 35 p. deep rose-lilac 10 20

830 Rajah Annamalai Chettiar

831 Gandhi marching to Dandi

1980 (30 Sept). *Rajah Annamalai Chettiar (statesman and educationalist) Commemoration. P* 14 × 14½.
982 **830** 35 p. deep lilac 10 15

(Des S. Ramachandran)

1980 (2 Oct). *"Dandi March" (Gandhi's defiance of Salt Tax Law) Commemoration. T* **831** *and similar vert design. P* 14½ × 14.
983 35 p. black, turquoise-blue and gold .. 10 20
a. Horiz pair. Nos. 983/4 .. .. .. 20 40
984 35 p. black, deep mauve and gold 10 20
Design:—No. 983, Type **831**; No. 984, Gandhi picking up handful of salt at Dandi.

No. 984 with the deep mauve omitted is a chemically produced fake.

Nos. 983/4 were printed together, *se-tenant*, in horizontal pairs throughout the sheet.

832 Jayaprakash Narayan **833** Great Indian Bustard

(Des Directorate of Advertising and Visual Publicity, New Delhi)

1980 (8 Oct). *Jayaprakash Narayan (politician and freedom fighter) Commemoration. Wmk Large Star and "INDIA GOVT" in sheet. P* 14 × 14½.
985 **832** 35 p. chocolate 15 20

(Des J. Irani)

1980 (1 Nov). *International Symposium on Bustards, Jaipur. P* 13.
986 **833** 2 r. 30, multicoloured .. .. 75 1·00

834 Arabic Commemorative Inscription

(Des B. Makhmoor)

1980 (3 Nov). *Moslem Year* 1400 *A.H. Commemoration. P* 13.
987 **834** 35 p. multicoloured 10 20

835 Girls Dancing **836** Dhyan Chand

(Des P. Paul)

1980 (14 Nov). *Children's Day. P* 13½ × 13.
988 **835** 35 p. multicoloured 20 30

1980 (3 Dec). *Dhyan Chand (hockey player) Commemoration. P* 14 × 14½.
989 **836** 35 p. red-brown 40 30

837 Gold Mining **838** M. A. Ansari

1980 (20 Dec). *Centenary of Kolar Gold Fields, Karnataka. P* 13.
990 **837** 1 r. multicoloured 30 20

1980 (25 Dec). *M. A. Ansari (medical practitioner and politician) Commemoration. Wmk Large Star and "INDIA GOVT" in sheet. P* 14 × 14½.
991 **838** 35 p. dull olive 10 15

839 India Government Mint, Bombay **840** Bride from Tamil Nadu

1980 (27 Dec). *150th Anniv of India Government Mint. Bombay. P* 13.
992 **839** 35 p. black, silver and dull blue 10 15

1980 (30 Dec). *Brides in Traditional Costume. T* **840** *and similar vert designs. Multicoloured. P* 13.
993 1 r. Type **840** 25 40
994 1 r. Bride from Rajasthan 25 40
995 1 r. Bride from Kashmir 25 40
996 1 r. Bride from Bengal 25 40
993/6 .. .. *Set of* 4 90 1·40

841 Mazharul Haque **842** St. Stephen's College

1981 (2 Jan). *Mazharul Haque (politician) Commemoration. Wmk Large Star and "INDIA GOVT" in sheet. P* 14 × 14½.
997 **841** 35 p. chalky blue 10 20

1981 (1 Feb). *Centenary of St. Stephen's College, Delhi. Wmk Large Star and "INDIA GOVT" in sheet. P* 14 × 14½.
998 **842** 35 p. dull scarlet 10 20

843 Gommateshwara **844** G. V. Mavalankar

1981 (9 Feb). *Millenium of Gommateshwara (statue at Shravanabelgola. P* 14 × 14½.
999 **843** 1 r. multicoloured 15 25

1981 (27 Feb). *25th Death Anniv of G. V. Mavalankar (parliamentarian). P* 14 × 14½.
1000 **844** 35 p. Venetian red 10 25

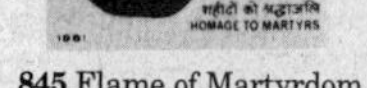

845 Flame of Martyrdom **846** Heinrich von Stephan and U.P.U. Emblem

(Des D. Dey)

1981 (23 Mar). *"Homage to Martyrs". P* 14 × 14½.
1001 **845** 35 p. multicoloured 10 20

1981 (8 Apr). *150th Birth Anniv of Heinrich von Stephan (founder of U.P.U.). P* 14½ × 14.
1002 **846** 1 r. red-brown and new blue 15 40

847 Disabled Child being helped by Able-bodied Child **848** Bhil

(Des K. Raha)

1981 (20 Apr). *International Year for Disabled Persons. P* 14½ × 14.
1003 **847** 1 r. black and blue 15 25

(Des from photographs by A. Pareek (No. 1004), S. Dutta (No. 1005). S. Theodore Baskaran (No. 1006), Kikrumielie Angami (No. 1007))

1981 (30 May). *Native Tribes. T* **848** *and similar vert designs. Multicoloured. P* 14.
1004 1 r. Type **848** 20 25
1005 1 r. Dandami Maria 20 25
1006 1 r. Toda 20 25
1007 1 r. Khlamngam Naga 20 25
1004/7 .. .. *Set of* 4 70 90

849 Stylised Trees **850** Nilmoni Phukan

(Des M. Bardhan)

1981 (15 June). *Conservation of Forests. P* 14 × 14½.
1008 **849** 1 r. multicoloured 15 15

1981 (22 June). *Nilmoni Phukan (poet) Commemoration. P* 14 × 14½.
1009 **850** 35 p. red-brown 10 15

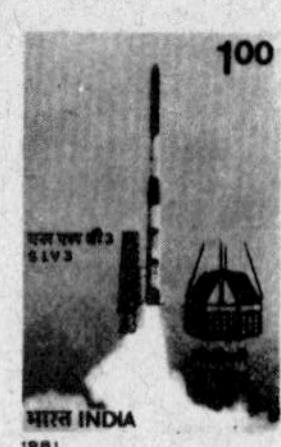

851 Sanjay Gandhi **852** Launch of "SLV 3" and Diagram of "Rohini"

(Des C. Pakrashi)

1981 (23 June). *First Death Anniv of Sanjay Gandhi (politician). P* 13.
1010 **851** 35 p. multicoloured 10 15

1981 (18 July). *Launch of "SLV 3" Rocket with "Rohini" Satellite. P* 14 × 14½.
1011 **852** 1 r. black, pink and pale blue 15 15

853 Games Logo **854** Flame of the Forest

(Des M. Chaudhury (No. 1013))

1981 (28 July). *Asian Games, New Delhi (1st issue). T* **853** *and similar horiz design. Multicoloured. P* 13½ × 13.
1012 1 r. Type **853** 40 25
1013 1 r. Games emblem and stylised hockey players 40 25

See also Nos. 1026, 1033, 1057, 1059 and 1061/6.

(Des from photographs by K. Vaid (35 p., 2 r.), R. Bedi (others))

1981 (1 Sept). *Flowering Trees. T* **854** *and similar vert designs. Multicoloured. P* 13 × 13½.
1014 35 p. Type **854** 15 10
1015 50 p. Crateva 25 20
1016 1 r. Golden Shower 35 25
1017 2 r. Bauhinia 50 55
1014/17 .. .. *Set of* 4 1·10 90

855 W.F.D. Emblem and Wheat **856** *Stichophthalma camadeva*

(Des M. Bardhan)

1981 (16 Oct). *World Food Day. P* 14 × 14½.
1018 **855** 1 r. greenish yellow and Prussian blue 15 15

(Des from paintings by M. Mandal)

1981 (20 Oct). *Butterflies. T* **856** *and similar multicoloured designs. P* 13.
1019 35 p. Type **856** 35 10
1020 50 p. *Cethosia biblis* 55 25
1021 1 r. *Cyrestis achates (vert)* 75 35
1022 2 r. *Teinopalpus imperialis (vert)* .. .. 1·00 1·00
1019/22 .. .. *Set of* 4 2·40 1·50

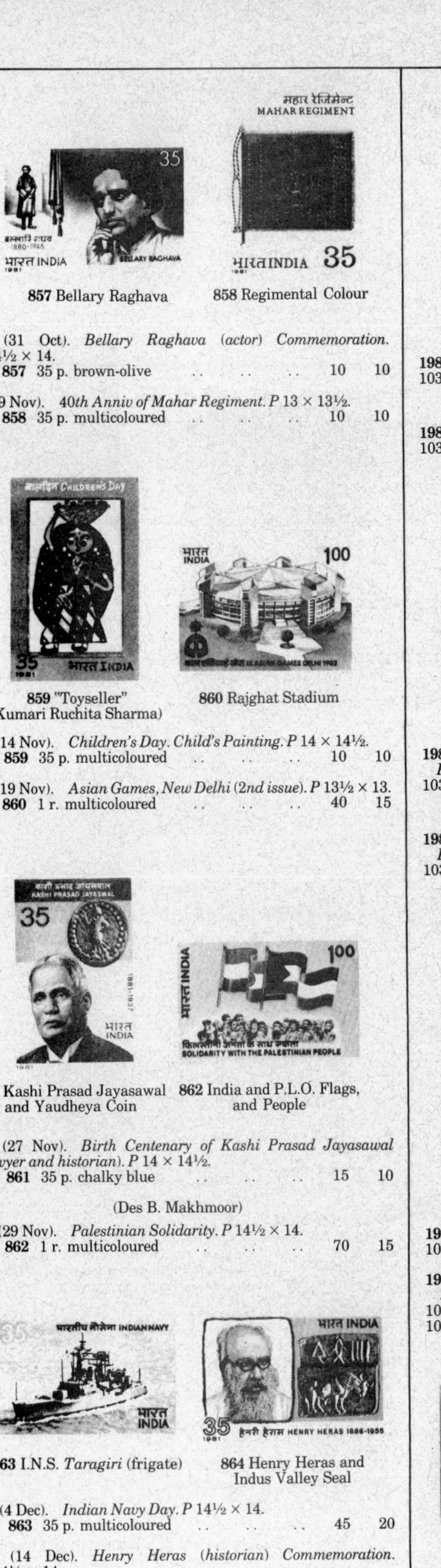

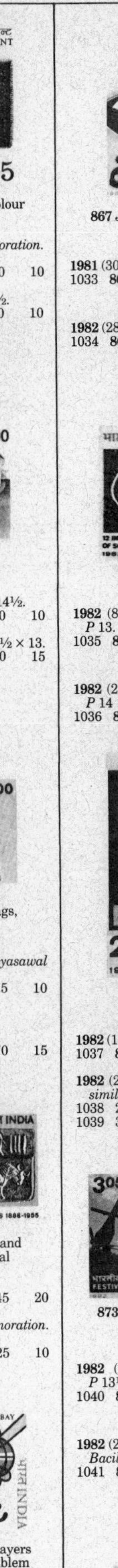
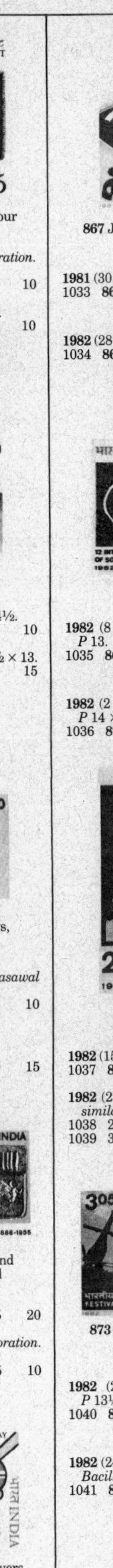

857 Bellary Raghava

858 Regimental Colour

1981 (31 Oct). *Bellary Raghava (actor) Commemoration. P* 14½ × 14.
1023 **857** 35 p. brown-olive 10 10

1981 (9 Nov). *40th Anniv of Mahar Regiment. P* 13 × 13½.
1024 **858** 35 p. multicoloured 10 10

859 "Toyseller" (Kumari Ruchita Sharma)

860 Rajghat Stadium

1981 (14 Nov). *Children's Day. Child's Painting. P* 14 × 14½.
1025 **859** 35 p. multicoloured 10 10

1981 (19 Nov). *Asian Games, New Delhi (2nd issue). P* 13½ × 13.
1026 **860** 1 r. multicoloured 40 15

861 Kashi Prasad Jayasawal and Yaudheya Coin

862 India and P.L.O. Flags, and People

1981 (27 Nov). *Birth Centenary of Kashi Prasad Jayasawal (lawyer and historian). P* 14 × 14½.
1027 **861** 35 p. chalky blue 15 10

(Des B. Makhmoor)

1981 (29 Nov). *Palestinian Solidarity. P* 14½ × 14.
1028 **862** 1 r. multicoloured 70 15

863 I.N.S. *Taragiri* (frigate)

864 Henry Heras and Indus Valley Seal

1981 (4 Dec). *Indian Navy Day. P* 14½ × 14.
1029 **863** 35 p. multicoloured 45 20

1981 (14 Dec). *Henry Heras (historian) Commemoration. P* 14½ × 14.
1030 **864** 35 p. deep rose-lilac 25 10

865 Map of South-East Asia showing Cable Route

866 Stylised Hockey-players and Championship Emblem

1981 (24 Dec). *I.O.C.O.M. (Indian Ocean Commonwealth Cable) Submarine Telephone Cable. P* 13½ × 13.
1031 **865** 1 r. multicoloured 55 15

(Des C. Lal)

1981 (29 Dec). *World Cup Hockey Championship, Bombay. P* 13½ × 13.
1032 **866** 1 r. multicoloured 30 15

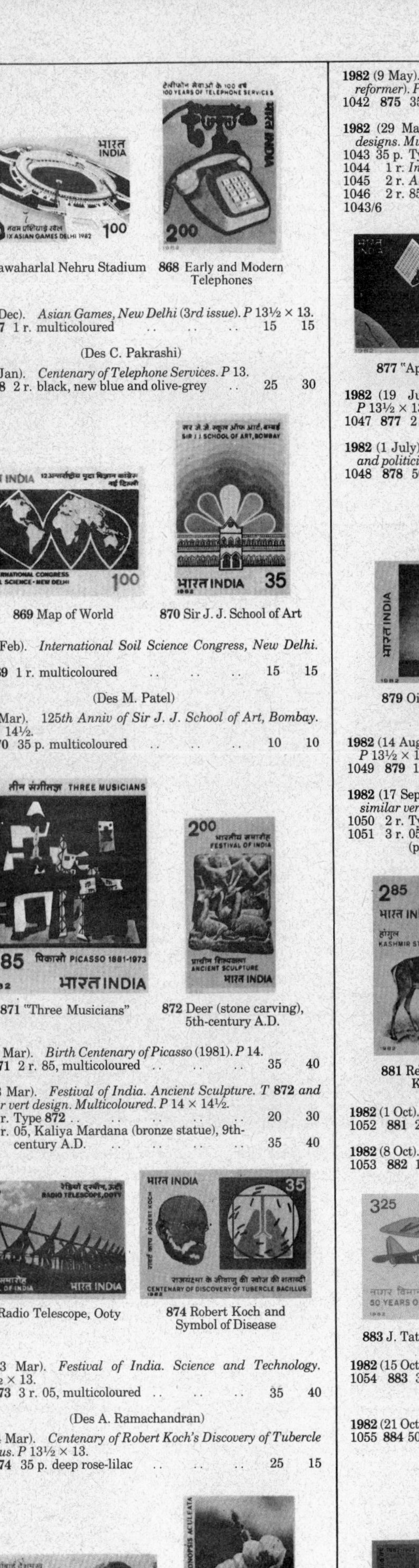

867 Jawaharlal Nehru Stadium

868 Early and Modern Telephones

1981 (30 Dec). *Asian Games, New Delhi (3rd issue). P* 13½ × 13.
1033 **867** 1 r. multicoloured 15 15

(Des C. Pakrashi)

1982 (28 Jan). *Centenary of Telephone Services. P* 13.
1034 **868** 2 r. black, new blue and olive-grey .. 25 30

869 Map of World

870 Sir J. J. School of Art

1982 (8 Feb). *International Soil Science Congress, New Delhi. P* 13.
1035 **869** 1 r. multicoloured 15 15

(Des M. Patel)

1982 (2 Mar). *125th Anniv of Sir J. J. School of Art, Bombay. P* 14 × 14½.
1036 **870** 35 p. multicoloured 10 10

871 "Three Musicians"

872 Deer (stone carving), 5th-century A.D.

1982 (15 Mar). *Birth Centenary of Picasso* (1981). *P* 14.
1037 **871** 2 r. 85, multicoloured 35 40

1982 (23 Mar). *Festival of India. Ancient Sculpture. T* **872** *and similar vert design. Multicoloured. P* 14 × 14½.
1038 2 r. Type **872** 20 30
1039 3 r. 05, Kaliya Mardana (bronze statue), 9th-century A.D. 35 40

873 Radio Telescope, Ooty

874 Robert Koch and Symbol of Disease

1982 (23 Mar). *Festival of India. Science and Technology. P* 13½ × 13.
1040 **873** 3 r. 05, multicoloured 35 40

(Des A. Ramachandran)

1982 (24 Mar). *Centenary of Robert Koch's Discovery of Tubercle Bacillus. P* 13½ × 13.
1041 **874** 35 p. deep rose-lilac 25 15

875 Durgabai Deshmukh

876 *Meconopsis aculeata*

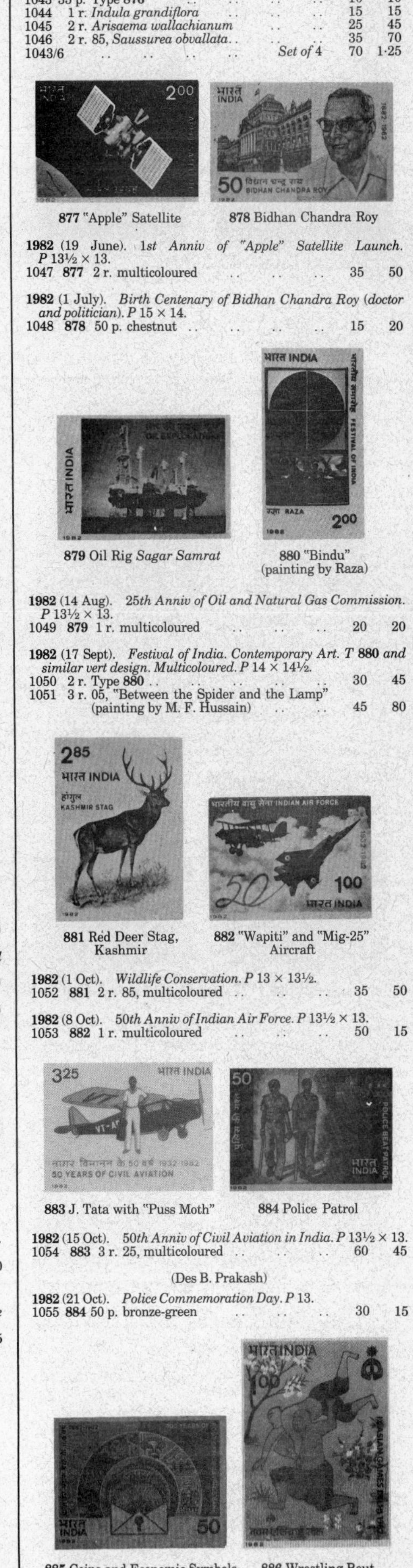

1982 (9 May). *First Death Anniv of Durgabai Deshmukh (social reformer). P* 14½ × 14.
1042 **875** 35 p. blue 10 20

1982 (29 May). *Himalayan Flowers. T* **876** *and similar vert designs. Multicoloured. P* 14.
1043 35 p. Type **876** 10 10
1044 1 r. *Indula grandiflora* 15 15
1045 2 r. *Arisaema wallachianum* 25 45
1046 2 r. 85, *Saussurea obvallata* 35 70
1043/6 .. .. *Set of* 4 70 1·25

877 "Apple" Satellite

878 Bidhan Chandra Roy

1982 (19 June). *1st Anniv of "Apple" Satellite Launch. P* 13½ × 13.
1047 **877** 2 r. multicoloured 35 50

1982 (1 July). *Birth Centenary of Bidhan Chandra Roy (doctor and politician). P* 15 × 14.
1048 **878** 50 p. chestnut 15 20

879 Oil Rig *Sagar Samrat*

880 "Bindu" (painting by Raza)

1982 (14 Aug). *25th Anniv of Oil and Natural Gas Commission. P* 13½ × 13.
1049 **879** 1 r. multicoloured 20 20

1982 (17 Sept). *Festival of India. Contemporary Art. T* **880** *and similar vert design. Multicoloured. P* 14 × 14½.
1050 2 r. Type **880** 30 45
1051 3 r. 05, "Between the Spider and the Lamp" (painting by M. F. Hussain) 45 80

881 Red Deer Stag, Kashmir

882 "Wapiti" and "Mig-25" Aircraft

1982 (1 Oct). *Wildlife Conservation. P* 13 × 13½.
1052 **881** 2 r. 85, multicoloured 35 50

1982 (8 Oct). *50th Anniv of Indian Air Force. P* 13½ × 13.
1053 **882** 1 r. multicoloured 50 15

883 J. Tata with "Puss Moth"

884 Police Patrol

1982 (15 Oct). *50th Anniv of Civil Aviation in India. P* 13½ × 13.
1054 **883** 3 r. 25, multicoloured 60 45

(Des B. Prakash)

1982 (21 Oct). *Police Commemoration Day. P* 13.
1055 **884** 50 p. bronze-green 30 15

885 Coins and Economic Symbols

886 Wrestling Bout

(Des S. Jha)

1982 (23 Oct). *Centenary of Post Office Savings Bank*. *P* 13.
1056 **885** 50 p. brown and cinnamon 10 10

(Des A. Ramachandran)

1982 (30 Oct). *Asian Games, New Delhi* (4*th issue*). *P* 13½ × 14.
1057 **886** 1 r. multicoloured 15 15

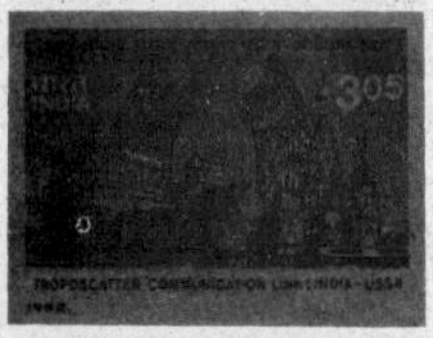

887 Troposcatter Communication Link
888 Arjuna shooting Arrow at Fish 

1982 (2 Nov). 1*st Anniv of Troposcatter Communication Link between India and U.S.S.R. P* 13.
1058 **887** 3 r. 05, multicoloured 30 40

(Des A. Ramachandran)

1982 (6 Nov). *Asian Games, New Delhi* (5*th issue*). *P* 13½ × 14.
1059 **888** 1 r. multicoloured 15 15

889 "Mother and Child"
890 Stylised Cyclists 

(Des D. Sharma)

1982 (14 Nov). *Children's Day. P* 14 × 14½.
1060 **889** 50 p. multicoloured 10 10

(Des C. Pakrashi (50 p.), B. Prakash (3 r. 25))

1982 (19 Nov). *Asian Games, New Delhi* (6*th issue*). *T* **890** *and similar horiz designs. Multicoloured. P* 13.
1061 50 p. Type **890** 10 10
1062 2 r. Javelin-throwing 25 30
1063 2 r. 85, Discus-throwing 30 45
1064 3 r. 25, Football 40 55
1061/4 .. .. *Set of* 4 90 1·25

891 Yachting
892 Chetwode Building 

(Des C. Pakrashi)

1982 (25 Nov). *Asian Games, New Delhi* (7*th issue*). *T* **891** *and similar horiz design. Multicoloured. P* 13.
1065 2 r. Type **891** 25 30
1066 2 r. 85, Rowing 30 40

1982 (10 Dec). 50*th Anniv of Indian Military Academy*. *P* 13.
1067 **892** 50 p. multicoloured 10 20

893 Purushottamdas Tandon
894 Darjeeling Himalayan Railway 

1982 (15 Dec). *Birth Centenary of Purushottamdas Tandon. P* 12½ × 13.
1068 **893** 50 p. yellow-brown 10 20

1982 (18 Dec). *Centenary of Darjeeling Himalayan Railway*. *P* 13.
1069 **894** 2 r. 85, multicoloured 80 80

895 Vintage Rail Coach and Silhouette of Steam Engine
896 Antarctic Camp 

(Des C. Pakrashi)

1982 (30 Dec). *"Inpex 82" Stamp Exhibition. T* **895** *and similar multicoloured design. P* 13 (50 *p*.) *or* 13½ × 14 (2 *r*.).
1070 50 p. Type **895** 20 25
1071 2 r. 1854 ½ a. stamp and 1947 3½ a. Independence commemorative (33 × 44 *mm*) 50 75

1983 (9 Jan). *First Indian Antarctic Expedition*. *P* 13.
1072 **896** 1 r. multicoloured 70 65

1983 (25 Jan). *As Nos.* 968/9, *but new face value. W* **374** (*sideways*). *P* 12½ × 13.
1073 50 p. red-brown (Gandhi) 65 25
a. Wmk upright .. ..
1074 50 p. deep ultramarine (Nehru) 65 25
a. Wmk upright .. ..

897 Roosevelt with Stamp Collection
898 "Siberian (Great White) Cranes at Bharatpur" (Diane Pierce) 

1983 (30 Jan). *Birth Centenary of Franklin D. Roosevelt* (*American statesman*) (1982). *P* 12½ × 13.
1075 **897** 3 r. 25, bistre-brown 45 70

1983 (7 Feb). *International Crane Workshop, Bharatpur*. *P* 13.
1076 **898** 2 r. 85, multicoloured 65 90

899 Jat Regiment Uniforms Past and Present
900 Non-aligned Summit Logo 

(Des C. Lal)

1983 (16 Feb). *Presentation of Colours to Battalions of the Jat Regiment*. *P* 13.
1077 **899** 50 p. multicoloured 20 25

(Des N. Srivastava)

1983 (7 Mar). 7*th Non-aligned Summit Conference, New Delhi. T* **900** *and similar horiz design*. *P* 13.
1078 1 r. bistre, orange-brown and black 20 25
1079 2 r. multicoloured 30 60
Design:—2 r. Nehru.

901 Shore Temple, Mahabalipuram
902 Acropolis and Olympic Emblems 

(Des R. Pasricha)

1983 (14 Mar). *Commonwealth Day. T* **901** *and similar horiz design. Multicoloured*. *P* 13.
1080 1 r. Type **901** 15 25
1081 2 r. Gomukh, Gangotri Glacier 30 60

(Des B. Makhmoor)

1983 (25 Mar). *International Olympic Committee Session, New Delhi*. *P* 13.
1082 **902** 1 r. multicoloured 15 20

903 "St. Francis and Brother Falcon" (statue by Giovanni Collina)
904 Karl Marx and *Das Kapital* 

1983 (4 Apr). 800*th Birth Anniv of St. Francis of Assisi*. *P* 13.
1083 **903** 1 r. bistre-brown 15 20

1983 (5 May). *Death Centenary of Karl Marx*. *P* 13.
1084 **904** 1 r. brown 15 20

905 Darwin and Map of Voyage

(Des M. Mandal)

1983 (18 May). *Death Centenary* (1982) *of Charles Darwin* (*naturalist*). *P* 13.
1085 **905** 2 r. multicoloured 40 60

906 Swamp Deer
907 Globe and Satellite 

1983 (30 May). 50*th Anniv of Kanha National Park*. *P* 13.
1086 **906** 1 r. multicoloured 15 25

(Des M. Mandal)

1983 (18 July). *World Communications Year*. *P* 13 × 12½.
1087 **907** 1 r. multicoloured 15 20

908 Simon Bolivar

1983 (24 July). *Birth Bicentenary of Simon Bolivar* (*South American statesman*). *P* 12½ × 13.
1088 **908** 2 r. multicoloured 40 70

909 Meera Behn
910 Ram Nath Chopra 

(Des C. Pakrashi (No. 1091))

1983 (9 Aug–28 Dec). *India's Struggle for Freedom* (1*st series*). *T* **909** *and similar designs. P* 14 × 13½ (*No.* 1091) *or* 13 (*others*).
1089 50 p. dull vermilion and dull green .. 15 40
a. Horiz pair. Nos. 1089/90 .. .. 30 80
1090 50 p. lt brown, dull green & dull vermilion 15 40
1091 50 p. multicoloured 10 20
1092 50 p. reddish brn, yell-grn & red-orge (18.10) 10 10
1093 50 p. olive-sepia, green and orange (18.10) .. 10 10
1094 50 p. olive-green, yellow-grn & orge (28.12) 10 10
1089/94 .. .. *Set of* 6 60 1·10

Designs: *Vert*—No. 1089, Type **909**; No. 1090, Mahadev Desai; No. 1092, Hemu Kalani (revolutionary); No. 1093, Acharya Vinoba Bhave (social reformer); No. 1094, Surendranath Banerjee (political reformer). *Horiz* (43 × 31 *mm*)—No. 1091, Quit India Resolution.

Nos. 1089/90 were printed together, *se-tenant*, in horizontal pairs throughout the sheet.

See also Nos. 1119/24, 1144/9, 1191/4, 1230/5, 1287/96 and 1345/9.

1983 (17 Aug). *Ram Nath Chopra* (*pharmacologist*) *Commemoration*. *P* 12½ × 13.
1095 **910** 50 p. Venetian red 10 20

911 Nanda Devi Mountain
912 Great Indian Hornbill 

1983 (27 Aug). 25*th Anniv of Indian Mountaineering Federation*. *P* 13.
1096 **911** 2 r. multicoloured 30 50

(Des J. Irani)

1983 (15 Sept). *Centenary of Natural History Society, Bombay*. *P* 13.
1097 **912** 1 r. multicoloured 15 15

913 View of Garden **914** Golden Langur

1983 (23 Sept). *Rock Garden, Chandigarh. P* 13.
1098 **913** 1 r. multicoloured 15 15

1983 (1 Oct). *Indian Wildlife. Monkeys. T* **914** *and similar horiz design. Multicoloured. P* 13.
1099 1 r. Type **914**.. .. .. 15 20
1100 2 r. Liontail Macaque 30 45

915 Ghats of Varanasi **916** Krishna Kanta Handique

1983 (3 Oct). *Fifth General Assembly of World Tourism Organization. P* 14 × 13½.
1101 **915** 2 r. multicoloured 30 30

1983 (7 Oct). *Krishna Kanta Handique (scholar) Commemoration. P* 13 × 12½.
1102 **916** 50 p. deep blue 10 20

918 Woman and Child (from "Festival" by Kashyap Premsawala) **920** *Udan Khatola*, First Indian Hot Air Balloon

1983 (14 Nov). *Children's Day. P* 13 × 13½.
1103 **918** 50 p. multicoloured 10 10

1983 (21 Nov). *Bicentenary of Manned Flight. T* **920** *and similar vert design. Multicoloured. P* 13.
1104 1 r. Type **920**.. .. .. 20 20
1105 2 r. Montgolfier balloon 30 35

921 Tiger **922** Commonwealth Logo

1983 (22 Nov). *Ten Years of "Project Tiger". P* 13 × 13½.
1106 **921** 2 r. multicoloured 45 60

(Des K. Raha (1 r.))

1983 (23 Nov). *Commonwealth Heads of Government Meeting, New Delhi. T* **922** *and similar vert design. Multicoloured. P* 13 × 12½.
1107 1 r. Type **922**.. .. .. 10 15
1108 2 r. Early 19th-century Goanese couple .. 25 30

923 "Pratiksha" **925** Lancer in Ceremonial Uniform

1983 (5 Dec). *Birth Cent of Nanda Lal Bose (artist). P* 13 × 12½.
1109 **923** 1 r. multicoloured 15 15

1984 (7 Jan). *Bicentenary of 7th Light Cavalry Regiment. P* 13 × 12½.
1110 **925** 1 r. multicoloured 65 25

926 Troopers in Ceremonial Uniform, and Tank **927** Society Building and William Jones (founder)

1984 (9 Jan). *Presentation of Regimental Guidon to the Deccan Horse. P* 13 × 13½.
1111 **926** 1 r. multicoloured 60 45

1984 (15 Jan). *Bicentenary of Asiatic Society. P* 13.
1112 **927** 1 r. emerald and bright purple.. .. 20 20

928 Insurance Logo **929** "Sea Harrier" Aircraft

(Des S. Jha)

1984 (1 Feb). *Centenary of Postal Life Insurance. P* 13 × 13½.
1113 **928** 1 r. multicoloured 15 20

(Des Capt. A. Dhir and S. Dheer)

1984 (12 Feb). *President's Review of the Fleet. T* **929** *and similar horiz designs. Multicoloured. P* 13½ × 13.
1114 1 r. Type **929**.. .. .. .. 20 25
a. Block of 4. Nos. 1114/17 70
1115 1 r. I.N.S. *Vikrant* (aircraft carrier) .. 20 25
1116 1 r. I.N.S. *Vela* (submarine) 20 25
1117 1 r. Destroyer 20 25
1114/17 .. .. .. *Set of* 4 70 90
Nos. 1114/7 were printed in *se-tenant* blocks of four within the sheet, forming a composite design.

930 I.L.A. Logo and Hemispheres

(Des J. Irani)

1984 (20 Feb). *12th International Leprosy Congress. P* 13.
1118 **930** 1 r. multicoloured 15 15

(Des C. Pakrashi (Nos. 1119, 1121/4))

1984 (21 Feb–10 May). *India's Struggle for Freedom (2nd series). Vert portraits as T* **909**. *P* 13.
1119 50 p. dp brownish olive, yell-grn & brt orge 10 15
1120 50 p. bistre-brown, emerald & brt orge (23.4) 10 15
1121 50 p. multicoloured (10.5) 10 15
1122 50 p. multicoloured (10.5) 10 15
1123 50 p. multicoloured (10.5) 10 15
1124 50 p. multicoloured (10.5) 10 15
1119/24 .. .. *Set of* 6 55 80
Designs:—No. 1119, Vasudeo Balvant Phadke (revolutionary); No. 1120, Baba Kanshi Ram (revolutionary); No. 1121, Tatya Tope; No. 1122, Nana Sahib; No. 1123, Begum Hazrat Mahal; No. 1124, Mangal Pandey.

932 "Salyut 7"

(Des R. Pasricha)

1984 (3 Apr). *Indo-Soviet Manned Space Flight. P* 14.
1125 **932** 3 r. multicoloured 45 45

935 G. D. Birla **936** Basketball

1984 (11 June). *90th Birth Anniv of G. D. Birla (industrialist). P* 13.
1126 **935** 50 p. chocolate 10 20

(Des K. Reha and S. Jha)

1984 (28 July). *Olympic Games, Los Angeles. T* **936** *and similar multicoloured designs. P* 13.
1127 50 p. Type **936** 10 10
1128 1 r. High jumping 15 15
1129 2 r. Gymnastics (*horiz*) 30 35
1130 2 r. 50, Weightlifting (*horiz*) 35 40
1127/30 .. .. *Set of* 4 75 90

937 Gwalior **938** B.V. Paradkar and Newspaper

1984 (3 Aug). *Forts. T* **937** *and similar multicoloured designs. P* 13½ × 13 (50 *p.*, 2 *r.*) *or* 13 × 13½ (*others*).
1131 50 p. Type **937** 20 15
1132 1 r. Vellore (*vert*) 25 15
1133 1 r. 50, Simhagad (*vert*) 40 40
1134 2 r. Jodphur 55 60
1131/4 .. .. *Set of* 4 1·25 1·10

1984 (14 Sept). *B. V. Paradkar (journalist) Commemoration. P* 13 × 13½.
1135 **938** 50 p. reddish brown 10 10

939 Dr. D. N. Wadia and Institute of Himalayan Geology, Dehradun **940** "Herdsman and Cattle in Forest" (H. Kassam)

1984 (23 Oct). *Birth Centenary (1983) of Dr. D. N. Wadia (geologist). P* 13.
1136 **939** 1 r. multicoloured 15 20

1984 (14 Nov). *Children's Day. P* 13 × 13½.
1137 **940** 50 p. multicoloured 15 20

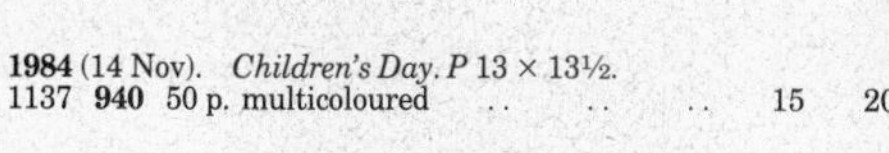

941 Indira Gandhi

(Des C. Lal)

1984 (19 Nov). *Prime Minister Indira Gandhi Commemoration (1st issue). P* 15 × 14.
1138 **941** 50 p. black, lavender and bright orange 25 25
See also Nos. 1151, 1167 and 1170.

942 Congress Emblem **943** Dr. Rajendra Prasad at Desk

1984 (20 Nov). *12th World Mining Congress, New Delhi. P* 13 × 13½.
1139 **942** 1 r. black and orange-yellow .. 15 15

1984 (3 Dec). *Birth Centenary of Dr. Rajendra Prasad (former President). P* 13.
1140 **943** 50 p. multicoloured 15 15

944 Mrinalini (rose) **945** "Fergusson College" (Gopal Deuskar)

1984 (23 Dec). *Roses. T* **944** *and similar vert design. Multicoloured. P* 13.
1141 1 r. 50, Type **944** 30 30
1142 2 r. Sugandha 40 40

1985 (2 Jan). *Centenary of Fergusson College, Pune. P* 13.
1143 **945** 1 r. multicoloured 15 15

1985 (10 Jan–24 Dec). *India's Struggle for Freedom* (3rd *series*). *Portraits as T* **909**. *P* 13.
1144 50 p. chestnut, deep green & bright orange 10 15
1145 50 p. chocolate, emerald & brt orange (21.7) 10 15
1146 50 p. reddish brown, emer & red-orge (22.7) 10 15
1147 50 p. olive-sepia, emer & reddish orge (2.12) 10 15
1148 50 p. royal blue, emerald & brt orge (23.12) 10 15
1149 50 p. grey-black, emerald & brt orge (24.12) 10 15
1144/9 .. .. *Set of* 6 55 80
Designs: *Vert*—No. 1144, Narhar Vishnu Gadgil (politician); No. 1145, Jairamdas Doulatram (journalist); No. 1147, Kakasaheb Kalelkar (author); No. 1148, Master Tara Singh (politician); No. 1149, Ravishankar Maharaj (politician). *Horiz*—No. 1146, Jatindra and Nellie Sengupta (politicians).

947 Gunner and Howitzer from Mountain Battery

1985 (15 Jan). *50th Anniv of Regiment of Artillery. P* 13½ × 13.
1150 **947** 1 r. multicoloured 70 60

948 Indira Gandhi making speech

(Des R. Chopra)

1985 (31 Jan). *Indira Gandhi Commemoration* (2nd *issue*). *P* 14.
1151 **948** 2 r. multicoloured 45 55

949 Minicoy Lighthouse **950** Medical College Hospital

1985 (2 Feb). *Centenary of Minicoy Lighthouse. P* 13.
1152 **949** 1 r. multicoloured 50 20

1985 (20 Feb). *150th Anniv of Medical College, Calcutta. P* 13½ × 13.
1153 **950** 1 r. yellow, reddish brown and deep reddish purple 25 15

951 Medical College, Madras **952** Riflemen of 1835 and 1985, and Map of North-East India

1985 (6 Mar). *150th Anniv of Medical College, Madras. P* 13½ × 13.
1154 **951** 1 r. yellow-brown and reddish brown .. 25 15

(Des A. Sharma)

1985 (29 Mar). *150th Anniv of Assam Rifles. P* 13½ × 13.
1155 **952** 1 r. multicoloured 55 40

953 Potato Plant **954** Baba Jassa Singh Ahluwalia

(Des Indian Council of Agricultural Research)

1985 (1 Apr). *50th Anniv of Potato Research in India. P* 13.
1156 **953** 50 p. deep brown and grey-brown .. 25 25

1985 (4 Apr). *Death Bicentenary* (1983) *of Baba Jassa Singh Ahluwalia (Sikh leader). P* 13.
1157 **954** 50 p. deep reddish purple 25 25

955 St. Xavier's College **956** White-winged Wood Duck

1985 (12 Apr). *125th Anniv of St. Xavier's College, Calcutta. P* 13.
1158 **955** 1 r. multicoloured 15 15

1985 (18 May). *Wildlife Conservation. White-winged Wood Duck. P* 14.
1159 **956** 2 r. multicoloured .. .. 1·00 1·00

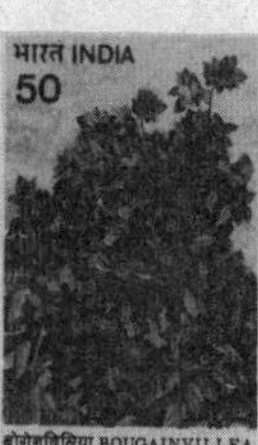

957 "Mahara" **958** Yaudheya Copper Coin, c 200 B.C.

1985 (5 June). *Bougainvillea. T* **957** *and similar vert design. Multicoloured. P* 13.
1160 50 p. Type **957** 10 10
1161 1 r. "H. B. Singh" 15 15

1985 (7 June). *Festival of India* (1st *issue*). *P* 13.
1162 **958** 2 r. multicoloured 40 45

MINIMUM PRICE

The minimum price quote is 10p which represents a handling charge rather than a basis for valuing common stamps. For further notes about prices see introductory pages.

959 Statue of Didarganj Yakshi (deity) **962** Swami Haridas

1985 (13 June). *Festival of India* (2nd *issue*). *P* 13.
1163 **959** 1 r. multicoloured 15 15

1985 (19 Sept). *Swami Haridas (philosopher) Commemoration. P* 13.
1164 **962** 1 r. multicoloured 30 15
Although not officially issued until 19 September 1985 examples of No. 1164 are known to have circulated from 27 November 1984, the date on which it was originally scheduled for release.

963 Stylised Mountain Road

1985 (10 Oct). *25th Anniv of Border Roads Organization. P* 13.
1165 **963** 2 r. brt carmine, bluish violet & black 40 40

964 Nehru addressing General Assembly

1985 (24 Oct). *40th Anniv of United Nations Organization. P* 13.
1166 **964** 2 r. multicoloured 25 30

965 Indira Gandhi with Crowd

1985 (31 Oct). *Indira Gandhi Commemoration* (3rd *issue*). *P* 14.
1167 **965** 2 r. brownish black and black .. 50 50

966 Girl using Home Computer **967** Halley's Comet

1985 (14 Nov). *Children's Day. P* 13½ × 13.
1168 **966** 50 p. multicoloured 15 20

1985 (19 Nov). *19th General Assembly of International Astronomical Union, New Delhi. P* 13 × 13½.
1169 **967** 1 r. multicoloured 20 25

968 Indira Gandhi **969** St. Stephen's Hospital

1985 (19 Nov). *Indira Gandhi Commemoration (4th issue). P 14.*
1170 **968** 3 r. multicoloured 70 70

1985 (25 Nov). *Centenary of St. Stephen's Hospital, Delhi. P 13.*
1171 **969** 1 r. black and buff 15 15

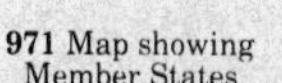

971 Map showing Member States

972 Shyama Shastri

1985 (8 Dec). *1st Summit Meeting of South Asian Association for Regional Co-operation, Dhaka, Bangladesh. T* **971** *and similar multicoloured design. P* 13½ × 13 (1 r.) *or* 14 (3 r.).
1172 1 r. Type **971** 25 15
1173 3 r. Flags of member nations (44 × 32 *mm*) .. 60 50

1985 (21 Dec). *Shyama Shastri (composer) Commemoration. P 13.*
1174 **972** 1 r. multicoloured 35 20

975 Young Runners and Emblem

(Des J. Irani)

1985 (24 Dec). *International Youth Year. P* 13½ × 13.
1175 **975** 2 r. multicoloured 25 30

976 Handel and Bach

1985 (27 Dec). *300th Birth Annivs of George Frederick Handel and Johann Sebastian Bach (composers). P* 13 × 13½.
1176 **976** 5 r. multicoloured 85 65

977 A. O. Hume (founder) and Early Congress Presidents

978 Bombay and Duncan Dry Docks, Bombay

(Des C. Pakrashi)

1985 (28 Dec). *Centenary of Indian National Congress. T* **977** *and similar vert designs showing miniature portraits of Congress Presidents. P 14.*
1177 **977** 1 r. black, bright orange, lt green & grey 25 25
a. Block of 4. Nos. 1177/80 90
1178 – 1 r. black, bright orange and light green 25 25
1179 – 1 r. black, bright orange and light green 25 25
1180 – 1 r. black, bright orange, lt green & grey 25 25
1177/80 .. .. *Set of* 4 90 90

Nos. 1178/80 each show sixteen miniature portraits. The individual stamps can be distinguished by the position of the face value and inscription which are at the top on Nos. 1177/8 and at the foot on Nos. 1179/80. No. 1180 shows a portrait of Prime Minister Rajiv Gandhi in a grey frame at bottom right.

(Des Capt. A. Dhir)

1986 (11 Jan). *250th Anniv of Naval Dockyard, Bombay. P* 13½ × 13.
1181 **978** 2 r. 50, multicoloured 75 75

979 Hawa Mahal and Jaipur 1904 2 a. Stamp

980 I.N.S. *Vikrant* (aircraft carrier)

1986 (14 Feb). *"INPEX '86" Philatelic Exhibition, Jaipur. T* **979** *and similar horiz design. Multicoloured. P* 13½ × 13.
1182 50 p. Type **979** 25 15
1183 2 r. Mobile camel post office, Thar Desert 50 60

(Des A. Sharma)

1986 (16 Feb). *Completion of 25 Years Service by I.N.S.* Vikrant. *P* 13 × 13½.
1184 **980** 2 r. multicoloured 65 65

981 Humber-Sommer Biplane and Later Mail Planes

982 Triennale Emblem

(Des R. Pasricha)

1986 (18 Feb). *75th Anniversary of First Official Airmail Flight, Allahabad – Naini. T* **981** *and similar horiz design. Multicoloured. P* 13½ × 13 (50 *p.*) *or* 13 (3 *r.*).
1185 50 p. Type **981** 25 20
1186 3 r. Modern Air India mail plane and Humber-Sommer biplane (37 × 24 *mm*) 80 1·10

1986 (22 Feb). *6th Triennale Art Exhibition, New Delhi. P* 13 × 13½.
1187 **982** 1 r. black, brt purple & orange-yellow 35 20

983 Chaitanya Mahaprabhu

984 Main Building, Mayo College

1986 (13 Mar). *500th Birth Anniv of Chaitanya Mahaprabhu (religious leader). P 13.*
1188 **983** 2 r. multicoloured 75 55

1986 (12 Apr). *Mayo College (public school), Ajmer, Commem. P* 13½ × 13.
1189 **984** 1 r. multicoloured 35 30

985 Two Footballers

987 Swami Sivananda

(Des Vandana Joshi)

1986 (31 May). *World Cup Football Championship, Mexico. P 13.*
1190 **985** 5 r. multicoloured .. .. 1·00 75

1986 (14 Aug–30 Dec). *India's Struggle for Freedom (4th series). Vert portraits as T* **909**. *P 13.*
1191 50 p. sepia, emerald and orange-red .. 20 20
1192 50 p. olive-sepia, emerald & orge-red (26.12) 20 20
1193 50 p. slate-blk, emer & reddish orge (29.12) 20 20
1194 50 p. red-brown, emerald & orge-red (30.12) 20 20
1191/4 .. .. *Set of* 4 70 70

Designs:—No. 1191, Bhim Sen Sachar; No. 1192, Alluri Seeta Rama Raju; No. 1193, Sagarmal Gopa; No. 1194, Veer Surendra Sai.

1986 (8 Sept). *Birth Centenary of Swami Sivananda (spiritual leader). P 13.*
1195 **987** 2 r. multicoloured 75 60

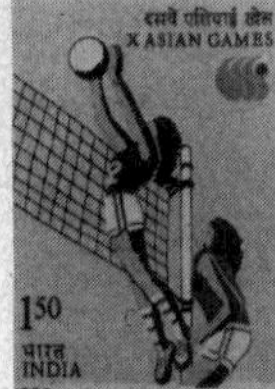

988 Volleyball

989 Madras G.P.O.

(Des Mohinder Dhadwal)

1986 (16 Sept). *Asian Games, Seoul, South Korea. T* **988** *and similar vert design. Multicoloured. P* 13 × 13½.
1196 1 r. 50, Type **988** 50 35
1197 3 r. Hurdling .. .. 1·00 65

1986 (9 Oct). *Bicentenary of Madras G.P.O. P 13.*
1198 **989** 5 r. black and Indian red .. .. 1·50 1·50

990 Parachutist

991 Early and Modern Policemen

(Des Nenu Bagga)

1986 (17 Oct). *225th Anniv of 8th Battalion of Coast Sepoys (now 1st Battalion Parachute Regiment). P* 13 × 13½.
1199 **990** 3 r. multicoloured .. .. 1·25 1·25

(Des A. Ali)

1986 (21 Oct). *125th Anniv of Indian Police. T* **991** *and similar vert design showing early and modern police. P* 13 × 13½.
1200 1 r. 50, multicoloured .. .. 75 1·00
a. Horiz pair. Nos. 1200/1 .. .. .. 1·50 2·00
1201 2 r. multicoloured .. .. 75 1·00

Nos. 1200/1 were printed together, *se-tenant*, in horizontal pairs with the 2 r. at left, each pair forming a composite design.

992 Hand holding Flower and World Map

993 "Girl Rock Climber" (Sujasha Dasgupta)

(Des B. Raj)

1986 (24 Oct). *International Peace Year. P* 13½ × 13.
1202 **992** 5 r. multicoloured 90 85

1986 (14 Nov). *Children's Day. P* 13 × 13½.
1203 **993** 50 p. multicoloured 30 25

994 Windmill

1986 (15 Nov)–**88**. *Science and Technology. T* **994** *and similar designs. W* **374** *(sideways on* 5, 50 *r.). P 13.*
1211 35 p. vermilion (27.2.87) 10 10
1212 40 p. rose-red (15.10.88) 10 10
1213 60 p. emerald and scarlet (27.2.87) .. 10 10
a. Wmk sideways.. .. .. 10 10
1217 5 r. deep brown & reddish orange (1.1.88) 35 40
1219 20 r. bistre-brown and blue (30.11.88) .. 1·40 1·50
1220 50 r. black, turquoise-blue and cerise .. 3·25 3·50
1211/20 .. .. *Set of* 6 4·50 5·00

Designs: *Horiz* (20 × 17 *mm*)—35 p. Family planning. (37 × 20 *mm*)—60 p. Indian family; 20 r. Bio gas production. *Vert* (17 × 20 *mm*)—40 p. Television set, dish aerial and transmitter. (20 × 37 *mm*)—5 r. Solar energy.

Numbers have been left for further values in this new definitive series.

995 Growth Monitoring **996** Tansen

1986 (11 Dec). *40th Anniv of United Nations Children's Fund. T* **995** *and similar horiz design. Multicoloured. P* 13½×13.

1221 50 p. Type **995** 30 25
1222 5 r. Immunization .. .. 1·25 1·25

1986 (12 Dec). *Tansen (musician and composer) Commem. P* 13.

1223 **996** 1 r. multicoloured 40 15

997 Indian Elephant **998** St. Martha's Hospital

(Des Pratibha Pandey)

1986 (15 Dec). *50th Anniv of Corbett National Park. T* **997** *and similar horiz design. Multicoloured. P* 13½×13.

1224 1 r. Type **997** 40 25
1225 2 r. Gharial .. .. 85 1·00

1986 (30 Dec). *Centenary of St. Martha's Hospital, Bangalore. P* 13½×13.

1226 **998** 1 r. Prussian blue, vermilion and black 40 35

999 Yacht *Trishna* and Route Map **1000** Map of Southern Africa and Logo

1987 (10 Jan). *Indian Army Round the World Yacht Voyage, 1985–7. P* 13½×13.

1227 **999** 6 r. 50, multicoloured .. .. .. 1·75 1·25

1987 (25 Jan). *Inauguration of AFRICA Fund. P* 14.

1228 **1000** 6 r. 50, black .. .. 1·75 1·50

1001 Emblem **1002** Blast Furnace

1987 (11 Feb). *29th Congress of International Chamber of Commerce, New Delhi. P* 13×13½.

1229 **1001** 5 r. bluish violet, new blue and rosine 1·50 85

1987 (13 Feb–12 Dec). *India's Struggle for Freedom (5th series). Vert portraits as T* **909**. *P* 13.

1230 60 p. bistre-brown, emerald & reddish orge 10 15
1231 60 p. deep violet, emerald & orge-red (18.3) 10 15
1232 60 p. red-brown, dp green & orge-red (21.3) 10 15
1233 60 p. bl, yellowish grn & reddish orge (25.4) 10 15
1234 60 p. yellowish brn, emer & orge-red (17.6) 10 15
1235 60 p. brown, emerald and orange-red (22.8) 10 15
1236 60 p. brown-red, emerald and reddish orange (31.12) 10 10
1230/6 .. .. *Set of* 7 60 90

Designs:—No. 1230, Hakim Ajmal Khan; No. 1231, Lala Har Dayal; No. 1232, M. N. Roy; No. 1233, Tripuraneni Ramaswamy Chowdary; No. 1234, Dr. Kailas Nath Katju; No. 1235, S. Satyamurti; No. 1236, Pandit Hriday Nath Kunzru.

(Des P. Biswas)

1987 (28 Mar). *Centenary of South Eastern Railway. T* **1002** *and similar multicoloured designs. P* 13×13½ *(vert) or* 13½×13 *(horiz).*

1237 1 r. Type **1002** 20 15
1238 1 r. 50, Metre-gauge tank locomotive, No. 691, 1887 *(horiz)* 25 25
1239 2 r. Electric train on viaduct, 1987 .. 35 35
1240 4 r. Steam locomotive, *c* 1900 *(horiz)* .. 60 90
1237/40 .. .. *Set of* 4 1·25 1·50

1003 Kalia Bhomora Bridge, Tezpur, Assam **1004** Madras Christian College

1987 (14 Apr). *Inauguration of Brahmaputra Bridge. P* 13½×13.

1241 **1003** 2 r. multicoloured 25 25

1987 (16 Apr). *150th Anniv of Madras Christian College. P* 13.

1242 **1004** 1 r. 50, black and brown-lake 15 15

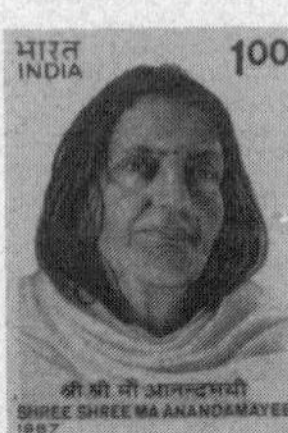

1005 Shree Shree Ma Anandamayee **1006** "Rabindranath Tagore" (self-portrait)

1987 (1 May). *Shree Shree Ma Anandamayee (Hindu spiritual leader) Commem. P* 13×13½.

1243 **1005** 1 r. bistre-brown 15 10

1987 (8 May). *Rabindranath Tagore (poet) Commem. P* 14.

1244 **1006** 2 r. multicoloured 30 25

1007 Garwhal Rifles Uniforms of 1887 **1008** J. Krishnamurti

1987 (10 May). *Centenary of Garwhal Rifles Regiment. P* 13×13½.

1245 **1007** 1 r. multicoloured 30 10

1987 (11 May). *J. Krishnamurti (philosopher) Commem. P* 13×13½.

1246 **1008** 60 p. sepia 30 30

1009 Regimental Uniforms of 1887 **1010** Hall of Nations, Pragati Maidan, New Delhi

1987 (3 June). *Centenary of 37th Dogra Regt (now 7th Battalion (1 Dogra)), Mechanised Infantry Regt. P* 13½×13.

1247 **1009** 1 r. multicoloured 30 15

(Des P. Biswas (Nos. 1248/9), Nenu Bagga (No. **MS**1250)

1987 (15 June)–**89**. *"India–89" International Stamp Exhibition, New Delhi (1st issue). T* **1010** *and similar horiz design. Multicoloured. P* 13½×13.

1248 50 p. Exhibition logo 10 10
a. Booklet pane. No. 1248×4 (20.1.89) 15
1249 5 r. Type **1010** 45 50
a. Booklet pane. No. 1249×4 (20.1.89) 1·50
MS1250 156×58 mm. Nos. 1248/9 *(sold at 8 r.)* 70 1·00

See also Nos. 1264/8, 1333/4, 1341/2 and 1358/61.

1011 "Sadyah-Snata" Sculpture, Sanghol **1012** Flag and Stylized Birds with "40" and "80"

1987 (3 July). *Festival of India, U.S.S.R. P* 13.

1251 **1011** 6 r. 50, multicoloured .. .. .. 1·00 75

1987 (15 Aug). *40th Anniv of Independence. P* 13×13½.

1252 **1012** 60 p. reddish orange, dp green & new bl 10 10

1013 Sant Harchand Singh Longowal **1014** Guru Ghasidas

1987 (20 Aug). *Sant Harchand Singh Longowal (Sikh leader) Commemoration. P* 13×13½.

1253 **1013** 1 r. multicoloured 15 10

1987 (1 Sept). *Guru Ghasidas (Hindu leader) Commemoration. P* 13.

1254 **1014** 60 p. deep Indian red 10 10

1015 Thakur Anukul Chandra **1016** University of Allahabad

1987 (2 Sept). *Thakur Anukul Chandra (spiritual leader) Commemoration. P* 13×13½.

1255 **1015** 1 r. multicoloured 25 10

1987 (23 Sept). *Centenary of Allahabad University. P* 13.

1256 **1016** 2 r. multicoloured 30 25

1017 Pankha Offering **1018** Chhatrasal on Horseback

1987 (1 Oct). *Phoolwalon Ki Sair Festival, Delhi. P* 13×13½.

1257 **1017** 2 r. multicoloured 30 25

1987 (2 Oct). *Chhatrasal (Bundela ruler) Commemoration. P* 14.

1258 **1018** 60 p. chestnut 15 10

1019 Family and Stylized Houses **1020** Map of Asia and Logo

1987 (5 Oct). *International Year of Shelter for the Homeless. P* 13½×13.

1259 **1019** 5 r. multicoloured 45 50

1987 (14 Oct). *Asia Regional Conference of Rotary International. T* **1020** *and similar horiz design. P* 13½×13.

1260 60 p. chestnut and emerald 10 10
1261 6 r. 50, multicoloured 60 65

Design:—6 r. 50, Oral Polio vaccination.

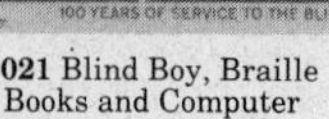

1021 Blind Boy, Braille Books and Computer **1022** Iron Pillar, Delhi

1987 (15 Oct). *Centenary of Service to Blind. T* **1021** *and similar horiz design. P* 13½×13.
1262 1 r. multicoloured 15 10
1263 2 r. deep blue and new blue 35 25
Design:—2 r. Eye donation.

1987 (17 Oct)–**89**. *"India–89" International Stamp Exhibition, New Delhi (2nd issue). Delhi Landmarks. T* **1022** *and similar horiz designs. Multicoloured. P* 13½×13.
1264 60 p. Type **1022** 10 10
a. Booklet pane. No. 1264×4 (20.1.89) 20
1265 1 r. 50, India Gate 15 15
a. Booklet pane. No. 1265×4 (20.1.89) 45
1266 5 r. Dewan-e-Khas, Red Fort 45 50
a. Booklet pane. No. 1266×4 (20.1.89) 1·50
1267 6 r. 50, Old Fort 60 65
a. Booklet pane. No. 1267×4 (20.1.89) 2·00
1264/7 .. .. *Set of* 4 1·10 1·25
MS1268 100×86 mm. Nos. 1264/7 (*sold at* 15 *r.*) 1·40 1·50

1023 Tyagmurti Goswami Ganeshdutt

1024 "My Home" (Siddharth Deshprabha)

1987 (2 Nov). *Tyagmurti Goswami Ganeshdutt (spiritual leader and social reformer) Commemoration. P* 13×13½.
1269 **1023** 60 p. brown-red 15 10

1987 (14 Nov). *Children's Day. P* 13½×13.
1270 **1024** 60 p. multicoloured 20 10

1025 Chinar

1026 Logo (from sculpture "Worker and Woman Peasant" by V. Mukhina)

(Des O. Ravindran, A. Mehta, T. D. Singh, Sudha Chowdhary)

1987 (19 Nov). *Indian Trees. T* **1025** *and similar multicoloured designs. P* 13×13½ (*vert*) *or* 13½×13 (*horiz*).
1271 60 p. multicoloured 10 10
1272 1 r. 50, multicoloured 20 20
1273 5 r. black, dull yellow-green and chestnut 55 55
1274 6 r. 50, brown, carmine-red & yellow-green 70 70
1271/4 .. .. *Set of* 4 1·40 1·40
Designs: *Horiz*—1 r. 50, Pipal; 6 r. 50, Banyan. *Vert*—5 r. Sal.

1987 (21 Nov). *Festival of U.S.S.R., India. P* 14.
1275 **1026** 5 r. multicoloured 50 50

1027 White Tiger

1028 Execution of Veer Narayan Singh

1987 (29 Nov). *Wildlife. T* **1027** *and similar multicoloured design. P* 13×13½ (1 *r.*) *or* 13½×13 (5 *r.*).
1276 1 r. Type **1027** 15 10
1277 5 r. Snow Leopard (*horiz*) 60 65

(Des S. Samanta)

1987 (10 Dec). *Veer Narayan Singh (patriot) Commemoration. P* 13½×13.
1278 **1028** 60 p. deep brown 10 10

OMNIBUS ISSUES

Details, together with prices for complete sets, of the various Omnibus issues from the 1935 Silver Jubilee series to date are included in a special section following Zululand at the end of the catalogue.

1029 Rameshwari Nehru

1030 Father Kuriakose Elias Chavara

1987 (10 Dec). *Rameshwari Nehri (women's rights campaigner) Commemoration. P* 13×13½.
1279 **1029** 60 p. red-brown 15 10

1987 (20 Dec). *Father Kuriakose Elias Chavara (founder of Carmelites of Mary Immaculate) Commemoration. P* 13×13½.
1280 **1030** 60 p. bistre-brown 15 10

1031 Dr. Rajah Sir Muthiah Chettiar

1032 Golden Temple, Amritsar

1987 (21 Dec). *Dr. Rajah Sir Muthiah Chettiar (politician) Commemoration. P* 13.
1281 **1031** 60 p. slate 15 10

1987 (26 Dec). 400*th Anniv of Golden Temple, Amritsar. P* 13×13½.
1282 **1032** 60 p. multicoloured 20 10

1033 Rukmini Devi and Dancer

1034 Dr. Hiralal

1987 (27 Dec). *Rukmini Devi (Bharatanatyam dance pioneer) Commemoration. P* 13½×13.
1283 **1033** 60 p. deep rose-red 20 10

1987 (31 Dec). *Dr. Hiralal (historian) Commemoration. P* 13×13½.
1284 **1034** 60 p. deep violet-blue 15 10

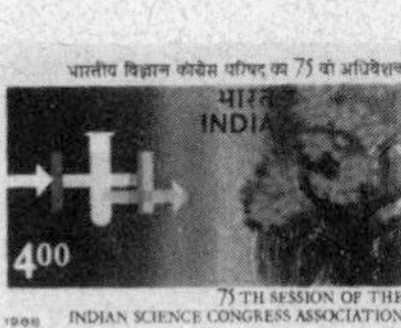

1035 Light Frequency Experiment and Bodhi Tree

1036 Rural Patient

1988 (7 Jan). 75*th Session of Indian Science Congress Association. P* 13.
1285 **1035** 4 r. multicoloured 50 60

(Des M. Sharma)

1988 (28 Jan). 13*th Asian Pacific Dental Congress. P* 13×13½.
1286 **1036** 4 r. multicoloured 40 40

1988 (2 Feb–6 Oct). *India's Struggle for Freedom (6th series). Vert portraits as T* **909**. *P* 13.
1287 60 p. black, emerald and reddish orange .. 10 10
1288 60 p. chestnut, emerald & brt orange (4.2) 10 10
1289 60 p. brt carmine, emer & orge-red (27.2) .. 10 10
1290 60 p. blackish purple, emer & brt orge (7.3) 10 10
1291 60 p. plum, dp green & reddish orge (18.6) 10 10
1292 60 p. slate-blk, dp grn & reddish orge (19.6) 10 10
1293 60 p. deep lilac, dp green & orge-red (28.6) 10 10
1294 60 p. dp bluish green, grn & orge-red (6.9) 10 10
1295 60 p. red-brown, emerald & orge-red (6.10) 10 10
1296 60 p. magenta, dp green & brt orange (5.12) 10 10
1287/96 .. .. *Set of* 10 70 70
Designs:—No. 1287, Mohan Lal Sukhadia; No. 1288, Dr. S. K. Sinha; No. 1289, Chandra Shekhar Azad; No. 1290, G. B. Pant; No. 1291, Dr. Anugrah Narain Singh; No. 1292, Kuladhor Chaliha; No. 1293, Shivprasad Gupta; No. 1294, Sarat Chandra Bose; No. 1295, Baba Kharak Singh; No. 1296, Sheikh Mohammad Abdullah.

1037 U Tirot Singh

1038 Early and Modern Regimental Uniforms

1988 (3 Feb). *U Tirot Singh (Khasis leader) Commemoration. P* 13×13½.
1297 **1037** 60 p. bistre-brown 10 10

1988 (19 Feb). *Bicentenary of 4th Battalion of the Kumaon Regiment. P* 14.
1298 **1038** 1 r. multicoloured 20 15

1039 Balgandharva

1040 Soldiers and Infantry Combat Vehicle

1988 (22 Feb). *Birth Centenary of Balgandharva (actor). P* 13×13½.
1299 **1039** 60 p. bistre-brown 10 10

1988 (24 Feb). *Presentation of Colours to Mechanised Infantry Regiment. P* 13½×13.
1300 **1040** 1 r. multicoloured 25 15

1041 B. N. Rau

1042 Mohindra Government College

1988 (26 Feb). *B. N. Rau (constitutional lawyer) Commemoration. P* 13.
1301 **1041** 60 p. grey-black 10 10

1988 (14 Mar). *Mohindra Government College, Patiala. P* 13×13½.
1302 **1042** 1 r. cerise 10 10

1043 Dr. D. V. Gundappa

1044 Rani Avantibai

1988 (17 Mar). *Dr. D. V. Gundappa (scholar) Commemoration. P* 13½×13.
1303 **1043** 60 p. slate 10 10

1988 (20 Mar). *Rani Avantibai of Ramgarh Commemoration. P* 13×13½.
1304 **1044** 60 p. cerise 10 10

1045 *Malayala Manorama* Office, Kottayam

1046 Maharshi Dadhichi

1988 (23 Mar). *Centenary of* Malayala Manorama *(newspaper). P* 13.
1305 **1045** 1 r. black and new blue 10 10

1988 (26 Mar). *Maharshi Dadhichi (Hindu saint) Commemoration. P* 13×13½.
1306 **1046** 60 p. Indian red 10 10

1047 Mohammad Iqbal **1048** Samarth Ramdas

(Des Alka Sharma)

1988 (21 Apr). *50th Death Anniv of Mohammad Iqbal (poet). P* 13.
1307 **1047** 60 p. gold and rosine 10 10

1988 (1 May). *Samarth Ramdas (Hindu spiritual leader) Commem. P* 13.
1308 **1048** 60 p. deep yellow-green 10 10

1049 Swati Tirunal Rama Varma **1050** Bhaurao Patil and Class

1988 (2 May). *175th Birth Anniv of Swati Tirunal Rama Varma (composer). P* 13×13½.
1309 **1049** 60 p. deep mauve 10 10

1988 (9 May). *Bhaurao Patil (educationist) Commemoration. P* 13½×13.
1310 **1050** 60 p. reddish brown 10 10

1051 "Rani Lakshmi Bai" (M. F. Husain)

1988 (9 May). *Martyrs from First War of Independence. P* 13×13½.
1311 **1051** 60 p. multicoloured 10 10

1052 Broad Peak **1053** Child with Grandparents

(Des R. Pasricha (1 r. 50, 4 r.), N. Roerich (5 r.))

1988 (19 May). *Himalayan Peaks. T* **1052** *and similar horiz designs. P* 13½×13.
1312 1 r. 50, reddish lilac, deep violet and blue 20 20
1313 4 r. multicoloured 40 45
1314 5 r. multicoloured 50 55
1315 6 r. 50, multicoloured 60 65
1312/15 . . . . . . *Set of* 4 1·50 1·75
Designs:—4 r. K 2 (Godwin Austen); 5 r. Kanchenjunga; 6 r.50, Nanda Devi.

(Des Neeta Verma)

1988 (24 May). *"Love and Care for Elders". P* 13×13½.
1316 **1053** 60 p. multicoloured 10 10

1054 Victoria Terminus, Bombay **1055** Lawrence School, Lovedale

1988 (30 May). *Centenary of Victoria Terminus Station, Bombay. P* 13½×13.
1317 **1054** 1 r. multicoloured 10 10

1988 (31 May). *130th Anniv of Lawrence School, Lovedale. P* 13.
1318 **1055** 1 r. red-brown and deep green . . 10 10

1056 Khejri Tree

1988 (5 June). *World Environment Day. P* 14.
1319 **1056** 60 p. multicoloured 10 10

1988 (15 June). *As No.* 732, *but new face value. W* **374**. *P* 12½ × 13.
1320 60 p. grey-black (Gandhi) 10 10

1057 Rani Durgawati **1058** Acharya Shanti Dev

1988 (24 June). *Rani Durgawati (Gondwana ruler) Commemoration. P* 13.
1322 **1057** 60 p. deep rose-red 10 10

1988 (28 July). *Acharya Shanti Dev (Buddhist scholar) Commemoration. P* 13×13½.
1323 **1058** 60 p. red-brown 10 10

1059 Y. S. Parmar

1988 (4 Aug). *Dr. Yashwant Singh Parmar (former Chief Minister of Himachal Pradesh) Commemoration. P* 13×13½.
1324 **1059** 60 p. slate-violet 10 10

1060 Arm pointing at Proclamation in Marathi

(Des Contract Advertising (India) Ltd)

1988 (16 Aug). *40th Anniv of Independence. Bal Gangadhar Tilak (patriot) Commemoration. T* **1060** *and similar horiz design. Multicoloured. P* 13×13½.
1325 60 p. Type **1060** 10 10
a. Vert pair. Nos. 1325/6 . . . . 20 20
1326 60 p. Battle scene 10 10
Nos. 1325/6 were printed together, *se-tenant*, in vertical pairs throughout the sheet, each pair forming a composite design showing a painting by M. F. Husain.

1061 Durgadas Rathore **1062** Gopinath Kaviraj

1988 (26 Aug). *150th Birth Anniv of Durgadas Rathore (Regent of Marwar). P* 13×13½.
1327 **1061** 60 p. reddish brown 10 10

1988 (7 Sept). *Gopinath Kaviraj (scholar) Commemoration. P* 13×13½.
1328 **1062** 60 p. bistre-brown 10 10

1063 Lotus and Outline Map of India **1064** Indian Olympic Association Logo

1988 (14 Sept). *Hindi Day. P* 13×13½.
1329 **1063** 60 p. orange-verm, grn & reddish brn 10 10

(Des C. Parameswaran (5 p.))

1988 (17 Sept). *"Sports–1988" and Olympic Games, Seoul. T* **1064** *and similar design. P* 13.
1330 60 p. brown-purple 10 10
1331 5 r. multicoloured 40 45
Design: *Horiz*—5 r. Various sports.

1065 Jerdon's Courser **1066** *Times of India* Front Page

1988 (7 Oct). *Wildlife Conservation. Jerdon's Courser. P* 13×13½.
1332 **1065** 1 r. multicoloured 15 10

(Des C. Pakrashi (4 r.), C. Meena (5 r.))

1988 (9 Oct)–**89**. *"India–89" International Stamp Exhibition, New Delhi (3rd issue). General Post Offices. Horiz designs as T* **1022**. *Multicoloured. P* 13½×13.
1333 4 r. Bangalore G.P.O. 30 35
a. Booklet pane. No. 1333×6 (20.1.89) 1·75
1334 5 r. Bombay G.P.O. 40 45
a. Booklet pane. No. 1334×6 (20.1.89) 2·25

(Des A. Nath)

1988 (3 Nov). *150th Anniv of* The Times of India. *P* 14.
1335 **1066** 1 r. 50, black, gold and lemon . . 15 15

1067 "Maulana Abul Kalam Azad" (K. Hebbar)

1988 (11 Nov). *Birth Centenary of Maulana Abul Kalam Azad (politician). P* 13½×13.
1336 **1067** 60 p. multicoloured 10 10

1068 Nehru

1988 (14 Nov). *Birth Centenary of Jawaharlal Nehru* (1989) (*1st issue*). *T* **1068** *and similar design. P* 13×13½ (60 p.) or 13½×13 (1 r.).
1337 60 p. grey-black, red-orange & deep green .. 10 10
1338 1 r. multicoloured 10 10
Design: *Vert*—1 r. "Jawaharlal Nehru" (Svetoslav Roerich).
See also No. 1393

1069 Birsa Munda

(Des S. Samantha)

1988 (15 Nov). *Birsa Munda (Munda leader) Commemoration. P* 13½ × 13.
1339 **1069** 60 p. reddish brown 10 10

1070 Bhakra Dam

1988 (15 Dec). *25th Anniv of Dedication of Bhakra Dam. P* 14.
1340 **1070** 60 p. bright carmine 15 20

1071 Dead Letter Office Cancellations of 1886

1072 K. M. Munshi

1988 (20 Dec)–**89**. *"India–89" International Stamp Exhibition, New Delhi (4th issue). Postal Cancellations. T* **1071** *and similar horiz design. P* 13½×13.
1341 60 p. dp cinnamon, black & carm-vermilion 15 15
a. Booklet pane. No. 1341×6 (20.1.89) 90
1342 6 r. 50, orange-brown and black .. .. 85 1·00
a. Booklet pane. No. 1342×6 (20.1.89) 5·00
Design:—6 r. 50, Travelling post office handstamp of 1864.

1988 (30 Dec). *Birth Centenary of K. M. Munshi (author and politician)* (1987). *P* 13½ × 13.
1343 **1072** 60 p. deep olive 15 15

1073 Mannathu Padmanabhan

1074 Lok Sabha Secretariat

1989 (2 Jan). *Mannathu Padmanabhan (social reformer) Commemoration. P* 13 × 13½.
1344 **1073** 60 p. olive-brown 15 15

1989 (2 Jan–11 May). *India's Struggle for Freedom (7th series). Vert portraits as T* **909**. *P* 13.
1345 60 p. blk, dull yellowish grn & reddish orge 15 15
1346 60 p. red-orange, dp grn & dp lilac (8.3.89) 15 15
1347 60 p. grey-black, bottle-green and bright orange (13.4.89) 15 15
1348 60 p. bistre-brown, emerald and reddish orange (13.4.89) 15 15
1349 60 p. brown, dp green & orge-red (11.5.89) 15 15
1345/9 .. .. *Set of* 5 70 70
Designs:—No. 1345, Hare Krushna Mahtab; No. 1346, Balasaheb Gangadhar Kher; No. 1347, Raj Kumari Amrit Kaur; No. 1348, Saifuddin Kitchlew; No. 1349, Asaf Ali.

1989 (10 Jan). *60th Anniv of Lok Sabha Secretariat (formerly Legislative Assembly Department). P* 13½ × 13.
1355 **1074** 60 p. brown-olive 15 15

1075 Goddess Durga seated on Lion (5th-cent terracotta plaque)

1076 Baldev Ramji Mirdha

1989 (11 Jan). *125th Anniv of Lucknow Museum. P* 14.
1356 **1075** 60 p. deep blue and new blue 15 15

1989 (17 Jan). *Birth Centenary of Baldev Ramji Mirdha (nationalist). P* 13 × 13½.
1357 **1076** 60 p. slate-green 15 15

1077 Girl with Stamp Collection

1078 St. John Bosco and Boy

(Des K. Radhakrishnan (60 p.), M. Jain (1 r. 50))

1989 (20 Jan). *"India–89" International Stamp Exhibition, New Delhi (5th issue). Philately. T* **1077** *and similar horiz designs. P* 13½×13.
1358 60 p. orge-yellow, rose-red & dp violet-blue 10 10
a. Booklet pane. No. 1358×6 35
1359 1 r. 50, brownish grey, orge-yellow & blk 15 15
a. Booklet pane. No. 1359×6 80
1360 5 r. dull vermilion and blue 50 50
a. Booklet pane. No. 1360×6 .. .. 2·75
1361 6 r. 50, black, red-brown & turquoise-blue 60 60
a. Booklet pane. No. 1361×6 .. .. 3·25
1358/61 .. .. *Set of* 4 1·25 1·25
Designs:—1 r. 50, Dawk gharry, c. 1842; 5 r. Travancore 1888 2 ch. conch shell stamp; 6 r. 50, Early Indian philatelic magazines.

1989 (31 Jan). *St. John Bosco (founder of Salesian Brothers) Commemoration. P* 13.
1362 **1078** 60 p. carmine 15 15

1079 Modern Tank and 19th-century Sowar

1080 Dargah Sharif, Ajmer

(Des P. Biswas)

1989 (8 Feb). *Third Cavalry Regiment. P* 13½ × 13.
1363 **1079** 60 p. multicoloured 20 15

1989 (13 Feb). *Dargah Sharif (Sufi shrine), Ajmer. P* 13½ × 13.
1364 **1080** 1 r. multicoloured 20 20

1081 Task Force and Indian Naval Ensign

1989 (15 Feb). *President's Review of the Fleet. P* 14.
1365 **1081** 6 r. 50, multicoloured 80 80

COVER PRICES

Cover factors are quoted at the beginning of each country for most issues to 1945. An explanation of the system can be found on page x. The factors quoted do not, however, apply to philatelic covers.

1082 Shaheed Laxman Nayak and Barbed Wire Fence

1083 Rao Gopal Singh

1989 (29 Mar). *Shaheed Laxman Nayak Commemoration. P* 13½×13.
1366 **1082** 60 p. dp brown, dp green & red-orange 10 10

1989 (30 Mar). *Rao Gopal Singh Commemoration. P* 13×13½.
1367 **1083** 60 p. olive-brown 10 10

1084 Sydenham College

1085 Bishnu Ram Medhi

1989 (19 Apr). *75th Anniv of Sydenham College, Bombay* (1988). *P* 13½×13.
1368 **1084** 60 p. grey-black 10 10

1989 (24 Apr). *Birth Centenary of Bishnu Ram Medhi (politician)* (1988). *P* 13.
1369 **1085** 60 p. yellowish green, deep blue-green and orange-red 10 10

1086 Dr. N. S. Hardikar

1087 "Advaita" in Devanagari Script

1989 (13 May). *Birth Centenary of Dr. Narayana Subbarao Hardikar (nationalist). P* 13×13½.
1370 **1086** 60 p. orange-brown 10 10

1989 (17 May). *Sankaracharya (philosopher) Commemoration. P* 14.
1371 **1087** 60 p. multicoloured 10 10

1088 Gandhi Bhavan, Punjab University

1089 Scene from Film *Raja Harischandra*

1989 (19 May). *Punjab University, Chandigarh. P* 13½×13.
1372 **1088** 1 r. light brown and turquoise-blue .. 10 10

1989 (30 May). *75 Years of Indian Cinema. P* 14.
1373 **1089** 60 p. black and yellow 10 10

1090 Cactus and Cogwheels

1091 Early Class and Modern University Students

1989 (20 June). *Centenary of Kirloskar Brothers Ltd (engineering group). P* 13½×13.
1374 **1090** 1 r. multicoloured 10 10

1989 (27 June). *Centenary of First D.A.V. College. P* 13½×13.
1375 **1091** 1 r. multicoloured 10 10

1092 Post Office, Dakshin Gangotri Base, Antarctica

1093 First Allahabad Bank Building

(Des S. Samantha)

1989 (11 July). *Opening of Post Office, Dakshin Gangotri Research Station, Antarctica. P* 14.
1376 **1092** 1 r. multicoloured 10 10

1989 (19 July). *125th Anniv of Allahabad Bank* (1990). *P* 14.
1377 **1093** 60 p. maroon and new blue 10 10

1094 Nehru inspecting Central Reserve Police, Neemuch, 1954

1095 Dairy Cow

1989 (27 July). *50th Anniv of Central Reserve Police Force (formerly Crown Representative's Police). P* 13½×13.
1378 **1094** 60 p. brown 10 10

1989 (18 Aug). *Centenary of Military Farms. P* 13½×13.
1379 **1095** 1 r. multicoloured 10 10

1096 Mustafa Kemal Atatürk

1097 Dr. S. Radhakrishnan

1989 (30 Aug). *50th Death Anniv of Mustafa Kemal Atatürk (Turkish statesman)* (1988). *P* 13×13½.
1380 **1096** 5 r. multicoloured 40 45

1989 (11 Sept). *Birth Centenary of Dr. Sarvepalli Radhakrishnan (former President)* (1988). *P* 13½×13.
1381 **1097** 60 p. grey-black 10 10

1098 Football Match

1099 Dr. P. Subbarayan

1989 (23 Sept). *Centenary of Mohun Bagan Athletic Club. P* 13½×13.
1382 **1098** 1 r. multicoloured 10 10

1989 (30 Sept). *Birth Centenary of Dr. P. Subbarayan (politician). P* 13×13½.
1383 **1099** 60 p. orange-brown 10 10

1100 Shyamji Krishna Varma

1101 Sayajirao Gaekwad III

1989 (4 Oct). *Shyamji Krishna Varma (nationalist) Commemoration. P* 13.
1384 **1100** 60 p. purple-brown, dp grn & orge-red 10 10

1989 (6 Oct). *50th Death Anniv of Maharaja Sayajirao Gaekwad III of Baroda. P* 13×13½.
1385 **1101** 60 p. brownish grey 10 10

1102 Symbolic Bird with Letter

1103 Namakkal Kavignar

1989 (14 Oct). *"Use Pincode" Campaign. P* 14.
1386 **1102** 60 p. multicoloured 10 10

1989 (19 Oct). *Namakkal Kavignar (writer) Commemoration. P* 13×13½.
1387 **1103** 60 p. brownish black 10 10

1104 Diagram of Human Brain

1105 Pandita Ramabai and Original Sharada Sadan Building

1989 (21 Oct). *18th International Epilepsy Congress and 14th World Congress on Neurology, New Delhi. P* 13½×13.
1388 **1104** 6 r. 50, multicoloured 50 55

1989 (26 Oct). *Pandita Ramabai (women's education pioneer) Commemoration. P* 13½×13.
1389 **1105** 60 p. light brown 10 10

1106 Releasing Homing Pigeons

1107 Acharya Narendra Deo

1989 (3 Nov). *Orissa Police Pigeon Post. P* 13½×13.
1390 **1106** 1 r. Indian red 10 10

1989 (6 Nov). *Birth Centenary of Acharya Narendra Deo (reformer). P* 13.
1391 **1107** 60 p. brown, emerald and red-orange 10 10

1108 Acharya Kripalani

1989 (11 Nov). *Acharya Kripalani (politician) Commemoration. P* 13½×13.
1392 **1108** 60 p. grey-blk, myrtle-grn & orge-red 10 10

1109 Nehru

(Des S. Debnath)

1989 (14 Nov). *Birth Centenary of Jawaharlal Nehru (2nd issue). P* 14×15.
1393 **1109** 1 r. dull brown, purple-brown and buff 10 10

1110 Meeting Logo

1111 Sir Gurunath Bewoor

1989 (19 Nov). *8th Asian Track and Field Meeting, New Delhi. P* 14.
1394 **1110** 1 r. black, reddish orge & yellowish grn 10 10

1989 (20 Nov). *Sir Gurunath Bewoor (former Director-General, Posts and Telegraphs) Commemoration. P* 13×13½.
1395 **1111** 60 p. light brown 10 10

1112 Balkrishna Sharma Navin

1113 Abstract Painting of Houses

1989 (8 Dec). *Balkrishna Sharma Navin (politician and poet) Commemoration. P* 13×13½.
1396 **1112** 60 p. black 10 10

1989 (15 Dec). *Centenary of Bombay Art Society* (1988). *P* 13½×13.
1397 **1113** 1 r. multicoloured 10 10

1114 Likh Florican

1989 (20 Dec). *Wildlife Conservation. Likh Florican. P* 13×13½.
1398 **1114** 2 r. multicoloured 15 20

Index to Indian Stamp Designs from 1947

The following index is intended to facilitate the identification of all Indian stamps from 1947 onwards. Portrait stamps are usually listed under surnames only, views under the name of the town or city and other issues under the main subject or a prominent word and date chosen from the inscription. Simple abbreviations have occasionally been resorted to and when the same design or subject appears on more than one stamp, only the first of each series is indicated.

OFFICIAL STAMPS

Stamps overprinted "POSTAL SERVICE" or "I.P.N." were not used as postage stamps, and are therefore omitted.

Service.
(O 1)

(Optd by the Military Orphanage Press, Calcutta)

1866 (1 Aug)–**72**. *Optd with Type* O 1. *P* 14. (*a*) *No wmk.*
O 1 **11** ½ a. blue .. .. — 85·00
O 2 ½ a. pale blue .. £550 65·00
a. Optd inverted
O 3 1 a. brown .. — 75·00
O 4 1 a. deep brown .. — 65·00
O 5 8 a. carmine .. 8·00 16·00

(*b*) *Wmk Elephant's Head, T* 13
O 6 **11** ½ a. blue .. 85·00 18·00
O 7 ½ a. pale blue .. 85·00 12·00
a. Opt inverted
b. No dot on "i" (No. 50 on pane) .. — £190
c. No stop (No. 77 on pane) .. — £190
O 8 **12** 8 p. purple (1.72) .. 16·00 28·00
a. No dot on "i" .. £160
b. No stop .. £160
O 9 **11** 1 a. brown .. 90·00 15·00
O10 1 a. deep brown .. 90·00 28·00
a. No dot on "i" .. — £300
b. No stop .. — £300
O11 2 a. orange .. 85·00 35·00
O12 2 a. yellow .. 85·00 35·00
a. Opt inverted
b. Imperf
O13 4 a. green .. 85·00 45·00
a. Opt inverted
O14 **17** 4 a. green (Die I) .. £650 £180

A variety with wide and more open capital "S" occurs six times in sheets of all values except No. O8. Price four times the normal.

Reprints exist of Nos. O6, O9 and O14; the latter is Die II instead of Die I.

Reprints of the overprint have also been made, in different setting, on the 8 pies, purple, no watermark.

O 2

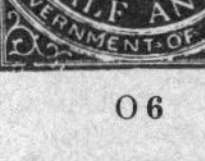
O 6

O 3

O 4

(No. O15 surch at Calcutta, others optd at Madras)

1866 (Oct). *Fiscal stamps surch or optd. Wmk Crown over* "INDIA".

(*a*) *Surch as in Type* O 2. *Thick blue glazed paper. Imperf × perf* 14
O15 O 2 2 a. purple .. £350 £225

(*b*) *Optd* "SERVICE POSTAGE" *in two lines as in Types* O 3/4 *and similar type. Imperf × perf* 14
O16 O 3 2 a. purple (G.) .. £650 £325
O17 O 4 4 a. purple (G.) .. £1400 £750
O18 — 8 a. purple (G.) .. £3500 £1800

(*c*) *Optd* "SERVICE POSTAGE" *in semi-circle. Wmk Large Crown. P* 15½ × 15
O19 O 6 ½ a. mauve/*lilac* (G.) .. £275 75·00
a. Opt double .. £1700

So-called reprints of Nos. O15 to O18 are known, but in these the surcharge differs entirely in the spacing, etc., of the words; they are more properly described as Government imitations. The imitations of No. O15 have surcharge in *black* or in *green*. No. O19 exists with reprinted overprint which has a full stop after "POSTAGE".

PRINTERS. The following stamps up to No. O108 were overprinted by De La Rue and thereafter Official stamps were printed or overprinted by the Security Printing Press at Nasik.

Service. (O 7)

On H. S. M. (O 8)

On H. S. M. (O 9)

1867–73. *Optd with Type* O 7. *Wmk Elephant's Head. T* 13. *P* 14.
O20 **11** ½ a. blue (Die I) .. 10·00 40
O21 ½ a. pale blue (Die I) .. 12·00 50
O22 ½ a. blue (Die II) (1873) .. 85·00 30·00
O23 1 a. brown .. 10·00 45
O24 1 a. deep brown .. 12·00 50
O25 1 a. chocolate .. 13·00 65
O26 2 a. yellow .. 6·00 2·50
O27 2 a. orange .. 4·50 2·25
O28 **17** 4 a. pale green (Die I) .. 6·00 2·00
O29 4 a. green (Die I) .. 3·00 1·50
O30 **11** 8 a. rose (Die II) (1868) .. 3·25 1·50
O30*a* 8 a. pale rose (Die II) .. 3·25 1·50

Prepared for use, but not issued
O30*b* **18** 6 a. 8 p. slate .. £140

1874–82. *Optd with Type* O 8. (*a*) *In black.*
O31 **11** ½ a. blue (Die II) .. 4·00 20
O32 1 a. brown .. 4·50 20
O33 2 a. yellow .. 15·00 4·50
O33*a* 2 a. orange .. 14·00 3·75
O34 **17** 4 a. green (Die I) .. 4·00 2·50
O35 **11** 8 a. rose (Die II) .. 3·50 1·75

(*b*) *Optd in blue-black*
O36 **11** ½ a. blue (Die II) (1882) .. £190 30·00
O37 1 a. brown (1882) .. £350 75·00

1883–99. *Wmk Star, T* 34. *P* 14. *Optd with Type* O 9.
O37*a* **40** 3 p. aniline carmine (1899) .. 20 10
O38 **23** ½ a. deep blue-green .. 30 10
a. Opt double .. — £425
O39 ½ a. blue-green .. 20 10
O40 **25** 1 a. brown-purple .. 35 10
a. Opt inverted .. £225 £300
b. Opt double .. — £425
c. Opt omitted (in horiz pair with normal) .. £500
O41 1 a. plum .. 25 10
O42 **27** 2 a. pale blue .. 1·40 10
O43 2 a. blue .. 1·60 10
O44 **29** 4 a. olive-green .. 2·50 10
O44*a* 4 a. slate-green .. 2·00 10
O45 **31** 8 a. dull mauve .. 5·50 60
O46 8 a. magenta .. 2·75 25
O47 **37** 1 r. green and rose (1892) .. 12·00 1·40
O48 1 r. green and carmine (1892) .. 3·50 40
O37*a*/48 .. *Set of* 7 9·25 90

1900 *Colours changed. Optd with Type* O 9.
O49 **23** ½ a. pale yellow-green .. 45 20
O49*a* ½ a. yellow-green .. 60 25
ab. Opt double .. £400
O50 **25** 1 a. carmine .. 80 10
a. Opt inverted .. — £400
b. Opt double .. — £450
O51 **27** 2 a. pale violet .. 10·00 25
O52 2 a. mauve .. 13·00 40
O49/52 .. *Set of* 3 10·00 40

1902–9. *Stamps of King Edward VII optd with Type* O 9.
O54 **41** 3 p. grey (1903) .. 70 20
O55 3 p. slate-grey (1905) .. 70 30
a. No stop after 'M' .. 35·00 25·00
O56 **42** ½ a. green .. 90 15
O57 **43** 1 a. carmine .. 70 10
O58 **44** 2 a. violet .. 2·50 15
O59 2 a. mauve .. 1·75 10
O60 **47** 4 a. olive .. 2·50 10
O61 4 a. pale olive .. 3·00 10
O62 **48** 6 a. olive-bistre (1909) .. 1·50 10
O63 **49** 8 a. mauve .. 5·00 50
O64 8 a. magenta .. 6·50 45
O65 **51** 1 r. green and carmine (1905) .. 4·00 15
O54/65 .. *Set of* 8 15·00 1·25

1906. *New types. Optd with Type* O 9.
O66 **53** ½ a. green .. 25 10
a. No stop after 'M' .. 24·00 20·00
O67 **54** 1 a. carmine .. 65 10
a. No stop after 'M' .. 30·00 20·00

On
H. S.
M.
(O 9*a*)

1909. *Optd with Type* O 9*a*.
O68 **52** 2 r. carmine and yellow-brown .. 7·50 60
O68*a* 2 r. rose-red and yellow-brown .. 7·00 80
O69 5 r. ultramarine and violet .. 14·00 1·50
O70 10 r. green and carmine .. 16·00 8·50
O70*a* 10 r. green and scarlet .. 35·00 7·00
O71 15 r. blue and olive-brown .. 55·00 28·00
O72 25 r. brownish orange and blue .. £140 60·00
O68/72 .. *Set of* 5 £210 85·00

SERVICE (O 10)(14 mm)

SERVICE (O 11) (21½) mm)

NINE PIES (O 12)

1912–13. *Stamps of King George V (wmk Single Star, T* 34) *optd with Type* O 10 *or* O 11 (*rupee values*).
O73 **55** 3 p. grey .. 15 10
O74 3 p. slate-grey .. 15 10
O75 3 p. blue-slate .. 40 10
a. Opt omitted (in pair with normal)
O76 **56** ½ a. yellow-green .. 15 10
a. Overprint double .. 85·00
O77 ½ a. pale blue-green .. 20 10
O80 **57** 1 a. rose-carmine .. 50 10
O81 1 a. carmine .. 40 10
O82 1 a. aniline carmine .. 40 10
a. Overprint double .. — £400
O83 **59** 2 a. mauve .. 45 10
O84 2 a. purple .. 45 10
O85 **63** 4 a. deep olive .. 1·00 10
O86 4 a. olive-green .. 1·00 10
O87 **64** 6 a. yellow-bistre .. 1·50 1·75
O88 6 a. deep bistre-brown .. 3·25 2·25
O89 **65** 8 a. purple .. 2·25 25
O89*a* 8 a. mauve .. 2·25 25
O90 8 a. bright aniline mauve .. 11·00 1·75
O91 **67** 1 r. red-brown and blue-green (1913) .. 2·25 25
O92 2 r. rose-carmine and brown (1913) .. 3·00 1·60
O93 5 r. ultramarine and violet (1913) .. 11·00 8·50
O94 10 r. green and scarlet (1913) .. 27·00 25·00
O95 15 r. blue and olive (1913) .. 65·00 75·00
O96 25 r. orange and blue (1913) .. £160 90·00
O73/96 .. *Set of* 13 £250 £180

1921. *No.* O80 *surch with Type* O 12.
O97 **57** 9 p. on 1 a. rose-carmine .. 15 15

1922. *No.* 197 *optd with Type* O 10.
O98 **57** 1 a. chocolate .. 40 10

ONE
RUPEE

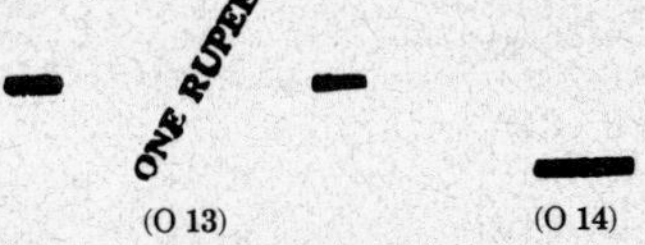

(O 13) (O 14)

1925. *Official stamps surcharged.*
(*a*) *Issue of* 1909, *as Type* O 13
O 99 **52** 1 r. on 15 r. blue and olive .. 4·25 2·50
O100 1 r. on 25 r chestnut and blue .. 17·00 35·00
O101 2 r. on 10 r green and scarlet .. 3·75 3·00
O101*a* 2 r. on 10 r. green and carmine .. £140 45·00

(*b*) Issue of 1912, *with Type* O 14
O102 **67** 1 r. on 15 r. blue and olive .. 17·00 38·00
O103 1 r. on 25 r. orange and blue .. 5·00 6·50
a. Surch inverted .. £350

(*c*) Issue of 1912, *as Type* O 13
O104 **67** 2 r. on 10 r. green and scarlet .. £600

Examples of the above showing other surcharge errors are believed to be of clandestine origin.

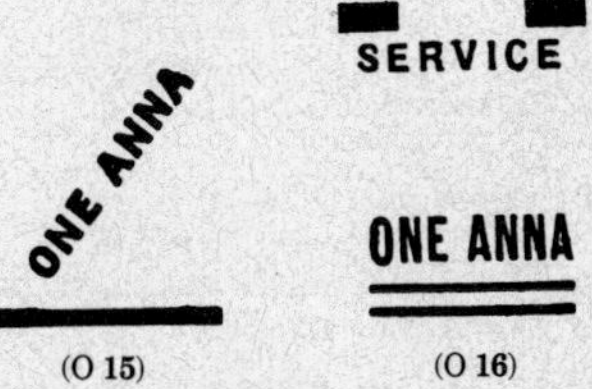

(O 15) (O 16)

1926. *No.* O62 *surch with Type* O 15.
O105 **48** 1 a. on 6 a. olive-bistre .. 25 25

1926. *Postage stamps of* 1911–22 (*wmk Single Star*), *surch as Type* O 16.
O106 **58** 1 a. on 1½ a. chocolate (A) .. 20 10
O107 1 a. on 1½ a. chocolate (B) .. 45 30
a. Error. On 1 a. chocolate (197) .. £150
O108 **61** 1 a. on 2½ a. ultramarine .. 60 1·25

The surcharge on No. O108 has no bars at top.

Examples of Nos. O106/7 with inverted or double surcharges are believed to be of clandestine origin.

SERVICE (O 17)(13½ mm)

SERVICE (O 18) (19½ mm)

1926–31. *Stamps of King George V (wmk Multiple Star, T* 69) *optd with Types* O 17 *or* O 18 (*rupee values*).
O109 **55** 3 p. slate (1.10.29) .. 15 10
O110 **56** ½ a. green (1931) .. 70 10
O111 **57** 1 a. chocolate .. 15 10
O112 **70** 2 a. purple .. 20 10
O113 **71** 4 a. sage-green .. 25 10
O115 **65** 8 a. reddish purple .. 60 10
O116 **66** 12 a. claret (1927) .. 60 30
O117 **67** 1 r. chocolate and green (1930) .. 1·25 30
O118 2 r. carmine and orange (1930) .. 6·00 3·75
O120 10 r. green and scarlet (1931) .. 65·00 45·00
O109/20 .. *Set of* 10 65·00 45·00

1930. *As No.* O111, *but optd as Type* O 10 (*14 mm*).
O125 **57** 1 a. chocolate .. 48·00 4·00

1932–36. *Stamps of King George V (wmk Mult Star, T* 69) *optd with Type* O 17.
O126 **79** ½ a. green (1935) .. 50 10
O127 **80** 9 p. deep green .. 20 10
O127*a* **81** 1 a. chocolate (1936) .. 35 10
O128 **82** 1¼ a. mauve .. 20 10
O129 **70** 2 a. vermilion .. 75 25
O130 **59** 2 a. vermilion (1935) .. 1·25 1·10
O130*a* 2 a. vermilion (*small die*) (1936) .. 75 10
O131 **61** 2½ a. orange (22.4.32) .. 15 10
O132 **63** 4 a. sage-green (1935) .. 75 10
O133 **64** 6 a. bistre (1936) .. 13·00 4·50
O126/33 .. *Set of* 9 15·00 4·75

1937–39. *Stamps of King George VI optd as Types* O 17 *or* O 18 *(rupee values).*

No.	Type	Description	Unused	Used
O135	91	½ a. red-brown (1938)	5·00	15
O136		9 p. green (1937)	5·00	10
O137		1 a. carmine (1937)	1·00	10
O138	93	1 r. grey and red-brown (5.38)	50	10
O139		2 r. purple and brown (5.38)	1·50	85
O140		5 r. green and blue (10.38)	2·50	2·00
O141		10 r. purple and claret (1939)	13·00	4·00
O135/41		*Set of* 7	26·00	6·50

(O 19)

(O 20)

1939 (May). *Stamp of King George V, surch with Type* O **19**.

No.	Type	Description	Unused	Used
O142	82	1 a. on 1¼ a. mauve	2·75	15

(Des T. I. Archer)

1939 (1 June)–**42**. *Typo. W* **69**. *P* 14.

No.	Type	Description	Unused	Used
O143	O 20	3 p. slate	20	10
O144		½ a. red-brown	30	10
O144*a*		½ a. purple (1942)	20	10
O145		9 p. green	25	10
O146		1 a. carmine	25	10
O146*a*		1 a. 3 p. yellow-brown (1941)	2·75	40
O146*b*		1½ a. dull violet (1942)	65	10
O147		2 a. vermilion	60	10
O148		2½ a. bright violet	60	15
O149		4 a. brown	60	10
O150		8 a. slate-violet	90	20
O143/50		*Set of* 11	6·50	90

1948 (Aug). *First Anniv Indian Independence. Mahatma Gandhi postage stamps optd* "SERVICE", *as Type* O **17**.

No.	Type	Description	Unused	Used
O150*a*	305	1½ a. brown	42·00	30·00
O150*b*		3½ a. violet	£550	£350
O150*c*		12 a. grey-green	£1350	£1350
O150*d*	306	10 r. purple-brown and lake	£6000	

O 21 Asokan Capital O 22

(Des T. I. Archer)

1950 (2 Jan)–**51**. *Typo* (O **21**) *or litho* (O **22**). *W* **69**. *P* 14.

No.	Type	Description	Unused	Used
O151	O 21	3 p. slate-violet (1.7.50)	10	10
O152		6 p. purple-brown (1.7.50)	10	10
O153		9 p. green (1.7.50)	20	10
O154		1 a. turquoise (1.7.50)	35	10
O155		2 a. carmine (1.7.50)	55	10
O156		3 a. red-orange (1.7.50)	1·50	50
O157		4 a. lake (1.7.50)	6·00	10
O158		4 a. ultramarine (1.10.51)	40	10
O159		6 a. bright violet (1.7.50)	1·50	40
O160		8 a. red-brown (1.7.50)	1·50	10
O161	O 22	1 r. violet	1·50	10
O162		2 r. rose-carmine	1·00	25
O163		5 r. bluish green	2·00	1·50
O164		10 r. reddish brown	4·00	8·50
O151/64		*Set of* 14	18·00	10·50

1957 (1 Apr)–**58**. *Value in naye paise. Typo* (*t*) *or litho* (*l*). *W* **69**. *P* 14.

No.	Type	Description	Unused	Used
O165	O 21	1 n.p. slate (*l*)	10	10
		a. Slate-black (*l*)	10	10
		b. Greenish slate (*t*)	10	10
O166		2 n.p. blackish violet (*t*)	10	10
O167		3 n.p. chocolate (*t*)	10	10
O168		5 n.p. green (*l*)	10	10
		a. Deep emerald (*t*)	10	10
O169		6 n.p. turquoise-blue (*t*)	10	10
O170		13 n.p. scarlet (*t*)	10	10
O171		15 n.p. reddish violet (*l*) (6.58)	25	25
		a. Reddish violet (*t*)	35	40
O172		20 n.p. red (*l*)	10	10
		a. Vermilion (*t*)	15	10
O173		25 n.p. violet-blue (*l*)	15	10
		a. Ultramarine (*t*)	25	10
O174		50 n.p. red-brown (*l*)	25	10
		a. Reddish brown (*t*)	35	25
O165/74		*Set of* 10	1·00	75

1958–71. *As Nos.* O165/74*a and* O161/4 *but W* **374** (*upright*). *Litho* (*l*) *or typo* (*t*). *P* 14.

No.	Type	Description	Unused	Used
O175	O 21	1 n.p. slate-black (*t*) (1.59)	10	10
O176		2 n.p. blackish violet (*t*) (1.59)	10	10
O177		3 n.p. chocolate (*t*) (11.58)	10	10
O178		5 n.p. deep emerald (*t*) (11.58)	10	10
O179		6 n.p. turquoise-blue (*t*) (5.59)	10	10
O180		10 n.p. deep grey-green (*l*) (1963)	25	25
		a. Deep grey-green (*t*) (1966?)	40	30
O181		13 n.p. scarlet (*t*) (1963)	15	60
O182		15 n.p. deep violet (*t*) (11.58)	10	10
		a. Light reddish violet (*t*) (1961)	10	10
O183		20 n.p. vermilion (*t*) (5.59)	10	10
		a. Red (*t*) (1966?)	40	25
O184		25 n.p. ultramarine (*t*) (7.59)	10	10
O185		50 n.p. reddish brown (*t*) (6.59)	15	10
		a. Chestnut (*l*) (1966?)	40	25
O186	O 22	1 r. reddish violet (*l*) (2.59)	15	10
O187		2 r. rose-carmine (*l*) (1960)	25	10
		a. Wmk sideways. *Pale rose-carmine* (*l*) (1969?)	35	40
O188	O 22	5 r. slate-green (*l*) (7.59)	50	40
		a. Wmk sideways. *Deep grey-green* (*l*) (1969?)	60	70
O189		10 r. brown-lake (*l*) (7.59)	1·25	80
		a. Wmk sideways (*l*) (1971)	1·75	2·00
O175/89		*Set of* 15	2·75	2·25

O 23 (*see also* Type O **26**)

शरणार्थी
सहायता
REFUGEE
RELIEF

(O 24)

O 25

1967 (20 Mar)–**74**? *Photo. W* **374** (*sideways*). *P* 15 × 14.

No.	Type	Description	Unused	Used
O190	O 23	2 p. violet (1974?)	10	15
O191		5 p. green (1974?)	15	10
O192		10 p. myrtle-green (1974?)	25	10
O193		15 p. plum (2.7.73)	40	15
O194		20 p. red (1974?)	2·00	2·00
O195		30 p. ultramarine (1973)	60	35
O196		50 p. chestnut (2.7.73)	1·00	1·00
O197		1 r. dull purple (20.3.67)	15	10
		a. Deep slate-purple (1969)	25	10
O190/7		*Set of* 8	4·25	3·25

1967 (15 Nov)–**74**(?). *Wmk Large Star and* "INDIA GOVT" *in sheet*. Photo. P* 15 × 14. *No gum.*

No.	Type	Description	Unused	Used
O200	O 23	2 p. violet	10	15
O201		3 p. chocolate	10	25
O202		5 p. green	10	10
		a. Yellowish green (1969)	10	10
O203		6 p. turquoise-blue	25	40
O204		10 p. myrtle-green	10	15
		a. Bronze-green (1969)	20	15
O205		15 p. plum	10	15
O206		20 p. red	10	10
O207		25 p. carmine-red (1974?)	1·50	1·50
O208		30 p. ultramarine	10	10
O209		50 p. chestnut	10	10
O200/9		*Set of* 10	2·00	2·50

*The arrangement of this watermark in the sheet results in the words and the star appearing upright, inverted or sideways.

1971. *Obligatory Tax. Refugee Relief.*

(*a*) *Provisional issue. No.* O202 *optd with Type* O **24**.

No.	Type	Description	Unused	Used
O210	O 23	5 p. yellowish green	10	10
		a. Green	10	10

(*b*) *Issue for Bangalore. No.* O202 *optd with T* **602**

No.	Type	Description	Unused	Used
O211	O 23	5 p. yellowish green	65	30
		a. Opt inverted	3·00	

(*c*) *Issue for Goa. No.* O202 *optd with T* **606**

No.	Type	Description	Unused	Used
O212	O 23	5 p. yellowish green		

(*d*) *Definitive issue. Wmk Large Star and* "INDIA GOVT" *in sheet*. Litho. P* 15 × 14. *No gum.*

No.	Type	Description	Unused	Used
O213	O 25	5 p. yellowish-green	10	10
		a. Yellow-green	10	10

*See note below No. O209.

The surcharge on mail for the relief of refugees from the former East Pakistan referred to in the note after No. 651 also applied to official mail. The cost of the stamps used by each Government Department was charged against its budget and the additional charge for refugee stamps meant that each Department had to spend less to keep within its budget.

O 26

O 27

O 28

1976 (1 Apr)–**80**. *Redrawn, showing face-value in figures only and smaller Capital with Hindi motto beneath. P* 14 (2, 5, 10 *r.*) *or* 15 × 14 (*others*). (*a*) *Wmk Large Star and* "INDIA GOVT" *in sheet.* No gum.*

No.	Type	Description	Unused	Used
O214	O 26	2 p. deep violet-blue	10	30
O215		5 p. yellowish green	10	15
O216		10 p. myrtle-green	10	20
		a. Deep dull green (1978)	10	15
O217		15 p. deep purple	10	15
O218		20 p. Indian red	10	15
O219		25 p. rose-carmine	20	40
		a. Bright crimson (1978)	25	45
O220		30 p. chalky blue (1.5.79)	40	40
O221		35 p. violet (6.12.80)	10	10
O222		50 p. chestnut	35	35
O223		1 r. deep brownish purple (13.8.80)	60	25

(*b*) *W* **374** (*sideways*)

No.	Type	Description	Unused	Used
O224	O 26	1 r. deep brownish purple	35	40
O225	–	2 r. rose-red (date?)	70	70
		a. Wmk upright	25	60
O226	–	5 r. deep green (date?)	1·25	1·75
		a. Wmk upright (1978)	60	1·25
O227	–	10 r. brown-lake (date?)	1·25	2·50
		a. Wmk upright	1·75	3·00
O214/27a		*Set of* 14	4·00	6·50

The 2, 5 and 10 r. are larger, size as Type O **22**.

*See note below No. 720. The 2 p. value is only known on the first type of watermark, the 35, 50 p. and 1 r. values on the second and the remaining values on both.

1981 (Feb). *Redrawn showing revised border design and inscriptions, with face value figures now in bottom corners. Wmk Large Star and* "INDIA GOVT" *in sheet. P* 15 × 14.

No.	Type	Description	Unused	Used
O228	O 27	2 r. rose-red	25	25
O229		5 r. deep green	50	55
O230		10 r. brown-lake	1·00	1·10
O228/30		*Set of* 3	1·50	1·75

1981 (10 Dec). *As Nos.* O215/19, O221/3 *and* O228/30 *but printed on cream paper with simulated perforations as Type* O **28**. *Unwatermarked. Imperf.*

No.	Type	Description	Unused	Used
O231	O 28	5 p. dull yellowish green	15	15
O232		10 p. deep green	15	15
O233		15 p. deep reddish violet	15	15
O234		20 p. dull vermilion	15	15
O235		25 p. bright rose	40	25
O236		35 p. violet	25	15
O237		50 p. orange-brown	40	25
O238		1 r. deep dull purple	45	25
O239		2 r. orange-vermilion	55	60
O240		5 r. deep dull green	1·00	1·25
O241		10 r. lake-brown	1·40	2·00
O231/41		*Set of* 11	4·50	4·75

Some values have been seen unofficially pin-perforated.

1982 (22 Nov). *As Nos.* 215/23 *and* 228/30. *Wmk Large Star and* "INDIA GOVT" *in sheet. P* 12½ × 13.

No.	Type	Description	Unused	Used
O242	O 26	5 p. light green	10	15
O243		10 p. deep dull green	10	15
O244		15 p. blackish purple	10	15
O245		20 p. Indian red	10	15
O246		25 p. cerise	10	20
O247		30 p. deep ultramarine	10	20
O248		35 p. bluish violet	10	15
O249		50 p. reddish brown	15	20
O250		1 r. deep purple-brown	20	25
O251	O 27	2 r. rose-red	35	60
O252		5 r. grey-green	65	1·25
O253		10 r. chocolate	1·25	2·00
O242/53		*Set of* 12	3·00	5·00

1984 (16 Apr)–**88**. *As Nos.* O215/23, O228/30 *and new values. W* **374** (*sideways*). *P* 13.

No.	Type	Description	Unused	Used
O254	O 26	5 p. yellowish green	10	10
O255		10 p. deep dull green	10	10
		a. Wmk upright		
O256		15 p. blackish purple	10	10
O257		20 p. Indian red	10	10
O258		25 p. rose-carmine (1986)	10	10
O259		30 p. deep ultramarine	10	10
O260		35 p. bluish violet	10	10
O261		40 p. bright violet (15.10.88)	10	10
O262		50 p. reddish brown	10	10
O263		60 p. deep brown (15.4.88)	10	10
O264		1 r. deep purple-brown	10	10
O265	O 27	2 r. rose-red	15	20
O266		5 r. grey-green	35	40
O267		10 r. chocolate	65	70
O254/67		*Set of* 14	1·50	1·60

INDIA USED ABROAD

In the years following 1858 the influence of the Indian Empire, political, military and economic, extended beyond its borders into neighbouring states, the Arabian Gulf, East Africa and the Far East. Such influence often led to the establishment of Indian civil post offices in the countries concerned w.ere unoverprinted stamps of India were used.

Such offices operated in the following countries. An * indicates that details will be found under that heading elsewhere in the catalogue.

ADEN*

Unoverprinted stamps of India used from 1854 until 1937.

BAHRAIN*

Unoverprinted stamps of India used from 1884 until 1933.

BRITISH EAST AFRICA*

Unoverprinted stamps of India used during August and September 1890.

FRENCH INDIAN SETTLEMENTS

The first Indian post office, at Chandernagore, was open by 1784 to be followed by offices in the other four Settlements. By an agreement with the French, dating from 1814, these offices handled mail destined for British India, Great Britain, the British Empire and most other foreign destinations except France and the French colonies. In later years the system was expanded by a number of sub-offices and it continued to operate until the French territories were absorbed into India on 2 May 1950 (Chandernagore) or 1 November 1954.

Chandernagore. Open by 1784. Used numeral cancellations "B86" or "86".
- Sub-offices:
  - Gondalpara (opened 1906)
  - Lakhiganj (opened 1909)
  - Temata (opened 1891)

Karikal. Open by 1794. Used numeral cancellations "C147", "147" or "6/M–21".
- Sub-offices:
  - Ambagarattur (opened 1904)
  - Kottuchari (opened 1901)
  - Nedungaon (opened 1903)
  - Puraiyar Road (opened 1901)
  - Settur (opened 1905)
  - Tirumalrayapatnam (opened 1875 – used numeral cancellation "6/M-21/1")
  - Tiramilur (opened 1898)

Mahe. Open by 1795. Used numeral cancellations "C192" or "9/M-14".

Pondicherry. Opened 1787. Used numeral cancellations "C111", "111" (also used elsewhere), "6/M-19" (also used elsewhere) or "6/M-20".
- Sub-offices:
  - Ariyankuppam (opened 1904)
  - Bahoor (opened 1885)
  - Mudaliarpet (opened 1897)
  - Muthialpet (opened 1885)
  - Pondicherry Bazaar (opened 1902)
  - Pondicherry Railway Station (opened 1895)
  - Olugarai (opened 1907)
  - Vallinur (opened 1875) – used numeral cancellation "M-19/1"

Yanam. Opened 1876. Used numeral cancellation "5/M-4".

IRAN

The British East Company was active in the Arabian Gulf from the early years of the 17th century with their first factory (trading centre) being established at Jask in 1619. After 1853 this commercial presence was converted into a political arm of the Indian Government culminating in the appointment of a Political Resident to Bushire in 1862.

The first Indian post office in Iran (Persia) opened at Bushire on 1 May 1864 with monthly mail services operating to the Resident there and to the British Legation at Tehran. Further offices in the other Gulf ports followed, but, unless otherwise stated below, all were closed on 1 April 1923.

Abadan. Opened during First World War.
Ahwaz. Opened March 1915.
Bandar Abbas. Opened 1 April 1867. Used numeral cancellations "22" or "1/K-5"
Bushire. Opened 1 May 1864. Used numeral cancellations "140", "308", "26" (also used elsewhere) or "K-5".
Chabbar. Opened August 1913. Closed 1920.
Henjam. Opened 1913.
Jask. Opened 1880.
Linga. Opened 1 April 1867. Used numeral cancellations "21" or "2/K-5".
Mohammera. Opened 19 July 1892.
Maidan-i-Naphtun. Opened during First World War. Closed 1920.

IRAQ*

Unoverprinted stamps of India used from 1868 until 1918.

KUWAIT*

Unoverprinted stamps of India used from 1904 until 1923.

MALAYSIA (STRAITS SETTLEMENTS)*

Unoverprinted stamps of India used from 1854 until 1867.

MUSCAT*

Unoverprinted stamps of India used from 1864 until 1947.

NEPAL

A post office was opened in the British Residency at Kathmandu in 1816 following the end of the Gurkha War. Stamps of India were used from 1854, initially with "B137", "137" or "C-37" numeral cancellations. The Residency Post Office continued to provide the overseas mail service after Nepal introduced its own issues in 1881.

In 1920 the Residency Post Office became the British Legation Post Office. On the independence of India in 1947 the service was transferred to the Indian Embassy and continued to function until 1965.

PORTUGUESE INDIA

A British post office was open in Damaun by 1823 and Indian stamps were used there until November 1883, some with "13" and "3/B-19" numeral cancellations.

No other British post offices were opened in the Portuguese territories, but from 1854 Indian stamps were sold by the local post offices. Between 1871 and 1877 mail intended for, or passing through, British India required combined franking of India and Portuguese India issues. After 1877 the two postal administrations accepted the validity of each other's stamps.

SOMALILAND PROTECTORATE*

Unoverprinted stamps of India used from 1887 until 1903.

TIBET

The first Indian post office in Tibet accompanied the Tibetan Frontier Commission in 1903. The Younghusband Military Expedition to Lhasa in the following year operated a number of Field Post Offices which were replaced by civil post offices at Gartok (opened 23 September 1906), Gyantse (opened March 1905), Pharijong (opened 1905) and Yatung (opened 1905). All Indian post offices in Tibet closed on 1 April 1955 except Gyantse which, it is believed, did not operate after 1943.

TRUCIAL STATES (DUBAI)*

Unoverprinted stamps of India used from 1909 until 1947.

ZANZIBAR*

Unoverprinted stamps of India used from 1875 until 1895.

CHINA EXPEDITIONARY FORCE

Following the outbreak of the Boxer Rising in North China the Peking Legations were besieged by the rebels in June 1900. An international force, including an Indian Army division, was assembled for their relief. The Legations were relieved on 14 August 1900, but operations against the Boxers continued in North China with Allied garrisons at key cities and along the Peking–Tientsin–Shanhaikwan railway. The last Indian Army battalion did not leave North China until 1923.

Field Post Offices accompanied the Indian troops and commenced operations on 23 July 1900 using unoverprinted Indian postage and official stamps. The unoverprinted postage issues were replaced in mid-August by stamps overprinted "C.E.F." to prevent currency speculation. The use of unoverprinted official stamps continued as they were not valid for public postage.

PRICES FOR STAMPS ON COVER

Nos. C1/10	*from* × 15
No. C10*a*	†
Nos. C11/22	*from* × 8
Nos. C23/34	*from* × 20

C. E. F.

(C 1)

Stamps of India overprinted with Type C 1, *in black*

1900 (Aug). *Stamps of Queen Victoria.*

C 1	**40**	3 p. carmine	20	30
		a. No stop after "C" (R. 1/2)		
C 2	**23**	½ a. green	30	20
		a. Opt double		
C 3	**25**	1 a. brown-purple	70	60
C 4	**27**	2 a. ultramarine	1·75	2·75
C 5	**36**	2½ a. green	2·25	5·50
C 6	**28**	3 a. orange	2·50	9·00
		a. Opt double, one albino	75·00	
C 7	**29**	4 a. olive-green	2·00	4·50
		a. Opt double, one albino	75·00	
C 8	**31**	8 a. magenta	2·00	7·00
C 9	**32**	12 a. purple/*red*	4·25	12·00
		a. Opt double, one albino	75·00	
C10	**37**	1 r. green and carmine	5·50	8·50
C1/10		*Set of* 10	19·00	45·00

Prepared, but not issued

C10*a*	**26**	1 a. 6 p. sepia	£150	

1904 (27 Feb).

C11	**25**	1 a. carmine	18·00	6·00

1904. *Stamps of King Edward VII.*

C12	**41**	3 p. grey	75	1·50
		a. Opt double, one albino	£140	
		b. Opt triple, one albino	£250	
		c. *Slate-grey*	1·00	1·75
C13	**43**	1 a. carmine	1·25	60
		a. Opt double, one albino	75·00	
C14	**44**	2 a. pale violet	4·00	1·50
C15	**45**	2½ a. ultramarine	2·50	5·00
C16	**46**	3 a. orange-brown	3·00	4·00
C17	**47**	4 a. olive-green	7·00	11·00
C18	**49**	8 a. magenta	6·00	7·00
		a. *Mauve*	50·00	
C19	**50**	12 a. purple/*red*	9·00	19·00
C20	**51**	1 r. green and carmine	9·00	22·00
C12/20		*Set of* 9	38·00	65·00

1909. "POSTAGE & REVENUE."

C21	**53**	½ a. green (No. 149)	1·25	50
		a. Opt double, one albino	75·00	
C22	**54**	1 a. carmine (No. 150)	1·00	25

1913–21. *Stamps of King George V. Wmk Star.*

C23	**55**	3 p. slate-grey (1913)	1·00	5·00
C24	**56**	½ a. green	1·00	2·25
C25	**57**	1 a. aniline carmine	1·40	1·00
C26	**58**	1½ a. chocolate (Type A)	8·50	30·00
		a. Opt double, one albino	75·00	
C27	**59**	2 a. mauve	3·50	18·00
		a. Opt triple	£275	
C28	**61**	2½ a. bright blue	5·00	11·00
C29	**62**	3 a. orange-brown	11·00	42·00
C30	**63**	4 a. olive-green	16·00	70·00
C32	**65**	8 a. mauve	14·00	£110
C33	**66**	12 a. claret	14·00	65·00
C34	**67**	1 r. red-brown and blue-green	38·00	£110
C23/34		*Set of* 11	£100	£425

On No. C27a two of the overprints are only lightly inked.

BRITISH RAILWAY ADMINISTRATION

As a vital communications link the North China Railway (Peking – Tientsin – Shanhaikwan) was captured by Russian forces during operations against the Boxers. Control of the line was subsequently, in February 1901, assigned to the China Expeditionary Force and a British Railway Administration was set up to run it. By international agreement the line was to provide postal services for the other national contingents and also, to a lesser extent, for the civilian population. Travelling post offices were introduced and, on 20 April 1901, a late letter service for which an additional fee of 5 c. was charged.

Type **32** of China

B.R.A.
5
Five Cents

(BR 35)

1901 (20 Apr). *No.* 108 *of China surch with Type* BR **35**.

BR133	**32**	5 c. on ½ c. brown (Bk.)	£125	65·00
		a. Surch inverted	£5000	£1500
		b. Surch in green	£100	90·00

No. BR133 was used for the collection of the 5 c. late letter fee and was affixed to correspondence by a postal official at the railway station. It was cancelled with a violet circular postmark showing "RAILWAY POST OFFICE" at top and the name of the station (PEKING, TIENTSIN, TONGKU, TONGSHAN or SHANHAIKWAN) at foot. With the exception of official mail it could only be used in combination with Indian stamps overprinted "C.E.F.", stamps from the other allied contingents or of the Chinese Imperial Post (*Price used on cover*: No. BR133 *from* £170, No. BR133b *from* £225).

The late fee charge was abolished on 20 May 1901 and No. BR133 was then withdrawn. The British Railway Administration continued to run the line, and its travelling post offices, until it was returned to its private owners in September 1902.

PRICES OF SETS

Set prices are given for many issues, generally those containing three stamps or more. Definitive sets include one of each value or major colour change, but do not cover different perforations, die types or minor shades. Where a choice is possible the set prices are based on the cheapest versions of the stamps included in the listings.

INDIAN EXPEDITIONARY FORCES 1914–22

PRICES FOR STAMPS ON COVER

Nos. E1/13	*from* × 10

I. E. F.

(E 1)

1914. *Stamps of India (King George V) optd with Type* E **1**.

E 1	**55**	3 p. slate-grey	15	25
		a. No stop after "F"	17·00	17·00
		b. No stop after "E"	40·00	40·00
		c. Opt double	30·00	25·00
E 2	**56**	½ a. yellow-green	20	20
		a. No stop after "F"	38·00	38·00
		b. Opt double	£140	£200
E 3	**57**	1 a. aniline carmine	25	20
		a. No stop after "F"	25·00	25·00
E 4		1 a. carmine	1·10	80
E 5	**59**	2 a. mauve	50	30
		a. No stop after "F"	50·00	50·00
		b. No stop after "E"	£100	£100
E 6	**61**	2½ a. ultramarine	70	1·00
		a. No stop after "F"	£100	£110
E 7	**62**	3 a. orange-brown	70	60
		a. No stop after "F"	£100	£110
E 8	**63**	4 a. olive-green	60	60
		a. No stop after "F"	£120	£130
E 9	**65**	8 a. purple	1·00	1·00
		a. No stop after "F"	£150	£160
E10		8 a. mauve	6·00	7·00
E11	**66**	12 a. dull claret	6·00	8·50
		a. No stop after "F"	£170	£180
		b. Opt double, one albino	50·00	
E12		12 a. claret	2·25	5·00
E13	**67**	1 r. red-brown and blue-green	2·50	4·00
		a. Opt double, one albino	£100	
E1/13		*Set of* 10	8·00	12·00

INDIAN CUSTODIAN FORCES IN KOREA

भारतीय
संरक्षा कटक
कोरिया

(K 1)

1953 (17 Oct). *Stamps of India optd with Type* K **1**.

K 1	**307**	3 p. slate-violet	40	2·00
K 2	**308**	6 p. purple-brown	40	2·00
K 3	**309**	9 p. yellow-green	40	2·00
K 4	**328**	1 a. turquoise	45	2·00
K 5	**311**	2 a. carmine	90	2·00
K 6	**313**	2½ a. lake	1·00	3·50
K 7	**312**	3 a. brown-orange	1·25	3·50
K 8	**314**	4 a. bright blue	1·75	4·00
K 9	**315**	6 a. violet	5·00	8·50
K10	**316**	8 a. turquoise-green	3·25	8·50
K11	**317**	12 a. dull blue	4·50	14·00
K12	**318**	1 r. dull violet and green	6·00	17·00
K1/12		*Set of* 12	20·00	60·00

INDIAN U.N. FORCE IN CONGO

U.N. FORCE
(INDIA)
CONGO

(U 1)

1962 (15 Jan). *Stamps of India optd with Type* U **1**. *W* **69** *(sideways) (13 n.p.) or W* **374** *(others).*

U1	**361**	1 n.p. blue-green	30	60
U2		2 n.p. light brown	35	50
U3		5 n.p. bright green	35	35
U4		8 n.p. light blue-green	50	30
U5		13 n.p. bright carmine-red	55	40
U6		50 n.p. orange	60	70
U1/6		*Set of* 6	2·40	2·50

INDIAN U.N. FORCE IN GAZA (PALESTINE) UNEF

UNEF

(G 1)

1965 (15 Jan). *No.* 492 *of India optd with Type* G **1**.

G1	**449**	15 p. slate (C.)	15	1·25

INTERNATIONAL COMMISSION IN INDO-CHINA

अन्तर्राष्ट्रीय आयोग कम्बोज (N 1) — अन्तर्राष्ट्रीय आयोग लाओस (N 2) — अन्तर्राष्ट्रीय आयोग वियत नाम (N 3)

1954 (1 Dec). *Stamps of India. W* **69**.

(*a*) *Optd as Type* N **1**, *for use in Cambodia*

N 1	**307**	3 p. slate-violet	30	1·25
N 2	**328**	1 a. turquoise	65	75
N 3	**311**	2 a. carmine	70	80
N 4	**316**	8 a. turquoise-green	2·00	3·50
N 5	**317**	12 a. dull blue	2·25	4·00

(b) Optd as Type N 2, for use in Laos

N 6 **307** 3 p. slate-violet .. .. 30 1·25
N 7 **328** 1 a. turquoise 65 75
N 8 **311** 2 a. carmine 70 80
N 9 **316** 8 a. turquoise-green .. .. 2·00 3·50
N10 **317** 12 a. dull blue .. .. 2·25 4·00

(c) Optd as Type N 3, for use in Vietnam

N11 **307** 3 p. slate-violet .. .. 30 1·25
N12 **328** 1 a. turquoise 65 75
N13 **311** 2 a. carmine 70 80
N14 **316** 8 a. turquoise-green .. .. 2·00 3·50
N15 **317** 12 a. dull blue .. .. 2·25 4·00
N1/15 .. .. *Set of* 15 15·00 28·00

1957 (1 Apr). *Stamps of India. W* **69** *(sideways).*

(a) Optd as Type N 1, for use in Cambodia

N16 **361** 2 n.p. light brown 20 20
N17 6 n.p. grey 35 25
N18 13 n.p. bright carmine-red 50 40
N19 50 n.p. orange .. .. 1·25 1·25
N20 75 n.p. reddish purple .. .. 1·50 1·25

(b) Optd as Type N 2, for use in Laos

N21 **361** 2 n.p. light brown 20 20
N22 6 n.p. grey 35 25
N23 13 n.p. bright carmine-red 50 40
N24 50 n.p. orange .. .. 1·25 1·25
N25 75 n.p. reddish purple .. .. 1·50 1·25

(c) Optd as Type N 3, for use in Vietnam

N26 **361** 2 n.p. light brown 20 20
N27 6 n.p. grey 35 25
N28 13 n.p. bright carmine-red 50 40
N29 50 n.p. orange .. .. 1·25 1·25
N30 75 n.p. reddish purple .. .. 1·50 1·25
N16/30 .. .. *Set of* 15 10·00 9·00

1962–65. *Stamps of India. W* **374**.

(a) Optd as Type N 1, for use in Cambodia

N32 **361** 2 n.p. light brown .. .. 15 2·25

(b) Optd as Type N 2, for use in Laos

N38 **361** 2 n.p. light brown .. .. 15 2·25
N39 3 n.p. deep brown (1.8.63) 10 20
N40 5 n.p. bright green (1.8.63) 10 15
N41 50 n.p. orange (1965) .. .. 1·50 2·25
N42 75 n.p. reddish purple (1965) .. .. .. 1·50 2·50

(c) Optd as Type N 3, for use in Vietnam

N43 **361** 1 n.p. blue-green 10 20
N44 2 n.p. light brown .. .. 15 2·25
N45 3 n.p. deep brown (1963?) 10 20
N46 5 n.p. bright green (1963) 10 15
N47 50 n.p. orange (1965) .. .. 1·50 2·25
N48 75 n.p. reddish-purple (1965) .. .. .. 1·50 2·50
N32/48 .. .. *Set of* 12 6·00 15·00

ICC (N 4) ICC (N 5)

1965 (15 Jan). *No. 492 of India optd with Type N 4, for use in Laos and Vietnam.*

N49 **449** 15 p. slate (C.) .. .. 20 1·25

1968 (2 Oct). *Nos. 504/5, 506, 509/10, 515 and 517/18 etc of India optd as Type N* **5**, *in red, for use in Laos and Vietnam.*

N50 2 p. red-brown 10 55
N51 3 p. brown-olive 10 55
N52 5 p. cerise 10 20
N53 10 p. new blue 50 50
N54 15 p. bronze-green 50 50
N55 60 p. deep grey 35 90
N56 1 r. red-brown and plum .. .. .. 50 1·25
N57 2 r. new blue and deep slate-violet .. .. 1·00 3·50
N50/7 .. .. *Set of* 8 2·75 7·00

INDIAN NATIONAL ARMY

The following are stated to have been used in the Japanese-occupied areas of India during the drive on Imphal. Issued by the Indian National Army.

Typo. No gum. Perf 11½ or imperf. 1 p. violet, 1 p. maroon, 1 a. green.

JAPANESE OCCUPATION OF THE ANDAMAN AND NICOBAR ISLANDS

The Andaman Islands in the Bay of Bengal were occupied on the 23 March 1942 and the Nicobar Islands in July 1942. Civil administration was resumed in October 1945.

The following Indian stamps were surcharged with large figures preceded by a decimal point:—

Postage stamps—.3 on ½ a. (No. 248), .5 on 1 a. (No. 250), .10 on 2 a. (No. 236*b*), .30 on 6 a. (No. 274).

Official stamps—.10 on 1 a. 3 p. (No. O146*b*), .20 on 3 p. (No. O143) from booklet panes, .20 in red on 3 p. (No. O143).

INDIAN CONVENTION STATES

The following issues resulted from a series of postal conventions agreed between the Imperial Government and the state administrations of Patiala (1 October 1884), Gwalior, Jind and Nabha (1 July 1885), and Chamba and Faridkot (1 January 1887).

Under the terms of these conventions the British Indian Post Office supplied overprinted British India issues to the state administrations which, in turn, had to conform to a number of conditions covering the issue of stamps, rates of postage and the exchange of mail.

Such overprinted issues were valid for postage within the state of issue, to other "Convention States" and to destinations in British India.

Stamps of Chamba, Gwalior, Jind, Nabha and Patiala ceased to be valid for postage on 1 January 1951, when they were replaced by those of the Republic of India, valid from 1 April 1950.

Stamps of India overprinted

In the Queen Victoria issues we omit varieties due to broken type, including the numerous small "A" varieties which may have come about through damaged type. We do, however, list the small "G", small "R" and tall "R" in "GWALIOR" as these were definitely the result of the use of type of the wrong size.

Variations in the length of the words due to unequal spacing when setting are also omitted.

CHAMBA

PRICES FOR STAMPS ON COVER

Nos. 1/27	*from* × 12
Nos. 28/120	*from* × 8
Nos. O1/86	*from* × 15

CHAMBA STATE (1) CHAMBA (2)

1886–95. *Queen Victoria. Optd with T* **1**.

1 **23** ½ a. blue-green 10 20
a. "CHMABA" £125 £140
b. "8TATE" £190
c. Opt double .. ..
2 **25** 1 a. brown-purple 15 30
a. "CHMABA" £250 £275
b. "8TATE" £275
3 1 a. plum 40 35
4 **26** 1½ a. sepia (1895) .. .. 60 2·50
5 **27** 2 a. dull blue 30 65
b. "CHMABA" £700 £750
c. "8TATE" £700
6 2 a. ultramarine 45 85
7 **36** 2½ a. green (1895) .. .. 13·00 28·00
8 **28** 3 a. orange (1887) .. .. 3·00 8·00
9 3 a. brown-orange (1891) .. .. .. 40 1·25
a. "CHMABA" £1600 £1600
b. Opt inverted .. ..
10 **29** 4 a. olive-green .. .. 50 1·40
a. "CHMABA" £600 £700
b. "8TATE" £850
11 4 a. slate-green .. .. 1·10 2·25
12 **21** 6 a. olive-bistre (1890) .. .. .. 90 2·50
13 6 a. bistre-brown .. .. 1·75 3·50
14 **31** 8 a. dull mauve (1887) .. .. .. 2·00 4·00
a. "CHMABA" £1400 £1500
15 8 a. magenta (1895) .. .. 1·25 3·25
16 **32** 12 a. purple/*red* (1890) .. .. .. 1·60 3·25
a. "CHMABA" £1900
b. "SLATE" £2500
17 **33** 1 r. slate (1887) .. .. 19·00 45·00
a. "CHMABA" £3500
18 **37** 1 r. green and carmine (1895) .. .. 1·25 3·25
19 **38** 2 r. carmine and yellow-brown (1895) .. 42·00 80·00
20 3 r. brown and green (1895) .. .. 48·00 80·00
21 5 r. ultramarine and violet (1895) .. 55·00 95·00
a. Opt double, one albino .. .. .. 95·00
1/21 .. .. *Set of* 15 £160 £300

1900–4. *Colours changed.*

22 **40** 3 p. carmine 10 20
23 3 p. grey (1904) 15 45
a. Opt inverted .. .. 45·00
24 **23** ½ a. pale yellow-green (1902) 15 45
25 ½ a. yellow-green (1903) 10 30
26 **25** 1 a. carmine (1902) 10 20
27 **27** 2 a. pale violet (1903) .. .. .. 5·00 10·00
22/7 .. .. *Set of* 5 5·00 10·50

1903–5. *King Edward VII. Optd with T* **1**.

28 **41** 3 p. pale grey 10 30
29 3 p. slate-grey (1905) 10 30
30 **42** ½ a. green 10 20
31 **43** 1 a. carmine 10 15
32 **44** 2 a. pale violet (1904) 25 60
33 2 a. mauve 30 55
34 **46** 3 a. orange-brown (1905) .. .. .. 70 1·50
35 **47** 4 a. olive (1904) .. .. 90 2·25
36 **48** 6 a. olive-bistre (1905) .. .. .. 1·40 3·75
37 **49** 8 a. dull mauve (1904) .. .. .. 1·25 3·50
38 8 a. magenta .. .. 2·50 5·50
39 **50** 12 a. purple/*red* (1905) .. .. .. 1·60 4·50
40 **51** 1 r. green and carmine (1904) .. .. 1·75 4·75
28/40 .. .. *Set of* 10 7·50 19·00

1907. *Nos. 149/50 of India optd with T* **1**.

41 **53** ½ a. green 15 60
42 **54** 1 a. carmine 20 60

1913. *King George V optd with T* **1**.

43 **55** 3 p. slate-grey 10 25
44 **56** ½ a. green 10 25
45 **57** 1 a. rose-carmine 50 70
46 1 a. aniline carmine 10 30
47 **59** 2 a. mauve 25 80
48 **62** 3 a. orange-brown .. .. 50 1·60
49 **63** 4 a. olive .. .. 60 1·25
50 **64** 6 a. olive-bistre .. .. 60 2·00
51 **65** 8 a. purple .. .. 80 2·75
52 **66** 12 a. dull claret .. .. 1·25 4·75
53 **67** 1 r. brown and green .. .. .. 4·00 6·00
a. Opt double, one albino .. .. .. 25·00
43/53 .. .. *Set of* 10 7·50 18·00

1921. *No. 192 of India optd with T* **2**.

54 **57** 9 p. on 1 a. rose-carmine .. .. .. 80 5·50

1923–27. *Optd with T* **1**. *New values, etc.*

55 **57** 1 a. chocolate 10 50
56 **58** 1½ a. chocolate (Type A) .. .. .. 13·00 40·00
57 1½ a. chocolate (Type B) (1924) .. .. 25 1·50
58 1½ a. rose-carmine (Type B) (1927) .. .. 60 3·25
59 **61** 2½ a. ultramarine .. .. 50 2·50
60 2½ a. orange (1927) .. .. 70 3·25
61 **62** 3 a. ultramarine (1924) .. .. .. 1·10 4·00
55/61 .. .. *Set of* 7 14·50 50·00

Nos. 58 and 60 with inverted overprint are of clandestine origin.

CHAMBA STATE (3) CHAMBA STATE (4)

1927–37. *King George V (Nasik printing, wmk Mult Star). Optd at Nasik with T* **3** *or* **4** *(1 r.).*

62 **55** 3 p. slate (1928) 10 30
63 **56** ½ a. green (1928) 10 40
64 **80** 9 p. deep green (1932) .. .. .. 45 1·75
65 **57** 1 a. chocolate 10 10
66 **82** 1¼ a. mauve (1932) 25 65
67 **58** 1½ a. rose-carmine (B) (1932) .. .. 65 1·75
68 **70** 2 a. purple (1928) 30 55
69 **61** 2½ a. orange (1932) .. .. 40 1·90
70 **62** 3 a. bright blue (1928) .. .. .. 60 2·75
71 **71** 4 a. sage-green (1928) .. .. .. 40 1·00
72 **64** 6 a. bistre (1937) .. .. 24·00 65·00
73 **65** 8 a. reddish purple (1928) .. .. .. 60 2·75
74 **66** 12 a. claret (1928) .. .. 85 3·75
75 **67** 1 r. chocolate and green (1928) .. .. 2·25 5·50
62/75 .. .. *Set of* 14 28·00 80·00

The 9 p. exists printed by lithography or typography.

1935–36. *New types and colours. Optd with T* **3**.

76 **79** ½ a. green .. .. 25 1·40
77 **81** 1 a. chocolate 30 40
78 **59** 2 a. vermilion (No. 236*a*) .. .. .. 20 3·00
79 2 a. vermilion (*small die*, No. 236*b*) .. 65·00 70·00
80 **62** 3 a. carmine .. .. 1·00 2·50
81 **63** 4 a. sage-green (1936) .. .. .. 80 1·90
76/81 .. .. *Set of* 6 65·00 70·00

CHAMBA STATE (5) CHAMBA (6) CHAMBA (7)

1938. *King George VI. Nos. 247/64 optd with T* **3** *(3 p. to 1 a.), T* **5** *(2 a. to 12 a.) or T* **4** *(rupee values).*

82 **91** 3 p. slate .. .. 1·25 2·50
83 ½ a. red-brown .. .. 60 1·60
84 9 p. green .. .. 1·25 3·25
85 1 a. carmine 80 65
86 **92** 2 a. vermilion .. .. 1·10 3·50
87 – 2½ a. bright violet .. .. 1·25 5·00
88 – 3 a. yellow-green .. .. 3·75 7·50
89 – 3½ a. bright blue .. .. 1·75 6·50
90 – 4 a. brown .. .. 5·00 5·00
91 – 6 a. turquoise-green .. .. 7·00 15·00
92 – 8 a. slate-violet .. .. 4·50 10·00
93 – 12 a. lake .. .. 3·00 14·00
94 **93** 1 r. grey and red-brown .. .. .. 12·00 18·00
95 2 r. purple and brown .. .. .. 20·00 50·00
96 5 r. green and blue .. .. 42·00 85·00
97 10 r. purple and claret .. .. .. 95·00 £190
98 15 r. brown and green £180 £325
99 25 r. slate-violet and purple £275 £450
82/99 .. .. *Set of* 18 £600 £1000

1942–47. *Optd with T* **6** *(to 12 a.), "CHAMBA" only, as in T* **5** *(14 a.) or T* **7** *(rupee values). (a) Stamps of 1937.*

100 **91** ½ a. red-brown .. .. 5·00 5·50
101 1 a. carmine .. .. 6·00 6·50
102 **93** 1 r. grey and red-brown .. .. .. 18·00 20·00
103 2 r. purple and brown .. .. .. 20·00 50·00
104 5 r. green and blue .. .. 45·00 80·00
105 10 r. purple and claret .. .. .. 75·00 £160
106 15 r. brown and green £180 £275
107 25 r. slate-violet and purple £275 £400
100/107 .. .. *Set of* 8 £550 £900

(b) Stamps of 1940–43

108 **100*a*** 3 p. slate .. .. 40 1·10
109 ½ a. purple (1943) 50 80
110 9 p. green .. .. 40 1·50
111 1 a. carmine (1943) 80 90
112 **101** 1½ a. dull violet (1943) .. .. .. 60 2·25
113 2 a. vermilion (1943) .. .. .. 1·25 2·50
114 3 a. bright violet .. .. 1·60 3·50
115 3½ a. bright blue .. .. 2·25 7·50
116 **102** 4 a. brown .. .. 2·50 3·75
117 6 a. turquoise-green .. .. 4·50 13·00
118 8 a. slate-violet .. .. 5·50 14·00
119 12 a. lake .. .. 8·50 20·00
120 **103** 14 a. purple (1947) .. .. 4·00 4·00
108/120 .. .. *Set of* 13 28·00 65·00

The 3 a. exists printed by lithography or typography.

OFFICIAL STAMPS

SERVICE

CHAMBA STATE (O 1)

1886–98. *Queen Victoria. Optd with Type* O 1.
O 1 **23** ½ a. blue-green 10 10
a. "CHMABA" .. .. .. 90·00 95·00
b. "SERV CE" £350
c. "8TATE" £180
O 2 **25** 1 a. brown-purple 20 20
a. "CHMABA" £160 £170
b. "SERV CE" £500
c. "8TATE" £250
d. "SERVICE" double £275 £275
O 3 **25** 1 a. plum 20 10
O 4 **27** 2 a. dull blue 50 70
a. "CHMABA" £475 £525
O 5 2 a. ultramarine (1887) 40 70
O 6 **28** 3 a. orange (1890) .. ..
O 7 3 a. brown-orange (1891) .. .. 1·25 3·50
a. "CHMABA" £1000 £1100
O 8 **29** 4 a. olive-green 45 90
a. "CHMABA" £475 £525
b. "SERV CE" £1100
c. "8TATE" £900
O 9 4 a. slate-green .. .. .. 65 1·10
O10 **21** 6 a. olive-bistre (1890) .. .. 1·25 3·25
O11 6 a. bistre-brown .. ..
O12 **31** 8 a. dull mauve (1887) .. .. 70 1·60
a. "CHMABA" £1500 £1600
O13 8 a. magenta (1895) .. .. 70 1·25
O14 **32** 12 a. purple/*red* (1890) .. .. 7·00 15·00
a. "CHMABA" £1900
b. "SLATE" .. ..
O15 **33** 1 r. slate (1890) .. .. .. 11·00 30·00
a. "CHMABA" £1600
O16 **37** 1 r. green and carmine (1898) .. 4·75 9·50
O1/16 .. .. *Set of* 10 24·00 55·00

Printings up to and including that of December 1895 had the "SERVICE" overprint applied to sheets of stamps already overprinted with Type **1**. From the printing of September 1898 onwards both "SERVICE" and "CHAMBA STATE" were overprinted at the same time. Nos. O6, O8 and O12 only exist using the first method, and No. O16 was only printed using the second.

1902–4. *Colours changed. Optd as Type* O 1.
O17 **40** 3 p. grey (1904) 15 35
O18 **23** ½ a. pale yellow-green 15 75
O19 ½ a. yellow-green 60 35
O20 **25** 1 a. carmine 15 40
O21 **27** 2 a. pale violet (1903) .. .. 5·00 8·50
O17/21 .. .. *Set of* 4 5·25 9·00

1903–5. *King Edward VII. Stamps of India optd as Type* O 1.
O22 **41** 3 p. pale grey 15 10
O23 3 p. slate-grey (1905) 10 25
O24 **42** ½ a. yellow-green 10 10
O25 **43** 1 a. carmine 10 10
O26 **44** 2 a. pale violet (1904) 75 40
O27 2 a. mauve 40 40
O28 **47** 4 a. olive (1905) .. .. .. 1·25 3·00
O29 **49** 8 a. dull mauve (1905) .. .. 1·25 3·50
O30 8 a. magenta .. .. .. 3·50 5·00
O31 **51** 1 r. green and carmine (1905) .. 1·25 2·75
O22/31 .. .. *Set of* 7 4·00 9·00

The 2 a. mauve King Edward VII, overprinted "On H.M.S.", was discovered in Calcutta, but was not sent to Chamba, and is an unissued variety. (*Price un.* £18.)

1907. *Nos.* 149/50 *of India, optd with Type* O 1.
O32 **53** ½ a. green 15 20
a. Opt inverted £1400 £1400
O33 **54** 1 a. carmine 40 40

The error, No. O32a was due to an inverted cliché which was corrected after a few sheets had been printed.

1913–14. *King George V Official stamps (wmk Single Star) optd with T* 1.
O34 **55** 3 p. slate-grey 10 15
O35 3 p. grey 15 25
O36 **56** ½ a. yellow-green 10 10
O37 ½ a. pale blue-green 20 15
O38 **57** 1 a. aniline carmine 10 10
O39 1 a. rose-carmine .. .. .. 1·00 20
O40 **59** 2 a. mauve (1914) .. .. .. 75 2·25
O41 **63** 4 a. olive .. .. 65 2·00
O42 **65** 8 a. purple .. .. 1·10 3·00
O43 **67** 1 r. brown and green (1914) .. 2·50 5·50
a. Opt double, one albino .. ..
O34/43 .. .. *Set of* 7 4·75 11·50

No. O36 with inverted overprint and No. O39 with double or inverted overprint (on gummed side) are of clandestine origin.

1914. *King George V. Optd with Type* O 1.
O44 **59** 2 a. mauve .. .. 5·00
O45 **63** 4 a. olive .. .. 10·00

1921. *No.* O97 *of India optd with T* 2 *at top.*
O46 **57** 9 p. on 1 a. rose-carmine .. .. 15 1·50

1925. *As* 1913–14. *New colour.*
O47 **57** 1 a. chocolate 35 40

CHAMBA STATE
SERVICE
(O 2)

CHAMBA STATE
SERVICE
(O 3)

1927–39. *King George V (Nasik printing, wmk Mult Star), optd at Nasik with Type* O 2 *or* O 3 *(rupee values).*
O48 **55** 3 p. slate (1928) 15 25
O49 **56** ½ a. green (1928) 25 15
O50 **80** 9 p. deep green(1932) .. .. 30 2·00
O51 **57** 1 a. chocolate 10 10
O52 **82** 1¼ a. mauve (1932) .. .. .. 1·10 40
O53 **70** 2 a. purple (1928) 40 40
O54 **71** 4 a. sage-green (1928) 40 40
O55 **65** 8 a. reddish purple (1930) .. .. 1·25 2·75
O56 **66** 12 a. claret (1928) .. .. .. 1·10 5·00
O57 **67** 1 r. chocolate and green (1930) .. 6·00 7·00
O58 2 r. carmine and orange (1939) .. 11·00
O59 5 r. ultramarine and purple (1939) .. 24·00
O60 10 r. green and scarlet (1939) .. 32·00
O48/60 .. .. *Set of* 13 70·00

1935–39. *New types and colours. Optd with Type* O 2.
O61 **79** ½ a. green 25 30
O62 **81** 1 a. chocolate 40 30
O63 **59** 2 a. vermilion .. .. .. 1·25 80
O64 2 a. vermilion (*small die*) (1939) .. 60 2·25
O65 **63** 4 a. sage-green (1936) .. .. 60 1·00
O61/5 .. .. *Set of* 5 2·75 4·25

1938–40. *King George VI. Optd with Type* O 2 *or* O 3 *(rupee values).*
O66 **91** 9 p. green .. .. 2·75 3·75
O67 1 a. carmine .. .. 2·00 1·00
O68 **93** 1 r. grey and red-brown (1940?) .. £550 £650
O69 2 r. purple and brown (1939) .. 35·00 80·00
O70 5 r. green and blue (1939) .. .. 60·00 £130
O71 10 r. purple and claret (1939) .. £110 £225
O66/71 .. .. *Set of* 6 £700 £950

CHAMBA
SERVICE
(O 4)

1940–43. (*a*) *Official stamps optd with T* 6.
O72 **O 20** 3 p. slate 55 40
O73 ½ a. red-brown .. .. .. 4·00 2·00
O74 ½ a. purple (1943) 60 60
O75 9 p. green .. .. 75 1·25
O76 1 a. carmine (1941) 55 50
O77 1 a. 3 p. yellow-brown (1941) .. 20·00 10·00
O78 1½ a. dull violet (1943) .. .. 2·75 2·00
O79 2 a. vermilion .. .. .. 1·75 1·40
O80 2½ a. bright violet (1941) .. .. 1·25 4·50
O81 4 a. brown .. .. 2·50 3·50
O82 8 a. slate-violet .. .. .. 4·50 7·00

(*b*) *Postage stamps optd with Type* O 4.
O83 **93** 1 r. grey and red-brown (1942) .. 20·00 32·00
O84 2 r. purple and brown (1942) .. 30·00 50·00
O85 5 r. green and blue (1942) .. 60·00 90·00
O86 10 r. purple and claret (1942) .. £110 £160
O72/86 .. .. *Set of* 15 £225 £325

FARIDKOT

For earlier issues, see under INDIAN FEUDATORY STATES

PRICES FOR STAMPS ON COVER

Nos. 1/17	*from* × 20
Nos. O1/15	*from* × 25

FARIDKOT
STATE
(1)

1887 (1 Jan)–**1900.** *Queen Victoria. Optd with T* 1.
1 **23** ½ a. deep green 15 30
a. "ARIDKOT" .. .. ..
b. "FAR DKOT" .. .. .. — £350
2 **25** 1 a. brown-purple 35 75
3 1 a. plum 50 60
4 **27** 2 a. blue .. .. 1·25 2·00
5 2 a. deep blue .. .. .. 1·40 2·75
6 **28** 3 a. orange .. .. 2·25 3·00
7 3 a. brown-orange (1893) .. .. 1·00 1·75
8 **29** 4 a. olive-green .. .. .. 1·60 3·75
a. "ARIDKOT" £425
9 4 a. slate-green .. .. .. 1·60 5·00
10 **21** 6 a. olive-bistre .. .. .. 5·50 10·00
a. "ARIDKOT" £500
11 6 a. bistre-brown .. .. .. 1·75 5·50
12 **31** 8 a. dull mauve .. .. .. 2·50 9·50
a. "ARIDKOT" £850
13 8 a. magenta .. .. 4·00 18·00
14 **32** 12 a. purple/*red* (1900) .. .. 25·00 90·00
15 **33** 1 r. slate .. .. 22·00 70·00
a. "ARIDKOT" £1400
16 **37** 1 r. green and carmine (1893) .. 12·00 20·00
1/16 .. .. *Set of* 10 60·00 £180

The ½ a., 1 a., 2 a., 3 a., 4 a., 8 a. and 1 r. (No. 16) are known with broken "O" (looking like a "C") in "FARIDKOT".

1900. *Optd with T* 1.
17 **40** 3 p. carmine .. .. 50 7·00

OFFICIAL STAMPS

SERVICE

FARIDKOT
STATE
(O 1)

1886–98. *Queen Victoria. Optd with Type* O 1.
O 1 **23** ½ a. deep green 15 30
a. "SERV CE" £450
O 2 **25** 1 a. brown-purple 40 75
O 3 1 a. plum 45 55
a. "SERV CE" £550
O 4 **27** 2 a. dull blue .. .. .. 80 3·25
a. "SERV CE" £650
O 5 2 a. deep blue .. .. .. 70 3·25
O 6 **28** 3 a. orange .. .. 3·00 3·25
O 7 3 a. brown-orange (12.98) .. .. 1·00 6·50
O 8 **29** 4 a. olive-green .. .. .. 1·40 4·25
a. "SERV CE" £750
b. "ARIDKOT" .. .. ..
O 9 4 a. slate-green .. .. .. 2·25 7·50
O10 **21** 6 a. olive-bistre .. .. .. 18·00 28·00
a. "ARIDKOT" £400
b. "SERVIC" £700
O11 **21** 6 a. bistre-brown .. .. .. 10·00 12·00
O12 **31** 8 a. dull mauve .. .. .. 2·25 7·00
a. "SERV CE" £900
O13 8 a. magenta .. .. 4·50 20·00
O14 **33** 1 r. slate .. .. 22·00 48·00
O15 **37** 1 r. green and carmine (12.98) .. 38·00 £100
O1/15 .. .. *Set of* 9 65·00 £160

The ½ a., 1 a., 2 a., 3 a., 4 a., 8 a. and 1 r. (No. O15) are known with the broken "O".

Printings up to and including that of November 1895 had the "SERVICE" overprint applied to sheets already overprinted with Type **1**. From December 1898 onwards "SERVICE" and "FARIDKOT STATE" were overprinted at one operation to provide fresh supplies of Nos. O1/3, O7 and O15.

This State ceased to use overprinted stamps after 31 March 1901.

GWALIOR

PRICES FOR STAMPS ON COVER

Nos. 1/3	*from* × 10
Nos. 4/11	—
Nos. 12/66	*from* × 5
Nos. 67/128	*from* × 4
Nos. 129/37	*from* × 5
Nos. O1/94	*from* × 10

OVERPRINTS. From 1885 to 1926 these were applied by the Government of India Central Printing Press, Calcutta, and from 1927 at the Security Press, Nasik, *unless otherwise stated.*

गवालियर

GWALIOR
(1)

GWALIOR
गवालियर
(2)

GWALIOR
Small "G"

GWALIOR
Small "R"

GWALIOR
Tall "R"
(original state)

GWALIOR
Tall "R"
(damaged state)

OVERPRINT VARIETIES OF TYPE 2.

Small "G"—Occurs on R.7/11 from June 1900 printing of ½, 1, 2, 3, 4 a. and 3 p. (No. 38), and on an unknown position from May 1901 printing of 2, 3 and 5 r.

Small "R"—Occurs on R. 9/3 from June 1900 printing of 3 p. to 4 a. and on R.2/3 from May 1901 printing of 2, 3 and 5 r.

Tall "R" —Occurs on R.20/2 from printings between June 1900 and May 1907. The top of the letter is damaged on printings from February 1903 onwards.

1885–97. *Queen Victoria.* I. *Optd. with T* 1.

(*a*) *Space between two lines of overprint* 13 *mm. Hindi inscription* 13 *to* 14 *mm long* (May 1885)
1 **23** ½ a. blue-green .. .. .. 32·00 11·00
2 **25** 1 a. brown-purple .. .. .. 38·00 16·00
3 **27** 2 a. dull blue .. .. .. 30·00 11·00
1/3 .. .. *Set of* 3 90·00 35·00

A variety exists of the ½ a. in which the space between the two lines of overprint is only 9½ mm but this is probably from a proof sheet.

(*b*) *Space between two lines of overprint* 15 *mm on* 4 *a. and* 6 *a. and* 16 *to* 17 *mm on other values* (June 1885)

A. *Hindi inscription* 13 *to* 14 *mm long*
B. *Hindi inscription* 15 *to* 15½ *mm long*

No.	Type	Value	A		B	
4	**23**	½ a. blue-green	20·00	—	35·00	—
5	**25**	1 a. brown-purple	24·00	—	45·00	—
6	**26**	1½ a. sepia	32·00	—	55·00	—
7	**27**	2 a. dull blue	24·00	—	45·00	—
8	**17**	4 a. green	35·00	—	70·00	—
9	**21**	6 a. olive-bistre	35·00	—	70·00	—
10	**31**	8 a. dull mauve	32·00	—	65·00	—
11	**33**	1 r. slate	32·00	—	65·00	—
4/11		*Set of* 8	£200	—	£400	—

The two types of overprint on these stamps occur in the same settings, with about a quarter of the stamps in each sheet showing the long inscription (B). Nos. 4/7 and 10/11 were overprinted in sheets of 240 and Nos. 8/9 in sheets of 320. *Se-tenant* pairs exist and are rare.

II. *Optd with T* 2

A. *Hindi inscription* 13 *to* 14 *mm long*
B. *Hindi inscription* 15 *to* 15½ *mm long*

(*a*) *In red* (Sept 1885)

No.	Type	Value	A		B	
12	**23**	½ a. blue-green	20	20	35	50
13	**27**	2 a. dull blue	6·00	6·00	14·00	14·00
14	**17**	4 a. green	12·00	9·00	35·00	30·00
15	**33**	1 r. slate	7·50	9·50	20·00	24·00
12/15		*Set of* 4	22·00	22·00	60·00	60·00

No. 14 was overprinted in sheets of 320, about 80 stamps being Type B. The remaining three values were from a setting of 240 containing 166 as Type A and 74 as Type B.

Reprints have been made of Nos. 12 to 15, but the majority of the specimens have the word "REPRINT" overprinted upon them.

(b) In black (1885–97)

			A		B	
16 **23**	½ a. blue-green (1889)	35	25	15	10
	a. Opt double	—	—	£300	—
	b. "GWALICR"	†		50·00	60·00
	c. Small "G"	†		35·00	35·00
	d. Small "R"	†		35·00	—
	e. Tall "R"	†		35·00	35·00
17 **24**	9 p. carmine (1891)	26·00	40·00	40·00	50·00
18 **25**	1 a. brown-purple	15	15	35	20
19	1 a. plum	†		25	10
	a. Small "G"	†		40·00	40·00
	d. Small "R"	†		40·00	—
	e. Tall "R"	†		40·00	—
20 **26**	1½ a. sepia	15	25	20	25
21 **27**	2 a. dull blue	1·50	70	30	10
	a. "R" omitted	†		£250	—
22	2 a. deep blue	2·25	1·10	90	20
	a. Small "G"	†		80·00	80·00
	d. Small "R"	†		80·00	—
	e. Tall "R"	†		80·00	80·00
23 **36**	2½ a. yellow-green (1896)	†		2·50	6·50
	a. "GWALICR"	†		£325	—
24 **28**	3 a. orange	2·75	2·25	14·00	8·50
25	3 a. brown-orange	2·00	1·10	30	15
	a. Small "G"	†		95·00	95·00
	d. Small "R"	†		£100	—
	e. Tall "R"	†		70·00	70·00
26 **29**	4 a. olive-green (1889)	1·50	75	1·25	75
27	4 a. slate-green	1·60	75	60	30
	a. Small "G"	†		£110	£110
	d. Small "R"	†		£110	—
	e. Tall "R"	†		90·00	—
28 **21**	6 a. olive-bistre	1·75	2·00	1·50	1·75
29	6 a. bistre-brown	45	1·40	60	1·50
30 **31**	8 a. dull mauve	4·50	7·50	55	55
31	8 a. magenta (1897)	†		2·50	2·25
32 **32**	12 a. purple/*red* (1891)	3·00	6·50	90	55
	a. Pair, with and without opt	†		—	—
	e. Tall "R"	†		£225	£225
33 **33**	1 r. slate (1889)	48·00	—	65	70
34 **37**	1 r. green and carmine (1896)	†		2·00	2·50
	a. "GWALICR"	†		£400	—
35 **38**	2 r. carmine and yellow-brown (1896)	†		5·00	3·00
	a. Small "G"	†		£120	£100
	d. Small "R"	†		£120	£100
36	3 r. brown and green (1896)	†		7·00	3·50
	a. Small "G"	†		£130	£110
	d. Small "R"	†		£130	£110
37	5 r. ultramarine and violet (1896)	†		12·00	6·50
	a. Small "G"	†		£140	£120
	d. Small "R"	†		£140	£120
16/37	*Set of* 16			50·00	60·00

Printings to 1891 continued to use the setting showing both types, but subsequently a new setting containing Type B overprints only was used.

The ½ a., 1 a., 2 a. and 3 a. exist with space between "I" and "O" of "GWALIOR".

1899–1911. *(a) Optd with T* **2** (B).

38 **40**	3 p. carmine	10	15
	a. Opt inverted	£300	£180
	b. Small "G"	35·00	35·00
	d. Small "R"	35·00	
	e. Tall "R"	22·00	
39	3 p. grey (1904)	5·50	30·00
	e. Tall "R"	£125	
40 **23**	½ a. pale yellow-green (1901)	10	35
	e. Tall "R"	40·00	
40*f*	½ a. yellow-green (1903)	55	1·25
	fe. Tall "R"	55·00	
41 **25**	1 a. carmine (1901)	15	35
	e. Tall "R"	45·00	
42 **27**	2 a. pale violet (1901)	35	90
	e. Tall "R"	65·00	
43 **36**	2½ a. ultramarine (1903)	65	1·25
	e. Tall "R"	80·00	
38/43	*Set of* 6	6·25	30·00

(b) Optd as T **2**, *but* "GWALIOR" 13 *mm long. Optd spaced* 2¾ *mm*

44 **38**	3 r. brown and green (1911)	75·00	85·00
45	5 r. ultramarine and violet (1910)	45·00	48·00

1903–11. *King Edward VII. Optd as T* **2**.

A. "GWALIOR" 14 *mm long. Overprint spaced* 1¾ *mm*
B. "GWALIOR" 13 *mm long. Overprint spaced* 2¾ *mm* (1908–11)

		A		B	
46 **41**	3 p. pale grey	10	10	35	10
	e. Tall "R"	13·00	—	†	
	f. Slate-grey (1905)	10	10	35	15
	fe. Tall "R"	17·00	—	†	
48 **42**	½ a. green	10	10	†	
	e. Tall "R"	13·00	14·00	†	
49 **43**	1 a. carmine	10	10	75	50
	e. Tall "R"	15·00	—	†	
50 **44**	2 a. pale violet (1904)	45	30	†	
	e. Tall "R"	30·00	—	†	
	f. Mauve	40	15	35	10
	fe. Tall "R"	35·00	—	†	
52 **45**	2½ a. ultramarine (1904)	7·50	20·00	45	2·50
	e. Tall "R"	£225	—	†	
53 **46**	3 a. orange-brown (1904)	50	15	80	10
	e. Tall "R"	55·00	—	†	
54 **47**	4 a. olive	1·10	40	†	
	e. Tall "R"	65·00	65·00	†	
	f. Pale olive	1·75	50	1·75	45
	fe. Tall "R"	80·00	—	†	
56 **48**	6 a. olive-bistre (1904)	2·25	1·75	2·25	60
	e. Tall "R"	£175	—	†	
57 **49**	8 a. dull mauve (1905)	1·40	65	3·00	1·25
	e. Tall "R"	£110	—	†	
	f. Magenta	†		6·00	1·25
59 **50**	12 a. purple/*red* (1905)	1·75	2·75	1·50	2·75
	e. Tall "R"	£200	—	†	
60 **51**	1 r. green & carmine (1905)	1·40	1·75	1·90	1·00
	e. Tall "R"	£200	—	†	
61 **52**	2 r. carmine and yellow-brown (1906)	30·00	38·00	8·50	10·00
62 **52**	3 r. brown and green (1910)	†		22·00	27·00
	a. Red-brown and green	†		29·00	35·00
63	5 r. ultram & vio (1911)	†		15·00	20·00
46/63	*Set of* 14			50·00	60·00

1907–08. *Nos.* 149 *and* 150 *of India optd as T* **2**.

(a) "GWALIOR" 14 *mm long. Overprint spaced* 1¾ *mm*

64 **53**	½ a. green	10	10
	e. Tall "R"	22·00	

(b) "GWALIOR" 13 *mm long. Overprint spaced* 2¾ *mm* (1908)

65 **53**	½ a. green	20	10
66 **54**	1 a. carmine	20	10

1912–14. *King George V. Optd as T* **2**.

67 **55**	3 p. slate-grey	10	10
	a. Opt double	†	£300
68 **56**	½ a. green	15	10
	a. Opt inverted	—	£225
69 **57**	1 a. aniline carmine	15	10
	a. Opt double	25·00	
70 **59**	2 a. mauve	25	10
71 **62**	3 a. orange-brown	40	15
72 **63**	4 a. olive (1913)	40	25
73 **64**	6 a. olive-bistre	65	55
74 **65**	8 a. purple (1913)	50	25
75 **66**	12 a. dull claret (1914)	75	1·10
76 **67**	1 r. brown and green (1913)	1·25	40
	a. Opt double, one albino	40·00	
	b. Opt double	£250	
77	2 r. carmine-rose and brown (1913)	4·50	1·50
	a. Opt double one albino	60·00	
78	5 r. ultramarine and violet (1913)	15·00	6·50
	a. Opt double, one albino	60·00	
67/78	*Set of* 12	21·00	10·00

GWALIOR
(3)

1921. *No.* 192 *of India optd with T* **3**.

79 **57**	9 p. on 1 a. rose-carmine	10	35

No. 79 with inverted overprint is of clandestine origin.

1923–7. *Optd as T* **2**. *New colours and values.*

80 **57**	1 a. chocolate	15	10
81 **58**	1½ a. chocolate (B) (1925)	45	45
82	1½ a. rose-carmine (B) (1927)	10	15
83 **61**	2½ a. ultramarine (1925)	70	1·00
84	2½ a. orange (1927)	20	30
85 **62**	3 a. ultramarine (1924)	35	45
80/5	*Set of* 6	1·75	2·25

No. 82 with inverted overprint is of clandestine origin.

GWALIOR
गवालियर
(4)

GWALIOR
गवालियर
(5)

1928–36. *King George V (Nasik printing, wmk Mult Star), optd at Nasik with T* **4** *or* **5** *(rupee values).*

86 **55**	3 p. slate (1932)	25	10
87 **56**	½ a. green (1930)	25	10
88 **80**	9 p. deep green (1932)	1·00	20
89 **57**	1 a. chocolate	15	10
90 **82**	1¼ a. mauve (1936)	15	10
91 **70**	2 a. purple	15	10
92 **62**	3 a. bright blue	40	35
93 **71**	4 a. sage-green	70	55
94 **65**	8 a. reddish purple	90	65
95 **66**	12 a. claret	85	1·25
96 **67**	1 r. chocolate and green	1·00	1·50
97	2 r. carmine and orange	2·50	2·50
98	5 r. ultramarine and purple (1929)	11·00	17·00
99	10 r. green and scarlet (1930)	24·00	30·00
100	15 r. blue and olive (1930)	42·00	48·00
101	25 r. orange and blue (1930)	75·00	80·00
86/101	*Set of* 16	£140	£160

The 9 p. exists printed by lithography or typography.

1935–36. *New types and colours. Optd with T* **4**.

102 **79**	½ a. green (1936)	15	10
103 **81**	1 a. chocolate	10	10
104 **59**	2 a. vermilion (1936)	25	70
102/4	*Set of* 3	45	80

1938–48. *King George VI. Nos.* 247/50, 253, 255/6, *and* 259/64 *optd with T* **4** *or* **5** *(rupee values).*

105 **91**	3 p. slate	2·00	10
106	½ a. red-brown	2·00	10
107	9 p. green (1939)	22·00	2·50
108	1 a. carmine	2·50	15
109 –	3 a. yellow-green (1939)	2·75	2·25
110 –	4 a. brown	15·00	1·25
111 –	6 a. turquoise-green (1939)	2·25	4·00
112 **93**	1 r. grey and red-brown (1942)	2·25	1·50
113	2 r. purple and brown (1948)	10·00	6·00
114	5 r. green and blue (1948)	38·00	22·00
115	10 r. purple and claret (1948)	38·00	35·00
116	15 r. brown and green (1948)	£100	£110
117	25 r. slate-violet and purple (1948)	95·00	90·00
105/117	*Set of* 13	£300	£250

1942–5. *King George VI. Optd with T* **4**.

118 **100a**	3 p. slate	35	10
119	½ a. purple (1943)	35	10
120	9 p. green	35	10
121	1 a. carmine (1943)	30	10
	a. Opt double	—	75·00
122 **101**	1½ a. dull violet	1·25	20
123	2 a. vermilion	45	20
124	3 a. bright violet	75	30
125 **102**	4 a. brown	65	20
126	6 a. turquoise-green (1945)	11·00	10·00
127	8 a. slate-violet (1944)	2·50	2·50
128	12 a. lake (1943)	5·00	8·50
118/128	*Set of* 11	21·00	20·00

The 1½ a. and 3 a. exist printed by lithography or typography.

GWALIOR
गवालियर
(6)

1949. *King George VI. Optd with T* **6** *at the Alizah Printing Press, Gwalior.*

129 **100a**	3 p. slate	60	50
130	½ a. purple	60	50
131	1 a. carmine	75	60
132 **101**	2 a. vermilion	7·00	1·50
133	3 a. bright violet	18·00	14·00
134 **102**	4 a. brown	2·00	2·50
135	6 a. turquoise-green	27·00	27·00
136	8 a. slate-violet	60·00	38·00
137	12 a. lake	£170	80·00
129/137	*Set of* 9	£250	£140

OFFICIAL STAMPS

गवालियर
सरविस
(O 1)

गवालियर
सरविस
(O 2)

1895–96. *Queen Victoria. Optd with Type* O 1.

O 1 **23**	½ a. blue-green	10	10
	a. Hindi characters transposed	19·00	19·00
	b. 4th Hindi character omitted	£125	30·00
	c. Opt double	—	£375
O 2 **25**	1 a. brown-purple	2·00	20
O 3	1 a. plum	65	10
	a. Hindi characters transposed	27·00	27·00
	b. 4th Hindi character omitted	—	40·00
O 4 **27**	2 a. dull blue	70	15
O 5	2 a. deep blue	80	15
	a. Hindi characters transposed	45·00	
	b. 4th Hindi character omitted	55·00	70·00
O 6 **29**	4 a. olive-green	1·40	60
	a. Hindi characters transposed	£190	£190
	b. 4th Hindi character omitted	—	£400
O 7	4 a. slate-green	1·00	45
	a. Hindi characters transposed	£170	
O 8 **31**	8 a. dull mauve	1·40	1·25
O 9	8 a. magenta	80	70
	a. Hindi characters transposed	£600	£650
	b. 4th Hindi character omitted		
O10 **37**	1 r. green and carmine (1896)	2·75	3·00
	a. Hindi characters transposed	£1100	
O1/10	*Set of* 6	5·25	4·00

In the errors listed above it is the last two Hindi characters that are transposed, so that the word reads "Sersiv". The error occurs on R.19/1 in the sheet from the early printings up to May 1896.

1901–04. *Colours changed.*

O23 **40**	3 p. carmine (1902)	20	30
O24	3 p. grey (1904)	75	1·25
O25 **23**	½ a. pale yellow-green	1·00	15
O26	½ a. yellow-green	15	10
O27 **25**	1 a. carmine	75	10
O28 **27**	2 a. pale violet (1903)	55	1·25
O23/8	*Set of* 5	2·10	2·75

1903–08. *King Edward VII. Optd as Type* O 1.

(a) Overprint spaced 10 *mm* (1903–5)

O29 **41**	3 p. pale grey	30	10
	a. Slate-grey (1905)	20	10
O31 **42**	½ a. green	70	10
O32 **43**	1 a. carmine	30	10
O33 **44**	2 a. pale violet (1905)	1·00	40
	a. Mauve	50	15
O35 **47**	4 a. olive (1905)	3·75	80
O36 **49**	8 a. dull mauve (1905)	2·50	70
	a. Magenta	3·25	1·40
O38 **51**	1 r. green and carmine (1905)	1·75	1·10
O29/38	*Set of* 7	8·75	2·50

(b) Overprint spaced 8 *mm* (1907–8)

O39 **41**	3 p. pale grey	1·50	15
	a. Slate-grey	2·00	40
O41 **42**	½ a. green	1·25	10
O42 **43**	1 a. carmine	35	10
O43 **44**	2 a. mauve	3·75	35
O44 **47**	4 a. olive	2·50	70
O45 **49**	8 a. dull mauve	2·75	2·75
O46 **51**	1 r. green and carmine (1908)	5·00	4·00
O39/46	*Set of* 7	15·00	7·00

1907–08. *Nos.* 149 *and* 150 *of India optd as Type* O 1.

(a) Overprint spaced 10 *mm* (1908)

O47 **53**	½ a. green	1·50	10
O48 **54**	1 a. carmine	1·50	10

(b) Overprint spaced 8 *mm* (1907)

O49 **53**	½ a. green	55	10
O50 **54**	1 a. carmine	20·00	3·00

1913-23. *King George V. Optd with Type* O 1.

O51 **55**	3 p. slate-grey	15	10
O52 **56**	½ a. green	15	10
	a. Opt double	65·00	
O53 **57**	1 a. rose-carmine	1·50	20
	a. Aniline carmine	15	10
	ab. Opt double	55·00	
O54	1 a. chocolate (1923)	1·40	10
O55 **59**	2 a. mauve	30	10
O56 **63**	4 a. olive	40	25
O57 **65**	8 a. purple	50	50
O58 **67**	1 r. brown and green	5·50	5·50
O51/58	*Set of* 8	7·50	6·00

1921. *No. O97 of India optd with T* **3**.
O59 **57** 9 p. on 1 a. rose-carmine 10 15

1927–35. *King George V (Nasik printing, wmk Mult Star), optd at Nasik as Type* O **1** *(but top line measures 13 mm instead of 14 mm) or with Type* O **2** *(rupee values).*
O61 **55** 3 p. slate 10 10
O62 **56** ½ a. green 10 10
O63 **80** 9 p. deep green (1932) 10 15
O64 **57** 1 a. chocolate 10 10
O65 **82** 1¼ a. mauve (1933) 35 15
O66 **70** 2 a. purple 15 15
O67 **71** 4 a. sage-green 35 25
O68 **65** 8 a. reddish purple (1928) 40 30
O69 **67** 1 r. chocolate and green 60 60
O70 2 r. carmine and orange (1935) 1·60 3·50
O71 5 r. ultramarine and purple (1932) 10·00 32·00
O72 10 r. green and scarlet (1932) 35·00 65·00
O61/72 *Set of* 12 45·00 90·00

1936–37. *New types. Optd as Type* O **1** *(13 mm).*
O73 **79** ½ a. green 10 10
O74 **81** 1 a. chocolate 10 10
O75 **59** 2 a. vermilion 15 15
O76 2 a. vermilion (*small die*) 1·25 70
O77 **63** 4 a. sage-green (1937) 30 30
O73/7 *Set of* 5 1·60 1·10

1938. *King George VI. Optd as Type* O **1** *(13 mm).*
O78 **91** ½ a. red-brown 2·75 25
O79 1 a. carmine 1·10 15

ग्वालियर (O 3) 1A——1A (O 4)

1940–42. *Official stamps optd with Type* O **3**.
O80 O **20** 3 p. slate 50 10
O81 ½ a. red-brown 2·50 25
O82 ½ a. purple (1942) 50 10
O83 9 p. green (1942) 70 45
O84 1 a. carmine 1·40 10
O85 1 a. 3 p. yellow-brown (1942) 4·50 1·60
O86 1½ a. dull violet (1942) 80 30
O87 2 a. vermilion 80 30
O88 4 a. brown (1942) 90 90
O89 8 a. slate-violet (1942) 2·25 2·50
O80/9 *Set of* 10 13·00 6·00

1942. *Stamp of 1932 (King George V) optd with Type* O **1** *and surch with Type* O **4**.
O90 **82** 1 a. on 1¼ a. mauve 5·00 2·25

1942–47. *King George VI. Optd with Type* O **2**.
O91 **93** 1 r. grey and red-brown 5·00 5·00
O92 2 r. purple and brown 14·00 24·00
O93 5 r. green and blue (1943) 38·00 85·00
O94 10 r. purple and claret (1947) 90·00 £170
O91/4 *Set of* 4 £130 £250

JIND

For earlier issues, see under INDIAN FEUDATORY STATES

PRICES FOR STAMPS ON COVER
Nos. 1/4 *from* × 15
Nos. 5/16 —
Nos. 17/40 *from* × 10
Nos. 41/149 *from* × 6
Nos. O1/86 *from* × 12

JHIND STATE (1) JEEND STATE (2) JHIND STATE (3)

1885. *Queen Victoria. Optd with T* **1**.
1 **23** ½ a. blue-green 45 1·00
a. Opt inverted 55·00 60·00
2 **25** 1 a. brown-purple 7·50 10·00
a. Opt inverted £325 £375
3 **27** 2 a. dull blue 4·00 6·00
a. Opt inverted £200
4 **17** 4 a. green 20·00 28·00
5 **31** 8 a. dull mauve £150
a. Opt inverted £2500
6 **33** 1 r. slate £150
a. Opt inverted £2500
1/6 *Set of* 6 £300

All six values exist with reprinted overprint. In these, words "JHIND" and "STATE" are 8 and 9 mm in length respectively, whereas in the originals the words are 9 and 9½ mm.

1885. *Optd with T* **2**.
7 **23** ½ a. blue-green (R.) 32·00
8 **25** 1 a. brown-purple 32·00
9 **27** 2 a. dull blue (R.) 40·00
10 **17** 4 a. green (R.) 55·00
11 **31** 8 a. dull mauve 60·00
12 **33** 1 r. slate (R.) 65·00
7/12 *Set of* 6 £250

1886. *Optd with T* **3**, *in red.*
13 **23** ½ a. blue-green 13·00
a. "JEIND" for "JHIND" £400
14 **27** 2 a. dull blue 14·00
a. "JEIND" for "JHIND" £500
15 **17** 4 a. green 17·00
a. Opt double, one albino 30·00
16 **33** 1 r. slate 28·00
a. "JEIND" for "JHIND" £1000
13/16 *Set of* 4 65·00

1886–99. *Optd with T* **3**.
17 **23** ½ a. blue-green (1888) 10 10
a. Opt inverted £150
18 **25** 1 a. brown-purple 15 10
a. "JEIND" for "JHIND" £250
19 1 a. plum (1899) 60 35
20 **26** 1½ a. sepia (1896) 50 85
21 **27** 2 a. dull blue (1891) 40 40
22 2 a. ultramarine 40 40
23 **28** 3 a. brown-orange (1891) 40 45
24 **29** 4 a. olive-green (1891) 90 80
25 4 a. slate-green 1·50 1·75
26 **21** 6 a. olive-bistre (1891) 2·00 3·75
27 6 a. bistre-brown 50 2·25
28 **31** 8 a. dull mauve 90 2·50
a. "JEIND" for "JHIND" £900
29 8 a. magenta (1897) 1·25 2·50
30 **32** 12 a. purple/*red* (1896) 1·25 3·00
31 **33** 1 r. slate (1891) 6·00 15·00
32 **37** 1 r. green and carmine (1897) 5·00 12·00
33 **38** 2 r. carmine and yellow-brown (1896) £120 £200
34 3 r. brown and green (1896) £175 £250
35 5 r. ultramarine and violet (1896) £225 £300
17/35 *Set of* 14 £475 £700

Varieties exist in which the word "JHIND" measures 10½ mm and 9¾ mm instead of 10 mm. Such varieties are to be found on Nos. 17, 18, 21, 24, 28 and 31.

1900–4. *Colours changed.*
36 **40** 3 p. carmine 15 50
37 3 p. grey (1904) 10 55
38 **23** ½ a. pale yellow-green (1902) 45 1·40
39 ½ a. yellow-green (1903) 1·75 3·50
40 **25** 1 a. carmine (1902) 15 1·40
36/40 *Set of* 4 75 3·50

1903–9. *King Edward VII. Optd with T* **3**.
41 **41** 3 p. pale grey 10 10
42 3 p. slate-grey (1905) 10 20
43 **42** ½ a. green 10 30
44 **43** 1 a. carmine 35 45
45 **44** 2 a. pale violet 55 70
46 2 a. mauve (1906) 35 55
47 **45** 2½ a. ultramarine (1909) 20 1·40
48 **46** 3 a. orange-brown 25 35
a. Opt double 85·00 £125
49 **47** 4 a. olive 90 1·50
50 4 a. pale olive 65 1·50
51 **48** 6 a. bistre (1905) 1·10 2·25
52 **49** 8 a. dull mauve 1·40 2·50
53 8 a. magenta 2·75 4·25
54 **50** 12 a. purple/*red* (1905) 1·40 3·00
55 **51** 1 r. green and carmine (1905) 1·60 2·75
41/55 *Set of* 11 6·75 13·00

1907–9. *Nos. 149/50 of India optd with T* **3**.
56 **53** ½ a. green 10 15
57 **54** 1 a. carmine (1909) 10 25

1913. *King George V. Optd with T* **3**.
58 **55** 3 p. slate-grey 10 70
59 **56** ½ a. green 10 45
60 **57** 1 a. aniline carmine 10 25
61 **59** 2 a. mauve 15 1·25
62 **62** 3 a. orange-brown 1·50 5·00
63 **64** 6 a. olive-bistre 3·25 11·00
58/63 *Set of* 6 4·75 16·00

JIND STATE (4) JIND STATE (5) JIND STATE (6)

1914–27. *King George V. Optd with T* **4**.
64 **55** 3 p. slate-grey 15 20
65 **56** ½ a. green 20 15
66 **57** 1 a. aniline carmine 15 15
67 **58** 1½ a. chocolate (Type A) (1922) 30 1·25
68 1½ a. chocolate (Type B) (1924) 30 1·25
69 **59** 2 a. mauve 25 45
70 **61** 2½ a. ultramarine (1922) 30 1·75
71 **62** 3 a. orange-brown 30 1·10
72 **63** 4 a. olive 30 1·25
73 **64** 6 a. olive-bistre 45 2·25
74 **65** 8 a. purple 60 1·75
75 **66** 12 a. dull claret 55 2·25
76 **67** 1 r. brown and green 2·25 3·75
a. Opt double, one albino 25·00
77 2 r. carmine and yellow-brown (1927) 4·00 16·00
78 5 r. ultramarine and violet (1927) 22·00 55·00
64/78 *Set of* 15 28·00 80·00

No. 71 with inverted overprint is of clandestine origin.

1922. *No. 192 of India optd "JIND" in block capitals.*
79 **57** 9 p. on 1 a. rose-carmine 1·75 6·50

1924–27. *Optd with T* **4**. *New colours.*
80 **57** 1 a. chocolate 25 50
81 **58** 1½ a. rose-carmine (Type B) (1927) 15 1·25
82 **61** 2½ a. orange (1927) 30 2·25
83 **62** 3 a. bright blue (1925) 50 2·75
80/3 *Set of* 4 1·00 6·00

Nos. 81/2 with inverted overprint are of clandestine origin.

1927–37. *King George V (Nasik printing, wmk Mult Star), optd at Nasik with T* **5** *or* **6** *(rupee values).*
84 **55** 3 p. slate 10 10
85 **56** ½ a. green (1929) 10 20
86 **80** 9 p. deep green (1932) 15 40
87 **57** 1 a. chocolate (1928) 10 10
88 **82** 1¼ a. mauve (1932) 15 30
89 **58** 1½ a. rose-carmine (Type B) (1930) 20 85
90 **70** 2 a. purple (1928) 20 25
91 **61** 2½ a. orange (1930) 20 1·75
92 **62** 3 a. bright blue (1930) 30 1·50
93 **83** 3½ a. ultramarine (1937) 35 2·75
94 **71** 4 a. sage-green (1928) 35 70
95 **64** 6 a. bistre (1937) 40 3·25
96 **65** 8 a. reddish purple (1930) 45 1·50
97 **66** 12 a. claret (1930) 70 3·00
98 **67** 1 r. chocolate and green (1930) 80 1·75
99 2 r. carmine and orange (1930) 8·00 22·00
100 5 r. ultramarine and purple (1928) 9·00 15·00
101 10 r. green and carmine (1928) 12·00 18·00
102 15 r. blue and olive (1929) 45·00 £110
103 25 r. orange and blue (1929) 65·00 £175
84/103 *Set of* 20 £125 £300

1934. *New types and colours. Optd with T* **5**.
104 **79** ½ a. green 10 15
105 **81** 1 a. chocolate 15 15
106 **59** 2 a. vermilion 25 30
107 **62** 3 a. carmine 40 40
108 **63** 4 a. sage-green 45 65
104/8 *Set of* 5 1·25 1·50

1937–38. *King George VI. Nos. 247/64 optd with T* **5** *or T* **6** *(rupee values).*
109 **91** 3 p. slate 1·25 75
110 ½ a. red-brown 35 85
111 9 p. green (1937) 50 1·50
112 1 a. carmine (1937) 30 35
113 **92** 2 a. vermilion 60 3·50
114 – 2½ a. bright violet 60 3·50
115 – 3 a. yellow-green 1·25 3·50
116 – 3½ a. bright blue 65 4·00
117 – 4 a. brown 1·75 4·00
118 – 6 a. turquoise-green 85 5·50
119 – 8 a. slate-violet 1·75 5·50
120 – 12 a. lake 1·50 7·50
121 **93** 1 r. grey and red-brown 6·00 8·00
122 2 r. purple and brown 13·00 20·00
123 5 r. green and blue 28·00 26·00
124 10 r. purple and claret 50·00 45·00
125 15 r. brown and green £160 £300
126 25 r. slate-violet and purple £200 £350
109/126 *Set of* 18 £400 £700

JIND (7)

1941–43. *King George VI. Optd with T* **7**. (a) *Stamps of* 1937.
127 **91** 3 p. slate 5·00 5·00
128 ½ a. red-brown 1·00 30
129 9 p. green 5·00 5·50
130 1 a. carmine 1·00 2·00
131 **93** 1 r. grey and red-brown 5·50 8·50
132 2 r. purple and brown 9·00 13·00
133 5 r. green and blue 26·00 32·00
134 10 r. purple and claret 48·00 48·00
135 15 r. brown and green £100 90·00
136 25 r. slate-violet and purple £150 £250
127/136 *Set of* 10 £300 £400

(b) *Stamps of* 1940–43
137 **100a** 3 p. slate (1942) 40 50
138 ½ a. purple (1943) 40 50
139 9 p. green (1942) 40 60
140 1 a. carmine (1942) 45 45
141 **101** 1 a. 3 p. yellow-brown 65 1·75
142 1½ a. dull violet (1942) 2·00 1·50
143 2 a. vermilion 85 1·10
144 3 a. bright violet (1942) 2·00 1·75
145 3½ a. bright blue 1·60 2·75
146 **102** 4 a. brown 1·60 1·60
147 6 a. turquoise-green 2·00 3·50
148 8 a. slate-violet 1·90 3·50
149 12 a. lake 4·50 5·50
137/149 *Set of* 13 17·00 22·00

The 1½ a. and 3 a. exist printed by lithography or typography.

OFFICIAL STAMPS

SERVICE

SERVICE (O 14) SERVICE (O 15) JHIND STATE (O 16)

1885. *Queen Victoria. Nos. 1/3 of Jind optd with Type* O **14**.
O1 **23** ½ a. blue-green 25 25
a. Opt Type **1** inverted 55·00 35·00
O2 **25** 1 a. brown-purple 15 10
a. Opt Type **1** inverted 8·00 7·00
O3 **27** 2 a. dull blue 17·00 21·00
a. Opt Type **1** inverted £375

The three values have had the overprint reprinted in the same way as the ordinary stamps of 1885. See note after No. 6.

1885. *Nos. 7/9 of Jind optd with Type* O **15**.
O7 **23** ½ a. blue-green (R.) 38·00
O8 **25** 1 a. brown-purple 38·00
O9 **27** 2 a. dull blue (R.) 42·00
O7/9 *Set of* 3 £100

1886. *Optd with Type* O **16**, *in red.*
O10 **23** ½ a. blue-green 10·00
a. "ERVICE"
b. "JEIND" £300
O11 **27** 2 a. dull blue 14·00
a. "ERVICE"
b. "JEIND" £450

1886–1902. *Optd with Type* O **16**.
O12 **23** ½ a. blue-green (1888) 40 10
O13 **25** 1 a. brown-purple 10·00
a. "ERVICE"
b. "JEIND" £250
O14 1 a. plum (1902) 2·00 15
O15 **27** 2 a. dull blue (1893) 60 40
O16 2 a. ultramarine 45 25
O17 **29** 4 a. olive-green (1892) 40 35
O18 4 a. slate-green 1·25 1·10
O19 **31** 8 a. dull mauve (1892) 1·50 2·00
O20 8 a. magenta (1897) 2·00 4·00
O21 **37** 1 r. green and carmine (1896) 6·00 12·00
O12/21 *Set of* 6 9·50 13·00

Varieties mentioned in note after No. 35 exist on Nos. O12, O15, O17 and O20.

Printings up to and including that of October 1897 had the

"SERVICE" overprint. Type O 15, applied to sheets already overprinted with Type 3. From the printing of December 1899 onwards "SERVICE" and "JHIND STATE" were overprinted at one operation, as Type O 16, to provide fresh supplies of Nos. O12, O14 and O21.

1902. *Colour changed. Optd with Type* O **16**.

O22	**23**	½ a. yellow-green	25	15

1903–6. *King Edward VII stamps of India optd with Type* O **16**.

O23	**41**	3 p. pale grey	10	10
O24		3 p. slate-grey (1906)	10	10
O25	**42**	½ a. green	1·25	10
		a. "HIND"	£550	£150
O26	**43**	1 a. carmine	60	10
		a. "HIND"	—	£130
O27	**44**	2 a. pale violet	60	30
O28		2 a. mauve	20	10
O29	**47**	4 a. olive	40	45
O30	**49**	8 a. dull mauve	7·00	5·00
O31		8 a. magenta	2·25	1·50
O32	**51**	1 r. green and carmine (1906)	2·50	2·25
O23/32		*Set of* 7	6·50	4·00

1907. *Nos.* 149/50 *of India optd with Type* O **16**.

O33	**53**	½ a. green	15	10
O34	**54**	1 a. carmine	15	10

1914–27. *King George V. Official stamps of India optd with T* **4**.

O35	**55**	3 p. slate-grey	10	10
O36	**56**	½ a. green	10	10
O37	**57**	1 a. aniline carmine	10	10
O38		1 a. pale rose-carmine	15	10
O39	**59**	2 a. mauve	15	10
O40	**63**	4 a. olive	20	15
O41	**64**	6 a. yellow-bistre (1927)	40	1·75
O42	**65**	8 a. purple	25	65
O43	**67**	1 r. brown and green	90	1·50
O44	**67**	2 r. carmine and yellow-brown (1927)	5·50	18·00
O45		5 r. ultramarine and violet (1927)	15·00	40·00
O35/45		*Set of* 10	20·00	55·00

No. O40 with double overprint is of clandestine origin.

1924. *As* 1914-27. *New colour.*

O46	**57**	1 a. chocolate	10	10

JIND STATE SERVICE (O 17) JIND STATE SERVICE (O 18) JIND SERVICE (O 19)

1927–37. *King George V (Nasik printing, wmk Mult Star), optd with Types* O **17** *or* O **18** *(rupee values).*

O47	**55**	3 p. slate (1928)	10	15
O48	**56**	½ a. green (1929)	10	35
O49	**80**	9 p. deep green (1932)	30	15
O50	**57**	1 a. chocolate	10	10
O51	**82**	1¼ a. mauve (1932)	15	15
O52	**70**	2 a. purple (1929)	15	15
O53	**61**	2½ a. orange (1937)	25	1·75
O54	**71**	4 a. sage-green (1929)	15	15
O55	**64**	6 a. bistre (1937)	40	3·00
O56	**65**	8 a. reddish purple (1929)	35	1·10
O57	**66**	12 a. claret (1928)	50	2·50
O58	**67**	1 r. chocolate and green (1928)	80	1·50
O59		2 r. carmine and orange (1930)	9·00	7·50
O60		5 r. ultramarine and purple (1929)	10·00	40·00
O61		10 r. green and carmine (1928)	18·00	28·00
O47/61		*Set of* 15	35·00	75·00

The 9 p. exists printed by lithography or typography.

1934. *Optd with Type* O **17**.

O62	**79**	½ a. green	15	10
O63	**81**	1 a. chocolate	10	10
O64	**59**	2 a. vermilion	15	15
O65	**63**	4 a. sage-green	1·00	30
O62/5		*Set of* 4	1·00	60

1937–40. *King George VI. Optd with Types* O **17** *or* O **18** *(rupee values).*

O66	**91**	½ a. red-brown (1938)	28·00	30
O67		9 p. green	60	1·50
O68		1 a. carmine	40	30
O69	**93**	1 r. grey and red-brown (1940)	14·00	18·00
O70		2 r. purple and brown (1940)	28·00	40·00
O71		5 r. green and blue (1940)	60·00	75·00
O72		10 r. purple and claret (1940)	£100	£170
O66/72		*Set of* 7	£200	£275

1939–43. (*a*) *Official stamps optd with T* **7**.

O73	O **20**	3 p. slate	30	20
O74		½ a. red-brown	2·00	60
O75		½ a. purple (1943)	30	30
O76		9 p. green	1·25	1·25
O77		1 a. carmine	1·25	15
O78		1½ a. dull violet (1942)	1·50	40
O79		2 a. vermilion	55	25
O80		2½ a. bright violet	65	2·00
O81		4 a. brown	85	75
O82		8 a. slate-violet	1·25	1·50
		(*b*) *Postage stamps optd with Type* O **19**		
O83	**93**	1 r. grey and red-brown (1942)	14·00	16·00
O84		2 r. purple and brown (1942)	20·00	32·00
O85		5 r. green and blue (1942)	50·00	75·00
O86		10 r. purple and claret (1942)	90·00	£130
O73/86		*Set of* 14	£160	£225

NABHA

PRICES FOR STAMPS ON COVER

Nos. 1/3	*from* × 15
Nos. 4/6	—
Nos. 10/36	*from* × 10
Nos. 37/117	*from* × 6
Nos. O1/68	*from* × 12

NABHA STATE (1) NABHA STATE (2)

1885 (May). *Queen Victoria. Optd with T* **1**.

1	**23**	½ a. blue-green	75	1·50
2	**25**	1 a. brown-purple	12·00	32·00
3	**27**	2 a. dull blue	7·00	13·00
4	**17**	4 a. green	32·00	55·00
5	**31**	8 a. dull mauve	£170	
6	**33**	1 r. slate	£150	
1/6		*Set of* 6	£325	

All six values have had the overprint reprinted. On the reprints the words "NABHA" and "STATE" both measure 9¼ mm in length, whereas on the originals these words measure 11 and 10 mm respectively. The varieties with overprint double come from the reprints.

1885 (Nov)–**1900**. *Optd with T* **2**. (*a*) *In red.*

10	**23**	½ a. blue-green	15	40
11	**27**	2 a. dull blue	50	90
12	**17**	4 a. green	18·00	45·00
13	**33**	1 r. slate	50·00	80·00
10/13		*Set of* 4	60·00	£110
		(*b*) *In black* (Nov 1885–97)		
14	**23**	½ a. blue-green (1888)	10	10
15	**24**	9 p. carmine (1892)	35	1·25
16	**25**	1 a. brown-purple	30	25
17		1 a. plum	20	10
18	**26**	1½ a. sepia (1891)	25	75
		a. "ABHA" for "NABHA"	£170	
19	**27**	2 a. dull blue (1888)	35	40
20		2 a. ultramarine	25	45
21	**28**	3 a. orange (1889)	1·90	4·00
22		3 a. brown-orange	55	50
23	**29**	4 a. olive-green (1888)	50	60
24		4 a. slate-green	50	50
25	**21**	6 a. olive-bistre (1889)	1·25	2·50
26		6 a. bistre-brown	80	1·40
27	**31**	8 a. dull mauve	65	1·25
28	**32**	12 a. purple/*red* (1889)	80	1·50
		a. Opt double, one albino		
29	**33**	1 r. slate (1888)	5·50	15·00
30	**37**	1 r. green and carmine (1893)	2·50	3·50
		a. "N BHA" for "NABHA"		
31	**38**	2 r. carmine and yellow-brown (1897)	65·00	90·00
32		3 r. brown and green (1897)	65·00	90·00
33		5 r. ultramarine and violet (1897)	75·00	£110
14/33		*Set of* 15	£190	£275
		(*c*) *New value. In black* (Nov 1900)		
36	**40**	3 p. carmine	10	10

1903–09. *King Edward VII. Optd with T* **2**.

37	**41**	3 p. pale grey	10	15
37*a*		3 p. slate-grey (1906)	10	15
38	**42**	½ a. green	10	15
		a. "NABH"	£400	
39	**43**	1 a. carmine	15	20
40	**44**	2 a. pale violet	30	45
40*a*		2 a. mauve	35	20
40*b*	**45**	2½ a. ultramarine (1909)	18·00	45·00
41	**46**	3 a. orange-brown	30	30
42	**47**	4 a. olive	50	1·10
43	**48**	6 a. olive-bistre	50	2·25
44	**49**	8 a. dull mauve	1·25	2·50
44*a*		8 a. magenta	2·75	4·00
45	**50**	12 a. purple/*red*	1·00	3·50
46	**51**	1 r. green and carmine	1·50	3·00
37/46		*Set of* 11	21·00	50·00

1907. *Nos.* 149/50 *of India optd with T* **2**.

47	**53**	½ a. green	20	30
48	**54**	1 a. carmine	35	65

1913. *King George V. Optd with T* **2**.

49	**55**	3 p. slate	10	10
50	**56**	½ a. green	10	10
51	**57**	1 a. aniline carmine	15	10
52	**59**	2 a. mauve	20	30
53	**62**	3 a. orange-brown	25	35
54	**63**	4 a. olive	30	65
55	**64**	6 a. olive-bistre	40	1·50
56	**65**	8 a. purple	55	1·40
57	**66**	12 a. dull claret	70	2·50
58	**67**	1 r. brown and green	1·60	2·25
		a. Opt double, one albino		
49/58		*Set of* 10	4·00	8·00

1924. *As* 1913. *New colour.*

59	**57**	1 a. chocolate	70	80

No. 59 with inverted or double overprint is of clandestine origin.

NABHA STATE (3) NABHA STATE (4)

1927–36. *King George V (Nasik printing, wmk Mult Star), optd as T* **3** *or* **4** *(rupee values).*

60	**55**	3 p. slate (1932)	15	15
61	**56**	½ a. green (1928)	15	20
61*a*	**80**	9 p. deep green (1934)	25	90
62	**57**	1 a. chocolate	15	15
63	**82**	1¼ a. mauve (1936)	15	65
64	**70**	2 a. purple (1932)	45	35
65	**61**	2½ a. orange (1932)	25	1·50
66	**62**	3 a. bright blue (1930)	40	1·00
67	**71**	4 a. sage-green (1932)	1·25	1·00
71	**67**	2 r. carmine and orange (1932)	8·50	25·00
72		5 r. ultramarine and purple (1932)	32·00	65·00
60/72		*Set of* 11	40·00	85·00

The 9 p. exists printed by lithography or typography.

1936–37. *New types and colours. Optd as T* **3**.

73	**79**	½ a. green	15	25
74	**81**	1 a. chocolate	15	30
75	**62**	3 a. carmine (1937)	80	2·00
76	**63**	4 a. slate-green (1937)	80	1·25
73/6		*Set of* 4	1·60	3·25

NABHA STATE (5) NABHA (6)

1938. *King George VI. Nos.* 247/64 *optd as T* **3** *(3 p. to 1 a.), T* **5** *(2 a. to 12 a.) or T* **4** *(rupee values).*

77	**91**	3 p. slate	4·25	30
78		½ a. red-brown	1·10	30
79		9 p. green	13·00	4·00
80		1 a. carmine	80	30
81	**92**	2 a. vermilion	65	2·50
82	–	2½ a. bright violet	75	3·00
83	–	3 a. yellow-green	85	2·25
84	–	3½ a. bright blue	90	4·50
85	–	4 a. brown	1·60	2·25
86	–	6 a. turquoise-green	1·40	5·00
87	–	8 a. slate-violet	1·75	5·50
88	–	12 a. lake	2·25	7·00
89	**93**	1 r. grey and red-brown	6·50	10·00
90		2 r. purple and brown	11·00	30·00
91		5 r. green and blue	38·00	70·00
92		10 r. purple and claret	75·00	£150
93		15 r. brown and green	£140	£275
94		25 r. slate-violet and purple	£180	£325
77/94		*Set of* 18	£425	£800

1941–45. *King George VI. Optd with T* **6**. (*a*) *Stamps of* 1937.

95	**91**	3 p. slate (1942)	20·00	1·50
96		½ a. red-brown (1942)	50·00	2·00
97		9 p. green (1942)	11·00	5·00
98		1 a. carmine (1942)	10·00	2·00
95/8		*Set of* 4	80·00	9·50
		(*b*) *Stamps of* 1940-43		
105	**100*a***	3 p. slate (1942)	50	40
106		½ a. purple (1943)	85	40
107		9 p. green (1942)	85	40
108		1 a. carmine (1945)	40	1·00
109	**101**	1 a. 3 p. yellow-brown	60	60
110		1½ a. dull violet (1942)	60	60
111		2 a. vermilion (1943)	60	1·10
112		3 a. bright violet (1943)	1·25	2·50
113		3½ a. bright blue (1944)	3·75	7·50
114	**102**	4 a. brown	1·40	1·00
115		6 a. turquoise-green (1943)	3·00	9·50
116		8 a. slate-violet (1943)	3·00	7·00
117		12 a. lake (1943)	4·00	10·00
105/117		*Set of* 13	18·00	38·00

The 1½ a. exists printed by lithography or typography.

OFFICIAL STAMPS

SERVICE (O 8) SERVICE NABHA STATE (O 9)

1885 (May). *Nos.* 1/3 *of Nabha optd with Type* O **8**.

O1	**23**	½ a. blue-green	60	30
O2	**25**	1 a. brown-purple	15	15
		a. Opt Type O **8** double	†	£450
O3	**27**	2 a. dull blue	29·00	45·00
O1/3		*Set of* 3	29·00	45·00

The three values have had the overprint reprinted in the same way as the ordinary stamps of 1885.

1885 (Nov)–**97**. *Optd with Type* O **9**. (*a*) *In red.*

O 4	**23**	½ a. blue-green	1·25	1·75
O 5	**27**	2 a. deep blue	45	55
		(*b*) *In black* (Nov 1885–97)		
O 6	**23**	½ a. blue-green (1888)	10	10
		a. "SERVICE." with stop	65·00	2·25
		b. "S ATE" for "STATE"		
O 7	**25**	1 a. brown-purple	15	10
O 8		1 a. plum	20	10
		a. "SERVICE." with stop	4·50	75
		b. "NABHA STATE" double	—	£200
O 9	**27**	2 a. dull blue (1888)	25	25
O10		2 a. ultramarine	50	50
O11	**28**	3 a. orange (1889)	7·00	14·00
O12		3 a. brown-orange	5·50	13·00
O13	**29**	4 a. olive-green (1888)	50	35
O14		4 a. slate-green	60	40
O15	**21**	6 a. olive-bistre (1889)	5·50	6·00
O16		6 a. bistre-brown	£160	
O17	**31**	8 a. dull mauve (1889)	55	70
O18	**32**	12 a. purple/*red* (1889)	4·00	6·50
O19	**33**	1 r. slate (1889)	17·00	55·00
O20	**37**	1 r. green and carmine (1.97)	14·00	24·00
O6/20		*Set of* 10	42·00	95·00

Printings up to and including that of August 1895 had the "SERVICE" overprint applied to sheets of stamps already overprinted with Type **2**. From the printing of January 1897 onwards the two parts of the overprint were applied at one operation. This method was only used for printings of the ½ a., 1 a. and 1 r. (O20).

1903–06. *King Edward VII stamps of India optd with Type* O **9**.

O24	**41**	3 p. pale grey (1906)	1·40	2·50
O25		3 p. slate-grey (1906)	65	1·75
O26	**42**	½ a. green	30	10
O27	**43**	1 a. carmine	10	10
O28	**44**	2 a. pale violet	40	40
O29		2 a. mauve	40	40
O30	**47**	4 a. olive	1·10	45
O32	**49**	8 a. dull mauve	90	90
O33		8 a. magenta	2·75	1·75
		a. Opt double, one albino		
O34	**51**	1 r. green and carmine	1·50	2·00
O24/34		*Set of* 7	4·50	5·00

1907. *Nos.* 149/50 *of India optd with Type* O **9**.

O35	**53**	½ a. green	10	10
O36	**54**	1 a. carmine	15	20

1913. *King George V. Optd with Type* O 9.
O37 **63** 4 a. olive .. 10·00
O38 **67** 1 r. brown and green .. 50·00
a. Opt double, one albino .. 80·00

1913. *Official stamps of India optd with T* 2.
O39 **55** 3 p. slate-grey .. 20 1·50
O39*a* 3 p. bluish slate .. 20 1·50
O40 **56** ½ a. green .. 15 10
O41 **57** 1 a. aniline carmine .. 15 10
O42 **59** 2 a. mauve .. 25 15
O43 **63** 4 a. olive .. 35 25
O44 **65** 8 a. dull mauve .. 60 60
O46 **67** 1 r. brown and green .. 1·75 1·75
O39/46 .. *Set of* 7 3·00 4·00

NABHA STATE SERVICE (O 10) NABHA SERVICE (O 11)

1932–42?. *King George V (Nasik printing, wmk Mult Star), optd at Nasik with Type* O 10.
O47 **55** 3 p. slate .. 10 15
O50 **81** 1 a. chocolate (1935) .. 10 15
O50*a* **63** 4 a. sage-green (1942?) .. 10·00 2·00
O51 **65** 8 a. reddish purple (1937) .. 75 1·50
O47/51 .. *Set of* 4 10·00 3·50

1938. *King George VI. Optd as Type* O 10.
O54 **91** 9 p. green .. 1·50 1·75
O55 1 a. carmine .. 2·25 50

1940–43. (*a*) *Official stamps optd with T* 6.
O56 **O 20** 3 p. slate (1942) .. 40 30
O57 ½ a. red-brown (1942) .. 50 30
O57*a* ½ a. purple (1943) .. 65 30
O58 9 p. green .. 65 20
O59 1 a. carmine (1942) .. 30 20
O61 1½ a. dull violet (1942) .. 40 40
O62 2 a. vermilion (1942) .. 40 45
O64 4 a. brown (1942) .. 1·50 1·75
O65 8 a. slate-violet (1942) .. 2·25 4·50

(*b*) *Postage stamps optd with Type* O 11.
O66 **93** 1 r. grey and red-brown (1942) .. 6·50 15·00
O67 2 r. purple and brown (1942) .. 17·00 45·00
O68 5 r. green and blue (1942) .. 90·00 £120
O56/68 .. *Set of* 11 £110 £170

PATIALA

PRICES FOR STAMPS ON COVER
Nos. 1/6 *from* × 10
Nos. 7/34 *from* × 5
Nos. 35/45 *from* × 6
Nos. 46/115 *from* × 4
Nos. O1/84 *from* × 12

PUTTIALLA STATE (1) (2) PUTTIALLA STATE (2) PATIALA STATE (3)

1884. *Queen Victoria. Optd with T* 1, *in red.*
1 **23** ½ a. blue-green .. 80 70
a. Opt double, one sideways .. £400 £250
2 **25** 1 a. brown-purple .. 15·00 14·00
a. Opt double
b. Optd in red and in black .. £250
3 **27** 2 a. dull blue .. 5·00 5·00
4 **17** 4 a. green .. 14·00 14·00
5 **31** 8 a. dull mauve .. £125 £250
a. Opt inverted .. £2250
b. Optd in red and in black .. 30·00
ba. Ditto. Opts inverted .. £1400
6 **33** 1 r. slate .. 65·00 £125
1/6 .. *Set of* 6 £200 £375

Nos. 5a and 5ba each occur once in the setting of 120. The 8 a. value also exists with a trial overprint (showing the words more curved) reading downwards (*Price* £250 *unused*), which should not be confused with No. 5a.

1885. *Optd with T* 2. (*a*) *In red.*
7 **23** ½ a. blue-green .. 30 20
a. "AUTTIALLA" .. 10·00 11·00
b. "STATE" only
c. Wide spacing between lines .. 1·25 1·50
8 **27** 2 a. dull blue .. 85 30
a. "AUTTIALLA" .. 18·00
b. Wide spacing between lines .. 5·00 5·00
9 **17** 4 a. green .. 1·00 1·00
a. Optd in red and in black .. £125
b. Wide spacing between lines .. 45·00
10 **33** 1 r. slate .. 4·50 15·00
a. "AUTTIALLA" .. £200
b. Wide spacing between lines .. 50·00

(*b*) *In black*
11 **25** 1 a. brown-purple .. 15 10
a. Optd in red and in black .. 2·75 12·00
b. "AUTTIALLA" .. 27·00
ba. Ditto. Optd in red and in black .. £550
c. Opt double .. £110 £120
d. Wide spacing between lines .. 18·00
12 **31** 8 a. dull mauve .. 6·00 10·00
a. "AUTTIALLA" .. £170
b. Opt double, one albino .. 45·00
c. Wide spacing between lines .. 45·00
7/12 .. *Set of* 6 11·50 23·00

The ½, 2 and 4 a. (T **29**), and 1 r. (all overprinted in black), are proofs.

All six values exist with reprinted overprints, and the error "AUTTIALLA STATE" has been reprinted in complete sheets on all values and in addition in black on the ½, 2, 4 a., and 1 r. Nearly all these however, are found with the word "REPRINT" overprinted upon them. On the genuine "AUTTIALLA" errors the word "STATE" is 8½ mm long; on the reprints only 7¾ mm.

Nos. 7/8 and 10/12 exist with error "PUTTILLA", but their status is uncertain.

1891–96. *Optd with T* 3.
13 **23** ½ a. blue-green (1892) .. 10 10
14 **24** 9 p. carmine .. 25 55
15 **25** 1 a. brown-purple .. 25 10
16 1 a. plum .. 30 20
a. "PATIALA" omitted .. £110 £110
17 **26** 1½ a. sepia .. 25 40
18 **27** 2 a. dull blue (1896) .. 40 15
19 2 a. ultramarine .. 60 35
20 **28** 3 a. brown-orange .. 40 35
21 **29** 4 a. olive-green (1896) .. 35 40
a. "PATIALA" omitted .. £180 £140
22 4 a. slate-green .. 35 40
23 **21** 6 a. bistre-brown .. 40 1·25
24 6 a. olive-bistre .. 1·00 3·75
25 **31** 8 a. dull mauve
26 8 a. magenta (1896) .. 55 1·75
27 **32** 12 a. purple/*red* .. 65 2·00
28 **37** 1 r. green and carmine (1896) .. 3·50 8·00
29 **38** 2 r. carmine and yellow-brown (1895) 70·00
30 3 r. brown and green (1895) .. 85·00
31 5 r. ultramarine and violet (1895) .. 95·00
13/31 .. *Set of* 14 £225

1899–1902. *Colours changed and new value. Optd with T* 3.
32 **40** 3 p. carmine (1899) .. 10 10
a. Pair, one without opt
33 **23** ½ a. pale yellow-green .. 10 15
34 **25** 1 a. carmine .. 15 15
32/4 .. *Set of* 3 30 35

1903–06. *King Edward VII. Optd with T* 3.
35 **41** 3 p. pale grey .. 10 10
36 3 p. slate-grey (1906) .. 10 10
37 **42** ½ a. green .. 15 10
38 **43** 1 a. carmine .. 10 10
a. Horiz pair, one without opt .. £450
39 **44** 2 a. pale violet .. 20 15
a. Mauve .. 1·40 40
40 **46** 3 a. orange-brown .. 20 15
41 **47** 4 a. olive (1905) .. 90 60
42 **48** 6 a. olive-bistre (1905) .. 65 1·40
43 **49** 8 a. dull mauve (1906) .. 1·25 80
44 **50** 12 a. purple/*red* (1906) .. 1·10 2·25
45 **51** 1 r. green and carmine (1905) .. 1·25 1·40
35/45 .. *Set of* 10 5·25 6·25

1912. *Nos.* 149/50 *of India optd with T* 3.
46 **53** ½ a. green .. 10 10
47 **54** 1 a. carmine .. 15 10

1912–26. *King George V. Optd with T* 3.
48 **55** 3 p. slate-grey .. 10 10
49 **56** ½ a. green .. 10 10
50 **57** 1 a. aniline carmine .. 15 10
51 **58** 1½ a. chocolate (Type A) (1922) .. 30 50
52 **59** 2 a. mauve .. 15 20
53 **62** 3 a. orange-brown .. 45 55
54 **63** 4 a. olive .. 50 65
55 **64** 6 a. yellow-brown .. 1·25 1·25
a. Yellow-bistre .. 60 1·00
56 **65** 8 a. purple .. 65 65
57 **66** 12 a. dull claret .. 85 1·75
58 **67** 1 r. brown and green .. 2·50 3·00
a. Opt double, one albino
59 2 r. carmine and yellow-brown (1926) .. 6·00 22·00
60 5 r. ultramarine and violet (1926) .. 16·00 28·00

1923–6. *As* 1912–26. *New colours.*
61 **57** 1 a. chocolate .. 15 10
62 **62** 3 a. ultramarine (1926) .. 35 1·00
48/62 .. *Set of* 15 26·00 55·00

PATIALA STATE (4) PATIALA STATE (5)

1928–34. *King George V (Nasik printing, wmk Mult Star) optd at Nasik with T* 4 *or* 5 (*rupee values*).
63 **55** 3 p. slate (1932) .. 25 10
64 **56** ½ a. green .. 10 10
65 **80** 9 p. deep green (1934) .. 15 20
66 **57** 1 a. chocolate .. 20 15
67 **82** 1¼ a. mauve (1932) .. 35 15
68 **70** 2 a. purple .. 20 20
69 **61** 2½ a. orange (1934) .. 55 90
70 **62** 3 a. bright blue (1929) .. 35 65
71 **71** 4 a. sage-green .. 55 65
72 **65** 8 a. reddish purple (1933) .. 1·40 1·40
73 **67** 1 r. chocolate and green (1929) .. 1·60 2·25
74 2 r. carmine and orange .. 3·25 11·00
63/74 .. *Set of* 12 8·00 16·00

The 9 p. exists printed by lithography or typography.

1935–7. *Optd with T* 4.
75 **79** ½ a. blue-green (1937) .. 15 10
76 **81** 1 a. chocolate (1936) .. 15 10
77 **59** 2 a. vermilion (No. 236*a*) (1936) .. 15 20
78 **62** 3 a. carmine .. 1·10 1·25
79 **63** 4 a. sage-green .. 35 60
75/9 .. *Set of* 5 1·60 2·00

PATIALA STATE (6) PATIALA (7) PATIALA (8)

1937–8. *King George VI. Nos.* 247/64 *optd with T* 4 (3 *p. to* 1 *a.*), *T* 6 (2 *a. to* 12 *a.*), *or T* 5 (*rupee values*).
80 **91** 3 p. slate .. 20·00 50
81 ½ a. red-brown .. 3·25 20
82 9 p. green (1937) .. 1·40 40
83 1 a. carmine (1937) .. 40 20
84 **92** 2 a. vermilion .. 80 2·00
85 – 2½ a. bright violet .. 1·10 3·75
86 – 3 a. yellow-green .. 1·10 2·50
87 – 3½ a. bright blue .. 1·50 7·00
88 – 4 a. brown .. 4·50 4·50
89 – 6 a. turquoise-green .. 6·00 8·00
90 – 8 a. slate-violet .. 6·00 8·00
91 – 12 a. lake .. 7·00 12·00
92 **93** 1 r. grey and red-brown .. 13·00 17·00
93 2 r. purple and brown .. 17·00 32·00
94 5 r. green and blue .. 26·00 48·00
95 10 r. purple and claret .. 48·00 95·00
96 15 r. brown and green .. 80·00 £170
97 25 r. slate-violet and purple .. £120 £250
80/97 .. *Set of* 18 £325 £600

1941–6. *King George VI. Optd with T* 7 *or* 8 (*rupee value*).

(*a*) *Stamps of* 1937
98 **91** 3 p. slate .. 7·50 50
99 ½ a. red-brown .. 6·50 20
100 9 p. green .. 55·00 2·50
101 1 a. carmine .. 13·00 50
102 **93** 1 r. grey and red-brown (1946) .. 7·00 13·00
98/102 .. *Set of* 5 80·00 15·00

(*b*) *Stamps of* 1940-43
103 **100*a*** 3 p. slate (1942) .. 45 15
104 ½ a. purple (1943) .. 45 15
105 9 p. green (1942) .. 45 15
a. Vert pair, one without opt .. £1500
106 1 a. carmine (1944) .. 35 10
107 **101** 1 a. 3 p. yellow-brown .. 1·00 1·00
108 1½ a. violet (1942) .. 1·25 30
109 2 a. vermilion (1944) .. 1·25 20
110 3 a. bright violet (1944) .. 1·25 70
111 3½ a. bright blue (1944) .. 3·25 5·00
112 **102** 4 a. brown (1944) .. 1·25 70
113 6 a. turquoise-green (1944) .. 1·40 3·50
114 8 a. slate-violet (1944) .. 1·75 3·50
115 12 a. lake (1945) .. 4·00 8·50
103/15 .. *Set of* 13 16·00 22·00

The 1½ a. exists printed by lithography or typography.

OFFICIAL STAMPS

SERVICE (O 2) SERVICE (O 3)

1884. *Nos.* 1/3 *of Patiala optd with Type* O 2, *in black.*
O1 **23** ½ a. blue-green .. 4·25 15
O2 **25** 1 a. brown-purple .. 25 10
a. Opt Type 1 inverted .. £375 £120
b. Opt Type 1 double .. — 70·00
c. "SERVICE" double .. £375 £170
d. "SERVICE" inverted .. — £450
O3 **27** 2 a. dull blue .. £1500 42·00

1885–90. (*a*) *No.* 7 *of Patiala optd with Type* O 2, *in black.*
O4 **23** ½ a. blue-green .. 15 10
a. "SERVICE" double .. — £250
b. "AUTTIALLA" .. 45·00 13·00

(*b*) *No.* 11 *of Patiala optd with Type* O 2, *in black*
O5 **25** 1 a. brown-purple .. 25 10
a. "SERVICE" double .. £300 £300
b. "SERVICE" double, one inverted .. — £275
c. "AUTTIALLA" .. £250 38·00
d. "PUTTIALLA STATE" double .. — £300

(*c*) *As No.* 7 *of Patiala, but optd in black, and No.* 8, *optd with Type* O 3
O6 **23** ½ a. blue-green (Bk.) (1890) .. 30 10
O7 **27** 2 a. dull blue (R.) .. 15 10
a. "SERVICE" double, one inverted .. 30·00

There are reprints of Nos. O4, O5 and O7. The first has the word "SERVICE" in the large type in *red* instead of the small type in *black*, and the second has the word in the large type in *black* in place of the small type. The 2 a. with Type O 3, in *black*, is a proof. The ½ a. "AUTTIALLA" has also been reprinted, but nearly all the above have been overprinted "REPRINT".

No. O7 exists with error "PUTTILLA", but its status is uncertain.

SERVICE

PATIALA STATE (O 4) PATIALA STATE SERVICE (O 5) PATIALA STATE SERVICE (O 6)

1891 (Nov)–1900. *Optd with Type* O 4, *in black.*
O 8 **23** ½ a. blue-green (9.95) .. 10 10
a. "SERVICE" inverted .. 50·00
b. "I" of "SERVICE" omitted .. £350
c. First "T" of "STATE" omitted .. £125 £125
O 9 **25** 1 a. plum (10.1900) .. 1·25 10
a. "SERVICE" inverted .. 55·00
O10 **27** 2 a. dull blue (12.98) .. 1·00 60
a. Deep blue .. 1·10 90
b. "SERVICE" inverted .. 55·00
O12 **28** 3 a. brown-orange .. 20 40
a. "I" of "SERVICE" omitted
O13 **29** 4 a. olive-green .. 20 30
a. Slate-green (9.95) .. 20 15
b. "I" of "SERVICE" omitted
O15 **21** 6 a. bistre-brown .. 60 35
O16 **31** 8 a. dull mauve .. 50 45
a. Magenta (12.98) .. 40 50
b. "I" of "SERVICE" omitted .. £1100
O18 **32** 12 a. purple/*red* .. 45 50
a. "I" of "SERVICE" omitted
O19 **33** 1 r. slate .. 55 55
a. "I" of "SERVICE" omitted
O8/19 .. *Set of* 9 4·00 2·75

Stamps from the first printing of November 1891 (Nos. O12/13, O15/16, O18/19) had the "SERVICE" overprint, as Type O 3, applied to sheets already overprinted with Type **3**. Subsequent printings of Nos. O8/10*a*, O13*a* and O16*a* had both overprints applied at one operation as shown on Type O **4**.

The errors with "SERVICE" inverted occur from a trial printing, in two operations, during 1894, which was probably not issued. Some of the "I" omitted varieties may also come from the same trial printing.

1902 (Jan)–**03**. *Optd with Type* O **4**.

O20	**25**	1 a. carmine	10	10
O21	**37**	1 r. green and carmine (5.03)	5·00	9·00

1903–10. *King Edward VII stamps of India optd with Type* O **4**.

O22	**41**	3 p. pale grey	10	10
		a. Slate-grey (1909)	10	10
O24	**42**	½ a. green	10	10
O25	**43**	1 a. carmine	10	10
O26	**44**	2 a. pale violet (1905)	15	10
		a. Mauve	15	10
O28	**46**	3 a. orange-brown	1·25	1·50
O29	**47**	4 a. olive (1905)	25	20
O30	**49**	8 a. dull mauve	45	45
		a. Magenta (1910)	90	55
O32	**51**	1 r. green and carmine (1906)	70	70
O22/32		*Set of* 8	2·75	2·75

1907. *Nos.* 149/50 *of India optd with Type* O **4**.

O33	**53**	½ a. green	10	10
O34	**54**	1 a. carmine	10	10

1913–26. *King George V. Official stamps of India optd with T* **3**.

O35	**55**	3 p. slate-grey	10	10
		a. Bluish slate (1926)	15	10
O36	**56**	½ a. green	10	10
O37	**57**	1 a. carmine	10	10
O38		1 a. brown (1925)	1·75	35
O39	**59**	2 a. mauve	25	10
O40	**63**	4 a. olive	20	25
O41	**64**	6 a. yellow-bistre (1926)	40	1·25
O42	**65**	8 a. purple	35	40
O43	**67**	1 r. brown and green	1·00	1·40
O44		2 r. carmine and yellow-brown (1926)	4·00	12·00
O45		5 r. ultramarine and violet (1926)	8·00	16·00
O35/45		*Set of* 11	14·50	28·00

1927–36. *King George V (Nasik printing, wmk Mult Star), optd at Nasik with* Type O **5** *or Type* O **6** (*rupee values*).

O47	**55**	3 p. slate	10	10
		a. Blue opt	40	40
O48	**56**	½ a. green (1932)	15	15
O49	**57**	1 a. chocolate	10	10
O50	**82**	1¼ a. mauve (1932)	15	10
O51	**70**	2 a. purple	15	20
O52		2 a. vermilion (1933)	20	25
O53	**61**	2½ a. orange (1933)	20	25
O54	**71**	4 a. sage-green (1935)	20	25
O55	**65**	8 a. reddish purple (1929)	50	55
O56	**67**	1 r. chocolate and green (1929)	1·50	1·10
O57		2 r. carmine and orange (1936)	3·00	9·00
O47/57		*Set of* 11	5·50	10·50

1935–9. *New types. Optd with Type* O **5**.

O58	**79**	½ a. green (1936)	10	10
O59	**81**	1 a. chocolate (1936)	10	10
O60	**59**	2 a. vermilion	15	15
O61		2 a. vermilion (*small die*) (1939)	1·50	50
O62	**63**	4 a. sage-green (1936)	20	20
O58/62		*Set of* 5	1·90	90

1937–39. *King George VI. Optd with Types* O **5** *or* O **6** (*rupee values*).

O63	**91**	½ a. red-brown (1938)	1·00	20
O64		9 p. green (1938)	12·00	35·00
O65		1 a. carmine	1·00	20
O66	**93**	1 r. grey and red-brown (1939)	2·00	3·00
O67		2 r. purple and brown (1939)	8·00	8·00
O68		5 r. green and blue (1939)	20·00	35·00
O63/8		*Set of* 6	40·00	70·00

1A ____ 1A (O **7**)

1A SERVICE 1A (O **8**)

PATIALA SERVICE (O **9**)

1939–40. *Stamp of* 1932 (*King George V*).

(*a*) *Optd with Types* O **5** *and* O **7**

O69	**82**	1 a. on 1¼ a. mauve	2·00	1·00

(*b*) *Optd with T* **4** *and* O **8**

O70	**82**	1 a. on 1¼ a. mauve (1940)	1·10	1·25

"SERVICE" measures 9¼ mm on No. O69 but only 8¾ mm on O70.

1939–44. (*a*) *Official stamps optd with T* **7**.

O71	O **20**	3 p. slate (1940)	20	10
O72		½ a. red-brown	70	10
O73		½ a. purple (1942)	15	10
O74		9 p. green	15	15
O75		1 a. carmine	20	10
O76		1 a. 3 p. yellow-brown (1941)	50	25
O77		1½ a. dull violet (1944)	60	15
O78		2 a. vermilion (1940)	1·25	15
O79		2½ a. bright violet (1940)	35	60
O80		4 a. brown (1943)	50	40
O81		8 a. slate-violet (1944)	1·00	1·60

(*b*) *Postage stamps optd with Type* O **9**

O82	**93**	1 r. grey and red-brown (1943)	6·00	3·75
O83		2 r. purple and brown (1944)	11·00	17·00
O84		5 r. green and blue (1944)	17·00	27·00
O71/84		*Set of* 14	35·00	45·00

INDIAN FEUDATORY STATES

These stamps were only valid for use within their respective states, *unless otherwise indicated*.

Postage stamps of the Indian States, current at that date, were replaced by those of the Republic of India on 1 April 1950.

Unless otherwise stated, all became obsolete on 1 May 1950 (with the exception of the "Anchal" stamps of Travancore-Cochin, which remained current until 1 July 1951 or Sept 1951 for the Official issues).

ALWAR

PRICES FOR STAMPS ON COVER	
Nos. 1/2	*from* × 25
No. 3	*from* × 50
No. 4	—
No. 5	*from* × 50

1 (1 a.).

1877. *Litho. Rouletted.*
1 1 ¼ a. grey-blue .. .. 1·75 40
a. Ultramarine .. .. 1·60 40
b. Imperf between (pair) .. .. — 40·00
c. Bright greenish blue .. .. 15·00 7·00
2 1 a. brown .. .. 2·00 80
a. Imperf between (pair) .. .. 45·00 45·00
b. Red-brown .. .. 1·40 60
c. Chocolate .. .. 9·00 8·00

1899–1901. *Redrawn. P 12. (a) Wide margins between stamps.*
3 1 ¼ a. slate-blue .. .. 4·50 2·00
a. Imperf between (horiz pair) .. £300
b. Imperf between (vert pair) £325
4 ¼ a. emerald-green £550
(b) Narrower margins (1901)
5 1 ¼ a. emerald-green .. .. .. 2·00 1·40
a. Imperf between (horiz pair) .. £190
b. Imperf between (vert pair) £190 £200
c. Imperf horiz (vert pair) £200
d. Imperf (pair) £200
e. Pale yellow-green .. .. .. 5·00 1·90
ea. Imperf (pair) £275

In the redrawn type only the bottom outer frameline is thick, whereas in the original 1877 issue the left-hand frameline is also thick, as shown in Type **1**.

The stamps of Alwar became obsolete on 1 July 1902.

BAHAWALPUR

See after **PAKISTAN**

BAMRA

PRICES FOR STAMPS ON COVER	
Nos. 1/6	—
Nos. 8/40	*from* × 25

Raja Sir Sudhal Deo, 1869–1903

GUM. The stamps of Bamra were issued without gum.

BAMRA postage — 1 (¼ a.)
BAMRA postage — 1*a*
BAMRA postage — 2 (½ a.)
BAMRA postage — 3 (1 a.)
BAMRA postage — 4 (2 a.)
BAMRA postage — 5 (4 a.)
BAMRA postage — 6 (8 a.)

(*illustrations actual size*)

(Typo Jagannata Ballabh Press, Deogarh)

1888. *Imperf.*
1 1 ¼ a. black/*yellow* £130
a. "g" inverted (R.5/1) £1600
b. Last native character inverted .. £1700
c. Last native character as Type 1*a* .. £1700
2 2 ½ a. black/*rose* .. .. .. 70·00
a. "g" inverted (R.5/1) £1400
3 3 1 a. black/*blue* .. .. .. 42·00
a. "g" inverted (R.5/1) £1300
b. Scroll inverted (R.8/4) £1100
4 4 2 a. black/*green* .. .. 60·00 £120
a. "a" omitted (R.8/3) £1400
b. Scroll inverted (R.8/4) £1200
5 5 4 a. black/*yellow* .. .. .. 48·00
a. "a" omitted (R.8/3) £1300
b. Scroll inverted (R.8/4) £1100
6 6 8 a. black/*rose* .. .. .. 38·00
a. "a" omitted (R.8/3) £1250
b. Horiz pair, one printed on back .. £325
c. Scroll inverted (R.8/4) £1000

These stamps were all printed from the same plate of 96 stamps, 12 × 8, but for some values only part of the plate was used. There are 96 varieties of the ½, 4 and 8 a., 72 of the 1 a., 80 of the 2 a. and not less than 88 of the ¼ a.

The scroll ornament can be found pointing to either the right or the left.

There are two forms of the third native character. In the first five horizontal rows it is as in T 1 and in the last three rows as in T 4.

These stamps have been reprinted: the ¼ a. and ½ a. in blocks of 8 varieties (all showing scroll pointing to right), and all the values in blocks of 20 varieties (all showing scroll pointing to left). On the reprints the fourth character is of a quite different shape.

8

1890 (July)–**93**. *Black on coloured paper. Nos. 24/5 and 39/40 show face value as "One Rupee". (a) "Postage" with capital "P".*
8 8 ¼ a. on *rose-lilac* .. .. .. 1·00 1·40
a. "Eeudatory" .. .. .. 10·00 14·00
b. "Quatrer" .. .. .. 10·00 14·00
c. Inverted "e" in "Postage" .. 10·00 14·00
9 ¼ a. on *bright rose* 50 70
10 ¼ a. on *reddish purple* 65 80
a. First "a" in "anna" inverted .. 27·00 30·00
b. "AMRA" inverted .. .. 42·00 42·00
c. "M" and second "A" in "BAMRA" inverted .. .. 50·00 50·00
11 ½ a. on *dull green* 70 90
a. "Eeudatory" .. .. .. 30·00 32·00
12 ½ a. on *blue-green* .. .. 1·40 1·40
13 1 a. on *bistre-yellow* .. .. 1·25 1·25
a. "Eeudatory" .. .. .. 60·00 65·00
14 1 a. on *orange-yellow* .. .. 32·00 32·00
a. "annas" for "anna" .. .. 90·00 90·00
15 2 a. on *rose-lilac* .. .. .. 6·00 10·00
a. "Eeudatory" .. .. .. 95·00 £110
16 2 a. on *bright rose* .. .. 1·60 1·60
17 2 a. on *dull rose* .. .. .. 3·50 2·25
18 4 a. on *rose-lilac* £325 £350
a. "Eeudatory" £1200 £1200
19 4 a. on *dull rose* .. .. .. 2·50 2·50
a. "Eeudatory" £275 £275
b. "BAMBA" £275 £275
20 4 a. on *bright rose* .. .. 2·25 3·00
20*a* 4 a. on *deep pink* .. .. 11·00 9·00
21 8 a. on *rose-lilac* .. .. .. 15·00 24·00
a. "Foudatory" and "Postagc" .. £120 £120
b. "BAMBA" £120 £120
22 8 a. on *bright rose* .. .. 5·50 6·50
23 8 a. on *dull rose* .. .. .. 7·00 8·00
24 1 r. on *rose-lilac* .. .. .. 32·00 42·00
a. "Eeudatory" £250 £250
b. "BAMBA" £160 £160
c. "Postagc" £160 £160
25 1 r. on *bright rose* .. .. 15·00 18·00
a. Small "r" in "rupee" £160 £160
(b) "postage" with small "p" (1891–93)
26 8 ¼ a. on *bright rose* 50 70
27 ¼ a. on *reddish purple* 50 50
28 ½ a. on *dull green* .. .. 80 1·00
a. First "a" in "anna" inverted .. 14·00 15·00
29 ½ a. on *blue-green* .. .. 1·40 1·50
a. First "a" in "anna" inverted .. 14·00 15·00
30 1 a. on *bistre-yellow* .. .. 1·40 1·25
31 1 a. on *orange-yellow* .. .. 32·00 32·00
32 2 a. on *bright rose* .. .. 1·60 2·00
33 2 a. on *dull rose* .. .. .. 3·50 1·50
34 4 a. on *dull rose* .. .. .. 3·75 2·75
35 4 a. on *bright rose* .. .. 3·25 3·50
35*a* 4 a. on *deep pink* .. .. 14·00 11·00
36 8 a. on *rose-lilac* .. .. .. 26·00 35·00
37 8 a. on *bright rose* .. .. 5·50 7·00
38 8 a. on *dull rose* .. .. .. 7·50 8·50
39 1 r. on *rose-lilac* .. .. .. 40·00 55·00
40 1 r. on *bright rose* .. .. 20·00 22·00
a. Small "r" in "rupee" £190 £190
b. Small "r" in "rupee" and native characters in the order 2, 3, 1, 4, 5 £1400 £1400

There are 10 settings of Type **8**. The first setting (of 20 varieties) has capital "P" throughout. The remaining settings (of 16 varieties) have capital "P" and small "p" mixed.

For the first setting the 8 a. and 1 r. values were printed within the same block, the ten lefthand stamps being 8 a. values and the ten righthand stamps 1 r.

The various stamps were distributed between the settings as follows:

Setting I—Nos. 8/c, 11/a, 13/a, 15/a, 18/19a, 21, 24/a.
Setting II—Nos. 19, 19b, 21/b, 24, 24b/c, 34, 36, 39
Setting III—Nos. 9, 11, 13, 16, 26, 28, 30, 32
Setting IV—Nos. 20, 22, 25, 35, 37, 40
Setting V—Nos. 10, 10b/c, 20*a*, 27, 35*a*
Setting VI—Nos. 11, 12, 28, 28a, 29/a
Setting VII—Nos. 10/a, 12, 17, 19, 23, 25a, 27, 29, 33/4, 38, 40a/b
Setting VIII—Nos. 17, 33
Setting IX—Nos. 10/a, 12, 14/a, 17, 19, 23, 27, 29, 31, 33/4, 38
Setting X—Nos. 19, 34

There are 4 sizes of the central ornament, which represents an elephant's trunk holding a stick:—(*a*) 4 mm long; (*b*) 5 mm; (*c*) 6½ mm; (*d*) 11 mm. These ornaments are found pointing to right or left, either upright or inverted.

Ornaments (*a*) are found in all settings; (*b*) in all settings from Settings III to X; (*c*) in Settings I and II; and (*d*) only in Setting I.

The stamps of Bamra have been obsolete since 1 January 1895.

BARWANI

PRICES FOR STAMPS ON COVER	
Nos. 1/2	*from* × 3
Nos. 3/43	*from* × 5

PROCESS. All Barwani stamps are typographed from clichés and are in sheets of 4, *unless otherwise indicated*.

Issues to about 1930 were printed by the Barwani State Printing Press, and subsequently by the *Times of India* Press, Bombay.

GUM. Nos. 1/31 were issued without gum.

BOOKLET PANES. Those stamps which were printed in sheets of 4 were issued in stamp booklets, binding holes appearing in the side margin.

1 Rana Ranjitsingh 2 Rana Ranjitsingh 3

1921 (Mar?). *Clear impression. Medium wove paper. P 7 all round.*
1 1 ¼ a. blue-green (dull *to* deep) .. .. 60·00 £120
2 ½ a. dull blue £130 £170
a. Imperf (pair) .. .. .. — £650

1921 (June?). *Blurred impression. Soft wove paper. P 7 on two or three sides.*
3 1 ¼ a. green (*shades*) .. .. .. 11·00 30·00
4 ½ a. ultramarine (dull *to* pale) .. .. 16·00 45·00

NOTE. As the small sheets of Barwani stamps were often not perforated all round, many of the earlier stamps are perforated on two or three sides only. Owing to the elementary method of printing, the colours vary greatly in depth, even within a single sheet.

1921. *Clear impression. Vertically laid bâtonné paper. Imperf.*
5 1 ¼ a. green (*shades*) .. .. .. 7·50
6 ½ a. green (*shades*) .. .. .. 3·00
a. Perf 11 at top or bottom only .. 3·00

It is suggested that No. 5 may be an error due to printing from the wrong plate.

1922 (?). *Clear impression. Thickish glazed wove paper. P 7 on two or three sides.*
7 1 ¼ a. dull blue .. .. 55·00

1922. *Smooth, soft medium wove paper. P 7 on two or three sides.*
(a) Clear impression
8 1 ¼ a. deep grey-blue .. .. .. 16·00
(b) Poor impression
9 1 ¼ a. steel blue .. .. 8·00

Examples of No. 9 exist with perforations on all four sides.

1922. *P 11 on two or three sides.*
(a) Thick, glazed white wove paper
10 2 1 a. vermilion (*shades*) .. .. .. 1·25 8·50
a. Imperf between (vert pair) £125
11 2 a. purple (*to* violet) .. .. .. 1·60 8·50
a. Doubly printed £125
b. Imperf between (pair) £100 £100
(b) Thick, toned wove paper
12 2 2 a. purple .. .. 9·50 20·00

1922. *Poor impression. Thin, poor wove paper. Pin-perf 8½ on two or three sides.*
13 1 ¼ a. grey (*to* grey-blue) .. .. .. 1·25
a. Imperf (pair) £100
b. Imperf between (vert pair) .. .. 90·00

1923. *Thin, smooth, unglazed wove paper. P 11 on two or three sides.*
14 1 ½ a. green (pale *to* deep) .. .. .. 1·10 7·00
a. Imperf between (pair) £150
15 2 1 a. brown-red £1500 £1500

1923. *Poor impression. Thick, soft wove paper. P 7 on two or three sides.*
16 1 ½ a. green (pale *to* deep) .. .. .. 18·00

No. 16 also exists perforated on all four sides.

1923 (Mar?). *Poor quality wove paper. P 7 on two or three sides.*
17 1 ¼ a. black .. .. 35·00 70·00
a. Imperf between (horiz pair) £550

1923 (May?). *Horizontally laid bâtonné paper. P 12.*
18 1 ¼ a. rose (*shades*) .. .. .. 80 4·50
a. Imperf between (vert or horiz pair) .. £150
b. Pin perf 6 .. .. .. 45·00 26·00
c. Perf compound of 12 and 6 .. .. 24·00
d. Perf 7 .. .. 85·00
da. On wove paper .. .. ..

No. 18 was issued in sheets of 12 (3 panes of 4) and was printed on paper showing a sheet watermark of Britannia and a double-lined inscription. No. 18d was only issued in booklet panes of 4.

1925 (?). *Vertically laid bâtonné paper. P 11.*
19 1 ¼ a. blue (pale *to* deep) .. .. .. 80 4·50
a. *Tête-bêche* (horiz pair) .. ..

No. 19 was issued in sheets of 8 and was printed on paper with a sheet watermark of a shell and an inscription "SHELL" in double-lined capitals.

1927. *Very poor impression. Thin, brittle wove paper. P 7.*

20	1	¼ a. milky blue (*shades*)	9·00	17·00
21		½ a. yellow-green (*shades*)	10·00	
		a. Imperf between (horiz pair)	£250	
22	3	4 a. orange-brown	48·00	
		a. Imperf between (horiz pair)	£325	
20/2		*Set of* 3	60·00	

On Nos. 20/1 the portrait is nearly invisible.

1927. *Thick wove paper. Sewing maching perf* 6–10.

23	3	4 a. yellow-brown	60·00	
		a. Perf 7	20·00	
		b. *Orange-brown*	70·00	

1928–32 (?). *Thick glazed paper. (a) P* 7.

24	1	¼ a. deep bright blue	6·50	
25		½ a. bright yellow-green	8·50	
		(*b*) *P* 10½ (*rough*) (Nov 1928)		
26	1	¼ a. ultramarine	2·50	
		a. *Tête-bêche* (horiz pair)	8·00	
		b. Horiz pair, one stamp printed on reverse		
27		½ a. apple-green	3·25	
		a. *Tête-bêche* (vert pair)	8·00	
		(*c*) *P* 11 (*clean-cut*) (1929-32?)		
28	1	¼ a. bright blue	1·50	4·50
		a. Indigo	1·50	4·50
		ab. Imperf between (horiz pair)	38·00	
		b. Deep dull blue	1·10	4·50
		ba. Imperf between (vert pair)	85·00	
		c. Ultramarine	2·00	5·50
29		½ a. myrtle-green	1·25	4·50
		a. Imperf between (horiz pair)	80·00	
		b. Turquoise-green	3·25	5·50
		ba. Imperf between (vert pair)	£125	
30	2	1 a. rose-carmine (1931)	8·50	14·00
		a. Imperf between (vert pair)	—	£250
31	3	4 a. salmon (*to* orange) (1931)	35·00	55·00
		a. Imperf between (horiz pair)	£450	
28/31		*Set of* 4	40·00	70·00

No. 26 was printed in sheets of 8 (4 × 2) with the two centre pairs *tête-bêche* while No. 27 in similar sheets, had the two horizontal rows *tête-bêche*. Both sheets are always found with one long side imperforate.

Nos. 28/31 were printed in sheets of 8 the two lower values existing either 4 × 2 or 2 × 4 and the two higher values 4 × 2 only. No *tête-bêche* pairs were included in these printings. It is believed that a small printing of No. 31 was produced in sheets of 4, but details are uncertain.

4 Rana Devi Singh 5

1932–47. *Medium to thick wove paper.*

A. *Close setting* (2½–4½ *mm*). *P* 11, 12 *or compound* (1932–8?)
B. *Wide setting* (6–7 *mm*). *P* 11 (1938–48)

			A		B	
32	4	¼ a. slate	70	5·50	1·90	7·50
33		½ a. blue-green	1·25	5·50	2·00	6·00
34		1 a. brown	1·50	5·50	4·50	6·50
		a. Imperf between (horiz pair)	—	—	†	
		b. Chocolate. Perf 8½ (1947)	†		10·00	17·00
35		2 a. purple (*shades*)	3·00	10·00	†	
		a. Rose-carmine	†		75·00	£110
36		4 a. olive-green	6·00	16·00	16·00	20·00
32A/6A		*Set of* 5	11·00	38·00		

The measurements given in the heading indicate the vertical spacing between impressions. There are eight settings of this interesting issue: four "Close" where the over-all stamp dimensions from centre to centre of perfs vary in width from 21½ to 23 mm and in height from 25 to 27½ mm; three "Wide", width 23–23½ mm and height 29–30 mm and one "Medium" (26½ × 31 mm) (No. 34*b* only).

1935–48. *P* 11.

A. *Close setting* (3–4½ *mm*). *Thick, cream-surfaced wove paper*
B. *Wide setting* (7–10 *mm*). *Medium to thick wove paper* (1938–48)

			A		B	
37	1	¼ a. black	1·40	—	2·50	10·00
38		½ a. blue-green	9·00	12·00	†	
		a. Yellowish green	5·00	9·00	3·75	12·00
39	2	1 a. brown (*shades*)	7·00	10·00	5·50	9·00
		a. Perf 8½ (5 mm) (1948)	†		7·00	16·00
40		2 a. bright purple	†		40·00	75·00
41		2 a. rose-carmine (1945?)	†		16·00	50·00
42	3	4 a. sage-green	16·00	27·00	14·00	22·00
		a. Pale sage-green (1945?)	†		8·50	15·00

There were two "Close" settings (over-all stamp size 25 × 29 mm) and six "Wide" settings with over-all sizes 26½–31½ × 31–36½ mm. There was also one "Medium" setting (26½ × 31 mm) but this was confined to the 1 a. perf 8½, No. 39a.

1938. *P* 11.

43	5	1 a. brown	9·50	25·00

Stamps printed in red with designs similar to Types 3 and 5 were intended for fiscal use.

The stamps of Barwani became obsolete on 1 July 1948.

OMNIBUS ISSUES

Details, together with prices for complete sets, of the various Omnibus issues from the 1935 Silver Jubilee series to date are included in a special section following Zululand at the end of the catalogue.

BHOPAL

PRICES FOR STAMPS ON COVER

Nos. 1/100	*from* × 10
Nos. O301/57	*from* × 15

The correct English inscription on these stamps is "H.H. NAWAB SHAH JAHAN BEGAM". In the case of Nos. 22 and 23 the normal stamps are spelt "BEGAN" and specimens with "BEGAM" are "errors".

As the stamps were printed from lithographic stones on which each unit was drawn separately by hand, numerous errors of spelling occurred. These are constant on all sheets and are listed. Some of our illustrations inadvertently include errors of spelling.

ILLUSTRATIONS. Types **1/3***a* and **6/12***a* are shown actual size.

EMBOSSING. Nos. 1/99 were only valid for postage when embossed with the device, in Urdu, of the ruling Begam. On T **1/3** and **6** to **12***a*. this was intended to fill the central part of the design. Almost all varieties can be found with the embossing inverted or sideways, as well as upright.

Shah Jahan

Sultan Jahan

(*actual size*)

The various basic types were often in concurrent use but for greater convenience the following list is arranged according to types instead of being in strict chronological order.

GUM. Nos. 1/99 were issued without gum.

Nawab Shah Jahan Begam, 16 November 1868–15 June 1901

1 (¼ a.)

1872. *Litho. (a) Double frame. Sheets of* 20 (5 × 4)

1	1	¼ a. black	£225	£225
		a. "BFGAM" (R.3/1)	£1000	£1000
		b. "BEGAN" (R.2/2, R.4/4)	£600	£600
		c. "EGAM" (R.4/5)	£1000	£1000
2		½ a. red	10·00	18·00
		a. "BFGAM" (R.3/1)	60·00	75·00
		b. "BEGAN" (R.2/2, R.4/4)	40·00	50·00
		c. "EGAM" (R.4/5)	60·00	75·00

2 (½ a.)

(*b*) *Single frame. Sheets of* 20 (4 × 5)

3	2	¼ a. black	—	£3000
4		½ a. red	6·00	10·00
		a. "NWAB" (R.2/2)	35·00	45·00

3 (¼ a.)

3*a* (¼ a.)

1878 (Jan). *All lettered* "EEGAM" *for* "BEGAM". *Sheets of* 20 (4 × 5).

(*a*) *Plate* 1. *Frame lines extend horiz and vert between stamps throughout sheet*

5	3	¼ a. black	1·60	4·00
		(*b*) *Plate* 2. *Frame lines normal*		
5*a*	3*a*	¼ a. black	1·60	4·00

Apart from the frame line difference between Types **3** and **3***a* the stamps can also be distinguished by the differences in the value tablets, notably the thin vertical line in the centre in Type **3***a* compared with the slightly diagonal and heavier line in Type **3**.

4 (¼ a.)

5 (½ a.)

1878 (June?)–**79**. *Value in parenthesis* (*Nos.* 6/7). *Sheets of* 32 (4 × 8). *Imperf.*

6	4	¼ a. green (1879)	6·00	8·00
7		¼ a. green (*perf*) (1879)	7·00	10·00
8	5	½ a. red	2·75	4·25
		a. "JAHN" (R.5/2)	22·00	
		b. "NWAB" (R.3/2, R.4/2)	14·00	
		c. "EEGAM" (R.1/3)	22·00	
9		½ a. brown	18·00	24·00
		a. "JAHN" (R.5/2)	£110	
		b. "NWAB" (R.3/2, R.4/2)	70·00	
		c. "EEGAM" (R.1/3)	£110	

The ¼ a. shows the "N" of "NAWAB" reversed on R.6/4 and the "N" of "JAHAN" reversed on R.1/2–4 and R.2/2–4.

1880. *T* **5** *redrawn; value not in parenthesis. Sheets of* 32 (4 × 8)

	(*a*) *Imperf*		
10	¼ a. blue-green	4·00	
	a. "NAWA" (R.2/2–4)	20·00	
	b. "CHAH" (R.8/3)	45·00	
11	½ a. brown-red	6·00	9·00
	(*b*) *Perf*		
12	¼ a. blue-green	4·50	
	a. "NAWA" (R.2/2–4)	25·00	
	b. "CHAH" (R.8/3)	55·00	
13	½ a. brown-red	3·25	

The ¼ a. shows the "N" of "NAWAB" reversed on R.8/4.

1884. *T* **5** *again redrawn. Sheets of* 32 (4 × 8), *some with value in parenthesis, others not. Perf.*

14	¼ a. greenish blue	2·50	5·00
	a. "ANAWAB" (R.8/1–4)	16·00	

In this plate there is a slanting dash under and to left of the letters "JA" of "JAHAN," instead of a character like a large comma, as on all previous varieties of this design. With the exception of R.1/1 all stamps in the sheet show "N" of "JAHAN" reversed.

1895. *T* **5** *again redrawn. Sheets of* 8 (2 × 4). *Laid paper.*

15	¼ a. red (*imperf*)	1·25	1·00
16	¼ a. red (*perf*)	—	£150

In these cases where the same design has been redrawn several times, and each time in a number of varieties of type, it is not easy to distinguish the various issues. Nos. 6 and 7 may be distinguished from Nos. 10 and 12 by the presence or absence of the parenthesis marks (); 8, 9 and 11 differ principally in colour; 8 and 15 are very much alike, but differ in the value as well as in paper.

6 (1 a.)

1881. *Sheets of* 24 (4 × 6). *Imperf.*

17	6	¼ a. black	1·10	3·50
		a. "NWAB" (R.6/2–4)	4·50	
18		½ a. red	1·25	2·75
		a. "NWAB" (R.6/2–4)	4·50	
19		1 a. brown	1·10	3·00
		a. "NWAB" (R.6/2–4)	4·50	
20		2 a. blue	1·00	3·00
		a. "NWAB" (R.6/2–4)	4·50	
21		4 a. buff	5·50	15·00
		a. "NWAB" (R.6/2–4)	18·00	
17/21		*Set of* 5	9·00	24·00

In this issue all values were produced from the same drawing, and therefore show exactly the same varieties of type. The value at foot in this and all the following issues is given in only one form.

7 (½ a.)

1886. *Similar to T* **6** *but normally lettered* (*incorrectly*) "BEGAN"; *larger lettering. Sheets of* 32 (4 × 8). (*a*) *Imperf.*

22	7	½ a. pale red	70	2·50
		a. "BEGAM" (R.2/1)	7·50	
		b. "NWAB" (R.3/4)	7·50	
		(*b*) *Perf*		
23	7	½ a. pale red	75·00	
		a. "BEGAM" (R.2/1)	£275	
		b. "NWAB" (R.3/4)	£275	

8 (4 a.)

1886. *T 8. T 6 redrawn. Sheets of 24 (4 × 6). The "M" of "BEGAM" is an inverted "W". The width of the stamps is rather greater than the height. (a) Wove paper. Imperf.*

24 8 4 a. yellow £200
a. "EEGAM" (R.2/3–4, R.3/3–4, R.4/2, R.4/4, R.6/1) £300

(b) Laid paper

25 8 4 a. yellow (*imperf*) .. .. 5·00
a. "EEGAM" (R.2/3–4, R.3/3–4, R.4/2, R.4/4, R.6/1) .. .. .. 10·00
26 4 a. yellow (*perf*) .. .. 2·50 6·00
a. "EEGAM" (R.2/3–4, R.3/3–4, R.4/2, R.4/4, R.6/1) .. .. .. 5·00 10·00

1889. *T 6 again redrawn. Sheets of 32 (4 × 8) lettered "BEGAN."*

27 ¼ a. black (*perf*) .. .. 70 1·25
a. "EEGAN" (R.7/3) .. .. 8·00 10·00
28 ¼ a. black (*imperf*) .. .. 1·10 1·50
a. "EEGAN" (R.7/3) .. .. 12·00 14·00

9 (¼ a.)

1889–90. *T 9. T 6 again redrawn. Sheets of 24 (4 × 6), all with "M" like an inverted "W". Wove paper. (a) Imperf.*

29 9 ¼ a. black 55 70
30 1 a. brown .. .. 85 1·25
a. "EEGAM" (R.2/3) .. .. 8·50 10·00
b. "BBGAM" (R.3/1) .. .. 8·50 10·00
31 2 a. blue 75 90
a. "BBEGAM" (R.1/2) .. .. 6·50 7·50
b. "NAWAH" (R.4/2) .. .. 6·50 7·50
32 4 a. orange-yellow .. .. 1·25 1·75
29/32 .. .. *Set of* 4 3·00 4·00

(b) Perf

33 9 ¼ a. black 70 85
34 1 a. brown .. .. 1·00 1·40
a. "EEGAM" (R.2/3) .. .. 9·00 11·00
b. "BBGAM" (R.3/1) .. .. 9·00 11·00
35 2 a. blue .. .. 75 1·10
a. "BBEGAM" (R.1/2) .. .. 6·50 8·00
b. "NAWAH" (R.4/2) .. .. 6·50 8·00
36 4 a. orange-yellow .. .. 1·50 2·75
33/6 .. .. *Set of* 4 3·50 5·50

Nos. 32 and 36 are nearly square, in many cases rather larger in height than in width.

1891. *As last, but sheets of 32 (4 × 8).*

37 9 ½ a. red (*imperf*) .. .. 75 1·00
38 ½ a. red (*perf*) .. .. 75 1·25

1894–98. *T 6 again redrawn; (a) Sheets of 24 (4 × 6), almost all showing a character inside the octagon below, as in T 9. Wove paper.*

39 1 a. deep brown (*imperf*) .. .. .. 1·60 1·25
a. Red-brown .. .. 20·00
b. Printed both sides .. .. .. — £350
41 1 a. deep brown (*perf*) .. .. 2·00 1·75

10 (1 a.)

(b) As Nos. 39/41, but printed from a fresh transfer (?), showing the lines blurred and shaky. Wove paper. Imperf (1898)

42 10 1 a. purple-brown .. .. 2·00 2·75
a. "NAWAH" (R.4/1) .. .. 13·00 15·00
43 1 a. purple-brown/*buff* .. .. .. 2·00 2·75
a. "NAWAH" (R.4/1) .. .. 13·00 15·00
b. Printed on both sides .. ..

The above are known without embossing.

NEW INFORMATION

The editor is always interested to correspond with people who have new information that will improve or correct the Catalogue.

11 (¼ a.)

1895. *Sheets of 8 (2 × 4), lettered "EEGAM". White laid paper.*

44 11 ¼ a. black (*imperf*) .. .. 1·25 1·10
a. "A" inserted (R.4/2) .. .. .. 5·00 5·00
45 ¼ a. black (*perf*) .. .. 24·00 12·00
a. "NAW B" (R.4/2) £200 £150

On the perf stamp the second "A" in "NAWAB" was missing on R.4/2 in the setting. This letter was later inserted for the imperf printing varying progressively from small to large.

12 (½ a.)

1895. *Narrow label at bottom. Sheets of 8 (2 × 4), lettered "W W" for "H H". Laid paper.*

46 12 ½ a. black (*imperf*) .. .. 80 1·00

12*a*

1895. *Sheets of 8 (2 × 4). Laid paper.*

47 12*a* ½ a. red (*imperf*) 85 90

No. 47 is a combination of Types 1 and 6, having the double outer frame to the octagon and the value in one form only.

13 (¼ a.)

(14 (¼ a.)

1884. *Sheets of 32 (4 × 8). Perf.*

48 13 ¼ a. blue-green £125 £150
a. "JAN" (R.2/1–2, R.3/1, R3/3–4, R.4/1–3, R.5/1–3) £125
b. "BEGM" (R.2/3–4) £350
c. "NWAB" and "JAN" (R.3/2) £600
ca. "NWAB" and "JN" (R.5/4) £600
d. "SHAHAN" (R.4/4) £600
e. "JAHA" (R.6/2–4) £275

1895. *T 14, double-lined frame round each stamp. Sheets of 6 (2 × 3), lettered "JAN". Laid paper.*

49 14 ¼ a. bright green (*imperf*) .. .. .. 1·50 2·25

15 (½ a.)

16 (¼ a.)

1884. *Sheets of 32 (4 × 8). Laid paper.*

50 15 ¼ a. blue-green (*imperf*) .. .. .. 45·00 55·00
a. "NWAB" (R.1/1) £225
b. "SAH" (R.1/4) £225
c. "NAWA" and "JANAN" (R.3/2) £225
51 ¼ a. blue-green (*perf*) 30 70
a. "NWAB" (R.1/1) .. .. 3·00
b. "SAH" (R.1/4) .. .. 3·00
c. "NAWA" and "JANAN" (R.3/2) .. .. 3·00
d. Imperf between (vert pair) £100
52 ½ a. black (*imperf*) 50 60
a. "NWAB" (R.1/1) .. .. 5·00
b. "SAH" (R.1/4) .. .. 5·00
c. "NAWA" and "JANAN" (R.3/2) .. .. 5·00
53 15 ½ a. black (*perf*) 30 70
a. "NWAB" (R.1/1) .. .. 3·00
b. "SAH" (R.1/4) .. .. 3·00
c. "NAWA" and "JANAN" (R.3/2) .. .. 3·00

The ¼ a. of this issue is in *blue-green*, or *greenish blue*. Both values were printed from the same stone, the value alone being altered. There are therefore the same varieties of each. These are the only stamps of this design on laid paper.

Both values show the "N" of "NAWAB" reversed on R.1/1–4, R.2/1–4, R.3/1–4 and the "N" of "JAHAN" reversed on R.1/1–4, R.2/1–4, R.3/4.

1886. *T 15 redrawn. Sheets of 32 (4 × 8). Wove paper.*

54 ¼ a. green (*imperf*) 25 80
a. "NAWA" (R.6/3–4) .. .. 1·50
b. "NWAB" (R.1/1) .. .. 2·50
c. "NWABA" (R.7/4) .. .. 2·50
d. "NAWAA" (R.6/2) .. .. 2·50
e. "BEGAAM" and "NWABA" (R.7/3) .. 2·50
55 ¼ a. green (*perf*) .. .. 50 1·10
a. "NAWA" (R.6/3–4) .. .. 3·75
b. "NWAB" (R.1/1) .. .. 5·50
c. "NWABA" (R.7/4) .. .. 5·50
d. "NAWAA" (R.6/2) .. .. 5·50
e. "BEGAAM" and "NWABA" (R.7/3) .. 5·50
56 ½ a. red (*imperf*) 40 50
a. "SAH" (R.1/4) .. .. 3·00
b. "NAWABA" (R.6/3–4) .. .. .. 2·50

The ¼ a. varies from *yellow-green* to *deep green*.

All examples of the ¼ a. value show the "N" of "NAWAB" reversed. On the same value the "N" of "JAHAN" is reversed on all positions except R.3/2, R.4/1, R.4/3. On the ½ a. both "N"s are always reversed.

1888. *T 15 again redrawn. Sheets of 32 (4 × 8), letters in upper angles smaller. "N" of "NAWAB" correct. Wove paper.*

57 ¼ a. deep green (*imperf*) 35 55
a. "SAH" (R.6/2) .. .. 3·25
b. "NAWA" (R.4/4) .. .. 3·25
58 ¼ a. deep green (*perf*) 45 65
a. "SAH" (R.6/2) .. .. 4·00
b. "NAWA" (R.4/4) .. .. 4·00

Nos. 50 to 58 have the dash under the letter "JA" as in No. 14.

1891. *T 15 again redrawn. Sheets of 32 (4 × 8), lettered "NWAB." Wove paper. (a) Imperf.*

59 ½ a. red 40 50
a. "SAH" (R.2/4) .. .. 3·00

(b) P 3 to 4½, or about 7

60 ½ a. red 60 70
a. "SAH" (R.2/4) .. .. 4·50

Nos. 59 and 60 have the comma under "JA". The "N" of "JAHAN" is reversed on R.1/1–3, R.2/1–2.

1894. *T 15 again redrawn; letters in corners larger than in 1888, value in very small characters. Sheets of 32 (4 × 8), all with "G" in left-hand lower corner. Wove paper.*

61 ¼ a. green (*imperf*) 55 60
a. "NAWAH" (R.4/4) .. .. 5·50
b. Value in brackets (R.1/1) .. .. .. 5·50
62 ¼ a. green (*perf*) 70 80
a. "NAWAH" (R.4/4) .. .. 7·00
b. Value in brackets (R.1/1) .. .. .. 7·00

Nos. 61 and 62 have neither the dash nor the comma under "JA".

1896. *T 16; oval narrower, stops after "H.H.", space after "NAWAB". The line down the centre is under the first "H" of "SHAH" or between "HA" instead of being under the second "H" or between "AH". Sheets of 32 (4 × 8). Wove paper. Imperf.*

63 16 ¼ a. bright green 25 25
a. "SHAN" (R.1/1) .. .. 2·50
64 ¼ a. pale green 30 30
a. "SHAN" (R.1/1) .. .. 3·00
65 ¼ a. black 30 30
a. "SHAN" (R.1/1) .. .. 3·00

1899. *T 15 redrawn. Sheets of 32 (4 × 8), the first "A" of "NAWAB" always absent. Numerous defective and malformed letters. Wove paper. Imperf.*

66 ½ a. black .. .. 1·40 2·00
a. "NWASBAHJANNI" (R.2/4) .. .. .. 10·00 13·00
b. "SBAH" (R.3/3, R.4/3–4, R.5/1–2, R.6/4) 5·00 6·50
c. "SBAN" (R.8/2) .. .. 10·00 13·00
d. "NWIB" (R.3/2) .. .. 10·00 13·00
e. "BEIAM" (R.4/4) .. .. 10·00 13·00
f. "SHH" (R.6/3) .. .. 10·00 13·00
g. "SBAH" and "BBGAM" (R.3/4) .. .. 10·00 13·00
h. "BBGAM" (R.1/3) .. .. 10·00 13·00

17 (8 a.)

(18 (¼ a.)

1890. *T 17. Sheets of 10 (2 × 5). Single-line frame to each stamp.*

(a) Wove paper

67 17 8 a. slate-green (*imperf*) .. .. .. 22·00 30·00
a. "HAH" (R.3/1, R.4/1, R.5/1) .. .. 42·00
b. "JABAN" (R.2/2) .. .. 42·00
68 8 a. slate-green (*perf*) .. .. .. 22·00 30·00
a. "HAH" (R.3/1, R.4/1, R.5/1) .. .. 42·00
b. "JABAN" (R.2/2) .. .. 42·00

(b) Thin laid paper

69 17 8 a. green-black (*imperf*) .. .. .. 30·00 38·00
a. "HAH" (R.3/1, R.4/1, R.5/1) .. .. 50·00
b. "JABAN" (R.2/2) .. .. 50·00
70 8 a. green-black (*perf*) .. .. .. 30·00 38·00
a. "HAH" (R.3/1, R.4/1, R.5/1) .. .. 50·00
b. "JABAN" (R.2/2) .. .. 50·00

The "N" of "NAWAB" is reversed on R.5/2 and the "N" of "JAHAN" on R.1/1–2, R.2/2, R.3/2, R.4/2 and R.5/2.

1893. *T 17 redrawn. No frame to each stamp, but a frame to the sheet. Sheets of 10 (2 × 5). (a) Wove paper.*
71 8 a. green-black (*imperf*) .. 14·00 15·00
72 8 a. green-black (*perf*) .. 18·00 22·00
(b) Thin laid paper. Imperf
73 8 a. green-black .. 90·00 £100

1898. *Defective transfer from the stone of 1893. Lettering irregular. Sheets of 10 (2 × 5). Wove paper. Imperf.*
74 8 a. green-black .. 22·00 26·00
a. Reversed "E" in "BEGAM" (R.1/2, R.3/2) 50·00
75 8 a. black .. 22·00 26·00
a. Reversed "E" in "BEGAM" (R.1/2, R.3/2) 50·00

1896–1901. *Sheets of 32 (4 × 8). (a) Wove paper. Imperf.*
76 **18** ¼ a. black .. 50 50
(b) Printed from a fresh transfer (?), lines shaky (1899)
77 **18** ¼ a. black .. 1·25 1·25
(c) The same, on thick wove paper (1901)
78 **18** ¼ a. black .. £100 £100

Nawab Sultan Jahan Begam, 16 June 1901–17 May 1926

19 (¼ a.)

20

1902. *T 19. With the octagonal embossed device of the previous issues. Sheets of 16 (4 × 4) ¼ a. or 8 (2 × 4) others. Thin, yellowish wove paper. Imperf.*
79 **19** ¼ a. rose .. 2·25 4·00
80 ¼ a. rose-red .. 1·50 3·00
81 ½ a. black .. 2·00 4·00
a. Printed both sides .. £325
82 1 a. brown .. 2·50 5·50
83 1 a. red-brown .. 2·50 5·50
84 2 a. blue .. 6·50 8·00
85 4 a. orange .. 32·00 45·00
86 4 a. yellow .. 28·00 40·00
87 8 a. lilac .. 45·00 70·00
88 1 r. rose .. 95·00 £110
79/88 .. *Set of* 7 £160 £210

1903. *With a circular embossed device. Sheets of 16 (4 × 4) ¼ a. (two plates) or 8 (2 × 4) (others).*

A. Wove paper. B. Laid paper

No.	Type	Stamp	A		B	
89	**19**	¼ a. rose-red	75	1·50	50	—
90		¼ a. red	65	1·25	30	1·25
91		½ a. black	50	1·50	60	1·75
92		1 a. brown	1·00	2·50	20·00	—
93		1 a. red-brown	2·00	—	—	—
94		2 a. blue	2·50	7·50	38·00	—
95		4 a. orange		†	90·00	90·00
96		4 a. yellow	14·00	28·00	55·00	55·00
97		8 a. lilac	32·00	50·00	£275	—
98		1 r. rose	40·00	65·00	£275	—
89A/98A		*Set of* 7	80·00	£140		

1903. *No. 71 optd with initial of the new Begam in red.*
99 8 a. green-black .. 42·00 45·00
a. Opt inverted .. £100 £100

Some of the previous stamps remained on sale (and probably in use) after the issue of the series of 1902, and some of these were afterwards put on sale with the new form of embossing; fresh plates were made of some of the old designs, in imitation of the earlier issues, and impressions from these were also sold with the new embossed device. We no longer list these doubtful items.

(Recess Perkins, Bacon & Co)

1908. *P* 13½.
100 **20** 1 a. green .. 1·50 1·00
a. Printed both sides .. £100
b. Imperf (pair)

The ordinary postage stamps of Bhopal became obsolete on 1 July 1908.

OFFICIAL STAMPS

SERVICE (O 1)   SERVICE (O 2)

(Recess and optd Perkins, Bacon)

1908–11. *As T 20, but inscribed* "H.H. BEGUM'S SERVICE" *at left. No wmk. P 13 to 14. Overprinted. (a) With Type O 1.*
O301 ½ a. yellow-green .. 1·25 10
a. Pair, one without overprint .. £175
b. Opt double, one inverted .. 90·00
ba. Ditto. Imperf (pair) .. £110
c. Opt inverted .. £100 £100
d. Imperf between (horiz pair) .. £275
O302 1 a. carmine-red .. 1·50 15
a. Opt inverted .. 70·00 70·00
b. Imperf (pair) .. 85·00
c. Red .. 1·75 10
O303 2 a. ultramarine .. 13·00 10
a. Imperf (pair) .. 50·00
O304 4 a. brown (1911) .. 8·00 15
O301/4 .. *Set of* 4 21·00 40

(b) With Type O 2
O305 ½ a. yellow-green .. 3·00 15
O306 1 a. carmine-red .. 5·00 90
O307 2 a. ultramarine .. 3·00 25
a. Opt inverted .. 25·00
O308 4 a. brown (1911) .. 65·00 25
a. Opt inverted .. 20·00 60·00
b. Opt double .. 75·00
c. Imperf (pair) .. 75·00
d. Imperf (pair) and opt inverted .. 75·00
O305/8 .. *Set of* 4 70·00 1·40

The two overprints differ in the shape of the letters, noticeably in the "R"

Nawab Mohammad Hamidullah. Khan
17 May 1926 to transfer of administration to India, 1 June 1949

SERVICE
(O 3) (O 4)

(Des T. I. Archer. Litho Indian Govt Ptg Wks, Nasik)

1930 (1 July)–**31.** *Type O 4 (25½ × 30½ mm) optd with Type O 3. P 14.*
O309 O 4 ½ a. sage-green (1931) .. 1·75 15
O310 1 a. carmine-red .. 3·00 10
O311 2 a. ultramarine .. 3·00 10
O312 4 a. chocolate .. 2·75 20
O309/12 .. *Set of* 4 9·50 50

The ½ a., 2 a. and 4 a. are inscribed "POSTAGE" at left.

(Litho Perkins, Bacon)

1932–34. *As Type O 4 (21 × 25 mm), but inscr* "POSTAGE" *at left. Optd with Type O 1. (a)* "BHOPAL STATE" *at right. P 13.*
O313 ¼ a. orange .. 1·40 25
a. Perf 11½ (1933) .. 3·25 15
b. Perf 14 (1934) .. 8·50 25
c. Perf 13½ (1934) .. 8·50 25
ca. Vert pair, one without opt .. 85·00
(b) "BHOPAL GOVT" *at right. P 13½*
O314 ½ a. yellow-green .. 1·75 10
O315 1 a. carmine-red .. 2·75 10
a. Vert pair, one without opt .. £160
O316 2 a. ultramarine .. 3·50 45
O317 4 a. chocolate .. 2·75 60
a. Perf 14 (1934) .. 8·50 40
O313/17 .. *Set of* 5 11·00 1·10

No. O317 is comb-perforated and No. O317a line-perforated.

¼A (O 5)   THREE PIES (O 6)   ONE ANNA (O 7)

1935–36. *Nos. O314, O316 and O317 surch as Types O 5 to O 7.*
O318 O 5 ¼ a. on ½ a. yellow-green (R.) .. 8·50 4·00
a. Surch inverted .. 65·00 50·00
O319 O 6 3 p. on ½ a. yellow-green (R.) .. 80 80
a. "THEEE PIES" (R. 7/10) .. 32·00 32·00
b. "THRFE" for "THREE" (R. 10/6) 32·00 32·00
c. Surch inverted .. 40·00 35·00
O320 O 5 ¼ a. on 2 a. ultramarine (R.) .. 7·50 4·00
a. Surch inverted .. 65·00 50·00
O321 O 6 3 p. on 2 a. ultramarine (R.) .. 65 70
a. Surch inverted .. 40·00 35·00
b. "THEEE PIES" (R. 7/10) .. 32·00 32·00
ba. Ditto. Surch inverted .. £225 £225
c. "THRFE" for "THREE" (R. 10/6) 32·00 32·00
ca. Ditto. Surch inverted .. £225 £225
O322 O 5 ¼ a. on 4 a. chocolate (R.) .. £325 90·00
O323 ¼ a. on 4 a. chocolate (No. O317a) (Blk.) (23.5.36) .. 20·00 9·00
O324 O 6 3 p. on 4 a. chocolate (R.) .. 40·00 22·00
a. "THEEE PIES" (R. 7/10) .. £190 £190
c. "THRFE" for "THREE" (R. 10/6) £190 £190
O325 3 p. on 4 a. chocolate (No. O317a) (Blk.) (25.5.36) .. 1·75 1·25
a. "THRER" for "THREE" (R. 8/2) £120 90·00
b. "FHREE" for "THREE" (R. 3/10, 10/1) .. £120 90·00
c. "PISE" for "PIES" (R. 10/10) .. £150 £150
d. "PIFS" for "PIES" (R. 7/9) .. £120 90·00
O326 O 7 1 a. on ½ a. yellow-green (V.) .. 65 80
a. Surch inverted .. 35·00 35·00
b. First "N" in "ANNA" inverted (R. 4/5) .. 38·00 38·00
ba. Ditto. Surch inverted .. £225 £225
O327 1 a. on 2 a. ultramarine (R.) .. 75 55
a. Surch inverted .. 38·00 32·00
b. First "N" in "ANNA" inverted (R. 4/5) .. 38·00 38·00
ba. Ditto. Surch inverted .. £225 £225
O327*d* 1 a. on 2 a. ultramarine (V.) .. 38·00 38·00
da. Surch inverted .. 85·00 85·00
db. First "N" in "ANNA" inverted (R. 4/5) .. £250 £250
dc. Ditto. Surch inverted .. £400 £400
O328 1 a. on 2 a. ultram (Blk.) (25.5.36) .. 60 65
a. "ANNO" .. £600
O329 1 a. on 4 a. chocolate (B.) .. 90 1·10
a. First "N" in "ANNA" inverted (R. 4/5) .. 38·00 38·00
b. Perf 14 .. 3·00 1·50
ba. Ditto. First "N" in "ANNA" inverted (R. 4/5) .. 65·00 55·00

Nos. O318 to O325 are arranged in composite sheets of 100 (10 × 10). The two upper horizontal rows of each value are surcharged as Type O **5** and the next five rows as Type O **6**. The remaining three rows are also surcharged as Type O **6** but in a slightly narrower setting.

The surcharge on No. O323 differs from Type O **5** in the shape of the figures and letter.

O 8

(Des T. I. Archer. Litho Indian Govt Ptg Wks, Nasik (No. O330). Typo Bhopal Govt Ptg Wks (others))

1935–39. *As Type* O **8**.
(a) Litho. Inscr "BHOPAL GOVT POSTAGE". *Optd* "SERVICE" *(13½ mm). P 13½.*
O330 1 a. 3 p. blue and claret .. 35 15
(b) Typo. Inscr "BHOPAL STATE POSTAGE". *Optd* "SERVICE" *(11 mm). P 12*
O331 1 a. 6 p. blue and claret (1937) .. 30 20
a. Imperf between (pair) .. 75·00 75·00
b. Opt omitted .. 65·00 60·00
c. Opt double, one inverted .. £125 £125
d. Imperf (pair) .. — 70·00
e. Blue printing double .. — 60·00
O332 1 a. 6 p. claret (1939) .. 75 20
a. Imperf between (pair) .. 75·00 75·00
b. Opt omitted .. — £125
c. Opt double, one inverted .. — £125
d. Opt double .. — £125

PRINTERS. From No. O333 all issues were printed by the Bhopal Govt Ptg Wks in typography.

O 9

O 10 The Moti Mahal

1936 (July)–**38.** *Optd* "SERVICE". *P 12.*
O333 O **9** ¼ a. orange (Br.) .. 30 15
a. Imperf between (vert pair) .. 80·00
b. Opt inverted .. 85·00 85·00
c. Black opt .. 6·00 1·00
ca. Ditto. Opt inverted .. — £140
O334 ¼ a. yellow (Br.) (1938) .. 35 10
O335 1 a. scarlet .. 30 10
a. Imperf between (horiz pair) .. 45·00 45·00
b. Imperf between (vert pair) .. — 75·00
c. Imperf between (block of four) £130 £130

1936–49. *As Type* O **10** *(various palaces). P 12.*
(a) Optd "SERVICE" *(13½ mm)*
O336 ½ a. purple-brown and yellow-green .. 30 15
a. Imperf between (vert pair) .. — 65·00
ab. Imperf between (horiz pair) .. — 65·00
b. Opt double .. 90·00 65·00
c. Frame double .. 40·00 12·00
d. Purple-brown and green (1938) .. 30 15
(b) Optd "SERVICE" *(11 mm)*
O337 2 a. brown and blue (1937) .. 35 15
a. Imperf between (vert pair) .. — 80·00
ab. Imperf between (horiz pair) .. — 65·00
b. Opt inverted .. 85·00 85·00
c. Pair, one without opt .. £140
d. As c. but opt inverted .. £275
O338 2 a. green and violet (1938) .. 1·50 15
a. Imperf between (vert pair) .. — 65·00
b. Imperf between (vert strip of 3) 50·00 55·00
c. Frame double .. — 65·00
d. Centre double .. — 65·00
O339 4 a. blue and brown (1937) .. 80 50
a. Imperf between (horiz pair) .. — £150
b. Opt omitted .. — £100
c. Opt double .. — £100
d. Blue and reddish brown (1938) .. 1·00 50
da. Frame double .. — 90·00
O340 8 a. bright purple and blue (1938) .. 1·25 65
a. Imperf between (vert pair) .. — £110
b. Opt omitted .. — 80·00
c. Opt double .. — 85·00
d. Imperf vert (horiz pair) and opt omitted .. — £100
e. Imperf (pair) and opt omitted .. — £100
O341 1 r. blue and reddish purple (Br.) (1938) .. 2·50 1·60
a. Imperf horiz (vert pair) .. — £400
b. Opt in black (1942) .. 10·00 6·00
ba. Light blue and bright purple .. 25·00 25·00
bb. Laid paper .. £160
O336/41 .. *Set of* 6 6·00 2·75
(c) Optd "SERVICE" *(11½ mm) with serifs*
O342 1 r. dull blue and bright purple (Blk.) (1949) .. 30·00 42·00
a. "SREVICE" for "SERVICE" (R. 6/6) 85·00 £110
b. "SERVICE" omitted .. £275
(d) Optd "SERVICE" *(13½ mm) with serifs*
O343 8 a. bright purple and blue (1949) .. 40·00 55·00
a. "SERAICE" for "SERVICE" (R. 6/5) £150 £175
b. Fig "1" for "I" in "SERVICE" (R. 7/1) £150 £175

The ½ a. is inscr "BHOPAL GOVT" below the arms, other values have "BHOPAL STATE".

Designs:—(37½ × 22½ *mm*) 2 a. The Moti Masjid; 4 a. Taj Mahal and Be-Nazir Palaces. (39 × 24 *mm*)—8 a. Ahmadabad Palace. (45½ × 27½ *mm*)—1 r. Rait Ghat.

O 11 Tiger

O 13 The Moti Mahal

1940. *As Type* O **11** *(animals). P* 12.
O344 ¼ a. bright blue .. .. 2·00 20
O345 1 a. bright purple (Spotted Deer) .. .. 7·50 40

1941. *As Type* O **8** *but coloured centre inscr* "SERVICE"; *bottom frame inscr* "BHOPAL STATE POSTAGE". *P* 12.
O346 1 a. 3 p. emerald-green 30 20
a. Imperf between (pair) £150 £150

1944–47. *As Type* O **13** *(various palaces). P* 12.
O347 ½ a. green 40 30
a. Imperf (pair) .. .. — 35·00
b. Imperf between (vert pair) .. .. — 60·00
c. Doubly printed .. .. — 50·00
O348 2 a. violet .. .. 2·25 80
a. Imperf (pair) .. .. — 35·00
c. *Bright purple* (1945) 75 70
d. *Mauve* (1947) .. .. 4·50 2·75
e. Error. Chocolate (imperf) .. .. 70·00 70·00
O349 4 a. chocolate .. .. 1·25 50
a. Imperf (pair) .. .. — 45·00
b. Imperf vert (horiz pair) .. .. — 75·00
c. Doubly printed .. .. — 60·00
O347/9 .. .. *Set of* 3 2·10 1·25

Design inscr "BHOPAL STATE":—2 a. The Moti Masjid; 4 a. Be-Nazir Palaces.

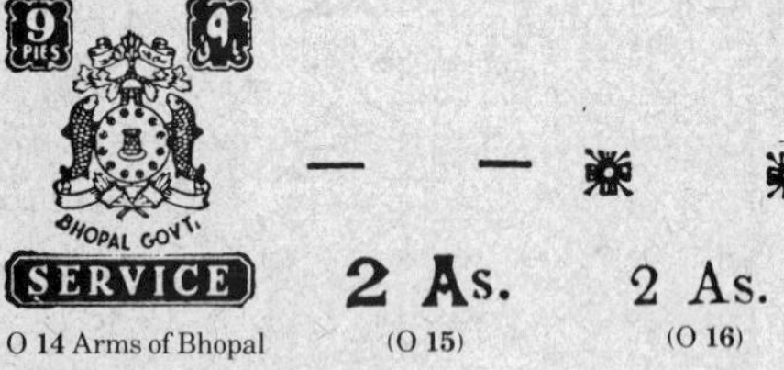
O 14 Arms of Bhopal (O 15) (O 16)

1944–49. *P* 12.
O350 O **14** 3 p. bright blue 20 12
a. Imperf between (pair) .. .. 45·00 45·00
b. Stamp doubly printed .. .. 30·00
O351 9 p. chestnut (*shades*) (1945) .. 3·00 75
a. Imperf (pair) .. .. .. — 65·00
b. *Orange-brown* .. .. .. 1·50 2·00
O352 1 a. purple (1945) .. .. .. 1·00 20
a. Imperf horiz (vert pair) .. .. — 85·00
b. *Violet* (1946) .. .. .. 2·00 70
O353 1½ a. claret (1945) 75 30
a. Imperf between (pair) .. .. — 80·00
O354 3 a. yellow .. .. 1·50 1·75
a. Imperf (pair) .. .. .. — 65·00
b. Imperf horiz (vert pair) .. .. — 80·00
c. Imperf vert (horiz pair) .. ..
d. *Orange-brown* (1949) .. .. 27·00 22·00
O355 6 a. carmine (1945) .. .. .. 6·00 12·00
a. Imperf (pair) .. .. .. — 70·00
b. Imperf horiz (vert pair) .. .. — 80·00
c. Imperf vert (horiz pair) .. .. — 80·00
O350/5 .. .. *Set of* 6 9·50 13·50

1949 (July). *Surch with Type* O **15**. *P* 12.
O356 O **14** 2 a. on 1½ a. claret .. .. .. 90 1·75
a. Stop omitted .. .. .. 8·00 10·00
b. Imperf (pair) £110 £120
ba. Stop omitted (pair) £300 £325
c. "2" omitted (in pair with normal) £150

The "stop omitted" variety occurs on positions 60 and 69 in the sheet of 81.

1949. *Surch with Type* O **16**. *Imperf*.
O357 O **14** 2 a. on 1½ a. claret £250 £300
a. Perf 12 .. .. .. £350 £300

BHOR

PRICES FOR STAMPS ON COVER
Nos. 1/2 *from* × 40
No. 3 *from* × 6

GUM. The stamps of Bhor were issued without gum.

1

2

1879. *Handstamped. Very thick to thin native paper. Imperf.*
1 **1** ½ a. carmine (*shades*) .. .. .. 1·75 2·75
a. *Tête-bêche* (pair) £300
2 **2** 1 a. carmine (*shades*) .. .. .. 2·50 3·75

3 Pant Sachiv Shankarro Chimnâji

1901. *Typo. Wove paper. Imperf.*
3 **3** ½ a. red .. .. 6·00 28·00

BIJAWAR

PRICES FOR STAMPS ON COVER
The stamps of Bijawar are very rare used on cover.

1 Maharaja Sir Sarwant Singh Bahadur 2

(Typo Lakshmi Art Ptg Works, Bombay)

1935 (1 July)–**36**. (*a*) *P* 11.
1 **1** 3 p. brown .. .. 1·00 70
a. Imperf (pair) .. .. 5·50
b. Imperf between (vert pair) .. .. 50·00
2 6 p. carmine 80 70
a. Imperf (pair) .. .. 55·00
b. Imperf between (vert or horiz pair) 50·00
3 9 p. violet .. .. 70 1·10
a. Imperf (pair) .. .. 90·00
b. Imperf between (vert or horiz pair) 50·00
4 1 a. blue .. .. 80 1·25
a. Imperf (pair) .. .. 55·00
b. Imperf between (vert or horiz pair) 55·00
c. Imperf vert (horiz strip of 3) .. 85·00
5 2 a. deep green .. .. 1·25 1·90
a. Imperf (pair) .. .. 85·00
b. Imperf horiz (vert pair) .. .. 11·00
c. Imperf between (vert pair) .. .. 25·00
d. Imperf between (horiz pair) .. 40·00
1/5 .. .. *Set of* 5 4·00 5·00

(*b*) *Roul* 7 (1936)
6 **1** 3 p. brown .. .. 50 1·25
a. Printed on gummed side £200
7 6 p. carmine .. .. 70 2·75
8 9 p. violet .. .. 2·00 13·00
9 1 a. blue .. .. 2·50 16·00
10 2 a. deep green .. .. 2·50 20·00
6/10 .. .. *Set of* 5 7·00 48·00

1937 (May). *Typo. P* 9.
11 **2** 4 a. orange .. .. 2·75 25·00
a. Imperf between (vert pair) £130
b. Imperf (pair) £225
12 6 a. lemon .. .. 2·75 25·00
a. Imperf between (vert pair) £130
b. Imperf (pair) £225
13 8 a. emerald-green .. .. 3·50 30·00
a. Imperf (pair) £225
14 12 a. greenish blue .. .. 4·50 35·00
a. Imperf (pair) £250
15 1 r. bright violet .. .. 14·00 55·00
a. "1 Rs" for "1 R" (R. 1/2) .. .. 42·00 £150
b. Imperf (pair) £250
ba. "1 Rs" for "1 R" (R. 1/2) £650
11/15 .. .. *Set of* 5 25·00 £150

The stamps of Bijawar were withdrawn in 1941.

BUNDI

PRICES FOR STAMPS ON COVER
No. 1 *from* × 2
No. 2 *from* × 4
Nos. 3/53 *from* × 10
Nos. 54/63 *from* × 5
Nos. 64/78 *from* × 2
Nos. 79/92 *from* × 10
Nos. O1/52 *from* × 15
Nos. O53/9 *from* × 20

GUM. Nos. 1/17 were issued without gum.

ILLUSTRATIONS. Types **1/10** and **12/19** are shown actual size.

In Nos. 1 to 17 characters denoting the value are below the dagger, except in Nos. 2a, 11 and 17.

All Bundi stamps until 1914 are imperforate.

1

1894 (May). *Each stamp with a distinct frame and the stamps not connected by the framing lines. Three vertical lines on dagger. Laid or wove paper.*
1 **1** ½ a. slate-grey £3000 £1500
a. Last two letters of value below the rest .. .. — £3000

2 (Block of four stamps)

1894 (Dec). *Stamps joined together, with no space between them. Two vertical lines on dagger. Thin wove paper.*
2 **2** ½ a. slate-grey .. .. 19·00 19·00
a. Value at top, name below £140 £140
b. Right upper ornament omitted .. £600 £600
c. Last two letters of value below the rest £475 £475
d. Left lower ornament omitted .. £600 £600

3

1896 (Nov). *Dagger shorter, lines thicker. Stamps separate. Laid paper.*
3 **3** ½ a. slate-grey .. .. 3·50 4·25
a. Last two letters of value below the rest £275 £275

4 (1 anna)

5 (2 annas)

6 (2 annas)

1897–98. *No shading in centre of blade of dagger. The stamps have spaces between them, but are connected by the framing lines, both vertically and horizontally. Laid paper.*

I. *Blade of dagger comparatively narrow, and either triangular, as in T* **4** *and* **6**, *or with the left-hand corner not touching the bar behind it, as in T* **5** (1897–98)
4 **4** 1 a. Indian red .. .. 7·50 11·00
5 **5** 1 a. red .. .. 7·50 11·00
6 2 a. green .. .. 9·00 13·00
7 **6** 2 a. yellow-green .. .. 9·00 13·00
8 **5** 4 a. green .. .. 20·00 27·00
9 8 a. Indian red .. .. 48·00 70·00
10 1 r. yellow/*blue* .. .. 90·00 £120
4/10 .. .. *Set of* 5 £150 £210

7

II. *Blade varying in shape, but as a rule not touching the bar; value above and name below the dagger, instead of the reverse* (Jan 1898)

11 7 4 a. emerald-green .. .. .. 14·00
a. Yellow-green .. .. .. 10·00

8 (½ anna)

9 (8 annas)

III. *Blade wider and (except on the ½ a.) almost diamond shaped; it nearly always touches the bar* (1898–1900)

12 8 ½ a. slate-grey (5.2.98) .. 90 1·25
13 9 1 a. Indian red (7.98) .. 1·10 1·40
14 2 a. pale green (9.11.98) .. 6·50 6·50
a. First two characters of value (= two) omitted .. £450 £450
15 8 a. Indian red (7.98) .. 4·50 6·50
16 1 r. yellow/*blue* (7.98) .. 7·50 12·00
a. On wove paper .. 7·50 12·00
12/16 .. *Set of* 5 18·00 24·00

10

IV. *Inscriptions as on No. 11; point of dagger to left* (9.11.98)

17 10 4 a. green .. 9·00 12·00
a. Yellow-green .. 7·00 10·00

All the above stamps are lithographed in large sheets, containing as many varieties of type as there are stamps in the sheets.

11 Raja protecting Sacred Cows

Type 11 was produced from separate clichés printed as a block of four. The same clichés were used for all values, but not necessarily in the same order within the block. The Devanagri inscriptions, "RAJ BUNDI" at top and the face value at bottom, were inserted into the basic clichés as required so that various differences exist within the 58 settings which have been identified.

The denominations may be identified from the following illustrations. The ½ a., 3 a. and rupee values can be easily distinguished by their colours.

Bottom tablets:—

¼ a. 1 a.

2 a. 2½ a.

4 a. 6 a.

8 a. 10 a.

12 a. 1 r.

The nine versions of the inscriptions are as follows:

A B

Top tablet

Type A. Top tablet has inscription in two separate words with a curved line over the first character in the second. The second word has three characters.
Bottom tablet has short line above the first character in the second word.

Type B. Top tablet as Type A, but without the curved line over the first character in the second word.
Bottom tablet as Type A.

C

Type C. Top tablet as Type B, but with large loop beneath the first character in the second word. This loop is usually joined to the main character, but is sometimes detached as in the illustration.
Bottom tablet as Type A.

D Top tablet E Bottom tablet

Type D. Top tablet in thinner lettering with the inscription shown as one word of six characters. The fourth character has a curved line above it, as in Type A, and a loop beneath, as in Type C.
Bottom tablet as Type A, but thinner letters.

Type E. Top tablet as Type C.
Bottom tablet shows a redrawn first character to the second word. This has the line at top extending over the entire character.

F
Bottom tablet

Type F. Top tablet as Type B.
Bottom tablet as Type E, but first character in second word differs.

G H

Type G. Top tablet as Type C, but without dot over first character in second word. There are now four characters in the second word.
Bottom tablet as Type E.

Type H. Top tablet as Type G, but with characters larger and bolder.
Bottom tablet as Type E, but with characters larger and bolder.

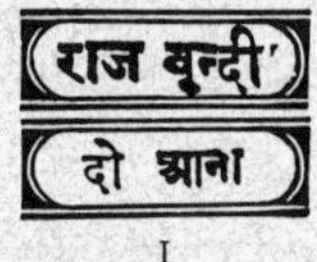

I

Type I. Top tablet as Type H.
Bottom tablet as Type E.

Some settings contained more than one inscription type within the block of four so that *se-tenant* examples are known of Type B with Type C (¼, 1, 2, 4, 8, 10 and 12 a.), Type C with Type E (¼, ½ and 4 a.) and Type E with Type F (½ and 4 a.). Type F only exists from this mixed setting.

1914 (Oct)–**41**. *T* **11**. *Typo. Ungummed paper except for Nos. 73/8.*

I. *Rouletted in colour*

(*a*) *Inscriptions as Type* A. *Thin wove paper* (1916–23)

18 ½ a. black .. 2·00 9·00
19 1 a. vermilion .. 2·00 8·00
20 2 a. emerald .. 1·60
a. Deep green (coarse ptg on medium wove paper) (1923) .. 1·60 6·00
21 2½ a. chrome-yellow (*shades*) (1917) .. 4·00 12·00
22 3 a. chestnut (1917) .. 5·50 14·00
23 4 a. yellow-green .. 17·00
24 6 a. cobalt (1917) .. 11·00 27·00
25 1 r. reddish violet (1917) .. 15·00 38·00

A special printing of the 1 a. took place in late 1917 in connection with the "OUR DAY" Red Cross Society Fund. This had the "RAJ BUNDI" inscription in the bottom tablet with the face value below it. The top tablet carried four Devanagri characters for "OUR DAY". No evidence has been found to suggest that this 1 a. stamp was used for postal purposes (*Price*, £140 *unused*).

(*b*) *Inscriptions as Type* B. *Thin wove or pelure paper* (1914–23)

25*a* ¼ a. cobalt (1916) .. 1·60 7·00
26 ¼ a. ultramarine (*shades*) (1917) .. 1·50 3·25
a. Indigo (1923) .. 1·50 3·25
b. Error. Black (1923)
27 ½ a. black .. 2·00 3·25
28 1 a. vermilion (1915) .. 2·50
a. Carmine (1923) .. 3·25 4·50
b. Red (shades) (1923) .. 3·75
29 2 a. emerald (*shades*) (1915) .. 3·25 8·00
30 2½ a. olive-yellow (1917) .. 4·50 12·00
31 3 a. chestnut (1917) .. 4·00 10·00
32 4 a. apple-green (1915) .. 3·50 14·00
32*a* 4 a. olive-yellow (1917) .. 70·00 90·00
33 6 a. pale ultramarine (*shades*) (1917) .. 7·50 24·00
a. Deep ultramarine (1917) .. 7·50
34 8 a. orange (1915) .. 7·50 28·00
35 10 a. olive-sepia (1917) .. £160
36 12 a. sage-green (1917) .. £300
36*a* 1 r. lilac (*shades*) (1915) .. 20·00

(*c*) *Inscriptions as Type* C. *Thin to medium wove paper* (1917–41)

37 ¼ a. ultramarine (*shades*) (1923) .. 1·75 3·00
a. Indigo (1923) .. 1·75 3·00
b. Error. Black (1923)
c. Cobalt (medium wove paper) (1937) .. 7·00 7·00
38 ½ a. black .. 1·25 2·50
39 1 a. orange-red .. 4·50 6·50
a. Carmine (1923) .. 4·00 5·50
b. Deep red (medium wove paper) (1936) .. 5·00 6·00
40 2 a. emerald .. 5·00 9·00
a. Sage-green .. 5·50
41 4 a. yellow-green (*shades*) .. 20·00 35·00
a. Olive-yellow .. 60·00 80·00
b. Bright apple-green (medium wove paper) (1936) .. 70·00 70·00
42 8 a. reddish orange .. 9·00 25·00
43 10 a. brown-olive .. 13·00 28·00
a. Olive-sepia .. 30·00
b. Yellow-brown .. 30·00
44 12 a. sage-green .. 6·00 28·00
45 1 r. lilac .. 22·00 45·00
46 2 r. red-brown and black .. 40·00 75·00
a. Chocolate and black (medium wove paper) (1936) .. 48·00 85·00
47 3 r. blue and red-brown .. 70·00 £125
a. Grey-blue and chocolate (medium wove paper) (1941) .. 90·00
ab. Chocolate (inscriptions) inverted .. £3000
48 4 r. emerald and scarlet .. £150 £250
49 5 r. scarlet and emerald .. £160 £275

(*d*) *Inscriptions as Type* D. *Thin wove paper* (1918?)

50 2½ a. buff (*shades*) .. 11·00 20·00
51 3 a. red-brown .. 15·00 15·00
a. Semi-circle and dot omitted from 4th character .. 32·00 32·00
52 10 a. bistre .. 24·00 42·00
a. 4th character turned to left instead of downwards .. 45·00
53 12 a. grey-olive .. 32·00
a. 4th character turned to left instead of downwards .. 60·00

(*e*) *Inscriptions as Type* E. (i) *Medium wove paper* (1930–37)

54 ¼ a. deep slate .. 14·00 12·00
54*a* ¼ a. indigo (*thin wove paper*) (1935) .. 6·00 9·00
b. Cobalt (1937) .. 10·00 10·00
55 ½ a. black .. 8·00 11·00
56 1 a. carmine-red .. 15·00 16·00
57 3 a. chocolate (*shades*) (1936) .. 10·00 16·00
58 4 a. yellow-olive (1935) .. £130 90·00
a. Bright apple-green (1936) .. £130 90·00

(ii) *Very thick wove paper* (1930–32)

59 ¼ a. indigo (1932) .. 7·00 8·00
60 ½ a. black .. 26·00
61 1 a. bright scarlet (1931) .. 7·00 9·00
a. Carmine-red .. 26·00

(iii) *Thin horizontally laid paper* (1935)

32 ¼ a. indigo .. 4·00 7·00
63 1 a. scarlet-vermilion .. 6·50 11·00

Nos. 62 and 63 exist in *tête-bêche* blocks of four on the same or opposite sides of the paper.

(*f*) *Inscriptions as Type* F. *Medium wove paper* (1935)

63*a* ½ a. black .. 25·00
63*b* 4 a. yellow-olive .. £250 £180

(*g*) *Inscriptions as Type* G. (i) *Horizontally laid paper* (1935)

64 ½ a. black .. 80·00 80·00
a. Vert laid paper .. 75·00 75·00
65 1 a. scarlet .. 70·00 50·00
66 4 a. bright green .. 20·00 35·00

(ii) *Medium wove paper* (1936)

66*a* ½ a. black .. 4·00 12·00
66*b* 4 a. yellow-green .. £275 £250

(*h*) *Inscriptions as Type* H. *Medium wove paper* (1935–41)

67 ¼ a. ultramarine .. 1·25 7·00
68 ½ a. black (1938) .. 75·00 75·00
69 1 a. deep red .. 5·00 13·00
a. Rosine (1938) .. 7·00 16·00
70 4 a. emerald (1938) .. 17·00 27·00
71 4 r. yellow-green and vermilion (1941) .. £180
72 5 r. vermilion and yellow-green (1941) .. £250

No. 70 shows the currency spelt as "ANE" with the last letter missing and an accent over the Devanagri "N".

II. *P* 11.

(*a*) *Inscriptions as Type* H. *Medium wove paper with gum* (1939–41)

No.	Description	Unused	Used
73	¼ a. ultramarine	25·00	35·00
	a. Greenish blue (1941)	1·75	20·00
74	½ a. black	24·00	24·00
75	1 a. scarlet-vermilion (1940)	£120	60·00
	a. Rose (1940)	12·00	27·00
76	2 a. yellow-green (1941)	15·00	55·00

(*b*) *Inscriptions as Type* I. *Medium wove paper with gum* (1940)

No.	Description	Unused	Used
77	½ a. black	£120	95·00
78	2 a. bright apple-green	42·00	42·00

FISCAL USE. Collectors are warned that the low values of the later settings of Type **11** were extensively used for fiscal purposes. Stamps which have been fraudulently cleaned of pen-cancels, regummed or provided with forged postmarks are frequently met with. Particular care should be exercised with examples of Nos. 64/5, 68/70, 74/5*a* and 77.

20

1941–45. *Typo. P* 11.

No.	Type	Description	Unused	Used
79	**20**	3 p. bright blue	75	2·00
80		6 p. deep blue	90	2·25
81		1 a. orange-red	1·00	2·50
82		2 a. chestnut	4·00	7·00
		a. Deep brown (*no gum*) (1945)	8·00	8·50
83		4 a. bright green	6·00	20·00
84		8 a. dull green	10·00	55·00
85		1 r. deep blue	17·00	65·00
79/85		*Set of* 7	35·00	£130

The first printing only of Nos. 79/85 is usual with gum; all further printings, including No. 82*a*, are without gum.

21 Maharao Rajah Bahadur Singh

22 Bundi

(Typo *Times of India* Press, Bombay)

1947. *P* 11.

No.	Type	Description	Unused	Used
86	**21**	¼ a. blue-green	55	10·00
87		½ a. violet	45	10·00
88		1 a. yellow-green	45	10·00
89	–	2 a. vermilion	1·00	20·00
90	–	4 a. orange	1·25	27·00
91	**22**	8 a. ultramarine	2·25	
92		1 r. chocolate	6·00	
86/92		*Set of* 7	10·50	

On the 2 and 4 a. the Rajah is in Indian dress.

OFFICIAL STAMPS

PRICES. Prices for Nos. O1/52 are for unused examples. Used stamps are generally worth a small premium over the prices quoted.

बूंदी

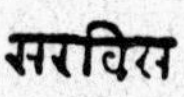

(O 1)

BUNDI

SERVICE

(O 2)

BUNDI

SERVICE

(O 3)

1915–41. *T* **11** *handstamped as Types* O **1/3**. *Ungummed paper except Nos.* O47/52.

A. *Optd with Type* O **1**. B. *Optd with Type* O **2**. C. *Optd with Type* O **3**.

I. *Rouletted in colour*

(*a*) *Inscriptions as Type* A. *Thin wove paper.*

No.	Description	A	B	C
O 1	½ a. black	£100	†	†
	a. Red opt	70·00	†	†
O 1*b*	2 a. emerald	1·75	†	†
	ba. Deep green (*coarse ptg on medium wove paper*)	6·50	11·00	85·00
	bb. Red opt	9·00	11·00	†
O 2	2½ a. chrome-yellow (*shades*)	2·00	5·50	85·00
	a. Red opt	45·00	55·00	†
O 3	3 a. chestnut	2·50	13·00	†
	a. Green opt	40·00	†	†
	b. Red opt	—	—	†
O 4	6 a. cobalt	24·00	24·00	85·00
	a. Red opt	80·00	85·00	£100
O 5	1 r. reddish violet	32·00	32·00	†
	a. Red opt	£110	£120	†

(*b*) *Inscriptions as Type* B. *Thin wove or pelure paper*

No.	Description	A	B	C
O 6	¼ a. ultramarine (*shades*)	1·10	1·60	6·00
	a. Red opt	1·25	4·00	45·00
O 7	½ a. black	2·50	4·50	16·00
	a. Red opt	2·50	11·00	50·00
O 8	1 a. vermilion	4·00	†	†
	a. Red opt	—	†	†
	b. Carmine	5·00	5·00	18·00
	c. Red (*shades*)	—	5·50	—
O 9	2 a. emerald (*shades*)	10·00	15·00	†
	a. Red opt	—	35·00	†
O 9*b*	3 a. chestnut (R.)	—	†	†
O10	4 a. apple-green	11·00	28·00	†
	a. Red opt	75·00	†	†
O10*b*	4 a. olive-yellow	85·00	95·00	†
	ba. Red opt	—	£180	†
O11	6 a. pale ultramarine (*shades*)	11·00	35·00	†
	a. Red opt	75·00	75·00	†
	b. Deep ultramarine	30·00	45·00	†
	ba. Red opt	85·00	85·00	†
O12	8 a. orange	32·00	45·00	£100
	a. Red opt	£100	†	†
O13	10 a. olive-sepia	£110	£140	£170
	a. Red opt	£200	£225	£250
O14	12 a. sage-green	£140	£150	£170
	a. Red opt	†	†	£250
O14*b*	1 r. lilac	£150	†	†

(*c*) *Inscriptions as Type* C. *Thin to medium wove paper.*

No.	Description	A	B	C
O15	¼ a. ultramarine (*shades*)	1·25	1·50	7·50
	a. Red opt	75	5·00	†
	b. Green opt	2·50	14·00	†
	c. Cobalt (*medium wove paper*)	35·00	32·00	£100
	ca. Red opt	22·00	18·00	75·00
O16	½ a. black	2·50	2·50	8·50
	a. Red opt	75	8·00	45·00
	b. Green opt	1·40	†	†
O17	1 a. orange-red	1·25	—	†
	a. Carmine	11·00	4·00	10·00
	b. Deep red (*medium wove paper*)	22·00	27·00	45·00
O18	2 a. emerald	4·50	7·00	†
	a. Red opt	†	30·00	†
	b. Sage-green	7·00	13·00	45·00
O19	4 a. yellow-green (*shades*)	8·00	21·00	†
	b. Red opt	—	†	†
	c. Olive-yellow	65·00	75·00	†
	ca. Red opt	—	£120	†
O20	8 a. reddish orange	14·00	24·00	85·00
	a. Red opt	85·00	†	†
O21	10 a. brown-olive	28·00	40·00	£110
	a. Red opt	£110	£120	£140
O22	12 a. sage-green	32·00	45·00	£120
	a. Red opt	†	†	£160
O23	1 r. lilac	£100	†	†
	a. Red opt	£140	†	†
O24	2 r. red-brown and black	£160	£180	†
	a. Red opt	†	£300	†
	b. Chocolate and black (*medium wove paper*)	£275	£250	†
O25	3 r. blue and red-brown	£200	£200	†
	a. Red opt	£300	†	†
	b. Grey-blue and chocolate (*medium wove paper*)	£300	£300	†
	ba. Red opt	£325	†	†
O26	4 r. emerald and scarlet	£275	£300	†
O27	5 r. scarlet and emerald	£275	£300	†

(*d*) *Inscriptions as Type* D. *Thin wove paper*

No.	Description	A	B	C
O28	2½ a. buff (*shades*)	15·00	18·00	†
	b. Red opt	80·00	—	†
O29	3 a. red-brown	18·00	24·00	†
	a. Variety as No. 51a	35·00	45·00	†
	b. Red opt	†	£120	†
O30	10 a. bistre	26·00	48·00	£150
	a. Variety as No. 52a	55·00	95·00	£225
	b. Red opt	£150	†	†
O31	12 a. grey-olive	32·00	55·00	£150
	a. Variety as No. 53a	65·00	£100	£225
	b. Red opt	£150	£180	†

(*e*) *Inscriptions as Type* E. (i) *Medium wove paper*

No.	Description	A	B	C
O32	¼ a. deep slate	30·00	15·00	†
	a. Red opt	27·00	27·00	†
O32*b*	¼ a. indigo (*thin wove paper*)	12·00	27·00	†
	ba. Red opt	20·00	22·00	†
	bb. Green opt	17·00	22·00	†
	c. Cobalt	48·00	42·00	£100
	ca. Red opt	35·00	30·00	75·00
O33	½ a. black	20·00	13·00	†
	a. Red opt	25·00	10·00	†
	b. Green opt	†	£100	†
O34	1 a. carmine-red	26·00	28·00	85·00
O35	3 a. chocolate (*shades*)	80·00	85·00	£110
	a. Red opt	£150	£160	†
O35*b*	4 a. yellow-olive	†	£180	†

(ii) *Very thick wove paper*

No.	Description	A	B	C
O36	¼ a. indigo	9·00	11·00	†
	a. Red opt	12·00	12·00	†
	b. Green opt	16·00	†	†
O37	½ a. black	28·00	28·00	†
O38	1 a. bright scarlet	13·00	11·00	75·00

(iii) *Thin horizontally laid paper*

No.	Description	A	B	C
O39	¼ a. indigo	35·00	40·00	†
	a. Red opt	5·00	8·00	75·00
O40	1 a. scarlet-vermilion	15·00	18·00	†
	a. Red opt	£100	£110	†

Nos. O39/40a exist in *tête-bêche* blocks of four on the same or opposite sides of the paper.

(*f*) *Inscriptions as Type* F. *Medium wove paper*

No.	Description	A	B	C
O40*b*	½ a. black	—	—	†
	ba. Red opt	—	—	†
O40*c*	4 a. yellow-olive	†	£225	†

(*g*) *Inscriptions as Type* G. (i) *Horizontally laid paper*

No.	Description	A	B	C
O41	½ a. black (red opt)	£110	£110	†
	a. Vert laid paper	£100	£110	†
	ab. Red opt	£100	60·00	£140
O42	4 a. bright green	£120	£140	†
	a. Red opt	£140	£160	†

(ii) *Medium wove paper*

No.	Description	A	B	C
O42*b*	½ a. black	70·00	80·00	†
	ba. Red opt	£150	£150	†

(*h*) *Inscriptions as Type* H. *Medium wove paper*

No.	Description	A	B	C
O43	¼ a. ultramarine	30·00	75·00	†
	a. Red opt	£150	£170	†
O44	½ a. black	£120	£130	†
	a. Red opt	£100	†	£200
O45	1 a. rosine	85·00	85·00	£170
O46	4 a. emerald	£125	£150	£200
	a. Red opt	£160	†	£225

II. *P* 11. (*a*) *Inscriptions as Type* H. *Medium wove paper with gum*

No.	Description	A	B	C
O47	¼ a. ultramarine	45·00	75·00	90·00
	a. Red opt	55·00	85·00	†
	b. Greenish blue	70·00	70·00	90·00
	c. Ditto. Red opt	£100	†	†
O48	½ a. black	45·00	55·00	£100
	a. Red opt	55·00	£100	£100
O49	1 a. scarlet-vermilion	£200	£225	£225
	a. Rose	75·00	65·00	£100
O50	2 a. yellow-green	90·00	85·00	75·00

(*b*) *Inscriptions as Type* I. *Medium wove paper with gum*

No.	Description	A	B	C
O51	½ a. black	£110	£130	£150
	a. Red opt	£110	£140	†
O52	2 a. bright apple-green	£110	£130	†

Until 1941 it was the general practice to carry official mail free but some of the above undoubtedly exist postally used.

1941. *Nos. 79 to 85 optd* "SERVICE".

No.	Type	Description	Unused	Used
O53	**20**	3 p. bright blue (R.)	2·00	3·50
O54		6 p. deep blue (R.)	4·50	5·00
O55		1 a. orange-red	4·00	5·50
O56		2 a. brown	7·00	8·50
O57		4 a. bright green	24·00	55·00
O58		8 a. dull green	60·00	£110
O59		1 r. deep blue (R.)	75·00	£130
O53/9		*Set of* 7	£160	£275

On 25 March 1948 Bundi became part of the Rajasthan Union.

BUSSAHIR (BASHAHR)

PRICES FOR STAMPS ON COVER

Nos. 1/21	*from* × 8
Nos. 22/23	*from* × 2
Nos. 24/43	*from* × 8

1 2 3 4 5 6 7 8 (9)

The initials are those of the Tika Raghunath Singh, son of the then Raja, who was the organiser and former director of the State Post Office.

(Litho at the Bussahir Press by Maulvi Karam Bakhsh, Rampur)

1895 (20 June). *Laid paper. Optd with T* **9** *in pale greenish blue* (B.), *rose* (R.), *mauve* (M.) *or lake* (L.). *With or without gum.*

(*a*) *Imperf.*

No.	Type	Description	Unused	Used
1	**1**	¼ a. pink (R.M.) (1.9.95)	£275	
2	**2**	½ a. grey (R.M.)	£160	
3	**3**	1 a. vermilion (M.)	70·00	
4	**4**	2 a. orange-yellow (R.M.L.)	20·00	65·00
5	**5**	4 a. slate-violet (R.M.L.)	30·00	
		a. Without monogram	85·00	
6	**6**	8 a. red-brown (B.M.L.)	30·00	65·00
		a. Without monogram	80·00	
		b. Thick paper	60·00	
7	**7**	12 a. green (L.)	£100	
8	**8**	1 r. ultramarine (R.M.L.)	35·00	
		a. Without monogram	90·00	

(*b*) *Perf with a sewing machine; gauge and size of holes varying between 7 and 11½*

9 1 ¼ a. pink (B.M.) .. .. 20·00 55·00
a. Without monogram .. .. .. 80·00 80·00
10 2 ½ a. grey (R.) .. .. 14·00 55·00
a. Without monogram £125
11 3 1 a. vermilion (M.) .. .. .. 14·00 55·00
12 4 2 a. orange-yellow (B.R.M.) .. .. 18·00 55·00
a. Without monogram .. .. .. — £100
13 5 4 a. slate-violet (B.R.M.) .. .. .. 15·00 60·00
a. Without monogram .. .. .. 60·00
14 6 8 a. red-brown (B.R.M.) .. .. .. 15·00 60·00
a. Without monogram .. .. .. 70·00
15 7 12 a. green (R.M.L.) .. .. .. 30·00 65·00
a. Without monogram .. .. .. 75·00
16 8 1 r. ultramarine (R.M.) .. .. .. 20·00 60·00
a. Without monogram .. .. .. 80·00
9/16 .. .. *Set of* 8 £130 £425

1899. *As* 1895, *but pin-perf or rouletted.*
17 3 1 a. vermilion (M.) £100 £125
18 4 2 a. orange-yellow (M.L.) .. .. 30·00 65·00
a. Without monogram .. .. 85·00
19 5 4 a. slate-violet (B.R.M.L.) £100
20 7 12 a. green (R.) £180
21 8 1 r. ultramarine (R.) £180

Nos. 1 to 21 were in sheets of 24. They seem to have been overprinted and perforated as required. Those first issued for use were perforated, but they were subsequently supplied imperf, both to collectors and for use. Nos. 17 to 21 were some of the last supplies. No rule seems to have been observed as to the colour of the overprinted monogram; pale blue, rose and mauve were used from the first. The pale blue varies to greenish blue or blue-green, and appears quite green on the yellow stamps. The lake is possibly a mixture of the mauve and the rose—it is a quite distinct colour and apparently later than the others. Specimens without overprint are either remainders left in the Treasury or copies that have escaped accidentally; they have been found sticking to the backs of others that bore the overprint.

Varieties may also be found doubly overprinted, in two different colours.

10

11

12

T **11**. Lines of shading above and at bottom left and right of shield.
T **12**. White dots above shield and ornaments in bottom corners.

13 14 15 16

(Printed at the Bussahir Press by Maulvi Karam Bakhsh)

1896–97. *Wove paper. Optd with monogram "R.S.", T* 9, *in rose. Recess singly from line-engraved dies. With or without gum. Various perfs.*
22 10 ¼ a. deep violet (1897) .. .. .. — £225
23 11 ½ a. grey-blue £300 £100
23*a* ½ a. deep blue (1897) .. .. .. — £160

No. 23 exists sewing-machine perf about 10 and also perf 14½–16. Nos. 22 and 23*a* are pin-perf.

1896–1900. *As Nos.* 22/3, *but lithographed in sheets of various sizes. No gum.*

(*a*) *Imperf*
24 10 ¼ a. slate-violet (B.R.M.L.) .. .. 2·50
25 11 ½ a. blue (*shades*) (R.M.L.) .. .. 2·50 14·00
a. Without monogram .. ..
b. Laid paper (B.L.) .. .. .. 20·00
26 13 1 a. olive (*shades*) (R.M.L.) .. .. 9·00 14·00

(*b*) *Pin-perf or rouletted*
27 10 ¼ a. slate-violet (R.M.L.) .. .. 4·50 8·00
28 11 ½ a. blue (*shades*) (R.M.L.) .. .. 8·00 14·00
29 13 1 a. olive (*shades*) (R.M.L.) .. .. 11·00 16·00
30 14 2 a. orange-yellow (B.) £200 £225

The ¼ a. and ½ a. are in sheets of 24, the 1 a. and 2a. in blocks of 4.

1900–01. ¼ *a.*, 1 *a, colours changed;* ½ *a. redrawn type;* 2 *a. with dash before "STATE" and characters in lower left label;* 4 *a. new value. No gum.*

(*a*) *Imperf*
31 10 ¼ a. vermilion (B.M.) .. .. .. 1·25 3·00
a. Without monogram .. ..
31*b* 12 ½ a. blue (M.) .. .. 5·00
ba. Without monogram .. .. .. 15·00
32 13 1 a. vermilion (B.M.) .. .. .. 2·00 4·50
a. Without monogram .. .. .. 10·00
33 15 2 a. ochre (M.) (9.00) .. .. .. 15·00
34 2 a. yellow (B.M.) (11.00) .. .. .. 15·00
a. Without monogram .. .. .. 20·00
35 2 a. orange (B.M.) (1.01) .. .. .. 14·00
a. Without monogram .. .. .. 20·00
36 16 4 a. claret (B.R.M.) .. .. .. 20·00 45·00
a. Without monogram .. .. .. 24·00

(*b*) *Pin-perf or rouletted*
37 10 ¼ a. vermilion (B.M.) .. .. .. 1·25 4·00
37*a* 12 ½ a. blue (M.) .. .. 11·00 18·00
38 13 1 a. vermilion (B.M.) .. .. .. 1·25 4·50
39 1 a. brown-red (M.) (3.01) .. .. .. — 80·00
40 15 2 a. ochre (B.M.) (9.00) .. .. .. 15·00
41 2 a. yellow (B.R.M.) (11.00) .. .. 16·00 25·00
42 2 a. orange (B.M.) (1.01) .. .. .. 16·00 25·00
43 16 4 a. claret (B.R.M.) .. .. .. 21·00

The ¼ a., ½ a. and 1 a. are in sheets of 24; the 2 a. in sheets of 50 differing throughout in the dash and the characters added at lower left; the 4 a. in sheets of 28.

(17)

The stamps formerly catalogued with large overprint "R.N.S." (T 17) are now believed never to have been issued for use.

Remainders are also found with overprint "P.S.", the initials of Padam Singh who succeeded Raghunath Singh in the direction of the Post Office, and with the original monogram "R.S." in a damaged state, giving it the appearance of a double-lined "R."

The stamps of Bussahir have been obsolete since 1 April 1901. Numerous remainders were sold after this date, and all values were later reprinted in the colours of the originals, or in fancy colours, from the original stones, or from new ones. Printings were also made from new types, similar to those of the second issue of the 8 a., 12 a., and 1 r. values, in sheets of 8.

Reprints are frequently found on laid paper.

Collectors are warned against obliterated copies bearing the Rampur postmark with date "19 MA 1900." Many thousand remainders and reprints were thus obliterated for export after the closing of the State Post Office.

CHARKHARI

PRICES FOR STAMPS ON COVER	
Nos. 1/4	*from* × 2
Nos. 5/26	*from* × 20
Nos. 27/44	*from* × 3
Nos. 45/53	*from* × 100
Nos. 54/5	*from* × 5
No. 56	*from* × 2

1

¼ ½ 1 2 4
¼ ½ 1 2 4

The top row shows the figures of value used in the stamps of 1894–97, and the bottom row those for the 1904 issue. In the 4 a. the figure slopes slightly to the right in the first issue, and to the left in the second.

1894. *Typo from a single die. No gum. Imperf.*
1 1 ¼ anna, rose £900 £700
2 1 annas, dull green £1600 £2250
3 2 annas, dull green £1800
4 4 annas, dull green £1200

Nos. 1/2 are known pin-perforated.

1897. *Inscr "ANNA". No gum. Imperf.*
5 1 ¼ a. magenta .. .. 5·00 6·50
a. Purple .. .. 1·75 2·50
b. Violet .. .. 1·75 2·50
6 ½ a. purple .. .. 2·25 3·50
a. Violet .. .. 3·50 4·00
7 1 1 a. blue-green .. .. 4·00 5·00
a. Turquoise-blue .. .. 4·00 4·50
b. Indigo .. .. 7·00 9·00
8 2 a. blue-green .. .. 7·00 9·00
a. Turquoise-blue .. .. 7·00 8·00
b. Indigo .. .. 9·00 13·00
9 4 a. blue-green .. .. 6·00 10·00
a. Turquoise-blue .. .. 6·00 9·00
b. Indigo .. .. 16·00 20·00
ba. Figure of value sideways .. ..
5/9 .. .. *Set of* 5 19·00 25·00

Minor varieties may be found with the first "A" in "ANNA" not printed.

All values are known on various coloured papers, but these are proofs or trial impressions.

1904. *Numerals changed as illustrated above. No gum.*
10 1 ¼ a. violet .. .. 2·50 3·50
11 ½ a. violet .. .. 3·50 4·50
12 1 a. green .. .. 8·00 12·00
13 2 a. green .. .. 18·00 20·00
14 4 a. green .. .. 15·00 22·00
10/14 .. .. *Set of* 5 42·00 55·00

Stamps of this issue can be found showing part of the paper-marker's watermark. "Mercantile Script Extra Strong John Haddon & Co.".

2 (Right-hand sword over left)

POSTAGE STAMP
Type I

POSTAGE STAMP
Type II

Type I. "P" of "POSTAGE" in same size as other letters. "E" small with long upper and lower arms. White dot often appears on one or both of the sword hilts.
Type II. "P" larger than the other letters. "E" large with short upper and lower arms. No dots occur on the hilts.

1909–19. *Litho in Calcutta. Wove paper. P* 11. (*a*) *Type* I.
15 2 1 p. chestnut .. .. 30·00 38·00
a. Pale chestnut .. .. 1·75 25·00
b. Orange-brown .. .. 3·00 25·00
16 1 p. turquoise-blue 30 40
a. Imperf between (horiz pair) £140
b. Greenish blue (1911) 35 40
c. Pale turquoise-green 60 70
17 ½ a. vermilion 90 90
a. Deep rose-red 75 90
18 1 a. sage-green .. .. 1·40 1·40
a. Yellow-olive .. .. 85 1·00
19 2 a. grey-blue .. .. 2·00 3·00
a. Dull violet-blue .. .. 3·00 3·00
20 4 a. deep green .. .. 2·75 4·00
21 8 a. brown-red .. .. 3·50 10·00
22 1 r. pale chestnut .. .. 7·00 13·00
15*a*/22 .. .. *Set of* 8 17·00 50·00

(*b*) *Type* II
24 2 1 p. turquoise-blue 85 85
25 ½ a. vermilion 70 70
a. Imperf (pair) £250
b. Deep rose-red .. .. 1·40 1·60
26 1 a. yellow-olive (1919) .. .. .. 1·25 1·50
a. Sage-green .. .. 1·25 1·50
24/6 .. .. *Set of* 3 2·40 2·50

No. 15, from the original printing, shows an upstroke to the "1", not present on other brown printings of this value.

See also Nos. 31/44.

3

"ᒧI" below Swords. Right sword overlaps left. Double frame lines.

4

"JI" below Swords. Left sword overlaps right. Single frame line.

1912–17. *Handstamped. Wove paper. No gum. Imperf.*
27 3 1 p. violet .. .. — 60·00
a. Dull purple .. .. — 60·00
28 4 1 p. violet (1917) .. .. 8·00 6·00
a. Dull purple .. .. 9·00 6·00
b. *Tête-bêche* (pair) .. .. .. 60·00 60·00
c. Laid paper .. .. — £100

5 (*actual size* 63 × 25 *mm*)

6 (Left-hand sword over right)

1922. *Handstamped. No gum.* (*a*) *Wove paper. Imperf.*
29 5 1 a. violet .. .. 50·00 65·00
a. Dull purple .. .. 60·00 70·00

(*b*) *Laid paper. P* 11
30 5 1 a. violet .. .. 55·00 80·00
a. Imperf .. .. 90·00 £100

(Typo State Ptg Press, Charkhari)

1930–45. *No gum. Imperf.*
31 6 1 p. deep blue .. .. 20 6·00
a. Vert pair, top ptd inverted on back, bottom normal upright .. .. 12·00
b. *Tête-bêche* (pair) .. .. .. 80·00
32 1 p. dull *to* light green (*pelure*) (1943) .. 28·00 65·00
33 1 p. violet (1943) .. .. 9·00 45·00
a. *Tête-bêche* (pair) .. .. .. 45·00
34 ½ a. deep olive .. .. 30 6·00
35 ½ a. red-brown (1940) .. .. .. 1·00 10·00
a. *Tête-bêche* (pair) £150
36 ½ a. black (*pelure*) (1943) .. .. .. 35·00 65·00
37 ½ a. red (1943) .. .. 13·00 25·00
a. *Tête-bêche* (pair) .. .. .. 40·00
38 ½ a. grey-brown .. .. 60·00 75·00
39 1 a. green .. .. 50 6·00
a. Emerald .. .. 10·00 18·00
40 1 a. chocolate (1940) .. .. .. 1·25 10·00
a. *Tête-bêche* (pair) .. .. .. 65·00
b. Lake-brown .. .. — 18·00
41 1 a. red (1940) .. .. 48·00 55·00
a. Carmine .. .. — 55·00
42 2 a. light blue .. .. 1·25 8·00
a. *Tête-bêche* (pair) .. .. .. 9·00
43 2 a. greenish grey (1941?) .. .. .. 24·00 38·00
a. *Tête-bêche* (pair) .. .. .. 55·00
43*b* 2 a. yellow-green (1945) .. .. .. — £200
44 4 a. carmine .. .. 4·00 12·00
a. *Tête-bêche* (pair) .. .. .. 14·00

½ As.

7 Imlia Palace (8)

(Typo Batliboi Litho Works, Bombay)

1931 (25 June). *T* **7** *and similar designs. P* 11, 11½, 12 *or compound.*

45 ½ a. blue-green 25 10
 a. Imperf between (horiz or vert pair) .. 20·00 10·00
46 1 a. blackish brown 25 10
 a. Imperf between (horiz or vert pair) .. 10·00 8·00
47 2 a. violet 20 10
 a. Imperf between (horiz or vert pair) .. 18·00 18·00
 b. Doubly printed .. .. 8·00
48 4 a. olive-green 25 10
 a. Imperf between (vert pair) .. 35·00
49 8 a. magenta 25 10
 a. Imperf between (horiz or vert pair) .. 22·00 11·00
50 1 r. green and rose 75 12
 a. Imperf between (vert pair) .. 70·00 70·00
 b. Green (centre) omitted .. .. — 60·00
51 2 r. red and brown .. .. 1·00 20
 a. Imperf horiz (vert pair) .. 38·00 13·00
52 3 r. chocolate and blue-green .. 1·75 25
 a. Imperf between (horiz pair) .. — 80·00
 b. *Tête-bêche* (pair) .. 70·00 15·00
 c. Chocolate (centre) omitted .. 17·00
53 5 r. turquoise and purple .. 2·25 45
 a. Imperf between (horiz pair) .. 80·00
 b. Centre inverted .. 25·00 18·00
 c. Centre doubly printed .. — 25·00
45/53 .. .. *Set of* 9 6·00 1·25

Designs:—½ a. The Lake; 2 a. Industrial School; 4 a. Bird's-eye view of City; 8 a. The Fort; 1 r. Guest House. 2 r. Palace Gate; 3 r. Temples at Rainpur; 5 r. Goverdhan Temple.

This issue was the subject of speculative manipulation, large stocks being thrown on the market cancelled-to-order at very low prices and unused at less than face value. The issue was an authorized one but was eventually withdrawn by the State authorities.

1940. *Nos*. 21/2 *surch as T* **8**.

54 2 ½ a. on 8 a. brown-red .. .. 20·00 60·00
 a. No space between "½" and "As." .. 25·00 60·00
 b. Surch inverted £225
 c. "1" of "½" inverted £190
55 1 a. on 1 r. chestnut .. .. 38·00 90·00
 a. Surch inverted £250
56 "1 ANNA" on 1 r. chestnut £275 £325

COCHIN

(6 puttans = 5 annas. 12 pies = 1 anna; 16 annas = 1 rupee)

Stamps of Cochin were also valid for postage in Travancore.

PRICES FOR STAMPS ON COVER

Nos. 1/3	*from* × 30
Nos. 4/5	*from* × 10
Nos. 6/6b	*from* × 3
Nos. 7/9	*from* × 20
Nos. 11/22	*from* × 15
Nos. 26/128	*from* × 8
Nos. O1/105	*from* × 15

1 2

(Dies eng P. Orr & Sons, Madras; typo Cochin Govt, Ernakulam)

1892 (1 April). *No wmk, or wmk large Umbrella in the sheet. P* 12.

1 1 ½ put. buff .. .. 1·25 1·00
 a. *Orange-buff* .. .. 1·75 1·00
 b. *Yellow* .. .. 1·75 1·25
 c. Imperf (pair) ..
2 1 put. purple .. .. 2·00 1·00
3 2 2 put. deep violet .. .. 1·00 1·00
1/3 .. .. *Set of* 3 3·75 2·75

1896 (End). *Similar to T* 1, *but* 28 × 33 *mm. P* 12.

(*a*) *Wmk Arms and inscription in sheet*

4 1 put. violet .. .. 28·00 40·00

(*b*) *Wmk Conch Shell to each stamp*

5 1 put. deep violet .. .. 16·00 22·00

This stamp was originally printed for provisional use as a fiscal; afterwards it was authorized for postal use.

(*c*) *On laid paper*

6 1 ½ put. orange-buff £375 £110
 a. *Orange* .. .. — £110
 b. *Yellow* .. .. — £110

WATERMARKS. Prior to the 1911–23 issue, printed by Perkins, Bacon & Co, little attention was paid to the position of the watermark. Inverted and sideways watermarks are frequently found in the 1898 and 1903 issues.

1897. *Wmk a small Umbrella on each stamp. P* 12.

7 1 ½ put. buff .. .. 2·00 1·25
 a. *Orange* .. .. 1·50 1·00
 ab. *Orange*. Imperf (pair) ..
 b. *Yellow* .. .. 1·75 1·00
8 1 put. purple .. .. 2·50 1·75
9 2 2 put. deep violet .. .. 2·50 2·00
 a. Imperf (pair) ..
 b. Doubly printed .. † —
 c. Printed both sides ..
 d. *Tête-bêche* (pair) .. £2250
7/9 .. .. *Set of* 3 5·50 4·25

The paper watermarked with a small umbrella is more transparent than that of the previous issue. The wmk is not easy to distinguish.

The 1 put. in deep violet was a special printing for fiscal use only.

3

4

5

6

1898. *Thin yellowish paper. Wmk small Umbrella on each stamp. With or without gum. P* 12.

11 3 3 pies, blue .. .. 1·00 50
 a. Imperf between (horiz pair) .. £325
 b. Imperf between (vert pair) .. £450
 c. Doubly printed ..
12 4 ½ put. green .. .. 2·00 40
 a. Imperf between (horiz pair) ..
 b. Stamp sideways (in pair) ..
13 5 1 put. pink .. .. 1·75 60
 a. *Tête-bêche* (pair) .. £1800 £1800
 b. Laid paper .. — £1600
 ba. Laid paper. *Tête-bêche* (pair) .. — £5500
 c. *Red* .. .. 1·75 50
 d. *Carmine-red* .. .. 2·25 60
14 6 2 put. deep violet .. .. 3·00 1·00
 a. Imperf between (vert pair) .. £300
11/14 .. .. *Set of* 4 7·00 2·00

1903. *Thick white paper. Wmk small Umbrella on each stamp. With or without gum. P* 12.

16 3 3 pies, blue 25 10
 a. Doubly printed .. — £175
17 4 ½ put. green 75 10
 a. Stamp sideways (in pair) .. £650 £650
 b. Doubly printed .. — £175
18 5 1 put. pink .. .. 1·25 10
 a. *Tête-bêche* (pair) .. — £2250
19 6 2 put. deep violet .. .. 1·40 20
 a. Double impression .. £375 £175
16/19 .. .. *Set of* 4 3·25 40

2 2

(7) (7*a*)

1909. *T* 3 (*paper and perf of* 1903), *surch with T* **7**. *Wmk is always sideways. No gum.*

22 3 2 on 3 pies, rosy mauve 15 25
 a. Surch T **7** inverted .. 70·00 70·00
 b. Surch T **7a** £275 £190
 c. Stamps *tête-bêche* .. £100 £100
 d. Stamps and surchs *tête-bêche* .. £140 £140

Varieties a, c and d were caused by the inversion of one stamp (No. 7) in the plate and the consequent inversion of the corresponding surcharge to correct the error.

8 Raja Sir Sri Rama Varma I

8*a*

(Recess Perkins, Bacon & Co)

1911–13. *Currency in pies and annas. W* **8a**. *P* 14.

26 8 2 p. brown 25 10
 a. Imperf (pair) ..
27 3 p. blue 25 10
 a. Perf 14 × 12½ .. 25·00 2·50
28 4 p. green 90 10
28*a* 4 p. apple-green .. .. 2·50 40
29 9 p. carmine .. .. 1·10 10
 a. Wmk sideways ..
30 1 a. brown-orange .. .. 1·60 10
31 1½ a. purple .. .. 3·75 40
32 2 a. grey (1913) .. .. 7·50 40
33 3 a. vermilion (1913) .. 28·00 32·00
26/33 .. .. *Set of* 8 38·00 32·00

9 Maharaja Sir Sri Rama Varma II 10

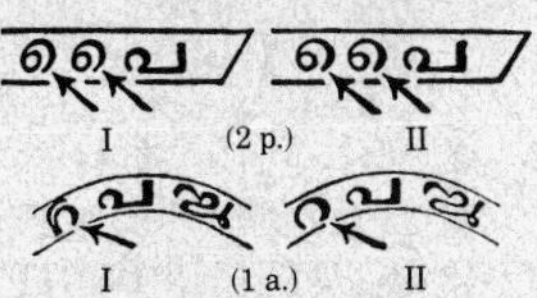

(Recess Perkins, Bacon & Co)

1916–30. *W* **8a**. *P* 13½ *to* 14.

35 10 2 p. brown (Die I) (*a*) (*b*) (*c*) .. 2·50 10
 a. Imperf (pair) ..
 b. Die II (*b*) (*c*) (1930) .. 75 10
36 4 p. green (*a*) (*b*) .. 95 10
37 6 p. red-brown (*a*) (*b*) (*c*) (1922) .. 1·00 10
38 8 p. sepia (*b*) (1923) .. 1·40 10
39 9 p. carmine (*a*) .. 7·00 15
40 10 p. blue (*b*) (1923) .. 1·25 10
41 9 1 a. orange (Die I) (*a*) .. 5·00 25
 a. Die II (*a*) (*b*) (1922) .. 8·00 25
42 10 1½ a. purple (*b*) (1923) .. 2·25 10
43 2 a. grey (*a*) (*b*) (*d*) .. 3·75 10
44 2¼ a. yellow-green (*a*) (*d*) (1922) .. 3·75 50
45 3 a. vermilion (*a*) (*b*) .. 11·00 35
35/45 .. .. *Set of* 11 34·00 1·50

Four different perforating heads were used for this issue: (*a*) comb 13.9; (*b*) comb 13.6; (*c*) line 13.8; (*d*) line 14.2. Values on which each perforation occur are shown above. Stamps with perforation (*a*) are on hand-made paper, while the other perforations are on softer machine-made paper with a horizontal mesh.

2 2 2

Two pies Two pies Two pies

(11) (12) (13)

2 2

Two Pies Two Pies

(14) (15)

1922–29. *T* **8** (*P* 14), *surch with T* **11/15**.

46 11 2 p. on 3 p. blue 40 30
 a. Surch double .. £175
47 12 2 p. on 3 p. blue .. .. 1·50 60
 a. Surch double .. £300
 b. Capital "P" in "Pies" .. 22·00 16·00
 ba. Surch double ..
48 13 2 p. on 3 p. blue (6.24) .. 2·50 30
 a. Capital "P" in "Pies" .. 28·00 12·00
 b. Perf 14 × 12½ .. 14·00 16·00
 ba. Ditto. Capital "P" in "Pies" .. £150 £150
49 14 2 p. on 3 p. blue (1929) .. 2·00 2·50
 a. Surch double .. £200
 b. Surch with Type **15**. .. 65·00 75·00
 ba. Ditto. Surch double ..

There are four settings of these overprints. The first (July 1922) consisted of 39 stamps with Type **11**, and 9 with Type **12**, and in Type **11** the centre of the "2" is above the "o" of "Two". In the second setting (May 1924) there were 36 of Type **11** and 12 of Type **12**, and the centre of the figure is above the space between "Two" and "Pies". The third setting (June 1924) consists of stamps with Type **13** only.

The fourth setting (1929) was also in sheets of 48, No. 49b being the first stamp in the fourth row.

ONE ANNA
ഒരു അണ

ANCHAL &
REVENUE

(16)

Three Pies
൩ 3
മൂന്നു പൈ

(17)

1928. *Surch with T* **16**.

50 10 1 a. on 2¼ a. yellow-green (*a*) .. 5·00 12·00
 a. "REVENUF" for "REVENUE" .. 45·00 65·00
 b. Surch double ..

1932–33. *Surch as T* **17**. *W* **8a**. *P* 13½.

51	**10**	3 p. on 4 p. green (*b*)	1·00	75
52		3 p. on 8 p. sepia (*b*)	1·00	1·10
53		9 p. on 10 p. blue (*b*)	1·50	1·10
51/3		*Set of* 3	3·00	2·50

18 Maharaja Sir Sri Rama Varma III

(Recess Perkins, Bacon & Co)

1933–38. *T* **18** (*but frame and inscription of* 1 *a. as T* **9**). *W* **8a**. *P* 13 × 13½.

54	**18**	2 p. brown (1936)	50	10
55		4 p. green	60	10
56		6 p. red-brown	70	10
57	–	1 a. brown-orange	70	10
58	**18**	1 a. 8 p. carmine	3·00	2·25
59		2 a. grey (1938)	1·50	10
60		2¼ a. yellow-green	1·50	10
61		3 a. vermilion (1938)	3·00	40
62		3 a. 4 p. violet	1·50	1·25
63		6 a. 8 p. sepia	1·75	2·75
64		10 a. blue	3·00	3·75
54/64		*Set of* 11	16·00	9·50

For stamps in this design, but lithographed, see Nos. 67/71.

1934. *Surcharged as T* **14**. *W* **8a**. *P* 13½.

65	**10**	6 p. on 8 p. sepia (R.) (*b*)	75	50
66		6 p. on 10 p. blue (R.) (*b*)	1·75	65

"DOUBLE PRINTS". The errors previously listed under this description are now identified as blanket offsets, a type of variety outside the scope of this catalogue. Examples occur on issues from 1938 onwards.

SPACING OF OVERPRINTS AND SURCHARGES. The typeset overprints and surcharges issued from 1939 onwards show considerable differences in spacing. Except for specialists, however, these differences have little significance as they occur within the same settings and do not represent separate printings.

(Litho The Associated Printers, Madras)

1938. *W* **8a** (A) *P* 11 *or* (B) *P* 13 × 13½.

			A		B	
67	**18**	2 p. brown	1·00	10	5·50	35
68		4 p. green	85	10	8·00	4·00
69		6 p. red-brown	2·25	10	—	£1100
70		1 a. brown-orange	40·00	45·00	42·00	48·00
71		2¼ a. sage-green	6·00	10	12·00	1·40
67/71		*Set of* 5	45·00	45·00	†	

Most examples of Nos. 70A/B were used fiscally. Collectors are warned against examples which have been cleaned and regummed or provided with forged postmarks.

ANCHAL
(19)

THREE PIES
(20)

SURCHARGED

ANCHAL

ONE ANNA
THREE PIES
(21)

NINE PIES
(22)

ANCHAL

ANCHAL

NINE PIES
(23)

SURCHARGED
NINE PIES
(24)

ANCHAL
(25)

1939–44. *T* **18** *variously optd or surch.*

I. *Recess-printed stamps. Nos.* 57/8

72	3 p. on 1 a. 8 p. carmine (T **20**)	90·00	45·00
73	3 p. on 1 a. 8 p. carmine (T **21**)	2·00	4·50
74	6 p. on 1 a. 8 p. carmine (T **20**)	2·00	8·00
75	1 a. brown-orange (T **19**)	1·50	10
76	1 a. 3 p. on 1 a. 8 p. carmine (T **21**)	1·00	25
72/6	*Set of* 5	90·00	50·00

II. *Lithographed stamps. Nos.* 68 *and* 70. A. *P* 11. B. *P* 13 × 13½

		A		B	
77	3 p. on 4 p. (T **21**)	5·00	1·00	12·00	1·40
78	6 p. on 1 a. (T **22**)	£130	85·00	†	
79	6 p. on 1 a. (T **23**)	£140	90·00	30·00	18·00
80	9 p. on 1 a. (T **22**)	45·00	55·00	†	
81	9 p. on 1 a. (T **23**)	†		85·00	18·00
82	9 p. on 1 a. (T **24**)	†		10·00	1·40
83	1 a. (T **19**)	65·00	30	—	95·00
84	1 a. (T **25**)	1·25	1·50	10·00	50

26 Maharaja Sri Kerala Varma I

27 (*The actual measurement of this wmk is* 6¼ × 3⅝ *in.*)

(Litho The Associated Printers, Madras)

1943. *Frame of* 1 *a. inscr* "ANCHAL & REVENUE". A. *P* 11. B. *P* 13 × 13½. (*a*) *W* **8a**.

			A		B	
85	**26**	2 p. grey-brown	—	£650	1·00	10
85*a*		4 p. green	†		£160	£100
85*b*		1 a. brown-orange	†		60·00	55·00
85/*b*		*Set of* 3	†		£200	£140

(*b*) *W* **27**

			A		B	
86	**26**	2 p. grey-brown	—	£650	24·00	20
87		4 p. green	3·00	1·00	8·00	7·00
88		6 p. red-brown	8·00	1·00	1·00	10
89		9 p. ultramarine	16·00	1·00	†	
		a. Imperf between (horiz pair)	£750	—	†	
90		1 a. brown-orange	20·00	30·00	£175	£110
91		2¼ a. yellow-green	24·00	5·00	10·00	35

Part of W **27** appears on many stamps in each sheet, while others are entirely without wmk.

Most examples of Nos. 85*b* and 90A/B were used fiscally. Collectors are warned against examples which have been cleaned and regummed or provided with forged postmarks.

1944. *T* **26** *variously opt or surch.* A. *P* 11. B. *P* 13 × 13½

(*a*) *W* **8a**.

		A		B	
92	3 p. on 4 p. (T **21**)	†		40·00	5·00
92*a*	9 p. on 1 a. (T **23**)	†		4·00	65
92*b*	9 p. on 1 a. (T **24**)	†		1·10	40
92*c*	1 a. on 3 p. on 1 a. (T **21**)	†		£2250	£1500

(*b*) *W* **27**

		A		B	
93	2 p. on 6 p. (T **20**)	1·00	75	1·00	60
94	3 p. on 4 p. (T **20**)	1·25	10	†	
95	3 p. on 4 p. (T **21**)	†		1·40	10
96	3 p. on 6 p. (T **20**)	80	15	80	15
97	4 p. on 6 p. (T **20**)	†		3·00	2·00

28 Maharaja Sri Ravi Varma **29**

I

II

(Litho The Associated Printers, Madras)

1944–48. *W* **27**. *No gum.* (*a*) *Type* I. *P* 11.

98	**28**	9 p. ultramarine (1944)	6·00	1·25

(*b*) *Type* II. *P* 13

98*a*	**28**	9 p. ultramarine (1946)	4·00	2·25
		ab. Perf 13 × 13½	9·00	1·00
99		1 a. 3 p. magenta (1948)	6·00	1·75
		a. Perf 13 × 13½	50·00	12·00
100		1 a. 9 p. ultramarine (*shades*) (1948)	10·00	1·75
98*a*/100		*Set of* 3	18·00	4·00

Nos. 98*a*/100 are line-perforated, Nos. 98ab and 99a comb-perforated.

(Litho The Associated Printers, Madras)

1946–48. *Frame of* 1 *a. inscr* "ANCHAL & REVENUE". *W* **27**. *No gum* (*except for stamps perf* 11). *P* 13.

101	**29**	2 p. chocolate	75	10
		a. Imperf horiz (vert pair)	£700	£700
		c. Perf 11	8·00	60
		d. Perf 11 × 13	£250	£110
102		3 p. carmine	50	10
103		4 p. grey-green	£1000	45·00
104		6 p. red-brown (1947)	14·00	1·40
		a. Perf 11	£120	1·00
105		9 p. ultramarine	50	10
		a. Imperf between (horiz pair)	—	£800
106	**29**	1 a. orange (1948)	5·00	10·00
		a. Perf 11	£350	
107		2 a. black	45·00	1·40
		a. Perf 11	90·00	2·25
108		3 a. vermilion	30·00	40
101/8		*Set of* 8	£1000	50·00

30 Maharaja Sri Kerala Varma II

(Litho The Associated Printers, Madras)

1948–50. *W* **27**. *P* 11.

109	**30**	2 p. grey-brown	1·00	10
		a. Imperf vert (horiz pair)	—	£650
110		3 p. carmine	1·00	10
		a. Imperf between (vert pair)	—	£650
111		4 p. green	3·00	15
		a. Imperf vert (horiz pair)	£250	£275
112		6 p. chestnut	5·00	10
		a. Imperf vert (horiz pair)	£700	
113		9 p. ultramarine	1·10	10
114		2 a. black	20·00	25
115		3 a. orange-red	24·00	35
		a. Imperf vert (horiz pair)	£1100	
116		3 a. 4 p. violet (1950)	90·00	£225
109/16		*Set of* 8	£130	£225

31 Chinese Nets **32** Dutch Palace

(Litho The Associated Printers, Madras)

1949. *W* **27**. *P* 11.

117	**31**	2 a. black	60	2·00
		a. Imperf vert (horiz pair)	£400	
118	**32**	2¼ a. green	60	2·50
		a. Imperf vert (horiz pair)	£400	

SIX PIES

ആറു പൈ
(33)

പൈ Normal

പൈ Error

Due to similarities between two Malayalam characters some values of the 1948 provisional issue exist with an error in the second word of the Malayalam surcharge. On Nos. 119, 122 and O103 this occurs twice in the setting of 48. No. 125 shows four examples and No. O104b one. Most instances are as illustrated above, but in two instances on the setting for No. 125 the error occurs on the second character.

1949. *Surch as T* **33**. (i) *On* 1944–48 *issue. P* 13.

119	**28**	6 p. on 1 a. 3 p. magenta	1·25	90
		a. Incorrect character	12·00	7·00
120		1 a. on 1 a. 9 p. ultramarine (R.)	1·00	40

(ii) *On* 1946–48 *issue*

121	**29**	3 p. on 9 p. ultramarine	5·00	7·00
122		6 p. on 1 a. 3 p. magenta	5·00	5·00
		a. Surch double	†	£300
		b. Incorrect character	35·00	35·00
123		1 a. on 1 a. 9 p. ultramarine (R.)	3·00	50
		a. Surch in black	—	£650
		b. Black surch with smaller native characters 7½ mm instead of 10 mm long	—	£900

(iii) *On* 1948–50 *issue*

124	**30**	3 p. on 9 p. ultramarine	1·75	1·50
		a. Larger native characters 20 mm instead of 16½ mm long	1·75	40
		ab. Imperf between (vert pair)	—	£700
		b. Surch double	£275	
125		3 p. on 9 p. ultramarine (R.)	2·00	60
		a. Incorrect character	10·00	5·00
126		6 p. on 9 p. ultramarine (R.)	1·00	60
119/26		*Set of* 8	18·00	13·00

Nos. 122/3 were not issued without surcharge.

1949. *Surch as T* **20**. *W* **27**. *P* 13.
127 **29** 6 p. on 1 a. orange .. .. .. 45·00 65·00
128 9 p. on 1 a. orange .. .. .. 30·00 55·00

From 1 July 1949 Cochin became part of the combined state of Travancore-Cochin.

OFFICIAL STAMPS

(O 1) (O 2 Small "ON") (O 3 "G" without serif)

1913. *Optd with Type* O **1** (3 *p.*) *or* O **2** (*others*).
O1 **8** 3 p. blue (R.) .. .. 65·00 10
a. Black opt .. .. — £650
O2 4 p. green (*wmk sideways*) .. .. 8·00 10
a. Opt inverted .. .. .. — £190
O3 9 p. carmine .. .. 38·00 10
a. Wmk sideways .. .. .. 13·00 10
O4 1½ a. purple .. .. 22·00 10
a. Opt double.. .. .. .. £300
O5 2 a. grey .. .. 13·00 10
O6 3 a. vermilion .. .. 26·00 15
O7 6 a. violet .. .. 22·00 2·00
O8 12 a. ultramarine .. .. .. 26·00 5·00
O9 1½ r. deep green.. .. .. .. 22·00 28·00
O1/9 .. .. *Set of* 9 £200 32·00

1919–33. *Optd as Type* O **3**.
O10 **10** 4 p. green (*a*) (*b*) .. .. .. 3·25 10
a. Opt double £300
O11 6 p. red-brown (*a*) (*b*) (1922) .. .. 5·00 10
a. Opt double £300
O12 8 p. sepia (*b*) (1923) .. .. .. 9·00 10
O13 9 p. carmine (*a*) (*b*) .. .. .. 22·00 10
O14 10 p. blue (*b*) (1923) .. .. .. 9·00 10
O15 1½ a. purple (*a*) (*b*) (1921) .. .. 5·50 10
O16 2 a. grey (*b*) (1923) .. .. .. 28·00 10
O17 2¼ a. yellow-green (*a*) (*b*) (1922) .. 8·00 10
a. Opt double .. .. — £300
O18 3 a. vermilion (*a*) (*b*) (*c*) .. .. 13·00 25
a. Opt inverted .. .. — £300
O19 6 a. violet (*a*) (*b*) (1924) .. .. 20·00 50
O19*a* 12 a. ultramarine (*a*) (*b*) (1929) .. 15·00 2·75
O19*b* 1½ r. deep green (*a*) (*b*) (1933) .. 22·00 45·00
O10/19*b* .. .. *Set of* 12 £140 45·00

(O 4 27½ mm high) (O 5 Straight back to "C") (O 6 Circular "O"; "N" without serifs)

1923 (Jan)–**24.** *T* **8** *and* **10** *surch with Type* O **4**.
O20 8 p. on 9 p. carmine (No. O3) £225 15
a. "Pies" for "pies" (R. 4/8) .. .. £475 45·00
b. Wmk sideways £110 10
ba. "Pies" for "pies" (R. 4/8) .. .. £275 16·00
c. Surch double .. .. .. — £275
O21 8 p. on 9 p. carmine (*a*) (*b*) (No. O13) (11.24) .. .. 70·00 10
a. "Pies" for "pies" (R. 4/8) .. .. £175 11·00
b. Surch double .. .. .. — £275

Varieties with smaller "i" or "t" in "Eight" and small "i" in "Pies" are also known from a number of positions in the setting.

1925 (Apr). *T* **10** *surch as Type* O **4**.
O22 10 p. on 9 p. carmine (*b*) (No. O13) .. 65·00 15
a. Surch inverted .. .. ..
b. Surch double .. .. .. — £275
c. Surch 25 mm high (*a*) .. .. — 75
ca. Surch double .. .. .. — £300

1929. *T* **8** *surch as Type* O **4**.
O23 10 p. on 9 p. carmine (No. O3a) .. .. £325 7·00
a. Surch double .. .. .. — £300

1929–31. *Optd with Type* O **5**.
O24 **10** 4 p. green (*b*) (1931) .. .. .. 22·00 1·10
a. Inverted "S" .. .. .. 75·00 9·00
O25 6 p. red-brown (*b*) (*c*) (*d*) (1930) .. 10·00 10
a. Inverted "S" .. .. .. 50·00 3·50
O26 8 p. sepia (*b*) (1930) .. .. .. 6·00 10
a. Inverted "S" .. .. .. 35·00 3·50
O27 10 p. blue (*b*) .. .. 6·00 10
a. Inverted "S" .. .. .. 35·00 4·00
O28 2 a. grey (*b*) (1930) .. .. .. 12·00 10
a. Inverted "S" .. .. .. 55·00 5·00
O29 3 a. vermilion (*b*) (1930) .. .. 8·00 15
a. Inverted "S" .. .. .. 48·00 6·00
O30 6 a. violet (*b*) (*d*) (1930) .. .. 50·00 3·00
a. Inverted "S" .. .. .. £190 48·00
O24/30 .. .. *Set of* 7 95·00 4·00

No. O32b

1933. *Nos.* O26/7 *surch as T* **14**, *in red.*
O32 **10** 6 p. on 8 p. sepia (*b*) .. .. .. 1·75 10
a. Inverted "S" .. .. .. 12·00 3·50
b. "3" for "S" in "Pies" .. ..
O33 6 p. on 10 p. blue (*b*) .. .. .. 4·00 10
a. Inverted "S" .. .. .. 30·00 3·50

The inverted "S" varieties occur on R.2/1 of one setting of this overprint only.

1933–38. *Recess-printed stamps of* 1933–38 *optd.*

(*a*) *With Type* O **5**
O34 **18** 4 p. green .. .. 1·50 10
O35 6 p. red-brown (1934) .. .. .. 1·75 10
O36 1 a. brown-orange .. .. .. 7·50 10
O37 1 a. 8 p. carmine .. .. .. 2·00 10
O38 2 a. grey .. .. 8·00 10
O39 2¼ a. yellow-green .. .. .. 4·00 10
O40 3 a. vermilion .. .. .. 18·00 10
O41 3 a. 4 p. violet .. .. .. 1·50 15
O42 6 a. 8 p. sepia .. .. .. 1·50 15
O43 10 a. blue .. .. 1·50 20
O34/43 .. .. *Set of* 10 42·00 90

(*b*) *With Type* O **6** (*typo*)
O44 **18** 1 a. brown-orange (1937) .. .. .. 35·00 10
O45 2 a. grey-black (1938) .. .. .. 15·00 20
O46 3 a. vermilion (1938) .. .. .. 10·00 35
O44/6 .. .. *Set of* 3 55·00 60

(O 7 Curved back to "c") (O 8)

(O 9 Circular "O"; N with serifs) (O 10 Oval "O") (O 11)

1938–44. *Lithographed stamps of* 1938. *W* **8***a*, *optd.*

(*a*) *With Type* O **7** *or* O **8** (1 *a*). I. *P* 11. II. *P* 13 × 13½.

			I		II	
O47	**18**	4 p. green ..	9·00	60	8·00	1·25
		a. Inverted "S" ..	9·50	70	†	
O48		6 p. red-brown ..	6·00	15	†	
		a. Inverted "S" ..	6·50	20	†	
O49		1 a. brown-orange ..	£150	2·50	†	
O50		2 a. grey-black ..	5·00	30	†	
		a. Inverted "S" ..	5·50	35	†	

(*b*) *With Type* O **9** (*litho*) *or* O **10** (6 *p.*)

			I		II	
O51	**18**	6 p. red-brown ..	†		3·50	90
O52		1 a. brown-orange ..	1·25	10	†	
O53		3 a. vermilion ..	2·75	25	†	

(*c*) *With Type* O **11**

			I		II	
O53*a*	**18**	6 p. red-brown ..	£600	£250	†	

The inverted "S" varieties, Nos. O47a, O48a and O50a, occur 21 times in the setting of 48.

1942–43. *Unissued stamps optd with Type* O **10**. *Litho. W* **27**. I. *P* 11. II. *P* 13×13½.

			I		II	
O54	**18**	4 p. green ..	50·00	10·00	70	50
O55		6 p. red-brown ..	70·00	10·00	18·00	90
		a. Optd both sides ..	†		—	75·00
O56		1 a. brown-orange ..	16·00	5·00	1·40	2·00
		a. Optd both sides ..	†		—	—
O56*b*		2 a. grey-black (1943) ..	40·00	50	†	
		ba. Opt omitted ..	—	£450	†	
O56*c*		2¼ a. sage-green (1943) ..	£400	3·00	†	
O56*d*		3 a. vermilion (1943) ..	10·00	3·00	†	

1943. *Official stamps variously surch with T* **20** *or* **21**.

(i) *On* 1½ *a. purple, of* 1919–33
O57 **10** 9 p. on 1½ a. (*b*) (T **20**) .. .. .. £140 8·00

(ii) *On recess-printed* 1 *a.* 8 *p. carmine of* 1933–44 (*Type* O **5** *opt*)
O58 3 p. on 1 a. 8 p. (T **21**) 80 30
O59 9 p. on 1 a. 8 p. (T **20**) .. .. .. 80·00 18·00
O60 1 a. 9 p. on 1 a. 8 p. (T **20**) .. .. 1·00 60
O61 1 a. 9 p. on 1 a. 8 p. (T **21**) 80 20

(iii) *On lithographed stamps of* 1938–44. *T* **18**. I. *P* 11. II. *P* 13 × 13½

(*a*) *W* **8***a*

		I		II	
O62	3 p. on 4 p. (Types O **7** and **20**)	†		10·00	2·50
	a. Surch double	†		£225	£130
O63	3 p. on 4 p. (Types O **7** and **21**)	†		50·00	26·00
O64	3 p. on 1 a. (Types O **9** and **20**)	1·75	50	†	
O65	9 p. on 1 a. (Types O **9** and **20**)	£110	25·00	†	
O66	1 a. 3 p. on 1 a. (Types O **9** and **21**) ..	£110	55·00	†	

(*b*) *W* **27**

		I		II	
O67	3 p. on 4 p. (Types O **10** and **20**)	†		48·00	30·00
O67*a*	3 p. on 4 p. (Types O **10** and **21**)	†		£170	—
O67*b*	3 p. on 1 a. (Types O **10** and **20**)	90·00	45·00	70·00	38·00

1944. *Optd with Type* O **10**. *W* **27**. *P* 13 × 13½.
O68 **26** 4 p. green .. .. 6·00 60
a. Perf 11 .. .. 50·00 2·25
b. Perf 13 .. .. — 38·00
O69 6 p. red-brown 70 10
a. Opt double .. .. — 55·00
b. Perf 11 .. .. 60 10
c. Perf 13 .. .. 10·00 2·00
O70 1 a. brown-orange .. .. .. £950 35·00
O71 2 a. black .. .. 1·25 20
O72 2¼ a. yellow-green .. .. .. 1·50 20
a. Optd both sides .. .. .. — 90·00
O73 3 a. vermilion .. .. 2·25 40
a. Perf 11 .. .. 2·50 40

Stamps perforated 13 × 13½ are from a comb machine; those perforated 13 from a line perforator.

1944. *Optd with Type* O **10** *and variously surch as Types* **20** *and* **21**. *W* **27**.

			I		II	
O74	**26**	3 p. on 4 p. (T **20**) ..	5·00	40	1·25	10
		b. Optd Type O **10** on both sides ..	—	90·00	†	
O75		3 p. on 4 p. (T **21**) ..	£225	£100	4·00	25
O76		3 p. on 1 a. (T **20**) ..	†		7·50	1·25
O77		9 p. on 6 p. (T **20**) ..	†		4·00	20
		a. Stamp printed both sides ..	†		—	—
O78		9 p. on 6 p. (T **21**) ..	†		1·50	15
O79		1 a. 3 p. on 1 a. (T **20**) ..	†		3·00	15
O80		1 a. 3 p. on 1 a. (T **21**) ..	†		2·25	10
O74/80		.. .. *Set of* 7	†		21·00	1·90

1946–47. *Stamps of* 1944–48 *optd with Type* O **10**. *Type* II. *P* 13.
O81 **28** 9 p. ultramarine 75 10
a. Stamp printed both sides .. .. — £160
b. Perf 13 × 13½ .. .. .. 1·00 10
O82 1 a. 3 p. magenta (1947) 45 10
a. Opt double .. .. .. 16·00 12·00
b. Optd both sides, opt double on reverse .. .. .. 25·00
O83 1 a. 9 p. ultramarine (1947) 35 15
a. Opt double .. .. ..
O81b/83 .. .. *Set of* 3 1·40 30

1948. *Stamps of* 1946–48 *and unissued values optd with Type* O **2**. *P* 13.
O84 **29** 3 p. carmine 30 10
a. Stamp printed both sides .. .. † —
O85 4 p. grey-green .. .. .. 13·00 4·00
O86 6 p. red-brown .. .. .. 3·00 15
O87 9 p. ultramarine .. .. .. 1·00 10
O88 1 a. 3 p. magenta .. .. .. 1·60 20
O89 1 a. 9 p. ultramarine .. .. .. 1·60 40
O90 2 a. black .. .. 9·00 1·50
O91 2¼ a. yellow-green .. .. .. 10·00 1·10
O84/91 .. .. *Set of* 8 35·00 6·50

1949. *Stamps of* 1948–50 *and unissued values optd with Type* O **7**.
O92 **30** 3 p. carmine 30 10
a. "C" for "G" in opt .. .. 4·00 2·50
O93 4 p. green 50 15
a. Imperf between (pair) .. .. — £600
b. Optd on reverse .. .. .. 40·00 40·00
c. "C" for "G" in opt .. .. 6·00 2·50
O94 6 p. chestnut .. .. 1·00 10
a. Imperf between (vert pair) .. — £750
b. "C" for "G" in opt .. .. 8·00 2·50
O95 9 p. ultramarine 50 10
a. "C" for "G" in opt .. .. 6·00 2·50
O96 2 a. black 60 15
a. "C" for "G" in opt .. .. 7·00 3·00
O97 2¼ a. yellow-green .. .. .. 1·25 1·25
a. "C" for "G" in opt .. .. 10·00 8·00
O98 3 a. orange-red .. .. .. 1·10 30
a. "C" for "G" in opt .. .. 9·00 5·00
O99 3 a. 4 p. violet .. .. .. 9·00 9·00
a. "C" for "G" in opt .. .. 60·00 60·00
O92/9 .. .. *Set of* 8 12·00 8·75

The "C" for "G" variety occurs on R. 1/4. Nos. O92/9, O103/4 and O104b also exist with a flat back to "G" which occurs twice on the sheet.

1949. *Official stamps surch as T* **33**. (i) *On* 1944 *issue.*
O100 **28** 1 a. on 1 a. 9 p. ultramarine (R.) .. 60 15

(ii) *On* 1948 *issue*
O101 **29** 1 a. on 1 a. 9 p. ultramarine (R.) .. 9·00 3·00

(iii) *On* 1949 *issue*
O103 **30** 6 p. on 3 p. carmine 30 25
a. Imperf between (vert pair) .. — £550
b. Surch double .. .. .. — £250
c. "C" for "G" in opt .. .. 4·00 4·00
d. Incorrect character .. .. 5·00 5·00
O104 9 p. on 4 p. green (18 *mm long*) .. 50 40
a. Imperf between (horiz pair) .. £450
b. Larger native characters, 22 mm long 60 40
ba. Ditto. Imperf between (horiz pair) £450 £450
bb. Incorrect character .. .. 7·00 7·00
c. "C" for "G" in opt .. .. 6·00 6·00
ca. Ditto. Larger native characters, 22 mm long .. .. .. 6·00 6·00
O100/4 .. .. *Set of* 4 9·50 3·25

1949. *No.* 124*a*, *but with lines of surch* 17½ *mm apart, optd* "SERVICE".
O105 **30** 3 p. on 9 p. ultramarine 60 35

For later issues see TRAVANCORE-COCHIN

DHAR

PRICES FOR STAMPS ON COVER
The stamps of Dhar are rare used on cover.

1

2

अर्धा बलड. No. 1c   अधा लबड. No. 1d   आर्धा डबल. No. 2

1897–1900. *Type-set. Colour-fugitive paper. With oval handstamp in black. No gum. Imperf.*
1 1 ½ p. black/*red* (three characters at bottom left) .. 70 80
a. Handstamp omitted .. £110
b. Line below upper inscription (R.2/2) 50·00 50·00
c. Character transposed (R.2/3) .. 13·00 14·00
d. Character transposed (R.2/5) .. 50·00
2 ½ p. black/*red* (four characters at bottom left) .. 70 90
a. Handstamp omitted .. £100
3 ¼ a. black/*orange* .. 70 1·25
a. Handstamp omitted .. £110
4 ½ a. black/*magenta* .. 85 1·40
a. Handstamp omitted .. £125 £125
b. Line below upper inscription (R.2/2) 80·00 90·00
5 1 a. black/*green* .. 2·00 4·00
a. Handstamp omitted .. £175
b. Printed both sides
c. Line below upper inscription (R.2/2) £110 £125
6 2 a. black/*yellow* .. 14·00 29·00
e. Top right corner ornament transposed with one from top of frame (R.2/5) .. £100 £125
1/6 .. *Set of* 6 16·00 32·00

Nos. 1/6 were each issued in sheets of 10 (5 × 2), but may, on the evidence of a single sheet of the ½ pice value, have been printed in sheets of 20 containing two of the issued sheets *tête-bêche*.

Research has identified individual characteristics for stamps printed from each position in the sheet.

The same research suggests that the type remained assembled during the entire period of production, being amended as necessary to provide the different values. Seven main settings have been identified with changes sometimes occurring during their use which form sub-settings.

The distribution of stamps between the main settings was as follows:

Setting I—½ p.
Setting II—½ a., 1 a.
Setting III—1 a.
Setting IV—½ p., ½ a., 1 a.
Setting V—½ p.
Setting VI—½ p. (No. 2), ¼ a.
Setting VII—2 a.

The listed constant errors all occurred during Setting IV.

In No. 1c the three characters forming the second word in the lower inscription are transposed to the order (2) (3) (1) and in No. 1d to the order (3) (2) (1).

On Nos. 1b, 4b and 5c the line which normally appears above the upper inscription is transposed so that it appears below the characters.

All values show many other constant varieties including mistakes in the corner and border ornaments, and also both constant and non-constant missing lines, dots and characters.

Examples of complete forgeries and faked varieties on genuine stamps exist.

(Typo at Bombay)

1898–1900. *P* 11 *to* 12.
7 2 ½ a. carmine .. 1·25 2·00
a. Imperf (pair) .. 35·00
b. *Deep rose* .. 90 1·75
8 1 a. claret .. 90 1·75
9 1 a. reddish violet .. 2·00 5·00
a. Imperf between (pair) .. £300
b. Imperf (pair) .. 75·00
10 2 a. deep green .. 3·25 9·50
7/10 .. *Set of* 4 6·50 16·00

The stamps of Dhar have been obsolete since 31 March 1901.

DUNGARPUR

PRICES FOR STAMPS ON COVER
Nos. 1/15 *from* × 2

1 State Arms

(Litho Shri Lakshman Bijaya Printing Press, Dungarpur)

1933–48. *P* 11 × 11½ (2 *a.*) *or* 11 (*others*).
1 1 ¼ a. bistre-yellow .. — 48·00
2 ¼ a. rose (1936) .. — £100
3 ¼ a. red-brown (1937) .. — 90·00
4 1 a. pale turquoise-blue .. — 48·00
5 1 a. rose (1938) .. — £300
6 1 a. 3 p. deep reddish violet (1935) .. — 65·00
7 2 a. deep dull green (1948) .. — 80·00
8 4 a. rose-red (1934) .. — £120

Nos. 2 and 5 are known in a *se-tenant* strip of 3, the centre stamp being the 1 a. value.

2

3

4

Maharawal Sir Shri Lakshman Singh Bahadur

Two dies of ½ a.:
Die I. Large portrait. Width of face 5 mm.
Die II. Small portrait. Width of face 4.5 mm.

(Typo L. V. Indap & Co, Bombay)

1932–46. *T* 2 (*various frames*) *and* 3/4. *Various perfs.*
9 2 ¼ a. orange (*p* 12, 11, 10½ *or* 10) (1939) .. £120 20·00
10 ½ a. vermilion (Die I) (*p* 12, 11 *or* 10½) .. 85·00 20·00
a. Die II (*p* 10) (1944) .. 85·00 20·00
b. Imperf between (vert pair) .. † —
11 1 a. deep blue (*p* 12, 11, 10½ *or* 10) (1936) 85·00 13·00
12 3 1 a. 3 p. bright mauve (*p* 10½ *or* 10) (1944) £150 55·00
13 4 1½ a. deep violet (*p* 10) (1946) .. £150 65·00
14 2 2 a. bright green (*p* 12) (1943) .. £180 £110
a. Pin-perf 11½ ..
15 4 a. brown (*p* 12, 10½ *or* 10) (1941) .. £150 45·00

Stamps perforated 12, 11, 11½ and 10½ were printed in sheets of 12 (4 × 3) which were imperforate along the top, bottom and, sometimes, at right so that examples exist with one or two adjacent sides imperforate. Stamps perforated 10 were printed in sheets of 4 either imperforate at top, bottom and right-hand side or fully perforated.

DUTTIA (DATIA)

PRICES FOR STAMPS ON COVER
Nos. 1/15 —
Nos. 16/40 *from* × 30

All the stamps of Duttia were impressed with a circular handstamp (as a rule in *blue*) before issue.

This handstamp shows the figure of Ganesh in the centre, surrounded by an inscription in Devanagari reading "DATIYA STET POSTAJ 1893". Stamps could not be used for postage without this control mark.

PROCESS. Nos. 1/15 were type-set and printed singly. Nos. 16/40 were typo from plates comprising 8 or more clichés.

GUM. The stamps of Duttia (*except No.* 25b) were issued without gum.

1 (4 a.) Ganesh.

2 (½ a.)

2*a* (2 a.)

1893. *Each with control handstamp as shown on T* 2. *Imperf.*
1 1 ¼ a. black/*orange* .. £1600
a. Without handstamp .. £1400
2 ½ a. black/*blue-green* .. £1750
a. Without handstamp .. £1400
3 2 1 a. red .. £1600
4 1 2 a. black/*yellow* .. £1500
5 4 a. black/*rose* .. £1250

1896? *Rosettes in lower corners. Imperf.*
5*a* 2*a* ½ a. black/*green* .. £3000
5*b* 2 a. grey-blue/*yellow* .. £1900

1897? *Imperf.*
6 2 ½ a. black/*green* .. 13·00 55·00
a. Value in one group .. 26·00
b. Ditto. *Tête-bêche* (horiz pair) .. £375
7 1 a. black/*white* .. 45·00 75·00
a. *Tête-bêche* (pair) .. £550
b. Laid paper .. 10·00
8 2 a. black/*yellow* .. 16·00 60·00
9 2 a. black/*lemon* .. 24·00
10 4 a. black/*rose* .. 15·00 50·00
a. *Tête-bêche* (pair) .. £140

3 (½ a.)

4 (¼ a.)

1897. *Name spelt "DATIA." Imperf.*
12 3 ½ a. black/*green* .. 48·00
13 1 a. black/*white* .. £100
14 2 a. black/*yellow* .. 55·00
a. *Tête-bêche* (vert pair) .. £750
15 4 a. black/*rose* .. 50·00
a. *Tête-bêche* (vert pair) .. £750
12/15 .. *Set of* 4 £225

1899–1906.
(*a*) *Rouletted in colour or in black, horizontally and at end of rows*
16 4 ¼ a. vermilion .. 1·40
a. *Rose-red* .. 1·25
b. *Pale rose* .. 1·10
c. *Lake* .. 1·25 3·50
d. *Carmine* .. 2·00
e. *Brownish red* .. 3·50
ea. *Tête-bêche* (pair) .. £2250
17 ½ a. black/*blue-green* .. 1·25 3·50
a. *On deep green* .. 1·75
b. *On yellow-green* (*pelure*) .. 1·75 4·50
c. *On dull green* (1906) .. 1·25
18 1 a. black/*white* .. 1·10 3·50
19 2 a. black/*lemon-yellow* .. 2·50
a. *On orange-yellow* .. 3·00
b. *On buff-yellow* .. 1·75 5·50
c. *On pale yellow* (1906) .. 2·25 5·50
20 4 a. black/*deep rose* .. 1·40 5·50
a. *Tête-bêche* (pair) ..

(*b*) *Rouletted in colour between horizontal rows, but imperf at top and bottom and at ends of rows*
20*b* 4 ¼ a. brownish red .. 13·00
21 1 a. black/*white* .. 8·00

1904–5. *Without rouletting.*
22 4 ¼ a. red .. 1·75
23 ½ a. black/*green* .. 7·00
24 1 a. black (1905) .. 5·00 12·00

1911. *P* 13½. *Stamps very wide apart.*
25 4 ¼ a. carmine .. 2·50
a. Imperf horiz (vert pair) .. £110
b. Stamps closer together (with gum) 4·25 9·50
c. As b. Imperf vert (horiz pair) .. 90·00
25*d* 1 a. black .. £140

1912? *Printed close together.* (*a*) *Coloured roulette × imperf.*
26 4 ½ a. black/*green* .. 5·00
(*b*) *Printed wide apart. P* 13½ × *coloured roulette.* (¼ *a.*) *or* 13½ × *imperf* (½ *a.*)
27 4 ¼ a. carmine .. 1·90
28 ½ a. black/*dull green* .. 4·50 12·00

1916. *Colours changed. Imperf.*
29 4 ¼ a. deep blue .. 2·50 6·00
30 ½ a. green .. 2·75 8·00
31 1 a. purple .. 3·50 9·00
a. *Tête-bêche* (pair) .. 18·00
32 2 a. brown .. 7·00 15·00
33 2 a. lilac .. 5·00 15·00
34 4 a. Venetian red (date?) .. 50·00

1918. *Colours changed.* (*a*) *Imperf.*
35 4 ½ a. blue .. 1·00 3·25
36 1 a. pink .. 1·40 4·50
(*b*) *P* 11½
37 4 ¼ a. black .. 3·50

1920. *Rouletted.*
38 4 ¼ a. blue .. 1·00 3·00
a. Roul × perf 7 .. 24·00 24·00
39 ½ a. pink .. 1·25 3·75
a. Roul × perf 7 .. 65·00

1920? *Rough perf about* 7.
40 4 ½ a. dull red .. 4·00 9·00

FARIDKOT

PRICES FOR STAMPS ON COVER
Nos. N1/4 *from* × 10
Nos. N5/8 *from* × 30

GUM. The stamps of Faridkot (Nos. N1/8) were issued without gum.

N 1 (1 folus)

N 2 (1 paisa)

N 3

1879–86. *Rough, handstamped impression. Imperf.*

(a) Native thick laid paper

N1 N 1 1 f. ultramarine .. .. .. 27·00 30·00
N2 N 2 1 p. ultramarine .. .. .. 55·00 60·00

(b) Ordinary laid paper

N3 N 1 1 f. ultramarine .. .. .. 14·00 16·00
N4 N 2 1 p. ultramarine .. .. .. 38·00 48·00

(c) Wove paper, thick to thinnish

N5 N 1 1 f. ultramarine .. .. .. 1·00 1·50
a. *Tête-bêche* (pair) £100
N6 N 2 1 p. ultramarine .. .. .. 1·50 3·25

(d) Thin wove whity brown paper

N7 N 2 1 p. ultramarine .. .. .. 13·00 15·00

(e) Wove paper

N8 N 3 1 p. ultramarine .. .. .. 1·25
a. *Tête-bêche* (pair) £100

It is doubtful whether stamps of Type N 3 were ever used for postage.

Impressions of these types in various colours, the ½ a. labels, and the later printings from re-engraved dies, were never in circulation at all.

Faridkot became a convention state and from 1887 used the Indian stamps overprinted which are listed under the Convention States.

HYDERABAD

PRICES FOR STAMPS ON COVER

Nos. 1/3	*from* × 10
Nos. 4/12	—
Nos. 13/60	*from* × 5
Nos. O1/53	*from* × 10

The official title of the State in English was The Dominions of the Nizam and in Urdu "Sarkar-i-Asafia" (State of the successors of Asaf). This Urdu inscription appears in many of the designs.

1

2

(Eng Mr. Rapkin. Plates by Nissen & Parker, London. Recess Mint, Hyderabad)

1869 (8 Sept). *P* 11½.

1 1 1 a. olive-green .. .. 8·50 6·00
a. Imperf between (horiz pair) .. £110
b. Imperf horiz (vert pair) £120 £100
c. Imperf (pair) £120 £120

Reprints in the colour of the issue, and also in fancy colours, were made in 1880 on white wove paper, perforated 12½.

1870 (16 May). *Locally engraved; 240 varieties of each value; wove paper. Recess. P* 11½.

2 2 ½ a. brown .. .. 4·00 4·00
3 2 a. sage-green .. .. 30·00 25·00

Stamps exist showing traces of lines in the paper, but they do not appear to be printed on true laid paper.

Reprints of both values were made in 1880 on white wove paper, perforated 12½: the ½ a. in grey-brown, yellow-brown, sea-green and dull blue, and the 2 a. in bright green and in blue-green.

3

A Normal 2 a. B Variety

In A the coloured lines surrounding each of the four labels join a coloured circle round their inner edge, in B this circle is missing.

C 3 a. D

C. Normal
D. Character omitted

(Plates by Bradbury, Wilkinson & Co. Recess Mint, Hyderabad)

1871–1909. *(a) No wmk.* (i) *Rough perf* 11½.

4 3 ½ a. red-brown .. .. .. 15·00 15·00
5 1 a. purple-brown .. .. .. 65·00 70·00
6 2 a. green (A) £250
7 3 a. ochre-brown .. .. .. 27·00 30·00
8 4 a. slate .. .. .. 80·00 85·00
9 8 a. deep brown .. .. ..
10 12 a. dull blue £160

(ii) *Pin-perf* 8–9

11 3 ½ a. red-brown .. .. .. — £125
12 1 a. drab .. .. .. £150 85·00

(iii) *P* 12½

13 3 ½ a. orange-brown 20 10
a. Imperf vert (horiz pair) .. — 60·00
ab. Imperf horiz (vert pair) .. — £110
b. *Brick-red* 20 10
ba. Imperf vert (horiz pair) .. — 60·00
bb. Doubly printed .. .. — 75·00
c. *Rose-red* 25 10
d. Error. Magenta .. .. 35·00 8·00
14 1 a. purple-brown .. .. 1·50 1·75
a. Doubly printed .. .. 85·00
b. *Drab* 20 10
ba. Imperf (pair) .. .. — £120
bb. Doubly printed .. .. 85·00
c. *Grey-black* 30 10
d. *Black* (1909) 30 10
da. Doubly printed .. .. 85·00
db. Imperf vert (horiz pair) .. — £120
dc. Imperf horiz (vert pair) .. — £120
15 2 a. green (A) 50 10
a. *Deep green* (A) 75 10
b. *Blue-green* (A) 60 10
ba. *Blue-green* (B) .. .. 65·00 48·00
c. *Pale green* (A) 70 10
ca. *Pale green* (B) .. .. 55·00 40·00
d. *Sage-green* (A) (1909) .. 50 15
da. *Sage-green* (B) .. .. — 40·00
16 3 a. ochre-brown (C) 70 30
a. *Chestnut* (C) 40 25
aa. Character omitted (D) .. 85·00 55·00
17 4 a. slate .. .. 1·50 70
a. Imperf horiz (vert pair) .. £300 £300
b. *Greenish grey* 70 50
ba. Imperf vert (horiz pair) .. £325
c. *Olive-green* .. .. 2·00 1·00
18 8 a. deep brown .. .. 1·25 1·25
a. Imperf vert (horiz pair) .. £350
19 12 a. pale ultramarine .. .. 2·25 2·50
a. *Grey-green* .. .. 2·00 2·25
13/19 .. .. .. *Set of* 7 4·75 4·00

(b) W **7**. *P* 12½

19*b* 3 1 a. black (1909) .. .. 60·00 5·00
19*c* 2 a. sage-green (A) (1909) .. — 24·00
ca. Sage-green (B) .. ..

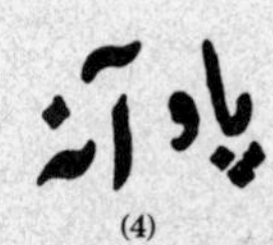
(4)

5

1898. *Surch with T* **4**. *P* 12½.

20 3 ¼ a. on ½ a. orange-brown 50 75
a. Surch inverted .. .. 25·00 20·00
b. Pair, one without surcharge .. £200

(Des Khusrat Ullah. Recess Mint, Hyderabad)

1900 (20 Sept). *P* 12½.

21 5 ¼ a. deep blue .. .. .. 2·75 1·75
a. *Pale blue* .. .. .. 2·75 1·75

6

7

(Plates by Allan G. Wyon, London. Recess Mint, Hyderabad.)

1905 (7 Aug). *Wmk T* **7**. *P* 12½.

22 6 ¼ a. dull blue .. .. .. 1·25 15
a. Imperf (pair) .. .. 28·00 40·00
b. *Dull ultramarine* .. .. 3·25 40
ba. Perf 11 × 12½ .. .. 15·00 15·00
c. *Pale blue-green* .. .. 8·00 1·25
23 ½ a. orange .. .. .. 2·50 25
a. Perf 11 .. .. ..
b. *Vermilion* .. .. 1·50 25
ba. Imperf (pair) .. .. 26·00 40·00
c. *Yellow* .. .. 50·00 15·00

1908–11. *W* **7**. *Various perfs, also compound.*

A. *Perf* 12½. B. *Perf* 11½, 12

			A		B	
24	6	¼ a. grey	45	10	1·75	10
		a. Imperf between (horiz pair)	85·00	85·00	†	
		b. Imperf between (vert pair)	—	85·00	†	
25		½ a. green	75	10	1·90	10
		a. *Pale green*	75	10	1·90	10
		b. *Blue-green*	5·00	90	†	
		c. Imperf between (vert pair)	85·00	—	†	
26	6	1 a. carmine	1·00	10	2·00	15
		a. Double impression, Perf 12½ × 11	—	—	†	
27		2 a. lilac	70	10	2·50	60
28		3 a. brown-orange (1909)	1·10	15	5·50	1·25
29		4 a. olive-green (1909)	1·00	15	6·50	1·50
30		8 a. purple (1911)	3·00	1·60	—	—
31		12 a. blue-green (1911)	20·00	12·00	3·50	4·50

C. *Perf* 11. D. *Perf* 13½

			C		D	
24	6	¼ a. grey	20·00	12·00	†	
25		½ a. green	†		40·00	20·00
26		1 a. carmine	14·00	8·00	†	
27		2 a. lilac	2·25	25	1·10	10
		a. Imperf between (horiz pair)	†		—	£100
		b. *Rose-lilac*	†		1·10	10
28		3 a. brown-orange (1909)	85	25	85	10
29		4 a. olive-green (1909)	13·00	3·25	65	10
		a. Imperf between (pair)	£150	£150	†	
30		8 a. purple (1911)	1·60	75	90	20
31		12 a. blue-green (1911)	—	—	2·25	65

1912. *New plates eng by Bradbury, Wilkinson & Co. Perfs as before, or compound.*

			A		B	
32	6	¼ a. grey-black	60	10	50	10
		a. Imperf horiz (vert pair)	—	85·00	†	
34		½ a. deep green	40	10	1·75	30
		a. Imperf between (pair)	—	85·00	†	
		b. Laid paper. Imperf (pair)	45·00	45·00	†	

			C		D	
32	6	¼ a. grey-black	65	10	20	10
		b. Imperf between (horiz pair)	—	85·00	†	
		c. Imperf between (vert pair)	—	85·00	†	
33		¼ a. brown-purple (*shades*)	†		15	10
		a. Imperf horiz (vert pair)	†		—	85·00
34		½ a. deep green	2·50	10	—	—
		a. Imperf between (pair)	—	—	—	—

In Wyon's ¼ a. stamp the fraction of value is closer to the end of the label than in the B.W. issue. In the Wyon ¼ a. and ½ a. the value in English and the label below are further apart than in the B.W.

Wyon's ¼ a. measures 19½ × 20 mm and the ½ a. 19½ × 20½ mm; both stamps from the Bradbury plates measure 19¾ × 21½ mm.

8 Symbols

9

1915. *Inscr* "Post & Receipt". *Various perfs as above, and compound.*

			A		C	
35	8	½ a. green	4·00	30	60	10
		a. Imperf between (pair)	—	—	—	75·00
		b. Imperf (pair)	60·00	50·00	†	
36		1 a. carmine	4·50	65	75	15
		a. Imperf between (pair)	—	—	†	
		b. Imperf (pair)	65·00	55·00	†	
		c. Perf 12½ × 11	5·50	3·50	†	
		d. *Scarlet*	—	—	—	9·00

			D	
35	8	½ a. green	50	10
		a. Imperf between (pair)	42·00	42·00
		c. *Emerald-green*	3·00	1·00
36		1 a. carmine	75	10
		a. Imperf between (pair)	75·00	
		d. *Scarlet*	1·00	10
		da. Imperf between (horiz pair)	—	75·00
		db. Imperf horiz (vert pair)	—	75·00

For ½ a. claret, see No. 58.

1927 (1 Feb). *As W* **7** *but larger. P* 13½.

37 9 1 r. yellow .. .. 7·00 11·00

10 (4 pies)

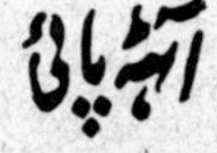
11 (8 pies)

1930 (6 May). *Surch as T* **10** *and* **11**. *W* **7**. *P* 13½.

38 6 4 p. on ¼ a. grey-black (R.) .. .. 32·00 8·50
a. Perf 11 .. .. .. — £150
b. Perf 12½ .. .. .. — 55·00
39 4 p. on ¼ a. brown-purple (R.) .. 10 10
a. Imperf between (pair) £275 £275
b. Surch double .. .. .. † —
c. Perf 11 .. .. .. — £300
d. Black surch £300 £300
40 8 8 p. on ½ a. green (R.) 10 10
a. Imperf between (horiz pair) .. — £100
b. Perf 11 .. .. .. £150 £100
c. Perf 12½ .. .. .. — £200

12 Symbols

13 The Char Minar

14 Bidar College

(Plates by De La Rue. Recess Stamps Office, Hyderabad)

1931 (12 Nov)–**47.** *T* **12** *to* **14** *(and similar types).* *W* **7**. *Wove paper. P* 13½.
41 12 4 p. black 15 10
a. Laid paper (1947) .. .. .. 2·50 3·75
b. Imperf (pair) .. .. .. 48·00 65·00
42 8 p. green 15 10
a. Imperf between (vert pair) .. .. — £550
b. Imperf (pair) .. .. .. 60·00 80·00
c. Laid paper (1947) .. .. .. 2·75 3·50
43 13 1 a. brown (*shades*) 15 10
a. Imperf between (horiz pair) .. .. — £550
44 – 2 a. violet (*shades*) 80 10
a. Imperf (pair) £130 £170
45 – 4 a. ultramarine 75 15
a. Imperf (pair) £160 £200
46 – 8 a. orange .. .. 1·60 80
a. Yellow-orange (1944) .. .. 40·00 25·00
47 14 12 a. scarlet .. .. 3·00 4·00
48 – 1 r. yellow .. .. 3·00 2·50
41/8 .. .. *Set of* 8 8·50 7·00

Designs (*as T* **14**): *Horiz*—2 a. High Court of Justice; 4 a. Osman Sagar Reservoir. *Vert*—8 a. Entrance to Ajanta Caves; 1 r. Victory Tower, Daulatabad.

Nos. 41a and 42c have a large sheet watermark "NIZAM's GOVERNMENT" and arms, but this does not appear on all stamps.

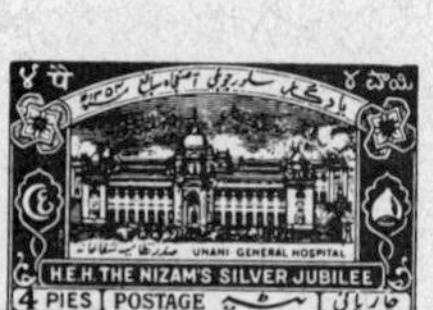

15 Unani General Hospital

16 Family Reunion

(Litho Indian Security Printing Press, Nasik)

1937 (13 Feb). *Various horiz designs as T* **15**, *inscr* "H.E.H. THE NIZAM'S SILVER JUBILEE". *P* 14.
49 4 p. slate and violet 15 25
50 8 p. slate and brown 15 35
51 1 a. slate and orange-yellow 20 30
52 2 a. slate and green 50 85
49/52 .. .. *Set of* 4 90 1·60

Designs:—8 p. Osmania General Hospital; 1 a. Osmania University; 2 a. Osmania Jubilee Hall.

(Des T. I. Archer. Typo)

1945 (6 Dec). *Victory. W* **7** (*very faint*). *Wove paper. P* 13½.
53 16 1 a. blue 10 10
a. Imperf between (vert pair) £475
b. Laid paper 25 35

No. 53b has a large sheet wmk reading "HYDERABAD GOVERNMENT", in circular frame, but parts of this do not appear on all stamps.

17 Town Hall

18 Power House, Hyderabad

(Des. T. I. Archer. Litho Government Press)

1947 (17 Feb). *Reformed Legislature. P* 13½.
54 17 1 a. black 20 20
a. Imperf between (pair) .. .. — £650

(Des T. I. Archer. Typo)

1947–49. *As T* **18** (*inscr* "H. E. H. THE NIZAM'S GOVT. POSTAGE"). *W* **7**. *P* 13½.
55 1 a. 4 p. green 40 30
56 3 a. greenish blue 40 40
a. Bluish green 50 40
57 6 a. sepia .. .. 3·00 4·00
a. Red-brown (1949) .. .. .. 18·00 22·00
ab. Imperf (pair) .. .. .. 75·00
55/7 .. .. *Set of* 3 3·50 4·25

Designs:—3 a. Kaktyai Arch, Warangal Fort; 6 a. Golkunda Fort.

1947. *As 1915 issue but colour changed. P* 13½.
58 8 ½ a. claret 50 50
a. Imperf between (horizontal pair) .. — £275
b. Imperf between (vert pair) .. — £300

An Independence commemorative set of four, 4 p., 8 p., 1 a. and 2 a., was prepared in 1947, but not issued.

1948. *As T* **12** ("POSTAGE" *at foot*). *Recess. W* **7**. *P* 13½.
59 6 p. claret .. .. 1·25 1·00

Following intervention by the forces of the Dominion of India during September 1948 the Hyderabad postal system was taken over by the Dominion authorities, operating as an agency of the India Post Office.

1949. *T* **12** ("POSTAGE" *at top*). *Litho. W* **7**. *P* 13½.
60 12 2 p. bistre-brown .. .. .. 1·00 85
a. Imperf between (horizontal pair) .. — £475
b. Imperf (pair) £475 £475

No. 60 was prepared by altering a plate of No. 41, each impression being amended individually.

OFFICIAL STAMPS

Official stamps became valid for postage within India from 1910.

سرکاری سرکاری سرکاری

(O 1) (O 1*a*) (O 2)

1873. I. *Handstamped as Type* O **1**. A. *In red.* B. *In black.*
(A / B)
O1 1 1 a. olive-green .. .. 27·00 16·00 — —
O2 2 ½ a. brown .. .. — 85·00 — 65·00
O3 2 a. sage-green .. .. — £150 — 80·00

Varieties of Type O 1 occur.

Imitations of these overprints on genuine stamps and on reprints are found horizontally or vertically in various shades of red, in magenta and in black.

II. *T* **3** *optd as Type* O **1**. A. *In red.* B. *In black.*
(*a*) *Rough perf* 11½.
(A / B)
O 4 ½ a. red-brown .. .. .. — — — —
O 5 1 a. purple-brown .. .. — — £100 £100
O 6 2 a. green (A) .. .. .. — — — £300
O 7 4 a. slate .. .. .. — — — —
O 8 8 a. deep brown .. .. — — — £350

(*b*) *Pin perf* 8–9
O 8*a* 1 a. drab .. .. .. † 6·00 60·00

(*c*) *P* 12½
O 9 ½ a. red-brown .. .. 3·00 2·50 1·75 1·00
a. Opt inverted .. .. † — —
O11 1 a. purple-brown .. .. 12·00 10·00 — 3·00
O12 1 a. drab .. .. .. 3·00 — 1·25 85
a. Opt inverted .. .. † — —
O13 2 a. green (*to* deep) (A) .. 5·50 5·50 2·25 1·75
a. Opt inverted .. .. † — —
b. Inner circle missing (B) † 65·00 —
O14 3 a. ochre-brown .. .. — — 5·00 —
O15 4 a. slate .. .. .. 14·00 10·00 4·00 4·00
O16 8 a. deep brown .. .. 20·00 — 12·00 9·00
a. Imperf between (pair) .. £350 — †
O17 12 a. blue .. .. .. 20·00 — 14·00 —

The use of Official Stamps (Sarkari) was discontinued in 1878, but was resumed in 1909, when the current stamps were overprinted from a new die.

1909–11. *Optd with Type* O **1***a*. (*a*) *On Type* **3**. *P* 12½.
O18 ½ a. orange-brown .. .. 30·00 4·00
a. Opt inverted .. ..
O19 1 a. black .. .. 20·00 10
O20 2 a. sage-green (A) .. .. 20·00 15
a. Optd on No. 15*da* (B) .. .. .. — 10·00
b. Stamp doubly printed .. .. .. — 80·00
O20*c* 3 a. ochre-brown .. .. 2·00 70
O20*d* 4 a. olive-green .. .. — 3·25
O20*e* 8 a. deep brown .. .. — 22·00
O20*f* 12 a. grey-green .. .. — 35·00

(*b*) *On Type* **6**. A. *Perf* 12½. B. *Perf* 11½, 12. C. *Perf* 11
(A / B)
O21 ½ a. orange .. .. .. — 1·25 †
a. Vermilion .. .. 30·00 15 †
b. Opt inverted .. .. — 90·00 †
c. Imperf between (vert pair) — 90·00 †
O22 ½ a. green (W.) .. .. 6·00 10 7·00 15
a. Pale green (W.) .. .. 6·00 10 7·00 15
b. Opt inverted .. .. — 45·00 — 38·00
c. Imperf between (vert pair) — 75·00 †
d. Imperf between (horiz pair) — 70·00 †
e. Stamp doubly printed .. — 70·00 †
f. Perf 13½ .. .. .. — 28·00 †
O23 1 a. carmine .. .. .. 15·00 10 20·00 30
a. Opt double .. .. 65·00 — †
b. Perf 12½×11 .. .. — 3·00 †
c. Stamp doubly printed .. † — 70·00
O24 2 a. lilac .. .. .. 18·00 10 25·00 75
O25 3 a. brown-orange .. .. 35·00 9·00 55·00 14·00
a. Opt inverted .. .. — 75·00 †
b. Perf 13½ .. .. .. — 35·00 †
O26 4 a. olive-green (1911) .. 15·00 20 25·00 1·75
O27 8 a. purple (1911) .. .. 12·00 45 22·00 1·50
O28 12 a. blue-green (1911) .. 8·00 50 13·00 90
a. Perf 12×12½ .. .. † — —
b. Imperf between (horiz pair) .. .. — £300 †
(C)
O22 ½ a. green (W.) .. ..
a. Pale green (W.) .. .. ..
O22*g* ½ a. deep green (B.W.) .. .. .. 60·00
O23 1 a. carmine .. .. — 4·50
O24 2 a. lilac .. ..
O25 3 a. brown-orange .. .. .. — 16·00
O26 4 a. olive-green (1911) .. .. .. — 7·00
O28 12 a. blue-green (1911) .. .. ..

The Wyon and Bradbury, Wilkinson stamps are distinguished above and below by the use of the letters (W.) and (B.W.) respectively.

1911–12. *T* **6** *optd with Type* O **2**. *Various perfs, also compound.*
A. *Perf* 12½. B. *Perf* 11½, 12
(A / B)
O29 ¼ a. grey (W.) .. .. .. 20·00 45 15·00 15
O30 ¼ a. grey-black (B.W.) .. .. 80 15 2·00 15
a. Opt inverted .. .. — 45·00 — —
b. Pair, one without opt .. — — — —
c. Imperf between (vert pair) — 75·00 †
O32 ½ a. pale green (W.) .. .. 13·00 35 — 15
O33 ½ a. deep green (B.W.) .. .. 70 10 — 25
a. Opt inverted .. .. — 18·00 †
c. Perf 11 × 12½ .. .. 25·00 25·00 †
O34 1 a. carmine .. .. .. 65 10 2·50 15
a. Opt inverted .. .. — 25·00 †
b. Perf 11 × 12½ .. .. 25·00 25·00 †
c. Imperf horiz (vert pair) .. — 90·00 †
O35 2 a. lilac .. .. .. 1·25 10 6·00 60
O36 3 a. brown-orange .. .. 4·50 50 6·00 80
a. Opt inverted .. .. — 55·00 †
O37 4 a. olive-green .. .. 4·00 50 2·75 50
a. Opt inverted .. .. — 55·00 — —
O38 8 a. purple .. .. .. — — — —
O39 12 a. blue-green .. .. .. — — — —

C. *Perf* 11. D. *Perf* 13½
(C / D)
O29 ¼ a. grey (W.) .. .. .. 30·00 18·00 — —
O30 ¼ a. grey-black (B.W.) 45 15 55 10
d. Imperf between (horiz pair) † — 75·00
O31 ¼ a. brown-pur (*shades*) (B.W.) — — 35 10
a. Imperf horiz (vert pair) .. † — 75·00
b. Imperf between (horiz pair) † — 85·00
O32 ½ a. pale green (W.) .. .. † — —
O33 ½ a. deep green (B.W.) 70 10 70 10
a. Opt inverted .. .. — 20·00 †
b. Imperf between (horiz pair) † — 60·00
d. Imperf horiz (vert pair) .. — 85·00 †
e. Yellow-green .. .. † — 50
O34 1 a. carmine .. .. .. 65 10 — —
O35 2 a. lilac .. .. .. 75 10 2·50 10
a. Imperf between (horiz pair) † — £100
b. Rose-lilac .. .. .. † 1·75 10
O36 3 a. brown-orange .. .. 6·00 40 7·50 15
a. Opt inverted .. .. — 60·00 — 55·00
O37 4 a. olive-green .. .. 1·60 25 1·40 10
a. Opt inverted .. .. † — 55·00
O38 8 a. purple .. .. .. — 14·00 2·00 20
O39 12 a. blue-green .. .. .. — — 3·25 30

1917–20. *T* **8** *optd with Type* O **2**. *Various perfs as above, also compound.*
(A / C)
O40 ½ a. green .. .. .. — 2·75 2·25 30
a. Opt inverted .. .. † — 19·00
b. Pair, one without opt .. † — —
O41 1 a. carmine .. .. .. — 2·75 2·50 15
a. Opt inverted .. .. † — 14·00
e. Scarlet (1920) .. .. † — 15·00
(D)
O40 ½ a. green 55 10
a. Opt inverted .. .. — 18·00
b. Pair, one without opt .. .. .. — 75·00
c. Imperf between (horiz pair) .. .. — 55·00
d. Imperf between (vert pair) .. .. — 65·00
e. Perf 11×13½ or 13½×11 .. .. 25·00 25·00
f. Emerald-green .. .. .. 2·50 40
O41 1 a. carmine 80 10
a. Opt inverted .. .. — 22·00
b. Opt double .. .. — 50·00
c. Imperf horiz (vert pair) .. .. — 75·00
d. Stamp printed double .. .. .. — 60·00
e. Scarlet (1920) 60 10
ea. Stamp printed double .. .. .. — 60·00
eb. Imperf between (horiz pair) .. .. — 65·00
ec. Imperf between (vert pair) .. .. — 65·00

1930–34. *T* **6** *and* **8** *optd as Type* O **2** *and surch at top of stamp, in red, as T* **10** *or* **11**.
O42 4 p. on ¼ a. grey-black (O30) (1934) .. .. 90·00 17·00
O43 4 p. on ¼ a. brown-purple (O31) 45 10
b. Imperf between (horiz pair) .. .. — 85·00
c. Imperf between (vert pair) .. .. — 85·00
d. Imperf horiz (vert pair) .. .. — 85·00
e. Red surch double .. .. .. — 50·00
f. Black opt double .. .. .. — £110
O44 8 p. on ½ a. green (O40) 40 10
c. Imperf between (horiz pair) .. .. — 85·00
ca. Imperf between (vert pair) .. .. — 85·00
d. Red surch double .. .. .. — 50·00
e. Stamp doubly printed .. .. .. — 85·00
f. Black opt double .. .. .. — £110
O45 8 p. on ½ a. yellow-green (O33*e*) .. .. 45·00 50·00

For Nos. O42/5 the red surcharge was intended to appear on the upper part of the stamp, above the official overprint, Type O **2**, but surcharge and overprint are not infrequently found superimposed on one another.

1934–44. *Nos.* 41/8 *optd with Type* O **2**.
O46 4 p. black 50 10
a. Imperf (pair) .. .. .. 60·00
b. Imperf between (vert pair) £500 £500
c. Imperf between (horiz pair) .. .. — £500
O47 8 p. green 20 10
a. Opt inverted .. .. .. — £150
b. Imperf between (horiz pair) .. .. — £500
c. Opt double .. .. .. — £120
d. Imperf (pair) £100 £125
O48 1 a. brown 30 10
a. Imperf between (vert pair) £400 £400
b. Imperf between (horiz pair) .. .. — £400
c. Imperf (pair) £150 £175
d. Opt double .. .. .. — £150
O49 2 a. violet .. .. 1·50 10
a. Imperf between (horiz pair) .. .. — £550
O50 4 a. ultramarine .. .. .. 1·00 10
O51 8 a. orange (1935) .. .. .. 4·00 50
a. Yellow-orange (1944) .. .. — 35·00
O52 12 a. scarlet (1935) .. .. .. 4·00 1·25
O53 1 r. yellow (1935) .. .. .. 5·00 2·00
O46/53 .. .. *Set of* 8 15·00 3·75

1947. *No.* 58 *optd with Type* O 2.
O54 8 ½ a. claret .. .. 3·00 2·00
a. Pair, one without opt

1949. *No.* 60 *optd with Type* O 2.
O55 12 2 p. bistre-brown .. .. .. 3·25 2·50

1950. *No.* 59 *optd with Type* O 2.
O56 6 p. claret .. .. 3·50 4·00

IDAR

PRICES FOR STAMPS ON COVER
Nos. 1/2*b* *from* × 2
Nos. 3/6 *from* × 3

The Idar postal service carried Official mail only.

1 Maharaja Shri Himatsinhji 2

(Typo M. N. Kothari & Sons, Bombay)

1939 (21 Feb). *P* 11. (*a*) *White panels.*
1 1 ½ a. emerald .. .. .. 5·00 12·00
a. Imperf between (pair) £350
b. Yellow-green .. .. .. 4·50 12·00
ba. Imperf between (horiz pair) .. £350
c. Pale yellow-green (thick paper) .. 9·00 14·00

(*b*) *Coloured panels*
2 1 ½ a. emerald .. .. .. 6·50 14·00
a. Yellow-green .. .. .. 5·50 14·00
b. Pale yellow-green (thick paper) .. 13·00 16·00

In No. 2 the whole design is composed of half-tone dots. In No. 1 the dots are confined to the oval portrait.

Covers have been seen which indicate that No. 1 may have been issued as early as 1934.

(Typo Purshottum Ghellaji Mehta & Co., Himmatnagar)

1944 (21 Oct). *P* 12.
3 2 ½ a. blue-green .. .. .. 85 18·00
a. Imperf between (vert pair) £120
b. Yellow-green .. .. .. 85 22·00
ba. Imperf between (vert pair) .. .. 12·00
4 1 a. violet .. .. .. 65 18·00
a. Imperf (pair) £200
b. Imperf vert (horiz pair) £225
5 2 a. blue .. .. .. 85 25·00
a. Imperf between (vert pair) .. 55·00
b. Imperf between (horiz pair) .. 95·00
6 4 a. vermilion .. .. .. 2·40 30·00
a. Doubly printed £200
3/6 .. .. .. *Set of* 4 4·25 80·00

Nos. 1 to 6 are from booklet panes of 4 stamps, producing single stamps with one or two adjacent sides imperf.

The 4 a. violet is believed to be a colour trial.

INDORE

(HOLKAR STATE)

PRICES FOR STAMPS ON COVER
Nos. 1/15 *from* × 20
Nos. 16/43 *from* × 6
Nos. S1/7 *from* × 40

1 Maharaja Tukoji Rao II Holkar XI

(Litho Waterlow & Sons)

1886 (6 Jan). *P* 15. (*a*) *Thick white paper.*
1 1 ½ a. bright mauve .. .. .. 3·50 4·50

(*b*) *Thin white or yellowish paper*
2 1 ½ a. pale mauve .. .. .. 1·10 1·25
a. Dull mauve .. .. .. 1·25 1·50

2 Type I 2*a* Type II

TYPES 2 AND 2a. In addition to the difference in the topline character (marked by arrow), the two Types can be distinguished by the difference in the angles of the 6-pointed stars and the appearance of the lettering. In Type I the top characters are smaller and more cramped than the bottom; in Type II both are in the same style and similarly spaced.

1889. *Handstamped. No gum. Imperf.*
3 2 ½ a. black/*pink* .. .. .. 8·00 8·00
4 2*a* ½ a. black/*pink* .. .. .. 1·40 1·75
a. *Tête-bêche* (pair) £110

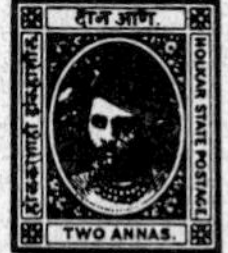

3 Maharaja Shivaji Rao Holkar XII 4 Maharaja Tukoji Rao III Holkar XIII 5

(Recess Waterlow)

1889–92. *Medium wove paper. P* 14 *to* 15.
5 3 ¼ a. orange (9.2.92) 20 20
a. Imperf between (horiz pair) .. — £400
b. Very thick wove paper 70 45
c. Yellow 25 20
6 ½ a. dull violet .. .. .. 1·00 60
a. Brown-purple 20 15
b. Imperf between (vert pair) .. £350
7 1 a. green (7.2.92) 65 50
a. Imperf between (pair) £450 £450
b. Very thick wove paper
8 2 a. vermilion (7.2.92) .. .. 1·50 1·00
a. Very thick wove paper .. .. 4·75 3·00
5/8 .. .. .. *Set of* 4 2·25 1·60

(Recess Perkins, Bacon & Co)

1904–20. *P* 13½, 14.
9 4 ¼ a. orange 20 10
10 5 ½ a. lake (1909) .. .. .. 3·50 10
a. Brown-lake (*shades*) .. .. 4·50 15
b. Imperf (pair) .. .. 16·00
11 1 a. green .. .. .. 1·60 10
a. Imperf (pair) £125
b. Perf 12½ (1920) .. .. † 38·00
12 2 a. brown .. .. .. 5·00 25
a. Imperf (pair) .. .. 75·00
13 3 a. violet .. .. .. 6·00 1·00
14 4 a. ultramarine .. .. .. 6·00 80
a. Dull blue .. .. .. 5·00 70
9/14 .. .. .. *Set of* 6 19·00 2·00

पाव आना.

(6) 7 Maharaja Yeshwant Rao II Holkar XIV

1905 (June). *No.* 6*a surch* "QUARTER ANNA" *in Devanagari, as T* 6.
15 3 ¼ a. on ½ a. brown-purple .. .. 1·50 10·00

NOTE. From 1 March 1908 the use of Indore stamps was restricted to official mail. Nos. S1/7 were withdrawn and replaced by Nos. 9/14.

(Recess Perkins, Bacon & Co)

1927–37. *P* 13 *to* 14.
16 7 ¼ a. orange (*a*) (*d*) (*e*) 25 10
17 ½ a. claret (*a*) (*d*) (*e*) 25 10
18 1 a. green (*a*) (*d*) (*e*) 35 10
19 1¼ a. green (*c*) (*d*) (1933) 50 15
20 2 a. sepia (*a*) .. .. .. 2·50 80
21 2 a. bluish green (*d*) (1936) .. 3·00 60
a. Imperf (pair) .. .. 25·00 60·00
22 3 a. deep violet (*a*) .. .. 1·50 4·50
23 3 a. Prussian blue (*d*) (1935?) .. 12·00
a. Imperf (pair) .. .. 30·00 £110
24 3½ a. violet (*d*) (1934) .. .. 4·00 8·00
a. Imperf (pair) .. .. 40·00 £110
25 4 a. ultramarine (*a*) .. .. 3·25 2·25
26 4 a. yellow-brown (*d*) (1937) .. 10·00 1·50
a. Imperf (pair) .. .. 30·00 90·00
27 8 a. slate-grey (*a*) .. .. 5·50 5·00
28 8 a. red-orange (*d*) (1937) .. .. 9·50 7·50
29 12 a. carmine (*d*) (1934) .. .. 5·00 10·00
30 – 1 r. black and light blue (*b*) .. 8·00 14·00
31 – 2 r. black and carmine (*b*) .. 27·00 27·00
32 – 5 r. black & brown-orange (*b*) .. 38·00 38·00

Nos. 30/32 are as Type 7, but larger, size 23 × 28 mm.

Five different perforating heads were used for this issue: (*a*) comb 13·6; (*b*) comb 13·9; (*c*) line 13·2; (*d*) line 13·8; (*e*) line 14·2. Values on which each perforation occur are indicated above.

Nos. 21a, 23a, 24a and 26a are plate proofs which were provisionally used for postage *circa* 1938–42. A plate proof of the 1 r. in green and carmine is also known postally used (*Price for pair £30 unused, £150 used*).

MINIMUM PRICE

The minimum price quote is 10p which represents a handling charge rather than a basis for valuing common stamps. For further notes about prices see introductory pages.

(8) 9

1940 (1 Aug). *Surch in words as T* 8.
33 7 ¼ a. on 5 r. black and brown-orange (*b*) 1·40 25
a. Surch double (Blk. + G.) .. .. — £400
34 ½ a. on 2 r. black and carmine (*b*) .. 2·50 50
35 1 a. on 1¼ a. green (*c*) (*d*) (*e*) .. 3·00 35
b. Surch inverted (*d*) .. .. 80·00
c. Surch double (*c*) £275
33/5 .. .. .. *Set of* 3 6·00 1·00

(Typo "*Times of India*" Press, Bombay)

1941–46. *P* 11.
36 9 ¼ a. red-orange .. .. .. 1·00 10
37 ½ a. claret .. .. .. 1·00 10
38 1 a. green .. .. .. 3·00 10
39 1¼ a. yellow-green .. .. .. 7·50 30
a. Imperf (pair) £190
40 2 a. turquoise-blue .. .. .. 7·00 1·00
41 4 a. yellow-brown (1946) .. .. 7·00 5·00

Larger size (23 × 28 *mm*)
42 2 r. black and carmine (1943) .. 11·00 55·00
43 5 r. black and yellow-orange (1943) .. 13·00 70·00
36/43 .. .. .. *Set of* 8 45·00 £120

OFFICIAL STAMPS

SERVICE **SERVICE**

(S 1) (S 2)

1904–6. (*a*) *Optd with Type* S 1.
S1 4 ¼ a. orange (1906) 10 15
S2 5 ½ a. lake 10 10
a. Opt inverted .. .. .. 14·00 18·00
b. Opt double .. .. .. 14·00
c. Imperf (pair) .. .. .. 32·00
d. Brown-lake 10 10
da. Opt inverted .. .. .. 14·00
e. Pair, one without opt £350
S3 1 a. green 10 10
S4 2 a. brown (1905) 30 20
a. Pair, one without opt £500
S5 3 a. violet (1906) .. .. .. 1·75 1·10
a. Imperf (pair) £250
S6 4 a. ultramarine (1905) .. .. 2·00 1·40

(*b*) *Optd with Type* S 2
S7 5 ½ a. lake 10 35
a. Opt double £125
S1/7 .. .. .. *Set of* 6 3·75 2·75

Types S 1 and S 2 differ chiefly in the shape of the letter "R".

JAIPUR

PRICES FOR STAMPS ON COVER
No. 1 *from* × 3
No. 2 *from* × 2
Nos. 3/5 *from* × 10
Nos. 6/70 *from* × 4
Nos. 71/80 *from* × 6

Nos. O1/34 *from* × 8

1 Chariot of the Sun God, Surya 2

½ a. 36 varieties (2 plates). Plate I, 12 stamps 2½ mm apart horizontally; Plate II, 24 stamps 4½ mm apart.
1 a. and 2 a. 12 varieties.

1904. *Litho.*
(*a*) *Value at sides in small letters and characters. Roughly perf* 14
1 1 ½ a. pale blue (Plate I) .. .. 45·00 75·00
a. Ultramarine .. .. .. 65·00 85·00
b. Imperf, *ultramarine* £350
2 ½ a. grey-blue (Plate II) .. .. — £200
a. Imperf £325 £425
b. Ultramarine .. .. .. — £250
3 1 a. dull red .. .. .. 2·50 7·00
a. Scarlet .. .. .. 2·75 7·00
4 2 a. pale green .. .. .. 2·50 8·50
a. Emerald-green .. .. .. 3·50

(*b*) *Value in larger letters and characters. 24 varieties on one plate. Roughly perf* 14
5 2 ½ a. pale blue .. .. .. 2·75 3·50
a. Deep blue .. .. .. 3·00 3·75
b. Ultramarine .. .. .. 3·00 3·75
c. Imperf £300 £300

3 Chariot of the Sun God, Surya

(Recess Perkins, Bacon & Co)

1904. *P* 12.

6 3 ½ a. blue .. 3·00 4·00
a. Perf 12½ .. 11·00 8·00
b. Perf comp of 12 and 12½ .. 14·00 14·00
7 1 a. brown-red .. 35·00 35·00
a. Perf 12½ .. 60·00 60·00
b. Perf comp of 12 and 12½ .. £120 £120
c. *Carmine* .. 2·25 2·25
ca. Imperf between (vert pair) .. £300 £350
cb. Perf comp of 12 and 12½ .. 10·00 10·00
8 2 a. deep green .. 6·50 8·00
a. Perf 12½ .. 55·00 48·00
b. Perf comp of 12 and 12½ .. 25·00 25·00

Nos. 6b, 7b, 7cb and 8b occur on the bottom two rows of sheets otherwise perforated 12.

1905–8. *Wmk* "JAs WRIGLEY & SON Ld. 219" "SPECIAL POSTAGE PAPER LONDON" *or* "PERKINS BACON & Co Ld LONDON" *in sheet. P* 13½.

9 3 ¼ a. olive-yellow (1906) .. 20 15
10 ½ a. blue .. 70 70
a. *Indigo* .. 40 40
11 1 a. brown-red (1906) .. 4·25 4·25
a. *Bright red* (1908) .. 50 40
12 2 a. deep green .. 1·25 1·00
13 4 a. chestnut .. 2·50 2·50
14 8 a. bright violet .. 3·50 3·50
15 1 r. yellow .. 7·00 7·50
a. *Orange-yellow* .. 8·00 9·00
b. *Yellow-ochre* .. 10·00 12·00
9/15 .. *Set of* 7 13·00 14·00

4 Chariot of the Sun God, Surya

३ आना

(5)

(Typo Jail Press, Jaipur)

1911. *Thin wove paper. No gum. Imperf. Six varieties of each value.*

16 4 ¼ a. green .. 1·25 1·60
a. Printed double .. 5·00
ab. Ditto, one inverted ..
b. "¼" inverted at right upper corner 5·00
c. No stop after "STATE" .. 5·00
17 ¼ a. greenish yellow .. 30 40
a. "¼" inverted in right upper corner 1·50
b. No stop after "STATE" .. 1·50
18 ½ a. ultramarine .. 30 40
a. Printed double .. 2·00
b. No stop after "STATE" .. 75
c. Large "J" in "JAIPUR" .. 75
d. "⅓" for "½" at lower left .. 1·50
19 ½ a. grey-blue .. 85 85
a. No stop after "STATE" .. 1·60
b. Large "J" in "JAIPUR" .. 1·60
c. "⅓" for "½" at lower left .. 2·75
20 1 a. rose-red .. 30 40
a. Printed double .. 90·00
21 2 a. greyish green .. 3·00 5·50
a. *Deep green* .. 3·00 5·50
ab. Printed double .. 90·00

One sheet of the ¼ a. is known in blue.

(Typo Jail Press, Jaipur)

1913–18. *Paper-maker's wmk* "DORLING & CO. LONDON" *in sheet. P* 11.

22 3 ¼ a. pale olive-yellow .. 15 30
a. Imperf horiz (vert pair) .. £180 £180
b. Imperf vert (horiz pair) .. — £200
23 ¼ a. olive .. 15 35
a. Imperf between (horiz pair) .. £180
b. Imperf vert (horiz pair) .. £200
c. Imperf horiz (vert pair) .. £180
24 ¼ a. bistre .. 15 35
a. Imperf between (horiz pair) .. £180
b. Imperf between (vert pair) .. — £180
c. Imperf horiz (vert pair) .. — £180
d. Doubly printed .. † —
25 ½ a. pale ultramarine .. 15 25
a. Imperf vert (horiz pair) .. — £250
b. *Blue* .. 20 30
ba. Imperf between (horiz pair) .. £200
26 1 a. carmine (1918) .. 75 80
a. Imperf between (vert pair) .. — £225
b. Imperf horiz (vert pair) .. — £225
27 1 a. rose-red .. 1·60 3·25
a. Imperf between (vert pair) .. £250
28 1 a. scarlet .. 30 60
a. Imperf between (vert pair) .. £250 £250
29 2 a. green (1918) .. 85 1·40
30 4 a. chocolate .. 1·10 2·25
31 4 a. pale brown .. 1·40 2·50
a. Imperf vert (horiz pair) .. £300
22/31 .. *Set of* 5 2·25 4·00

1926. *Surch with T* 5.

32 3 3 a. on 8 a. bright violet (R.) .. 90 1·40
a. Surch inverted .. £160 £140
33 3 a. on 1 r. yellow (R.) .. 1·10 2·00
a. Surch inverted .. £160 £140
c. *Yellow-ochre* .. 4·50

1928. *As* 1913–18 *issue. Wmk* "DORLING & CO. LONDON" (½ *a.*, 1 *a.*, 2 *a.*) *or* "OVERLAND BANK" (*all values*) *in sheet. No gum. P* 12.

34 3 ½ a. ultramarine .. 4·00 4·00
a. Perf comp of 12 and 11 .. 11·00 7·50
35 1 a. rose-red .. 18·00 13·00
a. Imperf between (vert pair) .. £300
36 3 1 a. scarlet .. 22·00 12·00
a. Perf comp of 12 and 11 .. 30·00 20·00
37 2 a. green .. 48·00 24·00
a. Perf comp of 12 and 11 .. 85·00 55·00
38 8 a. bright violet ..
39 1 r. orange-vermilion .. £160 £200

The "OVERLAND BANK" paper has a coarser texture. The ½ a. and 2 a. values also exist on this paper perforated 11, but such stamps are difficult to distinguish from examples of Nos. 25 and 29.

6 Chariot of the Sun God, Surya

7 Maharaja Sir Man Singh Bahadur

8 Sowar in Armour

(Des T. I. Archer. Litho Indian Security Printing Press, Nasik)

1931 (14 Mar). *Investiture of Maharaja. T* 6/8 *and similar designs. No wmk. P* 14.

40 ¼ a. black and deep lake .. 40 45
41 ½ a. black and violet .. 20 10
42 1 a. black and blue .. 2·75 3·25
43 2 a. black and buff .. 2·50 3·00
44 2½ a. black and carmine .. 20·00 26·00
45 3 a. black and myrtle .. 12·00 26·00
46 4 a. black and olive-green .. 10·00 22·00
47 6 a. black and deep blue .. 7·00 22·00
48 8 a. black and chocolate .. 10·00 30·00
49 1 r. black and pale olive .. 20·00 55·00
50 2 r. black and yellow-green .. 16·00 65·00
51 5 r. black and purple .. 25·00 75·00
40/51 .. *Set of* 12 £100 £300

Designs: *Vert*—1 a. Elephant and state banner; 2½ a. Common Peafowl; 8 a. Sireh-Deorhi Gate. *Horiz*—3 a. Bullock carriage; 4 a. Elephant carriage; 6 a. Albert Museum; 1 r. Chandra Mahal; 2 r. Amber Palace; 5 r. Maharajas Jai Singh and Sir Man Singh.

Eighteen of these sets were issued for presentation purposes with a special overprint "INVESTITURE—MARCH 14, 1931" in red.

10 Maharaja Sir Man Singh Bahadur

One Rupee

(11)

(Des T. I. Archer. Litho Indian Security Printing Press, Nasik)

1932–46. *P* 14. (*a*) *Inscr* "POSTAGE & REVENUE".

52 10 1 a. black and blue .. 30 20
53 2 a. black and buff .. 45 30
54 4 a. black and grey-green .. 1·25 1·75
55 8 a. black and chocolate .. 2·00 2·50
56 1 r. black and yellow-bistre .. 11·00 30·00
57 2 r. black and yellow-green .. 42·00 £110
52/7 .. *Set of* 6 50·00 £130

(*b*) *Inscr* "POSTAGE"

58 7 ¼ a. black and brown-lake .. 25 10
59 ¾ a. black and brown-red (1943?) .. 1·00 45
60 1 a. black and blue (1943?) .. 1·50 30
61 2 a. black and buff (1943?) .. 1·50 50
62 2½ a. black and carmine .. 55 40
63 3 a. black and green .. 55 35
64 4 a. black and grey-green (1943?) .. 3·00 15·00
65 6 a. black and deep blue .. 1·40 7·00
a. *Black and pale blue* (1946) .. 3·00 15·00
66 8 a. black and chocolate (1946) .. 6·00 20·00
67 1 r. black and yellow-bistre (1946) .. 12·00 35·00
58/67 .. *Set of* 10 23·00 70·00

1936. *Nos.* 57 *and* 51 *surch with T* 11.

68 10 1 r. on 2 r. black and yellow-green (R.) 2·50 15·00
69 – 1 r. on 5 r. black and purple .. 2·25 12·00

पाव आना

(12)

13 Maharaja and Amber Palace

1938 (Dec). *No.* 41 *surch* "QUARTER ANNA" *in Devanagari, T* 12.

70 7 ¼ a. on ½ a. black and violet (R.) .. 2·50 3·50

(Recess D.L.R.)

1947 (Dec)–**48.** *Silver Jubilee of Maharaja's Accession to Throne. Various designs as T* 13. *P* 13½ × 14.

71 ¼ a. red-brown and green (5.48) .. 15 65
72 ½ a. green and violet .. 15 65
73 ¾ a. black and lake (5.48) .. 15 65
74 1 a. red-brown and ultramarine .. 30 85
75 2 a. violet and scarlet .. 20 85
76 3 a. green and black (5.48) .. 30 1·10
77 4 a. ultramarine and brown .. 45 1·10
78 8 a. vermilion and brown .. 60 1·75
79 1 r. purple and green (5.48) .. 1·00 4·50
71/9 .. *Set of* 9 2·75 11·00

Designs:—¼ a. Palace Gate; ¾ a. Map of Jaipur; 1 a. Observatory; 2 a. Wind Palace; 3 a. Coat of Arms; 4 a. Amber Fort Gate; 8 a. Chariot of the Sun; 1 r. Maharaja's portrait between State flags.

3 PIES

= =

(14)

1947 (Dec). *No.* 41 *surch with T* 14.

80 7 3 p. on ½ a. black and violet (R.) .. 5·50 11·00
a. "PIE" for "PIES" .. 28·00 38·00
b. Bars at left vertical .. 32·00 42·00
c. Surch inverted .. 30·00 28·00
d. Surch inverted and "PIE" for "PIES" £120 £100
e. Surch double, one inverted .. 42·00 40·00
f. As variety e, but inverted surch showing "PIE" for "PIES" .. £180 £160

OFFICIAL STAMPS

SERVICE (O 1) SERVICE (O 2)

1928 (13 Nov)–**31.** *T* 3 *typographed. No gum* (*except for Nos. O6/a*). *P* 11, 12, *or compound. Wmk* "DORLING & CO. LONDON" (4 *a.*) *or* "OVERLAND BANK" (*others*). (*a*) *Optd with Type* O 1.

O 1 ¼ a. olive .. 45 80
a. *Bistre* .. 30 40
O 2 ½ a. pale ultramarine (Blk.) .. 25 10
a. Imperf between (horiz pair) .. £180 £180
b. Imperf between (vert pair) .. — £225
c. Opt inverted .. — £200
d. Opt double (R. and Blk.) .. — £300
O 3 ½ a. pale ultramarine (R.) (13.10.30) 1·25 15
a. Imperf horiz (vert pair) ..
b. Stamp doubly printed ..
O 3c 1 a. rose-red .. 35 20
d. Imperf between (horiz pair) .. — £225
O 4 1 a. scarlet .. 75 50
a. Opt inverted .. £225 £225
b. Imperf between (horiz pair) .. — £225
O 5 2 a. green .. 40 40
a. Imperf between (vert pair) .. — £250
b. Imperf between (horiz pair) .. £250 £250
O 6 4 a. pale brown (with gum) .. 2·00 2·25
a. *Chocolate* (with gum) .. 2·00 2·25
O 7 8 a. bright violet (R.) (13.10.30) .. 18·00 38·00
O 8 1 r. orange-vermilion .. 35·00 90·00

(*b*) *Optd with Type* O 2

O 9 ½ a. ultramarine (Blk.) (11.2.31) .. 95·00 15
a. Imperf vert (horiz pair) .. — £300
O10 ½ a. ultramarine (R.) (15.10.30) .. £120 15
a. Imperf between (vert pair) .. — £300
O11 8 a. bright violet (11.2.31) .. £200 £130
O12 1 r. orange-vermilion (11.2.31) .. £225 £160

SERVICE (O 3) आध आना (O 4)

1931–7. *Nos.* 41/3 *and* 46 *optd at Nasik with Type* O 3, *in red.*

O13 7 ½ a. black and violet .. 20 10
O14 – 1 a. black and blue .. £160 1·50
O15 8 2 a. black and buff (1936) .. 2·00 2·25
O16 – 4 a. black and olive-green (1937) .. 5·00 6·00
O13/16 .. *Set of* 4 £160 8·75

1932. *No.* O5 *surch with Type* O 4.

O17 3 ½ a. on 2 a. green .. £100 40

1932–7. *Nos.* 52/6 *optd at Nasik with Type* O 3, *in red.*

O18 10 1 a. black and blue .. 60 10
O19 2 a. black and buff .. 50 10
O20 4 a. black and grey-green (1937) .. 50·00 3·25
O21 8 a. black and chocolate .. 1·50 1·10
O22 1 r. black and yellow-bistre .. 6·00 7·50
O18/22 .. *Set of* 5 50·00 11·00

1932–46. *Stamps of* 1932–46, *inscr* "POSTAGE".

(*a*) *Optd at Nasik with Type* O 3, *in red*

O23 7 ¼ a. black and brown-lake (1936) .. 30 10
O24 ¾ a. black and brown-red (1944) .. 1·00 25
O25 1 a. black and blue (1941?) .. 3·50 30
O26 2 a. black and buff .. 3·00 50
O27 2½ a. black and carmine (1946) .. 4·00 20·00
O28 4 a. black and grey-green (1942) .. 2·25 90
O29 8 a. black and chocolate (1943) .. 2·25 2·00
O30 1 r. black and yellow-bistre (date?) .. £250
O23/9 .. *Set of* 7 14·50 22·00

(*b*) *Optd locally as Type* O 2 (16 *mm long*), *in black*

O31 7 ¼ a. black and red-brown (1936) .. 45·00 40·00

9 PIES

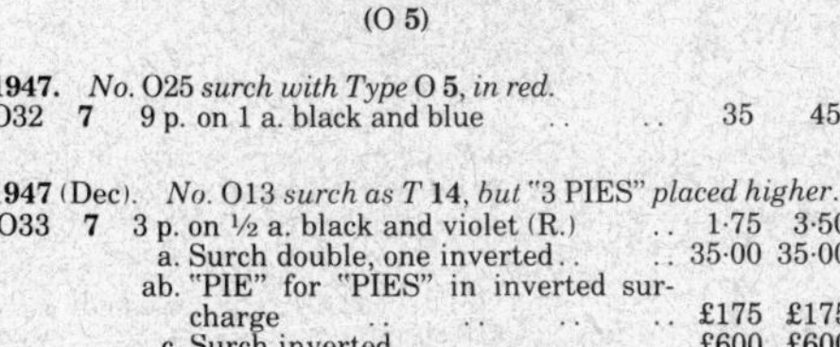

(O 5)

1947. *No. O25 surch with Type* O **5**, *in red.*

O32	**7**	9 p. on 1 a. black and blue	35	45

1947 (Dec). *No. O13 surch as T* **14**, *but "3 PIES" placed higher.*

O33	**7**	3 p. on ½ a. black and violet (R.)	1·75	3·50
		a. Surch double, one inverted	35·00	35·00
		ab. "PIE" for "PIES" in inverted surcharge	£175	£175
		c. Surch inverted	£600	£600

1949. *No. O13 surch* "THREE-QUARTER ANNA" *in Devanagari, as T* **12**, *but with two bars on each side.*

O34	**7**	¾ a. on ½ a. black and violet (R.)	4·50	5·00
		a. Surch double	£550	£550

There are three different types of surcharge in the setting of 30, which vary in one or other of the Devanagari characters.

On 30 March 1949 Jaipur became part of the Rajasthan Union.

JAMMU AND KASHMIR

PRICES FOR STAMPS ON COVER

Nos. 1/49	*from* × 4
No. 50	*from* × 2
Nos. 52/88	*from* × 3
Nos. 90/101	*from* × 10
Nos. 101*b*/23	*from* × 5
Nos. 124/36	*from* × 10
Nos. 138/9	*from* × 100
Nos. 140/61*a*	*from* × 15
Nos. 162/8	*from* × 5
Nos. O1/18	*from* × 30

ILLUSTRATIONS. Designs of Jammu and Kashmir are illustrated actual size.

1 (½ a.)

2 (1 a.)

3 (4 a.)

Characters denoting the value (on the circular stamps only) are approximately as shown in the central circles of the stamps illustrated above.

These characters were taken from Punjabi merchants' notation and were not familiar to most of the inhabitants of the state. Type **1** was certainly the ½ anna value, but there has long been controversy over the correct face values of Types **2** and **3**.

The study of surviving material suggests that, to some extent, this confusion involved contemporary post office officials. Although covers posted at Jammu, where the stamps were in use for twelve years, show Type **2** used as the 1 a. value and Type **3** as the 4 a., those originating from Srinagar (Kashmir) during 1866–68 show both Types **2** and **3** used as 1 a. stamps.

In the following listing we have followed contemporary usage at Jammu and this reflects the prevailing opinion amongst modern authorities.

GUM. The stamps of Jammu and Kashmir were issued without gum.

PRICES. Prices for the circular stamps, Nos. 1/49, are for cut-square examples. Cut-to-shape examples are worth from 10% to 20% of these prices, according to condition.

A. *Handstamped in watercolours*

1866 (23 Mar)–**67.** *Native paper, thick to thin, usually having the appearance of laid paper and tinted grey or brown. For Jammu and Kashmir.*

1	**1**	½ a. grey-black	£100	55·00
2	**2**	1 a. grey-black	£275	
3	**3**	4 a. grey-black	£225	
4	**2**	1 a. royal blue	£400	£225
4*a*	**1**	½ a. ultramarine		
5	**2**	1 a. ultramarine	£190	55·00
6	**3**	4 a. ultramarine	£425	£170
7		4 a. indigo (1867)	£1300	£425

1869–72. *Reissued for use in Jammu only.*

8	**1**	½ a. red	45·00	
9	**2**	1 a. red	70·00	
10	**3**	4 a. red	30·00	42·00
11	**1**	½ a. orange-red	£100	
12	**2**	1 a. orange-red	£100	
13	**3**	4 a. orange-red	48·00	
13*a*		4 a. carmine-red		
13*b*		4 a. orange (1872)		

1869–76. *Special Printings.*

14	**1**	½ a. deep black	14·00	
15	**2**	1 a. deep black	£120	
16	**3**	4 a. deep black	90·00	
17	**1**	½ a. bright blue	80·00	
18	**2**	1 a. bright blue	75·00	
19	**3**	4 a. bright blue	80·00	
20	**1**	½ a. emerald-green	60·00	
21	**2**	1 a. emerald-green	65·00	
22	**3**	4 a. emerald-green	65·00	
23*a*	**1**	½ a. yellow	£275	
24	**2**	1 a. yellow	£350	
25	**3**	4 a. yellow	£350	
25*a*		4 a. deep blue-black (1876)	£425	£200

These special printings were available for use, but little used.

B. *Handstamped in oil colours. Heavy blurred prints*

1877–78. (*a*) *Native paper.*

26	**1**	½ a. red	20·00	26·00
27	**2**	1 a. red	22·00	
28	**3**	4 a. red	£130	£375
29	**1**	½ a. black	16·00	26·00
32		½ a. slate-blue	70·00	
34	**2**	1 a. slate-blue	16·00	
35	**1**	½ a. sage-green	£100	
36	**2**	1 a. sage-green	£110	
37	**3**	4 a. sage-green	£110	

(*b*) *European laid paper, medium to thick*

38	**1**	½ a. red	—	£250
39	**3**	4 a. red	£300	
41	**1**	½ a. black	15·00	26·00
44		½ a. slate-blue	15·00	
45	**2**	1 a. slate-blue	32·00	
46	**3**	4 a. slate-blue	£250	
47		4 a. sage-green	£750	
48	**1**	½ a. yellow	95·00	

(*c*) *Thick yellowish wove paper*

49	**1**	½ a. red (1878)	—	£375

Forgeries exist of the ½ a. and 1 a. in types which were at one time supposed to be authentic.

Reprints and imitations (of which some of each were found in the official remainder stock) exist in a great variety of fancy colours, both on native paper, usually thinner and smoother than that of the originals, and on various thin European *wove* papers, on which the originals were never printed.

The imitations, which do not agree in type with the above illustrations, are also to be found on *laid* paper.

All the reprints, etc. are in oil colours or printer's ink. The originals in oil colour are usually blurred, particularly when on native paper. The reprints, etc. are usually clear.

(3*a*)

1877. *Provisional. Seal obliterator of Jammu handstamped in red watercolour on pieces of native paper, and used as a ½ anna stamp.*

50	**3*a***	(½ a.) rose-red	—	£450

FOR USE IN JAMMU

½ a. ½ a.

1 a. **4** ½ a.

T 4 to 11 have a star at the top of the oval band; the characters denoting the value are in the upper part of the inner oval. All are dated 1923, corresponding with A.D. 1866.

T **4.** *Printed in blocks of four, three varieties of ½ anna and one of 1 anna.*

1867. *In watercolour on native paper.*

52	½ a. grey-black	£140	65·00
53	1 a. grey-black	£750	£300
54	½ a. indigo	70·00	80·00
55	1 a. indigo	90·00	65·00
56	½ a. deep ultramarine	70·00	60·00
57	1 a. deep ultramarine	£100	75·00
58	½ a. deep violet-blue	65·00	48·00
59	1 a. deep violet-blue	£150	95·00

1868–77. *In watercolour on native paper.*

60	½ a. red (*shades*)	3·00	2·50
61	1 a. red (*shades*)	5·00	5·00
62	½ a. orange-red	80·00	20·00
63	1 a. orange-red	80·00	20·00
64	½ a. orange	75·00	70·00
65	1 a. orange	£275	£200

1874–6. *Special printings; in watercolour on native paper.*

66	½ a. bright blue	£170	85·00
67	1 a. bright blue	85·00	90·00
68	½ a. emerald-green	£700	£550
69	1 a. emerald-green	£1000	£600
69*a*	½ a. jet-black	80·00	£100
69*b*	1 a. jet-black	£550	£475

1877. *In oil colour.* (*a*) *Native paper.*

70	½ a. red	8·00	5·00
71	1 a. red	17·00	13·00
72	½ a. brown-red	—	28·00
73	1 a. brown-red	—	80·00
74	½ a. black	—	£250
75	1 a. black	—	£400
76	½ a. deep blue-black	—	£550
77	1 a. deep blue-black	—	£2500

(*b*) *Laid paper (medium or thick)*

78	½ a. red	—	£300

(*c*) *Thick wove paper*

79	½ a. red	—	£275
80	1 a. red		

(*d*) *Thin laid, bâtonné paper*

84	½ a. red	—	£800
85	1 a. red	—	£2750

The circular and rectangular stamps listed under the heading "Special Printings' did not supersede those in *red*, which was the normal colour for Jammu down to 1878. It is not known for what reason other colours were used during that period, but these stamps were printed in 1874 or 1875 and were certainly put into use. The rectangular stamps were again printed in *black* (jet-black, as against the greyish black of the 1867 printings) at that time, and impressions of the two periods can also be distinguished by the obliterations, which until 1868 were in *magenta* and after that in *black*.

There are reprints of these, in *oil* colour, *brown-red* and *bright blue*, on native paper; they are very clearly printed, which is not the case with the originals in *oil* colour.

FOR USE IN KASHMIR

5

1866 (Sept(?)). *Printed from a single die. Native laid paper.*

86	**5**	½ a. black	£1000	£275

Forgeries of this stamp are commonly found, copied from an illustration in *Le Timbre-Poste.*

6 (½ a.)

7 (1 a.)

1867. *Native laid paper.*

87	**6**	½ a. black	£700	85·00
88	**7**	1 a. black	£1200	£180

Printed in sheets of 25 (5 × 5), the four top rows being ½ a. and the bottom row 1 a.

8 (¼ a.)

9 (2 a.)

10 (4 a.)

11 (8 a.)

1867. *Native laid paper.*

No.	Type	Description	Unused	Used
90	8	¼ a. black	50	50
91	6	½ a. ultramarine	80	50
92		½ a. violet-blue	1·00	70
93	7	1 a. ultramarine	£2500	£1000
94		1 a. orange	6·00	4·00
95		1 a. brown-orange	5·00	4·00
96		1 a. orange-vermilion	5·50	4·50
97	9	2 a. yellow	6·50	5·00
98		2 a. buff	7·00	5·00
99	10	4 a. emerald-green	14·00	12·00
		a. *Tête-bêche* (pair)	£400	
100		4 a. sage-green	80·00	35·00
100*a*		4 a. myrtle-green	£450	£450
101	11	8 a. red	15·00	14·00
		a. *Tête-bêche* (pair)	£400	

Of the above, the ½ a. and 1 a. were printed from the same plate of 25 as Nos. 87/8, the ¼ a. and 2 a. from a new plate of 10 (5 × 2), the top row being ¼ a. and the lower 2 a., and the 4 a. and 8 a. from single dies. Varieties at one time catalogued upon European papers were apparently never put into circulation, though some of them were printed while these stamps were still in use.

Nos. 86 to 101 are in watercolour.

FOR USE IN JAMMU AND KASHMIR

In the following issues there are 15 varieties on the sheets of the ⅛ a., ¼ a. and ½ a.; 20 varieties of the 1 a. and 2 a. and 8 varieties of the 4 a. and 8 a. The value is in the lower part of the central oval.

12 (¼ a.)

13 (½ a.)

14 (1 a.)

15 (2 a.)

16 (4 a.)

17 (8 a.)

1878–79. *Provisional printings.*

I. *Ordinary white laid paper, of varying thickness*

(*a*) *Rough perf* 10 *to* 12 (i) *or* 13 *to* 16 (ii)

No.	Type	Description	Unused	Used
101*b*	12	¼ a. red (i)		
102	13	½ a. red (i)	12·00	8·00
103	14	1 a. red (ii)	£650	
104	13	½ a. slate-violet (i)	45·00	45·00
104*a*	14	1 a. violet (ii)		

(*b*) *Imperf*

No.	Type	Description	Unused	Used
105	13	½ a. slate-violet (*shades*)	12·00	12·00
106	14	1 a. slate-purple	18·00	18·00
107		1 a. mauve	19·00	19·00
108	15	2 a. violet	19·00	19·00
109		2 a. bright mauve	19·00	19·00
110		2 a. slate-blue	27·00	27·00
111		2 a. dull blue	38·00	38·00
112	12	¼ a. red	12·00	12·00
113	13	½ a. red	5·00	5·00
114	14	1 a. red	5·50	5·50
115	15	2 a. red	35·00	32·00
116	16	4 a. red	45·00	40·00

II. *Medium wove paper.* (*a*) *Rough perf* 10 *to* 12

No.	Type	Description	Unused	Used
117	13	½ a. red	—	60·00

(*b*) *Imperf*

No.	Type	Description	Unused	Used
117*b*	12	¼ a. red		
118	13	½ a. red	5·00	4·50
119	14	1 a. red	5·50	5·50
120	15	2 a. red	27·00	8·50

III. *Thick wove paper. Imperf*

No.	Type	Description	Unused	Used
121	13	½ a. red	18·00	
122	14	1 a. red	25·00	11·00
123	15	2 a. red	10·00	11·00

1879. *Definitive issue. Thin wove paper, fine to coarse.*

(*d*) *Rough perf* 10 *to* 12

No.	Type	Description	Unused	Used
124	13	½ a. red	70·00	55·00

(*b*) *Imperf*

No.	Type	Description	Unused	Used
125	12	¼ a. red	1·25	1·25
126	13	½ a. red	50	50
127	14	1 a. red	1·25	1·25
		a. Bisected (½ a.) (on cover)		† £2500
128	15	2 a. red	1·75	1·75
129	16	4 a. red	3·00	3·50
130	17	8 a. red	3·50	4·00

1880 (Mar). *Provisional printing in watercolour on thin bâtonné paper. Imperf.*

No.	Type	Description	Unused	Used
130*a*	12	¼ a. ultramarine	£450	£325

1881–83. *As Nos.* 124 *to* 130. *Colour changed.*

(*a*) *Rough perf* 10 *to* 12

No.	Type	Description	Unused	Used
130*b*	13	½ a. orange		

(*b*) *Imperf*

No.	Type	Description	Unused	Used
131	12	¼ a. orange	6·00	4·00
132	13	½ a. orange	18·00	11·00
133	14	1 a. orange	12·00	6·00
		a. Bisected (½ a.) (on cover)		† £2500
134	15	2 a. orange	13·00	7·00
135	16	4 a. orange	20·00	
136	17	8 a. orange	32·00	

No. 127a was used at Leh in April 1883 and No. 133a was used there later.

Nos. 125/30 and 132/6 were re-issued between 1890 and 1894 and used concurrently with the stamps which follow. Such re-issues can be identified by the "three-circle" cancellations, introduced in December 1890.

18 (⅛ a.)

1883–94. *New colours. Thin wove papers, toned, coarse to fine, or fine white* (1889). *Imperf.*

No.	Type	Description	Unused	Used
138	18	⅛ a. yellow-brown	12	20
139		⅛ a. yellow	12	20
140	12	¼ a. sepia	30	12
141		¼ a. brown	20	12
		a. Double impression	£1100	
142		¼ a. pale brown	20	12
		a. Error. Green	40·00	
143	13	½ a. dull blue	4·00	
144		½ a. bright blue	40·00	
145		½ a. vermillion	50	25
146		½ a. rose	50	40
147		½ a. orange-red	45	20
148	14	1 a. greenish grey	30	30
149		1 a. bright green	40	45
		a. Double impression		
150		1 a. dull green	25	25
151		1 a. blue-green	50	
152	15	2 a. red/*yellow*	50	50
153		2 a. red/*yellow-green*	70	80
154		2 a. red/*deep green*	3·00	3·00
155	16	4 a. deep green	1·75	1·75
156		4 a. green	1·75	1·75
157		4 a. pale green	2·00	2·00
158		4 a. sage-green	1·75	
159	17	8 a. pale blue	4·00	4·00
159*a*		8 a. deep blue	6·00	5·50
160		8 a. bright blue	5·50	5·50
161		8 a. indigo-blue	7·50	7·50
161*a*		8 a. slate-lilac	10·00	10·00

Well-executed forgeries of the ¼ a. to 8 a. have come from India, mostly postmarked; they may be detected by the type, which does not agree with any variety on the genuine sheets, and also, in the low values, by the margins being filled in with colour, all but a thin white frame round the stamp. The forgeries of the 8 a. are in sheets of eight like the originals.

Other forgeries of nearly all values also exist, showing all varieties of type. All values are on thin, coarse wove paper.

In February 1890, a forgery, in watercolour, of the ½ a. orange appeared, and many have been found genuinely used (*Price* £2).

Nos. 143 and 144 were never issued.

Examples of the ¼ a. brown, ½ a. orange-red and 1 a. green on wove paper exist with clean-cut perf 12.

There is a reference in the Jammu and Kashmir State Administration Report covering 1890–91 to the re-introduction of perforating and the machine-gumming of paper at the Jammu printing works.

The few known examples, the ¼ a. being only recorded used, the others unused or used, would appear to date from this period, but there is, as yet, no direct confirmation as to their status.

1887–94. *Thin creamy laid paper. Imperf.*

No.	Type	Description	Unused	Used
162	18	⅛ a. yellow	14·00	15·00
163	12	¼ a. brown	9·00	6·00
164	13	½ a. brown-red (March 1887)	—	35·00
165		½ a. orange-red	6·00	4·75
166	14	1 a. grey-green	£120	£110
168	17	8 a. blue (*Printed in watercolour*)	£150	£150
		a. On wove paper	£100	£100

19

T **19** represents a ¼ a. stamp, which exists in sheets of twelve varieties, in *red* and *black*, on thin wove and laid papers, also in *red* on native paper, but which does not appear ever to have been issued for use. It was first seen in 1886.

The ¼ a. *brown*, and the 4 a. *green*, exist on ordinary white laid paper; the ½ a. *red* on native paper; the ¼ a. in *bright green*, on thin white wove (this may be an error in the colour of the 4 a.); and the 8 a. in *lilac* on thin white wove. None of these are known to have been in use.

OFFICIAL STAMPS

1878. I. *White laid paper.* (*a*) *Rough perf* 10 *to* 12.

No.	Type	Description	Unused	Used
O1	13	½ a. black		

(*b*) *Imperf*

No.	Type	Description	Unused	Used
O2	13	½ a. black	35·00	35·00
O3	14	1 a. black	40·00	40·00
O4	15	2 a. black	45·00	50·00

II. *Medium wove paper. Imperf*

No.	Type	Description	Unused	Used
O5	14	1 a. black		

1880–94. *Thin wove papers, toned, coarse to fine, or fine white* (1889). *Imperf.*

No.	Type	Description	Unused	Used
O 6	12	¼ a. black	20	25
		a. Double print	£120	
O 7	13	½ a. black	12	15
O 8	14	1 a. black	20	15
O 9	15	2 a. black	25	25
O10	16	4 a. black	35	40
O11	17	8 a. black	40	45

1887–94. *Thin creamy laid paper. Imperf.*

No.	Type	Description	Unused	Used
O12	12	¼ a. black	2·00	2·50
O13	13	½ a. black	1·50	2·00
O14	14	1 a. black	1·50	2·00
O15	15	2 a. black	18·00	
O16	16	4 a. black	30·00	35·00
O17	17	8 a. black	26·00	35·00

1889. *Stout white wove paper. Imperf.*

No.	Type	Description	Unused	Used
O18	12	¼ a. black	90·00	

The stamps of Jammu and Kashmir have been obsolete since 1 November 1894.

JASDAN

PRICES FOR STAMPS ON COVER

No. 1	*from* × 2
No. 2	*from* × 3
No. 3	*from* × 5
No. 4	—
No. 5	*from* × 5

1 Sun

(Typo L. V. Indap & Co, Bombay)

1942 (15 Mar)–**47**(?). *Stamps from booklet panes. Various perfs.*

No.	Type	Description	Unused	Used
1	1	1 a. myrtle-green (*p* 10½ × *imperf*)	£150	£160
2		1 a. light green (*p* 10½ × *imperf*)	50·00	80·00
3		1 a. pale yellow-green (*p* 8½ × *imperf*)	5·00	38·00
4		1 a. dull yellow-green (*p* 10)	6·50	
5		1 a. bluish green (*p* 9)	6·00	38·00

Nos. 1/3 were issued in panes of four with the stamps imperforate on one or two sides; Nos. 4/5 were in panes of eight perforated all round.

A 1 a. rose with the arms of Jasdan in the centre is a fiscal stamp.

Jasdan was merged with the United State of Kathiawar on 15 February 1948 and renamed the United State of Saurashtra.

JHALAWAR

PRICES FOR STAMPS ON COVER

Nos. 1/2	*from* × 25

(Figure of an Apsara, "RHEMBA", a dancing nymph of the Hindu Paradise)

1 (1 paisa)　　2 (¼ anna)

1887–90. *Typo in horizontal strips of 12. Laid paper. No gum.*

No.	Type	Description	Unused	Used
1	**1**	1 p. yellow-green	1·25	3·00
		a. Blue-green	15·00	8·00
2	**2**	¼ a. green (*shades*)	60	1·25

The stamps formerly listed as on wove paper are from sheets on laid paper, with the laid lines almost invisible.

The stamps of Jhalawar have been obsolete since 1 November 1900.

JIND

PRICES FOR STAMPS ON COVER
Nos. J1/34 *from* × 50

ILLUSTRATIONS. Designs of Jind are illustrated actual size.

J **1** (½ a.)

J **2** (1 a.)

J **3** (2 a.)

J **4** (4 a.)

J **5** (8 a.)

(The letter "R" on stamp is the initial of Raghbir Singh, at one time Rajah)

(Litho Jind State Rajah's Press, Sungroor)

1874. *Thin yellowish paper. Imperf.*

No.	Type	Description	Unused	Used
J1	J **1**	½ a. blue	4·00	2·00
		a. No frame to value. (Retouched all over)	£225	£140
J2	J **2**	1 a. rosy mauve	7·00	6·00
J3	J **3**	2 a. yellow	1·00	2·50
J4		2 a. brown-buff	38·00	26·00
J5	J **4**	4 a. green	18·00	5·00
J6	J **5**	8 a. dull purple	£225	70·00
J6*a*		8 a. bluish violet	£125	55·00
J7		8 a. slate-blue	£125	55·00

1876. *Bluish laid card-paper. No gum. Imperf.*

No.	Type	Description	Unused	Used
J 8	J **1**	½ a. blue	25	1·25
J 9	J **2**	1 a. purple	1·10	2·75
J10	J **3**	2 a. brown	65	3·50
J11	J **4**	4 a. green	1·00	4·00
J11*a*	J **5**	8 a. bluish violet	8·00	13·00
J12		8 a. slate-blue	7·00	10·00
J13		8 a. steel-blue	9·00	15·00

Stocks of the ½ a. (No. J8) and 2 a. (No. J4) were perforated 12 in 1885 for use as fiscal stamps.

J **6** (¼ a.)

J **7** (½ a.)

J **8** (1 a.)

J **9** (2 a.)

J **10** (4 a.)

J **11** (8 a.)

(Litho Jind State Rajah's Press, Sungroor)

1882–85. *Types* J **6** *to* J **11**. *25 varieties of each value. No gum.* A. *Imperf* (1882–4). B. *P* 12 (1885). (*a*) *Thin yellowish wove paper.*

No.	Description	A		B	
J15	¼ a. buff (*shades*)	25	75	35	75
J16	¼ a. red-brown	30	60	1·25	—
	a. Doubly printed	35·00	—	†	
J17	½ a. lemon	50	50	40·00	40·00
J18	½ a. buff	70	1·00	40	1·25
J19	½ a. brown-buff	70	60	1·25	1·75
J20	1 a. brown (*shades*)	80	1·50	1·00	1·75
J21	2 a. blue	1·25	2·50	1·25	3·00
J22	2 a. deep blue	90	1·00	1·75	2·50
J23	4 a. sage-green	80	90	2·50	3·50
J24	4 a. blue-green	1·40	1·90	2·00	—
	a. Imperf between (pair)	†		£400	—
J25	8 a. red	3·00	2·75	5·50	—
	(*b*) *Various thick laid papers*				
J26	¼ a. brown-buff	1·50	—	6·00	—
J27	½ a. lemon	1·50	—	35·00	18·00
J27*a*	½ a. brown-buff	—	—	†	
J28	1 a. brown	1·50	2·50	2·00	—
J29	2 a. blue	18·00	20·00	18·00	20·00
J30	8 a. red	2·50	5·50	2·50	4·50
	(*c*) *Thick white wove paper*				
J31	¼ a. brown-buff	8·00	—	†	
J32	½ a. brown-buff	18·00	—	†	
J33	1 a. brown	3·50	—	—	—
J34	8 a. red	4·50	5·50	6·00	—

The perforated stamps ceased to be used for postal purposes in July 1885, but are said to have been used later as fiscals. Other varieties exist, but they must either be fiscals or reprints, and it is not quite certain that all of those listed above were issued as early as 1885.

Jind became a convention state and from 1885 used the Indian stamps overprinted which are listed under the Convention States.

KISHANGARH

PRICES FOR STAMPS ON COVER

Nos. 1/3	—
Nos. 4/91	*from* × 8
Nos. O1/32	*from* × 30

GUM. The stamps of Kishangarh were issued without gum, *except for* Nos. 42/50 and O 17/24.

1

1899. *Medium wove paper. Typo from a plate of eight impressions.*

No.	Type	Description	Unused	Used
1	**1**	1 a. green (*imperf*)	18·00	35·00
2		1 a. green (*pin-perf*)	38·00	

1900. *Thin white wove paper. Printed from a single die. Imperf.*

No.	Type	Description	Unused	Used
3	**1**	1 a. blue	£350	

ILLUSTRATIONS. Types **2** to **10***a* are shown actual size.

2 (¼ a.)

3 (½ a.)

4 (1 a.)

5 (2 a.)
Maharaja Sardul Singh

6 (4 a.)

7 (1 r.)

8 (2 r.)

9 (5 r.)

1899–1901. *Thin white wove paper.* (*a*) *Imperf.*

No.	Type	Description	Unused	Used
4	**2**	¼ a. green	£180	
5		¼ a. carmine	3·00	
		a. Rose-pink	30	75
6		¼ a. magenta	5·00	
		a. Doubly printed	75·00	
7	**3**	½ a. lilac	42·00	60·00
8		½ a. red	£500	£375
9		½ a. green	21·00	24·00
10		½ a. pale yellow-olive	28·00	28·00
		a. Bistre-brown	28·00	28·00
11		½ a. slate-blue	12·00	14·00
		a. Pair, one stamp sideways	£1000	
		b. Deep blue	2·50	3·00
		c. Light blue	55	75
12	**4**	1 a. slate	2·75	3·50
		a. Laid paper	30·00	
12*b*		1 a. pink	50·00	90·00
13		1 a. mauve	3·00	2·50
		a. Laid paper	30·00	
14		1 a. brown-lilac	1·10	90
		a. Laid paper	27·00	
15	**5**	2 a. dull orange	4·00	4·50
		a. Laid paper	£175	£175
16	**6**	4 a. chocolate	4·00	
		a. Lake-brown	4·00	6·00
		b. Chestnut	4·00	6·00
		c. Laid paper (*shades*)	50·00	50·00
17	**7**	1 r. brown-lilac	20·00	25·00
18		1 r. dull green	17·00	
19	**8**	2 r. brown-red	60·00	
		a. Laid paper	55·00	
20	**9**	5 r. mauve	50·00	
		a. Laid paper	60·00	
		(*b*) *Pin-perf* 12½ *or* 14		
21	**2**	¼ a. green	£110	£160
		a. Imperf between (pair)	£400	
22		¼ a. carmine	1·25	2·00
		a. Rose-pink	25	40
		ab. *Tête-bêche* (horiz pair)	£200	
		b. Rose		
23		¼ a. magenta	5·00	7·00
		a. Bright purple		
		ab. Doubly printed		
24	**3**	½ a. green	17·00	21·00
		a. Imperf between (pair)	£140	
25		½ a. pale yellow-olive	12·00	15·00
		a. Imperf vert (horiz pair)	£140	
		b. Bistre-brown	12·00	15·00
26		½ a. deep blue	1·40	1·75
		a. Light blue	40	40
		ab. Doubly printed	65·00	65·00
27	**4**	1 a. slate	3·25	1·60
		a. Laid paper	30·00	16·00
27*b*		1 a. pink	55·00	£100
28		1 a. mauve	80	90
		a. Laid paper	30·00	13·00
29		1 a. brown-lilac	75	60
		a. Laid paper	30·00	13·00
30	**5**	2 a. dull orange	4·00	5·00
31	**6**	4 a. chocolate	2·00	3·75
		a. Lake-brown	2·50	3·75
		b. Chestnut	3·50	4·25
		c. Laid paper (*shades*)	38·00	38·00
32	**7**	1 r. dull green	10·00	14·00
		a. Laid paper	70·00	
33		1 r. pale olive-yellow	£225	£225
34	**8**	2 r. brown-red	35·00	40·00
		a. Laid paper	40·00	
35	**9**	5 r. mauve	30·00	40·00
		a. Laid paper	60·00	

All the above, both imperf and pin-perf, exist in vertical *tête-bêche* pairs imperf between from the centre of the sheet. *Prices from* 3 × *normal, unused.* No. 22ab is an error.

FISCAL STAMPS. Many of the following issues were produced in different colours for fiscal purposes. Such usage is indicated by the initials "M.C.", punched hole or violet Stamp Office handstamp.

10 (¼ a.)

10*a* (1 r.)

1901. *Toned wove paper. Pin-perf.*
36 **10** ¼ a. dull pink . . . . 8·00 6·00
37 **4** 1 a. violet . . . . 32·00 27·00
38 **10*a*** 1 r. dull green . . . . 14·00 14·00
36/8 . . *Set of* 3 48·00 42·00

These were printed from plates: Nos. 36 and 37 in sheets of 24, No. 38 in sheets of 16. All the others, except Nos. 1, 2 and 3, were printed singly, sometimes on paper with spaces ruled in pencil.

The 1 a. (No. 37) differs from T 4 in having an inscription in native characters below the words "ONE ANNA".

11 (½ a.)

12 Maharaja Sardul Singh

1903. *Litho. Thick white wove glazed paper. Imperf.*
39 **11** ½ a. pink . . . . 4·00 3·00
a. Printed both sides . . — £850
40 **12** 2 a. dull yellow . . . . 3·00 4·00

12*a* (8 a.)

1904. *Printed singly. Thin paper. Pin-perf.*
41 **12*a*** 8 a. grey . . . . 5·00 7·50
a. *Tête-bêche* (pair) . . 24·00
b. Doubly printed . . 85·00

13 Maharaja Madan Singh 14

(Recess Perkins Bacon & Co)

1904–5. *With gum. P* 12½.
42 **13** ¼ a. carmine 40 35
a. Perf 13½ . . 35 35
43 ½ a. chestnut . . 60 65
a. Perf 13½ . . 30 30
44 1 a. blue . . . . 1·60 1·10
a. Perf 13½ . . 35 55
45 2 a. orange-yellow . . 8·00 7·00
a. Perf 13½ . . 14·00 10·00
46 4 a. brown . . 9·00 7·50
a. Perf 13½ . . 8·00 8·00
b. Perf 12 . . 22·00 22·00
47 8 a. violet (1905) . . 6·00 9·00
48 1 r. green . . 12·00 13·00
49 2 r. olive-yellow . . 14·00 30·00
50 5 r. purple-brown . . 21·00 45·00
42/50 . . *Set of* 9 60·00 £100

Stamps in other colours, all perforated 13½, are colour trials.

1912. *Printed from half-tone blocks. No ornaments to left and right of value in English; large ornaments on either side of value in Hindi. Small stop after* "STATE". (*a*) *Thin wove paper. Rouletted.*
51 **14** 2 a. deep violet ("TWO ANNA") . . 3·00 6·00
a. *Tête-bêche* (vert pair) . . 7·00
b. Imperf (pair) . . £110

No. 51 is printed in four rows, each inverted in respect to that above and below it.

(*b*) *Thick white chalk-surfaced paper. Rouletted*
52 **14** 2 a. lilac ("TWO ANNA") . . £250 £160

(*c*) *Thick white chalk-surfaced paper. Rouletted in colour* (*Medallion only in half-tone*)
53 **14** ¼ a. ultramarine . . 8·00 10·00

1913. *No ornaments on either side of value in English. Small ornaments in bottom label. With stop after* "STATE". *Thick white chalk-surfaced paper. Rouletted.*
54 **14** 2 a. purple ("TWO ANNAS") . . 2·50 5·00

QUARTER ANNA / POSTAGE & REVENUE / KISHANGARH STATE / पाव आना

15

पाव अना

No. 59e. This occurs on R. 3/3 on one setting only

2 TWO ANNAS 2 — No. 60. Small figures

2 TWO ANNAS 2 — No. 60b. Large figures

(Typo Diamond Soap Works, Kishangarh)

1913 (Aug). *Thick surfaced paper. Half-tone centre. Type-set inscriptions. Rouletted. Inscr* "KISHANGARH".
59 **15** ¼ a. pale blue 20 25
a. Imperf (pair) . . 7·00
b. Roul × imperf (horiz pair) . . 22·00
c. "OUARTER" . . 5·00 5·50
ca. As last, imperf (pair) . . 28·00
cb. As last, roul × imperf . . 50·00
d. "KISHANGAHR" . . 5·00 5·50
da. As last, imperf (pair) . . 28·00
db. As last, roul × imperf . . 50·00
e. Character omitted . . 7·00 7·00
ea. As last, imperf (pair) . . 32·00
60 2 a. purple . . 8·00 16·00
a. "KISHANGAHR" . . 70·00 85·00
b. Large figures "2" . . 40·00 50·00

1913–16. *Stamps printed far apart, horizontally and vertically, otherwise as No.* 54, *except as noted below.*
63 **14** ¼ a. blue 20 40
64 ½ a. green (1915) . . 20 50
a. Printed both sides . . £125
b. Imperf (pair) . . £125 £125
c. *Emerald-green* (1916) . . 1·75 2·75
65 1 a. red . . . . 1·00 1·75
a. Without stop* . . 1·25 2·25
ab. Imperf (pair) . . £150
66 2 a. purple ("TWO ANNAS") (1915) . . 6·00 7·00
67 4 a. bright blue . . 6·00 8·00
68 8 a. brown . . 7·00 22·00
69 1 r. mauve . . 12·00 35·00
70 2 r. deep green . . 35·00 75·00
71 5 r. brown . . 65·00 £120
63/71 . . *Set of* 9 £120 £250

*For this issue, ornaments were added on either side of the English value (except in the ¼ a.) and the inscription in the right label was without stop, except in the case of No. 65.

In Nos. 70 and 71 the value is expressed as "RUPIES" instead of "RUPEES".

Initial printings of the ¼ a., 1 a. and 4 a. values were in sheets of 20 containing two pairs of 10 separated by a central gutter margin. Stamps from these sheets measure 20 × 25½ mm and have heavier screening dots on the perforation margins than on the designs. Subsequent printings of these stamps, and of the other values in the set, were from single pane sheets of 20 on which the designs measured 19½ × 24¾ mm and with the screening dots uniform across the sheet.

16 Maharaja Yagyanarain Singhji 17

1928–36. *Thick surfaced paper. Typo. Pin-perf.*
72 **16** ¼ a. light blue . . . . 35 1·00
73 ½ a. yellow-green . . 45 60
a. *Deep green* . . 1·50 1·50
ab. Imperf (pair) . . 40·00 40·00
ac. Imperf between (vert or horiz pair) 40·00 40·00
74 **17** 1 a. carmine . . 60 1·00
a. Imperf (pair) . . 60·00 60·00
75 2 a. purple . . 3·00 5·50
75*a* 2 a. magenta (1936) . . 5·00 8·00
ab. Imperf (pair) . . 75·00
76 **16** 4 a. chestnut . . 1·25 1·75
a. Imperf (pair) . .
77 8 a. violet . . 3·50 11·00
78 1 r. light green . . 7·50 24·00
79 2 r. lemon-yellow (1929) . . 22·00 48·00
80 5 r. claret (1929) . . 25·00 60·00
a. Imperf (pair) . . £100
72/80 . . *Set of* 9 55·00 £140

The 4 a. to 5 r. are slightly larger than, but otherwise similar to, the ¼ a. and ½ a. The 8 a. has a dotted background covering the whole design.

1943–47. *As last, but thick, soft, unsurfaced paper. Poor impression. Typo. Pin-perf.*
81 **16** ¼ a. pale dull blue (1945) . . 1·00 2·50
a. Imperf (pair) . . 28·00
82 ¼ a. greenish blue (1947) . . 1·00 2·25
a. Imperf (pair) . . 28·00
83 ½ a. deep green (1944) . . 80 1·10
a. Imperf (pair) . . 25·00 25·00
b. Imperf between (vert or horiz pair) 35·00
84 ½ a. yellow-green (1946) . . 1·90 2·50
a. Imperf (pair) . . 25·00 25·00
b. Imperf between (vert or horiz pair) 35·00
85 **17** 1 a. carmine-red (1944) . . 2·25 1·60
a. Double print
b. Imperf (pair) . . 25·00 25·00
c. Imperf between (vert or horiz pair) 35·00
d. *Red-orange* (1947) . . 25·00 16·00
da. Imperf (pair) . . 50·00 50·00
86 2 a. bright magenta . . 5·00 7·50
a. Imperf (pair) . . 35·00 35·00
87 2 a. maroon (1947) . . 35·00 15·00
a. Imperf (pair) . . 40·00 40·00
b. Imperf between (vert or horiz pair) 55·00
88 **16** 4 a. brown (1944) . . 20·00 15·00
a. Imperf (pair) . .
89 8 a. violet (1945) . . 32·00 55·00
90 1 r. green (1945) . . 40·00 75·00
a. Imperf (pair) . . £150
90*b* 2 r. yellow (date?) . .
ba. Imperf (pair) . .
91 5 r. claret (1945) . . £200 £250
a. Imperf (pair) . . £275

OFFICIAL STAMPS

ON
K S
D

(O 1)

1918. *Handstamped with Type* O 1.

(*a*) *Stamps of* 1899–1901. (i) *Imperf*
O 1 **2** ¼ a. green . . — 80·00
O 2 ¼ a. rose-pink . . — 5·00
O 3 **4** 1 a. mauve . . — 25·00
O 3a 1 a. brown-lilac . . 20·00 4·50
O 4 **6** 4 a. chocolate . . — 40·00

(ii) *Pin-perf*
O 5 **2** ¼ a. green . . — 65·00
O 6 ¼ a. rose-pink . . 1·00 45
O 7 **3** ½ a. light blue . . — 22·00
O 8 **4** 1 a. mauve . . 12·00 1·50
O 9 1 a. brown-lilac . . 10·00 1·50
O10 **5** 2 a. dull orange . . — 70·00
O11 **6** 4 a. chocolate . . 18·00 16·00
O12 **7** 1 r. dull green . . 60·00 60·00
O13 **8** 2 r. brown-red . . — £450
O14 **9** 5 r. mauve . . — £500

(*b*) *Stamps of* 1903 *and* 1904
O15 **12** 2 a. dull yellow . . 20·00 7·00
a. Stamp printed both sides . . — £375
b. Red opt . . 80·00 60·00
O16 **12*a*** 8 a. grey . . 24·00 20·00
a. Red opt . . — 50·00

(*c*) *Stamps of* 1904–5. *P* 13½ (¼ *a. to* 4 *a.*) *or* 12½ (*others*)
O17 **13** ¼ a. carmine . . — 75·00
O18 ½ a. chestnut . . 60 35
O19 1 a. blue . . 7·00 4·00
a. Red opt . . 8·50 7·00
O20 2 a. orange-yellow . . — £375
O21 4 a. brown . . 22·00 17·00
a. Red opt . . 25·00 19·00
O22 8 a. violet . . £100 85·00
a. Red opt . . — 85·00
O23 1 r. green . . £225 £200
a. Red opt . . — £180
O24 5 r. purple-brown . .

(*d*) *Stamps of* 1913
O25 **15** ¼ a. pale blue . . 6·00
a. "OUARTER" . . 22·00
b. "KISHANGAHR" . . 22·00
c. Character omitted . . 22·00
d. Imperf (pair) . . 65·00
O26 **14** 2 a. purple (No. 54) . . — 38·00
a. Red opt . . 60·00 20·00
O27 **15** 2 a. purple . . £130 £140
a. "KISHANGAHR" . . £300
b. Large figures "2" . . £225

(*e*) *Stamps of* 1913–16
O28 **14** ¼ a. blue . . 50 50
a. Red opt . . 1·50 1·50
O29 ½ a. green . . 75 75
a. Red opt . . 1·50 1·50
O30 1 a. red . . 2·75 2·75
a. Without stop . . 1·00 1·00
ab. Red opt . . — 45·00
O31 2 a. purple . . 5·50 4·00
a. Red opt . . 50·00 28·00
O32 4 a. bright blue . . 18·00 15·00
a. Red opt . . — 26·00
O33 8 a. brown . . 50·00 35·00
a. Red opt . . — 60·00
O34 1 r. lilac . . £125 £125
O35 2 r. deep green . .
O36 5 r. brown . . £550

This overprint is found inverted as often as it is upright; and many other "errors" exist.

On 25 March 1948 Kishangarh became part of the Rajasthan Union.

LAS BELA

PRICES FOR STAMPS ON COVER
Nos. 1/12 *from* × 8

1

2

(Litho Thacker & Co, Bombay)

1897–98. *Thick paper. Pin-perf.*

1	1	½ a. black on *white*	9·00	5·50

1898–1900. *Pin-perf.*

2	1	½ a. black on *greyish blue* (1898)	7·50	4·50
3		½ a. black on *greenish grey* (1899)	6·50	4·00
		a. "BFLA" for "BELA"	60·00	
		b. Imperf between (horiz strip of 3)		
4		½ a. black on *thin white surfaced paper* (1899)	15·00	
5		½ a. black on *slate* (1900)	20·00	
		a. Imperf between (pair)	£250	

1901–2. *Pin-perf.*

6	1	½ a. black on *pale grey*	7·00	6·00
		a. "BFLA" for "BELA"	55·00	
7		½ a. black on *pale green* (1902)	11·00	12·00
8	2	1 a. black on *orange*	10·00	11·00

There are at least 14 settings of the above ½ a. stamps, the sheets varying from 16 to 30 stamps.

1904. *Stamps printed wider apart. Pin-perf.*

11	1	½ a. black on *pale blue*	7·00	6·00
		a. Imperf between (pair)	£275	
12		½ a. black on *pale green*	7·00	6·00

There are three plates of the above two stamps, each consisting of 18 varieties.

All the coloured papers of the ½ a. show coloured fibres, similar to those in granite paper.

The stamps of Las Bela have been obsolete since 1 April 1907.

MORVI

PRICES FOR STAMPS ON COVER
Nos. 1/19 *from* × 6

1

2

3

Maharaja Sir Lakhdirji Waghji

1931 (1 April). *Typo. P* 12.

(*a*) *Printed in blocks of four. Stamps* 10 *mm apart* (*Nos.* 1/2) *or* 6½ *mm apart* (*No.* 3). *Perf on two or three sides*

1	1	3 p. deep red	3·00	8·50
2		½ a. blue	16·00	22·00
3		2 a. yellow-brown	60·00	
1/3		*Set of* 3	70·00	

(*b*) *Printed in two blocks of four. Stamps* 5½ *mm apart. Perf on four sides*

4	1	3 p. bright scarlet	3·00	6·00
		a. Error. Dull blue	3·75	10·00
		b. Ditto. Double print	£275	
		c. Ditto. Printed on gummed side	£275	
5		½ a. dull blue	1·75	4·00
6		1 a. brown-red	2·75	7·50
7		2 a. yellow-brown	4·00	11·00
4/7		*Set of* 4	9·00	26·00

1932–33. *Horizontal background lines wider apart and portrait smaller than in T* 1. *Typo. P* 11.

8	2	3 p. carmine-rose (*shades*)	65	1·90
9		6 p. green	90	2·50
		a. Imperf between (horiz pair)	£1000	
		b. Emerald-green	60	2·25
10		1 a. ultramarine (*to deep*)	1·25	4·50
		a. Imperf between (vert pair)	£800	
11		2 a. bright violet (1933)	10·00	16·00
		a. Imperf between (vert pair)	£800	
8/11		*Set of* 4	11·00	22·00

1934. *Typo. London ptg. P* 14.

12	3	3 p. carmine	60	1·00
13		6 p. emerald-green	60	1·75
14		1 a. purple-brown	1·00	3·25
		a. Imperf between (horiz pair)	†	£750
15		2 a. bright violet	1·40	5·00
12/15		*Set of* 4	3·00	10·00

1935–48. *Typo. Morvi Press ptg. Rough perf* 11.

16	3	3 p. scarlet (*shades*)	40	1·10
		a. Imperf between (horiz pair)	£750	
17		6 p. grey-green	60	1·75
		a. Emerald-green	3·75	10·00
18		1 a. brown	10·00	12·00
		a. Pale yellow-brown	14·00	20·00
		b. Chocolate	12·00	17·00
19		2 a. dull violet (*to deep*)	2·50	8·50
16/19		*Set of* 4	12·00	21·00

Nos. 17*a*, 18*a* and 18*b* were issued between 1944 and 1948.

Morvi was incorporated in the Union of Saurashtra on 15 February 1948.

MINIMUM PRICE

The minimum price quote is 10p which represents a handling charge rather than a basis for valuing common stamps. For further notes about prices see introductory pages.

NANDGAON

PRICES FOR STAMPS ON COVER
The stamps of Nandgaon are very rare used on cover.

GUM. The stamps of Nandgaon were issued without gum.

1

1892 (Feb). *Litho. Imperf.*

1	1	½ a. blue	1·50	55·00
		a. Dull blue	2·50	
		b. Optd with T 2	85·00	
2		2 a. rose	11·00	£110

Collectors are warned against copies of T 1 with faked postmarks. Genuinely used they are very rare.

(2)

3 (2 a.)

("M.B.D." = Rajah Machant Balram Das)

1893–94. *Typo.*

(i) *Printed wide apart on the sheet, no wavy lines between stamps*

(*a*) *Optd with T* 2 *in purple or grey*

3	3	2 a. red	14·00	

(*b*) *Without overprint*

4	3	½ a. green	8·00	22·00
5		2 a. red	4·00	22·00

(ii) *Printed closer together, wavy lines between stamps*

(*a*) *Optd with T* 2 *in purple or grey*

6	3	½ a. green	2·25	3·50
		a. Sage-green	2·25	
7		1 a. rose (*laid paper*)	11·00	32·00
8		1 a. rose (*wove paper*)	4·50	10·00
9		2 a. dull carmine	5·00	10·00

(*b*) *Without overprint*

10	3	½ a. green	12·00	22·00
11		1 a. rose (*laid paper*)	£120	
12		1 a. rose (*wove paper*)	20·00	38·00

It has been stated that no stamps were regularly issued for postal use without the "control" mark, T 2, but it is very doubtful if this is correct. The overprint probably indicates official use.

The 1 a. exists in *ultramarine* and in *brown*, but these appear to be reprints.

The stamps of Nandgaon have been obsolete since 1 January 1895.

NAWANAGAR

PRICES FOR STAMPS ON COVER
The stamps of Nawanagar are very rare used on cover.

GUM. The stamps of Nawanagar were issued without gum.

1 (1 docra)

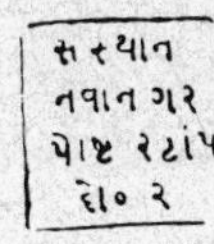
2 (2 docra)

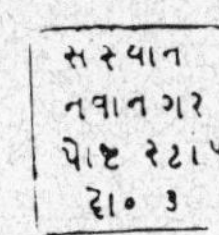
3 (3 docra)

1877. *Typo in sheets of* 32. *Laid paper.* (*a*) *Imperf.*

1	1	1 doc. blue (*shades*)	40	14·00
		a. *Tête-bêche* (pair)	£1000	
		b. Doubly printed	80·00	

(*b*) *Perf* 12½ (*line*) *or* 11 (*harrow*)

2	1	1 doc. slate-blue	45·00	70·00
		a. *Tête-bêche* (pair) (*p* 11)	£1250	

1877. *T* 2 *and* 3. *Type-set in black. Wove paper. Thick horizontal and vertical frame lines.*

A. *Stamp* 14½–15 *mm wide.* B. *Stamp* 16 *mm wide.* C. *Stamp* 19 *mm wide.*

		A		B		C	
2*b*	1 doc. *deep mauve*	£110		£110		†	90·00
2*c*	2 doc. *green*	†		†		†	£900
2*d*	3 doc. *yellow*	†		†		£1700	£1000

Prices for the 1 doc. and 2 doc. values are for used, no unused examples being known.

1880. *As last, but thin frame lines, as illustrated.*
D. *Stamp* 15 *to* 18 *mm wide.* E. *Stamp* 14 *mm wide.*

		D		E	
3	1 doc. *deep mauve*	80	3·50	†	
	a. On rose	80	—	80	2·00
4	1 doc. *magenta*	†		80	—
5	2 doc. *yellow-green*	1·10	5·00	1·10	4·00
	a. On blue-green	2·25	—	3·50	—
	b. Error. Yellow	£300	—	†	
6	3 doc. *orange-yellow*	3·00	—	†	
	a. On yellow	4·50	9·00	2·50	6·00
	ab. On yellow. Laid paper	75·00	—	40·00	—

There are several different settings of each value of this series.

No. 5b occurs in the sheet of the 3 doc. value from one setting only.

4 (1 docra)

1893. *Typo in sheets of* 36. *P* 12. (*a*) *Thick paper.*

8	4	1 doc. black	1·10	
		a. Imperf (pair)	£200	
9		3 doc. orange	2·25	

(*b*) *Thick laid paper*

10	4	1 doc. black	£140	

(*c*) *Thin wove paper*

11	4	1 doc. black *to* grey	35	1·75
		a. Imperf between (pair)	£225	
		b. Imperf (pair)	£200	
12		2 doc. green	50	2·00
		a. Imperf (pair)	£200	
		b. Imperf between (vert pair)		
13		3 doc. orange-yellow	90	2·75
		a. Imperf between (pair)	£225	
		b. Orange	60	2·75
		ba. Imperf (pair)	£200	
		bb. Imperf vert (horiz pair)		

(*d*) *Thin, soft wove paper*

14	4	1 doc. black		
15		2 doc. deep green	3·00	
16		3 doc. brown-orange	4·00	

Cancellations for postal purposes were intaglio seals, applied in black. Other forms of cancellation were only used on remainders.

The stamps of Nawanagar became obsolete on 1 January 1895.

NEPAL

Nepal being an independent state, its stamps will be found listed in Part 21 (*South-East Asia*) of this catalogue.

ORCHHA

PRICES FOR STAMPS ON COVER

Nos. 1/2	—
Nos. 3/7	*from* × 8
Nos. 8/30	*from* × 50
Nos. 31/45	*from* × 4

A set of four stamps, ½ a. red, 1 a. violet, 2 a. yellow and 4 a. deep blue-green, in a design similar to T 2, was prepared in 1897 with State authority but not put into use. These exist both imperforate and pin-perforated.

1

2

(T **1/2** litho Shri Pratap Prabhakar)

1913. *Background to arms unshaded. Very blurred impression. Wove paper. No gum. Imperf.*

1	1	½ a. green	18·00	35·00
2		1 a. red	16·00	

1914–17. *Background shaded with short horizontal lines. Clearer impression. Wove paper. No gum. Imperf.*

3	2	¼ a. bright ultramarine	60	2·25
		a. Grey-blue	35	1·50
		b. Deep blue	1·25	1·75
		ba. Laid paper	£275	
4		½ a. green (*shades*)	40	1·50
		a. Dull green	1·40	2·50
		b. Apple-green	1·90	2·50
5		1 a. scarlet	1·60	2·75
		a. Indian red	2·00	5·50
		b. Carmine	2·50	4·25
		ba. Laid paper	£120	
6		2 a. red-brown (1916)	4·50	9·00
		a. Light brown	7·00	9·00
		b. Chestnut	9·00	11·00
7		4 a. ochre (1917)	8·00	14·00
		a. Yellow-orange	8·00	14·00
		b. Yellow	8·00	14·00
3/7		*Set of* 5	13·00	26·00

There are two sizes of T **2** in the setting of 8 (4 × 2). In each value stamps from the upper row are slightly taller than those from the lower.

3 Maharaja Vir Singh Deo Bahadur **4**

(Typo Lakshmi Art Ptg Wks, Bombay)

1935 (1 Apr). *Thick, chalk-surfaced wove paper. P* 9½, 10, 10 × 9½, 11, 11 × 9½, 11½, 11½ × 11, 11½ × 12, 12 *or* 12 × 11.

No.	Type	Description	Unused	Used
8	**3**	¼ a. purple and slate	20	30
		a. Ordinary paper	20	30
		ab. Imperf between (vert pair)	10·00	
		ac. Imperf vert (horiz pair)	28·00	
9		½ a. olive-grey and emerald	30	30
		a. Imperf (pair)		
10		¾ a. magenta and deep myrtle-green	30	30
11		1 a. myrtle-green and purple-brown	35	35
		a. Imperf (pair)	—	45·00
12		1¼ a. slate and mauve	35	35
		a. Imperf (pair)	—	95·00
13		1½ a. brown and scarlet	35	35
		a. Imperf between (vert pair)		
		b. Imperf between (horiz pair)		
14		2 a. blue and red-orange	35	35
		a. Imperf (pair)	9·00	
15		2½ a. olive-brown and dull orange	35	35
		a. Imperf (pair)	9·00	
16		3 a. bright blue and magenta	35	35
17		4 a. deep reddish purple and sage-green	40	55
		a. Imperf (pair)	7·50	
18		6 a. black and pale ochre	45	60
		a. Imperf (pair)	7·50	
19		8 a. brown and purple	50	65
		a. Imperf (pair)	7·50	
20		12 a. bright emerald and bright purple	55	80
		a. Imperf (pair)	7·50	
21		12 a. pale greenish blue and bright purple	13·00	18·00
22		1 r. chocolate and myrtle-green	65	1·00
		a. Imperf (pair)	8·00	
		b. Imperf between (horiz pair)		
23	**4**	1 r. chocolate and myrtle-green	1·25	2·25
		a. Imperf (pair)		
24	**3**	2 r. purple-brown and bistre-yellow	90	1·40
		a. Imperf (pair)	9·00	
25		3 r. black and greenish blue	1·00	1·60
		a. Imperf (pair)	9·00	
26		4 r. black and brown	1·40	2·00
		a. Imperf (pair)	9·00	
27		5 r. bright blue and plum	2·00	3·00
		a. Imperf (pair)	9·00	
28		10 r. bronze-green and cerise	4·25	6·50
		a. Imperf (pair)	10·00	
		b. Imperf between (horiz pair)		
29		15 r. black and bronze-green	8·00	12·00
		a. Imperf (pair)	11·00	
30		25 r. red-orange and blue	10·00	15·00
		a. Imperf (pair)	14·00	
8/20, 22/30		*Set of* 22	30·00	45·00

Values to 5 r. except the 1 a., are inscribed "POSTAGE", and the remaining values "POSTAGE & REVENUE".

The central portrait of Type **3** is taken from a half-tone block and consists of large square dots. The portrait of Type **4** has a background of lines.

Owing to a lack of proper State control considerable quantities of these stamps circulated at below face value and the issue was subsequently withdrawn, supplies being exchanged for the 1939–42 issue. We are, however, now satisfied that the lower values at least did genuine postal duty until 1939.

Used prices are for stamps cancelled-to-order, postally used examples being worth considerably more.

5 H.H. The Maharaja of Orchha **6**

(Litho Indian Security Printing Press, Nasik)

1939–42? *P* 13½ × 14 (*T* **5**) *or* 14 × 13½ (*T* **6**).

No.	Type	Description	Unused	Used
31	**5**	¼ a. chocolate	65	18·00
32		½ a. yellow-green	65	13·00
33		¾ a. bright blue	65	25·00
34		1 a. scarlet	65	7·00
35		1¼ a. blue	85	25·00
36		1½ a. mauve	1·25	30·00
37		2 a. vermilion	1·10	18·00
38		2½ a. turquoise-green	1·40	
39		3 a. slate-violet	1·75	28·00
40		4 a. slate	2·25	11·00
41		8 a. magenta	4·00	40·00
42	**6**	1 r. grey-green	7·50	
43		2 r. bright violet	18·00	
44		5 r. yellow-orange	55·00	
45		10 r. turquoise-green (1942)	£170	
46		15 r. slate-lilac (date ?)		
47		25 r. claret (date ?)		

POONCH

PRICES FOR STAMPS ON COVER

Nos. 1/2	*from* × 3
Nos. 3/62	*from* × 10
Nos. O1/10	*from* × 30

GUM. The stamps of Poonch were issued without gum, except for some examples of Nos. 7/10.

The stamps of Poonch are all imperforate, and handstamped in watercolours.

ILLUSTRATIONS. Designs of Poonch are illustrated actual size.

1

2

1876. *T* **1** (22 × 21 *mm*). *Yellowish white, wove paper.*

No.	Type	Description	Unused	Used
1		6 p. red	—	85·00

1877. *As T* **1** (19 × 17 *mm*). *Same paper.*

No.	Type	Description	Unused	Used
1*a*		½ a. red	£3500	£1100

1879. *T* **2** (21 × 19 *mm*). *Same paper.*

No.	Type	Description	Unused	Used
2		½ a. red	—	£750

3 (½ a.)

4 (1 a.)

5 (2 a.)

6 (4 a.)

1880. *Yellowish white, wove paper.*

No.	Type	Description	Unused	Used
3	**3**	½ a. red	22·00	11·00
4	**4**	1 a. red	25·00	14·00
5	**5**	2 a. red	28·00	24·00
6	**6**	4 a. red	32·00	27·00

1884. *Toned wove bâtonné paper.*

No.	Type	Description	Unused	Used
7	**3**	½ a. red	3·50	3·50
8	**4**	1 a. red	6·00	
9	**5**	2 a. red	8·00	8·00
10	**6**	4 a. red	11·00	

These are sometimes found gummed.

7 (1 pice)

1884–87. *Various papers.* (*a*) *White laid bâtonné or ribbed bâtonné.*

No.	Type	Description	Unused	Used
11	**7**	1 p. red	7·50	7·50
12	**3**	½ a. red	1·25	1·50
13	**4**	1 a. red	1·40	
14	**5**	2 a. red	2·25	2·50
15	**6**	4 a. red	4·75	
		(*b*) *Thick white laid paper*		
22	**7**	1 p. red	8·00	
23	**3**	½ a. red	16·00	
24	**4**	1 a. red	22·00	
25	**5**	2 a. red	28·00	
26	**6**	4 a. red	35·00	
		(*c*) *Yellow wove bâtonné*		
27	**7**	1 p. red	2·25	2·00
		a. Pair, one stamp sideways		
28	**3**	½ a. red	2·50	2·50
29	**4**	1 a. red	8·50	
30	**5**	2 a. red	2·50	3·25
31	**6**	4 a. red	2·25	
		(*d*) *Orange-buff wove bâtonné*		
32	**7**	1 p. red	40	60
		a. Pair, one stamp sideways	13·00	
33	**3**	½ a. red	10·00	
34	**5**	2 a. red	15·00	
35	**6**	4 a. red	8·00	
		(*e*) *Yellow laid paper*		
36	**7**	1 p. red	1·00	1·00
37	**3**	½ a. red	2·00	
38	**4**	1 a. red	8·00	
39	**5**	2 a. red	11·00	11·00
40	**6**	4 a. red	15·00	
		(*f*) *Yellow laid bâtonné*		
41	**7**	1 p. red	6·00	4·50
		(*g*) *Buff laid or ribbed bâtonné paper thicker than* (*d*)		
42	**4**	1 a. red	20·00	
43	**6**	4 a. red	28·00	
		(*h*) *Blue-green laid paper* (1887)		
44	**3**	½ a. red	11·00	
45	**4**	1 a. red	2·00	2·75
46	**5**	2 a. red	10·00	
47	**6**	4 a. red	16·00	
		(*i*) *Yellow-green laid paper*		
48	**3**	½ a. red		
		(*j*) *Blue-green wove bâtonné*		
49	**7**	1 p. red	16·00	20·00
50	**4**	1 a. red	35	65
		(*k*) *Lavender wove bâtonné*		
51	**4**	1 a. red	20·00	
52	**5**	2 a. red	35	65
		(*l*) *Various coloured papers*		
53	**7**	1 p. red/*grey-blue laid*	3·00	3·00
54		1 p. red/*lilac laid*	45·00	48·00
55		1 p. red/*blue wove bâtonné*	45	45
		a. Pair, one stamp sideways		

1888. *Printed in aniline rose on various papers.*

No.	Type	Description	Unused	Used
56	**7**	1 p. on *blue wove bâtonné*	1·75	
57		1 p. on *buff laid*	3·50	
58	**3**	½ a. on *white laid*	5·50	
59	**4**	1 a. on *green laid*	9·00	8·00
60		1 a. on *green wove bâtonné*	3·00	2·50
61	**5**	2 a. on *lavender wove bâtonné*	3·00	2·50
62	**6**	4 a. on *yellow laid*	7·00	7·00

OFFICIAL STAMPS

1888. (*a*) *White laid bâtonné paper.*

No.	Type	Description	Unused	Used
O 1	**7**	1 p. black	70	80
		a. Pair, one stamp sideways	9·00	
		b. *Tête-bêche* (pair)	12·00	
O 2	**3**	½ a. black	70	1·00
O 3	**4**	1 a. black	70	1·00
O 4	**5**	2 a. black	1·10	1·25
O 5	**6**	4 a. black	2·25	2·50
		(*b*) *White toned wove bâtonné paper*		
O 6	**7**	1 p. black	1·40	
O 7	**3**	½ a. black	2·00	2·00
		a. Pair, one stamp sideways	£400	
O 8	**4**	1 a. black	6·00	6·00
O 9	**5**	2 a. black	3·25	3·25
O10	**6**	4 a. black	6·50	

The stamps of Poonch have been obsolete since 1894.

RAJASTHAN

Rajasthan was formed in 1948–49 from a number of States in Rajputana; these included Bundi, Jaipur and Kishangarh, whose posts continued to function more or less separately until ordered by the Indian Government to close on 1 April 1950.

PRICES FOR STAMPS ON COVER

Nos. 1/7	*from* × 15
Nos. 8/10	—
Nos. 11/12	*from* × 5
Nos. 13/14	—
Nos. 15/25	*from* × 4
Nos. 26/42	*from* × 3
No. 43	*from* × 5
Nos. 44/60	*from* × 3
No. 61	*from* × 5
Nos. 62/5	—

BUNDI

(**1**)

1949. *Nos.* 86/92 *of Bundi.* (*a*) *Handstamped with T* **1**.

A. *In black.* B. *In violet.* C. *In blue*

No.	Description	A	B	C
1	¼ a. blue-green	1·75	1·75	15·00
	a. Pair, one without opt	55·00	†	†
2	½ a. violet	1·75	1·75	12·00
	a. Pair, one without opt	†	65·00	†
3	1 a. yellow-green	1·75	7·00	14·00
	a. Pair, one without opt	†	65·00	†
4	2 a. vermilion	5·00	18·00	—
5	4 a. orange	14·00	7·00	25·00
6	8 a. ultramarine	2·50	2·25	18·00
7	1 r. chocolate	—	£100	35·00

The above prices are for unused, used stamps being worth about three times the unused prices. Most of these handstamps are known, sideways, inverted or double.

(*b*) *Machine-printed as T* **1** *in black*

No.	Description		
8	¼ a. blue-green		
9	½ a. violet		
10	1 a. yellow-green		

No.	Type	Description	Unused	Used
11		2 a. vermilion	1·75	18·00
		a. Opt inverted	£100	
12		4 a. orange	2·00	18·00
		a. Opt double	£100	
13		8 a. ultramarine	38·00	
		a. Opt inverted	£150	
14		1 r. chocolate	7·00	

JAIPUR

राजस्थान

RAJASTHAN

(2)

1950 (26 Jan). *T* **7** *of Jaipur optd with T* **2**.

No.	Description	Unused	Used
15	¼ a. black and brown-lake (No. 58) (B.)	2·50	6·00
16	½ a. black and violet (No. 41) (R.)	2·50	6·00
17	¾ a. black and brown-red (No. 59) (Blue-blk.)	2·75	6·50
	a. Opt in pale blue	8·00	16·00
18	1 a. black and blue (No. 60) (R.)	3·25	9·00
19	2 a. black and buff (No. 61) (R.)	3·25	10·00
20	2½ a. black and carmine (No. 62) (B.)	3·25	9·00
21	3 a. black and green (No. 63) (R.)	3·75	16·00
22	4 a. black and grey-green (No. 64) (R.)	4·25	20·00
23	6 a. black and pale blue (No. 65*a*) (R.)	4·75	24·00
24	8 a. black and chocolate (No. 66) (R.)	8·00	30·00
25	1 r. black and yellow-bistre (No. 67) (R.)	10·00	48·00
15/25	*Set of* 11	42·00	£160

KISHANGARH

1948–49. *Various stamps of Kishangarh handstamped with T* **1** *in red.*

No.	Type	Description	Unused	Used
		(*a*) *On stamps of* 1899–1901		
26		¼ a. rose-pink (No. 5*a*) (B.)	65·00	
26*a*		¼ a. rose-pink (No. 22*a*)	—	55·00
27		½ a. deep blue (No. 26)	65·00	
28		1 a. lilac (No. 29)	25·00	
29		1 a. brown-lilac (No. 29*b*)	14·00	25·00
		b. Imperf (pair)	40·00	55·00
		c. Violet handstamp	—	85·00
		d. Black handstamp	—	£110
30		4 a. chocolate (No. 31)	30·00	38·00
		a. Violet handstamp	—	£140
31		1 r. dull green (No. 32)	80·00	85·00
31*a*		2 r. brown-red (No. 34)	£100	
32		5 r. mauve (No. 35)	£100	£100
		(*b*) *On stamps of* 1904–05		
33	**13**	½ a. chestnut	—	35·00
33*a*		1 a. blue	—	55·00
34		4 a. brown	12·00	
		a. Blue handstamp	90·00	
35	**12*a***	8 a. grey	42·00	60·00
36	**13**	8 a. violet	11·00	
37		1 r. green	11·00	
38		2 r. olive-yellow	16·00	
39		5 r. purple-brown	17·00	
		a. Blue handstamp	£110	
		(*c*) *On stamps of* 1912–16		
40	**14**	½ a. green (No. 64)	—	40·00
41		1 a. red	—	40·00
42		2 a. deep violet (No. 51)	65·00	
43		2 a. purple (No. 66)	1·40	5·00
44		4 a. bright blue	—	£140
45		8 a. brown	5·00	
46		1 r. mauve	10·00	
47		2 r. deep green	10·00	
48		5 r. brown	95·00	
		(*d*) *On stamps of* 1928–36		
49	**16**	½ a. yellow-green	30·00	
49a		2 a. magenta	—	70·00
50		4 a. chestnut	40·00	
51		8 a. violet	6·00	25·00
52		1 r. light green	18·00	
53		2 r. lemon-yellow	14·00	
54		5 r. claret	14·00	
		(*e*) *On stamps of* 1943–47		
55	**16**	¼ a. pale dull blue	26·00	26·00
56		¼ a. greenish blue	26·00	26·00
		a. Imperf (pair)	80·00	
57		½ a. deep green	13·00	13·00
		a. Violet handstamp	—	55·00
57*b*		½ a. yellow-green	20·00	20·00
		ba. Imperf (pair)	80·00	
		bb. Blue handstamp	—	55·00
58	**17**	1 a. carmine-red	16·00	16·00
		a. Violet handstamp	—	65·00
58*b*		1 a. orange-red (*imperf*)	45·00	
		ba. Blue handstamp	55·00	
59		2 a. bright magenta	35·00	35·00
60		2 a. maroon (*imperf*)	42·00	
61	**16**	4 a. brown	1·75	5·00
62		8 a. violet	14·00	28·00
63		1 r. green	6·00	
64		2 r. yellow	95·00	
65		5 r. claret	48·00	

A 1 a. value in deep violet-blue was issued for revenue purposes, but is known postally used (*Price* £35 *used*).

NEW INFORMATION

The editor is always interested to correspond with people who have new information that will improve or correct the Catalogue.

RAJPIPLA

PRICES FOR STAMPS ON COVER

The stamps of Rajpipla are very rare used on cover.

1 (1 pice)

2 (2 a.)

3 (4 a.)

1880. *Litho. With or without gum* (1 *p.*) *or no gum* (*others*). *P* 11 (1 *p.*) *or* 12½.

No.	Type	Description	Unused	Used
1	**1**	1 p. blue	60	9·00
2	**2**	2 a. green	8·50	25·00
		a. Imperf between (pair)	£450	£450
3	**3**	4 a. red	4·25	15·00
1/3		*Set of* 3	12·00	45·00

These stamps became obsolete in 1886.

SIRMOOR

PRICES FOR STAMPS ON COVER

The stamps of Sirmoor are very rare used on cover.

1 (1 pice)

2

3 Raja Sir Shamsher Parkash

1876 (June)–**80**. *Litho. P* 11½.

No.	Type	Description	Unused	Used
1	**1**	1 p. pale green	5·00	
2		1 p. blue (on *laid* paper) (1880)	4·00	55·00
		a. Imperf between (pair)	£160	
		b. Imperf (pair)	£160	

(Litho at Calcutta)

1892. *Thick wove paper. P* 11½.

No.	Type	Description	Unused	Used
3	**2**	1 p. yellow-green	45	50
		a. Imperf between (pair)	65·00	
		b. Deep green	35	40
		ba. Imperf between (pair)	65·00	65·00
4		1 p. blue	45	45
		a. Imperf between (pair)	55·00	55·00
		b. Imperf (pair)	70·00	

These were originally made as reprints, about 1891, to supply collectors, but there being very little demand for them they were put into use. The design was copied (including the perforations) from an illustration in a dealer's catalogue.

A

B

C

D

There were seven printings of the 3 and 6 pies, six of the 1 anna, and four of the 2 annas, the last being used overprinted for official use (Nos. 99/102), all in sheets of seventy, made up of groups of transfers showing two or more minor varieties. There are two distinct varieties of the 3 p. and 6 p., as shown in Types A and B, C and D. Of these B and D are the types of the sixth printing of those values, and A and C those of all the other printings.

A and C have large white dots evenly placed between the ends of the upper and lower inscriptions; B has small white dots, and less space between the ends of the inscriptions; D has large spaces, and large white dots *not* in the centres of the spaces, especially at the left side.

The last printing of each value is only known with the Waterlow overprint, T **18**.

Roman figures denote printings.

(Litho Waterlow & Sons)

1885–96. *P* 14 *to* 15.

No.	Type	Description	Unused	Used
5	**3**	3 p. chocolate (A), I, IV	35	25
6		3 p. brown (B), VI	15	15
7		3 p. orange (A), II, III, IV, V	65	15
8		3 p. orange (B), VI	15	10
		a. Imperf (pair)	£425	
9		6 p. blue-green (C), I	1·90	85
10		6 p. bright green (C), III	30·00	30·00
11		6 p. green (C), II, IV	70	45
12		6 p. deep green (C), V	25	20
13		6 p. yellowish green (D), VI	40	70
14		1 a. bright blue, I	65	70
15		1 a. dull blue, III	5·50	4·50
16		1 a. steel-blue, IV	45·00	45·00
17		1 a. grey-blue, V	1·25	60
18	**3**	1 a. slate-blue, VI	50	1·00
19		2 a. pink, I	4·00	7·00
20		2 a. carmine, V	3·50	3·00
21		2 a. rose-red, VI	3·25	3·75

3 p. orange Printings III and IV are rare, being worth at least six times the value of other printings.

4 Indian Elephant

5 Raja Sir Shamsher Parkash

(Recess Waterlow & Sons)

1895–99. *P* 12 *to* 15 *and compounds.*

No.	Type	Description	Unused	Used
22	**4**	3 p. orange-brown	50	30
23		6 p. green	50	30
		a. Imperf between (vert pair)	£1000	
24		1 a. blue	80	30
25		2 a. rose	1·00	1·00
26		3 a. yellow-green	6·50	11·00
27		4 a. deep green	4·50	6·50
28		8 a. deep blue	6·00	8·00
29		1 r. vermilion	10·00	18·00
22/9		*Set of* 8	27·00	40·00

(Recess Waterlow & Sons)

1899. *P* 13 *to* 15.

No.	Type	Description	Unused	Used
30	**5**	3 a. yellow-green	1·25	7·00
31		4 a. deep green	1·75	7·00
32		8 a. deep blue	2·25	8·50
33		1 r. vermilion	4·00	13·00
30/3		*Set of* 4	8·25	32·00

OFFICIAL STAMPS

NOTE. The varieties occurring in the machine-printed "On S.S.S." overprints may, of course, also be found in the inverted and double overprints, and many of them are known thus.

Roman figures denote printings of the basic stamps (Nos. 7/21). Where more than one printing was overprinted the prices quoted are for the commonest.

I. MACHINE-PRINTED

On

S. S.

S.

(11)

1890. *Optd with T* **11**. (*a*) *In black.*

No.	Type	Description	Unused	Used
50	**3**	6 p. green, II	£250	£250
		a. Stop before first "S"		
51		2 a. pink, I	42·00	65·00
		a. Stop before first "S"	£110	
		(*b*) *In red*		
52	**3**	6 p. green, II	5·50	1·75
		a. Stop before first "S"	42·00	25·00
53		1 a. bright blue, I	20·00	9·00
		a. Stop before first "S"	80·00	60·00
		(*c*) *Doubly optd in red and in black*		
53*b*	**3**	6 p. green, II	£900	
		c. Stop before first "S" (R.)		

On S. S. S. (12)

On S. S. S. (13)

1891. *Optd with T* **12**. (*a*) *In black.*

No.	Type	Description	Unused	Used
54	**3**	3 p. orange, II	1·25	8·00
		a. Opt inverted	£180	
55		6 p. green, II	1·50	1·50
		a. Opt double	£100	
		b. No stop after lower "S"	20·00	20·00
		c. Raised stop before lower "S"	45·00	45·00
56		1 a. bright blue, I	£100	£100
57		2 a. pink, I	11·00	
		(*b*) *In red*		
58	**3**	6 p. green, II	13·00	3·00
		a. Opt inverted	£110	95·00
		b. Opt double	£110	95·00
59		1 a. bright blue, I	12·00	18·00
		a. Opt inverted	—	£160
		b. Opt double	—	£160
		c. No stop after lower "S"	70·00	80·00

1892–97. *Optd with T* 13. (*a*) *In black.*
60 3 3 p. orange, III, V, VI 40 40
a. Opt inverted £140
b. First "S" inverted and stop raised .. 5·00 5·00
c. No stop after lower "S" .. .. 5·00 5·00
d. Raised stop after second "S" .. 16·00 12·00
61 6 p. green, IV, V.. .. .. .. 1·40 50
a. First "S" inverted and stop raised .. 16·00 8·00
b. Raised stop after second "S" .. 16·00 8·00
62 1 a. blue, IV, V .. .. 7·00 1·00
a. Opt double £170
b. First "S" inverted and stop raised .. 18·00 10·00
c. No stop after lower "S" .. .. 55·00 55·00
d. Raised stop after second "S" .. 27·00 12·00
63 2 a. pink, I, V .. .. 7·00 7·00
a. Opt inverted £225 £225
b. First "S" inverted and stop raised .. 35·00 35·00
c. No stop after lower "S" .. .. 35·00 35·00
d. Raised stop after second "S" .. 50·00 50·00

(*b*) *In red*
64 3 6 p. green, II, III, IV .. .. .. 1·60 50
a. Opt inverted .. .. .. 80·00 80·00
b. First "S" inverted and stop raised .. 12·00 5·00
65 1 a. blue, I, IV .. .. 6·50 1·00
a. Opt inverted .. .. .. £100 80·00
b. Opt double £130
c. First "S" inverted and stop raised .. 18·00 8·00
d. No stop after lower "S" .. .. 18·00 8·00

(*c*) *Doubly overprinted in black and red*
65*e* 3 6 p. bright green, III .. ..

There are six settings of this overprint. The inverted "S" occurs in the 2nd and 5th settings, and the missing stop in the 2nd setting of all values except the 6 p. In the 5th setting occurs the raised stop after second "S".

On On
S. S. S. S.
S. S.
(14) (15)

1896. *Optd as T* 14.
66 3 3 p. orange, VI .. .. 5·50 1·25
a. Comma after first "S".. .. .. 38·00 30·00
b. Opt inverted .. ..
c. Opt double .. .. † £200
67 6 p. green, V, VI .. .. 5·50 60
a. Comma after first "S".. .. .. 40·00 18·00
b. Comma after lower "S" .. .. 40·00 18·00
c. "S" at right inverted .. .. .. 55·00 38·00
68 1 a. grey-blue, V .. .. 5·50 1·25
a. Comma after first "S".. .. .. 50·00 22·00
b. Comma after lower "S" .. .. 50·00 22·00
c. "S" at right inverted .. .. .. — 40·00
69 2 a. carmine, V .. .. 15·00 14·00
a. Comma after first "S".. .. .. £100 £100

There are four settings of this overprint, (1) 23 mm high, includes the comma after lower "S"; (2) and (3) 25 mm high, with variety, comma after first "S"; (4) 25 mm high, with variety, "S" at right inverted.

1898 (Nov). *Optd with T* 15.
70 3 6 p. green, V, VI .. .. .. 75·00 5·50
a. Small "S" at right .. .. .. — 25·00
b. Comma after lower "S" .. .. — 50·00
c. Lower "S" inverted and stop raised — 50·00
71 1 a. grey-blue, V .. .. .. 85·00 7·00
a. Small "S" at right .. .. .. — 38·00
b. Small "S" without stop .. .. — 60·00

There are two settings of this overprint. Nos. 70a and 71a/b occur in the first setting, and Nos. 70b/c in the second setting.

On On
S. S. S. S.
S. S.
(16) (17)

1899. *Optd with T* 16.
72 3 3 p. orange, VI .. .. 85·00 5·50
73 6 p. deep green, V .. .. — 11·00

1899 (Dec)–**1900.** *Optd as T* 17.
74 3 3 p. orange, VI .. .. — 4·00
a. Raised stop after lower "S" .. .. — 45·00
75 6 p. green, V, VI .. .. — 4·00
a. Raised stop after lower "S" .. .. — 45·00
b. Comma after first "S".. .. .. — 55·00
76 1 a. blue, I, V, VI .. .. — 5·00
a. Raised stop after lower "S" .. .. — 65·00
77 2 a. carmine, V .. .. — 65·00
a. Raised stop after lower "S" .. .. — £225

There are two settings of this overprint: (1) 22 mm high, with raised stop variety; (2) 23 mm high, with "comma" variety on the 6 pies.

On On
S. S. S S
S. S
(18) (19)

(Optd by Waterlow & Sons)

1900. *Optd with T* 18.
78 3 3 p. orange .. .. 1·00 2·00
79 6 p. green 40 45
80 1 a. blue 35 50
81 2 a. carmine .. .. 3·25 11·00

Nos. 78/81 were from printing VII which was not issued without the overprint.

II. HANDSTAMPED

The words "On" and each letter "S" struck separately (except for Type 22 which was applied at one operation).

1894. *Handstamped with T* 19. (*a*) *In black.*
82 3 3 p. orange, V .. .. 3·00 3·50
a. "On" sideways.. .. .. .. 60·00
83 6 p. green, IV, V .. .. 5·00 6·00
a. "On" only .. .. 60·00 60·00
84 1 a. blue, I, III, IV, V .. .. .. 7·00 7·50
85 2 a. carmine, V .. .. 13·00 14·00
a. "On" only .. .. 60·00
b. "On" sideways.. .. .. .. 70·00

(*b*) *In red*
86 3 6 p. green, IV .. .. 40·00 45·00
86*a* 1 a. grey-blue, V £100 £100

1896. *Handstamped with letters similar to those of T* 13, *with stops, but irregular.*
87 3 3 p. orange, III, V, VI .. .. .. 55·00 45·00
88 6 p. green, II, IV, V .. .. .. 55·00 45·00
a. "On" omitted .. .. 90·00
88*b* 1 a. grey-blue, V .. .. 65·00 65·00
89 2 a. carmine, V .. .. 85·00

1897. *Handstamped with letters similar to those of T* 14, *with stops, but irregular.*
90 3 3 p. orange, VI .. .. 8·00 12·00
a. "On" double .. .. 65·00
91 6 p. deep green, V .. .. 25·00 25·00
a. "On" only .. .. — 70·00
92 1 a. grey-blue, V .. .. 60·00 60·00
a. "On" only .. .. — 70·00
93 2 a. carmine, V .. .. 45·00 45·00

In No. 90a the second "On" is over the lower "S".

ON on
S S S S
S S
(20) (21)

1896. (*a*) *Handstamped with T* 20.
94 3 3 p. orange, V .. .. 50·00 50·00
95 2 a. carmine, V .. .. 55·00 55·00

(*b*) *Handstamped with T* 21
96 3 3 p. orange, V .. .. 75·00 75·00
97 6 p. green .. ..
98 1 a. blue, I, III .. .. 80·00
98*a* 2 a. carmine, V .. .. 90·00

On On
S S S S
S S
(22) (23)

(*c*) *Handstamped with T* 22
99 3 3 p. orange, VI .. .. 85·00
100 6 p. deep green, V £120
101 1 a. grey-blue, V £160
101*a* 2 a. carmine, V £200

1899. *Handstamped with T* 23.
102 3 3 p. orange, IV, V, VI .. .. .. 11·00 7·00
103 6 p. green, IV, V, VI .. .. .. 14·00 14·00
104 1 a. blue, I, V .. .. 25·00 22·00
105 2 a. rose-red, I, V, VI .. .. .. 22·00 20·00

COVER PRICES

Cover factors are quoted at the beginning of each country for most issues to 1945. An explanation of the system can be found on page x. The factors quoted do not, however, apply to philatelic covers.

On
S S
S
(24)

1901 (?). *Handstamped with T* 24.
105*a* 3 6 p. yellowish green, VI .. .. .. — £110

III. MIXED MACHINE-PRINTED AND HANDSTAMPED

1896. (i) *Handstamped "On" as in T* 19, *and machine-printed opt T* 13 *complete.*
106 3 6 p. deep green, V .. ..

(ii) *Handstamped opt as T* 14, *and machine-printed opt T* 13, *complete*
107 3 6 p. deep green, V .. ..

Various other types of these handstamps are known to exist, but in the absence of evidence of their authenticity we do not list them. It is stated that stamps of T 4 were never officially overprinted.

The stamps of Sirmoor have been obsolete since 1 April 1902.

SORUTH

PRICES FOR STAMPS ON COVER

Nos. 1/15	*from* × 5
Nos. 16/57	*from* × 10
Nos. O1/13	*from* × 20
Nos. 58/61	*from* × 10
Nos. O14/22	*from* × 10

The name "Saurashtra" corrupted to "Sorath" or "Soruth", was originally used for all the territory later known as Kathiawar. Strictly speaking the name should have been applied only to a portion of Kathiawar including the state of Junagadh. As collectors have known these issues under the heading of "Soruth" for so long, we retain the name.

The currency was 40 docras = 1 koree but early stamps are inscribed in "annas of a koree", one "anna" being a sixteenth of a koree.

GUM. Nos. 1/47 of Soruth were issued without gum.

A. JUNAGADH

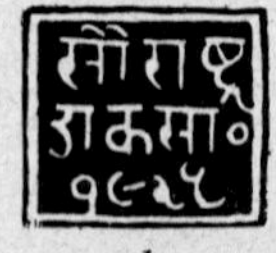

1

(="Saurashtra Post 1864–65")

1864 (Nov). *Handstamped in water-colour. Imperf.*
1 1 (1 a.) black/*azure* (laid) .. .. .. £600 35·00
2 (1 a.) black/*grey* (laid) .. .. .. £600 35·00
3 (1 a.) black/*azure* (wove).. .. .. — £140
4 (1 a.) black/*cream* (wove) .. .. .. — £375

ILLUSTRATIONS. Types 2 to 11 are shown actual size.

2 (1 a.) 3 (1 a.)
4 (4 a.) 5 (4 a.)

(Type-set at Junagadh Sarkari Saurashtra Nitiprakash Ptg Press)

1868–75. *T* 2 *to* 5 (*two characters, Devanagri and Gujerati respectively for "1" and "4" as shown in the illustrations*). *Imperf.*

A. *Inscriptions in Gujerati characters*
5 1 a. black/*yellowish* (wove) .. .. ..

B. *Inscriptions in Devanagri characters* (*as in the illustrations*)

I. *Accents over first letters in top and bottom lines. Wove paper*
6 1 a. red/*green* .. .. — £1100
7 1 a. red/*blue* .. .. — £1100
8 1 a. black/*pink* .. .. £180 48·00
9 2 a. black/*yellow* (1869) .. .. .. — £1200

II. *Accents over second letters in top and bottom lines* (1869–75).

(a) Wove paper

No.	Type	Description	Unused	Used
10	2	1 a. black/*pink*	£140	40·00
		a. Printed both sides	†	—

(b) Laid paper

No.	Type	Description	Unused	Used
10*b*	2	1 a. black/*white*		
11		1 a. black/*azure* (1870)	45·00	8·00
12	3	1 a. black/*azure*	85·00	16·00
		a. Printed both sides	†	—
13		1 a. red/*white* (1875)	12·00	13·00
14	4	4 a. black/*white*	95·00	£100
15	5	4 a. black/*white*	£120	£120

Official imitations, consisting of 1 a. carmine-red on white wove and white laid, 1 a. black on blue wove, 4 a. black on white wove, 4 a. black on blue wove, 4 a. red on white laid—all imperforate; 1 a. carmine-red on white laid, 1 a. black on blue wove, 4 a. black on white laid and blue wove—all perforated 12, were made in 1890. Entire sheets of originals have 20 stamps, the imitations only 4 or 16.

6

7

(Dies eng John Dickinson & Sons, London. Typo Junagadh Sarkari Saurashtra Nitiprakash Ptg Press)

1877. *Imperf.*

(a) Medium laid paper, lines wide apart
(b) Thick laid paper, lines wide apart
(c) Thick laid paper, lines close together

No.	Type	Description	Unused	Used
16	6	1 a. green *(a)*	30	30
17		1 a. green *(b)*	30	30
18		1 a. green *(c)*	30	30
		a. Printed both sides	£275	
19	7	4 a. vermilion *(a)*	80	1·00
20		4 a. vermilion/*toned (b)*	80	1·00
		a. Printed both sides	£275	
21		4 a. scarlet/*bluish (b)*	80	1·00

1886. *P* 12. *(a) Wove paper.*

No.	Type	Description	Unused	Used
22	6	1 a. green	65	65
		a. Imperf (pair)	28·00	32·00
		b. Error. Blue	—	£600
		c. Imperf horiz (vert pair)	50·00	
23	7	4 a. red	2·25	2·50
		a. Imperf (pair)	60·00	70·00

(b) Toned laid paper

No.	Type	Description	Unused	Used
24	6	1 a. green	15	15
25		1 a. emerald-green	85	55
		a. Error. Blue	—	£600
26	7	4 a. red	80	60
27		4 a. carmine	1·00	80

(c) Bluish white laid paper

No.	Type	Description	Unused	Used
28	6	1 a. green	90	1·25
		a. Imperf between (pair)	65·00	
29		4 a. scarlet	2·75	4·50

There is a very wide range of colours in both values. The laid paper is found both vertical and horizontal.

The 1 a. was issued in sheets of 20 varieties, with marginal inscriptions; the 4 a. is in horizontal strips of 5 varieties.

(Indian currency)

Three pies.
ત્રણ પાઇ.

(8)

One anna.
એક આનો.

(9)

1913. *Surch in Indian currency with T* 8 *or* 9. *P* 12.

(a) On yellowish wove paper

No.	Type	Description	Unused	Used
34	6	3 p. on 1 a. emerald	10	15
		a. Imperf (pair)		

(b) On white wove paper

No.	Type	Description	Unused	Used
35	6	3 p. on 1 a. emerald	10	15
		a. Imperf between (pair)	£100	£100
		b. Surch inverted	35·00	20·00
		c. Surch double	†	—
36	7	1 a. on 4 a. carmine	1·50	2·25
		a. Imperf (pair)		
		b. Surch both sides	£400	
		c. Capital "A" in "Anna"	10·00	

(c) On white laid paper

No.	Type	Description	Unused	Used
37	6	3 p. on 1 a. emerald	60·00	30·00
		a. Imperf (pair)	—	£100
38	7	1 a. on 4 a. red	6·00	14·00
		a. Capital "A" in "Anna"	70·00	£100
		b. Surch inverted	£350	
		c. Surch double	£350	
		d. Surch double, one inverted	£350	

(d) On toned wove paper

No.	Type	Description	Unused	Used
39	7	1 a. on 4 a. red	90	1·75
		a. Imperf (pair)		
		b. Capital "A" in "Anna"	6·00	
		c. Surch inverted	£350	
		d. Imperf between (horiz pair)		

10

11

(Dies eng Thacker & Co, Bombay. Typo Junagadh State Press)

1914 (1 Sept). *New plates. T* 6/7 *redrawn as T* 10/11. *Wove paper. P* 12.

No.	Type	Description	Unused	Used
40	10	3 p. bright green	35	35
		a. Imperf (pair)	1·60	3·00
		b. Imperf vert (horiz pair)	35·00	
		c. Laid paper	1·40	1·40
		ca. Imperf (pair)	5·00	7·00
41	11	1 a. red	60	60
		a. Imperf (pair)	9·50	16·00
		b. Imperf between (pair)	£175	
		c. Laid paper	35·00	20·00

12 Nawab Sir Mahabatkhanji III 13

(Dies eng Popatlal Bhimji Pandya. Typo Junagadh State Press)

1923 (1 Sept). *Blurred impression. Laid paper. Pin-perf* 12.

No.	Type	Description	Unused	Used
42	12	1 a. red	3·00	5·00

Sheets of 16 stamps (8 × 2).

ત્રણ પાઇ

(14)

ત્રણ પાઈ

(14*a*)

1923 (1 Sept). *Surch with T* 14.

No.	Type	Description	Unused	Used
43	12	3 p. on 1 a. red	2·50	5·00
		a. Surch with T 14*a*	3·25	6·50

Four stamps in the setting have surch. T 14*a*, i.e. with top of last character curved to right.

1923 (Oct). *Blurred impression. Wove paper. Pin-perf* 12, *small holes.*

No.	Type	Description	Unused	Used
44	13	3 p. mauve	35	40

1924. *Clear impression. P* 12, *large holes. Wove paper.*

No.	Type	Description	Unused	Used
45	13	3 p. mauve (1.24)	50	35
46	12	1 a. red (4.24)	2·75	3·50
		a. Imperf (pair)	30·00	50·00
		b. Pin perf	2·00	2·50

The first plate of the 3 p., which printed No. 44, produced unsatisfactory impressions, so it was replaced by a second plate, from which No. 45 comes. Sheets printed from the first plate had very large margins.

The 1 a. is also from a new plate, giving a clearer impression. Sheets of 16 stamps (4 × 4).

1929. *Clear impression. P* 12, *large holes. Laid paper.*

No.	Type	Description	Unused	Used
47	13	3 p. mauve	85	75
		a. Imperf (pair)	2·50	5·50
		b. Perf 11	1·25	1·25
		ba. Imperf between (horiz pair)	3·00	7·50

The laid paper shows a sheet watermark of the State Arms within a circular inscription.

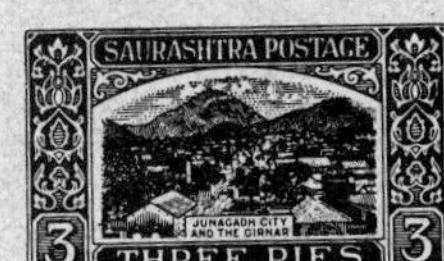

15 Junagadh City

16 Lion

17 Nawab Sir Mahabatkhanji III

18 Kathi Horse

(Litho Indian Security Printing Press, Nasik)

1929 (1 Oct). *P* 14. *Inscr* "POSTAGE".

No.	Type	Description	Unused	Used
49	15	3 p. black and blackish green	50	10
50	16	½ a. black and deep blue	4·50	10
51	17	1 a. black and carmine	2·75	85
52	18	2 a. black and dull orange	6·50	1·40
		a. Grey and dull yellow	25·00	1·10
53	15	3 a. black and carmine	2·00	2·25
54	16	4 a. black and purple	9·00	10·00
55	18	8 a. black and yellow-green	10·00	11·00
56	17	1 r. black and pale blue	2·75	11·00
49/56		*Set of* 8	34·00	32·00

1936. *As T* 17, *but inscr* "POSTAGE AND REVENUE". *P* 14.

No.	Type	Description	Unused	Used
57	17	1 a. black and carmine	2·25	90

OFFICIAL STAMPS

SARKARI

(O 1)

1929 (1 Oct). *Optd with Type* O 1, *in vermilion, at Nasik.*

No.	Type	Description	Unused	Used
O1	15	3 p. black and blackish green	50	10
		a. Red opt	50	10
O2	16	½ a. black and deep blue	1·25	10
		a. Red opt	1·75	15
O3	17	1 a. black and carmine (No. 51)	60	10
		a. Red opt	1·00	15
O4	18	2 a. black and dull orange	2·00	25
		a. Grey and dull yellow	8·00	60
		b. Red opt	9·00	1·25
O5	15	3 a. black and carmine	45	20
		a. Red opt	6·00	1·50
O6	16	4 a. black and purple	1·50	40
		a. Red opt	9·00	1·00
O7	18	8 a. black and yellow-green	1·75	80
O8	17	1 r. black and pale blue	2·25	7·00
O1/8		*Set of* 8	9·00	8·00

SARKARI

(O 2)

SARKARI

(O 3)

1932. *Optd with Types* O 2 (3 *a.*, 1 *r.*) *or* O 3 (others), *all in red, at Junagadh State Press.*

No.	Type	Description	Unused	Used
O 9	15	3 a. black and carmine	32·00	7·00
		a. Optd with Type O 3	12·00	12·00
O10	16	4 a. black and purple	15·00	15·00
O11	18	8 a. black and yellow-green	20·00	16·00
O12	17	1 r. black and pale blue	55·00	55·00
		a. Optd with Type O 3	20·00	35·00

1938. *No.* 57 *optd with Type* O 1, *in vermilion.*

No.	Type	Description	Unused	Used
O13	17	1 a. black and carmine	3·00	35
		a. Brown-red opt	3·00	55

The state was occupied by Indian troops on 9 November 1947.

B. UNITED STATE OF SAURASHTRA

Under the new Constitution of India the United State of Saurashtra was formed on 15 February 1948, comprising 31 former states and 191 estates of Kathiawar, including Jasdan, Morvi, Nawanagar and Wadhwan. A referendum was held in Junagadh which then joined the United State on 20 January 1949. However, it is believed that the following issues were in use only in Junagadh.

The following issues were surcharged at the Junagadh State Press.

POSTAGE & REVENUE

ONE ANNA

(19)

Postage & Revenue

ONE ANNA

(20)

1949. *Stamps of* 1929 *surch. (a) With T* 19 *in red.*

No.	Type	Description	Unused	Used
58	16	1 a. on ½ a. black and deep blue (6.49)	5·00	2·50
		a. Surch double	—	£180
		b. "AFNA" for "ANNA" and inverted "N" in "REVENUE"	£700	
		c. Larger first "A" in "ANNA"	80·00	60·00

(b) With T 20 *in green*

No.	Type	Description	Unused	Used
59	18	1 a. on 2 a. grey and dull yellow (2.49)	3·50	10·00

No. 58c occurs on position 10.

A number of other varieties occur on No. 58, including: small "V" in "REVENUE" (No. 8); small "N" in "REVENUE" (Nos. 9, 13 and 14); small "E" in "POSTAGE" (No. 12); thick "A" in "POSTAGE" (No. 19); inverted "N" in "REVENUE" and small second "A" in "ANNA" (No. 25); small "O" in "ONE" (No. 26); small "V" and "U" in "REVENUE" (No. 28); small "N" in "ONE" (No. 37).

In No. 59 no stop after "ANNA" is known on Nos. 4, 17, 25, 34 and 38 and small "N" in "ONE" on Nos. 9, 11, 26 and 31.

21

(Typo Waterlow)

1949 (Sept). *Court Fee stamps of Bhavnagar state optd* "SAURASHTRA" *and further optd* "U.S.S. REVENUE & POSTAGE" *as in T* 21, *in black. Typo. P* 11.

No.	Type	Description	Unused	Used
60	21	1 a. purple	4·00	3·00
		a. "POSTAGE" omitted	£180	£180
		b. Opt double	£225	£250

Minor varieties include small "S" in "POSTAGE" (Nos. 9 and 49); small "N" in "REVENUE" (Nos. 15 and 55); small "U" in "REVENUE" (Nos. 18 and 58); small "V" in "REVENUE" (Nos. 24, 37, 64 and 77); and small "O" in "POSTAGE" (Nos. 31 and 71).

Various missing stop varieties also occur.

POSTAGE & REVENUE
ONE ANNA

(22)

1950 (Mar). *Stamp of* 1929 *surch with T* **22**.
61 **15** 1 a. on 3 p. black and blackish green .. 20·00 20·00
a. "P" of "POSTAGE" omitted .. £200 £200
b. "O" of "ONE" omitted £250

Other minor varieties include small "S" in "POSTAGE" with small "V" in "REVENUE" (Nos. 14 and 26) and small "V" in "REVENUE" (No. 11).

OFFICIAL STAMPS

1948–49. *Nos.* O4/O7 *surch* "ONE ANNA" (2¼ *mm high*).
O14 **18** 1 a. on 2 a. grey & dull yell (B.) (7.48) £1500 17·00
O15 **15** 1 a. on 3 a. black and carmine (9.48) .. £1400 26·00
a. Surch double .. .. .. † £800
O16 **16** 1 a. on 4 a. black and purple (1.49) .. £160 20·00
a. "ANNE" for "ANNA" £1600 £300
b. "ANNN" for "ANNA" £1600 £300
O17 **18** 1 a. on 8 a. black and yellow-green (1.49) £160 17·00
a. "ANNE" for "ANNA" £1600 £275
b. "ANNN" for "ANNA" £1600 £275

Numerous minor varieties of fount occur in this surcharge.

The spelling errors occur on positions 24 ("ANNE") and 35 ("ANNN").

1948 (Nov). *Handstamped* "ONE ANNA" (4 *mm high*).
O18 **17** 1 a. on 1 r. (No. O8) .. .. .. £325 20·00
O19 1 a. on 1 r. (No. O12a) .. .. .. £120 23·00
a. Optd on No. O12 .. .. .. — 38·00

A used copy of No. O12a is known surcharged in black as on Nos. O14/17. This may have come from a proof sheet.

1949 (Jan). *Postage stamps optd with Type* O **3**, *in red.*
O20 **15** 3 p. black and blackish green .. .. £160 7·00
O21 **16** ½ a. black and deep blue .. .. £250 6·50
O22 **18** 1 a. on 2 a. grey and dull yellow (No. 59) 25·00 8·00

Various wrong fount letters occur in the above surcharges.

MANUSCRIPT OVERPRINTS. Nos. 49, 50, 58, 59 and 60 are known with manuscript overprints reading "Service" or "SARKARI" (in English or Gujerati script), usually in red. Such provisionals were used at Gadhda and Una between June and December 1949 (*Price from £70 each, used on piece*).

The United State of Saurashtra posts were integrated with the Indian Postal Service on 1 April 1950.

TRAVANCORE

PRICES FOR STAMPS ON COVER	
Nos. 1/77	*from* × 10
Nos. O1/108	*from* × 15

(16 cash = 1 chuckram; 28 chuckrams = 1 rupee)

"Anchel" or "Anchal" = Post Office Department.

The stamps of Travancore were valid on mail posted to Cochin.

PRINTERS. All stamps of Travancore were printed by the Stamp Manufactory, Trivandrum, *unless otherwise stated.*

PRINTING METHODS. The dies were engraved on brass from which electrotypes were made and locked together in a forme for printing the stamps. As individual electrotypes became worn they were replaced by new ones and their positions in the forme were sometimes changed. This makes it difficult to plate the early issues. From 1901 plates were made which are characterised by a frame (or "Jubilee" line) round the margins of the sheets.

Up to the 6 cash of 1910 the dies were engraved by Dharmalingham Asari.

SHADES. We list only the main groups of shades but there are many others in view of the large number of printings and the use of fugitive inks. Sometimes shade variation is noticeable within the same sheet.

1 Conch or Chank Shell

1888 (16 Oct). *As T* 1, *but each value differs slightly. Laid paper. P* 12.
1 **1** 1 ch. ultramarine (*shades*) .. .. 1·50 1·50
2 2 ch. red .. .. 3·00 4·00
3 4 ch. green .. .. 8·00 8·00
1/3 .. .. *Set of* 3 11·00 12·00

The paper bears a large sheet watermark showing a large conch shell surmounted by "GOVERNMENT" in large outline letters, in an arch with "OF TRAVANCORE" at foot in a straight line. Many stamps in the sheet are without watermark.

These stamps on laid paper in abnormal colours are proofs.

2

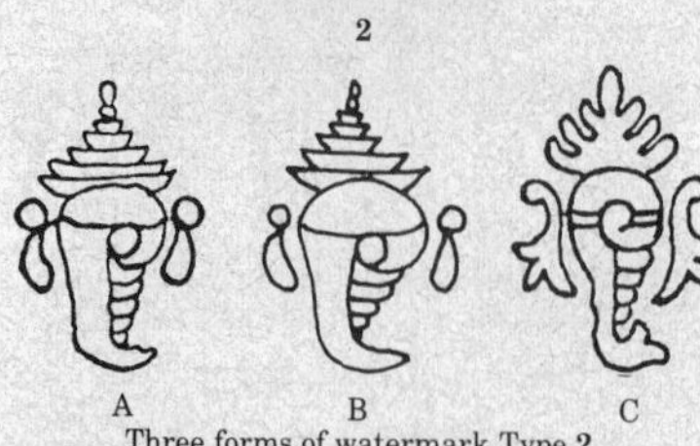

A B C

Three forms of watermark Type **2**.
(*as seen from the back of the stamp*)

WATERMARKS AND PAPERS.

Type A appeared upright on early printings of the 1, 2 and 4 ch. values on odd-sized sheets which did not fit the number of shells. Later it was always sideways with 15 mm between the shells on standard-sized sheets of 84 (14 × 6) containing 60 shells (10 × 6). It therefore never appears centred on the stamps and it occurs on hand-made papers only.

Type B is similar in shape but can easily be distinguished as it is invariably upright, with 11 mm between the shells, and is well centred on the stamps. It also occurs only on handmade papers. It was introduced in 1904 and from 1914, when Type A was brought back into use, it was employed concurrently until 1924.

Type C is quite different in shape and occurs on machine-made papers. There are two versions. The first, in use from 1924 to 1939, has 84 shells 11 mm apart and is always upright and well centred. The second, introduced in 1929 and believed not to have been used after 1930, has 60 shells (12 × 5) 15 mm apart and is invariably badly centred so that some stamps in the sheet are without watermark. This second version is normally found upright, but a few sideways watermark varieties are known and listed as Nos. 35g, 37c, O31j and O32i. We do not distinguish between the two versions of Type C in the lists, but stamps known to exist in the second version are indicated in footnotes. The machine-made paper is generally smoother and of more even texture.

NO WATERMARK VARIETIES. Some of these were formerly listed but we have now decided to omit them as they do not occur in full sheets. They arise in the following circumstances: (*a*) on sheets with wmk A; (*b*) on sheets with the wide-spaced form of wmk C; and (*c*) on late printings of the pictorial issues of 1939–46. They are best collected in pairs, with and without watermark.

DATES OF ISSUE. In the absence of more definite information the dates quoted usually refer to the first reported date of new printings on different watermarks but many were not noted at the time and the dates of these are indicated by a query. Dated postmarks on single stamps are difficult to find.

3

4

5

6

7

8

1889–1904. *Wove paper. Wmk* A (*upright or sideways*). *P* 12 (*sometimes rough*).
4 **1** ½ ch. slate-lilac (1894) 75 15
a. Doubly printed .. .. .. — £100
b. Reddish lilac 40 10
ba. Imperf between (vert pair) .. £100 £100
bb. Doubly printed .. .. .. — £100
c. Purple (1899) 55 10
ca. Doubly printed .. .. .. — £100
d. Dull purple (1904) 55 10
5 **5** ¾ ch. black (14.3.01) 65 10
6 **1** 1 ch. ultramarine 60 15
a. *Tête-bêche* (pair) £2000 £2000
b. Doubly printed .. .. .. — £160
c. Imperf vert (horiz pair).. .. — £160
d. Pale ultramarine (1892) .. 1·50 15
e. Violet-blue (1901) .. .. 1·75 30
7 2 ch. salmon (1890) .. .. .. 1·90 25
a. Rose (1891) .. .. .. 1·60 15
ab. Imperf (pair) .. .. .. — £160
b. Pale pink (1899) .. .. 1·50 25
ba. Imperf between (vert pair) .. 85·00
bb. Doubly printed £150
c. Red (1904) .. .. .. 1·10 15
ca. Imperf between (horiz pair) .. — £120
8 4 ch. green .. .. 1·25 40
a. Yellow-green (1901) .. .. 1·50 40
b. Dull green (1904) .. .. 3·50 45
ba. Doubly printed .. .. .. — £160

Nos. 6, 6*d*, 7 and 8 occur with the watermark upright and sideways. No. 7*a* is known only with the watermark upright. The remainder exist only with the watermark sideways.

The sheet sizes were as follows:

½ ch. 56 (14 × 4) except for No. 4*d* which was 84 (14 × 6), initially without border, later with border.

¾ ch. 84 (14 × 6) with border.

1 ch. No. 6, 80 (10 × 8) and later 84 (14 × 6) without border and then with border; No. 6*d*, 96 (16 × 6); No. 6*e*, 84 (14 × 6) with border.

2 ch. No. 7, 80 (10 × 8); No. 7*a*, 70 (10 × 7); Nos. 7*b*, 7*c*, 60 (10 × 6).

4 ch. No. 8, 60 (10 × 6); Nos. 8*a*/*b*, 84 (14 × 6) with border.

After 1904 all stamps in Types **3** to **8** were in standard-sized sheets of 84 (14 × 6) with border.

For later printings watermarked Type A, see Nos. 23/30.

1904–20. *Wmk* B, *upright* (*centred*). *P* 12, *sometimes rough.*
9 **3** 4 ca. pink (11.08).. .. .. .. 10 10
a. Imperf between (vert pair) .. 90·00 90·00
10 **1** 6 ca. chestnut (2.10) 25 10
a. Imperf between (horiz pair) .. — 90·00
11 ½ ch. reddish lilac 15 10
a. Reddish violet (6.10) 15 10
b. Lilac 20 10
c. "CHUCRRAM" .. .. .. 3·50 3·00
12 **4** 10 ca. pink (1920) .. .. .. 13·00 3·00
13 **5** ¾ ch. black 35 10
14 **1** 1 ch. bright blue .. ..
a. Blue .. .. 1·60 25
b. Deep blue .. .. 1·60 25
c. Indigo (8.10) 40 10
d. *Chalky blue* (1912) .. .. .. 1·25 20
15 1¼ ch. claret (*shades*) (10.14) 25 10
a. Imperf between (horiz pair) .. 95·00 95·00
16 2 ch. salmon .. .. 10·00 3·00
a. Red (8.10) 40 10
17 **6** 3 ch. violet (11.3.11) 85 10
a. Imperf between (vert pair) .. 90·00 90·00
b. Imperf between (vert strip of 3) .. — £130
18 **1** 4 ch. dull green .. .. 3·00 1·50
a. Slate-green .. .. 1·10 35
19 **7** 7 ch. claret (1916) .. .. .. 1·60 40
a. Error. Carmine-red .. .. — 50·00
20 **8** 14 ch. orange-yellow (1916) .. .. 2·40 80
a. Imperf vert (horiz strip of 3) .. £160

1/4

(9)

1 C

(10)

1906. *Surch as T* **9**. *Wmk* B.
21 **1** ¼ on ½ ch. reddish lilac 10 10
a. Reddish violet 10 10
b. Lilac 10 10
c. "CHUCRRAM" .. .. 3·00 3·00
d. Surch inverted .. .. 25·00 20·00
22 ⅜ on ½ ch. reddish lilac 20 10
a. Reddish violet 10 10
b. Lilac 10 10
c. "CHUCRRAM" .. .. 3·00 3·00
d. Surch inverted .. .. — 30·00
e. Surch double .. .. ..
f. "8" omitted .. .. .. — 40·00

1914–22. *Reversion to wmk A* (*sideways*). *P* 12 (*sometimes rough*).
23 **3** 4 ca. pink (1915) .. .. .. 3·50 20
24 **4** 5 ca. olive-bistre (30.10.21) 25 10
a. Imperf between (horiz pair) .. 40·00 40·00
b. Imperf between (horiz strip of 3) .. 85·00 85·00
c. "TRAVANCOPE" .. .. — 8·00
25 **1** 6 ca. orange-brown (2.15) .. .. 1·75 15
26 ½ ch. reddish violet (12.14) 70 15
a. "CHUCRRAM" .. .. .. 5·00 3·25
b. Imperf between (horiz pair) .. 85·00
27 **4** 10 ca. pink (26.10.21) 25 10
28 **1** 1 ch. grey-blue (5.22) .. .. .. 3·25 35
a. Deep blue .. .. 3·25 35
29 1¼ ch. claret (12.19) .. .. .. 4·00 15
30 **6** 3 ch. reddish lilac (8.22) .. .. 4·00 45

1921 (Mar). *Surch as T* **10**. *Wmk* A.
31 **3** 1 c. on 4 ca. pink 10 10
a. Surch inverted .. .. .. 12·00 8·00
32 **1** 5 c. on 1 ch. grey-blue (R.) 10 10
a. Deep blue 10 10
b. Stamp printed both sides .. ..
c. Imperf between (vert pair).. .. — 90·00
d. Surch inverted .. .. .. 12·00 7·00
e. Surch double .. .. .. 24·00 16·00
f. On wmk B. *Deep blue* .. .. 12·00 12·00

ALBINO OVERPRINT VARIETIES. Stamps with overprint double, one albino are frequently found in the provisional and official issues of Travancore, and are only worth a small premium over the normal prices.

1924–39. *Wmk* C. *Machine-made paper. P* 12.
33 **4** 5 ca. olive-bistre (18.6.25) .. .. 3·50 80
a. Imperf between (horiz pair) .. 60·00
b. "TRAVANCOPE" .. .. .. — 7·00
34 5 ca. chocolate (1930) 75 20
a. Imperf between (horiz pair) .. 30·00
b. Imperf between (vert pair) .. .. — 65·00
35 **1** 6 ca. brown-red (3.24) .. .. .. 2·50 10
a. Imperf between (horiz pair) .. 18·00 18·00
b. Imperf between (vert pair) .. .. 55·00 55·00
c. Printed both sides .. .. .. 50·00
d. Perf 12½ .. .. 4·00 70
e. Perf comp of 12 and 12½ .. .. 8·00 4·00
f. Perf 12½ × 11 .. .. .. — 45·00
g. Wmk sideways .. .. .. — 9·00
36 ½ ch. reddish violet (date?) .. .. 4·00 4·25
a. "CHUCRRAM" .. .. .. 30·00

37 4 10 ca. pink (8.24) 75 10
a. Imperf between (horiz pair) .. 55·00
b. Imperf between (vert pair) .. .. 16·00 18·00
c. Wmk sideways (16.9.28) .. .. — 3·50
38 5 ¾ ch. black (4.10.32) .. .. .. 4·00 35
39 ¾ ch. mauve (16.11.32) 25 10
a. Imperf between (horiz pair) .. — 65·00
b. Perf 12½ (8.37) .. .. .. 4·00 70
ba. Imperf between (horiz pair) .. 60·00
c. Perf comp of 12 and 12½ .. .. 8·50 4·25
40 ¾ ch. reddish violet (1939) .. .. 1·00 10
a. Perf 12½ .. .. 3·75 70
b. Perf comp of 12 and 12½ .. .. 6·00 2·00
c. Perf 11 .. .. — 45·00
d. Perf comp of 12 and 11 .. .. — 45·00
41 1 1 ch. slate-blue (8.26) .. .. .. 1·10 10
a. Indigo .. .. 1·75 10
b. Imperf between (horiz pair) .. — 85·00
c. Imperf between (vert pair) .. .. — 85·00
d. Perf 12½ .. .. 7·00 90
42 1½ ch. rose (1932) 60 10
a. Imperf between (horiz strip of 3) .. 85·00
b. Perf 12½ .. .. 12·00 2·75
c. Perf comp of 12 and 12½ .. .. — 16·00
43 2 ch. carmine-red (4.6.29) .. .. 5·50 30
44 6 3 ch. violet (4.25) .. .. .. 2·00 15
a. Imperf between (vert pair) .. .. 70·00 70·00
b. Perf 12½ .. .. — 8·50
c. Perf comp of 12 and 12½ .. .. — 12·00
45 1 4 ch. grey-green (5.4.34) .. .. .. 4·00 35
46 7 7 ch. claret (1925) .. .. .. 4·50 1·25
a. Carmine-red (date?) .. .. .. 60·00 55·00
b. Brown-purple (1932) .. .. 7·00 2·00
ba. Perf. 12½ .. .. 8·00 8·00
bb. Perf comp of 12 and 12½ .. .. 8·00 8·00
46*c* 8 14 ch. orange-yellow (*p* 12½) (date?) .. 85·00

It is believed that the 12½ perforation and the perf 12 and 12½ compound were introduced in 1937 and that the 11 perforation came later, probably in 1939.

The 5 ca. chocolate, 6 ca., 10 ca. and 3 ch. also exist on the wide-spaced watermark (60 shells to the sheet of 84).

11 Sri Padmanabha Shrine

12 State Chariot

13 Maharaja Sir Bala Rama Varma

(Des M. R. Madhawan Unnithan. Plates by Calcutta Chromotype Co. Typo Stamp Manufactory, Trivandrum)

1931 (6 Nov). *Coronation. Cream or white paper. Wmk C. P* 11½, 12.
47 11 6 ca. black and green 25 25
a. Imperf between (horiz pair) .. £175 £200
48 12 10 ca. black and ultramarine 25 25
49 13 3 ch. black and purple 30 30
47/9 .. .. *Set of* 3 70 70

1 c (14)

(15)

16 Maharaja Sir Bala Rama Varma and Subramania Shrine

1932 (14 Jan). (i) *Surch as T* **14**. (*a*) *Wmk* A (*sideways*).
50 1 1 c. on 1¼ ch. claret 10 15
a. Imperf between (horiz pair) .. 70·00
b. Surch inverted .. .. .. 4·25 6·00
c. Surch double .. .. .. 24·00 24·00
d. Pair, one without surch .. .. 70·00 80·00
e. "c" omitted .. .. 45·00 45·00
51 2 c. on 1¼ ch. claret 10 10
a. Surch inverted .. .. .. 4·25 6·00
b. Surch double .. .. .. 24·00
c. Surch double, one inverted .. .. 55·00
d. Surch treble .. .. .. 55·00
e. Surch treble, one inverted .. .. 70·00 70·00
f. Pair, one without surch .. .. 75·00 75·00
g. "2" omitted .. .. 45·00 45·00
h. "c" omitted .. .. 45·00 45·00
i. Imperf between (horiz pair) .. 70·00

(*b*) *Wmk* B (*upright*)
52 1 1 c. on 1¼ ch. claret 75 75
a. Surch inverted .. .. .. 17·00
b. Surch double .. .. .. 24·00
53 2 c. on 1¼ ch claret .. .. .. 1·75 2·00

(*c*) *Wmk* C
54 1 1 c. on 1¼ ch. claret .. .. .. 6·00 5·50
a. Surch inverted .. .. .. 28·00 28·00
55 2 c. on 1¼ ch. claret .. .. .. 6·50 4·50

(ii) *Surch as T* **10**. *Wmk* B
56 1 2 c. on 1¼ ch. claret .. .. .. 4·25 7·50

1932 (5 Mar). *Surch as T* **15**. *Wmk* C.
57 4 1 c. on 5 ca. chocolate 10 10
a. Imperf between (horiz pair) .. 85·00
b. Surch inverted .. .. .. 7·50 10·00
c. Surch inverted on back only .. 35·00
d. Pair, one without surch .. .. 65·00
e. "1" omitted .. .. 35·00
f. "C" omitted .. .. — 35·00
g. "TRAVANCOPE" .. .. .. 8·50
58 1 c. on 5 ca. slate-purple 20 15
a. Surch inverted .. .. .. — 85·00
b. "1" inverted .. .. 48·00 48·00
59 2 c. on 10 ca. pink 10 10
a. Imperf between (horiz pair) .. 75·00
b. Surch inverted .. .. .. 5·00 7·00
c. Surch double .. .. .. 16·00 18·00
d. Surch double, one inverted .. .. 42·00 42·00
e. Surch double, both inverted .. 30·00

No. 58 was not issued without the surcharge.

(Plates by Indian Security Printing Press, Nasik. Typo Stamp Manufactory, Trivandrum)

1937 (29 Mar). *Temple Entry Proclamation. T* **16** *and similar horiz designs. Wmk* C. *P* 12.
60 6 ca. carmine 15 15
a. Imperf between (horiz strip of 3) .. £325
b. Perf 12½ 85 55
c. Compound perf .. .. .. 16·00 16·00
61 12 ca. bright blue 30 15
a. Perf 12½ 70 40
ab. Imperf between (vert pair) .. £300
b. Compound perf .. .. .. 22·00
62 1½ ch. yellow-green 35 30
a. Imperf between (vert pair) .. £225
b. Perf 12½ .. .. 8·50 3·50
c. Compound perf .. .. ..
63 3 ch. violet 75 30
a. Perf 12½ .. .. 1·25 60
60/3 .. .. *Set of* 4 1·40 80

Designs:—Maharaja's portrait and temples—12 ca. Sri Padmanabha; 1½ ch. Mahadeva; 3 ch. Kanyakumari.

COMPOUND PERFS. This term covers stamps perf compound of 12½ and 11, 12 and 11 or 12 and 12½, and where two or more combinations exist the prices are for the commonest. Such compounds can occur on values which do not exist perf 12 all round.

17 Lake Ashtamudi

18 Maharaja Sir Bala Rama Varma

(Des Nilakantha Pellai. Plates by Indian Security Printing Press, Nasik. Typo Stamp Manufactory, Trivandrum)

1939 (9 May). *Maharaja's 27th Birthday. T* **17/18** *and similar designs. Wmk* C. *P* 12½.
64 1 ch. yellow-green 45 10
a. Imperf between (horiz pair) .. .. 15·00
b. Perf 11 .. .. 1·75 10
ba. Imperf between (vert pair) .. .. 13·00 16·00
bb. Imperf between (vert strip of 3) .. 15·00
c. Perf 12 .. .. 2·75 40
ca. Imperf between (horiz pair) .. .. 15·00
cb. Imperf between (vert pair) .. .. 15·00
d. Compound perf .. .. .. 3·75 1·50
da. Imperf between (vert pair) .. .. 35·00
65 1½ ch. scarlet 45 50
a. Doubly printed .. .. .. 70·00
b. Imperf between (horiz pair) .. .. 17·00
c. Imperf between (vert pair) .. .. 15·00
d. Perf 11 .. .. 3·00 6·00
da. Imperf horiz (vert pair) .. .. 8·00
e. Perf 12 .. .. 7·00 2·50
f. Perf 13½ .. .. 10·00 20·00
g. Compound perf .. .. .. 12·00 3·50
h. Imperf (pair) .. .. .. 20·00
66 2 ch. orange 85 20
a. Perf 11 .. .. 5·00 30
b. Perf 12 .. .. 17·00 3·75
c. Compound perf .. .. .. 17·00 3·75
67 3 ch. brown 95 10
a. Doubly printed .. .. .. — 40·00
b. Imperf between (horiz pair) .. .. 17·00 22·00
c. Perf 11 .. .. 5·00 25
ca. Doubly printed .. .. .. 28·00 28·00
d. Perf 12 .. .. 7·00 90
da. Imperf between (vert pair) .. .. 48·00 48·00
e. Compound perf .. .. .. 5·50 1·00
68 4 ch. red 75 40
a. Perf 11 .. .. 7·00 50
b. Perf 12 .. .. 7·50 1·40
c. Compound perf .. .. .. 30·00 30·00
69 7 ch. pale blue .. .. .. 1·50 3·25
a. Perf 11 .. .. 18·00 8·00
ab. Blue .. .. 18·00 8·50
b. Compound perf .. .. .. 25·00 10·00
70 14 ch. turquoise-green .. .. .. 1·75 8·50
a. Perf 11 .. .. 3·50 16·00
64/70 .. .. *Set of* 7 6·00 11·50

Designs: *Vert as T* **18**—1½ ch., 3 ch. Portraits of Maharaja in different frames. *Horiz as T* **17**—4 ch. Sri Padmanabha Shrine; 7 ch. Cape Comorin; 14 ch. Pachipari Reservoir.

19 Maharaja and Aruvikara Falls

2 CASH

(20)

(Des Nilakantha Pellai. Plates by Indian Security Printing Press, Nasik. Typo Stamp Manufactory, Trivandrum)

1941 (20 Oct). *Maharaja's 29th Birthday. T* **19** *and similar horiz design. Wmk* C. *P* 12½.
71 6 ca. blackish violet .. .. .. 1·25 10
a. Perf 11 .. .. 1·75 10
ab. Imperf between (vert pair) .. .. 15·00
ac. Imperf horiz (vert pair) .. .. 19·00
b. Perf 12 .. .. 5·00 1·00
ba. Imperf between (horiz pair) .. .. 14·00
bb. Imperf between (vert pair) .. .. 16·00
bc. Imperf between (vert strip of 3) .. 15·00
c. Compound perf .. .. .. 2·25 70
72 ¾ ch. brown .. .. 1·25 10
a. Perf 11 .. .. 1·75 10
ab. Imperf between (horiz pair) .. .. 40·00
ac. Imperf between (vert pair) .. .. 14·00 18·00
ad. Imperf between (vert strip of 3) .. 14·00
ae. Block of four imperf between (horiz and vert) .. .. 48·00
b. Perf 12 .. .. 9·00 3·25
c. Compound perf .. .. .. 3·25 1·10

Design:—¾ ch. Maharaja and Marthanda Varma Bridge, Alwaye.

1943 (17 Sept). *Nos.* 65, 71 (*colour changed*) *and* 72 *surch as T* **20**. *P* 12½.
73 2 ca. on 1½ ch. scarlet 15 10
a. Imperf between (vert pair) .. .. 22·00
b. "2" omitted .. .. 85·00 85·00
c. "CA" omitted £125
d. "ASH" omitted £125
e. Perf 11 .. .. 10 10
ea. "CA" omitted £125
f. Compound perf 55 55
fa. Imperf between (vert pair) .. .. 45·00
fb. "2" omitted .. .. 90·00
74 4 ca. on ¾ ch. brown 90 10
a. Perf 11 .. .. 90 10
b. Perf 12 .. .. — 35·00
c. Compound perf .. .. .. 2·50 1·00
75 8 ca. on 6 ca. scarlet .. .. .. 1·00 10
a. Perf 11 .. .. 75 10
ab. Imperf between (horiz pair) .. .. 20·00
b. Perf 12 .. .. — 28·00
c. Compound perf .. .. .. 4·50 3·25
73/5 .. .. *Set of* 3 1·50 25

21 Maharaja Sir Bala Rama Varma

SPECIAL

(22)

(Des Nilakantha Pellai. Plates by Indian Security Printing Press, Nasik. Typo Stamp Manufactory, Trivandrum)

1946 (24 Oct). *Maharaja's 34th Birthday. Wmk* C. *P* 12½.
76 21 8 ca. carmine .. .. 4·00 1·50
a. Perf 11 .. .. 50 50
b. Perf 12 .. .. 9·00 3·00
ba. Imperf between (horiz pair) .. .. 22·00 28·00
bb. Imperf between (horiz strip of 3) 35·00
c. Compound perf .. .. ..

1946. *No.* O103 *revalidated for ordinary postage with opt T* **22**, *in orange. P* 12½.
77 19 6 ca. blackish violet .. .. .. 4·00 1·50
a. Perf 11 .. .. 13·00 4·25
b. Compound perf .. .. .. 5·00 2·25

OFFICIAL STAMPS

GUM. Soon after 1911 the Official stamps were issued without gum. Thus only the initial printings of the 1, 2, 3 and 4 ch. values were gummed. As Nos. O38/9, O41/2 and O95 were overprinted on stamps intended for normal postage these, also, have gum.

PRINTINGS. Sometimes special printings of postage stamps were made specifically for overprinting for Official use, thus accounting for Official stamps appearing with watermarks or in shades not listed in the postage issues.

SETTINGS. These are based on the study of complete sheets of 84, and the measurements given are those of the majority of stamps on the sheet. Examples are known showing different measurements as each overprint was set individually in loose type, but these are not included in the listings.

On

S S

(O 1)

On

S S

(O 2)

Rounded "O"

1911 (16 Aug)–**26**. *Contemporary stamps optd with Type* O 1 (13 *mm wide*). *P* 12, *sometimes rough*. (*a*) *Wmk* B (*upright*) (16.8.11–21).
O 1 3 4 ca. pink (1916) 10 10
a. Opt inverted .. .. .. — 32·00
b. Opt double .. .. .. 50·00 35·00
c. "S S" inverted .. .. .. 12·00 6·00
d. Imperf (pair) .. .. .. 85·00 85·00
O 2 1 6 ca. chestnut (date ?) .. .. .. 24·00 24·00
O 3 ½ ch. reddish lilac (R.) (1919) 70 35
a. "CHUCRRAM" .. .. .. 7·50 4·50

O 4 4 10 ca. pink (1921) .. .. .. 7·00 2·00
a. "O" inverted .. .. .. 20·00 7·50
b. Left "S" inverted .. .. 20·00 7·50
c. Right "S" inverted .. .. 20·00 7·50
O 5 1 1 ch. chalky blue (R.) 35 10
a. Imperf between (vert pair) .. — 80·00
b. Opt inverted .. .. .. 7·00 4·25
c. Opt double .. .. .. 55·00 48·00
d. "nO" for "On" .. .. .. 75·00 75·00
e. "O" inverted .. .. .. 4·00 1·10
f. Left "S" inverted .. .. 4·00 1·10
g. Right "S" inverted .. .. 4·00 1·10
h. "S S" inverted .. .. .. — 18·00
O 6 2 ch. red 30 10
a. Opt inverted .. .. .. 8·00 8·00
b. "O" inverted .. .. .. 5·00 1·10
c. Left "S" inverted .. .. 5·00 1·10
d. Right "S" inverted .. .. 5·00 1·10
O 7 2 ch. red (B.) (date ?) .. .. — 35·00
O 8 6 3 ch. violet 30 10
a. Imperf between (vert pair) .. 75·00 75·00
b. Imperf vert (horiz pair) .. 75·00
c. Opt inverted .. .. .. 10·00 10·00
d. Opt double .. .. .. 50·00 50·00
e. Right "S" inverted .. .. 4·50 1·00
f. Right "S" omitted .. .. 50·00 50·00
g. Left "S" omitted .. .. .. 50·00 50·00
O 9 3 ch. violet (B.) (date ?) .. .. 45·00 24·00
O10 1 4 ch. slate-green 55 10
a. Imperf between (pair) .. .. 75·00 75·00
b. Opt inverted .. .. .. 20·00 11·00
c. Opt double .. .. .. 60·00 60·00
d. "O" inverted .. .. .. 7·00 2·40
e. Left "S" inverted .. .. 7·00 2·40
f. Right "S" inverted .. .. 7·00 2·40
g. Left "S" omitted .. .. .. 50·00 50·00
O11 4 ch. slate-green (B.) (1921) .. .. — 18·00
a. "O" inverted .. .. .. — 45·00
b. Left "S" inverted .. .. — 45·00
c. Right "S" inverted .. .. — 45·00

(*b*) *Wmk* A (*sideways*) (1919–25)

O12 3 4 ca. pink .. .. 1·75 15
a. Imperf (pair) .. .. .. 95·00 95·00
b. Opt inverted .. .. .. 25·00 15·00
c. "O" inverted .. .. .. 12·00 4·00
d. Left "S" inverted .. .. 12·00 4·00
e. Right "S" inverted .. .. 12·00 4·00
O13 4 ca. pink (B.) (1921) .. .. 14·00 75
a. "O" inverted .. .. .. — 14·00
O14 4 5 ca. olive-bistre (1921) 25 10
a. Opt inverted .. .. .. 10·00 8·00
b. "O" inverted .. .. .. 2·75 1·25
c. Left "S" inverted .. .. 2·75 1·25
d. Right "S" inverted .. .. 2·75 1·25
O15 1 6 ca. orange-brown (1921) 15 10
a. Imperf between (vert pair) .. — 75·00
b. Opt inverted .. .. .. 10·00 8·00
c. Opt double .. .. .. 38·00 38·00
d. "O" inverted .. .. .. 3·00 90
e. Left "S" inverted .. .. 3·00 90
f. Right "S" inverted .. .. 3·00 90
O16 6 ca. orange-brown (B.) (1921) .. 7·50 1·25
a. Opt inverted .. .. .. 60·00 60·00
b. "O" inverted .. .. .. 30·00 12·00
c. Left "S" inverted .. .. 30·00 12·00
d. Right "S" inverted .. .. 30·00 12·00
O17 ½ ch. reddish violet (R.) (date?) .. 30 10
a. Reddish lilac (date?) 30 10
b. Imperf between (horiz pair) .. 60·00 60·00
c. Imperf between (vert pair) .. 42·00 42·00
d. Stamp doubly printed .. .. 48·00
e. Opt inverted .. .. .. 9·00 3·00
f. Opt double, both inverted .. 65·00
g. "CHUCRRAM" .. .. .. 4·00 2·75
h. "On" omitted .. .. .. — 65·00
i. Right "S" inverted .. .. — 12·00
j. Right "S" omitted .. .. — 65·00
O18 4 10 ca. pink (3.21) 25 10
a. Scarlet (1925?) .. .. .. — 6·00
b. Opt inverted .. .. .. — 10·00
c. Opt double .. .. .. 45·00 35·00
d. "O" inverted .. .. .. 4·00 1·50
e. Left "S" inverted .. .. 4·00 1·50
f. Right "S" inverted .. .. 4·00 1·50
g. Imperf between (horiz pair) .. — 65·00
O19 10 ca. pink (B.) (date ?) .. .. 20·00 6·00
a. Opt inverted .. .. .. — 45·00
b. "O" inverted .. .. .. — 24·00
O20 1 1 ch. grey-blue (R.) (date ?) .. .. 1·90 60
a. Deep blue .. .. .. 1·90 60
b. "O" inverted .. .. .. 14·00 6·00
c. Left "S" inverted .. .. 14·00 6·00
d. "On" omitted .. .. ..
O21 1¼ ch. claret (12.19) 35 10
a. Stamp doubly printed .. .. — £100
b. Opt inverted .. .. .. 9·00 8·00
c. Opt double .. .. .. 45·00
d. "O" inverted .. .. .. 6·50 1·75
e. Left "S" inverted .. .. 6·50 2·00
f. Right "S" inverted .. .. 6·50 2·00
g. Error. Carmine .. .. .. 50·00
O22 1¼ ch. claret (B.) (1921) .. .. — 27·00
a. "O" inverted .. .. .. — 60·00
b. Left "S" inverted .. .. — 60·00
c. Right "S" inverted .. .. — 60·00

(*c*) *Wmk* C (1925–30)

O23 4 5 ca. olive-bistre (1926) 25 15
a. Imperf between (horiz pair) .. 75·00 75·00
b. Opt inverted .. .. .. 11·00 10·00
c. "O" inverted .. .. .. 2·50 1·25
d. Left "S" inverted .. .. 2·50 1·25
e. Right "S" inverted .. .. 2·50 1·25
O23*f* 5 ca. chocolate (1930) .. .. .. 24·00
fa. Opt inverted .. .. .. — 70·00
O24 10 ca. pink (1926) .. .. .. 1·50 15
a. Imperf between (vert pair) .. — 70·00
b. Opt inverted .. .. .. 35·00 35·00
c. "O" inverted .. .. .. 11·00 2·00
d. Left "S" inverted .. .. 11·00 2·00
e. Right "S" inverted .. .. 11·00 2·00
f. Stamp doubly printed .. ..

O25 1 1¼ ch. claret (1926) .. .. .. 3·50 40
a. "O" inverted .. .. .. 16·00 3·00
b. Left "S" inverted .. .. 16·00 3·50
c. Right "S" inverted .. .. 16·00 3·50
d. Opt double .. .. .. — 48·00
O26 7 7 ch. claret .. .. .. 1·50 30
a. "O" inverted .. .. .. 11·00 2·50
b. Left "S" inverted .. .. 11·00 2·50
c. Right "S" inverted .. .. 11·00 2·50
d. Error. Carmine-red .. .. 60·00
O27 8 14 ch. orange-yellow .. .. .. 1·75 40
a. "O" inverted .. .. .. 12·00 3·00
b. Left "S" inverted .. .. 12·00 3·00
c. Right "S" inverted .. .. 12·00 3·00

1926–30. *Contemporary stamps optd with Type* O **2** (16½ *mm wide*). *Wmk* C. *P* 12.

O28 4 5 ca. olive-bistre .. .. .. 1·50 25
a. Right "S" inverted .. .. 8·50 3·00
O29 5 ca. chocolate (1930) 15 15
a. Imperf between (vert pair) .. — 90·00
b. Opt inverted .. .. .. 16·00
c. "O" inverted .. .. .. 2·00 1·75
d. Left "S" inverted .. .. 2·00 1·75
O30 1 6 ca. brown-red (date?) .. .. 2·25 80
a. "O" inverted .. .. .. 12·00 4·50
b. Left "S" inverted .. .. 12·00 4·50
c. Opt double .. .. .. — 75·00
O31 4 10 ca. pink 25 10
a. Imperf between (horiz pair) .. 40·00 40·00
b. Imperf between (vert pair) .. 30·00 30·00
c. Imperf vert (horiz strip of 3) .. — 65·00
d. Opt inverted .. .. .. 9·00 9·00
e. "Ou" for "On" .. .. .. 32·00 32·00
f. "O" inverted .. .. .. 3·50 1·25
g. Left "S" inverted .. .. 3·50 1·25
h. Right "S" inverted .. .. 3·50 1·25
i. Left "S" omitted .. .. 25·00 25·00
j. Wmk sideways .. .. .. — 5·00
O32 1 1¼ ch. claret (*shades*) .. .. 1·60 30
a. Imperf between (horiz pair) .. 60·00 65·00
b. Imperf between (vert pair) .. 60·00 65·00
c. Opt inverted .. .. .. 18·00 18·00
d. "O" inverted .. .. .. 12·00 2·50
e. Left "S" inverted .. .. 12·00 2·50
f. Right "S" inverted .. .. 12·00 2·50
g. Left "S" omitted .. .. .. 55·00 55·00
h. Right "S" omitted .. .. 55·00 55·00
i. Wmk sideways .. .. .. — 7·00
O33 6 3 ch. violet .. .. .. 7·00 70
a. Opt inverted .. .. .. — 65·00
b. "O" inverted .. .. .. 28·00 16·00
c. "O" omitted .. .. .. 55·00 55·00
d. "Ou" for "On" .. .. .. 75·00 75·00
e. Left "S" inverted .. .. — 20·00
O34 7 7 ch. claret (date?) .. .. .. 42·00 1·75
O35 8 14 ch. orange-yellow .. .. .. 20·00 85
a. Imperf between (vert pair) .. £140
b. "O" inverted .. .. .. 45·00 7·00

The 5 ca. olive-bistre, 3 ch. and 7 ch. exist only with the normal watermark spaced 11 mm; the 5 ca. chocolate and 14 ch. exist only with the wide 15 mm spacing; the 6 ca., 10 ca. and 1¼ ch. exist in both forms.

On On On
S S S S S S
(O 3) (O 4) (O 5)
Italic "S S"

1930. *Wmk* C. *P* 12. (*a*) *Optd with Type* O 3.

O36 4 10 ca. pink .. .. 75·00 55·00
O37 1 1¼ ch. carmine-rose .. .. 2·75 2·25

(*b*) *Optd with Type* O 4

O38 5 ¾ ch. black (R.) 30 10
a. Left "S" omitted .. .. .. 38·00
b. Right "S" omitted .. .. 38·00
c. Large roman "S" at left .. .. — 35·00

(*c*) *Optd with Type* O 5

O39 5 ¾ ch. black (R.) 25 10
a. Opt inverted .. .. .. — 80·00
b. "n" omitted .. .. .. 42·00 42·00
O40 1 4 ch. slate-green (R.) .. .. .. 19·00 8·00

On On On
S S S S S S
(O 6) (O 7) (O 8)
Oval "O"

1930–39 (?). *Contemporary stamps overprinted. P* 12.

(*a*) *With Type* O **6** (16 *mm high*) (i) *Wmk* A

O41 3 4 ca. pink .. .. 8·50 15·00
a. Large right "S" as Type O **2** .. 50·00 60·00

(ii) *Wmk* B

O42 3 4 ca. pink .. .. 11·00 18·00
a. Large right "S" as Type O **2** .. 60·00 70·00

(iii) *Wmk* C

O43 1 6 ca. brown-red (1932) 25 10
a. Opt inverted .. .. .. 16·00
b. Opt double .. .. .. 35·00 35·00
c. "O" inverted .. .. .. 8·00 5·00
O44 4 10 ca. pink .. .. 1·50 1·10

O45 5 ¾ ch. mauve (1933) 90 10
a. Imperf between (horiz pair) .. 50·00 40·00
b. Imperf between (horiz strip of 3) — 60·00
c. Imperf between (vert pair) .. — 45·00
d. Stamp doubly printed .. .. — 75·00
e. Perf 12½ .. .. .. 3·25 40
f. Perf comp of 12 and 12½ .. 6·00 85
g. Right "S" inverted .. .. — 12·00
O46 1 1¼ ch. carmine-rose .. .. 8·50 1·75
a. Opt double .. .. .. 75·00 55·00
b. Large right "S" as Type O **2** .. 55·00 32·00
O47 4 ch. grey-green .. .. .. 1·50 1·75
O48 4 ch. grey-green (R.) (27.10.30) .. 70 15
a. Imperf between (horiz pair) .. 60·00 60·00
b. Opt double .. .. .. 24·00 24·00
c. "O" inverted .. .. .. 20·00 13·00
d. Large right "S" as Type O **2** .. 27·00 20·00
e. Imperf between (vert pair) .. 60·00
O49 8 14 ch. orange-yellow (1931) .. .. 3·25 90
a. Imperf between (vert pair) .. — 60·00

For the 1½ ch. and 3 ch., and for Nos. O43 and O48/9 but perf 12½, see Nos. O66/70 (new setting combining Types O **6** and O **8**).

(*b*) *With Type* O **7** (14 *mm high*). *Wmk* C

O50 3 4 ca. pink .. .. 6·00 11·00
a. "O" inverted .. .. .. 30·00 40·00
O51 4 5 ca. chocolate (1932) .. .. 12·00 9·00
a. Opt inverted .. .. .. 65·00 65·00
O52 1 6 ca. brown-red 15 10
a. Imperf between (vert pair) .. 45·00 45·00
b. Opt inverted .. .. .. 25·00
c. Opt double .. .. .. — 38·00
d. "nO" for "On" .. .. .. 70·00 70·00
e. Right "S" inverted .. .. 10·00 7·00
f. Left "S" omitted .. .. .. — 60·00
g. Large "n" as Type O **5** .. .. 16·00 10·00
h. Large italic left "S" as Type O **5** 16·00 10·00
i. Perf 12½ .. .. .. — 4·25
j. Perf compound of 12 and 12½ .. — 8·50
O53 ½ ch. reddish violet (1932) 25 15
a. "CHUCRRAM" .. .. .. 7·50 5·50
b. "Ou" for "On" .. .. .. 38·00 38·00
c. Left "S" omitted .. .. .. — 60·00
d. "O" of "On" omitted .. .. 80·00
O54 ½ ch. reddish violet (R.) (1935) .. 15 10
a. Imperf between (vert pair) .. 55·00 55·00
b. "CHUCRRAM" .. .. .. 3·00 3·00
c. Left "S" inverted .. .. — 12·00
O55 4 10 ca. pink (date?) .. .. .. 1·40 65
a. Imperf between (horiz pair) .. 10·00 11·00
b. Imperf between (vert pair) .. 10·00 11·00
c. "O" inverted .. .. .. 16·00 12·00
d. Right "S" inverted .. .. 16·00 12·00
O56 5 ¾ ch. mauve (1933?) 25 10
a. Imperf between (vert pair) .. — 55·00
b. "Ou" for "On" .. .. .. 38·00 38·00
c. "O" inverted .. .. .. 12·00 10·00
d. Right "S" inverted .. .. — 10·00
e. Opt double .. .. .. — 55·00
f. Perf comp of 12 and 12½ .. 14·00 9·00
O57 1 1 ch. deep blue (R.) (1935) 85 15
a. Slate-blue 80 15
b. Imperf between (horiz pair) .. 45·00 45·00
c. Imperf between (vert pair) .. 25·00 25·00
d. Perf 12½ .. .. .. 6·00 1·90
e. Perf comp of 12 and 12½ .. 9·00 3·00
O58 1¼ ch. claret .. .. .. 1·10 50
O59 1½ ch. rose (1933) 35 10
a. Imperf between (vert pair) .. — 60·00
b. Opt double .. .. .. 45·00 45·00
c. "O" inverted .. .. .. 3·75 2·50
e. Large "n" as type O **5** .. .. 26·00 16·00
f. Large italic left "S" as Type O **5** 26·00 16·00
g. Left "S" inverted .. .. — 14·00
h. Perf 12½ .. .. .. — 5·50
i. Perf comp of 12 and 12½ .. — 7·50
ia. Stamp doubly printed .. .. — 85·00
O60 6 3 ch. reddish violet (1933) .. .. 1·10 40
a. "O" inverted .. .. .. 12·00 7·00
O61 3 ch. violet (R.) (1934) 60 10
a. Imperf between (horiz pair) .. 45·00 32·00
b. Imperf between (vert pair) .. 45·00 32·00
c. Opt inverted .. .. .. — 30·00
d. "O" inverted .. .. .. 12·00 8·00
e. Perf 12½ .. .. .. — 1·90
ea. Imperf between (vert pair) .. — 75·00
f. Perf comp of 12 and 12½ .. — 4·00
fa. Imperf between (horiz pair) .. — 75·00
O62 1 4 ch. grey-green (1934) .. .. — £110
O63 4 ch. grey-green (R.) (1935?) 80 15
a. "Ou" for "On" .. .. .. 35·00 35·00
O64 7 7 ch. claret (*shades*) .. .. .. 1·10 25
a. Imperf between (vert pair) .. 24·00 24·00
b. "O" inverted .. .. .. 26·00 13·00
c. Left "S" inverted .. .. 26·00 13·00
d. Perf 12½ .. .. .. — 3·25
e. Perf comp of 12 and 12½ .. — 5·50
ea. Imperf between (vert pair) .. — 45·00
eb. Imperf between (vert strip of 3) .. 60·00 60·00
O65 8 14 ch. orange (1933) .. .. .. 1·50 40
a. Imperf between (horiz pair) .. 26·00 32·00
b. Imperf between (vert pair) .. 55·00
c. Opt inverted .. .. .. — £110

(*c*) *New setting combining Type* O **8** (18 *mm high*) *in top row with Type* O **6** (16 *mm high*) *for remainder. Wmk* C (dates?)

A. *Type* O **8**. B. *Type* O **6**

			A		B	
O66 1	6 ca. brown-red	..	5·00	2·25	†	
	a. Perf 12½ ..	..	5·00	2·25	1·75	50
	ab. Imperf between (vert pair)	..		†	50·00	50·00
	ac. "O" inverted	..		†	14·00	8·00
	g. Perf comp of 12 and 12½	..		†	—	9·00
O67	1½ ch. rose ..	..	11·00	4·25	2·75	35
	a. Perf 12½ ..	..	17·00	5·00	5·50	45
	ab. "O" inverted	..		†	24·00	10·00
	c. Perf comp of 12 and 12½ ..	..		†	—	12·00
O68 6	3 ch. violet (R.) ..	..	20·00	7·00	4·00	65
	a. Perf 12½ ..	..	26·00	8·50	7·50	75
	b. Perf comp of 12 and 12½ ..	..	38·00	11·00	14·00	2·75

O69 1 4 ch. grey-green (R.) .. 28·00 16·00 †
a. Perf 12½ .. .. 20·00 11·00 6·00 2·00
ab. Imperf between (horiz pair) † — 80·00
O70 8 14 ch. orange-yellow .. 22·00 8·00 †
a. Perf 12½ .. .. 15·00 6·00 4·25 75

Nos. O66B and O69/70B naturally exist but are not distinguishable from Nos. O43 and O48/9.

Nos. O66/70A/B in vertical *se-tenant* pairs are very scarce.

As with the postage issues it is believed that the 12½ and compound perforations were issued between 1937 and 1939.

1 ch

8 c — (O 9)

1 ch — Wrong fount "1 c"

1932. *Official stamps surch as T* **14** *or with Type* O **9**. *P* 12.

(a) With opt Type O **1** (i) *Wmk* A

O71 4 6 c. on 5 ca. olive-bistre .. .. 11·00 5·50
a. "O" inverted .. .. 35·00 17·00
b. Left "S" inverted .. .. 35·00 17·00
c. Right "S" inverted .. .. 35·00 17·00

(ii) *Wmk* C

O72 4 6 c. on 5 ca. olive-bistre .. .. 5·00 2·25
a. "O" inverted .. .. 17·00 7·50
b. Left "S" inverted .. .. 17·00 7·50
c. Right "S" inverted .. .. 17·00 7·50
O73 12 c. on 10 ca. pink .. .. 38·00

(b) With opt Type O **2**. *Wmk* C

O74 4 6 c. on 5 ca. olive-bistre .. .. 1·40 50
a. Opt and surch inverted .. 32·00
b. Surch inverted .. .. 26·00
c. Left "S" inverted .. .. 9·50 4·25
d. Right "S" inverted .. .. 9·50 4·25
e. "6" omitted .. .. — 45·00
O75 6 c. on 5 ca. chocolate 15 15
a. Surch inverted .. .. 9·00 9·00
b. Surch double .. .. 55·00
c. Surch double, one inverted .. 55·00
d. "O" inverted .. .. 2·25 2·25
e. Left "S" inverted .. .. 2·25 2·25
O76 12 c. on 10 ca. pink 20 15
a. Opt inverted .. .. 6·50 6·50
b. Surch inverted .. .. 7·00 7·00
c. Opt and surch inverted .. 22·00 22·00
d. Pair, one without surch .. £160
e. "O" inverted .. .. 2·50 2·50
f. Left "S" inverted .. .. 1·75 1·75
g. "Ou" for "On" .. .. 42·00 42·00
i. "c" omitted .. .. 32·00 32·00
O77 1 1 ch. 8 c. on 1¼ ch. claret .. 60 20
a. Surch inverted .. .. — 35·00
b. "O" inverted .. .. 4·50 2·00
c. Left "S" inverted .. .. 4·50 2·00
d. Right "S" inverted .. .. 4·50 2·00
e. Wrong fount "1 c" .. .. 15·00 12·00

(c) With opt Type O **3**. *Wmk* C

O78 4 12 c. on 10 ca. pink .. .. — £160
O79 1 1 ch. 8 c. on 1¼ ch. carmine-rose .. 28·00 20·00
a. "n" omitted £120
b. Wrong fount "1 c" .. .. 90·00 70·00

(d) With opt Type O **6**. *Wmk* C

O80 4 12 c. on 10 ca. pink .. .. 22·00 7·00
O81 1 1 ch. 8 c. on 1¼ ch. carmine-rose .. 35·00 11·00
a. Wrong fount "1 c" .. .. 90·00 45·00
b. "h" omitted
c. *Brown-red* .. .. — 11·00

(e) With opt Type O **7**. *Wmk* C

O82 4 6 c. on 5 ca. chocolate 15 15
a. Opt inverted .. .. 30·00 30·00
b. Surch inverted .. .. 11·00 12·00
c. Right "S" omitted .. .. 50·00 50·00
d. Two quads for right "S" .. £450
e. Right "S" inverted .. .. 16·00
O83 12 c. on 10 ca. pink 15 15
a. Opt inverted .. .. 7·00 7·00
b. Surch inverted .. .. 6·00 6·00
c. Opt and surch inverted .. 30·00 30·00
d. Opt double .. .. — 50·00
e. "O" inverted .. .. 7·00 7·00
f. Right "S" inverted .. .. 7·00 7·00
g. "On" omitted .. .. — 50·00
h. "n" omitted .. .. — 50·00
i. "c." omitted .. .. 22·00 22·00
j. Surch double .. .. — 45·00
O84 1 1 ch. 8 c. on 1¼ ch. claret .. 35 25
a. Imperf between (vert pair) .. — 90·00
b. Opt omitted .. .. — £160
c. Surch inverted .. .. 14·00 14·00
d. Surch double .. .. 35·00
e. "O" inverted .. .. 4·00 2·50
f. Wrong fount "1 c" .. .. 14·00 12·00

SERVICE — (O 10) 13 mm

SERVICE — (O 11) 13½ mm

SERVICE 8 CASH — (O 12)

1939–41. *Nos.* 35 *and* 40 *with type-set opt, Type* O **10**. *P* 12½.

O85 1 6 ca. brown-red (1941) 70 10
a. Perf 11 .. .. 1·00 40
b. Perf 12 .. .. 70 25
c. Compound perf 70 70
O86 5 ¾ ch. reddish violet .. .. 28·00 17·00
a. Perf 12 .. .. 7·00 70
b. Compound perf .. .. 35·00 22·00

1939 (9 Nov). *Maharaja's 27th Birthday. Nos.* 64/70 *with type-set opt, Type* O **10**. *P* 12½.

O87 1 ch. yellow-green .. .. 1·00 15
O88 1½ ch. scarlet .. .. 1·00 50
a. "SESVICE" .. .. 38·00 22·00
b. Perf 12 .. .. 7·00 1·75
ba. "SESVICE" .. .. — 50·00
bb. Imperf between (horiz pair) .. — 70·00
c. Compound perf .. .. 3·75 1·10
O89 2 ch. orange .. .. 1·00 90
a. "SESVICE" .. .. 50·00 50·00
b. Compound perf .. .. 20·00 20·00
O90 3 ch. brown .. .. 1·00 10
a. "SESVICE" .. .. 28·00 17·00
b. Perf 12 .. .. 2·00 40
ba. "SESVICE" .. .. 50·00 25·00
c. Compound perf .. .. 3·50 1·40
O91 4 ch. red .. .. 2·25 1·00
O92 7 ch. pale blue .. .. 3·00 1·40
O93 14 ch. turquoise-green .. .. 4·00 1·25
O87/93 .. *Set of* 7 12·00 4·50

1940 (?)**–45.** *Nos.* 40*a and* 42*b optd with Type* O **11**. *P* 12½.

O94 5 ¾ ch. reddish violet .. .. 4·00 15
a. Imperf between (horiz pair) .. 55·00
b. Perf 11 .. .. 12·00 1·00
c. Perf 12 .. .. 4·50 15
d. Compound perf .. .. 10·00 75
O95 1 1½ ch. rose (1945) .. .. 7·50 7·50
a. Perf 12 .. .. 2·00 1·00
b. Compound perf .. .. 11·00 11·00

1942 (?). *Nos.* 64/70 *optd with Type* O **11**. *P* 12½.

O 96 1 ch. yellow-green 25 10
a. Imperf between (vert pair) .. 26·00 26·00
b. Opt inverted .. .. — 20·00
c. Opt double .. .. 20·00
d. Perf 11 .. .. 35 10
da. Imperf between (vert pair) .. 15·00
db. Opt double .. .. 35·00 35·00
e. Perf 12 .. .. 1·60 30
ea. Imperf between (vert pair) .. 35·00 35·00
eb. Stamp doubly printed .. 70·00
ec. Opt inverted .. .. — 35·00
ed. Opt double .. .. 18·00
f. Compound perf .. .. 2·25 1·00
g. "S" inverted .. .. — 25·00
O 97 1½ ch. scarlet 60 10
a. Imperf between (horiz pair) .. 32·00
b. Perf 11 .. .. 85 15
ba. Imperf between (vert pair) .. 40·00 40·00
bb. Imperf between (vert strip of 3) .. 32·00
bc. Imperf between (horiz pair) .. — 40·00
c. Perf 12 .. .. 1·75 25
ca. Imperf between (vert strip of 3) .. 55·00
d. Compound perf .. .. 1·50 25
e. Imperf (pair) .. .. 25·00
O 98 2 ch. orange 60 30
a. Perf 11 .. .. 2·00 45
ab. Imperf between (vert pair)
b. Perf 12 .. .. 20·00 20·00
ba. Imperf between (vert pair) .. 90·00 90·00
c. Compound perf .. .. 25·00 25·00
O 99 3 ch. brown 35 10
a. Imperf between (vert pair)
b. Perf 11 .. .. 75 10
c. Perf 12 .. .. 1·60 40
ca. Imperf between (vert pair) .. 80·00 80·00
d. Compound perf .. .. 7·00 75
O100 4 ch. red 60 35
a. Perf 11 .. .. 1·40 45
b. Perf 12 .. .. 5·00 1·75
c. Compound perf .. .. 25·00 14·00
O101 7 ch. pale blue .. .. 2·00 35
a. Perf 11 .. .. 3·75 1·40
b. Perf 12 .. .. 8·50 5·00
c. Compound perf .. .. 10·00 3·50
d. *Blue* (p 11) .. .. 3·75 1·75
da. Perf 12 .. .. 4·00 2·25
db. Compound perf .. .. 14·00 6·50
O102 14 ch. turquoise-green .. .. 3·50 70
a. Perf 11 .. .. 4·75 1·50
b. Perf 12 .. .. 5·25 2·40
c. Compound perf .. .. 25·00 4·50
O96/102 .. *Set of* 7 6·50 1·75

1942. *Maharaja's 29th Birthday. Nos* 71/2 *optd with Type* O **11**. *P* 12½.

O103 6 ca. blackish violet 25 10
a. Perf 11 .. .. 70 25
b. Perf 12 .. .. 10·00 1·75
c. Compound perf .. .. 1·50 70
O104 ¾ ch. brown 50 10
a. Imperf between (vert pair) .. — 80·00
b. Perf 11 .. .. 1·75 10
c. Perf 12 .. .. 10·00 1·25
d. Compound perf .. .. 3·00 85

1943. *Surch with Type* O **12**. *P* 12½.

O105 19 8 ca. on 6 ca. scarlet 40 10
a. Perf 11 .. .. 75 10
ab. Surch inverted .. .. — £275
b. Compound perf .. .. 2·75 1·25

1945. *Nos.* 73/4 *optd with Type* O **11**. *P* 12½.

O106 2 ca. on 1½ ch. scarlet 20 10
a. Perf 11 .. .. 15 10
ab. Pair, one without surch .. £110
b. Compound perf 70 70
ba. "2" omitted .. .. 80·00 80·00
O107 4 ca. on ¾ ch. brown 70 10
a. Perf 11 .. .. 40 10
b. Compound perf .. .. 1·10 70

1947. *Maharaja's 34th Birthday. Optd with Type* O **11**. *P* 11.

O108 21 8 ca. carmine .. .. 1·10 70
a. Imperf between (horiz pair) .. 35·00
ab. Imperf between (vert pair) .. — 60·00
b. Opt double .. .. — 85·00
c. Perf 12½ .. .. 3·00 1·10
ca. Stamp doubly printed .. 30·00
d. Perf 12 .. .. 3·50 1·10
da. Stamp doubly printed .. 32·00

From 1 July 1949 Travancore formed part of the new State of Travancore-Cochin and stamps of Travancore surcharged in Indian currency were used.

TRAVANCORE-COCHIN

On 1 July 1949 the United State of Travancore and Cochin was formed ("U.S.T.C.") and the name was changed to State of Travancore-Cochin ("T.C.") by the new constitution of India on 26 January 1950.

PRICES FOR STAMPS ON COVER	
Nos. 1/13	*from* × 8
Nos. O1/17	*from* × 15

NO WATERMARK VARIETIES. These were formerly listed but we have now decided to omit them as they do not occur in full sheets. They are best collected in pairs, with and without watermarks.

COMPOUND PERFS. The notes above Type **17** of Travancore also apply here.

VALIDITY OF STAMPS. From 6 June 1950 the stamps of Travancore-Cochin were valid on mail from both Indian and state post offices to destinations in India and abroad.

ONE ANNA
ഒരണ
(1)

2 p. on 6 ca.

രണ്ടു പൈസ — Normal

രണ്ടു പൈസ — Variety: 1st character of 2nd group as 1st character of 1st group

1949 (1 July). *Stamps of Travancore surch in "PIES" or "ANNAS" as T* **1**. *P* 12½.

1 19 2 p. on 6 ca. blackish violet (R.) 50 20
a. Surch inverted .. .. 18·00
b. Character error .. .. 45·00 40·00
c. "O" inverted .. .. 13·00 11·00
d. Perf 11 .. .. 35 15
da. Imperf between (vert pair) .. 40·00 40·00
db. Pair, one without surch .. 45·00
dc. Character error .. .. 42·00 38·00
e. Perf 12 .. .. 15 10
ea. Imperf between (horiz pair) .. 14·00
eb. Imperf between (vert pair) .. 5·00 7·00
ec. Surch inverted .. .. 32·00
ed. Character error .. .. 45·00 40·00
ee. Imperf between (vert strip of 3) .. 17·00
ef. Block of four imperf between (horiz and vert) .. .. 22·00
eg. "O" inverted .. .. 13·00 11·00
f. Perf 14 .. .. — £225
g. Imperf (pair) .. .. 8·50 12·00
h. Compound perf .. .. — 18·00
2 21 4 p. on 8 ca. carmine 50 10
a. Surch inverted .. .. 20·00
b. "S" inverted .. .. 30·00 25·00
c. Perf 11 .. .. 40 10
ca. Imperf between (vert pair) .. 50·00 50·00
cb. Surch inverted .. .. 38·00
cc. Pair, one without surch .. 50·00 50·00
cd. "FOUP" for "FOUR" .. 48·00 40·00
ce. "S" inverted .. .. 30·00 25·00
d. Perf 12 .. .. 30 30
da. Imperf between (vert pair) .. 12·00
db. Pair, one without surch .. 45·00
dc. "FOUP" for "FOUR" .. 48·00 40·00
dd. "S" inverted .. .. 32·00 27·00
de. Surch inverted .. .. 45·00
e. Imperf (pair) .. .. 50·00
f. Compound perf .. .. — 18·00
g. Perf 13½ .. .. — £225
3 17 ½ a. on 1 ch. yellow-green 70 25
a. "NANA" for "ANNA" .. 55·00 45·00
b. Inverted "H" in "HALF" .. — 42·00
c. Perf 11 .. .. 55 15
ca. Imperf between (vert pair) .. 16·00
cb. Surch inverted .. .. — 40·00
cc. "NANA" for "ANNA" .. 65·00 48·00
cd. Inverted "H" in "HALF" .. — 42·00
d. Perf 12 .. .. 25 15
da. Imperf between (horiz pair) .. 11·00 12·00
db. Imperf between (vert pair) .. 4·50 6·00
dc. Surch inverted .. .. 5·00
dd. "NANA" for "ANNA" .. 65·00 48·00
de. Block of four imperf between (horiz and vert) .. .. 22·00
e. Perf 14 .. .. — £225
f. Imperf (pair) .. .. 8·50 12·00
g. Compound perf .. .. — 18·00
4 18 1 a. on 2 ch. orange 70 25
a. Perf 11 .. .. 20 15
ab. Surch double .. .. 45·00
b. Perf 12 .. .. 90 25
ba. Imperf between (horiz pair) .. 4·25
bb. Imperf between (vert pair) .. 4·25 6·00
bc. Block of four imperf between (horiz and vert) .. .. 22·00
c. Perf 13½ .. .. 55·00 2·00
d. Imperf (pair) .. .. 8·50
e. Compound perf .. .. 20·00 14·00
5 – 2 a. on 4 ch. red (68) 75 35
a. Surch inverted .. .. — £100
b. "O" inverted .. .. 14·00 10·00
c. Perf 11 .. .. 75 35
ca. "O" inverted .. .. — 13·00
d. Perf 12 .. .. 1·25 55
da. "O" inverted .. .. 18·00 13·00
e. Compound perf .. .. 18·00 18·00

6 18 3 a. on 7 ch. pale blue (69) .. .. 5·50 2·50
a. Perf 11 .. .. 4·00 1·50
ab. Blue .. .. 20·00 4·00
b. Perf 12 .. .. 3·75 2·50
c. Compound perf .. .. .. — 22·00
ca. Blue .. .. — 30·00
7 – 6 a. on 14 ch. turquoise-green (70) .. 4·00 6·00
a. Accent omitted from native surch .. 70·00 70·00
b. Perf 11 .. .. 3·50 6·00
ba. Accent omitted from native surch .. 75·00 75·00
c. Perf 12 .. .. 6·50 7·50
ca. Accent omitted from native surch .. 80·00 80·00
d. Compound perf .. .. .. 15·00 15·00
da. Accent omitted from native surch .. 95·00
e. Imperf (pair) .. .. ..
1/7 .. .. *Set of* 7 8·00 7·50

There are two settings of the ½ a. surcharge. In one the first native character is under the second downstroke of the "H" and in the other it is under the first downstroke of the "A" of "HALF". They occur on stamps perf 12½, 11 and 12 equally commonly and also on the Official stamps.

U. S. T. C. (2) **T.-C.** (3) **SIX PIES** (4)

1949. *No. 106 of Cochin optd with T* **2**.
8 29 1 a. orange .. .. 4·50 30·00
a. No stop after "S" .. .. .. 45·00
b. Raised stop after "T" .. .. 45·00

1950 (1 Apr). *No. 106 of Cochin optd with T* **3**.
9 29 1 a. orange .. .. 5·50 26·00
a. No stop after "T" .. .. .. 45·00
b. Opt inverted £150
ba. No stop after "T" £1500

The no stop variety occurs on No. 5 in the sheet and again on No. 8 in conjunction with a short hyphen.

1950 (1 Apr). *No. 9 surch as T* **4**.
10 29 6 p. on 1 a. orange .. .. .. 1·60 8·00
a. No stop after "T" .. .. .. 17·00
b. Error. Surch on No. 8 .. .. 40·00
ba. No stop after "S" £250
bb. Raised stop after "T" £250
11 9 p. on 1 a. orange .. .. .. 1·40 8·00
a. No stop after "T" .. .. .. 17·00
b. Error. Surch on No. 8 .. .. 90·00
ba. No stop after "S" £450
bb. Raised stop after "T" £450

5 Conch or Chank Shell

6 Palm Trees

(Litho Indian Security Printing Press, Nasik)

1950. *W* **69** *of India. P* 14.
12 5 2 p. rose-carmine .. .. .. 45 1·10
13 6 4 p. ultramarine .. .. .. 70 2·50

The ordinary issues of Travancore-Cochin became obsolete on 1 July 1951.

OFFICIAL STAMPS

VALIDITY. Travancore-Cochin official stamps were valid for use throughout India from 30 September 1950.

SERVICE (O 1) **SERVICE** (O 2)

1949–51. *Stamps of Travancore surch with value as T* **1** *and optd* "SERVICE". *No gum. P* 12½. *(a) With Type* O **1**.

(i) *Wmk* C *of Travancore*
O 1 19 2 p. on 6 ca. blackish violet (R.) .. 30 10
a. Imperf between (vert pair) .. .. 50·00 50·00
b. Character error .. .. .. 22·00 18·00
c. "O" inverted .. .. .. 12·00 9·00
d. Pair, one without surch .. .. 55·00
e. Perf 11 .. .. 25 10
ea. Imperf between (vert pair) .. .. 50·00 50·00
eb. Character error .. .. .. 30·00 24·00
ec. "O" inverted .. .. .. 12·00 9·00
f. Perf 12 .. .. 20 20
fa. Imperf between (horiz pair) .. 6·00
fb. Imperf between (vert pair) .. .. 6·00
fc. Character error .. .. .. 26·00 22·00
fd. "O" inverted .. .. .. 12·00
fe. Block of four imperf between (horiz and vert) .. .. 22·00
g. Imperf (pair) .. .. .. 8·00 11·00
ga. Character error £110
O 2 21 4 p. on 8 ca. carmine 70 30
a. "FOUB" for "FOUR" .. .. 60·00 40·00
b. Perf 11 .. .. 45 15
ba. "FOUB" for "FOUR" .. .. 45·00 32·00
c. Perf 12 .. .. 50 15
ca. "FOUB" for "FOUR" .. .. 50·00 38·00
d. Compound perf .. .. .. 14·00 14·00

O 3 17 ½ a. on 1 ch. yellow-green 25 15
a. Pair, one without surch .. .. 38·00
b. Surch inverted .. .. .. 16·00
c. "NANA" for "ANNA" .. .. 65·00 40·00
d. Perf 11 .. .. 70 15
da. Pair, one without surch .. .. 55·00
db. Surch inverted .. .. .. 48·00
dc. "NANA" for "ANNA" .. .. 65·00 45·00
e. Perf 12 .. .. 3·75 1·25
ea. "NANA" for "ANNA" .. .. 95·00 75·00
eb. Pair, one without surch .. .. 50·00
f. Compound perf .. .. .. — 15·00
O 4 18 1 a. on 2 ch. orange .. .. 9·00 5·00
a. Surch inverted .. .. .. 80·00
b. Pair, one without surch £300
c. Perf 11 .. .. 8·00 6·00
O 5 – 2 a. on 4 ch. red (68) 65 40
b. Perf 11 .. .. 2·25 45
c. Perf 12 .. .. 2·25 90
ca. O inverted .. .. .. — 22·00
cb. Pair, one without surch .. .. 95·00
d. Compound perf .. .. .. — 24·00
e. Imperf (pair) .. .. .. 12·00
O 6 – 3 a. on 7 ch. pale blue (69) .. .. 2·00 60
a. Imperf between (vert pair) .. .. 14·00
b. Blue .. .. 11·00 3·50
c. Perf 11 .. .. 1·75 60
ca. Blue .. .. 11·00 3·50
d. Perf 12 .. .. 1·60 1·60
da. Imperf between (horiz pair) .. 10·00
db. Imperf between (vert pair) .. .. 8·00
dc. Block of four imperf between (horiz and vert) .. .. 22·00
dd. Blue .. .. 10·00 3·00
e. Imperf (pair) .. .. .. 11·00
O 7 – 6 a. on 14 ch. turquoise-green (70) .. 4·50 1·75
a. Imperf between (vert pair) .. .. 24·00
b. Perf 11 .. .. 5·00 1·25
c. Perf 12 .. .. 14·00 5·00
ca. Imperf between (horiz pair) .. 20·00
cb. Imperf between (vert pair) .. .. 24·00
cc. Block of four imperf between (horiz and vert) .. .. 45·00
d. Imperf (pair) .. .. .. 14·00
O1/7 .. .. *Set of* 7 12·50 7·00

(ii) *W* **27** *of Cochin*
O 8 19 2 p. on 6 ca. blackish violet (R.) .. 10 15
a. Type O 1 double .. .. .. 15·00
b. Perf 11 .. .. 30 40
c. Perf 12 .. .. 40 50
O 9 – 2 a. on 4 ch. red (68) 50 35
a. Perf 11 .. .. 40 35
ab. Imperf between (vert pair) .. .. 85·00 85·00
b. Compound perf .. .. .. — 27·00

(*b*) *With Type* O **2**

(i) *Wmk* C *of Travancore*
O10 21 4 p. on 8 ca. carmine 15 10
a. "FOUB" for "FOUR" .. .. 50·00 30·00
b. 2nd "E" of "SERVICE" in wrong fount .. .. — 35·00
c. "S" in "PIES" inverted .. .. — 35·00
d. Imperf between (vert pair) .. — 45·00
e. Perf 11 .. .. 15 10
ea. Imperf between (horiz pair) .. 4·50
eb. Imperf between (vert pair) .. .. 15·00
ec. "FOUB" for "FOUR" .. .. 50·00 30·00
ed. 2nd "E" of "SERVICE" in wrong fount .. .. — 35·00
ee. "S" in "PIES" inverted .. .. — 35·00
ef. Block of four imperf between (horiz and vert) .. .. 22·00
f. Perf 12 .. .. 15 15
fa. Imperf between (horiz pair) .. 2·00
fb. Imperf between (vert pair) .. .. 2·00
fc. Block of four imperf between (horiz and vert) .. .. 9·00 13·00
fd. "FOUB" for "FOUR" .. .. 50·00 30·00
ff. 2nd "E" of "SERVICE" in wrong fount .. .. 50·00 35·00
g. Perf 13½ .. .. 2·50 1·25
h. Compound perf .. .. .. 8·00 8·00
i. Imperf (pair) .. .. .. 7·00
ia. 2nd "E" of "SERVICE" in wrong fount .. .. 80·00
O11 17 ½ a. on 1 ch. yellow-green 25 10
a. "AANA" for "ANNA" .. .. 60·00 40·00
b. Perf 11 .. .. 10 10
ba. Imperf between (horiz pair) .. 22·00 22·00
bb. Imperf between (vert pair) .. .. 5·50
bc. Block of four imperf between (horiz and vert) .. .. 27·00
bd. "AANA" for "ANNA" .. .. 60·00 40·00
c. Perf 12 .. .. 25 10
ca. Imperf between (horiz pair) .. 3·50
cb. Imperf between (vert pair) .. .. 3·50 5·00
cc. "AANA" for "ANNA" .. .. 55·00 38·00
cd. Block of four imperf between (horiz and vert) .. .. 20·00
d. Compound perf .. .. .. 13·00 10·00
da. "AANA" for "ANNA" .. .. — 65·00
e. Imperf (pair) .. .. .. 6·00 8·00
O12 18 1 a. on 2 ch. orange 20 20
a. Imperf between (vert pair) .. .. — 45·00
b. Perf 11 .. .. 60 50
ba. Imperf between (horiz pair) .. 5·50 7·50
bb. Imperf between (vert pair) .. .. 22·00 22·00
c. Perf 12 .. .. 30 20
ca. Imperf between (horiz pair) .. 3·50
cb. Imperf between (vert pair) .. .. 3·00 5·00
cc. Block of four imperf between (horiz and vert) .. .. 16·00
d. Compound perf .. .. .. 13·00 13·00
e. Imperf (pair) .. .. .. 14·00
O13 – 2 a. on 4 ch. red (68) .. .. 1·75 80
a. "O" inverted .. .. .. 28·00 20·00
b. Perf 11 .. .. 1·10 1·10
ba. "O" inverted .. .. .. 24·00 20·00
c. Perf 12 .. .. 3·50 1·10
ca. Imperf between (vert pair) .. .. 80·00 85·00
cb. "O" inverted .. .. .. 45·00 22·00
d. Compound perf .. .. .. 16·00 12·00

O14 – 3 a. on 7 ch. pale blue (69) .. .. 2·25 75
a. "S" inverted in "SERVICE" .. 45·00 32·00
b. First "E" inverted .. .. .. 85·00 75·00
c. "C" inverted .. .. .. 75·00 65·00
d. Second "E" inverted .. .. 85·00 75·00
e. Perf 11 .. .. 1·10 75
ea. "S" inverted in "SERVICE" .. 45·00 32·00
f. Perf 12 .. .. 2·75 1·25
fa. "S" inverted in "SERVICE" .. 55·00 38·00
g. Compound perf .. .. .. — 25·00
h. Imperf (pair) .. .. .. 32·00
O15 – 6 a. on 14 ch. turquoise-green (70) .. 1·10 1·50
a. Accent omitted from native surch .. 16·00 12·00
b. "S" inverted in "SERVICE" .. 55·00 38·00
c. Perf 11 .. .. 6·50 2·25
ca. Accent omitted from native surch .. 42·00 22·00
cb. "S" inverted in "SERVICE" .. 75·00 45·00
d. Perf 12 .. .. 17·00 2·75
da. Accent omitted from native surch .. 75·00 25·00
db. "S" inverted in "SERVICE" .. £100 45·00
e. Compound perf .. .. .. 32·00 32·00
O10/15 .. .. *Set of* 6 3·25 2·75

(ii) *W* **27** *of Cochin*
O16 17 ½ a. on 1 ch. yellow-green 30 25
a. Perf 11 .. .. 10 10
b. Perf 12 .. .. 12·00 6·50
c. Compound perf. .. .. .. 8·00 3·50
O17 18 1 a. on 2 ch. orange 30 25
a. Perf 11 .. .. 50 40
b. Perf 12 .. .. 10·00 5·00
c. Perf 13½ .. .. 2·50 1·50
d. Compound perf .. .. .. 3·75 3·75

Nos. O2, O10, O12 and O17 have the value at top in English and at bottom in native characters with "SERVICE" in between. All others have "SERVICE" below the surcharge.

Type O **2** was overprinted at one operation with the surcharges.

The Official stamps became obsolete in September 1951.

WADHWAN

PRICES FOR STAMPS ON COVER
No. 1 —
Nos. 2/6 *from* × 50

1

1888. (*a*) *Thin toned wove paper.*

(i) *Irregular perf* 12½ (*small holes*)
1 1 ½ pice, black (II) .. .. .. 18·00
a. Imperf between (pair) .. ..

(ii) *P* 12½ (*large holes*)
2 1 ½ pice, black (I, III) .. .. .. 8·00 27·00

(*b*) *Medium toned wove paper*
3 1 ½ pice, black (III) (*p* 12½) .. .. 6·50 20·00
4 ½ pice, black (V) (*p* 12) .. .. 4·50 5·50

1892 (?). *Thick wove paper. P* 12.
5 1 ½ pice, black/*toned* (VI, VII) .. .. 4·00 4·50
6 ½ pice, black/*white* (IV) .. .. 4·00 4·50
a. Perf compound of 12 and 11 .. 10·00

The stamps were lithographed from seven stones (as indicated by Roman figures), in sheets of from 20 to 42 units, distinguishable by flaws.

The stamps of Wadhwan became obsolete on 1 January 1895.

Ionian Islands

The British occupation of the Ionian Islands was completed in 1814 and the archipelago was placed under the protection of Great Britain by the Treaty of Paris in 1815. The United States of the Ionian Islands were given local self-government, which included responsibility for the postal services. Crowned-circle handstamps were, however, supplied in 1844, although it is believed these were intended for use on prepaid mail to foreign destinations.

Examples of the Great Britain 1855 1d. red-brown stamp are known used at Corfu, but there is little information available concerning such usage.

For illustrations of the handstamp types see BRITISH POST OFFICES ABROAD notes, following GREAT BRITAIN.

CEPHALONIA

CROWNED-CIRCLE HANDSTAMPS

CC1 CC 1 CEPHALONIA (19.4.1844) .. *Price on cover* £1000

CORFU

CROWNED-CIRCLE HANDSTAMPS

CC2 CC 1 CORFU (19.4.1844) .. .. *Price on cover* £500
CC3 CC 1 CORFU (G. or B.) (1844) .. *Price on cover* —

Stamps of GREAT BRITAIN *cancelled with No.* CC2.
Z1 1d. red-brown (1855) Die II, *wmk* Large Crown, *perf* 14 .. .. £700

ZANTE

CROWNED-CIRCLE HANDSTAMPS

CC4 CC 1 ZANTE (G. or B.) (19.4.1844) .. *Price on cover* £1000

Nos. CC1/2 were later, *circa* 1860/1, struck in green (Cephalonia) or red (Corfu).

It is believed that examples of No. CC4 in black are from an unauthorised use of this handstamp. A similar handstamp, but without "PAID AT" was introduced in 1861.

PRICES FOR STAMPS ON COVER	
Nos. 1/3	*from* × 10

1

(Recess Perkins, Bacon & Co)

1859 (15 June). *Imperf.*
1 **1** (½d.) orange (no wmk) .. .. .. 70·00 £500
2 (1d.) blue (wmk "2") .. .. .. 18·00 £175
3 (2d.) carmine (wmk "1") .. .. .. 13·00 £175

On 30 May 1864, the islands were ceded to Greece, and these stamps became obsolete.

Great care should be exercised in buying used stamps, on or off cover, as forged postmarks are plentiful.

Iraq

Indian post offices were opened at Baghdad and Basra, then part of the Turkish Empire, on 1 January 1868. Unoverprinted stamps of India were used, Baghdad being allocated numeral cancellations "356", "18" and "K-6", and Basra (also spelt Bussorah, Busreh, Busrah, Busra) "357", "19" and "1/K-6".

Both offices closed in November 1914, but Basra re-opened the following month when Indian stamps overprinted "I.E.F." were used.

(Currency. 16 annas = 1 rupee)

I. ISSUES FOR BAGHDAD

PRICES FOR STAMPS ON COVER	
Nos 1/25	*from* × 6

BRITISH OCCUPATION

British and Indian troops occupied the port of Basra on 22 November 1914 to protect the oil pipeline. They then advanced up the rivers, and after a hard campaign took Baghdad from the Turks on 11 March 1917.

IN BRITISH BAGHDAD OCCUPATION 2 Ans

(1)

1917 (1 Sept). *Stamps of Turkey, surch as T* **1** *in three operations.*

(a) Pictorial designs of 1914. *T* **32**, *etc., and* **31**
1 **32** ¼ a. on 2 pa. claret (Obelisk) .. .. 80·00 90·00
a. "IN BRITISH" omitted £4000
2 **34** ¼ a. on 5 pa. dull purple (Leander's Tower) 55·00 60·00
a. Value omitted £3500
3 **36** ½ a. on 10 pa. green (Lighthouse garden) £500 £500
4 **31** ½ a. on 10 pa. green (Mosque of Selim) .. £850 £1000
5 **37** 1 a. on 20 pa. red (Castle) £300 £300
a. "BAGHDAD" double £1300
6 **38** 2 a. on 1 pi. bright blue (Mosque) .. 90·00 £100

(b) As (a), but overprinted with small five-pointed Star
7 **37** 1 a. on 20 pa. red (B.) £170 £180
a. "OCCUPATION" omitted £2750
8 **38** 2 a. on 1 pi. bright blue (R.) £2000 £2750

(c) Postal Jubilee stamps (Old G.P.O.). P 12½
9 **60** ½ a. on 10 pa. carmine £275 £300
a. Perf 13½ £375 £400
10 1 a. on 20 pa. blue £750 £800
a. Value omitted £4250
b. Perf 13½ £650 £700
11 2 a. on 1 pi. black and violet .. .. 75·00 80·00
a. "BAGHDAD" omitted £2250
b. Perf 13½ .. .. .. 55·00 60·00

(d) T **30** *(G.P.O., Constantinople) with opt T* **26**.
12 **30** 2 a. on 1 pi. ultramarine £250 £300

(e) Stamps optd with Star and Arabic date "1331" within Crescent. T **53** *(except No. 16, T* **57**, *five-pointed Star)*
13 **30** ½ a. on 10 pa. green (R.) .. .. .. 55·00 60·00
14 1 a. on 20 pa. rose £300 £325
a. Value omitted £3750 £3750
b. Optd with T **26** also £3750 £3750
c. First "D" of "BAGHDAD" omitted £2250
15 **23** 1 a. on 20 pa. rose (No. 554a) £300 £325
a. Value omitted £4250
16 **21** 1 a. on 20 pa. carmine (No. 732) .. £2500 £3000
17 **30** 2 a. on 1 pi. ultramarine (R.) .. .. 65·00 70·00
a. "BAGHDAD" omitted .. .. † —
18 **21** 2 a. on 1 pi. dull blue (No. 543) (R.) .. £110 £120
a. "OCCUPATION" omitted .. ..

(f) Stamps with similar opt, but date between Star and Crescent (Nos. 19 and 22, T **54**; *others T* **55**, *five-pointed Star)*
19 **23** ½ a. on 10 pa. grey-green (No. 609a) (R.) 70·00 75·00
a. "OCCUPATION" omitted £3000
20 **60** ½ a. on 10 pa. carmine (*p* 12½) (B.) .. £100 £110
a. Perf 13½ £175 £175
21 **30** 1 a. on 20 pa. rose .. .. .. 65·00 70·00
22 **28** 1 a. on 20 pa. rose (Plate II) (No. 617) .. £275 £300
23 **15** 1 a. on 10 pa. on 20 pa. claret (No. 630) £140 £140
a. "OCCUPATION" omitted £2250 £2250
24 **30** 2 a. on 1 pi. ultramarine (R.) £120 £130
a. "OCCUPATION" omitted £3500
b. "BAGHDAD" omitted £3500
25 **28** 2 a. on 1 pi. ultramarine (Pl. II) (No. 649) £900 £950

The last group *(f)* have the Crescent obliterated by hand in violet-black ink, as this included the inscription, "Tax for the relief of children of martyrs".

II. ISSUES FOR MOSUL

PRICES FOR STAMPS ON COVER	
Nos. 1/8	*from* × 40

BRITISH OCCUPATION

A British and Indian force, designated Indian Expeditionary Force "D", occupied Mosul on 1 November 1918.

POSTAGE

I.E.F. 'D'

1 Anna 4 4

(1) I (*normal*) II (*small*)

(a) Central design shows large "tougra" or sign-manual of El Ghazi 7 mm high.
(b) Smaller "tougra" of Sultan Rechad 5½ mm high.

1919 (1 Feb). *Turkish Fiscal stamps surch as T* **1** *by Govt Press, Baghdad. P* 11½ (½ *a.*), 12 (1 *a.*), *or* 12½ (*others*).
1 ½ a. on 1 pi. green and red .. .. 1·40 1·40
2 1 a. on 20 pa. black/*red* (*a*) .. .. 1·40 1·40
a. Imperf between (horiz pair) £600
b. Surch double £500
3 1 a. on 20 pa. black/*red* (*b*) .. .. 4·00 3·00
b. Surch double £600
4 2½ a. on 1 pi. mauve and yellow (*b*) .. 1·50 1·50
a. No bar to fraction (R. 2/4) .. .. 25·00 35·00
b. Surch double £650
5 3 a. on 20 pa. green (*a*) .. .. 1·60 1·60
6 3 a. on 20 pa. green and orange (*b*) .. 24·00 35·00
7 4 a. on 1 pi. deep violet (*a*) (I) .. .. 3·00 3·50
a. "4" omitted £1400
c. Surch double £750
ca. Surch double, one with "4" omitted .. £2000
7*d* 4 a. on 1 pi. deep violet (*a*) (II) .. .. 4·00 4·50
8 8 a. on 10 pa. lake (*a*) .. .. 4·00 4·50
a. Surch inverted £500 £500
b. Surch double £500 £500
c. No comma after "D" .. .. 22·00 30·00
d. Surch inverted. No comma after "D" ..
e. Error. 8 a. on 1 pi. deep violet .. £1700

In December 1925 the League of Nations awarded the vilayet of Mosul to Iraq.

III. ISSUES FOR IRAQ

PRICES FOR STAMPS ON COVER	
Nos. 1/18	*from* × 4
Nos. 41/154	*from* × 2
Nos. O19/171	*from* × 2

BRITISH OCCUPATION

IN BRITISH IRAQ 1An. OCCUPATION

(1)

A

B

1918 (1 Sept)–**21**. *Turkish pictorial issue of* 1914, *surch as T* **1** *by Bradbury Wilkinson. P* 12.

(a) No wmk. Tougra as A (1 Sept 1918–20)
1 **34** ¼ a. on 5 pa. dull purple 25 25
2 **36** ½ a. on 10 pa. green 25 15
3 **37** 1 a. on 20 pa. red 25 10
4 **34** 1½ a. on 5 pa. dull purple (1920) .. 60 50
5 **38** 2½ a. on 1 pi. bright blue 80 60
a. Surch inverted £2500
6 **39** 3 a. on 1½ pi. grey and rose .. 40 25
a. Surch double (Bk. + R.) £1700 £2250
7 **40** 4 a. on 1¾ pi. red-brown and grey .. 45 25
a. Centre inverted .. .. † £9000
8 **41** 6 a. on 2 pi. black and green .. 90 1·25
9 **42** 8 a. on 2½ pi. green and orange .. 90 60
a. Surch inverted .. .. † £4000
10 **43** 12 a. on 5 pi. deep lilac .. .. 1·50 1·25
11 **44** 1 r. on 10 pi. red-brown .. .. 2·00 1·40
12 **45** 2 r. on 25 pi. yellow-green .. .. 5·00 2·50
13 **46** 5 r. on 50 pi. rose .. .. 20·00 13·00
14 **47** 10 r. on 100 pi. indigo .. .. 27·00 17·00
1/14 .. .. .. *Set of* 14 55·00 35·00
1/3, 5/14 Perf "Specimen" .. .. *Set of* 13 £250

(b) No wmk. Tougra as B *(one device instead of two)* (1921)
15 **44** 1 r. on 10 pi. red-brown .. .. 90·00 19·00

(c) Wmk Mult Script CA (1921)
16 **36** ½ a. on 10 pa. green 40 50
17 **34** 1½ a. on 5 pa. dull purple 50 50
18 **45** 2 r. on 25 pi. yellow-green .. .. 10·00 7·50
16/18 .. .. .. *Set of* 3 10·00 7·75
16/18 Optd "Specimen" .. .. *Set of* 3 50·00

Designs: *Horiz*—5 pa. Leander's Tower; 10 pa. Lighthouse-garden, Stamboul; 20 pa. Castle of Europe; 1 pi. Mosque of Sultan Ahmed; 1½ pi. Martyrs of Liberty Monument; 1¾ pi. Fountains of Suleiman; 2 pi. Cruiser *Hamidiye*; 2½ pi. Candilli, Bosphorus; 5 pi. Former Ministry of War; 10 pi. Sweet Waters of Europe; 25 pi. Suleiman Mosque; 50 pi. Bosphorus at Rumeli Hisar; 100 pi. Sultan Ahmed's Fountain.

No. 7a is only recorded with telegraph cancellation.

LEAGUE OF NATIONS MANDATE

On 25 April 1920 the Supreme Council of the Allies assigned to the United Kingdom a mandate under the League of Nations to administer Iraq.

The Emir Faisal, King of Syria in 1920, was proclaimed King of Iraq on 23 August 1921.

King Faisal I
23 August 1921–8 September 1933

2 Sunni Mosque, Muadhdham

3 Winged Cherub

4 Allegory of Date Palm

(Des Miss Edith Cheesman (½ a., 1 a., 4 a., 6 a., 8 a., 2 r., 5 r., 10 r.) and Mrs. C. C. Garbett (Miss M. J. Maynard) (remainder). Recess Bradbury, Wilkinson)

1923 (May)–**25**. *T* **2**/**4** *and similar designs. Wmk Mult Script CA (sideways on* 1½ *a.,* 4 *a.,* 8 *a.,* 5 *r.). P* 12.
41 **2** ½ a. olive-green 15 10
42 – 1 a. brown 20 10
43 **3** 1½ a. lake 25 10
44 – 2 a. orange-buff 30 15
45 – 3 a. grey-blue 50 15
46 – 4 a. violet 80 25
47 – 6 a. greenish blue 90 30
48 – 8 a. olive-bistre .. .. .. 1·00 30
49 **4** 1 r. brown and blue-green .. .. 1·75 70
50 **2** 2 r. black .. .. .. 9·50 7·00
51 2 r. olive-bistre (1925) .. .. 11·00 3·25
52 – 5 r. orange .. .. .. 19·00 13·00
53 – 10 r. lake .. .. .. 25·00 20·00
41/53 .. .. .. *Set of* 13 65·00 40·00
41/53 Optd "Specimen" .. .. *Set of* 13 £225

Designs: *Horiz (as T* **2**)—1 a. Gufas on the Tigris; 2 a. Bull from Babylonian wall-sculpture; 3 a. Arch of Ctesiphon; 6 a., 10 r. Shiar Mosque, Kadhimain. *Vert (as T* **3**)—4 a., 8 a., 5 r. Tribal Standard, Dulaim Camel Corps.

With the exception of Nos. 49 and 50, later printings of these stamps and of No. 78 are on a thinner paper.

10 11 12
King Faisal I

(Recess Bradbury, Wilkinson)

1927. *Wmk Mult Script CA. P 12.*
78 **10** 1 r. red-brown (Optd S. £30) 4·00 50
See note below No. 53.

(Recess Bradbury, Wilkinson)

1931. *Wmk Mult Script CA. P 12.*
80 **11** ½ a. green 10 10
81 1 a. red-brown 15 10
82 1½ a. scarlet 40 30
83 2 a. orange 20 10
84 3 a. blue 40 10
85 4 a. slate-purple 80 70
86 6 a. greenish blue 80 60
87 8 a. deep green 1·00 70
88 **12** 1 r. chocolate 2·50 90
89 2 r. yellow-brown 4·00 2·50
90 5 r. orange 18·00 22·00
91 10 r. scarlet 45·00 55·00
92 **10** 25 r. violet £500 £650
80/91 *Set of* 12 65·00 75·00
80/92 Perf "Specimen" *Set of* 13 £500

(New Currency. 1000 fils = 1 dinar)

10 Fils (13) ½ Dinar (14)

(Surcharged at Govt Ptg Wks, Baghdad)

1932 (1 Apr). *Nos. 80/92 and 46 surch in "Fils" or "Dinar" as T* **13** *or* **14**.
106 **11** 2 f. on ½ a. green (R.) 15 10
107 3 f. on ½ a. green 15 10
a. Surch double £140
b. Surch inverted £140
108 4 f. on 1 a. red-brown (G.) 35 25
109 5 f. on 1 a. red-brown 25 10
a. Inverted Arabic "5" 27·00 32·00
110 8 f. on 1½ a. scarlet 35 30
a. Surch inverted £140
111 10 f. on 2 a. orange 35 10
a. Inverted Arabic "1" 18·00 18·00
112 15 f. on 3 a. blue 35 1·00
113 20 f. on 4 a. slate-purple 1·00 1·00
a. Surch inverted
114 – 25 f. on 4 a. violet (No. 46) 1·00 90
a. "Flis" for "Fils" £300 £350
b. Inverted Arabic "5" £300 £350
c. Vars a and b in *se-tenant* pair £800
115 **11** 30 f. on 6 a. greenish blue 1·25 60
116 40 f. on 8 a. deep green 1·75 1·75
117 **12** 75 f. on 1 r. chocolate 1·75 1·75
a. Inverted Arabic "5" 25·00 32·00
118 100 f. on 2 r. yellow-brown 5·50 3·75
119 200 f. on 5 r. orange 11·00 8·50
120 ½ d. on 10 r. scarlet 32·00 42·00
a. No bar in English "½" £600 £650
121 **10** 1 d. on 25 r. violet 80·00 95·00
106/121 *Set of* 16 £120 £140

3 FILS
15

1932 (9 May). *T* **10** *to* **12**, *but with values altered to "FILS" or "DINAR" as in T* **15**. *Wmk Mult Script CA. P 12.*
138 **11** 2 f. ultramarine 15 10
139 3 f. green 15 10
140 4 f. brown-purple 15 10
141 5 f. grey-green 15 10
142 8 f. scarlet 20 10
143 10 f. yellow 20 10
144 15 f. blue 25 10
145 20 f. orange 30 15
146 25 f. mauve 45 15
147 30 f. bronze-green 50 15
148 40 f. violet 55 55
149 **12** 50 f. brown 55 20
150 75 f. dull ultramarine 1·60 1·25
151 100 f. deep green 2·25 50
152 200 f. scarlet 9·00 2·75
153 **10** ½ d. deep blue 23·00 18·00
154 1 d. claret 55·00 42·00
138/154 *Set of* 17 85·00 60·00
138/54 Perf "Specimen" *Set of* 17 £175

OFFICIAL STAMPS

ON STATE SERVICE
(O 1)

1920 (1 May)–**23**. *As Nos. 1/18, but surch includes additional wording "ON STATE SERVICE" as Type* O **1** *in black.*

(*a*) *No wmk. Tougra as* A (1920)
O19 **36** ½ a. on 10 pa. blue-green 55 15
O20 **37** 1 a. on 20 pa. red 55 15
O21 **34** 1½ a. on 5 pa. purple-brown 1·00 25
O22 **38** 2½ a. on 1 pi. blue 80 80
O23 **39** 3 a. on 1½ pi. black and rose 1·25 50
O24 **40** 4 a. on 1¾ pi. red-brown and grey-blue 1·75 75
O25 **41** 6 a. on 2 pi. black and green 2·50 1·25
O26 **42** 8 a. on 2½ pi. yellow-green & orge-brn 2·25 1·25
O27 **43** 12 a. on 5 pi. purple 2·25 1·75
O28 **44** 1 r. on 10 pi. red-brown 3·25 2·50
O29 **45** 2 r. on 25 pi. olive-green 11·00 7·50
O30 **46** 5 r. on 50 pi. rose-carmine 24·00 17·00
O31 **47** 10 r. on 100 pi. slate-blue 45·00 45·00
O19/31 *Set of* 13 85·00 70·00

(*b*) *No wmk. Tougra as* B (*No.* 15) (1922)
O32 **44** 1 r. on 10 pi. red-brown 10·00 7·00

(*c*) *Wmk Mult Script CA* (1921–23)
O33 **36** ½ a. on 10 pa. green 15 10
O34 **37** 1 a. on 20 pa. red 15 15
O35 **34** 1½ a. on 5 pa. purple-brown 30 30
O36 **40** 4 a. on 1¾ pi. red-brown and grey-blue 60 50
O37 **41** 6 a. on 2 pi. black and green (1923) 5·50 18·00
O38 **42** 8 a. on 2½ pi. yellow-green & orge-brn 1·25 1·25
O39 **43** 12 a. on 5 pi. purple (1923) 4·00 16·00
O40 **45** 2 r. on 25 pi. olive-green (1923) 17·00 35·00
O33/40 *Set of* 8 26·00 65·00
O33/40 Perf/Optd "Specimen" *Set of* 8 £120

ON STATE SERVICE
(O 2)

ON STATE SERVICE
(O 3)

1923. *Optd with Types* O **2** (*horiz designs*) *or* O **3** (*vert designs*).
O54 **2** ½ a. olive-green 35 10
O55 – 1 a. brown 35 10
O56 **3** 1½ a. lake 1·00 35
O57 – 2 a. orange-buff 50 20
O58 – 3 a. grey-blue 1·50 30
O59 – 4 a. violet 2·00 40
O60 – 6 a. greenish blue 2·50 1·25
O61 – 8 a. olive-bistre 2·75 1·00
O62 **4** 1 r. brown and blue-green 3·00 1·25
O63 **2** 2 r. black (R.) 13·00 6·00
O64 – 5 r. orange 32·00 17·00
O65 – 10 r. lake 50·00 45·00
O54/65 *Set of* 12 95·00 65·00
O54/65 Optd "Specimen" *Set of* 12 £200

ON STATE SERVICE رسمي
(O 4)

ON STATE SERVICE رسمي
(O 5)

1924–25. *Optd with Types* O **4** (*horiz designs*) *or* O **5** (*vert designs*).
O66 **2** ½ a. olive-green 20 10
O67 – 1 a. brown 20 10
O68 **3** 1½ a. lake 20 10
O69 – 2 a. orange-buff 40 10
O70 – 3 a. grey-blue 40 10
O71 – 4 a. violet 90 10
O72 – 6 a. greenish blue 95 20
O73 – 8 a. olive-bistre 1·25 35
O74 **4** 1 r. brown and blue-green 5·50 1·00
O75 **2** 2 r. olive-bistre (1925) 15·00 3·75
O76 – 5 r. orange 32·00 22·00
O77 – 10 r. lake 48·00 42·00
O66/77 *Set of* 12 90·00 65·00
O66/77 Optd "Specimen" *Set of* 12 £200

1927. *Optd with Type* O **5**.
O79 **10** 1 r. red-brown (Optd S. £30) 3·50 80

ON STATE SERVICE

ON STATE SERVICE رسمي
(O 6)

رسمي
(O 7)

1931. *Optd.* (*a*) *As Type* O **6**.
O 93 **11** ½ a. green 15 90
O 94 1 a. red-brown 20 10
O 95 1½ a. scarlet 4·50 7·50
O 96 2 a. orange 50 10
O 97 3 a. blue 85 50
O 98 4 a. slate-purple 95 40
O 99 6 a. greenish blue 2·25 5·50
O100 8 a. deep green 2·75 5·50

(*b*) *As Type* O **7**, *horizontally*
O101 **12** 1 r. chocolate 6·00 7·50
O102 2 r. yellow-brown 11·00 20·00
O103 5 r. orange 28·00 45·00
O104 10 r. scarlet 50·00 80·00

(*c*) *As Type* O **7**, *vertically upwards*
O105 **10** 25 r. violet £550 £700
O93/104 *Set of* 12 95·00 £150
O93/105 Perf "Specimen" *Set of* 13 £500

1932 (1 Apr). *Official issues of 1924–25 and 1931 surch in* "FILS" *or* "DINAR", *as T* **13** *or* **14**.
O122 **11** 3 f. on ½ a. green 75 1·00
a. Pair, one without surch £250
O123 4 f. on 1 a. red-brown (G.) 60 10
O124 5 f. on 1 a. red-brown 60 10
a. Inverted Arabic "5" 27·00 23·00
O125 **3** 8 f. on 1½ a. lake (No. O68) 90 40
O126 **11** 10 f. on 2 a. orange 90 10
a. Inverted Arabic "1" 17·00 17·00
b. "10" omitted † —
O127 **11** 15 f. on 3 a. blue 1·50 35
O128 20 f. on 4 a. slate-purple 1·25 25
O129 25 f. on 4 a. slate-purple 1·75 40
O130 – 30 f. on 6 a. greenish blue (No. O72) 1·75 65
O131 **11** 40 f. on 8 a. deep green 1·75 80
a. "Flis" for "Fils" £175 £250
O132 **12** 50 f. on 1 r. chocolate 1·75 1·40
a. Inverted Arabic "5" 40·00 40·00
O133 75 f. on 1 r. chocolate 3·50 3·75
a. Inverted Arabic "5" 35·00 35·00
O134 **2** 100 f. on 2 r. olive-bistre 3·50 2·75
O135 – 200 f. on 5 r. orange (No. O76) 8·50 11·00
O136 – ½ d. on 10 r. lake (No. O77) 35·00 42·00
a. No bar in English "½" £400 £450
O137 **10** 1 d. on 25 r. violet 80·00 £100
O122/37 *Set of* 16 £120 £150

1932 (9 May). *Optd.* (*a*) *As Type* O **6**.
O155 **11** 2 f. ultramarine 40 10
O156 3 f. green 40 10
O157 4 f. brown-purple 60 10
O158 5 f. grey-green 60 10
O159 8 f. scarlet 60 10
O160 10 f. yellow 85 10
O161 15 f. blue 1·25 10
O162 20 f. orange 1·25 10
O163 25 f. mauve 1·00 15
O164 30 f. bronze-green 1·75 20
O165 40 f. violet 2·50 20

(*b*) *As Type* O **7**, *horizontally*
O166 **12** 50 f. brown 1·75 20
O167 75 f. dull ultramarine 1·75 90
O168 100 f. deep green 3·75 35
O169 200 f. scarlet 11·00 5·50

(*c*) *As Type* O **7**, *vertically upwards*
O170 **10** ½ d. deep blue 11·00 13·00
O171 1 d. claret 42·00 55·00
O155/71 *Set of* 17 70·00 70·00
O155/71 Perf "Specimen" *Set of* 17 £300

The British Mandate was given up on 3 October 1932 and Iraq became an independent kingdom. Later issues will be found listed in Part 19 (*Middle East*) of this catalogue.

Ireland (Republic)

All the issues of Ireland are listed together here, in this section of the Gibbons Catalogue, purely as a matter of convenience to collectors.

PRICES FOR STAMPS ON COVER TO 1945

Nos. 1/15	*from* × 5
Nos. 17/21	*from* × 3
Nos. 22/5*a*	*from* × 4
Nos. 26/9*a*	*from* × 5
Nos. 30/43	*from* × 4
Nos. 44/6	—
Nos. 47/63	*from* × 5
Nos. 64/6	*from* × 3
Nos. 67/70	*from* × 6
Nos. 71/82	*from* × 2
Nos. 83/8	*from* × 3
Nos. 89/98	*from* × 2
Nos. 99/104	*from* × 3
Nos. 105/37	*from* × 2
Nos. D1/4	*from* × 7
Nos. D5/14	*from* × 6

PROVISIONAL GOVERNMENT

16 January—6 December 1922

Stamps of Great Britain overprinted. T 104/8, W 100; T 109, W 110

Rialtas Sealadaċ na hÉireann 1922
(1)

Rialtas Sealadaċ na hÉireann 1922.
(2)

Rialtas Sealadaċ na hÉireann 1922
(3)

("Provisional Government of Ireland, 1922")

1922 (17 Feb). *T* **104** *to* **108** (*W* **100**) *and* **109** *of Great Britain overprinted in black.*

(*a*) *With T* **1**, *by Dollard Printing House, Ltd. Optd in black**
1 **105** ½d. green 35 25
a. Opt inverted £400 £550
2 **104** 1d. scarlet 45 25
a. Opt inverted £250 £300
b. Opt double, both inverted, one albino £350
3 1d. carmine-red 75 40
4 2½d. bright blue 1·00 3·75
5 **106** 3d. bluish violet 2·50 3·75
6 4d. grey-green 2·50 6·50

7 **107** 5d. yellow-brown .. .. 3·50 8·00
8 **108** 9d. agate .. .. 9·00 17·00
9 10d. turquoise-blue .. .. 6·50 12·00
1/9 .. .. *Set of* 8 23·00 45·00

*All values except 2½d. and 4d. are known with greyish black overprint, but these are difficult to distinguish.

The ½d. with red overprint is a trial or proof printing (*Price* £150).

Bogus inverted T 1 overprints exist on the 2d., 4d., 9d. and 1s. values.

(*b*) *With T* **2**, *by Alex Thom & Co, Ltd*

10 **105** 1½d. red-brown .. .. 1·75 75
a. Error. "PENCF" £350 £275
12 **106** 2d. orange (Die I) .. .. 1·50 50
a. Opt inverted £175 £225
13 2d. orange (Die II) .. .. 1·75 60
a. Opt inverted £300 £400
14 **107** 6d. reddish purple, C .. .. .. 6·50 4·50
15 **108** 1s. bistre-brown .. .. 8·00 9·00
10/15 .. .. *Set of* 5 17·00 13·00

Varieties occur throughout the T **2** overprint in the relative positions of the lines of the overprint, the "R" of "Rialtas" being over either the "Se" or "S" of "Sealadac" or intermediately.

(*c*) *With T* **3**

17 **109** 2s. 6d. chocolate-brown .. .. .. 30·00 48·00
18 2s. 6d. sepia-brown .. .. .. 42·00 60·00
19 5s. rose-red .. .. 48·00 75·00
21 10s. dull grey-blue £120 £180
17/21 .. .. *Set of* 3 £180 £275

1922 (1 April–July). *Optd by Dollard with T* **1**, *in red or carmine.*

22 **104** 2½d. bright blue (R.) .. .. .. 85 2·50
23 **106** 4d. grey-green (R.) .. .. .. 5·50 14·00
24 4d. grey-green (C.) (July) .. .. 35·00 48·00
25 **108** 9d. agate (R.) .. .. 11·00 14·00
25*a* 9d. agate (C.) (July) .. .. .. 85·00 80·00
22/5 .. .. *Set of* 3 15·00 27·00

1922 (19 June–Aug). *Optd as T* **2**, *in black, by Harrison & Sons, for use in horiz and vert coils.*

26 **105** ½d. green .. .. 1·50 8·00
27 **104** 1d. scarlet .. .. 1·10 4·00
28 **105** 1½d. red-brown (21.6) .. .. .. 3·75 24·00
29 **106** 2d. bright orange (Die I) .. .. 12·00 27·00
29*a* 2d. bright orange (Die II) (August) .. 12·00 18·00
26/9*a* .. .. *Set of* 5 27·00 75·00

The Harrison overprint measures 15 × 17 mm (maximum) against the 14½ × 16 mm of T **2** (Thom printing) and is a much bolder black than the latter, while the individual letters are taller, the "i" of "Rialtas" being specially outstanding.

The "R" of "Rialtas" is always over the "Se" of "Sealadac".

1922. *Optd by Thom.*

(*a*) *As T* **2** *but bolder, in dull to shiny blue-black or red* (June–Nov)

30 **105** ½d. green .. .. 1·25 80
31 **104** 1d. scarlet 50 30
a. "Q" for "O" (No. 357ab) £1200 £1100
b. Reversed "Q" for "O" (No. 357ac) .. £350 £250
32 **105** 1½d. red-brown .. .. 3·00 3·25
33 **106** 2d. orange (Die I) .. .. .. 16·00 2·50
34 2d. orange (Die II) .. .. .. 2·50 70
35 **104** 2½d. blue (R.) .. .. 6·50 15·00
36 **106** 3d. violet .. .. 2·00 2·75
37 4d. grey-green (R.) .. .. .. 2·00 3·50
38 **107** 5d. yellow-brown .. .. .. 3·50 5·50
39 6d. reddish purple, C .. .. .. 5·00 2·25
40 **108** 9d. agate (R.) .. .. 9·50 13·00
41 9d. olive-green (R.) .. .. .. 4·00 13·00
42 10d. turquoise-blue .. .. .. 25·00 42·00
43 1s. bistre-brown .. .. 6·00 8·50
30/43 .. .. *Set of* 14 70·00 95·00

Both 2d. stamps exist with the overprint inverted but there remains some doubt as to whether they were issued.

These Thom printings are distinguishable from the Harrison printings by the size of the overprint, and from the previous Thom printings by the intensity and colour of the overprint, the latter being best seen when the stamp is looked through with a strong light behind it.

(*b*) *As with T* **3**, *but bolder, in shiny blue-black* (Oct–Dec)

44 **109** 2s. 6d. chocolate-brown £175 £200
45 5s. rose-red £170 £225
46 10s. dull grey-blue £800 £900
44/6 .. .. *Set of* 3 £1000 £1200

The above differ from Nos. 17/21 not only in the bolder impression and colour of the ink but also in the "h" and "é" of "héireann" which are closer together.

Rialtas Sealadac na hÉireann 1922.

(4)

Saorstát Éireann 1922

(5 Wide date) ("Irish Free State 1922")

1922 (21 Nov–Dec). *Optd by Thom with T* **4** (*wider setting*) *in shiny blue-black.*

47 **105** ½d. green .. .. 1·00 1·75
a. Opt in jet-black .. .. .. 95·00 85·00
48 **104** 1d. scarlet .. .. 1·50 2·25
49 **105** 1½d. red-brown (4 December) .. .. 2·75 6·50
50 **106** 2d. orange (Die II) .. .. .. 8·50 4·00
51 **108** 1s. olive-bistre (4 December) .. .. 35·00 42·00
47/51 .. .. *Set of* 5 42·00 48·00

The overprint T 4 measures 15¾ × 16 mm (maximum).

IRISH FREE STATE

6 December 1922—29 December 1937

1922 (Dec)–**23.**

(*a*) *Optd by Thom with T* **5**, *in dull to shiny blue-black or red*

52 **105** ½d. green 15 25
a. No accent in "Saorstat" £900 £900
b. Accent inserted by hand .. .. 80·00 90·00
53 **104** 1d. scarlet 15 25
aa. No accent in "Saorstat" £5000 £5000
a. No accent and final "t" missing .. £5000 £4500
b. Accent inserted by hand £125 £150
c. Accent and "t" inserted £225 £250
d. Reversed "Q" for "O" (No. 357ac) .. £300 £250
54 **105** 1½d. red-brown .. .. 2·00 8·00
55 **106** 2d. orange (Die II) .. .. .. 1·00 2·00
56 **104** 2½d. bright blue (R.) (6.1.23) .. .. 2·25 6·50
a. No accent £140 £170
57 **106** 3d. bluish violet (6.1.23) .. .. 3·00 12·00
a. No accent £250 £275
58 4d. grey-green (R.) (16.1.23) .. .. 2·00 3·75
a. No accent £150 £170
59 **107** 5d. yellow-brown .. .. .. 2·50 4·00
60 6d. reddish purple, C .. .. .. 2·00 1·75
a. Accent inserted by hand £700 £700
61 **108** 9d. olive-green (R.) .. .. .. 2·50 5·00
a. No accent £250 £275
62 10d. turquoise-blue .. .. .. 10·00 28·00
63 1s. bistre-brown .. .. 7·00 9·00
a. No accent £5000 £6000
b. Accent inserted by hand £600 £650
64 **109** 2s. 6d. chocolate-brown .. .. .. 32·00 45·00
a. Major Re-entry £800 £900
b. No accent £350 £400
c. Accent reversed £350 £400
65 5s. rose-red .. .. 55·00 90·00
a. No accent £450 £500
b. Accent reversed £500 £550
66 10s. dull grey-blue £140 £200
a. No accent £2000 £2500
b. Accent reversed £2750 £3500
52/66 .. .. *Set of* 15 £225 £350

The accents inserted by hand are in dull black. The reversed accents are grave (thus "à") instead of acute ("á"). A variety with "S" of "Saorstat" directly over "é" of "éireann", instead of to left, may be found in all values except the 2½d. and 4d. In the 2s. 6d., 5s. and 10s. it is very slightly to the left in the "S" over "é" variety, bringing the "á" of "Saorstat" directly above the last "n" of "éireann".

(*b*) *Optd with T* **5**, *in dull or shiny blue-black, by Harrison, for use in horiz or vert coils* (7.3.23)

67 ½d. green .. .. 1·50 9·00
a. Long "1" in "1922" .. .. .. 20·00 45·00
68 1d. scarlet .. .. 2·75 7·50
a. Long "1" in "1922" .. .. .. 65·00 £120
69 1½d. red-brown .. .. 7·00 30·00
a. Long "1" in "1922" .. .. .. 75·00 £190
70 2d. orange (Die II) .. .. .. 3·00 7·50
a. Long "1" in "1922" .. .. .. 17·00 38·00
67/70 .. .. *Set of* 4 13·00 48·00

In the Harrison overprint the characters are rather bolder than those of the Thom overprint, and the foot of the "1" of "1922" is usually rounded instead of square. The long "1" in "1922" has a serif at foot. The second "e" of "éireann" appears to be slightly raised.

PRINTERS. The following and all subsequent issues to No. 148 were printed at the Government Printing Works, Dublin, *unless otherwise stated.*

6 "Sword of Light" 7 Map of Ireland 8 Arms of Ireland

9 Celtic Cross 10

(Des J. J. O'Reilly, T **6**; J. Ingram, T **7**; Miss M. Girling, T **8**; and Miss L. Williams, T **9**. Typo. Plates made by Royal Mint, London)

1922 (6 Dec)–**34.** W **10.** *P* 15 × 14.

71 **6** ½d. bright green (20.4.23) 40 20
a. Imperf × perf 14, wmk sideways (11.34) .. .. 27·00 42·00
72 **7** 1d. carmine (23.2.23) 30 10
a. Perf 15 × imperf (single perf) (1933) 80·00 £130
c. Perf 15 × imperf (7.34) .. .. 17·00 35·00
d. Booklet pane. Three stamps plus three printed labels (21.8.31) .. £180
73 1½d. claret (2.2.23) .. .. .. 1·25 1·75
74 2d. grey-green (6.12.22) 35 10
a. Imperf × perf 14, wmk sideways (11.34) .. .. 48·00 70·00
b. Perf 15 × imperf (1934) £8500 £1500
75 **8** 2½d. red-brown (7.9.23) .. .. .. 2·50 2·75
76 **9** 3d. ultramarine (16.3.23) .. .. 1·00 75
77 **8** 4d. slate-blue (28.9.23) .. .. 2·00 3·25
78 **6** 5d. deep violet (11.5.23) .. .. 9·00 9·00
79 6d. claret (21.12.23) .. .. .. 3·50 3·50
80 **8** 9d. deep violet (26.10.23) .. .. 14·00 13·00
81 **9** 10d. brown (11.5.23) .. .. .. 8·50 17·00
82 **6** 1s. light blue (15.6.23) .. .. .. 26·00 4·00
71/82 .. .. *Set of* 12 60·00 50·00

No. 72a is imperf vertically except for a single perf at each top corner. It was issued for use in automatic machines.

See also Nos. 111/22 and 227/8.

Saorstát Éireann 1922

(11 Narrow Date) 12 Daniel O'Connell

1925 (Aug)–**28.** *T* **109** *of Great Britain* (*Bradbury, Wilkinson printing*) *optd at the Government Printing Works, Dublin or by Harrison and Sons.* (*a*) *With T* **11** *in black or grey-black* (25.8.25).

83 2s. 6d. chocolate-brown .. .. .. 32·00 55·00
a. Wide and narrow date (pair) (1927) .. £250
84 5s. rose-red .. .. 50·00 80·00
a. Wide and narrow date (pair) (1927) .. £400
85 10s. dull grey-blue £100 £180
a. Wide and narrow date (pair) (1927) .. £1100
83/5 .. .. *Set of* 3 £160 £275

The varieties with wide and narrow date *se-tenant* are from what is known as the "composite setting," in which some stamps showed the wide date, as T **5**, while in others the figures were close together, as in T **11**.

Single specimens of this printing with wide date may be distinguished from Nos. 64 to 66 by the colour of the ink, which is black or grey-black in the composite setting and blue-black in the Thom printing.

The type of the "composite" overprint usually shows distinct signs of wear.

(*b*) *As T* **5** (*wide date*) *in black* (1927–28)

86 2s. 6d. chocolate-brown (9.12.27) .. .. 35·00 40·00
a. Circumflex accent over "a" £200 £250
b. No accent over "a" £300 £350
c. Flat accent on "a" £300 £350
87 5s. rose-red (2.28) .. .. .. 55·00 80·00
a. Circumflex accent over "a" £300 £350
c. Flat accent on "a" £350 £400
88 10s. dull grey-blue (15.2.28) £140 £140
a. Circumflex accent over "a" £800 £900
c. Flat accent on "a" £900 £1000
86/8 .. .. *Set of* 3 £200 £225

This printing can be distinguished from the Thom overprints in dull black, by the clear, heavy impression (in deep black) which often shows in relief on the back of the stamp.

The variety showing a circumflex accent over the "a" occurred on R.9/2. The overprint in this position finally deteriorated to such an extent that some examples of the 2s. 6d. were without accent (No. 86b). A new cliché was then introduced with the accent virtually flat and which also showed damage to the "a" and the crossbar of the "t".

(Des L. Whelan. Typo)

1929 (22 June). *Catholic Emancipation Centenary.* **W10.** *P* 15 × 14.

89 **12** 2d. grey-green 40 20
90 3d. blue .. .. 4·00 7·00
91 9d. bright violet .. .. 4·00 3·75
89/91 .. .. *Set of* 3 7·50 10·00

13 Shannon Barrage 14 Reaper

(Des E. L. Lawrenson. Typo)

1930 (15 Oct). *Completion of Shannon Hydro-Electric Scheme.* W **10.** *P* 15 × 14.

92 **13** 2d. agate 50 15

(T **14** and **15** des G. Atkinson. Typo)

1931 (12 June). *Bicentenary of the Royal Dublin Society.* **W 10.** *P* 15 × 14.

93 **14** 2d. blue 40 15

15 The Cross of Cong 16 Adoration of the Cross 17 Hurler

1932 (12 May). *International Eucharistic Congress.* **W 10.** *P* 15 × 14.

94 **15** 2d. grey-green 50 25
95 3d. blue .. .. 2·00 5·00

(T **16** to **19** des R. J. King. Typo)

1933 (18 Sept). *"Holy Year".* **W 10.** *P* 15 × 14.

96 **16** 2d. grey-green 40 15
97 3d. blue .. .. 2·00 2·00

1934 (27 July). *Golden Jubilee of the Gaelic Athletic Association.* **W 10.** *P* 15 × 14.

98 **17** 2d. green 55 15

1935 (Mar–July). *T* **109** *of Great Britain* (*Waterlow printings*) *optd as T* **5** (*wide date*), *at the Government Printing Works, Dublin.*

99 **109** 2s. 6d. chocolate (No. 450) .. .. 45·00 48·00
a. Flat accent on "a" (R. 9/2) £200 £200
100 5s. bright rose-red (No. 451) .. .. 80·00 80·00
a. Flat accent on "a" (R. 9/2) £275 £250
101 10s. indigo (No. 452) £350 £350
a. Flat accent on "a" (R. 9/2) £800 £650
99/101 .. .. *Set of* 3 £425 £425

18 St. Patrick

19 Ireland and New Constitution

1937 (8 Sept). *W* **10**. *P* 14 × 15.
102 **18** 2s. 6d. emerald-green .. .. £120 55·00
103 5s. maroon £150 £100
104 10s. deep blue .. .. £120 50·00
102/4 .. .. *Set of* 3 £350 £180
See also Nos. 123/5.

EIRE

29 December 1937—17 April 1949

1937 (29 Dec). *Constitution Day. W* **10**. *P* 15 × 14.
105 **19** 2d. claret 50 20
106 3d. blue .. .. 3·75 2·75
For similar stamps see Nos. 176/7.

20 Father Mathew

(Des S. Keating. Typo)

1938 (1 July). *Centenary of Temperance Crusade. W* **10**. *P* 15 × 14.
107 **20** 2d. black 80 25
108 3d. blue .. .. 6·00 6·00

21 George Washington, American Eagle and Irish Harp

22

(Des G. Atkinson. Typo)

1939 (1 Mar). *150th Anniv of U.S. Constitution and Installation of First U.S. President. W* **10**. *P* 15 × 14.
109 **21** 2d. scarlet 75 40
110 3d. blue .. .. 4·00 3·75

SIZE OF WATERMARK. T **22** can be found in various sizes from about 8 to 10 mm high. This is due to the use of two different dandy rolls supplied by different firms and to the effects of paper shrinkage and other factors such as pressure and machine speed.

White line above left value tablet joining horizontal line to ornament (R. 3/7)

1940–68. *Typo. W* **22**. *P* 15 × 14 *or* 14 × 15 (2*s.* 6*d. to* 10*s.*).
111 **6** ½d. bright green (24.11.40) .. .. 1·25 40
112 **7** 1d. carmine (26.10.40) 30 10
a. From coils. Perf 14×imperf (9.40) 50·00 55·00
b. From coils. Perf 15×imperf (20.3.46) .. .. 27·00 13·00
c. Booklet pane. Three stamps plus three printed labels £650
113 1½d. claret (1.40) .. .. .. 7·00 25
114 2d. grey-green (1.40) 30 10
115 **8** 2½d. red-brown (3.41) .. .. .. 7·00 10
116 **9** 3d. blue (12.40) 40 10
117 **8** 4d. slate-blue (12.40) 40 10
118 **6** 5d. deep violet (7.40) 50 10
119 6d. claret (3.42) 65 15
aa. Chalky paper (1967) 85 20
119*a* 8d. scarlet (12.9.49) 70 50
120 **8** 9d. deep violet (7.40) 90 45
121 **9** 10d. brown (7.40) 60 35
121*a* 11d. rose (12.9.49) .. .. .. 80 1·00
122 **6** 1s. light blue (6.40) .. .. .. 85·00 10·00
123 **18** 2s. 6d. emerald-green (10.2.43) .. 28·00 1·25
a. Chalky paper (1968?) .. .. 1·50 2·00
124 5s. maroon (15.12.42) .. .. .. 26·00 2·00
a. Line flaw .. .. 32·00
b. Chalky paper (1968?) .. .. 3·50 2·75
ba. Purple .. .. 3·00 2·75
125 10s. deep blue (7.45) .. .. .. 55·00 5·00
a. Chalky paper (1968) .. .. 8·00 7·50
ab. Blue .. .. 7·00 7·50
111/25 .. .. *Set of* 17 £100 19·00
There is a wide range of shades and also variation in paper used in this issue.
See also Nos. 227/8.

1941
i gcuimne
aiséirge
1916

(**23** *Trans* "In memory of the rising of 1916")

24 Volunteer and G.P.O., Dublin

1941 (12 Apr). *25th Anniv of Easter Rising* (1916). *Provisional issue. T* **7** *and* **9** (2*d. in new colour*), *optd with T* **23**.
126 **7** 2d. orange (G.) .. .. 1·40 20
127 **9** 3d. blue (V.) .. .. 35·00 7·00

(Des V. Brown. Typo)

1941 (27 Oct). *25th Anniv of Easter Rising* (1916). *Definitive issue. W* **22**. *P* 15 × 14.
128 **24** 2½d. blue-black 50 15

25 Dr. Douglas Hyde

26 Sir William Rowan Hamilton

27 Bro. Michael O'Clery

(Des S. O'Sullivan. Typo)

1943 (31 July). *50th Anniv of Founding of Gaelic League. W* **22**. *P* 15 × 14.
129 **25** ½d. green 35 20
130 2½d. claret 40 10

(Des S. O'Sullivan from a bust by Hogan. Typo)

1943 (13 Nov). *Centenary of Announcement of Discovery of Quaternions. W* **22**. *P* 15 × 14.
131 **26** ½d. green 40 25
132 2½d. brown 40 10

(Des R. J. King. Typo)

1944 (30 June). *Tercentenary of Death of Michael O'Clery. (Commemorating the "Annals of the Four Masters"). W* **22** (*sideways*). *P* 14 × 15.
133 **27** ½d. emerald-green 10 10
134 1s. red-brown 30 10
Although issued as commemoratives these two stamps were kept in use as part of the current issue, replacing Nos. 111 and 122.

28 Edmund Ignatius Rice

29 "Youth Sowing Seeds of Freedom"

(Des S. O'Sullivan. Typo)

1944 (29 Aug). *Death Centenary of Edmund Rice (founder of Irish Christian Brothers). W* **22**. *P* 15 × 14.
135 **28** 2½d. slate 35 15

(Des R. J. King. Typo)

1945 (15 Sept). *Centenary of Death of Thomas Davis (founder of Young Ireland Movement). W* **22**. *P* 15 × 14.
136 **29** 2½d. blue 50 15
137 6d. claret .. .. 6·00 3·75

30 "Country and Homestead"

(Des R. J. King. Typo)

1946 (16 Sept). *Birth Centenaries of Davitt and Parnell (land reformers). W* **22**. *P* 15 × 14.
138 **30** 2½d. scarlet 50 15
139 3d. blue .. .. 2·25 2·50

31 Angel Victor over Rock of Cashel

(Des R. J. King. Recess Waterlow (1d. to 1s. 3d. until 1961), D.L.R. (8d., 1s. 3d. from 1961 and 1s. 5d.))

1948 (7 Apr)–**65**. *Air. T* **31** *and similar horiz designs. W* **22**. *P* 15 (1*s.* 5*d.*) *or* 15 × 14 (*others*).
140 **31** 1d. chocolate (4.4.49) .. .. .. 2·25 2·75
141 – 3d. blue .. .. 3·50 2·00
142 – 6d. magenta .. .. 1·00 70
142*a* – 8d. lake-brown (13.12.54) .. .. 4·00 3·00
143 – 1s. green (4.4.49) .. .. .. 1·50 70
143*a* **31** 1s. 3d. red-orange (13.12.54) .. .. 4·25 85
143*b* 1s. 5d. deep ultramarine (1.4.65) .. 3·50 80
140/143*b* .. .. *Set of* 7 18·00 10·00
Designs:—3d., 8d. Lough Derg; 6d. Croagh Patrick; 1s. Glendalough.

35 Theobald Wolfe Tone

(Des K. Uhlemann. Typo)

1948 (19 Nov). *150th Anniv of Insurrection. W* **22**. *P* 15 × 14.
144 **35** 2½d. reddish purple .. .. 1·00 10
145 3d. violet .. .. 3·50 3·25

REPUBLIC OF IRELAND

18 April 1949

36 Leinster House and Arms of Provinces

37 J. C. Mangan

(Des Muriel Brandt. Typo)

1949 (21 Nov). *International Recognition of Republic. W* **22**. *P* 15 × 14.
146 **36** 2½d. reddish brown 60 10
147 3d. bright blue .. .. 3·25 2·50

(Des R. J. King. Typo)

1949 (5 Dec). *Death Centenary of James Clarence Mangan (poet). W* **22**. *P* 15 × 14.
148 **37** 1d. green .. .. 1·00 15

38 Statue of St. Peter, Rome

39 Thomas Moore

40 Irish Harp

(Recess Waterlow & Sons)

1950 (11 Sept). *Holy Year. W* **22**. *P* 12½.
149 **38** 2½d. violet 50 40
150 3d. blue .. .. 8·00 8·00
151 9d. brown .. .. 8·00 9·50
149/51 .. .. *Set of* 3 15·00 16·00

PRINTERS. Nos. 152 to 200 were recess-printed by De La Rue & Co, Dublin, *unless otherwise stated.*

(Eng W. Vacek)

1952 (10 Nov). *Death Centenary of Thomas Moore (poet). W* **22**. *P* 13.
152 **39** 2½d. reddish purple 50 10
153 3½d. deep olive-green .. .. 1·00 2·75

(Des F. O'Ryan. Typo Government Printing Works, Dublin)

1953 (9 Feb). *"An Tostal" (Ireland at Home) Festival. W* **22** (*sideways*). *P* 14 × 15.
154 **40** 2½d. emerald-green 80 35
155 1s. 4d. blue .. .. 12·00 20·00

41 Robert Emmet

42 Madonna and Child (Della Robbia)

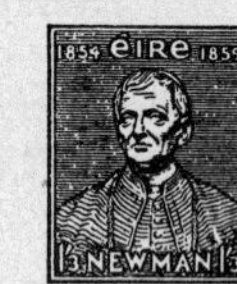
43 Cardinal Newman (first Rector)

(Eng L. Downey)

1953 (21 Sept). *150th Death Anniv of Emmet (patriot). W* **22**. *P* 13.
156 **41** 3d. deep bluish green .. .. 2·50 15
157 1s. 3d. carmine .. .. 45·00 8·00

(Eng A. R. Lane)

1954 (24 May). *Marian Year. W* **22**. *P* 15.
158 **42** 3d. blue .. .. 1·50 10
159 5d. myrtle-green .. .. 3·00 4·00

(Des L. Whelan. Typo Govt Printing Works, Dublin)

1954 (19 July). *Centenary of Founding of Catholic University of Ireland. W* **22**. *P* 15 × 14.
160 **43** 2d. bright purple .. .. 1·50 10
161 1s. 3d. blue .. .. 8·50 4·50

44 Statue of Commodore Barry **45** John Redmond **46** Thomas O'Crohan

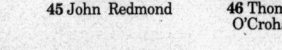

(Des and eng H. Woyty-Wimmer)

1956 (16 Sept). *Barry Commemoration. W* **22.** *P* 15.
162 **44** 3d. slate-lilac .. .. 1·00 10
163 1s. 3d. deep blue .. .. 5·00 7·00

1957 (11 June). *Birth Centenary of John Redmond (politician). W* **22.** *P* 14 × 15.
164 **45** 3d. deep blue .. .. 1·00 10
165 1s. 3d. brown-purple .. .. 6·00 8·00

1957 (1 July). *Birth Centenary of Thomas O'Crohan (author). W* **22.** *P* 14 × 15.
166 **46** 2d. maroon .. .. 1·25 10
a. Wmk sideways .. .. † —
167 5d. violet .. .. 1·25 5·00

47 Admiral Brown **48** "Father Wadding" (Ribera) **49** Tom Clarke

(Des S. O'Sullivan. Typo Govt Printing Works, Dublin)

1957 (23 Sept). *Death Centenary of Admiral William Brown. W* **22.** *P* 15 × 14.
168 **47** 3d. blue .. .. 2·00 20
169 1s. 3d. carmine .. .. 28·00 12·00

1957 (25 Nov). *300th Death Anniv of Father Luke Wadding (theologian). W* **22.** *P* 15.
170 **48** 3d. deep blue .. .. 1·50 10
171 1s. 3d. lake .. .. 10·50 6·50

1958 (28 July). *Birth Centenary of Thomas J. ("Tom") Clarke (patriot). W* **22.** *P* 15.
172 **49** 3d. deep green .. .. 1·75 10
173 1s. 3d. red-brown .. .. 5·25 11·00

50 Mother Mary Aikenhead **51** Arthur Guinness

(Eng Waterlow. Recess Imprimerie Belge de Securité, Brussels subsidiary of Waterlow & Sons)

1958 (20 Oct). *Death Centenary of Mother Mary Aikenhead (foundress of Irish Sisters of Charity). W* **22.** *P* 15 × 14.
174 **50** 3d. Prussian blue .. .. 1·00 10
175 1s. 3d. rose-carmine .. .. 11·00 8·50

(Typo Govt Printing Works, Dublin)

1958 (29 Dec). *21st Anniv of the Irish Constitution.* **W22.** *P* 15 × 14.
176 **19** 3d. brown 50 10
177 5d. emerald-green .. .. 1·25 4·00

1959 (20 July). *Bicentenary of Guinness Brewery. W* **22.** *P* 15.
178 **51** 3d. brown-purple .. .. 2·50 10
179 1s. 3d. blue .. .. 7·50 8·50

52 "The Flight of the Holy Family"

(Des K. Uhlemann)

1960 (20 June). *World Refugee Year. W* **22.** *P* 15.
180 **52** 3d. purple 25 10
181 1s. 3d. sepia .. .. 45 2·50

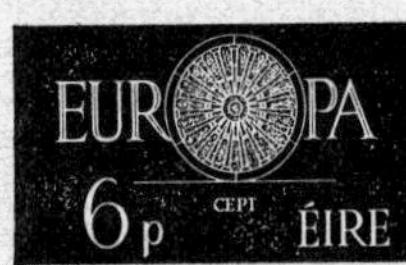

53 Conference Emblem

(Des P. Rahikainen)

1960 (19 Sept). *Europa. W* **22.** *P* 15.
182 **53** 6d. light brown .. .. 2·00 1·00
183 1s. 3d. violet .. .. 6·50 11·00
The ink of No. 183 is fugitive.

54 Dublin Airport, De Havilland "Dragon" and Boeing "720" jet aircraft **55** St. Patrick

(Des J. Flanagan and D. R. Lowther)

1961 (26 June). *25th Anniv of Aer Lingus. W* **22.** *P* 15.
184 **54** 6d. blue .. .. 75 2·50
185 1s. 3d. green .. .. 1·25 4·00

(Recess B.W.)

1961 (25 Sept). *Fifteenth Death Centenary of St. Patrick. W* **22.** *P* 14½.
186 **55** 3d. blue 35 10
187 8d. purple .. .. 60 1·75
188 1s. 3d. green 60 85
186/8 .. .. *Set of* 3 1·40 2·40

56 J. O'Donovan and E. O'Curry

(Recess B.W.)

1962 (26 Mar). *Death Centenaries of O'Donovan and O'Curry (scholars). W* **22.** *P* 15.
189 **56** 3d. carmine 30 10
190 1s. 3d. purple .. .. 1·25 1·50

57 Europa "Tree"

(Des L. Weyer)

1962 (17 Sept). *Europa. W* **22.** *P* 15.
191 **57** 6d. carmine-red 45 80
192 1s. 3d. turquoise 70 95

58 Campaign Emblem

(Des K. Uhlemann)

1963 (21 Mar). *Freedom from Hunger. W* **22.** *P* 15.
193 **58** 4d. deep violet 30 10
194 1s. 3d. scarlet .. .. 1·25 1·50

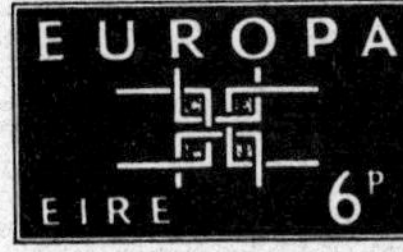

59 "Co-operation"

(Des A. Holm)

1963 (16 Sept). *Europa. W* **22.** *P* 15.
195 **59** 6d. carmine 40 50
196 1s. 3d. blue .. .. 1·00 2·00

60 Centenary Emblem

(Des P. Wildbur. Photo Harrison & Sons)

1963 (2 Dec). *Centenary of Red Cross. W* **22.** *P* 14½ × 14.
197 **60** 4d. red and grey 30 10
198 1s. 3d. red, grey and light emerald .. 65 1·25

61 Wolfe Tone

(Des P. Wildbur)

1964 (13 Apr). *Birth Bicentenary of Wolfe Tone (revolutionary). W* **22.** *P* 15.
199 **61** 4d. black 75 10
200 1s. 3d. ultramarine .. .. 1·50 1·25

62 Irish Pavilion at Fair

(Des A. Devane. Photo Harrison & Sons)

1964 (20 July). *New York World's Fair. W* **22.** *P* 14½ × 14.
201 **62** 5d. blue-grey, brown, violet & yellow-ol 40 10
a. Brown omitted* £1000
202 1s. 5d. blue-grey, brown, turquoise-blue and light yellow-green .. .. .. 85 1·50
*No. 201a comes from the top row of a sheet and shows part of the brown cross which would appear in the sheet margin. As the second horizontal row was normal it would appear that the brown cylinder was incorrectly registered.

63 Europa "Flower" **64** "Waves of Communication"

(Des G. Bétemps. Photo Harrison)

1964 (14 Sept). *Europa. W* **22** *(sideways). P* 14 × 14½.
203 **63** 8d. olive-green and blue 85 75
204 1s. 5d. red-brown and orange .. .. 1·60 2·00

(Des P. Wildbur. Photo Harrison)

1965 (17 May). *I.T.U. Centenary. W* **22.** *P* 14½ × 14.
205 **64** 3d. blue and green 30 10
206 8d. black and green .. .. .. 70 1·25

PRINTERS. Nos. 207 onwards were photogravure-printed by the Stamping Branch of the Revenue Commissioners, Dublin *unless otherwise stated.*

65 W. B. Yeats (poet) **66** I.C.Y. Emblem

(Des R. Kyne, from drawing by S. O'Sullivan)

1965 (14 June). *Yeats' Birth Centenary. W* **22** *(sideways). P* 15.
207 **65** 5d. black, orange-brown and deep green 60 10
208 1s. 5d. black, grey-green and brown .. 1·50 1·50

1965 (16 Aug). *International Co-operation Year. W* **22.** *P* 15.
209 **66** 3d. ultramarine and new blue 50 10
210 10d. deep brown and brown .. .. 1·00 3·00

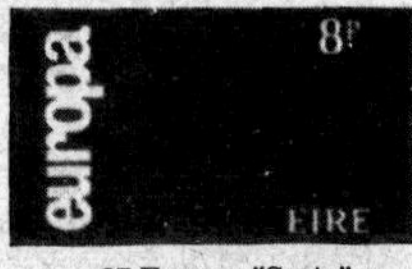

67 Europa "Sprig"

(Des H. Karlsson)

1965 (27 Sept). *Europa. W* **22.** *P* 15.
211 **67** 8d. black and brown-red 75 75
212 1s. 5d. purple and light turquoise-blue 1·25 1·50

MINIMUM PRICE

The minimum price quote is 10p which represents a handling charge rather than a basis for valuing common stamps. For further notes about prices see introductory pages.

68 James Connolly

69 "Marching to Freedom"

(Des E. Delaney (No. 216), R. Kyne, after portraits by S. O'Sullivan (others))

1966 (12 Apr). *50th Anniv of Easter Rising. T* **68/9** *and similar horiz portraits. W* **22.** *P* 15.

213		3d. black and greenish blue	20	10
		a. Horiz pair. Nos. 213/14	50	1·75
214		3d. black and bronze-green	20	10
215		5d. black and yellow-olive	20	10
		a. Horiz pair. Nos. 215/16	50	1·75
216		5d. black, orange and blue-green	20	10
217		7d. black and light orange-brown	55	2·00
		a. Horiz pair. Nos. 217/18	1·50	10·00
218		7d. black and blue-green	55	2·00
219		1s. 5d. black and turquoise	55	1·50
		a. Horiz pair. Nos. 219/20	2·00	10·00
220		1s. 5d. black and bright green	55	1·50
213/20		*Set of* 8	4·00	6·50

Designs:—No. 213, Type **68**; No. 214, Thomas J. Clarke; No. 215, P. H. Pearse; No. 216, Type **69**; No. 217, Eamonn Ceannt; No. 218, Sean MacDiarmada; No. 219, Thomas MacDonagh; No. 220, Joseph Plunkett.

Nos. 213/14, 215/16, 217/18 and 219/20 were each printed together, *se-tenant*, in horizontal pairs throughout the sheet.

76 R. Casement

77 Europa "Ship"

(Des R. Kyne)

1966 (3 Aug). *50th Death Anniv of Roger Casement (patriot). W* **22** *(sideways). P* 15.

221	**76**	5d. black	10	10
222		1s. red-brown	10	35

(Des R. Kyne, after G. and J. Bender)

1966 (26 Sept). *Europa. W* **22** *(sideways). P* 15.

223	**77**	7d. emerald and orange	30	35
224		1s. 5d. emerald and light grey	50	90

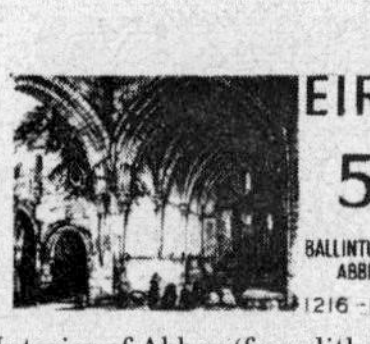

78 Interior of Abbey (from lithograph)

79 Cogwheels

1966 (8 Nov). *750th Anniv of Ballintubber Abbey. W* **22.** *P* 15.

225	**78**	5d. red-brown	10	10
226		1s. black	10	25

1966–67. *As Nos.* 116, 118 *but photo. Smaller design (17 × 21 mm). Chalk-surfaced paper. W* **22.** *P* 15.

227	**9**	3d. blue (1.8.67)	50	15
228	**6**	5d. bright violet (1.12.66)	30	15

No. 228 was only issued in booklets at first but was released in sheets on 1.4.68 in a slightly brighter shade. In the sheet stamps the lines of shading are more regular.

(Des O. Bonnevalle)

1967 (2 May). *Europa. W* **22** *(sideways). P* 15.

229	**79**	7d. light emerald, gold and pale cream	25	30
230		1s. 5d. carmine-red, gold and pale cream	35	55

80 Maple Leaves

(Des P. Hickey)

1967 (28 Aug). *Canadian Centennial. W* **22.** *P* 15.

231	**80**	5d. multicoloured	10	10
232		1s. 5d. multicoloured	10	35

81 Rock of Cashel (from photo by Edwin Smith)

1967 (25 Sept). *International Tourist Year. W* **22** *(inverted). P* 15.

233	**81**	7d. sepia	10	15
234		10d. slate-blue	10	30

82 1 c. Fenian Stamp Essay

83 24 c. Fenian Stamp Essay

1967 (23 Oct). *Centenary of Fenian Rising. W* **22** *(sideways). P* 15.

235	**82**	5d. black and light green	10	10
236	**83**	1s. black and light pink	10	25

84 Jonathan Swift

85 Gulliver and Lilliputians

(Des M. Byrne)

1967 (30 Nov). *300th Birth Anniv of Jonathan Swift. W* **22** *(sideways). P* 15.

237	**84**	3d. black and olive-grey	10	10
238	**85**	1s. 5d. blackish brown and pale blue	10	15

86 Europa "Key"

(Des H. Schwarzenbach and M. Biggs)

1968 (29 Apr). *Europa. W* **22.** *P* 15.

239	**86**	7d. brown-red, gold and brown	15	40
240		1s. 5d. new blue, gold and brown	25	70

87 St Mary's Cathedral, Limerick

(Des from photo by J. J. Bambury. Recess B.W.)

1968 (26 Aug). *800th Anniv of St. Mary's Cathedral, Limerick. W* **22.** *P* 15.

241	**87**	5d. Prussian blue	10	10
242		10d. yellow-green	10	25

88 Countess Markievicz

89 James Connolly

1968 (23 Sept). *Birth Centenary of Countess Markievicz (patriot). W* **22.** *P* 15.

243	**88**	3d. black	10	10
244		1s. 5d. deep blue and blue	10	15

1968 (23 Sept). *Birth Centenary of James Connolly (patriot). W* **22** *(sideways). P* 15.

245	**89**	6d. deep brown and chocolate	10	20
246		1s. blksh grn, apple-grn & myrtle-grn	10	10

90 Stylised Dog (brooch)

91 Stag

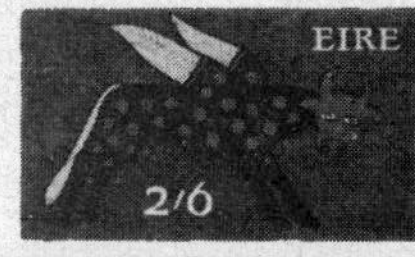

92 Winged Ox (Symbol of St. Luke)

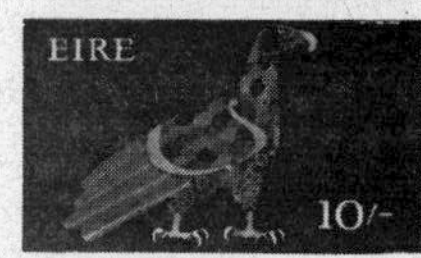

93 Eagle (Symbol of St. John The Evangelist)

(Des H. Gerl)

1968–70. *Pence values expressed with "p". W* **22** *(sideways on ½d. to 1s. 9d.). P* 15.

247	**90**	½d. red-orange (7.6.69)	10	25
248		1d. pale yellow-green (7.6.69)	15	10
		a. Coil stamp. Perf 14 × 15 (8.70?)	90	3·00
249		2d. light ochre (14.10.68)	20	10
		a. Coil stamp. Perf 14 × 15 (8.70?)	90	3·50
250		3d. blue (7.6.69)	35	10
		a. Coil stamp. Perf 14 × 15 (8.70?)	90	3·50
251		4d. deep brown-red (31.3.69)	25	10
252		5d. myrtle-green (31.3.69)	30	35
253		6d. bistre-brown (24.2.69)	20	10
254	**91**	7d. brown and yellow (7.6.69)	45	2·25
255		8d. chocolate & orange-brown (14.10.68)	45	50
256		9d. slate-blue and olive-green (24.2.69)	50	10
257		10d. chocolate and bluish violet (31.3.69)	1·00	50
258		1s. chocolate and red-brown (31.3.69)	40	10
259		1s. 9d. black & lt turquoise-bl (24.2.69)	3·00	70
260	**92**	2s. 6d. multicoloured (14.10.68)	2·00	25
261		5s. multicoloured (24.2.69)	3·25	55
262	**93**	10s. multicoloured (14.10.68)	7·00	2·25
247/62		*Set of* 16	17·00	6·50

The 1d., 2d., 3d., 5d., 6d., 9d., 1s. and 2s. 6d. exist with PVA gum as well as gum arabic. The coil stamps exist on PVA only, and the rest on gum arabic only.

See also Nos. 287/301, 339/59 and 478/83.

94 Human Rights Emblem

95 Dail Eireann Assembly

1968 (4 Nov). *Human Rights Year. W* **22** *(sideways). P* 15.

263	**94**	5d. yellow, gold and black	10	10
264		7d. yellow, gold and red	10	25

(Des M. Byrne)

1969 (21 Jan). *50th Anniv of Dail Eireann (First National Parliament). W* **22** *(sideways). P* 15 × 14½.

265	**95**	6d. myrtle-green	10	10
266		9d. Prussian blue	10	20

96 Colonnade

97 Quadruple I.L.O. Emblems

(Des L. Gasbarra and G. Belli; adapted Myra Maguire)

1969 (28 Apr). *Europa. W* **22.** *P* 15.

267	**96**	9d. grey, ochre and ultramarine	30	60
268		1s. 9d. grey, gold and scarlet	40	80

(Des K. C. Dābczewski)

1969 (14 July). *50th Anniv of International Labour Organization. W* **22** *(sideways). P* 15.

269	**97**	6d. black and grey	10	10
270		9d. black and yellow	10	15

98 "The Last Supper and Crucifixion" (Evie Hone Window, Eton Chapel)

(Des R. Kyne)

1969 (1 Sept). *Contemporary Irish Art* (*1st issue*). *W* **22** (*sideways*). *P* 15 × 14½.
271 **98** 1s. multicoloured 15 70

See also Nos. 280, 306, 317, 329, 362, 375, 398, 408, 452, 470 and 498.

99 Mahatma Gandhi

1969 (2 Oct). *Birth Centenary of Mahatma Gandhi*. *W* **22**. *P* 15.
272 **99** 6d. black and green 15 10
273 1s. 9d. black and yellow 25 65

100 Symbolic Bird in Tree

(Des D. Harrington)

1970 (23 Feb). *European Conservation Year*. *W* **22**. *P* 15.
274 **100** 6d. bistre and black 10 10
275 9d. slate-violet and black 10 50

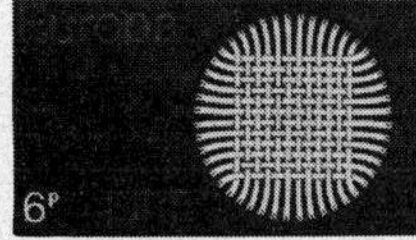

101 "Flaming Sun"

(Des L. le Brocquy)

1970 (4 May). *Europa*. *W* **22**. *P* 15.
276 **101** 6d. bright violet and silver 20 10
277 9d. brown and silver 35 70
278 1s. 9d. deep olive-grey and silver .. 75 1·10
276/8 .. .. *Set of* 3 1·10 1·75

102 "Sailing Boats" (Peter Monamy)

103 "Madonna of Eire" (Mainie Jellett)

(Des P. Wildbur and P. Scott)

1970 (13 July). *250th Anniv of Royal Cork Yacht Club*. *W* **22**. *P* 15.
279 **102** 4d. multicoloured 10 10

1970 (1 Sept). *Contemporary Irish Art* (*2nd issue*). *W* **22** (*sideways*). *P* 15.
280 **103** 1s. multicoloured 10 20

104 Thomas MacCurtain

106 Kevin Barry

(Des P. Wildbur)

1970 (26 Oct). *50th Death Anniversaries of Irish Patriots*. *T* **104** *and similar vert design*. *W* **22** (*sideways*). *P* 15.
281 9d. black, bluish violet and greyish black .. 35 25
a. Pair. Nos. 281/2 .. .. 1·25 2·00
282 9d. black, bluish violet and greyish black .. 35 25
283 2s. 9d. black, new blue and greyish black .. 85 1·50
a. Pair. Nos. 283/4 .. .. 4·50 13·00
284 2s. 9d. black, new blue and greyish black .. 85 1·50
281/4 .. .. *Set of* 4 5·25 3·25

Designs:—Nos. 281 and 283, Type **104**; others, Terence MacSwiney.

Nos. 281/2 and 283/4 were each printed together, *se-tenant*, in horizontal and vertical pairs throughout the sheet.

(Des P. Wildbur)

1970 (2 Nov). *50th Death Anniv of Kevin Barry* (*patriot*). *W* **22** (*inverted*). *P* 15.
285 **106** 6d. olive-green 10 10
286 1s. 2d. royal blue 15 70

106a Stylized Dog (Brooch)

107 "Europa Chain"

Two types of 10 p.:
I. Outline and markings of the ox in lilac.
II. Outline and markings in brown.

1971 (15 Feb)–**75**. *Decimal Currency. Designs as Nos.* 247/62 *but with* "p" *omitted as in T* **106a**. *W* **22** (*sideways on* 10, 12, 20 *and* 50 *p.*). *P* 15.
287 **106a** ½p. bright green 10 10
a. Wmk sideways .. .. 7·00 10·00
ab. Booklet pane of 6 .. .. 40·00
288 1p. blue 60 10
a. Coil stamp. Perf 14×14½ .. 75 50
b. Coil strip. Nos. 288a, 289a and 291a *se-tenant* .. .. 2·00
c. Wmk sideways 35 40
ca. Booklet pane of 6 .. .. 2·00
cb. Booklet pane. No. 288c×5 plus one *se-tenant* label (11.3.74) .. 2·00
289 1½p. lake-brown 20 15
a. Coil stamp. Perf 14×14½ .. 40 40
b. Coil strip. Nos. 289a, 291a, 294a and 290a *se-tenant* (24.2.72) .. 2·00
c. Coil strip. Nos. 289a×2, 290a and 295ab *se-tenant* (29.1.74) 2·00
290 2p. myrtle-green 20 10
a. Coil stamp. Perf 14×14½ (24.2.72) 40 40
b. Wmk sideways (27.1.75) .. 45 50
ba. Booklet pane. No. 290b×5 plus one *se-tenant* label (27.1.75) .. 2·25
291 2½p. sepia 25 10
a. Coil stamp. Perf 14×14½ (20.2.71) 50 50
b. Wmk sideways .. .. 1·50 2·25
ba. Booklet pane of 6 .. .. 2·50
292 3p. cinnamon 15 10
293 3½p. orange-brown 15 10
294 4p. pale bluish violet 15 10
a. Coil stamp. Perf 14×14½ (24.2.72) .. .. .. 1·25 60
295 **91** 5p. brown and yellow-olive .. 70 20
295*a* **106a** 5p. bright yellow-green (29.1.74) .. 2·25 45
ab. Coil stamp. Perf 14×14½ (29.1.74) .. .. .. 1·25 90
ac. Wmk sideways (11.3.74) .. 70 85
ad. Booklet pane. No. 295ac×5 plus one *se-tenant* label (11.3.74) .. 3·50
ae. Booklet pane. No. 295ac×6 (11.3.74) .. .. .. 13·00
296 **91** 6p. blackish brown and slate .. 3·00 30
296*a* 7p. indigo and olive-green (29.1.74) 4·75 1·00
297 7½p. chocolate and reddish lilac .. 50 20
298 9p. black and turquoise-green .. 1·50 35
299 **92** 10p. multicoloured (I) .. .. 14·00 7·00
299*a* 10p. multicoloured (II) .. .. 10·00 70
299*b* 12p. multicoloured (29.1.74) .. 1·50 45
300 20p. multicoloured .. .. .. 2·00 10
301 **93** 50p. multicoloured .. .. .. 4·00 65
287/301 .. .. *Set of* 18 26·00 4·50

The ½, 1, 2, 2½p. and 5 p. (No. 295*a*) with watermark sideways all come from stamp booklets and exist with one or two sides imperforate.

See also Nos. 339/59 and 478/83.

(Des H. Haflidason; adapted P. Wildbur)

1971 (3 May). *Europa*. *W* **22** (*sideways*). *P* 15.
302 **107** 4p. sepia and olive-yellow 25 10
303 6p. black and new blue .. .. .. 1·25 1·50

108 J. M. Synge

109 "An Island Man" (Jack B. Yeats)

(Des R. Kyne from a portrait by Jack B. Yeats)

1971 (19 July). *Birth Centenary of J. M. Synge* (*playwright*). *W* **22**. *P* 15.
304 **108** 4p. multicoloured 15 10
305 10p. multicoloured 25 70

(Des P. Wildbur)

1971 (30 Aug). *Contemporary Irish Art* (*3rd issue*). *Birth Centenary of J. B. Yeats* (*artist*). *W* **22**. *P* 15.
306 **109** 6p. multicoloured 45 55

110 Racial Harmony Symbol

111 "Madonna and Child" (statue by J. Hughes)

(Des P. Wildbur. Litho Harrison)

1971 (18 Oct). *Racial Equality Year*. *No wmk*. *P* 14 × 14½.
307 **110** 4p. red 20 10
308 10p. black 50 75

(Des R. Kyne)

1971 (15 Nov). *Christmas*. *W* **22**. *P* 15.
309 **111** 2½p. black, gold and deep bluish green 10 10
310 6p. black, gold and ultramarine .. 35 65

112 Heart

(Des L. le Brocquy)

1972 (7 Apr). *World Health Day*. *W* **22** (*sideways*). *P* 15.
311 **112** 2½p. gold and brown 30 15
312 12p. silver and grey .. .. .. 80 1·75

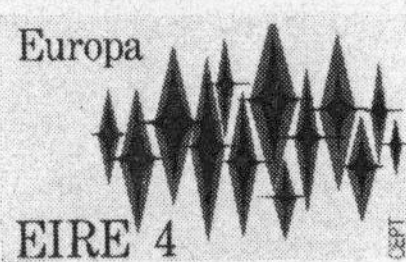

113 "Communications"

(Des P. Huovinen and P. Wildbur)

1972 (1 May). *Europa*. *W* **22** (*sideways*). *P* 15.
313 **113** 4p. orange, black and silver .. .. 1·00 15
314 6p. blue, black and silver .. .. 1·50 2·75

114 Dove and Moon

115 "Black Lake" (Gerard Dillon)

(Des P. Scott)

1972 (1 June). *The Patriot Dead*, 1922–23. *W* **22**. *P* 15.
315 **114** 4p. grey-blue, light orange & deep blue 10 10
316 6p. dp yellow-grn, lemon & dp dull grn 25 40

(Des P. Wildbur)

1972 (10 July). *Contemporary Irish Art* (*4th issue*). *W* **22** (*sideways*). *P* 15.
317 **115** 3p. multicoloured 25 30

116 "Horseman" (Carved Slab)

117 Madonna and Child (from Book of Kells)

(Des P. Scott)

1972 (28 Aug). *50th Anniv of Olympic Council of Ireland. W* **22.** *P* 15.

318	**116**	3p. bright yellow, black and gold	10	10
319		6p. salmon, black and gold	20	45

WATERMARK. All issues from here onwards are on unwatermarked paper.

(Des P. Scott)

1972 (16 Oct). *Christmas. P* 15.

320	**117**	2½p. multicoloured (*shades*)	10	10
321		4p. multicoloured	20	10
322		12p. multicoloured	45	65
320/2		.. .. *Set of* 3	65	70

118 2d. Stamp of 1922

119 Celtic Head Motif

(Des Stamping Branch of the Revenue Commissioners, Dublin)

1972 (6 Dec). *50th Anniv of the First Irish Postage Stamp. P* 15.

323	**118**	6p. light grey and grey-green	30	40
MS324		72 × 104 mm. No. 323 × 4	7·00	11·00

(Des L. le Brocquy)

1973 (1 Jan). *Entry into European Communities. P* 15.

325	**119**	6p. multicoloured	40	75
326		12p. multicoloured	60	1·00

120 Europa "Posthorn"

(Des L. Anisdahl; adapted R. Kyne)

1973 (30 Apr). *Europa. P* 15.

327	**120**	4p. bright blue	35	10
328		6p. black	1·25	1·50

121 "Berlin Blues II" (W. Scott)

122 Weather Map

(Adapted by R. Scott)

1973 (9 Aug). *Contemporary Irish Art (5th issue). P* 15 × 14½.

329	**121**	5p. ultramarine and grey-black ..	30	15

(Des R. Ballagh)

1973 (4 Sept). *I.M.O./W.M.O. Centenary. P* 14½ × 15.

330	**122**	3½p. multicoloured	25	10
331		12p. multicoloured	1·00	90

123 Tractor ploughing

124 "Flight into Egypt" (Jan de Cock)

(Des P. Scott)

1973 (5 Oct). *World Ploughing Championships, Wellington Bridge. P* 15 × 14½.

332	**123**	5p. multicoloured	15	10
333		7p. multicoloured	50	50

(Des D. Kiely)

1973 (1 Nov). *Christmas. P* 15.

334	**124**	3½p. multicoloured	10	10
335		12p. multicoloured	60	80

125 Daunt Island Lightship and Ballycotton Lifeboat, 1936

126 "Edmund Burke" (statue by J. H. Foley)

(Des M. Byrne from painting by B. Gribble)

1974 (28 Mar). *150th Anniv of Royal National Lifeboat Institution. P* 15 × 14½.

336	**125**	5p. multicoloured	20	15

(Des P. Wildbur)

1974 (29 Apr). *Europa. P* 14½ × 15.

337	**126**	5p. black and pale violet-blue	30	10
338		7p. black and light emerald	1·25	1·50

Two types of 50p.:

Type I. Fine screen (Cyls 1)

Type II. Coarse screen (Cyls 2)

1974–83. *Designs as Nos. 287 etc. No wmk. P* 15.

339	**106*a***	½p. bright green (5.6.78)	10	10
340		1p. blue (14.2.75)	10	10
		a. Coil stamp. Perf 14×14½ (21.3.77)	40	40
		b. Coil strip. Nos. 340a, 341a×2 and 344a *se-tenant* (21.3.77) ..	1·40	
341		2p. myrtle-green (7.4.76)	10	10
		a. Coil stamp. Perf 14×14½ (21.3.77)	40	40
342		3p. cinnamon (14.2.75)	10	10
343		3½p. orange-brown (9.10.74) ..	4·25	4·25
344		5p. bright yellow-green (16.8.74) ..	30	10
		a. Coil stamp. Perf 14 × 14½ (21.3.77)	85	85
345	**91**	6p. blackish brn & slate (16.10.74)	2·50	1·25
346	**106*a***	6p. slate (17.6.75)	20	10
347	**91**	7p. indigo and olive-green (27.9.74)	2·00	20
348	**106*a***	7p. deep yellow-green (17.6.75) ..	35	10
		a. Booklet pane. No. 348 × 5 plus *se-tenant* label (21.3.77) ..	7·50	
349	**91**	8p. dp brown & dp orge-brn (17.6.75)	1·50	50
350	**106*a***	8p. chestnut (14.7.76)	25	10
351	**91**	9p. black & turquoise-green (12.74)	2·00	20
352	**106*a***	9p. greenish slate (14.7.76) ..	25	10
352*a*		9½p. vermilion (3.12.79)	20	10
353	**92**	10p. multicoloured (II) (12.74) ..	3·50	30
354	**91**	10p. black and violet-blue (14.7.76)	1·75	10
354*a*	**106*a***	10p. deep mauve (8.6.77)	60	10
355	**91**	11p. black and rose-carmine (14.7.76)	45	10
355*a*		12p. black and bright green (8.6.77)	1·10	10
355*b*	**106*a***	12p. yellowish green (26.3.80) ..	30	10
355*c*	**91**	13p. reddish brn & red-brn (26.3.80)	35	15
356	**92**	15p. multicoloured (17.6.74) ..	1·00	30
356*a*	**106*a***	15p. ultramarine (10.7.80)	30	10
356*b*	**91**	16p. black & dull yellow-grn (10.7.80)	40	15
356*c*	**92**	17p. multicoloured (8.6.77)	90	10
357		20p. multicoloured (13.6.74) ..	1·00	10
358	**93**	50p. multicoloured (I) (12.74) ..	1·25	25
		a. Type II (1983)	1·50	1·50
359		£1 multicoloured (17.6.75) ..	1·75	25
339/59		.. .. *Set of* 29	25·00	8·00

For 18p., 19p., 22p., 24p., 26p. and 29p. values printed by lithography, see Nos. 478/83.

Stamps with one or two sides imperf come from the booklet pane.

127 "Oliver Goldsmith" (statue by J. H. Foley)

128 "Kitchen Table" (Norah McGuiness)

(Des P. Wildbur)

1974 (24 June). *Death Bicentenary of Oliver Goldsmith (writer). P* 14½ × 15.

360	**127**	3½p. black and olive-yellow	25	10
361		12p. black and bright yellowish green ..	1·00	60

(Design adapted by Norah McGuiness. Photo Harrison)

1974 (19 Aug). *Contemporary Irish Art (6th issue). P* 14 × 14½.

362	**128**	5p. multicoloured	20	10

129 Rugby Players

130 U.P.U. "Postmark"

(Design adapted from Irish Press photograph. Eng C. Slania. Recess (3½p.) or recess and photo (12p.) Harrison)

1974 (9 Sept). *Centenary of Irish Rugby Football Union. P* 14½ × 14.

363	**129**	3½p. greenish black	25	10
		a. Deep greenish blue	5·50	2·50
364		12p. multicoloured	1·50	1·50

No. 363a is from a second printing using a recut plate on which the engraving was deeper.

(Des R. Ballagh)

1974 (9 Oct). *Centenary of Universal Postal Union. P* 14½ × 15.

365	**130**	5p. light yellowish green and black ..	20	10
366		7p. light ultramarine and black ..	30	35

131 "Madonna and Child" (Bellini)

132 "Peace"

(Des P. Wildbur)

1974 (14 Nov). *Christmas. P* 14½ × 15.

367	**131**	5p. multicoloured	15	10
368		15p. multicoloured	75	55

(Des Alexandra Wejchert)

1975 (24 Mar). *International Women's Year. P* 14½ × 15.

369	**132**	8p. brt reddish purple & ultramarine ..	25	65
370		15p. ultramarine and bright green ..	40	1·10

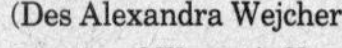

133 "Castletown Hunt" (R. Healy)

(Des R. Kyne)

1975 (28 Apr). *Europa. P* 15 × 14½.

371	**133**	7p. grey-black	40	15
372		9p. dull blue-green	1·00	1·25

134 Putting

(Des from photographs by J. McManus)

1975 (26 June). *Ninth European Amateur Golf Team Championship, Killarney. P* 15 × 14½.
373 **134** 6p. multicoloured (*shades*) 50 45
374 – 9p. multicoloured (*shades*) .. .. 1·25 1·25
The 9p. is similar to T **134** but shows a different view of the putting green.

135 "Bird of Prey" (sculpture by Oisin Kelly) **136** Nano Nagle (founder) and Waifs

(Design adapted by the artist)

1975 (28 June). *Contemporary Irish Art* (7*th issue*). *P* 15 × 14½.
375 **135** 15p. yellow-brown 45 60

(Des Kilkenny Design Workshops)

1975 (1 Sept). *Bicentenary of Presentation Order of Nuns. P* 14½ × 15.
376 **136** 5p. black and pale blue.. .. .. 15 10
377 7p. black and light stone 20 20

137 Tower of St. Anne's Church, Shandon **138** St. Oliver Plunkett (commemorative medal by Imogen Stuart)

(Des P. Scott)

1975 (6 Oct). *European Architectural Heritage Year. T* **137** *and similar vert design. P* 12½.
378 **137** 5p. blackish brown 15 10
379 6p. multicoloured 35 85
380 – 7p. steel-blue 35 10
381 – 9p. multicoloured 40 80
378/81 .. .. *Set of* 4 1·10 1·75
Design:—Nos. 380/1, Interior of Holycross Abbey, Co. Tipperary.

(Design adapted by the artist. Recess Harrison)

1975 (13 Oct). *Canonisation of Oliver Plunkett. P* 14 × 14½.
382 **138** 7p. black 10 10
383 15p. chestnut 35 45

139 "Madonna and Child" (Fra Filippo Lippi) **140** James Larkin (from a drawing by Seán O'Sullivan)

(Des P. Wildbur)

1975 (13 Nov). *Christmas. P* 15.
384 **139** 5p. multicoloured 10 10
385 7p. multicoloured 15 10
386 10p. multicoloured 30 30
384/6 .. .. *Set of* 3 50 40

(Des P. Wildbur)

1976 (21 Jan). *Birth Centenary of James Larkin* (*Trade Union leader*). *P* 14½ × 15.
387 **140** 7p. deep bluish green and pale grey .. 20 10
388 11p. sepia and yellow-ochre 50 40

141 Alexander Graham Bell **142** 1847 Benjamin Franklin Essay

(Des R. Ballagh)

1976 (10 Mar). *Telephone Centenary. P* 14½ × 15.
389 **141** 9p. multicoloured 15 10
390 15p. multicoloured 35 35

(Des L. le Brocquy; graphics by P. Wildbur. Litho Irish Security Stamp Printing Ltd)

1976 (17 May). *Bicentenary of American Revolution. T* **142** *and similar horiz designs. P* 14½ × 14.
391 7p. ultramarine, light red and silver .. 15 10
a. Silver (inscr) omitted .. .. .. † £200
392 8p. ultramarine, light red and silver .. 25 70
393 9p. violet-blue, orange and silver .. 25 10
394 15p. light rose-red, grey-blue and silver .. 30 45
a. Silver (face-value and inscr) omitted .. £500 £600
391/4 .. .. *Set of* 4 85 1·10
MS395 95 × 75 mm. Nos. 391/4 .. .. 5·00 7·00
a. Silver omitted £1200
Designs:—7p. Thirteen stars; 8p. Fifty stars; 9, 15p. Type **142**.
No. **MS**395 exists with the sheet margins overprinted in blue to commemorate "Stampa 76", the Irish National Stamp Exhibition.

143 Spirit Barrel

(Des P. Hickey)

1976 (1 July). *Europa. Irish Delft. T* **143** *and similar horiz design. Multicoloured. P* 15 × 14.
396 9p. Type **143** 25 10
397 11p. Dish 55 55

144 "The Lobster Pots, West of Ireland" (Paul Henry)

(Des R. McGrath)

1976 (30 Aug). *Contemporary Irish Art* (8*th issue*). *P* 15.
398 **144** 15p. multicoloured 40 50

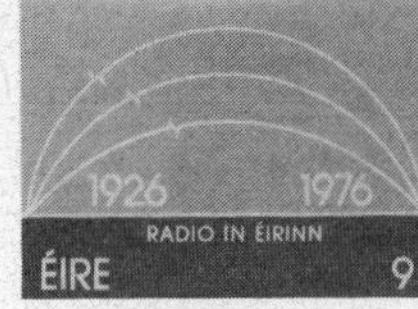

145 Radio Waves

(Des G. Shepherd and A. O'Donnell. Litho De La Rue Smurfit Ltd, Dublin)

1976 (5 Oct). *50th Anniv of Irish Broadcasting Service. T* **145** *and similar vert design. P* 14½ × 14 (9*p.*) *or* 14 × 14½ (11*p.*).
399 9p. light new blue and bottle-green 15 10
400 11p. agate, orange-red and light new blue .. 40 80
Design:—11p. Transmitter, radio waves and globe.

146 "The Nativity" (Lorenzo Monaco)

(Des R. McGrath)

1976 (11 Nov). *Christmas. P* 15 × 14½.
401 **146** 7p. multicoloured 10 10
402 9p. multicoloured 15 10
403 15p. multicoloured 40 40
401/3 .. .. *Set of* 3 55 50

147 16th Century Manuscript **148** Ballynahinch, Galway

(Des P. Hickey)

1977 (9 May). *Centenaries of National Library* (8*p.*) *and National Museum* (10*p.*). *T* **147** *and similar horiz design. Multicoloured. P* 15 × 14½.
404 8p. Type **147** 20 20
405 10p. Prehistoric stone 30 30

(Des E. van der Grijn. Litho Irish Security Stamp Printing Ltd)

1977 (27 June). *Europa. T* **148** *and similar vert design. Multicoloured. P* 14 × 15.
406 10p. Type **148** 25 20
407 12p. Lough Tay, Wicklow .. .. .. 60 1·10

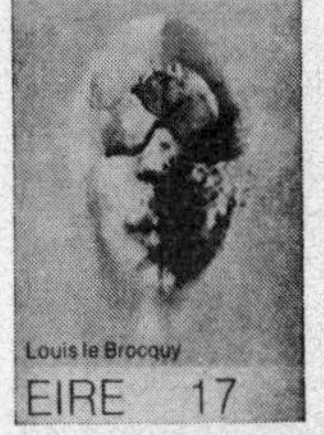

149 "Head" (Louis le Brocquy) **150** Guide and Tents

(Design adapted by the artist. Litho Irish Security Stamp Ptg Ltd)

1977 (8 Aug). *Contemporary Irish Art* (9*th issue*). *P* 14 × 14½.
408 **149** 17p. multicoloured 35 50

(Des R. Ballagh)

1977 (22 Aug). *Scouting and Guiding. T* **150** *and similar horiz design. Multicoloured. P* 15 × 14½.
409 8p. Type **150** 30 10
410 17p. Tent and Scout saluting .. .. .. 70 1·00

151 "The Shanachie" (drawing by Jack B. Yeats) **152** "Electricity" (Golden Jubilee of Electricity Supply Board)

(Des L. Miller (10p.), R. Ballagh (12p.). Litho Irish Security Stamp Printing Ltd)

1977 (12 Sept). *Anniversaries. T* **151** *and similar horiz design. P* 14 × 14½ (10*p.*) *or* 14½ × 14 (12*p.*).
411 10p. black 20 10
412 12p. black 40 80
Designs and events:—10p. Type **151** (Golden Jubilee of Irish Folklore Society); 12p. The philosopher Eriugena (1100th Death Anniv).

(Des R. Ballagh (10p.), P. Hickey (12p.), B. Blackshaw (17p.). Photo Stamping Branch of the Revenue Commissioners (12p.); Litho Irish Security Stamp Ptg Ltd (others))

1977 (10 Oct). *Golden Jubilees. T* **152** *and similar horiz designs. P* 15 × 14½ (12*p.*) *or* 15 × 14 (*others*).
413 10p. multicoloured 15 10
414 12p. multicoloured 25 70
415 17p. grey-black and grey-brown 30 60
413/15 .. .. *Set of* 3 60 1·25
Designs:—12p. Bulls (from contemporary coinage) (Jubilee of Agricultural Credit Corporation); 17p. Greyhound (Jubilee of Greyhound Track Racing).

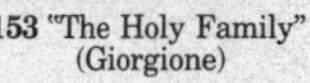

153 "The Holy Family" (Giorgione) **154** *Bremen* in Flight

(Des R. McGrath)

1977 (3 Nov). *Christmas. P* 14½ × 15.
416 **153** 8p. multicoloured 10 10
417 10p. multicoloured 15 10
418 17p. multicoloured 30 65
416/18 .. .. *Set of* 3 45 70

(Des R. Ballagh. Litho Irish Security Stamp Ptg Ltd)

1978 (13 Apr). *50th Anniv of First East–West Transatlantic Flight. P* 14 × 14½.
419 **154** 10p. bright blue and black 15 10
420 – 17p. olive-brown and black 35 50
The 17p. is as T **154**, but shows a different sky and sea.

155 Spring Gentian

156 Catherine McAuley

(Des Wendy Walsh. Litho Irish Security Stamp Ptg Ltd)

1978 (12 June). *Wild Flowers. T* **155** *and similar vert designs. Multicoloured. P* 14 × 15.
421 8p. Type **155** 20 15
422 10p. Strawberry tree 25 10
423 11p. Large-flowered Butterwort 40 50
424 17p. St. Dabeoc's Heath .. .. .. 85 1·40
421/4 .. .. *Set of* 4 1·50 1·90

(Des R. Ballagh (10p.), R. Kyne (11p.), E. van der Grijn (17p.). Litho Irish Security Stamp Ptg Ltd)

1978 (18 Sept). *Anniversaries and Events. T* **156** *and similar multicoloured designs. P* 14½ × 14 (11*p*.) *or* 14 × 14½ (*others*).
425 10p. Type **156** 15 10
426 11p. Doctor performing vaccination (*horiz*) .. 25 45
427 17p. "Self Portrait" 35 65
425/7 .. .. *Set of* 3 65 1·10
Events:—10p. Birth bicentenary of Catherine McAuley (founder of Sisters of Mercy); 11p. Global Eradication of Smallpox; 17p. Birth centenary of Sir William Orpen (painter).

157 Diagram of Drilling Rig

158 Farthing

(Des R. Ballagh. Litho Irish Security Stamp Ptg Ltd)

1978 (18 Oct). *Arrival Onshore of Natural Gas. P* 14 × 14½.
428 **157** 10p. maroon, turquoise-green and bistre 15 15

(Des P. Wildbur and R. Mercer)

1978 (26 Oct). *50th Anniv of Irish Currency. T* **158** *and similar horiz designs. P* 15 × 14½.
429 8p. black, copper and deep bluish green .. 15 15
430 10p. black, silver and blue-green 15 10
431 11p. black, copper and chocolate 25 45
432 17p. black, silver and deep blue 40 85
429/32 .. .. *Set of* 4 85 1·40
Designs:—10p. Florin; 11p. Penny; 17p. Half-crown.

159 "The Virgin and Child" (Guercino)

160 Conolly Folly, Castletown

(Des P. Wildbur)

1978 (16 Nov). *Christmas. P* 14½ × 15.
433 **159** 8p. purple-brown, gold and pale turquoise-green 15 10
434 10p. purple-brown, chocolate and pale turquoise-green 15 10
435 17p. purple-brown, deep blue-green and pale turquoise-green 30 75
433/5 .. .. *Set of* 3 55 75

(Des R. McGrath)

1978 (6 Dec). *Europa. Architecture. T* **160** *and similar horiz design. P* 15 × 14½.
436 10p. lake-brown and red-brown 20 15
437 11p. green and deep green 25 40
Design:—11p. Dromoland Belvedere.

161 Athletes in Cross-country Race

162 "European Communities" (in languages of member nations)

(Des R. Mercer. Litho Irish Security Stamp Ptg Ltd)

1979 (20 Aug). *7th World Cross-country Championships, Limerick. P* 14½ × 14.
438 **161** 8p. multicoloured 15 25

(Des P. Wildbur)

1979 (20 Aug). *First Direct Elections to European Assembly. P* 14½ × 15.
439 **162** 10p. dull turquoise-green 15 15
440 11p. reddish violet 15 25

163 Sir Rowland Hill

164 Winter Wren (*Troglodytes troglodytes*)

(Des C. Harrison. Litho Irish Security Stamp Ptg Ltd)

1979 (20 Aug). *Death Centenary of Sir Rowland Hill. P* 14 × 14½.
441 **163** 17p. black, brownish grey and red 25 40

(Des Wendy Walsh. Litho Irish Security Stamp Ptg Ltd)

1979 (30 Aug). *Birds. T* **164** *and similar horiz designs. Multicoloured. P* 14½ × 14.
442 8p. Type **164** 25 40
443 10p. Great Crested Grebe (*Podiceps cristatus*) 35 10
444 11p. White-fronted Goose (*Anser albifrons flavirostris*) 35 50
445 17p. Peregrine Falcon (*Falco peregrinus*) .. 70 1·25
442/5 .. .. *Set of* 4 1·50 2·00

165 "A Happy Flower" (David Gallagher)

(Des P. Wildbur. Litho Irish Security Stamp Ptg Ltd)

1979 (13 Sept). *International Year of the Child. Paintings by Children. T* **165** *and similar multicoloured designs. P* 14 × 14½ (11*p*.) *or* 14½ × 14 (*others*).
446 10p. Type **165** 15 10
447 11p. "Myself and My Skipping Rope" (Lucy Norman) (*vert*) 20 30
448 17p. "Swans on a Lake" (Nicola O'Dwyer) .. 30 45
446/8 .. .. *Set of* 3 60 75

166 Pope John Paul II

(Des P. Byrne. Litho Irish Security Stamp Ptg Ltd)

1979 (29 Sept). *Visit of Pope John Paul II. P* 14½ × 14.
449 **166** 12p. multicoloured 25 15

167 Brother and Child

(Des R. Kyne (9½p.), P. Scott (11p.), R. Mercer (20p.). Phot Stamping Branch of the Revenue Commissioners, Dublin (11p.) Litho Irish Security Stamp Ptg Ltd (others))

1979 (4 Oct). *Commemorations. T* **167** *and similar designs P* 14½ × 14 (9½*p*.), 14½ × 15 (11*p*.) *or* 14 × 14½ (*others*).
450 9½p. black and pale claret 12 1
451 11p. black, reddish orange and bright blue .. 15 4
452 20p. multicoloured .. .. 40 1·0
450/2 .. .. *Set of* 3 60 1·4
Designs and commemorations: *Horiz*—9½p. Type **16** (centenary of Hospitaller Order of St. John of God in Ireland); 20p "Seated Figure" (sculpture by F. E. McWilliam) (Contemporar Irish Art (10th issue)). *Vert*—11p. Windmill and Sun (International Energy Conservation Month).

168 Patrick Pearse, "Liberty" and General Post Office, Dublin

169 Madonna and Child (panel painting from Domnach Airgid Shrine)

(Des R. Ballagh)

1979 (10 Nov). *Birth Centenary of Patrick Pearse (patriot P* 15 × 14½.
453 **168** 12p. multicoloured 15 1

(Des Ewa Gargulinska)

1979 (15 Nov). *Christmas. P* 14½ × 15.
454 **169** 9½p. multicoloured 10 1
455 20p. multicoloured 25 4

170 Bianconi Long Car, 1836

171 John Baptist de la Salle (founder)

(Des P. Wildbur. Litho Irish Security Stamp Ptg Ltd)

1979 (6 Dec). *Europa. Communications. T* **170** *and similar horiz design. Multicoloured. P* 14½ × 14.
456 12p. Type **170** 20 20
457 13p. Transatlantic cable, Valentia, 1866 .. 25 80

(Des P. Wildbur. Litho Irish Security Stamp Ptg Ltd)

1980 (19 Mar). *Centenary of arrival of De La Salle Order. P* 14 × 14½.
458 **171** 12p. multicoloured 15 20

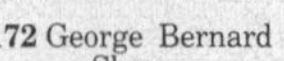

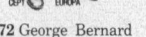

172 George Bernard Shaw

173 Stoat

(Des P. Byrne. Litho Irish Security Stamp Ptg Ltd)

1980 (7 May). *Europa. Personalities. T* **172** *and similar multicoloured design. P* 14 × 14½.
459 12p. Type **172** 30 20
460 13p. Oscar Wilde (28 × 38 *mm*) 30 70

(Des Wendy Walsh. Litho Irish Security Stamp Ptg Ltd)

1980 (30 July). *Wildlife. T* **173** *and similar vert designs. Multicoloured. P* 14 × 14½.
461 12p. Type **173** 20 10
462 15p. Arctic Hare 25 10
463 16p. Red Fox 30 20
464 25p. Red Deer 50 70
461/4 .. .. *Set of* 4 1·10 1·00
MS465 73 × 97 mm. Nos. 461/4 .. .. 2·50 3·50
No. **MS**465 exists with the sheet margins overprinted to commemorate "STAMPA 80", the Irish National Stamp Exhibition, in black or red.

174 Playing Bodhran and Whistle

175 Sean O'Casey

(Des J. Dixon and P. Wildbur. Litho Irish Security Stamp Ptg Ltd)

1980 (25 Sept). *Traditional Music and Dance. T* **174** *and similar vert designs. Multicoloured. P* 14 × 14½.

466	12p. Type **174** . .	10	10
467	15p. Playing Uilleann pipes . .	15	15
468	25p. Dancing . .	30	65
466/8 . .	*Set of* 3	45	75

(Des P. Wildbur (12p.), P. Scott (25p.). Litho Irish Security Stamp Ptg Ltd)

1980 (23 Oct). *Commemorations. T* **175** *and similar vert design. P* 14 × 14½.

469	12p. multicoloured . .	10	10
470	25p. black, buff and drab . .	25	40

Designs and commemorations:—12p. Type **175** (Birth centenary of Sean O'Casey (playwright)); 25p. "Gold Painting No. 57" (Patrick Scott) (Contemporary Irish Art (11th issue)).

176 Nativity Scene (painting by Geraldine McNulty)

177 Boyle Air-pump, 1659

(Des P. Wildbur)

1980 (13 Nov). *Christmas. P* 14½ × 15.

471	**176**	12p. multicoloured . .	15	10
472		15p. multicoloured . .	15	10
473		25p. multicoloured . .	30	50
471/3 . .		*Set of* 3	50	55

(Des P. Wildbur. Litho Irish Security Stamp Ptg Ltd)

1981 (12 Mar). *Irish Science and Technology. T* **177** *and similar vert designs. Multicoloured. P* 14 × 14½.

474	12p. Type **177** . .	15	10
475	15p. Ferguson tractor, 1936 . .	15	10
476	16p. Parsons turbine, 1884 . .	15	40
477	25p. Holland submarine, 1878 . .	30	60
474/7 . .	*Set of* 4	65	1·10

(Litho Irish Security Stamp Ptg Ltd)

1981 (27 Apr)–**82**. *No wmk. P* 14 × 14½.

478	**106***a*	18p. dull claret . .	35	10
479		19p. light blue . .	40	30
480		22p. dull turquoise-blue (1.9.81) . .	65	10
481		24p. drab (29.10.81) . .	65	25
482		26p. blue-green (1.4.82) . .	1·50	30
483		29p. purple (1.4.82) . .	1·50	1·50
478/83		*Set of* 6	4·50	2·25

178 "The Legend of the Cock and the Pot"

179 Cycling

(Des P. Byrne. Litho Irish Security Stamp Ptg Ltd)

1981 (4 May). *Europa. Folklore. Paintings by Maria Simonds-Gooding. T* **178** *and similar vert design. P* 14 × 14½.

491	18p. black, orange-yellow and carmine . .	25	10
492	19p. black, yellow-orange and yellow . .	25	40

Design:—19p. "The Angel with the Scales of Judgement".

(Des R. Ballagh. Litho Irish Security Stamp Ptg Ltd)

1981 (24 June). *50th Anniv of "An Óige" (Irish Youth Hostel Association). T* **179** *and similar multicoloured designs. P* 14 × 14½ (15, 30*p*.) *or* 14½ × 14 (*others*).

493	15p. Type **179** . .	30	30
494	18p. Hill-walking (*horiz*) . .	35	10
495	19p. Mountaineering (*horiz*) . .	35	40
496	30p. Rock-climbing . .	50	50
493/6 . .	*Set of* 4	1·40	1·10

180 Jeremiah O'Donovan Rossa

181 "Railway Embankment" (W. J. Leech)

(Des C. Harrison. Litho Irish Security Stamp Ptg Ltd)

1981 (31 Aug). *150th Birth Anniv of Jeremiah O'Donovan Rossa (politician). P* 14 × 14½.

497	**180**	15p. multicoloured . .	30	20

(Des P. Wildbur. Litho Irish Security Stamp Ptg Ltd)

1981 (31 Aug). *Contemporary Irish Art (12th issue). P* 14½ × 14.

498	**181**	30p. multicoloured . .	60	50

182 James Hoban and White House

183 "Arkle" (steeplechaser)

(Des B. Thompson. Litho Irish Security Stamp Ptg Ltd)

1981 (29 Sept). *150th Death Anniv of James Hoban (White House architect). P* 14½ × 14.

499	**182**	18p. multicoloured . .	30	15

(Des Wendy Walsh and P. Wildbur. Litho Irish Security Stamp Ptg Ltd)

1981 (23 Oct). *Famous Irish Horses. T* **183** *and similar horiz designs. Multicoloured. Ordinary paper (18p.) or chalk-surfaced paper (others). P* 14½ × 14.

500	18p. Type **183** . .	50	50
	a. Pair. Nos. 500/1 . .	1·00	1·00
501	18p. "Boomerang" (showjumper) . .	50	50
502	22p. "King of Diamonds" (Draught horse) . .	60	30
503	24p. "Ballymoss" (flatracer) . .	60	50
504	36p. "Coosheen Finn" (Connemara pony) . .	80	70
500/4 . .	*Set of* 4	2·75	2·25

The 18p values were printed together, *se-tenant*, in horizontal and vertical pairs throughout the sheet.

184 "Nativity" (F. Barocci)

185 Eviction Scene

(Des P. Wildbur. Litho Irish Security Stamp Ptg Ltd)

1981 (19 Nov). *Christmas. Chalk-surfaced paper. P* 14 × 14½.

505	**184**	18p. multicoloured . .	25	10
506		22p. multicoloured . .	35	10
507		36p. multicoloured . .	60	85
505/7 . .		*Set of* 3	1·10	85

(Des R. Mercer (18p.), P. Wildbur (22p.). Litho Irish Security Stamp Ptg Ltd)

1981 (10 Dec). *Anniversaries. T* **185** *and similar multicoloured design. Chalk-surfaced paper. P* 14 × 14½ (18*p*.) *or* 14½ × 14 (22*p*.).

508	18p. Type **185** . .	30	15
509	22p. Royal Dublin Society emblem (*horiz*) . .	35	30

Anniversaries—18p. Centenary of Land Law (Ireland) Act; 22p. 250th of Royal Dublin Society (organization for the advancement of agriculture, industry, art and science).

186 Upper Lake, Killarney National Park

187 "The Stigmatization of St Francis" (Sassetta)

(Des P. Wildbur. Litho Irish Security Stamp Ptg Ltd)

1982 (26 Feb). *50th Anniv of Killarney National Park. T* **186** *and similar horiz design. Multicoloured. P* 14½ × 14.

510	18p. Type **186** . .	35	15
511	36p. Eagle's Nest . .	75	65

(Des P. Wildbur (22p.), M. Craig (24p.). Litho Irish Security Stamp Ptg Ltd)

1982 (2 Apr). *Religious Anniversaries. T* **187** *and similar horiz design. Chalk-surfaced paper. P* 14 × 14½ (22*p*.) *or* 14½ × 14 (24*p*.).

512	22p. multicoloured . .	45	15
513	24p. olive-brown . .	55	45

Designs and anniversaries:—22p. Type **187** (800th birth anniv of St Francis of Assisi (founder of Franciscan Order)); 24p. Francis Makemie (founder of American Presbyterianism) and old Presbyterian Church, Ramelton, Co Donegal (300th anniv of ordination).

188 The Great Famine, 1845–50

189 Pádraic Ó Conaire (writer) (Birth Centenary)

(Des P. Wildbur. Litho Irish Security Stamp Ptg Ltd)

1982 (4 May). *Europa. Historic Events. T* **188** *and similar design. Chalk-surfaced paper. P* 14 × 14½ (26*p*.) *or* 14½ × 14 (29*p*.).

514	26p. black and stone . .	70	25
515	29p. multicoloured . .	70	70

Design: *Horiz*—29p. The coming of Christianity to Ireland.

(Des P. Wildbur. Litho Irish Security Stamp Ptg Ltd)

1982 (16 June). *Anniversaries of Cultural Figures. T* **189** *and similar vert designs. Chalk-surfaced paper. P* 14 × 14½.

516	22p. black and light blue . .	40	25
517	26p. black and sepia . .	55	25
518	29p. black and blue . .	65	75
519	44p. black and greenish grey . .	85	1·25
516/19 . .	*Set of* 4	2·25	2·25

Designs and anniversaries:—26p. James Joyce (writer) (birth centenary); 29p. John Field (musician) (birth bicentenary); 44p. Charles Kickham (writer) (death centenary).

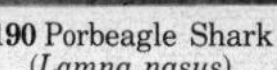

190 Porbeagle Shark (*Lamna nasus*)

191 Galway Hooker

(Des Wendy Walsh and P. Wildbur. Litho Irish Security Stamp Ptg Ltd)

1982 (29 July). *Marine Life. T* **190** *and similar horiz designs. Multicoloured. Chalk-surfaced paper. P* 14½ × 14.

520	22p. Type **190** . .	40	70
521	22p. Oyster (*Ostrea edulis*) . .	40	70
522	26p. Salmon (*Salmo salár*) . .	55	30
523	29p. Dublin Bay prawn (*Nephrops norvegicus*)	60	1·25
520/3 . .	*Set of* 4	1·75	2·75

(Des P. Wildbur. Litho Irish Security Stamp Ptg Ltd)

1982 (21 Sept). *Irish Boats. T* **191** *and similar multicoloured designs. Ordinary paper (26p.) or chalk-surfaced paper (others). P* 14 × 14½ (*Nos.* 524 *and* 527) *or* 14½ × 14 (*others*).

524	22p. Type **191** . .	65	70
525	22p. Currach (*horiz*) . .	65	70
526	26p. *Asgard II* (*horiz*) . .	75	30
527	29p. Howth 17-Footer . .	1·00	1·25
524/7 . .	*Set of* 4	2·75	2·75

192 "Irish House of Commons" (painting by Francis Wheatley)

193 "Madonna and Child" (sculpture)

(Des P. Wildbur (22p.) or R. Ballagh (26p.). Litho Irish Security Stamp Ptg Ltd)

1982 (14 Oct). *Bicentenary of Grattan's Parliament (22p.) and Birth Centenary of Eamon de Valera (26p.). T* **192** *and similar multicoloured design. P* 14½ × 14 *(22p.) or* 14 × 14½ *(26p.).*
528 22p. Type **192** 30 60
529 26p. Eamon de Valera (*vert*) 35 35

(Des P. Wildbur. Litho Irish Security Stamp Ptg Ltd)

1982 (11 Nov). *Christmas. P* 14 × 14½.
530 **193** 22p. multicoloured 30 35
531 26p. multicoloured 35 25

194 Aughnanure Castle

195 Ouzel Galley Goblet

(Des M. Craig and P. Wildbur. Litho Irish Security Stamp Ptg Ltd)

1982 (15 Dec)–**88**. *Irish Architecture. T* **194** *and similar designs. Chalk-surfaced paper* (24, 28, 32, 37, 39, 46*p.*, £1 (*No.* 550*b*), £2)) *or ordinary paper (others). P* 15 × 14 (15, 20, 22, 23, 24, 26, 39, 46, 50*p.*, £1 (*No.* 550), £2) *or* 14 × 15 *(others).*
532 1p. dull violet-blue (6.7.83) 10 10
a. Chalk-surfaced paper (9.87) 10 10
533 2p. deep yellow-green (6.7.83) 10 10
a. Chalk-surfaced paper (27.6.85) . . 10 10
ab. Booklet pane. Nos. 533a, 543a and 545a, each × 2 . . . . 2·50
ac. Booklet pane. Nos. 533a, 543a and 545a, each × 4 . . . . 4·50
ad. Booklet pane. Nos. 533a × 2, 535b × 3, 544*a* × 3 and 545*b* × 4 (8.9.86) . . . . 3·00
ae. Booklet pane. Nos. 533a × 4, 535b, 544*a* × 2 and 545*b* × 5 (24.11.88) 3·00
534 3p. black (6.7.83) 10 10
a. Chalk-surfaced paper (2.88) 10 10
535 4p. maroon (16.3.83) 10 10
a. Booklet pane. Nos. 535 × 3, 543 × 4 and 1 label (15.8.83) . . . . 3·00
b. Chalk-surfaced paper (9.7.84) . . 10 10
ba. Booklet pane. Nos. 535b × 3, 543a × 5 and 545a × 4 . . . . 5·50
536 5p. olive-sepia (6.7.83) 10 10
a. Chalk-surfaced paper (8.87) 10 10
537 6p. deep grey-blue (16.3.83) 10 10
a. Chalk-surfaced paper (11.85) . . 10 10
538 7p. dull yellow-green (16.3.83) . . 15 15
a. Chalk-surfaced paper (3.88) 10 10
539 10p. black (6.7.83) 20 15
a. Chalk-surfaced paper (3.87) . . 15 10
540 12p. purple-brown (6.7.83) 30 20
a. Chalk-surfaced paper (5.87) . . 20 15
541 15p. deep yellow-green (6.7.83) . . 20 10
542 20p. deep brown-purple (16.3.83) . . 45 30
a. Chalk-surfaced paper (12.84) . . 30 20
543 22p. chalky blue 50 30
a. Chalk-surfaced paper (9.7.84) . . 35 20
544 23p. yellow-green (16.3.83) 35 40
544*a* 24p. bistre-brown (27.6.85) 35 40
ab. Ordinary paper (9.87) 50 60
545 26p. blackish brown 60 15
a. Chalk-surfaced paper (9.7.84) . . 40 10
545*b* 28p. maroon (27.6.85) 40 45
ba. Ordinary paper (10.87) 60 65
546 29p. deep yellow-green 45 30
547 30p. black (16.3.83) 65 60
a. Chalk-surfaced paper (3.87) . . 45 40
547*b* 32p. bistre-brown (1.5.86) 50 55
547*c* 37p. chalky blue (27.6.85) 55 60
547*d* 39p. maroon (1.5.86) 60 65
548 44p. black and grey . . . . 1·00 1·10
a. Chalk-surfaced paper (4.85) . . 65 70
548*b* 46p. olive-green and brownish grey (1.5.86) 70 75
ba. Ordinary paper (9.87) . . . . 1·10 1·25
549 50p. dull ultramarine and grey (16.3.83) 1·25 1·25
a. Chalk-surfaced paper (12.84) . . 75 80
550 £1 bistre-brown and grey . . . . 5·50 2·25
a. Chalk-surfaced paper (9.84) . . 6·00 3·25
550*b* £1 chalky blue & brownish grey (27.6.85) 1·50 1·60
ba. Ordinary paper (1.88) . . . . 1·50 1·60
550*c* £2 grey-olive and black (26.7.88) . . 3·00 3·25
551 £5 crimson and grey . . . . 11·00 11·50
a. Chalk-surfaced paper (8.87) . . 7·50 7·75
532/51 . . . . . . *Set of* 28 23·00 20·00

Designs: *Horiz* (*as T* **194**)—1p. to 5p. Central Pavilion, Dublin Botanic Gardens; 6p. to 12p. Dr. Steevens' Hospital, Dublin; 28p. to 37p. St. MacDara's Church (37 × 21 *mm*)—46p., £1 (No. 550) Cahir Castle: 50p., £2 Casino, Marino; £5 Central Bus Station, Dublin. *Vert* (*as T* **194**)—15p. to 22p. Type **194**; 23p. to 26p., 39p. Cormac's Chapel. (21 × 37 *mm*)—44p., £1 (No. 550*b*) Killarney Cathedral.

The following stamps first appeared in booklet panes, but were later issued in sheets: Nos. 533a (7.86), 535b (7.85), 543a (10.84) and 545a (1.85).

Stamps from booklet panes Nos. 533ab/ae and 535a/ba come with one side imperforate. No. 535ba comes from £2 Discount booklet and shows "Booklet Stamp" printed over the gum on the reverse of each stamp.

NEW INFORMATION

The editor is always interested to correspond with people who have new information that will improve or correct the Catalogue.

(Des P. Wildbur (22p.), C. Harrison (26p.). Litho Irish Security Stamp Ptg Ltd)

1983 (23 Feb). *Bicentenaries of Dublin Chamber of Commerce (22p.) and Bank of Ireland (26p.). T* **195** *and similar multi-coloured design. P* 14 × 14½ *(22p.) or* 14½ × 14 *(26p.).*
552 22p. Type **195** 30 30
553 26p. Bank of Ireland building (*horiz*) 35 30

196 Pádraig O Siochfhradha (writer and teacher) (Birth cent)

197 Neolithic Carved Pattern, Newgrange Tomb

(Des C. Harrison (26p.), R. Ballagh (29p.). Litho Irish Security Stamp Ptg Ltd)

1983 (7 Apr). *Anniversaries. T* **196** *and similar vert design. Multi-coloured. P* 14 × 14½.
554 26p. Type **196** 40 45
555 29p. Young Boys' Brigade member (Centenary) 45 65

(Des L. le Brocquy (26p.), P. Wildbur (29p.). Litho Irish Security Stamp Ptg Ltd)

1983 (4 May). *Europa. T* **197** *and similar horiz design. P* 14½ × 14.
556 26p. grey-black and gold . . . . 1·00 30
557 29p. black, blackish brown and gold . . . . 1·50 1·50

Design:—29p. Sir William Rowan Hamilton's formulae for the multiplication of quaternions.

198 Kerry Blue Terrier

(Des Wendy Walsh and L. Miller. Litho Irish Security Stamp Ptg Ltd)

1983 (23 June). *Irish Dogs. T* **198** *and similar horiz designs. Multicoloured. P* 14½ × 14.
558 22p. Type **198** 45 35
559 26p. Irish Wolfhound 55 25
560 26p. Irish Water Spaniel 55 25
561 29p. Irish Terrier 70 70
562 44p. Irish Setters . . . . . . 1·00 80
558/62 . . . . *Set of* 5 3·00 2·10
MS563 142 × 80 mm. Nos. 558/62 . . . . 3·50 4·25

No. **MS**563 exists with the sheet margins overprinted in blue to commemorate "STAMPA 83", the Irish National Stamp Exhibition.

199 Animals (Irish Society for the Prevention of Cruelty to Animals)

200 Postman with Bicycle

(Des Wendy Walsh (No. 564), B. Murphy (No. 566), K. Uhlemann (No. 567), R. Ballagh (others). Litho Irish Security Stamp Ptg Ltd)

1983 (11 Aug). *Anniversaries and Commemorations. T* **199** *and similar designs. P* 14½ × 14 (*Nos.* 564, 566) *or* 14 × 14½ *(others).*
564 **199** 22p. multicoloured 40 35
565 – 22p. multicoloured 40 35
566 – 26p. multicoloured 50 25
567 – 26p. multicoloured 50 25
568 – 44p. grey-blue and black 70 70
564/8 . . . . *Set of* 5 2·25 1·75

Designs: *Vert*—No. 565, Sean Mac Diarmada (patriot) (birth cent); No. 567, "St. Vincent de Paul in the Streets of Paris" (150th anniv of Society of St. Vincent de Paul); No. 568, "Andrew Jackson" (Frank McKelvey) (President of the United States). *Horiz*—No. 566, "100" (Centenary of Industrial Credit Company).

(Des R. Ballagh. Litho Irish Security Stamp Ptg Ltd)

1983 (15 Sept). *World Communications Year. T* **200** *and similar vert design. Multicoloured. P* 14 × 14½.
569 22p. Type **200** 35 30
570 29p. Dish antenna 50 60

201 Weaving

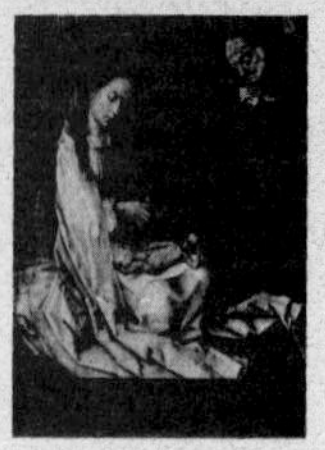

202 "La Natividad" (R. van der Weyden)

(Des R. Mercer. Litho Irish Security Stamp Ptg Ltd)

1983 (13 Oct). *Irish Handicrafts. T* **201** *and similar vert designs. Multicoloured. P* 14 × 14½.
571 22p. Type **201** 35 35
572 26p. Basketmaking 45 25
573 29p. Irish crochet 50 50
574 44p. Harpmaking 70 70
571/4 . . . . *Set of* 4 1·75 1·60

(Des and litho Irish Security Stamp Ptg Ltd)

1983 (30 Nov). *Christmas. P* 14 × 14½.
575 **202** 22p. multicoloured 35 25
576 26p. multicoloured 45 25

203 *Princess* (Dublin and Kingstown Railway)

(Des C. Rycroft. Litho Irish Security Stamp Ptg Ltd)

1984 (30 Jan). 150*th Anniv of Irish Railways. T* **203** *and similar horiz designs. Multicoloured. Ordinary paper (26p., miniature sheet) or chalk-surfaced paper (others). P* 15 × 14.
577 23p. Type **203** 70 60
578 26p. *Macha* (Great Southern Railway) . . 70 25
579 29p. *Kestrel* (Great Northern Railway) . . 80 70
580 44p. Two-car electric unit (Coras Iompair Eireann) . . . . . . 1·00 90
577/80 . . . . *Set of* 4 3·00 2·25
MS581 129 × 77 mm. Nos. 577/80 . . . . 3·00 4·00

No. **MS**581 exists with the sheet margins overprinted in black to commemorate "STAMPA 84", the Irish National Stamp Exhibition.

204 *Sorbus hibernica*

(Des Wendy Walsh and P. Wildbur. Litho Irish Security Stamp Ptg Ltd)

1984 (1 Mar). *Irish Trees. T* **204** *and similar horiz designs. Multi-coloured. P* 15 × 14.
582 22p. Type **204** 60 40
583 26p. *Taxus baccata fastigiata* 70 30
584 29p. *Salix hibernica* 80 75
585 44p. *Betula pubescens* . . . . . . 1·00 1·25
582/5 . . . . *Set of* 4 2·75 2·40

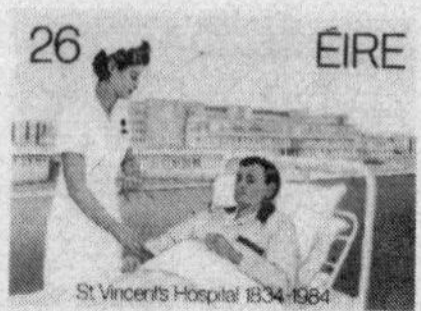

205 St. Vincent's Hospital, Dublin

(Des B. Donegan, adapted by C. Vis (26p.), B. Murphy (44p.). Litho Irish Security Stamp Ptg Ltd)

1984 (12 Apr). 150*th Anniv of St. Vincent's Hospital and Bicentenary of Royal College of Surgeons. T* **205** *and similar horiz design. Multicoloured. P* 15 × 14.
586 26p. Type **205** 35 25
587 44p. Royal College and logo 60 85

206 C.E.P.T. 25th Anniversary Logo

(Des J. Larrivière. Litho Irish Security Stamp Ptg Ltd)

1984 (10 May). *Europa. P* 15 × 14.
588 **206** 26p. blue, deep dull blue and black .. 60 30
589 29p. light green, blue-green and black .. 80 95

207 Flags on Ballot Box

208 John McCormack

(Des R. Ballagh. Litho Irish Security Stamp Ptg Ltd)

1984 (10 May). *Second Direct Elections to European Assembly. P* 15 × 14.
590 **207** 26p. multicoloured 40 35

(Des R. Mercer and J. Sharpe. Litho Irish Security Stamp Ptg Ltd)

1984 (6 June). *Birth Centenary of John McCormack (tenor). P* 14 × 15.
591 **208** 22p. multicoloured 40 40

209 Hammer-throwing

(Des L. le Brocquy and P. Wildbur. Litho Irish Security Stamp Ptg Ltd)

1984 (21 June). *Olympic Games, Los Angeles. T* **209** *and similar horiz designs. P* 15 × 14.
592 22p. deep mauve, black and gold 30 40
593 26p. violet, black and gold 35 40
594 29p. bright blue, black and gold 40 55
592/4 .. .. *Set of* 3 95 1·25
Designs:—26p. Hurdling; 29p. Running.

210 Hurling

211 Galway Mayoral Chain (500th Anniv of Mayoral Charter)

(Des C. Harrison. Litho Irish Security Stamp Ptg Ltd)

1984 (23 Aug). *Centenary of Gaelic Athletic Association. T* **210** *and similar multicoloured design. P* 15 × 14 *(22p.) or* 14 × 15 *(26p.).*
595 22p. Type **210** 40 40
596 26p. Irish football *(vert)* 45 40

(Des P. Wildbur. Litho Irish Security Stamp Ptg Ltd)

1984 (18 Sept). *Anniversaries. T* **211** *and similar multicoloured design. P* 14 × 15 *(26p.) or* 15 × 14 *(44p.).*
597 26p. Type **211** 35 30
598 44p. St. Brendan (from 15th-cent Bodleian manuscript) (1500th birth anniv) *(horiz)* 60 80

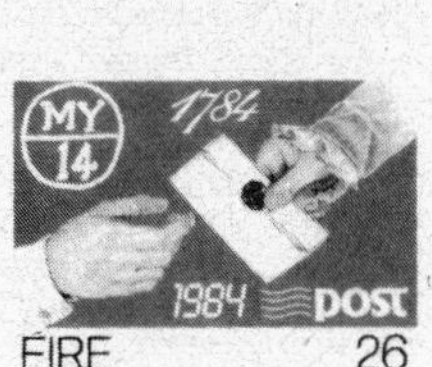

212 Hands passing Letter

213 "Virgin and Child" (Sassoferrato)

(Litho Irish Security Stamp Ptg Ltd)

1984 (19 Oct). *Bicentenary of the Irish Post Office. P* 15 × 14.
599 **212** 26p. multicoloured 35 40

(Des O'Connor O'Sullivan Advertising (17p.), P. Wildbur (others). Litho Irish Security Stamp Ptg Ltd)

1984 (26 Nov). *Christmas. T* **213** *and similar multicoloured design. Chalk-surfaced paper. P* 15 × 14 *(17p.) or* 14 × 15 *(others).*
600 17p. Christmas star *(horiz)* 30 10
601 22p. Type **213** 40 45
602 26p. Type **213** 50 30
600/2 .. .. *Set of* 3 1·10 70
No. 600 represented a special concession rate for Christmas card postings to addresses within Ireland and Great Britain between 26 November and 8 December 1984.

214 "Love" and Heart-shaped Balloon

215 Dunsink Observatory (Bicentenary)

(Des Susan Dubsky (22p.), Patricia Jorgensen (26p.). Litho Irish Security Stamp Ptg Ltd)

1985 (31 Jan). *Greetings Stamps. T* **214** *and similar multicoloured design. Chalk-surfaced paper. P* 15 × 14 *(22p.) or* 14 × 15 *(26p.).*
603 22p. Type **214** 40 25
604 26p. Bouquet of hearts and flowers *(vert)* .. 50 25

(Des R. Ballagh (22, 44p.), K. Thomson (26p.), M. Lunt (37p.). Litho Irish Security Stamp Ptg Ltd)

1985 (14 Mar). *Anniversaries. T* **215** *and similar designs. Multicoloured. Chalk-surfaced paper. P* 15 × 14 *(26p.) or* 14 × 15 *(others).*
605 22p. Type **215** 40 30
606 26p. "A Landscape at Tivoli, Cork, with Boats" (Nathanial Grogan) (800th anniv of city of Cork) *(horiz)* 45 20
607 37p. Royal Irish Academy (Bicentenary) .. 70 70
608 44p. Richard Crosbie's balloon flight (Bicentenary of first aeronautic flight by an Irishman) 75 75
605/8 .. .. *Set of* 4 2·10 1·75

216 Common Blue

217 Charles Villiers Stanford (composer)

(Des I. Loe. Litho Irish Security Stamp Ptg Ltd)

1985 (11 Apr). *Butterflies. T* **216** *and similar vert designs. Multicoloured. Chalk-surfaced paper. P* 14 × 15.
609 22p. Type **216** 70 50
610 26p. Red Admiral 80 45
611 28p. Brimstone 85 85
612 44p. Marsh Fritillary .. .. 1·25 1·50
609/12 .. .. *Set of* 4 3·25 3·00

(Des P. Hickey and J. Farrar. Litho Irish Security Stamp Ptg Ltd)

1985 (16 May). *Europa. Irish Composers. T* **217** *and similar horiz design. Multicoloured. Chalk-surfaced paper. P* 15 × 14.
613 26p. Type **217** .. .. 1·00 35
614 37p. Turlough Carolan (composer and lyricist) .. .. 1·50 1·40

218 George Frederick Handel

219 U.N. Patrol of Irish Soldiers, Congo, 1960 (25th Anniv. of Irish Participation in U.N. Peace-keeping Force)

(Des K. Uhlemann and J. Farrar. Litho Irish Security Stamp Ptg Ltd)

1985 (16 May). *European Music Year. Composers. T* **218** *and similar vert designs. Multicoloured. Chalk-surfaced paper. P* 14 × 15.
615 22p. Type **218** 70 65
a. Pair. Nos. 615/16 .. .. .. 1·40 1·25
616 22p. Guiseppe Domenico Scarlatti 70 65
617 26p. Johann Sebastian Bach 70 25
615/17 .. .. *Set of* 3 1·90 1·40
Nos. 615/16 were printed together, *se-tenant*, in horizontal and vertical pairs throughout the sheet.

(Des B. Donegan and J. Farrar (22p.), R. Ballagh (26p.), B. Donegan (44p.). Litho Irish Security Stamp Ptg Ltd)

1985 (20 June). *Anniversaries. T* **219** *and similar multicoloured designs. Chalk-surfaced paper. P* 15 × 14 *(22p.) or* 14 × 15 *(others).*
618 22p. Type **219** 65 45
619 26p. Thomas Ashe (patriot) (birth cent) *(vert)* 70 45
620 44p. "Bishop George Berkeley" (James Lathan) (philosopher, 300th birth anniv) *(vert)* .. .. 1·10 85
618/20 .. .. *Set of* 3 2·25 1·60

220 Group of Young People

(Des J. Farrar and N. Mooney. Litho Irish Security Stamp Ptg Ltd)

1985 (1 Aug). *International Youth Year. T* **220** *and similar multicoloured design. Chalk-surfaced paper. P* 15 × 14 *(22p.) or* 14 × 15 *(26p.).*
621 22p. Type **220** 45 40
622 26p. Students and young workers *(vert)* .. 55 45

221 Visual Display Unit

(Des B. Donegan (44p.), C. Rycraft (others). Litho Irish Security Stamp Ptg Ltd)

1985 (3 Oct). *Industrial Innovation. T* **221** *and similar horiz designs. Multicoloured. Chalk-surfaced paper. P* 15 × 14.
623 22p. Type **221** 55 40
624 26p. Turf cutting with hand tool and with modern machinery 60 45
625 44p. "The Key Man" (Sean Keating) (150th anniv of Institution of Engineers of Ireland) 90 75
623/5 .. .. *Set of* 3 1·90 1·40

222 Lighted Candle and Holly

223 "Virgin and Child in a Landscape" (Adrian van Ijsenbrandt)

(Des R. Mahon (No. 626). Litho Irish Security Stamp Ptg Ltd)

1985 (26 Nov). *Christmas. T* **222** *and designs as T* **223** *showing paintings. Multicoloured. Chalk-surfaced paper. P* 15 × 14 *(26p.) or* 14 × 15 *(others).*
626 22p. Type **222** 50 50
a. Sheetlet. No. 626 × 16 .. .. .. 7·00
627 22p. Type **223** .. .. 70 1·00
a. Pair. Nos. 627/8 .. .. 1·40 2·00
628 22p. "The Holy Family" (Murillo) .. .. 70 1·00
629 26p. "The Adoration of the Shepherds" (Louis le Nain) *(horiz)* 75 25
626/9 .. .. *Set of* 4 2·40 2·50
No. 626 was only issued in sheetlets of 16 sold at £3, providing a discount of 52p. off the face value of the stamps.
Nos. 627/8 were printed together, *se-tenant*, in horizontal and vertical pairs throughout the sheet.

224 Stylised Love Bird with Letter

225 Hart's Tongue Fern

(Des R. Hoek (22p.), T. Monaghan (26p.). Litho Irish Security Stamp Ptg Ltd)

1986 (30 Jan). *Greetings Stamps. T* **224** *and similar vert design. Multicoloured. Chalk-surfaced paper. P* 14 × 15.
630 22p. Type **224** 70 60
631 26p. Heart-shaped pillar-box 80 50

(Des I. Loe. Litho Irish Security Stamp Ptg Ltd)

1986 (20 Mar). *Ferns. T* **255** *and similar vert designs. Multicoloured. Chalk-surfaced paper. P* 14 × 15.
632 24p. Type **225** 70 70
633 28p. Rusty-back Fern 85 70
634 46p. Killarney Fern .. .. 1·25 1·60
632/4 .. .. *Set of* 3 2·50 2·75

226 "Harmony between Industry and Nature"

227 Boeing "747" over Globe showing Aer Lingus Routes

(Des G. van Gelderen. Litho Irish Security Stamp Ptg Ltd)

1986 (1 May). *Europa. Protection of the Environment. T* **226** *and similar multicoloured design. Chalk-surfaced paper. P* 14×15 (28*p*.) *or* 15×14 (39*p*.).

635 28p. Type **226** .. .. 1·25 40
636 39p. Butterfly and tractor in field ("Preserve hedgerows") (*horiz*) .. .. .. 1·75 2·25

(Des R. Ballagh. Litho Irish Security Stamp Ptg Ltd)

1986 (27 May). *50th Anniv of Aer Lingus (airline). T* **227** *and similar horiz design. Multicoloured. Chalk-surfaced paper. P* 15×14.

637 28p. Type **227** .. .. 1·25 50
638 46p. De Havilland "Dragon" *Iolar* (first aircraft) .. .. 1·75 1·75

228 Grand Canal at Robertstown

229 *Severn* (19th-century paddle-steamer)

(Des B. Matthews. Litho Irish Security Stamp Ptg Ltd)

1986 (27 May). *Irish Waterways. T* **228** *and similar multicoloured designs. Chalk-surfaced paper. P* 14×15 (28*p*.) *or* 15×14 (*others*).

639 24p. Type **228** 85 70
640 28p. Fishing in County Mayo (*vert*) 95 60
641 30p. Motor cruiser on Lough Derg .. .. 1·25 1·50
639/41 .. .. *Set of* 3 2·75 2·50

(Des C. Rycraft. Litho Irish Security Stamp Ptg Ltd)

1986 (10 July). *150th Anniv of British and Irish Steam Packet Company. T* **229** *and similar horiz design. Multicoloured. P* 15×14.

642 24p. Type **229** 75 80
643 28p. M.V. *Leinster* (modern ferry) 85 60

230 Kish Lighthouse and Helicopter

231 J. P. Nannetti (first president) and Linotype Operator (Dublin Council of Trade Unions centenary)

(Des R. Ballagh. Litho Irish Security Stamp Printing Ltd)

1986 (10 July). *Irish Lighthouses. T* **230** *and similar vert design. Multicoloured. P* 14×15.

644 24p. Type **230** 75 75
645 30p. Fastnet Lighthouse .. .. 1·25 1·25

(Des R. Ballagh (Nos. 646/7), M. Cameron (No. 648), A. Mazer (Nos. 649/50). Litho Irish Security Stamp Ptg Ltd)

1986 (21 Aug). *Anniversaries and Commemorations. T* **231** *and similar designs. Ordinary paper* (24*p*.) *or chalk-surfaced paper* (*others*). *P* 14×15 (*Nos.* 646/7, 649) *or* 15×14 (*others*).

646 24p. multicoloured 60 60
647 28p. black and brownish grey 70 60
648 28p. multicoloured 70 60
649 30p. multicoloured 70 60
650 46p. multicoloured .. .. 1·00 1·25
646/50 .. .. *Set of* 5 3·25 3·25

Designs: *Vert*—No. 647, Arthur Griffith (statesman); No. 649, Clasped hands (International Peace Year). *Horiz*—No. 648, Woman surveyor (Women in Society); No. 650, Peace dove (International Peace Year).

232 William Mulready and his Design for 1840 Envelope

233 "The Adoration of the Shepherds" (Francesco Pascucci)

(Des C. Harrison (24p.), A. Mazer from aquatints by M. A. Hayes (others). Litho Irish Security Stamp Ptg Ltd)

1986 (2 Oct). *Birth Bicentenaries of William Mulready (artist)* (24*p*). *and Charles Bianconi (originator of Irish mail coach service)* (*others*). *T* **232** *and similar multicoloured designs. Chalk-surfaced paper. P* 14×15 (28*p*.) *or* 15×14 (*others*).

651 24p. Type **232** 55 60
652 28p. Bianconi car outside Hearns Hotel, Clonmel (*vert*) 65 55
653 39p. Bianconi car on the road .. .. 85 1·00
651/3 .. .. *Set of* 3 1·90 2·00

(Des C. O'Neill (21p.). Litho Irish Security Stamp Ptg Ltd)

1986 (20 Nov). *Christmas. T* **233** *and similar multicoloured design. Chalk-surfaced paper. P* 15×14 (21*p*.) *or* 14×15 (28*p*.).

654 21p. Type **233** 65 85
a. Sheetlet. No. 654×12 .. .. .. 7·00
655 28p. "The Adoration of the Magi" (Frans Francken III) (*vert*) 65 55

No. 654 was only issued in sheetlets of 12 sold at £2.50, providing a discount of 2p. off the face value of the stamps.

234 "Butterfly and Flowers" (Tara Collins)

235 Cork Electric Tram

(Litho Irish Security Stamp Ptg Ltd)

1987 (27 Jan) *Greetings Stamps. Children's Paintings. T* **234** *and similar multicoloured design. Chalk-surfaced paper. P* 15×14 (24*p*.) *or* 14×15 (28*p*.).

656 24p. Type **234** 60 65
657 28p. "Postman on Bicycle delivering Hearts" (Brigid Teehan) (*vert*) 80 60

(Des C. Rycraft. Litho Irish Security Stamp Ptg Ltd)

1987 (4 Mar). *Irish Trams. T* **235** *and similar horiz designs. Multicoloured. Chalk-surfaced paper. P* 15×14.

658 24p. Type **235** 55 50
659 28p. Dublin Standard tram 55 50
660 30p. Howth (G.N.R.) tram 55 50
661 46p. Galway horse tram .. .. .. 1·00 90
658/61 .. .. *Set of* 4 2·40 2·10
MS662 131×85 mm. Nos. 658/61 .. .. 2·50 2·40

236 Ships from Crest (Bicentenary of Waterford Chamber of Commerce)

237 Bord na Mona Headquarters and "The Turf Cutter" sculpture (John Behan), Dublin

(Des K. Uhlemann (24p.), J Farrer (28p.), A. Mazer and Wendy Walsh (30p.), M. Cameron (39p.). Litho Irish Security Stamp Ptg Ltd)

1987 (9 Apr). *Anniversaries. T* **236** *and similar designs. Chalk-surfaced paper. P* 14×15 (30*p*.) *or* 15×14 (*others*).

663 24p. black, ultramarine and deep grey-green 60 50
664 28p. multicoloured 70 60
665 30p. multicoloured 70 75
666 39p. multicoloured .. .. 85 1·00
663/6 .. .. *Set of* 4 2·50 2·50

Designs: *Horiz*—28p. Canon John Hayes and symbols of agriculture and development (birth centenary and 50th anniv of Muintir na Tire programme); 39p. Mother Mary Martin and International Missionary Training Hospital, Drogheda (50th anniv of Medical Missionaries of Mary). *Vert*—30p. *Calceolaria burbidgei* and College crest (300th anniv of Trinity College Botanic Gardens, Dublin).

(Des M. Lunt. Litho Harrison)

1987 (14 May). *Europa. Modern Architecture. T* **237** *and similar horiz design. Multicoloured. P* 15×14.

667 28p. Type **237** 70 60
668 39p. St. Mary's Church, Cong 90 75

238 Kerry Cow

239 Fleadh Nua, Ennis

(Des B. Driscoll. Litho Irish Security Stamp Ptg Ltd)

1987 (2 July). *Irish Cattle. T* **238** *and similar horiz designs. Multicoloured. Chalk-surfaced paper. P* 15×14.

669 24p. Type **238** 45 50
670 28p. Friesian cow and calf 55 60
671 30p. Hereford bullock 55 60
672 39p. Shorthorn bull 70 75
669/72 .. .. *Set of* 4 2·00 2·25

(Des R. Ballagh. Litho Irish Security Stamp Ptg Ltd)

1987 (27 Aug). *Festivals. T* **239** *and similar multicoloured designs. Chalk-surfaced paper. P* 14×15 (*vert*) *or* 15×14 (*horiz*).

673 24p. Type **239** 55 50
674 28p. Rose of Tralee International Festival .. 65 60
675 30p. Wexford Opera Festival (*horiz*) .. 70 60
676 46p. Ballinasloe Horse Fair (*horiz*) .. .. 1·00 90
673/6 .. .. *Set of* 4 2·75 2·40

240 Flagon (1637), Arms and Anniversary Ornament (1987) (350th Anniv of Dublin Goldsmiths' Company)

241 Scenes from "The Twelve Days of Christmas" (carol)

(Des B. Donegan (No. 677), R. Ballagh (No. 678), A. Mazer and Breda Mathews (No. 679), Libby Carton (No. 680). Litho Harrison (46p.) or Irish Security Stamp Ptg Ltd (others))

1987 (1 Oct). *Anniversaries and Commemorations. T* **240** *and similar designs. Ordinary paper* (46*p*.) *or chalk-surfaced paper* (*others*). *P* 15×14 (*horiz*) *or* 14×15 (*vert*).

677 **240** 24p. multicoloured 45 50
678 – 24p. grey and black 45 50
679 – 28p. multicoloured 55 60
680 – 46p. multicoloured 85 90
677/80 .. .. *Set of* 4 2·10 2·25

Designs: *Vert*—24p. (No. 678) Cathal Brugha (statesman); 46p. Woman chairing board meeting (Women in Society). *Horiz*—28p. Arms of Ireland and inscription (50th anniv of Constitution).

(Des M. Cameron (21p.), A. Mazer (others). Litho Irish Security Stamp Ptg Ltd)

1987 (17 Nov). *Christmas. T* **241** *and similar multicoloured designs. Chalk-surfaced paper. P* 15×14 (21*p*.) *or* 14×15 (*others*).

681 21p. Type **241** 35 40
a. Sheetlet. No. 681×14 .. .. .. 5·00
682 24p. The Nativity (detail, late 15th-cent Waterford Vestments) (*vert*) 45 50
683 28p. Figures from Neapolitan crib, *c* 1850 (*vert*) 55 60
681/3 .. .. *Set of* 3 1·25 1·40

No. 681 represents a special rate for greetings cards within Ireland and to all E.E.C. countries. It was only issued in sheetlets of 14 stamps and 1 label sold at £2.90, providing an additional discount of 4p. off the face value of the stamps.

242 Acrobatic Clowns spelling "LOVE"

243 "Robert Burke" (Sidney Nolan) and Map of Burke and Wills Expedition Route

(Des M. Cameron (24p.), Aislinn Adams (28p.). Litho Irish Security Stamp Ptg Ltd)

1988 (27 Jan). *Greetings Stamps. T* **242** *and similar multicoloured design. Chalk-surfaced paper. P* 15×14 (24*p*.) *or* 14×15 (28*p*.).

684 24p. Type **242** 55 50
685 28p. Pillar box and hearts (*vert*) 70 55

(Des A. Mazer. Litho Irish Security Stamp Ptg Ltd)

1988 (1 Mar). *Bicentenary of Australian Settlement. T* **243** *and similar horiz design. Multicoloured. Chalk-surfaced paper. P* 15×14.

686 24p. Type **243** 45 50
687 46p. "Eureka Stockade" (mural detail, Sidney Nolan) 85 90

244 Past and Present Buildings of Dublin

245 Showjumping

(Des S. Conlin. Litho Irish Security Stamp Ptg Ltd)

1988 (1 Mar). *Dublin Millennium. Chalk-surfaced paper. P* 15×14.

688 **244** 28p. multicoloured 50 55
a. Booklet pane. No. 688×4 .. .. 1·90

No. 688a was printed with either Irish or English inscriptions in the centre of the pane and came from £2.24 stamp booklets. Loose panes could also be purchased from the Philatelic Bureau, Dublin, and its agents.

(Des Ann Flynn Litho Irish Security Stamp Ptg Ltd)

1988 (7 Apr). *Olympic Games, Seoul. T* **245** *and similar horiz design. Multicoloured. Chalk-surfaced paper. P* 15×14.

689 28p. Type **245** 80 90
a. Sheetlet. Nos. 689/90, each × 5 .. 7·00
690 28p. Cycling 80 90

Nos. 689/90 were printed together, *se-tenant*, in a sheetlet containing five of each design and two stamp-size labels.

246 William T. Cosgrave (statesman)

247 Air Traffic Controllers and "A320" Airbus

(Des R. Ballagh (24p.), J. Farrer (30p.), K. Uhlemann (50p.). Litho Irish Security Stamp Ptg Ltd)

1988 (7 Apr). *Anniversaries and Events. T* **246** *and similar designs. Chalk-surfaced paper. P* 14×15 *(vert) or* 15×14 *(horiz).*

691 24p. brownish grey and black 50 45
692 30p. multicoloured 60 55
693 50p. multicoloured .. .. .. 1·00 90
691/3 .. .. *Set of* 3 1·90 1·75

Designs: *Horiz*—30p. Members with casualty and ambulance (50th anniv of Order of Malta Ambulance Corps). *Vert*—50p. Barry Fitzgerald (actor) (birth centenary).

(Des C. Rycraft (28p.), M. Cameron (39p.). Litho Irish Security Stamp Ptg Ltd)

1988 (12 May). *Europa. Transport and Communications. T* **247** *and similar horiz design. Multicoloured. Chalk-surfaced paper. P* 15×14.

694 28p. Type **247** 50 55
695 39p. Globe with stream of letters from Ireland to Europe 65 70

248 *Sirius* (paddle-steamer) (150th anniv of regular transatlantic steamship services)

249 Cottonweed

(Des C. Rycraft. Litho Irish Security Stamp Ptg Ltd)

1988 (12 May). *Transatlantic Transport Anniversaries. T* **248** *and similar horiz design. Multicoloured. Chalk-surfaced paper. P* 15×14.

696 24p. Type **248** 40 45
697 46p. *Mercury* and *Maia* (Short-Mayo composite aircraft) in Foynes Harbour (50th anniv of first commercial transatlantic flight) 80 85

(Des Frances Poskitt. Litho Irish Security Stamp Ptg Ltd)

1988 (21 June). *Endangered Flora of Ireland. T* **249** *and similar vert designs. Multicoloured. Chalk-surfaced paper. P* 14×15.

698 24p. Type **249** 55 45
699 28p. Hart's Saxifrage 65 55
700 46p. Purple Milk-Vetch .. .. .. 1·00 85
698/700 .. .. *Set of* 3 2·00 1·60

250 Garda on Duty

251 Computer and Abacus (Institute of Chartered Accountants in Ireland Centenary)

(Des D. Teskey. Litho Irish Security Stamp Ptg Ltd)

1988 (23 Aug). *Irish Security Forces. T* **250** *and similar horiz designs. Multicoloured. Chalk-surfaced paper. P* 15×14.

701 28p. Type **250** 50 55
a. Strip of 4. Nos. 701/4 .. .. 1·75
702 28p. Army unit with personnel carrier .. 50 55
703 28p. Navy and Air Corps members with fisheries control ship 50 55
704 28p. Army and navy reservists 50 55
701/4 .. .. *Set of* 4 1·75 2·00

Nos. 701/4 were printed together, both horizontally and vertically *se-tenant*, throughout the sheet of 20 (4 × 5).

(Des C. Rycraft (24p.), K. King and A. Mazer (46p.). Litho Irish Security Stamp Ptg Ltd)

1988 (6 Oct). *Anniversaries. T* **251** *and similar multicoloured design. Chalk-surfaced paper. P* 14×15 *(24p.) or* 15×14 *(46p.).*

705 24p. Type **251** 40 45
706 46p. *Duquesa Santa Ana* off Donegal *(horiz)* (400th anniv of Spanish Armada) .. 80 85

252 "President Kennedy" (James Wyeth)

253 St. Kevin's Church, Glendalough

(Des A. Mazer. Litho Irish Security Stamp Ptg Ltd)

1988 (24 Nov). *25th Death Anniv of John F. Kennedy (American statesman). Chalk-surfaced paper. P* 15×14.

707 **252** 28p. multicoloured 50 55

(Des Ann Flynn (21p.), B. Donegan (others). Litho Irish Security Stamp Ptg Ltd)

1988 (24 Nov). *Christmas. T* **253** *and similar vert designs. Multicoloured. Chalk-surfaced paper. P* 14×15.

708 21p. Type **253** 35 40
a. Sheetlet. No. 708 × 14 .. .. 5·00
709 24p. The Adoration of the Magi 40 45
710 28p. The Flight into Egypt 50 55
711 46p. The Holy Family 80 85
708/11 .. .. *Set of* 4 1·90 2·00

No. 708 represents a special rate for greetings cards within Ireland and to all E.E.C. countries. It was only issued in sheetlets of 14 stamps and 1 label sold at £2.90, providing an additional discount of 4p. off the face value of the stamps.

The designs of Nos. 709/11 are from a 15th-century French Book of Hours.

254 Spring Flowers spelling "Love" in Gaelic

255 Italian Garden, Garinish Island

(Des Susan Dubsky (24p.), A. Mazer (28p.). Litho Irish Security Stamp Ptg Ltd)

1989 (24 Jan). *Greetings Stamps. T* **254** *and similar multicoloured design. Chalk-surfaced paper. P* 15×14 *(24p.) or* 14×15 *(28p.).*

712 24p. Type **254** 40 45
713 28p. "The Sonnet" (William Mulready) *(vert)* 50 55

(Des Frances Poskitt. Litho Irish Security Stamp Ptg Ltd)

1989 (11 Apr). *National Parks and Gardens. T* **255** *and similar horiz designs. Multicoloured. Chalk-surfaced paper. P* 15×14.

714 24p. Type **255** 55 45
715 28p. Lough Veagh, Glenveagh National Park 70 55
716 32p. Barnaderg Bay, Connemara National Park 80 60
717 50p. St. Stephen's Green, Dublin .. .. 1·10 90
714/17 .. .. *Set of* 4 2·75 2·25

256 "Silver Stream", 1908

257 Ring-a-ring-a-roses

(Des C. Rycraft. Litho Irish Security Stamp Ptg Ltd)

1989 (11 Apr). *Classic Irish Cars. T* **256** *and similar horiz designs. Multicoloured. Chalk-surfaced paper. P* 15×14.

718 24p. Type **256** 40 45
a. Booklet pane. Nos. 718/19, each ×2 .. 1·75
b. Booklet pane. Nos. 718/21 .. .. 2·40
719 28p. Benz "Comfortable", 1898 .. .. 50 55
720 39p. "Thomond", 1929 .. .. .. 75 80
721 46p. Chambers' 8 h.p. model, 1905 .. 95 1·10
718/21 .. .. *Set of* 4 2·40 2·75

Booklet panes Nos. 718a/b come from £2.41 stamp booklets and stamps from them have one or two adjacent sides imperforate. Such panes were also available loose from the Philatelic Bureau, Dublin, and its agents

(Des C. Harrison. Litho Irish Security Stamp Ptg Ltd)

1989 (11 May). *Europa. Children's Games. T* **257** *and similar horiz design. Multicoloured. Chalk-surfaced paper. P* 15×14.

722 28p. Type **257** 70 55
723 39p. Hopscotch .. .. 90 1·00

Nos. 722/3 were each issued in sheets of 10 showing additional illustrations in the left-hand sheet margin.

258 Irish Red Cross Flag (50th anniv)

259 Saints Kilian, Totnan and Colman (from 12th-century German manuscript)

(Des Q Design (24p.), R. Hoek (28p.). Litho Irish Security Stamp Ptg Ltd)

1989 (11 May). *Anniversaries and Events. T* **258** *and similar vert design. Chalk-surfaced paper. P* 14×15.

724 24p. vermilion and black 55 55
725 28p. new blue, black and lemon 70 70

Design:—28p. Circle of twelve stars (third direct elections to European Parliament).

(Des P. Effert. Litho Irish Security Stamp Ptg Ltd)

1989 (15 June). *1300th Death Anniv of Saints Kilian, Totnan and Colman. Chalk-surfaced paper. P* 13½.

726 **259** 28p. multicoloured 50 55
a. Booklet pane. No. 726×4 with margins all round .. .. 2·00

A stamp in a similar design was issued by West Germany.

No. 726a exists with text in Irish, English, German or Latin on the pane margin.

260 19th-century Mail Coach passing Cashel

261 Crest and 19th-century Dividers (150th anniv of Royal Institute of Architects of Ireland)

(Des Katie O'Sullivan and B. Donegan. Litho Irish Security Stamp Ptg Ltd)

1989 (27 July). *Bicentenary of Irish Mail Coach Service. Chalk-surfaced paper. P* 15×14.

727 **260** 28p. multicoloured 50 55

(Des R. Ballagh (24p.), A. Mazer (28p.), K. Uhlemann (30p.), Carey Clarke (46p.). Litho Irish Security Stamp Ptg Ltd)

1989 (27 July). *Anniversaries and Commemorations. T* **261** *and similar designs. Chalk-surfaced paper. P* 15×14 *(30p.) or* 14×15 *(others).*

728 24p. grey and black 40 45
729 28p. multicoloured 50 55
730 30p. multicoloured 50 55
731 46p. orange-brown 80 85
728/31 .. .. *Set of* 4 2·00 2·10

Designs: *Vert*—24p. Sean T. O'Kelly (statesman) (drawing by Sean O'Sullivan); 46p. Jawaharlal Nehru (birth centenary). *Horiz*—30p. Margaret Burke-Sheridan (soprano) (portrait by De Gennaro) and scene from *La Bohème* (birth centenary)

262 "*NCB Ireland* rounding Cape Horn" (Des Fallon)

263 Willow Red Grouse

(Des I. Caulder. Litho Irish Security Stamp Ptg Ltd)

1989 (31 Aug). *First Irish Entry in Whitbread Round the World Yacht Race. Chalk-surfaced paper. P* 15×14.

732 **262** 28p. multicoloured 50 55

(Des R. Ward. Litho Irish Security Stamp Ptg Ltd)

1989 (5 Oct). *Game Birds. T* **263** *and similar square designs. Multicoloured. Chalk-surfaced paper. P* 13½.

733 24p. Type **263** 40 45
734 28p. Lapwing 50 55
735 39p. Woodcock 65 70
736 46p. Ring-necked Pheasant 80 85
733/6 .. .. *Set of* 4 2·10 2·25
MS737 128×92 mm. Nos. 733/6 .. .. 2·25 2·50

No. **MS**737 exists overprinted on the margins to commemorate "STAMPA 89", the Irish National Stamp Exhibition.

264 "The Annunciation" **265** Logo (Ireland's Presidency of the European Communities)

(Des Jacinta Fitzgerald (21p.), J. McEvoy from 13th-century Flemish Psalter (others). Litho Irish Security Stamp Ptg Ltd)

1989 (14 Nov). *Christmas. T* **264** *and similar vert designs. Multicoloured. Chalk-surfaced paper. P* 14×15.

No.	Description	Unused	Used
738	21p. Children decorating crib	35	40
	a. Sheetlet. No. 738×14	5·00	
739	24p. Type **264**	40	45
740	28p. "The Nativity"	50	55
741	46p. "The Adoration of the Magi"	80	85
738/41	*Set of* 4	1·90	2·25

No. 738 represents a special rate for greetings cards within Ireland and to all E.E.C. countries. It was only issued in sheetlets of 14 stamps and 1 label sold at £2.90, providing an additional discount of 4p. off the face value of the stamps.

(Des B. Donegan (30p.), Q Design (50p.). Litho Irish Security Stamp Ptg Ltd)

1990 (9 Jan). *European Events. T* **265** *and similar horiz design. Multicoloured. Chalk-surfaced paper. P* 15×14.

No.	Description	Unused	Used
742	30p. Type **265**	50	55
743	50p. Logo and outline map of Ireland (European Tourism Year)	85	90

266 Dropping Messages from Balloon

(Des Aislinn Adams (26p.), Patricia Sleeman and R. Vogel (30p.). Litho Irish Security Stamp Ptg Ltd)

1990 (30 Jan). *Greetings Stamps. T* **266** *and similar vert design. Chalk-surfaced paper. P* 14×15.

No.	Description	Unused	Used
744	26p. multicoloured	45	50
745	30p. rosine, pale buff and reddish brown	50	55

Design:—30p. Heart and "Love" drawn in lipstick.

POSTAGE DUE STAMPS

From 1922 to 1925 Great Britain postage due stamps in both script and block watermarks were used without overprint.

D 1

D 2

D 3

(Des Ruby McConnell. Typo Govt Printing Works, Dublin)

1925 (20 Feb). *W* **10**. *P* 14 × 15.

No.	Type	Description	Unused	Used
D1	D 1	½d. emerald-green	9·00	15·00
D2		1d. carmine	12·00	1·50
		a. Wmk sideways	£110	50·00
D3		2d. deep green	20·00	3·00
		a. Wmk sideways	35·00	11·00
D4		6d. plum	3·75	5·00
D1/4		*Set of* 4	40·00	22·00

1940–70. *W* **22**. *P* 14 × 15.

No.	Type	Description	Unused	Used
D 5	D 1	½d. emerald-green (1942)	28·00	18·00
D 6		1d. carmine (1941)	85	50
D 7		1½d. vermilion (1953)	1·50	5·00
D 8		2d. deep green (1940)	1·75	50
D 9		3d. blue (10.11.52)	1·50	80
D10		5d. blue-violet (3.3.43)	2·00	2·75
D11		6d. plum (21.3.60)	1·75	1·25
		a. Wmk sideways (1968)	50	75
D12		8d. orange (30.10.62)	6·50	7·00
D13		10d. bright purple (27.1.65)	7·00	7·50
D14		1s. apple-green (10.2.69)	7·00	7·00
		a. Wmk sideways (1970)	30·00	8·50
D5/14		*Set of* 10	50·00	45·00

1971 (15 Feb). *As Nos. D5/14, but with values in decimal currency and colours changed. W* **22**. *P* 14 × 15.

No.	Type	Description	Unused	Used
D15	D 1	1p. sepia	30	35
		a. Wmk sideways	1·50	1·50
D16		1½p. light emerald	30	85
D17		3p. stone	90	1·00
D18		4p. orange	90	1·00
D19		5p. greenish blue	95	1·25
D20		7p. bright yellow	30	1·00
D21		8p. scarlet	30	1·00
D15/21		*Set of* 7	3·50	5·75

1978 (20 Mar). *As Nos.* D17/19, *but no wmk. P* 14 × 15.

No.	Type	Description	Unused	Used
D22	D 1	3p. stone	2·00	4·00
D23		4p. orange	3·50	5·50
D24		5p. greenish blue	2·00	3·50
D22/4		*Set of* 3	6·75	11·50

The above are on whiter paper and the colours are brighter.

1980 (11 June)–**85**. *Photo. Chalk-surfaced paper. P* 15.

No.	Type	Description	Unused	Used
D25	D 2	1p. apple green	10	20
D26		2p. dull blue	10	20
D27		4p. myrtle-green	10	20
D28		6p flesh	15	30
D29		8p. chalky blue	20	40
D30		18p. green	40	65
D31		20p. Indian red (22.8.85)	75	1·00
D32		24p. bright yellowish green	60	1·00
D33		30p. deep violet blue (22.8.85)	1·25	1·75
D34		50p. cerise (22.8.85)	1·75	2·50
D25/34		*Set of* 10	4·75	7·50

(Des Q Design. Litho Irish Security Stamp Ptg Ltd)

1988 (6 Oct). *Chalk-surfaced paper. P* 14 × 15.

No.	Type	Description	Unused	Used
D35	D 3	1p. black, orange-vermilion & lemon	10	10
D36		2p. black, orange-verm & purple-brn	10	10
D37		3p. black, orange-vermilion and plum	10	10
D38		4p. black, orange-vermilion & brt vio	10	10
D39		5p. black, orge-vermilion & royal blue	10	10
D40		17p. black, orange-verm & dp yell-grn	25	30
D41		20p. black, orange-vermilion & slate-bl	30	35
D42		24p. black, orange-verm & dp turq-grn	35	40
D43		30p. black, orange-vermilion & dp grey	45	50
D44		50p. black, orge-verm & brownish grey	75	80
D45		£1 black, orge-vermilion & bistre-brn	1·50	1·60
D35/45		*Set of* 11	3·75	4·00

THOMOND AND LONG ISLAND

Labels inscribed "Principality of Thomond" appeared on the philatelic market in the early 1960s. Thomond is the name of a district in western Ireland. The area does not have its own administration or postal service and the labels were not recognised by the Department of Posts & Telegraphs, Dublin.

Local carriage labels were issued for Long Island, County Cork in April 1973; they were intended to cover the cost of taking mail from the island to the nearest mainland post office. A local service operated for a few weeks before it was suppressed by the Irish Post Office. As the stamps were not accepted for national or international mail they are not listed here.

"Bow" flaw (R.18/12)

1927 (3 Nov). *Wmk Mult Script CA. P* 14.

No.	Type	Description	Unused	Used
107	**18**	½d. green, **O** (Optd S. £45)	15	10
		a. Bow flaw	20·00	

40

41

42

Die I

Die II

(Recess D.L.R.)

1929–32. *Wmk Mult Script CA. P* 14.

No.	Type	Description	Unused	Used
108	**40**	1d. scarlet (Die I)	25	10
		a. Die II (1932)	25	10
109	**41**	1½d. chocolate	30	15
110	**42**	9d. maroon	2·50	1·00
108/10		*Set of* 3	2·75	1·10
108/10 Perf "Specimen"		*Set of* 3	75·00	

In Die I the shading below JAMAICA is formed of thickened parallel lines, and in Die II of diagonal cross-hatching.

43 Coco Palms at Don Christopher's Cove

44 Wag Water River, St. Andrew

45 Priestman's River, Portland

(Dies eng and recess Waterlow)

1932. *Wmk Mult Script CA (sideways on 2d. and 2½d.). P* 12½.

No.	Type	Description	Unused	Used
111	**43**	2d. black and green (late 1932)	4·00	1·25
		a. Imperf between (vert pair)	£3000	
112	**44**	2½d. turquoise-blue & ultram (5.3.32)	80	70
		a. Imperf between (vert pair)	£3250	£3250
113	**45**	6d. grey-black and purple (2.32)	3·50	1·25
111/13		*Set of* 3	7·50	3·00
111/13 Perf "Specimen"		*Set of* 3	75·00	

1935 (6 May). *Silver Jubilee. As Nos. 91/4 of Antigua, but ptd by B.W. P* 11 × 12.

No.	Description	Unused	Used
114	1d. deep blue and scarlet	20	15
	d. Flagstaff on right-hand turret	30·00	
115	1½d. ultramarine and grey-black	25	35
	a. Extra flagstaff	70·00	£100
	b. Short extra flagstaff	45·00	
	c. Lightning conductor	40·00	
116	6d. green and indigo	2·75	5·00
	a. Extra flagstaff	£160	£200
	b. Short extra flagstaff	£100	
	c. Lightning conductor	85·00	
117	1s. slate and purple	2·75	5·00
	a. Extra flagstaff	£275	£350
	b. Short extra flagstaff	£150	
	c. Lightning conductor	£125	
114/17	*Set of* 4	5·50	9·50
114/17 Perf "Specimen"	*Set of* 4	70·00	

For illustrations of plate varieties see Omnibus section following Zululand.

1937 (12 May). *Coronation. As Nos. 13/15 of Aden.*

No.	Description	Unused	Used
118	1d. scarlet	30	15
119	1½d. grey-black	50	30
120	2½d. bright blue	80	70
118/20	*Set of* 3	1·40	1·00
118/20 Perf "Specimen"	*Set of* 3	55·00	

46 King George VI

47 Coco Palms at Don Christopher's Cove

48 Bananas

49 Citrus Grove

50 Kingston Harbour

51 Sugar Industry

52 Bamboo Walk

53 King George VI

53*a* Tobacco Growing and Cigar Making

Repaired chimney (Plate 1 R. 11/1)

(Recess D.L.R. (T **46**, 5s. and 10s.), Waterlow (others))

1938–52. *T* **46** *to* **53a** *and as Nos. 88, 112/113, but with inset portrait of King George VI, as in T* **47**. *Wmk Mult Script CA. P* 13½ × 14 (½d., 1d., 1½d.), 14 (5s., 10s.) *or* 12½ (*others*).

No.	Type	Description	Unused	Used
121	**46**	½d. blue-green (10.10.38)	10	10
		a. Wmk sideways	†	£1800
121*b*		½d. orange (25.10.51)	20	20
122		1d. scarlet (10.10.38)	10	10
122*a*		1d. blue-green (25.10.51)	30	10
123		1½d. brown (10.10.38)	10	10
124	**47**	2d. grey and green	10	10
		a. Perf 13 × 13½	35	20
		b. Perf 12½ × 13 (1951)	50	20
125	**44**	2½d. greenish blue and ultramarine	1·25	90
126	**48**	3d. ultramarine and green	30	30
126*a*		3d. greenish blue & ultram (15.8.49)	95	55
126*b*		3d. green and scarlet (1.7.52)	70	20
127	**49**	4d. brown and green	15	10
128	**45**	6d. grey and purple	35	10
		a. Perf 13½ × 13 (10.10.50)	45	10
129	**50**	9d. lake	15	15
130	**51**	1s. green and purple-brown	50	10
		a. Repaired chimney	90·00	50·00
131	**52**	2s. blue and chocolate	4·50	50
132	–	5s. slate-blue and yellow-orange	5·00	2·00
		a. Perf 14¼, line (1941)	£1800	£125
		b. Perf 13 (24.10.49)	6·00	3·00
		ba. Blue and orange (10.10.50)	4·00	2·75
133	**53**	10s. myrtle-green	10·00	6·00
		aa. Perf 13 (10.10.50)	7·00	5·00
133*a*	**53*a***	£1 chocolate and violet (15.8.49)	22·00	26·00
121/33*a*		*Set of* 18	35·00	30·00
121/33 Perf "Specimen"		*Set of* 13	£180	

No. 132a shows the emergency use of a line perforation machine, exact gauge 14.15, after the De La Rue works were damaged in December 1940. The normal comb measures 13.8 × 13.7.

SELF-GOVERNMENT

54 Courthouse, Falmouth

55 King Charles II and King George VI

56 Institute of Jamaica

(Recess Waterlow)

1945 (20 Aug)–**46.** *New Constitution. T* **54/6** *and similar designs. Wmk Mult Script CA. P* 12½.

No.	Type	Description	Unused	Used
134	**54**	1½d. sepia	15	15
		a. Perf 12½ × 13 (1946)	85	25
135	**55**	2d. green	2·25	70
		a. Perf 12½ × 13 (1945)	15	30
136	**56**	3d. ultramarine	15	20
		a. Perf 13 (1946)	70	80
137	–	4½d. slate	15	25
		a. Perf 13 (1946)	70	80
138	–	2s. red-brown	25	40
139	–	5s. indigo	50	70
140	**56**	10s. green	70	1·25
134/140		*Set of* 7	1·75	3·25
134/40 Perf "Specimen"		*Set of* 7	£140	

Designs: *Vert (as T* **54**)—2s. "Labour and Learning". *Horiz (as T* **56**)—4½d. House of Assembly; 5s. Scroll, flag and King George VI.

1946 (14 Oct). *Victory. As Nos. 28/9 of Aden. P* 13½ × 14.

No.	Description	Unused	Used
141	1½d. purple-brown	40	10
	a. Perf 13½	25	20
142	3d. blue	40	20
	a. Perf 13½	30	1·00
141/2 Perf "Specimen"	*Set of* 2	48·00	

1948 (1 Dec). *Royal Silver Wedding. As Nos. 30/1 of Aden.*

No.	Description	Unused	Used
143	1½d. red-brown	20	10
144	£1 scarlet	23·00	42·00

1949 (10 Oct). *75th Anniv of Universal Postal Union. As Nos. 114/17 of Antigua.*

No.	Description	Unused	Used
145	1½d. red-brown	25	15
146	2d. deep blue-green	45	55
147	3d. deep blue	45	70
148	6d. purple	55	80
145/8	*Set of* 4	1·50	2·00

1951 (16 Feb). *Inauguration of B.W.I. University College. As Nos. 118/19 of Antigua.*

No.	Description	Unused	Used
149	2d. black and red-brown	20	15
150	6d. grey-black and purple	30	15

60 Scout Badge and Map of Caribbean

61 Scout Badge and Map of Jamaica

(Litho B.W.)

1952 (5 Mar). *First Caribbean Scout Jamboree. Wmk Mult Script CA. P* 13½ × 13 (2*d.*) *or* 13 × 13½ (6*d.*).

No.	Type	Description	Unused	Used
151	**60**	2d. blue, apple-green and black	15	10
152	**61**	6d. yellow-green, carmine-red and black	15	30

1953 (2 June). *Coronation. As No. 47 of Aden.*

No.	Description	Unused	Used
153	2d. black and deep yellow-green	10	10

62 Coco Palms at Don Christopher's Cove

(Recess Waterlow)

1953 (25 Nov). *Royal Visit. Wmk Mult Script CA. P* 12½ × 13.

No.	Type	Description	Unused	Used
154	**62**	2d. grey-black and green	10	10

63 Man-o'-War at Port Royal

(Recess D.L.R.)

1955 (10 May). *Tercentenary Issue. T* **63** *and similar horiz designs. Wmk Mult Script CA. P* 12½.

155 2d. black and olive-green 20 10
156 2½d. black and deep bright blue 15 35
157 3d. black and claret 15 30
158 6d. black and carmine-red 20 20
155/8 .. .. *Set of* 4 65 80

Designs:—2½d. Old Montego Bay; 3d. Old Kingston; 6d. Proclamation of Abolition of Slavery, 1838.

67 Palms

71 Mahoe

75 Blue Mountain Peak

79 Arms of Jamaica

80 Arms of Jamaica

(Recess B.W. (T **79/80**), D.L.R. (others))

1956 (1 May)–**58**. *T* **67, 71, 75, 79/80** *and similar designs. Wmk Mult Script CA. P* 13 (½*d. to* 6*d.*), 13½ (8*d. to* 2*s.*) *or* 11½ (3*s. to* £1).

159 **67** ½d. black and deep orange-red 10 10
160 – 1d. black and emerald 10 10
161 – 2d. black and carmine-red (2.8.56) .. 10 10
162 – 2½d. black and deep bright blue (2.8.56) 15 40
163 **71** 3d. emerald and red-brown (17.12.56) 15 10
164 – 4d. bronze-green and blue (17.12.56) .. 15 10
165 – 5d. scarlet and bronze-green (17.12.56) 20 1·00
166 – 6d. black and deep rose-red (3.9.56) .. 1·25 10
167 **75** 8d. ultramarine & red-orge (15.11.56) 15 10
168 – 1s. yellow-green and blue (15.11.56) .. 30 10
169 – 1s. 6d. ultram & reddish pur (15.11.56) 30 10
170 – 2s. blue & bronze-green (15.11.56) .. 1·50 55
a. *Grey-blue & dp bronze-grn* (24.4.58) 2·25 65
171 **79** 3s. black and blue (2.8.56) 50 60
172 5s. black and carmine-red (15.8.56) .. 1·00 75
173 **80** 10s. black and blue-green (15.8.56) .. 8·00 4·50
174 £1 black and purple (15.8.56) .. 14·00 4·75
159/74 .. .. *Set of* 16 25·00 12·00

Designs:—*Vert* (*as T* **67, 71**)—1d. Sugar Cane; 2d. Pineapples; 2½d. Bananas; 4d. Breadfruit; 5d. Ackee; 6d. Streamertail. *Horiz.* (*as T* **75**)—1s. Royal Botanic Gardens, Hope; 1s. 6d. Rafting on the Rio Grande; 2s. Fort Charles.

1958 (22 Apr). *Inauguration of British Caribbean Federation. As Nos.* 135/7 *of Antigua.*

175 2d. deep green 25 10
176 5d. blue 40 70
177 6d. scarlet 40 20
175/7 .. .. *Set of* 3 95 85

81 "Britannia" flying over *City of Berlin*, 1860

83 1s. Stamps of 1860 and 1956

(Recess Waterlow)

1960 (4 Jan). *Stamp Centenary. T* **81, 83** *and similar design. W w* **12.** *P* 13 × 13½ (1*s.*) *or* 13½ × 14 (*others*).

178 2d. blue and reddish purple 15 10
179 6d. carmine and olive-green 20 10
180 1s. red-brown, yellow-green and blue .. 20 10
178/80 .. .. *Set of* 3 50 20

Design: *As T* **81**—6d. Postal mule-cart and motor-van.

INDEPENDENT

1962 1962 INDEPENDENCE (84)

INDEPENDENCE 1962 (85)

86 Military Bugler and Map

(Des V. Whiteley. Photo D.L.R. (2, 4d., 1s. 6d., 5s.))

1962 (8 Aug)–**63**. *Independence.*

(*a*) *Nos.* 159/60, 162, 171, 173/4 *optd as T* **84** *and Nos.* 163, 165/8, 170 *optd with T* **85**

181 **67** ½d. black and deep orange-red .. 10 30
182 – 1d. black and emerald 10 10
183 – 2½d. black and deep bright blue .. 10 75
184 **71** 3d. emerald and red-brown 10 10
185 – 5d. scarlet and bronze-green 15 60
186 – 6d. black and deep rose-red 75 10
187 **75** 8d. ultram & red-orge (opt at upper left) 15 10
a. Opt at lower left (17.9.63?) .. 15 15
188 – 1s. yellow-green and blue 15 10
189 – 2s. blue and bronze-green 80 60
a. *Dp blue & dp bronze-green* (20.8.63) 1·50 70
190 **79** 3s. black and blue .. .. .. 90 1·50
191 **80** 10s. black and blue-green .. .. 2·00 4·00
192 £1 black and purple .. .. .. 2·75 5·50

(*b*) *Horiz designs as T* **86.** *W w* **12.** *P* 13

193 2d. multicoloured 15 10
194 4d. multicoloured 15 10
195 1s. 6d. black and red 65 85
196 5s. multicoloured .. .. 1·25 2·00
181/96 .. .. *Set of* 16 9·00 15·00

Designs:—2, 4d. Type **86**; 1s. 6d. Gordon House and banner; 5s. Map, factories and fruit.

89 Kingston Seal, Weightlifting, Boxing, Football and Cycling

(Photo Harrison)

1962 (11 Aug). *Ninth Central American and Caribbean Games, Kingston. T* **89** *and similar horiz designs. W w* **12.** *P* 14½ × 14.

197 1d. sepia and carmine-red 10 10
198 6d. sepia and greenish blue 10 10
199 8d. sepia and bistre 10 10
200 2s. multicoloured 20 40
197/200 .. .. *Set of* 4 35 50

Designs:—6d. Kingston seal, diving, sailing, swimming and water polo; 8d. Kingston seal, pole-vaulting, javelin throwing, discus throwing, relay-racing and hurdling; 2s. Kingston coat of arms and athlete.

An imperf miniature sheet exists, but this was never available at face value or at any post office.

93 Farmer and Crops

94 Carole Joan Crawford ("Miss World 1963")

(Des M. Goaman. Litho D.L.R.)

1963 (4 June). *Freedom from Hunger. P* 12½.

201 **93** 1d. multicoloured 15 10
202 8d. multicoloured 50 20

1963 (4 Sept). *Red Cross Centenary. As Nos.* 147/8 *of Antigua.*

203 2d. red and black 15 10
204 1s. 6d. red and blue 40 65

1963–64. *As Nos.* 181/90, *but wmk w* **12.**

205 **67** ½d. black and deep orange-red (3.12.63*) 10 15
206 – 1d. black and emerald (3.4.64) .. 10 15
207 – 2½d. black and deep bright blue (3.4.64) 25 80
208 **71** 3d. emerald and red-brown (17.12.63*) 15 15
209 – 5d. scarlet and bronze-green (3.4.64) .. 30 1·25
210 **75** 8d. ultramarine and red-orange (3.4.64) 20 55
211 – 1s. yellow-green and blue (21.12.63*) .. 35 75
212 – 2s. deep blue and deep bronze-green (3.4.64) .. .. 60 2·00
213 **79** 3s. black and blue (5.2.64) .. .. 2·00 7·50
205/13 .. .. *Set of* 9 3·50 12·00

The overprint on the 8d., 1s. and 2s. is at lower left, the others are as before.

*These are the earliest known dates recorded in Jamaica.

(Des and photo D.L.R.)

1964 (14 Feb–25 May). *"Miss World 1963" Commemoration. P* 13.

214 **94** 3d. multicoloured 10 10
215 1s. multicoloured 10 10
216 1s. 6d. multicoloured 15 20
214/16 .. .. *Set of* 3 30 25
MS216*a* 153 × 101 mm. Nos. 214/16. Imperf (25.5.64) .. .. 80 1·00

95 *Lignum Vitae*

97 Blue Mahoe

103 Gypsum Industry

109 Arms of Jamaica

111 Multiple "J" and Pineapple

(Des V. Whiteley. Photo Harrison)

1964 (4 May)–**68**. *T* **95, 97, 103, 109** *and similar designs. W* **111**. *P* 14½ (1*d.*, 2*d.*, 2½*d.*, 6*d.*, 8*d.*), 14×14½ (1½*d.*, 3*d.*, 4*d.*, 10*s.*), 14½×14 (9*d.*, 1*s.*, 3*s.*, 5*s.*, £1) *or* 13½×14½ (1*s.* 6*d.*, 2*s.*).

217 1d. violet-blue, dp green & lt brn (*shades*) 10 10
218 1½d. multicoloured 15 10
219 2d. red, yellow and grey-green 15 10
220 2½d. multicoloured 45 60
221 3d. yellow, black and emerald 15 10
222 4d. ochre and violet 35 10
223 6d. multicoloured .. .. .. 1·25 10
a. Blue omitted .. .. .. 35·00
b. Value omitted .. .. ..
224 8d. mult (yellowish green background) .. 1·25 60
a. Red (beak) omitted .. .. 75·00
b. *Greyish green background* (16.7.68) 2·50 1·50
225 9d. blue and yellow-bistre 45 10
226 1s. black and light brown 20 10
a. Light brown omitted £150
ab. Value only omitted .. ..
b. Black omitted £350
ba. "NATIONAL STADIUM" etc omitted £400
227 1s. 6d. black, light blue and buff .. 75 15
228 2s. red-brown, black and light blue .. 1·25 15
229 3s. blue and dull green .. .. 1·00 80
a. Perf 13½×14½ 35 65
230 5s. black, ochre and blue .. .. 1·10 50
231 10s. multicoloured .. .. .. 1·25 1·00
a. Blue ("JAMAICA", etc) omitted .. £170
232 £1 multicoloured .. .. .. 1·50 1·00
217/32 .. .. *Set of* 16 9·50 4·25

Designs:—*Horiz.* (*As T* **95**)—1½d. Ackee; 2½d. Land shells; 3d. National flag over Jamaica; 4d. *Murex antillarum*; 6d. *Papilio homerus*; 8d. Streamertail. *As T* **103**—1s. National Stadium; 1s. 6d. Palisadoes International Airport; 2s. Bauxite mining; 3s. Blue Marlin (sport fishing); 5s. Exploration of sunken city, Port Royal; £1 Queen Elizabeth II and national flag.

No. 223b. Two left half sheets are known with the black printing shifted downwards to such an extent that the value is omitted from the top row.

Nos. 226a/ab came from a sheet on which the two bottom rows had the colour omitted with the next row showing it missing from the lower third of the stamps.

A similar sheet, but with the colour missing from the top two rows and part of the third produced Nos 226b/ba.

112 Scout Belt

113 Globe, Scout Hat and Scarf

114 Scout Badge and Alligator

(Photo Harrison)

1964 (27 Aug). *Sixth Inter-American Scout Conference, Kingston. W* **111.** *P* 14 (1*s.*) *or* 14½ × 14 (*others*).
233 **112** 3d. red, black and pink 10 10
234 **113** 8d. bright blue, olive and black 10 20
235 **114** 1s. gold, deep blue and light blue .. 10 20
233/5 .. .. *Set of* 3 25 35

115 Gordon House, Kingston

118 Eleanor Roosevelt

(Des V. Whiteley. Photo Harrison)

1964 (16 Nov). *Tenth Commonwealth Parliamentary Conference, Kingston. T* **115** *and similar horiz designs. W* **111.** *P* 14½ × 14.
236 3d. black and yellow-green 10 10
237 6d. black and carmine-red 10 10
238 1s. 6d. black and bright blue 15 20
236/8 .. .. *Set of* 3 20 25

Designs:—6d. Headquarters House, Kingston; 1s. 6d. House of Assembly, Spanish Town.

(Des V. Whiteley. Photo Harrison)

1964 (10 Dec). *16th Anniv of Declaration of Human Rights. W* **111.** *P* 14½ × 14.
239 **118** 1s. black, red and light green 10 10

119 Guides' Emblem on Map

120 Guide Emblems

(Photo Harrison)

1965 (17 May). *Golden Jubilee of Jamaica Girl Guides Association. W* **111** (*sideways on* 3*d.*). *P* 14 × 14½ (3*d.*) *or* 14 (1*s.*).
240 **119** 3d. yellow, green and light blue .. 10 10
241 **120** 1s. yellow, black and apple-green .. 10 15

121 Uniform Cap

122 Flag-bearer and Drummer

(Photo Harrison)

1965 (23 Aug). *Salvation Army Centenary. W* **111.** *P* 14 × 14½ (3*d.*) *or* 14½ × 14 (1*s.* 6*d.*).
242 **121** 3d. multicoloured 10 10
243 **122** 1s. 6d. multicoloured 15 20

123 Paul Bogle, William Gordon and Morant Bay Court House

124 Abeng-blower, "Telstar", Morse Key and I.T.U. Emblem

(Photo Enschedé)

1965 (29 Dec). *Centenary of Morant Bay Rebellion. No wmk. P* 14 × 13.
244 **123** 3d. light brown, ultramarine and black 10 10
245 1s. 6d. lt brown, yellow-green & black 10 10
246 3s. light brown, rose and black .. 15 30
244/6 .. .. *Set of* 3 25 40

(Photo Harrison)

1965 (29 Dec). *I.T.U. Centenary. W* **111.** *P* 14 × 14½.
247 **124** 1s. black, grey-blue and red 40 15

ROYAL VISIT
MARCH 1966

(**125**)

126 Sir Winston Churchill

1966 (3 Mar). *Royal Visit. Nos.* 221, 223, 226/7 *optd with T* **125.**
248 3d. yellow, black and emerald 15 10
249 6d. multicoloured 55 10
250 1s. black and light brown 55 10
251 1s. 6d. black, light blue and buff 70 60
248/51 .. .. *Set of* 4 1·75 65

(Des Jennifer Toombs. Photo Harrison)

1966 (18 April). *Churchill Commemoration. W* **111.** *P* 14.
252 **126** 6d. black and olive-green 35 20
253 1s. bistre-brown and deep violet-blue .. 65 70

127 Statue of Athlete and Flags

131 Bolivar's Statue and Flags of Jamaica and Venezuela

(Des V. Whiteley. Photo Harrison)

1966 (4 Aug). *Eighth British Empire and Commonwealth Games. T* **127** *and similar horiz designs. W* **111.** *P* 14½ × 14.
254 3d. multicoloured 10 10
255 6d. multicoloured 10 10
256 1s. multicoloured 10 10
257 3s. bright gold and deep blue 20 35
a. Dull gold and deep blue .. ..
254/7 .. .. *Set of* 4 35 45
MS258 128×103 mm. Nos. 254/7. Imperf .. 3·75 6·00

Designs:—6d. Racing cyclists; 1s. National Stadium, Kingston; 3s. Games emblem.

No. **MS**258 has been seen with the whole printing inverted except for the brown background.

(Des and photo Harrison)

1966 (5 Dec). *150th Anniv of "Jamaica Letter". W* **111.** *P* 14 × 15.
259 **131** 8d. multicoloured 10 10

132 Jamaican Pavilion

133 Sir Donald Sangster (Prime Minister)

(Des V. Whiteley. Photo Harrison)

1967 (28 Apr). *World Fair, Montreal. W* **111.** *P* 14½.
260 **132** 6d. multicoloured 10 10
261 1s. multicoloured 10 10

(Des and photo Enschedé)

1967 (28 Aug). *Sangster Memorial Issue. P* 13½.
262 **133** 3d. multicoloured 10 10
263 1s. 6d. multicoloured 10 10

134 Traffic Duty

135 Personnel of the Force

(Des V. Whiteley. Photo Enschedé)

1967 (28 Nov). *Centenary of the Constabulary Force. T* **134/5** *and similar horiz design. Multicoloured. W* **111.** *P* 13½ × 14.
264 3d. Type **134** 10 10
a. Wmk sideways 20 20
265 1s. Type **135** 15 10
266 1s. 6d. Badge and Constables of 1867 and 1967 (*as T* **134**) 20 15
264/6 .. .. *Set of* 3 40 25

1968 (8 Feb). *M.C.C.'s West Indies Tour. As Nos. 445/7 of Guyana, but inscr. "JAMAICA". Multicoloured. W* **111** (*sideways*). *P* 14.
267 6d. Wicket-keeping 20 30
a. Horiz strip of 3. Nos. 267/9 .. .. 1·50
268 6d. Batting 20 30
269 6d. Bowling 20 30
267/9 .. .. *Set of* 3 55 80

Nos. 267/9 were issued in small sheets of 9 comprising three *se-tenant* strips as No. 267a.

Nos. 267/9 exist on PVA gum as well as on gum arabic.

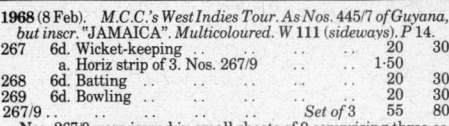

137 Sir Alexander and Lady Bustamante

(Des and photo Harrison)

1968 (23 May). *Labour Day. W* **111.** *P* 14.
270 **137** 3d. rose and black 10 10
271 1s. olive and black 10 10

138 Human Rights Emblem over Map of Jamaica

(Photo Harrison)

1968 (3 Dec). *Human Rights Year. T* **138** *and similar multicoloured designs. W* **111.** *P* 14.
272 3d. Type **138** 10 10
a. Gold (flame) omitted .. .. .. 90·00
273 1s. Hands cupping Human Rights emblem (*vert*) 10 10
274 3s. Jamaican holding "Human Rights" .. 15 25
a. Gold (flame) omitted £100
272/4 .. .. *Set of* 3 25 30

Three designs, showing 3d. Bowls of Grain, 1s. Abacus, 3s. Hands in Prayer, were prepared but not issued (*Price for set of 3 mint* £100).

141 ILO Emblem

142 Nurse, and Children being weighed and measured

(Des V. Whiteley. Litho Format)

1969 (23 May). *50th Anniv of International Labour Organization. P* 14.
275 **141** 6d. orange-yellow and blackish brown 10 10
276 3s. bright emerald and blackish brown 20 30

(Des and photo Harrison)

1969 (30 May). *20th Anniv of W.H.O. T* **142** *and similar designs. W* **111.** *P* 14.
277 6d. grey, brown and orange 10 10
278 1s. black, sepia and blue-green 10 10
279 3s. grey-black, brown and pale bright blue 20 30
277/9 .. .. *Set of* 3 30 35

Designs: *Horiz*—1s. Malaria eradication. *Vert*—3s. Trainee nurse.

(New Currency. 100 cents = 1 dollar)

C-DAY
8th September
1969
1c

(**145**)

146 "The Adoration of the Kings" (detail, Foppa)

1969 (8 Sept). *Decimal currency. Nos.* 217, 219, 221/3 *and* 225/32 *surch as T* **145.** *Sterling values unobliterated except* 1 c. *to* 4 c. *and* 8 c.
280 1 c. on 1d. violet-blue, dp green & lt brown .. 10 10
281 2 c. on 2d. red, yellow and grey-green .. 10 10
282 3 c. on 3d. yellow, black and emerald .. 10 10
283 4 c. on 4d. ochre and violet 25 10
a. "8t" of "8th" omitted (R. 10/1) .. .. 25·00

284 5 c. on 6d. multicoloured 50 10
a. Blue omitted .. .. 35·00
285 8 c. on 9d. blue and yellow-bistre 10 10
286 10 c. on 1s. black and light brown 10 10
287 15 c. on 1s. 6d. black, light blue and buff .. 30 45
288 20 c. on 2s. red-brown, black & lt blue .. 40 55
289 30 c. on 3s. blue and dull green .. .. 1·50 2·00
290 50 c. on 5s. black, ochre and blue .. .. 1·25 2·00
291 $1 on 10s. multicoloured .. .. .. 1·50 3·25
292 $2 on £1 multicoloured .. .. .. 1·50 6·00
280/92 .. .. .. Set of 13 6·50 13·00
No. 281 exists with PVA gum as well as gum arabic.

(Des J. Cooter. Litho D.L.R.)

1969 (25 Oct). *Christmas. Paintings. T* **146** *and similar vert designs. Multicoloured. W* **111**. *P* 13.
293 2 c. Type **146** 10 10
294 5 c. "Madonna, Child and St. John" (Raphael) 10 10
295 8 c. "The Adoration of the Kings" (detail, Dosso Dossi) 10 10
293/5 .. .. Set of 3 15 20

149 Half Penny, 1869

151 George William Gordon

(Des G. Drummond. Litho P.B.)

1969 (27 Oct). *Centenary of First Jamaican Coins. T* **149** *and similar horiz design. W* **111**. *P* 12½.
296 3 c. silver, black and mauve 15 25
b. Wmk sideways 10 10
297 15 c. silver, black and light emerald 10 10
Design:—15 c. One penny, 1869.

(Des G. Vasarhelyi. Litho Enschedé)

1970 (11 Mar). *National Heroes. T* **151** *and similar vert designs. Multicoloured. P* 12 × 12½.
298 1 c. Type **151** 10 10
a. Yellow (from flags) omitted £175
299 3 c. Sir Alexander Bustamante 10 10
300 5 c. Norman Manley 10 10
301 10 c. Marcus Garvey 10 10
302 15 c. Paul Bogle 12 15
298/302 .. .. Set of 5 30 30

156 "Christ appearing to St. Peter" (Carracci)

2c ■

(159)

(Des G. Drummond. Photo Enschedé)

1970 (23 Mar). *Easter. T* **156** *and similar vert designs. Multicoloured. W* **111**. *P* 12 × 12½.
303 3 c. Type **156** 10 10
304 10 c. "Christ Crucified" (Antonello da Messina) 10 10
305 20 c. Easter Lily 20 25
303/5 .. .. Set of 3 30 30

1970 (16 July). *No.* 219 *surch with T* **159**.
306 2 c. on 2d. red, yellow and grey-green .. 15 20

160 *Lignum Vitae*

161 Cable Ship *Dacia*

1970 (7 Sept–2 Nov). *Decimal Currency. Designs as Nos.* 217/32 *but inscr as T* **160** *in new currency. W* **111** *(sideways on* 2, 4, 15, 20 *c. and* $1*). P* 14½ (1, 5 *c.*), 14 × 14½ (4 *c.*, $1), 13½ × 14½ (15, 20 *c.*) *or* 14½ × 14 *(others)*.
307 1 c. violet-blue, deep green & lt brown .. 15 10
308 2 c. red, yellow and grey-green (as 2d.) .. 15 10
309 3 c. yellow, black and emerald (as 3d.) .. 15 10
310 4 c. ochre and violet (as 4d.) 40 10
311 5 c. multicoloured (as 6d.) .. .. 1·50 10
312 8 c. blue and yellow-bistre (as 9d.) .. 20 10
a. Wmk sideways 20 45
313 10 c. black and light brown (as 1s.) .. 20 10
314 15 c. black, light blue and buff (as 1s. 6d.) (2.11) 80 45
315 20 c. red-brown, black & lt blue (as 2s.) (2.11) 90 75
316 30 c. blue and dull green (as 3s.) (2.11) .. 1·25 60
317 50 c. black, ochre and blue (as 5s.) (2.11) .. 1·25 2·00
318 $1 multicoloured (as 10s.) (2.11) .. 1·25 2·25
319 $2 multicoloured (as £1) (2.11) .. .. 1·50 2·50
307/19 .. .. Set of 13 8·50 8·00

(Des G. Drummond. Litho J.W.)

1970 (12 Oct). *Centenary of Telegraph Service. T* **161** *and similar horiz designs. W* **111** *(sideways). P* 14½ × 14.
320 3 c. yellow, red and black 15 10
321 10 c. black and turquoise 20 10
322 50 c. multicoloured .. .. 50 1·00
320/2 .. .. Set of 3 75 1·10
Designs:—10 c. Bright's cable gear aboard *Dacia*; 50 c. Morse key and chart.

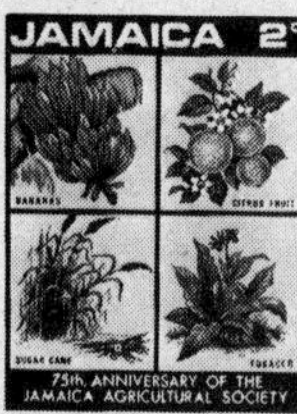

164 Bananas, Citrus, Sugar-Cane and Tobacco

165 *The Projector* (1845)

(Des G. Drummond. Litho Questa)

1970 (2 Nov). *75th Anniv of Jamaican Agricultural Society. W* **111**. *P* 14.
323 **164** 2 c. multicoloured 10 15
324 10 c. multicoloured 15 10

(Des V. Whiteley. Litho Format)

1970 (21 Nov). *125th Anniv of Jamaican Railways. T* **165** *and similar horiz designs. Multicoloured. W* **111** *(sideways). P* 13½.
325 3 c. Type **165** 25 10
326 15 c. Steam locomotive No. 54 (1944) .. 70 30
327 50 c. Diesel locomotive No. 102 (1967) .. 1·75 2·00
325/7 .. .. Set of 3 2·40 2·25

168 Church of St. Jago de la Vega

169 Henry Morgan and Ships

(Des R. Granger Barrett. Litho J.W.)

1971 (22 Feb). *Centenary of Disestablishment of the Church of England in Jamaica. T* **168** *and similar vert design. Multicoloured. W* **111**. *P* 14½.
328 3 c. Type **168** 10 10
329 10 c. Type **168** 10 10
330 20 c. Type **168** 15 25
331 30 c. Emblem of Church of England in Jamaica 20 45
328/31 .. .. Set of 4 35 70

(Des J.W. Litho Questa)

1971 (10 May). *Pirates and Buccaneers. T* **169** *and similar horiz designs. Multicoloured. W* **111** *(sideways). P* 14.
332 3 c. Type **169** 20 10
333 15 c. Mary Read, Anne Bonny and trial pamphlet 45 15
334 30 c. Pirate schooner attacking merchantman 1·00 1·25
332/4 .. .. Set of 3 1·50 1·40

170 1s. Stamp of 1919 with Frame Inverted

171 Satellite and Dish Aerial

(Des Jennifer Toombs. Litho J.W.)

1971 (30 Oct). *Tercentenary of Post Office Establishment. T* **170** *and similar designs. W* **111** *(sideways, except* 50 *c.). P* 13½.
335 3 c. black and lake 10 10
336 5 c. grey-black and bright green 10 10
337 8 c. black and violet 15 10
338 10 c. brown, black and indigo 15 10
339 20 c. multicoloured 25 35
340 50 c. ochre, black and slate 45 80
335/40 .. .. Set of 6 1·00 1·25
Designs: *Horiz*—3 c. Dummer packet letter, 1705; 5 c. Pre-stamp inland letter, 1793; 8 c. Harbour St. P.O., Kingston, 1820; 10 c. Modern stamp and cancellation; 20 c. British stamps used in Jamaica, 1859.

(Des Cable & Wireless Ltd. Litho J.W.)

1972 (17 Feb). *Opening of Jamaican Earth Satellite Station. W* **111**. *P* 14 × 13½.
341 **171** 3 c. multicoloured 15 10
342 15 c. multicoloured 20 15
343 50 c. multicoloured .. .. .. 55 1·25
341/3 .. .. Set of 3 80 1·25

172 Causeway, Kingston Harbour

173 Air Jamaica Hostess and Aircraft

(Des J.W. Litho Format)

1972 (17 Apr–2 Oct). *Multicoloured designs as T* **172** *(1 to 6 c.) or* **173** *(8 c. to $2). W* **111** *(sideways on horiz designs). P* 14½ × 14 (1, 2 *c.*), 14 × 14½ (3, 4, 5, 6 *c.*) *or* 13½ *(others)*.
344 1 c. Pimento (*vert*) (5.6) 10 10
345 2 c. Red Ginger (*vert*) (5.6) 10 10
346 3 c. Bauxite Industry (5.6) 10 10
347 4 c. Type **172** 10 10
348 5 c. Oil Refinery (5.6) 10 10
349 6 c. Senate Building, University of the West Indies (5.6) 10 10
350 8 c. National Stadium (5.6) 10 10
351 9 c. Devon House (5.6) 10 10
352 10 c. Type **173** 10 10
353 15 c. Old Iron Bridge, Spanish Town (*vert*) (2.10) 35 10
354 20 c. College of Arts, Science and Technology (2.10) 25 15
355 30 c. Dunn's River Falls (*vert*) (2.10) 35 15
356 50 c. River rafting (5.6) 60 40
357 $1 Jamaica House (2.10) 75 65
358 $2 Kings House (2.10) .. .. 1·00 1·25
344/58 .. .. Set of 15 3·25 2·75

TENTH
ANNIVERSARY
INDEPENDENCE
1962-1972

(174)

175 Arms of Kingston

1972 (8 Aug). *Tenth Anniv of Independence. Nos.* 346, 352 *and* 356 *optd as T* **174**.
359 3 c. Bauxite Industry 10 10
360 10 c. Type **173** 10 10
361 50 c. River rafting .. .. 40 1·25
359/61 .. .. Set of 3 45 1·25

(Des R. Granger Barrett. Litho J.W.)

1972 (4 Dec). *Centenary of Kingston as Capital. W* **111** *(sideways on* 50 *c.). P* 13½ × 14 *(*5 *and* 30 *c.) or* 14 × 13½ *(*50 *c.)*.
362 **175** 5 c. multicoloured 10 10
363 30 c. multicoloured 20 25
364 – 50 c. multicoloured 40 75
362/4 .. .. Set of 3 60 1·00
The 50 c. is as T **175**, but horiz.

176 Small Indian Mongoose on Map

(Des R. Granger Barrett. Litho Questa)

1973 (9 Apr). *Centenary of Introduction of the Mongoose. T* **176** *and similar horiz designs. W* **111** *(sideways). P* 14 × 14½.
365 8 c. light apple-green, yellow-green and black 10 10
366 40 c. light cobalt, light blue and black .. 25 50
367 60 c. salmon-pink, brownish salmon & black 50 1·00
365/7 .. .. Set of 3 75 1·40
MS368 165 × 95 mm. Nos. 365/7 .. .. 1·50 3·00
Designs:—40 c. Mongoose and rat; 60 c. Mongoose and chicken.

177 *Euphorbia punicea*

(Des Sylvia Goaman. Litho Questa)

1973 (9 July). *Flora. T* **177** *and similar diamond-shaped designs. Multicoloured.* W **111**. P 14.
369 1 c. Type **177** 10 10
370 6 c. *Hylocereus triangularis* 15 10
371 9 c. *Columnea argentea* 15 10
372 15 c. *Portlandia grandiflora* 25 15
373 30 c. *Samyda pubescens* 50 60
374 50 c. *Cordia sebestena* .. .. 80 1·25
369/74 .. .. *Set of* 6 1·75 2·00

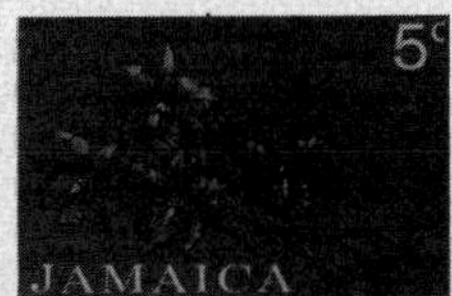

178 *Broughtonia sanguinea*

(Des Sylvia Goaman. Litho B.W.)

1973 (8 Oct). *Orchids. T* **178** *and similar multicoloured designs.* W **111** *(sideways on* 5 c., $1, **MS**379). P 14 × 13½ (5 c., $1) *or* 13½ × 14 *(others)*.
375 5 c. Type **178** 20 10
376 10 c. *Arpophyllum jamaicense (vert)* 35 10
377 20 c. *Oncidium pulchellum (vert)* 75 25
378 $1 *Brassia maculata* .. .. 2·00 2·75
375/8 .. .. *Set of* 4 3·00 2·75
MS379 161 × 95 mm. Nos. 375/8. P 12 .. .. 3·00 4·00

179 *Mary*, 1808–15 180 "Journeys"

(Des J. Cooter. Litho J.W.)

1974 (8 Apr). *Mail Packet Boats. T* **179** *and similar horiz designs. Multicoloured.* W **111** *(sideways on Nos.* 380/3, *upright on* **MS**384). P 13½ (5 c., 50 c.) *or* 14 *(others)*.
380 5 c. Type **179** 20 10
a. Perf 14 .. .. 3·00 1·75
381 10 c. *Queensbury*, 1814–27 .. .. 25 10
382 15 c. *Sheldrake*, 1829–34 .. .. 45 40
383 50 c. *Thames*, 1842 .. .. 1·75 2·25
380/3 .. .. *Set of* 4 2·40 2·50
MS384 133 × 159 mm. Nos. 380/4. P 13½ *(sold at* 90 c.) .. .. 3·25 4·50

(Des R. Granger Barrett. Litho Questa)

1974 (1 Aug). *National Dance Theatre Company. T* **180** *and similar vert designs showing dance-works. Multicoloured.* W **111**. P 13½.
385 5 c. Type **180** 10 10
386 10 c. "Jamaican Promenade" 10 10
387 30 c. "Jamaican Promenade" 25 30
388 50 c. "Misa Criolla" 45 80
385/8 .. .. *Set of* 4 70 1·10
MS389 161 × 102 mm. Nos. 385/8 *(sold at* $1) .. 1·50 2·25

181 U.P.U. Emblem and Globe

(Des V. Whiteley. Litho J.W.)

1974 (9 Oct). *Centenary of Universal Postal Union.* W **111** *(sideways)*. P 14.
390 **181** 5 c. multicoloured 10 10
391 9 c. multicoloured 10 10
392 50 c. multicoloured 35 80
390/2 .. .. *Set of* 3 50 80

182 Senate Building and Sir Hugh Wooding 183 Commonwealth Symbol

(Des R. Granger Barrett. Litho Questa)

1975 (13 Jan). *25th Anniv of University of West Indies. T* **182** *and similar horiz design. Multicoloured.* W **111** *(sideways)*. P 14.
393 5 c. Type **182** 10 10
394 10 c. University Chapel and H.R.H. Princess Alice 10 10
395 30 c. Type **182** 15 25
396 50 c. As 10 c. 30 60
393/6 .. .. *Set of* 4 50 80

(Des C. Abbott. Litho Questa)

1975 (29 Apr). *Heads of Commonwealth Conference. T* **183** *and similar square designs. Multicoloured.* W **111**. P 13½.
397 5 c. Type **183** 10 10
398 10 c. Jamaican coat of arms 10 10
399 30 c. Dove of Peace 15 30
400 50 c. Jamaican flag 30 80
397/400 .. .. *Set of* 4 50 1·10

184 *Graphium marcellinus* 185 Koo Koo or Actor Boy

(Des J. Cooter. Litho Questa)

1975 (25 Aug). *Butterflies (1st series). T* **184** *and similar vert designs showing the family Papilionidae. Multicoloured.* W **111**. P 14.
401 10 c. Type **184** 55 20
402 20 c. *Papilo thoas melonius* .. .. 1·10 85
403 25 c. *Papilo thersites* .. .. 1·25 1·40
404 30 c. *Papilo homerus* .. .. 1·40 1·75
401/4 .. .. *Set of* 4 4·00 3·75
MS405 134 × 179 mm. Nos. 401/4 *(sold at* 95 c.) 5·00 7·00
See also Nos. 429/**MS**433 and 443/**MS**447.

(Des C. Abbott. Litho J.W.)

1975 (3 Nov). *Christmas. T* **185** *and similar vert designs showing Belisario prints of "John Canoe" (Christmas) Festival (1st series). Multicoloured.* W **111**. P 14.
406 8 c. Type **185** 10 10
407 10 c. Red Set-girls 10 10
408 20 c. French Set-girls 15 15
409 50 c. Jaw-bone or House John Canoe 35 70
406/9 .. .. *Set of* 4 55 90
MS410 138 × 141 mm. Nos. 406/9. P 13½ *(sold at* $1) .. .. 1·25 2·50
See also Nos. 421/**MS**424.

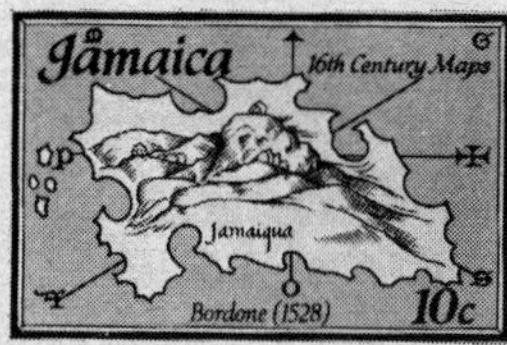

186 Bordone Map, 1528

(Des L. Curtis. Litho Questa)

1976 (12 Mar). *16th Century Maps of Jamaica. T* **186** *and similar horiz designs.* W **111** *(sideways)*. P 13½.
411 10 c. brown, light stone and light vermilion 20 10
412 20 c. multicoloured 35 25
413 30 c. multicoloured 60 75
414 50 c. multicoloured .. .. 85 1·25
411/14 .. .. *Set of* 4 1·75 2·10
Designs—20 c. Porcacchi map, 1576; 30 c. DeBry map, 1594; 50 c. Langenes map, 1598.
See also Nos. 425/8.

187 Olympic Rings

(Des Sir H. McDonald: adapted V. Whiteley Studio. Litho Walsall)

1976 (14 June). *Olympic Games, Montreal.* W **111** *(sideways)*. P 13½.
415 **187** 10 c. multicoloured 10 10
416 20 c. multicoloured 15 15
417 25 c. multicoloured 15 20
418 50 c. multicoloured 30 75
415/18 .. .. *Set of* 4 60 1·10

1976 (9 Aug). *West Indian Victory in World Cricket Cup. As Nos.* 559/60 *of Barbados.* P 14.
419 10 c. Map of the Caribbean 40 40
420 25 c. Prudential Cup .. .. 85 1·00

(Des C. Abbott. Litho J.W.)

1976 (8 Nov). *Christmas. Belisario Prints (2nd series). Multicoloured designs as T* **185**. W **111**. P 13½.
421 10 c. Queen of the set-girls 10 10
422 20 c. Band of the Jaw-bone John Canoe 15 10
423 50 c. Koo Koo (actor-boy) 30 50
421/3 .. .. *Set of* 3 40 60
MS424 110 × 140 mm. Nos. 421/3. P 14 × 14½ *(sold at* 90 c.) .. .. 70 2·00

(Des L. Curtis. Litho J.W.)

1977 (28 Feb). *17th Century Maps of Jamaica. Designs as T* **186**. W **111** *(sideways)*. P 13.
425 9 c. multicoloured 20 10
426 10 c. multicoloured 20 10
427 25 c. grey-black, pale blue and bright blue .. 50 60
428 40 c. grey-black, light turquoise and grey-blue 70 85
425/8 .. .. *Set of* 4 1·40 1·40
Designs:—9 c. Hickeringill map, 1661; 10 c. Ogilby map, 1671; 25 c. Visscher map, 1680; 40 c. Thornton map, 1689.

(Des J. Cooter. Litho J.W.)

1977 (9 May). *Butterflies (2nd series). Multicoloured designs as T* **184** *showing the families Nymphalidae and Pieridae.* W **111**. P 13½.
429 10 c. *Eurema elathea* 35 10
430 20 c. *Dynamine egaea egaea* 75 55
431 25 c. *Atlantea pantoni* .. .. 1·00 1·25
432 40 c. *Hypolinnas misippus* .. .. 1·50 2·00
429/32 .. .. *Set of* 4 3·25 3·50
MS433 139 × 122 mm. Nos. 429/32. P 14½ *(sold at* $1.05) .. .. 4·50 7·00

188 Map, Scout Emblem and Streamertail 189 Trumpeter

(Des Daphne Padden. Litho Questa)

1977 (5 Aug). *Sixth Caribbean Jamboree, Jamaica. Multicoloured; background colours given.* W **111** *(sideways)*. P 13½.
434 **188** 10 c. new blue 20 10
435 20 c. light yellow-green 40 15
436 25 c. orange 45 20
437 50 c. light magenta .. .. 75 1·10
434/7 .. .. *Set of* 4 1·60 1·25

(Des C. Abbott. Litho Questa)

1977 (19 Dec). *50th Anniv of Jamaica Military Band. T* **189** *and similar multicoloured designs.* W **111** *(sideways on horiz designs)*. P 14.
438 9 c. Type **189** 15 10
439 10 c. Clarinet players 15 10
440 20 c. Two kettle drummers *(vert)* 40 35
441 25 c. Cellist and trumpeter *(vert)* 55 65
438/41 .. .. *Set of* 4 1·10 1·00
MS442 120 × 137 mm. Nos. 438/41. Wmk sideways *(sold at* 75 c.) .. .. 2·50 3·75

(Des J. Cooter. Litho Walsall)

1978 (17 Apr). *Butterflies (3rd series). Multicoloured designs as T* **184**. W **111**. P 14.
443 10 c. *Callophrys crethona* 25 10
444 20 c. *Siproeta stelenes stelenes* 50 20
445 25 c. *Urbanus proteus* 65 35
446 50 c. *Anaea troglodyta portia* .. .. 1·40 1·60
443/6 .. .. *Set of* 4 2·50 2·00
MS447 100 × 125 mm. Nos. 443/6 *(sold at* $1.15) 2·50 2·75
a. Error. Imperf £175

190 Half-figure with Canopy 191 Norman Manley (statue)

(Des J. Cooter. Litho J.W.)

1978 (10 July). *Arawak Artefacts (1st series). T* **190** *and similar vert designs.* W **111**. P 13½ × 13.
448 10 c. deep brown, yellow and black 10 10
449 20 c. deep brown, mauve and black 10 10
450 50 c. deep brown, apple-green and black .. 30 35
448/50 .. .. *Set of* 3 40 45
MS451 135 × 90 mm. Nos. 448/50. P 14 *(sold at* 90 c.) 60 85
Designs:—20 c. Standing figure; 50 c. Birdman.
See also Nos. 479/83.

(Des and litho J.W.)

1978 (25 Sept). *24th Commonwealth Parliamentary Conference. T* **191** *and similar vert designs. Multicoloured.* W **111**. P 13.
452 10 c. Type **191** 10 10
453 20 c. Sir Alexander Bustamante (statue) .. 10 10
454 25 c. City of Kingston Crest 15 15
455 40 c. Gordon House Chamber, House of Representatives 25 35
452/5 .. .. *Set of* 4 50 60

192 Band and Banner

193 "Negro Aroused" (sculpture by Edna Manley)

(Des V. Whiteley. Litho J.W.)

1978 (4 Dec). *Christmas. Centenary of Salvation Army. T* **192** *and similar horiz designs. Multicoloured.* W **111** *(sideways). P* 14.

456 10 c. Type **192** 15 10
457 20 c. Trumpeter 15 10
458 25 c. Banner 15 20
459 50 c. William Booth (founder) 35 50
456/9 .. .. *Set of* 4 70 75

(Des G. Hutchins. Litho J.W.)

1978 (11 Dec). *International Anti-Apartheid Year.* W **111**. *P* 13.

460 **193** 10 c. multicoloured 10 10

194 Tennis, Montego Bay

195 Arms and Map of Jamaica

(Des and litho Harrison ($5). Des Walsall. Litho J.W. (others))

1979 (15 Jan)–**84**. *Vert designs as T* **194**, *and T* **195**. *Multicoloured. White ordinary paper* (15, 65, 75 c., $5) *or cream chalk-surfaced paper (others).* W **111** *(sideways on* $5). *P* 14½ × 14 ($5) *or* 13½ *(others).*

461 1 c. Type **194** (26.11.79) 10 10
462 2 c. Golf, Tryall, Hanover (26.11.79) 10 10
a. White ordinary paper (8.84) 25 10
463 4 c. Horse riding, Negril Beach (26.11.79) .. 10 10
a. White ordinary paper (8.84) 25 10
464 5 c. Old waterwheel, Tryall, Hanover (26.11.79) 15 10
a. White ordinary paper (27.8.82) 25 10
465 6 c. Fern Gully, Ocho Rios (26.11.79) .. 10 10
466 7 c. Dunn's River Falls, Ocho Rios (26.11.79) 15 10
467 8 c. Jamaican Tody (bird) (28.4.80) 40 10
468 10 c. Jamaican Mango (bird) (28.4.80) .. 40 10
a. White ordinary paper (27.8.82) 50 10
469 12 c. Yellow-billed Amazon (28.4.80) 40 10
470 15 c. Streamertail (bird) (28.4.80) 40 10
471 35 c. White-chinned Thrush (28.4.80) 55 10
472 50 c. Jamaican Woodpecker (28.4.80) 70 15
473 65 c. Rafting, Martha Brae Trelawny (28.4.80) 25 15
474 75 c. Blue Marlin Fleet, Port Antonio (28.4.80) 30 20
475 $1 Scuba Diving, Ocho Rios (28.4.80) .. 30 15
a. White ordinary paper (27.8.82) 60 30
476 $2 Sailing boats, Montego Bay (28.4.80) .. 50 35
a. White ordinary paper (27.8.82) 90 50
477 $5 Type **195** .. .. 1·00 1·25
461/77 .. .. *Set of* 17 5·00 2·50

TENTH ANNIVERSARY AIR JAMAICA 1st APRIL 1979

(196)

197 Grinding Stone, *circa* 400 BC.

1979 (2 Apr). *10th Anniv of Air Jamaica. No. 352 optd with T* **196**.

478 10 c. Type **173** 10 15

(Des D. Bowen. Litho Questa)

1979 (23 Apr). *Arawak Artefacts (2nd series). T* **197** *and similar multicoloured designs.* W **111** *(sideways on* 10, 20 *and* 25 c.). *P* 14.

479 5 c. Type **197** 10 10
480 10 c. Stone implements, *c.* 500 AD *(horiz)* .. 10 10
481 20 c. Cooking pot, *c.* 300 AD *(horiz)* 10 15
482 25 c. Serving boat, *c.* 300 AD *(horiz)* 10 20
483 50 c. Storage jar fragment, *c.* 300 AD 20 35
479/83 .. .. *Set of* 5 45 70

NEW INFORMATION

The editor is always interested to correspond with people who have new information that will improve or correct the Catalogue.

198 1962 1s. 6d. Independence Commemorative Stamp

(Des J.W. from a local design by J. Mahfood. Litho Walsall)

1979 (13 Aug). *Death Centenary of Sir Rowland Hill. T* **198** *and similar horiz designs showing stamps and Sir Rowland Hill.* W **111** *(sideways). P* 14.

484 10 c. black, scarlet-vermilion & brt scarlet .. 10 10
485 20 c. orange-yellow and yellowish brown .. 15 15
486 25 c. mauve and blue 20 20
487 50 c. multicoloured 30 40
484/7 .. .. *Set of* 4 65 70
MS488 146 × 94 mm. No. 485 *(sold at* 30 c.) .. 20 35

Designs:—20 c. 1920 1s. with frame inverted; 25 c. 1860 6d.; 50 c. 1968 3d. Human Rights Year commemorative.

199 Group of Children

(Des J.W. Litho Harrison)

1979 (1 Oct). *Christmas. International Year of the Child. T* **199** *and similar multicoloured designs.* W **111** *(sideways on* 10, 25 *and* 50 c.). *P* 14.

489 10 c. Type **199** 10 10
490 20 c. Doll *(vert)* 10 10
491 25 c. "The Family" (painting by child) .. 15 15
492 50 c. "House on the Hill" (painting by child) .. 25 40
489/92 .. .. *Set of* 4 50 60

200 Date Tree Hall, 1886 (original home of Institute)

(Des G. Drummond. Litho Walsall)

1980 (25 Feb). *Centenary of Institute of Jamaica. T* **200** *and similar multicoloured designs.* W **111** *(sideways on* 5, 15 *and* 50 c.). *P* 13½.

493 5 c. Type **200** 10 10
494 15 c. Institute building, 1980 .. .. .. 10 10
495 35 c. Microfilm reader *(vert)* 20 20
496 50 c. Hawksbill Turtle and Green Turtle .. 25 25
497 75 c. Jamaican Owl *(vert)* 40 50
493/7 .. .. *Set of* 5 90 1·00

201 Don Quarrie (200 Metres, 1976)

(Des BG Studio. Litho Walsall)

1980 (21 July). *Olympic Games, Moscow. Jamaican Olympic Athletics Gold Medal Winners. T* **201** *and similar horiz designs. Multicoloured.* W **111** *(sideways). P* 13.

498 15 c. Type **201** 15 10
499 35 c. Arthur Wint (4 × 400 Metres Relay, 1952) 25 30
a. Horiz strip of 4. Nos. 499/502 90
500 35 c. Leslie Laing (4 × 400 Metres Relay, 1952) 25 30
501 35 c. Herbert McKenley (4 × 400 Metres Relay, 1952) 25 30
502 35 c. George Rhoden (4 × 400 Metres Relay, 1952) 25 30
498/502 .. .. *Set of* 5 90 1·10

Nos. 499/502 were printed together, *se-tenant*, in horizontal strips of 4 throughout the sheet.

202 Parish Church

203 Blood Cup Sponge

(Des J.W. Litho Harrison)

1980 (24 Nov). *Christmas. Churches (1st series). T* **202** *and similar horiz designs. Multicoloured.* W **111** *(sideways). P* 14.

503 15 c. Type **202** 10 10
504 20 c. Coke Memorial Church 10 10
505 25 c. Church of the Redeemer 15 10
506 $5 Holy Trinity Cathedral .. .. .. 1·00 2·00
503/6 .. .. *Set of* 4 1·10 2·10
MS507 120 × 139 mm. Nos. 503/6. P 14½ *(sold at* $5.70) .. .. 1·75 2·75

See also Nos. 537/40 and 570/2.

(Des J. Mahfood. Litho Walsall)

1981 (27 Feb). *Marine Life (1st series). T* **203** *and similar multicoloured designs.* W **111** *(sideways on* 45 *and* 75 c.). *P* 14.

508 20 c. Type **203** 15 10
509 45 c. Tube Sponge *(horiz)* 25 30
510 60 c. Black Coral 35 40
511 75 c. Tyre Reef *(horiz)* 40 55
508/11 .. .. *Set of* 4 1·00 1·25

See also Nos. 541/5.

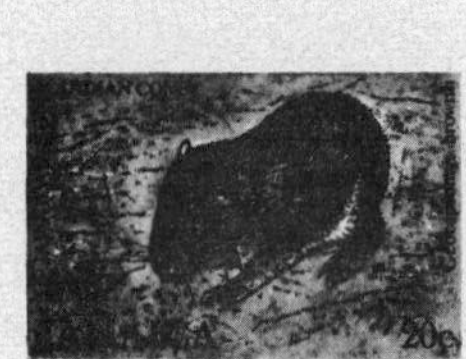

204 Brown's Hutia (or Indian Coney)

205 White Orchid

(Des D. Bowen. Litho Questa)

1981 (25 May). *Brown's Hutia (or Indian Coney). T* **204** *and similar horiz designs. Multicoloured.* W **111**. *P* 14.

512 20 c. Hutia facing right 15 20
a. Horiz strip of 4. Nos. 512/15 55
513 20 c. Type **204** 15 20
514 20 c. Hutia facing left and eating 15 20
515 20 c. Hutia family 15 20
512/15 .. .. *Set of* 4 55 70

Nos. 512/15 were printed together, *se-tenant*, in horizontal strips of 4 throughout the sheet.

(Des J.W. Litho Format)

1981 (29 July). *Royal Wedding. T* **205** *and similar vert designs. Multicoloured.* W w 14 *(sideways). P* 13½ ($5) *or* 15 *(others).*

516 20 c. Type **205** 20 10
a. Perf 15 × 14½ 25 25
ab. Booklet pane. Nos. 516a/19a .. .. 3·50
517 45 c. Royal Coach 35 20
a. Perf 15 × 14½ 50 50
518 60 c. Prince Charles and Lady Diana Spencer 50 30
a. Perf 15 × 14½ 60 60
519 $5 St. James' Palace .. .. .. 1·25 1·50
a. Perf 15 × 14½ .. .. 2·50 3·50
516/19 .. .. *Set of* 4 2·10 1·90
MS520 98 × 85 mm. No. 519. Wmk upright. P 13½ 1·90 2·40

Nos. 516/18 also exist perforated 13½ *(price for set of* 3 £2.25 *mint or used)* from additional sheetlets of 5 stamps and one label. No. 519 exists from both normal sheets and sheetlets.

Nos. 516a/19a are from $6.25 stamp booklets.

206 Blind Man at Work

207 W.F.D. Emblem on 1964 1½d. Definitive

(Des G. Vasarhelyi. Litho J.W.)

1981 (14 Sept). *International Year for Disabled Persons. T* **206** *and similar horiz designs. Multicoloured.* W **111** *(sideways). P* 13.

521 20 c. Type **206** 15 15
522 45 c. Painting with the mouth 40 40
523 60 c. Deaf student communicating with sign language 50 50
524 $1.50, Basketball players .. .. .. 1·25 1·25
521/4 .. .. *Set of* 4 2·10 2·10

(Des J. Mahfood. Litho J.W.)

1981 (16 Oct). *World Food Day. Stamps on Stamps. T* **207** *and similar designs showing W.F.D. emblems on various definitives.* W **111** *(sideways on* 20 c., $2 *and* $4). *P* 13.

525 20 c. multicoloured 30 15
526 45 c. black, rose and orange 60 40
527 $2 black, violet-blue and green .. .. 1·75 1·40
528 $4 black, green and light brown .. .. 3·00 2·50
525/8 .. .. *Set of* 4 5·00 4·00

Designs: *Vert as T* **207**—45 c. 1922 1d. (40 × 26 *mm.*)—$2 As 1938 3d. but with W.F.D. emblem replacing King's head; $4 As 1938 1s. but with W.F.D. emblem replacing King's head.

Nos. 525/8 were so designed that the face values obliterated those on the stamps depicted.

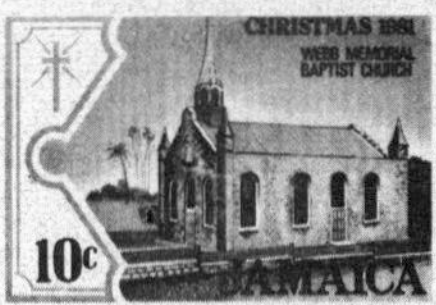

208 "Survival" (song title) **209** Webb Memorial Baptist Church

(Litho Format)

1981 (20 Oct). *Bob Marley (musician) Commemoration. T* **208** *and similar vert designs inscribed with song titles. In black and vermilion* ($5.25) *or multicoloured (others). W w* **14** *(sideways). P* 15.

529 1 c. Type **208** 10 10
530 2 c. "Exodus" 10 10
531 3 c. "Is this Love" 10 10
532 15 c. "Coming in from the Cold"* 30 15
533 20 c. "Positive Vibration"† 40 20
534 60 c. "War" 90 55
535 $3 "Could you be Loved" .. .. .. 6·00 3·00
529/35 .. .. *Set of* 7 7·00 3·50
MS536 134 × 110 mm. $5.25, Bob Marley (wmk upright) .. .. 4·00 4·75

*Part of initial "C" of song title inscription does not show on the design.
†Incorrectly inscribed "OSITIVE VIBRATION".

(Des J.W. Litho Questa)

1981 (11 Dec). *Christmas. Churches* (2*nd series*). *T* **209** *and similar horiz designs. Multicoloured. W* **111** *(sideways). P* 14.

537 10 c. Type **209** 10 10
538 45 c. Church of God in Jamaica 30 15
539 $5 Bryce United Church .. .. .. 2·25 2·50
537/9 .. .. *Set of* 3 2·40 2·50
MS540 120 × 168 mm. Nos. 537/9 (wmk upright). P 12 .. .. 3·00 3·25

210 Gorgonian Coral **211** Cub Scout

(Des J. Mahfood; adapted PAD Studio. Litho Questa)

1982 (22 Feb). *Marine Life* (2*nd series*). *T* **210** *and similar multicoloured designs. W* **111** *(sideways on* 45, 60, 75 *c. and* $3). *P* 14.

541 20 c. Type **210**.. .. .. 25 10
542 45 c. Hard Sponge and diver (*horiz*).. .. 45 25
543 60 c. American Manatee (*horiz*) 60 40
544 75 c. Plume Worm (*horiz*) 70 50
545 $3 Coral Banded Shrimp (*horiz*) .. .. 2·00 1·60
541/5 .. .. *Set of* 5 3·50 2·50

(Des L. Curtis. Litho J.W.)

1982 (12 July). 75*th Anniv of Boy Scout Movement. T* **211** *and similar vert designs. Multicoloured. W* **111**. *P* 13½ × 13.

546 20 c. Type **211** 35 15
547 45 c. Scout camp 65 35
548 60 c. "Out of Many, One People" 85 45
549 $2 Lord Baden-Powell .. .. .. 1·60 1·50
546/9 .. .. *Set of* 4 3·00 2·25
MS550 80 × 130 mm. Nos. 546/9 .. .. .. 3·50 4·00

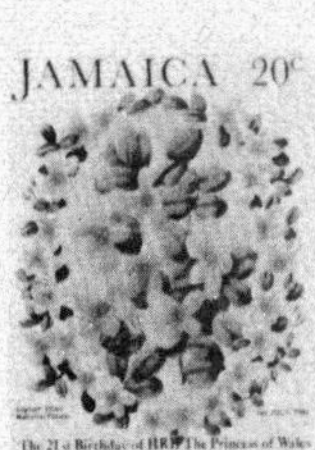

212 *Lignum vitae* (national flower) **213** Prey Captured

(Des R. Sauer. Litho Questa)

1982 (30 Aug). 21*st Birthday of Princess of Wales. T* **212** *and similar vert designs. W* **111**. *P* 14½ × 14.

551 20 c. Type **212** 20 20
a. Booklet pane. Nos. 551/3.. .. .. 1·00
552 45 c. Carriage ride 35 35
553 60 c. Wedding 50 50
554 75 c. *Saxifraga longifolia* 70 70
a. Booklet pane. Nos. 554/6.. .. .. 4·00
555 $2 Princess of Wales .. .. .. 1·50 1·50
556 $3 *Viola gracilis major* .. .. .. 2·00 2·00
551/6 .. .. *Set of* 6 4·75 4·75
MS557 106 × 75 mm. $5 Honeymoon photograph 3·00 3·50

Nos. 554 and 556 were printed in small sheets of 6 including one *se-tenant*, stamp-size, label. The other values were printed in sheets of 40.

1982 (13 Sept). *Birth of Prince William of Wales. Nos.* 551/7 *optd with T* **171** *of Antigua.*

558 20 c. Type **212** 20 20
a. Booklet pane. Nos. 558/60 .. .. 1·00
559 45 c. Carriage ride 35 35
560 60 c. Wedding 50 50
561 75 c. *Saxifraga longifolia* 70 70
a. Booklet pane. Nos. 561/3.. .. .. 4·00
562 $2 Princess of Wales .. .. .. 1·50 1·50
563 $3 *Viola gracilis major* .. .. .. 2·00 2·00
558/63 .. .. *Set of* 6 4·75 4·75
MS564 106 × 75 mm. $5 Honeymoon photograph 3·50 3·50

(Des N. Arlott. Litho Questa)

1982 (25 Oct). *Jamaican Birds* (1*st series*). *Jamaican Lizard Cuckoo. T* **213** *and similar vert designs. Multicoloured. W* **111**. *P* 14½.

565 $1 Type **213** 80 80
a. Horiz strip of 5. Nos. 565/9 .. .. 3·50
566 $1 Searching for prey 80 80
567 $1 Calling prior to prey search 80 80
568 $1 Adult landing 80 80
569 $1 Adult flying in 80 80
565/9.. .. .. *Set of* 5 3·50 3·50

Nos. 565/9 were printed in horizontal *se-tenant* strips of 5 throughout the sheet.

See also Nos. 642/5 and 707/10.

(Des and litho J.W.)

1982 (8 Dec). *Christmas. Churches* (3*rd series*). *Horiz designs as T* **209**. *Multicoloured. W* **111** *(sideways). P* 13.

570 20 c. United Pentecostal Church 15 10
571 45 c. Disciples of Christ Church 30 25
572 75 c. Open Bible Church 55 70
570/2 .. .. *Set of* 3 90 95

214 Queen Elizabeth II **215** Folk Dancing

(Des D. Miller. Litho Walsall)

1983 (14 Feb). *Royal Visit. T* **214** *and similar vert design. Multicoloured. W* **111**. *P* 14.

573 $2 Type **214** .. .. 2·00 2·00
574 $3 Coat of Arms .. .. 2·75 2·75

(Des Walsall. Litho Format)

1983 (14 Mar). *Commonwealth Day. T* **215** *and similar horiz designs. Multicoloured. W* **111** *(sideways). P* 14.

575 20 c. Type **215** 15 15
576 45 c. Bauxite mining 35 35
577 75 c. World map showing position of Jamaica 45 45
578 $2 Coat of arms and family.. .. .. 1·25 1·40
575/8 .. .. *Set of* 4 2·00 2·10

216 General Cargo Ship at Wharf **217** Norman Manley and Sir Alexander Bustamante

(Des A. Theobald. Litho Format)

1983 (17 Mar). 25*th Anniv of International Maritime Organization. T* **216** *and similar horiz designs. Multicoloured. P* 14.

579 15 c. Type **216** 45 20
580 20 c. *Veendam* (cruise liner) at Kingston .. 60 25
581 45 c. Container ship entering port 90 55
582 $1 Tanker passing International Seabed Headquarters Building .. .. .. 1·50 1·75
579/82 .. .. *Set of* 4 3·00 2·50

(Des D. Miller. Litho Harrison)

1983 (25 July). 21*st Anniv of Independence. W* **111**. *P* 14.

583 **217** 15 c. multicoloured 15 15
584 20 c. multicoloured 15 20
585 45 c. multicoloured 30 40
583/5 .. .. *Set of* 3 55 70

218 Ship-to-Shore Radio **219** "Racing at Caymanas" (Sidney Mclaren)

(Des Walsall. Litho Harrison)

1983 (18 Oct). *World Communications Year. T* **218** *and similar horiz designs. Multicoloured. W* **111** *(sideways). P* 14.

586 20 c. Type **218** 15 15
587 45 c. Postal services 35 40
588 75 c. Telephone communications 55 70
589 $1 T.V. via satellite .. .. 75 1·00
586/9 .. .. *Set of* 4 1·50 2·00

(Des D. Miller. Litho J.W.)

1983 (12 Dec). *Christmas. Paintings. T* **219** *and similar multicoloured designs. W* **111** *(sideways on* 15 *c.,* 20 *c.). P* 13 × 13½ (15 *c.,* 20 *c.) or* 13½ × 13 *(others).*

590 15 c. Type **219** 10 10
591 20 c. "Seated Figures" (Karl Parboosingh) .. 10 10
592 75 c. "The Petitioner" (Henry Daley) (*vert*) .. 30 25
593 $2 "Banana Plantation" (John Dunkley) (*vert*) .. .. 70 1·00
590/3 .. .. *Set of* 4 1·00 1·25

220 Sir Alexander Bustamante **221** "D.H. 60G Gipsy Moth" Seaplane

(Des D. Miller. Litho Questa)

1984 (24 Feb). *Birth Centenary of Sir Alexander Bustamante. T* **220** *and similar vert design. Multicoloured. W* **111**. *P* 14.

594 20 c. Type **220** 15 20
a. Horiz pair. Nos. 594/5 .. .. .. 30 40
595 20 c. Birthplace, Blenheim 15 20

Nos. 594/5 were printed together, *se-tenant*, in horizontal pairs throughout the sheet.

(Des A. Theobald. Litho Questa)

1984 (11 June). *Seaplanes and Flying Boats. T* **221** *and similar horiz designs. Multicoloured. W* **111** *(sideways). P* 14.

596 25 c. Type **221** 35 15
597 55 c. Consolidated "Commodore" flying boat .. 50 35
598 $1.50, Sikorsky "S-38" flying boat .. .. 1·00 1·00
599 $3 Sikorsky "S-40" flying boat .. .. 1·50 1·75
596/9 .. .. *Set of* 4 3·00 3·00

5c

222 Cycling **223**

(Des G. Vasarhelyi. Litho J.W.)

1984 (11 July). *Olympic Games, Los Angeles. T* **222** *and similar horiz designs. Multicoloured. W* **111** *(sideways). P* 14.

600 25 c. Type **222** 10 10
601 55 c. Relay running 20 25
602 $1.50, Start of race .. .. 60 1·00
603 $3 Finish of race .. .. 1·10 1·50
600/3 .. .. *Set of* 4 1·75 2·50
MS604 135 × 105 mm. Nos. 600/3 (*sold at* $5.40). P 13 × 13½ .. .. 1·90 2·00

1984 (7 Aug). *Nos.* 465 *and* 469 *surch as T* **223**.

605 5 c. on 6 c. Fern Gully, Ocho Rios 10 10
606 10 c. on 12 c. Yellow-billed Amazon 15 15

224 Head of Jamaican Boa Snake

(Des I. Loe. Litho Questa)

1984 (22 Oct). *Jamaican Boa Snake. T* **224** *and similar horiz designs. Multicoloured. W* **111** *(sideways). P* 14½.

607 25 c. Type **224** 15 15
608 55 c. Boa snake on branch over stream .. 35 35
609 70 c. Snake with young 40 40
610 $1 Snake on log 50 50
607/10 .. .. *Set of* 4 1·25 1·25
MS611 133 × 97 mm. As Nos. 607/10 but without W.W.F. emblem (*sold at* $2.60) .. .. .. 1·25 1·25

225 *Enterprise* (1845) **226** "Accompong Madonna" (Namba Roy)

(Des D. Hartley-Marjoram. Litho Enschedé)

1984 (16 Nov). *Railway Locomotives (1st series). T* **225** *and similar horiz designs. Multicoloured. W* **111** *(sideways). P* 13½×13.

612 25 c. Type **225** 35 15
613 55 c. Tank locomotive (1880) 50 30
614 $1.50, Kitson-Meyer tank locomotive (1904) 85 75
615 $3 Super-heated locomotive (1916) .. 1·50 1·50
612/15 .. .. *Set of* 4 2·75 2·50
See also Nos. 634/7.

(Des G. Vasarhelyi. Litho Harrison)

1984 (6 Dec). *Christmas. Sculptures. T* **226** *and similar vert designs. Multicoloured. W* **111**. *P* 14.

616 20 c. Type **226** 15 10
617 25 c. "Head" (Alvin Marriott) 20 10
618 55 c. "Moon" (Edna Manley) 30 25
619 $1.50, "All Women are Five Women" (Mallica Reynolds (Kapo)) 55 65
616/19 .. .. *Set of* 4 1·10 90

227 Brown Pelicans flying

228 The Queen Mother at Belfast University

(Des N. Arlott. Litho Walsall)

1985 (15 Apr). *Birth Bicentenary of John J. Audubon (ornithologist). Brown Pelican. T* **227** *and similar vert designs. Multicoloured. W* **111**. *P* 13½×13.

620 20 c. Type **227** 30 10
621 55 c. Diving for fish 45 15
622 $2 Young pelican taking food from adult .. 75 65
623 $5 "Brown Pelican" (John J. Audubon) .. 1·25 1·60
620/3 .. .. *Set of* 4 2·50 2·25
MS624 100×100 mm. Nos. 620/3 (*sold at* $7.85) .. .. 2·50 2·75

(Des A. Theobald ($5), C. Abbott (others). Litho Questa)

1985 (7 June). *Life and Times of Queen Elizabeth the Queen Mother. T* **228** *and similar vert designs. Multicoloured. W* **111**. *P* 14½×14.

625 25 c. With photograph album, 1963 .. .. 10 10
626 55 c. With Prince Charles at Garter Ceremony, Windsor Castle, 1983 .. .. 15 15
627 $1.50, Type **228** 35 40
628 $3 With Prince Henry at his christening (from photo by Lord Snowdon) 65 70
625/8 .. .. *Set of* 4 1·10 1·25
MS629 91×74 mm. $5 With the Queen, Prince Philip and Princess Anne at Ascot. Wmk sideways .. .. 1·25 1·40

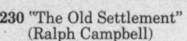

229 Maps and Emblems

(Des D. Miller. Litho Harrison)

1985 (30 July). *International Youth Year and 5th Pan-American Scout Jamboree. W* **111** *(sideways). P* 14.

630 **229** 25 c. multicoloured 10 10
631 55 c. multicoloured 15 15
632 70 c. multicoloured 20 20
633 $4 multicoloured .. .. .. 90 1·10
630/3 .. .. *Set of* 4 1·25 1·40

(Des D. Hartley. Litho Harrison)

1985 (30 Sept). *Railway Locomotives (2nd series). Horiz designs as T* **225**. *Multicoloured. W* **111** *(sideways). P* 14.

634 25 c. Baldwin locomotive No. 16 .. .. 35 10
635 55 c. Rogers locomotive 60 15
636 $1.50, Locomotive *The Projector* .. .. 1·00 75
637 $4 Diesel locomotive No. 102 .. .. 1·75 1·75
634/7 .. .. *Set of* 4 3·25 2·50

230 "The Old Settlement" (Ralph Campbell)

231 Bustamante Children's Hospital

(Litho Format)

1985 (9 Dec). *Christmas. Jamaican Paintings. T* **230** *and similar multicoloured designs. W* **111** *(sideways on* 20, 75 *c.). P* 14.

638 20 c. Type **230** 10 10
639 55 c. "The Vendor" (Albert Huie) (*vert*) .. 15 15
640 75 c. "Road Menders" (Gaston Tabois) .. 15 20
641 $4 "Woman, must I not be about my Father's business?" (Carl Abrahams) (*vert*) 90 95
638/41 .. .. *Set of* 4 1·10 1·25

(Des N. Arlott. Litho B.D.T.)

1986 (10 Feb). *Jamaican Birds (2nd series). Vert designs as T* **213**. *Multicoloured. W* **111**. *P* 14.

642 25 c. Chestnut-bellied Cuckoo 30 10
643 55 c. Jamaican Becard 40 25
644 $1.50, White-eyed Thrush 60 60
645 $5 Rufous-tailed Flycatcher .. .. 1·50 2·00
642/5 .. .. *Set of* 4 2·50 2·75

(Des A. Theobald. Litho Harrison)

1986 (21 Apr). *60th Birthday of Queen Elizabeth II. Vert designs as T* **110** *of Ascension. Multicoloured. W* **111**. *P* 14½×14.

646 20 c. Princess Elizabeth and Princess Margaret, 1939 .. .. 10 10
647 25 c. With Prince Charles and Prince Andrew, 1962 .. .. 10 10
648 70 c. Queen visiting War Memorial, Montego Bay, 1983 .. .. 15 20
649 $3 On state visit to Luxembourg, 1976 .. 65 70
650 $5 At Crown Agents Head Office, London, 1983 .. .. 1·25 1·40
646/50 .. .. *Set of* 5 1·90 2·10

(Des D. Miller. Litho Questa)

1986 (19 May). *"Ameripex '86" International Stamp Exhibition, Chicago. T* **231** *and similar vert designs. Multicoloured. W* **111**. *P* 14½×14.

651 25 c. Type **231** 10 10
652 55 c. Air Jamaica jet airliner and map of holiday resorts 15 15
653 $3 Norman Manley Law School 70 80
654 $5 Bauxite and agricultural exports .. 2·00 2·00
651/4 .. .. *Set of* 4 2·75 2·75
MS655 85×106 mm. Nos. 651/4 (*sold at* $8.90) .. 2·75 3·25

(Des D. Miller. Litho Walsall)

1986 (23 July). *Royal Wedding. Square design as T* **112** *of Ascension. Multicoloured. W* **111**. *P* 14½×14.

656 20 c. Prince Andrew and Miss Sarah Ferguson, Ascot, 1985 .. .. 15 10
657 $5 Prince Andrew making speech, Fredericton, Canada, 1985 .. .. 1·40 1·50

232 Richard "Shrimpy" Clarke

5c

(**233**)

(Des G. Vasarhelyi. Litho Questa)

1986 (27 Oct). *Jamaican Boxing Champions. T* **232** *and similar vert designs. Multicoloured. W* **111**. *P* 14.

658 45 c. Type **232** 15 15
659 70 c. Michael McCallum 20 20
660 $2 Trevor Berbick 50 55
661 $4 Richard "Shrimpy" Clarke, Michael McCallum and Trevor Berbick .. .. 95 1·25
658/61 .. .. *Set of* 4 1·60 1·90

1986 (3 Nov). *Nos.* 472/3 *surch as T* **233**.

662 5 c. on 50 c. Jamaican Woodpecker .. 10 10
663 10 c. on 65 c. Rafting, Martha Brae Trelawny 15 15

234 *Heliconia wagneriana*

235 Crown Cone

(Des Annette Robinson. Litho B.D.T.)

1986 (1 Dec). *Christmas. Flowers (1st series). T* **234** *and similar multicoloured designs. W* **111** *(sideways on* 25 *c.,* $5). *P* 13½.

664 20 c. Type **234** 10 10
665 25 c. *Heliconia psittacorum* (*horiz*) 10 10
666 55 c. *Heliconia rostrata* 20 15
667 $5 *Strelitzia reginae* (*horiz*) .. .. 1·60 2·25
664/7 .. .. *Set of* 4 1·75 2·25
See also Nos. 703/6 and 739/42.

(Des A. Riley. Litho Format)

1987 (23 Feb). *Sea Shells. T* **235** *and similar vert designs. Multicoloured. W* **111**. *P* 15.

668 35 c. Type **235** 20 10
669 75 c. Measled Cowrie 30 20
670 $1 Trumpet Triton 40 40
671 $5 Rooster Tail Conch .. .. .. 1·40 1·75
668/71 .. .. *Set of* 4 2·10 2·25

236 Norman Manley

237 Arms of Jamaica

(Des C. Slania (1 c. to 90 c.). Litho Enschedé)

1987 (18 May)–**88**. *Vert portraits as T* **236** *and T* **237**. *W* **111** *(sideways on $1 to $5). Cream paper* (2 *c. to* 9 *c.* (*Nos.* 673A/80A)). *P* 12½×13 (1 *to* 90 *c.*) *or* 13×13½ ($1 *to* $5). A. *Without imprint*. B. *With imprint date at foot* (6.6.88).

No.	Type	Value	A		B	
672	**236**	1 c. scarlet and pale pink	10	10	†	
673		2 c. brt carm & pale rose-pk	10	10	†	
674		3 c. yellow-ol & pale stone	10	10	†	
675		4 c. myrtle-grn & pale grn	10	10	†	
676		5 c. slate-blue and pale bluish grey	10	10	10	10
677		6 c. dull ultramarine and pale lavender-grey ..	10	10	†	
678		7 c. reddish vio & pale mve	10	10	†	
679		8 c. dp mag & pale rose-pk	10	10	†	
680		9 c. olive-sepia & pale brn	10	10	†	
681	–	10 c. dp rose-red & pale pink	10	10	†	
682	–	20 c. reddish orange & flesh	10	10	10	10
683	–	30 c. brt green & pale green	10	10	†	
684	–	40 c. dp turquoise-green & pale turquoise-green ..	10	10	†	
685	–	50 c. grey-ol & pale ol-grey	10	10	†	
686	–	60 c. brt blue & pale azure	10	15	†	
687	–	70 c. bluish violet & pale vio	15	20	†	
688	–	80 c. reddish violet and pale rose-lilac	15	20	†	
689	–	90 c. light reddish brown and pale grey-brown ..	15	20	†	
690	**237**	$1 olive-sepia and cream	20	25	†	
691		$2 bright orange & cream	35	40	†	
692		$5 brown-ol & pale stone	90	95	†	
693		$10 dp turq-bl & pale azure	1·90	2·00	†	
672/93 ..		.. .. *Set of* 22	4·75	5·25		

Designs:—10 c. to 90 c. Sir Alexander Bustamante.

238 Jamaican Flag and Coast at Sunset

239 Marcus Garvey

(Des D. Miller. Litho Walsall)

1987 (27 July). *25th Anniv of Independence. T* **238** *and similar multicoloured design. W* **111** *(sideways on* 70 *c.). P* 14.

694 55 c. Type **238** 20 15
695 70 c. Jamaican flag and inscription (*horiz*) .. 25 20

(Des D. Miller. Litho Walsall)

1987 (17 Aug). *Birth Centenary of Marcus Garvey (founder of Universal Negro Improvement Association). T* **239** *and similar vert design, both black, emerald and lemon. W* **111**. *P* 14.

696 25 c. Type **239** 15 15
a. Horiz pair. Nos. 696/7 .. .. .. 30 30
697 25 c. Statue of Marcus Garvey 15 15
Nos. 696/7 were printed together, *se-tenant*, in horizontal pairs throughout the sheet.

240 Salvation Army School for the Blind

241 Hibiscus Hybrid

(Des L. Curtis. Litho Walsall)

1987 (8 Oct). *Centenary of Salvation Army in Jamaica. T* **240** *and similar horiz designs. Multicoloured.* W **111** *(sideways). P* 13 × 13½.

698	25 c. Type **240**	15	10
699	55 c. Col. Mary Booth and Bramwell Booth Memorial Hall	25	15
700	$3 Welfare Service lorry, 1929	80	80
701	$5 Col. Abram Davey and S.S. *Alene*, 1887	1·60	1·75
698/701	*Set of* 4	2·50	2·50
MS702	100 × 80 mm. Nos. 698/701 (*sold at* $8.90)	2·50	2·75

(Des Annette Robinson. Litho Harrison)

1987 (30 Nov). *Christmas. Flowers (2nd series). T* **241** *and similar vert designs. Multicoloured.* W **111**. *P* 14½ × 14.

703	20 c. Type **241**	10	10
704	25 c. *Hibiscus elatus*	10	10
705	$4 *Hibiscus cannabinus*	90	95
706	$5 *Hibiscus rosasinensis*	1·25	1·40
703/6	*Set of* 4	2·00	2·25

242 Chestnut-bellied Cuckoo, Black-billed Parrot and Jamaican Euphonia

243 Blue Whales

(Des N. Arlott. Litho Walsall)

1988 (22 Jan). *Jamaican Birds (3rd series). T* **242** *and similar vert designs. Multicoloured.* W **111**. *P* 14.

707	45 c. Type **242**	40	40
	a. Horiz pair. Nos. 707/8	80	80
708	45 c. Jamaican White-eyed Vireo, Rufous-throated Solitaire and Yellow-crowned Elaenia	40	40
709	$5 Snowy Plover, Little Blue Heron and Great White Heron	1·75	1·75
	a. Horiz pair. Nos. 709/10	3·50	3·50
710	$5 Common Stilt, Snowy Egret and Black-crowned Night Heron	1·75	1·75
707/10	*Set of* 4	4·00	4·00

The two designs of each value were printed together, *se-tenant*, in horizontal pairs throughout the sheets, each pair forming a composite design.

(Des A. Riley. Litho Harrison)

1988 (14 Apr). *Marine Mammals. T* **243** *and similar horiz designs. Multicoloured.* W **111** *(sideways). P* 14.

711	20 c. Type **243**	15	10
712	25 c. Gervais's Whales	15	10
713	55 c. Killer Whales	30	15
714	$5 Common Dolphins	1·75	1·75
711/14	*Set of* 4	2·10	1·90

(Des D. Hartley. Litho Walsall)

1988 (6 June). *West Indian Cricket. Horiz designs as T* **186** *of Barbados, each showing portrait, cricket equipment and early belt buckle. Multicoloured.* W **111** *(sideways). P* 14.

715	25 c. Jackie Hendriks	15	10
716	55 c. George Headley	30	15
717	$2 Michael Holding	70	55
718	$3 R. K. Nunes	85	90
719	$4 Allan Rae	1·10	1·25
715/19	*Set of* 5	2·75	2·75

244 Jamaican Red Cross Workers with Ambulance

245 Boxing

(Des S. Noon. Litho Walsall)

1988 (8 Aug). *125th Anniv of International Red Cross. T* **244** *and similar vert design. Multicoloured.* W **111**. *P* 14½ × 14.

720	55 c. Type **244**	15	15
721	$5 Henri Dunant (founder) in field hospital	1·00	1·10

(Des P. Broadbent. Litho B.D.T.)

1988 (24 Aug). *Olympic Games, Seoul. T* **245** *and similar horiz designs. Multicoloured.* W **111** *(sideways). P* 14.

722	25 c. Type **245**	10	10
723	45 c. Cycling	10	10
724	$4 Athletics	85	90
725	$5 Hurdling	1·00	1·10
722/5	*Set of* 4	1·75	2·00
MS726	127 × 87 mm. Nos. 722/5 (*sold at* $9.90)	2·10	2·25

246 Bobsled Team Members and Logo

(Des D. Miller. Litho B.D.T.)

1988 (4 Nov). *Jamaican Olympic Bobsled Team. T* **246** *and similar horiz designs. Multicoloured.* W **111** *(sideways). P* 14.

727	25 c. Type **246**	10	15
	a. Horiz pair. Nos. 727/8	15	30
728	25 c. Two-man bobsled	10	15
729	$5 Bobsled team members (*different*) and logo	1·00	1·25
	a. Horiz pair. Nos. 729/30	2·00	2·50
730	$5 Four-man bobsled	1·00	1·25
727/30	*Set of* 4	1·90	2·50

Nos. 727/8 and 729/30 were printed together, *se-tenant*, in horizontal pairs throughout the sheets.

+25c

HURRICANE GILBERT RELIEF FUND

(247)

1988 (11 Nov). *Hurricane Gilbert Relief Fund. Nos.* 722/5 *surch as T* **247** *by Format. A. In red. B. In black.*

		A		B	
731	25 c. + 25 c. Type **245**	10	15	10	15
732	45 c. + 45 c. Cycling	20	25	20	25
733	$4 + $4 Athletics	1·75	1·90	1·75	1·90
734	$5 + $5 Hurdling	2·10	2·25	2·10	2·25
731/4	*Set of* 4	3·75	4·00	3·75	4·00

248 Nurses and Firemen

(Des S. Noon. Litho Format)

1988 (24 Nov). *Year of the Worker. T* **248** *and similar horiz designs. Multicoloured.* W **111** *(sideways). P* 14.

735	25 c. Type **248**	10	10
736	55 c. Woodcarver	15	15
737	$3 Textile workers	75	80
738	$5 Workers on fish farm	1·00	1·10
735/8	*Set of* 4	1·75	1·90

(Des Annette Robinson. Litho Format)

1988 (15 Dec). *Christmas. Flowers (3rd series). Multicoloured designs as T* **241**. W **111** *(sideways on 55 c., $4). P* 14.

739	25 c. *Euphorbia pulcherrima*	10	10
740	55 c. *Spathodea campanulata (horiz)*	15	15
741	$3 *Hylocereus triangularis*	75	80
742	$4 *Broughtonia sanguinea (horiz)*	85	90
739/42	*Set of* 4	1·60	1·75

249 Old York Castle School

250 *Syntomidopsis variegata*

(Des A. Theobald. Litho B.D.T.)

1989 (19 Jan). *Bicentenary of Methodist Church in Jamaica. T* **249** *and similar horiz designs.* W **111** *(sideways). P* 13½.

743	25 c. black and bright blue	10	10
744	45 c. black and rosine	10	10
745	$5 black and yellow-green	1·00	1·10
743/5	*Set of* 3	1·00	1·10

Designs:—45 c. Revd. Thomas Coke and Parade Chapel, Kingston; $5 Father Hugh Sherlock and St. John's Church.

(Des I. Loe. Litho B.D.T.)

1989 (30 Aug). *Jamaican Moths (1st series). T* **250** *and similar vert designs. Multicoloured.* W **111**. *P* 14 × 13½.

746	25 c. Type **250**	15	10
747	55 c. *Himantoides undata-perkinsi*	15	15
748	$3 *Hypercompe nigriplaga*	1·00	1·00
749	$5 *Sthenognatha toddi*	1·40	1·40
746/9	*Set of* 4	2·40	2·40

POSTAL FISCALS

Revenue stamps were authorised for postal use by Post Office notice of 12 October 1887.

CONDITION. The note at the beginning also applies to Nos. F1/6.

F 1

(Typo D.L.R.)

1865–71 (Issued). *P* 14. (*a*) *Wmk Pineapple (T 7).*

F1	F 1	1d. rose (1865)	70·00	90·00
		a. Imperf (pair)	£500	

(*b*) *Wmk Crown CC*

F2	F 1	1d. rose (1868)	50·00	50·00

(*c*) *Wmk CA over Crown (Type w 7 sideways, covering two stamps)*

F3	F 1	1d. rose (1870 or 1871)	17·00	7·00
		a. Imperf		

F 2

F 3

(Typo D.L.R.)

1855–74 (Issued). *Glazed paper. P* 14. (*a*) *No wmk.*

F4	F 2	1½d. blue/*blue* (1857)	45·00	45·00
		a. Imperf (1855)		
		b. Blue on white	50·00	55·00
F5		3d. purple/*blue* (1857)	42·00	50·00
		a. Imperf (1855)		
		b. Purple on lilac (1857)	42·00	50·00
		ba. Imperf (1855)		
		c. Purple on white (1857)	45·00	50·00

(*b*) *Wmk Crown CC*

F6	F 2	3d. purple/*lilac* (1874)	8·00	13·00

All the above stamps *imperf* are exceedingly rare postally used.

1858 (1 Jan). (Issued). *No wmk. P* 15½ × 15.

F7	F 3	1s. rose/*bluish*	65·00	70·00
F8		5s. lilac/*bluish*	£325	£375
F9		10s. green/*bluish*	£375	£425

Telegraph stamps were also used postally, but no authority was given for such use.

OFFICIAL STAMPS

OFFICIAL (O 1)   OFFICIAL (O 2)

1890 (1 April). *No.* 16 *optd with Type* O 1 *by C. Vendryes, Kingston.*

(*a*) "OFFICIAL" 17 *to* 17½ *mm long*

O1	8	½d. green	4·50	1·00
		a. "O" omitted	£450	
		b. One "I" omitted		
		c. Both "I"s omitted	£500	£500
		d. "L" omitted	—	£550
		e. Opt inverted	65·00	70·00
		f. Opt double	65·00	70·00
		g. Opt. double, one inverted	£325	£325
		h. Opt double, one vertical	£550	
		j. Pair, overprints *tête-bêche*		

(*b*) "OFFICIAL" 15 *to* 16 *mm long*

O2	8	½d. green	20·00	20·00
		a. Opt double	£500	

There were four (or possibly five) settings of this overprint, all but one being of the longer type. There are numerous minor varieties, due to broken type, etc. (*e.g.* a broken "E" used for "F").

Stamps with the 17–17½ mm opt were reissued in 1894 during a temporary shortage of No. O3.

1890–1. *Optd with Type* O **2** *by D.L.R. Wmk Crown CA. P* 14.

O3	8	½d. green (1891)	2·25	15
O4	11	1d. rose (1.4.90)	3·25	40
O5		2d. grey (1.4.90)	3·50	1·00
O3/5		*Set of* 3	8·00	1·40
O3/5 Optd "Specimen"		*Set of* 3	£100	

Jordan
see Transjordan

Kenya

INDEPENDENT

1 Cattle Ranching

2 Wood-carving

3 National Assembly

(Des V. Whiteley. Photo Harrison)

1963 (12 Dec). *Independence. T* **1/3** *and similar designs. P* 14 × 15 (*small designs*) *or* 14½ (*others*).

No.	Description		
1	5 c. brown, deep blue, green and bistre	10	15
2	10 c. brown	10	10
3	15 c. magenta	25	10
4	20 c. black and yellow-green	15	10
5	30 c. black and yellow	15	10
6	40 c. brown and light blue	15	20
7	50 c. crimson, black and green	15	10
8	65 c. deep turquoise-green and yellow	55	65
9	1 s. multicoloured	20	10
10	1 s. 30, brown, black and yellow-green	1·25	10
11	2 s. multicoloured	50	15
12	5 s. brown, ultramarine and yellow-green	1·25	40
13	10 s. brown and deep blue	5·00	1·25
14	20 s. black and rose	5·50	4·00
1/14	*Set of* 14	14·00	6·00

Designs: As *T* **1/2**—15 c. Heavy industry; 20 c. Timber industry; 30 c. Jomo Kenyatta and Mt Kenya; 40 c. Fishing industry; 50 c. Kenya flag; 65 c. Pyrethrum industry. *As T* **3**—1 s. 30, Tourism (Treetops Hotel); 2 s. Coffee industry; 5 s. Tea industry; 10 s. Mombasa Port; 20 s. Royal College, Nairobi.

The 10 c. was produced in coils of 1000 in addition to normal sheets.

REPUBLIC

4 Cockerel

(Des M. Goaman. Photo J. Enschedé)

1964 (12 Dec). *Inauguration of Republic T* **4** *and similar vert designs. Multicoloured. P* 13 × 12½.

No.	Description		
15	15 c. Type **4**	15	15
16	30 c. President Kenyatta	25	10
17	50 c. Lion	35	10
18	1 s. 30, Hartlaub's Turaco	2·00	50
19	2 s. 50, Nandi flame	2·25	3·75
15/19	*Set of* 5	4·25	4·00

5 Thomson's Gazelle

6 Sable Antelope

7 Greater Kudu

(Des Rena Fennessy. Photo Harrison)

1966 (12 Dec)–**71.** *Various designs as T* **5/7**. *Chalk-surfaced paper. P* 14 × 14½ (5 c. *to* 70 c.) *or* 14½ (*others*).

No.	Description		
20	5 c. orange, black and sepia	10	15
21	10 c. black and apple-green	10	10
	a. Glazed, ordinary paper (13.7.71)	50	50
22	15 c. black and orange	10	10
	a. Glazed, ordinary paper (13.7.71)	50	50
23	20 c. ochre, black and blue	10	10
	a. Glazed, ordinary paper (22.1.71)	80	60
24	30 c. Prussian blue, blue and black	10	10
25	40 c. black and yellow-brown	15	15
	a. Glazed, ordinary paper (19.2.71)	1·00	50
26	50 c. black and red-orange	15	10
	a. Glazed, ordinary paper (19.2.71)	5·50	60
27	65 c. black and light green	1·25	2·00
28	70 c. black and claret (15.9.69)	2·25	90
	a. Glazed, ordinary paper (19.2.71)	6·50	5·00
29	1 s. olive-brown, black and slate-blue	20	10
	a. Glazed, ordinary paper (22.1.71)	1·25	55
30	1 s. 30, indigo, light olive-green and black	1·75	15
31	1 s. 50, black, orange-brown and dull sage-green (15.9.69)	2·00	2·00
	a. Glazed, ordinary paper (22.1.71)	4·00	5·50
32	2 s. 50, yellow, black and olive-brown	2·00	90
	a. Glazed, ordinary paper (22.1.71)	4·00	5·50
33	5 s. yellow, black and emerald	1·00	60
	a. Glazed, ordinary paper (22.1.71)	4·00	5·50
34	10 s. yellow-ochre, black and red-brown	2·50	2·00
35	20 s. yellow-ochre, yellow-orange, blk & gold	7·50	6·50
20/35	*Set of* 16	19·00	13·00
21a/33a	*Set of* 10	25·00	22·00

Designs: *As T* **5/6**—15 c. Aardvark ("Ant Bear"); 20 c. Lesser Bushbaby; 30 c. Warthog; 40 c. Common Zebra; 50 c. African Buffalo; 65 c. Black Rhinoceros; 70 c. Ostrich. *As T* **7**—1 s. 30, African Elephant; 1 s. 50, Bat-eared Fox; 2 s. 50, Cheetah; 5 s. Savanna Monkey ("Vervet Monkey"); 10 s. Giant Ground Pangolin; 20 s. Lion.

On chalk-surfaced paper, all values except 30 c., 50 c. and 2 s. 50 exist with PVA gum as well as gum arabic but the 70 c. and 1 s. 50 exist with PVA gum only. The stamps on glazed, ordinary paper exist with PVA gum only.

Nos. 21 and 26 exist in coils constructed from normal sheets.

8 Rose Dawn

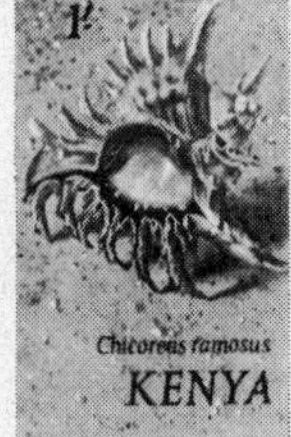

9 Rock Shell

2/- (10)

50 c. A. Inscr "*Janthina globosa*".
B. Inscr "*Janthina janthina*".

70 c. C. Inscr "*Nautilus pompileus*".
D. Inscr "*Nautilus pompilius*".

(Des Rena Fennessy. Photo Harrison)

1971 (15 Dec)–**74.** *T* **8/9** *and similar vert designs showing sea-shells. Multicoloured.* (*a*) *Size as T* **8**. *P* 14½ × 14.

No.	Description		
36	5 c. Type **8**	10	15
37	10 c. Bishop's Cap (yellow-green background)	10	10
	a. Olive-green background (21.1.74)	25	10
38	15 c. Strawberry Shell	15	10
39	20 c. Black Prince	15	10
40	30 c. Mermaid's Ear	20	10
41	40 c. Top Shell	20	10
42	50 c. Violet Shell (A)	30	10
43	50 c. Violet Shell (B) (21.1.74)	6·50	80
44	60 c. Cameo	30	25
45	70 c. Pearly Nautilus (C)	45	1·00
46	70 c. Pearly Nautilus (D) (21.1.74)	6·50	3·50
	(*b*) *Size as T* **9**. *P* 14		
47	1 s. Type **9** (yellow-buff background)	25	10
	a. Buff background (21.1.74)	20	10
48	1 s. 50, Triton	60	10
49	2 s. 50, Neptune's Trumpet	80	10
50	5 s. Turban Shell (pale ol-yell background)	1·25	10
	a. Pale olive-bistre background (13.6.73)	1·00	10
51	10 s. Cloth of Gold	2·50	15
52	20 s. Spider Shell (grey background)	6·00	75
	a. Bluish slate background (12.9.73)	3·75	35
36/52	*Set of* 17	22·00	6·00

1975 (17 Nov). *Nos.* 48/9 *and* 52 *surch as T* **10**.

No.	Description		
53	2 s. on 1 s. 50, Triton	2·50	1·75
54	3 s. on 2 s. 50, Neptune's Trumpet	9·00	13·00
55	40 s. on 20 s. Spider Shell	6·00	9·50
53/5	*Set of* 3	15·00	22·00

The surcharge on No. 55 does not have a dot beneath the stroke following the face value.

For commemorative stamps, issued between 1964 and 1976, inscribed "UGANDA KENYA TANGANYIKA AND ZANZIBAR" (or "TANZANIA UGANDA KENYA") see under KENYA, UGANDA AND TANGANYIKA.

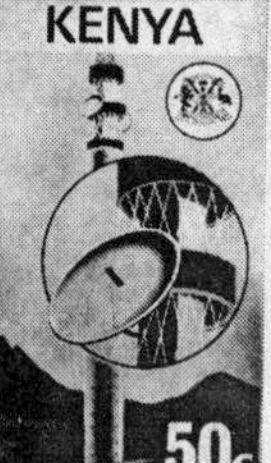

11 Microwave Tower

12 Akii Bua, Ugandan Hurdler

(Des H. Nickelsen. Litho Format)

1976 (15 Apr). *Telecommunications Development. T* **11** *and similar multicoloured designs. P* 14.

No.	Description		
56	50 c. Type **11**	10	10
57	1 s. Cordless switchboard (*horiz*)	10	10
58	2 s. Telephones	20	30
59	3 s. Message Switching Centre (*horiz*)	25	45
56/9	*Set of* 4	55	75
MS60	120 × 120 mm. Nos. 56/9. Imperf	1·60	2·00

(Des Beryl Moore. Litho Format)

1976 (7 July*). *Olympic Games, Montreal. T* **12** *and similar horiz designs. Multicoloured. P* 14½.

No.	Description		
61	50 c. Type **12**	10	10
62	1 s. Filbert Bayi, Tanzanian runner	15	10
63	2 s. Steve Muchoki, Kenyan boxer	45	35
64	3 s. Olympic flame and East African flags	60	50
61/4	*Set of* 4	1·10	85
MS65	129 × 154 mm. Nos. 61/4. P 13	5·00	5·00

*This is the local date of issue; the Crown Agents released the stamps two days earlier.

13 Diesel Train, Tanzania–Zambia Railway

14 Nile Perch

(Des H. Moghul. Litho Format)

1976 (4 Oct). *Railway Transport. T* **13** *and similar horiz designs. Multicoloured. P* 14½.

No.	Description		
66	50 c. Type **13**	35	10
67	1 s. Nile Bridge, Uganda	60	15
68	2 s. Nakuru Station, Kenya	2·25	1·25
69	3 s. Class "A" steam locomotive, 1896	2·50	1·75
66/9	*Set of* 4	5·00	3·00
MS70	154 × 103 mm. Nos. 66/9. P 13	8·00	7·50

(Des Adrienne Kennaway. Litho Format)

1977 (10 Jan). *Game Fish of East Africa. T* **14** *and similar vert designs. Multicoloured. P* 14*.

No.	Description		
71	50 c. Type **14**	20	10
72	1 s. Tilapia	30	10
73	3 s. Sailfish	1·50	75
74	5 s. Black Marlin	1·75	1·00
71/4	*Set of* 4	3·25	1·75
MS75	153 × 129 mm. Nos. 71/4	8·00	3·50

*On No. **MS**75 the right-hand side of the 5 s. value is perforated 13½.

15 Maasai Manyatta (village), Kenya

(Des Rena Fennessy. Litho Questa)

1977 (15 Jan). *Second World Black and African Festival of Arts and Culture, Nigeria. T* **15** *and similar horiz designs. Multicoloured. P* 13½.

No.	Description		
76	50 c. Type **15**	15	10
77	1 s. "Heartbeat of Africa" (Ugandan dancers)	25	10
78	2 s. Makonde sculpture, Tanzania	90	85
79	3 s. "Early Man and Technology" (skinning hippopotamus)	1·10	1·40
76/9	*Set of* 4	2·25	2·10
MS80	132 × 109 mm. Nos. 76/9	4·00	4·00

16 Rally-car and Villagers

(Litho Questa)

1977 (5 Apr). *25th Anniv of Safari Rally. T* **16** *and similar horiz designs. Multicoloured. P* 14.

81 50 c. Type **16** 20 10
82 1 s. President Kenyatta starting rally .. 30 10
83 2 s. Car fording river .. .. 70 1·00
84 5 s. Car and elephants .. .. .. 1·25 1·75
81/4 .. .. *Set of* 4 2·25 2·50
MS85 126 × 93 mm. Nos. 81/4 .. .. .. 4·00 4·75

17 Canon Kivebulaya

(Des Beryl Moore. Litho Questa)

1977 (30 June). *Centenary of Ugandan Church. T* **17** *and similar horiz designs. Multicoloured. P* 14 × 13½.

86 50 c. Type **17** 10 10
87 1 s. Modern Namirembe Cathedral 10 10
88 2 s. The first Cathedral 30 45
89 5 s. Early congregation, Kigezi 50 85
86/9 .. .. *Set of* 4 85 1·25
MS90 126 × 94 mm. Nos. 86/9 .. .. .. 1·75 2·75

18 Sagana Royal Lodge, Nyeri, 1952

(Des G. Vasarhelyi (50s.), J. Cooter (others). Litho Questa)

1977 (20 July). *Silver Jubilee. T* **18** *and similar multicoloured designs. P* 13½.

91 2 s. Type **18** 30 30
92 5 s. Treetops Hotel (*vert*) 65 65
93 10 s. Queen Elizabeth and President Kenyatta 90 1·25
94 15 s. Royal visit, 1972 .. .. 1·25 1·75
91/4 .. .. *Set of* 4 2·75 3·50
MS95 Two sheets: (a) 140 × 60 mm, No. 94; (b) 152 × 127 mm, 50 s. Queen and Prince Philip in Treetops Hotel .. .. *Set of* 2 4·00 4·50

19 Pancake Tortoise

(Des Rena Fennessy. Litho Questa)

1977 (26 Sept). *Endangered Species. T* **19** *and similar horiz designs. Multicoloured. P* 14.

96 50 c. Type **19** 30 10
97 1 s. Nile Crocodile 40 10
98 2 s. Hunter's Hartebeest .. .. .. 1·40 75
99 3 s. Red Colobus .. .. 1·75 1·00
100 5 s. Dugong .. .. 2·00 1·50
96/100 .. .. *Set of* 5 5·25 3·00
MS101 127 × 101 mm. Nos. 97/100 .. .. 7·00 7·00

20 Kenya–Ethiopia Border Point

(Litho Questa)

1977 (10 Nov). *Nairobi–Addis Ababa Highway. T* **20** *and similar horiz designs. Multicoloured. P* 14.

102 50 c. Type **20** 15 10
103 1 s. Archer's Post 20 10
104 2 s. Thika Flyover 75 60
105 5 s. Marsabit Game Lodge .. .. .. 1·75 1·50
102/5 .. .. *Set of* 4 2·50 2·00
MS106 144 × 91 mm. Nos. 102/5 .. .. .. 3·75 4·00

21 Gypsum

22 Amethyst

(Des Rena Fennessy. Photo Harrison)

1977 (10 Dec*). *Minerals. Multicoloured designs.*

(*a*) *Vert as T* **21**. *P* 14½ × 14

107 10 c. Type **21** 35 10
108 20 c. Trona 40 10
109 30 c. Kyanite 50 10
110 40 c. Amazonite 50 10
111 50 c. Galena 50 10
112 70 c. Silicified wood 75 15
113 80 c. Fluorite 75 15

(*b*) *Horiz as T* **22**. *P* 14

114 1 s. Type **22** 75 10
a. Gold (face value and inscr) omitted ..
115 1 s. 50, Agate .. .. 1·25 10
a. Gold (face vaue and inscr) omitted ..
116 2 s. Tourmaline .. .. 1·25 20
a. Gold (face value and inscr) omitted ..
117 3 s. Aquamarine .. .. 1·25 30
118 5 s. Rhodolite Garnet .. .. 1·25 60
119 10 s. Sapphire .. .. 1·75 1·25
120 20 s. Ruby .. .. 4·50 2·25
121 40 s. Green Grossular Garnet .. .. .. 7·50 7·50
107/21 .. .. *Set of* 15 21·00 11·50

*This is the local issue date. The stamps were released in London on 9 December.

23 Joe Kadenge (Kenya) and Forwards

(Des H. Moghul. Litho Questa)

1978 (10 Apr). *World Cup Football Championship, Argentina. T* **23** *and similar horiz designs showing footballers. Multicoloured. P* 14 × 13½.

122 50 c. Type **23** 10 10
123 1 s. Mohamed Chuma (Tanzania) and Cup presentation 10 10
124 2 s. Omari Kidevu (Zanzibar) and goalmouth scene 40 60
125 3 s. Polly Ouma (Uganda) and three forwards 50 85
122/5 .. .. *Set of* 4 1·00 1·40
MS126 136 × 81 mm. Nos. 122/5 .. .. .. 2·25 2·75

24 Boxing

(Des H. Moghul. Photo Heraclio Fournier)

1978 (17 July). *Commonwealth Games, Edmonton. T* **24** *and similar horiz designs. Multicoloured. P* 13 × 14.

127 50 c. Type **24** 15 10
128 1 s. Welcoming Olympic Games Team, 1968 20 10
129 3 s. Javelin throwing 60 80
130 5 s. President Kenyatta admiring boxer's trophy .. .. 75 1·25
127/30 .. .. *Set of* 4 1·50 2·00

25 "Overloading is Dangerous"

(Litho Walsall)

1978 (18 Sept). *Road Safety. T* **25** *and similar horiz designs. Multicoloured. P* 13½.

131 50 c. Type **25** 20 10
132 1 s. "Speed does not pay" 35 10
133 1 s. 50, "Ignoring Traffic Signs may cause death" 45 20
134 2 s. "Slow down at School Crossing" 70 55
135 3 s. "Never cross a continuous line" 85 70
136 5 s. "Approach Railway Level Crossing with extreme caution" .. .. 1·40 1·50
131/6 .. .. *Set of* 6 3·50 2·75

26 President Kenyatta at Mass Rally, 1963

27 Freedom Fighters, Namibia

(Des Beryl Moore. Litho J.W.)

1978 (16 Oct). *Kenyatta Day. T* **26** *and similar horiz designs. Multicoloured. P* 14.

137 50 c. "Harambee Water Project" 15 10
138 1 s. Handing over of Independence Instruments, 1963 .. .. 25 10
139 2 s. Type **26** 40 30
140 3 s. "Harambee, 15 Great Years" 60 55
141 5 s. "Struggle for Independence, 1952" .. 80 80
137/41 .. .. *Set of* 5 2·00 1·60

(Des L. Curtis. Litho Questa)

1978 (11 Dec*). *International Anti-Apartheid Year. T* **27** *and similar horiz designs. P* 14 × 14½.

142 50 c. multicoloured 15 10
143 1 s. black and cobalt 25 10
144 2 s. multicoloured 45 30
145 3 s. multicoloured 60 55
146 5 s. multicoloured 80 80
142/6 .. .. *Set of* 5 2·00 1·60

Designs:—1 s. International seminar on apartheid, racial discrimination and colonialism in South Africa; 2 s. Steve Biko's tombstone; 3 s. Nelson Mandela; 5 s. Bishop Lamont.

*This is the local date of issue; the Crown Agents released the stamps the previous day.

28 Children Playing

(Des Beryl Moore. Litho Walsall)

1979 (5 Feb). *International Year of the Child. T* **28** *and similar horiz designs. Multicoloured. P* 13½ × 14.

147 50 c. Type **28** 15 10
148 2 s. Child fishing 40 40
149 3 s. Children singing and dancing 60 60
150 5 s. Children working with camels 85 85
147/50 .. .. *Set of* 4 1·75 1·75

29 "The Lion and the Jewel"

30 Blind Telephone Operator

(Des Beryl Moore. Litho Enschedé)

1979 (6 Apr). *Kenya National Theatre. T* **29** *and similar horiz designs. Multicoloured. P* 13 × 13½.

151 50 c. Type **29** 10 10
152 1 s. Scene from "Utisi" 20 10
153 2 s. "Entertainment past and present" (programmes from past productions) .. 30 30
154 3 s. Kenya National Theatre 45 45
155 5 s. Nairobi City Players production of "Genesis" 75 75
151/5 .. .. *Set of* 5 1·75 1·50

(Litho Harrison)

1979 (29 June*). *50th Anniv of Salvation Army Social Services. T* **30** *and similar multicoloured designs. P* 13½ × 13 (50 c., 1s.) *or* 13 × 13½ (*others*).

156 50 c. Type **30** 15 10
157 1 s. Care for the Aged 20 10
158 3 s. Village polytechnic (*horiz*) 60 60
159 5 s. Vocational training (*horiz*) 85 85
156/9 .. .. *Set of* 4 1·60 1·40

*This is the local date of issue; the Crown Agents released the stamps on 4 June.

31 "Father of the Nation" (Kenyatta's funeral procession)

32 British East Africa Company 1890 1 a. Stamp

(Des H. Moghul. Litho Questa)

1979 (21 Aug*). *1st Death Anniv of President Kenyatta. T* **31** *and similar vert designs. Multicoloured. P* 13½ × 14.
160 50 c. Type **31** 10 10
161 1 s. "First President of Kenya" (Kenyatta receiving independence) 15 10
162 3 s. "Kenyatta the politician" (speaking at rally) 35 45
163 5 s. "A true son of Kenya" (Kenyatta as a boy carpenter) 60 85
160/3 .. .. *Set of* 4 1·00 1·25
*This is the local date of issue; the Crown Agents did not release the stamps until 29 August.

(Des J.W. Litho Harrison)

1979 (27 Nov). *Death Centenary of Sir Rowland Hill. T* **32** *and similar vert designs showing stamps. P* 14 × 14½.
164 50 c. multicoloured 10 10
165 1 s. multicoloured 15 10
166 2 s. black, magenta and yellow-ochre 20 35
167 5 s. multicoloured 55 90
164/7 .. .. *Set of* 4 90 1·25
Designs:—1 s. Kenya, Uganda and Tanganyika 1935 1 s.; 2 s. Penny Black; 5 s. 1964 Inauguration of Republic 2 s. 50, commemorative.

33 Roads, Globe and Conference Emblem

(Des H. Moghul. Litho Questa)

1980 (10 Jan). *I.R.F. (International Road Federation) African Highway Conference, Nairobi. T* **33** *and similar horiz designs. Multicoloured. P* 14 × 13½.
168 50 c. Type **33** 10 10
169 1 s. New weighbridge, Athi River 15 10
170 3 s. New Nyali Bridge, Mombasa 40 55
171 5 s. Highway to Jomo Kenyatta International Airport 70 95
168/71 .. .. *Set of* 4 1·25 1·50

34 Mobile Unit in action, Masailand **35** Statue of Sir Rowland Hill

(Des Beryl Moore. Litho Questa)

1980 (20 Mar). *Flying Doctor Service. T* **34** *and similar multi-coloured designs. P* 14½.
172 50 c. Type **34** 10 10
173 1 s. Donkey transport to Turkana airstrip (*vert*) 15 10
174 3 s. Surgical team in action at outstation (*vert*) 40 70
175 5 s. Emergency airlift from North Eastern Province .. .. 65 1·10
172/5 .. .. *Set of* 4 1·25 1·75
MS176 146 × 133 mm. Nos. 172/5 .. .. .. 1·50 2·00

(Des J.W. Litho Questa)

1980 (6 May). *"London 1980" International Stamp Exhibition. P* 14.
177 **35** 25 s. multicoloured .. .. .. 1·50 2·50
MS178 114 × 101 mm. No. 177 .. .. .. 1·60 2·75

36 Pope John Paul II **37** *Taeniura lymma*

(Des Sister Frances Randal. Litho Italian Govt Ptg Works, Rome)

1980 (8 May). *Papal Visit. T* **36** *and similar multicoloured designs. P* 13.
179 50 c. Type **36** 30 10
180 1 s. Pope John Paul II, cathedral and coat of arms (*vert*) 40 10
181 5 s. Pope John Paul II, Papal and Kenyan flags on dove symbol (*vert*) 85 70
182 10 s. President Moi, Pope John Paul II and map of Africa .. .. 1·40 1·40
179/82 .. .. *Set of* 4 2·75 2·00

(Des Adrienne Kennaway. Litho Harrison)

1980 (27 June). *Marine Life. T* **37** *and similar vert designs. Multicoloured. P* 14.
183 50 c. Type **37** 15 10
184 2 s. *Amphiprion allardi* 45 30
185 3 s. *Chromodoris quadricolor* 60 50
186 5 s. *Eretmochelys imbricata* .. .. .. 1·00 85
183/6 .. .. *Set of* 4 2·00 1·50

38 National Archives

(Des A. Odhuno; adapted L. Curtis. Litho Questa)

1980 (9 Oct). *Historic Buildings. T* **38** *and similar horiz designs. Multicoloured. P* 14.
187 50 c. Type **38** 10 10
188 1 s. Provincial Commissioner's Office, Nairobi 15 10
189 1 s. 50, Nairobi House 20 20
190 2 s. Norfolk Hotel 25 35
191 3 s. McMillan Library 35 45
192 5 s. Kipande House 55 80
187/92 .. .. *Set of* 6 1·40 1·75

39 "Disabled Enjoys Affection"

(Des H. Moghul. Litho Enschedé)

1981 (10 Feb). *International Year for Disabled Persons. T* **39** *and similar horiz designs. Multicoloured. P* 14 × 13.
193 50 c. Type **39** 15 10
194 1 s. President Moi presenting Kenyan flag to Disabled Olympic Games team captain 20 10
195 3 s. Blind people climbing Mount Kenya, 1975 .. .. 55 65
196 5 s. Disabled artist at work .. .. .. 85 1·00
193/6 .. .. *Set of* 4 1·60 1·60

40 Longonot Complex

(Des H. Moghul. Litho Harrison)

1981 (15 Apr). *Satellite Communications. T* **40** *and similar horiz designs. Multicoloured. P* 14 × 14½.
197 50 c. Type **40** 15 10
198 2 s. "Intelsat V" 50 35
199 3 s. "Longonot I" 60 55
200 5 s. "Longonot II" 85 85
197/200 .. .. *Set of* 4 1·90 1·60

41 Kenyatta Conference Centre **42** St. Paul's Cathedral

(Des L. Curtis. Litho Questa (**MS**206) or J.W. (others))

1981 (17 June*). *O.A.U. (Organisation of African Unity) Summit Conference, Nairobi. T* **41** *and similar horiz designs in black, bistre-yellow and new blue (1s.) or multicoloured (others). P* 13½.
201 50 c. Type **41** 15 10
202 1 s. "Panaftel" earth stations 20 10
203 3 s. Parliament Building 40 40
204 5 s. Jomo Kenyatta International Airport .. 65 65
205 10 s. O.A.U. flag .. .. 1·00 1·00
201/5 .. .. *Set of* 5 2·25 2·00
MS206 110 × 110 mm. No. 205. P 14½ × 14 .. 1·10 1·50
*This is the local date of issue; the Crown Agents did not release the stamps until 24 June.

(Des A. Theobald. Litho Questa)

1981 (29 July). *Royal Wedding. T* **42** *and similar vert designs. Multicoloured. P* 14.
207 50 c. Prince Charles and President Daniel Arap Moi 15 10
208 3 s. Type **42** 30 20
209 5 s. Royal Yacht *Britannia* 55 35
210 10 s. Prince Charles on safari in Kenya 80 70
207/10 .. .. *Set of* 4 1·60 1·25
MS211 85 × 102 mm. 25 s. Prince Charles and Lady Diana Spencer .. .. 2·00 2·00
Nos. 207/10 also exist perforated 12 (*price for set of* 4 £2·25 *mint or used*) from additional sheetlets of five stamps and one label.
Insufficient supplies of No. **MS**211 were received by 29 July for a full distribution, but subsequently the miniature sheet was freely available.

43 Giraffe **44** "Technical Development"

(Des Rena Fennessy. Litho Questa)

1981 (31 Aug). *Rare Animals. T* **43** *and similar vert designs. Multicoloured. P* 14½.
212 50 c. Type **43** 15 10
213 2 s. Bongo 35 20
214 5 s. Roan Antelope 70 55
215 10 s. Agile Mangabey .. .. 1·25 1·10
212/15 .. .. *Set of* 4 2·25 1·75

(Des H. Moghul, adapted L. Curtis. Litho Questa)

1981 (16 Oct). *World Food Day. T* **44** *and similar vert designs. Multicoloured. P* 14.
216 50 c. Type **44** 10 10
217 1 s. "Mwea rice projects" 15 10
218 2 s. "Irrigation schemes" 30 25
219 5 s. "Breeding livestock" 60 70
216/19 .. .. *Set of* 4 1·00 90

45 Kamba **46** *Australopithecus boisei*

(Des Adrienne Kennaway. Litho Harrison)

1981 (18 Dec). *Ceremonial Costumes (1st series). T* **45** *and similar vert designs. Multicoloured. P* 14½ × 13½.
220 50 c. Type **45** 15 10
221 1 s. Turkana 20 10
222 2 s. Giriama 50 25
223 3 s. Masai 70 40
224 5 s. Luo .. .. 1·10 85
220/4 .. .. *Set of* 5 2·40 1·40
See also Nos. 329/33, 413/17 and 515/19.

(Des Adrienne Kennaway. Litho Format)

1982 (19 Jan). *"Origins of Mankind". Skulls. T* **46** *and similar horiz designs. Multicoloured. P* 13½ × 14.
225 50 c. Type **46** 40 10
226 2 s. *Homo erectus* 80 25
227 3 s. *Homo habilis* .. .. 1·00 60
228 5 s. *Proconsul africanus* .. .. 1·40 1·00
225/8 .. .. *Set of* 4 3·25 1·75

47 Tree-planting

(Des L. Curtis. Litho Harrison)

1982 (9 June). *75th Anniv of Boy Scout Movement (Nos. 229, 231 233 and 235) and 60th Anniv of Girl Guide Movement (Nos. 230, 232, 234 and 236). T* **47** *and similar horiz designs. Multicoloured P* 14½.
229 70 c. Type **47** 20 10
a. Horiz pair. Nos. 229/30 .. .. .. 40 40
230 70 c. Paying homage 20 10
231 3 s. 50, "Be Prepared" 50 20
a. Horiz pair. Nos. 231/2 .. .. .. 1·00 1·00

32 3 s. 50, "International Friendship" 50 20
33 5 s. Helping disabled 70 50
a. Horiz pair. Nos. 233/4 .. .. .. 1·40 1·75
34 5 s. Community service 70 50
35 6 s. 50, Paxtu Cottage (Lord Baden-Powell's home) 90 60
a. Horiz pair. Nos. 235/6 .. .. .. 1·75 2·00
36 6 s. 50, Lady Baden-Powell 90 60
29/36 .. .. Set of 8 4·00 4·50
MS237 112 × 112 mm. Nos. 229, 231, 233 and 235 2·50 3·00

The two designs of each value were printed together, *se-tenant*, in horizontal pairs throughout the sheet.

48 Footballer displaying Shooting Skill

(Des local artist. Litho Harrison)

1982 (5 July). *World Cup Football Championships, Spain. T* **48** *and similar triangular designs showing footballers silhouetted against world map. Multicoloured. P* 12½.

238 70 c. Type **48** 40 15
239 3 s. 50, Heading 85 65
240 5 s. Goalkeeping .. .. 1·25 1·00
241 10 s. Dribbling .. .. 1·75 2·00
238/41 .. .. Set of 4 3·75 3·50
MS242 101 × 76 mm. 20 s. Tackling. P 13 × 14 .. 3·00 3·50

70c

49 Cattle Judging **50** Micro-wave Radio System **(51)**

(Des H. Moghul. Litho Harrison)

1982 (28 Sept). *80th Anniv of Agricultural Society of Kenya. T* **49** *and similar vert designs. Multicoloured. P* 14½.

243 70 c. Type **49** 35 10
244 2 s. 50, Farm machinery 80 60
245 3 s. 50, Musical ride .. .. 1·00 90
246 6 s. 50, Agricultural Society emblem .. 1·50 1·75
243/6 .. .. Set of 4 3·25 3·00

(Des H. Moghul. Photo Courvoisier)

1982 (21 Oct). *I.T.U. Plenipotentiary Conference, Nairobi. T* **50** *and similar vert designs. Multicoloured. P* 11½.

247 70 c. Type **50** 30 10
248 3 s. 50, Sea-to-shore service link 80 85
249 5 s. Rural telecommunications system .. 1·25 1·50
250 6 s. 50, I.T.U. emblem .. .. .. 1·60 1·75
247/50 .. .. Set of 4 3·50 3·75

1982 (22 Nov). *No. 113 surch with T* **51**, *in white on a black panel.*

251 70 c. on 80 c. Fluorite 30 30

52 Container Cranes

(Des R. Vigurs. Litho Questa)

1983 (20 Jan). *5th Anniv of Kenya Ports Authority. T* **52** *and similar horiz designs. P* 14.

252 70 c. Type **52** 35 10
253 2 s. Port by night 80 45
254 3 s. 50, Container cranes (*different*) .. .. 1·25 85
255 5 s. Map of Mombasa Port .. .. .. 1·50 1·25
252/5 .. .. Set of 4 3·50 2·25
MS256 125 × 85 mm. Nos. 252/5 .. .. .. 3·50 4·00

53 Shada Zamb[...] **54** Waridi Kikuba

(Des Rena Fennessy. Photo Harrison)

1983 (15 Feb)–**85**. *Flowers. Multicoloured.*

(*a*) *Vert designs as T* **53**. *P* 14½ × 14

257 10 c. Type **53** 15 10
258 20 c. Kilua Kingulima 25 10
259 30 c. Mwalika Mwiya 25 10
260 40 c. Ziyungi Buluu 25 10
261 50 c. Kilua Habashia 25 10
262 70 c. Chanuo Kato 30 10
262*a* 80 c. As 40 c. (7.8.85) 70 15
262*b* 1 s. Waridi Kikuba (5.8.85*) 70 15

(*b*) *Vert designs as T* **54**. *P* 14

263 1 s. Type **54** 25 10
264 1 s. 50, Mshomoro Mtambazi 45 20
265 2 s. Papatuo Boti 50 20
266 2 s. 50, Tumba Mboni 70 20
266*a* 3 s. Mkuku Mrembo (12.8.85) .. .. 1·00 50
267 3 s. 50, Mtongo Mbeja 75 50
a. Gold (inscr and face value) omitted ..
267*b* 4 s. Mnukia Muuma (7.8.85) .. .. 1·25 1·00
268 5 s. Nyungu Chepuo 80 45
268*a* 7 s. Mlua Miba (7.8.85) .. .. .. 1·75 1·75
269 10 s. Muafunili .. .. 1·50 1·25
270 20 s. Mbake Nyanza .. .. .. 2·25 2·00
271 40 s. Njuga Pagwa .. .. 4·00 4·75
257/71 .. .. Set of 20 16·00 12·00

*Earliest known postmark date.

55 Coffee Plucking **56** Examining Parcels

(Des C. Fernandes. Litho Harrison)

1983 (14 Mar). *Commonwealth Day. T* **55** *and similar multi-coloured designs. P* 14 × 14½ (70 c., 2 s.) *or* 14½ × 14 (*others*).

272 70 c. Type **55** 10 10
273 2 s. President Daniel Arap Moi 15 20
274 5 s. Satellite view of Earth (*horiz*) 45 45
275 10 s. Masai dance (*horiz*) .. .. .. 90 1·00
272/5 .. .. Set of 4 1·40 1·50

(Des H. Moghul. Litho Harrison)

1983 (11 May). *30th Anniv of Customs Co-operation Council. T* **56** *and similar vert designs. Multicoloured. P* 14.

276 70 c. Type **56** 15 10
277 2 s. 50, Customs Headquarters, Mombasa .. 35 25
278 3 s. 50, Customs Council Headquarters, Brussels 45 35
279 10 s. Customs patrol boat .. .. .. 1·40 1·40
276/9 .. .. Set of 4 2·10 1·90

57 Communications via Satellite **58** Ships in Kilindini Harbour

(Litho Harrison)

1983 (4 July). *World Communications Year. T* **57** *and similar multicoloured designs. P* 14 × 14½ (70 c., 2 s. 50) *or* 14½ × 14 (*others*).

280 70 c. Type **57** 30 10
281 2 s. 50, "Telephone and Postal Services" .. 60 50
282 3 s. 50, Communications by sea and air (*horiz*) 80 80
283 5 s. Road and rail communications (*horiz*) .. 1·25 1·25
280/3 .. .. Set of 4 2·75 2·40

(Litho Harrison)

1983 (22 Sept). *25th Anniv of Intergovernmental Maritime Organization. T* **58** *and similar horiz designs. Multicoloured. P* 14.

284 70 c. Type **58** 40 10
285 2 s. 50, Life-saving devices 85 40
286 3 s. 50, Mombasa container terminal .. 1·00 60
287 10 s. Marine park .. .. 2·00 2·00
284/7 .. .. Set of 4 3·75 2·75

59 President Moi signing Visitors' Book

(Litho Harrison)

1983 (31 Oct). *29th Commonwealth Parliamentary Conference. T* **59** *and similar multicoloured designs. P* 14.

288 70 c. Type **59** 15 10
289 2 s. 50, Parliament building, Nairobi (*vert*) .. 35 35
290 5 s. State opening of Parliament (*vert*) .. 70 60
288/90 .. .. Set of 3 1·10 90
MS291 122 × 141 mm. Nos. 288/90 .. .. 1·10 1·60

60 Kenyan and British Flags

(Des A. Theobald. Litho Harrison)

1983 (10 Nov). *Royal Visit. T* **60** *and similar horiz designs. Multi-coloured. P* 14.

292 70 c. Type **60** 25 10
293 3 s. 50, Sagana State Lodge 80 35
294 5 s. Treetops Hotel .. .. 1·25 70
295 10 s. Queen Elizabeth II and President Moi .. 2·00 1·75
292/5 .. .. Set of 4 4·00 2·50
MS296 126 × 100 mm. 25 s. Designs as Nos. 292/5, but without face values. Imperf .. .. 2·50 3·00

61 President Moi **62** White-backed Night Heron

(Des and litho Harrison)

1983 (9 Dec). *20th Anniv of Independence. T* **61** *and similar horiz designs. Multicoloured. P* 14½.

297 70 c. Type **61** 10 10
298 2 s. President Moi planting tree 20 20
299 3 s. 50, Kenyan flag and emblem 35 35
300 5 s. School milk scheme 50 50
301 10 s. People of Kenya .. .. 1·00 1·10
297/301 .. .. Set of 5 1·90 2·00
MS302 126 × 93 mm. 25 s. Designs as Nos. 297 and 299/301, but without face values. Imperf .. 1·75 2·75

(Des Agnes Odero. Litho Harrison)

1984 (6 Feb). *Rare Birds of Kenya. T* **62** *and similar vert designs. Multicoloured. P* 14½ × 13½.

303 70 c. Type **62** 55 15
304 2 s. 50, Quail Plover .. .. .. 1·00 65
305 3 s. 50, Taita Olive Thrush .. .. .. 1·25 90
306 5 s. Mufumbiri Shrike ("Yellow Gonolek") 1·50 1·25
307 10 s. White-winged Apalis .. .. .. 2·00 2·50
303/7 .. .. Set of 5 5·75 5·00

63 Radar Tower **64** Running

(Des C. Fernandes. Litho Harrison)

1984 (2 Apr). *40th Anniv of International Civil Aviation Organiz-ation. T* **63** *and similar multicoloured designs. P* 14.

308 70 c. Type **63** 10 10
309 2 s. 50, Kenya School of Aviation (*horiz*) .. 30 30
310 3 s. 50, Aircraft taking off from Moi airport (*horiz*) 40 45
311 5 s. Air traffic control centre 55 60
308/11 .. .. Set of 4 1·25 1·25

(Des and litho Harrison)

1984 (21 May). *Olympic Games, Los Angeles. T* **64** *and similar horiz designs. P* 14½.

312 70 c. black, bright yellow-green and bronze-green 15 10
313 2 s. 50, black, bright magenta and reddish violet 40 25
314 5 s. black, pale turquoise-blue and steel blue 70 55
315 10 s. black, bistre-yellow and brown .. .. 1·40 1·25
312/15 .. .. Set of 4 2·40 1·90
MS316 130 × 121 mm. 25 s. Designs as Nos. 312/15 but without face values. Imperf .. .. 2·50 3·00

Designs:—2 s. 50, Hurdling; 5 s. Boxing; 10 s. Hockey.

65 Conference and Kenya Library Association Logos

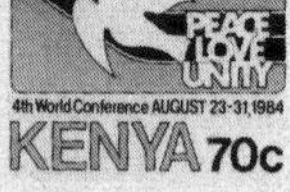

66 Doves and Cross

(Des and litho Harrison)

1984 (28 June). *50th Conference of the International Federation of Library Associations. T* **65** *and similar horiz designs. Multicoloured. P* 14½.

317 70 c. Type **65** 10 10
318 3 s. 50, Mobile library 40 40
319 5 s. Adult library 55 55
320 10 s. Children's library .. .. .. 1·00 1·25
317/20 .. .. *Set of* 4 1·75 2·00

(Des K. Bisley. Litho Harrison)

1984 (23 Aug). *4th World Conference on Religion and Peace. T* **66** *and similar vert designs, each showing a different central symbol. Multicoloured. P* 14½.

321 70 c. Type **66** 20 10
322 2 s. 50, Arabic inscription 55 50
323 3 s. 50, Peace emblem 85 75
324 6 s. 50, Star and Crescent .. .. .. 1·25 1·50
321/4 .. .. *Set of* 4 2·50 2·50

67 Export Year Logo

68 Knight and Nyayo National Stadium

(Litho Harrison)

1984 (1 Oct). *Kenya Export Year. T* **67** *and similar multicoloured designs. P* 14½.

325 70 c. Type **67** 20 10
326 3 s. 50, Forklift truck with air cargo (*horiz*) 85 75
327 5 s. Loading ship's cargo .. .. .. 1·25 1·00
328 10 s. Kenyan products (*horiz*) .. .. .. 2·00 2·50
325/8 .. .. *Set of* 4 4·00 4·00

(Litho Harrison)

1984 (5 Nov). *Ceremonial Costumes (2nd series). Vert designs as T* **45**. *Multicoloured. P* 14½ × 13½.

329 70 c. Luhya 25 10
330 2 s. Kikuyu 60 35
331 3 s. 50, Pokomo 85 70
332 5 s. Nandi .. .. 1·25 1·00
333 10 s. Rendile .. .. 1·75 2·00
329/33 .. .. *Set of* 5 4·25 3·75

(Litho Harrison)

1984 (21 Dec). *60th Anniv of World Chess Federation. T* **68** *and similar horiz designs. Multicoloured. P* 14½.

334 70 c. Type **68** 40 10
335 2 s. 50, Rook and Fort Jesus 90 50
336 3 s. 50, Bishop and National Monument .. 1·25 80
337 5 s. Queen and Parliament Building .. 1·50 1·00
338 10 s. King and Nyayo Fountain .. .. 2·00 2·25
334/8 .. .. *Set of* 5 5·50 4·25

69 Cooking with Wood-burning Stove and Charcoal Fire

(Des H. Moghul. Litho J.W.)

1985 (22 Jan). *Energy Conservation. T* **69** *and similar horiz designs. Multicoloured. P* 13½.

339 70 c. Type **69** 10 10
340 2 s. Solar energy panel on roof 20 20
341 3 s. 50, Production of gas from cow dung .. 35 45
342 10 s. Ploughing with oxen .. .. .. 1·00 1·50
339/42 .. .. *Set of* 4 1·40 2·00
MS343 110 × 85 mm. 20 s. Designs as Nos. 339/42, but without face values .. .. .. 2·25 2·50

70 Crippled Girl Guide making Table-mat

(Litho J.W.)

1985 (27 Mar). *75th Anniv of Girl Guide Movement. T* **70** *and similar horiz designs. Multicoloured. P* 13½.

344 1 s. Type **70** 25 10
345 3 s. Girl Guides doing community service .. 60 35
346 5 s. Lady Olave Baden-Powell (founder) .. 80 65
347 7 s. Girl Guides gardening .. .. .. 1·00 1·25
344/7 .. .. *Set of* 4 2·40 2·10

71 Stylised Figures and Globe

72 Man with Malaria

(Des and litho Harrison)

1985 (8 May). *World Red Cross Day. T* **71** *and similar horiz designs. P* 14½.

348 1 s. black and rosine 25 10
349 4 s. multicoloured 85 55
350 5 s. multicoloured .. .. 1·10 65
351 7 s. multicoloured .. .. 1·40 1·25
348/51 .. .. *Set of* 4 3·25 2·25

Designs:—4 s. First aid team; 5 s. Hearts containing crosses ("Blood Donation"); 7 s. Cornucopia ("Famine Relief").

(Des H. Moghul. Litho Harrison)

1985 (25 June). *7th International Congress of Protozoology, Nairobi. T* **72** *and similar vert designs. Multicoloured. P* 14½.

352 1 s. Type **72** 25 10
353 3 s. Child with Leishmaniasis 85 40
354 5 s. Cow with Trypanosomiasis .. .. 1·10 70
355 7 s. Dog with Babesiosis .. .. .. 1·40 1·25
352/5 .. .. *Set of* 4 3·25 2·25

73 Repairing Water Pipes

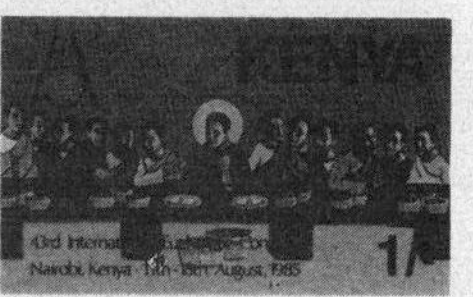

74 The Last Supper

(Des J. Tobula and Harrison. Litho Harrison)

1985 (15 July). *United Nations Women's Decade Conference. T* **73** *and similar vert designs. Multicoloured. P* 14½.

356 1 s. Type **73** 10 10
357 3 s. Traditional food preparation 30 35
358 5 s. Basket-weaving 50 55
359 7 s. Dressmaking 65 70
356/9 .. .. *Set of* 4 1·40 1·50

(Des Eucharistic Congress Secretariat. Litho J.W.)

1985 (17 Aug*). *43rd International Eucharistic Congress, Nairobi. T* **74** *and similar horiz designs. Multicoloured. P* 13½.

360 1 s. Type **74** 25 10
361 3 s. Village family ("The Eucharist and the Christian Family") 65 40
362 5 s. Congress altar, Uhuru Park 85 65
363 7 s. St. Peter Claver's Church, Nairobi .. 1·25 1·10
360/3 .. .. *Set of* 4 2·75 2·00
MS364 117 × 80 mm. 25 s. Pope John Paul II .. 3·50 3·50

* This is the local date of issue. The Crown Agents released the stamps on 15 August and this date also appears on first day covers serviced by Kenya Posts and Telecommunications Corporation.

75 Black Rhinoceros

(Des Rena Fennessy. Litho Harrison)

1985 (10 Dec). *Endangered Animals. T* **75** *and similar horiz designs. Multicoloured. P* 14½.

365 1 s. Type **75** 40 10
366 3 s. Cheetah .. .. 1·00 55
367 5 s. De Brazza's Monkey .. .. .. 1·50 85
368 10 s. Grevy's Zebra .. .. 2·00 2·00
365/8 .. .. *Set of* 4 4·50 3·25
MS369 129 × 122 mm. 25 s. Endangered species (122 × 114 *mm*). Imperf .. .. .. 3·50 4·00

76 *Borassus aethiopum*

77 Dove and U.N. Logo (from poster)

(Des Rena Fennessy. Litho Questa)

1986 (24 Jan). *Indigenous Trees. T* **76** *and similar horiz designs Multicoloured. P* 14½.

370 1 s. Type **76** 25 1
371 3 s. *Acacia xanthophloea* 75 5
372 5 s. *Ficus natalensis* .. .. 1·00 8
373 7 s. *Spathodea nilotica* .. .. .. 1·50 1·5
370/3 .. .. *Set of* 4 3·25 2·7
MS374 117 × 96 mm. 25 s. Landscape with trees (109 × 90 *mm*). Imperf .. .. 3·25 4·0

(Des Advertising Link. Litho Questa)

1986 (30 Apr*). *International Peace Year. T* **77** *and simila multicoloured designs. P* 14½.

375 1 s. Type **77** 10 1
376 3 s. U.N. General Assembly (*horiz*) .. 30 3
377 7 s. Nuclear explosion 65 7
378 10 s. Quotation from Wall of Isaiah, U.N. Building, New York (*horiz*) .. .. 1·00 1·1
375/8 .. .. *Set of* 4 1·90 2·0

*This is the local date of issue. The Crown Agents released th stamps on 17 April and this date also appears on first day cover serviced by Kenya Posts and Telecommunications Corporatior

78 Dribbling the Ball

79 Rural Post Office and Telephone

(Des C. Fernandes. Litho Harrison)

1986 (8 May). *World Cup Football Championship, Mexico. T* 7 *and similar multicoloured designs. P* 14½.

379 1 s. Type **78** 20 1
380 3 s. Scoring from a penalty 50 3
381 5 s. Tackling 75 5
382 7 s. Cup winners .. .. 1·00 8
383 10 s. Heading the ball .. .. 1·40 1·5
379/83 .. .. *Set of* 5 3·50 3·0
MS384 110 × 86 mm. 30 s. Harambee Stars football team (102 × 78 *mm*). Imperf .. .. .. 3·25 3·7

(Des H. Moghul. Litho Cartor, France)

1986 (11 June). *"Expo '86" World Fair, Vancouver. T* **79** *anc similar horiz designs. Multicoloured. P* 13½ × 13.

385 1 s. Type **79** 20 1
386 3 s. Container depot, Embakasi 60 3
387 5 s. Aircraft landing at game park airstrip .. 90 5
388 7 s. Container ship .. .. 1·25 1·1
389 10 s. Transporting produce to market .. 1·50 1·5
385/9 .. .. *Set of* 5 4·00 3·2

On 15 July 1986 Kenya was scheduled to release a set of five stamps, 1, 3, 4, 7 and 10 s., for the Commonwealth Games a Edinburgh. A political decision was taken at the last momen not to issue the stamps, but this instruction did not reach some o the sub-post offices until the morning of 15 July. About twc hundred stamps, mainly the 1 s. value, were sold by these sub-post offices before the instruction arrived. Examples of the 1 s. exist used on commercial mail from Kenyatta College sub-post office from 17 July 1986 onwards.

80 Telephone, Computer and Dish Aerial

(Des H. Moghul. Litho Harrison)

1986 (16 Sept). *African Telecommunications. T* **80** *and similar horiz designs. Multicoloured. P* 14½.

390 1 s. Type **80** 15 10
391 3 s. Telephones of 1876, 1936 and 1986 .. 45 35
392 5 s. Dish aerial, satellite, telephones and map of Africa 70 70
393 7 s. Kenyan manufacture of telecommunications equipment .. .. 1·00 1·00
390/3 .. .. *Set of* 4 2·10 2·00

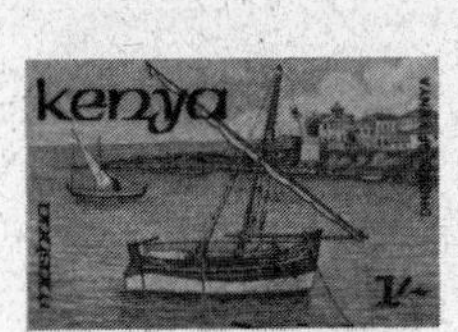

81 Mashua

82 The Nativity

(Des Mukund Arts. Litho Mardon Printers Ltd, Zimbabwe)

1986 (30 Oct). *Dhows of Kenya. T* **81** *and similar horiz designs. Multicoloured. P* 14½.

394 1 s. Type **81** 25 10
395 3 s. Mtepe 60 45
396 5 s. Dau La Mwao .. .. 1·00 70
397 10 s. Jahazi .. .. 1·50 2·00
394/7 .. .. *Set of* 4 3·00 3·00
MS398 118 × 80 mm. 25 s. Lamu dhow and map of Indian Ocean .. .. 3·50 4·00

(Des Mukund Arts. Photo Courvoisier)

1986 (5 Dec). *Christmas. T* **82** *and similar multicoloured designs. Granite paper. P* 11½.

399 1 s. Type **82** 15 10
400 3 s. Shepherd and sheep 45 35
401 5 s. Angel and slogan "LOVE PEACE UNITY" (*horiz*) 75 60
402 7 s. The Magi riding camels (*horiz*) .. .. 90 1·10
399/402 .. .. *Set of* 4 2·00 1·90

83 Immunization

84 Akamba Woodcarvers

(Des Judith D'Inca. Litho Harrison)

1987 (6 Jan). *40th Anniv of United Nations Children's Fund. T* **83** *and similar vert designs. Multicoloured. P* 14.

403 1 s. Type **83** 15 10
404 3 s. Food and nutrition 40 35
405 4 s. Oral rehydration therapy 55 45
406 5 s. Family planning 65 60
407 10 s. Female literacy .. .. 1·25 1·25
403/7 .. .. *Set of* 5 2·75 2·50

(Des C. Fernandes. Litho Questa)

1987 (25 Mar). *Tourism. T* **84** *and similar horiz designs. Multicoloured. P* 14½.

408 1 s. Type **84** 20 10
409 3 s. Tourists on beach 40 40
410 5 s. Tourist and guide at view point 60 60
411 7 s. Pride of lions .. .. 1·00 1·00
408/11 .. .. *Set of* 4 2·00 1·90
MS412 118 × 81 mm. 30 s. Geysers .. .. .. 3·50 4·00

(Des Mukund Arts. Litho Harrison)

1987 (20 May). *Ceremonial Costumes (3rd series). Vert designs as T* **45**. *Multicoloured. P* 14½ × 13½.

413 1 s. Embu 10 10
414 3 s. Kisii 20 25
415 5 s. Samburu 35 40
416 7 s. Taita 50 55
417 10 s. Boran 70 75
413/17 .. .. *Set of* 5 1·60 1·90

85 Telecommunications by Satellite

86 Volleyball

(Des Mukund Arts. Litho Harrison)

1987 (1 July). *10th Anniv of Kenya Posts and Telecommunications Corporation. T* **85** *and similar triangular designs. Multicoloured. P* 13½.

418 1 s. Type **85** 10 10
419 3 s. Rural post office, Kajiado 20 25
420 4 s. Awarding trophy, Welfare Sports 30 35
421 5 s. Village and telephone box 35 40
422 7 s. Speedpost labels and outline map of Kenya 50 55
418/22 .. .. *Set of* 5 1·25 1·50
MS423 110 × 80 mm. 25 s. Corporation flag .. 1·75 1·90

Nos. 418/22 were each printed as horizontal *tête-bêche* pairs within the sheet.

(Des C. Fernandes. Litho D.L.R.)

1987 (5 Aug). *4th All-Africa Games, Nairobi. T* **86** *and similar multicoloured designs. P* 14½ × 14.

424 1 s. Type **86** 10 10
425 3 s. Cycling 20 25
426 4 s. Boxing 30 35
427 5 s. Swimming 35 40
428 7 s. Steeplechasing 50 55
424/8 .. .. *Set of* 5 1·25 1·50
MS429 117 × 80 mm. 30 s. Kasarani Sports Complex (*horiz*). P 14 × 14½ .. .. 2·10 2·25

87 *Aloe volkensii*

(Des Advertising Link. Litho Cartor, France)

1987 (10 Nov). *Medicinal Herbs. T* **87** *and similar vert designs. Multicoloured. P* 13½ × 14.

430 1 s. Type **87** 10 10
431 3 s. *Cassia didymobotrya* 25 25
432 5 s. *Erythrina abyssinica* 40 40
433 7 s. *Adenium obesum* 60 70
434 10 s. Herbalist's clinic 80 90
430/4 .. .. *Set of* 5 2·00 2·10

88 *Iolaus sidus*

89 King Swallowtail

(Des Rena Fennessy. Photo Harrison)

1988 (15 Feb)–**89**. *Butterflies. Multicoloured.*

(*a*) *Vert designs as T* **88**. *P* 15 × 14

434*a* 10 c. *Cyrestis camillus* (1.9.89) 10 10
435 20 c. Type **88** 10 10
436 40 c. Painted Lady 10 10
437 50 c. Black-barred Red-tip 10 10
438 70 c. Blue-spot Commodore 10 10
439 80 c. African Clouded Yellow 10 10
440 1 s. Orange and Lemon 10 10

(*b*) *Vert designs as T* **89**. *P* 14½

441 2 s. Type **89** 10 10
442 2 s. 50, Variable Colotis 15 20
443 3 s. Taita Swallowtail 15 20
444 3 s. 50, Citrus Swallowtail 20 25
445 4 s. Green Swallowtail 20 25
446 5 s. Taita Silver-barred Charaxes 25 30
447 7 s. Taita Glider 40 45
448 10 s. Club-tailed Charaxes 55 60
449 20 s. Mocker Swallowtail .. .. 1·10 1·25
450 40 s. Blue-spotted Charaxes .. .. 2·10 2·25
434*a*/50 .. .. *Set of* 17 5·00 5·50

Examples of the 1 s. value were used in error at Kisumu from 2 February 1988.

90 Samburu Lodge and Crocodiles

(Des Advertising Link. Litho Questa)

1988 (31 May). *Kenyan Game Lodges. T* **90** *and similar horiz designs. Multicoloured. P* 14½.

451 1 s. Type **90** 10 10
452 3 s. Naro Moru River Lodge and rock climbing 25 25
453 4 s. Mara Serena Lodge and zebra with foal 30 30
454 5 s. Voi Safari Lodge and buffalo 35 35
455 7 s. Kilimanjaro Buffalo Lodge and giraffes 50 50
456 10 s. Meru Mulika Lodge and rhinoceroses 65 65
451/6 .. .. *Set of* 6 1·90 1·90

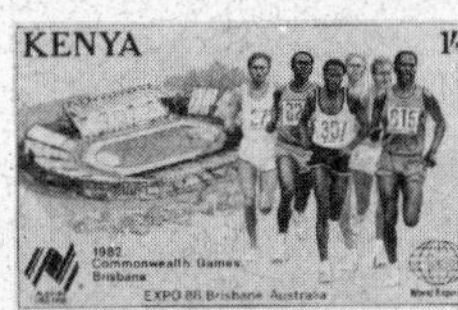

91 Athletes and Stadium, Commonwealth Games, Brisbane, 1982

(Des D. Ashby. Litho Harrison)

1988 (10 June). *"Expo '88" World Fair, Brisbane, and Bicentenary of Australian Settlement. T* **91** *and similar horiz designs. Multicoloured. P* 14½.

457 1 s. Type **91** 10 10
458 3 s. Flying Doctor Service aircraft 20 25
459 4 s. H.M.S. *Sirius* (frigate), 1788 .. .. 25 30
460 5 s. Ostrich and emu 30 35
461 7 s. Queen Elizabeth II, President Arap Moi of Kenya and Prime Minister Hawke of Australia 45 50
457/61 .. .. *Set of* 5 1·10 1·40
MS462 117×80 mm. 30 s. Entrance to Kenya Pavilion .. .. 1·90 2·00

92 W.H.O. Logo and Slogan

93 Handball

(Des Mukund Arts. Litho National Printing & Packaging, Zimbabwe)

1988 (1 July). *40th Anniv of World Health Organization. T* **92** *and similar horiz designs. P* 14½.

463 1 s. greenish blue, gold and ultramarine .. 10 10
464 3 s. multicoloured 30 25
465 5 s. multicoloured 40 35
466 7 s. multicoloured 60 50
463/6 .. .. *Set of* 4 1·25 1·10

Designs:—3 s. Mother with young son and nutritious food; 5 s. Giving oral vaccine to baby; 7 s. Village women drawing clean water from pump.

(Des H. Moghul. Litho D.L.R.)

1988 (1 Aug). *Olympic Games, Seoul. T* **93** *and similar vert designs. Multicoloured. P* 14½×14.

467 1 s. Type **93** 10 10
468 3 s. Judo 20 25
469 5 s. Weightlifting 30 35
470 7 s. Javelin 45 50
471 10 s. Relay racing 60 65
467/71 .. .. *Set of* 5 1·40 1·60
MS472 110×78 mm. 30 s. Tennis .. .. .. 1·90 2·00

94 Calabashes

95 Pres. Arap Moi taking Oath, 1978

(Des Mukund Arts. Litho D.L.R.)

1988 (20 Sept). *Kenyan Material Culture. T* **94** *and similar multicoloured designs. P* 14½×14 *(vert) or* 14×14½ *(horiz).*

473 1 s. Type **94** 10 10
474 3 s. Milk gourds 20 25
475 5 s. Cooking pots (*horiz*) 30 35
476 7 s. Winnowing trays (*horiz*) 45 50
477 10 s. Reed baskets (*horiz*) 60 65
473/7 .. .. *Set of* 5 1·40 1·60
MS478 118×80 mm. 25 s. Gourds, calabash and horn (*horiz*) .. .. 1·50 1·60

(Des Mukund Arts. Litho Harrison)

1988 (13 Oct). *10th Anniv of "Nyayo" Era. T* **95** *and similar horiz designs. Multicoloured. P* 13½×14½.

479 1 s. Type **95** 10 10
480 3 s. Building soil conservation barrier 30 25
481 3 s. 50, Passengers boarding bus 30 25
482 4 s. Metalwork shop 40 30
483 5 s. Moi University, Eldoret 50 45
484 7 s. Aerial view of hospital 65 70
485 10 s. Pres. Arap Moi and Mrs. Thatcher at Kapsabet Telephone Exchange .. .. 80 1·00
479/85 .. .. *Set of* 7 2·75 2·75

96 Kenya Flag

(Des Mukund Arts. Photo Courvoisier)

1988 (9 Dec). *25th Anniv of Independence. T* **96** *and similar horiz designs. Multicoloured. Granite paper. P* 11½.

486 1 s. Type **96** 10 10
487 3 s. Coffee picking 20 25
488 5 s. Proposed Kenya Posts and Telecommunications Headquarters building 30 35
489 7 s. Kenya Airways *Harambee Star* "A310-300" Airbus 45 50
490 10 s. New diesel locomotive No. 9401 .. .. 60 65
486/90 .. .. *Set of* 5 1·40 1·60

97 Gedi Ruins, Malindi

(Des Mukund Arts. Litho National Printing & Packaging, Zimbabwe)

1989 (15 Mar). *Historic Monuments. T* **97** *and similar multicoloured designs. P* 14½.

491	1 s. 20, Type **97**	15	10
492	3 s. 40, Vasco Da Gama Pillar, Malindi (*vert*)	30	30
493	4 s. 40, Ishiakani Monument, Kiunga	40	40
494	5 s. 50, Fort Jesus, Mombasa	50	50
495	7 s. 70, She Burnan Omwe, Lamu (*vert*)	65	70
491/5	*Set of* 5	1·75	1·75

98 125th Anniversary and Kenya Red Cross Logos

99 Female Giraffe and Calf

(Des H. Moghul. Litho Cartor, France)

1989 (8 May). *125th Anniv of International Red Cross. T* **98** *and similar horiz designs. Multicoloured. P* 14×13½.

496	1 s. 20, Type **98**	15	10
497	3 s. 40, Red Cross workers with car crash victim	30	30
498	4 s. 40, Disaster relief team distributing blankets	40	40
499	5 s. 50, Henri Dunant (founder)	50	50
500	7 s. 70, Blood donor	65	70
496/500	*Set of* 5	1·75	1·75

(Des Doreen McGuinness. Litho Walsall)

1989 (12 July). *Reticulated Giraffe. T* **99** *and similar vert designs. Multicoloured. P* 14½.

501	1 s. 20, Type **99**	15	10
502	3 s. 40, Giraffe drinking	30	30
503	4 s. 40, Two giraffes	40	40
504	5 s. 50, Giraffe feeding	50	55
501/4	*Set of* 4	1·25	1·25
MS505	80×110 mm. 30 s. Designs as Nos. 501/4, but without face values	2·50	2·75

Designs from No. **MS**505 are without the Worldwide Fund for Nature logo.

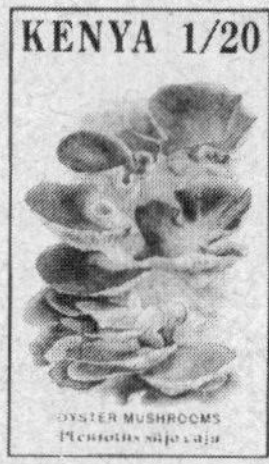

100 Oyster Mushrooms

101 Independence Monuments

(Des Dvora Bochman. Litho Questa)

1989 (6 Sept). *Mushrooms. T* **100** *and similar vert designs. Multicoloured. P* 14½.

506	1 s. 20, Type **100**	15	10
507	3 s. 40, Chestnut Mushrooms	30	30
508	4 s. 40, White Button Mushrooms	40	40
509	5 s. 50, Termite Mushrooms	50	50
510	7 s. 70, Shiitake Mushrooms	60	65
506/10	*Set of* 5	1·75	1·75

(Des Conference and Exhibitions Secretariat, Nairobi. Litho Cartor, France)

1989 (9 Nov). *Birth Centenary of Jawaharlal Nehru (Indian statesman). T* **101** *and similar vert designs. Multicoloured. P* 13½×14.

511	1 s. 20, Type **101**	10	10
512	3 s. 40, Nehru with graduates and open book	20	25
513	5 s. 50, Jawaharlal Nehru	35	40
514	7 s. 70, Industrial complex and cogwheels	50	55
511/14	*Set of* 4	1·00	1·10

(Des Mukund Arts. Litho Harrison)

1989 (8 Dec). *Ceremonial Costumes (4th series). Vert designs as T* **45**. *Multicoloured. P* 14½×13½.

515	1 s. 20, Kipsigis	10	10
516	3 s. 40, Rabai	20	25
517	5 s. 50, Duruma	35	40
518	7 s. 70, Kuria	50	55
519	10 s. Bajuni	60	65
515/19	*Set of* 5	1·50	1·75

POSTAGE DUE STAMPS

The Postage Due stamps of Kenya, Uganda and Tanganyika were used in Kenya until 2 January 1967.

D 3

(Litho D.L.R.)

1967 (3 Jan)–**70**. *Chalk-surfaced paper. P* 14 × 13½.

D13	D 3	5 c. scarlet	15	1·00
		a. Perf 14. *Dull scarlet*, **O** (16.12.69)	15	1·75
D14		10 c. green	20	1·00
		a. Perf 14, **O** (16.12.69)	30	1·75
D15		20 c. blue	40	1·25
		a. Perf 14. *Deep blue*, **O** (16.12.69)	30	2·25
D16		30 c. brown	55	1·75
		a. Perf 14. *Light red-brown*, **O** (16.12.69)	45	3·00
D17		40 c. bright purple	65	2·75
		a. Perf 14. *Pale bright purple*, **O** (16.12.69)	45	4·25
D18		1 s. bright orange	1·50	4·00
		a. Perf 14. *Dull bright orange*, **O** (18.2.70)	1·00	5·50
D13/18		*Set of* 6	3·00	10·50
D13a/18a		*Set of* 6	2·40	17·00

1971 (13 July)–**73**. *P* 14 × 15. (*a*) *Chalk-surfaced paper* (13.7.71).

D19	D 3	10 c. green	2·50	3·00
D20		20 c. deep dull blue	3·25	3·75
D21		30 c. red-brown	3·75	4·50
D22		1 s. dull bright orange	5·50	16·00
D19/22		*Set of* 4	13·50	24·00

(*b*) *Glazed, ordinary paper* (20.2.73)

D23	D 3	5 c. bright scarlet	70	1·75
D24		10 c. dull yellow-green	70	1·75
D25		20 c. deep blue	70	2·25
D27		40 c. bright purple	70	3·50
D28		1 s. bright orange	1·25	6·00
D23/8		*Set of* 5	3·50	14·00

1973 (12 Dec). *Glazed, ordinary paper. P* 15.

D29	D 3	5 c. red	20	1·25
D30		10 c. emerald	20	1·25
D31		20 c. deep blue	30	1·75
D32		30 c. red-brown	30	2·00
D33		40 c. bright purple	2·00	3·50
D34		1 s. bright orange	95	5·00
D29/34		*Set of* 6	3·50	13·50

1979 (27 Mar). *Chalk-surfaced paper. P* 14.

D35	D 3	10 c. bright emerald	40	1·25
D36		20 c. deep dull blue	60	1·50
D37		30 c. dull red-brown	60	1·25
D38		40 c. bright reddish purple	75	2·00
D39		80 c. dull red	45	1·25
D40		1 s. bright reddish orange	45	1·50
D35/40		*Set of* 6	3·00	8·00

1983 (Dec). *W w* **14**. *P* 14.

D41	D 3	10 c. yellowish green	10	10
D42		20 c. deep blue	10	10
D43		40 c. bright purple	1·25	1·50
D41/3		*Set of* 3	1·25	1·50

(Litho Harrison)

1985 (7 Aug)–**87**. *Ordinary paper. P* 14½ × 14.

D44	D 3	30 c. red-brown (9.1.87)	10	10
D45		40 c. bright magenta (9.1.87)	10	10
D46		80 c. dull vermilion (9.1.87)	10	10
D47		1 s. bright orange (1986)	10	10
D48		2 s. violet	10	10
D44/8		*Set of* 5	25	30

No. D47 was issued by the Crown Agents with Nos. D44/6, but was available in Kenya by November 1986.

OFFICIAL STAMPS

Intended for use on official correspondence of the Kenya Government only but there is no evidence that they were so used.

OFFICIAL

(O 4)

(15 c. 30 c. opt typo; others in photogravure)

1964 (1 Oct). *Nos.* 1/5 *and* 7 *optd with Type* O 4.

O21	5 c. brown, deep blue, green and bistre	10
O22	10 c. brown	10
O23	15 c. magenta	15
O24	20 c. black and yellow-green	20
O25	30 c. black and yellow	30
O26	50 c. crimson, black and green	1·00
O21/26	*Set of* 6	1·75

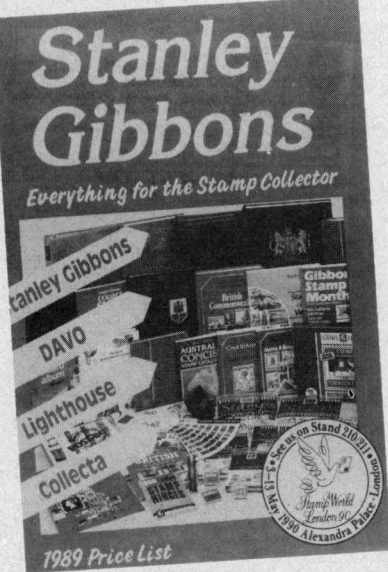

Kenya, Uganda and Tanganyika (Tanzania)

For earlier issues see BRITISH EAST AFRICA and UGANDA.
For the issues of the Mandated Territory of Tanganyika and the war-time issues that preceded them, see TANGANYIKA.

PRICES FOR STAMPS ON COVER TO 1945	
Nos. 1/43	*from* × 3
Nos. 44/75	*from* × 2
Nos. 76/95	*from* × 3
Nos. 96/105	—
Nos. 110/23	*from* × 2
Nos. 124/7	*from* × 3
Nos. 128/30	*from* × 5
Nos. 131/54	*from* × 3
Nos. D1/12	*from* × 8

PRINTERS. All the stamps issued between 1903 and 1927 were typographed by De La Rue & Co. Ltd, London.

USED HIGH VALUES. Beware of cleaned fiscally cancelled copies with faked postmarks.

EAST AFRICA AND UGANDA

1

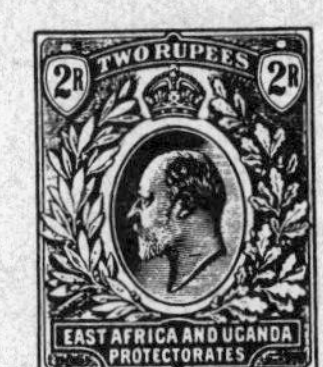

2

1903–4. *P* 14. (*a*) *Wmk Crown CA*.

1	1	½ a. green	1·40	3·75
2		1 a. grey and red	1·75	30
3		2 a. dull and bright purple	6·00	2·50
4		2½ a. blue	12·00	27·00
5		3 a. brown-purple and green	13·00	20·00
6		4 a. grey-green and black	11·00	14·00
7		5 a. grey and orange-brown	18·00	32·00
8		8 a. grey and pale blue	18·00	27·00
		(*b*) *Wmk Crown CC*		
9	2	1 r. green, **OC**	13·00	28·00
10		2 r. dull and bright purple, **O**	40·00	45·00
11		3 r. grey-green and black, **O**	50·00	75·00
12		4 r. grey and emerald-green, **O** ..	70·00	95·00
13		5 r. grey and red, **O**	70·00	95·00
14		10 r. grey and ultramarine, **OC** ..	£110	£140
15		20 r. grey and stone, **O** (Optd S. £120)	£450	£500
16		50 r. grey and red-brown, **O** (Optd S. £250)	£1100	£1300
1/13 ..		.. .. *Set of* 13	£275	£400
1/14 Optd "Specimen"		.. .. *Set of* 14	£250	

1904–07. *Wmk Mult Crown CA. P* 14.

17	1	½ a. grey-green, **OC**	2·50	60
18		1 a. grey and red, **OC**	1·75	20
19		2 a. dull and bright purple, **OC** ..	2·50	90
20		2½ a. blue, **O**	13·00	20·00
21		2½ a. ultramarine and blue, **O**	7·50	16·00
22		3 a. brown-purple and green, **OC** ..	3·75	10·00
23		4 a. grey-green and black, **OC** ..	7·50	10·00
24		5 a. grey and orange-brown, **OC** ..	6·50	13·00
25		8 a. grey and pale blue, **OC**	7·00	8·00
26	2	1 r. green, **C** (1907)	26·00	40·00
27		2 r. dull and bright purple, **C** (1906) ..	30·00	38·00
28		3 r. grey-green and black, **C** (1907) ..	40·00	65·00
29		4 r. grey and emerald-green, **C** (1907)	45·00	80·00
30		5 r. grey and red, **C** (1907)	45·00	70·00
31		10 r. grey and ultramarine, **C** (1907) ..	£110	£140
32		20 r. grey and stone, **C** (1907)	£500	£600
33		50 r. grey and red-brown, **C** (1907) ..	£1300	£1500
17/30 ..		.. .. *Set of* 13	£200	£325

(New Currency. 100 cents = 1 rupee)

1907–08. *Wmk Mult Crown CA. P* 14.

34	1	1 c. brown, **O** (1908)	20	15
35		3 c. grey-green, **O**	2·75	25
		a. Blue-green, **O**	3·75	1·75
36		6 c. red, **O**	2·75	10
37		10 c. lilac and pale olive, **C**	9·00	8·00
38		12 c. dull and bright purple, **C**	3·75	2·75
39		15 c. bright blue, **O**	9·00	8·00
40		25 c. grey-green and black, **C**	3·75	6·00
41		50 c. grey-green and orange-brown, **C** ..	6·50	10·00
42		75 c. grey and pale blue, **C** (1908) ..	4·50	16·00
34/42 ..		.. .. *Set of* 9	38·00	45·00
34/42 Optd "Specimen"		.. .. *Set of* 9	£180	

Original

Redrawn

1910. *T* 1 *redrawn. Printed from a single plate. Wmk Mult Crown CA. P* 14.

43	6 c. red, **O**	3·75	20

In the redrawn type a fine white line has been cut around the value tablets and above the name tablet separating the latter from the leaves above, EAST AFRICA AND UGANDA is in shorter and thicker letters and PROTECTORATES in taller letters than in No. 36.

3

4

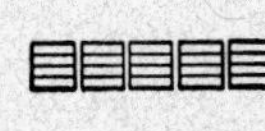
4
cents
(5)

1912–21. *Wmk Mult Crown CA. P* 14.

44	3	1 c. black, **O**	20	55
45		3 c. green, **O**	2·00	25
		a. Deep blue-green, **O** (1917)	2·50	40
46		6 c. red, **O**	50	15
		a. Scarlet, **O** (1917)	7·50	90
47		10 c. yellow-orange, **O**	2·00	20
		a. Orange, **O** (1921)	4·75	75
48		12 c. slate-grey, **O**	2·75	50
49		15 c. bright blue, **O**	2·75	55
50		25 c. black and red/*yellow*, **C**	45	90
		a. White back (5.14) (Optd S. £25) ..	50	1·75
		b. On lemon (1916) (Optd S. £25) ..	7·50	8·00
		c. On orange-buff (1921)	18·00	8·50
		d. On pale yellow (1921)	6·50	2·75
51		50 c. black and lilac, **C**	1·50	80
52		75 c. black/*green* **C**	1·50	8·50
		a. White back (5.14) (Optd S. £25) ..	90	7·50
		b. On blue-grn, ol back (Optd S. £25)	6·00	3·75
		c. On emerald, olive back (1919) ..	38·00	65·00
		d. On emerald back (1921)	10·00	17·00
53	4	1 r. black/*green*, **C**	1·75	3·25
		a. On emerald back (1919)	5·00	20·00
54		2 r. red and black/*blue*, **C**	20·00	27·00
55		3 r. violet and green, **C**	20·00	35·00
56		4 r. red and green/*yellow*, **C**	42·00	65·00
		a. On pale yellow	55·00	75·00
57		5 r. blue and dull purple, **C**	42·00	70·00
58		10 r. red and green/*green*, **C**	75·00	£110
59		20 r. black and purple/*red*, **C**	£250	£250
60		20 r. purple and blue/*blue*, **C** (1918) ..	£225	£225
61		50 r. carmine & grn, **CO** (Optd S. £160)	£600	£600
		a. Dull rose-red and dull greyish green, **O**	£700	£700
62		100 r. pur & blk/*red*, **C** (Optd S. £300)	£2750	£1700
63		500 r. grn & red/*grn*, **C** (Optd S. £650)	£12000	
44/58 ..		.. .. *Set of* 15	£190	£275
44/60 Optd "Specimen"		.. .. *Set of* 17	£500	

For values in this series overprinted "G.E.A." (German East Africa) see Tanganyika Nos. 45/62.

1919 (7 Apr). *T* **3** *surch with T* **5** *by the Swift Press, Nairobi*.

64	4 c. on 6 c. scarlet (*shades*)	20	15
	a. Bars omitted	23·00	35·00
	b. Surch double	70·00	85·00
	c. Surch inverted	£120	£150
	d. Pair, one without surch	£300	£325
64 H/S "Specimen"	.. ..	55·00	

1921–22. *Wmk Mult Script CA. P* 14.

65	3	1 c. black, **O**	35	50
66		3 c. green, **O**	1·25	2·75
		a. Blue-green, **O**	5·50	6·50
67		6 c. carmine-red, **O**	1·25	3·00
68		10 c. orange, **O** (12.21)	3·75	30
69		12 c. slate-grey, **O**	3·25	23·00
70		15 c. bright blue, **O**	3·25	9·50
71		50 c. black and dull purple, **C**	9·50	32·00
72	4	2 r. red and black/*blue*, **C**	45·00	80·00
73		3 r. violet and green, **C**	75·00	£110
74		5 r. blue and dull purple, **C**	80·00	£125
75		50 r. carmine and green, **C** (Optd S. £200)	£1800	£2250
65/74		.. .. *Set of* 10	£200	£350
65/74 Optd "Specimen"		.. .. *Set of* 10	£225	

For values in this series overprinted "G.E.A." see Tanganyika Nos. 63/73.

KENYA AND UGANDA

(New Currency. 100 cents = 1 shilling)

6

7

1922 (1 Nov)–**27**. *Wmk Script CA. P* 14.

(*a*) *Wmk upright. Ordinary paper*

76	6	1 c. pale brown	50	65
		a. Deep brown (1923)	90	1·60
77		5 c. dull violet	1·75	20
		a. Bright violet	2·50	70
78		5 c. green (1927)	2·00	10
79		10 c. green	1·25	10
80		10 c. black (5.27)	1·75	10
81		12 c. jet-black	4·75	20·00
		a. Grey-black	1·50	14·00
82		15 c. rose-carmine	80	10
83		20 c. dull orange-yellow	2·50	10
		a. Bright orange	2·50	10
84		30 c. ultramarine	1·25	20
85		50 c. grey	1·75	10
86		75 c. olive	2·25	7·50

(*b*) *Wmk sideways. Chalky paper*

87	7	1 s. green	2·75	1·75
88		2 s. dull purple	7·50	6·00
89		2 s. 50 c. brown (1.10.25)	18·00	60·00
90		3 s. brownish grey	15·00	6·00
		a. Jet-black	25·00	23·00
91		4 s. grey (1.10.25)	18·00	60·00
92		5 s. carmine-red	22·00	18·00
93		7 s. 50 c. orange-yellow (1.10.25) ..	55·00	£130
94		10 s. bright blue	48·00	48·00
95		£1 black and orange	£150	£190
96		£2 green and purple (1.10.25) (S. £120)	£700	
97		£3 purple and yellow (1.10.25) (S. £140)	£850	
98		£4 black & magenta (1.10.25) (S. £180)	£1400	
99		£5 black and blue (S. £225)	£1800	
100		£10 black and green (S. £275)	£7500	
101		£20 red and green (1.10.25) (S. £450)	£12000	
102		£25 black and red (S. £475) ..	£13000	
103		£50 black and brown (S. £550) ..	£17000	
104		£75 purple and grey (1.10.25) (S. £650)	£32000	
105		£100 red and black (1.10.25) (S. £700)	£35000	
76/95		.. .. *Set of* 20	£325	£475
76/95 Optd "Specimen"		.. .. *Set of* 20	£475	

Specimen copies of Nos. 96/105 are all overprinted.

KENYA, UGANDA AND TANGANYIKA

The postal administrations of Kenya, Tanganyika and Uganda were amalgamated on 1 January 1933. On the independence of the three territories the combined administration became the East African Posts and Telecommunications Corporation.

8 South African Crowned Cranes

9 Dhow on Lake Victoria

10 Lion

11 Kilimanjaro

12 Jinja Railway Bridge by Ripon Falls

13 Mt. Kenya

14 Lake Naivasha

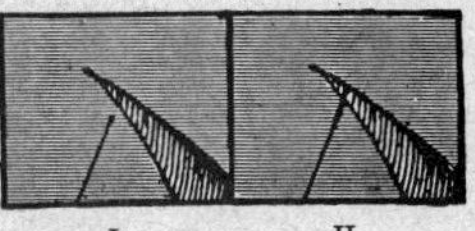
I II

(Des 1 c., 20 c., 10 s., R. C. Luck, 10 c., £1, A. Ross, 15 c., 2 s., G. Gill Holmes, 30 c., 5 s., R. N. Ambasana. 65 c., L. R. Cutts. T **10** typo, remainder recess D.L.R.).

1935 (1 May)–**36**. *Wmk Mult Script CA. P* 12 × 13 (**10**), 14 (**9** *and* **14**) *and* 13 (*remainder*).

110	8	1 c. black and red-brown	15	30
111	9	5 c. black and green (I)	40	10
		a. Perf 13 × 12 (I)	£300	85·00
		b. Rope joined to sail (II) (perf 14) ..	7·50	2·25
		c. Rope joined to sail (II) (perf 13 × 12)	£300	75·00
112	10	10 c. black and yellow, **C**	2·25	10
113	11	15 c. black and scarlet	75	10
114	8	20 c. black and orange	85	10
115	12	30 c. black and blue	80	65
116	9	50 c. bright purple and black (I)	75	10
117	13	65 c. black and brown	90	2·00
118	14	1 s. black and green	75	35
		a. Perf 13 × 12 (1936)	£750	75·00
119	11	2 s. lake and purple	4·25	3·50
120	14	3 s. blue and black	5·00	13·00
		a. Perf 13 × 12	£1200	
121	12	5 s. black and carmine	15·00	23·00
122	8	10 s. purple and blue	40·00	48·00
123	10	£1 black and red, **C**	£130	£130
110/23		.. .. *Set of* 14	£180	£200
110/23 Perf "Specimen"		.. .. *Set of* 14	£200	

Line through "0" of 1910 (R.4/2)

1935 (6 *May*). *Silver Jubilee. As T* **13** *of Antigua*.

124	20 c. light blue and olive-green	25	10
	h. Dot by flagstaff	20·00	
	i. Dash by turret	20·00	
125	30 c. brown and deep blue	1·75	1·50
	f. Diagonal line by turret	40·00	
	g. Dot to left of chapel	40·00	
	i. Dash by turret	40·00	

126 65 c. green and indigo .. .. .. 1·75 2·00
f. Diagonal line by turret .. .. 45·00
g. Dot to left of chapel .. .. .. 45·00
127 1 s. slate and purple .. .. .. 1·75 1·40
f. Diagonal line by turret .. .. 50·00
l. Line through "0" of 1910 .. .. 60·00
124/7 .. .. *Set of* 4 5·00 4·50
124/7 Perf "Specimen" .. .. *Set of* 4 85·00

For illustrations of the other plate varieties see Omnibus section following Zululand.

1937 (12 May). *Coronation As T* **2** *of Aden.*
128 5 c. green 25 10
129 20 c. orange 55 15
130 30 c. bright blue 85 85
128/30 .. .. *Set of* 3 1·50 1·00
128/30 Perf "Specimen" .. .. *Set of* 3 55·00

15 Dhow on Lake Victoria

Retouch on 1 c. (Pl 2, R. 9/6)

Retouch on 10 c. and 1s. (Pl 7B, R. 5/10 and 6/7)

With dot

Dot removed

In the 50 c., on Frame-plate 3, the dot was removed by retouching on all but five stamps (R.5/2, 6/1, 7/2, 7/4, and 9/1). In addition, other stamps show traces of the dot where the retouching was not completely effective.

PERFORATIONS. In this issue, to aid identification, the perforations are indicated to the nearest quarter.

(T **10** typo, others recess D.L.R.)

1938 (11 Apr)–**54**. *As T* **8** *to* **14** (*but with portrait of King George VI in place of King George V, as in T* **15**). *Wmk Mult Script CA.*
131 **8** 1 c. black and red-brown (*p* 13¼) (2.5.38) 40 25
a. Perf 13¼ × 13¾. *Black & chocolate-brown* (1942) 10 30
ab. Retouched value tablet .. .. 32·00 32·00
ac. Black & dp chocolate-brown (1946) 80 55
ad. Ditto. Retouched tablet .. .. 32·00 32·00
ae. Black and red-brown (26.9.51) .. 30 70
132 **15** 5 c. black and green (II) (*p* 13 × 11¾) .. 30 10
133 5 c. reddish brown & orange (*p* 13 × 11¾) (1.6.49) 35 90
a. Perf 13 × 12½ (14.6.50) 45 80
134 **14** 10 c. red-brn & orge (*p* 13 × 11¾) (2.5.38) 35 10
a. Perf 14 (1941) .. .. .. 50·00 5·50
135 10 c. black and green (*p* 13 × 11¾) (1.6.49) 20 20
a. Mountain retouch .. .. .. 32·00 13·00
b. Perf 13 × 12½ (14.6.50) 40 10
136 10 c. brown and grey (*p* 13 × 12½) (1.4.52) 35 15
137 **11** 15 c. black and rose-red (*p* 13¼) (2.5.38) 1·50 10
a. Perf 13¾ × 13¼ (2.43) .. .. 65 1·00
138 15 c. black & green (*p* 13¾ × 13¼) (1.4.52) 60 65
139 **8** 20 c. black and orange (*p* 13¼) (2.5.38) .. 9·00 15
a. Perf 14 (1941) .. .. .. 23·00 1·50
b. Perf 13¼ × 13¾ (1.6.42) 85 10
ba. Deep black and deep orange (8.51) 2·00 30
140 **15** 25 c. blk & carm-red (*p* 13 × 12½) (1.4.52) 1·25 60
141 **12** 30 c. black & dull vio-bl (*p* 13¼) (2.5.38) 18·00 40
a. Perf 14 (1941) .. .. .. 90·00 11·00
b. Perf 13¼ × 13¾ (9.42) 30 10
142 30 c. dull pur & brn (*p* 13¼ × 13¾) (1.4.52) 55 10
143 **8** 40 c. black and blue (*p* 13¼ × 13¾) (1.4.52) .. .. .. 1·00 90
144 **15** 50 c. pur & blk (II) (*p* 13 × 11¾) (2.5.38) 2·00 10
a. Rope not joined to sail (I) £180 £140
b. Dull claret and black (29.7.47) .. 2·00 25
c. Brown-purple and black (4.48) .. 2·25 25
d. Reddish purple and black (28.4.49) 2·25 25
e. Ditto. Perf 13 × 12½ (10.49) .. 85 15
ea. Dot removed (14.6.50) .. .. 7·50 10
eb. Ditto. In pair with normal .. .. £150 60·00
145 **14** 1 s. black & yellowish brn (*p* 13 × 11¾) (2.5.38) 75 10
a. Black and brown (9.42) .. .. 1·25 30
ab. Mountain retouch (7.49) .. .. 90·00 45·00
b. Perf 13 × 12½ (10.49) .. .. 1·00 10
ba. Deep black and brown (*clearer impression*) (14.6.50) 90 30
146 **11** 2 s. lake-brn & brn-pur (*p* 13¼) (2.5.38) 55·00 1·50
a. Perf 14 (1941) .. .. .. 42·00 7·50
b. Perf 13¾ × 13¼ (24.2.44) .. .. 5·00 10
147 **14** 3 s. dull ultramarine & blk (*p* 13 × 11¾) (2.5.38) .. .. .. 11·00 70
a. Deep violet-blue and black (29.7.47) 14·00 2·00
b. Ditto. Perf 13 × 12½ (14.6.50) .. 6·00 85
148 **12** 5 s. black and carmine (*p* 13¼) (2.5.38) 70·00 6·00
a. Perf 14 (1941) .. .. .. 16·00 1·25
b. Perf 13¼ × 13¾ (24.2.44) .. .. 6·00 25
149 **8** 10 s. purple and blue (*p* 13¼) (2.5.38) .. 80·00 15·00
a. Perf 14. *Reddish purple & blue* (1941) .. .. .. 42·00 20·00
b. Perf 13¼ × 13¾ (24.2.44) .. .. 12·00 2·50
150 **10** £1 blk & red (*p* 11¾ × 13), **C** (12.10.38) £170 60·00
a. Perf 14, **C** (1941) .. .. .. 10·00 7·50
ab. Ordinary paper (24.2.44) .. .. 10·00 7·00
b. Perf 12½. **C** (21.1.54) .. .. 10·00 18·00
131/150ab (*cheapest*) .. .. *Set of* 20 42·00 12·00
131/150 Perf "Specimen" .. .. *Set of* 13 £250

Stamps perf 14, together with Nos. 131a, 137a, 139b, 141b, 146b, 148b and 149b, are known as "Blitz perfs", the differences in perforation being the result of air raid damage to the De La Rue works in which the perforators normally used were destroyed.

10c
KENYA
TANGANYIKA
UGANDA

(**16**)

A screw head in the surcharging forme appears as a crescent moon (R. 20/4)

1941 (1 July)–**42**. *Pictorial Stamps of South Africa variously surch as T* **16** *by Government Printer, Pretoria. Inscr alternately in English and Afrikaans.*

		Unused pair	*Used pair*
151	5 c. on 1d. grey and carmine (No. 56) ..	60	1·50
152	10 c. on 3d. ultramarine (No. 59)	1·00	2·00
153	20 c. on 6d. green and vermilion (No. 61*a*) ..	60	1·75
154	70 c. on 1s. brown and chalky blue (No. 62) (20.4.42)	1·75	2·00
	a. Crescent moon flaw	30·00	
151/4	.. .. .. *Set of 4 pairs*	3·50	6·50
151/4	Handstamped "Specimen" *Set of 4 pairs*	£170	

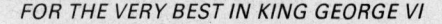

946 (11 Nov). *Victory. As Nos. 28/9 of Aden.*

		Unused	Used
55	20 c. red-orange	10	10
56	30 c. blue	10	10
55/6	Perf "Specimen" *Set of* 2	45·00	

Examples of Nos. 155/6 were prereleased at Lindi on 15 October 1946.

948 (1 Dec). *Royal Silver Wedding. As Nos. 30/1 of Aden.*

57	20 c. orange	15	10
58	£1 scarlet	30·00	35·00

949 (10 Oct). *75th Anniv of Universal Postal Union. As Nos. 114/17 of Antigua.*

59	20 c. red-orange	15	10
60	30 c. deep blue	40	25
61	50 c. grey	40	10
62	1 s. red-brown	75	40
59/62	*Set of* 4	1·50	70

17 Lake Naivasha

(Recess D.L.R.)

952 (1 Feb). *Visit of Princess Elizabeth and Duke of Edinburgh. Wmk Mult Script CA. P* 13 × 12½.

63	**17**	10 c. black and green	10	30
64		1 s. black and brown	20	1·75

1953 (2 June). *Coronation. As No. 47 of Aden.*

165	20 c. black and red-orange	15	10

1954 (28 Apr). *Royal Visit. As No. 171 but inscr* "ROYAL VISIT 1954" *below portrait.*

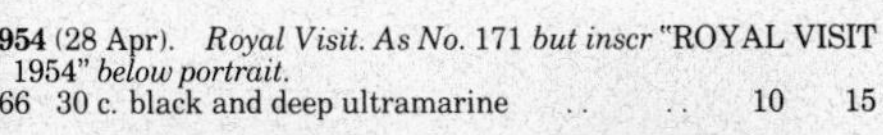

166	30 c. black and deep ultramarine	10	15

18 Owen Falls Dam

19 Giraffe

20 Royal Lodge, Sagana

21 Queen Elizabeth II

(Des G. Gill Holmes (10, 50 c.), H. Grieme (15 c., 1 s. 30, 5 s.), R. McLellan Sim (10 s.), De La Rue (65 c., 2 s., £1), O.C. Meronti (others). Recess D.L.R.)

1954 (1 June)–**59**. *Designs as T* **18/21**. *Wmk Mult Script CA. P* 13 (£1); *others*, 12½ × 13 (*vert*) *or* 13 × 12½ (*horiz*).

167	5 c. black and deep brown	10	10
	a. Vignette inverted	—	£12000
168	10 c. carmine-red	20	10
169	15 c. black and light blue (28.3.58)	35	20
	a. Redrawn. Stop below "c" of "15 c" (29.4.59)	35	10
170	20 c. black and orange	20	10
	a. Imperf (pair)	£450	£500
171	30 c. black and deep ultramarine	25	10
172	40 c. bistre-brown (28.3.58)	1·25	20
173	50 c. reddish purple	15	10
	a. *Claret* (23.1.57)	20	10
174	65 c. bluish green & brown-purple (1.12.55)	2·25	40
175	1 s. black and claret	20	10
176	1 s. 30, orange and deep lilac (1.12.55)	2·75	10
177	2 s. black and green	1·50	15
	a. *Black and bronze-green* (19.4.56)	2·00	45
178	5 s. black and orange	4·00	45
179	10 s. black and deep ultramarine	7·00	1·00
180	£1 brown-red and black	15·00	5·00
	a. *Venetian red and black* (19.4.56)	25·00	6·00
167/80	*Set of* 14	30·00	7·00

Designs: *Vert as T* **18/19**—5, 30 c. Type **18**; 10, 50 c. Type **19**; 20, 40 c., 1 s. Lion. *Horiz as T* **20**—15 c., 1 s. 30, 5 s. African Elephants; 65 c., 2 s. Kilimanjaro.

Only one used copy of No. 167a is known.

25 Map of E. Africa showing Lakes

(Recess Waterlow)

1958 (30 July). *Centenary of Discovery of Lakes Tanganyika and Victoria by Burton and Speke. W w* **12**. *P* 12½.

181	**25**	40 c. blue and deep green	20	15
182		1 s. 30 c. green and violet	25	50

26 Sisal

27 Cotton

28 Mt Kenya and Giant Plants

29 Queen Elizabeth II

(Des M. Goaman. Photo (5 c. to 65 c.), recess (others) D.L.R.)

1960 (1 Oct). *Designs as T* **26/9**. W w **12**. *P* 15 × 14 (5 c. *to* 65 c.), 13 (20 *s.*) *or* 14 (*others*).

183	5 c. Prussian blue	10	10
184	10 c. yellow-green	10	10
185	15 c. dull purple	10	10
186	20 c. magenta	10	10
187	25 c. bronze-green	1·25	45
188	30 c. vermilion	10	10
189	40 c. greenish blue	15	10
190	50 c. slate-violet	15	10
191	65 c. yellow-olive	30	45
192	1 s. deep reddish violet and reddish purple	30	10
193	1 s. 30, chocolate and brown-red	90	10
194	2 s. deep grey-blue and greenish blue	90	15
195	2 s. 50, olive-green and deep bluish green	1·50	1·50
196	5 s. rose-red and purple	3·00	45
197	10 s. blackish green and olive-green	4·00	2·50
	a. Imperf (pair)	£125	
198	20 s. violet-blue and lake	8·50	8·50
183/198	*Set of* 16	19·00	13·00

Designs: *Vert as T* **26/7**—15 c. Coffee; 20 c. Blue Wildebeest; 25 c. Ostrich; 30 c. Thomson's Gazelle; 40 c. Manta Ray; 50 c. Common Zebra; 65 c. Cheetah. *Horiz as T* **28**—1 s. 30, Murchison Falls and Hippopotamus; 2 s. Mt Kilimanjaro and Giraffe; 2 s. 50, Candelabra Tree and Black Rhinoceros; 5 s. Crater Lake and Mountains of the Moon; 10 s. Ngorongoro Crater and African Buffalo.

The 10 c. and 50 c. exist in coils with the designs slightly shorter in height, a wider horizontal gutter every eleven stamps and, in the case of the 10 c. only, printed with a coarser 200 screen instead of the normal 250. (*Price* 10 *c.* 5*p. unused.*) Plate 2 of 30 c. shows coarser 200 screen. (*Price* 25*p. unused.*)

30 Land Tillage

(Des V. Whiteley. Photo Harrison)

1963 (21 Mar). *Freedom from Hunger. T* **30** *and similar horiz design. P* 14½.

199	**30**	15 c. blue and yellow-olive	10	10
200	–	30 c. red-brown and yellow	20	10
201	**30**	50 c. blue and orange-brown	30	10
202	–	1 s. 30, red-brown and light blue	55	50
199/202		*Set of* 4	1·00	65

Design:—30 c., 1 s. 30, African with Corncob.

31 Scholars and Open Book

(Photo Harrison)

1963 (28 June). *Founding of East African University. P* 14½.

203	**31**	30 c. lake, violet, black and greenish blue	10	10
204		1 s. 30, lake, blue, red & lt yellow-brown	10	10

32 Red Cross Emblem

(Des V. Whiteley. Photo Harrison)

1963 (2 Sept). *Centenary of Red Cross. P* 14½.

205	**32**	30 c. red and blue	65	10
206		50 c. red and yellow-brown	85	35

PRINTERS. All the following stamps were printed in photogravure by Harrison, *unless otherwise stated.*

33 Chrysanthemum Emblems **34**

35 East African "Flags"

(Des V. Whiteley)

1964 (21 Oct). *Olympic Games. Tokyo. P* 14½.

207	**33**	30 c. yellow and reddish violet	10	10
208	**34**	50 c. deep reddish violet and yellow	10	10
209	**35**	1 s. 30, orange-yellow, dp green & lt blue	10	10
210		2 s. 50, magenta, deep violet-blue & lt bl	20	35
207/10		*Set of* 4	35	40

KENYA, UGANDA AND TANZANIA

The following stamps were issued by the East African Postal Administration for use in Uganda, Kenya and Tanzania, excluding Zanzibar.

36 Rally Badge

37 Cars *en route*

1965 (15 Apr*). *13th East African Safari Rally. P* 14.

211	**36**	30 c. black, yellow and turquoise	10	10
212		50 c. black, yellow and brown	10	10
		a. Imperf (pair)		
213	**37**	1 s. 30, dp bluish green, yell-ochre & blue	15	10
214		2 s. 50, dp bluish green, brn-red & lt blue	25	45
211/14		*Set of* 4	50	50

*This is the local release date. The Crown Agents in London issued the stamps the previous day.

38 I.T.U. Emblem and Symbols

1965 (17 May). *I.T.U. Centenary. P* 14½.

215	**38**	30 c. gold, chocolate and magenta	10	10
216		50 c. gold, chocolate and grey	15	10
217		1 s. 30, gold, chocolate and blue	30	10
218		2 s. 50, gold, chocolate & turquoise-grn	55	80
215/18		*Set of* 4	1·00	1·00

39 I.C.Y. Emblem

1965 (4 Aug). *International Co-operation Year. P* 14½ × 14.

219	**39**	30 c. deep bluish green and gold	10	10
220		50 c. black and gold	15	10
221		1 s. 30, ultramarine and gold	30	10
222		2 s. 50, carmine-red and gold	75	1·50
219/22		*Set of* 4	1·25	1·60

40 Game Park Lodge, Tanzania

(Des Rena Fennessy)

1966 (4 Apr). *Tourism. T* **40** *and similar horiz designs. Multi-coloured. P* 14½.

223	30 c. Type **40**		10	10
224	50 c. Murchison Falls, Uganda		20	10
	a. Blue omitted		£150	
225	1 s. 30, Lesser Flamingoes, Lake Nakuru, Kenya		90	15
226	2 s. 50, Deep Sea Fishing, Tanzania		1·00	70
223/6 . .	. . . .	*Set of* 4	2·00	85

41 Games Emblem

(Des Harrison)

1966 (2 Aug). *Eighth British Empire and Commonwealth Games Jamaica. P* 14½.

227	**41**	30 c. black, gold, turq-green & grey . .		10	10
228		50 c. black, gold, cobalt and cerise . .		10	10
229		1 s. 30, blk, gold, rosine & dp bluish grn		15	10
230		2 s. 50, black, gold, lake and ultramarine		25	35
227/30		. . . .	*Set of* 4	50	40

42 U.N.E.S.C.O. Emblem

(Des Harrison)

1966 (3 Oct). *20th Anniv of U.N.E.S.C.O. P* 14½ × 14.

231	**42**	30 c. black, emerald and red		15	10
232		50 c. black, emerald and light brown . .		20	10
233		1 s. 30, black, emerald and grey . .		45	15
234		2 s. 50, black, emerald and yellow . .		1·00	1·25
231/4 . .		. . . .	*Set of* 4	1·60	1·25

43 D.H. "Dragon Rapide"

(Des R. Granger Barrett)

1967 (23 Jan). *21st Anniv of East African Airways. T* **43** *and similar horiz designs. P* 14½.

235	30 c. slate-violet, greenish blue & myrtle-grn		15	10
236	50 c. multicoloured		20	10
	a. Red omitted		£150	
237	1 s. 30, multicoloured		60	15
238	2 s. 50, multicoloured		1·10	1·60
235/8 . .	. . . .	*Set of* 4	1·90	1·75

Designs:—50 c. "Super VC-10"; 1 s. 30, "Comet 4"; 2 s. 50, "F-27 Friendship".

44 Pillar Tomb **45** Rock Painting

(Des Rena Fennessy)

1967 (2 May). *Archaeological Relics. T* **44/5** *and similar designs. P* 14½.

239	30 c. ochre, black and deep reddish purple . .		15	10
240	50 c. orange-red, black and greyish brown . .		30	10
241	1 s. 30, black, greenish, yellow and deep yellow-green		55	10
242	2 s. 50, black, ochre and brown-red . .		1·00	1·00
239/42	. . . .	*Set of* 4	1·75	1·10

Designs:—1 s. 30, Clay head; 2 s. 50, Proconsul skull.

48 Unified Symbols of Kenya, Tanzania, and Uganda

(Des Rena Fennessy)

1967 (1 Dec). *Foundation of East African Community. P* 14½ × 14.

243	**48**	5 s. gold, black and grey	40	1·00

49 Mountaineering

(Des Rena Fennessy)

1968 (4 Mar). *Mountains of East Africa. T* **49** *and similar horiz designs. Multicoloured. P* 14.

244	30 c. Type **49**		10	10
245	50 c. Mount Kenya		15	10
246	1 s. 30, Mount Kilimanjaro		30	10
247	2 s. 50, Ruwenzori Mountains		55	1·00
244/7 . .	. . . .	*Set of* 4	1·00	1·10

50 Family and Rural Hospital

(Des Rena Fennessy. Litho D.L.R.)

1968 (13 May). *20th Anniv of World Health Organization. T* **50** *and similar horiz designs. P* 13½.

248	30 c. deep yellow-green, lilac and chocolate . .		10	10
249	50 c. slate-lilac, lilac and black . .		10	10
250	1 s. 30, yellow-brown, lilac and chocolate . .		15	10
251	2 s. 50, grey, black and reddish lilac . .		25	60
248/51	. . . .	*Set of* 4	50	75

Designs:—50 c. Family and nurse; 1 s. 30, Family and microscope; 2 s. 50, Family and hypodermic syringe.

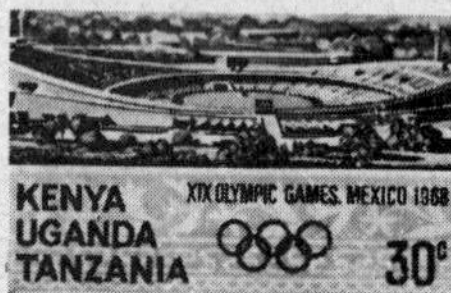

51 Olympic Stadium, Mexico City

(Des V. Whiteley)

1968 (14 Oct). *Olympic Games, Mexico. T* **51** *and similar designs. P* 14.

252	30 c. light green and black		10	10
253	50 c. black and blue-green		10	10
254	1 s. 30, carmine-red, black and grey . .		15	10
255	2 s. 50, blackish brown and yellow-brown . .		25	60
252/5 . .	. . . .	*Set of* 4	50	75

Designs: *Horiz*—50 c. High-diving boards; 1 s. 30, Running tracks. *Vert*—2 s. 50, Boxing ring.

52 M.V. *Umoja*

(Des A. Grosart)

1969 (20 Jan). *Water Transport. T* **52** *and similar horiz designs. P* 14.

256	30 c. deep blue, light blue and slate-grey . .		15	10
	a. Slate-grey omitted		24·00	
257	50 c. multicoloured		20	10
258	1 s. 30, bronze-grn, greenish blue & blue . .		45	15
259	2 s. 50, red-orange, dp blue & pale blue . .		1·00	1·00
256/9 . .	. . . .	*Set of* 4	1·60	1·10

Designs:—50 c. S.S. *Harambee*; 1 s. 30, M.V. *Victoria*; 2 s. 50, *St. Michael*.

MINIMUM PRICE

The minimum price quote is 10p which represents a handling charge rather than a basis for valuing common stamps. For further notes about prices see introductory pages.

53 I.L.O. Emblem and Agriculture **54** Pope Paul VI and Ruwenzori Mountains

(Des Rena Fennessy)

1969 (14 Apr). *50th Anniv of International Labour Organization T* **53** *and similar horiz designs. P* 14.

260	30 c. black, green and greenish yellow . .		10	10
261	50 c. black, plum, cerise and rose		10	10
262	1 s. 30, black, orange-brown & yellow-orange		10	10
263	2 s. 50, black, ultramarine & turquoise-blue		20	30
260/3 . .	. . . .	*Set of* 4	35	40

Designs:—50 c. I.L.O. emblem and building work; 1 s. 30, I.L.O. emblem and factory workers; 2 s. 50, I.L.O. emblem and shipping.

(Des Harrison)

1969 (31 July). *Visit of Pope Paul VI to Uganda. P* 14.

264	**54**	30 c. black, gold and royal blue . .		10	10
265		70 c. black, gold and claret		15	10
266		1 s. 50, black, gold and deep blue . .		25	20
267		2 s. 50, black, gold and violet		40	75
264/7 . .		. . . .	*Set of* 4	75	95

55 Euphorbia Tree shaped as Africa and Emblem **56** Marimba

(Des Rena Fennessy. Litho B.W.)

1969 (8 Dec). *Fifth Anniv of African Development Bank. P* 13½.

268	**55**	30 c. dp bluish green, gold & blue-green		10	10
269		70 c. dp bluish green, gold & reddish pur		10	10
270		1 s. 50, dp bluish grn, gold & lt turq-bl		10	10
271		2 s. 50, dp bluish grn, gold & orge-brn		20	25
268/71		. . . .	*Set of* 4	35	35

(Des Rena Fennessy. Litho B.W.)

1970 (16 Feb). *Musical Instruments. T* **56** *and similar horiz designs. P* 11 × 12.

272	30 c. buff, yellow-brown and bistre-brown . .		10	10
273	70 c. olive-green, yellow-brown and yellow . .		15	10
274	1 s. 50, chocolate and yellow		20	10
275	2 s. 50, salmon, yellow and chocolate . .		50	50
272/5 . .	. . . .	*Set of* 4	80	60

Designs:—70 c. Amadinda; 1 s. 50, Nzomari; 2 s. 50, Adeudeu.

57 Satellite Earth Station **58** Athlete

(Des V. Whiteley. Litho J.W.)

1970 (18 May). *Inauguration of East African Satellite Earth Station. T* **57** *and similar horiz designs. P* 14½ × 14.

276	30 c. multicoloured		10	10
277	70 c. multicoloured		15	10
278	1 s. 50, black, slate-violet and pale orange . .		20	10
279	2 s. 50, multicoloured		45	50
276/9 . .	. . . .	*Set of* 4	75	60

Designs:—70 c. Transmitter in daytime; 1 s. 50, Transmitter at night; 2 s. 50, Earth and satellite.

(Des Rena Fennessy. Litho Walsall)

1970 (13 July). *Ninth Commonwealth Games. P* 14 × 14½.

280	**58**	30 c. orange-brown and black		10	10
281		70 c. olive-green and black		10	10
282		1 s. 50, slate-lilac and black		10	10
283		2 s. 50, turquoise-blue and black . .		20	30
280/3 . .		. . . .	*Set of* 4	35	40

59 "25" and U.N. Emblem

(Des Rena Fennessy)

1970 (19 Oct). *25th Anniv of United Nations. P* 14½.
284 **59** 30 c. multicoloured 10 10
285 70 c. multicoloured 10 10
286 1 s. 50, multicoloured 20 10
287 2 s. 50, multicoloured 45 70
284/7 .. .. *Set of* 4 70 80

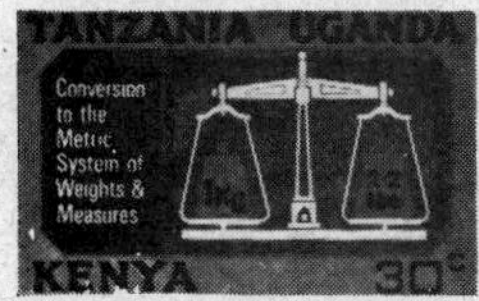

60 Balance and Weight Equivalents

(Des and litho J.W.)

1971 (4 Jan). *Conversion to Metric System. T* **60** *and similar horiz designs. Multicoloured. P* 14½ × 14.
288 30 c. Type **60** 10 10
289 70 c. Fahrenheit and Centigrade Thermometers 10 10
290 1 s. 50, Petrol Pump and Liquid Capacities .. 15 10
291 2 s. 50, Surveyors and Land Measures .. 35 65
288/91 .. .. *Set of* 4 60 70

61 Class "11" Locomotive

(Des Rena Fennessy)

1971 (5 Apr). *Railway Transport. T* **61** *and similar horiz designs. Multicoloured. P* 14.
292 30 c. Type **61** 25 10
293 70 c. Class "90" locomotive 40 10
294 1 s. 50, Class "59" locomotive .. .. 1·25 50
295 2 s. 50, Class "30" locomotive .. .. 2·25 2·75
292/5 .. .. *Set of* 4 3·75 3·00
MS296 120 × 88 mm. Nos. 292/5 .. .. .. 6·50 9·00

62 Syringe and Cow

(Des Rena Fennessy. Litho)

1971 (5 July). *O.A.U. Rinderpest Campaign. T* **62** *and similar horiz design. P* 14.
297 **62** 30 c. black, pale yell-brn & pale yell-grn 10 10
298 – 70 c. black, pale slate-blue & pale yell-brn 10 10
299 **62** 1 s. 50, black, plum & pale yellow-brn 15 10
300 – 2 s. 50, black, brown-red & pale yell-brn 25 50
297/300 .. .. *Set of* 4 45 60
Design:—70 c., 2 s. 50, As T **62**, but with bull facing right.

63 Livingstone meets Stanley

(Des and litho J.W.)

1971 (28 Oct). *Centenary of Livingstone and Stanley meeting at Ujiji. P* 13½ × 14.
301 **63** 5 s. multicoloured 30 75

64 President Nyerere and Supporters

(Des G. Drummond. Litho J.W.)

1971 (9 Dec). *Tenth Anniv of Tanzanian Independence. T* **64** *and similar horiz designs. Multicoloured. P* 13½.
302 30 c. Type **64** 10 10
303 70 c. Ujamaa village 10 10
304 1 s. 50, Dar es Salaam University 20 20
305 2 s. 50, Kilimanjaro airport .. .. .. 45 1·40
302/5 .. .. *Set of* 4 70 1·50

65 Flags and Trade Fair Emblem

(Des Trade Fair Publicity Agents. Litho Questa)

1972 (23 Feb). *All-Africa Trade Fair. P* 13½ × 14.
306 **65** 30 c. multicoloured 10 10
307 70 c. multicoloured 10 10
308 1 s. 50, multicoloured 10 10
309 2 s. 50, multicoloured 25 55
306/9 .. .. *Set of* 4 40 60

66 Child with Cup

(Des Rena Fennessy. Litho Questa)

1972 (24 Apr). *25th Anniv of UNICEF. T* **66** *and similar horiz designs. Multicoloured. P* 14 × 14½.
310 30 c. Type **66** 10 10
311 70 c. Children with ball 10 10
312 1 s. 50, Child at blackboard 10 10
313 2 s. 50, Child and tractor 25 50
310/13 .. .. *Set of* 4 35 60

67 Hurdling

(Des G. Vasarhelyi. Litho J.W.)

1972 (28 Aug). *Olympic Games, Munich. T* **67** *and similar horiz designs. Multicoloured. P* 14.
314 40 c. Type **67** 10 10
315 70 c. Running 10 10
316 1 s. 50, Boxing 20 10
317 2 s. 50, Hockey .. .. 30 1·00
314/17 .. .. *Set of* 4 60 1·10
MS318 131 × 98 mm. Nos. 314/17 .. .. .. 2·50 4·50

68 Kobs

(Des G. Drummond. Litho D.L.R.)

1972 (9 Oct). *Tenth Anniv of Ugandan Independence. T* **68** *and similar horiz designs. Multicoloured. P* 14.
319 40 c. Type **68** 10 10
320 70 c. Conference Centre 10 10
321 1 s. 50, Makerere University 25 20
322 2 s. 50, Coat of Arms .. .. 70 1·25
319/22 .. .. *Set of* 4 1·00 1·40
MS323 132 × 120 mm. Nos. 319/22. P 13 × 14 .. 2·75 3·50

69 Community Flag

(Des Rena Fennessy. Litho)

1972 (1 Dec). *Fifth Anniv of East African Community. P* 14½ × 14.
324 **69** 5 s. multicoloured .. .. 75 1·25

NEW INFORMATION

The editor is always interested to correspond with people who have new information that will improve or correct the Catalogue.

70 Run-of-the-wind Anemometer

71 "Learning by Serving"

(Des P. Powell. Litho)

1973 (1 Mar*). *I.M.O./W.M.O. Centenary. T* **70** *and similar multicoloured designs. P* 14½.
325 40 c. Type **70** 10 10
326 70 c. Weather balloon (*vert*) 15 10
327 1 s. 50, Meteorological rocket 25 15
328 2 s. 50, Satellite receiving aerial .. .. 55 1·10
325/8 .. .. *Set of* 4 90 1·25

No. 325 exists with country name at foot instead of at top, and also with country name omitted (or with imprint or plate numbers in lieu). These are because of faulty registration of the perforation comb.

*This is the local release date. The Crown Agents in London did not place the stamps on sale until 5 March.

(Des Rena Fennessy. Litho)

1973 (16 July). *24th World Scout Conference, Nairobi. T* **71** *and similar vert designs. P* 14.
329 40 c. multicoloured 15 10
330 70 c. Venetian red, reddish violet and black .. 20 10
331 1 s. 50, cobalt, reddish violet and black .. 45 30
332 2 s. 50, multicoloured .. .. 1·00 1·50
329/32 .. .. *Set of* 4 1·60 1·75

Designs:—70 c. Baden-Powell's grave, Nyeri; 1 s. 50, World Scout emblem; 2 s. 50, Lord Baden-Powell.

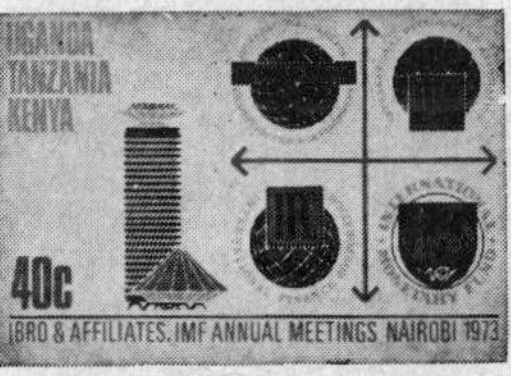

72 Kenyatta Conference Centre

(Des Marketing Communications Ltd, Nairobi; adapted J. Cooter. Litho D.L.R.)

1973 (29 Sept*). *I.M.F./World Bank Conference. T* **72** *and similar designs. P* 13½ × 14 (1 s. 50) *or* 14 × 13½ (*others*).
333 40 c. sage-green, light greenish grey & black 10 10
334 70 c. orange-brown, greenish grey and black 10 10
335 1 s. 50, multicoloured 25 35
336 2 s. 50, orange, greenish grey and black .. 35 65
333/6 .. .. *Set of* 4 65 1·00
MS337 166 × 141 mm. Nos. 333/6. Imperf .. 1·40 2·50

Designs:—Nos. 334/6 show different arrangements of Bank emblems and the Conference Centre, the 1 s. 50 being vertical.

*This is the local release date. The Crown Agents in London issued the stamps on 24 September.

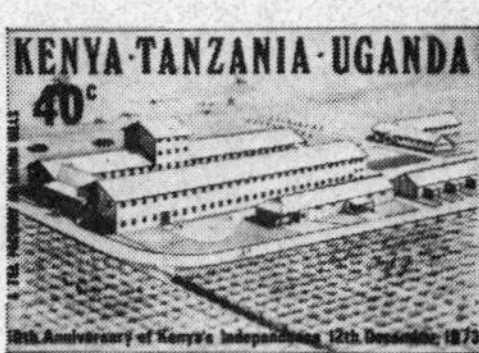

73 Police Dog-handler **74** Tea Factory

(Des C. Abbott. Litho Questa)

1973 (24 Oct)–**74**. *50th Anniv of Interpol. T* **73** *and similar vert designs. P* 14.
338 40 c. yellow, blue and black 25 10
339 70 c. turquoise-green, orange-yellow & black 40 10
340 1 s. 50, light violet, yellow and black .. 70 70
341 2 s. 50, light yellow-green, red-orange and black (I) .. .. 2·75 3·75
342 2 s. 50, light yellow-green, red-orange, and black (II) (25.2.74) .. .. .. 2·75 3·75
338/42 .. .. *Set of* 5 6·25 7·50

Designs:—70 c. East African Policeman; 1 s. 50, Interpol emblem; 2 s. 50, Interpol H.Q.

Nos. 341/2. Type I inscribed "St. Clans"; Type II corrected to "St. Cloud".

(Des G. Drummond. Litho Enschedé)

1973 (12 Dec). *10th Anniv of Kenya's Independence. T* **74** *and similar horiz designs. Multicoloured. P* 13 × 13½.
343 40 c. Type **74** 10 10
344 70 c. Kenyatta Hospital 10 15
345 1 s. 50, Nairobi Airport 20 15
346 2 s. 50, Kindaruma hydro-electric scheme .. 50 1·25
343/6 .. .. *Set of* 4 75 1·40

75 Party H.Q.

(Des PAD Studio. Litho D.L.R.)

1974 (12 Jan). *Tenth Anniv of Zanzibar's Revolution. T* **75** *and similar horiz designs. Multicoloured. P* 13½.

347	40 c. Type **75**	10	10
348	70 c. Housing scheme	10	10
349	1 s. 50, Colour T.V.	25	20
350	2 s. 50, Amaan Stadium	55	1·25
347/50	*Set of* 4	85	1·40

76 "Symbol of Union"

(Des Jennifer Toombs. Litho Questa)

1974 (26 Apr). *Tenth Anniv of Tanganyika–Zanzibar Union. T* **76** *and similar horiz designs. Multicoloured. P* 14½.

351	40 c. Type **76**	10	10
352	70 c. Handclasp and map	15	10
353	1 s. 50, "Communications"	35	25
354	2 s. 50, Flags of Tanu, Tanzania and Afro-Shirazi Party	85	1·25
351/4	*Set of* 4	1·25	1·40

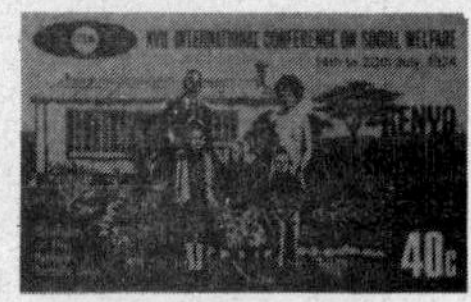

77 East African Family ("Stability of the Home")

(Des locally; adapted PAD Studio. Litho)

1974 (15 July). *17th Social Welfare Conference, Nairobi. T* **77** *and similar horiz designs. P* 14½.

355	40 c. greenish yellow, lake-brown and black	10	10
356	70 c. multicoloured	10	10
357	1 s. 50, olive-green, yellow-green and black	20	30
358	2 s. 50, light rose, reddish violet and black	45	1·25
355/8	*Set of* 4	70	1·50

Designs:—70 c. Dawn and drummer (U.N. Second Development Plan); 1 s. 50, Agricultural scene (Rural Development Plan); 2 s. 50, Transport and telephone ("Communications").

78 New Postal H.Q., Kampala

(Des Rena Fennessy. Litho)

1974 (9 Oct). *Centenary of Universal Postal Union. T* **78** *and similar horiz designs. Multicoloured. P* 14½.

359	40 c. Type **78**	10	10
360	70 c. Mail-train and post-van	15	10
361	1 s. 50, U.P.U. Building, Berne	15	15
362	2 s. 50, Loading mail into "VC-10"	30	80
359/62	*Set of* 4	60	95

79 Family-planning Clinic

(Des C. Abbott. Litho)

1974 (16 Dec). *World Population Year. T* **79** *and similar horiz designs. P* 14.

363	40 c. multicoloured	10	10
364	70 c. deep reddish violet and scarlet	10	10
365	1 s. 50, multicoloured	15	15
366	2 s. 50, apple-green, blue-green & bluish blk	30	90
363/6	*Set of* 4	55	1·00

Designs:—70 c. "Tug of war"; 1 s. 50, Population "scales"; 2 s. 50, W.P.Y. emblem.

80 Seronera Wild-Life Lodge, Tanzania

(Des R. Granger Barrett. Litho)

1975 (26 Feb*). *East Africa Game Lodges. T* **80** *and similar horiz designs. Multicoloured. P* 14.

367	40 c. Type **80**	15	10
368	70 c. Mweya Safari Lodge, Uganda	20	10
369	1 s. 50, "Ark"—Aberdare Forest Lodge, Kenya	35	25
370	2 s. 50, Paraa Safari Lodge, Uganda	80	1·50
367/70	*Set of* 4	1·40	1·75

*This is the local release date. The Crown Agents in London issued the stamps on 24 February.

81 Kitana (wooden comb), Bajun of Kenya

82 International Airport, Entebbe

(Des Mrs. Gombe of the E.A.P.T.; adapted C. Abbott. Litho Questa)

1975 (5 May). *African Arts. T* **81** *and similar vert designs. Multicoloured. P* 13½.

371	50 c. Type **81**	10	10
372	1 s. Earring, Chaga of Tanzania	15	10
373	2 s. Okoco (armlet), Acholi of Uganda	20	35
374	3 s. Kitete (Kamba gourd), Kenya	40	85
371/4	*Set of* 4	70	1·10

(Des PAD Studio. Litho State Ptg Wks, Warsaw)

1975 (28 July). *O.A.U. Summit Conference, Kampala. T* **82** *and similar multicoloured designs. P* 11.

375	50 c. Type **82**	10	10
376	1 s. Map of Africa and flag (*vert*)	10	10
377	2 s. Nile Hotel, Kampala	20	65
378	3 s. Martyrs' Shrine, Namugongo (*vert*)	30	1·00
375/8	*Set of* 4	60	1·60

83 Ahmed ("Presidential" Elephant)

84 Maasai Manyatta (village), Kenya

(Des locally. Litho State Ptg Wks, Warsaw)

1975 (11 Sept). *Rare Animals. T* **83** *and similar vert designs. Multicoloured. P* 11.

379	50 c. Type **83**	20	10
380	1 s. Albino buffalo	30	10
381	2 s. Ahmed in grounds of National Museum	85	1·00
382	3 s. Abbott's Duiker	1·10	1·75
379/82	*Set of* 4	2·25	2·75

(Des Rena Fennessy. Litho Questa)

1975 (3 Nov). *Second World Black and African Festival of Arts and Culture, Nigeria* (1977). *T* **84** *and similar horiz designs. Multicoloured. P* 13½ × 14.

383	50 c. Type **84**	10	10
384	1 s. "Heartbeat of Africa" (Ugandan dancers)	15	10
385	2 s. Makonde sculpture, Tanzania	35	55
386	3 s. "Early Man and Technology" (skinning hippopotamus)	60	1·00
383/6	*Set of* 4	1·10	1·50

For similar stamps see Nos. 76/80 of Kenya and the corresponding issues of Tanzania and Uganda.

85 Fokker "Friendship" at Nairobi Airport

(Des local artist. Litho State Security Ptg Wks, Warsaw)

1976 (2 Jan). *30th Anniv of East African Airways. T* **85** *and similar triangular designs. Multicoloured. P* 11½.

387	50 c. Type **85**	35	10
	a. Black (aircraft) and blue omitted	†	£550
388	1 s. "DC 9" at Kilimanjaro Airport	45	15
389	2 s. Super "VC 10" at Entebbe Airport	1·40	1·25
390	3 s. East African Airways Crest	2·00	2·00
387/90	*Set of* 4	3·75	3·00

Two black plates were used for each of Nos. 387/9: one for the frame and the other for the centre. No. 387a, three used copies of which are known, has the printing from the blue and centre black plates omitted.

Further commemorative issues were released during 1976–7 using common designs, but inscribed for one republic only. These are listed under KENYA, TANZANIA, or UGANDA.

Co-operation between the postal services of the three member countries virtually ceased after 30 June 1977, the postal services of Kenya, Tanzania and Uganda then operating independently.

OFFICIAL STAMPS

For use on official correspondence of the Tanganyika Government.

OFFICIAL
(O 1)

1959 (1 July). *Nos.* 167/71, 173 *and* 175/80 *optd as Type* O **1**.

O 1	5 c. black and deep brown	10	1
O 2	10 c. carmine-red	10	1
O 3	15 c. black and light blue (No. 169a)	10	1
O 4	20 c. black and orange	10	1
	a. Opt double	—	£47
O 5	30 c. black and deep ultramarine	10	1
O 6	50 c. reddish purple	10	1
O 7	1 s. black and claret	15	1
O 8	1 s. 30, orange and deep lilac	45	2
O 9	2 s. black and bronze-green	70	4
O10	5 s. black and orange	1·50	1·2
O11	10 s. black and deep ultramarine	2·00	2·5
O12	£1 brown-red and black	6·00	10·0
O1/12	*Set of* 12	10·00	13·0

The 30 c., 50 c. and 1 s. exist with overprint double, but wit the two impressions almost coincident.

OFFICIAL (O 2) **OFFICIAL** (O 3)

1960 (18 Oct). *Nos.* 183/6, 188, 190, 192 *and* 196 *optd with Typ* O **2** (*cents values*) *or* O **3**.

O13	5 c. Prussian blue	10	1
O14	10 c. yellow-green	10	1
O15	15 c. dull purple	10	1
O16	20 c. magenta	10	1
O17	30 c. vermilion	10	1
O18	50 c. slate-violet	10	1
O19	1 s. deep reddish violet and reddish purple	20	1
O20	5 s. rose-red and purple	3·00	6
O13/20	*Set of* 8	3·25	8

POSTAGE DUE STAMPS

D 1

D 2

(Typo Waterlow)

1928–33. *Wmk Mult Script CA. P* 15 × 14.

D1	D 1	5 c. violet	90	2
D2		10 c. vermilion	90	1
D3		20 c. yellow-green	90	2·5
D4		30 c. brown (1931)	5·50	6·5
D5		40 c. dull blue	4·50	9·0
D6		1 s. grey-green (1933)	28·00	45·0
D1/6		*Set of* 6	38·00	55·0
D1/6 Optd/Perf "Specimen"		*Set of* 6	90·00	

(Typo D.L.R.)

1935 (1 May)–**60**. *Wmk Mult Script CA. P* 14.

D 7	D 2	5 c. violet	70	4
D 8		10 c. scarlet	30	1
D 9		20 c. green	40	1
D10		30 c. brown	60	5
		a. *Bistre-brown* (19.7.60)	1·00	1·7
D11		40 c. ultramarine	1·50	3·0
D12		1 s. grey	8·00	12·0
D7/12		*Set of* 6	10·50	14·5
D7/12 Perf "Specimen"		*Set of* 6	70·00	

Kiribati

(*formerly* Gilbert Islands)

INDEPENDENT

15 Kiribati Flag

(Des G. Drummond. Litho Questa)

1979 (12 July). *Independence. T* **15** *and similar horiz design. Multicoloured. W* w **14** *(sideways). P* 14.

84 10 c. Type **15** 10 20
85 45 c. Houses of Parliament and Maneaba ni Maungatabu (House of Assembly) .. 30 50

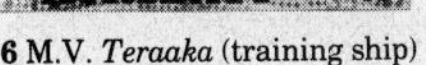

16 M.V. *Teraaka* (training ship)

17 Gilbert and Ellice Islands 1911 ½d. Stamp

(Des J. Cooter. Litho Questa)

1979 (12 July)–**80**. *Horiz designs as T* **16**. *Multicoloured. W* w **14** *(sideways). P* 14.

86 1 c. Type **16** 10 10
87 3 c. M.V. *Tautunu* (inter-island freighter) 10 10
88 5 c. Hibiscus 10 10
89 7 c. Catholic Cathedral, Tarawa 10 10
90 10 c. Maneaba, Bikenibeu 10 10
91 12 c. Betio Harbour 15 15
92 15 c. Eastern Reef Heron 35 20
93 20 c. Flamboyant Tree 20 20
94 25 c. Moorish Idol (fish) 30 30
95 30 c. Frangipani 25 25
96 35 c. G.I.P.C. Chapel, Tangintebu 25 25
97 50 c. *Hypolimnas bolina elliciana* (butterfly) .. 75 55
98 $1 *Tabakea* (Tarawa Lagoon ferry).. .. 70 75
99 $2 Evening scene .. .. 80 1·00
99a $5 National flag (27.8.80) .. .. .. 5·00 7·50
86/99a .. .. *Set of* 15 8·00 10·50

See also Nos. 121/35.

(Des J.W. Litho Questa)

1979 (27 Sept). *Death Centenary of Sir Rowland Hill. T* **17** *and similar vert designs showing stamps. Multicoloured. W* w **14**. *P* 14.

100 10 c. Type **17** 10 10
101 20 c. Gilbert and Ellice Islands 1956 2s. 6d. definitive 15 20
102 25 c. Great Britain 1902 2s. 6d. 15 20
103 45 c. Gilbert and Ellice Islands 1924 10s. .. 25 35
100/3 .. .. *Set of* 4 60 75
MS104 113 × 110 mm. Nos. 100/3 .. .. 65 85

18 Boy with Clam Shell

(Des D. Bowen. Litho Enschedé)

1979 (28 Nov). *International Year of the Child. T* **18** *and similar multicoloured designs. W* w **14** *(sideways on 20 c.). P* 13 × 13½ *(20 c.) or* 13½ × 13 *(others)*.

105 10 c. Type **18** 10 10
106 20 c. Child climbing coconut tree (*horiz*) .. 10 10
107 45 c. Girl reading 15 20
108 $1 Child in costume 30 50
105/8 .. .. *Set of* 4 55 75

19 Downrange Station, Christmas Island

(Des J. Cooter. Litho Format)

1980 (20 Feb). *Satellite Tracking. T* **19** *and similar multicoloured designs. P* 14½.

109 25 c. Type **19** 10 10
110 45 c. Map of South Pacific showing trajectory of Experimental Communications Satellite 15 15
111 $1 Rocket launch, Tanegashima, Japan (*vert*) 30 35
109/11 .. .. *Set of* 3 50 55

ALTERED CATALOGUE NUMBERS

Any Catalogue numbers altered from the last edition are shown as a list in the introductory pages.

20 T.S. *Teraaka*

(Litho Format)

1980 (30 Apr). *"London 1980" International Stamp Exhibition. T* **20** *and similar horiz designs. Multicoloured. P* 14½.

112 12 c. Type **20** 10 10
113 25 c. Loading Air Tungaru aeroplane, Bonriki Airport 10 10
114 30 c. Radio Operator 15 10
115 $1 Bairiki Post Office 30 35
112/15 .. .. *Set of* 4 50 50
MS116 139 × 116 mm. Nos. 112/15. P 14 × 14½ 55 75

Nos. 112/15 were each printed in sheets of 12 containing *se-tenant* stamp-size labels in positions 4 and 6.

21 *Achaea janata*

(Des J. Cooter. Litho Questa)

1980 (27 Aug). *Moths. T* **21** *and similar horiz designs. Multicoloured. P* 14.

117 12 c. Type **21** 15 10
118 25 c. *Ethmia nigroapicella* 20 15
119 30 c. *Utetheisa pulchelloides* 20 15
120 50 c. *Anua coronata* 25 25
117/20 .. .. *Set of* 4 70 60

1980 (27 Aug)–**81**. *As Nos. 86/99a but no wmk.*

121 1 c. Type **16** (4.81) 10 15
122 3 c. M.V. *Tautunu* (inter-island freighter) (6.1.81) 10 15
123 5 c. Hibiscus 10 15
124 7 c. Catholic Cathedral, Tarawa 10 15
125 10 c. Maneaba, Bikenibeu (19.11.80) 10 15
126 12 c. Betio Harbour (11.12.80) 15 15
127 15 c. Eastern Reef Heron (11.12.80) 35 20
128 20 c. Flamboyant Tree (6.1.81) 20 30
129 25 c. Moorish Idol (19.11.80) 25 30
130 30 c. Frangipani (4.81) 25 30
131 35 c. G.I.P.C. Chapel, Tangintebu (4.81) .. 25 30
132 50 c. *Hypolimnas bolina elliciana* (butterfly) (4.81) 75 70
133 $1 *Tabakea* (Tarawa Lagoon ferry) (11.12.80).. .. .. 90 1·50
134 $2 Evening scene (11.12.80) .. .. 1·40 2·25
135 $5 National flag (11.12.80) .. .. 2·50 4·00
121/35 .. .. *Set of* 15 6·50 9·50

22 Captain Cook Hotel, Christmas Island

(Des J. Cooter. Litho Format)

1980 (19 Nov). *Development. T* **22** *and similar horiz designs. Multicoloured. P* 13½ × 14.

136 10 c. Type **22** 10 10
137 20 c. Sports Stadium 10 10
138 25 c. International Airport, Bonriki 15 10
139 35 c. National Library and Archives 15 10
140 $1 Otintai Hotel 30 40
136/40 .. .. *Set of* 5 65 65

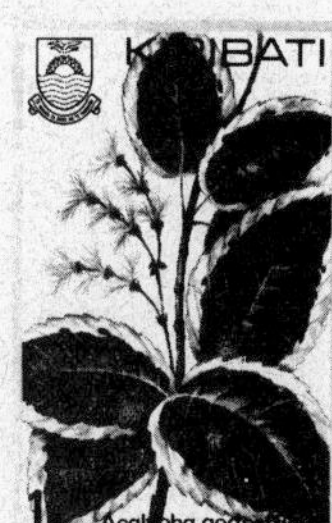

23 *Acalypha godseffiana*

(Des J. Cooter. Litho Format)

1981 (18 Feb). *Flowers. T* **23** *and similar vert designs. Multicoloured. W* w **15**. *P* 14 × 13½.

141 12 c. Type **23** 10 10
142 30 c. *Hibiscus schizopetalus* 15 15
143 35 c. *Calotropis gigantea* 15 15
144 50 c. *Euphorbia pulcherrima* 20 20
141/4 .. .. *Set of* 4 55 55

25 Maps of Abaiang and Marakei, and String Figures

(Des J. Cooter. Litho Format)

1981 (6 May). *Island Maps (1st series). T* **25** *and similar horiz designs. Multicoloured. W* w **15** *(sideways). P* 13½ × 14.

145 12 c. Type **25** 15 10
146 30 c. Maps of Little Makin and Butaritari, and village house 25 10
147 35 c. Map of Maiana, and coral road 30 15
148 $1 Map of Christmas Island, and Captain Cook's H.M.S. *Resolution* 90 75
145/8 .. .. *Set of* 4 1·40 1·00

See also Nos. 201/4, 215/18, 237/40 , 256/60 and 270/3.

26 *Katherine*

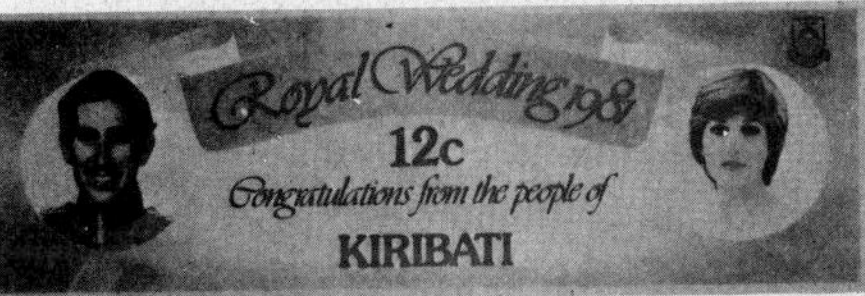

27 Prince Charles and Lady Diana Spencer

(Des D. Shults. Litho Questa)

1981 (29 July–26 Nov). *Royal Wedding. Horiz designs as T* **26**, *showing Royal Yachts, and T* **27**. *Multicoloured. (a) W* w **15**. *P* 14.

149 12 c. Type **26** 15 15
a. Sheetlet. No. 149 × 6 and No. 150 .. 1·00
150 12 c. Type **27** 30 30
151 50 c. *Osborne* 45 45
a. Sheetlet No. 151 × 6 and No. 152 .. 3·00
152 50 c. Type **27** 75 75
153 $2 *Britannia* .. .. 75 1·00
a. Sheetlet. No. 153 × 6 and No. 154 .. 6·00
154 $2 Type **27** .. .. 2·50 3·50
149/154 .. .. *Set of* 6 4·50 5·50
MS155 120 × 109 mm. $1.20, Type **27**. Wmk sideways. P 12 (26 Nov) .. .. .. 2·00 2·25

(*b*) *Booklet stamps. No wmk. P* 12 (26 Nov)

156 12 c. Type **26** 15 15
a. Booklet pane. No. 156 × 4 60
157 50 c. Type **27** 75 80
a. Booklet pane. No. 157 × 2 .. .. 1·50

Nos. 49/54 were printed in sheetlets of seven stamps of the same face value, each containing six of the "Royal Yacht" design and one as Type **27**.

Nos. 156/7 come from $1.96 stamp booklets.

28 Tuna Bait Breeding Centre, Bonriki Fish Farm

(Des G. Drummond. Litho Questa)

1981 (19 Nov). *Tuna Fishing Industry. T* **28** *and similar horiz designs. Multicoloured. W* w **15**. *P* 14.

158 12 c. Type **28** 15 10
159 30 c. Tuna fishing 25 20
160 35 c. Cold storage, Betio 25 25
161 50 c. Government Tuna Fishing Vessel *Nei Manganibuka* 50 50
158/61 .. .. *Set of* 4 1·00 95
MS162 134 × 99 mm. Nos. 158/61. Wmk sideways 1·25 1·40

29 Pomarine Skua

(Des G. Drummond. Litho Questa)

1982 (18 Feb)–**85**. *Birds. Multicoloured designs as T* **29**. *P* 14.

163 1 c. Type **29** 10 10
164 2 c. Mallard 10 10
165 4 c. White-winged Petrel 10 10
166 5 c. Blue-faced Booby 10 10
167 7 c. Friendly Quail Dove 10 10
168 8 c. Common Shoveler 10 10
169 12 c. Polynesian Reed Warbler 10 10
170 15 c. American Golden Plover 10 15
171 20 c. Eastern Reef Heron 15 20
171*a* 25 c. Common Noddy (31.1.83) 20 25
172 30 c. Brown Booby 25 30
173 35 c. Audubon's Shearwater 30 35
174 40 c. White-throated Storm Petrel (*vert*) .. 35 40
175 50 c. Bristle-thighed Curlew (*vert*) 40 45
175*a* 55 c. White Tern (*inscr* "Fairy Tern") (*vert*) (19.11.85) 45 50
176 $1 Kuhl's Lory (*vert*) 85 90
177 $2 Long-tailed Koel (*vert*) .. .. .. 1·60 1·75
178 $5 Great Frigate Bird (*vert*) .. .. .. 4·25 4·50
163/78 .. .. *Set of* 18 8·50 9·25

30 De Havilland "DH114 (Heron)"

31 Mary of Teck, Princess of Wales, 1893

(Des G. Drummond. Litho Format)

1982 (18 Feb). *Inauguration of Air Tungaru Airline. T* **30** *and similar horiz designs. Multicoloured. W w* **15** (*sideways*). *P* 14.

179 12 c. Type **30** 10 10
180 30 c. Britten-Norman "Trislander" 20 20
181 35 c. Casa "212 (Aviocar)" 25 25
182 50 c. Boeing "727" 35 35
179/82 .. .. *Set of* 4 75 75

(Des D. Shults and J. Cooter. Litho Format)

1982 (19 May). *21st Birthday of Princess of Wales. T* **31** *and similar vert designs. Multicoloured. W w* **15**. *P* 13½ × 14.

183 12 c. Type **31** 10 10
184 50 c. Coat of Arms of Mary of Teck 30 30
185 $1 Diana, Princess of Wales 50 50
183/5 .. .. *Set of* 3 75 75

The 12 c. design is incorrectly dated; Mary of Teck became Princess of Wales in 1901.

1982 (14 July). *Birth of Prince William of Wales. Nos.* 183/5 *optd with T* **19** *of St. Kitts.*

186 12 c. Type **31** 15 15
187 50 c. Coat of arms of Mary of Teck 35 35
a. Opt inverted .. .. 14·00
188 $1 Diana, Princess of Wales 55 55
186/8 .. .. *Set of* 3 95 95

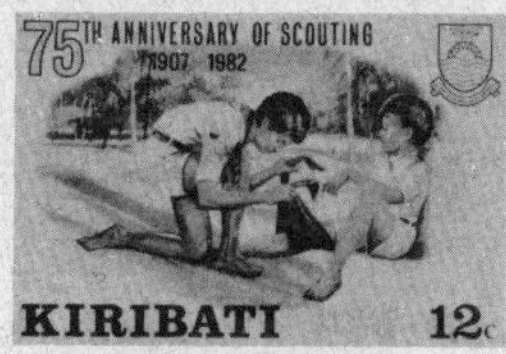

32 First Aid Practice

(Des J. Cooter. Litho Format)

1982 (12 Aug). *75th Anniv of Boy Scout Movement. T* **32** *and similar horiz designs. Multicoloured. W w* **15** (*sideways*). *P* 13½ × 14.

189 12 c. Type **32** 15 15
190 25 c. Boat repairs 30 30
191 30 c. On parade 35 35
192 50 c. Gilbert Islands 1977 8 c. Scouting stamp and "75" 60 60
189/92 .. .. *Set of* 4 1·25 1·25

33 Queen and Duke of Edinburgh with Local Dancer

(Des PAD Studio. Litho Walsall)

1982 (23 Oct). *Royal Visit. T* **33** *and similar horiz designs. Multicoloured. W w* **15** (*sideways*). *P* 14.

193 12 c. Type **33** 15 15
194 25 c. Queen, Duke of Edinburgh and outrigger canoe 20 20
195 35 c. New Philatelic Bureau building 30 30
193/5 .. .. *Set of* 3 60 60
MS196 88 × 76 mm. 50 c. Queen Elizabeth II .. 60 60

On No. **MS**196 the captions on the map for the islands of Teraina and Tabuaeren have been transposed.

34 "Obaia, The Feathered" (Kiribati legend)

(Des J.W. Litho Format)

1983 (14 Mar). *Commonwealth Day. T* **34** *and similar horiz designs. Multicoloured. W w* **15** (*sideways*). *P* 14.

197 12 c. Type **34** 15 10
198 30 c. Robert Louis Stevenson Hotel, Abemama 20 20
199 50 c. Container ship off Betio 25 25
200 $1 Map of Kiribati 45 65
197/200 .. .. *Set of* 4 95 1·10

(Des J. Cooter. Litho Format)

1983 (19 May). *Island Maps* (*2nd series*). *Multicoloured designs as T* **25**. *W w* **15** (*sideways on* 12 *and* 25 *c.*). *P* 13½ × 14 (*horiz*) *or* 14 × 13½ (*vert*).

201 12 c. Beru, Nikunau and canoe 15 20
202 25 c. Abemama, Aranuka, Kuria and fish .. 25 30
203 35 c. Nonouti and reef fishing (*vert*) 35 40
204 50 c. Tarawa and House of Assembly (*vert*) .. 50 55
201/4 .. .. *Set of* 4 1·10 1·25

35 Collecting Coconuts

(Des G. Drummond. Litho Questa)

1983 (8 Aug). *Copra Industry. T* **35** *and similar horiz designs. Multicoloured. W w* **15**. *P* 14.

205 12 c. Type **35** 20 20
206 25 c. Selecting coconuts for copra 35 35
207 30 c. Removing husks 40 40
208 35 c. Drying copra 45 45
209 50 c. Loading copra at Betio 55 55
205/9 .. .. *Set of* 5 1·75 1·75

36 War Memorials

(Des J. Cooter. Litho Format)

1983 (17 Nov). *40th Anniv of Battle of Tarawa. T* **36** *and similar horiz designs. Multicoloured. W w* **15** (*sideways*). *P* 14.

210 12 c. Type **36** 15 20
211 30 c. Maps of Tarawa and Pacific Ocean .. 35 40
212 35 c. Gun emplacement 40 45
213 50 c. Modern and war-time landscapes .. 60 65
214 $1 Aircraft carrier U.S.S. *Tarawa* .. .. 1·00 1·10
210/14 .. .. *Set of* 5 2·25 2·50

(Des J. Cooter. Litho Format)

1984 (14 Feb). *Island Maps* (*3rd series*). *Multicoloured designs as T* **25**. *W w* **15** (*sideways*). *P* 13½ × 14.

215 12 c. Teraina and Captain Fanning's ship *Betsey*, 1798 .. .. 20 15
216 30 c. Nikumaroro and Hawksbill Turtle .. 40 35
217 35 c. Kanton and local postmark 45 40
218 50 c. Banaba and Flying Fish 65 55
215/18 .. .. *Set of* 4 1·50 1·25

37 Tug *Riki*

(Des J. Cooter. Litho J.W.)

1984 (9 May). *Kiribati Shipping Corporation. T* **37** *and similar horiz designs. Multicoloured. W w* **15** (*sideways*). *P* 14.

219 12 c. Type **37** 15 15
220 35 c. Ferry *Nei Nimanoa* 35 35
221 50 c. Ferry *Nei Tebaa* 60 65
222 $1 Cargo ship *Nei Momi* .. .. .. 1·10 1·10
219/22 .. .. *Set of* 4 2·00 2·00
MS223 115 × 98 mm. Nos. 219/222. P 13 × 13½ 2·75 3·00

NEW INFORMATION

The editor is always interested to correspond with people who have new information that will improve or correct the Catalogue.

38 Water and Sewage Schemes

(Des J. Cooter. Litho Format)

1984 (21 Aug). *"Ausipex" International Stamp Exhibitio[n], Melbourne. T* **38** *and similar horiz designs. Multicolou[red]. W w* **15** (*sideways*). *P* 13½ × 14.

224 12 c. Type **38** 20
225 30 c. *Nouamake* (game fishing boat) 40
226 35 c. Overseas training schemes 50
227 50 c. International communications link .. 65
224/7 .. .. *Set of* 4 1·60

39 "Tabakea supporting Banaba"

(Des Jennifer Toombs. Litho Format)

1984 (21 Nov). *Kiribati Legends* (*1st series*). *T* **39** *and simila[r] horiz designs. Multicoloured. W w* **15** (*sideways*). *P* 14.

228 12 c. Type **39** 20
229 30 c. "Nakaa, Judge of the Dead" 35
230 35 c. "Naareau and Dragonfly" 45
231 50 c. "Whistling Ghosts" 55
228/31 .. .. *Set of* 4 1·40

See also Nos. 245/8.

40 Tang

(Des G. Drummond. Litho Questa)

1985 (19 Feb). *Reef Fishes. T* **40** *and similar horiz designs. Multi[coloured]. W w* **15**. *P* 14.

232 12 c. Type **40** 40
233 25 c. White-barred Triggerfish 65
234 35 c. Surgeon Fish 75
235 80 c. Squirrel Fish .. .. 1·25
232/5 .. .. *Set of* 4 2·75
MS236 140 × 107 mm. Nos. 232/5. Wmk sideways 2·75

(Des J. Cooter. Litho J.W.)

1985 (9 May). *Island Maps* (*4th series*). *Horiz designs as T* **25**. *Multicoloured. W w* **15** (*sideways*). *P* 13½.

237 12 c. Tabuaeran and Great Frigate Bird .. 35
238 35 c. Rawaki and germinating coconuts .. 60
239 50 c. Arorae and Xanthid Crab 75
240 $1 Tamana and fish hook .. .. .. 1·25
237/40 .. .. *Set of* 4 2·75

41 Youths playing Football on Beach

(Des R. Stokes. Litho Cambec Press, Melbourne)

1985 (5 Aug). *International Youth Year. T* **41** *and simila[r] multicoloured designs. P* 13½.

241 15 c. Type **41** 35
242 35 c. Logos of I.Y.Y. and Kiribati Youth Year 65
243 40 c. Girl preparing food (*vert*) 70
244 55 c. Map illustrating Kiribati's youth exchange links 90
241/4 .. .. *Set of* 4 2·40

(Des Jennifer Toombs. Litho Questa)

1985 (19 Nov). *Kiribati Legends* (*2nd series*). *Horiz designs as T* **39**. *Multicoloured. P* 14.

245 15 c. "Nang Kineia and the Tickling Ghosts" 40
246 35 c. "Auriaria and Tituabine" 70
247 40 c. "The first coming of Babai at Arorae" .. 85
248 55 c. "Riiki and the Milky Way" .. .. .. 1·00
245/8 .. .. *Set of* 4 2·75

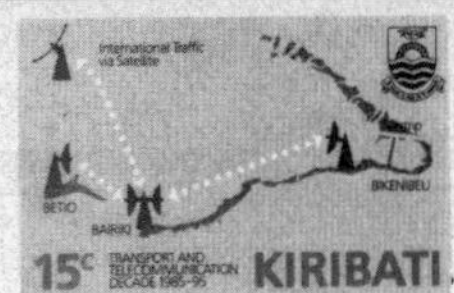

42 Map showing Telecommunications Satellite Link

(Litho Walsall)

985 (9 Dec). *Transport and Telecommunications Decade* (1*st issue*). *T* 42 *and similar horiz design. Multicoloured. P* 14.
49 15 c. Type 42 .. .. 40 40
50 40 c. M.V. *Moanaraoi* (Tarawa-Suva service) 85 85
See also Nos. 268/9, 293/4 and 314/15.

(Des A. Theobald. Litho Questa)

986 (21 Apr). 60*th Birthday of Queen Elizabeth II. Vert designs as T* 110 *of Ascension. Multicoloured. P* 14½×14.
51 15 c. Princess Elizabeth in Girl Guide uniform, Windsor Castle, 1938 .. .. 15 15
52 35 c. At Trooping the Colour, 1980 .. .. 30 35
53 40 c. With Duke of Edinburgh in Kiribati, 1982 .. .. 35 40
54 55 c. At banquet, Austrian Embassy, London, 1966 .. .. 50 55
55 $1 At Crown Agents Head Office, London, 1983 .. .. 90 95
51/5 .. .. *Set of* 5 2·00 2·10

(Des J. Cooter. Litho Questa)

986 (17 June). *Island Maps* (5*th series*). *Horiz designs as T* 25. *Multicoloured. P* 13½×14.
56 15 c. Manra and Coconut Crab 40 20
57 30 c. Birnie and McKean Islands and cowrie shells 60 35
58 35 c. Orona and Red-footed Booby 70 50
59 40 c. Malden Island and whaling ship, 1844 .. 85 90
60 55 c. Vostok, Flint and Caroline Islands and *Vostok*, 1820 .. .. 1·10 1·40
56/60 .. .. *Set of* 5 3·25 3·00

43 *Lepidodactylus lugubris*

44 Maps of Australia and Kiribati

(Des G. Drummond. Litho Questa)

986 (26 Aug). *Geckos. T* 43 *and similar horiz designs. Multicoloured. P* 14.
61 15 c. Type 43 .. .. 40 25
62 35 c. *Gehyra mutilata* 70 50
63 40 c. *Hemidactylus frenatus* 90 90
64 55 c. *Gehyra oceanica* .. .. 1·25 1·40
61/4 .. .. *Set of* 4 3·00 2·75

(Des D. Miller. Litho Format)

986 (29 Dec). *America's Cup Yachting Championship. T* 44 *and similar vert designs. Multicoloured. P* 13½×14.
65 15 c. Type 44 .. .. 12 15
a. Horiz strip of 3. Nos. 265/7 .. .. 1·75
66 55 c. America's Cup and map of course .. 50 55
67 $1.50, *Australia II* (1983 winner) .. .. 1·25 1·40
65/7 .. .. *Set of* 3 1·75 1·90
Nos. 265/7 were printed together, *se-tenant*, in horizontal trips of 3 throughout the sheet with the $1.50 at left and the 5 c. at centre of each strip.

45 Freighter *Moamoa*

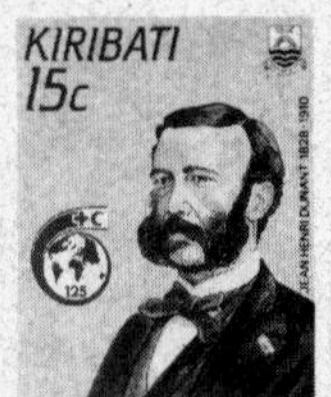

46 Henri Dunant (founder)

(Des and litho Questa)

1987 (31 Mar). *Transport and Telecommunications Decade* (2*nd issue*). *T* 45 *and similar horiz design. Multicoloured. P* 13½×14.
268 30 c. Type 45 .. .. 50 50
269 55 c. Telephone switchboard and automatic exchange 75 75

(Des J. Cooter. Litho Format)

1987 (22 Sept). *Island Maps* (6*th series*). *Multicoloured designs as T* 25, *but vert. P* 14×13½.
270 15 c. Starbuck and Red-tailed Tropic Bird .. 20 15
271 30 c. Enderbury and White Tern 30 30
272 55 c. Tabiteuea and Pandanus Tree 55 55
273 $1 Onotoa and okai (house) 95 95
270/3 .. .. *Set of* 4 1·75 1·75

(Des G. Drummond. Litho Format)

1987 (27 Oct). *Skinks. Horiz designs as T* 43. *Multicoloured. P* 15.
274 15 c. *Emoia nigra* 20 15
275 35 c. *Cryptoblepharus sp.* 35 35
276 40 c. *Emoia cyanura* 40 40
277 $1 *Lipinia noctua* 95 95
274/7 .. .. *Set of* 4 1·75 1·75
MS278 130×114 mm. Nos. 274/7 .. .. 2·60 2·25

1987 (30 Nov). *Royal Ruby Wedding. Nos* 251/5 *optd with T* 119 *of Ascension in silver.*
279 15 c. Princess Elizabeth in Girl Guide uniform, Windsor Castle, 1938 .. .. 15 15
280 35 c. At Trooping the Colour, 1980 .. .. 30 35
281 40 c. With Duke of Edinburgh in Kiribati, 1982 .. .. 35 40
282 55 c. At banquet, Austrian Embassy, London, 1966 .. .. 50 55
283 $1 At Crown Agents Head Office, London, 1983 .. .. 90 95
279/83 .. .. *Set of* 5 2·00 2·10

(Des A. Theobald. Litho Questa)

1988 (9 May). 125*th Anniv of International Red Cross. T* 46 *and similar vert designs. Multicoloured. P* 14½×14.
284 15 c. Type 46 .. .. 15 20
285 35 c. Red Cross workers in Independence parade, 1979 .. .. 35 40
286 40 c. Red Cross workers with patient .. 40 45
287 55 c. Gilbert & Ellice Islands 1970 British Red Cross Centenary 10 c. stamp .. 50 55
284/7 .. .. *Set of* 4 1·25 1·40

47 Causeway built by Australia

(Des CPE Australia Ltd ($2), D. Miller (others). Litho CPE Australia Ltd, Melbourne ($2), Format (others))

1988 (30 July). *Bicentenary of Australian Settlement and "Sydpex '88" National Stamp Exhibition, Sydney. T* 47 *and similar horiz designs. Multicoloured. P* 14½.
288 15 c. Type 47 .. .. 15 20
289 35 c. Capt. Cook and Pacific map 35 40
290 $1 Obverse of Australian $10 Bicentenary banknote .. .. 95 1·00
a. Horiz pair. Nos. 290/1 .. .. 1·75 1·75
291 $1 Reverse of $10 Bicentenary banknote 95 1·00
288/91 .. .. *Set of* 4 2·10 2·40
MS292 95 × 76 mm. $2 *Logistic Ace* (container ship) (37 × 26 *mm*). P 13½ × 14 .. .. 1·90 2·00
Nos. 290/1 were printed together, *se-tenant*, in horizontal pairs throughout the sheet.
No. **MS**292 also commemorates the 150th anniversary of the first screw-driven steamship.

48 Manual Telephone Exchange and Map of Kiritimati

(Des A. Theobald. Litho Questa)

1988 (28 Dec). *Transport and Communications Decade* (3*rd issue*). *T* 48 *and similar horiz design. Multicoloured. W w* 14 (*sideways*). *P* 14.
293 35 c. Type 48 .. .. 35 40
294 45 c. Betio–Bairiki Causeway 45 50

49 *Hound* (brigantine), 1835

50 Eastern Reef Heron

(Des E. Nisbet. Litho Questa)

1989 (26 May). *Nautical History. T* 49 *and similar horiz designs. Multicoloured. W w* 16 (*sideways*). *P* 14½.
295 15 c. Type 49 .. .. 30 25
296 30 c. *Phantom* (brig), 1854 .. .. .. 45 40
297 40 c. H.M.S. *Alacrity* (schooner), 1873 .. 60 60
298 $1 *Charles W. Morgan* (whaling ship), 1851 .. .. 1·40 1·40
295/8 .. .. *Set of* 4 2·50 2·50

(Des D. Johnstone. Litho Questa)

1989 (28 June). *Birds with Young. T* 50 *and similar vert designs. Multicoloured. W w* 16. *P* 14½.
299 15 c. Type 50 .. .. 25 25
a. Vert pair. Nos. 299/300 .. .. 50 50
300 15 c. Eastern Reef Heron chicks in nest .. 25 25
301 $1 White-tailed Tropic Bird .. .. 1·40 1·40
a. Vert pair. Nos. 301/2 .. .. 2·75 2·75
302 $1 Young White-tailed Tropic Bird .. 1·40 1·40
299/302 .. .. *Set of* 4 3·00 3·00
Nos. 299/300 and 301/2 were each printed together, *se-tenant*, in vertical pairs throughout the sheets, each pair forming a composite design.

51 House of Assembly

52 Telecommunications Centre

(Des D. Miller. Litho Cartor, France)

1989 (12 July). 10*th Anniv of Independence. T* 51 *and similar vert design. Multicoloured. W w* 16 (*inverted*). *P* 13½×14.
303 15 c. Type 51 .. .. 25 25
304 $1 Constitution .. .. 1·25 1·25

(Des A. Theobald ($2.50), D. Miller (others). Litho Questa)

1989 (20 July). 20*th Anniv of First Manned Landing on Moon. Multicoloured designs as T* 126 *of Ascension. W w* 16 (*sideways on* 50, 60 *c.*). *P* 14×13½ (20, 75 *c.*) *or* 14 (*others*).
305 20 c. "Apollo 10" on launch gantry 30 30
306 50 c. Crew of "Apollo 10" (30×30 *mm*) .. 70 70
307 60 c. "Apollo 10" emblem (30×30 *mm*) .. 80 80
308 75 c. "Apollo 10" splashdown, Hawaii .. 95 95
305/8 .. .. *Set of* 4 2·50 2·50
MS309 82×100 mm. $2.50, "Apollo 11" command module in lunar orbit. P 14×13½ .. .. 3·25 3·50

(Des D. Miller. Litho Walsall)

1989 (7 Aug*). *"Philexfrance 89" International Stamp Exhibition, Paris, and "World Stamp Expo '89", Washington* (1*st issue*). *Sheet* 104×86 *mm containing vert design as T* 125 *of Ascension. Multicoloured. W w* 16. *P* 14×13½.
MS310 $2 Gilbert and Ellice Islands 1949 75th anniv of U.P.U. 3d. stamp .. .. .. 2·25 2·50
*This is the local date of issue. The agents, Caphco Ltd, placed stocks on sale in London and Paris from 7 July.

(Des D. Miller, adapted Walsall. Litho Walsall)

1989 (25 Sept). *"Philexfrance 89" International Stamp Exhibition, Paris, and "World Stamp Expo '89", Washington* (2*nd issue*). *Vert designs as T* 127 *of Ascension showing Statue of Liberty. Multicoloured. W w* 14. *P* 14×13½.
311 35 c. Examining fragment of Statue .. 35 40
a. Sheetlet. Nos. 311/13 95
312 35 c. Workman drilling Statue 35 40
313 35 c. Surveyor with drawing 35 40
311/13 .. .. *Set of* 3 95 1·10
Nos. 311/13 were printed, *se-tenant*, in sheetlets of 3.

(Des L. Curtis. Litho Questa)

1989 (16 Oct). *Transport and Communications Decade* (4*th issue*). *T* 52 *and similar horiz design. Multicoloured. W w* 16 (*sideways*). *P* 14.
314 30 c. Type 52 .. .. 30 35
315 75 c. *Mataburo* (inter-island freighter) .. 70 75

(53)

54 Virgin and Child (detail, "The Adoration of the Holy Child" (Denys Calvert))

1989 (21 Oct). *"Melbourne Stampshow '89". Nos.* 301/2 *optd with T* 53.
316 $1 White-tailed Tropic Bird .. .. 95 1·00
a. Vert pair. Nos. 316/17 .. .. 1·90 2·00
317 $1 Young White-tailed Tropic Bird .. 95 1·00

(Des D. Miller. Litho Questa)

1989 (1 Dec). *Christmas. T* 54 *and similar vert designs showing paintings. Multicoloured. W w* 16. *P* 14.
318 10 c. Type 53 .. .. 10 10
319 15 c. "The Adoration of the Holy Child" (Denys Calvert) 15 20
320 55 c. "The Holy Family and St. Elizabeth" (Rubens) 50 55
321 $1 "Madonna with Child and Maria Magdalena" (School of Correggio) .. 95 1·00
318/21 .. .. *Set of* 4 1·50 1·60

POSTAGE DUE STAMPS

D 1 Kiribati Coat of Arms

(Litho Format)

1981 (27 Aug). *P* 14.

No.	Type	Description		Mint	Used
D1	D 1	1 c. black and magenta		10	10
D2		2 c. black and greenish blue		10	10
D3		5 c. black and bright green		10	10
D4		10 c. black and chestnut		10	10
D5		20 c. black and bright blue		15	20
D6		30 c. black and brown-ochre		25	30
D7		40 c. black and purple		35	40
D8		50 c. black and deep blue-green		40	45
D9		$1 black and orange-red		85	90
D1/9			*Set of* 9	2·00	2·25

OFFICIAL STAMPS

O.K.G.S. (O 1) **O.K.G.S.** (O 2)

1981 (May). *Optd with Type* O **1**. A. *On Nos.* 86, 90/3, 95 *and* 97/9*a*, *W* w **14** (*sideways*). B. *On Nos.* 121/35. *No wmk.*

No.	Description	A		B	
O 1	1 c. Type **16**	1·75	2·00	10	10
O 2	3 c. M.V. *Tautunu* (inter-island freighter)	†		10	10
O 3	5 c. Hibiscus	†		10	10
O 4	7 c. Catholic Cathedral, Tarawa	†		10	10
O 5	10 c. Maneaba, Bikenibeu	12·00	12·00	10	10
	a. Opt double	†		15·00	—
O 6	12 c. Betio Harbour	3·00	3·00	15	15
O 7	15 c. Reef Egret	11·00	11·00	15	20
O 8	20 c. Flamboyant Tree	10·00	10·00	20	25
O 9	25 c. Moorish Idol	†		25	30
O10	30 c. Frangipani	7·00	7·00	30	35
	a. Opt double	†		20·00	—
O11	35 c. G.I.P.C. Chapel, Tangintebu	†		35	40
O12	50 c. *Hypolimnas bolina eliciana* (butterfly)	5·00	5·00	50	55
	a. Opt double	†		60·00	—
	b. Opt inverted	†		60·00	—
O13	$1 *Tabakea* (Tarawa Lagoon ferry)	9·00	9·00	1·00	1·00
O14	$2 Evening scene	11·00	11·00	2·00	2·25
	a. Opt double	†		£110	—
O15	$5 National flag	3·75	3·75	4·00	4·25
	a. Opt inverted	£150	—	†	
O1A/15A	*Set of* 10	65·00	65·00		
O1B/15B	*Set of* 15			8·00	9·00

1983. *Nos.* 86, 90/3, 95, 97/9 *and* 131 *optd with Type* O **2**.

No.	Description	Mint	Used
O16	1 c. Type **16**	3·50	3·50
O17	10 c. Maneaba, Bikenibeu	11·00	8·00
O18	12 c. Betio Harbour	4·00	4·00
O19	15 c. Eastern Reef Heron	13·00	13·00
O20	20 c. Flamboyant Tree	6·50	6·50
O21	30 c. Frangipani	8·00	5·00
O21*a*	35 c. G.I.P.C. Chapel, Tangintebu	†	—
O22	50 c. *Hypolimnas bolina elliciana* (butterfly)	5·50	4·00
O23	$1 *Tabakea* (Tarawa Lagoon ferry)	10·00	8·00
O24	$2 Evening scene	16·00	10·00

1983 (28 June). *Nos.* 169, 172/3, 175 *and* 177 *optd with Type* O **2**.

No.	Description		Mint	Used
O25	12 c. Polynesian Reed Warbler		30	30
O26	30 c. Brown Booby		50	50
O27	35 c. Audubon's Shearwater		60	60
O28	50 c. Bristle-thighed Curlew		80	80
O29	$2 Long-tailed Koel		2·75	2·75
O25/9		*Set of* 5	4·50	4·50

Kuwait

Kuwait, an independent Arab shaikhdom since 1756, placed itself under British protection in 1899 to counter the spread of Ottoman influence in the Arabian Gulf.

The first, somewhat limited, postal service, via Bushire, commenced with the appointment of a Political Agent to Kuwait in August 1904. Because of diplomatic problems this system continued until 21 January 1915 when a regular Indian post office was established.

Limited supplies of Indian stamps were used by the Political Agency postal service, but these became available to the general public from 21 January 1915. Stamps seen postally used from Kuwait before 1923 are usually ½ a., 1 a., 1 r. or 5 r. values, with the occasional Official issue. Much more common are values to 15 r., both postage and Official, used telegraphically.

Before 1910 the name of the shaikhdom was spelt "KOWEIT" and this spelling appears on various circular postmarks used between 1915 and 1923. The more modern version of the name was first used for a postal cancellation in 1923.

1915 "KOWEIT"

1923 "KUWAIT"

On 1 August 1921 responsibility for the Kuwait postal service passed to the Iraq Post Office, but later it reverted to Indian administration some time before 1929.

PRICES FOR STAMPS ON COVER TO 1945

Nos. 1/15	*from* × 5
Nos. 16/29	*from* × 3
Nos. 31/51	*from* × 2
Nos. 52/63	*from* × 4
Nos. O1/27	*from* × 10

USED HIGH VALUES. It is necessary to emphasize that used prices quoted for high value stamps are for postally used examples.

KUWAIT (1) KUWAIT (2)

1923 (1 Apr)–**24**. *Stamps of India (King George V), optd with T* **1** *or* **2** *(rupee values, 15½ mm). Star wmk. P* 14.

No.	Type	Description	Unused	Used
1	**56**	½ a. green	60	2·50
		a. Opt double	£200	
		b. Vert pair, one without opt	£400	
2	**57**	1 a. chocolate	1·25	1·25
		a. Opt double	£200	
		b. Opt omitted (lower stamp of vert pair)	£650	
3	**58**	1½ a. chocolate (A)	1·00	4·00
4	**59**	2 a. violet	1·25	50
		a. Bright purple		
5	**61**	2 a. 6 p. ultramarine	1·75	6·50
6	**62**	3 a. orange-brown	3·75	15·00
7		3 a. ultramarine (1924)	9·00	1·50
8	**63**	4 a. deep olive	7·00	20·00
		a. Olive-green		
9	**64**	6 a. yellow-bistre	8·50	13·00
10	**65**	8 a. purple	8·00	20·00
		a. Mauve		
11	**66**	12 a. claret	14·00	22·00
12	**67**	1 r. brown and green	14·00	9·00
		a. Red-brown and blue-green	18·00	13·00
13		2 r. carmine and yellow-brown	40·00	90·00
14		5 r. ultramarine and violet	80·00	£200
15		10 r. green and scarlet	£120	£450
1/15		*Set of* 15	£275	£750

Essays of the overprint using the obsolete spelling "KOWEIT" were prepared in 1923 and can be found on the original 14 values of the postage stamps and on the 13 stamps of the Official series. (*Price per set of* 27 *unused* £19000).

Nos. 1/4 and 6/7 are all known with inverted overprint. It is doubtful if such errors were actually sold at the Kuwait Post Office, although some are known on registered or ordinary covers.

From 22 April 1929 the post office in Kuwait was again placed under the control of the Iraq Mandate postal administration.

KUWAIT (3) KUWAIT (4)

1929–37. *Stamps of India (King George V, Nasik printing), optd with T* **3** *or* **4** *(rupee values). Mult Star wmk. P* 14.

No.	Type	Description	Unused	Used
16	**56**	½ a. green	1·00	1·25
16*a*	**79**	½ a. green (1934)	4·50	60
17	**57**	1 a. chocolate	7·00	1·25
17*a*	**81**	1 a. chocolate (1934)	4·50	40
18	**70**	2 a. purple	1·25	40
19		2 a. vermilion	23·00	48·00
19*a*	**59**	2 a. vermilion (1934)	13·00	5·00
19*b*		2 a. vermilion (*small die*) (1937)	2·75	1·40
20	**62**	3 a. bright blue	2·75	1·25
21		3 a. carmine	5·50	4·00
22	**71**	4 a. sage-green	25·00	48·00
22*a*	**63**	4 a. sage-green (1934)	5·00	7·50
22*b*	**64**	6 a. bistre (1937)	13·00	24·00
23	**65**	8 a. reddish purple	9·00	13·00
24	**66**	12 a. claret (1933)	18·00	35·00
25	**67**	1 r. chocolate and green	10·00	22·00
		a. Extended 'T'	£180	
26		2 r. carmine and orange	13·00	50·00
		a. Extended 'T'	£200	
27		5 r. ultramarine and purple (1937)	80·00	£160
		a. Extended 'T'	£325	
28		10 r. green and scarlet (1934)	£180	£325
		a. Extended 'T'	£650	
29		15 r. blue and olive (1937)	£450	£700
		a. Extended 'T'	£850	
16/29		*Set of* 20	£800	£1250

The 'T' of 'KUWAIT' shows a ¾ mm downward extension on R. 3/2, lower left pane.

1933 (Feb)–**34**. *Air. Stamps of India optd as T* **2** (16½ *mm*).

No.	Type	Description	Unused	Used
31	**72**	2 a. deep blue-green	11·00	20·00
32		3 a. blue	1·25	2·00
		a. Stamp doubly printed	£850	£650
33		4 a. drab	£100	£200
34		6 a. bistre (2.34)	1·25	4·00
31/4		*Set of* 4	£100	£200

1939. *Nos.* 247/8, 251, 253, 255/63 *of India optd with T* **3** *or* **4** *(rupee values).*

No.	Type	Description	Unused	Used
36	**91**	½ a. red-brown	4·00	75
38		1 a. carmine	4·00	75
39	**92**	2 a. vermilion	4·00	1·50
41	–	3 a. yellow-green	3·25	1·25
43	–	4 a. brown	14·00	7·50
44	–	6 a. turquoise-green	12·00	6·00
45	–	8 a. slate-violet	18·00	18·00
46	–	12 a. lake	17·00	20·00
47	**93**	1 r. grey and red-brown	3·50	1·90
		a. Extended 'T'	£180	
48		2 r. purple and brown	3·75	6·50
		a. Extended 'T'	£180	
49		5 r. green and blue	12·00	15·00
		a. Extended 'T'	£225	
50		10 r. purple and claret	70·00	60·00
		a. Opt double	£300	
		b. Extended 'T'	£400	
51		15 r. brown and green	£100	£150
		a. Extended 'T'	£550	
36/51		*Set of* 13	£240	£250

On later printings the extended 'T' variety was corrected in two stages.

Following the rebellion in Iraq control of the Kuwait postal service was assumed by the Indian authorities.

Unoverprinted stamps of INDIA were used in Kuwait between 1941 and 1945.

1945. *Stamps of India (King George VI, on white background) optd with T* **3**.

No.	Type	Description	Unused	Used
52	**100a**	3 p. slate	70	1·00
53		½ a. purple	70	70
54		9 p. green	70	2·50
55		1 a. carmine	70	70
56	**101**	1½ a. dull violet	70	2·00
57		2 a. vermilion	70	1·00
58		3 a. bright violet	70	1·50
59		3½ a. bright blue	1·50	1·75
60	**102**	4 a. brown	70	1·00
60*a*		6 a. turquoise-green	9·50	8·50
61		8 a. slate-violet	1·50	80
62		12 a. lake	3·00	1·50
63	**103**	14 a. purple	6·00	11·00
52/63		*Set of* 13	24·00	30·00

Following a short period of Pakistani control, from August 1947 the Kuwait postal service passed to British administration on 1 April 1948.

KUWAIT 1 ANNA (5)

KUWAIT 5 RUPEES (6)

NOTE. From 1948 onwards, for stamps with similar surcharges, but without name of country, see British Postal Agencies in Eastern Arabia.

1948 (1 Apr)–**49**. *Stamps of Great Britain (K.G. VI), surch as T* **5** *or* **6** *(rupee values).*

No.	Type	Description	Unused	Used
64	**128**	½ a. on ½d. pale green	10	30
65		1 a. on 1d. pale scarlet	10	30
66		1½ a. on 1½d. pale red-brown	10	30
67		2 a. on 2d. pale orange	10	30
68		2½ a. on 2½d. light ultramarine	10	40
69		3 a. on 3d. pale violet	10	10
		a. Pair, one surch albino		
70	**129**	6 a. on 6d. purple	15	10
71	**130**	1 r. on 1s. bistre-brown	25	40
72	**131**	2 r. on 2s. 6d. yellow-green	70	2·00
73		5 r. on 5s. red	1·50	4·00
73*a*	**132**	10 r. on 10s. ultramarine (4.7.49)	30·00	6·00
64/73*a*		*Set of* 11	30·00	13·00

KUWAIT 2½ ANNAS (7)

KUWAIT 15 RUPEES (8)

1948 (26 Apr). *Royal Silver Wedding. Nos.* 493/4 *of Great Britain surch with T* **7** *or* **8**.

No.	Type	Description	Unused	Used
74	**137**	2½ a. on 2½d. ultramarine	30	10
75	**138**	15 r. on £1 blue	30·00	27·00
		a. Short bars (R.3/4)	£125	

No. 75a has the bars cancelling the original face value 3 mm long instead of the 3½ mm of the normal surcharge.

1948 (29 July). *Olympic Games. Nos.* 495/8 *of Great Britain surch as T* **7**, *but in one line* (6 *a.*) *or two lines (others).*

No.	Type	Description	Unused	Used
76	**139**	2½ a. on 2½d. ultramarine	45	70
77	**140**	3 a. on 3d. violet	55	90
78	**141**	6 a. on 6d. bright purple	70	95
79	**142**	1 r. on 1s. brown	85	1·25
76/9		*Set of* 4	2·25	3·50

1949 (10 Oct). *75th Anniv of U.P.U. Nos.* 499/502 *of Great Britain surch* "KUWAIT" *and new values.*

No.	Type	Description	Unused	Used
80	**143**	2½ a. on 2½d. ultramarine	40	40
81	**144**	3 a. on 3d. violet	65	55
82	**145**	6 a. on 6d. bright purple	80	55
83	**146**	1 r. on 1s. brown	1·25	50
80/3		*Set of* 4	2·75	1·75

KUWAIT 2 RUPEES Type I — KUWAIT 2 RUPEES Type II (8*a*)

KUWAIT 10 RUPEES Type I — KUWAIT 10 RUPEES Type II (8*b*)

2 r. Type I. Type-set surcharge. "2" level with "RUPEES". Surcharge sharp.

Type II. Plate-printed surcharge. "2" raised. Surcharge worn.

10 r. Type I. Type-set surcharge. "1" and "O" spaced. Surcharge sharp and clean.

Type II. Plate-printed surcharge. "1" and "O" closer together. Surcharge appears heavy and worn, see especially "A", "R" and "P".

KUWAIT Extra bar in centre (R. 7/2)

KUWAIT Extra bar at top (R. 2/2)

1950 (2 Oct)–**55**. *Nos.* 503/11 *of Great Britain surch as T* **5** *or* **8a/b** *(rupee values).*

No.	Type	Description	Unused	Used
84	**128**	½ a. on ½d. pale orange (3.5.51)	15	70
85		1 a. on 1d. light ultramarine (3.5.51)	15	30
86		1½ a. on 1½d. pale green (3.5.51)	15	90
87		2 a. on 2d. pale red-brown (3.5.51)	15	35
88		2½ a. on 2½d. pale scarlet (3.5.51)	20	40
89	**129**	4 a. on 4d. light ultramarine	20	25
90	**147**	2 r. on 2s. 6d. yellow-green (I) (3.5.51)	8·00	4·00
		a. Extra bar in centre	£200	£200
		b. Type II surch (1955)	£160	42·00
91	**148**	5 r. on 5s. red (3.5.51)	12·00	5·00
		a. Extra bar at top	£150	£150
92	**149**	10 r. on 10s. ultramarine (I) (3.5.51)	24·00	5·50
		a. Type II surch (1953)	£180	50·00
84/92		*Set of* 9	40·00	15·00

No. 92a is known with surch spaced 10 mm apart instead of 9 mm.

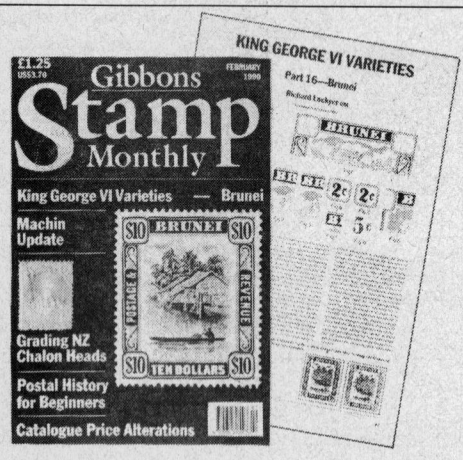

1952 (10 Dec)–**54.** *Stamps of Great Britain (Queen Elizabeth II). Wmk Tudor Crown, surch as T* **5** *(in two lines only on 2½ and 6 a.).*

93	**154**	½ a. on ½d. orange-red (31.8.53) ..	15	10
94		1 a. on 1d. ultramarine (31.8.53) ..	15	10
95		1½ a. on 1½d. green ..	15	10
96		2 a. on 2d. red-brown (31.8.53) ..	35	10
97	**155**	2½ a. on 2½d. carmine-red ..	15	10
98		3 a. on 3d. deep lilac (B.) (18.1.54) ..	40	10
99	**156**	4 a. on 4d. ultramarine (2.11.53) ..	1·25	35
100	**157**	6 a. on 6d. reddish purple (18.1.54) ..	85	10
101	**160**	12 a. on 1s. 3d. green (2.11.53) ..	4·50	1·75
102	**159**	1 r. on 1s. 6d. grey-blue (2.11.53) ..	4·50	10
93/102		.. *Set of* 10	11·00	2·10

1953 (3 June). *Coronation. Stamps of Great Britain surch "KUWAIT" and new values.*

103	**161**	2½ a. on 2½d. carmine-red ..	2·25	75
104	**162**	4 a. on 4d. ultramarine ..	3·00	80
105	**163**	12 a. on 1s. 3d. deep yellow-green ..	4·00	2·00
106	**164**	1 r. on 1s. 6d. deep grey-blue ..	4·00	80
103/6		.. *Set of* 4	12·00	4·00

KUWAIT 2 RUPEES I

KUWAIT 2 RUPEES II

(9)

KUWAIT 5 RUPEES I

KUWAIT 5 RUPEES II

(10)

KUWAIT 10 RUPEES I

KUWAIT 10 RUPEES II

(11)

Type I (**9/11**). Type-set overprints. Bold (generally thicker) letters with sharp corners and straight edges. Bars close together and usually slightly longer than in Type II.

Type II (**9/11**). Plate-printed overprints. Thinner letters, rounder corners and rough edges. Bars wider apart.

1955–57. *Nos.* 536/8 *of Great Britain surch.*

			I (23.9.55)		II (10.10.57)	
107	**166**	2 r. on 2s. 6d. black-brown	5·00	1·00	50·00	7·00
108	**167**	5 r. on 5s. rose-red	8·00	3·25	75·00	24·00
109	**168**	10 r. on 10s. ultramarine ..	10·00	4·00	£130	75·00
107/9		.. *Set of* 3	21·00	7·50	£225	95·00

1956. *Stamps of Great Britain (Queen Elizabeth II). Wmk St. Edward's Crown, surch as T* **5** *(in two lines only on 2½ and 6 a.).*

110	**154**	½ a. on ½d. orange-red ..	10	10
111		1 a. on 1d. ultramarine ..	15	10
112		1½ a. on 1½d. green ..	15	10
113		2 a. on 2d. red-brown ..	15	10
114	**155**	2½ a. on 2½d. carmine-red ..	30	15
116	**156**	4 a. on 4d. ultramarine ..	4·50	1·00
117	**157**	6 a. on 6d. reddish purple ..	1·00	15
118	**160**	12 a. on 1s. 3d. green ..	9·50	4·00
119	**159**	1 r. on 1s. 6d. grey-blue ..	1·50	10
110/19		.. *Set of* 9	15·00	5·00

(New Currency. 100 naye paise = 1 rupee)

KUWAIT NP 1 NP (12) KUWAIT 3 NP NP (13) KUWAIT 75 NP (14)

1957 (1 June)–**58.** *Stamps of Great Britain (Queen Elizabeth II). W* **165**, *St. Edward's Crown, surch as T* **12** *(1, 15, 25, 40, 50 n.p.),* **14** *(75 n.p.) or* **13** *(others).*

120	**157**	1 n.p. on 5d. brown ..	10	30
121	**154**	3 n.p. on ½d. orange-red ..	20	45
122		6 n.p. on 1d. ultramarine ..	20	45
123		9 n.p. on 1½d. green ..	25	20
124		12 n.p. on 2d. light red-brown ..	30	40
125	**155**	15 n.p. on 2½d. carmine-red (Type I) ..	30	10
		a. Type II (11.58) ..	28·00	40·00
126		20 n.p. on 3d. deep lilac (B.) ..	30	10
127	**156**	25 n.p. on 4d. ultramarine ..	1·50	2·25
128	**157**	40 n.p. on 6d. reddish purple ..	65	10
129	**158**	50 n.p. on 9d. bronze-green ..	4·25	2·75
130	**160**	75 n.p. on 1s. 3d. green ..	4·25	3·00
120/30		.. *Set of* 11	11·00	9·00

15 Shaikh Abdullah as-Salim as-Sabah

(Recess D.L.R.)

1958 (1 Feb). *P* 12½.

131	**35**	5 n.p. bluish green ..	20	10
132		10 n.p. rose-red ..	25	10
136		40 n.p. maroon ..	75	20
131/6		.. *Set of* 3	1·10	25

Nos. 131/6 were only valid for internal use in Kuwait prior to 1 February 1959. Further values were added to this series following the closure of the British Agency Post Offices on 31 January 1959. Responsibility of the postal service then passed to the Kuwait Government and later issues are listed in Part 19 (*Middle East*) of this catalogue.

OFFICIAL STAMPS

KUWAIT SERVICE (O 1) KUWAIT SERVICE (O 2)

1923–24. *Stamps of India (King George V), optd with Type* O **1** *or* O **2** *(rupee values, 15½–16 mm). Star Wmk. P* 14.

O 1	**56**	½ a. green ..	35	7·00
		a. Opt double, one albino ..	75·00	
O 2	**57**	1 a. chocolate ..	40	4·50
		a. Opt double, one albino ..	75·00	
O 3	**58**	1½ a. chocolate (A) ..	1·00	12·00
O 4	**59**	2 a. violet ..	3·00	11·00
		a. Bright purple ..		
O 5	**61**	2 a. 6p. ultramarine ..	2·50	22·00
O 6	**62**	3 a. orange-brown ..	3·25	32·00
O 7		3 a. ultramarine (1924) ..	2·50	19·00
O 8	**63**	4 a. olive-green ..	3·00	30·00
O 9	**65**	8 a. purple ..	4·50	30·00
		a. Mauve ..		
O10	**67**	1 r. brown and green ..	10·00	55·00
		a. Opt double, one albino ..		
O11		2 r. carmine and yellow-brown ..	16·00	80·00
O12		5 r. ultramarine and violet ..	48·00	£180
		a. Opt double, one albino ..		
O13		10 r. green and scarlet ..	90·00	£325
O14		15 r. blue and olive ..	£150	£450
O1/14		.. *Set of* 14	£300	£1100

1929–33. *Stamps of India (Nasik printing) optd as Types* O **1** *(spaced 10 mm) or* O **2** *(14½ mm × 19–20 mm wide). Mult Star wmk. P* 14.

O16	**57**	1 a. chocolate ..	1·25	10·00
O17	**70**	2 a. purple ..	40·00	80·00
O19	**62**	3 a. blue ..	1·60	15·00
O20	**71**	4 a. sage-green ..	4·25	40·00
O21	**65**	8 a. reddish purple ..	3·25	48·00
O22	**66**	12 a. claret ..	14·00	70·00
O23	**67**	1 r. chocolate and green ..	4·00	90·00
O24		2 r. carmine and orange ..	7·00	£140
O25		5 r. ultramarine and purple ..	25·00	£300
O26		10 r. green and scarlet ..	50·00	£450
O27		15 r. blue and olive ..	£100	£800
O16/27		.. *Set of* 11	£200	£1800

Labuan

CROWN COLONY

Stamps of STRAITS SETTLEMENTS were used from 1867 until 1879. Covers of 1864 and 1865 are known from Labuan franked with stamps of INDIA or HONG KONG.

PRICES FOR STAMPS ON COVER

Nos. 1/4	—
Nos. 5/10	*from* × 15
Nos. 11/13	—
Nos. 14/21	*from* × 10
Nos. 22/5	—
Nos. 26/38	*from* × 10
Nos. 39/47	*from* × 100
Nos. 49/50	*from* × 10
Nos. 51/7	*from* × 60
Nos. 62/74	*from* × 15
Nos. 75/9	*from* × 30
Nos. 80/8	*from* × 20
Nos. 89/97	*from* × 15
Nos. 98/110	*from* × 10
Nos. 111/35	*from* × 30
Nos. 136/40	—
Nos. D1/9	*from* × 15

1

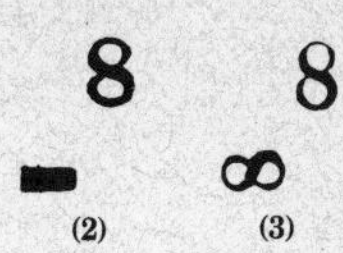

(2) (3)

(Recess D.L.R.)

1879 (May). *Wmk CA over Crown, sideways. P* 14.

1	**1**	2 c. blue-green ..	£500	£450
2		6 c. orange-brown ..	£110	90·00
3		12 c. carmine ..	£650	£350
4		16 c. blue ..	32·00	38·00

This watermark is always found sideways, and extends over two stamps, a single specimen showing only a portion of the Crown or the letters CA, these being tall and far apart. This paper was chiefly used for long fiscal stamps.

1880 (Jan)–**82.** *Wmk Crown CC. P* 14.

5	**1**	2 c. yellow-green ..	8·50	10·00
6		6 c. orange-brown ..	50·00	55·00
7		8 c. carmine (4.82) ..	50·00	55·00
8		10 c. brown ..	45·00	55·00
9		12 c. carmine ..	£130	£140
10		16 c. blue (1881) ..	45·00	40·00
5/10		.. *Set of* 6	£300	£325

1880 (Aug). (*a*) *No.* 9 *surch, with numerals in centre, in black, and the original value obliterated, as T* **2**, *in red or black.*

11	8 c. on 12 c. carmine ..	£500	£400
	a. "8" inverted ..	£550	£450
	b. "12" not obliterated ..	£600	£500
	c. As b. with "8" inverted ..		

(*b*) *No.* 4 *surch with two upright figures and No.* 9 *surch with numeral in centre, and another across the original value as T* **3**.

12	6 c. on 16 c. blue (R.) ..	£850	£500
	a. With one "6" only ..		
13	8 c. on 12 c. carmine ..	£550	£450
	a. Both "8's" upright ..		
	b. Upright "8" inverted ..	£700	£550

EIGHT CENTS (4) Eight Cents (5) One Dollar A.S.H. (6)

1881 (Mar). *No.* 9 *surch as T* **4**.

14	8 c. on 12 c. carmine ..	£110	£130

1881 (June). *No.* 9 *surch as T* **5**.

15	8 c. on 12 c. carmine ..	48·00	50·00
	a. Surch double ..	£325	£325
	b. Surch inverted ..	£3000	
	c. "Eighr" ..	£5000	

The error "Eighr" occurred on R. 2/1 of the first printing, but was soon corrected.

1883. *Wmk Crown CA. P* 14.

17	**1**	2 c. green ..	8·00	9·00
		a. Imperf between (horiz pair) ..	£2500	
18		8 c. carmine ..	80·00	45·00
19		10 c. yellow-brown ..	17·00	25·00
20		16 c. blue ..	50·00	55·00
21		40 c. amber ..	8·00	15·00
17/21		.. *Set of* 5	£150	£130

1883 (May). *No.* 10 *surch "One Dollar A.S.H." by hand, as T* **6**.

22	**1**	$1 on 16 c. blue (R.) ..	£1900	

The initials are those of the postmaster, Mr. A. S. Hamilton.

2 CENTS (7) 2 Cents (8) 2 Cents (9)

1885 (June). *Nos.* 18 *and* 10 *handstamped as T* **7**.

23	**1**	2 c. on 8 c. carmine ..	45·00	
24		2 c. on 16 c. blue ..	£500	£450

1885 (June). *No.* 20 *surch as T* **8**.

25	**1**	2 c. on 16 c. blue ..	65·00	70·00
		a. Surch double ..	—	£1200

1885 (Sept). *No.* 18 *handstamped diag as T* **9**.

26	**1**	2 c. on 8 c. carmine ..	25·00	35·00

1885–86. *Wmk Crown CA. P* 14.

30	**1**	2 c. rose-red (9.85) ..	1·25	3·50
		a. Pale rose-red (5.86) ..	1·25	3·50
31		8 c. deep violet (9.85) ..	12·00	7·00
		a. Mauve (5.86) ..	10·00	7·50
32		10 c. sepia (5.86) ..	4·50	10·00
33		16 c. grey (5.86) ..	45·00	38·00
30/3		.. *Set of* 4	55·00	50·00
30/3 Optd "Specimen"		*Set of* 4	£300	

ISSUES OF BRITISH NORTH BORNEO COMPANY

From 1 January 1890 while remaining a Crown Colony, the administration of Labuan was transferred to the British North Borneo Co, which issued the following stamps.

6 Cents (10) **Two CENTS** (11) **Six CENTS** (12)

1891 (Aug). *T* 1 *surch as T* 10. *P* 14.

34 6 c. on 8 c. deep violet (No. 31) .. .. 26·00 22·00
a. Surch inverted .. .. 40·00 35·00
b. Surch double £130
c. Surch double, one inverted £200
d. "Cents" omitted £200 £200
e. Imperf between (horiz pair) .. ..
35 6 c. on 8 c. mauve (No. 31*a*) .. .. 3·50 3·75
a. Surch inverted .. .. 20·00 20·00
b. Surch double, one inverted .. ..
c. Surch double, both inverted .. £225
d. "6" omitted £200
e. Pair, one without surcharge .. £300 £300
f. Inverted. "Cents" omitted .. £200
g. Pair, one without surch, one surch inverted £325
36 6 c. on 8 c. mauve (R.) (No. 31*a*) .. £275 £130
a. Surch inverted £275 £130
37 6 c. on 16 c. blue (No. 4) .. £1300 £1100
a. Surch inverted £2000 £1600
38 6 c. on 40 c. amber (No. 21) .. £1600 £1700
a. Surch inverted £2100 £1900

There are two different versions of Type 10 with the lines of the surcharge either 1 mm or 2 mm apart.

(Recess D.L.R.)

1892–93. *No wmk. P* 14.

39 1 2 c. rose-lake .. .. 90 3·25
40 6 c. bright green .. .. 4·00 4·50
41 8 c. violet .. .. 2·25 3·75
a. Pale violet (1893) .. .. 2·75 3·75
43 10 c. brown .. .. 3·25 5·50
a. Sepia-brown (1893) .. .. 3·25 6·00
45 12 c. bright blue .. .. 3·25 4·50
46 16 c. grey .. .. 3·25 5·00
47 40 c. ochre .. .. 15·00 20·00
a. Brown-buff (1893) .. .. 17·00 26·00
39/47 .. .. *Set of* 7 29·00 42·00

The 6 c., 12 c., 16 c. and 40 c. are in sheets of 10, as are all the earlier issues. The other values are in sheets of 30.

1892 (Dec). *Nos.* 47 *and* 46 *surch locally as T* 11 *or* 12.

49 1 2 c. on 40 c. ochre (13 December) .. 85·00 60·00
a. Surch inverted £130 £225
50 6 c. on 16 c. grey (20 December) .. £140 90·00
a. Surch inverted £170 £160

There are 10 types of each of these surcharges.

CANCELLED-TO-ORDER. Prices are separately indicated, in a third price column, for stamps showing the recognisable black bars remainder cancellation. Earlier issues of the Company administration were also so treated, but, as postal cancellations were used, these cannot be identified.

(Litho D.L.R.)

1894 (April). *No wmk. P* 14.

51 1 2 c. carmine-pink .. .. 1·10 3·50 20
52 6 c. bright green .. .. 5·50 6·50 20
a. Imperf between (horiz pair) .. £2000
53 8 c. bright mauve .. .. 5·00 5·00 20
54 10 c. brown .. .. 8·50 7·50 20
55 12 c. pale blue .. .. 10·00 13·00 25
56 16 c. grey .. .. 14·00 19·00 25
57 40 c. orange-buff .. .. 16·00 25·00 30
51/57 .. .. *Set of* 7 55·00 70·00 1·25
51/57 H/S "Specimen" .. *Set of* 7 £100

Collectors are warned against forgeries of this issue.

PERFORATION. There are a number of small variations in the perforation of the Waterlow issues of 1894 to 1905 which we believe to be due to irregularity of the pins rather than different perforators.

In the following lists, stamps perf 12, 12½, 13 or compound are described as perf 12–13, stamps perf 13½, 14 or compound are described as perf 13½–14 and those perf 14½, 15 or compound are listed as perf 14½–15. In addition the 13½–14 perforation exists compound with 14½–15 and with 12–13, whilst perf 16 comes from a separate perforator.

13

LABUAN 40 CENTS (14)

1894 (May)–**96.** *T* 24/32 *of North Borneo (colours changed), with "LABUAN" engraved on vignette plate as T* 13 *(8, 12, 24 c.) or horizontally (others). P* 14½–15.

(a) Name and central part of design in black

62 24 1 c. grey-mauve .. .. 1·50 3·00 20
a. Imperf between (vert pair) .. £275 £200
b. Perf 13½–14 .. .. 3·00 4·00
c. Perf 13½–14, comp 14½–15 ..
d. Perf 13½–14, comp 12–13 .. 7·00 6·00 —
e. Perf 12–13 .. ..
63 25 2 c. blue .. .. 2·25 3·25 20
a. Imperf (pair) £275
b. Perf 13½–14 .. .. 2·25 3·50 —
c. Perf 13½–14, comp 14½–15 ..
d. Perf 13½–14, comp 12–13 ..
e. Perf 12–13 .. ..
64 26 3 c. ochre .. .. 2·00 4·50 20
a. Perf 13½–14 .. .. 2·75 4·50 —
b. Perf 13½–14, comp 14½–15 ..
c. Perf 13½–14, comp 12–13 ..
d. Perf 12–13 .. ..
65 27 5 c. green .. .. 9·00 8·50 20
a. Perf 13½–14 .. .. 11·00 4·00 —
ab. Imperf between (horiz pair) ..
b. Perf 13½–14, comp 12–13 .. 10·00
67 28 6 c. brown-lake .. .. 2·25 4·50 20
a. Imperf (pair) .. .. £350 — £225
b. Perf 13½–14 .. .. — — 1·25
c. Perf 13½–14, comp 14½–15 .. — — 70
d. Perf 13½–14, comp 12–13 ..
e. Perf 12–13 .. ..
68 29 8 c. rose-red .. .. 8·00 12·00 30
a. Perf 13½–14 .. .. 8·00 12·00 —
69 8 c. pink (1896) .. .. 5·00 12·00 30
a. Perf 13½–14 .. .. 9·00
70 30 12 c. orange-vermilion .. .. 11·00 22·00 30
a. Perf 13½–14 .. .. — 25·00 2·00
b. Perf 12–13 .. ..
c. Perf 13½–14, comp 12–13 ..
71 31 18 c. olive-brown .. .. 15·00 22·00 30
a. Perf 13½–14 .. .. 18·00
72 18 c. olive-bistre (1896) .. .. 18·00 22·00 30
a. Perf 13½–14 .. .. 18·00 22·00 —
b. Perf 13½–14, comp 12–13 ..

(b) Name and central part in blue

73 32 24 c. pale mauve .. .. 11·00 20·00 30
a. Perf 13½–14 .. .. 11·00 20·00 —
74 24 c. dull lilac (1896) .. .. 11·00 20·00 30
a. Perf 13½–14 .. .. 11·00 20·00 —
62/74 .. .. *Set of* 9 50·00 85·00 2·00
62/74 Optd "Specimen" .. *Set of* 9 £120

1895 (June). *No.* 83 *of North Borneo* ($1 *inscr* "STATE OF NORTH BORNEO") *surch as T* 14.

75 32*c* 4 c. on $1 scarlet .. .. 90 1·10 30
76 10 c. on $1 scarlet .. .. 1·25 1·40 30
77 20 c. on $1 scarlet .. .. 8·00 6·00 30
78 30 c. on $1 scarlet .. .. 10·00 11·00 30
79 40 c. on $1 scarlet .. .. 8·00 8·00 30
75/9 .. .. *Set of* 5 25·00 25·00 1·40
75/9 Optd "Specimen" .. *Set of* 5 80·00

No. 76 exists with the figures of the surcharge 2½ mm away from "CENTS". The normal setting has a space of 4 mm. Examples of the narrow setting have, so far, only been seen on cancelled-to-order stamps.

LABUAN (15) **1846 JUBILEE 1896** (16) **4 CENTS** (17)

1896. *T* 32*a to* 32*c of North Borneo (as Nos.* 81 *to* 83, *but colours changed) optd with T* 15.

80 25 c. green .. .. 13·00 13·00 50
a. Opt omitted .. .. 7·00 — 1·25
b. Imperf (pair) .. ..
ba. Opt omitted .. .. 20·00
bb. Stamps ptd double, one inverted
81 50 c. maroon .. .. 15·00 16·00 50
a. Opt omitted .. .. 8·00 — 1·25
b. Imperf (pair) .. ..
ba. Opt omitted .. .. 20·00
bb. Stamps ptd double
82 $1 blue .. .. 24·00 16·00 50
a. Opt omitted .. .. 10·00 — 1·25
b. Imperf (pair) .. ..
ba. Opt omitted .. .. 20·00
80/82 Optd "Specimen" .. *Set of* 3 60·00

Nos. 80bb and 81bb are from waste sheets subsequently sold by the British North Borneo Company to collectors.

1896 (24 Sept). *Jubilee of Cession of Labuan to Gt Britain. Nos.* 62 *to* 68 *optd with T* 16. *P* 14½–15.

83 1 c. black and grey-mauve .. .. 10·00 12·00 50
a. Opt double .. .. £100 £100 —
b. Opt in orange .. .. £110 £110 —
c. "JEBILEE" .. .. — £250 £180
d. "JUBILE" (R. 3/10) ..
e. Perf 13½–14 .. .. 10·00
f. Perf 13½–14, comp 12–13 .. 10·00 8·50 —
g. Perf 12–13 .. ..
84 2 c. black and blue .. .. 12·00 10·00 50
a. Imperf horiz (vert pair) .. £200
b. "JEBILEE" £350 £375
c. "JUBILE" (R. 3/10) ..
d. Perf 13½–14 .. .. 12·00 10·00 —
e. Perf 13½–14, comp 14½–15 ..
f. Perf 13½–14, comp 12–13 ..
85 3 c. black and ochre .. .. 13·00 15·00 50
a. Opt double £100 £100
b. Opt treble £650
c. "JEBILEE" .. .. — £700 —
d. Perf 13½–14 .. .. 20·00 20·00 —
e. Perf 13½–14, comp 14½–15 ..
86 5 c. black and green .. .. 22·00 14·00 50
a. Opt double .. .. £120 £120 —
b. Perf 13½–14 .. .. 22·00 14·00 —
c. Perf 13½–14, comp 12–13 ..
87 6 c. black and brown-lake .. .. 11·00 13·00 50
a. Opt double .. .. £150 £150 —
b. "JUBILE" (R. 3/10) .. £700
c. Perf 13½–14, comp 14½–15 ..
88 8 c. black and pink .. .. 14·00 8·50 50
a. Perf 13½–14 .. .. 14·00 8·50 2·75
b. Perf 13½–14, comp 14½–15 ..
83/88 .. .. *Set of* 6 75·00 60·00 —
83/88 Optd "Specimen" .. *Set of* 6 £140

No. 84b is known in a vertical strip of 3 imperf horizonally except at the base of the bottom stamp.

1897 (Apr)–**1901.** *T* 34/45 *of North Borneo (colours changed) with "LABUAN" engraved on vignette plate as T* 13 *(8, 10, 12 24 c.) or horizontally (others). Name and central part in black (24 c. in blue). P* 13½–14.

89 34 1 c. greyish purple (*p* 14½–15) .. 2·25 2·75 20
a. Perf 13½–14, comp 14½–15 ..
b. Brown (1901) .. .. 2·25 3·50 —
ba. Perf 14½–15 .. .. 2·75
bb. Perf 16 .. .. 5·50 7·00 —
90 35 2 c. blue .. .. 4·50 2·25 20
a. Imperf between (vert pair) .. † † £200
b. Perf 14½–15 .. ..
c. Perf 13½–14, comp 12–13 .. 12·00
d. Perf 16 .. ..
91 36 3 c. ochre .. .. 5·00 5·50 20
a. Imperf between (vert pair) .. † † —
b. Perf 14½–15 .. .. 5·50 4·50 —
c. Perf 13½–14, comp 12–13 ..
92 38 5 c. green .. .. 12·00 14·00 25
a. Perf 14½–15 .. .. 15·00 18·00 —
b. Perf 13½–14, comp 12–13 ..
93 39 6 c. brown-lake .. .. 4·50 10·00 25
a. Imperf between (vert pair) .. † † £200
b. Perf 14½–15 .. .. 3·00 11·00 —
c. Perf 13½–14, comp 12–13 .. — — 3·00
94 40 8 c. rose-red .. .. — — 30
a. Perf 14½–15 .. .. 11·00 7·00 —
b. Perf 13½–14, comp 12–13 .. — — 2·75
c. Vermilion .. .. 4·50 — 30
ca. Perf 16 .. .. — — 3·00
95 42 12 c. vermilion .. .. 22·00 30·00 40
a. Perf 14½–15 .. .. 12·00 24·00 —
96 44 18 c. olive-bistre .. .. 15·00 18·00 40
a. Imperf between (vert pair) .. † † —
b. Perf 16 .. .. 12·00 20·00 —
97 45 24 c. grey-lilac .. .. 9·00 18·00 40
a. Perf 14½–15 .. .. 7·50
89/97 .. .. *Set of* 9 55·00 90·00 2·25
89/97 Optd "Specimen" .. *Set of* 9 £120

The 12, 18 and 24 c. above were errors; in the 12 c., "LABUAN" is over the value at the top; the 18 c. has "POSTAL REVENUE" instead of "POSTAGE AND REVENUE", and the 24 c. is without "POSTAGE AND REVENUE".

1897 (Nov)–**98.** *(a) Types of North Borneo (colours changed), with "LABUAN" engraved on the vignette plate as in T* 13. *P* 13½–14.

98 42 12 c. black and vermilion (3.98) .. † — 1·50
a. Perf 14½–15 .. .. 18·00 22·00 —
b. Perf 13½–14, comp 14½–15 ..
c. Perf 16 .. .. 22·00
99 46 18 c. black and olive-bistre ..
a. Perf 14½–15 .. .. 50·00 60·00 —
b. Perf 16 .. .. † — 6·50
100 47 24 c. blue and lilac-brown .. 12·00 27·00 —
a. Perf 14½–15 .. .. 12·00 27·00 —
b. Perf 13½–14, comp 12–13 ..
c. Perf 16 .. ..
d. Blue and ochre (*p* 14½–15) ..
98/100 Optd "Specimen" .. *Set of* 2 38·00

In the 12 c. "LABUAN" is now correctly placed at foot of stamp. The 18 c. and 24 c. have the inscriptions on the stamps corrected, but the 18 c. still has "LABUAN" *over* the value at foot, and was further corrected as follows.

(b) As No. 99, *but* "LABUAN" *at top*

101 46 18 c. black and olive-bistre (Optd S. £25) 22·00 27·00
a. Perf 14½–15 .. .. 22·00 27·00
b. Perf 13½–14, comp 12–13 .. 16·00 22·00
c. Perf 12–13 .. ..

1899. *Surch with T* 17. *(a) P* 14½–15.

102 38 4 c. on 5 c. (No. 92a) .. .. 12·00 20·00
103 39 4 c. on 6 c. (No. 93b) .. .. 12·00 14·00
a. Perf 13½–14 .. .. 16·00
b. Perf 13½–14, comp 12–13 ..
104 40 4 c. on 8 c. (No. 94a) .. .. — 25·00
a. Perf 13½–14 .. .. 11·00 20·00
b. Perf 13½–14, comp 12–13 .. 17·00
c. Perf 12–13 .. ..
105 42 4 c. on 12 c. (No. 98a) .. .. 12·00 20·00
a. Perf 13½–14 .. .. 18·00
b. Perf 16 .. .. 18·00 25·00
c. Perf 13½–14, comp 12–13 ..
106 46 4 c. on 18 c (No. 101a) .. .. 12·00 15·00
a. Surch double £225 £275
107 47 4 c. on 24 c. (No. 100a) .. .. 11·00 16·00
a. Perf 13½–14 .. .. 11·00 20·00
b. Perf 13½–14, comp 12–13 .. 14·00 14·00
c. Perf 16 .. .. 20·00

(b) P 14

108 32*a* 4 c. on 25 c. (No. 80) .. .. 5·50 7·50
109 32*b* 4 c. on 50 c. (No. 81) .. .. 5·50 7·50
110 32*c* 4 c. on $1 (No. 82) .. .. 5·50 7·50
102/110 Optd "Specimen" .. *Set of* 9 £120

The 1 c., 2 c. and 3 c. values of this set were also surcharged "4 CENTS" but were not issued. They exist overprinted "Specimen" (*Price £75 the set of three*).

1900–02. *Types of North Borneo with* "LABUAN" *engraved on the vignette plate as in T* 13, *in green on* 16 *c. P* 13½–14.

111 35 2 c. black and green .. .. 3·50 2·50 20
a. Perf 13½–14, comp 12–13 ..
112 37 4 c. black and yellow-brown .. 3·50 10·00 25
a. Imperf between (vert pair) .. £200
b. Perf 13½–14, comp 12–13 ..
113 4 c. black and carmine (8.1900) ..
a. Perf 14½–15 .. .. 5·50 2·50 20
b. Perf 13½–14, comp 12–13 .. 5·00 2·50 —
c. Perf 16 .. .. 10·00 3·00 —
114 38 5 c. black and pale blue ..
a. Perf 13½–14, comp 12–13 .. 13·00 18·00 50
115 41 10 c. brown & slate-lilac (*p* 14½–15) (1902) ..
116 43 16 c. green and chestnut (1902) .. 20·00 32·00 40
a. Perf 13½–14, comp 12–13 .. 25·00 — 1·50
b. Perf 12–13 .. .. 25·00 32·00 —
c. Perf 14½–15 .. ..
111/16 Optd "Specimen" .. *Set of* 6 £100

18 **4 cents** (19)

(Recess Waterlow)

1902 (Sept)–**03**. *P* 13½–14.
116*d* **18** 1 c. black and purple (10.03) .. 1·50 2·50 20
da. Perf 14½–15 .. — 3·75 —
117 2 c. black and green .. 1·50 2·00 20
a. Perf 14½–15 .. — 3·50 —
117*b* 3 c. black and sepia (10.03) .. 1·60 2·50 20
118 4 c. black and carmine .. 1·50 2·00 20
a. Perf 14½–15 ..
119 8 c. black and vermilion .. 1·00 3·00 20
a. Perf 14½–15 ..
120 10 c. brown and slate-blue 1·50 3·50 20
a. Imperf between (vert pair) † † £300
b. Perf 14½–15 ..
121 12 c. black and yellow .. 2·00 4·00 20
a. Perf 16 .. 2·00
122 16 c. green and brown .. 1·50 4·50 20
a. Imperf between (vert pair) .. † — —
123 18 c. black and pale brown 1·50 5·00 20
124 25 c. green and greenish blue .. 1·50 5·50 20
a. Perf 14½–15 ..
b. Error. Black and greenish blue .. — † £180
125 50 c. dull purple and lilac 7·00 13·00 30
a. Perf 13½–14, comp 12–13 .. 8·00
126 $1 claret and orange .. 2·50 13·00 40
a. Perf 14½–15 ..
116*d*/26 .. *Set of* 12 22·00 55·00 2·40
116*d*/26 Optd "Specimen" .. *Set of* 12 £150

1904 (Dec). *Issues of* 1895 *and* 1897–8 *surch with T* **19**.

(*a*) *P* 14½–15.
127 **38** 4 c. on 5 c. (No. 92a) .. 12·00 20·00 1·00
128 **39** 4 c. on 6 c. (No. 93b) .. 10·00 20·00 1·00
129 **40** 4 c. on 8 c. (No. 94a) .. 12·00 20·00 1·00
130 **42** 4 c. on 12 c. (No. 98a) .. 14·00 20·00 1·00
a. Perf 16 .. 15·00 20·00
131 **46** 4 c. on 18 c. (No. 101) (*p* 13½–14) .. 12·00 20·00 1·00
a. Perf 13½–14, comp 12–13 .. 15·00
b. Perf 12–13 ..
132 **47** 4 c. on 24 c. (No. 100a) .. 10·00 20·00 1·00
a. Perf 13½–14 .. 10·00
b. Perf 13½–14, comp 12–13 .. 15·00
c. Perf 16 .. 20·00

(*b*) *P* 14
133 **32*a*** 4 c. on 25 c. (No. 80) .. 8·00 17·00 1·00
134 **32*b*** 4 c. on 50 c. (No. 81) .. 8·00 17·00 1·00
a. Surch double .. £200
b. Surch triple ..
135 **32*c*** 4 c. on $1 (No. 82) .. 8·00 17·00 1·00

LABUAN (20) **LABUAN** (21)

1905 (Feb–Nov). *Nos.* 81, 83 (*in Labuan colour*), *and* 84/6 *of North Borneo optd locally with T* **20** (25 c., $2) *or* **21** *others*).
136 **32*a*** 25 c. indigo .. £600 † £350
137 **32*c*** $1 blue .. † £350
138 **32*d*** $2 dull green .. £2250 † £700
139 **14** $5 bright purple .. £2750 † £700
140 **15** $10 brown (11.05) .. † † £3000
Dangerous forgeries exist.
The overprint on No. 138 is 12 mm long.
No. 137 is said to have been issued in 1899.

POSTAGE DUE STAMPS

POSTAGE DUE

(D 1)

1901. *Optd with Type* D 1, *reading vertically upwards. P* 13½–14.
D1 **35** 2 c. black and green (111) .. 7·50 9·00 30
a. Opt double .. £160
b. Perf 13½–14, comp 12–13 ..
D2 **36** 3 c. black and ochre (91) .. 11·00 40·00 40
a. Perf 13½–14, comp 12–13 ..
D3 **37** 4 c. black and carmine (113) .. 13·00 40·00 40
a. Opt double .. † † £130
b. Perf 14½–15 .. 13·00
D4 **38** 5 c. black and pale blue (114) .. 17·00 40·00 50
a. Perf 14½–15 .. 17·00
b. Perf 13½–14, comp 12–13 ..
D5 **39** 6 c. black and brown-lake (93) .. 10·00 40·00 50
a. Perf 14½–15 ..
b. Perf 16 .. 18·00
D6 **40** 8 c. black and vermilion (94c) .. 18·00 40·00 60
a. Frame inverted (*p* 14½–15) † † £2750
b. Perf 14½–15 .. 14·00
c. Perf 16 .. 20·00
d. Black and rose-red (94) .. 25·00
da. Perf 14½–15 .. — — 6·50
db. Perf 13½–14, comp 12–13 ..
D7 **42** 12 c. black and vermilion (98) .. 35·00 38·00 2·00
a. Opt reading downwards † † £160
b. Perf 14½–15 .. 38·00
D8 **46** 18 c. blk & ol-bistre (101) (*p* 14½–15) 11·00 40·00 1·00
D9 **47** 24 c. blue and lilac-brown (100) .. 18·00 40·00 1·00
a. Perf 13½–14, comp 12–13 ..
b. Perf 14½–15 .. 20·00
ba. Blue and ochre .. 24·00
c. Perf 16 .. 18·00
D1/9 .. *Set of* 9 £120 £300 6·00

By Letters Patent dated 30 October 1906, Labuan was incorporated with Straits Settlements and ceased issuing its own stamps. In 1946 it became part of the Colony of North Borneo.

Lagos

A British Consul was established at Lagos during 1851 as part of the anti-slavery policy, but the territory was not placed under British administration until the treaty of August 1861.

Although a postal service had been established by the British G.P.O. in 1851 no postal markings were supplied to Lagos until 1859. The British G.P.O. retained control of the postal service until 1874, when it became the responsibility of the colonial authorities.

For illustrations of handstamp types see BRITISH POST OFFICES ABROAD notes, following GREAT BRITAIN.

CROWNED-CIRCLE HANDSTAMPS

CC1 CC 4 LAGOS (19.2.1859) .. *Price on cover* £1000

PRICES FOR STAMPS ON COVER

Nos. 1/9	*from* × 6
Nos. 10/41	*from* × 5
No. 42	*from* × 15
Nos. 44/53	*from* × 5
Nos. 54/63	*from* × 4

PRINTERS. All the stamps of Lagos were typographed by D.L.R.

1

1874 (10 June)–**75**. *Wmk Crown CC. P* 12½.
1 **1** 1d. lilac-mauve .. 48·00 28·00
2 2d. blue .. 48·00 26·00
3 3d. red-brown (3.75) .. 90·00 40·00
4 3d. red-brown and chestnut .. 75·00 45·00
5 4d. carmine .. 60·00 40·00
6 6d. blue-green .. 75·00 10·00
8 1s. orange (value 15½ mm) (3.75) .. £275 £120
9 1s. orange (value 16½ mm) .. £225 55·00
1/9 .. *Set of* 6 £475 £175

1876. *Wmk Crown CC. P* 14.
10 **1** 1d. lilac-mauve .. 32·00 14·00
11 2d. blue .. 35·00 11·00
12 3d. red-brown .. 90·00 18·00
13 3d. chestnut .. £110 30·00
14 4d. carmine .. £150 11·00
a. Wmk sideways .. £800 £120
15 6d. green .. 70·00 6·00
16 1s. orange (value 16½ mm long) .. £425 60·00
10/16 .. *Set of* 6 £700 £130

1882 (June). *Wmk Crown CA. P* 14.
17 **1** 1d. lilac-mauve .. 15·00 10·00
18 2d. blue .. £100 4·75
19 3d. chestnut .. 10·00 5·00
20 4d. carmine .. 90·00 10·00
17/20 .. *Set of* 4 £190 27·00

1884 (Dec)–**86**. *New values and colours. Wmk Crown CA. P* 14.
21 **1** ½d. dull green (2.86) .. 40 20
22 1d. rose-carmine .. 60 25
23 2d. grey .. 28·00 5·00
24 4d. pale violet .. 55·00 8·50
25 6d. olive-green .. 5·00 16·00
26 1s. orange (3.85) .. 5·00 12·00
27 2s. 6d. olive-black (10.86) .. £275 £250
28 5s. blue (10.86) .. £550 £350
29 10s. purple-brown (10.86) .. £1200 £800
21/9 .. *Set of* 9 £1800 £1250
27/9 Optd "Specimen" .. *Set of* 3 £500
We would warn collectors against clever forgeries of Nos. 27 to 29 on genuinely watermarked paper.

2½ PENNY A

2½ PENNY B

1887 (Mar)–**1902**. *Wmk Crown CA. P* 14.
30 **1** 2d. dull mauve and blue .. 1·25 1·00
31 2½d. ultramarine (A) (12.90) .. 1·25 1·75
a. Larger letters of value (B) .. 18·00 17·00
b. Blue (A) .. 80·00 50·00
32 3d. dull mauve and chestnut (4.91) 2·50 3·25
33 4d. dull mauve and black .. 2·00 1·75
34 5d. dull mauve and green (2.94) 2·00 11·00
35 6d. dull mauve and mauve .. 4·50 3·00
a. Dull mauve and carmine (10.02) 4·50 12·00
36 7½d. dull mauve and carmine (2.94) 2·00 18·00
37 10d. dull mauve and yellow (2.94) 2·75 13·00
38 1s. yellow-green and black .. 3·00 12·00
a. Blue-green and black .. 4·00 14·00
39 2s. 6d. green and carmine .. 22·00 35·00
40 5s. green and blue .. 32·00 70·00
41 10s. green and brown .. 60·00 £110
30/41 .. *Set of* 12 £120 £250
30/41 Optd "Specimen" .. *Set of* 12 £275

HALF PENNY

(2)

3

1893 (Aug). *No.* 33 *surch with T* **2**.
42 **1** ½d. on 4d. dull mauve and black .. 2·25 2·50
a. Surch double .. 55·00 55·00
b. Surch treble .. 75·00
c. Error. ½d. on 2d. (No. 30) .. £11000 £11000
There were four settings of this surcharge, a scarce setting in which "HALF PENNY" is 16½ mm and three others in which the length is 16 mm. Of No. 42c, one copy is known unused and one used.

1904 (22 Jan–Nov). *Wmk Crown CA. P* 14.
44 **3** ½d. dull green and green .. 1·50 5·50
45 1d. purple and black/*red* .. 60 15
46 2d. dull purple and blue .. 6·00 12·00
47 2½d. dull purple and blue/*blue* (B) .. 1·00 1·50
a. Smaller letters of value as A .. 3·00 7·50
48 3d. dull purple and brown .. 1·00 2·75
49 6d. dull purple and mauve .. 30·00 10·00
50 1s. green and black .. 32·00 28·00
51 2s. 6d. green and carmine .. 70·00 £100
52 5s. green and blue .. £150 £250
53 10s. green and brown (Nov) .. £300 £550
44/53 .. *Set of* 10 £550 £850
44/53 Optd "Specimen" .. *Set of* 10 £250

1904–05. *Wmk Mult Crown CA. P* 14
54 **3** ½d. dull green and green, **OC** (30.10.04) 2·00 1·75
55 1d. purple and black/*red* **OC** (22.10.04) 30 10
56 2d. dull purple and blue, **OC** (2.05) .. 1·75 75
57 2½d. dull purple and blue/*blue* (B), **C** (13.10.05) .. 1·50 13·00
a. Smaller letters of value as A .. 55·00 £100
58 3d. dull purple and brown, **OC** (27.4.05) 2·50 90
59 6d. dull purple and mauve, **OC** (31.10.05) .. 2·50 1·25
60 1s. green and black, **OC** (15.10.04) .. 3·00 1·75
61 2s. 6d. green and carmine, **OC** (3.12.04) 10·00 17·00
62 5s. green and blue, **OC** (1.05) .. 14·00 48·00
63 10s. green and brown, **OC** (3.12.04) .. 45·00 90·00
54/63 .. *Set of* 10 75·00 £150

Lagos was incorporated into the Colony and Protectorate of Southern Nigeria, previously formed from Niger Coast Protectorate and part of the Niger Company territories, on 16 February 1906. Stamps of Lagos were then authorised for use throughout Southern Nigeria.

Leeward Islands

Issues superseding the earlier issues, or in concurrent use with the later issues (from 1903), of Antigua, British Virgin Islands, Dominica (to 31 December 1939), Montserrat, Nevis, St. Christopher and St. Kitts-Nevis.

PRICES FOR STAMPS ON COVER TO 1945

Nos. 1/8	*from* × 10
Nos. 9/16	*from* × 12
Nos. 17/19	*from* × 8
Nos. 20/8	*from* × 5
Nos. 29/35	*from* × 4
Nos. 36/45	*from* × 5
Nos. 46/57	*from* × 4
Nos. 58/87	*from* × 5
Nos. 88/91	*from* × 6
Nos. 92/4	*from* × 10
Nos. 95/114	*from* × 5

PRINTERS. All the stamps of Leeward Islands were typographed by De La Rue & Co, Ltd, London, *except where otherwise stated.*

1

2

1890. *Name and value in second colour. Wmk Crown CA. P* 14.
1 **1** ½d. dull mauve and green .. 70 40
2 1d. dull mauve and rose .. 1·25 10
3 2½d. dull mauve and blue .. 2·75 15
4 4d. dull mauve and orange .. 2·75 7·00
5 6d. dull mauve and brown .. 4·50 6·50
6 7d. dull mauve and slate .. 1·75 8·50
7 **2** 1s. green and carmine .. 11·00 26·00
8 5s. green and blue .. £130 £200
1/8 .. *Set of* 8 £140 £225
1/8 Optd "Specimen" .. *Set of* 8 £200
The colours of this issue are fugitive.

THE KING GEORGE VI ALBUM

Stanley Gibbons proudly present a superb reprint of the prestigious King George VI Stamp Album.

Attractively bound in rich red buckram with matching head and tail bands and gold blocked on the front and spine it is presented in a matching library slip case. The pages are of superior quality cream cartridge interleaved throughout with glassine and fully guarded to allow for expansion. They are attractively laid out and written up to provide the perfect setting for a straightforward collection of this popular period and include spaces for watermark changes, officials, postage dues and express and special delivery issues.

Item 3419 **King George VI Stamp Album**

THE NEW IMPERIAL ALBUM

Another old favourite reprinted and reintroduced by popular demand!

The two-volume New Imperial, successor to the Imperial Album first published in 1873, provides spaces for the stamps of the British Empire, Egypt and Iraq, from SG 1 up to the end of the reign of King George V (1840 to mid-1936).

Provision is made for major variations of watermark, perforation and shade as well as postage dues, officials, special delivery stamps etc. Pages are attractively laid out in traditional style with spaces for stamps on the right hand page and, on the facing leaf, an illustrated catalogue for easy identification.

The New Imperial is bound in red buckram and gold blocked on the front and spine. The superior quality cartridge leaves are fully guarded to allow for expansion. Boxed.

Item 3275 **New Imperial Album** (two volume set)

Please note that neither of these albums is designed to be used with hingeless mounts.

For further details visit your favourite stamp shop or write to:

Stanley Gibbons Publications Ltd.,
5 Parkside, Christchurch Road, Ringwood, Hampshire BH24 3SH. Telephone 0425 472363

SUPERB KGVI

SG110. A sup. u/m plate block of 4 from the 1st printing showing R9/6 (Right pane) D I flaw. A MAJOR RARITY – ORIGINALLY ONLY THOUGHT TO EXIST ON THE OLIVE BACK PRINTING. BRILLIANT EXHIBITION ITEM

For this and other items of similar status, phone or write:

GOLDCAST (PHILATELICS)

FOR THE VERY BEST IN KING GEORGE VI

43 LONDON STREET, SOUTHPORT
MERSEYSIDE PR9 0TH. Tel: (0704) 43985

WE ALSO WISH TO BUY ITEMS OF SIMILAR QUALITY

LEEWARD IS.

King George VI

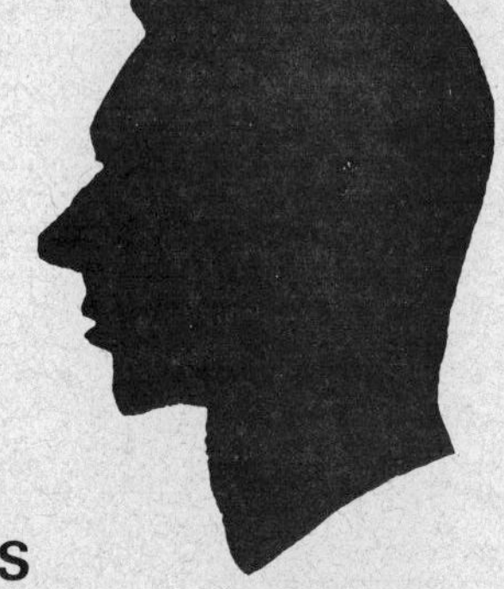

- **BASIC STAMPS**
  in Multiples,
  Plate Blocks,
  Sheets & Panes
- **VARIETIES**
  per S.G., B. & K.,
  Halward, or unlisted
- **LISTED SHADES and ALL PRINTINGS**

Send us your Wants Lists, stating: mint, unmounted mint (N/H) or fine used. Prices and/or photocopies by return post or fax.

No matter how simple or specialised your requirements in King George VI philately, we will try to help you.

We do not stock postal history, but we do stock postmarks (all reigns).

Contact **Stuart Babbington** or **Dickon Pollard** at:

J. EDWARD SELLARS (Philatelists) LTD.
Eclipse Office Park, High Street,
Staple Hill, Bristol BS16 5EL, England
Tel: 0272 560408
Fax: 0272 701329

SEXAGENARY 1897 VR

(3)

One Penny

(4)

One Penny

(5)

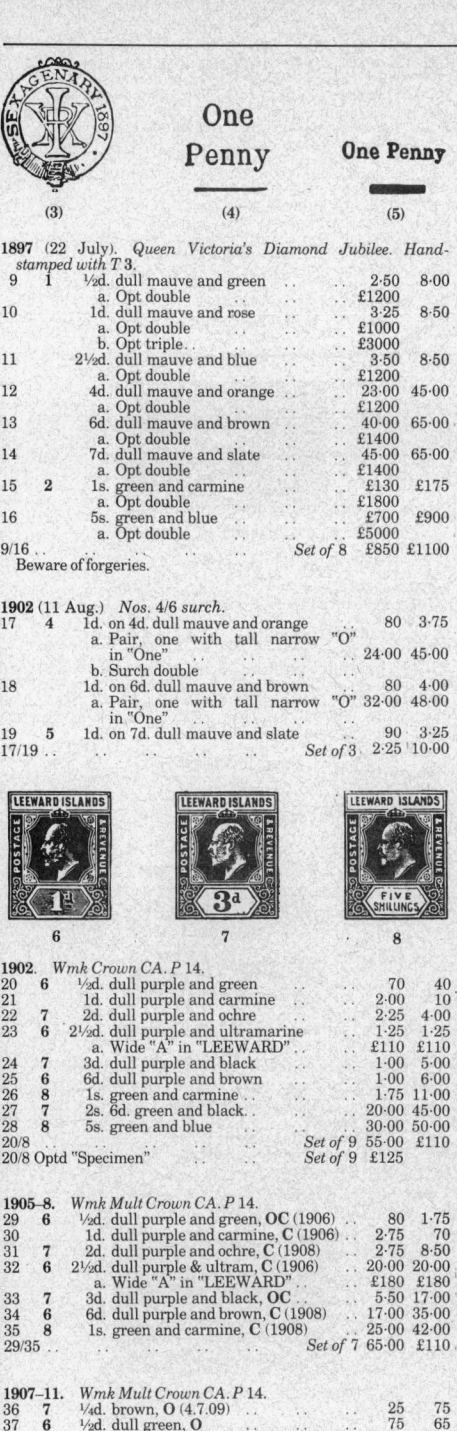

1897 (22 July). *Queen Victoria's Diamond Jubilee. Handstamped with T* 3.

9 1 ½d. dull mauve and green .. .. 2·50 8·00
a. Opt double £1200
10 1d. dull mauve and rose .. .. 3·25 8·50
a. Opt double £1000
b. Opt triple £3000
11 2½d. dull mauve and blue .. .. 3·50 8·50
a. Opt double £1200
12 4d. dull mauve and orange .. .. 23·00 45·00
a. Opt double £1200
13 6d. dull mauve and brown .. .. 40·00 65·00
a. Opt double £1400
14 7d. dull mauve and slate .. .. 45·00 65·00
a. Opt double £1400
15 2 1s. green and carmine £130 £175
a. Opt double £1800
16 5s. green and blue £700 £900
a. Opt double £5000
9/16 .. .. *Set of* 8 £850 £1100
Beware of forgeries.

1902 (11 Aug.) *Nos. 4/6 surch.*

17 4 1d. on 4d. dull mauve and orange .. 80 3·75
a. Pair, one with tall narrow "O" in "One" .. .. 24·00 45·00
b. Surch double
18 1d. on 6d. dull mauve and brown .. 80 4·00
a. Pair, one with tall narrow "O" in "One" .. 32·00 48·00
19 5 1d. on 7d. dull mauve and slate .. 90 3·25
17/19 .. .. *Set of* 3 2·25 10·00

LEEWARD ISLANDS POSTAGE & REVENUE 1d — 6

LEEWARD ISLANDS POSTAGE & REVENUE 3d — 7

LEEWARD ISLANDS POSTAGE & REVENUE FIVE SHILLINGS — 8

1902. *Wmk Crown CA. P* 14.

20 6 ½d. dull purple and green 70 40
21 1d. dull purple and carmine .. .. 2·00 10
22 7 2d. dull purple and ochre .. .. 2·25 4·00
23 6 2½d. dull purple and ultramarine .. 1·25 1·25
a. Wide "A" in "LEEWARD" .. £110 £110
24 7 3d. dull purple and black .. .. 1·00 5·00
25 6 6d. dull purple and brown .. .. 1·00 6·00
26 8 1s. green and carmine .. .. 1·75 11·00
27 7 2s. 6d. green and black .. .. 20·00 45·00
28 8 5s. green and blue .. .. 30·00 50·00
20/8 .. .. *Set of* 9 55·00 £110
20/8 Optd "Specimen" .. .. *Set of* 9 £125

1905–8. *Wmk Mult Crown CA. P* 14.

29 6 ½d. dull purple and green, **OC** (1906) .. 80 1·75
30 1d. dull purple and carmine, **C** (1906) .. 2·75 70
31 7 2d. dull purple and ochre, **C** (1908) .. 2·75 8·50
32 6 2½d. dull purple & ultram, **C** (1906) .. 20·00 20·00
a. Wide "A" in "LEEWARD" .. £180 £180
33 7 3d. dull purple and black, **OC** .. 5·50 17·00
34 6 6d. dull purple and brown, **C** (1908) .. 17·00 35·00
35 8 1s. green and carmine, **C** (1908) .. 25·00 42·00
29/35 .. .. *Set of* 7 65·00 £110

1907–11. *Wmk Mult Crown CA. P* 14.

36 7 ¼d. brown, **O** (4.7.09) 25 75
37 6 ½d. dull green, **O** 75 65
38 1d. bright red, **O** .. .. 1·00 35
a. Rose-carmine .. .. 10·00 55
39 7 2d. grey, **O** (1911) .. .. 1·00 6·00
40 6 2½d. bright blue, **O** .. .. 1·40 2·50
a. Wide "A" in "LEEWARD" .. £100 £100
41 7 3d. purple/*yellow*, **C** (1910) .. 1·00 4·25
42 6 6d. dull and bright purple, **C** (1911) .. 3·00 5·50
43 8 1s. black/*green*, **C** (1911) .. 2·75 14·00
44 7 2s. 6d. black and red/*blue*, **C** (1911) .. 24·00 42·00
45 8 5s. green and red/*yellow*, **C** (1911) .. 26·00 48·00
36/45 .. .. *Set of* 10 55·00 £110
36/45 Optd "Specimen" .. .. *Set of* 10 £170

10

11

12

13

1912–22. *Wmk Mult Crown CA. P* 14.

46 10 ¼d. brown, **O** 30 20
a. Pale brown 30 40
47 11 ½d. yellow-green, **O** (2.13) .. .. 1·00 40
a. Deep green .. .. .. 1·25 50
48 1d. carmine-red, **O** 75 20
a. Bright scarlet (1915) 90 25
49 10 2d. slate-grey, **O** (2.13) .. .. 60 1·40
50 11 2½d. bright blue, **O** .. .. 2·75 6·50
a. Deep bright blue .. .. 3·50 4·00
51 10 3d. purple/*yellow*, **C** (2.13) .. .. 40 3·75
a. White back (Optd S. £35) (11.13) .. 27·00 45·00
b. On lemon (1916) .. .. 1·10 7·00
c. On orange-buff .. .. 80 4·50
d. On pale yellow (Optd S. £30) (1919) 18·00 32·00
52 4d. blk & red/*pale yell*, **C** (Die II) (1922) 70 9·50
53 11 6d. dull and bright purple, **C** (2.13) .. 1·00 5·00
54 12 1s. black/*green*, **C** (2.13) .. 1·00 4·50
a. White back (Optd S.£35) (11.13) .. 22·00 35·00
b. On blue-green, olive back (Optd S. £35) (1914) .. .. 90 5·50
55 10 2s. pur & blue/*blue*, **C** (Die II) (1922) .. 3·00 14·00
56 2s. 6d. black and red/*blue*, **C** (2.13) .. 11·00 25·00
57 12 5s. green and red/*yellow*, **C** (1915) .. 20·00 45·00
a. White back (Optd S. £40) (11.13) .. 30·00 48·00
b. On lemon (1916) .. .. 10·00 35·00
c. On orange-buff (1920?) .. .. 65·00 £100
46/57 .. .. *Set of* 12 28·00 90·00
46/57 Optd "Specimen" .. .. *Set of* 12 £225

1921–32. *Wmk Mult Script CA, except* £1 (*Mult Crown CA*). *P* 14.

(*a*) *Die* II (1921–29)

58 10 ¼d. brown, **O** (1.4.22) 25 70
59 11 ½d. blue-green, **O** (1921) 15 20
60 1d. carmine-red, **O** (1921) 20 10
61 1d. bright violet, **O** (8.22) 25 20
62 1d. bright scarlet, **O** (1929) 35 15
63 10 1½d. carmine-red, **O** (1926) 40 45
64 1½d. red-brown, **O** (1929) 20 10
65 2d. slate-grey, **O** (6.22) 50 25
66 11 2½d. orange-yellow, **O** (7.23) .. .. 3·75 24·00
67 2½d. bright blue, **O** (1927) 75 30
68 10 3d. light ultramarine, **O** (7.23) .. .. 2·00 16·00
a. Deep ultramarine .. .. 14·00 25·00
69 3d. purple/*yellow*, **C** (1927) .. .. 40 3·50
70 4d. black and red/*pale yellow*, **C** (1924) 1·25 9·00
71 5d. dull purple and olive-green, **C** (1.4.22) .. .. .. 40 3·75
72 11 6d. dull and bright purple, **C** (1923) .. 7·00 17·00
73 12 1s. black/*emerald*, **C** (1923) .. .. 1·25 5·00
74 10 2s. purple and blue/*blue*, **C** (1.4.22) .. 16·00 30·00
a. Red-purple and blue/blue, **C** (1926) 7·00 24·00
75 2s. 6d. black and red/*blue*, **C** (1923) .. 6·50 22·00
76 3s. bright green and violet, **C** (1.4.22) 8·00 22·00
77 4s. black and red, **C** (1.4.22) .. 8·00 30·00
78 12 5s. green and red/*pale yellow*, **C** (1923) 28·00 48·00
79 13 10s. green and red/*green*, **C** (1928) .. 48·00 60·00
a. Break in scroll £125
b. Broken crown and scroll £125
80 £1 purple and black/*red*, **C** (1928) .. £210 £225
a. Break in scroll £350
b. Broken crown and scroll £350
58/80 .. .. *Set of* 22 £300 £450
58/80 Optd/Perf "Specimen" .. .. *Set of* 23 £550

For illustrations of the varieties on Nos. 79/80 see above No. 44 of Bermuda.

(*b*) *Reversion to Die* I (*Plate* 23) (1931–32)

81 10 ¼d. brown, **O** .. .. .. 60 5·50
82 11 ½d. blue-green, **O** (1931) .. .. 2·25 12·00
83 1d. bright, scarlet, **O** .. .. 1·75 10
84 10 1½d. red-brown, **O** .. .. 1·50 1·75
85 11 2½d. bright blue, **O** .. .. 3·50 3·50
86 6d. dull and bright purple, **C** .. 10·00 28·00
87 12 1s. black/*emerald*, **C** .. .. 20·00 30·00
81/7 .. .. *Set of* 7 35·00 70·00

1935 (6 May). *Silver Jubilee. As Nos.* 91/4 *of Antigua but printed by Waterlow. P* 11 × 12.

88 1d. deep blue and scarlet 45 40
89 1½d. ultramarine and grey 55 60
90 2½d. brown and deep blue .. .. 90 2·50
91 1s. slate and purple .. .. 4·25 9·00
j. Kite and vertical log .. .. 55·00
k. Kite and horizontal log .. .. 55·00
88/91 .. .. *Set of* 4 5·50 11·00
88/91 Perf "Specimen" .. .. *Set of* 4 70·00

For illustrations of plate varieties see Omnibus section following Zululand.

1937 (12 May). *Coronation. As Nos.* 13/15 *of Aden.*

92 1d. scarlet 30 15
93 1½d. buff 30 25
94 2½d. bright blue 30 35
92/4 .. .. *Set of* 3 80 65
92/4 Perf "Specimen .. .. *Set of* 3 45·00

14

15

(Die A)

(Die B)

In Die B the figure "1" has a broader top and more projecting serif.

VARD ISLI

"D I" shaved at foot (R. 7/3 of left pane) (all ptgs between Sept 1947 and July 1949)

Broken second "E" in "LEEWARD" (R. 4/1 of right pane) (Pl. 3 ptgs from December 1943 until corrected in June 1949)

1938 (25 Nov)–**51**. *T* 14 (*and similar type, but with shaded value tablet*, ½*d.*, 1*d.*, 2½*d.*, 6*d.*) *and* 15 (10*s.*, £1). *P* 14.

(*a*) *Wmk Mult Script CA*

95 ¼d. brown, **O** 10 10
a. Deep brown, **C** (13.6.49) 10 15
96 ½d. emerald 15 15
97 ½d. slate-grey, **C** (1.7.49) 30 10
98 1d. scarlet (Die A) .. .. 3·75 80
99 1d. scarlet (*shades*) (Die B) (1940) .. 40 30
a. "D I" flaw (9.47) .. .. 38·00
b. Carmine (9.42) .. .. 40 2·75
c. Red (13.9.48) 90 90
ca. "D I" flaw .. .. 42·00
100 1d. blue-green, **C** (1.7.49) 55 10
a. "D I" flaw .. .. 38·00
101 1½d. chestnut 15 10
102 1½d. yellow-orange and black, **C** (1.7.49) .. 50 10
103 2d. olive-grey 15 10
a. Slate-grey (11.42) .. .. 2·50 2·50
104 2d. scarlet, **C** (1.7.49) .. .. 1·40 15
a. Vermilion (24.10.51) .. .. 4·50 3·75
105 2½d. bright blue .. .. .. 1·60 35
a. Light bright blue (11.42) 20 10
106 2½d. black and purple, **C** (1.7.49) .. 55 10
107 3d. orange, **C** .. .. .. 25·00 1·25
a. Pale orange, **O** (11.42) 15 20
108 3d. bright blue, **C** (1.7.49) 65 10
109 6d. deep dull and bright purple, **C** .. 5·50 2·25
a. Purple and deep magenta, **CO** (8.42) 85 55
ab. Broken "E" .. .. 45·00
110 1s. black/*emerald*, **CO** 80 35
a. Grey and black/emerald, **O** (8.42) .. 13·00 1·75
b. Black and grey/emerald, **O** (11.42) .. 65·00 10·00
111 2s. reddish purple and blue/*blue*, **CO** .. 6·00 40
a. Deep purple and blue/blue, **O** (29.9.47) 3·00 90
112 5s. green and red/*yellow*, **CO** .. 13·00 11·00
a. Broken "E" £100
b. Bright green & red/yellow, **C** (24.10.51) 17·00 13·00
113 10s. bluish green and deep red/*green*, **CO** £100 70·00
a. Pale green & dull red/green, **O** (12.43) 45·00 28·00
ae. Broken lower right scroll £450
b. Dp green & dp verm/grn, **O** (10.5.44) 55·00 38·00

(*b*) *Wmk Mult Crown CA*

114 £1 brown-purple and black/*red*, **C** .. £170 £150
a. Purple and black/carmine, **C** (3.42) .. 45·00 30·00
ae. Broken lower right scroll £350
af. Gash in chin £150
b. Brown-pur & blk/salmon, **C** (3.12.43) 20·00 20·00
c. Perf 13. *Violet & blk/scar*, **C** (13.12.51) 22·00 28·00
ca. Wmk sideways (*p* 13) £2500
95/114*b* .. .. .. *Set of* 19 75·00 55·00
95/114 Perf "Specimen" .. .. *Set of* 13 £250

Nos. 96, 98/9 and 99*b* exist in coils constructed from normal sheets.

For illustration of Nos. 113ae and 114ae/af see above No. 116 of Bermuda.

1946 (1 Nov). *Victory. As Nos.* 28/9 *of Aden.*

115 1½d. brown 15 10
116 3d. red-orange 15 10
115/16 Perf "Specimen" .. .. *Set of* 2 45·00

1949 (2 Jan). *Royal Silver Wedding. As Nos.* 30/1 *of Aden.*

117 2½d. ultramarine 10 10
118 5s. green .. .. .. 3·75 2·50

1949 (10 Oct). *75th Anniv of Universal Postal Union. As Nos.* 114/17 *of Antigua.*

119 2½d. blue-black 15 10
120 3d. deep blue 40 40
121 6d. magenta 40 30
122 1s. blue-green 45 30
119/22 .. .. *Set of* 4 1·25 1·00

1951 (16 Feb). *Inauguration of B.W.I. University College. As Nos.* 118/19 *of Antigua.*

123 3 c. orange and black 15 10
124 12 c. rose-carmine and reddish violet .. 20 10

1953 (2 June). *Coronation. As No.* 47 *of Aden.*

125 3 c. black and green 10 25

16 Queen Elizabeth II 17

1954. (22 Feb). *Chalk-surfaced paper. Wmk Mult Script CA. P* 14 (*T* 16) *or* 13 (*T* 17)

126 16 ½ c. brown 10 10
127 1 c. grey 10 10
128 2 c. green 10 10
129 3 c. yellow-orange and black 10 10
130 4 c. rose-red 10 10
131 5 c. black and brown-purple 15 10
132 6 c. yellow-orange 15 10
133 8 c. ultramarine 35 10
134 12 c. dull and reddish purple 35 10
135 24 c. black and green 40 10
136 48 c. dull purple and ultramarine .. 3·50 2·75
137 60 c. brown and green .. .. 3·50 2·00
138 $1.20, yellow-green and rose-red .. 3·50 2·75

139 17 $2.40, bluish green and red .. .. 3·50 5·00
140 $4.80, brown-purple and black .. 4·00 6·50
126/40 .. .. *Set of* 15 17·00 17·00

The 3 c., 4 c., 6 c., 8 c., 24 c., 48 c., 60 c. and $1.20 have their value tablets unshaded.

The stamps of Leeward Islands were withdrawn and invalidated on 1 July 1956.

Lesotho

(*formerly* Basutoland)

INDEPENDENT KINGDOM

31 Moshoeshoe I and Moshoeshoe II

(Des and photo Harrison)

1966 (4 Oct). *Independence. P* 12½ × 13.
106 **31** 2½ c. light brown, black and red .. 10 10
107 5 c. light brown, black and new blue .. 10 10
108 10 c. light brown, black and emerald .. 10 10
109 20 c. light brown, black and bright purple 10 10
106/9 .. .. *Set of* 4 20 20

LESOTHO

(32)

33 "Education, Culture and Science"

1966 (1 Nov). *Stamps of Basutoland optd as T* **32**. A., *Nos.* 69/71 *and* 73/9 (*Script CA wmk*), B, *Nos.* 84/96 *and unissued* 1 *r.* (*wmk* w **12**).

			A		B	
110	½ c. grey-black and sepia	..	10	10	†	
111	1 c. grey-blk and bluish grn	..	10	10	10	10
112	2 c. deep bright blue & orange		20	10	†	
113	2½ c. pale yell-grn & rose-red	..	†		20	10
114	3½ c. ind & dp ultram	..	20	10	†	
115	5 c. chestnut & dp grey-grn	..	20	10	20	10
116	10 c. bronze-green and purple		20	10	†	
117	12½ c. brown & turq-green	..	1·50	35	30	20
118	25 c. deep ultram & crimson	..	40	20	†	
119	50 c. black and carmine-red	..	1·00	65	80	50
120	1 r. black and maroon	..	1·00	1·75	1·00	75
	a. "LSEOTHO"	..	60·00	—	40·00	—
	b. Opt double	..	80·00	—	†	
	ba. Ditto. "LSEOTHO"	..	—	—	†	
110A/120A	*Set of* 10		4·25	3·00		
111B/120B	*Set of* 6				2·25	1·40

(Des V. Whiteley. Litho D.L.R.)

1966 (1 Dec). *20th Anniv of U.N.E.S.C.O. P* 14½ × 14.
121 **33** 2½ c. orange-yellow and emerald-green 10 10
122 5 c. light green and olive 15 10
123 12½ c. light blue and red.. .. 35 10
124 25 c. red-orange and deep greenish blue 60 25
121/4 .. .. *Set of* 4 1·10 40

34 Maize

35 Moshoeshoe II

(Des and photo Harrison)

1967 (1 Apr). *Designs as T* **34/5**. *No Wmk. P* 14½ × 13½ (2 *r.*) *or* 13½ × 14½ (*others*).
125 ½ c. bluish green and light bluish violet .. 10 10
126 1 c. sepia and rose-red 10 10
127 2 c. orange-yellow and light green .. 10 10
128 2½ c. black and ochre 10 10
129 3½ c. chalky blue and yellow 10 10
130 5 c. bistre and new blue 10 10
131 10 c. yellow-brown and bluish grey .. 10 10
132 12½ c. black and red-orange 20 10
133 25 c. black and bright blue 55 20
134 50 c. black, new blue and turquoise .. 3·00 45
135 1 r. multicoloured .. .. .. 1·25 75
136 2 r. black, gold and magenta .. 1·50 1·75
125/36 .. .. .. *Set of* 12 6·00 3·00

Designs: *Horiz as T* **34**—1 c. Cattle; 2 c. Agaves (wrongly inscr "Aloes"); 2½ c. Basotho Hat; 3½ c. Merino Sheep ("Wool"); 5 c. Basotho Pony; 10 c. Wheat; 12½ c. Angora Goat ("Mohair"); 25 c. Maletsunyane Falls; 50 c. Diamonds; 1 r. Arms of Lesotho.

See also Nos. 147/59 and 191/203.

46 Students and University

(Des V. Whiteley. Photo Harrison)

1967 (7 Apr). *First Conferment of University Degrees. P* 14 × 14½.
137 **46** 1 c. sepia, ultram & light yellow-orange 10 10
138 2½ c. sepia, ultram & light greenish blue 10 10
139 12½ c. sepia, ultramarine and rose .. 10 10
140 25 c. sepia, ultramarine and light violet 15 10
137/40 .. .. *Set of* 4 25 15

47 Statue of Moshoeshoe I

(Des and photo Harrison)

1967 (4 Oct). *First Anniv of Independence. T* **47** *and similar triangular designs. P* 14½ × 14.
141 2½ c. black and light yellow-green 10 10
142 12½ c. multicoloured 15 10
143 25 c. black, green and light ochre 25 15
141/3 .. .. *Set of* 3 40 25

Designs:—12½ c. Lesotho flag; 25 c. Crocodile (national emblem).

50 Lord Baden-Powell and Scout Saluting

(Des V. Whiteley. Photo Harrison)

1967 (1 Nov). *60th Anniv of Scout Movement. P* 14 × 14½.
144 **50** 15 c. multicoloured 15 10

51 W.H.O. Emblem and World Map

(Des G. Vasarhelyi. Photo Harrison)

1968 (7 Apr). *20th Anniv of World Health Organization. T* **51** *and similar horiz design. P* 14 × 14½.
145 2½ c. blue, gold and carmine-red 10 10
a. Gold (emblem) omitted .. ..
146 25 c. multicoloured 15 10

Design:—25 c. Nurse and child.

53 Basotho Hat

54 Sorghum

1968–69. *As Nos.* 125/36 *and T* **54**, *but wmk* **53** (*sideways on* 2 *r.*).
147 ½ c. bluish green & lt bluish vio (26.11.68) 10 10
a. Blue-green and violet (30.9.69) .. 15 10
148 1 c. sepia and rose-red (26.11.68) .. 10 10
149 2 c. orange-yellow & lt green (26.11.68) 10 10
a. Orange-yellow & yell-grn (30.9.69) 20 20
150 2½ c. black and ochre (21.10.68) .. 15 10
a. Black and yellow-ochre (30.9.69) .. 25 25
151 3 c. chocolate, green & yell-brn (1.8.68) 15 15
152 3½ c. chalky blue and yellow (26.11.68) .. 15 10
153 5 c. bistre and new blue (22.7.68) .. 20 10
154 10 c. yell-brn & pale bluish grey (26.11.68) 15 10
155 12½ c. black and red-orange (30.9.69) .. 60 35
156 25 c. black and bright blue (30.9.69) .. 1·25 1·00
157 50 c. black, new blue & turquoise (30.9.69) 4·50 1·50
158 1 r. multicoloured (26.11.68) .. .. 3·50 3·00
159 2 r. black, gold and magenta (30.9.69) .. 16·00 14·00
147/59 .. .. *Set of* 13 24·00 18·00

55 Running Hunters

(Des Jennifer Toombs. Photo Harrison)

1968 (1 Nov). *Rock Paintings. T* **55** *and similar designs. W* **53** (*sideways on* 5 *c.*, 15 *c.*). *P* 14 × 14½ (5 *c.*, 15 *c.*) *or* 14½ × 14 (*others*).
160 3 c. yellow-brown. lt blue-green & blackish green 15 10
161 3½ c. greenish yellow, yellow-olive and sepia 20 10
162 5 c. Venetian red, yell-ochre & blackish brn 25 10
163 10 c. yellow, rose and deep maroon.. .. 35 10
164 15 c. light buff, pale olive-yell & blackish brn 65 25
165 20 c. yellow-grn, greenish yellow & blackish brown 75 35
166 25 c. yellow, orange-brown and black .. 90 50
160/6 .. .. *Set of* 7 2·75 1·25

Designs: *Horiz*—3½ c. Baboons; 10 c. Archers; 20 c. Eland; 25 c. Hunting scene. *Vert*—5 c. Javelin throwing; 15 c. Blue Cranes.

62 Queen Elizabeth II Hospital

(Des C. R. Househam and G. Drummond. Litho P.B.)

1969 (11 Mar). *Centenary of Maseru (capital). T* **62** *and similar horiz designs. Multicoloured. W* **53** (*sideways*). *P* 14 × 13½.
167 2½ c. Type **62** 10 10
168 10 c. Lesotho Radio Station.. .. .. 10 10
169 12½ c. Leabua Jonathan Airport 10 10
170 25 c. Royal Palace 15 15
167/70 .. .. *Set of* 4 25 20

66 Rally Car passing Mosotho Horseman

(Des P. Wheeler. Photo Harrison)

1969 (26 Sept). *Roof of Africa Car Rally. T* **66** *and similar horiz designs. W* **53**. *P* 14.
171 2½ c. yellow, mauve and plum 10 10
172 12½ c. cobalt, greenish yellow and olive-grey 15 10
173 15 c. blue, black and mauve 15 10
174 20 c. black, red and yellow 15 10
171/4 .. .. *Set of* 4 45 30

Designs:—12½ c. Rally car on mountain road; 15 c. Chequered flags and mountain scenery; 20 c. Map of rally route and Rally Trophy.

71 Gryponyx and Footprints

75 Moshoeshoe I, when a Young Man

(Des Jennifer Toombs. Photo Harrison)

1970 (5 Jan). *Prehistoric Footprints* (1*st series.*) *T* **71** *and similar designs. W* **53** (*sideways*). P 14 × 14½ (3 *c.*) *or* 14½ × 14 (*others*).
175 3 c. pale brown, yellow-brown and sepia .. 25 20
176 5 c. dull purple, pink and sepia 35 30

177	10 c. pale yellow, black, and sepia	50	35
178	15 c. olive-yellow, black and sepia	75	1·00
179	25 c. cobalt and black	1·75	2·00
175/9	*Set of* 5	3·25	3·50

Designs: (60 × 23 *mm*)—3 c. Dinosaur footprints at Moyeni. (40 × 24 *mm*)—10 c. Plateosauravus and footprints; 15 c. Tritylodon and footprints; 25 c. Massospondylus and footprints.

See also Nos. 596/8.

(Des G. Vasarhelyi. Litho D.L.R.)

1970 (11 Mar). *Death Centenary of King Moshoeshoe I. T* **75** *and similar vert design. W* **53**. *P* 13½.

180	2½ c. pale green and magenta	10	10
181	25 c. pale blue and chesnut	15	10

Design:—25 c. Moshoeshoe I as an old man.

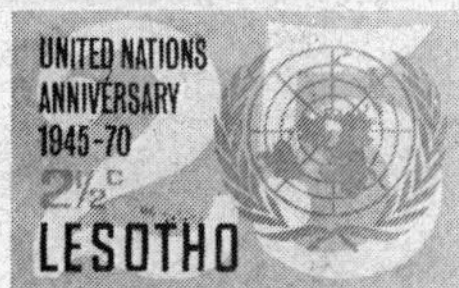

77 U.N. Emblem and "25"

1970 (26 June). *25th Anniv of United Nations. T* **77** *and similar horiz designs. W* **53** (*sideways*). *P* 14½ × 14.

182	2½ c. light pink, light blue and maroon	10	10
183	10 c. multicoloured	10	10
184	12½ c. brown-red, cobalt and drab	10	10
185	25 c. multicoloured	15	10
182/5	*Set of* 4	20	20

Designs:— 10 c. U.N. Building; 12½ c. "People of the World"; 25 c. Symbolic dove.

78 Basotho Hat Gift Shop, Maseru

(Des G. Drummond. Litho Questa)

1970 (27 Oct). *Tourism. T* **78** *and similar horiz designs. Multicoloured. W* **53** (*sideways*). *P* 14.

186	2½ c. Type **78**	10	10
187	5 c. Trout fishing	15	10
188	10 c. Pony trekking	20	10
189	12½ c. Skiing	30	10
190	20 c. Holiday Inn, Maseru	35	50
186/90	*Set of* 5	90	70

79 Maize **80** Lammergeier

(Des Harrison. Litho Questa)

1971 (4 Jan–1 Apr). *As Nos. 147/58 but in new format omitting portrait of Moshoeshoe II, as in T* **79**. *4 c. and 2 r. in new designs. W* **53** (*sideways except 2 r.*). *P* 14.

191	½ c. blue-green and light bluish violet	10	10
192	1 c. brown and orange-red	10	10
193	2 c. yellow and green	10	10
194	2½ c. black, olive-green and yellow-ochre	10	10
195	3 c. brown, green and yellow-ochre	10	10
196	3½ c. indigo and yellow	10	10
196*a*	4 c. multicoloured (1.4.71)	20	10
197	5 c. yellow-brown and pale blue	15	10
198	10 c. orange-brown and grey-blue	15	10
199	12½ c. chocolate and yellow-orange	25	30
200	25 c. slate and pale bright blue	60	40
201	50 c. black, pale blue and turquoise-green	2·75	1·25
202	1 r. multicoloured	2·50	2·25
203	2 r. yellow-brown and ultramarine	2·75	3·00
191/203	*Set of* 14	9·00	7·00

Designs: *Horiz*—4 c. National flag. *Vert*—2 r. Statue of Moshoeshoe I.

For 2 r. value without watermark see No. 401.

(Des R. Granger Barrett. Litho J.W.)

1971 (1 Mar). *Birds. T* **80** *and similar vert designs. Multicoloured. W* **53**. *P* 14.

204	2½ c. Type **80**	80	10
205	5 c. Bald Ibis	1·50	90
206	10 c. Rufous Rockjumper	2·00	1·25
207	12½ c. Blue Bustard	2·25	1·40
208	15 c. Painted Snipe	3·00	2·50
209	20 c. Golden-breasted Bunting	3·00	2·50
210	25 c. Ground Woodpecker	3·00	2·75
204/10	*Set of* 7	14·00	10·00

81 Lionel Collett Dam

(Des G. Drummond. Litho J.W.)

1971 (15 July). *Soil Conservation. T* **81** *and similar horiz designs. Multicoloured. W* **53** (*sideways*). *P* 14.

211	4 c. Type **81**	10	10
212	10 c. Contour ridges	10	10
213	15 c. Earth dams	15	10
214	25 c. Beaver dams	25	35
211/14	*Set of* 4	55	50

82 Diamond Mining

(Des J.W. Litho Questa)

1971 (4 Oct). *Development. T* **82** *and similar horiz designs. Multicoloured. W* **53** (*sideways*). *P* 14.

215	4 c. Type **82**	20	10
216	10 c. Pottery	20	10
217	15 c. Weaving	25	15
218	20 c. Construction	30	30
215/18	*Set of* 4	85	50

83 Mail Cart **84** Sprinting

(Des D. B. Picton-Phillips. Litho Questa)

1972 (3 Jan). *Post Office Centenary. T* **83** *and similar designs. W* **53** (*sideways on* 5, 10 *and* 20 *c.*). *P* 14 × 13½ (15 *c.*) *or* 13½ × 14 (*others*).

219	5 c. pale pink and black	15	10
220	10 c. multicoloured	15	10
221	15 c. pale drab, light blue and black	30	15
222	20 c. multicoloured	45	70
219/22	*Set of* 4	95	80

Designs: *Horiz*—10 c. Postal bus; 20 c. Maseru P.O. *Vert*—15 c. Cape of Good Hope 4d. stamp of 1876.

(Des J. W. Litho Questa)

1972 (1 Sept). *Olympic Games. Munich. T* **84** *and similar vert designs. Multicoloured. W* **53**. *P* 14.

223	4 c. Type **84**	10	10
224	10 c. Shot putting	10	10
225	15 c. Hurdling	15	10
226	25 c. Long-jumping	15	20
223/6	*Set of* 4	35	35

85 "Adoration of the Shepherds" (Matthias Stomer)

(Des and litho J.W.)

1972 (1 Dec). *Christmas. W* **53** (*sideways*). *P* 14.

227	**85**	4 c. multicoloured	10	10
228		10 c. multicoloured	10	10
229		25 c. multicoloured	15	20
227/9		*Set of* 3	20	25

O.A.U.
10th Anniversary
Freedom in Unity

86 W.H.O. Emblem (**87**)

(Des. J. Cooter. Litho Questa)

1973 (7 Apr). *25th Anniv of W.H.O. W* **53** (*sideways*). *P* 13½.

230	**86**	20 c. greenish blue and yellow	20	15

1973 (25 May). *Tenth Anniv of O.A.U. Nos.* 194 *and* 196*a*/8 *optd with T* **87** *by Govt Printer, Maseru.*

231	2½ c. black, olive-green and yellow-ochre	10	10
232	4 c. multicoloured	10	10
	a. Horiz pair, one without opt	£150	
233	5 c. yellow-brown and pale blue	10	10
234	10 c. orange-brown and grey-blue	15	15
231/4	*Set of* 4	35	35

88 Basotho Hat and W.F.P. Emblem

(Des locally; adapted J. Cooter. Litho Format)

1973 (1 June). *Tenth Anniv of World Food Programme. T* **88** *and similar horiz designs. Multicoloured. W* **53** (*sideways*). *P* 13½.

235	4 c. Type **88**	10	10
236	15 c. School feeding	20	15
237	20 c. Infant feeding	20	20
	a. Imperf (pair)		
238	25 c. "Food for Work"	25	25
235/8	*Set of* 4	65	60

89 Mountain Beauty **90** Kimberlite Volcano

(Des A. McLeod; artwork G. Drummond. Litho Questa)

1973 (3 Sept). *Butterflies. T* **89** *and similar horiz designs. Multicoloured. W* **53** (*sideways*). *P* 14.

239	4 c. Type **89**	25	10
240	5 c. Christmas Butterfly	35	25
241	10 c. Painted Lady	70	50
242	15 c. Yellow Pansy	1·00	1·00
243	20 c. Blue Pansy	1·00	1·00
244	25 c. African Monarch	1·50	1·75
245	30 c. Orange Tip	1·75	2·00
239/45	*Set of* 7	6·00	6·00

(Des PAD Studio. Litho Questa)

1973 (1 Oct). *International Kimberlite Conference. T* **90** *and similar multicoloured designs. W* **53** (*sideways on* 10 *and* 15 *c.*). *P* 13½.

246	10 c. Map of diamond mines (*horiz*)	75	50
247	15 c. Kimberlite-diamond rock (*horiz*)	1·00	1·00
248	20 c. Type **90**	1·25	1·25
249	30 c. Diamond prospecting	2·00	2·75
246/9	*Set of* 4	4·50	5·00

Type **90** is incorrectly inscribed "KIMERLITE VOLCANO".

91 "Health" **92** Open Book and Wreath

(Des R. Granger Barrett. Litho Questa)

1974 (18 Feb). *Youth and Development. T* **91** *and similar horiz designs. Multicoloured. W* **53** (*sideways*). *P* 13½.

250	4 c. Type **91**	10	10
251	10 c. "Education"	10	10
252	20 c. "Agriculture"	10	10
253	25 c. "Industry"	15	20
254	30 c. "Service"	20	25
250/4	*Set of* 5	50	55

(Des PAD Studio. Litho Questa)

1974 (7 Apr). *Tenth Anniv of U.B.L.S. T* **92** *and similar vert designs. Multicoloured. W* **53**. *P* 14.

255	10 c. Type **92**	10	10
256	15 c. Flags, mortar-board and scroll	10	10
257	20 c. Map of Africa	15	10
258	25 c. King Moshoeshoe II capping a graduate	15	15
255/8	*Set of* 4	40	30

NEW INFORMATION

The editor is always interested to correspond with people who have new information that will improve or correct the Catalogue.

93 Senqunyane River Bridge, Marakabei

(Des J. Cooter. Litho Questa)

1974 (26 June). *Rivers and Bridges. T* **93** *and similar horiz designs. Multicoloured. W* **53** *(sideways). P* 14½.

259 4 c. Type **93** 10 10
260 5 c. Tsoelike River and bridge 10 10
261 10 c. Makhaleng River Bridge 20 10
262 15 c. Seaka Bridge, Orange/Senqu River . . 35 35
263 20 c. Masianokeng Bridge, Phuthiatsana River 40 40
264 25 c. Mahobong Bridge, Hlotse River 45 45
259/64 . . . . *Set of* 6 1·50 1·25

94 U.P.U. Emblem

(Des R. Granger Barrett. Litho Enschedé)

1974 (6 Sept). *Centenary of Universal Postal Union. T* **94** *and similar horiz designs. W* **53** *(sideways). P* 13½ × 13.

265 4 c. light emerald and black 10 10
266 10 c. orange, greenish yellow and black . . 10 10
267 15 c. multicoloured 15 15
268 20 c. multicoloured 20 20
265/8 . . . . *Set of* 4 45 40

Designs:—10 c. Map of air-mail routes; 15 c. Post Office H.Q., Maseru; 20 c. Horseman taking rural mail.

On No. 266 the inscriptions for the airstrips at Makhotlong and Mohlanapeng were transposed in error.

95 Siege of Thaba-Bosiu

(Des Jennifer Toombs. Litho Enschedé)

1974 (25 Nov). *150th Anniv of Establishment of Thaba-Bosiu as Capital. T* **95** *and similar multicoloured designs. W* **53** *(sideways on 4 and 5 c.). P* 12½ × 12 *(4 and 5 c.) or* 12 × 12½ *(others)*.

269 4 c. Type **95** 10 10
270 5 c. The wreath-laying 10 10
271 10 c. Moshoeshoe I *(vert)* 25 10
272 20 c. Makoanyane, the warrior *(vert)* 65 30
269/72 . . . . *Set of* 4 1·00 40

96 Mamokhorong

(Des PAD Studio. Litho Questa)

1975 (25 Jan). *Basotho Musical Instruments. T* **96** *and similar horiz designs. Multicoloured. W* **53** *(sideways). P* 14.

273 4 c. Type **96** 10 10
274 10 c. Lesiba 10 10
275 15 c. Setolotolo 15 20
276 20 c. Meropa 15 20
273/6 . . . . *Set of* 4 40 45
MS277 108 × 92 mm. Nos. 273/6 . . . . . . 1·25 2·00

97 Horseman in Rock Archway

98 Morena Moshoeshoe I

(Des J. Cooter. Litho Questa)

1975 (15 Apr). *Sehlabathebe National Park. T* **97** *and similar horiz designs. Multicoloured. W* **53** *(sideways). P* 14.

278 4 c. Type **97** 15 10
279 5 c. Mountain view through arch 15 10
280 15 c. Antelope by stream 35 30
281 20 c. Mountains and lake 40 35
282 25 c. Tourists by frozen waterfall 50 50
278/82 . . . . *Set of* 5 1·40 1·10

(Des G. Vasarhelyi. Litho Questa)

1975 (10 Sept). *Leaders of Lesotho. T* **98** *and similar vert designs. W* **53**. *P* 14.

283 3 c. black and light blue 10 10
284 4 c. black and light mauve 10 10
285 5 c. black and pink 10 10
286 6 c. black and light grey-brown 10 10
287 10 c. black and light claret 10 10
288 15 c. black and light orange-red 20 20
289 20 c. black and dull green 25 30
290 25 c. black and azure 25 40
283/90 . . . . *Set of* 8 1·00 1·10

Designs:—4 c. King Moshoeshoe II; 5 c. Morena Letsie I; 6 c. Morena Lerotholi; 10 c. Morena Letsie II; 15 c. Morena Griffith; 20 c. Morena Seeiso Griffith Lerotholi; 25 c. Mofumahali Mantsebo Seeiso, O.B.E.

The 25 c. also commemorates International Women's Year.

99 Mokhibo Dance

(Des PAD Studio. Litho Questa)

1975 (17 Dec). *Traditional Dances. T* **99** *and similar horiz designs. Multicoloured. W* **53** *(sideways). P* 14 × 14½.

291 4 c. Type **99** 10 10
292 10 c. Ndlamo 10 10
293 15 c. Baleseli 25 30
294 20 c. Mohobelo 30 35
291/4 . . . . *Set of* 4 60 65
MS295 111 × 100 mm. Nos. 291/94 . . . . 1·90 2·50

100 Enrolment

(Des L. Curtis. Litho Questa)

1976 (20 Feb). *25th Anniv of the Lesotho Red Cross. T* **100** *and similar horiz designs. Multicoloured. W* **53** *(sideways). P* 14.

296 4 c. Type **100** 25 10
297 10 c. Medical aid 40 10
298 15 c. Rural service 65 45
299 25 c. Relief supplies 80 55
296/9 . . . . *Set of* 4 1·90 1·00

101 Tapestry **102** Football

(Des V. Whiteley Studio. Litho Format)

1976 (2 June)–**78**. *Multicoloured designs as T* **101**. *W* **53** *(sideways on 2 to 50 c.). P* 14.

300 2 c. Type **101** 10 10
301 3 c. Mosotho horseman 10 10
302 4 c. Map of Lesotho 25 10
303 5 c. Lesotho Brown diamond 35 10
304 10 c. Lesotho Bank 25 10
305 15 c. Lesotho and O.A.U. flags 55 20
306 25 c. Sehlabathebe National Park 70 35
307 40 c. Pottery 70 50
308 50 c. Prehistoric rock art . . . . . . 1·25 90
309 1 r. King Moshoeshoe II *(vert)* . . . . 1·40 1·75
300/309 . . . . *Set of* 10 5·00 3·50

For 25 c., 40 c. and 50 c. values on unwatermarked paper, see Nos. 398/400.

(Des P. Powell. Litho Questa)

1976 (9 Aug). *Olympic Games, Montreal. T* **102** *and similar vert designs. Multicoloured. W* **53**. *P* 14.

310 4 c. Type **102** 10 10
311 10 c. Weightlifting 10 10
312 15 c. Boxing 15 10
313 25 c. Throwing the discus 30 25
310/13 . . . . *Set of* 4 55 40

103 "Rising Sun" **104** Telephones, 1876 and 1976

(Des L. Curtis. Litho Questa)

1976 (4 Oct). *Tenth Anniv of Independence. T* **103** *and similar vert designs. Multicoloured. W* **53**. *P* 14.

314 4 c. Type **103** 10 10
315 10 c. Open gates 10 10
316 15 c. Broken chains 15 10
317 25 c. Aeroplane over hotel 20 25
314/17 . . . . *Set of* 4 45 35

(Des and litho J.W.)

1976 (6 Dec). *Telephone Centenary. T* **104** *and similar horiz designs. Multicoloured. W* **53** *(sideways). P* 13.

318 4 c. Type **104** 10 10
319 10 c. Early handset and telephone-user, 1976 10 10
320 15 c. Wall telephone and telephone exchange 15 15
321 25 c. Stick telephone and Alexander Graham Bell 30 40
318/21 . . . . *Set of* 4 55 55

105 *Aloe striatula* **106** Large-toothed Rock Hyrax

(Des D. Findlay. Litho Walsall)

1977 (14 Feb). *Aloes and Succulents. T* **105** *and similar vert designs. Multicoloured. W* **53** *(inverted). P* 14.

322 3 c. Type **105** 20 10
323 4 c. *Aloe aristata* 25 10
324 5 c. *Kniphofia caulescens* 30 10
325 10 c. *Euphorbia pulvinata* 45 10
326 15 c. *Aloe saponaria* 80 40
327 20 c. *Caralluma lutea* . . . . 1·10 65
328 25 c. *Aloe polyphylla* . . . . 1·60 90
322/8 . . . . *Set of* 7 4·25 2·00

(Des D. Findlay. Litho Questa)

1977 (25 Apr). *Animals. T* **106** *and similar horiz designs. Multicoloured. W* **53** *(sideways). P* 14.

329 4 c. Type **106** 20 10
330 5 c. Cape Porcupine 25 10
331 10 c. Zorilla (polecat) 40 10
332 15 c. Klipspringer 90 70
333 25 c. Chacma Baboon . . . . 1·40 1·10
329/33 . . . . *Set of* 5 2·75 1·75

107 "Rheumatic Man" **108** *Barbus holubi*

(Des C. Abbott. Litho Questa)

1977 (4 July). *World Rheumatism Year. T* **107** *and similar vert designs showing the "Rheumatic Man". W* **53**. *P* 14.

334 4 c. yellow and red 10 10
335 10 c. new blue and deep blue 10 10
336 15 c. yellow and blue-green 25 10
337 25 c. orange-red and black 40 45
334/7 . . . . *Set of* 4 75 55

Designs:—10 c. Man surrounded by "pain"; 15 c. Man surrounded by "chain"; 25 c. Man supporting globe.

(Des D. Findlay. Litho Questa)

1977 (28 Sept). *Fish. T* **108** *and similar horiz designs. Multicoloured. W* **53** *(sideways). P* 14.

338 4 c. Type **108** 15 10
339 10 c. *Labeo capensis* 30 10
340 15 c. *Salmo gairdneri* 60 35
341 25 c. *Oreodaimon quathlambae* 85 60
338/41 . . . . *Set of* 4 1·75 1·00

(109) **110** Black and White Heads

1977 (7 Dec*). *No.* 198 *surch with T* **109** *by Govt Printer, Maseru.*

342	3 c. on 10 c. yellow-brown and pale bluish grey	1·25	80

*Earliest known date of use.

(Des Jennifer Toombs. Litho Walsall)

1977 (12 Dec). *Decade for Action to Combat Racism. T* **110** *and similar vert designs. W* **53**. *P* 14.

343	4 c. chocolate and mauve	10	10
344	10 c. chocolate and light new blue	10	10
345	15 c. chocolate and light orange	15	15
346	25 c. chocolate and light turquoise-green ..	25	25
343/6	.. .. *Set of* 4	55	45

Designs:—10 c. Jigsaw pieces; 15 c. Cogwheels; 25 c. Handshake.

(Des D. Findlay. Litho Questa)

1978 (13 Feb). *Flowers. Vert designs similar to T* **105**. *Multicoloured. W* **53**. *P* 14.

347	2 c. *Papaver aculeatum*	10	10
348	3 c. *Diascia integerrima*	10	10
349	4 c. *Helichrysum trilineatum*	10	10
350	5 c. *Zaluzianskya maritima*	10	10
351	10 c. *Gladiolus natalensis*	20	20
352	15 c. *Chironia krebsii*	30	30
353	25 c. *Wahlenbergia undulata*	50	80
354	40 c. *Brunsvigia radulosa*	85	1·50
347/54	.. .. *Set of* 8	2·00	2·75

111 Edward Jenner performing Vaccination

112 Tsoloane Falls

(Des G. Hutchins. Litho J.W.)

1978 (8 May). *Global Eradication of Smallpox. T* **111** *and similar vert design. Multicoloured. W* **53**. *P* 13.

355	5 c. Type **111**	10	10
356	25 c. Head of child and W.H.O. emblem ..	30	25

(Des Kobus De Beer Art Studio. Litho Questa)

1978 (28 July). *Waterfalls. T* **112** *and similar vert designs. Multicoloured. W* **53**. *P* 14.

357	4 c. Type **112**	15	10
358	10 c. Qiloane Falls	25	10
359	15 c. Tsoelikana Falls	45	25
360	25 c. Maletsunyane Falls	75	60
357/60	.. .. *Set of* 4	1·40	90

113 Wright *Flyer*, 1903

114 *Orthetrum farinosum*

(Des L. Curtis. Litho Harrison)

1978 (9 Oct). *75th Anniv of Powered Flight. T* **113** *and similar horiz design. W* **53** *(sideways). P* 14½ × 14.

361	5 c. black, brown-ochre and new blue ..	10	10
362	25 c. multicoloured	30	20

Design:—25 c. Wilbur and Orville Wright.

(Des D. Findlay. Litho Questa)

1978 (18 Dec). *Insects. T* **114** *and similar vert designs. Multicoloured. W* **53**. *P* 14.

363	4 c. Type **114**	10	10
364	10 c. *Phymateus viridipes*	20	10
365	15 c. *Belonogaster lateritius*	30	20
366	25 c. *Sphodromantis gastrica*	50	45
363/6	.. .. *Set of* 4	1·00	70

115 Oudehout Branch in flower

116 Mampharoane

(Des D. Findlay. Litho Questa)

1979 (26 Mar). *Trees. T* **115** *and similar vert designs showing branches in flower. Multicoloured. W* **53**. *P* 14.

367	4 c. Type **115**	15	10
368	10 c. Wild Olive	20	10
369	15 c. Blinkblaar	35	60
370	25 c. Cape Holly	70	1·25
367/70	.. .. *Set of* 4	1·25	1·75

(New Currency. 100 lisente = 1(màloti)

(Des D. Findlay. Litho Questa)

1979 (1 June). *Reptiles. T* **116** *and similar horiz designs. Multicoloured. P* 14. A. *No wmk.* B. *W* **53** *(sideways).*

		A		B	
371	4 s. Type **116**	10	10	10	10
372	10 s. Qoaane	20	10	20	10
373	15 s. Leupa	30	35	30	50
374	25 s. Masumu	60	65	60	90
371/4	.. .. .. *Set of* 4	1·10	1·00	1·10	1·40

117 Basutoland 1933 1d. Stamp

118 Detail of Painting "Children's Games" by Brueghel

(Des J.W. Litho Format)

1979 (22 Oct). *Death Centenary of Sir Rowland Hill. T* **117** *and similar vert designs showing stamps. P* 14.

375	4 s. multicoloured	10	10
376	15 s. multicoloured	20	20
377	25 s. black, yellow-orange and olive-bistre ..	30	30
375/7	.. .. *Set of* 3	55	50
MS378	118 × 95 mm. 50 s. multicoloured ..	60	80

Designs:—15 s. Basutoland 1962 ½ c. definitive; 25 s. Penny Black; 50 s. 1972 15 c. Post Office Centenary commemorative.

(Des C. Abbott. Litho Questa)

1979 (10 Dec). *International Year of the Child. T* **118** *and similar vert designs showing details of the painting "Children's Games" by Brueghel. W* **53**. *P* 14.

379	4 s. multicoloured	10	10
380	10 s. multicoloured	10	10
381	15 s. multicoloured	15	15
379/81	.. .. *Set of* 3	25	25
MS382	113 × 88 mm. 25 s. multicoloured *(horiz)* (wmk sideways)	40	45

119 Beer Strainer, Broom and Mat

(Des Kobus de Beer Art Studio. Litho Walsall)

1980 (18 Feb). *Grasswork. T* **119** *and similar horiz designs. Multicoloured. W* **53** *(sideways). P* 14.

383	4 s. Type **119**	10	10
384	10 s. Winnowing Basket	10	10
385	15 s. Basotho Hat	15	15
386	25 s. Grain storage	25	25
383/6	.. .. *Set of* 4	50	45

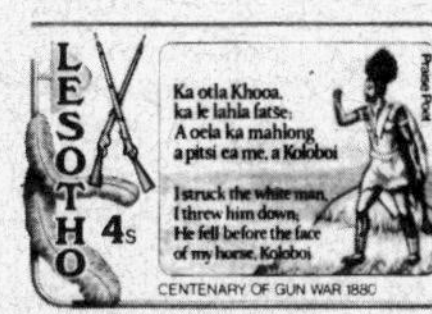

120 Praise Poet

(Des BG Studio. Litho Walsall)

1980 (6 May). *Centenary of Gun War. T* **120** *and similar horiz designs. Multicoloured. P* 14.

387	4 s. Type **120**	10	10
388	5 s. Lerotholi (commander of Basotho Army)	10	10
389	10 s. Ambush at Qalabane	15	10
390	15 s. Snider and Martini-Henry rifles ..	25	25
391	25 s. Map showing main areas of action ..	35	35
387/91	.. .. *Set of* 5	85	70

121 Olympic Flame, Flags and Kremlin (122)

(Des G. Vasarhelyi. Litho Format)

1980 (20 Sept). *Olympic Games, Moscow. T* **121** *and similar horiz designs. Multicoloured. P* 14½.

392	25 s. Type **121**	25	25
	a. Horiz strip of 5. Nos. 392/6	1·10	
393	25 s. Doves, flame and flags	25	25
394	25 s. Football	25	25
395	25 s. Running	25	25
396	25 s. Opening ceremony	25	25
392/6	.. .. *Set of* 5	1·10	1·10
MS397	110 × 85 mm. 1 m. 40, Ancient and modern athletes carrying Olympic torch	1·10	1·25

Nos. 392/6 were printed together, *se-tenant*, in horizontal strips of 5 throughout the sheet.

1980. *As Nos.* 203 *and* 306/8, *but without wmk.*

398	25 c. Sehlabathebe National Park	1·50	
399	40 c. Pottery	6·00	
400	50 c. Prehistoric rock art	6·00	
401	2 r. Statue of Moshoeshoe I (yellow-brown and ultramarine)	2·50	4·50
398/401	.. .. *Set of* 4	14·50	

Two opt types of No. 409:

Type I Cancelling bars centred on depth of "M1" (stamps surcharged in individual panes of 25 and from the righthand panes of those surcharged in sheets of 50 (2 panes 5 × 5)).

Type II. Lower cancelling bar aligns with foot of "M1" (stamps from lefthand panes of those surcharged in sheets of 50).

1980 (20 Oct)–**81**. *As Nos.* 300/5, 309 *and* 398/401 *surch as T* **122** *or with new figures of value* (5 *s.* (*No.* 410A), 6, 75 *s.*, 1 *and* 2 *m.*). A. *By typo (locally).* B. *By litho (London).*

(*a*) *W* **53** (*sideways on* 2, 3, 6, 10, 40, 50 *and* 75 *s.*)

		A		B	
402	2 s. on 2 c. Type **101** ..	10	10	10	10
403	3 s. on 3 c. Mosotho horseman	10	10	10	10
404	6 s. on 4 c. Map of Lesotho	10	10	10	10
	a. Surch double	†	—	†	
	b. Albino surch	†	—	†	
405	10 s. on 10 c. Lesotho Bank ..	80	10	5·00	5·50
405*a*	25 s. on 25 c. Sehlabathebe National Park	5·00	5·00	†	
406	40 s. on 40 c. Pottery ..	45	50	45	50
407	50 s. on 50 c. Prehistoric rock art	1·25	—	50	55
408	75 s. on 15 c. Lesotho and O.A.U. flags	70	75	†	
409	1 m. on 1 r. King Moshoeshoe II (I) (Sil.)	95	1·00	†	
	a. Surch double, one inverted	55·00	—	†	
	b. Opt Type II	3·75	4·00	†	
	(*b*) *No wmk*				
410	5 s. on 5 c. Lesotho Brown diamond	10	10	10	10
	a. Third surch (Basotho hat and "5 s.") double	—	—	†	
	b. Basotho hat and "5 s." surch albino	—	—	†	
	c. Basotho hat and "5 s." omitted	25·00	—	†	
	d. Second surch ("6 s." and bars) albino	28·00	—	†	
411	10 s. on 10 c. Lesotho Bank	†		10	10
412	25 s. on 25 c. Sehlabathebe National Park	25	30	25	30
	a. Surch double	20·00	—	†	
413	40 s. on 40 c. Pottery	5·00	5·00	†	
414	50 s. on 50 c. Prehistoric rock art	50	55	†	
415	75 s. on 15 c. Lesotho and O.A.U. flags	†		70	75
416	1 m. on 1 r. King Moshoeshoe II (Blk. and Sil.)	†		95	1·00
417	2 m. on 2 r. Statue of Moshoeshoe I	1·90	2·00	1·90	2·00
402/17	.. .. .. *Set of* 12			4·50	4·75

No. 410A is a further surcharge on No. 410B. Initially sheets of No. 410B were locally surcharged "6 s.", but this was later obliterated by a Basotho hat emblem and a further "5 s." surcharge added, both in typography.

The surcharge on No. 416 is similar to that on No. 409 but has the cancelling bars printed in black and the new face value in silver.

On each value except the 5 s. and 1 m. stamps, the design of the surcharge on the local printing is identical to that on the London printing. Stamps from the local printing can easily be identified from those of the London printing as indentations are clearly visible on the reverse of stamps with the typographed surcharge.

It is believed that the local surcharges were not placed on general sale before 1 December 1980. No. 410A did not appear until 20 January 1981.

123 Beer Mug

124 Queen Elizabeth the Queen Mother and Prince Charles

(Des G. Vasarhelyi (No. **MS**422), Kobus de Beer Art Studio (others). Litho Format (No. **MS**422), Questa (others)).

1980 (20 Nov). *Pottery. T* **123** *and similar horiz designs. Multicoloured. W* **53** *(sideways). P* 14.
418 4 s. Type **123** 10 10
419 10 s. Beer brewing pot 10 10
420 15 s. Water pot 15 15
421 25 s. Pot shapes 25 30
418/21 .. .. *Set of* 4 50 50
MS422 150 × 110 mm. 40 s. × 4 Wedgwood plaques of Prince Philip; Queen Elizabeth II; Prince Charles; Princess Anne (*each* 22 × 35 *mm*). P 14 × 14½ .. .. 1·00 1·40
No. **MS**422 was issued to commemorate the 250th birth anniversary of Josiah Wedgwood.

(Des G. Vasarhelyi. Litho Format)

1980 (1 Dec). *80th Birthday of Queen Elizabeth the Queen Mother. T* **124** *and similar multicoloured designs. P* 14½.
423 5 s. Type **124** 25 25
a. Horiz strip of 3. Nos. 423/5 .. .. 1·60
424 10 s. Queen Elizabeth the Queen Mother .. 30 30
425 1 m. Basutoland 1947 Royal Visit 2d. commemorative and flags (54 × 44 *mm*) 1·25 1·25
423/5 .. .. *Set of* 3 1·60 1·60
Nos. 423/5 were printed together, *se-tenant*, in horizontal strips of 3 throughout small sheets of nine stamps.

125 Lesotho Evangelical Church, Morija

(Des G. Vasarhelyi. Litho Format (75 s., 1 m. 50), Harrison (others))

1980 (8 Dec). *Christmas. T* **125** *and similar horiz designs. Multicoloured. No wmk (75 s.) or W* **53** *(others). P* 14 × 14½.
426 4 s. Type **125** 10 10
427 15 s. St. Agnes' Anglican Church, Teyateyaneng 10 10
428 25 s. Cathedral of Our Lady of Victories, Maseru 15 10
429 75 s. University Chapel, Roma 45 50
426/9 .. .. *Set of* 4 65 60
MS430 110 × 85 mm. 1 m. 50, Nativity scene (43 × 29 *mm*). No wmk. P 14½ .. .. 1·00 1·25

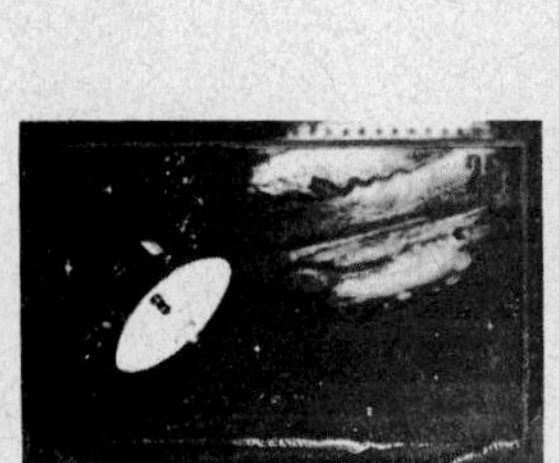

126 "Voyager" Satellite and Jupiter

127 Greater Kestrel

(Des G. Vasarhelyi. Litho Format)

1981 (15 Mar). *Space Exploration. T* **126** *and similar horiz designs. Multicoloured. P* 13½ × 14.
431 25 s. Type **126** 40 30
a. Horiz strip of 5. Nos. 431/5 .. .. 1·75
432 25 s. "Voyager" and Saturn 40 30
433 25 s. "Voyager" passing Saturn 40 30
434 25 s. "Space Shuttle" releasing satellite .. 40 30
435 25 s. "Space Shuttle" launch 40 30
431/5 .. .. *Set of* 5 1·75 1·40
MS436 111 × 85 mm. 1 m. 40, Saturn .. .. 1·75 1·50
Nos. 431/5 were printed together, *se-tenant*, in horizontal strips of 5 throughout the sheet.

(Des G. Vasarhelyi. Litho Format)

1981 (20 Apr–Dec). *Birds. Multicoloured designs as T* **127**. *P* 14½.
437 1 s. Type **127** 10 10
a. Perf 13 (12.81) 20 10
438 2 s. Speckled Pigeon (*horiz*) 10 10
a. Perf 13 (12.81) 35 10
439 3 s. South African Crowned Crane 15 10
440 5 s. Bokmakierie Shrike 15 10
a. Perf 13 (12.81) 40 10
441 6 s. Cape Robin Chat 20 10
442 7 s. Yellow Canary 20 10
443 10 s. Red-billed Pintail (*horiz*) 30 10
a. Perf 13 (12.81) 50 10
444 25 s. Malachite Kingfisher 65 15
445 40 s. Yellow-tufted Malachite Sunbird (*horiz*) 75 30
446 60 s. Cape Longclaw (*horiz*) .. .. 1·00 45
447 75 s. Hoopoe (*horiz*) .. .. 1·50 50
448 1 m. Red Bishop (*horiz*) .. .. 1·75 1·00
449 2 m. Egyptian Goose (*horiz*) .. .. 2·75 3·00
450 5 m. Lilac-breasted Roller (*horiz*) .. .. 5·50 7·00
437/50 .. .. *Set of* 14 14·00 11·50
Nos. 437/41 and 443 exist with different imprint dates below the designs.
For these stamps watermarked w 14 see Nos. 500/13.

128 Wedding Bouquet from Lesotho

(Des J.W. Litho Format)

1981 (22 July). *Royal Wedding. T* **128** *and similar vert designs. Multicoloured. P* 14.
451 25 s. Type **128** 40 40
a. Booklet pane. No. 451 × 3 plus printed label .. .. 1·10
b. Booklet pane. Nos. 451/3 plus printed label .. .. 2·10
452 50 s. Prince Charles riding 75 75
a. Booklet pane. No. 452 × 3 plus printed label .. .. 2·25
453 75 s. Prince Charles and Lady Diana Spencer 1·00 1·00
a. Booklet pane. No. 453 × 3 plus printed label .. .. 3·00
451/3 .. .. *Set of* 3 1·90 1·90
Nos. 451/3 also exist imperforate from a restricted printing (*price for set of* 3 £6 *mint*).

129 Prince Charles and Lady Diana Spencer

(Des G. Vasarhelyi. Litho Format)

1981 (5 Sept). *Royal Wedding* (*2nd issue*). *Sheet* 115 × 90 *mm. P* 14½.
MS454 **129** 1 m. 50, multicoloured .. .. 2·40 2·40
No. **MS**454 also exists imperforate from a restricted printing (*price* £5 *mint*).

130 "Santa planning his Annual Visit"

131 Duke of Edinburgh, Award Scheme Emblem and Flags

1981 (5 Oct). *Christmas. Paintings by Norman Rockwell* (*6 to 60 s.*) *or Botticelli* (*1 m. 25*). *T* **130** *and similar multicoloured designs. P* 13½.
455 6 s. Type **130** 10 10
456 10 s. "Santa reading his Mail" 15 10
457 15 s. "The Little Spooners" 20 15
458 20 s. "Raleigh Rockwell Travels" 30 20
459 25 s. "Ride 'em Cowboy" 35 25
460 60 s. "The Discovery" 80 75
455/60 .. .. *Set of* 6 1·75 1·40
MS461 111 × 85 mm. 1 m. 25, "Mystic Nativity" (48 × 31 *mm*). P 13½ × 14 .. .. 1·75 1·90

(Des G. Vasarhelyi. Litho Format)

1981 (5 Nov). *25th Anniv of Duke of Edinburgh Award Scheme. T* **131** *and similar multicoloured designs. P* 14½.
462 6 s. Type **131** 10 10
463 7 s. Tree planting 10 10
464 25 s. Gardening 30 30
465 40 s. Mountain climbing 50 50
466 75 s. Award Scheme emblem 85 85
462/6 .. .. *Set of* 5 1·75 1·75
MS467 111 × 85 mm. 1 m. 40, Duke of Edinburgh (45 × 30 *mm*) .. .. 1·60 1·60

132 Wild Cat

(Des G. Vasarhelyi. Litho Format)

1981 (16 Nov). *Wildlife. T* **132** *and similar multicoloured designs. P* 13½ (6, 25 *s.*) *or* 14½ (*others*).
468 6 s. Type **132** 15 10
469 20 s. Chacma Baboon (44 × 31 *mm*) 30 30
470 25 s. Eland 35 35
471 40 s. Cape Porcupine (44 × 31 *mm*) 60 60
472 50 s. Oribi (44 × 31 *mm*) 75 75
468/72 .. .. *Set of* 5 1·90 1·90
MS473 111 × 85 mm. 1 m. 50, Black-backed Jackal (47 × 31 *mm*). P 13½ × 14 .. .. 1·60 1·90

133 Scout Bugler

(Des G. Vasarhelyi. Litho Format)

1982 (5 Mar). *75th Anniv of Boy Scout Movement. T* **133** *and similar horiz designs. Multicoloured. P* 13½.
474 6 s. Type **133** 25 25
a. Booklet pane. Nos. 474/8 × 2 and **MS**479 6·50
475 30 s. Scouts hiking 50 50
476 40 s. Scout sketching 60 60
477 50 s. Scout with flag 65 65
478 75 s. Scouts saluting 80 80
474/8 .. .. *Set of* 5 2·50 2·50
MS479 117 × 92 mm. 1 m. 50, Lord Baden-Powell 2·00 2·50

134 Jules Rimet Trophy with Footballers and Flags of 1930 Finalists (Argentina and Uruguay)

(Des G. Vasarhelyi. Litho Format)

1982 (14 Apr). *World Cup Football Championship, Spain. T* **134** *and similar horiz designs showing World Football Cup with players and flags of countries in past finals* (*Nos. 480/90*). *Multicoloured. P* 14½.
480 15 s. Type **134** 20 20
a. Sheetlet. Nos. 480/91 .. .. 2·10
481 15 s. Jules Rimet Trophy with Czechoslovakia and Italy, 1934 .. .. 20 20
482 15 s. Jules Rimet Trophy with Hungary and Italy, 1938 .. .. 20 20
483 15 s. Jules Rimet Trophy with Brazil and Uruguay, 1950 .. .. 20 20
484 15 s. Jules Rimet Trophy with Hungary and West Germany, 1954 .. .. 20 20
485 15 s. Jules Rimet Trophy with Sweden and Brazil, 1958 .. .. 20 20
486 15 s. Jules Rimet Trophy with Czechoslovakia and Brazil, 1962 .. .. 20 20
487 15 s. Jules Rimet Trophy with West Germany and England, 1966 .. .. 20 20
488 15 s. Jules Rimet Trophy with Italy and Brazil, 1970 .. .. 20 20
489 15 s. World Cup with Holland and West Germany, 1974 .. .. 20 20
490 15 s. World Cup with Holland and Argentina, 1978 .. .. 20 20
491 15 s. World Cup and map of World on footballs 20 20
480/91 .. .. *Set of* 12 2·10 2·10
MS492 118 × 93 mm. 1 m. 25, Bernabeu Stadium, Madrid (47 × 35 *mm*). P 13½ .. .. 2·00 2·25
Nos. 480/91 were printed together, *se-tenant*, in a sheetlet of 12.

135 Portrait of George Washington

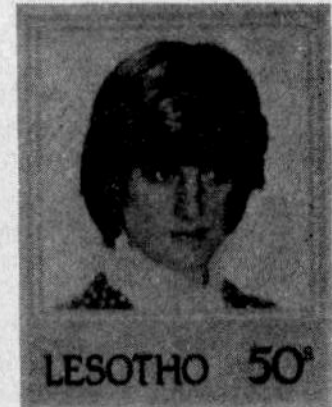

136 Lady Diana Spencer in Tetbury, May 1981

(Des G. Vasarhelyi. Litho Format)

1982 (7 June). *250th Birth Anniv of George Washington.* T **135** *and similar horiz designs. Multicoloured. P* 14 × 13½.

493 6 s. Type **135** 10 10
494 7 s. Washington with step-children and dog 10 10
495 10 s. Washington with Indian chief 15 10
496 25 s. Washington with troops 35 35
497 40 s. Washington arriving in New York .. 50 50
498 1 m. Washington on parade .. .. .. 1·25 1·25
493/8 .. .. *Set of* 6 2·25 2·25
MS499 117 × 92 mm. 1 m. 25, Washington crossing the Delaware .. .. 1·50 1·50

1982 (14 June). *As Nos.* 437/50 *but W w* **14** (*sideways on Nos.* 500, 502/5 *and* 507).

500 1 s. Type **127** 10 15
501 2 s. Speckled Pigeon (*horiz*) 10 15
502 3 s. South African Crowned Crane 10 15
503 5 s. Bokmakierie Shrike 10 10
504 6 s. Cape Robin Chat 10 10
505 7 s. Yellow Canary 10 10
506 10 s. Red-billed Pintail (*horiz*) 15 10
507 25 s. Malachite Kingfisher 35 25
508 40 s. Yellow-tufted Malachite Sunbird (*horiz*) 55 35
509 60 s. Cape Longclaw (*horiz*) 80 60
510 75 s. Hoopoe (*horiz*) .. .. 1·25 85
511 1 m. Red Bishop (*horiz*) .. .. 1·60 1·75
512 2 m. Egyptian Goose (*horiz*) .. .. .. 2·75 3·50
513 5 m. Lilac-breasted Roller (*horiz*) .. .. 5·50 8·50
500/13 .. .. *Set of* 14 12·00 15·00

(Des Jennifer Toombs. Litho Format)

1982 (1 July). *21st Birthday of Princess of Wales.* T **136** *and similar vert designs. Multicoloured. W w* **14**. A. *P* 13½. B. *P* 13½ × 14.

	A		B	
514 30 s. Lesotho coat of arms ..	50	50	30	30
515 50 s. Type **136**	45	50	75	80
516 75 s. Wedding picture at Buckingham Palace	75	80	70	70
517 1 m. Formal portrait	1·00	1·25	1·00	1·25
514/17 .. .. *Set of* 4	2·40	2·75	2·40	2·75

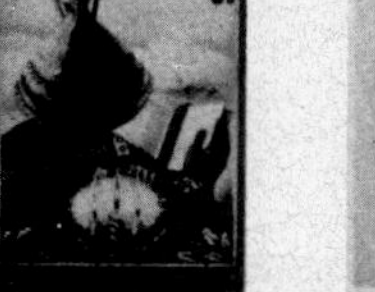

137 Mosotho reading Sesotho Bible **138** Birthday Greetings

(Des G. Vasarhelyi. Litho Format)

1982 (20 Aug). *Centenary of Sesotho Bible,* T **137** *and similar multicoloured designs. P* 14½.

518 6 s. Type **137** 10 10
a. Horiz strip of 3. Nos. 518/20 90
519 15 s. Sesotho Bible and Virgin Mary holding infant Jesus 20 20
520 1 m. Sesotho Bible and Cathedral (62 × 42 *mm*) 70 80
518/20 .. .. *Set of* 3 90 1·00

Nos. 518/20 were printed together, *se-tenant,* in horizontal strips of 3 throughout the sheet.

(Des G. Vasarhelyi. Litho Questa)

1982 (30 Sept). *Birth of Prince William of Wales.* T **138** *and similar vert design. Multicoloured. P* 14 × 13½.

521 6 s. Type **138** 15 15
a. Sheetlet. No. 521 and 522 × 5 .. .. 4·00
522 60 s. Princess Diana and Prince William of Wales 80 80

Nos. 521/2 come from sheetlets of 6 containing one 6 s. and five 60 s. stamps.

139 "A Partridge in a Pear Tree"

(Litho Format)

1982 (1 Dec). *Christmas. "The Twelve Days of Christmas".* T **139** *and similar horiz designs depicting Walt Disney cartoon characters. Multicoloured. P* 11.

523 2 s. Type **139** 10 10
a. Horiz pair. Nos. 523/4 .. .. .. 10 10
524 2 s. "Two turtle doves" 10 10
525 3 s. "Three French hens" 10 10
a. Horiz pair. Nos. 525/6 .. .. .. 10 10
526 3 s. "Four calling birds" 10 10
527 4 s. "Five golden rings" 10 10
a. Horiz pair. Nos. 527/8 .. .. .. 10 15
528 4 s. "Six geese a-laying" 10 10
529 75 s. "Seven swans a-swimming" 90 95
a. Horiz pair. Nos. 529/30 .. .. .. 1·75 1·90
530 75 s. "Eight maids a-milking" 90 95
523/30 .. .. *Set of* 8 1·90 2·10
MS531 126 × 101 mm. 1 m. 50, "Nine ladies dancing, ten lords a-leaping, eleven pipers piping, twelve drummers drumming". P 13½ .. .. 1·75 2·00

Nos. 523/4, 525/6, 527/8 and 529/30 were each printed in horizontal *se-tenant* pairs throughout the sheet.

140 *Lepista cafforum*

(Des G. Vasarhelyi. Litho Format)

1983 (11 Jan). *Fungi.* T **140** *and similar horiz designs. Multicoloured. P* 14½.

532 10 s. Type **140** 10 10
a. *Tête-bêche* (vert pair) 15 20
b. Booklet pane. Nos. 532/5 .. .. .. 1·75
c. Booklet pane. Nos. 532/3 40
533 30 s. *Broomeia congregata* 25 30
a. *Tête-bêche* (vert pair) 50 60
534 50 s. *Afroboletus luteolus* 45 50
a. *Tête-bêche* (vert pair) .. .. .. 90 1·00
535 75 s. *Lentinus tuber-regium* 60 75
a. *Tête-bêche* (vert pair) .. .. .. 1·25 1·50
532/5 .. .. *Set of* 4 1·25 1·50

Nos. 532/5 were each printed in sheets of 36 stamps plus 4 labels as the fourth horizontal row. The stamps in horizontal rows two, six, eight and ten were inverted, forming vertical *tête-bêche* pairs.

141 Ba-Leseli Dance

(Des J.W. Litho Format)

1983 (14 Mar). *Commonwealth Day.* T **141** *and similar multicoloured designs. P* 14½.

536 5 s. Type **141** 10 10
537 30 s. Tapestry weaving 35 40
538 60 s. Queen Elizabeth II (*vert*) 70 85
539 75 s. King Moshoeshoe II (*vert*) .. .. .. 90 1·10
536/9 .. .. *Set of* 4 1·75 2·25

142 "Dancers in a Trance" (rock painting from Ntloana Tsoana)

(Des G. Drummond. Litho Format)

1983 (20 May). *Rock Paintings.* T **142** *and similar multicoloured designs. P* 14½.

540 6 s. Type **142** 15 10
541 25 s. "Baboons", Sehonghong 40 35
542 60 s. "Hunters attacking Mountain Reedbuck", Makhetha 90 95
543 75 s. "Eland", Lehaha la Likhomo .. .. 1·25 1·40
540/3 .. .. *Set of* 4 2·40 2·50
MS544 166 × 84 mm. Nos. 540/3 and 10 s. "Cattle herding", Sehonghong (52 × 52 *mm*) .. .. 2·40 2·75

143 Montgolfier Balloon, 1783

(Des J.W. Litho Format)

1983 (11 July). *Bicentenary of Manned Flight.* T **143** *and similar multicoloured designs. P* 14½.

545 7 s. Type **143** 10 10
a. Booklet pane. Nos. 545/8 .. .. .. 2·40
546 30 s. Wright brothers and *Flyer* 35 40
547 60 s. First airmail flight 70 75
548 1 m. "Concorde" .. .. 1·50 1·50
545/8 .. .. *Set of* 4 2·40 2·50
MS549 180 × 92 mm. Nos. 545/8 and 6 s. Dornier "228" of Lesotho Airways (60 × 60 *mm*) .. .. 2·40 2·75

144 Rev. Eugene Casalis

(Des G. Vasarhelyi. Litho Questa)

1983 (5 Sept). *150th Anniv of Arrival of the French Missionaries.* T **144** *and similar horiz designs. Multicoloured. P* 13½ × 14.

550 6 s. Type **144** 10 10
a. *Tête-bêche* (vert pair) 10 15
551 25 s. The founding of Morija 30 35
a. *Tête-bêche* (vert pair) 60 70
552 40 s. Baptism of Libe 50 55
a. *Tête-bêche* (vert pair) .. .. .. 1·00 1·10
553 75 s. Map of Lesotho 90 95
a. *Tête-bêche* (vert pair) .. .. .. 1·75 1·90
550/3 .. .. *Set of* 4 1·60 1·75

Nos. 550/3 were each issued in sheets of 20 containing two panes (2 × 5) separated by a vertical gutter. Within these sheets horizontal rows two and four are inverted forming *tête-bêche* vertical pairs.

145 Mickey Mouse and Pluto Greeted by Friends

(Litho Questa)

1983 (18 Oct). *Christmas.* T **145** *and similar horiz designs showing Disney cartoon characters in scenes from "Old Christmas" (Washington Irving's sketchbook). Multicoloured. P* 14 × 13½.

554 1 s. Type **145** 10 10
555 2 s. Donald Duck and Pluto 10 10
556 3 s. Donald Duck with Huey, Dewey and Louie 10 10
557 4 s. Goofy, Donald Duck and Mickey Mouse 10 10
558 5 s. Goofy holding turkey, Donald Duck and Mickey Mouse 10 10
559 6 s. Goofy and Mickey Mouse 10 10
560 75 s. Donald and Daisy Duck .. .. .. 1·00 70
561 1 m. Goofy and Clarabell .. .. .. 1·60 1·25
554/61 .. .. *Set of* 8 2·75 2·00
MS562 132 × 113 mm. 1 m. 75, Scrooge McDuck, Pluto and Donald Duck .. .. 2·25 2·00

146 African Monarch

(Des and litho Format)

1984 (20 Jan). *Butterflies.* T **146** *and similar horiz designs. Multicoloured. P* 14.

563 1 s. Type **146** 10 10
564 2 s. Mountain Beauty 10 10
565 3 s. Orange Tip 15 10
566 4 s. Blue Pansy 15 10
567 5 s. Yellow Pansy 15 10
568 6 s. African Migrant 15 10
569 7 s. African Leopard 15 10
570 10 s. Suffused Acraea 20 10
571 15 s. Painted Lady 25 10
572 20 s. Lemon Traveller 30 10
573 30 s. Foxy Charaxes 35 20
574 50 s. Broad-bordered Grass Yellow 50 30
575 60 s. Meadow White 55 35
576 75 s. Queen Purple Tip 60 40
577 1 m. Diadem 85 70
578 5 m. Christmas Butterfly .. .. 3·50 3·50
563/78 .. .. *Set of* 16 7·00 5·50

147 "Thou Shalt not have Strange Gods before Me"

(Des G. Vasarhelyi. Litho Format)

1984 (30 Mar). *Easter. The Ten Commandments.* T **147** *and similar vert designs. Multicoloured. P* 13½ × 14.

579 20 s. Type **147** 25 25
a. Sheetlet. Nos. 579/88 .. .. 2·25
580 20 s. "Thou shalt not take the name of the Lord thy God in vain" 25 25
581 20 s. "Remember thou keep holy the Lord's Day" 25 25
582 20 s. "Honour thy father and mother" .. 25 25
583 20 s. "Thou shalt not kill" 25 25
584 20 s. "Thou shalt not commit adultery" .. 25 25
585 20 s. "Thou shalt not steal" 25 25
586 20 s. "Thou shalt not bear false witness against thy neighbour" 25 25
587 20 s. "Thou shalt not covet thy neighbour's wife" 25 25
588 20 s. "Thou shalt not covet thy neighbour's goods" 25 25
579/88 .. .. *Set of* 10 2·25 2·25
MS589 102 × 73 mm. 1 m. 50, Moses with Tablets (45 × 28 *mm*). P 14. .. .. 1·50 1·60

Nos. 579/88 were printed together in small sheets of 12 including 2 *se-tenant* stamp-size labels.

148 Torch Bearer

(Des G. Vasarhelyi. Litho Format)

1984 (3 May). *Olympic Games, Los Angeles.* T **148** *and similar horiz designs. Multicoloured. P* 13½ × 14.

590 10 s. Type **148** 10 10
591 30 s. Horse-riding 30 35
592 50 s. Swimming 50 55
593 75 s. Basketball 70 75
594 1 m. Running .. .. 95 1·10
590/4 .. .. *Set of* 5 2·25 2·50
MS595 101 × 72 mm. 1 m. 50, Olympic Flame and flags .. .. 1·50 1·60

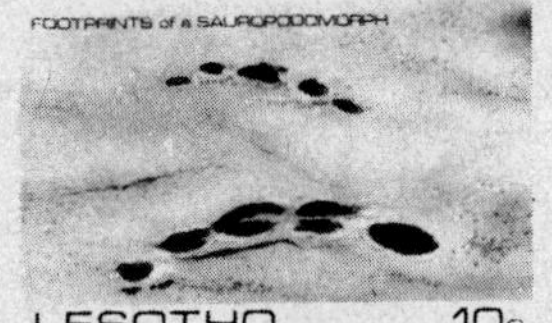

149 Sauropodomorph Footprints

(Des G. Drummond. Litho Format)

1984 (2 July). *Prehistoric Footprints (2nd series).* T **149** *and similar horiz designs. Multicoloured. P* 13½ × 14.

596 10 s. Type **149** 45 10
597 30 s. Lesothosaurus footprints .. .. 1·25 45
598 50 s. Footprint of carnivorous dinosaur .. 1·50 75
596/8 .. .. *Set of* 3 3·00 1·10

150 Wells Fargo Coach, 1852

(Des G. Vasarhelyi. Litho Format)

1984 (5 Sept). *"Ausipex" International Stamp Exhibition, Melbourne, and Bicentenary of First Mail Coach Run.* T **150** *and similar horiz designs. Multicoloured. P* 14.

599 6 s. Type **150** 10 10
a. Sheetlet. Nos. 599 × 4 and No. 603 .. 70
600 7 s. Basotho mail cart, *circa* 1900 .. 10 10
a. Sheetlet. No. 600 × 4 and No. 603 .. 80
601 10 s. Bath mail coach, 1784 .. .. 10 10
a. Sheetlet. No. 601 × 4 and No. 603 .. 90
602 30 s. Cobb coach, 1853.. .. .. .. 30 35
a. Sheetlet. No. 602 × 4 and No. 603 .. 1·60
603 50 s. Exhibition logo and Royal Exhibition Buildings, Melbourne (82 × 25 *mm*) .. 50 55
599/603 .. .. *Set of* 5 95 1·10
MS604. 147 × 98 mm. 1 m. 75, G.B. Penny Black, Basutoland 1934 "OFFICIAL" optd 6d. and Western Australia 1854 4d. with frame inverted (82 × 25 *mm*) .. .. 1·90 2·00

In addition to the listed sheetlets, Nos. 599/602 also exist in separate sheets of 50. No. 603 only comes from the sheetlets.

151 "The Orient Express" (1900)

(Des Walsall. Litho Format)

1984 (5 Nov). *Railways of the World.* T **151** *and similar horiz designs. Multicoloured. P* 14 × 13½.

605 6 s. Type **151** 20 10
606 15 s. German State Railways Class "05" No. 05001 (1935) 25 20
607 30 s. Caledonian Railway *Cardean* (1906) .. 50 35
608 60 s. Santa Fe "Super Chief" (1940) 85 65
609 1 m. L.N.E.R. "Flying Scotsman" (1934) .. 1·25 1·00
605/9 .. .. *Set of* 5 2·75 2·00
MS610 108 × 82 mm. 2 m. South African Railways "The Blue Train" (1972) .. .. 2·75 2·50

152 Eland Calf

153 Crown of Lesotho

(Des G. Drummond. Litho Format)

1984 (20 Dec). *Baby Animals.* T **152** *and similar horiz designs. Multicoloured. P* 14 × 13½ (1 *m.*) *or* 15 (*others*).

611 15 s. Type **152**.. .. .. 25 20
612 20 s. Young Chacma Baboons 30 25
613 30 s. Oribi calf 45 30
614 75 s. Young Natal Red Hares .. .. 1·00 75
615 1 m. Black-backed Jackal pups (46 × 27 *mm*) 1·25 1·25
611/15 .. .. *Set of* 5 3·00 2·50

(Des G. Vasarhelyi. Litho Format)

1985 (30 Jan). *Silver Jubilee of King Moshoeshoe II.* T **153** *and similar vert designs. Multicoloured. P* 15.

616 6 s. Type **153**.. .. .. 10 10
617 30 s. King Moshoeshoe in 1960 .. .. 20 25
618 75 s. King Moshoeshoe in traditional dress, 1985 .. .. 50 55
619 1 m. King Moshoeshoe in uniform, 1985 .. 70 75
616/19 .. .. *Set of* 4 1·25 1·50

154 Christ condemned to Death

(Des G. Vasarhelyi. Litho Format)

1985 (8 Mar). *Easter. The Stations of the Cross.* T **154** *and similar vert designs. Multicoloured. P* 11.

620 20 s. Type **154**.. .. .. 15 15
a. Sheetlet. Nos. 620/33 .. .. .. 1·75
621 20 s. Christ carrying the Cross 15 15
622 20 s. Falling for the first time 15 15
623 20 s. Christ meets Mary 15 15
624 20 s. Simon of Cyrene helping to carry the Cross 15 15
625 20 s. Veronica wiping the face of Christ .. 15 15
626 20 s. Christ falling a second time 15 15
627 20 s. Consoling the women of Jerusalem .. 15 15
628 20 s. Falling for the third time 15 15
629 20 s. Christ being stripped 15 15
630 20 s. Christ nailed to the Cross 15 15
631 20 s. Dying on the Cross 15 15
632 20 s. Christ taken down from the Cross .. 15 15
633 20 s. Christ being laid in the sepulchre .. 15 15
620/33 .. .. *Set of* 14 1·75 1·75
MS634 138 × 98 mm. 2 m. "The Crucifixion" (Mathias Grünewald). P 13½ × 14 .. .. 1·90 2·00

Nos. 620/33 were printed together, *se-tenant*, in a sheetlet of 14 stamps with one stamp-sized label which appears in the central position.

155 Duchess of York with Princess Elizabeth, 1931

(Des G. Vasarhelyi. Litho Format)

1985 (30 May). *Life and Times of Queen Elizabeth the Queen Mother.* T **155** *and similar multicoloured designs. P* 13½ × 14.

635 10 s. Type **155**.. .. .. 15 10
636 30 s. The Queen Mother in 1975 .. .. 40 40
637 60 s. Queen Mother with Queen Elizabeth and Princess Margaret, 1980 .. .. 70 70
638 2 m. Four generations of Royal Family at Prince Henry's christening, 1984 .. 2·75 2·75
635/8 .. .. *Set of* 4 3·50 3·50
MS639 139 × 98 mm. 2 m. Queen Elizabeth with the Princess of Wales and her children at Prince Henry's christening (37 × 50 *mm*) .. .. 2·40 2·50

156 B.M.W. "732i"

157 American Cliff Swallow

(Litho Format)

1985 (10 June). *Century of Motoring.* T **156** *and similar multicoloured designs. P* 14 × 13½.

640 6 s. Type **156**.. .. .. 15 10
641 10 s. Ford "Crown Victoria" 20 15
642 30 s. Mercedes-Benz "500SE" 55 40
643 90 s. Cadillac "Eldorado Biarritz" .. .. 1·50 1·25
644 2 m. Rolls-Royce "Silver Spirit" .. .. 2·50 2·50
640/4 .. .. *Set of* 5 4·50 4·00
MS645 139 × 98 mm. 2 m. Rolls-Royce "Silver Ghost Tourer", 1907 (37 × 50 *mm*). P 13½ × 14 .. 2·75 3·00

(Litho Format)

1985 (5 Aug). *Birth Bicentenary of John J. Audubon (ornithologist).* T **157** *and similar multicoloured designs showing original paintings. P* 15.

646 5 s. Type **157**.. .. .. 15 10
647 6 s. Great Crested Grebe (*horiz*) 15 10
648 10 s. Vesper Sparrow (*horiz*).. .. .. 30 15
649 30 s. Greenshank (*horiz*) 55 40
650 60 s. Stilt Sandpiper (*horiz*) 95 85
651 2 m. Glossy Ibis (*horiz*) .. .. .. 2·50 2·75
646/51 .. .. *Set of* 6 4·25 3·75

Nos. 646/51 were reissued in February 1986 in sheetlets containing five stamps and one label.

158 Two Youths Rock-climbing

159 U.N. (New York) 1951 1 c. Definitive and U.N. Flag

(Des Walsall. Litho Format)

1985 (26 Sept). *International Youth Year and 75th Anniv of Girl Guide Movement.* T **158** *and similar vert designs. Multicoloured. P* 15.

652 10 s. Type **158**.. .. .. 20 10
653 30 s. Young technician in hospital laboratory 50 40
654 75 s. Three guides on parade.. .. .. 1·00 90
655 2 m. Guide saluting .. .. 2·40 2·40
652/5 .. .. *Set of* 4 3·75 3·50
MS656 138 × 98 mm. 2 m. "Olave, Lady Baden-Powell" (Grace Wheatley) (37 × 50 *mm*). P 13½ × 14 .. .. 2·40 2·75

(Des G. Vasarhelyi. Litho Format)

1985 (15 Oct). *40th Anniv of United Nations Organization.* T **159** *and similar designs. P* 15.

657 10 s. multicoloured 20 10
658 30 s. multicoloured 50 35
659 50 s. multicoloured 85 60
660 2 m. black and bronze-green.. .. .. 2·75 2·75
657/60 .. .. *Set of* 4 4·00 3·50

Designs: *Vert*—30 s. Ha Sofonia Earth Satellite Station; 2 m. Maimonides (physician, philosopher and scholar). *Horiz*—50 s. Lesotho Airways aircraft at Maseru Airport.

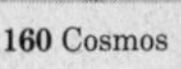

160 Cosmos

161 Male Lammergeier on Watch

(Des G. Drummond. Litho Format)

1985 (11 Nov). *Wild Flowers. T* **160** *and similar vert designs. Multicoloured. P* 15.
661 6 s. Type **160** 20 10
662 10 s. Small Agapanthus 35 10
663 30 s. Pink Witchweed.. .. .. 75 40
664 60 s. Small Iris .. .. 1·25 1·00
665 90 s. Wild Geranium or Cranesbill .. .. 1·75 1·50
666 1 m. Large Spotted Orchid .. .. .. 2·50 2·00
661/6 .. .. *Set of* 6 6·25 4·50

(Des Walt Disney Productions. Litho Questa)

1985 (2 Dec). *150th Birth Anniv of Mark Twain. As T* **118** *of Anguilla, but vert, showing Walt Disney cartoon characters illustrating various Mark Twain quotations. Multicoloured. P* 11.
667 6 s. Mrs. Jumbo and Baby Dumbo 20 10
668 50 s. Uncle Scrooge and Goofy reading newspaper 70 40
669 90 s. Winnie the Pooh, Tigger, Piglet and Owl .. .. 1·00 70
670 1 m. 50, Goofy at ship's wheel .. .. 1·60 1·25
667/70 .. .. *Set of* 4 3·25 2·25
MS671 127 × 102 mm. 1 m. 25, Mickey Mouse as astronaut. P 13½×14 .. .. 2·25 2·00
No. 669 was printed in sheetlets of 8 stamps.

(Des Walt Disney Productions. Litho Format)

1985 (2 Dec). *Birth Bicentenaries of Grimm Brothers (folklorists). Designs as T* **119** *of Anguilla, but vert, showing Walt Disney cartoon characters in scenes from "The Wishing Table". Multicoloured. P* 11.
672 10 s. The tailor (Donald Duck) 25 10
673 60 s. The second son (Dewey) with magic donkey and gold coins 85 55
674 75 s. The eldest son (Huey) with wishing table laden with food .. .. .. 1·00 65
675 1 m. The innkeeper stealing the third son's (Louie) magic cudgel .. .. .. 1·40 85
672/5 .. .. *Set of* 4 3·25 2·00
MS676 127 × 102 mm. 1 m. 50, The tailor and eldest son with wishing table. P 13½×14 .. 2·50 3·00
No. 673 was printed in sheetlets of 8 stamps.

(Des G. Drummond. Litho Format)

1986 (20 Jan). *Flora and Fauna of Lesotho. T* **161** *and similar vert designs. Multicoloured. P* 15.
677 7 s. Type **161** 35 10
678 9 s. Prickly Pear 35 10
679 12 s. Stapelia 40 15
680 15 s. Pair of Lammergeiers 70 25
681 35 s. Pig's Ears 75 40
682 50 s. Male Lammergeier in flight .. .. 1·60 80
683 1 m. Adult and juvenile Lammergeiers .. 2·25 2·00
684 2 m. Columnar cereus .. .. .. 3·00 3·25
677/84 .. .. *Set of* 8 8·50 6·25
MS685 125×106 mm. 2 m. Verreaux's Eagle .. 5·00 5·50

162 Two Players chasing Ball

163 International Year of the Child Gold Coin

(Des Lori Anzalone. Litho Questa)

1986 (17 Mar). *World Cup Football Championship, Mexico. T* **162** *and similar vert designs. Multicoloured. P* 14.
686 35 s. Type **162** 55 40
687 50 s. Goalkeeper saving goal.. .. .. .. 75 55
688 1 m. Three players chasing ball .. .. 1·75 1·75
689 2 m. Two players competing for ball .. 2·75 2·75
686/9 .. .. *Set of* 4 5·25 5·00
MS690 104×74 mm. 3 m. Player heading ball .. 4·25 4·75

(Des W. Hanson. Litho Questa)

1986 (5 Apr). *Appearance of Halley's Comet. Horiz designs as T* **123** *of Anguilla. Multicoloured. P* 14.
691 9 s. Galileo and 200 inch Hale telescope, Mount Palomar Observatory, California 20 10
692 15 s. Halley's Comet and "Pioneer Venus 2" spacecraft 30 15
693 70 s. Halley's Comet of 684 A.D. (from Nuremberg Chronicle, 1493) 85 60
694 3 m. Comet and landing of William the Conqueror, 1066 .. .. 2·75 3·00
691/4 .. .. *Set of* 4 3·75 3·50
MS695 101×70 mm. 4 m. Halley's Comet over Lesotho .. .. 3·75 4·25

(Litho Format)

1986 (Apr). *First Anniv of New Currency* (1980). *T* **163** *and similar horiz designs. Multicoloured. P* 13½×14.
696 30 s. Type **163** .. .. 6·50 5·50
a. Horiz strip of 5. Nos. 696/700 .. .. 30·00
697 30 s. Five maloti banknote .. .. .. 6·50 5·50
698 30 s. Fifty lisente coin .. .. .. 6·50 5·50
699 30 s. Ten maloti banknote .. .. .. 6·50 5·50
700 30 s. One sente coin .. .. 6·50 5·50
696/700 .. .. *Set of* 5 30·00 25·00
Nos. 696/700 were printed together, *se-tenant*, in horizontal strips of 5 throughout the sheet.
These stamps were prepared in 1980, but were not issued at that time. Due to increased postal rates a severe shortage of 30 s. stamps occurred in 1986 and Nos. 696/700 were sold for postal purposes from mid-April until early August.

(Des L. Nardo. Litho Questa)

1986 (21 Apr). *60th Birthday of Queen Elizabeth II. Vert designs as T* **125** *of Anguilla. P* 14.
701 90 s. black and yellow 60 60
702 1 m. multicoloured 65 65
703 2 m. multicoloured .. .. 1·40 1·40
701/3 .. .. *Set of* 3 2·40 2·40
MS704 119×85 mm. 4 m. black and grey-brown 3·00 3·50
Designs:—90 s. Princess Elizabeth in pantomime; 1 m. Queen at Windsor Horse Show, 1971; 2 m. At Royal Festival Hall, 1971; 4 m. Princess Elizabeth in 1934.

(Des J. Iskowitz. Litho Questa)

1986 (5 May). *Centenary of Statue of Liberty. Multicoloured designs as T* **211** *of Dominica, showing the Statue of Liberty and immigrants to the U.S.A. Multicoloured. P* 14.
705 15 s. Bela Bartok (composer).. .. .. 35 15
706 35 s. Felix Adler (philosopher) 45 30
707 1 m. Victor Herbert (composer) .. .. 1·50 85
708 3 m. David Niven (actor) .. .. .. 2·75 2·50
705/8 .. .. *Set of* 4 4·50 3·50
MS709 103×74 mm. 3 m. Statue of Liberty (*vert*) 2·75 3·25

(Des Walt Disney Productions. Litho Format)

1986 (25 May). *"Ameripex" International Stamp Exhibition, Chicago. Horiz designs as T* **212** *of Dominica showing Walt Disney cartoon characters delivering mail. Multicoloured. P* 11.
710 15 s. Mickey Mouse and Goofy as Japanese mail runners 15 15
711 35 s. Mickey Mouse and Pluto with mail sledge 35 30
712 1 m. Goofy as postman riding Harley-Davidson motorcycle 80 70
713 2 m. Donald Duck operating railway mailbag apparatus .. .. 1·50 1·40
710/13 .. .. *Set of* 4 2·50 2·25
MS714 127×101 mm. 4 m. Goofy driving mail to aircraft. P 14×13½ .. .. 3·50 3·75

9s (164) 9s (165) 15s (166) 35s (167) 35s (167*a*)

35s
Small "s"

Nos. 720a, 720ba, 721a, 721ca. Occurs eleven times in the sheet of 40 on R. 1/5, 1/6, 1/8, 1/9, 2/6, 2/7, 2/8, 3/5, 4/4, 4/6 and 4/8 for Nos. 720a and 720ba or R. 1/4, 2/4, 4/4, 5/4, 6/4, 7/1, 7/4, 9/1, 9/3, 10/1 and 10/2 for Nos. 721a and 721ca.
No. 728a. Occurs thirteen times in the sheet of 49 on R. 6/2 to 7 and on all positions in Row 7.

9s (168) 35s (169) 20s (170)

1986 (6 June)–**88**. *Various stamps surch* (*a*) *As T* **164**/**7***a* *by Lesotho Ads, Maseru.* (i) *On Nos.* 440, 447, 500/1, 506/7 *and* 509.
715 9 s. on 10 s. Red-billed Pintail (*horiz*) (No. 506) (Type **164**) .. .. 1·25 1·25
a. Surch on No. 443 ("1982" imprint date) .. .. 2·25 2·25
b. Surch double .. .. † —
c. Surch double, one inverted .. .. † —
716 15 s. on 1 s. Type **127** (No. 500) (22.8.86) 4·00 3·00
a. Surch on No. 437 .. .. ..
b. Surch on No. 437a .. .. .. 5·00 6·00
717 15 s. on 2 s. Speckled Pigeon (*horiz*) (22.8.86) .. .. 4·00 4·50
a. Surch double .. .. 60·00
718 15 s. on 5 s. Bokmakierie Shrike ("1982" imprint date) (2.11.87) 40 35
719 15 s. on 60 s. Cape Longclaw (*horiz*) (No. 509) (22.8.86) .. .. .. 2·75 2·75
a. Surch on No. 446 .. .. .. 45·00 20·00
720 35 s. on 25 s. Malachite Kingfisher (No. 507) (9.87) .. .. 15·00 20·00
a. Small "s" .. .. 32·00 35·00
b. Surch on No. 444 .. .. .. 50·00 50·00
ba. Small "s" £100 £100
721 35 s. on 75 s. Hoopoe (*horiz*) (No. 447) (Type **167**) (9.87) .. .. .. 16·00 16·00
a. Small "s" .. .. 32·00 32·00
b. Surch double .. .. 55·00
c. Surch on No. 510 .. .. .. £110 95·00
ca. Small "s" £200
721*d* 35 s. on 75 s. Hoopoe (*horiz*) (No. 447) (Type **167***a*) (1.88) .. .. 75·00

(ii) *On Nos.* 563/5, 567, 573 *and* 575/6
722 9 s. on 30 s. Foxy Charaxes (Type **164**) (1.7.86) 15 10
a. Surch with Type **165** .. .. 6·50 4·50
ab. Surch double .. .. † —
723 9 s. on 60 s. Meadow White (Type **165**) (1.7.86) .. .. 4·00 4·00
a. Surch double .. .. 50·00
b. Surch double, one inverted .. .. 50·00
724 15 s. on 1 s. Type **146** (25.6.86) .. .. 2·75 2·75
725 15 s. on 2 s. Mountain Beauty (25.6.86) .. 20 20
726 15 s. on 3 s. Orange Tip (25.6.86) 20 20
727 15 s. on 5 s. Yellow Pansy (14.8.87) .. 20 20
a. Surch double .. .. 32·00
728 35 s. on 75 s. Queen Purple Tip (15.8.86) 35 35
a. Small "s" .. .. 1·50 1·50

(*b*) *As T* **168**/**70** *by Epic Printers, Maseru.*
(i) *On Nos.* 440 *and* 444
729 9 s. on 5 s. Bokmakierie Shrike ("1982" imprint date) (30.12.87) 15 20
730 16 s. on 25 s. Malachite Kingfisher (No. 444) (3.88) .. .. 1·00 1·00
a. Surch on No. 507 .. .. .. £225
731 35 s. on 25 s. Malachite Kingfisher (No. 444) (15.12.87) 60 60
a. Surch on No. 507 .. .. .. 13·00 10·00

(ii) *On Nos.* 566 *and* 569
732 20 s. on 4 s. Blue Pansy (30.12.87) 30 30
a. Surch double, one inverted .. .. 12·00 9·00
733 40 s. on 7 s. African Leopard (30.12.87) .. 50 50

(iii) *On No.* 722
734 3 s. on 9 s. on 30 s. Foxy Charaxes (2.2.88) 15 15
a. Surch Type **164** double .. .. † —
735 7 s. on 9 s. on 30 s. Foxy Charaxes (2.2.88) 25 25
715/35 .. .. *Set of* 21 45·00 50·00

(Des D. Miller. Litho Questa)

1986 (23 July). *Royal Wedding. Vert designs as T* **213** *of Antigua. Multicoloured. P* 14.
736 50 s. Prince Andrew and Miss Sarah Ferguson 40 40
737 1 m. Prince Andrew 70 70
738 3 m. Prince Andrew piloting helicopter .. 2·00 2·00
736/8 .. .. *Set of* 3 2·75 2·75
MS739 88×88 mm. 4 m. Prince Andrew and Miss Sarah Ferguson (*different*) .. .. .. 3·25 3·50

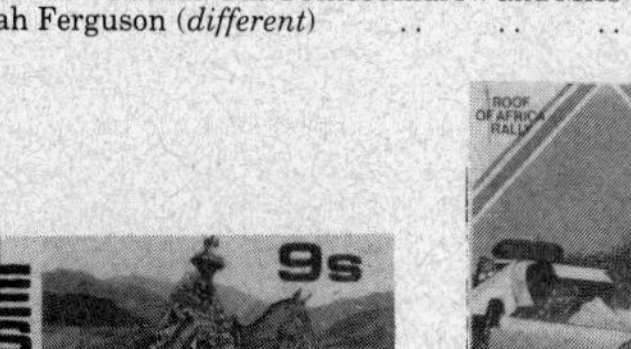

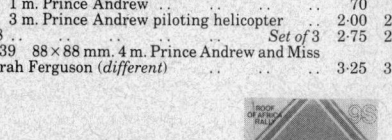

171 Basotho Pony and Rider

172 Rally Car

(Des B. Bundock. Litho Format)

1986 (3 Oct). *20th Anniv of Independence. T* **171** *and similar horiz designs. Multicoloured. P* 15.
740 9 s. Type **171** 25 10
741 15 s. Basotho woman spinning mohair .. 30 15
742 35 s. Crossing river by rowing boat.. .. 45 30
743 3 m. Thaba Tseka Post Office .. .. 2·40 2·50
740/3 .. .. *Set of* 4 3·00 2·75
MS744 109×78 mm. 4 m. King Moshoeshoe I .. 4·50 4·75

(Des Walt Disney Co. Litho Format)

1986 (4 Nov). *Christmas. Multicoloured designs as T* **220** *of Antigua, but vert, showing Walt Disney cartoon characters. P* 11.
745 15 s. Chip n'Dale pulling Christmas cracker 15 15
746 35 s. Mickey and Minnie Mouse 35 30
747 1 m. Pluto pulling Christmas taffy 75 70
748 2 m. Aunt Matilda baking .. .. .. 1·40 1·40
745/8 .. .. *Set of* 4 2·40 2·25
MS749 126×102 mm. 5 m. Huey and Dewey with gingerbread house. P 13½×14 .. .. .. 3·75 4·00

(Litho Questa)

1987 (28 Apr). *Roof of Africa Motor Rally. T* **172** *and similar vert designs. Multicoloured. P* 14.
750 9 s. Type **172** 10 10
751 15 s. Motorcyclist 15 10
752 35 s. Motorcyclist (*different*) 30 25
753 4 m. Rally car (*different*) .. .. .. 2·50 2·50
750/3 .. .. *Set of* 4 2·75 2·75

173 Lawn Tennis

174 Isaac Newton and Reflecting Telescope

(Des Y. Berry. Litho Questa)

1987 (29 May). *Olympic Games, Seoul* (1988) (*1st issue*). *T* **173** *and similar vert designs. Multicoloured. P* 14.
754 9 s. Type **173** 10 10
755 15 s. Judo 10 10
756 20 s. Athletics.. .. .. 15 15
757 35 s. Boxing 20 25
758 1 m. Diving 55 60
759 3 m. Ten-pin bowling .. .. .. 1·60 1·75
754/9 .. .. *Set of* 6 2·40 2·75
MS760 Two sheets, each 75×105 mm. (a) 2 m. Lawn tennis (*different*). (b) 4 m. Football *Set of* 2 *sheets* 3·25 3·50
Nos. 754/60 incorrectly show the Lesotho flag with white field and emblem at top right.
Similar stamps, with face values of 5, 10, 25, 40, 50 s., 3 m. 50 and a 4 m. miniature sheet showing the correct flag with white field and emblem at top left, were placed on philatelic sale from 30 November 1987. They were not, however, according to the Lesotho Philatelic Bureau, sold through post offices and agencies for postal purposes (*Price for set of* 6 £2.40, *mint; miniature sheet* £2.75 *mint*).
See also Nos. 838/42.

(Des Mary Walters. Litho Format)

1987 (30 June). *Great Scientific Discoveries. T* **174** *and similar horiz designs. Multicoloured. P* 15.

761 5 s. Type **174** . . 10 10
762 9 s. Alexander Graham Bell and first telephone . . 10 10
763 75 s. Robert Goddard and liquid fuel rocket . . 40 45
764 4 m. Chuck Yeager and "X-1" rocket plane . . 2·25 2·40
761/4 . . *Set of* 4 2·50 2·75
MS765 98 × 68 mm. 4 m. "Mariner 10" spacecraft 2·25 2·75

175 Grey Rhebuck

176 Scouts hiking

(Des G. Drummond. Litho Format)

1987 (14 Aug). *Flora and Fauna. T* **175** *and similar multicoloured designs. P* 15.

766 5 s. Type **175** . . 15 10
767 9 s. Cape Clawless Otter . . 15 10
768 15 s. Cape Grey Mongoose . . 20 10
769 20 s. Free State Daisy (*vert*) . . 25 15
770 35 s. River Bells (*vert*) . . 40 25
771 1 m. Turkey Flower (*vert*) . . 90 80
772 2 m. Sweet Briar (*vert*) . . 1·75 2·00
773 3 m. Mountain Reedbuck . . 2·00 2·25
766/73 . . *Set of* 8 5·25 5·00
MS774 114 × 98 mm. (a) 2 m. Pig-Lily (*vert*). (b) 4 m. Cape Wildebeest . . *Set of* 2 *sheets* 3·75 4·25

(Des Mary Walters. Litho Questa)

1987 (10 Sept). *World Scout Jamboree, Australia. T* **176** *and similar vert designs. Multicoloured. P* 14.

775 9 s. Type **176** . . 10 10
776 15 s. Scouts playing football . . 15 10
777 35 s. Kangaroos . . 25 25
778 75 s. Scout saluting . . 50 45
779 4 m. Australian scout windsurfing . . 2·25 2·50
775/9 . . *Set of* 5 3·00 3·00
MS780 96 × 66 mm. 4 m. Outline map and flag of Australia . . 2·75 3·25

177 Spotted Trunkfish and Columbus' Fleet

178 "Madonna and Child" (detail)

(Des I. MacLaury. Litho Questa)

1987 (14 Dec). *500th Anniv of Discovery of America by Columbus* (1992). *T* **177** *and similar horiz designs. Multicoloured. P* 14.

781 9 s. Type **177** . . 10 10
782 15 s. Green Turtle and ships . . 10 10
783 35 s. Columbus watching Common Dolphins from ship . . 20 25
784 5 m. White-tailed Tropic Bird and fleet at sea . . 2·75 3·00
781/4 . . *Set of* 4 2·75 3·00
MS785 105 × 76 mm. 4 m. *Santa Maria* and Cuban Amazon in flight . . 2·25 2·40
No. 782 is inscribed "Carribbean" in error.

(Litho Questa)

1987 (21 Dec). *Christmas. T* **178** *and similar vert designs showing religious paintings by Raphael. Multicoloured. P* 14.

786 9 s. Type **178** . . 10 10
787 15 s. "Marriage of the Virgin" . . 15 10
788 35 s. "Coronation of the Virgin" (detail) . . 30 25
789 90 s. "Madonna of the Chair" . . 70 80
786/9 . . *Set of* 4 1·10 1·10
MS790 75 × 100 mm. 3 m. "Madonna and Child enthroned with Five Saints" (detail) . . 1·60 1·75

179 Lesser Pied Kingfisher

40TH WEDDING ANNIVERSARY
H.M. QUEEN ELIZABETH II
H.R.H. THE DUKE OF EDINBURGH

(**180**)

(Des G. Drummond. Litho Format)

1988 (5 Apr). *Birds. T* **179** *and similar horiz designs. Multicoloured. Without printer's imprint. P* 15.

791 2 s. Type **179** . . 10 10
792 3 s. Three-banded Plover . . 10 10
793 5 s. Spur-winged Goose . . 10 10
794 10 s. Clapper Lark . . 10 10
795 12 s. Red-eyed Bulbul . . 10 10
796 16 s. Cape Weaver . . 10 10
797 20 s. Paradise Sparrow ("Red-headed Finch") . . 10 10
798 30 s. Mountain Chat . . 10 15
799 40 s. Stonechat . . 15 20
800 55 s. Pied Barbet . . 20 25
801 60 s. Cape Glossy Starling . . 25 30
802 75 s. Cape Sparrow . . 30 35
803 1 m. Cattle Egret . . 40 45
804 3 m. Giant Kingfisher . . 1·25 1·40
805 10 m. Helmet Guineafowl . . 4·00 4·25
791/805 . . *Set of* 15 6·25 7·00
For these stamps showing Questa imprint at bottom left see Nos. 887/99.

1988 (3 May). *Royal Ruby Wedding. Nos.* 701/4 *optd with T* **180** *in silver.*

806 90 s. black and yellow . . 55 55
807 1 m. multicoloured . . 60 60
808 2 m. multicoloured . . 1·00 1·00
806/8 . . *Set of* 3 1·90 1·90
MS809 119 × 85 mm. 4 m. black and grey-brown 2·25 2·50

181 Mickey Mouse and Goofy outside Presidential Palace, Helsinki

(Des Walt Disney Co. Litho Questa)

1988 (2 June). *"Finlandia '88" International Stamp Exhibition, Helsinki. T* **181** *and similar horiz designs showing Walt Disney cartoon characters in Finland. Multicoloured. P* 14 × 13½.

810 1 s. Type **181** . . 10 10
811 2 s. Goofy and Mickey Mouse in sauna . . 10 10
812 3 s. Goofy and Mickey Mouse fishing in lake . . 10 10
813 4 s. Mickey and Minnie Mouse and Finlandia Hall, Helsinki . . 10 10
814 5 s. Mickey Mouse photographing Goofy at Sibelius Monument, Helsinki . . 10 10
815 10 s. Mickey Mouse and Goofy pony trekking . . 10 10
816 3 m. Goofy, Mickey and Minnie Mouse at Helsinki Olympic Stadium . . 1·40 1·50
817 5 m. Mickey Mouse and Goofy meeting Santa at Arctic Circle . . 2·25 2·40
810/17 . . *Set of* 8 3·50 3·75
MS818 Two sheets, each 127 × 102 mm. (a) 4 m. Mickey Mouse and nephew as Lapps. (b) 4 m. Daisy Duck, Goofy, Mickey and Minnie Mouse by fountain, Helsinki . . *Set of* 2 *sheets* 3·75 4·00

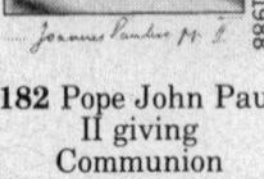

182 Pope John Paul II giving Communion

183 Large-toothed Rock Hyrax

(Litho Questa)

1988 (1 Sept). *Visit of Pope John Paul II. T* **182** *and similar multicoloured designs. P* 14.

819 55 s. Type **182** . . 35 30
820 2 m. Pope leading procession . . 1·25 1·25
821 3 m. Pope at airport . . 1·75 1·75
822 4 m. Pope John Paul II . . 2·25 2·25
819/22 . . *Set of* 4 5·00 5·00
MS823 98 × 79 mm. 5 m. Archbishop Morapeli (*horiz*) . . 2·25 2·40

(Des L. Watkins. Litho B.D.T.)

1988 (13 Oct). *Small Mammals of Lesotho. T* **183** *and similar vert designs. Multicoloured. P* 14.

824 16 s. Type **183** . . 15 10
825 40 s. Ratel and Honey Guide (bird) . . 35 25
826 75 s. Small-spotted Genet . . 55 40
827 3 m. Yellow Mongoose . . 1·75 2·00
824/7 . . *Set of* 4 2·50 2·50
MS828 110 × 78 mm. 4 m. Meerkat . . 1·90 2·00

184 "Birth of Venus" (detail) (Botticelli)

(Litho Questa)

1988 (17 Oct). *Famous Paintings. T* **184** *and similar vert designs. Multicoloured. P* 13½ × 14.

829 15 s. Type **184** . . 10 10
830 25 s. "View of Toledo" (El Greco) . . 15 15
831 40 s. "Maids of Honour" (detail) (Velasquez) 25 25
832 50 s. "The Fifer" (Manet) . . 30 30
833 55 s. "Starry Night" (detail) (Van Gogh) . . 30 30
834 75 s. "Prima Ballerina" (Degas) . . 40 40
835 2 m. "Bridge over Water Lilies" (Monet) . . 95 95
836 3 m. "Guernica" (detail) (Picasso) . . 1·50 1·50
829/36 . . *Set of* 8 3·50 3·50
MS837 Two sheets, each 110 × 95 mm. (a) 4 m. "The Presentation of the Virgin in the Temple" (Titian). (b) 4 m. "The Miracle of the Newborn Infant" (Titian) . . *Set of* 2 *sheets* 3·75 4·00

185 Wrestling

(Des J. Martin. Litho B.D.T.)

1988 (11 Nov). *Olympic Games, Seoul (2nd issue). T* **185** *and similar multicoloured designs. P* 14.

838 12 s. Type **185** . . 10 10
839 16 s. Show jumping (*vert*) . . 10 10
840 55 s. Shooting . . 35 30
841 3 m. 50, As 16 s. (*vert*) . . 1·75 1·75
838/41 . . *Set of* 4 2·00 2·00
MS842 108 × 77 mm. 4 m. Olympic flame (*vert*) . . 1·90 2·00

186 Yannick Noah and Eiffel Tower, Paris

(Des J. McDaniels. Litho Questa)

1988 (18 Nov). *75th Anniv of International Tennis Federation. T* **186** *and similar multicoloured designs. P* 14.

843 12 s. Type **186** . . 15 15
844 20 s. Rod Laver and Sydney Harbour Bridge and Opera House . . 15 15
845 30 s. Ivan Lendl and Prague . . 25 25
846 65 s. Jimmy Connors and Tokyo (*vert*) . . 45 45
847 1 m. Arthur Ashe and Barcelona (*vert*) . . 60 60
848 1 m. 55, Althea Gibson and New York (*vert*) 90 90
849 2 m. Chris Evert and Vienna (*vert*) . . 1·25 1·25
850 2 m. 40, Boris Becker and Houses of Parliament, London (*vert*) . . 1·50 1·50
851 3 m. Martina Navratilova and Golden Gate Bridge, San Francisco . . 1·75 1·75
843/51 . . *Set of* 9 6·25 6·25
MS852 98 × 72 mm. 4 m. Steffi Graf and Berlin 2·40 2·75
No. 844 is inscribed "SIDNEY" in error.

(Litho Questa)

1988 (1 Dec). *Christmas. 500th Birth Anniv of Titian (artist). Multicoloured designs as T* **238** *of Antigua, but inscr* "CHRISTMAS 1988". *P* 13½ × 14.

853 12 s. "The Averoldi Polyptych" (detail) . . 10 10
854 20 s. "Christ and the Adulteress" (detail) . . 15 15
855 35 s. "Christ and the Adulteress" (different detail) . . 20 20
856 45 s. "Angel of the Annunciation" . . 25 25
857 65 s. "Saint Dominic" . . 35 35
858 1 m. "The Vendramin Family" (detail) . . 50 50
859 2 m. "Mary Magdalen" . . 95 95
860 3 m. "The Tribute Money" . . 1·50 1·50
853/60 . . *Set of* 8 3·50 3·50
MS861 (a) 94 × 110 mm. 5 m. "Mater Dolorosa". P 13½ × 14. (b) 110 × 94 mm. 5 m. "Christ and the Woman taken in Adultery" (*horiz*). P 14 × 13½ . . *Set of* 2 *sheets* 5·00 5·50

MINIMUM PRICE

The minimum price quote is 10p which represents a handling charge rather than a basis for valuing common stamps. For further notes about prices see introductory pages.

187 Pilatus "PC-6 Turbo Porter"

(Des K. Grommel. Litho Questa)

1989 (30 Jan). *125th Anniv of International Red Cross. Aircraft. T* **187** *and similar multicoloured designs. P* 14.
862 12 s. Type **187** 15 10
863 20 s. Unloading medical supplies from Cessna "Caravan" 15 10
864 55 s. De Havilland "DHC-6 Otter" 35 30
865 3 m. Douglas "DC-3" .. .. .. 1·75 1·75
862/5 .. .. *Set of* 4 2·25 2·00
MS866 109×80 mm. 4 m. Red Cross logo and Douglas "DC-3" (*vert*) .. .. 2·25 2·40

(Litho Questa)

1989 (19 June). *Japanese Art. Paintings by Hiroshige. Horiz designs as T* **250** *of Antigua. Multicoloured. P* 14×13½.
867 12 s. "Dawn Mist at Mishima" 10 10
868 16 s. "Night Snow at Kambara" 10 10
869 20 s. "Wayside Inn at Mariko Station" .. 10 10
870 35 s. "Shower at Shono" 15 20
871 55 s. "Snowfall on the Kisokaido near Oi" .. 25 30
872 1 m. "Autumn Moon at Seba" 40 50
873 3 m. 20, "Evening Moon at Ryogoku Bridge" 1·50 1·60
874 5 m. "Cherry Blossoms at Arashiyama" .. 2·25 2·40
867/74 .. .. *Set of* 8 4·50 4·75
MS875 Two sheets, each 102×76 mm. (a) 4 m. "Listening to the Singing Insects at Dokanyama". (b) 4 m. "Moonlight, Nagakubo" *Set of* 2 *sheets* 3·75 4·00
Nos. 867/74 were each printed in sheetlets of 10 containing two horizontal strips of 5 stamps separated by printed labels commemorating Emperor Hirohito.

188 Mickey Mouse as General

189 *Paxillus involutus*

(Des Walt Disney Company. Litho Questa)

1989 (10 July). *"Philexfrance 89" International Stamp Exhibition, Paris. T* **188** *and similar multicoloured designs showing Walt Disney cartoon characters in French military uniforms of the Revolutionary period. P* 13½×14.
876 1 s. Type **188** 10 10
877 2 s. Ludwig von Drake as infantryman .. 10 10
878 3 s. Goofy as grenadier 10 10
879 4 s. Horace Horsecollar as cavalryman .. 10 10
880 5 s. Pete as hussar 10 10
881 10 s. Donald Duck as marine 10 10
882 3 m. Gyro Gearloose as National Guard .. 1·40 1·50
883 5 m. Scrooge McDuck as admiral .. 2·25 2·40
876/83 .. .. *Set of* 8 3·75 4·00
MS884 Two sheets, each 127×102 mm. (a) 4 m. Mickey and Minnie Mouse as King Louis XVI and Marie Antoinette with Goofy as a National Guard (*horiz*). P 14×13½. (b) 4 m. Mickey Mouse as drummer. P 13½×14 .. *Set of* 2 *sheets* 3·75 4·00

(Litho Questa)

1989 (5 Sept)–**90**. *As Nos.* 793, 795/7 *and* 803/5, *but with printer's imprint at bottom left. P* 14.
887 5 s. Spur-winged Goose (18.1.90) .. 10 10
889 12 s. Red-eyed Bulbul 10 10
890 16 s. Cape Weaver (20.12.89) 10 10
891 20 s. Paradise Sparrow ("Red-headed Finch") (12.89) 10 10
897 1 m. Cattle Egret (1990) 40 45
898 3 m. Giant Kingfisher (1990) .. .. 1·25 1·40
899 10 m. Helmet Guineafowl (1990) .. .. 4·00 4·25
887/99 .. .. *Set of* 7 5·25 5·75

(Des S. Wood. Litho Questa)

1989 (8 Sept). *Fungi. T* **189** *and similar vert designs. Multicoloured. P* 14.
900 12 s. Type **189** 10 10
901 16 s. *Ganoderma applanatum* 10 10
902 55 s. *Suillus granulatus* 25 30
903 5 m. *Stereum hirsutum* .. .. .. 2·25 2·40
900/3 .. .. *Set of* 4 2·25 2·40
MS904 96×69 mm. 4 m. *Scleroderma flavidum* 1·90 2·00

190 Sesotho Huts

191 Marsh Sandpiper

(Des S. Wood. Litho Questa)

1989 (18 Sept). *Maloti Mountains. T* **190** *and similar vert designs. Multicoloured. P* 14.
905 1 m. Type **190** 45 50
a. Horiz strip of 4. Nos. 905/8 .. .. 1·60
906 1 m. American Aloe and mountains .. 45 50
907 1 m. River valley with waterfall 45 50
908 1 m. Sesotho tribesman on ledge 45 50
905/8 .. .. *Set of* 4 1·60 1·75
MS909 86×117 mm. 4 m. Spiral Aloe .. 1·90 2·00
Nos. 905/8 were printed together, *se-tenant*, in horizontal strips on 4 throughout the sheet forming a composite design.

(Des Tracy Pederson. Litho Questa)

1989 (18 Sept). *Migrant Birds. T* **191** *and similar multicoloured designs. P* 14.
910 12 s. Type **191** 10 10
911 65 s. Little Stint 30 35
912 1 m. Ringed Plover 45 50
913 4 m. Curlew Sandpiper .. .. .. 1·90 2·00
910/13 .. .. *Set of* 4 2·40 2·50
MS914 97×69 mm. 5 m. Ruff (*vert*) .. .. 2·25 2·40

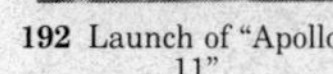

192 Launch of "Apollo 11"

193 English Penny Post Paid Mark, 1680

(Des G. Welker. Litho Questa)

1989 (6 Nov). *20th Anniv of First Manned Landing on Moon. T* **192** *and similar multicoloured designs. P* 14.
915 12 s. Type **192** 10 10
916 16 s. Lunar module *Eagle* landing on Moon (*horiz*) 10 10
917 40 s. Neil Armstrong leaving *Eagle* .. 20 25
918 55 s. Edwin Aldrin on Moon (*horiz*) .. 25 30
919 1 m. Aldrin performing scientific experiment (*horiz*) 45 50
920 2 m. *Eagle* leaving Moon (*horiz*) .. 90 95
921 3 m. Command module *Columbia* in Moon orbit (*horiz*) .. .. 1·40 1·50
922 4 m. Command module on parachutes .. 1·90 2·00
915/22 .. .. *Set of* 8 4·75 5·00
MS923 81×111 mm. 5 m. Astronaut on Moon 2·25 2·40

(Des U. Purins. Litho B.D.T.)

1989 (17 Nov). *"World Stamp Expo '89" International Stamp Exhibition, Washington. Stamps and Postmarks. T* **193** *and similar horiz designs. P* 14.
924 75 s. brown-lake, black and stone 35 40
a. Sheetlet. Nos. 924/32 .. .. 2·75
925 75 s. black, grey and rosine 35 40
926 75 s. dull violet, black and cinnamon .. 35 40
927 75 s. red-brown, black and cinnamon .. 35 40
928 75 s. black and olive-yellow 35 40
929 75 s. multicoloured 35 40
930 75 s. black and bright brown-lilac .. 35 40
931 75 s. black, bright carmine and pale brown 35 40
932 75 s. brt carmine, black & greenish yellow 35 40
924/32 .. .. *Set of* 9 2·75 3·25
Designs:— No. 925, German postal seal and feather, 1807; 926, British Post Offices in Crete 1898 20 pa. stamp; 927, Bermuda 1848 Perot 1d. provisional; 928, U.S.A. Pony Express cancellation, 1860; 929, Finland 1856 5 k. stamp; 930, Fiji 1870 *Fiji Times* 1d. stamp, 1870; 931, Sweden newspaper wrapper handstamp, 1823; 932, Bhor 1879 ½ a. stamp.
Nos. 924/32 were printed together, *se-tenant*, in sheetlets of 9.

(Des Design Element. Litho Questa)

1989 (17 Nov). *"World Stamp Expo '89" International Stamp Exhibition, Washington (2nd issue). Sheet* 78×61 *mm containing horiz design as T* **257** *of Antigua. Multicoloured. P* 14.
MS933 4 m. Cathedral Church of Saints Peter and Paul, Washington .. .. 1·90 2·00

POSTAGE DUE STAMPS

1966 (1 Nov). *Nos.* D9/10 *of Basutoland optd as T* **32** *but smaller.*
D11 D **2** 1 c. carmine 15 50
a. "LSEOTHO" (R.4/7) .. .. 25·00
D12 5 c. deep reddish violet 20 90
a. "LSEOTHO" (R.4/7) .. .. 45·00
No. D11 exists with the overprint centred near the foot of the stamp (just above "POSTAGE DUE") (*price £50 mint*). It is believed that this comes from a proof sheet which was issued in the normal way. It contains the "LSEOTHO" error, which only occurred in the first printing.

D 1 D 2

(Litho B.W.)

1967 (18 Apr). *No wmk. P* 13½.
D13 D **1** 1 c. blue .. .. 15 1·00
D14 2 c. brown-rose .. .. .. 15 1·10
D15 5 c. emerald .. .. .. 20 1·25
D13/15 .. .. *Set of* 3 45 3·00

1976 (30 Nov). *W* **53** (*sideways*). *P* 13½.
D17 D **1** 2 c. rose-red .. .. .. 70 1·50
D18 5 c. emerald .. .. .. 1·25 2·00

(Des G. Vasarhelyi. Litho)

1986. *No wmk. P* 13×13½.
D19 D **2** 2 s. light green 10 10
D20 5 s. new blue 10 10
D21 25 s. violet 10 10
D19/21 .. .. *Set of* 3 20 20

Appendix

The following stamps have either been issued in excess of postal needs, or have not been made available to the public in reasonable quantities at face value. Miniature sheets, imperforate stamps etc., are excluded from this section.

1981–83

15th Anniv of Independence. Classic Stamps of the World. 10 m. × 40, each embossed on gold foil.

MADAGASCAR

and the British Empire
1840-1936
— Bought & Sold—

SG 36Aa

RARE AND UNUSUAL STAMPS FOR SERIOUS COLLECTORS.

Want Lists filled from our comprehensive, 30 volume stock of stamps, varieties and postal history (**references please**).

&

We hold several British Empire **public auctions** annually.
Subscription: £25

George W. Holschauer
Colonial Stamp Co.

5410 Wilshire Blvd., Suite 202
Los Angeles, CA 90036, U.S.A.
(213) 933-9435• FAX(213) 939-9930

Members: IFSDA,PTS,ASDA,Int'l Soc. of Appraisers

FINE STAMPS DESERVE FINE ALBUMS

Many of the world's leading collections are housed in Stanley Gibbons peg-fitting albums – albums which have stood the test of time from the Devon, now in its 35th year of production to the Philatelic which has been housing the great collections of the world for over a century! The elegant binders are all manufactured to the highest specifications and embody all that is best in traditional quality and craftsmanship. Their easy-action peg-fitting mechanism ensures that leaves can be added, removed or rearranged without fuss.

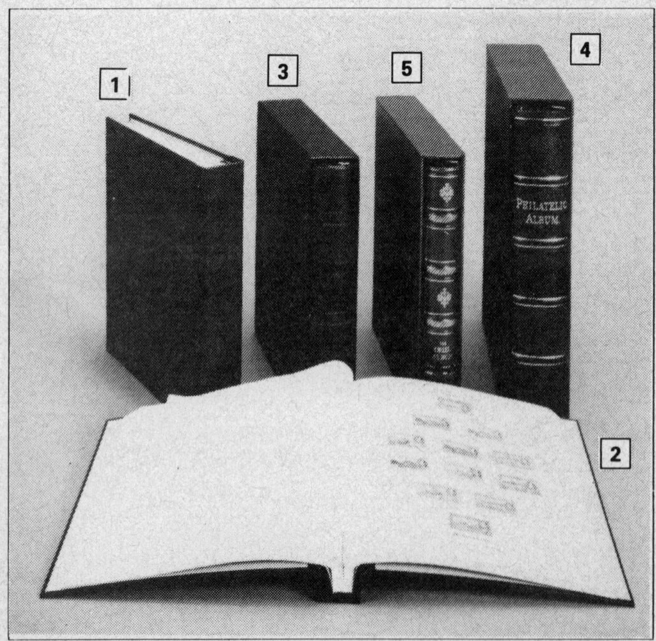

(1) **THE DEVON** (Item 2834)
A strong elegant, large-capacity binder containing 100 fine quality cartridge leaves ($10\frac{3}{8}$in. × $9\frac{3}{4}$in.). Choice of maroon, green, black or blue. Ideal for collections where that extra capacity is required. Transparent interleaving available, boxed.

(2) **THE EXETER** (Item 2832)
A quality binder in a choice of red, blue or green containing 40 leaves ($10\frac{3}{8}$in. × $9\frac{3}{4}$in.) of fine white cartridge. All leaves are double linen-hinged with transparent facing so that leaves lie flat when the album is opened.

(3) **THE PLYMOUTH** (Item 0392)
Maroon, black, green or blue, a connosseur's album in a strong matching slip-case. Supplied with 40 double linen-hinged leaves ($10\frac{3}{8}$in. × $9\frac{3}{4}$in.) with glassine facing for additional protection.

(4) **THE PHILATELIC** (Item 3921)
The largest album in the Stanley Gibbons range, it not only accommodates more stamps per page than other albums but also allows sheets, blocks, etc. to be arranged and mounted on its $12\frac{7}{8}$in × $10\frac{3}{4}$in. leaves. Bound in handsome deep green cloth with leather corners and spine, supplied with 80 double linen-hinged, transparent faced leaves and presented in a sturdy deep green slip-case.

(5) **THE ORIEL** (Item 0395)
Supreme among luxury blank albums, the Oriel will enhance the very finest collection. Half bound in rich red leather with gold tooling, each album contains 50 superior gilt-edged double linen-hinged leaves ($10\frac{3}{8}$in. × $9\frac{5}{8}$in.) with transparent facings and is supplied in a luxury matching slip-case. The most prestigious home for your stamps.

Additional binders and leaves are available for all Stanley Gibbons peg-fitting albums.

For further details visit your favourite stamp shop or write to:

Stanley Gibbons Publications Ltd.,
5 Parkside, Christchurch Road,
Ringwood, Hampshire BH24 3SH.
Telephone 0425 472363

Long Island

PRICES FOR STAMPS ON COVER

Most covers from Long Island are philatelic, but these are worth from ×2 (Nos. 1/3) or from ×6 (others).

The Turkish island of Chustan (or Keustan) in the Gulf of Smyrna was occupied by the Royal Navy during April 1916 and renamed Long Island.

The following stamps were provided by the Civil Administrator, Lieut-Cmdr H. Pirie-Gordon, for the postal service inaugurated on 7 May 1916.

(1)

2

1916 (7 May). *Turkish fiscal stamps surch by typewriter as in T* **1**. *No wmk. P* 12.

1 ½d. on 20 pa. green and buff (new value in red, remainder of surch in black) £2250 £4000
2 1d. on 10 pa. carmine and buff £2500 £4000
3 2½d. on 1 pi. violet and buff (R.) £2500 £4000

Quantities issued: ½d. 25; 1d. 20; 2½d. 25.

1916 (7 May). *Typewritten as T* **2** *in various colours of ribbon and carbon. Each stamp initialled by the Civil Administrator. No gum. Imperf.*

(*a*) *On pale green paper with horizontal grey lines. No wmk. Sheets of* 16 *or* 12 *with stamps initialled in red ink.*

4 ½d. black £425
a. "G.R.I." double £1300
b. "7" for "&" .. ..
5 ½d. blue £475
a. "G.R.I." double £1500
b. "7" for "&" .. ..
6 ½d. mauve £450
a. "G.R.I." double £1500
b. "7" for "&" £1500

Quantity issued: 140 in all.

(*b*) *On thin horiz laid paper with sheet wmk of* "SILVER LINEN" *in double-lined capitals. Sheets of* 20 *with stamps initialled in red ink.*

7 ½d. black £250
a. "postage" for "Postage" £600
8 ½d. blue £250
9 ½d. mauve £150
a. "postage" for "Postage" £500
b. "7" for "&" £500
10 1d. black £110
a. "7" for "&" £425
b. "Rvevue" for "Revenue" .. ..
11 1d. blue £110
c. "postage" for "Postage" £375
e. "G.R?I?" for "G.R.I." £750
f. "ONR" for "ONE" £375
12 1d. mauve £110 £200
a. "7" for "&" £425
e. "G.R?I?" for "G.R.I." .. .. .. † £750
f. "ONR" for "ONE" £500
g. "Postegg" for "Postage" £500
13 1d. red £100 £175
a. "7" for "&" £425
f. "ONR" for "ONE" £425 £600
14 2½d. black £400
15 2½d. blue £400 £500
16 2½d. mauve £400
17 6d. black (*inscr* "SIX PENCE") £500
19 6d. mauve (*inscr* "SIX PENCE") £160 £250
a. "SIXPENCE" (one word) £500
20 1s. black £100
a. "ISLANA" for "ISLAND" £400
b. "Postge" for "Postage" £500 £600
c. "Rebenue for "Revenue" £500
21 1s. blue £200
22 1s. mauve .. .. 90·00
b. "ISLANA" for "ISLAND" £425
c. "Rebenue" for "Revenue" £550

Quantities issued (all colours); ½d. 280; 1d. 1068; 2½d. 80; 6d. 100; 1s. 532.

(*c*) *On thin wove paper. No wmk. Sheets of* 24 *with stamps initialled in indelible pencil.*

23 ½d. black £150
25 ½d. mauve £400
26 1d. black £170 £200
27 1d. red £450 £500
30 2d. black £140
a. "ISTAD" for "ISLAND" £1200
b. Error. 1d. and 2d. *se-tenant* £1600
c. Initialled in red ink .. .. .. — £300
31 2d. mauve £140
a. Error. 1d. and 2d. *se-tenant* £2000
32 2½d. black £250 £300
33 2½d. blue £600
34 2½d. mauve £400 £450
35 6d. black £140 £200
a. "Rvenne" for "Revenue" £450
b. Error. 2d. and 6d. *se-tenant*, also "ISLND" for "ISLAND" £1800
36 6d. blue £400
b. Error. 2d. and 6d. *se-tenant*, also "ISLND" for "ISLAND" .. ..

Quantities issued (all colours); ½d. 144; 1d. 144; 2d. 288; 2½d. 144; 6d. 240.

TOP COPIES AND CARBONS. It is believed that the production sequence of the typewritten stamps was as follows:

Nos. 4/6 Three sheets of black top copies, two of 12 and one of 16
Three sheets of blue carbons, two of 12 and one of 16
Five sheets of mauve carbons, all of 12

Nos. 7/9 *Sheets of* 20
Three sheets of black top copies
Three sheets of blue carbons
Eight sheets of mauve carbons

Nos. 10/13 *Sheets of* 20
Eleven sheets of red top copies
Fifteen sheets of black carbons
Six sheets of blue carbons
Twenty-two sheets of mauve carbons

Nos. 14/16 *Sheets of* 20
One sheet of black top copies
One sheet of blue carbons
Two sheets of mauve carbons

Nos. 17/19 *Sheets of* 20
One sheet of black top copies
One sheet of blue carbons*
Three sheets of mauve carbons

Nos. 20/22 *Sheets of* 20
Five sheets of black top copies
Nine sheets of black carbons
Two sheets of blue carbons
Twelve sheets of mauve carbons

Nos. 23/5 *Sheets of* 24
One sheet of black top copies
Three sheets of black carbons
One sheet of blue carbons*
One sheet of mauve carbons

Nos. 26/9 *Sheets of* 24
One sheet of red top copies
Three sheets of black carbons
One sheet of blue carbons*
One sheet of mauve carbons*

Nos. 30/1 *Sheets of* 24
Two sheets of black top copies
Six sheets of black carbons (inc one as No. 30c)
Four sheets of mauve carbons

Nos. 32/4 *Sheets of* 24
One sheet of black top copies
Three sheets of black carbons
One sheet of blue carbons
One sheet of mauve carbons

Nos. 35/6 *Sheets of* 24
Two sheets of black top copies
Six sheets of black carbons
Two sheets of blue carbons

*These carbons are described in written records, but their existence has yet to be confirmed by actual examples.

Madagascar

PRICES FOR STAMPS ON COVER

Nos. 1/47	*from* × 5
Nos. 50/6	*from* × 20
Nos. 57/62	*from* × 30

BRITISH CONSULAR MAIL

After May 1883 mail from the British community at Antananarivo, the capital, was sent by runner to the British Consulate at Tamatave for forwarding via the French Post Office.

In March of the following year the British Vice-Consul at Antananarivo, Mr. W. C. Pickersgill, reorganised this service and issued stamps for use on both local and overseas mail. Such stamps were only gummed at one of the top corners. This was to facilitate their removal from overseas mail where they were replaced by Mauritius stamps (at Port Louis) or by French issues (at the Vice-Consulate) for transmission via Tamatave and Reunion. Local mail usually had the stamps removed also, being marked with a "PAID" or a Vice-Consular handstamp, although a few covers have survived intact.

CONDITION. Due to the type of paper used, stamps of the British Consular Mail are usually found with slight faults, especially thins. Our prices are for average examples, really fine stamps being worth a premium.

USED STAMPS. Postmarks are not usually found on these issues. Cancellations usually take the form of a manuscript line or cross in crayon, ink or pencil or as five parallel horizontal bars in black or red, approximately 15 mm long.

COVER PRICES

Cover factors are quoted at the beginning of each country for most issues to 1945. An explanation of the system can be found on page x. The factors quoted do not, however, apply to philatelic covers.

1

2

1884 (Mar). *Typo locally. Rouletted vertically in colour. No gum, except on one upper corner. With circular consular handstamp reading* "BRITISH VICE-CONSULATE ANTANANARIVO" *around Royal arms in black.*

(*a*) *Inscr* "LETTER".

1 **1** 6d. (½ oz) magenta £300 £325
a. Violet handstamp £700 £750
2 1s. (1 oz) magenta £225 £250
3 1s. 6d. (1½ oz) magenta £225 £250
4 2s. (2 oz) magenta £500 £525

(*b*) *Inscr* "POSTAL PACKET"

5 **1** 1d. (1 oz) magenta £140 £150
a. Without handstamp £1000 £1100
6 2d. (2 oz) magenta £160 £160
7 3d. (3 oz) magenta £140 £150
8 4d. (1 oz amended in ms to "4 oz") magenta £550 £600
a. Without manuscript amendment ..
ab. Violet handstamp £750 £800
ac. Without handstamp £1200 £1200

Nos. 1/8 were printed in horizontal strips of four, each strip containing two impressions of the setting. Each strip contained two stamps with normal stops after "B.C.M." and two with a hollow stop after "B" (1d., 4d., 6d. and 2s.) or after "M" (2d., 3d., 1s. and 1s. 6d.).

Several values are known with the handstamp either inverted or double.

1886. *Manuscript provisionals.*

(*a*) *No.* 2 *with* "SHILLING" *erased and* "PENNY" *written above in red ink*

9 **1** 1d. on 1s. (1 oz) magenta .. ..

(*b*) *No.* 2 *surch* "4½d." *and* "W.C.P." *in red ink with a line through the original value*

10 **1** 4½d. on 1 s. (1 oz) magenta .. ..

1886. *As No.* 1, *but colour changed. Handstamped with circular* "BRITISH VICE-CONSULATE ANTANANARIVO" *in black.*

11 **1** 6d. (½ oz) rose-red £275 £275

1886. *As No.* 8, *but handstamped* "BRITISH CONSULAR MAIL ANTANANARIVO" *in black* (B) *or violet* (V)

	B		V	
12 **1** 4d. (1 oz) magenta	£1200	£1200	£1300	£1300

1886. *Typo locally. Rouletted vertically in colour. No gum, except on one upper corner.*

I. "POSTAGE" 29½ *mm long. Stops after* "POSTAGE" *and value*

(*a*) *Handstamped* "BRITISH VICE-CONSULATE ANTANANARIVO" *in black* (B) *or violet* (V)

	B		V	
14 **2** 1d. rose	55·00	55·00	£150	£150
15 1½d. rose	£225	£225	£225	£250
16 2d. rose	60·00	60·00	£150	£150
17 3d. rose	£350	£350	£150	£150
18 4½d. rose	£350	£350	£160	£160
19 8d. rose	£450	£450	£375	£375
20 9d. rose	—	£1500	£525	£525

(*b*) *Handstamped* "BRITISH CONSULAR MAIL ANTANANARIVO" *in black*

21 **2** 1d. rose .. .. 40·00 45·00
22 1½d. rose .. .. 40·00 45·00
23 2d. rose .. .. 40·00 45·00
24 3d. rose .. .. 40·00 45·00
a. Handstamp in red .. .. .. — £1600
25 4½d. rose .. .. 45·00 50·00
a. Handstamp in red .. .. .. — £1400
26 8d. rose .. .. 55·00 65·00
a. Handstamp in violet £700 £700
27 9d. rose .. .. 55·00 65·00
a. Without handstamp £750
b. Handstamp in violet £110 £110

II. "POSTAGE" 29½ *mm long. No stops after* "POSTAGE" *or value*

(*a*) *Handstamped* "BRITISH VICE-CONSULATE ANTANANARIVO" *in violet*

28 **2** 1d. rose £500 £500
29 1½d. rose £600 £600
30 3d. rose £800 £800
31 4½d. rose £500 £525
32 6d. rose £500 £525

(*b*) *Handstamped* "BRITISH CONSULAR MAIL ANTANANARIVO" *in black* (B) *or violet* (V)

	B		V	
33 1d. rose	40·00	45·00	50·00	55·00
a. Without handstamp ..	£300			
34 1½d. rose	40·00	45·00	55·00	60·00
a. Without handstamp ..	£300			
35 2d. rose	40·00	45·00	55·00	60·00

36	3d. rose	.. .. ..	40·00	45·00	55·00	60·00
	a. Without handstamp	..	£700			
37	4½d. rose	.. .. ..	45·00	50·00	60·00	65·00
	a. Without handstamp	..	£800			
38	6d. rose	.. .. ..	45·00	50·00	£125	£125
	a. Without handstamp	..	£900			

III. "POSTAGE" 24½ *mm long. No stop after* "POSTAGE", *but stop after value.*

(*a*) *Handstamped* "BRITISH VICE-CONSULATE ANTANANARIVO" *in violet*

39	**2**	4d. rose	£250	£275
40		8d. rose	£450	£450
41		1s. 6d. rose	£1200	£1300
42		2s. rose	£800	£800
		a. Handstamp in black		

(*b*) *Handstamped* "BRITISH CONSULAR MAIL ANTANANARIVO" *in black* (B) *or violet* (V)

		B		V	
43	4d. rose	60·00	65·00	£150	£150
	a. Without handstamp	£650			
44	8d. rose	£150	£150	£175	£175
	a. Without handstamp	£700			
45	1s. rose	£100	£100	£500	£500
	a. Without handstamp	£750			
46	1s. 6d. rose	£175	£175	£600	£600
	a. Without handstamp	£1000			
47	2s. rose	£275	£275	£700	£700
	a. Without handstamp	£1000			

The above were also printed in horizontal strips of four.

The stamps of the British Consular Mail were suppressed in 1887, but the postal service continued with the charges paid in cash.

BRITISH INLAND MAIL

In January 1895 the Malagasy government agreed that a syndicate of British merchants at Antananarivo, including the Vice-Consul, should operate an inland postal service during the war with France. Mail was sent by runner to the port of Vatomandry and forwarded via Durban where Natal stamps were added.

Nos. 50/62 were cancelled with dated circular postmarks inscribed "BRITISH MAIL".

4

5 Malagasy Runners

(Typeset London Missionary Society Press, Antananarivo)

1895 (Jan). *Rouletted in black.* (*a*) *Thick laid paper*

50	4	4d. black	20·00	12·00
		a. "FUOR" for "FOUR"	—	£550

(*b*) *Wove paper*

51	4	1d. blue-grey	20·00	12·00
52		6d. pale yellow	20·00	12·00
53		8d. salmon	20·00	12·00
54		1s. fawn	30·00	12·00
55		2s. bright rose	30·00	14·00
		a. Italic "2" at left	£110	60·00
56		4s. grey	45·00	12·00
50/6		*Set of* 7	£170	75·00

There are six types of each value, printed in blocks of 6 (2×3) separated by gutters, four times on each sheet; the upper and lower blocks being *tête-bêche*.

Nos. 50a and 55a occur in the sixth position in their respective blocks. No. 50a was soon corrected.

(Typo John Haddon & Co, London)

1895 (Mar). *The inscription in the lower label varies for each value. P* 12.

57	**5**	2d. blue	5·00	15·00
		a. Imperf between (pair)	£400	
58		4d. rose	5·00	15·00
		a. Imperf between (pair)	£250	
59		6d. green	5·00	15·00
		a. Imperf between (pair)	£400	
60		1s. slate-blue	6·50	20·00
		a. Imperf between (pair)	£400	
61		2s. chocolate	7·00	22·00
		a. Imperf between (pair)	£400	
62		4s. bright purple	10·00	30·00
		a. Imperf between (pair)		
57/62		*Set of* 6	35·00	£100

This post was suppressed when the French entered Antananarivo on 30 September 1895.

PRICES OF SETS

Set prices are given for many issues, generally those containing three stamps or more. Definitive sets include one of each value or major colour change, but do not cover different perforations, die types or minor shades. Where a choice is possible the set prices are based on the cheapest versions of the stamps included in the listings.

Malawi

(*formerly* Nyasaland)

INDEPENDENT

44 Dr. H. Banda (Prime Minister) and Independence Monument

(Des M. Goaman. Photo Harrison)

1964 (6 July). *Independence. T* **44** *and similar horiz designs. P* 14½.

211	3d. yellow-olive and deep sepia	10	10
212	6d. red, gold, blue, carmine and lake	10	10
213	1s. 3d. red, green, black and bluish violet	10	10
214	2s. 6d. multicoloured	15	20
	a. Blue omitted	£180	
211/14	*Set of* 4	25	25

Designs:—6d. Banda and rising sun. 1s. 3d. Banda and Malawi flag; 2s. 6d. Banda and Malawi coat of arms.

Six examples of No. 214a are known from the top horizontal row of an otherwise normal sheet.

48 Tung Tree

49 Christmas Star and Globe

(Des V. Whiteley. Photo Harrison)

1964 (6 July)–**65**. *As Nos.* 199/210 *of Nyasaland but inscr* "MALAWI" *and T* **48** (*9d.*). *No wmk. P* 14½.

215	½d. reddish violet	10	20
216	1d. black and green	10	10
217	2d. light red-brown	10	10
218	3d. red-brown, yellow-green & bistre-brown	15	10
219	4d. black and orange-yellow	25	15
220	6d. bluish violet, yellow-green and light blue	35	10
221	9d. bistre-brown, green and yellow	30	15
222	1s. brown, turquoise-blue and pale yellow	25	10
223	1s. 3d. bronze-green and chestnut	50	40
224	2s. 6d. brown and blue	1·10	1·00
225	5s. blue, green, yellow and sepia	65	2·00
225*a*	5s. blue, green, yellow and sepia (1.6.65)	2·00	90
226	10s. green, orange-brown and black	1·50	2·00
227	£1 deep reddish purple and yellow	5·50	5·50
215/27	*Set of* 14	11·00	11·00

No. 225*a* is inscribed "LAKE MALAWI" instead of "LAKE NYASA".

See also Nos. 252/62.

(Des V. Whiteley. Photo Harrison)

1964 (1 Dec). *Christmas. P* 14½.

228	**49**	3d. blue-green and gold	10	10
		a. Gold (star) omitted	90·00	
229		6d. magenta and gold	10	10
230		1s. 3d. reddish violet and gold	10	10
231		2s. 6d. blue and gold	20	25
228/31		*Set of* 4	30	25
MS231*a*		83 × 126 mm. Nos. 228/31. Imperf	1·00	1·75

No. 228a comes from a sheet on which 41 examples had the gold colour omitted due to a paper fold.

50 Coins

(51)

(Des V. Whiteley. Photo Enschedé)

1965 (1 Mar). *Malawi's First Coinage. Coins in black and silver. P* 13½.

232	**50**	3d. green	10	10
233		9d. magenta	10	10
		a. Silver omitted	†	—
234		1s. 6d. purple	10	10
235		3s. blue	15	20
232/5		*Set of* 4	35	20
MS235*a*		126 × 104 mm. Nos. 232/5. Imperf	1·00	1·10

1965 (14 June). *Nos.* 223/4 *surch as T* **51**.

236	1s. 6d. on 1s. 3d. bronze-green and chestnut	10	10
237	3s. on 2s. 6d. brown and blue	20	15

On No. 237 "3/–" occurs below the bars.

52 Chilembwe leading Rebels

(Des M. Goaman. Photo Harrison)

1965 (20 Aug). *50th Anniv of* 1915 *Rising. P* 14 × 14½.

238	**52**	3d. violet and light olive-green	10	10
239		9d. olive-brown and red-orange	10	10
240		1s. 6d. red-brown and grey-blue	10	10
241		3s. turquoise-green and slate-blue	15	15
238/41		*Set of* 4	25	20
MS241*a*		127 × 83 mm. Nos. 238/41	6·00	7·00

53 "Learning and Scholarship"

(Des H. E. Baxter. Photo Harrison)

1965 (6 Oct). *Opening of Malawi University. P* 14½.

242	**53**	3d. black and emerald	10	10
243		9d. black and magenta	10	10
244		1s. 6d. black and reddish violet	10	10
245		3s. black and blue	15	20
242/5		*Set of* 4	25	20
MS246		127 × 84 mm. Nos. 242/5	3·50	3·50

54 *Papilio ophidicephalus mkuwadzi*

(Des V. Whiteley. Photo Enschedé)

1966 (15 Feb). *Malawi Butterflies. T* **54** *and similar horiz designs. Multicoloured. P* 13½.

247	4d. Type **54**	50	10
248	9d. *Papilio magdae*	75	10
249	1s. 6d. *Epamera handmani*	1·10	30
250	3s. *Amauris crawshayi*	2·50	2·75
247/50	*Set of* 4	4·25	2·75
MS251	130 × 100 mm. Nos. 247/50	12·00	11·00

55 Cockerels

56 Burley Tobacco

57 *Cyrestis camillus sublineatus* (butterfly)

(New values des V. Whiteley (1s. 6d.), M. Goaman (£2). Photo Harrison)

1966–67. *As Nos.* 215 *etc. but W* **55** (*sideways on ½d., 2d.*), *and new values and designs* (*1s. 6d., £2*). *P* 14½.

252	–	½d. reddish violet (1.4.66)	10	10
253	–	1d. black and green (1.4.66)	15	10
254	–	2d. light red-brown (4.6.66)*	15	10
255	–	3d. red-brn, yell-grn & bis-brn (4.3.67)*	20	10
256	–	6d. bluish violet, yell-grn & lt bl (2.7.66)*	25	10
257	**48**	9d. bistre-brown, green & yell (5.12.66)*	35	10
258	–	1s. brown, turquoise-bl & pale yell (1.4.66)	25	10
259	**56**	1s. 6d. chocolate & yellow-grn (15.11.66)	30	10

260 – 5s. blue, green, yellow & sepia (6.10.66)* 7·50 2·00
261 – 10s. green, orange-brown & blk (6.10.66)* 15·00 8·00
262 57 £2 black, orange-yellow, pale yellow and slate-violet (7.9.66) . . . . . . 22·00 24·00
252/62 . . . . *Set of* 11 42·00 30·00

*These are local dates of issue. The Crown Agents, in London, did not distribute these printings until some time later.
No. 260 is inscribed "LAKE MALAWI".
The 2d. exists with both PVA gum and gum arabic.

58 British Central Africa 6d. Stamp of 1891 59 President Banda

(Des V. Whiteley. Photo Harrison)

1966 (4 May–10 June). *75th Anniv of Postal Services. W* **55**. *P* 14½.
263 **58** 4d. grey-blue and yellow-green . . 10 10
264 9d. grey-blue and claret 10 10
265 1s. 6d. grey-blue and reddish lilac . . 15 10
266 3s. grey-blue and new blue 25 30
263/6 . . . . *Set of* 4 45 35
MS267 83 × 127 mm. Nos. 263/6 (10 June) . . 4·00 3·25

REPUBLIC

(Des M. Goaman. Photo Harrison)

1966 (6 July). *Republic Day. W* **55**. *P* 14 × 14½.
268 **59** 4d. brown, silver and emerald 10 10
269 9d. brown, silver and magenta . . 10 10
270 1s. 6d. brown, silver and violet . . 10 10
271 3s. brown, silver and blue 15 15
268/71 . . . . *Set of* 4 25 20
MS272 83 × 127 mm. Nos. 268/71 . . . . 1·75 2·25

60 Bethlehem

(Des and photo Harrison)

1966 (12 Oct). *Christmas. W* **55**. *P* 14½.
273 **60** 4d. myrtle-green and gold 10 10
274 9d. brown-purple and gold 10 10
275 1s. 6d. orange-red and gold 15 10
276 3s. blue and gold 40 50
273/6 . . . . *Set of* 4 65 55

61 *Ilala I*

(Des Mrs. H. Breggar. Photo Harrison)

1967 (4 Jan). *Lake Malawi Steamers. T* **61** *and similar horiz designs. W* **55**. *P* 14½.
277 4d. black, yellow and bright green 20 10
a. Yellow omitted . . . . . .
278 9d. black, yellow and magenta 25 10
279 1s. 6d., black, red and violet 40 15
280 3s. black, red and bright blue . . . . 1·00 1·25
277/80 . . . . *Set of* 4 1·75 1·40

Designs:—9d. *Dove*; 1s. 6d. *Chauncy Maples I* (wrongly inscr "Chauncey"); 3s. *Gwendolen*.

62 Turquoise-gold Chichlid

(Des R. Granger Barrett. Photo Enschedé)

1967 (3 May). *Lake Malawi Chichlids. T* **62** *and similar horiz designs. Multicoloured. W* **55** (*sideways*). *P* 12½ × 12.
281 4d. Type **62** 15 10
282 9d. Red Finned chichlid 20 10
283 1s. 6d. Zebra chichlid 30 10
284 3s. Golden chichlid . . . . . . 1·00 1·00
a. Imperf (pair) £140
281/4 . . . . *Set of* 4 1·50 1·10

63 Rising Sun and Gearwheel

(Des Jennifer Toombs. Litho D.L.R.)

1967 (5 July). *Industrial Development. P* 13½ × 13.
285 **63** 4d. black and emerald 10 10
286 9d. black and carmine 10 10
287 1s. 6d. black and reddish violet . . 10 10
288 3s. black and bright blue 15 15
285/8 . . . . *Set of* 4 25 20
MS289 134 × 108 mm. Nos. 285/8 . . . . 75 1·40

64 Mary and Joseph beside Crib

(Des Jennifer Toombs. Photo Harrison)

1967 (21 Nov–1 Dec). *Christmas. W* **55**. *P* 14 × 14½.
290 **64** 4d. royal blue and turquoise-green . . 10 10
291 9d. royal blue and light red 10 10
292 1s. 6d. royal blue and yellow 10 10
293 3s. royal blue and new blue 15 15
290/3 . . . . *Set of* 4 25 20
MS294 114 × 100 mm. Nos. 290/3. Wmk sideways. P 14 × 13½ (1 Dec) . . . . . . 1·00 2·50

65 *Calotropis procera*

(Des G. Drummond. Litho D.L.R.)

1968 (24 Apr). *Wild Flowers. T* **65** *and similar horiz designs. Multicoloured. W* **55** (*sideways*). *P* 13½ × 13.
295 4d. Type **65** 15 10
296 9d. *Borreria dibrachiata* 15 10
297 1s. 6d. *Hibiscus rhodanthus* 15 10
298 3s. *Bidens pinnatipartita* 20 20
295/8 . . . . *Set of* 4 60 25
MS299 135 × 91 mm. Nos. 295/8 . . . . 1·25 2·50

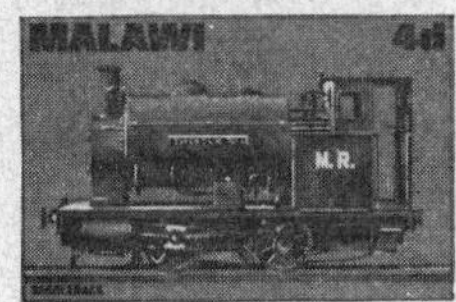

66 Saddleback Steam Locomotive, *Thistle* No. 1

(Des R. Granger Barrett. Photo Harrison)

1968 (24 July). *Malawi Locomotives. T* **66** *and similar horiz designs. W* **55**. *P* 14 × 14½.
300 4d. grey-green, slate-blue and red 25 10
301 9d. red, slate-blue and myrtle-green . . 30 10
302 1s. 6d. multicoloured 55 15
303 3s. multicoloured . . . . . . 1·00 1·00
300/3 . . . . *Set of* 4 1·90 1·25
MS304 120 × 88 mm. Nos. 300/3. P 14½ . . 3·00 5·50

Designs:—9d. Class "G" steam locomotive; 1s. 6d. Diesel locomotive *Zambesi*; 3s. Diesel railcar.

67 "The Nativity" (Piero della Francesca)

(Des and photo Harrison)

1968 (6 Nov). *Christmas. Paintings. T* **67** *and similar horiz designs. Multicoloured. W* **55** (*sideways on* 4*d*.). *P* 14 × 14½.
305 4d. Type **67** 10 10
306 9d. "The Adoration of the Shepherds" (Murillo) 10 10
307 1s. 6d. "The Adoration of the Shepherds" (Reni) 10 10
308 3s. "Nativity with God the Father and Holy Ghost" (Pittoni) 15 10
305/8 . . . . *Set of* 4 25 20
MS309 115 × 101 mm. Nos. 305/8. P 14 × 13½ 35 1·40

68 Scarlet-chested Sunbird 69 Nyasa Lovebird

70 Carmine Bee Eater

(Des V. Whiteley. Photo Harrison)

1968 (13 Nov). *Birds. T* **68**/**70** *and similar designs. Multicoloured. W* **55** (*sideways on* 1*d. to* 4*d. and* 3*s. to* £1). *P* 14½.
310 1d. Type **68** 15 10
311 2d. Violet Starling 15 10
312 3d. White-browed Robin Chat 20 10
313 4d. Red-billed Fire Finch 35 20
a. Red omitted . . . . . .
314 6d. Type **69** 45 10
315 9d. Yellow-rumped Bishop 50 50
316 1s. Type **70** 60 15
317 1s. 6d. Grey-headed Bush Shrike . . 5·00 5·50
318 2s. Paradise Whydah . . . . . . 5·00 6·50
319 3s. African Paradise Flycatcher . . 4·50 3·75
320 5s. Bateleur . . . . 4·50 3·75
321 10s. Saddle-bill Stork . . . . . . 5·50 7·50
322 £1 Purple Heron . . . . . . 11·00 15·00
323 £2 Knysna Turaco . . . . . . 35·00 45·00
310/323 . . . . . . *Set of* 14 65·00 80·00

Sizes:—2d. to 4d. as T **68**; 9d. as T **69**; 1s. 6d., 2s., £2 as T **70**; 3s. to £1 as T **70** but vertical.
No. 310 exists in coils, constructed from normal sheets.

71 I.L.O. Emblem

(Des G. Drummond. Photo, emblem die-stamped Harrison)

1969 (5 Feb). *50th Anniv of the International Labour Organization. W* **55** (*sideways on No.* **MS**328). *P* 14.
324 **71** 4d. gold and myrtle-green 10 10
325 9d. gold and chocolate 10 10
326 1s. 6d. gold and blackish brown . . 10 10
327 3s. gold and indigo 15 15
324/7 . . . . *Set of* 4 25 20
MS328 127 × 89 mm. Nos. 324/7 . . . . 2·25 6·50

72 White-fringed Ground Orchid 73 African Development Bank Emblem

(Des J.W. Litho B.W.)

1969 (9 July). *Orchids of Malawi. T* **72** *and similar horiz designs. Multicoloured. W* **55**. *P* 13½ × 13.
329 4d. Type **72** 15 10
330 9d. Red Ground orchid 20 10
331 1s. 6d. Leopard Tree orchid 30 10
332 3s. Blue Ground orchid . . . . . . 60 1·75
329/32 . . . . *Set of* 4 1·10 1·75
MS333 118 × 86 mm. Nos. 329/32 . . . . 1·10 3·50

(Des G. Vasarhelyi. Litho D.L.R.)

1969 (10 Sept). *Fifth Anniv of African Development Bank. W* **55**. *P* 14.
334 **73** 4d. yellow, yellow-ochre and chocolate 10 10
335 9d. yellow, yellow-ochre & myrtle-green 10 10
336 1s. 6d. yellow, yell-ochre & blackish brn 10 10
337 3s. yellow, yellow-ochre and indigo . . 15 15
334/7 . . . . *Set of* 4 20 20
MS338 102 × 137 mm. Nos. 334/7 . . . . 40 90

OMNIBUS ISSUES

Details, together with prices for complete sets, of the various Omnibus issues from the 1935 Silver Jubilee series to date are included in a special section following Zululand at the end of the catalogue.

74 Dove over Bethlehem

75 Elegant Grasshopper

(Des Jennifer Toombs. Photo Harrison)

1969 (5 Nov). *Christmas. W* **55**. *P* 14½ × 14.
339 **74** 2d. black and olive-yellow 10 10
340 4d. black and deep turquoise 10 10
341 9d. black and scarlet 10 10
342 1s. 6d. black & deep bluish violet .. 10 10
343 3s. black and ultramarine 15 15
339/43 .. .. *Set of* 5 25 20
MS344 130 × 71 mm. Nos. 339/43 .. .. 1·00 1·75
a. Ultramarine (background of 3s.) omitted £400

(Des V. Whiteley. Litho Format)

1970 (4 Feb). *Insects of Malawi. T* **75** *and similar vert designs. Multicoloured. W* **55**. *P* 14.
345 4d. Type **75** 15 10
346 9d. Beam Blister beetle 15 10
347 1s. 6d. Pumpkin ladybird 20 10
348 3s. Praying mantis 35 45
345/8 .. .. *Set of* 4 75 55
MS349 86 × 137 mm. Nos. 345/8 .. .. .. 1·25 2·25

Rand Easter Show
1970

(76)

1970 (18 Mar). *Rand Easter Show. No.* 317 *optd with T* **76**.
350 1s. 6d. multicoloured 15 50

77 Runner

(Des J. Cooter. Litho B.W.)

1970 (3 June). *Ninth British Commonwealth Games, Edinburgh. W* **55**. *P* 13.
351 **77** 4d. royal blue and blue-green 10 10
352 9d. royal blue and carmine 10 10
353 1s. 6d. royal blue and dull yellow .. 10 10
354 3s. royal blue and new blue 15 15
351/4 .. .. *Set of* 4 25 20
MS355 146 × 96 mm. Nos. 351/4 .. .. .. 55 90

(New Currency, 100 tambalas = 1 kwacha)

10t

(78)

79 *Aegocera trimenii*

1970 (2 Sept). *Decimal Currency. Nos.* 316 *and* 318 *surch as T* **78**.
356 10 t. on 1s. multicoloured 30 25
a. Surch double .. .. † —
357 20 t. on 2s. multicoloured 95 80

(Des R. Granger Barrett. Litho B.W.)

1970 (30 Sept). *Moths. T* **79** *and similar horiz designs. Multicoloured. W* **55**. *P* 11 × 11½.
358 4d. Type **79** 20 10
359 9d. *Epiphora bauhiniae* 30 10
360 1s. 6d. *Parasa karschi* 50 10
361 3s. *Teracotona euprepia* .. .. .. 1·25 2·00
358/61 .. .. *Set of* 4 2·00 2·00
MS362 112 × 92 mm. Nos. 358/61 .. .. 3·50 4·50

80 Mother and Child

30t
Special
United
Kingdom
Delivery
Service

(81)

(Des Brother W. Meyer. Litho J.W.)

1970 (4 Nov). *Christmas. W* **55** *(sideways). P* 14.
363 **80** 2d. black and light yellow 10 10
364 4d. black and emerald 10 10
365 9d. black and orange-red 10 10
366 1s. 6d. black and light purple 10 10
367 3s. black and blue 15 15
363/7 .. .. *Set of* 5 25 25
MS368 166 × 100 mm. Nos. 363/7 .. .. 65 1·60

1971 (8 Feb). *No.* 319 *surch with T* **81**.
369 30 t. on 3s. multicoloured .. .. .. 20 1·75

No. 369 was issued for use on letters carried by an emergency airmail service from Malawi to Great Britain during the British postal strike. The fee of 30 t. was to cover the charge for delivery by a private service, and ordinary stamps to pay the normal airmail fee had to be affixed as well.

The strike ended on 8 March, when private delivery services were withdrawn.

82 Decimal Coinage and Cockerel

(Des V. Whiteley. Litho Format)

1971 (15 Feb). *Decimal Coinage. W* **55** *(sideways). P* 14.
370 **82** 3 t. multicoloured 10 10
371 8 t. multicoloured 10 10
372 15 t. multicoloured 15 10
373 30 t. multicoloured 25 30
370/3 .. .. *Set of* 4 45 35
MS374 140 × 101 mm. Nos. 370/73 .. .. 80 1·75

83 Greater Kudu

84 Eland

(Des and litho J.W.)

1971 (15 Feb)–**74**. *Decimal Currency. Antelopes. Vert designs as T* **83** *(1 t. to 8 t.), or T* **84** *(others). Multicoloured. W* **55** *(sideways on 1 t. to 8 t.). P* 13½ × 14 *(1 t to 8 t.) or* 14½ *(others).*
375 1 t. Type **83** 10 10
a. Coil stamp. P 14½×14 .. .. 15 30
b. Perf 14† (12.11.74) 40 40
376 2 t. Nyala 15 10
377 3 t. Mountain Reedbuck 20 10
a. Perf 14† (12.11.74) 55 55
378 5 t. Puku 40 10
a. Perf 14† (12.11.74) 55 55
379 8 t. Impala 45 10
380 10 t. Type **84** 60 10
381 15 t. Klipspringer .. .. 1·00 20
382 20 t. Suni .. .. 1·50 50
383 30 t. Roan Antelope .. .. .. 2·75 60
384 50 t. Waterbuck 90 65
385 1 k. Bushbuck .. .. 2·00 85
386 2 k. Red Forest Duiker .. .. .. 3·50 1·50
387 4 k. Common Duiker .. .. .. 17·00 17·00
375/87 .. .. .. *Set of* 13 27·00 19·00

No. 387 is incorrectly inscr "Gray Duiker".

† These actually gauge 14·2 × 14 instead of 13·7 × 14 and are line-perforated; in blocks they can easily be distinguished as in alternate rows across the sheet the horizontal perfs have two holes where they cross the vertical perfs; the watermark is also sideways inverted.

85 Christ on the Cross

87 *Holarrhena febrifuga*

(Des G. Drummond. Litho Questa)

1971 (7 Apr). *Easter. Details from Painting "The Small Passion" by Dürer. T* **85** *and similar vert design. W* **55**. *P* 13½.
388 3 t. black and green 10 10
a. Pair. Nos. 388/9 .. .. .. 10 10
389 3 t. black and green 10 10
390 8 t. black and orange-red 10 10
a. Pair. Nos. 390/1 .. .. .. 20 20
391 8 t. black and orange-red 10 10
392 15 t. black and violet 15 15
a. Pair. Nos. 392/3 .. .. .. 30 30
393 15 t. black and violet 15 15
394 30 t. black and bright blue 25 2
a. Pair. Nos. 394/5 .. .. .. 50 5
395 30 t. black and bright blue 25 2
388/95 .. .. *Set of* 8 1·00 1·0
MS396 Two sheets each 95 × 145 mm (a) Nos. 388, 390, 392 and 394; (b) Nos. 389, 391, 393 and 395 2·50 2·7

Designs:—Nos. 388, 390, 392 and 394, Type **85**; Nos. 389, 39 393 and 395, The Resurrection.

Nos. 388/9, 390/1, 392/3 and 394/5 were each printed together, se *tenant*, in pairs throughout the sheet.

(Des G. Drummond. Litho J.W.)

1971 (14 July). *Flowering Shrubs and Trees. T* **87** *and simila vert designs. Multicoloured. W* **55**. *P* 14.
397 3 t. Type **87** 10
398 8 t. *Brachystegia spiciformis* 15
399 15 t. *Securidaca longepedunculata* 25
400 30 t. *Pterocarpus rotundifolius* 40 5
397/400 .. .. *Set of* 4 80 5
MS401 102 × 135 mm. Nos. 397/400 .. .. 1·25 2·0

88 Drum Major

89 "Madonna and Child" (William Dyce)

(Des J.W. Litho Questa)

1971 (5 Oct). *50th Anniv of Malawi Police Force. W* **5** *P* 14 × 14½.
402 **88** 30 t. multicoloured .. .. .. 65 1·

(Des J. Cooter. Litho Format)

1971 (10 Nov). *Christmas. T* **89** *and similar vert designs. Mul coloured. W* **55**. *P* 14½.
403 3 t. Type **89** 10
404 8 t. "The Holy Family" (M. Schöngauer) .. 15
405 15 t. "The Holy Family with St. John" (Raphael) 25
406 30 t. "The Holy Family" (Bronzino) 55
403/6 .. .. *Set of* 4 95 1·
MS407 101 × 139 mm. Nos. 403/6 .. .. 1·40 2·

90 Vickers "Viscount"

(Des R. Granger Barrett. Litho Questa)

1972 (9 Feb). *Air. Malawi Aircraft. T* **90** *and similar hor designs. Multicoloured. W* **55** *(sideways). P* 13½.
408 3 t. Type **90** 25
409 8 t. Hawker Siddeley "748" 40
410 15 t. Britten-Norman "Islander" 65
411 30 t. B.A.C. "One-Eleven" .. .. .. 1·10 1·
408/11 .. .. *Set of* 4 2·25 1·
MS412 143 × 94 mm. Nos. 408/11 .. .. 5·00 4·

91 Figures (Chencherere Hill)

92 Boxing

(Des R. Granger Barrett. Litho Format)

1972 (10 May). *Rock Paintings. T* **91** *and similar horiz desig W* **55** *(sideways). P* 13½.
413 3 t. apple-green, grey-green and black .. 20
414 8 t. red, grey and black 35
415 15 t. multicoloured 60
416 30 t. multicoloured .. .. 90 1·
413/16 .. .. *Set of* 4 1·90 1·
MS417 121 × 97 mm. Nos. 413/16. P 15 .. .. 2·75 2·

Designs:—8 t. Lizard and cat (Chencherere Hill); 15 t. Sc matics (Diwa Hill); 30 t. Sun through rain (Mikolongwe Hill).

(Des local artist. Litho Harrison)

1972 (9 Aug). *Olympic Games, Munich. W* **55** *(sideway P* 14 × 14½.
418 **92** 3 t. multicoloured 10
419 8 t. multicoloured 10
420 15 t. multicoloured 15
421 30 t. multicoloured 35
418/21 .. .. *Set of* 4 60
MS422 110 × 92 mm. Nos. 418/21. P 14 × 13½ .. 1·25 1

93 Arms of Malawi

94 "Adoration of the Kings" (Orcagna)

(Des G. Drummond. Litho Questa)

972 (20 Oct). *Commonwealth Parliamentary Conference. W* **55**. *P* 13½.
23 **93** 15 t. multicoloured 30 35

(Des V. Whiteley. Litho Questa)

972 (8 Nov). *Christmas. T* **94** *and similar vert designs. Multicoloured. W* **55**. *P* 14½ × 14.
24 3 t. Type **94** 10 10
25 8 t. "Madonna and Child Enthroned" (Florentine School) 10 10
26 15 t. "Virgin and Child" (Crivelli) 20 10
27 30 t. "Virgin and Child with St. Anne" (Flemish School) 45 70
24/7 .. .. *Set of* 4 70 80
IS428 95 × 121 mm. Nos. 424/7 .. .. .. 1·10 2·00

MALAŴI". All issues from No. 429 onwards have a circumflex ccent over the "W", to give the correct pronunciation of "Malavi".

95 *Charaxes bohemani*

(Des PAD Studio. Litho Questa)

973 (7 Feb–5 Apr). *Butterflies. T* **95** *and similar horiz designs. Multicoloured. W* **55** (*sideways*). *P* 13½ × 14.
29 3 t. Type **95** 20 10
30 8 t. *Uranothauma crawshayi* 45 10
31 15 t. *Charaxes acuminatus* 65 25
32 30 t. Inscr "EUPHAEDRA ZADDACHI" .. 3·00 5·50
33 30 t. Corrected to "AMAURIS ANSORGEI" (5 Apr) .. .. 3·00 5·50
29/33 .. .. *Set of* 5 6·50 10·00
IS434 145 × 95 mm. Nos. 429/32 .. .. 7·00 9·50

96 Livingstone and Map

(Des J.W. Litho Format)

73 (1 May). *Death Centenary of David Livingstone* (*1st issue*). *W* **55** (*sideways*). *P* 13½ × 14.
5 **96** 3 t. multicoloured 10 10
6 8 t. multicoloured 15 10
7 15 t. multicoloured 25 10
8 30 t. multicoloured 40 60
5/8 .. .. *Set of* 4 80 70
S439 144 × 95 mm. Nos. 435/8 .. .. 80 1·50
See also Nos. 450/**MS**451.

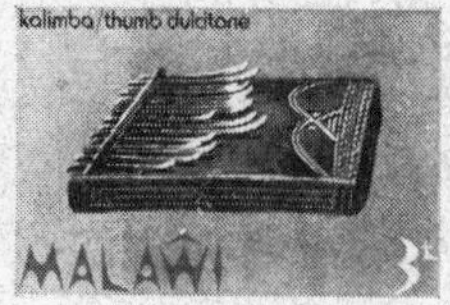

97 Thumb Dulcitone

(Des Jennifer Toombs. Litho Questa)

73 (8 Aug). *Musical Instruments. T* **97** *and similar multicoloured designs. W* **55** (*sideways on* 8, 15 *t. and* **MS**444). *P* 14.
0 3 t. Type **97** 10 10
1 8 t. Hand zither (*vert*) 15 10
2 15 t. Hand drum (*vert*) 20 10
3 30 t. One-stringed fiddle 40 60
0/3 .. .. *Set of* 4 70 65
S444 120 × 103 mm. Nos. 440/3 .. .. 1·75 1·90

98 The Magi

(Des J.W. Litho Format)

1973 (7 Nov). *Christmas. W* **55** (*sideways*). *P* 13½.
445 **98** 3 t. greenish blue, dp lilac & dull ultram 10 10
446 8 t. salmon-red, bluish lilac & red-brn 10 10
447 15 t. reddish mve, greenish bl & dp mve 15 10
448 30 t. orange-yell, bluish lilac & lt lake-brn 30 55
445/8 .. .. *Set of* 4 50 60
MS449 165 × 114 mm. Nos. 445/8 .. .. 75 1·40

99 Stained-glass Window, Livingstonia Mission

(Des PAD Studio. Litho Questa)

1973 (12 Dec). *Death Centenary of David Livingstone* (*2nd issue*). *W* **55** (*sideways*). *P* 13½.
450 **99** 50 t. multicoloured .. .. .. 45 1·00
MS451 71 × 77 mm. No. 450 .. .. .. 80 1·60

100 Largemouth Black Bass

(Des Sylvia Goaman. Litho Questa)

1974 (20 Feb). *35th Anniv of Malawi Angling Society. T* **100** *and similar horiz designs. Multicoloured. W* **55** (*sideways*). *P* 14.
452 3 t. Type **100** 20 10
453 8 t. Rainbow Trout 25 10
454 15 t. Lake Salmon 45 20
455 30 t. Tiger Fish 75 75
452/5 .. .. *Set of* 4 1·50 95
MS456 169 × 93 mm. Nos. 452/5 .. .. 1·50 1·60

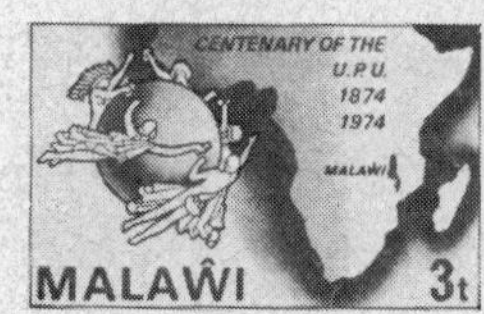

101 U.P.U. Monument and Map of Africa

(Des J. Cooter. Litho J.W.)

1974 (24 Apr). *Centenary of Universal Postal Union. W* **55** (*sideways*). *P* 13½ (*Nos.* 460/**MS**461) *or* 14½ × 14 (*others*).
457 **101** 3 t. green and ochre 10 10
a. Perf 13½ (pair) .. .. ..
458 8 t. red and ochre 10 10
459 15 t. violet and ochre 15 10
460 30 t. indigo and ochre 30 70
457/60 .. .. *Set of* 4 60 80
MS461 115 × 146 mm. Nos. 457/60 .. .. 65 1·75
a. Perf 14½ × 14 .. .. .. † —

No. 457a comes from normal sheets and not No. **MS**461. It can also be identified as a marginal single.

102 Capital Hill, Lilongwe

(Des PAD Studio. Litho Questa)

1974 (3 July). *Tenth Anniv of Independence. W* **55** (*sideways*). *P* 14.
462 **102** 3 t. multicoloured 10 10
463 8 t. multicoloured 10 10
464 15 t. multicoloured 10 10
465 30 t. multicoloured 25 35
462/5 .. .. *Set of* 4 40 40
MS466 120 × 86 mm. Nos. 462/5 .. .. 45 90

103 "Madonna of the Meadow" (Bellini)

104 Arms of Malawi

(Des Jennifer Toombs. Litho Enschedé)

1974 (4 Dec). *Christmas. T* **103** *and similar horiz designs. Multicoloured. W* **55** (*sideways*). *P* 13 × 13½.
467 3 t. Type **103** 10 10
468 8 t. "The Holy Family with Sts. John and Elizabeth" (Jordaens) 10 10
469 15 t. "The Nativity" (Pieter de Grebber) .. 15 10
470 30 t. "Adoration of the Shepherds" (Lorenzo di Credi) 30 50
467/70 .. .. *Set of* 4 50 50
MS471 163 × 107 mm. Nos. 467/70 .. .. 60 1·25

(Des and litho Harrison)

1975 (1 Feb)–**84**. *Coil stamp. W* **55** (*sideways*). *P* 14½ × 14
472 **104** 1 t. deep blue 10 20
472*a* 5 t. bright carmine (20.9.84) 10 15

105 African Snipe

106 Spur-winged Goose

(Des J.W. Litho Questa)

1975 (19 Feb). *Birds. T* **105/6** *and similar multicoloured designs. W* **55** (*sideways on* 2, 3, 8, 50 *t.*, 1 *k.*, 4 *k.*). *White, ordinary paper.*

(*a*) *Size as T* **105**. *P* 13½ × 14 (1, 5 *t.*) *or* 14 × 13½ (*others*)
473 1 t. Type **105** 25 40
474 2 t. Double-banded Sandgrouse 40 30
475 3 t. Blue Quail .. .. 1·00 40
476 5 t. Bare-throated Francolin .. .. .. 2·00 15
477 8 t. Harlequin Quail .. .. 2·50 20

(*b*) *Size as T* **106**. *P* 14
478 10 t. Type **106** .. .. 4·50 50
479 15 t. Barrow's Bustard .. .. .. 2·75 1·50
480 20 t. Comb Duck .. .. 1·00 80
481 30 t. Helmet Guineafowl .. .. .. 1·25 70
482 50 t. African Pigmy Goose .. .. .. 2·00 1·60
483 1 k. Garganey .. .. 3·00 3·25
484 2 k. White-faced Whistling Duck .. .. 10·00 9·50
485 4 k. African Green Pigeon .. .. .. 13·00 15·00
473/85 .. .. *Set of* 13 40·00 30·00
See also Nos. 501/4

107 M.V. *Mpasa*

108 *Habenaria splendens*

(Des R. Granger Barrett. Litho J.W.)

1975 (12 Mar). *Ships of Lake Malawi* (*1st series*). *T* **107** *and similar horiz designs. Multicoloured. W* **55** (*sideways*). *P* 13½.
486 3 t. Type **107** 15 10
487 8 t. M.V. *Ilala II* 25 10
488 15 t. M.V. *Chauncy Maples II* 40 20
489 30 t. M.V. *Nkwazi* 65 80
486/9 .. .. *Set of* 4 1·25 1·00
MS490 105 × 142 mm. Nos. 486/9. P 14 .. .. 1·75 2·75
See also Nos. 728/32.

(Des Sylvia Goaman. Litho Questa)

1975 (6 June). *Malawi Orchids. T* **108** *and similar vert designs. Multicoloured. W* **55**. *P* 14.
491 3 t. Type **108** 15 10
492 10 t. *Eulophia cucullata* 25 10
493 20 t. *Disa welwitschii* 40 20
494 40 t. *Angraecum conchiferum* 70 85
491/4 .. .. *Set of* 4 1·40 1·00
MS495 127 × 111 mm. Nos. 491/4 .. .. 2·00 3·00

109 Thick-tailed Bushbaby

10th ACP
Ministerial
Conference
1975

(110)

(Des R. Granger Barrett. Litho Walsall)

1975 (3 Sept). *Malawi Animals. T* **109** *and similar vert designs. Multicoloured. W* **55** *(inverted). P* 14.
496 3 t. Type **109** 10 10
497 10 t. Leopard 35 10
498 20 t. Roan Antelope 55 30
499 40 t. Common Zebra . . . . 1·00 1·75
496/9 . . . . *Set of* 4 1·75 2·00
MS500 88 × 130 mm. Nos. 496/9. W **55** (sideways) 2·25 2·75

1975 (1 Oct). *As Nos.* 473 *etc, but no wmk. Toned, chalk-surfaced paper.*
501 3 t. Blue Quail . . . . 1·75 80
502 10 t. Type **106** . . . . 1·75 90
503 15 t. Barrow's Bustard . . . . . . 1·75 1·50
504 2 k. White-faced Whistling Duck . . 9·50 9·50
501/4 . . . . *Set of* 4 13·00 11·50

Nos. 505/13 vacant.

1975 (9 Dec). *Tenth Africa, Caribbean and Pacific Ministerial Conference. No.* 482 *optd with T* **110**.
514 50 t. African Pigmy Goose . . . . . . 75 1·10

111 "A Castle with the Adoration of the Magi"

112 Alexander Graham Bell

(Des PAD Studio. Litho J.W.)

1975 (12 Dec). *Christmas. T* **111** *and similar horiz designs showing religious medallions. Multicoloured. W* **55** *(sideways). P* 13 × 13½.
515 3 t. Type **111** 10 10
516 10 t. "The Nativity" 15 10
517 20 t. "The Adoration of the Magi" 20 10
518 40 t. "The Angel appearing to the Shepherds" 50 70
515/18 . . . . *Set of* 4 80 80
MS519 98 × 168 mm. Nos. 515/18. P 14 . . . . 1·50 2·50

(Des C. Abbott. Litho Questa)

1976 (24 Mar). *Centenary of the Telephone. W* **55**. *P* 14.
520 **112** 3 t. black and dull green 10 10
521 10 t. black and magenta 10 10
522 20 t. black and light reddish violet . . 20 10
523 40 t. black and bright blue 50 70
520/3 . . . . *Set of* 4 80 80
MS524 137 × 114 mm. Nos. 520/3 . . . . 1·10 1·75

113 President Banda

114 Bagnall Diesel Shunter

(Des PAD Studio. Litho J.W.)

1976 (2 July). *Tenth Anniv of the Republic. Multicoloured; frame colour given. W* **55**. *P* 13.
525 **113** 3 t. green 10 10
526 10 t. magenta 10 10
527 20 t. new blue 20 10
528 40 t. dull ultramarine 50 70
525/8 . . . . *Set of* 4 80 80
MS529 102 × 112 mm. Nos. 524/8. P 13½ . . . . 95 1·50

(Des G. Drummond. Litho Questa)

1976 (1 Oct). *Malawi Locomotives. T* **114** *and similar horiz designs. Multicoloured. W* **55** *(sideways). P* 14½ × 14.
530 3 t. Type **114** 15 10
531 10 t. "Shire" Class diesel locomotive . . 40 10
532 20 t. Nippon Sharyo diesel locomotive . . 80 45
533 40 t. Hunslet diesel locomotive . . . . 1·75 2·00
530/3 . . . . *Set of* 4 2·75 2·25
MS534 130 × 118 mm. Nos. 530/3 . . . . 2·75 3·50

Blantyre
Mission
Centenary
1876-1976

(115)

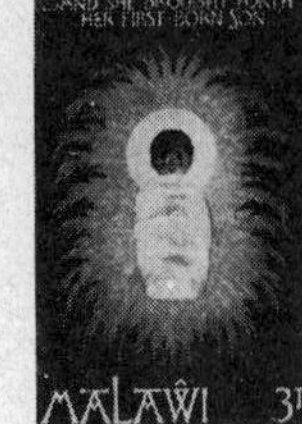

116 Child on Bed of Straw

1976 (22 Oct). *Centenary of Blantyre Mission. Nos.* 503 *and* 481 *optd with T* **115**.
535 15 t. Barrow's Bustard 55 70
536 30 t. Helmet Guineafowl . . . . . . 85 1·40

(Des Jennifer Toombs. Litho Walsall)

1976 (6 Dec). *Christmas. W* **55**. *P* 14.
537 **116** 3 t. multicoloured 10 10
538 10 t. multicoloured 10 10
539 20 t. multicoloured 20 10
540 40 t. multicoloured 40 60
537/40 . . . . *Set of* 4 70 70
MS541 135 × 95 mm. Nos. 537/40 . . . . 1·00 1·75

117 Man and Woman

118 Chileka Airport

(Des G. Hutchins. Litho Questa)

1977 (1 Apr). *Handicrafts. T* **117** *and similar multicoloured designs showing wood-carvings. W* **55** *(sideways on* 10 *and* 20 *t.). P* 14.
542 4 t. Type **117** 10 10
543 10 t. Elephant *(horiz)* 15 10
544 20 t. Rhino *(horiz)* 20 10
545 40 t. Deer 50 70
542/5 . . . . *Set of* 4 80 80
MS546 153 × 112 mm. Nos. 542/5. Wmk sideways 1·50 2·25

(Des Harrison. Litho Walsall)

1977 (12 July). *Transport. T* **118** *and similar horiz designs. Multicoloured. W* **55** *(sideways). P* 14½ × 14.
547 4 t. Type **118** 15 10
548 10 t. Blantyre-Lilongwe Road 25 10
549 20 t. M.V. *Ilala II* 80 30
550 40 t. Blantyre-Nacala rail line . . . . 1·50 1·40
547/50 . . . . *Set of* 4 2·40 1·60
MS551 127 × 83 mm. Nos. 547/50 . . . . 2·40 2·75

119 *Pseudotropheus johanni*

120 "Madonna and Child with St. Catherine and the Blessed Stefano Maconi" (Borgognone)

(Des R. Granger Barrett. Litho J.W.)

1977 (4 Oct). *Fish of Lake Malawi. T* **119** *and similar horiz designs. Multicoloured. P* 13½. *A. No wmk. B. W* **55** *(sideways).*

		A		B	
552	4 t. Type **119** . .	20	10	15	10
553	10 t. *Pseudotropheus livingstoni*	30	10	25	20
554	20 t. *Pseudotropheus zebra* . .	85	25	—	1·50
555	40 t. *Genyochromis mento* . .	95	95	95	95
552/5 . .	*Set of* 4	2·10	1·25	†	
MS556	147 × 99 mm. Nos. 552/5. P 13	2·10	2·75	2·25	3·25

(Des G. Hutchins. Litho Enschedé)

1977 (21 Nov). *Christmas. T* **120** *and similar vert designs. Multicoloured; frame colours given. No wmk. P* 14 × 13½.
557 4 t. deep blue-green 10 10
558 10 t. light vermilion 10 10
559 20 t. dull violet 20 10
560 40 t. blue 50 70
557/60 . . . . *Set of* 4 80 80
MS561 150 × 116 mm. Nos. 557/60 . . . . 1·75 2·50

Designs:—10 t. "Madonna and Child with the Eternal Father and Angels" (Borgognone); 20 t. Bottigella altarpiece (detail, Foppa); 40 t. "Madonna of the Fountain" (van Eyck).

121 "Entry of Christ into Jerusalem" (Giotto)

122 Nyala

(Des G. Hutchins. Litho Cartor S.A., France)

1978 (1 Mar). *Easter T* **121** *and similar vert designs showing paintings by Giotto. Multicoloured. P* 12 × 12½.
562 4 t. Type **121** 10 1
563 10 t. "The Crucifixion" 10 1
564 20 t. "Descent from the Cross" 20 1
565 40 t. "Jesus appears before Mary" 40 5
562/5 . . . . *Set of* 4 70 7
MS566 150 × 99 mm. Nos. 562/5 . . . . 1·00 1·6

(Des G. Hutchins. Litho Enschedé)

1978 (1 June). *Wildlife. T* **122** *and similar multicoloured designs. P* 13½ × 13 *(4, 40 t.) or* 13 × 13½ *(others).*
567 4 t. Type **122** 25 1
568 10 t. Lion *(horiz)* 60 1
569 20 t. Common Zebra *(horiz)* 85 4
570 40 t. Mountain Reedbuck . . . . . . 1·40 1·2
567/70 . . . . *Set of* 4 2·75 1·7
MS571 173 × 113 mm. Nos. 567/70 . . . . 3·50 4·0

123 Malamulo Seventh Day Adventist Church

124 *Vanilla polylepis*

(Des and litho Walsall)

1978 (15 Nov). *Christmas. Churches. T* **123** *and similar horiz designs. Multicoloured. W* **55** *(sideways). P* 13½.
572 4 t. Type **123** 10 1
573 10 t. Likoma Cathedral 10 1
574 20 t. St. Michael's and All Angels', Blantyre . . 20 1
575 40 t. Zomba Catholic Cathedral 40 6
572/5 . . . . *Set of* 4 70 7
MS576 190 × 105 mm. Nos. 572/5 . . . . 70 1·5

(Des G. Drummond. Litho J.W.)

1979 (2 Jan)–**82**. *Orchids. Vert designs as T* **124**. *Multicoloured. W* **55**. *P* 13½.
577 1 t. Type **124** 20 1
578 2 t. *Cirrhopetalum umbellatum* 20 1
579 5 t. *Calanthe natalensis* 20 1
580 7 t. *Ansellia gigantea* 25 1
581 8 t. *Tridactyle bicaudata* 25 1
582 10 t. *Acampe pachyglossa* 30 1
583 15 t. *Eulophia quartiniana* 35 1
584 20 t. *Cyrtorchis arcuata (variabilis)* 40 2
585 30 t. *Eulophia tricristata* 55 2
586 50 t. *Disa hamatopetala* 70 5
587 75 t. *Cynorchis glandulosa* . . . . . . 1·00 1·0
588 1 k. *Aerangis kotschyana* . . . . . . 1·25 8
589 1 k. 50, *Polystachya dendrobiiflora* . . . . 1·50 1·4
590 2 k. *Disa ornithantha* . . . . 1·75 1·6
591 4 k. *Cyrtorchis praetermissa* . . . . . . 3·00 3·5
577/91 . . . . *Set of* 15 11·00 9·0

125 Tsamba

126 Train crossing Viaduct

(Des L. Curtis. Litho Questa)

1979 (21 Jan). *National Tree Planting Day. T* **125** *and similar vert designs. Multicoloured. W* **55**. *P* 13½.
592 5 t. Type **125** 15 1
593 10 t. Mulanje Cedar 20 1
594 20 t. Mlombwa 30 2
595 40 t. Mbawa 60 7
592/5 . . . . *Set of* 4 1·10 9
MS596 118 × 153 mm. Nos. 592/5 . . . . 1·10 1·6

(Des J.W. Litho Questa)

79 (17 Feb). *Opening of Salima-Lilongwe Railway. T* **126** *and similar horiz designs. Multicoloured. W* **55** *(sideways)* (5 t.) *or no wmk (others). P* 14½.

7	5 t. Type **126**..	25	10
3	10 t. Diesel railcar at station	40	10
9	20 t. Train rounding bend	60	30
)	40 t. Diesel train passing through cutting ..	85	1·25
7/600	*Set of* 4	1·90	1·50
S601	153 × 103 mm. Nos. 597/600. W **55** (sideways)	3·00	3·50

Examples of an unissued 4 t. value as Type **126** and of a niature sheet containing this 4 t. value exist from supplies nt to Malawi before it was decided to increase the internal stage rate to 5 t.

127 Young Child

(Des BG Studio. Litho Questa)

79 (10 July). *International Year of the Child. T* **127** *and similar horiz designs showing young children. Multicoloured; background colours given. W* **55** *(sideways). P* 13½.

2	5 t. green	10	10
3	10 t. red	10	10
4	20 t. mauve	20	10
5	40 t. blue	40	60
2/5	*Set of* 4	65	70

128 1964 3d. Independence Commemorative Stamp

(Des J.W. Litho Enschedé)

79 (17 Sept). *Death Centenary of Sir Rowland Hill. T* **128** *and similar horiz designs showing 1964 Independence commemorative stamps. Multicoloured. W* **55** *(sideways). P* 13 × 13½.

6	5 t. Type **128** ..	10	10
7	10 t. 6d. value ..	10	10
8	20 t. 1s. 3d. value	20	10
9	40 t. 2s. 6d. value	35	60
6/9	*Set of* 4	65	70
S610	163 × 108 mm. Nos. 606/9	65	1·10

129 River Landscape

130 Limbe Rotary Club Emblem

(Des BG Studio. Litho Format)

79 (15 Nov). *Christmas. T* **129** *and similar horiz designs showing landscapes. Multicoloured. W* **55** *(sideways). P* 13½ × 14.

1	5 t. Type **129** ..	10	10
2	10 t. Sunset	10	10
3	20 t. Forest and hill	20	10
4	40 t. Plain and mountain	40	50
1/14	*Set of* 4	70	65

(Des L. Curtis. Litho J.W.)

80 (23 Feb). *75th Anniv of Rotary International. T* **130** *and similar vert designs. W* **55**. *P* 13½.

5	5 t. multicoloured	10	10
6	10 t. multicoloured	10	10
7	20 t. multicoloured	20	10
8	40 t. ultramarine and gold	50	85
5/18	*Set of* 4	80	1·00
S619	105 × 144 mm. Nos. 615/18. P 14 × 14½.	1·25	1·50

Designs:—10 t. Blantyre Rotary Club pennant; 20 t. Lilongwe tary Club pennant; 40 t. Rotary International emblem.

131 Mangochi District Post Office

132 Agate Nodule

(Des C. Abbott. Litho Walsall)

1980 (6 May). *"London 1980" International Stamp Exhibition. T* **131** *and similar horiz designs. W* **55** *(sideways). P* 14½ × 14.

620	5 t. black and blue-green	10	10
621	10 t. black and vermilion	10	10
622	20 t. black and violet ..	15	10
623	1 k. black and deep blue	65	1·00
620/3	*Set of* 4	80	1·10
MS624	114 × 89 mm. Nos. 620/3 ..	1·60	2·25

Designs:–10 t. New Blantyre Sorting Office; 20 t. Mail Transfer Hut, Walala; 1 k. First Nyasaland Post Office, Chiromo.

(Des G. Drummond. Litho J.W.)

1980 (20 Aug). *Gemstones. T* **132** *and similar vert designs. Multicoloured. W* **55**. *P* 13.

625	5 t. Type **132** ..	15	10
626	10 t. Sunstone ..	20	10
627	20 t. Smoky Quartz	40	15
628	1 k. Kyanite crystal	1·75	2·00
625/8	*Set of* 4	2·25	2·00

133 Elephants

134 Suni

(Des C. Abbott. Litho J.W.)

1980 (10 Nov). *Christmas. Children's Paintings. T* **133** *and similar horiz designs. Multicoloured. W* **55** *(sideways). P* 13.

629	5 t. Type **133** ..	10	10
630	10 t. Flowers ..	10	10
631	20 t. "Shire" class diesel train	20	10
632	1 k. Malachite Kingfisher	70	1·10
629/32	*Set of* 4	1·00	1·10

(Des G. Drummond. Litho Questa)

1981 (4 Feb). *Wildlife. T* **134** *and similar horiz designs. Multicoloured. W* **55** *(sideways). P* 14.

633	7 t. Type **134** ..	15	10
634	10 t. Blue Duiker	20	10
635	20 t. African Buffalo ..	30	15
636	1 k. Lichtenstein's Hartebeest	1·25	1·60
633/6	*Set of* 4	1·75	1·75

135 "Kanjedza II" Standard "A" Earth Station

(Des L. Curtis. Litho Harrison)

1981 (2 May). *International Communications. T* **135** *and similar horiz designs. Multicoloured. W* **55** *(sideways). P* 14½.

637	7 t. Type **135** ..	10	10
638	10 t. Blantyre International Gateway Exchange	15	10
639	20 t. "Kanjedza I" standard "B" earth station	25	15
640	1 k. "Satellite communications"	1·50	1·50
637/40	*Set of* 4	1·75	1·60
MS641	101 × 151 mm. Nos. 637/40	2·00	2·50

136 Maize

137 "The Adoration of the Shepherds" (Murillo)

(Des Jennifer Toombs. Litho Harrison)

1981 (11 Sept). *World Food Day. Agricultural Produce. T* **136** *and similar horiz designs. Multicoloured. W* **55** *(sideways). P* 14.

642	7 t. Type **136** ..	15	10
643	10 t. Rice	20	10
644	20 t. Finger-millet	30	20
645	1 k. Wheat	1·00	1·40
642/5	*Set of* 4	1·50	1·50

(Des BG Studio. Litho J.W.)

1981 (26 Nov). *Christmas. Paintings. T* **137** *and similar multicoloured designs. W* **55** *(sideways on 10 and 20 t.). P* 13½ × 13 *(7 t., 1 k.) or* 13 × 13½ *(others).*

646	7 t. Type **137** ..	15	10
647	10 t. "The Holy Family" (Lippi) *(horiz)*	20	10
648	20 t. "The Adoration of the Shepherds" (Louis le Nain) *(horiz)*	35	15
649	1 k. "The Virgin and Child, St. John the Baptist and an Angel" (Paolo Morando)	90	1·25
646/9	*Set of* 4	1·40	1·40

138 Impala Herd

(Des A. Theobald. Litho Harrison)

1982 (15 Mar). *National Parks. Wildlife. T* **138** *and similar horiz designs. Multicoloured. W* **55** *(sideways). P* 14½ × 14.

650	7 t. Type **138** ..	20	10
651	10 t. Lions	35	10
652	20 t. Greater Kudu	50	15
653	1 k. Greater Flamingoes	2·25	2·25
650/3	*Set of* 4	3·00	2·25

139 Kamuzu Academy

140 Attacker challenging Goalkeeper

(Des PAD Studio. Litho Questa)

1982 (1 July). *Kamuzu Academy. T* **139** *and similar horiz designs showing buildings. W* **55** *(sideways). P* 14½.

654	7 t. multicoloured	10	10
655	20 t. multicoloured	15	10
656	30 t. multicoloured	25	25
657	1 k. multicoloured	65	1·00
654/7	*Set of* 4	1·00	1·25

(Des and litho Harrison)

1982 (8 Sept). *World Cup Football Championship, Spain. T* **140** *and similar vert designs. Multicoloured. W* **55**. *P* 14 × 15.

658	7 t. Type **140** ..	20	10
659	20 t. FIFA World Cup trophy ..	40	25
660	30 t. Football stadium..	50	60
658/60	*Set of* 3	1·00	85
MS661	80 × 59 mm. 1 k. Football	1·25	1·60

141 Blantyre War Memorial, St. Paul's Church

(Des W. Fenton. Litho Format)

1982 (5 Nov). *Remembrance Day. T* **141** *and similar horiz designs. Multicoloured. W* **55** *(sideways). P* 14½ × 14.

662	7 t. Type **141** ..	10	10
663	20 t. Zomba war memorial	15	10
664	30 t. Chichiri war memorial ..	20	20
665	1 k. Lilongwe war memorial ..	65	1·50
662/5	*Set of* 4	1·00	1·75

142 Kwacha International Conference Centre

143 "Christ and St. Peter"

(Des Walsall. Litho Format)

1983 (14 Mar). *Commonwealth Day. T* **142** *and similar horiz designs. Multicoloured. W* **55** *(sideways). P* 14.

666 7 t. Type **142** 10 10
667 20 t. Tea-picking, Mulanje 20 10
668 30 t. World map showing position of Malawi 30 30
669 1 k. President Dr. H. Kamuzu Banda .. 80 1·25
666/9 .. .. *Set of* 4 1·25 1·50

(Des C. Abbott. Litho Format)

1983 (4 Apr). *500th Birth Anniv of Raphael. Details from the cartoon for "The Miraculous Draught of Fishes" Tapestry. T* **143** *and similar multicoloured designs. W* **55** *(sideways on 30 t.). P* 14.

670 7 t. Type **143** 15 10
671 20 t. "Hauling in the Catch" 35 20
672 30 t. "Fishing Village" (*horiz*).. .. .. 50 60
670/2 .. .. *Set of* 3 90 80
MS673 110 × 90 mm. 1 k. "Apostle" .. .. 1·10 1·25

144 Pair by Lake **145** Kamuzu International Airport

(Des N. Arlott. Litho Questa)

1983 (11 July). *African Fish Eagle. T* **144** *and similar vert designs. Multicoloured. W* **55**. *P* 14.

674 30 t. Type **144** 55 60
a. Horiz strip of 5. Nos. 674/8 .. .. 2·50
675 30 t. Making gull-like call 55 60
676 30 t. Diving on prey 55 60
677 30 t. Carrying fish 55 60
678 30 t. Feeding on catch.. .. .. .. 55 60
674/8.. .. .. *Set of* 5 2·50 2·75

Nos. 674/8 were printed together, *se-tenant*, in horizontal strips of 5 throughout the sheet, the backgrounds of each design forming a composite picture of Lake Malawi.

(Des A. Theobald. Litho Questa)

1983 (31 Aug). *Bicentenary of Manned Flight. T* **145** *and similar horiz designs. Multicoloured. W* **55** *(sideways). P* 14.

679 7 t. Type **145** 10 10
680 20 t. Kamuzu International Airport (*different*) 25 15
681 30 t. BAC "One Eleven" 40 30
682 1 k. Flying boat at Cape Maclear .. .. 1·10 1·25
679/82 .. .. *Set of* 4 1·75 1·60
MS683 100 × 121 mm. Nos. 679/82 .. .. 2·00 3·00

146 *Clerodendrum myricoides* **147** *Melanochromis auratus*

(Des R. Reader. Litho J.W.)

1983 (1 Nov). *Christmas. Flowers. T* **146** *and similar vert designs. Multicoloured. P* 13 (20 *t.*) *or* 14 (*others*).

684 7 t. Type **146** 25 10
a. Perf 13 .. .. 15·00
685 20 t. *Gloriosa superba* 50 15
686 30 t. *Gladiolus laxiflorus* 70 30
687 1 k. *Aframomum angustifolium* .. .. 1·50 2·00
684/7 .. .. *Set of* 4 2·75 2·25

(Des L. Curtis. Litho Harrison)

1984 (2 Jan). *Fishes. T* **147** *and similar horiz designs. Multicoloured. W* **55** *(sideways). P* 14½ × 14.

688 1 t. Type **147** 10 15
689 2 t. *Haplochromis compressiceps* 10 15
690 5 t. *Labeotropheus fuelleborni* 15 10
691 7 t. *Pseudotropheus lombardoi* 15 10
692 8 t. Gold *Pseudotropheus zebra* 15 10
693 10 t. *Trematocranus jacobfreibergi* 15 10
694 15 t. *Melanochromis crabro* 20 10
695 20 t. Marbled *Pseudotropheus zebra* 20 10
696 30 t. *Labidochromis caeruleus* 30 20
697 40 t. *Haplochromis venustus* 40 25
698 50 t. *Aulonacara of* Thumbi 45 30
699 75 t. *Melanochromis vermivorus* 65 40
700 1 k. *Pseudotropheus zebra* 75 60
701 2 k. *Trematocranus spp.* .. .. .. 1·50 1·50
702 4 k. *Aulonacara of* Mbenje .. .. .. 2·25 3·00
688/702 .. .. *Set of* 15 6·50 6·25

Nos. 688 and 691/7 exist with different imprint dates at foot.

148 Smith's Red Hare **149** Running

(Des Garden Studios. Litho Format)

1984 (2 Feb). *Small Mammals. T* **148** *and similar horiz designs. Multicoloured. W* **55** *(sideways). P* 14.

703 7 t. Type **148**.. .. .. 25 10
704 20 t. Gambian Sun Squirrel 50 15
705 30 t. South African Hedgehog 70 30
706 1 k. Large-spotted Genet .. .. .. 1·75 2·25
703/6 .. .. *Set of* 4 3·00 2·50

(Des C. Collins. Litho Harrison)

1984 (1 June). *Olympic Games, Los Angeles. T* **149** *and similar vert designs. Multicoloured. W* **55** *(sideways). P* 14.

707 7 t. Type **149** 10 10
708 20 t. Boxing 25 15
709 30 t. Cycling 35 25
710 1 k. Long jumping .. .. 1·00 1·25
707/10 .. .. *Set of* 4 1·50 1·50
MS711 90 × 128 mm. Nos. 707/10. Wmk upright 1·50 2·50

150 *Euphaedra neophron* **151** "The Virgin and Child" (Duccio)

(Des and photo Courvoisier)

1984 (1 Aug). *Butterflies. T* **150** *and similar vert designs. Granite paper. P* 11½.

712 7 t. multicoloured 45 10
713 20 t. lemon, blackish brown and red 75 15
714 30 t. multicoloured .. .. 1·00 50
715 1 k. multicoloured .. .. 2·25 2·25
712/15 .. .. *Set of* 4 4·00 2·75

Designs:—20 t. *Papilio dardanus*; 30 t. *Antanartia schaeneia*; 1 k. *Spindasis*.

(Des C. Abbott. Litho Harrison)

1984 (22 Oct). *Christmas. Religious Paintings. T* **151** *and similar vert designs. Multicoloured. W* **55**. *P* 14½.

716 7 t. Type **151** 20 10
717 20 t. "Madonna and Child" (Raphael) .. 50 15
718 30 t. "The Virgin and Child" (ascr to Lippi) .. 70 30
719 1 k. "The Wilton Diptych" .. .. .. 1·50 1·50
716/19 .. .. *Set of* 4 2·75 1·75

152 *Leucopaxillus gracillimus*

(Des A. Jardine. Litho Harrison)

1985 (23 Jan). *Fungi. T* **152** *and similar horiz designs. Multicoloured. W* **55** *(sideways). P* 14½ × 14.

720 7 t. Type **152** 40 10
721 20 t. *Limacella guttata* 75 15
722 30 t. *Termitomyces eurrhizus* .. .. 1·00 25
723 1 k. *Xerulina asprata* .. .. .. 1·90 2·25
720/3 .. .. *Set of* 4 3·50 2·50

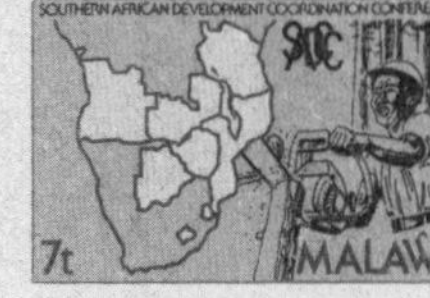

153 Map showing Member States, and Lumberjack (Forestry)

(Des A. Theobald. Litho Harrison)

1985 (1 Apr). *5th Anniv of Southern African Development Co-ordination Conference. T* **153** *and similar horiz designs showing map and aspects of development. W* **55** *(sideways). P* 14.

724 7 t. black, yellowish green and pale green 20 10
725 15 t. black, scarlet-vermilion & salmon pink 35 15
726 20 t. blk, bright bluish violet & bright mauve 85 35
727 1 k. black, bright blue and cobalt .. 1·25 1·40
724/7 .. .. *Set of* 4 2·40 1·75

Designs:—15 t. Radio mast (Communications); 20 t. Diesel locomotive (Transport); 1 k. Trawler and net (Fishing).

154 M.V. *Ufulu* **155** Stierling's Woodpecker

(Des L. Curtis. Litho Cartor S.A., France)

1985 (3 June). *Ships of Lake Malawi* (2nd series). *T* **154** *an[d] similar horiz designs. Multicoloured. W* **55** *(sideways[)]. P* 13½ × 13.

728 7 t. Type **154**.. .. .. 40 1
729 15 t. M.V. *Chauncy Maples II* 65 1
730 20 t. M.V. *Mtendere* 80 2
731 1 k. M.V. *Ilala II* .. .. 2·00 2·2
728/31 .. .. *Set of* 4 3·50 2·5
MS732 120 × 84 mm. Nos. 728/31. P 13 × 12 .. 3·50 3·7

(Des M. Stringer. Litho Harrison)

1985 (1 Aug). *Birth Bicentenary of John J. Audubon (ornitho[l]ogist). T* **155** *and similar vert designs. Multicoloured. W* **55** *P* 14.

733 7 t. Type **155**.. .. .. 45 1
734 15 t. Lesser Seedcracker 70 1
735 20 t. East Coast Akelat 85 3
736 1 k. Boehm's Bee Eater .. .. .. 1·75 2·5
733/6 .. .. *Set of* 4 3·25 2·7
MS737 130 × 90 mm. Nos. 733/6. Wmk sideways .. .. 3·25 3·2

156 "The Virgin of Humility" (Jaime Serra) **157** Halley's Comet and Path of *Giotto* Spacecraft

(Photo Courvoisier)

1985 (14 Oct). *Christmas. Nativity Paintings. T* **156** *an[d] similar vert designs. Multicoloured. Granite paper. P* 11½.

738 7 t. Type **156** 10 1
739 15 t. "The Adoration of the Magi" (Stefano da Zevio) 20 1
740 20 t. "Madonna and Child" (Gerard van Honthorst) 25 2
741 1 k. "Virgin of Zbraslav" (Master of Vissy Brod) .. .. 1·00 9
738/41 .. .. *Set of* 4 1·40 1·2

(Des N. Shewring. Litho Walsall)

1986 (10 Feb). *Appearance of Halley's Comet. T* **157** *and simila[r] vert designs. Multicoloured. W* **55**. *P* 14½ × 14.

742 8 t. Type **157**.. .. .. 10 1
743 15 t. Halley's Comet above Earth 15 1
744 20 t. Comet and dish aerial, Malawi .. 20 2
745 1 k. *Giotto* spacecraft .. .. .. 85 1·0
742/5 .. .. *Set of* 4 1·10 1·2

158 Two Players competing for Ball **159** President Banda

(Des and photo Courvoisier)

1986 (26 May). *World Cup Football Championship, Mexic[o]. T* **158** *and similar horiz designs. Multicoloured. Granit[e] paper. P* 11½.

746 8 t. Type **158**.. .. .. 10 1
747 15 t. Goalkeeper saving goal 15 1
748 20 t. Two players competing for ball (*different*) 20 2
749 1 k. Player kicking ball 90 7
746/9 .. .. *Set of* 4 1·25 1·(
MS750 108 × 77 mm. Nos. 746/9 .. .. .. 1·90 2·2

(Des and litho Harrison)

1986 (30 June). *20th Anniv of the Republic. T* **159** *and simila[r] vert designs. Multicoloured. P* 14.

751 8 t. Type **159**.. .. .. 15 1
752 15 t. National flag 20 1
753 20 t. Malawi coat of arms 25 2
754 1 k. Kamuzu Airport and emblem of national airline .. .. 1·00 1·(
751/4 .. .. *Set of* 4 1·40 1·2

160 "Virgin and Child" (Botticelli)

161 Wattled Crane

(Des and photo Courvoisier)

986 (15 Dec). *Christmas. T* **160** *and similar vert designs showing paintings. Multicoloured. Granite paper. P* 11½.

55   8 t. Type **160**.   10   10
56   15 t. "Adoration of the Shepherds" (Guido Reni)   15   10
57   20 t. "Madonna of the Veil" (Carlo Dolci) . .   25   20
58   1 k. "Adoration of the Magi" (Jean Bourdichon) . . . .   1·10   1·10
55/8 . . . . *Set of* 4   1·40   1·25

(Des W. Oliver. Litho Walsall)

987 (16 Feb)–**88**. *Wattled Crane. T* **161** *and similar horiz designs. Multicoloured. P* 14×14½. (*a*) *W* **55** (*sideways*).

59   8 t. Type **161**.   30   10
60   15 t. Two cranes   45   10
61   20 t. Cranes at nest   55   30
62   75 t. Crane in lake . . . .   1·00   1·50
59/62 . . . . *Set of* 4   2·10   1·75

(*b*) *W w* **14** (*sideways*) (10.88)

63   8 t. Type **161**   20   10
64   15 t. Two cranes   25   10
65   20 t. Cranes at nest   25   10
66   75 t. Cranes in lake   60   70
63/6 . . . . *Set of* 4   1·10   90

162 Locomotive *Shamrock* No. 2, 1902

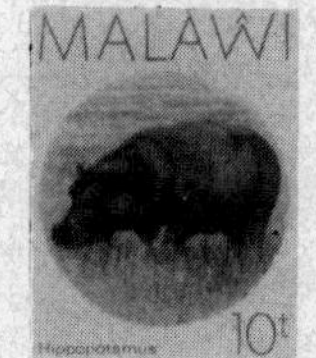

163 Hippopotamus grazing

(Des and litho Cartor S.A., France)

987 (25 May). *Steam Locomotives. T* **162** *and similar horiz designs. Multicoloured. P* 14×13½.

67   10 t. Type **162**.   30   10
68   25 t. "D" class, No. 8, 1914   45   15
69   30 t. *Thistle* No. 1, 1902   50   20
70   1 k. "Kitson" class, No. 6, 1903 . . . .   1·25   1·00
67/70 . . . . *Set of* 4   2·25   1·25

(Des and photo Courvoisier)

987 (24 Aug). *Hippopotamus. T* **163** *and similar vert designs. Multicoloured. Granite paper. P* 12½.

71   10 t. Type **163**.   20   10
72   25 t. Hippopotami in water   45   15
73   30 t. Female and calf in water   55   20
74   1 k. Hippopotami and egret. . . . . .   1·00   1·25
71/4 . . . . *Set of* 4   2·00   1·50
1S775   78×101 mm. Nos. 771/4 . . . . . .   2·00   2·25

164 *Stathmostelma spectabile*

165 Malawi and Staunton Knights

(Des and litho Harrison)

987 (19 Oct). *Christmas. Wild Flowers. T* **164** *and similar vert designs. Multicoloured. P* 14.

76   10 t. Type **164**.   15   10
77   25 t. *Pentanisia schweinfurthii*   30   15
78   30 t. *Chironia krebsii*.   35   20
79   1 k. *Ochna macrocalyx*   85   90
76/9 . . . . *Set of* 4   1·50   1·25

(Des Jennifer Toombs. Litho Walsall)

988 (8 Feb). *Chess. T* **165** *and similar vert designs showing local and Staunton chess pieces. Multicoloured. W w* **16**. *P* 14½×14.

80   15 t. Type **165**   25   10
81   35 t. Bishops   40   25
82   50 t. Rooks   55   30
83   2 k. Queens . . . .   1·50   1·75
80/3 . . . . *Set of* 4   2·50   2·25

166 High Jumping

167 Eastern Forest Scrub Warbler

(Des and litho Harrison)

1988 (13 June). *Olympic Games, Seoul. T* **166** *and similar vert designs. Multicoloured. P* 14.

784   15 t. Type **166**   10   10
785   35 t. Javelin throwing   20   20
786   50 t. Tennis   25   25
787   2 k. Shot-putting . . . .   1·00   1·00
784/7 . . . . *Set of* 4   1·40   1·40
MS788   91×121 mm. Nos. 784/7 . . . . . .   1·40   1·60

(Des N. Arlott (10 k.), Courvoisier (others). Litho Questa (10 k.) or photo Courvoisier (others))

1988 (25 July–3 Oct). *Birds. T* **167** *and similar vert designs. Multicoloured. W w* **14** *(sideways) (10 k.) or no wmk (others). Granite paper (1 t. to 4 k.). P* 15×14½ *(10 k.) or* 11½ *(others).*

789   1 t. Type **167**   10   10
790   2 t. Yellow-throated Woodland Warbler . .   10   10
791   5 t. Moustached Green Tinkerbird . .   10   10
792   7 t. Waller's Red-winged Starling . .   10   10
793   8 t. Oriole-Finch   10   10
794   10 t. Starred Robin   10   10
795   15 t. Bar-tailed Trogon   10   10
796   20 t. Green-backed Twin-spot   10   10
797   30 t. African Grey Cuckoo Shrike   10   15
798   40 t. Black-fronted Bush Shrike   15   20
799   50 t. White-tailed Crested Flycatcher . .   20   25
800   75 t. Green Barbet   30   35
801   1 k. Lemon Dove ("Cinnamon Dove") . .   40   45
802   2 k. Silvery-cheeked Hornbill   75   80
803   4 k. Crowned Eagle . . . .   1·50   1·60
804   10 k. Anchieta's Sunbird (3 Oct) . . . .   3·75   4·00
789/804 . . . . *Set of* 16   6·75   7·50

(Des D. Miller (15 t.), L. Curtis and D. Miller (35 t.), A. Theobald and D. Miller (50 t.), E. Nisbet and D. Miller (2 k.). Litho B.D.T.)

1988 (24 Oct). *300th Anniv of Lloyd's of London. Multicoloured designs as T* **123** *of Ascension. W w* **14** *(sideways on 35, 50 t.). P* 14.

805   15 t. Rebuilt Royal Exchange, 1844 . .   10   10
806   35 t. Opening ceremony, Nkula Falls Hydro-electric Power Station   20   20
807   50 t. Air Malawi "1-11" airliner (*horiz*) . .   25   25
808   2 k. *Seawise University* (formerly *Queen Elizabeth*) on fire, Hong Kong, 1972 . .   1·00   1·00
805/8 . . . . *Set of* 4   1·40   1·40

168 "Madonna in the Church" (Jan van Eyck)

169 *Serranochromis robustus*

(Des and litho Harrison)

1988 (28 Nov). *Christmas. T* **168** *and similar vert designs showing paintings. Multicoloured. P* 14.

809   15 t. Type **168**   10   10
810   35 t. "Virgin, Infant Jesus and St. Anna" (da Vinci).   15   20
811   50 t. "Virgin and Angels" (Cimabue) . .   20   25
812   2 k. "Virgin and Child" (Baldovinetti Apenio)   85   90
809/12 . . . . *Set of* 4   1·10   1·25

(Des and litho Harrison)

1989 (10 Apr). *50th Anniv of Malawi Angling Society. T* **169** *and similar horiz designs. Multicoloured. P* 14.

813   15 t. Type **169**   15   10
814   35 t. Lake Salmon   20   20
815   50 t. Yellow Fish   30   30
816   2 k. Tiger Fish . . . .   1·25   1·25
813/16 . . . . *Set of* 4   1·75   1·75

170 Independence Arch, Lilongwe

(Des and litho Harrison)

1989 (26 June). *25th Anniv of Independence. T* **170** *and similar horiz designs. Multicoloured. P* 14.

817   15 t. Type **170**   10   10
818   35 t. Grain silos   15   20
819   50 t. Capital Hill, Lilongwe   20   25
820   2 k. Reserve Bank Headquarters   85   90
817/20 . . . . *Set of* 4   1·10   1·25

171 Blantyre Digital Telex Exchange

(Des and litho Harrison)

1989 (30 Oct). *25th Anniv of African Development Bank. T* **171** *and similar horiz designs. Multicoloured. P* 14.

821   15 t. Type **171**   10   10
822   40 t. Dzalanyama steer   15   20
823   50 t. Mikolongwe heifer   20   25
824   2 k. Zebu bull   85   90
821/4 . . . . *Set of* 4   1·10   1·25

POSTAGE DUE STAMPS

D 1

(Litho Bradbury, Wilkinson)

1967 (1 Sept). *W* **55**. *P* 11½.

D 6   D 1   1d. carmine   15   1·25
D 7   2d. sepia   20   1·25
D 8   4d. reddish violet   25   1·50
D 9   6d. blue   25   1·75
D10   8d. emerald   35   1·90
D11   1s. black   45   2·25
D6/11 . . . . *Set of* 6   1·50   9·00

1971 (15 Feb). *As Nos.* D6/11 *but values in tambalas. W* **55**. *P* 11½.

D12   D 1   2 t. greenish drab   20   1·25
D13   4 t. bright mauve   30   1·25
D14   6 t. royal blue   30   1·50
D15   8 t. dull green   35   1·50
D16   10 t. blackish brown   40   1·50
D12/16 . . . . *Set of* 5   1·40   6·25

(Litho Walsall)

1975–84. *Design redrawn, with circumflex accent over "W" of "MALAWI". P* 14. (*a*) *W* **55** *(sideways)*.

D17   D 1   2 t. chestnut (15.9.75) . . . . . .   1·00   4·00
D18   2 t. brown (14.6.82)   10   10
D19   4 t. deep mauve (14.6.82)   10   10
D20   6 t. royal blue (9.84)   10   10
D21   8 t. green (9.84)   10   10
D22   10 t. black (14.6.82)   10   10
D17/22 . . . . *Set of* 6   1·10   4·00

(*b*) *No wmk*

D23   D 1   2 t. brown (19.10.77) . . . . . .   1·00   1·50
D24   4 t. mauve (19.10.77) . . . . . .   1·00   1·50
D25   8 t. green (15.12.78)   85   1·75
D26   10 t. brownish grey (19.10.77) . . . .   1·50   2·00
D23/6 . . . . *Set of* 4   4·00   6·00

Malaysia

The Federation of Malaysia was set up on 16 September 1963, ·d consisted of the former Malayan Federation, the State of Singa- ·re and the two former Crown Colonies in Borneo, Sabah (North ·rneo) and Sarawak. Singapore left the federation to become an ·dependent republic on 9 August 1965.

Malaysia now consists of thirteen States (11 in Peninsular ·alaysia and two in Borneo), together with the Federal Territories ·Kuala Lumpur and Labuan.

The philatelic history of the component parts of the federation is ·ost complex. Under this heading are now listed previous issues ·ade by the States of the Federation with the exception of ·ABUAN, SABAH (NORTH BORNEO) and SARAWAK. These, ·gether with SINGAPORE, continue to appear in the normal ·phabetical sequence.

The method adopted is to show the general issues for the area ·st, before dealing with the issues for the individual States. The ·ction is divided as follows:

I. STRAITS SETTLEMENTS
II. FEDERATED MALAY STATES
III. MALAYAN POSTAL UNION
IV. MALAYA (BRITISH MILITARY ADMINISTRATION)
V. MALAYAN FEDERATION
VI. MALAYSIA
VII. MALAYSIAN STATES—Johore, Kedah, Kelantan, Malacca, Negri Sembilan (with Sungei Ujong), Pahang, Penang, Perak, Perlis, Selangor, Trengganu
VIII. JAPANESE OCCUPATION
IX. THAI OCCUPATION

I. STRAITS SETTLEMENTS

The three original Settlements, Malacca, Penang (with Province ·ellesley) and Singapore (including Christmas Island and Cocos ·eeling) Islands) were formed into a Crown Colony during 1867. ·abuan was attached to the colony in 1896, becoming the fourth ·ttlement in 1906.

The first known prestamp cover with postal markings from ·enang (Prince of Wales Island) is dated March 1806 and from ·alacca, under British civil administration, February 1841. The ·vil post office at Singapore opened on 1 February 1823.

The stamps of India were used at all three post offices from ·e in 1854 until the Straits Settlements became a separate ·lony on 1 September 1867.

The Indian stamps were initially cancelled by dumb ·literators and their use in the Straits Settlements can only be ·entified from complete covers. In 1856 cancellations of the ·andard Indian octagonal type were issued, numbered "B 109" ·r Malacca, "B 147" for Penang and "B 172" for Singapore.

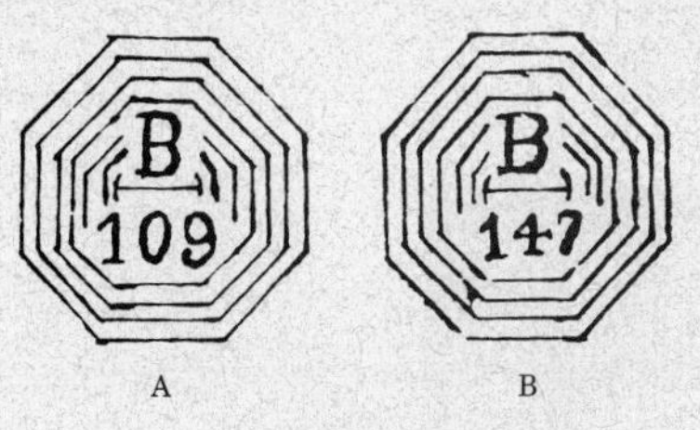

A B

C

The Penang and Singapore octagonals were replaced by a ·plex type, consisting of a double-ringed datestamp and a ·mond-shaped obliterator containing the office number, in ·63 and 1865 respectively.

D

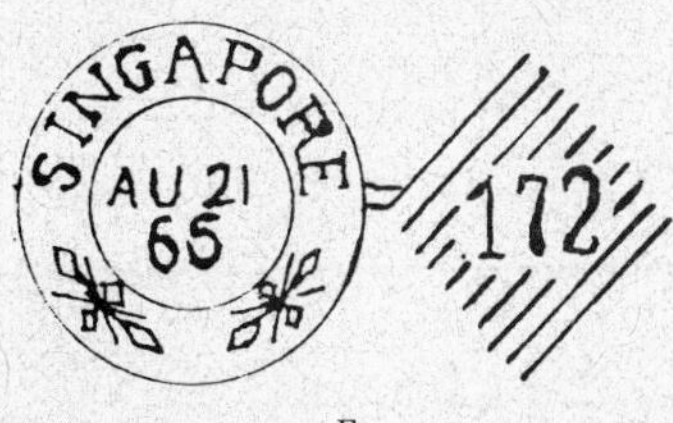

E

·RICES. Catalogue prices in this section are for stamps with ·arly legible, if partial, examples of the postmarks.

MALACCA

Stamps of INDIA *cancelled with Type* A.

1854. (*Nos.* 2/34).
Z1 ½ a. blue (Die I) .. £450
Z2 1 a. red (Die I) .. £350
Z3 1 a. dull red (Die II) .. £400
Z4 2 a. green .. £600
Z5 4 a. blue and red (Head Die II) (*cut-to-shape*) .. £700

1855. (*Nos.* 35/6).
Z6 8 a. carmine (Die I)/*blue glazed* .. 95·00

1856–64. (*Nos.* 37/49).
Z7 ½ a. pale blue (Die I) .. 55·00
Z8 1 a. brown .. 45·00
Z9 2 a. yellow-buff .. 45·00
Z10 2 a. yellow .. 55·00
Z11 4 a. green .. 85·00
Z12 8 a. carmine (Die I) .. 70·00

1860. (*Nos.* 51/3).
Z13 8 p. purple/*bluish* .. £120
Z14 8 p. purple/*white* .. 65·00

1865. (*Nos.* 54/65).
Z15 4 a. green .. 70·00

PENANG

Stamps of INDIA *cancelled with Type* B.

1854. (*Nos.* 2/34).
Z20 ½ a. blue (Die I) .. 65·00
Z21 1 a. red (Die I) .. 55·00
Z22 2 a. green .. 85·00
Z23 4 a. blue and pale red (Head Die I) .. £500
Z24 4 a. blue and red (Head Die II) .. £550
Z25 4 a. blue and red (Head Die III) .. £450

1855. (*Nos.* 35/6).
Z26 4 a. black/*blue glazed* .. 20·00
Z27 8 a. carmine (Die I)/*blue glazed* .. 24·00
a. Bisected (4 a.) (1860) (on cover) .. £15000

1856–64. (*Nos.* 37/49).
Z28 ½ a. pale blue (Die I) .. 22·00
Z29 1 a. brown .. 14·00
Z30 2 a. dull pink .. 20·00
Z31 2 a. yellow-buff .. 18·00
Z32 2 a. yellow .. 18·00
Z33 2 a. orange .. 20·00
Z34 4 a. black .. 12·00
Z35 8 a. carmine (Die I) .. 18·00

1860. (*Nos.* 51/3).
Z36 8 p. purple/*white* .. 35·00

Stamps of INDIA *cancelled with Type* D.

1856–64. (*Nos.* 37/49).
Z40 1 a. brown .. 10·00
Z41 2 a. yellow .. 15·00
Z42 4 a. black .. 12·00
Z43 4 a. green .. 32·00
Z44 8 a. carmine (Die I) .. 14·00

1860. (*Nos.* 51/3).
Z45 8 p. purple/*white* .. 25·00
Z46 8 p. mauve .. 22·00

1865. (*Nos.* 54/65).
Z47 8 p. purple
Z48 1 a. deep brown .. 10·00
Z49 2 a. yellow .. 12·00
Z50 4 a. green .. 35·00
Z51 8 a. carmine (Die I)

1866–67. (*Nos.* 69/72)
Z52 4 a. green (Die I) .. 30·00

SINGAPORE

Stamps of INDIA *cancelled with Type* C.

1854. (*Nos.* 2/34).
Z60 ½ a. blue (Die I) .. 50·00
Z61 1 a. red (Die I) .. 50·00
Z62 1 a. dull red (Die II) .. 70·00
Z63 1 a. red (Die III) .. £350
Z64 2 a. green .. 55·00
a. Bisected (1 a.) (1857) (on cover)
Z65 4 a. blue and pale red (Head Die I) .. £450
Z66 4 a. blue and red (Head Die II) .. £500
Z67 4 a. blue and red (Head Die III) .. £400

1855. (*Nos.* 35/6).
Z68 4 a. black/*blue glazed* .. 12·00
a. Bisected (2 a.) (1859) (on cover) .. £4000
Z69 8 a. carmine/*blue glazed* .. 14·00
a. Bisected (4 a.) (1859) (on cover) .. £16000

1856–64. (*Nos.* 37/49).
Z70 ½ a. pale blue (Die I) .. 8·00
Z71 1 a. brown .. 10·00
a. Bisected (½ a.) (1859) (on cover) .. £15000
Z72 2 a. dull pink .. 16·00
Z73 2 a. yellow-buff .. 11·00
Z74 2 a. yellow .. 11·00
Z75 2 a. orange .. 12·00
Z76 4 a. black .. 9·00
a. Bisected diagonally (2 a.) (1859) (on cover) .. £5500
Z77 4 a. green .. 30·00
Z78 8 a. carmine (Die I) .. 11·00
a. Bisected (4 a.) (1859) (on cover) .. £16000

1860. (*Nos.* 51/3).
Z79 8 p. purple/*bluish* .. £100
Z80 8 p. purple/*white* .. 18·00
a. Bisected diagonally (4 p.) (1862) (on cover) £16000
Z81 8 p. mauve .. 18·00

1865. (*Nos.* 54/65).
Z82 ½ a. blue (Die I) .. 10·00
Z83 8 p. purple .. 32·00
Z84 1 a. deep brown .. 9·00
Z85 2 a. yellow .. 10·00
Z86 2 a. orange .. 10·00
Z87 4 a. green .. 30·00
Z88 8 a. carmine (Die I) .. £110

1866–67. (*Nos.* 69/72).
Z89 4 a. green (Die I) .. 25·00
Z90 6 a. 8 p. slate .. 35·00

OFFICIAL STAMPS

1866–67. (*Nos.* O6/14).
Z91 ½ a. pale blue .. 70·00
Z92 2 a. yellow .. £140

Stamps of INDIA *cancelled with Type* E.

1856–64. (*Nos.* 37/49).
Z100 1 a. brown .. £120
Z101 2 a. yellow .. £150
Z102 4 a. black .. £150
Z103 8 a. carmine (Die I) .. £150

1860. (*Nos.* 51/3).
Z104 8 p. purple/*white* .. £150

1865. (*Nos.* 54/65).
Z105 2 a. yellow .. £120
Z106 2 a. orange .. £120
Z107 4 a. green .. £160

PRICES FOR STAMPS ON COVER	
Nos. 1/9	*from* × 10
Nos. 11/19	*from* × 8
Nos. 20/47	*from* × 7
Nos. 48/9	*from* × 10
Nos. 50/71	*from* × 5
No. 72	—
Nos. 73/8	*from* × 6
No. 80	*from* × 10
Nos. 82/5	*from* × 5
Nos. 86/7	*from* × 10
Nos. 88/94	*from* × 5
Nos. 95/105	*from* × 6
Nos. 106/9	*from* × 10
Nos. 110/21	*from* × 5
No. 122	—
Nos. 123/6	*from* × 4
Nos. 127/38	*from* × 3
Nos. 139/40	—
Nos. 141/51	*from* × 12
Nos. 152/67	*from* × 3
Nos. 168/9	—
Nos. 193/212	*from* × 3
Nos. 213/15	—
Nos. 216/17	*from* × 10
Nos. 218/40*a*	*from* × 3
Nos. 240*b*/*d*	—
Nos. 241/55	*from* × 15
Nos. 256/9	*from* × 4
Nos. 260/98	*from* × 3
Nos. D1/6	*from* × 20

PRINTERS. All Straits Settlements issues were printed in typography by De La Rue & Co, Ltd, London, *unless otherwise stated*.

THREE HALF CENTS (1)   32 CENTS (2)

1867 (1 Sept). *Stamps of India surch as T* **1** *or* **2** (24 *c.*, 32 *c.*) *by De La Rue. Wmk Elephant's Head. P* 14.

1	**11**	1½ c. on ½ a. blue (Die I) (R.)	50·00	£150
2		2 c. on 1 a. brown (R.)	50·00	50·00
3		3 c. on 1 a. brown (B.)	55·00	55·00
4		4 c. on 1 a. brown (Bk.)	£110	£150
5		6 c. on 2 a. yellow (P.)	£225	£150
6		8 c. on 2 a. yellow (G.)	70·00	30·00

7 **17** 12 c. on 4 a. green (R.) £325 £175
a. Surch double £650
8 **11** 24 c. on 8 a. rose (Die II) (B.) .. .. £150 60·00
9 32 c. on 2 a. yellow (Bk.).. .. .. .. £150 60·00
The 32 c. was re-issued for postal use in 1884.
No. 7a is only known unused.

1869 (?). *No.* 1 *with* "THREE HALF" *deleted and* "2" *written above, in black manuscript.*
10 2 on 1½ c. on ½ a. blue £3750 £2250
This stamp has been known from very early days and was apparently used at Penang, but nothing is known of its history.

5 6 7

8 9

1867 (Dec)–**72**. *Wmk Crown CC. P* 14. *Ornaments in corners differ for each value.*

No.	Type	Description	Unused	Used
11	**5**	2 c. brown (6.68)	9·00	1·60
		a. Yellow-brown	10·00	1·75
		b. Deep brown ..	35·00	7·00
12		4 c. rose (7.68) ..	14·00	4·00
		a. Deep rose	20·00	4·50
13		6 c. dull lilac (1.68)	38·00	10·00
		a. Bright lilac ..	38·00	10·00
14	**6**	8 c. orange-yellow	55·00	5·50
		a. Orange	55·00	7·00
15		12 c. blue ..	55·00	4·50
		a. Ultramarine	55·00	7·50
16	**7**	24 c. blue-green ..	50·00	3·50
		a. Yellow-green	80·00	16·00
17	**8**	30 c. claret (12.72)	70·00	7·00
18	**9**	32 c. pale red	£180	45·00
19		96 c. grey ..	£130	24·00
		a. Perf 12½ (6.71)	£1000	£225

Five Cents. (10) Seven Cents. (11)

1879 (May). *Nos.* 14*a and* 18 *surch with T* **10** *and* **11**.

No.	Type	Description	Unused	Used
20	**6**	5 c. on 8 c. orange	50·00	70·00
		a. No stop after "Cents"	£300	£325
		b. "F i" spaced ..	£350	£350
21	**9**	7 c. on 32 c. pale red	50·00	60·00
		a. No stop after "Cents"	£275	£300

10 cents. (12)

10 (*a*) 10 (*b*) 10 (*c*) 10 (*d*)

10 (*e*) 10 (*f*) 10 (*g*) 10 (*h*)

10 (*i*) 10 (*j*) 10 (*jj*) 10 (*k*) 10 (*l*)

(*a*) "1" thin curved serif and thin foot, "0" narrow.
(*b*) "1" thick curved serif and thick foot; "0" broad. Both numerals heavy.
(*c*) "1" as (*a*); "0" as (*b*)
(*d*) "1" as (*a*) but thicker; "0" as (*a*)
(*e*) As (*a*) but sides of "0" thicker.
(*f*) "1" as (*d*); "0" as (*e*)
(*g*) As (*a*) but "0" narrower.
(*h*) "1" thin, curved serif and thick foot; "0" as (*g*)
(*i*) "1" as (*b*); "0" as (*a*)
(*j*) "1" as (*d*); "0" as (*g*) but raised.
(*jj*) "1" as (*a*) but shorter, and with shorter serif and thicker foot; "0" as (*g*) but level with "1".
(*k*) "1" as (*jj*); "0" as (*d*)
(*l*) "1" straight serif; "0" as (*d*).

1880 (Mar). *No.* 17 *surch with T* **12** (*showing numerals* (*a*) *to* (*jj*)).

No.	Description	Unused	Used
22	10 c. on 30 c. claret (*a*)..	80·00	40·00
23	10 c. on 30 c. claret (*b*)..	80·00	35·00
24	10 c. on 30 c. claret (*c*)..	£800	£225
25	10 c. on 30 c. claret (*d*)..	£325	90·00
26	10 c. on 30 c. claret (*e*)..	£1300	£375
27	10 c. on 30 c. claret (*f*)..	£1300	£375
28	10 c. on 30 c. claret (*g*)..	£450	£175
29	10 c. on 30 c. claret (*h*)..	£1300	£375
30	10 c. on 30 c. claret (*i*) ..	£1300	£375
31	10 c. on 30 c. claret (*j*) ..	£1300	£375
32	10 c. on 30 c. claret (*jj*).	£1300	£375

Nos. 22/32 come from the same setting of 60 (6 × 10) containing twenty examples of No. 22 (R.1/1-2, 1/4, 1/6, 2/1-6, 3/1, 3/3, 3/5, 4/1, 4/3-4, 10/1, 10/3-5), twenty-two of No. 23 (R.4/1, 5/1-6, 6/1-6, 7/1, 8/2-4, 9/1-5), six of No. 25 (R.1/5, 3/2, 3/4, 4/2, 4/5, 10/2), four of No. 28 (R.7/2-5), two of No. 24 (R.9/6, 10/6) and one each of Nos. 26 (R.3/2), 27 (R.1/3), 29 (R.7/6), 30 (R.8/1), 31 (R.8/6) and 32 (R.8/5).

No. 23 is known with large stop after "cents" and also with stop low.

1880 (April). *No.* 17 *surch as T* **12**, *but without "cents.", showing numerals* (*a*) *to* (*c*), (*g*), (*j*), (*k*) *and* (*l*).

No.	Description	Unused	Used
33	10 on 30 c. claret (*a*)..	65·00	45·00
34	10 on 30 c. claret (*b*)..	75·00	30·00
35	10 on 30 c. claret (*c*)..	£225	£100
36	10 on 30 c. claret (*g*)..	£500	£200
37	10 on 30 c. claret (*i*) ..	£1000	£375
38	10 on 30 c. claret (*k*)..	£1000	£500
39	10 on 30 c. claret (*l*) ..	£1000	£500

Nos. 33/9 were surcharged from an amended setting of 60 (6 × 10) of which only 54 positions have been identified. Of those known No. 33 occurs on twenty-two (R.6/1-6, 7/1-6, 8/1-6, 9/2, 9/6, 10/2-3), No. 34 on nineteen (R.1/2-6, 2/2-6, 3/2-6, 4/3-5, 5/6), No. 35 on seven (R.4/2, 4/6, 5/1-5), No. 36 on three (R.9/3-5) and Nos. 37 (R.10/6), 38 (R.10/4) and 39 (R.10/5) on one each.

The top four and bottom two positions in the first vertical column have not been identified. A single example in the Royal Collection shows the "1" as (*b*) and "0" as (*g*) which may come from one of these positions, but this has not been confirmed.

5 cents. (13) 5 cents. (14) 5 cents. (15)

1880 (Aug). *No.* 14*a surch with T* **13** *to* **15**.

No.	Type	Description	Unused	Used
41	**13**	5 c. on 8 c. orange	55·00	70·00
42	**14**	5 c. on 8 c. orange	50·00	65·00
43	**15**	5 c. on 8 c. orange	£150	£170

Surcharged in a setting of 60 (6 × 10) with T **13** on rows one to four, T **14** on rows five to nine and T **15** on row ten.

10 cents. (16) 5 cents. (17)

1880–81. *Nos.* 13, 15/*a and* 17 *surch with T* **16**.

No.	Description	Unused	Used
44	10 c. on 6 c. lilac (11.81)	28·00	6·00
	a. Surch double		— £1000
45	10 c. on 12 c. ultramarine (1.81)	38·00	16·00
	a. Blue	26·00	9·00
46	10 c. on 30 c. claret (12.80)	£130	60·00

A second printing of the 10 c. on 6 c. has the surcharge heavier and the "10" usually more to the left or right of "cents".

1882 (Jan). *No.* 12 *surch with T* **17**.
47 5 c. on 4 c. rose £160 £180

18 19

1882 (Jan). *Wmk Crown CC. P* 14.

No.	Type	Description	Unused	Used
48	**18**	5 c. purple-brown	55·00	55·00
49	**19**	10 c. slate (Optd S. £150)	£170	50·00

1882. *Wmk Crown CA. P* 14.

No.	Type	Description	Unused	Used
50	**5**	2 c. brown (Aug)	£170	25·00
51		4 c. rose (April) ..	80·00	4·00
52	**6**	8 c. orange (Sept)	2·00	35
53	**19**	10 c. slate (Oct) ..	2·00	45

For the 4 c. in deep carmine see No. 98.

TWO CENTS 20*a* "S" wide TWO CENTS 20*b* "E" and "S" wide TWO CENTS 20*c* "N" wide

TWO CENTS 20*d* All letters narrow TWO CENTS 20*e* "EN" and "S" wide TWO CENTS 20*f* "E" wide

1883 (Apr). *Nos.* 52 *and* 18 *surch with T* **20***a*/*f*.

No.	Type	Description	Unused	Used
54	**20*a***	2 c. on 8 c. orange	55·00	42·00
55	**20*b***	2 c. on 8 c. orange	55·00	42·00
56	**20*c***	2 c. on 8 c. orange	55·00	42·00
57	**20*d***	2 c. on 8 c. orange	55·00	42·00
		a. Surch double	£1300	£800
58	**20*e***	2 c. on 8 c. orange	£120	90·00
59	**20*a***	2 c. on 32 c. pale red	£275	85·00
60	**20*f***	2 c. on 32 c. pale red	£275	85·00
		a. Surch double		

The 8 c. was surcharged using one of two triplet settings, either 54 + 55 + 56 or 57 + 57 + 57, applied to rows 2 to 10. A single handstamp, either No. 57 or No. 58, was then used to complete row 1. The 32 c. was surcharged in the same way with a triplet of 59 + 60 + 59 and a single handstamp as No. 60.

2 Cents. (21) 4 Cents (22) 8 Cents (23)

1883 (June–July). *Nos.* 51 *and* 15 *surch with T* **21**.

No.	Description	Unused	Used
61	2 c. on 4 c. rose	35·00	42·00
	a. "s" of "Cents" inverted ..	£850	£1000
62	2 c. on 12 c. blue (July)	90·00	55·00
	a. "s" of "Cents" inverted ..	£1600	£1400

1883 (July)–**91**. *Wmk Crown CA. P* 14.

No.	Type	Description	Unused	Used
63	**5**	2 c. pale rose	10·00	1·40
		a. Bright rose (1889)	1·00	15
64		4 c. pale brown ..	9·00	1·25
		a. Deep brown	13·00	2·75
		b. Olive-bistre	£350	£275
65	**18**	5 c. blue (8.83) ..	2·25	30
66	**5**	6 c. lilac (11.84)	12·00	6·50
		a. Violet	1·60	1·50
67	**6**	12 c. brown-purple	25·00	5·00
68	**7**	24 c. yellow-green (2.84)	40·00	3·25
		a. Blue-green ..	2·75	2·00
69	**8**	30 c. claret (9.91)	7·00	3·75
70	**9**	32 c. orange-vermilion (1.87)	5·50	1·50
71		96 c. olive-grey (8.88)	60·00	32·00
63*a*/71		*Set of* 9	£100	42·00
63/65, 67		Optd "Specimen" .. *Set of* 4	£400	

For the 12 c. in claret see No. 102.

1884 (Feb–Aug). *Nos.* 65, 15 *and* 67 *surch with T* **22** *or* **23**.

No.	Type	Description	Unused	Used
72	**18**	4 c. on 5 c. blue (Aug) ..	£1700	£2250
73		4 c. on 5 c. blue (R.) (Aug)	65·00	60·00
74	**6**	8 c. on 12 c. blue	£110	70·00
75		8 c. on 12 c. brown-purple (Aug)	£110	80·00
		a. Inverted "8"	†	—

No. 75 is known with "s" of "Cents" low.

1884 (Aug). *No.* 65 *surch with T* **20***d*/*f*.

No.	Type	Description	Unused	Used
76	**20*d***	2 c. on 5 c. blue ..	60·00	75·00
77	**20*e***	2 c. on 5 c. blue ..	60·00	75·00
		a. Pair, with and without surch		
		b. Surch double		
78	**20*f***	2 c. on 5 c. blue ..	60·00	75·00

Surcharged as a triplet, 77 + 76 + 78. On No. 76 "TS" are dropped below the line.

8 (24) 3 CENTS (25) THREE CENTS (26)

1884 (Sept). *No.* 75 *additionally surch with large numeral as T* **24** *in black.*

No.	Type	Description	Unused	Used
80	**6**	8 on 8 c. on 12 c. dull purple	90·00	£100
		a. Surch T **24** double	£1900	
		b. Surch T **24** in blue	£3000	

A similar "4" surcharge in red on No. 73 exists from a trial printing from which seven examples are known, all used on an official's correspondence (*Price* £7000 *used*).

1885. *No.* 65 *and T* **9** *in new colour, wmk Crown CA, surch with T* **25** *or* **26**.

No.	Type	Description	Unused	Used
82	**25**	3 c. on 5 c. blue (Sept)	60·00	£175
		a. Surch double	£1400	
83	**26**	3 c. on 32 c. pl mag (Dec) (Optd S. £100)	1·40	2·50
		a. Deep magenta	90	90

The surcharge on No. 82 was applied locally by a triplet setting. No. 83 was surcharged by De La Rue in complete panes.

3 cents (27) 2 Cents (28)

1886 (Apr). *No.* 48 *surch with T* **27**.
84 **18** 3 c. on 5 c. purple-brown .. .. 95·00 £110
The surcharge on No. 84 was applied by a triplet setting.

1887 (July). *No.* 65 *surch with T* **28**.

No.	Type	Description	Unused	Used
85	**18**	2 c. on 5 c. blue..	11·00	23·00
		a. "C" of "Cents" omitted		— £1600
		b. Surch double	£400	£325

The surcharge on No. 85 was applied by a triplet setting.

10 CENTS (29) THIRTY CENTS (30)

1891 (Nov). *Nos.* 68 *and* 70 *surch with T* **29** *and* **30**.

No.	Type	Description	Unused	Used
86	**7**	10 c. on 24 c. yellow-green	1·50	1·25
		a. Narrow "0" in "10" (R. 4/6)	25·00	28·00
87	**9**	30 c. on 32 c. orange-vermilion	4·00	3·50

The "R" of "THIRTY" and "N" of "CENTS" are found wide or narrow and in all possible combinations.

ONE CENT (31) ONE CENT (32)

1892. *Stamps of* 1882–91 (*wmk Crown CA*) *surch with T* **31**.

No.	Description	Unused	Used
88	1 c. on 2 c. rose (March)	1·25	1·50
89	1 c. on 4 c. brown (April)	3·75	3·75
	a. Surch double	£600	
90	1 c. on 6 c. lilac (Feb)..	1·00	2·00
	a. Surch double, one inverted	£650	£550

91 1 c. on 8 c. orange (Jan) .. .. 1·00 60
92 1 c. on 12 c. brown-purple (Mar) .. .. 4·00 9·00
88/92 .. .. *Set of* 5 10·00 15·00

The three settings used for Nos. 88/92 contained various combinations of the following varieties: "ON" of "ONE" and "N" of "CENT" wide; "O" wide, "N" of "ONE" narrow and "N" of "CENT" wide; "O" narrow and both letters "N" wide; "ON" narrow, and "N" of "CENT" wide; "O" wide and both letters "N" narrow; "ON" wide and "N" of "CENT" narrow; "ON" and "N" of "CENT" narrow; "O" narrow "N" of "ONE" wide and "N" of "CENT" narrow. Antique "N" and "E" letters also occur.

1892–94. *Colours changed. Wmk Crown CA. P 14. Surch with T* **32** *and* **26** *by De la Rue.*
93 **6** 1 c. on 8 c. green (3.92) 40 75
94 **9** 3 c. on 32 c. carmine-rose (6.94) .. .. 1·00 70
a. Surch omitted £2250
93/94 Optd "Specimen" .. .. *Set of* 2 85·00

No. 94a comes from a sheet found at Singapore on which all stamps in the upper left pane had the surcharge omitted. Five of the vertical inter-panneau pairs still exist with the surcharge omitted on the upper stamp (*Price* £10000 *unused*). The only used example of the error is on cover.

33

34

4
cents.
(35)

1892 (Mar)–**99.** *Wmk Crown CA. P* 14.
95 **33** 1 c. green (9.92) 40 20
96 3 c. carmine-rose (2.95) .. .. .. 4·00 30
97 3 c. brown (3.99) .. .. 2·00 25
a. Yellow-brown .. .. .. 2·25 40
98 **5** 4 c. deep carmine (7.99) .. .. .. 2·00 85
99 **18** 5 c. brown (6.94) .. .. 2·00 70
100 5 c. magenta (7.99) .. .. .. 1·60 1·75
101 **6** 8 c. ultramarine (6.94) .. .. .. 2·50 30
a. Bright blue .. .. 3·00 35
102 12 c. claret (3.94) .. .. 7·00 7·50
103 **33** 25 c. purple-brown and green .. .. 11·00 3·50
a. Dull purple and green .. .. 11·00 3·25
104 50 c. olive-green and carmine .. .. 17·00 2·50
105 **34** $5 orange and carmine (10.98) .. £275 £275
99/105 .. .. *Set of* 11 £300 £275
99/101, 103/5 Optd "Specimen" .. *Set of* 10 £250

1898 (26 Dec). *T* **18** *and* **6** *surch with T* **35** *at Singapore.*
106 4 c. on 5 c. brown (No. 99) .. .. .. 75 4·00
107 4 c. on 5 c. blue (No. 65) .. .. .. 1·25 4·00
a. Surch double .. .. .. — £700
108 4 c. on 8 c. ultramarine (No. 101) .. .. 80 2·50
a. Surch double £575 £500
b. Bright blue (No. 101*a*) 50 70
106/8*b* .. .. *Set of* 3 2·25 7·00

Nos. 107 and 108*b* exist with stop spaced 1½ mm from the "S".

FOUR CENTS
(36)

37

38

1899 (Mar). *T* **18** *(wmk Crown CA. P 14), surch with T* **36** *by De La Rue.*
109 4 c. on 5 c. carmine (Optd S. £30) 30 15
a. Surch omitted £8500

No. 109a is only known unused.

1902 (Apr)–**03.** *Wmk Crown CA. P* 14.
110 **37** 1 c. grey-green (7.02) 20 60
a. Pale green .. .. 2·00 90
111 3 c. dull purple and orange 45 15
112 4 c. purple/*red* (9.02) .. .. .. 1·75 25
113 **38** 5 c. dull purple (8.02) .. .. .. 1·75 45
114 8 c. purple/*blue* .. .. 3·00 20
115 10 c. purple and black/*yellow* (9.02) .. 8·50 70
116 **37** 25 c. dull purple and green (8.02) .. 6·50 3·50
117 **38** 30 c. grey and carmine (7.02) .. .. 12·00 8·00
118 **37** 50 c. deep green and carmine (9.02) .. 11·00 11·00
a. Dull green and carmine .. .. 15·00 13·00
119 **38** $1 dull green and black (9.02) .. .. 20·00 38·00
120 **37** $2 dull purple and black (9.02) .. .. 40·00 40·00
121 **38** $5 dull green and brown-orange (10.02) £120 90·00
122 **37** $100 pur & grn/*yell* (3.03) (Optd S. £225) £5000
110/21 .. .. *Set of* 12 £200 £170
110/21 Optd "Specimen" .. .. *Set of* 12 £200

39

40

41

42

(Des N. Trotter and W. Egerton)

1903 (Dec)–**04.** *Wmk Crown CA. P* 14.
123 **39** 1 c. grey-green .. .. 30 2·50
124 **40** 3 c. dull purple (1.04) .. .. .. 3·75 2·00
125 **41** 4 c. purple/*red* (4.04) 85 30
126 **42** 8 c. purple/*blue* (7.04) .. .. .. 15·00 1·25
123/6 .. .. *Set of* 4 18·00 5·00
123/6 Optd "Specimen" .. .. *Set of* 4 £100

1904 (Aug)–**10.** *Wmk Multiple Crown CA. P* 14.
127 **39** 1 c. deep green, **OC** (9.04) 60 10
128 **40** 3 c. dull purple, **OC** 30 25
a. Plum, **O** (2.08) .. .. .. 2·50 55
129 **41** 4 c. purple/*red*, **OC** (6.05) 80 15
130 **38** 5 c. dull purple, **OC** (12.06) .. .. 2·50 2·00
131 **42** 8 c. purple/*blue*, **OC** (8.05) .. .. 4·50 25
132 **38** 10 c. purple & black/*yellow* **OC** (8.05) .. 2·00 25
133 **37** 25 c. dull purple and green, **OC** (1.05) .. 7·00 8·50
134 **38** 30 c. grey and carmine, **OC** (3.05) .. 13·00 2·50
135 **37** 50 c. dull green & carm, **OC** (10.05) .. 9·00 6·00
136 **38** $1 dull green and black, **OC** (3.05) .. 16·00 7·50
137 **37** $2 dull purple and black, **C** (10.05) .. 60·00 60·00
138 **38** $5 dull grn & brn-orge **OC** (10.05) .. 75·00 75·00
139 **37** $25 grey-green and black, **C** (7.06) (Optd S. £125) £800 £700
140 $100 purple & green/*yellow*, **C** (6.10) .. £6500
127/38 .. .. *Set of* 12 £170 £150

STRAITS
SETTLEMENTS.
(43)

Straits Settlements.
(44)

STRAITS
SETTLEMENTS.

FOUR CENTS.
(45)

1906 (Dec)–**07.** *T* **18** *of Labuan (Nos. 116c etc.) optd with T* **43** *or* **44** *(10 c.), or additionally surch with T* **45**, *in black (No. 145), claret (No. 151) or brown-red (others) at Singapore. P* 13½–14.
141 1 c. black and purple (p 14½–15) .. .. 35·00 65·00
142 2 c. black and green £125 £150
a. Perf 14½–15 .. .. £125
143 3 c. black and sepia (1.07) .. .. .. 14·00 55·00
144 4 c. on 12 c. black and yellow .. .. 1·00 4·00
a. No stop after "CENTS" (R. 1/8, 6/8) .. £100
145 4 c. on 16 c. green and brown (Blk.) .. 1·00 3·00
a. "STRAITS SETTLEMENTS" in both brown-red and black £450 £400
b. Ditto. In vert pair with normal .. £1800
146 4 c. on 18 c. black and pale brown .. .. 75 3·00
a. No stop after "CENTS" (R. 1/8, 6/8) .. 90·00
b. "FOUR CENTS" and bar double .. £3000
c. "FOUR CENTS" and bar 1½ mm below normal position (pair with normal) .. £250
147 8 c. black and vermilion .. .. .. 75 4·00
148 10 c. brown and slate .. .. 2·50 3·50
a. No stop after "SETTLEMENTS" (R. 1/4, 6/4) £110
149 25 c. green and greenish blue (1.07) .. 3·25 12·00
a. Perf 14½–15 .. .. 60·00
b. Perf 13½–14 comp 14½–15 .. ..
150 50 c. dull purple and lilac (1.07) .. .. 8·00 30·00
151 $1 claret and orange (Claret) (1.07) .. 32·00 55·00
a. Perf 14½–15 .. ..
141/51 .. .. *Set of* 11 £200 £350

Nos. 141/51 were overprinted by a setting of 50 (10×5) applied twice to the sheets of 100. The "FOUR CENTS" surcharges were applied separately by a similar setting.

No. 145a shows impressions of Type **43** in both brown-red and black. It is known from one complete sheet and the top half of another.

No. 146b occurred on row 5 from one sheet only. No. 146c occurred on R. 4/10 and 9/10 of the first printing.

The 2 c. also exists perf 14 all round and is rare.

46

47

1906 (Sept)–**11.** *Wmk Mult Crown CA. P* 14.
152 **39** 1 c. blue-green, **O** (3.10) .. .. 4·00 70
153 **40** 3 c. red, **O** (6.08) 80 10
154 **41** 4 c. red, **O** (7.07) .. .. 4·00 75
155 4 c. dull purple, **OC** (2.08) 70 10
156 4 c. claret, **O** (9.11) 75 80
157 **38** 5 c. orange, **O** (4.09) .. .. .. 2·75 40
158 **42** 8 c. blue, **O** .. .. 1·00 25
159 **38** 10 c. purple/*yellow*, **OC** (7.08) .. .. 1·00 15
160 **46** 21 c. dull purple and claret, **C** (11.10) .. 4·50 20·00
161 **37** 25 c. dull and bright purple, **C** (7.09) .. 5·00 2·75
162 **38** 30 c. purple & orange-yell, **C** (11.09) .. 14·00 1·25
163 **46** 45 c. black/*green*, **C** (11.10) .. .. 2·50 3·50
164 **37** 50 c. black/*green*, **C** (4.10) .. .. 3·50 1·00
165 **38** $1 black and red/*blue*, **C** (10.10) .. 9·50 3·50
166 **37** $2 green and red/*yellow*, **C** (12.09) .. 15·00 15·00
167 **38** $5 green and red/*green*, **C** (11.09) .. 55·00 45·00
168 **47** $25 purple and blue/*blue*, **C** (5.11) (Optd S. £150) £700 £475
169 $500 purple and orange, **C** (5.10) (Optd S. £850) £35000
152/67 .. .. *Set of* 16 £110 85·00
153/67 Optd "Specimen" .. .. *Set of* 15 £200

Beware of dangerous forgeries of No. 169.

48

49

50

51

52

53

54

1912–23. $25, $100 *and* $500 *as T* **47**, *but with head of Kin George V. Wmk Mult Crown CA. P* 14.
193 **48** 1 c. green, **O** (9.12) .. .. .. 1·50 4
a. Pale green (1.14) .. .. .. 1·75 3
b. Blue-green (1917) .. .. .. 2·00 4
194 1 c. black, **O** (2.19) 20 2
195 **52** 2 c. green, **O** (10.19) 35 2
196 **49** 3 c. red, **O** (2.13) 90 3
a. Scarlet (2.17) 25 1
197 **50** 4 c. dull purple, **C** (3.13) 70 3
a. Wmk sideways .. .. .. — £100
198 4 c. rose-scarlet, **O** (2.19) 70 1
a. Carmine .. .. 1·00 2
199 **51** 5 c. orange, **O** (8.12) .. .. .. 1·25 4
a. Yellow-orange .. .. .. 1·50 4
200 **52** 6 c. dull claret, **O** (3.20) .. .. .. 1·75 5
a. Deep claret .. .. 4·25 2·5
201 8 c. ultramarine, **O** (3.13) 50 2
202 **51** 10 c. purple/*yellow*, **C** (8.12) 70 3
a. White back (9.13) (Optd S. £27) .. 50 5
b. On lemon (1916) (Optd S. £42) .. 8·00 9
203 10 c. deep bright blue, **O** (2.19) .. .. 4·75 2
a. Bright blue .. .. 3·75 3
204 **53** 21 c. dull and bright purple, **C** (11.13) .. 4·00 6·5
205 **54** 25 c. dull purple and mauve, **C** (7.14) .. 4·25 2·7
206 25 c. dull purple and violet, **C** (1919) .. 14·00 2·7
207 **51** 30 c. dull purple and orange, **C** (12.14) .. 3·25 1·5
208 **53** 45 c. black/*green*, **C** (*white back*) (12.14) 4·25 11·(
a. On blue-green, olive back (7.18) (Optd S. £27) .. .. .. 2·75 7·5
b. On emerald back (6.22) .. .. 2·75 12·(
209 **54** 50 c. black/*green*, **C** (7.14) .. .. 5·50 1·7
a. On blue-green, olive back (1918) .. 7·50 2·7
b. On emerald back (10.21) .. .. 7·50 2·7
c. On emerald back (Die II) (3.23) (Optd S. £27) .. .. 2·75 2·7
210 **51** $1 black and red/*blue*, **C** (10.14) .. 6·50 5·(
211 **54** $2 green and red/*yellow*, **C** (7.15) (Optd S. £28) .. .. .. 9·50 15·(
a. White back (7.14) .. .. .. 5·00 16·(
b. On orange-buff (1920) .. .. 30·00 40·(
c. On pale yellow (1921) .. .. 35·00 45·(
212 **51** $5 green and red/*green*, **C** (4.15) (Optd S. £28) .. .. 55·00 25·(
a. White back, **OC** (11.13) .. .. 48·00 21·(
b. On blue-green, olive back (1918) .. 70·00 26·(
c. On emerald back (6.21) .. .. 90·00 50·(
d. Die II (1923) (Optd S. £55) .. .. 55·00 35·(
213 – $25 purple & blue/*blue*, **C** (Optd S. £100) £550 £2(
a. Break in scroll £950
b. Broken crown and scroll £950
214 – $100 carm & blk/*blue*, **C** (Optd S. £225) £2500
a. Break in scroll £3500
b. Broken crown and scroll £3500
215 – $500 purple and orange-brown, **C** (8.12) (Optd S. £500) £19000
a. Break in scroll £23000
b. Broken crown and scroll £23000
193/212 .. .. *Set of* 20 85·00 60·(
193/210, 211*a*, 212*a* Optd "Specimen" *Set of* 19 £375

The 6 c. is similar to T **52**, but the head is in a beaded oval as i T **53**. The 2 c., 6 c. (and 12 c. below) have figures of value on circular ground while in the 8 c. this is of oval shape.

For illustrations of the varieties on Nos. 213/15 see above N 44 of Bermuda.

RED CROSS

2c.
(55)

MALAYA-
BORNEO
EXHIBITION.
(56)

1917 (1 May). *Surch with T* **55**.
216 **49** 2 c. on 3 c. scarlet .. .. .. 1·00 14·(
a. No stop (R. 2/3) .. .. .. £110 £1(
217 **50** 2 c. on 4 c. dull purple .. .. .. 1·00 14·(
a. No stop (R. 2/3) .. .. .. £110 £1(

Nos. 216a and 217a occur in the first setting only.

Type I Type II

Two types of duty plate in the 25 c. In Type II the solid shading forming the back of the figure 2 extends to the top of the curve; the upturned end of the foot of the 2 is short; two background lines above figure 5; c close to 5; STRAITS SETTLEMENTS in taller letters.

1921–33. *Wmk Mult Script CA. P 14.*

No.	Type	Description	Unused	Used
218	48	1 c. black, **O** (3.22)	25	10
219	52	2 c. green, **O** (5.21)	20	10
220		2 c. brown, **O** (12.25)	3·00	2·25
221	49	3 c. green, **O** (9.23)	90	60
222	50	4 c. carmine-red, **O** (10.21)	2·00	2·75
223		4 c. bright violet, **O** (8.24)	25	10
224		4 c. orange, **O** (8.29)	85	10
225	51	5 c. orange, **O** (Die II) (5.21)	45	25
		a. Die I (7.22)	55	15
226		5 c. brown, **O** (Die II) (2.32)	70	10
		a. Die I (1933)	1·25	10
227	52	6 c. dull claret, **O** (10.22)	65	15
228		6 c. rose-pink, **O** (2.25)	8·00	3·75
229		6 c. scarlet, **O** (1.27)	1·75	10
230	51	10 c. bright blue, **O** (Die I) (3.21)	1·40	30
231		10 c. purple/*yellow*, **C** (Die I) (6.25)	2·25	3·25
		a. Die II. *On pale yellow* (11.26)	1·25	10
		b. Die I. *On pale yellow* (1933)	1·50	15
232	52	12 c. bright blue, **O** (1.22)	70	10
233	53	21 c. dull and bright purple, **C** (2.23)	4·50	20·00
234	54	25 c. dull purple and mauve, **C** (Die I, Type I) (5.23)	20·00	38·00
		a. Die II. Type I (9.23)	11·00	2·50
		b. Die II. Type II (1927)	3·25	1·40
235	51	30 c. dull purple & orge, **C** (Die I) (5.21)	12·00	18·00
		a. Die II (1923)	2·00	40
236	53	35 c. dull purple & orge-yellow, **C** (8.22)	8·50	5·00
		a. Dull purple and orange	3·50	5·50
237		35 c. scarlet and purple, **C** (4.31)	6·00	7·00
238	54	50 c. black/*emerald*, **C** (9.25)	1·25	40
239	51	$1 black and red/*blue*, **C** (6.22)	4·75	45
240	54	$2 green and red/*pale yellow*, **C** (5.25)	9·00	8·00
240*a*	51	$5 green and red/*green*, **C** (8.26)	48·00	25·00
240*b*	–	$25 pur & bl/*bl*, **C** (5.23) (Optd S. £100)	£300	75·00
		ba. Break in scroll	£550	
		bb. Broken crown and scroll	£550	
240*c*	–	$100 carmine and black/*blue*, **C** (5.23) (Optd S. £175)	£1200	£600
		ca. Break in scroll	£1700	
		cb. Broken crown and scroll	£1700	
240*d*	–	$500 purple and orange-brown, **C** (4.23) (Optd S. £325)	£12000	
		da. Break in scroll	£14000	
		db. Broken crown and scroll	£14000	
218/40*a*		*Set of* 24	95·00	70·00
218/40*a* Optd/Perf "Specimen"		*Set of* 24	£350	

Nos. 240*b*/*d* are as Type **47**, but with portrait of George V.

An 8 c. in carmine was prepared but not issued (Optd "Specimen" £125).

The paper of No. 231b is the normal *pale yellow* at the back, but with a bright yellow surface. No. 231 is on paper of a *pale lemon* tint and the impression is smudgy.

For illustrations of the varieties on Nos. 240*b*/*d* see above No. 44 of Bermuda.

1922 (31 Mar). *T* **48** *and* **50** *to* **54**, *overprinted with T* **56**.

(a) Wmk Mult Crown CA

No.	Description	Unused	Used
241	2 c. green	13·00	42·00
242	4 c. scarlet	2·75	12·00
243	5 c. orange	3·25	10·00
244	8 c. ultramarine	1·75	6·00
245	25 c. dull purple and mauve (No. 202)	3·00	16·00
246	45 c. black/*blue-green* (*olive back*)	3·00	15·00
	a. On green (*white back*)	9·50	28·00
247	$1 black and red/*blue*	95·00	£275
248	$2 green and red/*orange-buff*	22·00	75·00
	a. On pale yellow	48·00	£130
249	$5 green and red/*blue-green* (*olive back*)	£190	£275

(b) Wmk Mult Script CA

No.	Description	Unused	Used
250	1 c. black	50	5·00
251	2 c. green	1·40	10·00
252	4 c. carmine-red	1·75	13·00
253	5 c. orange (Die II)	2·50	23·00
254	10 c. bright blue (Die I)	2·25	15·00
255	$1 black and red/*blue* (Die II)	15·00	65·00
241/55	*Set of* 11	£225	£450

Nos. 241/55 were overprinted by stereo which repeated a setting of 12 (6 × 2) five times. The following varieties therefore occur five times on each sheet: (a) Small second "A" in "MALAYA." (b) No stop. (c) No hyphen. (d) Oval last "O" in "BORNEO," (e) "EXH.BITION."

1935 (6 May). *Silver Jubilee. As Nos.* 91/4 *of Antigua but ptd by Waterlow & Sons. P* 11 × 12.

No.	Description	Unused	Used
256	5 c. ultramarine and grey	45	20
257	8 c. green and indigo	1·25	1·25
258	12 c. brown and deep blue	2·75	1·50
259	25 c. slate and purple	2·75	3·00
256/9	*Set of* 4	6·50	5·50
256/9 Perf "Specimen"	*Set of* 4	80·00	

57

58

1936 (1 Jan)–**37.** *Chalk-surfaced paper. Wmk Mult Script CA. P* 14.

No.	Type	Description	Unused	Used
260	57	1 c. black (1.1.37)	15	20
261		2 c. green (1.2.36)	20	15
262		4 c. orange (15.6.36)	30	30
263		5 c. brown (1.8.36)	20	10
264		6 c. scarlet (1.2.36)	70	25
265		8 c. grey	30	20
266		10 c. dull purple (1.7.36)	70	20
267		12 c. bright ultramarine (1.9.36)	2·00	1·75
268		25 c. dull purple and scarlet (1.2.36)	1·00	25
269		30 c. dull purple and orange	1·25	1·75
270		40 c. scarlet and dull purple	1·25	2·00
271		50 c. black/*emerald* (1.9.36)	1·50	70
272		$1 black and red/*blue* (1.7.36)	6·00	70
273		$2 green and scarlet (1.4.36)	10·00	7·00
274		$5 green and red/*emerald* (1.1.37)	27·00	10·00
260/74		*Set of* 15	48·00	23·00
260/74 Perf "Specimen"		*Set of* 15	£150	

1937 (12 May). *Coronation. As Nos.* 13/15 *of Aden.*

No.	Description	Unused	Used
275	4 c. orange	30	10
276	8 c. grey-black	55	10
277	12 c. bright blue	65	50
275/7	*Set of* 3	1·40	55
275/7 Perf "Specimen"	*Set of* 3	50·00	

1937–41. *Chalk-surfaced or ordinary paper* (**O**). *Wmk Mult Script CA. P* 14 *or* 15 × 14 (15 *c.*). *(a) Die I (printed at two operations).*

No.	Type	Description	Unused	Used
278	58	1 c. black (1.1.38)	1·25	10
279		2 c. green (6.12.37)	5·00	10
280		4 c. orange (1.1.38)	4·50	10
281		5 c. brown (19.11.37)	6·00	10
282		6 c. scarlet (10.1.38)	3·50	10
283		8 c. grey (26.1.38)	24·00	10
284		10 c. dull purple (8.11.37)	2·75	10
285		12 c. ultramarine (10.1.38)	2·75	10
286		25 c. dull purple and scarlet (11.12.37)	25·00	70
287		30 c. dull purple and orange (1.12.37)	25·00	95
288		40 c. scarlet and dull purple (20.12.37)	8·00	1·75
289		50 c. black/*emerald* (26.1.38)	4·50	10
290		$1 black and red/*blue* (26.1.38)	5·00	15
291		$2 green and scarlet (26.1.38)	17·00	3·00
292		$5 green and red/*emerald* (26.1.38)	22·00	3·00

(b) Die II (printed at one operation)

No.	Type	Description	Unused	Used
293	58	2 c. green (28.12.38)	13·00	10
294		2 c. orange (6.10.41)	60	2·25
295		3 c. green, **O** (5.9.41)	2·00	1·75
296		4 c. orange (29.10.38)	26·00	10
297		5 c. brown (18.2.39)	9·50	10
298		15 c. ultramarine, **O** (6.10.41)	3·25	6·00
278/98		*Set of* 18	£150	18·00
278/92, 294/5, 298 Perf "Specimen"		*Set of* 18	£275	

Die I. Lines of background outside central oval touch the oval and the foliage of the palm tree is usually joined to the oval frame. The downward-pointing palm frond, opposite the King's eye, has two points.

Die II. Lines of background are separated from the oval by a white line and the foliage of the palm trees does not touch the outer frame. The palm frond has only one point.

The 6 c. grey, 8 c. scarlet and $5 purple and orange were issued only with the BMA overprint, but the 8 c. without opt is known although in this state it was never issued (*Price* £8).

POSTAGE DUE STAMPS

D 1

1924 (1 Jan)–**26.** *Wmk Mult Script CA. P* 14.

No.	Type	Description	Unused	Used
D1	D 1	1 c. violet	3·00	4·50
D2		2 c. black	3·00	1·25
D3		4 c. green (5.26)	2·00	4·50
D4		8 c. scarlet	4·50	55
D5		10 c. orange	4·50	85
D6		12 c. bright blue	7·00	65
D1/6		*Set of* 6	22·00	11·00
D1/6 Optd "Specimen"		*Set of* 6	£200	

For later issues of Postage Due stamps, see MALAYAN POSTAL UNION.

The Straits Settlements were occupied by the Japanese in 1942. After the Second World War the stamps of MALAYA (BRITISH MILITARY ADMINISTRATION) were used. In 1946 Singapore became a separate Crown Colony and Labuan was transferred to North Borneo. Separate stamps were issued for Malacca and Penang, which both joined the Malayan Federation on 1 February 1948.

II. FEDERATED MALAY STATES

On 1 July 1896, the States of Negri Sembilan, Pahang, Perak and Selangor were organised on a federal basis to be known as the Federated Malay States. For the time being each State continued with individual issues, but stamps for the use of the Federation replaced these in 1900.

PRICES FOR STAMPS ON COVER

Nos. 1/13	*from* × 12
No. 14	—
Nos. 15/22	*from* × 10
Nos. 23/5	*from* × 3
Nos. 26	—
Nos. 27/50	*from* × 6
No. 51	—
Nos. 52/81	*from* × 5
No. 82	—
Nos. D1/6	*from* × 10

PRINTERS. All issues of the Federated Malay States were printed in typography by De La Rue & Co, Ltd, London, *unless otherwise stated.*

FEDERATED MALAY STATES (1) FEDERATED MALAY STATES (2)

1900. *Optd with T* **1** *(cent values) or* **2** *(dollar values).*

(a) Stamps of Negri Sembilan (T **3***)*

No.	Description	Unused	Used
1	1 c. dull purple and green	1·40	3·00
2	2 c. dull purple and brown	22·00	40·00
3	3 c. dull purple and black	1·90	3·25
4	5 c. dull purple and olive-yellow	55·00	75·00
5	10 c. dull purple and orange	1·75	9·00
6	20 c. green and olive	45·00	55·00
7	25 c. green and carmine	£110	£140
8	50 c. green and black	50·00	65·00
1/8	*Set of* 8	£250	£350
1/8 Optd "Specimen"	*Set of* 8	£150	

(b) Stamps of Perak (T **44** *and* **45***)*

No.	Description	Unused	Used
9	5 c. dull purple and olive-yellow	10·00	35·00
10	10 c. dull purple and orange	42·00	55·00
11	$1 green and pale green	95·00	£110
12	$2 green and carmine	80·00	£100
13	$5 green and ultramarine	£180	£225
14	$25 green and orange (Optd S. £250)	£3500	
11/13 Optd "Specimen"	*Set of* 3	£100	

The stamps of STRAITS SETTLEMENTS were used in Federated Malay States from 16 July 1900 until replaced by the 1900–1 issue.

3

4

1900–1. *P* 14. *(a) T* **3**. *Wmk Crown CA, sideways* (1901).

No.	Description	Unused	Used
15	1 c. black and green	70	1·25
	a. Grey and green	25	30
	b. Grey-brown and green	2·50	25
16	3 c. black and brown	2·50	70
	a. Grey and brown	1·25	35
	b. Grey-brown and brown	1·25	20
17	4 c. black and carmine	6·00	1·25
	a. Grey and carmine	4·00	1·25
	b. Grey-brown and carmine	6·50	30
18	5 c. green and carmine/*yellow*	1·50	2·00
19	8 c. black and ultramarine	20·00	5·00
	a. Grey and ultramarine	18·00	3·50
	b. Grey-brown and ultramarine	20·00	2·75
20	10 c. black and claret	35·00	4·00
	a. Grey and claret	28·00	3·00
	b. Black and purple	45·00	3·25
	c. Grey and purple	30·00	3·25
	d. Grey-brown and purple	35·00	2·00
21	20 c. mauve and black	17·00	6·00
22	50 c. black and orange-brown	60·00	30·00
	a. Grey and orange-brown	55·00	25·00
	b. Grey-brown and orange-brown	55·00	22·00
15/22	*Set of* 8	£110	32·00
15/22 Optd "Specimen"	*Set of* 8	£200	

Later printings in 1903–4 show the two upper lines of shading in the background at the corner nearest to the "S" of "STATE" blurred and running into one another, whereas in earlier printings these lines are distinct. Two plates were used for printing the central design of T **3**. In Plate 1 the lines of background are regular throughout, but in Plate 2 they are lighter around the head and back of the tiger. The 5 c. was the only value with single wmk to be printed from Plate 2. Stamps with multiple wmk were printed for a short time from Plate 1, and show the two blurred lines of background near "S" of "STATE," but the majority of these stamps were printed from Plate 2 and later plates.

(b) T **4**. *Wmk Crown CC* (1900)

No.	Description	Unused	Used
23	$1 green and pale green	60·00	65·00
24	$2 green and carmine	65·00	70·00
25	$5 green and bright ultramarine	£100	£110
	a. Green and pale ultramarine	£100	£110
26	$25 green and orange (Optd S. £225)	£850	£575
23/5 Optd "Specimen"	*Set of* 3	£140	

Two dies for 1 c. green and 4 c. scarlet

Die I. "Head" and duty plates. Thick frame line below "MALAY" and in the 1 c. the "c" is thin whilst in the 4 c. it is thick.

Die II. Single working plate. Thin frame line below "MALAY" and in the 1 c. the "c" is thicker whilst in the 4 c. it is thinner.

1904 (10 Oct)–**22.** *T* **3** *and* **4** *(dollar values). Wmk Mult Crown CA (sideways on T* **3***). Ordinary paper except where otherwise indicated. P* 14.

No.	Description	Unused	Used
27	1 c. grey and green	27·00	4·00
	a. Grey-brown and green	9·00	70
28	1 c. green (Die I) (8.7.06)	5·00	30

29 1 c. green (Die II) .. 75 20
a. Yellow-green .. 5·50 40
b. Blue-green .. 9·00 45
30 1 c. deep brown (21.1.19) .. 2·25 90
31 2 c. green (18.2.19) .. 50 30
32 3 c. grey and brown, **O** (10.04) .. 13·00 1·00
a. Grey-brown and brown, **OC** (12.05) .. 7·00 30
33 3 c. brown (11.7.06) .. 4·50 15
34 3 c. carmine (2.2.09) .. 2·00 10
a. Scarlet (1.17) .. 5·50 25
35 3 c. grey (29.10.18) .. 1·00 20
36 4 c. grey and scarlet, **O** .. 13·00 95
a. Grey and rose, **C** .. 8·00 85
b. Grey-brown and scarlet, **O** .. 11·00 75
c. Black and scarlet, **O** .. 12·00 80
d. Black and rose, **O** .. 3·25 25
e. Black and deep rose (aniline), **O** (1909) 26·00 3·25
f. Jet-black and rose, **O** (1914) .. 9·00 55
37 4 c. scarlet (Die I) (11.2.19) .. 2·00 1·75
38 4 c. scarlet (Die II) (15.4.19) .. 80 15
a. Wmk upright (2.22) .. † £450
39 5 c. green and carmine/*yellow*, **CO** (5.06) .. 3·75 1·50
a. Deep green and carmine/yellow, **O** .. 2·75 1·50
b. On orange-buff, **O** (1921) .. 6·50 3·00
c. On pale yellow (4.22) .. 3·00 1·75
40 6 c. orange (11.2.19) .. 2·00 1·50
41 8 c. grey and ultramarine, **O** (3.05) .. 20·00 8·00
a. Grey-brown & ultramarine, **OC** (12.05) 12·00 3·50
b. Wmk upright, **O** (3.07) .. 5·00 3·50
42 8 c. ultramarine (8.3.10) .. 13·00 90
a. Deep blue (1918) .. 13·00 1·25
43 10 c. grey-brown and claret, **OC** .. 16·00 55
a. Black and claret, **O** .. 6·50 25
b. Grey-brown and purple, **O** (1905) .. 22·00 95
c. Black and purple, **O** .. 11·00 95
d. Jet-black and bright purple, **O** (1914) 27·00 1·75
44 10 c. deep blue (3.6.19) .. 6·00 80
a. Bright blue .. 6·50 85
b. Wmk upright (inverted) ..
45 20 c. mauve and black, **OC** (3.05) .. 1·25 35
46 35 c. scarlet/*pale yellow* (25.8.22) .. 7·50 12·00
47 50 c. grey and orange, **O** (3.05) .. 32·00 2·75
a. Grey-brown & orange-brn, **OC** (1906) 17·00 3·00
b. Grey and orange-brown, **C** .. 27·00 3·00
c. Black and orange-brown, **C** .. 40·00 4·75
d. Jet-black and orange-brown, **C** (1914) 50·00 4·75
e. Wmk upright (inverted) .. † —
48 $1 grey-green and green, **C** (11.07) .. 30·00 25·00
a. Green and pale green .. 30·00 25·00
49 $2 green and carmine, **C** (4.12.07) .. 55·00 75·00
50 $5 green and blue, **C** (1.08) .. 80·00 85·00
51 $25 green and orange, **C** (8.10) .. £650 £350
27/50 .. *Set of* 22 £225 £190
28, 30/1, 33/5, 37, 40, 42, 44, 46 Optd "Specimen"
.. *Set of* 11 £350

Nos. 29/*b*, 30, 31, 33, 34/*a* and 35 were printed from single working plates and all the rest from double plates.

Most examples of No. 47e have fiscal cancellations, but at least one is known postally used.

1922–34. *Wmk Mult Script CA (sideways in T* 3). *P* 14.
52 3 1 c. deep brown, **O** (1.8.22) .. 2·50 2·25
53 1 c. black, **O** (12.6.23) .. 50 20
54 2 c. brown, **O** (5.8.25) .. 4·00 2·25
55 2 c. green, **O** (15.6.26) .. 45 10
56 3 c. grey, **O** (27.12.22) .. 2·50 4·25
57 3 c. green, **O** (22.1.24) .. 2·25 2·00
58 3 c. brown, **O** (31.5.27) .. 60 40
59 4 c. carmine-red, **O** (Die II) (27.11.23) .. 2·75 45
60 4 c. orange, **O** (9.11.26) .. 55 10
a. No watermark .. £200 £100
61 5 c. mauve/*pale yellow*, **O** (17.3.22) .. 75 20
62 5 c. brown, **O** (1.3.32) .. 1·40 10
63 6 c. orange, **O** (2.5.22) .. 55 45
64 6 c. scarlet, **O** (9.11.26) .. 80 10
65 10 c. bright blue, **O** (23.10.23) .. 1·25 6·00
66 10 c. black and blue, **O** (18.1.24*) .. 2·00 75
67 10 c. purple/*pale yellow*, **C** (14.7.31) .. 4·00 40
68 12 c. ultramarine, **O** (12.9.22) .. 1·25 10
69 20 c. dull purple and black, **OC** (3.4.23) .. 4·00 35
70 25 c. purple & bright magenta, **C** (3.9.29) 2·50 75
71 30 c. purple and orange-yellow, **C** (3.9.29) 3·25 95
72 35 c. scarlet/*pale yellow*, **O** (6.11.28) .. 3·75 11·00
73 35 c. scarlet and purple, **C** (29.9.31) .. 12·00 12·00
74 50 c. black and orange, **C** (24.4.24) .. 13·00 4·50
a. Black and orange-brown .. 13·00 4·50
75 50 c. black/*green*, **C** (16.6.31) .. 4·00 2·00
76 4 $1 pale green and green, **C** (2.2.26) .. 17·00 40·00
a. Grey-green and emerald, **C** (5.10.26) 9·00 17·00
77 3 $1 black and red/*blue*, **C** (10.3.31) .. 10·00 2·50
78 4 $2 green and carmine, **C** (17.8.26) .. 10·00 38·00
79 3 $2 green and red/*yellow*, **C** (6.2.34) .. 27·00 26·00
80 4 $5 green and blue, **C** (24.2.25) .. 60·00 85·00
81 3 $5 green and red/*green*, **C** (7.34) .. £110 £120
82 4 $25 green & orge, **C** (14.2.28) (Optd S. £90) £550 £250
52/81 .. *Set of* 30 £250 £300
52/81 Optd/Perf "Specimen" .. *Set of* 30 £550

Nos. 52, 56 and 59 were printed from single working plates and the rest from double plates.

*No. 66 was released in London by the Crown Agents some months earlier but this is the official date of issue in the States.

The 5 c. in mauve on white Script paper is the result of soaking early printings of No. 61 in water.

POSTAGE DUE STAMPS

D 1

(Typo Waterlow)

1924 (1 Dec)–**26.** *Wmk Mult Script CA (sideways). P* 15 × 14.
D1 D 1 1 c. violet .. 3·50 4·50
D2 2 c. black .. 1·75 2·00
D3 4 c. green (27.4.26) .. 2·25 4·25
D4 8 c. red .. 4·25 12·00
D5 D 1 10 c. orange .. 7·50 11·00
D6 12 c. blue .. 8·50 18·00
D1/6 .. *Set of* 6 25·00 48·00
D1/6 Optd "Specimen" .. *Set of* 6 £140

The issues of the Federated Malay States were replaced by stamps for the individual States from 1935 onwards.

III. MALAYAN POSTAL UNION

The Malayan Postal Union was organised in 1934 and, initially, covered the Straits Settlements and the Federated Malay States. Stamps of the Straits Settlements together with issues for the individual States continued to be used, but Malayan Postal Union postage due stamps were introduced in 1936.

Following the end of the Second World War the use of these postage dues spread throughout Malaya and to Singapore.

PRICES FOR STAMPS ON COVER TO 1945	
Nos. D1/6	*from* × 10
Nos. D7/13	*from* × 4

POSTAGE DUE STAMPS

D 1

10 cents
(D 2)

(Typo Waterlow until 1961, then D.L.R.)

1936 (June)–**38.** *Wmk Mult Script CA. P* 15 × 14.
D1 D 1 1 c. slate-purple (4.38) .. 3·00 70
D2 4 c. green (9.36) .. 5·50 1·00
D3 8 c. scarlet .. 2·50 3·50
D4 10 c. yellow-orange .. 2·00 25
D5 12 c. pale ultramarine (9.36) .. 3·75 6·00
D6 50 c. black (1.38) .. 13·00 5·00
D1/6 .. *Set of* 6 27·00 15·00
D1/6 Perf "Specimen" .. *Set of* 6 £100

For use in Negri Sembilan, Pahang, Perak, Selangor and Straits Settlements including Singapore.

1945–49. *New values and colours. Wmk Mult Script CA. P* 15 × 14.
D 7 D 1 1 c. purple .. 2·75 1·75
D 8 3 c. green .. 9·00 11·00
D 9 5 c. scarlet .. 12·00 7·50
D10 8 c. yell-orange (1949) (Perf S. £75) .. 24·00 16·00
D11 9 c. yellow-orange .. 55·00 45·00
D12 15 c. pale ultramarine .. 60·00 35·00
D13 20 c. blue (1948) (Perf S. £75) .. 14·00 7·00
D7/13 .. *Set of* 7 £160 £110

1951 (8 Aug)–**63.** *Wmk Mult Script CA. P* 14.
D14 D 1 1 c. violet (21.8.52) .. 25 50
D15 2 c. deep slate-blue (16.11.53) .. 25 65
a. Perf 12½ (15.11.60) .. 40 5·00
b. Perf 12½. Chalky paper (10.7.62) .. 35 3·00
ba. Ditto. Imperf between (vert pair) ..
D16 3 c. deep green (21.8.52) .. 12·00 10·00
D17 4 c. sepia (16.11.53) .. 45 1·75
a. Perf 12½ (15.11.60) .. 60 6·50
b. Perf 12½. *Bistre-brown.* Chalky paper (10.7.62) .. 70 5·50
D18 5 c. vermilion .. 24·00 10·00
D19 8 c. yellow-orange .. 1·75 3·00
D20 12 c. bright purple (1.2.54) .. 1·00 2·00
a. Perf 12½. Chalky paper (10.7.62) .. 1·50 12·00
D21 20 c. blue .. 4·00 6·00
a. Perf 12½. *Deep blue* (10.12.57) .. 3·00 24·00
b. Perf 12½. *Deep blue.* Chalky paper (15.10.63) .. 3·00 22·00
D14/21 .. *Set of* 8 38·00 30·00

Nos. D7 to D21b were for use in the Federation and Singapore, and from 1963 throughout Malaysia.

1964 (14 Apr)–**65.** *Chalk-surfaced paper. Wmk w* **12** *(sideways on* 1 c.). *P* 12½.
D22 D 1 1 c. maroon .. 30 5·50
a. Perf 12. Wmk upright (4.5.65) .. 25 5·50
D23 2 c. deep slate-blue .. 45 8·00
a. Perf 12 (9.3.65) .. 35 12·00
D24 4 c. bistre-brown .. 75 7·50
a. Perf 12 (9.3.65) .. 40 9·00
D25 8 c. yellow-orange (*p* 12) (4.5.65) .. 2·00 9·50
D27 12 c. bright purple .. 1·50 13·00
a. Perf 12 (4.5.65) .. 1·75 20·00
D28 20 c. deep blue .. 2·50 30·00
a. Perf 12 (4.5.65) .. 2·75 38·00
D22/8 .. *Set of* 6 6·25 65·00

1964 (Dec). *As No.* D19 *surch locally with Type* D 2.
D29 D 1 10 c. on 8 c. yellow-orange .. 25 1·50

First supplies of this stamp differed from No. D19 in that they had been climatically affected but later a fresh printing of No. D19 was surcharged.

1967? *Unsurfaced paper. Wmk w* **12.** *P* 15 × 14.
D30 D 1 50 c. black .. £450 £400

Nos. D22/9 were for use throughout Malaysia and Singapore. They were superseded on 15 August 1966 by the postage dues inscribed "MALAYSIA", but continued in use, together with No. D30, for Singapore until 31 January 1968 when they were replaced by Singapore Postage Dues.

IV. MALAYA (BRITISH MILITARY ADMINISTRATION)

For use throughout all Malay States and in Singapore. From 1948 this general issue was gradually replaced by individual issues for each state.

B M A
MALAYA
(1)

1945–48. *T* **58** *of Straits Settlements optd with T* **1.** *Values* 1 c. to 15 *c. from Die I (double-plate printing) or Die II (single-plate printing). Wmk Mult Script CA. P* 14 *or* 15 × 14 (*No.* 11).
1 1 c. black, **CO** (I) (R.) .. 10 1
2 2 c. orange, **OC** (II) .. 10 1
3 2 c. orange, **O** (I) (1946) .. 3·50 2·5
4 3 c. yellow-green, **O** (II) .. 10 1
a. Blue-green, **OC** (II) (1947) .. 40 1
5 5 c. brown, **C** (II) .. 15 1
6 6 c. grey, **OC** (II) .. 10 1
7 8 c. scarlet, **O** (II) .. 10 1
8 10 c. slate-purple, **C** (I) .. 10 1
a. Purple, **OC** (I) (1945) .. 25 1
b. Magenta, **C** (I) (1948) .. 40 1
9 10 c. purple, **C** (II) (1948) .. 8·00 4
10 12 c. bright ultramarine, **C** (I) .. 1·75 2·5
11 15 c. bright ultramarine, **O** (II) .. 2·00 4·5
12 15 c. bright ultramarine, **OC** (II) (R.) .. 20 1
a. Blue, **OC** (II) (R.) (1947) .. 11·00 7
13 25 c. dull purple and scarlet, **OC** .. 50 1
a. Opt double .. £1500
14 50 c. black/*emerald*, **CO** (I) (R.) (1946) .. 40 1
15 $1 black and red, **O** .. 1·25 1
16 $2 green and scarlet, **O** .. 1·50 4
17 $5 green and red/*emerald*, **C** .. 48·00 48·0
18 $5 purple and orange, **O** .. 3·00 1·5
1/18 .. *Set of* 15 50·00 48·0
1/11, 13/16, 18 Perf "Specimen" .. *Set of* 14 £350

The 8 c. grey with "B M A" opt was prepared but not officiall issued (*Price* £100 *unused*).

Nos. 3 and 9 do not exist without the overprint.

Nos. 1, 2, 6, 7, 8*a* and 13 exist also on thin, rough ordinary pape

No. 8*a* with reddish purple medallion and dull purple frame i from a printing with the head in fugitive ink which discolours wit moisture.

Stamps in the Crown Colony Victory design were prepared fo the Malayan Union in 1946, but not issued. Examples of the 8 carmine from this issue were stolen from stock awaitin destruction.

V. MALAYAN FEDERATION

The Malayan Federation, formed on 1 February 1948 b Malacca, Penang, the four Federated Malay States and the fiv Unfederated States, became an independent member of th British Commonwealth on 31 August 1957.

Commemoratives and a limited series of definitives were issue by the Federation and were used concurrently with the stamp from the individual States.

1 Tapping Rubber

4 Map of the Federation

(Centre recess, frame litho (6 c., 25 c.); centre litho, frame recess (12 c.); recess (30 c.), D.L.R.)

1957 (5 May)–**63.** *T* 1, 4 *and similar designs. W* w **12.** *P* 13×12½ (*No.* 4) *or* 13 (*others*).
1 6 c. deep blue, red, yellow and grey-blue .. 15 1
a. Indigo, red, yellow and grey-blue (20.6.61) 25 1
b. Indigo, red, yellow & slate-blue (12.2.63) 15 1
c. Yellow (star and crescent) omitted .. 35·00
2 12 c. red, yellow, blue, black and scarlet .. 25 1
3 25 c. maroon, red, yellow & dull greenish blue 40 1
4 30 c. orange-red and lake .. 40 2
a. Perf 13. *Orange-red & deep lake* (20.6.61) 40 1
ab. Orange-red and lake (10.7.62) .. 40 1
1/4 .. *Set of* 4 1·10 1

Designs: *Horiz*—12 c. Federation coat of arms; 25 c. Tin dredger

5 Prime Minister Tunku Abdul Rahman and Populace greeting Independence

(Des A. B. Saman. Recess Waterlow)

1957 (31 Aug). *Independence Day. Wmk Mult Script CA. P* 12½.
5 5 10 c. bistre-brown .. 10 10

6 United Nations Emblem **7** United Nations Emblem

(Recess D.L.R.)

58 (5 Mar). *U.N. Economic Commission for Asia and Far East Conference, Kuala Lumpur. W* w **12.** *P* 13½ (12 *c.*) *or* 12½ (30 *c.*).
6 | 12 c. carmine-red 30 40
7 | 30 c. maroon 40 20

8 Merdeka Stadium, Kuala Lumpur **9** The Yang di-Pertuan Agong (Tuanku Abdul Rahman)

(Photo Harrison)

58 (31 Aug). *First Anniv of Independence. W* w **12.** *P* 13½ × 14½ (10 *c.*) *or* 14½ × 13½ (30 *c.*).
8 | 10 c. green, yellow, red and blue .. 15 10
9 | 30 c. red, yellow, violet-blue and green .. 40 10

10 "Human Rights" **11** Malayan with Torch of Freedom

(Des J. P. Hendroff. Litho (10 c.), photo (30 c.) D.L.R.)

58 (10 Dec). *Tenth Anniv of Declaration of Human Rights.*

(*a*) *W* w **12.** *P* 12½ × 13
) **10** 10 c. blue, black, carmine and orange .. 10 10

(*b*) *Wmk Mult Script CA. P* 13 × 12½
11 30 c. deep green 30 15

12 Mace and Malayan Peoples

(Photo Enschedé)

59 (12 Sept). *Inauguration of Parliament. No wmk. P* 13 × 14.
2 **12** 4 c. rose-red 10 10
3 10 c. violet 10 10
4 25 c. yellow-green 35 20
2/14 .. .. *Set of* 3 50 25

13 **14**

(Recess D.L.R.)

960 (7 Apr). *World Refugee Year. W* w **12.** *P* 13½ (12 *c.*) *or* 12½ × 13 (30 *c.*).
5 **13** 12 c. purple 10 25
6 **14** 30 c. deep green 10 10

OMNIBUS ISSUES

Details, together with prices for complete sets, of the various Omnibus issues from the 1935 Silver Jubilee series to date are included in a special section following Zululand at the end of the catalogue.

15 Seedling Rubber Tree and Map **16** The Yang di-Pertuan Agong (Tuanku Syed Putra)

(Photo Japanese Govt Ptg Wks)

1960 (19 Sept). *Natural Rubber Research Conference and 15th International Rubber Study Group Meeting, Kuala Lumpur. T* **15** *and similar vert design. No wmk. P* 13.
17 6 c. yellow-green, black, orange & red-brown 20 15
18 30 c. yellow-green, black, orange & bright blue 50 10
No. 18 is inscribed "INTERNATIONAL RUBBER STUDY GROUP 15th MEETING KUALA LUMPUR" at foot.

(Photo Harrison)

1961 (4 Jan). *Installation of Yang di-Pertuan Agong, Tuanku Syed Putra. W* w **12.** *P* 14 × 14½.
19 **16** 10 c. black and blue 10 10

17 Colombo Plan Emblem **18** Malaria Eradication Emblem

(Photo Japanese Govt Ptg Works)

1961 (30 Oct). *Colombo Plan Conference, Kuala Lumpur. P* 13.
20 **17** 12 c. black and magenta .. .. .. 35 1·00
21 25 c. black and apple-green 80 90
22 30 c. black and turquoise-blue 70 25
20/2 .. .. *Set of* 3 1·75 2·00

(Photo Harrison)

1962 (7 Apr). *Malaria Eradication. W* w **13.** *P* 14 × 14½.
23 **18** 25 c. orange-brown 20 25
24 30 c. deep lilac 20 10
25 50 c. ultramarine 40 15
23/5 .. .. *Set of* 3 70 45

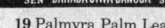

19 Palmyra Palm Leaf **20** "Shadows of the Future"

(Photo Harrison)

1962 (21 July). *National Language Month. W* w **13** (*upright or inverted*). *P* 13½.
26 **19** 10 c. light brown and deep reddish violet 15 10
27 20 c. light brown and deep bluish green 25 25
28 50 c. light brown and magenta .. 45 60
26/8 .. .. *Set of* 3 75 80

(Photo Enschedé)

1962 (1 Oct). *Introduction of Free Primary Education. W* w **13.** *P* 13½.
29 **20** 10 c. bright purple 10 10
30 25 c. ochre 30 30
31 30 c. emerald 80 10
29/31 .. .. *Set of* 3 1·10 40

21 Harvester and Fisherman **22** Dam and Pylon

(Photo Courvoisier)

1963 (21 Mar). *Freedom from Hunger. P* 11½.
32 **21** 25 c. carmine and apple-green 85 70
33 30 c. carmine and crimson .. .. 1·50 30
34 50 c. carmine and bright blue .. .. 1·50 1·00
32/4 .. .. *Set of* 3 3·50 1·75

(Photo Harrison)

1963 (26 June). *Cameron Highlands Hydro-Electric Scheme. W* w **13.** *P* 14.
35 **22** 20 c. green and reddish violet 35 10
36 30 c. blue-green and ultramarine 45 20

The definitive general issue for Malaysia and the low value sets for the individual states superseded the stamps of the Malayan Federation by 15 November 1965.

VI. MALAYSIA

On 16 September 1963, the Malayan Federation, Sabah (North Borneo), Sarawak and Singapore formed the Federation of Malaysia. Singapore left the Federation on 9 August 1965, and became an independent republic.

Individual issues for the component States continued, but were restricted to low value definitives and the occasional "State" commemorative. The higher value definitives and the vast majority of commemoratives were issued on a "National" basis.

A. NATIONAL ISSUES

General issues for use throughout the Malaysian Federation.

1 Federation Map **2** Bouquet of Orchids

(Photo Harrison)

1963 (16 Sept). *Inauguration of Federation. W* w **13.** *P* 14½.
1 **1** 10 c. yellow and bluish violet 15 10
a. Yellow omitted .. .. 85·00
2 12 c. yellow and deep green 60 60
3 50 c. yellow and chocolate 75 10
1/3 .. .. *Set of* 3 1·40 65

(Photo Enschedé)

1963 (3 Oct). *Fourth World Orchid Conference, Singapore. No wmk. P* 13 × 14.
4 **2** 6 c. multicoloured .. .. .. 80 1·00
5 25 c. multicoloured .. .. .. 1·25 25

4 Parliament House, Kuala Lumpur

(Des V. Whiteley. Photo Harrison)

1963 (4 Nov). *Ninth Commonwealth Parliamentary Conference, Kuala Lumpur. W* w **13** (*inverted*). *P* 13½.
7 **4** 20 c. deep magenta and gold 25 35
8 30 c. deep green and gold 25 15

5 "Flame of Freedom" and Emblems of Goodwill, Health and Charity **6** Microwave Tower and I.T.U. Emblem

(Photo Harrison)

1964 (10 Oct). *Eleanor Roosevelt Commemoration. W* w **13.** *P* 14½ × 13½.
9 **5** 25 c. black, red and greenish blue .. 15 10
10 30 c. black, red and deep lilac 15 10
11 50 c. black, red and ochre-yellow .. 15 10
9/11 .. .. *Set of* 3 40 15

(Photo Courvoisier)

1965 (17 May). *I.T.U. Centenary. P* 11½.
12 **6** 2 c. multicoloured 15 60
13 25 c. multicoloured 60 40
14 50 c. multicoloured .. .. .. 1·25 10
12/14 .. .. *Set of* 3 1·75 1·00

7 National Mosque **8** Air Terminal

(Photo Harrison)

1965 (27 Aug). *Opening of National Mosque, Kuala Lumpur.* W w **13**. P 14 × 14½.

15 **7** 6 c. carmine 10 10
16 15 c. red-brown 10 10
17 20 c. deep bluish green 10 10
15/17 .. .. *Set of* 3 25 20

(Photo Harrison)

1965 (30 Aug). *Opening of International Airport, Kuala Lumpur.* W w **13**. P 14½ × 14.

18 **8** 15 c. black, yellow-green and new blue .. 15 10
a. Yellow-green omitted .. .. 20·00
19 30 c. black, yellow-green and magenta .. 25 20

9 Crested Wood Partridge

17 Sepak Raga (ball game) and Football

(Des A. Fraser-Brunner. Photo Harrison)

1965 (9 Sept). *T* **9** *and similar vert designs. Multicoloured.* W w **13**. P 14½.

20 25 c. Type **9** 50 10
21 30 c. Blue-backed Fairy Bluebird 60 10
a. Blue omitted .. .. 95·00
22 50 c. Black-eyed Oriole 70 10
a. Yellow omitted .. .. 55·00
b. Imperf (pair) £200
c. Scarlet (inscr and berries) omitted .. 30·00
23 75 c. Rhinoceros Hornbill .. .. .. 1·25 10
a. Scarlet omitted* .. .. 45·00
24 $1 Zebra Dove .. .. 1·75 10
25 $2 Great Argus Pheasant .. .. .. 4·00 30
a. Imperf (pair) £200
26 $5 Asiatic Paradise Flycatcher .. .. 12·00 1·10
27 $10 Blue-tailed Pitta .. .. 28·00 5·50
a. Imperf (pair) £275
20/7 .. .. *Set of* 8 45·00 6·50

*The inscription at foot is omitted and the background appears paler.

All values except the 75 c. and $10 exist with PVA gum as well as gum arabic.

(Des E. A. F. Anthony. Litho Japanese Govt Ptg Wks)

1965 (14 Dec). *Third South East Asian Peninsular Games. T* **17** *and similar vert designs.* P 13 × 13½.

28 25 c. black and olive-green 40 90
29 30 c. black and bright purple 40 20
30 50 c. black and light blue 70 30
28/30 .. .. *Set of* 3 1·40 1·25

Designs:—30 c. Running; 50 c. Diving.

20 National Monument

21 The Yang di-Pertuan Agong (Tuanku Ismail Nasiruddin Shah)

(Photo Harrison)

1966 (8 Feb). *National Monument, Kuala Lumpur.* W w **13**. P 13½.

31 **20** 10 c. multicoloured 15 10
a. Blue omitted .. .. .. 35·00
32 20 c. multicoloured 25 15

(Photo Japanese Govt Ptg Wks)

1966 (11 Apr). *Installation of Yang di-Pertuan Agong, Tuanku Ismail Nasiruddin Shah.* P 13½.

33 **21** 15 c. black and light yellow 10 10
34 50 c. black and greenish blue 20 15

22 School Building

23 "Agriculture"

(Photo D.L.R.)

1966 (21 Oct). *150th Anniv of Penang Free School.* W w **13** (*sideways*). P 13.

35 **22** 20 c. multicoloured 25 10
36 50 c. multicoloured 60 10

The 50 c. is also inscr "ULANG TAHUN KE-150" at foot and bears a shield at bottom left corner.

(Des Enche Ng Peng Nam. Photo Japanese Govt Ptg Wks)

1966 (1 Dec). *First Malaysia Plan. T* **23** *and similar horiz designs. Multicoloured.* P 13½.

37 15 c. Type **23** 20 10
38 15 c. "Rural Health" 20 10
39 15 c. "Communications" 75 10
40 15 c. "Education" 20 10
41 15 c. "Irrigation" 20 10
37/41 .. .. *Set of* 5 1·40 50

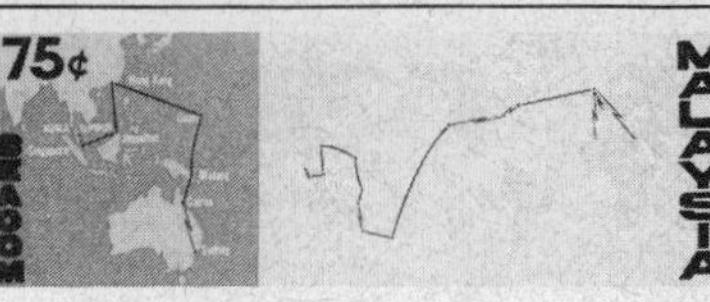

28 Cable Route Maps

(Des Enche Ng Peng Nam. Photo Japanese Govt Ptg Wks)

1967 (30 Mar). *Completion of Malaysia–Hong Kong Link of SEACOM Telephone Cable.* P 13½.

42 **28** 30 c. multicoloured 80 25
43 75 c. multicoloured .. .. 2·50 2·50

29 Hibiscus and Paramount Rulers

(Photo Harrison)

1967 (31 Aug). *Tenth Anniv of Independence.* W w **13**. P 14½.

44 **29** 15 c. multicoloured 20 10
45 50 c. multicoloured 50 30

30 Mace and Shield

31 Straits Settlements 1867 8 c. and Malaysia 1965 25 c. Definitive

(Des Enche Ng Peng Nam. Photo Harrison)

1967 (8 Sept). *Centenary of Sarawak Council.* W w **13**. P 14½.

46 **30** 15 c. multicoloured 10 10
47 50 c. multicoloured 20 20

(Des Enche Ng Peng Nam. Photo Japanese Govt Ptg Works)

1967 (2 Dec). *Stamp Centenary. T* **31** *and similar shaped designs. Multicoloured.* P 11½.

48 25 c. Type **31** .. .. 1·00 1·25
49 30 c. Straits Settlements 1867 24 c. and Malaysia 1965 30 c. definitive .. .. 1·00 75
50 50 c. Straits Settlements 1867 32 c. and Malaysia 1965 50 c. definitive .. .. 1·40 1·00
48/50 .. .. *Set of* 3 3·00 2·75

Nos. 48/50 were each printed in sheets with the stamps arranged *tête-bêche*.

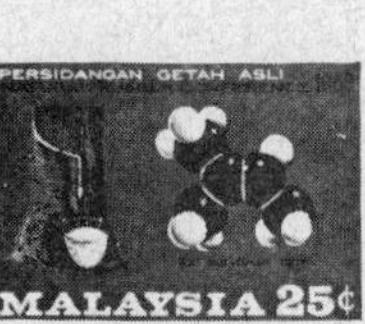

34 Tapping Rubber, and Molecular Unit

37 Mexican Sombrero and Blanket with Olympic Rings

(Litho B.W.)

1968 (29 Aug). *Natural Rubber Conference, Kuala Lumpur. T* **34** *and similar horiz designs. Multicoloured.* W w **13**. P 12.

51 25 c. Type **34** 25 10
52 30 c. Tapping rubber, and export consignment 40 20
53 50 c. Tapping rubber, and aircraft tyres .. 40 10
51/3 .. .. *Set of* 3 95 35

(Litho B.W.)

1968 (12 Oct). *Olympic Games, Mexico. T* **37** *and similar vert design. Multicoloured.* W w **13**. P 12 × 11½.

54 30 c. Type **37** 20 10
55 75 c. Olympic rings and Mexican embroidery 40 20

39 Tunku Abdul Rahman against background of Pandanus Weave **40**

(Photo Japanese Govt Ptg Wks)

1969 (8 Feb). *Solidarity Week. T* **39**/**40** *and similar multicoloured design.* P 13½.

56 15 c. Type **39** 15 10
57 20 c. Type **40** 20 40
58 50 c. Tunku Abdul Rahman with pandanus pattern (*horiz*) 20 20
56/8 .. .. *Set of* 3 50 55

42 Peasant Girl with Sheaves of Paddy

(Des Enche Hoessein Anas. Photo Harrison)

1969 (8 Dec). *National Rice Year.* W w **13**. P 13½.

59 **42** 15 c. multicoloured 15 10
60 75 c. multicoloured 45 55

43 Satellite tracking Aerial

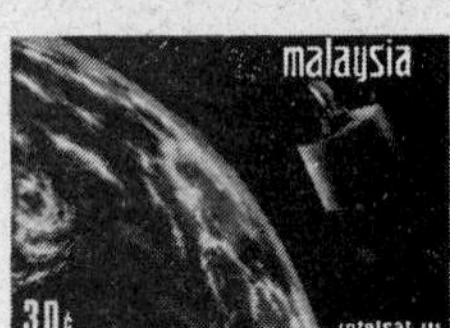

44 "Intelsat III" in Orbit

(Photo Enschedé)

1970 (6 Apr). *Satellite Earth Station.* W w **13**. P 14 × 13 (15 c.) *or* 13½ × 13 (30 c.).

61 **43** 15 c. multicoloured 65 15
a. *Tête-bêche* (horiz pair) .. .. 1·25 1·25
62 **44** 30 c. multicoloured* .. .. 75 1·00
63 30 c. multicoloured* .. .. 75 1·00
61/3 .. .. *Set of* 3 2·00 2·00

No. 61 was issued horizontally *tête-bêche* in the sheets.

*Nos. 62/3 are of the same design, differing only in the lettering colours (No. 62 white; No. 63 gold).

45 Blue-banded King Crow Butterfly

46 Emblem

(Des V. Whiteley. Litho B.W. (to 1976) or Harrison)

1970 (31 Aug–16 Nov). *Butterflies. T* **45** *and similar vert designs. Multicoloured.* P 13 × 13½.

64 25 c. Type **45** 70 10
65 30 c. Saturn 80 10
66 50 c. Common Nawab .. .. 1·25 10
67 75 c. Great Mormon .. .. 1·50 10
68 $1 Orange Albatross (16.11) .. .. 1·50 10
69 $2 Raja Brooke's Birdwing (16.11) .. 3·00 10
70 $5 Centaur Oak Bird (16.11) .. .. 4·50 1·00
71 $10 Royal Assyrian (16.11) .. .. 8·00 4·25
64/71 .. .. *Set of* 8 19·00 5·00

See also Nos. 144/5.

(Litho Harrison)

1970 (7 Sept). *50th Anniv of International Labour Organization.* P 14 × 13½.

72 **46** 30 c. grey and new blue 10 20
73 75 c. pink and new blue 20 30

47 U.N. Emblem encircled by Doves

50 The Yang di-Pertuan Agong (Tuanku Abdul Halim Shah)

(Des Enche Ng Peng Nam. Litho D.L.R.)

1970 (24 Oct). *25th Anniv of United Nations. T* **47** *and similar horiz designs.* P 13 × 12½.

74 25 c. gold, black and brown 35 40
75 30 c. multicoloured 45 35
76 50 c. black and dull yellow-green 75 75
74/6 .. .. *Set of* 3 1·40 1·40

Designs:—30 c. Line of doves and U.N. emblem; 50 c. Doves looping U.N. emblem.

(Des Union Art Corp. Photo Harrison)

1971 (20 Feb). *Installation of Yang di-Pertuan Agong (Paramount Ruler of Malaysia). P* 14½ × 14.

77 **50** 10 c. black, gold and lemon 20 15
  a. Gold (value and inscr) omitted .. £160
78 15 c. black, gold and bright mauve .. 20 10
79 50 c. black, gold and new blue .. .. 60 1·50
77/9 .. .. *Set of* 3 90 1·60

51 Bank Negara Complex

(Photo Harrison)

1971 (15 May). *Opening of Bank Negara Building. P* 13½ *(and around design).*

80 **51** 25 c. black and silver 70 80
81 50 c. black and gold 70 95

52 Aerial view of Parliament Buildings

(Des Union Art Corp. Litho Harrison)

1971 (13 Sept). *17th Commonwealth Parliamentary Association Conference, Kuala Lumpur. T* **52** *and similar multicoloured design. P* 13½ *(25 c.) or* 12½ × 13 *(75c.).*

82 25 c. Type **52** 65 50
83 75 c. Ground view of Parliament Buildings (73 × 23½ *mm*) .. .. 1·25 1·50

53 **54** **55**
Malaysian Carnival

(Des locally. Litho Harrison)

1971 (18 Sept). *Visit A.S.E.A.N.* Year. P* 14½.

84 **53** 30 c. multicoloured 85 25
  a. Horiz strip of 3. Nos. 84/6 .. .. 2·25
85 **54** 30 c. multicoloured 85 25
86 **55** 30 c. multicoloured 85 25
84/6 .. .. *Set of* 3 2·25 70

*A.S.E.A.N. = Association of South East Asian Nations.
Nos. 84/6 were printed together, *se-tenant*, in horizontal strips of 3 throughout the sheet, forming a composite design.

56 Trees, Elephant and Tiger

57 Athletics

(Des from children's drawings. Litho Harrison)

1971 (2 Oct). *25th Anniv of U.N.I.C.E.F. T* **56** *and similar multicoloured designs. P* 12½.

87 15 c. Type **56** 75 10
  a. Horiz strip of 5. Nos. 87/91 .. .. 3·25
88 15 c. Cat and kittens 75 10
89 15 c. Sun, flower and bird (22 × 29 *mm*) .. 75 10
90 15 c. Monkey, elephant and lion in jungle .. 75 10
91 15 c. Spider and butterflies 75 10
87/91 .. .. *Set of* 5 3·25 45

Nos. 87/91 were issued in horizontal *se-tenant* strips of 5 throughout the sheet.

(Des Union Art Corp. Litho B.W.)

1971 (11 Dec). *Sixth S.E.A.P.* Games, Kuala Lumpur. T* **57** *and similar horiz designs. Multicoloured. P* 14½ × 14.

92 25 c. Type **57** 35 40
93 30 c. Sepak Raga players 50 50
94 50 c. Hockey 80 95
92/4 .. .. *Set of* 3 1·50 1·75

*S.E.A.P. = South East Asian Peninsula.

58 **59** **60**
Map and Tourist Attractions

(Des locally. Litho Harrison)

1972 (31 Jan). *Pacific Area Tourist Association Conference. P* 14 × 14½.

95 **58** 30 c. multicoloured 85 20
  a. Horiz strip of 3. Nos. 95/7 .. .. 2·25
96 **59** 30 c. multicoloured 85 20
97 **60** 30 c. multicoloured 85 20
95/7 .. .. *Set of* 3 2·25 55

Nos. 95/7 were printed together, *se-tenant*, in horizontal strips of 3 throughout the sheet forming a composite design.

61 Kuala Lumpur City Hall

(Des from colour transparencies. Litho Harrison)

1972 (1 Feb). *City Status for Kuala Lumpur. T* **61** *and similar horiz design. Multicoloured. P* 14½ × 14.

98 25 c. Type **61** .. .. 80 1·00
99 50 c. City Hall in floodlights .. .. 1·10 1·00

62 SOCSO Emblem

63 W.H.O. Emblem

(Des B.W. Litho Harrison)

1973 (2 July). *Social Security Organisation. P* 13½.

100 **62** 10 c. multicoloured 15 15
101 15 c. multicoloured 25 10
102 50 c. multicoloured .. .. .. 60 1·40
100/2 .. .. *Set of* 3 90 1·50

(Des Union Advertising. Litho B.W.)

1973 (1 Aug). *25th Anniv of W.H.O. T* **63** *and similar vert design. P* 13.

103 30 c. multicoloured 45 25
104 75 c. multicoloured .. .. .. 1·25 1·75

64 Fireworks, National Flag and Flower

65 Emblems of Interpol and Royal Malaysian Police

(Des Clover Associates. Litho Harrison)

1973 (31 Aug). *Tenth Anniv of Malaysia. P* 13½.

105 **64** 10 c. multicoloured 25 15
106 15 c. multicoloured 30 10
107 50 c. multicoloured .. .. .. 1·25 1·50
105/7 .. .. *Set of* 3 1·60 1·60

(Des Union Advertising. Litho Harrison)

1973 (15 Sept). *50th Anniv of Interpol. T* **65** *and similar vert design. Multicoloured. P* 13½.

108 25 c. Type **65** .. .. 1·00 50
109 75 c. Emblems within "50" .. .. 1·75 2·00

66 Aeroplane and M.A.S. Emblem

(Des Art Dept, Malaysia Airline System. Litho Harrison)

1973 (1 Oct). *Foundation of Malaysia Airline System. P* 14½.

110 **66** 15 c. multicoloured 25 10
111 30 c. multicoloured 45 60
112 50 c. multicoloured .. .. .. 75 1·60
110/12 .. .. *Set of* 3 1·25 2·10

67 Kuala Lumpur

(Des Malaysian Advertising Services. Litho B.W.)

1974 (1 Feb). *Establishment of Kuala Lumpur as Federal Territory. P* 12½ × 13.

113 **67** 25 c. multicoloured 40 75
114 50 c. multicoloured .. .. .. 85 1·50

68 Development Projects

69 Scout Badge and Map

(Des Malaysian Advertising Services. Litho Rosenbaum Bros, Vienna)

1974 (25 Apr). *Seventh Annual Meeting of Asian Development Bank's Board of Governors, Kuala Lumpur. P* 13½.

115 **68** 30 c. multicoloured 25 50
116 75 c. multicoloured .. .. .. 80 1·75

(Des Malaysian Advertising Services. Litho Harrison)

1974 (1 Aug). *Malaysian Scout Jamboree. T* **69** *and similar multicoloured designs. P* 13 × 13½ *(15 c.) or* 14 × 13½ *(others).*

117 10 c. Type **69** 30 20
118 15 c. Scouts saluting and flags (46 × 24 *mm*) 35 25
119 50 c. Scout badge .. .. 1·25 2·00
117/19 .. .. *Set of* 3 1·75 2·25

70 Coat of Arms and Power Installations

(Des Malaysian Advertising Services. Litho Harrison)

1974 (1 Sept). *25th Anniv of National Electricity Board. T* **70** *and similar multicoloured design. P* 14 *(30 c.) or* 14 × 14½ *(75 c.).*

120 30 c. Type **70** 30 50
121 75 c. National Electricity Board Building (37 × 27 *mm*) .. .. 1·00 1·75

71 U.P.U. and Post Office Emblems within "100"

(Des Clover Associates. Litho Harrison)

1974 (9 Oct). *Centenary of Universal Postal Union. P* 14½ × 14.

122 **71** 25 c. dull yell-grn, brt yell & lt rose-carm 20 35
123 30 c. lt new blue, brt yell & lt rose-carm 25 35
124 75 c. brownish orange, bright yellow and light rose-carmine .. .. .. 65 1·75
122/4 .. .. *Set of* 3 1·00 2·25

72 Gravel Pump in Tin Mine

73 Hockey-players, World Cup and Federation Emblem

(Des Malaysian Advertising Service. Litho D.L.R.)

1974 (31 Oct). *Fourth World Tin Conference, Kuala Lumpur. T* **72** *and similar horiz designs. Multicoloured. P* 13½.

125 15 c. Type **72** 55 15
126 20 c. Open-cast mine 75 60
127 50 c. Dredger within "ingot" .. .. 1·75 2·25
125/7 .. .. *Set of* 3 2·75 2·75

(Des Malaysian Advertising Services. Litho Harrison)

1975 (1 Mar). *Third World Cup Hockey Championships. P* 13½ × 13.

128 **73** 30 c. multicoloured 90 60
129 75 c. multicoloured .. .. .. 2·10 2·25

74 Congress Emblem **75** Emblem of M.K.P.W. (Malayan Women's Organisation)

(Des Malaysian Advertising Services. Litho Harrison)

1975 (1 May). *25th Anniv of Malaysian Trade Union Congress. P* 14 × 14½.

130 **74** 20 c. multicoloured 20 25
131 25 c. multicoloured 30 30
132 30 c. multicoloured 45 60
130/2 .. .. *Set of* 3 85 1·00

(Des Malaysian Advertising Services. Litho Harrison)

1975 (25 Aug). *International Women's Year. P* 14.

133 **75** 10 c. multicoloured 15 25
134 15 c. multicoloured 30 25
135 50 c. multicoloured .. .. .. 1·25 2·25
133/5 .. .. *Set of* 3 1·50 2·50

76 Ubudiah Mosque, Kuala Kangsar **77** Plantation and Emblem

(Des Malaysian Advertising Services. Litho Harrison)

1975 (22 Sept). *Koran Reading Competition. T* **76** *and similar horiz designs. Multicoloured. P* 14.

136 15 c. Type **76** 70 15
a. Horiz strip of 5. Nos. 136/40 .. .. 3·25
137 15 c. Zahir Mosque, Alor Star 70 15
138 15 c. National Mosque, Kuala Lumpur .. 70 15
139 15 c. Sultan Abu Bakar Mosque, Johore Bahru 70 15
140 15 c. Kuching State Mosque, Sarawak .. 70 15
136/40 .. .. *Set of* 5 3·25 65

The above were printed together, horizontally *se-tenant* throughout the sheet.

(Des E. Sulaiman bin Haji Hassan and E. Hoh Lian Yong. Litho Harrison)

1975 (22 Oct). *50th Anniv of Malaysian Rubber Research Institute. T* **77** *and similar horiz designs. Multicoloured. P* 14 × 14½.

141 10 c. Type **77** 25 15
142 30 c. Latex cup and emblem 70 70
143 75 c. Natural rubber in test-tubes .. .. 1·40 2·25
141/3 .. .. *Set of* 3 2·10 2·75

77a *Hebomoia glaucippe aturia* **78** Scrub Typhus

(Photo Harrison)

1976 (19 Jan). *Coil Stamps. T* **77a** *and similar horiz design. Multicoloured. P* 13½.

144 10 c. Type **77a** .. .. 40 2·00
145 15 c. *Precis orithya wallacei* .. .. .. 45 2·50

(Des Lap Loy Fong (25 c.), Lee Eng Kee (others). Litho Harrison)

1976 (6 Feb). *75th Anniv of the Institute of Medical Research. T* **78** *and similar vert designs. Multicoloured. P* 14.

146 20 c. Type **78** 25 15
147 25 c. Malaria diagnosis 40 20
148 $1 Beri-beri .. .. 1·60 2·50
146/8 .. .. *Set of* 3 2·00 2·50

79 The Yang di-Pertuan Agong (Tuanku Yahya Petra) **80** State Council Complex

(Des Union Advertising. Photo Harrison)

1976 (28 Feb). *Installation of Yang di-Pertuan Agong. P* 14½ × 13½.

149 **79** 10 c. black, bistre and yellow 25 10
150 15 c. black, bistre and bright mauve .. 40 10
151 50 c. black, bistre and ultramarine .. 2·25 2·50
149/51 .. .. *Set of* 3 2·75 2·50

(Des Aini bin Abdul Rahman. Litho Harrison)

1976 (17 Aug). *Opening of the State Council Complex and Administrative Building, Sarawak. P* 12½.

152 **80** 15 c. grey-green and light yellow .. 35 10
153 20 c. grey-green and light bright mauve 45 40
154 50 c. grey-green and pale blue .. .. 1·00 1·40
152/4 .. .. *Set of* 3 1·60 1·75

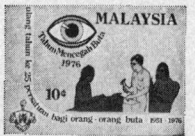

81 E.P.F. Building **82** Blind People at Work

(Litho Harrison)

1976 (18 Oct). *25th Anniv of Employees' Provident Fund. T* **81** *and similar multicoloured designs. P* 14½ (25 *c.*) *or* 13½ × 14½ (*others*).

155 10 c. Type **81** 15 10
156 25 c. E.P.F. emblems (27 × 27 *mm*) 25 35
157 50 c. E.P.F. Building at night .. .. .. 60 1·00
155/7 .. .. *Set of* 3 90 1·40

(Des Malayan Association for the Blind, Messrs Advertising Sales Promotion and Hexxon Grafic. Litho Harrison)

1976 (20 Nov). *25th Anniv of Malayan Association for the Blind. T* **82** *and similar horiz design. Multicoloured. P* 13½ × 14½.

158 10 c. Type **82** 15 15
159 75 c. Blind man and shadow .. .. .. 1·25 1·60

83 Independence Celebrations, 1957 **84** F.E.L.D.A. Village Scheme

(Des Hexxon Grafic. Photo Harrison)

1977 (14 Jan). *First Death Anniversary of Tun Abdul Razak (Prime Minister). T* **83** *and similar horiz designs, each sepia and gold. P* 14.

160 15 c. Type **83** 40 15
a. Horiz strip of 5. Nos. 160/4 .. .. 1·75
161 15 c. "Education" 40 15
162 15 c. Tun Razak and map ("Development") .. 40 15
163 15 c. "Rukunegara" (National Philosophy) .. 40 15
164 15 c. A.S.E.A.N. meeting 40 15
160/4 .. .. *Set of* 5 1·75 65

The above were printed together, horizontally *se-tenant* throughout the sheet.

(Des Halim Teh and Basyuni Sumrah. Litho Harrison)

1977 (7 July). *21st Anniv of Federal Land Development Authority (F.E.L.D.A.). T* **84** *and similar horiz design. Multicoloured. P* 13½ × 14.

165 15 c. Type **84** 25 10
166 30 c. Oil Palm settlement 60 70

85 Figure "10" **86** Games Logos

(Des Hexxon Grafic. Litho Harrison)

1977 (8 Aug). *Tenth Anniv of A.S.E.A.N. (Association of South East Asian Nations). T* **85** *and similar horiz design. Multicoloured. P* 13½ × 14½.

167 10 c. Type **85** 10 10
168 75 c. Flags of members 60 65

(Des PTM Communications & Co. Litho Harrison)

1977 (19 Nov). *9th South East Asia Games, Kuala Lumpur. T* **86** *and similar horiz designs. Multicoloured. P* 13½ × 14½.

169 10 c. Type **86** 10 10
170 20 c. "Ball" 20 10
171 75 c. Symbolic athletes .. .. 75 1·10
169/71 .. .. *Set of* 3 95 1·10

87 Islamic Development Bank Emblem **88** Mobile Post Office

(Des Queen's Advertising. Litho J.W.)

1978 (15 Mar). *Islamic Development Bank Board of Governors Meeting, Kuala Lumpur. P* 14.

172 **87** 30 c. multicoloured 15 15
173 75 c. multicoloured 50 55

(Des Hexxon Grafic. Litho J.W.)

1978 (10 July). *4th Commonwealth Postal Administrations Conference, Kuala Lumpur. T* **88** *and similar horiz designs. Multicoloured. P* 13½ × 13.

174 10 c. Type **88** 20 10
175 25 c. G.P.O., Kuala Lumpur 55 55
176 50 c. Postal delivery by motor-cycle 80 85
174/6 .. .. *Set of* 3 1·40 1·40

89 Boy Scout Emblem **90** Dome of the Rock, Jerusalem

(Des Aini bin Abdul Rahman. Litho J.W.)

1978 (26 July). *4th Malaysian Boy Scout Jamboree, Sarawak. T* **89** *and similar horiz design. Multicoloured. P* 13½ × 13.

177 15 c. Type **89** 30 10
178 $1 Bees and honeycomb .. .. .. 1·60 1·00

(Des Union Advertising. Litho Harrison)

1978 (21 Aug). *"Freedom for Palestine". P* 12½.

179 **90** 15 c. multicoloured 35 10
180 30 c. multicoloured 60 40

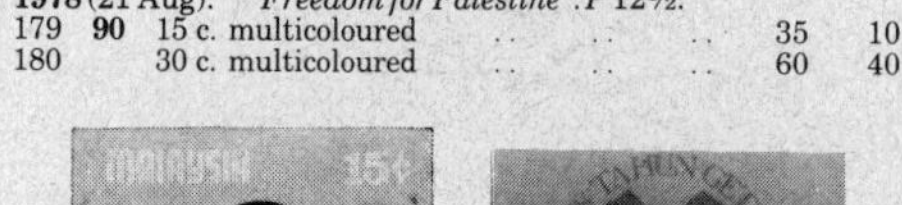

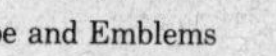

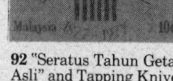

91 Globe and Emblems **92** "Seratus Tahun Getah Asli" and Tapping Knives Symbol

(Litho Harrison)

1978 (30 Sept). *Global Eradication of Smallpox. P* 13½ × 14½.

181 **91** 15 c. black, rosine and new blue 15 20
182 30 c. black, rosine and yellowish green .. 20 10
183 50 c. black, rosine and rose-pink 35 45
181/3 .. .. *Set of* 3 60 65

(Des Azmi bin Anuar. Litho J.W.)

1978 (28 Nov). *Centenary of Rubber Industry. T* **92** *and similar horiz designs. P* 13½ × 13.

184 10 c. gold and blue-green 10 10
185 20 c. ultramarine, brown & brt yellow-green 10 10
186 75 c. gold and blue-green 45 65
184/6 .. .. *Set of* 3 55 75

Designs:—20 c. Rubber tree seedling and part of "maxi stump"; 75 c. Graphic design of rubber tree, latex cup and globe arranged to form "100".

93 Sultan of Selangor's New Palace

(Des Queen's Advertising. Litho Harrison)

1978 (7 Dec). *Inauguration of Shah Alam New Town as State Capital of Selangor. T* **93** *and similar horiz designs. Multicoloured. P* 13½ × 14½.

187 10 c. Type **93** 10 10
188 30 c. Shah Alam (aerial view) 15 10
189 75 c. Shah Alam 45 60
187/9 .. .. *Set of* 3 65 70

94 Tiger

95 Multiple "POS" in Octagon

(Des Ong Soo Keat; adapted Malaysian Advertising Services. Litho Asher and Co, Melbourne)

1979 (4 Jan). *Wildlife. Multicoloured designs as T* **94.** *W* **95** *(inverted on $10 or sideways on others). P* 14½.

190	30 c. Type **94**	50	10
191	40 c. Malayan Flying Lemur	50	10
192	50 c. Lesser Malay Chevrotain	55	10
193	75 c. Leathery Pangolin	70	10
194	$1 Malayan Turtle	1·00	10
195	$2 Malayan Tapir	1·40	10
196	$5 Gaur	3·25	60
197	$10 Orang-Utan *(vert)*	6·00	3·00
190/7	*Set of* 8	12·50	3·50

For these stamps without watermark, see Nos. 272/9.

96 View of Central Bank of Malaysia

97 I.Y.C. Emblem

(Des Union Advertising. Litho J.W.)

1979 (26 Jan). *20th Anniv of Central Bank of Malaysia. T* **96** *and similar vert design showing view of bank building. P* 13.

198	10 c. multicoloured	10	10
199	75 c. multicoloured	40	45

(Des Queen's Advertising. Litho Harrison)

1979 (24 Feb). *International Year of the Child. T* **97** *and similar vert designs. P* 14½ × 14.

200	10 c. gold, blue and salmon	20	10
201	15 c. multicoloured	30	10
202	$1 multicoloured	1·50	1·25
200/2	*Set of* 3	1·75	1·25

Designs:—15 c. Children of different races holding hands in front of globe; $1 Children taking part in various activities.

98 Dam and Power Station

99 Exhibition Emblem

(Des National Electricity Board. Litho Harrison)

1979 (19 Sept). *Opening of Hydro-Electric Power Station, Temengor. T* **98** *and similar horiz designs showing views of power station and dam. P* 13½ × 14½.

203	15 c. multicoloured	15	15
204	25 c. multicoloured	25	45
205	50 c. multicoloured	45	75
203/5	*Set of* 3	75	1·25

(Des Malaysian Advertising Services. Litho J.W.)

1979 (20 Sept). *World Telecommunications Exhibition, Geneva. T* **99** *and similar designs. P* 14 (50 c.) *or* 13 *(others).*

206	10 c. orange, ultramarine and silver	10	15
207	15 c. multicoloured	15	10
208	50 c. multicoloured	40	90
206/8	*Set of* 3	60	1·10

Designs: (34 × 24 *mm*)—15 c. Telephone receiver joining one half of World to the other. (39 × 28 *mm*)—50 c. Communications equipment.

100 Tuanku Haji Ahmad Shah

101 Pahang and Sarawak Maps within Telephone Dials

(Des Malaysian Advertising Services. Litho Harrison)

1980 (10 July). *Installation of Yang di-Pertuan Agong (Tuanku Haji Ahmad Shah). P* 14.

209	**100**	10 c. black, gold and yellow	10	10
210		15 c. black, gold and bright purple	15	10
211		50 c. black, gold and new blue	40	90
209/11		*Set of* 3	60	1·00

(Des Malaysian Advertising Services. Litho J.W.)

1980 (31 Aug). *Kuantan-Kuching Submarine Cable Project. T* **101** *and similar horiz designs. Multicoloured. P* 13.

212	10 c. Type **101**	10	10
213	15 c. Kuantan and Kuching views within telephone dials	15	10
214	50 c. Pahang and Sarawak Maps within telephone receiver	35	50
212/14	*Set of* 3	50	60

102 Bangi Campus

103 Mecca

(Des Malaysian Advertising Services. Litho J.W.)

1980 (2 Sept). *10th Anniv of National University of Malaysia. T* **102** *and similar horiz designs. Multicoloured. P* 13.

215	10 c. Type **102**	15	15
216	15 c. Jalan Pantai Baru campus	20	10
217	75 c. Great Hall	65	1·25
215/17	*Set of* 3	90	1·40

(Des Malaysian Advertising Services. Litho J.W.)

1980 (9 Nov). *Moslem Year 1400 A.H. Commemoration. P* 13.

218	**103**	15 c. multicoloured	10	10
219		50 c. multicoloured	30	60

The 50 c. value is as T 103 but the inscriptions are in Roman lettering and the country name is to the left of the design.

104 Disabled Child learning to Walk

105 Industrial Scene

(Des Malaysian Advertising Services. Litho J.W.)

1981 (14 Feb). *International Year for Disabled Persons. T* **104** *and similar vert designs. Multicoloured. P* 13½ × 13.

220	10 c. Type **104**	25	15
221	15 c. Disabled woman sewing	40	10
222	75 c. Disabled athlete throwing javelin	1·25	1·25
220/2	*Set of* 3	1·75	1·40

(Des Malaysian Advertising Services. Litho J.W.)

1981 (2 May). *"Expo '81" Industrial Training Exposition, Kuala Lumpur and Seminar, Genting Highlands. T* **105** *and similar horiz designs. Multicoloured. P* 13½ × 13.

223	10 c. Type **105**	10	10
224	15 c. Worker and bulldozer	15	10
225	30 c. Workers at ship-building yard	25	25
226	75 c. Agriculture and fishing produce, workers and machinery	65	70
223/6	*Set of* 4	1·00	1·00

106 "25"

(Des A. Yusof and Malaysian Advertising Services. Litho J.W.)

1981 (17 June). *25th Anniv of Malaysian National Committee for World Energy Conferences. T* **106** *and similar horiz designs. Multicoloured. P* 13½ × 13.

227	10 c. Type **106**	15	15
228	15 c. Drawings showing importance of energy sources in industry	15	10
229	75 c. Symbols of various energy sources	65	1·25
227/9	*Set of* 3	85	1·40

107 Drawing showing development of Sabah from Village to Urbanised Area

(Des Creative Concepts. Litho J.W.)

1981 (31 Aug). *Centenary of Sabah. T* **107** *and similar horiz design. Multicoloured. P* 12.

230	15 c. Type **107**	50	15
231	80 c. Drawing showing traditional and modern methods of agriculture	1·25	2·00

108 *Samanea saman*

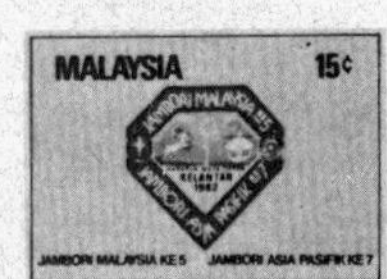

109 Jamboree Emblem

(Des Yusof bin Hadji Saman. Litho J.W.)

1981 (16 Dec). *Trees. T* **108** *and similar multicoloured designs. P* 14.

232	15 c. Type **108**	45	10
233	50 c. *Dyera costulata (vert)*	1·00	70
234	80 c. *Dryobalanops aromatica (vert)*	1·25	2·00
232/4	*Set of* 3	2·40	2·50

(Des P. Lim (15 c.), Datuk Syed Hashim bin Abdullah (others). Litho J.W.)

1982 (10 Apr). *5th Malaysian/7th Asia–Pacific Boy Scout Jamboree. T* **109** *and similar horiz designs. Multicoloured. P* 13½ × 13.

235	15 c. Type **109**	30	10
236	50 c. Malaysian flag and scout emblem	70	60
237	80 c. Malaysian and Asia–Pacific scout emblems	1·10	1·90
235/7	*Set of* 3	1·90	2·40

110 A.S.E.A.N. Building and Emblem

111 Dome of the Rock, Jerusalem

(Litho J.W.)

1982 (8 Aug). *15th Anniv Ministerial Meeting of A.S.E.A.N. (Association of South East Asian Nations). T* **110** *and similar horiz design. Multicoloured. P* 14.

238	15 c. Type **110**	15	10
239	$1 Flags of member nations	60	85

(Litho J.W.)

1982 (21 Aug). *"Freedom for Palestine". P* 13½.

240	**111**	15 c. gold, blue-green and black	65	15
241		$1 silver, pale turquoise-green & blk	2·10	1·25

112 Views of Kuala Lumpur in 1957 and 1982

(Des Ministry of Information. Litho Rosenbaum Bros, Vienna)

1982 (31 Aug). *25th Anniv of Independence. T* **112** *and similar horiz designs. Multicoloured. P* 14 × 13½.

242	10 c. Type **112**	10	10
243	15 c. Malaysian industries	15	15
244	50 c. Soldiers on parade	40	40
245	80 c. Independence ceremony	70	1·10
242/5	*Set of* 4	1·25	1·60
MS246	120 × 190 mm. Nos. 242/5	2·25	2·75

113 Shadow Play

(Des N. Ajib. Litho J.W.)

1982 (30 Oct). *Traditional Games. T* **113** *and similar horiz designs. Multicoloured. P* 13.

247	10 c. Type **113**	25	15
248	15 c. Cross Top	25	10
249	75 c. Kite flying	1·00	1·75
247/9	*Set of* 3	1·40	1·75

114 Sabah Hats

(Litho Harrison)

1982 (26 Nov). *Malaysian Handicrafts. T* **114** *and similar horiz designs. Multicoloured. P* 13 × 13½.

250	10 c. Type **114**	10	15
251	15 c. Gold-threaded cloth	10	10
252	75 c. Sarawak pottery	65	1·25
250/2	*Set of* 3	75	1·40

115 Gas Exploitation Logo

116 Flag of Malaysia

(Litho Security Printers (M), Malaysia)

1983 (22 Jan). *Export of Liquefied Natural Gas from Bintulu Field, Sarawak. T* **115** *and similar horiz designs. Multicoloured. P* 12.
253 15 c. Type **115** 35 10
254 20 c. *Tenaga Satu* (liquid gas tanker).. .. .. 60 30
255 $1 Gas drilling equipment .. .. .. 1·75 2·00
253/5 .. .. *Set of* 3 2·40 1·90

(Litho J.W.)

1983 (14 Mar). *Commonwealth Day. T* **116** *and similar horiz designs. Multicoloured. P* 13½ × 14.
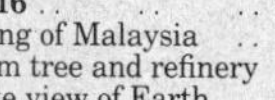
256 15 c. Type **116** 10 10
257 20 c. The King of Malaysia 15 15
258 40 c. Oil palm tree and refinery 25 25
259 $1 Satellite view of Earth .. .. .. 60 1·00
256/9 .. .. *Set of* 4 1·00 1·40
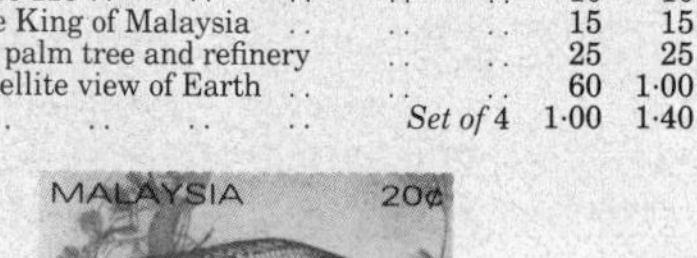

117 *Tilapia nilotica*

(Des and litho Security Printers (M), Malaysia)

1983 (15 June). *Freshwater Fishes. T* **117** *and similar horiz designs. Multicoloured. P* 12.
260 20 c. Type **117**.. .. .. 15 20
a. Horiz pair. Nos. 260/1 .. .. 30 40
b. Perf 13½×14 .. .. 1·75 1·00
ba. Horiz pair. Nos. 260b/1b .. .. .. 3·50 2·00
261 20 c. *Cyprinus carpie* 15 20
b. Perf 13½×14 .. .. 1·75 1·00
262 40 c. *Puntius gonionotus* 25 35
a. Horiz pair. Nos. 262/3 .. .. 50 70
b. Perf 13½×14 .. .. 3·00 2·50
ba. Horiz pair. Nos. 262b/3b .. .. .. 6·00 5·00
263 40 c. *Ctenopharyngodon idellus* 25 35
b. Perf 13½×14 .. .. 3·00 2·50
260/3 .. .. *Set of* 4 70 1·00
Nos. 260/1 and 262/3 were each printed together, *se-tenant*, in horizontal pairs throughout the sheet.

118 Lower Pergau River Bridge

(Des Malaysian Public Works Dept. Litho Security Printers (M), Malaysia)

1983 (11 July). *Opening of East–West Highway. T* **118** *and similar horiz designs. Multicoloured. P* 13½ × 13.
264 15 c. Type **118** 40 10
265 20 c. Perak river reservoir bridge 50 25
266 $1 Map showing East–West highway .. 1·75 2·00
264/6 .. .. *Set of* 3 2·40 2·10

119 Northrop "RF-5E" Fighter

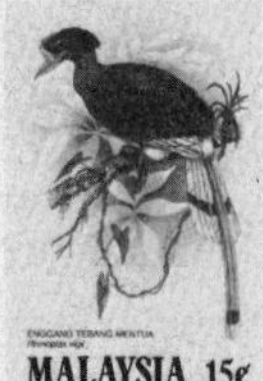

120 Helmeted Hornbill

(Des and litho J.W.)

1983 (16 Sept). *50th Anniv of Malaysian Armed Forces. T* **119** *and similar horiz designs. Multicoloured. P* 13.
267 15 c. Type **119** 25 10
268 20 c. Missile boat 40 20
269 40 c. Battle of Pasir Panjang 65 65
270 80 c. Trooping the Colour .. .. 1·10 1·40
267/70 .. .. *Set of* 4 2·25 2·10
MS271 130 × 85 mm. Nos. 267/70. P 13½ .. 2·25 3·00

1983 (3 Oct)–**85**.* *As Nos.* 190/7 *but without wmk.*
272 30 c. Type **94** (1984) 75 15
273 40 c. Malayan Flying Lemur (6.10.83) 80 15
274 50 c. Lesser Malay Chevrotain (10.4.84) .. 90 15
275 75 c. Leathery Pangolin (19.10.85) .. .. 5·00 5·50
276 $1 Malayan Turtle (5.10.83) .. .. .. 1·75 15
277 $2 Malayan Tapir .. .. 2·75 70
278 $5 Gaur (1985) .. .. 9·00 8·00
279 $10 Orang-Utan (*vert*) (3.84) .. .. .. 12·00 10·00
272/9 .. .. *Set of* 8 30·00 22·00
*There was no official release date for these stamps. Dates shown are the earliest recorded from postmarks and may be revised should earlier examples be reported.

(Des P. Ket. Litho Security Printers (M), Malaysia)

1983 (26 Oct). *Hornbills of Malaysia. T* **120** *and similar vert designs. Multicoloured. P* 13½.
280 15 c. Type **120** 40 10
281 20 c. Wrinkled Hornbill 55 25
282 50 c. Long-crested Hornbill 85 60
283 $1 Rhinoceros Hornbill .. .. 1·60 2·00
280/3 .. .. *Set of* 4 3·00 2·75

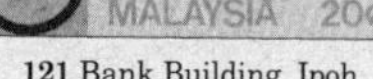
121 Bank Building, Ipoh

122 Sky-scraper and Mosque, Kuala Lumpur

(Des P. Hoong. Litho Security Printers (M), Malaysia)

1984 (26 Jan). *25th Anniv of Bank Negara. T* **121** *and similar horiz design. Multicoloured. P* 13½ × 14.
284 20 c. Type **121** 25 25
285 $1 Bank building, Alor Setar .. .. .. 85 1·60

(Des Mara Institute of Technology. Litho Security Printers (M), Malaysia)

1984 (1 Feb). *10th Anniv of Federal Territory of Kuala Lumpur. T* **122** *and similar multicoloured designs. P* 13½ × 14 (80 c.) *or* 14 × 13½ (*others*).
286 20 c. Type **122** 35 20
287 40 c. Aerial view 65 70
288 80 c. Gardens and clock-tower (*horiz*).. .. 1·25 1·60
286/8 .. .. *Set of* 3 2·00 2·25

123 Map showing Industries

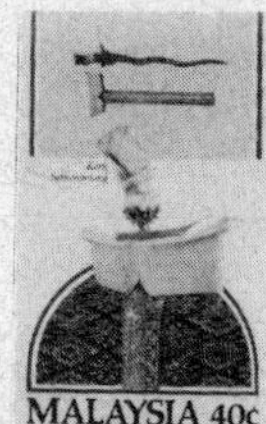

124 Semenanjung Keris

(Litho Security Printers (M), Malaysia)

1984 (16 Apr). *Formation of Labuan Federal Territory. T* **123** *and similar vert design. Multicoloured. P* 13½×14.
289 20 c. Type **123** 35 25
290 $1 Flag and map of Labuan.. .. .. .. 1·25 1·75

(Des P. Ket. Litho Harrison)

1984 (30 May). *Traditional Malay Weapons. T* **124** *and similar vert designs. Multicoloured. P* 13½ × 14.
291 40 c. Type **124** 50 50
a. Block of 4. Nos. 291/4 .. .. .. 1·75
292 40 c. Pekakak keris 50 50
293 40 c. Jawa keris 50 50
294 40 c. Lada tumbuk 50 50
291/4 .. .. *Set of* 4 1·75 1·75
Nos. 291/4 were printed in *se-tenant* blocks of four throughout the sheet.

125 Map of World and Transmitter

126 Facsimile Service

(Des Dept of Broadcasting. Litho Harrison)

1984 (23 June). *20th Anniv of Asia–Pacific Broadcasting Union. T* **125** *and similar horiz design. Multicoloured. P* 13½ × 14½.
295 20 c. Type **125** 30 25
296 $1 Clasped hands within "20" .. .. .. 1·25 2·00

(Des Mark Johan and Associates. Litho Security Printers (M), Malaysia)

1984 (29 Oct). *Opening of New General Post Office, Kuala Lumpur. T* **126** *and similar horiz designs. Multicoloured. P* 12.
297 15 c. Type **126** 25 15
298 20 c. New G.P.O. building 35 30
299 $1 Mailbag conveyor .. .. 1·25 2·00
297/9 .. .. *Set of* 3 1·75 2·25

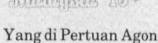

127 Yang di Pertuan Agong (Tuanku Mahmood)

128 White Hibiscus

(Des P. Ket. Litho Security Printers (M), Malaysia)

1984 (15 Nov). *Installation of Yang di Pertuan Agong (Tuanku Mahmood). T* **127** *and similar design. P* 12.
300 **127** 15 c. multicoloured 25 15
301 20 c. multicoloured 25 15
302 – 40 c. multicoloured 50 65
303 – 80 c. multicoloured .. .. .. 80 1·50
300/3 .. .. *Set of* 4 1·60 2·25
Design: *Horiz* — 40 c., 80 c. Yang di Pertuan Agong and Federal Crest.

(Litho Security Printers (M), Malaysia)

1984 (12 Dec). *Hibiscus. T* **128** *and similar vert designs. Multicoloured. P* 13½.
304 10 c. Type **128** 30 10
305 20 c. Red Hibiscus 55 20
306 40 c. Pink Hibiscus 75 75
307 $1 Orange Hibiscus .. .. 1·60 2·00
304/7 .. .. *Set of* 4 3·00 2·75

129 Parliament Building

130 Banded Lingsang

(Des P. Ket. Litho Security Printers (M), Malaysia)

1985 (30 Mar). *25th Anniv of Federal Parliament. T* **129** *and similar multicoloured design. P* 13½×14 (20 c.) *or* 14×13½ ($1).
308 20 c. Type **129**.. .. .. 25 15
309 $1 Parliament Building (*different*) (*horiz*) 1·25 1·25

(Des P. Ket. Litho J.W.)

1985 (25 Apr). *Protected Animals of Malaysia* (1*st series*). *T* **130** *and similar multicoloured designs. P* 14.
310 10 c. Type **130**.. .. .. 30 10
311 40 c. Slow Loris (*vert*) 55 55
312 $1 Spotted Giant Flying Squirrel (*vert*) .. 1·25 1·50
310/12 .. .. *Set of* 3 1·90 1·90
See also Nos. 383/6.

131 Stylised Figures

132 F.M.S.R. "No. 1" Steam Locomotive, 1885

(Des Amir bin Osman. Litho Security Printers (M), Malaysia)

1985 (15 May). *International Youth Year. T* **131** *and similar horiz design. Multicoloured. P* 13.
313 20 c. Type **131**.. .. .. 25 15
314 $1 Young workers .. .. 1·00 1·25

(Des AMW Communications Management. Litho Security Printers (M), Malaysia).

1985 (1 June). *Centenary of Malayan Railways. T* **132** *and similar horiz designs. P* 13.
315 15 c. black, carmine-verm & pale orange .. 30 10
316 20 c. multicoloured 40 15
317 $1 multicoloured .. .. 1·10 1·75
315/17 .. .. *Set of* 3 1·60 1·75
MS318 119×59 mm. 80 c. multicoloured. P 13½×13 .. .. 1·25 2·00
Designs: *Horiz* (*as T* **132**)—20 c. Class "20" diesel locomotive, 1957; $1 Class "23" diesel locomotive, 1983. (48×31 *mm*)—80 c. Class "56" steam locomotive, 1938.

133 Blue Proton "Saga 1.3s"

134 Penang Bridge

(Des and litho J.W.)

1985 (9 July). *Production of Proton "Saga" (Malaysian national car). T* **133** *and similar horiz designs. Multicoloured. P* 14.
319 20 c. Type **133**.. .. .. 20 15
320 40 c. White Proton "Saga 1.3s" 30 35
321 $1 Red Proton "Saga 1.5s".. .. .. .. 60 1·25
319/21 .. .. *Set of* 3 1·00 1·60

(Des Kathy's Design. Litho Security Printers (M), Malaysia)

1985 (14 Sept). *Opening of Penang Bridge. T* **134** *and similar horiz designs. Multicoloured. P* 12 ($1) *or* 13 (*others*).
322 20 c. Type **134**.. .. .. 20 15
323 40 c. Penang Bridge and location map .. 35 35
324 $1 Symbolic bridge linking Penang to mainland (40×24 *mm*).. .. .. .. 70 1·00
322/4 .. .. *Set of* 3 1·10 1·40

135 Offshore Oil Rig

136 Sultan Azlan Shah and Perak Royal Crest

(Des Andamaz Enterprise. Litho Security Printers (M), Malaysia)

1985 (4 Nov). *Malaysian Petroleum Production. T* **135** *and similar multicoloured designs. P* 12.

325	15 c. Type **135**	10	10
326	20 c. Malaysia's first oil refinery (*horiz*)	15	15
327	$1 Map of Malaysian offshore oil and gas fields (*horiz*)	60	65
325/7	*Set of* 3	70	80

(Des Kathy's Design. Litho J.W.)

1985 (9 Dec). *Installation of the Sultan of Perak. P* 14.

328 **136**	15 c. multicoloured	10	10
329	20 c. multicoloured	15	15
330	$1 multicoloured	70	1·10
328/30	*Set of* 3	85	1·25

137 Crested Fireback Pheasant

138

(Des P. Ket. Litho Security Printers (M), Malaysia)

1986 (11 Mar). *Protected Birds of Malaysia. T* **137** *and similar multicoloured designs. W* **138** (*sideways on* 40 *c.*). *Phosphorised paper. P* 13½.

331	20 c. Type **137**	50	50
	a. Horiz pair. Nos. 331/2	1·00	1·00
332	20 c. Malaya Peacock-pheasant	50	50
333	40 c. Bulwer's Pheasant (*horiz*)	75	75
	a. Horiz pair. Nos. 333/4	1·50	1·50
	b. Perf 12	1·50	1·75
	ba. Horiz pair. Nos. 333b/4b	3·00	3·50
334	40 c. Great Argus Pheasant (*horiz*)	75	75
	b. Perf 12	1·50	1·75
331/4	*Set of* 4	2·25	2·25

Nos. 331/2 and 333/4 were each printed together, *se-tenant*, in horizontal pairs throughout the sheets.

139 Two Indonesian Dancers

140 Stylized Competitors

(Des AMC Advertising Agencies. Litho Questa)

1986 (14 Apr). *Pacific Area Travel Association Conference, Malaysia. T* **139** *and similar vert designs. Multicoloured. P* 15 × 14.

335	20 c. Type **139**	10	15
	a. Horiz strip of 3. Nos. 335/7	30	
336	20 c. Dyak dancer and longhouse, Malaysia	10	15
337	20 c. Dancers and church, Philippines	10	15
338	40 c. Thai dancer and temple	20	30
	a. Horiz strip of 3. Nos. 338/40	60	
339	40 c. Chinese dancer, Singapore	20	30
340	40 c. Indian dancer and Hindu temple stairway	20	30
335/40	*Set of* 6	80	1·25

Nos. 335/7 and 338/40 were each printed together, *se-tenant*, in horizontal strips of 3 throughout the sheets.

(Des Design Excelsior. Litho Security Printers (M), Malaysia)

1986 (19 Apr). *Malaysia Games. T* **140** *and similar multicoloured designs. W* **138** (*sideways on* 20 *c.*). *Phosphorised paper. P* 12.

341	20 c. Type **140**	35	15
342	40 c. Games emblems (*vert*)	55	55
343	$1 National and state flags (*vert*)	1·25	1·50
341/3	*Set of* 3	2·00	2·00

141 Rambutan

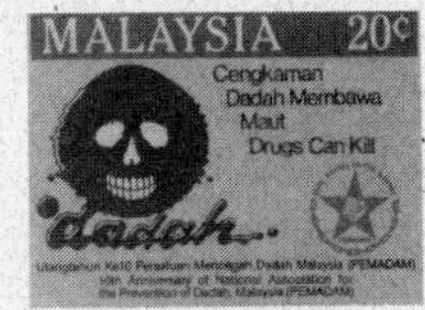

142 Skull and Slogan "Drugs Can Kill"

(Des P. Ket)

1986 (5 June). *Fruits of Malaysia. T* **141** *and similar vert designs. Multicoloured.*

(*a*) *Litho Security Printers (M), Malaysia. W* **138**. *Phosphorised paper. P* 12.

344	40 c. Type **141**	15	20
345	50 c. Pineapple	20	25
346	80 c. Durian	35	40
347	$1 Mangostene	40	45

(*b*) *Photo Harrison. W* **77** *of Brunei. P* 13½.

348	$2 Star Fruit	80	85
349	$5 Banana	2·10	2·25
350	$10 Mango	4·00	4·25
351	$20 Papaya	8·25	8·50
344/51	*Set of* 8	14·50	15·00

PHOSPHORISED PAPER. From No. 352 onwards all stamps were on phosphorised paper, *unless otherwise stated.*

(Des Kathy's Design. Litho Security Printers (M), Malaysia)

1986 (26 June). 10*th Anniv of National Association for Prevention of Drug Addiction. T* **142** *and similar multicoloured designs. W* **138** (*sideways on* $1). *P* 13.

352	20 c. Type **142**	15	15
353	40 c. Bird and slogan "Stay Free From Drugs"	25	25
354	$1 Addict and slogan "Drugs Can Destroy" (*vert*)	60	1·00
352/4	*Set of* 3	90	1·25

143 MAS Logo and Map showing Routes

144 Building Construction

(Des PTM Thompson Advertising. Litho Security Printers (M), Malaysia)

1986 (31 July). *Inaugural Flight of Malaysian Airlines Kuala Lumpur–Los Angeles Service. T* **143** *and similar horiz designs. Multicoloured. W* **138** (*sideways*). *P* 14 × 13½.

355	20 c. Type **143**	15	15
356	40 c. Logo, stylized aircraft and route diagram	25	25
357	$1 Logo and stylized aircraft	60	70
355/7	*Set of* 3	90	1·00

(Des M. Chin. Litho Security Printers (M), Malaysia)

1986 (3 Nov). 20*th Anniv of National Productivity Council and* 25*th Anniv of Asian Productivity Organization* (40 *c.*, $1). *T* **144** *and similar multicoloured designs. W* **138** (*sideways on* 40 *c.*, $1). *P* 13½ × 14 (20 *c.*) *or* 14 × 13½ (*others*).

358	20 c. Type **144**	25	15
359	40 c. Planning and design (*horiz*)	40	25
360	$1 Computer-controlled car assembly line (*horiz*)	70	70
358/60	*Set of* 3	1·25	1·00

145 Old Seri Menanti Palace, Negri Sembilan

(Des P. Ket. Litho Security Printers (M), Malaysia)

1986 (20 Dec). *Historic Buildings of Malaysia. T* **145** *and similar horiz designs. Multicoloured. W* **138** (*sideways*). *P* 13.

361	15 c. Type **145**	10	10
362	20 c. Old Kenangan Palace, Perak	15	15
363	40 c. Old Town Hall, Malacca	25	25
364	$1 Astana, Kuching, Sarawak	60	70
361/4	*Set of* 4	95	1·10

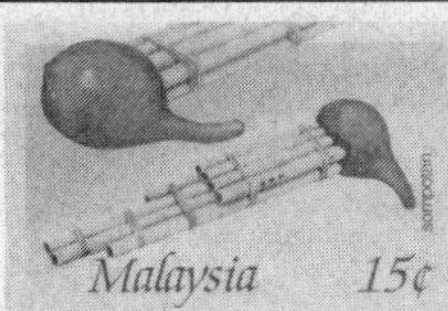

146 Sompotan (bamboo pipes)

(Des Kathy Wong. Litho Security Printers (M), Malaysia)

1987 (7 Mar). *Malaysian Musical Instruments. T* **146** *and similar multicoloured designs. W* **138** (*sideways on* 50, 80 *c.*). *P* 12.

365	15 c. Type **146**	10	10
366	20 c. Sapih (four-stringed chordophone)	15	15
367	50 c. Serunai (pipes) (*vert*)	30	30
368	80 c. Rebab (three-stringed fiddle) (*vert*)	45	45
365/8	*Set of* 4	90	90

147 Modern Housing Estate

(Litho Security Printers (M), Malaysia)

1987 (6 Apr). *International Year of Shelter for the Homeless. T* **147** *and similar horiz design. Multicoloured. W* **138**. *P* 12.

369	20 c. Type **147**	15	15
370	$1 Stylised families and houses	60	65

148 Drug Addict and Family

(Des Kathy's Design. Litho Security Printers (M), Malaysia)

1987 (8 June). *International Conference on Drug Abuse, Vienna. T* **148** *and similar horiz designs. Multicoloured. W* **138** (*sideways*). *P* 13.

371	20 c. Type **148**	10	10
	a. Vert pair. Nos. 371/2	15	20
372	20 c. Hands holding drugs and damaged internal organs	10	10
373	40 c. Healthy boy and broken drug capsule	20	25
	a. Vert pair. Nos. 373/4	40	50
374	40 c. Drugs and healthy internal organs	20	25
371/4	*Set of* 4	50	65

Nos. 371/2 and 373/4 were printed together, *se-tenant*, in vertical pairs throughout the sheet, each pair forming a composite design.

149 Spillway and Power Station

(Des Kathy's Design. Litho Security Printers (M), Malaysia)

1987 (13 July). *Opening of Sultan Mahmud Hydro-electric Scheme, Kenyir, Trengganu. T* **149** *and similar horiz design. Multicoloured. W* **138**. *P* 12.

375	20 c. Type **149**	10	10
376	$1 Dam, spillway and reservoir	45	50

150 Crossed Maces and Parliament Building, Kuala Lumpur

151 Dish Aerial, Satellite and Globe

(Des R. Zahabuddin. Litho Security Printers (M), Malaysia)

1987 (1 Sept). 33*rd Commonwealth Parliamentary Conference. T* **150** *and similar horiz design. Multicoloured. W* **138**. *P* 12.

377	20 c. Type **150**	10	10
378	$1 Parliament building and crossed maces emblem	45	50

(Des Mark Design. Litho Security Printers (M), Malaysia)

1987 (26 Oct). *Asia/Pacific Transport and Communications Decade. T* **151** *and similar horiz designs. Multicoloured. W* **138** *(sideways). P* 13.

379 15 c. Type **151** 10 10
380 20 c. Diesel train and car 10 10
381 40 c. Container ships and lorry 20 25
382 $1 Malaysian Airlines jumbo jet, Kuala Lumpur Airport 45 50
379/82 *Set of* 4 75 85

152 Temminck's Golden Cat

153 Flags of Member Nations and "20"

(Des Ong Soo Keat. Litho Security Printers (M), Malaysia)

1987 (14 Nov). *Protected Animals of Malaysia (2nd series). T* **152** *and similar horiz designs. Multicoloured. W* **138** *(sideways on* 15, 20, 40 *c.). P* 13.

383 15 c. Type **152** 10 10
384 20 c. Flatheaded Cat 10 10
385 40 c. Marbled Cat 20 25
386 $1 Clouded Leopard 45 60
383/6 *Set of* 4 75 95

(Des P. Ket. Litho Security Printers (M), Malaysia)

1987 (14 Dec). *20th Anniv of Association of South East Asian Nations. T* **153** *and similar horiz design. Multicoloured. W* **138**. *P* 13.

387 20 c. Type **153** 10 10
388 $1 Flags of member nations and globe 45 50

154 Mosque and Portico

155 Aerial View

(Des R. Zahabuddin. Litho Security Printers (M), Malaysia)

1988 (11 Mar). *Opening of Sultan Salahuddin Abdul Aziz Shah Mosque. T* **154** *and similar multicoloured designs. W* **138** *(sideways on* 15, 20 *c.). P* 12.

389 15 c. Type **154** 10 10
390 20 c. Dome, minarets and Sultan of Selangor 10 10
391 $1 Interior and dome (*vert*) 45 50
389/91 *Set of* 3 55 65

(Des Azmi bin Kassim. Litho Security Printers (M), Malaysia)

1988 (4 Apr). *Sultan Ismail Hydro-electric Power Station, Paka, Trengganu. T* **155** *and similar horiz design. Multicoloured. W* **138** *(sideways). P* 13.

392 20 c. Type **155** 10 10
393 $1 Power station and pylons 45 50

156 Black-naped Blue Monarch

157 Outline Map and Products of Sabah

(Des Ong Soo Keat. Litho Security Printers (M), Malaysia)

1988 (30 June). *Protected Birds of Malaysia (2nd series). T* **156** *and similar vert designs. Multicoloured. W* **138**. *P* 13.

394 20 c. Type **156** 10 10
a. Horiz pair. Nos. 394/5 15 20
395 20 c. Scarlet-backed Flowerpecker 10 10
396 50 c. Yellow-backed Sunbird 20 25
a. Horiz pair. Nos. 396/7 40 50
397 50 c. Black and Red Broadbill 20 25
394/7 *Set of* 4 50 65

The two designs of each value were printed together, *se-tenant*, in horizontal pairs throughout the sheets.

(Des P. Ket. Litho Security Printers (M), Malaysia)

1988 (31 Aug). *25th Anniv of Sabah and Sarawak as States of Malaysia. T* **157** *and similar vert designs. Multicoloured. W* **138**. *P* 13.

398 20 c. Type **157** 10 10
a. Horiz pair. Nos. 398/9 15 20
399 20 c. Outline map and products of Sarawak 10 10
400 $1 Flags of Malaysia, Sabah and Sarawak (30×40 *mm*) 40 45
398/400 *Set of* 3 50 60

Nos. 398/9 were printed together, *se-tenant*, in horizontal pairs throughout the sheet.

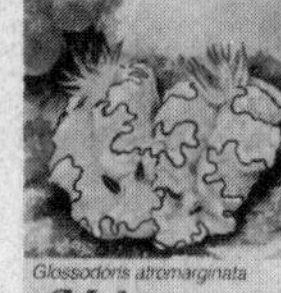

158 *Glossodoris atromarginata*

159 Sultan's Palace, Malacca

(Litho Security Printers (M), Malaysia)

1988 (17 Dec). *Marine Life (1st series). T* **158** *and similar vert designs. Multicoloured. W* **138**. *P* 12.

401 20 c. Type **158** 15 15
a. Horiz strip of 5. Nos. 401/5 70
402 20 c. *Phyllidia ocellata* 15 15
403 20 c. *Chromodoris annae* 15 15
404 20 c. *Flabellina macassarana* 15 15
405 20 c. *Fryeria ruppelli* 15 15
401/5 *Set of* 5 70 70
MS406 100×75 mm. $1 *Pomacanthus annularis* (50×40 *mm*). P 14 70 80

Nos. 401/5 were printed together, *se-tenant*, in horizontal strips of 5 throughout the sheet, forming a composite background design.

See also Nos. 410/13.

(Des P. Ket. Litho Security Printers (M), Malaysia)

1989 (15 Apr). *Declaration of Malacca as Historic City. T* **159** *and similar multicoloured designs. W* **138** *(sideways on* 20 *c.). P* 13.

407 20 c. Type **159** 15 10
408 20 c. Independence Memorial Building 15 10
409 $1 Porta De Santiago Fortress (*vert*) 65 70
407/9 *Set of* 3 85 80

160 *Tetralia nigrolineata*

161 Map of Malaysia and Scout Badge

(Des P. Ket. Litho Security Printers (M), Malaysia)

1989 (29 June). *Marine Life (2nd series). Crustaceans. T* **160** *and similar horiz designs. Multicoloured. W* **138** *(sideways). P* 12.

410 20 c. Type **160** 10 10
a. Horiz pair. Nos. 410/11 15 20
411 20 c. *Neopetrolisthes maculatus* (crab) 10 10
412 40 c. *Periclimenes holthuisi* (shrimp) 15 20
a. Horiz pair. Nos. 412/13 30 40
413 40 c. *Synalpheus neomeris* (shrimp) 15 20
410/13 *Set of* 4 40 35

Nos. 410/11 and 412/13 were each printed together, *se-tenant*, in horizontal pairs throughout the sheets.

(Des T. Teh. Litho Security Printers (M), Malaysia)

1989 (26 July). *7th National Scout Jamboree. T* **161** *and similar multicoloured designs. W* **138** *(sideways on* 10, 20 *c.). P* 13.

414 10 c. Type **161** 10 10
415 20 c. Saluting national flag 10 10
416 80 c. Scouts around camp fire (*horiz*) 35 40
414/16 *Set of* 3 40 45

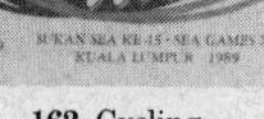

162 Cycling

163 Sultan Azlan Shah

(Litho Security Printers (M), Malaysia)

1989 (20 Aug). *15th South East Asian Games, Kuala Lumpur. T* **162** *and similar multicoloured designs. W* **138** *(sideways on* 50 *c.,* $1). *P* 13.

417 10 c. Type **162** 10 10
418 20 c. Athletics 10 10
419 50 c. Swimming (*vert*) 25 30
420 $1 Torch bearer (*vert*) 45 50
417/20 *Set of* 4 70 75

(Des R. Zahabuddin. Litho Security Printers (M), Malaysia)

1989 (18 Sept). *Installation of Sultan Azlan Shah as Yang di Pertuan Agong. W* **138** *(sideways). P* 13.

421 **163** 20 c. multicoloured 10 10
422 40 c. multicoloured 15 20
423 $1 multicoloured 45 50
421/3 *Set of* 3 60 70

164 Kuala Lumpur Skyline

165 Clock Tower, Kuala Lumpur City Hall and Big Ben

(Litho Security Printers (M), Malaysia)

1989 (18 Oct). *Commonwealth Heads of Government Meeting. T* **164** *and similar multicoloured designs. W* **138** *(sideways on* 50 *c.). P* 13.

424 20 c. Type **164** 10 10
425 50 c. Traditional dancers (*vert*) 25 30
426 $1 National flag and map showing Commonwealth countries 45 50
424/6 *Set of* 3 75 80

(Des AMC-Melewar Zecha Communications. Litho Security Printers (M), Malaysia)

1989 (2 Dec). *Inaugural Malaysia Airlines "747" Non-stop Flight to London. T* **165** *and similar horiz designs, each showing Malaysia Airlines Boeing "747-400". Multicoloured. W* **138**. *P* 13.

427 20 c. Type **165** 10 10
a. Horiz pair. Nos. 427/9 15 15
428 20 c. Parliament Buildings, Kuala Lumpur, and Palace of Westminster 10 10
429 $1 World map showing route 45 50
427/9 *Set of* 3 55 60

Nos. 427/8 were printed together, *se-tenant*, in horizontal pairs throughout the sheet.

166 Sloth and Map of Park

167 Outline Map of South-east Asia and Logo

(Des Jermaine. Litho Security Printers (M), Malaysia)

1989 (28 Dec). *50th Anniv of National Park. T* **166** *and similar vert design. Multicoloured. W* **138**. *P* 12 (20 *c.*) *or* 13 ($1).

430 20 c. Type **166** 10 10
431 $1 Pair of Crested Argus Pheasants 45 50

(Des A. Kassim. Litho Security Printers (M), Malaysia)

1990 (1 Jan). *"Visit Malaysia Year". T* **167** *and similar horiz designs. Multicoloured. W* **138** *(sideways). P* 12.

432 20 c. Type **167** 10 10
433 50 c. Traditional drums 25 30
434 $1 Scuba diving, windsurfing and yachting 45 50
432/4 *Set of* 3 70 75

POSTAGE DUE STAMPS

Until 15 August 1966 the postage due stamps of MALAYAN POSTAL UNION were in use throughout MALAYSIA.

D 1

D 2

(Litho Harrison)

1966 (15 Aug)–**71**. *Ordinary paper. W* w **13** *(upright). P* 14½ × 14.

No.	Type	Description	Unused	Used
D1	D 1	1 c. rose	10	45
D2		2 c. indigo	20	1·00
D3		4 c. apple-green	30	1·00
D4		8 c. blue-green	60	3·25
		a. Bright blue-green, **C** (1.6.71)	1·50	3·25
D5		10 c. bright blue	45	1·50
		a. Chalky paper (1.6.71)	1·50	4·00
D6		12 c. reddish violet	45	1·25
D7		20 c. red-brown	45	2·75
		a. Brown-purple, **C** (22.4.69)	1·50	4·75
D8		50 c. brownish bistre	1·25	4·00
		a. Olive-bistre, **C** (1.6.71)	1·75	6·50
D1/8		*Set of* 8	3·25	13·50

1972 (23 May). *Glazed paper. W* w **13** *(sideways). P* 14½ × 14.

No.	Type	Description	Unused	Used
D12	D 1	8 c. turquoise-green	2·00	5·00
D13		10 c. dull ultramarine	2·00	5·00
D15		20 c. pale chocolate	2·75	5·50
D16		50 c. pale olive-bistre	3·25	7·00
D12/16		*Set of* 4	9·00	20·00

1980–86. *No wmk. P* 14½×14.

No.	Type	Description	Unused	Used
D17	D 1	2 c. indigo	10	40
D18		8 c. blue-green	15	60
D19		10 c. dull ultramarine	20	70
D19*a*		12 c. reddish lilac (1986)		
D20		20 c. pale chocolate	25	1·00
D21		50 c. pale olive-bistre	55	1·75

(Des Kathy Wong. Litho Security Printers (M), Malaysia)

1986 (15 Sept). *P* 12×11½.

No.	Type	Description	Unused	Used
D22	D 2	5 c. cerise and rose-lilac	10	10
D23		10 c. brownish black & pale olive-grey	10	10
D24		20 c. dull vermilion and cinnamon	10	10
D25		50 c. dp turquoise-green & turq-bl	20	25
D26		$1 ultramarine and cobalt	40	45
D22/6		*Set of* 5	60	70

B. FEDERAL TERRITORY ISSUES

Kuala Lumpur, previously part of Selangor state, was established as a Federal Territory on 1 February 1974.

The following stamps were produced for use there, corresponding to the low value definitives provided for the states of the federation.

The island of Labuan, formerly part of Sabah, became the second Federal Territory on 16 April 1984, when Nos. K1/13 replaced the low value definitives of Sabah previously used there.

K **1** *Rafflesia hasseltii*

K **2** Coffee

(Des M. Yusof bin Mohammed; adapted Malaysian Advertising Services. Litho Asher and Co., Melbourne)

1979 (30 Apr). *Flowers. Horiz designs as Type* K **1**. *Multicoloured. W* **95** *(sideways). P* 15 × 14½.

No.	Description	Unused	Used
K1	1 c. Type K **1**	10	10
K2	2 c. *Pterocarpus indicus*	10	10
K3	5 c. *Lagerstroemia speciosa* (Type I)	10	10
K4	10 c. *Durio zibethinus*	10	10
K5	15 c. *Hibiscus rosa-sinensis*	15	10
K6	20 c. *Rhododendron scortechinii*	15	10
K7	25 c. *Phaeomeria speciosa*	15	10
K1/7	*Set of* 7	65	20

For higher values used in conjunction with this series see Nos. 190/7.

PRICES OF SETS

Set prices are given for many issues, generally those containing three stamps or more. Definitive sets include one of each value or major colour change, but do not cover different perforations, die types or minor shades. Where a choice is possible the set prices are based on the cheapest versions of the stamps included in the listings.

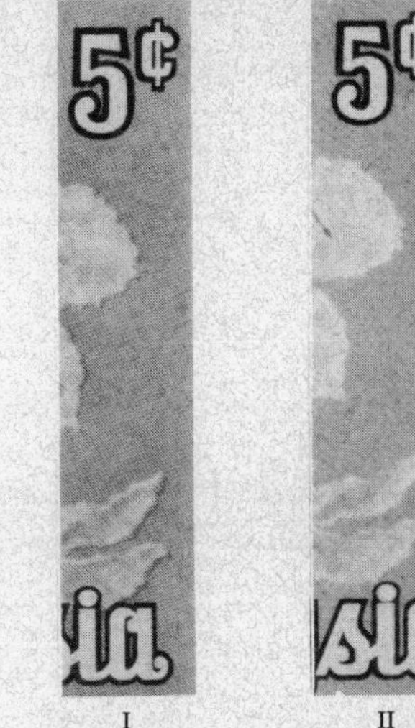

I II

Two types of 5 c.:

Type I. "5" over "i" and "c" to right of "a" in "Malaysia" (Nos. K3 and K10).

Type II. "5" over "s" and "c" aligns on "a" of "Malaysia" (No. K10*a*).

1983–85.* *As Nos.* K3/7 *but without wmk.*

No.	Description	Unused	Used
K10	5 c. *Lagerstroemia speciosa* (I) (turquoise-green background) (12.12.84)	5·00	3·25
K10*a*	5 c. *Lagerstroemia speciosa* (II) (turquoise-blue background) (1.85)	1·40	90
K11	10 c. *Durio zibethinus* (9.84)	35	15
K12	15 c. *Hibiscus rosa-sinensis* (5.11.83)	35	15
K13	20 c. *Rhododendron scortechinii* (blackish brown background) (1983)	7·50	
K13*a*	20 c. *Rhododendron scortechinii* (bronze-green background) (13.11.83)	45	35
K14	25 c. *Phaeomeria speciosa* (1.85)	3·75	2·00

*There was no official release date for these stamps. Dates shown are the earliest recorded from postmarks and may be revised if earlier examples are reported.

The 10 c., 15 c. and 20 c. (No. K13*a*) are also from redrawn plates and show the inscriptions or the face value in slightly different positions.

(Des Kathy Wong. Litho Security Printers (M), Malaysia)

1986 (25 Oct). *Agricultural Products of Malaysia. Vert designs as Type* K **2**. *Multicoloured. W* **138**. *P* 12.

No.	Description	Unused	Used
K15	1 c. Type K **2**	10	10
K16	2 c. Coconuts	10	10
K17	5 c. Cocoa	10	10
K18	10 c. Black pepper	10	10
K19	15 c. Rubber	10	10
K20	20 c. Oil palm	10	10
K21	30 c. Rice	10	15
K15/21	*Set of* 7	40	45

VII. MALAYSIAN STATES

PRINTERS. All Malaysian States stamps were printed in typography by De La Rue and Co, Ltd, London, *unless otherwise stated.*

JOHORE

A British adviser was appointed to Johore in 1914. The state joined the Federation of Malaya on 1 February 1948.

Until 1 January 1899 mail for addresses outside Malaya had the external postage paid by stamps of the STRAITS SETTLEMENTS.

PRICES FOR STAMPS ON COVER TO 1945

Nos. 1/2	—
Nos. 3/5	*from* × 10
No. 6	*from* × 15
Nos. 7/8	—
Nos. 9/15	*from* × 20
No. 16	—
Nos. 17/20	*from* × 10
Nos. 21/31	*from* × 6
Nos. 32/8	*from* × 10
Nos. 39/53	*from* × 4
Nos. 54/60	*from* × 3
Nos. 61/74	*from* × 5
Nos. 75/7	—
Nos. 78/87	*from* × 8
No. 88	*from* × 10
Nos. 89/102	*from* × 6
Nos. 103/25	*from* × 5
Nos. 126/8	—
Nos. 129/30	*from* × 6
Nos. D1/5	*from* × 10

(1)

1876 (July). *No.* 11 *of Straits Settlements handstamped with T* **1**.

No.	Type	Description	Unused	Used
1	**1**	2 c. brown	£6000	£3000

No. 1 is known with the handstamp double.

From September 1878 to August 1884 no overprinted stamps were supplied by Singapore to Johore.

JOHORE
(2)

JOHORE
(3) ("H" and "E" wide. "J" raised. Opt 16 mm long)

JOHORE
(4) ("H" wide, "E" narrow. Opt 16 mm long)

JOHORE
(5) ("H" and "E" wide. Opt 16¾mm long)

JOHORE.
(6)

JOHORE
(7)

JOHORE
(8)

1884 (June)–**86**. *No.* 63 *of Straits Settlements optd with T* **2/8**.

No.	Type	Description	Unused	Used
2	**2**	2 c. pale rose	£900	
3	**3**	2 c. pale rose (8.84)	£250	£120
		a. Opt double	£850	
4	**4**	2 c. pale rose (8.84)	£300	£120
		a. Opt double		
5	**5**	2 c. pale rose (8.84)	£275	£120
		a. Opt double	—	£500
6	**6**	2 c. pale rose (3.85)	55·00	65·00
7	**7**	2 c. pale rose (1885)	£750	
8	**8**	2 c. pale rose (4.86)	27·00	38·00

Nos. 3 to 7 were from triplet settings, either 3+4+5 or three examples of the same overprint. Nos. 2 and 8 are probably single unit handstamps.

JOHOR
(9) (All letters narrow)

JOHOR
(10)

JOHOR
(11) ("H" wide)

JOHOR
(12)

JOHOR
(13)

JOHOR.
(14)

JOHOR
(15)

JOHOR
(16)

1884 (Aug)–**91**. *Nos.* 63/*a of Straits Settlements optd with T* **9/16**.

No.	Type	Description	Unused	Used
9	**9**	2 c. pale rose	6·50	8·00
10	**10**	2 c. pale rose (10.84)	4·25	4·25
		a. Thin, narrow "J" (R. 6/6)	50·00	50·00
		b. Bright rose (1890)	17·00	23·00
		ba. Thin, narrow "J" (R. 6/6)	90·00	£100
11	**11**	2 c. pale rose (2.85)	26·00	26·00

12	12	2 c. pale rose (1886)	20·00	20·00
		a. Opt double	£625	
13	13	2 c. pale rose (1886)	24·00	24·00
14	14	2 c. pale rose (1888)	30·00	25·00
		a. Thin, narrow "J"	£150	£175
		b. Opt double	£450	
15	15	2 c. bright rose (9.90)	4·25	4·25
16	16	2 c. bright rose (1891)	£4500	

Settings:
No. 9 — various triplets with the length of the overprint varying from 12 to 15 mm
No. 10 — triplet or 60 (6×10)
No. 11 — triplet 11 + 9 + 9
No. 12 — triplet
No. 13 — triplet
No. 14 — 30 (3×10)
No. 15 — 60 (6×10)
No. 16 — not known. As no used examples are known it is possible that this stamp was not issued.

JOHOR Two CENTS (17) JOHOR Two CENTS (18)

JOHOR Two CENTS (19) JOHOR Two CENTS (20)

1891 (May). *No. 68 of Straits Settlements surch as T* **17/20**.

17	17	2 c. on 24 c. green	22·00	32·00
		a. "CENST" (R. 5/4)	£350	£225
18	18	2 c. on 24 c. green	50·00	55·00
		a. Thin, narrow "J" (R. 6/6)	£120	£120
19	19	2 c. on 24 c. green	20·00	38·00
20	20	2 c. on 24 c. green	48·00	55·00

Nos. 17/20 come from the same setting of 60. Type **12** occurs on horizontal rows 1 to 5, Type **13** on row 6, Type **14** on rows 7, 8 and 9 and Type **15** on row 10.

21 Sultan Aboubakar

3 cents. (22) KEMAHKOTAAN (23)

1891 (16 Nov)–**94**. *No wmk. P* 14.

21	21	1 c. dull purple and mauve (7.94)	30	50
22		2 c. dull purple and yellow	30	1·50
23		3 c. dull purple and carmine (7.94)	55	50
24		4 c. dull purple and black	2·75	3·50
25		5 c. dull purple and green	8·00	20·00
26		6 c. dull purple and blue	10·00	20·00
27		$1 green and carmine	32·00	65·00
21/7		*Set of* 7	48·00	£100

1894 (Mar). *Surch with T* **22**.

28	21	3 c. on 4 c. dull purple and black	75	50
		a. No stop (R. 5/11)	28·00	28·00
29		3 c. on 5 c. dull purple and green	80	2·00
		a. No stop (R. 5/11)	32·00	35·00
30		3 c. on 6 c. dull purple and blue	1·00	2·00
		a. No stop (R. 5/11)	35·00	38·00
31		3 c. on $1 green and carmine	9·50	26·00
		a. No stop (R. 5/11)	£100	£130
28/31		*Set of* 4	11·00	27·00

1896 (Mar). *Coronation of Sultan Ibrahim. Optd with T* **23**.

32	21	1 c. dull purple and mauve	45	85
		a. "KETAHKOTAAN"	2·50	5·00
33		2 c. dull purple and yellow	45	1·00
		a. "KETAHKOTAAN"	2·50	5·50
34		3 c. dull purple and carmine	55	1·00
		a. "KETAHKOTAAN"	2·50	6·50
35		4 c. dull purple and black	80	2·25
		a. "KETAHKOTAAN"	2·50	5·50
36		5 c. dull purple and green	5·50	7·50
		a. "KETAHKOTAAN"	2·75	7·50
37		6 c. dull purple and blue	2·50	6·00
		a. "KETAHKOTAAN"	2·50	6·00
38		$1 green and carmine	27·00	55·00
		a. "KETAHKOTAAN"	27·00	65·00
32/8		*Set of* 7	32·00	65·00
32a/8a		*Set of* 7	38·00	90·00

The two spellings of the overprint occur in separate sheets.

24 Sultan Ibrahim **25**

26 **27**

1896 (26 Aug)–**99**. *W* **27**. *P* 14.

39	24	1 c. green	70	45
40		2 c. green and blue	40	20
41		3 c. green and purple	1·25	40
		a. Green and dull claret		
42		4 c. green and carmine	50	35
43		4 c. yellow and red (1899)	75	50
44		5 c. green and brown	75	1·25
45		6 c. green and yellow	80	1·60
46	25	10 c. green and black (1898)	7·00	28·00
47		25 c. green and mauve (1898)	9·00	25·00
48		50 c. green and carmine (1898)	12·00	28·00
49	24	$1 dull purple and green (1898)	18·00	40·00
50	26	$2 dull purple and carmine (1898)	18·00	38·00
51		$3 dull purple and blue (1898)	26·00	60·00
52		$4 dull purple and brown (1898)	28·00	60·00
53		$5 dull purple and yellow (1898)	60·00	90·00
39/53		*Set of* 15	£170	£350

3 cents. (28) 10 cents. (29)

1903 (Apr). *Surch with T* **28** *or* **29**.

54	24	3 c. on 4 c. yellow and red	50	1·10
		a. Original value uncancelled	3·00	10·00
55		10 c. on 4 c. green and carmine	2·50	4·50
		a. Tall "1" in "10" (R. 9/12)	50·00	70·00
		b. Original value uncancelled	20·00	45·00
		ba. As b, with tall "1" in "10" (R. 9/12)	£550	£650

The bars on these stamps were ruled by hand with pen and ink.

50 Cents. (30) One Dollar (31)

1903 (Oct). *Surch with T* **30** *or* **31**.

56	26	50 c. on $3 dull purple and blue	18·00	45·00
57		$1 on $2 dull purple and carmine	48·00	70·00
		a. "e" of "One" inverted (R. 7/9)	£950	

10 CENTS. (32)

1904. *Surch as T* **32**.

58	24	10 c. on 4 c. yellow and red (Apr)	22·00	35·00
		a. Surcharge double	£4750	
59		10 c. on 4 c. green and carmine (Aug)	9·00	24·00
60	26	50 c. on $5 dull purple and yellow (May)	50·00	85·00
58/60		*Set of* 3	75·00	£130

33 **34** **35** Sultan Sir Ibrahim

1904 (Sept). *W* **27**. *P* 14.

61	33	1 c. dull purple and green, **OC**	25	30
62		2 c. dull purple and orange, **OC**	85	1·25
63		3 c. dull purple and olive-black, **O**	65	40
64		4 c. dull purple and carmine, **O**	4·25	1·25
65		5 c. dull purple and sage-green, **O**	60	2·50
66	35	8 c. dull purple and blue, **O**	2·50	3·25
67	34	10 c. dull purple and black, **OC**	14·00	7·50
68		25 c. dull purple and green, **O**	3·50	13·00
69		50 c. dull purple and red, **O**	20·00	14·00
70	33	$1 green and mauve, **O**	12·00	35·00
71	35	$2 green and carmine, **O**	17·00	38·00
72		$3 green and blue, **O**	20·00	55·00
73		$4 green and brown, **O**	22·00	60·00
74		$5 green and orange, **O**	32·00	60·00
75	34	$10 green and black, **O**	45·00	90·00
76		$50 green and ultramarine, **O**	£130	£180
77		$100 green and scarlet, **O**	£250	£375
61/75		*Set of* 15	£170	£350

1910 (Dec)–**19**. *Wmk Mult Rosettes (vertical). P* 14.

78	33	1 c. dull purple and green, **C** (1912)	15	15
79		2 c. dull purple and orange, **C** (1912)	1·75	65
80		3 c. dull purple and olive-black, **C** (1912)	2·50	65
		a. Wmk horizontal (1910)	7·50	7·00
81		4 c. dull purple and carmine, **C** (1912)	1·50	55
		a. Wmk horizontal (1910)	15·00	12·00
82		5 c. dull purple and sage-green, **C** (1912)	1·25	50
83	35	8 c. dull purple and blue, **C** (1912)	3·75	4·25
84	34	10 c. dull purple and black, **C** (1912)	10·00	2·50
		a. Wmk horizontal (1911)	18·00	26·00
85		25 c. dull purple and green, **C** (1912)	3·25	13·00
86		50 c. dull purple and red, **C** (1919)	35·00	60·00
87	33	$1 green and mauve, **C** (1918)	48·00	55·00
78/87		*Set of* 10	95·00	£120

3 CENTS. (36) **37** Sultan Sin Ibrahim and Sultana

1912 (Mar). *No. 66 surch with T* **36**.

88		3 c. on 8 c. dull purple and blue, **O**	1·75	2·50
		a. "T" of "CENTS" omitted	£550	
		b. Bars double		

No. 88b shows the bars printed twice with the upper pair partly erased.

1918–21. *Chalk-surfaced paper. Wmk Mult Crown CA. P* 14.

89	33	2 c. dull purple and green (1919)	40	80
90		2 c. purple and orange (1921)	50	80
91		4 c. dull purple and red	55	20
92		5 c. dull purple and sage-green (1920)	2·00	2·50
93	34	10 c. dull purple and blue	1·50	1·40
94		21 c. dull purple and orange (1919)	2·75	3·50
95		25 c. dull purple and green (1920)	8·00	13·00
96		50 c. dull purple and red (1920)	11·00	17·00
97	33	$1 green and mauve	9·00	25·00
98	35	$2 green and carmine	18·00	35·00
99		$3 green and blue	28·00	55·00
100		$4 green and brown	30·00	60·00
101		$5 green and orange	45·00	70·00
102	34	$10 green and black	85·00	£130
89/102		*Set of* 14	£225	£375
89/102 Optd "Specimen"		*Set of* 14	£300	

1922–40. *Chalk-surfaced paper. Wmk Mult Script CA. P* 14.

103	33	1 c. dull purple and black	25	20
104		2 c. purple and sepia (1924)	75	1·40
105		2 c. green (1928)	25	25
106		3 c. green (1925)	1·50	2·75
107		3 c. purple and sepia (1928)	95	1·50
108		4 c. purple and carmine (1924)	2·25	15
109		5 c. dull purple and sage-green	30	30
110		6 c. dull purple and claret	40	40
111	34	10 c. dull purple and blue	13·00	18·00
112		10 c. dull purple and yellow	25	25
113	33	12 c. dull purple and blue	1·00	1·25
114		12 c. ultramarine (1940)	16·00	10·00
115	34	21 c. dull purple and orange (1928)	2·50	3·00
116		25 c. dull purple and myrtle	1·40	1·00
117	35	30 c. dull purple and orange (1936)	2·25	2·75
118		40 c. dull purple and brown (1936)	2·75	3·25
119	34	50 c. dull purple and red	2·00	1·25
120	33	$1 green and mauve	2·00	85
121	35	$2 green and carmine (1923)	4·75	3·50
122		$3 green and blue (1925)	23·00	50·00
123		$4 green and brown (1926)	42·00	70·00
124		$5 green and orange	32·00	48·00
125	34	$10 green and black (1924)	£100	£150
126		$50 green and ultram (Optd S. £150)	£400	
127		$100 green and scarlet (Optd S. £275)	£1000	
128	35	$500 blue and red (1926) (Optd S. £750)	£16000	
103/25		*Set of* 23	£225	£325
103/25 Optd/Perf "Specimen"		*Set of* 23	£400	

(Recess Waterlow)

1935 (15 May). *Wmk Mult Script CA (sideways). P* 12½.

129	37	8 c. bright violet and slate	1·00	40
129 Perf "Specimen"			35·00	

38 Sultan Sir Ibrahim **39**

(Recess D.L.R.)

1940 (Feb). *Wmk Mult Script CA. P* 13½.

130	38	8 c. black and pale blue	2·75	15
130 Perf "Specimen"			35·00	

1948 (1 Dec). *Royal Silver Wedding. As Nos. 30/1 of Aden.*

131		10 c. violet	15	15
132		$5 green	24·00	30·00

1949 (2 May)–**55**. *Wmk Mult Script CA. Chalk-surfaced paper. P* 17½ × 18.

133	34	1 c. black	10	10
134		2 c. orange	10	10
		a. Orange-yellow (22.1.52)	10	20
135		3 c. green	35	30
		a. Yellow-green (22.1.52)	70	80
136		4 c. brown	10	10
136*a*		5 c. bright purple (1.9.52)	25	20
137		6 c. grey	20	10
		a. Pale grey (22.1.52)	25	20
		ac. Error. St. Edward's Crown W 9*b*	£500	
138		8 c. scarlet	35	90
138*a*		8 c. green (1.9.52)	75	1·25
139		10 c. magenta	20	10
		aa. Imperf (pair)	£750	
139*a*		12 c. scarlet (1.9.52)	1·25	2·00
140		15 c. ultramarine	70	10
141		20 c. black and green	45	1·00
141*a*		20 c. bright blue (1.9.52)	80	10
142		25 c. purple and orange	30	10
142*a*		30 c. scarlet and purple (5.9.55)	1·25	1·75
142*b*		35 c. scarlet and purple (1.9.52)	1·25	1·00
143		40 c. red and purple	1·75	4·50
144		50 c. black and blue	50	10
145		$1 blue and purple	2·00	75
146		$2 green and scarlet	9·50	3·50
147		$5 green and brown	22·00	8·50
133/47		*Set of* 21	40·00	23·00

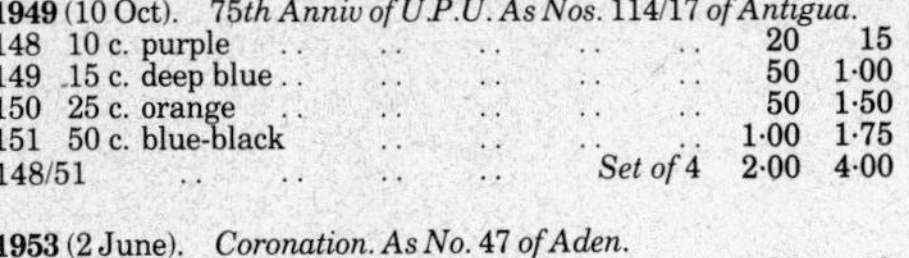

1949 (10 Oct). *75th Anniv of U.P.U. As Nos.* 114/17 *of Antigua.*

148	10 c. purple	20	15
149	15 c. deep blue	50	1·00
150	25 c. orange	50	1·50
151	50 c. blue-black	1·00	1·75
148/51	*Set of* 4	2·00	4·00

1953 (2 June). *Coronation. As No.* 47 *of Aden.*

152	10 c. black and reddish purple	25	10

40 Sultan Sir Ibrahim

41 Sultan Sir Ismail and Johore Coat of Arms

(Recess D.L.R.)

1955 (1 Nov). *Diamond Jubilee of Sultan. Wmk Mult Script CA. P* 14.

153 **40**	10 c. carmine-red	10	10

(Photo Courvoisier)

1960 (10 Feb). *Coronation of Sultan. No wmk. P* 11½.

154 **41**	10 c. multicoloured	10	10

1960. *As T* **9/19** *of Kedah, but with portrait of Sultan Ismail. P* 13½ ($1); *others* 12½ × 13 (*vert*) *or* 13 × 12½ (*horiz*).

155	1 c. black (7.10.60)	10	20
156	2 c. orange-red (7.10.60)	10	15
157	4 c. sepia (19.8.60)	10	10
158	5 c. carmine-lake (7.10.60)	10	10
159	8 c. myrtle-green (9.12.60)	1·25	90
160	10 c. deep maroon (10.6.60)	15	10
161	20 c. blue (9.12.60)	15	10
162	50 c. black and bright blue (19.8.60)	20	10
163	$1 ultramarine and reddish purple (9.12.60)	1·25	1·00
164	$2 bronze-green and scarlet (9.12.60)	3·25	5·50
165	$5 brown and bronze-green (7.10.60)	11·00	15·00
155/65	*Set of* 11	16·00	21·00

In No. 161 there are only two figures in the boat, the steersman being missing. In the 20 c. value for all the other States there are three figures.

The 6, 12, 25 and 30 c. values used with this issue were Nos. 1/4 of Malayan Federation.

42 *Vanda hookeriana* (Inset portrait of Sultan Ismail)

(Des A. Fraser-Brunner. Photo Harrison)

1965 (15 Nov). *T* **42** *and similar horiz designs. W* w **13** (*upright*). *P* 14½.

166	1 c. Type **42**	10	25
	a. Black (orchid's name and part of flower) omitted	50·00	
167	2 c. *Arundina graminifolia*	10	20
168	5 c. *Paphiopedilum niveum*	10	10
	b. Yellow (flower) omitted	18·00	
169	6 c. *Spathoglottis plicata*	15	10
170	10 c. *Arachnis flos-aeris*	20	10
171	15 c. *Rhyncostylis retusa*	55	10
	b. Green (face value and leaves) omitted		
172	20 c. *Phalaenopsis violacea*	80	25
	a. Bright purple (blooms) omitted	35·00	
166/72	*Set of* 7	1·75	80

The 2 c. to 15 c. exist with both PVA gum and gum arabic.

The 2 c. with black (name of state, arms and head) omitted is listed under Sarawak No. 213a as there is some evidence that a sheet was issued there; if it also exists from any of the other states it would, of course, be identical.

The higher values used with this issue were Nos. 20/27 of Malaysia (National Issues).

1970. *As No.* 166 *and* 170 *but W* w **13** (*sideways*).

173	1 c. multicoloured (20.11)	30	1·25
174	10 c. multicoloured (27.5)	40	1·00

44 Malayan Jezebel (Inset portrait of Sultan Ismail)

45 *Rafflesia hasseltii* (Inset portrait of Sultan Ismail)

(Des V. Whiteley)

1971 (1 Feb)–**78**. *Butterflies. T* **44** *and similar horiz designs. Multicoloured. No wmk. P* 13½ × 13.

(*a*) *Litho by Bradbury, Wilkinson*

175	1 c. Type **44**	10	20
176	2 c. Black-veined Tiger	20	20
177	5 c. Clipper Butterfly	35	10
178	6 c. Lime Butterfly	35	15
179	10 c. Great Orange Tip	35	10
180	15 c. Blue Pansy Butterfly	50	10
181	20 c. Wanderer	60	10
175/81	*Set of* 7	2·25	75

(*b*) *Photo by Harrison* (1977–78)

182	1 c. Type **44**	50	60
183	2 c. Black-veined Tiger	35	70
184	5 c. Clipper Butterfly	1·50	30
185	10 c. Great Orange Tip	75	15
186	15 c. Blue Pansy	1·50	25
187	20 c. Wanderer	2·00	75
182/7	*Set of* 6	6·00	2·50

The higher values used with this issue were Nos. 64/71 of Malaysia (National Issues).

DIFFERENCES BETWEEN LITHO AND PHOTO PRINTINGS. Stamps from the photogravure printings can be easily identified by the appearance of certain features. The differences are most easily observed on the face values and inscriptions. Stamps printed by lithography show straight edges to letters and figures, but when those produced by photogravure are examined under a magnifying glass it will be seen that these edges are broken by the photogravure screen.

In addition the backgrounds and portraits of those stamps of this series printed by lithography show a regular screen of dots, a feature not visible on those printed by the photogravure process.

A number of instances have come to light of photogravure stamps which have had the top colour "removed" by means of an eraser.

(Des M. Yusof bin Mohammed; adapted Malaysian Advertising Services. Litho Asher and Co., Melbourne)

1979 (30 Apr). *Flowers. Horiz designs as T* **45.** *Multicoloured. W* **95** *of Malaysia* (*sideways*). *P* 15 × 14½.

188	1 c. Type **45**	10	10
189	2 c. *Pterocarpus indicus*	10	10
190	5 c. *Lagerstroemia speciosa*	10	10
191	10 c. *Durio zibethinus*	10	10
192	15 c. *Hibiscus rosa-sinensis*	15	10
193	20 c. *Rhododendron scortechinii*	15	10
194	25 c. *Phaeomeria speciosa*	15	10
188/94	*Set of* 7	65	25

For higher values used in conjunction with this series see Nos. 190/7 of Malaysia.

1983 (July)–**85.*** *As Nos.* 190/3 *but without wmk.*

197	5 c. *Lagerstroemia speciosa* (20.11.83)	35	30
198	10 c. *Durio zibethinus* (11.7.85)	50	40
199	15 c. *Hibiscus rosa-sinensis* (12.83)	45	15
200	20 c. *Rhododendron scortechinii* (blackish brown background)		
200*a*	20 c. *Rhododendron scortechinii* (bronze-green background) (13.11.83)	55	35

*There was no official release date for these stamps. Dates shown are the earliest recorded from postmarks and may be revised if earlier examples are reported.

On Nos. 197/9 and 200*a* the "Johor" inscription is in rounded instead of square-ended letters.

WATERMARKED AND UNWATERMARKED PRINTINGS. The first printing of the 20 c. value on unwatermarked paper (of which examples have, so far, been reported from the Federal Territory and all states except Perlis) was from the same plates and in the same shades as the original watermarked issue.

Subsequent no watermark printings of the 20 c. and all no watermark printings of the other values were in changed shades and can be readily identified as follows:

5 c. No watermark printing has the frame in turquoise-blue instead of the dull blue of the watermarked version.

10 c. No watermark printing shows a purple-brown background instead of the sepia of the watermarked.

15 c. No watermark printing shows stronger highlights in the design and more detail on the flowers and leaves.

20 c. Later no watermark printings have a bronze-green background instead of the blackish brown shown on the watermarked and first no watermark stamps.

25 c. No watermark printing has a deep background with more detail on the flower. The latin inscription has also been moved downwards to a more central position up the side of the vignette.

Differences also occur in the plates used to apply the state names, rulers' portraits or crests. Notes on these are provided under the individual issues.

46 Coconuts (Inset portrait of Sultan Mahmood)

(Des Kathy Wong. Litho Security Printers (M), Malaysia)

1986 (25 Oct). *Agricultural Products of Malaysia. Vert designs as T* **46.** *Multicoloured. W* **138.** *Phosphorised paper. P* 12.

202	1 c. Coffee	10	10
203	2 c. Type **46**	10	10
204	5 c. Cocoa	10	10
205	10 c. Black pepper	10	10
206	15 c. Rubber	10	10
207	20 c. Oil palm	10	10
208	30 c. Rice	10	15
202/8	*Set of* 7	40	45

ALTERED CATALOGUE NUMBERS

Any Catalogue numbers altered from the last edition are shown as a list in the introductory pages.

POSTAGE DUE STAMPS

D 1

(Typo Waterlow)

1938 (1 Jan). *Wmk Mult Script CA. P* 12½.

D1	D 1	1 c. carmine	6·50	23·00
D2		4 c. green	19·00	32·00
D3		8 c. orange	24·00	70·00
D4		10 c. brown	24·00	38·00
D5		12 c. purple	27·00	85·00
D1/5		*Set of* 5	90·00	£225
D1/5 Perf "Specimen"		*Set of* 5	£100	

KEDAH

Suzerainty over Kedah was transferred by Thailand to Great Britain on 15 July 1909. A British adviser was appointed in 1923.

The state joined the Federation of Malaya on 1 February 1948.

Stamps of THAILAND were used in Kedah at Alor Star (from 1883), Kuala Muda (from 1907), Kulim (from 1907) and Langkawi (from 1908) until 1909. Issues of the FEDERATED MALAY STATES were used in Kedah from 16 July 1909 until 1912.

PRICES FOR STAMPS ON COVER TO 1945

Nos. 1/14	*from* × 7
Nos. 15/23	*from* × 5
Nos. 24/40	*from* × 3
Nos. 41/8	*from* × 10
Nos. 49/51	—
Nos. 52/9	*from* × 4
Nos. 60/8	*from* × 3
Nos. 68*a*/9*a*	*from* × 4

1 Sheaf of Rice

2 Malay ploughing

3 Council Chamber, Alor Star

1912 (16 June). *Wmk Mult Crown CA (sideways on* 10 *c. to* $5). *P* 14.

No.	Type	Description	Unused	Used
1	1	1 c. black and green	25	25
2		3 c. black and red	2·25	30
3		4 c. rose and grey	8·00	25
4		5 c. green and chestnut	2·00	3·00
5		8 c. black and ultramarine	1·00	2·00
6	2	10 c. blue and sepia	1·75	90
7		20 c. black and green	2·75	4·00
8		30 c. black and rose	2·25	9·00
9		40 c. black and purple	3·50	14·00
10		50 c. brown and blue	7·50	13·00
11	3	$1 black and red/*yellow*	10·00	18·00
12		$2 green and brown	10·00	40·00
13		$3 black and blue/*blue*	45·00	80·00
14		$5 black and red	45·00	75·00
1/14		*Set of* 14	£120	£225
1/14 Optd "Specimen"		*Set of* 14	£275	

Due to an increase in postal notes 1 c. and 4 c. stamps of STRAITS SETTLEMENTS were used in Kedah for some months from March 1919.

(i)

(ii)

DOUBLE AND SINGLE PLATES. (i) Printed from separate plates for frame and centre, with dotted shading extending close to the central sheaf. Soft impression of centre with little clear detail.

(ii) Printed from single plate, with white space around sheaf. Centre more deeply etched with sharp image.

1919 (June)–**21**. *New colours and values. Wmk Mult Crown CA (sideways on* 21 *c.,* 25 *c.). P* 14.

No.	Type	Description	Unused	Used
15	1	1 c. brown (i) (8.19)	55	45
18		2 c. green (ii)	50	20
19		3 c. deep purple (i) (1920)	65	70
20		4 c. rose (i)	1·50	20
21		4 c. red (ii) (1920)	2·00	20
22	2	21 c. purple (8.19)	5·50	28·00
23		25 c. blue and purple (1921)	1·75	18·00
15/23		*Set of* 6	9·50	42·00
15/23 Optd "Specimen"		*Set of* 6	£130	

ONE

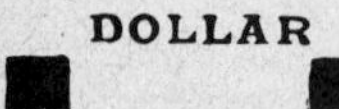

DOLLAR

(4)

MALAYA-
BORNEO
EXHIBITION.

(5)

(Surch by Ribeiro & Co, Penang)

1919 (Mar). *Surch as T* 4.

No.	Type	Description	Unused	Used
24	3	50 c. on $2 green and brown	40·00	48·00
		a. "C" of "CENTS" inserted by hand-stamp (R. 6/4)	£950	£1000
25		$1 on $3 black and blue/*blue*	20·00	60·00

Two centre plate dies of Type **2** wmkd Mult Script CA:

Die I

Die II

The common centre plate used for Type **2** was re-engraved in 1926. Stamps from this re-engraved Die II show considerably more detail of the ground and have the oxen, ploughman's hat and his clothing much more deeply cut.

1921–27. *Wmk Mult Script CA (sideways on* 10 *c. to* $5). *P* 14.

No.	Type	Description	Unused	Used
26	1	1 c. brown (ii)	40	20
27		2 c. dull green (ii) (Die I)*	25	20
28		3 c. deep purple (ii)	80	70
29		4 c. deep carmine (ii)	5·00	20
30	2	10 c. blue and sepia (I)	90	75
		a. Die II (1927)	4·00	2·00
31		20 c. black and yellow-green (I)	1·50	2·00
32		21 c. mauve and purple (I)	2·00	9·50
33		25 c. blue and purple (I)	2·25	4·50
		a. Die II (1927)	10·00	3·00
34		30 c. black and rose (I) (1922)	2·50	3·75
		a. Die II (1927)	10·00	2·50
35		40 c. black and purple (I)	2·50	16·00
		a. Die II (1927)	18·00	14·00
36		50 c. brown and grey-blue (I)	1·75	4·50
		a. Die II (1927)	10·00	3·00
37	3	$1 black and red/*yellow* (1924)	6·50	7·50
38		$2 myrtle and brown	13·00	48·00
39		$3 black and blue/*blue*	30·00	48·00
40		$5 black and deep carmine	45·00	75·00
26/40		*Set of* 15	95·00	£180
26/40 Optd "Specimen"		*Set of* 15	£250	

* For 2 c. Die II, see No. 69.

1922 (31 Mar). *Optd as T* **5** *at Singapore.*

I. "BORNEO" 14 *mm. long.*

(*a*) *Wmk Mult Crown CA*

No.	Type	Description	Unused	Used
41	1	2 c. green (ii)	3·50	14·00
42	2	21 c. mauve and purple (I)	17·00	70·00
43		25 c. blue and purple (I)	18·00	70·00
		a. Overprint inverted	£850	
44		50 c. brown and grey-blue (I)	18·00	85·00

(*b*) *Wmk Mult Script CA*

No.	Type	Description	Unused	Used
45	1	1 c. brown (ii)	2·25	13·00
46		3 c. purple (ii)	3·00	24·00
47		4 c. deep carmine (ii)	3·00	25·00
48	2	10 c. blue and sepia (I)	4·50	32·00
41/8		*Set of* 8	60·00	£300

There are setting variations in the size and shape of the letters, stop raised, stop omitted, etc., etc.

II. "BORNEO" 15–15½ *mm long. Wmk Mult Crown CA*

No.	Type	Description	Unused	Used
49	2	21 c. mauve and purple (I)	17·00	75·00
50		25 c. blue and purple (I)	22·00	85·00
51		50 c. brown and grey-blue (I)	45·00	£130
49/51		*Set of* 3	75·00	£250

1922–36. *New colours, etc. Wmk Mult Script CA (sideways on* 12, 35 *c.). P* 14.

No.	Type	Description	Unused	Used
52	1	1 c. black (ii) (Die I)*	15	10
53		3 c. green (ii) (1924)	1·50	65
54		4 c. violet (ii) (1926)	90	10
55		5 c. yellow (ii)	1·50	10
56		6 c. carmine (ii) (Die I) (1926)*	70	65
57		8 c. grey-black (10.36)	8·00	10
58	2	12 c. black and indigo (II) (1926)	2·00	4·00
59		35 c. purple (II) (1926)	4·50	22·00
52/9		*Set of* 8	17·00	25·00
52/9 Optd/Perf "Specimen"		*Set of* 8	£130	

*For 1 c. and 6 c. Die II, see Nos. 68*a* and 69*a*.

MINIMUM PRICE

The minimum price quote is 10p which represents a handling charge rather than a basis for valuing common stamps. For further notes about prices see introductory pages.

6 Sultan Abdul Hamid Halimshah

(Recess Waterlow)

1937 (30 June). *Wmk Mult Script CA. P* 12½.

No.	Type	Description	Unused	Used
60	6	10 c. ultramarine and sepia	1·25	15
61		12 c. black and violet	13·00	12·00
62		25 c. ultramarine and purple	3·75	4·50
63		30 c. green and scarlet	6·50	9·50
64		40 c. black and purple	1·25	11·00
65		50 c. brown and blue	2·50	4·50
66		$1 black and green	2·50	9·00
67		$2 green and brown	65·00	70·00
68		$5 black and scarlet	25·00	55·00
60/8		*Set of* 9	£110	£160
60/8 Perf "Specimen"		*Set of* 9	£170	

I

II

I

II

1938–40. *As Nos.* 52, 27 *and* 56, *but redrawn as Dies* II.

No.	Type	Description	Unused	Used
68*a*	1	1 c. black	45·00	4·00
69		2 c. bright green (1940)	85·00	10·00
69*a*		6 c. carmine-red (1940)	28·00	45·00
68*a*/9*a*		*Set of* 3	£140	55·00

1 c. Die II. Figures "1" have square-cut corners instead of rounded, and larger top serif. Larger "C". Line perf.

2 c. Die II. Figures "2" have circular instead of oval drops and the letters "c" are thin and tall instead of thick and rounded. Size of design: 19½ × 23 mm instead of about 18½ × 22½ mm. Line perf.

6 c. Die II. Design measures 19¼ × 22¼ mm instead of 18¾ × 22½ mm (No. 56). Note also shade of Die II. Line perf.

1948 (1 Dec). *Royal Silver Wedding. As Nos.* 30/1 *of Aden.*

No.	Description	Unused	Used
70	10 c. violet	20	20
71	$5 carmine	22·00	32·00

1949 (10 Oct). *75th Anniv of U.P.U. As Nos.* 114/17 *of Antigua.*

No.	Description	Unused	Used
72	10 c. purple	25	20
73	15 c. deep blue	50	1·25
74	25 c. orange	65	1·25
75	50 c. blue-black	1·25	2·25
72/5	*Set of* 4	2·40	4·50

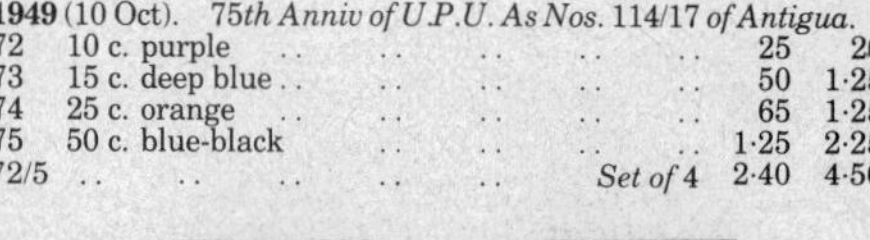

7 Sheaf of Rice

8 Sultan Badlishah

1950 (1 June)–**55.** *Wmk Mult Script CA. Chalk-surfaced paper. P* 17½ × 18.

No.	Type	Description	Unused	Used
76	7	1 c. black	10	30
77		2 c. orange	10	15
78		3 c. green	20	85
79		4 c. brown	10	10
79*a*		5 c. bright purple (1.9.52)	35	30
		ab. Bright mauve (24.9.53)	35	30
80		6 c. grey	10	15
81		8 c. scarlet	30	1·75
81*a*		8 c. green (1.9.52)	75	1·75
		ab. Deep green (24.9.53)	1·75	2·50
82		10 c. magenta	15	10
82*a*		12 c. scarlet (1.9.52)	85	2·50
83		15 c. ultramarine	40	35
84		20 c. black and green	40	2·50
84*a*		20 c. bright blue (1.9.52)	85	10
85	8	25 c. purple and orange	30	25
85*a*		30 c. scarlet and purple (5.9.55)	1·25	1·25
85*b*		35 c. scarlet and purple (1.9.52)	85	1·50
86		40 c. red and purple	1·00	6·00
87		50 c. black and blue	50	10
88		$1 blue and purple	2·25	1·50
89		$2 green and scarlet	14·00	17·00
90		$5 green and brown	20·00	22·00
76/90		*Set of* 21	40·00	50·00

1953 (2 June). *Coronation. As No.* 47 *of Aden.*

No.	Description	Unused	Used
91	10 c. black and reddish purple	20	10

9 Copra

10 Pineapples

11 Ricefield

12 Masjid Alwi Mosque, Kangar

13 East Coast Railway

14 Tiger

15 Fishing Prau

16 Aborigines with Blowpipes

17 Government Offices

18 Bersilat

19 Weaving

(Recess D.L.R.)

1957. *Inset portrait of Sultan Badlishah*. W w **12**. P 13×12½ (1 c. *to* 8 c.), 12½×13 (10 c., 20 c.), 12½ (50 c., $2, $5) *or* 13½ ($1).

No.	Type	Description	Unused	Used
92	**9**	1 c. black (21.8)	10	35
93	**10**	2 c. orange-red (25.7)	10	40
94	**11**	4 c. sepia (21.8)	10	10
95	**12**	5 c. carmine-lake (21.8)	10	15
96	**13**	8 c. myrtle-green (21.8)	2·00	3·50
97	**14**	10 c. deep brown (4.8)	15	10
98	**15**	20 c. blue (26.6)	30	45
99	**16**	50 c. black and blue (25.7)	40	85
100	**17**	$1 ultramarine & reddish purple (25.7)	2·75	5·00
101	**18**	$2 bronze-green and scarlet (21.8)	8·00	12·00
102	**19**	$5 brown and bronze-green (26.6)	13·00	18·00
92/102		*Set of* 11	24·00	35·00

The 6, 12, 25 and 30 c. values used with this issue were Nos. 1/4 of Malayan Federation.

20 Sultan Abdul Halim Mu'Adzam Shah

21 Sultan Abdul Halim Shah

(Photo Harrison)

1959 (20 Feb). *Installation of the Sultan*. W w **12**. *P* 14 × 14½.

No.	Type	Description	Unused	Used
103	**20**	10 c. multicoloured	10	10

1959 (1 July)–**62**. *As Nos. 92/102 but with inset portrait of Sultan Abdul Halim Shah as in T* **21**.

No.	Type	Description	Unused	Used
104	**21**	1 c. black	10	30
105	**10**	2 c. orange-red	10	30
106	**11**	4 c. sepia	10	10
107	**12**	5 c. carmine-lake	10	10
108	**13**	8 c. myrtle-green	2·50	1·25
109	**14**	10 c. deep brown	20	10
109*a*		10 c. deep maroon (19.12.61)	70	10
110	**15**	20 c. blue	20	10
111	**16**	50 c. black and blue (*p* 12½)	25	35
		a. Perf 12½ × 13 (14.6.60)	25	10
112	**17**	$1 ultramarine and reddish purple	1·25	2·25
113	**18**	$2 bronze-green and scarlet	4·50	8·00
114	**19**	$5 brown and bronze-green (*p* 12½)	9·50	16·00
		a. Perf 13 × 12½ (26.11.62)	7·50	10·00
104/14		*Set of* 12	15·00	20·00

22 *Vanda hookeriana*

23 Black-veined Tiger

1965 (15 Nov). *As Nos. 166/72 of Johore but with inset portrait of Sultan Abdul Halim Shah as in T* **22**. W w **13** (*upright*).

No.	Description	Unused	Used
115	1 c. multicoloured	10	25
	a. Black omitted (orchid's name and part of flower)	45·00	
116	2 c. multicoloured	10	20
	b. Yellow (flower) omitted	40·00	
117	5 c. multicoloured	10	10
	a. Black (country name and head) omitted	60·00	
118	6 c. multicoloured	15	10
119	10 c. multicoloured	20	10
	a. Red omitted	£130	
	b. Green (leaves) omitted	£130	
120	15 c. multicoloured	55	10
121	20 c. multicoloured	80	40
	a. Bright purple (blooms) omitted	75·00	
	b. Yellow (leaves) omitted	15·00	
115/21	*Set of* 7	1·75	1·00

The 1 c. to 15 c. exist with PVA gum as well as gum arabic.

The 6 c. value exists with black (country name, arms and head) omitted and is listed under Sarawak where it was issued.

The higher values used with this issue were Nos. 20/27 of Malaysia (National Issues).

1970 (27 May). *As Nos.* 115 *and* 119 *but* W w **13** (*sideways*).

No.	Type	Description	Unused	Used
122	**22**	1 c. multicoloured	45	1·50
123	–	10 c. multicoloured	65	1·50

1971 (1 Feb)–**78**. *As Nos.* 175/87 *of Johore but with portrait of Sultan Abdul Halim Shah as in T* **23**. (*a*) *Litho by Bradbury, Wilkinson*.

No.	Description	Unused	Used
124	1 c. multicoloured	10	25
125	2 c. multicoloured	20	25
126	5 c. multicoloured	35	10
127	6 c. multicoloured	35	15
128	10 c. multicoloured	35	10
129	15 c. multicoloured	50	10
130	20 c. multicoloured	60	20
124/30	*Set of* 7	2·25	95

(*b*) *Photo by Harrison* (1977–78)

No.	Description	Unused	Used
130*a*	2 c. multicoloured	6·00	7·00
131	5 c. multicoloured	70	25
132	10 c. multicoloured	1·75	15
133	15 c. multicoloured	75	30
134	20 c. multicoloured	1·50	75
130*a*/4	*Set of* 5	9·50	7·50

The higher values used with this issue were Nos. 64/71 of Malaysia (National Issues).

For differences between litho and photo printings, see after Johore No. 187.

24 *Pterocarpus indicus*

25 Sultan Abdul Halim Shah

1979 (30 Apr). *As Nos. 188/94 of Johore but with portrait of Sultan Abdul Halim Shah as in T* **24**.

No.	Description	Unused	Used
135	1 c. *Rafflesia hasseltii*	10	10
136	2 c. Type **24**	10	10
137	5 c. *Lagerstroemia speciosa*	10	10
138	10 c. *Durio zibethinus*	10	10
139	15 c. *Hibiscus rosa-sinensis*	15	10
140	20 c. *Rhododendron scortechinii*	15	10
141	25 c. *Phaeomeria speciosa*	15	10
135/41	*Set of* 7	65	25

For higher values used in conjunction with this series see Nos. 190/7 of Malaysia (National Issues).

(Des and litho Security Printers (M), Malaysia)

1983 (15 July). *Silver Jubilee of Sultan. T* **25** *and similar multicoloured designs. P* 13×13½ (20 *c.*) *or* 13½×13 (*others*).

No.	Description	Unused	Used
142	20 c. Type **25**	40	25
143	40 c. Paddy fields (*horiz*)	50	30
144	60 c. Paddy fields and Mount Jerai (*horiz*)	65	80
142/4	*Set of* 3	1·40	1·25

1983 (22 Feb)–**85**.* *As Nos. 138/40 but without wmk*.

No.	Description	Unused	Used
148	10 c. *Durio zibethinus* (27.6.85)	7·50	70
149	15 c. *Hibiscus rosa-sinensis* (12.84)	85	50
150	20 c. *Rhododendron scortechinii* (blackish brown background)		
150*a*	20 c. *Rhododendron scortechinii* (bronze-green background) (16.12.83)	30	15

*There was no official release date for these stamps. Dates shown are the earliest recorded from postmarks and may be revised if earlier examples are reported.

For details of the shade differences between watermarked and unwatermarked printings see after Johore No. 200*a*.

Nos. 148/9 and 150*a* show "kedah" nearer to "malaysia" than on Nos. 135/41 and 150.

OMNIBUS ISSUES

Details, together with prices for complete sets, of the various Omnibus issues from the 1935 Silver Jubilee series to date are included in a special section following Zululand at the end of the catalogue.

26 Cocoa

1986 (25 Oct). *As Nos. 202/8 of Johore but with portrait of Sultan Abdul Halim Shah as in T* **26**.

No.	Description	Unused	Used
152	1 c. Coffee	10	10
153	2 c. Coconuts	10	10
154	5 c. Type **26**	10	10
155	10 c. Black pepper	10	10
156	15 c. Rubber	10	10
157	20 c. Oil palm	10	10
158	30 c. Rice	10	15
152/8	*Set of* 7	40	45

KELANTAN

Suzerainty over Kelantan was transferred by Thailand to Great Britain on 15 July 1909. A British adviser was appointed in 1923.

The state joined the Federation of Malaya on 1 February 1948.

Until 1909 the stamps of THAILAND were used by the post offices at Kota Bharu and Batu Mengkebang. From 1909 until the introduction of Kelantan stamps in 1911 the issues of the FEDERATED MALAY STATES were in use.

PRICES FOR STAMPS ON COVER TO 1945

Nos. 1/11	*from* × 4
No. 12	—
Nos. 13/23	*from* × 7
Nos. 30/8	*from* × 10
Nos. 39/*a*	*from* × 4
Nos. 40/54	*from* × 8

1

MALAYA
BORNEO
EXHIBITION
(2)

1911 (Jan). *Wmk Mult Crown CA. P* 14.

1 **1** 1 c. yellow-green, **O** .. 80 70
a. Blue-green, **O** .. 70 30
2 3 c. red, **O** .. 1·00 15
3 4 c. black and red, **O** .. 80 15
4 5 c. green and red/*yellow,* **O** .. 3·00 20
5 8 c. ultramarine, **O** .. 5·00 1·00
6 10 c. black and mauve, **O** .. 10·00 25
7 30 c. dull purple and red, **O** .. 9·00 2·50
a. Purple and carmine, **C** .. 22·00 11·00
8 50 c. black and orange, **C** .. 4·75 2·50
9 $1 green and emerald, **C** .. 35·00 48·00
10 $2 green and carmine, **C** .. 1·00 4·00
11 $5 green and blue, **C** .. 4·00 7·50
12 $25 green and orange, **C** .. 38·00 75·00
1/12 .. *Set of* 12 95·00 £130
1/12 Optd "Specimen" .. *Set of* 12 £200

1915. *Colours changed. Wmk Mult Crown CA. P* 14.

13 **1** $1 green and brown, **C** (Optd S. £45) 27·00 2·00

1921–28. *Wmk Mult Script CA. P* 14.

14 **1** 1 c. dull green, **C** .. 3·75 60
15 1 c. black, **O** (1923) .. 40 50
16 2 c. brown, **O** (1922) .. 2·75 3·50
16*a* 2 c. green, **O** (1926) .. 90 40
16*b* 3 c. brown, **O** (1927) .. 2·25 1·50
17 4 c. black and red, **O** (1922) .. 50 10
18 5 c. green and red/*pale yellow,* **O** (1922) 50 10
19 6 c. claret, **O** (1922) .. 2·50 2·50
19*a* 6 c. scarlet, **O** (1928) .. 4·00 5·50
20 10 c. black and mauve, **O** .. 2·00 10
21 30 c. purple and carmine, **C** (1926) .. 4·00 5·50
22 50 c. black and orange, **C** (1925) .. 5·00 22·00
23 $1 green and brown, **C** (1924) .. 24·00 40·00
14/23 .. *Set of* 13 45·00 75·00
14/23 Optd "Specimen" .. *Set of* 13 £225

For the 4 c., 5 c. and 6 c. surcharged, see issues under "Japanese Occupation".

1922 (31 Mar). *Optd with T* **2** *by Govt Survey Office, Khota Bharu.*

(a) Wmk Mult Crown CA

30 **1** 4 c. black and red .. 2·75 27·00
31 5 c. green and red/*pale yellow* .. 4·25 27·00
32 30 c. dull purple and red .. 4·50 45·00
33 50 c. black and orange .. 7·50 50·00
34 $1 green and brown .. 20·00 80·00
35 $2 green and carmine .. 45·00 £140
36 $5 green and blue .. £130 £300

(b) Wmk Mult Script CA

37 **1** 1 c. green .. 2·50 22·00
a. Opt double .. £1800
38 10 c. black and mauve .. 4·75 38·00
30/8 .. *Set of* 9 £200 £650

3 Sultan Ismail 4

(Recess D.L.R.)

1928–33. *Wmk Mult Script CA. P* 12.

39 **3** $1 blue (Perf S. £40) .. 7·50 48·00
a. Perf 14 (1933) .. 30·00 40·00

(Recess B.W.)

1937 (July)–**40.** *Wmk Mult Script CA. P* 12.

40 **4** 1 c. grey-olive and yellow .. 25 40
41 2 c. green .. 55 10
42 4 c. scarlet .. 2·00 45
43 5 c. red-brown .. 3·00 10
44 6 c. lake (10.37) .. 4·50 80
45 8 c. grey-olive .. 2·75 10
46 10 c. purple (10.37) .. 9·00 2·75
47 12 c. blue .. 1·75 3·00
48 25 c. vermilion and violet .. 3·75 3·50
49 30 c. violet and scarlet (10.37) .. 18·00 16·00
50 40 c. orange and blue-green .. 6·00 16·00
51 **4** 50 c. grey-olive and orange (10.37) .. 26·00 9·00
52 $1 violet and blue-green (10.37) .. 15·00 12·00
53 $2 red-brown and scarlet (3.40) .. £140 £250
54 $5 vermilion and lake (3.40) .. £225 £400
40/54 .. *Set of* 15 £400 £650
40/54 Perf "Specimen" .. *Set of* 15 £375

For above issue surcharged see issues under "Japanese Occupation".

1948 (1 Dec). *Royal Silver Wedding. As Nos.* 30/1 *of Aden.*

55 10 c. violet .. 25 60
56 $5 carmine .. 23·00 48·00

1949 (10 Oct). *75th Anniv of Universal Postal Union. As Nos.* 114/17 *of Antigua.*

57 10 c. purple .. 25 30
58 15 c. deep blue .. 50 90
59 25 c. orange .. 60 2·25
60 50 c. blue-black .. 1·25 2·25
57/60 .. *Set of* 4 2·40 5·00

5 Sultan Ibrahim

6 Sultan Yahya Petra and Crest of Kelantan

Normal

No. 62a

Tiny stop (R. 1/2)

1951 (11 July)–**55.** *Chalk-surfaced paper. Wmk Mult Script CA. P* 17½ × 18.

61 **5** 1 c. black .. 10 30
62 2 c. orange .. 10 35
a. Tiny stop .. 5·00
b. Orange-yellow (11.5.55) .. 10 30
63 3 c. green .. 50 90
64 4 c. brown .. 10 15
65 5 c. bright purple (1.9.52) .. 35 40
a. Bright mauve (9.12.53) .. 25 40
66 6 c. grey .. 10 20
67 8 c. scarlet .. 30 2·50
68 8 c. green (1.9.52) .. 75 1·75
69 10 c. magenta .. 15 10
70 12 c. scarlet (1.9.52) .. 75 2·25
71 15 c. ultramarine .. 60 50
72 20 c. black and green .. 45 4·00
73 20 c. bright blue (1.9.52) .. 80 25
74 25 c. purple and orange .. 40 55
75 30 c. scarlet and purple (5.9.55) .. 1·25 1·75
76 35 c. scarlet and purple (1.9.52) .. 90 1·50
77 40 c. red and purple .. 1·25 6·50
78 50 c. black and blue .. 50 40
79 $1 blue and purple .. 2·50 1·50
80 $2 green and scarlet .. 11·00 20·00
81 $5 green and brown .. 30·00 38·00
a. Green and sepia (8.12.53) .. 40·00 48·00
61/81 .. *Set of* 21 48·00 75·00

1953 (2 June). *Coronation. As No.* 47 *of Aden.*

82 10 c. black and reddish purple .. 20 15

1957 (26 June)–**63.** *As Nos.* 92/102 *of Kedah but with inset portrait of Sultan Ibrahim.*

83 **9** 1 c. black (21.8.57) .. 10 20
84 **10** 2 c. orange-red (25.7.57) .. 10 40
a. Red-orange (17.11.59) .. 90 2·75
85 **11** 4 c. sepia (21.8.57) .. 10 10
86 **12** 5 c. carmine-lake (21.8.57) .. 10 10
87 **13** 8 c. myrtle-green (21.8.57) .. 80 1·50
88 **14** 10 c. deep brown (4.8.57) .. 15 10
89 10 c. deep maroon (19.4.61) .. 2·50 2·75
90 **15** 20 c. blue .. 20 25
91 **16** 50 c. black and blue (*p* 12½) (25.7.57) .. 25 35
a. Perf 12½ × 13 (28.6.60) .. 25 25
92 **17** $1 ultramarine & reddish pur (25.7.57) 1·75 1·50
93 **18** $2 bronze-grn & scar (*p* 12½) (21.8.57) 3·25 6·00
a. Perf 13 × 12½ (9.4.63) .. 3·50 10·00
94 **19** $5 brown and bronze-green (*p* 12½) .. 9·00 12·00
a. Perf 13 × 12½ (13.8.63) .. 11·00 16·00
83/94 .. *Set of* 12 16·00 22·00

The 6, 12, 25 and 30 c. values used with this issue were Nos. 1/4 of Malayan Federation.

(Photo Harrison)

1961 (17 July). *Coronation of the Sultan. W w* **12**. *P* 15 × 14.

95 **6** 10 c. multicoloured .. 10 10

7 Sultan Yahya Petra

8 *Vanda hookeriana*

(Recess D.L.R.)

1961–63. *As Nos.* 92/8 *of Kedah but with inset portrait of Sultan Yahya Petra as in T* **7**. *W w* **13**. *P* 12½×13 *(vert) or* 13×12½ *(horiz).*

96 1 c. black (1.3.62) .. 10 40
97 2 c. orange-red (1.3.62) .. 10 45
98 4 c. sepia (1.3.62) .. 10 10
99 5 c. carmine-lake (1.3.62) .. 10 10
100 8 c. myrtle-green (1.3.62) .. 1·50 2·00
a. Deep green (15.1.63) .. 2·50 2·75
101 10 c. deep maroon (2.12.61) .. 15 10
102 20 c. blue (1.3.62) .. 30 30
96/102 .. *Set of* 7 2·00 3·00

1965 (15 Nov). *As Nos.* 166/72 *of Johore but with inset portrait of Sultan Yahya Petra as in T* **8**. *W w* **13** *(upright).*

103 1 c. multicoloured .. 10 20
b. Magenta omitted .. 50·00
104 2 c. multicoloured .. 10 20
105 5 c. multicoloured .. 15 10
106 6 c. multicoloured .. 25 20
107 10 c. multicoloured .. 20 10
a. Red omitted .. 26·00
108 15 c. multicoloured .. 65 20
109 20 c. multicoloured .. 1·00 60
a. Bright purple (blooms) omitted .. 32·00
b. Yellow (leaves) omitted .. 20·00
103/9 .. *Set of* 7 2·25 1·40

The 5 c. and 10 c. exist with PVA gum as well as gum arabic.

The higher values used with this issue were Nos. 20/27 of Malaysia (National Issues).

1970 (20 Nov). *As Nos.* 103 *and* 107 *but W w* **13** *(sideways).*

110 **8** 1 c. multicoloured .. 20 85
111 – 10 c. multicoloured .. 90 1·25

9 Clipper Butterfly

10 *Lagerstroemia speciosa*

1971 (1 Feb)–**78.** *As Nos.* 175/87 *of Johore but with portrait of Sultan Yahya Petra and arms, as in T* **9**. *(a) Litho by Bradbury, Wilkinson.*

112 1 c. multicoloured .. 10 30
113 2 c. multicoloured .. 20 30
114 5 c. multicoloured .. 35 10
115 6 c. multicoloured .. 35 10
116 10 c. multicoloured .. 35 10
117 15 c. multicoloured .. 50 10
a. Black (state inscription, portrait and arms) omitted .. 65·00
118 20 c. multicoloured .. 60 25
112/18 .. *Set of* 7 2·25 1·00

(b) Photo by Harrison (1977–78)

119 1 c. multicoloured .. 20 60
120 5 c. multicoloured .. 1·50 35
121 10 c. multicoloured .. 1·75 30
122 15 c. multicoloured .. 3·00 65
119/22 .. *Set of* 4 5·75 1·75

The higher values used with this issue were Nos. 64/71 of Malaysia (National Issues).

For differences between litho and photo printings, see after Johore No. 187.

On No. 117a only the country inscription, portrait and arms are omitted, the remainder of the black printing being as normal. The design was produced using two black plates, one for the main design, value and inscription and the other to apply the state name, head and arms. It is this plate which is omitted from No. 117a.

1979 (30 Apr). *As Nos.* 188/94 *of Johore but with portrait of Sultan Yahya Petra as in T* **10**.

123 1 c. *Rafflesia hasseltii* .. 10 15
124 2 c. *Pterocarpus indicus* .. 10 15
125 5 c. Type **10** .. 10 10
126 10 c. *Durio zibethinus* .. 10 10
127 15 c. *Hibiscus rosa-sinensis* .. 15 10
128 20 c. *Rhododendron scortechinii* .. 15 10
129 25 c. *Phaeomeria speciosa* .. 15 15
123/9 .. *Set of* 7 65 55

For higher values used in conjunction with this series see Nos. 190/7 of Malaysia (National Issues).

11 Sultan Tengku Ismail Petra

12 Black Pepper

(Des M. A. B. bin Saman. Litho Harrison)

980 (30 Mar). *Coronation of Sultan Tengku Ismail Petra. P* 14.
30 **11** 10 c. multicoloured .. 15 10
31 15 c. multicoloured .. 20 15
32 50 c. multicoloured .. 50 75
30/2 .. *Set of* 3 75 90

983–86.* *As Nos.* 125/6 *and* 128 *but without wmk.*
35 5 c. Type **10** (1986) .. 90 65
36 10 c. *Durio zibethinus* (18.9.84) .. 25 15
38 20 c. *Rhododendron scortechinii* (blackish brown background) (1983) ..
38*a* 20 c. *Rhododendron scortechinii* (bronze-green background) (5.10.83) .. 40 15

*There was no official release date for these stamps. Dates hown are the earliest recorded from postmarks and may be evised if earlier examples are reported.
For details of the shade differences between watermarked and nwatermarked printings see after Johore No. 200*a*.
On Nos. 135/6 and 138*a* the portrait and state arms have been edrawn smaller.

986 (25 Oct). *As Nos.* 202/8 *of Johore but with portrait of Sultan Ismail Petra as in T* **12**.
40 1 c. Coffee .. 10 10
41 2 c. Coconuts .. 10 10
42 5 c. Cocoa .. 10 10
43 10 c. Type **12** .. 10 10
44 15 c. Rubber .. 10 10
45 20 c. Oil palm .. 10 10
46 30 c. Rice .. 10 15
40/6 .. *Set of* 7 40 45

MALACCA

One of the Straits Settlements.
Issues from 1965 are inscribed "MELAKA".

1948 (1 Dec). *Royal Silver Wedding. As Nos.* 30/1 *of Aden.*
1 10 c. violet .. 25 30
2 $5 brown .. 24·00 35·00

1949 (1 Mar)–**52.** *As T* **58** *of Straits Settlements, but inscr* "MALACCA" *at foot. Wmk Mult Script CA. Chalk-surfaced paper. P* 17½ × 18.
3 1 c. black .. 10 40
4 2 c. orange .. 15 45
5 3 c. green .. 15 1·00
6 4 c. brown .. 15 10
6*a* 5 c. bright purple (1.9.52) .. 45 60
7 6 c. grey .. 15 25
8 8 c. scarlet .. 25 1·75
8*a* 8 c. green (1.9.52) .. 85 2·00
9 10 c. purple .. 15 10
9*a* 12 c. scarlet (1.9.52) .. 95 1·50
10 15 c. ultramarine .. 30 60
11 20 c. black and green .. 30 2·50
11*a* 20 c. bright blue (1.9.52) .. 1·25 90
12 25 c. purple and orange .. 25 50
12*a* 35 c. scarlet and purple (1.9.52) .. 1·00 1·50
13 40 c. red and purple .. 1·25 7·50
14 50 c. black and blue .. 50 45
15 $1 blue and purple .. 4·00 6·50
16 $2 green and scarlet .. 9·00 15·00
17 $5 green and brown .. 20·00 32·00
3/17 .. *Set of* 20 35·00 60·00

1949 (10 Oct). *75th Anniv of U.P.U. As Nos.* 114/17 *of Antigua.*
18 10 c. purple .. 15 45
19 15 c. deep blue .. 45 1·75
20 25 c. orange .. 45 2·50
21 50 c. blue-black .. 1·00 3·75
18/21 .. *Set of* 4 1·90 7·50

1953 (2 June). *Coronation. As No.* 47 *of Aden.*
22 10 c. black and reddish purple .. 15 10

1 Queen Elizabeth II

2 Copra

1954 (9 June)–**57.** *Chalk-surfaced paper. Wmk Mult Script CA. P* 17½×18.
23 **1** 1 c. black (27.4.55) .. 10 20
24 2 c. yellow-orange (27.4.55) .. 20 30
25 4 c. brown .. 30 10
a. Pale brown (24.4.57) .. 80 90
26 5 c. bright purple (12.7.54) .. 30 50
27 6 c. grey .. 10 15
28 8 c. green (5.1.55) .. 20 50
29 10 c. brown-purple (1.7.54) .. 15 10
a. Reddish purple (27.3.57) .. 35 15
30 12 c. rose-red (5.1.55) .. 20 65
31 20 c. bright blue (5.1.55) .. 20 15
32 25 c. brown-purple & yellow-orge (27.4.55) 20 20
33 30 c. rose-red and brown-purple (5.9.55) .. 20 15
34 35 c. rose-red and brown-purple (8.9.54) .. 20 35
35 50 c. black and bright blue (5.1.55) .. 25 25
36 $1 bright blue and brown-purple (8.9.54) 2·25 3·50
37 $2 emerald and scarlet (27.4.55) .. 10·00 14·00
38 $5 emerald and brown (27.4.55) .. 10·00 17·00
23/38 .. *Set of* 16 22·00 35·00

1957. *As Nos.* 92/102 *of Kedah but with inset portrait of Queen Elizabeth II.*
39 **9** 1 c. black (21.8) .. 10 40
40 **10** 2 c. orange-red (25.7) .. 10 40
41 **11** 4 c. sepia (21.8) .. 10 10
42 **12** 5 c. carmine-lake (21.8) .. 10 10
43 **13** 8 c. myrtle-green (21.8) .. 1·25 2·25
44 **14** 10 c. deep brown (4.8) .. 15 10
45 **15** 20 c. blue (26.6) .. 25 40
46 **16** 50 c. black and blue (25.7) .. 25 50
47 **17** $1 ultramarine and reddish purple (25.7) .. 2·00 2·50
48 **18** $2 bronze-green and scarlet (21.8) .. 4·50 10·00
49 **19** $5 brown and bronze-green (26.6) .. 7·50 11·00
39/49 .. *Set of* 11 14·50 25·00

The 6, 12, 25 and 30 c. values used with this issue were Nos. 1/4 of Malayan Federation.

(Recess D.L.R.)

1960 (15 Mar)–**62.** *As Nos.* 39/49, *but with inset picture of Melaka tree and Pelandok (mouse deer) as in T* **2**. *W w* **12**. *P* 13 × 12½ (1 *c. to* 8 *c.*, $2, $5), 12½ × 13 (10 *c. to* 50 *c.*) *or* 13½ ($1).
50 1 c. black .. 10 30
51 2 c. orange-red .. 10 30
52 4 c. sepia .. 10 10
53 5 c. carmine-lake .. 10 10
54 8 c. myrtle-green .. 1·25 70
55 10 c. deep maroon .. 15 10
56 20 c. blue .. 20 10
57 50 c. black and blue .. 25 25
a. Black and ultramarine (9.1.62) .. 25 10
58 $1 ultramarine and reddish purple .. 1·50 1·50
59 $2 bronze-green and scarlet .. 3·50 3·50
60 $5 brown and bronze-green .. 7·50 4·50
50/60 .. *Set of* 11 13·00 10·00

3 *Vanda hookeriana*

4 Lime Butterfly

1965 (15 Nov)–**68.** *As Nos.* 166/72 *of Johore but with Arms of Malacca inset and inscr* "MELAKA" *as in T* **3**. *W w* **13** (*upright*).
61 1 c. multicoloured .. 10 30
62 2 c. multicoloured .. 10 30
63 5 c. multicoloured .. 10 10
b. Yellow (flower) omitted .. 13·00
c. Red omitted .. 20·00
64 6 c. multicoloured .. 15 10
65 10 c. multicoloured .. 15 10
66 15 c. multicoloured .. 65 40
67 20 c. multicoloured (purple-brn background) 1·00 40
a. Red-brown background (2.4.68) .. 1·25 40
61/7 .. *Set of* 7 2·00 1·00

The 5 c., 6 c., 10 c. and 20 c. exist with PVA gum as well as gum arabic.
The higher values used with this issue were Nos. 20/27 of Malaysia (National Issues).

1970. *As Nos.* 61 *and* 65 *but W w* **13** (*sideways*).
68 **3** 1 c. multicoloured (27.5.70) .. 50 2·00
69 – 10 c. multicoloured (20.11.70) .. 1·75 2·00

1971 (1 Feb)–**78.** *As Nos.* 175/87 *of Johore but with arms of Malacca and inscr* "melaka", *as in T* **4**. (*a*) *Litho by Bradbury, Wilkinson.*
70 1 c. multicoloured .. 10 30
71 2 c. multicoloured .. 20 30
72 5 c. multicoloured .. 35 10
73 6 c. multicoloured .. 35 20
74 10 c. multicoloured .. 35 10
75 15 c. multicoloured .. 50 10
76 20 c. multicoloured .. 60 40
70/6 .. *Set of* 7 2·25 1·25

(*b*) *Photo by Harrison* (1977–78)
77 1 c. multicoloured .. 1·25 1·75
78 5 c. multicoloured .. 60 15
79 10 c. multicoloured .. 1·50 15
80 15 c. multicoloured .. 2·00 30
81 20 c. multicoloured .. 2·00 1·50
77/81 .. *Set of* 5 6·50 3·50

The higher values used with this issue were Nos. 64/71 of Malaysia (National Issues).
For differences between litho and photo printings, see after Johore No. 187.

5 *Durio zibethinus*

6 Rubber

1979 (30 Apr). *As Nos.* 188/94 *of Johore but with Arms of Malacca and inscr* "melaka" *as in T* **5**.
82 1 c. *Rafflesia hasseltii* .. 10 10
83 2 c. *Pterocarpus indicus* .. 10 10
84 5 c. *Lagerstroemia speciosa* .. 10 10
85 10 c. Type **5** .. 10 10
86 15 c. *Hibiscus rosa-sinensis* .. 15 10
87 20 c. *Rhododendron scortechinii* .. 15 10
88 25 c. *Phaeomeria speciosa* .. 15 20
82/8 .. *Set of* 7 65 60

For higher values used in conjunction with this series see Nos. 190/7 of Malaysia (National Issues).

1983 (26 Oct)–**86.*** *As Nos.* 85/7 *but without wmk.*
92 10 c. Type **5** (19.4.85) .. 2·00 1·00
93 15 c. *Hibiscus rosa-sinensis* (9.86) .. 70 45
94 20 c. *Rhododendron scortechinii* (blackish brown background) ..
94*a* 20 c. *Rhododendron scortechinii* (bronze-green background) (13.6.84) .. 85 50

*There was no official release date for these stamps. Dates shown are the earliest recorded from postmarks and may be revised if earlier examples are reported.
For details of the shade differences between watermarked and unwatermarked printings see after Johore No. 200*a*.
On Nos. 92/3 and 94*a* the distance between the coat of arms and the value is greater than on Nos. 85, 87 and 94.

1986 (25 Oct). *As Nos.* 202/8 *of Johore but with Arms of Malacca and inscr* "MELAKA" *as in T* **6**.
96 1 c. Coffee .. 10 10
97 2 c. Coconuts .. 10 10
98 5 c. Cocoa .. 10 10
99 10 c. Black pepper .. 10 10
100 15 c. Type **6** .. 10 10
101 20 c. Oil palm .. 10 10
102 30 c. Rice .. 10 15
96/102 .. *Set of* 7 40 45

NEGRI SEMBILAN

A federation of smaller states reconstituted in 1886. Sungei Ujong, taken under British protection in 1874, was absorbed into Negri Sembilan in 1895. Negri Sembilan joined the Federated Malay States in 1896.

A. SUNGEI UJONG

Until 1 January 1899, when the Federated Malay States joined the U.P.U., mail for addresses outside Malaya was franked with the stamps of the STRAITS SETTLEMENTS.

PRICES FOR STAMPS ON COVER

Nos. 1/14	—
Nos. 15/27	*from* × 25
Nos. 28/36	*from* × 8
Nos. 37/49	*from* × 10
Nos. 50/5	*from* × 25

(1)

1878. *No. 11 of Straits Settlements handstamped with T* **1**.
1 2 c. brown £1600 £1400
This overprint on India No. 54 is bogus.

SUNGEI (2) ("Narrow letters)
SUNGEI (3) ("N" wide)
SUNGEI (4) ("S" wide)
UJONG (5) ("N" wide)
UJONG (6) (Narrow letters, "UJ" close together)
UJONG (7) Narrow letters, evenly spaced)

1881. *No. 11 of Straits Settlements optd with T* **2/7**.
2 **2+5** 2 c. brown £2000 £2000
3 **3+5** 2 c. brown £1500 £1500
4 **2+6** 2 c. brown £100
a. Opt Type **6** double £750
5 **4+6** 2 c. brown £325
6 **2+7** 2 c. brown £175

The two lines of this surcharge were applied as separate operations. On Nos. 2/3 "SUNGEI" was printed as a triplet, probably 2+3+3, "UJONG" being added by a single unit handstamp. Nos. 4 and 5 come from a similar triplet, 4+4+5, completed by another single unit handstamp. No. 6 comes from a single type triplet with the second line added as a triplet instead of by a single unit handstamp.

The 10 c. slate overprinted Types **2** + **7** is bogus.

SUNGEI (8) ("N" and "E" wide)
SUNGEI (9) ("SUN" and "E" wide)
SUNGEI (10) ("SUN" wide)
SUNGEI (11) ("S" wide)
SUNGEI (12) (Narrow letters)
UJONG (13) ("U" and "NG" wide)
UJONG (14) (Narrow letters)

1881. *No. 11 of Straits Settlements optd with T* **8/14**.
7 **8+13** 2 c. brown .. .. 85·00
8 **9+13** 2 c. brown .. .. 85·00
9 **10+13** 2 c. brown .. .. 85·00
10 **11+14** 2 c. brown £110
a. "S" inverted £1200
11 **12+14** 2 c. brown .. .. 85·00

Nos. 7/11 also had the two lines of the overprint applied at separate operations. "SUNGEI" as a triplet, either 7+8+9 or 10+11+11, and "UJONG" as a single unit.

S.U.

(15)

1882. *Nos. 50/1 of Straits Settlements optd as T* **15**.
12 2 c. brown (with stops).. .. .. .. £110
13 2 c. brown (without stops) £100 £140
14 4 c. rose (with stops) £1400 £1400

Each of the above was applied by a triplet setting.

Examples of Straits Settlements No. 11 with a similar overprint, including stops, are trials which were not issued.

SUNGEI (16) ("S" and "E" wide)
SUNGEI (17) ("E" wide)
UJONG (18) ("N" wide)

1882 (Dec)–**84**. *Nos. 12 and 50/3 of Straits Settlements optd with T* **11/12**, **14** *and* **16/18**.
15 **12+14** 2 c. brown £180 £130
16 **11+14** 2 c. brown £250 £190
17 **12+14** 2 c. rose (1884) .. .. .. 75·00 90·00
18 **11+14** 2 c. rose (1884) .. .. .. 75·00 90·00
19 **16+14** 2 c. rose (1884) .. .. .. 55·00 65·00
20 **17+14** 2 c. rose (1884) .. .. .. 65·00 75·00
21 **12+18** 2 c. rose (1884) .. .. .. 65·00 75·00
a. Opt Type **18** double .. ..
22 **12+14** 4 c. rose £650 £650
23 **11+14** 4 c. rose £900 £900
24 **12+14** 8 c. orange £650 £900
25 **11+14** 8 c. orange £900 £900
26 **12+14** 10 c. slate £250 £250
27 **11+14** 10 c. slate £350 £350

Nos. 15/27 had the two lines of the overprint applied by separate triplets. Settings so far identified are Nos. 15+16+15, 17+18+19, 19+20+21, 22+23+22, 24+25+24 and 26+27+26.

The 4 c. rose overprinted Types **16**+**14** is now believed to be a trial.

UJONG. (19) (With stop. Narrow letters)
UJONG. (20) (With stop "N" wide)
UJONG (21) (Without stop. Narrow letters)

1883–84. *Nos.* 50 *and* 63/4 *of Straits Settlements optd with T* **12**, **16/17** *and* **19/21**.
28 **12+19** 2 c. brown .. .. 27·00 60·00
29 **16+19** 2 c. brown .. .. 27·00 60·00
30 **12+20** 2 c. brown .. .. 27·00 60·00
31 **16+21** 2 c. rose (1884) .. .. .. 40·00 50·00
32 **17+21** 2 c. rose (1884) .. .. .. 40·00 50·00
33 **12+21** 2 c. rose (1884) .. .. .. 40·00 50·00
34 **16+21** 4 c. brown (1884) .. .. .. 95·00 £125
35 **17+21** 4 c. brown (1884) .. .. .. 95·00 £125
36 **12+21** 4 c. brown (1884) .. .. .. 95·00 £125

Nos. 28/36 had the two lines of the overprint applied by separate triplets. Settings were Nos. 28+29+30, 31+32+33 and 34+35+36.

The 8 c. orange overprinted Types **12**+**19** is now believed to be a trial.

Sungei Ujong (22)
SUNGEI UJONG (23)
SUNGEI UJONG (24)
SUNGEI UJONG (25)
SUNGEI UJONG (26)
SUNGEI UJONG (27)
SUNGEI UJONG (28)
SUNGEI UJONG. (29)
SUNGEI UJONG (30)

1885–90. *No. 63 of Straits Settlements optd with T* **22/30**.
37 **22** 2 c. rose .. .. 22·00 32·00
a. Opt double £275 £275
38 **23** 2 c. rose .. .. 15·00 30·00
39 **24** 2 c. rose (1886) .. .. .. 70·00 80·00
40 **25** 2 c. rose (1886) .. .. .. 70·00 90·00
a. Opt double .. .. ..
41 **26** 2 c. rose (1886) .. .. .. 65·00 75·00
a. Opt double .. .. ..
42 **27** 2 c. rose (1887) .. .. .. 7·50 22·00
43 **28** 2 c. rose (1889) .. .. .. 4·50 6·50
a. Narrow "E" (2 mm wide) (R. 3/4 and 4/3) .. .. .. 35·00
b. Antique "N" in "UJONG" (R. 10/6) .. 55·00
44 **29** 2 c. rose (1889) .. .. .. 35·00 38·00
a. "UNJOG" (R. 7/3) £1800 £1500
45 **30** 2 c. rose (1890) .. .. .. 12·00 12·00
a. Antique "G" in "SUNGEI" (R. 6/1) .. 75·00
b. Antique "G" in "UJONG" (R. 8/3) .. 75·00

All the above overprints had both lines applied at the same operation. Nos. 37/42 were from different triplet settings. The first printing of No. 43 was from a triplet, but this was followed by further settings of 60 (6 × 10), the first containing No. 43a and the second Nos. 43a/b. Nos. 44/5 were both from settings of 60.

SUNGEI UJONG Two CENTS (31)
SUNGEI UJONG Two CENTS (32)
SUNGEI UJONG Two CENTS (33)
SUNGEI UJONG Two CENTS (34)

1891. *No. 68 of Straits Settlements surch with T* **31/4**.
46 **31** 2 c. on 24 c. green £275 £300
47 **32** 2 c. on 24 c. green £110 £140
48 **33** 2 c. on 24 c. green £275 £300
49 **34** 2 c. on 24 c. green .. .. .. 70·00 95·00
a. Antique "G" in "SUNGEI" (R. 6/1) .. £250
b. Antique "G" in "UJONG" (R. 8/3) .. £250

Nos. 46/9 come from the same setting of 60 on which "SUNGEI UJONG" was from the same type as No. 45. No. 46 occurs in row 1, No. 47 from rows 2 to 4, No. 48 from row 5 and No. 49 from rows 6 to 10.

35

3 CENTS

(36)

37

1891–94. *Wmk Crown CA. P* 14.
50 **35** 2 c. rose .. .. 13·00 20·0
51 2 c. orange (1894).. .. .. .. 1·40 4·2
52 5 c. blue (1893) .. .. 4·50 5·5
50/2 .. .. *Set of* 3 17·00 27·0
50/2 Optd "Specimen" .. .. *Set of* 3 60·00

1894. *Surch as T* **36** *by De La Rue.*
53 **35** 1 c. on 5 c. green 65 7
54 3 c. on 5 c. rose .. .. 1·75 4·0

1895. *Wmk Crown CA. P* 14.
55 **37** 3 c. dull purple and carmine .. .. 4·00 7
53/5 Optd "Specimen" .. .. *Set of* 3 60·00

B. NEGRI SEMBILAN

Stamps of the STRAITS SETTLEMENTS were used in Negri Sembilan during 1891, until replaced by the stamps listed below. Until the Federated Malay States joined the U.P.U. On 1 January 1899 Straits Settlements stamps continued to be used for mail to addresses outside Malaya.

PRICES FOR STAMPS ON COVER TO 1945

No. 1	*from* × 200
Nos. 2/4	*from* × 8
Nos. 5/14	*from* × 5
Nos. 15/20	*from* × 6
Nos. 21/49	*from* × 4

Negri Sembilan

(1)

2

3

1891 (Aug?). *No. 63 of Straits Settlements optd with T* **1**.
1 2 c. rose .. .. 2·25 4·00

1891–94. *Wmk Crown CA. P* 14.
2 **2** 1 c. green (1893) .. .. .. 2·50 1·0
3 2 c. rose .. .. 3·25 3·75
4 5 c. blue (1894) .. .. 20·00 22·0
2/4 .. .. *Set of* 3 23·00 24·0
2/4 Optd "Specimen".. .. .. *Set of* 3 70·00

1895–99. *Wmk Crown CA. P* 14.
5 **3** 1 c. dull purple and green (1899) .. 3·25 2·50
6 2 c. dull purple and brown (1898) .. 22·00 50·00
7 3 c. dull purple and carmine .. .. 2·50 60
8 5 c. dull purple and orange-yellow (1897) 4·50 5·00
9 8 c. dull purple and ultramarine (1898) .. 17·00 12·00
10 10 c. dull purple and orange (1897) .. 22·00 11·00
11 15 c. green and violet (1896) .. .. 26·00 35·00
12 20 c. green and olive (1897) .. .. 28·00 32·00
13 25 c. green and carmine (1896) .. .. 45·00 60·00
14 50 c. green and black (1896) .. .. 48·00 48·00
5/14 .. .. *Set of* 10 £200 £225
5/14 Optd "Specimen" .. .. *Set of* 10 £160

Four cents. (4)

Four cents. (5)

1898 (Dec)–**1900**. (*a*) *Surch as T* **4**.
15 **3** 1 c. on 15 c. green and violet (1900) .. 75·00 £130
a. Raised stop (R. 5/1 and R. 10/1 of each pane) £180 £275
16 **2** 4 c. on 1 c. green .. .. 1·00 7·50
17 **3** 4 c. on 3 c. dull purple and carmine .. 3·00 11·00
a. Pair, one without surch £1200 £1400
b. Surch double £400 £350
ba. Ditto. "Four cents" albino .. ..
c. Surch inverted £250 £250
d. "cents" repeated at left £200 £250
e. "Four" repeated at right £200 £250
f. Without bar £450 £350
g. Bar double .. .. † £475
18 **2** 4 c. on 5 c. blue .. .. 1·00 7·00

On Nos. 15 and 17 the bar is at the top of the stamp.

The surcharges were applied as a setting of 30 (6 × 5).

(*b*) *Surch as T* **5**
19 **3** 4 c. on 8 c. dull pur & ultram (G.) (12.98) 1·90 3·0
a. Pair, one without surch £1200 £120
b. Surch double £650
c. Surch double (G.+R.) £700 £70
20 4 c. on 8 c. dull purple & ultramarine (Bk.) £375 £425

Pending the arrival of the permanent Federated Malay States issue the stamps of SELANGOR, FEDERATED MALAY STATES provisional overprints, STRAITS SETTLEMENTS and PERAK were used at various times between October 1899 and April 1901.

The general issues for FEDERATED MALAY STATES were used in Negri Sembilan from 29 April 1901 until 1935.

6 Arms of Negri Sembilan 7

1935 (2 Dec)–**41**. *Chalk-surfaced or ordinary paper* (**O**). *Wmk Mult Script CA. P* 14.

21 **6** 1 c. black (1.1.36) 25 10
22 2 c. green (1.1.36) 70 20
23 2 c. orange (11.12.41) .. .. .. 50 15·00
24 3 c. green (21.8.41) .. .. .. 80 5·00
25 4 c. orange 25 10
26 5 c. brown (5.12.35) 40 10
27 6 c. scarlet (1.1.37) .. .. .. 3·25 1·75
a. Stop omitted at right (R.10/9) .. 80·00 70·00
28 6 c. grey, **O** (18.12.41) .. .. 2·25 30·00
a. Stop omitted at right (R.10/9) .. 50·00 £120
29 8 c. grey .. .. 1·60 10
30 10 c. dull purple (1.1.36) 30 10
31 12 c. bright ultramarine (1.1.36) .. 1·00 25
32 15 c. ultramarine, **O** (1.10.41) .. .. 2·25 23·00
33 25 c. dull purple and scarlet (1.4.36) .. 60 70
34 30 c. dull purple and orange (1.1.36) .. 3·00 2·00
35 40 c. scarlet and dull purple .. .. 85 2·00
36 50 c. black/*emerald* (1.2.36) .. .. 2·75 1·25
37 $1 black and red/*blue* (1.4.36) .. .. 1·60 1·75
38 $2 green and scarlet (16.5.36) .. .. 17·00 15·00
39 $5 green and red/*emerald* (16.5.36) .. 13·00 32·00
21/39 .. .. *Set of* 19 45·00 £120
21/39 Perf "Specimen" .. .. *Set of* 19 £200

An 8 c. scarlet was issued but only with opt during Japanese Occupation of Malaya. Unoverprinted specimens result from leakages.

During shortages in 1941 stamps of STRAITS SETTLEMENTS (2 c.), SELANGOR (2 c., 8 c.), PERAK (2 c., 25 c., 50 c.) and PAHANG (8 c.) were issued in Negri Sembilan.

1948 (1 Dec). *Royal Silver Wedding. As Nos.* 30/1 *of Aden.*

40 10 c. violet 15 15
41 $5 green .. .. 17·00 28·00

1949 (1 Apr)–**55**. *Chalk-surfaced paper. Wmk Mult Script CA. P* 17½ × 18.

42 **7** 1 c. black 10 10
43 2 c. orange 10 10
44 3 c. green 10 25
45 4 c. brown 10 10
46 5 c. bright purple (1.9.52) 30 35
a. Bright mauve (25.8.53) 25 25
47 6 c. grey 15 10
a. Pale grey (25.8.53) 15 10
48 8 c. scarlet 20 75
49 8 c. green (1.9.52) .. .. .. 1·50 1·25
50 10 c. purple 15 10
51 12 c. scarlet (1.9.52) .. .. .. 1·50 1·50
52 15 c. ultramarine 50 10
53 20 c. black and green 25 75
54 20 c. bright blue (1.9.52) 80 10
55 25 c. purple and orange 25 10
56 30 c. scarlet and purple (5.9.55) .. 1·25 1·25
57 35 c. scarlet and purple (1.9.52) .. 70 1·00
58 40 c. red and purple .. .. .. 65 2·50
59 50 c. black and blue 40 10
60 $1 blue and purple .. .. .. 2·00 50
61 $2 green and scarlet .. .. .. 7·00 5·00
62 $5 green and brown .. .. .. 32·00 23·00
42/62 .. .. *Set of* 21 45·00 35·00

1949 (10 Oct). *75th Anniv of U.P.U. As Nos.* 114/17 *of Antigua.*

63 10 c. purple 20 10
64 15 c. deep blue 45 70
65 25 c. orange .. .. 50 1·50
66 50 c. blue-black .. .. 80 2·50
63/6 .. .. *Set of* 4 1·75 4·25

1953 (2 June). *Coronation. As No.* 47 *of Aden.*

67 10 c. black and reddish purple 20 10

1957 (26 June)–**63**. *As Nos.* 92/102 *of Kedah but with inset Arms of Negri Sembilan.*

68 **9** 1 c. black (21.8.57) 10 10
69 **10** 2 c. orange-red (25.7.57) 10 10
70 **11** 4 c. sepia (21.8.57) 10 10
71 **12** 5 c. carmine-lake (21.8.57) 10 10
72 **13** 8 c. myrtle-green (21.8.57) 85 70
73 **14** 10 c. deep brown (4.8.57) 15 10
74 10 c. deep maroon (10.1.61) 25 10
75 **15** 20 c. blue 20 10
76 **16** 50 c. black and blue (*p* 12½) (25.7.57) .. 20 20
a. Perf 12½ × 13 (19.7.60) 20 10
77 **17** $1 ultramarine & reddish pur (25.7.57) 1·25 45
78 **18** $2 bronze-green & scarlet (*p* 12½) (21.8.57) .. .. .. 3·00 5·50
a. Perf 13 × 12½ (15.1.63) .. .. 3·75 7·50
79 **19** $5 brown and bronze-green (*p* 12½) .. 8·00 11·00
a. Perf 13 × 12½ (6.3.62) .. .. 8·50 8·50
ab. Perf 13 × 12½. *Brown and yellow-olive* (13.11.62) .. .. .. 85·00 42·00
68/79 .. .. *Set of* 12 13·00 13·50

The 6, 12, 25 and 30 c. values used with this issue were Nos. 1/4 of Malayan Federation.

8 Tuanku Munawir 9 *Vanda hookeriana*

(Photo Enschedé)

1961 (17 Apr). *Installation of Tuanku Munawir as Yang di-Pertuan Besar of Negri Sembilan. No wmk. P* 14 × 13.

80 **8** 10 c. multicoloured 10 10

1965 (15 Nov)–**69**. *As Nos.* 166/72 *of Johore but with Arms of Negri Sembilan inset and inscr* "NEGERI SEMBILAN" *as in T* **9**. *W w* **13** (*upright*).

81 1 c. multicoloured 10 20
82 2 c. multicoloured 10 20
83 5 c. multicoloured 10 10
b. Yellow omitted .. .. .. 20·00
84 6 c. multicoloured 15 10
85 10 c. multicoloured 15 10
86 15 c. multicoloured 55 10
87 20 c. jet-black and multicoloured 80 65
a. Blackish brown & mult (19.12.69) .. 1·25 15
81/7 .. .. *Set of* 7 1·75 65

The 2 c., 6 c., 15 c. and 20 c. exist with PVA gum as well as gum arabic.

The higher values used with this issue were Nos. 20/27 of Malaysia (National Issues).

See also No. 90.

10 Negri Sembilan Crest and Tuanku Ja'afar 11 Great Orange Tip

(Des Z. Noor. Photo Japanese Govt Ptg Wks)

1968 (8 Apr). *Installation of Tuanku Ja'afar as Yang di-Pertuan Besar of Negri Sembilan. P* 13.

88 **10** 15 c. multicoloured 15 25
89 50 c. multicoloured 30 90

1970 (27 May). *As No.* 81 *but with W w* **13** (*sideways*).

90 **9** 1 c. multicoloured .. .. .. 45 1·25

1971 (1 Feb)–**78**. *As Nos.* 175/87 *of Johore but with Arms of Negri Sembilan and inscr* "negeri sembilan", *as in T* **11**.

(*a*) *Litho by Bradbury, Wilkinson*

91 1 c. multicoloured 10 30
92 2 c. multicoloured 20 30
93 5 c. multicoloured 35 10
94 6 c. multicoloured 35 15
95 10 c. multicoloured 35 10
96 15 c. multicoloured 50 10
97 20 c. multicoloured 60 15
91/7 .. .. *Set of* 7 2·25 85

(*b*) *Photo by Harrison* (1977–78)

98 2 c. multicoloured 45 70
99 5 c. multicoloured 40 15
100 10 c. multicoloured .. .. 2·00 10
101 15 c. multicoloured .. .. 2·75 30
102 20 c. multicoloured .. .. 1·50 85
98/102 .. .. *Set of* 5 6·50 1·90

The higher values used with issue were Nos. 64/71 of Malaysia (National Issues).

For differences between litho and photo printings, see after Johore No. 187.

12 *Hibiscus rosa-sinensis* 13 Oil Palm

1979 (30 Apr). *As Nos.* 188/94 *of Johore but with Arms of Negri Sembilan and inscr* "negeri sembilan" *as in T* **12**.

103 1 c. *Rafflesia hasseltii* 10 10
104 2 c. *Pterocarpus indicus* 10 10
105 5 c. *Lagerstroemia speciosa* 10 10
106 10 c. *Durio zibethinus* 10 10
107 15 c. Type **12** 15 10
108 20 c. *Rhododendron scortechinii* 15 10
109 25 c. *Phaeomeria speciosa* 15 10
103/9 .. .. *Set of* 7 65 40

For higher values used in conjunction with this series see Nos. 190/7 of Malaysia (National Issues).

1983 (Oct)–**84**.* *As Nos.* 105/8 *but without wmk.*

112 5 c. *Lagerstroemia speciosa* (25.5.84) .. 1·50 75
113 10 c. *Durio zibethinus* (24.10.84) .. 25 20
114 15 c. Type **12** (11.8.84) 75 45
115 20 c. *Rhododendron scortechinii* (blackish brown background) .. .. ..
115*a* 20 c. *Rhododendron scortechinii* (bronze-green background) (1983) 30 15

*There was no official release date for these stamps. Dates shown are the earliest recorded from postmarks and may be revised if earlier examples are reported.

For details of the shade differences between watermarked and unwatermarked printings see after Johore No. 200*a*.

Nos. 112/14 and 115*a* show a larger crest, further from the face value than on Nos. 105/8 and 115.

1986 (25 Oct). *As Nos.* 202/8 *of Johore but with Arms of Negri Sembilan and inscr* "NEGERI SEMBILAN" *as in T* **13**.

117 1 c. Coffee 10 10
118 2 c. Coconuts 10 10
119 5 c. Cocoa 10 10
120 10 c. Black pepper 10 10
121 15 c. Rubber 10 10
122 20 c. Type **13** 10 10
123 30 c. Rice 10 15
117/23 .. .. *Set of* 7 40 45

PAHANG

The first British Resident was appointed in 1888. Pahang joined the Federated Malay States in 1896.

Until 1 January 1899, when the Federated Malay States joined the U.P.U., mail for addresses outside Malaya was franked with stamps of the STRAITS SETTLEMENTS.

PRICES FOR STAMPS ON COVER TO 1945

Nos. 1/3	*from* × 9
Nos. 4/6	*from* × 15
Nos. 7/10	*from* × 5
Nos. 11/13	*from* × 12
Nos. 14/16	*from* × 6
Nos. 17/18	*from* × 4
Nos. 19/24	*from* × 3
No. 25	*from* × 8
Nos. 26/7	—
No. 28	*from* × 8
Nos. 29/46	*from* × 4

PAHANG (1) PAHANG (2) PAHANG (2*a*) (Antique letters)

1889 (Jan). *Nos. 52/3 and 63 of Straits Settlements optd with T* **1**.
1 2 c. rose .. .. 55·00 32·00
2 8 c. orange £1600 £1300
3 10 c. slate £250 £250

All three values were overprinted from a triplet setting, but the 2 c. also exists from a similar setting of 30 or 60.

1889. *No. 63 of Straits Settlements optd with T* **2**.
4 2 c. rose .. .. 3·75 5·50
a. Opt Type **2***a*. Antique letters £375

No. 4 was overprinted from a setting of 60. No. 4a usually occurs on R. 10/1, but has also been found on R. 8/1 as the result of revision to the setting.

PAHANG (3) PAHANG (4)

1890. *No. 63 of Straits Settlements optd.*
5 **3** 2 c. rose £1300 £800
6 **4** 2 c. rose .. .. 45·00 14·00

No. 5 may have been overprinted from a triplet setting. No. 6 was from a setting of 60.

PAHANG Two CENTS (5) PAHANG Two CENTS (6)

PAHANG Two CENTS (7) PAHANG Two CENTS (8)

1891. *No. 68 of Straits Settlements surch with T* **5/8**.
7 **5** 2 c. on 24 c. green .. .. .. 42·00 65·00
8 **6** 2 c. on 24 c. green £250
9 **7** 2 c. on 24 c. green .. .. .. 70·00 £100
10 **8** 2 c. on 24 c. green £250

Nos. 7/10 come from one setting used to surcharge the panes of sixty. No. 7 occurs in rows 1 to 5, No. 8 on row 6, No. 9 on rows 7 to 9 and No. 10 on row 10.

9

10

1891–95. *Wmk Crown CA. P* 14.
11 **9** 1 c. green (1895) .. .. .. 3·50 2·50
12 2 c. rose .. .. 1·50 90
13 5 c. blue (1893) .. .. 6·50 14·00
11/13 .. .. *Set of* 3 10·50 16·00
11/13 Optd "Specimen" .. .. *Set of* 3 60·00

OMNIBUS ISSUES

Details, together with prices for complete sets, of the various Omnibus issues from the 1935 Silver Jubilee series to date are included in a special section following Zululand at the end of the catalogue.

Following an increase of postage rates on 1 March 1894 1 cent stamps of STRAITS SETTLEMENTS were used in Pahang until the autumn of the following year.

1895–99. *Wmk Crown CA. P* 14.
14 **10** 3 c. dull purple and carmine .. .. 2·25 90
15 4 c. dull purple and carmine (1899) .. 7·50 3·50
16 5 c. dull purple and olive-yellow (1897) .. 13·00 12·00
14/16 .. .. *Set of* 3 21·00 15·00
14/16 Optd "Specimen" .. .. *Set of* 3 60·00

1897 (2 Aug). *No. 13 bisected, surch in red manuscript at Kuala Lipis and initialled "JFO". (a) Bisected horizontally.*
17 2 c. on half of 5 c. blue (surch "2" and bar across "5") .. .. — £450
17*a* 3 c. on half of 5 c. blue (surch "3") .. — £450

(b) Bisected diagonally
18 2 c. on half of 5 c. blue (surch "2" and bar across "5") £700 £250
a. Unsevered pair. Nos. 18 and 18*c* .. £3500 £1100
b. Surch in black manuscript .. .. — £1500
18*c* 3 c. on half of 5 c. blue (surch "3") .. £700 £250
cb. Surch in black manuscript £3500 £1500

The initials are those of John Fortescue Owen, the District Treasurer at Kuala Lipis.

Nos. 17 and 18 only occur on the bottom half of the 5 c. and Nos. 17*a* and 18*c* on the top half.

Pahang. (11) Pahang. (12)

1898–99. *(a) Nos. 72/5 of Perak optd with T* **11**.
19 10 c. dull purple and orange .. .. 13·00 22·00
20 25 c. green and carmine .. .. .. 48·00 70·00
21 50 c. dull purple and greenish black .. £110 £120
22 50 c. green and black (1899) .. .. 80·00 85·00

(b) Nos. 76 and 79 of Perak optd with T **12**
23 $1 green and pale green £120 £130
24 $5 green and ultramarine £425 £475

Pahang Four cents (13) Four cents. (14)

1898. *(a) T* **44** *of Perak surch with T* **13**.
25 4 c. on 8 c. dull purple and ultramarine .. 2·50 5·50
a. Surch inverted £1300 £650
b. Surch double £450

(b) T **13** *on plain paper (no stamp), but issued for postage*
26 4 c. black .. .. — £650
27 5 c. black £425

1899. *No. 16 surch with T* **14**.
28 **10** 4 c. on 5 c. dull purple and olive-yellow .. 6·50 23·00

Pending the arrival of the permanent Federated Malay States issue the stamps of SELANGOR, FEDERATED MALAY STATES provisional overprints and PERAK were used at various times between November 1899 and July 1902.

The general issues for the FEDERATED MALAY STATES were used in Pahang from July 1902 until 1935.

15 Sultan Sir Abu Bakar

16 Sultan Sir Abu Bakar

1935 (2 Dec)–**41**. *Chalk-surfaced or ordinary paper* (**O**). *Wmk Mult Script CA. P* 14.
29 **15** 1 c. black (1.1.36) 10 20
30 2 c. green (1.1.36) 40 15
31 3 c. green, **OC** (21.8.41) .. .. .. 70 4·25
32 4 c. orange 20 10
33 5 c. brown (5.12.35) 50 10
34 6 c. scarlet (1.1.37) .. .. 3·25 2·25
35 8 c. grey 50 10
36 8 c. scarlet (11.12.41) .. .. .. 70 22·00
37 10 c. dull purple (1.1.36) 30 10
38 12 c. bright ultramarine (1.1.36) .. .. 1·50 1·75
39 15 c. ultramarine, **O** (1.10.41) .. .. 1·75 25·00
40 25 c. dull purple and scarlet (1.4.36) .. 80 1·00
41 30 c. dull purple and orange (1.1.36) .. 55 80
42 40 c. scarlet and dull purple .. .. 75 1·40
43 50 c. black/*emerald* (1.2.36) .. .. 3·25 1·50
44 $1 black and red/*blue* (1.4.36) .. .. 2·25 4·50
45 $2 green and scarlet (16.5.36) .. .. 17·00 26·00
46 $5 green and red/*emerald* (16.5.36) .. 8·00 42·00
29/46 .. .. *Set of* 18 38·00 £120
29/46 Perf "Specimen" .. .. *Set of* 18 £180

A 2 c. orange and a 6 c. grey were prepared but not officially issued. (*Price mint £4 each*).

During shortages in 1941 stamps of STRAITS SETTLEMENTS (2 c.), SELANGOR (2 c., 8 c.) and PERAK (2 c.) were issued in Pahang.

1948 (1 Dec). *Royal Silver Wedding. As Nos. 30/1 of Aden.*
47 10 c. violet 15 40
48 $5 green .. .. 20·00 40·00

1949 (10 Oct). *75th Anniv of Universal Postal Union. As Nos. 114/17 of Antigua.*
49 10 c. purple 20 20
50 15 c. deep blue 35 70
51 25 c. orange .. .. 35 1·10
52 50 c. blue-black .. .. 70 2·00
49/52 .. .. *Set of* 4 1·40 3·50

1950 (1 June)–**56**. *Wmk Mult Script CA. Chalk-surfaced paper. P* $17\frac{1}{2}\times18$.
53 **16** 1 c. black 10 10
54 2 c. orange 10 10
55 3 c. green 20 25
56 4 c. brown 15 10
a. Chocolate (24.3.54) 70 40
57 5 c. bright purple (1.9.52) 25 20
a. Bright mauve (10.9.53) 25 15
58 6 c. grey 15 10
59 8 c. scarlet .. .. 20 1·00
60 8 c. green (1.9.52) 85 75
61 10 c. magenta 15 10
62 12 c. scarlet (1.9.52) .. .. 85 1·25
63 15 c. ultramarine 30 10
64 20 c. black and green .. .. 25 1·75
65 20 c. bright blue (1.9.52) 75 10
a. Ultramarine (8.3.56) .. .. .. 1·25 90
66 25 c. purple and orange 20 10
67 30 c. scarlet and brown-purple (5.9.55) .. 1·25 35
a. Scarlet and purple (8.3.56) .. .. 3·25 95
68 35 c. scarlet and purple (1.9.52) 60 25
69 40 c. red and purple .. .. 90 5·50
70 50 c. black and blue 40 10
71 $1 blue and purple .. .. 2·00 80
72 $2 green and scarlet .. .. 9·50 15·00
73 $5 green and brown .. .. 25·00 32·00
a. Green and sepia (24.3.54) .. .. 30·00 45·00
53/73 .. .. *Set of* 21 40·00 55·00

1953 (2 June). *Coronation. As No. 47 of Aden.*
74 10 c. black and reddish purple 20 10

1957 (26 June)–**62**. *As Nos. 92/102 of Kedah but with inset portrait of Sultan Sir Abu Bakar.*
75 **9** 1 c. black (21.8.57) 10 10
76 **10** 2 c. orange-red (25.7.57) 10 10
77 **11** 4 c. sepia (21.8.57) 10 10
78 **12** 5 c. carmine-lake (21.8.57) 10 10
79 **13** 8 c. myrtle-green (21.8.57) 80 80
80 **14** 10 c. deep brown (4.8.57) 15 10
81 10 c. deep maroon (21.2.61) 35 10
82 **15** 20 c. blue 20 10
83 **16** 50 c. black and blue (*p* $12\frac{1}{2}$) (25.7.57) .. 20 10
a. Perf $12\frac{1}{2}\times13$ (17.5.60) 20 10
84 **17** $1 ultramarine & reddish pur (25.7.57) 1·25 85
85 **18** $2 bronze-grn & scar (*p* $12\frac{1}{2}$) (21.8.57) 3·00 5·50
a. Perf $13\times12\frac{1}{2}$ (13.11.62) .. .. 3·75 7·00
86 **19** $5 brown and bronze-green (*p* $12\frac{1}{2}$) .. 6·00 8·50
a. Perf $13\times12\frac{1}{2}$ (17.5.60) .. .. 8·00 8·50
b. Perf $13\times12\frac{1}{2}$. *Brown and yellow-olive* (23.10.62) .. .. .. 15·00 20·00
75/86 .. .. *Set of* 12 11·00 14·00

The 6, 12, 25 and 30 c. values used with this issue were Nos. 1/4 of Malayan Federation.

17 *Vanda hookeriana*

18 Blue Pansy Butterfly

1965 (15 Nov). *As Nos. 166/72 of Johore but with inset portrait of Sultan Sir Abu Bakar as in T* **17**. *W w* **13** *(upright).*
87 1 c. multicoloured 10 20
c. Grey (flower name, etc) omitted .. 18·00
88 2 c. multicoloured 10 15
89 5 c. multicoloured 10 10
c. Red (leaves, etc) omitted .. .. 22·00
90 6 c. multicoloured 15 10
91 10 c. multicoloured 15 10
a. Red omitted .. .. 22·00
92 15 c. multicoloured 55 10
93 20 c. multicoloured 80 25
87/93 .. .. *Set of* 7 1·75 80

The 2 c., 5 c. and 6 c. exist with PVA gum as well as gum arabic.

The higher values used with this issue were Nos. 20/27 of Malaysia (National Issues).

1970 (27 May). *As Nos.* 87 *and* 91 *but W w* **13** *(sideways).*
94 **17** 1 c. multicoloured .. .. .. 15 1·25
95 – 10 c. multicoloured .. .. .. 55 1·75

(Litho B.W.)

1971 (1 Feb). *As Nos. 175/81 of Johore but with portrait of Sultan Sir Abu Bakar and arms, as in T* **18**.
96 1 c. multicoloured 10 15
97 2 c. multicoloured 20 15
98 5 c. multicoloured 35 10
99 6 c. multicoloured 35 10
100 10 c. multicoloured 35 10
101 15 c. multicoloured 50 10
102 20 c. multicoloured 60 10
96/102 .. .. *Set of* 7 2·25 60

The higher values used with this issue were Nos. 64/71 of Malaysia (National Issues).

19 Sultan Haji Ahmad Shah

20 *Rhododendron scortechinii*

(Des Union Advertising. Litho Harrison)

1975 (8 May). *Installation of the Sultan. P* 14 × 14½.

103 **19** 10 c. slate-green, light lilac and gold .. 35 15
104 15 c. greenish black, yellow & dp green .. 40 10
105 50 c. black, light violet-bl & greenish blk 1·40 1·75
103/5 .. .. *Set of* 3 1·90 1·75

(Photo Harrison)

1977 (5 Sept)–**78**. *As Nos.* 97/8, 100/2 *but with portraits of Sultan Haji Ahmad Shah.*

106 2 c. multicoloured (1978) .. .. .. 25·00 25·00
107 5 c. multicoloured 35 10
108 10 c. multicoloured (10.2.78) 50 10
109 15 c. multicoloured (13.1.78) 50 20
a. Black (face value, etc.)* omitted .. .. 60·00
110 20 c. multicoloured (1978) 90 80
106/10 .. .. *Set of* 5 25·00 25·00

*There were two black cylinders used for No. 109, one to apply the portrait and state details, the other the face value and parts of the main design.

The higher values used with this issue were Nos. 64/71 of Malaysia (National Issues).

1979 (30 Apr). *As Nos.* 188/94 *of Johore but with portrait of Sultan Haji Ahmad Shah as in T* **20**.

111 1 c. *Rafflesia hasseltii* 10 10
112 2 c. *Pterocarpus indicus* 10 10
113 5 c. *Lagerstroemia speciosa* 10 10
114 10 c. *Durio zibethinus* 10 10
115 15 c. *Hibiscus rosa-sinensis* 15 10
116 20 c. Type **20** 15 10
117 25 c. *Phaeomeria speciosa* 15 10
111/17 .. .. *Set of* 7 65 40

For higher values used in conjunction with this series see Nos. 190/7 of Malaysia (National Issues).

1983 (5 Oct)–**85**.* *As Nos.* 113/16 *but without wmk.*

120 5 c. *Lagerstroemia speciosa* (17.11.83) .. 30 15
121 10 c. *Durio zibethinus* (8.1.85) .. .. 1·75 80
123 20 c. Type **20** (blackish brown background) ..
123*a* 20 c. Type **20** (bronze-green background) (20.8.84) 25 15

*There was no official release date for these stamps. Dates shown are the earliest recorded from postmarks and may be revised if earlier examples are reported.

For details of the shade differences between watermarked and unwatermarked printings see after Johore No. 200*a*.

On Nos. 120/1 and 123*a* "pahang" is one millimetre nearer "malaysia" than on Nos. 113/16 and 123.

21 Rice

1986 (25 Oct). *As Nos.* 202/8 *of Johore but with portrait of Sultan Ahmad Shah as in T* **21**.

125 1 c. Coffee 10 10
126 2 c. Coconuts 10 10
127 5 c. Cocoa 10 10
128 10 c. Black pepper 10 10
129 15 c. Rubber 10 10
130 20 c. Oil Palm 10 10
131 30 c. Type **21** 10 15
125/31 .. .. *Set of* 7 40 45

PENANG

One of the Straits Settlements.
Issues from 1965 are inscribed "PULAU PINANG".

1948 (1 Dec). *Royal Silver Wedding. As Nos.* 30/1 *of Aden.*

1 10 c. violet 25 10
2 $5 brown .. .. 24·00 24·00

1949 (21 Feb)–**52**. *As T* **58** *of Straits Settlements, but inscr* "PENANG" *at foot. Wmk Mult Script CA. Chalk-surfaced paper. P* 17½ × 18.

3 1 c. black 10 10
4 2 c. orange 10 10
5 3 c. green 10 15
6 4 c. brown 10 10
7 5 c. bright purple (1.9.52) 40 60
8 6 c. grey 15 10
9 8 c. scarlet .. .. 25 1·60
10 8 c. green (1.9.52) .. .. 55 1·00
11 10 c. purple 15 10
12 12 c. scarlet (1.9.52) .. .. 55 2·00
13 15 c. ultramarine 20 30
14 20 c. black and green .. .. 20 1·00
15 20 c. bright blue (1.9.52) 45 15
16 25 c. purple and orange 25 10
17 35 c. scarlet and purple (1.9.52) 60 70
18 40 c. red and purple .. .. 55 4·75
19 50 c. black and blue 40 15
20 $1 blue and purple .. .. 3·00 25
21 $2 green and scarlet .. .. 5·00 60
22 $5 green and brown .. .. 18·00 80
3/22 .. .. *Set of* 20 28·00 13·00

1949 (10 Oct). *75th Anniv of U.P.U. As Nos.* 114/17 *of Antigua.*

23 10 c. purple 15 10
24 15 c. deep blue 35 40
25 25 c. orange 35 50
26 50 c. blue-black .. .. 1·00 1·40
23/6 .. .. *Set of* 4 1·75 2·10

1953 (2 June). *Coronation. As No.* 47 *of Aden.*

27 10 c. black and reddish purple 25 10

1954 (9 June)–**57**. *As T* **1** *of Malacca (Queen Elizabeth II) but inscr* "PENANG" *at foot. Chalk-surfaced paper. Wmk Mult Script CA. P* 17½×18.

28 1 c. black (5.1.55) 10 20
29 2 c. yellow-orange (8.9.54) 20 15
30 4 c. brown (1.9.54) 15 10
a. *Yellow-brown* (17.7.57) 60 60
31 5 c. bright purple (1.10.54) 60 30
a. *Bright mauve* (17.7.57) 50 70
32 6 c. grey 15 10
33 8 c. green (5.1.55) 20 90
34 10 c. brown-purple (1.9.54) 15 10
35 12 c. rose-red (5.1.55) .. .. 20 1·25
36 20 c. bright blue (1.9.54) 20 10
37 25 c. brown-purple & yellow-orange (1.12.54) 20 10
38 30 c. rose-red and brown-purple (5.9.55) .. 20 10
39 35 c. rose-red and brown-purple (8.9.54) .. 25 15
40 50 c. black and bright blue (1.12.54) 25 10
41 $1 bright blue and brown-purple (1.10.54) 2·00 10
42 $2 emerald and scarlet (1.10.54) .. .. 4·00 2·50
43 $5 emerald and brown (5.1.55) .. .. 14·00 3·00
28/43 .. .. *Set of* 16 21·00 8·00

1957. *As Nos.* 92/102 *of Kedah, but with inset portrait of Queen Elizabeth II.*

44 **9** 1 c. black (21.8) 10 20
45 **10** 2 c. orange-red (25.7) 10 25
46 **11** 4 c. sepia (21.8) 10 10
47 **12** 5 c. carmine-lake (21.8) 10 10
48 **13** 8 c. myrtle-green (21.8) 80 40
49 **14** 10 c. deep brown (4.8) 15 10
50 **15** 20 c. blue (26.6) 20 20
51 **16** 50 c. black and blue (25.7) 25 10
52 **17** $1 ultramarine and reddish purple (25.7) .. .. 1·75 25
53 **18** $2 bronze-green and scarlet (21.8) .. 3·00 4·00
54 **19** $5 brown and bronze-green (26.6) .. 6·00 2·75
44/54 .. .. *Set of* 11 11·00 7·50

The note after No. 86 of Pahang also applies here.

1 Copra

2 *Vanda hookeriana*

(Recess D.L.R.)

1960 (15 Mar). *As Nos.* 44/54, *but with inset Arms of Penang as in T* **1**. *W w* **12**. *P* 13 × 12½ (1 *c. to* 8 *c.*, $2, $5), 12½ × 13 (10 *c. to* 50 *c.*) *or* 13½ ($1).

55 1 c. black 10 10
56 2 c. orange-red 10 10
57 4 c. sepia 10 10
58 5 c. carmine-lake 10 10
59 8 c. myrtle-green 80 80
60 10 c. deep maroon 15 10
61 20 c. blue 20 10
62 50 c. black and blue 20 10
a. Imperf (pair) £250
63 $1 ultramarine and reddish purple .. .. 1·00 10
64 $2 bronze-green and scarlet .. .. .. 2·25 1·25
65 $5 brown and bronze-green .. .. .. 6·50 2·25
55/65 .. .. *Set of* 11 10·00 4·25

No. 62*a* comes from a sheet purchased at the Penang Post Office which had the upper five horizontal rows imperforate.

1965 (15 Nov)–**68**. *As Nos.* 166/72 *of Johore but with Arms of Penang inset and inscr* "PULAU PINANG" *as in T* **2**. *W w* **13** *(upright).*

66 1 c. multicoloured 10 10
67 2 c. multicoloured 10 10
68 5 c. multicoloured 10 10
b. Yellow (flower) omitted .. .. .. 15·00
c. Red omitted .. .. 20·00
d. Blue (background and inscr) omitted .. 22·00
da. Blue and yellow omitted .. .. .. 35·00
69 6 c. multicoloured 10 10
b. Yellow omitted .. .. 15·00
70 10 c. grey and multicoloured 15 10
a. *Jet-black and multicoloured* (12.11.68) 15 10
71 15 c. multicoloured 55 10
b. Green (value and leaves) omitted .. 65·00
72 20 c. multicoloured 80 10
a. Bright purple (blooms) omitted £100
b. Yellow (leaves) omitted £100
66/72 .. .. *Set of* 7 1·75 35

The 2 c., 5 c., 6 c., 10 c. and 20 c. exist with PVA gum as well as gum arabic.

The higher values used with this issue were Nos. 20/27 of Malaysia (National Issues).

1970. *As Nos.* 66 *and* 70 *but W w* **13** *(sideways).*

73 **2** 1 c. multicoloured (27.5.70) .. .. 15 1·25
74 – 10 c. multicoloured (20.11.70) .. .. 1·75 1·75

3 Wanderer

4 *Phaeomeria speciosa*

1971 (1 Feb)–**78**. *As Nos.* 175/87 *of Johore, but with Arms of Penang and inscr* "pulau pinang", *as in T* **3**.

(*a*) *Litho by Bradbury Wilkinson*

75 1 c. multicoloured 10 15
76 2 c. multicoloured 20 15
77 5 c. multicoloured 35 10
78 6 c. multicoloured 35 10
79 10 c. multicoloured 35 10
80 15 c. multicoloured 50 10
81 20 c. multicoloured 60 15
75/81 .. .. *Set of* 7 2·25 60

(*b*) *Photo by Harrison* (1977–78)

81*a* 1 c. multicoloured .. .. 2·75 90
82 5 c. multicoloured 80 20
83 10 c. multicoloured .. .. 1·50 20
84 15 c. multicoloured .. .. 1·75 30
85 20 c. multicoloured .. .. 2·00 60
81*a*/5 .. .. *Set of* 5 8·00 2·00

The higher values used with this issue were Nos. 64/71 of Malaysia (National Issues).

For differences between litho and photo printings, see after Johore No. 187.

1979 (30 Apr). *As Nos.* 188/94 *of Johore but with Arms of Penang and inscr* "pulau pinang" *as in T* **4**.

86 1 c. *Rafflesia hasseltii* 10 10
87 2 c. *Pterocarpus indicus* 10 10
88 5 c. *Lagerstroemia speciosa* 10 10
89 10 c. *Durio zibethinus* 10 10
90 15 c. *Hibiscus rosa-sinensis* 15 10
91 20 c. *Rhododendron scortechinii* 15 10
92 25 c. Type **4** 15 10
86/92 .. .. *Set of* 7 65 20

For higher values used in conjunction with this series see Nos. 190/7 of Malaysia (National Issues).

1983–85.* *As Nos.* 88/91 *but without wmk.*

95 5 c. *Lagerstroemia speciosa* (1.84) 25 15
96 10 c. *Durio zibethinus* (2.7.85) .. .. 4·00 90
97 15 c. *Hibiscus rosa-sinensis* (27.12.83) .. 1·25 60
98 20 c. *Rhododendron scortechinii* (blackish brown background) (21.10.85) .. .. 13·00
98*a* 20 c. *Rhododendron scortechinii* (bronze-green background) (3.84) 25 15

*There was no official release date for these stamps. Dates shown are the earliest recorded from postmarks and may be revised if earlier examples are reported.

For details of the shade differences between watermarked and unwatermarked printings see after Johore No. 200*a*.

On Nos. 95/7 and 98*a* the state arms are larger than on the watermarked printing and No. 98.

5 Cocoa

1986 (25 Oct). *As Nos.* 202/8 *of Johore but with Arms of Penang and inscr* "PULAU PINANG" *as in T* **5**.

100 1 c. Coffee 10 10
101 2 c. Coconuts 10 10
102 5 c. Type **5** 10 10
103 10 c. Black pepper 10 10
104 15 c. Rubber 10 10
105 20 c. Oil palm 10 10
106 30 c. Rice 10 15
100/6 .. .. *Set of* 7 40 45

PERAK

Perak accepted a British Resident in 1874, although he was later murdered.

The state joined the Federated Malay States in 1896.

> The stamps of the STRAITS SETTLEMENTS were used in Perak during 1877/8.
>
> Until 1 January 1899, when the Federated Malay States joined the U.P.U., mail for addresses outside Malaya was franked with stamps of the STRAITS SETTLEMENTS.

PRICES FOR STAMPS ON COVER TO 1945

No. 1	—
Nos. 2/9	*from* × 50
Nos. 10/13	*from* × 20
Nos. 14/16	*from* × 5
Nos. 17/22	*from* × 15
No. 23	—
Nos. 24/5	—
Nos. 26/8	*from* × 10
No. 29	*from* × 50
No. 30	*from* × 15
Nos. 31/2	—
Nos. 33/40	*from* × 12
Nos. 43/60	*from* × 6
Nos. 61/5	*from* × 12
Nos. 66/79	*from* × 10
No. 80	—
Nos. 81/7	*from* × 5
Nos. 88/102	*from* × 4
Nos. 103/21	*from* × 3

The Official stamps of Perak are rare used on cover.

(1)

1878. *No. 11 of Straits Settlements handstamped with T* **1**.

1 2 c. brown £950 £850

PERAK (2) (14½ mm long) — PERAK (3) (11 mm long) — PERAK (4) (10¼ mm long)

PERAK (5) (17 mm long) — PERAK (6) ("RA" narrow) — PERAK (7) ("R" narrow)

PERAK (8) ("P" and "K" wide) — PERAK (9) (12 to 13½ mm long)

1880–81. *No. 11 (wmk Crown CC) of Straits Settlements optd with T* **2/9**.

2 **2** 2 c. brown £300 £180
3 **3** 2 c. brown £275 £150
4 **4** 2 c. brown £150 £120
5 **5** 2 c. brown (1881) .. .. 22·00 27·00
6 **6** 2 c. brown (1881) .. .. 65·00 75·00
7 **7** 2 c. brown (1881) .. .. 60·00 75·00
8 **8** 2 c. brown (1881) £120 £110
9 **9** 2 c. brown (1881) .. .. 60·00 70·00

Of the above No. 2 is from a single unit overprint, No. 5 from a setting of sixty and the remainder from settings applied as horizontal strips of three. Nos. 6/8 come from mixed triplets, either 6 + 7 + 7 or 7 + 7 + 8. No. 4 is believed to come from a single unit overprint in addition to a triplet.

PERAK (10) ("A" wide) — PERAK (11) ("E" wide)

1882–83. *Nos. 50 (wmk Crown CA) and 63 of Straits Settlements optd with T* **9/11**.

10 **9** 2 c. brown .. .. 9·50 15·00
    a. Opt double £400
11 2 c. rose (1883) .. .. 7·50 13·00
12 **10** 2 c. rose (1883) .. .. 8·50 15·00
13 **11** 2 c. rose (1883) .. .. 8·50 15·00
    a. Opt double £450

The above were all overprinted as triplet settings. Those for the 2 c. rose were 11 + 12 + 13, 13 + 11 + 11 and 13 + 11 + 12.

2 CENTS PERAK (12) — 2 CENTS (13)

1883 (July). *No. 51 (wmk Crown CA) of Straits Settlements surch.*

(a) Surch with T **12**

14 2 c. on 4 c. rose £1300
    a. On Straits Settlements No. 12 (wmk Crown CC) .. ..

(b) Optd as T **9** *or* **11** *and surch with T* **13**

15 **11** 2 c. on 4 c. rose £400 £250
16 **9** 2 c. on 4 c. rose £275 £200

It is believed that No. 14 occurred on the top row of the sheet with the remaining nine rows surcharged with a triplet containing 15 + 16 + 16.

PERAK (14) ("E" wide) — PERAK (15) ("E" narrow) — PERAK (16) (12½–13 mm long)

PERAK (17) (12–12½ mm long) — PERAK (18) (10½ mm long) — PERAK (19) (10 mm long)

PERAK (20) (13 mm long)

1884–91. *No. 63 of Straits Settlements optd with T* **14/20**.

17 **14** 2 c. rose 70 70
    a. Opt double .. .. — £500
    b. Opt inverted £275 £400
18 **15** 2 c. rose .. .. 18·00 20·00
    b. Opt inverted £475 £600
19 **16** 2 c. rose (1886) .. .. 85 3·50
    a. Optd "FERAK" £150 £170
20 **17** 2 c. rose (1886) .. .. 1·75 6·50
    a. Opt double £1000
21 **18** 2 c. rose (1886) .. .. 35·00 50·00
22 **19** 2 c. rose (1890) .. .. 6·50 16·00
23 **20** 2 c. rose (1891) £1250

Settings:
Nos. 17/18 – triplets (either 17 + 17 + 17 or 18 + 17 + 17)
– 30 (3 × 10) (containing twenty-eight as No. 17 and two as No. 18)
– 60 (6 × 10) (containing either fifty-seven as No. 17 and three as No. 18 or all as No. 17)
No. 19 – 60 (6 × 10) (No. 19a occurs on one position of the setting, it is often found amended in manuscript)
No. 20 – triplet
No. 21 – triplet
No. 22 – 60 (6 × 10)
No. 23 – not known

1 CENT (21)

1886. *No. 17 surch with T* **21**.

24 **14** 1 c. on 2 c. rose £1200

ONE CENT PERAK (22) — ONE CENT PERAK. (23) — ONE CENT PERAK. (24) ("N" wide in "ONE" and "CENT")

1886. *No. 63 of Straits Settlements surch with T* **22/4**.

25 **22** 1 c. on 2 c. rose £250
26 **23** 1 c. on 2 c. rose .. .. 23·00 32·00
    a. Surch double £450
27 **24** 1 c. on 2 c. rose .. .. 30·00 38·00

Nos. 26/7 are from a triplet setting, 26 + 27 + 26, used on the top nine rows of the sheet. No. 25 may have been used on the bottom row.

1 CENT PERAK (25) — One CENT PERAK (26) — ONE CENT PERAK (27)

1886. *No. 63 of Straits Settlements surch with T* **25**.

28 1 c. on 2 c. rose .. .. 38·00 45·00
    a. Surch double £1500

No. 28 comes from a triplet setting.

1886. *No. 63 of Straits Settlements surch with T* **26**.

29 1 c. on 2 c. rose .. .. 85 3·50
    a. "One" inverted £1200
    b. Surch double £750

No. 29 comes from a triplet setting. It is believed that No. 29a occurred when the type was dropped and "One" replaced upside down.

1887. *No. 63 of Straits Settlements surch with T* **27** *in blue.*

30 1 c. on 2 c. rose .. .. 11·00 17·00
    a. Optd in black £1000 £750

No. 30 was printed from a setting of 60.

1 CENT PERAK (28) — 1 CENT PERAK (29)

1887. *No. 63 of Straits Settlements surch with T* **28**.

31 1 c. on 2 c. rose £150 £175

No. 31 comes from a triplet setting.

1887. *No. 63 of Straits Settlements surch with T* **29**.

32 1 c. on 2 c. rose £600 £900

The size of setting used for No. 32 is not known.

One CENT PERAK (30) — One CENT PERAK (31) — One CENT PERAK (32) — One CENT PERAK (33)

One CENT PERAK (34) — One CENT PERAK (35) — One CENT PERAK (36) — One CENT PERAK (37)

1887–89. *No. 63 of Straits Settlements surch with T* **30/7**.

33 **30** 1 c. on 2 c. rose .. .. 45 1·00
    a. Surch double .. ..
34 **31** 1 c. on 2 c. rose (1889) .. .. .. 55·00 65·00
35 **32** 1 c. on 2 c. rose (1889) .. .. .. 5·50 9·00
    a. "PREAK" (R. 6/1) £200 £200
36 **33** 1 c. on 2 c. rose (1889) .. .. .. 3·50 4·25
37 **34** 1 c. on 2 c. rose (1889) .. .. .. 3·50 4·50
38 **35** 1 c. on 2 c. rose (1889) £250 £250
39 **36** 1 c. on 2 c. rose (1889) .. .. .. 65·00 80·00
40 **37** 1 c. on 2 c. rose (1889) .. .. .. 8·50 10·00

Settings. No. 33 originally appeared as a triplet, then as a block of 30 (3 × 10) and, finally, as part of a series of composite settings of 60. Specialists recognise four such composite settings:

Setting I contained No. 33 in Rows 1 to 4, R. 5/1 to 5/5 and Row 7; No. 34 on R. 5/6, 6/1 and 6/2; No. 35 on R. 6/3–6; No. 36 on Row 8; No. 37 on Rows 9 and 10.

Setting II was similar, but had the example of No. 33 on R. 3/5 replaced by No. 38 and those on R. 7/4 and R. 7/6 by No. 39.

Setting III contained No. 33 in Rows 1 to 5; No. 35 in Row 6; No. 36 in Row 7; No. 37 in Rows 8 and 9; No. 40 in Row 10.

Setting IV was similar, but showed the "PREAK" error on R. 6/1 corrected.

ONE CENT. (38) — ONE CENT (39)

1889–90. *No. 17 surch with T* **38/9**.

41 **38** 1 c. on 2 c. rose .. .. 80·00 80·00
42 **39** 1 c. on 2 c. rose (1890) .. .. .. — £120

PERAK Two CENTS (40) — PERAK One CENT (41)

1891. *Nos. 63, 66 and 68 of Straits Settlements surch.*

(a) As T **30**, **32/4** *and* **37**, *but with* "PERAK" *at top and a bar through the original value*

43 **30** 1 c. on 6 c. lilac .. .. 27·00 24·00
44 **32** 1 c. on 6 c. lilac .. .. 45·00 50·00
45 **33** 1 c. on 6 c. lilac .. .. 65·00 70·00
46 **34** 1 c. on 6 c. lilac .. .. 45·00 50·00
47 **37** 1 c. on 6 c. lilac .. .. 45·00 50·00

(b) With T **40** *and as T* **32/4** *and* **37** *but with* "PERAK" *at top, all with a bar through the original value*

48 **40** 2 c. on 24 c. green .. .. 8·00 8·00
49 **32** 2 c. on 24 c. green .. .. 50·00 50·00
50 **33** 2 c. on 24 c. green .. .. 48·00 48·00
51 **34** 2 c. on 24 c. green .. .. 23·00 20·00
52 **37** 2 c. on 24 c. green .. .. 42·00 42·00

(c) With T **41** *and as T* **30**, **34** *and* **37**, *but with* "PERAK" *at top.*

(i) *Without bar over original value*

53 **30** 1 c. on 2 c. rose £130
    a. Narrow "O" in "One" (R. 3/3) £1200
54 **41** 1 c. on 2 c. rose £550
55 **34** 1 c. on 2 c. rose £200
56 **37** 1 c. on 2 c. rose £450

(ii) *With bar through original value*

57 **30** 1 c. on 2 c. rose .. .. 55 1·00
    a. Narrow "O" in "One" (R. 3/3) .. .. 13·00 22·00
58 **41** 1 c. on 2 c. rose .. .. 2·50 5·00
59 **34** 1 c. on 2 c. rose .. .. 55 1·00
60 **37** 1 c. on 2 c. rose .. .. 4·25 6·00

Settings. Nos. 43/7 were arranged as Setting IV described under Nos. 33/40.

Nos. 48/52 were similar except that Type **40** replaced Type **30** on the first five rows.

The first printing of the 1 c. on 2 c. was without a bar through the original face value. Both printings, Nos. 53/60, were from the same setting with Type **30** on Rows 1 to 5, **41** on Row 6, **34** on Rows 7 to 9 and **37** on Row 10.

42

3 CENTS

(43)

92 (1 Jan)–**95.** *Wmk Crown CA. P* 14.

1	**42**	1 c. green	2·00	15
2		2 c. rose	1·00	30
3		2 c. orange (9.9.95)	35	3·25
4		5 c. blue	2·75	4·50
1/4		*Set of* 4	5·50	7·50
1/4 Optd "Specimen"		*Set of* 4	75·00	

95 (18 Apr). *Surch with T* **43**.

	42	3 c. on 5 c. rose (Optd S. £25)	45	1·00

44

45

895 (2 Sept)–**99.** *P* 14. (*a*) *Wmk Crown CA.*

6	**44**	1 c. dull purple and green	70	40
7		2 c. dull purple and brown	75	40
3		3 c. dull purple and carmine	1·50	20
9		4 c. dull purple and carmine (1899)	4·00	3·75
0		5 c. dull purple and olive-yellow	2·25	55
1		8 c. dull purple and ultramarine	20·00	65
2		10 c. dull purple and orange	5·50	45
3		25 c. green and carmine (1897)	70·00	11·00
4		50 c. dull purple and greenish black	24·00	24·00
5		50 c. green and black (2.99)	80·00	80·00
		(*b*) *Wmk Crown CC*		
6	**45**	$1 green and pale green (1896)	55·00	60·00
7		$2 green and carmine (1896)	£100	£100
8		$3 green and ochre (1898)	80·00	£100
9		$5 green and ultramarine (1896)	£250	£225
0		$25 green and orange (1899?) (S. £120)	£2750	£750
6/76		*Set of* 11	£225	£160
6/79 Optd "Specimen"		*Set of* 14	£225	

Pending the arrival of the permanent Federated Malay States issue the stamps of FEDERATED MALAY STATES provisional overprints, SELANGOR and STRAITS SETTLEMENTS were used at various times between June 1900 and February 1901.

The general issues for the FEDERATED MALAY STATES were used in Perak from 1901 until 1935.

One Cent.

(46)

ONE CENT.

(47)

Three Cent.

(48)

Three Cent.

(49)

900. *Stamps of* 1895–99 *surch.*

1	**46**	1 c. on 2 c. dull purple and brown (13 July*)	40	1·00
		a. Antique "e" in "One" (R. 5/2)	35·00	45·00
		b. Antique "e" in "Cent" (R. 9/4)	32·00	42·00
2	**47**	1 c. on 4 c. dull purple and carmine	45	2·75
		a. Surch double	£600	
3	**46**	1 c. on 5 c. dull purple & ol-yell (30 June*)	50	4·25
		a. Antique "e" in "One" (R. 5/2)	35·00	50·00
		b. Antique "e" in "Cent" (R. 9/4)	32·00	48·00
4	**48**	3 c. on 8 c. dull purple & ultram (26 Sept*)	2·50	2·75
		a. Antique "e" in "Cent" (R. 9/4)	55·00	60·00
		b. No stop after "Cent" (R. 9/5)	60·00	65·00
		c. Surch double	£150	£150
5		3 c. on 50 c. green and black (7 Sept*)	80	3·25
		a. Antique "e" in "Cent" (R. 9/4)	55·00	65·00
		b. No stop after "Cent" (R. 9/5)	55·00	65·00
6	**49**	3 c. on $1 green and pale green (21 Oct*)	45·00	75·00
		a. Small "t" in "Cent"	£160	£200
		b. Surch double		
7		3 c. on $2 green and carmine (24 Oct*)	26·00	55·00
1/7		*Set of* 7	65·00	£130

*Earliest known postmark date.

With the exception of No. 86a, whose sheet position is not known, the remaining surcharge varieties all occur in the left-hand pane.

50 Sultan Iskandar 51

1935 (2 Dec)–**37.** *Chalk-surfaced paper. Wmk Mult Script CA. P* 14.

88	**50**	1 c. black (1.1.36)	15	10
89		2 c. green (1.1.36)	20	10
90		4 c. orange	30	10
91		5 c. brown (5.12.35)	20	10
92		6 c. scarlet (1.1.37)	3·50	1·75
93		8 c. grey	40	10
94		10 c. dull purple (1.1.36)	20	15
95		12 c. bright ultramarine (1.1.36)	60	90
96		25 c. dull purple and scarlet (1.4.36)	75	85
97		30 c. dull purple and orange (1.1.36)	80	1·50
98		40 c. scarlet and dull purple	2·00	4·25
99		50 c. black/*emerald* (1.2.36)	3·00	80
100		$1 black and red/*blue* (1.4.36)	2·00	80
101		$2 green and scarlet (16.5.36)	8·00	8·50
102		$5 green and red/*emerald* (16.5.36)	28·00	22·00
88/102		*Set of* 15	45·00	38·00
88/102 Perf "Specimen"		*Set of* 15	£150	

1938 (2 May)–**41.** *Chalk-surfaced or ordinary paper* (**O**). *Wmk Mult Script CA. P* 14.

103	**51**	1 c. black (4.39)	2·00	10
104		2 c. green (13.1.39)	1·75	10
105		2 c. orange, **OC** (30.10.41)	35	4·75
106		3 c. green, **OC** (21.8.41)	60	35
107		4 c. orange (5.39)	13·00	10
108		5 c. brown (1.2.39)	1·50	10
109		6 c. scarlet (12.39)	15·00	10
110		8 c. grey (1.12.38)	12·00	10
111		8 c. scarlet (12.41)	1·00	17·00
112		10 c. dull purple (17.10.38)	9·00	10
113		12 c. bright ultramarine (17.10.38)	8·00	2·00
114		15 c. bright ultramarine, **O** (10.41)	1·75	12·00
115		25 c. dull purple and scarlet (12.39)	48·00	4·25
116		30 c. dull purple and orange (17.10.38)	5·50	3·00
117		40 c. scarlet and dull purple	22·00	2·00
118		50 c. black/*emerald* (17.10.38)	14·00	75
119		$1 black and red/*blue* (7.40)	60·00	14·00
120		$2 green and scarlet (9.40)	75·00	45·00
121		$5 green and red/*emerald* (1.41)	£170	£190
103/21		*Set of* 19	£425	£275
103/21 Perf "Specimen"		*Set of* 19	£250	

During shortages in 1941 stamps of STRAITS SETTLEMENTS (2 c.), SELANGOR (2 c., 3 c.) and PAHANG (8 c.) were issued in Perak.

1948 (1 Dec). *Royal Silver Wedding. As Nos.* 30/1 *of Aden.*

122	10 c. violet	15	10
123	$5 green	20·00	20·00

1949 (10 Oct). *75th Anniv of Universal Postal Union. As Nos.* 114/17 *of Antigua.*

124	10 c. purple	15	10
125	15 c. deep blue	45	35
126	25 c. orange	45	45
127	50 c. blue-black	1·25	1·50
124/7	*Set of* 4	2·10	2·10

52 Sultan Yussuf 'Izzuddin Shah

53 Sultan Idris Shah

1950 (17 Aug)–**56.** *Chalk-surfaced paper. Wmk Mult Script CA. P* 17½×18.

128	**52**	1 c. black	10	10
129		2 c. orange	10	10
130		3 c. green	75	10
		a. Yellowish green (15.11.51)	75	90
131		4 c. brown	10	10
		a. Yellow-brown (20.6.56)	35	10
132		5 c. bright purple (1.9.52)	35	20
		a. Bright mauve (10.11.54)	35	15
133		6 c. grey	10	10
134		8 c. scarlet	25	75
135		8 c. green (1.9.52)	1·00	60
136		10 c. purple	10	10
		a. Brown-purple (20.6.56)	25	10
137		12 c. scarlet (1.9.52)	1·00	80
138		15 c. ultramarine	25	10
139		20 c. black and green	30	20
140		20 c. bright blue (1.9.52)	75	10
141		25 c. purple and orange	30	10
142		30 c. scarlet and purple (5.9.55)	1·25	20
143		35 c. scarlet and purple (1.9.52)	70	25
144		40 c. red and purple	85	3·00
145		50 c. black and blue	40	10
146		$1 blue and purple	3·00	15
147		$2 green and scarlet	5·50	70
148		$5 green and brown	20·00	6·00
128/48		*Set of* 21	35·00	13·00

1953 (2 June). *Coronation. As No.* 47 *of Aden.*

149	10 c. black and reddish purple	20	10

1957 (26 June)–**61.** *As Nos.* 92/102 *of Kedah but with inset portrait of Sultan Yussuf 'Izzuddin Shah.*

150	1 c. black (21.8.57)	10	15
151	2 c. orange-red (25.7.57)	10	10
	a. Red-orange (15.12.59)	10	30
152	4 c. sepia (21.8.57)	10	10
153	5 c. carmine-lake (21.8.57)	10	10
154	8 c. myrtle-green (21.8.57)	1·40	30
155	10 c. deep brown (4.8.57)	15	10
156	10 c. deep maroon (21.2.61)	25	10
157	20 c. blue	20	10
158	50 c. black and blue (*p* 12½) (25.7.57)	25	10
	a. Perf 12½ × 13 (24.5.60)	20	10
159	$1 ultramarine and reddish purple (25.7.57)	1·60	10
160	$2 bronze-green & scar (*p* 12½) (21.8.57)	2·50	1·50
	a. Perf 13 × 12½ (21.2.61)	2·50	1·25
161	$5 brown and bronze-green (*p* 12½)	6·00	4·50
	a. Perf 13 × 12½ (24.5.60)	6·00	2·50
150/61	*Set of* 12	11·00	3·75

The 6, 12, 25 and 30 c. values used with this issue were Nos. 1/4 of Malayan Federation.

(Photo Harrison)

1963 (26 Oct). *Installation of the Sultan of Perak. W w* **13**. *P* 14½.

162	**53**	10 c. red, black, blue and yellow	10	10

54 *Vanda hookeriana*

55 Malayan Jezebel

1965 (15 Nov)–**68.** *As Nos.* 166/72 *of Johore but with inset portrait of Sultan Idris as in T* **54**. *W w* **13** (*upright*).

163	1 c. multicoloured	10	20
164	2 c. multicoloured	10	15
165	5 c. pale black and multicoloured	10	10
	a. Grey-black and multicoloured (2.4.68)	10	10
	b. Yellow (flower) omitted	15·00	
166	6 c. multicoloured	15	10
167	10 c. multicoloured	15	10
168	15 c. multicoloured	55	10
	a. Black (country name and head) omitted	80·00	
	c. Magenta (background) omitted	60·00	
169	20 c. multicoloured	80	10
	a. Bright purple (blooms) omitted	22·00	
163/9	*Set of* 7	1·75	55

No. 168a comes from a horizontal strip of three, the centre stamp having the black completely omitted. The two outer stamps show the colour partly omitted.

The 2 c. to 15 c. exist with PVA gum as well as gum arabic.

The higher values used with this issue were Nos. 20/27 of Malaysia (National Issues).

1970. *As Nos.* 163 *and* 167, *but W w* **13** (*sideways*).

170	**54**	1 c. multicoloured (27.5.70)	50	1·25
171	–	10 c. multicoloured (20.11.70)	2·25	1·75

1971 (1 Feb)–**78.** *As Nos.* 175/87 *of Johore, but with portrait of Sultan Idris and arms, as in T* **55**.

	(*a*) *Litho by Bradbury, Wilkinson*		
172	1 c. multicoloured	10	15
173	2 c. multicoloured	20	20
174	5 c. multicoloured	35	10
175	6 c. multicoloured	35	10
176	10 c. multicoloured	35	10
177	15 c. multicoloured	50	10
178	20 c. multicoloured	60	10
172/8	*Set of* 7	2·25	60
	(*b*) *Photo by Harrison* (1977–78)		
179	1 c. multicoloured	30	50
180	5 c. multicoloured	1·50	15
181	10 c. multicoloured	1·25	15
182	15 c. multicoloured	2·50	25
183	20 c. multicoloured	1·50	45
179/83	*Set of* 5	6·50	1·40

The higher values used with this issue were Nos. 64/71 of Malaysia (National Issues).

For differences between litho and photo printings, see after Johore, No. 187.

56 *Rafflesia hasseltii*

57 Coffee

1979 (30 Apr). *As Nos.* 188/94 *of Johore but with portrait of Sultan Idris as in T* **56**.

184	1 c. Type **56**	10	10
185	2 c. *Pterocarpus indicus*	10	10
186	5 c. *Lagerstroemia speciosa*	10	10
187	10 c. *Durio zibethinus*	10	10
188	15 c. *Hibiscus rosa-sinensis*	15	10
189	20 c. *Rhododendron scortechinii*	15	10
190	25 c. *Phaeomeria speciosa*	15	10
184/90	*Set of* 7	65	20

For higher values used in conjunction with this series see Nos. 190/7 of Malaysia (National Issues).

1983 (15 Oct)–**84.*** *As Nos.* 186/9 *but without wmk.*

193	5 c. *Lagerstroemia speciosa* (9.9.83)	25	15
194	10 c. *Durio zibenthinus* (1984)	25	15
195	15 c. *Hibiscus rosa-sinensis* (9.9.83)	1·50	65
196	20 c. *Rhododendron scortechinii* (blackish brown background)		
196*a*	20 c. *Rhododendron scortechinii* (bronze-green background) (20.3.84)	20	10

*There was no official release date for these stamps. Dates shown are the earliest recorded from postmarks and may be revised if earlier examples are reported.

For details of the shade differences between watermarked and unwatermarked printings see after Johore No. 200*a*.

On Nos. 193/5 and 196*a* the portrait and arms are redrawn smaller.

1986 (25 Oct). *As Nos. 202/8 of Johore but with portrait of Sultan Azlan Shah as in T* **57**.

198 1 c. Type **57** 10 10
199 2 c. Coconuts 10 10
200 5 c. Cocoa 10 10
201 10 c. Black pepper 10 10
202 15 c. Rubber 10 10
203 20 c. Oil palm 10 10
204 30 c. Rice 10 15
198/204 *Set of* 7 40 45

OFFICIAL STAMPS

P.G.S. (O 1) **Service.** (O 2)

1889 (1 Nov). *Stamps of Straits Settlements optd with Type* O **1**. *Wmk Crown CC (Nos. O6 and O8) or Crown CA (others).*

O1 2 c. rose 2·00 2·50
a. Overprint double £850 £850
b. Wide space between "G" and "S" 35·00 45·00
c. No stop after "S" 35·00 45·00
O2 4 c. brown 6·50 10·00
a. Wide space between "G" and "S" 55·00 70·00
b. No stop after "S" 70·00 90·00
O3 6 c. lilac 18·00 27·00
a. Wide space between "G" and "S" 75·00 95·00
O4 8 c. orange 22·00 45·00
a. Wide space between "G" and "S" 85·00 £110
O5 10 c. slate 65·00 65·00
a. Wide space between "G" and "S" £150 £160
O6 12 c. blue (CC) 90·00 £100
a. Wide space between "G" and "S" £350
O7 12 c. brown-purple (CA) £140 £160
a. Wide space between "G" and "S" £400
O8 24 c. green (CC) £375 £400
a. Wide space between "G" and "S" £1200
O9 24 c. green (CA) 90·00 £100
a. Wide space between "G" and "S" £350

Nos. O1/9 were overprinted from a setting of 30 (3 × 10). The variety "wide space between G and S" occurs on R. 10/3 and R. 10/6 of the original printing. A later printing of the 2 c. and 4 c. values had this variety corrected, but was without a stop after "S" on R. 10/1 and R. 10/4.

1894 (1 June). *No. 64 optd with Type* O **2**.

O10 5 c. blue 17·00 80
a. Overprint inverted £225 £180

1897. *No. 70 optd with Type* O **2**.

O11 5 c. dull purple and olive-yellow 1·40 35
a. Overprint double £160 £180

PERLIS

Suzerainty over Perlis was transferred by Thailand to Great Britain in 1909. A British adviser was appointed in 1930.

The State joined the Federation of Malaya on 1 February 1948.

The stamps of THAILAND were used in Perlis at Kangar (Muang Perlis) until 1909. Issues of the FEDERATED MALAY STATES were in use from 10 July 1909 until 1912 and these were replaced by the stamps of KEDAH between 1912 and 1951.

1948 (1 Dec). *Royal Silver Wedding. As Nos. 30/1 of Aden.*

1 10 c. violet 25 80
2 $5 brown 25·00 42·00

1949 (10 Oct). *75th Anniv of U.P.U. As Nos. 114/17 of Antigua.*

3 10 c. purple 25 60
4 15 c. deep blue 50 1·75
5 25 c. orange 55 1·75
6 50 c. blue-black 90 3·50
3/6 *Set of* 4 2·00 7·00

1 Raja Syed Putra

2 *Vanda hookeriana*

1951 (26 Mar)–**55**. *Chalk-surfaced paper. Wmk Mult Script CA. P* 17½ × 18.

7 **1** 1 c. black 10 40
8 2 c. orange 10 40
9 3 c. green 40 1·25
10 4 c. brown 15 20
11 5 c. bright purple (1.9.52) 30 65
12 6 c. grey 15 25
13 8 c. scarlet 30 1·50
14 8 c. green (1.9.52) 75 1·50
15 10 c. purple 15 20
16 12 c. scarlet (1.9.52) 75 1·75
17 15 c. ultramarine 70 1·50
18 20 c. black and green 70 2·25
19 20 c. bright blue (1.9.52) 85 65
20 25 c. purple and orange 50 90
21 30 c. scarlet and purple (5.9.55) 1·75 4·00
22 35 c. scarlet and purple (1.9.52) 75 2·50
23 40 c. red and purple 1·25 7·00
24 50 c. black and blue 70 90
25 $1 blue and purple 3·00 6·50
26 $2 green and scarlet 7·00 17·00
27 $5 green and brown 30·00 40·00
7/27 *Set of* 21 45·00 80·00

1953 (2 June). *Coronation. As No. 47 of Aden.*

28 10 c. black and reddish purple 25 1·00

1957 (26 June)–**62**. *As Nos. 92/102 of Kedah but with inset portrait of Raja Syed Putra.*

29 **9** 1 c. black (21.8.57) 10 10
30 **10** 2 c. orange-red (25.7.57) 10 15
31 **11** 4 c. sepia (21.8.57) 10 10
32 **12** 5 c. carmine-lake (21.8.57) 10 10
33 **13** 8 c. myrtle-green (21.8.57) 1·10 80
34 **14** 10 c. deep brown (4.8.57) 15 15
35 10 c. deep maroon (14.3.61) 30 15
36 **15** 20 c. blue 20 35
37 **16** 50 c. black and blue (*p* 12½) (25.7.57) 20 60
a. Perf 12½ × 13 (8.5.62) 40 60
38 **17** $1 ultram & reddish purple (25.7.57) 2·00 3·50
39 **18** $2 bronze-green and scarlet (25.7.57) 3·50 5·00
40 **19** $5 brown and bronze-green (21.8.57) 6·00 7·50
29/40 *Set of* 12 12·50 16·00

The 6, 12, 25 and 30 c. values used with this issue were Nos. 1/4 of Malayan Federation.

1965 (15 Nov). *As Nos. 166/72 of Johore but with inset portrait of Tunku Bendahara Abu Bakar as in T* **2**.

41 1 c. multicoloured 10 40
42 2 c. multicoloured 10 50
43 5 c. multicoloured 15 10
44 6 c. multicoloured 20 10
45 10 c. multicoloured 20 10
46 15 c. multicoloured 55 35
47 20 c. multicoloured 80 65
41/7 *Set of* 7 1·90 2·00

The 6 c. exists with PVA gum as well as gum arabic.

The higher values used with this issue were Nos. 20/27 of Malaysia (National Issues).

3 Black-veined Tiger

4 Raja Syed Putra

1971 (1 Feb)–**78**. *As Nos. 175/87 of Johore but with portrait of Raja Syed Putra and Arms, as in T* **3**.

(*a*) *Litho by Bradbury, Wilkinson*

48 1 c. multicoloured 10 35
49 2 c. multicoloured 20 40
50 5 c. multicoloured 35 10
51 6 c. multicoloured 35 20
52 10 c. multicoloured 35 10
53 15 c. multicoloured 50 25
54 20 c. multicoloured 60 55
48/54 *Set of* 7 2·25 1·75

(*b*) *Photo by Harrison* (1977–78)

54*a* 10 c. multicoloured
55 15 c. multicoloured 2·75 1·0
55*a* 20 c. multicoloured 8·50 9·0

The higher values used with this issue were Nos. 64/71 c Malaysia (National Issues).

For differences between litho and **photo printings**, see afte Johore No. 187.

(Des Citizen Studio and Engravers. Litho Enschedé)

1971 (28 Mar). *25th Anniv of Installation of Raja Syed Putra P* 13½ × 13.

56 **4** 10 c. multicoloured 20 3
57 15 c. multicoloured 20 2
58 50 c. multicoloured 70 1·4
56/8 *Set of* 3 1·00 1·7

5 *Pterocarpus indicus*

6 Coconuts

1979 (30 Apr). *As Nos. 188/94 of Johore but with portrait of Raja Syed Putra as in T* **5**.

59 1 c. *Rafflesia hasseltii* 10 2(
60 2 c. Type **5** 10 2(
61 5 c. *Lagerstroemia speciosa* 10 1(
62 10 c. *Durio zibethinus* 10 1(
63 15 c. *Hibiscus rosa-sinensis* 15 1(
64 20 c. *Rhododendron scortechinii* 15 1
65 25 c. *Phaeomeria speciosa* 15 2
59/65 *Set of* 7 65 8

For higher values used in conjunction with this series see Nos 190/7 of Malaysia (National Issues).

1983–84*. *As No. 64 but without wmk.*

71 20 c. *Rhododendron scortechinii* (**blackish brown background**)
71*a* 20 c. *Rhododendron scortechinii* (**bronze-green background**) (**4.12.84**) 1·00 1·0

*There was no official release date for these stamps. Date shown are the earliest recorded from **postmarks** and may b revised if earlier examples are reported.

For details of the shade differences between watermarked an unwatermarked printings see after Johore No. 200*a*.

No. 71*a* shows **the Sultan's head larger than on Nos. 64 and 7** and has "perlis" in **rounded, instead of square-ended, letters.**

1986 (25 Oct). *As Nos. 202/8 of Johore but with portrait of Raja Syed Putra as in T* **6**.

73 1 c. Coffee 10 1
74 2 c. Type **6** 10 1
75 5 c. Cocoa 10 1
76 10 c. Black pepper 10 1
77 15 c. Rubber 10 1
78 20 c. Oil palm 10 1
79 30 c. Rice 10 1
73/9 *Set of* 7 40 4

SELANGOR

The first British Resident was appointed in 1874. Selangor joined the Federated Malay States in 1896.

The stamps of the STRAITS SETTLEMENTS were used in Selangor from 1879 until 1881.

Until 1 January 1899, when the Federated Malay States joined the U.P.U., mail for addresses outside Malaya was franked with stamps of the STRAITS SETTLEMENTS.

PRICES FOR STAMPS ON COVER TO 1945

Nos. 1/8	—
Nos. 9/19	*from* × 6
Nos. 20/30	*from* × 8
Nos. 31/3	*from* × 20
Nos. 34/6	*from* × 15
Nos. 37/8	*from* × 10
Nos. 38*a*/40	—
Nos. 41/2	*from* × 4
No. 43	—
Nos. 44/8	*from* × 5
Nos. 49/53	*from* × 20
Nos. 54/66	*from* × 6
Nos. 66*a*/7	*from* × 4
Nos. 68/85	*from* × 3
Nos. 86/7	*from* × 4

The Straits Settlements 1867 2 c. brown with Crown CC watermark (No. 11) has been known since 1881 overprinted in black with a crescent and star over a capital S, all within an oval, similar in style to the overprints listed for Perak and Sungei Ujong.

The status of this item remains unclear, but it may well represent the first issue of distinctive stamps for Selangor. This overprint should not be confused with a somewhat similar cancellation used on Selangor stamps of the same period. This cancellation differs in having a circular frame with the capital S shown above the crescent and star. It is usually struck in red.

A similar overprint in red on the Straits Settlements 2 c. brown with Crown CA watermark is known to be bogus.

SELANGOR
(1) ("S" inverted and narrow letters)

SELANGOR
(2) ("S" wide)

SELANGOR
(3) (narrow letters)

SELANGOR
(4) ("N" wide)

SELANGOR
(5) ("SE" and "AN" wide)

SELANGOR
(6) ("SEL" and "N" wide)

SELANGOR
(7) ("SELAN" wide)

1881–82. *No. 11 (wmk Crown CC) of Straits Settlements optd with T* **1/7**.

1	**1**	2 c. brown	£100	£120
2	**2**	2 c. brown	40·00	50·00
3	**3**	2 c. brown	40·00	42·00
4	**4**	2 c. brown	—	£1800
5	**5**	2 c. brown (1882)	75·00	80·00
6	**6**	2 c. brown (1882)	75·00	80·00
7	**7**	2 c. brown (1882)	75·00	80·00

Nos. 1/3 and 5/7 have been identified as coming from triplet settings, either Nos. 1 + 2 + 3, 2 + 3 + 3 or 5 + 6 + 7. The setting for No. 4 is unknown.

S.
(8)

1882. *No. 50 (wmk Crown CA) of Straits Settlements optd with T* **8**.

8	**8**	2 c. brown	—	£1000

SELANGOR
(9) ("SEL" and "NG" wide)

SELANGOR
(10) ("E" and "ANG" wide)

SELANGOR
(11) ("ELANG" wide)

SELANGOR
(12) ("S" and "L" wide)

SELANGOR
(13) ("S" and "A" wide)

SELANGOR
(14) ("E" wide)

SELANGOR
(15) ("EL" wide)

SELANGOR
(16) ("SE" and "N" wide)

SELANGOR
(17) ("S" and "N" wide)

1882–83. *No. 50 (wmk Crown CA) of Straits Settlements optd with T* **2/3** *and* **9/17**.

9	**9**	2 c. brown	70·00	70·00
10	**10**	2 c. brown	70·00	70·00
11	**11**	2 c. brown	70·00	70·00
12	**2**	2 c. brown (1883)	60·00	60·00
13	**3**	2 c. brown (1883)	60·00	60·00
14	**12**	2 c. brown (1883)	—	£1200
15	**13**	2 c. brown (1883)	£150	£150
16	**14**	2 c. brown (1883)	80·00	80·00
17	**15**	2 c. brown (1883)	80·00	80·00
18	**16**	2 c. brown (1883)	55·00	55·00
19	**17**	2 c. brown (1883)	55·00	55·00

The above were all printed from triplet settings. Those so far identified are Nos. 9 + 10 + 11, 12 (with defective "G") + 13 + 13, 15 + 16 + 17 and 18 + 12 + 19. No. 14 occurs as the first position of a triplet, but the second and third units are not yet known.

SELANGOR
(18) ("E" and "A" wide)

SELANGOR
(19) ("A" wide)

SELANGOR
(20) ("L" wide)

SELANGOR
(21) ("L" narrow)

SELANGOR
(22) ("A" narrow)

SELANGOR
(23) (wide letters)

1883–85. *No. 63 of Straits Settlements optd with T* **2**, **4**, **12**, **14/15** *and* **18/23**.

20	**12**	2 c. rose	55·00	55·00
21	**14**	2 c. rose	45·00	45·00
		a. Opt double		
22	**4**	2 c. rose (1884)	50·00	48·00
23	**15**	2 c. rose (1884)	45·00	45·00
24	**2**	2 c. rose (1884)	50·00	55·00
25	**18**	2 c. rose (1884)	50·00	50·00
26	**19**	2 c. rose (1884)	75·00	55·00
27	**20**	2 c. rose (1884)	90·00	70·00
28	**21**	2 c. rose (1885)	45·00	55·00
29	**22**	2 c. rose (1885)	42·00	48·00
30	**23**	2 c. rose (1885)	65·00	60·00

The above come from triplet settings with Nos. 20 + 21 + 21, 22 + 22 + 23, 24 + 25 + 23 and 28 + 29 + 28 so far identified. The triplets for Nos. 26, 27 and 30 are not known, although the first two may come from the same setting.

SELANGOR
(24)

Selangor
(25)

SELANGOR
(26)

SELANGOR
(27)

SELANGOR
(28)

SELANGOR
(29)

SELANGOR
(30)

SELANGOR
(31)

SELANGOR
(32)

SELANGOR
(33)

SELANGOR
(34)

1885–91. *No. 63 of Straits Settlements optd with T* **24/34**.

31	**24**	2 c. rose	2·25	5·00
		a. Opt double	—	£600
32	**25**	2 c. rose	£400	£450
33	**26**	2 c. rose	7·00	10·00
34	**27**	2 c. rose (1886)	25·00	25·00
		a. Opt double	†	£600
35	**28**	2 c. rose (horiz opt without stop) (1887)	2·75	2·25
36		2 c. rose (horiz opt with stop) (1887)	15·00	15·00
37	**29**	2 c. rose (1889)	90·00	60·00
38	**30**	2 c. rose (vert opt) (1889)	26·00	5·50
38*a*		2 c. rose (horiz opt) (1889)	£2000	
39	**31**	2 c. rose (diagonal opt) (1889)	£650	
40	**32**	2 c. rose (1889)	£150	20·00
41	**28**	2 c. rose (vert opt without stop) (1890)	8·00	11·00
42	**33**	2 c. rose (1890)	60·00	2·25
43	**34**	2 c. rose (1891)	£180	£130

Settings:

Nos. 31/4 – each in triplet containing three examples of the same stamp
No. 35 – triplet or 60 (6 × 10)
No. 36 – 60 (6 × 10)
Nos. 37/8 – 60 (6 × 10) containing both overprints in an unknown combination, but with No. 38 predominating
No. 38*a*/9 – not known
Nos. 40/3 – each in 60 (6 × 10)

SELANGOR *Two* CENTS
(35)

SELANGOR *Two* CENTS
(36)

SELANGOR Two CENTS
(37)

SELANGOR Two CENTS
(38)

SELANGOR Two CENTS
(39)

1891. *No. 68 of Straits Settlements, surch with T* **35/9**, *each with bar obliterating old value.*

44	**35**	2 c. on 24 c. green	10·00	23·00
45	**36**	2 c. on 24 c. green	80·00	£110
46	**37**	2 c. on 24 c. green	80·00	£110
47	**38**	2 c. on 24 c. green	55·00	75·00
		a. "SELANGCR"		
48	**39**	2 c. on 24 c. green	80·00	£110

Nos. 44/8 come from the one setting used to surcharge the panes of sixty. No. 44 occurs in rows 1 to 5, No. 45 on row 6, No. 46 on row 7, No. 47 on rows 8 and 9, and No. 48 on row 10.

The error, No. 47a, occurs in the first printing only and is No. 45 (R.8/3) on the pane.

40

3 CENTS
(41)

1891 (Nov)–**95.** *Wmk Crown CA. P* 14.

49	**40**	1 c. green (1893)	70	25
50		2 c. rose	2·00	45
51		2 c. orange (1895)	65	40
52		5 c. blue (1892)	7·50	3·75
49/52		*Set of* 4	9·75	4·25
49/52 Optd "Specimen"		*Set of* 4	70·00	

1894. *Surch with T* **41**.

53	**40**	3 c. on 5 c. rose (Optd S. £30)	75	30

42

43

1895–99. *Wmk Crown CA or Crown CC (dollar values). P* 14.

54	**42**	3 c. dull purple and carmine	3·50	20
55		5 c. dull purple and olive-yellow	65	30
56		8 c. dull purple and ultramarine (1898)	40·00	7·00
57		10 c. dull purple and orange	5·00	25
58		25 c. green and carmine (1896)	48·00	27·00
59		50 c. green and black (1896)	£130	70·00
60		50 c. dull purple & greenish black (1898)	18·00	15·00
61	**43**	$1 green and yellow-green	28·00	40·00
62		$2 green and carmine (1897)	85·00	85·00
63		$3 green and ochre (1897)	£160	£120
64		$5 green and blue	75·00	£100
65		$10 green and purple (1899) (S. £90)	£250	£200
66		$25 green and orange (1899?) (S. £175)	£850	
54/62		*Set of* 9	£325	£225
54/64 Optd "Specimen"		*Set of* 11	£190	

Pending the arrival of the permanent Federated Malay States issue the stamps of STRAITS SETTLEMENTS and PERAK were used at various times between July 1900 and March 1901.

The general issues for the FEDERATED MALAY STATES were used in Selangor from 1901 until 1935.

One cent.
(44)

Three cents.
(45)

1900 (Oct). *Nos. 55 and 59 surch with T* **44** *or* **45**.

66*a*	**42**	1 c. on 5 c. dull purple & ol-yell (31 Oct*)	38·00	45·00
66*b*		1 c. on 50 c. green and black (22 Oct*)	80	12·00
		bc. "cent" repeated at left	£850	
67		3 c. on 50 c. green and black (30 Oct*)	6·00	14·00
		a. Antique "t" in "cents"	85·00	£120

*Earliest known postmark date.

It is believed that these stamps were surcharged from settings of 30, repeated four times to complete the sheet of 120.

No. 66bc occurred on two separate vertical strips of five stamps where two impressions of the setting overlapped.

The position in the setting of No. 67a is not known.

46 Mosque at Palace, Klang

47 Sultan Suleiman

(Des E. J. McNaughton)

1935 (2 Dec)–**41.** *Chalk-surfaced or ordinary paper* (**O**). *Wmk Mult Script CA (sideways on T* **46**). *P* 14 *or* 14 × 14½ *(No. 70).*

68	**46**	1 c. black (1.1.36)	20	10
69		2 c. green (1.1.36)	20	10
70		2 c. orange, **OC** (21.8.41)	25	1·10
		a. Perf 14, **O** (9.41)	7·00	1·50
71		3 c. green, **OC** (21.8.41)	50	2·00
72		4 c. orange	20	10
73		5 c. brown (5.12.35)	20	10
74		6 c. scarlet (1.1.37)	2·75	10
75		8 c. grey	40	10
76		10 c. dull purple (1.1.36)	40	10
77		12 c. bright ultramarine (1.1.36)	1·50	10
78		15 c. bright ultramarine, **O** (1.10.41)	2·75	18·00
79		25 c. dull purple and scarlet (1.4.36)	1·50	60
80		30 c. dull purple and orange (1.1.36)	1·25	85
81		40 c. scarlet and dull purple	1·75	1·25
82		50 c. black/*emerald* (1.2.36)	1·50	15
83	**47**	$1 black and rose/*blue* (1.4.36)	4·00	40
84		$2 green and scarlet (16.5.36)	14·00	7·00
85		$5 green and red/*emerald* (16.5.36)	40·00	23·00
68/85		*Set of* 18	65·00	50·00
68/85 Perf "Specimen"		*Set of* 18	£250	

Supplies of an unissued 8 c. scarlet were diverted to Australia in 1941. Examples circulating result from leakages of this supply.

48 Sultan Hisamud-din Alam Shah **49**

1941. *Wmk Mult Script CA. P* 14.
86 **48** $1 black and red/*blue*, **C** (15.4.41) .. 5·50 5·00
87 $2 grn & scar, **C** (7.7.41) (Perf S. £70) 30·00 27·00

A $5 green and red on emerald, T **24**, was issued overprinted during the Japanese occupation of Malaya. Unoverprinted examples are known, but were not issued thus (*Price* £55).

During shortages in 1941 stamps of STRAITS SETTLEMENTS (2 c.) and PERAK (25 c.) were issued in Selangor.

1948 (1 Dec). *Royal Silver Wedding. As Nos.* 30/1 *of Aden.*
88 10 c. violet 20 10
89 $5 green .. .. 23·00 14·00

1949 (12 Sept)–**55.** *Chalk-surfaced paper. Wmk Mult Script CA. P* 17½ × 18.
90 **49** 1 c. black 10 10
91 2 c. orange 10 10
92 3 c. green 20 65
93 4 c. brown 10 10
94 5 c. bright purple (1.9.52) 25 20
a. Bright mauve (17.9.53) 20 10
95 6 c. grey 10 10
96 8 c. scarlet 25 65
97 8 c. green (1.9.52) 65 50
98 10 c. purple 10 10
99 12 c. scarlet (1.9.52) .. .. 80 1·25
100 15 c. ultramarine 35 10
101 20 c. black and green 30 10
102 20 c. bright blue (1.9.52) 80 10
103 25 c. purple and orange 25 10
104 30 c. scarlet and purple (5.9.55) .. 1·25 50
105 35 c. scarlet and purple (1.9.52) 70 80
106 40 c. scarlet and purple .. .. .. 90 2·00
107 50 c. black and blue 40 10
108 $1 blue and purple .. .. 2·00 10
109 $2 green and scarlet .. .. 5·00 15
110 $5 green and brown .. .. 24·00 80
90/110 .. .. *Set of* 21 35·00 7·00

1949 (10 Oct). *75th Anniv of Universal Postal Union. As Nos.* 114/17 *of Antigua.*
111 10 c. purple 15 10
112 15 c. deep blue 45 45
113 25 c. orange 50 80
114 50 c. blue-black .. .. 1·10 80
111/14 .. .. *Set of* 4 2·00 1·90

1953 (2 June). *Coronation. As No.* 47 *of Aden.*
115 10 c. black and reddish purple 20 10

1957 (26 June)–**61.** *As Nos.* 92/102 *of Kedah but with inset portrait of Sultan Hisamud-din Alam Shah.*
116 1 c. black (21.8.57) 10 20
117 2 c. orange-red (25.7.57) 10 15
a. Red-orange (10.11.59) 40 70
118 4 c. sepia (21.8.57) 10 10
119 5 c. carmine-lake (21.8.57) 10 10
120 8 c. myrtle-green (21.8.57) .. .. .. 1·10 25
121 10 c. deep brown (4.8.57) 15 10
122 10 c. deep maroon (9.5.61) 60 10
123 20 c. blue 25 10
124 50 c. black and blue (*p* 12½) (25.7.57) .. 25 10
a. Perf 12½ × 13 (10.5.60) 25 10
125 $1 ultramarine and reddish purple (25.7.57) 1·25 10
126 $2 bronze-green & scarlet (*p* 12½) (21.8.57) 2·25 85
a. Perf 13 × 12½ (6.12.60) .. .. .. 2·00 1·25
127 $5 brown and bronze-green (*p* 12½) .. 6·50 1·50
a. Perf 13 × 12½ (10.5.60) .. .. .. 4·25 1·00
116/27a .. .. *Set of* 12 9·00 2·50

The 6, 12, 25 and 30 c. values used with this issue were Nos. 1/4 of Malayan Federation.

50 Sultan Salahuddin Abdul Aziz Shah **51**

(Photo Harrison)

1961 (28 June). *Coronation of the Sultan.* W w **12**. *P* 15 × 14.
128 **50** 10 c. multicoloured 10 10
a. Black ptg misplaced £110

No. 128a is "The Double-headed Sultan" error, from one sheet where the majority of the stamps showed considerable black printing misplacement.

1961–62. *As Nos.* 92/8 *of Kedah but with inset portrait of Sultan Salahuddin Abdul Aziz as in T* **51**. W w **13**. *P* 12½ × 13 (*vert*) *or* 13 × 12½ (*horiz*).
129 1 c. black (1.3.62) 10 30
130 2 c. orange-red (1.3.62) 10 20
131 4 c. sepia (1.3.62) 10 10
132 5 c. carmine-lake (1.3.62) 10 10
133 8 c. myrtle-green (1.3.62) 60 70
134 10 c. deep maroon (1.11.61) 10 10
135 20 c. blue (1.3.62) 20 10
129/35 .. .. *Set of* 7 1·00 1·25

52 *Vanda hookeriana* **53** Clipper Butterfly

1965 (15 Nov). *As Nos.* 166/72 *of Johore but with inset portrait of Sultan Salahuddin Abdul Aziz Shah as in T* **52**.
136 1 c. multicoloured 10 10
b. Magenta omitted .. .. 24·00
137 2 c. multicoloured 10 15
b. Yellow (flower) omitted .. .. .. 15·00
138 5 c. multicoloured 10 10
b. Yellow (flower) omitted .. .. .. 15·00
c. Red (leaves, etc) omitted .. .. 22·00
139 6 c. multicoloured 15 10
140 10 c. multicoloured 15 10
a. Red omitted .. .. 24·00
141 15 c. multicoloured 55 10
b. Green (value and leaves) omitted .. 90·00
142 20 c. multicoloured 80 10
a. Bright purple (blooms) omitted .. 23·00
b. Yellow (leaves) omitted .. .. 15·00
136/42 .. .. *Set of* 7 1·75 40

The 2 c. to 20 c. values exist with PVA gum as well as gum arabic.

The higher values used with this issue were Nos. 20/27 of Malaysia (National Issues).

1970 (20 Nov). *As Nos.* 136 *etc. but* W w **13** (*sideways*).
143 **52** 1 c. multicoloured 30 85
144 10 c. multicoloured .. .. .. 1·25 15
145 – 20 c. multicoloured .. .. .. 2·00 1·50
143/5 .. .. *Set of* 3 3·25 2·25

1971 (1 Feb)–**78.** *As Nos.* 175/87 *of Johore but with portrait of Sultan Salahuddin Abdul Aziz Shah and Arms, as in T* **53**.

(*a*) *Litho by Bradbury, Wilkinson*
146 1 c. multicoloured 10 15
147 2 c. multicoloured 20 20
148 5 c. multicoloured 35 10
149 6 c. multicoloured 35 10
150 10 c. multicoloured 35 10
a. Black (state inscr, portrait and arms) omitted .. .. 60·00
151 15 c. multicoloured 50 10
152 20 c. multicoloured 60 10
146/52 .. .. *Set of* 7 2·25 50

(*b*) *Photo by Harrison* (1977–78)
153 1 c. multicoloured 25 60
154 5 c. multicoloured .. .. 1·50 15
155 10 c. multicoloured .. .. 1·75 15
156 15 c. multicoloured .. .. 1·75 25
157 20 c. multicoloured .. .. 1·75 55
153/7 .. .. *Set of* 5 6·25 1·50

The higher values used with this issue were Nos. 64/71 of Malaysia (National Issues).

For differences between litho and photo printings see after Johore No. 187.

A used example of No. 150 has been seen with the magenta apparently missing.

For explanation of No. 150a, see note below No. 122 of Kelantan.

54 *Lagerstroemia speciosa* **55** Sultan Salahuddin Abdul Aziz Shah and Royal Crest

1979 (30 Apr). *As Nos.* 188/94 *of Johore but with portrait of Sultan Salahuddin Abdul Aziz Shah as in T* **54**.
158 1 c. *Rafflesia hasseltii* 10 10
159 2 c. *Pterocarpus indicus* 10 10
160 5 c. Type **54** 10 10
161 10 c. *Durio zibethinus* 10 10
162 15 c. *Hibiscus rosa-sinensis* 15 10
163 20 c. *Rhododendron scortechinii* 15 10
164 25 c. *Phaeomeria speciosa* 15 10
158/64 .. .. *Set of* 7 65 20

For higher values used in conjunction with this series see Nos. 190/7 of Malaysia (National Issues).

1983 (6 Oct)–**85.*** *As Nos.* 160/3 *but without wmk.*
166 5 c. Type **54** (20.11.83) 25 15
167 10 c. *Durio zibethinus* (3.85) .. .. 1·25 60
168 15 c. *Hibiscus rosa-sinensis* (20.11.83) .. 1·25 60
169 20 c. *Rhododendron scortechinii* (blackish brown background)
169*a* 20 c. *Rhododendron scortechinii* (bronze-green background) (12.12.83) 60 40

*There was no official release date for these stamps. Dates shown are the earliest recorded from postmarks and may be revised if earlier examples are reported.

For details of the shade differences between watermarked and unwatermarked printings see after Johore No. 200*a*.

On Nos. 166/8 and 169*a* the ruler's headdress is bolder than on Nos. 160/3 and 169.

(Des P. Ket. Litho Security Printers (M), Malaysia)

1985 (5 Sept). *Silver Jubilee of Sultan. P* 13.
173 **55** 15 c. multicoloured 35 10
174 20 c. multicoloured 45 15
175 $1 multicoloured .. .. .. 1·50 1·25
173/5 .. .. *Set of* 3 2·10 1·25

56 Black Pepper

1986 (25 Oct). *As Nos.* 202/8 *of Johore but with portrait of Sultan Salahuddin Abdul Aziz Shah as in T* **56**.
176 1 c. Coffee 10 10
177 2 c. Coconuts 10 10
178 5 c. Cocoa 10 10
179 10 c. Type **56** 10 10
180 15 c. Rubber 10 10
181 20 c. Oil palm 10 10
182 30 c. Rice 10 15
176/82 .. .. *Set of* 7 40 45

TRENGGANU

Suzerainty over Perlis was transferred by Thailand to Great Britain in 1909. A British adviser was appointed in 1919.
The state joined the Federation of Malaya on 1 February 1948.

PRICES FOR STAMPS ON COVER TO 1945	
Nos. 1/17	*from* × 8
No. 18	—
Nos. 19/22	*from* × 6
Nos. 23/33	*from* × 8
Nos. 34/6	—
Nos. 37/47	*from* × 15
Nos. 48/60	*from* × 6
Nos. D1/4	*from* × 10

RED CROSS

2c.

1 Sultan Zain ul ab din 2 (3)

1910 (14 Dec)–**19.** *T* **1** *and* **2** ($5 *and* $25). *Wmk Mult Crown CA. P* 14.
1 1 1 c. blue-green, **O** .. 50 1·00
a. Green, **O** .. 75 1·00
2 2 c. brown and purple, **C** (1915) .. 40 90
3 3 c. carmine-red, **O** .. 1·75 1·50
4 4 c. orange, **O** .. 2·25 5·00
5 4 c. red-brown and green, **C** (1915) .. 2·00 3·75
5*a* 4 c. carmine-red, **O** (1919) .. 60 1·75
6 5 c. grey, **O** .. 1·25 2·00
7 5 c. grey and brown, **C** (1915) .. 2·25 2·00
8 8 c. ultramarine, **O** .. 1·25 5·50
9 10 c. purple/*yellow* .. 4·00 6·00
a. On pale yellow .. 3·00 1·75
10 10 c. green and red/*yellow*, **O** (1915) .. 1·00 2·25
11 20 c. dull and bright purple, **C** .. 2·50 3·25
12 25 c. green and dull purple, **C** (1915) .. 3·75 16·00
13 30 c. dull purple and black, **C** (1915) .. 5·00 22·00
14 50 c. black/*green*, **C** .. 4·00 5·50
15 $1 black and carmine/*blue*, **C** .. 9·00 16·00
16 $3 green and red/*green*, **C** (1915) .. 55·00 £110
17 2 $5 green and dull purple, **C** (1912) .. 90·00 £200
18 $25 rose-carmine and green, **C** (1912) (Optd S. £150) .. £700
1/17 .. *Set of* 18 £160 £350
1/17 Optd "Specimen" .. *Set of* 18 £375

1917 (June)–**18.** *Surch with T* **3**.
19 1 2 c. on 3 c. carmine-red .. 30 2·00
a. Comma after "2 c." .. 3·00 10·00
b. "SS" in "CROSS" inverted .. £180 £180
c. "CSOSS" for "CROSS" .. 50·00 70·00
d. "2" in thick block type .. 11·00 23·00
e. Surch inverted .. £400 £400
f. Pair, one without surch .. £1100
20 2 c. on 4 c. orange .. 70 8·50
a. Comma after "2 c." .. 10·00 35·00
b. "SS" in "CROSS" inverted .. £650 £450
c. "CSOSS" for "CROSS" .. £110 £140
d. Surch double .. £400
21 2 c. on 4 c. red-brown and green (1918) .. 1·10 15·00
a. Pair, one without surch .. £1000
22 2 c. on 8 c. ultramarine (1917) .. 50 15·00
a. Comma after "2 c." .. 9·00 50·00
b. "SS" in "CROSS" inverted .. £550
c. "CSOSS" for "CROSS" .. 90·00 £100
d. "RED CROSS" double .. £300

The surcharges on Nos. 19/22 were arranged in settings of 18 (6×3) applied three times to cover the top nine rows of the sheet with the tenth row completed by a further impression so that "RED CROSS" from the centre row of the setting appears on the bottom sheet margin. Specialists recognise four different settings:

Setting I — Shows "CSOSS" for "CROSS" on R. 2/1, "SS" inverted on R. 2/5 and comma after "2 c." on both R. 3/3 and 3/5. It was used for the 3 c., 4 c. orange and 8 c. The error on R. 2/5 was later corrected.

Setting II — This shows the error on R. 2/1 corrected, but the comma varieties now occur on R. 1/3 and 1/5. Used for 3 c., 4 c. orange and 8 c.

Setting III — Both comma varieties corrected. Used for all values including 4 c. red-brown and green.

Setting IV — This shows a thick black "2" on R. 2/2. Used for the 3 c. only.

During a temporary shortage between March and August 1921 2 c., 4 c. and 6 c. stamps of the STRAITS SETTLEMENTS were authorised for use in Trengganu.

2 CENTS

4 Sultan Suleiman 5 (6)

1921. *Chalk-surfaced paper. P* 14. (*a*) *Wmk Mult Crown CA*.
23 4 $1 purple and blue/*blue* .. 11·00 14·00
24 $3 green and red/*emerald* .. 50·00 90·00
25 5 $5 green and red/*pale yellow* .. 60·00 £120

(*b*) *Wmk Mult Script CA*
26 4 2 c. green .. 60 15
27 4 c. carmine-red .. 60 10
28 5 c. grey and deep brown .. 2·00 2·50
29 10 c. bright blue .. 2·00 15
30 20 c. dull purple and orange .. 2·00 1·50
31 25 c. green and deep purple .. 2·25 2·00
32 30 c. dull purple and black .. 3·25 1·00
33 50 c. green and bright carmine .. 3·50 1·00
34 5 $25 purple and blue (S. £70) .. £450 £550
35 $50 green and yellow (S. £150) .. £950 £1300
36 $100 green and scarlet (S. £300) .. £3250
23/33 .. *Set of* 11 £120 £200
23/33 Optd "Specimen" .. *Set of* 11 £250

1922 (31 Mar). *Optd* "MALAYA-BORNEO EXHIBITION" *as T* **56** *of Straits Settlements at Singapore*.
37 4 2 c. green .. 75 17·00
38 4 c. carmine-red .. 3·00 19·00
39 1 5 c. grey and brown .. 2·50 22·00
40 10 c. green and red/*yellow* .. 2·50 23·00
41 20 c. dull and bright purple .. 2·00 30·00
42 25 c. green and dull purple .. 2·00 30·00
43 30 c. dull purple and black .. 2·25 30·00
44 50 c. black/*green* .. 2·50 30·00
45 $1 black and carmine/*blue* .. 10·00 55·00
46 $3 green and red/*green* .. £110 £300
47 2 $5 green and dull purple .. £190 £500
37/47 .. *Set of* 11 £300 £950
Minor varieties of this overprint exist as in Straits Settlements.

1924–38. *New values, etc. Chalk-surfaced paper. Wmk Mult Script CA. P* 14.
48 4 1 c. black (1926) .. 35 25
49 3 c. green (1926) .. 50 75
50 3 c. brown (1938) .. 6·50 4·50
51 5 c. purple/*yellow* (1926) .. 1·00 45
52 6 c. orange .. 2·25 25
53 8 c. grey (1938) .. 6·50 50
54 12 c. bright ultramarine (1926) .. 3·25 3·25
55 35 c. carmine/*yellow* (1926) .. 3·50 8·00
56 $1 purple and blue/*blue* (1929) .. 9·00 3·50
57 $3 green and red/*green* (1926) .. 25·00 48·00
58 5 $5 green and red/*yellow* (1938) .. £200 £650
48/58 .. *Set of* 11 £225 £650
48/58 Optd/Perf "Specimen" .. *Set of* 11 £300
The 2 c. yellow, 6 c. grey, 8 c. red and 15 c. blue were prepared, but not officially issued.

1941 (1 May). *Nos.* 51 *and* 29 *surch as T* **6**.
59 4 2 c. on 5 c. purple/*yellow* .. 6·00 4·50
60 8 c. on 10 c. bright blue .. 7·00 4·50

1948 (1 Dec). *Royal Silver Wedding. As Nos.* 30/1 *of Aden*.
61 10 c. violet .. 15 25
62 $5 carmine .. 20·00 35·00

1949 (10 Oct). *75th Anniv of Universal Postal Union. As Nos.* 114/17 *of Antigua*.
63 10 c. purple .. 20 35
64 15 c. deep blue .. 55 1·60
65 25 c. orange .. 55 2·25
66 50 c. blue-black .. 90 2·50
63/6 .. *Set of* 4 2·00 6·00

7 Sultan Ismail

8 *Vanda hookeriana*

1949 (27 Dec)–**55.** *Chalk-surfaced paper. Wmk Mult Script CA. P* 17½ × 18.
67 7 1 c. black .. 10 20
68 2 c. orange .. 10 20
69 3 c. green .. 20 80
70 4 c. brown .. 10 15
71 5 c. bright purple (1.9.52) .. 25 50
72 6 c. grey .. 15 15
73 8 c. scarlet .. 20 1·25
74 8 c. green (1.9.52) .. 65 1·00
a. Deep green (11.8.53) .. 1·00 2·00
75 10 c. purple .. 15 10
76 12 c. scarlet (1.9.52) .. 65 1·50
77 15 c. ultramarine .. 30 25
78 20 c. black and green .. 30 1·25
79 20 c. bright blue (1.9.52) .. 80 25
80 25 c. purple and orange .. 25 55
81 30 c. scarlet and purple (5.9.55) .. 1·25 1·25
82 35 c. scarlet and purple (1.9.52) .. 70 1·00
83 40 c. red and purple .. 1·00 7·00
84 50 c. black and blue .. 40 45
85 $1 blue and purple .. 2·00 2·25
86 $2 green and scarlet .. 7·00 13·00
87 $5 green and brown .. 32·00 35·00
67/87 .. *Set of* 21 45·00 60·00

1953 (2 June). *Coronation. As No.* 47 *of Aden*.
88 10 c. black and reddish purple .. 20 25

1957 (26 June)–**63.** *As Nos.* 92/102 *of Kedah, but with inset portrait of Sultan Ismail*.
89 1 c. black (21.8.57) .. 10 20
90 2 c. orange-red (25.7.57) .. 15 30
a. Red-orange (21.2.61) .. 3·50 5·00
91 4 c. sepia (21.8.57) .. 10 10
92 5 c. carmine-lake (21.8.57) .. 10 10
93 8 c. myrtle-green (21.8.57) .. 3·25 60
94 10 c. deep brown (4.8.57) .. 15 10
94*a* 10 c. deep maroon (21.2.61) .. 80 10
95 20 c. blue .. 20 15
96 50 c. black and blue (*p* 12½) (25.7.57) .. 20 55
a. Perf 12½ × 13 (17.5.60) .. 25 60
ab. Black and ultramarine (20.3.62) .. 30 35
97 $1 ultramarine and reddish purple (25.7.57) 2·25 2·25
98 $2 bronze-green and scarlet (21.8.57) .. 4·00 6·00
99 $5 brown and bronze-green .. 6·00 8·00
a. Perf 13 × 12½ (13.8.63) .. 6·00 8·50
89/99a .. *Set of* 12 15·00 16·00
The 6, 12, 25 and 30 c. values used with this issue were Nos. 1/4 of Malayan Federation.

1965 (15 Nov). *As Nos.* 166/72 *of Johore but with inset portrait of Sultan Ismail Nasiruddin Shah as in T* **8**.
100 1 c. multicoloured .. 10 20
101 2 c. multicoloured .. 10 20
102 5 c. multicoloured .. 10 10
103 6 c. multicoloured .. 15 15
104 10 c. multicoloured .. 20 10
105 15 c. multicoloured .. 55 10
106 20 c. multicoloured .. 80 15
a. Bright purple (blooms) omitted .. 27·00
100/6 .. *Set of* 7 1·75 75
The 5 c. value exists with PVA gum as well as gum arabic.
No. 101a, formerly listed here, is now listed as Sarawak No. 213a.
The higher values used with this issue were Nos. 20/27 of Malaysia (National Issues).

9 Sultan of Trengganu

10 Lime Butterfly

(Des Enche Nik Zainal Abidin. Photo Harrison)

1970 (16 Dec). *25th Anniv of Installation of H.R.H. Tuanku Ismail Nasiruddin Shah as Sultan of Trengganu. P* 14½ × 13½.
107 9 10 c. multicoloured .. 25 40
108 15 c. multicoloured .. 30 50
109 50 c. multicoloured .. 65 1·60
107/9 .. *Set of* 3 1·10 2·25

1971 (1 Feb)–**78.** *As Nos.* 175/87 *of Johore but with portrait of Sultan Ismail Nasiruddin Shah and Arms, as in T* **10**.

(*a*) *Litho by Bradbury, Wilkinson*
110 1 c. multicoloured .. 10 40
111 2 c. multicoloured .. 20 40
112 5 c. multicoloured .. 35 10
113 6 c. multicoloured .. 35 15
114 10 c. multicoloured .. 35 10
115 15 c. multicoloured .. 50 10
116 20 c. multicoloured .. 60 30
110/16 .. *Set of* 7 2·25 1·40

(*b*) *Photo by Harrison* (1977–78)
116*a* 5 c. multicoloured ..
117 10 c. multicoloured .. 2·00 75
117*a* 15 c. multicoloured .. 2·50 90
The higher values used with this issue were Nos. 64/71 of Malaysia (National Issues).
For differences between litho and photo printings, see after Johore No. 187.

11 *Durio zibethinus*

12 Sultan Mahmud

1979 (30 Apr). *As Nos.* 188/94 *of Johore but with portrait of Sultan Ismail Nasiruddin Shah as in T* **11**.
118 1 c. *Rafflesia hasseltii* .. 10 15
119 2 c. *Pterocarpus indicus* .. 10 15
120 5 c. *Lagerstroemia speciosa* .. 10 10
121 10 c. Type **11** .. 10 10
122 15 c. *Hibiscus rosa-sinensis* .. 15 10
123 20 c. *Rhododendron scortechinii* .. 15 10
124 25 c. *Phaeomeria speciosa* .. 15 10
118/24 .. *Set of* 7 65 50
For higher values used in conjunction with this series see Nos. 190/7 of Malaysia (National Issues).

(Des Malaysian Advertising Services. Litho Harrison)

1981 (21 Mar). *Installation of Sultan Mahmud. P* 14.
125 12 10 c. black, gold and new blue .. 15 35
126 15 c. black, gold and yellow .. 20 25
127 50 c. black, gold and bright purple .. 50 1·10
125/7 .. *Set of* 3 75 1·50

1983 (Oct)–**86.*** *As Nos.* 121/4 *but without wmk*.
131 10 c. Type **11** (5.2.86) .. 10·00 1·50
132 15 c. *Hibiscus rosa-sinensis* (24.1.85) .. 1·75 1·00
133 20 c. *Rhododendron scortechinii* (blackish brown background)
133*a* 20 c. *Rhododendron scortechinii* (bronze-green background) (2.3.84) .. 3·50 2·25
134 25 c. *Phaeomeria speciosa* (13.11.83) .. 25 15
*There was no official release date for these stamps. Dates shown are the earliest recorded from postmarks and may be revised if earlier examples are reported.
For details of the shade differences between watermarked and unwatermarked printings see after Johore No. 200*a*.
On Nos. 131/2, 133*a* and 134 the portrait and state arms have been redrawn smaller.

13 Rubber

1986 (25 Oct). *As Nos. 202/8 of Johore but with portrait of Sultan Mahmud and inscr* "TERENGGANU" *as in T* **13**.

135	1 c. Coffee	10	10
136	2 c. Coconuts..	10	10
137	5 c. Cocoa	10	10
138	10 c. Black pepper	10	10
139	15 c. Type **13**	10	10
140	20 c. Oil palm..	10	10
141	30 c. Rice	10	15
135/41	.. .. *Set of* 7	40	45

POSTAGE DUE STAMPS

D 1

1937 (10 Aug). *Wmk Mult Script CA. P* 14.

D1	D 1	1 c. scarlet	6·50	40·00
D2		4 c. green	6·50	40·00
D3		8 c. yellow	45·00	£225
D4		10 c. brown	55·00	85·00
D1/4		.. .. *Set of* 4	£100	£350
D1/4 Perf "Specimen"		.. .. *Set of* 4	£130	

VIII. JAPANESE OCCUPATION

PRICES FOR STAMPS ON COVER

Nos. J1/110	*from* × 6
Nos. J111/13	—
Nos. J114/25	*from* × 10
Nos. J128/85	*from* × 12
Nos. J186/8	*from* × 15
Nos. J189/203	*from* × 10
Nos. J203*b/v*	*from* × 12
Nos. J204/16	*from* × 20
Nos. J217/57	*from* × 12
Nos. J258/70	*from* × 10
Nos. J270*a/g*	—
Nos. J271/84	*from* × 20
Nos. JD1/7	*from* × 20
Nos. JD8/16	*from* × 30
Nos. JD17/28	*from* × 12
Nos. JD29/41	*from* × 30
Nos. JK1/29	*from* × 10

A. MALAYA

For convenience we have included in one list the stamps of various States which could be used throughout Malaya and those which were issued and used in one State or district only, the latter being indicated by footnotes.

Collectors are warned against forgeries of the various overprints, particularly on the scarcer stamps.

The stamps listed below were all valid for postal use. A number of others overprinted with Types **2** or **4** were subsequently made available by favour and are known as "request stamps". Although they had postal validity they were not on sale to the public.

(1)
"Seal of Post Office of Malayan Military Dept"

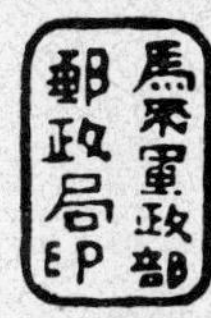

(2) (Upright)

(Handstamped at Singapore)

1942 (16 Mar). *Stamps of Straits Settlements optd with T* **1**, *in red.*

J1 **58** 1 c. black 8·50 11·00
J2 2 c. orange 9·50 12·00
J3 3 c. green 35·00 50·00
J4 8 c. grey 14·00 15·00
J5 15 c. ultramarine 13·00 13·00

The overprint Type **1** has a double-lined frame, although the two lines are not always apparent, as in the illustration. Three chops were used, differing slightly in the shape of the characters, but forgeries also exist. It is distinguishable from Type **2** by its extra width, measuring approximately 14 mm against 12½ mm.

(Handstamped at Singapore and Kuala Lumpur)

1942 (3 Apr). *Stamps optd with T* **2**. (*a*) *On Straits Settlements.*

J 6 **58** 1 c. black (R.) 2·50 2·50
a. Black opt £100 £120
b. Violet opt £120 £120
J 7 2 c. green (V.) £750 £750
J 8 2 c. orange (R.) 2·25 2·25
a. Black opt 40·00 45·00
b. Violet opt 45·00 40·00
c. Brown opt £140 £160
J 9 3 c. green (R.) 2·50 2·25
a. Black opt £110 £130
b. Violet opt £120 £140
J10 5 c. brown (R.) 12·00 13·00
a. Black opt £140 £140
J12 8 c. grey (R.) 2·50 2·25
a. Black opt £110 £130
J13 10 c. dull purple (R.) 18·00 20·00
a. Brown opt £250 £250
J14 12 c. ultramarine (R.) 55·00 65·00
J15 15 c. ultramarine (R.) 3·25 2·75
a. Violet opt £140 £150
J17 30 c. dull purple and orange (R.) £550 £575
J18 40 c. scarlet and dull purple (R.) 55·00 65·00
a. Brown opt £140 £140
J19 50 c. black/*emerald* (R.) 32·00 32·00
J20 $1 black and red/*blue* (R.) 55·00 60·00
J21 $2 green and scarlet (R.) £100 £110
J22 $5 green and red/*emerald* (R.) £130 £140

(*b*) *On Negri Sembilan*

J23 **6** 1 c. black (R.) 12·00 13·00
a. Violet opt 15·00 15·00
b. Brown opt 11·00 12·00
c. Black opt 15·00 22·00
J24 2 c. orange (R.) 8·50 8·50
a. Violet opt 24·00 20·00
b. Black opt 18·00 19·00
c. Brown opt 19·00 20·00
J25 3 c. green (R.) 12·00 14·00
a. Violet opt 20·00 24·00
b. Violet opt (sideways) £110 £110
c. Brown opt 24·00 27·00
J27 5 c. brown 13·00 13·00
a. Brown opt 11·00 11·00
b. Red opt 8·50 9·50
c. Violet opt 24·00 24·00
J29 6 c. grey 85·00 85·00
a. Brown opt £275 £275
J31 8 c. scarlet 15·00 27·00
J32 10 c. dull purple 35·00 38·00
a. Red opt 28·00 28·00
b. Brown opt 75·00 75·00
J32*c* 12 c. bright ultramarine (Br.) £400 £400
J33 15 c. ultramarine (R.) 11·00 8·00
a. Violet opt 22·00 22·00
J34 25 c. dull purple and scarlet 22·00 22·00
a. Red opt 50·00 60·00
b. Brown opt £100 £120
J35 **6** 30 c. dull purple and orange 70·00 80·00
a. Brown opt £275 £275
J36 40 c. scarlet and dull purple £375 £375
a. Brown opt £525 £550
J37 50 c. black/*emerald* 90·00 £100
J38 $1 black and red/*blue* 60·00 70·00
a. Red opt 80·00 90·00
b. Brown opt £250 £250
J39 $5 green and red/*emerald* £250 £275
a. Red opt £275 £300

(*c*) *On Pahang*

J40 **15** 1 c. black 18·00 20·00
a. Red opt 18·00 20·00
b. Violet opt 75·00 85·00
c. Brown opt 65·00 65·00
J41 3 c. green 45·00 50·00
a. Red opt £200 £250
b. Violet opt £300 £300
J42 5 c. brown 6·50 5·00
a. Red opt 48·00 55·00
b. Brown opt 70·00 70·00
c. Violet opt £140 £140
J44 8 c. grey 85·00 85·00
J45 8 c. scarlet 12·00 9·00
a. Red opt 38·00 38·00
b. Violet opt 38·00 42·00
c. Brown opt 45·00 48·00
J46 10 c. dull purple 24·00 26·00
a. Red opt 35·00 40·00
b. Brown opt £110 £120
J47 12 c. bright ultramarine £750 £750
a. Red opt £900 £900
J48 15 c. ultramarine 35·00 35·00
a. Red opt 55·00 55·00
b. Violet opt £250 £250
c. Brown opt £120 £140
J49 25 c. dull purple and scarlet 16·00 22·00
J50 30 c. dull purple and orange 12·00 18·00
a. Red opt £130 £150
J51 40 c. scarlet and dull purple 14·00 18·00
a. Brown opt 85·00 90·00
b. Red opt 24·00 24·00
J52 50 c. black/*emerald* £110 £120
a. Red opt £225 £250
J53 $1 black and red/*blue* (R.) 60·00 65·00
a. Black opt £110 £110
b. Brown opt £350 £350
J54 $5 green and red/*emerald* £475 £525
a. Red opt £550 £600

(*d*) *On Perak*

J55 **51** 1 c. black 16·00 16·00
a. Violet opt 42·00 45·00
b. Brown opt 48·00 48·00
J57 2 c. orange 11·00 12·00
a. Violet opt 42·00 45·00
b. Red opt 17·00 16·00
c. Brown opt 38·00 38·00
J58 3 c. green 20·00 20·00
a. Violet opt 95·00 £100
b. Brown opt 80·00 85·00
c. Red opt 85·00 85·00
J59 5 c. brown 5·00 5·00
a. Brown opt 15·00 15·00
b. Violet opt 60·00 70·00
c. Red opt 55·00 65·00
J61 8 c. grey 20·00 20·00
a. Red opt £110 £120
b. Brown opt £110 £120
J62 8 c. scarlet 11·00 28·00
a. Violet opt £110
J63 10 c. dull purple 10·00 17·00
a. Red opt 55·00 60·00
J64 12 c. bright ultramarine 55·00 65·00
J65 15 c. ultramarine 13·00 18·00
a. Red opt 35·00 35·00
b. Violet opt 80·00 80·00
c. Brown opt 75·00 75·00
J66 25 c. dull purple and scarlet 10·00 15·00
J67 30 c. dull purple and orange 17·00 28·00
a. Brown opt 75·00 80·00
b. Red opt 32·00 35·00
J68 40 c. scarlet and dull purple £120 £130
a. Brown opt £250 £250
J69 50 c. black/*emerald* 25·00 30·00
a. Red opt 32·00 35·00
b. Brown opt 70·00 70·00
J70 $1 black and red/*blue* £160 £190
a. Brown opt £600
J71 $2 green and scarlet £950 £950
J72 $5 green and red/*emerald* £400
a. Brown opt £700

(*e*) *On Selangor*

J73 **46** 1 c. black, S 5·50 6·50
a. Red opt, SU 9·50 11·00
b. Violet opt, SU 21·00 26·00
J74 2 c. green, U £325 £325
a. Violet opt, U £450 £450
J75 2 c. orange (*p* 14 × 15), S 24·00 27·00
a. Red opt, U 55·00 60·00
b. Violet opt, U 90·00 70·00
c. Brown opt, S 25·00 28·00
J76 2 c. orange (*p* 14), S 30·00 35·00
a. Red opt, U 65·00 65·00
b. Violet opt, U £150 £150
J77 3 c. green, SU 9·50 11·00
a. Red opt, SU 9·50 11·00
b. Violet opt, S 35·00 38·00
c. Brown opt, SU 9·50 9·50
J78 5 c. brown, S 4·25 3·75
a. Red opt, S 9·00 10·00
b. Violet opt, SU 17·00 19·00
c. Brown opt, SU 30·00 30·00
J79 6 c. scarlet, S £120 £120
a. Red opt, S £140 £140
b. Brown opt, S £225
J80 8 c. grey, S 9·50 11·00
a. Red opt, SU 16·00 18·00
b. Violet opt, U 22·00 24·00
c. Brown opt, S 32·00 22·00
J81 **46** 10 c. dull purple, S 9·00 12·00
a. Red opt, S 27·00 27·00
b. Brown opt, S 22·00 18·00
J82 12 c. bright ultramarine, S 22·00 20·00
a. Red opt, S 45·00 45·00
b. Brown opt, S 48·00 48·00
J83 15 c. ultramarine, S 10·00 12·00
a. Red opt, SU 22·00 24·00
b. Violet opt, U 80·00 75·00
c. Brown opt, S 22·00 22·00
J84 25 c. dull purple and scarlet, S 55·00 65·00
a. Red opt, S 45·00 50·00
J85 30 c. dull purple and orange, S 10·00 17·00
a. Brown opt, S 70·00 70·00
J86 40 c. scarlet and dull purple, S 35·00 38·00
a. Brown opt, S 85·00 75·00
J87 50 c. black/*emerald*, S 24·00 27·00
a. Red opt, S 40·00 45·00
b. Brown opt, S 55·00 60·00
J88 **47** $1 black and red/*blue* 26·00 30·00
a. Red opt 80·00 85·00
J89 $2 green and scarlet 30·00 40·00
a. Red opt £130 £140
J91 $5 green and red/*emerald* 40·00 50·00

On T **22** the overprint is normally sideways (with "top" to either right or left), but on T **24** it is always upright.

S=Sideways
U=Upright
SU=Sideways or upright (our prices being for the cheaper).

(*f*) *On Trengganu* (*all Script wmk*)

J 92 **4** 1 c. black 75·00 75·00
a. Red opt £110 £120
b. Brown opt £140 £140
J 93 2 c. green £110 £120
a. Red opt £130 £140
b. Brown opt £150 £150
J 94 2 c. on 5 c. purple/*yellow* (No. 59) 70·00 70·00
a. Red opt 42·00 42·00
J 95 3 c. brown 75·00 75·00
a. Brown opt £200 £200
J 96 4 c. carmine-red £120 95·00
J 97 5 c. purple/*yellow* 6·50 8·50
a. Red opt 13·00
J 98 6 c. orange 6·50 12·00
a. Red opt 16·00
b. Brown opt 75·00 75·00
J 99 8 c. grey 7·50 10·00
a. Brown to red opt 24·00
J100 8 c. on 10 c. bright blue (No. 60) 11·00 15·00
a. Red opt 21·00
J101 10 c. bright blue 8·00 12·00
a. Red opt 24·00
b. Brown opt 85·00 85·00
J102 12 c. bright ultramarine 6·50 11·00
a. Red opt 22·00
J103 20 c. dull purple and orange 7·50 12·00
a. Red opt 14·00
J104 25 c. green and deep purple 6·50 12·00
a. Red opt 17·00
b. Brown opt 65·00 65·00
J105 30 c. dull purple and black 6·50 12·00
a. Red opt 15·00
J106 35 c. carmine/*yellow* 8·50 12·00
a. Red opt 14·00
J107 50 c. green and bright carmine 38·00 45·00
J108 $1 purple and blue/*blue* £750 £750
J109 $3 green and red/*green* 35·00 48·00
a. Red opt 40·00
J110 **5** $5 green and red/*yellow* 95·00 £120
J111 $25 purple and blue £500
a. Red opt £1100
J112 $50 green and yellow £2500
J113 $100 green and scarlet £700

Nos. J92/113 were issued in Trengganu only.

Specialists recognise nine slightly different chops as Type **2**. Of these nine two are believed to have been used in Singapore and the remainder at Kuala Lumpur.

(3 "Seal of the Government Office of the Malacca Military Dept." (approx size))

1942 (23 Apr). *Stamps of Straits Settlements handstamped as T* **3**, *in red, each impression covering four stamps.*

			Single Un.	*Single* Used
J114	**58**	1 c. black	48·00	45·00
J115		2 c. orange	45·00	45·00
J116		3 c. green	45·00	45·00
J117		5 c. brown	75·00	80·00
J118		8 c. grey	80·00	70·00
J119		10 c. dull purple	50·00	50·00
J120		12 c. ultramarine	65·00	65·00
J121		15 c. ultramarine	48·00	48·00
J123		40 c. scarlet and dull purple	£225	£225
J124		50 c. black/*emerald*	£450	£450
J125		$1 black and red/*blue*	£550	£550

Nos. J114 to J125 were issued in Malacca only. Blocks of 4 showing the complete handstamp are worth from six times the price of a single stamp.

DAI NIPPON
2602
MALAYA
(4)

DAI NIPPON
2602
MALAYA
2 Cents
(5)

SELANGOR
EXHIBITION
DAI NIPPON
2602
MALAYA
(6)

1942. *Optd with T* **4**. *(a) On Straits Settlements.*

J128 **58** 2 c. orange 50 50
a. Opt inverted .. .. 7·00 9·00
b. Opt double, one inverted .. .. 35·00 40·00
J129 3 c. green .. .. 32·00 40·00
J130 8 c. grey .. .. 1·75 1·75
a. Opt inverted .. .. 13·00 20·00
J131 15 c. blue .. .. 5·50 4·00

(b) On Negri Sembilan

J132 **6** 1 c. black 80 60
a. Opt inverted .. .. 8·00 12·00
b. Opt double, one inverted .. .. 26·00 32·00
J133 2 c. orange .. .. 1·00 50
J134 3 c. green 75 45
J135 5 c. brown 45 55
J136 6 c. grey .. .. 1·00 1·00
a. Opt inverted .. .. — £500
b. Stop omitted at right (R.10/9) .. 30·00 32·00
J137 8 c. scarlet .. .. 1·75 1·25
J138 10 c. dull purple .. .. 3·00 3·00
J139 15 c. ultramarine .. .. 4·00 3·00
J140 25 c. dull purple and scarlet .. .. 2·00 4·50
J141 30 c. dull purple and orange .. .. 3·00 3·00
J142 $1 black and red/*blue* .. .. .. 80·00 90·00

(c) On Pahang

J143 **15** 1 c. black 70 50
J144 5 c. brown 55 70
J145 8 c. scarlet .. .. 17·00 2·25
J146 10 c. dull purple .. .. 8·50 5·00
J147 12 c. bright ultramarine .. .. .. 1·00 2·00
J148 25 c. dull purple and scarlet .. .. 3·50 5·50
J149 30 c. dull purple and orange .. .. 80 2·00

(d) On Perak

J151 **51** 2 c. orange 60 70
a. Opt inverted .. .. 12·00 15·00
J152 3 c. green 50 60
a. Opt inverted .. .. 10·00 13·00
J154 8 c. scarlet 60 40
a. Opt inverted .. .. 4·50 5·50
b. Opt double, one inverted £120 £140
c. Opt omitted (in pair with normal) £250
J155 10 c. dull purple .. .. 4·00 5·00
J156 15 c. ultramarine .. .. 2·75 2·00
J158 50 c. black/*emerald* .. .. .. 1·75 2·75
J159 $1 black and red/*blue* £200 £250
J160 $5 green and red/*emerald* .. .. 24·00 38·00
a. Opt inverted £250 £300

(e) On Selangor

J162 **46** 3 c. green 40 60
J165 12 c. bright ultramarine .. .. .. 1·10 2·50
J166 15 c. ultramarine .. .. 2·75 2·00
J168 40 c. scarlet and dull purple .. .. 2·00 2·50
J170 **48** $2 green and scarlet .. .. .. 9·00 15·00

On T **22** the overprint is sideways, with "top" to left or right.

(f) On Trengganu (all Script wmk)

J172 **4** 1 c. black .. .. 4·00 5·00
J173 2 c. green £100 £140
J174 2 c. on 5 c. purple/*yellow* (No. 59) .. 4·50 4·75
J175 3 c. brown .. .. 7·00 9·00
J176 4 c. carmine-red .. .. 4·50 6·50
J177 5 c. purple/*yellow* .. .. .. 4·00 5·50
J178 6 c. orange .. .. 4·00 6·50
J179 8 c. grey .. .. 45·00 14·00
J180 8 c. on 10 c. bright blue (No. 60) .. 3·50 5·00
J181 12 c. bright ultramarine .. .. .. 3·50 6·50
J182 20 c. dull purple and orange .. .. 5·00 7·50
J183 25 c. green and deep purple .. .. 5·50 9·50
J184 30 c. dull purple and black .. .. 5·50 9·50
J185 $3 green and red/*green* .. .. .. 35·00 65·00

Nos. J172/85 were issued in Trengganu only.

1942. *No.* 108 *of Perak surch with T* **5**.

J186 **51** 2 c. on 5 c. brown .. .. .. 1·25 1·00

1942 (3 Nov). *Agri-horticultural Exhibition. Nos.* 294 *and* 283 *of Straits Settlements optd with T* **6**.

J187 **58** 2 c. orange .. .. 6·50 9·00
a. "C" for "G" in "SELANGOR" .. £130 £150
b. Opt inverted £300 £325
J188 8 c. grey .. .. 5·50 8·00
a. "C" for "G" in "SELANGOR" .. £130 £150
b. Opt inverted £300 £325

Nos. J187/8 were only issued in Selangor.

DAI NIPPON
2602
(7)

DAI NIPPON
2602
(8)

1942 (13 May). *Stamps of Kedah (Script wmk) optd. (a) With T* **7**.

J189 **1** 1 c. black (R.) .. .. 1·40 2·25
J190 2 c. bright green (R.) .. .. .. 16·00 22·00
J191 4 c. violet (R.) .. .. 1·75 1·50
J192 5 c. yellow (R.) .. .. 1·10 1·60
a. Black opt £150 £150
J193 6 c. carmine-red .. .. 1·25 2·25
J194 8 c. grey-black (R.) .. .. .. 1·90 1·50

(b) With T **8**

J195 **6** 10 c. ultramarine and sepia (R.) .. 3·25 4·00
J196 12 c. black and violet (R.) .. .. 7·50 12·00
J197 25 c. ultramarine and purple (R.) .. 3·25 5·00
a. Black opt £140 £150
J198 30 c. green and scarlet (R.) .. .. 32·00 45·00
J199 40 c. black and purple (R.) .. .. 9·00 16·00
J200 50 c. brown and blue (R.) .. .. 10·00 18·00
J201 $1 black and green (R.) £100 £110
a. Opt inverted £350 £350
J202 **6** $2 green and brown (R.) .. .. 90·00 £100
J203 $5 black and scarlet (R.) .. .. 30·00 32·00
a. Black opt £325 £325

Nos. J189 to J203a were issued in Kedah only.

奥川
(8*a*)
Okugawa Seal

内堀
(8*b*)
Ochiburi Seal

奥川亮印
(8*c*)
Okugawa-Ryo Seal

1942 (30 Mar). *Straits Settlements stamps optd.*

(a) As T **8***a* *(three forms of this seal)*

J203*b* **58** 1 c. black .. .. 5·50 5·50
J203*c* 2 c. orange .. .. 13·00 13·00
J203*d* 3 c. green .. .. 11·00 12·00
J203*e* 5 c. brown .. .. 12·00 12·00
J203*f* 8 c. grey .. .. 14·00 14·00
J203*g* 10 c. dull purple .. .. .. 22·00 22·00
J203*h* 12 c. ultramarine .. .. .. 13·00 14·00
J203*i* 15 c. ultramarine .. .. .. 14·00 15·00
J203*j* 40 c. scarlet and dull purple .. 50·00 55·00
J203*k* 50 c. black/*emerald* .. .. .. 75·00 80·00
J203*l* $1 black and red/*blue* £120 £130
J203*m* $2 green and scarlet £225 £250
J203*n* $5 green and red/*emerald* .. £650 £750

(b) With T **8***b*

J203*o* **58** 1 c. black .. .. 24·00 32·00
J203*p* 2 c. orange .. .. 24·00 32·00
J203*q* 3 c. green .. .. 24·00 32·00
J203*r* 5 c. brown £325 £325
J203*s* 8 c. grey .. .. 20·00 24·00
J203*t* 10 c. dull purple .. .. .. 20·00 24·00
J203*u* 12 c. ultramarine .. .. .. 20·00 24·00
J203*v* 15 c. ultramarine .. .. .. 20·00 24·00

Nos. J203*b*/*v* were issued only in Penang.

We have seen the 2 c. orange and 3 c. green overprinted with T *8c* supported by Expert Committee certificates and the 1 c. is also reported to exist. These are believed to be revenue stamps that have done postal duty without authorisation.

DAI NIPPON
2602
PENANG
(9)

DAI NIPPON
YUBIN
2 Cents
(10)
("Japanese Postal Service")

1942 (15 Apr). *Straits Settlements stamps optd with T* **9**.

J204 **58** 1 c. black (R.) .. .. 1·00 1·00
a. Opt inverted .. .. 75·00 75·00
J205 2 c. orange .. .. 3·50 2·75
a. "PE" for "PENANG" .. .. .. 40·00 45·00
b. Opt inverted .. .. 85·00
c. Opt double .. ..
J206 3 c. green (R.) .. .. 1·25 1·50
J207 5 c. brown (R.) .. .. 1·00 1·25
a. "N PPON" .. .. 70·00
b. Opt double .. ..
J208 8 c. grey (R.) .. .. 2·25 1·40
a. "N PPON" .. .. 30·00 35·00
b. Opt double, one inverted .. .. 85·00
J209 10 c. dull purple (R.) .. .. .. 1·50 2·00
a. Opt double £130
J210 12 c. ultramarine (R.) .. .. .. 2·00 3·25
a. "N PPON" £170
b. Opt double £170
c. Opt double, one inverted .. .. — £300
J211 15 c. ultramarine (R.) .. .. .. 1·75 2·00
a. "N PPON" .. .. 70·00 80·00
b. Opt inverted £225 £225
c. Opt double £225
J212 40 c. scarlet and dull purple .. .. 2·00 4·50
J213 50 c. black/*emerald* (R.) .. .. 2·50 6·50
J214 $1 black and red/*blue* .. .. 4·00 10·00
J215 $2 green and scarlet .. .. .. 16·00 30·00
J216 $5 green and red/*emerald* £225 £300

Nos. J204/16 were issued in Penang and Wellesley Province only.

1942 (Dec). *Perak stamps surch or optd only, as in T* **10**.

J217 **51** 1 c. black .. .. 2·00 2·75
a. Opt inverted .. .. 19·00 24·00
J218 2 c. on 5 c. brown .. .. .. 2·00 3·00
a. "DAI NIPPON YUBIN" inverted .. 17·00 20·00
b. Ditto and "2 Cents" omitted .. 30·00 42·00
J219 8 c. scarlet .. .. 2·75 1·00
a. Opt inverted .. .. 10·00 14·00

In December 1942 contemporary Japanese 3, 5, 8 and 25 s. stamps were issued without overprint in Singapore and the 1, 2, 4, 6, 7, 10, 30 and 50 s. and 1 y. values were issued in February 1943.

大日本郵便
(11)

大口本郵便
(11*a*) Error. Second Character Sideways

大日本郵便
("Japanese Postal Service")
(12)

6 cts.
(14)

6 cts.
(15)

2 Cents
(16)

6 cts.
(17)

$1.00
(18)

1943–45. *Stamps of the various Malayan territories optd with T* **11** *or* **12** *(so-called "Kanji" characters), in black or red, some stamps surch in addition as T* **14** *to* **18**. *(a) On Straits Settlements (opt T* **11**).

J221 **58** 8 c. grey (Blk.) 70 50
a. Opt inverted .. .. 27·00 30·00
b. Red opt 80 80
J222 12 c. ultramarine .. .. 55 1·60
J223 40 c. scarlet and dull purple .. .. 65 1·25

(b) On Negri Sembilan (opt T **11**)

J224 **6** 1 c. black 25 40
a. Opt inverted .. .. 7·00 11·00
b. Error. T **11***a* .. .. .. 13·00 14·00
ba. T **11***a* inverted £350
J225 2 c. on 5 c. brown (T **14**) 40 45
J226 6 c. on 5 c. brown (T **15**) 40 60
J227 25 c. dull purple and scarlet .. .. 1·10 2·25

(c) On Pahang (opt T **11**)

J228 **15** 6 c. on 5 c. brown (T **14**) 50 75
J229 6 c. on 5 c. brown (T **15**) .. .. 1·00 1·25

(d) On Perak (opt T **11**)

J230 **51** 1 c. black 70 60
a. Error. T **11***a* .. .. .. 90·00 95·00
J232 2 c. on 5 c. brown (T **14**) 50 50
a. Opt and surch inverted .. .. 18·00 27·00
b. Opt only inverted .. .. .. 18·00 27·00
c. Error. T **11***a* .. .. .. 32·00 35·00
J233 2 c. on 5 c. brown (T **16**) 45 45
a. Opt and surch inverted .. .. 18·00 27·00
b. Surch only inverted .. .. .. 18·00 27·00
c. Error. T **11***a* .. .. .. 24·00 26·00
ca. Opt and surch inverted £600
cb. Surch only inverted £550
J235 5 c. brown 45 40
a. Opt inverted .. .. 25·00 28·00
b. Error. T **11***a* £180 £300
J237 8 c. scarlet 55 50
a. Opt inverted .. .. 15·00 22·00
b. Error. T **11***a* .. .. .. 48·00 55·00
ba. T **11***a* inverted £550
J238 10 c. dull purple 60 50
J239 30 c. dull purple and orange .. .. 1·25 2·25
J240 50 c. black/*emerald* .. .. .. 3·00 5·50
J241 $5 green and red/*emerald* .. .. 35·00 50·00

(e) On Selangor

(i) *Opt T* **11** *placed horizontally either way on T* **46** *and vertically on T* **48**

J242 **46** 1 c. black 70 70
J243 3 c. green 40 45
a. Error. T **11***a* .. .. .. 15·00 19·00
J244 12 c. bright ultramarine 45 80
a. Error. T **11***a* .. .. .. 17·00 22·00
J245 15 c. ultramarine .. .. 2·75 3·00
a. Error. T **11***a* .. .. .. 27·00 32·00
J246 **48** $1 black and red/*blue* .. .. .. 3·00 5·50
a. Error. T **11***a* £190 £225
b. Opt inverted £225 £225
J247 $2 green and scarlet .. .. .. 10·00 16·00
J248 $5 green and red/*emerald* .. .. 22·00 42·00
a. Opt inverted £225 £225

(ii) *Opt T* **12**

J249 **46** 1 c. black (R.) 35 50
J250 2 c. on 5 c. brown (T **15**) (R.) 20 50
J251 3 c. on 5 c. brown (T **15**) 20 60
a. "s" in "cts" inverted .. .. 25·00 38·00
b. Comma after "cts" .. .. .. 25·00 38·00
J252 5 c. brown (R.) 30 60
J253 6 c. on 5 c. brown (T **15**) 20 60
J254 6 c. on 5 c. brown (T **17**) 15 50
a. "6" inverted £400
J255 15 c. ultramarine .. .. 4·00 4·00
J256 $1.00 on 10 c. dull purple (T **18**) .. 25 1·00
J257 $1.50 on 30 c. dull purple and orange (T **18**) .. .. 25 1·00

(f) On Trengganu (opt T **11**)

J258 **4** 1 c. black .. .. 4·00 9·00
J259 2 c. green .. .. 4·50 12·00
J260 2 c. on 5 c. purple/*yellow* (No. 59) .. 3·50 11·00
J261 5 c. purple/*yellow* .. .. .. 3·50 11·00
J262 6 c. orange .. .. 5·50 13·00
J263 8 c. grey .. .. 30·00 38·00
J264 8 c. on 10 c. bright blue (No. 60) .. 12·00 24·00
J265 10 c. bright blue .. .. 55·00 90·00
J266 12 c. bright ultramarine .. .. .. 6·50 17·00
J267 20 c. dull purple and orange .. .. 8·50 17·00
J268 25 c. green and deep purple .. .. 6·50 20·00
J269 30 c. dull purple and black .. .. 6·50 20·00
J270 35 c. carmine/*yellow* .. .. .. 6·50 20·00

Nos. J258/70 were issued in Trengganu only.

大日本
マライ郵便
50 セント
(18*a*)

大日本
マライ郵便
1ドル
(18*b*)

大日本
マライ郵便
1½ドル
(18*c*)

1944 (16 Dec). *Stamps intended for use on Red Cross letters. Surch with T* **18***a*/*c in red. (a) On Straits Settlements.*

J270*a* **58** 50 c. on 50 c. black/*emerald* .. .. 5·00 11·00
J270*b* $1 on $1 black and red/*blue* .. .. 8·00 16·00
J270*c* $1.50 on $2 green and scarlet .. .. 15·00 38·00

(b) On Johore

J270*d* **29** 50 c. on 50 c. dull purple and red .. 6·00 10·00
J270*e* $1.50 on $2 green and carmine .. 5·00 8·00

(c) On Selangor

J270*f* **48** $1 on $1 black and red/*blue* .. .. 4·00 9·00
J270*g* $1.50 on $2 green and scarlet .. .. 5·50 10·00

No. J270*a*/*g* were issued in Singapore but were withdrawn after one day, probably because supplies of Nos. J256/7 were received and issued on the 18 December.

19 Tapping Rubber

20 Fruit

24 Japanese Shrine, Singapore

(Litho in Batavia)

1943. *T* **19/20, 24** *and similar designs. P* 12½.
J271 **19** 1 c. grey-green (1 Oct) 15 25
J272 **20** 2 c. pale emerald (1 June) 15 15
J273 **19** 3 c. drab (1 Oct) 15 15
J274 – 4 c. carmine-rose (29 Apr) 15 15
J275 – 8 c. dull blue (29 Apr) 15 15
J276 – 10 c. brown-purple (1 Oct) 15 15
J277 **24** 15 c. violet (1 Oct) 35 50
J278 – 30 c. olive-green (1 Oct) 35 35
J279 – 50 c. blue (1 Oct) 75 65
J280 – 70 c. blue (1 Oct) 7·50 7·00
J271/80 *Set of* 10 8·50 8·00

Designs: *Vert*—4 c. Tin dredger; 8 c. War memorial; 10 c. Huts; 30 c. Sago palms; 50 c. Straits of Johore. *Horiz*—70 c. Malay Mosque, Kuala Lumpur.

28 Ploughman

29 Rice-planting

1943 (1 Sept). *Savings Campaign. Litho. P* 12½.
J281 **28** 8 c. violet 5·50 2·25
J282 15 c. scarlet 5·00 2·25

(Des Hon Chin. Litho)

1944 (15 Feb). *"Re-birth" of Malaya. P* 12½.
J283 **29** 8 c. rose-red 6·00 2·25
J284 15 c. magenta 4·00 2·50

POSTAGE DUE STAMPS

Postage Due stamps of the various Malayan territories overprinted.

1942 (3 Apr). *Handstamped with T* **2** *in black.*

(*a*) *On Malayan Postal Union*
JD 1 D 1 1 c. slate-purple 6·50 9·00
a. Red opt 15·00 18·00
b. Brown opt 32·00 38·00
JD 2 3 c. green 8·00 10·00
a. Red opt 28·00 40·00
JD 3 4 c. green 7·00 7·00
a. Red opt 16·00 22·00
b. Brown opt 40·00 45·00
JD 4 8 c. scarlet 10·00 12·00
a. Red opt 32·00 30·00
b. Brown opt 40·00 40·00
JD 5 10 c. yellow-orange 11·00 13·00
a. Red opt 18·00 22·00
b. Brown opt 20·00 26·00
JD 6 12 c. ultramarine 12·00 15·00
a. Red opt 35·00 40·00
JD 7 50 c. black 30·00 35·00
a. Red opt 75·00 85·00

(*b*) *On Johore*
JD 8 D 1 1 c. carmine (R.) 45·00
a. Black opt 35·00
JD 9 4 c. green (R.) 45·00
a. Black opt 45·00
JD10 8 c. orange (R.) 55·00
a. Black opt 35·00
JD11 10 c. brown (R.) 20·00
a. Black opt 12·00
JD12 12 c. purple (R.) 25·00
a. Black opt 19·00

The above were issued only in Johore.

(*c*) *On Trengganu*
JD13 D 1 1 c. scarlet 35·00 48·00
JD14 4 c. green 40·00 45·00
a. Red opt 35·00 45·00
JD15 8 c. yellow 12·00 25·00
JD16 10 c. brown 12·00 25·00

Nos. JD13/16 were issued in Trengganu only.

1942 (23 Apr). *Handstamped on Malayan Postal Union with T* **3**, *in red, each impression covering four stamps.*
JD17 D 1 1 c. slate-purple 60·00 60·00
JD18 4 c. green 85·00 85·00
JD19 8 c. scarlet £600 £600
JD20 10 c. yellow-orange £100 £100
JD21 12 c. ultramarine £125 £140
JD22 50 c. black £600 £700

Nos. JD17/22 were issued in Malacca only. Prices quoted are for single stamps. Blocks of four showing the complete handstamp are worth from six times the price of a single stamp.

1942. *Optd on Malayan Postal Union with T* **4**, *in black.*
JD23 D 1 1 c. slate-purple 85 1·40
JD24 3 c. green 3·25 4·50
JD25 4 c. green 3·25 4·50
JD26 8 c. scarlet 3·25 5·00
JD27 10 c. yellow-orange 1·60 3·00
JD28 12 c. ultramarine 1·60 3·50

1943–45. *Optd with T* **11**. (*a*) *On Malayan Postal Union.*
JD29 D 1 1 c. slate-purple 30 1·00
JD30 3 c. green 30 1·10
JD31 4 c. green 18·00 22·00
JD32 5 c. scarlet 50 1·40
JD33 D 1 9 c. yellow-orange 60 1·75
a. Opt inverted 24·00 25·00
JD34 10 c. yellow-orange 60 2·00
a. Opt inverted 38·00 38·00
JD35 12 c. ultramarine 60 2·25
JD36 15 c. ultramarine 60 2·25

(*b*) *On Johore*
JD37 D 1 1 c. carmine 1·25 4·00
a. Error. Optd with T **11*a*** 40·00 70·00
JD38 4 c. green 1·25 4·00
a. Error. Optd with T **11*a*** 40·00 70·00
JD39 8 c. orange 2·75 6·50
a. Error. Optd with T **11*a*** 55·00 90·00
JD40 10 c. brown 2·25 9·00
a. Error. Optd with T **11*a*** 55·00 90·00
JD41 12 c. purple 3·00 9·00
a. Error. Optd with T **11*a*** 55·00 90·00

Nos. JD37/41 were used only in Johore. Postage stamps of Johore optd with Type **4** were authorised for use for revenue purposes only.

B. KELANTAN

40 CENTS
(JK 1)

$1.00
(JK 2)

Sunagawa Seal

Handa Seal

1942 (June). *Kelantan stamps surch as Type* JK **1** *or* JK **2** (*dollar values*). (*a*) *With Sunagawa Seal in red.*
JK 1 **4** 1 c. on 50 c. grey-olive and orange £100 £110
JK 2 2 c. on 40 c. orange and blue-green £120 £130
JK 3 4 c. on 30 c. violet and scarlet £600 £650
JK 4 5 c. on 12 c. blue (R.) 80·00 90·00
JK 5 6 c. on 25 c. vermilion and violet 80·00 £100
JK 6 8 c. on 5 c. red-brown (R.) 90·00 £100
JK 7 10 c. on 6 c. lake 60·00 65·00
JK 8 12 c. on 8 c. grey-olive (R.) 38·00 48·00
JK 9 25 c. on 10 c. purple (R.) £700 £750
JK10 30 c. on 4 c. scarlet £950 £1000
JK11 40 c. on 2 c. green (R.) 42·00 50·00
JK12 50 c. on 1 c. grey-olive and yellow £600 £650
JK13 **1** $1 on 4 c. black & red (R., bars Blk.) 40·00 50·00
JK14 $2 on 5 c. green and red/*yellow* 40·00 50·00
JK15 $5 on 6 c. scarlet 40·00 50·00

(*b*) *With Handa Seal in red*
JK16 **4** 12 c. on 8 c. grey-olive (R.) 80·00 90·00

1 Cents
(JK 3)

1942. *Kelantan stamps surcharged as Type* JK **3**.

(*a*) *With Sunagawa Seal in red*
JK17 **4** 1 c. on 50 c. grey-olive and orange 50·00 55·00
a. "Cente" for "Cents" (R. 5/1) £300
JK18 2 c. on 40 c. orange and blue-green 50·00 55·00
a. "Cente" for "Cents" (R. 5/1) £300
JK19 5 c. on 12 c. blue (R.) 40·00 45·00
a. "Cente" for "Cents" (R. 5/1) £250
JK20 8 c. on 5 c. red-brown (R.) 35·00 35·00
a. "Cente" for "Cents" (R. 5/1) £225
JK21 10 c. on 6 c. lake 40·00 50·00
a. "Cente" for "Cents" (R. 5/1) £250
JK22 12 c. on 8 c. grey-olive (R.) 48·00 55·00
a. "Cente" for "Cents" (R. 5/1) £275
JK23 30 c. on 4 c. scarlet £650 £700
a. "Cente" for "Cents" (R. 5/1)
JK24 40 c. on 2 c. green (R.) 55·00 65·00
a. "Cente" for "Cents" (R. 5/1) £325
JK25 50 c. on 1 c. grey-olive and yellow £275 £300
a. "Cente" for "Cents" (R. 5/1)

(*b*) *With Handa Seal in red*
JK26 **4** 1 c. on 50 c. grey-olive and orange 65·00 75·00
a. "Cente" for "Cents" (R. 5/1) £375
JK27 2 c. on 40 c. orange and blue-green 60·00 75·00
a. "Cente" for "Cents" (R. 5/1) £375
JK28 8 c. on 5 c. red-brown (R.) 50·00 65·00
a. "Cente" for "Cents" (R. 5/1) £300
JK29 10 c. on 6 c. lake 60·00 75·00
a. "Cente" for "Cents" (R. 5/1) £375

All the above were overprinted with the personal Seals of Sunagawa, the Governor, or of Handa, the Assistant Governor, to indicate that these were Japanese stamps. Some of these also exist without the seals and come from remainder stocks sent to Singapore and Kuala Lumpur after Kelantan was ceded to Thailand.

IX. THAI OCCUPATION

Stamps issued for use in the four Malay States of Kedah, Kelantan, Perlis and Trengganu, ceded by Japan to Thailand on 19 October 1943 and restored to British rule on the defeat of the Japanese.

PRICES FOR STAMPS ON COVER	
Nos. TK1/5	*from* × 25
Nos. TM1/6	*from* × 20
Nos. TT1/29	*from* × 10

A. KELANTAN

TK 1

(Ptd at Khota Baru)

1943 (15 Nov). *Surch with value and inscr in black. No gum. P* 11.
TK1 TK 1 1 c. violet 45·00 55·00
TK2 2 c. violet 45·00 55·00
a. Violet omitted £300
TK3 4 c. violet 45·00 55·00
a. Violet omitted
TK4 8 c. violet 45·00 55·00
a. Violet omitted £250
TK5 10 c. violet 45·00 70·00

The above bear sheet watermarks in the form of "STANDARD" in block capitals with curved "CROWN" above and "AGENTS" below in double-lined capitals. This watermark occurs four times in the sheet.

These stamps but with centres printed in red were for fiscal use.

B. MALAYA

TM 1 War Memorial

(Litho Defence Ministry, Bangkok)

1943 (Dec). *Thick opaque, or thin semi-transparent paper. Gummed or ungummed. P* 12½.
TM1 TM 1 1 c. yellow 6·00 7·00
TM2 2 c. red-brown 2·50 4·25
a. Imperf (pair) £225
b. Perf 11½×11
TM3 3 c. green 4·50 7·00
a. Perf 11½×11
TM4 4 c. purple 2·75 4·50
a. Perf 11½×11
TM5 8 c. carmine 2·00 5·50
a. Perf 11½×11
TM6 15 c. blue 5·00 8·00
a. Perf 11½×11

5 c. and 10 c. stamps in this design were prepared, but never issued.

C. TRENGGANU

TRENGGANU
(TT 1)

(Overprinted at Trengganu Survey Office)

1944 (1 Oct). *Various stamps optd with Type* TT **1**.

(i) *On Trengganu stamp optd with T* **2**
TT 1 **4** 8 c. grey (J99) 90·00 55·00

(ii) *On stamps optd with T* **4**. (*a*) *Pahang*
TT 2 **15** 12 c. bright ultramarine (J147) 90·00 55·00

(*b*) *Trengganu*
TT 3 **4** 2 c. on 5 c. purple/*yellow* (J174)* 90·00 90·00
TT 4 8 c. on 10 c. bright bl (J180) (inverted) 55·00 55·00
TT 5 12 c. brt ultramarine (J181) (inverted) 55·00 55·00

*This is spelt "TRENGANU" with one "G".

(iii) *On stamps optd with T* **11**. (*a*) *Straits Settlements*
TT 6 **58** 12 c. ultramarine (J222) 90·00 90·00
TT 7 40 c. scarlet and dull purple (J223) 90·00 90·00

(*b*) *On Perak*
TT 8 **51** 30 c. dull purple and orange (J239) £190 90·00

(*c*) *On Selangor*
TT 9 **46** 3 c. green (J243) 55·00 50·00
TT10 12 c. bright ultramarine (J244) (L. to R.) 50·00 45·00
TT11 12 c. bright ultramarine (J244) (R. to L.) 42·00 40·00
a. Error. T **11*a*** £650 £650

(iv) *On Selangor stamps optd with T* **12**
TT12 **46** 2 c. on 5 c. brown (J250) 90·00 90·00
TT13 3 c. on 5 c. brown (J251) 90·00 90·00

(v) *On pictorials of* 1943 (*Nos.* J271 *etc.*)
TT14 **19** 1 c. grey-green 95·00 £120
TT15 **20** 2 c. pale emerald 95·00 60·00
TT16 **19** 3 c. drab £100 £100
TT17 **21** 4 c. carmine-rose £100 £100
TT18 **22** 8 c. dull blue £190 £190
TT19 **23** 10 c. brown-purple
TT20 **24** 15 c. violet £120 95·00
TT21 **25** 30 c. olive-green £120 70·00
TT22 **26** 50 c. blue £180 £180
TT23 **27** 70 c. blue £325 £325

(vi) *On Savings Campaign stamps* (*Nos.* J281/2)
TT24 **28** 8 c. violet £180 £180
TT25 15 c. scarlet £180 £180

(vii) *On stamps of Japan*
TT26 – 5 s. claret (No. 396) £130 £150
TT27 – 25 s. brown and chocolate (No. 329) 65·00 50·00
TT28 – 30 s. blue-green (No. 330) £130 90·00

(viii) *On Trengganu Postage Due stamp optd with T* **2**
TT29 D 1 1 c. scarlet (JD13) £550 £550

Maldive Islands

PRICES FOR STAMPS ON COVER TO 1945

Nos. 1/6	*from* × 10
Nos. 7/10	*from* × 50
Nos. 11/20	*from* × 20

BRITISH PROTECTORATE

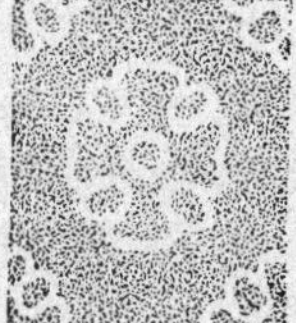

MALDIVES

(1)   2 Minaret, Juma Mosque, Malé   3

1906. *Stamps of Ceylon optd with T* **1**. *Wmk Mult Crown CA. P* 14.

No.	Type	Description	Unused	Used
1	**44**	2 c. orange-brown, **O**	11·00	20·00
2	**45**	3 c. green, **O**	15·00	20·00
3		4 c. orange and ultramarine, **O**	32·00	60·00
4	**46**	5 c. dull purple, **C**	4·50	6·50
5	**48**	15 c. blue, **O**	50·00	80·00
6		25 c. bistre, **O**	60·00	80·00
1/6		*Set of* 6	£150	£225

(Recess D.L.R.)

1909 (May). *T* **2** (18½ × 22½ *mm*). *W* **3**. *P* 14.

No.	Type	Description	Unused	Used
7	**2**	2 c. orange-brown	2·25	70
8		3 c. deep myrtle	40	70
9		5 c. purple	40	35
10		10 c. carmine	2·00	80
7/10		*Set of* 4	4·50	2·25

4

(Photo Harrison)

1933. *T* **2** *redrawn (reduced to* 18 × 21½ *mm). W* **4**. *P* 15 × 14.

No.	Type	Description	Unused	Used
11	**2**	2 c. grey	90	90
12		3 c. red-brown	70	1·50
13		5 c. claret (*vert wmk*)	10·00	13·00
14		5 c. mauve (*horiz wmk*)	4·00	7·00
15		6 c. scarlet	1·25	1·60
16		10 c. green	55	55
17		15 c. black	2·50	4·50
18		25 c. brown	3·00	4·50
19		50 c. purple	2·75	2·75
20		1 r. deep blue	4·25	2·75
11/20		*Set of* 10	27·00	35·00

All values exist with both vert and horiz wmks.

(New Currency. 100 larees=1 rupee)

5 Palm Tree and Dhow

(Recess B.W.)

1950 (24 Dec). *P* 13.

No.	Type	Description	Unused	Used
21	**5**	2 l. olive-green	50	40
22		3 l. blue	2·50	40
23		5 l. emerald-green	2·50	50
24		6 l. red-brown	35	20
25		10 l. scarlet	35	20
26		15 l. orange	35	25
27		25 l. purple	35	25
28		50 l. violet	40	25
29		1 r. chocolate	6·50	13·00
21/9		*Set of* 9	12·00	14·00

7 Fish

8 Native Products

(Recess B.W.)

1952. *P* 13.

No.	Type	Description	Unused	Used
30	**7**	3 l. blue	30	15
31	**8**	5 l. emerald	10	10

The Maldive Islands became a republic on 1 January 1953, but reverted to a sultanate in 1954.

9 Malé Harbour

10 Fort and Building

(Recess B.W.)

1956 (Feb). *P* 13½ (*T* **9**) *or* 11½ × 11 (*T* **10**).

No.	Type	Description	Unused	Used
32	**9**	2 l. purple	10	10
33		3 l. slate	10	10
34		5 l. red-brown	10	10
35		6 l. blackish violet	10	10
36		10 l. emerald	10	10
37		15 l. chocolate	10	10
38		25 l. rose-red	10	10
39		50 l. orange	10	10
40	**10**	1 r. bluish green	15	10
41		5 r. blue	60	20
42		10 r. magenta	85	40
32/42		*Set of* 11	1·75	80

11 Cycling

12 Basketball

(Des C. Bottiau. Recess and typo B.W.)

1960 (20 Aug). *Olympic Games. P* 11½ × 11 (*T* **11**) *or* 11 × 11½ (*T* **12**).

No.	Type	Description	Unused	Used
43	**11**	2 l. purple and green	10	10
44		3 l. greenish slate and purple	10	10
45		5 l. red-brown and ultramarine	10	10
46		10 l. emerald-green and brown	10	10
47		15 l. sepia and blue	10	10
48	**12**	25 l. rose-red and olive	10	10
49		50 l. orange and violet	10	10
50		1 r. emerald and purple	20	35
43/50		*Set of* 8	60	65

13 Tomb of Sultan

14 Custom House

(Recess B.W.)

1960 (15 Oct). *T* **13, 14** *and similar horiz designs. P* 11½ × 11.

No.	Description	Unused	Used
51	2 l. purple	10	10
52	3 l. emerald-green	10	10
53	5 l. orange-brown	10	10
54	6 l. bright blue	10	10
55	10 l. carmine	10	10
56	15 l. sepia	10	10
57	25 l. deep violet	10	10
58	50 l. slate-grey	10	10
59	1 r. orange	15	10
60	5 r. deep ultramarine	1·50	60
61	10 r. grey-green	3·50	1·25
51/61	*Set of* 11	5·00	2·00

Designs:—5 l. Cowrie shells; 6 l. Old Royal Palace; 10 l. Road to Juma Mosque, Malé; 15 l. Council house; 25 l. New Government Secretariat; 50 l. Prime Minister's office; 1 r. Old Ruler's tomb; 5 r. Old Ruler's tomb (distant view); 10 r. Maldivian Port.

Higher values were also issued, intended mainly for fiscal use.

24 "Care of Refugees"

(Recess B.W.)

1960 (15 Oct). *World Refugee Year. P* 11½ × 11.

No.	Type	Description	Unused	Used
62	**24**	2 l. deep violet, orange and green	10	10
63		3 l. brown, green and red	10	10
64		5 l. deep green, sepia and red	10	10
65		10 l. bluish green, reddish violet and red	10	10
66		15 l. reddish violet, grey-green and red	10	10
67		25 l. blue, red-brown and bronze-green	10	10
68		50 l. yellow-olive, rose-red and blue	10	10
69		1 r. carmine, slate and violet	15	35
62/9		*Set of* 8	30	45

MINIMUM PRICE

The minimum price quote is 10p which represents a handling charge rather than a basis for valuing common stamps. For further notes about prices see introductory pages.

25 Coconuts

26 Map of Malé

(Photo Harrison)

1961 (20 Apr). *P* 14 × 14½ (*Nos.* 70/74) *or* 14½ × 14 (*others*).

No.	Type	Description	Unused	Used
70	**25**	2 l. yellow-brown and deep green	10	10
71		3 l. yellow-brown and bright blue	10	10
72		5 l. yellow-brown and magenta	10	10
73		10 l. yellow-brown and red-orange	10	10
74		15 l. yellow-brown and black	10	10
75	**26**	25 l. multicoloured	10	10
76		50 l. multicoloured	10	10
77		1 r. multicoloured	20	30
70/7		*Set of* 8	45	55

27 5 c. Stamp of 1906

30 Malaria Eradication Emblem

(Des M. Shamir. Photo Harrison)

1961 (9 Sept). *55th Anniv of First Maldivian Stamp. T* **27** *and similar horiz designs. P* 14½ × 14.

No.	Description	Unused	Used
78	2 l. brown-purple, ultramarine & lt green	10	10
79	3 l. brown-purple, ultramarine & lt green	10	10
80	5 l. brown-purple, ultramarine & lt green	10	10
81	6 l. brown-purple, ultramarine & lt green	10	10
82	10 l. green, claret and maroon	10	10
83	15 l. green, claret and maroon	10	10
84	20 l. green, claret and maroon	10	10
85	25 l. claret, green and black	10	10
86	50 l. claret, green and black	20	35
87	1 r. claret, green and black	35	65
78/87	*Set of* 10	75	1·25
MS87*a*	114 × 88 mm. No. 87 (block of four). Imperf	1·50	2·75

Designs:—2 to 6 l. Type **27**; 10 to 20 l. 1906 3 c. and posthorn; 25 l. to 1 r. 1906 2 c. and olive sprig.

(Recess B.W.)

1962 (7 Apr). *Malaria Eradication. P* 13½ × 13.

No.	Type	Description	Unused	Used
88	**30**	2 l. chestnut	10	10
89		3 l. emerald	10	10
90		5 l. turquoise-blue	10	10
91		10 l. red	10	10
92	–	15 l. deep purple-brown	10	10
93	–	25 l. deep blue	10	10
94	–	50 l. deep green	10	10
95	–	1 r. purple	25	25
88/95		*Set of* 8	50	45

Nos. 92/5 are as T **30**, but have English inscriptions at the side.

31 Children of Europe and America   33 Sultan Mohamed Farid Didi

(Des C. Bottiau. Photo Harrison)

1962 (9 Sept). *15th Anniv of U.N.I.C.E.F. T* **31** *and similar horiz design. Multicoloured. P* 14½ × 14.

No.	Description	Unused	Used
96	2 l. Type **31**	10	10
97	6 l. Type **31**	10	10
98	10 l. Type **31**	10	10
99	15 l. Type **31**	10	10
100	25 l. Children of Middle East and Far East	10	10
101	50 l. As 25 l.	10	10
102	1 r. As 25 l.	10	20
103	5 r. As 25 l.	45	1·50
96/103	*Set of* 8	70	1·75

(Photo Harrison)

1962 (29 Nov). *Ninth Anniv of Enthronement of Sultan. P* 14 × 14½.

No.	Type	Description	Unused	Used
104	**33**	3 l. orange-brown and bluish green	10	10
105		5 l. orange-brown and indigo	10	10
106		10 l. orange-brown and blue	10	10
107		20 l. orange-brown and olive-green	10	10
108		50 l. orange-brown and deep magenta	10	10
109		1 r. orange-brown and slate-lilac	15	25
104/9		*Set of* 6	35	45

34 Angel Fish

(Des R. Hegeman. Photo Enschedé)

1963 (2 Feb). *Tropical Fish. T* **34** *and similar triangular designs. Multicoloured. P* 13½.

No.	Type	Description	Unused	Used
110		2 l. Type **34**	10	10
111		3 l. Type **34**	10	10
112		5 l. Type **34**	10	10
113		10 l. Moorish Idol	10	10
114		25 l. As 10 l.	10	10
115		50 l. Soldier Fish	10	10
116		1 r. Surgeon Fish	30	30
117		5 r. Butterfly Fish	2·50	3·50
110/17		*Set of* 8	2·75	3·75

39 Fishes in Net **40** Handful of Grain

(Photo State Ptg Wks, Vienna)

1963 (21 Mar). *Freedom from Hunger. P* 12.

No.	Type	Description	Unused	Used
118	**39**	2 l. brown and deep bluish green	25	40
119	**40**	5 l. brown and orange-red	45	40
120	**39**	7 l. brown and turquoise	55	40
121	**40**	10 l. brown and blue	70	40
122	**39**	25 l. brown and brown-red	2·50	2·75
123	**40**	50 l. brown and violet	4·00	5·00
124	**39**	1 r. brown and deep magenta	7·00	9·00
118/24		*Set of* 7	14·00	17·00

41 Centenary Emblem **42** Maldivian Scout Badge

(Photo Harrison)

1963 (Oct). *Centenary of Red Cross. P* 14 × 14½.

No.	Type	Description	Unused	Used
125	**41**	2 l. red and deep purple	25	40
126		15 l. red and deep bluish green	50	45
127		50 l. red and deep brown	1·25	85
128		1 r. red and indigo	2·00	1·25
129		4 r. red and deep brown-olive	6·50	14·00
125/9		*Set of* 5	9·50	15·00

(Photo Enschedé)

1964. *World Scout Jamboree, Marathon* (1963). *P* 13½.

No.	Type	Description	Unused	Used
130	**42**	2 l. green and violet	10	10
131		3 l. green and bistre-brown	10	10
132		25 l. green and blue	10	10
133		1 r. green and crimson	45	85
130/3		*Set of* 4	60	95

43 Mosque, Malé **44** Putting the Shot

(Recess B.W.)

1964 (10 Aug). *"Maldives Embrace Islam". W w* **12**. *P* 11½.

No.	Type	Description	Unused	Used
134	**43**	2 l. purple	10	10
135		3 l. emerald-green	10	10
136		10 l. carmine	10	10
137		40 l. deep dull purple	10	10
138		60 l. blue	15	10
139		85 l. orange-brown	20	15
134/9		*Set of* 6	50	40

(Litho Enschedé)

1964 (Oct). *Olympic Games, Tokyo. T* **44** *and similar horiz design. W w* **12**. *P* 14 × 13½.

No.	Type	Description	Unused	Used
140		2 l. deep maroon and turquoise-blue	10	10
141		3 l. crimson and chestnut	10	10
142		5 l. bronze-green and deep green	10	10
143		10 l. slate-violet and reddish purple	10	10
144		15 l. sepia and yellow-brown	10	10
145		25 l. indigo and deep blue	20	10
146		50 l. deep olive-green and yellow-olive	45	20
147		1 r. deep maroon and olive-grey	85	40
140/7		*Set of* 8	1·60	70
MS147*a*		126 × 140 mm. Nos. 145/7. Imperf	1·75	2·25

Designs:—2 to 10 l. Type **44**; 15 l. to 1 r. Running.

46 Telecommunications Satellite

(Des M. Shamir. Photo Harrison)

1965 (1 July). *International Quiet Sun Years. P* 14½.

No.	Type	Description	Unused	Used
148	**46**	5 l. blue	10	10
149		10 l. brown	15	10
150		25 l. green	25	10
151		1 r. deep magenta	50	35
148/51		*Set of* 4	90	50

On 26 July 1965, Maldive Islands became independent and left the British Commonwealth.

INDEPENDENT SULTANATE

Sultan Mohamed Farid Didi
29 November 1953–10 November 1968

47 Isis (wall carving, Abu Simbel) **48** President Kennedy and Doves

(Des M. and G. Shamir. Litho Harrison)

1965 (1 Sept). *Nubian Monuments Preservation. T* **47** *and similar vert design. W w* **12**. *P* 14½.

No.	Type	Description	Unused	Used
152	**47**	2 l. bluish green and brown-purple	10	10
153	–	3 l. lake and deep green	10	10
154	**47**	5 l. dull green and brown-purple	10	10
155	–	10 l. steel-blue and orange	10	10
156	**47**	15 l. red-brown and deep violet	10	10
157	–	25 l. reddish purple and deep blue	15	10
158	**47**	50 l. yellow-green and sepia	25	15
159	–	1 r. ochre and myrtle-green	50	30
152/9		*Set of* 8	1·00	70

Design:—3, 10, 25 l., 1 r. Rameses II on throne (wall carving, Abu Simbel).

(Photo State Ptg Wks, Vienna)

1965 (10 Oct). *Second Death Anniv of President Kennedy. T* **48** *and similar horiz design. P* 12.

No.	Type	Description	Unused	Used
160	**48**	2 l. black and mauve	10	10
161		5 l. bistre-brown and mauve	10	10
162		25 l. indigo and mauve	10	10
163	–	1 r. brt reddish purple, yellow & bl-grn	25	25
164	–	2 r. bronze-green, yellow & blue-green	40	40
160/4		*Set of* 5	75	75
MS164*a*		150 × 130 mm. No. 164 in block of four. Imperf	2·75	3·00

Design:—1 r., 2 r. Pres. Kennedy and hands holding olive-branch.

49 "XX" and U.N. Flag **50** I.C.Y. Emblem

(Des O. Adler. Photo State Ptg Wks, Vienna)

1965 (24 Nov). *20th Anniv of U.N. P* 12.

No.	Type	Description	Unused	Used
165	**49**	3 l. turquoise-blue and red-brown	10	10
166		10 l. turquoise-blue and violet	10	10
167		1 r. turquoise-blue and bronze-green	35	35
165/7		*Set of* 3	40	40

(Des M. and G. Shamir. Photo State Ptg Wks, Vienna)

1965 (20 Dec). *International Co-operation Year. P* 12.

No.	Type	Description	Unused	Used
168	**50**	5 l. brown and yellow-bistre	10	10
169		15 l. brown and slate-lilac	15	10
170		50 l. brown and yellow-olive	35	25
171		1 r. brown and orange-red	1·00	1·00
172		2 r. brown and new blue	1·75	2·00
168/72		*Set of* 5	3·00	3·00
MS173		101 × 126 mm. Nos. 170/2. Imperf	4·50	5·00

51 Seashells

(Des M. and G. Shamir. Photo State Ptg Wks, Vienna)

1966 (1 June). *T* **51** *and similar multicoloured designs. P* 12.

No.	Type	Description	Unused	Used
174		2 l. Type **51**	10	10
175		3 l. Yellow flowers	10	10
176		5 l. Seashells (*different*)	15	10
177		7 l. Camellias	15	10
178		10 l. Type **51**	20	10
179		15 l. Crab Plover and Seagull	75	15
180		20 l. Yellow flowers	50	15
181		30 l. Type **51**	70	15
182		50 l. Crab Plover and Seagull	1·75	30
183		1 r. Type **51**	1·25	30
184		1 r. Camellias	1·25	30
185		1 r. 50, Yellow flowers	2·00	65
186		2 r. Camellias	2·75	90
187		5 r. Crab Plover and Seagull	7·00	4·50
188		10 r. Seashells (*different*)	11·00	9·00
174/88		*Set of* 15	27·00	15·00

The 3 l., 7 l., 20 l., 1 r. (No. 184), 1 r. 50 and 2 r. are diamond-shaped (43½ × 43½ mm); the others are horizontal designs as T **51**.

52 Maldivian Flag

(Des M. and G. Shamir. Litho Harrison)

1966 (26 July). *First Anniv of Independence. P* 14 × 14½.

No.	Type	Description	Unused	Used
189	**52**	10 l. green, red and turquoise	10	10
190		1 r. green, red, brown & orange-yellow	30	30

53 "Luna 9" on Moon

(Des M. and G. Shamir. Litho Harrison)

1966 (1 Nov). *Space Rendezvous and Moon Landing. T* **53** *and similar horiz designs. W w* **12**. *P* 15 × 14.

No.	Type	Description	Unused	Used
191		10 l. light brown, grey-blue and bright blue	10	10
192		25 l. green and carmine	10	10
193		50 l. orange-brown and green	15	15
194		1 r. turquoise-blue and chestnut	35	35
195		2 r. green and violet	65	65
196		5 r. rose-pink and deep turquoise-blue	1·60	1·60
191/6		*Set of* 6	2·50	2·50
MS197		108 × 126 mm. Nos. 194/6. Imperf	3·25	3·75

Designs:—25 l., 1 r., 5 r. "Gemini 6" and "7" rendezvous in space; 2 r. "Gemini" spaceship as seen from the other spaceship; 50 l. Type **53**.

54 U.N.E.S.C.O. Emblem, and Owl on Book **55** Sir Winston Churchill and Cortège

(Litho Harrison)

1966 (15 Nov). *20th Anniv of U.N.E.S.C.O. T* **54** *and similar vert designs. W w* **12**. *Multicoloured. P* 15 × 14.

No.	Type	Description	Unused	Used
198		1 l. Type **54**	10	15
199		3 l. U.N.E.S.C.O. emblem, and globe and microscope	10	15
200		5 l. U.N.E.S.C.O. emblem, and mask, violin and palette	10	15
201		50 l. Type **54**	40	30
202		1 r. Design as 3 l.	75	65
203		5 r. Design as 5 l.	4·50	6·00
198/203		*Set of* 6	5·00	6·50

(Des M. and G. Shamir. Litho Harrison)

1967 (1 Jan). *Churchill Commemoration. T* **55** *and similar horiz design. Flag in red and blue. P* 14½ × 13½.
204 **55** 2 l. olive-brown . . 10 15
205 – 10 l. turquoise-blue . . 20 10
206 **55** 15 l. green . . 35 10
207 – 25 l. violet . . 60 10
208 – 1 r. brown . . 2·25 75
209 **55** 2 r. 50, crimson . . 5·50 6·00
204/9 . . *Set of* 6 8·00 6·50
Design:—10 l., 25 l., 1 r. Churchill and catafalque.

IMPERFORATE STAMPS. From No. 210 onwards some sets and perforated miniature sheets exist imperforate from limited printings.

56 Footballers and Jules Rimet Cup

(Des M. and G. Shamir. Photo Govt Printer, Israel)

1967 (22 Mar). *England's Victory in World Cup Football Championships. T* **56** *and similar horiz designs. P* 14 × 13½.
210 2 l. greenish blue, black and red . . 10 10
211 3 l. red, black and yellow-olive . . 10 10
212 5 l. greenish yellow, black & reddish violet 10 10
213 25 l. orange, black and emerald . . 10 10
214 50 l. green, black and orange . . 30 15
215 1 r. orange, black and greenish blue . . 75 35
216 2 r. brown, red, royal blue and black . . 1·50 1·25
210/16 . . *Set of* 7 2·50 1·75
MS217 100 × 121 mm. Nos. 214/16. Imperf . . 3·50 4·25
Designs:—3 l. to 50 l. Various football scenes; 1 r. Type **56**; 2 r. Emblem on Union Jack, and Clock Tower, Westminster.

57 Clown Butterfly Fish

(Des M. and G. Shamir. Photo Govt Printer, Israel)

1967 (1 May). *Tropical Fishes. T* **57** *and similar horiz designs. Multicoloured. P* 14.
218 2 l. Type **57** . . 10 15
219 3 l. Striped Puffer . . 10 15
220 5 l. Blue Spotted Boxfish . . 15 10
221 6 l. Picasso Fish . . 15 15
222 50 l. Blue Angelfish . . 1·00 15
223 1 r. Blue Spotted Boxfish . . 2·25 55
224 2 r. Blue Angelfish . . 3·00 3·00
218/24 . . *Set of* 7 6·00 3·75

58 Hawker Siddeley "HS748" over Airport Building

(Des M. and G. Shamir. Photo Govt Printer, Israel)

1967 (26 July). *Inauguration of Hulule Airport. T* **58** *and similar horiz design. P* 14 × 13½.
225 2 l. reddish violet and yellow-olive . . 10 20
226 5 l. deep green and lavender . . 10 10
227 10 l. reddish violet and light turquoise-green 10 10
228 15 l. deep green and yellow-ochre . . 10 10
229 30 l. deep ultramarine and light blue . . 20 10
230 50 l. deep brown and magenta . . 35 15
231 5 r. deep ultramarine and yellow-orange . . 2·00 3·00
232 10 r. deep brown and blue . . 3·75 4·75
225/32 . . *Set of* 8 6·00 7·50
Designs:—2 l., 10 l., 30 l., 5 r. T **58**; 5 l., 15 l., 50 l., 10 r. Airport building and aircraft. Higher values were also issued, intended mainly for fiscal use.

59 "Man and Music" Pavilion

International Tourist Year 1967

(60)

(Des M. and G. Shamir. Photo Govt Printer, Israel)

1967 (Sept). *World Fair, Montreal. T* **59** *and similar horiz design. Multicoloured. P* 14 × 13½.
233 2 l. Type **59** . . 10 10
234 5 l. "Man and His Community" Pavilion . . 10 10
235 10 l. Type **59** . . 10 10
236 50 l. As 5 l. . . 20 20
237 1 r. Type **59** . . 40 40
238 2 r. As 5 l. . . 70 70
233/8 . . *Set of* 6 1·25 1·25
MS239 102 × 137 mm. Nos. 237/8. Imperf . . 2·25 2·25

1967 (1 Dec). *International Tourist Year. Nos. 225/32 optd as T* **60** *(in one or three lines), in gold.*
240 2 l. reddish violet and yellow-olive . . 10 20
241 5 l. deep green and lavender . . 10 15
242 10 l. reddish violet and light turquoise-green 10 15
243 15 l. deep green and yellow-ochre . . 10 15
244 30 l. deep ultramarine and light blue . . 15 20
245 50 l. deep brown and magenta . . 15 20
246 5 r. deep ultramarine and yellow-orange . . 2·00 2·50
247 10 r. deep brown and blue . . 3·50 4·25
240/7 . . *Set of* 8 5·50 7·00

61 Cub signalling and Lord Baden-Powell

62 French Satellite "A 1"

(Litho Harrison)

1968 (1 Jan). *Maldivian Scouts and Cubs. T* **61** *and similar vert design. P* 14 × 14½.
248 **61** 2 l. brown, green and yellow . . 10 20
249 – 3 l. carmine, bright blue and light blue 10 20
250 **61** 25 l. bluish violet, lake and orange-red . . 75 25
251 – 1 r. blackish green, chest & apple-green 2·50 1·40
248/51 . . *Set of* 4 3·00 1·90
Design:—3 l., 1 r. Scouts and Lord Baden-Powell.

(Des M. and G. Shamir. Photo Govt Printer, Israel)

1968 (27 Jan). *Space Martyrs. Triangular designs as T* **62**. *P* 14.
252 2 l. magenta and ultramarine . . 10 20
253 3 l. violet and yellow-brown . . 10 20
254 7 l. olive-brown and lake . . 10 20
255 10 l. deep blue, pale drab and black . . 10 15
256 25 l. bright emerald and reddish violet 30 15
257 50 l. blue and orange-brown . . 55 30
258 1 r. purple-brown and deep bluish green 75 50
259 2 r. deep brown, pale blue and black . . 1·25 1·25
260 5 r. magenta, light drab and black . . 2·25 2·25
252/60 . . *Set of* 9 4·75 4·75
MS261 110 × 155 mm. Nos. 258/9. Imperf . . 3·25 3·25
Designs:—2 l., 50 l. Type **62**; 3 l., 25 l. "Luna 10"; 7 l., 1 r. "Orbiter" and "Mariner"; 10 l., 2 r. Astronauts White, Grissom and Chaffee; 5 r. Cosmonaut V. M. Komarov.

63 Putting the Shot

64 "Adriatic Seascape" (Bonington)

(Des M. Shamir. Litho Harrison)

1968 (Feb). *Olympic Games, Mexico* (1967) (*1st issue*). *T* **63** *and similar vert design. Multicoloured. P* 14½.
262 2 l. Type **63** . . 10 10
263 6 l. Throwing the discus . . 10 10
264 10 l. Type **63** . . 10 10
265 15 l. As 6 l. . . 10 10
266 1 r. Type **63** . . 35 35
267 2 r. 50, As 6 l. . . 65 65
262/7 . . *Set of* 6 1·10 1·10
See also Nos. 294/7.

(Des M. Shamir. Litho Govt Printer, Israel)

1968 (1 Apr). *Paintings. T* **64** *and similar horiz designs. Multicoloured. P* 14.
268 50 l. Type **64** . . 20 15
269 1 r. "Ulysses deriding Polyphemus" (Turner) 40 35
270 2 r. "Sailing Boat at Argenteuil" (Monet) 85 85
271 5 r. "Fishing Boats at Les Saintes-Maries" (Van Gogh) . . 2·75 2·75
268/71 . . *Set of* 4 3·75 3·75

65 *Graf Zeppelin* and Montgolfier's Balloon

(Des M. Shamir. Photo Govt Printer, Israel)

1968 (1 June). *Development of Civil Aviation. T* **65** *and similar horiz designs. P* 14 × 13½.
272 2 l. orange-brown, yellow-green & ultram . . 10 20
273 3 l. turquoise-blue, violet & orange-brown . . 10 20
274 5 l. slate-green, crimson and turquoise-blue . . 15 15
275 7 l. bright blue, purple and red-orange . . 20 15
276 10 l. brown, turquoise-blue and bright purple . . 20 15
277 50 l. crimson, slate-green and yellow-olive . . 1·00 20
278 1 r. emerald, blue and vermilion . . 1·75 45
279 2 r. maroon, bistre and bright blue . . 7·50 7·00
272/9 . . *Set of* 8 10·00 7·75
Designs:—3 l., 1 r. Boeing "707" and Douglas "DC-3"; 5 l., 50 l. Wright Brothers aircraft and Lilienthal's glider; 7 l., 2 r. Projected Boeing Supersonic "733" and "Concorde"; 10 l. Type **65**.

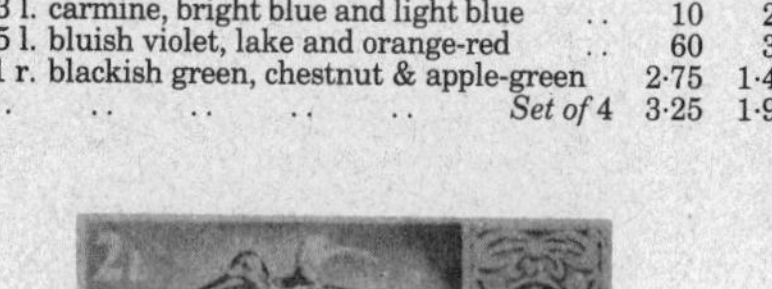

66 W.H.O. Building, Geneva

International Boy Scout Jamboree, Farragut Park, Idaho, U.S.A. August 1-9, 1967

(67)

(Litho Harrison)

1968 (15 July). *20th Anniv of World Health Organisation. P* 14½ × 13½.
280 **66** 10 l. violet, turquoise-bl & lt greenish bl 20 10
281 25 l. bronze-green, yell-brn & orge-yell . . 45 10
282 1 r. deep brown, emerald & brt green . . 1·50 65
283 2 r. bluish violet, magenta and mauve . . 3·00 3·25
280/3 . . *Set of* 4 4·50 3·50

1968 (1 Aug). *First Anniv of Scout Jamboree, Idaho. Nos. 248/51 optd with T* **67**.
284 2 l. brown, green and yellow . . 10 20
285 3 l. carmine, bright blue and light blue . . 10 20
286 25 l. bluish violet, lake and orange-red . . 60 30
287 1 r. blackish green, chestnut & apple-green 2·75 1·40
284/7 . . *Set of* 4 3·25 1·90

68 Curlew and Redshank

1968 (24 Sept). *T* **68** *and similar horiz designs. Photo. Multicoloured. P* 14 × 13½.
288 2 l. Type **68** . . 15 25
289 10 l. Conches . . 40 15
290 25 l. Shells . . 75 20
291 50 l. Type **68** . . 2·50 55
292 1 r. Conches . . 2·50 70
293 2 r. Shells . . 2·75 3·00
288/93 . . *Set of* 6 8·00 4·25

69 Throwing the Discus

(Des M. Shamir. Photo Govt Printer, Israel)

1968 (12 Oct). *Olympic Games, Mexico (2nd issue). T* **69** *and similar multicoloured designs. P* 14.
294 10 l. Type **69** . . 10 10
295 50 l. Running . . 10 10
296 1 r. Cycling . . 35 35
297 2 r. Basketball . . 75 75
294/7 . . *Set of* 4 1·10 1·10

INDEPENDENT REPUBLIC

11 November 1968

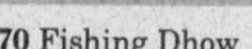

70 Fishing Dhow

71 "The Thinker" (Rodin)

(Photo Harrison)

1968 (11 Nov). *Republic Day. T* **70** *and similar horiz design. P* 14 × 14½.

298 10 l. brown, ultramarine and lt yellow-green .. 40 15
299 1 r. green, red and bright blue .. .. 1·25 60

Design:—1 r. National flag, crest and map.

(Des M. Shamir. Litho Rosenbaum Brothers, Vienna)

1969 (10 Apr). *U.N.E.S.C.O. "Human Rights". T* **71** *and similar vert designs, showing sculptures by Rodin. Multicoloured. P* 13½.

300 6 l. Type **71** 15 10
301 10 l. "Hands" 15 10
302 1 r. 50, "Eve" .. .. 1·25 1·00
303 2 r. 50, "Adam" .. .. 1·75 1·75
300/3 .. .. *Set of* 4 3·00 2·75
MS304 112 × 130 mm. Nos. 302/3. Imperf .. 3·00 3·50

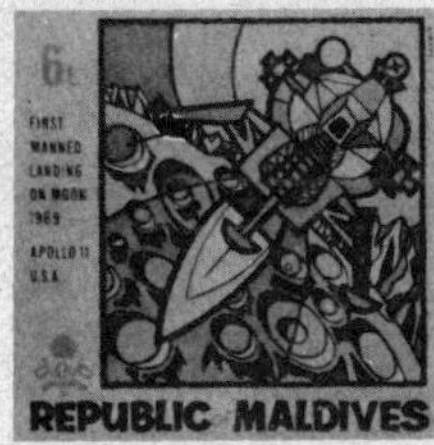

72 Module nearing Moon's Surface

(Des M. Shamir. Litho Govt Printer, Israel)

1969 (25 Sept). *First Man on the Moon. T* **72** *and similar square designs. Multicoloured. P* 14.

305 6 l. Type **72** 10 10
306 10 l. Astronaut with hatchet 10 10
307 1 r. 50, Astronaut and module 70 70
308 2 r. 50, Astronaut using camera .. .. 1·25 1·00
305/8 .. .. *Set of* 4 1·75 1·60
MS309 101 × 130 mm. Nos. 305/8. Imperf .. 1·75 2·50

Gold Medal Winner
Mohamed Gammoudi
5000 m. run
Tunisia
REPUBLIC OF MALDIVES

(73)

1969 (1 Dec). *Gold-medal Winners, Olympic Games, Mexico (1968). Nos. 295/6 optd with T* **73**, *or similar inscr honouring P. Trentin (cycling) of France.*

310 50 l. multicoloured 40 40
311 1 r. multicoloured 60 60

74 Red-striped Butterfly Fish

(Des M. Shamir. Litho)

1970 (Jan). *Tropical Fish. T* **74** *and similar diamond-shaped designs. Multicoloured. P* 10½.

312 2 l. Type **74** 15 25
313 5 l. Spotted Triggerfish 20 15
314 25 l. Scorpion Fish 55 20
315 50 l. Forceps Fish .. .. 1·00 40
316 1 r. Imperial Angelfish .. .. 1·75 70
317 2 r. Regal Angelfish .. .. 2·75 2·75
312/17 .. .. *Set of* 6 5·75 4·00

75 Columbia Dauman Victoria, 1899

(Des M. Shamir. Litho)

1970 (1 Feb). *"75 Years of the Automobile". T* **75** *and similar horiz designs. Multicoloured. P* 12.

318 2 l. Type **75** 10 15
319 5 l. Duryea phaeton, 1902 .. .. 15 15
320 7 l. Packard S-24, 1906 .. .. 15 15
321 10 l. Autocar Runabout, 1907 .. .. 15 15
322 25 l. Type **75** 45 15
323 50 l. As 5 l. .. .. 1·00 30
324 1 r. As 7 l. .. .. 1·75 65
325 2 r. As 10 l. .. .. 2·75 2·75
318/25 .. .. *Set of* 8 5·75 4·00
MS326 95 × 143 mm. Nos. 324/5. P 11½ .. 3·25 3·50

76 U.N. Headquarters, New York

77 Ship and Light Buoy

(Des M. Shamir. Litho Rosenbaum Brothers, Vienna)

1970 (26 June). *25th Anniv of United Nations. T* **76** *and similar horiz designs. Multicoloured. P* 13½.

327 2 l. Type **76** 10 20
328 10 l. Surgical operation (W.H.O.) 30 10
329 25 l. Student, actress and musician (U.N.E.S.C.O.) 65 15
330 50 l. Children at work and play (U.N.I.C.E.F.) 75 25
331 1 r. Fish, corn and farm animals (F.A.O.) .. 1·00 65
332 2 r. Miner hewing coal (I.L.O.) .. .. 2·00 2·25
327/32 .. .. *Set of* 6 4·25 3·25

(Des M. Shamir. Litho)

1970 (26 July). *10th Anniv of Inter-governmental Maritime Consultative Organization. T* **77** *and similar vert design. Multicoloured. P* 13½.

333 50 l. Type **77** 45 40
334 1 r. Ship and lighthouse .. .. 1·00 85

78 "Guitar-player and Masqueraders" (A. Watteau)

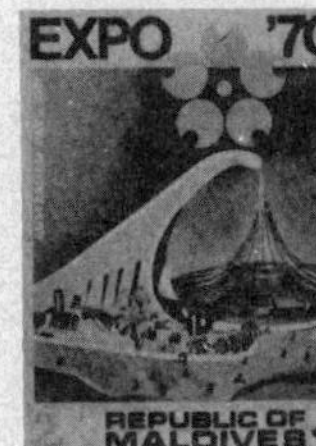

79 Australian Pavilion

(Des M. Shamir. Litho Govt Printer, Israel)

1970 (1 Aug). *Famous Paintings showing the Guitar. T* **78** *and similar vert designs. Multicoloured. P* 14.

335 3 l. Type **78** 10 20
336 7 l. "Spanish Guitarist" (E. Manet) 10 20
337 50 l. "Costumed Player" (Watteau) 30 25
338 1 r. "Mandoline-player" (Roberti) 60 45
339 2 r. 50, "Guitar-player and Lady" (Watteau) 1·75 1·75
340 5 r. "Mandoline-player" (Frans Hals) .. 3·00 3·00
335/40 .. .. *Set of* 6 5·00 5·25
MS341 132 × 80 mm. Nos. 339/40. Roul .. .. 4·25 4·75

(Des M. Shamir. Litho Rosenbaum Brothers, Vienna)

1970 (1 Aug). *"EXPO 70" World Fair, Osaka, Japan. T* **79** *and similar vert designs. Multicoloured. P* 13½.

342 2 l. Type **79** 10 20
343 3 l. West German Pavilion 10 20
344 10 l. U.S.A. Pavilion 10 10
345 25 l. British Pavilion 10 10
346 50 l. Soviet Pavilion 20 20
347 1 r. Japanese Pavilion 40 40
342/7 .. .. *Set of* 6 80 1·10

80 Learning the Alphabet

(Des M. Shamir. Litho Govt Printer, Israel)

1970 (7 Sept). *International Education Year. T* **80** *and similar horiz designs. Multicoloured. P* 14.

348 5 l. Type **80** 10 10
349 10 l. Training teachers 10 10
350 25 l. Geography lesson 15 15
351 50 l. School inspector 25 20
352 1 r. Education by television 40 35
348/52 .. .. *Set of* 5 80 70

MINIMUM PRICE

The minimum price quote is 10p which represents a handling charge rather than a basis for valuing common stamps. For further notes about prices see introductory pages.

Philympia
London 1970

(81)

82 Footballers

1970 (18 Sept). *"Philympia 1970" Stamp Exhibition, London. Nos. 306/***MS***309 optd with T* **81**, *in silver.*

353 10 l. multicoloured 10 10
354 1 r. 50, multicoloured 65 65
355 2 r. 50, multicoloured .. .. 1·00 1·00
353/5 .. .. *Set of* 3 1·50 1·50
MS356 101 × 130 mm. Nos. 305/8 optd. Imperf .. 4·00 5·00

(Des M. Shamir. Litho Rosenbaum Brothers, Vienna)

1970 (Dec). *World Cup Football Championships, Mexico. T* **82** *and similar vert designs, each showing football scenes and outline of the Jules Rimet Trophy. P* 13½.

357 3 l. multicoloured 10 20
358 6 l. multicoloured 10 20
359 7 l. multicoloured 10 20
360 25 l. multicoloured 50 15
361 1 r. multicoloured .. .. 1·25 80
357/61 .. .. *Set of* 5 1·75 1·40

83 Little Boy and U.N.I.C.E.F. Flag

84 Astronauts Lovell, Haise and Swigert

(Des M. Shamir. Litho State Printing Works, Budapest)

1971 (1 Apr). *25th Anniv of U.N.I.C.E.F. T* **83** *and similar vert design. Multicoloured. P* 12.

362 5 l. Type **83** 10 10
363 10 l. Little girl with U.N.I.C.E.F. balloon .. 10 10
364 1 r. Type **83** 55 45
365 2 r. As 10 l. .. .. 1·25 1·40
362/5 .. .. *Set of* 4 1·75 1·90

(Des M. Shamir. Litho Govt Printer, Israel)

1971 (27 Apr). *Safe Return of "Apollo 13". T* **84** *and similar vert designs. Multicoloured. P* 14.

366 5 l. Type **84** 10 10
367 20 l. Explosion in Space 10 10
368 1 r. Splashdown 40 40
366/8 .. .. *Set of* 3 45 45

85 "Multiracial Flower"

86 "Mme. Charpentier and her Children" (Renoir)

(Des M. Shamir. Litho)

1971 (3 May). *Racial Equality Year. P* 14.

369 **85** 10 l. multicoloured 10 10
370 25 l. multicoloured 10 10

1971 (Aug). *Famous Paintings showing "Mother and Child". T* **86** *and similar vert designs. Multicoloured. Litho. P* 12.

371 5 l. Type **86** 10 10
372 7 l. "Susanna van Collen and her Daughter" (Rembrandt) 10 10
373 10 l. "Madonna nursing the Child" (Titian) .. 10 10
374 20 l. "Baroness Belleli and her Children" (Degas) 25 15
375 25 l. "The Cradle" (Morisot) 30 15
376 1 r. "Helena Fourment and her Children" (Rubens) .. .. 1·00 60
377 3 r. "On the Terrace" (Renoir) .. .. .. 2·50 2·50
371/7 .. .. *Set of* 7 3·75 3·25

87 Alan Shepard

88 "Ballerina" (Degas)

(Photo State Ptg Works, Vienna)

1971 (11 Nov). *Moon Flight of "Apollo 14". T* **87** *and similar vert designs. Multicoloured. P* 12½.

378	6 l. Type **87**	20	10
379	10 l. Stuart Roosa	20	10
380	1 r. 50, Edgar Mitchell	2·00	1·75
381	5 r. Mission insignia	4·50	4·25
378/81	*Set of* 4	6·25	5·50

(Litho Rosenbaum Brothers, Vienna)

1971 (19 Nov). *Famous Paintings showing "Dancers". T* **88** *and similar vert designs. Multicoloured. P* 14.

382	5 l. Type **88**	15	10
383	10 l. "Dancing Couple" (Renoir)	20	10
384	2 r. "Spanish Dancer" (Manet)	2·00	2·00
385	5 r. "Ballerinas" (Degas)	3·50	3·50
386	10 r. "La Goulue at the Moulin Rouge" (Toulouse-Lautrec)	5·50	5·50
382/6	*Set of* 5	10·00	10·00

ROYAL VISIT 1972

(89)

90 Book Year Emblem

1972 (13 Mar). *Visit of Queen Elizabeth II and Prince Philip. Nos.* 382/6 *optd with T* **89**.

387	5 l. multicoloured	15	10
388	10 l. multicoloured	20	10
389	2 r. multicoloured	3·00	3·00
390	5 r. multicoloured	5·50	5·50
391	10 r. multicoloured	7·50	7·50
387/91	*Set of* 5	15·00	15·00

(Des M. Shamir. Litho Bradbury, Wilkinson)

1972 (1 May). *International Book Year. P* 13 × 13½.

392 **90**	25 l. multicoloured	15	10
393	5 r. multicoloured	1·60	2·00

91 Scottish Costume

93 Cross-country Skiing

92 Stegosaurus

(Des M. Shamir. Litho State Printing Works, Budapest)

1972 (15 May). *National Costumes of the World. T* **91** *and similar vert designs. Multicoloured. P* 12.

394	10 l. Type **91**	10	10
395	15 l. Netherlands	10	10
396	25 l. Norway	20	15
397	50 l. Hungary	40	30
398	1 r. Austria	75	60
399	2 r. Spain	1·75	1·50
394/9	*Set of* 6	3·00	2·40

(Des M. Shamir. Litho Rosenbaum Brothers, Vienna)

1972 (31 May). *Prehistoric Animals. T* **92** *and similar horiz designs. Multicoloured. P* 14.

400	2 l. Type **92**	15	20
401	7 l. Edaphosaurus	25	15
402	25 l. Diplodocus	50	35
403	50 l. Triceratops	70	50
404	2 r. Pteranodon	2·25	2·75
405	5 r. Tyrannosaurus	4·50	4·75
400/5	*Set of* 6	7·50	8·00

An imperforate miniature sheet containing Nos. 404/5 also exists, but was never freely available.

(Des M. Shamir. Litho Rosenbaum Brothers, Vienna)

1972 (June). *Winter Olympic Games, Sapporo, Japan. T* **93** *and similar vert designs. Multicoloured. P* 14.

406	3 l. Type **93**	10	10
407	6 l. Bob-sleighing	10	10
408	15 l. Speed-skating	15	10
409	50 l. Ski-jumping	55	25
410	1 r. Figure-skating (pair)	80	60
411	2 r. 50, Ice-hockey	2·25	2·00
406/11	*Set of* 6	3·50	2·75

94 Scout Saluting

95 Cycling

(Des M. Shamir. Litho Govt Printer, Israel)

1972 (1 Aug). *13th World Scout Jamboree, Asagiri, Japan* (1971). *T* **94** *and similar vert designs. Multicoloured. P* 14.

412	10 l. Type **92**	30	10
413	15 l. Scout signalling	40	10
414	50 l. Scout blowing bugle	1·75	65
415	1 r. Scout beating drum	2·50	1·40
412/15	*Set of* 4	4·50	2·00

PRINTERS AND PROCESS. *Unless otherwise stated,* all the following issues to No. 1277 were lithographed by Format International Security Printers Ltd, London.

1972 (30 Oct). *Olympic Games, Munich. T* **95** *and similar vert designs. Multicoloured. P* 14½ × 14.

416	5 l. Type **95**	10	10
417	10 l. Running	10	10
418	25 l. Wrestling	15	10
419	50 l. Hurdling	30	25
420	2 r. Boxing	1·00	1·00
421	5 r. Volleyball	2·10	2·10
416/21	*Set of* 6	3·25	3·25
MS422	92 × 120 mm. 3 r. As 50 l.; 4 r. As 10 l. P 15	4·50	5·00

96 Globe and Conference Emblem

97 "Flowers" (Van Gogh)

(Litho Harrison)

1972 (15 Nov). *U.N. Environmental Conservation Conference, Stockholm. P* 14½.

423 **96**	2 l. multicoloured	10	20
424	3 l. multicoloured	10	20
425	15 l. multicoloured	20	15
426	50 l. multicoloured	60	35
427	2 r. 50, multicoloured	2·75	2·75
423/7	*Set of* 5	3·25	3·25

(Des M. Shamir)

1973 (Mar). *Floral Paintings. T* **97** *and similar vert designs. Multicoloured. P* 13½.

428	1 l. Type **97**	10	20
429	2 l. "Flowers in Jug" (Renoir)	10	20
430	3 l. "Chrysanthemums" (Renoir)	10	20
431	50 l. "Mixed Bouquet" (Bosschaert)	20	15
432	1 r. As 3 l.	45	40
433	5 r. As 2 l.	2·25	2·00
428/33	*Set of* 6	2·75	2·75
MS434	120 × 94 mm. 2 r. as 50 l.; 3 r. Type **97**. P 15	3·50	4·00

LEMECHEV
MIDDLE-WEIGHT
GOLD MEDALLIST

(98)

99 Animal Care

1973 (Apr). *Gold-medal Winners, Munich Olympic Games. Nos.* 420/**MS**422 *optd with T* **98** *or similar commemorative inscr, in blue.*

435	2 r. multicoloured	1·75	1·25
436	5 r. multicoloured	2·75	2·25
MS437	92 × 120 mm. 3 r. multicoloured; 4 r. multicoloured	4·50	5·50

Overprints:—2 r. Type **98**; 5 r. "JAPAN GOLD MEDAL WINNERS" (volleyball). Miniature sheet:—3 r. "EHRHARDT 100 METER HURDLES GOLD MEDALLIST"; 4 r. "SHORTER MARATHON GOLD MEDALLIST".

(Des M. Shamir)

1973 (Aug). *International Scouting Congress, Nairobi and Addis Ababa. T* **99** *and similar horiz designs. Multicoloured. P* 14½.

438	1 l. Type **99**	10	15
439	2 l. Lifesaving	10	15
440	3 l. Agricultural training	10	15
441	4 l. Carpentry	10	15
442	5 l. Playing leapfrog	10	15
443	1 r. As 2 l.	1·75	65
444	2 r. As 4 l.	3·00	2·25
445	3 r. Type **99**	4·25	3·25
438/45	*Set of* 8	8·50	6·25
MS446	101 × 79 mm. 5 r. As 3 l.	6·50	8·00

100 *Makaira herscheli*

1973 (Aug). *Fishes. T* **100** *and similar horiz designs. Multicoloured. P* 14½.

447	1 l. Type **100**	10	15
448	2 l. *Katsuwonus pelamys*	10	15
449	3 l. *Thunnus thynnus*	10	15
450	5 l. *Coryphaena hippurus*	10	15
451	60 l. *Lutjanus gibbus*	40	25
452	75 l. As 60 l.	50	30
453	1 r. 50, *Variola louti*	1·10	75
454	2 r. 50, As 5 l.	1·60	95
455	3 r. *Plectropoma maculatum*	1·75	1·40
456	10 r. *Scomberomorus commerson*	4·75	4·75
447/56	*Set of* 10	9·00	8·00
MS457	119 × 123 mm. 4 r. As 2 l.; 5 r. Type **100**	8·00	10·00

Nos. 451/2 are smaller, size 29 × 22 mm.

101 Golden-fronted Leafbird

102 *Lantana camara*

(Des M. Shamir)

1973 (Oct). *Fauna. T* **101** *and similar diamond-shaped designs. Multicoloured. P* 14½.

458	1 l. Type **101**	10	15
459	2 l. Indian Flying Fox	10	15
460	3 l. Land tortoise	10	15
461	4 l. *Kallima inachus* (butterfly)	15	15
462	50 l. As 3 l.	40	25
463	2 r. Type **101**	3·00	2·75
464	3 r. As 2 l.	3·00	2·75
458/64	*Set of* 7	6·25	5·75
MS465	66 × 74 mm. 5 r. As 4 l.	10·00	10·00

(Litho Questa)

1973 (19 Dec). *Flowers of the Maldive Islands. T* **102** *and similar vert designs. Multicoloured. P* 14.

466	1 l. Type **102**	10	10
467	2 l. *Nerium oleander*	10	10
468	3 l. *Rosa polyantha*	10	10
469	4 l. *Hibiscus manihot*	10	10
470	5 l. *Bougainvillea glabra*	10	10
471	10 l. *Plumera alba*	10	10
472	50 l. *Poinsettia pulcherrima*	55	20
473	5 r. *Ononis natrix*	3·75	3·00
466/73	*Set of* 8	4·00	3·25
MS474	110 × 100 mm. 2 r. As 3 l.; 3 r. As 10 l.	3·25	3·75

103 "Tiros" Weather Satellite

(Des M. Shamir)

1974 (10 Jan). *Centenary of World Meteorological Organization. T* **103** *and similar horiz designs. Multicoloured. P* 14½.

475 1 l. Type **103** .. 10 10
476 2 l. "Nimbus" satellite .. 10 10
477 3 l. *Nomad* (weather ship) .. 10 10
478 4 l. Scanner, A.P.T. Instant Weather Picture equipment .. 10 10
479 5 l. Richard's wind-speed recorder .. 10 10
480 2 r. Type **103** .. 2·00 1·25
481 3 r. As 3 l. .. 2·25 1·50
475/81 *Set of* 7 4·00 2·75
MS482 110 × 79 mm. 10 r. As 2 l. .. 7·00 9·00

104 "Apollo" Spacecraft and Pres. Kennedy

(Des M. Shamir)

1974 (1 Feb). *American and Russian Space Exploration Projects. T* **104** *and similar horiz designs. Multicoloured. P* 14½.

83 1 l. Type **104** .. 10 15
84 2 l. "Mercury" capsule and John Glenn .. 10 15
85 3 l. "Vostok 1" and Yuri Gagarin .. 10 15
86 4 l. "Vostok 6" and Valentina Tereshkova .. 10 15
87 5 l. "Soyuz 11" and "Salyut" space-station .. 10 15
88 2 r. "Skylab" space laboratory .. 2·00 1·75
89 3 r. As 2 l. .. 2·50 2·00
83/9 *Set of* 7 4·25 4·00
MS490 103 × 80 mm. 10 r. Type **104** .. 6·50 8·50

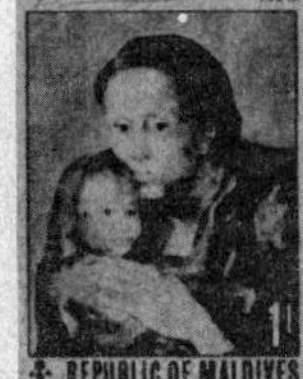

105 Copernicus and "Skylab" Space Laboratory

106 "Maternity" (Picasso)

(Des G. Vasarhelyi)

1974 (10 Apr). *500th Birth Anniv of Nicholas Copernicus (astronomer). T* **105** *and similar horiz designs. Multicoloured. P* 14½.

491 1 l. Type **105** .. 10 15
492 2 l. Orbital space-station of the future .. 10 15
493 3 l. Proposed "Space-shuttle" craft .. 10 15
494 4 l. "Mariner 2" Venus probe .. 10 15
495 5 l. "Mariner 4" Mars probe .. 10 15
496 25 l. Type **105** .. 45 15
497 1 r. 50, As 2 l. .. 2·00 1·75
498 5 r. As 3 l. .. 4·50 4·50
491/8 *Set of* 8 6·50 6·50
MS499 106 × 80 mm. 10 r. "Copernicus" orbital observatory .. 8·00 11·00

(Des M. Shamir. Litho Questa)

1974 (May). *Paintings by Picasso. T* **106** *and similar vert designs. Multicoloured. P* 14.

500 1 l. Type **106** .. 10 10
501 2 l. "Harlequin and Friend" .. 10 10
502 3 l. "Pierrot Sitting" .. 10 10
503 20 l. "Three Musicians" .. 10 10
504 75 l. "L'Aficionado" .. 20 20
505 5 r. "Still Life" .. 2·00 1·75
500/5 *Set of* 6 2·25 2·00
MS506 100 × 101 mm. 2 r. As 20 l.; 3 r. As 5 r. .. 2·50 3·25

107 U.P.U. Emblem, Steam and Diesel Locomotives

108 Footballers

(Des M. Shamir)

1974 (May). *Centenary of Universal Postal Union. T* **107** *and similar horiz designs. Multicoloured. P* 14½.

507 1 l. Type **107** .. 10 10
508 2 l. Paddle-steamer and modern mailboat .. 10 10
509 3 l. Airship and Boeing "747" airliner .. 10 10
510 1 r. 50, Mailcoach and motor van .. 85 85
511 2 r. 50, As 2 l. .. 1·60 1·60
512 5 r. Type **107** .. 3·50 3·50
507/12 *Set of* 6 5·50 5·50
MS513 126 × 105 mm. 4 r. Type **107** .. 4·50 6·00

Nos. 507/12 were first issued in sheets of 50, but were later released in small sheets of five stamps and one label. These small sheets were perforated 13½.

(Des M. Shamir)

1974 (June). *World Cup Football Championships, West Germany. T* **108** *and similar vert designs, showing football scenes. P* 14½.

514 1 l. multicoloured .. 10 15
515 2 l. multicoloured .. 10 15
516 3 l. multicoloured .. 10 15
517 4 l. multicoloured .. 10 15
518 75 l. multicoloured .. 65 40
519 4 r. multicoloured .. 1·75 1·50
520 5 r. multicoloured .. 2·25 2·25
514/20 *Set of* 7 4·50 4·25
MS521 88 × 95 mm. 10 r. multicoloured .. 5·00 5·50

109 "Capricorn"

110 Churchill and Bomber Aircraft

(Des G. Vasarhelyi)

1974 (3 July). *Signs of the Zodiac. T* **109** *and similar horiz designs. Multicoloured. P* 14½.

522 1 l. Type **109** .. 10 15
523 2 l. "Aquarius" .. 10 15
524 3 l. "Pisces" .. 10 15
525 4 l. "Aries" .. 10 15
526 5 l. "Taurus" .. 10 15
527 6 l. "Gemini" .. 10 15
528 7 l. "Cancer" .. 10 15
529 10 l. "Leo" .. 10 15
530 15 l. "Virgo" .. 15 15
531 20 l. "Libra" .. 15 15
532 25 l. "Scorpio" .. 15 15
533 5 r. "Sagittarius" .. 6·00 4·50
522/33 *Set of* 12 6·00 5·50
MS534 119 × 99 mm. 10 r. "The Sun" (49 × 37 *mm*). P 13½ .. 10·00 12·00

(Des M. Shamir)

1974 (30 Nov). *Birth Centenary of Sir Winston Churchill. T* **110** *and similar horiz designs. Multicoloured. P* 14½.

535 1 l. Type **110** .. 10 15
536 2 l. Churchill as pilot .. 10 15
537 3 l. Churchill as First Lord of the Admiralty 10 15
538 4 l. Churchill and H.M.S. *Indomitable* (aircraft carrier) .. 10 15
539 5 l. Churchill and fighter aircraft .. 10 15
540 60 l. Churchill and anti-aircraft battery .. 1·50 80
541 75 l. Churchill and tank in desert .. 1·75 90
542 5 r. Churchill and flying-boat .. 7·50 6·50
535/42 *Set of* 8 10·00 8·00
MS543 113 × 83 mm. 10 r. As 4 l. .. 12·00 12·00

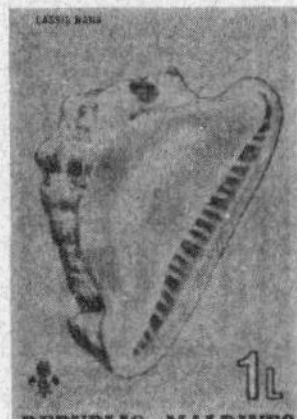

111 *Cassia nana*

112 Royal Throne

(Des M. Shamir)

1975 (25 Jan). *Seashells and Cowries. T* **111** *and similar multicoloured designs. P* 14 × 13½ (60 *l.*, 75 *l.*) *or* 14½ (*others*).

544 1 l. Type **111** .. 10 15
545 2 l. *Murex triremus* .. 10 15
546 3 l. *Harpa major* .. 10 15
547 4 l. *Lambis chiragra* .. 10 15
548 5 l. *Conus pennaceus* .. 10 15
549 60 l. *Cypraea diliculum* (22 × 30 *mm*) .. 1·25 65
550 75 l. *Clanculus pharaonis* (22 × 30 *mm*) .. 1·50 80
551 5 r. *Chicoreus ramosus* .. 5·50 4·50
544/51 *Set of* 8 7·50 6·00
MS552 152 × 126 mm. 2 r. As 3 l.; 3 r. as 2 l. .. 6·50 8·00

(Des M. Shamir. Litho Questa)

1975 (22 Feb). *Historical Relics and Monuments. T* **112** *and similar multicoloured designs. P* 14.

553 1 l. Type **112** .. 10 10
554 10 l. Candlesticks .. 10 10
555 25 l. Lamp-tree .. 15 10
556 60 l. Royal umbrellas .. 30 20
557 75 l. Eid-Miskith Mosque (*horiz*) .. 35 25
558 3 r. Tomb of Al-Hafiz Abu-al Barakath-al Barubari (*horiz*) .. 1·60 1·75
553/8 *Set of* 6 2·25 2·25

113 Guavas

114 *Phyllangia*

(Des M. Shamir)

1975 (Mar). *Fruits. T* **113** *and similar vert designs. Multicoloured. P* 14½.

559 2 l. Type **113** .. 10 15
560 4 l. Maldive mulberry .. 10 15
561 5 l. Mountain apples .. 10 15
562 10 l. Bananas .. 15 15
563 20 l. Mangoes .. 25 15
564 50 l. Papaya .. 55 20
565 1 r. Pomegranates .. 1·00 40
566 5 r. Coconut .. 5·50 5·00
559/66 *Set of* 8 6·75 5·75
MS567 136 × 102 mm. 2 r. As 10 l.; 3 r. As 2 l. .. 5·50 6·50

(Des M. Shamir)

1975 (6 June). *Marine Life. T* **114** *and similar triangular designs. Multicoloured. P* 14½.

568 1 l. Type **114** .. 10 10
569 2 l. *Madrepora oculata* .. 10 10
570 3 l. *Acropora gravida* .. 10 10
571 4 l. *Stylotella* .. 10 10
572 5 l. *Acrophora cervicornis* .. 10 10
573 60 l. *Strongylocentrotus purpuratus* .. 55 55
574 75 l. *Pisaster ochracëus* .. 65 65
575 5 r. *Marthasterias glacialis* .. 3·75 3·75
568/75 *Set of* 8 4·75 4·75
MS576 155 × 98 mm. 4 r. As 1 l. Imperf .. 7·00 8·50

115 Clock Tower and Customs Building within "10"

14th Boy Scout Jamboree
July 29 – August 7, 1975

(**116**)

(Des M. Shamir)

1975 (26 July). *10th Anniv of Independence. T* **115** *and similar horiz designs. Multicoloured. P* 14½.

577 4 l. Type **115** .. 10 10
578 5 l. Government Offices .. 10 10
579 7 l. Waterfront .. 10 10
580 15 l. Mosque and minaret .. 10 10
581 10 r. Sultan Park and museum .. 4·00 5·00
577/81 *Set of* 5 4·00 5·00

1975 (26 July). *"Nordjamb 75" World Scout Jamboree, Norway. Nos.* 443/5 *and* **MS**446 *optd with T* **116**.

582 1 r. multicoloured .. 30 30
583 2 r. multicoloured .. 50 50
584 3 r. multicoloured .. 1·00 1·00
582/4 *Set of* 3 1·60 1·60
MS585 101 × 79 mm. 5 r. multicoloured .. 3·75 4·50

117 Madura Prau

118 *Brahmaea wallichii*

(Des M. Shamir)

1975 (Aug). *Ships. T* **117** *and similar multicoloured designs. P* 14½.

586 1 l. Type **117** .. 10 10
587 2 l. Ganges patela .. 10 10
588 3 l. Indian palla (*vert*) .. 10 10
589 4 l. Odhi (dhow) (*vert*) .. 10 10
590 5 l. Maldivian schooner .. 10 10
591 25 l. *Cutty Sark* .. 35 20
592 1 r. Maldivian baggala (*vert*) .. 85 70
593 5 r. Freighter *Maldive Courage* .. 3·75 3·75
586/93 *Set of* 8 4·75 4·50
MS594 99 × 85 mm. 10 r. As 1 l. .. 6·50 8·00

(Des M. Shamir)

1975 (7 Sept). *Butterflies. T* **118** *and similar horiz designs. Multicoloured. P* 14½.

595 1 l. Type **118** .. 10 10
596 2 l. *Teinopalpus imperialis* .. 10 10
597 3 l. *Cethosia biblis* .. 10 10
598 4 l. *Hestia jasonia* .. 10 10
599 5 l. *Apatura ilia* .. 10 10
600 25 l. *Kallima horsfieldi* .. 55 35
601 1 r. 50, *Hebomoia leucippe* .. 2·50 2·50
602 5 r. *Papilio memnon* .. 7·00 6·00
595/602 *Set of* 8 9·00 8·00
MS603 134 × 97 mm. 10 r. As 25 l. .. 14·00 15·00

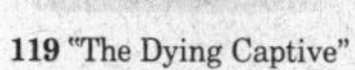

119 "The Dying Captive"

120 Beaker and Vase

1975 (9 Oct). *500th Birth Anniv of Michelangelo. T* **119** *and similar vert designs. Multicoloured. P* 14½.
604 1 l. Type **119** 10 10
605 2 l. Detail of "The Last Judgement" 10 10
606 3 l. "Apollo" 10 10
607 4 l. Detail of Sistine Chapel ceiling 10 10
608 5 l. "Bacchus" 10 10
609 1 r. Detail of "The Last Judgement" (*different*) 55 20
610 2 r. "David" 1·10 90
611 5 r. "Cumaean Sibyl" 2·75 2·50
604/11 *Set of* 8 4·00 3·50
MS612 123 × 113 mm. 10 r. As 2 r. 5·00 7·00
The 1, 3, 5 l. and 2, 10 r. are sculptures; the other values show details of the frescoes in the Sistine Chapel.

(Des M. Shamir. Litho Questa)

1975 (Dec). *Maldivian Lacquerware. T* **120** *and similar vert designs. Multicoloured. P* 14.
613 2 l. Type **120** 10 10
614 4 l. Boxes 10 10
615 50 l. Jar with lid 40 20
616 75 l. Bowls with covers 50 30
617 1 r. Craftsman at work 65 40
613/17 *Set of* 5 1·50 90

121 Map of Maldives

122 Cross-country Skiing

(Des M. Shamir. Litho Questa)

1975 (25 Dec). *Tourism. T* **121** *and similar horiz designs. Multicoloured. P* 14.
618 4 l. Type **121** 10 10
619 5 l. Motor launch and small craft 10 10
620 7 l. Sailing boats 10 10
621 15 l. Underwater fishing 10 10
622 3 r. Hulule Airport 1·40 1·40
623 10 r. Motor cruisers 4·00 4·00
618/23 *Set of* 6 5·00 5·00

(Des M. Shamir)

1976 (10 Jan). *Winter Olympic Games, Innsbruck, Austria. T* **122** *and similar vert designs. Multicoloured. P* 15.
624 1 l. Type **122** 10 10
625 2 l. Speed ice-skating 10 10
626 3 l. Pairs figure-skating 10 10
627 4 l. Four-man bobsleigh 10 10
628 5 l. Ski-jumping 10 10
629 25 l. Women's figure-skating 15 10
630 1 r. 15, Slalom skiing 65 65
631 4 r. Ice-hockey 2·25 2·00
624/31 *Set of* 8 3·00 2·75
MS632 93 × 117 mm. 10 r. Downhill skiing 5·00 6·50

123 "General Burgoyne" (Reynolds)

124 Thomas Edison

1976 (15 Feb). *Bicentenary of American Revolution. T* **123** *and similar multicoloured designs. P* 15.
633 1 l. Type **123** 10 10
634 2 l. "John Hancock" (Copley) 10 10
635 3 l. "Death of General Montgomery" (Trumbull) (*horiz*) 10 10
636 4 l. "Paul Revere" (Copley) 10 10
637 5 l. "Battle of Bunker Hill" (Trumbull) (*horiz*) 10 10
638 2 r. "The Crossing of the Delaware" (Sully) (*horiz*) 1·75 1·50
639 3 r. "Samuel Adams" (Copley) 2·25 1·75
640 5 r. "Surrender of Cornwallis" (Trumbull) (*horiz*) 2·75 2·25
633/40 *Set of* 8 6·25 5·00
MS641 147 × 95 mm. 10 r. "Washington at Dorchester Heights" (Stuart) 8·00 10·00

1976 (10 Mar). *Telephone Centenary. T* **124** *and similar horiz designs. Multicoloured. P* 15.
642 1 l. Type **124** 10 10
643 2 l. Alexander Graham Bell 10 10
644 3 l. Telephones of 1919, 1937 and 1972 10 10
645 10 l. Cable entrance into station 10 10
646 20 l. Equaliser circuit assembly 15 10
647 1 r. *Salernum* (cable ship) 70 55
648 10 r. "Intelsat IV-A" and Earth Station 4·25 4·25
642/8 *Set of* 7 4·75 4·50
MS649 156 × 105 mm. 4 r. Early telephones 4·25 4·75

MAY 29TH–JUNE 6TH
"INTERPHIL" 1976
(125)

126 Wrestling

1976 (29 May). *"Interphil 76" International Stamp Exhibition, Philadelphia. Nos. 638/*MS*641 optd with T* **125**, *in blue (5 r.) or silver (others).*
650 2 r. multicoloured 1·25 1·25
651 3 r. multicoloured 1·75 1·75
652 5 r. multicoloured 2·25 2·25
650/2 *Set of* 3 4·75 4·75
MS653 147 × 95 mm. 10 r. multicoloured 6·50 8·00

(Des M. Shamir)

1976 (June). *Olympic Games, Montreal. T* **126** *and similar vert designs. Multicoloured. P* 15.
654 1 l. Type **126** 10 10
655 2 l. Putting the shot 10 10
656 3 l. Hurdling 10 10
657 4 l. Hockey 10 10
658 5 l. Running 10 10
659 6 l. Javelin-throwing 10 10
660 1 r. 50, Discus-throwing 1·25 1·25
661 5 r. Volleyball 3·00 3·00
654/61 *Set of* 8 4·00 4·00
MS662 135 × 106 mm. 10 r. Throwing the hammer 5·00 7·00

127 *Dolichos lablab*

128 "Viking" approaching Mars

(Des M. Shamir. Litho Questa)

1976 (26 July)–**77**. *Vegetables. T* **127** *and similar vert designs. Multicoloured. P* 14.
663 2 l. Type **127** 10 10
664 4 l. *Moringa pterygosperma* 10 10
665 10 l. *Solanum melongena* 10 10
666 20 l. *Moringa pterygosperma* (1977) 75 75
667 50 l. *Cucumis sativus* 80 65
668 75 l. *Trichosanthes anguina* 85 75
669 1 r. *Momordica charantia* 95 85
670 2 r. *Trichosanthes anguina* (1977) 3·00 3·50
663/70 *Set of* 8 6·00 6·00

1976 (2 Dec). *"Viking" Space Mission. T* **128** *and similar horiz design. Multicoloured. P* 14.
671 5 r. Type **128** 2·50 2·50
MS672 121 × 89 mm. 20 r. Landing module on Mars 8·00 10·00

129 Coronation Ceremony

1977 (6 Feb). *Silver Jubilee of Queen Elizabeth II. T* **129** *and similar horiz designs. Multicoloured. P* 14 × 13½.
673 1 l. Type **129** 10 10
674 2 l. Queen and Prince Philip 10 10
675 3 l. Royal couple with Princes Andrew and Edward 10 10
676 1 r. 15, Queen with Archbishops 25 25
677 3 r. State coach in procession 65 55
678 4 r. Royal couple with Prince Charles and Princess Anne 90 90
673/8 *Set of* 6 1·75 1·60
MS679 120 × 77 mm. 10 r. Queen and Prince Charles 3·00 3·25
Nos. 673/8 also exist perf 12 (*Price per set of* 6 £1·75 *mint or used*) from additional sheetlets of five stamps and one label in changed colours.

130 Beethoven and Organ

(Des M. Shamir)

1977 (26 Mar). *150th Death Anniv of Ludwig van Beethove(n) (composer). T* **130** *and similar horiz designs. Multicoloured. P* 1(4)
680 1 l. Type **130** 10 1
681 2 l. Portrait and manuscript of *Moonlight Sonata* 10 1
682 3 l. With Goethe at Teplitz 10 1
683 4 l. Portrait and string instruments 10 1
684 5 l. Beethoven's home, Heiligenstadt 10 1
685 25 l. Hands and gold medals 40 1
686 2 r. Portrait and part of *Missa solemnis* 2·00 1·4
687 5 r. Portrait and hearing-aids 3·75 2·5
680/7 *Set of* 8 5·75 3·7
MS688 121 × 92 mm. 4 r. Death mask and room where composer died 3·25 4·5

131 Printed Circuit and I.T.U. Emblem

132 "Miss Anne Ford" (Gainsborough)

(Des M. Shamir. Litho Questa)

1977 (17 May). *Inauguration of Satellite Earth Station. T* **13**(1) *and similar horiz designs. Multicoloured. P* 14.
689 10 l. Type **131** 10 1
690 90 l. Central telegraph office 45 4
691 10 r. Satellite Earth station 5·00 5·0
689/91 *Set of* 3 5·00 5·0
MS692 100 × 85 mm. 5 r. "Intelsat IV-A" satellite over Maldives 2·75 3·5

(Des M. Shamir. Litho Questa)

1977 (20 May). *Artists' Birth Anniversaries. T* **132** *and simila(r) vert designs. Multicoloured. P* 14.
693 1 l. Type **132** (250th anniv) 10 1
694 2 l. Group painting by Rubens (400th anniv) 10 1
695 3 l. "Girl with Dog" (Titian) (500th anniv) 10 1
696 4 l. "Mrs. Thomas Graham" (Gainsborough) 10 1
697 5 l. "Artist with Isabella Brant" (Rubens) 10 1
698 95 l. Portrait by Titian 40 4
699 1 r. Portrait by Gainsborough 40 4
700 10 r. "Isabella Brant" (Rubens) 3·50 3·0
693/700 *Set of* 8 4·00 3·7
MS701 152 × 116 mm. 5 r. "Self-portrait" (Titian) 2·00 2·7

133 Lesser Frigate Birds

134 Charles Lindbergh

(Des M. Shamir)

1977 (26 July). *Birds. T* **133** *and similar vert designs. Multi(coloured). P* 14½.
702 1 l. Type **133** 10 1
703 2 l. Crab Plover 10 1
704 3 l. White-tailed Tropic Bird 10 1
705 4 l. Wedge-tailed Shearwater 10 1
706 5 l. Grey Heron 10 1
707 20 l. White Tern 30 2
708 95 l. Cattle Egret 1·25 9
709 1 r. 25, Black-naped Tern 1·75 1·4
710 5 r. Pheasant Coucal 6·50 6·5
702/10 *Set of* 9 9·00 8·2
MS711 124 × 117 mm. 10 r. Green Heron 14·00 16·0

(Des M. Shamir)

1977 (31 Oct). *50th Anniv of Lindbergh's Transatlantic Flig(ht) and 75th Anniv of First Navigable Airships. T* **134** *and simila(r) multicoloured designs. P* 14½.
712 1 l. Type **134** 10 1
713 2 l. Lindbergh and *Spirit of St. Louis* 10 1
714 3 l. "Mohawk" aircraft (*horiz*) 10 1
715 4 l. Julliot's airship *Lebaudy I* (*horiz*) 10 1
716 5 l. Airship *Graf Zeppelin* and portrait of Zeppelin 10 1
717 1 r. Airship *Los Angeles* (*horiz*) 60 3
718 3 r. Lindbergh and Henry Ford 1·40 1·0
719 10 r. Vickers rigid airship 3·50 2·7
712/19 *Set of* 8 5·00 3·7
MS720 148 × 114 mm. 5 r. *Spirit of St. Louis*, Statue of Liberty and Eiffel Tower; 7 r. 50, Airship *L* 31 over German battleship 7·00 8·0

ALTERED CATALOGUE NUMBERS

Any Catalogue numbers altered from the las(t) edition are shown as a list in the introductor(y) pages.

135 Boat Building

136 Rheumatic Heart

(Des M. Shamir. Litho J.W.)

1977 (11 Nov). *Occupations. T* **135** *and similar multicoloured designs. P* 13½ × 13 (2 *r.*) *or* 13 × 13½ (*others*).

721 6 l. Type **135** 15 10
722 15 l. Fishing 25 10
723 20 l. Cadjan weaving 30 10
724 90 l. Mat weaving 80 45
725 2 r. Lace making (*vert*) .. .. 1·50 1·50
721/5 .. .. *Set of* 5 2·75 2·00

(Des M. Shamir. Litho Questa)

1977 (Dec). *World Rheumatism Year. T* **136** *and similar vert designs. Multicoloured. P* 14.

726 1 l. Type **136** 10 10
727 50 l. Rheumatic shoulder 20 10
728 2 r. Rheumatic fingers 85 75
729 3 r. Rheumatic knee .. .. 1·10 1·00
726/9 .. .. *Set of* 4 2·00 1·75

137 Lilienthal's Glider

138 Newgate Prison

(Des M. Shamir. Litho Questa)

1978 (27 Feb). *75th Anniv of First Powered Aircraft. T* **137** *and similar horiz designs. Multicoloured. P* 13 × 13½.

730 1 l. Type **137** 10 15
731 2 l. Chanute's glider 10 15
732 3 l. Wright testing glider, 1900 .. .. .. 10 15
733 4 l. Roe's aircraft 10 15
734 5 l. Wright demonstrating aircraft to King Alfonso of Spain 10 15
735 10 l. Roe's second biplane 15 15
736 20 l. Wright Brothers and A. G. Bell 20 15
737 95 l. Hadley's triplane 85 60
738 5 r. "BE 2"s at Upavon, 1914 .. .. .. 3·75 3·25
730/8 .. .. *Set of* 9 4·50 4·50
MS739 98 × 82 mm. 10 r. Wright Brothers' *Flyer* 6·50 8·00

1978 (15 Mar). *World Eradication of Smallpox. T* **138** *and similar multicoloured designs. P* 14.

740 15 l. Foundling Hospital, London (*horiz*) .. 25 10
741 50 l. Type **138** 70 30
742 2 r. Edward Jenner .. .. 2·00 1·75
740/2 .. .. *Set of* 3 2·75 2·00

139 Television Set

140 Mas Odi

(Des M. Shamir. Litho J.W.)

1978 (29 Mar). *Inauguration of Television in Maldives. T* **139** *and similar multicoloured designs. P* 13 × 13½ (1 *r.* 50) *or* 13½ × 13 (*others*).

743 15 l. Type **139** 20 10
744 25 l. Television aerials 25 15
745 1 r. 50, Control desk (*horiz*) .. .. .. 1·25 1·10
743/5 .. .. *Set of* 3 1·50 1·25

(Des M. Shamir)

1978 (27 Apr). *Ships. T* **140** *and similar multicoloured designs. P* 14½.

746 1 l. Type **140** 10 10
747 2 l. Battela 10 10
748 3 l. Bandu odi (*vert*) 10 10
749 5 l. *Maldive Trader* (freighter) 10 10
750 1 r. *Fath-hul Baaree* (brigantine) (*vert*) .. 35 20
751 1 r. 25, Mas dhoni 55 40
752 3 r. Baggala (*vert*) .. .. 1·25 70
753 4 r. As No. 751 .. .. 1·60 90
746/53 .. .. *Set of* 8 3·50 2·10
MS754 152 × 138 mm. 1 r. As No. 747; 4 r. As No. 751 .. .. 2·50 3·00

141 Ampulla

142 Capt. Cook

(Des M. Shamir. Litho Questa)

1978 (15 May). *25th Anniv of Coronation of Queen Elizabeth II. T* **141** *and similar vert designs. Multicoloured. P* 14.

755 1 l. Type **141** 10 10
756 2 l. Sceptre with dove 10 10
757 3 l. Golden orb 10 10
758 1 r. 15, St. Edward's Crown 15 15
759 2 r. Sceptre with cross 30 25
760 5 r. Queen Elizabeth II 80 70
755/60 .. .. *Set of* 6 1·10 1·00
MS761 108 × 106 mm. 10 r. Anointing spoon .. 2·00 2·00

Nos. 755/60 were also each issued in small sheets of three stamps and one label, perf 12, in changed colours.

(Des M. Shamir)

1978 (15 July). *250th Birth Anniv of Capt. James Cook and Bicentenary of Discovery of Hawaii. T* **142** *and similar multicoloured designs. P* 14½.

762 1 l. Type **142** 10 10
763 2 l. Statue of Kamehameha I of Hawaii .. 10 10
764 3 l. H.M.S. *Endeavour* 10 10
765 25 l. Route of Cook's third voyage 35 35
766 75 l. H.M.S. *Resolution*, H.M.S. *Discovery* and map of Hawaiian Islands (*horiz*) .. 85 85
767 1 r. 50, Cook meeting Hawaiian islanders on ship (*horiz*) .. .. 1·60 1·60
768 10 r. Death of Cook (*horiz*) .. .. .. 7·00 7·00
762/8 .. .. *Set of* 7 9·00 9·00
MS769 100 × 92 mm. 5 r. H.M.S. *Endeavour* (*different*) .. .. 11·00 12·00

143 *Schizophrys aspera*

144 "Four Apostles"

1978 (30 Aug). *Crustaceans. T* **143** *and similar multicoloured designs. P* 14.

770 1 l. Type **143** 10 10
771 2 l. *Atergatis floridus* 10 10
772 3 l. *Perenon planissimum* 10 10
773 90 l. *Portunus granulatus* 50 40
774 1 r. *Carpilius maculatus* 50 40
775 2 r. *Huenia proteus* .. .. 1·00 1·00
776 25 r. *Etisus laevimanus* .. .. 9·00 10·00
770/6 .. .. *Set of* 7 10·00 11·00
MS777 147 × 146 mm. 2 r. *Panulirus longipes* (*vert*) 1·50 1·75

(Des BG Studio. Litho Questa)

1978 (28 Oct). *450th Death Anniv of Albrecht Dürer (artist). T* **144** *and similar designs. P* 14.

778 10 l. multicoloured 10 10
779 20 l. multicoloured 10 10
780 55 l. multicoloured 20 20
781 1 r. black, cinnamon and brown 30 30
782 1 r. 80, multicoloured 50 50
783 3 r. multicoloured .. .. 1·00 1·00
778/83 .. .. *Set of* 6 1·90 1·90
MS784 141 × 122 mm. 10 r. multicoloured .. 4·50 4·75

Designs: *Vert*—20 l. "Self-portrait at 27", 55 l. "Madonna and Child with a Pear"; 1 r. 80, "Hare"; 3 r. "Great Piece of Turf"; 10 r. "Columbine". *Horiz*— 1 r. "Rhinoceros".

145 T.V. Tower and Building

146 Human Rights Emblem

(Des M. Shamir)

1978 (11 Nov). *Tenth Anniv of Republic. T* **145** *and similar horiz designs. Multicoloured. P* 14½.

785 1 l. Fishing boat 10 10
786 5 l. Montessori School 10 10
787 10 l. Type **145** 10 10
788 25 l. Islet 15 10
789 50 l. Boeing "737" 20 10
790 95 l. Beach scene 30 20
791 1 r. 25, Dhow at night 50 35
792 2 r. President's official residence 75 60
793 5 r. Masjidh Afeefuddin (mosque) .. .. 1·75 1·50
785/93 .. .. *Set of* 9 3·50 2·50
MS794 119 × 88 mm. 3 r. Fisherman casting net 2·00 2·50

1978 (10 Dec). *30th Anniv of Declaration of Human Rights. P* 14.

795 **146** 30 l. pale magenta, dp mauve and green 15 15
796 90 l. yellow-ochre, red-brown and green 40 40
797 1 r. 80, lt greenish blue, dp blue & grn .. 70 70
795/7 .. .. *Set of* 3 1·10 1·10

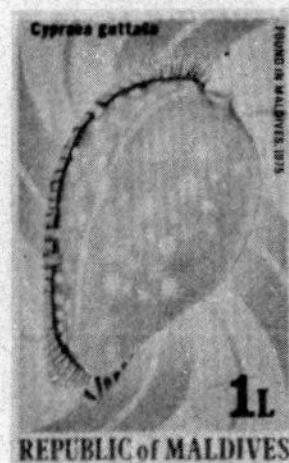

147 *Cypraea guttata*

148 Delivery by Bellman

(Des M. Shamir. Litho Questa)

1979 (Jan). *Shells. T* **147** *and similar vert designs. Multicoloured. P* 14.

798 1 l. Type **147** 10 10
799 2 l. *Conus imperialis* 10 10
800 3 l. *Turbo marmoratus* 10 10
801 10 l. *Lambis truncata* 10 10
802 1 r. *Cypraea leucodon* 40 40
803 1 r. 80, *Conus figulinus* 75 75
804 3 r. *Conus gloria-maris* .. .. 1·10 1·10
798/804 .. .. *Set of* 7 2·25 2·25
MS805 141 × 110 mm. 5 r. *Vasum turbinellus* .. 3·00 3·50

(Des M. Shamir. Litho Questa)

1979 (28 Feb). *Death Centenary of Sir Rowland Hill. T* **148** *and similar multicoloured designs. P* 14.

806 1 l. Type **148** 10 10
807 2 l. Mail coach, 1840 (*horiz*) 10 10
808 3 l. First London letter box, 1855 .. .. 10 10
809 1 r. 55, Penny Black stamps and posthorn .. 65 65
810 5 r. Maldives 15 c. stamp, 1906, and carrier pigeon .. .. 2·00 2·00
806/10 .. .. *Set of* 5 2·50 2·50
MS811 132 × 107 mm. 10 r. Sir Rowland Hill .. 4·00 4·50

Nos. 806/10 were also each issued in small sheets of five stamps and one label, perf 12, in changed colours.

149 Girl with Teddy Bear

150 "White Feathers"

(Des M. Sharmir. Litho Questa)

1979 (10 May). *International Year of the Child (1st issue). T* **149** *and similar vert designs. Multicoloured. P* 14.

812 5 l. Type **149** 10 10
813 1 r. 25, Boy with model sailing boat 40 40
814 2 r. Boy with toy rocket 45 40
815 3 r. Boy with toy airship 60 60
812/15 .. .. *Set of* 4 1·40 1·25
MS816 108 × 109 mm. 5 r. Boy with toy train .. 1·60 2·00

See also Nos. 838/**MS**847.

(Des M. Shamir)

1979 (25 June). *25th Death Anniv of Henri Matisse (artist). T* **150** *and similar horiz designs. Multicoloured. P* 14.

817 20 l. Type **150** 10 10
818 25 l. "Joy of Life" 10 10
819 30 l. "Eggplants" 10 10
820 1 r. 50, "Harmony in Red" 40 35
821 5 r. "Still-life" .. .. 1·10 85
817/21 .. .. *Set of* 5 1·60 1·25
MS822 135 × 95 mm. 4 r. "Water Pitcher" .. 1·25 1·50

151 Sari with Overdress

152 *Gloriosa superba*

(Des M. Shamir. Litho Questa)

1979 (22 Aug). *National Costumes. T* **151** *and similar vert designs. Multicoloured. P* 14.

823 50 l. Type **151** 25 25
824 75 l. Sashed apron dress 40 40
825 90 l. Serape 45 45
826 95 l. Ankle-length printed dress 55 55
823/6 .. .. *Set of* 4 1·50 1·50

(Des M. Shamir. Litho Questa)

1979 (29 Oct). *Flowers. T* **152** *and similar vert designs. Multicoloured. P* 14.

827 1 l. Type **152** 10 10
828 3 l. *Hibiscus tiliaceus* 10 10
829 50 l. *Barringtonia asiatica* 20 20
830 1 r. *Abutilon indicum* 40 40
831 5 r. *Guettarda speciosa* .. .. 1·75 1·75
827/31 .. .. *Set of* 5 2·10 2·10
MS832 94 × 85 mm. 4 r. *Pandanus odoratissimus* 1·75 2·25

153 Weaving

(Litho Questa)

1979 (11 Nov). *Handicraft Exhibition. T* **153** *and similar horiz designs. Multicoloured. P* 14.

833 5 l. Type **153** 10 10
834 10 l. Lacquerwork 10 10
835 1 r. 30, Tortoiseshell jewellery 45 40
836 2 r. Carved woodwork 70 60
833/6 .. .. *Set of* 4 1·10 1·00
MS837 125 × 85 mm. 5 r. Gold and silver jewellery 1·50 2·25

154 Mickey Mouse attacked by Bird

(Des Walt Disney Productions)

1979 (10 Dec). *International Year of the Child (2nd issue). T* **154** *and similar multicoloured designs. P* 11.

838 1 l. Goofy delivering parcel on motor-scooter (*vert*) 10 10
839 2 l. Type **154** 10 10
840 3 l. Goofy half-covered with letters 10 10
841 4 l. Pluto licking Minnie Mouse's envelopes 10 10
842 5 l. Mickey Mouse delivering letters on roller-skates (*vert*) 10 10
843 10 l. Donald Duck placing letter in mail-box 10 10
844 15 l. Chip and Dale carrying letter 10 10
845 1 r. 50, Donald Duck on monocycle (*vert*) .. 75 75
846 5 r. Donald Duck with ostrich in crate (*vert*) 2·25 2·25
838/46 .. .. *Set of* 9 3·00 3·00
MS847 127 × 102 mm. 4 r. Pluto putting parcel in mail-box. P 13½ .. .. 3·25 3·25

155 Post-Ramadan Dancing

(Litho Questa)

1980 (19 Jan). *National Day. T* **155** *and similar horiz designs. Multicoloured. P* 14.

848 5 l. Type **155** 10 10
849 15 l. Musicians and dancer, Eeduu Festival .. 10 10
850 95 l. Sultan's ceremonial band 30 25
851 2 r. Dancer and drummers, Circumcision Festival 55 35
848/51 .. .. *Set of* 4 90 65
MS852 131 × 99 mm. 5 r. Swordsmen .. .. 1·40 1·75

156 Leatherback Turtle (*Dermochelys coriacea*)

157 Paul Harris (founder)

(Des M. Shamir. Litho Questa)

1980 (17 Feb). *Turtle Conservation Campaign. T* **156** *and similar horiz designs. Multicoloured. P* 14.

853 1 l. Type **156** 10 10
854 2 l. Flatback turtle (*Chelonia depressa*) .. 10 10
855 5 l. Hawksbill turtle (*Eretmochelys imbricata*) 10 10
856 10 l. Loggerhead turtle (*Caretta caretta*) .. 10 10
857 75 l. Olive Ridley turtle (*Lepidochelys olivacea*) 30 20
858 10 r. Atlantic Ridley turtle (*Lepidochelys kempii*) .. .. 3·25 2·75
853/8 .. .. *Set of* 6 3·25 2·75
MS859 85 × 107 mm. 4 r. Green turtle (*Chelonia mydas*) .. .. 1·50 2·00

(Des J.W. Litho Questa)

1980 (7 Apr). *75th Anniv of Rotary International. T* **157** *and similar vert designs. Multicoloured. P* 14.

860 75 l. Type **157** 25 10
861 90 l. Family (Humanity) 30 20
862 1 r. Wheat (Hunger) 30 25
863 10 r. Caduceus of Hermes (Health) .. .. 3·00 2·75
860/3 .. .. *Set of* 4 3·50 3·00
MS864 109 × 85 mm. 5 r. Globe .. .. .. 1·50 2·00

LONDON 1980

(158)

159 Swimming

1980 (6 May). *"London 1980" International Stamp Exhibition. Nos.* 809/**MS**811 *optd with T* **158**.

865 1 r. 55, multicoloured 65 55
866 5 r. multicoloured .. .. 1·60 1·25
MS867 132 × 107 mm. 10 r. multicoloured .. 3·75 4·25

On No. **MS**867 the overprint is horizontal.

(Des J.W. Litho Questa)

1980 (4 June). *Olympic Games, Moscow. T* **159** *and similar horiz designs. Multicoloured. P* 14.

868 10 l. Type **159** 10 10
869 50 l. Running 20 15
870 3 r. Putting the shot .. .. 90 1·00
871 4 r. High jump .. .. 1·10 1·25
868/71 .. .. *Set of* 4 2·00 2·25
MS872 105 × 85 mm. 5 r. Weightlifting .. .. 1·25 2·00

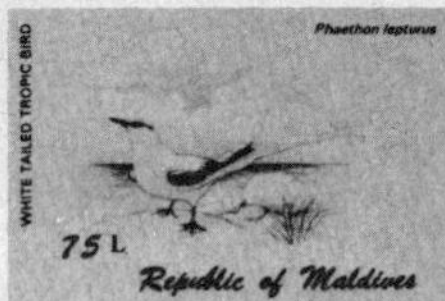

160 White-tailed Tropic Bird

(Des A. Abbas. Litho Questa)

1980 (10 July). *Birds. T* **160** *and similar horiz designs. Multicoloured. P* 14.

873 75 l. Type **160** 25 15
874 95 l. Sooty Tern 35 30
875 1 r. Common Noddy 35 30
876 1 r. 55, Curlew 50 40
877 2 r. Wilson's Petrel 60 40
878 4 r. Caspian Tern .. .. 1·10 75
873/8 .. .. *Set of* 6 2·75 2·10
MS879 124 × 85 mm. 5 r. Red-footed Booby and Brown Booby .. .. 3·50 3·75

161 Seal of Ibrahim II

(Litho Questa)

1980 (26 July). *Seals of the Sultans. T* **161** *and similar horiz designs. Each purple-brown and black. P* 14.

880 1 l. Type **161** 10 10
881 2 l. Mohammed Imadudeen II 10 10
882 5 l. Bin Haji Ali 10 10
883 1 r. Kuda Mohammed Rasgefaanu 30 25
884 2 r. Ibrahim Iskander I 50 45
880/4 .. .. *Set of* 5 80 70
MS885 131 × 95 mm. 3 r. Ibrahim Iskander I (*different*) .. .. 85 1·25

162 Queen Elizabeth the Queen Mother

(Des and litho Questa)

1980 (29 Sept). *Queen Mother's 80th Birthday. P* 14.

886 **162** 4 r. multicoloured .. .. 1·50 1·25
MS887 85 × 110 mm. **162** 5 r. multicoloured .. 2·00 2·50

163 Munnaru

(Des A. Abbas and M. Hassan)

1980 (9 Nov). *1400th Anniv of Hegira. T* **163** *and similar horiz designs. Multicoloured. P* 15.

888 5 l. Type **163** 10 10
889 10 l. Hukuru Miskiiy mosque.. .. .. .. 10 10
890 30 l. Medhuziyaaraiy (shrine of saint) .. 25 15
891 55 l. Writing tablets with verses of Koran .. 30 25
892 90 l. Mother teaching child Koran 50 45
888/92 .. .. *Set of* 5 1·10 85
MS893 124 × 101 mm. 2 r. Map of Maldives and coat of arms .. .. 80 1·25

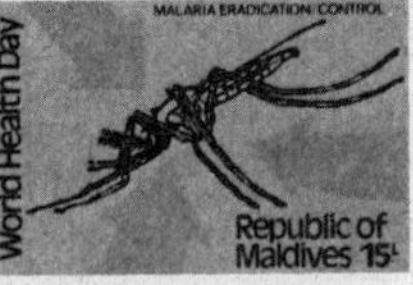

164 Malaria Eradication

(Des J.W. Litho Questa)

1980 (30 Nov). *World Health Day. T* **164** *and similar horiz designs. P* 14.

894 15 l. black, yellow and vermilion 10 10
895 25 l. multicoloured 10 10
896 1 r. 50, orange-brown, yellow-ochre & black 60 45
897 5 r. multicoloured .. .. 1·50 1·40
894/7 .. .. *Set of* 4 2·10 1·75
MS898 68 × 85 mm. 4 r. black, greenish blue and azure .. .. 1·25 1·75

Designs:—25 l. Food (Nutrition); 1 r. 50, Molar and toothbrush (Dental health); 4, 5 r. People and medical equipment (Clinics).

165 White Rabbit

(Des Walt Disney Productions)

1980 (22 Dec). *Scenes from Film "Alice in Wonderland". T* **165** *and similar horiz designs. Multicoloured. P* 11.

899 1 l. Type **165** 10 10
900 2 l. Alice falling into Wonderland 10 10
901 3 l. Alice too big to go through door 10 10
902 4 l. Alice and Tweedledum and Tweedledee 10 10
903 5 l. Alice and the caterpillar.. .. .. 10 10
904 10 l. Cheshire cat 10 10
905 15 l. Alice painting the roses 10 10
906 2 r. 50, Alice and the Queen of Hearts .. 1·25 85
907 4 r. Alice on trial .. .. 1·75 1·40
899/907 .. .. *Set of* 9 3·00 2·25
MS908 126 × 101 mm. 5 r. Alice at the Mad Hatter's tea-party. P 13½.. .. .. .. 3·25 3·25

166 Indian Ocean Ridley Turtle

167 Pendant Lamp

(Des A. Abbas and Maniku. Litho Questa)

1980 (29 Dec). *Marine Life. T* **166** *and similar horiz designs. Multicoloured. P* 14.

909 90 l. Type **166** 90 50
910 1 r. 25, Angel fishes .. .. 1·10 75
911 2 r. Spiny lobster .. .. 1·50 1·10
909/11 .. .. *Set of* 3 3·25 2·10
MS912 140 × 94 mm. 4 r. Fishes .. .. .. 1·50 2·00

1981 (7 Jan). *National Day. T* **167** *and similar multicoloured designs. P* 14½.

913 10 l. Tomb of Ghaazee Muhammad Thakurufaan (*horiz*) 10 10
914 20 l. Type **167** 10 10
915 30 l. Chair used by Muhammad Thakurufaan 15 10
916 95 l. Muhammad Thakurufaan's palace (*horiz*) 35 20
917 10 r. Cushioned divan .. .. 2·75 2·75
913/17 .. .. *Set of* 5 3·00 2·75

168 Prince Charles and Lady Diana Spencer **169** First Majlis Chamber

(Des and litho J.W.)

1981 (22 June). *Royal Wedding. T* **168** *and similar vert designs. Multicoloured. P* 14.

918 1 r. Type **168** 30 25
919 2 r. Buckingham Palace 45 40
920 5 r. Prince Charles, polo player .. .. 1·00 1·00
918/20 .. *Set of* 3 1·60 1·50
MS921 95 × 83 mm. 10 r. State coach .. 2·25 2·50

Nos. 918/20 also exist perforated 12 (*Price for set of* 3 £1.60 *mint or used*) from additional sheets of five stamps and one label. These stamps have changed background colours.

(Des I. Azeez)

1981 (27 June). *50th Anniv of Citizens' Majlis (grievance rights). T* **169** *and similar multicoloured designs. P* 14½.

922 95 l. Type **169** 30 30
923 1 r. Sultan Muhammed Shamsuddin III .. 35 35
MS924 137 × 94 mm. 4 r. First written constitution (*horiz*) .. .. 2·00 2·50

170 "Self-portrait with a Palette" **171** Airmail Envelope

(Des J.W. Litho Questa)

1981 (July). *Birth Centenary of Pablo Picasso. T* **170** *and similar vert designs. Multicoloured. P* 13½ × 14.

925 5 l. Type **170** 10 10
926 10 l. "Woman in Blue" 10 10
927 25 l. "Boy with Pipe" 15 10
928 30 l. "Card Player" 15 10
929 90 l. "Sailor" 35 30
930 3 r. "Self-portrait" 75 75
931 5 r. "Harlequin" .. .. 1·25 1·25
925/31 .. *Set of* 7 2·50 2·40
MS932 106 × 130 mm. 10 r. "Child holding a Dove". Imperf .. .. 3·00 3·50

(Des and litho Questa)

1981 (9 Sept). *75th Anniv of Postal Service. P* 14.

933 **171** 25 l. multicoloured 15 10
934 75 l. multicoloured 35 30
935 5 r. multicoloured .. .. 1·25 1·40
933/5 .. *Set of* 3 1·60 1·60

172 Aircraft taking off **173** Homer

(Des A. Abbas. Litho Questa)

1981 (11 Nov). *Male International Airport. T* **172** *and similar horiz designs. Multicoloured. P* 14.

936 5 l. Type **172** 10 10
937 20 l. Passengers leaving aircraft 20 15
938 1 r. 80, Refuelling 75 75
939 4 r. Plan of airport .. .. 1·40 1·40
936/9 .. *Set of* 4 2·25 2·10
MS940 106 × 79 mm. 5 r. Aerial view of airport .. 1·50 2·00

(Des J.W.)

1981 (18 Nov). *International Year of Disabled People. T* **173** *and similar vert designs. Multicoloured. P* 14½.

941 2 l. Type **173** 10 10
942 5 l. Miguel Cervantes 10 10
943 1 r. Beethoven .. .. 1·25 75
944 5 r. Van Gogh .. .. 2·50 2·50
941/4 .. *Set of* 4 3·50 3·00
MS945 116 × 91 mm. 4 r. Helen Keller and Anne Sullivan .. .. 2·00 2·75

174 Preparation of Maldive Fish **175** Collecting Bait

(Des Central Art Palace. Litho Questa)

1981 (25 Nov). *Decade for Women. T* **174** *and similar vert designs. Multicoloured. P* 14.

946 20 l. Type **174** 10 10
947 90 l. 16th century Maldive women 25 25
948 1 r. Farming 30 30
949 2 r. Coir rope making 55 55
946/9 .. *Set of* 4 1·10 1·10

(Des I. Azeez. Litho Questa)

1981 (10 Dec). *Fishermen's Day. T* **175** *and similar horiz designs. Multicoloured. P* 14.

950 5 l. Type **175** 15 10
951 15 l. Fishing boats 25 20
952 90 l. Fisherman with catch 50 40
953 1 r. 30, Sorting fish 70 55
950/3 .. *Set of* 4 1·40 1·10
MS954 147 × 101 mm. 3 r. Loading fish for export 1·00 1·50

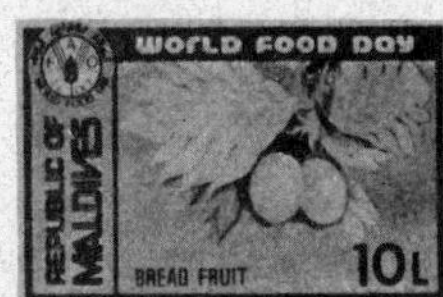

176 Bread Fruit

(Des Design Images. Litho Questa)

1981 (30 Dec). *World Food Day. T* **176** *and similar horiz designs. Multicoloured. P* 14.

955 10 l. Type **176** 15 10
956 25 l. Hen with chicks 30 15
957 30 l. Maize 30 20
958 75 l. Skipjack Tuna 50 40
959 1 r. Pumpkin 60 40
960 2 r. Coconuts .. .. 1·00 1·00
955/60 .. *Set of* 6 2·50 2·00
MS961 110 × 85 mm. 5 r. Eggplant .. .. 1·75 2·25

177 Pluto and Cat **178** Balmoral

(Des Walt Disney Productions)

1982 (29 Mar). *50th Anniv of Pluto (Walt Disney cartoon character). T* **177** *and similar multicoloured design. P* 13½.

962 4 r. Type **177** .. .. 2·00 2·00
MS963 127 × 101 mm. 6 r. Pluto (scene from *The Pointer*) .. .. 2·50 2·50

(Des PAD Studio. Litho Questa)

1982 (1 July). *21st Birthday of Princess of Wales. T* **178** *and similar vert designs. Multicoloured. P* 14½ × 14.

964 95 l. Type **178** 20 20
965 3 r. Prince and Princess of Wales 55 55
966 5 r. Princess on aircraft steps 85 85
964/6 .. *Set of* 3 1·40 1·40
MS967 103 × 75 mm. 8 r. Princess of Wales .. 1·50 1·60

Nos. 964/6 also exist in sheetlets of 5 stamps and 1 label.

Nos. 964/7 and the sheetlets exist imperforate from a restricted printing.

COMMONWEALTH MEMBER
9 July 1982

179 Scout saluting and Camp-site **180** Footballer

(Des D. Miller. Litho Questa)

1982 (9 Aug). *75th Anniv of Boy Scout Movement. T* **179** *and similar horiz designs. Multicoloured. P* 14.

968 1 r. 30, Type **179** 40 40
969 1 r. 80, Lighting a fire 50 50
970 4 r. Life-saving .. .. 1·10 1·10
971 5 r. Map-reading .. .. 1·40 1·40
968/71 .. *Set of* 4 3·00 3·00
MS972 128 × 66 mm. 10 r. Scout emblem and flag of the Maldives .. .. 2·00 2·50

(Des M. and S. Gerber Studio. Litho Questa)

1982 (4 Oct). *World Cup Football Championship, Spain. T* **180** *and similar square designs. P* 13½.

973 90 l. multicoloured 40 30
974 1 r. 50, multicoloured 55 45
975 3 r. multicoloured 85 85
976 5 r. multicoloured .. .. 1·25 1·25
973/6 .. *Set of* 4 2·75 2·50
MS977 94 × 63 mm. 10 r. multicoloured .. .. 2·50 3·25

1982 (18 Oct). *Birth of Prince William of Wales. Nos.* 964/7 *optd with T* **171** *of Antigua.*

978 95 l. Type **178** 20 20
979 3 r. Prince and Princess of Wales 55 55
980 5 r. Princess on aircraft steps 85 85
978/80 .. *Set of* 3 1·40 1·40
MS981 103 × 75 mm. 8 r. Princess of Wales .. 2·25 2·50

Nos. 978/80 also exist in sheetlets of 5 stamps and 1 label.

Nos. 978/81 and the sheetlets exist imperforate from a restricted printing.

181 Basic Education Scheme **182** Koch isolates the Bacillus

(Des and litho Harrison)

1982 (15 Nov). *National Education. T* **181** *and similar horiz designs. Multicoloured. P* 14.

982 90 l. Type **181** 15 20
983 95 l. Primary education 15 20
984 1 r. 30, Teacher training 20 25
985 2 r. 50, Printing educational material .. 40 45
982/5 .. *Set of* 4 80 1·00
MS986 100 × 70 mm. 6 r. Thaana typewriter keyboard .. .. 1·00 1·60

(Des Artists International)

1982 (22 Nov). *Centenary of Robert Koch's Discovery of Tubercle Bacillus. T* **182** *and similar multicoloured designs. P* 14.

987 5 l. Type **182** 10 10
988 15 l. Micro-organism and microscope 10 10
989 95 l. Dr. Robert Koch in 1905 .. .. 25 25
990 3 r. Dr. Koch and plates from publication .. 65 65
987/90 .. *Set of* 4 95 95
MS991 77 × 61 mm. 5 r. Koch in his laboratory (*horiz*) .. .. 80 1·25

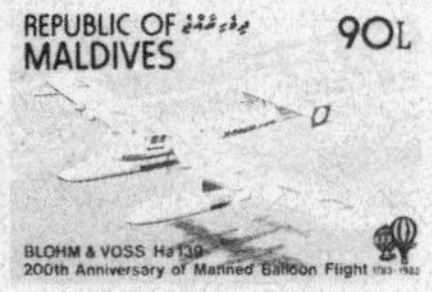

183 Blohm and Voss "Ha 139" Seaplane

(Des W. Wright. Litho Questa)

1983 (28 July). *Bicentenary of Manned Flight. T* **183** *and similar horiz designs. Multicoloured. P* 14.

992 90 l. Type **183** 75 50
993 1 r. 45, Macchi-Castoldi "MC.72" .. .. 1·25 1·00
994 4 r. Boeing "F4B-3" .. .. 2·50 2·00
995 5 r. *La France* airship .. .. 2·75 2·25
992/5 .. *Set of* 4 6·50 5·25
MS996 110 × 85 mm. 10 r. Nadar's *Le Geant* .. 3·00 4·00

184 "Curved Dash" Oldsmobile, 1902

(Des Publishers Graphics Inc)

1983 (Aug). *Classic Motor Cars. T* **184** *and similar horiz designs. Multicoloured. P* 14½.

997 5 l. Type **184** 10 10
998 30 l. Aston Martin "Tourer", 1932 .. .. 25 15
999 40 l. Lamborghini "Muira", 1966 .. .. 30 20
1000 1 r. Mercedes-Benz "300SL", 1945 .. .. 55 40
1001 1 r. 45, Stutz "Bearcat", 1913 .. .. 80 75
1002 5 r. Lotus "Elite", 1958 .. .. 2·50 2·25
997/1002 .. *Set of* 6 4·00 3·50
MS1003 132 × 103 mm. 10 r. Grand Prix "Sunbeam", 1924. P 14½ .. .. 5·50 5·50

Nos. 997/1002 were each issued in sheets of 9, including one *se-tenant* label.

185 Rough-toothed Dolphin

(Des D. Miller. Litho Questa)

1983 (6 Sept). *Marine Mammals. T* **185** *and similar horiz designs. Multicoloured. P* 14.
1004 30 l. Type **185** 55 30
1005 40 l. Indo-Pacific Hump-backed Dolphin .. 70 35
1006 4 r. Finless Porpoise .. .. .. 3·00 2·00
1007 6 r. Pygmy Sperm Whale .. .. .. 3·75 3·25
1004/7 .. .. *Set of* 4 7·25 5·50
MS1008 82 × 90 mm. 5 r. Striped Dolphin .. 2·50 3·25

186 Dish Aerial

(Des PAD Studio. Litho Questa)

1983 (9 Oct). *World Communications Year. T* **186** *and similar horiz designs. Multicoloured. P* 14.
1009 50 l. Type **186** 15 10
1010 1 r. Land, sea and air communications .. 45 45
1011 2 r. Ship-to-shore communication 55 55
1012 10 r. Air traffic controller .. .. .. 1·90 2·00
1009/12 .. .. *Set of* 4 2·75 2·75
MS1013 91 × 76 mm. 20 r. Telecommunications 3·75 4·50

187 "La Donna Gravida"

(Des M. Diamond. Litho Questa)

1983 (25 Oct). *500th Birth Anniv of Raphael. T* **187** *and similar vert designs showing paintings. Multicoloured. P* 13½.
1014 90 l. Type **187** 20 25
1015 3 r. "Giovanna d'Aragona" (detail) .. 60 65
1016 4 r. "Woman with Unicorn" 80 85
1017 6 r. "La Muta" .. .. 1·25 1·40
1014/17 .. .. *Set of* 4 2·50 2·75
MS1018 121 × 97 mm. 10 r. "The Knight's Dream" (detail) .. .. 1·90 2·75

188 Refugee Camp

(Litho Questa)

1983 (29 Nov). *Solidarity with the Palestinians. T* **188** *and similar horiz designs each showing the Dome of the Rock, Jerusalem. Multicoloured. P* 13½ × 14.
1019 4 r. Type **188** .. .. 1·50 1·50
1020 5 r. Refugee holding dead child .. .. 1·60 1·60
1021 6 r. Child carrying food .. .. .. 1·90 1·90
1019/21 .. .. *Set of* 3 4·50 4·50

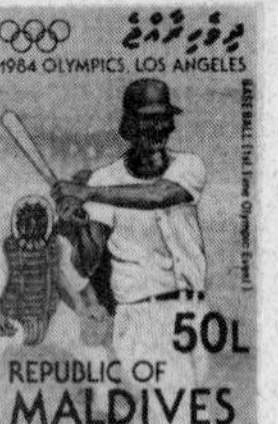

189 Education Facilities **190** Baseball

(Des I. Azeez. Litho Questa)

1983 (10 Dec). *National Development Programme. T* **189** *and similar horiz designs. Multicoloured. P* 13½.
1022 7 l. Type **189** 10 10
1023 10 l. Health service and education 10 10
1024 5 r. Growing more food .. .. .. 1·25 1·25
1025 6 r. Fisheries development .. .. .. 1·50 1·50
1022/5 .. .. *Set of* 4 2·50 2·50
MS1026 134 × 93 mm. 10 r. Air transport .. 2·25 2·75

(Des PAD Studio. Litho Questa)

1984 (10 Mar). *Olympic Games, Los Angeles. T* **190** *and similar vert designs. Multicoloured. P* 14.
1027 50 l. Type **190** 15 15
1028 1 r. 55, Backstroke swimming 40 40
1029 3 r. Judo 80 90
1030 4 r. Shot-putting .. .. 1·25 1·40
1027/30 .. .. *Set of* 4 2·40 2·50
MS1031 85 × 105 mm. 10 r. Team Handball .. 2·40 2·75

Rf1.45

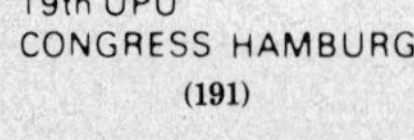

(191) (192)

1984 (19 June). *Universal Postal Union Congress, Hamburg. Nos.* 994/6 *optd as T* **191**.
1032 4 r. Boeing "F4B-3" .. .. 1·40 1·40
1033 5 r. *La France* airship .. .. .. 1·60 1·60
MS1034 110 × 85 mm. 10 r. Nadar's *Le Geant* .. 2·75 3·50

1984 (20 Aug). *Surch as T* **192**. A. *In black*. B. *In gold*.

(*a*) *On Nos.* 964/7

	A		B	
1035 1 r. 45 on 95 l. Type **178** ..	5·00	3·00	5·00	3·00
1036 1 r. 45 on 3 r. Prince and Princess of Wales	5·00	3·00	5·00	3·00
1037 1 r. 45 on 5 r. Princess on aircraft steps	5·00	3·00	5·00	3·00
1035/7 .. .. .. *Set of* 3	13·50	8·00	13·50	8·00
MS1038 103×75 mm. 1 r. 45 on 8 r. Princess of Wales	5·50	8·00	5·50	8·00

(*b*) *On Nos.* 978/81

	A		B	
1039 1 r. 45 on 95 l. Type **178** ..	5·00	3·00	5·00	3·00
1040 1 r. 45 on 3 r. Prince and Princess of Wales	5·00	3·00	5·00	3·00
1041 1 r. 45 on 5 r. Princess on aircraft steps	5·00	3·00	5·00	3·00
1039/41 .. .. *Set of* 3	13·50	8·00	13·50	8·00
MS1042 103×75 mm. 1 r. 45 on 8 r. Princess of Wales	5·50	8·00	5·50	8·00

Stamps from the sheetlets of five plus one label were also surcharged, either in black or gold, using a slightly different type.

193 Hands breaking Manacles **194** Island Resort and Sea Birds

1984 (26 Aug). *Namibia Day. T* **193** *and similar horiz designs. Multicoloured. P* 15.
1043 6 r. Type **193** .. .. 1·50 1·60
1044 8 r. Namibia family .. .. 2·00 2·10
MS1045 129 × 104 mm. 10 r. Map of Namibia .. 2·40 2·75

(Litho Questa)

1984 (12 Sept). *Tourism. T* **194** *and similar vert designs. Multicoloured. P* 14.
1046 7 l. Type **194** 10 10
1047 15 l. Dhow 10 10
1048 20 l. Snorkelling 10 10
1049 2 r. Wind-surfing 35 40
1050 4 r. Aqualung diving 70 75
1051 6 r. Night fishing .. .. 1·00 1·25
1052 8 r. Game fishing .. .. 1·40 1·50
1053 10 r. Turtle on beach .. .. 1·60 1·75
1046/53 .. .. *Set of* 8 4·75 5·25

195 Frangipani

1984 (21 Sept). *"Ausipex" International Stamp Exhibition, Melbourne. T* **195** *and similar horiz designs showing flowers. Multicoloured. P* 15.
1054 5 r. Type **195** .. .. 1·50 1·50
1055 10 r. Cooktown Orchid .. .. .. 3·25 3·25
MS1056 105 × 77 mm. 15 r. Sun Orchid .. .. 5·50 5·50

196 Facade of the Malé Mosque

1984 (11 Nov). *Opening of Islamic Centre. T* **196** *and similar multicoloured design. P* 15.
1057 2 r. Type **196** 45 50
1058 5 r. Malé Mosque and minaret (*vert*) .. .. 1·10 1·25

197 Air Maldives Boeing "737"

(Des G. Drummond. Litho Questa)

1984 (19 Nov). *40th Anniv of International Civil Aviation Authority. T* **197** *and similar horiz designs. Multicoloured. P* 14.
1059 7 l. Type **197** 10 10
1060 4 r. Airlanka Lockheed "L–1011 TriStar" .. 90 95
1061 6 r. Air Alitalia McDonnell Douglas "DC10–30" .. .. 1·25 1·40
1062 8 r. L.T.U. Lockheed "L–1011 TriStar" .. 1·75 1·90
1059/62 .. .. *Set of* 4 3·50 4·00
MS1063 110 × 92 mm. 15 r. Air Maldives Shorts "SC7 Skyvan" .. .. 3·25 4·00

198 Daisy Duck

(Litho Questa)

1984 (26 Nov–1 Dec). *50th Anniv of Donald Duck (Walt Disney cartoon character). T* **198** *and similar horiz designs. Multicoloured. P* 12 (5 *r*.) *or* 14 × 13½ (*others*).
1064 3 l. Type **198** 10 10
1065 4 l. Huey, Dewey and Louie 10 10
1066 5 l. Ludwig von Drake 10 10
1067 10 l. Gyro Gearloose 10 10
1068 15 l. Uncle Scrooge painting self portrait .. 10 10
1069 25 l. Donald Duck with camera 10 10
1070 5 r. Donald Duck and Gus Goose (1.12) .. 1·00 1·00
1071 8 r. Gladstone Gander .. .. .. 1·60 1·60
1072 10 r. Grandma Duck .. .. .. 2·00 2·00
1064/72 .. .. *Set of* 9 4·25 4·25
MS1073 102 × 126 mm. 15 r. Uncle Scrooge and Donald Duck in front of camera .. .. .. 2·75 3·25
MS1074 126 × 102 mm. 15 r. Uncle Scrooge (1.12) 2·75 3·25
No. 1070 was printed in sheetlets of 8 stamps.

199 "The Day" (detail) **200** "Edmond Iduranty" (Degas)

(Litho Questa)

1984 (10 Dec). *450th Death Anniv of Correggio (artist). T* **199** *and similar vert designs. Multicoloured. P* 14.
1075 5 r. Type **199** .. .. 95 1·00
1076 10 r. "The Night" (*detail*) .. .. .. 1·60 1·75
MS1077 60 × 80 mm. 15 r. "Portrait of a Man" .. 2·75 3·25

(Litho Questa)

1984 (15 Dec). *150th Birth Anniv of Edgar Degas (artist). T* **200** *and similar vert designs. P* 14.
1078 75 l. Type **200** 15 20
1079 2 r. "James Tissot" 45 50
1080 5 r. "Achille de Gas in Uniform" .. .. 1·10 1·25
1081 10 r. "Lady with Chrysanthemums" .. .. 2·25 2·50
1078/81 .. .. *Set of* 4 3·50 4·00
MS1082 100 × 70 mm. 15 r. "Self-portrait" .. 3·25 3·75

201 Pale-footed Shearwater

202 Squad Drilling

(Des I. MacLaury. Litho Questa)

1985 (9 Mar). *Birth Bicentenary of John J. Audubon (ornithologist) (1st issue). T* **201** *and similar multicoloured designs showing original paintings. P* 14.
1083 3 r. Type **201** 65 60
1084 3 r. 50, Little Grebe (*horiz*) . . 75 70
1085 4 r. Common Cormorant . . 90 85
1086 4 r. 50, White-faced Storm Petrel (*horiz*) . . 95 90
1083/6 . . *Set of* 4 3·00 2·75
MS1087 108×80 mm. 15 r. Red-necked Phalarope (*horiz*) . . 2·75 3·25
See also Nos. 1192/200.

(Des and litho Questa)

1985 (6 June). *National Security Service. T* **202** *and similar multicoloured designs. P* 13½×14 (*No.* 1092) *or* 14×13½ (*others*).
1088 15 l. Type **202** . . 15 10
1089 20 l. Combat patrol . . 15 10
1090 1 r. Fire fighting . . 35 25
1091 2 r. Coastguard cutter . . 65 55
1092 10 r. Independence Day Parade (*vert*) . . 2·00 2·50
1088/92 . . *Set of* 5 3·00 3·00
MS1093 128×85 mm. 10 r. Cannon on saluting base and National Security Service badge . . 1·90 2·25

GOLD MEDALIST
THERESA ANDREWS
USA

(**203**)

204 Queen Elizabeth the Queen Mother, 1981

1985 (17 July). *Olympic Games Gold Medal Winners, Los Angeles. Nos.* 1027/31 *optd as T* **203** *or in larger capitals* (50 *l.,* 10 *r.*).
1094 50 l. Type **190** (optd "JAPAN") . . 10 10
1095 1 r. 55, Backstroke swimming (opt T **203**) 30 35
1096 3 r. Judo (Optd "GOLD MEDALIST FRANK WIENEKE USA") . . 55 60
1097 4 r. Shot-putting (optd "GOLD MEDALIST CLAUDIA LOCH WEST GERMANY") . . 80 85
1094/7 . . *Set of* 4 1·60 1·75
MS1098 85×105 mm. 10 r. Team Handball (opt "U.S.A.") . . 1·90 2·00

(Des J.W. Litho Questa)

1985 (20 Aug). *Life and Times of Queen Elizabeth the Queen Mother. T* **204** *and similar multicoloured designs. P* 14.
1099 3 r. Type **204** . . 55 60
1100 5 r. Visiting the Middlesex Hospital (*horiz*) . . 95 1·00
1101 7 r. The Queen Mother . . 1·40 1·50
1099/101 . . *Set of* 3 2·50 2·75
MS1102 56×85 mm. 15 r. With Prince Charles at Garter Ceremony . . 2·75 3·00
Stamps as Nos. 1099/101, but with face values of 1 r., 4 r. and 10 r., exist from additional sheetlets of 5 plus a label issued 4 January 1986. These also have changed background colours and are perforated 12½×12 (4 r.) or 12×12½ (others) (*Price for set of stamps £2.50 mint*).

(Des Susan David. Litho Questa)

1985 (3 Sept). *300th Birth Anniv of Johann Sebastian Bach (composer). Vert designs as T* **206** *of Antigua. P* 14.
1103 15 l. multicoloured . . 10 10
1104 2 r. multicoloured . . 50 45
1105 4 r. multicoloured . . 90 85
1106 10 r. multicoloured . . 1·90 2·00
1103/6 . . *Set of* 4 3·00 3·00
MS1107 104×75 mm. 15 r. black and reddish orange . . 3·00 3·50
Designs:—15 l. Liro da braccio: 2 r. Tenor oboe; 4 r. Serpent; 10 r. Table organ; 15 r. Johann Sebastian Bach.

205 Mas Odi (fishing boat)

(Des H. Afeef. Litho Questa)

1985 (23 Sept). *Maldives Ships and Boats. T* **205** *and similar horiz designs. Multicoloured. P* 14.
1108 3 l. Type **205** . . 10 10
1109 5 l. Battela (dhow) . . 10 10
1110 10 l. Addu odi (dhow) . . 10 10
1111 2 r. 60, Modern dhoni (fishing boat) . . 25 30
1112 2 r. 70, Mas dhoni (fishing boat) . . 30 35
1113 3 r. Baththeli dhoni . . 30 35
1114 5 r. *Inter* 1 (inter-island vessel) . . 50 55
1115 10 r. Dhoni-style yacht . . 1·00 1·10
1108/15 . . *Set of* 8 2·40 2·75

206 Windsurfing

207 United Nations Building, New York

(Des H. Afeef. Litho Questa)

1985 (2 Oct). *10th Anniv of World Tourism Organization. T* **206** *and similar horiz designs. Multicoloured. P* 14.
1116 6 r. Type **206** . . 1·10 1·25
1117 8 r. Scuba diving . . 1·50 1·60
MS1118 171×114 mm. 15 r. Kuda Hithi Resort 2·75 3·00

(Litho Questa)

1985 (24 Oct). *40th Anniv of United Nations Organization and International Year of Peace. T* **207** *and similar multicoloured designs. P* 14.
1119 15 l. Type **207** . . 10 10
1120 2 r. Hands releasing peace dove . . 40 45
1121 4 r. U.N. Security Council meeting (*horiz*) 80 85
1122 10 r. Lion and lamb . . 1·90 2·00
1119/22 . . *Set of* 4 2·75 3·00
MS1123 76×92 mm. 15 r. U.N. Building and peace dove . . 2·75 3·00

208 Maldivian Delegate voting in U.N. General Assembly

(Des BG Studio. Litho Questa)

1985 (24 Oct). *20th Anniv of United Nations Membership. T* **208** *and similar horiz design. Multicoloured. P* 14.
1124 20 l. Type **208** . . 10 10
1125 15 r. U.N. and Maldivian flags, and U.N. Building, New York . . 2·75 3·00

209 Youths playing Drums

(Des BG Studio)

1985 (20 Nov). *International Youth Year. T* **209** *and similar multicoloured designs. P* 15.
1126 90 l. Type **209** . . 15 20
1127 6 r. Tug-of-war . . 1·10 1·25
1128 10 r. Community service (*vert*) . . 1·90 2·00
1126/8 . . *Set of* 3 2·75 3·00
MS1129 85×84 mm. 15 r. Raising the flag at youth camp (*vert*) . . 2·75 3·00

210 Quotation and Flags of Member Nations

(Litho Questa)

1985 (8 Dec) *1st Summit Meeting of South Asian Association for Regional Co-operation, Dhaka, Bangladesh. P* 14.
1130 **210** 3 r. multicoloured . . 55 60

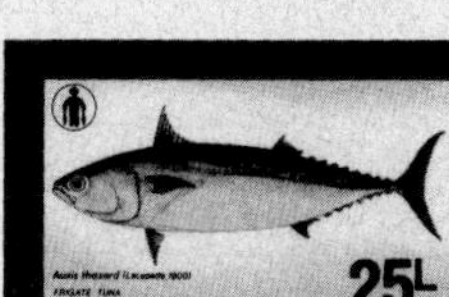

211 Frigate Tuna

212 Player running with Ball

(Litho Questa)

1985 (10 Dec). *Fishermen's Day. Species of Tuna. T* **211** *and similar horiz designs. Multicoloured. P* 14.
1131 25 l. Type **211** . . 10 10
1132 75 l. Little Tuna . . 15 15
1133 3 r. Dogtooth Tuna . . 55 60
1134 5 r. Yellowfin Tuna . . 95 1·00
1131/4 . . *Set of* 4 1·50 1·60
MS1135 130×90 mm. 15 r. Skipjack Tuna . . 2·75 3·00

(Des Walt Disney Productions. Litho Questa)

1985 (21 Dec). *150th Birth Anniv of Mark Twain. As T* **118** *of Anguilla, but vert, showing Walt Disney cartoon characters illustrating various Mark Twain quotations. Multicoloured. P* 12 (4 *r.*) *or* 13½×14 (*others*).
1136 2 l. Winnie the Pooh . . 10 10
1137 3 l. Gepetto and Figaro the cat . . 10 10
1138 4 l. Goofy and basket of broken eggs . . 10 10
1139 20 l. Goofy as doctor scolding Donald Duck 10 10
1140 4 r. Mowgli and King Louis . . 75 80
1141 13 r. The wicked Queen and mirror . . 2·50 2·75
1136/41 . . *Set of* 6 3·00 3·25
MS1142 126×101 mm. 15 r. Mickey Mouse as Tom Sawyer on comet's tail . . 2·75 3·00
No. 1140 was issued in sheetlets of 8 stamps.

(Des Walt Disney Productions. Litho Questa)

1985 (21 Dec). *Birth Bicentenaries of Grimm Brothers (folklorists). Horiz designs as T* **119** *of Anguilla showing Walt Disney cartoon characters in scenes from "Dr. Knowall". Multicoloured. P* 12 (3 *r.*) *or* 14×13½ (*others*).
1143 1 l. Donald Duck as Crabb driving oxcart . . 10 10
1144 5 l. Donald Duck as Dr. Knowall . . 10 10
1145 10 l. Dr. Knowall in surgery . . 10 10
1146 15 l. Dr. Knowall with Uncle Scrooge as a lord . . 10 10
1147 3 r. Dr. and Mrs. Knowall in pony trap . . 55 60
1148 14 r. Dr. Knowall and thief . . 2·75 3·00
1143/8 . . *Set of* 6 3·00 3·25
MS1149 126×101 mm. 15 r. Donald and Daisy Duck as Dr. and Mrs. Knowall . . 2·75 3·00
No. 1147 was printed in sheetlets of 8 stamps.

(Des W. Hanson. Litho Questa)

1986 (29 Apr). *Appearance of Halley's Comet (1st issue). Horiz designs as T* **123** *of Anguilla. Multicoloured. P* 14.
1150 20 l. N.A.S.A. space telescope and Comet . . 20 10
1151 1 r. 50, E.S.A. *Giotto* spacecraft and Comet 60 55
1152 2 r. Japanese *Planet A* spacecraft and Comet . . 80 65
1153 4 r. Edmond Halley and Stonehenge . . 1·50 1·40
1154 5 r. Russian *Vega* spacecraft and Comet . . 1·75 1·60
1150/4 . . *Set of* 5 4·25 3·75
MS1155 101×70 mm. 15 r. Halley's Comet . . 3·00 3·75
See also Nos. 1206/11.

(Des J. Iskowitz. Litho Questa)

1986 (5 May). *Centenary of Statue of Liberty. Multicoloured designs as T* **211** *of Dominica, showing the Statue of Liberty and immigrants to the U.S.A. P* 14.
1156 50 l. Walter Gropius (architect) . . 20 15
1157 70 l. John Lennon (musician) . . 55 40
1158 1 r. George Balanchine (choreographer) . . 60 45
1159 10 r. Franz Werfel (writer) . . 2·75 3·25
1156/9 . . *Set of* 4 3·75 3·75
MS1160 100×72 mm. 15 r. Statue of Liberty (*vert*) . . 3·00 3·75

(Des Walt Disney Productions)

1986 (22 May). *"Ameripex" International Stamp Exhibition, Chicago. Horiz designs as T* **212** *of Dominica, showing Walt Disney cartoon characters and U.S.A. stamps. Multicoloured. P* 11.
1161 3 l. Johnny Appleseed and 1966 Johnny Appleseed stamp . . 10 10
1162 4 l. Paul Bunyan and 1958 Forest Conservation stamp . . 10 10
1163 5 l. Casey and 1969 Professional Baseball Centenary stamp . . 10 10
1164 10 l. Ichabod Crane and 1974 "Legend of Sleepy Hollow" stamp . . 10 10
1165 15 l. John Henry and 1944 75th anniv of completion of First Transcontinental Railroad stamp . . 10 10
1166 20 l. Windwagon Smith and 1954 Kansas Territory Centenary stamp . . 10 10
1167 13 r. Mike Fink and 1970 Great Northwest stamp . . 2·40 2·75
1168 14 r. Casey Jones and 1950 Railroad Engineers stamp . . 2·75 3·00
1161/8 . . *Set of* 8 5·00 5·50
MS1169 Two sheets, each 127×101 mm. (a) 15 r. Davy Crockett and 1967 Davy Crockett stamp. (b) 15 r. Daisy Duck as Pocahontas saving Captain John Smith (Donald Duck). P 14×13½. . . *Set of* 2 *sheets* 5·50 7·00

(Litho Questa)

1986 (29 May). *60th Birthday of Queen Elizabeth II. Vert designs as T* **125** *of Anguilla. P* 14.
1170 1 r. black and chrome-yellow 35 25
1171 2 r. multicoloured 55 55
1172 12 r. multicoloured .. .. 2·75 2·75
1170/2 .. .. *Set of* 3 3·25 3·25
MS1173 120×85 mm. 15 r. black and grey-brown 3·75 4·25
Designs:—1 r. Royal Family at Girl Guides Rally, 1938; 2 r. Queen in Canada; 12 r. At Sandringham, 1970; 15 r. Princesses Elizabeth and Margaret at Royal Lodge, Windsor, 1940.
Nos. 1170/2 were each issued in sheetlets of five stamps and one stamp-size label.

(Des BG Studio. Litho Questa)

1986 (8 June). *World Cup Football Championship, Mexico. T* **212** *and similar vert designs. Multicoloured. P* 14.
1174 15 l. Type **212** 10 10
1175 2 r. Player gaining control of ball .. 40 45
1176 4 r. Two players competing for ball .. 75 80
1177 10 r. Player bouncing ball on knee.. .. 1·90 2·00
1174/7 .. .. *Set of* 4 2·75 3·00
MS1178 95×114 mm. 15 r. Player kicking ball .. 2·75 3·50

(Litho Questa)

1986 (1 July). *Royal Wedding. Vert designs as T* **213** *of Antigua. Multicoloured. P* 14.
1179 10 l. Prince Andrew and Miss Sarah Ferguson 10 10
1180 2 r. Prince Andrew.. .. .. 60 60
1181 12 r. Prince Andrew in naval uniform .. 2·75 3·00
1179/81 .. .. *Set of* 3 3·00 3·25
MS1182 88×88 mm. 15 r. Prince Andrew and Miss Sarah Ferguson (*different*) .. .. .. 3·25 3·75

213 Moorish Idol and Sea Fan

214 Servicing Aircraft

(Des Mary Walters)

1986 (22 Sept). *Marine Wildlife. T* **213** *and similar horiz designs. Multicoloured. P* 15.
1183 50 l. Type **213** 30 20
1184 90 l. Regal Angelfish 40 35
1185 1 r. Anemone Fish 50 40
1186 2 r. Tiger Cowrie and Stinging Coral .. 75 65
1187 3 r. Emperor Angelfish and Staghorn Coral .. .. 1·00 90
1188 4 r. Black-naped Tern .. .. .. 1·50 1·50
1189 5 r. Fiddler Crab and Staghorn Coral .. 1·50 1·50
1190 10 r. Hawksbill Turtle .. .. .. 2·50 2·50
1183/90 .. .. *Set of* 8 7·50 7·25
MS1191 Two sheets, each 107×76 mm. (a) 15 r. Long Nosed Butterfly Fish. (b) 15 r. Trumpet Fish .. .. *Set of 2 sheets* 6·50 7·50

(Litho Questa)

1986 (9 Oct). *Birth Bicentenary of John J. Audubon (ornithologist)* (1985) (*2nd issue*). *Multicoloured designs as T* **201** *showing original paintings. P* 14.
1192 3 l. Little Blue Heron (*horiz*) 10 10
1193 4 l. White-tailed Kite 10 10
1194 5 l. Greater Shearwater (*horiz*) 10 10
1195 10 l. Magnificent Frigate Bird 15 10
1196 15 l. Black-necked Grebe 25 10
1197 20 l. Goosander 30 10
1198 13 r. Peregrine Falcon (*horiz*) .. .. 4·50 4·00
1199 14 r. Prairie Chicken (*horiz*) .. .. 4·50 4·00
1192/9 .. .. *Set of* 8 9·00 7·50
MS1200 Two sheets, each 74×104 mm. (a) 15 r. Fulmar. (b) 15 r. White-fronted Goose (*horiz*) *Set of 2 sheets* 7·50 9·00
Nos. 1192/9 were each issued in sheetlets of five stamps and one stamp-size label, which appears in the centre of the bottom row.

1986 (25 Oct). *World Cup Football Championship Winners, Mexico. Nos.* 1174/8 *optd with T* **216** *of Antigua in gold.*
1201 15 l. Type **212** 10 10
1202 2 r. Player gaining control of ball .. 40 45
1203 4 r. Two players competing for ball .. 75 80
1204 10 r. Player bouncing ball on knee.. .. 1·90 2·00
1201/4 .. .. *Set of* 4 2·75 3·00
MS1205 95×114 mm. 15 r. Player kicking ball .. 2·75 3·50

1986 (30 Oct). *Appearance of Halley's Comet* (*2nd issue*). *Nos.* 1150/5 *optd with T* **218** *of Antigua in silver.*
1206 20 l. N.A.S.A. space telescope and Comet .. 10 10
1207 1 r. 50, E.S.A. *Giotto* spacecraft and Comet 30 35
1208 2 r. Japanese *Planet A* spacecraft and Comet 40 45
1209 4 r. Edmond Halley and Stonehenge .. 75 80
1210 5 r. Russian *Vega* spacecraft and Comet .. 95 1·00
1206/10 .. .. *Set of* 5 2·25 2·40
MS1211 101×70 mm. 15 r. Halley's Comet .. 2·75 3·50

(Des BG Studio)

1986 (4 Nov). *40th Anniv of U.N.E.S.C.O. T* **214** *and similar vert designs. Multicoloured. P* 15.
1212 1 r. Type **214**.. .. .. 20 25
1213 2 r. Boat building 40 45
1214 3 r. Children in classroom 55 60
1215 5 r. Student in laboratory .. .. .. 95 1·00
1212/15 .. .. *Set of* 4 1·90 2·10
MS1216 77×100 mm. 15 r. Diving bell on sea bed .. .. 2·75 3·50

215 *Hypholoma fasciculare*

216 Ixora

(Des Mary Walters)

1986 (31 Dec). *Fungi of the Maldives. T* **215** *and similar multicoloured designs. P* 15.
1217 15 l. Type **215** 20 10
1218 50 l. *Kuehneromyces mutabilis* (*vert*) .. 25 15
1219 1 r. *Amanita muscaria* (*vert*) 35 30
1220 2 r. *Agaricus campestris* 60 50
1221 3 r. *Amanita pantherina* (*vert*) 80 70
1222 4 r. *Coprinus comatus* (*vert*) 90 90
1223 5 r. *Pholiota spectabilis* .. .. .. 1·25 1·50
1224 10 r. *Pluteus cervinus* .. .. .. 2·25 2·50
1217/24 .. .. *Set of* 8 6·00 6·00
MS1225 Two sheets, each 100×70 mm. (a) 15 r. *Armillaria mellea.* (b) 15 r. *Stropharia aeruginosa* (*vert*) .. .. *Set of 2 sheets* 5·50 7·50

(Des Mary Walters)

1987 (29 Jan). *Flowers. T* **216** *and similar vert designs. Multicoloured. P* 15.
1226 10 l. Type **216** 10 10
1227 20 l. Frangipani 10 10
1228 50 l. Crinum.. .. .. 25 15
1229 2 r. Pink Rose 50 50
1230 4 r. Flamboyant Flower 80 80
1231 10 r. Ground Orchid.. .. .. .. 2·50 2·50
1226/31 .. .. *Set of* 6 3·75 3·75
MS1232 Two sheets, each 100×70 mm. (a) 15 r. Gardenia. (b) 15 r. Oleander *Set of 2 sheets* 4·75 6·50

217 Guides studying Wild Flowers

218 *Thespesia populnea*

(Des R. Vigurs)

1987 (4 Apr). *75th Anniv of Girl Guide Movement* (1985). *T* **217** *and similar horiz designs. Multicoloured. P* 15.
1233 15 l. Type **217** 10 10
1234 2 r. Guides with pet rabbits 40 40
1235 4 r. Guide observing spoonbill 80 80
1236 12 r. Lady Baden-Powell and Guide flag .. 2·50 2·50
1233/6 .. .. *Set of* 4 3·50 3·50
MS1237 104×78 mm. 15 r. Guides in sailing dinghy .. .. 2·75 3·00

(Litho Questa)

1987 (22 Apr). *Trees and Plants. T* **218** *and similar multicoloured designs. P* 14.
1238 50 l. Type **218** 10 10
1239 1 r. *Cocos nucifera* 15 20
1240 2 r. *Calophyllum mophyllum* 30 35
1241 3 r. *Xyanthosoma indica* (*horiz*) 45 50
1242 5 r. *Ipomoea batatas* (*horiz*) 80 85
1243 7 r. *Artocarpus altilis* .. .. .. 1·10 1·25
1238/43 .. .. *Set of* 6 2·50 3·00
MS1244 75×109 mm. 15 r. *Cocos nucifera* (*different*) .. .. 2·25 2·75

(Des J. Iskowitz)

1987 (4 May). *America's Cup Yachting Championship. Multicoloured designs as T* **222** *of Antigua. P* 15.
1245 15 l. *Intrepid*, 1970 .. .. 10 10
1246 1 r. *France II*, 1974.. .. .. .. 20 20
1247 2 r. *Gretel*, 1962 .. .. 40 45
1248 12 r. *Volunteer*, 1887 .. .. .. 2·00 2·25
1245/8 .. .. *Set of* 4 2·40 2·75
MS1249 113×83 mm. 15 r. Helmsman and crew on deck of *Defender*, 1895 (*horiz*) .. .. 2·25 2·75

NEW INFORMATION

The editor is always interested to correspond with people who have new information that will improve or correct the Catalogue.

219 *Precis octavia*

220 Isaac Newton experimenting with Spectrum

1987 (16 Dec). *Butterflies. T* **219** *and similar vert designs. Multicoloured. P* 15.
1250 15 l. Type **219** 15 1
1251 20 l. Common Rose 15 1
1252 50 l. *Teinopalpus imperialis* 20 2
1253 1 r. *Kallima horsfieldi* 30 3
1254 2 r. *Cethosia biblis* 50 5
1255 4 r. *Hestia jasonia* 85 8
1256 7 r. *Papilio memnon* .. .. .. 1·50 1·5
1257 10 r. Mountain Beauty .. .. .. 2·00 2·0
1250/7 .. .. *Set of* 8 5·00 5·0
MS1258 Two sheets, each 135×102 mm. (a) 15 r. *Acraea violae* (*acraeinae*). (b) 15 r. *Hebomoia leucippe* .. .. .. *Set of 2 sheets* 5·50 7·0

(Des J. Martin. Litho Questa)

1988 (10 Jan). *Great Scientific Discoveries. T* **220** *and simila multicoloured designs. P* 14.
1259 1 r. 50, Type **220** 45 4
1260 3 r. Euclid composing *Principles of Geometry* (*vert*) 70 7
1261 4 r. Mendel formulating theory of Genetic Evolution (*vert*) 85 8
1262 5 r. Galileo and moons of Jupiter .. .. 1·00 1·0
1259/62 .. .. *Set of* 4 2·75 2·7
MS1263 102×72 mm. 15 r. "Apollo" lunar module (*vert*) .. .. 2·75 3·5

221 Donald Duck and Weather Satellite

(Des Walt Disney Co. Litho Questa)

1988 (15 Feb). *Space Exploration. T* **221** *and simila multicoloured designs showing Walt Disney cartoo characters. P* 14×13½ (*horiz*) *or* 13½×14 (*vert*).
1264 3 l. Type **221** 10 1
1265 4 l. Minnie Mouse and navigation satellite 10 1
1266 5 l. Mickey Mouse's nephews talking via communication satellite 10 1
1267 10 l. Goofy in lunar rover (*vert*) 10 1
1268 20 l. Minnie Mouse delivering pizza to flying saucer (*vert*) 10 1
1269 13 r. Mickey Mouse directing spacecraft docking (*vert*) .. .. .. 1·60 1·7
1270 14 r. Mickey Mouse and "Voyager 2" .. 1·75 1·9
1264/70 .. .. *Set of* 7 3·25 3·5
MS1271 Two sheets, each 127×102 mm. (a) 15 r. Mickey Mouse at first Moon landing, 1969. (b) 15 r. Mickey Mouse and nephews in space station swimming pool (*vert*) .. *Set of 2 sheets* 3·50 3·7

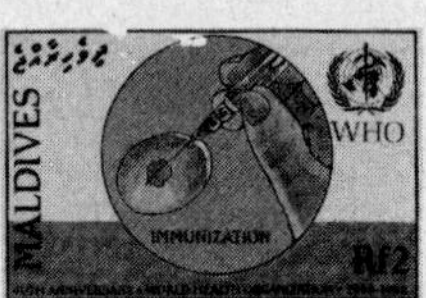

222 Syringe and Bacterium ("Immunization")

(Des Mary Walters. Litho Questa)

1988 (7 Apr). *40th Anniv of World Health Organization. T* **22** *and similar horiz design. Multicoloured. P* 14.
1272 2 r. Type **222** 25 3
1273 4 r. Tap ("Clean Water") 50 5

223 Water Droplet and Atoll

224 Globe, Carrier Pigeon and Letter

(Des I. Rasheed)

988 (9 May). *World Environment Day* (1987). *T* **223** *and similar multicoloured designs. P* 15.

274	15 l. Type **223**	10	10
275	75 l. Coral reef	10	10
276	2 r. Audubon's Shearwaters in flight	25	30
274/6	*Set of* 3	35	40
MS1277	105×76 mm. 15 r. Banyan Tree (*vert*)	1·75	1·90

(Litho Questa)

988 (31 May). *Transport and Telecommunications Decade. T* **224** *and similar horiz designs, each showing central globe. Multicoloured. P* 14.

278	2 r. Type **224**	25	30
279	3 r. Dish aerial and girl using telephone	35	40
280	5 r. Satellite, television, telephone and antenna tower	60	65
281	10 r. Car, ship and airliner	1·25	1·40
278/81	*Set of* 4	2·25	2·50

40TH WEDDING ANNIVERSARY
H.M.QUEEN ELIZABETH II
H.R.H. THE DUKE OF EDINBURGH

(225)

226 Discus-throwing

988 (7 July). *Royal Ruby Wedding. Nos.* 1170/3 *optd with T* **225** *in gold.*

282	1 r. black and chrome-yellow	15	15
283	2 r. multicoloured	25	30
284	12 r. multicoloured	1·40	1·90
282/4	*Set of* 3	3·25	3·50
MS1285	120×85 mm. 15 r. black and grey-brown	1·75	1·90

(Des B. Bundock. Litho Questa)

988 (16 July). *Olympic Games, Seoul. T* **226** *and similar multicoloured designs. P* 14.

286	15 l. Type **226**	10	10
287	2 r. 100 metres race	25	30
288	4 r. Gymnastics (*horiz*)	50	55
289	12 r. Three-day equestrian event (*horiz*)	1·40	1·50
286/9	*Set of* 4	2·00	2·10
MS1290	106×76 mm. 20 r. Tennis (*horiz*)	2·40	2·50

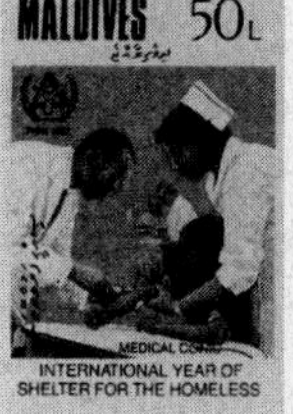

227 Immunization at Clinic

228 Breadfruit

(Des A. DiLorenzo. Litho Questa)

988 (20 July). *International Year of Shelter for the Homeless. T* **227** *and similar vert designs. Multicoloured. P* 14.

291	50 l. Type **227**	10	10
292	3 r. Prefab housing estate	35	40
MS1293	63×105 mm. 15 r. Building site	1·75	1·90

(Des G. Watkins. Litho Questa)

988 (30 July). *10th Anniv of International Fund for Agricultural Development. T* **228** *and similar multicoloured designs. P* 14.

294	7 r. Type **228**	85	90
295	10 r. Mangos (*vert*)	1·25	1·40
MS1296	103×74 mm. 15 r. Coconut palm, fishing boat and Yellowtail Tuna	1·75	1·90

(229)

230 Pres. Kennedy and Launch of "Apollo" Spacecraft

988 (1 Dec). *World Aids Day. Nos.* 1272/3 *optd with T* **229**.

297	2 r. Type **222**	25	30
298	4 r. Tap ("Clean Water")	50	55

(Des A. Nahigian. Litho Questa)

1989 (13 Feb). *25th Death Anniv of John F. Kennedy (American statesman). U.S. Space Achievements. T* **230** *and similar vert designs. Multicoloured. P* 14.

1299	5 r. Type **230**	60	65
	a. Horiz strip of 4. Nos. 1299/1302	2·10	
1300	5 r. Lunar module and astronaut on Moon	60	65
1301	5 r. Astronaut and buggy on Moon	60	65
1302	5 r. President Kennedy and spacecraft	60	65
1299/1302	*Set of* 4	2·10	2·40
MS1303	108 × 77 mm. 15 r. President Kennedy making speech	1·75	1·90

Nos. 1299/1302 were printed together, *se-tenant*, in horizontal strips of 4 throughout the sheet.

J. SCHULT
DDR

(231)

ASIA-PACIFIC
TELECOMMUNITY
10 YEARS

(232)

1989 (29 Apr). *Olympic Medal Winners, Seoul. Nos.* 1286/90 *optd as T* **231**.

1304	15 l. Type **226** (optd with T **231**)	10	10
1305	2 r. 100 metres race (optd "C. LEWIS USA")	25	30
1306	4 r. Gymnastics (*horiz*) (optd "MEN'S ALL AROUND V. ARTEMOV USSR")	50	55
1307	12 r. Three-day equestrian event (*horiz*) (optd "TEAM SHOW JUMPING W. GERMANY")	1·40	1·50
1304/7	*Set of* 4	2·00	2·25
MS1308	106×76 mm. 20 r. Tennis (*horiz*) (optd "OLYMPIC WINNERS MEN'S SINGLES GOLD M. MECIR CZECH. SILVER T. MAYOTTE USA BRONZE B. GILBERT USA")	3·50	3·50

On No. **MS**1308 the overprint appears on the sheet margin and not the 20 r. stamp.

(Litho Questa)

1989 (20 May). *500th Birth Anniv of Titian (artist). Vert designs as T* **238** *of Antigua showing paintings. Multicoloured. P* $13^1/_2$×14.

1309	15 l. "Benedetto Varchi"	10	10
1310	1 r. "Portrait of a Young Man"	10	15
1311	2 r. "King Francis I of France"	25	30
1312	5 r. "Pietro Aretino"	60	65
1313	15 r. "The Bravo"	1·75	1·90
1314	20 r. "The Concert" (detail)	2·40	2·50
1309/14	*Set of* 6	4·75	5·00
MS1315	Two sheets. (a) 112×96 mm. 20 r. "An Allegory of Prudence" (detail). (b) 96×110 mm. 20 r. "Francesco Maria della Rovere" *Set of* 2 *sheets*	4·75	5·00

1989 (10 July). *10th Anniv of Asia-Pacific Telecommunity. Nos.* 1279/80 *optd with T* **232** *in silver.*

1316	3 r. Dish aerial and girl using telephone	35	40
1317	5 r. Satellite, television, telephone and antenna tower	60	65

(Litho Questa)

1989 (2 Sept–16 Oct). *Japanese Art. Paintings by Hokusai. Horiz designs as T* **250** *of Antigua. Multicoloured. P* 14×$13^1/_2$.

1318	15 l. "Fuji from Hodogaya"	10	10
1319	50 l. "Fuji from Lake Kawaguchi"	10	10
1320	1 r. "Fuji from Owari"	10	15
1321	2 r. "Fuji from Tsukudajima in Edo"	25	30
1322	4 r. "Fuji from a Teahouse at Yoshida"	50	55
1323	6 r. "Fuji from Tagonoura"	70	75
1324	10 r. "Fuji from Mishima-goe"	1·25	1·40
1325	12 r. "Fuji from the Sumida River in Edo"	1·40	1·50
1318/25	*Set of* 8	4·00	4·25
MS1326	Two sheets, each 101×77 mm. (a) 18 r. "Fuji from Inume Pass" (2 Sept). (b) 18 r. "Fuji from Fukagawa in Edo" (16 Oct) *Set of* 2 *sheets*	2·10	2·25

Nos. 1318/25 were each printed in sheetlets of 10 containing two horizontal strips of 5 stamps separated by printed labels commemorating Emperor Hirohito.

233 Clown Triggerfish

(Des L. Birmingham. Litho Questa)

1989 (16 Oct). *Tropical Fishes. T* **233** *and similar horiz designs. Multicoloured. P* 14.

1327	20 l. Type **233**	10	10
1328	50 l. Bluestripe Snapper	10	10
1329	1 r. Blue Surgeonfish	10	15
1330	2 r. Oriental Sweetlips	25	30
1331	3 r. Wrasse	35	40
1332	8 r. Threadfin Butterflyfish	95	1·00
1333	10 r. Bicolour Parrotfish	1·25	1·40
1334	12 r. Sabre Squirrelfish	1·40	1·50
1327/34	*Set of* 8	4·00	4·25
MS1335	Two sheets, each 101×73 mm. (a) 15 r. Butterfly Perch. (b) 15 r. Semicircle Angelfish *Set of* 2 *sheets*	3·50	3·75

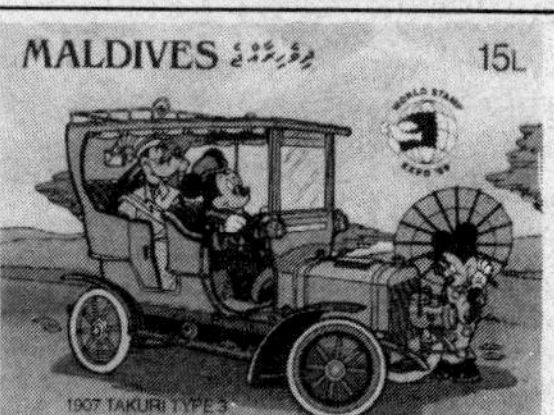

234 Goofy, Mickey and Minnie Mouse with Takuri "Type 3", 1907

(Des Walt Disney Co. Litho Questa)

1989 (17 Nov). *"World Stamp Expo '89" International Stamp Exhibition, Washington (1st issue). T* **234** *and similar horiz designs showing Walt Disney cartoon characters with Japanese cars. Multicoloured. P* 14×$13^1/_2$.

1336	15 l. Type **234**	10	10
1337	50 l. Donald and Daisy Duck in Mitsubishi "Model A", 1917	10	10
1338	1 r. Goofy in Datsun "Roadstar", 1935	10	15
1339	2 r. Donald and Daisy Duck with Mazda, 1940	25	30
1340	4 r. Donald Duck with Nissan "Bluebird 310", 1959	50	55
1341	6 r. Donald and Daisy Duck with Subaru "360", 1958	70	75
1342	10 r. Mickey Mouse and Pluto in Honda "5800", 1966	1·25	1·40
1343	12 r. Mickey Mouse and Goofy in Daihatsu "Fellow", 1966	1·40	1·50
1336/43	*Set of* 8	3·75	4·25
MS1344	Two sheets, each 127×102 mm. (a) 20 r. Daisy Duck with Chip n'Dale and Isuzu "Trooper II", 1981 (b) 20 r. Mickey Mouse with tortoise and Toyota "Supra", 1985 *Set of* 2 *sheets*	4·75	5·00

(Des Design Element. Litho Questa)

1989 (17 Nov). *"World Stamp Expo '89" International Stamp Exhibition, Washington (2nd issue). Landmarks of Washington. Sheet* 62×78 *mm containing multicoloured design as T* **257** *of Antigua, but vert. P* 14.

MS1345	8 r. Marine Corps Memorial, Arlington National Cemetery	95	1·00

235 Lunar Module *Eagle*

(Des W. Hanson. Litho Questa)

1989 (24 Nov). *20th Anniv of First Manned Landing on Moon. T* **235** *and similar multicoloured designs. P* 14.

1346	1 r. Type **235**	10	15
1347	2 r. Astronaut Aldrin collecting dust samples	25	30
1348	6 r. Aldrin setting up seismometer	70	75
1349	10 r. Pres. Nixon congratulating "Apollo 11" astronauts	1·25	1·40
1346/9	*Set of* 4	2·10	2·40
MS1350	107×75 mm. 18 r. Television picture of Armstrong about to step onto Moon (34×47 *mm*). P $13^1/_2$×14	2·10	2·25

Malta

:arly records of the postal services under the British Occupation re fragmentary, but it is known that an Island Postmaster was ppointed in 1802. A British Packet Agency was established in 806 and it later became customary for the same individual to old the two appointments together. The inland posts continued o be the responsibility of the local administration, but the verseas mails formed part of the British G.P.O. system.

The stamps of Great Britain were used on overseas mails from eptember 1857. Previously during the period of the Crimean Var letters franked with Great Britain stamps from the Crimea vere cancelled at Malta with a wavy line obliterator. Such ostmarks are known between April 1855 and September 1856.

The British G.P.O. relinquished control of the overseas posts on 1 December 1884 when Great Britain stamps were replaced by nose of Malta.

For illustrations of the postmark types see BRITISH POST)FFICES ABROAD notes, following GREAT BRITAIN.

Wavy Lines

855–56. *Stamps of* GREAT BRITAIN *cancelled with wavy lines obliteration as shown above.*

'1 1d. red-brown (1854), Die I, *wmk*, Small Crown, *perf* 16 .. .. £800
:2 1d. red-brown (1855), Die II, *wmk* Small Crown, *perf* 14 .. .. £800
a. Very blued paper
'3 1d. red-brown (1855), Die II, *wmk* Large Crown, *perf* 16 .. .. £800
4 2d. blue (1855), *wmk* Large Crown, *perf* 14 Plate No. 5
5 6d. (1854) embossed £4000
6 1s. (1847) embossed £4500

It is now established that this obliterator was sent to Malta and sed on mail in transit emanating from the Crimea.

857–59. *Stamps of* GREAT BRITAIN *cancelled* "M" *as Type* 1.

7 1d. red-brown (1841) £1000
8 1d. red-brown, Die I, *wmk* Small Crown, *perf* 16 .. 75·00
9 1d. red-brown, Die II, *wmk* Small Crown, *perf* 16 £800
10 1d. red-brown, Die II (1855), *wmk* Small Crown, *perf* 14 .. .. £150
11 1d. red-brown, Die II (1855), *wmk* Large Crown, *perf* 14 .. .. 85·00
:12 1d. rose-red (1857), *wmk* Large Crown, *perf* 14 .. 17·00
:13 2d. blue (1841), *imperf* £2500
:14 2d. blue (1854) *wmk* Small Crown, *perf* 16 .. £600
Plate No. 4.
:15 2d. blue (1855), *wmk* Large Crown, *perf* 14 *From* 55·00
Plate Nos. 5, 6.
'16 2d. blue (1858), *wmk* Large Crown, *perf* 16 .. £225
Plate No. 6.
:17 2d. blue (1858) (Plate Nos. 7, 8, 9) .. *From* 25·00
:18 4d. rose (1857) .. .. 35·00
a. Thick glazed paper £170
:19 6d. violet (1854), embossed £1600
:20 6d. lilac (1856) .. .. 40·00
a. Thick paper £190
21 6d. lilac (1856) (blued *paper*) £850
22 1s. green (1856) £150
a. Thick paper

859–84. *Stamps of* GREAT BRITAIN *cancelled* "A 25" *as in Types* 2, 5, 6, 8 *or* 11.

23 ½d. rose-red (1870–79) .. *From* 16·00
Plate Nos. 4, 5, 6, 8, 9, 10, 11, 12, 13, 14, 15, 19, 20.
24 1d. red-brown (1841), *imperf* £2000
25 1d. red-brown (1854), *wmk* Small Crown, *perf* 16 £225
26 1d. red-brown (1855), *wmk* Large Crown, *perf* 14 45·00
27 1d. rose-red (1857), *wmk* Large Crown, *perf* 14 .. 7·50
28 1d. rose-red (1861), Alphabet IV £450
30 1d. rose-red (1864–79) .. *From* 11·00
Plate Nos. 71, 72, 73, 74, 76, 78, 79, 80, 81, 82, 83, 84, 85, 86, 87, 88, 89, 90, 91, 92, 93, 94, 95, 96, 97, 98, 99, 100, 101, 102, 103, 104, 105, 106, 107, 108, 109, 110, 111, 112, 113, 114, 115, 116, 117, 118, 119, 120, 121, 122, 123, 124, 125, 127, 129, 130, 131, 132, 133, 134, 135, 136, 137, 138, 139, 140, 141, 142, 143, 144, 145, 146, 147, 148, 149, 150, 151, 152, 153, 154, 155, 156, 157, 158, 159, 160, 161, 162, 163, 164, 165, 166, 167, 168, 169, 170, 171, 172, 173, 174, 175, 176, 177, 178, 179, 180, 181, 182, 183, 184, 185, 186, 187, 188, 189, 190, 191, 192, 193, 194, 195, 196, 197, 198, 199, 200, 201, 202, 203, 204, 205, 206, 207, 208, 209, 210, 211, 212, 213, 214, 215, 216, 217, 218, 219, 220, 221, 222, 223, 224.
31 1½d. lake-red (1870–79) (Plate Nos. 1, 3) .. *From* £250
32 2d. blue (1841), *imperf* £3500
33 2d. blue (1855) *wmk* Large Crown *perf* 14 .. 35·00
34 2d. blue (1858–69) .. *From* 15·00
Plate Nos. 7, 8, 9, 12, 13, 14, 15.
35 2½d. rosy mauve (1875) (blued *paper*) .. *From* 50·00
Plate Nos. 1, 2.
36 2½d. rosy mauve (1875–76) (Plate Nos. 1, 2, 3) *From* 27·00
37 2½d. rosy mauve (*Error of Lettering*) .. £2250
38 2½d. rosy mauve (1876–79) .. *From* 18·00
Plate Nos. 3, 4, 5, 6, 7, 8, 9, 10, 11, 12, 13, 14, 15, 16, 17.
39 2½d. blue (1880–81) (Plate Nos. 17, 18, 19, 20) *From* 9·00
40 2½d. blue (1881) (Plate Nos. 21, 22, 23) .. *From* 6·00
41 3d. carmine-rose (1862) £100
42 3d. rose (1865) (Plate No. 4) .. .. 50·00
Z43 3d. rose (1867–73) .. .. *From* 18·00
Plate Nos. 4, 5, 6, 7, 8, 9, 10.
Z44 3d. rose (1873–76) .. .. *From* 17·00
Plate Nos. 11, 12, 14, 15, 16, 17, 18, 19, 20.
Z45 3d. rose (1881) (Plate Nos. 20, 21) .. *From* 50·00
Z46 3d. on 3d. lilac (1883) £400
Z47 4d. rose (or rose-carmine) (1857) .. .. 27·00
a. Thick glazed paper £110
Z48 4d. red (1862) (Plate Nos. 3, 4) .. *From* 35·00
Z49 4d. vermilion (1865–73) .. *From* 18·00
Plate Nos. 7, 8, 9, 10, 11, 12, 13, 14.
Z50 4d. vermilion (1876) (Plate No. 15) .. £190
Z51 4d. sage-green (1877) (Plate Nos. 15, 16) .. *From* 75·00
Z52 4d. grey-brown (1880) *wmk* Large Garter .. 90·00
Plate No. 17.
Z53 4d. grey-brown (1880) *wmk* Crown .. *From* 15·00
Plate Nos. 17, 18.
Z54 6d. violet (1854), embossed £1400
Z55 6d. lilac (1856) .. .. 40·00
a. Thick paper
Z56 6d. lilac (1862) (Plate Nos. 3, 4) .. *From* 35·00
Z57 6d. lilac (1865–67) (Plate Nos. 5, 6) .. *From* 32·00
Z58 6d. lilac (1865–67) (*Wmk error*)
Z59 6d. lilac (1867) (Plate No. 6) .. .. 40·00
Z60 6d. violet (1867–70) (Plate Nos. 6, 8, 9) .. *From* 32·00
Z61 6d. buff (1872–73) (Plate Nos. 11, 12) .. *From* £160
Z62 6d. chestnut (1872) (Plate No. 11) .. .. 32·00
Z63 6d. grey (1873) (Plate No. 12) .. .. 42·00
Z64 6d. grey (1873–80) .. .. *From* 24·00
Plate Nos. 13, 14, 15, 16, 17.
Z65 6d. grey (1881–82) (Plate Nos. 17, 18) .. *From* 15·00
Z66 6d. on 6d. lilac (1883) £140
Z67 8d. orange (1876) £250
Z68 9d. straw (1862) £475
Z69 9d. bistre (1862) £475
Z70 9d. straw (1865) £475
Z71 9d. straw (1867) £600
Z72 10d. red-brown (1867) £150
Z73 1s. (1847), embossed £1400
Z74 1s. green (1856) .. .. 70·00
Z75 1s. green (1856) (thick *paper*) £250
Z76 1s. green (1862) .. .. 55·00
Z77 1s. green ("K" *variety*) £2250
Z78 1s. green (1865) (Plate No. 4) .. .. 35·00
Z79 1s. green (1867–73) (Plate Nos. 4, 5, 6, 7) . *From* 8·50
Z80 1s. green (1873–77) .. *From* 28·00
Plate Nos. 8, 9, 10, 11, 12, 13.
Z81 1s. orange-brown (1880) (Plate No. 13) .. £225
Z82 1s. orange-brown (1881) (Plate Nos. 13, 14) *From* 30·00
Z83 2s. blue (*shades*) (1867) .. *From* 85·00
Z84 2s. brown (1880) £1700
Z85 5s. rose (1867–74) (Plate Nos. 1, 2) .. *From* £300
Z86 5s. rose (1882) (Plate No. 4), blue *paper* .. £1000
Z87 5s. rose (1882) (Plate No. 4), white *paper* .. £1000
Z88 10s. grey-green (1878) £1800

1880.

Z89 ½d. deep green .. .. 8·50
Z90 ½d. pale green .. .. 8·50
Z91 1d. Venetian red .. .. 7·50
Z92 1½d. Venetian red .. .. 75·00
Z93 2d. pale rose .. .. 25·00
Z94 2d. deep rose .. .. 25·00
Z95 5d. indigo .. .. 50·00

1881.

Z96 1d. lilac (14 *dots*) .. .. 13·00
Z97 1d. lilac (16 *dots*) .. .. 5·00

1883–4.

Z 98–Z102 ½d. slate-blue; 1½d., 2d, 2½d., 3d. *From* 8·50
Z103–Z107 4d. 5d., 6d., 9d., 1s. .. *From* 60·00
Z108 5s. rose (blued *paper*) £1000
Z109 5s. rose (white *paper*) £700

POSTAL FISCALS

Z110 1d. purple (1871) *wmk* Anchor £750
Z111 1d. purple (1881) *wmk* Orb £600

PRICES FOR STAMPS ON COVER TO 1945

Nos. 1/3	*from* × 3
Nos. 4/19	*from* × 5
Nos. 20/9	*from* × 6
No. 30	—
Nos. 31/3	*from* × 4
Nos. 34/7	*from* × 10
Nos. 38/88	*from* × 4
Nos. 92/3	*from* × 5
Nos. 97/103	*from* × 3
Nos. 104/5	—
Nos. 106/20	*from* × 3
No. 121	—
Nos. 122/38	*from* × 3
Nos. 139/40	—
Nos. 141/72	*from* × 4
Nos. 173/209	*from* × 3
Nos. 210/31	*from* × 2
Nos. D1/10	*from* × 30
Nos. D11/20	*from* × 15

CROWN COLONY

PRINTERS. Nos. 1/156. Printed by De La Rue; typographed *except where otherwise stated.*

1

Type 1

The first Government local post was established on 10 June 1853 and, as an experiment, mail was carried free of charge. During 1859 the Council of Government decided that a rate of ½d. per ½ ounce should be charged for this service and stamps in Type I were ordered for this purpose. Both the new rate and the stamps were introduced on 1 December 1860. Until 1 January 1885 the ½d. stamps were intended for the local service only; mail for abroad being handled by the British Post Office on Malta, using G.B. stamps.

Specialists now recognise 29 printings in shades of yellow and one in green during the period to 1884. These printings can be linked to the changes in watermark and perforation as follows:

Ptg 1—Blued paper without wmk. P 14.
Ptgs 2 and 3—White paper without wmk. P 14.
Ptgs 4 to 9, 11, 13 to 19, 22 to 24—Crown CC wmk. P 14.
Ptg 10—Crown CC wmk. P 12½ (rough).
Ptg 12—Crown CC wmk. P 12½ (clean-cut).
Ptgs 20 and 21—Crown CC wmk. P 14 × 12½.
Ptgs 25 to 28, 30—Crown CA wmk. P 14.
Ptg 29—In green (No. 20).

1860 (1 Dec)–**63.** *No wmk. P* 14. (*a*) *Blued paper.*

1 ½d. buff (1.2.60) £850 £425

(*b*) *Thin, hard white paper*

2 ½d. brown-orange (11.61) £750 £325
3 ½d. buff (1.63) £550 £275
a. Pale buff £550 £275

No. 1 is printed in fugitive ink. It is known imperforate but was not issued in that state (*Price* £9000 *unused*).

The printing on No. 2 gives a very blurred and muddy impression; on Nos. 3/3*a* the impression is clear.

Specks of carmine can often be detected with a magnifying glass on Nos. 2/3*a*, and also on No. 4. Examples also exist on which parts of the design are in pure rose, due to defective mixing of the ink.

(Des E. Fuchs)

1863–81. *Wmk Crown CC.* (*a*) *P* 14.

4 ½d. buff (6.63) .. .. 75·00 45·00
5 ½d. bright orange (11.64) .. .. £175 90·00
6 ½d. brown-red (4.67) .. .. £275 70·00
7 ½d. dull orange (4.70) .. .. £140 50·00
8 ½d. orange-buff (5.72) .. .. £130 50·00
9 ½d. golden yellow (aniline) (10.74) .. £250 £250
10 ½d. yellow-buff (9.75) .. .. 60·00 60·00
11 ½d. pale buff (3.77) .. .. 90·00 48·00
12 ½d. bright orange-yellow (4.80) .. 65·00 50·00
13 ½d. yellow (4.81) .. .. 60·00 45·00

(*b*) *P* 12½ *rough* (*No.* 14) *or clean-cut* (*No.* 15)

14 ½d. buff-brown (11.68) .. .. 80·00 65·00
a. Imperf between (vert pair)
15 ½d. yellow-orange (5.71) £200 £150

(*c*) *P* 14 × 12½

16 ½d. yellow-buff (7.78) .. .. £150 85·00
a. Perf 12½ × 14
17 ½d. yellow (2.79) .. .. £150 85·00

Examples of No. 4 from the 1863 printing are on thin, surfaced paper; later printings in the same shade were on unsurfaced paper.

The ink used for No. 5 is mineral and, unlike that on No. 9, does not stain the paper.

Some variations of shade on No. 6 may be described as chestnut. The ink of No. 6 is clear and never muddy, although some examples are over-inked. Deeper shades of No. 4, with which examples of No. 6 might be confused, have muddy ink.

1882 (Mar)–**84.** *Wmk Crown CA. P* 14.

18 ½d. orange-yellow .. .. 17·00 35·00
19 ½d. red-orange (9.84) .. .. 17·00 35·00

2

3

4

5

1885 (1 Jan)–**90.** *Wmk Crown CA. P* 14.

20 1 ½d. green .. .. 1·00 35
21 2 1d. rose .. .. 60·00 25·00
22 1d. carmine (*shades*) (1890) .. 1·75 35
23 3 2d. grey .. .. 3·25 1·25
24 4 2½d. dull blue .. .. 22·00 90
25 2½d. bright blue .. .. 22·00 90
26 2½d. ultramarine .. .. 22·00 90
27 3 4d. brown .. .. 7·50 3·00
a. Imperf (pair) £3750 £4000
28 1s. violet .. .. 28·00 9·00
29 1s. pale violet (1890) .. 42·00 15·00
20/29 .. .. *Set of* 6 55·00 14·00
20/28 Optd "Specimen" .. *Set of* 6 £1800

Although not valid for postage until 1 January 1885 these stamps were available at the G.P.O., Valletta from 27 December 1884.

Three unused examples of the ½d. green, No. 20, are known line perforated 12. It is believed that these originated from proof books, the stamp not being issued for use with this perforation.

1886 (1 Jan). *Wmk Crown CC. P* 14.

30	5	5s. rose (Optd S. £450)	£110	80·00

6 Harbour of Valletta **7** Gozo Fishing Boat **8** Galley of Knights of St. John

9 Emblematic figure of Malta **10** Shipwreck of St. Paul

(T **6/10** recess)

1899 (4 Feb)–**1901.** *P* 14. (*a*) *Wmk Crown CA (sideways on ¼d).*

31	**6**	¼d. brown (4.1.01)	1·50	1·25
		a. Red-brown	90	40
32	**7**	4½d. sepia	11·00	7·50
33	**8**	5d. vermilion	22·00	13·00
		(*b*) *Wmk Crown CC*		
34	**9**	2s. 6d. olive-grey	30·00	12·00
35	**10**	10s. blue-black	75·00	60·00
31/5		.. .. .. *Set of* 5	£120	85·0(
31/5 Optd "Specimen"		.. .. *Set of* 5	£300	

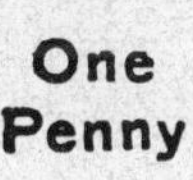

(11)

12

1902 (4 July). *Nos. 24 and 25 surch locally at Govt Ptg Office with T* **11**.

36	1d. on 2½d. dull blue (Optd S. £70).. ..	40	65
	a. Surch double	—	£2750
	b. "One Pnney" (R. 9/2)	27·00	42·00
	ba. Surch double, with "One Pnney" ..		
37	1d. on 2½d. bright blue	40	65
	a. "One Pnney" (R. 9/2)	27·00	42·00

(Des E. Fuchs)

1903 (12 Mar)–**4**. *Wmk Crown CA. P* 14.

38	**12**	½d. green	2·50	10
39		1d. black and red (7.5.03)	7·50	10
40		2d. purple and grey	12·00	6·00
41		2½d. maroon and blue (9.03)	13·00	1·75
42		3d. grey and purple (26.3.03)	80	50
43		4d. black and brown (19.5.04)	23·00	11·00
44		1s. grey and violet (6.4.03)	13·00	6·00
38/44		.. .. *Set of* 7	65·00	23·00
38/44 Optd "Specimen"		.. .. *Set of* 7	£150	

1904-14. *Wmk Mult Crown CA (sideways on ¼d.). P* 14.

45	**6**	¼d. red-brown (10.10.05)	75	15
		a. Deep brown (1910)	75	10
47	**12**	½d. green (6.11.04)	2·75	25
		a. Deep green (1909)	1·50	10
48		1d. black and red (24.4.05)	4·50	10
49		1d. red (2.4.07)	80	10
50		2d. purple and grey (22.2.05)	4·50	45
51		2d. grey (4.10.11)	1·25	3·00
52		2½d. maroon and blue (10.04)	6·50	40
53		2½d. bright blue (15.1.11)	4·00	1·25
54		4d. black and brown (1.4.06)	8·00	5·00
55		4d. black and red/*yellow* (21.11.11) ..	3·50	3·00
57	**7**	4½d. brown (27.2.05)	17·00	5·50
58		4½d. orange (2.8.12)	3·00	3·25
59	**8**	5d. vermilion (20.2.05)	18·00	3·75
60		5d. pale sage-green (1909)	3·00	3·25
		a. Deep sage-green (1914)	9·00	12·00
61	**12**	1s. grey and violet (14.12.04)	35·00	1·75
62		1s. black/*green* (15.3.11)	5·00	2·00
63		5s. green and red/*yellow*, **C** (22.3.11) ..	60·00	65·00
45/63		.. .. *Set of* 17	£150	90·00
45*a*, 47*a*, 49, 51, 53, 55, 58, 60, 62, 63 Optd "Specimen"		.. .. *Set of* 10	£400	

13

14

15

Lines omitted from Scroll (R. 2/4)

1914–21. *Wmk Mult Crown CA. P* 14.

69	**13**	¼d. brown, **O** (2.1.14)	20	10
		a. Deep brown (1919)	30	25
71		½d. green, **O** (20.1.14)	90	10
		aa. Wmk sideways	†	£3000
		a. Deep green (1919)	60	15
73		1d. carmine-red, **O** (15.4.14)	60	10
		a. Scarlet (1915)	1·25	30
75		2d. grey, **O** (12.8.14)	4·50	2·50
		a. Deep slate (1919)	8·00	8·00
77		2½d. bright blue, **O** (11.3.14)	70	20
78	**14**	3d. purple/*yellow*, **C** (1.5.20)	2·50	5·00
		a. On orange-buff	10·00	17·00
79	**6**	4d. black, **C** (21.8.15)	10·00	2·50
		a. Grey-black (1916)	17·00	7·00
80	**13**	6d. dull and bright purple, **C** (10.3.14) ..	7·00	10·00
		a. Dull purple and magenta (1918) ..	7·00	10·00
81	**14**	1s. black/*green* (*white back*), **C** (2.1.14)..	8·00	17·00
		a. On green, green back (Optd S. £45) (1915)	10·00	13·00
		ab. Wmk sideways	†	£1800
		b. On blue-green, olive back (1918) ..	11·00	16·00
		c. On emerald surface (1920)	8·50	14·00
		d. On emerald back (1921)	16·00	24·00
86	**15**	2s. purple & brt blue/*blue*, **C** (15.4.14) ..	50·00	28·00
		a. Break in scroll	£150	
		b. Broken crown and scroll	£150	
		c. Dull purple and blue/blue (1921) ..	50·00	40·00
		ca. Break in scroll	£140	
		cb. Broken crown and scroll	£140	
87	**9**	2s. 6d. olive-green, **O** (1919)	40·00	55·00
		a. Olive-grey (1920)	40·00	60·00
88	**15**	5s. green and red/*yellow*, **C** (21.3.17) ..	65·00	80·00
		a. Break in scroll	£200	
		b. Broken crown and scroll	£200	
69/88		.. .. *Set of* 12	£170	£180
69/88 (*excl.* 87) Optd "Specimen"		.. *Set of* 11	£500	

The design of Nos. 79/*a* differs in various details from that of Type **6**.

We have only seen one copy of No. 71aa; it is in used condition.

A 3d. purple on yellow on white back, Type **14**, was prepared for use but not issued. It exists overprinted "Specimen" (*price* £250).

For illustrations of the other varieties on Nos. 86 and 88 see above No. 44 of Bermuda.

WAR TAX

(16)

17

18

1917–18. *Optd with T* **16**, *by De La Rue.*

92	**13**	½d. deep green (14.12.17*)	20	15
93	**12**	3d. grey and purple (15.2.18*)	1·75	6·50
92/3 Optd "Specimen"		.. .. *Set of* 2	£150	

*These are the earliest known dates of use.

(T **17** recess)

1919 (6 Mar). *Wmk Mult Crown CA. P* 14.

96	**17**	10s. black (Optd S. £900)	£4000	£4250

1921 (16 Feb)–**22.** *Wmk Mult Script CA. P* 14.

97	**13**	¼d. brown, **O** (12.1.22)	40	9·00
98		½d. green, **O** (19.1.22)	90	8·00
99		1d. scarlet, **O** (24.12.21)	40	55
100	**18**	2d. grey, **O**	2·50	80
101	**13**	2½d. bright blue, **O** (15.1.22)	2·75	12·00
102		6d. dull purple & brt purple, **C** (19.1.22)	22·00	35·00
103	**15**	2s. purple and blue/*blue*, **C** (19.1.22) ..	60·00	£130
		a. Break in scroll	£170	
		b. Broken crown and scroll	£170	
		c. Lines omitted from scroll	£170	
104	**17**	10s. black, **O** (19.1.22)	£300	£475
97/104		.. .. *Set of* 8	£350	£600
97/104 Optd "Specimen"		.. .. *Set of* 8	£500	

For illustrations of varieties on No. 103 see above No. 69 or above No. 44 of Bermuda.

OMNIBUS ISSUES

Details, together with prices for complete sets, of the various Omnibus issues from the 1935 Silver Jubilee series to date are included in a special section following Zululand at the end of the catalogue.

(19)

(20)

1922 (12 Jan–Apr). *Optd with T* **19** *or* **20** *(large stamps), at Govt Printing Office, Valletta.* (*a*) *Wmk Crown CC.*

105	**10**	10s. blue-black, **O** (R.)	£160	£250
		(*b*) *Wmk Mult Crown CA*		
106	**13**	½d. green, **O**	20	35
107		2½d. bright blue, **O**	4·50	11·00
108	**14**	3d. purple/*orange-buff*, **C**	1·25	8·50
109	**13**	6d. dull and bright purple, **C**	1·25	8·50
110	**14**	1s. black/*emerald*, **C**	2·50	6·50
111	**15**	2s. dull purple and blue/*blue*, **C** (R.) ..	£200	£300
		a. Break in scroll	£500	
		b. Broken crown and scroll	£500	
112	**9**	2s. 6d. olive-grey, **O**	17·00	26·00
113	**15**	5s. green and red/*yellow*, **C**	50·00	65·00
		a. Break in scroll	£150	
		b. Broken crown and scroll	£150	
		c. Lines omitted from scroll.. ..	£150	
106/13		.. .. *Set of* 8	£250	£375
		(*c*) *Wmk Mult Script CA*		
114	**13**	¼d. brown, **O**	10	20
115		½d. green, **O** (29.4)	60	2·50
116		1d. scarlet, **O**	20	15
117	**18**	2d. grey, **O**	75	45
118	**13**	2½d. bright blue, **O** (15.1)	30	45
119		6d. dull and bright purple, **C** (19.4) ..	6·00	12·00
120	**15**	2s. dull purple & blue/*bl*, **C** (R.) (25.1)	35·00	55·00
		a. Break in scroll	£110	
		b. Broken crown and scroll	£110	
		c. Lines omitted from scroll.. ..	£110	
121	**17**	10s. black, **O** (R.) (9.3)	£100	£130
114/21		.. .. *Set of* 8	£130	£180

One Farthing

(21)

22

23

1922 (15 Apr). *No.* 100 *surch with T* **21**, *at Govt Printing Office, Valletta.*

122	**18**	¼d. on 2d. grey..	15	25

(Des C. Dingli (T **22**) and G. Vella (**23**))

1922 (1 Aug)–**26.** *Wmk Mult Script CA (sideways on T* **22**, *except No.* 140). *P* 14. (*a*) *Typo. Chalk-surfaced paper.*

123	**22**	¼d. brown (22.8.22)	30	40
		a. Chocolate-brown	30	15
124		½d. green	40	10
125		1d. orange and purple	1·00	15
126		1d. bright violet (25.4.24)	80	35
127		1½d. brown-red (1.10.23)	85	10
128		2d. bistre-brown and turquoise (28.8.22)	30	20
129		2½d. ultramarine (16.2.26)	1·00	4·50
130		3d. cobalt (28.8.22)	1·75	50
		a. Bright ultramarine	1·75	50
131		3d. black/*yellow* (16.2.26)	1·00	6·50
132		4d. yellow and bright blue (28.8.22) ..	1·00	1·60
133		6d. olive-green and reddish violet ..	1·75	1·25
134	**23**	1s. indigo and sepia	3·75	2·50
135		2s. brown and blue	5·50	8·50
136		2s. 6d. brt magenta & black (28.8.22)	6·00	8·50
137		5s. orange-yell & brt ultram (28.8.22)	14·00	24·00
138		10s. slate-grey and brown (28.8.22) ..	38·00	60·00
		(*b*) *Recess*		
139	**22**	£1 black and carmine-red (28.8.22) ..	£100	£160
140		£1 black and bright carmine (14.5.25)	£100	£160
123/39		.. .. *Set of* 17	£160	£250
123/39 Optd "Specimen"		.. .. *Set of* 17	£600	

No. 139 has the watermark sideways and No. 140 has it upright.

Two pence halfpenny

(24)

POSTAGE

(25)

1925. *Surch with T* **24**, *at Govt Printing Office, Valletta.*

141	**22**	2½d. on 3d. cobalt (3 Dec)	30	1·00
142		2½d. on 3d. bright ultramarine (9 Dec)	40	1·00

1926 (1 April). *Optd with T* **25**, *at Govt Printing Office, Valletta.*

143	**22**	¼d. brown	15	80
144		½d. green	15	15
145		1d. bright violet	40	25
146		1½d. brown-red..	45	25
147		2d. bistre-brown and turquoise ..	25	20
148		2½d. ultramarine	50	40
149		3d. black/*yellow*	30	50
		a. Opt inverted	£190	£375
150		4d. yellow and bright blue	3·00	5·00
151		6d. olive-green and violet	1·50	1·40
152	**23**	1s. indigo and sepia	4·50	6·50
153		2s. brown and blue	35·00	60·00

154	23	2s. 6d. bright magenta and black	9·00	22·00
155		5s. orange-yellow & brt ultramarine	8·00	24·00
156		10s. slate-grey and brown	6·00	14·00
143/156		*Set of* 14	60·00	£120

26

27 Valletta Harbour

28 St. Publius

33 St. Paul

(T **26** typo, others recess Waterlow)

1926 (6 Apr)–**27.** *T* **26/8, 33** *and similar designs. Inscr* "POSTAGE". *Wmk Mult Script CA. P* 15 × 14 (*T* **26**) *or* 12½ (*others*).

157	26	¼d. brown	20	15
158		½d. yellow-green (5.8.26)	30	15
159		1d. rose-red (1.4.27)	30	40
160		1½d. chestnut (7.10.26)	60	10
161		2d. greenish grey (1.4.27)	2·25	5·50
162		2½d. blue (1.4.27)	2·50	20
162*a*		3d. violet (1.4.27)	2·50	1·50
163		4d. black and red	2·75	7·00
164		4½d. lavender and ochre	2·50	2·50
165		6d. violet and scarlet (5.5.26)	2·50	2·00
166	27	1s. black	2·50	2·25
167	28	1s. 6d. black and green	5·00	8·00
168	–	2s. black and purple	5·50	13·00
169	–	2s. 6d. black and vermilion	10·00	22·00
170	–	3s. black and blue	13·00	25·00
171	–	5s. black and green (5.5.26)	18·00	30·00
172	33	10s. black and carmine (9.2.27)	48·00	75·00
157/72		*Set of* 17	£110	£170
157/72 Optd "Specimen"		*Set of* 17	£400	

Designs: *Vert*—2s. 6d. Gozo fishing boat; 3s. Neptune; *Horiz*—2s. Mdina (Notabile); 5s. Neolithic temple, Mnajdra.

AIR MAIL (34)

POSTAGE AND REVENUE (35)

POSTAGE AND REVENUE. (36)

1928 (1 Apr). *Air. Optd with T* **34**.

173	26	6d. violet and scarlet	1·75	1·25

1928 (1 Oct–Dec). *As Nos.* 157/72, *optd.*

174	35	¼d. brown	25	10
175		½d. yellow-green	25	10
176		1d. rose-red	1·50	1·00
177		1d. chestnut (5.12.28)	2·00	10
178		1½d. chestnut	75	20
179		1½d. rose-red (5.12.28)	2·00	10
180		2d. greenish grey	3·25	8·00
181		2½d. blue	1·25	10
182		3d. violet	1·25	30
183		4d. black and red	1·25	1·00
184		4½d. lavender and ochre	2·25	1·50
185		6d. violet and scarlet	2·25	1·00
186	36	1s. black (R.)	2·25	2·00
187		1s. 6d. black and green (R.)	5·00	9·00
188		2s. black and purple (R.)	15·00	28·00
189		2s. 6d. black and vermilion (R.)	13·00	23·00
190		3s. black and blue (R.)	17·00	30·00
191		5s. black and green (R.)	26·00	55·00
192		10s. black and carmine (R.)	45·00	75·00
174/92		*Set of* 19	£110	£200
174/92 Optd "Specimen"		*Set of* 19	£400	

1930 (20 Oct). *As Nos.* 157/172, *but inscr* "POSTAGE (&) REVENUE".

193	¼d. brown	20	10
194	½d. yellow-green	25	10
195	1d. chestnut	25	10
196	1½d. rose-red	50	10
197	2d. greenish grey	75	20
198	2½d. blue	1·25	10
199	3d. violet	1·50	20
200	4d. black and red	1·25	2·25
201	4½d. lavender and ochre	1·50	1·50
202	6d. violet and scarlet	1·25	75
203	1s. black	4·00	7·50
204	1s. 6d. black and green	5·00	12·00
205	2s. black and purple	6·50	15·00
206	2s. 6d. black and vermilion	13·00	30·00
207	3s. black and blue	20·00	42·00
208	5s. black and green	25·00	48·00
209	10s. black and carmine	60·00	80·00
193/209	*Set of* 17	£130	£225
193/209 Perf "Specimen"	*Set of* 17	£400	

1935 (6 May). *Silver Jubilee. As Nos.* 91/4 *of Antigua, but printed by B.W. P* 11 × 12.

210	½d. black and green	20	20
	a. Extra flagstaff	25·00	
	b. Short extra flagstaff	25·00	
	c. Lightning conductor	25·00	
211	2½d. brown and deep blue	1·75	2·00
	a. Extra flagstaff	£130	
	b. Short extra flagstaff	£100	
	c. Lightning conductor	90·00	
212	6d. light blue and olive-green	4·00	2·75
	a. Extra flagstaff	£180	
	b. Short extra flagstaff	£130	
	c. Lightning conductor	£120	
213	1s. slate and purple	7·50	11·00
	a. Extra flagstaff	£425	
	b. Short extra flagstaff	£275	
	c. Lightning conductor	£225	
210/13	*Set of* 4	12·00	14·00
210/13 Perf "Specimen"	*Set of* 4	£130	

For illustration of plate varieties see Omnibus section following Zululand.

Examples of the ½d., 6d. and 1s. values are known with the extra flagstaff erased from the stamp with a sharp point.

1937 (12 May). *Coronation. As Nos.* 13/15 *of Aden.*

214	½d. green	10	10
215	1½d. scarlet	25	15
	a. Brown-lake	£400	£425
216	2½d. bright blue	50	35
214/16	*Set of* 3	75	50
214/16 Perf "Specimen"	*Set of* 3	60·00	

37 Grand Harbour, Valletta

38 H.M.S. *St. Angelo*

39 Verdala Palace

40 Hypogeum, Hal Saflieni

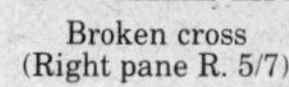

Broken cross (Right pane R. 5/7)

Damaged value tablet (R. 4/9)

Semaphore flaw (R. 2/7)

(Recess Waterlow)

1938 (17 Feb*)–**43.** *T* **37/40** *and similar designs. Wmk Mult Script CA* (*sideways on No.* 217). *P* 12½.

217	37	¼d. brown	10	10
218	38	½d. green	30	10
218*a*		½d. red-brown (8.3.43)	15	10
219	39	1d. red-brown	1·50	20
219*a*		1d. green (8.3.43)	20	10
220	40	1½d. scarlet	15	15
		a. Broken cross	10·00	
220*b*		1½d. slate-black (8.3.43)	20	15
		ba. Broken cross	10·00	
221	–	2d. slate-black	30	70
221*a*	–	2d. scarlet (8.3.43)	15	10
222	–	2½d. greyish blue	15	25
222*a*	–	2½d. dull violet (8.3.43)	60	10
223	–	3d. dull violet	20	60
223*a*	–	3d. blue (8.3.43)	30	10
224	–	4½d. olive-green and yellow-brown	50	10
225	–	6d. olive-green and scarlet	30	15
226	–	1s. black	50	30
227	–	1s. 6d. black and olive-green	3·25	3·50
228	–	2s. green and deep blue	3·00	2·75
229	–	2s. 6d. black and scarlet	5·00	4·00
		a. Damaged value tablet	50·00	
230	–	5s. black and green	5·00	5·50
		a. Semaphore flaw	35·00	
231	–	10s. black and carmine	11·00	14·00
217/231		*Set of* 21	29·00	29·00
217/31 Perf "Specimen"		*Set of* 21	£350	

Designs: *Horiz* (*as T* **39**)—2d. Victoria and citadel, Gozo; 2½d. De l'Isle Adam entering Mdina; 4½d. Ruins at Mnajdra; 1s. 6d. St. Publius; 2s. Mdina Cathedral; 2s. 6d. Statue of Neptune. *Vert* (*as T* **40**)—3d. St. John's Co-Cathedral; 6d. Statue of Manoel de Vilhena; 1s. Maltese girl wearing faldetta; 5s. Palace Square, Valletta; 10s. St. Paul.

*This is the local date of issue but the stamps were released in London on 15 February.

1946 (3 Dec). *Victory. As Nos.* 28/9 *of Aden, but inscr* "MALTA" *between Maltese Cross and George Cross.*

232	1d. green	10	10
233	3d. blue	10	10
232/3 Perf "Specimen"	*Set of* 2	50·00	

SELF-GOVERNMENT

(52)

"NT" joined (R. 4/10)

Halation flaw (Pl 2 R. 2/5) (ptg of 8 Jan 1953)

Cracked plate (Pl 2 R. 5/1) (ptg of 8 Jan 1953)

(Optd by Waterlow)

1948 (25 Nov)–**53.** *New Constitution. As Nos.* 217/31 *but optd as T* **52**; *reading up on* ½*d. and* 5*s., down on other values, and smaller on* ¼*d. value.*

234	37	¼d. brown	10	15
235	38	½d. red-brown	15	10
		a. "NT" joined	5·00	
236	39	1d. green	15	10
236*a*		1d. grey (R.) (8.1.53)	10	10
237	40	1½d. blue-black (R.)	20	10
		a. Broken cross	10·00	
237*b*		1½d. green (8.1.53)	10	10
		ba. Opt omitted	†	£10000
238	–	2d. scarlet	25	10
238*a*	–	2d. yellow-ochre (8.1.53)	10	10
		ab. Halation flaw	40·00	
		ac. Cracked plate	50·00	
239	–	2½d. dull violet (R.)	20	10
239*a*	–	2½d. scarlet-vermilion (8.1.53)	25	65
240	–	3d. blue (R.)	20	15
240*a*	–	3d. dull violet (R.) (8.1.53)	35	15
241	–	4½d. olive-green and yellow-brown	90	1·50
241*a*	–	4½d. olive-green & dp ultram (R.) (8.1.53)	50	90
242	–	6d. olive-green and scarlet	25	15
243	–	1s. black	80	40
244	–	1s. 6d. black and olive-green	2·25	45
245	–	2s. green and deep blue (R.)	3·50	1·50
246	–	2s. 6d. black and scarlet	6·50	2·50
247	–	5s. black and green (R.)	10·00	5·50
		a. "NT" joined	85·00	
248	–	10s. black and carmine	17·00	16·00
234/248		*Set of* 21	38·00	27·00

1949 (4 Jan). *Royal Silver Wedding. As Nos.* 30/1 *of Aden, but inscr* "MALTA" *between Maltese Cross and George Cross* (£1 *recess*).

249	1d. green	20	10
250	£1 indigo	40·00	35·00

1949 (10 Oct). *75th Anniv of Universal Postal Union. As Nos.* 114/17 *of Antigua, but inscr* "MALTA" (*recess*).

251	2½d. violet	25	10
252	3d. deep blue	1·00	35
253	6d. carmine-red	1·25	35
254	1s. blue-black	1·40	1·50
251/4	*Set of* 4	3·50	2·00

53 Queen Elizabeth II when Princess

54 "Our Lady of Mount Carmel" (attrib Palladino)

(T 53/4. Recess B.W.)

1950 (1 Dec). *Visit of Princess Elizabeth to Malta. Wmk Mult Script CA. P* 12 × 11½.

255	**53**	1d. green	10	10
256		3d. blue	20	10
257		1s. black	30	45
255/7		*Set of* 3	55	55

1951 (12 July). *Seventh Centenary of the Scapular. Wmk Mult Script CA. P* 12 × 11½.

258	**54**	1d. green	10	10
259		3d. violet	15	10
260		1s. black	30	40
258/60		*Set of* 3	50	50

1953 (3 June). *Coronation. As No.* 47 *of Aden.*

261	1½d. black and deep yellow-green	10	10

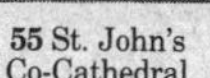

55 St. John's Co-Cathedral

56 "Immaculate Conception" (Caruana) (altar-piece, Cospicua)

(Recess Waterlow)

1954 (3 May). *Royal Visit. Wmk Mult Script CA. P* 12½.

262	**55**	3d. violet	15	10

(Photo Harrison)

1954 (8 Sept). *Centenary of Dogma of the Immaculate Conception. Wmk Mult Script CA. Chalk-surfaced paper. P* 14½ × 14.

263	**56**	1½d. emerald	10	10
264		3d. bright blue	10	10
265		1s. grey-black	10	10
263/5		*Set of* 3	15	15

57 Monument of the Great Siege, 1565

62 Auberge de Castile

(Recess Waterlow (2s. 6d. to £1). B.W. (others))

1956 (23 Jan)–**58**. *T* **57**, **62** *and similar designs. Wmk Mult Script CA. P* 14×13½ (2*s.* 6*d. to* £1) *or* 11½ (*others*).

266	¼d. violet	10	10
267	½d. orange	10	10
268	1d. black (9.2.56)	15	10
269	1½d. bluish green (9.2.56)	15	10
270	2d. brown (9.2.56)	15	10
	a. Deep brown (26.2.58)	15	10
271	2½d. orange-brown	30	30
272	3d. rose-red (22.3.56)	30	10
273	4½d. deep blue	40	20
274	6d. indigo (9.2.56)	30	10
275	8d. bistre-brown	1·00	1·00
276	1s. deep reddish violet	35	10
277	1s. 6d. deep turquoise-green	2·75	20
278	2s. olive-green	3·75	80
279	2s. 6d. chestnut (22.3.56)	4·50	2·25
280	5s. green (11.10.56)	8·00	2·75
281	10s. carmine-red (19.11.56)	40·00	10·00
282	£1 yellow-brown (5.1.57)	40·00	25·00
266/82	*Set of* 17	90·00	38·00

Designs:—*Vert*—½d. Wignacourt aqueduct horsetrough; 1d. Victory church; 1½d. War memorial; 2d. Mosta dome; 3d. The King's scroll; 4½d. Roosevelt's scroll; 8d. Vedette; 1s. Mdina gate; 1s. 6d. "Les Gavroches" (statue); 2s. Monument of Christ the King; 2s. 6d. Grand Master Cottoner's monument; 5s. Grand Master Perellos's monument; 10s. St. Paul; £1 Baptism of Christ. *Horiz*—6d. Neolithic Temples at Tarxien.

See also Nos. 314/15.

74 "Defence of Malta"

75 Searchlights over Malta

(Des E. Cremona. Photo Harrison)

1957 (15 Apr). *George Cross Commemoration. Cross in silver. T* **74/5** *and similar design. Wmk Mult Script CA. P* 14½ × 14 (3*d.*) *or* 14 × 14½ (*others*).

283	1½d. deep dull green	10	10
284	3d. vermilion	10	10
285	1s. reddish brown	10	10
283/5	*Set of* 3	25	15

Design: *Vert*—1s. Bombed buildings.

77 "Design"

(Des E. Cremona. Photo Harrison)

1958 (15 Feb). *Technical Education in Malta. T* **77** *and similar designs. W w* **12**. *P* 14 × 14½ (3*d.*) *or* 14½ × 14 (*others*).

286	1½d. black and deep green	10	10
287	3d. black, scarlet and grey	10	10
288	1s. grey, bright purple and black	10	10
286/8	*Set of* 3	25	15

Designs: *Vert*—3d. "Construction". *Horiz*—1s. Technical School, Paola.

80 Bombed-out Family

81 Sea Raid on Grand Harbour, Valletta

(Des E. Cremona. Photo Harrison)

1958 (15 Apr). *George Cross Commemoration. Cross in first colour, outlined in silver. T* **80/1** *and similar design. W w* **12**. *P* 14 × 14½ (3*d.*) *or* 14½ × 14 (*others*).

289	1½d. blue-green and black	10	10
290	3d. red and black	10	10
291	1s. reddish violet and black	10	10
	a. Silver (outline) omitted	60·00	
289/91	*Set of* 3	25	15

Design: *Horiz*—1s. Searchlight crew.

83 Air Raid Casualties

84 "For Gallantry"

(Des E. Cremona. Photo Harrison)

1959 (15 Apr). *George Cross Commemoration. T* **83/4** *and similar design. W w* **12**. *P* 14½ × 14 (3*d.*) *or* 14 × 14½ (*others*).

292	1½d. grey-green, black and gold	10	10
293	3d. reddish violet, black and gold	15	10
294	1s. blue-grey, black and gold	40	55
292/4	*Set of* 3	60	55

Design: *Vert*—1s. Maltese under bombardment.

86 Shipwreck of St. Paul (after Palombi)

87 Statue of St. Paul, Rabat, Malta

(Des E. Cremona. Photo Harrison)

1960 (9 Feb). *19th Centenary of the Shipwreck of St. Paul. T* **86/7** *and similar designs. W w* **12**. *P* 13 (1½*d.*, 3*d.*, 6*d.*) *or* 14 × 14½ (*others*).

295	1½d. blue, gold and yellow-brown	15	10
	a. Gold (dates and crosses) omitted	50·00	
296	3d. bright purple, gold and blue	15	10
297	6d. carmine, gold and pale grey	25	10
298	8d. black and gold	30	40
299	1s. maroon and gold	25	10
300	2s. 6d. blue, deep bluish green and gold	1·00	1·50
	a. Gold omitted	£250	
295/300	*Set of* 6	1·90	1·90

Designs: *Vert as T* **86**—3d. Consecration of St. Publius (first Bishop of Malta) (after Palombi); 6d. Departure of St. Paul (after Palombi). *Diamond shaped as T* **87**—1s. Angel with *Acts of the Apostles*; 2s. 6d. St. Paul with *Second Epistle to the Corinthians*.

92 Stamp of 1860

(Centre litho; frame recess. Waterlow)

1960 (1 Dec). *Stamp Centenary. W w* **12**. *P* 13½.

301	**92**	1½d. buff, pale blue and green	10	10
		a. Buff, pale bl & myrtle (white paper)	3·00	1·50
302		3d. buff pale blue and deep carmine	15	10
		a. Blank corner	£100	
303		6d. buff, pale blue and ultramarine	20	25
301/3		*Set of* 3	40	30

No. 302a shows the right-hand bottom corner of the 1860 stamp blank. It occurs on R. 4/7 from early trial plates and sheets containing the error should have been destroyed, but some were sorted into good stock and issued at a post office.

93 George Cross

(Photo Harrison)

1961 (15 Apr). *George Cross Commemoration. T* **93** *and similar designs showing medal. W w* **12**. *P* 15 × 14.

304	1½d. black, cream and bistre	15	10
305	3d. olive-brown and greenish blue	25	10
306	1s. olive-green, lilac & dp reddish violet	40	70
304/6	*Set of* 3	70	75

96 "Madonna Damascena"

(Photo Harrison)

1962 (7 Sept). *Great Siege Commemoration. T* **96** *and similar vert designs. W w* **12**. *P* 13 × 12.

307	2d. bright blue	10	10
308	3d. red	10	10
309	6d. bronze-green	10	10
310	1s. brown-purple	15	20
307/10	*Set of* 4	30	25

Designs:—3d. Great Siege Monument; 6d. Grand Master La Valette; 1s. Assault on Fort St. Elmo.

1963 (4 June). *Freedom from Hunger. As No.* 76 *of Aden.*

311	1s. 6d. sepia	4·50	2·75

1963 (2 Sept). *Red Cross Centenary. As No.* 147/8 *of Antigua.*

312	2d. red and black	25	12
313	1s. 6d. red and blue	3·75	3·75

1963 (15 Oct)–**64**. *As Nos.* 268 *and* 270, *but wmk w* **12**.

314	**59**	1d. black	40	30
315	**61**	2d. deep brown (11.7.64*)	1·50	1·75

*This is the earliest known date recorded in Malta.

100 Bruce, Zammit and Microscope

101 Goat and Laboratory Equipment

(Des E. Cremona. Photo Harrison)

1964 (14 April). *Anti-Brucellosis Congress. W w* **12**. *P* 14.

316	**100**	2d. light brown, black and bluish green	10	10
		a. Black (microscope, etc) omitted	£180	
317	**101**	1s. 6d. black and maroon	35	20

102 "Nicola Cotoner tending Sick Man" (M. Preti)

105 Maltese Cross
(*Upright*)

In this illustration the points of the crosses meet in a vertical line. When the watermark is sideways they meet in a horizontal line.

(Des E. Cremona. Photo Harrison)

1964 (5 Sept). *First European Catholic Doctors' Congress, Vienna. T* **102** *and similar horiz designs. W* **105** (*sideways*). *P* 13½ × 11½.

318		2d. red, black, gold and grey-blue	20	10
319		6d. red, black, gold and bistre	45	15
320		1s. 6d. red, black, gold and reddish violet	85	75
318/20		*Set of* 3	1·40	85

Designs:—6d. St. Luke and Hospital; 1s. 6d. Sacra Infermeria, Valletta.

INDEPENDENT

106 Dove and British Crown

109 "The Nativity"

(Des E. Cremona. Photo Harrison)

1964 (21 Sept). *Independence. T* **106** *and similar vert designs. W* **105**. *P* 14½ × 13½.

321		2d. olive-brown, red and gold	30	10
		a. Gold omitted	70·00	
322		3d. brown-purple, red and gold	30	10
		a. Gold omitted	£110	
323		6d. slate, red and gold	90	15
324		1s. blue, red and gold	90	15
325		1s. 6d. indigo, red and gold	2·50	1·50
326		2s. 6d. deep violet-blue, red and gold	2·50	2·75
321/6		*Set of* 6	6·50	4·00

Designs:—2d., 1s. Type **106**; 3d., 1s. 6d. Dove and Pope's Tiara; 6d., 2s. 6d. Dove and U.N. emblem.

No. 322a comes from a sheet on which the gold was misplaced downwards leaving the stamps on the top row without gold.

(Des E. Cremona. Photo D.L.R.)

1964 (3 Nov). *Christmas. W* **105** (*sideways*). *P* 13 × 13½.

327	**109**	2d. bright purple and gold	10	10
328		4d. bright blue and gold	20	15
329		8d. deep bluish green and gold	45	45
327/9		*Set of* 3	65	60

110 Neolithic Era

117 Galleys of Knights of St. John

119 British Rule

(Des E. Cremona. Photo Harrison)

1965 (7 Jan)–**70**. *Chalk-surfaced paper. T* **110**, **117**, **119** *and similar designs. W* **105**. *P* 14 × 14½ (*vert*) *or* 14½ (*horiz*).

330		½d. multicoloured	10	10
		a. "½d" (white) printed twice†	5·00	
		b. White (face value) omitted		
331		1d. multicoloured	10	10
		a. Gold (ancient lettering) omitted	40·00	
		b. White (Greek lettering and "PUNIC") omitted	38·00	
		d. "PUNIC" omitted		
332		1½d. multicoloured	10	10
333		2d. multicoloured	10	10
		a. Gold omitted	28·00	
		b. Imperf (pair)	£250	
334		2½d. multicoloured	20	10
		a. Orange omitted*	40·00	
		b. Gold ("SARACENIC") omitted	45·00	
335		3d. multicoloured	10	10
		a. Gold (windows) omitted	50·00	
		b. "MALTA" (silver) omitted	32·00	
		c. Imperf (pair)	£275	
336		4d. multicoloured	30	10
		a. "KNIGHTS OF MALTA" (silver) omitted	35·00	
		b. Black (shield surround) omitted	38·00	
		c. Imperf (pair)	£275	
337		4½d. multicoloured	40	20
337*b*		5d. multicoloured (1.8.70)	30	20
		ba. "FORTIFICATIONS" (gold) omitted	50·00	
338		6d. multicoloured	20	10
		a. "MALTA" (silver) omitted	42·00	
		b. Black omitted	45·00	
339		8d. multicoloured	20	10
		a. Gold (centre) omitted	28·00	
		b. Gold (frame) omitted	50·00	
339*c*		10d. multicoloured (1.8.70)	45	60
		ca. "NAVAL ARSENAL" (gold) omitted	50·00	
340		1s. multicoloured	30	10
		a. Gold (centre) omitted	50·00	
		b. Gold (framework) omitted	38·00	
341		1s. 3d. multicoloured	1·00	1·25
		a. Gold (centre) omitted	42·00	
		b. Gold (framework) omitted	50·00	
		c. Imperf (pair)	£325	
342		1s. 6d. multicoloured	60	10
		a. Head (black) omitted	£200	
		b. Gold (centre) omitted	35·00	
		c. Gold (frame) omitted	50·00	
343		2s. multicoloured	70	10
		a. Gold (centre) omitted	50·00	
		b. Gold (framework) omitted	42·00	
344		2s. 6d. multicoloured	70	50
345		3s. multicoloured	1·25	75
		a. Gold (framework) omitted	30·00	
346		5s. multicoloured	3·50	1·00
		a. Gold (framework) omitted	48·00	
347		10s. multicoloured	3·50	3·00
		a. Gold (centre) omitted	55·00	
348		£1 multicoloured	3·00	5·00
		a. Pink omitted	22·00	
330/48		*Set of* 21	15·00	11·50

Designs: *Vert*—1d. Punic era; 1½d. Roman era; 2d. Proto Christian era; 2½d. Saracenic era; 3d. Siculo Norman era; 4d. Knights of Malta; 5d. Fortifications; 6d. French occupation. *Horiz*—10d. Naval arsenal; 1s. Maltese corps of the British army; 1s. 3d. International Eucharistic congress, 1913; 1s. 6d. Self-government, 1921; 2s. Gozo civic council; 2s. 6d. State of Malta; 3s. Independence, 1964; 5s. HAFMED (Allied forces, Mediterranean); 10s. The Maltese Islands (map); £1 Patron saints.

*The effect of this is to leave the Saracenic pattern as a pink colour.

†Second impression is 6½ mm lower or 3 mm to the left, stamps with almost coincidental double impression are common.

The ½d. and 1d. had white printing plates. Two silver plates were used on the 4d., one for "KNIGHTS OF MALTA" and the other for "MALTA". Two gold plates were used for the 8d. to 10s., one for the framework and the other for the gold in the central part of the designs.

The ½d. to 4d., 1s. and 1s. 6d. to 5s. values exist with PVA gum as well as gum arabic and the 5d. and 10d. have PVA gum only.

129 "Dante" (Raphael)

(Des E. Cremona. Photo Govt Ptg Works, Rome)

1965 (7 July). *700th Birth Anniv of Dante. P* 14.

349	**129**	2d. indigo	10	10
350		6d. bronze-green	15	10
351		2s. chocolate	50	70
349/51		*Set of* 3	65	70

130 Turkish Camp

131 Turkish Fleet

(Des E. Cremona. Photo Harrison)

1965 (1 Sept). *400th Anniv of Great Siege. T* **130/1** *and similar designs. W* **105** (*sideways*). *P* 13 (6d., 1s.) *or* 14½ × 14 (*others*).

352		2d. olive-green, red and black	25	10
353		3d. olive-green, red, black and light drab	25	10
354		6d. multicoloured	50	10
		a. Gold (framework and dates) omitted	£160	
		b. Black (on hulls) omitted	£140	
355		8d. red, gold, indigo and blue	75	75
356		1s. red, gold and deep grey-blue	55	10
357		1s. 6d. ochre, red and black	1·00	30
358		2s. 6d. sepia, black, red and yellow-olive	1·50	2·00
352/8		*Set of* 7	4·25	2·75

Designs: *Square* (*as T* **130**)—3d. Battle scene; 8d. Arrival of relief force; 1s. 6d. "Allegory of Victory" (from mural by M. Preti); 2s. 6d. Victory medal. *Vert* (*as T* **131**)—1s. Grand Master J. de La Valette's arms.

137 "The Three Kings"

138 Sir Winston Churchill

(Des E. Cremona. Photo Enschedé)

1965 (7 Oct). *Christmas. W* **105** (*sideways*). *P* 11 × 11½.

359	**137**	1d. slate-purple and red	10	10
360		4d. slate-purple and blue	30	25
361		1s. 3d. slate-purple and bright purple	30	30
359/61		*Set of* 3	60	50

(Des E. Cremona. Photo Harrison)

1966 (24 Jan). *Churchill Commemoration. T* **138** *and similar square design. W* **105** (*sideways*). *P* 14½ × 14.

362	**138**	2d. black, red and gold	15	10
363	–	3d. bronze-green, yellow-olive and gold	15	10
364	**138**	1s. maroon, red and gold	20	10
		a. Gold (shading) omitted	£200	
365	–	1s. 6d. chalky blue, violet-blue and gold	35	40
362/5		*Set of* 4	75	55

Design:—3d., 1s. 6d. Sir Winston Churchill and George Cross.

140 Grand Master La Valette

145 President Kennedy and Memorial

(Des E. Cremona. Photo State Ptg Works, Vienna)

1966 (28 Mar). *400th Anniv of Valletta. T* **140** *and similar square designs. Multicoloured. W* **105** (*sideways*). *P* 12.

366		2d. Type **140**	10	10
367		3d. Pope Pius V	10	10
		a. Gold omitted	£225	
368		6d. Map of Valletta	10	10
369		1s. Francesco Laparelli (architect)	10	10
370		2s. 6d. Girolamo Cassar (architect)	20	30
366/70		*Set of* 5	40	45

(Des E. Cremona. Photo Harrison)

1966 (28 May). *President Kennedy Commemoration. W* **105** (*sideways*). *P* 15 × 14.

371	**145**	3d. olive, gold and black	10	10
		a. Gold inscr omitted	£200	
372		1s. 6d. Prussian blue, gold and black	10	10

146 "Trade"

(Des E. Cremona. Photo D.L.R.)

1966 (16 June). *Tenth Malta Trade Fair. W* **105** (*sideways*). *P* 13½.

373	**146**	2d. multicoloured	10	10
374		8d. multicoloured	20	25
375		2s. 6d. multicoloured	20	25
373/5		*Set of* 3	45	50

147 "The Child in the Manger"

148 George Cross

(Des E. Cremona. Photo D.L.R.)

1966 (7 Oct). *Christmas. W* **105**. *P* 13½.

376	**147**	1d. black, gold, turquoise-bl & slate-pur	10	10
377		4d. black, gold, ultramarine & slate-pur	10	10
378		1s. 3d. black, gold, brt pur & slate-pur	10	10
		a. Gold omitted	£100	
376/8		*Set of* 3	15	10

(Des E. Cremona. Photo Harrison)

1967 (1 Mar). *25th Anniv of George Cross Award to Malta. W* **105** *(sideways). P* 14½ × 14.

379	**148**	2d. multicoloured	10	10
380		4d. multicoloured	10	10
381		3s. multicoloured	15	15
379/81		.. .. *Set of* 3	15	15

149 Crucifixion of St. Peter

150 Open Bible and Episcopal Emblems

(Des E. Cremona. Photo Harrison)

1967 (28 June). *1900th Anniv of Martyrdom of Saints Peter and Paul. T* **149/50** *and similar design. W* **105** *(sideways). P* 13½ × 14½ *(8d.) or* 14½ *(others).*

382	2d. chestnut, orange and black	10	10
383	8d. yellow-olive, gold and black	10	10
384	3s. blue, light blue and black	15	10
382/4	.. .. *Set of* 3	20	15

Design:—*Square as T* **149**—3s. Beheading of St. Paul.

152 "St. Catherine of Siena"

156 Temple Ruins, Tarxien

(Des E. Cremona. Photo Enschedé)

1967 (1 Aug). *300th Death Anniv of Melchior Gafa (sculptor). T* **152** *and similar horiz designs. Multicoloured. W* **105** *(sideways). P* 13½ × 13.

385	2d. Type **152**	10	10
386	4d. "St. Thomas of Villanova"	10	10
387	1s. 6d. "Baptism of Christ" (detail)	10	10
388	2s. 6d. "St. John the Baptist" (from "Baptism of Christ")	10	10
385/8	.. .. *Set of* 4	20	15

(Des E. Cremona. Photo Harrison)

1967 (12 Sept). *15th International Historical Architecture Congress, Valletta. T* **156** *and similar square designs. Multicoloured. W* **105**. *P* 15 × 14½.

389	2d. Type **156**	10	10
390	6d. Facade of Palazzo Falzon, Notabile ..	10	10
391	1s. Parish Church, Birkirkara	10	10
392	3s. Portal, Auberge de Castille	15	15
389/92	.. .. *Set of* 4	20	20

160 "Angels" **161** "Crib" **162** "Angels"

(Des E. Cremona. Photo D.L.R.)

1967 (20 Oct). *Christmas. W* **105** *(sideways). P* 14.

393	**160**	1d. multicoloured	10	10
		a. In triptych with Nos. 394/5	10	10
		b. White stars (red omitted)	65·00	
394	**161**	8d. multicoloured	10	10
395	**162**	1s. 4d. multicoloured	10	10
393/5		.. .. *Set of* 3	10	10

Nos. 393/5 were issued in sheets of 60 of each value (arranged *tête-bêche*), and also in sheets containing the three values *se-tenant*, thus forming a triptych of the Nativity.

163 Queen Elizabeth II and Arms of Malta

(Des E. Cremona. Photo Harrison)

1967 (13 Nov). *Royal Visit. T* **163** *and similar designs. W* **105** *(sideways on 2d., 3s.). P* 14 × 15 *(4d.) or* 15 × 14 *(others).*

396	2d. multicoloured	10	10
	a. Cream omitted*		
397	4d. black, brown-purple and gold	10	10
398	3s. multicoloured	15	15
396/8	.. .. *Set of* 3	20	20

Designs: *Vert*—4d. Queen in Robes of Order of St. Michael and St. George. *Horiz*—3s. Queen and outline of Malta.

*This affects the Queen's face.

166 Human Rights Emblem and People **167**

(Des E. Cremona. Photo Harrison)

1968 (2 May). *Human Rights Year. W* **105**. *P* 12½ *(6d.) or* 14½ *(others).*

399	**166**	2d. multicoloured	10	10
400	**167**	6d. multicoloured	10	10
401	–	2s. multicoloured	10	10
399/401		.. .. *Set of* 3	15	10

The design of the 2s. value is a reverse of Type **166.**

169 Fair "Products"

(Des E. Cremona. Photo Harrison)

1968 (1 June). *Malta International Trade Fair. W* **105** *(sideways). P* 14½ × 14.

402	**169**	4d. multicoloured	10	10
403		8d. multicoloured	10	10
404		3s. multicoloured	15	10
402/4		.. .. *Set of* 3	20	15

170 Arms of the Order of St. John and La Valette

171 "La Valette" (A. de Favray)

172 La Valette's Tomb

173 Angels and Scroll bearing Date of Death

(Des E. Cremona. Photo Govt Printer, Israel)

1968 (1 Aug). *Fourth Death Centenary of Grand Master La Valette. W* **105** *(upright, 1s. 6d.; sideways, others). P* 13 × 14 *(1d., 1s. 6d.) or* 14 × 13 *(others).*

405	**170**	1d. multicoloured	10	10
406	**171**	8d. multicoloured	10	10
407	**172**	1s. 6d. multicoloured	10	10
408	**173**	2s. 6d. multicoloured	15	20
405/8		.. .. *Set of* 4	25	30

174 Star of Bethlehem and Angel waking Shepherds

177 "Agriculture"

(Des E. Cremona. Photo Harrison)

1968 (3 Oct). *Christmas. T* **174** *and similar shaped designs. Multicoloured. W* **105** *(sideways). P* 14½ × 14.

409	1d. Type **174**	10	10
410	8d. Mary and Joseph with shepherd watching over cradle	10	10
411	1s. 4d. Three Wise Men and Star of Bethlehem	10	10
409/11	.. .. *Set of* 3	15	15

The shortest side at top and the long side at the bottom both gauge 14½, the other three sides are 14. Nos. 409/11 were issued in sheets of 60 arranged in ten strips of six, alternately upright and inverted.

(Des E. Cremona. Photo Enschedé)

1968 (21 Oct). *Sixth Food and Agricultural Organization Regional Conference for Europe. T* **177** *and similar vert designs. Multicoloured. W* **105** *(sideways). P* 12½ × 12.

412	4d. Type **177**	10	10
413	1s. F.A.O. emblem and coin	10	10
414	2s. 6d. "Agriculture" sowing seeds	10	15
412/14	.. .. *Set of* 3	15	20

180 Mahatma Gandhi

181 I.L.O. Emblem

(Des E. Cremona. Photo Enschedé)

1969 (24 Mar). *Birth Centenary of Mahatma Gandhi. W* **105**. *P* 12 × 12½.

415	**180**	1s. 6d. blackish brown, black and gold	15	10

(Des E. Cremona. Photo Harrison)

1969 (26 May). *50th Anniv of International Labour Organization. W* **105** *(sideways). P* 13½ × 14½.

416	**181**	2d. indigo, gold and turquoise	10	10
417		6d. sepia, gold and chestnut	10	10

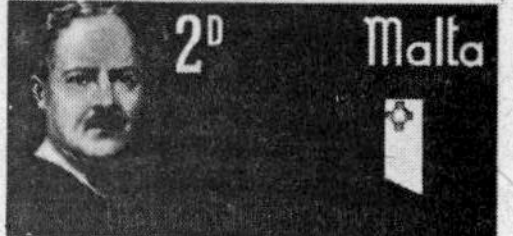

182 Robert Samut

(Des E. Cremona. Photo D.L.R.)

1969 (26 July). *Birth Centenary of Robert Samut (composer of Maltese National Anthem). W* **105** *(sideways). P* 13.

418	**182**	2d. multicoloured	10	10

183 Dove of Peace, U.N. Emblem and Sea-Bed

(Des E. Cremona. Photo D.L.R.)

1969 (26 July). *United Nations Resolution on Oceanic Resources. W* **105** *(sideways). P* 13.

419	**183**	5d. multicoloured	10	10

184 "Swallows" returning to Malta

(Des E. Cremona. Photo D.L.R.)

1969 (26 July). *Maltese Migrants' Convention. W* **105** *(sideways). P* 13.

420	**184**	10d. black, gold and yellow-olive ..	10	10

185 University Arms and Grand Master de Fonseca (founder)

(Des E. Cremona. Photo D.L.R.)

1969 (26 July). *Bicentenary of University of Malta. W* **105** *(sideways). P* 13.

421	**185**	2s. multicoloured	10	20

186 1919 Monument

187 Flag of Malta and Birds

(Des E. Cremona. Photo Enschedé)

1969 (20 Sept). *Fifth Anniv of Independence. T* **186/7** *and similar designs. W* **105** *(upright on 5d., sideways others). P* 13½ × 12½ *(2d.),* 12 × 12½ *(5d.), or* 12½ × 12 *(others).*

422		2d. multicoloured	10	10
423		5d. black, red and gold	10	10
424		10d. black, turquoise-blue and gold	10	10
425		1s. 6d. multicoloured	10	15
426		2s. 6d. black, olive-brown and gold	15	20
422/6		*Set of* 5	30	45

Designs:—*Vert as T* **187**—10d. "Tourism"; 1s. 6d. U.N. and Council of Europe emblems; 2s. 6d. "Trade and Industry".

191 Peasants playing Tambourine and Bagpipes

(Des E. Cremona. Litho D.L.R.)

1969 (8 Nov). *Christmas. Children's Welfare Fund. T* **191** *and similar horiz designs. Multicoloured. W* **105** *(sideways). P* 12½.

427		1d. + 1d. Type **191**	10	10
		a. Gold omitted	90·00	
		b. In triptych with Nos. 428/9	15	20
428		5d. + 1d. Angels playing trumpet and harp	10	10
429		1s. 6d. + 3d. Choir boys singing	10	15
427/9		*Set of* 3	15	20

Nos. 427/9 were issued in sheets of 60 of each value, and also in sheets containing the three values *se-tenant*, thus forming the triptych No. 427b.

194 "The Beheading of St. John" (Caravaggio)

(Des E. Cremona. Photo Enschedé)

1970 (21 Mar). *13th Council of Europe Art Exhibition. T* **194** *and similar multicoloured designs. W* **105** *(upright, 10d., 2s.; sideways, others). P* 14 × 13 *(1d., 8d.),* 12 *(10d., 2s.) or* 13 × 13½ *(others).*

430		1d. Type **194**	10	10
431		2d. "St. John the Baptist" (M. Preti) (45 × 32 *mm*)	10	10
432		5d. Interior of St. John's Co-Cathedral, Valletta (39 × 39 *mm*)	10	10
433		6d. "Allegory of the Order" (Neapolitan School) (45 × 32 *mm*)	10	10
434		8d. "St. Jerome" (Caravaggio)	10	20
435		10d. Articles from the Order of St. John in Malta (63 × 21 *mm*)	10	10
436		1s. 6d. "The Blessed Gerard receiving Godfrey de Bouillon" (A. de Favray) (45 × 35 *mm*)	15	25
437		2s. Cape and Stolone (16th-century) (63 × 21 *mm*)	20	35
430/37		*Set of* 8	60	85

202 Artist's Impression of Fujiyama

(Des E. Cremona. Photo D.L.R.)

1970 (29 May). *World Fair, Osaka. W* **105** *(sideways). P* 15.

438	**202**	2d. multicoloured	10	10
439		5d. multicoloured	10	10
440		3s. multicoloured	15	15
438/40		*Set of* 3	15	15

203 "Peace and Justice"

204 Carol-Singers, Church and Star

(Des J. Casha. Litho Harrison)

1970 (30 Sept). *25th Anniv of United Nations. W* **105**. *P* 14 × 14½.

441	**203**	2d. multicoloured	10	10
442		5d. multicoloured	10	10
443		2s. 6d. multicoloured	15	15
441/3		*Set of* 3	15	15

(Des E. Cremona. Photo Govt Printer, Israel)

1970 (7 Nov). *Christmas. T* **204** *and similar vert designs. Multicoloured. W* **105** *(sideways). P* 14 × 13.

444		1d. + ½d. Type **204**	10	10
445		10d. + 2d. Church, star and angels with Infant	10	15
446		1s. 6d. + 3d. Church, star and nativity scene	15	25
444/6		*Set of* 3	20	40

207 Books and Quill

208 Dun Karm, Books, Pens and Lamp

(Des H. Alden (1s. 6d.), A. Agius (2s.). Litho D.L.R.)

1971 (20 Mar). *Literary Anniversaries. Death Bicentenary* (1970) *of De Soldanis (historian)* (1s. 6d.) *and Birth Centenary of Dun Karm (poet)* (2s.). *W* **105** *(sideways). P* 13 × 13½.

447	**207**	1s. 6d. multicoloured	10	10
448	**208**	2s. multicoloured	10	15

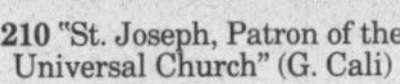

209 Europa "Chain"

(Des H. Haflidason; adapted E. Cremona. Litho Harrison)

1971 (3 May). *Europa. W* **105** *(sideways). P* 13½ × 14½.

449	**209**	2d. orange, black and yellow-olive	10	10
450		5d. orange, black and vermilion	10	10
451		1s. 6d. orange, black and slate	20	40
449/51		*Set of* 3	30	40

210 "St. Joseph, Patron of the Universal Church" (G. Cali)

211 *Centaurea spathulata*

(Des E. Cremona. Litho D.L.R.)

1971 (24 July). *Centenary of Proclamation of St. Joseph as Patron Saint of Catholic Church, and 50th Anniv of the Coronation of the Statue of "Our Lady of Victories". T* **210** *and similar horiz design. Multicoloured. W* **105** *(sideways). P* 13 × 13½.

452		2d. Type **210**	10	10
453		5d. Statue of "Our Lady of Victories" and galley	10	10
454		10d. Type **210**	10	10
455		1s. 6d. As 5d.	20	40
452/5		*Set of* 4	30	50

(Des Reno Psaila. Litho Harrison)

1971 (18 Sept). *National Plant and Bird of Malta. T* **211** *and similar horiz design. Multicoloured. W* **105** *(sideways on 5d. and 10d.). P* 14½ × 14.

456		2d. Type **211**	10	10
457		5d. Blue Rock Thrush	10	10
458		10d. As 5d.	20	10
459		1s. 6d. Type **211**	20	60
456/9		*Set of* 4	50	70

212 Angel

(Des E. Cremona. Litho Format)

1971 (8 Nov). *Christmas. T* **212** *and similar horiz designs. Multicoloured. W* **105** *(sideways). P* 13½ × 14.

460		1d. + ½d. Type **212**	10	10
461		10d. + 2d. Mary and the Child Jesus	15	20
462		1s. 6d. + 3d. Joseph lying awake	20	30
460/2		*Set of* 3	35	55
MS463		131 × 113 mm. Nos. 460/2. P 15	60	1·50

213 Heart and W.H.O. Emblem

214 Maltese Cross

(Des A. Agius. Litho Format)

1972 (20 Mar). *World Health Day. W* **105**. *P* 13½ × 14.

464	**213**	2d. multicoloured	10	10
465		10d. multicoloured	15	10
466		2s. 6d. multicoloured	40	80
464/6		*Set of* 3	55	85

(New Currency. 10 mils = 1 cent; 100 cents = 1 Maltese pound)

(Des G. Pace. Litho Format)

1972 (16 May). *Decimal Currency. T* **214** *and similar vert designs showing decimal coins. Multicoloured. W* **105**. *P* 14 *(2 m., 3 m., 2 c.),* 14½ × 14 *(5 m., 1 c., 5 c.) or* 13½ *(10 c., 50 c.).*

467		2 m. Type **214**	10	10
468		3 m. Bee on honeycomb	10	10
469		5 m. Earthen lampstand	10	10
470		1 c. George Cross	10	10
471		2 c. Classical head	10	10
472		5 c. Ritual altar	10	10
473		10 c. Grandmaster's galley	20	10
474		50 c. Great Siege Monument	50	1·25
467/74		*Set of* 8	85	1·25

Sizes:—2 m., 3 m. and 2 c. as T **214**; 5 m., 1 c. and 5 c. 22 × 27 mm; 10 c. and 50 c. 27 × 35 mm.

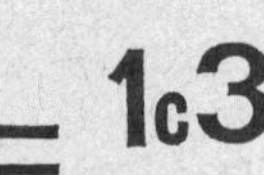

(215)

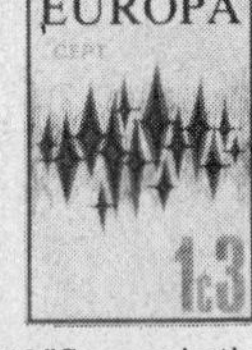

216 "Communications"

1972 (30 Sept). *Nos. 337a, 339 and 341 surch as T* **215**, *by Govt. Printing Works, Valletta.*

475		1 c. 3 on 5d. multicoloured	10	10
476		3 c. on 8d. multicoloured	10	10
		a. Surch inverted	45·00	
		b. Gold (frame) omitted	55·00	
477		5 c. on 1s. 3d. multicoloured	10	20
		a. Surch double	50·00	
		b. Surch inverted	25·00	
		c. Gold (centre) omitted	35·00	
475/7		*Set of* 3	20	35

PRINTERS. All stamps from No. 478 onwards were printed in lithography by Printex Ltd, Malta.

(Des P. Huovinen; adapted G. Pace)

1972 (11 Nov). *Europa. W* **105** *(sideways). P* 13.

478	**216**	1 c. 3, multicoloured	10	10
479		3 c. multicoloured	10	10
480		5 c. multicoloured	15	30
481		7 c. 5, multicoloured	20	60
478/81		*Set of* 4	50	90

Nos. 478/81 were each printed in sheets including two *se-tenant* stamp-size labels.

217 Angel

(Des E. Cremona)

1972 (9 Dec). *Christmas. T* **217** *and similar horiz designs. W* **105** *(sideways). P* 13½.

482		8 m. + 2 m. dull sepia, brownish grey and gold	10	10
483		3 c. + 1 c. plum, lavender and gold	15	35
484		7 c. 5 + 1 c. 5, indigo, azure and gold	20	45
482/4		*Set of* 3	35	75
MS485		137 × 113 mm. Nos. 482/4	1·40	2·50

Designs:—No. 483, Angel with tambourine; No. 484, Singing angel.

See also Nos. 507/10.

218 Archaeology

219 Europa "Posthorn"

(Des E. Cremona)

1973 (31 Mar)–**76.** *T* **218** *and similar designs. Multicoloured.* **W 105** *(sideways). P* 13½ × 14 *(Nos. 500/a) or* 13½ *(others).*

486	2 m. Type **218**	10	10
487	4 m. History	10	10
	a. Gold (inscr and decoration) omitted	75·00	
	b. Imperf (pair)	£325	
488	5 m. Folklore	10	10
489	8 m. Industry	10	10
490	1 c. Fishing industry	10	10
491	1 c. 3, Pottery	10	10
492	2 c. Agriculture	10	10
493	3 c. Sport	10	10
494	4 c. Yacht marina	15	10
495	5 c. Fiesta	15	10
496	7 c. 5, Regatta	25	10
497	10 c. Voluntary service	25	10
498	50 c. Education	75	1·00
499	£1 Religion	2·00	2·75
500	£2 Coat of arms *(horiz)*	14·00	16·00
	a. Gold omitted		
500*b*	£2 National Emblem *(horiz)* (28.1.76)	9·00	9·00
486/500*b*	*Set of* 16	24·00	26·00

Nos. 500/*b* are larger, 32 × 27 mm.

(Des L. Anisdahl; adapted G. Pace)

1973 (2 June). *Europa.* **W 105.** *P* 14.

501 **219**	3 c. multicoloured	15	10
502	5 c. multicoloured	15	35
503	7 c. 5, multicoloured	25	60
501/3	*Set of* 3	50	95

Nos. 501/3 were each printed in sheets containing two *se-tenant* stamp-size labels.

220 Emblem, and Woman holding Corn

221 Girolamo Cassar (architect)

(Des H. Alden)

1973 (6 Oct). *Anniversaries. T* **220** *and similar vert designs showing emblem and allegorical figures.* **W 105** *(sideways). P* 13½.

504	1 c. 3, multicoloured	10	10
505	7 c. 5, multicoloured	25	40
506	10 c. multicoloured	30	50
504/6	*Set of* 3	55	85

Anniversaries:—1 c. 3, Tenth Anniv of World Food Programme; 7 c. 5, 25th Anniv of W.H.O.; 10 c. 25th Anniv of Universal Declaration of Human Rights.

(Des E. Cremona)

1973 (10 Nov). *Christmas. Horiz designs as T* **217.** *Multicoloured.* **W 105** *(sideways). P* 13½.

507	8 m. + 2 m. Angels and organ pipes	15	10
508	3 c. + 1 c. Madonna and Child	25	40
509	7 c. 5 + 1 c. 5, Buildings and Star	45	65
507/9	*Set of* 3	75	1·00
MS510	137 × 112 mm. Nos. 507/9	3·25	5·00

(Des E. Cremona)

1974 (12 Jan). *Prominent Maltese. T* **221** *and similar vert designs.* **W 105.** *P* 14.

511	1 c. 3, dull myrtle-grn, dull grey-grn & gold	10	10
512	3 c. deep turquoise, grey-blue and gold	10	10
513	5 c. dull sepia, deep slate-green and gold	15	15
514	7 c. 5, slate-blue, light slate-blue and gold	20	30
515	10 c. purple, dull purple and gold	20	40
511/15	*Set of* 5	60	85

Designs:—3 c. Giuseppe Barth (ophthalmologist); 5 c. Nicolo' Isouard (composer); 7 c. 5, John Borg (botanist); 10 c. Antonio Sciortino (sculptor).

222 "Air Malta" Emblem

(Des E. Cremona)

1974 (30 Mar). *Air. T* **222** *and similar horiz design. Multicoloured.* **W 105** *(sideways). P* 13½.

516	3 c. Type **222**	10	10
517	4 c. Boeing "707"	15	10
518	5 c. Type **222**	15	10
519	7 c. 5, As 4 c.	20	10
520	20 c. Type **222**	45	60
521	25 c. As 4 c.	45	60
522	35 c. Type **222**	80	1·40
516/22	*Set of* 7	2·00	2·50

223 Prehistoric Sculpture

(Des E. Cremona)

1974 (13 July). *Europa. T* **223** *and similar designs.* **W 105** *(sideways on Nos. 523 and 525). P* 13½.

523	1 c. 3, slate-blue, grey-black and gold	10	10
524	3 c. light bistre-brown, grey-black and gold	10	15
525	5 c. purple, grey-black and gold	15	45
526	7 c. 5, dull green, grey-black and gold	30	80
523/6	*Set of* 4	55	1·40

Designs: *Vert*—3 c. Old Cathedral Door, Mdina; 7 c. 5, "Vetlina" (sculpture by A. Sciortino). *Horiz*—5 c. Silver Monstrance.

Nos. 523/6 were each printed in sheets including two *se-tenant* stamp-size labels.

224 Heinrich von Stephan (founder) and Land Transport

225 Decorative Star and Nativity Scene

(Des S. and G. Sullivan)

1974 (20 Sept). *Centenary of Universal Postal Union. T* **224** *and similar horiz designs.* **W 105.** *P* 13½ × 14.

527	1 c. 3, blue-green, lt violet-blue & yell-orge	25	10
528	5 c. brown, dull vermilion and yellow-green	25	10
529	7 c. 5, dp dull blue, lt violet-blue & yell-grn	25	20
530	50 c. purple, dull vermilion and yellow-orange	70	1·25
527/30	*Set of* 4	1·25	1·50
MS531	126 × 91 mm. Nos. 527/30	2·00	3·25

Designs (each containing portrait as T **224**):—5 c. *Washington* (paddle-steamer) and *Royal Viking Star* (liner); 7 c. 5, Balloon and Boeing "747"; 50 c. U.P.U. Buildings, 1874 and 1974.

(Des E. Cremona)

1974 (22 Nov). *Christmas. T* **225** *and similar vert designs, each with decorative star. Multicoloured.* **W 105** *(sideways). P* 14.

532	8 m. + 2 m. Type **225**	10	10
533	3 c. + 1 c. "Shepherds"	15	20
534	5 c. + 1 c. "Shepherds with gifts"	20	35
535	7 c. 5 + 1 c. 5, "The Magi"	30	40
532/5	*Set of* 4	65	95

REPUBLIC

226 Swearing-in of Prime Minister

(Des E. Cremona)

1975 (31 Mar). *Inauguration of Republic. T* **226** *and similar horiz designs.* **W 105** *(sideways). P* 14.

536	1 c. 3, multicoloured	10	10
537	5 c. rose-red and grey-black	20	10
538	25 c. multicoloured	60	1·00
536/8	*Set of* 3	75	1·10

Designs:—5 c. National flag; 25 c. Minister of Justice, President and Prime Minister.

227 Mother and Child ("Family Life")

(Des D. Friggieri)

1975 (30 May). *International Women's Year. T* **227** *and similar horiz design.* **W 105.** *P* 13½ × 14.

539	**227**	1 c. 3, light violet and gold	25	10
540	–	3 c. light blue and gold	35	10
541	**227**	5 c. dull olive-sepia and gold	60	20
542	–	20 c. chestnut and gold	2·75	4·00
539/42		*Set of* 4	3·50	4·00

Design:—3 c., 20 c. Office secretary ("Public Life").

228 "Allegory of Malta" (Francesco de Mura)

(Des E. Cremona)

1975 (15 July). *Europa. T* **228** *and similar horiz design. Multicoloured.* **W 105.** *P* 14 × 13½.

543	5 c. Type **228**	20	10
544	15 c. "Judith and Holofernes" (Valentin de Boulogne)	40	65

The 15 c. is a smaller design than the 5 c. (47 × 23 mm), though the perforated area is the same.

Nos. 543/4 were each printed in sheets including two *se-tenant* stamp-size labels.

229 Plan of Ggantija Temple

(Des R. England)

1975 (16 Sept). *European Architectural Heritage Year. T* **229** *and similar horiz designs.* **W 105** *(sideways). P* 13½.

545	1 c. 3, brownish black and light orange-red	10	10
546	3 c. dull purple, lt orange-red & blackish brn	20	10
547	5 c. blackish brown and light orange-red	40	35
548	25 c. dull grey-olive, light orange-red and brownish black	1·75	3·25
545/8	*Set of* 4	2·25	3·50

Designs:—3 c. Mdina skyline; 5 c. View of Victoria, Gozo; 25 c. Silhouette of Fort St. Angelo.

230 Farm Animals

231 "The Right to Work"

(Des E. Cremona)

1975 (4 Nov). *Christmas. T* **230** *and similar multicoloured designs.* **W 105** *(sideways). P* 13½.

549	8 m. + 2 m. Type **230**	30	25
	a. In triptych with Nos. 550/1	2·25	5·00
550	3 c. + 1 c. Nativity scene (50 × 23 *mm*)	60	75
551	7 c. 5 + 1 c. 5, Approach of the Magi	1·50	1·75
549/51	*Set of* 3	2·25	2·50

Nos. 549/51 were issued in sheets of 50 of each value, and also in sheets containing the three values horizontally *se-tenant*, thus forming the triptych No. 549a which is a composite design of "The Nativity" by Master Alberto.

(Des A. de Giovanni)

1975 (12 Dec). *First Anniv of Republic. T* **231** *and similar vert designs.* **W 105.** *P* 14.

552	1 c. 3, multicoloured	10	10
553	5 c. multicoloured	20	10
554	25 c. deep rose, light steel-blue and black	70	1·10
552/4	*Set of* 3	80	1·10

Designs:—5 c. "Safeguarding the Environment"; 25 c. National Flag.

232 "Festa Tar-Rahal"

233 Waterpolo

(Des M. Camilleri)

1976 (26 Feb). *Maltese Folklore. T* **232** *and similar multicoloured designs.* **W 105** *(sideways on 5 c. and 7 c. 5). P* 14.

555	1 c. 3, Type **232**	10	10
556	5 c. "L-Imnarja" *(horiz)*	15	10
557	7 c. 5, "Il-Karnival" *(horiz)*	45	70
558	10 c. "Il-Gimgha L-Kbira"	70	1·40
555/8	*Set of* 4	1·25	2·00

(Des H. Alden)

1976 (28 Apr). *Olympic Games, Montreal. T* **233** *and similar horiz designs. Multicoloured.* **W 105.** *P* 13½ × 14.

559	1 c. 7, Type **233**	10	10
560	5 c. Sailing	20	10
561	30 c. Athletics	65	1·50
559/61	*Set of* 3	85	1·50

234 Lace-making

(Des F. Portelli)

1976 (8 July). *Europa. T* **234** *and similar horiz design. Multicoloured.* **W 105** *(sideways). P* 13½ × 14.

562	7 c. Type **234**	20	30
563	15 c. Stone carving	25	40

Nos. 562/3 were each printed in sheets including two *se-tenant* stamp-size labels.

235 Nicola Cotoner

(Des E. Cremona)

1976 (14 Sept). *300th Anniv of School of Anatomy and Surgery. T* **235** *and similar horiz designs. Multicoloured. W* **105** *(sideways). P* 13½.

564	2 c. Type **235** ..	10	10
565	5 c. Arm ..	10	10
566	7 c. Giuseppe Zammit ..	15	10
567	11 c. Sacra Infermeria ..	25	65
564/7	.. *Set of* 4	50	75

1c7

236 St. John the Baptist and St. Michael

237 Jean de la Valette's Armour

(238)

(Des E. Cremona)

1976 (23 Nov). *Christmas. Designs showing portions of "Madonna and Saints" by Domenico di Michelino. Multicoloured. W* **105** *(sideways on No. 571). P* 13½ × 14 *(No. 571) or* 13½ *(others).*

568	1 c. + 5 m. Type **236** ..	15	20
569	5 c. + 1 c. Madonna and Child ..	50	70
570	7 c. + 1 c. 5, St. Christopher and St. Nicholas	65	1·00
571	10 c. + 2 c. Complete painting (32 × 27 *mm*) ..	75	1·40
568/71	.. *Set of* 4	1·90	3·00

(Des J. Briffa)

1977 (20 Jan). *Suits of Armour. T* **237** *and similar vert designs. Multicoloured. W* **105**. *P* 13½.

572	2 c. Type **237** ..	10	10
573	7 c. Aloph de Wignacourt's armour ..	20	10
574	11 c. Jean Jacques de Verdelin's armour ..	25	50
572/4	.. *Set of* 3	45	60

1977 (24 Mar). *No. 336 surch with T* **238** *by Govt Printing Press, Malta.*

575 **116**	1 c. 7 on 4d. multicoloured ..	25	25
	a. "KNIGHTS OF MALTA" (silver) omitted ..	65·00	

239 "Annunciation"

240 Map and Radio Aerial

(Des E. Cremona)

1977 (30 Mar). *400th Birth Anniversary of Rubens. Flemish tapestries (1st series) showing his paintings as T* **239**. *Multicoloured. W* **105** *(sideways). P* 14.

576	2 c. Type **239** ..	10	10
577	7 c. "Four Evangelists" ..	20	10
578	11 c. "Nativity" ..	40	45
579	20 c. "Adoration of the Magi" ..	65	1·00
576/9	.. *Set of* 4	1·25	1·50

See also Nos. 592/5, 615/18 and 638/40.

(Des H. Borg)

1977 (17 May). *World Telecommunication Day. T* **240** *and similar design. W* **105** *(sideways on 1 and 6 c.). P* 14 × 13½ *(1 and 6 c.) or* 13½ × 14 *(others).*

580	**240**	1 c. black, green and vermilion ..	10	10
581		6 c. black, grey-blue and vermilion ..	15	10
582	–	8 c. black, chestnut and vermilion ..	15	10
583	–	17 c. black, dull mauve and vermilion ..	30	40
580/3		.. *Set of* 4	55	55

Design: *Horiz*—8 and 17 c. Map, aerial and aeroplane tail-fin.

241 Ta' L-Isperanza

242 "Aid to Handicapped Workers" (detail from Workers' Monument)

(Des G. French)

1977 (5 July). *Europa. T* **241** *and similar horiz design. Multicoloured. W* **105** *(sideways). P* 13½.

584	7 c. Type **241** ..	30	15
585	20 c. Is-Salini ..	35	65

Nos. 584/5 were each printed in sheets including two *se-tenant* stamp-size labels.

(Des A. Agius)

1977 (12 Oct). *Maltese Worker Commemoration. T* **242** *and similar designs. W* **105** *(sideways on 20 c.). P* 13½.

586	2 c. orange-brown and light brown ..	10	10
587	7 c. chestnut and brown ..	15	10
588	20 c. multicoloured ..	40	60
586/8	.. *Set of* 3	55	60

Designs: *Vert*—7 c. "Stoneworker, modern industry and shipbuilding" (monument detail). *Horiz*—20 c. "Mother with Dead Son" and Service Medal.

243 The Shepherds

244 "Young Lady on Horseback and Trooper"

(Des E. Cremona)

1977 (16 Nov). *Christmas. T* **243** *and similar horiz designs. Multicoloured. W* **105** *(sideways). P* 13½ × 14.

589	1 c. + 5 m. Type **243** ..	10	20
	a. In triptych with Nos. 590/1 ..	40	
590	7 c. + 1 c. The Nativity ..	15	30
591	11 c. + 1 c. 5, Flight into Egypt ..	20	45
589/91	.. *Set of* 3	40	85

Nos. 589/91 were issued in sheets of 50 of each value, and also in sheets containing the three values *se-tenant*, thus forming the triptych No. 589a.

(Des E. Cremona)

1978 (26 Jan). *Flemish Tapestries (2nd series). Horiz designs similar to T* **239**. *Multicoloured. W* **105** *(sideways). P* 14.

592	2 c. "The Entry into Jerusalem" (artist unknown) ..	10	10
593	7 c. "The Last Supper" (after Poussin) ..	15	10
594	11 c. "The Raising of the Cross" (after Rubens)	20	25
595	25 c. "The Resurrection" (after Rubens) ..	60	80
592/5	.. *Set of* 4	90	1·10

(Des A. Camilleri)

1978 (7 Mar). *450th Death Anniv of Albrecht Dürer. T* **244** *and similar vert designs. W* **105**. *P* 14.

596	1 c. 7, black, vermilion and deep blue ..	10	10
597	8 c. black, vermilion and slate ..	15	10
598	17 c. black, vermilion and deep slate ..	40	45
	a. Vermilion (monogram) omitted ..	60·00	
596/8	.. *Set of* 3	55	55

Designs:—8 c. "The Bag-piper"; 17 c. "The Virgin and Child with a Monkey".

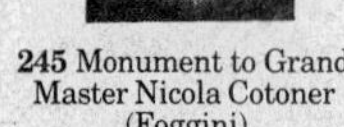

245 Monument to Grand Master Nicola Cotoner (Foggini)

246 Goalkeeper

(Des E. Cremona)

1978 (26 Apr). *Europa. Monuments. T* **245** *and similar vert design. Multicoloured. W* **105**. *P* 14 × 13½.

599	7 c. Type **245** ..	15	10
600	25 c. Monument to Grand Master Ramon Perellos (Mazzuoli) ..	35	55

Nos. 599/600 were each printed in sheets including two *se-tenant* stamp-size labels.

(Des A. de Giovanni)

1978 (6 June). *World Cup Football Championship, Argentina. T* **246** *and similar vert designs. Multicoloured. W* **105** *(sideways). P* 14 × 13½.

601	2 c. Type **246** ..	10	10
602	11 c. Players heading ball ..	15	10
603	15 c. Tackling ..	25	35
601/3	.. *Set of* 3	45	45
MS604	125 × 90 mm. Nos. 601/3 ..	1·00	2·00

247 Airliner over Megalithic Temple

(Des R. Caruana)

1978 (3 Oct). *Air. Horiz designs as T* **247**. *Multicoloured. W* **105** *(sideways). P* 13½.

605	5 c. Type **247** ..	15	10
606	7 c. Air Malta Boeing "720B" ..	15	10
607	11 c. Boeing "747" taking off from Luqa Airport	25	10
608	17 c. Type **247** ..	35	30
609	20 c. As 7 c. ..	50	40
610	75 c. As 11 c. ..	1·50	2·25
605/10	.. *Set of* 6	2·75	2·75

248 Folk Musicians and Village Church

249 Luzzu and Aircraft Carrier

(Des E. Cremona)

1978 (9 Nov). *Christmas. T* **248** *and similar multicoloured designs. W* **105** *(sideways). P* 13½ *(11 c.) or* 14 *(others).*

611	1 c. + 5 m. Type **248** ..	10	10
612	5 c. + 1 c. Choir of Angels ..	10	15
613	7 c. + 1 c. 5, Carol singers ..	15	20
614	11 c. + 3 c. Folk musicians, church, angels and carol singers (58 × 23 *mm*) ..	20	30
611/14	.. *Set of* 4	50	65

The 1, 5 and 7 c. values depict details of the complete design shown on the 11 c. value.

(Des E. Cremona)

1979 (24 Jan). *Flemish Tapestries (3rd series). Horiz designs as T* **239** *showing paintings by Rubens. Multicoloured. W* **105** *(sideways). P* 14.

615	2 c. "The Triumph of the Catholic Church" ..	10	10
616	7 c. "The Triumph of Charity" ..	10	10
617	11 c. "The Triumph of Faith" ..	20	20
618	25 c. "The Triumph of Truth" ..	55	55
615/18	.. *Set of* 4	80	80

(Des E. Cremona)

1979 (31 Mar). *End of Military Facilities Agreement. T* **249** *and similar vert designs. Multicoloured. W* **105** *(sideways). P* 13½.

619	2 c. Type **249** ..	10	10
620	5 c. Raising the flag ceremony ..	10	10
621	7 c. Departing soldier and olive sprig ..	15	10
622	8 c. Type **249** ..	30	40
623	17 c. As 5 c. ..	50	60
624	20 c. As 7 c. ..	50	60
619/24	.. *Set of* 6	1·40	1·60

MALTA 2c

250 Speronara (fishing boat) and Tail of Air Malta Airliner

251 Children on Globe

(Des E. Cremona)

1979 (9 May). *Europa. Communications. T* **250** *and similar vert design. Multicoloured. W* **105** *(sideways). P* 14.

625	7 c. Type **250** ..	15	10
626	25 c. Coastal watch tower and radio link towers	35	50

Nos. 625/6 were each printed in sheets including two *se-tenant* stamp-size labels.

(Des A. Bonnici (2 c.), A. Pisani (7 c.), M. French (11 c.))

1979 (13 June). *International Year of the Child. T* **251** *and similar multicoloured designs. W* **105** *(sideways). P* 14 × 13½ *(2 c.) or* 14 *(others).*

627	2 c. Type **251** ..	10	10
628	7 c. Children flying kites (27 × 33 *mm*) ..	15	10
629	11 c. Children in circle (27 × 33 *mm*) ..	20	35
627/9	.. *Set of* 3	35	45

252 Shells (*Gibbula nivosa*)

(Des R. Pitré)

1979 (10 Oct). *Marine Life. T* **252** *and similar horiz designs. Multicoloured. W* **105**. *P* 13½.

630	2 c. Type **252** ..	10	10
631	5 c. Loggerhead Turtle (*Garetta garetta*) ..	20	10
632	7 c. Dolphin Fish (*Coryphaena hippurus*) ..	25	10
633	25 c. Noble Pen Shell (*Pinna nobilis*) ..	90	1·25
630/3	.. *Set of* 4	1·25	1·25

253 "The Nativity" (detail)

(Des E. Cremona)

1979 (14 Nov). *Christmas. Paintings by G. Cali. T* **253** *and similar horiz designs. Multicoloured. W* **105**. *P* 14 × 13½.

634	1 c. + 5 m. Type **253**	10	10
635	5 c. + 1 c. "The Flight into Egypt" (detail)	10	15
636	7 c. + 1 c. 5, "The Nativity"	15	20
637	11 c. + 3 c. "The Flight into Egypt"	25	50
634/7	*Set of* 4	50	85

(Des E. Cremona)

1980 (30 Jan). *Flemish Tapestries (4th series). Horiz designs as T* **239** *taken from paintings. Multicoloured. W* **105** *(sideways). P* 14.

638	2 c. "The Institution of Corpus Domini" (Rubens)	10	10
639	8 c. "The Destruction of Idolatry" (Rubens)	20	20
MS640	114 × 86 mm. 50 c. "Grand Master Perellos with St. Jude and St. Simon" (unknown Maltese artist) (*vert*)	80	1·40

254 Hal Saflieni Hypogeum, Paola **255** Dun Gorg Preca

1980 (15 Feb). *International Restoration of Maltese Monuments Campaign. T* **254** *and similar multicoloured designs. W* **105** *(sideways on* 8 *and* 12 *c.). P* 14.

641	2 c. 5, Type **254**	10	10
642	6 c. Vilhena Palace, Mdina	25	15
643	8 c. Victoria Citadel, Gozo (*horiz*)	30	30
644	12 c. Fort St. Elmo, Valletta (*horiz*)	40	45
641/4	*Set of* 4	95	90

(Des R. Pitré)

1980 (12 Apr). *Birth Centenary of Dun Gorg Preca (founder of Society of Christian Doctrine). W* **105** *(sideways). P* 14 × 13½.

645	**255**	2 c. 5, black and grey	10	10

256 Ruzar Briffa (poet) **257** "Annunciation"

(Des V. Apap)

1980 (29 Apr). *Europa. Personalities. T* **256** *and similar horiz design. W* **105** *(sideways). P* 13½ × 14.

646	8 c. black, brown-ochre and bronze-green	15	10
647	30 c. brown, brown-olive and brown-lake	40	70

Design:—30 c. Nikiol Anton Vassalli (scholar and patriot).

Nos. 646/7 were each printed in sheets including two *se-tenant* stamp-size labels.

(Des R. Pitré)

1980 (7 Oct). *Christmas. Paintings by A. Inglott. T* **257** *and similar multicoloured designs. W* **105** *(sideways on* 12 *c.). P* 14 (12 *c.*) *or* 13½ (*others*).

648	2 c. + 5 m. Type **257**	10	10
649	6 c. + 1 c. "Conception"	15	10
650	8 c. + 1 c. 5, "Nativity"	20	25
651	12 c. + 3 c. "Annunciation", "Conception" and "Nativity" (47 × 38 *mm*)	25	30
648/51	*Set of* 4	60	60

The paintings from the 2, 6 and 8 c. values are united to form the triptych on the 12 c. value.

OMNIBUS ISSUES

Details, together with prices for complete sets, of the various Omnibus issues from the 1935 Silver Jubilee series to date are included in a special section following Zululand at the end of the catalogue.

258 Chess Pieces **259** Barn Owl (*Tyto alba*)

(Des H. Borg)

1980 (20 Nov). *Chess Olympiad and F.I.D.E. (International Chess Federation) Congress. T* **258** *and similar multicoloured designs. W* **105** *(sideways on* 30 *c.). P* 14 × 13½ (30 *c.*) *or* 13½ × 14 (*others*).

652	2 c. 5, Type **258**	20	10
653	8 c. Chess pieces (*different*)	50	15
654	30 c. Chess pieces (*vert*)	1·00	80
652/4	*Set of* 3	1·50	95

(Des M. Burlò)

1981 (20 Jan). *Birds. T* **259** *and similar vert designs. Multicoloured. W* **105** *(sideways). P* 13½.

655	3 c. Type **259**	30	10
656	8 c. Sardinian Warbler (*Sylvia melanocephala*)	50	15
657	12 c. Woodchat Shrike (*Lanius senator*)	60	45
658	23 c. British Storm Petrel (*Hydrobates pelagicus*)	1·10	85
655/8	*Set of* 4	2·25	1·40

260 Traditional Horse Race **261** Stylised "25"

(Des H. Borg)

1981 (28 Apr). *Europa. Folklore. T* **260** *and similar vert design. Multicoloured. W* **105** *(sideways). P* 14.

659	8 c. Type **260**	20	10
660	30 c. Attempting to retrieve flag from end of "gostra" (greasy pole)	40	65

The two values were each printed in sheets including two *se tenant* stamp-size labels.

(Des A. de Giovanni)

1981 (12 June). *25th Maltese International Trade Fair. W* **105** *(sideways). P* 13½.

661	**261**	4 c. multicoloured	15	15
662		25 c. multicoloured	50	60

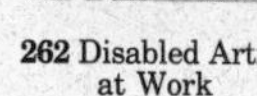

262 Disabled Artist at Work **263** Wheat Ear in Conical Flask

(Des A. Camilleri)

1981 (17 July). *International Year for Disabled Persons. T* **262** *and similar vert design. Multicoloured. W* **105** *(sideways). P* 13½.

663	3 c. Type **262**	15	10
664	35 c. Disabled child playing football	55	75

(Des R. Caruana)

1981 (16 Oct). *World Food Day. W* **105** *(sideways). P* 14.

665	**263**	8 c. multicoloured	15	15
666		23 c. multicoloured	60	50

264 Megalithic Building **265** Children and Nativity Scene

(Des F. Portelli)

1981 (31 Oct). *History of Maltese Industry. Horiz designs as T* **264**. *Multicoloured. W* **105**. *P* 14.

667	5 m. Type **264**	10	10
668	1 c. Cotton production	10	10
669	2 c. Early ship-building	10	10
670	3 c. Currency minting	10	10
671	5 c. "Art"	15	20
672	6 c. Fishing	15	20
673	7 c. Agriculture	20	25
674	8 c. Stone quarrying	25	30
675	10 c. Grape pressing	30	35
676	12 c. Modern ship-building	35	40
677	15 c. Energy	45	50
678	20 c. Telecommunications	60	65
679	25 c. "Industry"	75	80
680	50 c. Drilling for water	1·50	1·60
681	£1 Sea transport	3·00	3·25
682	£3 Air transport	8·75	9·00
667/82	*Set of* 16	15·00	16·00

(Des A. Bugeja)

1981 (18 Nov). *Christmas. T* **265** *and similar multicoloured designs. W* **105** *(sideways). P* 14.

683	2 c. + 1 c. Type **265**	15	10
684	8 c. + 2 c. Christmas Eve procession (*horiz*)	25	20
685	20 c. + 3 c. Preaching midnight sermon	50	60
683/5	*Set of* 3	80	80

266 Shipbuilding **267** Elderly Man and Has-Serh (home for elderly)

(Des N. Attard)

1982 (29 Jan). *Shipbuilding Industry. T* **266** *and similar vert designs showing different scenes. W* **105** *(sideways). P* 13½.

686	3 c. multicoloured	15	10
687	8 c. multicoloured	30	30
688	13 c. multicoloured	55	55
689	27 c. multicoloured	1·25	1·25
686/9	*Set of* 4	2·00	2·00

(Des R. Pitré)

1982 (16 Mar). *Care of Elderly. T* **267** *and similar horiz design. Multicoloured. W* **105**. *P* 14 × 13½.

690	8 c. Type **267**	40	20
691	30 c. Elderly woman and Has-Zmien (hospital for elderly)	1·40	1·40

268 Redemption of Islands by Maltese, 1428

(Des F. Portelli)

1982 (29 Apr). *Europa. Historical Events. T* **268** *and similar horiz design. Multicoloured. W* **105**. *P* 14 × 13½.

692	8 c. Type **268**	40	20
693	30 c. Declaration of rights by Maltese, 1802	1·00	1·40

Nos. 692/3 were each printed in sheets containing 2 *se-tenant* stamp-size labels.

269 Stylised Footballer

(Des R. Caruana)

1982 (11 June). *World Cup Football Championship, Spain. T* **269** *and similar horiz designs showing stylised footballers. W* **105**. *P* 14.

694	3 c. multicoloured	15	10
695	12 c. multicoloured	55	55
696	15 c. multicoloured	65	65
694/6	*Set of* 3	1·25	1·25
MS697	125 × 90 mm. Nos. 694/6	1·50	1·75

270 Angel appearing to Shepherds

(Des J. Mallia)

1982 (8 Oct). *Christmas. T* **270** *and similar multicoloured designs.* W **105** (*sideways*). *P* 14 (*No.* 700) *or* 13½ (*others*).
698 2 c. + 1 c. Type **270** 15 10
699 8 c. + 2 c. Nativity and Three Wise Men bearing gifts 40 40
700 20 c. + 3 c. Nativity scene (*larger* 45 × 37 *mm*) 85 85
698/700 .. .. *Set of* 3 1·25 1·25
The designs from the 2 and 8 c. values are united to form the design of the 20 c. stamp.

271 *Ta' Salvo Serafino* (oared brigantine), 1531

(Des N. Attard)

1982 (13 Nov). *Maltese Ships* (1*st series*). *T* **271** *and similar horiz designs. Multicoloured.* W **105**. *P* 14 × 13½.
701 3 c. Type **271** 25 10
702 8 c. *La Madonna del Rosaria* (tartane), 1740 .. .. 55 30
703 12 c. *San Paulo* (xebec), 1743 .. .. 75 55
704 20 c. *Ta' Pietro Saliba* (xprunara), 1798 .. 1·10 90
701/4 .. .. *Set of* 4 2·40 1·60
See also Nos. 725/8, 772/5, 792/5 and 809/12.

272 *Manning Wardle*, 1883

(Des R. Caruana)

1983 (21 Jan). *Centenary of Malta Railway. T* **272** *and similar horiz designs. Multicoloured.* W **105**. *P* 14 × 13½.
705 3 c. Type **272** 35 10
706 13 c. *Black Hawthorn*, 1884 .. .. .. 75 55
707 27 c. *Beyer Peacock*, 1895 .. .. .. 1·75 1·25
705/7 .. .. *Set of* 3 2·50 1·75

273 Peace Doves leaving Malta

(Des C. Cassar)

1983 (14 Mar). *Commonwealth Day. T* **273** *and similar multicoloured designs.* W **105** (*sideways on vert designs*). *P* 14 × 13½ (8, 12 *c.*) *or* 13½ × 14 (*others*).
708 8 c. Type **273** 30 30
709 12 c. Tourist landmarks 40 40
710 15 c. Holiday beach (*vert*) 50 50
711 23 c. Ship-building (*vert*) 70 75
708/11 .. .. *Set of* 4 1·75 1·75

274 Ggantija Megalithic Temples, Gozo

(Des T. Bugeja (8 c.), R. Caruana (30 c.))

1983 (5 May). *Europa. T* **274** *and similar horiz design. Multicoloured.* W **105**. *P* 14 × 13½.
712 8 c. Type **274** 50 30
713 30 c. Fort St. Angelo .. .. 1·50 1·10
Nos. 712/13 were each printed in sheets including two *se-tenant* stamp-size labels.

275 Dish Aerials (World Communications Year)

(Des D. Friggieri)

1983 (14 July). *Anniversaries and Events. T* **275** *and similar horiz designs. Multicoloured.* W **105** (*sideways*). *P* 13½ × 14.
714 3 c. Type **275** 35 15
715 7 c. Ships' prows and badge (25th anniv of I.M.O. Convention) 60 40
716 13 c. Container lorries and badge (30th anniv of Customs Co-operation Council) .. 80 60
717 20 c. Stadium and emblem (9th Mediterranean Games) .. .. 1·00 1·00
714/17 .. .. *Set of* 4 2·50 2·00

276 Monsignor Giuseppe de Piro

277 Annunciation

(Des E. Barthet)

1983 (1 Sept). 50*th Death Anniv of Monsignor Giuseppe de Piro.* W **105** (*sideways*). *P* 14.
718 **276** 3 c. multicoloured 10 10

(Des N. Attard)

1983 (6 Sept). *Christmas. T* **277** *and similar vert designs. Multicoloured.* W **105** (*sideways*). *P* 13½ × 14.
719 2 c. + 1 c. Type **277** 25 15
720 8 c. + 2 c. The Nativity 60 40
721 20 c. + 3 c. Adoration of the Magi .. .. 1·10 85
719/21 .. .. *Set of* 3 1·75 1·25

278 Workers at Meeting

(Des F. Portelli)

1983 (5 Oct). 40*th Anniv of General Workers' Union. T* **278** *and similar horiz designs. Multicoloured.* W **105**. *P* 14 × 13½.
722 3 c. Type **278** 25 10
723 8 c. Worker with family 50 30
724 27 c. Union H.Q. Building .. .. .. 1·50 1·40
722/4 .. .. *Set of* 3 2·00 1·75

(Des N. Attard)

1983 (17 Nov). *Maltese Ships* (2*nd series*). *Horiz designs as T* **271**. *Multicoloured.* W **105**. *P* 14 × 13½.
725 2 c. *Strangier* (full-rigged ship), 1813 .. 15 15
726 12 c. *Tigre* (topsail schooner), 1839 .. .. 70 60
727 13 c. *La Speranza* (brig), 1844 .. .. 80 70
728 20 c. *Wignacourt* (barque), 1844 .. .. 1·25 1·00
725/8 .. .. *Set of* 4 2·75 2·25

279 Boeing "737"

(Des R. Caruana)

1984 (26 Jan). *Air. T* **279** *and similar horiz designs. Multicoloured.* W **105**. *P* 14 × 13½.
729 7 c. Type **279** 20 25
730 8 c. Boeing "720B" 25 30
731 16 c. Vickers "Vanguard" 45 50
732 23 c. Vickers "Viscount" 65 70
733 27 c. Douglas "DC.3 Dakota" 80 85
734 38 c. A.W. "Atlanta" .. .. 1·10 1·25
735 75 c. Dornier "Wal" .. .. 2·25 2·40
729/35 .. .. *Set of* 7 5·25 5·75

280 C.E.P.T. 25th Anniversary Logo

281 Early Policeman

(Des J. Larrivière and L. Borg)

1984 (27 Apr). *Europa.* W **105**. *P* 13½.
736 **280** 8 c. green, black and gold 35 35
737 30 c. carmine-lake, black and gold .. 1·25 1·25
Nos. 736/7 were each printed in sheets including two *se-tenant* stamp-size labels.

(Des T. Bugeja)

1984 (14 June). 170*th Anniv of Malta Police Force. T* **281** *and similar vert designs. Multicoloured.* W **105**. *P* 14 × 13½.
738 3 c. Type **281** 40 15
739 8 c. Mounted police 80 55
a. Pale Venetian red (background) omitted .. .. 95·00
740 11 c. Motorcycle policeman .. .. .. 1·00 70
741 25 c. Policeman and fireman .. .. .. 2·00 1·50
738/41 .. .. *Set of* 4 3·75 2·75

282 Running

283 "The Visitation" (Pietro Caruana)

(Des L. Micallef)

1984 (26 July). *Olympic Games, Los Angeles. T* **282** *and similar vert designs. Multicoloured.* W **105** (*sideways*). *P* 14.
742 7 c. Type **282** 25 30
743 12 c. Gymnastics 50 60
744 23 c. Swimming .. .. 85 1·10
742/4 .. .. *Set of* 3 1·50 1·75

(Des L. Micallef)

1984 (5 Oct). *Christmas. Paintings from Church of Our Lady of Porto Salvo, Valletta. T* **283** *and similar multicoloured designs.* W **105** (*sideways on horiz designs*). *P* 14.
745 2 c. + 1 c. Type **283** 35 40
746 8 c. + 2 c. "The Epiphany" (Rafel Caruana) (*horiz*) 70 70
747 20 c. + 3 c. "Jesus among the Doctors" (Rafel Caruana) (*horiz*) .. .. 1·50 2·00
745/7 .. .. *Set of* 3 2·25 2·75

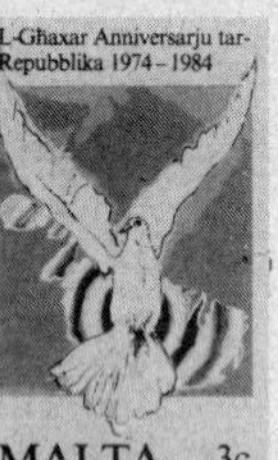

284 Dove on Map

285 1885 ½d. Green Stamp

(Des L. Micallef)

1984 (12 Dec). 10*th Anniv of Republic. T* **284** *and similar vert designs. Multicoloured.* W **105** (*sideways*). *P* 14.
748 3 c. Type **284** 30 15
749 8 c. Fort St. Angelo 60 40
750 30 c. Hands .. .. 2·10 2·50
748/50 .. .. *Set of* 3 2·75 2·75

(Des N. Attard)

1985 (2 Jan). *Centenary of Malta Post Office. T* **285** *and similar vert designs showing stamps of* 1885. *Multicoloured.* W **105**. *P* 14.
751 3 c. Type **285** 25 10
752 8 c. 1885 1d. rose 45 35
753 12 c. 1885 2½d. dull blue 60 65
754 20 c. 1885 4d. brown .. .. 90 1·25
751/4 .. .. *Set of* 4 2·00 2·10
MS755 165 × 90 mm. Nos. 751/4. Wmk sideways 2·00 2·50

286 Boy, and Hands planting Vine

(Des T. Bugeja)

1985 (7 Mar). *International Youth Year. T* **286** *and similar multicoloured designs.* W **105** (*sideways on* 13 *c.*). *P* 14.
756 2 c. Type **286** 10 15
757 13 c. Young people and flowers (*vert*) 55 60
758 27 c. Girl holding flame in hand .. .. 1·25 1·40
756/8 .. .. *Set of* 3 1·75 1·90

287 Nicolo Baldacchino (tenor) **288** Guzeppi Bajada and Manwel Attard (victims)

(Des L. Micallef)

1985 (25 Apr). *Europa. European Music Year. T* **287** *and similar vert design. Multicoloured. W* **105**. *P* 14.

759	8 c. Type **287**	1·00	30
760	30 c. Francesco Azopardi (composer)	2·00	1·25

Nos. 759/60 were each printed in sheets including two *se-tenant* stamp-size labels.

(Des L. Micallef)

1985 (7 June). *66th Anniv of 7 June 1919 Demonstrations. T* **288** *and similar multicoloured designs. W* **105** (*sideways on* 3 c., 7 c.). *P* 14.

761	3 c. Type **288**	25	15
762	7 c. Karmnu Abela and Wenzu Dyer (victims)	55	35
763	35 c. Model of projected Demonstration monument by Anton Agius (*vert*)	1·75	1·50
761/3	*Set of* 3	2·25	1·75

289 Stylized Birds **290** Giorgio Mitrovich (nationalist) (Death Centenary)

(Des D. Friggieri)

1985 (26 July). *40th Anniv of United Nations Organization. T* **289** *and similar horiz designs. Multicoloured. W* **105** (*sideways*). *P* 13½ × 14.

764	4 c. Type **289**	15	15
765	11 c. Arrow-headed ribbons	45	60
766	31 c. Stylized figures	1·25	1·90
764/6	*Set of* 3	1·75	2·40

(Des R. Pitre)

1985 (3 Oct). *Celebrities' Anniversaries. T* **290** *and similar vert design. Multicoloured. W* **105** (*sideways*). *P* 14.

767	8 c. Type **290**	40	35
768	12 c. Pietru Caxaru (poet and administrator) (400th death anniv)	70	90

291 The Three Wise Men **292** John XXIII Peace Laboratory and Statue of St. Francis of Assisi

(Des G. Bonnici)

1985 (10 Oct). *Christmas. T* **291** *and similar vert designs showing details of terracotta relief by Ganni Bonnici. Multicoloured. W* **105** (*sideways*). *P* 14.

769	2 c. + 1 c. Type **291**	35	40
770	8 c. + 2 c. Virgin and Child	75	75
771	20 c. + 3 c. Angels	1·50	1·50
769/71	*Set of* 3	2·40	2·40

(Des N. Attard)

1985 (27 Nov). *Maltese Ships (3rd series). Steamships. Horiz designs as T* **271**. *Multicoloured. W* **105**. *P* 14.

772	3 c. *Scotia* (paddle-steamer), 1844	30	15
773	7 c. *Tagliaferro* (screw steamer), 1882	60	45
774	15 c. *Gleneagles* (screw steamer), 1885	1·00	1·00
775	23 c. *L'Isle Adam* (screw steamer), 1886	1·50	1·50
772/5	*Set of* 4	3·00	2·75

(Des A. Agius (8 c.), T. Bugeja (11, 27 c.))

1986 (28 Jan). *International Peace Year. T* **292** *and similar horiz designs. Multicoloured. W* **105** (*sideways*). *P* 14 (8, 27 c.) *or* 13½ × 14 (11 c.).

776	8 c. Type **292**	70	35
777	11 c. Dove and hands holding olive branch (40 × 19 *mm*)	1·00	1·00
778	27 c. Map of Africa, dove and two heads	2·50	2·50
776/8	*Set of* 3	3·75	3·50

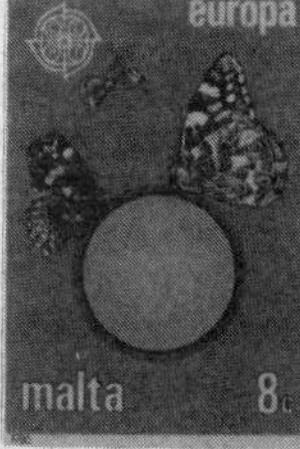

293 Symbolic Plant and Painted Lady, Red Admiral and Common Blue Butterflies **294** Heading the Ball

(Des M. Burló)

1986 (3 Apr). *Europa. Environmental Conservation. T* **293** *and similar vert design. Multicoloured. W* **105**. *P* 14.

779	8 c. Type **293**	1·00	40
780	35 c. Island, Neolithic frieze, sea and sun	2·25	3·00

Nos. 779/80 were each printed in sheets including two *se-tenant* stamp-size labels.

(Des T. Bugeja)

1986 (30 May). *World Cup Football Championship, Mexico. T* **294** *and similar horiz designs. Multicoloured. W* **105**. *P* 14.

781	3 c. Type **294**	30	15
782	7 c. Saving a goal	60	35
783	23 c. Controlling the ball	2·10	2·50
781/3	*Set of* 3	2·75	2·75
MS784	125 × 90 mm. Nos. 781/3. Wmk sideways	2·75	3·25

295 Father Diegu **296** "Nativity"

(Des L. Micallef)

1986 (28 Aug). *Maltese Philanthropists. T* **295** *and similar vert designs. Multicoloured. W* **105**. *P* 14.

785	2 c. Type **295**	25	15
786	3 c. Adelaide Cini	30	15
787	8 c. Alfonso Maria Galea	90	50
788	27 c. Vincenzo Bugeja	2·40	2·75
785/8	*Set of* 4	3·50	3·25

(Des L. Micallef)

1986 (10 Oct). *Christmas. T* **296** *and similar multicoloured designs showing paintings by Giuseppe D'Arena. W* **105** (*sideways on horiz designs*). *P* 14.

789	2 c. + 1 c. Type **296**	30	40
790	8 c. + 2 c. "Nativity" (detail) (*vert*)	90	90
791	20 c. + 3 c. "Epiphany"	1·75	2·00
789/91	*Set of* 3	2·75	3·00

(Des N. Attard)

1986 (19 Nov). *Maltese Ships (4th series). Horiz designs as T* **271**. *Multicoloured. W* **105**. *P* 14.

792	7 c. *San Paul* (freighter), 1921	70	35
793	10 c. *Knight of Malta* (cargo liner), 1930	1·00	70
794	12 c. *Valetta City* (freighter), 1948	1·25	1·00
795	20 c. *Saver* (freighter), 1959	1·75	2·00
792/5	*Set of* 4	4·25	3·50

297 European Robin

(Des R. Caruana)

1987 (26 Jan). *25th Anniv of Malta Ornithological Society. T* **297** *and similar multicoloured designs. W* **105** (*sideways on* 3, 23 c.). *P* 14.

796	3 c. Type **297**	30	20
797	8 c. Peregrine Falcon (*vert*)	75	55
798	13 c. Hoopoe (*vert*)	1·25	1·25
799	23 c. Cory's Shearwater	1·75	2·00
796/9	*Set of* 4	3·50	3·50

298 Aquasun Lido **299** 16th-century Pikeman

(Des R. England)

1987 (15 Apr). *Europa. Modern Architecture. T* **298** *and similar vert design. Multicoloured. W* **105**. *P* 14.

800	8 c. Type **298**	80	50
801	35 c. Church of St. Joseph, Manikata	2·40	2·75

Nos. 800/1 were each printed in sheets including two *se-tenant* stamp-size labels.

(Des L. Micallef)

1987 (10 June). *Maltese Uniforms (1st series). T* **299** *and similar vert designs. Multicoloured. W* **105** (*sideways*). *P* 14.

802	3 c. Type **299**	30	20
803	7 c. 16th-century officer	70	50
804	10 c. 18th-century standard bearer	90	80
805	27 c. 18th-century General of the Galleys	2·40	2·75
802/5	*Set of* 4	4·00	3·75

See also Nos. 832/5 and 851/4.

300 Maltese Scenes, Wheat Ears and Sun (European Environment Year)

(Des A. Camilleri)

1987 (18 Aug). *Anniversaries and Events. T* **300** *and similar horiz designs. Multicoloured. W* **105** (*sideways*). *P* 14.

806	5 c. Type **300**	45	45
807	8 c. Esperanto star as comet (Centenary of Esperanto)	65	50
808	23 c. Family at house door (International Year of Shelter for the Homeless)	1·75	2·00
806/8	*Set of* 3	2·50	2·75

(Des N. Attard)

1987 (16 Oct). *Maltese Ships (5th series). Horiz designs as T* **271**. *Multicoloured. W* **105**. *P* 14.

809	2 c. *Medina* (freighter), 1969	20	20
810	11 c. *Rabat* (container ship), 1974	80	70
811	13 c. *Ghawdex* (passenger ferry), 1979	90	80
812	20 c. *Pinto* (car ferry), 1987	1·40	1·60
809/12	*Set of* 4	3·00	3·00

301 "The Visitation"

(Des R. Caruana)

1987 (6 Nov). *Christmas. T* **301** *and similar horiz designs, each showing illuminated illustration, score and text from 16th-century choral manuscript. Multicoloured. W* **105** (*sideways*). *P* 14.

813	2 c. + 1 c. Type **301**	25	25
814	8 c. + 2 c. "The Nativity"	75	75
815	20 c. + 3 c. "The Adoration of the Magi"	1·50	1·50
813/15	*Set of* 3	2·25	2·25

302 Dr. Arvid Pardo (U.N. representative) **303** Ven. Nazju Falzon (Catholic catechist)

(Des S. Mallia)

1987 (18 Dec). *20th Anniv of United Nations Resolution on Peaceful Use of the Seabed. T* **302** *and similar vert design. Multicoloured. W* **105**. *P* 14.
816 8 c. Type **302** 60 40
817 12 c. U.N. emblem and sea 1·00 1·00
MS818 125×90 mm. Nos. 816/17. Wmk sideways. P 13×13½ 1·60 1·75

(Des E. Barthet)

1988 (23 Jan). *Maltese Personalities. T* **303** *and similar vert designs. Multicoloured. W* **105**. *P* 14.
819 2 c. Type **303** 10 15
820 3 c. Mgr. Sidor Formosa (philanthropist) 10 15
821 4 c. Sir Luigi Preziosi (ophthalmologist) 15 15
822 10 c. Fr. Anastasju Cuschieri (poet) 45 45
823 25 c. Mgr. Pietru Pawl Saydon (Bible translator) 1·25 1·50
819/23 *Set of* 5 1·75 2·25

304 "St. John Bosco with Youth" (statue) (Death Centenary)

305 Bus, Ferry and Airplane

(Des F. Portelli)

1988 (5 Mar). *Religious Anniversaries. T* **304** *and similar vert designs. Multicoloured. W* **105** *(sideways). P* 14.
824 10 c. Type **304** 50 50
825 12 c. "Assumption of Our Lady" (altarpiece by Perugino, Ta' Pinu, Gozo) (Marian Year) 60 60
826 14 c. "Christ the King" (statue by Sciortino) (75th anniv of International Eucharistic Congress, Valletta) 70 70
824/6 *Set of* 3 1·60 1·60

(Des F. Fenech)

1988 (9 Apr). *Europa. Transport and Communications. T* **305** *and similar vert design. Multicoloured. W* **105** *(sideways). P* 13½.
827 10 c. Type **305** 55 40
828 35 c. Control panel, dish aerial and pylons 1·50 1·75
Nos. 827/8 were each printed in sheets including two *se-tenant* stamp-size labels.

306 Globe and Red Cross Emblems (125th anniv of International Red Cross)

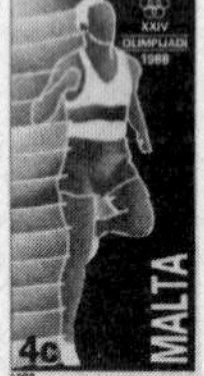

307 Athletics

(Des M. Cremona)

1988 (28 May). *Anniversaries and Events. T* **306** *and similar horiz designs. Multicoloured. W* **105**. *P* 13½.
829 4 c. Type **306** 20 15
830 18 c. Divided globe (Campaign for North-South Interdependence and Solidarity) 90 90
831 19 c. Globe and symbol (40th anniv of World Health Organization) 90 90
829/31 *Set of* 3 1·75 1·75

(Des L. Micallef)

1988 (23 July). *Maltese Uniforms (2nd issue). Vert designs as T* **299**. *Multicoloured. W* **105** *(sideways). P* 14.
832 3 c. Private, Maltese Light Infantry, 1800 15 15
833 4 c. Gunner, Malta Coast Artillery, 1802 20 15
834 10 c. Field Officer, 1st Maltese Provincial Battalion, 1805 50 50
835 25 c. Subaltern, Royal Malta Regiment, 1809 1·40 1·50
832/5 *Set of* 4 2·00 2·10

(Des R. Gauci)

1988 (17 Sept). *Olympic Games, Seoul. T* **307** *and similar vert designs. Multicoloured. W* **105** *(sideways). P* 14×13½.
836 4 c. Type **307** 15 15
837 10 c. Diving 35 40
838 35 c. Football 1·10 1·25
836/8 *Set of* 3 1·40 1·60

NEW INFORMATION

The editor is always interested to correspond with people who have new information that will improve or correct the Catalogue.

308 Shepherd with Flock

309 Commonwealth Emblem

(Des R. Gauci)

1988 (5 Nov). *Christmas. T* **308** *and similar vert designs. Multicoloured. W* **105**. *P* 14.
839 3 c. + 1 c. Type **308** 15 20
840 10 c. + 2 c. The Nativity 40 50
841 25 c. + 3 c. Three Wise Men 95 1·25
839/41 *Set of* 3 1·40 1·75

(Des F. Portelli)

1989 (28 Jan). *25th Anniv of Independence. T* **309** *and similar multicoloured designs. W* **105** *(sideways). P* 14 (25 c.) *or* 13½ *(others).*
842 2 c. Type **309** 10 10
843 3 c. Council of Europe flag 10 10
844 4 c. U. N. flag 15 15
845 10 c. Workers hands gripping ring and national flag 45 40
846 12 c. Scales and allegorical figure of Justice 50 45
847 25 c. Prime Minister Borg Olivier with Independence constitution (42 × 28 *mm*) 1·10 1·10
842/7 *Set of* 6 2·00 2·00

310 New State Arms

311 Two Boys flying Kite

(Des F. Portelli)

1989 (25 Mar). *W* **105**. *P* 14.
848 **310** £1 multicoloured 3·25 3·50

(Des R. Gauci)

1989 (6 May). *Europa. Children's Games. T* **311** *and similar vert design. Multicoloured. W* **105** *(sideways). P* 13½.
849 10 c. Type **311** 50 40
850 35 c. Two girls with dolls 1·50 1·60
Nos. 849/50 were each printed in sheets including two *se-tenant* stamp-size labels.

(Des L. Micallef)

1989 (24 June). *Maltese Uniforms (3rd series). Vert designs as T* **299**. *Multicoloured. W* **105** *(sideways). P* 14.
851 3 c. Officer, Maltese Veterans, 1815 15 15
852 4 c. Subaltern, Royal Malta Fencibles, 1839 20 20
853 10 c. Private, Malta Militia, 1856 50 50
854 25 c. Colonel, Royal Malta Fencible Artillery, 1875 1·40 1·40
851/4 *Set of* 4 2·00 2·00

312 Human Figures and Buildings

313 Angel and Cherub

(Des L. Casha)

1989 (17 Oct). *Anniversaries and Commemorations. T* **312** *and similar horiz designs showing logo and stylized human figures. Multicoloured. W* **105** *(sideways). P* 14.
855 3 c. Type **312** (20th anniv of U.N. Declaration on Social Progress and Development) 10 15
856 4 c. Workers and figure in wheelchair (Malta's Ratification of European Social Charter) 15 20
857 10 c. Family (40th anniv of Council of Europe) 35 40
858 14 c. Teacher and children (70th anniv of Malta Union of Teachers) 45 50
859 25 c. Symbolic knights (Knights of the Sovereign Military Order of Malta Assembly) 85 90
855/9 *Set of* 5 1·75 1·90

(Des J. Mallia)

1989 (11 Nov). *Christmas. T* **313** *and similar horiz designs showing vault paintings by Mattia Preti from St. John's Co-Cathedral, Valletta. Multicoloured. W* **105**. *P* 13½.
860 3 c. + 1 c. Type **313** 15 20
861 10 c. + 2 c. Two angels 40 45
862 20 c. + 3 c. Angel blowing trumpet 75 80
860/2 *Set of* 3 1·10 1·25

POSTAGE DUE STAMPS

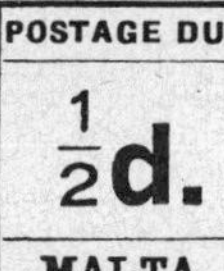

D 1

D 2

D 3 Maltese Lace

1925 (16 Apr). *Type-set by Govt. Printing Office, Valletta. Imperf.*
D 1 D 1 ½d. black 1·25 3·75
D 2 1d. black 1·75 2·50
D 3 1½d. black 2·25 3·50
D 4 2d. black 3·00 5·50
D 5 2½d. black 2·75 2·75
a. "2" of "½" omitted £900 £1200
D 6 3d. black/*grey* 6·50 11·00
D 7 4d. black/*buff* 4·00 9·00
D 8 6d. black/*buff* 4·00 10·00
D 9 1s. black/*buff* 7·50 15·00
D10 1s. 6d. black/*buff* 12·00 30·00
D1/10 *Set of* 10 40·00 80·00
Nos. D1/10 were each issued in sheets containing 4 panes (6×7) printed separately. Examples exist in *tête-bêche* pairs from the junction of the panes, price about four times that of a single stamp.
No. D5a occurred on R. 4/4 of the last 2½d. pane position to be printed. Forgeries exist, but can be detected by comparison with a normal example under ultra-violet light.

(Typo B.W.)

1925 (20 July). *Wmk Mult Script CA (sideways). P* 12.
D11 D **2** ½d. green 1·25 60
D12 1d. violet 1·25 45
D13 1½d. brown 1·50 1·25
D14 2d. grey 11·00 1·50
D15 2½d. orange 2·00 1·25
D16 3d. blue 2·75 1·25
D17 4d. olive-green 12·00 11·00
D18 6d. purple 2·25 2·75
D19 1s. black 4·75 9·00
D20 1s. 6d. carmine 6·50 13·00
D11/20 *Set of* 10 40·00 38·00
D11/20 Optd "Specimen" *Set of* 10 £200

1953 (5 Nov)–**63**. *Chalk-surfaced paper. Wmk Mult Script CA (sideways). P* 12.
D21 D **2** ½d. emerald 60 60
D22 1d. purple 60 70
a. Deep purple (17.9.63) 75 1·50
D23 1½d. yellow-brown 4·00 5·00
D24 2d. grey-brown (20.3.57) 7·00 7·00
a. Blackish brown (3.4.62) 8·50 8·50
D25 3d. deep slate-blue 1·50 2·00
D26 4d. yellow-olive 6·00 8·00
D21/6 *Set of* 6 18·00 21·00

1966 (Oct). *As No.* D24, *but wmk* w **12** *(sideways).*
D27 D **2** 2d. grey-brown 25·00 25·00

1967–70. *Ordinary paper. W* **105** *(sideways).*

(*a*) *P* 12, *line* (9.11.67)
D28 D **2** ½d. emerald 4·00 9·00
D29 1d. purple 4·00 9·00
D30 2d. blackish brown 4·00 9·00
D31 4d. yellow-olive 80·00 £120
D28/31 *Set of* 4 85·00 £130

(*b*) *P* 12½, *comb* (30.5.68–70)
D32 D **2** ½d. emerald 20 75
D33 1d. purple 20 55
D34 1½d. yellow-brown 35 1·25
a. Orange-brown (23.10.70) 90 2·00
D35 2d. blackish brown 70 70
a. Brownish black (23.10.70) 1·00 2·00
D36 2½d. yellow-orange 60 70
D37 3d. deep slate-blue 60 60
D38 4d. yellow-olive 1·00 80
D39 6d. purple 75 1·00
D40 1s. black 90 1·50
D41 1s. 6d. carmine 2·25 4·00
D32/41 *Set of* 10 6·75 10·50
The above are the local release dates. In the 12½ perforation the London release dates were 21 May for the ½d. to 4d. and 4 June for the 6d. to 1s. 6d.
Nos. D34*a* and D35*a* are on glazed paper.

(Des G. Pace. Litho Printex Ltd, Malta)

1973 (28 Apr). *W* **105**. *P* 13 × 13½.
D42 D **3** 2 m. grey-brown and reddish brown 10 10
D43 3 m. dull orange and Indian red 10 10
D44 5 m. rose and bright scarlet 10 10
D45 1 c. turquoise and bottle green 10 10
D46 2 c. slate and black 10 10
D47 3 c. light yellow-brown and red-brown 10 10
D48 5 c. dull blue and royal blue 15 20
D49 10 c. reddish lilac and plum 30 35
D42/9 *Set of* 8 70 85

Mauritius

GREAT BRITAIN STAMPS USED IN MAURITIUS. We no longer list the Great Britain stamps with obliteration "B 53" as there is no evidence that British stamps were available from the Mauritius Post Office.

PRICES FOR STAMPS ON COVER TO 1945

The classic issues, Nos. 1/34, are rare used on cover.

Nos. 35/41	*from* × 2
Nos. 42/72	*from* × 3
Nos. 74/5	†
Nos. 76/82	*from* × 5
Nos. 83/91	*from* × 6
Nos. 92/103	*from* × 4
Nos. 104/8	*from* × 3
Nos. 110/14	*from* × 10
Nos. 115/24	*from* × 8
Nos. 125/32	*from* × 7
No. 133	*from* × 4
Nos. 134/5	*from* × 10
No. 136	*from* × 8
Nos. 137/42	*from* × 6
Nos. 143/9	*from* × 5
Nos. 150/223	*from* × 3
No. 224	—
Nos. 225/7	*from* × 10
Nos. 228/44	*from* × 6
Nos. 245/8	*from* × 3
Nos. 249/63	*from* × 2
Nos. E1/6	*from* × 10
Nos. D1/7	*from* × 40
Nos. R1/4	*from* × 15

CROWN COLONY

Nos. 1/34b were printed in Mauritius.

1 ("POST OFFICE")

2 ("POST PAID")

3

(Engraved on copper by J. O. Barnard)

1847 (21 Sept). *Head of Queen on groundwork of diagonal and perpendicular lines. Imperf.*

1 1 1d. orange-red £375000 £140000
2 2d. deep blue £240000 £140000

A single plate contained one example of each value.

It is generally agreed that fifteen examples of No. 1 have survived (including two unused) and twelve of No. 2 (including four unused).

NOTE. Our prices for early Mauritius are for stamps in very fine condition. Exceptional copies are worth more, poorer copies considerably less.

(Engraved on copper by J. O. Barnard)

1848 (June). *T* **2**. 12 *varieties on the sheet. Imperf.*

A. *Earliest impressions. Design deep, sharp and clear. Diagonal lines predominate. Thick paper* (*Period of use:* 1d. 1853–54, 2d. 1848–49)

3 1d. orange-vermilion/*yellowish* £19000 £13000
4 2d. indigo-blue/*grey to bluish* £23000 £13000
a. "PENOE" for "PENCE £34000 £23000
5 2d. deep blue/*grey to bluish* £25000 £13000
a. "PENOE" for "PENCE" .. .. — £26000

B. *Early impressions. Design sharp and clear but some lines slightly weakened. Paper not so thick, grey to yellowish white or bluish* (*Period of use:* 1d. 1853–55, 2d. 1849–54).

6 1d. vermilion £11000 £5000
7 1d. orange-vermilion £12000 £5000
8 2d. blue £15000 £5500
a. "PENOE" for "PENCE" £18000 £9000
9 2d. deep blue £19000 £6000

C. *Intermediate impressions. White patches appear where design has worn. Paper yellowish white, grey or bluish, of poorish quality* (*Period of use:* 1d and 2d. 1854–57)

10 1d. bright vermilion £7500 £2000
11 1d. dull vermilion £7500 £2000
12 1d. red £7500 £1900
13 2d. deep blue £7000 £2000
14 2d. blue £5000 £2000
a. "PENOE" for "PENCE" (*shades*) *from* £10000 £4000
15 2d. light blue £5000 £2000

D. *Worn impressions. Much of design worn away but some diagonal lines distinct. Paper yellowish, grey or bluish, of poorish quality* (*Period of use:* 1d. 1857–59, 2d. 1855–58)

16 1d. red/*yellowish or grey* £1300 £275
17 1d. red-brown/*yellowish or grey* £1300 £275
18 1d. red/*bluish* £800 £275
19 1d. red-brown/*bluish* £750 £275
20 2d. blue (*shades*)/*yellowish or grey* £1300 £550
a. "PENOE" for "PENCE" .. .. *from* — £800
21 2d. grey-blue/*yellowish or grey* £1500 £550
22 2d. blue (*shades*)/*bluish* £1300 £500
a. Doubly printed .. ..

E. *Latest impressions. Almost none of design showing except part of Queen's head and frame. Paper yellowish, grey or bluish, of poorish quality* (*Period of use:* 1d. 1859, 2d. 1856–58)

23 1d. red £700 £275
24 1d. red-brown £750 £275
25 2d. grey-blue/*bluish* £750 £300
a. "PENOE" for "PENCE" £1300 £700

F. *Retouched impression. Retouching to Queen's head and frame. Paper bluish of poor quality* (*Period of use* 2d. 1857–58)

25*b* 2d. greyish blue/*bluish* .. .. ..

The "PENOE" stamp is No. 7 on the sheet.

Earliest known use of the 2d. value is on 19 June 1848, but the 1d. value is not known used before 27 September 1853.

(Engraved on copper by J. Lapirot)

1859 (March). 12 *varieties on the sheet. Imperf. Early impressions.*

26 3 2d. deep blue £3500 £1700
27 2d. blue £2500 £1500

1859 (July). *Intermediate prints. Lines of background, etc, partly worn away.*

28 3 2d. blue £1800 £600

1859 (Oct). *Worn impressions; bluish-paper.*

29 3 2d. blue £750 £375

4

5

(T 4. The 1848 plate re-engraved by R. Sherwin)

1859 (Oct). *Bluish paper. Imperf.*

30 4 2d. deep blue £22000 £3000

The 1d. plate was also re-engraved, but was not put into use. Reprints in black were made in 1877 from both 1d. and 2d. re-engraved plates. Coloured autotype illustrations were prepared from these reprints and 600 were included in the R.P.S.L. handbook on *British Africa* in 1900. Further reprints in black were made in 1911 after the plates had been presented to the R.P.S.L. and defaced.

(Lithographed by L. A. Dardenne)

1859 (Dec). *White laid paper. Imperf.*

31 5 1d. deep red £2000 £900
31*a* 1d. red £1500 £600
32 1d. dull vermilion £1000 £550
33 2d. slate-blue £2000 £600
33*a* 2d. blue £900 £400
34 2d. pale blue £800 £300
a. Heavy retouch on neck .. .. — £1000
b. Slight retouches (several varieties) — £550

6

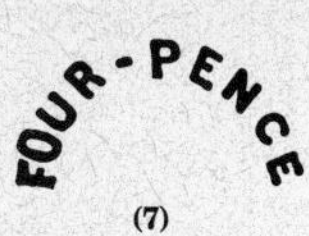

(7)

8

(Recess P.B.)

1854 (8 Apr)*. *Surch with T* **7**. *Imperf.*

35 6 4d. green £650 £350

*Although originally gazetted for use from the above date, research into the archives suggests that No. 35 was not actually issued until sometime in 1858, being mentioned in a further ordinance dated 30 April. The earliest dated postmark known is 27 March 1858.

1858–62. *No value expressed. Imperf.*

36 6 (4d.) green £450 £200
37 (6d.) vermilion .. .. 17·00 25·00
38 (9d.) dull magenta £450 £200
a. Reissued as (1d.) value (11.62) .. † £160

Examples of the design in dull magenta used as a 1d. value (No. 38a) can be identified by the use of the "B 53" cancellation.

Prepared for use, but not issued

39 6 (No value), red-brown (1859) .. .. 3·50
40 (No value), blue (1858) .. .. 2·75

Remainders of these were overprinted "L.P.E. 1890" in *red*, perforated at the London Philatelic Exhibition and sold as souvenirs.

(Recess P.B.)

1859. *Imperf.*

42 8 6d. blue .. .. £475 28·00
43 1s. vermilion .. .. £1800 45·00

1861. *Colours corrected. Imperf.*

44 8 6d. dull purple-slate .. .. .. 15·00 20·00
45 1s. yellow-green .. .. .. £180 70·00

1862. *Intermediate perf* 14 *to* 16.

46 8 6d. slate .. .. 14·00 24·00
a. Imperf between (pair) £2250
47 1s. deep green £1300 £300

9

10

(Typo D.L.R.)

1860–3. *No wmk. P* 14.

48 9 1d. purple-brown .. .. 75·00 14·00
49 2d. blue .. .. 90·00 20·00
50 4d. rose .. .. 90·00 15·00
51 6d. green (1862) .. .. .. £400 85·00
52 6d. slate (1863) .. .. .. £110 65·00
53 9d. dull purple .. .. .. 60·00 29·00
54 1s. buff (1862) .. .. .. £160 55·00
55 1s. green (1863) £400 £110

1863–72. *Wmk Crown CC. P* 14.

56 9 1d. purple-brown (1870) .. .. 26·00 6·50
57 1d. brown .. .. 38·00 5·00
58 1d. bistre .. .. 55·00 5·00
59 2d. pale blue .. .. 38·00 4·50
60 2d. bright blue .. .. .. 38·00 4·50
a. Imperf (pair) £1000 £1000
61 3d. deep red .. .. 65·00 19·00
61*a* 3d. dull red .. .. 30·00 8·00
62 4d. rose .. .. 50·00 1·75
63 6d. dull violet (1864) .. .. 70·00 23·00
64 6d. yellow-green (1865) .. .. 75·00 9·00
65 6d. blue-green .. .. .. 75·00 3·75
66 9d. yellow-green (1872) .. .. £100 85·00
67 10 10d. maroon (1872) .. .. .. 90·00 16·00
68 9 1s. yellow .. .. 95·00 12·00
69 1s. orange .. .. 95·00 12·00
70 1s. blue (1870) .. .. .. £130 18·00
71 5s. rosy mauve .. .. .. £110 30·00
72 5s. bright mauve (1865) .. .. £120 28·00

½ d HALF PENNY (11)

HALF PENNY (12)

Prepared for use, but not issued. No. 53 surch with T **11**

74 9 ½d. on 9d. dull purple (R.) £550
a. "PRNNY" .. ..
75 ½d. on 9d. dull purple (Bk.) £650

1876. *Nos. 53 and 67 surch with T* **12**.

76 9 ½d. on 9d. dull purple .. .. 2·75 6·00
a. Surch inverted £250
b. Surch double .. ..
77 10 ½d. on 10d. maroon .. .. .. 80 9·00

HALF PENNY (13) One Penny (14) One Shilling (15)

1877. *T* **9** *and* **10**, *wmk Crown CC, surch with T* **13**/**15**. *P* 14.

79 ½d. on 10d. rose (Apr) .. .. .. 2·00 16·00
80 1d. on 4d. rose-carmine (6 Dec) .. .. 7·50 12·00
81 1s. on 5s. rosy mauve (6 Dec) .. .. £160 80·00
82 1s. on 5s. bright mauve (6 Dec) .. .. £190 95·00

"CANCELLED" OVERPRINTS. Following the change of currency in 1878 various issues with face values in sterling were overprinted "CANCELLED" in serifed type and sold as remainders. The stamps involved were Nos. 53, 56/62, 64, 67/8, 71/2, 74/6, 79 and 81/2.

Examples of such overprints on stamps between Nos. 53 and 72 are worth about the same as the prices quoted for used, on Nos. 74/6 they are worth 12% of the unused price, on No. 79 65% and on Nos. 81/2 20%.

2 CENTS (16) 2 Rs.50 C. (17)

1878 (3 Jan). *T* **10** (*with lower label blank*) *surch with T* **16**. *Wmk Crown CC. P* 14.

83 2 c. dull rose .. .. 5·00 4·00

1878. *Surch as T* **16** *or* **17**. *Wmk Crown CC. P* 14.

84 9 4 c. on 1d. bistre .. .. .. 7·00 3·75
85 8 c. on 2d. blue .. .. .. 38·00 75
86 13 c. on 3d. orange-red .. .. .. 7·00 14·00
87 17 c. on 4d. rose .. .. .. 55·00 1·50
88 25 c. on 6d. slate-blue .. .. .. 90·00 4·75
89 38 c. on 9d. pale violet .. .. .. 18·00 27·00
90 50 c. on 1s. green .. .. .. 48·00 2·50
91 2 r. 50 c. on 5s. bright mauve .. .. 12·00 9·00
84/91 .. .. *Set of* 8 £250 55·00

18

19

20

21

22

23

24 25 26

(Type D.L.R.)

1879–80. *Wmk Crown CC. P* 14.
92 18 2 c. Venetian red .. .. 27·00 11·00
93 19 4 c. orange (1879) .. .. 40·00 3·25
94 20 8 c. blue .. .. 11·00 75
95 21 13 c. slate .. .. 90·00 65·00
96 22 17 c. rose .. .. 25·00 3·50
97 23 25 c. olive-yellow (1879) .. .. .. £110 8·00
98 24 38 c. bright purple £120 £120
99 25 50 c. green .. .. 2·50 1·75
100 26 2 r. 50 c. brown-purple .. .. .. 23·00 30·00
92/100 .. .. *Set of* 9 £400 £225

1882–83. *Wmk Crown CA. P* 14.
101 18 2 c. Venetian red .. .. 12·00 4·75
102 19 4 c. orange .. .. 35·00 2·50
103 23 25 c. olive-yellow (1883) .. .. .. 3·00 1·50
101/3 .. .. *Set of* 3 45·00 8·00

16 CENTS SIXTEEN CENTS
(27) (28)

(*a*) Surcharge 14 mm long and 3 high.
(*b*) Surcharge 15 mm long and 3½ high.
(*c*) Surcharge 15 mm long and 2½ high.

1883 (26 Feb). *No.* 96 *surch as T* **27**.
104 22 16 c. on 17 c. rose (*a*) .. .. .. 55·00 28·00
a. Surch double .. .. ..
105 16 c. on 17 c. rose (*b*) .. .. .. 60·00 28·00
106 16 c. on 17 c. rose (*c*) .. .. .. £120 70·00

1883 (14 July). *Wmk Crown CA. Surch with T* **28**. *P* 14.
107 22 16 c. on 17 c. rose .. .. 24·00 80

2 CENTS
(29)

30

2 CENTS
(31)

1885 (11 May). *No.* 98 *surch with T* **29**.
108 24 2 c. on 38 c. bright purple .. .. .. 55·00 32·00
a. Without bar .. .. — 70·00
b. Surch inverted £200 £200
c. Surch double £275

(Typo D.L.R.)

1885–91. *Wmk Crown CA. P* 14.
110 18 2 c. green 90 30
111 19 4 c. carmine 90 20
112 20 8 c. blue (1891) 65 65
113 30 16 c. chestnut .. .. 2·00 40
114 25 50 c. orange (1887) .. .. 26·00 7·50
110/14 .. .. *Set of* 5 27·00 8·00
110/14 *excl* 112 optd "Specimen" *Set of* 4 £225

1887 (6 July). *No.* 95 *surch with T* **31**.
115 21 2 c. on 13 c. slate (R.) .. .. .. 23·00 35·00
a. Surch inverted .. .. 70·00 85·00
b. Surch double .. .. — £225
c. Surch double, one on back of stamp £275

TWO CENTS TWO CENTS
(32) (33)

1891 (Sept). *Various stamps surcharged.*
117 32 2 c. on 4 c. (No. 111) 35 20
a. Surch inverted .. .. 50·00
b. Surch double .. .. 60·00 55·00
c. Surch double, one inverted .. .. 60·00 55·00
118 2 c. on 17 c. (No. 96) .. .. .. 42·00 45·00
a. Surch inverted £130
b. Surch double £200 £200
119 33 2 c. on 38 c. (No. 89) .. .. .. 1·00 3·50
a. Surch inverted £100
b. Surch double £225 £225
c. Surch double, one inverted .. .. 50·00
120 32 2 c. on 38 c. (No. 98) .. .. .. 2·00 2·50
a. Surch inverted £200
b. Surch double .. .. 55·00
c. Surch double, one inverted .. .. 55·00

Minor varieties are also known with portions of the surcharge missing, due to defective printing.

ONE CENT ONE CENT
(34) (35)

1893 (1 Jan). *Surch with T* 34/5. *Wmk Crown CA. P* 14.
123 18 1 c. on 2 c. pale violet (Optd S. £27) .. 25 35
124 30 1 c. on 16 c. chestnut 25 60

1893–4. *Wmk Crown CA. P* 14.
125 18 1 c. pale violet 25 40
126 30 15 c. chestnut 70 30
127 15 c. blue .. .. 3·50 40
125/7 .. .. *Set of* 3 4·00 1·00
125/7 Optd "Specimen" .. .. *Set of* 3 35·00

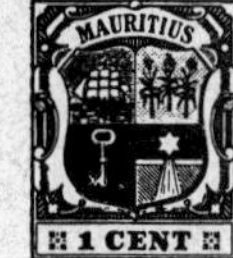

36 37

(Typo D.L.R.)

1895–9. *Wmk Crown CA. P* 14.
128 36 1 c. dull purple and ultramarine (8.7.97) 25 25
129 2 c. dull purple and orange (8.7.97) .. 1·75 10
130 3 c. dull purple and deep purple .. 50 30
131 4 c. dull purple and emerald .. .. 2·75 30
131*a* 6 c. green and rose-red (1899) .. .. 2·75 1·50
132 18 c. green and ultramarine (8.7.97) .. 6·50 5·00
128/32 .. .. *Set of* 6 13·00 6·50
128/32 Optd "Specimen" .. .. *Set of* 6 70·00

(Des R. S. du Verge. Typo D.L.R.)

1898 (21 Apr*). *Jubilee issue. Wmk CA over Crown, sideways. P* 14.
133 37 36 c. orange & ultramarine (Optd S. £40) 9·00 12·00
*Earliest known postmark.

6 CENTS 15 CENTS
(38) (39)

1899. *Nos.* 132/33 *surcharged.*
134 38 6 c. on 18 c. green and ultramarine (R.) 25 35
a. Surch inverted £170 £140
135 39 15 c. on 36 c. orange and ultramarine (B.) 1·00 70
a. Bar of surch omitted £130

The space between "6" and "CENTS" varies from 2½ to 4 mm.

40 Admiral Mahé de Labourdonnais, Governor of Mauritius, 1735–46

(Recess D.L.R.)

1899 (15 Dec). *Birth Bicentenary of Labourdonnais. Wmk Crown CC. P* 14.
136 40 15 c. ultramarine (Optd S. £60) .. .. 9·50 1·75

4 Cents 12 CENTS
(41) (42)

1900. *No.* 113 *surch with T* **41**.
137 30 4 c. on 16 c. chestnut .. .. .. 60 2·25

1900. *Wmk Crown CA. P* 14.
138 36 1 c. grey and black 50 10
139 2 c. dull and bright purple 30 10
140 4 c. purple and carmine/*yellow* .. .. 1·10 10
141 15 c. green and orange .. .. .. 5·25 6·00
138/41 .. .. *Set of* 4 6·50 6·00
138/41 Optd "Specimen" .. .. *Set of* 4 45·00

1902. *No.* 132 *surch with T* **42**.
142 36 12 c. on 18 c. green and ultramarine .. 80 5·00

The bar cancelling the original value seems in some cases to be one thick bar and in others two thin ones.

Postage & Revenue.
(43)

44

1902. *Various stamps optd with T* **43**.
143 4 c. purple and carmine/*yellow* (No. 140) .. 20 20
144 6 c. green and rose-red (No. 131*a*) .. .. 35 2·25
145 15 c. green and orange (No. 141) 45 30
146 25 c. olive-yellow (No. 103) .. .. .. 50 2·25
147 50 c. green (No. 99) .. .. 3·50 1·00
148 2 r. 50 c. brown-purple (No. 100) .. .. 32·00 45·00
143/48 .. .. *Set of* 6 35·00 45·00

1902. *No.* 133 *surch as T* **42**, *but with longer bar.*
149 37 12 c. on 36 c. orange and ultramarine .. 1·00 1·00
a. Surch inverted £200 £200

The note below No. 142 also applies to No. 149.

(Typo D.L.R.)

1902–5. *T* 36 *and* 44 (*rupee values*). *Wmk Crown CC* (1 *r.*) *or Crown CA* (*others*), *sideways on* 2 *r.* 50 *and* 5 *r. P* 14.
150 3 c. green and carmine/*yellow* 90 30
151 4 c. grey-green and violet 60 85
152 4 c. black and carmine/*blue* .. .. .. 2·50 10
153 5 c. dull and bright purple/*buff* .. .. 3·00 28·00
154 5 c. dull purple and black/*buff* .. .. 1·60 1·75
155 6 c. purple and carmine/*red* .. .. .. 1·25 15
156 8 c. green and black/*buff* .. .. .. 80 2·75
157 12 c. grey-black and carmine .. .. .. 1·50 70
158 15 c. black and blue/*blue* (1905) .. .. 25·00 1·25
159 25 c. green and carmine/*green*, **OC** .. .. 2·00 6·50
160 50 c. dull green and deep green/*yellow* .. 6·50 13·00
161 1 r. grey-black and carmine .. .. .. 30·00 20·00
162 2 r. 50, green and black/*blue* .. .. .. 11·00 30·00
163 5 r. purple and carmine/*red* .. .. .. 45·00 65·00
150/63 .. .. *Set of* 14 £110 £150
150/63 Optd "Specimen" .. .. *Set of* 14 £120

1904–7. T36 *and* 44 (1 *r.*). *Wmk Mult Crown CA. P* 14.
164 1 c. grey and black, **C** (1907) .. .. 5·00 80
165 2 c. dull and bright purple, **OC** (1905) .. 3·50 15
166 3 c. green and carmine/*yellow*, **C** .. .. 13·00 2·75
167 4 c. black and carmine/*blue*, **OC** .. .. 1·00 10
168 6 c. purple and carmine/*red*, **OC** 80 10
171 15 c. black and blue/*blue*, **C** (1907) .. .. 4·00 35
174 50 c. green and deep green/*yellow*, **C** .. 1·00 2·25
175 1 r. grey-black and carmine, **C** (1907) .. 18·00 23·00
164/75 .. .. *Set of* 8 42·00 26·00

46 (47)

(Typo D.L.R.)

1910. *Wmk Mult Crown CA. P* 14.
181 46 1 c. black, **O** 40 10
182 2 c. brown, **O** 90 10
183 3 c. green, **O** 40 10
184 4 c. pale yellow-green and carmine, **O** .. 70 10
185 47 5 c. grey and carmine, **O** .. .. .. 40 1·25
186 46 6 c. carmine-red, **O** 40 10
a. Pale red .. .. 2·50 25
187 8 c. orange, **O** .. .. 95 1·25
188 47 12 c. greyish slate, **O** 30 50
189 46 15 c. blue, **O** .. .. 4·50 10
190 47 25 c. black and red/*yellow*, **C** .. .. 1·75 8·50
191 50 c. dull purple and black, **C** .. .. 1·75 8·50
192 1 r. black/*green*, **C** .. .. 3·75 6·00
193 2 r. 50, black and red/*blue*, **C** .. .. 7·50 26·00
194 5 r. green and red/*yellow*, **C** .. .. 20·00 45·00
195 10 r. green and red/*green*, **C** .. .. 80·00 £120
181/95 .. .. *Set of* 15 £110 £190
181/95 Optd "Specimen" .. .. *Set of* 15 £200

In Nos. 188, 190 and 195, the value labels are as in T **49**.

48 49

(Typo D.L.R.)

1913–23. *T* **48** *and* **49** (12 *c.*, 25 *c. and* 10 *r.*). *Wmk Mult Crown CA. P* 14.
196 5 c. grey and carmine, **O** (1915) .. .. 90 1·00
197 5 c. slate-grey and carmine, **O** .. .. 6·00 6·00
198 12 c. greyish slate, **O** (1915) 90 30
199 25 c. black and red/*yellow*, **C** (1913) .. .. 40 1·40
a. White back (1916) .. .. .. 50 8·50
b. On orange-buff .. .. .. 27·00 50·00
c. On pale yellow (Die I) (Optd S. £25) .. 22·00 30·00
d. On pale yellow (Die II) (Optd S. £25) .. 50 12·00
200 50 c. dull purple and black, **C** (Die I) .. 15·00 30·00
201 1 r. black/*blue-green* (*olive back*), **C** (1917) .. 1·50 7·00
a. On emerald surface .. .. .. 5·50 28·00
b. On emerald back (Die II) (Optd S. £25) 1·25 6·00
202 2 r. 50, black and red/*blue*, **C** .. .. 11·00 22·00
203 5 r. green and red/*orange-buff*, **C** .. .. 26·00 48·00
a. On pale yellow (Die I) .. .. 26·00 48·00
b. On pale yellow (Die II) .. .. 27·00 55·00
204 10 r. green and red/*green*, **C** .. .. .. 30·00 55·00
a. On blue-green, olive back £650
b. On emerald surface .. .. .. 30·00 55·00
c. On emerald back (Die I) .. .. .. 25·00 50·00
d. On emerald back (Die II) (Opt S. £28) 18·00 50·00
196/204 .. .. *Set of* 8 65·00 £140
196/204 Optd "Specimen" (Die I) .. *Set of* 8 £150

MAURITIUS 12c
A

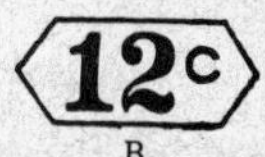

B

Two types of duty plate in the 12 c. In Type B the letters of "MAURITIUS" are larger; the extremities of the downstroke and the tail of the "2" are pointed, instead of square, and the "c" is larger.

1921–34. *Wmk Mult Script CA. P* 14. (*a*) *T* **46**.
205 1 c. black, **O** 35 55
206 2 c. brown, **O** 50 10

207 4 c. pale olive-green and carmine, O 1·50 1·75
208 4 c. green, O 90 10
209 6 c. carmine, O 9·50 6·00
210 6 c. bright mauve, O 90 10
210*a* 8 c. orange, O (1925) 2·25 6·50
211 10 c. grey, O (1922) 2·00 3·25
212 12 c. carmine-red, O 80 40
213 15 c. blue, O 4·75 1·50
214 20 c. blue, O (1922) 2·00 50
205/214 *Set of* 11 23·00 19·00
205/14 Optd "Specimen" *Set of* 11 £140

(*b*) *T* 48 *and* 49

215 5 c. grey and carmine, O (Die II) 15 10
215*a* 5 c. grey and carmine, O (Die I) (1932) 90 15
216 12 c. grey, O (A) 25 5·00
216*a* 12 c. pale grey, O (1928) (A) (Optd S. £24) 25 1·50
216*b* 12 c. grey, O (1934) (B) 30 10
217 12 c. carmine-red, O (1922) 15 2·25
218 25 c. black and red/*pale yellow*, C (Die II) 20 15
218*a* 25 c. black & red/*pale yellow*, C (Die I) (1932) 65 12·00
219 50 c. dull purple and black, C (Die II) 6·00 4·00
220 1 r. black/*emerald*, C (Die II) (1923) 55 40
220*a* 1 r. black/*emerald*, C (Die I) (1932) 5·50 14·00
221 2 r. 50 c. black and red/*blue*, C (1923) 7·00 6·00
222 5 r. green and red/*yellow*, C (1925) 13·00 35·00
223 10 r. green and red/*emerald*, C (1928) 32·00 60·00
215/223 *Set of* 9 55·00 95·00
215/23 Optd "Specimen" *Set of* 9 £140

1924. *As T* 44, *but Arms similar to T* 46. *Wmk Mult Script CA. P* 14.
224 50 r. dull purple and green, C £850 £1200
224 Optd "Specimen" £175

3
Cents

(50)

51

1925. *T* 46 *surch locally as T* 50.
225 3 c. on 4 c. green 1·75 2·50
226 10 c. on 12 c. carmine-red 15 10
227 15 c. on 20 c. blue 15 15
225/7 *Set of* 3 1·90 2·50
225/7 Optd "Specimen" *Set of* 3 60·00

1926. *Wmk Mult Script CA. P* 14.
228 **46** 2 c. purple/*yellow*, O 15 20
229 3 c. green, O 1·00 1·00
230 4 c. brown, O 35 60
231 10 c. carmine-red, O 1·75 80
232 12 c. grey, O 35 1·25
233 15 c. cobalt, O 45 25
234 20 c. purple, O 4·00 8·00
228/234 *Set of* 7 7·00 11·00
228/32, 234 Optd "Specimen" *Set of* 6 80·00

1926–34. *As T* 49 (*King*). *Wmk Mult Script CA. P* 14.
235 1 c. black, O 15 35
236 2 c. brown, O 15 10
237 3 c. green, O 20 30
238 4 c. sage-green and carmine, O (Die II) (1927) 25 30
238*a* 4 c. sage-green and carmine, O (Die I) (1932) 3·75 15·00
238*b* 4 c. green, O (Die I)(1933) 55 45
239 6 c. sepia, O (1927) 20 60
240 8 c. orange, O 25 4·75
241 10 c. carmine-red, O (Die II) 25 10
241*a* 10 c. carmine-red, O (Die I) (1932) 90 2·50
242 15 c. Prussian blue, O (1928) 45 20
243 20 c. purple, O (1927) 30 40
244 20 c. Prussian blue, O (Die I) (1933) 6·00 80
244*a* 20 c. Prussian blue, O (Die II) (1934) 7·50 30
235/244 *Set of* 11 8·00 7·00
235/244 (*excl* 238*a*, 241*a*). Optd/Perf "Specimen" *Set of* 11 £150

1935 (6 May). *Silver Jubilee. As Nos.* 91/4 *of Antigua.*
245 5 c. ultramarine and grey 15 10
g. Dot to left of chapel 18·00
h. Dot by flagstaff 18·00
246 12 c. green and indigo 1·00 10
g. Dot to left of chapel 30·00
247 20 c. brown and deep blue 2·50 20
g. Dot to left of chapel 40·00
248 1 r. slate and purple 16·00 22·00
h. Dot by flagstaff £100
245/8 *Set of* 4 17·00 22·00
245/8 Perf "Specimen" *Set of* 4 70·00

For illustrations of plate varieties see Omnibus section following Zululand.

PRICES OF SETS

Set prices are given for many issues, generally those containing three stamps or more. Definitive sets include one of each value or major colour change, but do not cover different perforations, die types or minor shades. Where a choice is possible the set prices are based on the cheapest versions of the stamps included in the listings.

Line by sceptre (R. 5/3)

1937 (12 May). *Coronation. As Nos.* 13/15 *of Aden.*
249 5 c. violet 25 10
250 12 c. scarlet 25 20
251 20 c. bright blue 30 10
a. Line by sceptre 22·00
249/51 *Set of* 3 70 35
249/251 Perf "Specimen" *Set of* 3 45·00

"IJ" flaw (R. 3/6)

Battered "A" (R. 6/1 of right pane)

(Typo D.L.R.)

1938–49. *T* 51 *and similar types. Wmk Mult Script CA. P* 14.
252 2 c. olive-grey (9.3.38) 15 10
a. Perf 15×14 (1942) 50 10
253 3 c. reddish purple and scarlet (27.10.38) 50 25
a. Reddish lilac and red (4.43) 50 40
254 4 c. dull green (26.2.38) 50 30
a. Deep dull green (4.43) 50 30
255 5 c. slate-lilac (23.2.38) 60 10
a. Pale lilac (*shades*) (4.43) 40 10
b. Perf 15×14 (1942) 15·00 10
256 10 c. rose-red (9.3.38) 50 15
a. Deep reddish rose (*shades*) (4.43) 45 10
b. Perf 15×14. *Pale reddish rose* (1942) 15·00 30
257 12 c. salmon (*shades*) (26.2.38) 40 10
a. Perf 15×14 (1942) 35·00 75
258 20 c. blue (26.2.38) 60 10
259 25 c. brown-purple, CO (2.3.38) 75 10
a. "IJ" flaw 28·00
260 1 r. grey-brown, CO (2.3.38) 2·00 50
a. Battered "A" 32·00
b. Drab, C (4.49) 2·50 70
261 2 r. 50, pale violet, CO (2.3.38) 10·00 4·50
a. Slate-violet, C (4.48) 25·00 13·00
262 5 r. olive-green, CO (2.3.38) 22·00 16·00
a. Sage-green, O (4.43) 22·00 16·00
263 10 r. reddish purple (*shades*), CO (2.3.38) 8·00 13·00
252/263 *Set of* 12 40·00 32·00
252/263 Perf "Specimen" *Set of* 12 £130

The stamps perf 15 × 14 were printed by Bradbury, Wilkinson from De La Rue plates and issued only in the colony in 1942. De La Rue printings of the 2 c. to 20 c. in 1943–45 were on thin, whiter paper. 1943–45 printings of the 25 c. to 10 r. were on unsurfaced paper.

1946 (20 Nov). *Victory. As Nos.* 28/9 *of Aden.*
264 5 c. lilac 10 10
265 20 c. blue 10 10
264/5 Perf "Specimen" *Set of* 2 45·00

52 1d. "Post Office" Mauritius and King George VI

(Recess B.W.)

1948 (22 Mar). *Centenary of First British Colonial Postage Stamp. P* 11½ × 11.
266 **52** 5 c. orange and magenta 10 10
267 12 c. orange and green 10 10
268 – 20 c. blue and light blue 10 10
269 – 1 r. blue and red-brown 10 15
266/9 *Set of* 4 35 30
266/9 Perf "Specimen" *Set of* 4 90·00

Design:–20 c., 1 r. As T **52** but showing 2d. "Post Office" Mauritius.

1948 (25 Oct). *Royal Silver Wedding. As Nos.* 30/1 *of Aden.*
270 5 c. violet 10 10
271 10 r. magenta 8·00 12·00

1949 (10 Oct). *75th Anniv of U.P.U. As Nos.* 114/17 *of Antigua.*
272 12 c. carmine 50 50
273 20 c. deep blue 60 50
274 35 c. purple 60 40
275 1 r. sepia 60 20
272/5 *Set of* 4 2·00 1·40

53 Sugar Factory

55 Aloe Plant

(Photo Harrison)

1950 (1 July). *T* **53**, **55** *and similar designs. Wmk Mult Script CA. Chalk surfaced paper. P* 13½ × 14½ (*horiz*), 14½ × 13½ (*vert*).
276 1 c. bright purple 10 40
277 2 c. rose-carmine 15 10
278 3 c. yellow-green 60 90
279 4 c. green 20 15
280 5 c. blue 15 10
281 10 c. scarlet 25 75
282 12 c. olive-green 1·25 30
283 20 c. ultramarine 25 15
284 25 c. brown-purple 40 40
285 35 c. violet 20 10
286 50 c. emerald-green 75 45
287 1 r. sepia 1·25 15
288 2 r. 50, orange 4·50 5·50
289 5 r. red-brown 4·50 8·00
290 10 r. dull blue 9·00 10·00
276/290 *Set of* 15 21·00 25·00

Designs: *Horiz*—2 c. Grand Port; 5 c. Rempart Mountain; 10 c. Transporting cane; 12 c. Mauritius Dodo and map; 35 c. Government House; 1 r. Timor Deer; 2 r. 50, Port Louis; 5 r. Beach scene; 10 r. Arms of Mauritius. *Vert*—4 c. Tamarind Falls; 20 c. Legend of Paul and Virginie (*inscr* "VIRGINIA"); 25 c. Labourdonnais statue; 50 c. Pieter Both Mountain.

The latitude is incorrectly shown on No. 282. This was corrected before the same design was used for No. 302*a*.

1953 (2 June). *Coronation. As No.* 47 *of Aden.*
291 10 c. black and emerald 25 10

68 Tamarind Falls

69 Historical Museum, Mahebourg

(Photo Harrison)

1953 (3 Nov)–**58.** *Designs previously used for King George VI issue, but with portrait of Queen Elizabeth II as in T* **68/9**. *Wmk Mult Script CA. Chalk-surfaced paper. P* 13½×14½ (*horiz*) *or* 14½×13½ (*vert*).
293 2 c. bright carmine (1.6.54) 10 10
294 3 c. yellow-green (1.6.54) 25 40
295 4 c. bright purple 10 20
296 5 c. Prussian blue (1.6.54) 10 10
297 10 c. bluish green 10 10
a. Yellowish green (9.2.55) 20 10
298 15 c. scarlet 10 10
299 20 c. brown-purple 15 10
300 25 c. bright ultramarine 30 10
a. Bright blue (19.6.57) 20 10
301 35 c. reddish violet (1.6.54) 20 10
302 50 c. bright green 20 30
302*a* 60 c. deep green (2.8.54) 3·50 10
ab. Bronze-green (27.8.58) 3·50 10
303 1 r. sepia 20 10
a. Deep grey-brown (19.6.57) 90 55
304 2 r. 50, orange (1.6.54) 7·00 4·00
305 5 r. red-brown (1.6.54) 6·50 2·50
a. Orange-brown (19.6.57) 9·50 3·00
306 10 r. deep grey-blue (1.6.54) 10·00 60
293/306 *Set of* 15 25·00 7·50

Designs: *Horiz*—2 c. Grand Port; 4 c. Sugar factory; 5 c. Rempart Mountain; 35 c. Government House; 60 c. Mauritius Dodo and map; 1 r. Timor Deer; 2 r. 50, Port Louis; 5 r. Beach scene; 10 r. Arms of Mauritius. *Vert*—3 c. Aloe plant; 20 c. Labourdonnais statue; 25 c. Legend of Paul and Virginie; 50 c. Pieter Both Mountain.

Nos. 296 and 300 exist in coils, constructed from normal sheets.

See also Nos. 314/16.

70 Queen Elizabeth II and King George III (after Lawrence)

(Litho Enschedé)

1961 (11 Jan). *150th Anniv of British Post Office in Mauritius. W* w **12**. *P* 13½ × 14.
307 **70** 10 c. black and brown-red 10 10
308 20 c. ultramarine and light blue 15 15
309 35 c. black and yellow 15 15
310 1 r. deep maroon and green 15 20
307/10 .. .. *Set of* 4 50 50

1963 (4 June). *Freedom from Hunger. As No.* 76 *of Aden.*
311 60 c. reddish violet 40 10

1963 (2 Sept). *Red Cross Centenary. As Nos.* 147/8 *of Antigua.*
312 10 c. red and black 15 10
313 60 c. red and blue 60 15

1963 (12 Nov)–**65**. *As Nos.* 297, 302*a and* 304 *but wmk* w **12**.
314 **68** 10 c. bluish green (1964) 15 10
a. Yellowish green (21.1.65) 25 10
315 – 60 c. bronze-green (28.5.64) .. .. 1·25 10
316 – 2 r. 50, orange .. .. 2·50 5·00
314/16 .. .. *Set of* 3 3·50 5·00

71 Bourbon White Eye

(Des D. M. Reid-Henry. Photo Harrison)

1965 (16 Mar). *Horiz designs as T* **71**. *W* w **12** *(upright). Multicoloured; background colours given. P* 14½ × 14.
317 2 c. lemon 10 15
a. Grey (leg) omitted .. .. 35·00
318 3 c. brown 10 15
a. Black (eye and beak) omitted .. .. 30·00
319 4 c. light reddish purple 10 15
a. Mauve-pink omitted* .. .. 30·00
b. Pale grey omitted .. .. 45·00
c. Orange omitted .. .. .. 75·00
320 5 c. grey-brown 70 10
321 10 c. light grey-green 25 10
322 15 c. pale grey 70 10
a. Red (beak) omitted .. .. 30·00
323 20 c. light yellow-bistre 70 10
324 25 c. bluish grey 80 10
325 35 c. greyish blue 75 10
326 50 c. light yellow-buff 35 25
327 60 c. light greenish yellow 40 10
328 1 r. light yellow-olive 75 10
a. Pale orange omitted .. .. 50·00
b. Light grey (ground) omitted .. .. 50·00
329 2 r. 50, pale stone .. .. .. 4·50 4·00
330 5 r. pale grey-blue .. .. .. 12·00 4·50
a. Brown-red omitted .. .. 60·00
331 10 r. pale bluish green .. .. .. 15·00 6·50
317/31 .. .. *Set of* 15 35·00 14·50

Designs:—3 c. Rodriguez Fody; 4 c. Olive White-eye; 5 c. Mascarene Paradise Flycatcher; 10 c. Mauritius Fody; 15 c. Mauritius Parakeet; 20 c. Mauritius Greybird; 25 c. Mauritius Kestrel; 35 c. Pink Pigeon; 50 c. Reunion Bulbul; 60 c. Mauritius Blue Pigeon (extinct); 1 r. Mauritius Dodo (extinct); 2 r. 50, Rodriguez Solitaire (extinct); 5 r. Mauritius Red Rail (extinct); 10 r. Broad-billed Parrot (extinct).

*On the 4 c. the background is printed in two colours so that in No. 319a the background colour is similar to that of the 5 c.

On No. 317a it is the deep grey which is missing, affecting the leg, beak and part of the branch. On No. 319c the missing orange affects the under breast of the bird, which appears much paler. On No. 328a the omission affects the legs and part of the body and on No. 330a the whole of the bird appears in the same colour as the legs.

The 50 c. and 2 r. 50 exist with PVA gum as well as gum arabic.

Nos. 320 and 324 exist in coils, constructed from normal sheets.

See also Nos. 340/1 and 370/5.

1965 (17 May). *I.T.U. Centenary. As Nos.* 166/7 *of Antigua.*
332 10 c. red-orange and apple-green 15 10
333 60 c. yellow and bluish violet 40 10

1965 (25 Oct). *International Co-operation Year. As Nos.* 168/9 *of Antigua.*
334 10 c. reddish purple and turquoise-green .. 15 10
335 60 c. deep bluish green and lavender 30 10

1966 (24 Jan). *Churchill Commemoration. As Nos.* 170/3 *of Antigua.*
336 2 c. new blue 10 35
337 10 c. deep green 25 10
338 60 c. brown .. .. 1·10 15
339 1 r. bluish violet .. .. 1·25 15
336/9 .. .. *Set of* 4 2·40 65

1966–67. *As Nos.* 320, 325 *but wmk* w **12** *sideways.*
340 5 c. grey-brown (1966) 10 10
341 35 c. greyish blue (27.6.67) 15 10
No. 340 exists in coils, constructed from normal sheets.

1966 (1 Dec). *20th Anniv of U.N.E.S.C.O. As Nos.* 196/8 *of Antigua.*
342 5 c. slate-violet, red, yellow and orange .. 15 20
343 10 c. orange-yellow, violet and deep olive .. 25 10
344 60 c. black, bright purple and orange 50 15
342/4 .. .. *Set of* 3 80 35

SELF-GOVERNMENT

86 Red-tailed Tropic Bird

(Des D. M. Reid-Henry. Photo Harrison)

1967 (1 Sept). *Self-Government. T* **86** *and similar horiz designs. Multicoloured. W* w **12**. *P* 14½.
345 2 c. Type **86** 10 15
346 10 c. Rodriguez Brush Warbler 10 10
347 60 c. Rose-ringed Parakeet (extinct) 15 10
348 1 r. Grey-rumped Swiftlet 25 10
345/8 .. .. *Set of* 4 55 20

SELF GOVERNMENT 1967

(90)

1967 (1 Dec). *Self-Government. As Nos.* 317/31 *but wmk sideways on Nos.* 352/3 *and* 357. *Optd with T* **90**. *P* 14 × 14½.
349 2 c. lemon 10 40
350 3 c. brown 10 40
351 4 c. light reddish purple 10 40
a. Orange omitted .. .. .. 22·00
352 5 c. grey-brown 10 10
353 10 c. light grey-green 10 10
354 15 c. pale grey 10 10
355 20 c. light yellow-bistre 15 10
356 25 c. bluish grey 15 10
357 35 c. greyish blue 20 10
358 50 c. light yellow-buff 25 15
359 60 c. light greenish yellow 25 10
360 1 r. light yellow-olive 35 10
361 2 r. 50, pale stone .. .. .. 1·00 2·00
362 5 r. pale grey-blue .. .. .. 1·50 3·25
363 10 r. pale bluish green .. .. .. 3·75 6·50
349/63 .. .. *Set of* 15 7·50 11·50

INDEPENDENT

91 Flag of Mauritius

(Litho D.L.R.)

1968 (12 Mar). *Independence. T* **91** *and similar horiz design. P* 13½ × 13.
364 **91** 2 c. multicoloured 10 25
365 – 3 c. multicoloured 10 25
366 **91** 15 c. multicoloured 10 10
367 – 20 c. multicoloured 10 10
368 **91** 60 c. multicoloured 10 10
369 – 1 r. multicoloured 20 10
364/9 .. .. *Set of* 6 45 65
Design:—3 c., 20 c. and 1 r. Arms and Mauritius Dodo emblem.

1968 (12 July). *As Nos.* 317/18, 322/3 *and* 327/8 *but background colours changed as below.*
370 2 c. olive-yellow 15 80
371 3 c. cobalt .. .. 80 1·50
372 15 c. cinnamon 55 20
a. Greenish blue omitted .. ..
373 20 c. buff .. .. 1·50 50
374 60 c. rose 90 15
375 1 r. reddish purple .. .. .. 1·75 1·00
370/5 .. .. *Set of* 6 5·00 3·75

93 Dominique rescues Paul and Virginie

(Des V. Whiteley, from prints. Litho Format)

1968 (2 Dec). *Bicentenary of Bernardin de St. Pierre's Visit to Mauritius. Multicoloured designs as T* **93**. *P* 13½.
376 2 c. Type **93** 10 30
377 15 c. Paul and Virginie crossing the river .. 10 10
378 50 c. Visit of Labourdonnais to Madame de la Tour *(horiz)* 20 10
379 60 c. Meeting of Paul and Virginie in Confidence *(vert)* 20 10
380 1 r. Departure of Virginie for Europe *(horiz)* 35 20
381 2 r. 50, Bernardin de St. Pierre *(vert)* .. 85 2·00
376/81 .. .. *Set of* 6 1·75 2·40

NEW INFORMATION

The editor is always interested to correspond with people who have new information that will improve or correct the Catalogue.

99 Batardé

(Des J. Vinson (3 c., 20 c., 1 r.), R. Granger Barrett (others). Photo Harrison)

1969 (12 Mar)–**73**. *W* w **12** *(sideways on* 2, 3, 4, 5, 10, 15, 60 *and* 75 *c.). Chalk-surfaced paper. P* 14.
382 2 c. multicoloured 10 30
a. Pale green printed double* .. .. 20·00
383 3 c. multicoloured 10 35
384 4 c. multicoloured 75 65
385 5 c. multicoloured 30 10
386 10 c. scarlet, black and flesh 75 10
387 15 c. ochre, black and cobalt 30 10
388 20 c. multicoloured 65 15
a. Glazed ordinary paper (20.2.73) 30 90
389 25 c. red, black and pale apple-green 30 40
a. Glazed ordinary paper (22.1.71) .. .. 3·00 80
390 30 c. multicoloured .. .. .. 1·50 50
a. Glazed, ordinary paper (20.2.73) .. 1·50 2·00
391 35 c. multicoloured 65 35
a. Glazed ordinary paper (3.2.71) 90 30
392 40 c. multicoloured .. .. .. 35 1·00
a. Glazed ordinary paper (20.2.73) .. .. 1·00 1·75
393 50 c. multicoloured .. .. .. 1·00 10
a. Red omitted .. .. .. 50·00
b. Glazed ordinary paper (22.1.71) .. 1·00 10
ba. Red printed double .. .. ..
394 60 c. black, rose and ultramarine .. .. 1·50 10
395 75 c. multicoloured .. .. .. 1·50 1·00
396 1 r. multicoloured 60 10
a. Glazed ordinary paper (22.1.71) .. .. 1·25 15
397 2 r. 50, multicoloured .. .. .. 2·75 4·25
a. Glazed ordinary paper (20.2.73) .. .. 2·00 5·00
398 5 r. multicoloured .. .. .. 4·50 6·00
a. Glazed ordinary paper (22.1.71) .. .. 6·00 5·00
399 10 r. multicoloured .. .. .. 2·50 4·00
382/99 .. .. *Set of* 18 18·00 17·00
388a/98a .. .. *Set of* 9 15·00 14·50

Designs:—3 c. Red Reef Crab; 4 c. Episcopal Mitre; 5 c. Bourse; 10 c. Starfish; 15 c. Sea Urchin; 20 c. Fiddler Crab; 25 c. Spiny Shrimp; 30 c. Single Harp Shells, and Double Harp Shell; 35 c. Argonaute; 40 c. Nudibranch; 50 c. Violet and Orange Spider Shells; 60 c. Blue Marlin; 75 c. *Conus clytospira*; 1 r. Dolphin; 2 r. 50, Spiny Lobster, 5 r. Sacré Chien Rouge; 10 r. Croissant Queue Jaune.

*No. 382a. occurs from a sheet on which a second printing of the pale green appears above the normal.

Nos. 385/6 and 389 exist in coils constructed from normal sheets.

See also Nos. 437/54 and 475/91.

117 Gandhi as Law Student **124** Frangourinier Cane-crusher (18th cent)

(Des J. W. Litho Format)

1969 (1 July). *Birth Centenary of Mahatma Gandhi. T* **117** *and similar vert designs. Multicoloured. W* w **12**. *P* 13½.
400 2 c. Type **117** 10 10
401 15 c. Gandhi as stretcher-bearer during Zulu Revolt 20 10
402 50 c. Gandhi as Satyagrahi in South Africa .. 25 20
403 60 c. Gandhi at No. 10 Downing Street, London 25 10
404 1 r. Gandhi in Mauritius, 1901 .. .. 30 10
405 2 r. 50, Gandhi, the "Apostle of Truth and Non-Violence" .. .. .. 80 1·00
400/5 .. .. *Set of* 6 1·75 1·25
MS406 153 × 153 mm. Nos. 400/5 .. .. 3·50 5·50

(Des V. Whiteley. Photo Enschedé)

1969 (22 Dec).* *150th Anniv of Telfair's Improvements to the Sugar Industry. T* **124** *and similar multicoloured designs. W* w **12** *(sideways on* 2 *c. to* 1 *r.), P* 11½ × 11 *(*2 *r.* 50*) or* 11 × 11½ *(others).*
407 2 c. Three-roller Vertical Mill 10 20
408 15 c. Type **124** 10 10
409 60 c. Beau Rivage Factory, 1867 .. .. 10 10
410 1 r. Mon Désert-Alma Factory, 1969 .. .. 10 10
411 2 r. 50, Dr. Charles Telfair *(vert)* 25 50
407/11 .. .. *Set of* 5 45 60
MS412 159 × 88 mm. Nos. 407/11†. Wmk sideways. P 11 × 11½ .. .. 1·25 2·00

*This was the local release date but the Crown Agents issued the stamps on 15 December.

† In the miniature sheet the 2 r. 50 is perf 11 at the top and imperf on the other three sides.

EXPO '70'
OSAKA

(128)

129 Morne Plage, Mountain and Lufthansa Airliner

1970 (7 Apr). *World Fair, Osaka. Nos.* 394 *and* 396 *optd with T* **128** *by Harrison & Sons.*

413	60 c. black, rose and ultramarine	10	10
414	1 r. multicoloured	10	10

(Des H. Rose. Litho G. Gehringer, Kaiserslautern, Germany)

1970 (2 May). *Inauguration of Lufthansa Flight, Mauritius-Frankfurt. T* **129** *and similar multicoloured design. P* 14.

415	25 c. Type **129**	10	10
416	50 c. Airliner and Map (*vert*)	10	10

131 Lenin as a Student 133 2d. "Post Office" Mauritius and original Post Office

(Photo State Ptg Works, Moscow)

1970 (15 May). *Birth Centenary of Lenin. T* **131** *and similar vert design. P* 12 × 11½.

417	15 c. blackish green and silver	10	10
418	75 c. blackish brown and gold	20	15

Design:—75 c. Lenin as Founder of U.S.S.R.

(Des and litho D.L.R.)

1970 (15 Oct). *Port Louis, Old and New. T* **133** *and similar horiz designs. Multicoloured. W* w **12** (*sideways*). *P* 14.

419	5 c. Type **133**	10	10
420	15 c. G.P.O. Building (built 1870)	10	10
421	50 c. Mail Coach (c. 1870)	10	10
422	75 c. Port Louis Harbour (1970)	15	10
423	2 r. 50, Arrival of Pierre A. de Suffren (1783)	35	60
419/23	.. .. *Set of* 5	60	70
MS424	165 × 95 mm. Nos. 419/23	2·75	5·50

138 U.N. Emblem and Symbols

(Des Jennifer Toombs. Litho Format)

1970 (24 Oct). *25th Anniv of United Nations. W* w **12** (*sideways*). *P* 14½.

425 **138**	10 c. multicoloured	10	10
426	60 c. multicoloured	10	10

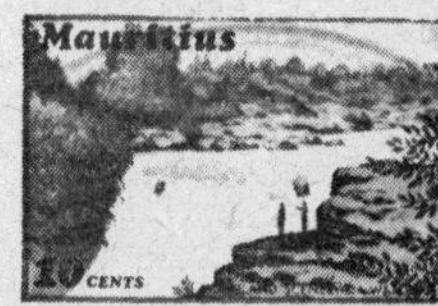

139 Rainbow over Waterfall

(Des R. Granger Barrett from local ideas (60 c.), R. Granger Barrett from local ideas and adapted by N. Mossae (others). Litho Format)

1971 (12 Apr). *Tourism. T* **139** *and similar horiz designs. Multicoloured. W* w **12** (*sideways*). *P* 14.

427	10 c. Type **139**	15	10
428	15 c. Trois Mamelles Mountains	15	10
429	60 c. Beach scene	30	10
430	2 r. 50, Marine life	1·00	1·50
427/30	.. .. *Set of* 4	1·40	1·50

Nos. 427/30 are inscribed on the reverse with details of tourist attractions in Mauritius.

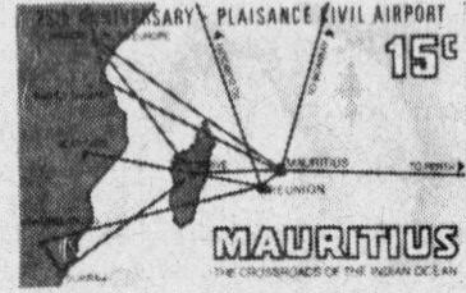

140 "Crossroads" of Indian Ocean

(Des R. Granger Barrett (60 c.) or V. Whiteley (others). Litho Harrison)

1971 (23 Oct). *25th Anniv of Plaisance Airport. T* **140** *and similar horiz designs. Multicoloured. W* w **12** (*sideways on* 15 *c.*). *P* 14.

431	15 c. Type **140**	10	10
432	60 c. "Boeing 707" and Terminal Buildings ..	25	10
433	1 r. Air Hostesses on gangway	30	10
434	2 r. 50, *Roland Garros* (aeroplane), Choisy Airfield, 1937	1·50	2·75
431/4	.. .. *Set of* 4	1·90	2·75

141 Princess Margaret Orthopaedic Centre

(Des and litho Harrison)

1971 (2 Nov). *Third Commonwealth Medical Conference. T* **141** *and similar horiz design. Multicoloured. W* w **12**. *P* 14 × 13½.

435	10 c. Type **141**	10	10
436	75 c. Operation Theatre in National Hospital	15	15

1972–74. *As Nos.* 382/99 *but W* w **12** *upright* (2, 3, 4, 5, 10, 15, 60, 75 *c.*) *or sideways* (*others*).

A. *Glazed, ordinary paper*. B. *Chalk-surfaced paper*

		A		B	
437	2 c. multicoloured	10	25	20	60
438	3 c. multicoloured	40	1·50	20	60
439	4 c. multicoloured	†		1·75	2·25
440	5 c. multicoloured	1·50	20	30	10
441	10 c. scarlet, black and flesh ..	2·00	20	1·50	20
442	15 c. ochre, black and cobalt ..	50	40	35	10
443	20 c. multicoloured	†		35	50
444	25 c. red, black & apple-green ..	†		35	55
445	30 c. multicoloured	†		1·25	1·75
446	35 c. multicoloured	†		3·00	50
	a. Orange-brown omitted ..	†		40·00	—
447	40 c. multicoloured	†		2·00	2·25
448	50 c. multicoloured	†		35	10
	a. Red omitted	†		—	—
449	60 c. black, rose & ultramarine	60	60	65	10
	a. Rose omitted	†		40·00	—
450	75 c. multicoloured	1·75	4·00	1·75	95
451	1 r. multicoloured	†		70	20
452	2 r. 50, multicoloured ..	†		2·00	3·50
453	5 r. multicoloured	†		3·00	2·00
	a. Greenish blue printed double	†		24·00	—
454	10 r. multicoloured	†		5·00	8·00
437/450A	.. .. *Set of* 7	6·25	6·50		
437/454B	.. .. *Set of* 18			22·00	22·00

Nos. 440B and 444B exist in coils, constructed from normal sheets.

Dates of issue:

Glazed paper—10.1.72, 5 c., 10 c.; 20.2.73, 2 c., 3 c., 15 c., 60 c., 75 c.

Chalk-surfaced paper—8.11.73, 10 c., 20 c., 30 c., 35 c., 40 c., 75 c., 1 r., 10 r.; 12.12.73, 25 c., 50 c., 2 r. 50, 5 r.; 25.2.74, 5 c., 15 c., 60 c.; 13.6.74, 2 c., 3 c., 4 c.

142 Queen Elizabeth and Prince Philip

(Des and photo Harrison)

1972 (24 Mar). *Royal Visit. T* **142** *and similar multicoloured design. W* w **12**. *P* 14.

455	15 c. Type **142**	15	10
456	2 r. 50, Queen Elizabeth II (*vert*)	1·75	2·00

143 Theatre Façade

(Des and litho Harrison)

1972 (26 June). *150th Anniversary of Port Louis Theatre. T* **143** *and similar horiz design. Multicoloured. W* w **12**. *P* 14.

457	10 c. Type **143**	10	10
458	1 r. Theatre Auditorium	20	10

144 Pirate Dhow

(Des and litho Harrison)

1972 (17 Nov). *Pirates and Privateers. T* **144** *and similar multicoloured designs. W* w **12** (*sideways on* 60 *c. and* 1 *r.*). *P* 14½ × 14 (60 *c.*, 1 *r.*) *or* 14 × 14½ (*others*).

459	15 c. Type **144**	35	10
460	60 c. Treasure chest (*vert*)	60	10
461	1 r. Lemene and *L'Hirondelle* (*vert*)	75	15
462	2 r. 50, Robert Surcouf	3·00	4·75
459/62	.. .. *Set of* 4	4·25	4·75

145 Mauritius University 146 Map and Hands

(Des and litho Harrison)

1973 (10 Apr). *Fifth Anniv of Independence. T* **145** *and similar horiz designs. Multicoloured. W* w **12** (*sideways*). *P* 14.

463	15 c. Type **145**	10	10
464	60 c. Tea Development	10	10
465	1 r. Bank of Mauritius	10	10
463/5	.. .. *Set of* 3	20	15

(Des and litho Harrison)

1973 (25 Apr). *O.C.A.M.* Conference. T* **146** *and similar multicoloured design. W* w **12** (*sideways on* 10 *c.*). *P* 14½ × 14 (10 *c.*) *or* 14 × 14½ (2 *r.* 50).

466	10 c. O.C.A.M. emblem (*horiz*)	10	10
467	2 r. 50, Type **146**	40	45

*O.C.A.M. = Organisation Commune Africaine Malgache et Mauricienne.

147 W.H.O. Emblem

(Des and litho Harrison)

1973 (20 Nov). *25th Anniv of W.H.O. W* w **12**. *P* 14.

468 **147**	1 r. multicoloured	10	10
	a. Wmk sideways	20	10

148 Meteorological Station, Vacoas.

(Des and litho Harrison)

1973 (27 Nov). *I.M.O./W.M.O. Centenary. W* w **12** (*sideways*). *P* 14.

469 **148**	75 c. multicoloured	20	20

149 Capture of the *Kent*, 1800 150 P. Commerson (naturalist)

(Des and litho Harrison)

1974 (21 Mar). *Birth Bicent of Robert Surcouf* (*privateer*). *W* w **12** (*sideways*). *P* 14.

470 **149**	60 c. multicoloured	30	30

(Des and litho Harrison)

1974 (18 Apr). *Death Bicent of Philibert Commerson* (1973). *W* w **12**. *P* 14½.

471 **150**	2 r. 50, multicoloured	25	40

151 Cow being Milked

(Des and litho Harrison)

1974 (23 Oct). *Eighth F.A.O. Regional Conference for Africa, Mauritius.* W w **12** (*sideways*). *P* 14.
472 **151** 60 c. multicoloured 10 10

152 Mail Train

(Des and litho Harrison)

1974 (4 Dec). *Centenary of Universal Postal Union.* *T* **152** *and similar horiz design. Multicoloured.* W w **12**. *P* 14.
473 15 c. Type **152** 30 15
474 1 r. New G.P.O., Port Louis 30 20

1975–77. *As Nos.* 382/99 *but* W w **14** (*sideways on* 2 *to* 15 *c.*, 60 *c. and* 75 *c.*). *Chalk-surfaced paper.*
475 2 c. multicoloured (16.8.77) .. .. .. 1·25 40
476 3 c. multicoloured (16.8.77) .. .. .. 1·25 40
477 4 c. multicoloured (16.8.77) .. .. .. 1·25 40
478 5 c. multicoloured (19.3.75) 40 40
479 15 c. ochre, black and cobalt (21.1.75) 60 55
480 20 c. multicoloured (19.3.76) 30 25
a. Grey (background) omitted £110
481 25 c. red, black and apple-green (19.3.75) .. 35 90
482 30 c. multicoloured (21.1.75) .. .. .. 35 1·50
a. Yellow omitted .. .. ..
483 35 c. multicoloured (19.3.76) 50 15
a. Orange-brown omitted .. .. .. 30·00
484 40 c. multicoloured (19.3.76) 50 50
485 50 c. multicoloured (19.3.76) 50 10
486 60 c. black, rose and ultramarine (16.8.77) .. 3·25 25
487 75 c. multicoloured (19.4.77) .. .. .. 1·25 40
488 1 r. multicoloured (19.3.76) 65 20
489 2 r. 50, multicoloured (16.8.77) .. .. 10·00 4·00
490 5 r. multicoloured (21.1.75) .. .. .. 5·00 11·00
491 10 r. multicoloured (21.1.75) .. .. .. 7·50 11·00
475/91 .. .. *Set of* 17 32·00 29·00
No. 492 vacant.

153 "Cottage Life" (F. Leroy)

(Des and litho Harrison)

1975 (6 Mar). *Aspects of Mauritian Life.* *T* **153** *and similar multicoloured designs showing paintings.* W w **14** (*sideways on* 15 *c.*, 60 *c. and* 2 *r.* 50). *P* 14.
493 15 c. Type **153** 10 10
494 60 c. "Milk Seller" (A. Richard) (*vert*) 20 10
a. Brown and stone (ornaments and frame) double .. ..
495 1 r. "Entrance of Port Louis Market" (Thuillier) 25 10
496 2 r. 50, "Washerwoman" (Max Boullée) (*vert*) 55 60
493/6 .. .. *Set of* 4 1·00 65

154 Mace across Map

(Des Harrison. Litho Questa)

1975 (21 Nov). *French-speaking Parliamentary Assemblies Conference. Port Louis.* W w **14** (*sideways*). *P* 14.
497 **154** 75 c. multicoloured 20 35

155 Woman with Lamp ("The Light of the World")

(Des A. H. Abdoolah; adapted Harrison. Litho Questa)

1975 (5 Dec). *International Women's Year.* W w **14** (*sideways*). *P* 14½.
498 **155** 2 r. 50, multicoloured .. .. 35 1·00

156 Parched Landscape

(Des Harrison (50 c.), J.W. Ltd (60 c.) Litho Questa)

1976 (26 Feb). *Drought in Africa.* *T* **156** *and similar design. Multicoloured.* W w **14** (*sideways on* 50 *c.*). P 14.
499 50 c. Type **156** 15 15
500 60 c. Map of Africa and carcass (*vert*) 15 15

157 *Pierre Loti*, 1953–70

(Des J. W. Litho Questa)

1976 (2 July). *Mail Carriers to Mauritius.* *T* **157** *and similar horiz designs. Multicoloured.* W w **14** (*sideways*). *P* 14½ × 14.
501 10 c. Type **157** 15 10
502 15 c. *Secunder*, 1907 .. .. 20 10
503 50 c. *Hindoostan*, 1842 .. .. 45 15
504 60 c. *St. Geran*, 1740 .. .. 50 15
505 2 r. 50, *Maën*, 1638 .. .. 2·00 3·75
501/5 .. .. *Set of* 5 3·00 3·75
MS506 115 × 138 mm. Nos. 501/5 .. .. .. 3·25 4·50

158 "The Flame of Hindi carried across the Seas"

159 Conference Logo and Map of Mauritius

(Des N. Nagalingum (Type **158**), C. R. Prakashi and R. B. Kailash (1 r. 20); adapted J. W. Litho Questa)

1976 (28 Aug). *Second World Hindi Convention.* *T* **158** *and similar horiz design. Multicoloured.* W w **14** (*sideways*). *P* 14.
507 10 c. Type **158** 10 10
508 75 c. Type **158** 10 15
509 1 r. 20, Hindi script 20 40
507/9 .. .. *Set of* 3 25 50

(Des J. W. Litho Questa)

1976 (22 Sept). *22nd Commonwealth Parliamentary Association Conference.* *T* **159** *and similar vert design. Multicoloured.* W w **14**. *P* 14.
510 1 r. Type **159** 15 10
511 2 r. 50, Conference logo 55 80

160 King Priest and Breastplate

161 Sega Scene

(Des J. W. Litho Walsall)

1976 (15 Dec). *Moenjodaro Excavations, Pakistan.* *T* **160** *and similar vert designs. Multicoloured.* W w **14**. *P* 14.
512 60 c. Type **160** 15 10
513 1 r. House with well and goblet 25 10
514 2 r. 50, Terracotta figurine and necklace .. 70 45
512/14 .. .. *Set of* 3 1·00 50

(Des BG Studio. Litho J.W.)

1977 (20 Jan). *Second World Black and African Festival of Arts and Culture, Nigeria.* W w **14** (*sideways*). *P* 13.
515 **161** 1 r. multicoloured 20 15

MINIMUM PRICE

The minimum price quote is 10p which represents a handling charge rather than a basis for valuing common stamps. For further notes about prices see introductory pages.

162 The Queen with Sceptre and Rod

163 *Hugonia tomentosa*

(Des L. Curtis. Litho Harrison)

1977 (7 Feb). *Silver Jubilee.* *T* **162** *and similar vert designs. Multicoloured.* W w **14** (*sideways*). *P* 14½ × 14.
516 50 c. The Queen at Mauritius Legislative Assembly, 1972 .. .. 20 10
517 75 c. Type **162** 25 10
518 5 r. Presentation of Sceptre and Rod 75 75
516/18 .. .. *Set of* 3 1·10 75

(Des Jennifer Toombs. Litho Questa)

1977 (22 Sept). *Indigenous Flowers.* *T* **163** *and similar multicoloured designs.* W w **14** (*sideways on* 20 *c. and* 1 *r.* 50). *P* 14.
519 20 c. Type **163** 10 10
520 1 r. *Ochna mauritiana* (*vert*) 20 10
521 1 r. 50, *Dombeya acutangula* 30 20
522 5 r. *Trochetia blackburniana* (*vert*) .. .. 1·00 1·25
519/22 .. .. *Set of* 4 1·40 1·40
MS523 130 × 130 mm. Nos. 519/22. Wmk sideways 2·50 3·50

164 "Twin Otter"

165 Portuguese Map of Mauritius, 1519

(Des A. Theobald. Litho Questa)

1977 (31 Oct). *Inaugural International Flight of Air Mauritius.* *T* **164** *and similar horiz designs. Multicoloured.* W w **14** (*sideways*). *P* 14½ × 14.
524 25 c. Type **164** 10 10
525 50 c. "Twin Otter" and Air Mauritius emblem 10 10
526 75 c. Piper "Navajo" and Boeing "747" .. 20 10
527 5 r. Boeing "707" .. .. 1·10 1·25
524/7 .. .. *Set of* 4 1·25 1·25
MS528 110 × 152 mm. Nos. 524/7 .. .. 2·00 2·75

(Des Harrison. Litho J.W.)

1978 (12 Mar)–**84**. *Designs as T* **165** *in light brown, chestnut and black* (25 *r.*) *or multicoloured* (*others*). W w **14** (*sideways on horiz designs*). *P* 13½. A. *Without imprint.* B. *With imprint date at foot.*

No.	Description	A		B	
529	10 c. Type **165**	10	10	10	10
530	15 c. Dutch Occupation, 1638–1710 (*horiz*)	10	10	†	
531	20 c. Van Keulen's map, *c.* 1700 (*horiz*)	25	10	†	
532	25 c. Settlement on Rodriguez, 1691	15	10	25	25
533	35 c. French charter, 1715	15	10	15	10
534	50 c. Construction of Port Louis, *c.* 1736 (*horiz*)	10	10	10	10
535	60 c. Pierre Poivre, *c.* 1767	10	10	†	
536	70 c. Bellin's map, 1763 (*horiz*)	10	10	†	
537	75 c. First coinage, 1794	25	20	10	10
538	90 c. Battle of Grand Port, 1810 (*horiz*)	10	10	†	
539	1 r. British landing, 1810 (*horiz*)	15	10	10	10
540	1 r. 20, Government House, *c.* 1840 (*horiz*)	10	10	†	
541	1 r. 25, Lady Gomm's ball, 1847	20	15	10	10
542	1 r. 50, Indian immigration, 1835 (*horiz*)	10	15	†	
543	2 r. Race course, *c.* 1870 (*horiz*)	40	25	50	15
544	3 r. Place d'Armes, *c.* 1880 (*horiz*)	25	30	†	
545	5 r. Royal Visit postcard, 1901 (*horiz*)	45	50	55	60
546	10 r. Royal College, 1914 (*horiz*)	80	85	†	
547	15 r. Unfurling Mauritian flag, 1968	1·25	1·40	†	
548	25 r. First Mauritian Governor-General and Prime Minister (*horiz*)	2·00	2·25	†	
529/48	*Set of* 20	6·25	6·25		

Dates of issue:—12.3.78, Nos. 529A/48A; 15.6.83, Nos. 537B, 541B, 543B; 1.84, No. 533B; 11.84, Nos. 529B, 532B, 534B; 4.85, No. 539B; 8.5.85, No. 545B.

Nos. 533B, 537B, 541B and 543B exist with different imprint dates.

For 35 c. as No. 533B, but perforated 14½ see No. 737 and for the 20 c., 25 c. and 2 r. watermarked w **16** see Nos. 740/52.

166 Mauritius Dodo 167 Problem of Infection, World War I

(Des Jennifer Toombs. Litho Questa)

1978 (21 Apr). *25th Anniv of Coronation. T* **166** *and similar vert designs. P* 15.

549   3 r. grey-blue, black and new blue 25 45
  a. Sheetlet, Nos. 549/51, each × 2 . . . . 1·75
550   3 r. multicoloured 25 45
551   3 r. grey-blue, black and new blue 25 45
549/51 . . . . *Set of* 3 65 1·25

Designs:—No. 549, Antelope of Bohun; 550, Queen Elizabeth II.

Nos. 549/51 were printed together in small sheets of 6, containing two *se-tenant* strips of 3 with horizontal gutter margin between.

(Des Jennifer Toombs. Litho Enschedé)

1978 (3 Aug). *50th Anniv of Discovery of Penicillin. T* **167** *and similar horiz designs. W w* **14** *(sideways). P* 13½ × 14.

552 20 c. multicoloured 15 10
553   1 r. multicoloured 35 10
554   1 r. 50, black, olive-bistre & dp bluish grn . . 55 20
555   5 r. multicoloured . . . . 1·50 1·25
552/5 . . . . *Set of* 4 2·25 1·40
MS556 150 × 90 mm. Nos. 552/5 . . . . 2·25 3·00

Designs:—1 r. First mould-growth, 1928; 1 r. 50, *Penicillium notatum*; 5 r. Sir Alexander Fleming.

168 Citrus Butterfly 169 Ornate Table

(Des G. Drummond. Litho Walsall)

1978 (21 Sept). *World Wildlife. T* **168** *and similar horiz designs. Multicoloured. W w* **14** *(sideways). P* 13½ × 14.

557 20 c. Type **168** 15 10
558   1 r. Geckos 20 10
559   1 r. 50 Greater Mascarene Flying Fox . . 30 30
560   5 r. Mauritius Kestrel . . . . . . 1·75 2·40
557/60 . . . . *Set of* 4 2·10 2·50
MS561 154 × 148 mm. Nos. 557/60 . . . . 3·00 4·50

(Des C. Abbott. Litho Questa)

1978 (21 Dec). *Bicentenary of Reconstruction of Chateau Le Réduit. T* **169** *and similar vert designs. Multicoloured. W w* **14**. *P* 14½ × 14.

562 15 c. Type **169** 10 10
563 75 c. Chateau Le Réduit 10 10
564   3 r. Le Réduit gardens 30 45
562/4 . . . . *Set of* 3 40 50

170 Whitcomb Diesel Locomotive "65H.P.", 1949 171 Father Laval and Crucifix

(Des G. Hutchins. Litho Questa)

1979 (1 Feb). *Railway Locomotives. T* **170** *and similar horiz designs. Multicoloured. W w* **14** *(sideways). P* 14½.

565 20 c. Type **170** 10 10
566   1 r. *Sir William*, 1922 . . . . . . 25 10
567   1 r. 50, Kitson type, 1930 . . . . . . 35 45
568   2 r. Garratt type, 1927 . . . . . . 50 85
565/8 . . . . *Set of* 4 1·10 1·25
MS569 128 × 128 mm. Nos. 565/8 . . . . 1·75 2·00

(Des J. W. Litho Questa)

1979 (30 Apr). *Beatification of Father Laval (missionary). T* **171** *and similar multicoloured designs. W w* **14** *(sideways on* 5 *r). P* 14.

570 20 c. Type **171** 10 10
571   1 r. 50, Father Laval 10 10
572   5 r. Father Laval's tomb (*horiz*) 35 50
570/2 . . . . *Set of* 3 40 55
MS573 150 × 96 mm. Nos. 570/2 (wmk upright) . . 90 1·40

172 Astronaut descending from Lunar Module 173 Great Britain 1855 4d. Stamp and Sir Rowland Hill

(Manufactured by Walsall)

1979 (20 July). *10th Anniv of Moon Landing. T* **172** *and similar vert designs. Multicoloured. Imperf × roul* 5*. *Self-adhesive (from booklets).*

574 20 c. Type **172** 15 15
  a. Booklet pane. Nos. 574/6 . . . . 2·25
  b. Booklet pane. Nos. 574/5, each × 3 . . 2·25
575   3 r. Astronaut performing experiment on Moon 70 80
576   5 r. Astronaut on Moon . . . . . . 1·50 2·25
574/6 . . . . *Set of* 3 2·10 2·75

*Nos. 574/6 are separated by various combinations of rotary-knife (giving a straight edge) and roulette.

(Des J. W. Litho Questa)

1979 (27 Aug). *Death Centenary of Sir Rowland Hill. T* **173** *and similar vert designs showing stamps and Sir Rowland Hill. Multicoloured. W w* **14**. *P* 14.

577 25 c. Type **173** 10 10
578   2 r. 1954 60 c. definitive 35 40
579   5 r. 1847 1d. "POST OFFICE" . . . . 70 1·00
577/9 . . . . *Set of* 3 1·00 1·25
MS580 120 × 89 mm. 3 r. 1847 2d. "POST OFFICE" 60 90

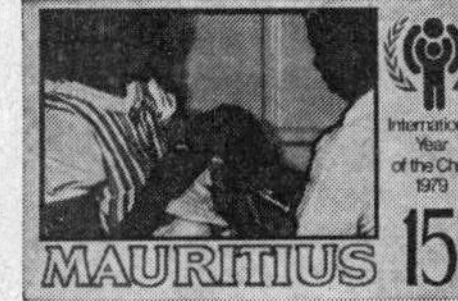

174 Young Child being Vaccinated

(Des V. Whiteley Studio. Litho Questa)

1979 (11 Oct). *International Year of the Child. T* **174** *and similar designs in black, ultramarine and bright blue* (1 *r.*) *or multi-coloured (others). W w* **14** *(sideways on* 15, 25 *c.,* 1 *r.* 50, *and* 3 *r.). P* 14½ × 14.

581 15 c. Type **174** 10 10
582 25 c. Children playing 10 10
583   1 r. I.Y.C. emblem (*vert*) 10 10
584   1 r. 50, Girls in chemistry laboratory . . 15 20
585   3 r. Boy operating lathe 30 50
581/5 . . . . *Set of* 5 60 75

175 The Liénard Obelisk 176 *Emirne*

(Des L. Curtis. Litho Questa)

1980 (24 Jan). *Pamplemousses Botanical Gardens. T* **175** *and similar horiz designs. Multicoloured. W w* **14** *(sideways). P* 14 × 14½.

586 20 c. Type **175** 10 10
587 25 c. Poivre Avenue 10 10
588   1 r. Varieties of Vacoas 15 10
589   2 r. Giant Water Lilies 25 30
590   5 r. Mon Plaisir (mansion) 45 85
586/90 . . . . *Set of* 5 90 1·25
MS591 152 × 105 mm. Nos. 586/90 . . . . 1·25 1·60

(Des J. W. Litho Walsall)

1980 (6 May). *"London 1980" International Stamp Exhibition. Mail-carrying Ships. T* **176** *and similar horiz designs. Multi-coloured. W w* **14** *(sideways). P* 14½ × 14.

592 25 c. Type **176** 10 10
593   1 r. *Boissevain* 10 10
594   2 r. *La Boudeuse* 20 10
595   5 r. *Sea Breeze* 40 45
592/5 . . . . *Set of* 4 65 65

PRICES OF SETS

Set prices are given for many issues, generally those containing three stamps or more. Definitive sets include one of each value or major colour change, but do not cover different perforations, die types or minor shades. Where a choice is possible the set prices are based on the cheapest versions of the stamps included in the listings.

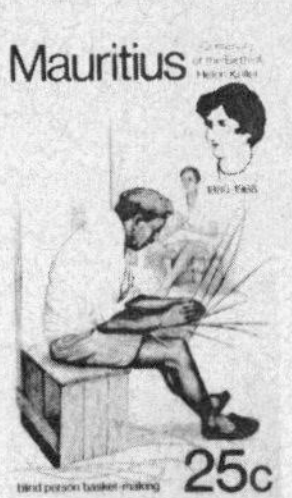

177 Blind Person Basket-making 178 Prime Minister Sir Seewoosagur Ramgoolam

(Des J. W. Litho Harrison)

1980 (27 June). *Birth Centenary of Helen Keller (campaigner for the handicapped). T* **177** *and similar vert designs. Multicoloured. W w* **14**. *P* 14.

596 25 c. Type **177** 10 10
597   1 r. Deaf child under instruction 15 10
598   2 r. 50, Helen reading braille 35 25
599   5 r. Helen at graduation, 1904 . . . . 65 70
596/9 . . . . *Set of* 4 1·10 90

(Des Walsall. Litho and gold foil embossed Questa)

1980 (18 Sept). *80th Birthday and 40th Year in Parliament of Prime Minister Sir Seewoosagur Ramgoolam. W w* **14**. *P* 13½.

600 **178** 15 r. multicoloured . . . . . . 1·25 1·40

No. 600 was printed in sheets of 4 stamps.

179 Headquarters, Mauritius Institute

(Des BG Studio. Litho J.W.)

1980 (1 Oct). *Centenary of Mauritius Institute. T* **179** *and similar horiz designs. Multicoloured. W w* **14** *(sideways). P* 13.

601 25 c. Type **179** 10 10
602   2 r. Rare copy of Veda 20 10
603   2 r. 50, Rare cone 25 15
604   5 r. "Le Torrent" (painting by Harpignies) . . 40 50
601/4 . . . . *Set of* 4 80 70

180 *Hibiscus liliiflorus* 181 Beau-Bassin/Rose Hill

(Des Jennifer Toombs. Litho Questa)

1981 (15 Jan). *Flowers. T* **180** *and similar vert designs. Multi-coloured. W w* **14**. *P* 14.

605 25 c. Type **180** 10 10
606   2 r. *Erythrospermum monticolum* 30 35
607   2 r. 50, *Chasalia boryana* 40 45
608   5 r. *Hibiscus columnaris* . . . . . . 70 1·00
605/8 . . . . *Set of* 4 1·25 1·75

(Des. L. Curtis. Litho J.W.)

1981 (10 Apr). *Coats of Arms of Mauritius Towns. T* **181** *and similar vert designs. Multicoloured. W w* **14**. *P* 13½ × 13.

609 25 c. Type **181** 10 10
610   1 r. 50, Curepipe 20 20
611   2 r. Quatre-Bornes 25 25
612   2 r. 50, Vacoas/Phoenix 30 30
613   5 r. Port Louis 55 55
609/13 . . . . *Set of* 5 1·25 1·25
MS614 130 × 130 mm. Nos. 609/13. *P* 14 . . . . 1·50 2·25

182 Prince Charles as Colonel-in-Chief, Royal Regiment of Wales 183 Emmanuel Anquetil and Guy Rozemont

(Des J. W. Litho Questa)

981 (22 July). *Royal Wedding. T* **182** *and similar vert designs. Multicoloured.* W w **14**. *P* 14.
15 25 c. Wedding bouquet from Mauritius 10 10
16 2 r. 50, Type **182** 40 15
17 10 r. Prince Charles and Lady Diana Spencer 1·25 90
15/17 .. .. *Set of* 3 1·50 1·00

(Des G. Vasarhelyi. Litho Questa)

1981 (27 Aug). *Famous Politicians and Physician* (5 *r*). *T* **183** *and similar horiz designs.* W w **14** (*sideways*). *P* 14½.
618 20 c. black and carmine 10 10
619 25 c. black and lemon 10 10
620 1 r. 25, black and emerald 20 15
621 1 r. 50, black and rose-red 25 15
622 2 r. black and ultramarine 30 20
623 2 r. 50, black and orange-brown 35 25
624 5 r. black and turquoise-blue 55 70
618/24 .. .. *Set of* 7 1·60 1·40

Designs:—25 c. Remy Ollier and Sookdeo Bissoondoyal; 1 r. 25, Maurice Curé and Barthélemy Ohsan; 1 r. 50, Sir Guy Forget and Renganaden Seeneevassen; 2 r. Sir Abdul Razak Mohamed and Jules Koenig; 2 r. 50, Abdoollatiff Mahomed Osman and Dazzi Rama (Pandit Sahadeo); 5 r. Sir Thomas Lewis and electrocardiogram.

184 Drummer and Piper **185** "Skills"

(Des Jennifer Toombs. Litho Format)

1981 (16 Sept). *Religion and Culture. T* **184** *and similar multi-coloured designs.* W w **14** (*sideways on* 20 *c. and* 5 *r.*). *P* 14 × 13½ (20 *c.*), 13½ × 14 (2 *r.*) *or* 13½ (5 *r.*).
625 20 c. Type **184** 10 10
626 2 r. Swami Sivananda (*vert*) 25 35
627 5 r. Chinese Pagoda .. .. 60 1·25
625/7 .. .. *Set of* 3 80 1·50

The 20 c. value commemorates the World Tamil Culture Conference (1980).

(Des BG Studio. Litho Questa)

1981 (15 Oct). *25th Anniv of Duke of Edinburgh Award Scheme. T* **185** *and similar vert designs. Multicoloured.* W w **14**. *P* 14.
628 25 c. Type **185** 10 10
629 1 r. 25, "Service" 10 10
630 5 r. "Expeditions" 25 30
631 10 r. Duke of Edinburgh 50 70
628/31 .. .. *Set of* 4 75 1·00

186 Ka'aba (sacred shrine, Great Mosque of Mecca) **187** Scout Emblem

(Des Jennifer Toombs. Litho Questa)

1981 (26 Nov). *Moslem Year* 1400 *A.H. Commemoration. T* **186** *and similar vert designs. Multicoloured.* W w **14**. *P* 14½ × 14.
632 25 c. Type **186** 10 10
633 2 r. Mecca 25 35
634 5 r. Mecca and Ka'aba .. .. .. 60 1·25
632/4 .. .. *Set of* 3 80 1·50

(Des C. Abbott. Litho Walsall)

1982 (22 Feb). *75th Anniv of Boy Scout Movement and 70th Anniv of Scouting in Mauritius. T* **187** *and similar horiz designs.* W w **14** (*sideways*). *P* 14 × 14½.
635 25 c. deep lilac and light green 10 10
636 2 r. deep brown and brown-ochre 30 30
637 5 r. deep green and yellow-olive 70 85
638 10 r. deep green and new blue .. .. 1·25 1·75
635/8 .. .. *Set of* 4 2·00 2·75

Designs:—2 r. Lord Baden-Powell and Baden-Powell House; 5 r. Grand Howl; 10 r. Ascent of Pieter Both.

188 Charles Darwin **189** Bride and Groom at Buckingham Palace

(Des L. Curtis. Litho Questa)

1982 (19 Apr). *150th Anniv of Charles Darwin's Voyage. T* **188** *and similar horiz designs. Multicoloured.* W w **14** (*sideways*). *P* 14.
639 25 c. Type **188** 10 10
a. Yellow (background to side panels) omitted .. ..
640 2 r. Darwin's telescope 30 40
641 2 r. 50, Darwin's elephant ride 35 50
642 10 r. H.M.S. *Beagle* beached for repairs .. 1·40 2·00
639/42 .. .. *Set of* 4 1·90 2·75

(Des Jennifer Toombs. Litho J. W.)

1982 (1 July). *21st Birthday of Princess of Wales. T* **189** *and similar vert designs. Multicoloured.* W w **14**. *P* 13.
643 25 c. Mauritius coat of arms 10 10
644 2 r. 50, Princess Diana in Chesterfield, November 1981 .. .. 30 30
645 5 r. Type **189** 50 60
646 10 r. Formal portrait .. .. 90 1·40
643/6 .. .. *Set of* 4 1·60 2·10

190 Prince and Princess of Wales with Prince William **191** Bois Fandamane Plant

(Des Harrison. Litho Walsall)

1982 (22 Sept). *Birth of Prince William of Wales.* W w **14** (*sideways*). *P* 14 × 14½.
647 **190** 2 r. 50, multicoloured 30 20

(Des Harrison. Litho Format)

1982 (15 Dec). *Centenary of Robert Koch's Discovery of Tubercle Bacillus. T* **191** *and similar vert designs. Multicoloured.* W w **14**. *P* 14.
648 25 c. Type **191** 10 10
649 1 r. 25, Central market, Port Louis 15 15
650 2 r. Bois Banane plant 25 30
651 5 r. Platte de Lézard plant 55 90
652 10 r. Dr. Robert Koch .. .. 1·00 1·75
648/52 .. .. *Set of* 5 1·75 2·75

192 Arms and Flag of Mauritius **193** Early Wall-mounted Telephone

(Des and litho J.W.)

1983 (14 Mar). *Commonwealth Day. T* **192** *and similar horiz designs. Multicoloured.* W w **14** (*sideways*). *P* 13.
653 25 c. Type **192** 10 10
654 2 r. 50, Satellite view of Mauritius 15 30
655 5 r. Harvesting sugar cane 30 75
656 10 r. Port Louis harbour .. .. .. 70 1·50
653/6 .. .. *Set of* 4 1·10 2·40

(Des G. Vasarhelyi. Litho Format)

1983 (24 June). *World Communications Year. T* **193** *and similar multicoloured designs.* W w **14** (*sideways on* 1 *r.* 25 *and* 10 *r.*). *P* 14.
657 25 c. Type **193** 10 10
658 1 r. 25, Early telegraph apparatus (*horiz*) .. 25 15
659 2 r. Earth satellite station 40 25
660 10 r. First hot air balloon in Mauritius, 1784 (*horiz*) .. .. 1·40 1·50
657/60 .. .. *Set of* 4 1·90 1·75

194 Map of Namibia **195** Fish Trap

(Des J. W. Litho Questa)

1983 (26 Aug). *Namibia Day. T* **194** *and similar vert designs. Multicoloured.* W w **14**. *P* 14.
661 25 c. Type **194** 10 10
662 2 r. 50, Hands breaking chains 40 30
663 5 r. Family and settlement 70 80
664 10 r. Diamond mining .. .. 1·25 1·75
661/4 .. .. *Set of* 4 2·25 2·50

(Des Walsall. Litho Format)

1983 (25 Sept). *Fishery Resources. T* **195** *and similar multi-coloured designs.* W w**14** (*sideways on* 1 *r. and* 10 *r.*). *P* 14.
665 25 c. Type **195** 15 10
666 1 r. Fishing boat (*horiz*) 30 15
667 5 r. Game fishing .. .. 70 1·00
668 10 r. Octopus drying (*horiz*) .. .. .. 1·10 2·00
665/8 .. .. *Set of* 4 2·00 2·75

196 Swami Dayananda **197** Adolf von Plevitz

(Des A. Theobald. Litho Questa)

1983 (3 Nov). *Death Centenary of Swami Dayananda. T* **196** *and similar vert designs. Multicoloured.* W w **14**. *P* 14.
669 25 c. Type **196** 10 10
670 35 c. Last meeting with father 10 10
671 2 r. Receiving religious instruction 20 25
672 5 r. Swami demonstrating strength 50 90
673 10 r. At a religious gathering .. .. .. 1·00 1·75
669/73 .. .. *Set of* 5 1·60 2·75

(Des L. Curtis. Litho Harrison)

1983 (8 Dec). *125th Anniv of the Arrival in Mauritius of Adolf von Plevitz (social reformer). T* **197** *and similar horiz designs. Multi-coloured.* W w **14** (*sideways*). *P* 14 × 14½.
674 25 c. Type **197** 10 10
675 1 r. 25, La Laura Government school 15 15
676 5 r. Von Plevitz addressing 1872 Commission of Enquiry 50 85
677 10 r. Von Plevitz with Indian farm workers .. 1·00 1·75
674/7 .. .. *Set of* 4 1·50 2·50

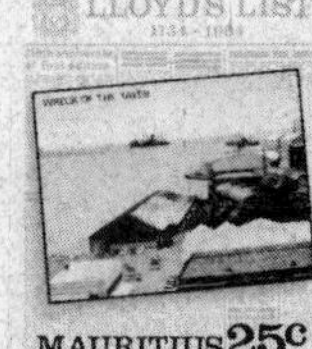

198 Courtship Chase **199** Wreck of S.S. *Tayeb*

(Des N. Arlott. Litho Format)

1984 (26 Mar). *Mauritius Kestrel. T* **198** *and similar multi-coloured designs.* W w **14** (*sideways on* 25 *c. and* 2 *r.* 50). *P* 14.
678 25 c. Type **198** 35 10
679 2 r. Kestrel in tree (*vert*) 75 40
680 2 r. 50, Young Kestrel 90 70
681 10 r. Head (*vert*) .. .. 2·00 3·00
678/81 .. .. *Set of* 4 3·50 3·75

(Des M. Joyce. Litho Questa)

1984 (23 May). *250th Anniv of "Lloyd's List" (newspaper). T* **199** *and similar vert designs. Multicoloured.* W w **14**. *P* 14½ × 14.
682 25 c. Type **199** 15 10
683 1 r. S.S. *Taher* 40 15
684 5 r. East Indiaman *Triton* .. .. .. 1·00 1·25
685 10 r. M.S. *Astor* .. .. 1·60 2·25
682/5 .. .. *Set of* 4 2·75 3·25

200 Blue Latan Palm **201** Slave Girl

(Des Jennifer Toombs. Litho Format)

1984 (23 July). *Palm Trees. T* **200** *and similar vert designs. Multi-coloured.* W w **14**. *P* 14½.
686 25 c. Type **200** 10 10
687 50 c. *Hyophorbe vaughanii* 15 10
688 2 r. 50, *Tectiphiala ferox* 70 45
689 5 r. Round Island Bottle-palm .. .. 1·25 1·50
690 10 r. *Hyophorbe amaricaulis* .. .. .. 2·00 2·25
686/90 .. .. *Set of* 5 3·75 4·00

(Des C. Abbott. Litho Walsall)

1984 (20 Aug). *150th Anniv of the Abolition of Slavery and of the Introduction of Indian Immigrants. T* **201** *and similar designs.* W w **14** (*sideways on* 2 *r.*, 10 *r.*). *P* 14½.
691 25 c. deep rose-lilac, rose-lilac and bistre .. 10 10
692 1 r. deep rose-lilac, rose-lilac and bistre .. 20 10
693 2 r. deep rose-lilac and rose-lilac 40 40
694 10 r. deep rose-lilac and rose-lilac .. .. 1·40 2·25
691/4 .. .. *Set of* 4 1·90 2·50

Designs: *Vert*—1 r. Slave market. *Horiz*—2 r. Indian immigrant family; 10 r. Arrival of Indian immigrants.

202 75th Anniversary Production of *Faust* and Leoville L'Homme

203 The Queen Mother on Clarence House Balcony

(Des Walsall. Litho Questa)

1984 (10 Sept). *Centenary of Alliance Francaise (cultural organization). T* **202** *and similar horiz designs. Multicoloured. W w* **14** *(sideways). P* 14½ × 14.

695 25 c. Type **202** 10 10
696 1 r. 25, Prize-giving ceremony and Aunauth Beejadbur 20 20
697 5 r. First headquarters and Hector Clarenc .. 70 1·10
698 10 r. Lion Mountain and Labourdonnais .. 1·25 2·00
695/8 .. .. *Set of* 4 2·00 3·00

(Des A. Theobald (15 r.), C. Abbott (others). Litho Questa)

1985 (7 June). *Life and Times of Queen Elizabeth the Queen Mother. T* **203** *and similar vert designs. Multicoloured. W w* **16**. *P* 14½ × 14.

699 25 c. The Queen Mother in 1926 .. .. 10 10
700 2 r. With Princess Margaret at Trooping the Colour 20 25
701 5 r. Type **203**.. .. .. 50 70
702 10 r. With Prince Henry at his christening (from photo by Lord Snowdon).. .. 1·00 1·25
699/702 .. .. *Set of* 4 1·60 2·00
MS703 91 × 73 mm. 15 r. Reopening the Stratford Canal, 1964. Wmk sideways .. .. 1·50 1·60

204 High Jumping

205 Adult and Fledgling Pink Pigeons

(Des Joan Thompson. Litho Walsall)

1985 (24 Aug). *2nd Indian Ocean Islands Games. T* **204** *and similar vert designs. Multicoloured. W w* **14**. *P* 14½.

704 25 c. Type **204**.. .. .. 10 10
705 50 c. Javelin-throwing 10 10
706 1 r. 25, Cycling 20 20
707 10 r. Wind surfing .. .. 1·25 1·75
704/7 .. .. *Set of* 4 1·50 1·90

(Des N. Arlott. Litho Walsall)

1985 (2 Sept). *Pink Pigeon. T* **205** *and similar vert designs. Multicoloured. W w* **16**. *P* 14.

708 25 c. Type **205**.. .. .. 30 10
709 2 r. Pink Pigeon displaying at nest .. 80 40
710 2 r. 50, On nest 90 70
711 5 r. Pair preening .. .. 1·50 2·00
708/11 .. .. *Set of* 4 3·25 2·75

206 Caverne Patates, Rodrigues

(Des D. Miller. Litho Walsall)

1985 (27 Sept). *10th Anniv of World Tourism Organization T* **206** *and similar horiz designs. Multicoloured. W w* **16** *(sideways). P* 14½.

712 25 c. Type **206**.. .. .. 10 10
713 35 c. Coloured soils, Chamarel 10 10
714 5 r. Serpent Island .. .. 80 1·00
715 10 r. Coin de Mire Island .. .. 1·40 2·00
712/15 .. .. *Set of* 4 2·10 2·75

207 Old Town Hall, Port Louis

(Des Jennifer Toombs. Litho J.W.)

1985 (22 Nov). *250th Anniv of Port Louis. T* **207** *and similar horiz designs. Multicoloured. W w* **16** *(sideways). P* 13 × 13½.

716 25 c. Type **207**.. .. .. 10 10
717 1 r. Al-Aqsa Mosque (180th anniv) .. 20 10
718 2 r. 50, Vase and trees (250th anniv of settlement of Tamil-speaking Indians) 40 30
719 10 r. Port Louis Harbour .. .. 1·25 1·75
716/19 .. .. *Set of* 4 1·75 2·00

208 Edmond Halley and Diagram

209 Maize (World Food Day)

(Des D. Hartley. Litho Walsall)

1986 (21 Feb). *Appearance of Halley's Comet. T* **208** *and similar horiz designs. Multicoloured. W w* **16** *(sideways). P* 14.

720 25 c. Type **208**.. .. .. 10 10
721 1 r. 25, Halley's Comet (1682) and Newton's Reflector.. .. .. 20 15
722 3 r. Halley's Comet passing Earth.. .. 40 45
723 10 r. *Giotto* spacecraft .. .. 1·25 1·50
720/3 .. .. *Set of* 4 1·75 2·00

(Des A. Theobald. Litho Harrison)

1986 (21 Apr). *60th Birthday of Queen Elizabeth II. Vert designs as T* **110** *of Ascension. Multicoloured. W w* **16**. *P* 14½ × 14.

724 25 c. Princess Elizabeth wearing badge of Grenadier Guards, 1942 .. .. 10 10
725 75 c. Investiture of Prince of Wales, 1969 .. 10 10
726 2 r. With Prime Minister of Mauritius, 1972 20 25
727 3 r. In Germany, 1978 .. .. 30 35
728 15 r. At Crown Agents Head Office, London, 1983 .. .. 1·50 1·60
724/8 .. .. *Set of* 5 1·90 2·10

(Des O. Bell. Litho Walsall)

1986 (25 July). *International Events. T* **209** *and similar vert designs. Multicoloured. W w* **16**. *P* 14.

729 25 c. Type **209**.. .. .. 10 10
730 1 r. African Regional Industrial Property Organization emblem (10th anniv) .. 20 10
731 1 r. 25, International Peace Year emblem .. 30 15
732 10 r. Footballer and Mauritius Football Association emblem (World Cup Football Championship, Mexico) .. .. 1·50 1·75
729/32 .. .. *Set of* 4 1·90 1·90

210 *Cryptopus elatus*

211 Hesketh Bell Bridge

(Des Harrison. Litho Walsall)

1986 (3 Oct). *Orchids. T* **210** *and similar vert designs. Multicoloured. W w* **16**. *P* 14½ × 14.

733 25 c. Type **210**.. .. .. 25 10
734 2 r. *Jumellea recta* 60 30
735 2 r. 50, *Angraecum mauritianum* 70 40
736 10 r. *Bulbophyllum longiflorum* .. .. 1·75 2·00
733/6 .. .. *Set of* 4 3·00 2·50

1986 (Nov). *As No.* 533B, *but printed litho by Questa. P* 14½.

737 35 c. French charter, 1715 .. .. 10 10

(Litho Questa)

1987 (11 Jan)–**89**. *As Nos.* 531/2, 534, 543/5 *and* 548 *but W w* **16** *(sideways on horiz designs). P* 14½.

740 20 c. Van Keulen's map, *c.* 1700 (*horiz*) .. 10 10
741 25 c. Settlement on Rodriguez, 1691 .. 10 10
743 50 c. Construction of Port Louis, *c.* 1736 (*horiz*) (16.1.89) 10 10
752 2 r. Race course, *c.* 1870 (*horiz*) .. 15 20
753 3 r. Place d'Armes, *c.* 1880 (*horiz*) (16.1.89) 25 30
754 5 r. Royal Visit postcard, 1901 (*horiz*) (16.1.89) 40 45
757 25 r. First Mauritian Governor-General and Prime Minister (*horiz*) (16.1.89) .. 2·00 2·25
740/57 .. .. *Set of* 7 2·75 3·25

No. 752 exists with different imprint dates below the design.

(Des D. Hartley. Litho Format)

1987 (22 May). *Mauritius Bridges. T* **211** *and similar horiz designs. Multicoloured. W w* **16** *(sideways). P* 14½.

758 25 c. Type **211**.. .. .. 10 10
759 50 c. Sir Colville Deverell Bridge 15 10
760 2 r. 50, Cavendish Bridge 50 35
761 5 r. Tamarin Bridge.. .. .. 90 80
762 10 r. Grand River North West Bridge .. 1·50 1·75
758/62 .. .. *Set of* 5 2·75 2·75

212 Supreme Court, Port Louis

213 Dodo Mascot

(Des N. Shewring. Litho Walsall)

1987 (2 June). *Bicentenary of the Mauritius Bar. T* **212** *and similar horiz designs. Multicoloured. W w* **16** *(sideways). P* 14 × 14½.

763 25 c. Type **212**.. .. .. 10 10
764 1 r. District Court, Flacq 15 10
765 1 r. 25, Statue of Justice 20 15
766 10 r. Barristers of 1787 and 1987 .. 1·00 1·25
763/6 .. .. *Set of* 4 1·25 1·40

(Des O. Bell. Litho Format)

1987 (5 Sept). *International Festival of the Sea. T* **213** *and similar multicoloured designs. W w* **16** *(sideways on* 25 c., 5 r.). *P* 14 × 14½ (*vert*) *or* 14½ × 14 (*horiz*).

767 25 c. Type **213**.. .. .. 10 10
768 1 r. 50, Yacht regatta (*horiz*) 35 20
769 3 r. Water skiing (*horiz*) 45 40
770 5 r. *Svanen* (barquentine) 85 85
767/70 .. .. *Set of* 4 1·50 1·40

214 Toys

215 Maison Ouvriere (Int Year of Shelter for the Homeless)

(Des G. Vasarhelyi. Litho Walsall)

1987 (30 Oct). *Industrialisation. T* **214** *and similar horiz designs. Multicoloured. W w* **14** *(sideways). P* 14.

771 20 c. Type **214**.. .. .. 10 10
772 35 c. Spinning factory 10 10
773 50 c. Rattan furniture 10 10
774 2 r. 50, Spectacle factory 35 35
775 10 r. Stone carving .. .. 1·00 1·25
771/5 .. .. *Set of* 5 1·40 1·60

(Des D. Miller. Litho Walsall)

1987 (30 Dec). *Art and Architecture. T* **215** *and similar horiz designs. W w* **16** *(sideways). P* 14 × 14½.

776 25 c. multicoloured 10 10
777 1 r. black and brownish grey 10 10
778 1 r. 25, multicoloured 10 15
779 2 r. multicoloured 20 25
780 5 r. *Svanen* (barquentine) 45 50
776/80 .. .. *Set of* 5 80 95

Designs:—1 r. "Paul et Virginie" (lithograph); 1 r. 25, Chateau de Rosnay; 2 r. "Vielle Ferme" (Boulle); 5 r. "Trois Mamelles".

216 University of Mauritius

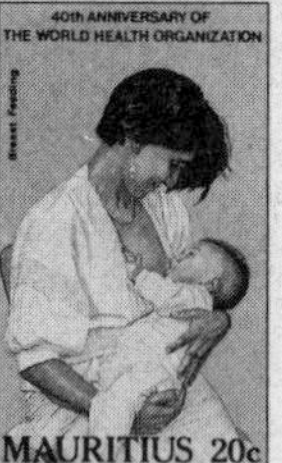

217 Breast Feeding

(Des A. Theobald. Litho B.D.T.)

1988 (11 Mar). *20th Anniv of Independence. T* **216** *and similar horiz designs. Multicoloured. W w* **14** *(sideways). P* 13½.

781 25 c. Type **216**.. .. .. 10 10
782 75 c. Anniversary gymnastic display .. 10 10
783 2 r. 50, Hurdlers and aerial view of Sir Maurice Rault Stadium 30 30
784 5 r. Air Mauritius aircraft at Sir Seewoosagur Ramgoolam International Airport 50 50
785 10 r. Governor-General Sir Veerasamy Ringadoo and Prime Minister Anerood Jugnauth 95 95
781/5 .. .. *Set of* 5 1·75 1·75

(Des D. Ashby. Litho B.D.T.)

1988 (1 July). *40th Anniv of World Health Organization. T* **217** *and similar vert designs. Multicoloured. W w* **14**. *P* 13½.

786 20 c. Type **217** 10 10
787 2 r. Baby under vaccination umbrella and germ droplets 30 25
788 3 r. Nutritious food 40 45
789 10 r. W.H.O. logo .. .. 1·10 1·10
786/9 .. .. *Set of* 4 1·60 1·60

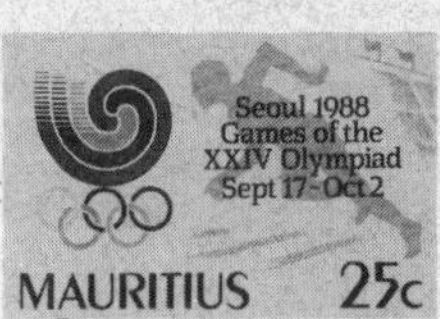

218 Modern Bank Building **219** Olympic Rings and Athlete

(Des N. Shewring (25 r.). Litho B.D.T.)

988 (1 Sept). *150th Anniv of Mauritius Commercial Bank Ltd. T* **218** *and similar multicoloured designs.* W w **14** *(sideways on 1, 25 r.). P* 13½.
90 25 c. black, blue-green and new blue .. 10 10
91 1 r. black and brown-lake .. 10 10
92 1 r. 25, multicoloured .. 15 15
93 25 r. multicoloured .. 2·50 2·75
90/3 .. *Set of* 4 2·50 2·75
Designs: *Horiz*—1 r. Mauritius Commercial Bank, 1897; 25 r. ifteen dollar bank note of 1838. *Vert*—1 r. 25, Bank arms.

(Des P. Broadbent. Litho B.D.T.)

988 (1 Oct). *Olympic Games, Seoul. T* **219** *and similar horiz designs. Multicoloured.* W w **14** *(sideways). P* 14.
94 25 c. Type **219** .. 10 10
95 35 c. Wrestling .. 10 10
96 1 r. 50, Long distance running .. 25 20
97 10 r. Swimming .. 1·00 1·10
94/7 .. *Set of* 4 1·25 1·25

220 Nature Park **221** La Tour Sumeire, Port Louis

(Des D. Miller. Litho Harrison)

1989 (11 Mar). *Protection of the Environment. T* **220** *and similar multicoloured designs.* W w **16** (40 c. *(sideways)*, 10 r.) *or* W w **14** (3 r. *(sideways)*, 4 r, 6 r). *P* 14.
802 40 c. Type **220** .. 10 10
811 3 r. Marine life .. 25 30
812 4 r. Fern Tree (*vert*) .. 30 35
814 6 r. Ecological scenery (*vert*) .. 45 50
815 10 r. *Phelsuma ornata* (gecko) on plant (*vert*) 80 85
802/15 .. *Set of* 5 1·75 1·90

(Des A. Theobald. Litho B.D.T.)

1989 (14 July). *Bicentenary of the French Revolution. T* **221** *and similar vert designs.* W w **14**. *P* 14.
818 30 c. black, emerald & pale greenish yellow 10 10
819 1 r. black, orange-brown and cinnamon .. 15 10
820 8 r. multicoloured .. 1·00 1·00
821 15 r. multicoloured .. 1·75 1·75
818/21 .. *Set of* 4 2·75 2·75
Designs:—1 r. Salle de Spectacle du Jardin; 8 r. Portrait of Comte de Malartic; 15 r. Bicentenary logo.

222 Cardinal Jean Margeot **223** Nehru

(Des L. Curtis. Litho B.D.T.)

1989 (13 Oct). *Visit of Pope John Paul II. T* **222** *and similar vert designs. Multicoloured.* W w **14**. *P* 14×13½.
822 30 c. Type **222** .. 10 10
823 40 c. Pope John Paul II and Prime Minister Jugnauth, Vatican, 1988 .. 10 10
824 3 r. Mère Marie Magdeleine de la Croix and Chapelle des Filles de Marie, Port Louis, 1864 .. 25 30
825 6 r. St. Francois d'Assise Church, Pamplemousses, 1756 .. 55 60
826 10 r. Pope John Paul II .. 90 95
822/6 .. *Set of* 5 1·60 1·75

(Des K. Clarkson. Litho B.D.T.)

1989 (14 Nov). *Birth Centenary of Jawaharlal Nehru (Indian statesman). T* **223** *and similar horiz designs. Multicoloured.* W w **16** *(sideways). P* 14.
827 40 c. Type **223** .. 10 10
828 1 r. 50, Nehru with daughter, Indira, and grandsons .. 15 20
829 3 r. Nehru and Gandhi .. 25 30
830 4 r. Nehru with Presidents Nasser and Tito 35 40
831 10 r. Nehru with children .. 90 95
827/31 .. *Set of* 5 1·50 1·75

224 Cane cutting

(Des D. Miller. Litho B.D.T.)

1990 (10 Jan). *350th Anniv of Introduction of Sugar Cane to Mauritius. T* **224** *and similar horiz designs. Multicoloured.* W w **16** *(sideways). P* 13½.
832 30 c. Type **224** .. 10 10
833 40 c. Sugar factory, 1867 .. 10 10
834 1 r. Mechanical loading of cane .. 10 10
835 25 r. Modern sugar factory .. 2·25 2·40
832/5 .. *Set of* 4 2·10 2·25

EXPRESS DELIVERY STAMPS

EXPRESS DELIVERY 15c. (E 1)

EXPRESS DELIVERY (INLAND) 15c. (E 2)

EXPRESS DELIVERY (INLAND) 15c. (E 3)

EXPRESS DELIVERY (INLAND) 15 c (E 4)

Type E 2. "(INLAND)" was inserted at a second printing on stamps already surcharged with Type E 1 (No. E1).
Type E 3. New setting made at one printing. More space above and below "(INLAND)".
Type E 4. New setting with smaller "15 c" and no stop.

1903–04. *No.* 136 *surch in red.*
E1 E 1 15 c. on 15 c. ultramarine .. 4·00 12·00
E2 E 2 15 c. on 15 c. ultramarine .. 11·00 18·00
a. "A" inverted .. £250 £275
E3 E 3 15 c. on 15 c. ultramarine .. 3·50 85
a. Surch inverted .. — £175
b. Surch double, both inverted
c. Imperf between (vert pair) .. £1500
E4 E 4 15 c. on 15 c. ultramarine (1904) .. £150 £160
a. Surch inverted
b. Surch double
c. Surch double, both inverted
d. "c" omitted .. — £1000

(FOREIGN) EXPRESS DELIVERY 18 CENTS (E 5)

1904. *T* **44** *(without value in label), wmk Crown CC, surch with Type* E **5**. *P* 14.
E5 18 c. green .. 1·50 8·00
a. Exclamation mark for "I" in "FOREIGN" £200

1904. *T* **44** *surch with Type* E **3**.
E6 15 c. grey-green (R.) .. 80 1·25
a. Surch inverted .. £160 £160
b. Surch double .. £160
c. Surch double, one "LNIAND" .. £160 £160

POSTAGE DUE STAMPS

D 1

POSTAGE DUE 10c (D 2)

(Typo Waterlow)

1933–54. *Wmk Mult Script CA. P* 15 × 14.
D1 D 1 2 c. black .. 35 50
D2 4 c. violet .. 40 65
D3 6 c. scarlet .. 40 80
D4 10 c. green .. 40 70
D5 20 c. bright blue .. 50 90
D6 50 c. deep magenta (1.3.54) .. 40 5·00
D7 1 r. orange (1.3.54) .. 65 7·00
D1/7 .. *Set of* 7 2·75 14·00
D1/5 Perf "Specimen" .. *Set of* 5 60·00

(Typo D.L.R.)

1966–72. *Chalk-surfaced paper. Wmk* w **12**. *P* 13½×14 (2 c.) *or* 15×14 *(others).*
D 8 D 1 2 c. black (11.7.67) .. 80 2·25
D 9 4 c. slate-lilac (7.1.69) .. 1·00 3·50
D10 6 c. red-orange (7.1.69) .. 1·00 4·00
a. Perf 13½×14 .. 18·00
D11 10 c. yellow-green (16.2.67) .. 30 85
D12 20 c. blue (3.1.66) .. 75 3·25
a. Deep blue (7.1.69) .. 60 3·25
D13 50 c. deep magenta (7.1.69) .. 75 5·00
a. Magenta (10.1.72) .. 75 5·50
D8/13 .. *Set of* 6 4·00 17·00

1982 (25 Oct). *Nos.* 530A/1A, 535A, 540A, 542A *and* 547A *optd as Type* D **2**, *by J. W. Dunn Printers Ltd.*
D14 10 c. on 15 c. Dutch Occupation, 1638–1710 .. 10 10
D15 20 c. on 20 c. Van Keulen's map, *circa* 1700 .. 10 10
D16 50 c. on 60 c. Pierre Poivre, *circa* 1767 .. 10 10
D17 1 r. on 1 r. 20, Government House, *circa* 1840 10 10
D18 1 r. 50 on 1 r. 50, Indian immigration, 1835 10 15
D19 5 r. on 15 r. Unfurling Mauritian flag, 1968 40 45
D14/19 .. *Set of* 6 80 90

FISCALS USED FOR POSTAGE

INLAND REVENUE (F 1)

INLAND (F 2)

REVENUE

MAURITIUS INLAND REVENUE 4c F 3

1889. *T* **19**, *wmk Crown CA, optd. P* 14.
R1 F 1 4 c. carmine .. 3·00 5·00
R2 F 2 4 c. lilac .. 2·50 9·50

(Typo D.L.R.)

1896. *Wmk Crown CA. P* 14.
R3 F 3 4 c. dull purple .. 13·00

Montserrat

A local post office operated on Montserrat from some time in the 18th century, although the first recorded postal marking does not occur until 1807. A branch of the British G.P.O. was established at Plymouth, the island capital, in 1852.

The stamps of Great Britain were used from 1858 until the overseas postal service reverted to local control on 1 April 1860.

In the interim period between 1860 and the introduction of Montserrat stamps in 1876 No. CC1 and a similar "uncrowned" handstamp were again used.

For illustrations of the handstamp and postmark types see BRITISH POST OFFICES ABROAD notes, following GREAT BRITAIN.

PLYMOUTH

CROWNED-CIRCLE HANDSTAMPS

CC1 CC 5 MONTSERRAT (R.) (15.7.1852) *Price on cover* £2500

Stamps of GREAT BRITAIN *cancelled* "A 08" *as Type* **2**.

1858 *to* **1860**.
Z1 1d. rose-red (1857), *perf* 14 .. .. £1100
Z2 4d. rose (1857)
Z3 6d. lilac (1856) .. £450
Z4 1s. green (1856)

PRICES FOR STAMPS ON COVER TO 1945

Nos. 1/2	*from* × 30
No. 3	†
Nos. 4/5	*from* × 6
Nos. 6/13	*from* × 8
Nos. 14/22	*from* × 4
No. 23	—
Nos. 24/33	*from* × 4
Nos. 35/47	*from* × 3
No. 48	—
Nos. 49/59	*from* × 3
Nos. 60/2	*from* × 15
Nos. 63/83	*from* × 3
Nos. 84/93	*from* × 4
Nos. 94/7	*from* × 3
Nos. 98/100	*from* × 8
Nos. 101/12	*from* × 5

1

(2)

3 (Die I)

(T **1** recess D.L.R.)

1876 (Sept). *Stamps of Antigua optd with T* **2**. *Wmk Crown CC. P* 14.
1 1 1d. red .. 17·00 15·00
a. Bisected (½d.) (on cover) .. † £1400
b. Inverted "S" .. £1600 £1600
2 6d. green .. 50·00 40·00
a. Bisect (used as 2½d.) (on cover)
b. Inverted "S" .. £2000 £2000
3 6d. blue-green .. £1100
a. Inverted "S" .. £5500

No. 1 was bisected and used for a ½d. in 1883. This bisected stamp is found surcharged with a small "½" in *black* and also in *red*; both were unofficial and they did not emanate from the Montserrat P.O. The 6d. in blue-green is only known unused.

(T **3** typo D.L.R.)

1880 (Jan). *Wmk Crown CC. P* 14.
4 3 2½d. red-brown .. £250 £175
5 4d. blue .. £140 40·00

1884–85. *Wmk Crown CA. P* 14.
6 3 ½d. dull green .. 1·00 5·00
7 1 1d. red .. 7·00 17·00
a. Inverted "S" .. £1300 £1300
b. Rose-red .. 13·00 14·00
ba. Bisected vert (½d.) (on cover) .. † £1300
9 3 2½d. red-brown .. £225 65·00
10 2½d. ultramarine (1885) .. 14·00 16·00
11 4d. blue .. £3250 £250
12 4d. mauve (1885) .. 3·00 3·00
10, 12 Optd "Specimen" .. *Set of* 2 £250

1884 (May). *Wmk Crown CA. P* 12.
13 1 1d. red .. 65·00 45·00
a. Inverted "S" .. £2750 £1900
b. Bisected (½d.) (on cover) .. † £1600

The stamps for Montserrat were temporarily superseded by the general issue for Leeward Islands in 1890, but the following issues were in concurrent use with the stamps inscribed "LEEWARD ISLANDS" until 1 July 1956, when Leeward Islands stamps were withdrawn and invalidated.

MINIMUM PRICE

The minimum price quote is 10p which represents a handling charge rather than a basis for valuing common stamps. For further notes about prices see introductory pages.

4 Device of the Colony

5 [image not detected: 5s MONTSERRAT 5s, POSTAGE REVENUE, FIVE SHILLINGS]

(Typo D.L.R.)

1903. (*a*) *Wmk Crown CA. P* 14.
14 4 ½d. grey-green and green .. 65 4·75
15 1d. grey-black and red .. 60 40
16 2d. grey and brown .. 5·00 8·50
17 2½d. grey and blue .. 1·50 1·75
18 3d. dull orange and deep purple .. 4·00 13·00
19 6d. dull purple and olive .. 4·00 20·00
20 1s. green and bright purple .. 10·00 16·00
21 2s. green and brown-orange .. 18·00 16·00
22 2s. 6d. green and black .. 15·00 30·00

(*b*) *Wmk Crown CC. P* 14
23 5 5s. black and scarlet .. 75·00 £140
14/23 .. *Set of* 10 £110 £225
14/23 Optd "Specimen" .. *Set of* 10 £160

1903–8. *Wmk Mult Crown CA. P* 14.
24 4 ½d. grey-green and green, **OC** .. 40 65
25 1d. grey-black and red, **C** (1908) .. 12·00 17·00
26 2d. grey and brown, **OC** .. 65 1·00
27 2½d. grey and blue, **C** (1905) .. 2·50 6·50
28 3d. dull orange and deep purple, **OC** .. 2·50 2·50
29 6d. dull purple and olive, **OC** .. 2·50 5·00
30 1s. green and bright purple, **C** (1908) .. 7·50 4·50
31 2s. green and orange, **C** (1908) .. 18·00 30·00
32 2s. 6d. green and black, **C** (1908) .. 28·00 30·00
33 5 5s. black and red, **C** (1907) .. 60·00 90·00
24/33 .. *Set of* 10 £110 £160

1908–13. *Wmk Mult Crown CA. P* 14.
35 4 ½d. deep green, **O** .. 1·25 80
36 1d. rose-red, **O** .. 1·40 30
38 2d. greyish-slate, **O** .. 1·75 8·00
39 2½d. blue, **O** .. 2·25 3·50
40 3d. purple/*yellow*, **C** .. 1·00 8·50
a. White back (1913) (Optd. S. £25) .. 2·25 15·00
43 6d. dull and deep purple, **C** .. 6·50 24·00
a. Dull and bright purple .. 7·50 24·00
44 1s. black/*green*, **C** .. 3·50 15·00
45 2s. purple and bright blue/*blue*, **C** .. 24·00 30·00
46 2s. 6d. black and red/*blue*, **C** .. 30·00 42·00
47 5 5s. red and green/*yellow*, **C** .. 48·00 55·00
35/47 .. *Set of* 10 £100 £150
35/47 Optd "Specimen" .. *Set of* 10 £190

7

8

WAR STAMP
(9)

(T **7/8** typo D.L.R.)

1914. *Wmk Mult Crown CA. P* 14.
48 7 5s. red and green/*yellow*, **C** .. 48·00 75·00
48 Optd "Specimen" .. 75·00

1916–23. *Wmk Mult Crown CA. P* 14.
49 8 ½d. green, **O** .. 20 1·00
50 1d. scarlet, **O** .. 35 75
a. Carmine-red .. 4·75 4·50
51 2d. grey, **O** .. 1·00 4·00
52 2½d. bright blue, **O** .. 1·50 7·00
53 3d. purple/*yellow*, **C** .. 75 5·00
a. On pale yellow (Optd S. £20) .. 75 5·50
54 4d. grey-black & red/*pl yellow*, **C** (1923) .. 4·75 16·00
55 6d. dull and deep purple, **C** .. 2·50 13·00
56 1s. black/*blue-green* (*olive back*), **C** .. 2·50 12·00
57 2s. purple and blue/*blue*, **C** .. 7·50 15·00
58 2s. 6d. black and red/*blue*, **C** .. 17·00 28·00
59 5s. green and red/*yellow*, **C** .. 27·00 48·00
49/59 .. *Set of* 11 55·00 £130
49/59 Optd "Specimen" .. *Set of* 11 £160

1917 (Oct)–**18**. *No.* 49 *optd with T* **9**.
60 8 ½d. green (R.) .. 10 60
61 ½d. green (Blk.) (1918) .. 15 90
a. Deep green .. 15 90
ab. "C" and "A" missing from wmk

No. 61ab shows the "C" omitted from one impression and the "A" missing from the next.

1919. *T* **8**. *Special printing in orange. Value and* "WAR STAMP" *as T* **9** *inserted in black at one printing*.
62 1½d. black and orange .. 10 25
60/2 Optd "Specimen" .. *Set of* 3 80·00

1922–9. *Wmk Mult Script CA. P* 14.
63 8 ¼d. brown, **O** .. 15 1·75
64 ½d. green, **O** .. 20 25
65 1d. bright violet, **O** .. 25 30
66 1d. carmine, **O** (1929) .. 75 70
67 1½d. orange-yellow, **O** .. 1·75 9·50
68 1½d. carmine, **O** .. 20 1·50
69 1½d. red-brown, **O** (1929) .. 70 50
70 2d. grey, **O** .. 45 1·00
71 2½d. deep bright blue, **O** .. 5·00 9·50
a. Pale bright blue (1926) (Optd S. £30) .. 60 90
72 2½d. orange-yellow, **O** (1923) .. 1·25 15·00
73 3d. dull blue, **O** (1923) .. 50 8·50
74 3d. purple/*yellow*, **C** (1927) .. 1·10 4·75
75 8 4d. black and red/*pale yellow*, **C** .. 60 3·75
76 5d. dull purple and olive, **C** .. 2·50 10·00
77 6d. pale and bright purple, **C** .. 90 5·00
78 1s. black/*emerald*, **C** .. 3·00 7·00
79 2s. purple and blue/*blue*, **C** .. 3·50 10·00
80 2s. 6d. black and red/*blue*, **C** .. 11·00 24·00
81 3s. green and violet, **C** .. 12·00 16·00
82 4s. black and scarlet, **C** .. 13·00 20·00
83 5s. green and red/*pale yellow*, **C** .. 18·00 25·00
63/83 .. *Set of* 21 55·00 £130
63/83 Optd/Perf "Specimen" .. *Set of* 21 £275

10 Plymouth

(Recess D.L.R.)

1932 (18 April). *Tercentenary. Wmk Mult Script CA. P* 14.
84 10 ½d. green .. 75 2·50
85 1d. scarlet .. 75 2·00
86 1½d. red-brown .. 1·25 1·75
87 2d. grey .. 1·25 8·00
88 2½d. ultramarine .. 1·25 8·50
89 3d. orange .. 1·50 8·50
90 6d. violet .. 2·25 14·00
91 1s. olive-brown .. 8·00 22·00
92 2s. 6d. purple .. 48·00 60·00
93 5s. chocolate .. £110 £130
84/93 .. *Set of* 10 £160 £225
84/93 Perf "Specimen" .. *Set of* 10 £275

1935 (6 May). *Silver Jubilee. As Nos.* 91/4 *of Antigua, but printed by Waterlow & Sons. P* 11 × 12.
94 1d. deep blue and scarlet .. 85 75
95 1½d. ultramarine and grey .. 75 2·00
96 2½d. brown and deep blue .. 2·25 1·25
97 1s. slate and purple .. 3·00 7·50
94/7 .. *Set of* 4 6·25 10·50
94/7 Perf "Specimen" .. *Set of* 4 70·00

1937 (12 May). *Coronation. As Nos.* 13/15 *of Aden*.
98 1d. scarlet .. 20 35
99 1½d. yellow-brown .. 30 25
100 2½d. bright blue .. 30 50
98/100 .. *Set of* 3 70 1·00
98/100 Perf "Specimen" .. *Set of* 3 45·00

11 Carr's Bay

12 Sea Island Cotton

13 Botanic Station

(Recess D.L.R.)

1938 (2 Aug)–**48**. *Wmk Mult Script CA*.
101 11 ½d. blue-green (*p* 13) .. 30 55
a. Perf 14 (1942) .. 10 10
102 12 1d. carmine (*p* 13) .. 35 35
a. Perf 14 (1943) .. 10 10
103 1½d. purple (*p* 13) .. 7·50 50
a. Perf 14 (1942) .. 10 10
104 13 2d. orange (*p* 13) .. 4·25 60
a. Perf 14 (1942) .. 10 10
105 12 2½d. ultramarine (*p* 13) .. 45 25
a. Perf 14 (1943) .. 20 10
106 11 3d. brown (*p* 13) .. 70 25
a. Perf 14, *Red-brown* (1942) .. 15 15
ab. Deep brown (1943) .. 3·00 3·75
107 13 6d. violet (*p* 13) .. 1·75 60
a. Perf 14 (1943) .. 60 20
108 11 1s. lake (*p* 13) .. 2·75 70
a. Perf 14 (1942) .. 40 20
109 13 2s. 6d. slate-blue (*p* 13) .. 5·00 70
a. Perf 14 (1943) .. 6·00 2·25
110 11 5s. rose-carmine (*p* 13) .. 16·00 7·00
a. Perf 14 (1942) .. 4·75 2·00
111 13 10s. pale blue (*p* 12) (1948) .. 12·00 16·00
112 11 £1 black (*p* 12) (1948) .. 12·00 20·00
101a/112 .. *Set of* 12 30·00 35·00
101/12 Perf "Specimen" .. *Set of* 12 £250

1946 (1 Nov). *Victory. As Nos.* 28/9 *of Aden*.
113 1½d. purple .. 10 10
114 3d. chocolate .. 10 10
113/14 Perf "Specimen" .. *Set of* 2 55·00

1949 (3 Jan). *Royal Silver Wedding. As Nos.* 30/1 *of Aden*.
115 2½d. ultramarine .. 10 10
116 5s. carmine .. 4·50 2·50

1949 (10 Oct). *75th Anniv of Universal Postal Union. As Nos.* 114/17 *of Antigua*.
117 2½d. ultramarine .. 15 20
118 3d. brown .. 30 20
119 6d. purple .. 30 20
120 1s. purple .. 35 25
117/20 .. *Set of* 4 1·00 75

(New Currency. 100 cents = 1 dollar)

1951 (16 Feb). *Inauguration of B.W.I. University College. As Nos. 118/19 of Antigua.*
121 3 c. black and purple . . 20 15
122 12 c. black and violet . . 20 20

14 Government House

18 Badge of Presidency

(Recess B.W.)

1951 (17 Sept). *T* **14**, **18** *and similar horiz designs. Wmk Mult Script CA. P* 11½ × 11.
123 **14** 1 c. black . . 10 35
124 – 2 c. green . . 15 30
125 – 3 c. orange-brown . . 30 30
126 – 4 c. carmine . . 25 20
127 – 5 c. reddish violet . . 25 25
128 **18** 6 c. olive-brown . . 25 20
129 – 8 c. deep blue . . 35 20
130 – 12 c. blue and chocolate . . 35 20
131 – 24 c. carmine and yellow-green . . 45 25
132 – 60 c. black and carmine . . 2·50 1·50
133 – $1.20, yellow-green and blue . . 4·50 2·50
134 – $2.40, black and green . . 4·50 10·00
135 **18** $4.80, black and purple . . 9·50 13·00
123/135 . . *Set of* 13 21·00 26·00

Designs:—2 c., $1.20, Sea Island cotton: cultivation; 3 c. Map of colony; 4, 24 c. Picking tomatoes; 5, 12 c. St. Anthony's Church; 8, 60 c. Sea Island cotton: ginning; $2.40, Government House.

1953 (2 June). *Coronation. As No. 47 of Aden.*
136 2 c. black and deep green . . 10 10

22 Government House

Types **16** and **18**: I. inscr "PRESIDENCY". II. inscr "COLONY".

(Recess B.W.)

1953 (15 Oct)–**62**. *As King George VI issue, but with portrait of Queen Elizabeth II as in T* **22**. *Wmk Mult Script CA. P* 11½×11.
136*a* – ½ c. deep violet (I) (3.7.56) . . 10 10
136*b* – ½c. deep violet (II) (1.9.58) . . 10 10
137 **22** 1 c. black . . 10 10
138 – 2 c. green . . 10 10
139 – 3 c. orange-brown (I) . . 15 10
139*a* – 3 c. orange-brown (II) (1.9.58) . . 25 15
140 – 4 c. carmine-red (1.6.55) . . 25 10
141 – 5 c. reddish lilac (1.6.55) . . 25 10
142 **18** 6 c. deep bistre-brown (I) (1.6.55) . . 15 10
142*a* 6 c. deep bistre-brown (II) (1.9.58) . . 40 15
ab. Deep sepia-brown (30.7.62) . . 1·00 60
143 – 8 c. deep bright blue (1.6.55) . . 20 10
144 – 12 c. blue and red-brown (1.6.55) . . 65 10
145 – 24 c. carmine-red and green (1.6.55) . . 70 10
145*a* – 48 c. yellow-olive and purple (15.10.57) 5·00 2·00
146 – 60 c. black and carmine (1.6.55) . . 3·75 80
147 – $1.20, green and greenish blue (1.6.55) 5·50 3·75
148 – $2.40, black and bluish green (1.6.55) 4·00 6·00
149 **18** $4.80, black & deep purple (I) (1.6.55) 6·00 10·00
149*a* $4.80, black & deep purple (II) (1.9.58) 6·00 7·00
136*a*/149*a* . . *Set of* 15 24·00 18·00

Extra designs:—½, 3 c. Map of colony; 48 c. Sea Island cotton: cultivation.

See also No. 157.

1958 (22 Apr). *Inauguration of British Caribbean Federation. As Nos. 135/7 of Antigua.*
150 3 c. deep green . . 15 15
151 6 c. blue . . 15 20
152 12 c. scarlet . . 20 10
150/2 . . *Set of* 3 45 40

1963 (8 July). *Freedom from Hunger. As No. 76 of Aden.*
153 12 c. reddish violet . . 30 15

1963 (2 Sept). *Red Cross Centenary. As Nos. 147/8 of Antigua.*
154 4 c. red and black . . 10 10
155 12 c. red and blue . . 25 25

1964 (23 April). *400th Birth Anniv of William Shakespeare. As No. 164 of Antigua.*
156 12 c. indigo . . 10 10

1964 (29 Oct). *As No. 138 but wmk* w **12**.
157 2 c. green . . 15 15

1965 (17 May). *I.T.U. Centenary. As Nos. 166/7 of Antigua.*
158 4 c. vermilion and violet . . 15 10
159 48 c. light emerald and carmine . . 30 20

23 Pineapple

24 Avocado

(Des Sylvia Goaman. Photo Harrison)

1965 (16 Aug). *T* **23/4** *and similar vert designs showing vegetables, fruit or plants. Multicoloured. W* w **12** (*upright*). *P* 15 × 14.
160 1 c. Type **23** . . 10 10
161 2 c. Type **24** . . 10 10
162 3 c. Soursop . . 10 10
163 4 c. Pepper . . 10 10
164 5 c. Mango . . 10 10
165 6 c. Tomato . . 10 10
166 8 c. Guava . . 10 10
167 10 c. Ochro . . 10 10
168 12 c. Lime . . 15 10
169 20 c. Orange . . 20 10
170 24 c. Banana . . 20 10
171 42 c. Onion . . 75 60
172 48 c. Cabbage . . 75 75
173 60 c. Pawpaw . . 1·25 90
174 $1.20, Pumpkin . . 2·00 1·75
175 $2.40, Sweet potato . . 4·50 2·50
176 $4.80, Egg plant . . 5·00 6·00
160/76 . . *Set of* 17 13·00 12·00

See also Nos. 213/22.

1965 (25 Oct). *International Co-operation Year. As Nos. 168/9 of Antigua.*
177 2 c. reddish purple and turquoise-green . . 10 10
178 12 c. deep bluish green and lavender . . 25 10

1966 (26 Jan). *Churchill Commemoration. As Nos. 170/3 of Antigua.*
179 1 c. new blue . . 10 10
a. Cerise (sky) omitted . . £175
180 2 c. deep green . . 10 10
181 24 c. brown . . 15 10
182 42 c. bluish violet . . 20 15
179/82 . . *Set of* 4 40 25

1966 (4 Feb). *Royal Visit. As Nos. 174/5 of Antigua.*
183 14 c. black and ultramarine . . 30 10
184 24 c. black and magenta . . 50 15

1966 (20 Sept). *Inauguration of W.H.O. Headquarters, Geneva. As Nos. 178/9 of Antigua.*
185 12 c. black, yellow-green and light blue . . 10 10
186 60 c. black, light purple and yellow-brown . . 25 15

1966 (1 Dec). *20th Anniv of U.N.E.S.C.O. As Nos. 196/8 of Antigua.*
187 4 c. slate-violet, red, yellow and orange . . 10 10
a. Orange omitted . . 50·00
188 60 c. orange-yellow, violet and deep olive . . 20 10
189 $1.80, black, bright purple and orange . . 70 70
187/9 . . *Set of* 3 80 75

On No. 187a the omission of the orange only affects the squares of the lower case letters so that they appear yellow, the same as the capital squares.

25 Yachting

$1.00
(26)

(Des and photo Harrison)

1967 (29 Dec). *International Tourist Year. T* **25** *and similar multicoloured designs. W* w **12** (*sideways on* 15 c.). *P* 14.
190 5 c. Type **25** . . 10 10
191 15 c. Waterfall near Chance Mountain (*vert*) 10 10
192 16 c. Fishing, skin-diving and swimming . . 10 10
193 24 c. Playing golf . . 15 10
190/3 . . *Set of* 4 30 20

1968 (6 May). *Nos.* 168, 170, 172 *and* 174/6 *surch as T* **26**. *W* w **12** (*upright*).
194 15 c. on 12 c. Lime . . 20 15
195 25 c. on 24 c. Banana . . 25 15
196 50 c. on 48 c. Cabbage . . 45 15
197 $1 on $1.20, Pumpkin . . 1·50 40
198 $2.50 on $2.40, Sweet potato . . 2·00 3·00
199 $5 on $4.80, Egg plant . . 2·50 3·75
194/9 . . *Set of* 6 6·00 7·00

See also Nos. 219 etc.

27 Sprinting

28 Sprinting, and Aztec Pillars

(Des G. Vasarhelyi. Photo Harrison)

1968 (31 July). *Olympic Games, Mexico. T* **27/8** *and similar designs. W* w **12** (*sideways on* $1). *P* 14.
200 15 c. deep claret, emerald and gold . . 10 10
201 25 c. blue, orange and gold . . 10 10
202 50 c. green, red and gold . . 10 10
203 $1 multicoloured . . 20 20
200/3 . . *Set of* 4 35 25

Designs: *Horiz as T* **27**—25 c. Weightlifting; 50 c. Gymnastics.

31 Alexander Hamilton

(Des and photo Harrison)

1968 (6 Dec*). *Human Rights Year. T* **31** *and similar horiz designs. Multicoloured. W* w **12**. *P* 14 × 14½.
204 5 c. Type **31** . . 10 10
205 15 c. Albert T. Marryshow . . 10 10
206 25 c. William Wilberforce . . 10 10
207 50 c. Dag Hammarskjöld . . 10 10
208 $1 Dr. Martin Luther King . . 25 30
204/8 . . *Set of* 5 40 45

*Although first day covers were postmarked 2 December, these stamps were not put on sale in Montserrat until 6 December.

32 "The Two Trinities" (Murillo)

33 "The Adoration of the Kings" (detail, Botticelli)

(Des and photo Harrison)

1968 (16 Dec). *Christmas. W* w **12** (*sideways*). *P* 14½ × 14.
209 **32** 5 c. multicoloured . . 10 10
210 **33** 15 c. multicoloured . . 10 10
211 **32** 25 c. multicoloured . . 10 10
212 **33** 50 c. multicoloured . . 15 20
209/12 . . *Set of* 4 30 25

1969–70. *As Nos.* 160/4, 167, 169 *and* 194/6 *but wmk* w **12** *sideways.*
213 1 c. Type **23** (24.6.69) . . 10 10
214 2 c. Type **24** (23.4.70) . . 60 60
215 3 c. Soursop (24.6.69) . . 20 15
216 4 c. Pepper (24.6.69) . . 25 15
217 5 c. Mango (23.4.70) . . 70 75
218 10 c. Ochro (24.6.69) . . 50 25
219 15 c. on 12 c. Lime (24.6.69) . . 60 40
220 20 c. Orange (17.3.69) . . 65 45
221 25 c. on 24 c. Banana (24.6.69) . . 90 85
222 50 c. on 48 c. Cabbage (24.6.69) . . 2·75 4·50
213/22 . . *Set of* 10 6·50 7·50

The 1 c., 3 c., 4 c., 10 c., 15 c. and 20 c. exist with PVA gum as well as gum arabic, but the 2 c. and 5 c. exist with PVA gum only.

34 Map showing "CARIFTA" Countries

35 "Strength in Unity"

(Des J. Cooter. Photo Harrison)

1969 (27 May). *First Anniv of CARIFTA (Caribbean Free Trade Area). W* w **12** (*sideways on T* **34**). *P* 14.
223 **34** 15 c. multicoloured . . 10 10
224 20 c. multicoloured . . 10 10
225 **35** 35 c. multicoloured . . 10 10
226 50 c. multicoloured . . 10 10
223/6 . . *Set of* 4 15 15

36 Telephone Receiver and Map of Montserrat

40 Dolphin

(Des R. Reid, adapted by V. Whiteley. Litho P.B.)

1969 (29 July). *Development Projects. T* **36** *and similar vert designs. Multicoloured. W* w **12**. *P* 13½.
227 15 c. Type **36** . . 10 10
228 25 c. School symbols and map . . 10 10
229 50 c. "HS 748" aircraft and map . . 15 10
230 $1 Electricity pylon and map . . 25 20
227/30 . . 35 30

(Des Harrison. Photo Enschedé)

1969 (1 Nov). *Game Fish. T* **40** *and similar horiz designs. Multicoloured. P* 13 × 13½.

231	5 c. Type **40**	15	10
232	15 c. Atlantic sailfish	30	10
233	25 c. Blackfin tuna	35	10
234	40 c. Spanish mackerel	55	15
231/4	*Set of* 4	1·25	30

41 King Caspar before the Virgin and Child (detail) (Norman 16th-cent stained glass window)

42 "Nativity" (Leonard Limosin)

(Des J. Cooter. Litho D.L.R.)

1969 (10 Dec). *Christmas. Paintings multicoloured; frame colours given.* W w **12** (*sideways on* 50 c.). *P* 13.

235	**41**	15 c. black, gold and violet	10	10
236		25 c. black and vermilion	10	10
237	**42**	50 c. black, ultramarine & yellow-orange	15	15
235/7		*Set of* 3	25	20

43 "Red Cross Sale"

(Des and litho J.W.)

1970 (13 Apr). *Centenary of British Red Cross. T* **43** *and similar horiz designs. Multicoloured.* W w **12** (*sideways*). *P* 14½ × 14.

238	3 c. Type **43**	10	10
239	4 c. School for deaf children	10	10
240	15 c. Transport services for disabled	10	10
241	20 c. Workshop	10	15
238/41	*Set of* 4	25	20

44 Red-footed Booby

45 "Madonna and Child with Animals" (Brueghel the Elder, after Dürer)

(Des V. Whiteley. Photo Harrison)

1970 (2 July)–74. *Birds. T* **44** *and similar multicoloured designs.* W w **12** (*sideways on vert designs and upright on horiz designs*). *P* 14 × 14½ (*horiz*) *or* 14½ × 14 (*vert*).

A. *Chalk-surfaced paper* (2.7.70).
B. *Glazed, ordinary paper* (30.10.74, $10; 22.1.71, *others*).

		A		B	
242	1 c. Type **44**	10	10	†	
243	2 c. American Kestrel	15	15	25	80
244	3 c. Magnificent Frigate Bird	15	15	†	
245	4 c. Great Egret	15	15	†	
246	5 c. Brown Pelican	15	10	30	60
247	10 c. Bananaquit	25	10	85	1·00
248	15 c. Smooth-billed Ani	30	15	2·25	2·25
249	20 c. Red-billed Tropic Bird	35	15	1·50	1·25
250	25 c. Montserrat Oriole	50	50	3·00	3·00
251	50 c. Green-throated Carib	1·75	85	3·50	3·50
252	$1 Antillean Crested Humming-bird	2·75	1·00	4·25	4·50
253	$2.50, Little Blue Heron	3·00	3·50	8·00	9·00
254	$5 Purple-throated Carib	7·00	9·00	13·00	15·00
254*a*	$10 Forest Thrush	†		15·00	15·00
242A/54A	*Set of* 13	15·00	14·00		
243B/54*a*B	*Set of* 11			45·00	48·00

The 1 c. 15 c., 20 c., 25 c., $1, $5 and $10 are horizontal, and the remainder are vertical designs.

See also Nos. 295/302.

(Des G. Drummond. Litho D.L.R.)

1970 (1 Oct).* *Christmas. T* **45** *and similar multicoloured design.* W w **12**. *P* 13½ × 14.

255	5 c. Type **45**	10	10
256	15 c. "The Adoration of the Shepherds" (Domenichino)	10	10
257	20 c. Type **45**	10	10
258	$1 As 15 c.	35	50
255/8	*Set of* 4	55	60

*This was the local date of issue but the stamps were released by the Crown Agents on 21 September.

46 War Memorial

47 Girl Guide and Badge

(Des V. Whiteley. Litho J.W.)

1970 (30 Nov). *Tourism. T* **46** *and similar horiz designs. Multicoloured.* W w **12** (*sideways*). *P* 14½ × 14.

259	5 c. Type **46**	10	10
260	15 c. Plymouth from Fort St. George	10	10
261	25 c. Carr's Bay	15	10
262	50 c. Golf Fairway	55	30
259/62	*Set of* 4	75	45
MS263	135 × 109 mm. Nos. 259/62	1·50	2·00

(Des V. Whiteley. Litho Questa)

1970 (31 Dec). *Diamond Jubilee of Montserrat Girl Guides. T* **47** *and similar vert design. Multicoloured.* W w **12**. *P* 14.

264	10 c. Type **47**	10	10
265	15 c. Brownie and Badge	10	10
266	25 c. As 15 c.	15	10
267	40 c. Type **47**	20	20
264/7	*Set of* 4	50	30

48 "Descent from the Cross" (Van Hemessen)

49 D.F.C. and D.F.M. in Searchlights

(Des J.W. Photo Enschedé)

1971 (22 Mar). *Easter. T* **48** *and similar vert design. Multicoloured.* W w **12**. *P* 13½.

268	5 c. Type **48**	10	10
269	15 c. "Noli me tangere" (Orcagna)	10	10
270	20 c. Type **48**	10	10
271	40 c. As 15 c.	15	15
268/71	*Set of* 4	25	30

(Des Col. A. Maynard. Litho Questa)

1971 (8 July). *Golden Jubilee of Commonwealth Ex-Services League. T* **49** *and similar vert designs. Multicoloured.* W w **12**. *P* 14.

272	10 c. Type **49**	10	10
273	20 c. M.C., M.M. and jungle patrol	15	10
274	40 c. D.S.C., D.S.M. and submarine action	20	15
275	$1 V.C. and soldier attacking bunker	50	70
272/5	*Set of* 4	85	85

50 "The Nativity with Saints" (Romanino)

51 Piper "Apache"

(Des G. Drummond. Litho Questa)

1971 (16 Sept). *Christmas. T* **50** *and similar vert design. Multicoloured.* W w **12**. *P* 14 × 13½.

276	5 c. Type **50**	10	10
277	15 c. "Choir of Angels" (Simon Marmion)	10	10
278	20 c. Type **50**	10	10
279	$1 As 15 c.	35	40
276/9	*Set of* 4	50	50

(Des and litho J.W.)

1971 (16 Dec). *14th Anniv of Inauguration of L.I.A.T. (Leeward Islands Air Transport). T* **51** *and similar horiz designs. Multicoloured.* W w **12** (*sideways*). *P* 13½.

280	5 c. Type **51**	10	10
281	10 c. Beech "Twin Bonanza"	15	15
282	15 c. De Havilland "Heron"	30	15
283	20 c. Britten Norman "Islander"	35	15
284	40 c. De Havilland "Twin Otter"	65	45
285	75 c. Hawker Siddeley "748"	2·00	2·25
280/5	*Set of* 6	3·25	3·00
MS286	203 × 102 mm. Nos. 280/5	10·00	11·00

52 "Chapel of Christ in Gethsemane", Coventry Cathedral

53 Lizard

(Des G. Drummond. Litho A. & M.)

1972 (9 Mar). *Easter. T* **52** *and similar horiz design. Multicoloured.* W w **12**. *P* 13.

287	5 c. Type **52**	10	10
288	10 c. "The Agony in the Garden" (Bellini)	10	10
289	20 c. Type **52**	10	10
290	75 c. As 10 c.	35	50
287/90	*Set of* 4	45	60

(Des G. Drummond. Litho Questa)

1972 (20 July). *Reptiles. T* **53** *and similar multicoloured designs.* W w **12** (*sideways on* 40 c. *and* $1). *P* 14½.

291	15 c. Type **53**	15	10
292	20 c. Mountain Chicken (frog)	20	10
293	40 c. Iguana (*horiz*)	35	20
294	$1 Tortoise (*horiz*)	2·00	2·00
291/4	*Set of* 4	2·40	2·00

1972 (21 July)–74. *As No.* 242 *etc., but* W w **12**, *sideways on horiz designs* (1, 15, 20, 25 c.) *and upright on vert designs* (*others*). *Glazed, ordinary paper.*

295	1 c. Type **44**	30	30
	a. Chalk-surfaced paper (4.2.74)	45	30
296	2 c. American Kestrel	50	25
	a. Chalk-surfaced paper (4.2.74)	90	30
297	3 c. Magnificent Frigate Bird	3·00	3·25
298	4 c. Great Egret (*chalk-surfaced paper*) (4.2.74)	75	1·50
299	5 c. Brown Pelican (8.3.73)	40	15
	a. Chalk-surfaced paper (4.2.74)	40	55
300	15 c. Smooth-billed Ani (8.3.73)	50	40
	a. Chalk-surfaced paper (2.10.73)	85	1·00
301	20 c. Red-billed Tropic Bird (*chalk-surfaced paper*) (2.10.73)	1·40	1·50
302	25 c. Montserrat Oriole (*chalk-surfaced paper*) (17.5.74)	3·25	3·50
295/302	*Set of* 8	9·00	9·75

In 1973–74, during shortages of the 5 c. value, letters can be found posted unstamped and franked with a "postage paid" mark. Other covers exist with the word "paid" in manuscript.

54 "Madonna of the Chair" (Raphael)

(Des J. Cooter. Litho Format)

1972 (18 Oct). *Christmas. T* **54** *and similar horiz designs. Multicoloured.* W w **12**. *P* 13½.

303	10 c. Type **54**	10	10
304	35 c. "Virgin and Child with Cherub" (Fungai)	15	10
305	50 c. "Madonna of the Magnificat" (Botticelli)	25	30
306	$1 "Virgin and Child with St. John and an Angel" (Botticelli)	40	65
303/6	*Set of* 4	70	90

55 Lime, Tomatoes and Pawpaw

56 *Passiflora herbertiana*

(Des (from photographs by D. Groves) and photo Harrison)

1972 (20 Nov). *Royal Silver Wedding. Multicoloured; background colour given.* W w **12**. *P* 14 × 14½.

307	**55**	35 c. rose	10	10
308		$1 bright blue	20	20

(Des J. Cooter. Litho Walsall)

1973 (9 Apr). *Easter. T* **56** *and similar vert designs showing passion-flowers. Multicoloured.* W w **12**. *P* 13½.

309	20 c. Type **56**	25	10
310	35 c. *P. vitifolia*	35	10
311	75 c. *P. amabilis*	1·40	1·40
312	$1 *P. alata-caerulea*	1·75	1·75
309/12	*Set of* 4	3·50	3·00

Nos. 309/12 are inscribed on the reverse with information about the passion-flower.

57 Montserrat Monastery, Spain

58 "Virgin and Child" (School of Gerard David)

(Des J. Cooter. Litho Format)

1973 (9 July). *480th Anniv of Columbus's Discovery of Montserrat. T* **57** *and similar horiz designs. Multicoloured. W* w **12**. *P* 13½.

313 10 c. Type **57** 15 10
314 35 c. Columbus sighting Montserrat 30 15
315 60 c. Columbus's ship off Montserrat .. .. 1·50 1·50
316 $1 Colony badge and map of voyage .. 1·75 1·75
313/16 .. .. *Set of* 4 3·50 3·00
MS317 126 × 134 mm. Nos. 313/16 .. .. 16·00 16·00

(Des J. Cooter. Litho Questa)

1973 (22 Oct). *Christmas. T* **58** *and similar vert designs. Multicoloured. W* w **12** (*sideways*). *P* 13½.

318 20 c. Type **58** 15 10
319 35 c. "The Holy Family with St. John" (Jordaens) 20 10
320 50 c. "Virgin and Child" (Bellini) 40 50
321 90 c. "Virgin and Child with Flowers" (Dolci) 70 1·00
318/21 .. .. *Set of* 4 1·25 1·40

1973 (14 Nov). *Royal Wedding. As Nos.* 165/6 *of Anguilla. Centre multicoloured. W* w **12** (*sideways*). *P* 13½.

322 35 c. sage-green 10 10
323 $1 violet-blue 20 20

59 Steel Band

(Des J. W. Litho Questa)

1974 (8 Apr). *25th Anniv of University of West Indies. T* **59** *and similar designs. Multicoloured. W* w **12** (*sideways on* 20 c., $1 *and* **MS**328).

324 20 c. Type **59** 15 10
325 35 c. Masqueraders (*vert*) 20 10
326 60 c. Student weaving (*vert*) .. .. .. 1·00 1·00
327 $1 University Centre, Montserrat .. .. 1·10 1·25
324/7 .. .. *Set of* 4 2·25 2·25
MS328 130 × 89 mm. Nos. 324/7 .. .. 4·00 7·50

60 Hands with Letters

02¢

(61)

(Des P. Powell. Litho Walsall)

1974 (3 July). *Centenary of Universal Postal Union. T* **60** *and similar horiz design. W* w **12**. *P* 14½ × 14.

329 **60** 1 c. multicoloured 10 10
330 – 2 c. lt rose-red, orange-verm & blk .. 10 10
331 **60** 3 c. multicoloured 10 10
332 – 5 c. lt yellow-orange, reddish orge & blk 10 10
333 **60** 50 c. multicoloured 20 20
334 – $1 pale blue, turquoise-blue and black 40 65
329/34 .. .. *Set of* 6 75 90

Designs:—2 c., 5 c., $1 Figures from U.P.U. Monument.

1974 (2 Oct). *Various stamps surch as T* **61**.

335 2 c. on $1 (No. 252B) 30 50
336 5 c. on 50 c. (No. 333) 40 60
337 10 c. on 60 c. (No. 326) .. .. .. 1·75 2·25
338 20 c. on $1 (No. 252B) 30 40
a. "2" with seriffs (Pl 1B R. 3/1) .. 10·00
b. Bottom bar of surch omitted (Pl 1B R. 5/1-5) .. .. 5·00
339 35 c. on $1 (No. 334) .. .. .. 75 1·25
335/9 .. .. *Set of* 5 3·25 4·50

PRICES OF SETS

Set prices are given for many issues, generally those containing three stamps or more. Definitive sets include one of each value or major colour change, but do not cover different perforations, die types or minor shades. Where a choice is possible the set prices are based on the cheapest versions of the stamps included in the listings.

62 Churchill and Houses of Parliament

63 Carib "Carbet"

(Des R. Granger Barrett. Litho D.L.R.)

1974 (30 Nov). *Birth Centenary of Sir Winston Churchill. T* **62** *and similar vert design. Multicoloured. No wmk. P* 13 × 13½.

340 35 c. Type **62** 15 10
341 70 c. Churchill and Blenheim Palace 20 20
MS342 81 × 85 mm. Nos. 340/1 .. .. 50 70

(Des C. Abbott. Litho Walsall)

1975 (3 Mar). *Carib Artefacts. T* **63** *and similar horiz designs.*

(*a*) *W* w **12** (*sideways*). *From sheets. P* 14

343 5 c. lake-brown, yellow and black 10 10
344 20 c. black, lake-brown and yellow 10 10
345 35 c. black, yellow and lake-brown 15 10
346 70 c. yellow, lake-brown and black 25 40
343/6 .. .. *Set of* 4 50 60

(*b*) *No wmk. Self-adhesive with advertisements on the reverse. From booklets. Rouletted*

347 5 c. lake-brown, yellow and black 12 25
a. Booklet pane. Nos. 347/50 *se-tenant* .. 90
348 20 c. black, lake-brown and yellow 15 25
a. Booklet pane. Nos. 348 × 3 and No. 349 × 3 90
349 35 c. black, yellow and lake-brown 15 25
350 70 c. yellow, lake-brown and black 55 70
347/50 .. .. *Set of* 4 90 1·25

Designs:—20 c. "Caracoli"; 35 c. Club or mace; 70 c. Canoe.

64 One-Bitt Coin

(Des J. Cooter. Litho Questa)

1975 (1 Sept). *Local Coinage, 1785–1801. T* **64** *and similar diamond-shaped designs. W* w **14** (*sideways*). *P* 13½.

351 5 c. black, light violet-blue and silver .. 10 10
352 10 c. black, salmon and silver 15 10
353 35 c. black, light blue-green and silver .. 20 15
354 $2 black, bright rose and silver .. .. 1·25 1·50
351/4 .. .. *Set of* 4 1·50 1·60
MS355 142 × 142 mm. Nos. 351/4 .. .. 1·75 2·75

Designs:—10 c. Eighth dollar; 35 c. Quarter dollar; $2 One dollar.

No. **MS**355 has details of the coins depicted printed on the reverse side, beneath the gum.

65 1d. and 6d. Stamps of 1876

66 "The Trinity"

(Des J. Cooter. Litho J. W.)

1976 (5 Jan). *Centenary of First Montserrat Postage Stamp. T* **65** *and similar horiz designs. W* w **12** (*sideways*). *P* 13.

356 5 c. deep carmine, yellowish green and black 10 10
357 10 c. light yellow-ochre, scarlet and black .. 15 10
358 40 c. multicoloured 40 40
359 55 c. deep mauve, yellowish green and black 50 50
360 70 c. multicoloured 70 70
361 $1.10, yellowish green, brt blue & grey-blk .. 1·00 1·00
356/61 .. .. *Set of* 6 2·50 2·50
MS362 170 × 159 mm. Nos. 356/61. P 13½ .. 3·50 4·50

Designs:—10 c. G.P.O. and bisected 1d. stamp; 40 c. Bisects on cover; 55 c. G.B. 6d. used in Montserrat and local 6d. of 1876; 70 c. Stamps for 2½d. rate, 1876; $1.10, Packet boat *Antelope* and 6d. stamp.

(Des J. Cooter. Litho Questa)

1976 (5 Apr). *Easter. Unissued stamps prepared for Easter* 1975 *with values and date obliterated by black bars. T* **66** *and similar vert designs showing paintings by Orcagna. Multicoloured. W* w **14**. *P* 13½.

363 15 c. on 5 c. Type **66** 10 10
a. Surch omitted .. .. 50·00
364 40 c. on 35 c. "The Resurrection" 15 15
a. Surch omitted .. .. 50·00
365 55 c. on 70 c. "The Ascension" 15 15
a. Surch omitted .. .. 50·00
366 $1.10 on $1 "Pentecost" 30 40
a. Surch omitted .. .. 50·00
363/6 .. .. *Set of* 4 55 65
MS367 160 × 142 mm. Nos. 363/6 .. .. 1·25 2·00
a. Surch omitted £200

For No. 363 the "1" was added to the original 5 c. to make 15 c.

2¢

(67)

68 White Frangipani

1976 (12 Apr). *Nos.* 244A, 246A *and* 247A *surch as T* **67**.

368 2 c. on 5 c. Brown Pelican 10 15
369 30 c. on 10 c. Bananaquit 15 20
370 45 c. on 3 c. Magnificent Frigate Bird .. 20 25
a. Surch triple .. ..
b. Surch double .. .. 40·00
368/70 .. .. *Set of* 3 40 55

(Des J. Cooter. Litho Questa)

1976 (5 July)–**80**. *Various horiz designs showing Flowering Trees as T* **68**. *Multicoloured. Ordinary paper. W* w **14** (*sideways*). *P* 13½.

371 1 c. Type **68** 10 10
372 2 c. Cannon-ball Tree 10 10
373 3 c. Lignum vitae 10 10
374 5 c. Malay apple 15 10
375 10 c. Jacaranda 20 10
376 15 c. Orchid Tree 25 10
a. Chalk-surfaced paper (8.80) 45 45
377 20 c. Manjak 25 10
a. Chalk-surfaced paper (8.80) 45 45
378 25 c. Tamarind 25 10
379 40 c. Flame of the Forest 35 20
380 55 c. Pink Cassia 40 25
381 70 c. Long John 50 30
382 $1 Saman 65 40
383 $2.50, Immortelle .. .. .. 1·25 1·50
384 $5 Yellow Poui .. .. 2·00 2·25
385 $10 Flamboyant .. .. 3·00 4·25
371/85 .. .. *Set of* 15 8·00 8·50

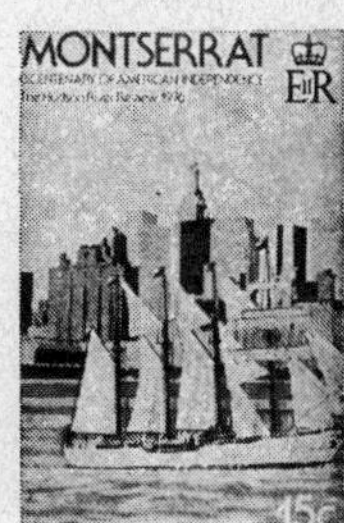

69 Mary and Joseph

70 Hudson River Review, 1976

(Des L. Curtis. Litho Format)

1976 (4 Oct). *Christmas. T* **69** *and similar vert designs. Multicoloured. W* w **14**. *P* 14.

386 15 c. Type **69** 10 10
387 20 c. The Shepherds 10 10
388 55 c. Mary and Jesus 15 15
389 $1.10, The Magi 30 50
386/9 .. .. *Set of* 4 50 65
MS390 95 × 135 mm. Nos. 386/9 .. .. 60 1·75

(Des and litho J.W.)

1976 (13 Dec). *Bicentenary of American Revolution. T* **70** *and similar vert designs. Multicoloured. W* w **14**. *P* 13.

391 15 c. Type **70** 30 15
392 40 c. } The *Raleigh* attacking 60 40
393 75 c. } H.M.S. *Druid*, 1777* 60 40
394 $1.25, Hudson River Review .. .. 1·10 60
391/4 .. .. *Set of* 4 2·40 1·40
MS395 95 × 145 mm. Nos. 391/4. P 13½ .. 2·50 2·75

*The date is wrongly given on the stamps as "1776".

Nos. 392/3 and 391 and 394 were printed in horizontal *se-tenant* pairs throughout the sheet, each pair forming a composite design.

71 The Crowning

72 *Ipomoea alba*

(Des G. Vasarhelyi. Litho J.W.)

1977 (7 Feb). *Silver Jubilee. T* **71** *and similar horiz designs. Multicoloured. W* w **14** (*sideways*). *P* 13.

396 30 c. Royal Visit, 1966 .. .. .. 15 15
397 45 c. Cannons firing salute 20 20
398 $1 Type **71** 35 60
396/8 .. .. *Set of* 3 60 85

(Des J. Cooter. Litho Questa)

1977 (1 June). *Flowers of the Night. T* **72** *and similar multi-coloured designs.* W w **14** (*sideways on* 40 *and* 55 c.). *P* 14.

399 15 c. Type **72** 15 10
400 40 c. *Epiphyllum hookeri* (*horiz*) 30 30
401 55 c. *Cereus hexagonus* (*horiz*) 40 45
402 $1.50, *Cestrum nocturnum* .. .. .. 1·25 1·25
399/402 .. .. *Set of* 4 1·90 1·90
MS403 126 × 130 mm. Nos. 399/402. Wmk sideways .. .. 2·25 2·75

73 Princess Anne laying Foundation Stone of Glendon Hospital

(Des BG Studio. Litho Questa)

1977 (3 Oct). *Development. T* **73** *and similar horiz designs. Multi-coloured.* W w **14** (*sideways*). *P* 14½ × 14.

404 20 c. Type **73** 15 10
405 40 c. *Statesman* (freighter) at Plymouth .. 25 15
406 55 c. Glendon Hospital 30 20
407 $1.50, Jetty at Plymouth Port .. .. 80 1·00
404/7 .. .. *Set of* 4 1·40 1·25
MS408 146 × 105 mm. Nos. 404/7 .. .. 2·00 2·25

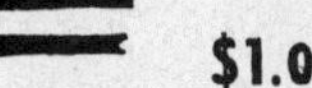

$1.00
SILVER JUBILEE 1977
ROYAL VISIT
TO THE CARIBBEAN

(74)

1977 (28 Oct). *Royal Visit. Nos.* 380/1 *and* 383 *surch locally with T* **74**.

409 $1 on 55 c. Pink Cassia 30 45
410 $1 on 70 c. Long John 30 45
411 $1 on $2.50, Immortelle 30 45
409/11 .. .. *Set of* 3 80 1·25

75 The Stable at Bethlehem 76 Four-eye Butterflyfish

(Des L. Curtis. Litho Walsall)

1977 (14 Nov). *Christmas. T* **75** *and similar vert designs. Multi-coloured.* W w **14**. *P* 14 × 14½.

412 5 c. Type **75** 10 10
413 40 c. The Three Kings 15 10
414 55 c. Three Ships 20 10
415 $2 Three Angels 55 75
412/15 .. .. *Set of* 4 80 85
MS416 119 × 115 mm. Nos. 412/15 .. .. 1·00 1·75

(Des J.W. Litho Walsall)

1978 (15 Mar). *Fish. T* **76** *and similar horiz designs. Multi-coloured.* W w **14** (*sideways*). *P* 14.

417 30 c. Type **76** 20 10
418 40 c. French Angelfish 25 15
419 55 c. Blue Tang 35 15
420 $1.50, Queen Triggerfish 80 90
417/20 .. .. *Set of* 4 1·40 1·10
MS421 152 × 102 mm. Nos. 417/20 .. .. 2·00 2·25

77 St. Paul's Cathedral 78 *Alpinia speciosa*

(Des G. Drummond. Litho J.W.)

1978 (2 June). *25th Anniv of Coronation. T* **77** *and similar horiz designs. Multicoloured.* W w **14** (*sideways*). *P* 13.

422 40 c. Type **77** 10 10
423 55 c. Chichester Cathedral 10 10
424 $1 Lincoln Cathedral 20 25
425 $2.50, Llandaff Cathedral 30 50
422/5 .. .. *Set of* 4 55 75
MS426 130 × 102 mm. Nos. 422/5. P 13½ × 14 .. 70 1·25

Nos. 422/5 were each printed in sheets including two *se-tenant* stamp-size labels.

(Des J. Cooter. Litho J.W.)

1978 (18 Sept). *Flowers. T* **78** *and similar vert designs. Multi-coloured.* W w **14**. *P* 13½ × 13.

427 40 c. Type **78** 20 10
428 55 c. *Allamanda cathartica* 25 15
429 $1 *Petrea volubilis* 45 45
430 $2 *Hippeastrum puniceum* 70 80
427/30 .. .. *Set of* 4 1·40 1·40

79 Private, 21st (Royal North British Fusiliers), 1796 80 Cub Scouts

(Des J.W. Litho Questa)

1978 (20 Nov). *Military Uniforms* (1*st series*). *T* **79** *and similar vert designs showing soldiers from British infantry regiments. Multicoloured.* W w **14**. *P* 14 × 14½.

431 30 c. Type **79** 15 15
432 40 c. Corporal, 86th (Royal County Down), 1831 .. .. 20 15
433 55 c. Sergeant, 14th (Buckinghamshire) 1837 30 20
434 $1.50, Officer, 55th (Westmorland), 1784 .. 75 80
431/4 .. .. *Set of* 4 2·00 1·75
MS435 140 × 89 mm. Nos. 431/4 .. .. .. 2·00 2·25

See also Nos. 441/5.

(Des J. W. Litho Walsall)

1979 (2 Apr). *50th Anniv of Boy Scout Movement on Montserrat. T* **80** *and similar multicoloured designs.* W w **14** (*sideways on* 40 *and* 55 c). *P* 14.

436 40 c. Type **80** 25 10
437 55 c. Scouts with signalling equipment .. 35 20
438 $1.25, Camp fire (*vert*) 60 55
439 $2 Oath ceremony (*vert*) .. .. .. 1·00 1·00
436/9 .. .. *Set of* 4 2·00 1·75
MS440 120 × 110 mm. Nos. 436/9 .. .. 2·25 2·25

(Des J.W. Litho Questa)

1979 (4 June). *Military Uniforms* (2*nd series*). *Vert designs as T* **79** *showing soldiers from infantry regiments. Multicoloured.* W w **14**. *P* 14 × 14½.

441 30 c. Private, 60th (Royal American), 1783 .. 15 15
442 40 c. Private, 1st West India, 1819 .. .. 20 15
443 55 c. Officer, 5th (Northumberland), 1819 .. 30 25
444 $2.50, Officer, 93rd (Sutherland Highlanders), 1830 .. .. 1·00 1·10
441/4 .. .. *Set of* 4 1·50 1·50
MS445 139 × 89 mm. Nos. 441/4 .. .. .. 2·00 2·50

81 Child reaching out to Adult

(Des G. Vasarhelyi. Litho Questa)

1979 (17 Sept). *International Year of the Child.* W w **14** (*sideways*). *P* 13½ × 14.

446 **81** $2 black, orange-brown and flesh 40 55
MS447 85 × 99 mm. No. 446 .. .. 50 2·00

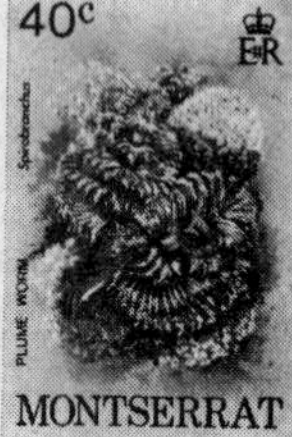

82 Sir Rowland Hill with Penny Black and Montserrat 1876 1d. Stamp 83 Plume Worm

(Des G. Vasarhelyi. Litho Questa)

1979 (1 Oct). *Death Centenary of Sir Rowland Hill and Centenary of U.P.U. Membership. T* **82** *and similar horiz designs. Multi-coloured.* W w **14** (*sideways*). *P* 14.

448 40 c. Type **82** 20 10
449 55 c. U.P.U. emblem and notice announcing Leeward Islands entry into Union .. 25 15
450 $1 1883 Letter following U.P.U. membership 35 45
451 $2 Great Britain Post Office Regulations notice and Sir Rowland Hill 60 70
448/51 .. .. *Set of* 4 1·25 1·25
MS452 135 × 154 mm. Nos. 448/51 .. .. 3·25 5·00

(Des G. Drummond. Litho Walsall)

1979 (26 Nov). *Marine Life. T* **83** *and similar vert designs. Multi-coloured.* W w **14**. *P* 14.

453 40 c. Type **83** 20 15
454 55 c. Sea Fans 30 20
455 $2 Coral and Sponge .. .. 80 1·00
453/5 .. .. *Set of* 3 1·10 1·25

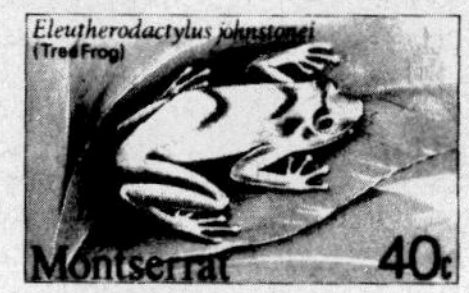

84 Tree Frog

(Des J. Cooter. Litho Rosenbaum Bros, Vienna)

1980 (4 Feb). *Reptiles and Amphibians. T* **84** *and similar horiz designs. Multicoloured.* W w **14** (*sideways*). *P* 13½.

456 40 c. Type **84** 20 15
457 55 c. Tree Lizard 25 25
458 $1 Crapaud 45 50
459 $2 Wood Slave 80 90
456/9 .. .. *Set of* 4 1·50 1·60

75th Anniversary of
Rotary International

85 *Marquess of Salisbury* and 1838 Handstamps (86)

(Des BG Studio. Litho Questa)

1980 (14 Apr). *"London 1980" International Stamp Exhibition. T* **85** *and similar horiz designs. Multicoloured.* W w **14** (*sideways*). *P* 14.

460 40 c. Type **85** 15 15
461 55 c. "H.S. 748" aircraft and 1976 55 c. definitive 20 25
462 $1.20, *La Plata* (liner) and 1903 5s. stamp 35 45
463 $1.20, *Lady Hawkins* (packet steamer) and 1932 Tercentenary 5s. commemorative 35 45
464 $1.20, *Avon* (paddle-steamer) and Penny Red stamp with "A 08" postmark .. 35 45
465 $1.20, "Aeronca" aeroplane and 1953 $1.20 definitive 35 45
460/5 .. .. *Set of* 6 1·60 2·00
MS466 115 × 110 mm. Nos. 460/5. P 12 .. .. 1·60 2·50

Nos. 460/5 were each printed in sheets of 4 stamps and two *se-tenant* stamp-size labels.

Some sheets of No. 462 showed the red colour omitted from the map in the right-hand label.

1980 (7 July). *75th Anniv of Rotary International. No.* 383 *optd with T* **86**.

467 $2.50, Immortelle 70 85

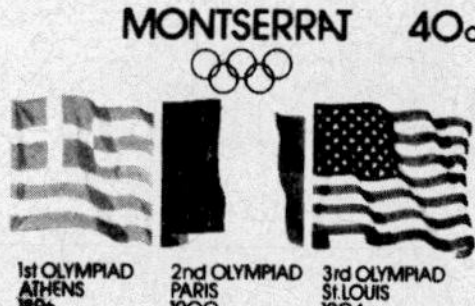

87 Greek, French and U.S.A. Flags

(Des A. Theobald. Litho Questa)

1980 (7 July). *Olympic Games, Moscow. T* **87** *and similar horiz designs. Multicoloured.* W w **14** (*sideways*). *P* 13½ × 14.

468 40 c. Type **87** 15 15
469 55 c. Union, Swedish and Belgian flags .. 15 15
470 70 c. French, Dutch and U.S.A. flags 20 20
471 $1 German, Union and Finnish flags .. 25 25
472 $1.50, Australian, Italian and Japanese flags 30 30
473 $2 Mexican, West German and Canadian flags 35 40
474 $2.50, "The Discus Thrower" (sculpture by Miron) 40 50
468/74 .. .. *Set of* 7 1·60 1·75
MS475 150 × 100 mm. Nos. 468/74 .. .. 1·60 3·00
a. Bottom row of stamps in miniature sheet imperf on 3 sides £475

Nos. 468/74 were each printed in small sheets of 4 including one *se-tenant* stamp-size label.

No. **MS**475a shows the three stamps in the bottom row of the miniature sheet imperforate vertically and with no perforations between the stamps and the bottom margin.

XX 5¢

(88)

89 S.S. *Lady Nelson*, 1928

1980 (30 Sept). *Nos.* 371, 373, 376 *and* 379 *surch as T* **88**.
476 5 c. on 3 c. Lignum vitae 10 10
a. Surch double, one inverted . . . . 45·00
477 35 c. on 1 c. Type **68** 20 15
a. Surch omitted (in vert pair with normal) . . . . 60·00
478 35 c. on 3 c. Lignum vitae 20 15
479 35 c. on 15 c. Orchid Tree 20 15
480 55 c. on 40 c. Flame of the Forest 25 15
a. Surch inverted . . . . 60·00
481 $5 on 40 c. Flame of the Forest . . . . 1·25 2·00
476/81 . . . . *Set of* 6 2·00 2·25
The surcharge omitted error, No. 477a, occurs on the lower stamp of a vertical pair. On the upper stamp the surcharge is at the foot of the design.

(Des J.W. Litho Walsall)

1980 (3 Nov). *Mail Packet Boats (1st series). T* **89** *and similar horiz designs. Multicoloured.* W w **14** (*sideways*). *P* 14.
482 40 c. Type **89** 20 15
483 55 c. R.M.S.P. *Chignecto*, 1913 . . . . 30 25
484 $1 R.M.S.P. *Solent*, 1878 . . . . 50 50
485 $2 R.M.S.P. *Dee*, 1841 . . . . 75 85
482/5 . . . . *Set of* 4 1·60 1·60
See also Nos. 615/19.

90 *Heliconius charitonius*

91 Spadefish

(Des J.W. Litho Questa)

1981 (2 Feb). *Butterflies. T* **90** *and similar square designs. Multicoloured.* W w **14** (*inverted*). *P* 14.
486 50 c. Type **90** 60 40
487 65 c. *Pyrgus oileus* 70 45
488 $1.50, *Phoebis agarithe* 90 85
489 $2.50, *Danaus plexippus* . . . . . . 1·25 1·10
486/9 . . . . *Set of* 4 3·00 2·50
Nos. 486/9 were each printed in sheets including two *se-tenant* stamp-size labels.

(Des G. Drummond. Litho J.W.)

1981 (20 Mar). *Fishes. Vert designs as T* **91**. *Multicoloured.* W w **14**. *P* 13½ × 13.
490 5 c. Type **91** 25 10
491 10 c. Hogfish 25 10
492 15 c. Creole Wrasse 35 10
493 20 c. Yellow Damselfish 35 10
494 25 c. Sergeant Major 40 10
495 35 c. Clown Wrasse 40 20
496 45 c. Schoolmaster 40 25
497 55 c. Striped Parrotfish 75 30
498 65 c. Bigeye 50 30
499 75 c. French Grunt 60 40
500 $1 Rock Beauty 75 55
501 $2 Blue Chromis . . . . . . 1·75 1·10
502 $3 Fairy Basslet and Blueheads . . . . 1·90 1·75
503 $5 Cherubfish . . . . . . 2·75 2·75
504 $7.50, Longspine Squirrelfish . . . . 4·75 4·75
505 $10 Longsnout Butterflyfish . . . . 6·50 6·50
490/505 . . . . . . *Set of* 16 21·00 17·00
For stamps watermarked with W w **15** see Nos. 555/70.

92 Fort St. George

(Des J. Cooter. Litho Format)

1981 (18 May). *Montserrat National Trust. T* **92** *and similar horiz designs. Multicoloured.* W w **14** (*sideways*). *P* 13½ × 14.
506 50 c. Type **92** 30 20
507 65 c. Bird sanctuary, Fox's Bay 45 35
508 $1.50, Museum 85 75
509 $2.50, Bransby Point Battery, *circa* 1780 . . 1·40 1·40
506/9 . . . . *Set of* 4 2·75 2·40

(Des D. Shults. Litho Questa)

1981 (17 July–19 Nov). *Royal Wedding. Horiz designs as T* **26/27** *of Kiribati. Multicoloured.* (a) W w **15**. *P* 14.
510 90 c. *Charlotte* 25 25
a. Sheetlet. No. 510 × 6 and No. 511 . . 2·25
511 90 c. Prince Charles and Lady Diana Spencer 1·00 1·00
512 $3 *Portsmouth* 60 60
a. Sheetlet. No. 512 × 6 and No. 513 . . 4·75
513 $3 As No. 511 . . . . . . 1·75 1·75
514 $4 *Britannia* 75 75
a. Sheetlet No. 514 × 6 and No. 515 . . 6·00
515 $4 As No. 511 . . . . . . 2·25 2·25
510/15 . . . . *Set of* 6 6·00 6·00
MS516 120 × 109 mm. $5 As No. 511. Wmk sideways. P 12 (19 Nov) . . . . . . 1·50 1·50

(*b*) *Booklet stamps. No wmk. P* 12 (19 Nov)
517 90 c. As No. 510 . . . . . . 45 45
a. Booklet pane. No. 517 × 4 . . . . 1·75
518 $3 As No. 513 . . . . . . 1·60 1·75
a. Booklet pane No. 518 × 2 . . . . 3·25
Nos. 510/15 were printed in sheetlets of seven stamps of the same face value, each containing six of the "Royal Yacht" design and one of the larger design showing Prince Charles and Lady Diana.
Nos. 517/18 come from $13.20 stamp booklets.

93 H.M.S. *Dorsetshire* and Seaplane

94 Methodist Church, Bethel

(Des Court House Advertising Ltd. Litho Questa)

1981 (31 Aug). *50th Anniv of Montserrat Airmail Service. T* **93** *and similar horiz designs. Multicoloured.* W w **14** (*sideways*). *P* 14.
519 50 c. Type **93** 30 30
520 65 c. Beechcraft "Twin Bonanza" aeroplane . . 45 45
521 $1.50, De Havilland "Dragon Rapide" R.M. *Lord Shaftesbury* aeroplane 85 85
522 $2.50, Hawker Siddeley Avro "748" aeroplane and maps of Montserrat and Antigua . . . . 1·25 1·25
519/22 . . . . *Set of* 4 2·50 2·50

(Des J. Cooter. Litho Walsall)

1981 (16 Nov). *Christmas. Churches. T* **94** *and similar vert designs. Multicoloured.* W w **14**. *P* 14 × 13½.
523 50 c. Type **94** 20 15
524 65 c. St George's Anglican Church, Harris . . 25 15
525 $1.50, St Peter's Anglican Church, St Peters 60 60
526 $2.50, St Patrick's R.C. Church, Plymouth 75 1·00
523/6 . . . . *Set of* 4 1·75 1·75
MS527 176 × 120 mm. Nos. 523/6 . . . . 2·40 2·75

95 Rubiaceae (*Rondeletia buxifolia*)

96 Plymouth

(Des local artist. Litho Questa)

1982 (18 Jan). *Plant Life. T* **95** *and similar multicoloured designs.* W w **14** (*sideways on* 65 *c. and* $2.50). *P* 14½.
528 50 c. Type **95** 30 30
529 65 c. Boraginaceae (*Heliotropium ternatum*) (*horiz*) 40 40
530 $1.50, Simarubaceae (*Picramnia pentandra*) 85 85
531 $2.50, Ebenaceae (*Diospyrus revoluta*) (*horiz*) 1·25 1·25
528/31 . . . . *Set of* 4 2·50 2·50

(Litho Format)

1982 (17 Apr). *350th Anniv of Settlement of Montserrat by Sir Thomas Warner.* W w **14** (*sideways*). *P* 14½.
532 **96** 40 c. green 30 30
533 55 c. red 35 35
534 65 c. chestnut 40 40
535 75 c. olive-grey 45 45
536 85 c. bright blue 50 50
537 95 c. bright orange 55 55
538 $1 bright reddish violet 60 60
539 $1.50, brown-olive 80 80
540 $2 deep claret . . . . . . 1·10 1·10
541 $2.50, bistre-brown . . . . . . 1·40 1·40
532/41 . . . . *Set of* 10 5·75 5·75
Nos. 532/41 are based on the 1932 Tercentenary set.

97 Catherine of Aragon, Princess of Wales, 1501

98 Local Scout

(Des D. Shults and J. Cooter. Litho Format)

1982 (16 June). *21st Birthday of Princess of Wales. T* **97** *and similar vert designs. Multicoloured.* W w **15**. *P* 13½ × 14.
542 75 c. Type **97** 20 15
543 $1 Coat of Arms of Catherine of Aragon . . 30 20
544 $5 Diana, Princess of Wales . . . . 1·50 1·75
542/4 . . . . *Set of* 3 1·75 1·90

(Des D. Shults. Litho Format)

1982 (13 Sept). *75th Anniv of Boy Scout Movement. T* **98** *and similar vert design. Multicoloured.* W w **15**. *P* 14.
545 $1.50, Type **98** 85 70
546 $2.50, Lord Baden-Powell . . . . . . 1·25 1·10

99 Annunciation

(Des Jennifer Toombs. Litho Walsall)

1982 (18 Nov). *Christmas. T* **99** *and similar horiz designs. Multicoloured.* W w **14** (*sideways*). *P* 14.
547 35 c. Type **99** 20 15
548 75 c. Shepherd's Vision 40 35
549 $1.50, The Stable 85 85
550 $2.50, Flight into Egypt . . . . . . 1·00 1·10
547/50 . . . . *Set of* 4 2·25 2·25

100 *Lepthemis vesiculosa*

101 Blue-headed Hummingbird

(Des J. Cooter. Litho Walsall)

1983 (19 Jan). *Dragonflies. T* **100** *and similar horiz designs. Multicoloured.* W w **14** (*sideways*). *P* 13½ × 14.
551 50 c. Type **100** 25 20
552 65 c. *Orthemis ferruginea* 30 25
553 $1.50, *Triacanthagyna trifida* 70 75
554 $2.50, *Erythrodiplax umbrata* . . . . 1·25 1·25
551/4 . . . . *Set of* 4 2·25 2·25

1983 (12 Apr). *As Nos.* 490/505, *but* W w **15** *and imprint date "1983" added. P* 13½ × 13.
555 5 c. Type **91** 15 10
556 10 c. Hogfish 15 10
559 25 c. Sergeant Major 25 20
560 35 c. Clown Wrasse 35 30
564 75 c. French Grunt 60 55
565 $1 Rock Beauty 70 65
568 $5 Cherubfish . . . . . . 2·75 3·00
570 $10 Longsnout Butterflyfish . . . . 5·50 6·00
555/70 . . . . *Set of* 8 9·50 10·00

(Des G. Drummond. Litho Format)

1983 (24 May). *Hummingbirds. T* **101** *and similar vert designs. Multicoloured.* W w **14**. *P* 14.
571 35 c. Type **101** 70 35
572 75 c. Green-throated Carib . . . . . . 1·00 55
573 $2 Antillean Crested Hummingbird . . 2·00 1·40
574 $3 Purple-throated Carib . . . . . . 2·50 1·75
571/4 . . . . *Set of* 4 5·50 3·50

102 Montserrat Emblem

(**103**)

(Litho Harrison)

1983 (25 July). W w **14**. *P* 14½.
575 **102** $12 royal blue and rose . . . . 4·25 5·00
576 $30 rose and royal blue . . . . 11·00 12·00

1983 (15 Aug). *Various stamps surch as T* **103**. (*a*) *Nos.* 491, 498, 501 (*all* W w 14), 559, 564 (*both* W w **15**).
577 40 c. on 25 c. Sergeant Major (No. 559) . . 20 20
a. Surch inverted . . . . 38·00
b. Surch on No. 494 . . . . . . 12·00 12·00
c. Error. Surch on 10 c. (No. 491) . . . . 26·00
d. Surch double . . . . 45·00

578 70 c. on 10 c. Hogfish (No. 491) 35 35
a. Surch inverted .. .. 38·00
b. Surch on No. 556.. .. .. .. 27·00 27·00
c. Surch omitted (in pair with normal) .. £130
d. Surch double .. .. 45·00
579 90 c. on 65 c. Bigeye (No. 498).. .. .. 50 55
a. Error. Surch on 10 c. (No. 491) ..
b. Error. Surch on 75 c. (No. 499) .. .. 80·00
c. Surch double .. .. 45·00
580 $1.15 on 75 c. French Grunt (No. 564) 60 65
a. Surch on No. 499.. .. .. .. 14·00 14·00
b. Error. Surch on 25 c. (No. 559) .. .. 40·00
c. Surch inverted .. .. 50·00
581 $1.50 on $2 Blue Chromis (No. 501) .. 80 85
a. Surch inverted .. .. 60·00
b. Error. Surch on 75 c. (No. 499) .. .. 80·00

(b) Nos. 512/15

582 70 c. on $3 *Portsmouth* 60 70
a. Sheetlet. No. 582 × 6 and No. 583 .. 4·00
b. Surch double .. .. 5·00
c. Surch inverted .. .. 20·00
d. Surch inverted (horiz pair) .. .. 40·00
583 70 c. on $3 Prince Charles and Lady Diana Spencer 60 70
b. Surch double .. .. 45·00
c. Surch inverted .. .. 90·00
584 $1.15 on $4 *Britannia* .. .. .. 1·00 1·10
a. Sheetlet. No. 584 × 6 and No. 585 .. 7·00
b. Surch double .. .. 23·00
c. Surch inverted .. .. 15·00
d. Surch inverted (horiz pair) .. .. 30·00
e. Error. Surch on $3 (No. 512) .. .. 6·50
585 $1.15 on $4 As No. 583 .. .. .. 1·00 1·10
b. Surch double .. .. 40·00
c. Surch inverted .. .. 65·00
e. Error. Surch on $3 (No. 513) .. .. 70·00
577/85 .. .. *Set of* 9 4·75 5·25

Nos. 582d and 584d show the long surcharge intended for Nos. 583 or 585 inverted across horizontal pairs of the smaller design. Nos. 583c and 585c show two examples of the smaller surcharge inverted.

104 Montgolfier Balloon, 1783 **105** Boys dressed as Clowns

(Des A. Theobald. Litho Format)

1983 (19 Sept). *Bicentenary of Manned Flight. T* **104** *and similar multicoloured designs. W w* **14** *(sideways on 75 c. to $2). P* 14.
586 35 c. Type **104** 15 15
587 75 c. De Havilland "Twin Otter" (*horiz*) .. 35 30
588 $1.50, Lockheed "Vega" (*horiz*) 70 75
589 $2 *R 34* airship (*horiz*) .. .. .. 1·00 1·25
586/9 .. .. *Set of* 4 2·00 2·25
MS590 109 × 145 mm. Nos. 586/9. Wmk sideways 2·10 2·50

Nos. 586/9 were re-issued on 15 December 1983 overprinted "INAUGURAL FLIGHT Montserrat-Nevis-St. Kitts". It is understood nearly all of these overprints were used on Flown First Flight/Day Covers (*Price for set of 4 on First Flight Cover £30*).

(Des Jennifer Toombs. Litho Format)

1983 (18 Nov). *Christmas. Carnival. T* **105** *and similar horiz designs. Multicoloured. W w* **15** *(sideways). P* 14.
591 55 c. Type **105** 25 20
592 90 c. Girls dressed as silver star bursts .. 40 35
593 $1.15, Flower girls 50 60
594 $2 Masqueraders .. .. 95 1·00
591/4 .. .. *Set of* 4 1·90 1·90

106 Statue of Discus-thrower **107** Cattle Egret

(Des Court House Studio. Litho Questa)

1984 (26 Mar). *Olympic Games, Los Angeles. T* **106** *and similar vert designs. Multicoloured. W w* **15** *(sideways). P* 14.
595 90 c. Type **106** 35 35
596 $1 Olympic torch 40 45
597 $1.15, Olympic stadium, Los Angeles .. 45 50
598 $2.50, Olympic and American flags.. .. 80 1·00
595/8 .. .. *Set of* 4 1·75 2·10
MS599 110 × 110 mm. Nos. 595/8. Wmk upright 1·75 2·25

(Des G. Drummond. Litho Walsall)

1984 (28 May). *Birds of Montserrat. T* **107** *and similar multicoloured designs. W w* **15** *(sideways on 5 c. to 90 c.). P* 14.
600 5 c. Type **107** 15 10
601 10 c. Carib Grackle 15 10
602 15 c. Moorhen ("Common Gallinule") .. 15 10
603 20 c. Brown Booby 20 10
604 25 c. Black-whiskered Vireo 20 10
605 40 c. Scaly-breasted Thrasher.. .. .. 35 20
606 55 c. Laughing Gull 50 25
607 70 c. Glossy Ibis 60 35
608 90 c. Green Heron 75 40
609 $1 Belted Kingfisher (*vert*) 90 55
610 $1.15, Bananaquit (*vert*) .. .. .. 1·10 75
611 $3 American Kestrel ("Sparrow Hawk") (*vert*).. .. .. 2·25 2·50
612 $5 Forest Thrush (*vert*) .. .. .. 3·50 4·00
613 $7.50, Black-crowned Night Heron (*vert*) .. 5·50 6·50
614 $10 Bridled Quail Dove (*vert*) .. .. 7·00 8·50
600/14 .. .. *Set of* 15 21·00 22·00

(Des J.W. Litho Format)

1984 (9 July). *Mail Packet Boats (2nd series). Multicoloured designs as T* **89**. *W w* **15** *(sideways). P* 14.
615 55 c. R.M.S.P. *Tagus*, 1907 .. .. .. 50 40
616 90 c. R.M.S.P. *Cobequid*, 1913 .. .. 75 65
617 $1.15, S.S. *Lady Drake*, 1942 .. .. 1·00 1·00
618 $2 M.V. *Factor*, 1948 .. .. .. 1·75 2·00
615/18 .. .. *Set of* 4 3·50 3·50
MS619 152 × 100 mm. Nos. 615/18.. .. 3·25 3·75

No. **MS**619 also commemorates the 250th anniversary of *Lloyd's List* (newspaper).

108 Hermit Crab and Top Shell

(Des G. Drummond. Litho Questa)

1984 (24 Sept). *Marine Life. T* **108** *and similar horiz designs. Multicoloured. W w* **15** *(sideways). P* 14.
620 90 c. Type **108** 75 50
621 $1.15, Rough File Shell 95 70
622 $1.50, True Tulip Snail .. .. .. 1·25 90
623 $2.50, West Indian Fighting Conch .. 2·00 1·75
620/3 .. .. *Set of* 4 4·50 3·50

109 "Bull Man" **110** Mango

(Des Jennifer Toombs. Litho Questa)

1984 (12 Nov). *Christmas. Carnival Costumes. T* **109** *and similar horiz designs. Multicoloured. W w* **15** *(sideways). P* 14.
624 55 c. Type **109** 25 25
625 $1.15, Masquerader Captain 70 70
626 $1.50, "Fantasy" Carnival Queen 80 85
627 $2.30, "Ebony and Ivory" Carnival Queen .. 1·25 1·40
624/7 .. .. *Set of* 4 2·75 2·75

(Des G. Drummond. Litho Format)

1985 (8 Feb). *National Emblems. T* **110** *and similar vert designs. Multicoloured. W w* **15**. *P* 14.
628 $1.15, Type **110**.. .. .. 1·00 75
629 $1.50, Lobster Claw .. .. 1·50 95
630 $3 Montserrat Oriole .. .. 2·75 1·90
628/30 .. .. *Set of* 3 4·75 3·75

IMPERFORATES AND MISSING COLOURS. Various issues between Nos. 631 and 695 exist either imperforate or with colours omitted. Such items are not listed as there is no evidence that they fulfil the criteria outlined on page xi of this catalogue.

111 *Oncidium urophyllum* **112** Queen Elizabeth the Queen Mother

(Des J. Cooter. Litho Format)

1985 (9 May). *Orchids of Montserrat. T* **111** *and similar vert designs. Multicoloured. W w* **15**. *P* 14.
631 90 c. Type **111**.. .. .. 80 55
632 $1.15, *Epidendrum difforme* 90 70
633 $1.50, *Epidendrum ciliare*.. .. .. 1·00 85
634 $2.50, *Brassavola cucullata* .. .. 1·40 1·40
631/4 .. .. *Set of* 4 3·75 3·25
MS635 120 × 140 mm. Nos. 631/4 .. .. 4·25 4·75

(Des D. Ewart ($2), Maxine Marsh (others). Litho Format)

1985 (7 Aug). *Life and Times of Queen Elizabeth the Queen Mother. Various vertical portraits as T* **112**. *P* 12½.
636 55 c. multicoloured 30 35
a. Horiz pair. Nos. 636/7 .. .. .. 60 70
637 55 c. multicoloured 30 35
638 90 c. multicoloured 50 55
a. Horiz pair. Nos. 638/9 .. .. .. 1·00 1·10
639 90 c. multicoloured 50 55
640 $1.15, multicoloured 65 70
a. Horiz pair. Nos. 640/1 .. .. .. 1·25 1·40
641 $1.15, multicoloured 65 70
642 $1.50, multicoloured 80 85
a. Horiz pair. Nos. 642/3 .. .. .. 1·60 1·60
643 $1.50, multicoloured 80 85
636/43 .. .. *Set of* 8 4·00 4·50
MS644 85 × 113 mm. $2 multicoloured; $2 multicoloured .. .. 2·10 2·25

The two designs of each value were issued, *se-tenant*, in horizontal pairs within the sheets. Each *se-tenant* pair shows a floral pattern across the bottom of the portraits which stops short of the left-hand edge on the left-hand stamp and of the right-hand edge on the right-hand stamp.

Designs as Nos. 636/7 and 642/3 but with face values of $3.50 × 2 and $6 × 2, also exist in additional miniature sheets from a restricted printing issued 10 January 1986.

113 Cotton Plants

(Des G. Drummond. Litho Format)

1985 (18 Oct). *Montserrat Sea Island Cotton Industry. T* **113** *and similar horiz designs. Multicoloured. W w* **15**. *P* 15.
645 90 c. Type **113**.. .. .. 65 60
646 $1 Operator at carding machine 70 65
647 $1.15, Threading loom 85 85
648 $2.50, Weaving with hand loom .. .. 1·75 2·00
645/8 .. .. *Set of* 4 3·50 3·75
MS649 148 × 103 mm. Nos. 645/8. Wmk sideways .. .. 3·50 3·75

CARIBBEAN ROYAL VISIT 1985

(**114**) **115** Black-throated Blue Warbler

1985 (25 Oct). *Royal Visit. Nos.* 514/15, 543, 587/8 *and* 640/1 *optd as T* **114** *or surch also.*
650 75 c. multicoloured (No. 587) .. .. 2·50 2·50
651 $1 multicoloured (No. 543) .. .. 4·00 3·00
652 $1.15, multicoloured (No. 640) .. .. 4·00 3·00
a. Horiz pair. Nos. 652/3 .. .. .. 8·00 7·00
653 $1.15, multicoloured (No. 641) .. .. 4·00 3·50
654 $1.50, multicoloured (No. 588) .. .. 5·50 5·00
655 $1.60 on $4 multicoloured (No. 514) .. 3·50 3·50
a. Sheetlet. No. 655 × 6 and No. 656 .. 28·00
ab. Sheetlet No. 655 × 6 and No. 656a .. 28·00
656 $1.60 on $4 multicoloured (No. 515) (surch $1.60 only) .. .. 10·00 10·00
a. Additionally optd "CARIBBEAN ROYAL VISIT—1985".. .. .. 10·00 10·00
650/6 .. .. *Set of* 7 30·00 28·00

No. 656 shows a new face value only; "CARIBBEAN ROYAL VISIT" being omitted from the surcharge. No. 656a is the corrected version issued subsequently.

(Des R. Vigurs. Litho Format)

1985 (29 Nov). *Leaders of the World. Birth Bicentenary of John J. Audubon (ornithologist). T* **115** *and similar vert designs showing original paintings. Multicoloured. P* 12½.
657 15 c. Type **115**.. .. .. 25 25
a. Horiz pair. Nos. 657/8 .. .. .. 50 50
658 15 c. Palm Warbler 25 25
659 30 c. Bobolink.. .. .. 30 30
a. Horiz pair. Nos. 659/60 .. .. .. 60 60
660 30 c. Lark Sparrow 30 30
661 55 c. Chipping Sparrow 40 40
a. Horiz pair. Nos. 661/2 .. .. .. 80 80
662 55 c. Northern Oriole.. .. .. .. 40 40
663 $2.50, American Goldfinch .. .. .. 1·50 1·50
a. Horiz pair. Nos. 663/4 .. .. .. 3·00 3·00
664 $2.50, Blue Grosbeak .. .. .. 1·50 1·50
657/64 .. .. *Set of* 8 4·50 4·50

Nos. 657/8, 659/60, 661/2 and 663/4 were printed together, *se-tenant*, in horizontal pairs throughout the sheets.

116 Herald Angel appearing to Goatherds   117 Lord Baden-Powell

(Des Jennifer Toombs. Litho Format)

1985 (2 Dec). *Christmas. T* **116** *and similar horiz designs showing a Caribbean Nativity. Multicoloured. P* 15.
665 70 c. Type **116** 40 45
666 $1.15, Three Wise Men following the Star 65 70
667 $1.50, Carol singing around War Memorial, Plymouth 80 85
668 $2.30, Praying to "Our Lady of Montserrat" Church of Our Lady, St. Patrick's Village . . . . 1·25 1·40
665/8 . . . . *Set of* 4 2·75 3·00

(Des G. Vasarhelyi. Litho Format)

1986 (11 Apr). *50th Anniv of Montserrat Girl Guide Movement. T* **117** *and similar vert designs. Multicoloured.* W w **15** (*sideways*). *P* 15.
669 20 c. Type **117** 25 25
a. Horiz pair. Nos. 669/70 . . . . . . 50 50
670 20 c. Girl Guide saluting 25 25
671 75 c. Lady Baden-Powell 65 65
a. Horiz pair. Nos. 671/2 . . . . . . 1·25 1·25
672 75 c. Guide assisting in old people's home . . 65 65
673 90 c. Lord and Lady Baden-Powell 80 80
a. Horiz pair. Nos. 673/4 . . . . . . 1·60 1·60
674 90 c. Guides serving meal in old people's home 80 80
675 $1.15, Girl Guides of 1936 . . . . . . 1·00 1·00
a. Horiz pair. Nos. 675/6 . . . . . . 2·00 2·00
676 $1.15, Two Guides saluting . . . . . . 1·00 1·00
669/76 . . . . *Set of* 8 4·75 4·75

Nos. 669/70, 671/2, 673/4 and 675/6 were each printed together, *se-tenant*, in horizontal pairs throughout the sheets.

(Des Court House Studio. Litho Format)

1986 (21 Apr). *60th Birthday of Queen Elizabeth II. Multicoloured designs as T* **167** *of British Virgin Islands. P* 12½.
677 10 c. Queen Elizabeth II 10 10
678 $1.50, Princess Elizabeth in 1928 . . . . 90 90
a. Wmk w **15** (sideways) . . . . . . 6·00
679 $3 In Antigua, 1977 . . . . . . 1·75 1·75
a. Wmk w **15** (sideways) . . . . . . 6·00
680 $6 In Canberra, 1982 (*vert*) . . . . 3·25 3·25
677/80 . . . . *Set of* 4 5·50 5·50
MS681 85 × 115 mm. $8 Queen with bouquet . . 4·50 5·00

118 King Harold and Halley's Comet, 1066 (from Bayeux Tapestry)

(Des Court House Studio. Litho Format)

1986 (9 May). *Appearance of Halley's Comet. T* **118** *and similar horiz designs. Multicoloured. P* 14 × 13½.
682 35 c. Type **118** 30 30
683 50 c. Comet of 1301 (from Giotto's "Adoration of the Magi") 40 40
684 70 c. Edmond Halley and Comet of 1531 . . 55 55
685 $1 Comets of 1066 and 1910 . . . . 70 70
686 $1.15, Comet of 1910 . . . . . . 80 80
687 $1.50, E.S.A. *Giotto* spacecraft and Comet 95 95
688 $2.30, U.S. Space Telescope and Comet . . 1·40 1·40
689 $4 Computer reconstruction of 1910 Comet 2·50 2·50
682/9 . . . . *Set of* 8 7·00 7·00
MS690 Two sheets, each 140 × 115 mm. (a) 40 c. Type **118**; $1.75, As No. 683; $2 As No. 684; $3 As No. 685. (b) 55 c. As No. 686; 60 c. As No. 687; 80 c. As No. 688; $5 As No. 689 *Set of 2 sheets* 7·00 8·00

(Des Court House Studio. Litho Format)

1986 (23 July–15 Oct). *Royal Wedding (1st issue). Multicoloured designs as T* **168** *of British Virgin Islands. P* 12½.
691 70 c. Prince Andrew 50 50
a. Pair. Nos. 691/2 . . . . 1·00 1·00
692 70 c. Miss Sarah Ferguson 50 50
693 $2 Prince Andrew wearing stetson (*horiz*) 1·25 1·25
a. Pair. Nos. 693/4 . . . . 2·50 2·50
694 $2 Miss Sarah Ferguson on skiing holiday (*horiz*) . . . . 1·25 1·25
691/4 . . . . *Set of* 4 3·25 3·25
MS695 115 × 85 mm. $10 Duke and Duchess of York on Palace balcony after wedding (*horiz*) (15.10) . . . . 5·00 5·50

Nos. 691/2 and 693/4 were printed together, *se-tenant*, in horizontal and vertical pairs throughout the sheets.

Nos. 691/4 imperforate come from souvenir stamp booklets.

See also Nos. 705/8.

119 *Antelope* (1793)

(Des T. Hadler. Litho Questa)

1986 (29 Aug). *Mail Packet Sailing Ships. T* **119** *and similar horiz designs. Multicoloured.* W w **15**. *P* 14.
696 90 c. Type **119** . . . . 1·00 80
697 $1.15, *Montagu* (1810) . . . . . . 1·25 1·00
698 $1.50, *Little Catherine* (1813) . . . . 1·75 1·75
699 $2.30, *Hinchingbrook* (1813) . . . . 2·25 2·50
696/9 . . . . *Set of* 4 5·75 5·50
MS700 165 × 123 mm. Nos. 696/9. Wmk sideways 6·00 6·50

120 Radio Montserrat Building, Dagenham

(Des G. Vasarhelyi. Litho Questa)

1986 (29 Sept). *Communications. T* **120** *and similar horiz designs. Multicoloured.* W w **15**. *P* 14.
701 70 c. Type **120** 70 60
702 $1.15, Radio Gem dish aerial, Plymouth . . 1·00 90
703 $1.50, Radio Antilles studio, O'Garro's . . 1·25 1·25
704 $2.30, Cable and Wireless building, Plymouth . . . . 1·75 2·00
701/4 . . . . *Set of* 4 4·25 4·25

Congratulations to
T.R.H. The Duke
& Duchess of York

(121)

1986 (14 Nov). *Royal Wedding (2nd issue). Nos. 691/4 optd as T* **121** *in silver.*
705 70 c. Prince Andrew 50 50
a. Pair. Nos. 705/6 . . . . 1·00 1·00
706 70 c. Miss Sarah Ferguson 50 50
707 $2 Prince Andrew wearing stetson (*horiz*) 1·25 1·25
a. Pair. Nos. 707/8 . . . . 2·50 2·50
708 $2 Miss Sarah Ferguson on skiing holiday (*horiz*) . . . . 1·25 1·25
705/8 . . . . *Set of* 4 3·25 3·25

(Des Court House Studio. Litho Format)

1986 (18 Nov). *Centenary of Statue of Liberty. Vert views of Statue as T* **171** *of British Virgin Islands in separate miniature sheets. Multicoloured. P* 14 × 13½.
MS709 Three sheets, each 85 × 115 mm. $3; $4.50; $5 . . . . . . *Set of 3 sheets* 7·00 8·00

122 Sailing and Windsurfing   123 Christmas Rose

(Des J. Cooter. Litho Format)

1986 (10 Dec). *Tourism. T* **122** *and similar horiz designs. Multicoloured. P* 15.
710 70 c. Type **122** 70 50
711 $1.15, Golf . . . . 1·50 1·00
712 $1.50, Plymouth market . . . . . . 1·75 1·75
713 $2.30, Air Recording Studios . . . . 2·00 2·50
710/13 . . . . *Set of* 4 5·50 5·25

(Des Jennifer Toombs. Litho Questa)

1986 (12 Dec). *Christmas. Flowering Shrubs. T* **123** *and similar vert designs. Multicoloured. P* 14.
714 70 c. Type **123** 60 40
715 $1.15, Candle Flower 85 70
716 $1.50, Christmas Tree Kalanchoe . . . . 1·25 1·00
717 $2.30, Snow on the Mountain . . . . 1·75 2·00
714/17 . . . . *Set of* 4 4·00 3·75
MS718 150 × 110 mm. Nos. 714/17. P 12 . . 4·00 4·50

124 Tiger Shark

5c ▬

(125)

(Des M. Hillier. Litho Questa)

1987 (2 Feb). *Sharks. T* **124** *and similar horiz designs. Multicoloured.* W w **15**. *P* 14.
719 40 c. Type **124** 60 40
720 90 c. Lemon Shark . . . . 1·25 70
721 $1.15, White Shark . . . . 1·40 1·25
722 $3.50, Whale Shark . . . . 3·25 3·50
719/22 . . . . *Set of* 4 6·00 5·25
MS723 150 × 102 mm. Nos. 719/22. Wmk sideways. P 12 . . . . 6·00 6·50

1987 (6 Apr). *Nos.* 601, 603, 607/8 *and* 611 *surch as T* **125**.
724 5 c. on 70 c. Glossy Ibis 10 10
725 $1 on 20 c. Brown Booby 60 60
726 $1.15 on 10 c. Carib Grackle 70 70
727 $1.50 on 90 c. Green Heron 85 85
728 $2.30 on $3 American Kestrel (*vert*) . . 1·25 1·50
724/8 . . . . *Set of* 5 3·25 3·50

(126)   127 Straight Line Sulpher

1987 (13 June). *"Capex '87" International Stamp Exhibition, Toronto. No.* **MS**690 *optd with T* **126** *in black and red.*
MS729 Two sheets. As No. **MS**690 *Set of 2 sheets* 6·50 7·00

No. **MS**729 also carries an overprint commemorating the exhibition on the lower sheet margins.

(Des M. Hillier. Litho Questa)

1987 (10 Aug). *Butterflies. T* **127** *and similar square designs. Multicoloured.* W w **15**. *P* 14.
730 90 c. Type **127** 85 50
731 $1.15, Red Rim . . . . 1·25 80
732 $1.50, Hammock Skipper . . . . . . 1·50 1·25
733 $2.50, Mimic . . . . 2·00 2·50
730/3 . . . . *Set of* 4 5·00 4·50

128 *Oncidium variegatum*

(Des R. Vigurs. Litho Questa)

1987 (13 Nov). *Christmas. Orchids. T* **128** *and similar multicoloured designs. P* 14 × 13½ (90 c., $1.50) *or* 13½ × 14 (*others*).
734 90 c. Type **128** 60 45
735 $1.15, *Vanilla planifolia* (*horiz*) 85 55
736 $1.50, *Gongora quinquenervis* . . . . 1·10 75
737 $3.50, *Brassavola nodosa* (*horiz*) . . . . 2·00 1·75
734/7 . . . . *Set of* 4 4·00 3·25
MS738 100 × 75 mm. $5 *Oncidium lanceanum* (*horiz*) . . . . 4·00 4·50

40th Wedding Anniversary
HM Queen Elizabeth II
HRH Duke of Edingburgh.
November 1987.
$2.30 ==

(129)   130 Free-tailed Bat

1987 (29 Nov). *Royal Ruby Wedding. Nos* 601. 604/5 *and* 608 *surch as T* **129**. A. *Surch* "Edingburgh". B. *Surch* "Edinburgh".

		A		B	
739	5 c. on 90 c. Green Heron . .	1·50	1·50	10	10
740	$1.15 on 10 c. Carib Grackle . .	3·25	3·25	50	55
741	$2.30 on 25 c. Black-whiskered Vireo	6·00	6·00	1·00	1·10
742	$5 on 40 c. Scaly-breasted Thrasher	9·00	9·00	2·25	2·40
739/42	. . . . *Set of* 4	18·00	18·00	3·50	3·75

Nos. 739A/42A were from the first printing using Type **129**. After the spelling mistake was noticed it was corrected on sheets subsequently surcharged.

(Des M. Pollard. Litho Questa)

1988 (8 Feb). *Bats. T* **130** *and similar vert designs. Multi-coloured. W w* **15** *(sideways). P* 14.
743 55 c. Type **130** 25 30
744 90 c. *Chiroderma improvisum* (fruit bat) . . 40 45
745 $1.15, Fisherman Bat 50 55
746 $2.30, *Brachyphylla cavernarum* (fruit bat) 1·00 1·10
743/6 . . . . *Set of* 4 1·90 2·10
MS747 133 × 110 mm. $2.50, Funnel-eared Bat. Wmk upright . . . . 1·25 1·50

131 Magnificent Frigate Bird **132** Discus throwing

(Des R. Vigurs. Litho Questa)

1988 (2 Apr). *Easter. Birds. T* **131** *and similar vert designs. Multicoloured. P* 14×13½.
748 90 c. Type **131** 60 45
749 $1.15, Caribbean Elaenia 80 65
750 $1.50, Glossy Ibis . . . . . . 1·00 1·00
751 $3.50, Purple-throated Carib . . . . 2·00 2·25
748/51 . . . . . . *Set of* 4 4·00 4·00
MS752 100 × 75 mm. $5 Brown Pelican . . 2·50 3·00

(Des R. Vigurs. Litho Questa)

1988 (29 July). *Olympic Games, Seoul. T* **132** *and similar horiz designs. Multicoloured. P* 13½×14.
753 90 c. Type **132** 40 45
754 $1.15, High jumping 50 55
755 $3.50, Athletics . . . . 1·60 1·75
753/5 . . . . . . *Set of* 3 2·25 2·50
MS756 103×77 mm. $5 Rowing . . . . 2·25 2·75

133 Golden Tulip **134** University Crest

(Des R. Vigurs. Litho Questa)

1988 (30 Aug). *Sea Shells. T* **133** *and similar horiz designs. Multicoloured. P* 14.
757 5 c. Type **133** 10 10
758 10 c. Little Knobby Scallop 10 10
759 15 c. Sozoni's Cone 10 10
760 20 c. Globular Coral Shell 10 10
761 25 c. Sundial 10 10
762 40 c. King Helmet 15 20
763 55 c. Channelled Turban 20 25
764 70 c. True Tulip Shell 30 35
765 90 c. Music Volute 35 40
766 $1 Flame Auger 40 45
767 $1.15, Rooster Tail Conch 45 50
768 $1.50, Queen Conch 60 65
769 $3 Teramachi's Slit Shell . . . . 1·25 1·40
770 $5 Florida Crown Conch . . . . 2·10 2·25
771 $7.50, Beau's Murex . . . . . . 3·00 3·25
772 $10 Triton's Trumpet . . . . . . 4·00 4·25
757/72 . . . . . . *Set of* 16 11·50 13·00

(Des R. Vigurs. Litho Questa)

1988 (14 Oct). 40*th Anniv of University of West Indies. P* 14×13½.
773 **134** $5 multicoloured . . . . . . 2·40 2·50

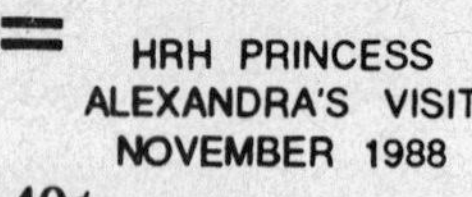

(135)

1988 (4 Nov). *Princess Alexandra's Visit. Nos.* 763, 766 *and* 769/70 *surch as T* **135**.
774 40 c. on 55 c. Channelled Turban 20 25
775 90 c. on $1 Flame Auger 40 45
776 $1.15 on $3 Teramachi's Slit Shell . . 50 55
a. Surch double . . . . 55·00
777 $1.50 on $5 Florida Crown Conch . . 60 65
774/7 . . . . . . *Set of* 4 1·50 1·75

136 Spotted Sandpiper

(Des R. Vigurs. Litho Questa)

1988 (4 Dec). *Christmas. Sea Birds. T* **136** *and similar horiz designs. Multicoloured. P* 13½×14.
778 90 c. Type **136** 60 45
779 $1.15, Turnstone 70 55
780 $3.50, Red-footed Booby . . . . 1·75 2·00
778/80 . . . . . . *Set of* 3 2·75 2·75
MS781 105×79 mm. $5 Audubon's Shearwater 2·75 3·00

137 Handicapped Children in Classroom

(Des R. Vigurs. Litho Questa)

1988 (16 Dec). 125*th Anniv of International Red Cross. P* 13½ × 14.
782 **137** $3.50, multicoloured . . . . . . 1·50 1·60

138 Drum Major in Ceremonial Uniform **139** Amazon Lily

(Des R. Vigurs. Litho Questa)

1989 (24 Feb). 75*th Anniv of Montserrat Defence Force* (1988). *Uniforms. T* **138** *and similar vert designs. Multicoloured. P* 14×13½.
783 90 c. Type **138** 60 45
784 $1.15, Field training uniform 75 65
785 $1.50, Cadet in ceremonial uniform . . 90 90
786 $3.50, Gazetted Police Officer in ceremonial uniform . . . . . . 2·00 2·25
783/6 . . . . . . *Set of* 4 3·75 3·75
MS787 102×76 mm. $5 Island Girl Guide Commissioner and Brownie . . . . 3·00 3·25

(Litho Questa)

1989 (21 Mar). *Easter. Lilies. T* **139** *and similar multicoloured designs. P* 13½×14 (90 *c.*) *or* 14×13½ (*others*).
788 90 c. Type **139** 50 50
789 $1.15, Salmon Blood Lily (*vert*) . . 70 70
790 $1.50, Amaryllis (*Hippeastrum vittatum*) (*vert*) 85 85
791 $3.50, Amaryllis (*Hippeastrum* hybrid) (*vert*) . . . . 1·90 1·90
788/91 . . . . . . *Set of* 4 3·50 3·50
MS792 103×77 mm. $5 Resurrection Lily (*vert*) 3·00 3·25

140 *Morning Prince* (schooner), 1942 **141** The Scarecrow

(Des R. Vigurs. Litho Questa)

1989 (30 June). *Shipbuilding in Montserrat. T* **140** *and similar horiz designs. Multicoloured. P* 13½×14.
793 90 c. Type **140** 40 45
794 $1.15, *Western Sun* (inter-island freighter) 55 60
795 $1.50, *Kim G* (inter-island freighter) under construction 70 75
796 $3.50, *Romaris* (island ferry), *c.* 1942 1·60 1·75
793/6 . . . . . . *Set of* 4 3·00 3·25

(Litho Questa)

1989 (22 Sept). 50*th Anniv of* The Wizard of Oz *(film). T* **141** *and similar multicoloured designs. P* 14.
797 90 c. Type **141** 40 45
798 $1.15, The Lion 55 60
799 $1.50, The Tin Man 70 75
800 $3.50, Dorothy . . . . 1·60 1·75
797/800 . . . . . . *Set of* 4 3·00 3·25
MS801 113×84 mm. $5 Characters from film (*horiz*) . . . . 2·40 2·50

Hurricane Hugo
Relief Surcharge $2.50

(142)

1989 (20 Oct). *Hurricane Hugo Relief Fund. Nos.* 795/6 *surch with T* **142**.
802 $1.50 + $2.50, *Kim G* (inter-island freighter) under construction . . 1·90 2·00
803 $3.50 + $2.50, *Romaris* (island ferry), *c.* 1942 . . . . 2·75 3·00

OFFICIAL STAMPS

O.H.M.S. (O 1) **O.H.M.S.** (O 2)

1976 (12 Apr). *Various stamps, some already surcharged, optd locally with Type* O **1**.

No.	Description	Unused	Used
O1	5 c. multicoloured (No. 246A)	†	65
O2	10 c. multicoloured (No. 247A)	†	75
	a. Opt double	†	25·00
	b. Horiz pair, one stamp without opt	†	£250
O3	30 c. on 10 c. multicoloured (No. 369)	†	1·50
	a. Opt double	†	40·00
O4	45 c. on 3 c. multicoloured (No. 370)	†	2·00
O5	$5 multicoloured (No. 254A)	†	£100
O6	$10 multicoloured (No. 254*a*B)	†	£550
O1/6	*Set of* 6	†	£600

These stamps were issued for use on mail from the Montserrat Philatelic Bureau. They were not available for sale in either unused or used condition.

1976 (1 Oct)–**80**. *Nos.* 374/8, 380/2 *and* 384/5 *optd with Type* O **2** locally.

No.	Description	Unused	Used
O 7	5 c. Malay Apple	†	15
	a. Opt inverted	†	—
	b. Missing stop after "S"	†	1·50
O 8	10 c. Jacaranda	†	20
	a. Missing stop after "S"	†	1·50
O 9	15 c. Orchid Tree	†	25
	a. Opt inverted	†	70·00
	b. Missing stop after "S"	†	1·50
O10	20 c. Manjak	†	30
	a. Opt inverted	†	70·00
	b. Chalk-surfaced paper (1980)	†	—
	c. Missing stop after "S"	†	1·50
O11	25 c. Tamarind	†	35
	a. Missing stop after "S"	†	1·50
O12	55 c. Pink Cassia	†	55
	a. Opt inverted	†	—
	b. Opt double	†	—
	c. Missing stop after "S"	†	2·50
O13	70 c. Long John	†	60
	a. Missing stop after "S"	†	3·50
O14	$1 Saman	†	85
	a. Missing stop after "S"	†	5·00
O15	$5 Yellow Poui	†	4·00
	a. Missing stop after "S"	†	13·00
O16	$10 Flamboyant (14.4.80)	†	7·00
	a. Missing stop after "S"	†	20·00
O7/16	*Set of* 10	†	13·00

Nos. O7/16 were not available in an unused condition, but were sold to the public cancelled-to-order.

The missing stop after "S" variety occurs on R. 1/3 and 3/5.

O.H.M.S. (O 3) O.H.M.S. (O 4) O.H.M.S. 45¢ (O 5)

1980 (7 July). *Nos.* 374/8, 380/2 *and* 384/5 *optd with Type* O **3** *in Great Britain*.

No.	Description	Unused	Used
O17	5 c. Malay Apple	†	10
	a. Opt double	†	—
O18	10 c. Jacaranda	†	10
O19	15 c. Orchid Tree	†	10
O20	20 c. Manjak	†	10
	a. Opt double	†	70·00
O21	25 c. Tamarind	†	15
O22	55 c. Pink Cassia	†	35
	a. Opt double	†	25·00
O23	70 c. Long John	†	45
O24	$1 Saman	†	60
O25	$5 Yellow Poui	†	2·75
O26	$10 Flamboyant	†	5·50
O17/26	*Set of* 10	†	9·00

Nos. O17/26 were not available in an unused condition, but were sold to the public cancelled-to-order. At least two values, the 20 c. and $1 are, however, known uncancelled.

These stamps were originally intended for issue on 3 November 1980, but certain values were placed on sale from 7 July onwards to meet shortages. Bulk supplies did not arrive on the island until early December 1980.

O.H. M.S.

Spaced "H" and "M" (R. 3/4)

1980 (30 Sept). *Nos.* 374/82, 384/5 *and* 476, *together with surcharges on Nos.* 372, 376 *and* 379, *optd as Type* O **4** *locally*.

No.	Description	Unused	Used
O27	5 c. Malay Apple	†	10
O28	5 c. on 3 c. Lignum vitae	†	10
O29	10 c. Jacaranda	†	10
O30	15 c. Orchid Tree	†	10
	a. Opt double	†	—
O31	20 c. Manjak	†	15
	a. Opt double	†	20·00
O32	25 c. Tamarind	†	15
O33	30 c. on 15 c. Orchid Tree	†	20
O34	35 c. on 2 c. Cannon-ball Tree	†	20
	a. Spaced "H" and "M"	†	3·50
O35	40 c. Flame of the Forest	†	25
O36	55 c. Pink Cassia	†	35
O37	70 c. Long John	†	50
O38	$1 Saman	†	60
O39	$2.50 on 40 c. Flame of the Forest	†	1·75
	a. "O.H.M.S." opt omitted	£160	
O40	$5 Yellow Poui	†	3·50
O41	$10 Flamboyant	†	6·50
	a. Opt double	†	75·00
O27/41	*Set of* 15	†	13·00

Nos. O27/41 were not available in an unused condition, but were sold to the public cancelled-to-order. No. O39a was, however, found amongst supplies of the postage series.

1981 (20 Mar). *Nos.* 490/4, 496, 498, 500, 502/3 *and* 505 *optd with Type* O **4**.

No.	Description	Unused	Used
O42	5 c. Type **91**	10	10
	a. Opt inverted	26·00	
O43	10 c. Hogfish	10	10
O44	15 c. Creole Wrasse	10	10
	a. Opt double	†	—
O45	20 c. Yellow Damselfish	15	15
O46	25 c. Sergeant Major	15	15
O47	45 c. Schoolmaster	25	20
	a. Opt double	38·00	
	ab. Opt double, one on reverse	22·00	
	b. Opt inverted	38·00	
O48	65 c. Bigeye	35	30
	a. Opt inverted	65·00	
O49	$1 Rock Beauty	65	65
O50	$3 Fairy Basslet and Blueheads	1·75	1·75
O51	$5 Cherubfish	3·00	3·00
O52	$10 Longsnout Butterflyfish	5·50	5·50
O42/52	*Set of* 11	11·00	11·00

1982 (17 Nov). *Nos.* 510/15 *surch as Type* O **5** (*in one line on Nos.* O54, O56 *and* O58).

No.	Description	Unused	Used
O53	45 c. on 90 c. *Charlotte*	25	30
	a. Sheetlet. No. O53 × 6 and No. O54	1·75	
	b. Surch double	25·00	
	c. Surch inverted	16·00	
	d. Surch inverted (horiz pair)	32·00	
	e. Horiz pair, one without surch	70·00	
O54	45 c. on 90 c. Prince Charles and Lady Diana Spencer	30	30
	b. Surch double	70·00	
	c. Surch inverted	50·00	
O55	75 c. on $3 *Portsmouth*	35	35
	a. Sheetlet. No. O55 × 6 and No. O56	2·25	
	b. Surch double	30·00	
	c. Surch inverted	22·00	
	d. Surch inverted (horiz pair)	27·00	
	e. Horiz pair, one without surch	70·00	
	f. Error. Surch on $4 (No. 514)	15·00	
	fa. Sheetlet. No. O55f × 6 and No. O56f	£150	
O56	75 c. on $3 Prince Charles and Lady Diana Spencer	45	45
	b. Surch double	75·00	
	c. Surch inverted	30·00	
	f. Error. Surch on $4 (No. 515)	70·00	
O57	$1 on $4 *Britannia*	50	50
	a. Sheetlet. No. O57 × 6 and No. O58	3·50	
	b. Surch double	32·00	
	c. Surch inverted	10·00	
	d. Surch inverted (horiz pair)	30·00	
	e. Horiz pair, one without surch		
O58	$1 on $4 Prince Charles and Lady Diana Spencer	60	60
	b. Surch double	80·00	
	c. Surch inverted	35·00	
O53/8	*Set of* 6	2·00	2·10

Nos. O53d, O55d and O57d show the long surcharge, intended for Nos. O54, O56 or O58, inverted across horizontal pairs of the smaller design. Nos. O54c, O56c and O58c show two examples as Type O **5** inverted on the same stamp.

70¢

O.H.M.S. (O 6) OHMS (O 7) OHMS (O 8)

1983 (19 Oct). *Nos.* 542/4 *surch as Type* O **6** *or optd only* ($1).

No.	Description	Unused	Used
O59	70 c. on 75 c. Type **97**	50	40
O60	$1 Coat of Arms of Catherine of Aragon	60	50
	a. Opt inverted	40·00	
O61	$1.50 on $5 Diana, Princess of Wales	85	80
O59/61	*Set of* 3	1·75	1·60

1985 (12 Apr). *Nos.* 600/12 *and* 614 *opt with Type* O **7** (*horizontally on Nos.* O71/5).

No.	Description	Unused	Used
O62	5 c. Type **107**	15	15
O63	10 c. Carib Grackle	15	15
O64	15 c. Moorhen	15	15
O65	20 c. Brown Booby	15	15
O66	25 c. Black-whiskered Vireo	20	15
O67	40 c. Scaly-breasted Thrasher	25	20
	a. Opt double	†	—
O68	55 c. Laughing Gull	35	25
O69	70 c. Glossy Ibis	45	35
O70	90 c. Green Heron	55	40
O71	$1 Belted Kingfisher	70	45
O72	$1.15, Bananaquit	80	60
O73	$3 American Kestrel	1·75	2·00
O74	$5 Forest Thrush	2·50	2·75
O75	$10 Bridled Quail Dove	4·75	5·50
O62/75	*Set of* 14	11·50	12·00

1989 (9 May). *Nos.* 757/70 *and* 772 *optd with Type* O **8**.

No.	Description	Unused	Used
O76	5 c. Type **133**	10	10
O77	10 c. Little Knobby Scallop	10	10
O78	15 c. Sozoni's Cone	10	10
O79	20 c. Globular Coral Shell	10	10
O80	25 c. Sundial	10	10
O81	40 c. King Helmet	15	20
O82	55 c. Channelled Turban	20	25
O83	70 c. True Tulip Shell	30	35
O84	90 c. Music Volute	35	40
O85	$1 Flame Auger	40	45
O86	$1.15, Rooster Tail Conch	45	50
O87	$1.50, Queen Conch	60	65
O88	$3 Teramachi's Slit Shell	1·25	1·40
O89	$5 Florida Crown Conch	2·10	2·25
O90	$10 Triton's Trumpet	4·00	4·25
O76/90	*Set of* 15	9·25	10·00

Morocco Agencies
(British Post Offices)

With the growth of trade and commerce during the 19th century European powers opened post offices or postal agencies in various ports along the Moroccan coast from the early 1850's onwards. French and, in the north, Spanish influence eventually became predominant, leading to the protectorates of 1912. The British, who had inaugurated a regular postal service between Gibraltar and Tangier or Tetuan in May 1778, established their first postal agency in 1857. German offices followed around the turn of the century.

Before 1892 there was no indigenous postal service and those towns where there was no foreign agency were served by a number of private local posts which continued to flourish until 1900. In November 1892 the Sultan of Morocco established the Cherifian postal service, but this was little used until after its reorganization at the end of 1911. The Sultan's post was absorbed by the French postal service on 1 October 1913. Issues of the local posts and of the Sultan's post can occasionally be found used on cover in combination with stamps of Gibraltar or the Morocco Agencies.

In 1857 the first British postal agency was established at Tangier within the precincts of the Legation and was run by the official interpreter. From 1 March 1858 all letters for Great Britain sent via the British mail packets from Gibraltar required franking with Great Britain stamps.

In 1872 the Tangier office was relocated away from the Legation and the interpreter was appointed British Postal Agent. At the same time the agency was placed under the control of the Gibraltar postmaster. When the colonial posts became independent of the British G.P.O. on 1 January 1886 Gibraltar retained responsibility for the Morocco Agencies. Further offices, each under the control of the local Vice-Consul, were opened from 1886 onwards.

I. GIBRALTAR USED IN MOROCCO

Details of the various agencies are given below. Type C, the "A26" killer, is very similar to postmarks used at Gibraltar during this period. In addition to the town name postmarks as Types A, B and D from Fez, Mazagan, Saffi and Tetuan were also inscribed "MOROCCO".

Postmark Types used on Gibraltar issues.

Type A
Circular datestamp

Type C
"A26" killer

Type B
Duplex cancellation

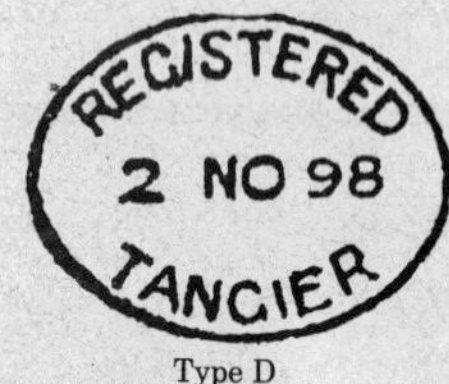

Type D
Registered oval

BISECTS. The 10 c., 40 c. and 50 c. values of the 1889 surcharges and of the 1889–96 issue are known bisected and used for half their value from various of the Morocco Agencies. These bisects were never authorised by the Gibraltar Post Office.

CASABLANCA

The British postal agency opened on 1 January 1887 and was initially supplied with ½d., 4d. and 6d. stamps from the Gibraltar 1886 overprinted on Bermuda issue and 1d., 2d. and 2½d. values from the 1886–87 set.

Stamps of GIBRALTAR *cancelled with Types* A (*without code or code* "C"), B (*without code or code* "A") *or* D.

1886 (*Nos.* 1/7).

Z1	½d. dull green	40·00
Z2	4d. orange-brown	£250
Z3	6d. deep lilac	

1886–87 (*Nos.* 8/14).

Z 4	½d. dull green	16·00
Z 5	1d. rose	20·00
Z 6	2d. brown-purple	40·00
Z 7	2½d. blue	30·00
Z 8	4d. orange-brown	65·00
Z10	1s. bistre	£250

1889 (*Nos.* 15/21).

Z11	5 c. on ½d. green	30·00
Z12	10 c. on 1d. rose	30·00
Z13	25 c. on 2d. brown-purple	35·00
Z14	25 c. on 2½d. bright blue	20·00
Z15	40 c. on 4d. orange-brown	65·00
Z16	50 c. on 6d. bright lilac	60·00
Z17	75 c. on 1s. bistre	£100

1889–96 (*Nos.* 22/33).

Z18	5 c. green	10·00
Z19	10 c. carmine	10·00
Z20	20 c. olive-green and brown	20·00
Z22	25 c. ultramarine	10·00
Z23	40 c. orange-brown	25·00
Z24	50 c. bright lilac	20·00
Z25	75 c. olive-green	50·00
Z26	1 p. bistre	50·00
Z28	1 p. bistre and ultramarine	25·00
Z29	2 p. black and carmine	35·00

FEZ

The British postal agency in this inland town opened on 24 February 1892 and was initially supplied with stamps up to the 50 c. value from the Gibraltar 1889–96 issue.

Stamps of GIBRALTAR *cancelled with Types* A (*without code*) *or* D.

1889–96 (*Nos.* 22/33).

Z31	5 c. green	15·00
Z32	10 c. carmine	22·00
Z33	20 c. olive-green and brown	35·00
Z35	25 c. ultramarine	28·00
Z36	40 c. orange-brown	50·00
Z37	50 c. bright lilac	40·00

LARAICHE

The British postal agency at Laraiche opened in March 1886, although the first postmark, an "A26" killer, was not supplied until May.

Stamps of GIBRALTAR *cancelled with Types* B (*without code*) *or* D.

1886 (*Nos.* 1/7).

Z39	½d. dull green	
Z40	1d. rose-red	
Z41	2½d. ultramarine	

1886–87 (*Nos.* 8/14).

Z42	½d. dull green	75·00
Z43	1d. rose	75·00
Z45	2½d. blue	80·00

1889 (*Nos.* 15/21).

Z47	5 c. on ½d. green	
Z48	10 c. on 1d. rose	
Z49	25 c. on 2½d. bright blue	

It is believed that the other surcharges in this series were not supplied to Laraiche.

1889–96 (*Nos.* 22/23).

Z50	5 c. green	20·00
Z51	10 c. carmine	20·00
Z52	20 c. olive-green and brown	
Z54	25 c. ultramarine	30·00
Z55	40 c. orange-brown	
Z56	50 c. bright-lilac	55·00
Z57	1 p. bistre and ultramarine	

MAZAGAN

This was the main port for the inland city of Marrakesh. The British postal agency opened on 1 March 1888 and was initially supplied with stamps from the Gibraltar 1886–87 series.

Stamps of GIBRALTAR *cancelled with Types* A (*codes* "A" *or* "C") *or* D (*without code, code* "A" *or code* "C").

1886–87 (*Nos.* 8/14).

Z58	½d. dull green	18·00
Z59	1d. rose	18·00
Z60	2d. brown-purple	
Z61	2½d. blue	25·00
Z62	4d. orange-brown	75·00
Z63	6d. lilac	90·00

1889 (*Nos.* 15/21).

Z64	5 c. on ½d. green	
Z65	10 c. on 1d. rose	
Z66	25 c. on 2½d. bright blue	

It is believed that the other surcharges in this series were not supplied to Mazagan.

1889–96 (*Nos.* 22/33).

Z67	5 c. green	14·00
Z68	10 c. carmine	12·00
Z69	20 c. olive-green and brown	30·00
Z70	25 c. ultramarine	35·00
Z71	40 c. orange-brown	
Z72	50 c. bright lilac	
Z74	1 p. bistre and ultramarine	
Z75	2 p. black and carmine	

MOGADOR

The British postal agency at this port opened in May 1887 and was initially supplied with stamps from the Gibraltar 1886–87 series.

Stamps of GIBRALTAR *cancelled with Types* A (*code* "C"), B (*code* "C") *or* D.

1886–87 (*Nos.* 8/14).

Z76	½d. dull green	18·00
Z77	1d. rose	25·00
Z78	2d. brown-purple	40·00
Z79	2½d. blue	25·00

1889 (*Nos.* 15/21).

Z80	5 c. on ½d. green	28·00
Z81	10 c. on 1d. rose	30·00
Z82	25 c. on 2½d. bright blue	30·00

It is believed that the other surcharges in this series were not supplied to Mogador.

1889–96 (*Nos.* 22/33).

Z83	5 c. green	10·00
Z84	10 c. carmine	12·00
Z85	20 c. olive-green and brown	
Z87	25 c. ultramarine	16·00
Z88	40 c. orange-brown	25·00
Z89	50 c. bright lilac	25·00

RABAT

The British postal agency at this port on the north-west coast of Morocco opened in March 1886, although the first cancellation, an "A26" killer, was not supplied until May. The initial stock of stamps was from the Gibraltar 1886 overprinted on Bermuda issue.

Stamps of GIBRALTAR *cancelled with Types* B (*code* "O") *or* D.

1886 (*Nos.* 1/7).

Z92	½d. dull green	
Z93	1d. rose-red	
Z94	2½d. ultramarine	£100

1886–87 (*Nos.* 8/14).

Z 95	½d. dull green	16·00
Z 96	1d. rose	16·00
Z 97	2d. brown-purple	45·00
Z 98	2½d. blue	20·00
Z101	1s. bistre	£300

1889 (*Nos.* 15/21).

Z102	5 c. on ½d. green	30·00
Z103	10 c. on 1d. rose	30·00
Z104	25 c. on 2½d. bright blue	35·00

It is believed that the other surcharges in this series were not supplied to Rabat.

1889–96 (*Nos.* 22/33).

Z105	5 c. green	11·00
Z106	10 c. carmine	11·00
Z107	20 c. olive-green and brown	20·00
Z108	25 c. ultramarine	12·00
Z109	40 c. orange-brown	25·00
Z110	50 c. bright lilac	25·00

SAFFI

The British postal agency at this port opened on 1 July 1891 and was supplied with stamps from the Gibraltar 1889–96 series.

Stamps of GIBRALTAR *cancelled with Types* B (*code* "C") *or* D (*code* "C").

1889–96 (*Nos.* 22/33).

Z111	5 c. green	14·00
Z112	10 c. carmine	14·00
Z113	20 c. olive-green and brown	20·00
Z115	25 c. ultramarine	14·00
Z116	40 c. orange-brown	
Z117	50 c. bright lilac	30·00
Z118	1 p. bistre and ultramarine	30·00
Z119	2 p. black and carmine	35·00

TANGIER

The British postal agency in Tangier opened on 1 April 1857 and from 1 March of the following year letters from it sent via the packet service to Great Britain required franking with Great Britain stamps.

No identifiable postmark was supplied to Tangier until 1872 and all earlier mail was cancelled with one of the Gibraltar marks. In April 1872 a postmark as Type A was supplied on which the "N" of "TANGIER" was reversed. A corrected version, with code letter "A", followed in 1878, but both were used as origin or arrival marks and the Great Britain stamps continued to be cancelled with Gibraltar obliterators. The Type A postmarks generally fell into disuse after 1880 and very few identifiable marks occur on mail from Tangier until the introduction of Gibraltar stamps in 1886.

Stamps of GIBRALTAR *cancelled with Types* A (*codes* "A" *or* "C"), B (*code* "A") *or* D.

1886 (*Nos.* 1/7).

Z120	½d. dull green	25·00
Z121	1d. rose-red	30·00
Z122	2d. purple-brown	£125
Z123	2½d. ultramarine	30·00
Z124	4d. orange-brown	£150
Z125	6d. deep lilac	£200
Z126	1s. yellow-brown	£500

1886–87 (*Nos.* 8/14).

Z127	½d. dull green	10·00
Z128	1d. rose	10·00
Z129	2d. brown-purple	35·00
Z130	2½d. blue	15·00
Z131	4d. orange-brown	60·00
Z132	6d. lilac	£100
Z133	1s. bistre	£225

1889 (*Nos.* 15/21).
Z134 5 c. on ½d. green .. .. 20·00
Z135 10 c. on 1d. rose .. .. 17·00
Z136 25 c. on 2d. brown-purple .. .. 25·00
Z137 25 c. on 2½d. bright blue .. .. 15·00
Z138 40 c. on 4d. orange-brown .. .. 70·00
Z139 50 c. on 6d. bright lilac .. .. 60·00
Z140 75 c. on 1s. bistre £100

1889–96 (*Nos.* 22/33).
Z141 5 c. green .. .. 5·00
Z142 10 c. carmine .. .. 5·00
Z143 20 c. olive-green and brown .. .. 16·00
Z144 20 c. olive-green .. ..
Z145 25 c. ultramarine .. .. 8·00
Z146 40 c. orange-brown .. .. 10·00
Z147 50 c. bright lilac .. .. 9·00
Z148 75 c. olive-green .. .. 40·00
Z149 1 p. bistre .. .. 50·00
Z150 1 p. bistre and ultramarine .. .. 15·00
Z151 2 p. black and carmine .. .. 35·00
Z152 5 p. slate-grey .. .. 80·00

TETUAN

The British postal agency in this northern town was opened in 1890 and was supplied with stamps from the Gibraltar 1889–96 series.

Stamps of GIBRALTAR *cancelled with Types* A (*code* "C"), B (*code* "C" *often inverted*) *or* D (*code* "C").

1889–96 (*Nos.* 22/33).
Z153 5 c. green .. .. 15·00
Z154 10 c. carmine .. .. 22·00
Z155 20 c. olive-green and brown .. .. 30·00
Z157 25 c. ultramarine .. .. 25·00
Z158 40 c. orange-brown .. .. 35·00
Z159 50 c. bright lilac .. .. 35·00
Z161 1 p. bistre and ultramarine .. ..

PRICES FOR STAMPS ON COVER TO 1945

Nos. 1/16	*from* × 7
Nos. 17/30	*from* × 3
Nos. 31/74	*from* × 3
Nos. 75/6	*from* × 4
Nos. 112/24	*from* × 4
No. 125	—
Nos. 126/35	*from* × 5
Nos. 136/42	*from* × 2
Nos. 143/59	*from* × 3
Nos. 160/75	*from* × 8
Nos. 191/9	*from* × 5
Nos. 200/1	*from* × 3
Nos. 202/11	*from* × 4
Nos. 212/15	*from* × 5
Nos. 216/24	*from* × 8
Nos. 225/6	*from* × 2
Nos. 227/30	*from* × 8
Nos. 231/52	*from* × 6

The above prices apply to stamps used on cover from Morocco. Examples of Nos. 31/76 and 231/52 used on cover in Great Britain after 1950 have little additional value.

II. GIBRALTAR ISSUES OVERPRINTED

With the reversion of Gibraltar to sterling in 1898 it became necessary to provide separate issues for the Morocco Agencies which continued to use Spanish currency.

The following were used in all the British postal agencies.

Morocco Agencies (1) — Morocco Agencies (2)

Agencies — "Λ" for "A" (Right-hand pane R.6/6)

Agencies — Long tail to "S" (Right-hand pane R.8/2)

1898 (1 June)–**1900**. *Stamps of Gibraltar optd with T* **1** (*wide* "M" *and ear of* "g" *projecting upwards*), *in black at* Gibraltar Chronicle *office*.
1 **7** 5 c. green 30 35
a. "Λ" for "A" .. .. 20·00 24·00
b. Long tail to "S" .. .. .. 20·00
2 10 c. carmine 30 20
b. Bisected (5 c.) (on cover) .. .. † £1100
c. "Λ" for "A" £300 £350
d. Long tail to "S" .. .. ..
e. Lines of opt 5 mm apart (6.00) ..
ea. Opt double £550
3 20 c. olive-green .. .. 2·75 2·75
a. Opt double £450
b. "Λ" for "A" .. .. 24·00 29·00
c. Long tail to "S" .. .. .. 24·00
d. Olive-green and brown .. .. 1·50 1·25
db. "Λ" for "A" .. .. 24·00 24·00
dc. Long tail to "S" .. .. .. 24·00
4 25 c. ultramarine .. .. 1·50 60
a. "Λ" for "A" £100 £120
b. Long tail to "S" .. .. ..
5 40 c. orange-brown (2.6.98) .. .. .. 2·50 3·25
a. "Λ" for "A" £150 £180
b. Long tail to "S" .. .. ..
c. Blue opt (7.98) .. .. 26·00 32·00
6 50 c. bright lilac (2.6.98) .. .. .. 14·00 23·00
a. "Λ" for "A" £250 £275
b. Long tail to "S" .. .. ..
c. Blue opt (7.98) .. .. 8·00 12·00
7 1 p. bistre and ultramarine (2.6.98) .. 8·00 20·00
a. "Λ" for "A" £180 £225
b. Long tail to "S" .. .. ..
c. Blue opt (7.98) £120 £110
8 **7** 2 p. black and carmine (4.6.98) .. .. 5·00 20·00
a. "Λ" for "A" £225 £275
b. Long tail to "S" .. .. ..
1/8 .. .. *Set of* 8 24·00 60·00

The blue overprint can be easily distinguished by looking through the stamp in front of a strong light.

The listed varieties of overprint occur from the first setting. They were corrected on the second setting of July 1898, which produced Nos. 5c, 6c, 7c and further supplies of No. 8. The corrected type was subsequently used to produce additional stocks of Nos. 1/2. Numerous more minor varieties exist from these settings.

No. 2e comes from two further printings in 1900 using a third setting on which the two lines of the overprint were 5 mm apart instead of the 4 mm space used previously.

Agencies — "CD" sideways flaw (Left-hand pane R.1/5)

Morocco — Broad top to "M" (Left-hand pane R.7/3)

Agencies — Hyphen between "nc" (Right-hand pane R.3/5)

1899 (Feb)–**1902**. *Stamps of Gibraltar optd with T* **2** (*narrow* "M" *and ear of* "g" *horizontal*), *in black by D.L.R., London*.
9 **7** 5 c. green (4.99) 25 15
a. "CD" sideways .. .. 5·00 5·00
b. Broad top to "M" .. .. .. 5·00 5·00
c. Hyphen between "nc" .. .. .. 5·00 5·00
10 10 c. carmine 35 15
a. "CD" sideways .. .. 5·00 5·00
b. Broad top to "M" .. .. .. 5·00 5·00
c. Hyphen between "nc" .. .. .. 5·00 5·00
d. Opt double £650
11 20 c. olive-green (5.02) .. .. .. 1·50 70
b. Broad top to "M" .. .. .. 15·00 15·00
c. Hyphen between "nc" .. .. .. 15·00 15·00
12 25 c. ultramarine (10.99) .. .. .. 3·00 90
a. "CD" sideways .. .. 17·00 15·00
b. Broad top to "M" .. .. .. 17·00 15·00
c. Hyphen between "nc" .. .. .. 17·00 15·00
13 40 c. orange-brown (3.02) .. .. .. 15·00 16·00
b. Broad top to "M" .. .. .. 75·00 85·00
c. Hyphen between "nc" .. .. .. 75·00 85·00
14 50 c. bright lilac (4.99) .. .. .. 5·50 3·50
b. Broad top to "M" .. .. .. 90·00 £100
c. Hyphen between "nc" .. .. .. 90·00 £100
15 1 p. bistre and ultramarine (4.99) .. 12·00 20·00
b. Broad top to "M" £100 £125
c. Hyphen between "nc" £100 £125
16 2 p. black and carmine (3.01) .. .. 18·00 35·00
b. Broad top to "M" £250 £300
c. Hyphen between "nc" £250 £300
9/16 .. .. *Set of* 8 50·00 70·00
9/16 Optd "Specimen" .. .. *Set of* 8 £225

1903–5. *As T* **8** *of Gibraltar, but with value in Spanish currency, optd with T* **2**. *Wmk Crown CA. P* 14.
17 5 c. grey-green and green (1.03) .. .. 2·50 60
a. "CD" sideways .. .. 20·00 20·00
b. Broad top to "M" .. .. .. 20·00 20·00
c. Hyphen between "nc" .. .. .. 20·00 20·00
18 10 c. dull purple/*red* (8.03) .. .. .. 2·00 30
a. "CD" sideways .. .. 20·00 20·00
b. Broad top to "M" .. .. .. 20·00 20·00
c. Hyphen between "nc" .. .. .. 20·00 20·00
19 20 c. grey-green and carmine (9.04) .. .. 7·00 26·00
a. "CD" sideways .. .. 50·00 90·00
b. Broad top to "M" .. .. .. 50·00 90·00
c. Hyphen between "nc" .. .. .. 50·00 90·00
20 25 c. purple and black/*blue* (1.7.03) 90 15
a. "CD" sideways .. .. 32·00 32·00
b. Broad top to "M" .. .. .. 32·00 32·00
c. Hyphen between "nc" .. .. .. 32·00 32·00
21 50 c. purple and violet (3.7.05) .. .. 48·00 95·00
a. "CD" sideways £250 £350
b. Broad top to "M" £250 £350
c. Hyphen between "nc" £250 £350
22 1 p. black and carmine (19.11.05) .. .. 45·00 £100
a. "CD" sideways £225 £350
b. Broad top to "M" £225 £350
c. Hyphen between "nc" £225 £350
23 2 p. black and blue (19.11.05) .. .. 48·00 90·00
a. "CD" sideways £250 £350
b. Broad top to "M" £250 £350
c. Hyphen between "nc" £250 £350
17/23 .. .. *Set of* 7 £130 £275
17/23 Optd "Specimen" .. .. *Set of* 7 £225

1905 (Jan)–**06**. *As Nos.* 17/23 *but wmk Mult Crown CA*.
24 5 c. grey-green and green, **OC** (4.05) .. 45 60
a. "CD" sideways .. .. 18·00 20·00
b. Broad top to "M" .. .. .. 18·00 20·00
c. Hyphen between "nc" £600 £650
25 10 c. dull purple/*red*, **OC** 65 25
a. "CD" sideways .. .. 20·00 20·00
b. Broad top to "M" .. .. .. 20·00 20·00
26 20 c. grey-green and carmine, **O** (1.06) .. 1·50 14·00
a. "CD" sideways .. .. 25·00 50·00
b. Broad top to "M" .. .. .. 25·00 50·00
27 25 c. purple and black/*blue*, **C** (6.06) .. 22·00 5·00
a. "CD" sideways £125 £110
b. Broad top to "M" £125 £110
28 50 c. purple and violet, **C** (7.06) .. .. 6·00 16·00
a. "CD" sideways £125 £175
b. Broad top to "M" £125 £175
29 1 p. black and carmine, **C** (11.05) .. .. 22·00 48·00
a. "CD" sideways £175 £225
b. Broad top to "M" £175 £225
30 2 p. black and blue, **C** (11.05) .. .. 15·00 32·00
a. "CD" sideways £160 £225
b. Broad top to "M" £160 £225
24/30 .. .. *Set of* 7 60·00 £100

Control of the British postal agencies in Morocco returned to the G.P.O., London, from 1 January 1907.

All the following issues are overprinted on Great Britain

III. BRITISH CURRENCY

Stamps overprinted "MOROCCO AGENCIES" only were primarily intended for use on parcels (and later, air-mail correspondence), and were on sale at British P.Os throughout Morocco including Tangier, until 1937.

PRICES. Our prices for used stamps with these overprints are for specimens used in Morocco. These stamps could be used in the United Kingdom, with official sanction, from the summer of 1950 onwards with U.K. postmarks are worth about 50 per cent less.

MOROCCO AGENCIES (4) — MOROCCO AGENCIES (5) — MOROCCO AGENCIES (6)

1907–13. *King Edward VII optd as T* **4** *or* **5** (2*s*. 6*d*.)

(*a*) *De La Rue printings*
31 ½d. pale yellowish green, **O** .. .. .. 75 4·50
32 1d. scarlet, **O** .. .. 2·25 2·50
33 2d. grey-green and carmine, **C** .. .. 2·50 4·50
34 4d. green and chocolate-brown, **C** .. .. 15·00 3·25
35 4d. orange, **O** (1912) .. .. 3·75 3·50
36 6d. dull purple, **C** .. .. 4·75 6·00
37 1s. dull green and carmine, **C** .. .. 11·00 15·00
38 2s. 6d. pale dull purple, **C** .. .. .. 48·00 65·00
39 2s. 6d. dull purple, **C** .. .. .. 48·00 70·00
31/39 .. .. *Set of* 8 75·00 95·00
37/8 Optd "Specimen" .. .. *Set of* 2 £160

(*b*) *Later printings* (1913)
40 4d. bright orange, **O** (No. 286) .. .. 8·00 15·00
41 2s. 6d. dull purple, **O** (No. 315) .. .. 55·00 85·00

1914–31. *King George V*. (*a*) *Optd with T* **4**. *W* **100**.
42 **105** ½d. green 20 45
43 **104** 1d. scarlet 50 10
44 **105** 1½d. red-brown (1921) .. .. .. 1·00 9·00
45 **106** 2d. orange (Die I) .. .. 1·00 35
46 3d. bluish violet (1921) .. .. .. 1·00 35
47 4d. grey-green (1921) .. .. 1·00 70
48 **107** 6d. reddish purple, **C** (1921) .. .. 3·00 12·00
49 **108** 1s. bistre-brown (1917) .. .. .. 5·00 75
a. Opt triple, two albino .. .. .. 90·00

(*b*) *Optd with T* **6**. (i) *Waterlow printing*
50 **109** 2s. 6d. sepia-brown (1914) .. .. 28·00 38·00
a. Re-entry £450 £450
b. Opt double, one albino £150

(ii) *De La Rue printings*
51 **109** 2s. 6d. yellow-brown (1917) .. .. 28·00 28·00
a. Opt double (1917) £1500 £1000
52 2s. 6d. grey-brown .. .. 25·00 40·00

(iii) *Bradbury Wilkinson printings*
53 **109** 2s. 6d. chocolate-brown .. .. .. 28·00 25·00
a. Opt double, one albino* £175
54 5s. rose-red (1931) .. .. 48·00 70·00
a. Opt triple, two albino
42/54 .. .. *Set of* 10 80·00 £110
49/50, 54 Optd "Specimen" .. .. *Set of* 3 £250

*The albino overprint is quite clear, with the "MOROCCO" appearing just below "AGENCIES" of the normal overprint and a little to the right as seen from the back; however, this occurs with a second faint albino impression just below the normal overprint.

MOROCCO AGENCIES (7) — S (A) — MOROCCO AGENCIES (8) — S (B)

(A) Opt 14 mm long; ends of "s" cut off diagonally.
(B) Opt 15½ mm long; ends of "s" cut off horizontally

1925–36. *King George V, optd with T* **7** (A) *or T* **8** (B). *W* **111**.

No.	Type	Description	A	A	B	B
55	**105**	½d. green	60	30	1·25	17·00
56		1½d. chestnut (1931) ..	9·00	13·00	†	
57	**106**	2d. orange	2·00	1·00	†	
58	**104**	2½d. blue	2·00	5·00	90·00	30·00
59	**106**	4d. grey-green (1.36) ..	†		3·50	30·00
60	**107**	6d. purple, **O** (1931) ..	2·00	8·00	40	60
61	**108**	1s. bistre-brown	15·00	5·00	48·00	55·00
55/61 (*cheapest*) *Set of* 7		.. ..	29·00	50·00		
61A Optd "Specimen"		.. ..	60·00			

1935 (8 May). *Silver Jubilee stamps. Optd* "MOROCCO AGENCIES" *only, as in T* **17**.
62 **123** ½d. green (B.) .. .. 1·00 1·75
63 1d. scarlet (B.) .. .. 1·10 3·25
64 1½d. red-brown (B.) .. .. 1·50 7·00
65 2½d. blue (R.) .. .. 1·50 2·50
62/5 .. .. *Set of* 4 4·50 13·00

1935–37. *King George V*. (*a*) *Harrison photo ptgs optd with T* **8**.
66 **119** 1d. scarlet (4.35) .. .. .. 2·50 1·25
67 **118** 1½d. red-brown (28.4.36) .. .. 2·00 10·00
68 **120** 2d. orange (1.5.36) 35 40
69 **119** 2½d. ultramarine (11.2.36) .. .. 1·75 4·25
70 **120** 3d. violet (2.3.36) 40 15
71 4d. deep grey-green (14.5.36) 40 15
72 **122** 1s. bistre-brown (31.8.36) 80 80

(*b*) *Waterlow re-engraved ptg optd with T* **6**
73 **109** 2s. 6d. chocolate-brown (No. 450) .. 28·00 28·00
74 5s. bright rose-red (No. 451) (2.3.37) .. 22·00 45·00
66/74 .. .. *Set of* 9 50·00 80·00
72/3 Optd "Specimen" .. .. *Set of* 2 £150

1936 (26 Oct)–**37**. *King Edward VIII, optd* "MOROCCO AGENCIES" *only, as in T* **18**.
A. MOROCCO 14½ mm long.
B. MOROCCO 15¼ mm long (5.1.37)

No.	Type	Description	A	A	B	B
75	**124**	1d. scarlet	10	25	1·50	4·00
76		2½d. bright blue	10	15	80	2·50

The first two printings of both values showed all the stamps with the short overprint, Nos. 75A/6A.

On 5 January 1937 a further printing of both values was placed on sale in London which had all stamps, 24 in all, from the bottom two horizontal rows (Rows 19 and 20) with the long overprint, Nos. 75B/6B. Subsequent printings increased the number of long overprints in the sheet to 25 by the addition of R. 8/9, and, finally, to 31 (R. 1/7, R. 7/1, R. 8/1, R. 13/3, 4 and 10, R 14/6, but without R. 8/9).

For the 1d. value all sheets from cylinder 2 show the first setting. Sheets from cylinder 6 were also used for the first, and for all subsequent settings. The 2½d. value was overprinted on sheets from cylinder 2 throughout.

In 1937 unoverprinted Great Britain stamps replaced overprinted "MOROCCO AGENCIES" issues as stocks became exhausted. In 1949 overprinted issues reappeared and were in use at Tetuan (Spanish Zone), the only remaining British P.O. apart from that at Tangier.

MOROCCO AGENCIES (9) MOROCCO AGENCIES (10)

1949 (16 Aug). *King George VI, optd with T* **9** *or* **10** (*2s. 6d., 5s.*).

No.	Type	Description	Unused	Used
77	**128**	½d. pale green	70	85
78		1d. pale scarlet	90	2·25
79		1½d. pale red-brown	1·25	1·75
80		2d. pale orange	1·25	2·25
81		2½d. light ultramarine	1·40	2·25
82		3d. pale violet	50	45
83	**129**	4d. grey-green	35	50
84		5d. brown	1·25	4·00
85		6d. purple	40	75
86	**130**	7d. emerald-green	40	5·00
87		8d. bright carmine	1·00	3·50
88		9d. deep olive-green	40	4·00
89		10d. turquoise-blue	40	3·00
90		11d. plum	70	2·75
91		1s. bistre-brown	1·50	2·25
92	**131**	2s. 6d. yellow-green	7·00	15·00
93		5s. red	21·00	30·00
77/93		*Set of* 17	35·00	70·00

1951 (3 May). *King George VI* (Nos. 503/7, 509/10), *optd with T* **9** *or* **10** (*2s. 6d., 5s.*).

No.	Type	Description	Unused	Used
94	**128**	½d. pale orange	35	25
95		1d. light ultramarine	35	25
96		1½d. pale green	35	40
97		2d. pale red-brown	35	45
98		2½d. pale scarlet	35	30
99	**147**	2s. 6d. yellow-green	7·00	12·00
100	**148**	5s. red	9·00	16·00
94/100		*Set of* 7	16·00	27·00

1952–55. *Queen Elizabeth II* (*Tudor Crown wmk*), *optd with T* **9**.

No.	Type	Description	Unused	Used
101	**154**	½d. orange-red (31.8.53)	10	10
102		1d. ultramarine (31.8.53)	15	20
103		1½d. green (5.12.52)	15	10
104		2d. red-brown (31.8.53)	20	30
105	**155**	2½d. carmine-red (5.12.52)	25	10
106	**156**	4d. ultramarine (1.3.55)	60	1·00
107	**157**	5d. brown (6.7.53)	65	60
108		6d. reddish purple (1.3.55)	50	1·00
109	**158**	8d. magenta (6.7.53)	1·25	1·00
110	**159**	1s. bistre-brown (6.7.53)	70	60
101/110		*Set of* 10	4·00	4·50

1956 (10 Sept). *Queen Elizabeth II* (*St. Edward's Crown wmk*), *optd with T* **9**.

No.	Type	Description	Unused	Used
111	**155**	2½d. carmine-red (No. 544)	55	2·00

Stamps overprinted "MOROCCO AGENCIES" were withdrawn from sale on 31 December 1956.

IV. SPANISH CURRENCY

Stamps surcharged in Spanish currency were sold at British P.Os. throughout Morocco until the establishment of the French Zone and the Tangier International Zone, when their use was confined to the Spanish Zone.

During this period further British postal agencies were opened at Alcazar (1907–1916), Fez–Mellah (Jewish quarter) (1909), Marrakesh (1909), Marrakesh–Mellah (Jewish quarter) (1912–14), and Mequinez (1907–1916).

MOROCCO AGENCIES MOROCCO AGENCIES

5 CENTIMOS (11) 6 PESETAS (12)

1907–13. *King Edward VII, surch as T* **11** (*5 c. to 1 p.*) *or* **12** (*3p. to 12 p.*). (a) *De La Rue printings.*

No.	Description	Unused	Used
112	5 c. on ½d. pale yellowish green, **O**	45	15
113	10 c. on 1d. scarlet, **O**	65	10
114	15 c. on 1½d. purple and green, **C**	70	15
	a. "1" of "15" omitted	£2750	
115	20 c. on 2d. grey-green and carmine, **C**	60	15
116	25 c. on 2½d. ultramarine, **O**	85	15
117	40 c. on 4d. green and chocolate-brown, **C**	90	1·75
118	40 c. on 4d. orange, **O** (1910)	35	60
119	50 c. on 5d. purple and ultramarine, **C**	1·10	75
120	1 p. on 10d. purple and carmine, **C**	5·50	5·50
	a. No cross on crown		
121	3 p. on 2s. 6d. pale dull purple, **C**	17·00	22·00
122	6 p. on 5s. carmine, **O**	42·00	45·00
123	12 p. on 10s. ultramarine, **O**	75·00	75·00
112/123	*Set of* 12	£130	£130
117, 123	Optd "Specimen" *Set of* 2	£160	

(*b*) *Harrison printing*

No.	Description	Unused	Used
124	25 c. on 2½d. bright blue (No. 283) (1912)	11·00	11·00

(*c*) *Somerset House printing*

No.	Description	Unused	Used
125	12 p. on 10s. bright blue (No. 319) (1913)	£130	£180

1912. *King George V, surch as T* **11**.

No.	Description	Unused	Used
126	5 c. on ½d. green (No. 339)	90	10
127	10 c. on 1d. scarlet (No. 342)	50	10
	a. No cross on crown	£100	50·00

MOROCCO AGENCIES 3 CENTIMOS (13) MOROCCO AGENCIES 10 CENTIMOS (14)

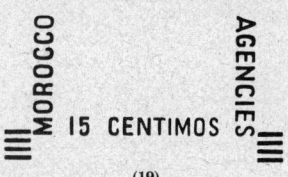

MOROCCO AGENCIES 15 CENTIMOS (15) MOROCCO AGENCIES 6 PESETAS (16)

1914–26. *King George V.* (*a*) *Surch as T* **11** (*5 c.*), **13** (*3 c. and 40 c*)*, **15** (*15 c.*) *and* **14** (*remainder*). *W* **100**.

No.	Type	Description	Unused	Used
128	**105**	3 c. on ½d. green (1917)	20	2·50
129		5 c. on ½d. green	30	10
130	**104**	10 c. on 1d. scarlet	30	10
131	**105**	15 c. on 1½d. red-brown (1915)	30	10
		a. Surch double, one albino		
132	**106**	20 c. on 2d. orange (Die I)	25	25
		a. Surch double, one albino	75·00	
133	**104**	25 c. on 2½d. blue (*shades*)	50	25
134	**106**	40 c. on 4d. grey-green (1917)	1·50	4·00
		a. Surch double, one albino		
135	**108**	1p. on 10d. turquoise-blue	1·25	3·00

*The surcharge on Nos. 134, 148 and 158 is as T **13** for the value and T **15** for "MOROCCO AGENCIES".

(*b*) *Surch as T* **16**. (i) *Waterlow printings*

No.	Type	Description	Unused	Used
136	**109**	6 p. on 5s. rose-carmine	27·00	48·00
		a. Surch double, one albino	£110	
		b. Surch triple, two albino		
137		6 p. on 5s. pale rose-carmine	£130	£180
		a. Surch double, one albino	£150	
138		12 p. on 10s. indigo-blue (R.)	£100	£150
		a. Surch double, one albino	£300	
		b. Surch triple, two albino		
136, 138		Optd "Specimen" *Set of* 2	£225	

(ii) *De La Rue printings*

No.	Type	Description	Unused	Used
139	**109**	3 p. on 2s. 6d. grey-brown (1918)	25·00	60·00
		a. Surch double, one albino		
140		3 p. on 2s. 6d. yellow-brown	25·00	70·00
		a. Surch double, one albino		
141		12 p. on 10s. blue (R.)	£110	£160
		a. Surch double, one albino		

(iii) *Bradbury Wilkinson printings*

No.	Type	Description	Unused	Used
142	**109**	3 p. on 2s. 6d. chocolate-brown (1926)	23·00	48·00
128/142		*Set of* 11	£140	£225

1925–31. *King George V, surch as T* **11**, **13**, **14** *or* **15**. *W* **111**.

No.	Type	Description	Unused	Used
143	**105**	5 c. on ½d. green (1931)	40	5·00
144	**104**	10 c. on 1d. scarlet (1929)	9·00	13·00
145	**105**	15 c. on 1½d. red-brown	7·00	14·00
146	**106**	20 c. on 2d. orange (1931)	3·00	5·50
		a. Surch double, one albino	85·00	
147	**104**	25 c. on 2½d. blue	65	30
148	**106**	40 c. on 4d. grey-green (1930)	65	25
		a. Surch double, one albino		
143/148		*Set of* 6	18·00	35·00

MOROCCO AGENCIES 10 CENTIMOS (17) MOROCCO 10 AGENCIES CENTIMOS (18)

1935 (8 May). *Silver Jubilee, surch as T* **17**.

No.	Type	Description	Unused	Used
149	**123**	5 c. on ½d. green (B.)	60	45
150		10 c. on 1d. scarlet (B)	2·75	2·25
		a. Pair, one with "CENTIMES"	£1100	
151		15 c. on 1½d. red-brown (B.)	1·25	7·00
152		25 c. on 2½d. blue (R.)	5·00	2·25
149/52		*Set of* 4	8·50	11·00

No. 150a occurred on R. 5/4 of a small second printing made in June 1935. The error can only be identified when *se-tenant* with a normal No. 150. Beware of forgeries.

1935–37. *King George V, surch as T* **11**, **13**, **14** *or* **15**.

No.	Type	Description	Unused	Used
153	**118**	5 c. on ½d. green (9.6.36)	65	4·00
154	**119**	10 c. on 1d. scarlet (11.36)	2·25	2·50
155	**118**	15 c. on 1½d. red-brown (4.35)	2·50	3·25
156	**120**	20 c. on 2d. orange (26.10.36)	30	25
157	**119**	25 c. on 2½d. ultramarine (8.9.36)	1·25	3·75
158	**120**	40 c. on 4d. deep grey-green (18.5.37)	35	3·00
159	**122**	1 p. on 10d. turquoise-blue (14.4.37)	45	25
153/159		*Set of* 7	7·00	15·00

1936 (26 Oct)–**37**. *King Edward VIII, surch as T* **18**.
A. "MOROCCO" 14¼ mm long.
B. "MOROCCO" 15¼ mm long (5.1.37)

No.	Type	Description	A Unused	A Used	B Unused	B Used
160	**124**	5 c. on ½d. green	10	10	†	
161		10 c. on 1d scarlet	35	45	1·00	2·00
162		15 c. on 1½d. red-brown	10	10	†	
163		25 c. on 2½d. bright blue	10	10	†	
160/3		*Set of* 4	50	60		

The first three printings of the 10 c. on 1d. (from cyls 4, 5 and 6) showed all stamps with the short surcharge (No. 161A).

On 5 January 1937 a further printing was placed on sale in London which had 49 stamps in the sheet (R. 1/2 to 11, R. 2/1, 5 and 6, 8 and 9, R. 3/5, R. 4/5, R. 5/4 and 5, 10, R. 6/6 and 7, R. 7/8, R. 8/8, R. 9/8, R. 11/7, 9, R.13/2 to 5, 7 and 8, R. 14/1, 7, R. 15/7, 11, R. 16/5, 10, R. 17/4, 10 and 11, R. 18/1, R. 19/2, R. 20/1 and 2, 3, 7, 9) with the long surcharge (No. 161B). The next printing increase the number of long surcharges in the sheet to 50 (R. 10/2), bu the final version, although retaining 50 long surcharges, showe them on R. 1/2 to 11, R. 17/5 to 8 and the entire rows 18, 19 an 20. The first two printings with long surcharges were fror cylinder 6 and the last from cylinder 13.

MOROCCO 15 CENTIMOS AGENCIES (19)

1937 (13 May). *Coronation, surch as T* **19**.

No.	Type	Description	Unused	Used
164	**126**	15 c. on 1½d. maroon (B.)	25	2

MOROCCO AGENCIES 10 CENTIMOS (20) MOROCCO AGENCIES 10 CENTIMOS (21)

1937 (June)–**52**. *King George VI, surch as T* **20**.

No.	Type	Description	Unused	Used
165	**128**	5 c. on ½d. green (B.)	35	15
166		10 c. on 1d. scarlet	35	10
167		15 c. on 1½d. red-brown (B.) (4.8.37)	35	25
168		25 c. on 2½d. ultramarine	40	40
169	**129**	40 c. on 4d. grey-green (9.40)	3·75	6·00
170	**130**	70 c. on 7d. emerald-green (9.40)	50	5·00
171		1 p. on 10d. turquoise-blue (16.6.52)	30	3·00
165/171		*Set of* 7	5·50	13·50

1940 (6 May). *Centenary of First Adhesive Postage Stamps, surch as T* **21**.

No.	Type	Description	Unused	Used
172	**134**	5 c. on ½d. green (B.)	25	80
173		10 c. on 1d. scarlet	40	1·00
174		15 c. on 1½d. red-brown (B.)	25	90
175		25 c. on 2½d. ultramarine	25	50
172/5		*Set of* 4	1·00	3·00

25 CENTIMOS MOROCCO AGENCIES (22) 45 PESETAS MOROCCO AGENCIES (23)

1948 (26 Apr). *Silver Wedding, surch with T* **22** *or* **23**.

No.	Type	Description	Unused	Used
176	**137**	25 c. on 2½d. ultramarine	30	15
177	**138**	45 p. on £1 blue	15·00	22·00

1948 (29 July). *Olympic Games, variously surch as T* **22**.

No.	Type	Description	Unused	Used
178	**139**	25 c. on 2½d. ultramarine	25	30
179	**140**	30 c. on 3d. violet	25	30
180	**141**	60 c. on 6d. bright purple	25	30
181	**142**	1 p. 20 c. on 1s. brown	45	30
		a. Surch double	£500	
178/81		*Set of* 4	1·10	1·10

1951 (3 May)–**52**. *King George VI, surch as T* **20**.

No.	Type	Description	Unused	Used
182	**128**	5 c. on ½d. pale orange	1·00	1·25
183		10 c. on 1d. light ultramarine	1·50	1·00
184		15 c. on 1½d. pale green	1·25	1·50
185		25 c. on 2½d. pale scarlet	1·25	1·50
186	**129**	40 c. on 4d. light ultramarine (26.5.52)	50	7·00
182/6		*Set of* 5	5·00	11·00

1954–55. *Queen Elizabeth II* (*Tudor Crown wmk*), *surch as T* **20**.

No.	Type	Description	Unused	Used
187	**154**	5 c. on ½d. orange-red (1.9.54)	10	25
188		10 c. on 1d. ultramarine (1.3.55)	25	30

1956. *Queen Elizabeth II* (*St. Edward's Crown wmk*), *surch as T* **20**.

No.	Type	Description	Unused	Used
189	**154**	5 c. on ½d. orange-red (June)	15	20
190	**156**	40 c. on 4d. ultramarine (15 Aug)	70	1·50

The British postal agency at Laraiche closed on 30 June 1938. Stamps surcharged in Spanish currency were withdrawn from sale when the Tetuan agency closed on 31 December 1956.

V. FRENCH CURRENCY

For use in the British postal agencies at Casablanca (closed 14.8.37), Fez (closed 8.1.38), Fez–Mellah (closed after 1930), Marrakesh (closed 14.8.37), Mazagan (closed 14.8.37), Mogador (closed 31.10.33), Rabat (closed 8.1.38) and Saffi (closed 14.8.37).

MOROCCO AGENCIES 25 CENTIMES (24) MOROCCO AGENCIES 1 FRANC (25)

1917–24. *King George V, surch as T* **24** *or* **25** *(1 f.).* W **100**.

191 **105** 3 c. on ½d. green (R.) 10 2·50
192 5 c. on ½d. green 10 10
193 **104** 10 c. on 1d. scarlet 75 15
194 **105** 15 c. on 1½d. red-brown 80 15
195 **104** 25 c. on 2½d. blue 30 15
196 **106** 40 c. on 4d. slate-green 70 25
197 **107** 50 c. on 5d. yellow-brown (1923) 70 2·50
198 **108** 75 c. on 9d. olive-green (1924) 50 75
199 1 f. on 10d. turquoise-blue 1·50 60
a. Opt double, one albino 85·00
191/9 *Set of* 9 4·75 6·50

1924–32. *King George V, surch as T* **25**, *but closer vertical spacing.*

200 **109** 3 f. on 2s 6d. chocolate brown 7·50 2·00
a. Major re-entry £250 £275
b. *Reddish brown* 20·00 10·00
201 6 f. on 5s. rose-red (1932) 38·00 35·00
200/1 Optd "Specimen" *Set of* 2 £140

1925–34. *King George V, surch as T* **24** *or* **25** *(1 f.).* W **111**.

202 **105** 5 c. on ½d. green 25 3·75
203 **104** 10 c. on 1d. scarlet 20 25
204 **105** 15 c. on 1½d. red-brown 85 1·75
205 **104** 25 c. on 2½d. blue 25 25
206 **106** 40 c. on 4d. grey-green 50 70
207 **107** 50 c. on 5d. yellow-brown 50 10
208 **108** 75 c. on 9d. olive-green 1·50 15
209 90 c. on 9d. olive-green 2·00 3·00
210 1 f. on 10d. turquoise-blue 70 10
211 1 f. 50 on 1s. bistre-brown (Optd S. £50) 2·50 2·25
202/211 *Set of* 10 8·50 11·00

1935 (8 May). *Silver Jubilee, surch as T* **17**, *but in French currency.*

212 **123** 5 c. on ½d. green (B.) 15 15
213 10 c. on 1d. scarlet (B.) 35 50
214 15 c. on 1½d. red-brown (B.) 15 50
215 25 c. on 2½d. blue (R.) 20 15
212/15 *Set of* 4 75 1·10

1935–37. *King George V, surch as T* **24** *or* **25** *(1 f.).*

216 **118** 5 c. on ½d. green (10.35) 45 85
217 **119** 10 c. on 1d. scarlet (2.3.36) 35 30
218 **118** 15 c. on 1½d. red brown 1·25 1·25
219 **119** 25 c. on 2½d. ultramarine (25.9.36) 25 15
220 **120** 40 c. on 4d. deep grey-green (2.12.36) 25 15
221 **121** 50 c. on 5d. yellow-brown (15.9.36) 25 15
222 **122** 90 c. on 9d. deep olive-green (15.2.37) 35 50
223 1 f. on 10d. turquoise-blue (10.2.37) 25 25
224 1 f. 50 on 1s. bistre-brown (20.7.37) (Optd S. £50) 25 50

1935–36. *King George V (Waterlow re-engraved ptgs), surch as T* **25**, *but closer vertical spacing.*

225 **109** 3 f. on 2s. 6d. chocolate-brown (No. 450) 4·75 11·00
226 6 f. on 5s. bright rose-red (No. 451) (17.6.36) 6·00 20·00
216/226 *Set of* 11 13·00 30·00
225/6 Optd "Specimen" *Set of* 2 £140

1936 (26 Oct). *King Edward VIII, surch as T* **18**, *but in French currency.*

227 **124** 5 c. on ½d. green 10 15
a. Bar through "POSTAGE" £400
228 15 c. on 1½d. red-brown 10 15

No. 227a was probably caused by a piece of printer's rule. It can be found on various stamps from Row 18, righthand pane.

1937 (13 May). *Coronation, surch as T* **19**, *but in French currency.*

229 **126** 15 c. on 1½d. maroon (B.) 25 20

1937 (June). *King George VI, surch as T* **20**, *but in French currency.*

230 **128** 5 c. on ½d. green (B.) 25 60

Stamps surcharged in French currency were withdrawn from sale on 8 January 1938.

VI. TANGIER INTERNATIONAL ZONE

By an agreement between Great Britain, France and Spain Tangier was declared an international zone in 1924. Stamps overprinted "Morocco Agencies" or surcharged in Spanish currency were used there until replaced by Nos. 231/4.

PRICES. Our note *re* U.K. usage (at beginning of Section III) also applies to "TANGIER" optd stamps.

TANGIER TANGIER
(26)

TANGIER
(27)

1927. *King George V, optd with T* **26**. W **111**.

231 **105** ½d. green 50 10
a. Opt double, one albino
232 **104** 1d. scarlet 40 10
a. Inverted "Q" for "O" (R. 20/3) £800
233 **105** 1½d. chestnut 2·00 2·00
234 **106** 2d. orange 2·75 10
a. Opt double, one albino 75·00
231/4 *Set of* 4 5·00 2·00

1934 (Dec)–**35**. *King George V, optd with T* **26**.

235 **118** ½d. green (2.35) 80 1·25
236 **119** 1d. scarlet 65 70
237 **118** 1½d. red-brown 15 10
235/7 *Set of* 3 1·40 1·75

1935 (8 May). *Silver Jubilee, optd with T* **27**.

238 **123** ½d. green (B.) 90 85
239 1d. scarlet 3·00 2·75
240 1½d. red-brown (B.) 1·00 15
238/40 *Set of* 3 4·50 3·50

1936 (26 Oct). *King Edward VIII, optd with T* **26**.

241 **124** ½d. green 10 10
242 1d. scarlet 10 10
243 1½d. red-brown 10 10
241/3 *Set of* 3 25 20

TANGIER TANGIER
(28)

TANGIER
(29)

1937 (13 May). *Coronation, optd with T* **28**.

244 **126** 1½d. maroon (B.) 40 15

1937. *King George VI, optd with T* **29**.

245 **128** ½d. green (B.) (June) 40 15
246 1d. scarlet (June) 40 20
247 1½d. red-brown (B.) (4 Aug) 55 10
245/7 *Set of* 3 1·25 40

TANGIER
(30)

TANGIER
(31)

1940 (6 May). *Centenary of First Adhesive Postage Stamps, optd with T* **30**.

248 **134** ½d. green (B.) 15 50
249 1d. scarlet 20 25
250 1½d. red-brown (B.) 40 20
248/50 *Set of* 3 65 85

1944. *King George VI, optd with T* **29**.

251 **128** ½d. pale green (B.) 1·00 50
252 1d. pale scarlet 2·00 1·00

1946 (11 June). *Victory, optd as T* **31**.

253 **135** 2½d. ultramarine 25 20
254 **136** 3d. violet 25 20

The opt on No. 254 is smaller (23 × 2½ mm).

1948 (26 Apr). *Royal Silver Wedding, optd with T* **30**.

255 **137** 2½d. ultramarine 30 15
a. Opt omitted (in vert pair with stamp optd at top) £2250
256 **138** £1 blue 24·00 27·00

No. 255a comes from a sheet in which the overprint is misplaced downwards resulting in the complete absence of the opt from the six stamps of the top row. On the rest of the sheet the opt falls at the top of each stamp instead of at the foot.

1948 (29 July). *Olympic Games, optd with T* **30**.

257 **139** 2½d. ultramarine 45 20
258 **140** 3d. violet 50 15
259 **141** 6d. bright purple 50 20
260 **142** 1s. brown 50 15
257/60 *Set of* 4 1·75 60

1949 (1 Jan). *King George VI, optd with T* **29**.

261 **128** 2d. pale orange 1·25 1·75
262 2½d. light ultramarine 35 60
263 3d. pale violet 35 20
264 **129** 4d. grey-green 1·25 3·75
265 5d. brown 75 3·25
266 6d. purple 35 30
267 **130** 7d. emerald-green 55 4·00
268 8d. bright carmine 85 4·00
269 9d. deep olive-green 50 3·50
270 10d. turquoise-blue 50 4·50
271 11d. plum 50 5·00
272 1s. bistre-brown 50 75
273 **131** 2s. 6d. yellow-green 4·00 7·50
274 5s. red 9·00 24·00
275 **132** 10s. ultramarine 35·00 55·00
261/275 *Set of* 15 48·00 £110

1949 (10 Oct). *75th Anniv of U.P.U., optd with T* **30**.

276 **143** 2½d. ultramarine 40 45
277 **144** 3d. violet 40 50
278 **145** 6d. bright purple 40 40
279 **146** 1s. brown 40 90
276/9 *Set of* 4 1·40 2·00

1950 (2 Oct)–**51**. *King George VI, optd with T* **29** *or* **30** *(shilling values).*

280 **128** ½d. pale orange (3.5.51) 30 20
281 1d. light ultramarine (3.5.51) 40 35
282 1½d. pale green (3.5.51) 45 2·00
283 2d. pale red-brown (3.5.51) 50 90
284 2½d. pale scarlet (3.5.51) 55 45
285 **129** 4d. light ultramarine 35 2·25
286 **147** 2s. 6d. yellow-green (3.5.51) 1·75 2·00
287 **148** 5s. red (3.5.51) 6·50 7·50
288 **149** 10s. ultramarine (3.5.51) 10·00 13·00
280/288 *Set of* 9 19·00 25·00

1952–54. *Queen Elizabeth II (Tudor Crown wmk), optd with T* **29**.

289 **154** ½d. orange-red (31.8.53) 10 10
290 1d. ultramarine (31.8.53) 15 10
291 1½d. green (5.12.52) 10 10
292 2d. red-brown (31.8.53) 20 10
293 **155** 2½d. carmine-red (5.12.52) 10 10
294 3d. deep lilac (B.) (18.1.54) 20 10
295 **156** 4d. ultramarine (2.11.53) 45 75
296 **157** 5d. brown (6.7.53) 60 90
297 6d. reddish purple (18.1.54) 45 10
298 7d. bright green (18.1.54) 80 1·60
299 **158** 8d. magenta (6.7.53) 80 1·50
300 9d. bronze-green (8.2.54) 1·25 65
301 10d. Prussian blue (8.2.54) 1·40 2·75
302 11d. brown-purple (8.2.54) 1·40 3·00
303 **159** 1s. bistre-brown (6.7.53) 50 25
304 **160** 1s. 3d. green (2.11.53) 65 45
305 **159** 1s. 6d. grey-blue (2.11.53) 80 1·25
289/305 *Set of* 17 9·00 12·00

1953 (3 June). C[illegible]

306 **161** 2½d. carmine-red [illegible]50 25
307 **162** 4d. ultramarine [illegible] 30
308 **163** 1s. 3d. deep yellow-gre[illegible] [illegible] 1·25
309 **164** 1s. 6d. deep grey-blue [illegible] 55
306/9 Se[illegible] [illegible] 2·10

1955 (23 Sept). *Queen Elizabeth II, optd with T* **30**.

310 **166** 2s. 6d. black-brown [illegible] [illegible]25
311 **167** 5s. rose-red 5·[illegible] [illegible]50
312 **168** 10s. ultramarine 18·00 [illegible]
310/12 *Set of* 3 24·00 30·[illegible]

1956. *Queen Elizabeth II (St. Edward's Crown wmk), optd with T* **29**.

313 **154** ½d. orange-red (21 March) 10 10
314 1d. ultramarine (13 April) 20 20
315 1½d. green (22 Oct) 40 75
316 2d. red-brown (25 July) 80 1·50
317 2d. light red-brown (10 Dec) 50 30
318 **155** 2½d. carmine-red (19 Dec) 40 30
319 3d. deep lilac (B.) (22 Oct) 40 40
320 **156** 4d. ultramarine (25 June) 65 2·00
321 **157** 6d. reddish purple (22 Oct) 50 45
322 **160** 1s. 3d. green (26 Nov) 1·75 11·00
313/22 *Set of* 10 5·00 15·00

1857-1957
TANGIER
(32)

1857-1957
TANGIER
(33)

1957 (1 Apr). *Centenary of British Post Office in Tangier.*

(a) Nos. 540/2 and 543b/56 optd as T **32** *or* **33** *(7d)*

323 **154** ½d. orange-red 10 10
324 1d. ultramarine 10 10
325 1½d. green 10 10
326 2d. light red-brown 10 10
327 **155** 2½d. carmine-red 15 10
328 3d. deep lilac (B.) 15 10
329 **156** 4d. ultramarine 25 20
330 **157** 5d. brown 25 35
331 6d. reddish purple 25 15
332 7d. bright green 30 30
333 **158** 8d. magenta 30 35
334 9d. bronze-green 30 25
a. "TANGIER" omitted £3500
335 10d. Prussian blue 30 30
336 11d. brown-purple 30 30
337 **159** 1s. bistre-brown 30 25
338 **160** 1s. 3d. green 45 50
339 **159** 1s. 6d. grey-blue 50 55

(b) Nos. 536/8 optd as T **32**

340 **166** 2s. 6d. black-brown 2·00 2·25
a. Hyphen omitted 60·00
b. Hyphen inserted 20·00
341 **167** 5s. rose-red 2·75 2·25
a. Hyphen omitted 60·00
b. Hyphen inserted 10·00
342 **168** 10s. ultramarine 3·00 3·00
a. Hyphen omitted 65·00
b. Hyphen inserted 13·00
323/42 *Set of* 20 10·00 10·00

Nos. 340a/b, 341a/b and 342a/b occur on stamp No. 34 in the sheet of 40 (4 × 10). They are best collected in marginal blocks of four from the bottom left corner of the sheet. Specialists recognise two forms of No. 340b; one where the hyphen on stamp No. 34 was inserted separately to correct the error, No. 340a; the other from a later printing where a new and corrected overprinting plate was used. (*Price* £10 *un.*)

All stamps overprinted "TANGIER" were withdrawn from sale on 30 April 1957.

Mosul
see Iraq

Muscat

An independent Arab Sultanate in Eastern Arabia with an Indian postal administration.

The Indian post office at Muscat town is officially recorded as having opened on 1 May 1864. Stamps of India were provided for its use, most surviving examples being of the ½ a. value, although others to the 8 a. are known.

The office was initially included in the Bombay Postal Circle and the first postmark, so far only recorded on stampless covers, was a single circle, 21½ mm in diameter, broken at the top by "MUSCAT" and with the date in two lines across the centre. This was followed by a cancellation showing the post office number, "309", within a diamond of 13, later 16, bars. It is believed that this was used in conjunction with a single ring date stamp inscribed "MUSCAT".

1864 Diamond

In 1869 the office was transferred to the Sind Circle, assigned a new number, "23", and issued with a duplex cancellation. Major reorganisation of the postal service in 1873 resulted in Muscat becoming office "K-4". For ten years from 1873 the cancellations do not, very confusingly, carry any indication of the year of use.

1869 Duplex

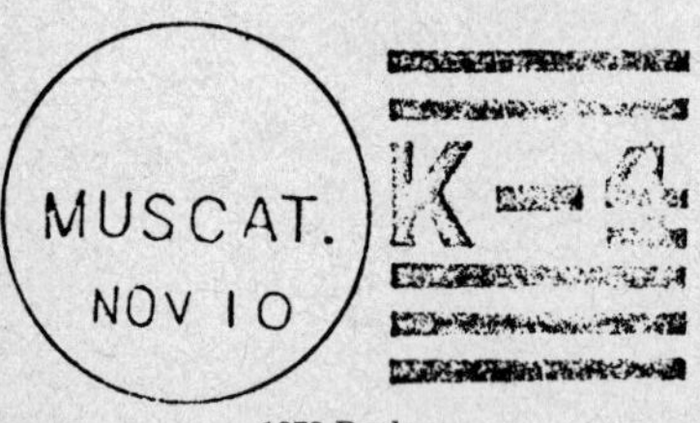

1873 Duplex

Muscat rejoined the Bombay Circle in 1879 and was issued with a cancellation showing a "B" within a square of horizontal bars. The date stamp used at this time was unique in that it carried the inscription "MASKAT", although the spelling reverted to the more usual form by 1882. The square cancellation had been replaced by a similar circular mark by 1884.

Subsequent postmarks were of various circular types, all inscribed "MUSCAT".

There was only one Indian post office in Muscat, but a further office did exist, from 12 April 1868, at the Muscat dependency of Guadur, a port on the Mekran coast of Baluchistan.

No cancellations have been reported from Guadur before its transfer to the Sind Circle in 1869. Cancellations are all similar in style to those for Muscat, Guadur being initially assigned number "24", although an office in Southern India is also known to have used this numeral. The 1869 duplex is interesting in that it is inscribed "GWADUR". Under the 1873 reorganisation the office became "4/K-1", this postmark using the "GUADUR" spelling.

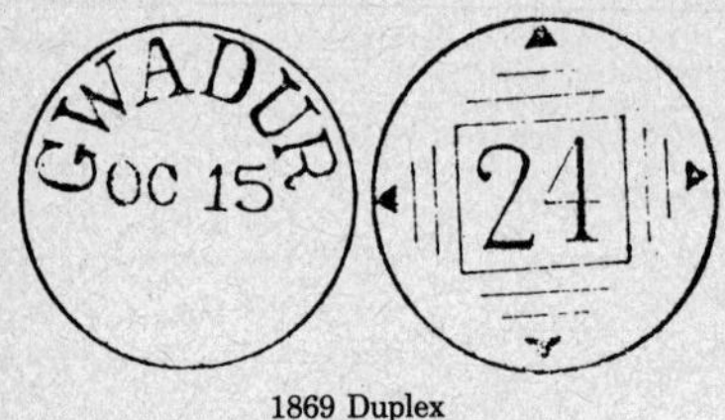

1869 Duplex

PRICES FOR STAMPS ON COVER	
Nos. 1/15	*from* × 100
Nos. O1/10	*from* × 100

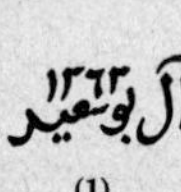

(1)

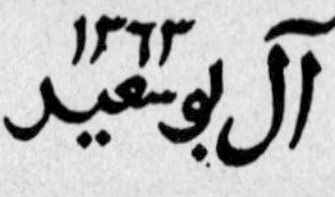

(2)

1944 (20 Nov). *Bicentenary of Al-Busaid Dynasty. Stamps of India optd ("AL BUSAID 1363" in Arabic script) as T* 1 *or* 2 *(rupee values).*

1	**100a**	3 p. slate	15	1·50
2		½ a. purple	15	1·50
3		9 p. green	15	1·50
4		1 a. carmine	15	1·50
5	**101**	1½ a. dull violet	15	1·50
6		2 a. vermilion	15	1·50
7		3 a. bright violet	15	1·50
8		3½ a. bright blue	15	1·50
9	**102**	4 a. brown	15	1·50
10		6 a. turquoise-green	25	1·50
11		8 a. slate-violet	15	2·00
12		12 a. lake	35	2·25
13	**103**	14 a. purple	15	2·75
14	**93**	1 r. grey and red-brown	20	3·75
15		2 r. purple and brown	20	8·00
1/15		*Set of* 15	2·25	30·00

OFFICIAL STAMPS

1944 (20 Nov). *Bicentenary of Al-Busaid Dynasty. Official stamps of India optd as T* 1 *or* 2 *(1 r).*

O 1	**O 20**	3 p. slate	15	2·50
O 2		½ a. purple	15	2·50
O 3		9 p. green	15	2·50
O 4		1 a. carmine	15	2·50
O 5		1½ a. dull violet	15	2·50
O 6		2 a. vermilion	15	2·50
O 7		2½ a. bright violet	15	2·50
O 8		4 a. brown	15	3·00
O 9		8 a. slate-violet	15	3·75
O10	**93**	1 r. grey and red-brown (No. O138)	75	9·00
O1/O10		*Set of* 10	1·90	30·00

From December 1947 there was a Pakistani postal administration and stamps of Pakistan were used until 31 March 1948. The subsequent British administration operated from 1 April 1948 to 29 April 1966 when the stamps of the BRITISH POSTAL AGENCIES IN EASTERN ARABIA were used.

Later issues for this area will be found listed under OMAN in Part 19 (*Middle East*) of this catalogue.

Nagaland

Labels inscribed "NAGALAND" with currency in cents and chaplees are considered to be propaganda labels.

Natal

PRICES FOR STAMPS ON COVER	
Nos. 1/7	*from* × 2
Nos. 9/25	*from* × 3
Nos. 26/56	*from* × 4
Nos. 57/8	—
Nos. 59/65	*from* × 4
Nos. 66/73	*from* × 5
Nos. 76/84	*from* × 4
Nos. 85/93	*from* × 3
Nos. 96/103	*from* × 6
Nos. 104/5	*from* × 5
Nos. 106/25	*from* × 6
Nos. 127/42	*from* × 4
Nos. 143/5a	—
Nos. 146/57	*from* × 4
No. 162	—
Nos. 165/71	*from* × 3
No. F1	—
Nos. O1/6	*from* × 10

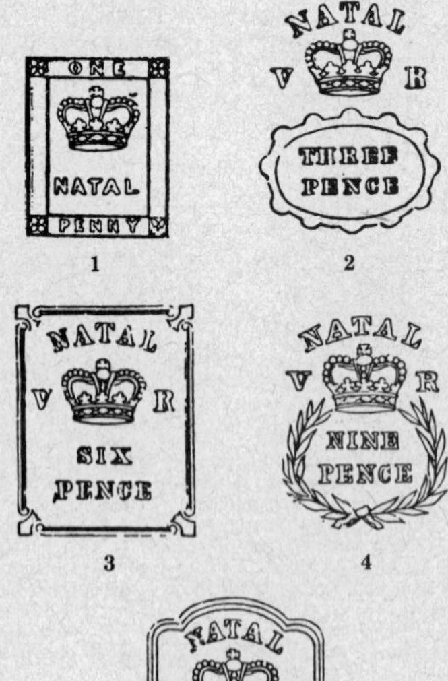

1 2 3 4

5

(Embossed in plain relief on coloured wove paper)

1857 (26 May, *the* 1*d. in* 1858). *Imperf.*

1	**1**	1d. rose	—	£1700
2		1d. buff	—	£950
3		1d. blue	—	£1100
4	**2**	3d. rose	—	£400
		a. *Tête-bêche* (pair)	—	£10000
5	**3**	6d. green	—	£1100
6	**4**	9d. blue	—	£7000
7	**5**	1s. buff	—	£5500

All the above have been reprinted more than once, and the early reprints of some values cannot always be distinguished with certainty from originals.

Stamps on surface-coloured paper, perforated 12½, are fiscals.

NOTE. The value of the above stamps depends on their dimensions, and the clearness of the embossing, but our prices are for fine used.

6

7

(Eng C. H. Jeens. Recess P.B.)

1859–60. *No wmk. P* 14.

9	**6**	1d. rose-red	£120	70·00
10		3d. blue	£100	42·00
		a. Imperf between (vert pair)		

No. 10a is only known from a cover of 1867 franked with two such pairs.

1861. *No wmk. Intermediate perf* 14 *to* 16.

11	**6**	3d. blue	£170	65·00

1862. *No wmk. Rough perf* 14 *to* 16.

12	**6**	3d. blue	85·00	32·00
		a. Imperf between (pair)	£1600	
		b. Imperf (pair)	—	£1100
13		6d. grey	£130	45·00

1862. *Wmk Small Star. Rough perf* 14 *to* 16.

15	**6**	1d. rose-red	£100	55·00

The 1d. and 3d. wmk. Star, imperf, are proofs, and are therefore not included. The 3d. wmk Star, perforated, is believed to exist only with forged watermark.

(Recess D.L.R.)

1863. *Thick paper. No wmk. P* 13.

18	**6**	1d. lake	75·00	27·00
19		1d. carmine-red	75·00	20·00

1864. *Wmk Crown CC. P* 12½.

20	**6**	1d. brown-red	£110	35·00
21		1d. rose	80·00	27·00
22		1d. bright-red	80·00	27·00
23		6d. lilac	50·00	15·00
24		6d. violet	38·00	25·00

(Typo D.L.R.)

1867 (April). *Wmk Crown CC. P* 14.

25	**7**	1s. green	£120	26·00

1869 (23 Aug). *Optd horiz in Natal. No wmk (3d.), wmk Crown CC (others). P* 14 *or* 14–16 *(3d.),* 12½ *(1d., 6d) or* 14 *(1s.).*

POSTAGE

Tall capitals

26	**6**	1d. rose	£225	50·00
27		1d. bright red	£225	50·00
28		3d. blue (No. 10)		
28*a*		3d. blue (No. 11)	£350	£190
28*b*		3d. blue (No. 12)	£225	70·00
29		6d. lilac	—	55·00
30		6d. violet	£300	55·00
31	**7**	1s. green	—	£950

Postage.

12¾ mm long

32	**6**	1d. rose	£225	50·00
33		1d. bright red	£225	50·00
		a. Opt double	—	£475
34		3d. blue (No. 10)	—	£200
34*a*		3d. blue (No. 11)	£350	£160
34*b*		3d. blue (No. 12)	£325	65·00
35		6d. lilac	£300	50·00
36		6d. violet	£225	50·00
37	**7**	1s. green	—	£350

Postage.

13¾ mm long

38	**6**	1d. rose	£350	95·00
39		1d. bright red	—	95·00
40		3d. blue (No. 10)		
40*a*		3d. blue (No. 11)		
40*b*		3d. blue (No. 12)	£800	£250
41		6d. lilac	—	£120
42		6d. violet	£700	£120
43	**7**	1s. green	—	£1400

Postage.

14½ to 15½ mm long

44	**6**	1d. rose	£350	£190
45		1d. bright red	£400	£170
46		3d. blue (No. 10)		
46*a*		3d. blue (No. 11)	—	£190
46*b*		3d. blue (No. 12)	—	£190
47		6d. lilac	—	60·00
48		6d. violet	£800	65·00
49	**7**	1s. green	—	£1400

POSTAGE.

With a stop

50 6 1d. rose .. .. 65·00 25·00
51 1d. bright red .. .. £120 25·00
52 3d. blue (No. 10) .. .. £170 45·00
53 3d. blue (No. 11) .. .. £100 38·00
54 3d. blue (No. 12) .. .. £130 32·00
a. Opt double .. .. — £600
54b 6d. lilac .. .. £100 38·00
55 6d. violet .. .. 85·00 38·00
56 7 1s. green .. .. £100 38·00

All values exist with this overprint at top or bottom of stamp.

POSTAGE

(8)

1870. *No. 25 optd with T 8.*

57 7 1s. green (C.) £3000
58 1s. green (Blk.) £1500 £950
a. Opt double £2750 £1000
59 1s. green (G.) .. .. 38·00 10·00

For 1s. orange, see No. 108.

POSTAGE POSTAGE POSTAGE POSTAGE POSTAGE

(9) (10) (11)

1870–73. *Optd with T 9. Wmk Crown CC. P 12½.*

60 6 1d. bright red .. .. 55·00 13·00
61 3d. bright blue (R.) .. .. 55·00 13·00
62 6d. mauve .. .. £100 25·00

1873 (July). *Optd up centre of stamp with T 10. Wmk Crown CC. P 14.*

63 7 1s. purple-brown .. .. 85·00 16·00

1874 (July). *No. 21 optd with T 11.*

65 7 1d. rose .. .. £120 42·00
a. Opt double .. ..

NATAL POSTAGE ONE PENNY — 12
NATAL POSTAGE THREE PENCE — 13
NATAL POSTAGE FOUR PENCE — 14
NATAL POSTAGE SIX PENCE — 15
NATAL POSTAGE FIVE SHILLINGS — 16

(Typo D.L.R.)

1874–78. *Wmk Crown CC. P 14.*

66 12 1d. dull rose .. .. 16·00 1·25
67 1d. bright rose .. .. 16·00 1·25
68 13 3d. blue .. .. 50·00 13·00
a. Perf 14 × 12½ £1300 £850
69 14 4d. brown (1878) .. .. 65·00 10·00
a. Perf 12½ .. .. £275 65·00
70 15 6d. lilac .. .. 27·00 6·00
71 16 5s. maroon .. .. 90·00 26·00
a. Perf 15½ × 15 .. .. £110 65·00
72 5s. rose .. .. 60·00 24·00
73 5s. carmine (H/S S. £160) .. .. .. 55·00 26·00

The 5s. stamps normally have wmk sideways.

POSTAGE (17) POSTAGE (18) ½ HALF (19)

1875. *Wmk Crown CC. P 14 (1s.) or 12½ (others). (a) Optd with T 17.*

76 6 1d. rose .. .. 70·00 35·00
a. Opt double £475 £425
77 1d. bright red .. .. 70·00 48·00

(b) *Optd with T 18 (14½ mm long, without stop)*

81 6 1d. rose .. .. 60·00 40·00
a. Opt inverted £700 £400
82 1d. yellow .. .. 65·00 65·00
83 6d. violet .. .. 42·00 5·50
a. Opt double .. .. — £550
b. Opt inverted £650 £150
84 7 1s. green .. .. 65·00 4·50
a. Opt double .. .. — £325

TYPE 19. There are several varieties of this surcharge, of which T 19 is an example. They may be divided as follows:

(*a*) "½" 4½ mm high, "2" has straight foot.
(*b*) As last but "½" is 4 mm high.
(*c*) As last but "2" has curled foot.
(*d*) "½" 3½ mm. high, "2" has straight foot.
(*e*) As last but "2" has curled foot.
(*f*) As last but "2" smaller.

As the "½" and "HALF" were overprinted separately, they vary in relative position, and are frequently overlapping.

1877 (13 Feb). *No. 66 surch as T 19.*

85 12 ½d. on 1d. rose (*a*) .. .. 17·00 55·00
a. "½" double .. ..
86 ½d. on 1d. rose (*b*) .. .. 85·00
87 ½d. on 1d. rose (*c*) .. .. 75·00
88 ½d. on 1d. rose (*d*) .. .. 40·00
89 ½d. on 1d. rose (*e*) .. .. 42·00
90 ½d. on 1d. rose (*f*) .. .. 42·00

POSTAGE Half-penny (21)
NATAL POSTAGE ONE HALF-PENNY — 23
ONE HALF-PENNY. (24)

1877–79. *T 6 (wmk Crown CC, P 12½) surch as T 21.*

91 ½d. on 1d. yellow .. .. 8·00 11·00
a. Surch inverted £200 £200
b. Surch double £200 £200
c. Surch omitted (lower stamp, vertical pair) £950 £850
d. "POSTAGE" omitted (in pair with normal) £1000
e. "S" of "POSTAGE" omitted £180 £170
f. "T" of "POSTAGE" omitted £180
92 1d. on 6d. violet .. .. 30·00 8·00
a. "S" of "POSTAGE" omitted £250 £150
93 1d. on 6d. rose .. .. 65·00 27·00
a. Surch inverted .. .. — £160
b. Surch double .. .. — £190
c. Surch double, one inverted £250 £250
d. Surch four times £325 £160
e. "S" of "POSTAGE" omitted £250

No. 93c. is known with one surcharge showing variety "S" of "POSTAGE" omitted.

Other minor varieties exist in these surcharges.

(Typo D.L.R.)

1880 (13 Oct). *Wmk Crown CC. P 14.*

96 23 ½d. blue-green .. .. 6·00 8·00
a. Imperf between (vert pair) .. ..

1882–89. *Wmk Crown CA. P 14.*

97 23 ½d. blue-green .. .. 60·00 13·00
a. Dull green 40 20
99 12 1d. rose (*shades*) 40 10
a. Carmine .. .. 1·90 15
100 13 3d. blue .. .. 75·00 17·00
101 3d. grey (11.89) .. .. 1·00 75
102 14 4d. brown .. .. 2·25 65
103 15 6d. mauve .. .. 2·75 70
97a/103 .. .. *Set of 6* 75·00 17·00
97a, 99a, 101/3 H/S "Specimen" .. *Set of 5* £250

1885 (26 Jan). *No. 99 surch with T 24.*

104 12 ½d. on 1d. rose .. .. 16·00 11·00

TWO PENCE (25)
NATAL POSTAGE TWO PENCE — 26
TWOPENCE HALFPENNY (27)

1886. *Surch with T 25 by D.L.R.*

105 13 2d. on 3d. grey .. .. 18·00 5·50

(Typo D.L.R.)

1887–89. *Wmk Crown CA. P 14.*

106 26 2d. olive-green Die I* (Optd S. £60) .. 17·00 65
107 2d. olive-green, Die II (H/S S. £60) .. 1·00 65

*The differences between Dies I and II are shown in the Introduction.

1888 (16 Mar). *As No. 84, but wmk Crown CA, optd with T 8, by D.L.R.*

108 7 1s. orange (C.) (H/S S. £90) .. .. 2·75 85
a. Opt double .. .. — £1500

1890. *Surch locally with T 27.*

109 14 2½d. on 4d. brown (H/S S. £50) .. .. 11·00 8·50
a. "TWOPENGE" .. .. 60·00 60·00
b. "HALFPENN" £225 £180
c. Surch double £250 £180
d. Surch inverted £325 £250

NATAL POSTAGE 2½d — 28
POSTAGE. Half-Penny (29)
POSTAGE. Varieties of long-tailed letters

(Typo D.L.R.)

1891 (June). *Wmk Crown CA. P 14.*

113 28 2½d. bright blue (H/S S. £60) .. .. 2·00 50

1895 (12 Mar). *No. 24 surch with T 29 in carmine.*

114 ½d. on 6d. violet (H/S S. £50) .. .. 90 2·00
a. "Ealf-Penny" .. .. 18·00 14·00
b. "Half-Pennv" and long "P" .. .. 14·00
ba. "Half Pennv" and long "T" and "A" .. 14·00
c. No stop after "POSTAGE" and long "P", "T" and "A" .. .. 15·00
d. Long "P" .. .. 2·00 3·50
e. Long "T" .. .. 2·00 3·50
f. Long "A" .. .. 2·00 3·50
g. Long "P" and "T" .. .. 2·50 4·00
h. Long "P" and "A" .. .. 2·00 3·50
i. Long "T" and "A" .. .. 2·00 3·50
k. Long "P", "T" and "A" .. .. .. 2·50 4·00
ka. Long "P", "T" and "A" with comma after "POSTAGE" .. .. 5·00
l. Surcharge double, one vertical £250

No. 114 is known with surcharge double and widely spaced, but the second surcharge is extremely faint.

HALF (30)
NATAL POSTAGE REVENUE ONE PENNY 1d — 31
NATAL POSTAGE REVENUE 5s FIVE SHILLINGS — 32

1895 (18 Mar). *No. 99 surch with T 30.*

125 HALF on 1d. rose (*shades*) (H/S S. £50) .. 70 75
a. Surch double £325 £325
b. "H" with longer left limb .. .. 20·00
c. Pair, one without surcharge .. ..

No. 125b occurs on the second, fourth, sixth etc., stamps of the first vertical row of the righthand pane. It was very soon corrected.

In some printings what appears to be a broken "E" (with the top limb removed) was used instead of "L" in "HALF" on the last stamp in the sheet (*Price* £30)

(Typo D.L.R.)

1902–3. *Inscr "POSTAGE REVENUE". Wmk Crown CA. P 14.*

127 31 ½d. blue-green 65 15
128 1d. carmine 70 15
129 1½d. green and black 80 80
130 2d. red and olive-green 80 25
131 2½d. bright blue .. .. 90 3·00
132 3d. purple and grey 80 30
133 4d. carmine and cinnamon .. .. 1·75 6·00
134 5d. black and orange .. .. .. 1·25 2·00
135 6d. green and brown-purple .. .. 1·25 1·10
136 1s. carmine and pale blue .. .. 3·50 1·10
137 2s. green and bright violet .. .. 35·00 9·00
138 2s. 6d. purple .. .. 30·00 12·00
139 4s. deep rose and maize .. .. .. 48·00 35·00
a. Imperf between (horiz pair)
127/139 .. .. *Set of 13* £110 65·00
127/39 Optd "Specimen" .. .. *Set of 13* £175

No. 139a is also imperforate between stamp and left-hand margin.

(Typo D.L.R.)

1902–3. *Wmk Crown CC. P 14.*

140 32 5s. dull blue and rose .. .. .. 16·00 7·50
141 10s. deep rose and chocolate .. .. 45·00 20·00
142 £1 black and bright blue .. .. £110 42·00
143 £1 10s. green & violet (Optd S. £65) .. £200 65·00
144 £5 mauve and black (Optd S. £100) .. £1300 £250
145 £10 green and orange (Optd S. £250) .. £5500 £2000
145a £20 red and green (Optd S. £400) £11000
140/2 Optd "Specimen" .. .. *Set of 3* £125

USED HIGH VALUES. Collectors are warned against fiscally used high value Natal stamps with penmarks cleaned off and forged postmarks added.

1904–8. *Wmk Mult Crown CA. P 14.*

146 31 ½d. blue-green .. .. 1·00 15
147 1d. rose-carmine .. .. 1·00 15
148 1d. deep carmine .. .. 2·00 20
149 2d. red and olive-green .. .. .. 1·00 3·25
152 4d. carmine and cinnamon .. .. 1·75 1·00
153 5d. black and orange (1908) .. .. 2·50 2·75
155 1s. carmine and pale blue .. .. 38·00 6·00
156 2s. dull green and bright violet .. .. 32·00 20·00
157 2s. 6d. purple .. .. 32·00 24·00
162 32 £1 10s. brown-orange and deep purple, C (1908) (Optd S. £175) £1100
146/157 .. .. *Set of 9* £100 50·00

1908–9. *Inscr "POSTAGE POSTAGE". Wmk Mult Crown CA. P 14.*

165 31 6d. dull and bright purple .. .. 4·50 2·00
166 1s. black/*green* .. .. 6·00 2·00
167 2s. purple and bright blue/*blue* .. .. 15·00 3·00
168 2s. 6d. black and red/*blue* .. .. 25·00 3·00
169 32 5s. green and red/*yellow* .. .. 18·00 15·00
170 10s. green and red/*green* .. .. 48·00 45·00
171 £1 purple and black/*red* £225 £150
165/71 .. .. *Set of 7* £300 £200
165/71 Optd "Specimen" .. .. *Set of 7* £250

FISCALS USED FOR POSTAGE

1869. *Embossed on coloured wove, surfaced paper. P 12½.*

F1 1 1d. yellow .. .. 50·00 80·00

Examples of 1d. yellow and 6d. rose values as Type **6**, 1s. purple-brown as Type **7** and various values between 5s. and £10 in the design illustrated above are believed to exist postally used, but, as such use was not authorised, they are not now listed.

OFFICIAL STAMPS

OFFICIAL

(O 1)

1904. *T* **31**, *wmk Mult Crown CA, optd with Type* O 1. *P* 14.

No.	Description	Unused	Used
O1	½d. blue-green	3·00	35
O2	1d. carmine	1·50	60
O3	2d. red and olive-green	11·00	7·50
O4	3d. purple and grey	6·50	4·00
O5	6d. green and brown-purple	22·00	22·00
O6	1s. carmine and pale blue	55·00	85·00
O1/6	.. .. *Set of* 6	90·00	£110

The use of stamps overprinted as above was discontinued after 30 May 1907. Stamps perforated with the letters "N.G.R." were for use on Government Railways.

Natal now uses the stamps of South Africa.

Nauru

Stamps of MARSHALL ISLANDS were used in Nauru from the opening of the German Colonial Post Office on 14 July 1908 until 8 September 1914.

Following the occupation by Australian forces the "N.W. PACIFIC ISLANDS" overprints on Australia (see NEW GUINEA) were used during the early months of 1916.

PRICES FOR STAMPS ON COVER TO 1945

Nos. 1/12	*from* × 10
Nos. 13/16	*from* × 3
Nos. 17/25	—
Nos. 26/39	*from* × 6
Nos. 40/3	*from* × 10
Nos. 44/7	*from* × 15

BRITISH MANDATE

NAURU (1) **NAURU** (2) **NAURU** (3)

1916 (2 Sept)–**23**. *Stamps of Great Britain* (1912–22) *overprinted at Somerset House.*

(*a*) *With T* **1** (12½ *mm long*) *at foot*

No.	Type	Description	Unused	Used
1	**105**	½d. green	30	2·25
		a. "NAUP.U"	£275	
		b. Double opt, one albino	70·00	
2	**104**	1d. bright scarlet	40	2·00
		a. "NAUP.U"	£450	
2*b*		1d. carmine-red	10·00	
		bb. Double opt, one albino	£200	
3	**105**	1½d. red-brown (1923)	55·00	80·00
4	**106**	2d. orange (Die I)	1·75	7·00
		a. "NAUP.U"	£300	
		b. Double opt, one albino	£100	
5		2d. orange (Die II) (1923)	70·00	£100
6	**104**	2½d. blue	2·75	5·00
		a. "NAUP.U"	£375	
		b. Double opt, one albino	£200	
7	**106**	3d. bluish violet	2·00	3·50
		a. "NAUP.U"	£375	
		b. Double opt, one albino	£200	
8		4d. slate-green	2·00	7·50
		a. "NAUP.U"	£475	
		b. Double opt, one albino	£200	
9	**107**	5d. yellow-brown	2·25	8·50
		a. "NAUP.U"	£550	
		b. Double opt, one albino	£140	
10		6d. purple, C	3·25	10·00
		a. "NAUP.U"	£500	
		b. Double opt, one albino	£225	
11	**108**	9d. agate	7·00	18·00
		a. Double opt, one albino	£225	
12		1s. bistre-brown (Optd S. £125) ..	7·00	18·00
		a. Double opt, one albino	£250	
1/12		.. .. *Set of* 11	70·00	£130

(*b*) *With T* **2** (13½ *mm long*) *at centre* (1923)

No.	Type	Description	Unused	Used
13	**105**	½d. green	4·50	48·00
14	**104**	1d. scarlet	24·00	40·00
15	**105**	1½d. red-brown	26·00	50·00
		a. Double opt, one albino	£140	
16	**106**	2d. orange (Die II)	45·00	80·00
13/16		.. .. *Set of* 4	85·00	£190

The "NAUP.U" errors occur on R.6/2 from Control I 16 only. The ink used on this batch of overprints was shiny jet-black.

There is a constant variety consisting of short left stroke to "N" which occurs on Nos. 1, 2, 2*b*, 4 (£30 *each*); 3 (£175); 5 (£200); 6, 7 (£38 *each*); 8, 9, 10 (£55 *each*); 11, 12 (£65 *each*). All unused prices.

(*c*) *T* **109** *optd with T* **3**. (i) *Waterlow printing*

No.	Description	Unused	Used
17	5s. rose-carmine	£2750	£2250
18	10s. indigo-blue (R.) (Optd S. £1400) ..	£6000	£5000
	a. Double opt, one albino	£8000	£8000

(ii) *De La Rue printing*

No.	Description	Unused	Used
19	2s. 6d. deep brown (Optd S. £250)	£500	£600
	a. Double opt, one albino	£1200	
	b. Treble opt, two albino	£1300	
20	2s. 6d. yellow-brown	65·00	90·00
21	2s. 6d. pale brown (worn plate) (Optd S. £250)	70·00	85·00
	a. Re-entry		
22	5s. bright carmine (*shades*) (Optd S. £250)	£110	£150
	a. Treble opt, two albino	£550	
23	10s. pale blue (R.)	£300	£400
	a. Treble opt. (Blk. + R. + albino) ..		
23*b*	10s. deep bright blue (R.)	£600	£650

(iii) *Bradbury, Wilkinson printing* (1919)

No.	Description	Unused	Used
24	2s. 6d. chocolate-brown	75·00	£100
	a. Major re-entry		
	b. Double opt, one albino	£300	
25	2s. 6d. pale brown	60·00	85·00
	a. Double opt, one albino	£275	

AUSTRALIAN MANDATE

PRINTERS. See note at beginning of Australia.

4 *Century* (freighter)

(Des R. A. Harrison. Eng T. S. Harrison. Recess Note Printing Branch of the Treasury, Melbourne and from 1926 by the Commonwealth Bank of Australia)

1924–48. *T* **4**. *No wmk. P* 11.
I. Rough surfaced, greyish paper (1924–34).
II. Shiny surfaced, white paper (1937–48).

No.	Description	I Unused	I Used	II Unused	II Used
26	½d. chestnut	60	2·75	6·50	11·00
	a. Perf 14 (1947)	†		1·25	5·00
27	1d. green	1·50	2·75	2·50	3·00
28	1½d. scarlet	2·25	3·50	90	1·50
29	2d. orange	2·25	6·00	1·50	6·00
30	2½d. slate-blue	4·00	11·00	†	
30*a*	2½d. greenish blue (1934) ..	4·00	11·00	†	
30*b*	2½d. dull blue (1948)	†		1·25	3·00
	ba. Imperf between (vert pair)	†		£3750	£3750
	bb. Imperf between (horiz pair)	†		£3750	£3750
31	3d. pale blue	2·50	6·50	†	
31*a*	3d. greenish grey (1947) ..	†		1·50	3·50
32	4d. olive-green	3·50	8·50	3·50	5·50
33	5d. brown	2·50	6·00	3·25	3·75
34	6d. dull violet	3·00	11·00	3·00	3·50
35	9d. olive-brown	4·75	17·00	7·50	14·00
36	1s. brown-lake	6·00	13·00	5·00	2·75
37	2s. 6d. grey-green	25·00	35·00	24·00	27·00
38	5s. claret	48·00	70·00	35·00	48·00
39	10s. yellow	80·00	£100	80·00	80·00
26I/39I	.. .. *Set of* 14	£180	£250	†	
26II/39II	.. .. *Set of* 15	†		£160	£180

HIS MAJESTY'S JUBILEE.

1910 - 1935

(5)

6

1935 (12 July). *Silver Jubilee. T* **4** (*shiny surfaced, white paper*) *optd with T* **5**.

No.	Description	Unused	Used
40	1½d. scarlet	60	80
41	2d. orange	1·00	4·00
42	2½d. dull blue	1·50	1·50
43	1s. brown-lake	4·00	3·50
40/3	.. .. *Set of* 4	6·50	9·00

(Recess John Ash, Melbourne)

1937 (10 May). *Coronation. P* 11.

No.	Type	Description	Unused	Used
44	**6**	1½d. scarlet	45	40
45		2d. orange	45	70
46		2½d. blue	45	30
47		1s. purple	60	70
44/7		.. .. *Set of* 4	1·75	1·90

7 Nauruan Netting Fish

8 Anibare Bay

15 Map of Nauru

(Recess Note Printing Branch, Commonwealth Bank, Melbourne, and from 1960 by Note Ptg Branch, Reserve Bank of Australia, Melbourne)

1954 (6 Feb)–**65**. *T* **7/8**, **15** *and similar designs. Toned paper. P* 13½×14½ (*horiz*) *or* 14½×13½ (*vert*).

No.	Description	Unused	Used
48	½d. deep violet	15	10
	a. Violet (8.5.61)	15	10
49	1d. bluish green	15	15
	a. Emerald-green (8.5.61)	15	15
	b. Deep green (1965)		
50	3½d. scarlet	1·50	15
	a. Vermilion (1958)	2·25	60
51	4d. grey-blue	1·50	45
	a. Deep blue (1958)	2·50	70
52	6d. orange	70	15
53	9d. claret	50	15
54	1s. deep purple	30	15
55	2s. 6d. deep green	2·50	60
56	5s. magenta	8·00	2·00
48/56	.. .. *Set of* 9	14·00	3·25

Designs: *Horiz*—3½d. Loading phosphate from cantilever; 4d. Great Frigate Bird; 6d. Nauruan canoe; 9d. Domaneab (meeting-house); 2s. 6d. Buada lagoon. *Vert*—1s. Palm trees.

Nos. 48*a*, 49*a*/*b*, 50*a* and 51*a* are on white paper.

16 Micronesian Pigeon

17 Poison Nut

20 Capparis

21 White Tern

(Recess (10d., 2s. 3d.) or photo (others) Note Ptg Branch, Reserve Bank of Australia, Melbourne)

1963–65. *T* **16/17**, **20/1** *and similar designs. P* 13½ × 13 (5*d.*), 13 × 13½ (8*d.*), 14 × 13½ (10*d.*), 15 × 14½ (1*s.* 3*d.*) *or* 13½ (*others*).

No.	Description	Unused	Used
57	2d. black, blue, red-brn & orge-yell (3.5.65)	1·00	1·00
58	3d. multicoloured (16.4.64)	75	35
59	5d. multicoloured (22.4.63)	75	75
60	8d. black and green (1.7.63)	1·50	80
61	10d. black (16.4.64)	50	30
62	1s. 3d. blue, black & yellow-green (3.5.65) ..	3·50	1·75
63	2s. 3d. ultramarine (16.4.64)	2·75	55
64	3s. 3d. multicoloured (3.5.65)	4·00	2·50
57/64	.. .. *Set of* 8	13·00	7·00

Designs: *Vert*—5d. "Iyo" (*calophyllum*). *Horiz*—8d. Black Lizard; 2s. 3d. Coral pinnacles; 3s. 3d. Finsch's Reed Warbler.

1965 (14 Apr). 50*th Anniv of Gallipoli Landing. As T* **184** *of Australia, but slightly larger* (22 × 34½ *mm*). *Photo.*

No.	Description	Unused	Used
65	5d. sepia, black and emerald	15	10

(New Currency. 100 cents = $1 Australian)

24 Anibare Bay

25 "Iyo" (*calophyllum*)

(Recess (1, 2, 3, 5, 8, 19, 25 c. and $1) or photo (others))

1966 (14 Feb–25 May). *Decimal Currency. Various stamps with values in cents and dollars as T* **24/5** *and some colours changed. Recess printed stamps on helecon paper.*

No.	Type	Description	Unused	Used
66	**24**	1 c. deep blue	15	10
67	**7**	2 c. brown-purple (25 May)	15	10
68	–	3 c. bluish green (as 3½d.) (25 May) ..	30	15
69	**25**	4 c. multicoloured	25	10
70	–	5 c. deep ultramarine (as 1s.) (25 May) ..	25	15
71	–	7 c. black and chestnut (as 8d.)	25	10
72	**20**	8 c. olive-green	30	10
73	–	10 c. red (as 4d.)	40	10
74	**21**	15 c. blue, black & yellow-green (25 May)	80	80
75	–	25 c. deep brown (as 2s. 3d.) (25 May) ..	45	40
76	**17**	30 c. multicoloured	70	30
77	–	35 c. multicoloured (as 3s. 3d.) (25 May) ..	1·25	35
78	**16**	50 c. multicoloured	2·50	80
79	–	$1 magenta (as 5s.)	2·00	1·00
66/79		.. .. *Set of* 14	8·50	3·75

The 25 c. is as No. 63, but larger, 27½ × 24½ mm.

REPUBLIC

Nauru became independent on 31 January 1968 and was later admitted into special membership of the Commonwealth.

REPUBLIC OF NAURU

(26)

1968 (31 Jan–15 May). *Nos. 66/79 optd with T* **26**.

80	**24**	1 c. deep blue (R.)	10	10
81	**7**	2 c. brown-purple	10	10
82	–	3 c. bluish green	15	10
83	**25**	4 c. multicoloured (15.5.68)	15	10
84	–	5 c. deep ultramarine (R.)	15	10
85	–	7 c. black and chestnut (R.) (15.5.68)	25	10
86	**20**	8 c. olive-green (R.)	25	10
87	–	10 c. red	30	15
88	**21**	15 c. blue, black and yellow-green	2·75	2·50
89	–	25 c. deep brown (R.)	30	15
90	**17**	30 c. multicoloured (15.5.68)	55	15
91	–	35 c. multicoloured (15.5.68)	1·25	30
92	**16**	50 c. multicoloured	2·00	50
93		$1 magenta	1·25	75
80/93		*Set of* 14	8·00	4·25

27 "Towards the Sunrise" **28** Planting Seedling, and Map

(Des H. Fallu (5 c.), Note Ptg Branch (10 c.). Photo Note Ptg Branch, Reserve Bank of Australia, Melbourne)

1968 (11 Sept). *Independence. P* 13½.

94	**27**	5 c. black, slate-lilac, orange-yellow and yellow-green	10	10
95	**28**	10 c. black, yellow-green and new blue	10	10

29 Flag of Independent Nauru **30** Island, "C" and Stars

(Des J. Mason. Photo Note Ptg Branch, Reserve Bank of Australia, Melbourne)

1969 (31 Jan). *P* 13½.

96	**29**	15 c. yellow, orange and royal blue	15	15

This is a definitive issue which was put on sale on the first anniversary of Independence.

(Des R. Brooks, Litho Format)

1972 (7 Feb). *25th Anniv of South Pacific Commission. P* 14½ × 14.

97	**30**	25 c. multicoloured	30	25

Independence 1968-1973

(31)

1973 (31 Jan). *Fifth Anniv of Independence. No.* 96 *optd with T* **31** *in gold.*

98	**29**	15 c. yellow, orange and royal blue	20	30

32 Denea **33** Artefacts and Map

(Des locally; adapted G. Vasarhelyi. Litho Format)

1973 (28 Mar*–25 July). *Various multicoloured designs as T* **32** *(1 to 5 c.) or T* **33** *(others). P* 14 *(1 to 5 c.),* 14½ × 14 *(7, 8, 10, 30, 50 c.) or* 14 × 14½ *(others).*

99	1 c. Ekwenababae	25	10
100	2 c. Kauwe Iud	40	10
101	3 c. Rimone	40	10
102	4 c. Type **32**	40	15
103	5 c. Erekogo	40	15
104	7 c. Ikimago (fish) (25.7)	30	10
105	8 c. Catching flying-fish (23.5)	30	10
106	10 c. Itsibweb (ball game) (23.5)	30	10
107	15 c. Nauruan wrestling (23.5)	35	15
108	20 c. Snaring Frigate Birds (23.5)	50	20
109	25 c. Nauruan girl (25.7)	50	25
110	30 c. Catching Noddy Birds (25.7)	85	40
111	50 c. Great Frigate Birds (25.7)	1·50	75
112	$1 Type **33**	1·75	75
99/112	*Set of* 14	7·00	3·00

The 1 to 5 c. show flowers, and the 7, 8, 10, 30, 50 c. are horiz designs.

*This is the local release date but the Crown Agents issued the stamps on 21 March.

34 Co-op Store **35** Phosphate Mining

(Des G. Vasarhelyi. Litho Format)

1973 (20 Dec). *50th Anniv of Nauru Co-operative Society. T* **34** *and similar multicoloured designs. P* 14 × 14½ *(50 c.) or* 14½ × 14 *(others).*

113	5 c. Type **34**	20	30
114	25 c. Timothy Detudamo (founder)	20	15
115	50 c. N.C.S. trademark (*vert*)	45	55
113/15	*Set of* 3	75	90

(Des G. Vasarhelyi (7 c. from original by J. Mason; 10 c. from original by K. Depaune). Litho Format)

1974 (21 May). *175th Anniv of First Contact with the Outside World. T* **35** *and similar horiz designs. Multicoloured. P* 13 × 13½ *(7, 35, 50 c.) or* 13½ × 13 *(others).*

116	7 c. M.V. *Eigamoiya* (bulk carrier)	1·25	90
117	10 c. Type **29**	1·00	25
118	15 c. Fokker Friendship *Nauru Chief*	1·00	30
119	25 c. Nauruan chief in early times	1·25	35
120	35 c. Capt. Fearn and H.M.S. *Hunter*	5·50	2·50
121	50 c. H.M.S. *Hunter* off Nauru	2·50	1·40
116/121	*Set of* 6	11·00	5·25

The 7, 35 and 50 c. are larger, 70 × 22 mm.

36 Map of Nauru **37** Rev. P. A. Delaporte

(Des G. Vasarhelyi. Litho Format)

1974 (23 July). *Centenary of Universal Postal Union. T* **36** *and similar multicoloured designs. P* 13½ × 14 *(5 c.),* 13 × 13½ *($1) or* 13½ × 13 *(others).*

122	5 c. Type **36**	20	20
123	8 c. Nauru Post Office	20	20
124	20 c. Nauruan postman	20	10
125	$1 U.P.U. Building and Nauruan flag	50	60
122/5	*Set of* 4	1·00	1·00
MS126	157 × 105 mm. Nos. 122/5. Imperf	3·50	5·50

The 8 and 20 c. are horiz (33 × 21 mm), and the $1 is vert (21 × 33 mm).

(Des J.W. Litho Format)

1974 (10 Dec). *Christmas and 75th Anniv of Rev. Delaporte's Arrival. P* 14½.

127	**37**	15 c. multicoloured	20	20
128		20 c. multicoloured	30	30

38 Map of Nauru, Lump of Phosphate Rock and Albert Ellis **39** Micronesian Outrigger

(Des M. and Sylvia Goaman. Litho Format)

1975 (23 July). *Phosphate Mining Anniversaries. T* **38** *and similar horiz designs. Multicoloured. P* 14½ × 14.

129	5 c. Type **38**	20	20
130	7 c. Coolies and mine	25	25
131	15 c. Electric railway, barges and ship	65	65
132	25 c. Modern ore extraction	80	80
129/32	*Set of* 4	1·75	1·75

Anniversaries:—5 c. 75th Anniv of discovery; 7 c. 70th Anniv of Mining Agreement; 15 c. 55th Anniv of British Phosphate Commissioners; 25 c. 5th Anniv of Nauru Phosphate Corporation.

(Des M. and Sylvia Goaman. Litho Format)

1975 (1 Sept). *South Pacific Commission Conference, Nauru (1st issue). T* **39** *and similar horiz designs. Multicoloured. P* 13½ × 14.

133	20 c. Type **39**	50	40
	a. Block of 4. Nos. 133/6	1·75	
134	20 c. Polynesian double-hull	50	40
135	20 c. Melanesian outrigger	50	40
136	20 c. Polynesian outrigger	50	40
133/6	*Set of* 4	1·75	1·40

Nos. 133/6 were printed in *se-tenant* blocks of four throughout the sheet.

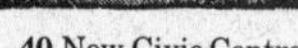

40 New Civic Centre **41** "Our Lady" (Yaren Church)

(Des M. and Sylvia Goaman. Litho Format)

1975 (29 Sept). *South Pacific Commission Conference, Nauru (2nd issue). T* **40** *and similar horiz design. Multicoloured. P* 14.

137	30 c. Type **40**	15	15
138	50 c. Domaneab (meeting-house)	30	30

(Des M. and Sylvia Goaman. Litho Format)

1975 (7 Nov). *Christmas. T* **41** *and similar vert design showing stained-glass window. Multicoloured. P* 14½ × 14.

139	5 c. Type **41**	10	10
140	7 c. "Suffer little children. . ." (Orro Church)	10	10
141	15 c. As 7 c.	15	15
142	25 c. Type **41**	25	25
139/42	*Set of* 4	45	45

42 Flowers floating towards Nauru

(Des M. and Sylvia Goaman. Litho Format)

1976 (31 Jan*). *30th Anniv of the Return from Truk. T* **42** *and similar horiz designs. Multicoloured. P* 14½.

143	10 c. Type **42**	10	10
144	14 c. Nauru encircled by garland	10	10
145	25 c. Finsch's Reed Warbler and maps	25	25
146	40 c. Return of the islanders	35	35
143/6	*Set of* 4	65	65

*This is the local date of issue; the Crown Agents released the stamps one day earlier.

43 3d. and 9d. Stamps of 1916

(Des M. and Sylvia Goaman. Litho Format)

1976 (6 May). *60th Anniv of Nauruan Stamps. T* **43** *and similar horiz designs. Multicoloured. P* 13½.

147	10 c. Type **43**	15	15
148	15 c. 6d. and 1s. stamps	20	15
149	25 c. 2s. 6d. stamp	30	25
150	50 c. 5s. "Specimen" stamp	40	35
147/50	*Set of* 4	95	80

Nos. 147/8 show stamps with errors: the 3d. "Short N" and the 6d. "P" for "R".

44 *Pandanus mei* and *Enna G* (cargo liner)

(Des M. and Sylvia Goaman. Litho Format)

1976 (26 July). *South Pacific Forum, Nauru. T* **44** *and similar horiz designs. Multicoloured. P* 13½.

151	10 c. Type **44**	15	10
152	20 c. *Tournefortia argentea* and Nauruan aircraft	20	15
153	30 c. *Thespesia populnea* and Nauru Tracking Station	25	15
154	40 c. *Cordia subcordata* and produce	35	25
151/4	*Set of* 4	85	60

45 Nauruan Choir **46** Nauru House and Coral Pinnacles

(Des G. Vasarhelyi. Litho Format)

1976 (17 Nov). *Christmas. T* **45** *and similar vert designs. Multicoloured. P* 13½.

155	15 c. Type **45**	10	10
	a. Horiz pair. Nos. 155/6	20	20
156	15 c. Nauruan choir	10	10
157	20 c. Angel in white dress	15	15
	a. Horiz pair. Nos. 157/8	30	30
158	20 c. Angel in red dress	15	15
155/8	*Set of* 4	50	50

Nos. 155/6 and 157/8 were printed horizontally *se-tenant* throughout the sheet, both forming composite designs.

(Des D. Gentleman. Photo Harrison)

1977 (25 Apr*). *Opening of Nauru House, Melbourne. T* **46** *and similar vert design. Multicoloured. P* 14.
159 15 c. Type **46** 15 15
160 30 c. Nauru House and Melbourne skyline 25 25
*This is the local release date. The London agency released the stamps on 14 April.

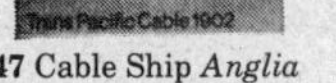

47 Cable Ship *Anglia* **48** Father Kayser and First Catholic Church

(Des D. Gentleman. Photo Harrison)

1977 (7 Sept). *75th Anniv of First Trans-Pacific Cable and 20th Anniv of First Artificial Earth Satellite. T* **47** *and similar vert designs. P* 14 × 14½.
161 7 c. multicoloured 20 10
162 15 c. light blue, grey and black 25 15
163 20 c. light blue, grey and black 25 15
164 25 c. multicoloured 25 15
161/4 *Set of* 4 85 45
Designs:—15 c. Tracking station, Nauru; 20 c. Stern of *Anglia*; 25 c. Dish aerial.

(Des D. Gentleman. Photo Harrison)

1977 (28 Nov). *Christmas. T* **48** *and similar vert designs. Multicoloured. P* 14½.
165 15 c. Type **48** 10 10
166 25 c. Congregational Church, Orro 15 15
167 30 c. Catholic Church, Arubo 15 15
165/7 *Set of* 3 30 30
No. 165 also commemorates the 75th anniversary of the Catholic Church on Nauru.

= 4c

49 Arms of Nauru (**50**)

(Des G. Vasarhelyi. Litho Format)

1978 (31 Jan). *Tenth Anniv of Independence. P* 14½.
168 **49** 15 c. multicoloured 10 10
169 60 c. multicoloured 20 20

1978 (29 Mar). *Nos. 159/60 surch as T* **50** *by Format.*
170 4 c. on 15 c. Type **46** 2·50 4·50
171 5 c. on 15 c. Type **46** 2·50 4·50
172 8 c. on 30 c. No. 160 2·50 4·50
173 10 c. on 30 c. No. 160 2·50 4·50
170/3 *Set of* 4 9·00 16·00

51 Collecting Shellfish **52** A.P.U. Emblem

(Des D. Gentleman. Photo Harrison)

1978 (17 May)–**79**. *Horiz designs as T* **51** *in brown, blue and black (4 c.), grey, black and light blue (20 c., $5) or multicoloured (others). P* 14½.
174 1 c. Type **51** 10 10
175 2 c. Coral outcrop (6.6.79) 15 10
176 3 c. Reef scene (6.6.79) 15 10
177 4 c. Girl with fish (6.6.79) 15 10
178 5 c. Eastern Reef Heron (6.6.79) 30 10
179 7 c. Catching fish, Buada Lagoon 15 10
180 10 c. Ijuw Lagoon 15 15
181 15 c. Girl framed by coral 15 20
182 20 c. Pinnacles, Anibare Bay reef 25 25
183 25 c. Pinnacle at Meneng 30 30
184 30 c. Head of Great Frigate Bird 60 35
185 32 c. White-capped Noddy in coconut palm 75 35
186 40 c. Wandering Tattler 90 45
187 50 c. Great Frigate Birds on perch 75 45
188 $1 Old coral pinnacles at Topside 70 55
189 $2 New pinnacles at Topside 95 1·00
190 $5 Blackened pinnacles at Topside 1·75 2·25
174/90 *Set of* 17 7·50 6·00

(Litho Toppan Ptg Co, Ltd)

1978 (28 Aug). *14th General Assembly of Asian Parliamentarians' Union. T* **52** *and similar vert design. P* 13.
191 15 c. multicoloured 20 25
192 20 c. black, deep ultramarine and gold 20 25
Design:—20 c. As T **52** but different background.

53 Virgin and Child **54** Baden-Powell and Cub Scout

(Des R. Vigurs. Litho Format)

1978 (1 Nov). *Christmas. T* **53** *and similar multicoloured design. P* 14.
193 7 c. Type **53** 10 10
194 15 c. Angel in sun-rise scene (*horiz*) 10 10
195 20 c. As 15 c. 15 15
196 30 c. Type **53** 20 20
193/6 *Set of* 4 40 40

(Des J. Charles. Litho Format)

1978 (1 Dec). *70th Anniv of Boy Scout Movement. T* **54** *and similar horiz designs. Multicoloured. P* 13½.
197 20 c. Type **54** 20 15
198 30 c. Baden-Powell and Boy Scout 25 20
199 50 c. Baden-Powell and Rover Scout 35 30
197/9 *Set of* 3 70 60

55 Wright *Flyer* over Nauru

(Des D. Gentleman. Litho Format)

1979 (24 Jan). *Flight Anniversaries. T* **55** *and similar horiz designs. Multicoloured. P* 14.
200 10 c. Type **55** 10 10
201 15 c. *Southern Cross* superimposed on nose of Boeing "727" 15 15
a. Pair. Nos. 201/2 30 30
202 15 c. *Southern Cross* and Boeing "727" (front view) 15 15
203 30 c. Wright *Flyer* over Nauru airfield 20 20
200/3 *Set of* 4 55 55
Commemorations:—10, 30 c. 75th anniversary of powered flight; 15 c. 50th anniversary of Kingsford-Smith's Pacific flight.
Nos. 201/2 were printed together, *se-tenant*, in horizontal and vertical pairs throughout the sheet.

56 Sir Rowland Hill and Marshall Islands 10 pf. Stamp of 1901

(Des R. Granger Barrett. Litho Format)

1979 (27 Feb). *Death Centenary of Sir Rowland Hill. T* **56** *and similar horiz designs showing stamps and Sir Rowland Hill. Multicoloured. P* 14½.
204 5 c. Type **56** 10 10
a. Imperf (pair) £375
205 15 c. "NAURU" opt on Great Britain 10s. "Seahorse" of 1916–23 20 20
a. Imperf (pair) £375
206 60 c. 1978 10th Anniversary of Independence 60 c. commemorative 40 40
a. Imperf (pair)
204/6 *Set of* 3 60 60
MS207 159 × 101 mm. Nos. 204/6 85 1·10
a. Error. Imperf £650

57 Dish Antenna, Transmitting Station and Radio Mast **58** Smiling Child

(Des G. Vasarhelyi. Litho Format)

1979 (22 Aug). *50th Anniv of International Consultative Radio Committee. T* **57** *and similar horiz designs. Multicoloured. P* 14½.
208 7 c. Type **57** 10 10
209 32 c. Telex operator 20 15
210 40 c. Radio operator 25 15
208/10 *Set of* 3 40 30

(Des G. Vasarhelyi. Litho Format)

1979 (3 Oct). *International Year of the Child. T* **58** *and similar vert designs showing smiling children. P* 14½.
211 8 c. multicoloured 10 10
a. Horiz strip of 5. Nos. 211/15 70
212 15 c. multicoloured 15 15
213 25 c. multicoloured 20 20
214 32 c. multicoloured 20 20
215 50 c. multicoloured 25 25
211/15 *Set of* 5 70 70
Nos. 211/15 were printed together, *se-tenant*, in horizontal strips of 5 throughout the sheet, forming a composite design.

59 Ekwenababae (flower), Scroll inscribed "Peace on Earth" and Star

(Des G. Vasarhelyi. Litho Format)

1979 (14 Nov). *Christmas. T* **59** *and similar horiz designs. Multicoloured. P* 14½.
216 7 c. Type **59** 10 10
217 15 c. *Thespia populnea* (flower), scroll inscribed "Goodwill toward Men" and star 10 10
218 20 c. Denea (flower), scroll inscribed "Peace on Earth" and star 10 10
219 30 c. Erekogo (flower), scroll inscribed "Goodwill toward Men" and star 20 20
216/19 *Set of* 4 40 40

60 Dassult "Falcon" over Melbourne

(Des G. Vasarhelyi. Litho Format)

1980 (28 Feb). *10th Anniv of Air Nauru. T* **60** *and similar horiz designs. Multicoloured. P* 14½.
220 15 c. Type **60** 25 15
221 20 c. Fokker "F28 (Fellowship)" over Tarawa 30 15
222 25 c. Boeing "727" over Hong Kong 30 15
223 30 c. Boeing "737" over Auckland 30 15
220/3 *Set of* 4 1·00 55

61 Steam Locomotive

(Des G. Vasarhelyi. Litho Format)

1980 (6 May). *10th Anniv of Nauru Phosphate Corporation. Railway Locomotives. T* **61** *and similar horiz designs. Multicoloured. P* 14½.
224 8 c. Type **61** 10 10
225 32 c. Electric locomotives 20 20
226 60 c. Diesel locomotive 35 35
224/6 *Set of* 3 60 60
MS227 168 × 118 mm. Nos. 224/6. P 13 1·10 1·40
No. **MS**227 also commemorates the "London 1980" International Stamp Exhibition.

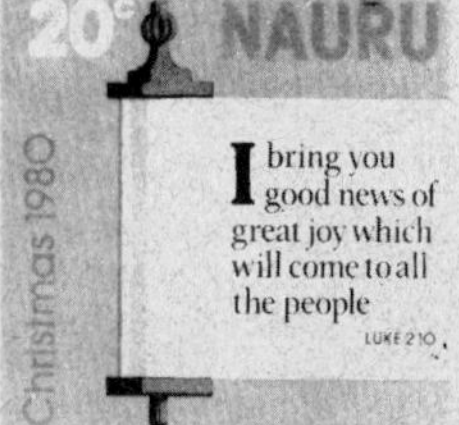

62 Verse 10 from Luke, Chapter 2 in English

(Des C. Abbott. Litho Format)

1980 (24 Sept). *Christmas. T* **62** *and similar square designs showing verses from Luke, chapter 2. Multicoloured. P* 14½.

228	20 c. Type **62**	10	10
	a. Horiz pair. Nos. 228/9	20	20
229	20 c. Verse 10 in Nauruan	10	10
230	30 c. Verse 14 in English	15	15
	a. Horiz pair. Nos. 230/1	30	30
231	30 c. Verse 14 in Nauruan	15	15
228/31	*Set of* 4	50	50

Nos. 228/9 and 230/1 were each printed together, *se-tenant*, in horizontal pairs throughout the sheet.

See also Nos. 248/51.

63 Nauruan, Australian, Union and New Zealand Flags on Aerial View of Nauru

(Des H. Woods. Litho Format)

1980 (3 Dec)–81. *20th Anniv of U.N. Declaration on the Granting of Independence to Colonial Countries and Peoples. T* **63** *and similar multicoloured designs. P* 14½ (25 *c.*) *or* 13½ (*others*).

232	25 c. Type **63**	15	15
233	30 c. U.N. Trusteeship Council (72 × 23 *mm*) (11.2.81)	15	15
234	50 c. Nauru independence ceremony, 1968 (72 × 23 *mm*)	25	25
232/4	*Set of* 3	50	50

The 25 c. value was printed in sheets including 5 *se-tenant* stamp-size labels; the other two values were each printed in sheets including 5 *se-tenant* half stamp-size labels.

64 Timothy Detudamo

(Des R. Granger Barrett. Litho Format)

1981 (11 Feb). *30th Anniv of Nauru Local Government Council. Head Chiefs. T* **64** *and similar horiz designs. Multicoloured. P* 14½.

235	20 c. Type **64**	15	15
236	30 c. Raymond Gadabu	15	15
237	50 c. Hammer DeRoburt	25	25
235/7	*Set of* 3	50	50

65 Casting Net by Hand

(Litho Questa)

1981 (22 May). *Fishing. T* **65** *and similar horiz designs. Multicoloured. P* 12 × 11½.

238	8 c. Type **65**	10	10
239	20 c. Outrigger canoe	20	15
240	32 c. Outboard motor boat	25	20
241	40 c. Trawler	30	25
238/41	*Set of* 4	75	60
MS242	167 × 116 mm. No. 241 × 4. P 14	1·90	2·00

No. **MS**242 was issued to commemorate the "WIPA 1981" International Stamp Exhibition, Vienna.

66 Bank of Nauru Emblem and Building **67** Inaugural Speech

(Des H. Woods. Litho Harrison)

1981 (21 July). *Fifth Anniv of Bank of Nauru. P* 14 × 14½.

243 **66**	$1 multicoloured	60	60

(Des G. Vasarhelyi. Litho Questa)

1981 (24 Oct). *U.N. Day. E.S.C.A.P. (United Nations Economic and Social Commission for Asia and the Pacific) Events. T* **67** *and similar square designs. Multicoloured. P* 14 × 14½.

244	15 c. Type **67**	15	15
245	20 c. Presenting credentials	15	15
246	25 c. Unveiling plaque	20	20
247	30 c. Raising U.N. flag	25	25
244/7	*Set of* 4	65	65

(Des C. Abbott. Litho Format)

1981 (14 Nov). *Christmas. Bible Verses. Square designs as T* **62.** *Multicoloured. P* 14½.

248	20 c. Matthew 1, 23 in English	15	15
	a. Horiz pair. Nos. 248/9	30	30
249	20 c. Matthew 1, 23 in Nauruan	15	15
250	30 c. Luke 2, 11 in English	20	20
	a. Horiz pair. Nos. 250/1	40	40
251	30 c. Luke 2, 11 in Nauruan	20	20
248/51	*Set of* 4	70	70

Nos. 248/9 and 250/1 were each printed together, *se-tenant*, in horizontal pairs throughout the sheet.

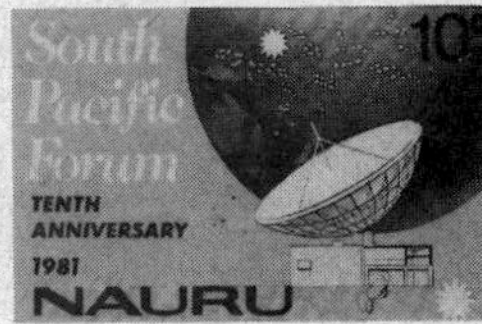

68 Earth Satellite Station

(Des M. Rickards. Litho Format)

1981 (9 Dec). *Tenth Anniv of South Pacific Forum. T* **68** *and similar horiz designs. Multicoloured. P* 13½ × 14.

252	10 c. Type **68**	20	20
253	20 c. *Enna G* (cargo liner)	25	25
254	30 c. Airliner	30	30
255	40 c. Local produce	40	40
252/5	*Set of* 4	1·00	1·00

69 Nauru Scouts leaving for 1935 Frankston Scout Jamboree

(Des C. Abbott. Litho Format)

1982 (23 Feb). *75th Anniv of Boy Scout Movement. T* **69** *and similar multicoloured designs. P* 14.

256	7 c. Type **69**	15	15
257	8 c. Two Nauru scouts on *Nauru Chief*, 1935 (*vert*)	15	15
258	15 c. Nauru scouts making pottery, 1935 (*vert*)	20	20
259	20 c. Lord Huntingfield addressing Nauru scouts, Frankston Jamboree, 1935	25	25
260	25 c. Nauru cub and scout, 1982	30	30
261	40 c. Nauru cubs, scouts and scouters, 1982	45	45
256/61	*Set of* 6	1·40	1·40
MS262	152 × 114 mm. Nos. 256/61. Imperf	1·40	1·50

No. **MS**262 also commemorates Nauru's participation in the "Stampex" National Stamp Exhibition, London.

Nos. 256/61 were each printed in sheets including four *se-tenant* stamp-size labels.

70 100kw Electricity Generating Plant under Construction (left side)

(Litho Irish Security Stamp Printing Ltd)

1982 (10 June). *Ocean Thermal Energy Conversion. T* **70** *and similar horiz designs. Multicoloured. P* 13½.

263	25 c. Type **70**	40	30
	a. Horiz pair. Nos. 263/4	80	60
264	25 c. 100kw Electricity Generating Plant under construction (right side)	40	30
265	40 c. Completed plant (left)	55	40
	a. Horiz pair. Nos. 265/6	1·10	80
266	40 c. Completed plant (right)	55	40
263/6	*Set of* 4	1·75	1·25

Nos. 263/4 and 265/6 were printed together, *se-tenant*, in horizontal pairs forming composite designs throughout sheets which also included two stamp-size and twelve half stamp-size labels.

71 S.S. *Fido*

72 Queen Elizabeth II on Horseback

(Des R. Littleford (5 c.), Debbie Ryder (10, 30 c.), Cecilia Eales (60 c.), Jane Evans ($1). Litho Format)

1982 (11 Oct). *75th Anniv of Phosphate Shipments. T* **71** *and similar horiz designs. Multicoloured. P* 14.

267	5 c. Type **71**	25	10
268	10 c. Steam locomotive *Nellie*	45	15
269	30 c. Modern "Clyde" class diesel loco	70	35
270	60 c. M.V. *Eigamoiya* (bulk carrier)	90	60
267/70	*Set of* 4	2·10	1·10
MS271	165 × 107 mm. $1 *Eigamoiya, Rosie-D* and *Kolle-D* (bulk carriers) (67 × 27 *mm*)	1·00	1·25

No. **MS**271 was issued to commemorate "ANPEX 82" National Stamp Exhibition, Brisbane.

(Des G. Vasarhelyi. Litho Format)

1982 (21 Oct). *Royal Visit. T* **72** *and similar multicoloured designs. P* 14½.

272	20 c. Type **72**	30	30
273	50 c. Prince Philip, Duke of Edinburgh	60	60
274	$1 Queen Elizabeth II and Prince Philip (*horiz*)	1·25	1·25
272/4	*Set of* 3	1·90	1·90

73 Father Bernard Lahn **74** Speaker of the Nauruan Parliament

(Des G. Vasarhelyi. Litho Format)

1982 (17 Nov). *Christmas. T* **73** *and similar horiz designs. Multicoloured. P* 14½.

275	20 c. Type **73**	30	30
276	30 c. Reverend Itubwa Amram	35	40
277	40 c. Pastor James Aingimen	40	50
278	50 c. Bishop Paul Mea	45	70
275/8	*Set of* 4	1·40	1·75

Nos. 275/8 were printed in sheets of 25 including 5 *se-tenant*, stamp-size, labels.

(Des G. Vasarhelyi. Litho Walsall)

1983 (23 Mar). *15th Anniv of Independence. T* **74** *and similar multicoloured designs. W* w **14** (*sideways on* 30, 50 *c.*). *P* 14.

279	15 c. Type **74**	15	15
280	20 c. Family Court in session	20	20
281	30 c. Law Courts building (*horiz*)	25	25
282	50 c. Parliamentary chamber (*horiz*)	40	40
279/82	*Set of* 4	90	90

75 Nauru Satellite Earth Station

(Des C. Abbott. Litho Questa)

1983 (11 May). *World Communications Year. T* **75** *and similar horiz designs. Multicoloured. W* w **14** (*sideways*). *P* 14.

283	5 c. Type **75**	10	10
284	10 c. Omni-directional range installation	15	15
285	20 c. Emergency short-wave radio	20	25
286	25 c. Radio Nauru control room	30	30
287	40 c. Unloading air mail	45	45
283/7	*Set of* 5	1·00	1·10

76 Return of Exiles from Truk on M.V. *Trienza*, 1946 **77** "The Holy Virgin, the Holy Child and St. John" (School of Raphael)

(Des D. Slater. Litho Format)

1983 (14 Sept). *Angam Day. T* **76** *and similar multicoloured designs. W* w **14** (*sideways on* 15 *c.*). *P* 13½ (15 *c.*) *or* 14 (*others*).

288	15 c. Type **76**	20	25
289	20 c. Mrs. Elsie Agio (exile community leader)	20	25
290	30 c. Child on scales	35	40
291	40 c. Nauruan children	45	50
288/91	*Set of* 4	1·10	1·25

Nos. 289/91 are vertical designs, each 25 × 41 mm.

(Des L. Curtis. Litho Questa)

1983 (16 Nov). *Christmas. T* **77** *and similar multicoloured designs.* W w **14** (*sideways on* 50 *c.*). *P* 14 × 14½ (50 *c.*) *or* 14½ × 14 (*others*).

292 5 c. Type **77** . . 10 10

293 15 c. "Madonna on the Throne surrounded by Angels" (School of Seville) . . 15 15

294 50 c. "The Mystical Betrothal of St. Catherine with Jesus" (School of Veronese) (*horiz*) 40 40

292/4 . . *Set of* 3 55 55

78 S.S. *Ocean Queen* **79** 1974 U.P.U. $1 Stamp

(Des Beverley Barnard and L. Curtis. Litho Questa)

1984 (23 May). *250th Anniv of "Lloyd's List" (newspaper). T* **78** *and similar vert designs. Multicoloured.* W w **14**. *P* 14½ × 14.

295 20 c. Type **78** . . 40 30

296 25 c. M.V. *Enna G* . . 45 35

297 30 c. M.V. *Baron Minto* . . 50 40

298 40 c. Sinking of M.V. *Triadic*, 1940 . . 65 55

295/8 . . *Set of* 4 1·75 1·40

(Des L. Curtis. Litho Format)

1984 (4 June). *Universal Postal Union Congress, Hamburg.* W w **14**. *P* 14.

299 **79** $1 multicoloured . . 1·10 1·25

80 Female Common Eggfly

(Des I. Loe. Litho B.D.T.)

1984 (24 July). *Butterflies. T* **80** *and similar horiz designs. Multicoloured.* W w **14** (*sideways*). *P* 14.

300 25 c. Type **80** . . 40 40

301 30 c. Male Common Eggfly . . 45 45

302 50 c. Wanderer . . 70 75

300/2 . . *Set of* 3 1·40 1·40

81 Coastal Scene **82** Buada Chapel

(Des A. Theobald. Litho Enschedé)

1984 (21 Sept). *Life in Nauru. T* **81** *and similar multicoloured designs.* W w **14** (*sideways on horiz designs*). *P* 13½ × 14 (1, 5, 10, 25, 40 *c.*, $2) *or* 14 × 13½ (*others*).

303 1 c. Type **81** . . 10 10

304 3 c. Nauruan woman (*vert*) . . 10 10

305 5 c. Modern trawler . . 10 10

306 10 c. Golfer on the links . . 10 10

307 15 c. Excavating phosphate (*vert*) . . 10 15

308 20 c. Surveyor (*vert*) . . 15 20

309 25 c. Air Nauru airliner . . 20 25

310 30 c. Elderly Nauruan (*vert*) . . 25 30

311 40 c. Loading hospital patient on to aircraft . . 35 40

312 50 c. Skin-diver with fish (*vert*) . . 40 45

313 $1 Tennis player (*vert*) . . 85 90

314 $2 Anabar Lagoon . . 1·60 1·75

303/14 . . *Set of* 12 3·75 4·25

Nos. 303/14 were each issued in sheets of 9 with decorative margins.

(Des L. Curtis. Litho Format)

1984 (14 Nov). *Christmas. T* **82** *and similar multicoloured designs.* W w **14** (*sideways on* 50 *c.*). *P* 14.

315 30 c. Type **82** . . 60 50

316 40 c. Detudamo Memorial Church . . 80 65

317 50 c. Candle-light service, Kayser College (*horiz*) . . 90 70

315/17 . . *Set of* 3 2·10 1·75

83 Air Nauru Jet on Tarmac

(Des L. Curtis. Litho Walsall)

1985 (26 Feb). *15th Anniv of Air Nauru. T* **83** *and similar multicoloured designs.* W w **14** (*sideways on* 20 *c.*, 40 *c.*). *P* 14.

318 20 c. Type **83** . . 55 35

319 30 c. Stewardess on aircraft steps (*vert*) . . 70 60

320 40 c. Fokker "F28" over Nauru . . 85 75

321 50 c. Freight being loaded onto Boeing "727" (*vert*) . . 1·00 85

318/21 . . *Set of* 4 2·75 2·25

84 Open Cut Mining **85** Mother and Baby on Beach

(Des L. Curtis. Litho B.D.T.)

1985 (31 July). *15th Anniv of Nauru Phosphate Corporation. T* **84** *and similar horiz designs. Multicoloured.* W w **14** (*sideways*). *P* 14.

322 20 c. Type **84** . . 55 55

323 25 c. Locomotive hauling crushed ore . . 70 70

324 30 c. Phosphate drying plant . . 70 70

325 50 c. Early steam locomotive . . 1·25 1·25

322/5 . . *Set of* 4 3·00 3·00

(Des A. Theobald. Litho Questa)

1985 (15 Nov). *Christmas. T* **85** *and similar vert design. Multicoloured.* W w **16** (*sideways*). *P* 14.

326 50 c. Beach scene . . 1·00 1·00

a. Horiz pair. Nos. 326/7 . . 2·00 2·00

327 50 c. Type **85** . . 1·00 1·00

Nos. 326/7 were printed in sheets of 16 made up of two strips of four *se-tenant* pairs, each pair forming a composite design. The two strips were divided by a horizontal gutter.

86 Adult Common Noddy with Juvenile

(Des N. Arlott. Litho Questa)

1985 (31 Dec). *Birth Bicentenary of John J. Audubon (ornithologist). Common "Brown" Noddy. T* **86** *and similar horiz designs. Multicoloured.* W w **16**. *P* 14.

328 10 c. Type **86** . . 35 35

329 20 c. Adult and immature birds in flight . . 50 50

330 30 c. Adults in flight . . 65 65

331 50 c. "Brown Noddy" (John J. Audubon) . . 80 80

328/31 . . *Set of* 4 2·10 2·10

87 Douglas Motor Cycle

(Des M. Joyce. Litho Questa)

1986 (5 Mar). *Early Transport on Nauru. T* **87** *and similar horiz designs. Multicoloured.* W w **16**. *P* 14.

332 15 c. Type **87** . . 40 40

333 20 c. Primitive lorry . . 50 50

334 30 c. German 2 ft gauge locomotive (1910) . . 65 65

335 40 c. "Baby" Austin car . . 75 75

332/5 . . *Set of* 4 2·10 2·10

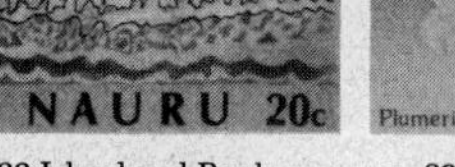

88 Island and Bank of Nauru **89** *Plumeria rubra*

(Des G. Vasarhelyi. Litho Format)

1986 (21 July). *10th Anniv of Bank of Nauru. Children's Paintings. T* **88** *and similar horiz designs. Multicoloured.* W w **16** (*sideways*). *P* 14.

336 20 c. Type **88** . . 30 30

337 25 c. Borrower with notes and coins . . 35 35

338 30 c. Savers . . 40 40

339 40 c. Customers at bank counter . . 55 55

336/9 . . *Set of* 4 1·40 1·40

(Des Doreen McGuinness. Litho Questa)

1986 (30 Sept). *Flowers. T* **89** *and similar horiz designs. Multicoloured.* W w **16**. *P* 14.

340 20 c. Type **89** . . 50 50

341 25 c. *Tristellateia australis* . . 60 60

342 30 c. *Bougainvillea cultivar* . . 70 70

343 40 c. *Delonix regia* . . 85 85

340/3 . . *Set of* 4 2·40 2·40

90 Carol Singers **91** Young Girls Dancing

(Des M. Joyce. Litho Questa)

1986 (8 Dec). *Christmas. T* **90** *and similar horiz design. Multicoloured.* W w **16** (*sideways*). *P* 14.

344 20 c. Type **90** . . 45 30

345 $1 Carol singers and hospital patient . . 2·00 1·75

(Des Joan Thompson. Litho Questa)

1987 (31 Jan). *Nauruan Dancers. T* **91** *and similar multicoloured designs.* W w **16** (*sideways on* 20, 30 *c.*). *P* 14.

346 20 c. Type **91** . . 30 25

347 30 c. Stick dance . . 45 50

348 50 c. Boy doing war dance (*vert*) . . 65 80

346/8 . . *Set of* 3 1·25 1·40

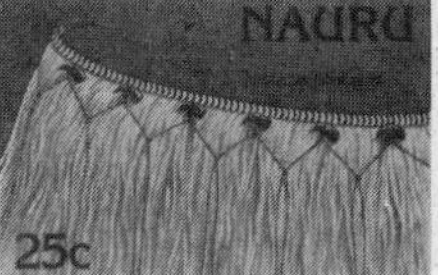

92 Hibiscus Fibre Skirt **93** U.P.U. Emblem and Air Mail Label

(Des L. Curtis. Litho B.D.T.)

1987 (30 July). *Personal Artifacts. T* **92** *and similar horiz designs. Multicoloured.* W w **16** (*sideways*). *P* 14.

349 25 c. Type **92** . . 45 45

350 30 c. Headband and necklets . . 50 50

351 45 c. Decorative necklets . . 70 70

352 60 c. Pandanus leaf fan . . 95 95

349/52 . . *Set of* 4 2·40 2·40

(Des D. Miller. Litho Format)

1987 (20 Oct). *World Post Day. T* **93** *and similar multicoloured design.* W w **16**. *P* 14½×14.

353 40 c. Type **93** . . 65 65

MS354 122×82 mm. $1 U.P.U. emblem and map of Pacific showing mail routes (114×74 *mm*). Wmk sideways. Imperf . . 1·25 1·40

94 Open Bible **95** Nauruan Children's Party

(Des Janet Boschen. Litho Walsall)

1987 (5 Nov). *Centenary of Nauru Congregational Church.* W w **14**. *P* 13×13½.

355 **94** 40 c. multicoloured . . 65 65

(Des M. Joyce. Litho Format)

1987 (27 Nov). *Christmas. T* **95** *and similar horiz design. Multicoloured.* W w **16** (*sideways*). *P* 14.

356 20 c. Type **95** . . 40 25

357 $1 Nauruan Christmas dinner . . 1·75 1·50

96 Loading Phosphate on Ship **97** Map of German Marshall Is. and 1901 5 m. Yacht Definitive

(Des B. Clinton. Litho CPE Australia Ltd, Melbourne)

1988 (31 Jan). *20th Anniv of Independence. T* **96** *and similar multicoloured designs. P* 13½×14 (25 *c.*), 14×13½ (40, 55 *c.*) *or* 13 ($1).

358 25 c. Type **96** . . 45 45

359 40 c. Tomano flower (*vert*) . . 70 70

360 55 c. Frigate Bird (*vert*) . . 1·00 1·00

361 $1 Arms of Republic (35×35 *mm*) . . 1·25 1·50

358/61 . . *Set of* 4 3·00 3·25

(Des O. Bell. Litho Format)

1988 (29 July). *80th Anniv of Nauru Post Office. T* **97** *and similar horiz designs. Multicoloured. W w* **16** *(sideways). P* 14.

362	30 c. Type **97**	30	35
363	50 c. Letter and post office of 1908	50	55
364	70 c. Nauru Post Office and airmail letter	65	70
362/4	*Set of* 3	1·25	1·40

98 "Itubwer" (mat)

99 U.P.U. Emblem and National Flag

(Des Jennifer Toombs. Litho CPE Australia Ltd, Melbourne)

1988 (1 Aug). *String Figures. T* **98** *and similar horiz designs. Multicoloured. P* 13½ × 14.

365	25 c. Type **98**	25	30
366	40 c. "Etegerer–the Pursuer"	40	45
367	55 c. "Holding up the Sky"	50	55
368	80 c. "Manujie's Sword"	75	80
365/8	*Set of* 4	1·75	1·90

(Des Elisabeth Innes. Litho CPE Australia Ltd, Melbourne)

1988 (1 Oct). *Centenary of Nauru's Membership of Universal Postal Union. P* 13½ × 14.

369	**99** $1 multicoloured	95	1·00

100 "Hark the Herald Angels"

101 Logo (15th anniv of Nauru Insurance Corporation)

(Des Elisabeth Innes. Litho CPE Australia Ltd, Melbourne)

1988 (28 Nov). *Christmas. T* **100** *and similar square designs showing words and music from "Hark the Herald Angels Sing". P* 13.

370	20 c. black, orange-vermilion and lemon	20	25
371	60 c. black, orange-vermilion and mauve	55	60
372	$1 black, orange-vermilion & bright green	95	1·00
370/2	*Set of* 3	1·50	1·60

(Litho Note Ptg Branch, Reserve Bank of Australia)

1989 (19 Nov). *Anniversaries and Events. T* **101** *and similar vert designs. Multicoloured. P* 14×15.

373	15 c. Type **101**	15	20
374	50 c. Logos (World Telecommunications Day and 10th anniv of Asian Pacific Telecommunity)	50	55
375	$1 Photograph of island scene (150 years of photography)	95	1·00
376	$2 Capitol and U.P.U. emblem (20th U.P.U. Congress, Washington)	1·90	2·00
373/6	*Set of* 4	3·25	3·50

Nevis
see St. Kitts-Nevis

New Brunswick

PRICES FOR STAMPS ON COVER

Nos. 1/6	*from* × 2
Nos. 7/19	*from* × 3

1 Royal Crown and Heraldic Flowers of the United Kingdom

(Recess P.B.)

1851 (5 Sept). *Blue paper. Imperf.*

No.	Type		Unused	Used
1	1	3d. bright red	£1800	£300
2		3d. dull red	£2500	£300
		a. Bisected (1½d.) (on cover)	†	£2750
2*b*		6d. mustard-yellow	†	£2500
3		6d. yellow	£5000	£800
4		6d. olive-yellow	£4500	£700
		a. Bisected (3d.) (on cover)	†	£3000
		b. Quartered (1½d.) (on cover)	†	£15000
5		1s. reddish mauve	£16000	£5500
6		1s. dull mauve	£14000	£4500
		a. Bisected (6d.) (on cover)	†	£25000
		b. Quartered (3d.) (on cover)	†	£20000

Reprints of all three values were made in 1890 on thin, hard, white paper. The 3d. is bright orange, the 6d. and 1s. violet-black.

Nos. 2a and 4b were to make up the 7½d. rate.

2 Locomotive

3

3*a* Charles Connell

4

5

6 Paddle-steamer *Washington*

7 King Edward VII when Prince of Wales

(Recess A.B.N. Co)

1860 (15 May)–**1863.** *No wmk. P* 12.

No.	Type		Unused	Used
7	2	1 c. brown-purple	30·00	27·00
8		1 c. purple	17·00	18·00
9		1 c. dull claret	17·00	18·00
		a. Imperf between (horiz pair)	£500	
10	3	2 c. orange (1863)	11·00	14·00
11		2 c. orange-yellow	12·00	14·00
12		2 c. deep orange	11·00	14·00
		a. Imperf between (vert pair)	£450	
13	3*a*	5 c. brown	£2750	
14	4	5 c. yellow-green	12·00	12·00
15		5 c. deep green	12·00	12·00
16		5 c. sap-green (deep yellowish green)	£300	40·00
17	5	10 c. red	30·00	22·00
		a. Bisected (5 c.) (on cover) (1860)	†	£900
18	6	12½ c. indigo	50·00	40·00
19	7	17 c. black	30·00	27·00

Beware of forged cancellations.

In March, 1868, issues of the Dominion of Canada replaced those of New Brunswick.

Newfoundland

The first local postmaster, at St. John's, was appointed in 1805, the overseas mails being routed via Halifax, Nova Scotia. A regular packet service was established between these two ports in 1840, the British G.P.O. assuming control of the overseas mails at the same time.

The responsibility for the overseas postal service reverted to the colonial administration on 1 July 1851.

For illustrations of the handstamp types see BRITISH POST OFFICES ABROAD notes, following GREAT BRITAIN.

ST. JOHN'S

CROWNED-CIRCLE HANDSTAMPS

CC1 CC **1a** ST. JOHNS NEWFOUNDLAND (R.) (27.6.1846) . . *Price on cover* £900

PRICES FOR STAMPS ON COVER TO 1945

Nos. 1/24*e*	*from* × 2
Nos. 25/43	*from* × 3
Nos. 44/54	*from* × 4
Nos. 55/61	*from* × 5
Nos. 62/5*a*	*from* × 2
Nos. 66/79	*from* × 3
Nos. 80/1	*from* × 2
No. 82	—
Nos. 83/94	*from* × 5
Nos. 95/127	*from* × 2
Nos. 130/41	*from* × 3
Nos. 142/3	—
Nos. 144/8*f*	*from* × 2
Nos. 149/62	*from* × 3
No. 163	—
Nos. 164/78	*from* × 2
Nos. 179/90	*from* × 3
No. 191	—
Nos. 192/220	*from* × 2
No. 221	—
Nos. 222/9	*from* × 3
Nos. 230/4	*from* × 2
No. 235	—
Nos. 236/91	*from* × 2
Nos. D1/6	*from* × 10

1

2

4

3

5

Royal Crown and Heraldic flowers of the United Kingdom

(Recess P.B.)

1857 (1 Jan–15 Feb). *No wmk. Thick paper. Imperf.*

No.	Type		Unused	Used
1	1	1d. brown-purple	75·00	£120
		a. Bisected (½d.) (on cover)	†	£6500
2	2	2d. scarlet-vermilion (15 Feb)	£11000	£4500
3	3	3d. yellowish green	£300	£375
4	4	4d. scarlet-vermilion	£6000	£2500
		a. Bisected (2d.) (on cover)		
5	1	5d. brown-purple	£180	£300
6	4	6d. scarlet-vermilion	£11000	£2750
7	5	6½d. scarlet-vermilion	£2250	£2750
8	4	8d. scarlet-vermilion	£190	£200
		a. Bisected (4d.) (on cover)	†	£2500
9	2	1s. scarlet-vermilion	£14000	£3750
		a. Bisected (6d.) (on cover)	†	£9500

The 6d. and 8d. differ from the 4d. in many details, as does also the 1s. from the 2d.

1860 (Aug). *Medium paper. Imperf.*

No.	Type		Unused	Used
10	2	2d. orange-vermilion	£250	£300
11	3	3d. green *to* deep green*	45·00	£120
12	4	4d. orange-vermilion	£1400	£500
		a. Bisected (2d.) (on cover)	†	£7500
13	1	5d. Venetian red	50·00	£190
14	4	6d. orange-vermilion	£2500	£600
15	2	1s. orange-vermilion	£20000	£7000
		a. Bisected (6d.) (on cover)		

*No. 11 includes stamps from the November 1861 printing which are very difficult to distinguish.

The 1s. on horizontally or vertically *laid* paper is now considered to be a proof.

BISECTS. Collectors are warned against buying bisected stamps of these issues without a reliable guarantee.

1861. *New colours. Imperf. (a)* 1st *printing. Soft paper* (July).

No.	Type		Unused	Used
16	2	2d. deep rose-lake	£150	£475
17	4	4d. deep rose-lake	50·00	£170
		a. Bisected (2d.) (on cover)		
18		6d. deep rose-lake	50·00	£180
		a. Bisected (3d.) (on cover)		
19	5	6½d. deep rose-lake	£200	£500
20	2	1s. deep rose-lake	£225	£500
		a. Bisected (6d.) (on cover)	†	£13000
		(b) 2nd printing. Hard paper (Nov)		
21	1	1d. chocolate-brown	£100	£175
		a. Red-brown	£3500	
22	2	2d. pale rose-lake	£110	£350
23	4	4d. pale rose-lake	16·00	80·00
24	1	5d. chocolate-brown	30·00	£250
		a. Red-brown	25·00	£150
24*b*	4	6d. pale rose-lake	14·00	£100
24*c*	5	6½d. pale rose-lake	48·00	£325
24*d*	4	8d. pale rose-lake	48·00	£350
24*e*	2	1s. pale rose-lake	20·00	£170

Stamps of the second printing of the pale rose-lake shades have a more transparent look due to the paper being generally thinner, but paper thickness alone is not a sure test for distinguishing the printings.

Stamps of this issue may be found with part of the paper-maker's watermark "STACEY WISE 1858".

Beware of buying used specimens of the stamps which are worth much less in unused condition, as many unused stamps have been provided with faked postmarks. A guarantee should be obtained.

6 Codfish

7 Common Seal on Ice-floe

8 Prince Consort

9 Queen Victoria

10 Schooner

11 Queen Victoria

(Recess A.B.N. Co)

1865 (15 Nov)–**75.** *P* 12. *(a) Thin yellowish paper.*

No.	Type		Unused	Used
25	6	2 c. yellowish green	£120	28·00
		a. Bisected (1 c.) (on cover)	†	£3750
26	7	5 c. brown	£500	£190
		a. Bisected (2½ c.) (on cover)		
27	8	10 c. black	£225	48·00
		a. Bisected (5 c.) (on cover)	†	£2750
28	9	12 c. red-brown	£325	£150
		a. Bisected (6 c.) (on cover)		
29	10	13 c. orange-yellow	65·00	48·00
30	11	24 c. blue	32·00	32·00
		(b) Medium white paper		
31	6	2 c. bluish green (*to* deep) (1870)	60·00	26·00
32	8	10 c. black (1875)	£150	23·00
33	9	12 c. chestnut (1870)	35·00	35·00
33*a*	11	24 c. blue (1870?)	£400	£140

12 King Edward VII when Prince of Wales

14 Queen Victoria

I

II

In Type II the white oval frame line is unbroken by the scroll containing the words "ONE CENT", the letters "N.F." are smaller and closer to the scroll, and there are other minor differences.

(Recess National Bank Note Co, New York)

1868 (Nov). *P* 12.
34 **12** 1 c. dull purple (I) .. .. .. 38·00 45·00

(Recess A.B.N. Co)

1868 (Nov)–**73**. *P* 12.
35 **12** 1 c. brown-purple (II) (5.71) .. .. 55·00 45·00
36 **14** 3 c. vermilion (7.70) £300 £100
37 3 c. blue (1.4.73) .. .. .. £350 14·00
38 **7** 5 c. black £190 £100
39 **14** 6 c. rose (7.70) .. .. 5·50 16·00

1876–79. *Rouletted.*
40 **12** 1 c. lake-purple (II) (1877) .. .. 65·00 38·00
41 **6** 2 c. bluish green (1879) .. .. .. £120 70·00
42 **14** 3 c. blue (1877) .. .. £250 3·00
43 **7** 5 c. blue .. .. £170 2·75
a. Imperf (pair) .. .. ..

15 King Edward VII when Prince of Wales

16 Codfish

17

18 Common Seal on Ice-floe

(Recess British American Bank Note Co, Montreal)

1880–82. *P* 12.
44 **15** 1 c. dull grey-brown .. .. .. 13·00 7·00
a. Dull brown .. .. 10·00 7·00
b. Red-brown .. .. 17·00 11·00
46 **16** 2 c. yellow-green (1882) .. .. .. 40·00 17·00
47 **17** 3 c. pale dull blue .. .. .. 30·00 5·00
a. Bright blue .. .. 35·00 1·00
48 **18** 5 c. pale dull blue .. .. .. £190 3·75

19 Newfoundland Dog

20 Atlantic Brigantine

21 Queen Victoria

(Recess British American Bank Note Co, Montreal)

1888 (Jan). *New colours and values. P* 12.
49 **19** ½ c. rose-red .. .. 5·00 6·00
50 **15** 1 c. blue-green .. .. 6·00 4·00
a. Green .. .. 5·00 1·25
b. Yellow-green .. .. .. 6·50 5·50
51 **16** 2 c. orange-vermilion .. .. .. 9·50 3·00
52 **17** 3 c. deep brown .. .. 23·00 70
53 **18** 5 c. deep blue .. .. 48·00 3·50
54 **20** 10 c. black .. .. 45·00 38·00
49/54 .. .. *Set of* 6 £120 45·00

For reissues of 1880/87 stamps in similar colours, see Nos. 62/65*a*.

(Recess B.A.B.N.)

1890 (Nov). *P* 12.
55 **21** 3 c. deep slate .. .. 15·00 75
a. Imperf (pair) .. .. ..
56 3 c. slate-grey (*to* grey) .. .. 17·00 75
a. Imperf horiz (vert pair) £500
57 3 c. slate-violet .. .. .. 17·00 2·00
58 3 c. grey-lilac .. .. 16·00 75
58*a* 3 c. brown-grey .. .. .. 16·00 4·50
58*b* 3 c. purple-grey .. .. .. 18·00 3·75

There is a very wide range of shades in this stamp, and those given only cover the main groups.

Stamps on pink paper are from a consignment recovered from the sea and which were affected by the salt water.

(Recess British American Bank Note Co, Montreal)

1894 (Aug–Dec). *Changes of colour. P* 12.
59 **19** ½ c. black (11.94) .. .. .. 3·00 3·50
59*a* **18** 5 c. bright blue (12.94) .. .. .. 40·00 1·50
60 **14** 6 c. crimson-lake (12.94) .. .. 7·50 14·00
61 **9** 12 c. deep brown .. .. .. 30·00 42·00

The 6 c. is printed from the old American Bank Note Company's plates.

1896–97. *Reissues. P* 12.
62 **19** ½ c. orange-vermilion .. .. .. 27·00 40·00
63 **15** 1 c. deep green .. .. 11·00 6·00
63*a* 1 c. deep brown .. .. 30·00 24·00
64 **16** 2 c. green .. .. 30·00 22·00
65 **17** 3 c. deep blue .. .. 28·00 7·00
65*a* 3 c. chocolate-brown .. .. .. 38·00 25·00
62/65*a* .. .. *Set of* 6 £150 £110

The above were *reissued* for postal purposes. The colours were generally brighter than those of the original stamps.

22 Queen Victoria

23 Jean Cabot

24 Cape Bonavista

25 Reindeer-hunting

26 Mining

27 Logging

28 Fishing

29 *Matthew* (Cabot)

30 Willow Grouse

31 Group of Grey Seals

32 Salmon-fishing

33 Seal of the Colony

34 Iceberg off St. John's

35 Henry VII

(Recess A.B.N. Co)

1897 (24 June). 400*th Anniv of Discovery of Newfoundland and* 60*th year of Queen Victoria's reign. P* 12.
66 **22** 1 c. green .. .. 80 2·00
67 **23** 2 c. bright rose .. .. 80 1·25
a. Bisected (1 c.) on cover .. .. † £400
68 **24** 3 c. bright blue .. .. 1·00 30
a. Bisected (1½ c.) on cover .. .. † £300
69 **25** 4 c. olive-green .. .. 5·00 1·25
70 **26** 5 c. violet .. .. 4·50 1·25
71 **27** 6 c. red-brown .. .. 3·75 1·50
a. Bisected (3 c.) on cover .. .. † £350
72 **28** 8 c. orange .. .. 11·00 6·00
73 **29** 10 c. sepia .. .. 17·00 1·75
74 **30** 12 c. deep blue .. .. 25·00 1·75
75 **31** 15 c. bright scarlet .. .. .. 10·00 9·00
76 **32** 24 c. dull violet-blue .. .. .. 16·00 11·00
77 **33** 30 c. slate-blue .. .. 26·00 32·00
78 **34** 35 c. red .. .. 48·00 48·00
79 **35** 60 c. black .. .. 8·50 7·00
66/79 .. .. *Set of* 14 £160 £110

The 60 c. surcharged "TWO—2—CENTS" in three lines is an essay made in December 1918.

ONE CENT

(36)

ONE CENT

(37)

ONE CENT

(38)

1897 (Oct). *T* **21** *surch with T* **36** *to* **38** *by Royal Gazette, St. Johns, on stamps of various shades.*
80 **36** 1 c. on 3 c. grey-purple .. .. .. 25·00 15·00
a. Surch double, one diagonal .. £1100
d. Vert pair, one without lower bar and "ONE CENT" £3500
81 **37** 1 c. on 3 c. grey-purple .. .. .. 80·00 70·00
82 **38** 1 c. on 3 c. grey-purple £450 £325

Nos. 80/2 occur in the same setting of 50 (10 × 5) applied twice to each sheet. Type **36** appeared in the first four horizontal rows, Type **37** on R. 5/1–8 and Type **38** on R. 5/9 and 10.

Trial surcharges in red or red and black were not issued. (*Price*: Type **36** *in red* £1100, *in red and black* £1100; Type **37** *in red* £2750, *in red and black* £3000; Type **38** *in red* £5000, *in red and black* £6000).

These surcharges exist on stamps of various shades, but those on brown-grey are clandestine forgeries, having been produced by one of the printers at the *Royal Gazette*.

39 Prince Edward later Duke of Windsor

40 Queen Victoria

41 King Edward VII when Prince of Wales

42 Queen Alexandra when Princess of Wales

43 Queen Mary when Duchess of York

44 King George V when Duke of York

(Recess A.B.N. Co)

1897–1918. *P* 12.
83 **39** ½ c. olive (8.97) 80 60
a. Imperf (pair) £225
84 **40** 1 c. carmine (4.12.87) .. .. 1·75 2·25
85 1 c. blue-green (6.98) .. .. 2·75 10
a. Yellow-green .. .. .. 4·25 10
b. Imperf horiz (vert pair) £170
86 **41** 2 c. orange (4.12.97) .. .. .. 80 1·40
a. Imperf (pair) .. .. ..
87 2 c. scarlet (6.98) .. .. .. 6·00 15
a. Imperf (pair) £225
b. Imperf between (pair) .. ..
88 **42** 3 c. orange (6.98) .. .. .. 5·00 10
a. Imperf horiz (vert pair) £250
b. Imperf (pair) £225
c. Red-orange/bluish (6.18) .. 16·00 2·75
89 **43** 4 c. violet (10.01) .. .. .. 17·00 2·25
a. Imperf (pair) £200
90 **44** 5 c. blue (6.99) .. .. .. 22·00 2·75
83/90 .. .. *Set of* 8 50·00 9·00

No. 88*c* was an emergency war-time printing made by the American Bank Note Co from the old plate, pending receipt of the then current 3 c. from England.

The imperforate errors of this issue are found used, but only as philatelic "by favour" items. It is possible that No. 86a only exists in this condition.

45 Map of Newfoundland

(Recess A.B.N. Co)

1908 (Sept). *P* 12.
94 **45** 2 c. lake .. .. 15·00 20

46 King James I

47 Arms of Colonisation Co

48 John Guy

49 *Endeavour* (immigrant ship), 1610

50 Cupids

51 Sir Francis Bacon

52 View of Mosquito

53 Logging Camp

54 Paper Mills

55 King Edward VII

56 King George V

(Litho Whitehead, Morris & Co, Ltd)

1910 (15 Aug). (*a*) *P* 12.

No.	Type	Description	Unused	Used
95	**46**	1 c. green	1·75	30
		a. "NFWFOUNDLAND" (Right pane R. 5/1)	27·00	42·00
		b. "JANES" (Right pane R. 5/2)	27·00	42·00
		c. Imperf between (horiz pair)	£275	£300
96	**47**	2 c. rose-carmine	2·50	40
97	**48**	3 c. olive	2·00	11·00
98	**49**	4 c. violet	8·00	11·00
99	**50**	5 c. bright blue	5·00	4·00
100	**51**	6 c. claret (A)	38·00	85·00
100*a*		6 c. claret (B)	18·00	38·00
101	**52**	8 c. bistre-brown	35·00	55·00
102	**53**	9 c. olive-green	35·00	55·00
103	**54**	10 c. purple-slate	38·00	55·00
104	**55**	12 c. pale red-brown	38·00	55·00
		a. Imperf (pair)	£400	
105	**56**	15 c. black	42·00	55·00
95/105		*Set of* 11	£200	£300

6 c. (A) "Z" in "COLONIZATION" reversed. (B) "Z" correct.

(*b*) *P* 12 × 14

No.	Type	Description	Unused	Used
106	**46**	1 c. green	2·00	2·50
		a. "NFWFOUNDLAND"	25·00	35·00
		b. "JANES"	25·00	35·00
		c. Imperf between (pair)	£450	£500
107	**47**	2 c. rose-carmine	2·75	35
		a. Imperf between (pair)	£400	
108	**50**	5 c. bright blue (*p* 14×12)	8·00	2·50

(*c*) *P* 12×11

No.	Type	Description	Unused	Used
109	**46**	1 c. green	1·25	20
		a. Imperf between (horiz pair)	£250	
		b. Imperf between (vert pair)	£300	
		c. "NFWFOUNDLAND"	22·00	32·00
		e. "JANES"	22·00	32·00

(*d*) *P* 12 × 11½

No.	Type	Description	Unused	Used
110	**47**	2 c. rose-carmine	80·00	80·00

(Dies eng Macdonald & Sons. Recess A. Alexander & Sons, Ltd)

1911 (7 Feb). *As T* **51** *to* **56**, *but recess printed. P* 14.

No.	Description	Unused	Used
111	6 c. claret (B)	13·00	25·00
112	8 c. yellow-brown	32·00	48·00
	a. Imperf between (horiz pair)	£400	
	b. Imperf (pair)	£300	
113	9 c. sage-green	28·00	48·00
	a. Imperf between (horiz pair)	£225	
114	10 c. purple-black	48·00	70·00
	a. Imperf between (horiz pair)	£300	
	b. Imperf (pair)	£250	
115	12 c. red-brown	40·00	55·00
116	15 c. slate-green	45·00	80·00
111/16	*Set of* 6	£180	£300

The 9 c. and 15 c. exist with papermaker's watermark "E. TOWGOOD FINE".

57 Queen Mary

58 King George V

59 Duke of Windsor when Prince of Wales

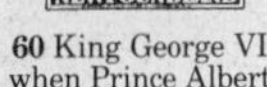

60 King George VI when Prince Albert

61 Princess Mary, the Princess Royal

62 Prince Henry Duke of Gloucester

63 Prince George, Duke of Kent

64 Prince John

65 Queen Alexandra

66 Duke of Connaught

67 Seal of Newfoundland

(1 c. to 5 c., 10 c. eng and recess D.L.R.; others eng Macdonald & Co, recess A. Alexander & Sons)

1911 (19 June)–**16.** *Coronation. P* 13½ × 14 (*comb*) (1 *c. to* 5 *c.*, 10 *c.*) *or* 14 (*line*) (*others*).

No.	Type	Description	Unused	Used
117	**57**	1 c. yellow-green	2·50	15
		a. Blue-green (1915)	1·75	15
118	**58**	2 c. carmine	1·60	15
		a. Rose-red (*blurred impression*). Perf 14 (1916)	3·00	55
119	**59**	3 c. red-brown	11·00	22·00
120	**60**	4 c. purple	14·00	21·00
121	**61**	5 c. ultramarine	3·75	80
122	**62**	6 c. slate-grey	10·00	22·00
123	**63**	8 c. aniline blue	45·00	70·00
		a. Greenish blue	45·00	75·00
124	**64**	9 c. violet-blue	9·00	24·00
125	**65**	10 c. deep green	16·00	27·00
126	**66**	12 c. plum	12·00	28·00
127	**67**	15 c. lake	12·00	28·00
117/27		*Set of* 11	£120	£225

The 2 c. rose-red, No. 118*a* is a poor war-time printing by Alexander & Sons.

Although No. 123 has a typical aniline appearance it is believed that the shade results from the thinning of non-aniline ink.

68 Reindeer

FIRST
TRANS-
ATLANTIC
AIR POST
April, 1919.

(69)

(Des J. H. Noonan. Recess D.L.R.)

1919 (2 Jan). *Newfoundland Contingent*, 1914–1918. *P* 14.

No.	Type	Description	Unused	Used
130	**68**	1 c. green (*a*) (*b*)	60	20
131		2 c. scarlet (*a*) (*b*)	70	30
		a. Carmine-red (*b*)	1·50	45
132		3 c. brown (*a*) (*b*)	80	15
		a. Red-brown (*b*)	1·50	20
133		4 c. mauve (*a*)	1·75	60
		a. Purple (*b*)	1·75	25
134		5 c. ultramarine (*a*) (*b*)	1·50	60
135		6 c. slate-grey (*a*)	4·00	18·00
136		8 c. bright magenta (*a*)	3·75	24·00
137		10 c. deep grey-green (*a*)	3·25	1·75
138		12 c. orange (*a*)	13·00	28·00
139		15 c. indigo (*a*)	13·00	30·00
		a. Prussian blue (*a*)	80·00	£130
140		24 c. bistre-brown (*a*)	16·00	24·00
141		36 c. sage-green (*a*)	7·00	16·00
130/41		*Set of* 12	60·00	£130

Each value bears with "Trail of the Caribou" the name of a different action: 1 c. Suvla Bay; 3 c. Gueudecourt; 4 c. Beaumont Hamel; 6 c. Monchy; 10 c. Steenbeck; 15 c. Langemarck; 24 c. Cambrai; 36 c. Combles; 2 c., 5 c., 8 c., and 12 c. inscribed "Royal Naval Reserve-Ubique".

Perforations. Two perforating heads were used: (*a*) comb 14 × 13.9; (*b*) line 14.1 × 14.1.

1919 (12 Apr). *Air. No.* 132 *optd with T* **69**, *by Robinson & Co Ltd, at the offices of the "Daily News".*

No.	Type	Description	Unused	Used
142	**68**	3 c. brown	£14000	£8000

These stamps franked correspondence carried by Lieut. H. Hawker on his Atlantic flight. 18 were damaged and destroyed, 95 used on letters, 11 given as presentation copies, and the remaining 76 were sold in aid of the Marine Disasters Fund.

1919 (19 April). *Nos.* 132 *optd in MS.* "Aerial Atlantic Mail. J.A.R.".

No.	Type	Description	Unused	Used
142*a*	**68**	3 c. brown	—	£20000

This provisional was made by W. C. Campbell, the Secretary of the Postal Department, and the initials are those of the Postmaster, J. A. Robinson, for use on correspondence intended to be carried on the abortive Morgan-Raynham Trans-Atlantic flight. The mail was eventually delivered by sea.

In addition to the 25 to 30 used examples, one unused, no gum, copy of No. 142*a* is known.

A single example of a similar overprint on the 2 c., No. 131, is known used on cover together with an unoverprinted example of the same value.

Trans-Atlantic
AIR POST,
1919.
ONE DOLLAR.

(70)

THREE
CENTS

(71)

1919 (9 June). *Air. No.* 75 *surch with T* **70** *by Royal Gazette, St. Johns.*

No.	Type	Description	Unused	Used
143	**31**	$1 on 15 c. bright scarlet	90·00	90·00
		a. No comma after "AIR POST"	£200	£225
		b. As Var a and no stop after "1919"	£425	£425
		c. As Var a and "A" of "AIR" under "a" of "Trans"	£425	£425

These stamps were issued for use on the mail carried on the first successful flight across the Atlantic by Capt. J. Alcock and Lieut. A. Brown, and on other projected Trans-Atlantic flights (Alcock flown cover, *Price* £2500).

The surcharge was applied in a setting of 25 of which 16 were normal, 7 as No. 143a, 1 as No. 143b and 1 as No. 143c.

1920 (Sept). *Nos.* 75 *and* 77/8 *surch as T* **71**, *by Royal Gazette* (2 *c. with only one bar, at top of stamp*).

A. Bars of surch 10½ mm apart. B. Bars 13½ mm apart.

No.	Type	Description	Unused	Used
144	**33**	2 c. on 30 c. slate-blue (23 Sept)	3·50	7·50
		a. Surch inverted	£500	
145	**31**	3 c. on 15 c. bright scarlet (A) (13 Sept)	80·00	80·00
		a. Surch inverted	£700	
146		3 c. on 15 c. bright scarlet (B) (13 Sept)	6·50	8·50
147	**34**	3 c. on 35 c. red (15 Sept)	4·00	7·50
		a. Surch inverted		
		b. Lower bar omitted	£110	£120
		c. "THREE" omitted	£1100	

Our prices for Nos. 147b and 147c are for stamps with lower bar or "THREE" entirely missing. The bar may be found in all stages of incompleteness and stamps showing broken bar are not of much value.

On the other hand, stamps showing either only the top or bottom of the letters "THREE" are scarce, though not as rare as No. 147c.

The 6 c. T **27**, surcharged "THREE CENTS," in red or black, is an essay. (*Price* £275). The 2 c. on 30 c. with red surcharge is a colour trial (*Price* £275).

AIR MAIL
to Halifax, N.S.
1921.

(72)

1921 (16 Nov). *Air. No.* 78 *optd with T* **72** *by Royal Gazette.*

I. 2¾ *mm between* "AIR" *and* "MAIL"

No.	Type	Description	Unused	Used
148	**34**	35 c. red	90·00	90·00
		a. No stop after "1921"	80·00	80·00
		b. No stop and first "1" of "1921" below "f" of "Halifax"	£180	£180
		c. As No. 148, inverted	£3000	
		d. As No. 148a, inverted	£3000	
		e. As No. 148b, inverted	£6000	

II. 1½ *mm between* "AIR" *and* "MAIL"

No.	Type	Description	Unused	Used
148*f*	**34**	35 c. red	£100	£100
		g. No stop after "1921"	£120	£120
		h. No stop and first "1" of "1921" below "f" of "Halifax"	£180	£180
		i. As No. 148f, inverted	£3750	
		k. As No. 148g, inverted	£4500	
		l. As No. 148h, inverted	£6000	

Type **72** was applied as a setting of 25 which contained ten stamps as No. 148a, seven as No. 148, four as No. 148*f*, two as No. 148g, one as No. 148b and one as No. 148h.

73 Twin Hills, Tor's Cove

74 South-West Arm, Trinity

75 Statue of the Fighting Newfoundlander, St. John's

(Recess D.L.R.)

1923 (9 July)–**26.** *T* **73/5** *and similar designs. P* 14 (*comb or line*).

No.	Description	Unused	Used
149	1 c. green	60	10
	a. Booklet pane of 8 (1926)	£250	
150	2 c. carmine	60	10
	a. Imperf (pair)	£160	
	b. Booklet pane of 8 (1926)	£140	
151	3 c. brown	55	10
152	4 c. deep purple	90	25
153	5 c. ultramarine	1·50	70
154	6 c. slate	1·50	5·00
155	8 c. purple	1·50	3·25
156	9 c. slate-green	13·00	25·00
157	10 c. violet	2·50	1·75
	a. Purple	3·00	2·25
158	11 c. sage-green	1·50	8·00
159	12 c. lake	2·00	7·50
160	15 c. Prussian blue	2·00	11·00
161	20 c. chestnut (28.4.24)	3·00	10·00
162	24 c. sepia (22.4.24)	27·00	48·00
149/62	*Set of* 14	50·00	£110

Designs: *Horiz* (*as T* **73**)—6 c. Upper Steadies, Humber River; 11 c. Shell Bird Island; 20 c. Placentia. (*As T* **74**)—8 c. Quidi Vidi, near St. John's; 9 c. Reindeer crossing lake; 12 c. Mount Moriah, Bay of Islands. *Vert* (*as T* **75**)—4 c. Humber River; 5 c. Coast at Trinity; 10 c. Humber River Cañon; 15 c. Humber River near Little Rapids; 24 c. Topsail Falls.

Perforations. Three perforating heads were used: comb 13.8 × 14 (all values); line 13.7 and 14, and combinations of these two (for all except 6, 8, 9 and 11 c.).

Air Mail
DE PINEDO
1927

(87)

1927 (18 May). *Air. No.* 79 *optd with T* **87**, *by Robinson & Co, Ltd.*

163	**35**	60 c. black (R.)	£16000	£5000

For the mail carried by De Pinedo to Europe 300 stamps were overprinted, 230 used on correspondence, 66 presented to De Pinedo, Government Officials, etc., and 4 damaged and destroyed. Stamps without overprint were also used.

88 Newfoundland and Labrador

89 S.S. *Caribou*

90 King George V and Queen Mary

91 Duke of Windsor when Prince of Wales

92 Express Train

93 Newfoundland Hotel, St. John's

94 Heart's Content

95 Cabot Tower, St. John's

96 War Memorial, St. John's

97 G.P.O., St. John's

98 Vickers "Vimy" Aircraft

99 Parliament House, St. John's

100 Grand Falls, Labrador

(Recess D.L.R.)

1928 (3 Jan)–**29.** *"Publicity" issue. P* 13 *to* 14.

164	**88**	1 c. deep green (*a*)	55	70
165	**89**	2 c. carmine (*b*)	1·00	40
166	**90**	3 c. brown (*b*) (*c*)	1·25	30
167	**91**	4 c. mauve (*b*)	1·50	1·00
		a. Rose-purple (1929)	3·75	4·50
168	**92**	5 c. slate-grey (*b*) (*c*)	5·00	2·75
169	**93**	6 c. ultramarine (*b*) (*c*)	1·50	7·50
170	**94**	8 c. red-brown (*c*)	1·50	9·00
171	**95**	9 c. deep green (*c*)	1·50	7·00
172	**96**	10 c. deep violet (*b*) (*c*)	3·00	4·25
173	**97**	12 c. carmine-lake (*c*)	1·50	8·00
174	**95**	14 c. brown-purple (*b*) (*c*)	3·00	5·00
175	**98**	15 c. deep blue (*c*)	2·50	14·00
176	**99**	20 c. grey-black (*b*) (*c*)	1·75	6·50
177	**97**	28 c. deep green (*c*)	14·00	30·00
178	**100**	30 c. sepia (*c*)	4·50	10·00
164/78		.. .. *Set of* 15	40·00	95·00

See also Nos. 179/87 and 198/208.

Perforations. Three perforating heads were used: (*a*) comb 14 × 13.9; (*b*) comb 13.5 × 12.75; (*c*) line 13.7 to 14 or compound.

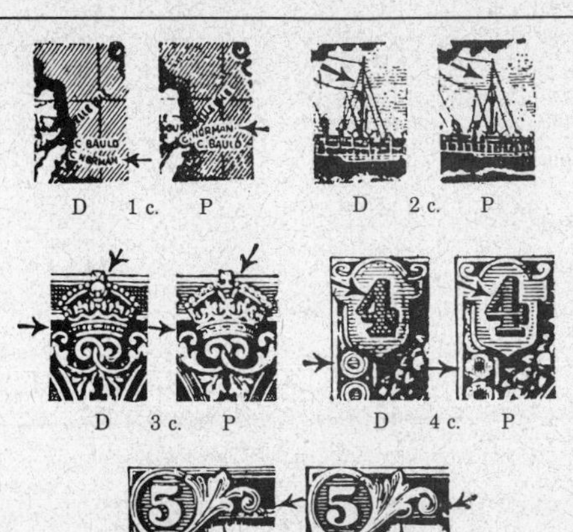

D 1 c. P D 2 c. P

D 3 c. P D 4 c. P

D 5 c. P

D 6 c. P D 10 c. P

D 15 c. P

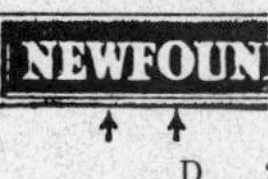

D 20 c. P

D. "De La Rue" printing

P. "Perkins, Bacon" printing

1929 (10 Aug)–**31.** *"Perkins, Bacon" printing. Former types re-engraved. No wmk. P* 13½ to 14.

179	**88**	1 c. green (*a*) (*d*) (26.9.29)	2·50	20
		a. Imperf between (vert pair) ..	£120	
		b. Imperf (pair)	£110	
180	**89**	2 c. scarlet (*b*) (*d*)	90	10
		a. Imperf (pair)	80·00	
181	**90**	3 c. red-brown (*c*)	80	10
		a. Imperf (pair)	90·00	
182	**91**	4 c. reddish purple (*c*) (26.8.29) ..	1·25	10
		a. Imperf (pair)	95·00	
183	**92**	5 c. deep grey-green (*c*) (14.9.29) ..	2·75	80
184	**93**	6 c. ultramarine (*b*) (*d*) (8.11.29) ..	2·00	6·50
185	**96**	10 c. violet (*c*) (5.10.29)	2·00	1·50
186	**98**	15 c. blue (*c*) (1.30)	15·00	55·00
187	**99**	20 c. black (*d*) (1.1.31)	15·00	32·00
179/87		.. .. *Set of* 9	38·00	85·00

Perforations. Four perforating heads were used: (*a*) comb 14 × 13.9; (*b*) comb 13.6 × 13.5; (*c*) comb 13.6 × 13.8; (*d*) line 13.7 to 14 or compound.

THREE
CENTS

(101)

Trans-Atlantic
AIR MAIL
By B. M.
"Columbia"
September
1930
Fifty Cents

(102)

(Surch by Messrs D. R. Thistle, St. John's)

1929 (23 Aug). *No.* 154 *surch with T* **101**.

188	3 c. on 6 c. slate (R.)	55	2·40
	a. Surch inverted	£600	£900
	b. Surch in black	£850	

1930 (25 Sept). *Air. No.* 141 *surch with T* **102** *by Messrs D. R. Thistle.*

191	**68**	50 c. on 36 c. sage-green	£4000	£4000

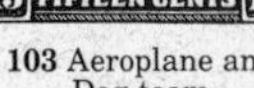

103 Aeroplane and Dog-team

104 Vickers-Vimy Biplane and early Sailing Packet

105 Routes of historic Transatlantic Flights

106

(Des A. B. Perlin. Recess P.B.)

1931. *Air. T* **103** *to* **105.** *P* 14. (*a*) *Without wmk* (2.1.31).

192	15 c. chocolate	3·00	7·00
	a. Imperf between (horiz or vert pair) ..	£400	
	b. Imperf (pair)	£350	
193	50 c. green	16·00	24·00
	a. Imperf between (horiz or vert pair) ..	£400	£350
	b. Imperf (pair)	£375	
194	$1 deep blue	32·00	60·00
	a. Imperf between (horiz or vert pair) ..	£400	
	b. Imperf (pair)	£350	
192/4	.. .. *Set of* 3	45·00	80·00

(*b*) *Wmk W* **106**, *sideways* (13.3.31)

195	15 c. chocolate	2·25	7·00
	a. Pair, with and without wmk	29·00	
	b. Imperf between (horiz or vert pair) ..	£375	
	ba. Ditto, one without wmk (vert pair) ..	£800	
	c. Imperf (pair)	£225	
	d. Wmk Cross (pair)	70·00	
196	50 c. green	15·00	40·00
	a. Imperf between (horiz or vert pair) ..	£400	
	b. Imperf (pair)	£250	
	c. Pair, with and without wmk		
197	$1 deep blue	48·00	85·00
	a. Imperf between (horiz or vert pair) ..	£450	
	b. Imperf horiz (vert pair)	£450	
	c. Pair, with and without wmk		
	d. Imperf (pair)	£300	
195/7	.. .. *Set of* 3	60·00	£120

"WITH AND WITHOUT WMK" PAIRS listed in the issues from No. 195a onwards must have one stamp *completely* without any trace of watermark.

1931 (25 March–July). *"Perkins, Bacon" printing (re-engraved types). W* **106** (*sideways on* 1 *c.*, 4 *c.*, 30 *c.*). *P* 13½ *to* 14.

198	**88**	1 c. green (7.31)	1·50	1·00
		a. Imperf between (horiz pair) ..	£600	
199	**89**	2 c. scarlet (7.31)	1·75	1·00
200	**90**	3 c. red-brown (7.31)	1·50	80
201	**91**	4 c. reddish purple (7.31)	1·50	70
202	**92**	5 c. deep grey-green (7.31)	5·00	6·50
203	**93**	6 c. ultramarine	9·00	16·00
204	**94**	8 c. chestnut (1.4.31)	9·00	18·00
205	**96**	10 c. violet (1.4.31)	4·00	6·50
206	**98**	15 c. blue (1.7.31)	17·00	38·00
207	**99**	20 c. black (1.7.31)	19·00	10·00
208	**100**	30 c. sepia (1.7.31)	13·00	24·00
198/208		.. .. *Set of* 11	70·00	£110

Perforations. Two perforating heads were used: comb 13.4 × 13.4 for 1 c.; comb 13.6 × 13.8 for other values.

107 Codfish

108 King George V

109 Queen Mary

110 Duke of Windsor when Prince of Wales

111 Reindeer

112 Queen Elizabeth II when Princess

113 Salmon

114 Newfoundland Dog

115 Harp Seal

116 Cape Race

117 Sealing Fleet

118 Fishing Fleet

(Recess P.B.)

1932 (1 Jan). *W* **106** *(sideways on vert designs). P* 13½ *(comb).*

209 **107** 1 c. green .. .. 1·00 15
a. Imperf (pair) .. .. 75·00
b. Perf 13 (line) .. .. 22·00 25·00
ba. Imperf between (vert pair) £110
bb. Booklet pane of 4 .. .. £100
210 **108** 2 c. carmine .. .. 1·10 10
a. Imperf (pair) .. .. 75·00
b. Booklet pane of 4 .. .. 27·00
c. Perf 13 (line) .. .. 15·00 20·00
ca. Booklet pane of 4 .. .. 75·00
211 **109** 3 c. orange-brown 70 10
a. Imperf (pair) .. .. 75·00
b. Booklet pane of 4 .. .. 80·00
c. Perf 13 (line) .. .. 24·00
ca. Booklet pane of 4 .. .. £110
d. Perf 14 (line). Small holes .. .. 18·00
da. Imperf between (vert pair) £100
db. Booklet pane of 4 .. .. 80·00
212 **110** 4 c. bright violet .. .. 1·75 70
213 **111** 5 c. maroon .. .. 2·00 45
a. Imperf (pair) £150
214 **112** 6 c. light blue .. .. 4·00 9·00
215 **113** 10 c. black-brown 55 25
a. Imperf (pair) .. .. 75·00
216 **114** 14 c. black .. .. 80 1·50
a. Imperf (pair) £120
217 **115** 15 c. claret .. .. 1·25 1·75
a. Imperf (pair) £130
b. Perf 14 (line) .. .. 10·00 14·00
218 **116** 20 c. green .. .. 1·00 50
a. Imperf (pair) £110
b. Perf 14 (line) .. .. 35·00
219 **117** 25 c. slate .. .. 1·25 1·75
a. Imperf (pair) £120
b. Perf 14 (line) .. .. 8·50 15·00
ba. Imperf between (vert pair) £250
220 **118** 30 c. ultramarine .. .. 15·00 22·00
a. Imperf (pair) £250
b. Imperf between (vert pair) £450
c. Perf 14 (line) £160
209/20 .. .. *Set of* 12 27·00 35·00

For similar stamps in different perforations see Nos. 222/8*a* and 276/89.

TRANS-ATLANTIC
WEST TO EAST
Per Dornier DO-X
May, 1932.
One Dollar and Fifty Cents

(119)

1932 (19 May). *Air. No.* 197 *surch as T* **119**, *by Messrs. D. R. Thistle. P* 14.

221 **105** $1.50 on $1 deep blue (R.) £180 £225
a. Surch inverted £7500

120 Queen Mother, when Duchess of York

121 Paper Mills

122 Bell Island

(Recess P.B.)

1932 (15 Aug)–**38**. *Wmk W* **106** *(sideways on vert designs). P* 13½ *(comb).*

222 **107** 1 c. grey 20 10
a. Imperf (pair) .. .. 50·00
b. Booklet pane of 4 .. .. 80·00
c. Perf 14 (line) .. .. 6·00
d. Perf 14 (line). Small holes .. .. 18·00
da. Booklet pane of 4 .. .. 80·00
e. Pair, with and without wmk .. .. 30·00
223 **108** 2 c. green 40 10
a. Imperf (pair) .. .. 60·00
b. Booklet pane of 4 .. .. 26·00
c. Perf 14 (line) .. .. 6·00
ca. Imperf between (horiz pair) £250
d. Perf 14 (line). Small holes .. .. 13·00
da. Booklet pane of 4 .. .. 50·00
e. Pair, with and without wmk .. .. 24·00
224 **110** 4 c. carmine (21.7.34) 40 10
a. Imperf (pair) .. .. 60·00
b. Perf 14 (line) .. .. 3·25
ba. Imperf between (horiz or vert pair) £120
225 **111** 5 c. violet (Die I) .. .. 2·00 45
a. Imperf (pair) .. .. 60·00
b. Perf 14 (line). Small holes .. .. 23·00
c. Die II 50 10
ca. Imperf (pair) .. .. 70·00
cb. Perf 14 (line) .. .. 18·00
cc. Imperf between (horiz pair) .. £180
cd. Pair, with and without wmk .. ..
226 **120** 7 c. red-brown .. .. 85 2·50
b. Perf 14 (line) .. ..
ba. Imperf between (horiz pair) .. £425
c. Imperf (pair) £120
227 **121** 8 c. brownish red .. .. 2·25 1·50
a. Imperf (pair) .. .. 75·00
228 **122** 24 c. bright blue .. .. 60 1·75
a. Imperf (pair) £160
b. Doubly printed £750
228*c* **118** 48 c. red-brown (1.1.38) .. .. .. 4·50 7·00
ca. Imperf (pair) .. .. 75·00
222/8*c* .. .. *Set of* 8 8·50 12·00

No. 223. Two dies exist of the 2 c. Die I was used for No. 210 and both dies for No. 223. The differences, though numerous, are very slight.

No. 225. There are also two dies of the 5 c., Die I only being used for No. 213 and both dies for the violet stamp. In Die II the antler pointing to the "T" of "POSTAGE" is taller than the one pointing to the "S" and the individual hairs on the underside of the caribou's tail are distinct.

For similar stamps in a slightly larger size and perforated 12½ or 13½ (5 c.) see Nos. 276/89.

(123) "L.&S."—Land and Sea

1933 (9 Feb). *Optd with T* **123** *for ordinary postal use, by Messrs D. R. Thistle. W* **106** *(sideways). P* 14.

229 **103** 15 c. chocolate .. .. 1·50 4·00
a. Pair, one without wmk .. .. 20·00
b. Opt reading up £1200
c. Vertical pair, one without surch .. £1800

124 Put to Flight

125 Land of Hearts Delight

(Des J. Scott. Recess P.B.)

1933 (31 May). *Air. T* **124/5** *and similar horiz designs. W* **106** *(sideways). P* 14 (*a*) *or* 11½ (*b*).

230 5 c. red-brown (*a*) .. .. 7·50 13·00
a. Imperf (pair) £130
b. Imperf between (horiz or vert pair) .. £1750
231 10 c. orange-yellow (*b*) .. .. .. 4·00 14·00
a. Imperf (pair) £110
232 30 c. light blue (*a*) .. .. 18·00 30·00
a. Imperf (pair) £250
233 60 c. green (*b*) .. .. 32·00 50·00
a. Imperf (pair) £250
234 75 c. yellow-brown (*a*) .. .. .. 32·00 50·00
a. Imperf (pair) £140
b. Imperf between (horiz or vert pair) .. £2250
230/4 .. .. *Set of* 5 85·00 £140

Designs:—30 c. Spotting the herd; 60 c. News from home; 75 c. Labrador.

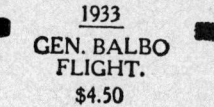

1933
GEN. BALBO
FLIGHT.
$4.50

(129)

(Surch by Robinson & Co, St. John's)

1933 (24 July). *Air. Balbo Transatlantic Mass Formation Flight. No.* 234 *surch with T* **129**. *W* **106**. *P* 14.

235 $4.50 on 75 c. yellow-brown £275 £325
a. Surch inverted £20000
b. Surch on 10 c. (No. 231) £20000

No. 235a. When this error was discovered the stamps were ordered to be officially destroyed but four copies which had been torn were recovered and skilfully repaired. In addition four undamaged examples exist and the price quoted is for one of these.

130 Sir Humphrey Gilbert

131 Compton Castle, Devon

132 Gilbert Coat of Arms

(Recess P.B.)

1933 (3 Aug). *350th Anniv of the Annexation by Sir Humphrey Gilbert. T* **130/2** *and similar designs. W* **106** *(sideways on vert designs). P* 13½ *(comb).**

236 1 c. slate 50 60
a. Imperf (pair) .. .. 45·00
237 2 c. green 60 35
a. Imperf (pair) .. .. 48·00
b. Doubly printed £300
238 3 c. chestnut .. .. 60 1·00
239 4 c. carmine 45 30
a. Imperf (pair) .. .. 45·00
240 5 c. violet 75 70
241 7 c. greenish blue .. .. 3·25 11·00
a. Perf 14 .. .. 15·00 35·00
242 8 c. vermilion .. .. 5·00 7·50
a. Brownish red £250
b. Bisected (4 c.) (on cover) .. .. .. † £350
243 9 c. ultramarine .. .. 3·75 6·50
a. Imperf (pair) £150
b. Perf 14 .. .. 15·00 30·00
244 10 c. brown-lake .. .. 3·75 4·00
a. Imperf (pair) £300
b. Perf 14 .. .. 20·00 35·00
245 14 c. grey-black .. .. 7·00 24·00
a. Perf 14 .. .. 16·00 40·00
246 15 c. claret .. .. 7·00 14·00
247 20 c. grey-green .. .. 5·50 12·00
a. Perf 14 .. .. 13·00 24·00
248 24 c. maroon .. .. 7·00 20·00
a. Imperf (pair) £120
b. Perf 14 .. .. 20·00 35·00
249 32 c. olive-black .. .. 6·00 30·00
a. Perf 14 .. .. 22·00 48·00
236/49 .. .. *Set of* 14 40·00 £110

Designs: *Horiz*—4 c. Eton College; 7 c. Gilbert commissioned by Elizabeth; 8 c. Fleet leaving Plymouth, 1583; 9 c. Arrival at St. John's; 10 c. Annexation, 5 August 1583; 20 c. Map of Newfoundland. *Vert*—5 c. Anchor token; 14 c. Royal Arms; 15 c. Gilbert in the *Squirrel*; 24 c. Queen Elizabeth I. 32 c. Gilbert's statue at Truro.

**Perforations*. Two perforating heads were used: comb 13.4 × 13.4 for all values; line 13.8 (listed above as 14) for a second printing of some values.

1935 (6 May). *Silver Jubilee. As Nos.* 91/4 *of Antigua, but ptd by B.W. P* 11 × 12.

250 4 c. rosine 50 45
251 5 c. bright violet 90 50
252 7 c. blue .. .. 1·00 3·75
253 24 c. olive-green .. .. 2·75 3·50
250/3 .. .. *Set of* 4 4·50 7·50
250/3 Perf "Specimen" .. .. *Set of* 4 £120

1937 (12 May). *Coronation Issue. As Nos.* 13/15 *of Aden but name and value uncoloured on coloured background and ptd by B.W. P* 11 × 11½.

254 2 c. green 90 90
255 4 c. carmine .. .. 1·10 50
256 5 c. purple .. .. 1·60 1·50
254/6 .. .. *Set of* 3 3·25 2·75
254/6 Perf "Specimen" .. .. *Set of* 3 70·00

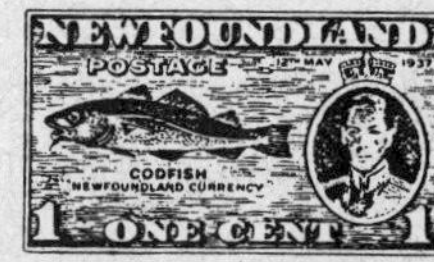

144 Codfish

Die I

Die II

No. 258. In Die II the shading of the King's face is heavier and dots have been added down the ridge of the nose. The top frame line is thicker and more uniform.

(Recess P.B.)

1937 (12 May). *Additional Coronation Issue. T* **144** *and similar horiz designs. W* **106**. A. *P* 14 *or* 13½ *(line).* B. *P* 13 *(comb).*

		A		B	
257	1 c. grey	55	15	12·00	24·00
	a. Pair, with and without wmk	18·00	—	—	—
258	3 c. orange-brown (I)	2·00	80	1·40	70
	a. Pair, with and without wmk	42·00		†	
	b. Die I. Imperf between (horiz or vert pair)	£350		†	
	c. Die II	1·40	90	1·75	90
	d. Die II. Imperf between (horiz or vert pair)	£450		†	
	e. Die II. Pair, with and without wmk	—	—	80·00	—
259	7 c. bright ultramarine	1·00	60	£175	£250
	a. Pair, with and without wmk	—	—	†	
260	8 c. scarlet	1·00	80	2·50	3·00
	a. Pair, with and without wmk	30·00		†	
	b. Imperf between (horiz or vert pair)	£500		†	
	c. Imperf (pair)	£250		†	
261	10 c. deep olive	2·75	3·00	3·25	4·50
	a. Pair, with and without wmk	45·00		†	
262	14 c. black	1·40	2·00	£2250	£1100
	a. Pair, with and without wmk	30·00		†	
263	15 c. claret	6·00	4·00	10·00	10·00
	a. Pair, with and without wmk	32·00	—	48·00	—
	b. Imperf between (vert pair)	£325		†	
264	20 c. green	2·25	3·00	2·50	4·50
	a. Pair, with and without wmk	85·00		†	
	b. Imperf between (vert pair)	£475		†	
265	24 c. light blue	2·25	2·50	9·00	9·00
	a. Pair, with and without wmk	85·00		†	
	b. Imperf between (vert pair)	£500		†	
266	25 c. slate	2·75	1·75	10·00	15·00
	a. Pair, with and without wmk	55·00		†	
267	48 c. slate-purple	6·00	4·00	15·00	24·00
	a. Pair, with and without wmk	90·00		†	
	b. Imperf between (vert pair)	£500		†	
257/67	*Set of* 11	24·00	20·00		

Designs:—3 c. Map of Newfoundland; 7 c. Reindeer; 8 c. Corner Brook paper mills; 10 c. Salmon; 14 c. Newfoundland dog; 15 c.

Harp Seal; 20 c. Cape Race; 24 c. Bell Island; 25 c. Sealing fleet; 48 c. The Banks fishing fleet.

The line perforation "A" was produced by two machines measuring respectively 13.7 and 14.1. The comb perforation "B" measures 13.3 × 13.2.

Three used examples of No. 259B have now been identified on separate covers.

155 King George VI **156** Queen Mother

(Recess P.B.)

1938 (12 May). *T* **155/6** *and similar vert designs. W* **106** *(sideways). P* 13½ *(comb).*

No.		Description	Unused	Used
268		2 c. green	1·00	15
		a. Pair, with and without wmk	£130	
		b. Imperf (pair)	65·00	
269		3 c. carmine	80	20
		a. Perf 14 (line)	£250	£120
		b. Pair, with and without wmk	£180	
		c. Imperf (pair)	55·00	
270		4 c. light blue	1·25	15
		a. Pair, with and without wmk	80·00	
		b. Imperf (pair)	65·00	
271		7 c. deep ultramarine	65	1·50
		a. Imperf (pair)	65·00	
268/71		*Set of* 4	3·25	1·75

Designs:—4 c. Queen Elizabeth II as princess; 7 c. Queen Mary.

For similar designs, perf 12½, see Nos. 277/281.

159 King George VI and Queen Elizabeth

(Recess B.W.)

1939 (17 June). *Royal Visit. No wmk. P* 13½.

No.		Description	Unused	Used
272	**159**	5 c. deep ultramarine	75	25

2

 **CENTS** 

(160)

1939 (20 Nov). *No. 272 surch as T* **160**, *at St. John's.*

No.		Description	Unused	Used
273	**159**	2 c. on 5 c. deep ultramarine (Br.)	1·10	20
274		4 c. on 5 c. deep ultramarine (C.)	70	20

161 Grenfell on the *Strathcona* (after painting by Gribble) **162** Memorial University College

(Recess C.B.N.)

1941 (1 Dec). *Sir Wilfred Grenfell's Labrador Mission. P* 12.

No.		Description	Unused	Used
275	**161**	5 c. blue	15	15

(Recess Waterlow)

1941–44. *W* **106** *(sideways on vert designs). P* 12½ *(line).*

No.		Description	Unused	Used
276	**107**	1 c. grey	20	15
277	**155**	2 c. green	20	10
278	**156**	3 c. carmine	25	10
		a. Pair, with and without wmk	55·00	
279	–	4 c. blue (As No. 270)	80	10
		a. Pair, with and without wmk	£100	
280	**111**	5 c. violet (Die I) (*p* 13½ *comb*)	£200	
		a. Perf 12½ (line) (6.42)		
		ab. Pair, with and without wmk	95·00	
		ac. Printed double		
		ad. Imperf vert (horiz pair)		
		b. Imperf (pair)		
281	–	7 c. deep ultramarine (As No. 271)	2·25	2·75
		a. Pair, with and without wmk	£100	
282	**121**	8 c. rose-red	1·00	1·75
		a. Pair, with and without wmk	£100	
283	**113**	10 c. black-brown	1·50	75
284	**114**	14 c. black	1·50	3·00
285	**115**	15 c. claret	3·25	4·00
286	**116**	20 c. green	3·50	3·50
287	**122**	24 c. blue	3·00	4·50
288	**117**	25 c. slate	3·75	4·75
289	**118**	48 c. red-brown (1944)	2·50	5·00
276/89		*Set of* 14	21·00	28·00

Nos. 276/89 are redrawn versions of previous designs with slightly larger dimensions; the 5 c., for example, measures 21 mm in width as opposed to the 20.4 mm of the Perkins Bacon printings.

No. 280. For Die I see note relating to No. 225.

(Recess C.B.N.)

1943 (2 Jan). *P* 12.

No.		Description	Unused	Used
290	**162**	30 c. carmine	1·00	80

TWO

CENTS

163 St. John's **(164)**

(Recess C.B.N.)

1943 (1 June). *Air. P* 12.

No.		Description	Unused	Used
291	**163**	7 c. ultramarine	15	20

1946 (21 Mar). *Surch locally with T* **164**.

No.		Description	Unused	Used
292	**162**	2 c. on 30 c. carmine	15	15

165 Queen Elizabeth II when Princess **166** Cabot off Cape Bonavista

(Recess Waterlow)

1947 (21 Apr). *Princess Elizabeth's 21st Birthday. W* **106** *(sideways). P* 12½.

No.		Description	Unused	Used
293	**165**	4 c. light blue	15	10
		a. Imperf vert (horiz pair)		

(Recess Waterlow)

1947 (23 June). *450th Anniv of Cabot's Discovery of Newfoundland. W* **106** *(sideways). P* 12½.

No.		Description	Unused	Used
294	**166**	5 c. mauve	15	25
		a. Imperf between (horiz pair)	£850	

POSTAGE DUE STAMPS

D 1

D **6**ac

(Litho John Dickinson & Co, Ltd)

1939 (1 May)–**49.** *P* 10.

No.		Description	Unused	Used
D1	D 1	1 c. green	1·75	5·50
		a. Perf 11 (1949)	3·00	8·50
D2		2 c. vermilion	5·00	5·00
		a. Perf 11 × 9 (1946)	6·50	11·00
D3		3 c. ultramarine	4·00	14·00
		a. Perf 11 × 9 (1949)	8·00	15·00
		b. Perf 9	£250	
D4		4 c. orange	5·00	9·00
		a. Perf 11 × 9 (May 1948)	10·00	25·00
D5		5 c. brown	5·50	16·00
D6		10 c. violet	6·00	11·00
		a. Perf 11 (W **106**) (1949)	11·00	45·00
		ab. Ditto. Imperf between (vert pair)	**£475**	
		ac. "POSTAGE LUE" (R 3/3 or 3/8)	**65·00**	**£140**
D1/6		*Set of* 6	**25·00**	**55·00**

On 1 April 1949, Newfoundland joined the Confederation of Canada whose stamps it now uses.

New Guinea

(*formerly* New Britain)

Stamps of Germany and later of GERMAN NEW GUINEA were used in New Guinea from 1888 until 1914.

During the interim period between the "G.R.I." surcharges and the "N.W. PACIFIC ISLANDS" overprints, stamps of AUSTRALIA perforated "OS" were utilised.

PRICES FOR STAMPS ON COVER

Nos.	
Nos. 1/30	*from* × 3
Nos. 31/2	—
Nos. 33/49	*from* × 3
Nos. 50/9	*from* × 2
Nos. 60/2	—
Nos. 63/4	*from* × 2
Nos. 64 *c/a*	—
Nos. 65/81	*from* × 5
Nos. 83/5	—
Nos. 86/97	*from* × 5
No. 99	—
Nos. 100/16	*from* × 4
Nos. 117/18	—
Nos. 119/24	*from* × 4
Nos. 125/203	*from* × 2
Nos. 204/5	—
Nos. 206/11	*from* × 8
Nos. 212/25	*from* × 2
Nos. O1/33	*from* × 8

AUSTRALIAN OCCUPATION

Stamps of German New Guinea surcharged

G.R.I. 2d. (1) **G.R.I. 1s.** (2) **G.R.I. 1d.** (3)

SETTINGS. The "G.R.I" issues of New Guinea were surcharged on a small hand press which could only accommodate one horizontal row of stamps at a time. In addition to complete sheets the surcharges were also applied to multiples and individual stamps which were first lightly affixed to plain paper backing sheets. Such backing sheets could contain a mixture of denominations, some of which required different surcharges.

Specialists recognise twelve settings of the low value surcharges (1d. to 8d.):

Setting 1 (Nos. 1/4, 7/11) shows the bottom of the "R" 6 mm from the top of the "d"

Setting 2 (Nos. 16/19, 22/6) shows the bottom of the "R" 5 mm from the top of the "d"

Setting 3 was used for the Official stamps (Nos. O1/2)

Setting 4, which included the 2½d. value for the first time, and Setting 5 showed individual stamps with either 6 mm or 5 mm spacing.

These five settings were for rows of ten stamps, but the remaining seven, used on odd stamps handed in for surcharging, were applied as strips of five only. One has, so far, not been reconstructed, but of the remainder three show the 6 mm spacing, two the 5 mm and one both.

On the shilling values the surcharges were applied as horizontal rows of four and the various settings divide into two groups, one with 3½ to 4½ mm between the bottom of the "R" and the top of numeral, and the second with 5½ mm between the "R" and numeral. The first group includes the very rare initial setting on which the space is 4 to 4½ mm.

G.R.I. 2d. "1" for "I" (Setting 1) **G.R.I. 1d.** Short "1" (Setting 1) **G.R.I. 1s.** Large "S" (Setting 1)

1914 (17 Oct)–**15.** *Stamps of* 1901 *surch.*

(*a*) *As T* **1**. "G.R.I." *and value* 6 *mm apart*

No.	Description	Unused	Used
1	1d. on 3 pf. brown	£200	£200
	a. "1" for "I"	£350	
	b. Short "1"	£350	
	c. "1" with straight top serif (Setting 6)	£400	
	d. "I" for "1" (Setting 12)	£450	
2	1d. on 5 pf. green	25·00	30·00
	a. "1" for "I"	£120	
	b. Short "1"	£110	
	c. "1" with straight top serif (Settings 6 and 9)	£140	
3	2d. on 10 pf. carmine	40·00	50·00
	a. "1" for "I"	£170	
4	2d. on 20 pf. ultramarine	30·00	35·00
	a. "1" for "I"	£140	
	e. Surch double, one "G.R.I." albino	£1750	
	f. Surch inverted	£2500	
5	2½d. on 10 pf. carmine (27.2.15)	60·00	£100
	a. Fraction bar omitted (Setting 9)	£1000	£1300
6	2½d. on 20 pf. ultramarine (27.2.15)	60·00	£100
7	3d. on 25 pf. black and red/*yellow*	£150	£175
	a. "1" for "I"	£325	
8	3d. on 30 pf. black and orange/*buff*	£175	£200
	a. "1" for "I"	£350	
	e. Surch double	£2500	£2500
9	4d. on 40 pf. black and carmine	£225	£250
	a. "1" for "I"	£450	
	e. Surch double	£850	£1100
	f. Surch inverted	£2500	
10	5d. on 50 pf. black and purple/*buff*	£350	£450
	a. "1" for "I"	£700	
	e. Surch double	£2500	
11	8d. on 80 pf. black and carmine/*rose*	£600	£750
	a. "1" for "I"	£1100	
	d. No stop after "d"	£1200	

(*b*) *As T* **2**. "G.R.I." *and value* 3½ *to* 4 *mm apart*

No.	Description	Unused	Used
12	1s. on 1 m. carmine	£1300	£1600
	a. Large "s"	£2750	£2750
13	2s. on 2 m. blue	£1500	£1800
	a. Large "s"	£3000	£3500
	c. Error. Surch "G.R.I. 5s."	£7500	
14	3s. on 3 m. violet-black	£2750	£3250
	a. Large "s"	£4250	
	b. No stop after "I" (Setting 3)	£5000	£5000
15	5s. on 5 m. carmine and black	£4750	£5250
	a. Large "s"	£6500	
	b. No stop after "I" (Setting 3)	£6500	£8000
	c. Error. Surch "G.R.I. 1s."	£12500	

G.R.I. 3d. Thick "3" (Setting 2) **G.R.I. 5d.** Thin "5" (Setting 2)

1914 (16 Dec)–**15.** *Stamps of* 1901 *surch.*

(*a*) *As T* **1**. "G.R.I." *and value* 5 *mm apart*

No.	Description	Unused	Used
16	1d. on 3 pf. brown	35·00	40·00
	a. "I" for "1" (Setting 11)	£100	
	b. Short "1" (Setting 2)	£150	
	c. "1" with straight top serif (Settings 2 and 6)	55·00	60·00
	e. Surch double	£250	£325
	f. Surch double, one inverted	£950	
	g. Surch inverted	£550	£850
	h. Error. Surch "G.R.I. 4d."	£3500	

7 1d. on 5 pf. green 12·00 15·00
b. Short "1" (Setting 2) £100 £110
c. "1" with straight top serif (Setting 2) 27·00 35·00
e. "d" inverted — £800
f. "1d" inverted — £1750
g. "G.R.I." without stops or spaces — £1750
h. "G.I.R." instead of "G.R.I." £2500 £2500
i. Surch double £600
8 2d. on 10 pf. carmine 16·00 20·00
e. No stop after "d" (Setting 2) 75·00 90·00
f. Stop before, instead of after, "G" (Settings 4 and 5) £2250
g. Surch double £2750 £2750
h. Surch double, one inverted — £1500
i. In vert pair with No. 20 £8000
j. In horiz pair with No. 20 £8000
k. Error. Surch ".GR.I. 1d." £2000 £2000
l. Error. Surch "G.I.R. 3d." £3500
9 2d. on 20 pf. ultramarine 20·00 25·00
e. No stop after "d" (Setting 2) 60·00 75·00
f. No stop after "I" (Setting 11) £350
g. "R" inverted (Settings 4 and 5) — £1750
h. Surch double £550 £1100
i. Surch double, one inverted £1100 £1200
j. Surch inverted £1500 £2500
k. Albino surch (in horiz pair with normal) £3250
l. In vert pair with No. 21 £4000 £5000
m. Error. Surch "G.R.I. 1d." £3500 £3250
0 2½d. on 10 pf. carmine (27.2.15) £175 £225
1 2½d. on 20 pf. ultramarine (27.2.15) £1000 £1200
2 3d. on 25 pf. black and red/*yellow* 75·00 85·00
e. Thick "3" £425
f. Surch double £1500 £2500
g. Surch inverted £1500 £2500
h. Surch omitted (in horiz pair with normal) £4500
i. Error. Surch "G.R.I. 1d." £4500
3 3d. on 30 pf. black and orange/*buff* 70·00 80·00
e. No stop after "d" (Setting 2) £350
f. Thick "3" £325
g. Surch double £800 £1000
h. Surch double, one inverted £1000 £1300
i. Surch double, both inverted £1600 £2500
j. Surch inverted £1400
k. Albino surch
l. Surch omitted (in vert pair with normal) £2750
m. Error. Surch "G.R.I. 1d." £2500 £3250
24 4d. on 40 pf. black and carmine 80·00 90·00
e. Surch double £800
f. Surch double, one inverted £1000
g. Surch double, both inverted £2000
h. Surch inverted £1300
i. Error. Surch "G.R.I. 1d." £1500
j. Error. Surch "G.R.I. 3d." double £3500
25 5d. on 50 pf. black and purple/*buff* £120 £130
e. Thin "5" £600 £1000
f. Surch double £800
g. Surch double, one inverted £1400
h. Surch double, both inverted £2250
i. Surch inverted £1300
j. Error. Surch "G.I.R. 3d." £4500
26 8d. on 80 pf. black and carmine/*rose* £400 £450
e. Surch double £1500 £1500
f. Surch double, one inverted £1500 £1500
g. Surch triple £1600 £1800
h. Surch inverted £1750 £2500
i. Error. Surch "G.R.I. 3d." £4500

(*b*) *As T* 2. "G.R.I." *and value* 5½ *mm apart*
27 1s. on 1 m. carmine £1750 £2250
28 2s. on 2 m. blue £1900 £2500
29 3s. on 3 m. violet-black £3000 £3750
a. "G.R.I." double £8500
30 5s. on 5 m. carmine and black £8000 £9000

1915. *Nos.* 18 *and* 19 *further surch as in T* 3.
31 "1" on 2d. on 10 pf. £8000 £8000
32 "1" on 2d. on 20 pf. £8000 £5000

OFFICIAL STAMPS

O. S.

G.R.I.

1d.

(O 3*a*)

1915 (27 Feb). *Stamps of* 1901 *surch as Type* O 3*a*. "G.R.I." *and value* 3½ *mm apart.*
O1 1d. on 3 pf. brown 25·00 45·00
a. "1" and "d" spaced 75·00
b. Surch double £2000
O2 1d. on 5 pf. green 75·00 £110
a. "1" and "d" spaced £150

German New Guinea Registration Labels surcharged

4

4*a*

G.R.I.

3d.

Sans serif "G" and different "3"

1915. *Registration Labels surch* "G.R.I. 3d." *in settings of five or ten and used for postage. Each black and red on buff. Inscr* "(Deutsch Neuguinea)" *spelt in various ways as indicated.*

I. *With name of town in sans-serif letters as T* 4
33 Rabaul "(Deutsch Neuguinea)" £100 £120
a. "G.R.I. 3d." double £1000 £1100
b. No bracket before "Deutsch" £375 £450
ba. No bracket and surch double £2500
d. "(Deutsch-Neuguinea)" £160 £180
da. "G.R.I. 3d." double £2500 £2500
db. No stop after "I" £550
dc. "G.R.I. 3d" inverted £2000
dd. No bracket before "Deutsch" £550
de. No bracket after "Neuguinea" £550
34 Deulon "(Deutsch Neuguinea)" £4250
35 Friedrich-Wilhelmshafen "(Deutsch Neuguinea)" £110 £200
a. No stop after "d" £275
b. "G" omitted £1750
c. Sans-serif "G" £2500
d. Sans-serif "G" and different "3" £2000
e. Surch inverted — £2250
f. "(Deutsch-Neuguinea)" £125 £225
fa. No stop after "d" £325
36 Herbertshöhe "(Deutsch Neuguinea)" £160 £275
a. No stop after "d" £375
b. No stop after "I" £650
c. "G" omitted £2250
d. Surch omitted (in horiz pair with normal) £3250
e. "(Deutsch Neu-Guinea)" £300
37 Käwieng "(Deutsch-Neuguinea)" £375
a. No bracket after "Neuguinea" £1500
b. "Deutsch Neu-Guinea" £140 £225
ba. No stop after "d" £325
bb. "G.R.I." double £1500
bc. "3d." double £1500
bd. "G" omitted £3000
38 Kieta "(Deutsch-Neuguinea)" £300 £425
a. No bracket before "Deutsch" £900 £1000
b. No stop after "d" £650
c. Surch omitted (righthand stamp of horiz pair) £2750
d. No stops after "R" and "I"
e. No stop after "I" £900
f. "G" omitted £2000
39 Manus "(Deutsch Neuguinea)" £170 £275
a. "G.R.I. 3d." double £1500
b. No bracket before "Deutsch" £600 £750
40 Stephansort "(Deutsch Neu-Guinea)" — £1500
a. No stop after "d" — £2500

II. *With name of town in letters with serifs as T* 4*a*
41 Friedrich Wilhelmshafen "(Deutsch-Neuguinea)" £140 £225
b. No stop after "d" £300 £400
c. No stop after "I" £550 £700
d. No bracket before "Deutsch" £550 £700
e. No bracket after "Neuguinea" £550 £700
42 Käwieng "(Deutsch Neuguinea)" £110 £190
a. No stop after "d" £275
43 Manus "(Deutsch-Neuguinea)" £1100 £1600
a. No stop after "I" £1900 £1900

Stamps of Marshall Islands surcharged

SETTINGS. The initial supply of Marshall Islands stamps, obtained from Nauru, was surcharged with Setting 2 (5 mm between "R" and "d") on the penny values and with the 3½ to 4 setting on the shilling stamps.

Small quantities subsequently handed in were surcharged, often on the same backing sheet as German New Guinea values, with Settings 6, 7 or 12 (all 6 mm between "R" and "d") for the penny values and with a 5½ mm setting for the shilling stamps.

1914 (16 Dec). *Stamps of* 1901 *surch.*

(*a*) *As T* 1. "G.R.I." *and value* 5 *mm apart*
50 1d. on 3 pf. brown 35·00 40·00
c. "1" with straight top serif (Setting 2) 80·00 90·00
d. ".GR.I." and "1" with straight top serif (Settings 4 and 5) — £2750
e. Surch inverted £1300
51 1d. on 5 pf. green 40·00 45·00
c. "1" with straight top serif (Settings 2 and 11) 90·00 £100
d. "I" for "1" (Setting 11) £325
e. "1" and "d" spaced £300
f. Surch double £800 £1300
g. Surch inverted £1000
52 2d. on 10 pf. carmine 12·00 16·00
e. No stop after "G" (Setting 2) £500
f. Surch double £800 £1300
g. Surch double, one inverted £800 £1300
h. Surch inverted £1200
i. Surch sideways £1900
53 2d. on 20 pf. ultramarine 13·00 18·00
e. No stop after "d" (Setting 2) 35·00
g. Surch double £700 £1300
h. Surch double, one inverted £1300 £1500
i. Surch inverted £1500 £1500
54 3d. on 25 pf. black and red/*yellow* £250 £325
e. No stop after "d" (Settings 2 and 11) £500 £650
f. Thick "3" £650
g. Surch double £1000 £1300
h. Surch double, one inverted £1000
i. Surch inverted £1500
55 3d. on 30 pf. black and orange/*buff* £275 £350
e. No stop after "d" (Setting 2) £550
f. Thick "3" £700
g. Surch inverted £1300 £1500
56 4d. on 40 pf. black and carmine 80·00 £100
e. No stop after "d" (Setting 2) £225 £275
f. "d" omitted (Setting 2) — £2000
g. Surch double £1200 £1300
h. Surch triple £2000
i. Surch inverted £1300
j. Error. Surch "G.R.I. 1d." £3000
k. Error. Surch "G.R.I. 3d." £3000
57 5d. on 50 pf. black and purple/*buff* £100 £130
e. Thin "5" £2000
f. "d" omitted (Setting 2) £600
g. Surch double £1500
h. Surch inverted £1800
58 8d. on 80 pf. black and carmine/*rose* £450 £550
e. Surch double £1500
f. Surch double, both inverted £1700 £2000
g. Surch triple £2500
h. Surch inverted £1400 £2000

(*b*) *As T* 2. "G.R.I." *and value* 3½-4 *mm apart*
59 1s. on 1 m. carmine £1400 £1700
b. No stop after "I" £2500
e. Surch double £5500
60 2s. on 2 m. blue £950 £1200
b. No stop after "I" £2000 £2500
e. Surch double £5500
f. Surch double, one inverted £4000 £4000
61 3s. on 3 m. violet-black £2500 £3000
b. No stop after "I" £3500
e. Surch double £5500 £6500
62 5s. on 5 m. carmine and black £4750 £5500
e. Surch double, one inverted — £8500

1915. *Nos.* 52 *and* 53 *further surch as in T* 3.
63 "1" on 2d. on 10 pf. carmine £140 £170
a. "1" double £5000
b. "1" inverted £5000 £5000
64 "1" on 2d. on 20 pf. ultramarine £2750 £2000
a. On No 53e. £4500 £2750
b. "1" inverted £6000 £6000

1915. *Stamps of* 1901 *surch.*

(*a*) *As T* 1. "G.R.I." *and value* 6 *mm apart*
64*c* 1d. on 3 pf. brown £425
cc. "1" with straight top serif (Setting 6) — £1100
cd. "I" for "1" (Setting 12) £550
ce. Surch inverted £2000
64*d* 1d. on 5 pf. green £425 £700
dc. "1" with straight top serif (Setting 6) £550
dd. "I" for "1" (Setting 12) £550
de. Surch inverted £2000
64*e* 2d. on 10 pf. carmine £650 £900
64*f* 2d. on 20 pf. ultramarine £550 £900
fe. Surch inverted £2000
64*g* 2½d. on 10 pf. carmine £3500
64*h* 2½d. on 20 pf. ultramarine £5000
64*i* 3d. on 25 pf. black and red/*yellow* £800 £1100
64*j* 3d. on 30 pf. black and orange/*buff* £850 £1100
je. Error. Surch "G.R.I. 1d." £3000
64*k* 4d. on 40 pf. black and carmine £800 £1100
ke. Surch double £2500
kf. Surch inverted £2500
64*l* 5d. on 50 pf. black and purple/*buff* £700 £1100
le. Surch double £2500
64*m* 8d. on 80 pf. black and carmine/*rose* £1100 £1300
me. Surch inverted £3000

(*b*) *As T* 2. "G.R.I." *and value* 5½ *mm apart*
64*n* 1s. on 1 m. carmine £3250
na. Large "s" (Setting 5) £4250
64*o* 2s. on 2 m. blue £2750
oe. Surch double, one inverted £8500
64*p* 3s. on 3 m. violet-black £4750
pe. Surch inverted £8500
64*q* 5s. on 5 m. carmine and black £7500
qa. Large "s" (Setting 5) £9000

Stamps of Australia overprinted

N. W. PACIFIC ISLANDS.	**N. W. PACIFIC ISLANDS.**	**N. W. PACIFIC ISLANDS.**
(*a*)	(*b*)	(*c*)

(**6**)

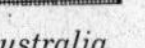

W 5 *of Australia*

W 2 *of Australia*

W 6 *of Australia*

1915–16. *Stamps of Australia optd in black as T* 6 (*a*), (*b*) *or* (*c*).

(i) *W* 5 *of Australia. P* 14 (4 Jan–15 March 1915)
65 5*a* ½d. green 1·00 4·25
66 ½d. bright green 1·50 4·50
67 1d. pale rose (Die I) (4.1) 2·75 3·00
68 1d. dull red (Die I) 3·50 3·25
69 1d. carmine-red (Die I) 3·25 3·25
a. Substituted cliché — £700
69*b* 1d. carmine-red (Die II) £250 £200
c. Substituted cliché £1100
70 4d. yellow-orange 3·25 7·50
a. Line through "FOUR PENCE" £400 £500
b. Pale orange-yellow
71 4d. chrome-yellow £300 £325
72 5d. brown 3·00 14·00

(ii) *W* **2** *of Australia. P* 12 (4 Jan 1915–March 1916)
73 **1** 2d. grey (Die I) .. .. .. 14·00 24·00
74 2½d. indigo (4.1.15) .. .. .. 2·75 13·00
76 3d. yellow-olive (Die I) .. .. .. 12·00 30·00
a. Die II £300 £350
ab. In pair with Die I £500 £550
77 3d. greenish olive (Die I) £190 £250
a. Die II £1300
ab. In pair with Die I £2250
78 6d. ultramarine .. .. .. 23·00 42·00
a. Retouched "E" £5000
79 9d. violet .. .. 27·00 48·00
81 1s. green .. .. 32·00 48·00
83 5s. grey and yellow (3.16) £750 £900
84 10s. grey and pink (12.15) £110 £160
85 £1 brown and ultramarine (12.15) .. £600 £750

(iii) *W* **5** *of Australia. P* 12 (Oct 1915–July 1916)
86 **1** 2d. grey (Die I) .. .. .. 5·50 11·00
87 2½d. indigo (7.16) £9000 £8000
88 6d. ultramarine .. .. .. 8·00 12·00
89 9d. violet (12.15) .. .. .. 9·50 14·00
90 1s. emerald (12.15) .. .. .. 8·00 20·00
91 2s. brown (12.15) .. .. .. 80·00 £100
92 5s. grey and yellow (12.15) .. .. 80·00 £100

(iv) *W* **6** *of Australia. P* 12 (Dec 1915–Aug 1916)
94 **1** 2d. grey (Die I) .. .. .. 4·00 9·00
a. In pair with Die IIA £175
96 3d. yellow-olive (Die I) .. .. .. 4·50 11·00
a. Die II .. .. 75·00 90·00
ab. In pair with Die I £140
97 2s. brown (8.16) .. .. .. 25·00 45·00
99 £1 brown and ultramarine (8.16) .. £400 £500

Dates for Nos. 67 and 74 are issue dates. All other dates are those of despatch. Nos. 65/6, 68/73, 76/81 were despatched on 15 March 1915.

For Die IIA of 2d. see note below Australia No. 45.

SETTINGS. Type **6** exists in three slightly different versions, illustrated above as (*a*), (*b*), *and* (*c*). These differ in the letters "S" of "ISLANDS" as follows:

(*a*) Both "SS" normal.
(*b*) First "S" with small head and large tail and second "S" normal.
(*c*) Both "SS" with small head and large tail.

Type **11**, which also shows the examples of "S" as the normal version, can be identified from Type **6**(*a*) by the relative position of the second and third lines of the overprint. On Type **6***a* the "P" of "PACIFIC" is exactly over the first "S" of "ISLANDS". On Type **11** the "P" appears over the space between "I" and "S".

It has been established, by the study of minor variations, that there are actually six settings of the "N.W. PACIFIC ISLANDS" overprint, including that represented by T **11**, but the following are the different arrangements of Type **6**(*a*), (*b*), and (*c*) which occur.

A. Horizontal rows 1 and 2 all Type (*a*). Row 3 all Type (*b*). Rows 4 and 5 all Type (*c*).

B. (½d. green only). As A, except that the types in the bottom row run (*c*) (*c*) (*c*) (*c*) (*b*) (*c*).

C. As A, but bottom row now shows types (*a*) (*c*) (*c*) (*c*) (*b*) (*c*).

Horizontal strips and pairs showing varieties (*a*) and (*c*), or (*b*) and (*c*) *se-tenant* are scarce.

The earliest printing of the 1d. and 2½d. values was made on sheets with margin attached on two sides, the later printings being on sheets from which the margins had been removed. In this printing the vertical distances between the overprints are less than in later printings, so that in the lower horizontal rows of the sheet the overprint is near the top of the stamp.

The settings used on King George stamps and on the Kangaroo type are similar, but the latter stamps being smaller the overprints are closer together in the vertical rows.

PURPLE OVERPRINTS. We no longer differentiate between purple and black overprints in the above series. In our opinion the two colours are nowadays insufficiently distinct to warrant separation.

PRICES. The prices quoted for Nos. 65 to 101 apply to stamps with opts Types **6** (*a*) or **6** (*c*). Stamps with opt Type **6** (*b*) are worth a 25 per cent premium. Vertical strips of three, showing (*a*), (*b*) and (*c*), are worth from four times the prices quoted for singles as Types **6** (*a*) or **6** (*c*).

One Penny
(10)

N. W.
PACIFIC
ISLANDS.
(11)

1918 (23 May). *Nos.* 72 *and* 81 *surch locally with T* **10**.
100 1d. on 5d. brown .. .. 90·00 80·00
101 1d. on 1s. green .. .. 90·00 80·00
Types **6** (*a*), (*b*), (*c*) occur on these stamps also.

1918–23. *Stamps of Australia optd with T* **11** ("P" *of* "PACIFIC" *over space between* "I" *and* "S" *of* "ISLANDS").

(i) *T* **5a** (*King*). *W* **5** *of Australia. P* 14
102 ½d. green .. .. 50 2·75
103 1d. carmine-red (Die I) .. .. .. 95 1·40
a. Substituted cliché £800 £500
b. Rosine. Rough paper, locally gummed (perfd "OS") £400 £150
103*c* 1d. carmine-red (Die II) .. .. .. £150 48·00
d. Substituted cliché £800 £500
e. Rosine. Rough paper, locally gummed (perfd "OS") .. .. — £500
104 4d. yellow-orange (1919) .. .. 3·25 16·00
a. Line through "FOUR PENCE" .. £1100 £1100
105 5d. brown (1919) .. .. .. 1·75 12·00

(ii) *T* **1** (*Kangaroo*). *W* **6** *of Australia. P* 12
106 2d. grey (Die I) (1919) .. .. .. 2·50 15·00
a. Die II .. .. 9·00 30·00
107 2½d. indigo (1919) .. .. .. 3·00 15·00
a. "1" of "½" omitted £5500 £5000
108 2½d. blue (1920) .. .. .. 6·00 22·00
109 3d. greenish olive (Die I) (1919) .. 14·00 17·00
a. Die II .. .. 35·00 50·00
ab. In pair with Die I £300
b. Light olive (Die II) (1923) .. .. 7·00 13·00
110 6d. ultramarine (1919) .. .. .. 4·50 14·00
111 6d. greyish ultramarine (1922) .. .. 40·00 60·00
112 9d. violet (1919) .. .. 6·50 30·00
113 1s. emerald .. .. 6·50 25·00
114 1s. pale blue-green .. .. .. 13·00 25·00
115 2s. brown (1919) .. .. .. 28·00 38·00
116 5s. grey and yellow (1919) .. .. 60·00 60·00
117 10s. grey and bright pink (1919) £150 £200
118 £1 brown and ultramarine (1922) .. £2750

(iii) *T* **5a**. *W* **6a** *of Australia* (*Mult Crown A*). *P* 14
119 ½d. green (1919) .. .. 40 3·50
Type **11** differs from Type **6** (*a*) in the position of the "P" of "PACIFIC", which is further to the left in Type **11**.

1921–22. *T* **5a** *of Australia. W* **5** *of Australia. Colour changes and new value. Optd with T* **11**.
120 1d. bright violet (1922) .. .. .. 1·00 5·00
121 2d. orange .. .. 2·50 4·50
122 2d. scarlet (1922) .. .. .. 3·50 8·00
123 4d. violet (1922) .. .. .. 22·00 40·00
a. "FOUR PENCE" in thinner letters .. £750
124 4d. ultramarine (1922) .. .. .. 10·00 38·00
a. "FOUR PENCE" in thinner letters .. £750
120/4 .. .. *Set of* 5 35·00 85·00

MANDATED TERRITORY OF NEW GUINEA

PRINTERS. See note at the beginning of Australia.

12 Native Village

(**13**)

(Des R. Harrison. Eng T. Harrison. Recess Note Printing Branch, Treasury, Melbourne, from 1926 Note Ptg Branch, Commonwealth Bank of Australia, Melbourne).

1925–28. *P* 11.
125 **12** ½d. orange .. .. 1·25 3·50
126 1d. green .. .. 1·50 3·50
126*a* 1½d. orange-vermilion (1926) .. .. 1·50 2·25
127 2d. claret .. .. 1·75 4·50
128 3d. blue .. .. 4·00 4·00
129 4d. olive-green .. .. 11·00 15·00
130 6d. dull yellow-brown .. .. .. 13·00 32·00
a. Olive-bistre (1927) .. .. .. 6·00 32·00
b. Pale yellow-bistre (1928) .. .. 4·50 32·00
131 9d. dull purple (*to violet*) .. .. 13·00 32·00
132 1s. dull blue-green .. .. .. 15·00 22·00
133 2s. brown-lake .. .. 28·00 38·00
134 5s. olive-bistre .. .. 48·00 65·00
135 10s. dull rose £110 £160
136 £1 dull olive-green £200 £250
125/36 .. .. *Set of* 13 £400 £550

1931 (8 June). *Air. Optd with T* **13**. *P* 11.
137 **12** ½d. orange .. .. 60 2·50
138 1d. green .. .. 1·25 2·50
139 1½d. orange-vermilion .. .. .. 1·00 4·00
140 2d. claret .. .. 1·00 7·00
141 3d. blue .. .. 1·50 8·00
142 4d. olive-green .. .. 1·25 7·50
143 6d. pale yellow-bistre .. .. .. 1·75 13·00
144 9d. violet .. .. 3·00 15·00
145 1s. dull blue-green .. .. .. 3·00 16·00
146 2s. brown-lake .. .. 7·00 25·00
147 5s. olive-bistre .. .. 20·00 48·00
148 10s. bright pink .. .. 65·00 85·00
149 £1 olive-grey £110 £140
137/49 .. .. *Set of* 13 £200 £325

14 Raggiana Bird of Paradise (Dates either side of value)

AIR
MAIL
(**15**)

(Recess John Ash, Melbourne)

1931 (2 Aug). *Tenth Anniv of Australian Administration. T* **14** (*with dates*). *P* 11.
150 **14** 1d. green 70 40
151 1½d. vermilion .. .. 4·00 8·50
152 2d. claret .. .. 2·50 2·00
153 3d. blue .. .. 3·00 4·00
154 4d. olive-green .. .. 5·00 11·00
155 5d. deep blue-green .. .. .. 3·50 12·00
156 6d. bistre-brown .. .. 3·00 12·00
157 9d. violet .. .. 5·50 14·00
158 1s. pale blue-green .. .. .. 5·00 14·00
159 2s. brown-lake .. .. 6·50 24·00
160 5s. olive-brown .. .. 35·00 48·00
161 10s. bright pink .. .. 75·00 £120
162 £1 olive-grey £140 £200
150/62 .. .. *Set of* 13 £250 £425

1931 (2 Aug). *Air. Optd with T* **15**.
163 **14** ½d. orange 45 75
164 1d. green .. .. 1·00 2·25
165 1½d. vermilion .. .. 1·40 5·50
166 2d. claret .. .. 1·00 2·75
167 3d. blue .. .. 2·75 3·25
168 4d. olive-green .. .. 3·00 5·00
169 5d. deep blue-green .. .. .. 3·50 6·50
170 6d. bistre-brown .. .. 6·00 18·00
171 9d. violet .. .. 7·50 15·00
172 1s. pale blue-green .. .. .. 6·50 15·00
173 2s. dull lake .. .. 10·00 38·00
174 **14** 5s. olive-brown .. .. 25·00 48·0
175 10s. bright pink .. .. 60·00 £10
176 £1 olive-grey £100 £17
163/76 .. .. *Set of* 14 £200 £35

1932 (30 June)–**1934.** *T* **14** (*redrawn without dates*). *P* 11.
177 1d. green 50 2
178 1½d. claret .. .. 60 5·0
179 2d. vermilion 55 2
179*a* 2½d. green (14.9.34) .. .. 3·50 9·0
180 3d. blue 90 8
180*a* 3½d. aniline carmine (14.9.34) .. .. 8·00 9·0
181 4d. olive-green .. .. 75 2·2
182 5d. deep blue-green 75 7
183 6d. bistre-brown .. .. 85 3·0
184 9d. violet .. .. 7·50 17·0
185 1s. blue-green .. .. 4·00 10·0
186 2s. dull lake .. .. 4·00 16·0
187 5s. olive .. .. 27·00 45·0
188 10s. pink .. .. 60·00 80·0
189 £1 olive-grey .. .. 90·00 £10
177/89 .. .. *Set of* 15 £190 £25

1932 (30 June)–**34.** *Air. T* **14** (*redrawn without dates*), *optd wi* *T* **15**. *P* 11.
190 ½d. orange .. .. 40 1·5
191 1d. green .. .. 40 1·5
192 1½d. claret .. .. 55 4·5
193 2d. vermilion 60 3
193*a* 2½d. green (14.9.34) .. .. 2·75 2·2
194 3d. blue .. .. 1·10 1·6
194*a* 3½d. aniline carmine (14.9.34) .. .. 3·50 3·2
195 4d. olive-green .. .. 2·50 5·5
196 5d. deep blue-green .. .. 4·25 7·5
197 6d. bistre-brown .. .. 2·75 9·0
198 9d. violet .. .. 5·50 9·0
199 1s. pale blue-green .. .. 4·50 7·5
200 2s. dull lake .. .. 5·50 24·0
201 5s. olive-brown .. .. 30·00 45·0
202 10s. pink .. .. 65·00 70·0
203 £1 olive-grey .. .. 75·00 55·0
190/203 .. .. *Set of* 16 £180 £20
Two sheets were reported of the ½d. without overprint but it believed they were not issued (*Price* £125 *un*.).

16 Bulolo Goldfields

(Recess John Ash, Melbourne)

1935 (1 May). *Air. P* 11.
204 **16** £2 bright violet £225 £17
205 £5 emerald-green £600 £50

HIS MAJESTY'S
JUBILEE.
1910 — 1935
(**17**)

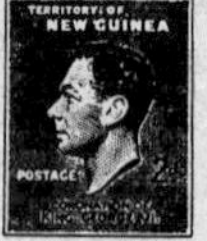

18

1935 (27 June). *Silver Jubilee. As Nos.* 177 *and* 179, *but shin paper. Optd with T* **17**.
206 1d. green 45 35
207 2d. vermilion 55 35

(Recess John Ash, Melbourne)

1937 (18 May). *Coronation. P* 11.
208 **18** 2d. scarlet 50 3
209 3d. blue 50 3
210 5d. green 50 3
a. Re-entry (design completely duplicated) .. .. 60·00 75·0
211 1s. purple 75 3
208/11 .. .. *Set of* 4 2·00 1·1

(Recess John Ash, Melbourne)

1939 (1 Mar). *Air. Inscr* "AIR MAIL POSTAGE" *at foot. P* 11.
212 **16** ½d. orange .. .. 80 3·2
213 1d. green .. .. 1·25 2·0
214 1½d. claret .. .. 80 5·0
215 2d. vermilion .. .. 3·00 3·0
216 3d. blue .. .. 3·50 8·0
217 4d. yellow-olive .. .. 3·00 7·5
218 5d. deep green .. .. 2·75 2·2
219 6d. bistre-brown .. .. 3·50 9·5
220 9d. violet .. .. 3·50 14·0
221 1s. pale blue-green .. .. 5·50 13·0
222 2s. dull lake .. .. 38·00 40·0
223 5s. olive-brown .. .. 80·00 85·0
224 10s. pink £225 £18
225 £1 olive-green £120 £13
212/25 .. .. *Set of* 14 £450 £45

OFFICIAL STAMPS

Australian stamps perforated "O S" exist with overprint Type 11 for use in New Guinea. We do not list such varieties.

O S (O 1) **O S** (O 2)

1925–31. *Optd with Type* O **1.** *P* 11.

No.	Type	Description	Unused	Used
O3	12	1d. green	80	4·00
O4		1½d. orange-vermilion (1931)	5·50	16·00
O5		2d. claret	1·60	3·75
O6		3d. blue	2·00	5·50
O7		4d. olive-green	3·00	8·50
O8		6d. olive-bistre	13·00	35·00
		a. Pale yellow-bistre (1931)	7·00	35·00
O9		9d. violet	3·75	35·00
O10		1s. dull blue-green	5·00	35·00
O11		2s. brown-lake	27·00	60·00
O3/11		*Set of* 9	50·00	£180

1931 (2 Aug). *Optd with Type* O **2.** *P* 11.

No.	Type	Description	Unused	Used
O12	14	1d. green	1·25	9·00
O13		1½d. vermilion	2·25	12·00
O14		2d. claret	2·75	7·00
O15		3d. blue	2·25	6·00
O16		4d. olive-green	2·25	8·50
O17		5d. deep blue-green	4·50	12·00
O18		6d. bistre-brown	7·50	17·00
O19		9d. violet	8·00	28·00
O20		1s. pale blue-green	12·00	28·00
O21		2s. brown-lake	35·00	70·00
O22		5s. olive-brown	£120	£180
O12/22		*Set of* 11	£180	£325

1932 (30 June)–**34.** *T* **14** (*redrawn without dates*), *optd with Type* O **2.** *P* 11.

No.	Description	Unused	Used
O23	1d. green	1·50	3·50
O24	1½d. claret	2·75	10·00
O25	2d. vermilion	2·75	2·75
O26	2½d. green (14.9.34)	2·75	7·50
O27	3d. blue	4·50	11·00
O28	3½d. aniline carmine (14.9.34)	3·00	10·00
O29	4d. olive-green	4·50	13·00
O30	5d. deep blue-green	4·50	13·00
O31	6d. bistre-brown	6·00	24·00
O32	9d. violet	10·00	35·00
O33	1s. pale blue-green	15·00	28·00
O34	2s. dull lake	35·00	80·00
O35	5s. olive-brown	£120	£170
O23/35	*Set of* 13	£190	£375

Civil Administration in New Guinea was suspended in 1942, following the Japanese invasion. It is believed that the Japanese intended to issue various New Guinea stamps overprinted with Japanese characters and an anchor, but such issues were never made available for postal purposes.

On resumption, after the Japanese defeat in 1945, Australian stamps were used until the appearance of the issue for the combined territories of PAPUA & NEW GUINEA.

New Hebrides

Stamps of NEW SOUTH WALES were used by various Postal Agencies in the New Hebrides from 1891 onwards. Similar Postal Agencies supplying the stamps of NEW CALEDONIA were opened from 1903 onwards.

PRICES FOR STAMPS ON COVER TO 1945

Nos. 1/8 (F1/5)	*from* × 10
No. 9	*from* × 2
Nos. 10/16 (F6/10)	*from* × 8
Nos. 18/28 (F11/32)	*from* × 6
Nos. 30/4 (F33/7)	*from* × 4
No. 35 (F32*a*)	—
Nos. 36/9	*from* × 3
Nos. 40/2 (F38/41)	*from* × 4
Nos. 43/51 (F42/52)	*from* × 5
Nos. 52/63 (F53/64)	*from* × 3
Nos. D1/10 (FD53/69)	*from* × 8

ANGLO-FRENCH CONDOMINIUM

The New Hebrides, an island group in the south-west Pacific, were recognised as an area of joint Anglo-French influence in 1878. The position was regularised by the Convention of 20 October 1906 which created a Condominium, the two nations having equal rights and shares in the administration of the islands.

Stamps inscribed in English or French were issued concurrently and had equal validity throughout the islands. A common currency was reflected in the face values from 1938.

Where common designs were used the main differences between stamps inscribed in English and those in French are as follows:
(a) Inscriptions in English or French.
(b) Position of cyphers. French issues normally have "RF" to the right or above the British royal cypher.
(c) French issues are without watermark, *unless otherwise stated.*

Inscriptions in English — Inscriptions in French

I. STAMPS INSCRIBED IN ENGLISH

NEW HEBRIDES. (1) — NEW HEBRIDES (2)

CONDOMINIUM. (1) — CONDOMINIUM (2)

1908 (29 Oct). *T* **23** *and* **24** *of Fiji optd with T* **1** *by Govt Printing Establishment, Suva. On the bicoloured stamps the word* "FIJI" *obliterated by a bar in the colour of the word. P* 14.

(*a*) *Wmk Multiple Crown CA*

No.	Description	Unused	Used
1	½d. green and pale green, **O** (No. 115)	1·00	7·50
1*a*	½d. green, **O** (No. 118)	40	4·50
2	1d. red, **O**	45	40
	a. Opt omitted (in vert pair with normal)	£5000	
3	1s. green and carmine, **C**	16·00	16·00

(*b*) *Wmk Crown CA*

No.	Description	Unused	Used
4	½d. green and grey-green	45·00	70·00
5	2d. dull purple and orange	60	70
6	2½d. dull purple and blue/*blue*	60	70
7	5d. dull purple and green	80	2·00
8	6d. dull purple and carmine	70	1·25
9	1s. green and carmine	£150	£200
1/9	*Set of* 9	£180	£250

1910 (15 Dec). *Types as last. Wmk Multiple Crown CA. P* 14. *Optd with T* **2** *by D.L.R.*

No.	Description	Unused	Used
10	½d. green, **O**	3·50	18·00
11	1d. red, **O**	10·00	8·50
12	2d. grey, **O**	60	3·00
13	2½d. bright blue, **O**	65	3·75
14	5d. dull purple and olive-green, **C**	65	5·00
15	6d. dull and deep purple, **C**	85	5·00
16	1s. black/*green*, **C** (R.)	85	6·50
10/16	*Set of* 7	15·00	45·00
10/16 Optd "Specimen"	*Set of* 7	£250	

3 Weapons and Idols

1d. (4)

(Des J. Giraud. Recess D.L.R.)

1911 (25 July). *Wmk Mult Crown CA. P* 14.

No.	Type	Description	Unused	Used
18	3	½d. green	85	1·60
19		1d. red	2·00	2·00
20		2d. grey	3·25	3·75
21		2½d. ultramarine	1·60	4·00
24		5d. sage-green	1·75	4·00
25		6d. purple	1·50	4·50
26		1s. black/*green*	1·50	7·00
27		2s. purple/*blue*	12·00	15·00
28		5s. green/*yellow*	24·00	45·00
18/28		*Set of* 9	40·00	75·00
18/28 Optd "Specimen"		*Set of* 9	£160	

1920 (June)–**21.** *Surch with T* **4** *at Govt Printing Establishment, Suva.*

(*a*) *On Nos.* 24 *and* 26/8

No.	Type	Description	Unused	Used
30	3	1d. on 5d. sage-green (10.3.21)	7·00	48·00
		a. Surch inverted	£1200	
31		1d. on 1s. black/*green*	1·00	10·00
32		1d. on 2s. purple/*blue*	1·00	10·00
33		1d. on 5s. green/*yellow*	1·00	10·00

(*b*) *On No.* F16

No.	Type	Description	Unused	Used
34	3	2d. on 40 c. red/*yellow*	1·00	11·00

(*c*) *On No.* F27

No.	Type	Description	Unused	Used
35	3	2d. on 40 c. red/*yellow*	£125	£275

1921 (Sept–Oct). *Wmk Mult Script CA. P* 14.

No.	Type	Description	Unused	Used
36	3	1d. scarlet	2·00	10·00
37		2d. slate-grey	3·25	17·00
39		6d. purple	11·00	40·00
36/9		*Set of* 3	15·00	60·00
36/9 Optd "Specimen"		*Set of* 3	65·00	

1924 (1 May). *Surch as T* **4**, *at Suva.*

No.	Type	Description	Unused	Used
40	3	1d. on ½d. green (No. 18)	2·00	14·00
41		3d. on 1d. scarlet (No. 36)	2·00	10·00
42		5d. on 2½d. ultramarine. (No. 21)	4·75	16·00
		a. Surch inverted	£1000	
40/2		*Set of* 3	8·00	35·00

5

(Recess D.L.R.)

1925 (June). *Wmk Mult Script CA. P* 14.

No.	Type	Description	Unused	Used
43	5	½d. (5 c.) black	60	4·00
44		1d. (10 c.) green	90	4·00
45		2d. (20 c.) slate-grey	1·50	2·25
46		2½d. (25 c.) brown	1·00	3·75
47		5d. (50 c.) ultramarine	1·50	2·50
48		6d. (60 c.) purple	2·75	7·00
49		1s. (1.25 fr.) black/*emerald*	2·75	10·00
50		2s. (2.50 fr.) purple/*blue*	6·00	15·00
51		5s. (6.25 fr.) green/*yellow*	6·00	18·00
43/51		*Set of* 9	20·00	60·00
43/51 Optd "Specimen"		*Set of* 9	£180	

CURRENCY. The currency used for the face values of issues to 1977 was an artificial, rather than an actual, monetary unit. The actual currencies in use being Australian dollars and the local franc.

6 Lopevi Is and Copra Canoe

(Des J. Kerhor. Recess B.W.)

1938 (1 June). *Gold Currency. Wmk Mult Script CA. P* 12.

No.	Type	Description	Unused	Used
52	6	5 c. blue-green	1·75	1·40
53		10 c. orange	1·25	50
54		15 c. bright violet	1·50	1·25
55		20 c. scarlet	1·60	80
56		25 c. reddish brown	1·60	1·00
57		30 c. blue	1·60	1·00
58		40 c. grey-olive	3·50	2·00
59		50 c. purple	1·60	50
60		1 f. red/*green*	4·00	6·00
61		2 f. blue/*green*	20·00	15·00
62		5 f. red/*yellow*	60·00	42·00
63		10 f. violet/*blue*	£150	70·00
52/63		*Set of* 12	£225	£130
52/63 Perf "Specimen"		*Set of* 12	£225	

(Recess Waterlow)

1949 (10 Oct). *75th Anniv of Universal Postal Union. As T* **21** *of Antigua, but inscribed* "NEW HEBRIDES". *Wmk Mult Script CA. P* 13½–14.

No.	Description	Unused	Used
64	10 c. red-orange	25	15
65	15 c. violet	30	15
66	30 c. ultramarine	30	15
67	50 c. purple	40	20
64/7	*Set of* 4	1·10	60

7 Outrigger Sailing Canoes

(Des C. Hertenberger (1 f. to 5 f.), R. Serres (others). Recess Waterlow)

1953 (30 Apr). *T* **7** *and similar horiz designs. Wmk Mult Script CA. P* 12½.

No.	Description	Unused	Used
68	5 c. green	25	10
69	10 c. scarlet	25	10
70	15 c. yellow-ochre	25	10
71	20 c. ultramarine	25	10
72	25 c. olive	25	10
73	30 c. brown	35	10
74	40 c. blackish brown	40	10
75	50 c. violet	45	10
76	1 f. orange	3·50	70
77	2 f. reddish purple	6·00	8·50
78	5 f. scarlet	12·00	26·00
68/78	*Set of* 11	21·00	32·00

Designs:—5 to 20 c. Type **7**; 25 to 50 c. Native carving; 1 to 5 f. Two natives outside hut.

1953 (2 June). *Coronation. As No.* 47 *of Aden.*

No.	Description	Unused	Used
79	10 c. black and carmine	20	25

10 Quirós Galleon and Map

(Photo Harrison)

1956 (20 Oct). *50th Anniv of Condominium. T* **10** *and similar horiz design. Wmk Mult Script CA. P* 14½ × 14.

No.	Description	Unused	Used
80	5 c. emerald	10	10
81	10 c. scarlet	10	10
82	20 c. deep bright blue	10	10
83	50 c. deep lilac	10	10
80/3	*Set of* 4	35	15

Designs:—5, 10 c. Type **10**; 20, 50 c. "Marianne", "Talking Drum" and "Britannia".

12 Port Vila: Iririki Islet   13 River Scene and Spear Fisherman

(Des H. Cheffer (T 12), P Gandon (others). Recess Waterlow)

1957 (3 Sept). *Wmk Mult Script CA. T* **12/13** *and similar horiz design. P* 13½.

No.	Type	Description	Unused	Used
84	12	5 c. green	15	10
85		10 c. scarlet	15	10
86		15 c. yellow-ochre	15	15
87		20 c. ultramarine	20	10
88	13	25 c. olive	20	10
89		30 c. brown	20	10
90		40 c. sepia	30	10
91		50 c. violet	30	10
92	–	1 f. orange	1·00	80
93	–	2 f. mauve	6·00	4·00
94	–	5 f. black	15·00	6·00
84/94		*Set of* 11	21·00	10·00

Design:—1 to 5 f. Woman drinking from coconut.

1963 (2 Sept). *Freedom from Hunger. As No. 76 of Aden.*

No.	Type	Description	Unused	Used
95		60 c. green	50	15

15 Red Cross Emblem

(Des V. Whiteley. Litho B.W.)

1963 (2 Sept). *Red Cross Centenary.* W w **12**. *P* 13½.

No.	Type	Description	Unused	Used
96	15	15 c. red and black	35	10
97		45 c. red and blue	45	10

16 Exporting Manganese, Forari   17 Cocoa Beans

(Des V. Whiteley, from drawings by J. White (10 c., 20 c.), K. Penny (40 c.), C. Robin (3 f.). Photo Harrison. Des C. Robin (5 c., 1 f.), J. White (15 c.), G. Vasarhelyi (25 c., 5 f.), A. Larkins, Turrell and Thomas (30 c., 50 c., 2 f.). Recess Govt Printing Works, Paris)

1963 (25 Nov)–**72**. *T* **16/17** *and similar horiz designs.* W w **12** (*10 c., 20 c., 40 c., 3 f.*) *or no wmk* (*others*). *P* 14 (*3 f.*), 12½ (*10 c., 20 c., 40 c.*) *or* 13 (*others*).

No.	Type	Description	Unused	Used
98		5 c. lake, purple-brown and greenish blue (15.8.66)	20	25
		*a. Lake and greenish blue** (29.2.72)	35·00	35·00
99		10 c. light brown, buff & emerald (16.8.65)	15	10
100		15 c. yellow-bistre, red-brown & deep violet	15	10
101		20 c. black, olive-grn & greenish bl (16.8.65)	45	10
102		25 c. reddish violet, orange-brown and crimson (15.8.66)	50	60
103		30 c. chestnut, bistre and violet	75	10
104		40 c. vermilion and deep blue (16.8.65)	80	1·40
105		50 c. green, yellow and greenish blue	60	10
106		1 f. red, black & deep bluish green (15.8.66)	2·50	1·75
107		2 f. black, brown-purple & yellow-olive	2·50	1·75
108		3 f. deep violet, orange-brown, emerald and black (16.8.65)	12·00	8·00
109		5 f. blue, deep blue and black (24.1.67)	18·00	14·00
98/109		*Set of* 12	35·00	26·00

Designs:—15 c. Copra; 20 c. Fishing from Palikulo Point; 25 c. Picasso Fish; 30 c. Nautilus shell; 40 c. Stingfish; 50 c. Blue-lined Surgeon (fish); 1 f. Cardinal Honeyeater; 2 f. Buff-bellied Flycatcher; 3 f. Thicket Warbler; 5 f. White-collared Kingfisher.

*In No. 98*a* the globe is printed in the same colour as the centre, instead of in purple-brown.

See also No. 129.

28 I.T.U. Emblem

(Des M. Goaman. Litho Enschedé)

1965 (17 May). *I.T.U. Centenary.* W w **12**. *P* 11 × 11½.

No.	Type	Description	Unused	Used
110	28	15 c. scarlet and drab	20	10
111		60 c. blue and light red	35	15

ALTERED CATALOGUE NUMBERS

Any Catalogue numbers altered from the last edition are shown as a list in the introductory pages.

29 I.C.Y. Emblem

(Des V. Whiteley. Litho Harrison)

1965 (24 Oct). *International Co-operation Year.* W w **12**. *P* 14½.

No.	Type	Description	Unused	Used
112	29	5 c. reddish purple and turquoise-green	15	10
113		55 c. deep bluish green and lavender	20	20

30 Sir Winston Churchill and St. Paul's Cathedral in Wartime

(Des Jennifer Toombs. Photo Harrison)

1966 (24 Jan). *Churchill Commemoration.* W w **12**. *P* 14.

No.	Type	Description	Unused	Used
114	30	5 c. black, cerise, gold and new blue	20	10
115		15 c. black, cerise, gold and deep green	40	10
116		25 c. black, cerise, gold and brown	50	10
117		30 c. black, cerise, gold and bluish violet	50	10
114/17		*Set of* 4	1·40	35

31 Footballer's Legs, Ball and Jules Rimet Cup

(Des V. Whiteley. Litho Harrison)

1966 (1 July). *World Cup Football Championships.* W w **12** (*sideways*). *P* 14.

No.	Type	Description	Unused	Used
118	31	20 c. violet, yellow-green, lake & yell-brn	20	10
119		40 c. chocolate, blue-grn, lake & yell-brn	30	10

32 W.H.O. Building

(Des M. Goaman. Litho Harrison)

1966 (20 Sept). *Inauguration of W.H.O. Headquarters, Geneva.* W w **12** (*sideways*). *P* 14.

No.	Type	Description	Unused	Used
120	32	25 c. black, yellow-green and light blue	20	10
121		60 c. black, light purple and yellow-brown	55	10

33 "Education"

(Des Jennifer Toombs. Litho Harrison)

1966 (1 Dec). *20th Anniv of U.N.E.S.C.O.* W w **12** (*sideways*). *T* **33** *and similar horiz designs. P* 14.

No.	Type	Description	Unused	Used
122		15 c. slate-violet, red, yellow and orange	20	10
123		30 c. orange-yellow, violet and deep olive	65	10
124		45 c. black, bright purple and orange	70	10
122/4		*Set of* 3	1·40	25

Designs:—30 c. "Science"; 45 c. "Culture".

36 The Coast Watchers

(Des R. Granger Barrett. Photo Enschedé)

1967 (26 Sept). *25th Anniv of the Pacific War. T* **36** *and similar horiz designs. Multicoloured.* W w **12**. *P* 14 × 13.

No.	Type	Description	Unused	Used
125		15 c. Type **36**	10	10
126		25 c. Map of war zone, U.S. marine and Australian soldier	10	15
127		60 c. H.M.A.S. *Canberra*	15	15
128		1 f. "Flying Fortress"	20	15
125/8		*Set of* 4	50	40

1967 (5 Dec). *New value with* W w **12** *sideways.*

No.	Type	Description	Unused	Used
129		60 c. vermilion and deep blue (as No. 104)	40	15

40 Globe and Hemispheres

(Des and eng J. Combet. Recess Govt Printing Works, Paris)

1968 (23 May). *Bicentenary of Bougainville's World Voyage. T* **40** *and similar horiz designs. P* 13.

No.	Type	Description	Unused	Used
130		15 c. emerald, slate-violet and red	10	10
131		25 c. deep olive, maroon and ultramarine	15	10
132		60 c. bistre-brown, brown-pur & myrtle-grn	15	10
130/2		*Set of* 3	35	20

Designs:—25 c. Ships *La Boudeuse* and *L'Etoile*, and map; 60 c. Bougainville, ship's figure-head and bougainvillea flowers.

43 "Concorde" and Vapour Trails   45 Kauri Pine

(Des S. W. Moss (25 c.), R. Granger Barrett (60 c.). Litho D.L.R.)

1968 (9 Oct). *Anglo-French "Concorde" Project. T* **43** *and similar horiz design.* W w **12** (*sideways*). *P* 14.

No.	Type	Description	Unused	Used
133		25 c. lt blue, orange-red & deep violet-blue	50	20
134		60 c. red, black and bright blue	60	25

Design:—60 c. "Concorde" in flight.

(Des V. Whiteley. Litho Format)

1969 (30 June). *Timber Industry.* W w **12**. *P* 14½.

No.	Type	Description	Unused	Used
135	45	20 c. multicoloured (*shades*)	10	10

No. 135 was issued in small sheets of 9 (3 × 3) printed on a simulated wood-grain background and with a decorative border showing various stages of the local timber industry. There is a wide range of shades on the printing.

46 Cyphers, Flags and Relay Runner receiving Baton   48 Diver on Platform

(Des C. Haley. Photo Delrieu)

1969 (13 Aug). *Third South Pacific Games, Port Moresby. T* **46** *and similar horiz design. Multicoloured. P* 12½.

No.	Type	Description	Unused	Used
136		25 c. Type **46**	10	10
137		1 f. Cyphers, flags and relay runner passing baton	15	10

(Des V. Whiteley. Litho P.B.)

1969 (15 Oct). *Pentecost Island Land Divers. T* **48** *and similar vert designs. Multicoloured.* W w **12** (*sideways*). *P* 12½.

No.	Type	Description	Unused	Used
138		15 c. Type **48**	10	10
139		25 c. Diver jumping	10	10
140		1 f. Diver at end of fall	20	10
138/40		*Set of* 3	30	15

51 U.P.U. Emblem and New Headquarters Building   52 General de Gaulle

(Des and eng J. Gauthier. Recess Govt Ptg Wks, Paris)

1970 (20 May). *Inauguration of New U.P.U. Headquarters Building. P* 13.

No.	Type	Description	Unused	Used
141	51	1 f. 05, slate, red-orange & bright purple	15	15

(Des V. Whiteley. Photo Govt Ptg Wks, Paris)

970 (20 July). *30th Anniv of New Hebrides' Declaration for the Free French Government. P* 13.
42 **52** 65 c. multicoloured 35 15
43 1 f. 10, multicoloured 45 15

35

(53)

54 "The Virgin and Child" (Bellini)

970 (15 Oct). *As No.* 101, *but W w* **12** (*sideways*) *and surch with T* **53**.
44 35 c. on 20 c. black, ol-grn & greenish black .. 20 25

(Des V. Whiteley. Litho Harrison)

970 (30 Nov). *Christmas. T* **54** *and similar vert design. Multi-coloured. W w* **12** (*sideways*). *P* 14½ × 14.
45 15 c. Type **54** 10 10
46 50 c. "The Virgin and Child" (Cima) 10 10

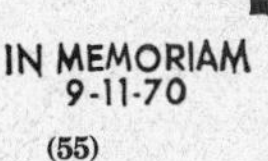

1890-1970

IN MEMORIAM
9-11-70

(55)

971 (19 Jan). *Death of General Charles de Gaulle. Nos.* 142/3 *optd with T* **55**, *vertical bars in black, inscriptions in gold.*
47 **52** 65 c. multicoloured 15 10
48 1 f. 10, multicoloured 15 15

56 Football

(Des G. Bétemps. Photo Delrieu)

971 (13 July). *Fourth South Pacific Games, Papeete, French Polynesia. T* **56** *and similar multicoloured design. P* 12½.
149 20 c. Type **56** 10 10
150 65 c. Basketball (*vert*) 20 10

57 Kauri Pine, Cone and Arms of Royal Society

58 "The Adoration of the Shepherds" (detail, Louis le Nain)

(Des P. Powell. Litho Harrison)

1971 (7 Sept). *Royal Society Expedition to New Hebrides*, 1971. *W w* **12** (*sideways*). *P* 14½ × 14.
151 **57** 65 c. multicoloured 15 10

(Des G. Drummond. Litho Questa)

1971 (23 Nov). *Christmas. T* **58** *and similar vert design. Multi-coloured. W w* **12**. *P* 14 × 13½.
152 25 c. Type **58** 10 10
153 50 c. "The Adoration of the Shepherds" (detail, Tintoretto) 15 15

59 "Drover" Mk III

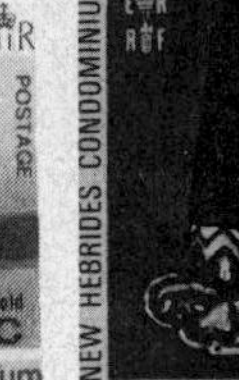

60 Ceremonial Headdress, South Malekula

(Des M. Goaman. Photo Delrieu)

1972 (29 Feb). *Aircraft. T* **59** *and similar horiz designs. Multi-coloured. P* 13.
154 20 c. Type **59** 35 15
155 25 c. "Sandringham" flying-boat 45 15
156 30 c. D.H. "Dragon Rapide" 45 15
157 65 c. "Caravelle" .. .. 1·25 1·25
154/7 .. .. *Set of* 4 2·25 1·50

(Des Odette Baillais (bird designs), Pierrette Lambert (others). Photo Govt Printing Works, Paris)

1972 (24 July). *T* **60** *and similar vert designs. Multicoloured. P* 12½ × 13.
158 5 c. Type **60** 10 10
159 10 c. Baker's Pigeon 25 10
160 15 c. Gong and carving, North Ambrym .. 15 15
161 20 c. Red-headed Parrot Finch 40 25
162 25 c. *Cribraria fischeri* (shell) 40 25
163 30 c. *Oliva rubrolabiata* (shell) 50 30
164 35 c. Chestnut-bellied Kingfisher 65 40
165 65 c. *Strombus plicatus* (shell) 75 60
166 1 f. Gong (North Malekula) and carving (North Ambrym) .. .. 1·25 1·00
167 2 f. Palm Lorikeet .. .. 4·00 4·00
168 3 f. Ceremonial headdress, South Malekula (*different*) .. .. 3·75 5·50
169 5 f. Green snail shell .. .. 7·50 11·00
158/69 *and* 199 .. .. .. *Set of* 13 27·00 35·00

61 "Adoration of the Kings" (Spranger)

62 Royal and French Cyphers

(Des G. Drummond. Litho J.W.)

1972 (25 Sept). *Christmas. T* **61** *and similar vert design. Multi-coloured. W w* **12**. *P* 14.
170 25 c. Type **61** 10 10
171 70 c. "The Virgin and Child in a Landscape" (Provoost) 10 10

(Des (from photographs by D. Groves) and photo Harrison)

1972 (20 Nov). *Royal Silver Wedding. Multicoloured; background colour given. W w* **12**. *P* 14 × 14½.
172 **62** 35 c. violet-black 15 10
173 65 c. yellow-olive 20 10

63 *Dendrobium teretifolium*

64 New Wharf at Vila

(Des Jennifer Toombs. Litho Questa)

1973 (26 Feb). *Orchids. T* **63** *and similar vert designs. Multi-coloured. W w* **12** (*sideways*). *P* 14 × 14½.
174 25 c. Type **63** 25 10
175 30 c. *Ephemerantha comata* 30 10
176 35 c. *Spathoglottis petri* 35 10
177 65 c. *Dendrobium mohlianum* 60 55
174/7 .. .. *Set of* 4 1·40 70

(Des PAD Studio. Litho Questa)

1973 (14 May). *Opening of New Wharf at Vila. P* 14 × 14½ (25 c.) *or* 14½ × 14 (70 c.).
178 **64** 25 c. multicoloured 20 10
179 – 70 c. multicoloured 40 30
The 70 c. is as T **64**, but in a horizontal format.

65 Wild Horses

66 Mother and Child

(Des Pierrette Lambert. Photo Govt Printing Works, Paris)

1973 (13 Aug). *Tanna Island. T* **65** *and similar horiz design. Multicoloured. P* 13 × 12½.
180 35 c. Type **65** 30 15
181 70 c. Yasur Volcano 55 20

(Des Moutouh (35 c.), Tatin d'Avesnières (70 c.); adapted PAD Studio. Litho Questa)

1973 (19 Nov). *Christmas. T* **66** *and similar vert design. Multi-coloured. W w* **12** (*sideways*). *P* 13½.
182 35 c. Type **66** 10 10
183 70 c. Lagoon scene 10 10

67 Pacific Pigeon

ROYAL VISIT
1974

(68)

(Des J. and H. Bregulla. Photo Govt Printing Works, Paris)

1974 (11 Feb). *Wild Life. T* **67** *and similar horiz designs. Multi-coloured. P* 13 × 12½.
184 25 c. Type **67** 95 35
185 35 c. Night Swallowtail (butterfly) .. .. 1·25 60
186 70 c. Green Sea Turtle .. .. 1·50 70
187 1 f. 15, Grey-headed Flying Fox .. .. 1·75 1·50
184/7 .. .. *Set of* 4 5·00 2·75

1974 (11 Feb). *Royal Visit of Queen Elizabeth II. Nos.* 164 *and* 167 *optd with T* **68**.
188 35 c. Chestnut-bellied Kingfisher (R.) 15 10
189 2 f. Palm Lorikeet 30 40

69 Old Post Office

(Des Odette Baillais. Photo Govt Printing Works, Paris)

1974 (6 May). *Inauguration of New Post Office, Vila. T* **69** *and similar triangular design. Multicoloured. P* 12.
190 35 c. Type **69** 15 40
a. *Tête-bêche* (pair). Nos. 190/1 .. .. 30 85
191 70 c. New Post Office 15 45
Nos. 190/1 were printed together, in *tête-bêche* pairs throughout the sheet.

70 Capt. Cook and Map

(Des J. Cooter. Litho J.W.)

1974 (1 Aug). *Bicentenary of Discovery. T* **70** *and similar horiz designs. Multicoloured. W w* **12** (*sideways on* 1 *f.* 15). *P* 11 (1 *f.* 15) *or* 13 (*others*).
192 35 c. Type **70** .. .. 1·75 1·25
a. Horiz strip of 3. Nos. 192/4 .. .. 5·00
193 35 c. William Wales and beach landing .. 1·75 1·25
194 35 c. William Hodges and island scene .. 1·75 1·25
195 1 f. 15, Capt Cook, map and H.M.S. *Resolution* (59 × 34 *mm*) .. .. .. 4·00 4·00
192/5 .. .. *Set of* 4 8·00 7·00
Nos. 192/4 were printed together, *se-tenant*, in horizontal strips of 3 throughout the sheet forming a composite design.

71 U.P.U. Emblem and Letters

72 "Adoration of the Magi" (Velazquez)

(Des Pierrette Lambert. Photo Govt Printing Works, Paris)

1974 (9 Oct). *Centenary of Universal Postal Union. P* 13 × 12½.
196 **71** 70 c. multicoloured 20 40

(Des J. Cooter. Litho Questa)

1974 (14 Nov). *Christmas. T* **72** *and similar multicoloured design. W* w **12** *(sideways on* 70 *c.). P* 14 × 13½ (35 *c.*) *or* 13½ × 14 (70 *c.*).
197 35 c. Type **72** 10 10
198 70 c. "The Nativity" (Gerard van Honthorst) (*horiz*) 10 10

73 Charolais Bull

74 Canoeing

(Des and eng J. Pheulpin. Recess Govt Printing Works, Paris)

1975 (29 Apr). *P* 13 × 12½.
199 **73** 10 f. bistre-brown, green & dull ultram 11·00 16·00

(Des J. Cooter. Litho Questa)

1975 (5 Aug). *World Scout Jamboree, Norway. T* **74** *and similar vert designs. Multicoloured. P* 13½.
200 25 c. Type **74** 30 10
201 35 c. Preparing meal 30 10
202 1 f. Map-reading 70 15
203 5 f. Fishing .. .. 3·00 2·50
200/3 .. .. *Set of* 4 4·00 2·50

75 "Pitti Madonna" (Michelangelo)

(Des PAD Studio. Litho Harrison)

1975 (11 Nov). *Christmas. Michelangelo's Sculptures. T* **75** *and similar vert designs. Multicoloured. W* w **12** *(sideways). P* 14½ × 14.
204 35 c. Type **75** 10 10
205 70 c. "Bruges Madonna" 15 10
206 2 f. 50, "Taddei Madonna" 60 50
204/6 .. .. *Set of* 3 75 55

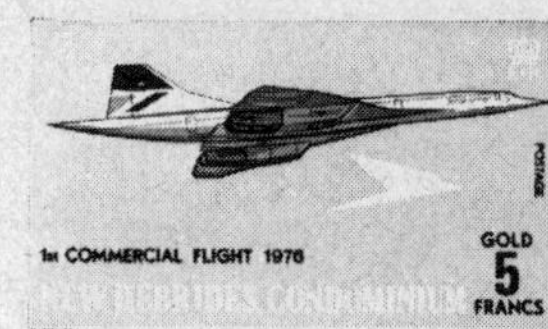

76 "Concorde"

(Des J. B. F. Chesnot. Typo Edila)

1976 (30 Jan). *First Commercial Flight of "Concorde". P* 13.
207 **76** 5 f. multicoloured .. .. 15·00 6·00

ALTERED CATALOGUE NUMBERS

Any Catalogue numbers altered from the last edition are shown as a list in the introductory pages.

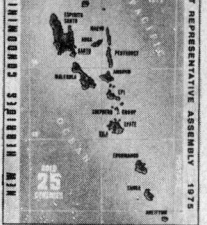

77 Telephones of 1876 and 1976

78 Map of the Islands

(Des J. Gauthier. Photo Delrieu)

1976 (31 Mar). *Telephone Centenary. T* **77** *and similar vert designs. Multicoloured. P* 13½.
208 25 c. Type **77** 15 10
209 70 c. Alexander Graham Bell 30 10
210 1 f. 15, Satellite and Nouméa Earth Station 50 50
208/10 .. .. *Set of* 3 85 60

(Des Odette Baillais. Photo Govt Printing Works, Paris)

1976 (29 June). *Constitutional Changes. T* **78** *and similar multicoloured designs. P* 13 (25 *c.*) *or* 13 × 12½ *(others).*
211 25 c. Type **78** 20 15
212 1 f. View of Santo (36 × 27 *mm*) 45 60
213 2 f. View of Vila (36 × 27 *mm*) .. .. 65 1·25
211/13 .. .. *Set of* 3 1·10 1·75
No. 211 shows the incorrect longitude, 116°E instead of 166°E.

79 "The Flight into Egypt" (Lusitano)

80 Royal Visit, 1974

(Des J. Cooter. Litho Walsall)

1976 (8 Nov). *Christmas. T* **79** *and similar vert designs. Multicoloured. W* w **14**. *P* 13½.
214 35 c. Type **79** 10 10
215 70 c. "Adoration of the Shepherds" 15 10
216 2 f. 50, "Adoration of the Magi" 45 50
214/16 .. .. *Set of* 3 60 55
Nos. 215/16 show retables by the Master of Santos-o-Novo.

(Des BG Studio. Litho Walsall)

1977 (7 Feb). *Silver Jubilee. T* **80** *and similar vert designs. Multicoloured. W* w **14**. *P* 13½.
217 35 c. Type **80** 15 10
218 70 c. Imperial State Crown 20 10
219 2 f. The Blessing 40 65
217/19 .. .. *Set of* 3 65 70

(New Currency: 100 centimes = 1 New Hebrides franc)

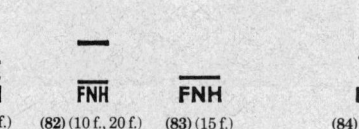

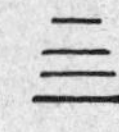

FNH (**81**) (5 f.) FNH (**82**) (10 f., 20 f.) FNH (**83**) (15 f.) 25 FNH (**84**)

1977 (1 July). *Currency change. Surch by Govt. Ptg Works, Paris. Nos.* 220/3 *as T* **81/3**, *others as T* **84**.
220 5 f. on 5 c. Type **60** 25 20
221 10 f. on 10 c. Baker's Pigeon 60 35
222 15 f. on 15 c. Gong and carving 55 50
223 20 f. on 20 c. Red-headed Parrot Finch .. 85 55
224 25 f. on 25 c. *Cribraria fischeri* (shell) .. 75 75
225 30 f. on 30 c. *Oliva rubrolabiata* (shell) .. 85 50
226 35 f. on 35 c. Chestnut-bellied Kingfisher .. 1·50 1·25
227 40 f. on 65 c. *Strombus plicatus* (shell) .. 1·25 1·50
228 50 f. on 1 f. Gong and carving .. .. 1·50 1·50
229 70 f. on 2 f. Palm Lorikeet .. .. .. 3·00 1·00
230 100 f. on 3 f. Ceremonial headdress .. .. 3·00 4·25
231 200 f. on 5 f. Green snail shell .. .. .. 7·00 12·00
232 500 f. on 10 f. Type **73** .. .. .. 17·00 22·00
220/32 .. .. *Set of* 13 35·00 42·00

FNH (**85**) (5 f.) FNH (**86**) (10 f.) FNH (**87**) (15 f.)

Two settings of 35 f. and 200 f. surcharges:
Setting I. Space of 1.4 mm between figures and "FNH".
Setting II. Space of 2.1 mm between figures and "FNH".

1977 (18 July)–**78**. *Nos.* 158/60, 162/5 *and* 169 *surch by I.P.V Port Vila, in typography with T* **85/7** *or similar surcharges.*
233 5 f. on 5 c. Type **60** (10.8.77) 50 1
a. Surch double .. .. ..
234 10 f. on 10 c. Baker's Pigeon (10.7.77) .. 50 1
235 15 f. on 15 c. Gong and carving (18.7.77) .. 2·50 1·2
b. Short bar in surcharge (5.8.77) .. 1·50 9
ba. Surch inverted .. .. ..
236 25 f. on 25 c. *Cribraria fischeri* (shell) (10.9.77) .. .. 45·00 20·0
a. "FHN" for "FNH" (R. 5/1) .. ..
237 30 f. on 30 c. *Oliva rubrolabiata* (shell) (Setting I) (10.9.77) .. .. .. £130 50·0
a. "FHN" for "FNH" (R. 5/1) .. ..
b. Setting II (6.1.78) .. .. ..
238 35 f. on 35 c. Chestnut-bellied Kingfisher (10.9.77) .. .. 2·00 5
239 40 f. on 65 c. *Strombus plicatus* (shell) (12.9.77) .. .. 1·50 5
240 200 f. on 5 f. Green snail shell (Setting I) (22.8.77) .. .. 17·00 17·0
a. Setting II (13.1.78) .. .. ..
241 500 f. on 10 f. Type **73** (14.9.77) .. .. 18·00 17·0
233/41 .. .. *Set of* 9 £190 95·0
50 f. and 100 f. local surcharges were also prepared but thes were not put on general sale, being available from the Philatel Bureau only (*Price for set of* 2 £40 *mint*, £40 *used*).
Dates are those on which the various values were surcharged.
Surcharges on Nos. 236/41 are similar to Type **84**, but with ne currency inscription as Type **86**.

89 Island of Erromango and Kauri Pine

90 "Tempi Madonna" (Raphael)

(Des L. Curtis. Litho J.W. (15, 30, 40 f.), Walsall (10, 35, 70, 500 f.), Questa (others))

1977 (6 Sept)–**78**. *Maps of the Islands. T* **89** *and similar ve designs. Multicoloured. W* w **14**. *P* 13½ × 13 (15, 30, 40 *f.*) *or* 1 (*others*).
242 5 f. Type **89** 15 1
243 10 f. Territory map and copra-making (9.5.78) 25 2
244 15 f. Espiritu Santo and cattle (23.11.77) .. 25 2
245 20 f. Efate and Vila P.O. 30 2
246 25 f. Malekula and headdresses (23.11.77) 35 4
247 30 f. Aoba, Maewo and pigs' tusks (23.11.77) 45 5
248 35 f. Pentecost and land diver (9.5.78) .. 50 6
249 40 f. Tanna and John Frum cross (23.11.77) 70 6
250 50 f. Shepherd Island and canoe 70 4
251 70 f. Banks Island and dancers (9.5.78) .. 1·75 1·4
252 100 f. Ambrym and idols .. .. .. 1·75 9
253 200 f. Aneityum and baskets .. .. 2·75 2·5
254 500 f. Torres Islands and archer fisherman (9.5.78) .. .. 6·00 7·5
242/54 .. .. *Set of* 13 14·00 14·0

(Des J.W. Litho Cartor S.A., France)

1977 (8 Dec). *Christmas. T* **90** *and similar vert designs. Multicoloured. W* w **14**. *P* 12.
255 10 f. Type **90** 10 10
256 15 f. "The Flight into Egypt" (Gerard David) 15 15
257 30 f. "Virgin and Child" (Batoni) 20 40
255/7 .. .. *Set of* 3 40 60

91 "Concorde" over New York

92 White Horse of Hanover

(Des BG Studio. Litho Rosenbaum Bros, Vienna)

1978 (9 May). *"Concorde" Commemoration. T* **91** *and similar horiz designs. Multicoloured. W* w 14 *(sideways). P* 13½.
258 10 f. Type **91** 65 65
259 20 f. "Concorde" over London 85 85
260 30 f. "Concorde" over Washington .. .. 1·10 1·10
261 40 f. "Concorde" over Paris .. .. .. 1·40 1·40
258/61 .. .. *Set of* 4 3·50 3·50

(Des Jennifer Toombs. Litho Questa)

1978 (2 June). *25th Anniv of Coronation. T* **92** *and similar vert designs. P* 15.

262 40 f. sepia, turquoise-blue and silver 35 55
 a. Sheetlet. Nos. 262/4, each × 2 .. .. 1·90
263 40 f. multicoloured 35 55
264 40 f. sepia, turquoise-blue and silver 35 55
262/4 .. .. *Set of* 3 95 1·50

Designs:—No. 262, Type **92**. No. 263, Queen Elizabeth II; No. 264, Gallic Cock.

Nos. 262/4 were printed together in small sheets of 6, containing two *se-tenant* strips of 3 with horizontal gutter margin between.

93 "Madonna and Child" (94)

(Des C. Abbott. Litho Questa)

1978 (1 Dec). *Christmas. Paintings by Dürer. T* **93** *and similar vert designs. Multicoloured. W* w **14**. *P* 14 × 13½.

265 10 f. Type **93** 10 10
266 15 f. "The Virgin and Child with St. Anne" .. 10 10
267 30 f. "Madonna of the Siskin" 10 10
268 40 f. "The Madonna of the Pear" 15 15
265/8 .. .. *Set of* 4 40 30

1979 (11 Jan). *1st Anniv of Internal Self-Government. As No.* 211 *surch as T* **94**.

269 **78** 10 f. on 25 c. multicoloured (blue background) 10 10
270 40 f. on 25 c. multicoloured (pale blue-green background) 20 20

95 1938 5 c. Stamp and Sir Rowland Hill 96 Chubwan Mask

(Des J.W. Litho Questa)

1979 (10 Sept). *Death Centenary of Sir Rowland Hill. T* **95** *and similar horiz designs showing stamps and Sir Rowland Hill. Multicoloured. W* w **14** (*sideways*). *P* 14.

271 10 f. Type **95** 10 10
272 20 f. 1969 25 c. Pentecost Island Land Divers commemorative 15 10
273 40 f. 1925 2d. (20 c.) 20 20
271/3 .. .. *Set of* 3 35 30
MS274 143 × 94 mm. No. 272 and as No. F286, but W w **14** (sideways) 75 90

(Des BG Studio. Litho Format)

1979 (16 Nov). *Festival of Arts. T* **96** *and similar vert designs. Multicoloured. W* w **14**. *P* 14.

275 5 f. Type **96** 10 10
276 10 f. Nal-Nal clubs and spears 10 10
277 20 f. Ritual puppet 15 10
278 40 f. Neqatmalow headdress 25 15
275/8 .. .. *Set of* 4 55 30

97 "Native Church" (Metas Masongo)

(Litho Delrieu)

1979 (4 Dec). *Christmas and International Year of the Child. Children's Drawings. T* **97** *and similar multicoloured designs. No wmk. P* 13 × 13½ (*horiz*) *or* 13½ × 13 (*vert*).

279 5 f. Type **97** 10 10
280 10 f. "Priest and Candles" (Herve Rutu) .. 10 10
281 20 f. "Cross and Bible" (Mark Deards) (*vert*) .. 10 10
282 40 f. "Green Candle and Santa Claus" (Dev Raj) (*vert*) 15 15
279/82 .. .. *Set of* 4 25 30

98 White-bellied Honeyeater

(Des G. Drummond. Litho Walsall)

1980 (27 Feb). *Birds. T* **98** *and similar horiz designs. Multicoloured. W* w **14** (*sideways*). *P* 14.

283 10 f. Type **98** 50 10
284 20 f. Scarlet Robin 70 10
285 30 f. Yellow-fronted White Eye 90 30
286 40 f. Fan-tailed Cuckoo .. .. 1·00 45
283/6 .. .. *Set of* 4 2·75 85

POSTAGE DUE STAMPS

POSTAGE DUE (D 1) POSTAGE DUE (D 2) POSTAGE DUE (D 3)

1925 (June). *Optd with Type* D **1**, *by D.L.R.*

D1 **5** 1d. (10 c.) green .. .. .. 38·00 1·00
D2 2d. (20 c.) slate-grey .. .. .. 45·00 1·00
D3 3d. (30 c.) red .. .. .. 50·00 2·50
D4 5d. (50 c.) ultramarine .. .. .. 55·00 4·50
D5 10d. (1 f.) carmine/*blue* .. .. .. 60·00 5·50
D1/5 .. .. *Set of* 5 £225 13·00
D1/5 Optd "Specimen" .. .. *Set of* 5 £225

1938 (1 June). *Optd with Type* D **2**, *by B.W.*

D 6 **6** 5 c. blue-green .. .. .. 9·00 13·00
D 7 10 c. orange .. .. .. 9·50 13·00
D 8 20 c. scarlet .. .. .. 15·00 17·00
D 9 40 c. grey-olive .. .. .. 23·00 26·00
D10 1 f. red/*green* .. .. .. 45·00 45·00
D6/10 .. .. *Set of* 5 90·00 £100
D6/10 Perf "Specimen" .. .. *Set of* 5 £120

1953 (30 Apr). *Nos.* 68/9, 71, 74 *and* 76 *optd with Type* D **3**, *by Waterlow.*

D11 5 c. green .. .. .. 3·00 3·50
D12 10 c. scarlet .. .. .. 1·25 3·25
D13 20 c. ultramarine .. .. .. 3·00 6·00
D14 40 c. blackish brown .. .. .. 7·00 13·00
D15 1 f. orange .. .. .. 6·00 15·00
D11/15 .. .. *Set of* 5 18·00 35·00

1957 (3 Sept). *Nos.* 84/5, 87, 90 *and* 92 *optd with Type* D **3**, *by Waterlow.*

D16 **12** 5 c. green .. .. .. 30 1·00
D17 10 c. scarlet .. .. .. 30 1·00
D18 20 c. ultramarine .. .. .. 1·25 1·50
D19 **13** 40 c. sepia .. .. .. 2·50 3·50
D20 – 1 f. orange .. .. .. 4·00 6·50
D16/20 .. .. *Set of* 5 7·50 12·00

II. STAMPS INSCRIBED IN FRENCH

NOUVELLES HEBRIDES (F 1) NOUVELLES-HEBRIDES (F 2)

1908 (21 Nov). *T* **15/17** *of New Caledonia optd with Types* **F 1** *or* **F 2** (1 *f.*), *by Govt Ptg Wks, Paris.*

F1 5 c. green .. .. .. 75 1·25
F2 10 c. carmine 80 80
F3 25 c. blue/*greenish* (R.) .. .. .. 2·75 2·25
F4 50 c. red/*orange* .. .. .. 4·00 3·25
F5 1 f. blue/*green* (R.) .. .. .. 7·00 6·50
F1/5 .. .. *Set of* 5 14·00 12·00

CONDOMINIUM (F 3) 10c. (F 4)

1910 (Aug)–**11**. *Nos.* F1/5 *further optd with Type* **F 3**, *or larger* (1 *f.*), *by Govt Ptg Wks, Paris.*

F 6 5 c. green 90 75
F 7 10 c. carmine 75 40
F 8 25 c. blue/*greenish* (R.) (1911) .. .. 1·50 2·50
F 9 50 c. red/*orange* (1911) .. .. 3·00 3·00
F10 1 f. blue/*green* (R.) .. .. 10·00 10·00
F6/10 .. .. *Set of* 5 14·50 15·00

All the above were released in Paris on 16 March 1910. The 5 c., 10 c. and 1 f. were issued in New Hebrides in August but the 25 c. and 50 c. were not received until 1911 after the issue of the definitive stamps and they were placed in reserve, although some may have been issued on request.

1911 (12 July). *Wmk Mult Crown CA. P* 14.

F11 **3** 5 c. green .. .. .. 70 1·50
F12 10 c. carmine 35 55
F13 20 c. greyish slate .. .. .. 95 1·25
F14 25 c. ultramarine .. .. .. 2·50 3·25
F15 30 c. brown/*yellow* .. .. .. 3·50 2·75
F16 40 c. red/*yellow* .. .. .. 1·40 2·75
F17 50 c. sage-green .. .. .. 2·00 2·75
F18 75 c. orange .. .. .. 5·00 7·50
F19 1 f. red/*blue* .. .. .. 2·00 2·25
F20 2 f. violet .. .. .. 7·00 10·00
F21 5 f. red/*green* .. .. .. 10·00 15·00
F11/21 .. .. *Set of* 11 32·00 45·00

1913. *As last but wmk* "R F" *in sheet or without wmk.*

F22 **3** 5 c. green .. .. .. 75 1·50
F23 10 c. carmine .. .. .. 75 1·00
F24 20 c. greyish slate .. .. .. 80 1·50
F25 25 c. ultramarine .. .. .. 75 2·00
F26 30 c. brown/*yellow* .. .. .. 1·50 3·50
F27 40 c. red/*yellow* .. .. .. 18·00 30·00
F28 50 c. sage-green .. .. .. 9·00 9·00
F29 75 c. orange .. .. .. 9·00 16·00
F30 1 f. red/*blue* .. .. .. 4·25 5·00
F31 2 f. violet .. .. .. 8·50 13·00
F32 5 f. red/*green* .. .. .. 11·00 18·00
F22/32 .. .. *Set of* 11 55·00 90·00

The above were placed on sale in Paris on 29 April 1912.

1920–21. *Surch as Type* **F 4**, *at Govt Printing Establishment, Suva, Fiji.* (*a*) *On stamps of* 1908–11 (June 1920).

F32*a* 5 c. on 50 c. red/*orange* (F4) £350 £350
F33 5 c. on 50 c. red/*orange* (F9) .. .. 1·75 4·00
F33*a* 10 c. on 25 c. blue/*greenish* (F8) .. .. 30 1·25

(*b*) *On stamps of* 1911–13 (10.3.21)

F34 **3** 5 c. on 40 c. red/*yellow* (F27) .. .. 22·00 40·00
F35 20 c. on 30 c. brown/*yellow* (F15) .. .. 7·50 23·00
F36 20 c. on 30 c. brown/*yellow* (F26) .. .. 10·00 25·00

(*c*) *On Inscr in English* (10.3.21)

F37 **3** 10 c. on 5d. sage-green (24) .. .. 12·00 18·00

1924 (1 May). *Stamps of* 1911–13 *surch as Type* **F 4**, *at Suva.*

F38 **3** 10 c. on 5 c. green (F22) .. .. 1·25 2·00
F39 30 c. on 10 c. carmine (F23) .. .. 1·25 1·50
F40 50 c. on 25 c. ultramarine (F14) .. .. 20·00 35·00
F41 50 c. on 25 c. ultramarine (F25) .. .. 2·50 10·00
F38/41 .. .. *Set of* 4 22·00 45·00

France Libre

F 5 (F 6)

(Recess D.L.R.)

1925 (June). *Wmk* "R F" *in sheet or without wmk. P* 14.

F42 **F 5** 5 c. (½d.) black .. .. .. 50 3·50
F43 10 c. (1d.) green .. .. .. 35 2·50
F44 20 c. (2d.) greyish slate .. .. .. 35 1·25
F45 25 c. (2½d.) brown .. .. .. 35 1·75
F46 30 c. (3d.) red .. .. .. 35 1·75
F47 40 c. (4d.) red/*yellow* .. .. .. 55 2·00
F48 50 c. (5d.) ultramarine .. .. .. 60 2·00
F49 75 c. (7½d.) yellow-brown .. .. .. 1·00 3·50
F50 1 f. (10d.) carmine/*blue* .. .. .. 1·75 3·00
F51 2 f. (1/8) violet .. .. .. 3·50 11·00
F52 5 f. (4s.) carmine/*green* .. .. .. 5·00 16·00
F42/52 .. .. *Set of* 11 13·00 42·00
F42/52 Optd "Specimen" .. .. *Set of* 11 £250

In July 1929 a batch of mail was carried by aircraft from Port Vila to the French cruiser *Tourville* for sorting and forwarding at Nouméa, New Caledonia. Stamps of the above issue (including those with English inscriptions) were affixed to covers and handstamped "PAR AVION" before cancellation.

1938 (1 June). *Gold Currency. Wmk* "R F" *in sheet or without wmk. P* 12.

F53 **6** 5 c. blue-green .. .. .. 1·00 1·25
F54 10 c. orange .. .. .. 1·00 75
F55 15 c. bright violet .. .. .. 1·00 1·25
F56 20 c. scarlet .. .. .. 1·00 1·00
F57 25 c. reddish brown .. .. .. 1·75 1·40
F58 30 c. blue .. .. .. 1·75 1·40
F59 40 c. grey-olive .. .. .. 1·00 2·50
F60 50 c. purple .. .. .. 1·00 1·00
F61 1 f. lake/*pale green* (*shades*) .. .. 1·50 2·25
F62 2 f. blue/*pale green* (*shades*) .. .. 11·00 11·00
F63 5 f. red/*yellow* .. .. .. 18·00 18·00
F64 10 f. violet/*blue* .. .. .. 55·00 55·00
F53/64 .. .. *Set of* 12 85·00 85·00
F53/64 Optd "Specimen" .. .. *Set of* 12 £275

1941 (15 Apr). *Adherence to General de Gaulle. Optd with Type* **F 6**, *at Nouméa, New Caledonia.*

F65 **6** 5 c. blue-green .. .. .. 3·25 7·00
F66 10 c. orange .. .. .. 3·75 6·00
F67 15 c. bright violet .. .. .. 4·50 8·00
F68 20 c. scarlet .. .. .. 5·00 8·00
F69 25 c. reddish brown .. .. .. 7·00 9·50
F70 30 c. blue .. .. .. 7·00 9·50
F71 40 c. grey-olive .. .. .. 7·00 11·00
F72 50 c. purple .. .. .. 7·00 8·00
F73 1 f. lake/*pale green* .. .. .. 8·50 10·00
F74 2 f. blue/*pale green* .. .. .. 9·50 14·00
F75 5 f. red/*yellow* .. .. .. 11·00 17·00
F76 10 f. violet/*blue* .. .. .. 13·00 18·00
F65/76 .. .. *Set of* 12 75·00 £110

1949 (10 Oct). *75th Anniv of U.P.U. As Nos.* 64/7. *Wmk* "R F" *in sheet or without wmk. P* 13½.

F77 10 c. red-orange .. .. .. 1·75 1·75
F78 15 c. violet .. .. .. 3·50 3·00
F79 30 c. ultramarine .. .. .. 4·50 5·00
F80 50 c. purple .. .. .. 5·00 5·50
F77/80 .. .. *Set of* 4 13·50 14·00

1953 (30 Apr). *As Nos.* 68/78. *Wmk* "R F" *in sheet or without wmk. P* 12½.

F81 **7** 5 c. green 15 10
F82 10 c. scarlet 20 10
F83 15 c. yellow-ochre 20 15
F84 20 c. ultramarine 30 30
F85 – 25 c. olive 30 30
F86 – 30 c. brown 40 35
F87 – 40 c. blackish brown 40 35
F88 – 50 c. violet 40 35
F89 – 1 f. orange .. .. .. 6·00 2·75
F90 – 2 f. reddish purple .. .. .. 12·00 17·00
F91 – 5 f. scarlet .. .. .. 24·00 40·00
F81/91 .. .. *Set of* 11 40·00 55·00

1956 (20 Oct). *Fiftieth Anniv of Condominium. As Nos.* 80/3. *Wmk "R F" in sheet or without wmk. P* 14½ × 14.
F92 **10** 5 c. emerald 60 40
F93 10 c. scarlet 60 40
F94 – 20 c. deep bright blue 60 55
F95 – 50 c. deep lilac .. .. 1·25 1·50
F92/5 .. .. *Set of* 4 2·75 2·50

1957 (3 Sept). *As Nos.* 84/94. *Wmk "R F" in sheet or without wmk. P* 13½.
F 96 **12** 5 c. green 45 15
F 97 10 c. scarlet 45 15
F 98 15 c. orange-yellow 70 25
F 99 20 c. ultramarine 70 25
F100 **13** 25 c. yellow-olive 80 25
F101 30 c. brown 90 40
F102 40 c. sepia 90 40
F103 50 c. reddish violet 90 35
F104 – 1 f. red-orange .. .. 4·75 2·00
F105 – 2 f. mauve .. .. 14·00 16·00
F106 – 5 f. black .. .. 26·00 27·00
F96/106 .. .. *Set of* 11 45·00 42·00

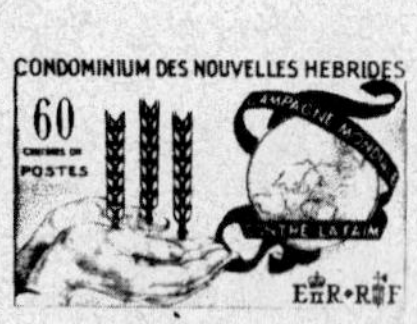

F **7** Emblem and Globe

F **8** Centenary Emblem

(Des and eng J. Derrey. Recess Govt Ptg Wks, Paris)

1963 (2 Sept). *Freedom from Hunger. P* 13.
F107 F **7** 60 c. deep bluish green and chestnut .. 9·00 6·50

(Des and eng J. Combet. Recess Govt Ptg Wks, Paris)

1963 (2 Sept). *Red Cross Centenary. P* 13.
F108 F **8** 15 c. red, grey and orange .. .. 5·50 3·75
F109 45 c. red, grey and yellow-bistre .. 10·50 12·00

1963 (25 Nov)–**72**. *As Nos.* 98/109 *and* 129. *No wmk. P* 12½ (10, 20, 40, 60 *c.*), 14 (3 *f.*) *or* 13 (*others*).
F110 5 c. lake, purple-brown and greenish blue (15.8.66) 40 30
a. *Lake and greenish blue* (29.2.72) .. 45·00 35·00
F111 10 c. lt brown, buff & emerald* (16.8.65) .. 80 80
F112 10 c. lt brown, buff and emerald (5.8.68) .. 30 15
F113 15 c. yellow-bistre, red-brown & dp violet .. 2·50 30
F114 20 c. black, ol-green & grnsh bl* (16.8.65) .. 2·25 2·50
F115 20 c. black, ol-green & grnsh bl (5.8.68) .. 60 25
F116 25 c. reddish violet, orange-brown and crimson (15.8.66) 60 40
F117 30 c. chestnut, bistre and violet .. 3·25 50
F118 40 c. vermilion and deep blue* (16.8.65) .. 3·50 4·00
F119 50 c. green, yellow and greenish blue .. 3·25 60
F120 60 c. vermilion and deep blue (5.12.67) .. 1·50 80
F121 1 f. red, black & dp bluish grn (15.8.66) .. 2·00 1·75
F122 2 f. black, brown-purple & yellow-olive .. 13·00 4·25
F123 3 f. multicoloured* (16.8.65) .. 11·00 14·00
F124 3 f. multicoloured (5.8.68) .. .. 5·50 6·00
F125 5 f. blue, deep blue and black (24.1.67) .. 15·00 16·00
F110/25 .. .. *Set of* 16 60·00 48·00

*Normally all French New Hebrides issues have the "RF" inscription on the right to distinguish them from the British New Hebrides stamps which have it on the left. The stamps indicated by an asterisk have "RF" wrongly placed on the left.

F **9** "Syncom" Communications Satellite, Telegraph Poles and Morse Key

(Des and eng J. Combet. Recess Govt Ptg Wks, Paris)

1965 (17 May). *Air. I.T.U. Centenary. P* 13.
F126 F **9** 15 c. blue, emerald and red-brown .. 4·50 3·00
F127 60 c. cerise, slate and deep bluish green 9·50 14·00

1965 (24 Oct). *International Co-operation Year. As Nos.* 112/13. *P* 14½.
F128 **29** 5 c. dp reddish purple & turquoise-grn 1·00 75
F129 55 c. deep bluish green and lavender .. 3·00 3·50

1966 (24 Jan). *Churchill Commemoration. As Nos.* 114/17. *P* 14.
F130 **30** 5 c. black, cerise, gold and new blue .. 85 35
F131 15 c. black, cerise, gold and deep green .. 2·25 50
F132 25 c. black, cerise, gold and brown .. 3·00 2·25
F133 30 c. black, cerise, gold and bluish violet 3·75 2·50
F130/3 .. .. *Set of* 4 9·00 5·00

1966 (1 July). *World Cup Football Championships. As Nos.* 118/19. *P* 14.
F134 **31** 20 c. violet, yellow-grn, lake & yell-brn .. 1·50 1·25
F135 40 c. chocolate, bl-grn, lake & yell-brn .. 2·00 1·75

1966 (20 Sept). *Inauguration of W.H.O. Headquarters, Geneva. As Nos.* 120/1. *P* 14.
F136 **32** 25 c. black, yellow-green and light blue 1·75 1·00
F137 60 c. black, mauve and yellow-ochre .. 2·50 1·75

1966 (1 Dec). *20th Anniv of U.N.E.S.C.O. As Nos.* 122/4. *P* 14.
F138 **33** 15 c. slate-violet, red, yellow and orange 1·00 50
F139 – 30 c. orange-yellow, violet & dp olive .. 1·75 1·50
F140 – 45 c. black, bright purple and orange .. 2·00 1·75
F138/40 .. .. *Set of* 3 4·25 3·50

1967 (26 Sept). *25th Anniv of the Pacific War. As Nos.* 125/8. *P* 14 × 13.
F141 15 c. Type **36** 30 25
F142 25 c. War Zone map, U.S. marine and Australian soldier 55 40
F143 60 c. H.M.A.S. *Canberra* 95 85
F144 1 f. "Flying Fortress" .. .. .. 1·50 1·50
F141/4 .. .. *Set of* 4 3·00 2·75

1968 (23 May). *Bicentenary of Bougainville's World Voyage. As Nos.* 130/2. *P* 13.
F145 **40** 15 c. emerald, slate-violet and red .. 20 20
F146 – 25 c. dp olive, maroon & ultramarine .. 40 40
F147 – 60 c. bistre-brn, brn-pur & myrtle-grn .. 90 90
F145/7 .. .. *Set of* 3 1·40 1·40

1968 (9 Oct). *Anglo-French "Concorde" Project. As Nos.* 133/4. *P* 14.
F148 **43** 25 c. lt blue, orange-red & dp violet-bl .. 2·00 1·25
F149 – 60 c. red, black and bright blue .. 3·50 2·50

1969 (30 June). *Timber Industry. As No.* 135. *P* 14½.
F150 **45** 20 c. multicoloured (*shades*) 15 20

1969 (13 Aug). *3rd South Pacific Games, Port Moresby, Papua New Guinea. As Nos.* 136/7. *Multicoloured. P* 12½.
F151 25 c. Type **46** 25 25
F152 1 f. Runner passing baton, and flags .. 1·25 1·00

1969 (15 Oct). *Pentecost Island Land Divers. As Nos.* 138/40. *Multicoloured. P* 12½.
F153 15 c. Type **48** 30 30
F154 25 c. Diver jumping 40 40
F155 1 f. Diver at end of fall .. .. .. 1·40 1·40
F153/5 .. .. *Set of* 3 1·90 1·90

1970 (20 May). *Inauguration of New U.P.U. Headquarters Building, Berne. As No.* 141. *P* 13.
F156 **51** 1 f. 05, slate, red-orange & brt purple .. 50 70

1970 (20 July). *30th Anniv of New Hebrides' Declaration for the Free French Government. As Nos.* 142/3. *P* 13.
F157 **52** 65 c. multicoloured 55 55
F158 1 f. 10, multicoloured .. .. .. 1·10 1·10

1970 (15 Oct). *No.* F115 *surch with T* **53**.
F159 35 c. on 20 c. black, ol-green & greenish blue 60 50

1970 (30 Nov). *Christmas. As Nos.* 145/6. *Multicoloured. P* 14½ × 14.
F160 15 c. Type **54** 15 15
F161 50 c. "The Virgin and Child" (G. Cima) .. 25 40

1971 (19 Jan). *Death of General Charles de Gaulle. Nos.* F157/8 *optd with T* **55**, *the vertical bars in black and inscriptions in gold.*
F162 **52** 65 c. multicoloured 75 55
a. Gold opt omitted .. .. ..
F163 1 f. 10, multicoloured .. .. .. 1·50 1·25
On No. F162a the vertical black bars are still present.

1971 (13 July). *4th South Pacific Games, Papeete, French Polynesia. As Nos.* 149/50. *Multicoloured. P* 12½.
F164 20 c. Type **56** 35 20
F165 65 c. Basketball (*vert*) 95 80

1971 (7 Sept). *Royal Society's Expedition to New Hebrides. As No.* 151. *P* 14½ × 14.
F166 **57** 65 c. multicoloured 50 50

1971 (23 Nov). *Christmas. As Nos.* 152/3. *Multicoloured. P* 14 × 13½.
F167 25 c. Type **58** 15 20
F168 50 c. "Adoration of the Shepherds" (J. Tintoretto) 30 35

1972 (29 Feb). *Aircraft. As Nos.* 154/7. *Multicoloured. P* 13.
F169 20 c. Type **59** 70 55
F170 25 c. "Sandringham" flying-boat 80 60
F171 30 c. DH "Dragon Rapide" 85 70
F172 65 c. "Caravelle" .. .. 2·75 2·75
F169/72 .. .. *Set of* 4 4·50 4·25

1972 (24 July). *As Nos.* 158/69. *Multicoloured. P* 12½ × 13.
F173 5 c. Type **60** 20 10
F174 10 c. Baker's Pigeon 80 15
F175 15 c. Gong and carving, North Ambrym .. 30 15
F176 20 c. Red-headed Parrot Finch .. .. 1·25 30
F177 25 c. *Cribraria fischeri* (shell) .. .. 1·00 30
F178 30 c. *Oliva rubrolabiata* (shell) .. .. 1·00 30
F179 35 c. Chestnut-bellied Kingfisher .. .. 1·75 40
F180 65 c. *Strombus plicatus* (shell) .. .. 1·75 60
F181 1 f. Gong, North Malekula and carving, North Ambrym .. .. .. 2·25 1·75
F182 2 f. Palm Lorikeet .. .. 10·00 8·00
F183 3 f. Ceremonial headdress, South Malekula (*different*) .. .. .. 8·00 9·00
F184 5 f. Green snail shell .. .. .. 14·00 17·00
F173/84 *and* F213 .. .. *Set of* 13 55·00 55·00

1972 (25 Sept). *Christmas. As Nos.* 170/1. *Multicoloured. P* 14.
F185 25 c. Type **61** 25 20
F186 70 c. "Virgin and Child" (Provoost) 50 45

1972 (20 Nov). *Royal Silver Wedding. As Nos.* 172/3. *W* w **12**. *P* 14 × 14½.
F187 **62** 35 c. multicoloured 75 50
F188 65 c. multicoloured .. .. .. 1·25 1·25

1973 (26 Feb). *Orchids. As Nos.* 174/7. *Multicoloured P* 14 × 14½.
F189 25 c. Type **63** 75 3
F190 30 c. *Ephemerantha comata* 80 5
F191 35 c. *Spathoglottis petri* 90 6
F192 65 c. *Dendrobium mohlianum* .. .. 2·75 3·0
F189/92 .. .. *Set of* 4 4·75 4·0

1973 (14 May). *Opening of New Wharf, Vila. As Nos.* 178/9. *Multicoloured. P* 14 × 14½ (25 *c.*) *or* 14½ × 14 (70 *c.*).
F193 25 c. Type **64** 75 50
F194 70 c. View of wharf (*horiz*) .. .. .. 1·50 1·75

1973 (13 Aug). *Tanna Island. As Nos.* 180/1. *Multicoloured P* 13 × 12½.
F195 35 c. Type **65** .. .. 1·50 7
F196 70 c. Yasur Volcano .. .. 2·50 1·5

1973 (19 Nov). *Christmas. As Nos.* 182/3. *Multicoloured P* 14 × 13½.
F197 35 c. Type **66** 45 3
F198 70 c. Lagoon scene .. .. 1·00 7

1974 (11 Feb). *Wild Life. As Nos.* 184/7. *Multicoloured P* 13 × 12½.
F199 25 c. Type **67** .. .. 2·50 7
F200 35 c. Night Swallowtail (butterfly) .. .. 3·75 1·5
F201 70 c. Green Sea Turtle .. .. .. 3·75 2·5
F202 1 f. 15, Grey-headed Flying Fox .. .. 4·50 5·0
F199/202 .. .. *Set of* 4 13·00 8·7

VISITE ROYALE
1974
(F **10**)

1974 (11 Feb). *Royal Visit of Queen Elizabeth II. Nos.* F179 *and* F182 *optd with Type* F **10**.
F203 35 c. Chestnut-bellied Kingfisher (R.) .. 1·00 4
F204 2 f. Palm Lorikeet .. .. 3·50 3·7

1974 (6 May). *Inauguration of New Post Office, Vila. As Nos.* 190/1. *Multicoloured. P* 12.
F205 35 c. Type **69** 50 65
a. *Tête-bêche* (pair). Nos. F205/6 .. 1·10 1·50
F206 70 c. New Post Office 60 85

1974 (1 Aug). *Bicentenary of Discovery. As Nos.* 192/5. *Multicoloured. P* 11 (1 *f.* 15) *or* 13 × 13½ (*others*).
F207 35 c. Type **70** .. .. 2·75 2·00
a. Horiz strip of 3. Nos. F207/9 .. 7·50
F208 35 c. William Wales and beach landing .. 2·75 2·00
F209 35 c. William Hodges and island scene .. 2·75 2·00
F210 1 f. 15, Capt. Cook, *Resolution* and map of islands (64 × 39 *mm*) .. .. .. 6·50 7·00
F207/10 .. .. *Set of* 4 12·50 11·50

1974 (9 Oct). *Centenary of Universal Postal Union. As No.* 196. *P* 13 × 12½.
F210*a* **71** 70 c. dp turquoise-blue, rosine & black 75 75

1974 (4 Nov). *Christmas. As Nos.* 197/8. *Multicoloured. P* 14 × 13½ (35 *c.*) *or* 13½ × 14 (70 *c.*).
F211 35 c. Type **72** 25 20
F212 70 c. "The Nativity" (G. van Honthorst) (*horiz*) 55 45

1975 (29 Apr). *As No.* 199. *P* 13 × 12½.
F213 **73** 10 f. bistre-brown, yellow-green & blue 20·00 26·00

1975 (5 Aug). *World Scout Jamboree, Norway. As Nos.* 200/3. *Multicoloured. P* 14 × 13½.
F214 25 c. Type **74** 55 20
F215 35 c. Preparing meal 75 30
F216 1 f. Map-reading .. .. 1·90 85
F217 5 f. Fishing .. .. 10·00 7·50
F214/17 .. .. *Set of* 4 12·00 8·00

1975 (11 Nov). *Christmas. As Nos.* 204/6. *Multicoloured, P* 14½ × 14.
F218 35 c. Type **75** 25 15
F219 70 c. "Bruges Madonna" 40 25
F220 2 f. 50, "Taddei Madonna" .. .. .. 2·25 2·75
F218/20 .. .. *Set of* 3 2·75 2·75

1976 (30 Jan). *First Commercial Flight of "Concorde". As No.* 207. *P* 13.
F221 **76** 5 f. multicoloured .. .. .. 17·00 11·00

1976 (31 Mar). *Telephone Centenary. As Nos.* 208/10. *Multicoloured. P* 13½.
F222 25 c. Type **77** 45 35
F223 70 c. Alexander Graham Bell .. .. 1·25 90
F224 1 f. 15, Satellite and Earth Station, Nouméa 1·60 2·00
F222/4 .. .. *Set of* 3 3·00 3·00

1976 (29 June). *Constitutional Changes. As Nos.* 211/13. *Multicoloured. P* 13 (25 *c.*) *or* 13 × 12½ (*others*).
F225 25 c. Type **78** 50 30
F226 1 f. Luganville (36 × 27 *mm*) .. .. 1·50 1·00
F227 2 f. Vila (36 × 27 *mm*) .. .. .. 2·50 1·90
F225/7 .. .. *Set of* 3 4·00 2·75
No. F225 shows the incorrect longitude, 116°E, instead of 166°E.
Nos. F226/7 exist with the inscription "PREMIERE ASSEMBLEE REPRESENTATIVE 1975" and the name of the city. These stamps were not available in the New Hebrides.

1976 (8 Nov). *Christmas. As Nos.* 214/16. *Multicoloured. P* 13½.
F228 35 c. Type **79** 25 15
F229 70 c. "Adoration of the Shepherds" 40 25
F230 2 f. 50, "Adoration of the Magi" .. .. 2·25 2·75
F228/30 .. .. *Set of* 3 2·75 2·75

1977 (7 Feb). *Silver Jubilee. As Nos.* 217/19. *Multicoloured. P* 13½.
F231 35 c. Type **80** 35 20
F232 70 c. Imperial State Crown 60 50
F233 2 f. The Blessing .. .. 1·00 1·25
F231/3 .. .. *Set of* 3 1·75 1·75

1977 (1 July). *Currency Change. Nos.* F173/84 *and* F214 *surch as T* **81/3** (Nos. F234/7) *or as T* **84** (*others*) *by Govt Ptg Wks, Paris.*
F234 5 f. on 5 c. Type **60** 35 35
F235 10 f. on 10 c. Baker's Pigeon 60 40
F236 15 f. on 15 c. Gong and carving, North Ambrym 60 60
F237 20 f. on 20 c. Red-headed Parrot Finch .. 1·25 85
F238 25 f. on 25 c. *Cribraria fischeri* (shell) .. 1·25 1·00
F239 30 f. on 30 c. *Oliva rubrolablata* (shell) .. 1·50 1·50
F240 35 f. on 35 c. Chestnut-bellied Kingfisher .. 2·00 1·50
F241 40 f. on 65 c. *Strombus plicatus* (shell) .. 2·00 2·00
F242 50 f. on 1 f. Gong, North Malekula, and carving, North Ambrym .. .. 2·00 2·00
F243 70 f. on 2 f. Palm Lorikeet .. .. .. 3·75 2·75
F244 100 f. on 3 f. Ceremonial headdress, South Malekula .. .. 4·25 4·50
F245 200 f. on 5 f. Green snail shell .. .. 12·00 15·00
F246 500 f. on 10 f. Type **73** .. .. .. 25·00 30·00
F234/46 .. .. *Set of* 13 50·00 55·00

1977 (18 July)–**78**. *Nos.* F173/5, F177/180, F184 *and* F213 *surch by I.P.V., Port Vila, in typography with T* **85/7** *or similar surcharges.*
F247 5 f. on 5 c. Type **60** (10.8.77) .. .. 1·00 1·00
F248 10 f. on 10 c. Baker's Pigeon (20.7.77) .. 1·25 55
F249 15 f. on 15 c. Gong and carving (18.7.77) 1·75 1·25
a. Short bar in surcharge (5.8.77) .. 2·25 2·25
F250 25 f. on 25 c. *Cribraria fischeri* (shell) (10.9.77) .. .. £100 55·00
a. "FHN" for "FNH" (R. 5/1) ..
F251 30 f. on 30 c. *Oliva rubrolabiata* (shell) (10.9.77) .. .. £170 48·00
a. "FHN" for "FNH" (R. 5/1) .. ..
F252 35 f. on 35 c. Chestnut-bellied Kingfisher (Setting I) (10.9.77) .. .. 4·00 4·25
a. "NH" for "FNH" (R. 4/2) .. ..
b. Setting II (6.1.78) .. ..
F253 40 f. on 65 c. *Strombus plicatus* (shell) (12.9.77) .. .. .. 4·50 4·50
F254 200 f. on 5 f. Green snail shell (Setting I) (22.8.77) .. .. 32·00 42·00
a. Setting II (13.1.78) ..
F255 500 f. on 10 f. Type **73** (14.9.77) .. .. 38·00 45·00
F247/55 .. .. *Set of* 9 £325 £180

Dates are those on which the various values were surcharged.

50 f., 70 f. and 100 f. local surcharges were also prepared, but were not put on general sale, being available from the Philatelic Bureau only.

1977 (7 Sept)–**78**. *Maps of the Islands. As Nos.* 242/54. *Multicoloured. P* 13½ × 13 (15, 30, 40 *f.*) *or* 14 (*others*).
F256 5 f. Type **89** 20 10
F257 10 f. Territory map and copra-making (9.5.78) 35 20
F258 15 f. Espiritu Santo and cattle (23.11.77) .. 40 20
F259 20 f. Efate and Vila Post Office 55 30
F260 25 f. Malekula and headdresses (23.11.77) 60 40
F261 30 f. Aoba, Maewo and pigs' tusks (23.11.77) 70 45
F262 35 f. Pentecost and land diver (9.5.78) .. 1·00 60
F263 40 f. Tanna and John Frum cross (23.11.77) 1·25 75
F264 50 f. Shepherd Island and canoe .. .. 1·50 75
F265 70 f. Banks Island and dancers (9.5.78) .. 2·50 1·50
F266 100 f. Ambrym and idols .. .. .. 2·50 2·25
F267 200 f. Aneityum and baskets .. .. 4·25 5·00
F268 500 f. Torres Islands and archer fisherman (9.5.78) .. .. 10·00 10·00
F256/68 .. .. .. *Set of* 13 23·00 20·00

1977 (8 Dec). *Christmas. As Nos.* 255/7. *Multicoloured. P* 12.
F269 10 f. Type **90** 20 20
F270 15 f. "The Flight into Egypt" (G. David) .. 35 35
F271 30 f. "Virgin and Child" (Pompeo Batoni) .. 85 85
F269/71 .. .. *Set of* 3 1·25 1·25

1978 (9 May). *"Concorde". As Nos.* 258/61. *Multicoloured. P* 13½.
F272 10 f. Type **91** .. .. 1·50 65
F273 20 f. "Concorde" over London .. .. 1·75 1·25
F274 30 f. "Concorde" over Washington .. .. 2·25 1·75
F275 40 f. "Concorde" over Paris .. .. 2·75 2·75
F272/5 .. .. .. *Set of* 4 7·50 5·75

1978 (2 June). *25th Anniv of Coronation. As Nos.* 262/4. *P* 15.
F276 **92** 40 f. sepia, turquoise-blue and silver .. 50 85
a. Sheetlet. Nos. F276/8 × 2 .. .. 2·75
F277 – 40 f. multicoloured 50 85
F278 – 40 f. sepia, turquoise-blue and silver .. 50 85
F276/8 .. .. .. *Set of* 3 1·40 2·25

Nos. F276/278 were printed together in small sheets of 6, containing two *se-tenant* strips of 3, with horizontal gutter margin between.

1978 (1 Dec). *Christmas. As Nos.* 265/8. *Multicoloured. P* 14 × 13½.
F279 10 f. Type **93** 20 20
F280 15 f. "The Virgin and Child with St. Anne" .. 25 30
F281 30 f. "The Madonna with the Goldfinch" .. 40 60
F282 40 f. "The Madonna with the Child" 50 70
F279/82 .. .. .. *Set of* 4 1·25 1·60

166°E
PREMIER GOUVERNEMENT AUTONOME
11.1.78 - 11.1.79
10 FNH

(F 11)

1979 (11 Jan). *1st Anniv of Internal Self-Government. As No.* F225 *surch as Type* **F 11**.
F283 **78** 10 f. on 25 c. multicoloured (blue background) 35 25
F284 40 f. on 25 c. multicoloured (pale blue-green background) .. .. .. 90 1·00

1979 (10 Sept). *Death Centenary of Sir Rowland Hill. As Nos.* 271/3. *Multicoloured. P* 14.
F285 10 f. Type **95** 30 35
F286 20 f. 1969 Land Divers 25 c. commemorative 45 55
F287 40 f. 1925 20 c. (2d.) 65 75
F285/7 .. .. .. *Set of* 3 1·25 1·50

For miniature sheet containing No. F286, see No. **MS**274.

1979 (16 Nov). *Festival of Arts. As Nos.* 275/8. *Multicoloured. P* 14.
F288 5 f. Type **96** 20 10
F289 10 f. Nal-Nal clubs and spears 25 15
F290 20 f. Ritual puppet 45 40
F291 40 f. Neqatmalow headdress .. .. 75 1·00
F288/91 .. .. .. *Set of* 4 1·50 1·50

1979 (4 Dec). *Christmas and International Year of the Child. As Nos.* 279/82. *Multicoloured. P* 13 × 13½ (*horiz*) *or* 13½ × 13 (*vert*).
F292 5 f. Type **97** 45 35
F293 10 f. "Priest and Candles" (Herve Rutu) .. 65 35
F294 20 f. "Cross and Bible" (Mark Deards) (*vert*) 1·00 1·00
F295 40 f. "Green Candle and Santa Claus" (Dev Raj) (*vert*) .. .. 1·90 2·00
F292/5 .. .. .. *Set of* 4 3·50 3·25

1980 (27 Feb). *Birds. As Nos.* 283/6. *Multicoloured. P* 14.
F296 10 f. Type **98** .. .. 1·00 35
F297 20 f. Scarlet Robin .. .. .. 1·25 80
F298 30 f. Yellow-fronted White Eye .. .. 1·50 1·50
F299 40 f. Fan-tailed Cuckoo .. .. .. 1·75 2·00
F296/9 .. .. .. *Set of* 4 5·00 4·25

POSTAGE DUE STAMPS

CHIFFRE TAXE (FD 1) — **CHIFFRE TAXE** (FD 2) — **TIMBRE-TAXE** (FD 3)

1925 (June). *Optd with Type* FD **1**, *by D.L.R.*
FD53 **F 5** 10 c. (1d.) green .. .. .. 38·00 2·00
FD54 20 c. (2d.) greyish slate .. .. 38·00 2·00
FD55 30 c. (3d.) red .. .. .. 38·00 2·00
FD56 50 c. (5d.) ultramarine .. .. 38·00 2·00
FD57 1 f. (10d.) carmine/*blue* .. .. 38·00 2·00
FD53/7 .. .. .. *Set of* 5 £170 9·00
FD53/7 Optd "Specimen" .. .. *Set of* 5 £200

Although on sale in Paris, the Postmaster would not issue any in unused condition for about a year and most copies are cancelled-to-order.

1938 (1 June). *Optd with Type* FD **2**, *by Bradbury, Wilkinson.*
FD65 **6** 5 c. blue-green .. .. .. 6·50 13·00
FD66 10 c. orange .. .. .. 8·50 13·00
FD67 20 c. scarlet .. .. .. 12·00 17·00
FD68 40 c. grey-olive .. .. .. 22·00 30·00
FD69 1 f. lake/*pale green* .. .. 30·00 42·00
FD65/9 .. .. .. *Set of* 5 70·00 £100
FD65/9 Optd "Specimen" .. *Set of* 5 £200

1941 (15 Apr). *Nos.* FD65/9 *optd with Type* **F 6** *at Nouméa, New Caledonia.*
FD77 **6** 5 c. blue-green .. .. .. 6·00 12·00
FD78 10 c. orange .. .. .. 6·00 12·00
FD79 20 c. scarlet .. .. .. 6·00 12·00
FD80 40 c. grey-olive .. .. .. 6·00 12·00
FD81 1 f. lake/*pale green* .. .. 10·00 12·00
FD77/81 .. .. .. *Set of* 5 30·00 55·00

1953 (30 Apr). *Optd with Type* FD **3**, *by Waterlow.*
FD92 **7** 5 c. green .. .. .. 2·25 4·00
FD93 10 c. scarlet .. .. .. 2·25 4·00
FD94 20 c. ultramarine .. .. .. 4·50 7·00
FD95 – 40 c. blackish brown .. .. 9·50 16·00
FD96 – 1 f. orange .. .. .. 14·00 20·00
FD92/6 .. .. .. *Set of* 5 29·00 45·00

1957 (3 Sept). *Optd with Type* FD **3**, *by Waterlow.*
FD107 **12** 5 c. green .. .. .. 1·00 2·75
FD108 10 c. scarlet .. .. .. 1·00 2·75
FD109 20 c. ultramarine .. .. .. 2·00 3·50
FD110 **13** 40 c. sepia .. .. .. 4·50 8·00
FD111 – 1 f. red-orange .. .. .. 6·00 12·00
FD107/11 .. .. .. *Set of* 5 13·00 26·00

The New Hebrides Condominium became an independent republic, within the Commonwealth, on 30 July 1980 and was renamed VANUATU.

New Republic

During the unrest following the death of Cetshwayo, the Zulu king, in 1884, a group of Boers from the Transvaal offered their support to his son, Dinizulu. The price for this support was the cession of a sizeable portion of Zulu territory to an independent Boer republic. The New Republic, centred on Vryheid, was proclaimed on 5 August 1884 with the remaining Zulu territory becoming a protectorate of the new administration.

Alarmed by these developments the British authorities annexed the southernmost part of the land grant, around St. Lucia Bay, to prevent access to the Indian Ocean. The remainder of the New Republic was, however, recognised as independent on 22 October 1886. Zululand was annexed by the British on 22 May 1887.

Difficulties beset the New Republic, however, and its Volksraad voted for union with the South African Republic (Transvaal). The two republics united on 21 July 1888. In 1903 the territory of the former New Republic was transferred to Natal.

Mail from Vryheid in 1884–85 was franked with issues of Transvaal (for dispatches made via Utrecht) or Natal (for those sent via Dundee). Issues of the New Republic were never accepted as internationally valid by these administrations so that all external mail continued to show Transvaal or Natal stamps used in combination with those of the republic.

PRICES FOR STAMPS ON COVER
Nos. 1/95 *from* × 10

1

Printed with a rubber handstamp on paper bought in Europe and sent out ready gummed and perforated.

1886 (7 Jan)–**87**. *Various dates indicating date of printing. P* 11½.

A. *Without Arms.* (i) *Yellow paper*
1 **1** 1d. black (9.1.86) .. .. — £2500
2 1d. violet (9.1.86) .. .. 10·00 12·00
a. "1d." omitted (in pair with normal) (24.4.86) £1500
3 2d. violet (9.1.86) .. .. 10·00 15·00
a. "d" omitted (13.10.86) .. ..
4 3d. violet (13.1.86) .. .. .. 23·00
a. "d" omitted (13.10.86) .. ..
5 4d. violet (30.8.86) .. .. .. 35·00
6 6d. violet (20.2.86) .. .. .. 30·00
a. "6d." omitted (in pair with normal) (2.7.86) .. ..
7 9d. violet (13.1.86) .. .. .. 30·00
8 1s. violet (30.8.86) .. .. .. 65·00
a. "1s." omitted (in pair with normal) (6.9.86) .. ..
9 1/s. violet (13.10.86) £500
10 1/6 violet (30.8.86) .. .. .. 65·00
11 1s. 6d. violet (6.9.86) £500
a. "d" omitted (13.10.86) .. .. 85·00
12 2s. violet (30.8.86) .. .. .. 38·00
a. *Tête-bêche* (pair) (6.9.86) £475
13 2/6 violet (13.1.86) £150
14 2s. 6d. violet (20.1.86) .. .. .. 95·00
15 4/s. violet (17.1.87) £400
16 5s. violet (1.86) .. .. .. 28·00 30·00
a. "S" omitted (in pair with normal) (7.3.86) £2000
17 5/6 violet (20.2.86) .. .. .. 35·00
18 5s. 6d. violet (13.1.86) £160
19 7/6 violet (13.1.86) £170
20 7s. 6d. violet (24.5.86) .. .. .. 95·00
21 10s. violet (13.1.86) .. .. .. 95·00
22 10s. 6d. violet (7.1.86) £170
a. "d" omitted (1.86) .. .. .. 48·00
23 13s. violet (24.11.86) £400
24 £1 violet (13.1.86) £120
25 30s. violet (13.1.86) .. .. .. 95·00
a. *Tête-bêche* (pair) (24.11.86) £700

(ii) *Blue granite paper*
26 **1** 1d. violet (20.1.86) .. .. .. 13·00 14·00
a. "d" omitted (24.11.86) £375
b. "1" omitted (in pair with normal) (24.11.86) .. ..
27 2d. violet (13.1.86) .. .. .. 13·00 14·00
a. "d" omitted (24.4.86) £750
b. "2d." omitted (in pair with normal) (24.4.86) .. ..
28 3d. violet (13.10.86) .. .. .. 16·00 18·00
a. *Tête-bêche* (pair) (13.10.86) £325
29 4d. violet (24.5.86) .. .. .. 13·00 16·00
30 6d. violet (24.5.86) .. .. .. 25·00 21·00
a. "6" omitted (in pair with normal) (24.5.86) £1500
31 9d. violet (6.9.86) .. .. .. 24·00
32 1s. violet (1.86) .. .. .. 28·00 30·00
a. *Tête-bêche* (pair) (21.5.86) £400
b. "1s." omitted (in pair with normal) (29.4.86) £1250
33 1s. 6d. violet (2.7.86) .. .. .. 35·00
a. *Tête-bêche* (pair) (6.9.86) £475
34 1/6 violet (6.9.86) £150
35 2s. violet (21.5.86) £120
36 2s. 6d. violet (19.8.86) £140
37 2/6 violet (19.8.86) £180
38 4/s. violet (17.1.87) £200
39 5s. 6d. violet (13.1.86) £170
40 5/6 violet (13.1.86) £200
a. "/" omitted (13.1.87) .. ..
41 7/6 violet (13.1.86) £200
41*a* 7s. 6d. violet (13.1.86) .. ..
42 10s. violet (1.86) £200 £200
a. *Tête-bêche* (pair) (2.7.86) £500
b. "s" omitted (13.1.86) .. ..
43 10s. 6d. violet (7.1.86) £200
a. *Tête-bêche* (pair) (13.1.86) .. ..
b. "d" omitted (2.7.86) £450
44 12s. violet (13.1.86) £300
45 13s. violet (17.1.87) £400
46 £1 violet (13.1.86) £250
47 30s. violet (13.1.86) £250

B. *With embossed Arms of New Republic.* (i) *Yellow paper*
48 **1** 1d. violet (20.1.86) .. .. .. 13·00 15·00
a. Arms inverted (20.1.86) .. .. 25·00 25·00
b. Arms *tête-bêche* (pair) (14.4.86) .. £100 £120

No.	Type	Description	Un.	Us.
49	1	2d. violet (2.12.86)	13·00	15·00
		a. Arms inverted (24.11.86)	23·00	28·00
50		4d. violet (2.12.86)	18·00	22·00
		a. Arms inverted (12.86)	95·00	60·00
		b. Arms *tête-bêche* (pair) (12.86)	£250	
51		6d. violet (2.12.86)	45·00	
		(ii) *Blue granite paper*		
52	1	1d. violet (20.1.86)	14·00	16·00
		a. Arms inverted (10.2.86)	35·00	40·00
		b. Arms *tête-bêche* (pair) (3.11.86)		
53		2d. violet (30.8.86)	14·00	16·00
		a. Arms inverted (30.8.86)	48·00	
		b. Arms *tête-bêche* (pair) (2.12.86)	£500	£500

Stamps as Type **1** were produced as and when stocks were required, each printing including in its design the date on which it was prepared. The dates quoted above for Nos. 1/53 are those on which the various stamps first appeared. Details of the various printing dates are given below. From these dates it can be seen that some values share common printing dates, and, it is believed, that the different values were produced *se-tenant* within the same sheet, at least in some instances. A reported proof sheet in the Pretoria Postal Museum, on yellow paper and embossed, contains 4 examples of the 6d. value and 3 each of the 3d., 4d., 9d., 1s., 1/6, 2/-, 2/6, 3s., 4s., 5s., 5/6, 7/6, 10/-, 10/6, £1 and 30/-.

The significance, if any, of the two coloured papers and the use of the embossing machine have never been satisfactorily explained. Both the different papers and the embossing machine were introduced in January 1886, and occur throughout the period that the stamps with dates were used.

PRINTINGS

Date	*Paper*	*Face value*	*Cat. No.*	*Un.*	*Us.*
Jan 86	*Yellow*	5s.	16	28·00	30·00
		10s. 6d.	22a	80·00	
	Blue	1s.	32		
		10s.	42	£200	£200
7 Jan 86	*Yellow*	10s. 6d.	22	£160	
	Blue	10s.	42		
		10s. 6d.	43	£450	
9 Jan 86	*Yellow*	1d.	1	—	£2500
		1d.	2	10·00	12·00
		2d.	3	10·00	15·00
13 Jan 86	*Yellow*	1d.	2	35·00	
		2d.	3	14·00	15·00
		3d.	4	40·00	
		9d.	7	£200	
		2/6	13	£160	
		5s. 6d.	18		
		7/6	19	£170	
		10s.	21		
		£1	24	£130	
		30s	25	95·00	
	Blue	2d.	27		
		5s. 6d.	39	£170	
		5/6	40	£200	
		7/6	41	£200	
		7s. 6d.	41*a*		
		10s.	42	£400	
		10s.	42b		
		10s. 6d.	43	£200	
		10s. 6d.	43a		
		12s.	44	£300	
		£1	46	£250	
		30s.	47	£250	
20 Jan 86	*Yellow*	1d.	2		
		2s. 6d.	14		
	Blue	1d.	26	£250	
	Yellow, embossed	1d.	48	32·00	
		1d.	48a	48·00	
	Blue, embossed	1d.	52	95·00	
Jan 20 86	*Blue*	1d.	26	23·00	
	Yellow, embossed	1d.	48a		
	Blue, embossed	1d.	52	£100	
24 Jan 86	*Blue*	1d.	26	18·00	
		2d.	27	30·00	
10 Feb 86	*Yellow*	1d.	2		
	Yellow, embossed	1d.	48		
		1d.	48a	48·00	
	Blue, embossed	1d.	52	£130	
		1d.	52a	35·00	
20 Feb 86	*Yellow*	6d.	6		
		2s. 6d.	14	£130	
		5/6	17	£120	
		5s. 6d.	18		
7 Mar 86	*Yellow*	1d.	2	£110	
		2/6	13		
		2s. 6d.	14	95·00	
		5s.	16	£200	85·00
		5s.	16a		
		5/6	17	35·00	
		5s. 6d.	18	£160	
	Blue	2d.	27	95·00	
		1s.	32		
17 Mar 86	*Yellow*	1d.	2	95·00	
	Yellow, embossed	1d.	48	48·00	
	Blue, embossed	1d.	52	95·00	
		1d.	52a	80·00	
26 Mar 86	*Blue, embossed*	1d.	52a	£130	
14 Apr 86	*Yellow*	1d.	2		
	Yellow, embossed	1d.	48	23·00	
		1d.	48a	£120	
		1d.	48b	£100	£120
	Blue, embossed	1d.	52	45·00	
		1d.	52a		
24 Apr 86	*Yellow*	1d.	2	£100	
		1d.	2a	£1500	
		5s.	16		
	Blue	2d.	27	28·00	
		2d.	27a	£750	
		2d.	27b		
		1s.	32		
29 Apr 86	*Blue*	1s.	32	£110	
		1s.	32b		
21 May 86	*Yellow*	6d.	6	£130	
	Blue	1d.	26	85·00	
		1s.	32	28·00	30·00
		1s.	32a	£400	
		1s.	32b	£1500	
		2s.	35	£325	
23 May 86	*Yellow, embossed*	1d.	48		
	Blue, embossed	1d.	52a	95·00	
24 May 86	*Yellow*	1d.	2	95·00	
		2d.	3	£120	
		5s.	16	70·00	
		7/6	19	£170	
		7s. 6d.	20	95·00	
	Blue	1d.	26	13·00	14·00
		2d.	27		
		4d.	29	85·00	
		6d.	30	£120	
		6d.	30a		
		1s.	32	£200	
		1s.	32b		
		2s.	35	£120	
26 May 86	*Yellow*	1d.	2		
	Blue	1d.	26	£110	
	Yellow, embossed	1d.	48	£250	
		1d.	48a	95·00	
	Blue, embossed	1d.	52	£130	
		1d.	52a	48·00	50·00
28 May 86	*Yellow, embossed*	1d.	48	32·00	
30 Jun 86	*Yellow*	1d.	2		
	Blue	1d.	26		
Jun 30 86	*Blue*	1d.	26	15·00	16·00
	Yellow, embossed	1d.	48	14·00	16·25
		1d.	48a	25·00	28·00
		1d.	48b	£200	£225
	Blue, embossed	1d.	52	45·00	40·00
2 Jul 86	*Yellow*	6d.	6		
		6d.	6a		
		9d.	7	95·00	95·00
	Blue	1s.	32		
		1s. 6d.	33	35·00	
		10s.	42	£400	
		10s.	42a	£500	
		10s. 6d.	43		
		10s. 6d.	43b		
7 Jul 86	*Yellow*	1d.	2		
	Blue	1d.	26		
		10s. 6d.	43		
	Yellow, embossed	1d.	48	25·00	
		1d.	48a	95·00	95·00
	Blue, embossed	1d.	52	14·00	16·00
		1d.	52a	55·00	40·00
Jul 7 86	*Blue, embossed*	1d.	52		
		1d.	52a		
4 Aug 86	*Yellow*	1d.	2		
	Yellow, embossed	1d.	48	55·00	
	Blue, embossed	1d.	52	35·00	
		1d.	52a		
19 Aug 86	*Yellow*	2/6	13		
		2s. 6d.	14	£140	
	Blue	2s. 6d.	36	£140	
		2/6	37	£180	
30 Aug 86	*Yellow*	1d.	2	10·00	12·00
		2d.	3	11·00	
		3d.	4	23·00	
		4d.	5	48·00	
		6d.	6	32·00	
		9d.	7	48·00	
		1s.	8	65·00	
		1/6	10	65·00	
		2s.	12	95·00	
		2/6	13	£150	
	Blue	1d.	26		
		2d.	27	13·00	14·00
	Yellow, embossed	1d.	48		
	Blue, embossed	2d.	53	42·00	
		2d.	53a	£110	
6 Sep 86	*Yellow*	1d.	2	12·00	
		2d.	3	8·50	9·00
		3d.	4	38·00	
		4d.	5	40·00	
		6d.	6	30·00	
		9d.	7	30·00	
		1s.	8	95·00	
		1s.	8a		
		1/6	10	70·00	
		1s. 6d.	11	£500	
		2s.	12	£100	
		2s.	12a	£475	
		2/6	13	£150	
		2s. 6d.	14		
		5s.	16	£140	
		7s. 6d.	20	£200	
		10s.	21	95·00	
		£1	24	£120	
	Blue	6d.	30	20·00	21·00
		9d.	31	95·00	
		1s.	32	65·00	
		1s.	32b	£1250	
		1s. 6d.	33	£140	
		1s. 6d.	33a	£475	
		1/6	34		
		2/6	37	£400	
		10s. 6d.	43		
13 Sep 86	*Yellow*	1d.	2		
	Yellow, embossed	1d.	48	48·00	
		1d.	48a	48·00	
	Blue, embossed	1d.	52	85·00	
6 Oct 86	*Yellow*	1d.	2		
	Blue	1d.	26	85·00	
	Yellow, embossed	1d.	48	23·00	18·00
		1d.	48a		
	Blue, embossed	1d.	52	45·00	18·00
		1d.	52a	85·00	
13 Oct 86	*Yellow*	1d.	2	12·00	12·00
		2d.	3	10·00	11·00
		2d.	3a		
		3d.	4	23·00	25·00
		3d.	4a		
		4d.	5	35·00	
		6d.	6	30·00	32·00
		9d.	7	35·00	
		1s.	8	70·00	
		1/s.	9	£500	
		1/6	10	£150	
		1s. 6d.	11a	85·00	
		2s.	12	38·00	
		2/6	13	£160	
		5s.	16	42·00	
		10s.	21	95·00	£100
		10s. 6d.	22a	48·00	
		£1	24	£120	
	Blue	2d.	27	13·00	14·0(
		3d.	28	16·00	18·0(
		3d.	28a	£325	
		4d.	29	28·00	28·0(
		1s.	32	28·00	
		1/6	34	£150	
		2s.	35	£120	
3 Nov 86	*Yellow*	1d.	2	28·00	
		9d.	7		
	Blue	1d.	26		
	Yellow, embossed	1d.	48	13·00	15·0(
		1d.	48a	25·00	28·0(
		1d.	48b	£100	£12(
	Blue, embossed	1d.	52	14·00	
		1d.	52a	35·00	40·0(
		1d.	52b		
13 Nov 86	*Yellow*	1d.	2	35·00	
24 Nov 86	*Yellow*	1d.	2	14·00	
		2d.	3	10·00	11·0(
		3d.	4	30·00	32·0(
		1/6	10		
		10s.	21	£200	
		13s.	23	£400	
		30s.	25	95·00	
		30s.	25a	£700	
	Blue	1d.	26	38·00	17·0(
		1d.	26a	£375	
		1d.	26b		
		2d.	27	18·00	
		2d.	27a		
		4d.	29	13·00	16·0(
		6d.	30	20·00	21·0(
		9d.	31	24·00	
		1s.	32	45·00	48·0(
		1/6	34	£160	
		2s.	35	£140	
	Yellow, embossed	2d.	49	£160	
		2d.	49a		
26 Nov 86	*Yellow*	1/6	10	£140	
2 Dec 86	*Yellow*	1d.	2		
		2d.	3		
	Yellow, embossed	1d.	48	13·00	15·0(
		1d.	48a	£160	
		2d.	49	13·00	15·0(
		2d.	49a	23·00	28·0(
		4d.	50	80·00	
		6d.	51	45·00	
	Blue, embossed	1d.	52	28·00	
		1d.	52a	£160	
		2d.	53	14·00	16·0(
		2d.	53a	48·00	
		2d.	53b	£500	£50(
Dec 86	*Yellow*	6d.	6		
	Blue	4d.	29		
		6d.	30		
	Yellow, embossed	4d.	50	18·00	22·00
		4d.	50a	93·00	60·00
		4d.	50b	£250	
		6d.	51	42·00	
4 Jan 87	*Yellow*	1d.	2	35·00	
		2d.	3	32·00	
		13s.	23	£400	
	Blue	1d.	26	13·00	14·00
		2d.	27	16·00	14·00
	Blue, embossed	2d.	53	42·00	
13 Jan 87	*Blue*	5/6	40	£400	
		5/6	40a		
		7/6	41	£400	
17 Jan 87	*Yellow*	1d.	2	38·00	
		2d.	3	30·00	
		3d.	4	45·00	
		4/s.	15	£200	
	Blue	1d.	26	75·00	
		4/s.	38	£200	
		13s.	45	£400	
		30s.	47	£250	
20 Jan 87	*Blue*	2d.	27	32·00	
	Yellow, embossed	2d.	49	50·00	
		2d.	49a	£140	
	Blue, embossed	2d.	53	42·00	
		2d.	53a	95·00	
Jan 20 87	*Yellow, embossed*	1d.	48a	£400	

1887 (Feb–Mar). *As T* **1**, *but without date. With embossed Arms.*

(*a*) *Blue granite paper*

No.	Description	Un.	Us.
72	1d. violet	14·00	14·0(
	a. Imperf between (pair)		
	b. Stamps *tête-bêche* (pair)	£325	
	c. Arms *tête-bêche* (pair)		
	d. Arms inverted	23·00	23·0(
	e. Arms omitted	£110	£11(
	f. Arms sideways		
73	2d. violet	8·50	8·5(
	a. Stamps *tête-bêche* (pair)	£325	
	b. Arms inverted	23·00	23·0(
	c. Arms omitted	£110	95·0(
	d. Arms *tête-bêche* (pair)		
74	3d. violet	13·00	13·0(
	a. Stamps *tête-bêche* (pair)	£375	
	b. Arms *tête-bêche* (pair)		
	c. Arms inverted	48·00	48·0(
75	4d. violet	13·00	13·0(
	a. Stamps *tête-bêche* (pair)	£325	
	b. Arms *tête-bêche* (pair)	£275	
	c. Arms inverted	85·00	
76	6d. violet	13·00	13·0(
	a. Arms inverted	85·00	
77	1/6 violet	14·00	14·00
	a. Arms inverted	80·00	
77*b*	2/6d. violet	—	£750
	(*b*) *Yellow paper* (March 1887)		
78	2d. violet (*arms omitted*)	13·00	
79	3d. violet	13·00	13·00
	a. Imperf between (pair)		
	b. Stamps *tête-bêche* (pair)	£325	£350
	c. Arms *tête-bêche* (pair)	£200	
	d. Arms inverted	23·00	23·00
	da. Double impression		
80	4d. violet	13·00	13·00
	a. Arms inverted	14·00	14·00

6d. violet .. .. 8·00 8·00
a. Arms *tête-bêche* (pair) £350
b. Arms inverted .. .. 42·00 42·00
c. Arms omitted .. .. 80·00
ca. Double impression
2 9d. violet .. .. 8·50 8·50
a. Arms inverted £200
b. Arms *tête-bêche* (pair) £350
3 1s. violet .. .. 8·50 8·50
a. Arms inverted .. .. 70·00
4 1/6 violet .. .. 17·00 14·0
5 2s. violet .. .. 18·00 16·00
a. Arms inverted .. .. 55·00 50·00
b. Arms omitted .. .. 70·00
6 2/6 violet .. .. 23·00 23·00
a. Arms inverted .. .. 28·00 28·00
7 3s. violet .. .. 42·00 42·00
a. Arms inverted .. .. 45·00 45·00
b. Stamps *tête-bêche* (pair) £450
8 4s. violet .. .. 11·00 11·00
a. Arms omitted (4*s*.)
b. Arms omitted (4/-) £130
9 5s. violet .. .. 13·00 13·00
a. Imperf between (pair)
b. Arms inverted .. .. — 80·00
0 5/6 violet .. .. 12·00 12·00
1 7/6 violet .. .. 14·00 17·00
a. Arms *tête-bêche* (pair)
a. Arms inverted .. .. 45·00
2 10s. violet .. .. 12·00 12·00
a. Imperf between (pair)
b. Arms *tête-bêche* (pair) £120
c. Arms inverted .. .. 23·00
d. Arms omitted .. .. £110 45·00
3 10/6 violet .. .. 16·00 16·00
a. Imperf between (pair)
b. Arms inverted
4 £1 violet .. .. 45·00 45·00
a. Stamps *tête-bêche* (pair) £350 £375
b. Arms inverted .. .. 55·00
5 30s. violet .. .. 85·00

New South Wales

PRICES FOR STAMPS ON COVER

Nos. 1/83	*from* × 2
Nos. 84/108	*from* × 3
Nos. 109/10	—
No. 110*b*	*from* × 3
Nos. 111/13	*from* × 2
No. 114	—
Nos. 115/24	*from* × 2
Nos. 125/6	—
Nos. 127/53	*from* × 2
Nos. 154/70	*from* × 3
Nos. 171/2	—
No. 173	*from* × 2
Nos. 174/81	—
Nos. 186/202	*from* × 2
Nos. 203/6	*from* × 10
Nos. 207/21	*from* × 5
Nos. 222/39	*from* × 6
Nos. 240/1	*from* × 2
Nos. 241*a*/3	*from* × 10
Nos. 244/52	—
Nos. 253/73	*from* × 10
Nos. 274/80	—
Nos. 281/4	*from* × 15
Nos. 285/7	*from* × 10
Nos. 287*c*/*d*	*from* × 2
Nos. 288/97	*from* × 10
Nos. 298/312	*from* × 12
Nos. 313/28	*from* × 10
No. 329	—
Nos. 330/45	*from* × 12
No. 346	—
Nos. 347/60	*from* × 12
No. O1	—
Nos. O2/12	*from* × 4
Nos. O13/18	—
Nos. O19/34	*from* × 20
Nos. O35/8	—
Nos. O39/47	*from* × 40
Nos. O48/53	—
Nos. O54/8	*from* × 20
No. O59	—
Nos. D1/7	*from* × 50
Nos. D8/10	—
Nos. D11/15	*from* × 50

SPECIMEN OVERPRINTS. Those listed are from U.P.U. distributions between 1892 and 1903. Further "Specimen" overprints exist, but these were used for other purposes.

1

2

(Eng Robert Clayton, Sydney)

1850 (1 Jan). *T* **1**. *Plate I. No clouds. (a) Soft yellowish paper.*
1 1d. crimson-lake £4000 £450
2 1d. carmine £3750 £400
3 1d. reddish rose £3500 £375
4 1d. brownish red £3750 £400

(b) Hard bluish paper
5 1d. pale red £3500 £350
6 1d. dull lake £3500 £350

1850 (Aug). *T* **2**. *Plate I, re-engraved by H. C. Jervis, commonly termed Plate II. With clouds. (a) Hard toned white to yellowish paper.*
7 1d. vermilion £2000 £300
8 1d. dull carmine £2000 £300
a. No trees on hill (No. 7) £4500 £450
b. Hill unshaded (No. 8) £4500 £450
c. Without clouds (No. 15) £4500 £450

(b) Hard greyish or bluish paper
9 1d. crimson-lake £2250 £300
10 1d. gooseberry-red £2750 £425
11 1d. dull carmine £2000 £250
12 1d. brownish red £2000 £250
a. No trees on hill (No. 7) £4500 £450
b. Hill unshaded (No. 8) £4500 £450
c. Without clouds (No. 15) £4500 £450

(c) Laid paper
13 1d. carmine £3500 £475
14 1d. vermilion £4000 £450
a. No trees on hill (No. 7) .. .. .. — £750
b. Hill unshaded (No. 8) .. .. .. — £750
c. Without clouds (No. 15) .. .. .. — £750

The varieties quoted with the letters "a", "b", "c" of course exist in each shade; the prices quoted are for the commonest shade, and the same applies to the following portions of this list.

The numbers given in brackets throughout indicate position on sheet.

3

4

A (Pl I)

Illustrations A, B, C, and D are sketches of the lower part of the inner circular frame, showing the characteristic variations of each plate.

(Eng John Carmichael)

1850 (1 Jan). *Plate I. Vertical-lined background. T* **3**.

(a) Early impressions, full details of clouds, etc.
15 2d. greyish blue £4000 £300
16 2d. deep blue .. .. — £350
a. Double lines on bale (No. 19) .. .. — £550

(b) Intermediate impressions
16*b* 2d. greyish blue £2750 £250
16*c* 2d. deep blue £3000 £275

(c) Later impressions, clouds, etc., mostly gone, T **4**
17 2d. blue £1900 £120
18 2d. dull blue £1500 £110

1850 (end Jan). *Stamps in the lower row partially retouched.*
19 2d. blue £2500 £190
20 2d. greyish blue £2250 £160

An interesting variety occurs on positions 9, 10, 11 and 19 in all five plates. It consists of ten loops of the engine-turning on each side of the design instead of the normal nine loops.

5

B (Pl II)

C (Pl III)

(Plate entirely re-engraved by H. C. Jervis)

1850 (Apr). *T* **5**. *Plate II. Horizontal-lined background. Bale on left side supporting the seated figure, dated. Dot in centre of the star in each corner. (a) Early impressions.*
21 2d. indigo £3250 £250
22 2d. lilac-blue .. .. — £1000
23 2d. grey-blue £3250 £200
24 2d. bright blue £3250 £200
a. Fan as in Pl III, but with shading outside (No. 1) .. .. .. — £375
b. Fan as in Pl III, but without shading, and inner circle intersects the fan (No. 2) .. — £375
c. Pick and shovel omitted (No. 10) .. — £375
d. "CREVIT" omitted (No. 13) .. .. — £500
e. No whip (Nos. 4, 8, and 20) .. .. — £300

(b) Worn impressions
25 2d. dull blue £1600 £100
26 2d. Prussian blue £1700 £150
a. Fan as in Pl III, but with shading outside (No. 1) .. .. .. — £300
b. Fan as in Pl III, but without shading, and inner circle intersects the fan (No. 2) .. — £300
c. Pick and shovel omitted (No. 10) .. — £300
d. "CREVIT" omitted (No. 13) .. .. — £350
e. No whip (Nos. 4, 8, and 20) .. .. — £200

1850 (Aug). *Bottom row retouched with dots and dashes in lower spandrels.*
27 2d. Prussian blue £2250 £180
28 2d. dull blue £2000 £110
a. No whip (No. 20) .. .. .. — £250
b. "CREVIT" omitted (No. 13) .. .. — £300

(Plate re-engraved a second time by H. C. Jervis)

1850 (Sept). *Plate III. Bale not dated and single-lined, except Nos. 7, 10 and 12, which are double-lined. No dots in stars.*
29 2d. ultramarine £1900 £140
30 2d. deep blue £1800 £140
a. No whip (Nos. 15 and 19) .. .. — £225
b. Fan with 6 segments (No. 20) .. .. — £375
c. Double lines on bale (No. 7, 10, and 12) — £225

(Plate re-engraved a third time by H. C. Jervis)

1851 (Jan). *Plate IV. Double-lined bale, and circle in centre of each star. (a) Hard bluish grey wove paper.*
31 2d. ultramarine £2250 £140
32 2d. Prussian blue £1900 £110
33 2d. bright blue £2000 £120
a. Hill not shaded (No. 12) .. .. — £200
b. Fan with 6 segments (No. 20) .. .. — £200
c. No clouds (No. 22) .. .. .. — £200
d. Retouch (No. 13) .. .. .. — £275
e. No waves (Nos. 9 and 17) .. .. — £190

(b) Stout yellowish vertically laid paper
34 2d. ultramarine £2250 £140
35 2d. Prussian blue £2500 £120
a. Hill not shaded (No. 12) .. .. — £225
b. Fan with 6 segments (No. 20) .. .. — £225
c. No clouds (No. 22) .. .. .. — £225
d. Retouch (No. 13) .. .. .. — £300
e. No waves (Nos. 9 and 17) .. .. — £200
f. "PENOE" (No. 24)

6

D (Pl V)

7

(Plate re-engraved a fourth time by H. C. Jervis)

1851 (Apr). *T* **6**. *Plate V. Pearl in fan. (a) Hard greyish wove paper.*
36 2d. ultramarine £2000 £120
37 2d. dull blue £2000 £120
a. Pick and shovel omitted (No. 17) .. — £250
b. Fan with 6 segments (No. 20) .. .. — £250

(b) Stout yellowish vertically laid paper
38 2d. dull ultramarine £3500 £250
a. Pick and shovel omitted (No. 17) .. — £400
b. Fan with 6 segments (No. 20) .. .. — £400

(Eng H. C. Jervis)

1850. *T* **7**. *(a) Soft yellowish wove paper.*
39 3d. yellow-green £2500 £200
40 3d. myrtle-green £10000 £1000
41 3d. emerald-green £2750 £200
a. No whip (Nos. 18 and 19) .. .. — £375
b. "SIGIIIUM" for "SIGILLUM" (No. 23) .. — £375

(b) Bluish to grey wove paper
42 3d. yellow-green £1900 £190
43 3d. emerald-green £1900 £190
b. No whip (Nos. 18 and 19) .. .. — £225
c. "SIGIIIUM" for "SIGILLUM" (No. 23) .. — £300

(c) Yellowish to bluish laid paper
43*d* 3d. bright green £5000 £400
43*e* 3d. yellowish green £4500 £350
f. No whip (Nos. 18 and 19) .. .. — £600
g. "SIGIIIUM" for "SIGILLUM" (No. 23) .. — £600

8

9

(Des A. W. Manning from sketch by W. T. Levine; eng on steel by John Carmichael, Sydney)

1851 (18 Dec)–**52**. *T* **8**. *Imperf. (a) Thick yellowish wove paper.*
44 1d. carmine £1700 £180
a. No leaves right of "SOUTH" .. .. — £350
b. Two leaves right of "SOUTH" .. .. — £350
c. "WALE" .. .. — £400

(b) Bluish medium wove paper (1852)
45 1d. carmine £1000 £120
46 1d. scarlet £1000 £120
47 1d. vermilion £900 £100
48 1d. brick-red £900 £100
a. No leaves right of "SOUTH" (Nos. 7 and 8) — £200
b. Two leaves right of "SOUTH" (No. 15) — £300
c. "WALE" (No. 9) .. .. .. — £300

(c) Thick vertically laid bluish paper (1852?)
49 1d. orange-brown £2750 £300
50 1d. claret £2750 £300
a. No leaves right of "SOUTH" .. .. — £500
b. Two leaves right of "SOUTH" .. .. — £500
c. "WALE" .. .. — £500

(Eng on steel by John Carmichael)

1851 (24 July). *T* **8**. *Plate I. Imperf. (a) Thick yellowish wove paper.*
51 2d. ultramarine .. .. £650 80·00

(b) Fine impressions, blue to greyish medium paper
52 2d. ultramarine .. .. £700 30·00
53 2d. chalky blue .. .. £600 30·00
54 2d. dark blue .. .. £600 30·00
55 2d. greyish blue .. .. £600 30·00

(c) Worn plate, blue to greyish medium paper
56 2d. ultramarine .. .. £425 30·00
57 2d. Prussian blue .. .. £425 30·00

(d) Worn plate, blue wove medium paper
58 2d. ultramarine .. .. £325 30·00
59 2d. Prussian blue .. .. £300 30·00

(Plate II eng H. C. Jervis)

53 (Oct). *T* **9.** *Plate II. Stars in corners. Imperf.*

(*a*) *Bluish medium to thick wove paper*
2d. deep ultramarine £900 £110
2d. indigo .. .. £1000 80·00
a. "WAEES" (No. 23) .. .. .. — £350

(*b*) *Worn plate, hard blue wove paper*
2d. deep Prussian blue £900 £100
a. "WAEES" (No. 23) .. .. .. — £325

55 (Sept). *Plate III, being Plate I re-engraved by H. C. Jervis. Background of crossed lines. Imperf.*

(*a*) *Medium bluish wove paper*
3 2d. Prussian blue .. .. £450 55·00
a. "WALES" covered with wavy lines (No. 3) — £150

(*b*) *Stout white wove paper*
4 2d. Prussian blue .. .. £450 55·00
a. "WALES" covered with wavy lines (No. 3) — £190

(Eng John Carmichael)

852 (3 Dec). *T* **8.** *Imperf.* (*a*) *Medium greyish blue wove paper.*
5 3d. deep green £1600 £200
6 3d. green £1300 £140
7 3d. dull yellow-green £1200 £100
a. "WAEES" (No. 37) .. .. .. — £350

(*b*) *Thick blue wove paper*
9 3d. emerald-green £1300 £200
1 3d. blue-green £1300 £200
a. "WAEES" (No. 37) .. .. .. — £500

853 (Apr). *As T* **8.** *Fine background. Imperf.*

(*a*) *Medium white wove paper*
2 6d. vandyke-brown .. .. — £900
a. "WALLS" (No. 8).. .. .. .. — £1500

(*b*) *Medium bluish grey wove paper*
3 6d. vandyke-brown £1700 £250
4 6d. yellow-brown £1800 £275
5 6d. chocolate-brown £1700 £250
6 6d. grey-brown £1600 £250
a. "WALLS" (No. 8).. .. .. .. — £500

853 (June). *Plate I re-engraved by H. C. Jervis. Coarse background. Imperf.*
7 6d. brown £1800 £300
8 6d. grey-brown £1700 £300

(Eng H. C. Jervis)

1853 (May). *Medium bluish paper. Imperf.*
9 8d. dull yellow £3250 £500
30 8d. orange-yellow £3250 £550
31 8d. orange £3500 £500
a. No bow at back of head (No. 9) .. .. — £1200
b. No leaves right of "SOUTH" (No. 21) .. — £1200
c. No lines in spandrel (Nos. 12, 22, and 32) — £800

10 13 14

NOTE. All watermarked stamps from No. 82 to No. 172 have double-lined figures, as T **10**.

1854 (Feb). *T* **8.** *Wmk* "**1**", *T* **10.** *Imperf. Yellowish wove paper.*
82 1d. red-orange .. .. £170 15·00
83 1d. orange-vermilion .. .. .. £170 15·00
a. No leaves right of "SOUTH" (Nos. 7 and 21) .. .. £325 85·00
b. Two leaves right of "SOUTH" (No. 15) .. £425 £120
c. "WALE" (No. 9) £425 £120

1854 (Jan). *Plate III. Wmk* "**2**". *Imperf.*
84 2d. ultramarine .. .. £100 10·00
85 2d. Prussian blue .. .. £100 10·00
86 2d. chalky blue .. .. £100 7·00
a. "WALES" partly covered .. .. £400 50·00

1854 (Mar). *Wmk* "**3**". *Imperf.*
87 3d. yellow-green .. .. £180 25·00
a. "WAEES" (No. 37) .. .. .. — £120
b. Error. Wmk "**2**" .. .. — £2250

(Eng John Carmichael)

1856 (1 Jan). *For Registered Letters. T* **13.** *No wmk. Imperf. Soft medium yellowish paper.*
88 (6d.) vermilion and Prussian blue £700 £150
a. Frame printed on back.. .. .. £2500 £1000
89 (6d.) salmon and indigo £700 £170
90 (6d.) orange and Prussian blue £700 £200
91 (6d.) orange and indigo £700 £180

1859 (Apr)–**60.** *Hard medium bluish wove paper, with manufacturer's wmk in sans-serif, double-lined capitals across sheet and only showing portions of letters on a few stamps in a sheet.*

(*a*) *Imperf.*
92 (6d.) orange and Prussian blue £700 £130
92*a* (6d.) vermilion and Prussian blue £850 £180

(*b*) *P* 12 (2.60)
93 (6d.) orange and Prussian blue .. .. £350 40·00
94 (6d.) orange and indigo .. .. .. £325 40·00

1860 (Feb)–**62.** *Coarse yellowish wove paper having the manufacturer's wmk in Roman capitals.* (*a*) *P* 12.
95 (6d.) rose-red and Prussian blue .. .. £250 35·00
96 (6d.) rose-red and indigo .. .. .. £325 80·00
97 (6d.) salmon and indigo .. .. ..

(*b*) *P* 13 (1862)
98 (6d.) rose-red and Prussian blue .. .. £225 50·00

1863 (May). *Yellowish wove paper. Wmk* "**6**". *P* 13.
99 (6d.) rose-red and Prussian blue .. .. 90·00 15·00
100 (6d.) rose-red and indigo .. .. .. £140 17·00
101 (6d.) rose-red and pale blue .. .. .. 65·00 15·00
a. Double impression of frame .. .. — £1500

(T **14/21** and **24** printed by the New South Wales Govt Ptg Dept from plates engraved by Perkins, Bacon & Co)

Two plates of the 2d. and 6d. were used. On Plate II of the 2d. the stamps are wider apart and more regularly spaced than on Plate I.

1856 (6 Apr). *Wmk* "**1**". *Imperf.*
102 **14** 1d. orange-vermilion .. .. .. £130 22·00
a. Error. Wmk "**2**" .. .. ..
103 1d. carmine-vermilion .. .. .. £130 22·00
104 1d. orange-red .. .. £130 22·00
a. Printed on both sides .. .. — £1400

1856 (7 Jan). *Plate I. Wmk* "**2**". *Imperf.*
105 **14** 2d. light ultramarine .. .. .. £140 8·00
106 2d. Prussian blue .. .. .. £130 8·00
107 2d. dull blue .. .. £130 8·00
108 2d. pale blue .. .. £130 8·00
a. Error. Wmk "**1**" .. .. .. — £4000
b. Error. Wmk "**5**" .. .. .. £450 60·00
c. Error. Wmk "**8**" .. .. ..

1858. *Plate I, retouched.*
109 **14** 2d. dull blue £1800 £450

1859 (3 Aug). *Lithographic transfer of Plate I.*
110 **14** 2d. pale cobalt-blue .. .. .. — £750
a. Retouched .. .. — £2500

1860 (Jan). *Plate II. Recess. Stamps printed wider apart.*
110*b* **14** 2d. blue .. .. £350 12·00

1856 (10 Oct). *Wmk* "**3**". *Imperf.*
111 **14** 3d. yellow-green .. .. .. £700 80·00
112 3d. bluish green .. .. .. £750 80·00
113 3d. dull green .. .. £750 80·00
a. Error, Wmk "**2**" .. .. .. — £3000

In the 3d. the value is in block letters on a white ground.

15 17

19 21

(6d. and 1s. des E. H. Corbould after sketches by T. W. Levinge)

1855 (1 Dec). *Wmk* "**5**". *Imperf.*
114 **15** 5d. dull green £1000 £475

1854 (Feb)–**59.** *Wmk* "**6**". *Imperf.*
115 **17** 6d. deep slate .. .. £450 32·00
116 6d. greenish grey .. .. .. £350 32·00
117 6d. slate-green £350 £100
a. Printed both sides .. .. ..
118 6d. bluish grey .. .. £400 55·00
119 6d. fawn .. .. £450 95·00
a. Error. Wmk "**8**" (15.8.59) £1500 £100
120 6d. grey .. .. £400 55·00
121 6d. olive-grey .. .. £400 32·00
122 6d. greyish brown .. .. .. £400 32·00
a. Error. Wmk "**8**" (15.8.59) £1500 £100

1855 (1 Dec). *Wmk* "**8**". *Imperf.*
125 **19** 8d. golden yellow £3000 £700
126 8d. dull yellow-orange £3000 £700

1854 (Feb). *Wmk* "**12**". *Imperf.*
127 **21** 1s. rosy vermilion .. .. .. £650 65·00
a. Error. Wmk "**8**" (20.6.57) £1900 £170
128 1s. pale red .. .. £650 65·00
129 1s. brownish red .. .. .. £700 75·00

1860 (Feb)–**63.** *Wmk double-lined figure of value. P* 12.
131 **14** 1d. orange-red .. .. £170 16·00
a. Imperf between (pair) .. ..
b. Double impression .. .. ..
132 1d. scarlet .. .. £100 16·00
133 2d. cobalt-blue (Pl I) £500 £140
a. Retouched .. .. — £1300
134 2d. greenish blue (Pl II) .. .. 90·00 10·00
136 2d. Prussian blue (Pl II) .. .. 90·00 10·00
a. Error. Wmk "**1**" .. .. .. — £2750
b. Retouched (*shades*) .. .. .. — £400
137 2d. Prussian blue (Pl I) (3.61) .. .. £110 11·00
138 2d. dull blue (Pl I) .. .. .. £100 10·00
139 3d. yellow-green (1860) .. .. .. £1000 55·00
140 3d. blue-green .. .. £550 42·00
141 **15** 5d. dull green (1863) .. .. .. £100 36·00
142 5d. yellowish green (1863) .. .. £100 36·00
143 **17** 6d. grey-brown .. .. £275 45·00
144 6d. olive-brown .. .. £275 55·00
145 **17** 6d. greenish grey .. .. .. £350 45·00
146 6d. fawn .. .. £325 65·00
147 6d. mauve .. .. £300 35·00
148 6d. violet .. .. £275 16·00
a. Imperf between (pair) .. .. ..
149 **19** 8d. lemon-yellow .. .. — £1400
150 8d. orange £2000 £600
151 8d. red-orange £2000 £600
152 **21** 1s. brownish red .. .. £450 48·00
153 1s. rose-carmine .. .. £450 48·00
a. Imperf between (pair) .. .. ..

No. 133 was made by perforating a small remaining stock of No. 108. Nos. 137/8 were printed from the original plate after its return from London, where it had been repaired.

1862–72. *Wmk double-lined figure of value.* (*a*) *P* 13.
154 **14** 1d. scarlet (1862) .. .. .. 55·00 8·00
155 1d. dull red .. .. 55·00 8·00
156 3d. blue-green (12.62) .. .. .. 45·00 11·00
157 3d. yellow-green .. .. 50·00 8·50
a. Error. Wmk "**6**" (7.72) .. .. 50·00 12·00
158 3d. dull green .. .. 50·00 8·00
a. Error. Wmk "**6**" (7.72) .. .. 55·00 15·00
160 **15** 5d. bluish green (12.63) .. .. .. 35·00 15·00
161 5d. bright yellow-green (8.65) .. .. 38·00 24·00
162 5d. sea-green (1866) .. .. .. 38·00 17·00
162*a* 5d. dark bluish green (11.70) .. .. 28·00 17·00
163 **17** 6d. reddish purple (Pl I) (7.62) .. .. 60·00 5·00
164 6d. mauve .. .. 60·00 5·00
165 6d. purple (Pl II) (1864) .. .. 55·00 4·50
a. Error. Wmk "**5**" (7.66) .. .. £350 25·00
b. Error. Wmk "**12**" (12.66) .. .. £275 20·00
166 6d. violet .. .. 55·00 6·00
167 6d. aniline mauve £900 £120
167*a* **19** 8d. red-orange .. .. £140 55·00
167*b* 8d. yellow-orange .. .. £140 40·00
167*c* 8d. bright yellow .. .. £140 40·00
168 **21** 1s. rose-carmine .. .. 70·00 7·50
169 1s. carmine .. .. 70·00 8·00
170 1s. crimson-lake .. .. 70·00 8·00

(*b*) *Perf compound* 12 × 13
171 **14** 1d. scarlet .. .. — £1700
172 2d. dull blue £2000 £250

23

1864 (June). *W* **23.** *P* 13.
173 **14** 1d. pale red .. .. 30·00 12·00

24 25

(Des E. H. Corbould, R.I.)

1861–88. *W* **25.** *Various perfs.*
174 **24** 5s. dull violet, *p* 12 (1861) £1000 £325
a. Perf 13 (1861) .. .. .. £160 28·00
175 5s. royal purple, *p* 13 (1872) .. .. £275 45·00
176 5s. deep rose-lilac, *p* 13 (1875) .. .. 95·00 28·00
177 5s. deep purple, *p* 13 (1880) .. .. £150 40·00
a. Perf 10 (1882) .. .. .. £150 45·00
178 5s. rose-lilac, *p* 10 (1883) .. .. £110 40·00
179 5s. purple, *p* 12 (1885) .. .. .. — 45·00
a. Perf 10 × 12 (1885) .. .. .. — £120
180 5s. reddish purple, *p* 10 (1886) .. .. £110 40·00
a. Perf 12 × 10 (1887) .. .. .. £275 45·00
181 5s. rose-lilac, *p* 11 (1888) .. .. — £120

This value was replaced by Nos. 261, etc. in 1888 but reissued in 1897, *see* Nos. 297*c*/*e*.

26 28 29

(Printed by De La Rue & Co, Ltd, London and perf at Somerset House, London)

1862–65. *Surfaced paper. P* 14. (i) *W* **23.**
186 **26** 1d. dull red (Pl I) (4.64) .. .. 80·00 28·00

(ii) *No wmk*
187 **26** 1d. dull red (Pl II) (1.65) .. .. 60·00 28·00
188 **28** 2d. pale blue (3.62) .. .. .. 60·00 28·00

(Printed from the De La Rue plates in the Colony)

1862 (12 Apr). *Wmk double-lined* "**2**". *P* 13.
189 **28** 2d. blue .. .. 45·00 7·00
a. Perf 12 .. .. £120 12·00
b. Perf 12 × 13 .. .. £400

1864–65. *W* **23.** *P* 13.
190 **26** 1d. dark red-brown (Pl I) .. .. 70·00 14·00
191 1d. brownish red (Pl II) .. .. .. 18·00 1·50
192 1d. brick-red (Pl II) .. .. .. 18·00 1·50
a. Highly surfaced paper (1865) .. £180
194 **28** 2d. pale blue .. .. £110 3·50

Plates I and II were made from the same die; they can only be distinguished by the colour or by the marginal inscription.

1865–66. *Thin wove paper. No wmk. P* 13.
195 **26** 1d. brick-red .. .. 90·00 15·00
196 1d. brownish red .. .. .. 90·00 15·00
197 **28** 2d. pale blue .. .. 40·00 3·00

1863–69. *W* **29.** *P* 13.
198 **26** 1d. pale red (3.69) .. .. .. 70·00 11·00
199 **28** 2d. pale blue .. .. 7·50 50
a. Perf 12 .. ..
200 2d. cobalt-blue .. .. 7·50 50
201 2d. Prussian blue .. .. .. 19·00 3·50

1862 (Sept). *Wmk double-lined* "**5**". *P* 13.
202 **28** 2d. dull blue .. .. 60·00 8·50

32

34

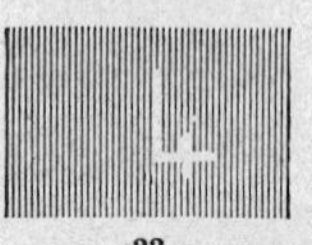
33

35

1867 (Sept)–**93.** *W* **33** *and* **35.**
203 **32** 4d. red-brown, *p* 13 .. .. .. 32·00 3·00
204 4d. pale red-brown, *p* 13 .. .. 32·00 3·00
205 **34** 10d. lilac, *p* 13 (Optd S. £25) .. 10·00 3·00
a. Imperf between (pair) £400
206 10d. lilac, *p* 11 (1893) .. .. 11·00 3·00
a. Perf 10 .. .. 14·00 4·50
b. Perf 10 and 11, compound .. 18·00 7·50
c. Perf 12 × 11 .. .. .. £110 15·00

36

37

38

NINEPENCE
(39)

From 1871 to 1903 the 9d. is formed from the 10d. by a *black* surch. (T 39), 15 mm long on Nos. 219 to 220h, and 13½ mm long on subsequent issues.

1871–85. *W* **36.**
207 **26** 1d. dull red, *p* 13 (8.71) .. .. 4·50 20
a. Imperf vert (horiz pair) .. ..
208 1d. salmon, *p* 13 .. .. .. 4·50 20
a. Perf 10 .. .. £250 15·00
b. Perf 13 × 10 .. .. .. 16·00 20
c. *Scarlet.* Perf 10 .. .. .. — £180
209 **28** 2d. Prussian-blue, *p* 13 (11.71) .. 5·50 20
a. Perf 11 × 12, comb .. .. £250 40·00
b. Imperf vert (horiz pair) .. .. — £500
210 2d. pale blue, *p* 13 .. .. .. 5·50 20
aa. "TWO PENCE" double impression at right .. .. .. — 30·00
a. Perf 10 .. .. £250 22·00
b. Perf 13 × 10 .. .. .. 6·00 20
c. Surfaced paper. Perf 13 .. ..
211 **14** 3d. yellow-green (3.74), *p* 13 .. 18·00 2·40
a. Perf 10 .. .. 65·00 5·50
b. Perf 11 .. .. £150 £100
c. Perf 12 .. .. — £150
d. Perf 10 × 12 .. .. .. £150 32·00
e. Perf 12 × 11 .. .. .. £120 32·00
212 3d. bright green, *p* 10 .. .. £120 11·00
a. Perf 10 × 13 .. .. .. £110 15·00
213 **32** 4d. pale red-brown (8.77), *p* 13 .. 45·00 6·00
214 4d. red-brown, *p* 13 .. .. .. 45·00 6·00
a. Perf 10 .. .. £180 50·00
b. Perf 13 × 10 .. .. .. 75·00 3·50
215 **15** 5d. bluish green (8.84), *p* 10 .. 15·00 8·00
a. Perf 12 (5.85) £250 £100
b. Perf 13×10 .. ..
c. Perf 10×12 .. .. .. 19·00 9·00
216 **37** 6d. bright mauve (1.72), *p* 13 .. 30·00 1·00
a. Imperf between (horiz pair) .. — £500
217 6d. pale lilac, *p* 13 .. .. .. 35·00 1·00
a. Perf 10 .. .. £180 12·00
b. Perf 13 × 10 .. .. .. 55·00 1·90
c. Imperf between (horiz pair). Perf 13 × 10 .. .. — £500
218 **19** 8d. yellow (3.77), *p* 13 .. .. 90·00 17·00
a. Perf 10 .. .. £250 24·00
b. Perf 13 × 10 .. .. .. £170 22·00
219 **34** 9d. on 10d. pale red-brown (8.71), *p* 13 18·00 4·50
220 **34** 9d. on 10d. red-brown, *p* 13 (Optd S. £25) 18·00 6·00
a. Perf 10 .. .. 9·00 4·50
b. Perf 12 .. .. 9·00 4·50
c. Perf 11 .. .. 24·00 7·00
d. Perf 10 × 12 .. .. .. £250 £160
e. Perf 10 × 11 .. .. .. 38·00 9·00
f. Perf 12 × 11 .. .. .. 12·00 5·50
g. Perf 11 × 12, comb .. .. 12·00 5·50
h. In black and blue. Perf 11 .. £110
221 **38** 1s. black (4.76), *p* 13 .. .. 80·00 2·50
a. Perf 10 .. .. £325 12·00
b. Perf 10 × 13 .. .. .. £170 4·50
c. Perf 11 .. ..
d. Imperf between (horiz pair) .. — £750

Collectors should note that the classification of perforations is that adopted by the Royal Philatelic Society, London. "Perf 12" denotes the perforation formerly called "11½, 12" and "perf 13" that formerly called "12½, 13".

40

41

1882–97. *W* **40.**
222 **26** 1d. salmon, *p* 10 .. .. .. 9·00 20
a. Perf 13 .. ..
b. Perf 10 × 13 .. .. .. 28·00 1·50
223 1d. orange *to* scarlet, *p* 13 .. ..
a. Perf 10 .. .. 7·00 20
ab. Imperf between (horiz pair) ..
b. Perf 10 × 13 .. .. .. £120 6·00
c. Perf 10 × 12 .. .. .. £250 65·00
d. Perf 10 × 11 .. .. .. £450 £120
e. Perf 12 × 11 .. .. .. — £120
f. Perf 11 × 12, comb .. .. 4·50 25
h. Perf 11 .. .. — £130
224 **28** 2d. pale blue, *p* 13 .. .. .. £450 90·00
a. Perf 10 .. .. 8·00 25
b. Perf 13 × 10 .. .. .. 65·00 2·00
225 2d. Prussian blue, *p* 10 .. .. 17·00 25
a. Perf 13 × 10 .. .. .. 65·00 1·90
b. Perf 12 .. .. — £225
c. Perf 11 .. .. — £100
d. Perf 12 × 11 .. .. .. — £100
e. Perf 12 × 10 .. .. .. £225 65·00
f. Perf 10 × 11 .. .. .. £450 £100
g. Perf 11 × 12, comb .. .. 12·00 15
226 **14** 3d. yellow-green (1886), *p* 10 .. 5·00 80
a. Perf 10 × 12 .. .. .. £160 15·00
b. Perf 11 .. .. 5·00 80
c. Perf 11 × 12 or 12 × 11 .. .. 5·00 80
d. Perf 12 .. .. 9·00 1·00
e. Imperf between (horiz pair) .. £130
f. Imperf (pair) £110
227 3d. bluish green, *p* 10 .. .. 5·00 80
a. Perf 11 .. .. 5·00 80
b. Perf 10 × 11 .. .. .. 15·00 1·50
c. Perf 12 × 11 .. .. .. 5·00 1·10
d. Perf 12 × 10 .. .. .. 75·00 3·00
228 3d. emerald-green, *p* 10 (1893) .. 55·00 7·50
a. Perf 10 × 11 .. .. .. 55·00 3·00
b. Perf 12 × 10 .. .. .. 80·00 8·00
229 **32** 4d. red-brown, *p* 10 .. .. .. 32·00 2·00
a. Perf 10 × 12 .. .. .. — £130
b. Perf 11 × 12, comb .. .. 42·00 1·25
230 4d. dark brown, *p* 10 .. .. .. 42·00 2·75
a. Perf 12 .. .. — 35·00
b. Perf 10 × 12 .. .. .. — 90·00
c. Perf 11 × 12, comb .. .. 14·00 1·00
231 **15** **5d. dull grn** *p* **10 (1890) (Optd S. £25)** 12·00 90
a. Perf 11×10 .. .. .. 30·00 2·00
b. Perf 12×10 (4.85) .. .. 80·00 3·50
232 **5d. bright green,** *p* **10 (4.82)** .. 32·00 4·50
a. Perf 11 (12.85) .. .. .. — 4·50
b. Perf 10×11 (12.85) .. .. 38·00 4·50
c. Perf 12×10 (4.85) .. .. £150 6·50
233 5d. blue-green, *p* 10 (4.82) .. .. 8·50 90
a. Perf 12 (4.85) .. .. .. 11·00 90
b. Perf 11 (12.85) .. .. .. 8·50 55
c. Perf 10×11 (12.85) .. .. 24·00 1·60
d. Perf 11×12 or 12×11 .. .. 6·50 55
e. Imperf (pair) £275
234 **37** 6d. pale lilac, *p* 10 .. .. .. 30·00 1·00
a. Perf 10×13 or 13×10 .. .. — £300
b. Perf 10×12 or 12×10 .. .. 38·00 1·50
235 6d mauve, *p* 10 .. .. .. 35·00 1·00
a. Perf 12 .. .. 80·00 2·50
b. Perf 11 .. .. 80·00 8·00
c. Perf 10×12 or 12×10 .. .. 32·00 1·00
ca. Imperf between (horiz pair) .. — £650
d. Perf 11×12 or 12×11 .. .. 32·00 1·40
e. Perf 10×11 .. .. .. 55·00 1·00
236 **19** 8d. yellow, *p* 10 (1883) .. .. £100 15·00
a. Perf 12 .. .. £150 24·00
b. Perf 11 .. .. £100 17·00
c. Perf 10×12 .. .. .. £130 22·00
236*d* **34** 9d. on 10d. red-brown, *p* 11×12 (1897) (Optd S. £25) .. .. .. 6·00 3·75
da. Perf 12 .. .. 9·00 5·00
db. Perf 11 .. .. 9·00 5·50
dc. Surch double, *p* 11 .. .. £140 £120
236*e* 10d. violet, *p* 11×12 (1897) (Optd S. £25) 10·00 3·25
ea. Perf 12×11½ .. .. .. 10·00 3·25
eb. Perf 12 .. .. 13·00 4·00
ec. Perf 11 .. .. 13·00 4·00
237 **38** 1s. black, *p* 10 .. .. .. 65·00 2·00
a. Perf 11 .. .. £200 9·00
b. Perf 10×12 .. ..
c. Perf 10×13 .. .. .. — 11·00
d. Perf 11×12, comb .. .. .. 65·00 2·00

1886–87. *W* **41.**
238 **26** 1d. scarlet, *p* 10 .. .. .. 11·00 3·75
a. Perf 11 × 12, comb .. .. 2·00 90
239 **28** 2d. deep blue, *p* 10 .. .. .. 32·00 5·00
a. Perf 11 × 12, comb .. .. 12·00 95
b. Imperf .. ..

1891 (July). *Wmk* "10" *as T* **35.** *P* 10.
240 **14** 3d. green (Optd S. £25) .. .. 12·00 80·00
241 3d. dark green .. .. 5·00 17·00

42

43

NOTE. The spacing between the Crown and "NSW" is 1 mm in T **42**, as against 2 mm in T **40**.

1903–8. *W* **42.**
241*a* **14** 3d. yellow-green, *p* 11 .. .. 6·00 90
b. Perf 12 .. .. 5·00 90
c. Perf 11 × 12 .. .. .. 5·00 90
242 3d. dull green, *p* 12 .. .. .. 19·00 1·75
a. Perf 11 × 12 .. .. .. 7·00 1·00
243 **15** 5d. dark blue-green, *p* 11 × 12 .. 5·00 90
a. Perf 11 .. .. 12·00 90
b. Perf 12 .. .. 19·00 3·50
c. Imperf (pair) £125
d. Wmk sideways .. .. ..

1885–86. *W* **41.** (i) *Overprinted* "POSTAGE", *in black.*
244 **43** 5s. green and lilac, *p* 13 .. ..
a. Perf 10 .. ..
b. Perf 12 × 10 .. .. .. £300 80·00
245 10s. claret and lilac, *p* 13 .. ..
a. Perf 12 .. .. £400 £120
246 £1 claret and lilac, *p* 13 .. .. — £2000
a. Perf 12 .. .. £2000 £900

(ii) *Overprinted in blue*
247 **43** 10s. claret and mauve, *p* 10 (Optd S. £60) £450 £100
a. Perf 12 .. .. £130 40·00
b. Perf 12 × 11 .. .. .. £225
248 £1 claret and rose-lilac, *p* 12 × 10 .. £2250 £1000

44

1894. *Overprinted* "POSTAGE" *in blue. W* **44.**
249 **43** 10s. claret and mauve, *p* 10 .. .. £200 38·00
249*a* 10s. claret and violet, *p* 12 .. .. £110 28·00
b. Perf 11 .. .. £100 28·00
c. Perf 12 × 11 .. .. .. £100 28·00
250 10s. aniline crimson & violet, *p* 12 × 11 £120 30·00
a. Perf 12 .. .. £140 40·00
250*b* £1 claret and violet, *p* 12 × 11 ..

1903–04. *Optd* "POSTAGE" *in blue. Chalk-surfaced paper. W* **44.**
250*c* **43** 10s. aniline crimson & violet, *p* 12 × 11
251 10s. rosine and violet, *p* 12 (1904) .. £100 28·00
a. Perf 11 .. .. £120 28·00
b. Perf 12 × 11 .. .. .. £120 28·00
252 10s. claret and violet, *p* 12 × 11 (1904) .. £170 28·00

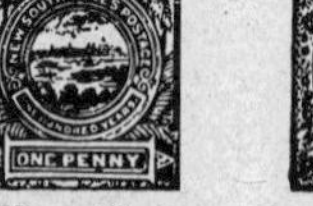

45 View of Sydney

46 Emu

47 Captain Cook

48 Queen Victoria and Arms of Colony

49 Superb Lyrebird

50 Eastern Grey Kangaroo

51 Map of Australia

52 Capt. Arthur Phillip, first Governor and Lord Carrington, Governor in 1888

es M. Tannenberg (1d., 6d.), Miss Devine (2d., 8d.), H. Barraclough (4d.), Govt Ptg Office (1s.), C. Turner (5s.), Mrs. F. Stoddard (20s.). Eng W. Bell).

88 (1 May)–**89.** *Centenary of New South Wales.* (*a*) *W* **40**. *P* 11 × 12.

3	**45**	1d. lilac (9.7.88) ..	3·75	10
		a. Perf 12 × 11½	17·00	90
		b. Perf 12	5·00	10
		c. Imperf (pair) ..		
		d. Mauve	3·75	10
		da. Imperf between (pair)		
		da. Perf 12 × 11½	6·00	25
		dc. Perf 12	5·50	25
4	**46**	2d. Prussian blue (1.9.88)	3·25	10
		a. Imperf (pair) ..	£100	
		b. Imperf between (pair)	£350	
		c. Perf 12 × 11½	7·00	10
		d. Perf 12	5·00	10
		e. Chalky blue ..	3·25	10
		ea. Perf 12 × 11½		
		eb. Perf 12	4·25	25
5	**47**	4d. purple-brown (8.10.88)	9·00	3·00
		a. Perf 12 × 11½	28·00	7·50
		b. Perf 12	24·00	3·25
		c. Perf 11	£300	90·00
		d. Red-brown ..	9·00	3·00
		da. Perf 12 × 11½	13·00	2·75
		db. Perf 12	13·00	2·75
		e. Orange-brown, p 12 × 11½ ..	13·00	2·75
		f. Yellow-brown, p 12 × 11½ ..	10·00	3·00
6	**48**	6d. carmine (26.11.88) ..	20·00	2·50
		a. Perf 12 × 11½	25·00	3·00
		b. Perf 12	21·00	2·50
7	**49**	8d. lilac-rose (17.1.89) ..	8·50	1·50
		a. Perf 12 × 11½	35·00	10·00
		b. Perf 12	8·50	1·75
		c. Magenta	75·00	9·00
		ca. Perf 12 × 11½	8·50	1·75
		cb. Perf 12	8·00	2·25
8	**50**	1s. maroon (21.2.89)	12·00	90
		a. Perf 12 × 11½	14·00	90
		b. Perf 12	18·00	90
		c. Violet-brown ..	12·00	90
		ca. Imperf (pair) ..	£550	
		cb. Perf 12 × 11½	38·00	1·25
		cc. Perf 12	38·00	90

(*b*) *W* **41**. *P* 11 × 12

59	**45**	1d. lilac (1888) ..	9·00	
		a. Mauve	7·50	10
60	**46**	2d. Prussian blue (1888)	40·00	3·00

(*c*) *W* **25**. *P* 10

61	**51**	5s. deep purple (13.3.89)	£225	45·00
		a. Deep violet ..	£200	42·00
62	**52**	20s. cobalt-blue ..	£300	£110
3/8 Optd "Specimen"		*Set of* 6	£150	

Nos. 255c and 261/2 are line perforated, the remainder are comb.

53

54

890. *W* **53** (*5s.*) *or* **54** (*20s.*). *P* 10.

63	**51**	5s. lilac ..	£150	25·00
		a. Perf 11	£225	35·00
		ab. Imperf between (horiz pair)		
		b. Perf 12	£300	35·00
		c. Perf 10 × 11 or 11 × 10	£225	25·00
		d. Mauve	£225	25·00
		da. Perf 11	£225	35·00
64	**52**	20s. cobalt-blue ..	£225	80·00
		a. Perf 11	£300	75·00
		b. Perf 11 × 10 ..		
		c. Ultramarine, p 11 ..	£225	75·00
		ca. Perf 12	£325	£130
		cb. Perf 11 × 12 or 12 × 11	£225	75·00
63/4 Optd "Specimen"		*Set of* 2	£225	

55 Allegorical figure of Australia

Halfpenny

(56)

SEVEN-PENCE
HALFPENNY

(57)

1890 (22 Dec). *W* **40**.

281	**55**	2½d. ultramarine, *p* 11 × 12 *comb* (Optd S. £25)	75	30
		a. Perf 12 × 11½, comb	45·00	
		b. Perf 12, comb	6·00	30

1891 (5 Jan). *Surch as T* **56** *and* **57**. *W* **40**.

282	**26**	½d. on 1d. grey, *p* 11 × 12 *comb*	50	30
		a. Surch omitted		
		b. Surch double	£120	
283	**37**	7½d. on 6d. brown, *p* 10	2·00	90
		a. Perf 11	2·00	90
		b. Perf 12	2·50	2·25
		c. Perf 11 × 12	2·25	2·00
		d. Perf 10 × 12	2·50	2·00
284	**38**	12½d. on 1s. red, *p* 10	2·50	2·25
		a. Perf 11	2·75	2·00
		b. Perf 11 × 12, comb	2·50	1·75
		c. Perf 12 × 11½, comb	1·75	1·75
		d. Perf 12, comb	3·25	1·75
282/4 Optd "Specimen"		*Set of* 3	70·00	

58

Die I

1892 (21 Mar)–**99.** *T* **58**. *Die I. Narrow* "H" *in* "HALF". *W* **40**.

285	½d. grey, *p* 10 ..	12·00	45
	a. Perf 11	60·00	5·00
	b. Perf 10 × 12	55·00	7·50
	c. Perf 11 × 12 (Optd S. £20)	70·00	10
	d. Perf 12	90·00	10
286	½d. slate, *p* 11 × 12 (1897)	80	10
	a. Perf 12 × 11½	80	10
	b. Perf 12	80	10
	c. Imperf between (horiz pair). Perf 11 × 12	£400	
287	½d. bluish green, *p* 11 × 12 (1899)	1·50	10
	a. Perf 12 × 11½	70	10
	b. Perf 12	80	10

The perforations 11 × 12, 12 × 11½, 12, are from comb machines.

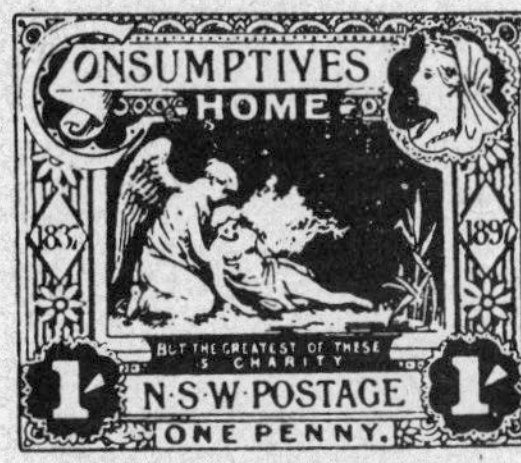

58*a*

58*b*

(Des C. Turner. Typo Govt Printing Office, Sydney)

1897. *Charity. T* **58a** *and* **58b**. *Wmk W* **40**. *P* 12 × 11 (*1d.*) *or* 11 (*2½d.*).

287*c*	**58*a***	1d. (1s.) green and brown (22.6)	40·00	40·00
287*d*	**58*b***	2½d. (2s. 6d.), gold, carmine & bl (28.6)	£150	£150
287*c/d* Optd "Specimen"		*Set of* 2	£200	

These stamps, sold at 1s. and 2s. 6d. respectively, paid postage of 1d. and 2½d. only, the difference being given to a Consumptives' Home.

59

60

61

Dies of the 1d.

Die I

Die II

1d. Die I. The first pearl on the crown on the left side is merged into the arch, the shading under the fleur-de-lis is indistinct, the "S" of "WALES" is open.

Die II. The first pearl is circular, the vertical shading under the fleur-de-lis clear, the "S" of "WALES" not so open.

Dies of the 2½d.

Die I

Die II

2½d. Die I. There are 12 radiating lines in the star on the Queen's breast.

Die II. There are 16 radiating lines in the star and the eye is nearly full of colour.

1897–99. *W* **40** (*sideways on 2½d.*).

288	**59**	1d. carmine (Die I), *p* 11 × 12 ..	1·75	10
		a. Perf 12 × 11½	2·00	10
289		1d. scarlet (Die I), *p* 11 × 12	1·75	10
		a. Perf 12 × 11½	4·50	40
		b. Perf 12	4·50	50
		ba. Imperf horiz (vert pair)		
290		1d. rose-carmine (Die II), *p* 11 × 12	1·75	10
		a. Perf 12 × 11½	1·50	10
		b. Perf 12	1·50	10
		c. Imperf between (pair)	£400	
291		1d. salmon-red (Die II), *p* 12 × 11½	1·75	10
		a. Perf 12	3·25	30
292	**60**	2d. deep dull blue, *p* 11 × 12	1·75	10
		a. Perf 12 × 11½	1·75	10
		b. Perf 12	4·50	10
293		2d. cobalt-blue, *p* 11 × 12	3·00	10
		a. Perf 12 × 11½	2·50	10
		b. Perf 12	3·00	10
294		2d. ultramarine, *p* 11 × 12	2·50	10
		a. Perf 12 × 11½	1·75	10
		b. Perf 12	1·75	10
		c. Imperf between (pair)		
295	**61**	2½d. purple (Die I), *p* 12 × 11	5·00	1·25
		a. Perf 11½ × 12	6·00	80
		b. Perf 11	6·00	1·75
296		2½d. deep violet (Die II), *p* 12 × 11	3·50	80
		a. Perf 11½ × 12	6·00	1·25
		b. Perf 12	3·25	1·25
297		2½d. Prussian blue, *p* 12 × 11	6·00	
		a. Perf 11½ × 12	4·00	80
		b. Perf 12	3·25	80
288, 292, 294/5 Optd "Specimen"		*Set of* 4	60·00	

The perforations 11 × 12, 12 × 11½ and 12 are from comb machines, the perforation 11 is from a single-line machine.

1897. *Reissue of T* **24**. *W* **25**. *P* 11.

297*c*	5s. reddish purple (*shades*)	30·00	12·00
	ca. Imperf between (pair)	£2750	
	d. Perf 12	38·00	20·00
	e. Perf 11 × 12 or 12 × 11 ..	30·00	19·00

1898–99. *W* **40**. *P* 11 × 12.

297*f*	**48**	6d. emerald-green (Optd S. £20)	25·00	5·00
		fa. Perf 12 × 11½	17·00	5·00
		fb. Perf 12	17·00	5·00
297*g*		6d. orange-yellow (1899)	13·00	3·00
		ga. Perf 12 × 11½	12·00	2·50
		gb. Perf 12	21·00	4·50
		gc. Yellow, p 12 × 11½ ..	13·00	1·25

1899(Oct). *Chalk-surfaced paper. W* **40** (*sideways on 2½d.*). *P* 12 × 11½ *or* 11½ × 12 (*2½d.*), *comb.*

298	**58**	½d. blue-green (Die I) ..	90	10
		a. Imperf (pair)	50·00	30·00
299	**59**	1d. carmine (Die II)	80	10
		a. Imperf horiz (vert pair)	£200	
300		1d. scarlet (Die II)	80	10
301		1d. salmon-red (Die II)	80	10
		a. Imperf (pair)	40·00	38·00
302	**60**	2d. cobalt-blue ..	1·75	10
		a. Imperf (pair)	40·00	
303	**61**	2½d. Prussian blue (Die II)	2·75	70
		a. Imperf (pair)	45·00	
303*b*	**47**	4d. red-brown ..	9·00	3·00
		c. Imperf (pair)	£200	
304		4d. orange-brown	9·00	3·00
305	**48**	6d. deep orange	8·00	90
		a. Imperf (pair)	£140	
306		6d. orange-yellow	8·00	90
307		6d. emerald-green	38·00	2·00
		a. Imperf (pair)	£175	
308	**49**	8d. magenta	9·00	2·50
309	**34**	9d. on 10d. dull brown ..	6·50	4·00
		a. Surcharge double ..	90·00	70·00
		b. Without surcharge	80·00	
310		10d. violet	10·00	2·75
311	**50**	1s. maroon	12·00	80
312		1s. purple-brown	12·00	1·25
		a. Imperf (pair)	£150	

62 Superb Lyrebird

63

1902. *Chalk-surfaced paper. W* **42** (*sideways on 2½d.*). *P* 12 × 11½ *or* 11½ × 12 (*2½d.*), *comb.*

313	**58**	½d. blue-green, (Die I) ..	2·75	10
		a. Perf 12 × 11	2·75	
314	**59**	1d. carmine (Die II)	80	10
315	**60**	2d. cobalt-blue ..	1·50	10
316	**61**	2½d. dark blue (Die II)	2·75	10
317	**47**	4d. orange-brown	18·00	3·25
318	**48**	6d. yellow-orange	15·00	90
319		6d. orange	14·00	90
320		6d. orange-buff ..	14·00	90
321	**49**	8d. magenta	9·00	1·75
322	**34**	9d. on 10d. brownish orange	6·50	3·50
323		10d. violet	18·00	3·00
324	**50**	1s. maroon	12·00	80
325		1s. purple-brown	13·00	80
326	**62**	2s. 6d. green (Optd S. £35)	42·00	14·00

(Typo Victoria Govt Printer, Melbourne)

1903 (18 July). *Wmk double-lined V over Crown. W* w **10**.

327	**63**	9d. brown & ultram, *p* 12¼ × 12½, *comb* (Optd S. £27) ..	7·50	1·75
328		9d. brown & dp blue, *p* 12¼ × 12½, *comb*	7·50	1·75
329		9d. brown and blue, *p* 11	£450	£275

Die II. Broad "H" in "HALF"

66

1905–10. *Chalk-surfaced paper. W* **66** *(sideways on 2½d.). P 12×11½ or 11½×12 (2½d.) comb, unless otherwise stated.*
330 **58** ½d. blue-green (Die I) .. 1·75 10
a. Perf 11½ × 11
331 ½d. blue-green (Die II) .. 90 10
a. Perf 11½ × 11 .. 1·75
332 **59** 1d. rose-carmine (Die II) .. 75 10
a. Perf. 11½ × 11 .. 1·75
333 **60** 2d. deep ultramarine .. 1·75 10
b. Perf 11½ × 11 .. 2·00
333*d* 2d. milky blue (1910) .. 1·75 10
da. Perf 11 .. 45·00
db. Perf 11½ × 11
334 **61** 2½d. Prussian blue (Die II) .. 2·75 80
335 **47** 4d. orange-brown .. 8·00 3·00
336 4d. red-brown .. 8·50 3·00
337 **48** 6d. dull yellow .. 11·00 1·00
a. Perf 11½ × 11 .. 19·00
338 6d. orange-yellow .. 11·00 90
a. Perf 11 × 11½ .. 25·00
339 6d. deep orange .. 8·00 90
a. Perf 11 .. £150
339*b* 6d. orange-buff .. 8·00 90
c. Perf 11½ × 11 .. 15·00 2·75
340 **49** 8d. magenta .. 8·50 2·00
341 8d. lilac-rose .. 8·50 2·25
342 **34** 10d. violet .. 13·00 2·75
a. Perf 11½ × 11 .. 12·00 2·50
b. Perf 11 .. 12·00 2·50
343 **50** 1s. maroon .. 11·00 85
344 1s. purple-brown (1908) .. 12·00 85
345 **62** 2s. 6d. blue-green .. 38·00 14·00
a. Perf 11½ × 11 .. 27·00 11·00
b. Perf 11 .. 30·00 15·00

67

1905 (Dec). *Chalk-surfaced paper. W* **67**. *P* 11.
346 **52** 20s. cobalt-blue .. £180 60·00
a. Perf 12 .. £180 60·00
b. Perf 11 × 12 or 12 × 11 .. £180 60·00

(Typo Victoria Govt Printer, Melbourne)

1906 (Sept). *Wmk double-lined "A" and Crown, W w* **11**. *P 12×12½, comb.*
347 **63** 9d. brown and ultramarine .. 6·00 1·10
a. Perf 11 .. 42·00 35·00
348 9d. yellow-brown and ultramarine .. 6·00 90

1907 (July). *W w* **11**. *P 12×11½ or 11½×12 (2½d.), comb, unless otherwise stated.*
349 **58** ½d. blue-green (Die I) .. 2·00 10
351 **59** 1d. dull rose (Die II) .. 1·75 10
352 **60** 2d. cobalt-blue .. 1·75 10
353 **61** 2½d. Prussian blue (Die II) .. 42·00
354 **47** 4d. orange-brown .. 8·00 3·00
355 **48** 6d. orange-buff .. 18·00 3·25
356 6d. dull yellow .. 17·00 3·25
357 **49** 8d. magenta .. 8·50 3·00
358 **34** 10d. violet, *p* 11 .. 18·00
359 **50** 1s. purple-brown .. 16·00 2·50
a. Perf 11
360 **62** 2s. 6d. blue-green .. 45·00 22·00

OFFICIAL STAMPS

O S (O 1) **O S** (O 2) **O S** (O 3)

The space between the letters is normally 7 mm as illustrated, except on the 5d. and 8d. (11–11½ mm), 5s. (12 mm) and 20s. (14 mm). Later printings of the 3d., W **40**, are 5½ mm, and these are listed. Varieties in the settings are known on the 1d. (8 and 8½ mm), 2d. (8½ mm) and 3d. (9 mm).
Varieties of Type O 1 exist with "O" sideways.

Nos. O1/35 overprinted with Type O 1

1879. *Wmk double-lined "6". P* 13.
O1 **14** 3d. dull green .. — £400

1879 (Oct)–**85.** *W* **36**. *P* 13.
O 2 **26** 1d. salmon .. 8·50 2·00
a. Perf 10 (5.81) .. £180 30·00
b. Perf 13 × 10 (1881) .. 20·00 3·50
O 3 **28** 2d. blue .. 10·00 1·25
a. Perf 10 (7.81) .. £225 32·00
b. Perf 13 × 10 (1881) .. 20·00 2·50
c. Perf 10 × 13 (1881) .. 45·00 7·00
d. Perf 11 × 12 (11.84?) .. — £225
O 4 **14** 3d. dull green (R.) (12.79) .. £200 £200
O 5 **14** 3d. dull green (3.80) .. £250 45·00
a. Perf 10 (1881) .. £140 40·00
b. *Yellow-green*. Perf 10 (10.81) .. £140 25·00
c. Ditto. Perf 13 × 10 (1881) .. £140 25·00
d. Ditto. Perf 12 (4.85) .. £200 50·00
e. Ditto. Perf 12 × 10 (4.85) .. £200 50·00
O 6 **32** 4d. red-brown .. £140 7·50
a. Perf 10 (1881) .. — £190
b. Perf 13 × 10 (1881) .. £200 90·00
c. Perf 10 × 13 (1881) .. £200 11·00
O 7 **15** 5d. green, *p* 10 (8.84) .. 14·00 7·50
O 8 **37** 6d. pale lilac .. £200 4·50
a. Perf 10 (1881) .. — 40·00
b. Perf 13 × 10 (1881) .. £150 40·00
O 9 **19** 8d. yellow (R.) (12.79) .. — £130
O10 8d. yellow (1880) .. — 9·00
a. Perf 10 (1881) .. £250 75·00
O11 **34** 9d. on 10d. brown, *p* 10 (30.5.80) (Optd S. £60) .. £250 £150
O12 **38** 1s. black (R.) .. £200 7·50
a. Perf 10 (1881) .. — 16·00
b. Perf 13 × 10 (1881) .. — 9·00
c. Perf 10 × 13 (1881) .. — 45·00
Other stamps are known with red overprint but their status is in doubt.

1880–88. *Wmk "5/-", W* **25**. *(a) P* 13.
O13 **24** 5s. deep purple (15.2.80) .. £400 65·00
a. Royal purple .. — £300
b. Deep rose-lilac .. — £300
(b) P 10
O14 **24** 5s. deep purple (9.82) .. £400 £160
b. Rose-lilac (1883) .. £275 £100
(c) P 10 × 12
O15 **24** 5s. purple (10.86)
(d) P 12 × 10
O16 **24** 5s. reddish purple (1886) .. £300 £100
(e) P 12
O17 **24** 5s. purple .. — £150
(f) P 11
O18 **24** 5s. rose-lilac (1888) .. £160 42·00

1880 (31 May). *Wmk "10", W* **35**. *P* 13.
O18*a* **34** 10d. lilac (Optd S. £60) .. £130 80·00
ab. Perf 10 and 11, compound .. £200 £180

1882–85. *W* **40**. *P* 10.
O19 **26** 1d. salmon .. 7·00 2·00
a. Perf 13 × 10 .. — £130
O20 1d. orange *to* scarlet .. 6·00 1·50
a. Perf 10 × 13 .. — £130
b. Perf 11 × 12, comb (1.84) .. 3·50 1·40
c. Perf 10 × 12 (4.85) .. — £110
d. Perf 12 × 11 (12.85)
O21 **28** 2d. blue .. 4·00 1·00
a. Perf 13 × 10
b. Perf 10 × 13 .. £190 75·00
c. Perf 11 × 12, comb (1.84) .. 4·00 1·00
d. Ditto. Opt double
e. Perf 12 × 11 (12.85)
O22 **14** 3d. yellow-green (7 *mm*) .. 4·50 2·25
a. Perf 12 (4.85) .. £120 80·00
b. Perf 12 × 10 (4.85)
O23 3d. bluish green (7 *mm*) .. 4·50 2·25
a. Perf 12 (4.85) .. £120 80·00
b. Perf 12 × 10 (4.85)
c. Perf 10 × 11 (12.85)
O24 3d. yellow-green (5½ *mm*) .. 4·50 2·25
a. Perf 12 × 10 or 10 × 12 (4.85) .. 4·50 2·25
b. Perf 10 × 11 or 11 × 10 (12.85)
O25 3d. bluish green (5½ *mm*) (Optd S. £35) 4·50 2·25
a. Perf 12 × 10 or 10 × 12 (4.85) .. 4·75 2·75
c. Perf 10 × 11 or 11 × 10 (12.85) .. 4·00 2·25
O26 **32** 4d. red-brown .. 25·00 2·50
a. Perf 11 × 12, comb (1.84) .. 7·00 2·25
b. Perf 10 × 12 (4.85) .. — 70·00
O27 4d. dark brown .. 11·00 2·25
a. Perf 11 × 12, comb (1.84) .. 7·00 2·25
b. Perf 12 (4.85) .. £200 £150
c. Perf 10 × 12 (4.85) .. £200 90·00
O28 **15** 5d. dull green (Optd S. £35) .. 8·50 4·00
a. Perf 12 × 10 (4.85)
O29 5d. blue-green .. 9·00 5·00
a. Perf 12 (4.85) .. £100
b. Perf 10 × 11 .. 9·00 5·00
O30 **37** 6d. pale lilac .. 14·00 1·75
a. Perf 11 (12.85) .. 15·00 1·50
O31 6d. mauve .. 14·00 1·75
a. Perf 12 (4.85) .. — 45·00
b. Perf 12 × 10 (4.85) .. 14·00 1·50
c. Perf 10 × 12 (4.85) .. 80·00 36·00
d. Perf 11 × 10 (12.85) .. 14·00 1·75
e. Perf 12 × 11 (12.85) .. 55·00 15·00
O32 **19** 8d. yellow .. 17·00 3·25
a. Perf 12 (4.85) .. £130 36·00
b. Perf 12 × 10 or 10 × 12 (4.85) .. 17·00 2·75
d. Perf 11 (12.85) .. 18·00 3·00
da. Opt double
db. Opt treble .. † —
O33 **38** 1s. black (R.) .. 17·00 2·50
a. Perf 10 × 13 .. — 55·00
b. Perf 11 × 12, comb (1.84) .. 17·00 2·50
c. Ditto. Opt double

1886–87. *W* **41**. *P* 10.
O34 **26** 1d. scarlet .. 20·00 3·00
O35 **28** 2d. deep blue
a. Perf 11 × 12

1887–89. *Nos. 247/8 overprinted in black. (a) With Type* O 1.
O36 **43** 10s. claret and mauve, *p* 12 .. — £300
(b) With Type O **2** *(April 1889)*
O37 **43** 10s. claret and mauve, *p* 12 (Optd S. £75) .. £1100 £500
a. Perf 10 .. £2000 £1300
(c) With Type O **3** *(Jan 1887)*
O38 **43** £1 claret and rose-lilac, *p* 12 × 10 .. £2250 £2250
a. Opt double

1888 (17 July)–**90.** *Optd as Type* O **1**. *(a) W* **40**. *P* 11 × 12.
O39 **45** 1d. lilac .. 1·50
a. Perf 12 .. 1·50
b. Mauve .. 1·50
ba. Perf 12 .. 1·50
O40 **46** 2d. Prussian blue (15.10.88) .. 2·00
a. Perf 12 .. 2·00
O41 **47** 4d. purple-brown (10.10.89) .. 4·00 7
a. Perf 12 .. 5·50 7
b. Perf 11
c. Red-brown .. 4·00 7
ca. Perf 12 .. 5·00 7
O42 **48** 6d. carmine (16.1.89) .. 4·50 8
a. Perf 12 .. 6·00 8
O43 **49** 8d. lilac-rose (1890) .. 10·00 3·7
a. Perf 12 .. — 5·0
O44 **50** 1s. maroon (9.1.90) .. 8·00 1·2
a. Perf 12 .. 9·00 1·2
b. Purple-brown .. 8·00 1·2
ba. Opt double
bb. Perf 12 .. 8·00 1·2
(b) W **41**. *P* 11 × 12 (1889)
O45 **45** 1d. mauve
O46 **46** 2d. blue
(c) W **25**. *P* 10
O47 **51** 5s. deep purple (9.1.90) .. £500 £4(
O48 **52** 20s. cobalt-blue (10.3.90) .. £1000 £4(
O39/44 Optd "Specimen" .. *Set of* 6 £200

1890 (Feb)–**91.** *Optd as Type* O **1**. *W* **53** *(5s.) or* **54** *(20s.) P* 1(
O49 **51** 5s. lilac .. £130 42·0
a. Mauve .. £150 45·0
b. Dull lilac, p 12 .. £550
O50 **52** 20s. cobalt-blue (3.91) .. £1500 £5(
O49/50 Optd "Specimen" .. *Set of* 2 £200

1891 (Jan)–**92.** *Nos. 281/5 optd as Type* O **1**. *W* **40**. *P* 11 × 12.
O54 **55** 2½d. ultramarine .. 2·75 1·5
O55 **26** ½d. on 1d. grey .. 30·00 20·0
O56 **37** 7½d. on 6d. brown, *p* 10 .. 20·00 15·0
O57 **38** 12½d. on 1s. red .. 40·00 25·0
O58 **58** ½d. grey (5.92) .. 2·50 1·7
a. Perf 10 .. 2·75 3·5
b. Perf 12 .. 2·50 2·0
c. Perf 12 × 11½ .. 4·00
O54/8 Optd "Specimen" .. *Set of* 5 £160
Official stamps were withdrawn from the government depart ments on 31 December 1894.

POSTAGE DUE STAMPS

D 1

(*Dies eng by A. Collingridge. Typo Govt Printing Office, Sydney*)

1891 (1 Jan)–**92.** *W* **40**. *P* 10.
D 1 **D 1** ½d. green (21.1.92) .. 2·50 2·0
D 2 1d. green .. 3·50 9
a. Perf 11 .. 3·75 9
b. Perf 12 .. 13·00 2·5
c. Perf 12 × 10 .. — 1·7
d. Perf 10 × 11 .. 6·50 9
e. Perf 11 × 12 or 12 × 11 .. 4·00 9
D 3 2d. green .. 5·50 8
a. Perf 11 .. 5·50 8
b. Perf 12 .. — 8·0
c. Perf 12 × 10 .. 15·00 3·0
d. Perf 10 × 11 .. 7·00 1·5
e. Perf 11 × 12 or 12 × 11 .. 5·50 8
D 4 3d. green .. 9·00 2·7
a. Perf 10 × 11 .. 9·00 2·7
D 5 4d. green .. 7·50 8
a. Perf 11 .. 8·50 8
b. Perf 10 × 11 .. 7·50 8
D 6 6d. green .. 14·00 2·0
D 7 8d. green .. 60·00 2·5
D 8 5s. green .. £120 30·0
a. Perf 11 .. £200 75·0
b. Perf 11 × 12 .. — £25
D 9 10s. green (early 1891) .. £180 45·0
a. Perf 12 × 10 .. £120 80·0
D10 20s. green (early 1891) .. £300 80·0
a. Perf 12 .. £300
b. Perf 12 × 10 .. £175 £10
D1/10 Optd "Specimen" .. *Set of* 10 £200

1900. *Chalk-surfaced paper. W* **40**. *P* 11.
D11 **D 1** ½d. emerald-green
D12 1d. emerald-green .. 3·50 1·7
a. Perf 12 .. 10·00 3·5
b. Perf 11 × 12 or 12 × 11 .. 3·50 1·0
D13 2d. emerald-green .. 6·50 2·7
a. Perf 12 .. — 12·0
b. Perf 11 × 12 or 12 × 11 .. 5·50 2·5
D14 3d. emerald-green, *p* 11 × 12 or 12 × 11 12·00 3·0
D15 4d. emerald-green .. 7·50 2·2

The six former colonies of New South Wales, Queensland South Australia, Tasmania, Victoria and Western Australi united to form the Commonwealth of Australia on 1 January 1901.

On 1 March 1901 control of the postal service passed to th federal administration. The first national postage due stamp appeared in July 1902, but it was not until January 1913 tha postage stamps inscribed "Australia" were issued.

ALTERED CATALOGUE NUMBERS

Any Catalogue numbers altered from the last edition are shown as a list in the introductory pages.

New Zealand

From 1831 mail from New Zealand was sent to Sydney, New South Wales, routed through an unofficial postmaster at Kororareka.

The first official post office opened at Kororareka in January 1840 to be followed by others at Auckland, Britannia, Coromandel Harbour, Hokianga, Port Nicholson, Russell and Waimate during the same year. New South Wales relinquished control of the postal service when New Zealand became a separate colony on 3 May 1841.

The British G.P.O. was responsible for the operation of the overseas mails from 11 October 1841 until the postal service once again passed under colonial control on 18 November 1848.

For illustrations of handstamp types see BRITISH POST OFFICES ABROAD notes, following GREAT BRITAIN.

AUCKLAND

CROWNED-CIRCLE HANDSTAMPS

CC1 CC 1 AUCKLAND NEW ZEALAND (R.) (31.10.1846) . . . . *Price on cover* £300

NELSON

CROWNED-CIRCLE HANDSTAMPS

CC2 CC 1 NELSON NEW ZEALAND (R.) (31.10.1846) *Price on cover* £1100

NEW PLYMOUTH

CROWNED-CIRCLE HANDSTAMPS

CC3 CC 1 NEW PLYMOUTH NEW ZEALAND (R. *or* Black) (31.10.1846) . . *Price on cover* £1500

CC3*a* CC 2 NEW PLYMOUTH NEW ZEALAND (R. *or* Black) (1854) . . *Price on cover* £1500

OTAGO

CROWNED-CIRCLE HANDSTAMPS

CC4 CC 2 OTAGO NEW ZEALAND (R.) (1851) *Price on cover* £1500

PETRE

CROWNED-CIRCLE HANDSTAMPS

CC5 CC 1 PETRE NEW ZEALAND (R.) (31.10.1846) *Price on cover* £1500

PORT VICTORIA

CROWNED-CIRCLE HANDSTAMPS

CC6 CC 2 PORT VICTORIA NEW ZEALAND (R.) (1851) . . . . . . *Price on cover* £1000

RUSSELL

CROWNED-CIRCLE HANDSTAMPS

CC7 CC 1 RUSSELL NEW ZEALAND (R.) (30.10.1846) *Price on cover* £1400

WELLINGTON

CROWNED-CIRCLE HANDSTAMPS

CC8 CC 1 WELLINGTON NEW ZEALAND (R.) (31.10.1846) . . . . *Price on cover* £500

A similar mark for Christchurch as Type CC **2** is only known struck, in black, as a cancellation after the introduction of adhesive stamps.

No. CC3*a* is a locally-cut replacement with the office name around the circumference, but a straight "PAID AT" in the centre.

PRICES FOR STAMPS ON COVER TO 1945

Nos. 1/125	*from* × 2
Nos. 126/36	*from* × 3
Nos. 137/9	*from* × 2
No. 140	—
No. 141	*from* × 2
No. 142	—
Nos. 143/8	*from* × 2
Nos. 149/51	*from* × 10
Nos. 152/84	*from* × 2
Nos. 185/6	—
Nos. 187/203	*from* × 3
Nos. 205/7*e*	—
Nos. 208/13	*from* × 2
Nos. 214/16*j*	—
Nos. 217/58	*from* × 3
No. 259	—
Nos. 260/9	*from* × 3
No. 270	—
Nos. 271/6	*from* × 3
Nos. 277/307	*from* × 2
Nos. 308/16	*from* × 3
No. 317	—
Nos. 318/28	*from* × 3
Nos. 329/48	—
No. 349	*from* × 5
Nos. 350/1	—
No. 352	*from* × 5
Nos. 353/69	—
Nos. 370/86	*from* × 2
No. 387	*from* × 4
Nos. 388/99	*from* × 3
Nos. 400/666	*from* × 2
Nos. E1/5	*from* × 5
No. E6	*from* × 10
Nos. D1/8	*from* × 3
Nos. D9/16	*from* × 5
Nos. D17/20	*from* × 3
Nos. D21/47	*from* × 6
Nos. O1/24	*from* × 12
Nos. O59/66	*from* × 4
Nos. O67/8	—
Nos. O69/81	*from* × 5
Nos. O82/7	—
Nos. O88/93	*from* × 20
Nos. O94/9	*from* × 12
Nos. O100/11	*from* × 5
Nos. O112/13	—
Nos. O115/19	*from* × 15
Nos. O120/33	*from* × 10
Nos. O134/51	*from* × 4
Nos. P1/7	*from* × 8
Nos. L1/9	*from* × 10
Nos. L9*a*/12	—
Nos. L13/20	*from* × 15
Nos. L21/3	—
Nos. L24/41	*from* × 12
No. F1	—
No. F2	*from* × 5
Nos. F3/144	—
Nos. F145/58	*from* × 3
Nos. F159/68	—
Nos. F169/79	*from* × 3
Nos. F180/6	—
Nos. F187/90	*from* × 2
Nos. F191/203	*from* × 3
Nos. F204/11	—
Nos. F212/18	*from* × 2
Nos. A1/3	*from* × 2

CROWN COLONY

1

2

(Eng by Humphreys. Recess P.B.)

1855 (18 July). *Wmk Large Star, W* w **1.** *Imperf.*

1	1	1d. dull carmine (*white paper*) . .	£25000	£8000
2		2d. dull blue (*blued paper*)	£10000	£550
3		1s. pale yellow-green (*blued paper*) . .	£25000	£5250
		a. Bisected (6d.) (on cover)	†	£20000

The 2d. and 1s. on white paper formerly listed are now known to be stamps printed on blued paper which have had the bluing washed out.

Nos. 3a and 6a. were used at Dunedin from March 1857 when the rate for ½ oz letters to Great Britain was reduced to 6d. All known examples are bisected vertically.

(Printed by J. Richardson, Auckland, N.Z.)

1855 (Dec). *First printing. Wmk Large Star. White paper. Imperf.*

3*b*	1	1d. orange	£15000	

1855 (Dec)–**57.** *No wmk. Blue paper. Imperf.*

4	1	1d. red	£6500	£1400
5		2d. blue (3.56)	£2250	£300
		a. Without value		
6		1s. green (9.57)	£10000	£3500
		a. Bisected (6d.) (on cover)	†	£15000

These stamps on blue paper may occasionally be found wmkd double-lined letters, being portions of the paper-maker's name.

1857 (Jan). *Wmk Large Star. White paper similar to the issue of July* 1855.

7	1	1d. dull orange	—	£12000

This stamp is in the precise shade of the 1d. of the 1858 printing by Richardson on *no wmk* white paper. An unsevered pair is known with Dunedin cancellation on a cover bearing arrival postmark of Auckland dated "19.1.1857".

1858–63. *Hard or soft white paper. No wmk.* (*a*) *Imperf.*

8	1	1d. dull orange (1858)	£1400	£325
8*a*		2d. deep ultramarine (1858)	£1500	£750
9		2d. pale blue	£700	£175
10		2d. blue	£700	£175
11		2d. dull deep blue	—	£175
12		6d. bistre-brown (Aug 1859)	£2250	£500
13		6d. brown	£1000	£300
14		6d. pale brown	£1000	£300
15		6d. chestnut	£2250	£500
16		1s. dull emerald-green	£6500	£1000
17		1s. blue-green	£6500	£1200
		(*b*) *Pin-roulette, about* 10 *at Nelson* (1862)		
18	1	1d. dull orange	—	£4500
19		2d. blue	—	£4500
20		6d. brown	—	£4500
21		1s. blue-green	—	£6500
		(*c*) *Serrated perf about* 16 *or* 18 *at Nelson* (1862)		
22	1	1d. dull orange	—	£3250
23		2d. blue	—	£2750
24		6d. brown	—	£2750
25		6d. chestnut	—	£5250
26		1s. blue-green	—	£4750
		(*d*) *Rouletted* 7 *at Auckland* (April 1859)		
27	1	1d. dull orange	£4250	£3000
28		2d. blue	£5250	£2750
29		6d. brown	£3500	£2750
		a. Imperf between (pair)	£10000	£9000
30		1s. dull emerald-green	£5500	£3500
31		1s. blue-green	£6500	£3500
		(*e*) *P* 13 *at Dunedin* (1863)		
31*a*	1	1d. dull orange	—	£2250
31*b*		2d. pale blue	£2750	£1750
32		6d. pale brown	—	£5000

Other forms of separation, in addition to those shown above, are known, both on the stamps of this issue and on those of 1862. Some of the varieties are extremely rare, only single copies being known.

The 2d. in a distinctive deep bright blue on white paper wmkd. Large Star is believed by experts to have been printed by Richardson in 1861 or 1862. This also exists doubly printed and with serrated perf.

(Printed by John Davies at the G.P.O., Auckland, N.Z.)

1862 (Feb–Dec). *Wmk Large Star.* (*a*) *Imperf.*

33	1	1d. orange-vermilion	£350	£120
34		1d. vermilion	£350	£120
35		1d. carmine-vermilion	£350	£150
36		2d. deep blue (Plate I)	£300	60·00
		a. Double print	—	£2250
37		2d. slate-blue (Plate I)	£1500	£180
37*a*		2d. milky blue (Plate I, worn)	—	£225
38		2d. pale blue (Plate I, worn)	£225	70·00
39		2d. blue (*to* deep) (Plate I, very worn) . .	£225	70·00
40		3d. brown-lilac (Dec 1862)	£275	£100
41		6d. black-brown	£600	75·00
42		6d. brown	£600	75·00
43		6d. red-brown	£500	65·00
44		1s. green	£750	£160
45		1s. yellow-green	£700	£150
46		1s. deep green	£850	£190

Nos. 37*a*/38 show some signs of wear on right of Queen's head and shades of No. 39 show moderate to advanced states of wear.

		(*b*) *Rouletted* 7 *at Auckland* (6.62)		
47	1	1d. orange-vermilion	£3000	£600
48		1d. vermilion	£1800	£600
48*a*		1d. carmine-vermilion	£2500	£700
49		2d. deep blue	£1700	£400
50		2d. slate-blue	£2750	£650
51		2d. pale blue	£1500	£500
52		3d. brown-lilac	£1700	£650
53		6d. black-brown	£2000	£400
54		6d. brown	£1700	£475
55		6d. red-brown	£1700	£400
56		1s. green	£2000	£550
57		1s. yellow-green	£3000	£550
58		1s. deep green	£3000	£650
		(*c*) *Serrated perf* 16 *or* 18 *at Nelson* (8.62)		
59	1	1d. orange-vermilion	—	£1000
60		2d. deep blue	—	£700
		a. Imperf between (pair)	£5000	£2500
61		2d. slate-blue		
62		3d. brown-lilac	£2500	£1400
63		6d. black-brown	—	£1500
64		6d. brown	—	£1500
65		1s. yellow-green	—	£2250
		(*d*) *Pin-perf* 10 *at Nelson* (8.62)		
66	1	2d. deep blue	—	£1700
67		6d. black-brown	—	£2750

The dates put to above varieties are the earliest that have been met with.

1862. *Wmk Large Star. P* 13 (*at Dunedin*).

68	1	1d. orange-vermilion	£550	£150
69		1d. carmine-vermilion	£550	£150
70		2d. deep blue (Plate I)	£275	30·00
71		2d. slate-blue (Plate I)	—	£700
72		2d. blue (Plate I)	£200	30·00
72*a*		2d. milky blue (Plate I)	—	£500
73		2d. pale blue (Plate I)	£200	30·00
74		3d. brown-lilac	£500	£120
75		6d. black-brown	£500	£110
		a. Imperf between (horiz pair)		
76		6d. brown	£450	48·00
77		6d. red-brown	£350	30·00
78		1s. dull green	£450	£190
79		1s. deep green	£500	£180
80		1s. yellow-green	£500	£160

See also Nos. 110/125 and the note that follows these.

1862. *Pelure paper. No wmk.* (*a*) *Imperf.*

81	1	1d. orange-vermilion	£5500	£1700
82		2d. ultramarine	£3250	£750
83		2d. pale ultramarine	£3250	£750
84		3d. lilac	£25000	†
85		6d. black-brown	£1200	£225
86		1s. deep green	£5500	£800

The 3d. is known only unused.

		(*b*) *Rouletted* 7 *at Auckland*		
87	1	1d. orange-vermilion	—	£4000
88		6d. black-brown	£2000	£450
89		1s. deep green	£3500	£1100
		(*c*) *P* 13 *at Dunedin*		
90	1	1d. orange-vermilion	£9500	£3000
91		2d. ultramarine	£4500	£550
92		2d. pale ultramarine	£4500	£550
93		6d. black-brown	£3500	£325
94		1s. deep green	£7000	£950
		(*d*) *Serrated perf* 15 *at Nelson*		
95	1	6d. black-brown	—	£3500

1863 (early). *Hard or soft white paper. No wmk.* (*a*) *Imperf.*

96	1	2d. dull deep blue (*shades*)	£2250	£800
		(*b*) *P* 13		
96*a*	1	2d. dull deep blue (*shades*)	£1600	£475

These stamps show slight beginnings of wear of the printing plate in the background to right of the Queen's ear, as one looks at the stamps. By the early part of 1864, the wear of the plate had spread, more or less, all over the background of the circle containing the head. The major portion of the stamps of this printing appears to have been consigned to Dunedin and to have been there perforated 13.

1864. *Wmk* "N Z", *W* **2.** (*a*) *Imperf.*

97	1	1d. carmine-vermilion	£700	£200
98		2d. pale blue (Plate I worn)	£750	£200
99		6d. red-brown	£2000	£475
100		1s. green	£900	£250
		(*b*) *Rouletted* 7 *at Auckland*		
101	1	1d. carmine-vermilion	£4500	£2750
102		2d. pale blue (Plate I worn)	£1400	£700
103		6d. red-brown	£4250	£2750
104		1s. green	£2750	£1000

(c) P 13 at Dunedin

04a	1	1d. carmine-vermilion	£5000	£3500
05		2d. pale blue (Plate I worn)	£550	£160
06		1s. green	£1100	£550
		a. Imperf between (horiz pair)	£7500	

(d) P 12½ at Auckland

06b	1	1d. carmine-vermilion	£3750	£2000
07		2d. pale blue (Plate I worn)	£200	50·00
08		6d. red-brown	£200	30·00
09		1s. yellow-green	£4000	£2000

864–67. *Wmk Large Star. P 12½ (at Auckland)*

10	1	1d. carmine-vermilion (1864)	80·00	17·00
11		1d. pale orange-vermilion	90·00	17·00
		a. Imperf (pair)	£1500	£1000
12		1d. orange	£225	38·00
13		2d. pale blue (Plate I worn) (1864)	80·00	14·00
14		2d. deep blue (Plate II) (1866)	80·00	14·00
		a. Imperf between (pair)	—	£2000
15		2d. blue (Plate II)	80·00	17·00
		a. Retouched (Plate II) (1867)	£130	19·00
		c. Imperf (pair) (Plate II)	£1200	£1200
		d. Retouched. Imperf (pair)	£1500	£1800
16		3d. brown-lilac (1864)	£700	£500
17		3d. lilac	65·00	17·00
		a. Imperf (pair)	£1300	£1000
18		3d. deep mauve	£300	45·00
		a. Imperf (pair)	£1500	£1000
19		4d. deep rose (1865)	£1600	£250
20		4d. yellow (1865)	75·00	38·00
21		4d. orange	£1000	£800
22		6d. red-brown (1864)	75·00	15·00
22a		6d. brown	75·00	15·00
		b. Imperf (pair)	£950	£950
23		1s. deep green (1864)	£450	£160
24		1s. green	£275	48·00
25		1s. yellow-green	£100	45·00

The above issue is sometimes difficult to distinguish from Nos. 8/80 because the vertical perforations usually gauge 12¾ and ometimes a full 13. However stamps of this issue invariably gauge 2½ horizontally, whereas the 1862 stamps measure a full 13.

The 1d., 2d. and 6d. were officially reprinted imperforate, ithout gum, in 1884 for presentation purposes. They can be istinguished from the errors listed by their shades which are pale range, dull blue and dull chocolate-brown respectively, and by the orn state of the plates from which they were printed.

871. *Wmk Large Star. (a) P 10.*

26	1	1d. brown	£375	50·00

(b) P 12½ × 10

27	1	1d. deep brown	—	£750

(c) P 10 × 12½

28	1	1d. brown	£100	14·00
		a. Perf 12½ comp 10 (1 side)	£225	60·00
29		2d. deep blue (Plate II)	—	£4500
		a. Perf 10*	†	£8000
30		2d. vermilion	£120	15·00
		a. Retouched	£160	19·00
		b. Perf 12½ comp 10 (1 side)	£650	£275
		c. Perf 10*	†	£8000
31		6d. deep blue	£950	£450
		a. Blue	£750	£275
		b. Imperf between (vert pair)	—	£4000
		c. Perf 12½ comp 10 (1 side)	£500	£200
		ca. Imperf vert (horiz pair)		

(d) P 12½

32	1	1d. red-brown	90·00	14·00
		a. Brown (shades, worn plate)	90·00	14·00
		b. Imperf horiz (vert pair)	—	£2500
33		2d. orange	50·00	15·00
		a. Retouched	£110	40·00
34		2d. vermilion	85·00	15·00
		a. Retouched	£150	50·00
35		6d. blue	85·00	17·00
36		6d. pale blue	50·00	17·00

In or about 1872 both 1d. and 2d. stamps were printed on some paper having a wmk of script letters "W.T. & Co." (=Wiggins Teape & Co) in the sheet, and other paper with the name "T. H. Saunders" in double-lined capitals in the sheet; portions of these letters are occasionally found on stamps.

*Only one used copy each of Nos. 129a and 130c have been reported.

1872. *No wmk. P 12½.*

137	1	1d. brown	£275	40·00
138		2d. vermilion	48·00	18·00
		a. Retouched	£150	25·00
139		4d. orange-yellow	£120	£350

1872. *Wmk* "N Z", *W* **2.** *P* 12½.

140	1	1d. brown	—	£2500
141		2d. vermilion	£300	65·00
		a. Retouched	£600	£150

1872. *Wmk Lozenges, with* "INVICTA" *in double-lined capitals four times in the sheet. P* 12½.

142	1	2d. vermilion	£2500	£550
		a. Retouched	£3750	£800

3

4

Des John Davies. Die eng on wood in Melbourne. Printed from electrotypes at Govt Ptg Office, Wellington)

1873 (1 Jan). (a) *Wmk* "NZ", *W* **2**.

143	3	½d. pale dull rose (*p* 10)	60·00	14·00
144		½d. pale dull rose (*p* 12½)	£180	55·00
145		½d. pale dull rose (*p* 12½ × 10)	£110	42·00

(b) No wmk

146	3	½d. pale dull rose (*p* 10)	60·00	20·00
147		½d. pale dull rose (*p* 12½)	£180	60·00
148		½d. pale dull rose (*p* 12½ × 10)	£150	55·00

As the paper used for Nos. 143/5 was originally intended for fiscal stamps which were more than twice as large, about one-third of the impressions fall on portions of the sheet showing no watermark, giving rise to varieties Nos. 146/8. In later printings of No. 151 a few stamps in each sheet are without watermark. These can be distinguished from No. 147 by the shade.

1875 (Jan). *Wmk Star, W* **4**.

149	3	½d. pale dull rose (*p* 12½)	11·00	90
		a. Imperf between (pair)	£600	£325
150		½d. dull pale rose (*p nearly* 12)	60·00	5·50

1892 (May). *Wmk "NZ and Star". W* **12***b*. *P* 12½.

151	3	½d. bright rose (*shades*)	5·00	25
		a. No wmk	7·00	2·25

5 6 7

8 9 10

11 12 **12***a* 6 mm

12*b* 7 mm **12***c* 4 mm

(T **5/10** eng De La Rue. T **11** and **12** des, eng & plates by W. R. Bock. Typo Govt Ptg Office, Wellington)

1874 (2 Jan)–**78**. *W* **12***a*. A. *White paper. (a) P* 12½.

152	5	1d. lilac	60·00	3·25
		a. Imperf	£400	
153	6	2d. rose	60·00	1·60
154	7	3d. brown	95·00	50·00
155	8	4d. maroon	£300	50·00
156	9	6d. blue	£200	10·00
157	10	1s. green	£1000	30·00

(b) Perf nearly 12

158	6	2d. rose (1878)	£600	£180

(c) Perf compound of 12½ and 10

159	5	1d. lilac	£150	40·00
160	6	2d. rose	£350	65·00
161	7	3d. brown	£160	55·00
162	8	4d. maroon	£350	£100
163	9	6d. blue	£225	40·00
164	10	1s. green	£1000	95·00
		aa. Imperf between (vert pair)	†	—

(d) Perf nearly 12 × 12½

164a	5	1d. lilac (1875)	£650	£250
165	6	2d. rose (1878)	£650	£190

B. *Blued paper. (a) P 12½*

166	5	1d. lilac	70·00	29·00
167	6	2d. rose	95·00	29·00
168	7	3d. brown	£225	75·00
169	8	4d. maroon	£425	£100
170	9	6d. blue	£325	48·00
171	10	1s. green	£1000	£190

(b) Perf compound of 12½ and 10

172	5	1d. lilac	£180	50·00
173	6	2d. rose	£500	80·00
174	7	3d. brown	£180	55·00
175	8	4d. maroon	£450	£110
176	9	6d. blue	£300	90·00
177	10	1s. green	£1000	£200

1875. *Wmk Large Star, W* w **1.** *P* 12½.

178	5	1d. deep lilac	£500	£100
179	6	2d. rose	£300	15·00

1878. *W* **12***a*. *P* 12 × 11½ *(comb)*.

180	5	1d. mauve-lilac	40·00	2·00
181	6	2d. rose	40·00	1·40
182	8	4d. maroon	£130	38·00
183	9	6d. blue	80·00	10·00
184	10	1s. green	£110	27·00
185	11	2s. deep rose (1 July)	£350	£275
186	12	5s. grey (1 July)	£375	£275

This perforation is made by a horizontal "comb" machine, giving a gauge of 12 horizontally and about 11¾ vertically. Single specimens can be found apparently gauging 11½ all round or 12 all round, but these are all from the same machine. The perforation described above as "nearly 12" was from a single-line machine.

13 14 15

16 17 18

19 20 21

22

Description of Watermarks

W12*a*. 6 mm between "N Z" and star; broad irregular star; comparatively wide "N"; "N Z" 11½ mm wide.

W12*b*. 7 mm between "N Z" and star; narrower star; narrow "N"; "N Z" 10 mm wide.

W12*c*. 4 mm between "N Z" and star; narrow star; wide "N"; "N Z" 11½ mm wide.

Description of Papers

1882–88.	Smooth paper with horizontal mesh. W **12***a*.
1888–98.	Smooth paper with vertical mesh. *W* **12***b*.
1890–91.	Smooth paper with vertical mesh. *W* **12***c*.
1898.	Thin yellowish toned, coarse paper with clear vertical mesh. *W* **12***b*. Perf 11 only.

In 1899–1900 stamps appeared on medium to thick white coarse paper but we do not differentiate these (except where identifiable by shade) as they are more difficult to distinguish.

PAPER MESH. This shows on the back of the stamp as a series of parallel grooves, either vertical or horizontal. It is caused by the use of a wire gauze conveyor-belt during paper-making.

Description of Dies

1d.

Die 1

Die 2

Die 3

1882. Die 1.	Background shading complete and heavy.
1886. Die 2.	Background lines thinner. Two lines of shading weak or missing left of Queen's forehead.
1889. Die 3.	Shading on head reduced; ornament in crown left of chignon clearer, with unshaded "arrow" more prominent.

PRICES OF SETS

Set prices are given for many issues, generally those containing three stamps or more. Definitive sets include one of each value or major colour change, but do not cover different perforations, die types or minor shades. Where a choice is possible the set prices are based on the cheapest versions of the stamps included in the listings.

2d.

Die 1

Die 2

Die 3

1882. Die 1. Background shading complete and heavy.

1886. Die 2. Weak line of shading left of forehead and missing shading lines below "TA".

1889. Die 3. As Die 2 but with comma-like white notch in hair below "&".

6d.

Die 1

Die 2

1882. Die 1. Shading heavy. Top of head merges into shading.

1892. Die 2. Background lines thinner. Shading on head more regular with clear line of demarcation between head and background shading.

STAMPS WITH ADVERTISEMENTS. During November 1891 the New Zealand Post Office invited tenders for the printing of advertisements on the reverse of the current 1d. to 1s. stamps. The contract was awarded to Messrs Miller, Truebridge & Reich and the first sheets with advertisements on the reverse appeared in February 1893.

Different advertisements were applied to the backs of the individual stamps within the sheets of 240 (four panes of 60).

On the first setting those in a vertical format were inverted in relation to the stamps and each of the horizontal advertisements had its base at the left-hand side of the stamp when seen from the back. For the second and third settings the vertical advertisements were the same way up as the stamps and the bases of those in the horizontal format were at the right as seen from the back. The third setting only differs from the second in the order of the individual advertisements.

The experiment was not, however, a success and the contract was cancelled at the end of 1893.

Des F. W. Sears (½d.), A. E. Cousins (2½d.), A. W. Jones (5d.); others adapted from 1874 issue by W. H. Norris. Dies eng A. E. Cousins (½d., 2½d., 5d.), W. R. Bock (others). Typo Govt Ptg Office)

1882–1900. *Inscr* "POSTAGE & REVENUE".

A. W 12*a*. *Paper with horiz mesh* (1.4.82–86). (*a*) *P* 12 × 11½

187 **14** 1d. rose *to* rose-red (Die 1) .. .. 35·00 4·00
a. Imperf (pair) £275
b. Imperf between (vert pair) ..
c. Die 2. *Pale rose to carmine-rose* (1886) 30·00 4·00
188 **15** 2d. lilac *to* lilac-purple (Die 1) .. .. 40·00 4·00
a. Imperf (pair) £300
b. Imperf between (vert pair) £300
c. Die 2. *Lilac* (1886) .. .. .. 50·00 5·00
189 **17** 3d. yellow (1884) .. .. .. 45·00 4·50
190 **18** 4d. blue-green .. .. .. 60·00 4·50
191 **20** 6d. brown (Die 1) .. .. .. 65·00 3·75
192 **21** 8d. blue (1885) .. .. .. 65·00 45·00
193 **22** 1s. red-brown .. .. .. 75·00 11·00

(*b*) *P* 12½ (1884?)

193*a* **14** 1d. rose *to* rose-red (Die 1) .. .. £170 70·00

B. W 12*b*. *Paper with vert mesh* (1888–95)

(*a*) *P* 12×11½ (1888–95)

194 **13** ½d. black (1.4.95) .. .. .. 25·00 48·00
195 **14** 1d. rose *to* rosine (Die 2) .. .. 35·00 3·50
a. Die 3. *Rose to carmine* (1889) .. 35·00 3·50
ab. Red-brn advert (1st setting) (2.93)
ac. Red advert (1st setting) (3.93) .. 45·00 10·00
ad. Blue advert (2nd setting) (4.93) .. 55·00 25·00
ae. Mauve advert (2nd setting) (5.93) 35·00 6·00
af. Green advert (2nd setting) (6.93)
ag. Brn-red advert (3rd setting) (9.93) 35·00 6·00
196 **15** 2d. lilac (Die 2) .. .. .. 40·00 3·50
a. Die 3. *Lilac to purple* (1889) .. 40·00 3·50
ab. Red advert (1st setting) (3.93) .. 60·00 15·00
ac. Mauve advert (2nd setting) (5.93) 50·00
ad. Sepia advert (2nd setting) (5.93) 50·00 20·00
ae. Green advert (2nd setting) (6.93) — 75·00
af. Brn-red advert (3rd setting) (9.93)
197 **16** 2½d. pale blue (1891) .. .. 38·00 5·50
a. Brn-red advert (2nd setting) (4.93) 38·00 10·00
b. Ultramarine (green advert. 2nd setting) (6.93) .. .. .. 48·00 12·00
198 **17** 3d. yellow .. .. .. 40·00 6·00
a. Brn-red advert (2nd setting) (4.93) 60·00 10·00
b. Sepia advert (2nd setting) (5.93)
199 **18** 4d. green *to* bluish green .. .. 48·00 2·75
a. Sepia advert (2nd setting) (5.93) 60·00 10·00
200 **19** 5d. olive-black (1.2.91) .. .. 40·00 9·00
a. Imperf (pair) £300
b. Brn-pur advert (3rd setting) (9.93) 60·00 25·00
201 **20** 6d. brown (Die 1) .. .. .. 60·00 2·25
a. Die 2 (1892) .. .. .. £110 50·00
ab. Sepia advert (2nd setting) (5.93)
ac. Brn-red advert (3rd setting) (9.93) £140 60·00
202 **21** 8d. blue .. .. .. 65·00 38·00
203 **22** 1s. red-brown .. .. .. 75·00 6·00
a. Black advert (2nd setting) (5.93) £300 £150
b. Brn-pur advert (3rd setting) (9.93) £100 15·00

(*b*) *Perf compound of* 12 *and* 12½ (1888–91)

204 **14** 1d. rose (Die 2) .. .. .. £190 75·00
a. Die 3 (1889) .. .. ..

(*c*) *P* 12½ (1888–89)

205 **14** 1d. rose (Die 3) (1889) .. .. £160 90·00
a. Mauve advert (2nd setting) (5.93)
206 **15** 2d. lilac (Die 2) .. .. .. £160 80·00
a. Die 3. *Deep lilac* (1889) .. .. £120 65·00
ab. Brn-red advert (3rd setting) (9.93) £120 75·00
207 **16** 2½d. blue (1891) .. .. .. £170 90·00

(*d*) *Mixed perfs* 12×11½ *and* 12½ (1891–93)

207*a* **14** 1d. rose (Die 3) .. .. ..
207*b* **15** 2d. lilac (Die 3) .. .. ..
ba. Brn-red advert (3rd setting) (9.93)
207*c* **18** 4d. green .. .. .. — 50·00
207*d* **19** 5d. olive-black .. .. .. — 95·00
207*e* **20** 6d. brown (Die 1) .. .. .. — £100
ea. Die 2 .. .. .. — £150

C. W 12*c*. *Paper with vert mesh* (1890). (*a*) *P* 12 × 11½

208 **14** 1d. rose (Die 3) .. .. .. 50·00 4·00
209 **15** 2d. purple (Die 3) .. .. .. 50·00 4·00
210 **16** 2½d. ultramarine (27.12) .. .. 48·00 7·50
211 **17** 3d. yellow .. .. .. 50·00 7·50
a. Lemon-yellow .. .. .. 50·00 8·00
212 **20** 6d. brown (Die 1) .. .. .. 95·00 15·00
213 **22** 1s. deep red-brown .. .. .. £110 27·00

(*b*) *P* 12½

214 **14** 1d. rose (Die 3) £170 £100
215 **15** 2d. purple (Die 3) .. .. .. £180 90·00
216 **16** 2½d. ultramarine .. .. .. £200 95·00

(*c*) *Perf compound of* 12 *and* 12½

216*a* **20** 6d. brown (Die 1) £180 £130

D. *Continuation of W* 12*b*. *Paper with vert mesh* (1891–1900)

(*a*) *Perf compound of* 10 *and* 12½ (1891–94)

216*b* **14** 1d. rose (Die 3) .. .. .. £175 85·00
ba. Red-brn advert (1st setting) (2.93) £175 £100
bb. Brn-red advert (2nd setting) (4.93) £150 70·00
bc. Mauve advert (2nd setting) (5.93) £150 70·00
bd. Green advert (2nd setting) (6.93) £200 £120
216*c* **15** 2d. lilac (Die 3) .. .. .. £150 55·00
216*d* **16** 2½d. blue (1893) .. .. .. £130 60·00
216*e* **17** 3d. yellow .. .. .. £150 70·00
216*f* **18** 4d. green £170 £140
216*g* **19** 5d. olive-black (1894) £180 £170
216*h* **20** 6d. brown (Die 1) £190 £190
i. Die 2 (1892) £150 £150
ia. Brn-pur advert (3rd setting) (9.93) £175 £175
216*j* **22** 1s. red-brown £170 £160

(*b*) *P* 10 (1891–95)

217 **13** ½d. black (1895) .. .. .. 2·50 15
218 **14** 1d. rose (Die 3) .. .. .. 3·00 10
a. Carmine .. .. .. 5·50 1·25
b. Imperf (pair) £250 £250
c. Imperf between (pair) £275
d. Imperf horiz (vert pair) £200
e. Mixed perfs 10 and 12½ £250 £120
f. Red-brown advert (1st setting) (2.93) .. .. .. 12·00 4·00
g. Red advert (1st setting) (3.93) .. 12·00 5·00
h. Brown-red advert (2nd and 3rd settings) (4.93) .. .. 6·00 2·50
i. Blue advert (2nd setting) (4.93) .. 45·00 20·00
j. Mauve advert (2nd setting) (5.93) .. .. .. 6·00 2·50
k. Green advert (2nd setting) (6.93) .. 45·00 16·00
l. Brown-purple advert (3rd setting) (9.93) .. .. 6·00 2·50
219 **15** 2d. lilac (Die 3) .. .. .. 6·00 10
a. Purple .. .. .. 7·50 15
b. Imperf between (pair) £180
c. Mixed perfs 10 and 12½ .. .. £200 90·00
d. Red-brown advert (1st setting) (2.93) .. .. .. 20·00 5·00
e. Red advert (1st setting) (3.93) .. 20·00 5·00
f. Brown-red advert (2nd and 3rd settings) (4.93) .. .. 10·00 2·50
g. Sepia advert (2nd setting) (5.93) .. 14·00 3·00
h. Green advert (2nd setting) (6.93) .. 30·00 8·00
i. Brown-purple advert (3rd setting) (9.93) .. .. 10·00 2·50

220 **16** 2½d. blue (1892) .. .. .. 35·00 3·50
a. Ultramarine .. .. .. 35·00 4·00
b. Mixed perfs 10 and 12½ .. .. £170 80·00
c. Mauve advert (2nd setting) (5.93) .. .. .. 35·00 6·00
d. Green advert (2nd setting) (6.93) 55·00 9·00
e. Brown-purple advert (3rd setting) (9.93) .. .. 35·00 6·00
221 **17** 3d. pale orange-yellow .. .. 35·00 5·50
a. Orange .. .. .. 35·00 5·50
b. Lemon-yellow .. .. .. 42·00 6·50
c. Mixed perfs 10 and 12½ £160 £120
d. Brown-red advert (2nd and 3rd settings) (4.93) .. .. 38·00 9·00
e. Sepia advert (2nd setting) (5.93) 75·00 22·00
f. Brown-purple advert (3rd setting) (9.93) .. .. 35·00 6·00
222 **18** 4d. green (1892) .. .. .. 45·00 2·50
a. Blue-green .. .. .. 50·00 3·50
b. Mixed perfs 10 and 12½ .. .. £190 80·00
c. Brown-red advert (2nd setting) (4.93) .. .. .. 60·00 4·00
d. Brown-purple advert (3rd setting) (9.93) .. .. 55·00 4·00
223 **19** 5d. olive-black (1893) .. .. 42·00 10·00
a. Brown-purple advert (3rd setting) (9.93) .. .. 65·00 14·00
224 **20** 6d. brown (Die 1) .. .. .. 80·00 12·00
a. Mixed perfs 10 and 12½ .. ..
b. Die 2 (1892) .. .. .. 45·00 3·50
ba. Black-brown .. .. .. 48·00 3·50
bb. Imperf (pair) £225
bc. Mixed perfs 10 and 12½ .. .. 90·00 50·00
bd. Sepia advert (2nd setting) (4.93) 60·00 9·00
be. Brown-red advert (3rd setting) (9.93) .. .. .. 60·00 9·00
bf. Brown-purple advert (3rd setting) (9.93) .. .. 60·00 9·00
225 **21** 8d. blue (brown-purple advert. 3rd setting) (9.93) .. .. .. 65·00 45·00
226 **22** 1s. red-brown .. .. .. 75·00 5·00
a. Imperf between (pair) £350
b. Mixed perfs 10 and 12½ £150 £110
c. Sepia advert (2nd setting) (5.93) £100 12·00
d. Black advert (2nd setting) (5.93) £175 £110
e. Brown-red advert (3rd setting) (9.93) .. .. .. £100 12·00
f. Brown-purple advert (3rd setting) (9.93) .. .. £100 12·00

(*c*) *Perf compound of* 11 *and* 10 (1895)

226*c* **13** ½d. black .. .. .. 16·00 7·50
226*d* **14** 1d. rose (Die 3) .. .. .. 35·00 4·00
226*e* **20** 6d. brown (Die 2) .. .. .. £160 70·00

(*d*) *Perf compound of* 10 *and* 11 (1895–97)

227 **13** ½d. black (1896) .. .. .. 3·25 20
a. Mixed perfs 10 and 11 .. .. 80·00 24·00
228 **14** 1d. rose (Die 3) .. .. .. 4·00 15
a. Mixed perfs 10 and 11 .. .. 85·00 45·00
229 **15** 2d. purple (Die 3) .. .. .. 7·50 15
a. Mixed perfs 10 and 11 .. .. 60·00 45·00
230 **16** 2½d. blue (1896) .. .. .. 35·00 3·50
a. Ultramarine .. .. .. 35·00 4·00
b. Mixed perfs 10 and 11 .. .. — 65·00
231 **17** 3d. lemon-yellow (1896) .. .. 50·00 5·50
232 **18** 4d. pale green (1896) .. .. 65·00 5·50
a. Mixed perfs 10 and 11 .. .. — 80·00
233 **19** 5d. olive-black (1897) .. .. 45·00 10·00
234 **20** 6d. deep brown (Die 2) (1896) .. 50·00 3·75
a. Mixed perfs 10 and 11
235 **22** 1s. red-brown (1896) .. .. 70·00 7·00
a. Mixed perfs 10 and 11 .. .. £140 70·00

(*e*) *P* 11 (1895–1900)

236 **13** ½d. black (1897) .. .. .. 2·50 15
a. Thin coarse toned paper (1898) .. 20·00 70
b. Ditto. Wmk sideways .. .. — £150
237 **14** 1d. rose (Die 3) .. .. .. 3·50 10
a. Deep carmine .. .. .. 5·50 75
b. Imperf between (pair) £300
c. Deep carmine/thin coarse toned (1898) .. .. .. 8·00 75
d. Ditto. Wmk sideways .. .. — £200
238 **15** 2d. mauve (Die 3) .. .. .. 7·00 15
a. Purple .. .. .. 7·00 15
b. Deep purple/thin coarse toned (1898) 8·00 55
c. Ditto. Wmk sideways .. .. — £180
239 **16** 2½d. blue (1897) .. .. .. 35·00 3·50
a. Thin coarse toned paper (1898) .. 45·00 10·00
240 **17** 3d. pale yellow (1897) .. .. 40·00 4·50
a. Pale dull yellow/thin coarse toned (1898) .. .. .. 45·00 6·00
b. Orange (1899) .. .. .. 40·00 5·00
c. Dull orange-yellow (1900) .. .. 40·00 5·00
241 **18** 4d. yellowish green .. .. .. 45·00 2·25
a. Bluish green (1897) .. .. .. 45·00 2·25
242 **19** 5d. olive-black/*thin coarse toned* (1899) 45·00 14·00
243 **20** 6d. brown (Die 2) (1897) .. .. 50·00 2·75
a. Black-brown .. .. .. 50·00 2·75
b. Brown/thin coarse toned (1898) .. 55·00 4·00
244 **21** 8d. blue (1898) .. .. .. 65·00 45·00
245 **22** 1s. red-brown (1897) .. .. .. 70·00 5·50

Only the more prominent shades have been included.

Stamps perf compound of 11 and 12½ exist but we do not list them as there is some doubt as to whether they are genuine.

For the ½d. and 2d. with double-lined watermark, see Nos. 271/2.

23 Mount Cook or Aorangi

24 Lake Taupo and Mount Ruapehu

25 Pembroke Peak, Milford Sound

26 Lake Wakatipu and Mount Earnslaw, inscribed "WAKITIPU"

27 Lake Wakatipu and Mount Earnslaw, inscribed "WAKATIPU"

28 Sacred Huia Birds

29 White Terrace, Rotomahana

30 Otira Gorge and Mount Ruapehu

31 Brown Kiwi

32 Maori War Canoe

33 Pink Terrace, Rotomahana

34 Kea and Kaka

35 Milford Sound

36 Mount Cook

(Des H. Young (½d.), J. Gaut (1d.), W. Bock (2d., 3d., 9d., 1s.), E. Howard (4d., 6d., 8d.), E. Luke (others). Eng A. Hill (2½d., 1s.), J. A. C. Harrison (5d.), Rapkin (others). Recess Waterlow)

1898 (5 Apr). *No wmk. P* 12 to 16.
246 **23** ½d. purple-brown .. .. .. 3·50 35
a. Imperf between (pair) £600 £600
b. Purple-slate .. .. 3·75 35
c. Purple-black .. .. 6·00 1·50
247 **24** 1d. blue and yellow-brown .. .. 2·00 20
a. Imperf between (pair) £600
b. Imperf vert (horiz pair) £450
c. Imperf horiz (vert pair) £450 £500
d. Blue and brown .. .. .. 2·50 65
da. Imperf between (pair) £600
248 **25** 2d. lake .. .. 20·00 20
a. Imperf vert (horiz pair) £400
b. Rosy lake .. .. 20·00 20
ba. Imperf between (pair) £550
bb. Imperf vert (horiz pair) £400
249 **26** 2½d. sky-blue (inscr "WAKITIPU") .. 6·00 18·00
a. Blue .. .. 6·00 18·00
250 **27** 2½d. blue (inscr "WAKATIPU") .. .. 11·00 1·25
a. Deep blue .. .. 11·00 1·50
251 **28** 3d. yellow-brown .. .. .. 20·00 4·75
252 **29** 4d. bright rose .. .. 12·00 14·00
a. Lake-rose .. .. 14·00 15·00
b. Dull rose .. .. 12·00 14·00
253 **30** 5d. sepia .. .. 48·00 80·00
a. Purple-brown .. .. .. 27·00 12·00
254 **31** 6d. green .. .. 48·00 22·00
a. Grass-green .. .. 55·00 32·00
255 **32** 8d. indigo .. .. 32·00 20·00
a. Prussian blue .. .. .. 32·00 20·00
256 **33** 9d. purple .. .. 32·00 20·00
257 **34** 1s. vermilion .. .. 55·00 14·00
a. Dull red .. .. 55·00 14·00
ab. Imperf between (pair) £1100
258 **35** 2s. grey-green .. .. 90·00 55·00
a. Imperf between (vert pair) £1100 £1100
259 **36** 5s. vermilion £200 £160
246/59 .. .. *Set of* 13 £450 £250

37 Lake Taupo and Mount Ruapehu

(Recess Govt Printer, Wellington)

1899 (May)–**03.** *Thick, soft ("Pirie") paper. No wmk. P* 11.
260 **27** 2½d. blue (6.99) .. .. .. 11·00 1·75
a. Imperf between (pair) £500
b. Imperf horiz (vert pair) £300
c. Deep blue .. .. 11·00 1·75
261 **28** 3d. yellow-brown (5.00) .. .. .. 19·00 65
a. Imperf between (pair) £600
b. Imperf vert (horiz pair) £350
c. Deep brown .. .. 19·00 65
ca. Imperf between (pair) £600
262 **37** 4d. indigo and brown (8.99) .. .. 7·00 1·25
a. Bright blue and chestnut .. .. 7·00 1·25
b. Deep blue and bistre-brown .. 7·00 1·25
263 **30** 5d. purple-brown (6.99) .. .. .. 18·00 2·25
a. Deep purple-brown .. .. .. 18·00 2·25
ab. Imperf between (pair) £700
264 **31** 6d. deep green .. .. 48·00 48·00
a. Yellow-green .. .. 65·00 70·00
265 6d. pale rose (5.5.00) .. .. .. 35·00 2·50
a. Imperf vert (horiz pair) £350
b. Rose-red .. .. 35·00 2·50
ba. Printed double £325
bb. Imperf between (pair) £500
bc. Imperf vert (horiz pair) £200
bd. Showing part of sheet wmk (7.02)* .. 60·00 25·00
c. Scarlet .. .. 45·00 8·00
ca. Imperf vert (horiz pair) £375
266 **32** 8d. indigo .. .. 26·00 8·00
a. Prussian blue .. .. .. 26·00 8·00
267 **33** 9d. deep purple (8.99) .. .. .. 38·00 20·00
a. Rosy purple .. .. 26·00 8·50
268 **34** 1s. red (5.00) .. .. 48·00 6·50
a. Dull orange-red .. .. .. 48·00 3·00
b. Dull brown-red .. .. .. 48·00 6·50
c. Bright red .. .. 55·00 18·00
269 **35** 2s. blue-green (7.99) .. .. .. 75·00 30·00
a. Laid paper (1.03) £160 £160
b. Grey-green .. .. 75·00 35·00
270 **36** 5s. vermilion (7.99) £200 £140
a. Carmine-red £300 £225
260/70 .. .. *Set of* 11 £425 £200

*No. 265bd is on paper without general watermark, but showing the words "LISBON SUPERFINE" wmkd once in the sheet; the paper was obtained from Parsons Bros, an American firm with a branch at Auckland.

38

1900. *Thick, soft ("Pirie") paper. Wmk double-lined "NZ" and Star, W* **38** *(sideways). P* 11.
271 **13** ½d. black .. .. 3·75 3·00
272 **15** 2d. bright purple .. .. 9·50 3·00

39 White Terrace, Rotomahana

41

40 Commemorative of the New Zealand Contingent in the South African War

(Des J. Nairn (1½d.). Recess Govt Printer, Wellington)

1900 (Mar–Dec). *Thick, soft ("Pirie") paper. W* **38**. *P* 11.
273 **23** ½d. pale yellow-green (7.3.00) .. .. 7·00 2·50
a. Yellow-green .. .. 4·50 10
b. Green .. .. 3·75 10
ba. Imperf between (pair) £275
c. Deep green .. .. 3·75 10
274 **39** 1d. crimson (7.3.00) .. .. .. 8·50 10
a. Rose-red .. .. 8·50 10
ab. Imperf between (pair) £550 £550
ac. Imperf vert (horiz pair) £275
b. Lake .. .. 15·00 2·50
275 **40** 1½d. khaki (7.12.00) £650 £475
a. Brown .. .. 45·00 45·00
ab. Imperf vert (horiz pair) £450
ac. Imperf (pair) £550
b. Chestnut .. .. 7·50 4·00
ba. Imperf vert (horiz pair) £450
bb. Imperf horiz (vert pair) £550
c. Pale chestnut .. .. 7·50 4·00
ca. Imperf (pair) £550

276 **41** 2d. dull violet (3.00) .. .. .. 6·00 2
a. Imperf between (pair) £650
b. Mauve .. .. 8·00 1·5
c. Purple .. .. 6·50 2
ca. Imperf between (pair) £450

The above ½d. stamps are slightly smaller than those of th previous printing. A new plate was made to print 240 stamp instead of 120 as previously, and to make these fit th watermarked paper the border design was redrawn and contra ted, the centre vignette remaining as before. The 2d. stamp also from a new plate providing smaller designs.

42

(Des G. Bach. Eng J. A. C. Harrison. Recess Waterlow)

1901 (1 Jan). *Universal Penny Postage. No wmk. P* 12 *to* 16.
277 **42** 1d. carmine .. .. 5·00 2·5

(Recess Govt Printer, Wellington)

1901 (Feb–Dec). *Thick, soft ("Pirie") paper. W* **38**. (*a*) *P* 11.
278 **42** 1d. carmine .. .. 5·00 1
a. Imperf vert (horiz pair) £225
b. Deep carmine .. .. .. 5·00 1
ba. Imperf vert (horiz pair) .. .. £225 -
c. Carmine-lake .. .. .. 18·00 7·5

(b) P 14
279 **23** ½d. green (11.01) .. .. 9·00 2·7
280 **42** 1d. carmine .. .. 35·00 7·5
a. Imperf vert (horiz pair) £225

(c) Perf compound of 11 *and* 14
281 **23** ½d. green .. .. 10·00 4·0
a. Deep green .. .. 10·00 4·0
282 **42** 1d. carmine .. .. £250 75·0

(d) P 11 *and* 14 *mixed**
283 **23** ½d. green .. .. 55·00 35·0
284 **42** 1d. carmine .. .. £250 75·0

*The term "mixed" is applied to stamps from sheets whic were at first perforated 14, or 14 and 11 compound, and eithe incompletely or defectively perforated. These sheets wer patched on the back with strips of paper, and re-perforated 11 i those parts where the original perforation was defective.

(Recess Govt Printer, Wellington)

1901 (Dec.) *Thin, hard ("Basted Mills") paper. W* **38**. (*a*) *P* 11
285 **23** ½d. green .. .. 50·00 50·0
286 **42** 1d. carmine .. .. 60·00 50·0

(*b*) *P* 14
287 **23** ½d. green .. .. 28·00 10·0
a. Imperf vert (horiz pair) £325
288 **42** 1d. carmine .. .. 14·00 2·0
a. Imperf between (pair) £275

(*c*) *Perf compound of* 11 *and* 14
289 **23** ½d. green .. .. 23·00 23·0
a. Deep green .. .. 23·00 23·0
290 **42** 1d. carmine .. .. 12·00 2·5

(*d*) *Mixed perfs*
291 **23** ½d. green .. .. 75·00 75·0
292 **42** 1d. carmine .. .. 75·00 50·0

(Recess Govt Printer, Wellington)

1902 (Jan). *Thin, hard ("Cowan") paper. No wmk.* (*a*) *P* 11.
293 **23** ½d. green .. .. 90·00 90·0

(*b*) *P* 14
294 **23** ½d. green .. .. 9·00 3·2
295 **42** 1d. carmine .. .. 15·00 1·2

(*c*) *Perf compound of* 11 *and* 14
296 **23** ½d. green .. .. 90·00 90·0
297 **42** 1d. carmine £110 £11

(*d*) *Mixed perfs*
298 **23** ½d. green .. .. 90·00 90·0
299 **42** 1d. carmine £120 £12

43 "Single" Wmk

(Recess Govt Printer, Wellington)

1902 (Apr). *Thin, hard ("Cowan") paper. W* **43**. (*a*) *P* 11.
300 **23** ½d. green .. .. 55·00 55·0
301 **42** 1d. carmine £550 £40

(b) P 14

2 23 ½d. green .. .. 2·25 15
a. Imperf vert (horiz pair) £170
b. Deep green .. .. 2·75 30
ba. Imperf vert (horiz pair) £170
c. Yellow-green .. .. 2·25 25
d. Pale yellow-green .. .. .. 9·50 2·00
3 42 1d. carmine .. .. 3·00 10
a. Imperf between (pair) £170
b. Booklet pane of 6 (21.8.02) £190
c. Pale carmine .. .. 3·00 10
ca. Imperf between (pair) £170
cb. Booklet pane of 6 .. .. .. £190
*d. Deep carmine** .. .. 28·00 3·75

(c) Perf compound of 11 and 14

4 23 ½d. green .. .. 14·00 25·00
a. Deep green .. .. 20·00 27·00
5 42 1d. carmine .. .. £100 80·00
*a. Deep carmine** £400 £300

(d) Mixed perfs

6 23 ½d. green .. .. 26·00 26·00
a. Deep green .. .. 30·00 30·00
7 42 1d. carmine .. .. 30·00 30·00
a. Pale carmine .. .. 30·00 30·00
*b. Deep carmine** £250 £250

*Nos. 303*d*, 305*a* and 307*b* were printed from a plate made by aterlow & Sons, known as the "Reserve" plate. The stamps do t show evidence of wearing and the area surrounding the per part of the figure is more deeply shaded.

A special plate, showing a minute dot between the horizontal ws, was introduced in 1902 to print booklet panes. A special aracteristic of the booklet plate was that the pearl in the top t-handed corner was large. Some panes exist with outer edges perforate.

(Recess Govt Printer, Wellington)

02 (28 Aug)–09. *Thin, hard ("Cowan") paper.* W **43** *(sideways on 3d., 5d., 6d., 8d., 1s. and 5s.). (a) P 11*

8 27 2½d. blue (5.03) .. .. 11·00 10·00
a. Deep blue .. .. 12·00 10·00
9 28 3d. yellow-brown .. .. 16·00 35
a. Bistre-brown .. .. 16·00 35
b. Pale bistre .. .. 25·00 2·75
0 37 4d. deep blue and deep brown/*bluish* (27.11.02) .. .. 8·50 32·00
a. Imperf vert (horiz pair) £450
1 30 5d. red-brown (4.03) .. .. .. 16·00 5·50
a. Deep brown .. .. 16·00 2·50
b. Sepia .. .. 30·00 12·00
2 31 6d. rose (9.02) .. .. 35·00 3·50
a. Rose-red .. .. 35·00 3·50
ab. Wmk upright £450 £300
b. Rose-carmine .. .. 35·00 3·50
ba. Imperf vert (horiz pair) £400
bb. Imperf horiz (vert pair) .. ..
c. Bright carmine-pink .. .. .. 48·00 5·00
d. Scarlet .. .. 48·00 15·00
3 32 8d. blue (2.03) .. .. 24·00 6·00
a. Steel-blue .. .. 24·00 6·00
ab. Imperf vert (horiz pair) £500
ac. Imperf horiz (vert pair) £500
4 33 9d. purple (5.03) .. .. 25·00 9·00
15 34 1s. brown-red (11.02) .. .. .. 48·00 4·00
a. Bright red .. .. 48·00 4·25
b. Orange-red .. .. 48·00 3·25
ba. Error. Wmk W **12b** .. .. .. † £1200
c. Orange-brown .. .. 60·00 6·50
16 35 2s. green (4.03) .. .. 70·00 32·00
a. Blue-green .. .. 70·00 32·00
17 36 5s. deep red (6.03) £190 £140
a. Wmk upright £200 £150
b. Vermilion £190 £140
ba. Wmk upright £200 £150

(b) P 14

18 40 1½d. chestnut (2.07) .. .. .. 11·00 27·00
19 41 2d. grey-purple (12.02) .. .. .. 5·50 40
a. Purple .. .. 5·50 40
ab. Imperf vert (horiz pair) £350
ac. Imperf horiz (vert pair) £350
b. Bright reddish purple .. .. .. 6·50 85
20 27 2½d. blue (1906) .. .. 7·00 1·25
a. Deep blue .. .. 7·00 1·50
21 28 3d. bistre-brown (1906) .. .. .. 23·00 90
a. Imperf vert (horiz pair) £450
b. Bistre .. .. 23·00 90
c. Pale yellow-bistre .. .. .. 40·00 8·00
22 37 4d. deep blue and deep brown/*bluish* (1903) .. .. 6·00 2·00
a. Imperf vert (horiz pair) £400
b. Imperf horiz (vert pair) £400
c. Centre inverted .. .. .. † £25000
d. Blue and chestnut/bluish .. .. 6·00 60
e. Blue and ochre-brown/bluish .. .. 6·00 60
23 30 5d. black-brown (1906) .. .. .. 40·00 14·00
a. Red-brown .. .. 22·00 5·50
24 31 6d. bright carmine-pink (1906) .. .. 55·00 5·50
a. Imperf vert (horiz pair) £400
b. Rose-carmine .. .. 55·00 6·00
25 32 8d. steel-blue (1907) .. .. .. 25·00 4·50
26 33 9d. purple (1906) .. .. 25·00 6·00
27 34 1s. orange-brown (1906) .. .. .. 55·00 4·50
a. Orange-red .. .. 50·00 4·50
b. Pale red .. .. 70·00 20·00
28 35 2s. green (1.06) .. .. 60·00 20·00
a. Blue-green .. .. 60·00 20·00
29 36 5s. deep red (1906) £190 £140
a. Wmk upright £200 £150
b. Dull red £190 £140
ba. Wmk upright £200 £150

(c) Perf compound of 11 and 14

330 40 1½d. chestnut (1907) £550
331 41 2d. purple (1903) £275
332 28 3d. bistre-brown (1906) £500 £450
333 37 4d. blue and yellow-brown (1903) .. £300 £300
334 30 5d. red-brown (1906) £400 £400
335 31 6d. rose-carmine (1907) £300 £200
336 32 8d. steel-blue (1907) £600 £600
337 33 9d. purple (1906) £800 £800
338 36 5s. deep red (1906) £1100 £1000

(d) Mixed perfs

339 40 1½d. chestnut (1907) £550
340 41 2d. purple (1903) £140
341 28 3d. bistre-brown (1906) £500 £450
342 37 4d. blue and chestnut/*bluish* (1904) £250 £250
a. Blue and yellow-brown/bluish .. £250 £250
343 30 5d. red-brown (1906) £400 £400
344 31 6d. rose-carmine (1907) £250 £200
a. Bright carmine-pink £250 £200
345 32 8d. steel-blue (1907) £550 £550
346 33 9d. purple (1906) £700 £700
347 35 2s. blue-green (1906) £800 £800
348 36 5s. vermilion (1906) £1100 £1000

Two sizes of paper were used for the above stamps:—

(1) A sheet containing 240 wmks, with a space of 9 mm between each.

(2) A sheet containing 120 wmks, with a space of 24 mm between each vertical row.

Size (1) was used for the ½d., 1d., 2d., and 4d., and size (2) for 2½d., 5d., 9d., and 2s. The paper in each case exactly fitted the plates, and had the watermark in register, though in the case of the 4d., the plate of which contained only 80 stamps, the paper was cut up to print it. The 3d., 6d., 8d., and 1s. were printed on variety (1), but with watermark sideways: by reason of this, specimens from the margins of the sheets show parts of the words "NEW ZEALAND POSTAGE" in large letters, and some copies have no watermark at all. For the 1½d. and 5s. stamps variety (1) was also used, but two watermarks appear on each stamp.

(Recess Govt Printer, Wellington)

1904. *Printed from new "dot" plates. Thin, hard ("Cowan") paper.* W **43** *(a) P 14.*

349 42 1d. rose-carmine .. .. 6·50 30
a. Pale carmine .. .. 6·50 30

(b) Perf compound of 11 and 14

350 42 1d. rose-carmine £120 £110

(c) Mixed perfs

351 42 1d. rose-carmine .. .. 20·00 20·00
a. Pale carmine .. .. 20·00 20·00

The above new plates have a minute dot between the stamps in the horizontal rows, but it is frequently cut out by the perforations. However, they can be further distinguished by the notes below.

In 1906 fresh printings were made from four new plates, two of which, marked in the margin "W1" and "W2", were supplied by Waterlow Bros and Layton, and the other two, marked "R1" and "R2", by W. R. Royle & Son. The intention was to note which pair of plates wore the best and produced the best results. They can be distinguished as follows:—

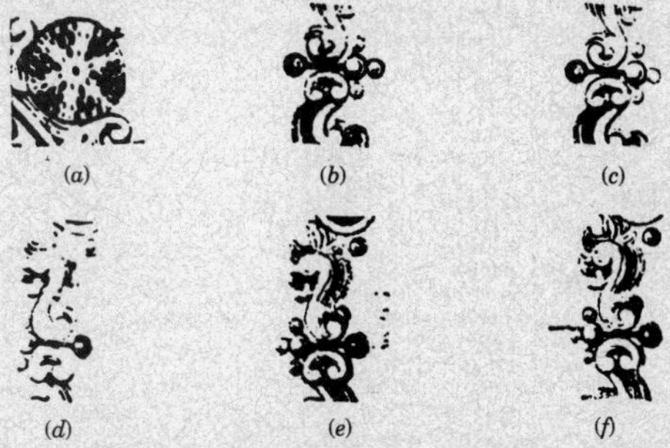

(*a*) Four o'clock flaw in rosette at top right corner. Occurs in all these plates but not in the original Waterlow plates.
(*b*) Pearl at right strong.
(*c*) Pearl at right weak.
(*d*) Dot at left and S-shaped ornament unshaded.
(*e*) S-shaped ornament with one line of shading within.
(*f*) As (*e*) but with line from left pearl to edge of stamp.

"Dot" plates comprise (*a*) and (*d*).
Waterlow plates comprise (*a*), (*b*) and (*e*).
Royle plates comprise (*a*), (*c*) and (*e*) and the line in (*f*) on many stamps but not all.

(Recess Govt Printer, Wellington)

1906. *Thin, hard ("Cowan") paper.* W **43**.

(a) Printed from new Waterlow plates. (i) P 14

352 42 1d. deep rose-carmine .. .. .. 15·00 70
a. Imperf between (pair) £200
b. Aniline carmine .. .. 14·00 70
ba. Imperf between (pair) £200
c. Rose-carmine .. .. 14·00 70

(ii) P 11

353 42 1d. aniline carmine £325 £325

(iii) Perf compound of 11 and 14

354 42 1d. rose-carmine £300 £300

(iv) Mixed perfs

355 42 1d. deep rose-carmine £225 £225

(b) Printed from new Royle plates. (i) P 14

356 42 1d. rose-carmine .. .. 8·00 90
a. Imperf horiz (vert pair) £225 £225
b. Bright rose-carmine .. .. .. 10·00 1·00

(ii) P 11

357 42 1d. bright rose-carmine £150 £150

(iii) Perf compound of 11 and 14

358 42 1d. rose-carmine .. .. 85·00 85·00

(iv) Mixed perfs

359 42 1d. rose-carmine .. .. £100 85·00

(v) P 14 × 14½ (comb)

360 42 1d. bright rose-carmine .. .. .. 60·00 35·00
a. Rose-carmine .. .. 60·00 35·00

Nos. 360/*a* are known both with and without the small dot. See also No. 437.

1905 (15 June)–**06.** *Stamps supplied to penny-in-the-slot machines.*

(i) *"Dot" plates of* 1904. (ii) *Waterlow "reserve" plate of* 1902

(a) Imperf top and bottom; zigzag roulette 9½ on one or both sides, two large holes at sides

361 42 1d. rose-carmine (i) £120
362 1d. deep carmine (ii) £140

(b) As last but rouletted 14½ (8.7.05)

363 42 1d. rose-carmine (i) £140
364 1d. deep carmine (ii) .. .. ..

(c) Imperf all round, two large holes each side (6.3.06)

365 42 1d. rose-carmine (i) £120
366 1d. deep carmine (ii) £140

(d) Imperf all round (21.6.06)

367 42 1d. deep carmine (ii) £130

(e) Imperf all round. Two small indentations on back of stamp (1.06)

368 42 1d. deep carmine (ii) £160 £130

(f) Imperf all round; two small pin-holes in stamp (21.6.06)

369 42 1d. deep carmine (ii) £140 £130

No. 365 *only* exists from strips of Nos. 361 or 363 (resulting from the use of successive coins) which have been separated by scissors. Similarly strips of Nos. 362 and 364 can produce single copies of No. 366 but this also exists in singles from a different machine.

Most used copies of Nos. 361/7 are forgeries and they should only be collected on cover.

44 Maori Canoe, *Te Arawa*

(Des L. J. Steele. Eng W. R. Bock. Typo Govt Printer, Wellington)

1906 (1–17 Nov). *New Zealand Exhibition, Christchurch.* T **44** *and similar horiz designs.* W **43** *(sideways). P 14.*

370 ½d. emerald-green .. .. 16·00 23·00
371 1d. vermilion .. .. 13·00 15·00
a. Claret £7000 £8000
372 3d. brown and blue .. .. 45·00 55·00
373 6d. pink and olive-green (17.11) £140 £225
370/3 .. .. *Set of* 4 £200 £275

Designs:—1d. Maori art; 3d. Landing of Cook; 6d. Annexation of New Zealand.

The 1d. in claret was the original printing, which was considered unsatisfactory.

46

47 (T **28** reduced)

48 (T **31** reduced)

49 (T **34** reduced)

(New plates (except 4d.), supplied by Perkins Bacon. Recess (T **46** typo) by Govt Printer, Wellington)

1907–8. *Thin, hard ("Cowan") paper.* W **43**. *(a) P 14 (line).*

374 23 ½d. green (1907) .. .. 30·00 6·00
a. Imperf (pair) £120
b. Yellow-green .. .. 20·00 2·00
c. Deep yellow-green .. .. .. 16·00 1·50
375 47 3d. brown (6.07) .. .. 48·00 17·00
376 48 6d. carmine-pink (3.07) .. .. .. 48·00 6·00
a. Red .. .. 75·00 26·00

(b) P 14 × 13, 13½ (comb)

377 23 ½d. green (1907) .. .. 18·00 3·50
a. Yellow-green .. .. 8·00 85
378 47 3d. brown (2.08) .. .. 48·00 22·00
a. Yellow-brown .. .. 48·00 25·00
379 37 4d. blue and yellow-brown/*bluish* (6.08) 27·00 20·00
380 48 6d. pink (2.08) .. .. £250 80·00
381 49 1s. orange-red (12.07) .. .. .. £130 45·00

(c) P 14 × 15 (comb)

382 23 ½d. yellow-green (1907) .. .. .. 12·00 60
383 46 1d. carmine (1.12.08) .. .. .. 30·00 50
384 47 3d. brown (8.08) .. .. 48·00 7·00
a. Yellow-brown .. .. 48·00 7·00
385 48 6d. carmine-pink (8.08) .. .. .. 48·00 8·00
386 49 1s. orange-red (8.08) .. .. .. £120 24·00
a. Deep orange-brown £300

The ½d. stamps of this 1907–8 issue have a minute dot in the margin between the stamps, where not removed by the perforation. (See note after No. 351*a*). Those perforated 14 can be distinguished from the earlier stamps, Nos. 302/*d*, by the absence of plate wear. This is most noticeable on the 1902 printings as a white patch at far left, level with the bottom of the "P" in "POSTAGE". Such damage is not present on the new plates used for Nos. 374/*c*.

Stamps of T **47**, **48** and **49** also have a small dot as described in note after No. 351*a*.

Stamps in T **46** are typographed but the design also differs from T **42**. The rosettes in the upper corners are altered and the lines on the globe diagonal instead of vertical. The paper is chalk-surfaced.

TYPOGRAPHY PAPERS 1909–30. De La Rue paper is chalk-surfaced and has a smooth finish. The watermark is as illustrated. The gum is toned and strongly resistant to soaking. **Jones paper** is chalk-surfaced and has a coarser texture, is poorly surfaced and the ink tends to peel. The outline of the watermark commonly shows on the surface of the stamp. The gum is colourless or only slightly toned and washes off readily. **Cowan paper** is chalk-surfaced and is white and opaque. The watermark is usually smaller than in the "Jones" paper and is often barely visible

Wiggins Teape paper is chalk-surfaced and is thin and hard. It has a vertical mesh with a narrow watermark, whereas the other papers have a horizontal mesh and a wider watermark.

50

51

52

(Eng. P.B. Typo Govt Printer, Wellington)

1909 (8 Nov)–**12**. *De La Rue chalk-surfaced paper with toned gum. W* **43**. *P* 14 × 15 (*comb*).
387 **50** ½d. yellow-green .. .. 2·75 10
aa. *Deep green* .. .. 2·75 20
a. Imperf (pair) £140
b. Booklet pane. Five stamps plus label in position 1 (4.10) £400
c. Ditto, but label in position 6 (4.10) .. £400
d. Booklet pane of 6 (4.10) £140
e. Ditto, but with coloured bars on selvedge (5.12) £140

Stamps with blurred and heavy appearance are from booklets.

(Eng W. R. Royle & Son, London. Recess Govt Printer, Wellington)

1909 (8 Nov)–**16**. *T* **51** *and similar portraits.*

(*a*) *W* **43**. *P* 14 × 14½ (*comb*)
388 2d. mauve .. .. 14·00 4·75
a. Deep mauve .. .. 17·00 4·75
389 3d. chestnut .. .. 17·00 30
390 4d. orange-red .. .. 22·00 20·00
a. Orange-yellow (1912) .. .. .. 7·00 2·00
391 5d. brown (1910) .. .. 13·00 60
a. Red-brown .. .. 11·00 60
392 6d. carmine (1910) .. .. 24·00 40
a. Deep carmine (29.10.13) .. .. .. 24·00 50
393 8d. indigo-blue .. .. 9·00 65
a. Deep bright blue .. .. 11·00 65
394 1s. vermilion (1910) .. .. 45·00 1·75
388/94 .. .. *Set of* 8 £130 27·00

(*b*) *W* **43**. *P* 14 (*line*)*
395 3d. chestnut (1910) .. .. 32·00 3·75
396 4d. orange (1910) .. .. 15·00 5·00
397 5d. brown .. .. 18·00 3·00
a. Red-brown (15.9.11) .. .. .. 20·00 3·50
398 6d. carmine .. .. 35·00 6·50
399 1s. vermilion .. .. 45·00 6·50
395/9 .. .. *Set of* 5 £130 22·00

(*c*) *W* **43** (*sideways*) (*paper with widely spaced watermark as used for Nos.* 308 *and* 320 – *see note below No.* 348). *P* 14 (*line*)*
400 8d. indigo-blue (8.16) .. .. 13·00 28·00
a. No wmk .. .. 50·00 75·00

(*d*) *W* **43**. *P* 14 × 13½ (*comb*)†
401 3d. chestnut (1915) .. .. 55·00 55·00
a. Vert pair. P 14 × 13½ and 14 × 14½ .. £225 £275
402 5d. red-brown (1916) .. .. 15·00 1·50
a. Vert pair. P 14 × 13½ and 14 × 14½ .. 50·00 70·00
403 6d. carmine (1915) .. .. 60·00 60·00
a. Vert pair. P 14 × 13½ and 14 × 14½ .. £225 £275
404 8d. indigo-blue (3.16) .. .. 18·00 1·75
a. Vert pair. P 14 × 13½ and 14 × 14½ .. 50·00 70·00
b. Deep bright blue .. .. 18·00 1·75
ba. Vert pair. P 14 × 13½ and 14 × 14½ .. 50·00 70·00
401/4 .. .. *Set of* 4 £130 £110

*In addition to showing the usual characteristics of a line perforation, these stamps may be distinguished by their vertical perforation which measures 13.8. Nos. 388/94 generally measure vertically 14 to 14.3. An exception is 13.8 one vertical side but 14 the other.

†The 3d. and 6d. come in full sheets perf 14 × 13½. The 3d., 5d. and 6d. values also exist in two combinations: (*a*) five top rows perf 14 × 13½ with five bottom rows perf 14 × 14½ and (*b*) four top rows perf 14 × 13½ with six bottom rows perf 14 × 14½. The 8d. perf 14 × 13½ only exists from combination (*b*).

(Eng P.B. Typo Govt Printer, Wellington)

1909 (8 Nov)–**26**. *P* 14 × 15 (*comb*).

(*a*) *W* **43**. *De La Rue chalk-surfaced paper with toned gum*
405 **52** 1d. carmine .. .. 1·00 10
a. Imperf (pair) £200
b. Booklet pane of 6 (4.10) £110
c. Ditto, but with coloured bars on selvedge (5.12) £110

(*b*) *W* **43**. *Jones chalk-surfaced paper with white gum*
406 **52** 1d. deep carmine (1924) .. .. .. 9·00 3·00
a. On unsurfaced paper. *Pale carmine* .. £275
b. Booklet pane of 6 with bars on selvedge (1.12.24) .. .. .. 95·00

(*c*) *W* **43**. *De La Rue unsurfaced medium paper with toned gum*
407 **52** 1d. rose-carmine (4.25) .. .. .. 22·00 50·00

(*d*) *W* **43** (*sideways*). *De La Rue chalk-surfaced paper with toned gum*
408 **52** 1d. bright carmine (4.25) .. .. .. 5·50 17·00
a. No wmk .. .. 18·00 32·00
b. Imperf (pair) .. .. 50·00

(*e*) *No wmk, but bluish "NZ" and Star lithographed on back. Art paper*
409 **52** 1d. rose-carmine (1925) .. .. .. 2·25 60
a. "NZ" and Star in black .. .. .. 8·00
b. "NZ" and Star colourless .. .. .. 24·00

(*f*) *W* **43**. *Cowan thick, opaque, chalk-surfaced paper with white gum*
410 **52** 1d. deep carmine (8.25) .. .. .. 4·25 70
a. Imperf (pair) .. .. 65·00 70·00
b. Booklet pane of 6 with bars and adverts on selvedge .. .. .. 45·00

(*g*) *W* **43**. *Wiggins Teape thin, hard, chalk-surfaced paper with white gum*
411 **52** 1d. rose-carmine (6.26) .. .. .. 18·00 7·50

Examples of No. 405 with a blurred and heavy appearance are from booklets.

No. 406a comes from a sheet on which the paper coating was missing from the right-hand half.

Many stamps from the sheets of No. 408 were without watermark or showed portions of "NEW ZEALAND POSTAGE" in double-lined capitals.

AUCKLAND EXHIBITION, 1913.
(59)

60

1913 (1 Dec). *Auckland Industrial Exhibition. Nos.* 387*aa*, 389, 392 *and* 405 *optd with T* **59** *by Govt Printer, Wellington.*
412 **50** ½d. deep green .. .. 10·00 20·00
413 **52** 1d. carmine .. .. 15·00 24·00
414 **51** 3d. chestnut £100 £160
415 6d. carmine £100 £170
412/15 .. .. *Set of* 4 £200 £350

These overprinted stamps were only available for letters in New Zealand and to Australia.

(Des H. L. Richardson. Recess Govt Printer, Wellington, from plates made in London by P.B.)

1915 (30 July)–**30**. *P* 14 × 14½, *comb* (*See notes below*).

(*a*) *W* **43**. *Cowan unsurfaced paper*
416 **60** 1½d. grey-slate .. .. 2·50 40
a. Perf 14 × 13½ .. .. 1·75 50
b. Vert pair, 416/a .. .. 35·00 50·00
417 2d. bright violet .. .. 6·50 17·00
a. Perf 14 × 13½ .. .. 6·50 17·00
b. Vert pair, 417/a .. .. 24·00 50·00
418 2d. yellow (15.1.16) .. .. 4·00 13·00
a. Perf 14 × 13½ .. .. 4·00 13·00
b. Vert pair, 418/a .. .. 18·00 48·00
419 2½d. blue .. .. 8·50 4·00
a. Perf 14 × 13½ (1916) .. .. .. 3·25 1·50
b. Vert pair, 419/a .. .. 35·00 65·00
420 3d. chocolate .. .. 6·00 60
a. Perf 14 × 13½ .. .. 6·00 50
b. Vert pair, 420/a .. .. 35·00 55·00
421 4d. yellow .. .. 4·25 28·00
a. Perf 14 × 13½ .. .. 4·25 28·00
b. Vert pair, 421/a .. .. 26·00 £120
c. Re-entry (Pl 20 R. 1/6) .. .. .. 30·00
d. Re-entry (Pl 20 R. 4/10) .. .. .. 35·00
422 4d. bright violet (7.4.16) .. .. .. 7·00 20
a. Perf 14 × 13½ .. .. 5·00 15
b. Imperf (pair) £950
c. Vert pair, 422/a .. .. 35·00 65·00
d. Re-entry (Pl 20 R. 1/6) .. .. .. 35·00
e. Re-entry (Pl 20 R. 4/10) .. .. .. 40·00
423 4½d. deep green .. .. 16·00 13·00
a. Perf 14 × 13½ .. .. 10·00 2·50
b. Vert pair, 423/a .. .. 48·00 65·00
424 5d. light blue (4.22) .. .. 15·00 13·00
a. Perf 14 × 13½ .. .. 6·00 40
b. Imperf (pair) £110 £120
c. Pale ultramarine (5.30) .. .. .. 11·00 6·00
ca. Perf 14 × 13½ .. .. 8·00 3·75
cb. Vert pair, 424c/ca .. .. .. 55·00 75·00
425 6d. carmine .. .. 5·50 30
a. Perf 14 × 13½ .. .. 5·50 20
b. Vert pair, 425/a (1916) .. .. .. 65·00 95·00
c. Imperf three sides (pair) £1200
d. Carm-lake. Perf 14 × 13½ (28.1.28) .. £500 £325
426 7½d. red-brown .. .. 27·00 30·00
a. Perf 14 × 13½ (10.20) .. .. .. 11·00 15·00
b. Vert pair, 426/a .. .. 50·00 75·00
427 8d. indigo-blue (19.4.21) .. .. .. 15·00 28·00
a. Perf 14 × 13½ .. .. 13·00 26·00
b. Vert pair, 427/a .. .. 38·00 70·00
428 8d. red-brown (*p* 14 × 13½) (2.22) .. .. 15·00 40
429 9d. sage-green .. .. 17·00 3·50
a. Perf 14 × 13½ .. .. 13·00 60
b. Vert pair, 429/a .. .. 70·00 £100
c. Imperf three sides (pair) £1300
d. Imperf (pair) £1000
e. Yellowish ol. Perf 14 × 13½ (12.25) .. 28·00 7·00
430 1s. vermilion .. .. 13·00 25
a. Perf 14 × 13½ .. .. 13·00 95
b. Imperf (pair) £2250
c. Vert pair, 430/a .. .. 75·00 £100
d. Pale orange-red .. .. 26·00 4·50
da. Imperf (pair) £325
db. Orange-brown (1.2.28) £850 £425
416/30 .. .. *Set of* 15 90·00 90·00

(*b*) *W* **43** (*sideways on 2d., 3d. and 6d.*). *Thin paper with widely spaced watermark as used for Nos.* 308 *and* 320 – *see note below No.* 348)
431 **60** 1½d. grey-slate (3.16) .. .. .. 1·25 3·00
a. No wmk .. .. 2·00 6·50
b. Perf 14 × 13½ .. .. 1·25 3·00
ba. No wmk .. .. 2·00 6·50
c. Vert pair, 431/b .. .. 20·00 35·00
ca. Vert pair, 431a/ba .. .. .. 28·00 50·00
432 2d. yellow (*p* 14, *line*) (6.16) .. .. 4·50 30·00
a. No wmk .. .. 28·00 60·00
433 3d. chocolate (*p* 14, *line*) (6.16) .. .. 5·50 7·00
a. No wmk .. .. 25·00 45·00
434 6d. carmine (*p* 14, *line*) (8.16) .. .. 6·00 35·
a. No wmk .. .. 35·00 70·
431/4 .. .. *Set of* 4 15·00 65·

The 1½d., 2½d., 4½d. and 7½d. have value tablets as shown T **60**. In the other values, the tablets are shortened, and the orr mental border at each side of the crown correspondingly extende

During the laying-down of plate 20 for the 4d., from t roller-die which also contained dies of other values, an impre sion of the 4½d. value was placed on R.1/6 and of the 2½d. R.4/10. These errors were subsequently corrected by re-entries the 4d. impression, but on R.1/6 traces of the original impressi can be found in the right-hand value tablet and above the t frame line, while on R.4/10 the foot of the "2" is visible in t left-hand value tablet with traces of "½" to its right.

Of this issue the 1½d., 2½d., 4d. (both), 4½d., 5d., 6d., 7½ 9d. and 1s are known from sheets perforated 14 × 13½ throug out and the 4d. violet, 5d., 6d. and 1s. from sheets perforat 14 × 14½ throughout.

All values from 1½d. to 1s. were also produced showing the u of the two different perforations within the same sheet as describ beneath No. 404ba. In most instances the top four rows we perforated 14 × 13½ and the bottom six 14 × 14½. For o printing of the 4d. violet and for all printings of the 5d. pa ultramarine with two perforations on the same sheet t arrangement differed in that the top five rows were perforat 14 × 14½ and the bottom five 14 × 13½.

With the exception of Nos. 432/4 any with perforatio measuring 14 × 14 or nearly must be classed as 14 × 14½, th being an irregularity of the comb machine, and not a product the 14-line machine.

61

62

WAR STAMP
(63)

Type **62** (from local plates) can be identified from Type **6** (prepared by Perkins Bacon) by the shading on the portrait. Th is diagonal on Type **62** and horizontal on Type **61**.

(Die eng W. R. Bock. Typo Govt Printer, Wellington, from plat made by P.B. (T **61**) or locally (T **62**))

1915 (30 July)–**34**. *P* 14 × 15.

(*a*) *W* **43**. *De La Rue chalk-surfaced paper with toned gum.*
435 **61** ½d. green 70
a. Booklet pane of 6 with bars on selvedge .. .. 95·00
b. Yellow-green .. .. 3·00
ba. Booklet pane of 6 with bars on selvedge .. .. 80·00
c. Very thick, hard, highly surfaced paper with white gum (12.15) .. 11·00 17·0
436 **62** 1½d. grey-black (4.16) .. .. .. 3·00
a. Black .. .. 4·50
437 **61** 1½d. slate (5.9.16) .. .. 5·50
438 1½d. orange-brown (9.18) .. .. .. 1·50
439 2d. yellow (9.16) 80
a. Pale yellow .. .. 3·50
440 3d. chocolate (5.19) .. .. 6·00
435/40 .. .. *Set of* 6 16·00

(*b*) *W* **43**. *Jones chalk-surfaced paper with white gum*
441 **61** ½d. green (10.24) .. .. 5·50 3·2
a. Booklet pane of 6 with bars on selvedge (1.12.24) .. .. .. 85·00
442 2d. dull yellow (7.24) .. .. 4·00 13·0
443 3d. deep chocolate (3.25) .. .. .. 15·00 4·5
441/3 .. .. *Set of* 3 22·00 19·0

(*c*) *No wmk, but bluish "NZ" and Star lithographed on back. Ar paper*
444 **61** ½d. apple-green (4.25) .. .. .. 1·25 5
a. "NZ" and Star almost colourless .. 4·25
445 2d. yellow (7.25) .. .. 5·50 26·0

(*d*) *W* **43**. *Cowan thick, opaque, chalk-surfaced paper with whit gum*
446 **61** ½d. green (8.25) 40 10
a. Booklet pane of 6 with bars and adverts on selvedge .. .. .. 85·00
ab. Booklet pane of 6 with bars on selvedge (1934) .. ..
b. Perf 14 (1927) 50 20
ba. Booklet pane of 6 with bars on selvedge (1928) .. .. .. 45·00
bb. Booklet pane of 6 with bars and adverts on selvedge (1928) .. .. 45·00
447 1½d. orange-brown (*p* 14) (8.29) .. .. 8·50 9·00
a. Perf 14 × 15 (7.33) .. .. .. 45·00 48·00
448 2d. yellow (8.25) .. .. 3·25 20
a. Perf 14 (1929) .. .. 2·75 10
449 3d. chocolate (8.25) .. .. 6·50 20
a. Perf 14 (1929) .. .. 7·50 1·25
446/9 .. .. *Set of* 4 17·00 9·00

(*e*) *W* **43**. *Wiggins Teape thin, hard, chalk-surfaced paper*
450 **61** 1½d. orange-brown (*p* 14) (1930) .. 27·00 55·00
451 2d. yellow (5.26) .. .. 6·50 14·00
a. Perf 14 (10.27) .. .. 6·00 14·00

The designs of these stamps also differ as described beneath No. 434.

Stamps from booklet panes often have blurred, heavy impressions. Different advertisements can be found on the listed booklet panes.

1915 (24 Sept). *No.* 435 *optd with T* **63**.
452 **61** ½d. green .. .. 1·40 20

64 "Peace" and Lion

65 "Peace" and Lion

es and typo D.L.R. from plates by P.B., Waterlow and D.L.R.)

20 (27 Jan). *Victory. T* **64/5** *and similar designs. W* **43** *sideways on ½d., 1½d., 3d. and 1s.). De La Rue halk-surfaced paper. P* 14.

3 ½d. green .. .. 1·50 75
a. *Pale yellow-green* .. .. .. 20·00 9·50
4 1d. carmine-red .. .. 3·00 25
a. *Bright carmine* .. .. 4·25 35
5 1½d. brown-orange .. .. 3·25 20
6 3d. chocolate .. .. 10·00 10·00
7 6d. violet .. .. 10·00 11·00
8 1s. orange-red .. .. 20·00 35·00
3/8 .. .. *Set of* 6 42·00 50·00

Designs: *Horiz (as T* **65**)—1½d. Maori chief. (*As T* **64**)—3d. on; 1s. King George V. *Vert (as T* **64**)—6d. "Peace" and rogress".

The above stamps were placed on sale in London in November, 19.

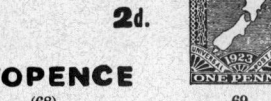

2d. **2d.**

TWOPENCE

(68)

69

22 (Mar). *Surch with T* **68**.
9 **64** 2d. on ½d. green (R.) .. .. .. 2·00 60

(Des and eng W. R. Bock. Typo Govt Printer, Wellington)

23 (1 Oct)–**25**. *Restoration of Penny Postage. W* **43**. *P* 14 × 15.

(a) De La Rue chalk-surfaced paper with toned gum.
0 **69** 1d. carmine .. .. 1·50 25

(b) Jones chalk-surfaced paper with white gum
1 **69** 1d. carmine (3.24) .. .. .. 3·75 2·25

(c) Cowan unsurfaced paper with very shiny gum
2 **69** 1d. carmine-pink (4.25) .. .. .. 26·00 22·00

The paper used for No. 462 is similar to that of Nos. 416/30.

70 Exhibition Buildings

(Des H. L. Richardson. Eng and typo Govt Printer, Wellington)

925 (17 Nov). *Dunedin Exhibition. W* **43**. *Cowan chalk-surfaced paper. P* 14 × 15.
63 **70** ½d. yellow-green/*green* .. .. .. 1·75 9·50
64 1d. carmine/*rose* .. .. .. 2·00 5·00
65 4d. mauve/*pale mauve* .. .. .. 35·00 60·00
a. "POSTAGF" at right (R.1/2, R.10/1) £120 £170
63/5 .. .. *Set of* 3 35·00 65·00

71

72

(Des H. L. Richardson; plates by B.W. (1d. from sheets), P.B. (1d. from booklets), Royal Mint, London (others). Typo Govt Printer, Wellington)

926 (12 July)–**34**. *W* **43**. *P* 14. (*a*) *Jones chalk-surfaced paper with white gum.*
66 **72** 2s. deep blue .. .. 42·00 42·00
67 3s. mauve .. .. 70·00 85·00

(b) Cowan thick, opaque, chalk-surfaced paper with white gum
68 **71** 1d. rose-carmine (15.11.26) 40 10
a. Imperf (pair) .. .. 45·00
b. Booklet pane of 6 with bars on selvedge (1928) .. .. .. 45·00
c. Booklet pane of 6 with bars and adverts on selvedge (1928) .. .. 45·00
d. Perf 14 × 15 (3.27) 45 10
da. Booklet pane of 6 with bars and adverts on selvedge (1934) .. .. 60·00
69 **72** 2s. light blue (5.27) .. .. .. 40·00 14·00
70 3s. pale mauve (9.27) .. .. .. 70·00 80·00
68/70 .. .. *Set of* 3 £100 85·00

(c) Wiggins Teape thin, hard, chalk-surfaced paper with white gum
71 **71** 1d. rose-carmine (6.30) .. .. .. 13·00 4·00

No. 468 exists in a range of colours including scarlet and deep armine to magenta but we have insufficient evidence to show hat these were issued.

73 Nurse

74 Smiling Boy

(Typo Govt Printing Office, Wellington)

1929–30. *Anti-Tuberculosis Fund. T* **73** *and similar type. W* **43**. *P* 14. (*a*) *Inscribed* "HELP STAMP OUT TUBERCULOSIS".
544 1d. + 1d. scarlet (11.12.29) .. .. .. 11·00 13·00

(*b*) *Inscribed* "HELP PROMOTE HEALTH"
545 1d. + 1d. scarlet (29.10.30) .. .. .. 16·00 22·00

(Des L. C. Mitchell. Dies eng and plates made Royal Mint, London (1d.), Govt Ptg Office, Wellington from W. R. Bock die (2d.). Typo Govt Ptg Office, Wellington)

1931 (31 Oct). *Health Stamps. W* **43** (*sideways*). *P* 14½ × 14.
546 **74** 1d. + 1d. scarlet .. .. .. 75·00 75·00
547 2d. + 1d. blue .. .. 75·00 65·00

75 New Zealand Lake Scenery

FIVE PENCE

(76)

(Des L. C. Mitchell. Plates, Royal Mint, London. Typo Govt Ptg Office)

1931 (10 Nov)–**35**. *Air. W* **43**. *P* 14 × 14½.
548 **75** 3d. chocolate .. .. 17·00 8·50
a. Perf 14 × 15 (4.35) £190 £425
549 4d. blackish purple .. .. .. 19·00 10·00
550 7d. brown-orange .. .. .. 20·00 7·00
548/50 .. .. *Set of* 3 50·00 23·00

1931 (18 Dec). *Air. Surch with T* **76**.
551 **75** 5d. on 3d. green (R.) .. .. .. 8·50 6·50

77 Hygeia, Goddess of Health

78 The Path to Health

(Des R. E. Tripe and W. J. Cooch. Eng H. T. Peat. Recess Govt Printing Office, Wellington)

1932 (18 Nov). *Health Stamp. W* **43**. *P* 14.
552 **77** 1d. + 1d. carmine .. .. .. 16·00 20·00

(Des J. Berry. Eng H. T. Peat. Recess Govt Printing Office, Wellington)

1933 (8 Nov). *Health Stamp. W* **43**. *P* 14.
553 **78** 1d. + 1d. carmine .. .. .. 7·00 11·00

TRANS-TASMAN
AIR MAIL
"FAITH IN AUSTRALIA."

(79)

80 Crusader

1934 (17 Jan). *Air. T* **75** *in new colour optd with T* **79**. *W* **43**. *P* 14 × 14½.
554 **75** 7d. light blue (B.) .. .. .. 30·00 38·00

(Des J. Berry. Recess D.L.R.)

1934 (25 Oct). *Health Stamp. W* **43**. *P* 14 × 13½.
555 **80** 1d. + 1d. carmine .. .. .. 4·00 7·00

81 Collared Grey Fantail

82 Brown Kiwi

83 Maori Woman

84 Maori Carved House

85 Mt Cook

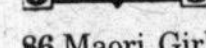
86 Maori Girl

87 Mitre Peak

88 Swordfish

89 Harvesting

90 Tuatara Lizard

91 Maori Panel

92 Tui

93 Capt. Cook at Poverty Bay

94 Mt Egmont

Die I Die II

"Captain Coqk"
(R. 1/4)

(Des J. Fitzgerald (½d., 4d.), C. H. and R. J. G. Collins (1d.), M. Matthews (1½d.), H. W. Young (2d.), L. C. Mitchell (2½d., 3d., 8d., 1s., 3s.), W. J. Cooch and R. E. Tripe (5d.), T. I. Archer (6d.), I. F. Calder (9d.) and I. H. Jenkins (2s.). Litho Waterlow (9d.). Recess D.L.R. (remainder))

1935 (1 May). *W* **43**.
556 **81** ½d. bright green, *p* 14 × 13½ .. .. 1·00 20
557 **82** 1d. scarlet (Die I), *p* 14 × 13½ .. 1·00 10
a. Perf 13½ × 14 .. .. .. 40·00 17·00
b. Die II. Perf 14 × 13½ .. .. 3·75 75
ba. Booklet pane of 6 with adverts on selvedge .. .. 25·00
558 **83** 1½d. red-brown, *p* 14 × 13½ .. .. 3·50 3·75
a. Perf 13½ × 14 .. .. .. 3·50 3·50
559 **84** 2d. orange, *p* 14 × 13½ .. .. 1·25 30
560 **85** 2½d. chocolate and slate, *p* 13–14 × 13½ 3·50 10·00
a. Perf 13½ × 14 .. .. .. 2·75 9·00
561 **86** 3d. brown, *p* 14 × 13½ .. .. 7·00 60
562 **87** 4d. black and sepia, *p* 14 .. .. 2·25 35
563 **88** 5d. ultramarine, *p* 13–14 × 13½ .. 8·00 11·00
a. Perf 13½ × 14 .. .. .. 13·00 12·00
564 **89** 6d. scarlet, *p* 13½ × 14 .. .. 3·50 2·00
565 **90** 8d. chocolate, *p* 14 × 13½ .. .. 3·50 2·25
566 **91** 9d. scarlet and black, *p* 14 × 14½ .. 8·00 2·50
567 **92** 1s. deep green, *p* 14 × 13½ .. .. 10·00 3·00
568 **93** 2s. olive-green, *p* 13–14 × 13½ .. 17·00 12·00
a. "CAPTAIN COQK" .. .. 28·00
b. Perf 13½ × 14 .. .. .. 24·00 15·00
ba. "CAPTAIN COQK" .. .. 38·00
569 **94** 3s. chocolate & yell-brn, *p* 13–14 × 13½ .. .. .. 15·00 27·00
a. Perf 13½ × 14 .. .. .. 14·00 25·00
556/69a .. .. *Set of* 14 75·00 65·00

In the 2½d., 5d., 2s. and 3s. perf 13–14 × 13½ the horizontal perforations of each stamp are in two sizes, one half of each horizontal side measuring 13 and the other 14.

See also Nos. 577/90 and 630/1.

95 Bell Block Aerodrome

96 King George V and Queen Mary

(Des J. Berry. Eng Stamp Printing Office, Melbourne. Recess Govt Printing Office, Wellington)

1935 (4 May). *Air. W* **43**. *P* 14.
570 **95** 1d. carmine 30 20
571 3d. violet .. .. 2·25 1·75
572 6d. blue .. .. 4·00 1·75
570/2 .. .. *Set of* 3 6·00 3·25

Following the success of the GB and Australia Concise Catalogues, Stanley Gibbons are pleased to announce the

NEW ZEALAND CONCISE CATALOGUE

In addition to New Zealand itself, this handy volume lists all issues of the Cook Islands, including Aitutaki and Penrhyn, Niue, Ross Dependency, Tokelau and the pre-independence issues of Western Samoa.

Like other Concise Catalogues, the New Zealand listings are based on 'Part 1' but with a host of additional features: these include inverted watermarks from 1874 onwards, Queen Victoria 'second sidefaces' with Advertisements ('Adsons') on the back, counter coil pairs, first day covers, booklets (from 1901) and more recent Post Office products such as presentation and souvenir packs, postcards and year books.

For further details visit your favourite stamp shop or write to:
Stanley Gibbons Publications Ltd.,
5 Parkside, Christchurch Road,
Ringwood, Hampshire BH24 3SH,
Telephone 0425 472363

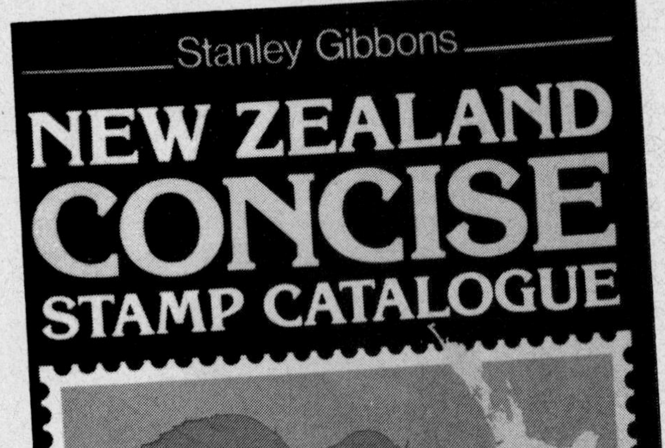

SATISFACTION

A well laid out and written up album page is a joy to behold – it may take a little time and trouble but it will give immeasurably more satisfaction and pleasure than any printed album page which just needs the spaces to be filled up.

To present your collection in the best possible way we recommend:

HOW TO ARRANGE AND WRITE UP A STAMP COLLECTION
by Stanley Phillips and C. P. Rang, revised by Michael Briggs

A classic philatelic work – first published in 1933 – thoroughly revised and fully up to date. Sound, constructive advice is given on how to present a stamp collection in the most attractive way – using a variety of different types of album and methods of writing up.

For further details visit your favourite stamp shop or write to:
Stanley Gibbons Publications Ltd., 5 Parkside,
Christchurch Road, Ringwood, Hampshire BH24 3SH.
Telephone 0425 472363

WHEN BUYING OR SELLING FINE INDIVIDUAL STAMPS AND SETS OF

NEW ZEALAND

. . . and other Commonwealth countries, serious collectors have come to rely on our friendly, personal service and competitive prices. Every month we mail (overseas by air) all regular clients with our monthly lists and Postal Bid Sale catalogues, in which we guarantee satisfaction on all purchases. **CAN WE HELP YOU TOO?**

Either write or phone for our current lists today! (Commonwealth Definitive Sets Buying List £2, refundable)

ROWLAND HILL STAMPS
27A Comberton Hill,
Kidderminster, Worcs DY10 1QN
Tel: 0562 824060

PTS
Established in stamp dealing since 1968

WANTS LISTS INVITED
Take advantage of our computerised booking service - simply list in SG order and state condition in which required

Kidderminster was the birth place of the great postal reformer who introduced the Penny Post and the Penny Black in 1840

A Choice of Albums for the New Zealand Collector

The Stanley Gibbons New Zealand One Country Album (Item 5262)
This elegant 4-ring album provides the perfect home for any straightforward NZ collection. Housed in a rich burgundy leather effect binder with gold tooling on the spine, the high quality cartridge leaves are laid out and written up to ensure that your collection is attractively displayed whatever its stage of development. Every stamp illustrated and identified by its SG catalogue number.

The Stanley Gibbons New Zealand Luxury Hingeless Album (Item 5288/9)
This impressive two-volume album represents the very ultimate in luxury, convenience and style, its padded binders are covered in navy blue leatherette rexine and decorated with the country's crest in traditional heraldic colours. The leaves are of the highest quality, tastefully laid out to give a superbly attractive display with a crystal clear mount already affixed in each space for the immediate insertion of your stamps. Each album is presented in its own matching slip case for added protection.
Item 5288 New Zealand Luxury Hingeless Album Volume 1 1855–1967
Item 5289 New Zealand Luxury Hingeless Album Volume 2 1967–date

For further details visit your favourite stamp shop or write to:
Stanley Gibbons Publications Ltd.,
5 Parkside, Christchurch Road, Ringwood, Hampshire BH24 3SH. Telephone 0425 472363

(Frame by J. Berry. Recess B.W.)

935 (7 May). *Silver Jubilee. W* **43**. *P* 11 × 11½.

3	**96**	½d. green	70	45
4		1d. carmine	90	20
5		6d. red-orange	10·00	15·00
3/5		*Set of* 3	10·50	15·00

7 "The Key to Health" **98** "Multiple Wmk"

(Des S. Hall. Recess John Ash, Melbourne)

935 (30 Sept). *Health Stamp. W* **43**. *P* 11.

76	**97**	1d. + 1d. scarlet	1·50	2·25

ATERMARKS. In W **43** the wmk units are in vertical columns idely spaced and the sheet margins are unwatermarked or wmkd NEW ZEALAND POSTAGE" in large letters.

In W **98** the wmk units are arranged alternately in horizontal ows closely spaced and are continued into the sheet margins.

Litho Govt Ptg Office, Wellington (9d.). Recess Waterlow or D.L.R. (others))

936–43. *W* **98**.

77	**81**	½d. bright green, *p* 14×13½	60	10
78	**82**	1d. scarlet (Die II), *p* 14×13½	30	10
79	**83**	1½d. red-brown, *p* 14×13½	3·00	1·25
80	**84**	2d. orange, *p* 14×13½	15	10
		b. Perf 12½† (6.41)	1·75	10
		c. Perf 14 (6.41)	6·00	70
		d. Perf 14×15 (6.41)	12·00	3·25
81	**85**	2½d. chocolate and slate, *p* 13–14×13½	75	2·25
		a. Perf 14	95	1·25
		b. Perf 14×13½ (1942)	50	1·75
82	**86**	3d. brown, *p* 14×13½	23·00	15
83	**87**	4d. black and sepia, *p* 14×13½	2·00	10
		a. Perf 12½* (1941)	9·00	70
		b. Perf 14, line (1941)	40·00	30·00
		c. Perf 14×14½ comb (7.42)	80	10
84	**88**	5d. ultramarine, *p* 13–14×13½	3·75	80
		b. Perf 12½*† (7.41, 1942)	11·00	95
		c. Perf 14×13½ (1942)	2·00	65
85	**89**	6d. scarlet, *p* 13½×14	2·75	10
		a. Perf 12½* (1941)	2·25	20
		b. Perf 14½×14 (1942)	65	10
86	**90**	8d. choc, *p* 14×13½ (*wmk sideways*)	2·50	75
		aa. Wmk upright (1939)	2·25	55
		a. Perf 12½* (*wmk sideways*) (1941)	2·00	60
		b. Perf 14×14½ (*wmk sideways*) (1943)	90	10
87	**91**	9d. red & grey, *p* 14×15 (*wmk sideways*)	27·00	1·75
		a. Red and grey-black. Perf 13½×14 (1.3.38)	27·00	1·50
88	**92**	1s. deep green, *p* 14×13½	1·50	10
		b. Perf 12½* (11.41)	32·00	8·50
89	**93**	2s. olive-green, *p* 13–14×13½	12·00	1·25
		a. "CAPTAIN COQK"	28·00	
		b. Perf 13½×14 (1938)	£140	2·00
		ba. "CAPTAIN COQK"	£140	
		c. Perf 12½*† (1941, 1942)	16·00	1·50
		ca. "CAPTAIN COQK"	25·00	
		d. Perf 14×13½ (1942)	8·50	85
		da. "CAPTAIN COQK"	35·00	
90	**94**	3s. chocolate & yell-brn, *p* 13–14×13½	16·00	3·00
		a. Perf 12½* (1941)	38·00	22·00
		b. Perf 14×13½ (1942)	6·00	1·50
77/90b		*Set of* 14	65·00	6·50

*†Stamps indicated with an asterisk were printed and perforated by Waterlow; those having a dagger were printed by D.L.R. and perforated by Waterlow. No. 580d was printed by D.L.R. and perforated by Harrison and No. 583b was printed by Waterlow and perforated by D.L.R. These are all known as "Blitz perfs" because De La Rue were unable to maintain supplies after their works were damaged by enemy action. All the rest, except the 9d., were printed and perforated by D.L.R.

On stamps printed and perforated by De La Rue the perf 14 × 13½ varies in the sheet and is sometimes nearer 13½. 2d. perf 14 × 15 is sometimes nearer 14 × 14½.

2½d., 5d., 2s. and 3s. In perf 13–14 × 13½ one half the length of each horizontal perforation measures 13 and the other 14. In perf 14 × 13½ the horizontal perforation is regular.

4d. No. 583b is line-perf measuring 14 exactly and has a blackish sepia frame. No. 583c is a comb-perf measuring 14 × 14.3 or 14 × 14.2 and the frame is a warmer shade.

2s. No. 589b is comb-perf and measures 13.5 × 13.75.

For 9d. typographed, see Nos. 630/1.

99 N.Z. Soldier at Anzac Cove **100** Wool

(Des L. C. Mitchell. Recess John Ash, Melbourne)

1936 (27 Apr). *Charity. 21st Anniv of "Anzac" Landing at Gallipoli. W* **43**. *P* 11.

591	**99**	½d. + ½d. green	25	90
592		1d. + 1d. scarlet	25	90

(Des L. C. Mitchell. Recess John Ash, Melbourne)

1936 (1 Oct). *Congress of British Empire Chambers of Commerce, Wellington. Industries Issue. T* **100** *and similar horiz designs. W* **43**. *P* 11½.

593		½d. emerald-green	15	25
594		1d. scarlet	15	20
595		2½d blue	90	4·00
596		4d. violet	80	3·50
597		6d. red-brown	90	3·25
593/7		*Set of* 5	2·50	10·00

Designs:—1d. Butter; 2½d. Sheep; 4d. Apples; 6d. Exports.

105 Health Camp **106** King George VI and Queen Elizabeth

(Des J. Berry. Recess John Ash, Melbourne)

1936 (2 Nov). *Health Stamp. W* **43**. *P* 11.

598	**105**	1d. + 1d. scarlet	65	2·75

(Recess B.W.)

1937 (13 May). *Coronation. W* **98**. *P* 14 × 13½.

599	**106**	1d. carmine	25	10
600		2½d. Prussian blue	1·25	1·10
601		6d. red-orange	1·50	1·00
599/601		*Set of* 3	2·75	2·00

107 Rock climbing **108** King George VI **108a**

(Des G. Bull and J. Berry. Recess John Ash, Melbourne)

1937 (1 Oct). *Health Stamp. W* **43**. *P* 11.

602	**107**	1d. + 1d. scarlet	1·50	2·50

(Des W. J. Cooch. Recess B.W.)

1938–44. *W* **98**. *P* 14 × 13½.

603	**108**	½d. green (1.3.38)	3·50	10
604		½d. brown-orange (10.7.41)	10	10
605		1d. scarlet (1.7.38)	3·50	10
606		1d. green (21.7.41)	10	10
607	**108a**	1½d. purple-brown (26.7.38)	16·00	70
608		1½d. scarlet (1.2.44)	10	10
609		3d. blue (26.9.41)	10	10
603/9		*Set of* 7	21·00	70

For other values see Nos. 680/89.

109 Children playing **110** Beach Ball

(Des J. Berry. Recess B.W.)

1938 (1 Oct). *Health Stamp. W* **98**. *P* 14 × 13½.

610	**109**	1d. + 1d. scarlet	1·40	1·40

(Des S. Hall. Recess Note Printing Branch, Commonwealth Bank of Australia, Melbourne)

1939 (16 Oct). *Health Stamps. Surcharged with new value. W* **43**. *P* 11.

611	**110**	1d. on ½d. + ½d. green	1·50	3·25
612		2d. on 1d. + 1d. scarlet	1·75	3·25

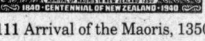

111 Arrival of the Maoris, 1350 **115** Signing Treaty of Waitangi, 1840

(Des L. C. Mitchell (½d., 3d., 4d.); J. Berry (others). Recess B.W.)

1940 (2 Jan–8 Mar). *Centenary of Proclamation of British Sovereignty. T* **111**, **115** *and similar designs. W* **98**. *P* 14 × 13½ (2½d.), 13½ × 14 (5d.) *or* 13½ (*others*).

613		½d. blue-green	25	10
614		1d. chocolate and scarlet	1·50	10
615		1½d. light blue and mauve	30	20
616		2d. blue-green and chocolate	1·50	10
617		2½d. blue-green and blue	45	20
618		3d. purple and carmine	2·00	25
619		4d. chocolate and lake	8·00	50
620		5d. pale blue and brown	3·75	2·00
621		6d. emerald-green and violet	7·50	25
622		7d. black and red	1·25	3·50
623		8d. black and red (8.3)	7·50	1·25
624		9d. olive-green and orange	6·00	75
625		1s. sage-green and deep green	11·00	2·25
613/25		*Set of* 13	45·00	10·00

Designs: *Horiz* (*as T* **111**)—1d. H.M.S. *Endeavour*, chart of N.Z., and Capt. Cook; 1½d. British Monarchs; 2d. Tasman with *Heemskerk* and chart; 3d. Landing of immigrants, 1840; 4d. Road, Rail, Sea and Air transport; 6d. *Dunedin* and "Frozen Mutton Route" to London; 7d., 8d. Maori council; 9d. Gold mining in 1861 and 1940. (*As T* **115**)—5d. H.M.S. *Britomart* at Akaroa, 1840. *Vert* (*as T* **111**)—1s. Giant Kauri tree.

1940 (1 Oct). *Health Stamps. As T* **110**, *but without extra surcharge. W* **43**. *P* 11.

626	**110**	1d. + ½d. blue-green	2·75	7·00
627		2d. + 1d. brown-orange	2·75	7·00

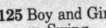

1D 1D ■ ■ (123) 2D Inserted "2" 1941 (124)

1941. *Surch as T* **123**.

628	**108**	1d. on ½d. green (1.5.41)	25	10
629	**108a**	2d. on 1½d. purple-brown (4.41)	25	10
		a. Inserted "2"	£450	£300

The surcharge on No. 629 has only one figure, at top left, and there is only one square to obliterate the original value at bottom right.

The variety "Inserted 2" occurs on the 10th stamp, 10th row. It is identified by the presence of remnants of the damaged "2", and by the spacing of "2" and "D" which is variable and different from the normal.

(Typo Govt Printing Office, Wellington)

1941. *As T* **91**, *but smaller* (17½ × 20½ *mm*). *P* 14 × 15. (*a*) *W* **43**.

630	**91**	9d. scarlet and black (5.41)	55·00	7·00

(*b*) *W* **98**

631	**91**	9d. scarlet and black (29.9.41)	1·75	75

1941 (4 Oct). *Health Stamps. Nos. 626/7 optd with T* **124**.

632	**110**	1d. + ½d. blue-green	25	1·25
633		2d. + 1d. brown-orange	25	1·25

125 Boy and Girl on Swing **126** Princess Margaret

(Des S. Hall. Recess Note Printing Branch, Commonwealth Bank of Australia, Melbourne)

1942 (1 Oct). *Health Stamps. W* **43**. *P* 11.

634	**125**	1d. + ½d. blue-green	15	35
635		2d. + 1d. orange-red	15	30

(Des J. Berry. Recess B.W.)

1943 (1 Oct). *Health Stamps. T* **126** *and similar triangular design. W* **98**. *P* 12.

636		1d. + ½d. green	10	20
		a. Imperf between (vert pair)	£3750	
637		2d. + 1d. red-brown	10	10
		a. Imperf between (vert pair)	£3750	£3750

Design:—2d. Queen Elizabeth II as Princess.

(128)

1944 (1 May). *No. 615 surch with T* **128**.

662		10d. on 1½d. light blue and mauve	10	10

ALTERED CATALOGUE NUMBERS

Any Catalogue numbers altered from the last edition are shown as a list in the introductory pages.

129 Queen Elizabeth II as Princess and Princess Margaret

130 Statue of Peter Pan, Kensington Gardens

(Recess B.W.)

1944 (9 Oct). *Health Stamps. W* **98.** *P* 13½.

663	**129**	1d. + ½d. green	10	10
664		2d. + 1d. blue	10	10

(Des J. Berry. Recess B.W.)

1945 (1 Oct). *Health Stamps. W* **98.** *P* 13½.

665	**130**	1d. + ½d. green and buff	10	10
666		2d. + 1d. carmine and buff	10	10

131 Lake Matheson

132 King George VI and Parliament House, Wellington

133 St. Paul's Cathedral

139 "St. George" (Wellington College War Memorial Window)

Printer's guide mark (R. 12/3)

Completed rudder (R. 2/4 of Pl 42883 and R. 3/2 of Pl 42796)

(Des J. Berry. Photo Harrison (1½d. and 1s.). Recess B.W. (1d. and 2d.) and Waterlow (others))

1946 (1 Apr). *Peace issue. T* **131/3, 139** *and similar designs. W* **98** *(sideways on* 1½*d.). P* 13 *(1d., 2d.),* 14 × 14½ *(1½d., 1s.),* 13½ *(others).*

667	½d. green and brown	10	15
	a. Printer's guide mark	1·50	
668	1d. green	10	10
669	1½d. scarlet	10	10
670	2d. purple	15	10
671	3d. ultramarine and grey	20	10
	a. Completed rudder	3·00	
672	4d. bronze-green and orange	20	15
673	5d. green and ultramarine	20	10
674	6d. chocolate and vermilion	15	10
675	8d. black and carmine	15	10
676	9d. blue and black	15	10
677	1s. grey-black	15	15
667/77	.. .. .. *Set of* 11	1·50	1·00

Designs: *Horiz* (*as T* 132)—2d. The Royal Family. (*As T* 131)—3d. R.N.Z.A.F. badge and aeroplanes; 4d. Army badge, tank and plough; 5d. Navy badge, H.M.N.Z.S. *Achilles* (cruiser) and *Dominion Monarch* (liner); 6d. N.Z. coat of arms, foundry and farm; 9d. Southern Alps and Franz Josef Glacier. *Vert* (*as T* 139)—1s. National Memorial Campanile.

142 Soldier helping Child over Stile

(Des J. Berry. Recess Waterlow)

1946 (24 Oct). *Health Stamps. W* **98.** *P* 13½.

678	**142**	1d. + ½d. green and orange-brown ..	10	10
		a. Yellow-green and orange-brown ..	3·00	3·00
679		2d. + 1d. chocolate and orange-brown	10	10

144 King George VI

145 Statue of Eros

Plate 1

Plate 2

(Des W. J. Cooch. Recess T **108a**, B.W.; T **144**, D.L.R.)

1947–52. *W* **98** *(sideways on "shilling" values). (a) P* 14 × 13½.

680	**108a**	2d. orange	15	10
681		4d. bright purple	35	10
682		5d. slate	50	35
683		6d. carmine	40	10
684		8d. violet	65	15
685		9d. purple-brown	70	10
		(b) P 14		
686	**144**	1s. red-brown and carmine (Plate 1) ..	1·40	20
		a. Wmk upright (Plate 1) ..	50	20
		b. Wmk upright (Plate 2) ..	85	15
687		1s. 3d. red-brown and blue (Plate 2) ..	70	30
		a. Wmk upright (14.1.52) ..	1·75	3·00
688		2s. brown-orange and green (Plate 1) ..	1·25	50
		a. Wmk upright (Plate 1) ..	1·00	1·50
689		3s. red-brown and grey (Plate 2) ..	1·75	1·00
680/9		.. .. *Set of* 10	6·00	2·25

In head-plate 2 the diagonal lines of the background have been strengthened and result in the upper corners and sides appearing more deeply shaded.

(Des J. Berry. Recess Waterlow)

1947 (1 Oct). *Health Stamps. W* **98** *(sideways). P* 13½.

690	**145**	1d. + ½d. green	10	10
691		2d. + 1d. carmine	10	10

146 Port Chalmers, 1848

148 First Church Dunedin

(Des J. Berry. Recess B.W.)

1948 (23 Feb). *Centennial of Otago. T* **146, 148** *and similar designs. W* **98** *(sideways on 3d.). P* 13½.

692	1d. blue and green	10	10
693	2d. green and brown	10	10
694	3d. purple	10	10
695	6d. black and rose	10	10
692/5	.. .. .. *Set of* 4	30	35

Designs: *Horiz*—2d. Cromwell, Otago; 6d. University of Otago.

150 Boy Sunbathing and Children Playing

151 Nurse and Child

(Des E. Linzell. Recess B.W.)

1948 (1 Oct). *Health Stamps. W* **98.** *P* 13½.

696	**150**	1d. + ½d. blue and green	10	10
697		2d. + 1d. purple and scarlet	10	10

1949 ROYAL VISIT ISSUE. Four stamps were prepared t commemorate this event: 2d. Treaty House, Waitangi; 3d. H.M.S *Vanguard*; 5d. Royal portraits; 6d. Crown and sceptre. The visit di not take place and the stamps were destroyed, although a fe examples of the 3d. later appeared on the market. A similar set wa prepared in 1952, but was, likewise, not issued.

(Des J. Berry. Photo Harrison)

1949 (3 Oct). *Health Stamps. W* **98.** *P* 14 × 14½.

698	**151**	1d. + ½d. green	10	1
699		2d. + 1d. ultramarine	10	1
		a. No stop below "D" of "1 D." ..	6·00	11·0

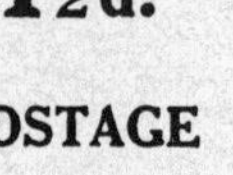

(152)

153 Queen Elizabeth II and Prince Charles

1950 (28 July). *As Type* **F 6**, *but without value, surch with T* **15** *W* **98** *(inverted). Chalk-surfaced paper. P* 14.

700	**F 6**	1½d. carmine	10	1

Originally issued with the watermark inverted, this late appeared with it upright.

(Des J. Berry and R. S. Phillips. Photo Harrison)

1950 (2 Oct). *Health Stamps. W* **98.** *P* 14 × 14½.

701	**153**	1d. + ½d. green	10	1
702		2d. + 1d. plum	10	1

154 Christchurch Cathedral

155 Cairn on Lyttleton Hills

(Des L. C. Mitchell (2d.), J. A. Johnstone (3d.) and J. Berry (others Recess B.W.)

1950 (20 Nov). *Centennial of Canterbury, N.Z. T* **154/5** *an similar designs. W* **98** *(sideways on 1d. and 3d.). P* 13½.

703	1d. green and blue	10	1
704	2d. carmine and orange	10	1
705	3d. dark blue and blue	10	1
706	6d. brown and blue	15	2
707	1s. reddish purple and blue	15	3
703/7	.. .. .. *Set of* 5	50	8

Designs: *Vert* (*as T* **154**)—3d. John Robert Godley. *Horiz* (*a T* **155**)—6d. Canterbury University College; 1s. Aerial view Timaru.

159 "Takapuna" class Yachts

(Des J. Berry and R. S. Phillips. Recess B.W.)

1951 (1 Nov). *Health Stamps. W* **98.** *P* 13½.

708	**159**	1½d. + ½d. scarlet and yellow.. ..	10	1
709		2d. + 1d. deep green and yellow ..	10	1

160 Princess Anne

161 Prince Charles

3D

(162)

(From photographs by Marcus Adams. Photo Harrison)

1952 (1 Oct). *Health Stamps. W* **98.** *P* 14 × 14½.

710	**160**	1½d. + ½d. carmine-red	10	1
711	**161**	2d. + 1d. brown	10	1

1952–53. *Nos.* 604 *and* 606 *surch as T* **162.**

712	**108**	1d. on ½d. brown-orange (11.9.53) ..	10	1
		a. "D" omitted..	†	–
713		3d. on 1d. green (12.12.52*) ..	10	1

*Earliest known date used.

163 Buckingham Palace   164 Queen Elizabeth II

(Des L. C. Mitchell (1s. 6d.), J. Berry (others). Recess D.L.R. (2d., 4d.), Waterlow (1s. 6d.) Photo Harrison (3d., 8d.))

1953 (25 May). *Coronation. T* **163/4** *and similar designs.* **W 98.** *P* 13 (2*d*., 4*d*.), 13½ (1*s*. 6*d*.) *or* 14 × 14½ (3*d*., 8*d*.).

714	2d. deep bright blue	15	15
715	3d. brown	15	10
716	4d. carmine	70	1·50
717	8d. slate-grey	60	70
718	1s. 6d. purple and ultramarine	1·25	80
714/18	*Set of* 5	2·50	2·75

Designs: *Horiz* (*as T* **163**)—4d. Coronation State Coach; 1s. 6d. St. Edward's Crown and Royal Sceptre. *Vert* (*as T* **164**)—8d. Westminster Abbey.

168 Girl Guides   169 Boy Scouts

(Des J. Berry. Photo Harrison)

1953 (7 Oct). *Health Stamps.* **W 98.** *P* 14 × 14½.

719	168	1½d. + ½d. blue	10	10
720	169	2d. + 1d. deep yellow-green	10	15

170 Queen Elizabeth II   171 Queen Elizabeth II and Duke of Edinburgh

(Des L. C. Mitchell. Recess Waterlow)

1953 (9 Dec). *Royal Visit.* **W 98.** *P* 13 × 14 (3*d*.) *or* 13½ (4*d*.).

721	170	3d. dull purple	10	10
722	171	4d. deep ultramarine	10	20

172   173 Queen Elizabeth II   174

Die I   Die II

(Des L. C. Mitchell (T **172/3**), J. Berry (T **174**). Recess D.L.R. (T **173**), B.W. (others))

1953 (15 Dec)–**58.** **W 98.** *P* 14 × 13½ (*T* **172**), 14 (*T* **173**) *or* 13½ (*T* **174**).

723	172	½d. slate-black (1.3.54)	15	20
724		1d. orange (1.3.54)	15	10
725		1½d. brown-lake	20	10
726		2d. bluish green (1.3.54)	20	10
727		3d. vermilion (1.3.54)	20	10
728		4d. blue (1.3.54)	40	15
729		6d. purple (1.3.54)	70	40
730		8d. carmine (1.3.54)	60	25
731	173	9d. brown and bright green (1.3.54)	60	10
732		1s. black & carm-red (Die I) (1.3.54)	65	10
		a. Die II (1958)	50·00	9·00
733		1s. 6d. black and bright blue (1.3.54)	1·75	15
733*a*		1s. 9d. black and red-orange (1.7.57)	5·50	50
733*b*	174	2s. 6d. brown (1.7.57)	22·00	4·00
734		3s. bluish green (1.3.54)	9·00	25
735		5s. carmine (1.3.54)	16·00	2·25
736		10s. deep ultramarine (1.3.54)	40·00	14·00
723/36		*Set of* 16	85·00	20·00

1s. Dies I and II. The two dies of the Queen's portrait differ in the shading on the sleeve at right. The long lines running upwards from left to right are strong in Die I and weaker in Die II. In the upper part of the shading the fine cross-hatching is visible in Die I only between the middle two of the four long lines, but in Die II it extends clearly across all four lines.

In the lower part of the shading the strength of the long lines in Die I makes the cross-hatching appear subdued, whereas in Die II the weaker long lines make the cross-hatching more prominent.

Centre plates 1A, 1B and 2B are Die I; 3A and 3B are Die II.

For stamps as T **172** but with larger figures of value see Nos. 745/51.

1958 NEW PAPER. A new white opaque paper first came into use in August 1958 and was used for later printings of Nos. 733*a*, 745, 747/9, O159, O161, O163/4, O166 and L54. It is slightly thicker than the paper previously used, but obviously different in colour (white, against cream) and opacity (the previous paper being *relatively* transparent).

175 Young Climber and Mts Aspiring and Everest

(Des J. Berry. Recess; vignette litho B.W.)

1954 (4 Oct). *Health Stamps.* **W 98.** *P* 13½.

737	175	1½d. + ½d. sepia and deep violet	10	10
738		2d. + 1d. sepia and blue-black	10	10

176 Maori Mail-carrier   177 Queen Elizabeth II

178 Douglas "DC 3" Airliner

(Des R. M. Conly (2d.), J. Berry (3d.), A. G. Mitchell (4d.). Recess D.L.R.)

1955 (18 July). *Centenary of First New Zealand Postage Stamps.* **W 98.** *P* 14 (2*d*.), 14 × 14½ (3*d*.) *or* 13 (4*d*.).

739	176	2d. sepia and deep green	10	10
740	177	3d. brown-red	10	10
741	178	4d. black and bright blue	15	25
739/41		*Set of* 3	20	35

179 Children's Health Camps Federation Emblem   180

(Des E. M. Taylor. Recess B.W.)

1955 (3 Oct). *Health Stamps.* **W 98** (*sideways*). *P* 13½ × 13.

742	179	1½d. + ½d. sepia and orange-brown	10	25
743		2d. + 1d. red-brown and green	10	15
744		3d. + 1d. sepia and deep rose-red	10	10
		a. Centre omitted		
742/4		*Set of* 3	25	45

1955–59. *As Nos. 724/30 but larger figures of value and stars omitted from lower right corner.*

745	180	1d. orange (12.7.56)	40	10
746		1½d. brown-lake (1.12.55)	60	60
747		2d. bluish green (19.3.56)	40	10
748		3d. vermilion (1.5.56)	85	10
749		4d. blue (3.2.58)	1·75	30
750		6d. purple (20.10.55)	5·50	10
751		8d. chestnut (1.12.59)	4·00	5·00
745/51		*Set of* 7	12·00	5·50

See note *re* white opaque paper after No. 736. No. 751 exists only on white paper.

181 "The Whalers of Foveaux Strait"   183 Takahe

(Des E. R. Leeming (2d.), L. C. Mitchell (3d.), M. R. Smith (8d.). Recess D.L.R.)

1956 (16 Jan). *Southland Centennial. T* **181, 183** *and similar design.* **W 98.** *P* 13½ × 13 (8*d*.) *or* 13 × 12½ (*others*).

752	2d. deep blue-green	10	10
753	3d. sepia	10	10
754	8d. slate-violet and rose-red	40	60
752/4	*Set of* 3	50	70

Design: *Horiz*—3d. "Farming".

184 Children picking Apples

(Des L. C. Mitchell, after photo by J. F. Louden. Recess B.W.)

1956 (24 Sept). *Health Stamps.* **W 98.** *P* 13 × 13½.

755	184	1½d. + ½d. purple-brown	10	20
		a. *Blackish brown*	60	4·00
756		2d. + 1d. blue-green	10	15
757		3d. + 1d. claret	10	10
755/7		*Set of* 3	25	40

185 New Zealand Lamb and Map   186 Lamb, *Dunedin* and *Port Brisbane* (refrigerated freighter)

(Des M. Goaman. Photo Harrison)

1957 (15 Feb). *75th Anniv of First Export of N.Z. Lamb.* **W 98** (*sideways on* 4*d*.). *P* 14 × 14½ (4*d*.) *or* 14½ × 14 (8*d*.).

758	185	4d. blue	40	45
759	186	8d. deep orange-red	60	65

187 Sir Truby King

(Des M. R. Smith. Recess B.W.)

1957 (14 May). *50th Anniv of Plunket Society.* **W 98.** *P* 13.

760	187	3d. bright carmine-red	10	10

188 Life-savers in Action   189 Children on Seashore

(Des L. Cutten (2d.), L. C. Mitchell (3d.). Recess Waterlow)

1957 (25 Sept). *Health Stamps.* **W 98** (*sideways*). *P* 13½.

761	188	2d. + 1d. black and emerald	10	10
762	189	3d. + 1d. ultramarine and rose-red	10	10
MS762*b*		Two sheets each 112 × 96 mm with Nos. 761 and 762 in blocks of 6 (2 × 3). *Per pair*	12·00	18·00
MS762*c*		As last but with wmk upright *Per pair*	16·00	32·00

2d

(190)

191 Girls' Life Brigade Cadet   192 Boys' Brigade Bugler

1958 (6 Jan–Mar). *No. 746 surch as T* **190.**

763	180	2d. on 1½d. brown-lake	15	10
		a. Smaller dot in surch	10	10
		b. Error. Surch on No. 725 (3.58)	£110	£150

Diameter of dot on No. 763 is 4¼ mm; on No. 763a 3¾ mm.
Forgeries of No. 763b are known.

(Des J. Berry. Photo Harrison)

1958 (20 Aug). *Health Stamps.* **W 98.** *P* 14 × 14½.

764	191	2d. + 1d. green	10	10
765	192	3d. + 1d. blue	10	10
MS765*a*		Two sheets each 104 × 124 mm with Nos. 764/5 in blocks of 6 (3 × 2). *Per pair*	12·00	11·00

(Des J. E. Lyle. Eng F. D. Manley. Recess Commonwealth Bank of Australia Note Ptg Branch)

1958 (27 Aug). *30th Anniv of First Air Crossing of the Tasman Sea. As T* **120** *of Australia, but inscr* "NEW ZEALAND". *W* **98** *(sideways). P* 14 × 14½.
766 6d. deep ultramarine 20 30

193 Seal of Nelson

(Des M. J. Macdonald. Recess B.W.)

1958 (29 Sept). *Centenary of City of Nelson. W* **98**. *P* 13½ × 13.
767 **193** 3d. carmine 10 10

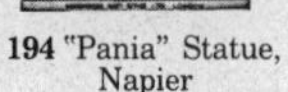
194 "Pania" Statue, Napier

195 Australian Gannets on Cape Kidnappers

(Des M. R. Smith (2d.), J. Berry (3d.), L. C. Mitchell (8d.). Photo Harrison)

1958 (3 Nov). *Centenary of Hawke's Bay Province. T* **194/5** *and similar design. W* **98** *(sideways on 3d.). P* 14½ × 14 *(3d.) or* 13½ × 14½ *(others).*
768 2d. yellow-green 10 10
769 3d. blue 15 10
770 8d. red-brown 45 75
768/70 .. .. .. *Set of* 3 60 80
Design:—*Vert* 8d. Maori sheep-shearer.

197 "Kiwi" Jamboree Badge

198 Careening H.M.S. *Endeavour* at Ship Cove

(Des Mrs. S. M. Collins. Recess B.W.)

1959 (5 Jan). *Pan-Pacific Scout Jamboree, Auckland. W* **98**. *P* 13½×13.
771 **197** 3d. sepia and carmine 10 10

(Des G. R. Bull and G. R. Smith. Photo Harrison)

1959 (2 Mar). *Centenary of Marlborough Province. T* **198** *and similar horiz designs. W* **98** *(sideways). P* 14½ × 14.
772 2d. green 15 10
773 3d. deep blue 15 10
774 8d. light brown 60 60
772/4 .. .. .. *Set of* 3 80 70
Designs:—3d. Shipping wool, Wairau Bar, 1857; 8d. Salt industry. Grassmere.

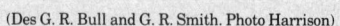

201 Red Cross Flag

(Photo Harrison)

1959 (3 June). *Red Cross Commemoration. W* **98** *(sideways). P* 14½×14.
775 **201** 3d. + 1d. red and ultramarine 10 10
a. Red Cross omitted £950

202 Grey Teal

203 New Zealand Stilt

(Des Display Section, G.P.O. Photo Harrison)

1959 (16 Sept). *Health Stamps. W* **98** *(sideways). P* 14 × 14½.
776 **202** 2d. + 1d. greenish yellow, ol & rose-red 15 15
777 **203** 3d. + 1d. black, pink and light blue .. 15 15
a. Pink ptg omitted .. .. .. 95·00
MS777*c*. Two sheets each 95 × 109 mm. with Nos. 776/7 in blocks of 6 (3 × 2). .. *Per pair* 6·00 14·00

204 "The Explorer"

205 "The Gold Digger"

(Des G. R. Bull and G. R. Smith. Photo Harrison)

1960 (16 May). *Centenary of Westland Province. T* **204/5** *and similar vert design. W* **98**. *P* 14 × 14½.
778 2d. deep dull green 15 10
779 3d. orange-red 15 10
780 8d. grey-black .. .. 40 1·50
778/80 .. .. .. *Set of* 3 60 1·50
Design:—8d. "The Pioneer Woman".

207 Manuka (Tea Tree)

214 National Flag

216 Trout

219 Taniwha (Maori Rock Drawing)

220 Butter Making

221 Tongariro National Park and Château

221*a* Tongariro National Park and Château

(Des Harrison (½d.), G. F. Fuller (1d., 3d., 6d.), A. G. Mitchell (2d., 4d., 5d., 8d., 3s., 10s., £1), P.O. Public Relations Division (7d.), P.O. Publicity Section (9d.), J. Berry (1s., 1s. 6d.), R. E. Barwick (1s. 3d.), J. C. Boyd (1s. 9d.), D. F. Kee (2s.), L. C. Mitchell (2s. 6d., 5s.). Photo D.L.R. (½d., 1d., 2d., 3d., 4d., 6d., 8d.) or Harrison (others))

1960 (11 July)–**66**. *T* **207**, **214**, **216**, **219/21*a*** *and similar designs. Ordinary or chalk-surfaced paper* (**C**). *W* **98** *(sideways on* 2½*d.,* 5*d.,* 1*s.,* 3*d.,* 1*s.* 6*d.,* 2*s.* 6*d.,* 3*s. and* 10*s.). P* 14 × 14½ (1*s.* 3*d.,* 1*s.* 6*d.,* 2*s.,* 5*s.,* £1) *or* 14½ × 14 *(others).*
781 **207** ½d. grey, green and cerise (1.9.60) .. 10 10
a. Grey omitted .. .. .. 30·00
b. Green omitted .. .. .. 45·00
782 – 1d. orge, green, lake & brn (1.9.60) 10 10
a. Orange omitted £110
b. Coil. Perf 14½×13. Wmk sideways (11.63) .. .. 70 1·50
c. Chalky paper (1965?) 10 15
783 – 2d. carmine, black, yellow and green 10 10
a. Black omitted £130
b. Yellow omitted £140
784 – 2½d. red, yellow, blk & grn, **C** (1.11.61) 45 10
a. Red omitted £110
b. Yellow omitted .. .. .. 40·00
c. Green omitted .. .. .. 55·00
d. Red and green omitted £225
785 – 3d. yellow, green, yellow-brown and deep greenish blue (1.9.60) .. 25 10
a. Yellow omitted .. .. .. 30·00
b. Green omitted .. .. .. 30·00
c. Yellow-brown omitted .. .. 30·00
e. Coil. Perf 14½×13. Wmk sideways (3.10.63) .. .. 70 1·25
f. Chalky paper (1965?) 25 25
786 – 4d. purple, buff, yellow-green & lt blue 30 10
a. Purple omitted .. .. .. 60·00
b. Buff omitted £130
d. Chalky paper (1965?) .. .. £150 7·00
787 – 5d. yellow, deep green, black and violet, **C** (14.5.62) 50 10
a. Yellow omitted .. .. .. 85·00
788 – 6d. lilac, grn & dp bluish grn (1.9.60) 40 10
a. No wmk .. .. 20·00 13·00
ab. Lilac omitted .. .. .. 55·00
ac. Green omitted .. .. .. 42·00
c. Chalky paper (1966?) 45 70

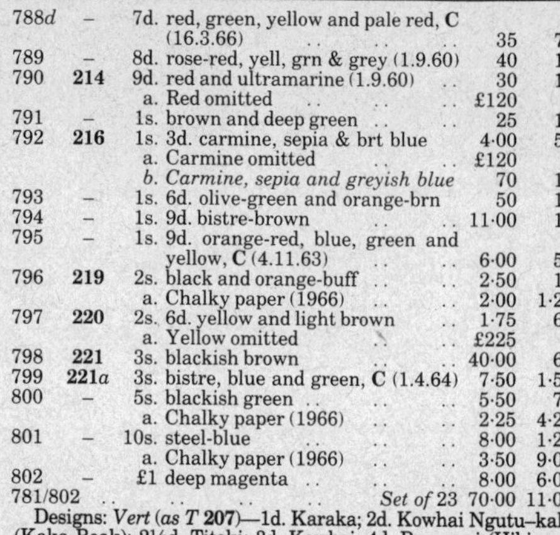
788*d* – 7d. red, green, yellow and pale red, **C** (16.3.66) 35 7
789 – 8d. rose-red, yell, grn & grey (1.9.60) 40 1
790 **214** 9d. red and ultramarine (1.9.60) .. 30 1
a. Red omitted £120
791 – 1s. brown and deep green 25 1
792 **216** 1s. 3d. carmine, sepia & brt blue 4·00 5
a. Carmine omitted £120
b. Carmine, sepia and greyish blue 70 1
793 – 1s. 6d. olive-green and orange-brn 50 1
794 – 1s. 9d. bistre-brown .. .. 11·00 1
795 – 1s. 9d. orange-red, blue, green and yellow, **C** (4.11.63) .. .. 6·00 5
796 **219** 2s. black and orange-buff .. .. 2·50 1
a. Chalky paper (1966) .. .. 2·00 1·2
797 **220** 2s. 6d. yellow and light brown .. 1·75 6
a. Yellow omitted £225
798 **221** 3s. blackish brown .. .. 40·00 6
799 **221*a*** 3s. bistre, blue and green, **C** (1.4.64) 7·50 1·5
800 – 5s. blackish green .. .. .. 5·50 7
a. Chalky paper (1966) .. .. 2·25 4·2
801 – 10s. steel-blue .. .. .. 8·00 1·2
a. Chalky paper (1966) .. .. 3·50 9·0
802 – £1 deep magenta .. .. .. 8·00 6·0
781/802 .. .. *Set of* 23 70·00 11·0
Designs: *Vert* (*as T* **207**)—1d. Karaka; 2d. Kowhai Ngutu–kak (Kaka Beak); 2½d. Titoki; 3d. Kowhai; 4d. Puarangi (Hibiscus 5d. Matua Tikumu (Mountain Daisy); 6d. Pikiarero (Clematis); 7 Koromiko; 8d. Rata. (*As T* **216**)—1s. 6d. Tiki. (*As T* **219**)—5s. Suth erland Falls; £1 Pohutu Geyser. *Horiz* (*as T* **214**)—1s. Timbe industry—1s. 9d. Aerial top dressing. (*As T* **221**)—10s. Tasma Glacier.
Nos. 782b and 785e were replaced by coils with uprigh watermark perf 14½×14 in 1966.

CHALKY PAPER. The chalk-surfaced paper is not only white but also thicker, making the watermark difficult to se Examples of the 4d. value can be found on a thick surfaced pape These should not be confused with the rare chalk-surface printing, No. 786d, which can be identified by its positiv reaction to the silver test.

225 Sacred Kingfisher

226 New Zealand Pigeon

(Des Display Section, G.P.O. Recess B.W.)

1960 (10 Aug). *Health Stamps. W* **98**. *P* 13½.
803 **225** 2d. + 1d. sepia and turquoise-blue .. 30 3
804 **226** 3d. + 1d. deep purple-brown and orange 30 3
MS804*b* Two sheets each 95 × 107 mm with Nos. 803 and 804 in blocks of 6. *P* 11½ × 11 *Per pair* 26·00 32·0

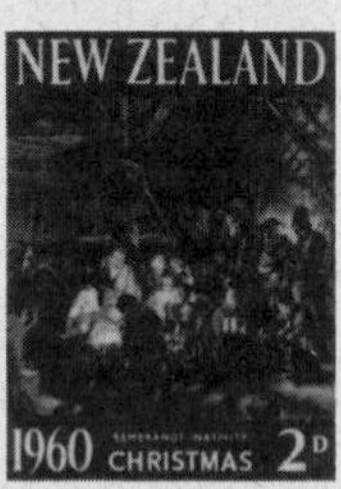

227 "The Adoration of the Shepherds" (Rembrandt)

(Photo Harrison)

1960 (1 Nov). *Christmas. W* **98**. *P* 12.
805 **227** 2d. red and deep brown/*cream* 15 1
a. Red omitted £300

228 Great Egret

229 New Zealand Falcon

(Des Display Section, G.P.O. Recess B.W.)

1961 (2 Aug). *Health Stamps. W* **98**. *P* 13½.
806 **228** 2d. + 1d. black and purple 20 20
807 **229** 3d. + 1d. deep sepia and yellow-green 20 20
MS807*a* Two sheets each 97 × 121 mm with Nos. 806/7 in blocks of 6 (3 × 2) .. *Per pair* 22·00 22·00

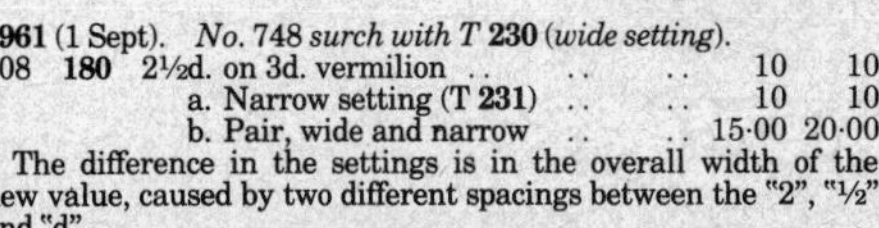

(230) (231) 232 "Adoration of the Magi" (Dürer)

1961 (1 Sept). *No. 748 surch with T* **230** (*wide setting*).
808 **180** 2½d. on 3d. vermilion 10 10
a. Narrow setting (T **231**) 10 10
b. Pair, wide and narrow .. .. 15·00 20·00
The difference in the settings is in the overall width of the new value, caused by two different spacings between the "2", "½" and "d".

(Photo Harrison)

1961 (16 Oct). *Christmas*. **W 98** (*sideways*). *P* 14½ × 14.
809 **232** 2½d. multicoloured 10 10

233 Morse Key and Port Hills, Lyttelton

(Des A. G. Mitchell (3d.) and L. C. Mitchell (8d.). Photo Harrison)

1962 (1 June). *Telegraph Centenary. T* **233** *and similar horiz design.* **W 98** (*sideways*). *P* 14½ × 14.
810 3d. sepia and bluish green 10 10
a. Green omitted £300
811 8d. black and brown-red 35 55
a. Imperf (pair) £800
b. Black omitted £300
Design:—8d. Modern teleprinter.
No. 811a comes from a sheet with the two top rows imperforate and the third row imperforate on three sides.

235 Red-fronted Parakeet 236 Tieke Saddleback

(Des Display Section, G.P.O. Photo D.L.R.)

1962 (3 Oct). *Health Stamps*. **W 98**. *P* 15 × 14.
812 **235** 2½d. + 1d. multicoloured 20 25
a. Orange omitted .. .. ..
813 **236** 3d. + 1d. multicoloured 20 25
a. Orange omitted £850
MS813*b* Two sheets each 96 × 101 mm with Nos. 812/3 in blocks of 6 (3 × 2) . .. *Per pair* 35·00 30·00

237 "Madonna in Prayer" (Sassoferrato)

(Photo Harrison)

1962 (15 Oct). *Christmas*. **W 98**. *P* 14½ × 14.
814 **237** 2½d. multicoloured 10 10

238 Prince Andrew 239

(Design after photographs by Studio Lisa, London. Recess D.L.R.)

1963 (7 Aug). *Health Stamps*. **W 98**. *P* 14.
815 **238** 2½d. + 1d. dull ultramarine .. 10 10
a. Ultramarine 15 10
b. Deep blue 25 35
816 **239** 3d. + 1d. carmine 10 10
MS816*a* Two sheets each 93×100 mm with Nos. 815/16 in blocks of 6 (3 × 2) .. *Per pair* 18·00 22·00

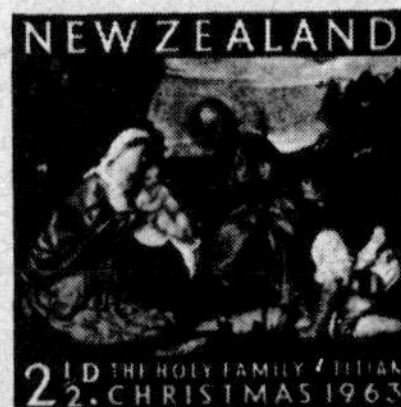

240 "The Holy Family" (Titian)

(Photo Harrison)

1963 (14 Oct). *Christmas*. **W 98** (*sideways*). *P* 12½.
817 **240** 2½d. multicoloured 10 10
a. Imperf (pair) £150
b. Yellow omitted £250

241 Steam Locomotive *Pilgrim* and "DG" Diesel Electric Loco 242 Diesel Express and Mt Ruapehu

(Des Commercial Art Section, N.Z. Railways. Photo D.L.R.)

1963 (25 Nov). *Railway Centenary*. **W 98** (*sideways*). *P* 14.
818 **241** 3d. multicoloured 30 10
a. Blue (sky) omitted £250
819 **242** 1s. 9d. multicoloured .. .. 1·60 80
a. Red (value) omitted £650

1963 (3 Dec). *Opening of COMPAC (Trans-Pacific Telephone Cable). As T* **174** *of Australia but inscr* "NEW ZEALAND". *No wmk. P* 13½.
820 8d. red, blue, black and yellow 50 90

243 Road Map and Car Steering-wheel 244 Silver Gulls

(Des L. C. Mitchell. Photo Harrison)

1964 (1 May). *Road Safety Campaign*. **W 98**. *P* 15 × 14.
821 **243** 3d. black, ochre-yellow and blue .. 10 10

(Des Display Section G.P.O., after Miss T. Kelly. Photo Harrison)

1964 (5 Aug). *Health Stamps. T* **244** *and similar horiz design. Multicoloured.* **W 98**. *P* 14½.
822 2½d. + 1d. Type **244** 10 15
a. Red (beak and legs) omitted .. .. 80·00
823 3d. + 1d. Little Penguin 10 15
MS823*a* Two sheets each 171 × 84 mm with Nos. 822/3 in blocks of 8 (4 × 2) . .. *Per pair* 38·00 45·00

7D POSTAGE

246 Rev. S. Marsden taking first Christian service at Rangihoua Bay, 1814 (247)

(Des L. C. Mitchell. Photo Harrison)

1964 (12 Oct). *Christmas*. **W 98** (*sideways*). *P* 14 × 13½.
824 **246** 2½d. multicoloured 10 10

1964 (14 Dec). *As Type* **F 6**, *but without value, surch with T* **247**. **W 98**. *Unsurfaced paper. P* 14 × 13½.
825 **F 6** 7d. carmine-red 25 70

ANZAC 1915 NEW ZEALAND 4D

248 Anzac Cove

(Des R. M. Conly. Photo Harrison)

1965 (14 Apr). *50th Anniv of Gallipoli Landing. T* **248** *and similar horiz design.* **W 98**. *P* 12½.
826 4d. yellow-brown 10 10
827 5d. green and red 10 25
Design:—5d. Anzac Cove and poppy.

250 I.T.U. Emblem and Symbols

(Photo Harrison)

1965 (17 May). *I.T.U. Centenary*. **W 98**. *P* 14½ × 14.
828 **250** 9d. blue and pale chocolate 30 35

(From photograph by Karsh. Photo Note Ptg Branch, Reserve Bank of Australia)

1965 (24 May). *Churchill Commemoration. As T* **186** *of Australia but inscr* "NEW ZEALAND". *P* 13½.
829 7d. black, pale grey and light blue 15 50

251 Wellington Provincial Council Building

(Des from painting by L. B. Temple (1867). Photo Harrison)

1965 (26 July). *Centenary of Government in Wellington.* **W 98** (*sideways*). *P* 14½ × 14.
830 **251** 4d. multicoloured 10 10

NEW ZEALAND 1965 4D POSTAGE·HEALTH 1D

252 Kaka 253 Collared Grey Fantail (after Miss T. Kelly)

(Des Display Section, G.P.O. Photo Harrison)

1965 (4 Aug). *Health Stamps*. **W 98**. *P* 14 × 14½.
831 **252** 3d. + 1d. multicoloured 20 15
832 **253** 4d. + 1d. multicoloured 20 15
a. Green ("POSTAGE HEALTH" and on leaves) omitted £110
MS832*b* Two sheets each 100 × 109 mm with Nos. 831/2 in blocks of 6 (3 × 2) .. *Per pair* 25·00 35·00

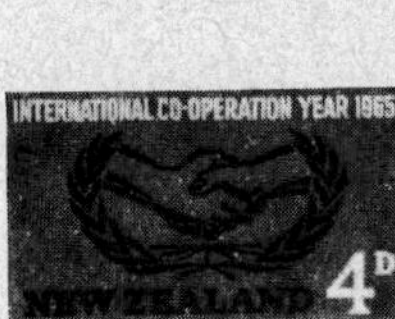

NEW ZEALAND CHRISTMAS 1965

254 I.C.Y. Emblem 255 "The Two Trinities" (Murillo)

(Litho D.L.R.)

1965 (28 Sept). *International Co-operation Year*. **W 98** (*sideways*). *P* 14.
833 **254** 4d. carmine-red and light yellow-olive 15 10

(Photo Harrison)

1965 (11 Oct). *Christmas*. **W 98**. *P* 13½ × 14.
834 **255** 3d. multicoloured 10 10
a. Gold (frame) omitted £600

256 Arms of New Zealand 259 "Progress" Arrowhead

(Des Display Section, G.P.O. Photo D.L.R.)

1965 (30 Nov). *11th Commonwealth Parliamentary Conference. T* **256** *and similar horiz designs. Multicoloured. P* 14.

835 4d. Type **256** 25 20
a. Blue (incl value) omitted £300
836 9d. Parliament House, Wellington and Badge 45 75
837 2s. Wellington from Mt Victoria 80 2·25
a. Carmine omitted £250
835/7 *Set of* 3 1·40 3·00

(Des Display Section, G.P.O. Photo Harrison)

1966 (5 Jan). *Fourth National Scout Jamboree, Trentham. W* **98**. *P* 14 × 15.

838 **259** 4d. gold and myrtle-green 10 10
a. Gold (arrowhead) omitted £450

260 New Zealand Bell Bird

262 "The Virgin with Child" (Maratta)

(Des Display Section, G.P.O. Photo Harrison)

1966 (3 Aug). *Health Stamps. T* **260** *and similar vert design. Multicoloured. W* **98** *(sideways). P* 14 × 14½.

839 3d. + 1d. Type **260** 15 20
840 4d. + 1d. Weka Rail 15 20
a. Deep brown (values and date) omitted £650
MS841 Two sheets each 107 × 91 mm. Nos. 839/40 in blocks of 6 (3 × 2) *Per pair* 16·00 28·00

In No. 840a besides the value, "1966" and "Weka" are also omitted and the bird, etc. appears as light brown.

(Photo Harrison)

1966 (3 Oct). *Christmas. W* **98** *(sideways). P* 14½.

842 **262** 3d. multicoloured 10 10
a. Red omitted £100

263 Queen Victoria and Queen Elizabeth II

264 Half-sovereign of 1867 and Commemorative Dollar Coin

(Des Display Section, G.P.O. Photo Harrison)

1967 (3 Feb). *Centenary of New Zealand Post Office Savings Bank. W* **98** *(sideways on 4d.). P* 14 × 14½.

843 **263** 4d. black, gold and maroon 10 10
844 **264** 9d. gold, silver, black, lt blue & dp grn 10 15

(New Currency. 100 cents = 1 dollar)

265 Manuka (Tea Tree)

266 Pohutu Geyser

1967 (10 July)–**70**. *Decimal Currency. Designs as* 1960–66 *issue, but with values inscr in decimal currency as T* **265/6**. *Chalky paper. W* **98** *(sideways on* 8 c., 10 c., 20 c., 50 c. *and* $2). *P* 13½ × 14 (½ c. *to* 3 c., 5 c. *and* 7 c.), 14½ × 14 (4 c., 6 c., 8 c., 10 c., 25 c., 30 c. *and* $1) *or* 14 × 14½ (15 c., 20 c., 50 c. *and* $2).

845 **265** ½ c. pale blue, yellow-green and cerise 10 10
846 – 1 c. yellow, carmine, green & lt brown (as 1d.) 10 10
a. Booklet pane. Five stamps plus one printed label 1·50
847 – 2 c. carmine, black, yellow and green (as 2d.) 10 10
848 – 2½ c. yellow, green, yellow-brown and deep bluish green (as 3d.) 10 10
a. Deep bluish green omitted* £400
b. Imperf (pair)† 50·00
849 – 3 c. purple, buff, yellow-green and light greenish blue (as 4d.) 10 10
850 – 4 c. yellow, deep green, black and violet (as 5d.) 30 10
851 – 5 c. lilac, yellow-olive and bluish green (as 6d.) 55 10
852 – 6 c. red, green, yellow and light pink (as 7d.) 70 10
853 – 7 c. rose-red, yellow, green and grey (as 8d.) 85 10
854 **214** 8 c. red and ultramarine 85 10
a. Red omitted £170
855 – 10 c. brown and deep green (as 1s.) 60 10
856 – 15 c. olive-green and orange-brown (as 1s. 6d.) 60 60
857 **219** 20 c. black and buff 2·00 10
858 **220** 25 c. yellow and light brown 6·00 90
859 **221***a* 30 c. olive-yellow, green & greenish blue 3·50 25
a. No wmk (1970) 3·50 3·75
860 – 50 c. blackish green (as 5s.) 4·00 75
861 – $1 Prussian blue (as 10s.) 14·00 1·25
862 **266** $2 deep magenta 8·50 10·00
845/62 *Set of* 18 35·00 13·00

*This occurred on one horizontal row of ten, affecting the background colour so that the value is also missing. In the row above and the row below, the colour was partially omitted. The price is for a vertical strip.

The 2½ c. value has been seen with the yellow omitted, but only on a used example.

†This comes from a sheet of which the six right-hand vertical rows were completely imperforate and the top, bottom and left-hand margins had been removed.

The 4 c., 30 c. and 50 c. exist with PVA gum as well as gum arabic. No. 859a exists with PVA gum only.

For $4 to $10 in the "Arms" type, see under Postal Fiscal stamps. See also Nos. 870, etc.

268 Running with Ball

(Des L. C. Mitchell. Photo Harrison)

1967 (2 Aug). *Health Stamps. Rugby Football. T* **268** *and similar multicoloured design. W* **98** *(sideways on* 2½ c.). *P* 14½ × 14 (2½ c.) *or* 14 × 14½ (3 c.).

867 2½ c. + 1 c. Type **268** 10 10
868 3 c. + 1 c. Positioning for a place-kick (*horiz*) 10 10
MS869 Two sheets; (*a*) 76 × 130 mm (867); (*b*) 130 × 76 mm (868). Containing blocks of six *Per pair* 18·00 22·00

270 *Kaita* (trawler) and Catch

271 Brown Trout

276 Dairy Farm, Mt Egmont and Butter Consignment

277 Fox Glacier, Westland National Park

(Des Display Section, G.P.O. (7, 8, 10, 18, 20, 25 c. and 28 c. from photo), R. M. Conly (7½ c.). Litho B.W. (7, 8, 18, 20 c.) or photo D.L.R. (7½ c.) and Harrison (10, 25, 28 c.). Others (15 c., $2) as before)

1967–69. *T* **270/1**, **276/7** *and similar designs. Chalky paper (except* 7, 8, 18, 20 c.). *No wmk* (7, 8, 20 c.) *or W* **98** *(sideways on* 7½, 10, 15, 25 c., *upright on* 18, 28 c., $2). *P* 13½ (7, 7½ c.), 13 × 13½ (8, 18, 20 c.), 14½ × 14 (10, 25 c.) *or* 14 × 14½ (15, 28 c., $2).

870 7 c. multicoloured (3.12.69) 75 75
871 7½ c. multicoloured* (29.8.67) 30 70
a. Wmk upright (10.68) 50 60
872 8 c. multicoloured (8.7.69) 75 70
873 10 c. multicoloured (2.4.68) 50 10
a. Green (background) omitted £200
874 15 c. apple-green, myrtle-green and carmine (as No. 856†) (19.3.68) 90 50
875 18 c. multicoloured (8.7.69) 1·40 55
876 20 c. multicoloured (8.7.69) 1·40 20
877 25 c. multicoloured (10.12.68) 6·00 2·00
878 28 c. multicoloured (30.7.68) 60 10
879 $2 black, ochre & pale blue (as No. 862) (10.12.68) 35·00 18·00
870/79 *Set of* 10 42·00 21·00

Designs: *Horiz*—8 c. Apples and orchard; 10 c. Forest and timber; 18 c. Sheep and the "Woolmark"; 20 c. Consignments of beef and herd of cattle.

*No. 871 was originally issued to commemorate the introduction of the brown trout into New Zealand.

† No. 874 is slightly larger than No. 856, measuring 21 × 25 mm and the inscriptions and numerals differ in size.

278 "The Adoration of the Shepherds" (Poussin)

279 Mount Aspiring, Aurora Australis and Southern Cross

280 Sir James Hector (founder)

(Photo Harrison)

1967 (3 Oct). *Christmas. W* **98** *(sideways). P* 13½ × 14.

880 **278** 2½ c. multicoloured 10 10

(Des J. Berry. Litho D.L.R.)

1967 (10 Oct). *Centenary of the Royal Society of New Zealand. W* **98** *(sideways on* 4 c.). *P* 14 (4 c) *or* 13 × 14 (8 c.).

881 **279** 4 c. multicoloured 15 20
882 **280** 8 c. multicoloured 15 25

281 Open Bible

282 Soldiers and Tank

(Des Display Section, G.P.O. Litho D.L.R.)

1968 (23 Apr). *Centenary of Maori Bible. W* **98**. *P* 13½.

883 **281** 3 c. multicoloured 10 10
a. Gold (inscr etc.) omitted £100

(Des L. C. Mitchell. Litho D.L.R.)

1968 (7 May). *New Zealand Armed Forces. T* **282** *and similar horiz designs. Multicoloured. W* **98** *(sideways). P* 14 × 13½.

884 4 c. Type **282** 30 15
885 10 c. Airmen, "Canberra" and "Kittyhawk" aircraft 50 25
886 28 c. Sailors and H.M.N.Z.S. *Achilles*, 1939, and H.M.N.Z.S. *Waikato*, 1968 70 1·40
884/6 *Set of* 3 1·40 1·60

285 Boy breasting Tape, and Olympic Rings

287 Placing Votes in Ballot Box

(Des L. C. Mitchell. Photo Harrison)

1968 (7 Aug). *Health Stamps. T* **285** *and similar horiz design. Multicoloured. P* 14½ × 14.

887 2½ c. + 1 c. Type **285** 10 10
888 3 c. + 1 c. Girl swimming and Olympic rings 10 10
a. Red (ring) omitted £750
MS889 Two sheets each 145 × 95 mm. Nos. 887/8 in blocks of six *Per pair* 13·00 20·00

No. 888a occurred in one miniature sheet. Six examples are known, one being used.

(Des J. Berry. Photo Japanese Govt Ptg Bureau, Tokyo)

1968 (19 Sept). *75th Anniv of Universal Suffrage in New Zealand. P* 13.

890 **287** 3 c. ochre, olive-green and light blue 10 10

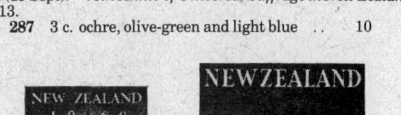

288 Human Rights Emblem

289 "The Nativity" (G. van Honthorst)

(Photo Japanese Govt Ptg Bureau, Tokyo)

1968 (19 Sept). *Human Rights Year. P* 13.

891 **288** 10 c. scarlet, yellow and deep green 10 25

(Photo Harrison)

1968 (1 Oct). *Christmas. W* **98** *(sideways). P* 14 × 14½.

892 **289** 2½ c. multicoloured 10 10

290 I.L.O. Emblem

(Photo Harrison)

1969 (11 Feb). *50th Anniv of International Labour Organization. W* **98** *(sideways). P* 14½ × 14.
893 **290** 7 c. black and carmine-red 15 30

291 Supreme Court Building, Auckland **292** Law Society's Coat of Arms

(Des R. M. Conly. Litho B.W.)

1969 (8 Apr). *Centenary of New Zealand Law Society. T* **291/2** *and similar design. P* 13½ × 13 (3 c.) *or* 13 × 13½ *(others).*
894 3 c. multicoloured *(shades)* 10 10
895 10 c. multicoloured 30 45
896 18 c. multicoloured *(shades)* 40 70
894/6 .. .. *Set of* 3 70 1·10
Design:—*Vert*—18 c. "Justice" (from Memorial Window in University of Canterbury, Christchurch).

295 Student being conferred with Degree

(Des R. M. Conly. Litho B.W.)

1969 (3 June). *Centenary of Otago University T* **295** *and similar multicoloured design. P* 13 × 13½ (3 c.) *or* 13½ × 13 (10 c.).
897 3 c. Otago University *(vert)* 10 10
898 10 c. Type **295** 20 25

296 Boys playing Cricket **298** Dr. Elizabeth Gunn (founder of First Children's Health Camp)

(Des R. M. Conly (4 c.); L. C. Mitchell (others). Litho B.W.)

1969 (6 Aug). *Health Stamps. T* **296** *and similar horiz design and T* **298**. *P* 12½ × 13 (*No.* 901) *or* 13 × 12½ *(others).*
899 2½ c. + 1 c. multicoloured 30 40
900 3 c. + 1 c. multicoloured 30 40
901 4 c. + 1 c. brown and ultramarine .. .. 30 1·00
899/901 .. .. *Set of* 3 80 1·60
MS902 Two sheets each 144 × 84 mm. Nos. 899/900 in blocks of six .. .. *Per pair* 20·00 35·00
Design:—3 c. Girls playing cricket.

299 Oldest existing House in New Zealand, and Old Stone Mission Store, Kerikeri

(Litho D.L.R.)

1969 (18 Aug). *Early European Settlement in New Zealand, and 150th Anniv of Kerikeri. T* **299** *and similar horiz design. Multicoloured. W* **98** *(sideways). P* 13 × 13½.
903 4 c. Type **299** 20 25
904 6 c. View of Bay of Islands .. .. .. 30 1·00

301 "The Nativity" (Federico Fiori (Barocci)) **302** Captain Cook, Transit of Venus and "Octant"

(Photo Harrison)

1969 (1 Oct). *Christmas. P* 13 × 14. A. *W* **98**. B. *No wmk.*

		A		B	
905 **301**	2½ c. multicoloured ..	10	10	10	10

(Des Eileen Mayo. Photo; portraits embossed Harrison)

1969 (9 Oct). *Bicentenary of Captain Cook's Landing in New Zealand. T* **302** *and similar horiz designs. P* 14½ × 14.
906 4 c. black, cerise and blue 75 35
907 6 c. slate-green, purple-brown & black .. 1·00 2·50
908 18 c. purple-brown, slate-green & black .. 2·50 2·50
909 28 c. cerise, black and blue .. .. .. 4·00 4·50
906/9 .. .. *Set of* 4 7·50 9·00
MS910 109 × 90 mm. Nos. 906/9 .. .. .. 18·00 30·00
Designs:—6 c. Sir Joseph Banks (naturalist) and outline of H.M.S. *Endeavour*; 18 c. Dr. Daniel Solander (botanist) and his plant; 28 c. Queen Elizabeth II and Cook's chart, 1769.
The miniature sheet exists additionally inscribed on the selvedge at bottom. "A SOUVENIR FROM NEW ZEALAND STAMP EXHIBITION, NEW PLYMOUTH 6TH–11TH OCTOBER. 1969" These were not sold from Post Offices.

306 Girl, Wheat Field and C.O.R.S.O. Emblem **307** Mother feeding her Child, Dairy Herd and C.O.R.S.O. Emblem

(Des L. C. Mitchell. Photo Japanese Govt Printing Bureau, Tokyo)

1969 (18 Nov). *25th Anniv of C.O.R.S.O. (Council of Organizations for Relief Services Overseas). P* 13.
911 **306** 7 c. multicoloured 20 75
912 **307** 8 c. multicoloured 20 75

308 "Cardigan Bay" (champion trotter)

(Des L. C. Mitchell. Photo Courvoisier)

1970 (28 Jan). *Return of "Cardigan Bay" to New Zealand. P* 11½.
913 **308** 10 c. multicoloured 20 25

309 Red Admiral Butterfly **310** Queen Elizabeth II and New Zealand Coat of Arms

(Des Enid Hunter (½ c., 1 c., 2 c., 18 c., 20 c.), Eileen Mayo (2½ c. to 7 c.), D. B. Stevenson (7½ c., 8 c.), M. Cleverley (10 c., 15 c., 25 c., 30 c., $1, $2), M. V. Askew (23 c., 50 c.). Photo Harrison (½ c. to 20 c.), Enschedé (23 c., 50 c.), Courvoisier ($1, $2) or Litho B.W. (25 c., 30 c.))

1970 (12 Mar)–**76**. *Various designs at T* **309/10**. *W* **98** *(sideways on* 10, 15 *and* 20 c.) *or No wmk* (23 c., to $2).

(a) Size as T **309**. *P* 13½ × 13
914 ½ c. multicoloured (2.9.70) 10 20
915 1 c. multicoloured (2.9.70) 10 10
a. Wmk sideways (booklets) (6.7.71) .. 60 80
b. Booklet pane. No. 915a × 3 with three *se-tenant* printed labels (6.7.71) .. .. 2·00
916 2 c. multicoloured (2.9.70) 10 10
a. Black (inscr, etc.) omitted .. .. 90·00
917 2½ c. multicoloured (2.9.70) 40 10
918 3 c. black, brown and orange (2.9.70) .. 15 10
a. Wmk sideways (booklets) (6.7.71) .. 40 60
919 4 c. multicoloured (2.9.70) 15 10
a. Wmk sideways (booklets) (6.7.71) .. 40 60
920 5 c. multicoloured (4.11.70) 45 10
921 6 c. blackish grn, yell-grn & carm (4.11.70) 45 20
922 7 c. multicoloured (4.11.70) 55 30
923 7½ c. multicoloured (4.11.70) .. .. .. 1·00 1·50
924 8 c. multicoloured (4.11.70) 65 30

(b) Size as T **310**. *Various Perfs*
925 10 c. multicoloured (*p* 14½×14) 40 15
926 15 c. black, flesh and pale brown (*p* 13½×13) (20.1.71) .. .. .. 1·50 40
927 18 c. chestnut, black and apple-green (*p* 13×13½) (20.1.71) .. .. .. 1·50 40
928 20 c. black & yell-brn (*p* 13½×13) (20.1.71) 1·50 15
929 23 c. multicoloured (*p* 13½×12½) (1.12.71) 80 15
930 25 c. multicoloured (*p* 13×13½) (1.9.71) .. 1·75 15
b. Perf 14 (11.76?) 70 40
931 30 c. multicoloured (*p* 13×13½) (1.9.71) .. 2·50 15
a. Perf 14 (9.76?) .. .. 2·50 2·25
932 50 c. multicoloured (*p* 13½×12½) (1.9.71) 80 20
a. Apple green (hill) omitted .. .. 25·00
b. Buff (shore) omitted .. .. .. 50·00
933 $1 multicoloured (*p* 11½) (14.4.71) .. 2·00 80
934 $2 multicoloured (*p* 11½) (14.4.71) .. 4·75 1·25
914/34 .. .. *Set of* 21 18·00 6·00
Designs: *Vert*—½ c. Glade Copper Butterfly; 1 c. Type **309**; 2 c. Tussock Butterfly; 2½ c. Magpie Moth; 3 c. Lichen Moth; 4 c. Puriri Moth; 5 c. Scarlet Parrot Fish; 6 c. Sea Horses; 7 c. Leather Jacket (fish); 7½ c. Garfish; 8 c. John Dory (fish); 18 c. Maori Club; 25 c. Hauraki Gulf Maritime Park; 30 c. Mt Cook National Park. *Horiz*—10 c. Type **310**; 15 c. Maori fish hook; 20 c. Maori tattoo pattern; 23 c. Egmont National Park; 50 c. Abel Tasman National Park; $1 Geothermal Power; $2 Agricultural Technology.
Although issued as a definitive, No. 925 was put on sale on the occasion of the Royal Visit to New Zealand.
See also Nos. 1008, etc.

311 Geyser Restaurant **312** U.N. H.Q. Building

(Des M. Cleverley. Photo Japanese Govt Printing Bureau, Tokyo)

1970 (8 Apr). *World Fair, Osaka. T* **311** *and similar horiz designs. Multicoloured. P* 13.
935 7 c. Type **311** 40 65
936 8 c. New Zealand Pavilion 40 65
937 18 c. Bush Walk 60 65
935/7 .. .. *Set of* 3 1·25 1·75

(Des R. M. Conly (3 c.), L. C. Mitchell (10 c.). Litho D.L.R.)

1970 (24 June). *25th Anniv of United Nations. T* **312** *and similar vert design. P* 13½.
938 3 c. multicoloured 10 10
939 10 c. scarlet and yellow 10 15
Design:—10 c. Tractor on horizon.

313 Soccer

(Des L. C. Mitchell. Litho D.L.R.)

1970 (5 Aug). *Health Stamps. T* **313** *and similar multicoloured design. P* 13½.
940 2½ c. + 1 c. Netball *(vert)* 10 15
941 3 c. + 1 c. Type **313** 10 15
MS942 Two sheets: *(a)* 102 × 125 mm (940); *(b)* 125 × 102 mm (941), containing blocks of six *Per pair* 15·00 22·00

314 "The Virgin adoring the Child" (Correggio) **315** "The Holy Family" (stained glass window, Invercargill Presbyterian Church)

(Litho D.L.R.)

1970 (1 Oct). *Christmas. T* **314/15** *and similar design. P* 12½.
943 2½ c. multicoloured 10 10
944 3 c. multicoloured 10 10
a. Green (inscr and value) omitted £150
945 10 c. black, orange and silver 30 70
943/5 .. .. *Set of* 3 35 70
Design: *Horiz*—10 c. Tower of Roman Catholic Church, Sockburn.

316 Chatham Islands Lily

(Des Eileen Mayo. Photo Japanese Govt Printing Bureau, Tokyo)

1970 (2 Dec). *Chatham Islands. T* **316** *and similar horiz design. Multicoloured. P* 13.
946 1 c. Type **316** 10 15
947 2 c. Shy Albatross 15 25

317 Country Women's Institute Emblem

(Des L. C. Mitchell. Photo Japanese Govt Ptg Bureau, Tokyo)

1971 (10 Feb). *50th Anniversaries of Country Women's Institutes and Rotary International in New Zealand. T* **317** *and similar horiz design. Multicoloured. P* 13.
948 4 c. Type **317** 10 10
949 10 c. Rotary emblem and map of New Zealand 10 20

318 *Rainbow II* (yacht)

(Des J. Berry (5 c.), G. F. Fuller (8 c.). Litho B.W.)

1971 (3 Mar). *One Ton Cup Racing Trophy. T* **318** *and similar horiz design. Multicoloured. P* 13½ × 13.
950 5 c. Type **318** 15 20
951 8 c. One Ton Cup 25 55

319 Civic Arms of Palmerston North

(Des R. M. Conly. Photo Japanese Govt Ptg Bureau, Tokyo)

1971 (12 May). *City Centenaries. T* **319** *and similar horiz designs. Multicoloured. P* 13.
952 3 c. Type **319** 10 10
953 4 c. Arms of Auckland 10 10
954 5 c. Arms of Invercargill 15 40
952/4 .. .. *Set of* 3 30 50

320 Antarctica on Globe **321** Child on Swing

(Des Eileen Mayo. Photo Japanese Govt Ptg Bureau, Tokyo)

1971 (9 June). *Tenth Anniv of Antarctic Treaty. P* 13.
955 **320** 6 c. multicoloured .. .. .. 1·50 1·50

(Des Eileen Mayo. Photo Japanese Govt Ptg Bureau, Tokyo)

1971 (9 June). *25th Anniv of U.N.I.C.E.F. P* 13.
956 **321** 7 c. multicoloured 50 70

(322) (322*a*) (322*b*)

T **322**. Photo, showing screening dots; thin bars, wide apart.
T **322***a*. Typo, without screening dots; thick bars, closer together.
T **322***b*. Typo; bars similar to T **322**.

1971–73. *No.* 917 *surcharged.*

(*a*) *In photogravure, by Harrison* (23.6.71*)
957 **322** 4 c. on 2½ c. multicoloured 15 10

(*b*) *Typographically, by Harrison* (13.7.72*)
957*a* **322***a* 4 c. on 2½ c. multicoloured 40 10
ab. Albino surch £110
ac. Surch double, one albino .. .. 15·00

(*c*) *Typographically, locally* (18.6.73*)
957*b* **322***b* 4 c. on 2½ c. multicoloured 15 10
*Earliest known postmarks.

323 Satellite-tracking Aerial

(Des M. Cleverley. Photo Courvoisier)

1971 (14 July). *Opening of Satellite Earth Station. T* **323** *and similar horiz design. P* 11½.
958 8 c. black, drab-grey and vermilion .. .. 60 1·00
959 10 c. black, turquoise-grn & pale bluish vio .. 65 1·00
Design:—10 c. Satellite.

324 Girls playing Hockey

(Des L. C. Mitchell. Litho Harrison)

1971 (4 Aug). *Health Stamps. T* **324** *and similar horiz designs. Multicoloured. W* **98** (*sideways on* 5 c.). *P* 13½ × 13.
960 3 c. + 1 c. Type **324** 20 20
961 4 c. + 1 c. Boys playing hockey 20 25
962 5 c. + 1 c. Dental Health .. .. .. 70 1·25
960/2 .. .. *Set of* 3 1·00 1·50
MS963 Two sheets each 122 × 96 mm. Nos. 960/1 in blocks of six .. .. .. *Per pair* 17·00 26·00

325 "Madonna bending over the Crib" (Maratta) **326** "Tiffany" Rose

(Des Enid Hunter (10 c.), D. A. Hatcher (others). Photo Harrison)

1971 (6 Oct). *Christmas. T* **325** *and similar vert designs. Multicoloured. P* 13 × 13½.
964 3 c. Type **325** 10 10
965 4 c. "The Annunciation" (stained-glass window) (21½ × 38 *mm*) 10 10
966 10 c. "The Three Kings" (21½ × 38 *mm*) .. 70 1·25
964/6 .. .. *Set of* 3 80 1·25

(Des A. G. Mitchell. Photo Courvoisier)

1971 (3 Nov). *First World Rose Convention, Hamilton. T* **326** *and similar vert designs showing roses. Multicoloured. P* 11½.
967 2 c. Type **326** 15 20
968 5 c. "Peace" 35 30
969 8 c. "Chrysler Imperial" .. .. .. 60 1·00
967/9 .. .. *Set of* 3 1·00 1·40

327 Lord Rutherford and Alpha Particles **328** Benz (1895)

(Des M. Cleverley. Litho B.W.)

1971 (1 Dec). *Birth Centenary of Lord Rutherford (scientist). T* **327** *and similar horiz design. Multicoloured. P* 13½ × 13.
970 1 c. Type **327** 25 35
971 7 c. Lord Rutherford and formula .. .. 85 1·25

(Des A. G. Mitchell. Litho B.W.)

1972 (2 Feb). *International Vintage Car Rally. T* **328** *and similar horiz designs. Multicoloured. P* 14.
972 3 c. Type **328** 20 10
973 4 c. Oldsmobile (1904) 25 10
974 5 c. Ford "Model T" (1914) 35 10
975 6 c. Cadillac Service car (1915) 55 45
976 8 c. Chrysler (1924) .. .. 1·25 1·00
977 10 c. Austin "7" (1923) .. .. 1·25 1·00
972/7 .. .. *Set of* 6 3·50 2·50

329 Coat of Arms of Wanganui **330** Black Scree Cotula

(Des M. Cleverley. Litho Harrison)

1972 (5 Apr). *Anniversaries. T* **329** *and similar designs. P* 13 × 13½ (3, 5 *and* 8 c.) *or* 13½ × 13 (*others*).
978 3 c. multicoloured 15 10
979 4 c. red-orange, brown-bistre and black .. 15 10
980 5 c. multicoloured 25 10
981 8 c. multicoloured .. .. 1·50 1·50
982 10 c. multicoloured .. .. 1·50 1·50
978/82 .. .. *Set of* 5 3·25 3·00
Designs and Events: *Vert*—3 c. Type **329** (Centenary of Wanganui Council govt); 5 c. De Havilland DH89 "Rapide" *Dominie* and Boeing "737" (25th Anniv National Airways Corp); 8 c. French frigate and Maori palisade (Bicent of landing by Marion du Fresne). *Horiz*—4 c. Postal Union symbol (Tenth Anniv of Asian-Oceanic Postal Union); 10 c. Stone cairn (150th Anniv of New Zealand Methodist Church).

(Des Eileen Mayo. Litho Harrison)

1972 (7 June). *Alpine Plants. T* **330** *and similar vert designs. Multicoloured. P* 13½.
983 4 c. Type **330** 30 10
984 6 c. North Island Eidelweiss 75 60
985 8 c. Haast's Buttercup .. .. 1·25 1·25
986 10 c. Brown Mountain Daisy .. .. .. 1·75 1·75
983/6 .. .. *Set of* 4 3·50 3·25

331 Boy playing Tennis **332** "Madonna with Child" (Murillo)

(Des L. C. Mitchell. Litho Harrison)

1972 (2 Aug). *Health Stamps. T* **331** *and similar vert design. P* 13 × 13½.
987 3 c. + 1 c. light grey and chestnut 20 25
988 4 c. + 1 c. light red-brown, grey and lemon 20 25
MS989 Two sheets each 107 × 123 mm. Nos. 987/8 in blocks of six .. .. .. *Per pair* 18·00 27·00
Design:—No. 988, Girl playing tennis.

(Des D. A. Hatcher. Photo Courvoisier)

1972 (4 Oct). *Christmas. T* **332** *and similar vert designs. Multicoloured. P* 11½.
990 3 c. Type **332** 10 10
991 5 c. "The Last Supper" (stained-glass window, St. John's Church, Levin) 15 10
992 10 c. Pohutukawa flower .. .. 55 1·00
990/2 .. .. *Set of* 3 70 1·00

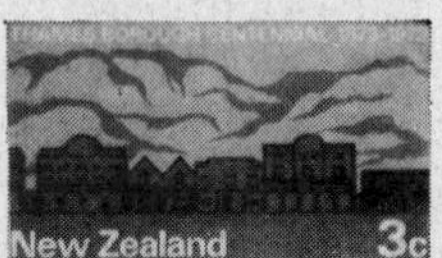

333 Lake Waikaremoana **334** Old Pollen Street

(Des D. A. Hatcher. Photo Courvoisier)

1972 (6 Dec). *Lake Scenes. T* **333** *and similar vert designs. Multicoloured. P* 11½.
993 6 c. Type **333** .. .. 1·00 1·25
994 8 c. Lake Hayes .. .. 1·10 1·25
995 18 c. Lake Wakatipu .. .. 2·00 2·25
996 23 c. Lake Rotomahana .. .. 2·25 2·75
993/6 .. .. *Set of* 4 5·75 6·75

(Des Miss V. Jepsen (3 c.), B. Langford (others). Litho Harrison)

1973 (7 Feb). *Commemorations. T* **334** *and similar horiz designs. Multicoloured* (*except* 8 c.). *P* 13½ × 13.
997 3 c. Type **334** 15 10
998 4 c. Coal-mining and pasture 15 10
999 5 c. Cloister 15 15
1000 6 c. Forest, birds and lake 50 70
1001 8 c. Rowers (light grey, indigo and gold) .. 45 1·00
1002 10 c. Graph and people .. .. 50 1·40
997/1002 .. .. *Set of* 6 1·75 3·00
Events:—3 c. Centennial of Thames Borough; 4 c. Centennial of Westport Borough; 5 c. Centennial of Canterbury University; 6 c. 50th Anniv of Royal Forest and Bird Protection Society; 8 c. Success of N.Z. Rowers in 1972 Olympics; 10 c. 25th Anniv of E.C.A.F.E.

335 Class "W" Locomotive **336** "Maori Woman and Child"

(Des R. M. Conly. Litho Harrison)

1973 (4 Apr). *New Zealand Steam Locomotives. T* **335** *and similar horiz designs. Multicoloured. P* 14 × 14½.

1003 3 c. Type **335** 45 10
1004 4 c. Class "X" 55 10
1005 5 c. Class "Ab" 60 10
1006 10 c. Class "Ja" .. .. 2·50 1·40
1003/6 .. .. *Set of* 4 3·50 1·50

1973–76. *As Nos.* 914 *etc., but no wmk.*

1008 1 c. multicoloured (7.9.73) 60 20
a. Booklet pane. No. 1008 × 3 with three *se-tenant* printed labels (8.74) .. 2·00
b. Red (wing markings) omitted .. £100
c. Blue (spots on wings) omitted .. 45·00
1009 2 c. multicoloured (6.73?) 25 10
1010 3 c. black, light brown and orange (1974) 1·50 40
1011 4 c. multicoloured (7.9.73) 50 10
a. Bright green (wing veins) inverted .. £275
b. Purple-brown omitted £170
c. Orange-yellow omitted £170
d. Greenish blue (background) omitted £140
e. Bright green (wing veins) omitted .. 6·00
f. Apple green (wings) omitted .. 90·00
1012 5 c. multicoloured (1973) .. .. 1·75 65
1013 6 c. blackish green, yellow-green and rose-carmine (7.9.73) 40 25
a. Yellow-grn (part of sea horse) omitted £160
1014 7 c. multicoloured (1974) .. .. 3·00 2·25
1015 8 c. multicoloured (1974) .. .. 3·75 1·50
a. Blue-green (background) omitted .. 80·00
1017 10 c. multicoloured, *p* 13½×13 (6.73?) .. 60 10
a. Silver (Arms) omitted £130
b. Imperf (vert pair) £180
c. Deep blue (Queen's head, face value, etc.) omitted £150
d. Red omitted .. .. 20·00
1018 15 c. black, flesh & pale brown, *p* 13½×13 (2.8.76) .. .. .. 1·25 10
1019 18 c. chestnut, black & apple-green (1974) 1·00 60
a. Black (inscr, etc.) omitted £160
1020 20 c. black and yellow-brown (1974) .. 80 10
1008/20 .. .. *Set of* 12 14·00 5·50

(Des and photo Courvoisier)

1973 (6 June). *Paintings by Frances Hodgkins. T* **336** *and similar vert designs. Multicoloured. P* 11½.

1027 5 c. Type **336** 40 15
1028 8 c. "Hilltop" 75 75
1029 10 c. "Barn in Picardy" .. .. .. 1·00 1·25
1030 18 c. "Self Portrait Still Life" .. .. 1·50 2·50
1027/30 .. .. *Set of* 4 3·25 2·50

337 Prince Edward

338 "Tempi Madonna" (Raphael)

(Des and litho Harrison)

1973 (1 Aug). *Health Stamps. P* 13 × 13½.

1031 **337** 3 c. + 1 c. dull yellowish green and reddish brown 25 25
1032 4 c. + 1 c. rose-red and blackish brown 25 25
MS1033 Two sheets each 96 × 121 mm with Nos. 1031/2 in blocks of 6 (3 × 2) .. *Per pair* 15·00 25·00

(Des A. G. Mitchell. Photo Enschedé)

1973 (3 Oct). *Christmas. T* **338** *and similar vert designs. Multicoloured. P* 12½ × 13½.

1034 3 c. Type **338** 10 10
1035 5 c. "Three Kings" (stained-glass window, St. Theresa's Church, Auckland) 10 10
1036 10 c. Family entering church 25 50
1034/6 .. .. *Set of* 3 40 50

339 Mitre Peak

340 Hurdling

(Des D. A. Hatcher. Photo Enschedé)

1973 (5 Dec). *Mountain Scenery. T* **339** *and similar multicoloured designs. P* 13 × 13½ (6, 8 c.) *or* 13½ × 13 (*others*).

1037 6 c. Type **339** 80 90
1038 8 c. Mt Ngauruhoe .. .. .. 1·00 1·50
1039 18 c. Mt Sefton (*horiz*) .. .. .. 1·75 3·00
1040 23 c. Burnett Range (*horiz*) .. .. 2·00 3·00
1037/40 .. .. *Set of* 4 5·00 7·50

(Des M. Cleverley. Litho Harrison)

1974 (9 Jan). *Tenth British Commonwealth Games, Christchurch. T* **340** *and similar vert designs.* 5 c. *black and violet-blue, others multicoloured. P* 13 × 14.

1041 4 c. Type **340** 10 10
1042 5 c. Ball-player 15 10
1043 10 c. Cycling 20 15
1044 18 c. Rifle-shooting 35 65
1045 23 c. Bowls 50 85
1041/5 .. .. *Set of* 5 1·10 1·60

No. 1042 does not show the Games emblem, and commemorates the Fourth Paraplegic Games, held at Dunedin.

341 Queen Elizabeth II

342 "Spirit of Napier" Fountain

(Des D. A. Hatcher and A. G. Mitchell. Litho Harrison)

1974 (5 Feb). *New Zealand Day. Sheet* 131 × 74 mm. *containing T* **341** *and similar horiz designs, size* 37 × 20 *mm. Multicoloured. P* 13.

MS1046 4 c. × 5 Treaty House, Waitangi; Signing Waitangi Treaty; Type **341**; Parliament Buildings Extensions; Children in Class .. .. .. 60 1·75

(Des Miss V. Jepsen. Photo Courvoisier)

1974 (3 Apr). *Centenaries of Napier and U.P.U. T* **342** *and similar vert designs. Multicoloured. P* 11½.

1047 4 c. Type **342** 10 10
1048 5 c. Clock Tower, Berne 10 15
1049 8 c. U.P.U. Monument, Berne 35 90
1047/9 .. .. *Set of* 3 50 1·00

343 Boeing Seaplane, 1919

344 Children, Cat and Dog

(Des R. M. Conly. Litho Harrison)

1974 (5 June). *History of New Zealand Airmail Transport. T* **343** *and similar horiz designs. Multicoloured. P* 14 × 13.

1050 3 c. Type **343** 25 10
1051 4 c. Lockheed "Electra", 1937 .. .. 30 10
1052 5 c. Bristol Freighter, 1958 .. .. 35 10
1053 23 c. Empire "S 30" flying-boat, 1940 .. 1·50 1·50
1050/3 .. .. *Set of* 4 2·25 1·60

(Des B. Langford. Litho Harrison)

1974 (7 Aug). *Health Stamps. P* 13 × 13½.

1054 **344** 3 c. + 1 c. multicoloured 15 25
1055 – 4 c. + 1 c. multicoloured 20 25
1056 – 5 c. + 1 c. multicoloured .. .. 90 1·10
1054/6 .. .. *Set of* 3 1·10 1·40
MS1057 145 × 123 mm. No. 1055 in block of ten 18·00 27·00

Nos. 1055/6 are as T **344**, showing children and pets.

345 "The Adoration of the Magi" (Konrad Witz)

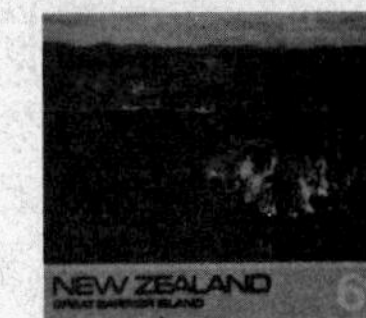

346 Great Barrier Island

(Des Eileen Mayo. Photo Courvoisier)

1974 (2 Oct). *Christmas. T* **345** *and similar horiz designs. Multicoloured. P* 11½.

1058 3 c. Type **345** 10 10
1059 5 c. "The Angel Window" (stained-glass window, Old St. Pauls Church, Wellington) 10 10
1060 10 c. Madonna Lily 30 50
1058/60 .. .. *Set of* 3 40 55

(Des D. A. Hatcher. Photo Enschedé)

1974 (4 Dec). *Off-shore Islands. T* **346** *and similar horiz designs. Multicoloured. P* 13½ × 13.

1061 6 c. Type **346** 30 40
1062 8 c. Stewart Island 40 80
1063 18 c. White Island .. .. .. 70 1·50
1064 23 c. The Brothers .. .. .. 1·00 2·00
1061/4 .. .. *Set of* 4 2·25 4·25

347 Crippled Child

(Des Miss V. Jepsen (3 c., 5 c.), A. G. Mitchell (10 c., 18 c.). Litho Harrison)

1975 (5 Feb). *Anniversaries and Events. T* **347** *and similar horiz designs. Multicoloured. P* 13½.

1065 3 c. Type **347** 10 10
1066 5 c. Farming family 15 10
1067 10 c. I.W.Y. symbols 20 55
1068 18 c. Medical School Building, Otago University 35 80
1065/8 .. .. *Set of* 4 70 1·40

Commemorations:—3 c. 40th Anniv of N.Z. Crippled Children Society; 5 c. 50th Anniv of Women's Division, Federated Farmers of N.Z.; 10 c. International Women's Year; 18 c. Centenary of Otago Medical School.

348 Scow *Lake Erie*

(Des R. M. Conly. Litho Harrison)

1975 (2 Apr). *Historic Sailing Ships. T* **348** *and similar horiz designs. P* 13½ × 13.

1069 4 c. black and red 20 10
1070 5 c. black and turquoise-blue 30 10
1071 8 c. black and yellow 40 35
1072 10 c. black and olive-yellow 40 40
1073 18 c. black and light brown 65 90
1074 23 c. black and slate-lilac .. .. 80 1·25
1069/74 .. .. *Set of* 6 2·50 2·75

Ships:—5 c. Schooner *Herald*; 8 c. Brigantine *New Zealander*; 10 c. Topsail schooner *Jessie Kelly*; 18 c. Barque *Tory*; 23 c. Full-rigged clipper *Rangitiki*.

349 Lake Summer Forest Park

(Des and photo Enschedé)

1975 (4 June). *Forest Park Scenes. T* **349** *and similar horiz designs. Multicoloured. P* 13.

1075 6 c. Type **349** 50 70
1076 8 c. North-west Nelson .. .. .. 60 1·00
1077 18 c. Kaweka .. .. 1·25 1·75
1078 23 c. Coromandel .. .. .. 1·50 2·00
1075/8 .. .. *Set of* 4 3·50 5·00

350 Girl feeding Lamb

351 "Virgin and Child" (Zanobi Machiavelli)

(Des Margaret Chapman. Litho Harrison)

1975 (6 Aug). *Health Stamps. T* **350** *and similar horiz designs. Multicoloured. P* 13½ × 13.

1079 3 c. + 1 c. Type **350** 15 15
1080 4 c. + 1 c. Boy with hen and chicks 15 15
1081 5 c. + 1 c. Boy with duck and duckling .. 50 95
1079/81 .. .. *Set of* 3 70 1·10
MS1082 123 × 146 mm. No. 1080 × 10 .. .. 14·00 20·00

(Des Enid Hunter. Photo Harrison)

1975 (1 Oct). *Christmas. T* **351** *and similar horiz designs. Multicoloured. P* 13 × 13½ (3 c.) *or* 13½ × 13 (*others*).

1083 3 c. Type **351** 10 10
a. Red omitted* .. ..
1084 5 c. "Cross in Landscape" (stained-glass window, Greendale Church) 15 10
a. Brown (face value) omitted £160
1085 10 c. "I saw three ships . . ." (carol) .. 35 65
1083/5 .. .. *Set of* 3 60 65

*This occurred in the last two vertical rows of the sheet with the red partially omitted on the previous row.

Used copies of No. 1083 have been seen with the orange ("Christmas 1975") omitted.

352 "Sterling Silver"

353 Queen Elizabeth II (photograph by W. Harrison)

353a Maripi (knife)

353b Paua

353c "Beehive" (section of Parliamentary Buildings, Wellington)

(Des A. G. Mitchell (1 to 14 c.), I. Hulse (20 c. to $2), R. Conly ($5). Photo Harrison (1 to 10 c.), Courvoisier (11 to 14 c.), Heraclio Fournier (20 c. to $5))

1975 (26 Nov)–**81**. *(a) Vert designs as T* **352** *showing garden roses. Multicoloured. P* 14½ (6 *to* 8 c.) *or* 14½ × 14 (*others*).

No.	Description	Unused	Used
1086	1 c. Type **352**	10	10
1087	2 c. "Lilli Marlene"	10	10
1088	3 c. "Queen Elizabeth"	50	10
	a. Perf 14½ (6.79)	40	10
1089	4 c. "Super Star"	10	10
1090	5 c. "Diamond Jubilee"	10	10
1091	6 c. "Cresset"	90	75
	a. Perf 14½ × 14 (8.76?)	10	10
1092	7 c. "Michele Meilland"	1·75	50
	a. Perf 14½ × 14 (6.76?)	30	10
1093	8 c. "Josephine Bruce"	1·75	75
	a. Perf 14½ × 14 (8.76?)	45	10
1094	9 c. "Iceberg"	15	15
	(b) Type **353**. *P* 14½ × 14 (7.12.77)		
1094*a*	10 c. multicoloured	85	20
	ab. Perf 14½ (2.79)	25	10
	(c) Vert designs as T **353a** *showing Maori artefacts. P* 11½ (24.11.76)		
1095	11 c. reddish brown, lemon & blackish brown	40	15
1096	12 c. reddish brown, lemon & blackish brown	30	10
1097	13 c. reddish brown, greenish blue and blackish brown	50	25
1098	14 c. reddish brown, lemon & blackish brown	30	15

Designs:—12 c. Putorino (flute); 13 c. Wahaika (club); 14 c. Kotiate (club).

No.	Description	Unused	Used
	(d) Horiz designs as T **353b** *showing seashells. Multicoloured. P* 13		
1099	20 c. Type **353***b* (29.11.78)	15	20
1100	30 c. Toheroa (29.11.78)	25	30
1101	40 c. Coarse Dosinia (29.11.78)	30	35
1102	50 c. Spiny Murex (29.11.78)	40	45
1103	$1 Scallop (26.11.79)	70	85
	a. Imperf between (vert pair)	£400	
1104	$2 Circular Saw (26.11.79)	1·00	1·75
	(e) Type **353c**. *P* 13 (2.12.81)		
1105	$5 multicoloured	3·00	2·00
	a. Imperf (vert pair)		
1086/105	*Set of* 21	8·00	6·00

Faked "missing colour errors" exist of No. 1094*a*, involving parts of the portrait.

A used example of No. 1099 exists with the black colour omitted so that the body of the shell appears in blue instead of green.

No. 1103a occurs on the top two rows of the sheet; the lower stamp being imperforate on three edges except for two perforation holes at the foot of each vertical side.

354 Family and League of Mothers Badge

(Des A. P. Derrick. Litho J.W.)

1976 (4 Feb). *Anniversaries and Metrication. T* **354** *and similar horiz designs. Multicoloured. P* 13½ × 14.

No.	Description	Unused	Used
1110	6 c. Type **354**	10	10
1111	7 c. Weight, temperature, linear measure and capacity	10	10
1112	8 c. *William Bryan* (immigrant ship), mountain and New Plymouth	15	10
1113	10 c. Two women shaking hands and Y.W.C.A. badge	15	40
1114	25 c. Map of the world showing cable links	30	1·25
1110/14	*Set of* 5	70	1·60

Anniversaries:—6 c. League of Mothers, 50th Anniv; 7 c. Metrication; 8 c. Centenary of New Plymouth; 10 c. 50th Anniv of New Zealand Y.W.C.A.; 25 c. Centenary of link with International Telecommunications Network.

355 Gig

356 Purakaunui Falls

(Des G. F. Fuller. Litho Harrison)

1976 (7 Apr). *Vintage Farm Transport. T* **355** *and similar horiz designs. Multicoloured. P* 13½ × 13.

No.	Description	Unused	Used
1115	6 c. Type **355**	15	20
1116	7 c. Thorneycroft lorry	20	10
1117	8 c. Scandi wagon	50	20
1118	9 c. Traction engine	30	40
1119	10 c. Wool wagon	30	75
1120	25 c. Cart	80	1·75
1115/20	*Set of* 6	2·00	2·75

(Des and photo Courvoisier)

1976 (2 June). *Waterfalls. T* **356** *and similar vert designs. Multicoloured. P* 11½.

No.	Description	Unused	Used
1121	10 c. Type **356**	40	10
1122	14 c. Marakopa Falls	75	55
1123	15 c. Bridal Veil Falls	80	60
1124	16 c. Papakorito Falls	90	70
1121/4	*Set of* 4	2·50	1·75

357 Boy and Pony

358 "Nativity" (Spanish carving)

(Des Margaret Chapman. Litho Harrison)

1976 (4 Aug). *Health Stamps. T* **357** *and similar vert designs. Multicoloured. P* 13 × 13½.

No.	Description	Unused	Used
1125	7 c. + 1 c. Type **357**	15	25
1126	8 c. + 1 c. Girl and calf	15	25
1127	10 c. + 1 c. Girls and bird	40	60
1125/7	*Set of* 3	65	1·00
MS1128	96 × 121 mm. Nos. 1125/7 × 2	6·00	9·00

(Des Margaret Chapman (18 c.), D. A. Hatcher (others). Photo Harrison)

1976 (6 Oct). *Christmas. T* **358** *and similar horiz designs. Multicoloured. P* 14 × 14½ (7 c.) *or* 14½ × 14 (*others*).

No.	Description	Unused	Used
1129	7 c. Type **358**	15	10
1130	11 c. "Resurrection" (stained-glass window, St. Joseph's Catholic Church, Grey Lynn)	25	30
1131	18 c. Angels	40	60
1129/31	*Set of* 3	70	85

359 Arms of Hamilton

360 Queen Elizabeth II

(Des P. L. Blackie. Litho Harrison)

1977 (19 Jan). *Anniversaries. T* **359** *and similar vert designs. Multicoloured. P* 13 × 13½.

No.	Description	Unused	Used
1132	8 c. Type **359**	15	10
	a. Horiz strip of 3, Nos. 1132/4	45	
1133	8 c. Arms of Gisborne	15	10
1134	8 c. Arms of Masterton	15	10
1135	10 c. A.A. emblem	15	20
	a. Horiz pair. Nos. 1135/6	30	90
1136	10 c. Arms of the College of Surgeons	15	20
1132/6	*Set of* 5	75	60

Events:—Nos. 1132/4, City Centenaries; No. 1135, 75th Anniv of the Automobile Association in New Zealand; No. 1136, 50th Anniv of Royal Australasian College of Surgeons.

Designs of each value were printed in the same sheet horizontally *se-tenant*.

(Des and photo Harrison from photographs by Warren Harrison)

1977 (23 Feb). *Silver Jubilee. Sheet* 178 × 82 *mm containing T* **360** *and similar vert designs showing different portraits. P* 14 × 14½.

No.	Description	Unused	Used
MS1137	8 c. × 5 multicoloured	70	1·50
	a. Imperf	£1400	
	ab. Ditto, and silver omitted	£2000	
	b. Silver omitted	£550	
	c. Indian red omitted	£250	

361 Physical Education and Maori Culture

(362)

(Des A. G. Mitchell. Litho Harrison)

1977 (6 Apr). *Education. T* **361** *and similar vert designs. Multicoloured. P* 13 × 13½.

No.	Description	Unused	Used
1138	8 c. Type **361**	30	50
	a. Horiz strip of 5, Nos. 1138/42	1·40	
1139	8 c. Geography, science and woodwork	30	50
1140	8 c. Teaching the deaf, kindergarten and woodwork	30	50
1141	8 c. Tertiary and language classes	30	50
1142	8 c. Home science, correspondence school and teacher training	30	50
1138/42	*Set of* 5	1·40	2·00

Nos. 1138/42 were printed horizontally *se-tenant* throughout the sheet.

1977 (Apr). *Coil Stamps. Nos.* 1010/11 *surch as T* **362** *by Govt Printer, Wellington.*

No.	Description	Unused	Used
1143	7 c. on 3 c. Lichen Moth (19.4)	20	40
1144	8 c. on 4 c. Puriri Moth (21.4)	20	40
	a. Bright green (wing veins) omitted	85·00	

Forged "7 c." surcharges, similar to No. 1143, but in smaller type, are known applied to Nos. 918 and 1010.

363 Karitane Beach

364 Girl with Pigeon

(Des D. A. Hatcher. Photo Heraclio Fournier)

1977 (1 June). *Seascapes. T* **363** *and similar horiz designs. Multicoloured. P* 14½.

No.	Description	Unused	Used
1145	10 c. Type **363**	20	10
1146	16 c. Ocean Beach, Mount Maunganui	35	35
1147	18 c. Piha Beach	40	40
1148	30 c. Kaikoura Coast	50	50
1145/8	*Set of* 4	1·25	1·25

(Des A. P. Derrick. Litho Harrison)

1977 (3 Aug). *Health Stamps. T* **364** *and similar vert designs. Multicoloured. P* 13 × 13½.

No.	Description	Unused	Used
1149	7 c. + 2 c. Type **364**	15	20
1150	8 c. + 2 c. Boy with frog	20	25
1151	10 c. + 2 c. Girl with butterfly	35	50
1149/51	*Set of* 3	65	85
MS1152	97 × 120 mm. Nos. 1149/51 × 2	5·50	10·00

Stamps from the miniature sheet are without white border and together form a composite design.

365 "The Holy Family" (Correggio)

(Des Margaret Chapman (23 c.), graphics for all values produced by printer. Photo Courvoisier)

1977 (5 Oct). *Christmas. T* **365** *and similar vert designs. Multicoloured. P* 11½.

No.	Description	Unused	Used
1153	7 c. Type **365**	15	10
1154	16 c. "Madonna and Child" (stained-glass window, St. Michael's and All Angels, Dunedin)	25	20
1155	23 c. "Partridge in a Pear Tree"	40	45
1153/5	*Set of* 3	70	65

366 Merryweather Manual Pump, 1860

367 Town Clock and Coat of Arms, Ashburton

(Des R. M. Conly. Litho Harrison)

1977 (7 Dec). *Fire Fighting Appliances. T* **366** *and similar horiz designs. Multicoloured. P* 14 × 13.

No.	Description	Unused	Used
1156	10 c. Type **366**	15	10
1157	11 c. 2-wheel hose, reel and ladder, 1880	15	10
1158	12 c. Shand Mason steam fire engine, 1873	20	15
1159	23 c. Chemical fire engine, 1888	30	30
1156/9	*Set of* 4	70	60

(Des P. L. Blackie (No. 1162), Harrison (No. 1163), P. J. Durrant (others), Litho Harrison)

1978 (8 Mar). *Centenaries. T* **367** *and similar multicoloured designs. P* 14.

1160 10 c. Type **367** 15 10
a. Horiz pair. Nos. 1160/1 .. .. .. 30 50
1161 10 c. Stratford and Mt Egmont 15 10
1162 12 c. Early telephone 15 15
1163 20 c. Bay of Islands (*horiz*) 20 30
1160/3 .. .. *Set of* 4 60 85

Centenaries commemorated are those of the towns of Ashburton and Stratford, of the telephone in New Zealand, and of the Bay of Islands County.

The 10 c. values were printed together, *se-tenant*, in horizontal pairs throughout the sheet.

368 Students and Ivey Hall, Lincoln College

369

370 Maui Gas Drilling Platform

(Des A. P. Derrick. Litho Harrison)

1978 (26 Apr). *Land Resources and Centenary of Lincoln College of Agriculture. T* **368** *and similar vert designs. Multicoloured. P* 14½.

1164 10 c. Type **368** 15 10
1165 12 c. Sheep grazing 20 25
1166 15 c. Fertiliser ground spreading 20 30
1167 16 c. Agricultural Field Days 20 30
1168 20 c. Harvesting grain 25 40
1169 30 c. Dairy farming 40 70
1164/9 .. .. *Set of* 6 1·25 1·90

(Photo Harrison)

1978 (3 May–9 June). *Coil Stamps. P* 14½ × 14 (10 *c.*) *or* 14 × 13 (*others*).

1170 **369** 1 c. bright purple (9.6) 10 20
1171 2 c. bright orange (9.6) 10 20
1172 5 c. red-brown (9.6) 10 20
1173 10 c. bright blue 10 20
1170/3 .. .. *Set of* 4 20 70

(Des R. M. Conly. Litho Harrison)

1978 (7 June). *Resources of the Sea. T* **370** *and similar vert designs. Multicoloured. P* 13 × 14.

1174 12 c. Type **370** 20 15
1175 15 c. Trawler 30 25
1176 20 c. Map of 200 mile fishing limit 40 35
1177 23 c. Humpback Whale and Bottle-nosed Dolphins 50 40
1178 35 c. Kingfish, snapper, grouper and squid .. 75 75
1174/8 .. .. *Set of* 5 1·90 1·75

371 First Health Charity Stamp

372 "The Holy Family" (El Greco)

373 Sir Julius Vogel

(Des A. G. Mitchell. Litho Harrison)

1978 (2 Aug). *Health Stamps. Health Services Commemorations. T* **371** *and similar vert design. P* 13 × 14.

1179 10 c. + 2 c. black, red and gold 25 25
1180 12 c. + 2 c. multicoloured 25 30
MS1181 97 × 124 mm. Nos. 1179/80 × 3 .. .. 3·50 4·75

Designs and commemorations:—10 c. Type **371** (50th anniversary of health charity stamps); 12 c. Heart operation (National Heart Foundation).

(Des R. M. Conly. Photo Courvoisier)

1978 (4 Oct). *Christmas. T* **372** *and similar multicoloured designs. P* 11½.

1182 7 c. Type **372** 10 10
1183 16 c. All Saints' Church, Howick 25 30
1184 23 c. Beach scene 30 45
1182/4 .. .. *Set of* 3 60 70

(Des A. G. Mitchell. Litho J.W.)

1979 (7 Feb). *Statesmen. T* **373** *and similar vert designs in sepia and drab. P* 13 × 13½.

1185 10 c. Type **373** 30 40
a. Horiz strip of 3, Nos. 1185/7 90
1186 10 c. Sir George Grey 30 40
1187 10 c. Richard John Seddon 30 40
1185/7 .. .. *Set of* 3 90 1·10

Nos. 1185/7 were printed together, *se-tenant*, in horizontal strips of 3 throughout the sheet.

Nos. 1185/7 have matt, almost invisible gum.

374 Riverlands Cottage, Blenheim

375 Whangaroa Harbour

(Des P. Leitch. Litho Enschedé)

1979 (4 Apr). *Architecture* (1*st series*). *T* **374** *and similar horiz designs. P* 13½ × 13.

1188 10 c. black, new blue and deep blue 10 10
1189 12 c. black, pale green and bottle green .. 15 20
1190 15 c. black and grey 20 25
1191 20 c. black, yellow-brown and sepia 25 30
1188/91 .. .. *Set of* 4 65 80

Designs:—12 c. The Mission House, Waimate North; 15 c. "The Elms", Tauranga; 20 c. Provincial Council Buildings, Christchurch.

See also Nos. 1217/20 and 1262/5.

(Photo Heraclio Fournier)

1979 (6 June). *Small Harbours. T* **375** *and similar multicoloured designs. P* 13.

1192 15 c. Type **375** 20 10
1193 20 c. Kawau Island 25 30
1194 23 c. Akaroa Harbour (*vert*) 30 35
1195 35 c. Picton Harbour (*vert*) 45 50
1192/5 .. .. *Set of* 4 1·10 1·10

376 Children with Building Bricks

(Des W. Kelsall. Litho J.W.)

1979 (6 June). *International Year of the Child. P* 14.

1196 **376** 10 c. multicoloured 15 10

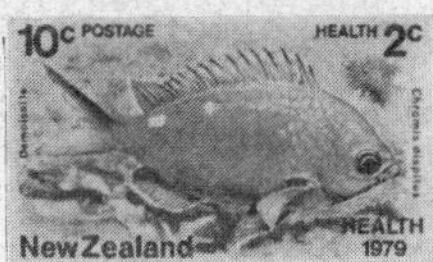

377 Demoiselle

4c

(378)

(Des P. Blackie (12 c.), G. Fuller (others). Litho Harrison)

1979 (25 July). *Health Stamps. Marine Life. T* **377** *and similar multicoloured designs. P* 13 × 13½ (12 *c.*) *or* 13½ × 13 (*others*).

1197 10 c. + 2 c. Type **377** 25 30
a. Horiz pair. Nos. 1197/8 .. .. 50 60
1198 10 c. + 2 c. Sea Urchin 25 30
1199 12 c. + 2 c. Fish and underwater cameraman (*vert*) 25 30
1197/9 .. .. *Set of* 3 70 80
MS1200 144 × 72 mm. Nos. 1197/9, each × 2. P 14 × 14½ (12 c.) or 14½ × 14 (others) .. .. 4·00 5·50

Nos. 1197/8 were printed together, *se-tenant*, in horizontal pairs throughout the sheet.

1979 (31 Aug)–**80**. *Nos.* 1091a, 1092a, 1093a *and* 1094ab *surch as T* **378** *by Govt Printer, Wellington.*

1201 4 c. on 8 c. "Josephine Bruce" (24.9.79) .. 10 10
1202 14 c. on 10 c. Type **353** 35 20
a. Surch double, one albino .. ..
1203 17 c. on 6 c. "Cresset" (9.10.79) 35 50
1203*a* 20 c. on 7 c. "Michele Meilland" (29.9.80) .. 20 10
1201/3*a* .. .. *Set of* 4 85 75

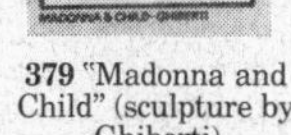

379 "Madonna and Child" (sculpture by Ghiberti)

380 Chamber, House of Representatives

(Des D. Hatcher. Photo Courvoisier)

1979 (3 Oct). *Christmas. T* **379** *and similar vert designs. Multicoloured. P* 11½.

1204 10 c. Type **379** 15 10
1205 25 c. Christ Church, Russell 30 40
1206 35 c. Pohutukawa (tree) 40 55
1204/6 .. .. *Set of* 3 75 90

(Des D. Hatcher. Litho J.W.)

1979 (26 Nov). *25th Commonwealth Parliamentary Conference, Wellington. T* **380** *and similar vert designs. Multicoloured. P* 13½.

1207 14 c. Type **380** 15 10
1208 20 c. Mace and Black Rod 20 20
1209 30 c. Wall hanging from the "Beehive" .. 30 45
1207/9 .. .. *Set of* 3 60 60

381 1855 1d. Stamp

(Des D. Hatcher (14 c. (all designs)), R. Conly (others). Litho Harrison)

1980 (17 Feb). *Anniversaries and Events. T* **381** *and similar designs. P* 13½ × 13 (14 *c.* (*all designs*)) *or* 14 (*others*).

1210 14 c. black, brown-red and yellow 20 20
a. Horiz strip of 3. Nos. 1210/12 60
ab. Black (inscription) omitted (*strip of* 3) .. 90·00
1211 14 c. black, deep turquoise-blue and yellow .. 20 20
1212 14 c. black, dull yellowish green and yellow .. 20 20
1213 17 c. multicoloured 20 25
1214 25 c. multicoloured 25 30
1215 30 c. multicoloured 25 35
1210/15 .. .. *Set of* 6 1·10 1·40
MS1216 146 × 96 mm. Nos. 1210/12. P 14½ × 14 (*sold at* 52 *c.*) .. .. 2·75 4·50

Designs and commemorations; (38 × 22 *mm*)—No. 1210, Type **381**; No. 1211, 1855 2d. stamp; No. 1212, 1855 1s. stamp (125th anniversary of New Zealand stamps). (40 × 23 *mm*)—No. 1213, Geyser, wood-carving and building (centenary of Rotorua (town)); No. 1214, *Earina autumnalis* and *thelymitra venosa* (International Orchid Conference, Auckland); No. 1215; Ploughing and Golden Plough Trophy (World Ploughing Championships, Christchurch).

The premium on No. **MS**1216 was used to help finance the "Zeapex 80" International Stamp Exhibition, Auckland.

Nos. 1210/12 were printed together, *se-tenant*, in horizontal strips of 3 throughout the sheet.

382 Ewelme Cottage, Parnell

383 Auckland Harbour

(Des P. Leitch. Litho Enschedé)

1980 (2 Apr). *Architecture* (2*nd series*). *T* **382** *and similar horiz designs. Multicoloured. P* 13½ × 12½.

1217 14 c. Type **382** 15 10
1218 17 c. Broadgreen, Nelson 25 30
1219 25 c. Courthouse, Oamaru 30 40
1220 30 c. Government Buildings, Wellington .. 35 45
1217/20 .. .. *Set of* 4 95 1·10

(Des D. Hatcher. Photo Heraclio Fournier)

1980 (4 June). *Large Harbours. T* **383** *and similar horiz designs. Multicoloured. P* 13.

1221 25 c. Type **383** 30 25
1222 30 c. Wellington Harbour 35 30
1223 35 c. Lyttelton Harbour 40 40
1224 50 c. Port Chalmers 65 65
1221/4 .. .. *Set of* 4 1·50 1·40

384 Surf-fishing

385 "Madonna and Child with Cherubim" (sculpture by Andrea della Robbia)

(Des Margaret Chapman. Litho Enschedé)

1980 (6 Aug). *Health Stamps. Fishing. T* **384** *and similar horiz designs. Multicoloured. P* 13 × 12½.

1225 14 c. + 2 c. Type **384** 25 30
a. Horiz pair. Nos. 1225/6 .. .. 50 60
1226 14 c. + 2 c. Wharf-fishing 25 30
1227 17 c. + 2 c. Spear-fishing 25 30
1225/7 .. .. *Set of* 3 70 80
MS1228 148 × 75 mm. Nos. 1225/7 each × 2. P 13½ × 13 .. .. 2·25 3·50

Nos. 1225/6 were printed together, *se-tenant*, in horizontal pairs throughout the sheet.

(Des P. Durrant. Photo Courvoisier)

1980 (1 Oct). *Christmas. T* **385** *and similar vert designs. Multicoloured. P* 11½.

1229 10 c. Type **385** 15 10
1230 25 c. St. Mary's Church, New Plymouth .. 25 25
1231 35 c. Picnic scene 40 45
1229/31 .. .. *Set of* 3 70 70

386 Te Heu Heu (chief)

387 Lt.-Col. the Hon W. H. A. Feilding and Borough of Feilding Crest

(Des R. Conly. Litho Heraclio Fournier)

1980 (26 Nov). *Maori Personalities. Vert designs as T* **386**. *Multi-coloured. P* 12½ × 13.

1232 15 c. Type **386** 10 10
1233 25 c. Te Hau (chief) 15 10
1234 35 c. Te Puea (princess) 20 10
1235 45 c. Ngata (politician) 30 15
1236 60 c. Te Ata-O-Tu (warrior) 35 20
1232/6 .. .. *Set of* 5 1·00 50

(Des R. Conly. Litho Harrison)

1981 (4 Feb). *Commemorations. T* **387** *and similar horiz design. P* 14½.

1237 20 c. multicoloured 20 20
1238 25 c. black and brown-ochre 25 25

Designs and Commemorations:—20 c. Type **387** (Centenary of Feilding (town)); 25 c. I.Y.D. emblem and cupped hands (International Year of the Disabled).

388 The Family at Play

389 Kaiauai River

(Des A. Derrick. Litho J.W.)

1981 (1 Apr). *"Family Life." T* **388** *and similar vert designs. Multicoloured. P* 13½ × 13.

1239 20 c. Type **388** 20 10
1240 25 c. The family, young and old 25 25
1241 30 c. The family at home 30 30
1242 35 c. The family at church 35 40
1239/42 .. .. *Set of* 4 1·00 95

(Des D. Hatcher. Photo Heraclio Fournier)

1981 (3 June). *River Scenes. T* **389** *and similar multicoloured designs. P* 13½ × 13 (30, 35 c.) *or* 13 × 13½ (*others*).

1243 30 c. Type **389** 30 30
1244 35 c. Mangahao 40 40
1245 40 c. Shotover (*horiz*) 45 45
1246 60 c. Cleddau (*horiz*) 75 75
1243/6 .. .. *Set of* 4 1·75 1·75

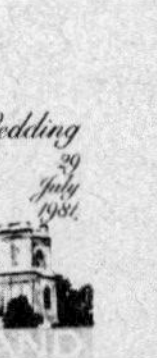

390 St. Paul's Cathedral

391 Girl with Starfish

(Des and litho Harrison)

1981 (29 July). *Royal Wedding. T* **390** *and similar horiz design. Multicoloured. P* 14½.

1247 20 c. Type **390** 20 30
a. Pair. Nos. 1247/8 .. .. 40 60
ab. Deep grey (inscriptions and date) omitted £800
1248 20 c. Prince Charles and Lady Diana Spencer 20 30

Nos. 1247/8 were printed together, *se-tenant*, in horizontal and vertical pairs throughout the sheet.

(Des P.O. Litho Harrison)

1981 (5 Aug). *Health Stamps. Children playing by the Sea. T* **391** *and similar vert designs. Multicoloured. P* 14½.

1249 20 c. + 2 c. Type **391** 25 35
a. Horiz pair. Nos. 1249/50 .. .. .. 50 70
1250 20 c. + 2 c. Boy fishing 25 35
1251 25 c. + 2 c. Children exploring rock pool .. 25 30
1249/51 .. .. *Set of* 3 70 90
MS1252 100 × 125 mm. Nos. 1249/51, each × 2 .. 2·00 2·50

The 20 c. values were printed together, *se-tenant*, in horizontal pairs throughout the sheet, forming a composite design.

The stamps from No. **MS**1252 were printed together, *se-tenant*, in two horizontal strips of 3, each forming a composite design.

392 "Madonna Suckling the Child" (painting, d'Oggiono)

393 Tauranga Mission House

(Des Margaret Chapman. Photo Courvoisier)

1981 (7 Oct). *Christmas. T* **392** *and similar vert designs. Multi-coloured. P* 11½.

1253 14 c. Type **392** 15 10
1254 30 c. St. John's Church, Wakefield 35 25
1255 40 c. Golden Tainui (flower) 45 35
1253/5 .. .. *Set of* 3 85 60

(Des A. Derrick. Litho Walsall)

1982 (3 Feb). *Commemorations. T* **393** *and similar vert designs. Multicoloured. P* 14½.

1256 20 c. Type **393** 25 10
a. Horiz pair. Nos. 1256/7 .. .. .. 50 60
1257 20 c. Water tower, Hawera 25 10
1258 25 c. Cat 35 35
1259 30 c. *Dunedin* (refrigerated sailing ship) .. 35 40
1260 35 c. Scientific research equipment 40 45
1256/60 .. .. *Set of* 5 1·40 1·60

Commemorations:—No. 1256, Centenary of Tauranga (town); No. 1257, Centenary of Hawera (town); No. 1258, Centenary of S.P.C.A. (Society for the Prevention of Cruelty to Animals in New Zealand); No. 1259, Centenary of Frozen Meat Exports; No. 1260, International Year of Science.

The 20 c. values were printed together, *se-tenant*, in horizontal pairs throughout the sheet.

394 Map of New Zealand

395 Alberton, Auckland

(Des A. G. Mitchell. Litho Leigh-Mardon Ltd, Melbourne)

1982 (1 Apr–13 Dec). *P* 12½.

1261 **394** 24 c. pale yellowish green and ultram 20 10
a. Perf 14½ × 14 (13.12.82) .. 20 10

(Des P. Leitch. Litho Walsall)

1982 (7 Apr). *Architecture (3rd series). T* **395** *and similar horiz designs. Multicoloured. P* 14 × 14½.

1262 20 c. Type **395** 20 15
1263 25 c. Caccia Birch, Palmerston North 25 25
1264 30 c. Railway station, Dunedin 30 30
1265 35 c. Post Office, Ophir 35 40
1262/5 .. .. *Set of* 4 1·00 1·00

396 Kaiteriteri Beach, Nelson (Summer)

397 Labrador

(Des D. Hatcher. Photo Heraclio Fournier)

1982 (2 June). *"The Four Seasons". New Zealand Scenes. T* **396** *and similar horiz designs. Multicoloured. P* 13 × 13½.

1266 35 c. Type **396** 40 40
1267 40 c. St. Omer Park, Queenstown (Autumn) 45 45
1268 45 c. Mt Ngauruhoe, Tongariro National Park (Winter) 50 50
1269 70 c. Wairarapa farm (Spring) 75 75
1266/9 .. .. *Set of* 4 1·90 1·90

(Des R. Conly. Litho Enschedé)

1982 (4 Aug). *Health Stamps. Dogs. T* **397** *and similar vert designs. Multicoloured. P* 13 × 13½.

1270 24 c. + 2 c. Type **397** 35 40
a. Horiz pair. Nos. 1270/1 .. .. .. 70 80
1271 24 c. + 2 c. Border Collie 35 40
1272 30 c. + 2 c. Cocker Spaniel 45 45
1270/2 .. .. *Set of* 3 1·10 1·25
MS1273 98 × 125 mm. Nos. 1270/2, each × 2. P 14 × 13½ .. .. 2·25 2·50

The 24 c. values were printed together, *se-tenant*, in horizontal pairs throughout the sheet.

398 "Madonna with Child and Two Angels" (paintings by Piero di Cosimo)

(Des Margaret Chapman. Photo Heraclio Fournier)

1982 (6 Oct). *Christmas. T* **398** *and similar vert designs. Multi-coloured. P* 14 × 13½.

1274 18 c. Type **398** 20 10
1275 35 c. Rangiatea Maori Church, Otaki 35 30
1276 45 c. Surf life-saving 50 40
1274/6 .. .. *Set of* 3 95 65

399 Nephrite

399a Grapes

399b Kokako

(Des P. Durrant (Nos. 1277/82), D. Little (Nos. 1283/7), Janet Marshall (Nos. 1288/97). Litho Leigh-Mardon Ltd. Melbourne)

1982 (1 Dec)–**89**. *Multicoloured. P* 14½×14 (*Nos.* 1277/87) *or* 14½ (*Nos.* 1288/97).

(*a*) *Minerals. T* **399** *and similar vert designs*

1277 1 c. Type **399** 10 10
a. Perf 12½ 25 10
1278 2 c. Agate 10 10
a. Perf 12½ 75 75
1279 3 c. Iron Pyrites 10 10
1280 4 c. Amethyst 10 10
1281 5 c. Carnelian 10 10
1282 9 c. Native Sulphur 10 10

(*b*) *Fruits. T* **399***a* *and similar vert designs*

1283 10 c. Type **399***a* (7.12.83) 20 10
1284 20 c. Citrus Fruit (7.12.83) 25 10
1285 30 c. Nectarines (7.12.83) 25 10
1286 40 c. Apples (7.12.83) 35 10
1287 50 c. Kiwifruit (7.12.83) 40 10

(*c*) *Native Birds. T* **399***b* *and similar vert designs*

1288 30 c. Kakapo (1.5.86) 30 15
1289 40 c. Mountain ("Blue") Duck (2.2.87) .. 40 15
1290 45 c. New Zealand Falcon (1.5.86) 60 20
1291 60 c. New Zealand Teal (2.2.87) 65 25
1292 $1 Type **399***b* (24.4.85) 65 20
1293 $2 Chatham Island Robin (24.4.85) .. 1·40 50
1294 $3 Stitchbird (23.4.86) .. .. .. 2·00 1·40
1295 $4 Saddleback (23.4.86) .. .. .. 2·75 2·00
1296 $5 Takahe (20.4.88) .. .. 3·25 2·50
1297 $10 Little Spotted Kiwi (19.4.89) .. 6·00 5·00
1277/97 .. .. *Set of* 21 18·00 13·00
1292/7 Optd "Specimen" .. .. *Set of* 6 7·50

Nos. 1292/7 overprinted "Specimen" come from a special "NEW ZEALAND 1990" Presentation Pack issued on 19 April 1989.

A miniature sheet containing No. 1293 was only available from the New Zealand stand at "PHILEXFRANCE '89" International Stamp Exhibition or the Philatelic Bureau at Wanganui.

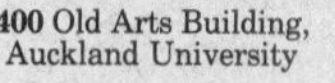

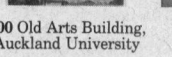

400 Old Arts Building, Auckland University

401 Queen Elizabeth II

(Des G. Emery (35 c.), P. Durrant (others). Litho Cambec Press, Melbourne (35 c.), J.W. (others))

1983 (2 Feb). *Commemorations. T* **400** *and similar vert designs. Multicoloured. P* 13 × 13½ (35 c.) *or* 14 × 13½ (*others*).

1303 24 c. Salvation Army Centenary logo .. 30 10
1304 30 c. Type **400** 40 35
1305 35 c. Stylised Kangaroo and Kiwi 45 35

1306	40 c. Rainbow Trout		50	45
1307	45 c. Satellite over Earth		55	50
1303/7		*Set of* 5	2·00	1·50

Commemorations:—24 c. Centenary of Salvation Army; 30 c. Centenary of Auckland University; 35 c. Closer Economic Relationship agreement with Australia; 40 c. Centenary of introduction of Rainbow Trout into New Zealand; 45 c. World Communications Year.

(Des P. Durrant. Litho Harrison)

1983 (14 Mar). *Commonwealth Day. T* **401** *and similar horiz designs. Multicoloured. P* 13½.

1308	24 c. Type **401**		20	10
1309	35 c. Maori rock drawing		30	40
1310	40 c. Woolmark and wool-scouring symbols		35	45
1311	45 c. Coat of arms		40	55
1308/11		*Set of* 4	1·10	1·40

402 "Boats, Island Bay" (Rita Angus) **403** Mt Egmont

(Des D. Hatcher. Litho Leigh-Mardon Ltd, Melbourne)

1983 (6 Apr). *Paintings by Rita Angus. T* **402** *and similar vert designs. Multicoloured. P* 14½.

1312	24 c. Type **402**		25	10
1313	30 c. "Central Otago Landscape"		30	45
1314	35 c. "Wanaka Landscape"		35	50
1315	45 c. "Tree"		45	70
1312/15		*Set of* 4	1·25	1·60

(Des P. Durrant. Photo Heraclio Fournier)

1983 (1 June). *Beautiful New Zealand. T* **403** *and similar multicoloured designs. P* 13.

1316	35 c. Type **403**		30	35
1317	40 c. Cooks Bay		35	40
1318	45 c. Lake Matheson (*horiz*)		40	45
1319	70 c. Lake Alexandrina (*horiz*)		65	70
1316/19		*Set of* 4	1·50	1·75

404 Tabby **405** "The Family of the Holy Oak Tree" (Raphael)

(Des R. Conly. Litho Harrison)

1983 (3 Aug). *Health Stamps. Cats. T* **404** *and similar vert designs. Multicoloured. P* 14.

1320	24 c. + 2 c. Type **404**		25	25
	a. Horiz pair. Nos. 1320/1		50	50
1321	24 c. + 2 c. Siamese		25	25
1322	30 c. + 2 c. Persian		40	30
1320/2		*Set of* 3	90	80
MS1323	100 × 126 mm. Nos. 1320/2, each × 2		1·50	1·75

The 24 c. values were printed together, *se-tenant*, in horizontal pairs throughout the sheet.

(Des R. Conly (45 c.), M. Wyatt (others). Photo Courvoisier)

1983 (5 Oct). *Christmas. T* **405** *and similar vert designs. Multicoloured. P* 12 × 11½.

1324	18 c. Type **405**		10	10
1325	35 c. St. Patrick's Church, Greymouth		30	35
1326	45 c. "The Glory of Christmas" (star and flowers)		40	45
1324/6		*Set of* 3	75	75

406 Geology

(Des R. Conly. Litho Cambec Press, Melbourne)

1984 (1 Feb). *Antarctic Research. T* **406** *and similar horiz designs. Multicoloured. P* 13½ × 13.

1327	24 c. Type **406**		25	10
1328	40 c. Biology		35	40
1329	58 c. Glaciology		50	55
1330	70 c. Meteorology		60	70
1327/30		*Set of* 4	1·60	1·60
MS1331	126 × 110 mm. Nos. 1327/30		1·75	2·25

407 *Mountaineer*, Lake Wakatipu **408** Mount Hutt

(Des M. Wyatt. Litho Cambec Press, Melbourne)

1984 (4 Apr). *New Zealand Ferry Boats. T* **407** *and similar horiz designs. Multicoloured. P* 13½ × 13.

1332	24 c. Type **407**		30	10
1333	40 c. *Waikana*, Otago		40	40
1334	58 c. *Britannia*, Waitemata		55	55
1335	70 c. *Wakatere*, Firth of Thames		65	65
1332/5		*Set of* 4	1·75	1·60

(Des D. Little. Litho Cambec Press, Melbourne)

1984 (6 June). *Ski-slope Scenery. T* **408** *and similar horiz designs. Multicoloured. P* 13½ × 13.

1336	35 c. Type **408**		40	40
1337	40 c. Coronet Park		45	45
1338	45 c. Turoa		50	50
1339	70 c. Whakapapa		75	75
1336/9		*Set of* 4	1·90	1·90

409 Hamilton's Frog

(Des A. G. Mitchell. Litho Cambec Press, Melbourne)

1984 (11 July). *Amphibians and Reptiles. T* **409** *and similar horiz designs. Multicoloured. P* 13½.

1340	24 c. Type **409**		30	30
	a. Horiz pair. Nos. 1340/1		60	60
1341	24 c. Great Barrier Skink		30	30
1342	30 c. Harlequin Gecko		35	35
1343	58 c. Otago Skink		70	70
1344	70 c. Gold-striped Gecko		75	75
1340/4		*Set of* 5	2·25	2·25

Nos. 1340/1 were printed together, *se-tenant*, in horizontal pairs throughout the sheet.

410 Clydesdales ploughing Field

(Des Margaret Chapman. Litho Harrison)

1984 (1 Aug). *Health Stamps. Horses. T* **410** *and similar horiz designs. Multicoloured. P* 14½.

1345	24 c. + 2 c. Type **410**		30	30
	a. Horiz pair. Nos. 1345/6		60	60
1346	24 c. + 2 c. Shetland ponies		30	30
1347	30 c. + 2 c. Thoroughbreds		45	35
1345/7		*Set of* 3	1·00	85
MS 1348	148 × 75 mm. Nos. 1345/7, each × 2		1·40	1·75

Nos. 1345/6 were printed together, *se-tenant*, in horizontal pairs throughout the sheet.

MACHINE LABELS. An automatic machine dispensing labels, ranging in value from 1 c. to $99.99, was installed at the Queen Street Post Office, Auckland, on 3 September 1984 for a trial period. The oblong designs, framed by simulated perforations at top and bottom and vertical rules at the sides, showed the "Southern Cross", face value and vertical column of six horizontal lines between the "NEW ZEALAND" and "POSTAGE" inscriptions. The trial period ended abruptly on 16 October 1984.

Similar labels, with the face value and inscriptions within a plain oblong, were introduced on 12 February 1986 and from 22 August 1988 they were printed on paper showing New Zealand flags.

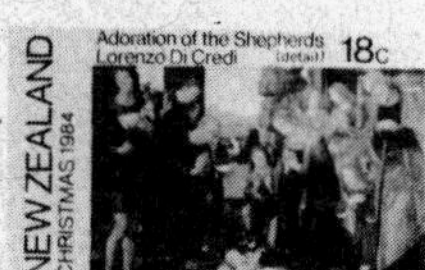

411 "Adoration of the Shepherds" (Lorenzo di Credi)

(Des R. Conly (45 c.), P. Durrant (others). Photo Heraclio Fournier)

1984 (26 Sept). *Christmas. T* **411** *and similar multicoloured designs. P* 13½ × 14 (18 c.) *or* 14 × 13½ (*others*).

1349	18 c. Type **411**		20	10
1350	35 c. Old St. Paul's, Wellington (*vert*)		40	35
1351	45 c. "The Joy of Christmas" (*vert*)		50	45
1349/51		*Set of* 3	1·00	80

412 Mounted Riflemen, South Africa, 1901

(Des R. Conly. Litho Harrison)

1984 (7 Nov). *New Zealand Military History. T* **412** *and similar horiz designs. Multicoloured. P* 15 × 14.

1352	24 c. Type **412**		30	10
1353	40 c. Engineers, France, 1917		45	45
1354	58 c. Tanks of 2nd N.Z. Divisional Cavalry, North Africa, 1942		60	60
1355	70 c. Infantryman in jungle kit, and 25-pounder gun, Korea and South-East Asia, 1950–72		70	75
1352/5		*Set of* 4	1·90	1·75
MS1356	122 × 106 mm. Nos. 1352/5		1·60	1·90

413 St. John Ambulance Badge

(Des Lindy Fisher. Litho J.W.)

1985 (16 Jan). *Centenary of St. John Ambulance in New Zealand. P* 14.

1357 **413**	24 c. black, gold and bright rosine		25	10
1358	30 c. black, sil & bright ultram		35	30
1359	40 c. black and grey		40	45
1357/9		*Set of* 3	90	75

The colours of the badge depicted are those for Bailiffs and Dames Grand Cross (24 c.), Knights and Dames of Grace (30 c.) and Serving Brothers and Sisters (40 c.).

414 Nelson Horse-drawn Tram, 1862 **415** Shotover Bridge

(Des. R. Conly. Litho Cambec Press, Melbourne)

1985 (6 Mar). *Vintage Trams. T* **414** *and similar horiz designs. Multicoloured. P* 13½.

1360	24 c. Type **414**		25	10
1361	30 c. Graham's Town steam tram, 1871		35	35
1362	35 c. Dunedin cable car, 1881		35	45
1363	40 c. Auckland electric tram, 1902		35	45
1364	45 c. Wellington electric tram, 1904		40	55
1365	58 c. Christchurch electric tram, 1905		50	75
1360/5		*Set of* 6	2·00	2·40

TARAPEX '86. To support this National Philatelic Exhibition the New Zealand Post Office co-operated with the organisers in the production of a set of "postage imprint labels". Five of the designs showed drawings of Maoris, taken from originals by Arthur Herbert Messenger and the sixth the Exhibition logo.

The sheetlets of 6 gummed and perforated labels were released by the Exhibition organisers on 3 April 1985. Although such labels were valid for postage, and could be so used by the general public, the sheetlets were not available from any New Zealand post office or from the Philatelic Bureau.

(Des R. Freeman. Photo Courvoisier)

1985 (12 June). *Bridges of New Zealand. T* **415** *and similar multicoloured designs. Granite paper. P* 11½.

1366	35 c. Type **415**		40	35
1367	40 c. Alexandra Bridge		45	40
1368	45 c. South Rangitikei Railway Bridge (*vert*)		50	50
1369	70 c. Twin Bridges (*vert*)		70	70
1366/9		*Set of* 4	1·90	1·75

416 Queen Elizabeth II (from photo by Camera Press) **417** Princess of Wales and Prince William

(Des B. Clinton. Litho Leigh-Mardon Ltd, Melbourne)

1985 (1 July). *Multicoloured, background colours given. P* 14½ × 14.

1370 **416**	25 c. rosine		50	10
1371	35 c. new blue		90	10

Examples of the 25 c. value exist with the orders on the sash omitted. These are believed to originate from unissued sheets sent for destruction in March 1986.

(Des D. Little. Litho Cambec Press, Melbourne)

1985 (31 July). *Health Stamps. T* **417** *and similar vert designs showing photographs by Lord Snowdon. Multicoloured. P* 13½.

1372 25 c. + 2 c. Type **417** 35 45
a. Horiz pair. Nos. 1372/3 .. .. 70 90
1373 25 c. + 2 c. Princess of Wales and Prince Henry 35 45
1374 35 c. + 2 c. Prince and Princess of Wales with Princes William and Henry .. 35 45
1372/4 .. .. *Set of* 3 95 1·25
MS1375 118 × 84 mm. Nos. 1372/4, each × 2 .. 1·40 1·75

Nos. 1372/3 were printed together, *se-tenant*, in horizontal pairs throughout the sheet.

418 The Holy Family in the Stable   **419** H.M.N.Z.S. *Philomel* (1914–47)

(Des Eileen Mayo. Photo Enschedé)

1985 (18 Sept). *Christmas. T* **418** *and similar vert designs. Multicoloured. P* 13½ × 12½.

1376 18 c. Type **418** 20 10
1377 40 c. The shepherds 40 55
1378 50 c. The angels 45 65
1376/8 .. .. *Set of* 3 95 1·10

Examples of the 18 c. and 50 c. stamps exist showing the spelling error "CRISTMAS". These are believed to originate from unissued sheets sent for destruction in March 1986. The New Zealand Post Office has stated that no such stamps were issued and that existing examples "were removed unlawfully during the destruction process".

(Des P. Durrant. Litho Cambec Press, Melbourne)

1985 (6 Nov). *New Zealand Naval History. T* **419** *and similar horiz designs. Multicoloured. P* 13½.

1379 25 c. Type **419** 45 10
1380 45 c. H.M.N.Z.S. *Achilles* (1936–46) .. 65 75
1381 60 c. H.M.N.Z.S. *Rotoiti* (1949–65) .. 85 1·00
1382 75 c. H.M.N.Z.S. *Canterbury* (from 1971) .. 95 1·25
1379/82 .. .. *Set of* 4 2·50 2·75
MS1383 124 × 108 mm. Nos. 1379/82 .. .. 2·50 3·00

420 Police Computer Operator   **421** Indian "Power Plus" 1000cc Motor Cycle (1920)

(Des A. Mitchell. Litho Leigh-Mardon Ltd, Melbourne)

1986 (15 Jan). *Centenary of New Zealand Police. T* **420** *and similar vert designs, each showing historical aspects above modern police activities. Multicoloured. P* 14½ × 14.

1384 25 c. Type **420** 25 30
a. Horiz strip of 5. Nos. 1384/8 .. 1·10
1385 25 c. Detective and mobile control room .. 25 30
1386 25 c. Policewoman and badge 25 30
1387 25 c. Forensic scientist, patrol car and policeman with child 25 30
1388 25 c. Police College, Porirua, patrol boat and dog handler 25 30
1384/8 .. .. *Set of* 5 1·10 1·40

Nos. 1384/8 were printed together, *se-tenant*, in horizontal strips of 5 throughout the sheet.

(Des M. Wyatt. Litho J.W.)

1986 (5 Mar). *Vintage Motor Cycles. T* **421** *and similar horiz designs. Multicoloured. P* 13 × 12½.

1389 35 c. Type **421** 40 30
1390 45 c. Norton "CS1" 500cc (1927) 50 35
1391 60 c. B.S.A. "Sloper" 500cc (1930) 65 50
1392 75 c. Triumph "Model H" 550cc (1915) .. 75 70
1389/92 .. .. *Set of* 4 2·10 1·75

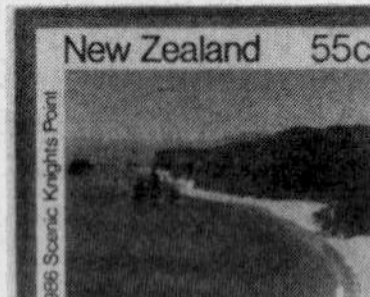

422 Tree of Life   **423** Knights Point

(Des Margaret Clarkson. Litho J.W.)

1986 (5 Mar). *International Peace Year. T* **422** *and similar horiz design. Multicoloured. P* 13 × 12½.

1393 25 c. Type **422** 30 30
a. Horiz pair. Nos. 1393/4 .. .. 60 60
1394 25 c. Peace dove 30 30

Nos. 1393/4 were printed together, *se-tenant*, in horizontal pairs throughout the sheet.

(Des P. Durrant. Photo Heraclio Fournier)

1986 (11 June). *Coastal Scenery. T* **423** *and similar horiz designs. Multicoloured. P* 14.

1395 55 c. Type **423** 55 45
1396 60 c. Becks Bay 55 45
1397 65 c. Doubtless Bay 60 50
1398 80 c. Wainui Bay 75 65
1395/8 .. .. *Set of* 4 2·25 1·90
MS1399 124 × 99 mm. No. 1398 (*sold at* $1.20) .. 85 90

The 40 c. premium on No. **MS**1399 was to support the 1990 Auckland International Stamp Exhibition.

No. **MS**1399 exists overprinted for "Stockholmia". Such miniature sheets were only available at this International Stamp Exhibition in Stockholm and were not placed on sale in New Zealand.

424 "Football" (Kylie Epapara)   **425** "A Partridge in a Pear Tree"

(Litho Leigh-Mardon Ltd, Melbourne)

1986 (30 July). *Health Stamps. Children's Paintings* (1st *series*). *T* **424** *and similar multicoloured designs. P* 14½ × 14 (30 *c.*) *or* 14 × 14½ (45 *c.*).

1400 30 c. + 3 c. Type **424** 30 30
a. Horiz pair. Nos. 1400/1 .. .. 60 60
1401 30 c. + 3 c. "Children at Play" (Phillip Kata) 30 30
1402 45 c. + 3 c. "Children Skipping" (Mia Flannery) (*horiz*) 40 40
1400/2 .. .. *Set of* 3 90 90
MS1403 144 × 81 mm. Nos. 1400/2, each × 2 .. 2·00 2·25

Nos. 1400/1 were printed together, *se-tenant*, in horizontal pairs throughout the sheet.

No. **MS**1403 exists overprinted for "Stockholmia". Such miniature sheets were only available at this International Stamp Exhibition in Stockholm and were not placed on sale in New Zealand.

See also Nos. 1433/6.

(Des Margaret Halcrow-Cross. Photo Heraclio Fournier)

1986 (17 Sept). *Christmas. "The Twelve Days of Christmas" (carol). T* **425** *and similar vert designs. Multicoloured. P* 14½.

1404 25 c. Type **425** 20 10
1405 55 c. "Two turtle doves" 45 45
1406 65 c. "Three French hens" 50 50
1404/6 .. .. *Set of* 3 1·00 95

426 Conductor and Orchestra   **427** Jetboating

(Des R. Freeman. Litho Leigh-Mardon Ltd, Melbourne)

1986 (5 Nov). *Music in New Zealand. T* **426** *and similar vert designs. P* 14½ × 14.

1407 30 c. multicoloured 25 10
1408 60 c. black, new blue and yellow-orange .. 45 50
1409 80 c. multicoloured 70 75
1410 $1 multicoloured 80 85
1407/10 .. .. *Set of* 4 2·00 2·00

Designs:—60 c. Cornet and brass band; 80 c. Piper and Highland pipe band; $1 Guitar and country music group.

(Des M. Wyatt. Litho Leigh-Mardon Ltd, Melbourne)

1987 (14 Jan). *Tourism. T* **427** *and similar vert designs. Multicoloured. P* 14½ × 14.

1411 60 c. Type **427** 50 45
1412 70 c. Sightseeing flights 60 55
1413 80 c. Camping 70 65
1414 85 c. Windsurfing 70 65
1415 $1.05, Mountaineering 90 80
1416 $1.30, River rafting .. .. .. 1·10 95
1411/16 .. .. *Set of* 6 4·00 3·75

428 Southern Cross Cup

(Des R. Proud. Litho Leigh-Mardon Ltd, Melbourne)

1987 (2 Feb). *Yachting Events. T* **428** *and similar horiz designs showing yachts. Multicoloured. P* 14 × 14½.

1417 40 c. Type **428** 35 15
1418 80 c. Admiral's Cup 70 70
1419 $1.05, Kenwood Cup .. .. .. 85 1·00
1420 $1.30, America's Cup .. .. .. 1·10 1·10
1417/20 .. .. *Set of* 4 2·75 2·75

429 Hand writing Letter and Postal Transport

(Des Communication Arts Ltd. Litho C.P.E. Australia Ltd, Melbourne)

1987 (1 Apr). *New Zealand Post Ltd Vesting Day. T* **429** *and similar horiz design. Multicoloured. P* 13½.

1421 40 c. Type **429** 40 50
a. Horiz pair. Nos. 1421/2 .. .. 80 1·00
1422 40 c. Posting letter, train and mailbox .. 40 50

Nos. 1421/2 were printed together, *se-tenant*, in horizontal pairs throughout the sheet.

430 Avro "626" and Wigram Airfield, 1937   **431** Urewera National Park and Fern Leaf

(Des P. Leitch. Litho Leigh-Mardon Ltd, Melbourne)

1987 (15 Apr). *50th Anniv of Royal New Zealand Air Force. T* **430** *and similar horiz designs. Multicoloured. P* 14 × 14½.

1423 40 c. Type **430** 35 15
1424 70 c. "P-40 Kittyhawk" over World War II Pacific airstrip 55 60
1425 80 c. Short "Sunderland" flying boat and Pacific lagoon 60 70
1426 85 c. A-4 "Skyhawk" and Mt Ruapehu .. 65 75
1423/6 .. .. *Set of* 4 2·00 2·00
MS1427 115 × 105 mm. Nos. 1423/6 .. .. 2·25 2·50

No. **MS**1427 overprinted on the selvedge with the "CAPEX" logo was only available from the New Zealand stand at this International Philatelic Exhibition in Toronto.

(Des Tracey Purkis. Litho Leigh-Mardon Ltd, Melbourne)

1987 (17 June). *Centenary of National Parks Movement. T* **431** *and similar vert designs. Multicoloured. P* 14½.

1428 70 c. Type **431** 65 55
1429 80 c. Mt Cook and buttercup 70 60
1430 85 c. Fiordland and pineapple shrub .. 75 65
1431 $1.30, Tongariro and tussock .. .. 1·25 95
1428/31 .. .. *Set of* 4 3·00 2·50
MS1432 123 × 99 mm. No. 1431 (*sold at* $1.70) .. 1·75 1·75

The 40 c. premium on No. **MS**1432 was to support the 1990 Auckland International Stamp Exhibition.

No. **MS**1432 overprinted on the selvedge with the "CAPEX" logo was only available from the New Zealand stand at this International Philatelic Exhibition in Toronto.

432 "Kite Flying" (Lauren Baldwin)   **433** "Hark the Herald Angels Sing"

(Adapted D. Little. Litho Leigh-Mardon Ltd, Melbourne)

1987 (29 July). *Health Stamps. Children's Paintings* (2nd *series*). *T* **432** *and similar multicoloured designs. P* 14½.

1433 40 c. + 3 c. Type **432** 35 35
a. Horiz pair. Nos. 1433/4 .. .. 70 70
1434 40 c. + 3 c. "Swimming" (Ineke Schoneveld) 35 35
1435 60 c. + 3 c. "Horse Riding" (Aaron Tylee) (*vert*) 50 50
1433/5 .. .. *Set of* 3 1·10 1·10
MS1436 100 × 117 mm. Nos. 1433/5, each × 2 .. 2·25 2·25

Nos. 1433/4 were printed together, *se-tenant*, in horizontal pairs throughout the sheet.

(Des Ellen Giggenbach. Litho Leigh-Mardon Ltd, Melbourne)

1987 (16 Sept). *Christmas. T* **433** *and similar vert designs. Multicoloured. P* 14½.

1437 35 c. Type **433** 30 10
1438 70 c. "Away in a Manger" 55 55
1439 85 c. "We Three Kings of Orient Are" .. 65 65
1437/9 .. .. *Set of* 3 1·40 1·25

MINIMUM PRICE

The minimum price quote is 10p which represents a handling charge rather than a basis for valuing common stamps. For further notes about prices see introductory pages.

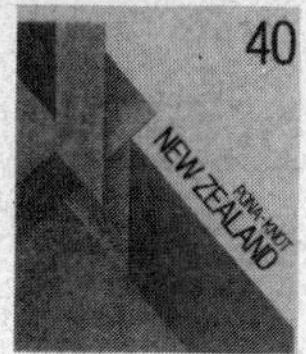

434 Knot ("Pona") **435** "Geothermal"

(Des Nga Puna Waihanga. Litho Security Printers (M), Malaysia)

1987 (4 Nov). *Maori Fibre-work. T* **434** *and similar vert designs. Multicoloured. W* **138** *of Malaysia. P* 12.

1440 40 c. Type **434** 35 10
1441 60 c. Binding ("Herehere") 45 45
1442 80 c. Plait ("Whiri") 60 65
1443 85 c. Cloak weaving ("Korowai") with flax fibre ("Whitau") 65 70
1440/3 .. .. *Set of* 4 1·90 1·75

(Des Fay McAlpine. Litho Leigh-Mardon Ltd, Melbourne)

1988 (13 Jan). *Centenary of Electricity. T* **435** *and similar horiz designs, each showing radiating concentric circles representing energy generation. P* 14 × 14½.

1444 40 c. multicoloured 30 35
1445 60 c. black, rosine and brownish black .. 40 45
1446 70 c. multicoloured 50 55
1447 80 c. multicoloured 55 60
1444/7 .. .. *Set of* 4 1·60 1·75

Designs:—60 c. "Thermal"; 70 c. "Gas"; 80 c. "Hydro".

436 Queen Elizabeth II and 1882 Queen Victoria 1d. Stamp **437** "Mangopare"

(Des A. G. Mitchell (40 c.), M. Conly and M. Stanley ($1). Litho Leigh-Mardon Ltd, Melbourne)

1988 (13 Jan). *Centenary of Royal Philatelic Society of New Zealand. T* **436** *and similar multicoloured designs. P* 14 × 14½.

1448 40 c. Type **436** 30 35
a. Horiz pair. Nos. 1448/9 .. .. .. 60 70
1449 40 c. As Type **436**, but 1882 Queen Victoria 2d. 30 35
MS1450 107 × 160 mm. $1 "Queen Victoria" (Chalon) (*vert*). P 14½ × 14 .. .. .. 70 75

Nos. 1448/9 were printed together, *se-tenant*, in horizontal pairs throughout the sheet.

No. **MS**1450 overprinted on the selvedge with the "SYDPEX" logo was only available from the New Zealand stand at this International Philatelic Exhibition in Sydney and from the Philatelic Bureau at Wanganui.

(Des S. Adsett. Litho Leigh-Mardon Ltd, Melbourne)

1988 (2 Mar). *Maori Rafter Paintings. T* **437** *and similar vert designs. Multicoloured. P* 14½.

1451 40 c. Type **437** 40 35
1452 40 c. "Koru" 40 35
1453 40 c. "Raupunga" 40 35
1454 60 c. "Koiri" 55 45
1451/4 .. .. *Set of* 4 1·60 1·40

438 "Good Luck" **439** Paradise Shelduck

(Des Communication Arts Ltd. Litho CPE Australia Ltd, Melbourne)

1988 (18 May). *Greetings Booklet Stamps. T* **438** *and similar multicoloured designs. P* 13½.

1455 40 c. Type **438** 25 30
a. Booklet pane. Nos. 1455/9 .. .. 1·10
1456 40 c. "Keeping in touch" 25 30
1457 40 c. "Happy birthday" 25 30
1458 40 c. "Congratulations" (41 × 27 *mm*) .. 25 30
1459 40 c. "Get well soon" (41 × 27 *mm*) .. 25 30
1455/9 .. .. *Set of* 5 1·10 1·40

Nos. 1455/9 only exist from $2 stamp booklets.

(Des Pauline Morse. Litho Leigh-Mardon Ltd, Melbourne)

1988 (7 June–2 Nov). *Native Birds. Multicoloured. P* 14½ × 14.

1460 10 c. Banded Dotterel (2.11) 10 10
1461 20 c. Yellowhead (2.11) 10 15
1462 30 c. Silvereye (2.11) 20 25
1463 40 c. Brown Kiwi (2.11) 25 30
1464 50 c. Kingfisher (2.11) 30 35
1465 60 c. Spotted Shag (2.11) 40 45
1466 70 c. Type **439** 45 50
1467 80 c. Fiordland Crested Penguin (2.11) .. 55 60
1468 90 c. South Island Robin (2.11) 60 65
1460/8 .. .. *Set of* 9 2·75 3·00

A miniature sheet containing No. 1466 was only available from the New Zealand stand at "WORLD STAMP EXPO '89" International Stamp Exhibition or the Philatelic Bureau, Wanganui.

440 Milford Track **441** Kiwi and Koala at Campfire

(Des H. Thompson. Litho Leigh-Mardon Ltd, Melbourne)

1988 (8 June). *Scenic Walking Trails. T* **440** *and similar vert designs. Multicoloured. P* 14½.

1469 70 c. Type **440** 50 55
1470 80 c. Heaphy Track 55 60
1471 85 c. Copland Track 60 65
1472 $1.30, Routeburn Track 90 95
1469/72 .. .. *Set of* 4 2·25 2·50
MS1473 124 × 99 mm. No. 1472 (*sold at* $1.70) 1·25 1·40

The 40 c. premium on No. **MS**1473 was to support the 1990 Auckland International Stamp Exhibition.

(Des R. Harvey. Litho Leigh-Mardon Ltd, Melbourne)

1988 (21 June). *Bicentenary of Australian Settlement. P* 14½.

1474 **441** 40 c. multicoloured 30 35

A stamp in a similar design was also issued by Australia.

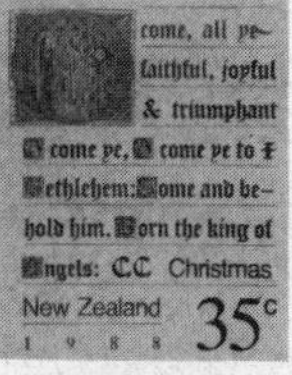

442 Swimming **443** "O Come All Ye Faithful"

(Des R. Proud. Litho Leigh-Mardon Ltd, Melbourne)

1988 (27 July). *Health Stamps. Olympic Games, Seoul. T* **442** *and similar horiz designs. Multicoloured. P* 14½.

1475 40 c. + 3 c. Type **442** 30 35
1476 60 c. + 3 c. Athletics 45 50
1477 70 c. + 3 c. Canoeing 50 55
1478 80 c. + 3 c. Show-jumping 60 65
1475/8 .. .. *Set of* 4 1·60 1·90
MS1479 120 × 90 mm. Nos. 1475/8 .. .. 1·90 2·00

(Des Fay McAlpine. Litho Leigh-Mardon Ltd, Melbourne)

1988 (14 Sept). *Christmas. Carols. T* **443** *and similar vert designs, each showing illuminated verses. Multicoloured. P* 14½.

1480 35 c. Type **443** 25 30
1481 70 c. "Hark the Herald Angels Sing" 50 55
1482 80 c. "Ding Dong Merrily on High" 55 60
1483 85 c. "The First Nowell" 60 65
1480/3 .. .. *Set of* 4 1·75 1·90

444 "Lake Pukaki" (John Gully) **445** Brown Kiwi

(Litho Leigh-Mardon Ltd, Melbourne)

1988 (5 Oct). *New Zealand Heritage (1st issue). The Land. T* **444** *and similar horiz designs showing 19th-century paintings. Multicoloured. P* 14 × 14½.

1484 40 c. Type **444** 30 35
1485 60 c. "On the Grass Plain below Lake Arthur" (William Fox) 40 45
1486 70 c. "View of Auckland" (John Hoyte) .. 50 55
1487 80 c. "Mt. Egmont from the Southward" (Charles Heaphy) 55 60
1488 $1.05, "Anakiwa, Queen Charlotte Sound" (John Kinder) 75 80
1489 $1.30, "White Terraces, Lake Rotomahana" (Charles Barraud) 90 95
1484/9 .. .. *Set of* 6 3·00 3·25

See also Nos. 1505/10 and 1524/9.

(Des A. Mitchell. Eng. G. Prosser of B.A.B.N. Recess Leigh-Mardon Ltd, Melbourne)

1988 (19 Oct). *Booklet Stamp. P* 14½ *(and around design)*.

1490 **445** $1 bronze-green 65 70
a. Booklet pane. No. 1490 × 6 .. .. 4·00

No. 1490 were only issued in $6 stamp booklets with the horizontal edges of the booklet pane imperforate. Each circular stamp is also separated by vertical perforations.

446 Humpback Whale and Calf **447** Clover

(Des Lindy Fisher. Litho Govt Ptg Office, Wellington)

1988 (2 Nov). *Whales. T* **446** *and similar horiz designs. Multicoloured. P* 13½.

1491 60 c. Type **446** 45 45
1492 70 c. Killer Whales 55 55
1493 80 c. Southern Right Whale 60 60
1494 85 c. Blue Whale 65 65
1495 $1.05, Southern Bottlenose Whale and calf 80 80
1496 $1.30, Sperm Whale 95 95
1491/6 .. .. *Set of* 6 3·50 3·50

Although inscribed "ROSS DEPENDENCY" Nos. 1491/6 were available from post offices throughout New Zealand.

(Des Heather Arnold. Litho Leigh-Mardon Ltd, Melbourne)

1989 (18 Jan). *Wild Flowers. T* **447** *and similar horiz designs. Multicoloured. P* 14½.

1497 40 c. Type **447** 35 35
1498 60 c. Lotus 45 45
1499 70 c. Montbretia 55 55
1500 80 c. Wild Ginger 60 60
1497/1500 .. .. *Set of* 4 1·75 1·75

448 Katherine Mansfield **449** Moriori Man and Map of Chatham Islands

(Des A. G. Mitchell. Litho Harrison)

1989 (1 Mar). *New Zealand Authors. T* **448** *and similar vert designs. Multicoloured. P* 12½.

1501 40 c. Type **448** 30 35
1502 60 c. James K. Baxter 40 45
1503 70 c. Bruce Mason 50 55
1504 80 c. Ngaio Marsh 55 60
1501/4 .. .. *Set of* 4 1·60 1·75

(Des D. Gunson. Litho Leigh-Mardon Ltd, Melbourne)

1989 (17 May). *New Zealand Heritage (2nd issue). The People. T* **449** *and similar horiz designs. P* 14 × 14½.

1505 40 c. multicoloured 30 35
1506 60 c. orge-brn, brownish grey & reddish brn 45 50
1507 70 c. yellow-grn, brownish grey & dp olive 50 55
1508 80 c. bright greenish blue, brownish grey and deep dull blue 60 65
1509 $1.05, grey, brownish grey & grey-black 80 85
1510 $1.30, bright rose-red, brownish grey, and lake-brown .. .. 1·00 1·10
1505/10 .. .. *Set of* 6 3·25 3·50

Designs:—60 c. Gold prospector; 70 c. Settler ploughing; 80 c. Whaling; $1.05, Missionary preaching to Maoris; $1.30, Maori village.

450 White Pine (Kahikatea) **451** Duke and Duchess of York with Princess Beatrice

(Des D. Gunson. Litho Questa)

1989 (7 June). *Native Trees. T* **450** *and similar vert designs. Multicoloured. P* 14 × 14½.

1511 80 c. Type **450** 60 65
1512 85 c. Red Pine (Rimu) 65 70
1513 $1.05, Totara 80 85
1514 $1.30, Kauri .. .. 1·00 1·10
1511/14 .. .. *Set of* 4 2·75 3·00
MS1515 102 × 125 mm. No. 1514 (*sold at* $1.80) 1·40 1·50

The 50 c. premium on No. **MS**1515 was to support the 1990 Auckland International Stamp Exhibition.

(Des and litho Leigh-Mardon Ltd, Melbourne)

1989 (26 July). *Health Stamps. T* **451** *and similar vert designs. Multicoloured. P* 14½.

1516 40 c. + 3 c. Type **451** 35 40
a. Horiz pair. Nos. 1516/17 .. .. 70 80
1517 40 c. + 3 c. Duchess of York with Princess Beatrice 35 40

1518 80 c. + 3 c. Princess Beatrice 60 65
1516/18 .. .. Set of 3 1·10 1·25
MS1519 120×89 mm. Nos. 1516/18, each ×2 .. 2·50 2·75

Nos. 1516/17 were printed together, *se-tenant*, in horizontal pairs throughout the sheet.

No. **MS**1519 overprinted on the selvedge with the "WORLD STAMP EXPO '89" logo was only available from the New Zealand stand at this International Philatelic Exhibition and from the Philatelic Bureau at Wanganui

452 One Tree Hill, Auckland, through Bedroom Window

453 Windsurfing

(Des H. Chapman. Litho Leigh-Mardon Ltd, Melbourne)

1989 (13 Sept). *Christmas. T* **452** *and similar vert designs showing Star of Bethlehem. Multicoloured. P* 14½.

1520 35 c. Type **452** 25 30
1521 65 c. Shepherd and dog in mountain valley 50 55
1522 80 c. Star over harbour 60 65
1523 $1 Star over globe 75 80
1520/3 .. .. Set of 4 1·90 2·10

(Des M. Bailey. Litho Leigh-Mardon Ltd, Melbourne)

1989 (11 Oct). *New Zealand Heritage (3rd issue). The Sea. T* **453** *and similar horiz designs. Multicoloured. P* 14×14½.

1524 40 c. Type **453** 30 35
1525 60 c. Fishes of many species 45 50
1526 65 c. Marlin and game fishing launch .. 50 55
1527 80 c. Rowing boat and yachts in harbour .. 60 65
1528 $1 Coastal scene 75 80
1529 $1.50, Container ship and tug .. .. 1·10 1·25
1524/9 .. .. Set of 6 3·25 3·75

454 Games Logo

(Des Heather Arnold. Litho Leigh-Mardon Ltd, Melbourne)

1989 (8 Nov). *14th Commonwealth Games, Auckland. T* **454** *and similar horiz designs. Multicoloured. P* 14½.

1530 40 c. Type **454** 30 35
1531 40 c. Goldie (games kiwi mascot) 30 35
1532 40 c. Gymnastics 30 35
1533 50 c. Weightlifting 35 40
1534 65 c. Swimming 50 55
1535 80 c. Cycling 60 65
1536 $1 Lawn bowling 75 80
1537 $1.80, Hurdling .. .. 1·40 1·50
1530/7 .. .. Set of 8 4·00 4·50

455 Short "S.30" Empire Flying Boat and Boeing "747"

456 Chief Kawiti signing Treaty

(Des R. Proud. Litho Enschedé)

1990 (17 Jan). *50th Anniv of Air New Zealand. P* 13×14½.

1539 **455** 80 c. multicoloured 60 65

(Des A. G. Mitchell from painting by L. C. Mitchell. Litho Enschedé)

1990 (17 Jan). *150th Anniv of Treaty of Waitangi. Sheet* 80×118 *mm, containing T* **456** *and similar multicoloured design. P* 13½.

MS1540 40 c. Type **456**; 40 c. Chief Hone Heke (first signatory) and Lieut-Governor Hobson (*horiz*) 60 65

Index to New Zealand Stamp Designs from 1946

The following index is intended to facilitate the identification of all New Zealand stamps from 1946 onwards. Portrait stamps are usually listed under surnames only, views under the name of the town or city and other issues under the main subject or a prominent word and date chosen from the inscription. Simple abbreviations have occasionally been resorted to and when the same design or subject appears on more than one stamp, only the first of each series is indicated.

EXPRESS DELIVERY STAMPS

E 1

(Typo Govt Printing Office, Wellington)

1903 (9 Feb). *Value in first colour. W* **43** *(sideways). P* 11.
E1 E 1 6d. red and violet .. .. .. 30·00 20·00

1926–36. *Thick, white, opaque chalk-surfaced "Cowan" paper. W* **43**.

(a) P 14 × 14½
E2 E 1 6d. vermilion and bright violet .. 28·00 17·00

(b) P 14 × 15 (1936)
E3 E 1 6d. carmine and bright violet .. .. 28·00 38·00

1937–39. *Thin, hard, chalk-surfaced "Wiggins Teape" paper.*

(a) P 14 × 14½
E4 E 1 6d. carmine and bright violet .. .. 45·00 25·00

(b) P 14 × 15 (1939)
E5 E 1 6d. vermilion and bright violet .. 70·00 70·00

E 2 Express Mail Delivery Van

(Des J. Berry. Eng Stamp Ptg Office, Melbourne Recess Govt Ptg Office, Wellington)

1939 (16 Aug). *W* **43**. *P* 14.
E6 E 2 6d. violet .. .. 1·50 1·75

POSTAGE DUE STAMPS

D 1

(I)

(II)

3D. (a) Large "D"   5D. (b) Small "D"

(Typo Govt Printing Office, Wellington)

1899 (1 Dec). *W* **12b**. *Coarse paper. P* 11.

I. Type I. *Circle of* 14 *ornaments*, 17 *dots over* "N.Z.", "N.Z." *large*.

(a) Large "D"
D1 D 1 ½d. carmine and green .. .. 11·00 20·00
a. No stop after "D" (Right pane R. 2/3) 80·00 £110
D2 8d. carmine and green .. .. 60·00 75·00
D3 1s. carmine and green .. .. 65·00 60·00
D4 2s. carmine and green £120 £130
D1/4 .. .. *Set of* 4 £225 £250

To avoid further subdivision the 1s. and 2s. are placed with the pence values, although the two types of "D" do not apply to the higher values.

(b) Small "D"
D6 D 1 5d. carmine and green .. .. .. 18·00 18·00
D7 6d. carmine and green .. .. .. 22·00 18·00
D8 10d. carmine and green .. .. .. 70·00 80·00
D6/8 .. .. *Set of* 3 £100 £100

II. Type II. *Circle of* 13 *ornaments*, 15 *dots over* "N.Z.", "N.Z." *small*.

(a) Large "D"
D 9 D 1 ½d. vermilion and green .. .. 2·25 11·00
a. No stop after "D" (Right pane R. 2/3) .. .. .. 50·00 75·00
D10 1d. vermilion and green .. .. 7·50 1·00
D11 2d. vermilion and green .. .. 45·00 9·00
D12 3d. vermilion and green .. .. 12·00 3·50
D9/12 .. .. *Set of* 4 60·00 23·00

(b) Small "D"
D14 D 1 1d. vermilion and green .. .. 11·00 1·25
D15 2d. vermilion and green .. .. 24·00 3·50
D16 4d. vermilion and green .. .. 24·00 9·00
D14/16 .. .. *Set of* 3 55·00 12·50

Nos. D9/16 were printed from a common frame plate of 240 (4 panes of 60) used in conjunction with centre plates of 120 (2 panes of 60) for the ½d. and 4d. or 240 for the other values. Sheets of the 1d. and 2d. each contained two panes with large "D" and two panes with small "D".

D 2

D 3

(Des W. R. Bock. Typo Govt Printing Office)

1902 (28 Feb). *No wmk. P* 11.
D17 D 2 ½d. red and deep green .. .. 85 5·00

1904–08. *"Cowan" unsurfaced paper. W* **43** *(sideways). (a) P* 11.
D18 D 2 ½d. red and green (4.04) .. .. 1·50 1·50
a. Imperf between (horiz pair) .. £500
D19 1d. red and green (5.12.05) .. .. 7·00 3·25
D20 2d. red and green (5.4.06) .. .. 90·00 90·00
D18/20 .. .. *Set of* 3 90·00 90·00

(b) P 14
D21 D 2 1d. carmine and green (12.06) .. 8·50 80
a. Rose-pink and green (9.07) .. 7·00 60
D22 2d. carmine and green (10.06) .. 7·50 3·25
a. Rose-pink and green (6.08) .. 4·25 65

1919 (Jan)–**20.** *"De La Rue" chalky paper. Toned gum. W* **43**. *P* 14 × 15.
D23 D 2 ½d. carmine and green (6.19) .. .. 3·25 1·50
D24 1d. carmine and green .. .. 4·00 20
D25 2d. carmine and green (8.20) .. .. 7·00 2·00
D23/5 .. .. *Set of* 3 13·00 3·25

1925 (May). *"Jones" chalky paper. White gum. W* **43**. *P* 14 × 15.
D26 D 2 ½d. carmine and green .. .. 30·00 30·00

1925 (July). *No wmk, but bluish* "N Z" *and Star lithographed on back. P* 14 × 15.
D27 **D 2** ½d. carmine and green .. .. 1·75 14·00
D28 2d. carmine and green .. .. 2·50 12·00

1925 (Nov)–**35.** *"Cowan" thick, opaque chalky paper. W* **43**.

(a) P 14 × 15
D29 D 2 ½d. carmine and green (12.26) .. 1·75 5·50
D30 1d. carmine and green .. .. 3·25 80
D31 2d. carmine and green (6.26) .. 12·00 3·75
D32 3d. carmine and green (6.35) .. .. 35·00 35·00
D29/32 .. .. .. *Set of* 4 45·00 40·00

(b) P 14
D33 D 2 ½d. carmine and green (10.28) .. 17·00 22·00
D34 1d. rose and pale yellow-green (6.28) .. 3·25 50
D35 2d. carmine and green (10.29) .. .. 6·50 1·75
D36 3d. carmine and green (5.28) .. .. 15·00 27·00
D33/6 .. .. *Set of* 4 38·00 45·00

1937–38. *"Wiggins Teape" thin, hard chalky paper. W* **43**. *P* 14 × 15.
D37 D 2 ½d. carmine and yellow-green (2.38) .. 10·00 20·00
D38 1d. carmine and yellow-green (1.37) .. 8·50 3·75
D39 2d. carmine and yellow-green (6.37) .. 12·00 6·50
D40 3d. carmine and yellow-green (11.37) 45·00 35·00
D37/40 .. .. *Set of* 4 70·00 60·00

(Des J. Berry. Typo Govt Printing Office, Wellington)

1939–49. *P* 15 × 14. *(a) W* **43** *(sideways)* (16.8.39).
D41 D 3 ½d. turquoise-green .. .. .. 3·00 3·50
D42 1d. carmine .. .. .. 1·25 30
D43 2d. bright blue .. .. .. 4·00 2·75
D44 3d. orange-brown .. .. .. 12·00 16·00
D41/4 .. .. *Set of* 4 18·00 20·00

(b) W **98** *sideways*
D45 D 3 1d. carmine (4.49) .. .. .. 3·00 2·00*
D46 2d. bright blue (12.46) .. .. 1·00 70
D47 3d. orange-brown (6.45) .. .. 3·00 5·00
a. Wmk upright (1943) .. .. 27·00 26·00
D45/6 .. .. *Set of* 3 6·25 7·00*

*The use of Postage Due stamps ceased in 1951, our used price for No. D45 being for stamps postmarked after this date (*price for examples clearly cancelled* 1949–51, £25).

OFFICIAL STAMPS

1892–1906. *Contemporary issues handstamped* "O.P.S.O." *diagonally. (a) Stamps of* 1873 *type. W* **12b**. *P* 12½.
O 1 3 ½d. rose (V.) .. .. .. — £400

(b) Stamps of 1882–97 *optd in rose or magenta. W* **12b**.
O 2 13 ½d. black (*p* 10) .. .. .. — £150
a. Violet opt .. .. .. — £180
O 3 ½d. black (*p* 10 × 11) .. .. — £150
O 4 14 1d. rose (*p* 12 × 11½) .. .. — £160
O 5 1d. rose (*p* 11) .. .. .. — £160
O 6 15 2d. purple (*p* 11) .. .. .. — £300
O 7 2d. mauve-lilac (*p* 10) .. .. — £300
a. Violet opt .. .. ..
O 8 16 2½d. blue (*p* 11) .. .. .. — £200
O 9 2½d. ultramarine (*p* 10) .. .. — £200
O10 2½d. ultramarine (*p* 10 × 11) .. — £200
O11 19 5d. olive-black (*p* 12 × 11½) .. — £350
O12 20 6d. brown (*p* 12 × 11½) .. .. — £425

(c) Stamps of 1898–1903 *optd in violet. P* 11. (i) *No wmk*
O13 23 ½d. green (*p* 14) (No. 294) .. — £140
O14 26 2½d. blue (*p* 12–16) (No. 249*a*) .. — £350
O15 27 2½d. blue (No. 260) .. .. — £275
O16 37 4d. indigo and brown (No. 262) .. — £325
O17 30 5d. purple-brown (No. 263) .. — £375
a. Green opt .. .. .. — £350
O18 32 8d. indigo (No. 266) .. .. — £400

(ii) *W* **38**
O19 42 1d. carmine (No. 278) .. .. — £150

(iii) *W* **43** *(sideways on 3d., 1s.)*
O20 42 1d. carmine (*p* 14) (No. 303) .. — £150
a. Green opt .. .. .. — £150
O21 27 2½d. blue (No. 308) .. .. — £250
O22 28 3d. yellow-brown (No. 309) .. — £350
O23 34 1s. orange-red (No. 315*b*) .. — £700
O24 35 2s. green (No. 316) .. .. — £1000

The letters signify "On Public Service Only," and stamps so overprinted were used by the Post Office Department on official correspondence between the department and places abroad.

MINIMUM PRICE

The minimum price quote is 10p which represents a handling charge rather than a basis for valuing common stamps. For further notes about prices see introductory pages.

OFFICIAL.

(O 3)

1907–08. *Stamps of* 1902–6 *optd with Type* O 3 *(vertically upwards). W* **43** *(sideways on 3d., 6d., 1s. and 5s.). P* 14.
O59 23 ½d. yellow-green .. .. .. 6·50 50
a. Perf compound of 11 and 14 .. 60·00
b. Mixed perfs .. .. .. 60·00
O60 42 1d. carmine (No. 303) (1908)* .. 5·50 6·00
a. Booklet pane of 6 .. .. .. 30·00
O60*b* 1d. rose-carmine (Waterlow) (No. 352) 5·50 30
ba. Perf compound of 11 and 14 .. £275 £225
bb. Mixed perfs £275 £225
O60*c* 1d. carmine (Royle) .. .. 5·50 25
ca. Perf compound of 11 and 14 .. £180 £160
cb. Mixed perfs £180 £160
O61 41 2d. purple .. .. .. 7·00 1·25
a. Bright reddish purple .. .. 6·50 1·00
ab. Mixed perfs £180 £180
O63 28 3d. bistre-brown .. .. .. 35·00 1·75
O64 31 6d. bright carmine-pink .. .. £110 15·00
a. Imperf vert (horiz pair) £750
b. Mixed perfs £400 £350
O65 34 1s. orange-red .. .. .. 85·00 15·00
O66 35 2s. blue-green .. .. .. 70·00 45·00
a. Imperf between (pair) £1100
b. Imperf vert (horiz pair) £900
O67 36 5s. deep red £150 £150
a. Wmk upright £700 £550

*Though issued in 1908, a large quantity of booklets was mislaid and not utilized until they were found in 1930.

1908–09. *Optd as Type* O **3**. *W* **43**.
O69 23 ½d. green (*p* 14 × 15) .. .. 6·00 1·25
O70 46 1d. carmine (*p* 14 × 15) .. .. 55·00 1·00
O71 48 6d. pink (*p* 14 × 13, 13½) .. .. £140 35·00
O72 6d. pink (*p* 14 × 15) (1909) .. .. £110 28·00
O72*a* F 4 £1 rose-pink (*p* 14) (No. F89) .. £600 £550

1910. *No.* 387 *optd with Type* O **3**.
O73 50 ½d. yellow-green .. .. .. 3·25 30
a. Opt inverted (reading downwards) † £1200

1910–16. *Nos.* 389 *and* 392/4 *optd with Type* O 3. *P* 14 × 14½.
O74 51 3d. chestnut .. .. .. 14·00 80
a. Perf 14 × 13½ (1915) .. .. 60·00 70·00
ab. Vert pair, O74/a £300 £350
O75 – 6d. carmine .. .. .. 18·00 3·75
a. Deep carmine (1913) .. .. 24·00 4·25
O76 – 8d. indigo-blue (R.) (5.16) .. 13·00 18·00
a. Perf 14 × 13½ .. .. .. 13·00 18·00
ab. Vert pair, O76/a .. .. 45·00 60·00
O77 – 1s. vermilion .. .. .. 45·00 12·00
O74/7 .. .. *Set of* 4 80·00 30·00

1910–25. *Optd with Type* O **3**. *(a) W* **43**. *De La Rue chalk-surfaced paper with toned gum.*
O78 52 1d. carmine (No. 405) .. .. 2·25 10

(b) W **43**. *Jones chalk-surfaced paper with white gum*
O79 52 1d. deep carmine (No. 406) (1925) .. 8·00 3·00

(c) No wmk, but bluish "NZ" and Star lithographed on back. Art paper
O80 52 1d. rose-carmine (No. 409) (1925) .. 5·00 6·50

(d) W **43**. *Cowan thick, opaque, chalk-surfaced paper with white gum*
O81 52 1d. deep carmine (No. 410) (1925) .. 6·00 1·25

1913–25. *Postal Fiscal stamps optd with Type* O **3**.

(i) *Chalk-surfaced De La Rue paper. (a) P* 14 (1913–14)
O82 F 4 2s. blue (30.9.14) .. .. 35·00 20·00
O83 5s. yellow-green (13.6.13) .. 65·00 65·00
O84 £1 rose-carmine (1913) £550 £450
O82/4 .. .. *Set of* 3 £575 £475

(b) P 14½ × 14, *comb* (1915)
O85 F 4 2s. deep blue (Aug) .. .. 35·00 20·00
a. No stop after "OFFICIAL" .. £120 80·00
O86 5s. yellow-green (Jan) .. .. 65·00 65·00
a. No stop after "OFFICIAL" .. £200 £200

(ii) *Thick, white, opaque chalk-surfaced Cowan paper. P* 14½ × 14 (1925)
O87 F 4 2s. blue .. .. .. 55·00 55·00
a. No stop after "OFFICIAL" .. £160 £160

The overprint on these last, and on Nos. O69 and O72*a*, is from a new set of type, giving a rather sharper impression than Type O 3, but otherwise resembling it closely.

1915 (12 Oct)–**34.** *Optd with Type* O **3**. *P* 14 × 15. *(a) On Nos.* 435/40 *(De La Rue chalk-surfaced paper with toned gum).*
O88 61 ½d. green .. .. .. 1·00 10
O89 62 1½d. grey-black (6.16) .. .. 4·75 2·50
O90 61 1½d. slate (12.16) .. .. .. 2·75 40
O91 1½d. orange-brown (4.19) .. .. 3·00 30
O92 2d. yellow (4.17) .. .. .. 3·00 10
O93 3d. chocolate (11.19) .. .. 6·50 35
O88/93 .. .. *Set of* 6 19·00 3·50

(b) On Nos. 441 *and* 443 *(Jones chalk-surfaced paper with white gum)*
O94 61 ½d. green (1924) .. .. .. 3·50 1·75
O95 3d. deep chocolate (1924) .. 26·00 4·00

(c) On Nos. 446/7 *and* 448a/9 *(Cowan thick, opaque, chalk-surfaced paper with white gum)*
O96 61 ½d. green (1925) 50 10
a. Perf 14 (1929) .. .. .. 1·25 35
ab. No stop after "OFFICIAL" .. 18·00 18·00
O97 1½d. orange-brown (*p* 14) (1929) .. 8·50 11·00
a. No stop after "OFFICIAL" .. 35·00 42·00
b. Perf 14 × 15 (1934) .. .. 17·00 20·00
O98 2d. yellow (*p* 14) (1931) .. .. 1·50 20
a. No stop after "OFFICIAL" .. 27·00 17·00

O99 **61** 3d. chocolate (1925) .. .. .. 3·50 40
a. No stop after "OFFICIAL" .. 35·00 22·00
b. Perf 14 (1930) .. .. .. 16·00 1·75
ba. No stop after "OFFICIAL" .. 60·00 28·00
O96/9 .. .. *Set of* 4 12·50 11·00

1915 (Dec)–**27**. *Optd with Type* O **3**. *P* 14×14½. (*a*) *Nos.* 420, 422, 425, 428 *and* 429*a*/30 (*Cowan unsurfaced paper*).
O100 **60** 3d. chocolate .. .. 3·00 70
a. Perf 14×13½ .. .. 3·00 70
ab. Vert pair, O100/a .. .. .. 35·00 50·00
O101 4d. bright violet (*p* 14×13½) (4.25) .. 12·00 2·00
a. Re-entry (Pl 20 R. 1/6) .. .. 40·00
b. Re-entry (Pl 20 R. 4/10) .. .. 45·00
c. Perf 14×14½ (4.27) .. .. 15·00 1·00
O102 6d. carmine (6.16) .. .. .. 4·00 75
a. Perf 14×13½ .. .. .. 3·75 60
ab. Vert pair, O102/a .. .. .. 50·00 50·00
O103 8d. red-brown (*p* 14×13½) (8.22) .. 70·00 80·00
O104 9d. sage-green (*p* 14×13½) (4.25) .. 35·00 30·00
O105 1s. vermilion (9.16) .. .. .. 5·50 2·00
a. Perf 14×13½ .. .. .. 15·00 7·00
ab. Vert pair, O105/a .. .. .. 65·00 90·00
c. Pale orange-red .. .. .. 24·00 6·50
O100/5 .. .. *Set of* 6 £120 £100

(*b*) *No.* 433 (*Thin paper with widely spaced sideways wmk*)
O106 **60** 3d. chocolate (*p* 14) (7.16) .. .. 3·00 4·00
a. No wmk .. .. 30·00 50·00

1927–33. *Optd with Type* O **3**. **W 43**. *P* 14.
O111 **71** 1d. rose-carmine (No. 468) .. .. 1·00 10
a. No stop after "OFFICIAL" .. 17·00 9·00
b. Perf 14 × 15 .. .. .. 1·25 10
O112 **72** 2s. light blue (No. 469) (2.28) .. 70·00 65·00
O113 **F 6** 5s. green (1933) £250 £250
O111/13 .. .. *Set of* 3 £300 £275

Official (O 4) Official (O 5)

1936–61. *Pictorial issue optd horiz or vert* (2s.) *with Type* O **4**.
(*a*) **W 43** (*Single "N Z" and Star*)
O115 **82** 1d. scarlet (Die I) (*p* 14 × 13½) .. 1·00 15
a. Perf 13½ × 14 .. .. .. 70·00 32·00
O116 **83** 1½d. red-brown (*p* 13½ × 14) .. .. 16·00 18·00
a. Perf 14 × 13½ £4000
O118 **92** 1s. deep green (*p* 14 × 13½) .. .. 18·00 18·00
O119 **F 6** 5s. green (*p* 14) (12.38) .. .. 50·00 17·00
O115/19 .. .. *Set of* 4 75·00 45·00

The watermark of No. O119 is almost invisible.

Only four examples of No. O116a exist. The error occurred when a sheet of No. 558a was found to have a block of four missing. This was replaced by a block of No. 558 and the sheet was then sent for overprinting.

(*b*) **W 98** (*Mult "N Z" and Star*)
O120 **81** ½d. bright green, *p* 14 × 13½ (7.37) .. 3·25 3·50
O121 **82** 1d. scarlet (Die II), *p* 14 × 13½ (11.36) 1·50 10
O122 **83** 1½d. red-brown, *p* 14 × 13½ (7.36) .. 6·00 4·00
O123 **84** 2d. orange, *p* 14 × 13½ (1.38) .. 1·00 10
a. Perf 12½ (1942) .. .. .. £110 32·00
c. Perf 14 (1942) .. .. .. 18·00 6·50
O124 **85** 2½d. chocolate and slate, *p* 13–14 × 13½ (26.7.38) .. .. .. 18·00 24·00
a. Perf 14 (1938) .. .. .. 6·00 9·00
O125 **86** 3d. brown, *p* 14 × 13½ (1.3.38) .. 30·00 2·00
O126 **87** 4d. black and sepia, *p* 14 × 13½ (8.36) 4·00 60
a. Perf 14 (8.41) .. .. .. 3·00 60
b. Perf 12½ (1941) .. .. .. 2·00 90
c. Perf 14 × 14½ (10.42) .. .. 3·00 40
O127 **89** 6d. scarlet, *p* 13½ × 14 (12.37) .. 4·50 40
a. Perf 12½ (1941) .. .. .. 5·00 2·25
b. Perf 14½ × 14 (7.42) .. .. 2·25 25
O128 **90** 8d. chocolate, *p* 12½ (*wmk sideways*) (1942) .. .. 7·00 7·00
a. Perf 14 × 14½ (*wmk sideways*) (1945) .. .. 5·50 6·50
b. Perf 14 × 13½ .. .. .. † £1600
O129 **91** 9d. red and grey-black (G.) (No. 587*a*), *p* 13½ × 14 (1.3.38) .. .. 48·00 35·00
O130 9d. scarlet and black (Blk.)(No.631), *p* 14 × 15 (1943) .. .. .. 13·00 18·00
O131 **92** 1s. deep green, *p* 14 × 13½ (2.37) .. 11·00 70
a. Perf 12½ (1942) .. .. .. 7·00 70
O132 **93** 2s. olive-green, *p* 13–14 × 13½ (5.37) 35·00 14·00
a. "CAPTAIN COQK" .. .. 40·00
b. Perf 13½ × 14 (1939) .. .. 70·00 5·50
ba. "CAPTAIN COQK" .. .. 75·00
c. Perf 12½ (1942) .. .. .. 55·00 20·00
ca. "CAPTAIN COQK" .. .. 75·00
d. Perf 14 × 13½ (1944) .. .. 22·00 7·00
da. "CAPTAIN COQK" .. ..
O133 **F 6** 5s. green, **C**, *p* 14 (3.43) .. .. 24·00 4·50
a. Perf 14 × 13½. *Yellow-green*, **O** (10.61) .. .. 15·00 15·00
O120/33 .. .. *Set of* 14 £150 80·00

The opt on No. O127a was sometimes applied at the top of the stamp, instead of always at the bottom, as on No. O127.

See notes on perforations after No. 590b.

1938–51. *Nos.* 603 *etc., optd with Type* O **4**.
O134 **108** ½d. green (1.3.38) .. .. .. 7·00 60
O135 ½d. brown-orange (1946) .. .. 1·25 80
O136 1d. scarlet (1.7.38) .. .. .. 7·00 15
O137 1d. green (10.7.41) 65 10
O138 **108*a*** 1½d. purple-brown (26.7.38) .. .. 55·00 18·00
O139 1½d. scarlet (2.4.51) .. .. .. 6·00 1·25
O140 3d. blue (16.10.41) .. .. .. 1·25 10
O134/40 .. .. *Set of* 7 70·00 19·00

1940 (2 Jan–8 Mar). *Centennial. Nos.* 613, *etc., optd with Type* O **5**.
O141 ½d. blue-green (R.) 50 35
a. "ff" joined, as Type O 4 .. .. 30·00 30·00
O142 1d. chocolate and scarlet .. .. 2·50 10
a. "ff" joined, as Type O 4 .. .. 35·00 30·00
O143 1½d. light blue and mauve .. .. 1·25 2·00
O144 2d. blue-green and chocolate .. .. 2·50 10
a. "ff" joined, as Type O 4 .. .. 35·00 30·00
O145 2½d. blue-green and ultramarine .. .. 2·00 2·75
a. "ff" joined, as Type O 4 .. .. 35·00 35·00
O146 3d. purple and carmine (R.) .. .. 6·00 80
a. "ff" joined, as Type O 4 .. .. 30·00 30·00
O147 4d. chocolate and lake .. .. 30·00 2·00
a. "ff" joined, as Type O 4 .. .. 70·00 38·00
O148 6d. emerald-green and violet .. .. 18·00 2·00
a. "ff" joined, as Type O 4 .. .. 50·00 38·00
O149 8d. black and red (8.3) .. .. 15·00 12·00
a. "ff" joined, as Type O 4 .. .. 50·00 50·00
O150 9d. olive-green and vermilion .. .. 7·00 7·00
O151 1s. sage-green and deep green .. .. 35·00 4·00
O141/51 .. .. *Set of* 11 £110 30·00

1947–49. *Nos.* 680, *etc., optd with Type* O **4**.
O152 **108*a*** 2d. orange 50 10
O153 4d. bright purple .. .. .. 2·00 50
O154 6d. carmine .. .. 5·50 40
O155 8d. violet .. .. 8·00 5·50
O156 9d. purple-brown .. .. .. 9·00 6·50
O157 **144** 1s. red-brown and carmine (*wmk upright*) (Plate 1) .. .. .. 10·00 85
a. Wmk sideways (Plate 1) (1949) .. 8·00 2·50
b. Wmk upright (Plate 2) .. .. 14·00 4·50
O158 2s. brown-orange and green (*wmk sideways*) (Plate 1) .. .. 16·00 9·00
a. Wmk upright (Plate 1) .. .. 20·00 14·00
O152/8 .. .. *Set of* 7 45·00 21·00

O 6 Queen Elizabeth II

6d (O 7)

(Des J. Berry. Recess B.W.)

1954 (1 Mar)–**63**. **W 98**. *P* 14 × 13½.
O159 **O 6** 1d. orange 30 15
O160 1½d. brown-lake .. .. .. 45 2·50
O161 2d. bluish green 30 15
O162 2½d. olive (1.3.63) .. .. .. 3·50 1·50
O163 3d. vermilion 30 10
O164 4d. blue 50 15
O165 9d. carmine .. .. 1·00 60
O166 1s. purple 50 10
O167 3s. slate (1.3.63) .. .. .. 32·00 45·00
O159/67 .. .. *Set of* 9 35·00 45·00

See note *re* white opaque paper after No. 736. Nos. O162 and O167 exist only on white paper.

1959 (1 Oct). *No.* O160 *surch with Type* O **7**.
O168 **O 6** 6d. on 1½d. brown-lake 20 85

1961 (1 Sept). *No.* O161 *surch as Type* O **7**.
O169 **O 6** 2½d. on 2d. bluish green .. .. 35 1·00

Owing to the greater use of franking machines by Government Departments, the use of official stamps was discontinued on 31 March 1965, but they remained on sale at the G.P.O. until 31 December 1965.

PROVISIONALS ISSUED AT REEFTON AND USED BY THE POLICE DEPARTMENT

1907 (Jan). *Current stamps of* 1906, *overwritten* "Official," *in red ink, and marked* "Greymouth—PAID—3" *inside a circular postmark stamp. P* 14.
P1 **23** ½d. green £425 £600
P2 **40** 1d. carmine £425 £650
P3 **38*a*** 2d. purple £650 £800
P4 **28** 3d. bistre £550 £700
P5 **31** 6d. pink £750 £850
P6 **34** 1s. orange-red £1000 £1200
P7 **35** 2s. green .. .. — £5000

LIFE INSURANCE DEPARTMENT

L 1 Lighthouse L 2

(Des W. B. Hudson and J. F. Rogers; eng A. E. Cousins. Typo Govt Printing Office, Wellington)

1891 (2 Jan)–**98**. A. *W* 12*c*. *P* 12×11½.
L 1 **L 1** ½d. bright purple .. .. .. 55·00 7·00
L 2 1d. blue .. .. 55·00 9·00
a. Wmk 12*b* .. .. .. 90·00 18·00
L 3 2d. brown-red .. .. 85·00 4·00
a. Wmk 12*b* .. .. .. 95·00 9·00
L 4 3d. deep brown .. .. .. £190 20·00
L 5 6d. green .. .. £275 60·00
L 6 1s. rose £650 £125
L1/6 .. .. *Set of* 6 £1100 £200

B. *W* 12*b* (1893–98). (*a*) *P* 10 (1893)
L 7 **L 1** ½d. bright purple .. .. .. 55·00 6·00
L 8 1d. blue .. .. 55·00 1·25
L 9 2d. brown-red .. .. 75·00 3·75
L7/9 .. .. *Set of* 3 £160 9·00

(*b*) *Perf compound of* 11 *and* 10 (1896)
L 9*a* **L 1** ½d. bright purple .. .. .. 90·00 24·00
L 9*b* 1d. blue .. .. 55·00 10·00

(*c*) *Perf compound of* 10 *and* 11 (1897)
L10 **L 1** ½d. bright purple .. .. .. — 60·00
L11 1d. blue

(*d*) *Mixed perfs* 10 *and* 11 (1897)
L12 **L 1** 2d. brown-red £550 £550

(*e*) *P* 11 (1897–98)
L13 **L 1** ½d. bright purple .. .. .. 55·00 2·50
a. Thin coarse toned paper (1898) .. 65·00 5·00
L14 1d. blue .. .. 55·00 75
a. Thin coarse toned paper (1898) .. 65·00 90
L15 2d. brown-red .. .. 70·00 3·00
a. Chocolate .. .. £110 20·00
b. Thin coarse toned paper (1898) .. 70·00 3·00
L13/15 .. .. *Set of* 3 £160 5·50

1902–04. **W 43** (*sideways*). (*a*) *P* 11.
L16 **L 1** ½d. bright purple (1903) .. .. 55·00 3·25
L17 1d. blue (1902) .. .. .. 55·00 90
L18 2d. brown-red (1904) .. .. .. 80·00 3·75
L16/18 .. .. *Set of* 3 £170 7·00

(*b*) *Perf compound of* 11 *and* 14
L19 **L 1** ½d. bright purple (1903) £1100
L20 1d. blue (1904) .. .. .. 90·00 10·00

Nos. L16/17 and L20 are known without watermark from the margins of the sheet.

1905–6. *Redrawn, with* "V.R." *omitted*. **W 43** (*sideways*). (*a*) *P* 11.
L21 **L 2** 2d. brown-red (12.05) .. .. .. £1200 80·00

(*b*) *P* 14
L22 **L 2** 1d. blue (1906) .. .. £150 28·00

(*c*) *Perf compound of* 11 *and* 14
L23 **L 2** 1d. blue (1906) £375 £150
a. Mixed perfs .. .. — £350

1913 (2 Jan)–**37**. *New values and colours*. **W 43**.
(*a*) *"De La Rue paper". P* 14 × 15
L24 **L 2** ½d. green .. .. 6·00 70
a. Yellow-green .. .. .. 6·00 70
L25 1d. carmine .. .. 6·00 60
a. Carmine-pink .. .. .. 11·00 90
L26 1½d. black (1917) .. .. .. 28·00 5·50
L27 1½d. chestnut-brown (1919) .. .. 1·25 2·25
L28 2d. bright purple .. .. .. 32·00 15·00
L29 2d. yellow (1920) .. .. .. 3·50 2·00
L30 3d. yellow-brown .. .. .. 32·00 22·00
L31 6d. carmine-pink .. .. .. 22·00 17·00
L24/31 .. .. *Set of* 8 £120 55·00

(*b*) *"Cowan" paper*. (i) *P* 14 × 15
L31*a* **L 2** ½d. yellow-green (1925) .. .. 12·00 3·00
L31*b* 1d. carmine-pink (1925) .. .. 17·00 3·00

(ii) *P* 14
L32 **L 2** ½d. yellow-green (1926) .. .. 5·50 1·50
L33 1d. scarlet (1931) .. .. .. 7·00 1·50
L34 2d. yellow (1937) .. .. .. 3·25 3·50
L35 3d. brown-lake (1931) .. .. 16·00 20·00
L36 6d. pink (1925) .. .. .. 18·00 18·00
L32/6 .. .. *Set of* 5 45·00 40·00

(*c*) *"Wiggins Teape" paper. P* 14 × 15
L36*a* **L 2** ½d. yellow-green (3.37) .. .. 2·25 4·00
L36*b* 1d. scarlet (3.37) .. .. .. 6·50 1·50
L36*c* 6d. pink (7.37) .. .. .. 22·00 26·00
L36*a*/*c* .. .. *Set of* 3 28·00 28·00

For descriptions of the various types of paper, see after No. 518.

In the 1½d. the word "POSTAGE" is in both the side-labels instead of at left only.

1944–47. **W 98**. *P* 14 × 15.
L37 **L 2** ½d. yellow-green (7.47) .. .. 1·50 3·25
L38 1d. scarlet (6.44) .. .. .. 1·50 1·25
L39 2d. yellow (1946) .. .. .. 3·50 3·25
L40 3d. brown-lake (10.46) .. .. 9·00 8·50
L41 6d. pink (7.47) .. .. .. 7·00 15·00
L37/41 .. .. *Set of* 5 20·00 28·00

L3 Castlepoint Lighthouse L 6 Cape Campbell Lighthouse

(Des J. Berry. Recess B.W.).

1947 (1 Aug)–**65**. *Type* L **3**, L **6** *and similar designs*. **W 98** (*sideways on* 1*d*., 2*d*., 2½*d*.). *P* 13½.
L42 ½d. grey-green and orange-red 80 60
L43 1d. olive-green and pale blue 50 30
L44 2d. deep blue and grey-black 70 25
L45 2½d. black and bright blue (*white opaque paper*) (4.11.63) .. .. .. 7·50 10·00
L46 3d. mauve and pale blue .. .. 2·00 35
L47 4d. brown and yellow-orange .. .. 1·75 40
a. Wmk sideways (*white opaque paper*) (13.10.65) .. .. .. 5·00 12·00
L48 6d. chocolate and blue .. .. .. 1·75 1·25
L49 1s. red-brown and blue .. .. .. 2·00 75
L42/49 .. .. *Set of* 8 15·00 12·50

Designs: *Horiz* (*as Type* L **3**)–1d Taiaroa lighthouse; 2d. Cape Palliser lighthouse; 6d. The Brothers lighthouse. *Vert* (*as Type* L **6**)–3d. Eddystone lighthouse; 4d. Stephens Island lighthouse; 1s. Cape Brett lighthouse.

2c 10c

(L 11) (L 12)

1967 (10 July)–**68**. *Decimal currency. Stamps of* 1947–65, *surch as Type* L **12** *or* L **11** (2 *c.*).

L50 1 c. on 1d. (No. L43) 1·75 4·00
a. Wmk upright (*white opaque paper*) (10.5.68) 1·60 3·25
L51 2 c. on 2½d. (No. L45) 3·50 8·00
L52 2½ c. on 3d. (No. L46) 1·75 4·50
a. Wmk sideways (*white opaque paper*) (4.68?) 2·50 4·50
L53 3 c. on 4d. (No. L47a) 3·50 4·75
L54 5 c. on 6d. (No. L48) 2·00 6·00
L55 10 c. on 1s. (No. L49) 3·00 11·00
a. Wmk sideways (*white opaque paper*) 1·25 4·00
L50/55a *Set of* 6 12·00 28·00

See note *re* white opaque paper below No. 736.
No. L54 exists on both ordinary and whiter paper.

L **13** Moeraki Point Lighthouse
L **14** Puysegur Point Lighthouse

(Des J. Berry. Litho B.W.)

1969 (27 Mar)–**77**. *Types* L **13/14** *and similar designs. No wmk. Chalk-surfaced paper* (8, 10 *c.*), *ordinary paper* (*others*). *P* 14 (8, 10 *c.*) *or* 13½ (*others*).

L56 ½ c. greenish yellow, red and deep blue 2·00 2·00
L57 2½ c. ultramarine, green and pale buff 1·00 1·25
L58 3 c. reddish brown and yellow 75 75
a. Chalk-surfaced paper (16.6.77) 80 1·50
L59 4 c. lt new blue, yellowish grn & apple-grn 1·00 1·00
a. Chalk-surfaced paper (16.6.77) 65 1·50
L60 8 c. multicoloured (17.11.76) 45 1·50
L61 10 c. multicoloured (17.11.76) 45 1·50
L62 15 c. black, light yellow and ultramarine 60 1·75
a. Perf 14. Chalk-surfaced paper (24.12.76) 1·50 1·75
L56/62a *Set of* 7 5·00 8·75

Designs: *Horiz*—4 c. Cape Egmont Lighthouse; *Vert*—3c. Baring Head Lighthouse; 8 c. East Cape; 10 c. Farewell Spit; 15 c. Dog Island Lighthouse.

(L **16**) L **17**

1978 (8 Mar). *No.* L 57 *surch with Type* L **16**. *Chalky paper.*

L63 L **14** 25 c. on 2½ c. ultramarine, grn & buff 75 1·25

(Des A. G. Mitchell. Litho Harrison)

1981 (3 June). *P* 14½.

L64 L **17** 5 c. multicoloured 10 10
L65 10 c. multicoloured 10 10
L66 20 c. multicoloured 15 15
L67 30 c. multicoloured 25 25
L68 40 c. multicoloured 35 30
L69 50 c. multicoloured 45 35
L64/9 *Set of* 6 1·25 1·00

Issues for the Government Life Insurance Department were withdrawn on 1 December 1989 when it became the privatised Tower Corporation.

POSTAL FISCAL STAMPS

As from 1 April 1882 fiscal stamps were authorised for postal use and conversely postage stamps became valid for fiscal use. Stamps in the designs of 1867 with "STAMP DUTY" above the Queen's head were withdrawn and although some passed through the mail quite legitimately they were mainly "philatelic" and we no longer list them. The issue which was specifically authorised in 1882 was the one which had originally been put on sale for fiscal use in 1880.

Although all fiscal stamps were legally valid for postage only values between 2s. and £1 were stocked at ordinary post offices. Other values could only be obtained by request from the G.P.O., Wellington or from offices of the Stamp Duties Department. Later the Arms types above £1 could also be obtained from the head post offices in Auckland, Christchurch, Dunedin and also a branch post office at Christchurch North where there was a local demand for them.

It seems sensible to list under Postal Fiscals the Queen Victoria stamps up to the £1 value and the Arms types up to the £5 because by 1931 the higher values were genuinely needed for postal purposes. Even the £10 was occasionally used on insured airmail parcels.

Although 2s. and 5s. values were included in the 1898 pictorial issue, it was the general practice for the Postal Department to limit the postage issues to 1s. until 1926 when the 2s. and 3s. appeared. These were then dropped from the fiscal issues and when in turn the 5s. and 10s. were introduced in 1953 and the £1 in 1960 no further printings of these values occurred in the fiscal series.

FORGED POSTMARKS. Our prices are for stamps with genuine postal cancellations. Beware of forged postmarks on stamps from which fiscal cancellations have been cleaned off.

Many small post offices acted as agents for government departments and it was the practice to use ordinary postal date-stamps on stamps used fiscally, so that when they are removed from documents they are indistinguishable from postally used specimens unless impressed with the embossed seal of the Stamp Duties Department.

Date-stamps very similar to postal date-stamps were sometimes supplied to offices of the Stamp Duties Department and it is not clear when this practice ceased. Prior to the Arms types the only sure proof of the postal use of off-cover fiscal stamps is when they bear a distinctive duplex, registered or parcel post cancellation, but beware of forgeries of the first two.

F 1 F 2 F 3

(Die eng W. R. Bock. Typo Govt Ptg Office)

1882 (Feb). *W* **12***a*. *P* 12 × 11½.

F1 F **1** 1d. lilac £160 £300
F2 1d. blue 75·00 25·00

The 1d. fiscal was specifically authorised for postal use in February 1882 owing to a shortage of the 1d. Type **5** and pending the introduction of the 1d. Type **14** on 1 April.

The 1d. lilac fiscal had been replaced by the 1d. blue in 1878 but postally used copies with 1882 duplex postmarks are known although most postally used examples are dated from 1890 and these must have been philatelic.

(Des and dies eng W. R. Bock. Typo Govt Ptg Office)

1882 (early). *W* **12***a*. *P* 12 × 11½.

F3 F **2** 1s. grey green
F4 F **3** 1s. grey-green and red

Copies of these are known postally used in 1882 and although not specifically authorised for postal use it is believed that their use was permitted where there was a shortage of the 1s. postage stamp.

The 2s. value Type F **3** formerly listed is not known with 1882–83 postal date-stamps.

WMK TYPE F 5. The balance of the paper employed for the 1867 issue was used for early printings of Type F **4** introduced in 1880 before changing over to the "N Z" and Star watermark. The values we list with this watermark are known with 1882–83 postal date stamps. Others have later dates and are considered to be philatelic but should they be found with 1882–83 postal dates we would be prepared to add them to the list.

In the following list the 4d., 6d., 8d. and 1s. are known with early 1882 postal date-stamps and, like Nos. F3/4, it is assumed that they were used to meet a temporary shortage of postage stamps.

F **4** F **5**

The 12s. 6d. value has the head in an oval (as Type **10**), and the 15s. and £1 values have it in a broken circle (as Type **7**).

(Dies eng W. R. Bock. Typo Govt Ptg Office)

1882 (1 Apr). *Type* F **4** *and similar types. "De La Rue" paper.*

A. *W* **12***a* (6 *mm*). (*a*) *P* 12 (1882)

F 5 4d. orange-red (*Wmk* F **5**) — £130
F 6 6d. lake-brown — £130
F 7 8d. green (*Wmk* F **5**)
F 8 1s. pink
F 9 2s. blue 50·00 4·50
F10 2s. 6d. grey-brown 85·00 4·50
a. Wmk F **5**
F11 3s. mauve £110 5·50
F12 4s. brown-rose £110 11·00
F13 5s. green £140 11·00
a. Yellow-green £140 11·00
F14 6s. rose £150 27·00
F15 7s. ultramarine £160 40·00
F16 7s. 6d. bronze-grey £160 45·00
F17 8s. deep blue £160 40·00
F18 9s. orange £150 45·00
F19 10s. brown-red £140 14·00
a. Wmk F **5**
F20 15s. green £190 45·00
F21 £1 rose-pink £190 45·00

(*b*) *P* 12½ (1886)

F22 2s. blue 50·00 4·50
F23 2s. 6d. grey-brown 85·00 4·50
F24 3s. mauve £110 5·50
F25 4s. purple-claret £110 11·00
a. Brown-rose £110 11·00
F26 5s. green £140 11·00
a. Yellow-green £140 11·00
F27 6s. rose £150 27·00
F28 7s. ultramarine £160 40·00
F29 8s. deep blue £160 40·00
F30 9s. orange £150 45·00
F31 10s. brown-red £140 14·00
F32 15s. green £190 45·00
F33 £1 rose-pink £190 45·00

B. *W* **12***b* (7 *mm*). *P* 12½ (1888)

F34 2s. blue 45·00 4·50
F35 2s. 6d. grey-brown 80·00 4·50
F36 3s. mauve £100 5·50
F37 4s. brown-rose £100 11·00
a. Brown-red £100 11·00
F38 5s. green £130 11·00
a. Yellow-green £130 11·00
F39 6s. rose £150 27·00
F40 7s. ultramarine £160 40·00
F41 7s. 6d. bronze-grey £160 45·00
F42 8s. deep blue £160 40·00
F43 9s. orange £150 45·00
F44 10s. brown-red £140 12·00
a. Maroon £140 12·00
F45 £1 pink £190 45·00

C. *W* **12***c* (4 *mm*). *P* 12½ (1890)

F46 2s. blue 75·00 11·00
F47 3s. mauve £150 27·00
F48 4s. brown-red £120 15·00
F49 5s. green £140 12·00
F50 6s. rose £160 27·00
F51 7s. ultramarine £170 40·00
F52 8s. deep blue £170 40·00
F53 9s. orange £150 45·00
F54 10s. brown-red £140 13·00
F55 15s. green £250 60·00

D. *Continuation of W* **12***b*. *P* 11 (1895–1901)

F56 2s. blue 27·00 5·50
F57 2s. 6d. grey-brown 80·00 4·50
a. Inscr "COUNTERPART" (1901)* £150 £110
F58 3s. mauve £100 5·50
F59 4s. brown-red £100 10·00
F60 5s. yellow-green £130 12·00
F61 6s. rose £140 27·00
F62 7s. pale blue £160 40·00
F63 7s. 6d. bronze-grey £160 45·00
F64 8s. deep blue £160 40·00
F65 9s. orange £150 45·00
a. Imperf between (horiz pair) £650
F66 10s. brown-red £140 12·00
a. Maroon £140 12·00
F67 15s. green £190 45·00
F68 £1 rose-pink £190 45·00

*The plate normally printed in yellow and inscribed "COUNTERPART" just above the bottom value panel, was for use on the counterparts of documents but was issued in error in the colour of the normal fiscal stamp and accepted for use.

E. *W* **43** (*sideways*)

(i) *Unsurfaced "Cowan" paper.* (*a*) *P* 11 (1903)

F69 2s. 6d. grey-brown 80·00 4·50
F70 3s. mauve £100 5·50
F71 4s. orange-red £100 10·00
F72 6s. rose £140 27·00
F73 7s. pale blue £160 40·00
F74 8s. deep blue £150 40·00
F75 10s. brown-red £130 14·00
a. Maroon £130 14·00
F76 15s. green £190 45·00
F77 £1 rose-pink £170 45·00

(*b*) *P* 14 (1906)

F78 2s. 6d. grey-brown 80·00 4·50
F79 3s. mauve £100 5·50
F80 4s. orange-red £100 7·50
F81 5s. yellow-green 70·00 7·50
F82 6s. rose £140 27·00
F83 7s. pale blue £150 40·00
F84 7s. 6d. bronze-grey £150 45·00
F85 8s. deep blue £150 40·00
F86 9s. orange £140 45·00
F87 10s. maroon £130 12·00
F88 15s. green £190 45·00
F89 £1 rose-pink £170 45·00

(*c*) *P* 14½ × 14, *comb* (*clean-cut*) (1907)

F90 2s. blue 25·00 4·00
F91 2s. 6d. grey-brown 80·00 4·50
F92 3s. mauve £100 5·50
F93 4s. orange-red 90·00 7·50
F94 6s. rose £140 27·00
F95 10s. maroon £130 12·00
F96 15s. green £170 45·00
F97 £1 rose-pink £170 45·00

(ii) *Chalk-surfaced "De La Rue" paper.* (*a*) *P* 14 (1913)

F 98 2s. blue 25·00 4·00
F 99 2s. 6d. grey-brown 27·00 4·50
F100 3s. purple 70·00 5·50
F101 4s. orange-red 70·00 7·00
F102 5s. yellow-green 70·00 7·50
F103 6s. rose £100 14·00
F104 7s. pale blue £100 15·00
F105 7s. 6d. bronze-grey £150 45·00
F106 8s. deep blue £130 24·00
F107 9s. orange £140 45·00
F108 10s. maroon £130 12·00
F109 15s. green £170 40·00
F110 £1 rose-carmine £170 45·00

(*b*) *P* 14½ × 14, *comb* (1913–21)

F111 2s. deep blue 25·00 4·00
F112 2s. 6d. grey-brown 27·00 4·50
F113 3s. purple 70·00 5·50
F114 4s. orange-red 70·00 7·00
F115 5s. yellow-green 70·00 7·50
F116 6s. rose £100 14·00
F117 7s. pale blue £100 15·00
F118 8s. deep blue £130 24·00
F119 9s. orange £130 45·00
F120 10s. maroon £130 12·00
F121 12s. 6d. deep plum (1921) £2250 £500
F122 15s. green £170 40·00
F123 £1 rose-carmine £170 45·00

The "De La Rue" paper has a smooth finish and has toned gum which is strongly resistant to soaking.

(iii) *Chalk-surfaced "Jones" paper. P* 14½ × 14, *comb* (1924)

F124 2s. deep blue 30·00 4·00
F125 2s. 6d. deep grey-brown 32·00 4·50
F126 3s. purple 80·00 5·50
F127 5s. yellow-green 80·00 7·50
F128 10s. brown-red £140 12·00
F129 12s. 6d deep purple £2250 £500
F130 15s. green £190 40·00

The "Jones" paper has a coarser texture, is poorly surfaced and the ink tends to peel. The outline of the watermark commonly shows on the surface of the stamp. The gum is colourless or only slightly toned and washes off readily.

(iv) *Thick, opaque, chalk-surfaced "Cowan" paper. P* 14½ × 14, *comb* (1925–30)

F131 2s. blue 25·00 4·00
F132 2s. 6d. deep grey-brown 27·00 4·50
F133 3s. mauve £100 10·00

F134 4s. orange-red .. .. 70·00 7·00
F135 5s. yellow-green .. .. 70·00 7·50
F136 6s. rose .. .. £100 14·00
F137 7s. pale blue .. .. £100 15·00
F138 8s. deep blue .. .. £130 24·00
a. Error. Blue (as 2s.) (1930) .. ..
F139 10s. brown-red .. .. £130 12·00
F140 12s. 6d. blackish purple £2250 £500
F141 15s. green .. .. £170 40·00
F142 £1 rose-pink .. .. £170 45·00

The "Cowan" paper is white and opaque and the watermark, which is usually smaller than in the "Jones" paper, is often barely visible.

(v) *Thin, hard, chalk-surfaced "Wiggins Teape" paper. P* 14½ × 14, *comb* (1926)

F143 4s. orange-red .. .. 75·00 7·00
F144 £1 rose-pink .. .. £180 80·00

The "Wiggins Teape" paper has a vertical mesh with narrow watermark, whereas other chalk-surfaced papers with this perforation have a horizontal mesh and wider watermark.

F 6

35/-

(F 7)

(Des H. L. Richardson. Typo Govt Ptg Office)

1931–40. *As Type* F **6** (*various frames*). W **43**. *P* 14.

(i) *Thick, opaque, chalk-surfaced "Cowan" paper, with horizontal mesh* (1931–35)

F145 1s. 3d. lemon (4.31) .. .. .. 10·00 32·00
F146 1s. 3d. orange-yellow .. .. .. 4·00 2·75
F147 2s. 6d. deep brown .. .. .. 12·00 1·75
F148 4s. red .. .. 14·00 2·25
F149 5s. green .. .. 15·00 3·50
F150 6s. carmine-rose .. .. 22·00 7·00
F151 7s. blue .. .. 25·00 8·50
F152 7s. 6d. olive-grey .. .. 55·00 55·00
F153 8s. slate-violet .. .. 28·00 18·00
F154 9s. brown-orange .. .. 30·00 20·00
F155 10s. carmine-lake .. .. 24·00 5·50
F156 12s. 6d. deep plum (9.35) £140 £140
F157 15s. sage-green .. .. 60·00 17·00
F158 £1 pink .. .. 60·00 15·00
F159 25s. greenish blue £200 £275
F160 30s. brown (1935) £250 £120
F161 35s. orange-yellow £2000 £2000
F162 £2 bright purple .. .. £300 50·00
F163 £2 10s. red £175 £200
F164 £3 green £300 £150
F165 £3 10s. rose (1935) £1200 £950
F166 £4 light blue (1935) £300 £120
F167 £4 10s. deep olive-grey (1935) £1300 £1000
F168 £5 indigo-blue .. .. £325 90·00

(ii) *Thin, hard "Wiggins Teape" paper with vertical mesh* (1936–40)

(*a*) *Chalk-surfaced* (1936–39)

F169 1s. 3d. pale orange-yellow .. .. .. 3·50 60
F170 2s. 6d. dull brown .. .. 16·00 1·25
F171 4s. pale red-brown .. .. 20·00 2·00
F172 5s. green .. .. 22·00 4·25
F173 6s. carmine-rose .. .. 25·00 8·00
F174 7s. pale blue .. .. 27·00 14·00
F175 8s. slate-violet .. .. 38·00 28·00
F176 9s. brown-orange .. .. 45·00 28·00
F177 10s. pale carmine-lake .. .. .. 38·00 5·50
F178 15s. sage-green .. .. 70·00 20·00
F179 £1 pink .. .. 55·00 17·00
F180 30s. brown (1.39) .. .. £225 95·00
F181 35s. orange-yellow £2500 £2000
F182 £2 bright purple (1937) .. .. .. £300 60·00
F183 £3 green (1937) £300 £150
F184 £5 indigo-blue (1937) £375 £110

(*b*) *Unsurfaced* (1940)

F185 7s. 6d. olive-grey .. .. £120 90·00

Not all values listed above were stocked at ordinary post offices as some of them were primarily required for fiscal purposes but all were valid for postage.

1939. *No.* F161 *surch with Type* F **7**.

F186 35/- on 35s. orange-yellow £300 £200

Because the 35s. orange-yellow could so easily be confused with the 1s. 3d. in the same colour it was surcharged.

1940 (June). *New values surch as Type* F **7**. W **43**. *"Wiggins Teape" chalk-surfaced paper. P* 14.

F187 3/6 on 3s. 6d. grey-green .. .. .. 26·00 8·50
F188 5/6 on 5s. 6d. lilac .. .. 35·00 24·00
F189 11/- on 11s. yellow .. .. £100 65·00
F190 22/- on 22s. scarlet £225 £160
F187/90 .. .. *Set of* 4 £325 £225

These values were primarily needed for fiscal use.

1940–58. *As Type* F **6** (*various frames*). W **98**.

(i) *P* 14. *"Wiggins Teape" chalk-surfaced paper with vertical mesh* (1940–56)

F191 1s. 3d. orange-yellow .. .. .. 3·50 30
F192 1s. 3d. yell & blk (*wmk inverted*) (14.6.55) 1·00 15
b. Error. Yellow & bl (wmk inverted) (7.56) 3·00 5·50
F193 2s. 6d. deep brown .. .. 5·00 15
F194 4s. red-brown .. .. 7·50 25
F195 5s. green .. .. 12·00 50
F196 6s. carmine-rose .. .. 22·00 2·50
F197 7s. pale blue .. .. 25·00 4·25
F198 7s. 6d. olive-grey (*wmk inverted*) (21.12.50) 48·00 45·00
F199 8s. slate-violet .. .. 32·00 13·00
F200 9s. brown-orange (1.46) .. .. .. 20·00 22·00
F201 10s. carmine-lake .. .. 20·00 2·25
F202 15s. sage-green .. .. 38·00 17·00
F203 £1 pink .. .. 24·00 3·50
F204 25s. greenish blue (1946) £275 £300
F205 30s. brown (1946) .. .. £180 95·00
F206 £2 bright purple (1946) .. .. .. 65·00 18·00
F207 £2 10s. red (*wmk inverted*) (9.8.51) .. £225 £190
F208 £3 green (1946) .. .. 80·00 45·00
F209 £3 10s. rose (11.48) £1200 £1000
F210 £4 light blue (*wmk inverted*) (12.2.52) .. £100 48·00
F211 £5 indigo-blue .. .. £130 45·00
F191/211 .. .. *Set of* 21 £2250 £1600

THREE SHILLINGS I.

THREE SHILLINGS II.

3s. 6d.

Type I. Broad serifed capitals

Type II. Taller capitals, without serifs

Surcharged as Type F **7**

F212 3/6 on 3s. 6d. grey-green (I) (1942) .. 18·00 5·00
F213 3/6 on 3s. 6d. grey-green (II) (6.53) .. 12·00 25·00
F214 5/6 on 5s. 6d. lilac (1944) .. .. .. 22·00 10·00
F215 11/- on 11s. yellow (1942) .. .. .. 55·00 40·00
F216 22/- on 22s. scarlet (1945) £170 £120
F212/16 .. .. *Set of* 5 £250 £180

(ii) *P* 14 × 13½. *"Wiggins Teape" unsurfaced paper with horizontal mesh* (1956–58)

F217 1s. 3d. yellow and black (11.56) .. .. 1·50 75
F218 £1 pink (20.10.58) .. .. 32·00 20·00

No. F192b had the inscription printed in blue in error but as many as 378,000 were printed.

From about 1949–53 inferior paper had to be used and for technical reasons it was necessary to feed the paper into the machine in a certain way which resulted in whole printings with the watermark inverted for most values. These are fully listed in the *New Zealand Concise Catalogue*. In the above list the prices are for the cheapest form.

F 8

1967 (10 July). *Decimal currency.* W **98** (*sideways*). *Unsurfaced paper. P* 14.

F219 F **8** $4 deep reddish violet .. .. 2·00 55
F220 $6 emerald .. .. 3·00 1·50
F221 $8 light greenish blue .. .. .. 4·00 3·50
F222 $10 deep ultramarine .. .. .. 5·00 3·50
F219/22 .. .. *Set of* 4 12·50 8·00

The original printings were line perf on paper with the sideways watermark inverted ("N Z" to right of star when viewed from the front). From 1968 the stamps were comb perforated with the sideways watermark normal. The prices quoted are for the cheaper printings. Both are listed in the *New Zealand Concise Catalogue*.

1986 (Apr). *As Nos.* F220/2 *but without wmk. Chalk-surfaced paper.*

F223 F **8** $6 bright green .. .. .. 4·00 4·50
F224 $8 light greenish blue .. .. .. 6·50 7·50
F225 $10 deep ultramarine .. .. .. 8·00 9·00
F223/5 .. .. *Set of* 3 17·00 19·00

No further printings were made of the $4 after the introduction of a $5 postage stamp in 1981.

ANTARCTIC EXPEDITIONS

VICTORIA LAND

These issues were made under authority of the New Zealand Postal Department and, while not strictly necessary, they actually franked correspondence to New Zealand. They were sold to the public at a premium.

1908 (15 Jan). *Shackleton Expedition. T* **42** *of New Zealand* (*p* 14), *optd* "King Edward VII Land", *in two lines, reading up, by Coulls, Culling and Co., Wellington.*

A1 1d. rose-carmine (No. 356 Royle) (G.) .. £400 35·00
a. Opt double .. .. — £1500
A1*b* 1d. rose-carmine (No. 352*c* Waterlow) (G.) .. £1300 £800

Nos. A1/1*b* were used on board the expedition ship, *Nimrod*, and at the Cape Royds base in McMurdo Sound. Due to adverse conditions Shackleton landed in Victoria Land rather than King Edward VII Land the intended destination.

1911 (9 Feb)–**13**. *Scott Expedition. Stamps of New Zealand optd* "VICTORIA LAND.", *in two lines by Govt Printer, Wellington.*

A2 **50** ½d. deep green (No. 387*aa*) (18.1.13) .. £500 £500
A3 **52** 1d. carmine (No. 405) .. .. .. 45·00 70·00
a. No stop after "LAND" £375 £550

Nos. A2/3 were used at the Cape Evans base on McMurdo Sound or on the *Terra Nova*.

ROSS DEPENDENCY

This comprises a sector of the Antarctic continent and a number of islands. It was claimed by Great Britain on 30 July 1923 and soon afterward put under the jurisdiction of New Zealand.

1 H.M.S. *Erebus*

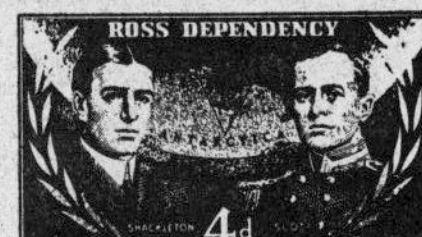

2 Shackleton and Scott

3 Map of Ross Dependency and New Zealand

4 Queen Elizabeth II

(Des E. M. Taylor (3d.), L. C. Mitchell (4d.), R. Smith (8d.), J.Berry (1s. 6d.). Recess D.L.R.)

1957 (11 Jan). W **98** *of New Zealand* (*Mult* N Z *and Star*). *P* 13 (1*s.* 6*d.*) *or* 14 (*others*).

1 **1** 3d. indigo .. .. 2·50 75
2 **2** 4d. carmine-red .. .. 2·50 75
3 **3** 8d. bright carmine-red and ultramarine .. 2·50 1·00
a. Bright carmine-red and blue .. .. 7·50 6·00
4 **4** 1s. 6d. slate-purple .. .. 2·50 1·25
1/4 .. .. *Set of* 4 9·00 3·25

(New Currency. 100 cents = 1 dollar)

5 H.M.S. *Erebus*

1967 (10 July). *Decimal currency. As Nos.* 1/4 *but with values inscr in decimal currency as T* **5**. *Chalky paper* (*except* 15 *c.*). W **98** *of New Zealand* (*sideways on* 7 *c.*). *P* 13 (15 *c.*) *or* 14 (*others*).

5 **5** 2 c. indigo .. .. 8·00 4·75
a. Deep blue .. .. 10·00 7·00
6 **2** 3 c. carmine-red .. .. 7·00 4·75
7 **3** 7 c. bright carmine-red and ultramarine .. 9·00 7·50
8 **4** 15 c. slate-purple .. .. 12·00 12·00
5/8 .. .. *Set of* 4 32·00 26·00

6 Great Skua   7 Scott Base

(Des M. Cleverley. Litho B.W.)

1972 (18 Jan)–**79**. *Horiz design as T* **6** (3 *to* 8 *c.*) *or* **7** (10, 18 *c.*). *Ordinary paper. P* 14½ × 14 (10, 18 *c.*) *or* 13 (*others*).

9 3 c. black, brownish grey and pale blue .. 1·10 1·10
a. Chalk-surfaced paper (2.79) 65 75
10 4 c. black, royal blue and violet 70 85
a. Chalk-surfaced paper (2.79) 40 60
11 5 c. black, brownish grey and rose-lilac .. 70 85
a. Chalk-surfaced paper (2.79) 30 60
12 8 c. black, yellow-brown and brownish grey 70 1·00
a. Chalk-surfaced paper (2.79) 40 70
13 10 c. black, turquoise-green and slate-green .. 1·00 1·50
a. Perf 13½ × 13. Chalk-surfaced paper (2.79) 40 80
14 18 c. black, violet and bright violet .. .. 2·25 2·50
a. Perf 13½ × 13. Chalk-surfaced paper (2.79) .. .. 50 1·25
9/14 .. .. *Set of* 6 5·75 7·00
9a/14a .. .. *Set of* 6 2·40 4·25

Designs:—4 c. "Hercules" aeroplane at Williams Field; 5 c. Shackleton's Hut; 8 c. Supply ship H.M.N.Z.S. *Endeavour*; 18 c. Tabular ice floe.

8 Adelie Penguins

(Des R. Conly. Litho Asher and Co, Melbourne)

1982 (20 Jan). *Horiz designs as T* **8**. *Multicoloured. P* 15½.

15 5 c. Type **8** 25 10
16 10 c. Tracked vehicles 15 10
17 20 c. Scott Base 20 20
18 30 c. Field party 25 30
19 40 c. Vanda Station 30 30
20 50 c. Scott's hut, Cape Evans 35 35
15/20 .. .. *Set of* 6 1·40 1·25

The post office at Scott Base closed on 30 September 1987 and Nos. 15/20 were withdrawn from sale at philatelic counters in New Zealand on 31 December 1987.

TOKELAU

Formerly known as the Union Islands, and administered as part of the Gilbert & Ellice Islands Colony, they were transferred to New Zealand on 4 November 1925 and then administered by Western Samoa. The islands were finally incorporated in New Zealand on 1 January 1949 and became a dependency. The name Tokelau was adopted on 7 May 1946.

> Stamps of GILBERT AND ELLICE ISLANDS were used in Tokelau from February 1911 until June 1926 when they were replaced by those of SAMOA. These were current until 1948.
> The post office on Atafu opened in 1911, but the cancellations for the other two islands, Fakaofo and Nukunono, did not appear until 1926.

1 Atafu Village and Map

(Des J. Berry from photographs by T. T. C. Humphrey. Recess B.W.)

1948 (22 June). *T* 1 *and similar horiz designs. Wmk T* **98** *of New Zealand (Mult N Z and Star). P* 13½.

1	½d. red-brown and purple	15	20
2	1d. chestnut and green	15	20
3	2d. green and ultramarine	15	20
1/3	*Set of* 3	40	55

Designs:–1d. Nukunono hut and map; 2d. Fakaofo village and map.

Covers are known postmarked 16 June 1948, but this was in error for 16 July.

1953 (15 June*). *Coronation. As No.* 715 *of New Zealand, but inscr* "TOKELAU ISLANDS".

4	**164** 3d. brown	3·50	3·75

*This is the date of issue in Tokelau. The stamps were released in New Zealand on 25 May.

ONE SHILLING (4)

6D TOKELAU ISLANDS (5)

1956 (27 Mar). *No.* 1 *surch with T* 4 *by Govt Printer, Wellington.*

5	1 1s. on ½d. red-brown and purple	4·00	3·50

1966 (8 Nov). *Postal fiscal stamps of New Zealand (Type* F **6**), *but without value, surch as T* 5 *by Govt Printer, Wellington. W* **98** *of New Zealand. P* 14.

6	6d. light blue	65	1·00
7	8d. light emerald	75	1·00
8	2s. light pink	85	1·40
6/8	*Set of* 3	2·00	3·00

(New Currency. 100 cents = 1 dollar (New Zealand))

(6) (7)

1967 (4 Sept*). *Decimal currency.*

(*a*) *Nos.* 1/3 *surch in decimal currency as T* 6 *by Govt Printer, Wellington*

9	1c. on 1d.	60	60
10	2 c. on 2d.	1·00	1·00
11	10 c. on ½d.	2·00	2·00

(*b*) *Postal Fiscal stamps of New Zealand (Type* F **6**), *but without value, surch as T* 7 *by Govt Printer, Wellington. W* **98** *of New Zealand (sideways). P* 14 (*line or comb*)

12	**F 6** 3 c. reddish lilac	50	30
13	5 c. light blue	50	30
14	7 c. light emerald	50	30
15	20 c. light pink	65	40
9/15	*Set of* 7	5·25	4·50

*This is the date of issue in Tokelau. The stamps were released in New Zealand on 10 July.

8 British Protectorate (1877)

12 H.M.S. *Dolphin*, 1765

(Des New Zealand P.O. artists from suggestions by Tokelau Administration. Litho B.W.)

1969 (8 Aug). *History of Tokelau. T* 8 *and similar horiz designs. W* **98** *of New Zealand. P* 13 × 12½.

16	5 c. ultramarine, yellow and black	25	10
17	10 c. vermilion, yellow and black	30	10
18	15 c. green, yellow and black	35	15
19	20 c. yellow-brown, yellow and black	40	15
16/19	*Set of* 4	1·10	45

Designs:—10 c. Annexed to Gilbert and Ellice Islands, 1916: 15 c. New Zealand Administration, 1925; 20 c. New Zealand Territory, 1948.

1969 (1 Oct). *Christmas. As T* **301** *of New Zealand, but inscr* "TOKELAU ISLANDS". *W* **98** *of New Zealand. P* 13½ × 14½.

20	**301** 2 c. multicoloured	10	15

1970 (1 Oct). *Christmas. As T* **314** *of New Zealand but inscr* "TOKELAU ISLANDS". *P* 12½.

21	**341** 2 c. multicoloured	10	20

(Des D. B. Stevenson. Litho B.W.)

1970 (9 Dec). *Discovery of Tokelau. T* **12** *and similar multicoloured designs. P* 13½.

22	5 c. Type **12**	1·50	35
23	10 c. H.M.S. *Pandora*, 1791	1·50	35
24	25 c. *General Jackson*, 1835 (*horiz*)	3·25	70
22/4	*Set of* 3	5·75	1·25

13 Fan

14 Windmill Pump

(Des Enid Hunter. Litho Harrison)

1971 (20 Oct). *Various horiz designs as T* **13** *showing handicrafts. Multicoloured. P* 14.

25	1 c. Type **13**	20	20
26	2 c. Hand-bag	30	30
27	3 c. Basket	40	40
28	5 c. Hand-bag	50	65
29	10 c. Shopping-bag	60	80
30	15 c. Fishing box	1·00	1·50
31	20 c. Canoe	1·25	2·00
32	25 c. Fishing hooks	1·25	2·00
25/32	*Set of* 8	5·00	7·00

(Des A. G. Mitchell. Litho Questa)

1972 (6 Sept). *25th Anniversary of South Pacific Commission. T* **14** *and similar vert designs. Multicoloured. P* 14 × 13½.

33	5 c. Type **14**	35	60
34	10 c. Community well	45	75
35	15 c. Pest eradication	55	1·00
36	20 c. Flags of member nations	60	1·25
33/6	*Set of* 4	1·75	3·25

On No. 35 "PACIFIC" is spelt "PACFIC".

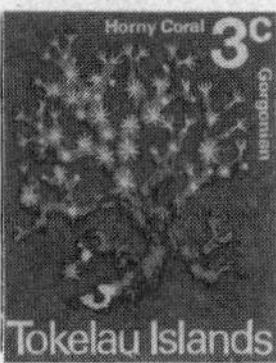

15 Horny Coral

16 Hump-back Cowrie

(Des Eileen Mayo. Litho B.W.)

1973 (12 Sept). *Coral. T* **15** *and similar vert designs. Multicoloured. P* 13.

37	3 c. Type **15**	1·00	80
38	5 c. Soft Coral	1·00	90
39	15 c. Mushroom Coral	1·75	1·50
40	25 c. Staghorn Coral	2·00	1·75
37/40	*Set of* 4	5·25	4·50

(Des G. F. Fuller. Litho Questa)

1974 (13 Nov). *"Shells of the Coral Reef". T* **16** *and similar horiz designs. Multicoloured. P* 14.

41	3 c. Type **16**	1·50	1·25
42	5 c. Tiger Cowrie	1·75	1·25
43	15 c. Mole Cowrie	3·00	2·75
44	25 c. Eyed Cowrie	4·00	3·00
41/4	*Set of* 4	9·00	7·50

17 Moorish Idol

18 Canoe Building

(Des Eileen Mayo. Litho Questa)

1975 (19 Nov). *Fishes. T* **17** *and similar vert designs. Multicoloured. P* 14.

45	5 c. Type **17**	50	1·00
46	10 c. Long-nosed Butterfly-fish	70	1·25
47	15 c. Lined Butterfly-fish	85	1·75
48	25 c. Red Fire-fish	1·10	2·00
45/8	*Set of* 4	2·75	5·50

(Des F. Paulo. Litho Questa)

1976 (27 Oct)–**81**. *T* **18** *and similar multicoloured designs showing local life. P* 14 × 13½ (9 *c. to* $1) *or* 13½ × 14 (*others*).

49	1 c. Type **18**	15	30
	a. Perf 14½ × 15 (15.7.81)	10	15
50	2 c. Reef fishing	20	60
51	3 c. Weaving preparation	25	25
	a. Perf 14½ × 15 (15.7.81)	10	15
52	5 c. Umu (kitchen)	30	45
	a. Perf 14½ × 15 (15.7.81)	10	15
53	9 c. Carving (*vert*)	10	35
	a. Perf 15 × 14½ (15.7.81)	10	15
54	20 c. Husking coconuts (*vert*)	15	40
	a. Perf 15 × 14½ (15.7.81)	15	20
55	50 c. Wash day (*vert*)	20	70
	a. Perf 15 × 14½ (15.7.81)	20	20
56	$1 Meal time (*vert*)	35	1·25
	a. Perf 15 × 14½ (15.7.81)	30	30
49a/56a	*Set of* 8	1·10	1·50

19 White Tern

20 Westminster Abbey

(Des F. Paulo. Litho Questa)

1977 (16 Nov). *Birds of Tokelau. T* **19** *and similar horiz designs. Multicoloured. P* 14½.

57	8 c. Type **19**	30	40
58	10 c. Turnstone	35	45
59	15 c. White-capped Noddy	60	70
60	30 c. Common Noddy	90	1·25
57/60	*Set of* 4	2·00	2·50

(Des Eileen Mayo. Litho Questa)

1978 (28 June). *25th Anniv of Coronation. T* **20** *and similar vert designs. Multicoloured. P* 14.

61	8 c. Type **20**	20	20
62	10 c. King Edward's Chair	20	20
63	15 c. Coronation regalia	30	35
64	30 c. Queen Elizabeth II	50	60
61/4	*Set of* 4	1·10	1·25

21 Canoe Race

22 Rugby

(Des F. Paulo. Photo Heraclio Fournier)

1978 (8 Nov). *Canoe Racing. T* **21** *and similar horiz designs showing races. P* 13½ × 14.

65	8 c. multicoloured	20	20
66	12 c. multicoloured	25	25
67	15 c. multicoloured	30	30
68	30 c. multicoloured	50	50
65/8	*Set of* 4	1·10	1·10

(Des F. Paulo. Photo Heraclio Fournier)

1979 (7 Nov). *Sports. T* **22** *and similar horiz designs. Multicoloured. P* 13½.

69	10 c. Type **22**	15	15
70	15 c. Cricket	40	60
71	20 c. Rugby (*different*)	40	65
72	30 c. Cricket (*different*)	60	80
69/72	*Set of* 4	1·40	2·00

23 Surfing

24 Pole Vaulting

(Des F. Paulo. Litho J.W.)

1980 (5 Nov). *Water Sports. T* **23** *and similar horiz designs. Multicoloured. P* 13.

73	10 c. Type **23**	10	10
74	20 c. Surfing (*different*)	12	15
75	30 c. Swimming	20	25
76	50 c. Swimming (*different*)	25	35
73/6	*Set of* 4	60	75

(Des F. Paulo. Photo Heraclio Fournier)

1981 (4 Nov). *Sports. T* **24** *and similar vert designs. Multicoloured. P* 14 × 13½.

77	10 c. Type **24**	10	10
78	20 c. Volleyball	20	20
79	30 c. Running	25	30
80	50 c. Volleyball (*different*)	30	35
77/80	*Set of* 4	75	85

25 Wood Carving

26 Octopus Lure

(Des R. Conly. Litho Enschedé)

1982 (5 May). *Handicrafts. T* **25** *and similar vert designs. Multicoloured. P* 14 × 13½.

81	10 s. Type **25**	10	10
82	22 s. Bow-drilling sea shell	15	25
83	34 s. Bowl finishing	20	35
84	60 s. Basket weaving	35	50
81/4	*Set of* 4	70	1·10

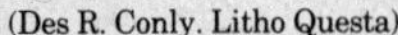

(Des R. Conly. Litho Questa)

1982 (3 Nov). *Fishing Methods. T* **26** *and similar vert designs. Multicoloured. P* 14.

85	5 s. Type **26**	10	10
86	18 s. Multiple-hook fishing	30	20
87	23 s. Ruvettus fishing	35	25
88	34 s. Netting flying fish	40	30
89	63 s. Noose fishing	50	40
90	75 s. Bonito fishing	60	45
85/90	*Set of* 6	2·00	1·50

27 Outrigger Canoe

28 Javelin Throwing

(Des R. Conly. Litho Cambec Press, Melbourne)

1983 (4 May). *Transport. T* **27** *and similar horiz designs. Multicoloured. P* 13 × 13½.

91	5 s. Type **27**	10	10
92	18 s. Wooden whaleboat	15	15
93	23 s. Aluminium whaleboat	15	20
94	34 s. *Alia* (fishing catamaran)	25	25
95	63 s. M.V. *Frysna* (freighter)	35	40
96	75 s. McKinnon "Goose" flying boat	45	50
91/6	*Set of* 6	1·25	1·40

(Des R. Conly. Litho Questa)

1983 (2 Nov). *Traditional Pastimes. T* **28** *and similar horiz designs. Multicoloured. P* 14.

97	5 s. Type **28**	10	10
98	18 s. String game	15	15
99	23 s. Fire making	15	20
100	34 s. Shell throwing	25	25
101	63 s. Hand-ball game	35	40
102	75 s. Mass wrestling	45	50
97/102	*Set of* 6	1·25	1·40

29 Planting and Harvesting

30 Convict Tang ("Manini")

(Des R. Conly. Litho J.W.)

1984 (2 May). *Copra Industry. T* **29** *and similar vert designs. Multicoloured. P* 13½ × 13.

103	48 s. Type **29**	40	45
	a. Horiz strip of 5. Nos. 103/7	1·90	
104	48 s. Husking and splitting	40	45
105	48 s. Drying	40	45
106	48 s. Bagging	40	45
107	48 s. Shipping	40	45
103/7	*Set of* 5	1·90	2·00

Nos. 103/7 were printed together, *se-tenant*, in horizontal strips of 5 throughout the sheet.

(Des R. Conly. Litho B.D.T.)

1984 (5 Dec). *Fishes. T* **30** *and similar horiz designs. Multicoloured. P* 15 × 14.

108	1 s. Type **30**	10	10
109	2 s. Flying Fish ("Hahave")	10	10
110	5 s. Fire Wrasse ("Uloulo")	10	10
111	9 s. Unicorn Fish ("Ume ihu")	10	10
112	23 s. Napoleon Fish ("Lafilafi")	15	20
113	34 s. Red Snapper ("Fagamea")	20	25
114	50 s. Yellow Fin Tuna ("Kakahi")	30	35
115	75 s. Castor-oil Fish ("Palu po")	50	55
116	$1 Grey Shark ("Mokoha")	65	70
117	$2 Black Marlin ("Hakula")	1·40	1·50
108/17	*Set of* 10	3·25	3·50

Examples of Nos. 108/17 are known postmarked at Nukunonu on 23 November 1984.

The 50 s., No. 114 was sold at the "STAMPEX 86" Stamp Exhibition, Adelaide, overprinted "STAMPEX 86 4–10 AUGUST 1986" in three lines. These overprinted stamps were not available from post offices in Tokelau. Used examples come from dealers' stocks subsequently sent to the islands for cancellation.

31 *Ficus tinctoria* ("Mati")

32 Administration Centre, Atafu

(Des R. Conly. Litho Wyatt and Wilson Ltd, Christchurch, N.Z.)

1985 (26 June). *Native Trees. T* **31** *and similar vert designs. Multicoloured. P* 13.

118	5 c. Type **31**	10	10
119	18 c. *Morinda citrifolia* ("Nonu")	15	15
120	32 c. Breadfruit Tree ("Ulu")	20	25
121	48 c. *Pandanus tectorius* ("Fala")	35	40
122	60 c. *Cordia subcordata* ("Kanava")	40	45
123	75 c. Coconut Palm ("Niu")	50	55
118/23	*Set of* 6	1·50	1·60

Nos. 118/23 were issued with matt, almost invisible PVA gum.

(Des R. Conly. Litho Questa)

1985 (4 Dec). *Tokelau Architecture* (1*st series*). *Public Buildings. T* **32** *and similar horiz designs. Multicoloured. P* 14.

124	5 c. Type **32**	10	10
125	18 c. Administration Centre, Nukunonu	15	15
126	32 c. Administration Centre, Fakaofo	20	25
127	48 c. Congregational Church, Atafu	35	40
128	60 c. Catholic Church, Nukunonu	40	45
129	75 c. Congregational Church, Fakaofo	50	55
124/9	*Set of* 6	1·50	1·60

33 Atafu Hospital

(Des R. Conly. Litho Cambec Press, Melbourne)

1986 (7 May). *Tokelau Architecture* (2*nd series*). *Hospitals and Schools. T* **33** *and similar horiz designs. Multicoloured. P* 13½.

130	5 c. Type **33**	10	10
131	18 c. St. Joseph's Hospital, Nukunonu	10	10
132	32 c. Fenuafala Hospital, Fakaofo	20	25
133	48 c. Matauala School, Atafu	35	40
134	60 c. Matiti School, Nukunonu	40	45
135	75 c. Fenuafala School, Fakaofo	55	60
130/5	*Set of* 6	1·50	1·60

34 Coconut Crab

(Des R. Conly. Litho Questa)

1986 (3 Dec). *Agricultural Livestock. T* **34** *and similar horiz designs. Multicoloured. P* 14.

136	5 c. Type **34**	10	10
137	18 c. Pigs	15	15
138	32 c. Chickens	25	25
139	48 c. Reef Hawksbill Turtle	40	40
140	60 c. Goats	45	45
141	75 c. Ducks	60	60
136/41	*Set of* 6	1·75	1·75

35 *Scaevola taccada* ("Gahu")

(Des R. Conly. Litho Questa)

1987 (6 May). *Tokelau Flora. T* **35** *and similar horiz designs. Multicoloured. P* 14.

142	5 c. Type **35**	15	10
143	18 c. *Hernandia nymphaeifolia* ("Puka")	20	15
144	32 c. *Pandanus tectorius* ("Higano")	35	30
145	48 c. *Gardenia taitensis* ("Tialetiale")	55	45
146	60 c. *Pemphis acidula* ("Gagie")	70	55
147	75 c. *Guettarda speciosa* ("Puapua")	80	70
142/7	*Set of* 6	2·50	2·00

36 Javelin-throwing

(Des F. Paulo. Litho Leigh-Mardon Ltd, Melbourne)

1987 (2 Dec). *Tokelau Olympic Sports. T* **36** *and similar horiz designs. Multicoloured. P* 14 × 14½.

148	5 c. Type **36**	10	10
149	18 c. Shot-putting	15	15
150	32 c. Long jumping	20	25
151	48 c. Hurdling	35	40
152	60 c. Sprinting	40	45
153	75 c. Wrestling	50	55
148/53	*Set of* 6	1·50	1·60

37 Small Boat Flotilla in Sydney Harbour

38 Island Maps and Ministerial Representatives

(Des and litho CPE Australia Ltd, Melbourne)

1988 (30 July). *Bicentenary of Australian Settlement and "Sydpex '88" National Stamp Exhibition, Sydney. T* **37** *and similar square designs. Multicoloured. P* 13.

154	50 c. Type **37**	40	40
	a. Horiz strip of 5. Nos. 154/8	1·75	
155	50 c. Sailing ships and liners	40	40
156	50 c. Sydney skyline and Opera House	40	40
157	50 c. Sydney Harbour Bridge	40	40
158	50 c. Sydney waterfront	40	40
154/8	*Set of* 5	1·75	1·75

Nos. 154/8 were printed together, *se-tenant*, in horizontal strips of five throughout the sheet, forming a composite aerial view of the re-enactment of First Fleet's arrival.

(Des F. Paulo. Litho Leigh-Mardon Ltd, Melbourne)

1988 (10 Aug). *Political Development. T* **38** *and similar horiz designs. Multicoloured. P* 14½.

159	5 c. Type **38** (administration transferred to N.Z. Foreign Affairs Ministry, 1975)	10	10
160	18 c. General Fono (island assembly) meeting, 1977	15	15
161	32 c. Arms of New Zealand (first visit by New Zealand Prime Minister, 1985)	20	25
162	48 c. U.N. logo (first visit by U.N. representative, 1976)	35	40
163	60 c. Canoe and U.N. logo (first Tokelau delegation to U.N., 1987)	40	45
164	75 c. Secretary and N.Z. flag (first islander appointed as Official Secretary, 1987)	50	55
159/64	*Set of* 6	1·50	1·60

39 Three Wise Men in Canoe and Star

(Des F. Paulo. Litho Govt Ptg Office, Wellington)

1988 (7 Dec). *Christmas. T* **39** *and similar horiz designs showing Christmas in Tokelau. Multicoloured. P* 13½.

165	5 c. Type **39**	10	10
166	20 c. Tokelau Nativity	15	20
167	40 c. Flight to Egypt by canoe	30	35
168	60 c. Children's presents	40	45
169	70 c. Christ child in Tokelauan basket	50	55
170	$1 Christmas parade	70	75
165/70	*Set of* 6	1·90	2·10

40 Launching Outrigger Canoe

(Des F. Paulo. Litho Leigh-Mardon Ltd, Melbourne)

1989 (28 June). *Food Gathering. T* **40** *and similar horiz designs. Multicoloured. P* 14×14½.

171	50 c. Type **40**	35	40
	a. Horiz strip of 3. Nos. 171/3	1·00	
172	50 c. Paddling canoe away from shore ..	35	40
173	50 c. Fishing punt and sailing canoe ..	35	40
174	50 c. Canoe on beach	35	40
	a. Horiz strip of 3. Nos. 174/6	1·00	
175	50 c. Loading coconuts into canoe	35	40
176	50 c. Tokelauans with produce	35	40
171/6	.. .. *Set of* 6	1·90	2·10

Nos. 171/3 and 174/6 were each printed together, *se-tenant*, in horizontal strips of three throughout the sheets, forming composite designs.

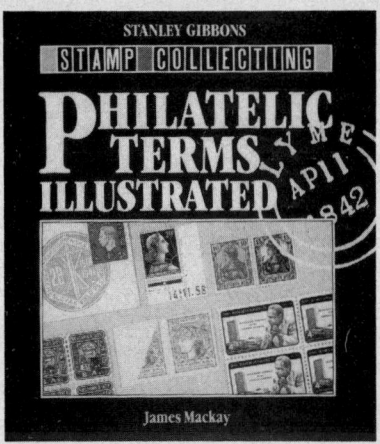

Niger Coast Protectorate

OIL RIVERS PROTECTORATE

A British consulate for the Bights of Benin and Biafra was established in 1849 on the off-shore Spanish island of Fernando Poo. In 1853 the appointment was divided with a consul for th Bight of Benin at Lagos. The consulate for the Bight of Biafra was transferred to Old Calabar in 1882.

A British protectorate was proclaimed over the coastal area, with the exceptions of the colony of Lagos and the centre of the Niger delta, in June 1885. It was not, however, until 1891 that steps were taken to set up an admininistration with a consul-general at Old Calabar and vice-consuls at some of the river ports.

The consulate-general at Old Calabar and the vice-consulates at Benin, Bonny, Brass, Forcados and Opobo acted as collection and distribution centres for mail from November 1891, but were not recognised as post offices until 20 July 1892.

For a few months from July 1892 local administrative handstamps, as Type Z 1, were in use either as obliterators or in conjunction with the c.d.s.

Z 1

These oval handstamps are usually found on the 1892 overprinted issue, but the following are known on unoverprinted stamps of Great Britain:

1892

BENIN

Stamps of GREAT BRITAIN *cancelled with oval postmark, Type* Z 1, *inscribed* "BENIN".

Z1 2½d. purple/*blue* (V.) .. ..

BONNY

Stamps of GREAT BRITAIN *cancelled with oval postmark, Type* Z 1, *inscribed* "BONNY".

Z2 2½d. purple/*blue* (V.) .. ..

BRASS RIVER

Stamps of GREAT BRITAIN *cancelled with oval postmark, Type* Z 1, *inscribed* "BRASS".

Z3 2½d. purple/*blue* (Blk.) .. ..

OLD CALABAR RIVER

Stamps of GREAT BRITAIN *cancelled with oval postmark, Type* Z 1, *inscribed* "OLD CALABAR".

Z4 2½d. purple/*blue* (Blk.) .. ..

Stamps of GREAT BRITAIN *cancelled* "BRITISH VICE-CONSULATE OLD CALABAR" *within double-lined circle.*

Z5 2½d. purple/*blue* (V.) £300
Z6 5d. dull purple and blue (V.) .. ..

For later use of Type Z 1 and the circular Vice-Consulate marks see note beneath No. 6.

Z 2.

Unoverprinted stamps of Great Britain remained officially valid for postage in the Protectorate until 30 September 1892, but were available from post offices in the Niger Company Territories up to the end of 1899. The two areas were so closely linked geographically that offices in the Protectorate continued to accept letters franked with Great Britain stamps until the reorganisation of 1900. The listing below covers confirmed examples, known on cover or piece, the prices quoted being for the latter.

1892 *to* 1899

Stamps of GREAT BRITAIN *cancelled with circular postmarks as Type* Z 2.

BENIN RIVER

Z 7 2d. green and carmine .. ..
Z 8 2½d. purple/*blue* .. ..
Z 9 3d. purple/*yellow* .. ..
Z10 5d. dull purple and blue .. ..
Z11 1s. green .. ..

BONNY RIVER

Z12 ½d. vermilion .. ..
Z13 2½d. purple/*blue* £150
Z14 5d. dull purple and blue .. ..
Z15 6d. deep purple/*red* .. ..

BRASS RIVER

Z16 1½d. dull purple and green .. ..
Z17 2½d. purple/*blue* £850
Z17*a* 2½d. purple/*blue* (squared-circle cancellation)
Z18 6d. purple/*red* £700

FORCADOS RIVER

Z19 1d. lilac £525
Z20 2½d. purple/*blue* .. ..
Z21 5d. dull purple and blue (m/s cancellation)
Z22 10d. dull purple and carmine .. ..

OLD CALABAR RIVER

Z23 ½d. vermilion .. ..
Z24 1d. lilac .. ..
Z25 1½d. dull purple and green .. .. ..
Z26 2d. green and vermilion .. .. ..
Z27 2½d. purple/*blue* .. ..
Z28 5d. dull purple and blue .. .. ..
Z29 6d. purple/*red* .. ..
Z30 1s. green .. ..

OPOBO RIVER

Z31 2½d. purple/*blue* .. ..
Z32 10d. dull purple and carmine .. ..

Some later covers are known franked with G.B. stamps, but the origin of the stamps involved is uncertain.

PRICES FOR STAMPS ON COVER

Nos. 1/6	*from* × 6
Nos. 7/36	*from* × 2
Nos. 37/44	—
Nos. 45/50	*from* × 10
Nos. 51/6	*from* × 12
Nos. 57/65	*from* × 2
Nos. 66/73	*from* × 12

BRITISH
PROTECTORATE

OIL RIVERS

(1)

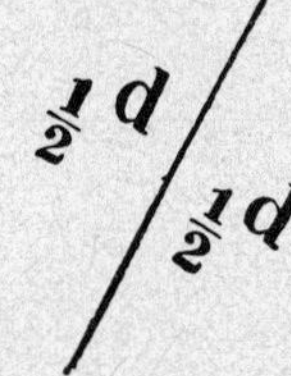

(2)

1892 (20 July)–**94**. *Stamps of Great Britain optd by D.L.R. with T* 1.

1 **71** ½d. vermilion .. .. 5·50 4·50
2 **57** 1d. lilac .. .. 5·50 4·50
a. Opt reversed "OIL RIVERS" at top £4000
b. Bisected (½d.) (on cover) .. .. † £2500
3 **73** 2d. green and carmine .. .. .. 11·00 8·00
a. Bisected (1d.) (on cover) .. .. † £5000
4 **74** 2½d. purple/*blue* .. .. .. 6·50 2·00
5 **78** 5d. dull purple & blue (No. 207*a* Die II) 7·50 7·50
a. On No. 207 (Die I) .. ..
6 **82** 1s. green .. .. 42·00 48·00
1/6 .. .. *Set of* 6 70·00 65·00
1/6 H/S "Specimen" .. .. .. *Set of* 6 £350

Nos. 2b and 3a were used at Bonny River during August and September 1894.

OVAL HANDSTAMPS. In addition to Nos. Z1/4 postmarks as Type Z 1 are also known used on the 1892–94 overprinted issue from the following offices:

Bakana (Nos. 2, 4/6)
Benin (Nos. 1/6)
Bonny (No. 2)
Brass (Nos. 3/5)
Buguma (Nos. 4 and 6)
Old Calabar (No. 4)
Opobo (Nos. 1/3)
Sombreiro River (Nos. 1/6)

The Vice-Consulate marks, as Nos. Z5/6, are also known struck on examples of No. 4 from Bonny, Forcados or Old Calabar.

Nos. 2 to 6 surcharged locally

1893 (3 Sept). *Issued at Old Calabar. Surch with T* 2 *and then bisected.*

7 ½d. on half of 1d. (R.) £150 £140
a. Unsevered pair £450 £425
ab. Surch inverted and dividing line reversed (unsevered pair) .. .. .. — £4000
b. Surch reversed (dividing line running from left to right) .. .. .. — £4500
c. Straight top to "1" in "½" £300 £300
d. "½" omitted .. ..
e. Surch double (in pair with normal) .. — £1200
f. *Se-tenant* pair. Nos. 7/8 .. .. .. — £7000
8 ½d. on half of 1d. (V.) £4000 £3750
a. Surch double (pair) £8000

The surcharge was applied in a setting covering one horizontal row at a time. Violet ink was used for the top row in the first sheet, but was then replaced with red.

HALF PENNY.

(3)

HALF PENNY.

(4)

1893 (Dec). *Issued at Old Calabar. Nos. 3/6 handstamped.*

(*a*) *With T* **3**

9 ½d. on 2d. (V.) £275 £275
a. Surch inverted £2750
b. Surch diagonal (up or down) £2250
c. Surch vertical (up or down) £1200
10 ½d. on 2½d. (Verm.) £6500
a. Surch in carmine £10000

(*b*) *With T* **4**

11 ½d. on 2½d. (G.) £300 £300
a. Surch double £2000
b. Surch diagonally inverted £1500
12 ½d. on 2½d. (Verm) £325 £325
13 ½d. on 2½d. (C.) £325 £325
a. Surch omitted (in pair) .. .. ..
14 ½d. on 2½d. (B.) £375 £375
15 ½d. on 2½d. (Blk.) £2500
a. Surch inverted .. ..
b. Surch diagonal inverted (up or down) .. £2500
16 ½d. on 2½d. (B.-Blk.) £2500

In T **3** "HALF" measures 9½ mm and "PENNY" 12½ mm with space 1½ mm between the words. Bar 14½ mm ending below the stop. The "F" is nearly always defective.

In T **4** "HALF" is 8½ mm, "PENNY" 12½ mm, spacing 2½ mm, and bar 16 mm, extending beyond the stop.

HALF PENN.Y

5 (Stop after "N")

HALF PENNY

6 (No stop after "N")

(*c*) *With T* **5**

17 ½d. on 2½d. (Verm.) £350 £35
a. Surch double .. .. — £130
b. Surch vertical (up) .. .. .. — £200

(*d*) *With T* **6**

18 ½d. on 2d. (V.) £650 £50
19 ½d. on 2½d. (Verm.) £225 £20
a. Surch inverted £1200
b. Surch double .. .. — £120
c. Surch diagonal (up or down) £1200
d. Surch omitted (in strip of 3) £5500
e. Surch vertical (up or down) £850
f. Surch diagonal, inverted (up or down) £1700

In T **5** the "P" and "Y" are raised, and the space between th words is about 4 mm. Bar is short, approx 13½ mm. T **6** is simila but without the stop after "N".

Half Penny

(7)

Half Penny

(8)

(*e*) *With T* **7**

20 ½d. on 2d. (V.) £225 £22
a. Surch double .. .. — £550
b. Surch vertical (up or down) £1500
c. Surch diagonal (up or down) £1400
d. Surch diagonal (inverted) £2750
21 ½d. on 2½d. (Verm.) £225 £20
a. Surch double £4000
b. Surch vertical (up or down) £1300
c. Surch inverted £1500
d. Surch diagonal (up or down) £1200
e. Surch diagonal, inverted (up) £3000
22 ½d. on 2½d. (B.) £4500 £400
23 ½d. on 2½d. (C.) .. ..
24 ½d. on 2½d. (V.) £2750

(*f*) *With T* **8**

25 ½d. on 2½d. (Verm.) £300 £325
a. Surch diagonal (up) £1600
26 ½d. on 2½d. (B.) .. ..
27 ½d. on 2½d. (G.) £275 £250
a. Surch double .. ..
28 ½d. on 2½d. (C.) .. .. — £80

In T **7** the "a" and "e" are narrow and have a short upward terminal hook. The "l" has a very small hook. The letters "nny" have curved serifs, and the distance between the words is 5½ mm

In T **8** the "a" and "e" are wider. The "l" has a wider hook. The letters "nny" have straight serifs, and the distance between the words is 4¼ mm.

HALF PENNY.

(9)

HALF PENNY

(10)

(*g*) *With T* **9**

29 ½d. on 2d. (V.) £300 £30
30 ½d. on 2d. (B.) £750 £70
a. Surch double .. ..
31 ½d. on 2½d. (Verm.) £450 £45
a. Surch double .. ..
32 ½d. on 2½d. (B.) £300 £30
33 ½d. on 2½d. (G.) £325 £32
a. Surch double (G.) £1100
b. Surch double (G. + Verm.) .. ..
34 ½d. on 2½d. (V.) £3500

(*h*) *With T* **10**

35 ½d. on 2½d. (G.) £500 £50
36 ½d. on 2½d. (Verm.) £4000

One Shilling

(11)

5/-

(12)

(*i*) *With T* **11**
37 1s. on 2d. (V.) £450 £400
a. Surch inverted £2500
b. Surch vertical (up or down) £2500
c. Surch diagonal (up or down) £2500
d. Surch diagonal, inverted (up or down) £2750
38 1s. on 2d. (Verm.) £550 £550
a. Surch inverted . . . .
b. Surch diagonal (up or down) £3750
c. Surch vertical (up or down) £3750
39 1s. on 2d. (Blk.) £5000
a. Surch inverted £8000
b. Surch vertical (up or down) £6500

There are two main types of the "One Shilling" surcharge:—
Type A. The "O" is over the "hi" of "Shilling" and the downstrokes of the "n" in "One", if extended, would meet the "ll" of "Shilling". The "g" is always raised. Type A is known in all three colours.
Type B. The "O" is over the first "i" of "Shilling" and the downstrokes of the "n" would meet the "li" of "Shilling". Type B is known in violet and vermilion.
There is a third, minor type of the black surcharge, but the differences are very slight.
Various types of the surcharges on Nos. 9 to 39 were printed on the same sheet, and different types in different colours may be found *se-tenant*. These are of great rarity.

(*j*) *As T* **12**
40 5s. on 2d. (V.) £9000 £8000
a. Surch inverted . . . .
b. Surch vertical (up or down) £10000 £10000
c. Surch diagonal (down) £11000
41 10s. on 5d. (Verm.) £7000 £7500
a. Surch inverted £10000
b. Surch vertical (up or down) £9500
c. Surch diagonal (down) . . . .
42 20s. on 1s (V.) £38000
a. Surch inverted £80000
43 20s. on 1s. (Verm.) £65000
44 20s. on 1s. (Blk.) . . . .

NIGER COAST PROTECTORATE

The name of the protectorate was changed from 12 May 1893.

PERFORATION. There are a number of small variations in the perforation of the Waterlow issues of 1893 to 1898 which were due to irregularity of the pins rather than different perforators.
In the following lists, stamps perf 12, 12½, 13 or compound are described as perf 12–13, stamps perf 13½, 14 or compound are described as perf 13½–14 and those perf 14½, 15 or compound are listed as perf 14½–15. In addition the 13½–14 perforation exists compound with 14½–15 and with 12–13, whilst perf 15½–16 comes from a separate perforator.

13

14

(Des G. D. Drummond. Recess Waterlow)

1894 (1 Jan). *T* **13** (*with* "OIL RIVERS" *obliterated and* "NIGER COAST" *in top margin*). *Various frames. No wmk. Thick and thin papers. P* 14½–15.
45 ½d. vermilion . . . . 4·00 3·75
a. Perf 13½–14 . . . .
46 1d. pale blue . . . . 3·75 3·25
a. Bisected (½d.) (on cover) . . . . † £550
b. Dull blue . . . . 3·75 3·25
ba. Bisected (½d.) (on cover) . . . . † £450
c. Perf 13½–14 . . . .
d. Perf 13½–14, comp 12–13 . . . .
47 2d. green . . . . 13·00 13·00
a. Imperf between (pair) . . . . — £3000
b. Bisected (1d.) (on cover) . . . . † £700
c. Perf 14½–15, comp 12–13 . . . .
d. Perf 13½–14 . . . . 13·00 13·00
e. Perf 13½–14, comp 12–13 . . . . — 18·00
d. Perf 12–13 . . . .
48 2½d. carmine-lake . . . . 3·50 3·50
a. Perf 13½–14 . . . .
b. Perf 13½–14, comp 12–13 . . . .
c. Perf 12–13 . . . .
49 5d. grey-lilac . . . . 8·00 9·00
a. Lilac (1894) . . . . 7·50 12·00
b. Perf 13½–14 . . . .
50 1s. black . . . . 14·00 12·00
a. Perf 14½–15, comp 12–13 . . . .
b. Perf 13½–14 . . . .
c. Perf 13½–14, comp 12–13 . . . .
45/50 . . . . *Set of* 6 40·00 42·00

There were three printings of each value, in November 1893, Jan 1894 and March 1894.
Nos. 46a, 46ba and 47b were used at Bonny River during August and September 1894.

(Recess Waterlow)

1894 (June). *T* **14** (*various frames*). *No wmk. P* 14½–15.
51 ½d. yellow-green . . . . 1·40 2·50
a. Deep green . . . . 1·60 3·25
b. Perf 14½–15, comp 13½–14 . . . .
c. Perf 13½–14 . . . .
d. Perf 13½–14, comp 12–13 . . . .
52 1d. orange-vermilion . . . . 6·00 6·50
a. Vermilion . . . . 3·75 3·25
b. Bisected diagonally (½d.) (on cover) . . † £500
c. Perf 15½–16 . . . .
d. Perf 13½–14 . . . .
e. Perf 13½–14, comp 12–13 . . . .
53 2d. lake . . . . 4·75 3·75
a. Bisected diagonally (1d.) (on cover) . .
b. Perf 13½–14 . . . .
54 2½d. blue . . . . 5·00 3·25
a. Pale blue . . . . 5·00 3·25
55 5d. purple . . . . 3·75 5·00
a. Deep violet . . . . 4·00 5·50
56 1s. black . . . .
a. Perf 13½–14 . . . . 7·50 7·00
b. Perf 13½–14, comp 12–13 . . . .
51/6 . . . . *Set of* 6 23·00 22·00

Nos. 52b and 53a were used at Bonny River during August and September 1894.

½ (15) 1 (16) ONE = = HALF PENNY (17)

1894. *Provisionals. Issued at Opobo.*

(*a*) *Nos. 46b and 46 bisected vertically and surch with T* **15** (May–June)
57 "½" on half of 1d dull blue (R.) (May) . . £500 £225
a. Surch inverted (in strip of 3 with normals) £6500
58 "½" on half of 1d. pale blue (R.) (June) . . £750 £225
a. Surch *tête-bêche* (pair) . . . .
b. Surcharge inverted £2000

(*b*) *No. 3 bisected vertically and surch*
(i) *With T* **16** (12 *mm high*) (June-Oct)
59 "1" on half of 2d. (Verm.) £475 £350
a. Surch double £900 £850
b. Surch inverted . . . . — £850

(ii) *Smaller* "1" (4¾ *mm high*)
60 "1" on half of 2d. (C.) . . . . . . — £2250

(iii) *Smaller* "1" (3¾ *mm high*)
61 "1" on half on 2d. (C.) . . . . . .
Nos. 60 and 61 exist *se-tenant*. (*Price* £18000 *used*.)

(*c*) *No. 52a bisected, surch with T* **15** (Aug–Sept)
62 ½ on half of 1d. vermilion (Blk.) £1000 £300
63 ½ on half of 1d. vermilion (V.) £1000 £275
64 ½ on half of 1d. vermilion (B.) £1000 £250
a. "½" double . . . . — £1000

The stamp is found divided down the middle and also diagonally.

1894 (10 Aug). *Issued at Old Calabar. No. 54 surch with T* **17** *and two bars through value at foot.*
65 ½d. on 2½d. blue £250 £200
a. Surch double £1500 £1300
b. "OIE" for "ONE" £1400 £1000
c. Ditto. Surch double . . . . . . — £2000

There are eight types in the setting of T **17**.

(Recess Waterlow)

1897 (Mar)–**98**. *As T* **14** (*various frames*). *Wmk Crown CA. P* 14½–15.
66 ½d. green (7.97) . . . . 1·00 1·00
a. Sage-green . . . . 1·25 1·75
b. Perf 13½–14 . . . . — 2·25
67 1d. orange-vermilion . . . . 1·50 1·00
a. Vermilion . . . . 1·75 1·00
b. Imperf between (pair) £1200
c. Perf 15½–16 . . . .
d. Perf 13½–14 . . . . — 1·75
68 2d. lake (7.97) . . . . 1·50 1·00
a. Perf 15½–16 . . . . — 2·00
69 2½d. slate-blue (8.97) . . . . . . 2·00 2·00
a. Deep bright blue . . . . . . 2·00 1·00
b. Perf 13½–14 . . . .
70 5d. red-violet (1898) . . . . . . 6·50 32·00
a. Purple . . . . 6·50 32·00
b. Perf 13½–14 . . . .
71 6d. yellow-brown (6.98) . . . . . . 7·00 6·50
a. Perf 13½–14 . . . .
72 1s. black (1898) . . . . 12·00 13·00
a. Perf 13½–14 . . . . 12·00 13·00
73 2s. 6d. olive-bistre (6.98) . . . . . .
a. Perf 15½–16 . . . .
b. Perf 13½–14 . . . . 20·00 42·00
74 10s. deep violet (6.98) . . . . . . 75·00 £130
a. Bright violet . . . . 80·00 £130
b. Perf 13½–14 . . . .
66/74 . . . . *Set of* 9 £110 £200
71, 73/4 Optd "Specimen" . . . . *Set of* 3 £225

Owing to temporary shortages in Southern Nigeria, the above issue was again in use at various times from 1902 until 1907.

On 1 January 1900 the Niger Coast Protectorate together with the southern portion of the Niger Company Territories became the protectorate of SOUTHERN NIGERIA.

Niger Company Territories

Following the development of trade along the Niger, British commercial interests formed the United African Company in 1879 which became, in 1886, the Royal Niger Company. A charter was granted to the Company in the same year to administer territory along the Rivers Niger and Benue over which a British protectorate had been proclaimed. The Company's territories extended to the Niger delta to provide access to the interior.
Post Offices were opened at Akassa (1887), Burutu (1896), Lokoja (1898) and Abutshi (1899). The stamps of Great Britain were used from 1888.
On the establishment of postal services in 1887 the Company arranged with the British G.P.O. that unstamped mail marked with their handstamps would be delivered in Great Britain, the recipients only being charged the normal rate of postage from West Africa. This system was difficult to administer, however, so the British authorities agreed to the supply of G.B. stamps for use at the Company post offices.
Initially the stamps on such covers were left uncancelled until the mail arrived in the United Kingdom, the Company handstamp being struck elsewhere on the address side. This method continued to be used until early 1896, although a number of covers from the twelve months prior to that date do show the Company handstamp cancelling the stamps. Some of these covers were later recancelled on arrival in Great Britain. From May 1896 the postage stamps were cancelled in the Niger Territories.
In the following listings no attempt has been made to cover the use of the Company marks on the reverse of envelopes.
Dates given are those of earliest known postmarks. Colour of postmarks in brackets. Where two or more colours are given, price is for cheapest. Illustrations are reduced to two-thirds linear of the actual size.

Stamps of GREAT BRITAIN *cancelled as indicated below.*

ABUTSHI

1899 (4 Oct *to* 31 Dec). *Cancelled as T* **8**, *but inscribed* "THE ROYAL NIGER CO. C. & L. ABUTSHI" *with* "CUSTOMS (date) OFFICE" *in central oval.*
Z1 ½d. vermilion (V.) £200
Z2 1d. lilac (V.) £150
Z3 2½d. purple/*blue* (V.) £225
Z4 5d. dull purple and blue (V.) £250
Z5 10d. dull purple and carmine (V.) £300
Z6 2s. 6d. deep lilac (V.) £350

AKASSA

The listings for Nos. Z7/15 are for *covers* on which the Akassa handstamp appears on the front, but is *not* used as a cancellation for the G.B. stamps. Examples of Nos. Z16/26 occur, from 1895–96, with the handstamp struck on the front of the cover away from the stamps, or, from 1896, used as a cancellation. The prices quoted are for *single stamps* showing the cancellation; covers from either period being worth considerably more. On Nos. Z27/42 the handstamp was used as a cancellation and the prices quoted are for *single stamps*.

1

2

1888. *Cancelled as T* **3** *but with Maltese cross each side of* "AKASSA". *Size* 36 × 22 *mm.*
Z 7 6d. deep purple/*red* . . . .

1890 (24 June). *Size* 39 × 24 *mm.*
Z 8 **1** 2½d. Purple/*blue* (V.) . . . . . .
Z 9 3d. purple/*yellow* (V.) . . . . . .
Z10 5d. dull purple and blue (V.) . . . .
Z11 6d. deep purple/*red* (V.) . . . .
Z12 10d. dull purple and carmine (V.) . .
Z12*a* 1s. green (V.) . . . . . .
Z13 2s. lilac (V.) . . . . . .

1894.
Z14 **2** 1d. lilac (V.) (July) . . . . . . 65·00
Z15 2½d. purple/*lilac* (V.) (3 Oct) . . . .

3

4

1895 (7 March). *Size* 39 × 25 *mm.*
Z16 **3** 2½d. purple/*blue* (V.) . . . . . .

1895 (1 June)–**99**.
Z17 **4** ½d. vermilion (V.) . . . . . . 22·00
Z18 1d. lilac (V.) . . . . . . 22·00
Z19 2d. green and vermilion (V.) £170
Z20 2½d. purple/*blue* (V.) . . . . . . 22·00
Z21 3d. purple/*yellow* (V.) £130
Z22 5d. dull purple and blue (V.) . . . . 23·00
Z23 6d. deep purple/*red* (V.) . . . . . . 50·00
Z24 9d. dull purple and blue (V.) £110
Z25 10d. dull purple and carmine (V.) . . . . 60·00
Z26 2s. 6d. deep lilac (V.) £110

1899 (20 May). *Cancelled as T* **4**, *but* "CUSTOMS DEPT" *in place of* "POST OFFICE".
Z27 1d. lilac (V.) £150
Z28 2½d. purple/*blue* (V.) £150

THE ROYAL NIGER COMPANY,
CHARTERED & LIMITED.
4 NOV. 1889
POST OFFICE,
AKASSA.
5

1897 (Jan) *to* **1899** (Dec).
Z29 5 ½d. vermilion (V.) .. .. 24·00
Z30 1d. lilac (V.) .. .. 23·00
a. "RECD" for year in postmark .. ..
Z31 2d. green and vermilion (V.) .. .. .. 55·00
Z32 2½d. purple/*blue* (V.) .. .. 32·00
a. "RECD" for year in postmark (1898) ..
Z33 3d. purple/*yellow* (V.) .. .. 90·00
Z34 4d. green and brown (V.) .. .. .. 60·00
Z35 4½d. green and carmine (V.) £425
Z36 5d. dull purple and blue (V.) .. .. 42·00
Z37 6d. deep purple/*red* (V.) .. .. .. 95·00
Z38 9d. dull purple and blue (V.) £140
Z39 10d. dull purple and carmine (V.) .. .. 60·00
Z40 1s. green (V.) £200
Z41 2s. 6d. deep lilac (V.) £120

1899 (9 Jan). *Cancelled as T* **7**, *but inscribed* "AKASSA".
Z42 5d. dull purple and blue (V.) .. ..

BURUTU

THE ROYAL NIGER COMPANY
CHARTERED & LIMITED.
31 MAR 1898
POST OFFICE.
BURUTU.

6

1897 (20 Jan) *to* **1898** (30 Oct). *Cancelled as T* **6**, "BURUTU" *in sans-serif caps. Size* 44 × 24 *mm.*
Z43 6 ½d. vermilion (V.) .. .. 40·00
Z44 1d. lilac (V.) .. .. 40·00
Z45 1½d. dull purple and green (V.) £110
Z46 2d. green and carmine (V.) .. .. .. 60·00
Z47 2½d. purple/*blue* (V.) .. .. 23·00
Z48 3d. purple/*yellow* (V.) .. .. 75·00
Z49 4d. green and brown (V.) .. .. .. 50·00
Z50 5d. dull purple and blue (V.) .. .. 42·00
Z51 6d. deep purple/*red* (V.) .. .. .. 75·00
Z52 9d. dull purple and blue (V.) £110
Z53 10d. dull purple and carmine (V.) .. .. 60·00
Z54 1s. green (V.) £225
Z55 2s. 6d. lilac (V.) £100

The 2½d. is also known with this postmark in blue (6.9.97) and violet-black (Apr 1898) and the ½d., 2½d., 3d., 5d. and 10d. with it in black.

1898 *to* **1899**. *Cancelled as T* **4**, *but inscribed* "BURUTU" *in serifed caps. Size* 44 × 27 *mm.*
Z56 ½d. vermilion (V., Blk.) .. .. 42·00
Z57 1d. lilac (V., Blk.) .. .. 42·00
Z58 2d. green and vermilion (V.) £110
Z59 2½d. purple/*blue* (V., Blk.) .. .. .. 35·00
Z60 3d. purple/*yellow* (V.) .. .. 90·00
Z61 4d. green and brown (V.) .. .. .. 70·00
Z62 4½d. green and carmine (V.) £450
Z63 5d. dull purple and blue (V.) .. .. 45·00
Z64 6d. deep purple/*red* (V.) £110
Z65 9d. dull purple and blue (V.) £140
Z66 10d. dull purple and carmine (V., Blk.) .. 65·00
Z67 2s. 6d. lilac (V., Blk.) £150

THE ROYAL NIGER COMPANY
Chartered & Limited.
9 JUL 1898
BURUTU

7

1898 (9 July) *to* **1899** (Feb).
Z68 7 1d. lilac (V.) .. ..
Z69 2½d. purple/*blue* (V.) £180

1899 (20 May). *Cancelled as T* **4**, *but inscribed* "CUSTOM DEPT. BURUTU".
Z70 1d. lilac (V.) .. ..

There is some doubt as to the use of this cancellation for postal purposes.

LOKOJA

8

1899 (30 June *to* 31 Dec).
Z71 8 ½d. vermilion (V.) .. .. 50·00
Z72 1d. lilac (V.) .. .. 45·00
Z73 2½d. purple/*blue* (V.) £150
Z74 5d. dull purple and blue (V.) £150
Z75 10d. dull purple and carmine (V.) £150
Z76 2s. 6d. deep lilac (V.) .. ..

AGENT GENERAL NIGER TERRITORIES

The listings for Nos. Z78/9 are for covers showing a handstamp struck on the address side, but *not* used as a cancellation for the G.B. stamp.

1894. *Cancelled as T* **8** *but inscribed* "AGENT GENERAL NIGER TERRITORIES".
Z78 2½d. purple/*blue* (V.) (3.10.94) .. .. .. 75·00

1895 (4 Aug). *Cancelled as T* **7** *but inscribed as last.*
Z79 2½d. purple/*blue* (V.).. .. .. 75·00

It is now believed that these cancellations may have been used at Asaba.

The British Government purchased the Royal Niger Company territories and from 1 January 1900 they were incorporated into the protectorates of Northern and Southern Nigeria. Of the post offices listed above only Lokoja was then situated in Northern Nigeria, the remainder joining Niger Coast in forming Southern Nigeria.

Issues for Northern Nigeria did not reach Lokoja until sometime in March 1900 and the post office there continued to use unoverprinted stamps of Great Britain until these supplies arrived.

Nigeria

Nigeria was formed on 1 January 1914 from the former protectorates of Northern and Southern Nigeria.

PRICES FOR STAMPS ON COVER TO 1945	
Nos. 1/10	*from* × 3
Nos. 11/13	—
Nos. 15/24	*from* × 3
No. 25	—
Nos. 25*a*/9*d*	*from* × 3
No. 29*e*	—
Nos. 30/3	*from* × 3
Nos. 34/59	*from* × 2

CROWN COLONY

1

2

(Typo D.L.R.)

1914–27. *Wmk Mult Crown CA. Ordinary paper* (½d. *to* 2½d.) *or chalk-surfaced paper* (*others*). *P* 14.

A. *Die I.* (1.6.14–21)
1 1 ½d. green 30 30
2 1d. carmine-red 50 10
a. Scarlet (6.17) .. .. 1·00 10
3 2d. grey .. .. 1·50 50
a. Slate-grey (1918) .. .. 2·50 55
4 2½d. bright blue 90 70
a. Dull blue (1915) .. ..
5 2 3d. purple/*yellow* (*white back*) .. 1·50 4·00
a. On yellow (*lemon back*) (8.15) .. 1·25 90
b. On deep yellow (*yellow back, thick paper*) (1915) (Optd S. £30) .. 12·00 7·00
c. On pale yellow (*orange-buff back*) (12.20) .. .. 3·00 11·00
d. On pale yellow (*pale yellow back*) (1921) .. .. 3·75 11·00
6 4d. black and red/*yellow* (*white back*) .. 1·00 3·50
a. On yellow (*lemon back*) (8.15) .. 80 2·75
b. On deep yellow (*yellow back, thick paper*) (1915) (Optd S. £30) .. 11·00 6·00
c. On pale yellow (*orange-buff back*) (1921) .. .. 3·50 4·75
d. On pale yellow (*pale yellow back*) (1921) .. .. 6·00 12·00
7 6d. dull and bright purple (*shades*) .. 1·75 2·00
8 1 1s. black /*pale blue-green* (*white back*) .. 80 2·75
a. On yellow-green (*white back*) ..
b. On pale blue-green (*yellow-green back*) (1915) .. .. 6·50 7·50
c. On pale blue-green (*blue-green back*) (1915) (Optd S. £30) .. .. 1·00 3·25
d. On pale blue-green (*pale olive back*) (1918) .. .. 8·50 10·00
e. On emerald-green (*pale olive back*) (12.20) .. .. 4·50 10·00
f. On emerald-green (*emerald-green back*) (1921) .. .. 1·00 6·50
9 2s. 6d. black and red/*blue* .. .. 5·00 3·00
10 2 5s. green and red/*yellow* (*white back*) .. 6·00 14·00
a. On yellow (*lemon back*) (8.15) .. 14·00 26·00
b. On deep yellow (*yellow back, thick paper*) (1915) (Optd S. £30) .. 17·00 30·00
c. On yellow (*orange-buff back*) (1921) 18·00 40·00
d. On pale yellow (*pale yellow back*) (1921) .. .. 32·00 55·00
11 1 10s. green and red/*blue-green* (*white back*) 35·00 60·00
a. On blue-green (*blue-green back*) (8.15) (Optd S. £35) .. .. 35·00 50·00
b. On blue-green (*pale olive back*) (1918) £800 £1100
c. On emerald green (*pale olive back*) (12.20) .. .. 55·00 80·00
d. On emerald-green (*emerald back*) (1921) .. .. 26·00 55·00
12 2 £1 deep purple and black/*red* £150 £180

B. *Change to Die II* (19.1.27)
13 2 £1 purple and black/*red* £160 £200
1/12 .. .. *Set of* 12 £170 £225
1/12 Optd "Specimen" .. .. *Set of* 12 £350

1921–32. *Wmk Mult Script CA. Ordinary paper* (½d. *to* 3d.) *or chalk-surfaced paper* (*others*). *P* 14.

A. *The basic issue. Die I for the* ½d., 1d., 2d., 2½d., 3d *and* 6d., *Die II remainder* (1921–26)
15 1 ½d. green (1921) 60 30
16 1d. rose-carmine (1921) 30 15
17 2d. grey (5.21) .. .. 1·50 90
18 2½d. bright blue (5.21) .. .. .. 50 1·50
19 2 3d. bright violet (1.24) .. .. .. 3·75 3·25
20 4d. black and red/*pale yellow* (10.23) .. 50 55
21 6d. dull and bright purple (5.21) .. 4·00 4·00
22 1 1s. black/*emerald* (7.24) 65 50
23 2s. 6d. black and red/*blue* (8.25) .. 6·00 12·00
24 2 5s. green and red/*yellow* (10.26) .. 10·00 32·00
25 1 10s. green and red/*green* (4.26) .. 42·00 75·00
15/25 .. .. *Set of* 11 65·00 £120
15/25 Optd "Specimen" .. .. *Set of* 11 £250

B. *Change to Die II* (1924–25)
25*a* 1 ½d. green (5.25) 60 35
25*b* 1d. rose-carmine (5.25) 30 20
25*c* 2d. grey (1924) .. .. 2·00 30
25*d* 2 3d. bright violet (5.25) .. .. .. 4·50 1·50
25*e* 6d. dull and bright purple (7.24) .. 3·00 2·50
25*a/e* .. .. *Set of* 5 9·50 4·25

C. *New value and colours changed. Die II* (1927–31)
26 2 1½d. orange (1.4.31) 90 15
27 1 2d. chestnut (1.10.27) .. .. .. 1·50 1·00
28 2d. chocolate (1.7.28) 25 15
29 2 3d. bright blue (1.4.31) .. .. .. 2·25 2·00
26/7, 29 .. .. *Set of* 3 4·25 3·00
26/7, 29 Optd/Perf "Specimen" .. *Set of* 3 75·00

D. *Reappearance of Die I* (*Key Plate* 23) (Mar to Aug 1932)
29*a* 1 2d. chocolate (Mar) .. .. .. 4·50 75
29*b* 2 4d. black and red/*pale yellow* .. .. 5·50 7·00
29*c* 1 2s. 6d. black and red/*blue* .. .. 24·00 25·00
29*d* 2 5s. green and red/*yellow* .. .. 38·00 65·00
29*e* 1 10s. green and red/*green* .. .. 70·00 £140
29*a/e* .. .. *Set of* 5 £120 £225

1935 (6 May). *Silver Jubilee. As Nos.* 91/4 *of Antigua but ptd by Waterlow. P* 11 × 12.
30 1½d. ultramarine and grey 45 20
31 2d. green and indigo .. .. .. 1·50 20
j. Kite and vertical log .. .. .. 30·00
32 3d. brown and deep blue .. .. .. 1·75 3·25
33 1s. slate and purple .. .. .. 2·75 9·50
30/3 .. .. *Set of* 4 5·75 12·00
30/3 Perf "Specimen" .. .. *Set of* 4 70·00

For illustration of plate variety see Omnibus section following Zululand.

3 Apapa Wharf

4 Fishing Village

5 Victoria-Buea Road

(Recess D.L.R.)

1936 (1 Feb). *Designs as T* **3/5**. *Wmk Mult Script CA.*

(*a*) *P* 11½ × 13
34 ½d. green 45 40
35 1d. carmine 25 25
36 1½d. brown 25 20
a. Perf 12½ × 13½ .. .. .. 22·00 2·00
37 2d. black 30 40
38 3d. blue 40 75
a. Perf 12½ × 13½ .. .. .. 60·00 22·00
39 4d. red-brown .. .. 90 2·00
40 6d. dull violet 40 60
41 1s. sage-green .. .. 1·10 4·50

(*b*) *P* 14
42 2s. 6d. black and ultramarine .. .. 3·50 11·00
43 5s. black and olive-green .. .. .. 6·00 17·00
44 10s. black and grey .. .. 38·00 48·00
45 £1 black and orange.. .. .. .. 70·00 £110
34/45 .. .. *Set of* 12 £110 £180
34/45 Perf "Specimen" .. .. *Set of* 12 £225

Designs: *Vert as T* **3/4**—1d. Cocoa; 1½d. Tin dredger; 2d. Timber industry; 4d. Cotton ginnery; 6d. Habe minaret; 1s. Fulani Cattle. *Horiz as T* **5**—5s. Oil Palms; 10s. River Niger at Jebba; £1, Canoe pulling.

1937 (12 May). *Coronation. As Nos.* 13/15 *of Aden, but printed by B.W. & Co. P* 11 × 11½.
46 1d. carmine 30 35
47 1½d. brown 50 45
48 3d. blue .. .. 90 1·50
46/8 .. .. *Set of* 3 1·50 2·00
46/8 Perf "Specimen" .. .. *Set of* 3 55·00

15 King George VI

16 Victoria-Buea Road

(Recess B.W. (T **15**), D.L.R. (others))

1938 (1 May)–**51**. *Designs as T* **15/16**. *Wmk Mult Script CA. P* 12 (*T* **15**) *or* 13 × 11½ (*others*).
49 15 ½d. green 10 10
a. Perf 11½ (15.2.50) 20 10
50 1d. carmine .. .. 15·00 2·00
a. Rose-red (1941) 15 10

No.	Type	Description	Unused	Used
50b	15	1d. bright purple (1.12.44)	10	10
		ba. Perf 11½ (15.2.50)	10	15
51		1½d. brown	10	10
		a. Perf 11½ (15.11.50)	10	10
52		2d. black	10	30
52aa		2d. rose-red (1.12.44)	10	25
		ab. Perf 11½ (15.2.50)	10	30
52a		2½d. orange (4.41)	10	30
53		3d. blue	10	10
		a. Wmk sideways	†	—
53b		3d. black (1.12.44)	10	10
54		4d. orange	40·00	2·50
54a		4d. blue (1.12.44)	10	45
55		6d. blackish purple	10	10
		a. Perf 11½ (17.4.51)	20	15
56		1s. sage-green	40	10
		a. Perf 11½ (15.2.50)	10	10
57		1s. 3d. light blue (1940)	30	10
		a. Perf 11½ (14.6.50)	30	35
		b. Wmk sideways (Perf 11½)	—	£1000
58	16	2s. 6d. black and blue	26·00	8·50
		a. Perf 13½ (6.42)	1·25	1·75
		ab. Perf 13½. *Black and deep blue* (1946)	20·00	15·00
		b. Perf 14 (1942)	1·25	90
		c. Perf 12 (15.8.51)	1·25	90
59	–	5s. black and orange	50·00	7·50
		a. Perf 13½ (8.42)	3·50	1·75
		b. Perf 14 (1948)	3·00	1·50
		c. Perf 12 (19.5.49)	2·75	90
49/59c		*Set of* 16	40·00	5·50
49/52aa, 53/9 Perf "Specimen"		*Set of* 15	£200	

Design: *Horiz as T* **16**—5s. R. Niger at Jebba.

1946 (21 Oct). *Victory. As Nos.* 28/9 *of Aden.*

No.	Description	Unused	Used
60	1½d. chocolate	10	10
61	4d. blue	15	30
60/1 Perf "Specimen"	*Set of* 2	55·00	

1948 (20 Dec). *Royal Silver Wedding. As Nos.* 30/1 *of Aden.*

No.	Description	Unused	Used
62	1d. bright purple	35	10
63	5s. brown-orange	5·00	7·00

1949 (10 Oct). *75th Anniv of Universal Postal Union. As Nos.* 114/17 *of Antigua.*

No.	Description	Unused	Used
64	1d. bright reddish purple	15	10
65	3d. deep blue	35	55
66	6d. purple	50	1·00
67	1s. olive	70	1·40
64/7	*Set of* 4	1·50	2·75

1953 (2 June). *Coronation. As No.* 47 *of Aden but ptd by B.W.*

No.	Description	Unused	Used
68	1½d. black and emerald	20	10

18 Old Manilla Currency

21 "Tin"

Die I Flat-bed | Die Ia Rotary

Two types of 1d.:

The Belgian rotary printings have thicker lines of shading giving blotches of black colour instead of fine lines, particularly in the stirrups.

Major re-entry showing duplication of steps of the terraces (Pl 3, R. 1/5)

Type A
Gap in row of dots

Type B
Unbroken row of dots

Two types of 2d. slate-violet:

Nos. 72c/cc. The original cylinder used was Type A (July 1956); later Type B (Sept 1957). The above illustrations will help classification, but two stamps per sheet of 60 of Type A show faint dots. However, one of these has the "2d." re-entry which does not exist in Type B sheets, and shades are distinctive.

Die I Flat-bed

Die 1a Rotary

Two types of 3d.:

As in the 1d. the Belgian rotary printings have thicker lines of shading and this is particularly noticeable in the dark hills in the background.

24 Ife Bronze

26 Victoria Harbour

29 New and Old Lagos

(Des M. Fievet. Recess Waterlow)

1953 (1 Sept)–**58**. *T* **18**, **21**, **24**, **26**, **29** *and similar designs. Wmk Mult Script CA. P* 14.

No.	Type	Description	Unused	Used
69	18	½d. black and orange	15	10
70	–	1d. black and bronze-green (Die I)	20	10
		a. Die Ia (1.9.58)	20	10
71	–	1½d. blue-green	35	10
72	21	2d. black and yellow-ochre	1·00	10
		a. Black and ochre (18.8.54)	85	10
		b. Re-entry	50·00	
72c		2d. slate-violet (Type A) (23.7.56)	1·25	35
		ca. Slate-blue (shades) (Type A)	2·00	10
		cb. Bluish grey (Type B) (25.9.57)	1·25	10
		cc. Grey (shades) (Type B)	1·50	10
73	–	3d. black and purple (Die I)	45	10
		a. Die Ia. *Black & reddish pur* (1.9.58)	45	10
		b. Imperf (pair)	£180	
74	–	4d. black and blue	60	10
75	24	6d. orange-brown and black	20	10
		a. Chestnut and black (18.8.54)	25	10
76	–	1s. black and maroon	40	10
77	26	2s. 6d. black and green	3·25	10
		a. Black and deep green (18.8.54)	3·50	15
78	–	5s. black and red-orange	3·25	50
79	–	10s. black and red-brown	3·75	1·00
80	29	£1 black and violet	9·00	3·75
69/80		*Set of* 13	21·00	5·50

Designs: *Horiz (as T* **18**)—1d. Bornu horsemen; 1½d. "Groundnuts"; 3d. Jebba bridge and R. Niger; 4d. "Cocoa"; 1s. "Timber". (*As T* **26**)—5s. "Palm-oil"; 10s. "Hides and skins".

Nos. 70a, 72*c*/*cc* and 73a were printed on rotary machines by a subsidary company, Imprimerie Belge de Securité, in Belgium.

Nos. 72*ca* and 72*cc* were only available in Nigeria.

MINIMUM PRICE

The minimum price quote is 10p which represents a handling charge rather than a basis for valuing common stamps. For further notes about prices see introductory pages.

ROYAL VISIT 1956

(30)

31 Victoria Harbour

1956 (28 Jan). *Royal Visit. No.* 72 *optd with T* **30**.

No.	Type	Description	Unused	Used
81	21	2d. black and ochre	15	10
		a. Opt inverted	£160	

(Recess Waterlow)

1958 (1 Dec). *Centenary of Victoria. W w* **12**. *P* 13½ × 14.

No.	Type	Description	Unused	Used
82	31	3d. black and purple	10	10

32 Lugard Hall

(Recess Waterlow)

1959 (14 Mar). *Attainment of Self-Government, Northern Region of Nigeria. T* **32** *and similar horiz design. W w* **12**. *P* 13½ (3*d.*) *or* 13½ × 14 (1*s.*).

No.	Description	Unused	Used
83	3d. black and purple	10	10
84	1s. black and green	20	20

Design:—1s. Kano Mosque.

INDEPENDENT FEDERATION

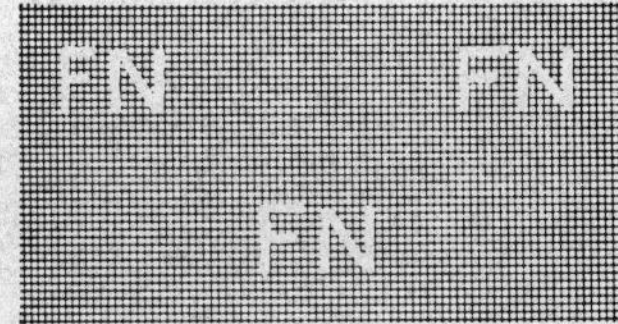

34

35 Legislative Building

38 Dove, Torch and Map

(Des L. J. Wittington (1d.), R. Crawford (3d.), R. D. Baxter (6d.), J. White (1s. 3d.), Photo Waterlow)

1960 (1 Oct). *Independence. T* **35**, **38** *and similar horiz designs. W* **34**. *P* 13½ (1*s.* 3*d.*) *or* 14 (*others*).

No.	Description	Unused	Used
85	1d. black and scarlet	10	10
86	3d. black and greenish blue	10	10
87	6d. green and red-brown	10	10
88	1s. 3d. bright blue and yellow	15	10
85/8	*Set of* 4	25	20

Designs: (*As T* **35**)—3d. African paddling canoe; 6d. Federal Supreme Court.

39 Groundnuts

48 Central Bank

1961 (1 Jan). *T* **39**, **48**, *and similar designs. W* **34**. *P* 15 × 14 (½*d. to* 1*s* 3*d.*) *or* 14½ (*others*).

No.	Description	Unused	Used
89	½d. emerald	10	20
90	1d. reddish violet	15	10
91	1½d. carmine-red	15	60
92	2d. deep blue	15	10
93	3d. deep green	15	10
94	4d. blue	15	20
95	6d. yellow and black	15	10
	a. Yellow omitted	—	£225
96	1s. yellow-green	80	10
97	1s. 3d. orange	25	10
98	2s. 6d. black and yellow	50	15
99	5s. black and emerald	50	25
100	10s. black and ultramarine	75	90
101	£1 black and carmine-red	5·00	3·50
89/101	*Set of* 13	8·00	5·50

Designs: *Vert* (*as T* **39**)—1d. Coal mining; 1½d. Adult education; 2d. Pottery; 3d. Oyo carver; 4d. Weaving; 6d. Benin mask; 1s. Yellow-casqued Hornbill; 1s. 3d. Camel train. *Horiz* (*as T* **48**)—5s. Nigeria Museum; 10s. Kano airport; £1 Lagos railway station.

PRINTERS. The above and all following issues to No. 206 were printed in photogravure by Harrison & Sons, *except where otherwise stated.*

52 Globe and Railway Locomotive **56** Coat of Arms

(Des M. Goaman)

1961 (25 July). *Admission of Nigeria into U.P.U. T* **52** *and similar horiz designs.* W **34**. *P* 14½.

102	1d. red-orange and blue	10	10
103	3d. olive-yellow and black	10	10
104	1s. 3d. blue and carmine-red	15	10
105	2s. 6d. deep green and blue	25	35
102/5	*Set of* 4	45	40

Designs:—3d. Globe and mail-van; 1s. 3d. Globe and aircraft; 2s. 6d. Globe and liner.

(Des S. Bodo (3d.), R. Hopeman (4d.), C. Adesina (6d.), M. Shamir (1s. 6d.), B. Enweonwu (2s. 6d.))

1961 (1 Oct). *First Anniv of Independence. T* **56** *and similar designs.* W **34**. *P* 14½.

106	3d. multicoloured	10	10
107	4d. yellow-green and yellow-orange	10	10
108	6d. emerald-green	15	10
109	1s. 3d. grey, emerald and blue	15	10
110	2s. 6d. green and grey-blue	20	20
106/10	*Set of* 5	55	35

Designs: *Horiz*—4d. Natural resources and map; 6d. Nigerian Eagle; 1s. 3d. Eagles in flight; 2s. 6d. Nigerians and flag.

A used copy of No. 106 has been seen with both the silver (large "Y" appearing grey) and the yellow (appearing white) omitted.

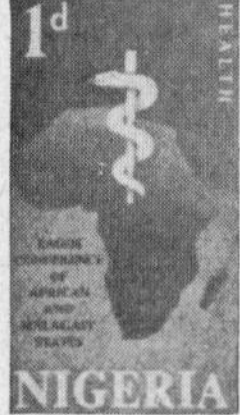

61 "Health" **66** Malaria Eradication Emblem and Parasites

(Des M. Shamir)

1962 (25 Jan). *Lagos Conference of African and Malagasy States. T* **61** *and similar vert designs.* W **34**. *P* 14 × 14½.

111	1d. yellow-bistre	10	10
112	3d. deep reddish purple	10	10
113	6d. deep green	10	10
114	1s. brown	10	10
115	1s. 3d. blue	10	15
111/15	*Set of* 5	20	25

Designs:—3d. "Culture"; 6d. "Commerce"; 1s. "Communications"; 1s. 3d. "Co-operation".

1962 (7 Apr). *Malaria Eradication. T* **66** *and similar horiz designs.* W **34**. *P* 14½.

116	3d. green and orange-red	10	10
117	6d. blue and bright purple	10	10
118	1s. 3d. magenta and violet-blue	10	10
119	2s. 6d. blue and yellow-brown	15	20
116/19	*Set of* 4	30	30

Designs:—6d. Insecticide spraying; 1s. 3d. Aerial spraying; 2s. 6d. Mother, child and microscope.

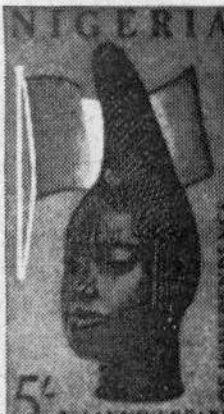

70 National Monument **71** Benin Bronze

(Des S. Bodo (3d.), B. Enweonwu (5s.))

1962 (1 Oct). *Second Anniv of Independence.* W **34**. *P* 14½ × 14 (3d.) *or* 14 × 14½ (5s.).

120	**70**	3d. emerald and blue	10	10
		a. Emerald omitted		
121	**71**	5s. red, emerald and violet	50	30

72 Fair Emblem **73** "Cogwheels of Industry"

(Des M. Goaman (1d., 2s. 6d.), J. O. Gbagbeolu and M. Goaman (6d.), R. Hegeman (1s.))

1962 (27 Oct). *International Trade Fair, Lagos.* W **34**. *T* **72/3** *and similar designs. P* 14½.

122	1d. olive-brown and orange-red	10	10
123	6d. carmine-red and black	10	10
124	1s. orange-brown and black	10	10
125	2s. 6d. ultramarine and yellow	15	20
122/5	*Set of* 4	25	25

Designs: *Horiz as T* **73**—1s. "Cornucopia of Industry"; 2s. 6d. Oilwells and *British Petroleum* (tanker).

76 "Arrival of Delegates" **77** Mace as Palm Tree

(Des S. Akosile (2½d.), M. Goaman (others))

1962 (5 Nov). *Eighth Commonwealth Parliamentary Conference, Lagos. T* **76/77** *and similar design.* W **34**. *P* 14½.

126	2½d. greenish blue	10	15
127	4d. indigo and rose-red	10	10
128	1s. 3d. sepia and lemon	15	20
126/8	*Set of* 3	25	35

Design: *Horiz*—4d. National Hall.

80 Tractor and Maize **81** Mercury Capsule and Kano Tracking Station

(Des M. Goaman)

1963 (21 Mar). *Freedom from Hunger. T* **80** *and similar design.* W **34**. *P* 14.

129	3d. olive-green	20	10
130	6d. magenta	35	10

Design: *Vert*—3d. Herdsman.

(Des R. Hegeman)

1963 (21 June). *"Peaceful Use of Outer Space". T* **81** *and similar vert design.* W **34**. *P* 14½ × 14.

131	6d. blue and yellow-green	10	10
132	1s. 3d. black and blue-green	10	10

Design:—1s. 3d. Satellite and Lagos Harbour.

83 Scouts shaking Hands

(Des S. Apostolou (3d.), G. Okiki (1s.))

1963 (1 Aug). *11th World Scout Jamboree, Marathon. T* **83** *and similar triangular-shaped design.* W **34**. *P* 14.

133	3d. red and bronze-green	10	10
134	1s. black and red	20	25
MS134*a*	93 × 95 mm. Nos. 133/4	1·00	1·00
	ab. Red omitted (on 3d. value)	£225	

Design:—1s. Campfire.

85 Emblem and First Aid Team **88** President Azikiwe and State House

(Des M. Goaman)

1963 (1 Sept). *Red Cross Centenary. T* **85** *and similar horiz designs.* W **34**. *P* 14½.

135	3d. red and deep ultramarine	20	10
136	6d. red and deep green	30	10
137	1s. 3d. red and deep sepia	70	35
135/7	*Set of* 3	1·10	45
MS137*a*	102 × 102 mm. No. 137 (block of four)	2·00	2·25

Designs:—6d. Emblem and "Hospital Services"; 1s. 3d. Patient and emblem.

(Des M. Shamir. Photo Govt Printer, Israel)

1963 (1 Oct). *Republic Day. T* **88** *and similar vert designs showing administrative buildings and President Azikiwe. P* 14 × 13.

138	3d. yellow-olive and grey-green	10	10
139	1s. 3d. yellow-brown and sepia	10	10
	a. Yellow-brown (portrait) omitted		
140	2s. 6d. turquoise-blue and deep violet-blue	15	15
138/40	*Set of* 3	25	20

Designs:—1s. 3d. Federal Supreme Court Building; 2s. 6d. Parliament Building.

89 Charter and Broken Whip **90** "Freedom of Worship"

(Des S. Apostolou (3d.), Mrs. F. P. Effiong (others). Photo D.L.R.)

1963 (10 Dec). *15th Anniv of Declaration of Human Rights. T* **89/90** *and similar designs.* W **34**. *P* 13.

141	3d. vermilion	10	10
142	6d. blue-green	10	10
143	1s. 3d. ultramarine	10	10
144	2s. 6d. bright purple	20	30
141/4	*Set of* 4	30	35

Designs: *Vert as T* **90**—1s. 3d. "Freedom from want"; 2s. 6d. "Freedom of speech".

93 Queen Nefertari **94** Rameses II

(Des M. Shamir)

1964 (8 Mar). *Nubian Monuments Preservation.* W **34**. *P* 14½.

145	**93**	6d. yellow-olive and emerald	15	10
146	**94**	2s. 6d. brown, deep olive and emerald	60	80

95 President Kennedy

(Des M. Shamir (1s. 3d.), M. Goaman (2s. 6d.), Mr. Bottiau (5s.). Photo Govt Printer, Israel (1s. 3d.); litho Lewin-Epstein, Bat Yam, Israel (others))

1964 (27 Aug). *President Kennedy Memorial Issue. T* **95** *and similar horiz designs. P* 13 × 14 (1s. 3d.) *or* 14 (*others*).

147	1s. 3d. light violet and black	20	15
148	2s. 6d. black, red, blue and green	40	40
149	5s. black, deep blue, red and green	70	1·00
147/9	*Set of* 3	1·10	1·40
MS149*a*	154 × 135 mm. No. 149 (block of four). Imperf	5·00	6·00

Designs:—2s. 6d. President Kennedy and flags; 5s. President Kennedy (U.S. coin head) and flags.

98 President Azikiwe **99** Herbert Macaulay

(Des S. Apostolou (3d.), W. H. Irvine (others). Photo Govt Printer, Israel (3d.); Harrison (others))

1964 (1 Oct). *First Anniv of Republic. T* **98** *or* **99** *and similar vert design. P* 14 × 13 (3d.) *or* 14½ (*others*).

150	3d. red-brown	10	10
151	1s. 3d. green	10	10
152	2s. 6d. deep grey-green	20	20
150/2	*Set of* 3	30	25

Design:—2s. 6d. King Jaja of Opobo.

101 Boxing Gloves

102 Hurdling

(Des A. Adalade (3d.), S. Medahunsi (6d.), M. Shamir (1s. 3d.), M. Goaman (2s. 6d.))

964 (10 Oct). *Olympic Games, Tokyo. T* **101** *and similar designs, and T* **102**. *W* **34**. *P* 14 (*2s. 6d.*) *or* 14½ (*others*).

.53 3d. sepia and olive-green 10 10
.54 6d. emerald and indigo 15 10
.55 1s. 3d. sepia and yellow-olive 20 10
.56 2s. 6d. sepia and chestnut 30 55
.53/6 .. .. *Set of* 4 60 65
MS156*a* 102 × 102 mm. No. 156 (block of four). Imperf .. .. 2·50 3·00

Designs: *Horiz*—6d. High-jumping. *Vert*—1s. 3d. Running.

105 Scouts on Hill-top

Des S. Apostolou (1d., 1s. 3d.), H. N. G. Cowham and Eagle Scout N. A. Lasisi (3d.), W. H. Irvine (6d.))

965 (1 Jan). *50th Anniv of Nigerian Scout Movement. T* **105** *and similar vert designs. P* 14 × 14½.

157 1d. brown 10 10
158 3d. red, black and emerald 15 10
159 6d. red, sepia and yellow-green 25 10
160 1s. 3d. bistre-brown, greenish yellow and black-green 40 45
157/60 .. .. *Set of* 4 75 55
MS160*a* 76 × 104 mm. No. 160 (block of four). Imperf .. .. 5·00 6·50

Designs:—3d. Scout badge on shield; 6d. Scout badges; 1s. 3d. Chief Scout and Nigerian scout.

109 "Telstar" **110** Solar Satellite

(Des M. Shamir. Photo Govt Printer, Israel)

1965 (1 Apr). *International Quiet Sun Years. P* 14 × 13.

161 **109** 6d. reddish violet and turquoise-blue .. 10 10
162 **110** 1s. 3d. green and reddish lilac 10 10

111 Native Tom-tom and Modern Telephone

(Des C. Botham (5s.), H. N. G. Cowham (others). Photo Enschedé)

1965 (2 Aug). *I.T.U. Centenary. T* **111** *and similar designs. P* 11½ × 11 (*1s. 3d.*) *or* 11 × 11½ (*others*).

163 3d. black, carmine and yellow-brown .. 15 10
164 1s. 3d. black, blue-green and chalky blue .. 1·25 1·00
165 5s. black, carmine, blue & brt greenish blue 3·75 4·50
163/5 .. .. *Set of* 3 4·50 5·00

Designs: *Vert*—1s. 3d. Microwave aerial. *Horiz*—5s. Telecommunications satellite and part of globe.

NEW INFORMATION

The editor is always interested to correspond with people who have new information that will improve or correct the Catalogue.

114 I.C.Y. Emblem and Diesel Locomotive **117** Carved Frieze

(Des W. H. Irvine. Photo D.L.R.)

1965 (1 Sept). *International Co-operation Year. T* **114** *and similar horiz designs. W* **34**. *P* 14 × 15.

166 3d. green, red and orange 75 10
167 1s. black, bright blue and lemon .. .. 1·00 40
168 2s. 6d. green, bright blue and yellow .. 4·50 4·00
166/8 .. .. *Set of* 3 5·50 4·00

Designs:—1s. Students and Lagos Teaching Hospital; 2s. 6d. Kainji (Niger) Dam.

(Des S. Apostolou (3d.), W. H. Irvine (others). Photo D.L.R.)

1965 (1 Oct). *2nd Anniv of Republic. T* **117** *and similar designs. P* 14 × 15 (*3d.*) *or* 15 × 14 (*others*).

169 3d. black, red and orange-yellow 10 10
170 1s. 3d. red-brown, dp green & lt ultramarine 45 20
171 5s. brown, blackish brown and light green .. 1·50 2·00
169/71 .. .. *Set of* 3 1·90 2·00

Designs: *Vert*—1s. 3d. Stone images at Ikom; 5s. Tada bronze.

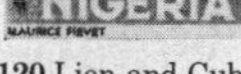

120 Lion and Cubs **121** African Elephants

132 Hippopotamus **133** African Buffalo

(Des M. Fievet. Photo Harrison (1d., 2d., 3d., 4d. (No. 177a), 9d.) or Delrieu (others))

1965 (1 Nov)–**66**. *T* **120/1**, **132/3** *and similar designs. Without printer's imprint. Chalk-surfaced paper* (*1d., 2d., 3d., 4d., 9d.*). *P* 12 × 12½ (*½d., 6d.*), 12½ × 12 (*1½d., 4d.*), 14 × 13½ (*1d., 2d., 3d., 9d.*) *or* 12½ (*others*).

172 ½d. multicoloured (1.11.65) 20 40
173 1d. multicoloured (1.11.65) 20 10
174 1½d. multicoloured (2.5.66) .. .. .. 3·50 3·75
175 2d. multicoloured (1.4.66) .. .. .. 2·00 15
176 3d. multicoloured (17.10.66) 50 10
177 4d. multicoloured (2.5.66) 50 90
 a. Perf 14 × 13½ (1966) 20 15
178 6d. multicoloured (2.5.66) .. .. .. 1·00 15
179 9d. Prussian blue and orange-red (17.10.66) 2·25 30
180 1s. multicoloured (2.5.66) .. .. .. 1·50 20
181 1s. 3d. multicoloured (2.5.66) .. .. .. 5·00 25
182 2s. 6d. orange-brown, buff and brown (2.5.66) 75 30
183 5s. chestnut, light yellow and brown (2.5.66) 1·50 80
 a. Pale chestnut, yellow and brown-purple (1966) .. .. 1·50 80
184 10s. multicoloured (2.5.66) .. .. .. 5·50 3·00
185 £1 multicoloured (2.5.66) .. .. .. 13·00 8·50
172/85 .. .. *Set of* 14 32·00 16·00

Designs: *Horiz* (*as T* **121**)—1½d. Splendid Sunbird; 2d. Village Weaver and Red-headed Malimbe; 3d. Cheetah; 4d. Leopards; 9d. Grey Parrots. (*As T* **133**)—1s. Blue-breasted Kingfishers; 1s. 3d. Crowned Cranes; 2s. 6d. Kobs; 5s. Giraffes. *Vert* (*as T* **120**)—6d. Saddle-bill Stork.

The 2d. and 3d. exist with PVA gum as well as gum arabic.

See also Nos. 220, etc.

The 1d., 3d., 4d. (No. 177a), 1s., 1s. 3d., 2s. 6d., 5s. and £1 values exist overprinted "F.G.N." (Federal Government of Nigeria) twice in black. They were prepared in November 1968 at the request of one of the State Governments for use as official stamps but the scheme was abandoned and meter machines were used instead. Some stamps held at Lagos Post Office were sold over the counter in error and passed through the post. The Director of Posts made limited stocks of all values, except the 1s., available from the Philatelic Bureau from 11 April 1969 "in order not to create an artificial scarcity", but they had no postal validity. Covers do, however, exist showing the 4d. value used by Lagos Federal Income Tax Office in April 1969 and others from the Office of the Secretary to the Military Government in 1973 carry the 3d., 4d. and 2s. 6d. values.

COMMONWEALTH
P. M. MEETING
11. JAN. 1966

(134) **135** Y.M.C.A. Emblem and H.Q., Lagos

1966 (11 Jan). *Commonwealth Prime Ministers' Meeting, Lagos. No* 98 *optd with T* **134** *by the Nigerian Security Printing and Minting Co, Lagos, in red.*

186 **48** 2s. 6d. black and yellow 20 30

(Des S. B. Ajayi. Litho Nigerian Security Printing & Minting Co Ltd)

1966 (1 Sept). *Nigerian Y.W.C.A.'s Diamond Jubilee. P* 14.

187 **135** 4d. yellow-orange, ultramarine, orange-brown and yellow-green 10 10
188 9d. yellow-orange, ultramarine, brown and turquoise-green 10 15

137 Telephone Handset and Linesman **139** "Education, Science and Culture"

(Des S. B. Ajayi (4d.), N. Lasisi (1s. 6d.), B. Enweonwu (2s. 6d))

1966 (1 Oct). *Third Anniv of Republic. T* **137** *and similar designs. W* **34**. *P* 14½ × 14.

189 4d. green 10 10
190 1s. 6d. black, brown and reddish violet .. 45 50
191 2s. 6d. indigo, blue, yellow and green .. 1·25 2·00
189/91 .. .. *Set of* 3 1·60 2·25

Designs: *Vert*—4d. Dove and flag. *Horiz*—2s. 6d. Niger Bridge, Jebba.

(Des V. Whiteley from sketch by B. Salisu)

1966 (4 Nov). *20th Anniv of U.N.E.S.C.O. W* **34** (*sideways*). *P* 14½ × 14.

192 **139** 4d. black, lake and orange-yellow .. 40 10
193 1s. 6d. black, lake and turquoise-green 1·50 1·75
194 2s. 6d. black, lake and rose-pink .. 2·50 3·75
192/4 .. .. *Set of* 3 4·00 5·00

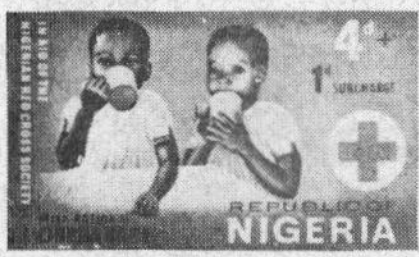

140 Children drinking

(Des V. Whiteley, after M. O. Afamefuna (4d.), I. U. Anawanti (1s. 6d.) and S. Adeyemi (2s. 6d.))

1966 (1 Dec). *Nigerian Red Cross. T* **140** *and similar designs. W* **34**. *P* 14 × 14½ (*1s. 6d.*) *or* 14½ × 14 (*others*).

195 4d. + 1d. black, reddish violet and red .. 30 25
196 1s. 6d. + 3d. multicoloured .. .. 1·00 3·25
197 2s. 6d. + 3d. multicoloured .. .. 1·25 3·75
195/7 .. .. *Set of* 3 2·25 6·50

Designs: *Vert*—1s. 6d. Tending patient. *Horiz*—2s. 6d. Tending casualties, and badge.

143 Surveying

(Des M. Goaman)

1967 (1 Feb). *International Hydrological Decade. T* **143** *and similar multicoloured design. W* **34**. *P* 14½ × 14 (*4d.*) *or* 14 × 14½ (*2s. 6d.*).

198 4d. Type **143** 10 10
199 2s. 6d. Water gauge on dam (*vert*) 25 60

145 Globe and Weather Satellite **147** Eyo Masqueraders

(Des M. Shamir (4d.), S. Bodo (1s. 6d.))

1967 (23 Mar). *World Meteorological Day. T* **145** *and similar horiz design. W* **34**. *P* 14½ × 14.

200 4d. magenta and blue 10 10
201 1s. 6d. black, yellow and blue 30 50

Design:—1s. 6d. Passing storm and sun.

(Des G. A. Okiki (4d.), A. B. Saka Lawal (1s. 6d.), S. Bodo (2s. 6d.). Photo Enschedé)

1967 (1 Oct). *4th Anniv of Republic. T* **147** *and similar multi-coloured designs. P* 11½ × 11 (*2s. 6d.*) *or* 11 × 11½ (*others*).

No.	Type	Description	Mint	Used
202		4d. Type **147**	20	10
203		1s. 6d. Crowd watching acrobat	1·25	1·25
204		2s. 6d. Stilt dancer (*vert*)	1·50	2·25
202/4		*Set of* 3	2·75	3·25

150 Tending Sick Animal

151 Smallpox Vaccination

(Des G. Drummond)

1967 (1 Dec). *Rinderpest Eradication Campaign. P* 14½ × 14.

No.	Type	Description	Mint	Used
205	**150**	4d. multicoloured	10	10
206		1s. 6d. multicoloured	30	65

PRINTERS AND PROCESS. Nos. 207/89 were printed in photogravure by the Nigerian Security Printing and Minting Co Ltd, *unless otherwise stated.*

(Des J. Owei. Litho)

1968 (7 Apr). *20th Anniv of World Health Organization. T* **151** *and similar horiz design. P* 14.

No.	Type	Description	Mint	Used
207		4d. magenta and black	10	10
208		1s. 6d. orange, lemon and black	30	40

Design:—1s. 6d. African and mosquito.

153 Chained Hands and Outline of Nigeria

155 Hand grasping at Doves of Freedom

(Des Jennifer Toombs)

1968 (1 July). *Human Rights Year. T* **153** *and similar design. P* 14.

No.	Type	Description	Mint	Used
209		4d. greenish blue, black and yellow	10	10
210		1s. 6d. myrtle-green, orange-red and black	20	30

Design: *Vert*—1s. 6d. Nigerian flag and Human Rights emblem.

(Des G. Vasarhelyi)

1968 (1 Oct). *5th Anniv of Federal Republic. P* 13½ × 14.

No.	Type	Description	Mint	Used
211	**155**	4d. multicoloured	10	10
212		1s. 6d. multicoloured	15	15

156 Map of Nigeria and Olympic Rings

158 G.P.O., Lagos

(Des J. Owei)

1968 (14 Oct). *Olympic Games, Mexico. T* **156** *and similar horiz design. P* 14.

No.	Type	Description	Mint	Used
213		4d. black, green and scarlet	10	10
214		1s. 6d. multicoloured	15	15

Design:—1s. 6d. Nigerian athletes, flag and Olympic rings.

(Des D.L.R.)

1969 (11 Apr). *Inauguration of Philatelic Service. P* 14.

No.	Type	Description	Mint	Used
215	**158**	4d. black and green	10	10
216		1s. 6d. black and blue	15	15

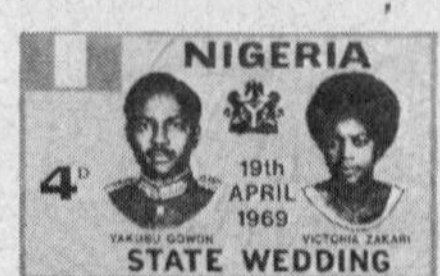

159 Yakubu Gowon and Victoria Zakari

(Des adapted from photo by Jackie Phillips. Litho)

1969 (20 Sept). *Wedding of General Gowon. P* 13 × 13½.

No.	Type	Description	Mint	Used
217	**159**	4d. chocolate and emerald	10	10
218		1s. 6d. black and emerald	15	15

1969–72. (*a*) *As No. 173 etc, but printed by Nigerian Security Printing and Minting Co Ltd. With printer's imprint* "N.S.P. & M. CO. LTD." *P* 13½ (*6d.*) *or P* 13 × 13½ (*others*).

No.	Type	Description	Mint	Used
220		1d. multicoloured	1·50	20
222		2d. multicoloured	1·25	30
		a. Smaller imprint* (13.1.71)	1·25	50
223		3d. multicoloured (7.71)	65	20
		a. Larger imprint* (22.10.71)	1·00	50
224		4d. multicoloured	3·50	25
		a. Smaller imprint*		
225		6d. multicoloured (1971)	1·00	40
226		9d. Prussian blue and orange-red (1970)	4·50	2·50
		a. "TD" of "LTD" omitted from imprint (Pl. 1B, R. 10/2)	15·00	
227		1s. multicoloured (8.71)	2·00	30
228		1s. 3d. multicoloured (1971)	6·50	2·50
229		2s. 6d. multicoloured (1972)	3·00	5·00
230		5s. multicoloured (1972)	3·00	6·00
220/30		*Set of* 10	24·00	16·00

*On No. 222a the designer's name measures 4¾ mm. On No. 223a the imprints measure 9 and 8½ mm respectively. The normal imprints on Nos. 222/3 both measure 5½ mm.

The date given for Nos. 222a and 223a are for the earliest known used copies.

†No. 224 has the left-hand imprint 6 mm long and the right-hand 5½ mm. On No. 224a the imprints are 5½ mm and 4½ mm respectively. The width of the design is also ½ mm smaller.

Imperforate proofs of similar 10s. and £1 values are known.

(*b*) *As Nos. 222 and 224, but redrawn, and printed by Enschedé. No printer's imprint; designer's name at right. P* 14½ × 13.

No.	Type	Description	Mint	Used
231		2d. multicoloured (9.70)	18·00	3·50
232		4d. multicoloured (3.71)	1·50	1·50

In the 2d. the face value is white instead of yellow, and in the 4d. the white lettering and value are larger.

160 Bank Emblem and "5th Anniversary"

161 Bank Emblem and Rays

(Des J. Owei (4d.), B. Salisu (1s. 6d.). Litho)

1969 (18 Oct). *Fifth Anniv of African Development Bank. P* 14.

No.	Type	Description	Mint	Used
233	**160**	4d. orange, black and blue	10	10
234	**161**	1s. 6d. lemon, black and plum	15	15

162 I.L.O. Emblem

164 Olumo Rock

(Des D. West)

1969 (15 Nov). *50th Anniv of International Labour Organisation. T* **162** *and similar horiz design. P* 14.

No.	Type	Description	Mint	Used
235		4d. black and bright reddish violet	10	10
236		1s. 6d. emerald and black	15	25

Design:—1s. 6d. World map and I.L.O. emblem.

(Des A. Onwudimegwu)

1969 (30 Dec). *International Year of African Tourism. T* **164** *and similar designs. P* 14.

No.	Type	Description	Mint	Used
237		4d. multicoloured	10	10
238		1s. black and bright emerald	15	10
239		1s. 6d. multicoloured	30	15
237/9		*Set of* 3	50	25

Designs: *Vert*—1s. Traditional musicians; 1s. 6d. Assob Falls.

167 Symbolic Tree

(Des E. Emokpae (4d., 1s., 2s.), B. Onobrakpeya (1s. 6d.). Photo Enschedé)

1970 (28 May). *"Stamp of Destiny"; End of Civil War. T* **167** *and similar designs. P* 11 × 11½ (*2s.*) *or* 11½ × 11 (*others*).

No.	Type	Description	Mint	Used
240		4d. gold, new blue and black	10	10
241		1s. multicoloured	10	10
242		1s. 6d. yellow-green and black	10	10
243		2s. multicoloured	15	20
240/3		*Set of* 4	30	30

Designs: *Vert*—1s. Symbolic Wheel; 1s. 6d. United Nigerians supporting Map. *Horiz*—2s. Symbolic Torch.

168 U.P.U. H.Q. Building

(Des A. Onwudimegwu)

1970 (29 June). *New U.P.U. Headquarters Building. P* 14.

No.	Type	Description	Mint	Used
244	**168**	4d. reddish violet and greenish yellow	10	10
245		1s. 6d. light greenish blue and deep blue	15	15

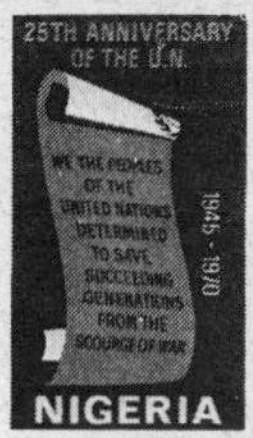

169 Scroll

170 Oil Rig

(Des A. Onwudimegwu)

1970 (1 Sept). *25th Anniv of United Nations. T* **169** *and similar vert design. P* 14.

No.	Type	Description	Mint	Used
246		4d. orange-brown, buff and black	10	10
247		1s. 6d. steel-blue, cinnamon and gold	15	15

Design:—1s. 6d. U.N. Building.

(Des E. Emokpae. Litho Enschedé)

1970 (30 Sept). *Tenth Anniv of Independence. T* **170** *and similar vert designs. Multicoloured. P* 13½ × 13.

No.	Type	Description	Mint	Used
248		2d. Type **170**	10	10
249		4d. University Graduate	15	10
250		6d. Durbar Horsemen	15	10
251		9d. Servicemen raising Flag	20	10
252		1s. Footballer	20	10
253		1s. 6d. Parliament Building	20	25
254		2s. Kainji Dam	50	70
255		2s. 6d. Agricultural Produce	50	75
248/55		*Set of* 8	1·75	1·75

171 Children and Globe

172 Ibibio Face Mask

(Des E. Emokpae and A. Onwudimegwu. Photo Enschedé)

1971 (21 Mar). *Racial Equality Year. T* **171** *and similar multi-coloured designs. P* 13 × 13½ (*4d., 2s.*) *or* 13½ × 13 (*others*).

No.	Type	Description	Mint	Used
256		4d. Type **171**	10	10
257		1s. Black and white men uprooting "Racism" (*vert*)	10	10
258		1s. 6d. The world in black and white (*vert*)	15	40
259		2s. Black and white men united	15	75
256/9		*Set of* 4	35	1·10

(Des A. Onwudimegwu)

1971 (30 Sept). *Antiquities of Nigeria. T* **172** *and similar vert designs. P* 13½ × 14.

No.	Type	Description	Mint	Used
260		4d. black and pale blue	10	10
261		1s. 3d. blackish brown and ochre	15	30
262		1s. 9d. emerald, sepia and olive-yellow	20	80
260/2		*Set of* 3	35	1·00

Designs:—1s. 3d. Benin bronze; 1s. 9d. Ife bronze.

173 Children and Symbol

174 Mast and Dish Aerial

(Des E. Emokpae)

1971 (11 Dec). *25th Anniv of U.N.I.C.E.F. T* **173** *and similar vert designs, each incorporating the U.N.I.C.E.F. symbol P* 13½ × 14.

No.	Type	Description	Mint	Used
263		4d. multicoloured	10	10
264		1s. 3d. yellow-orange, orge-red & carm-lake	10	40
265		1s. 9d. pale greenish blue & dp greenish blue	15	75
263/5		*Set of* 3	25	1·10

Designs:—1s. 3d. Mother and child; 1s. 9d. Mother carrying child.

(Des A. Onwudimegwu)

1971 (30 Dec). *Opening of Nigerian Earth Satellite Station. T* **174** *and similar horiz designs. P* 14.

No.	Type	Description	Mint	Used
266	**174**	4d. multicoloured	15	10
267	–	1s. 3d. green, blue and black	30	50
268	–	1s. 9d. brown, orange and black	40	1·00
269	–	3s. mauve, black and magenta	85	2·00
266/9		*Set of* 4	1·50	3·25

Designs:—Nos. 267/9, as T **174**, but showing different views of the Satellite Station.

The 4d. has been seen on a cover from Ilorin, postmarked 23.12.71.

175 Trade Fair Emblem

176 Traffic

(Des E. Emokpae (4d.), A. Onwudimegwu (others). Litho D.L.R.)

1972 (23 Feb). *All-Africa Trade Fair. T* **175** *and similar designs. P* 13.
270 4d. multicoloured 10 10
271 1s. 3d. deep lilac, lemon and gold 10 30
272 1s. 9d. yellow-orange, orange-yellow & black 15 75
270/2 .. .. *Set of* 3 20 1·00

Designs: *Horiz*—1s. 3d. Map of Africa with pointers to Nairobi. *Vert*—1s. 9d. Africa on globe.

(Des A. Onwudimegwu (4d., 3s.), E. Emokpae (1s. 3d.), J. Owei (1s. 9d.). Litho D.L.R.)

1972 (23 June). *Change to Driving on the Right. T* **176** *and similar horiz designs. Multicoloured (except 4d.). P* 13.
273 4d. Type **176** (yellow-orge, dp chest & black) 15 10
274 1s. 3d. Roundabout 70 70
275 1s. 9d. Highway .. .. 80 1·25
276 3s. Road junction .. .. 2·00 3·00
273/6 .. .. *Set of* 4 3·25 4·50

177 Nok Style Terracotta Head

178 Hides and Skins

(Des G. Okiki (1s. 3d.), A. Aiyegbusi (others). Litho D.L.R.)

1972 (1 Sept). *All-Nigeria Arts Festival. T* **177** *and similar multi-coloured designs. P* 13.
277 4d. Type **177** 10 10
278 1s. 3d. Bronze pot from Igbo-Ukwu 25 60
279 1s. 9d. Bone harpoon (*horiz*) .. .. .. 30 1·00
277/9 .. .. *Set of* 3 60 1·50

(New Currency. 100 kobo = 1 naira)

(Des E. Emokpae (8, 25, 30, 50 k., 1 n.), A. Onwudimegwu (others))

1973–74. *T* **178** *and similar designs. P* 14.

(*a*) *Photo. Left-hand imprint* 5¼ *mm long* (2 Jan–2 Apr)
280 1 k. multicoloured (deep green foliage) .. 20 20
*a. Light emerald foliage** (2.4.73) 20 10
281 2 k. black, pale turquoise-blue and bright purple 35 10
282 5 k. multicoloured (emerald hills) 60 25
*a. Bright yellow-green hills** (2.4.73) .. 50 10
283 10 k. black, orange-yellow and lilac 70 25
284 12 k. black, pale emerald and deep cobalt .. 5·00 5·00
285 18 k. multicoloured .. .. 4·50 2·00
286 20 k. multicoloured .. .. 7·50 3·00
287 30 k. black, chrome-yellow and new blue .. 7·50 4·50
288 50 k. multicoloured (black background and figure) .. .. 5·00 2·75
*a. Deep chocolate background and figure** (2.4.73) .. .. 1·50 90
289 1 n. multicoloured .. .. 12·00 12·00
280/9 .. .. *Set of* 10 35·00 25·00

(*b*) *Litho. Left-hand imprint* 6 *mm long* (2 Apr 1973†–74)
290 1 k. multicoloured (8.73) 10 10
291 2 k. black, pale turquoise-blue and bright purple (27.6.74)** .. .. 1·25 25
292 3 k. multicoloured 15 10
293 5 k. multicoloured (*shades*) (2.74) .. .. 1·25 25
294 7 k. multicoloured 30 25
295 8 k. multicoloured 40 10
296 10 k. black, orange-yellow and lilac (8.73) .. 2·25 15
297 12 k. black, green and cobalt (*shades*) .. 20 30
298 15 k. multicoloured 20 20
299 18 k. multicoloured 50 25
300 20 k. multicoloured 65 25
301 25 k. multicoloured 85 45
302 30 k. black, chrome-yellow and new blue .. 40 55
303 35 k. multicoloured .. .. 2·50 1·25
305 1 n. multicoloured (*shades*) .. .. .. 1·25 1·10
306 2 n. multicoloured (*shades*) .. .. .. 3·50 3·75
290/306 .. .. *Set of* 16 14·00 8·00

Designs: *Horiz*—2 k. Natural gas tanks; 3 k. Cement works; 5 k. Cattle-ranching; 7 k. Timber mill; 8 k. Oil refinery; 10 k. Cheetahs, Yankari Game Reserve; 12 k. New Civic Building; 15 k. Sugar-cane harvesting; 20 k. Vaccine production; 25 k. Modern wharf; 35 k. Textile machinery; 1 n. Eko Bridge; 2 n. Teaching Hospital, Lagos. *Vert*—18 k. Palm oil production; 30 k. Argungu Fishing Festival; 50 k. Pottery.

*On Nos. 280*a*, 282*a* and 288*a* other colours also differ, but the shades can best be identified by the distinctive features noted.

Used copies of No. 282*a* have been seen with orange omitted.

†Although First Day Covers of Nos. 290/306 were dated 1 April the stamps were not placed on sale until 2 April. Later, post-dated, covers included No. 291.

**This is the earliest known postmark date. No. 291 was not released by the Crown Agents in London until 11 September 1975.

Differences between printings:
1 k. In photogravure printings the stretched hide at left is in brownish black; on the litho stamps this hide is brown and yellow.
2 k. On the litho stamp the line of division between the black and pale blue colours of the gas tanks is a regular curve; on the photogravure printing it is horizontal and irregular. The litho stamp also has a wider mauve border at top.
5 k. The litho printing differs from the photogravure (Nos. 282/*a*) in having brown on the herdsman, instead of black.
10 k. The litho version has much less black on the cheetahs and tree trunk. It also shows black details at the left-hand end of the trunk, which do not appear on the photogravure version.
12 k. No. 284 is much darker than the litho version, especially within the building and amongst the trees at right.
18 k. The lithographed printing shows two oildrums in the foreground which are not present on the photogravure stamp.
20 k. The lithographed printing includes a brown plate not present on the photogravure version and this shows on the chemist. The liquid in the flasks is grey-blue instead of black. On the watermarked version, No. 348, the liquid is turquoise-blue.
30 k. No. 287 is much darker, with greater use of black in the design.
50 k. The litho version (No. 352) has solid shading on the potter's upper arm and lacks a black inner frame-line beneath the potter's wheel. No. 352 has a green printer's imprint at foot (instead of black) and its background is similar to that of No. 288*a*.
1 n. On the photogravure stamp the traffic is shown driving on the left. For the litho version the traffic is corrected to show it driving on the right.

See also Nos. 338/54.

PROCESS. From No. 307 onwards all stamps were lithographed by the Nigerian Security Printing and Minting Co Ltd.

179 Athlete

1973 (8 Jan). *Second All-African Games. Lagos. T* **179** *and similar multicoloured designs (except 5 k.). P* 13.
307 5 k. Type **179** (lt lilac, lt greenish bl & blk) .. 15 10
308 12 k. Football 25 50
309 18 k. Table-tennis .. .. 60 1·00
310 25 k. National Stadium (*vert*) .. .. .. 70 1·50
307/10 .. .. *Set of* 4 1·50 2·75

180 All-Africa House, Addis Ababa

181 Dr. Hansen

1973 (25 May). *Tenth Anniv of O.A.U. T* **180** *and similar vert designs. Multicoloured. P* 14.
311 5 k. Type **180** 10 10
312 18 k. O.A.U. flag 30 40
313 30 k. O.A.U. emblem and symbolic flight of ten stairs 50 80
311/13 .. .. *Set of* 3 70 1·10

(Des A. Onwudimegwu)

1973 (30 July). *Centenary of Discovery of Leprosy Bacillus. P* 14.
314 **181** 5 k. + 2 k. lt red-brown, flesh & black .. 20 35

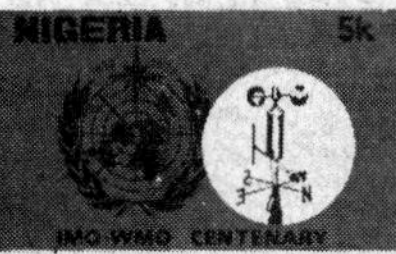

182 W.M.O. Emblem and Weather-vane

183 University Complex

(Des O. I. Oshiga)

1973 (4 Sept). *I.M.O./W.M.O. Centenary. P* 14.
315 **182** 5 k. multicoloured 15 10
316 30 k. multicoloured .. .. 85 1·75

(Des A. Onwudimegwu (5, 18 k.), C. Okechukwu (12 k.), O. I. Oshiga (30 k.))

1973 (17 Nov). *25th Anniv of Ibadan University. T* **183** *and similar multicoloured designs. P* 13½ × 14 (12 *k.*) *or* 14 × 13½ (*others*).
317 5 k. Type **183** 10 10
318 12 k. Students' population growth (*vert*) .. 25 30
319 18 k. Tower and students 35 55
320 30 k. Teaching Hospital 50 85
317/20 .. .. *Set of* 4 1·10 1·50

184 Lagos 1d. Stamp of 1874

(Des A. Onwudimegwu (30 k.), S. Eluare (others))

1974 (10 June). *Stamp Centenary. T* **184** *and similar horiz designs. P* 14 × 13½.
321 5 k. light emerald, yellow-orange and black 15 10
322 12 k. multicoloured 40 60
323 18 k. light yellowish green, mauve and black 70 1·00
324 30 k. multicoloured .. .. 1·60 2·50
321/4 .. .. *Set of* 4 2·50 3·75

Designs:—5 k. Graph of mail traffic growth; 12 k. Northern Nigeria £25 stamp of 1904; 30 k. Forms of mail transport.

185 U.P.U. Emblem on Globe

186 Starving and Well-fed Children

(Des S. Eluare (5 k.). A. Onwudimegwu (18 k.), O. I. Oshiga (30 k.))

1974 (9 Oct). *Centenary of Universal Postal Union. T* **185** *and similar horiz designs. P* 14.
325 5 k. lt greenish blue, yellow-orange & black 15 10
326 18 k. multicoloured 60 60
327 30 k. bistre-brown, lt greenish blue & black .. 1·25 1·75
325/7 .. .. *Set of* 3 1·75 2·25

Designs:—18 k. World transport map; 30 k. U.P.U. emblem and letters.

(Des A. Onwudimegwu (12 k.), S. Eluare (others))

1974 (25 Nov). *Freedom from Hunger Campaign. T* **186** *and similar designs. P* 14.
328 5 k. apple-green, buff and grey-black .. 10 10
329 12 k. multicoloured 40 50
330 30 k. multicoloured .. .. 1·10 1·75
328/30 .. .. *Set of* 3 1·40 2·00

Designs: *Horiz*—12 k. Poultry battery. *Vert*—30 k. Water-hoist.

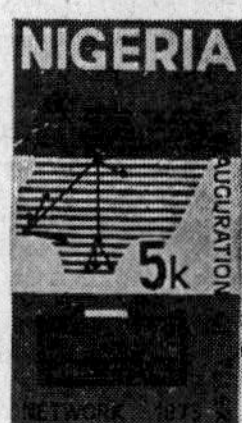

187 Telex Network and Teleprinter

188 Queen Amina of Zaria

(Des S. Eluare)

1975 (3 July). *Inauguration of Telex Network. T* **187** *and similar vert designs. P* 13½ × 14.
331 5 k. black, yellow-orange & light olive-green 10 10
332 12 k. black, lemon and orange-brown 20 20
333 18 k. multicoloured 30 30
334 30 k. multicoloured 50 50
331/4 .. .. *Set of* 4 1·00 1·00

Nos. 332/4 are as T **187** but have the motifs arranged differently.

(Des A. Onwudimegwu)

1975 (18 Aug). *International Women's Year. P* 14.
335 **188** 5 k. deep olive, light yellow and azure .. 15 10
336 18 k. purple, pale blue and light mauve .. 50 65
337 30 k. multicoloured .. .. 60 1·10
335/7 .. .. *Set of* 3 1·10 1·75

189

1975–82*. *As Nos.* 290 *etc., but W* **189** *(sideways on* 18, 50 *k.)*.
338 1 k. multicoloured (6.4.77) 25 25
339 2 k. black, pale turq-bl & bright purple (9.75) 50 10
340 3 k. multicoloured (10.75) 10 10
341 5 k. multicoloured (1.76) 50 10
342 7 k. multicoloured (16.5.80) 90 25
343 8 k. multicoloured (12.76) 45 25
344 10 k. blk, orange-yell & lilac (*shades*) (7.4.76) 70 10
346 15 k. multicoloured (5.82) .. ..
347 18 k. multicoloured (12.78) .. .. 1·50 85
348 20 k. multicoloured (9.79) .. .. 1·50 85
349 25 k. multicoloured (21.3.77) .. .. .. 1·50 25
352 50 k. multicoloured (2.9.77) .. .. .. 2·25 2·25
354 2 n. multicoloured (11.77) .. .. .. 5·00 5·00
*Earliest known dates of use.

190 Alexander Graham Bell

191 Child Writing

(Des A. Onwudimegwu)

1976 (10 Mar). *Telephone Centenary. T* **190** *and similar designs. W* **189** *(sideways on* 5 *and* 25 *k.)*. *P* 13½.
355 5 k. multicoloured 10 10
356 18 k. multicoloured 40 55
357 25 k. royal blue, pale blue and blackish brown 70 1·00
a. No wmk .. .. 10·00
355/7 .. .. *Set of* 3 1·10 1·50
Designs: *Horiz*—18 k. Gong and modern telephone system. *Vert*—25 k. Telephones, 1876 and 1976.

(Des A. Onwudimegwu (5 k.), S. Eluare (18 k.), N. Lasisi (25 k.))

1976 (20 Sept). *Launching of Universal Primary Education. T* **191** *and similar designs. W* **189** *(sideways on* 18 *and* 25 *k.)*. *P* 14.
358 5 k. lemon, light violet and bright mauve .. 10 10
359 18 k. multicoloured 45 60
360 25 k. multicoloured 70 85
358/60 .. .. *Set of* 3 1·10 1·40
Designs: *Vert*—18 k. Children entering school; 25 k. Children in class.

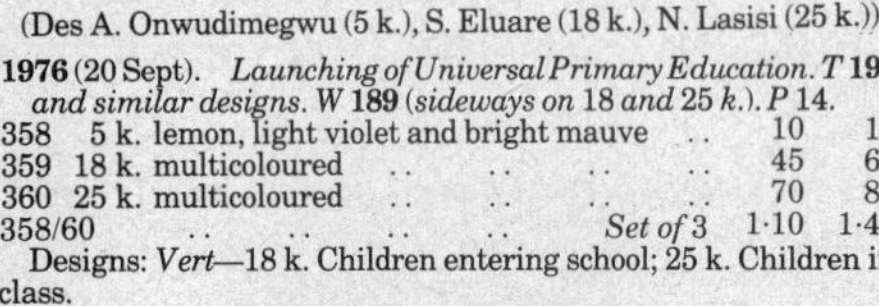

192 Festival Emblem

(Des O. I. Oshiga (5 k., 30 k.), A. Onwudimegwu (10 k., 12 k.), N. Lasisi (18 k.))

1976–77. *Second World Black and African Festival of Arts and Culture, Nigeria. T* **192** *and similar horiz designs. W* **189**. *P* 14.
361 5 k. gold and blackish brown (1.11.76) .. 15 10
362 10 k. lt red-brown, lt yellow & black (15.1.77) 35 40
363 12 k. multicoloured (15.1.77) 40 55
364 18 k. chrome-yellow, lt brown & blk (1.11.76) 60 80
365 30 k. magenta and black (15.1.77) .. .. 1·00 1·50
361/5 .. .. *Set of* 5 2·25 3·00
Designs:—10 k. National Arts Theatre; 12 k. African hair styles; 18 k. Musical instruments; 30 k. "Nigerian arts and crafts".

193 General Murtala Muhammed and Map of Nigeria

194 Scouts Saluting

(Des A. Onwudimegwu (5, 18 k.), O. I. Oshiga (30 k.))

1977 (12 Feb). *First Death Anniv of General Muhammed (Head of State). T* **193** *and similar vert designs. Multicoloured. W* **189** *(sideways on* 18 *and* 30 *k.)*. *P* 14.
366 5 k. Type **193** 10 10
367 18 k. General in dress uniform 20 35
368 30 k. General in battle dress 30 70
366/8 .. .. *Set of* 3 50 1·00

(Des N. Lasisi (18 k.), A. Onwudimegwu (others))

1977 (2 Apr). *First All-Africa Scout Jamboree, Jos, Nigeria. T* **194** *and similar horiz designs. Multicoloured. W* **189** *(sideways on* 5 *k.)*. *P* 14.
369 5 k. Type **194** 15 10
370 18 k. Scouts cleaning street 70 70
371 25 k. Scouts working on farm 85 95
372 30 k. Jamboree emblem and map of Africa .. 1·10 1·40
369/72 .. .. *Set of* 4 2·50 2·75

195 Trade Fair Complex

(Des S. Eluare (5 k.), A. Onwudimegwu (others))

1977 (27 Nov). *1st Lagos International Trade Fair. T* **195** *and similar horiz designs. W* **189**. *P* 14.
373 5 k. black, new blue and yellow-green .. 10 10
374 18 k. black, new blue and magenta 20 25
375 30 k. multicoloured 30 45
373/5 .. .. *Set of* 3 50 70
Designs:—18 k. Globe and Trade Fair emblem; 30 k. Weaving and basketry.

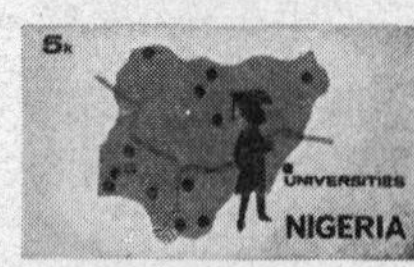

196 Map showing Nigerian Universities

(Des M. O. Shadare (5 k.), C. Okechukwu (12 k.), A. Onwudimegwu (18 k.), N. Lasisi (30 k.))

1978 (28 Apr). *Global Conference on Technical Co-operation between Developing Countries, Buenos Aires. T* **196** *and similar horiz designs. W* **189**. *P* 14.
376 5 k. multicoloured 10 10
377 12 k. multicoloured 15 15
378 18 k. multicoloured 25 25
379 30 k. yellow, bluish violet and black 45 60
376/9 .. .. *Set of* 4 80 1·00
Designs:—12 k. Map of West African highways and telecommunications; 18 k. Technologists undergoing training; 30 k. World map.

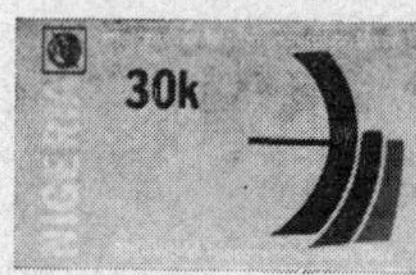

197 Microwave Antenna

1978 (17 May). *10th World Telecommunications Day. W* **189**. *P* 14.
380 **197** 30 k. multicoloured 50 60

198 Students on "Operation Feed the Nation"

199 Mother with Infected Child

(Des J. Salisu (5 k.), N. Lasisi (18 k.), A. Onwudimegwu (30 k.))

1978 (7 July). *"Operation Feed the Nation" Campaign. T* **198** *and similar multicoloured designs. W* **189** *(sideways on* 30 *k.)*. *P* 14.
381 5 k. Type **198** 10 10
382 18 k. Family backyard farm 20 20
383 30 k. Plantain farm (*vert*) 35 60
381/3 .. .. *Set of* 3 55 75

(Des G. Osuji (30 k.), N. Lasisi (others))

1978 (31 Aug). *Global Eradication of Smallpox. T* **199** *and similar designs. W* **189** *(sideways on* 30 *k.)*. *P* 14.
384 5 k. black, orange-brown and rose-lilac .. 10 10
385 12 k. multicoloured 20 20
386 18 k. black, lake-brown and greenish yellow .. 30 30
387 30 k. black, silver and rose-pink 50 50
384/7 .. .. *Set of* 4 1·00 1·00
Designs: *Horiz*—12 k. Doctor and infected child; 18 k. Group of children being vaccinated. *Vert*—30 k. Syringe.

200 Nok Terracotta Human Figure, Bwari (900 B.C.–200 A.D.)

201 Anti-Apartheid Emblem

(Des local artists)

1978 (27 Oct). *Antiquities. T* **200** *and similar designs. W* **189** *(sideways on* 5, 18 *and* 30 *k.)*. *P* 14.
388 5 k. black, new blue and carmine-red .. 10 10
389 12 k. multicoloured 10 10
390 18 k. black, greenish blue and carmine-red .. 15 15
391 30 k. multicoloured 20 20
388/91 .. .. *Set of* 4 45 45
Designs: *Horiz*—12 k. Igbo-Ukwu bronze snail shell, Igbo Isaiah (9th-century A.D.). *Vert*—18 k. Ife bronze statue of king (12th–15th century A.D.); 30 k. Benin bronze equestrian figure (about 1700 A.D.).

(Des A. Onwudimegwu)

1978 (10 Dec). *International Anti-Apartheid Year. W* **189** *(sideways)*. *P* 14.
392 **201** 18 k. black, greenish yellow & vermilion 15 15

202 Wright Brothers and *Flyer*

203 Murtala Muhammed Airport

(Des A. Onwudimegwu)

1978 (28 Dec). *75th Anniv of Powered Flight. T* **202** *and similar horiz design. W* **189**. *P* 14.
393 5 k. multicoloured 10 10
394 18 k. black, ultramarine and light blue .. 45 20
Design:—18 k. Nigerian Air Force formation.

(Des A. Onwudimegwu)

1979 (15 Mar). *Opening of Murtala Muhammed Airport. W* **189**. *P* 14.
395 **203** 5 k. black, grey-blk & brt greenish blue 10 10

204 Child with Stamp Album

205 Mother and Child

1979 (11 Apr). *10th Anniv of National Philatelic Service. W* **189**. *P* 14.
396 **204** 5 k. multicoloured 10 10

1979 (28 June). *International Year of the Child. T* **205** *and similar multicoloured designs. W* **189** *(sideways on* 25 *k.)*. *P* 14.
397 5 k. Type **205** 10 10
398 18 k. Children studying 30 30
399 25 k. Children playing (*vert*) 45 50
397/9 .. .. *Set of* 3 75 80

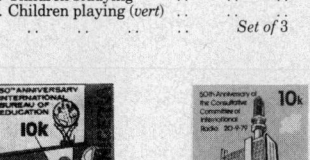

206 Trainee Teacher making Audio Visual Aid Materials

207 Necom House

(Des M. Shadare and O. Oshiga)

1979 (25 July). *50th Anniv of International Bureau of Education. T* **206** *and similar vert design. Multicoloured. W* **189** *(sideways)*. *P* 14.
400 10 k. Type **206** 10 10
401 30 k. Adult education class 25 30

(Des A. Onwudimegwu)

1979 (20 Sept). *50th Anniv of Consultative Committee of International Radio. W* **189** *(sideways)*. *P* 14.
402 **207** 10 k. multicoloured 15 20

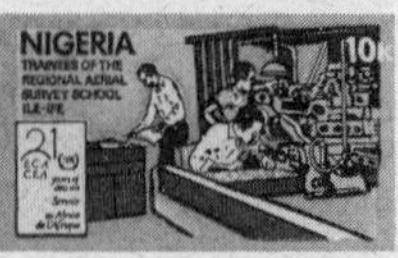

208 Trainees of the Regional Aerial Survey School, Ile-Ife

(Des A. Onwudimegwu)

1979 (12 Dec). *21st Anniv of the Economic Commission for Africa. W* **189**. *P* 14.
403 **208** 10 k. multicoloured 20 20

209 Football, Cup and Map of Nigeria

210 Wrestling

(Des G. Akinola (10 k.), Mrs. O. Adeyeye (30 k.))

1980 (8 Mar). *African Cup of Nations Football Competition, Nigeria. T* **209** *and similar multicoloured design. W* **189** *(sideways on 30 k.). P 14.*
404 10 k. Type **209** 15 10
405 30 k. Footballer (*vert*) 50 50

(Des M. Shadare (10 k.), Mrs. O. Adeyeye (others))

1980 (19 July). *Olympic Games, Moscow. T* **210** *and similar designs. W* **189** *(sideways on 10, 20 and 45 k.). P 14.*
406 10 k. multicoloured 10 10
407 20 k. black and bright yellow-green 10 10
408 30 k. black, reddish orange and blue 15 15
409 45 k. multicoloured 20 20
406/9 .. .. *Set of* 4 45 45
Designs: *Vert*—20 k. Long jump; 45 k. Netball. *Horiz*—30 k. Swimming.

211 Figures supporting O.P.E.C. Emblem

212 Steam Locomotive

(Des G. Oluwasegun)

1980 (15 Sept). *20th Anniv of O.P.E.C. (Organization of Petroleum Exporting Countries). T* **211** *and similar design. W* **189** *(sideways on 45 k.). P 14.*
410 10 k. black, ultramarine and greenish yellow 15 10
411 45 k. black, deep turquoise-blue and magenta 55 60
Design: *Vert*—45 k. O.P.E.C. emblem on globe.

1980 (2 Oct). *25th Anniv of Nigerian Railway Corporation. T* **212** *and similar horiz designs. Multicoloured. W* **189**. *P 14.*
412 10 k. Type **212** 25 10
413 20 k. Loading goods train 65 60
414 30 k. Freight train 75 70
412/14 .. .. *Set of* 3 1·50 1·25

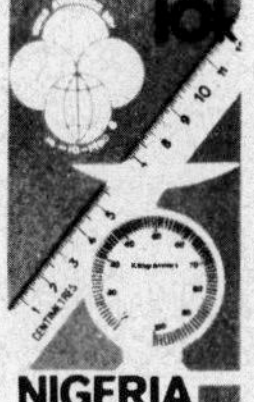

213 Metric Scales

214 "Communications" Symbols and Map of West Africa

(Des G. Akinola (10 k.), M. Shadare (30 k.))

1980 (14 Oct). *World Standards Day. T* **213** *and similar design. W* **189** *(sideways on 10 k.). P 14.*
415 10 k. red and black 10 10
416 30 k. multicoloured 35 40
Design: *Horiz*—30 k. Quality control.

1980 (5 Nov). *5th Anniv of E.C.O.W.A.S. (Economic Community of West African States). T* **214** *and similar horiz designs showing symbols of economic structure and map of West Africa. W* **189**. *P 14.*
417 10 k. black, yellow-orange and grey-olive .. 10 10
418 25 k. black, emerald and bright rose 10 10
419 30 k. black, greenish yellow and yellow-brown 15 15
420 45 k. black, turquoise-blue and bright blue .. 20 25
417/20 .. .. *Set of* 4 45 50
Designs:—25 k. "Transport"; 30 k. "Agriculture"; 45 k. "Industry".

215 Disabled Woman Sweeping

216 President launching "Green Revolution" (food production campaign)

(Des N. Lasisi (10 k.), G. Akinola (30 k.))

1981 (25 June). *International Year for Disabled Persons. T* **215** *and similar vert design. W* **189** *(sideways). P 14.*
421 10 k. multicoloured 15 10
422 30 k. black, chestnut and new blue 50 65
Design:—30 k. Disabled man filming.

(Des Mrs. A. Adeyeye (10 k.), G. Akinola (30 k.), S. Eluare (others))

1981 (16 Oct). *World Food Day. T* **216** *and similar designs. W* **189** *(sideways on 25 and 30 k.). P 14.*
423 10 k. multicoloured 10 10
424 25 k. black, greenish yellow and emerald .. 20 50
425 30 k. multicoloured 25 55
426 45 k. black, yellow-brown and orange-yellow 45 85
423/6 .. .. *Set of* 4 85 1·75
Designs: *Vert*—25 k. Food crops; 30 k. Harvesting tomatoes. *Horiz*—45 k. Pig farming.

217 Rioting in Soweto

218 "Preservation of Wildlife"

(Des G. Osuji)

1981 (10 Dec). *Anti-Apartheid Movement. T* **217** *and similar design. W* **189** *(sideways on 45 k.). P 14.*
427 30 k. multicoloured 35 45
428 45 k. black, vermilion and light green .. 50 80
Design: *Vert*—45 k. "Police brutality".

(Des G. Akinola)

1982 (22 Feb). *75th Anniv of Boy Scout Movement. T* **218** *and similar horiz design. Multicoloured. W* **189**. *P 14.*
429 30 k. Type **218** 55 55
430 45 k. Lord Baden-Powell taking salute .. 85 95

219 Early Inoculation

220 "Keep Your Environment Clean"

(Des G. Osuji (10 k.), C. Ogbebor (30 k.), N. Lasisi (45 k.))

1982 (24 Mar). *Centenary of Robert Koch's Discovery of Tubercle Bacillus. T* **219** *and similar designs. W* **189** *(sideways on 45 k.). P 14.*
431 10 k. multicoloured 20 15
432 30 k. grey-black, brown and turquoise-green .. 50 55
433 45 k. grey-black, light brown and bright green 80 85
431/3 .. .. *Set of* 3 1·40 1·40
Designs: *Horiz*—30 k. Technician and microscope. *Vert*—45 k. Patient being X-rayed.

(Des C. Ogbebor (10 k.), N. Lasisi (others))

1982 (10 June). *10th Anniv of U.N. Conference on Human Environment. T* **220** *and similar horiz designs. W* **189**. *P 14.*
434 10 k. multicoloured 15 10
435 20 k. yellow-orange, greenish grey and black .. 40 40
436 30 k. multicoloured 55 60
437 45 k. multicoloured 80 85
434/7 .. .. *Set of* 4 1·75 1·75
Designs:—20 k. "Check air pollution"; 30 k. "Preserve natural environment"; 45 k. "Reafforestation concerns all".

221 *Salamis parhassus*

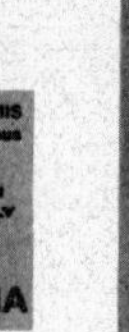

222 Carving of "Male and Female Twins"

(Des G. Akinola)

1982 (15 Sept). *Nigerian Butterflies. T* **221** *and similar horiz designs. Multicoloured. W* **189**. *P 14.*
438 10 k. Type **221** 15 10
439 20 k. *Papilio zalmoxis* 40 40
440 30 k. *Pachylophus beckeri* 55 60
441 45 k. *Papilio hesperus* 80 85
438/41 .. .. *Set of* 4 1·75 1·75

(Des C. Ogbebor (10 k.), G. Akinola (20 k.), S. Eluare (30 k.), N. Lasisi (45 k.))

1982 (18 Nov). *25th Anniv of National Museum. T* **222** *and similar multicoloured designs. W* **189** *(sideways on 10, 30, 45 k.). P 14.*
442 10 k. Type **222** 15 10
443 20 k. Royal bronze leopard (*horiz*) 35 45
444 30 k. Soapstone seated figure 55 80
445 45 k. Wooden helmet mask .. .. 90 1·40
442/5 .. .. *Set of* 4 1·75 2·50

223 Three Generations

224 Satellite View of Globe

(Des G. Akinola)

1983 (8 Mar). *Family Day. T* **223** *and similar multicoloured design. W* **189** *(sideways on 30 k.). P 14.*
446 10 k. Type **223** 15 10
447 30 k. Parents with three children (*vert*) .. 50 65

(Des N. Lasisi (30 k.), C. Ogbebor (others))

1983 (14 Mar). *Commonwealth Day. T* **224** *and similar designs. W* **189** *(sideways on 30, 45 k.). P 14.*
448 10 k. yellow-brown and black 15 10
449 25 k. multicoloured 45 50
450 30 k. black, magenta and pale grey 50 55
451 45 k. multicoloured 80 85
448/51 .. .. *Set of* 4 1·75 1·75
Designs: *Horiz*—25 k. National Assembly Buildings. *Vert*—30 k. Drilling for oil; 45 k. Athletics.

225 Corps Members on Building Project

226 Postman on Bicycle

(Des Mrs. A. Adeyeye (25 k.), G. Akinola (others))

1983 (25 May). *10th Anniv of National Youth Service Corps. T* **225** *and similar multicoloured designs. W* **189** *(sideways on 25, 30 k.). P 14.*
452 10 k. Type **225** 15 10
453 25 k. On the assault-course (*vert*) 45 50
454 30 k. Corps members on parade (*vert*) .. 50 60
452/4 .. .. *Set of* 3 1·00 1·10

(Des N. Lasisi (25 k.), O. Ogunfowora (30 k.), Mrs. A. Adeyeye (others))

1983 (20 July). *World Communications Year. T* **226** *and similar multicoloured designs. W* **189** *(sideways on 10 k.). P 14.*
455 10 k. Type **226** 15 10
456 25 k. Newspaper kiosk (*horiz*) 45 50
457 30 k. Town crier blowing elephant tusk (*horiz*) 50 55
458 45 k. T.V. newsreader (*horiz*) 80 85
455/8 .. .. *Set of* 4 1·75 1·75

227 Pink Shrimp

228 On Parade

(Des Hilda Woods (10 k.), G. Osuji (25 k.), Mrs. A. Adeyeye (30 k.), O. Ogunfowora (45 k.))

1983 (22 Sept). *World Fishery Resources. T* **227** *and similar horiz designs. W* **189**. *P 14.*
459 10 k. rose, new blue and black.. .. .. .. 15 10
460 25 k. multicoloured 35 50
461 30 k. multicoloured 40 55
462 45 k. multicoloured 65 85
459/62 .. .. *Set of* 4 1·40 1·75
Designs:—25 k. Long Neck Croaker; 30 k. Barracuda; 45 k. Fishing techniques.

(Des F. Nwaije (10 k.), Mrs A. Adeyeye (30 k.), G. Osuji (45 k.))

1983 (14 Oct). *Boys' Brigade Centenary and 75th Anniv of Movement in Nigeria. T* **228** *and similar multicoloured designs. W* **189** *(sideways on 10 k.). P 14.*
463 10 k. Type **228** 25 10
464 30 k. Members working on cassava plantation (*horiz*) 75 75
465 45 k. Skill training (*horiz*) .. .. 1·50 1·50
463/5 .. .. *Set of* 3 2·25 2·10

OMNIBUS ISSUES

Details, together with prices for complete sets, of the various Omnibus issues from the 1935 Silver Jubilee series to date are included in a special section following Zululand at the end of the catalogue.

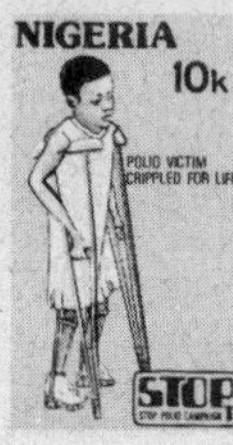

229 Crippled Child

230 Waterbuck

(Des S. Eluare (10 k.), G. Osuji (others))

1984 (29 Feb). *Stop Polio Campaign. T* **229** *and similar designs. W* **189** *(sideways on* 10 *k. and* 30 *k.). P* 14.

466	10 k. light blue, black and light brown ..	20	10
467	25 k. pale orange, black and greenish yellow ..	45	50
468	30 k. carmine-rose, black and orange-brown	55	60
466/8	.. .. *Set of* 3	1·10	1·10

Designs: *Horiz*—25 k. Child receiving vaccine. *Vert*—30 k. Healthy child.

(Des O. Ogunfowora (30 k.), Mrs. A. Adeyeye (45 k.), N. Lasisi (others))

1984 (25 May). *Nigerian Wildlife. T* **230** *and similar designs. W* **189** *(inverted on* 30 *k., sideways on* 10 *k.,* 45 *k.). P* 14.

469	10 k. light green, light brown and black ..	20	10
470	25 k. multicoloured	50	50
471	30 k. yellow-brown, black and light green ..	60	70
472	45 k. new blue, pale orange and black .	80	95
469/72	.. .. *Set of* 4	1·90	2·00

Designs: *Horiz*—25 k. Hartebeest; 30 k. African Buffalo. *Vert*—45 k. Diademed Monkey ("African Golden Monkey").

231 Obverse and Reverse of 1969 £1 Note

232 Boxing

1984 (2 July). *25th Anniv of Nigerian Central Bank. T* **231** *and similar horiz designs. W* **189** *(inverted on* 30 *k.). P* 14.

473	10 k. multicoloured	20	10
474	25 k. deep cinnamon, black and light green ..	45	50
475	30 k. light rose, black and grey-olive ..	55	60
473/5	.. .. *Set of* 3	1·10	1·10

Designs:—25 k. Central Bank; 30 k. Obverse and reverse of 1959 £5 note.

1984 (20 July). *Olympic Games, Los Angeles. T* **232** *and similar vert designs. Multicoloured. W* **189** *(sideways). P* 14.

476	10 k. Type **232**	15	10
477	25 k. Discus-throwing	35	50
478	30 k. Weightlifting	40	60
479	45 k. Cycling	60	90
476/9	.. .. *Set of* 4	1·40	1·90

233 Irrigation Project, Lesotho

234 Pin-tailed Whydah

(Des Mrs. A. Adeyeye (10 k.), S. Eluare (25 k.), Hilda Woods (30 k.), O. Ogunfowora (45 k.))

1984 (10 Sept). *20th Anniv of African Development Bank. T* **233** *and similar designs. W* **189** *(sideways on* 10 *k.). P* 14.

480	10 k. multicoloured	20	10
481	25 k. multicoloured	45	50
482	30 k. black, chrome yell & bright greenish bl	60	60
483	45 k. black, orange-brn & bright greenish bl ..	90	90
480/3	.. .. *Set of* 4	1·90	1·90

Designs: *Horiz*—25 k. Bomi Hills Road, Liberia; 30 k. School building project, Seychelles; 45 k. Coal mining, Niger.

(Des S. Eluare (25 k.), O. Ogunfowora (45 k.), F. Isibor (others))

1984 (24 Oct). *Rare Birds. T* **234** *and similar vert designs. Multicoloured. W* **189** *(sideways). P* 14.

484	10 k. Type **234**	50	10
485	25 k. Spur-winged Plover	1·25	60
486	30 k. Red Bishop	1·25	1·00
487	45 k. Double-spurred Francolin	1·25	1·40
484/7	.. .. *Set of* 4	3·75	2·75

235 Aircraft taking-off

236 Office Workers and Clocks ("Punctuality")

(Des. F. Isibor (10 k.), O. Ogunfowora (45 k.))

1984 (7 Dec). *40th Anniv of International Civil Aviation Organization. T* **235** *and similar horiz design. Multicoloured. W* **189** *(inverted on* 45 *k.). P* 14.

488	10 k. Type **235**	35	10
489	45 k. Aircraft circling globe	1·25	90

(Des O. Ogunfowora)

1985 (27 Feb). *"War against Indiscipline". T* **236** *and similar horiz design. Multicoloured. W* **189** *(inverted on* 20 *k.). P* 14.

490	20 k. Type **236**	30	35
491	50 k. Cross over hands passing banknotes ("Discourage Bribery")	70	75

237 Footballers receiving Flag from Major-General Buhari

238 Globe and O.P.E.C. Emblem

(Des F. Isibor (50 k.), G. Akinola (others))

1985 (5 June). *International Youth Year. T* **237** *and similar multicoloured designs. W* **189** *(sideways on* 50, 55 *k.). P* 14.

492	20 k. Type **237**	30	35
493	50 k. Girls of different tribes with flag (*vert*)	70	75
494	55 k. Members of youth organizations with flags (*vert*)	75	80
492/4	.. .. *Set of* 3	1·60	1·75

1985 (15 Sept). *25th Anniv of Organization of Petroleum Exporting Countries. T* **238** *and similar design. W* **189** *(sideways on* 20 *k.). P* 14.

495	20 k. greenish blue and orange-vermilion ..	50	35
496	50 k. black and ultramarine	1·00	75

Design: *Horiz*—50 k. World map and O.P.E.C. emblem.

239 Rolling Mill

240 Waterfall

1985 (25 Sept). *25th Anniv of Independence. T* **239** *and similar horiz designs. Multicoloured. W* **189**. *P* 14.

497	20 k. Type **239**	25	10
498	50 k. Map of Nigeria	45	25
499	55 k. Remembrance Arcade	45	25
500	60 k. Eleme, first Nigerian oil refinery ..	50	30
497/500	.. .. *Set of* 4	1·50	85
MS501	101×101 mm. Nos. 497/500. Wmk sideways	1·50	1·75

(Des S. Eluare (55 k.), F. Isibor (60 k.), Mrs. A. Adeyeye (others))

1985 (27 Sept). *World Tourism Day. T* **240** *and similar multicoloured designs. W* **189** *(sideways on* 20, 55, 60 *k., inverted on* 50 *k.). P* 14.

502	20 k. Type **240**	25	10
503	50 k. Pottery, carved heads and map of Nigeria (*horiz*)	35	25
504	55 k. Calabash carvings and Nigerian flag ..	35	25
505	60 k. Leather work	35	30
502/5	.. .. *Set of* 4	1·10	85

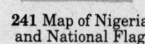

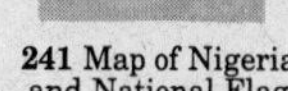

241 Map of Nigeria and National Flag

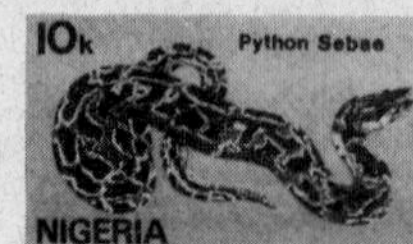

242 Rock Python

(Des N. Lasisi (20 k.), Mrs. A. Adeyeye (50 k.), O. Ogunfowora (55 k.))

1985 (7 Oct). *40th Anniv of United Nations Organization and 25th Anniv of Nigerian Membership. T* **241** *and similar designs. W* **189** *(sideways on* 20 *k., inverted on* 50 *k.). P* 14.

506	20 k. black, light green and pale blue ..	10	10
507	50 k. black, dull ultramarine and cerise ..	20	25
508	55 k. black, new blue and carmine	20	25
506/8	.. .. *Set of* 3	45	55

Designs: *Horiz*—50 k. United Nations Building, New York; 55 k. United Nations logo.

IMPERFORATE STAMPS. Nos. 509/12, 528/38, 543/6, 555/7 and 560/7 exist imperforate from restricted printings. Such printings may also exist for other issues.

(Des Hilda Woods (10, 30 k.), G. Akinola (20 k.), F. Isibor (25 k.))

1986 (15 Apr). *African Reptiles. T* **242** *and similar horiz designs. W* **189** *(inverted on* 10 *k.). P* 14.

509	10 k. multicoloured	20	10
510	20 k. black, orange-brown and pale new blue	25	25
511	25 k. multicoloured	35	40
512	30 k. multicoloured	35	40
509/12	.. .. *Set of* 4	1·00	1·00

Designs:—20 k. Long Snouted Crocodile; 25 k. Gopher Tortoise; 30 k. Chameleon.

243 Social Worker with Children

244 Emblem and Globe

(Des G. Akinola (1, 35 k.), S. Eluare (5 k.), O. Ogunfowora (10, 15 k.), Mrs. A. Adeyeye (40, 45 k.), G. Osuji (50 k.), C. Ogbebor (others))

1986 (16 June). *Nigerian Life. T* **243** *and similar multicoloured designs. W* **189** *(sideways on* 1, 10, 20, 40 *k. and inverted on* 2, 5, 25, 50 *k.,* 1, 2 *n.). P* 14.

513	1 k. Type **243**	10	10
514	2 k. Volkswagen motor assembly line (*horiz*)	10	10
515	5 k. Modern housing estate (*horiz*) ..	10	10
516	10 k. Harvesting oil palm fruit	10	10
517	15 k. Unloading freighter (*horiz*) ..	10	10
518	20 k. *Tecoma stans* (flower)	10	10
519	25 k. Hospital ward (*horiz*)	10	10
519*a*	30 k. Birom dancers	10	10
520	35 k. Telephonists operating switchboard (*horiz*)	10	10
521	40 k. Nkpokiti dancers	10	10
522	45 k. Hibiscus (*horiz*)	20	10
523	50 k. Post Office counter (*horiz*) ..	10	10
524	1 n. Stone quarry (*horiz*)	20	25
525	2 n. Students in laboratory (*horiz*) ..	35	40
513/25	.. .. *Set of* 14	1·50	1·60

Nos. 513/25 were originally scheduled for issue during 1984, but were delayed. The 5 k. and 20 k. appear to have been released for postal purposes during 1984 and are known postmarked from 2 November (5 k.) or 3 July (20 k.). The 30 k. value, No. 519*a*, was not included in the 1986 philatelic release.

(Des Mrs. A. Adeyeye)

1986 (20 June). *International Peace Year. T* **244** *and similar horiz design. Multicoloured. W* **189**. *P* 14.

526	10 k. Type **244**	10	10
527	20 k. Hands of five races holding globe ..	10	10

245 Goliath Beetle

246 Oral Rehydration Therapy

(Des Hilda Woods (25 k.), S. Eluare (others))

1986 (14 July). *Nigerian Insects. T* **245** *and similar horiz designs. Multicoloured. W* **189** *(inverted on* 20 *k.). P* 14.

528	10 k. Type **245**	20	10
529	20 k. Common Wasp	25	25
530	25 k. Cricket (*Acheta domestica*)	35	35
531	30 k. Carpet Beetle	55	65
528/31	.. .. *Set of* 4	1·25	1·25
MS532	119×101 mm. Nos. 528/31. Wmk sideways	1·50	1·75

(Des N. Lasisi (10 k.), F. Isibor (30 k.), Mrs. A. Adeyeye (others))

1986 (11 Nov). *40th Anniv of United Nations Children's Fund. T* **246** *and similar vert designs. W* **189** *(sideways). P* 14.

533	10 k. multicoloured	20	10
534	20 k. black, reddish brown & greenish yellow	25	25
535	25 k. multicoloured	30	30
536	30 k. multicoloured	45	45
533/6	.. .. *Set of* 4	1·10	1·00

Designs:—20 k. Immunisation; 25 k. Breast feeding; 30 k. Mother and child.

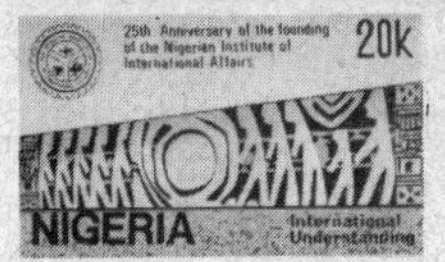

247 Stylized Figures on Wall ("International Understanding")

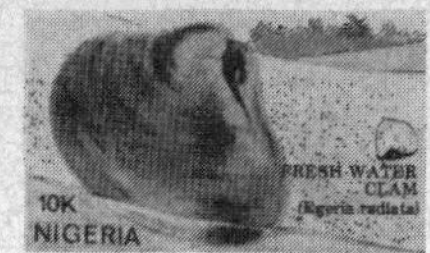

248 Freshwater Clam

(Des S. Eluare (20 k.), Hilda Woods (30 k.))

1986 (12 Dec). *25th Anniv of Nigerian Institute of International Affairs. T* **247** *and similar design. W* **189** *(sideways on 30 k.). P* 14.

537 20 k. black, greenish blue and light green .. 25 25
538 30 k. multicoloured 40 45
Design: *Vert*—30 k. "Knowledge" (bronze sculpture).

(Des G. Osuji (20 k.), F. Isibor (others))

1987 (31 Mar). *Shells. T* **248** *and similar horiz designs. W* **189** *(inverted on 10, 25 k.). P* 14.

539 10 k. multicoloured 15 10
540 20 k. black, reddish brown & pale rose-pink 25 25
541 25 k. multicoloured 25 25
542 30 k. multicoloured 30 35
539/42 .. .. *Set of* 4 85 85
Designs:—20 k. Periwinkle; 25 k. Bloody Cockle (inscr "BLODDY COCKLE"); 30 k. Mangrove Oyster.

249 *Clitoria ternatea*

250 Doka Hairstyle

(Des S. Eluare (10 k.), Hilda Woods (20 k.), Mrs. A. Adeyeye (others))

1987 (28 May). *Nigerian Flowers. T* **249** *and similar vert designs. W* **189** *(sideways). P* 14.

543 10 k. multicoloured 10 10
544 20 k. lake-brown, greenish yellow & emerald 15 10
545 25 k. multicoloured 15 15
546 30 k. multicoloured 20 20
543/6 .. .. *Set of* 4 55 45
Designs:—20 k. *Hibiscus tiliaceus*; 25 k. *Acanthus montanus*; 30 k. *Combretum racemosum*.

(Des G. Akinola (25 k.), S. Eluare (30 k.), Mrs. A. Adeyeye (others))

1987 (15 Sept). *Women's Hairstyles. T* **250** *and similar vert designs. W* **189** *(sideways). P* 14.

547 10 k. black, orange-brown and olive-grey .. 10 10
548 20 k. multicoloured 10 10
549 25 k. black, brown and vermilion 10 10
550 30 k. multicoloured 10 10
547/50 .. .. *Set of* 4 20 25
Designs:—20 k. Eting; 25 k. Agogo; 30 k. Goto.

251 Family sheltering under Tree

252 Red Cross Worker distributing Food

(Des S. Nwasike (20 k.), Mrs. A. Adeyeye (30 k.))

1987 (10 Dec). *International Year of Shelter for the Homeless. T* **251** *and similar vert design. Multicoloured. W* **189** *(sideways). P* 14.

551 20 k. Type **251** 10 10
552 30 k. Family and modern house 10 10

(Des G. Osuji)

1988 (17 Feb). *125th Anniv of International Red Cross. T* **252** *and similar vert design. Multicoloured. W* **189** *(sideways). P* 14.

553 20 k. Type **252** 10 10
554 30 k. Carrying patient to ambulance .. 10 20

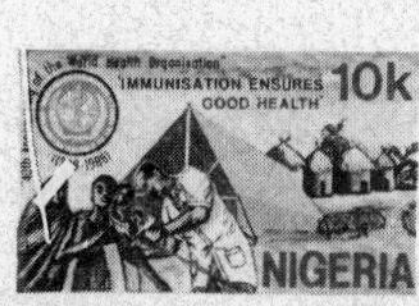

253 Doctor vaccinating Baby

254 O.A.U. Logo

(Des C. Ogbebor (10 k.), G. Osuji (others))

1988 (7 Apr). *40th Anniv of World Health Organization. T* **253** *and similar horiz designs. Multicoloured. W* **189** *(inverted). P* 14.

555 10 k. Type **253** 10 10
556 20 k. W.H.O. logo and outline map of Nigeria 10 10
557 30 k. Doctor and patients at mobile clinic .. 10 10
555/7 .. .. *Set of* 3 15 15

(Des O. Ojo (10 k.), Mrs. A. Adeyeye (20 k.))

1988 (25 May). *25th Anniv of Organization of African Unity. T* **254** *and similar vert design. W* **189** *(sideways). P* 14.

558 10 k. olive-bistre, emerald and bright orange 10 10
559 20 k. multicoloured 10 10
Design:—20 k. Four Africans supporting map of Africa.

255 Pink Shrimp

256 Weightlifting

(Des S. Eluare)

1988 (2 June). *Shrimps. T* **255** *and similar horiz designs. W* **189**. *P* 14.

560 10 k. multicoloured 10 10
561 20 k. black and pale yellow-olive 10 10
562 25 k. black, orange-vermilion & yell-brown 10 10
563 30 k. reddish orange, olive-bistre and black 10 10
560/3 .. .. *Set of* 4 20 20
MS564 120 × 101 mm. Nos. 560/3. Wmk sideways 20 20
Designs:—20 k. Tiger Shrimp; 25 k. Deepwater Roseshrimp; 30 k. Estuarine Prawn.

(Des G. Osuji (30 k.), Mrs. A. Adeyeye (others))

1988 (6 Sept). *Olympic Games, Seoul. T* **256** *and similar multicoloured designs. W* **189** *(sideways on 30 k.). P* 14.

565 10 k. Type **256** 10 10
566 20 k. Boxing 10 10
567 30 k. Athletics (*vert*) 10 10
565/7 .. .. *Set of* 3 15 15

257 Banknote Production Line

(Des Mrs. A. Adeyeye (25 k.), G. Akinola (30 k.), O. Ojo (others))

1988 (28 Oct). *25th Anniv of Nigerian Security Printing and Minting Co Ltd. T* **257** *and similar designs. W* **189** *(inverted on 10 k.). P* 14.

568 10 k. multicoloured 10 10
569 20 k. black, silver and emerald 10 10
570 25 k. multicoloured 10 10
571 30 k. multicoloured 10 10
568/71 .. .. *Set of* 4 20 20
Designs: *Horiz* (*as T* **257**)—20 k. Coin production line. *Vert* (*37 × 44 mm*)—25 k. Montage of products; 30 k. Anniversary logos.

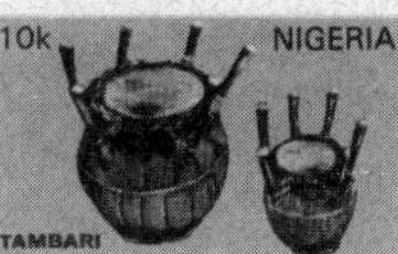

258 Tambari

259 Construction of Water Towers, Mali

(Des S. Nwasike (10 k.), N. Lasisi (20 k.), S. Eluare (others))

1989 (29 June). *Nigerian Musical Instruments. T* **258** *and similar horiz designs. W* **189** *(inverted). P* 14.

572 10 k. multicoloured 10 10
573 20 k. multicoloured 10 10
574 25 k. chestnut, bronze-green and black .. 10 10
575 30 k. red-brown and black 10 10
572/5 .. .. *Set of* 4 15 20
Designs:—20 k. Kundung, 25 k. Ibid; 30 k. Dundun.

(Des Hilda Woods (10 k.), F. Abdul (20, 25 k.), S. Eluare (30 k.))

1989 (10 Sept). *25th Anniv of African Development Bank. T* **259** *and similar multicoloured designs. W* **189** *(inverted on 10, 25 k. and sideways on 30 k.). P* 14.

576 10 k. Type **259** 10 10
577 20 k. Paddy field, Gambia 10 10
578 25 k. Bank Headquarters, Abidjan, Ivory Coast 10 10
579 30 k. Anniversary logo (*vert*) 10 10
576/9 .. .. *Set of* 4 15 20

260 Lighting Camp Fire

261 Etubom Costume

(Des F. Abdul (10 k.), Mrs. A. Adeyeye (20 k.))

1989 (16 Sept). *70th Anniv of Nigerian Girl Guides Association. T* **260** *and similar multicoloured design. W* **189** *(inverted on 10 k. and sideways on 20 k.). P* 14.

580 10 k. Type **260** 10 10
581 20 k. Guide on rope bridge (*vert*) 10 10

(Des S. Eluare (10 k.), Mrs. A. Adeyeye (20 k.), F. Abdul (others))

1989 (26 Oct). *Traditional Costumes. T* **261** *and similar vert designs. Multicoloured. W* **189** *(sideways). P* 14.

582 10 k. Type **261** 10 10
583 20 k. Fulfulde 10 10
584 25 k. Aso-Ofi 10 10
585 30 k. Fuska Kura 10 10
582/5 .. .. *Set of* 4 15 20

262 Dove with Letter and Map of Africa

1990 (18 Jan). *10th Anniv of Pan African Postal Union. T* **262** *and similar vert design. Multicoloured. W* **189** *(sideways). P* 14.

586 10 k. Type **262** 10 10
587 20 k. Parcel and map of Africa 10 10

POSTAGE DUE STAMPS

1d
NIGERIA
POSTAGE DUE

D 1

(Litho B.W.)

1959 (4 Jan). *Wmk Mult Script CA. P* 14½ × 14.

D1 D 1 1d. red-orange 10 40
D2 2d. red-orange 15 50
D3 3d. red-orange 20 75
D4 6d. red-orange .. .. 20 1·75
D5 1s. grey-black .. .. 45 2·75
D1/5 .. .. *Set of* 5 1·00 5·50

1961 (1 Aug). *W* **34**. *P* 14½ × 14.

D 6 D 1 1d. red 10 25
D 7 2d. light blue 10 30
D 8 3d. emerald 15 50
D 9 6d. yellow 30 70
D10 1s. blue (*shades*) .. .. 45 1·75
D6/10 .. .. *Set of* 5 1·00 3·25

(Typo Nigerian Security Printing & Minting Co)

1973 (3 May)–87. *New Currency. No wmk. P* 12½ × 13½.

D11 D 1 2 k. red 10 10
D12 3 k. blue 10 10
D13 5 k. orange-yellow (*shades*) 10 10
D14 10 k. light apple-green (*shades*) 10 10
a. Roul 9 (1987) .. .. ..
D11/14 .. .. *Set of* 4 20 20
No. D14a is known postally used at Ibadan in August 1987.

BIAFRA

The following stamps were issued by Biafra (the Eastern Region of Nigeria) during the civil war with the Federal Government, 1967–70.

They were in regular use within Biafra from the time when supplies of Nigerian stamps were exhausted; and towards the end of the conflict they began to be used on external mail carried by air via Libreville.

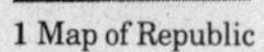
1 Map of Republic

2 Arms, Flag and Date of Independence

3 Mother and Child

(Typo and litho Mint, Lisbon)

1968 (5 Feb). *Independence. P* 12½.
1 **1** 2d. multicoloured 10 15
2 **2** 4d. multicoloured 10 25
3 **3** 1s. multicoloured 15 70
1/3 .. .. *Set of* 3 30 1·00

(4)

1968. *Nos.* 172/5 *and* 177/85 *of Nigeria optd as T* 4 (*without* "SOVEREIGN" *on* 10s.).
4 ½d. multicoloured (No. 172) .. .. 45 1·50
5 1d. multicoloured (No. 173) .. .. 1·25 2·75
a. Opt double £130
b. Opt omitted (in pair with normal) .. £275
6 1½d. multicoloured (No. 174) .. .. 3·75 5·00
7 2d. multicoloured (No. 175) .. .. 17·00 35·00
8 4d. multicoloured (No. 177a) .. .. 17·00 35·00
9 6d. multicoloured (No. 178) .. .. 3·50 4·50
10 9d. Prussian blue and orange-red (No. 179) 1·00 1·50
11 1s. multicoloured (Blk. + R.) (No. 180) .. 50·00 80·00
12 1s. 3d. multicoloured (Blk. + R.) (No. 181) 32·00 50·00
13 2s. 6d. orange-brown, buff and brown (Blk. + R.) (No. 182) .. .. 1·75 4·50
a. Red opt omitted £140
14 5s. chestnut, lt yell & brn (Blk. + R.) (No. 183) .. .. 1·75 4·50
a. Red opt omitted £140
b. Black opt omitted £130
c. *Pale chestnut, yellow & brn-pur* (No. 183*a*) .. .. 2·25 4·75
15 10s. multicoloured (No. 184) .. .. 9·00 22·00
16 £1 multicoloured (Blk. + R.) (No. 185) .. 10·00 22·00
a. Black ("SOVEREIGN BIAFRA") omitted £150
b. Red (coat of arms) omitted £150
4/16 .. .. *Set of* 13 £120 £225

Nos. 172/3 of Nigeria also exist surcharged "BIAFRA – FRANCE FRIENDSHIP 1968 SOVEREIGN BIAFRA", clasped hands and "+5/-" (½d.) or "+£1" (1d.). There is no evidence that these two surcharges were used for postage within Biafra (*Price for set of* 2 £20 *mint*).

5 Weapon Maintenance

8 Biafran Arms and Banknote

9 Orphaned Child

(Litho Mint, Lisbon)

1968 (30 May). *First Anniv of Independence. T* **5**, **8**/**9** *and similar vert designs. P* 12½.
17 4d. multicoloured 10 10
18 1s. multicoloured 15 20
19 2s. 6d. multicoloured 35 70
20 5s. multicoloured .. .. 50 1·00
a. Indigo (banknote) omitted .. .. 40·00
b. Red (from flag) omitted .. .. 40·00
21 10s. multicoloured .. .. 1·00 2·00
a. Bright green (from flag) omitted .. 30·00
17/21 .. .. *Set of* 5 1·75 3·50
Designs:—1s. Victim of atrocity; 2s. 6d. Nurse and refugees.

Nos. 17/21 also exist surcharged "HELP BIAFRAN CHILDREN" and different charity premium ranging from 2d. on the 4d. to 2s. 6d. on the 10s. There is no evidence that these surcharges were used for postage within Biafra (*Price for set of* 5 £1.50 *mint*).

In late 1968 a set of four values, showing butterflies and plants, was offered for sale outside Biafra. The same stamps also exist overprinted "MEXICO OLYMPICS 1968" and Olympic symbol. There is no evidence that either of these issues were used for postage within Biafra (*Price for set of* 4 £4 (*Butterflies and Plants*) *or* £3.50 (*Olympic overprints*), *both mint*).

CANCELLED-TO-ORDER. Many issues of Biafra, including the three unissued sets mentioned above, were available cancelled-to-order with a special "UMUAHIA" handstamp. This was the same diameter as postal cancellations, but differed from them by having larger letters, 3 mm. high, and the year date in full. Where such cancellations exist on issued stamps the used prices quoted are for c-t-o examples. Postally used stamps are worth considerably more.

16 Child in Chains and Globe

17 Pope Paul VI, Map of Africa and Papal Arms

1969 (30 May). *Second Anniv of Independence. Multicoloured; frame colours given. Litho. P* 13 × 13½.
35 **16** 2d. yellow-orange .. .. 35 1·50
36 4d. red-orange .. .. 35 1·50
a. Green (wreath) and orange (Sun) omitted .. ..
37 1s. new blue .. .. 65 2·50
38 2s. 6d. emerald .. .. 1·40 5·50
35/8 .. .. *Set of* 4 2·50 10·00
A miniature sheet with a face value of 10s. was also released.

1969 (25 Sept). *Visit of Pope Paul to Africa. T* **17** *and similar vert designs. Multicoloured. Litho. P* 13 × 13½.
39 4d. Type **17** .. .. 40 1·25
40 6d. Pope Paul VI, Map of Africa and arms of the Vatican .. .. 55 2·50
41 9d. Pope Paul VI, map of Africa and St. Peter's Basilica, Vatican .. .. .. 75 3·50
42 3s. Pope Paul VI, map of Africa and Statue of St. Peter .. .. 2·25 8·00
39/42 .. .. *Set of* 4 3·50 13·50
A miniature sheet with a face value of 10s. was also released.
No. 42 has a magenta background. This value is also known with the background in brown-red or brown.

Biafra was overrun by Federal troops on 10 January 1970 and surrender took place on 15 January.

On 17 December the French Agency released a Christmas issue consisting of Nos. 39/42 overprinted "CHRISTMAS 1969 PEACE ON EARTH AND GOODWILL TO ALL MEN" together with the miniature sheet overprinted "CHRISTMAS 1969" and surcharged £1. Later Nos. 35/38 were released overprinted in red "SAVE BIAFRA 9TH JAN 1970" with a premium of 8d., 1s. 4d., 4s., and 10s. respectively together with the miniature sheet with a premium of £1. We have no evidence that these issues were actually put on sale in Biafra before the collapse, but it has been reported that the 4d. Christmas issue and 2d. + 8d. Save Biafra exist genuinely used before capitulation.

Nos. 40/41 have been seen surcharged "+ 10/–HUMAN RIGHTS" and the United Nations emblem but it is doubtful if they were issued.

No. 81 of Nigeria has also been reported with the original "ROYAL VISIT 1956" overprint, together with "NIGERIA" from the basic stamp, obliterated and a "SERVICE" overprint added. Such stamps were not used for official mail in Biafra, although an example is known with the "UMUAHIA" c-t-o mark.

Niue

PRICES FOR STAMPS ON COVER TO 1945

No. 1	*from* × 2
Nos. 2/5	*from* × 8
Nos. 6/7	—
Nos. 8/9	*from* × 30
Nos. 10/12	—
Nos. 13/31	*from* × 3
Nos. 32/7c	—
Nos. 38/47	*from* × 5
Nos. 48/9	—
No. 50	*from* × 15
Nos. 51/4	—
Nos. 55/61	*from* × 8
Nos. 62/8	*from* × 12
Nos. 69/71	*from* × 3
Nos. 72/4	*from* × 10
Nos. 75/8	*from* × 8
Nos. 79/88	—
Nos. 89/97	*from* × 2

NEW ZEALAND DEPENDENCY

Stamps of New Zealand overprinted

NIUE

(1)

1902 (4 Jan). *Handstamped with T* 1, *in green or bluish green. Pirie paper. Wmk double-lined "N Z" and Star. W* 38 *of New Zealand. P* 11.
1 **42** 1d. carmine £375 £375
A few overprints were made with a *greenish violet* ink. These occurred only in the first vertical row and part of the second row of the first sheet overprinted owing to violet ink having been applied to the pad (*Price* £1400 *un*).

NIUE. ½ PENI. (2)   NIUE. TAHA PENI. 3 1d.   NIUE. 2½ PENI. (4)

1902 (4 Apr). *Type-set surcharges. T* **2**, **3**, *and* **4**.
(*i*) *Pirie paper. No wmk. P* 11.
2 **27** 2½d. blue (R.) .. .. 1·25 2·75
a. No stop after "PENI" .. .. 24·00 35·00
b. Surch double £2000

(ii) *Basted Mills paper. Wmk double-lined "N Z" and Star, W* **38** *of New Zealand.*
(*a*) *Perf* 14
3 **23** ½d. green (R.) .. .. 75 2·25
a. Spaced "U" and "E" (R. 3/3, 3/6, 8/3, 8/6) .. .. 4·00 7·50
b. Surch inverted £250 £375
c. Surch double .. ..
4 **42** 1d. carmine (B.) .. .. 5·00 7·50
a. Spaced "U" and "E" (R. 3/3, 3/6, 8/6) .. 35·00 45·00
b. No stop after "PENI" (R. 9/3) £110 £120
c. Varieties a. and b. on same stamp (R. 8/3) £110 £120
(*b*) *P* 11 *and* 14 *compound*
5 **42** 1d. carmine (B.) .. .. 75 1·40
a. Spaced "U" and "E" (R. 3/3, 3/6, 8/6) 5·50 7·50
b. No stop after "PENI" (R. 9/3) .. .. 25·00 32·00
c. Varieties a. and b. on same stamp (R. 8/3) .. .. 25·00 32·00
(*c*) *Mixed perfs*
6 **23** ½d. green (R.) £300
7 **42** 1d. carmine (B.) £300

1902 (2 May). *Type-set surcharges, T* **2**, **3**. *Cowan paper. Wmk single-lined "N Z" and Star, W* **43** *of New Zealand.* (*a*) *P* 14.
8 **23** ½d. green (R.) 65 80
a. Spaced "U" and "E" (R. 3/3, 3/6, 8/3, 8/6) .. .. 4·25 5·00
9 **42** 1d. carmine (B.) 50 65
a. Surch double £650
b. Spaced "U" and "E" (R. 3/3, 3/6, 8/6) 8·00 10·00
c. No stop after "PENI" (R. 5/3, 7/3, 9/3, 10/3, 10/6) .. .. 8·00 10·00
d. Varieties b. and c. on same stamp (R. 8/3) .. .. 25·00 32·00
e. "I" of "NIUE" omitted (R. 6/5 from end of last ptg) .. ..
(*b*) *Perf* 11 *and* 14 *compound*
10 **23** ½d. green (R.) .. ..
(*c*) *Mixed perfs*
11 **23** ½d. green (R.) £300
12 **42** 1d. carmine (B.) £160
a. Spaced "U" and "E" (R. 3/3, 3/6, 8/3, 8/6) £275
b. No stop after "PENI" (R. 5/3, 7/3, 9/3, 10/3, 10/6) £275

NIUE. (5)   Tolu e Pene. 6 3d.

Ono e Pene. 7 6d.   Taha e Sileni. 8 1s.

1903 (2 July). *Optd with name at top, T* **5**, *and values at foot, T* **6**/**8**, *in blue. W* **43** *of New Zealand. P* 11.
13 **28** 3d. yellow-brown .. .. .. 5·00 5·00
14 **31** 6d. rose-red .. .. 4·75 9·00
15 **34** 1s. brown-red ("Tahae" joined) £650
16 1s. bright red .. .. 20·00 24·00
a. *Orange-red* .. .. 25·00 32·00
13/16 .. .. *Set of* 3 27·00 35·00

NIUE. ½ PENI. (9)   NIUE. (10)

1911 (30 Nov). *½d. surch with T* **9**, *others optd at top as T* **5** *and values at foot as T* **7**, **8**. *W* **43** *of New Zealand. P* 14 × 14½.
17 **50** ½d. green (C.) 45 40
18 **51** 6d. carmine (B.) .. .. 2·00 7·00
19 1s. vermilion (B.) .. .. 6·50 28·00
17/19 .. .. *Set of* 3 8·00 32·00

1915 (Sept). *Surch as T* **4**. *W* **43** *of New Zealand. P* 14.
20 **27** 2½d. deep blue (C.) .. .. 8·00 15·00

1917 (Aug). *1d. surch as T* **3**, *3d. optd as T* **5** *with value as T* **6**. *W* **43** *of New Zealand.*
21 **52** 1d. carmine (*p* 14×15) (Br.) .. .. 5·00 5·50
a. No stop after "PENI" (R. 10/16) .. £130
22 **60** 3d. chocolate (*p* 14×14½) (B.) .. .. 45·00 70·00
a. No stop after "PENE" (R. 10/4) .. £450
b. Perf 14×13½ .. .. 60·00 85·00
c. Vert pair, Nos. 22/b £180

1917–21. *Optd with T* **10**. *W* **43** *of New Zealand.* (*a*) *P* 14 × 15.
23 **61** ½d. green (R.) (2.20) 50 70
24 **52** 1d. carmine (B.) (10.17) .. .. 1·75 2·50
25 **61** 1½d. slate (R.) (11.17) .. .. .. 80 1·75
26 1½d. orange-brown (R.) (2.19) .. .. 70 2·00
27 3d. chocolate (B.) (6.19) .. .. .. 1·40 9·00
(*b*) *P* 14 × 14½
28 **60** 2½d. deep blue (R.) (10.20) .. .. 90 2·50
a. Perf 14 × 13½ .. .. 1·60 3·75
b. Vert pair, Nos. 28/a .. .. .. 16·00 27·00

29 60 3d. chocolate (B.) (10.17) 1·25 1·50
a. Perf 14 × 13½ 1·60 2·50
b. Vert pair, Nos. 29/a 25·00 32·00
30 6d. carmine (B.) (8.21) 4·25 13·00
a. Perf 14 × 13½ 4·75 13·00
b. Vert pair, Nos. 30/a 35·00 50·00
31 1s. vermilion (B.) (10.18) 4·75 13·00
a. Perf 14 × 13½ 7·50 13·00
b. Vert pair, Nos. 31/a 38·00 55·00
23/31 *Set of* 9 14·50 40·00

1918–29. *Postal Fiscal stamps as Type* F **4** *of New Zealand optd with T* **10**. *W* **43** *of New Zealand (sideways).*

(i) *Chalk-surfaced "De La Rue" paper.* (a) *P* 14
32 5s. yellow-green (R.) (7.18) 65·00 80·00

(b) *P* 14½ × 14, *comb*
33 2s. deep blue (R.) (9.18) 15·00 32·00
34 2s. 6d. grey-brown (B.) (2.23) 17·00 32·00
35 5s. yellow-green (R.) (10.18) 20·00 45·00
36 10s. maroon (B.) (2.23) 70·00 90·00
37 £1 rose-carmine (B.) (2.23) £130 £150
33/7 *Set of* 5 £225 £300

(ii) *Thick, opaque, white chalk-surfaced "Cowan" paper. P* 14½ × 14
37*a* 5s. yellow-green (R.) (10.29) 20·00 45·00
37*b* 10s. brown-red (B.) (2.27) 70·00 90·00
37*c* £1 rose-pink (B.) (2.28) £130 £150
37*a/c* *Set of* 3 £200 £250

(Des, eng and recess P.B.)

1920 (23 Aug). *As T* **9** *to* **14** *of Cook Islands but inscr* "NIUE". *No wmk. P* 14.
38 ½d. black and green 2·00 3·25
39 1d. black and dull carmine 1·75 1·25
40 1½d. black and red 2·25 3·25
41 3d. black and blue 60 4·00
42 6d. red-brown and green 80 8·50
43 1s. black and sepia 1·50 9·00
38/43 *Set of* 6 8·00 26·00

Examples of the 6d. with inverted centre were not supplied to the Post Office.

1925–27. *Pictorial stamps as* 1920 *and new values as T* **16/17** *of Cook Islands, but inscr* "NIUE". *W* **43** *of New Zealand. P* 14.
44 ½d. black and green (1927) 1·00 3·75
45 1d. black and deep carmine (1925) 65 75
46 2½d. black and blue (10.27) 1·00 4·75
47 4d. black and violet (10.27) 2·00 7·00
44/7 *Set of* 4 4·25 14·50

1927–28. *Admiral type of New Zealand optd as T* **10**. *W* **43** *of New Zealand. P* 14.

(a) *"Jones" paper*
48 **72** 2s. deep blue (2.27) (R.) 15·00 42·00

(b) *"Cowan" paper*
49 **72** 2s. light blue (R.) (2.28) 14·00 30·00

1931 (Apr). *No.* 40 *surch as T* **18** *of Cook Is.*
50 2d. on 1½d. black and red 1·00 90

1931 (12 Nov). *Postal Fiscal stamps as Type* F **6** *of New Zealand optd as T* **10**. *W* **43** *of New Zealand. Thick, opaque, chalk-surfaced "Cowan" paper. P* 14.
51 2s. 6d. deep brown (B.) 5·50 11·00
52 5s. green (R.) 24·00 45·00
53 10s. carmine-lake (B.) 35·00 65·00
54 £1 pink (B.) 55·00 90·00
51/4 *Set of* 4 £110 £190

See also Nos. 79/82 for different type of overprint.

(Des L. C. Mitchell. Recess P.B.)

1932 (16 Mar). *As T* **20** *to* **26** *of Cook Is, but frames include* "NIUE" *as well as* "COOK ISLANDS." *No wmk. P* 13.
55 ½d. black and emerald 3·25 7·00
a. Perf 13×14×13×13 £250
56 1d. black and deep lake 1·00 25
57 2d. black and red-brown 75 2·25
a. Perf 14×13×13×13 90·00 £150
58 2½d. black and slate-blue 3·75 18·00
59 4d. black and greenish blue 6·50 18·00
a. Perf 14 6·50 15·00
60 6d. black and orange-vermilion 2·00 2·00
61 1s. black and purple (*p* 14) 2·00 5·00
55/61 *Set of* 7 17·00 45·00

Examples of the 2½d. with inverted centre were not supplied to the Post Office.

Nos. 55a and 57a are mixed perforations, each having one side perforated 14 where the original perforation, 13, was inadequate.

(Recess from Perkins, Bacon's plates at Govt Ptg Office, Wellington, N.Z.)

1932–36. *Pictorial types as* 1932, *but W* **43** *of New Zealand. P* 14.
62 ½d. black and emerald 50 75
63 1d. black and deep lake 50 30
64 2d. black and yellow-brown (1.4.36) 40 70
65 2½d. black and slate-blue 40 2·50
66 4d. black and greenish blue 70 1·25
67 6d. black and red-orange (1.4.36) 70 65
68 1s. black and purple (1.4.36) 4·00 12·00
62/68 *Set of* 7 6·50 16·00

Imperforate proofs of No. 65 are known used on registered mail from Niue postmarked 30 August 1945 or 29 October 1945.

See also Nos. 89/97.

1935 (7 May). *Silver Jubilee. Designs as Nos.* 63, 65 *and* 67 *(colours changed) optd as T* **27** *of Cook Is (wider vertical spacing on 6d.). W* **43** *of New Zealand. P* 14.
69 1d. red-brown and lake 60 1·50
a. Narrow "K" in "KING" 2·75 8·00
b. Narrow "B" in "JUBILEE" 2·75 8·00
70 2½d. dull and deep blue (R.) 3·00 2·50
a. Narrow first "E" in "GEORGE" 4·00 12·00
71 6d. green and orange 3·00 5·00
a. Narrow "N" in "KING" 12·00 32·00
69/71 *Set of* 3 6·00 8·00

For illustrations of varieties, see Cook Islands.

Examples of No. 70 imperforate horizontally are from proof sheets not issued through the Post and Telegraph Department (*Price* £400 *for vert pair*).

NIUE (13)   NIUE. (14)

1937 (13 May). *Coronation Issue. Nos.* 599/601 *of New Zealand optd with T* **13**.
72 1d. carmine 30 10
73 2½d. Prussian blue 40 20
74 6d. red-orange 40 10
72/4 *Set of* 3 1·00 35

1938 (2 May). *As T* **29** *to* **31** *of Cook Is., but frames inscr.* "NIUE COOK ISLANDS". *W* **43** *of New Zealand. P* 14.
75 1s. black and violet 3·25 4·00
76 2s. black and red-brown 7·00 7·00
77 3s. light blue and emerald-green 16·00 9·00
75/7 *Set of* 3 24·00 18·00

1940 (2 Sept). *As T* **32** *of Cook Islands, but additionally inscr.* "NIUE". *W* **98** *of New Zealand. P* 13½ × 14.
78 3d. on 1½d. black and purple 10 10

1941–67. *Postal Fiscal stamps as Type* F **6** *of New Zealand with thin opt, T* **14**. *P* 14.

(i) *Thin, hard, chalk-surfaced "Wiggins Teape" paper with vertical mesh* (1941–43). (a) *W* **43** *of New Zealand*
79 2s. 6d. deep brown (B.) (4.41) 25·00 22·00
80 5s. green (R.) (4.41) £170 £140
81 10s. pale carmine-lake (B.) (6.42) £100 £140
82 £1 pink (B.) (2.43?) £170 £200
79/82 *Set of* 4 £425 £450

(b) *W* **98** *of New Zealand* (1944–45)
83 2s. 6d. deep brown (B.) (3.45) 3·00 6·50
84 5s. green (R.) (11.44) 5·50 9·00
85 10s. carmine-lake (B.) (11.45) 40·00 50·00
86 £1 pink (B.) (6.42) 32·00 40·00
83/6 *Set of* 4 70·00 95·00

(ii) *Unsurfaced "Wiggins Teape" paper with horizontal mesh. W* **98** *of New Zealand* (1957–67)
87 2s. 6d. deep brown (*p* 14 × 13½) (1.11.57) 3·25 3·00
88 5s. pale yellowish green (*wmk sideways*) (6.67) 48·00 70·00

Nos. 83/5 were later printed with the watermark inverted for technical reasons and the prices quoted are for the cheapest form. They are fully listed in the *Two Reigns Catalogue*.

No. 88 came from a late printing made to fill demands from Wellington, but no supplies were sent to Niue. It exists in both line and comb perf.

1944–46. *As T* **20** *to* **25** *and* **29** *to* **31** *of Cook Is. but additionally inscr* "NIUE". *W* **98** *of New Zealand (sideways on* ½d., 1d., 1s. *and* 2s.).
89 ½d. black and emerald 50 60
90 1d. black and deep lake 50 60
91 2d. black and red-brown 2·00 1·50
92 2½d. black and slate-blue (1946) 60 85
93 4d. black and greenish blue 60 90
94 6d. black and red-orange 70 1·40
95 1s. black and violet 1·25 85
96 2s. black and red-brown (1945) 4·00 2·75
97 3s. light blue and emerald-green (1945) 8·50 6·00
89/97 *Set of* 9 17·00 14·00

1946 (1 June). *Peace. Nos.* 668, 670, 674/5 *of New Zealand optd as T* **14**, *but without stop (twice, reading up and down on 2d.).*
98 **132** 1d. green (Blk.) 10 10
99 – 2d. purple (B.) 10 10
100 – 6d. chocolate and vermilion (Blk.) 10 10
a. Opt double, one albino £200
101 **139** 8d. black and carmine (B.) 10 10
98/101 *Set of* 4 35 20

Nos. 102/112 are no longer used.

15 Map of Niue

16 H.M.S. *Resolution*

23 Bananas

24 Matapa Chasm

(Des J. Berry. Recess B.W.)

1950 (3 July). *T* **15/16**, **23/24** *and similar designs. W* **98** *of New Zealand (sideways inverted on* 1d., 2d., 3d., 4d., 6d. *and* 1s.). *P* 13½ × 14 (*horiz*), 14 × 13½ (*vert*).
113 ½d. orange and blue 10 10
114 1d. brown and blue-green 1·50 20
115 2d. black and carmine 10 10
116 3d. blue and violet-blue 10 10
117 4d. olive-green and purple-brown 10 10
118 6d. green and brown-orange 20 15
119 9d. orange and brown 10 15
120 1s. purple and black 10 10
121 2s. brown-orange and dull green 75 2·00
122 3s. blue and black 3·50 3·75
113/22 *Set of* 10 5·75 6·00

Designs: *Horiz* (*as T* **16**)—2d. Alofi landing; 3d. Native hut; 4d. Arch at Hikutavake; 6d. Alofi bay; 1s. Cave, Makefu. *Vert* (*as T* **18**)—9d. Spearing fish.

1953 (25 May). *Coronation. As Nos.* 715 *and* 717 *of New Zealand, but inscr* "NIUE".
123 3d. brown 65 30
124 6d. slate-grey 95 30

(New Currency. 100 cents = 1 dollar)

(25)

26

1967 (10 July–7 Aug). *Decimal currency.* (a) *Nos.* 113/22 *surch as T* **25**.
125 ½ c. on ½d. 10 10
126 1 c. on 1d. 80 15
127 2 c. on 2d. 10 10
128 2½ c. on 3d. 10 10
129 3 c. on 4d. 10 10
130 5 c. on 6d. 10 10
131 8 c. on 9d. 10 10
132 10 c. on 1s. 10 10
133 20 c. on 2s. 60 1·25
134 30 c. on 3s. 1·50 1·75
125/34 *Set of* 10 2·75 3·00

(b) *Arms type of New Zealand without value, surch as in T* **26**. *W* **98** *of New Zealand (sideways). P* 14.
135 **26** 25 c. deep yellow-brown 65 65
a. Rough perf 11 8·00 13·00
136 50 c. pale yellowish green 1·00 1·00
a. Rough perf 11 9·00 15·00
137 $1 magenta 80 1·50
a. Rough perf 11 13·00 15·00
138 $2 light pink 1·40 2·50
a. Rough perf 11 15·00 20·00
135/8 *Set of* 4 3·50 5·00
135a/8a *Set of* 4 40·00 55·00

The 25 c., $1 and $2 perf 14 exist both line and comb perforated. The 50 c. is comb perforated only. The perf 11 stamps resulted from an emergency measure in the course of printing.

1967 (3 Oct). *Christmas. As T* **278** *of New Zealand, but inscr* "NIUE".
139 2½ c. multicoloured 10 10

1969 (1 Oct). *Christmas. As T* **301** *of New Zealand, but inscr* "NIUE". *W* **98** *of New Zealand. P* 13½ × 14½.
140 2½ c. multicoloured 10 10

27 "Pua"

37 Kalahimu

(Des Mrs. K. W. Billings. Litho Enschedé)

1969 (27 Nov). *T* **27** *and similar vert designs. Multicoloured. P* 12½ × 13½.
141 ½ c. Type **27** 10 10
142 1 c. "Golden Shower" 10 10
143 2 c. Flamboyant 10 10
144 2½ c. Frangipani 10 10
145 3 c. Niue Crocus 10 10
146 5 c. Hibiscus 10 10
147 8 c. "Passion Fruit" 10 10
148 10 c. "Kampui" 10 10
149 20 c. Queen Elizabeth II (after Anthony Buckley) 1·00 1·25
150 30 c. Tapeu Orchid 1·75 1·75
141/150 *Set of* 10 3·00 3·00

(Des G. F. Fuller. Photo Enschedé)

1970 (19 Aug). *Indigenous Edible Crabs. T* **37** *and similar horiz designs. Multicoloured. P* 13½ × 12½.
151 3 c. Type **37** 10 10
152 5 c. Kalavi 10 10
153 30 c. Unga 30 25
151/3 *Set of* 3 45 40

1970 (1 Oct). *Christmas. As T* **314** *of New Zealand, but inscr* "NIUE".
154 2½ c. multicoloured 10 10

38 Outrigger Canoe and Aircraft over Jungle

39 Spotted Triller

(Des L. C. Mitchell. Litho B.W.)

1970 (9 Dec). *Opening of Niue Airport. T* **38** *and similar horiz designs. Multicoloured. P* 13½.
155 3 c. Type **38** 10 10
156 5 c. Cargo liner, and aircraft over harbour 15 10
157 8 c. Aircraft over Airport 15 20
155/7 *Set of* 3 35 35

(Des A. G. Mitchell. Litho B.W.)

1971 (23 June). *Birds. T* **39** *and similar horiz designs. Multicoloured. P* 13½.
158 5 c. Type **39** 15 10
159 10 c. Purple-capped Fruit Dove 70 15
160 20 c. Blue-crowned Lory 80 20
158/60 *Set of* 3 1·50 40

1971 (6 Oct). *Christmas. As T* **325** *of New Zealand, but inscr* "NIUE".
161 3 c. multicoloured 10 10

40 Niuean Boy **41** Octopus Lure

(Des L. C. Mitchell. Litho Harrison)

1971 (17 Nov). *Niuean Portraits. T* **40** *and similar vert designs. Multicoloured. P* 13 × 14.
162 4 c. Type **40** 10 10
163 6 c. Girl with garland 10 10
164 9 c. Man 10 10
165 14 c. Woman with garland 15 20
162/5 .. .. *Set of* 4 35 35

(Des A. G. Mitchell. Litho B.W.)

1972 (3 May). *South Pacific Arts Festival, Fiji. T* **41** *and similar multicoloured designs. P* 13½.
166 3 c. Type **41** 10 10
167 5 c. War weapons 15 10
168 10 c. Sika throwing (*horiz*) 20 10
169 25 c. Vivi dance (*horiz*) 30 20
166/9 .. .. *Set of* 4 65 40

42 Alofi Wharf

(Des A. G. Mitchell. Litho Questa)

1972 (6 Sept). *25th Anniversary of South Pacific Commission. T* **42** *and similar horiz designs. Multicoloured. P* 14.
170 4 c. Type **42** 10 10
171 5 c. Medical Services 15 10
172 6 c. Schoolchildren 15 10
173 18 c. Dairy cattle 25 20
170/3 .. .. *Set of* 4 60 40

1972 (4 Oct). *Christmas. As T* **332** *of New Zealand but inscr* "NIUE".
174 3 c. multicoloured 10 10

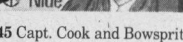

43 Kokio **44** "Large Flower Piece" (Jan Brueghel)

(Des G. F. Fuller. Litho Harrison)

1973 (27 June). *Fishes. T* **43** *and similar horiz designs. Multicoloured. P* 14 × 13½.
175 8 c. Type **43** 25 25
176 10 c. Loi 30 30
177 15 c. Malau 40 40
178 20 c. Palu 45 45
175/8 .. .. *Set of* 4 1·25 1·25

(Des and litho Enschedé)

1973 (21 Nov). *Christmas. T* **44** *and similar vert designs showing flower studies by the artists listed. Multicoloured. P* 14 × 13½.
179 4 c. Type **44** 10 10
180 5 c. Bollongier 10 10
181 10 c. Ruysch 15 15
179/81 .. .. *Set of* 3 25 20

45 Capt. Cook and Bowsprit **46** King Fataaiki

(Des A. G. Mitchell. Litho Questa)

1974 (20 June). *Bicentenary of Capt. Cook's Visit. T* **45** *and similar horiz designs each showing Cook's portrait. Multicoloured. P* 13½ × 14.
182 2 c. Type **45** 30 20
183 3 c. Niue landing place 30 25
184 8 c. Map of Niue 50 40
185 20 c. Ensign of 1774 and Administration Building 70 80
182/5 .. .. *Set of* 4 1·60 1·50

SELF-GOVERNMENT

(Des A. G. Mitchell. Litho Questa)

1974 (19 Oct). *Self-Government. T* **46** *and similar multicoloured designs. P* 14 × 13½ (4 *and* 8 c.) *or* 13½ × 14 (*others*).
186 4 c. Type **46** 10 10
187 8 c. Annexation Ceremony, 1900 .. .. 10 10
188 10 c. Legislative Assembly Chambers (*horiz*) 10 10
189 20 c. Village meeting (*horiz*) 15 15
186/9 .. .. *Set of* 4 35 30

47 Decorated Bicycles **48** Children going to Church

(Des B. C. Strong. Litho D.L.R.)

1974 (13 Nov). *Christmas. T* **47** *and similar vert designs. P* 12½.
190 3 c. multicoloured 10 10
191 10 c. multicoloured 10 10
192 20 c. dull red-brown, slate and black .. 20 15
190/2 .. .. *Set of* 3 30 20
Designs:—10 c. Decorated motorcycles; 20 c. Motor transport to church.

(Des Enid Hunter. Litho Questa)

1975 (29 Oct). *Christmas. T* **48** *and similar horiz designs. Multicoloured. P* 14.
193 4 c. Type **48** 10 10
194 5 c. Child with balloons on bicycle 10 10
195 10 c. Balloons and gifts on tree 15 15
193/5 .. .. *Set of* 3 25 20

49 Hotel Buildings **50** Preparing Ground for Taro

(Des B. C. Strong. Litho Harrison)

1975 (19 Nov). *Opening of Tourist Hotel. T* **49** *and similar horiz design. Multicoloured. P* 13½ × 13.
196 8 c. Type **49** 10 10
197 20 c. Ground-plan and buildings 15 15

(Des A. G. Mitchell. Litho Questa)

1976 (3 Mar). *T* **50** *and similar horiz designs showing food gathering. Multicoloured. P* 13½ × 14.
198 1 c. Type **50** 10 10
199 2 c. Planting taro 10 10
200 3 c. Banana gathering 10 10
201 4 c. Harvesting taro 10 10
202 5 c. Gathering shell fish 15 10
203 10 c. Reef fishing 15 10
204 20 c. Luku gathering 20 15
205 50 c. Canoe fishing 40 60
206 $1 Coconut husking 60 80
207 $2 Uga gathering .. .. .. 1·00 1·40
198/207 .. .. .. *Set of* 10 2·50 2·75
See also Nos. 249/58 and 264/73.

51 Water **52** Christmas Tree, Alofi

(Des A. G. Mitchell. Litho Questa)

1976 (7 July). *Utilities. T* **51** *and similar vert designs. Multicoloured. P* 14.
208 10 c. Type **51** 10 10
209 15 c. Power 15 15
210 20 c. Telecommunications 15 15
208/10 .. .. *Set of* 3 30 30

(Des A. G. Mitchell. Litho Questa)

1976 (15 Sept). *Christmas. T* **52** *and similar horiz design. Multicoloured. P* 14.
211 9 c. Type **52** 10 10
212 15 c. Church Service, Avatele 15 15

53 Queen Elizabeth II and Westminster Abbey

(Des and photo Heraclio Fournier)

1977 (7 June). *Silver Jubilee. T* **53** *and similar horiz design. Multicoloured. P* 13½.
213 $1 Type **53** .. .. 1·50 75
214 $2 Coronation regalia .. .. .. 2·00 1·00
MS215 72 × 104 mm. Nos. 213/14 .. .. 3·50 2·50
Stamps from the miniature sheet have a blue border.

54 Child Care **55** "The Annunciation"

(Des R. M. Conly. Litho Questa)

1977 (29 June). *Personal Services. T* **54** *and similar horiz designs. Multicoloured. P* 14½.
216 10 c. Type **54** 15 10
217 15 c. School dental clinic 20 20
218 20 c. Care of the aged 20 20
216/18 .. .. *Set of* 3 50 45

(Des and photo Heraclio Fournier)

1977 (15 Nov). *Christmas. T* **55** *and similar vert designs showing paintings by Rubens. Multicoloured. P* 13.
219 10 c. Type **55** 15 10
220 12 c. "Adoration of the Magi" 15 10
221 20 c. "Virgin in a Garland 25 20
222 35 c. "The Holy Family" 45 35
219/22 .. .. *Set of* 4 90 65
MS223 82 × 129 mm. Nos. 219/22 .. .. 1·50 1·75

12c

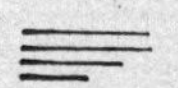

(56)

1977 (15 Nov). *Nos.* 198 *etc.,* 214, 216 *and* 218 *surch as T* **56** *by New Zealand Govt Printer.*
224 12 c. on 1 c. Type **50** 25 25
225 16 c. on 2 c. Planting taro 30 30
226 30 c. on 3 c. Banana gathering 50 40
227 35 c. on 4 c. Harvesting taro 55 45
228 40 c. on 5 c. Gathering shell fish 60 50
229 60 c. on 20 c. Luku gathering 85 65
230 70 c. on $1 Coconut husking 95 70
231 85 c. on $2 Uga gathering .. .. 1·00 70
232 $1.10 on 10 c. Type **54** .. .. 1·00 75
233 $2.60 on 20 c. Care of the aged .. 1·75 1·25
234 $3.20 on $2 Coronation regalia (Gold) .. 2·00 1·50
224/34 .. .. .. *Set of* 11 8·50 6·50

57 "An Island View in Atooi"

(Photo Heraclio Fournier)

1978 (18 Jan). *Bicentenary of Discovery of Hawaii. T* **57** *and similar horiz designs showing paintings by John Webber. Multicoloured. P* 13.
235 12 c. Type **57** 55 30
236 16 c. "View of Karakaooa, in Owhyhee" .. 65 40
237 20 c. "Offering before Capt. Cook in the Sandwich Islands" 70 45
238 30 c. "Tereoboo, King of Owhyhee bringing presents to Capt. Cook" 90 50
239 35 c. "Canoe in the Sandwich Islands, the rowers masked" .. .. 1·00 55
235/9 .. .. *Set of* 5 3·50 2·00
MS240 121 × 121 mm. Nos. 235/9 .. .. 4·25 4·25
Nos. 235/9 were each printed in small sheets of 6, including 1 *se-tenant* stamp-size label.

58 "The Deposition of Christ" (Caravaggio) 59 Flags of Niue and U.K.

(Photo Heraclio Fournier)

1978 (15 Mar). *Easter. Paintings from the Vatican Galleries. T* **58** *and similar vert design. Multicoloured. P* 13.
241 10 c. Type **58** 10 10
242 20 c. "The Burial of Christ" (Bellini) 25 25
MS243 102 × 68 mm. Nos. 241/2 .. .. .. 45 60

1978 (15 Mar). *Easter. Children's Charity. Designs as Nos.* 241/2 *in separate miniature sheets* 64 × 78 *mm, each with a face value of* 70 c. + 5 c. *P* 13.
MS244 As Nos. 241/2 .. .. *Set of* 2 *sheets* 1·75 2·00

(Photo Heraclio Fournier)

1978 (26 June). *25th Anniv of Coronation. T* **59** *and similar horiz designs. Multicoloured.* A. *White border.* B. *Turquoise-green border. P* 13.

		A		B	
245	$1.10 Type **59**	1·25	1·00	1·25	1·00
246	$1.10 Coronation portrait by Cecil Beaton	1·25	1·00	1·25	1·00
247	$1.10 Queen's personal flag for New Zealand	1·25	1·00	1·25	1·00
245/7	.. .. .. *Set of* 3	3·25	2·75	3·25	2·75
MS248	87 × 98 mm. Nos. 245/7	4·25	3·50	†	

Nos. 245/7 were printed together in small sheets of 6, containing two *se-tenant* strips of 3, with horizontal gutter margin between. The upper strip has white borders, the lower turquoise-green.

(Litho Questa)

1978 (27 Oct). *Designs as Nos.* 198/207 *but margin colours changed and silver frame. P* 13½ × 14.
249 12 c. Type **50** 20 20
250 16 c. Planting taro 20 20
251 30 c. Banana gathering 30 25
252 35 c. Harvesting taro 30 30
253 40 c. Gathering shell fish 40 30
254 60 c. Reef fishing 45 35
255 75 c. Luku gathering 50 40
256 $1.10, Canoe fishing.. .. .. .. 1·10 80
257 $3.20, Coconut husking .. .. .. 1·25 1·25
258 $4.20, Uga gathering .. .. 1·40 1·40
249/58 .. .. *Set of* 10 5·50 5·00
See also Nos. 264/73.

60 "Festival of the Rosary"

(Des and photo Heraclio Fournier)

1978 (30 Nov). *Christmas. 450th Death Anniv of Dürer. T* **60** *and similar horiz designs. Multicoloured. P* 13.
259 20 c. Type **60** 30 20
260 30 c. "The Nativity" 35 30
261 35 c. "Adoration of the Magi" 35 35
259/61 .. .. *Set of* 3 90 75
MS262 143 × 82 mm. Nos. 259/61 .. .. 1·25 1·50
Nos. 259/61 were each printed in small sheets of 6.

1978 (30 Nov). *Christmas. Children's Charity. Designs as Nos.* 259/61 *in separate miniature sheets* 74 × 66 *mm., each with a face value of* 60 c. + 5 c. *P* 13.
MS263 As Nos. 259/61 .. .. *Set of* 3 *sheets* 2·00 2·00

(Litho Questa)

1979 (26 Feb–28 May). *Air. Designs as Nos.* 249/58 *but gold frames and additionally inscr* "AIRMAIL". *P* 13½ × 14.
264 15 c. Planting taro 20 15
265 20 c. Banana gathering 25 15
266 23 c. Harvesting taro 30 15
267 50 c. Canoe fishing 70 20
268 90 c. Reef fishing 85 35
269 $1.35, Type **50** (30.3) .. .. .. 1·25 1·50
270 $2.10, Gathering shell fish (30.3) .. .. 2·00 2·25
271 $2.60, Luku gathering (30.3) .. .. 2·00 2·50
272 $5.10, Coconut husking (28.5) .. .. 2·25 3·50
273 $6.35, Uga gathering (28.5).. .. .. 2·50 4·50
264/73 .. .. *Set of* 10 11·00 14·00

PRINTERS. The following stamps were printed in photogravure by Heraclio Fournier, Spain, *except where otherwise stated.*

MINIMUM PRICE

The minimum price quote is 10p which represents a handling charge rather than a basis for valuing common stamps. For further notes about prices see introductory pages.

61 "Pietà" (Gregorio Fernandez) 62 "The Nurse and Child" (Franz Hals)

1979 (2 Apr). *Easter. Paintings. T* **61** *and similar horiz design. Multicoloured. P* 13.
274 30 c. Type **61** 30 25
275 35 c. "Burial of Christ" (Pedro Roldan) .. 35 25
MS276 82 × 82 mm. Nos. 274/5 .. .. .. 90 1·00

1979 (2 Apr). *Easter. Children's Charity. Designs as Nos.* 274/5 *in separate miniature sheets* 86 × 69 *mm., each with a face value of* 70 c. + 5 c. *P* 13.
MS277 As Nos. 274/5 .. .. *Set of* 2 *sheets* 1·75 1·75

1979 (31 May). *International Year of the Child. Details of Paintings. T* **62** *and similar vert designs. Multicoloured. P* 14 × 13½.
278 16 c. Type **62** 20 15
279 20 c. "Child of the Duke of Osuna" (Goya) .. 25 20
280 30 c. "Daughter of Robert Strozzi" (Titian) .. 40 35
281 35 c. "Children eating Fruit" (Murillo) .. 40 40
278/81 .. .. *Set of* 4 1·10 1·00
MS282 80 × 115 mm. Nos. 278/81. P 13 .. .. 1·25 1·50

1979 (31 May). *International Year of the Child. Children's Charity. Designs as Nos.* 278/81 *in separate miniature sheets* 99 × 119 *mm, each with a face value of* 70 c. + 5 c. *P* 13.
MS283 As Nos. 278/81 .. .. *Set of* 4 *sheets* 3·00 2·50

63 Penny Black Stamp 64 Cook's Landing at Botany Bay

1979 (3 July). *Death Centenary of Sir Rowland Hill. T* **63** *and similar vert designs. Multicoloured. P* 14 × 13½.
284 20 c. Type **63** 20 15
285 20 c. Sir Rowland Hill and original Bath mail coach 20 15
286 30 c. Basel 1845 2½ r. stamp 30 20
287 30 c. Sir Rowland Hill and Alpine village coach 30 20
288 35 c. U.S.A. 1847 5 c. stamp 35 25
289 35 c. Sir Rowland Hill and first Transatlantic U.S.A. mail vessel 35 25
290 50 c. France 1849 20 c. stamp.. .. .. 50 35
291 50 c. Sir Rowland Hill and French Post Office railway van, 1849 .. .. .. 50 35
292 60 c. Bavaria 1849 1 k. stamp.. .. .. 55 40
293 60 c. Sir Rowland Hill and Bavarian coach with mail 55 40
284/93 .. .. *Set of* 10 3·50 2·50
MS294 143 × 149 mm. Nos. 284/93 .. .. 3·50 3·75
Nos. 284/5, 286/7, 288/9, 290/1 and 292/3 were each printed together, *se-tenant*, in horizontal pairs throughout the sheet forming composite designs.

1979 (30 July). *Death Bicentenary of Captain Cook. T* **64** *and similar horiz designs. Multicoloured. P* 14.
295 20 c. Type **64** 35 30
296 30 c. Cook's men during a landing on Erromanga 50 40
297 35 c. H.M.S. *Resolution* and H.M.S. *Discovery* in Queen Charlotte's Sound .. 55 45
298 75 c. Death of Captain Cook, Hawaii 95 70
295/8 .. .. *Set of* 4 2·10 1·75
MS299 104 × 80 mm. Nos. 295/8. P 13½.. .. 2·50 3·00

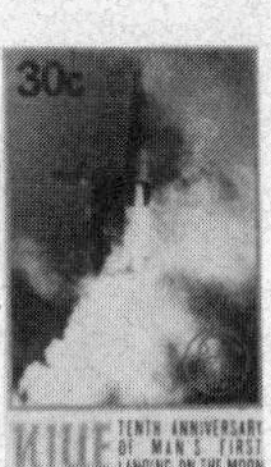

65 Launch of "Apollo 11" 66 "Virgin of Tortosa" (P. Serra)

1979 (27 Sept). *10th Anniv of Moon Landing. T* **65** *and similar vert designs. Multicoloured. P* 13½.
300 30 c. Type **65** 25 20
301 35 c. Lunar module on Moon 30 25
302 60 c. Helicopter, recovery ship and command module after splashdown 40 40
300/2 .. .. *Set of* 3 85 75
MS303 120 × 82 mm. Nos. 300/2 .. .. .. 1·00 1·40
Stamps from No. **MS**303 have the inscription in gold on a blue panel.

1979 (29 Nov). *Christmas. Paintings. T* **66** *and similar vert designs. Multicoloured. P* 13.
304 20 c. Type **66** 10 10
305 25 c. "Virgin with Milk" (R. di Mur) 15 15
306 30 c. "Virgin and Child" (S. di G. Sassetta) .. 20 20
307 50 c. "Virgin and Child" (J. Huguet) 25 25
304/7 .. .. *Set of* 4 60 60
MS308 95 × 113 mm. Nos. 304/7 .. .. .. 75 1·25

1979 (29 Nov). *Christmas. Children's Charity. Designs as Nos.* 304/7 *in separate miniature sheets,* 49 × 84 *mm, each with a face value of* 85 c. + 5 c. *P* 13.
MS309 As Nos. 304/7 .. .. *Set of* 4 *sheets* 1·50 2·00

HURRICANE
RELIEF
Plus 2c

(67)

68 "Pietà" (Bellini)

1980 (25 Jan). *Hurricane Relief. Various stamps surch as T* **67** *in black (Nos.* 310/19) *or silver* (320/30).

(*a*) *Nos.* 284/93 (*Death Centenary of Sir Rowland Hill*)
310 20 c. + 2 c. Type **63** 20 25
311 20 c. + 2 c. Sir Rowland Hill and original Bath mail coach 20 25
312 30 c. + 2 c. Basel 1845 2½ r. stamp 30 35
313 30 c. + 2 c. Sir Rowland Hill and Alpine village coach 30 35
314 35 c. + 2 c. U.S.A. 1847 5 c. stamp 35 40
315 35 c. + 2 c. Sir Rowland Hill and first Trans-atlantic U.S.A. mail vessel 35 40
316 50 c. + 2 c. France 1849 20 c. stamp 50 55
317 50 c. + 2 c. Sir Rowland Hill and French Post Office railway van, 1849.. .. .. 50 55
318 60 c. + 2 c. Bavaria 1849 1 k. stamp 60 65
319 60 c. + 2 c. Sir Rowland Hill and Bavarian coach with mail 60 65

(*b*) *Nos.* 295/8 (*Death Bicentenary of Captain Cook*)
320 20 c. + 2 c. Type **64** 20 25
321 30 c. + 2 c. Cook's men during a landing on Erromanga 30 35
322 35 c. + 2 c. H.M.S. *Resolution* and H.M.S. *Discovery* in Queen Charlotte's Sound .. 35 40
323 75 c. + 2 c. Death of Captain Cook, Hawaii .. 75 80

(*c*) *Nos.* 300/2 (*10th Anniv of Moon Landing*)
324 30 c. + 2 c. Type **65** 30 35
325 35 c. + 2 c. Lunar module on Moon 35 40
326 60 c. + 2 c. Helicopter, recovery ship and command module after splashdown .. 60 65

(*d*) *Nos.* 304/7 (*Christmas*)
327 20 c. + 2 c. Type **66** 20 25
328 25 c. + 2 c. "Virgin with Milk" (R. de Mur) .. 25 30
329 30 c. + 2 c. "Virgin and Child" (S. di G. Sassetta) 30 35
330 50 c. + 2c. "Virgin and Child" (J. Huguet) .. 50 55
310/30 .. .. *Set of* 21 7·50 8·00
On Nos. 310/19 "HURRICANE RELIEF" covers the two designs of each value.

1980 (2 Apr). *Easter. Paintings. T* **68** *and similar horiz designs showing "Pietà" paintings by various artists. Multicoloured. P* 13½ × 13.
331 25 c. Type **68** 15 15
332 30 c. Botticelli 20 20
333 35 c. Antony van Dyck 20 20
331/3 .. .. *Set of* 3 50 50
MS334 75 × 104 mm. As Nos. 331/3, but each with additional premium of "+ 2 c." 55 90
The premiums on No. **MS**334 were used to support Hurricane Relief.

1980 (2 Apr). *Easter. Hurricane Relief. Designs as Nos.* 331/3 *in separate miniature sheets,* 75 × 52 *mm, each with a face value of* 85 c. + 5 c. *P* 13 × 14.
MS335 As Nos. 331/3 .. .. *Set of* 3 *sheets* 1·25 1·75

69 Ceremonial Stool, New Guinea

1980 (30 July). *South Pacific Festival of Arts, New Guinea. T* **69** *and similar vert designs. Multicoloured. P* 13.
336 20 c. Type **69** 20 20
337 20 c. Ku-Tagwa plaque, New Guinea.. .. 20 20
338 20 c. Suspension hook, New Guinea 20 20
339 20 c. Ancestral board, New Guinea 20 20

340 25 c. Platform post, New Hebrides 25 25
341 25 c. Canoe ornament, New Ireland 25 25
342 25 c. Carved figure, Admiralty Islands .. 25 25
343 25 c. Female with child, Admiralty Islands .. 25 25
344 30 c. The God A'a, Rurutu (Austral Islands) .. 25 30
345 30 c. Statue of Tangaroa, Cook Islands .. 25 30
346 30 c. Ivory pendant, Tonga 25 30
347 30 c. Tapa (Hiapo) cloth, Niue.. .. .. 25 30
348 35 c. Feather box (Waka), New Zealand .. 30 35
349 35 c. Hei-Tiki amulet, New Zealand 30 35
350 35 c. House post, New Zealand 30 35
351 35 c. Feather image of god Ku, Hawaii .. 30 35
336/51 .. .. *Set of* 16 3·75 4·00
MS352 Four sheets, each 86 × 124 mm. (a) Nos. 336, 340, 344, 348; (b) Nos. 337, 341, 345, 349; (c) Nos. 338, 342, 346, 350; (d) Nos. 339, 343, 347, 351. Each stamp with an additional premium of 2 c. .. .. .. *Set of 4 sheets* 4·00 4·25

Nos. 336/9, 340/3, 344/7 and 348/51 were each printed together, *se-tenant*, in horizontal strips of 4 throughout the sheet.

ZEAPEX '80 AUCKLAND

(70) (71)

1980 (22 Aug). *"Zeapex '80" International Stamp Exhibition, Auckland. Nos.* 284, 286, 288, 290 *and* 292 *optd with T* **70** *and Nos.* 285, 287, 289, 291 *and* 293 *optd with T* **71**, *both in black on silver background.*
353 20 c. Type **63** 20 20
354 20 c. Sir Rowland Hill and original Bath mail coach 20 20
355 30 c. Basel 1845 2½ r. stamp 30 25
356 30 c. Sir Rowland Hill and Alpine village coach 30 25
357 35 c. U.S.A. 1847 5 c. stamp 35 25
358 35 c. Sir Rowland Hill and first Transatlantic U.S.A. mail vessel 35 25
359 50 c. France 1849 20 c. stamp.. .. .. 45 30
360 50 c. Sir Rowland Hill and French Post Office railway van, 1849 .. .. .. 45 30
361 60 c. Bavaria 1849 1 k. stamp.. .. .. 55 35
362 60 c. Sir Rowland Hill and Bavarian coach with mail 55 35
353/62 .. .. *Set of* 10 3·50 2·50
MS363 143 × 149 mm. Nos. 353/62, each additionally surcharged "+ 2 c." .. .. 3·75 3·25

72 Queen Elizabeth the Queen Mother

73 100 Metre Dash

1980 (15 Sept). 80*th Birthday of Queen Elizabeth the Queen Mother. P* 13.
364 **72** $1.10 multicoloured .. .. .. 1·25 1·50
MS365 55 × 80 mm. **72** $3 multicoloured.. .. 3·00 3·00

No. 364 was printed in small sheets of 6 including one *se-tenant* stamp-size label.

1980 (30 Oct). *Olympic Games, Moscow. T* **73** *and similar horiz designs. Multicoloured. P* 14 × 13½.
366 20 c. Type **73** 15 15
367 20 c. Allen Wells, Great Britain (winner of 100 metre dash).. .. .. .. 15 15
368 25 c. } 400 metre freestyle (winner, Ines Diers, 15 20
369 25 c. } D.D.R.) 15 20
370 30 c. } "Soling" Class Yachting (winner, 20 20
371 30 c. } Denmark) 20 20
372 35 c. } Football (winner, Czechoslovakia) .. 20 25
373 35 c. } 20 25
366/73 .. .. *Set of* 8 1·25 1·40
MS374 119 × 128 mm. Nos. 366/73, each stamp including premium of 2 c.. .. .. .. 1·60 2·00

Nos. 366/7, 368/9, 370/1 and 372/3 were each printed together, *se-tenant*, in horizontal pairs throughout the sheet, forming composite designs. On the 25 c. and 35 c. stamps the face value is at right on the first design and at left on the second in each pair. For the 30 c. No. 370 has a yacht with a green sail at left and No. 371 a yacht with a red sail.

74 "The Virgin and Child"

75 *Phalaenopsis sp.*

1980 (28 Nov). *Christmas and* 450*th Death Anniv of Andrea del Sarto (painter). T* **74** *and similar vert designs showing different "The Virgin and Child" works. P* 13.
375 20 c. multicoloured 15 15
376 25 c. multicoloured 15 15
377 30 c. multicoloured 20 20
378 35 c. multicoloured 20 20
375/8 .. .. *Set of* 4 60 60
MS379 87 × 112 mm. Nos. 375/8 .. .. .. 85 95

1980 (28 Nov). *Christmas. Children's Charity. Designs as Nos.* 375/8 *in separate miniature sheets* 62 × 84 *mm, each with a face value of* 80 *c.* + 5 *c. P* 13.
MS380 As Nos. 375/8 .. .. *Set of 4 sheets* 2·75 3·00

1981 (2 Apr)–**82**. *Flowers* (1st series). *Horiz designs as T* **75**. *Multicoloured. P* 13.
381 2 c. Type **75** 10 10
382 2 c. Moth Orchid 10 10
383 5 c. *Euphorbia pulcherrima* 10 10
384 5 c. Poinsettia 10 10
385 10 c. *Thunbergia alata* 10 10
386 10 c. Black-eyed Susan 10 10
387 15 c. *Cochlospermum hibiscoides* 15 15
388 15 c. Buttercup Tree 15 15
389 20 c. *Begonia sp.* 20 20
390 20 c. Begonia 20 20
391 25 c. *Plumeria sp.* 25 25
392 25 c. Frangipani 25 25
393 30 c. *Strelitzia reginae* (26 May) 30 30
394 30 c. Bird of Paradise (26 May) 30 30
395 35 c. *Hibiscus syriacus* (26 May) 30 30
396 35 c. Rose of Sharon (26 May).. .. .. 30 30
397 40 c. *Nymphaea sp.* (26 May) 35 35
398 40 c. Water Lily (26 May) 35 35
399 50 c. *Tibouchina sp.* (26 May).. .. .. 45 45
400 50 c. Princess Flower (26 May) 45 45
401 60 c. *Nelumbo sp.* (26 May) 55 55
402 60 c. Lotus (26 May) 55 55
403 80 c. *Hybrid hibiscus* (26 May) 75 75
404 80 c. Yellow Hibiscus (26 May) 75 75
405 $1 Golden Shower Tree (*Cassia fistula*) (9.12.81) .. .. 1·00 1·00
406 $2 *Orchid var.* (9.12.81) .. .. .. 2·50 2·50
407 $3 *Orchid sp.* (9.12.81) .. .. .. 3·50 3·50
408 $4 *Euphorbia pulcherrima poinsettia* (15.1.82) .. .. 3·00 3·25
409 $6 *Hybrid hibiscus* (15.1.82) .. .. 4·50 4·75
410 $10 Scarlet Hibiscus (*Hibiscus rosasinensis*) (12.3.82) .. .. 7·50 7·75
381/410 .. .. .. *Set of* 30 26·00 26·00

The two designs of the 2 c. to 80 c. show different drawings of the same flower, one inscribed with its name in Latin, the other giving the common name. These were printed together, *se-tenant*, in horizontal and vertical pairs throughout the sheet.

Nos. 405/10 are larger, 47 × 33 mm.

See also Nos. 527/36.

76 "Jesus Defiled" (El Greco)

77 Prince Charles

1981 (10 Apr). *Easter. Details of Paintings. T* **76** *and similar horiz designs. Multicoloured. P* 14.
425 35 c. Type **76** 30 30
426 50 c. "Pietà" (Fernando Gallego) 50 50
427 60 c. "The Supper of Emmaus" (Jacopo da Pontormo) 55 55
425/7 .. .. *Set of* 3 1·25 1·25
MS428 69 × 111 mm. As Nos. 425/7, but each with charity premium of 2 c. P 13½ .. .. .. 1·40 1·60

1981 (10 Apr). *Easter. Children's Charity. Designs as Nos.* 425/7 *in separate miniature sheets* 78 × 86 *mm, each with a face value of* 80 *c.* + 5 *c. P* 13½ × 14.
MS429 As Nos. 425/7 .. .. *Set of 3 sheets* 2·50 2·75

1981 (26 June). *Royal Wedding. T* **77** *and similar vert designs. Multicoloured. P* 14.
430 75 c. Type **77** 90 80
431 95 c. Lady Diana Spencer .. .. .. 1·00 90
432 $1.20, Prince Charles and Lady Diana .. 1·25 1·00
430/2 .. .. *Set of* 3 2·75 2·50
MS433 78 × 85 mm. Nos. 430/2 .. .. .. 3·00 3·25

Nos. 430/2 were each printed in small sheets of 6, including one *se-tenant* stamp-size label.

78 Footballer Silhouettes

+5c

(79)

1981 (16 Oct). *World Cup Football Championship, Spain* (1982). *T* **78** *and similar horiz designs showing footballer silhouettes. P* 13.
434 30 c. blue-green, gold & new blue (Type **78**) .. 20 20
435 30 c. blue-green, gold and new blue (gold figure 3rd from left of stamp) 20 20
436 30 c. blue-green, gold and new blue (gold figure 4th from left) 20 20
437 35 c. new blue, gold and reddish orange (gold figure 3rd from left) 25 25
438 35 c. new blue, gold and reddish orange (gold figure 4th from left) 25 25
439 35 c. new blue, gold and reddish orange (gold figure 2nd from left) 25 25
440 40 c. reddish orange, gold and blue-green (gold figure 3rd from left, displaying close control) 25 25
441 40 c. reddish orange, gold and blue-green (gold figure 2nd from left) 25 25
442 40 c. reddish orange, gold and blue-green (gold figure 3rd from left, heading) 25 25
434/42 .. .. *Set of* 9 1·90 1·90
MS443 162 × 122 mm. 30 c. + 3 c., 35 c. + 3 c., 40 c. + 3 c. (each × 3). As Nos. 434/42 .. .. .. 2·00 2·50

The three designs of each value were printed together, *se-tenant*, in horizontal strips of 3 throughout the sheets.

1981 (3 Nov). *International Year for Disabled Persons. Nos.* 430/3 *surch as T* **79**.
444 75 c. + 5 c. Type **77** .. .. 2·25 1·50
445 95 c. + 5 c. Lady Diana Spencer .. .. 2·75 1·75
446 $1.20 + 5 c. Prince Charles and Lady Diana 3·75 2·00
444/6 .. .. *Set of* 4 8·00 4·75
MS447 78 × 85 mm. As Nos. 444/6, each surcharged "+ 10 c." .. .. 8·00 5·25

Nos. 444/6 have commemorative inscription overprinted on the sheet margins.

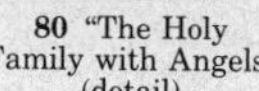

80 "The Holy Family with Angels" (detail)

81 Prince of Wales

1981 (11 Dec). *Christmas and* 375*th Birth Anniv of Rembrandt. T* **80** *and similar vert designs. Multicoloured. P* 14 × 13.
448 20 c. Type **80** 25 20
449 35 c. "Presentation in the Temple" 35 30
450 50 c. "Virgin and Child in Temple" 45 40
451 60 c. "The Holy Family" 50 45
448/51 .. .. *Set of* 4 1·40 1·25
MS452 79 × 112 mm. Nos. 448/51 .. .. .. 1·40 1·50

1982 (22 Jan). *Christmas. Children's Charity. Designs as Nos.* 448/51 *in separate miniature sheets* 66 × 80 *mm, each with a face value of* 80 *c.* + 5 *c. P* 14 × 13.
MS453 As Nos. 448/51 .. .. *Set of 4 sheets* 2·50 2·75

1982 (1 July). 21*st Birthday of Princess of Wales. T* **81** *and similar horiz designs. Multicoloured. P* 14.
454 50 c. Type **81** 55 55
455 $1.25, Prince and Princess of Wales .. 1·25 1·25
456 $2.50, Princess of Wales .. .. .. 2·00 2·00
454/6 .. .. *Set of* 3 3·50 3·50
MS457 81 × 101 mm. Nos. 454/6 .. .. .. 3·75 4·00

Nos. 454/6 were each printed in small sheets of 6 including one *se-tenant* stamp-size label.

The stamps from No. **MS**457 are without white borders.

(82)

83 Infant

1982 (23 July). *Birth of Prince William of Wales* (1st issue). *Nos.* 430/3 *optd as T* **82**.
458 75 c. Type **77** (optd with T **82**).. .. .. 2·25 1·75
a. Pair. Nos. 458/9 .. .. .. 4·50 3·50
459 75 c. Type **77** (optd "BIRTH OF PRINCE WILLIAM OF WALES 21 JUNE 1982") 2·25 1·75
460 95 c. Lady Diana Spencer (optd with T **82**) .. 3·25 2·25
a. Pair. Nos. 460/1 .. .. .. 6·50 4·50
461 95 c. Lady Diana Spencer (optd "BIRTH OF PRINCE WILLIAM OF WALES 21 JUNE 1982") .. .. .. 3·25 2·25
462 $1.20, Prince Charles and Lady Diana Spencer (optd with T **82**) .. .. 4·25 2·75
a. Pair. Nos. 462/3 .. .. .. 8·50 5·50
463 $1.20, Prince Charles and Lady Diana Spencer (optd "BIRTH OF PRINCE WILLIAM OF WALES 21 JUNE 1982") 4·25 2·75
458/63 .. .. *Set of* 6 18·00 12·00
MS464 78 × 85 mm. Nos. 430/2 each optd "PRINCE WILLIAM OF WALES 21 JUNE 1982" .. .. 8·50 6·00

Nos. 458/9, 460/1 and 462/3 were each printed *se-tenant* in small sheets of 6, containing three stamps overprinted with Type **82**, two with "BIRTH OF PRINCE WILLIAM OF WALES 21 JUNE 1982" and one stamp-size label.

1982 (10 Sept). *Birth of Prince William of Wales (2nd issue). Designs as Nos. 454/7 but with changed inscriptions. Multi-coloured. P 14.*
465 50 c. Type **81** 55 55
466 $1.25, Prince and Princess of Wales .. 1·25 1·25
467 $2.50, Princess of Wales .. .. .. 2·00 2·00
465/7 .. .. *Set of* 3 3·50 3·50
MS468 81 × 101 mm. As Nos. 465/7 .. .. 3·75 4·00
Nos. 465/7 were each printed in small sheets of 6 including one *se-tenant*, stamp-size, label.

1982 (3 Dec). *Christmas. Paintings of Infants by Bronzino, Murillo and Boucher. T* **83** *and similar horiz designs. P* 13 × 14½.
469 40 c. multicoloured 45 35
470 52 c. multicoloured 55 45
471 83 c. multicoloured 90 80
472 $1.05, multicoloured .. .. 1·10 95
469/72 .. .. *Set of* 4 2·75 2·25
MS473 110 × 76 mm. Designs as Nos. 469/72 (*each* 31 × 27 *mm*), but without portrait of Princess and Prince William. P 13½ .. .. 2·50 2·75

84 Prince and Princess of Wales with Prince William

85 Prime Minister Robert Rex

1982 (3 Dec). *Christmas. Children's Charity. Sheet* 72 × 58 *mm. P* 13 × 13½.
MS474 **84** 80 c. + 5 c. multicoloured 85 90
No. **MS**474 occurs with four different designs in the sheet margin.

1983 (14 Mar). *Commonwealth Day. T* **85** *and similar horiz designs. Multicoloured. P* 13.
475 70 c. Type **85** 65 70
476 70 c. H.M.S. *Resolution* and H.M.S. *Adventure* off Niue, 1774 .. .. .. 65 70
477 70 c. Passion flower 65 70
478 70 c. Limes 65 70
475/8 .. .. *Set of* 4 2·40 2·50
Nos. 475/8 were issued together, *se-tenant*, in blocks of four throughout the sheet.

86 Scouts signalling

XV WORLD JAMBOREE CANADA
(**87**)

1983 (28 Apr). *75th Anniv of Boy Scout Movement and 125th Birth Anniv of Lord Baden-Powell. T* **86** *and similar vert designs. Multicoloured. P* 13.
479 40 c. Type **86** 35 40
480 50 c. Planting sapling 45 50
481 83 c. Map-reading 85 90
479/81 .. .. *Set of* 3 1·50 1·60
MS482 137 × 90 mm. As Nos. 479/81, but each with premium of 3 c. .. .. 1·60 1·75

1983 (14 July). *15th World Scout Jamboree, Alberta, Canada. Nos.* 479/82 *optd with T* **87**, *in black on silver background.*
483 40 c. Type **86** 35 40
484 50 c. Planting sapling 45 50
485 83 c. Map-reading 85 90
483/5 .. .. *Set of* 3 1·50 1·60
MS486 137 × 90 mm. As Nos. 483/5, but each with premium of 3 c. .. .. 1·60 1·75

88 Black Right Whale

1983 (15 Aug). *Protect the Whales. T* **88** *and similar horiz designs. Multicoloured. P* 13 × 14.
487 12 c. Type **88** 35 25
488 25 c. Fin Whale 50 40
489 35 c. Sei Whale 70 60
490 40 c. Blue Whale 75 65
491 58 c. Bowhead Whale 90 75
492 70 c. Sperm Whale .. .. 1·25 1·00
493 83 c. Humpback Whale .. .. 1·50 1·25
494 $1.05, Minke Whale ("Lesser Rorqual") .. 1·75 1·50
495 $2.50, Grey Whale .. .. 3·00 2·75
487/95 .. .. *Set of* 9 9·50 8·25

89 Montgolfier Balloon, 1783

90 "The Garvagh Madonna"

1983 (14 Oct). *Bicentenary of Manned Flight. T* **89** *and similar horiz designs. Multicoloured. (a) Postage. P* 13½.
496 25 c. Type **89** 20 20
497 40 c. Wright Brothers' *Flyer*, 1903 .. .. 35 35
498 58 c. *Graf Zeppelin*, 1928 .. .. .. 50 50
499 70 c. Boeing "247", 1933 .. .. .. 65 65
500 83 c. "Apollo 8", 1968 .. .. 80 80
501 $1.05, Space shuttle *Columbia*, 1982 .. 95 95
496/501 .. .. *Set of* 6 3·00 3·00

(*b*) *Air. Inscr* "AIRMAIL"
MS502 118 × 130 mm. Nos. 496/501. P 13 .. 3·00 3·25

1983 (25 Nov). *Christmas. 500th Birth Anniv of Raphael. T* **90** *and similar vert designs. Multicoloured. P* 14 × 13½.
503 30 c. Type **90** 25 30
504 40 c. "Madonna of the Granduca" 30 35
505 58 c. "Madonna of the Goldfinch" 45 50
506 70 c. "The Holy Family of Francis I" 55 60
507 83 c. "The Holy Family with Saints" 65 70
503/7 .. .. *Set of* 5 2·00 2·25
MS508 120 × 114 mm. As Nos. 503/7 but each with a premium of 3 c. .. .. 2·25 2·50

1983 (30 Nov). *Various stamps surch as T* **200** *of Cook Islands.*

(*a*) *Nos.* 393/4, 399/404 *and* 407
509 52 c. on 30 c. *Strelitzia reginae* 40 45
510 52 c. on 30 c. Bird of Paradise 40 45
511 58 c. on 50 c. *Tibouchina sp.* 50 55
512 58 c. on 50 c. Princess Flower 50 55
513 70 c. on 60 c. *Nelumbo sp.* 55 60
514 70 c. on 60 c. Lotus 55 60
515 83 c. on 80 c. *Hybrid hibiscus* 70 75
516 83 c. on 80 c. Yellow Hibiscus 70 75
517 $3.70 on $3 *Orchid sp.* .. .. .. 3·00 3·25

(*b*) *Nos.* 431/2 *and* 455/6
518 $1.10 on 95 c. Lady Diana Spencer .. 3·00 2·25
a. Error. Surch on No. 458 .. .. .. 6·00 6·00
ab. Pair. Nos. 518a/b .. .. .. 15·00 15·00
b. Error. Surch on No. 459 .. .. .. 9·00 9·00
519 $1.10 on $1.25, Prince and Princess of Wales 2·25 2·00
520 $2.60 on $1.20, Prince Charles and Lady Diana .. .. 5·50 3·50
a. Error. Surch on No. 462 .. .. .. 6·00 6·00
ab. Pair. Nos. 520a/b .. .. .. 15·00 15·00
b. Error. Surch on No. 463 .. .. .. 9·00 9·00
521 $2.60 on $2.50, Princess of Wales .. 3·50 3·25
509/21 .. .. *Set of* 13 19·00 17·00

1983 (29 Dec). *Christmas. 500th Birth Anniv of Raphael. Children's Charity. Designs as Nos.* 503/7 *in separate miniature sheets,* 65 × 80 *mm, each with face value of* 85 *c.* + 5 *c. P* 13½.
MS522 As Nos. 503/7 .. .. *Set of* 5 *sheets* 3·25 3·50

91 Morse Key Transmitter

92 *Phalaenopsis sp.*

1984 (23 Jan). *World Communications Year. T* **91** *and similar vert designs. Multicoloured. P* 13 × 13½.
523 40 c. Type **91** 30 35
524 52 c. Wall-mounted phone 40 45
525 83 c. Communications satellite 60 65
523/5 .. .. *Set of* 3 1·10 1·25
MS526 114 × 90 mm. Nos. 523/5 .. .. 1·10 1·25

1984 (20 Feb–23 July). *Flowers (2nd series). Designs as Nos.* 381 *etc., but with gold frames and redrawn inscr as in T* **92**. *Multi-coloured. P* 13 (*Nos.* 537/42) *or* 13 × 13½ (*others*).
527 12 c. Type **92** 10 10
528 25 c. *Euphorbia pulcherrima* 15 20
529 30 c. *Cochlospermum hibiscoides* 20 25
530 35 c. *Begonia sp.* 25 30
531 40 c. *Plumeria sp.* 25 30
532 52 c. *Strelitzia reginae* 35 40
533 58 c. *Hibiscus syriacus* 35 40
534 70 c. *Tibouchina sp.* 45 50
535 83 c. *Nelumbo sp.* 55 60
536 $1.05, *Hybrid hibiscus* 70 75
537 $1.75, *Cassia fistula* (10.5) .. .. 1·10 1·25
538 $2.30, *Orchid var.* (10.5) .. .. .. 1·50 1·60
539 $3.90, *Orchid sp.* (10.5) .. .. .. 2·50 2·75
540 $5 *Euphorbia pulcherrima poinsettia* (18.6) 3·25 3·50
541 $6.60, *Hybrid hibiscus* (18.6) .. .. 4·25 4·50
542 $8.30, *Hibiscus rosasinensis* (23.7) .. 5·50 5·75
527/42 .. .. *Set of* 16 19·00 21·00
Nos. 537/42 are larger, 39 × 31 mm.

93 Discus-throwing

94 Koala

1984 (15 Mar). *Olympic Games, Los Angeles. T* **93** *and similar multicoloured designs showing ancient Greek sports. P* 14.
547 30 c. Type **93** 25 30
548 35 c. Sprinting (*horiz*) 30 35
549 40 c. Horse racing (*horiz*) 35 40
550 58 c. Boxing (*horiz*) 50 55
551 70 c. Javelin-throwing 60 65
547/51 .. .. *Set of* 5 1·75 2·00

1984 (24 Aug). *"Ausipex" International Stamp Exhibition, Melbourne (1st issue). P* 14. (*a*) *Postage. Vert designs as T* **94** *showing Koala Bears.*
552 25 c. multicoloured 30 30
553 35 c. multicoloured 35 35
554 40 c. multicoloured 40 40
555 58 c. multicoloured 55 55
556 70 c. multicoloured 65 65

(*b*) *Air. Vert designs showing Red Kangaroos*
557 83 c. multicoloured 75 75
558 $1.05, multicoloured 95 95
559 $2.50, multicoloured .. .. 2·25 2·25
552/9 .. .. *Set of* 8 5·50 5·50
MS560 110 × 64 mm. $1.75, Wallaby; $1.75, Koala Bear. P 13½ .. .. 3·25 3·50
See also Nos. **MS**566/7.

Discus Throw
Rolf Danneberg
Germany
(**95**)

96 Niue National Flag and Premier Sir Robert Rex

1984 (7 Sept). *Olympic Gold Medal Winners, Los Angeles. Nos.* 547/51 *optd as T* **95** *in red* (35 *c.*) *or gold* (*others*).
561 30 c. Type **93** (opt T **95**) 25 30
562 35 c. Sprinting (optd "1,500 Metres Sebastian Coe Great Britain") 30 35
563 40 c. Horse racing (optd "Equestrian Mark Todd New Zealand") 30 35
564 58 c. Boxing (optd "Boxing Tyrell Biggs United States") 45 50
565 70 c. Javelin-throwing (optd "Javelin Throw Arto Haerkoenen Finland") 55 60
561/5 .. .. *Set of* 5 1·75 1·90

1984 (20 Sept). *"Ausipex" International Stamp Exhibition, Melbourne (2nd issue). Designs as Nos.* 552/60 *in miniature sheets of six or four. Multicoloured. P* 13½.
MS566 109 × 105 mm. Nos. 552/6 and $1.75, Koala Bear (as No. **MS**560) .. .. .. 3·00 3·25
MS567 80 × 105 mm. Nos. 557/9 and $1.75, Wallaby (as No. **MS**560) .. .. 4·50 4·75

1984 (19 Oct). *10th Anniv of Self-Government. T* **96** *and similar horiz designs. Multicoloured. P* 13.
568 40 c. Type **96** 30 35
569 58 c. Map of Niue and Premier Rex 45 50
570 70 c. Premier Rex receiving proclamation of self-government 55 60
568/70 .. .. *Set of* 3 1·10 1·25
MS571 110 × 83 mm. Nos. 568/70 .. .. 1·25 1·40
MS572 100 × 74 mm. $2.50, As 70 c. (50 × 30 *mm*) .. .. 1·75 1·90

$2
Prince Henry
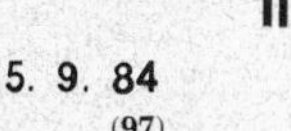
15. 9. 84
(**97**)

98 "The Nativity" (A. Vaccaro)

1984 (22 Oct). *Birth of Prince Henry. Nos.* 430 *and* 454 *optd as T* **97**.
573 $2 on 50 c. Type **81** (Sil.) .. .. .. 2·50 1·75
574 $2 on 75 c. Type **77** (R.) .. .. .. 2·50 1·75

1984 (23 Nov). *Christmas. T* **98** *and similar vert designs. Multicoloured. P* 13 × 13½.

575 40 c. Type **98** 30 35
576 58 c. "Virgin with Fly" (anon, 16th-century) 45 50
577 70 c. "The Adoration of the Shepherds" (B. Murillo) 55 60
578 83 c. "Flight into Egypt" (B. Murillo) .. 65 70
575/8 .. .. *Set of* 4 1·75 1·90
MS579 115 × 111 mm. As Nos. 575/8 but each stamp with a 5 c. premium .. .. 2·00 2·25
MS580 Four sheets, each 66 × 98 mm. As Nos. 575/8, but each stamp 30 × 42 mm. with a face value of 95 c. + 10 c. P 13½ *Set of 4 sheets* 3·00 3·25

99 House Wren

1985 (15 Apr). *Birth Bicentenary of John J. Audubon (ornithologist). T* **99** *and similar horiz designs showing original paintings. Multicoloured. P* 14.

581 40 c. Type **99** 70 35
582 70 c. Veery .. .. 1·00 60
583 83 c. Grasshopper Sparrow .. .. .. 1·10 70
584 $1.05, Henslow's Sparrow .. .. .. 1·50 85
585 $2.50, Vesper Sparrow .. .. .. 2·25 2·00
581/5 .. .. *Set of* 5 6·00 4·00
MS586 Five sheets, each 54 × 60 mm. As Nos. 581/5 but each stamp 34 × 26 mm with a face value of $1.75 and without the commemorative inscription .. .. .. *Set of 5 sheets* 7·50 8·50

100 The Queen Mother in Garter Robes

1985 (14 June). *Life and Times of Queen Elizabeth the Queen Mother. T* **100** *and similar horiz designs. Multicoloured. P* 13.

587 70 c. Type **100** 55 60
588 $1.15, In open carriage with the Queen .. 90 95
589 $1.50, With Prince Charles during 80th birthday celebrations .. .. .. 1·10 1·25
587/9 .. .. *Set of* 3 2·25 2·50
MS590 70 × 70 mm. $3 At her desk in Clarence House (38 × 35 *mm*) .. .. 2·25 2·50

Nos. 587/9 were each issued in sheetlets of five stamps and one stamp-size label at top left, showing the Queen Mother's arms.

For Nos. 587/9 in miniature sheet see No. **MS**627.

MINI SOUTH PACIFIC GAMES, RAROTONGA

(**101**)

1985 (26 July). *South Pacific Mini Games, Rarotonga. Nos.* 547/8 *and* 550/1 *surch as T* **101** *in black and gold.*

591 52 c. on 70 c. Javelin-throwing 40 45
592 83 c. on 58 c. Boxing 65 70
593 95 c. on 35 c. Sprinting 75 80
594 $2 on 30 c. Type **93** .. .. 1·50 1·60
591/4 .. .. *Set of* 4 3·00 3·25

On Nos. 591/4 the new face values and inscriptions are surcharged in black on gold panels. The Games emblem is in gold only.

PACIFIC ISLANDS CONFERENCE, RAROTONGA

(**102**)

103 "R. Strozzi's Daughter" (Titian)

1985 (26 July). *Pacific Islands Conference, Rarotonga. Nos.* 475/8 *optd with T* **102** *in black on silver.*

595 70 c. Type **85** 55 60
596 70 c. *Resolution* and *Adventure* off Niue, 1774 .. .. 55 60
597 70 c. Passion flower 55 60
598 70 c. Limes 55 60
595/8 .. .. *Set of* 4 2·00 2·25

No. 595 also shows an overprinted amendment to the caption which now reads "Premier Sir Robert Rex K.B.E.".

1985 (11 Oct). *International Youth Year. T* **103** *and similar vert designs. Multicoloured. P* 13.

599 58 c. Type **103** 65 50
600 70 c. "The Fifer" (E. Manet) 80 60
601 $1.15, "Portrait of a Young Girl" (Renoir) .. .. 1·25 1·25
602 $1.50, "Portrait of M. Berard" (Renoir) .. 1·50 1·50
599/602 .. .. *Set of* 4 3·75 3·50
MS603 Four sheets, each 63 × 79 mm. As Nos. 599/602 but each with a face value of $1.75 + 10 c. .. .. *Set of 4 sheets* 6·00 6·50

104 "Virgin and Child"

1985 (29 Nov). *Christmas. Details of Paintings by Correggio. T* **104** *and similar vert designs. Multicoloured. P* 13 × 13½.

604 58 c. Type **104** 50 50
605 85 c. "Adoration of the Magi" 70 70
606 $1.05, "Virgin with Child and St. John" .. 85 85
607 $1.45, "Virgin and Child with St. Catherine" .. .. 1·25 1·25
604/7 .. .. *Set of* 4 3·00 3·00
MS608 83 × 123 mm. As Nos. 604/7, but each stamp with a face value of 60 c. + 10 c. .. .. 2·10 2·25
MS609 Four sheets, each 80 × 90 mm. 65 c. Type **104**; 95 c. As No. 605; $1.20, As No. 606; $1.75, As No. 607 (each stamp 49 × 59 mm). Imperf .. *Set of 4 sheets* 3·50 3·75

105 "The Constellations" (detail)

106 Queen Elizabeth II and Prince Philip

1986 (24 Jan). *Appearance of Halley's Comet. T* **105** *and similar horiz designs showing details from ceiling painting "The Constellations" by Giovanni de Vecchi. Nos.* 611/13 *show different spacecraft at top left. P* 13½.

610 60 c. multicoloured 50 50
611 75 c. multicoloured (*Vega* spacecraft) .. 65 65
612 $1.10, multicoloured (*Planet A* spacecraft) 90 90
613 $1.50, multicoloured (*Giotto* spacecraft) .. 1·25 1·25
610/13 .. .. *Set of* 4 3·00 3·00
MS614 125 × 91 mm. As Nos. 610/13 but each stamp with a face value of 95 c. .. .. 3·00 3·25

Stamps from No. **MS**614 are without borders.

1986 (28 Apr). *60th Birthday of Queen Elizabeth II. T* **106** *and similar vert designs. Multicoloured. P* 14½ × 13.

615 $1.10, Type **106** .. .. 1·00 1·00
616 $1.50, Queen and Prince Philip at Balmoral 1·25 1·25
617 $2 Queen at Buckingham Palace .. .. 1·75 1·75
615/17 .. .. *Set of* 3 3·50 3·50
MS618 110 × 70 mm. As Nos. 615/17, but each stamp with a face value of 75 c. .. .. .. 1·60 1·75
MS619 58 × 89 mm. $3 Queen and Prince Philip at Windsor Castle .. .. 2·10 2·25

107 U.S.A. 1847 Franklin 5 c. Stamp and Washington Sculpture, Mt. Rushmore, U.S.A.

108 "Statue under Construction, Paris, 1883" (Victor Dargaud)

1986 (22 May). *"Ameripex '86" International Stamp Exhibition, Chicago. T* **107** *and similar vert design. Multicoloured. P* 14.

620 $1 Type **107** .. .. 1·25 1·25
a. Horiz pair. Nos. 620/1 .. .. .. 2·50 2·50
621 $1 Flags of Niue and U.S.A. and Mt. Rushmore sculptures .. .. 1·25 1·25

Nos. 620/1 were printed together, *se-tenant*, in horizontal pairs, within sheetlets of 8 stamps, each pair forming a composite design.

1986 (4 July). *Centenary of Statue of Liberty* (1*st issue*). *T* **108** *and similar vert design. Multicoloured. P* 13 × 13½.

622 $1 Type **108** .. .. 1·25 1·25
623 $2.50, "Unveiling of the Statue of Liberty" (Edmund Morand) .. .. 2·25 2·25
MS624 107 × 73 mm. As Nos. 622/3, but each stamp with a face value of $1.25 .. .. 2·50 3·00

See also No. **MS**648.

109 Prince Andrew, Miss Sarah Ferguson and Westminster Abbey

1986 (23 July). *Royal Wedding. T* **109** *and similar horiz design. Multicoloured. P* 13½ × 13.

625 $2.50, Type **109** .. .. 2·50 2·75
MS626 106 × 68 mm. $5 Prince Andrew and Miss Sarah Ferguson (43 × 30 *mm*) .. .. .. 4·50 4·75

1986 (4 Aug). *86th Birthday of Queen Elizabeth the Queen Mother. Nos.* 587/9 *in miniature sheet,* 109 × 83 *mm. P* 13.

MS627 Nos. 587/9 .. .. 2·75 3·00

110 Great Egret

111 "Virgin and Child" (Perugino)

1986 (4 Aug). *"Stampex '86" Stamp Exhibition, Adelaide. Australian Birds. T* **110** *and similar multicoloured designs. P* 13 × 13½ (40, 75 c., $1, $2.20) *or* 13½ × 13 (*others*).

628 40 c. Type **110** 70 40
629 60 c. Painted Finch (*horiz*) 80 50
630 75 c. Australian King Parrot .. .. .. 1·00 70
631 80 c. Variegated Wren (*horiz*) .. .. 1·25 75
632 $1 Peregrine Falcon .. .. .. 1·50 1·00
633 $1.65, Azure Kingfisher (*horiz*) .. .. 2·00 1·50
634 $2.20, Budgerigars .. .. 2·50 2·25
635 $4.25, Emu (*horiz*) .. .. 3·75 3·50
628/35 .. .. *Set of* 8 12·50 9·50

1986 (14 Nov). *Christmas. Paintings from the Vatican Museum. T* **111** *and similar vert designs. Multicoloured. P* 14.

636 80 c. Type **111** 65 65
637 $1.15, "Virgin of St. N. dei Frari" (Titian) 85 85
638 $1.80, "Virgin with Milk" (Lorenzo di Credi) .. .. 1·40 1·40
639 $2.60, "Madonna of Foligno" (Raphael) .. 1·90 1·90
636/9 .. .. *Set of* 4 4·25 4·25
MS640 87 × 110 mm. As Nos. 636/9, but each stamp with a face value of $1.50. P 13½ .. 4·00 4·25
MS641 70 × 100 mm. $7.50, As No. 639, but 27 × 43 mm. P 14½ × 13 .. .. 5·50 5·75

+10c

(**112**)

1986 (21 Nov). *Visit of Pope John Paul II to South Pacific. Nos.* 636/41 *surch as T* **112** *in black on silver.*

642 80 c. + 10 c. Type **111** 90 90
643 $1.15 + 10 c. "Virgin of St. N. dei Frari" (Titian) .. .. 1·25 1·25
644 $1.80 + 10 c. "Virgin with Milk" (Lorenzo di Credi) .. .. 2·00 2·00
645 $2.60 + 10 c. "Madonna of Foligno" (Raphael) .. .. 2·25 2·25
642/5 .. .. *Set of* 4 5·75 5·75
MS646 87 × 110 mm. As Nos. 642/5, but each stamp with a face value of $1.50 + 10 c. .. .. 5·00 6·00
MS647 70 × 100 mm. $7.50 + 50 c. As No. 645, but 27 × 43 mm .. .. 6·50 7·00

1987 (20 May). *Centenary of Statue of Liberty* (1986) (*2nd issue*). *Two sheets, each* 122×122 *mm, containing multicoloured designs as T* **63** *of Cook Islands* (*Penrhyn*). *Litho. P* 13½×14 (*horiz*) *or* 14×13½ (*vert*).

MS648 Two sheets (a) 75 c. Sailing ship under Brooklyn Bridge; 75 c. Restoring Statue's flame; 75 c. Steam-cleaning Statue's torch; 75 c. *Esmerelda* (Chilean cadet ship) off Manhattan; 75 c. Cadet barque at dusk. (b) 75 c. Statue of Liberty at night (*vert*); 75 c. Statue at night (side view) (*vert*); 75 c. Cleaning Statue's crown (*vert*); 75 c. Statue at night (rear view) (*vert*); 75 c. Cleaning a finial (*vert*) .. .. *Set of* 2 *sheets* 4·25 4·50

113 Boris Becker, Olympic Rings and Commemorative Coin

(Des G. Vasarhelyi. Litho Questa)

1987 (25 Sept). *Olympic Games, Seoul* (1988). *Tennis* (*1st issue*). *T* **113** *and similar horiz designs showing Boris Becker in play. P* 13½×14.

649	80 c. multicoloured	1·00	1·00
650	$1.15, multicoloured	1·25	1·25
651	$1.40, multicoloured	1·50	1·50
652	$1.80, multicoloured	1·75	1·75
649/52	.. .. *Set of* 4	5·00	5·00

(Des G. Vasarhelyi. Litho Questa)

1987 (20 Oct). *Olympic Games, Seoul* (1988). *Tennis* (*2nd issue*). *Horiz designs as T* **113**, *but showing Steffi Graf. P* 13½×14.

653	85 c. multicoloured	1·00	1·00
654	$1.05, multicoloured	1·25	1·25
655	$1.30, multicoloured	1·50	1·50
656	$1.75, multicoloured	1·75	1·75
653/6	.. .. *Set of* 4	5·00	5·00

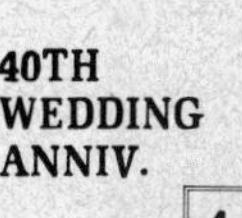

(114) 115 "The Nativity"

1987 (20 Nov). *Royal Ruby Wedding. Nos.* 616/17 *optd with T* **114**.

657	$4.85 on $1.50, Queen and Prince Philip at Balmoral	3·50	3·75
658	$4.85 on $2 Queen at Buckingham Palace ..	3·50	3·75

On Nos. 657/8 the original values are obliterated in gold.

1987 (4 Dec). *Christmas. Religious Paintings by Dürer. T* **115** *and similar horiz designs. Multicoloured. P* 13½.

659	80 c. Type **115**	55	60
660	$1.05, "Adoration of the Magi"	75	80
661	$2.80, "Celebration of the Rosary" ..	2·00	2·10
659/61	.. .. *Set of* 3	3·00	3·25
MS662	100×140 mm. As Nos. 659/61, but each size 48×37 mm with a face value of $1.30 ..	2·75	3·00
MS663	90×80 mm. $7.50, As No. 661, but size 51×33 mm	5·25	5·50

Nos. 659/61 each include a detail of an angel with lute as in T **115**. Stamps from the miniature sheets are without this feature.

116 Franz Beckenbauer in Action

(Des G. Vasarhelyi. Litho Questa)

1988 (20 June). *European Cup Football Championship, West Germany. T* **116** *and similar horiz designs. Multicoloured. P* 13½ × 14.

664	20 c. Type **116**	15	20
665	40 c. German "All Star" team in action ..	30	35
666	60 c. Bayern Munich team with European Cup, 1974	40	45
667	80 c. World Cup match, England, 1966 ..	55	60
668	$1.05, World Cup match, Mexico, 1970 ..	75	80
669	$1.30, Beckenbauer with pennant, 1974	90	95
670	$1.80, Beckenbauer and European Cup, 1974	1·25	4·25
664/70	.. .. *Set of* 7	3·75	4·25

NEW INFORMATION

The editor is always interested to correspond with people who have new information that will improve or correct the Catalogue.

Australia 24 Jan 88
French Open 4 June 88

(117) **118** Angels

1988 (14 Oct). *Steffi Graf's Tennis Victories. Nos.* 653/6 *optd as T* **117**.

671	85 c. multicoloured (optd with T **117**) ..	60	65
672	$1.05, mult (optd "Wimbledon 2 July 88 U S Open 10 Sept. 88")	75	80
673	$1.30, mult (optd "Women's Tennis Grand Slam: 10 September 88")	90	95
674	$1.75, multicoloured (optd "Seoul Olympic Games Gold Medal Winner")	1·25	1·40
671/4	.. .. *Set of* 4	3·25	3·50

1988 (28 Oct). *Christmas. T* **118** *and similar vert designs showing details from "The Adoration of the Shepherds" by Rubens. Multicoloured. P* 13½.

675	60 c. Type **118**	40	45
676	80 c. Shepherds	55	60
677	$1.05, Virgin Mary	75	80
678	$1.30, Holy Child	90	95
675/8	.. .. *Set of* 4	2·40	2·50
MS679	83 × 103 mm. $7.20, The Nativity (38 × 49 *mm*)	5·00	5·50

119 Astronaut and "Apollo 11" Emblem

(Des G. Vasarhelyi)

1989 (20 July). *20th Anniv of First Manned Landing on Moon. T* **119** *and similar horiz designs. Multicoloured. P* 14.

680	$1.50, Type **119**	1·10	1·25
	a. Horiz strip of 3. Nos. 680/2	3·00	
681	$1.50, Earth and Moon	1·10	1·25
682	$1.50, Astronaut and "Apollo 1" emblem	1·10	1·25
680/2	.. .. *Set of* 3	3·00	3·25
MS683	160×64 mm. As Nos. 680/2, but each stamp with a face value of $1.15. P 13	2·50	2·75

Nos. 680/2 were printed together, *se-tenant*, in horizontal strips of 3 throughout the sheet.

120 Priests

1989 (22 Nov). *Christmas. T* **120** *and similar multicoloured designs showing details from "Presentation in the Temple" by Rembrandt. P* 13.

684	70 c. Type **120**	50	55
685	80 c. Virgin and Christ Child in Simeon's arms	60	65
686	$1.05, Joseph	80	85
687	$1.30, Simeon and Christ Child	1·00	1·10
684/7	.. .. *Set of* 4	2·75	3·00
MS688	84×110 mm. $7.20, "Presentation in the Temple" (39×49 *mm*). P 13½	5·50	5·75

121 Fritz Walter

1990 (5 Feb). *World Cup Football Championship, Italy. German Footballers. T* **121** *and similar horiz designs. Multicoloured. P* 13½×13.

689	80 c. Type **121**	60	65
690	$1.15, Franz Beckenbauer	85	90
691	$1.40, Uwe Seeler	1·10	1·25
692	$1.80, German team emblem and signatures of former captains	1·40	1·50
689/92	.. .. *Set of* 4	3·50	3·75

OFFICIAL STAMPS

O.H.M.S. (O 1) **O.H.M.S.** (O 2)

1985 (1 July)–**87**. *Nos.* 408/10 *optd with Type* O **2** *in gold and Nos.* 527/42 *optd with Type* O **1** *in blue, all by foil embossing.*

O 1	12 c. Type **92**	10	10
O 2	25 c. *Euphorbia pulcherrima*	15	20
O 3	30 c. *Cochlospermum hibiscoides*	20	25
O 4	35 c. *Begonia sp.*	25	30
O 5	40 c. *Plumeria sp.*	25	30
O 6	52 c. *Strelitzia reginae*	35	40
O 7	58 c. *Hibiscus syriacus*	35	40
O 8	70 c. *Tibouchina sp.*	45	50
O 9	83 c. *Nelumbo sp.*	55	60
O10	$1.05, *Hybrid hibiscus*	70	75
O11	$1.75, *Cassia fistula*	1·10	1·25
O12	$2.30, *Orchid var.* (29.11.85)	1·50	1·60
O13	$3.90, *Orchid sp.* (29.11.85)	2·50	2·75
O14	$4 *Euphorbia pulcherrima poinsettia* (1.4.86)	2·75	3·00
O15	$5 *Euphorbia pulcherrima poinsettia* (1.4.86)	3·25	3·50
O16	$6 *Hybrid hibiscus* (29.4.87)	4·00	4·25
O17	$6.60, *Hybrid hibiscus* (15.9.86)	4·25	4·50
O18	$8.30, *Hibiscus rosasinensis* (15.9.86) ..	5·50	5·75
O19	$10 Scarlet Hibiscus (29.4.87)	6·00	6·25
O1/19	.. .. *Set of* 19	30·00	32·00

Norfolk Island

The stamps of TASMANIA were used on Norfolk Island from mid-1854 until May 1856, such use being identified by the "72" numeral cancellation. From 1877 the stamps of NEW SOUTH WALES were in regular use, being replaced by issues for AUSTRALIA from 1913 to 1947.

AUSTRALIAN ADMINISTRATION

PRINTERS. Nos. 1 to 42 were printed at the Note Printing Branch Reserve Bank of Australia (until 14 Jan 1960, known as the Note Printing Branch, Commonwealth Bank) by recess. See note at the beginning of Australia *re* imprints.

1 Ball Bay

1947 (10 June)–**59**. *Toned paper. P* 14.

1 **1** ½d. orange 35 15
 a. White paper (11.56) .. .. 1·50 2·50
2 1d. bright violet 50 15
 a. White paper (11.56) .. .. 6·50 9·00
3 1½d. emerald-green 50 20
 a. White paper (11.56) .. .. 12·00 15·00
4 2d. reddish violet 55 20
 a. White paper (11.56) £130 £120
5 2½d. scarlet 80 20
6 3d. chestnut 70 20
6*a* 3d. emerald-green (*white paper*) (6.7.59) 11·00 3·75
7 4d. claret 70 20
8 5½d. indigo 70 20
9 6d. purple-brown 70 20
10 9d. magenta 90 40
11 1s. grey-green 70 20
12 2s. yellow-bistre .. .. .. 4·00 1·00
12*a* 2s. deep blue (*white paper*) (6.7.59) .. 20·00 5·00
1/12*a* .. .. *Set of* 14 38·00 11·00

NOTE. Stamps of T **1**, perf 11, or in different colours, perf 11, are in the same category as those mentioned in Australia after No. 221.

2 Warder's Tower

3 Airfield

1953 (10 June). *T* **2**/**3** *and similar designs. P* 14½ × 15 (*vert*) *or* 15 × 14½ (*horiz*).

13 3½d. brown-lake .. .. 3·00 90
14 6½d. deep green .. .. 3·00 1·00
15 7½d. deep blue .. .. 4·00 3·00
16 8½d. chocolate .. .. 7·00 3·50
17 10d. reddish violet .. .. .. 5·00 75
18 5s. sepia .. .. 35·00 8·00
13/18 .. .. *Set of* 6 50·00 15·00

Designs: *Horiz* (*as T* **3**)—7½d. Old Stores (Crankmill); 5s. Bloody Bridge. *Vert* (*as T* **2**)—8½d. Barracks entrance; 10d. Salt House.

8 Norfolk Island Seal and Pitcairners Landing

Two types of 2s.:

Type I Type II

Alternate stamps on each horizontal row are with or without a dot in bottom right corner.

1956 (8 June). *Centenary of Landing of Pitcairn Islanders on Norfolk Island. P* 15 × 14½.

19 **8** 3d. deep bluish green 75 30
20 2s. violet (I) .. .. 1·50 50
 a. Type II .. .. 1·50 50
 b. Deep violet (I) .. .. .. 2·75 1·75
 ba. Type II .. .. 2·75 1·75

(9) (10) (11)

1958 (1 July). *Nos.* 15/16 *surch with T* **9**/**10**.

21 7d. on 7½d. deep blue .. .. .. 1·00 45
22 8d. on 8½d. chocolate .. .. .. 1·00 45

1959 (7 Dec). *150th Anniv of Australian Post Office. No.* 331 *of Australia surch with T* **11**.

23 5d. on 4d. slate (R.) 35 15

12 *Hibiscus insularis*

14 White Tern

16 Red Hibiscus

17 Queen Elizabeth II and Cereus

21 Rose Apple

22 Red-tailed Tropic Bird

(Design recess; centre typo (T **21**))

1960–62. *T* **12, 14, 16/17, 21/2** *and similar designs. P* 14½ *or* 14½ × 14 (10*s*.).

24 1d. bluish green (23.5.60) 15 10
25 2d. rose and myrtle-green (23.5.60) 20 10
26 3d. green (1.5.61) 70 15
27 5d. bright purple (20.6.60) 55 20
28 8d. red (20.6.60) 80 50
29 9d. ultramarine (23.5.60) 80 45
30 10d. brown and reddish violet (as No. 17) (27.2.61) .. .. 2·50 1·25
31 1s. 1d. carmine-red (16.10.61) 80 35
32 2s. sepia (1.5.61) .. .. 5·50 90
33 2s. 5d. deep violet (5.2.62) .. .. .. 1·00 40
34 2s. 8d. cinnamon and deep green (9.4.62) .. 2·00 55
35 5s. sepia and deep green (as No. 18) (27.2.61) 6·00 75
36 10s. emerald-green (14.8.61) (Optd S. £48) .. 48·00 20·00
24/36 .. .. *Set of* 13 60·00 23·00

Designs: *Vert* (*as T* **12**)—2d. *Lagunaria patersonii*; 5d. Lantana. (*As T* **21**); 1s. 1d. Fringed Hibiscus; 2s. 5d. Passion-flower. (*As T* **14**)—2s. Solander's Petrel.

Nos. 30 and 35 are redrawn.

The Specimen overprint on No. 36 is of similar status to those mentioned in the note at the beginning of Australia.

2/8

1/1 2/5

(23) (24) (25)

1960. *As Nos.* 13/15 *but colours changed, surch with T* **23**/**5**.

37 1s. 1d. on 3½d. deep ultramarine (26.9.60) 3·50 1·25
38 2s. 5d. on 6½d. bluish green (26.9.60) .. 3·50 1·25
39 2s. 8d. on 7½d. sepia (29.8.60) .. .. 7·00 2·25
37/9 .. .. *Set of* 3 12·50 4·25

26 Queen Elizabeth II and Map

27 "Tweed Trousers" (*Atypichthys latus*)

1960 (24 Oct). *Introduction of Local Government. P* 14.

40 **26** 2s. 8d. reddish purple .. .. .. 14·00 6·00

1960 (21 Nov). *Christmas. As No.* 328 *of Australia.*

41 5d. bright purple 60 30

1961 (20 Nov). *Christmas. As No.* 341 *of Australia.*

42 5d. slate-blue 30 20

PRINTERS. All the following issues to No. 233 were printed in photogravure by Harrison and Sons, Ltd, London except issues which are in the same designs as Australia, *and where otherwise stated.*

1962–63. *Fishes. Horiz designs as T* **27**. *P* 14½ × 14.

43 6d. sepia, yellow & dp bluish green (16.7.62) 1·00 25
44 11d. red-orange, brown and blue (25.2.63) .. 2·50 80
45 1s. blue, pink and yellow-olive (17.9.62) .. 1·00 25
46 1s. 3d. blue, red-brown and green (15.7.63) 2·50 1·00
47 1s. 6d. sepia, violet and light blue (6.5.63) .. 3·00 80
48 2s. 3d. dp blue, red & greenish yell (23.9.63) 3·00 80
43/8 .. .. *Set of* 6 11·50 3·50

Designs:—11d. "Trumpeter"; 1s. "Po'ov"; 1s. 3d. "Dreamfish"; 1s. 6d. "Hapoéka"; 2s. 3d. "Ophie" (*carangidae*).

1962 (19 Nov). *Christmas. As Nos.* 345 *of Australia.*

49 5d. ultramarine 30 15

1963 (11 Nov). *Christmas. As No.* 361 *of Australia.*

50 5d. red 25 15

33 Overlooking Kingston

37 Norfolk Pine

1964 (24 Feb–28 Sept). *Views. Horiz designs as T* **33**. *Multicoloured. P* 14½ × 14.

51 5d. Type **33** 50 15
52 8d. Kingston 75 20
53 9d. The Arches (Bumboras) (11.5) .. .. 1·75 15
54 10d. Slaughter Bay (28.9) .. .. .. 3·00 25
51/4 .. .. *Set of* 4 5·50 65

(Photo Note Ptg Branch, Reserve Bank of Australia, Melbourne)

1964 (1 July). *50th Anniv of Norfolk Island as Australian Territory. P* 13½.

55 **37** 5d. black, red and orange 10 10
56 8d. black, red and grey-green 15 10

1964 (9 Nov). *Christmas. As No.* 372 *of Australia.*

57 5d. green, blue, buff and violet 20 10

1965 (14 Apr). *50th Anniv of Gallipoli Landing. As T* **184** *of Australia, but slightly larger* (22 × 34½ *mm*). *Photo.*

58 5d. sepia, black and emerald 10 10

1965 (25 Oct). *Christmas. Helecon paper. As No.* 381 *of Australia.*

59 5d. multicoloured 10 10

(New Currency. 100 cents = $1 Australian)

38 *Hibiscus insularis*

39 Headstone Bridge

1966 (14 Feb). *Decimal currency. Various stamps surch in black on silver tablets, which vary slightly in size, obliterating old value as in T* **38**. *Surch typo.*

60 **38** 1 c. on 1d. bluish green (*value tablet* 4 × 5 *mm*) 20 10
 a. Value tablet larger, 5½ × 5½ mm 40 25
61 – 2 c. on 2d. rose and myrtle-green (No. 25) 20 10
62 **14** 3 c. on 3d. green 50 10
63 – 4 c. on 5d. bright purple (No. 27) .. 25 10
64 **16** 5 c. on 8d. red 30 10
65 – 10 c. on 10d. brown & reddish vio (No. 30) 40 15
66 – 15 c. on 1s. 1d. carmine-red (No. 31) .. 45 15
67 – 20 c. on 2s. sepia (No. 32) .. .. 3·50 1·50
68 – 25 c. on 2s. 5d. deep violet (No. 33) .. 1·25 40
69 **21** 30 c. on 2s. 8d. cinnamon and deep green 1·00 50
70 – 50 c. on 5s. sepia and deep green (No. 35) 4·50 75
71 **22** $1 on 10s. emerald-green (*value tablet* 7 × 6½ *mm*) .. .. .. 3·50 1·75
 a. Value tablet smaller, 6½ × 4 mm 3·50 1·75
60/71 .. .. *Set of* 12 14·00 5·00

1966 (27 June). *Horiz designs as T* **39**. *Multicoloured. P* 14½ × 14.

72 7 c. Type **39** 20 10
73 9 c. Cemetery Road 20 10

41 St. Barnabas' Chapel (interior)

42 St. Barnabas' Chapel (exterior)

1966 (23 Aug). *Centenary of Melanesian Mission. P* 14 × 14½.

74 **41** 4 c. multicoloured 10 10
75 **42** 25 c. multicoloured 15 10

43 Star over Philip Island

44 H.M.S. *Resolution*, 1774

(Des B.W.G. McCoy)

1966 (24 Oct). *Christmas. P* 14½.

76 **43** 4 c. multicoloured 10 10

(Des Harrison)

1967 (17 Apr)–**68.** *T* **44** *and similar horiz designs showing ships. Multicoloured. P* 14 × 14½.

77 1 c. Type **44** . . 10 10
78 2 c. *La Boussole* and *L'Astrolabe*, 1788 . . 15 10
79 3 c. H.M.S. *Supply*, 1788 . . 15 10
80 4 c. H.M.S. *Sirius*, 1790 . . 15 10
81 5 c. *Norfolk* (cutter), 1798 (14.8.67) . . 20 10
82 7 c. H.M.S. *Mermaid* (survey cutter), 1825 (14.8.67) . . 20 10
83 9 c. *Lady Franklin*, 1853 (14.8.67) . . 20 10
84 10 c. *Morayshire*, 1856 (14.8.67) . . 20 20
85 15 c. *Southern Cross*, 1866 (18.3.68) . . 45 30
86 20 c. *Pitcairn*, 1891 (18.3.68) . . 60 40
87 25 c. Norfolk Island whaleboat, 1895 (18.3.68) 1·00 50
88 30 c. *Iris* (cable ship), 1907 (18.6.68) . . 2·00 1·00
89 50 c. *Resolution*, 1926 (18.6.68) . . 3·00 1·75
90 $1 *Morinda*, 1931 (18.6.68) . . 5·50 2·50
77/90 . . *Set of* 14 12·50 6·25

1967 (7 June). *50th Anniv of Lions International. As No.* 411 *of Australia but colours changed.*
91 4 c. black, bluish green and olive-yellow . . 10 10

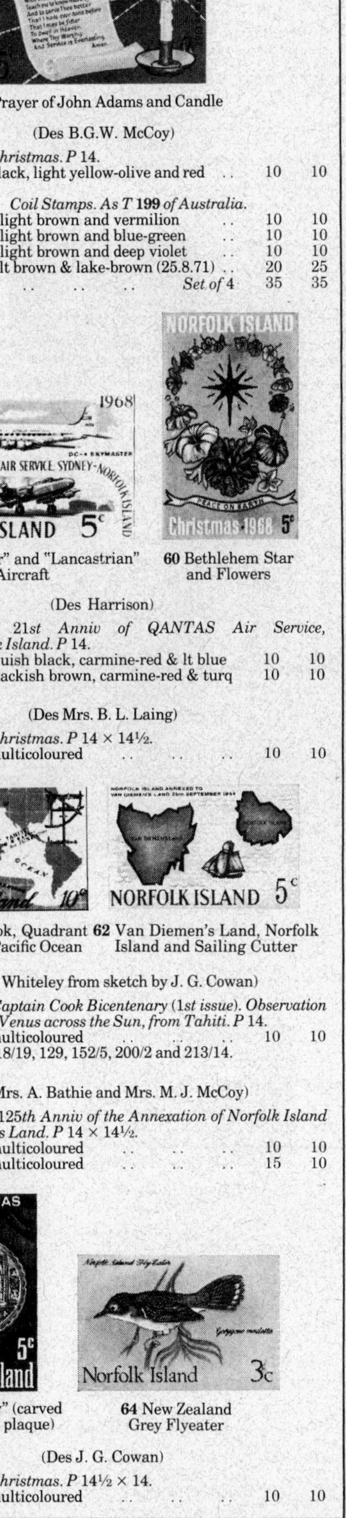

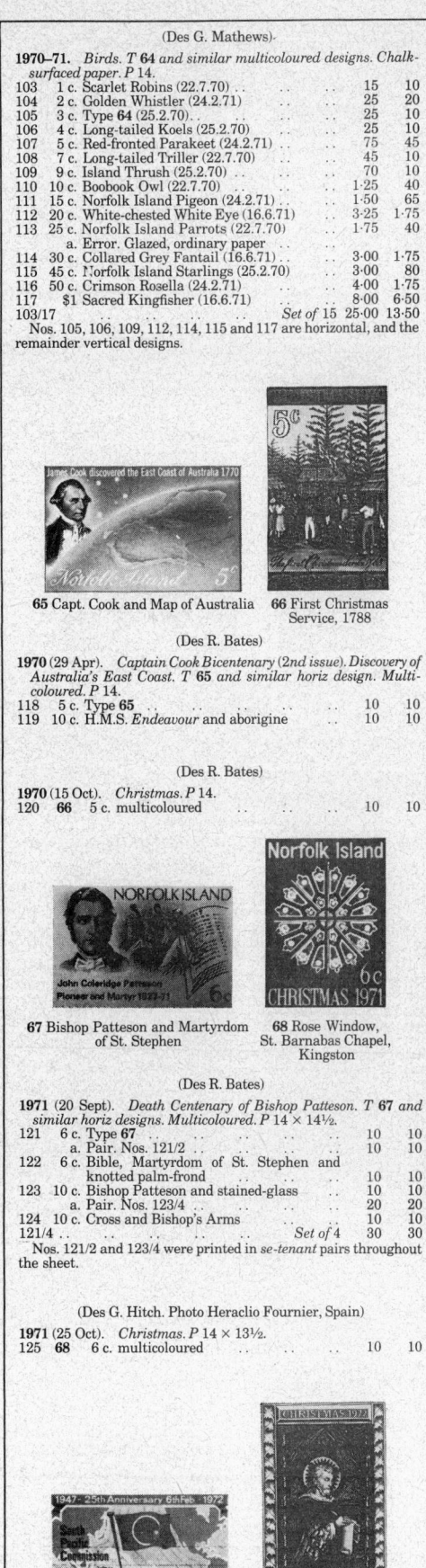

58 Prayer of John Adams and Candle

(Des B.G.W. McCoy)

1967 (16 Oct). *Christmas. P* 14.
92 **58** 5 c. black, light yellow-olive and red . . 10 10

1968 (5 Aug)–**71.** *Coil Stamps. As T* **199** *of Australia.*
93 3 c. black, light brown and vermilion . . 10 10
94 4 c. black, light brown and blue-green . . 10 10
95 5 c. black, light brown and deep violet . . 10 10
95*a* 6 c. black, lt brown & lake-brown (25.8.71) . . 20 25
93/5*a* . . *Set of* 4 35 35

59 "Skymaster" and "Lancastrian" Aircraft

60 Bethlehem Star and Flowers

(Des Harrison)

1968 (25 Sept). *21st Anniv of QANTAS Air Service, Sydney–Norfolk Island. P* 14.
96 **59** 5 c. bluish black, carmine-red & lt blue 10 10
97 7 c. blackish brown, carmine-red & turq 10 10

(Des Mrs. B. L. Laing)

1968 (24 Oct). *Christmas. P* 14 × 14½.
98 **60** 5 c. multicoloured . . 10 10

61 Captain Cook, Quadrant and Chart of Pacific Ocean

62 Van Diemen's Land, Norfolk Island and Sailing Cutter

(Des V. Whiteley from sketch by J. G. Cowan)

1969 (3 June). *Captain Cook Bicentenary (1st issue). Observation of the transit of Venus across the Sun, from Tahiti. P* 14.
99 **61** 10 c. multicoloured . . 10 10
See also Nos. 118/19, 129, 152/5, 200/2 and 213/14.

(Des Mrs. A. Bathie and Mrs. M. J. McCoy)

1969 (29 Sept). *125th Anniv of the Annexation of Norfolk Island to Van Diemen's Land. P* 14 × 14½.
100 **62** 5 c. multicoloured . . 10 10
101 30 c. multicoloured . . 15 10

63 "The Nativity" (carved mother-of-pearl plaque)

64 New Zealand Grey Flyeater

(Des J. G. Cowan)

1969 (27 Oct). *Christmas. P* 14½ × 14.
102 **63** 5 c. multicoloured . . 10 10

(Des G. Mathews)

1970–71. *Birds. T* **64** *and similar multicoloured designs. Chalk-surfaced paper. P* 14.
103 1 c. Scarlet Robins (22.7.70) . . 15 10
104 2 c. Golden Whistler (24.2.71) . . 25 20
105 3 c. Type **64** (25.2.70) . . 25 10
106 4 c. Long-tailed Koels (25.2.70) . . 25 10
107 5 c. Red-fronted Parakeet (24.2.71) . . 75 45
108 7 c. Long-tailed Triller (22.7.70) . . 45 10
109 9 c. Island Thrush (25.2.70) . . 70 10
110 10 c. Boobook Owl (22.7.70) . . 1·25 40
111 15 c. Norfolk Island Pigeon (24.2.71) . . 1·50 65
112 20 c. White-chested White Eye (16.6.71) . . 3·25 1·75
113 25 c. Norfolk Island Parrots (22.7.70) . . 1·75 40
a. Error. Glazed, ordinary paper . .
114 30 c. Collared Grey Fantail (16.6.71) . . 3·00 1·75
115 45 c. Norfolk Island Starlings (25.2.70) . . 3·00 80
116 50 c. Crimson Rosella (24.2.71) . . 4·00 1·75
117 $1 Sacred Kingfisher (16.6.71) . . 8·00 6·50
103/17 . . *Set of* 15 25·00 13·50
Nos. 105, 106, 109, 112, 114, 115 and 117 are horizontal, and the remainder vertical designs.

65 Capt. Cook and Map of Australia

66 First Christmas Service, 1788

(Des R. Bates)

1970 (29 Apr). *Captain Cook Bicentenary (2nd issue). Discovery of Australia's East Coast. T* **65** *and similar horiz design. Multicoloured. P* 14.
118 5 c. Type **65** . . 10 10
119 10 c. H.M.S. *Endeavour* and aborigine . . 10 10

(Des R. Bates)

1970 (15 Oct). *Christmas. P* 14.
120 **66** 5 c. multicoloured . . 10 10

67 Bishop Patteson and Martyrdom of St. Stephen

68 Rose Window, St. Barnabas Chapel, Kingston

(Des R. Bates)

1971 (20 Sept). *Death Centenary of Bishop Patteson. T* **67** *and similar horiz designs. Multicoloured. P* 14 × 14½.
121 6 c. Type **67** . . 10 10
a. Pair. Nos. 121/2 . . 10 10
122 6 c. Bible, Martyrdom of St. Stephen and knotted palm-frond . . 10 10
123 10 c. Bishop Patteson and stained-glass . . 10 10
a. Pair. Nos. 123/4 . . 20 20
124 10 c. Cross and Bishop's Arms . . 10 10
121/4 . . *Set of* 4 30 30
Nos. 121/2 and 123/4 were printed in *se-tenant* pairs throughout the sheet.

(Des G. Hitch. Photo Heraclio Fournier, Spain)

1971 (25 Oct). *Christmas. P* 14 × 13½.
125 **68** 6 c. multicoloured . . 10 10

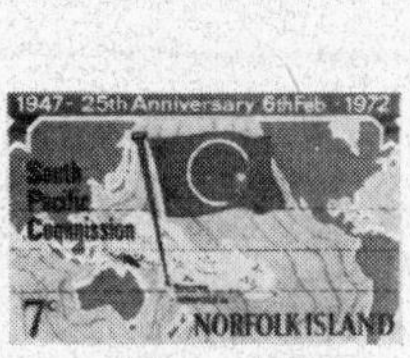

69 Map and Flag

70 "St. Mark" (stained-glass window, All Saints, Norfolk Is)

(Des G. Hitch)

1972 (7 Feb). *25th Anniv of South Pacific Commission. P* 14 × 14½.
126 **69** 7 c. multicoloured . . 15 10

(Des Mrs. M. J. McCoy)

1972 (16 Oct). *Christmas. P* 14.
127 **70** 7 c. multicoloured . . 10 10

71 Cross and Pines. (stained-glass window, All Saints Church)

72 H.M.S. *Resolution* in the Antarctic

(Des Harrison)

1972 (20 Nov). *Centenary of First Pitcairner-built Church. P* 14.
128 **71** 12 c. multicoloured . . 10 10
a. Purple (background to dates) omitted . .

(Des G. Hitch)

1973 (17 Jan). *Captain Cook Bicentenary (3rd issue). Crossing of the Antarctic Circle. P* 14.
129 **72** 35 c. multicoloured . . 3·00 1·75

73 Child and Christmas Tree

74 Protestant Clergyman's Quarters

(Des B. W. McCoy (T **73**), R. Westwood (35 c.))

1973 (22 Oct). *Christmas. T* **73** *and similar vert design. Multicoloured. P* 14.
130 7 c. Type **73** . . 20 10
131 12 c. Type **73** . . 25 10
132 35 c. Fir trees and star . . 70 80
130/2 . . *Set of* 3 1·00 90

(Des G. Hitch)

1973 (19 Nov)–**75.** *Historic Buildings. T* **74** *and similar horiz designs. Multicoloured. P* 14 × 14½.
133 1 c. Type **74** . . 10 10
134 2 c. Royal Engineers' Office (1.5.74) . . 10 10
135 3 c. Double Quarters for Free Overseers (19.2.75) . . 25 15
136 4 c. Guard House (12.7.74) . . 20 15
137 5 c. Entrance to Pentagonal Gaol . . 25 15
138 7 c. Pentagonal Gaol (1.5.74) . . 35 25
139 8 c. Prisoners' Barracks (19.2.75) . . 50 35
140 10 c. Officers' Quarters, New Military Barracks . . 50 35
141 12 c. New Military Barracks (1.5.74) . . 50 25
142 14 c. Beach Stores (12.7.74) . . 60 45
143 15 c. The Magazine (19.2.75) . . 80 50
144 20 c. Entrance, Old Military Barracks (12.7.74) 80 65
145 25 c. Old Military Barracks (19.2.75) . . 1·25 90
146 30 c. Old Stores (Crankmill) (1.5.74) . . 1·00 60
147 50 c. Commissariat Stores . . 1·25 1·75
148 $1 Government House (12.7.74) . . 2·25 3·50
133/48 . . *Set of* 16 9·00 9·00

75 Royal Couple and Map

(Des Harrison)

1974 (8 Feb). *Royal Visit. P* 14 × 14½.
149 **75** 7 c. multicoloured . . 40 15
150 25 c. multicoloured . . 1·25 75

76 Chichester's *Madame Elijah*

(Des B. McCoy. Litho State Bank Note Printing Works, Helsinki)

1974 (28 Mar). *First Aircraft Landing on Norfolk Island. P* 14.
151 **76** 14 c. multicoloured . . 1·00 70

MINIMUM PRICE

The minimum price quote is 10p which represents a handling charge rather than a basis for valuing common stamps. For further notes about prices see introductory pages.

77 "Captain Cook" (engraving by J. Basire)

78 Nativity Scene (pearl-shell pew carving)

(Des C. I. Buffett. Litho Questa)

1974 (8 Oct). *Captain Cook Bicentenary* (*4th issue*). *Discovery of Norfolk Is. T* **77** *and similar vert designs. Multicoloured. P* 14.

152 7 c. Type **77** .. .. 1·25 60
153 10 c. "H.M.S. *Resolution*" (H. Roberts) .. 2·25 1·40
154 14 c. Norfolk Island Pine .. .. .. 2·50 1·50
155 25 c. "Norfolk Island flax" (G. Raper) .. .. 3·00 2·25
152/5 .. .. *Set of* 4 8·00 5·25

(Des G. Hitch)

1974 (18 Oct). *Christmas. P* 14½.

156 **78** 7 c. multicoloured 15 10
157 30 c. multicoloured 60 75

79 Norfolk Pine

(Manufactured by Walsall)

1974 (16 Dec). *Centenary of Universal Postal Union. T* **79** *and similar "island"-shaped designs. Multicoloured. Imperf* (*backing-paper roul* 20). *Self-adhesive.*

158 10 c. Type **79** 35 40
159 15 c. Offshore islands 40 45
160 35 c. Crimson Rosella and Sacred Kingfisher 70 75
161 40 c. Pacific map 75 90
158/61 .. .. *Set of* 4 2·00 2·25
MS162 106 × 101 mm. Map of Norfolk Is. cut-to-shape with reduced-size replicas of Nos. 158/61 18·00 23·00

80 H.M.S. *Mermaid* (survey cutter)

(Manufactured by Walsall)

1975 (18 Aug). *150th Anniv of Second Settlement. T* **80** *and similar "island"-shaped design. Multicoloured. Imperf* (*backing-paper roul* 20). *Self-adhesive.*

163 10 c. Type **80** 25 20
164 35 c. Kingston, 1835 (from painting by T. Seller) 45 35

81 Star on Norfolk Island Pine

82 Memorial Cross

(Des Harrison)

1975 (6 Oct). *Christmas. P* 14.

165 **81** 10 c. multicoloured 15 10
166 15 c. multicoloured 20 10
167 35 c. multicoloured 30 35
165/7 .. .. *Set of* 3 60 45

(Des Harrison)

1975 (24 Nov). *Centenary of St. Barnabas Chapel. T* **82** *and similar horiz design. Multicoloured. P* 14.

168 30 c. Type **82** 20 15
169 60 c. Laying foundation stone and Chapel in 1975 .. .. 40 40

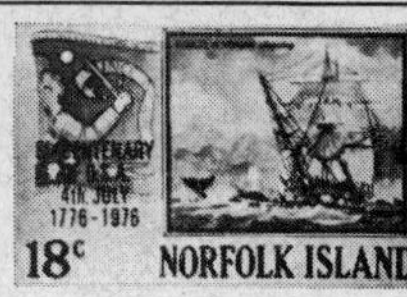

83 Launching of *Resolution*

84 Whaleship *Charles W. Morgan*

(Des Harrison)

1975 (1 Dec). *50th Anniv of Launching of Schooner "Resolution". T* **83** *and similar horiz design. Multicoloured. P* 14.

170 25 c. Type **83** 25 20
171 45 c. *Resolution* at sea 40 35

(Des Harrison)

1976 (5 July). *Bicentenary of American Revolution. T* **84** *and similar horiz designs. Multicoloured. P* 14.

172 18 c. Type **84** 25 15
173 25 c. Thanksgiving Service 35 20
174 40 c. "Flying Fortress" over Norfolk Is .. 65 35
175 45 c. California Quail 75 40
172/5 .. .. *Set of* 4 1·75 1·00

85 Swallow-tailed Tern and Sun

86 *Bassaris itea*

(Des Harrison)

1976 (4 Oct). *Christmas. P* 14.

176 **85** 18 c. multicoloured 25 15
177 25 c. multicoloured 40 15
178 45 c. multicoloured 85 35
176/8 .. .. *Set of* 3 1·40 60

(Des B. Hargreaves)

1976 (17 Nov)–**77**. *Butterflies and Moths. T* **86** *and similar horiz designs. Multicoloured. P* 14.

179 1 c. Type **86** 10 15
180 2 c. *Utetheisa pulchelloides vaga* (22.2.77) .. 10 15
181 3 c. *Agathia asterias jowettorum* (5.7.77) .. 10 10
182 4 c. *Cynthia kershawi* (5.7.77) 10 15
183 5 c. *Leucania loreyimima* 15 15
184 10 c. *Hypolimnas bolina nerina* 30 15
185 15 c. *Pyrrhorachis pyrrhogona subscrenulata* (22.2.77) 30 20
186 16 c. *Austrocarea iocephala millsi* 30 20
187 17 c. *Pseudocoremia christiani* (10.5.77) .. 35 20
188 18 c. *Cleora idiocrossa* 35 20
189 19 c. *Simplicia caeneusalis buffetti* (10.5.77) .. 35 20
190 20 c. *Austrocidaria ralstonae* (10.5.77) .. 40 20
191 30 c. *Hippotion scrofa* (22.2.77) 50 35
192 40 c. *Papilio ilioneus ilioneus* (10.5.77) .. 55 40
193 50 c. *Tiracola plagiata* (22.2.77) 70 50
194 $1 *Precis villida calybe* .. .. .. 1·00 75
195 $2 *Cepora perimale perimale* (5.7.77) .. 1·75 1·40
179/95 .. .. *Set of* 17 6·50 4·50

87 Queen's View, Kingston

(Des Harrison)

1977 (10 June). *Silver Jubilee. P* 14.

196 **87** 25 c. multicoloured 35 25

88 Hibiscus Flowers and Oil Lamp

89 Captain Cook (from a portrait by Nathaniel Dance)

(Des Mrs. M. J. McCoy)

1977 (4 Oct). *Christmas. P* 14 × 14½.

197 **88** 18 c. multicoloured 15 10
198 25 c. multicoloured 15 10
199 45 c. multicoloured 30 35
197/9 .. .. *Set of* 3 55 50

(Des Harrison)

1978 (18 Jan). *Captain Cook Bicentenary* (*5th issue*). *Discovery of Hawaii. T* **89** *and similar horiz designs. Multicoloured. P* 14½.

200 18 c. Type **89** 30 20
201 25 c. Discovery of Northern Hawaiian islands 40 30
202 80 c. British flag against island background .. 90 70
200/2 .. .. *Set of* 3 1·40 1·10

90 Guide Flag and Globe

(Manufactured by Walsall)

1978 (22 Feb). *50th Anniv of Girl Guides. T* **90** *and similar "island"-shaped designs. Multicoloured. Imperf* (*backing paper roul* 20). *Self-adhesive.*

203 18 c. Type **90** 20 15
204 25 c. Emblem and scarf badge 35 20
a. Horiz roul omitted (vert pair) ..
205 35 c. Emblem and Queen Elizabeth 45 25
a. Horiz roul omitted (vert pair) ..
206 45 c. Emblem and Lady Baden-Powell .. 55 35
203/6 .. .. *Set of* 4 1·40 85

Nos. 204a and 205a each come from sheets of 20 on which all the horizontal roulettes were omitted.

91 St. Edward's Crown

(Des Harrison)

1978 (29 June). *25th Anniv of Coronation. T* **91** *and similar horiz design. Multicoloured. P* 14½.

207 25 c. Type **91** 15 15
208 70 c. Coronation regalia 40 45

92 View of Duncombe Bay with Scout at Camp Fire

(Des S. Jensen. Manufactured by Walsall)

1978 (22 Aug). *50th Anniv of Boy Scouts. T* **92** *and similar "island"-shaped designs. Multicoloured. Imperf* (*backing paper roul* 20). *Self-adhesive.*

209 20 c. Type **92** 25 15
210 25 c. View from Kingston and emblem 40 20
211 35 c. View of Anson Bay and Link Badge .. 60 25
212 45 c. Sunset scene and Lord Baden-Powell .. 70 35
209/12 .. .. *Set of* 4 1·75 85

93 Chart showing Route of Arctic Voyage

94 Poinsettia and Bible

(Des G. Hitch)

1978 (29 Aug). *Captain Cook Bicentenary* (*6th issue*). *Northernmost Voyages. T* **93** *and similar horiz design. Multicoloured. P* 14½.

213 25 c. Type **93** 40 30
214 90 c. "H.M.S. *Resolution* and H.M.S. *Discovery* in Pack Ice" (painting by Webber) .. .. 1·25 80

(Des Mrs. M. J. McCoy)

1978 (3 Oct). *Christmas. T* **94** *and similar vert designs. Multicoloured. P* 14½ × 14.

215 20 c. Type **94** 15 10
216 30 c. Native Oak and Bible 20 15
217 55 c. Hibiscus and Bible 30 30
215/17 .. .. *Set of* 3 60 50

95 Cook and Village of Staithes near Marton

(Des Harrison)

1978 (27 Oct). *250th Birth Anniv of Captain Cook. T* **95** *and similar horiz design. Multicoloured. P* 14½.
218 20 c. Type **95** 35 25
219 80 c. Cook and Whitby Harbour .. .. 1·40 1·25

96 H.M.S. *Resolution* **97** Assembly Building

(Des G. Hitch)

1979 (14 Feb). *Death Bicentenary of Captain Cook. T* **96** *and similar horiz designs. Multicoloured. P* 14.
220 20 c. Type **96** 50 30
a. Pair. Nos. 220/1 .. .. 1·00 60
221 20 c. Cook (statue) 50 30
222 40 c. Cook's death 70 50
a. Pair. Nos. 222/3 .. .. 1·40 1·00
223 40 c. Cook's death (*different*) 70 50
220/23 .. .. *Set of* 4 2·40 1·60

The 20 c. designs depict the *Resolution* and Cook's statue on a map showing the last voyage. The 40 c. designs show Cook's death from an aquatint by John Clevely.

Nos. 220/1 and 222/3 were each printed together, *se-tenant*, in horizontal pairs throughout the sheets, forming composite designs.

1979 (10 Aug). *First Norfolk Island Legislative Assembly. P* 14½ × 14.
224 **97** $1 multicoloured 50 50

98 Tasmania 1853 1d. Stamp and Sir Rowland Hill

1979 (27 Aug). *Death Centenary of Sir Rowland Hill. T* **98** *and similar horiz designs showing stamps and Sir Rowland Hill. P* 14 × 14½.
225 20 c. new blue and sepia 20 10
226 30 c. brown-red and olive-grey 25 15
227 55 c. violet and indigo 40 30
225/7 .. .. *Set of* 3 75 50
MS228 142 × 91 mm. No. 227. P 14 .. .. 55 65
Designs:—30 c. Penny Red; 55 c. 1d. "Ball Bay".

99 I.Y.C. Emblem and Map of Pacific showing Norfolk Island as Pine Tree

(Des Claire Walters. Litho Asher and Co, Melbourne)

1979 (25 Sept). *International Year of the Child. P* 15.
229 **99** 80 c. multicoloured 40 45

100 Emily Bay **101** Lions International Emblem

1979 (5 Nov).* *Christmas. T* **100** *and similar horiz designs showing different aspects of Emily Bay. P* 12½ × 13.
230 15 c. multicoloured 15 15
a. Horiz strip of 3. Nos. 230/2 40
231 20 c. multicoloured 15 15
232 30 c. multicoloured 15 15
230/2 .. .. *Set of* 3 40 40
MS233 152 × 83 mm. Nos. 230/2. P 14 × 14½ .. 65 1·00

Nos. 230/2 were printed together, *se-tenant*, in horizontal strips of 3 throughout the sheet, forming a composite design.

*Although released by the Crown Agents in London on 2 October the stamps were not released locally until 5 November.

(Des Norfolk Island Lions Club. Litho Asher and Co, Melbourne)

1980 (25 Jan). *Lions Convention. P* 15.
234 **101** 50 c. multicoloured 35 30

102 Rotary International Emblem

(Des E. Lenthall. Litho Asher and Co, Melbourne)

1980 (21 Feb). *75th Anniv of Rotary International. P* 15.
235 **102** 50 c. multicoloured 35 30
a. Black (face value and "NORFOLK ISLAND") omitted .. .. ..

103 "D.H. 60 (Gypsy Moth)" *Mme Elijah*

(Des G. Hitch. Litho Harrison)

1980 (25 Mar)–**81**. *Aeroplanes. Horiz designs as T* **103**. *Multi-coloured. P* 14½ × 14.
236 1 c. Hawker Siddeley "H.S. 748" (3.3.81) .. 15 10
237 2 c. Type **103** 15 10
238 3 c. Curtis "P-40 Kittyhawk" 15 10
239 4 c. Chance Vought "F4U-1 Corsair" (19.8.80) 15 10
240 5 c. Grumman "TBF-1c Avenger" (19.8.80) .. 15 10
241 15 c. Douglas "SBD-5 Dauntless" (19.8.80) .. 20 20
242 20 c. Cessna "172" 25 25
243 25 c. Lockheed "Hudson" (3.3.81) 30 30
244 30 c. Lockheed "PV-1 Ventura" (13.1.81) .. 40 35
245 40 c. Avro "York" (3.3.81) 50 45
246 50 c. Douglas "DC-3" (13.1.81) 65 55
247 60 c. Avro "691 Lancastrian" (13.1.81) .. 75 65
248 80 c. Douglas "DC-4" (13.1.81) 95 85
249 $1 Beechcraft "Super King Air" (3.3.81) .. 1·25 90
250 $2 Fokker "F-27 Friendship" (19.8.80) .. 2·25 90
251 $5 Lockheed "C-130 Hercules" .. .. 5·50 2·00
236/51 .. .. *Set of* 16 12·00 6·50

104 Queen Elizabeth the Queen Mother

(Des K. Williams. Litho Harrison)

1980 (4 Aug). *80th Birthday of Queen Elizabeth the Queen Mother. P* 14.
252 **104** 22 c. multicoloured 30 20
253 60 c. multicoloured 65 40

105 Red-tailed Tropic Birds

(Des K. Williams. Litho Harrison)

1980 (28 Oct). *Christmas. Birds. T* **105** *and similar horiz designs. Multicoloured. P* 14 × 14½.
254 15 c. Type **105** 35 25
a. Horiz strip of 3. Nos. 254/6 95
255 22 c. White Terns 35 25
256 35 c. White-capped Noddys 35 25
257 60 c. White Terns (*different*) 60 45
254/7 .. .. *Set of* 4 1·50 1·10

Nos. 254/6 were printed together, *se-tenant*, in horizontal strips of 3 throughout the sheet.

106 *Morayshire* and View of Norfolk Island **107** Wedding Bouquet from Norfolk Island

(Des Jennifer Toombs. Litho Harrison)

1981 (5 June). *125th Anniv of Pitcairn Islanders' Migration to Norfolk Island. T* **106** *and similar horiz designs. Multicoloured. P* 14½.
258 5 c. Type **106** 15 15
259 35 c. Islanders arriving ashore 55 30
260 60 c. View of new settlement 85 45
258/60 .. .. *Set of* 3 1·40 80
MS261 183 × 127 mm. Nos. 258/60 .. .. 1·50 1·40

(Des J.W. Litho Harrison)

1981 (22 July). *Royal Wedding. T* **107** *and similar vert designs. Multicoloured. P* 14.
262 35 c. Type **107** 20 15
263 55 c. Prince Charles at horse trials 35 25
264 60 c. Prince Charles and Lady Diana Spencer 35 35
262/4 .. .. *Set of* 3 80 65

108 Uniting Church of Australia **109** Pair of White-chested White Eyes

(Des K. Williams. Litho Harrison)

1981 (15 Sept). *Christmas. Churches. T* **108** *and similar horiz designs. Multicoloured. P* 14½ × 14.
265 18 c. Type **108** 20 10
266 24 c. Seventh Day Adventist Church 25 15
267 30 c. Church of the Sacred Heart 30 20
268 $1 St. Barnabas Chapel 70 70
265/8 .. .. *Set of* 4 1·25 1·00

(Des P. Slater. Litho Questa)

1981 (10 Nov). *White-chested White Eye ("Silvereye"). T* **109** *and similar horiz designs. Multicoloured. P* 14 × 14½.
269 35 c. Type **109** 45 40
a. Horiz strip of 5. Nos. 269/73 .. .. 2·25
270 35 c. Bird on nest 45 40
271 35 c. Bird with egg 45 40
272 35 c. Parents with chicks 45 40
273 35 c. Fledgelings 45 40
269/73 .. .. *Set of* 5 2·25 2·00

Nos. 269/73 were printed together, *se-tenant*, in horizontal strips of 5 throughout the sheet.

110 Aerial View of Philip Island

(Des local artist. Litho Harrison)

1982 (12 Jan). *Philip and Nepean Islands. T* **110** *and similar horiz designs. Multicoloured. P* 14 × 13½.
274 24 c. Type **110** 25 25
a. Horiz strip of 5. Nos. 274/8 .. .. 1·10
275 24 c. Close-up view of Philip Island landscape 25 25
276 24 c. Gecko (*Phyllodactylus guentheri*), Philip Island 25 25
277 24 c. Sooty Tern (*Sterna fuscata*), Philip Island 25 25
278 24 c. Philip Island Hibiscus (*Hibiscus insularis*) 25 25
279 35 c. Aerial view of Nepean Island 35 35
a. Horiz strip of 5. Nos. 279/83 .. .. 1·60
280 35 c. Close-up view of Nepean Island landscape 35 35
281 35 c. Gecko (*Phyllodactylus guentheri*), Nepean Island 35 35
282 35 c. Blue-faced Boobies (*Sula dactylatra*), Nepean Island 35 35
283 35 c. *Carpobrotus glaucescens* (flower), Nepean Island 35 35
274/83 .. .. *Set of* 10 2·50 2·50

The five designs of each value were printed together, *se-tenant*, in horizontal strips of 5 throughout the sheet.

111 Sperm Whale

(Des Jennifer Toombs. Litho Harrison)

1982 (23 Feb). *Whales. T* **111** *and similar horiz designs. P* 14½.
284 24 c. multicoloured 45 35
285 55 c. multicoloured 85 75
286 80 c. black, mauve and stone .. .. .. 1·10 1·00
284/6 .. .. *Set of* 3 2·25 1·90
Designs:—55 c. Black Right Whale; 80 c. Humpback Whale.

MINIMUM PRICE

The minimum price quote is 10p which represents a handling charge rather than a basis for valuing common stamps. For further notes about prices see introductory pages.

112 *Diocet*, Wrecked 20 April 1873

(Litho Harrison)

1982 (18 May–27 July). *Shipwrecks. T* **112** *and similar horiz designs. Multicoloured. P* 14½ × 14.

287 24 c. H.M.S. *Sirius*, wrecked 19 March 1790 (27 July) 30 30
288 27 c. Type **112** 30 30
289 35 c. *Friendship*, wrecked 17 May 1835 (27 July) 40 40
290 40 c. *Mary Hamilton*, wrecked 6 May 1873 .. 50 50
291 55 c. *Fairlie*, wrecked 14 February 1840 (27 July) 65 70
292 65 c. *Warrigal*, wrecked 18 March 1918 .. 80 85
287/92 .. .. *Set of* 6 2·75 2·75

C-KURITY PAPER. The following issues up to No. 342 were all printed on this type of security paper, *unless otherwise stated.* It shows a pattern of blue fluorescent markings, resembling rosettes, on the reverse beneath the gum.

113 R.N.Z.A.F. "Hudson" dropping Christmas Supplies, 1942 — **114** 50th (Queen's Own) Regiment

(Des A. Theobald. Litho Walsall)

1982 (7 Sept). *Christmas. 40th Anniv of first Supply-plane Landings on Norfolk Island (Christmas Day 1942). T* **113** *and similar horiz designs. Multicoloured. P* 14.

293 27 c. Type **113** 30 35
294 40 c. "Hudson" landing Christmas supplies, 1942 .. .. 45 50
295 75 c. Christmas, 1942 .. .. 90 95
293/5 .. .. *Set of* 3 1·50 1·60

(Des W. Fenton. Litho Questa)

1982 (9 Nov). *Military Uniforms. T* **114** *and similar vert designs. Multicoloured. P* 14½ × 14.

296 27 c. Type **114** 30 35
297 40 c. 58th (Rutlandshire) Regiment 45 60
298 55 c. 80th (Staffordshire Volunteers) Battalion Company 65 80
299 65 c. 11th (North Devonshire) Regiment .. 80 1·00
296/9 .. .. *Set of* 4 2·00 2·50

115 *Panaeolus papilionaceus* — **116** Beechcraft "18" Aircraft

(Des Jane Thatcher. Litho Enschedé)

1983 (29 Mar). *Fungi. T* **115** *and similar vert designs. Multicoloured. P* 13½ × 13.

300 27 c. Type **115** 30 35
301 40 c. *Coprinus domesticus* 45 50
302 55 c. *Marasmius niveus* 65 70
303 65 c. *Cymatoderma elegans var. lamellatum* .. 80 85
300/3 .. .. *Set of* 4 2·00 2·25

(Des Walsall. Litho Format)

1983 (12 July). *Bicentenary of Manned Flight. T* **116** *and similar horiz designs. Multicoloured. P* 14½ × 14.

304 10 c. Type **116** 15 15
305 27 c. Fokker "F28 Fellowship" 30 35
306 45 c. French military "DC 4" 50 60
307 75 c. Sikorsky helicopter 90 95
304/7 .. .. *Set of* 4 1·60 1·90
MS308 105 × 100 mm. Nos. 304/7 .. .. 1·75 2·00

PRICES OF SETS

Set prices are given for many issues, generally those containing three stamps or more. Definitive sets include one of each value or major colour change, but do not cover different perforations, die types or minor shades. Where a choice is possible the set prices are based on the cheapest versions of the stamps included in the listings.

117 St. Matthew — **118** Cable Ship *Chantik*

(Des McCombie-Skinner Studio. Litho Format)

1983 (13 Sept). *Christmas. 150th Birth Anniv of Sir Edward Burne-Jones. T* **117** *and similar vert designs showing stained-glass windows from St. Barnabas Chapel, Norfolk Island. Multicoloured. P* 14.

309 5 c. Type **117** 10 10
310 24 c. St. Mark 30 30
311 30 c. Jesus Christ 40 40
312 45 c. St. Luke 55 55
313 85 c. St. John .. .. 1·10 1·10
309/13 .. .. *Set of* 5 2·25 2·25

(Des G. Drummond. Litho Format)

1983 (15 Nov). *World Communications Year. ANZCAN Cable. T* **118** *and similar horiz designs. Multicoloured. Ordinary paper. P* 14½ × 14.

314 30 c. Type **118** 40 40
315 45 c. *Chantik* during in-shore operations .. 55 55
316 75 c. Cable ship *Mercury* 95 95
317 85 c. Diagram of cable route .. .. .. 1·10 1·10
314/17 .. .. *Set of* 4 2·75 2·75

119 Popwood — **120** *Cheilodactylidae*

(Des I. Loe. Litho B.D.T.)

1984 (10 Jan–27 Mar). *Flowers. T* **119** *and similar vert designs. Multicoloured. P* 14.

318 1 c. Type **119** (27.3) 10 15
319 2 c. Strand Morning Glory 10 15
320 3 c. Native Phreatia 15 15
321 4 c. Philip Island Wisteria (27.3) 15 15
322 5 c. Norfolk Island Palm (27.3) 15 15
323 10 c. Evergreen 20 15
324 15 c. Bastard Oak (27.3) 30 20
325 20 c. Devil's Guts 35 25
326 25 c. White Oak 40 35
327 30 c. Ti (27.3) 55 40
328 35 c. Philip Island Hibiscus (27.3) 55 40
329 40 c. Native Wisteria 60 45
330 50 c. Native Jasmine 75 50
331 $1 Norfolk Island Hibiscus (27.3) .. .. 1·10 1·00
332 $3 Native Oberonia (27.3) .. .. .. 3·00 2·75
333 $5 Norfolk Island Pine .. .. .. 4·00 4·00
318/33 .. .. *Set of* 16 11·00 10·00

(Des Marg Towt. Litho Cambec Press, Melbourne)

1984 (17 Apr). *Reef Fishes. T* **120** *and similar horiz designs. Multicoloured. Ordinary paper. P* 13½ × 14.

334 30 c. Type **120** 40 45
335 45 c. *Pseudopeneus signatus* 60 65
336 75 c. *Acanthuridae* .. .. 1·00 1·10
337 85 c. *Chaeton ancinetus* .. .. 1·25 1·40
334/7 .. .. *Set of* 4 2·75 3·25

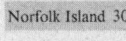

121 Owl with Eggs — **122** 1953 7½d. and 1974 Cook Bicent 10 c. Stamps

(Des P. Slater. Litho Questa)

1984 (17 July). *Boobook Owl. T* **121** *and similar vert designs. Multicoloured. P* 14.

338 30 c. Type **121** 55 50
a. Horiz strip of 5. Nos. 338/42 .. .. 2·50
339 30 c. Fledgeling 55 50
340 30 c. Young owl on stump 55 50
341 30 c. Adult on branch 55 50
342 30 c. Owl in flight 55 50
338/42 .. .. *Set of* 5 2·50 2·25

Nos. 338/42 were printed together, *se-tenant*, in horizontal strips of 5 throughout the sheet.

(Des D. Miller. Litho Harrison)

1984 (18 Sept). *"Ausipex" International Stamp Exhibition, Melbourne. T* **122** *and similar horiz designs. Multicoloured. W* w **14** (*sideways*). *P* 14.

343 30 c. Type **122** 30 35
344 45 c. John Buffett commemorative postal stationery envelope 45 55
345 75 c. Design from Presentation Pack for 1982 Military Uniforms issue .. .. .. 90 1·25
343/5 .. .. *Set of* 3 1·50 2·00
MS346 151 × 93 mm. Nos. 343/5. P 14½ .. .. 2·10 2·50

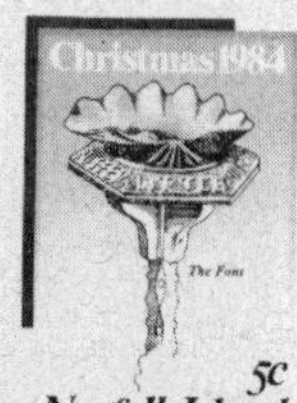

123 Font, Kingston Methodist Church — **124** The Revd. Nobbs teaching Pitcairn Islanders

(Des R. Murphy. Litho Questa)

1984 (9 Oct). *Christmas. Centenary of Methodist Church on Norfolk Island. T* **123** *and similar vert designs. Multicoloured. W* w **14**. *P* 14.

347 5 c. Type **123** 10 10
348 24 c. Church service in Old Barracks, Kingston, late 1800's 35 40
349 30 c. The Revd. & Mrs. A. H. Phelps and sailing ship 40 45
350 45 c. The Revd. A. H. Phelps and First Congregational Church, Chester, U.S.A. .. 60 65
351 85 c. Interior of Kingston Methodist Church .. 1·25 1·40
347/51 .. .. *Set of* 5 2·40 2·50

(Des D. Hopkins. Litho B.D.T.)

1984 (6 Nov). *Death Centenary of the Revd. George Hunn Nobbs (leader of Pitcairn community). T* **124** *and similar vert designs. Multicoloured. W* w **14**. *P* 14 × 15.

352 30 c. Type **124** 40 45
353 45 c. The Revd. Nobbs with sick islander .. 60 65
354 75 c. Baptising baby .. .. 1·00 1·10
355 85 c. Presented to Queen Victoria, 1852 .. 1·25 1·40
352/5 .. .. *Set of* 4 3·00 3·25

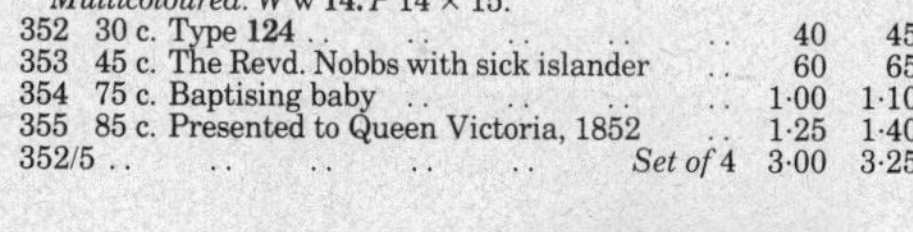

125 *Fanny Fisher* — **126** The Queen Mother (from photo by Norman Parkinson)

(Des D. Hopkins. Litho Cambec Press, Melbourne)

1985 (19 Feb). *19th-Century Whaling Ships (1st series). T* **125** *and similar horiz designs. Multicoloured. P* 13½ × 14.

356 5 c. Type **125** 20 10
357 33 c. *Costa Rica Packet* 55 40
358 50 c. *Splendid* 80 75
359 90 c. *Onward* .. .. 1·25 1·50
356/9 .. .. *Set of* 4 2·50 2·50

See also Nos. 360/3.

(Des D. Hopkins. Litho Cambec Press, Melbourne)

1985 (30 Apr). *19th-Century Whaling Ships (2nd series). Horiz designs as T* **125**. *Multicoloured. P* 13½ × 14.

360 15 c. *Waterwitch* 40 25
361 20 c. *Canton* 50 35
362 60 c. *Aladdin* .. .. 1·10 85
363 80 c. *California* .. .. 1·40 1·40
360/3 .. .. *Set of* 4 3·00 2·50

(Des A. Theobald ($1), C. Abbott (others). Litho Questa)

1985 (6 June). *Life and Times of Queen Elizabeth the Queen Mother. T* **126** *and similar vert designs. Multicoloured. W* w **16**. *P* 14½ × 14.

364 5 c. The Queen Mother (from photo by Dorothy Wilding) 10 10
365 33 c. With Princess Anne at Trooping the Colour 35 40
366 50 c. Type **126** 50 55
367 90 c. With Prince Henry at his christening (from photo by Lord Snowdon) .. .. 95 1·00
364/7 .. .. *Set of* 4 1·75 1·90
MS368 91 × 73 mm. $1 With Princess Anne at Ascot Races. Wmk sideways .. .. 1·10 1·25

127 "Swimming" — **128** Prize-winning Cow and Owner

(Des from children's paintings. Litho Cambec Press, Melbourne)

1985 (9 July). *International Youth Year. T* **127** *and similar horiz design. Multicoloured. P* 13½ × 14.
369 33 c. Type **127** 60 40
370 50 c. "A Walk in the Country" 90 55

(Des Flett Henderson & Arnold. Litho Cambec Press, Melbourne)

1985 (10 Sept). *125th Anniv of Royal Norfolk Island Agricultural and Horticultural Show. T* **128** *and similar horiz design. Multicoloured. P* 13½ × 14.
371 80 c. Type **128** 75 80
372 90 c. Show exhibits 85 90
MS373 132 × 85 mm. Nos. 371/2 .. .. .. 1·60 2·00

129 Shepherds with Flock **130** Long-spined Sea Urchin

(Des R. Murphy. Litho Cambec Press, Melbourne)

1985 (3 Oct). *Christmas. T* **129** *and similar vert designs. Multicoloured. P* 13½.
374 27 c. Type **129** 50 30
375 33 c. Mary and Joseph with donkey 60 40
376 50 c. The Three Wise Men 80 55
377 90 c. The Nativity .. .. 1·25 90
374/7 .. .. *Set of* 4 2·75 1·90

(Des L. Curtis. Litho Cambec Press, Melbourne)

1986 (14 Jan). *Marine Life. T* **130** *and similar horiz designs. Multicoloured. P* 13½ × 14.
378 5 c. Type **130** 10 10
379 33 c. Blue Starfish 30 35
380 55 c. Eagle Ray 50 55
381 75 c. Moray Eel 70 75
378/81 .. .. *Set of* 4 1·40 1·60
MS382 100 × 95 mm. Nos. 378/81 .. .. 1·75 2·00

131 *Giotto* Spacecraft **132** Isaac Robinson (U.S. Consul 1887–1908)

(Des G. Revell. Litho Leigh-Mardon Ltd, Melbourne)

1986 (11 Mar). *Appearance of Halley's Comet. T* **131** *and similar vert design. Multicoloured. P* 14½ × 15.
383 $1 Type **131** .. .. 1·50 1·25
a. Horiz pair. Nos. 383/4 .. .. .. 3·00 2·50
384 $1 Halley's Comet .. .. 1·50 1·25

Nos. 383/4 were printed together, *se-tenant*, in horizontal pairs throughout the sheet, each pair forming a composite design.

(Des G. Revell. Litho Cambec Press, Melbourne)

1986 (22 May). *"Ameripex '86" International Stamp Exhibition, Chicago. T* **132** *and similar multicoloured designs. P* 13½.
385 33 c. Type **132** 60 35
386 50 c. Ford "Model T" (first vehicle on island) (*horiz*) 80 50
387 80 c. Statue of Liberty .. .. .. 1·10 80
385/7 .. .. *Set of* 3 2·25 1·50
MS388 125 × 100 mm. Nos. 385/7 .. .. 2·25 2·50

No. 387 also commemorates the Centenary of the Statue of Liberty.

133 Princess Elizabeth and Dog **134** Stylized Dove and Norfolk Island

(Des Allison Ryves. Litho Cambec Press, Melbourne)

1986 (12 June). *60th Birthday of Queen Elizabeth II. T* **133** *and similar vert designs. Multicoloured. P* 13½.
389 5 c. Type **133** 10 10
390 33 c. Queen Elizabeth II 35 35
391 80 c. Opening Norfolk Island Golf Club .. 85 85
392 90 c. With Duke of Edinburgh in carriage .. 90 90
389/92 .. .. *Set of* 4 2·00 2·00

(Des Lyn Studham. Litho Cambec Press, Melbourne)

1986 (23 Sept). *Christmas. P* 13½ × 14.
393 **134** 30 c. multicoloured 25 30
394 40 c. multicoloured 35 40
395 $1 multicoloured 90 95
393/5 .. .. *Set of* 3 1·40 1·50

135 British Convicts, 1787 **136** Stone Tools

(Des Josephine Martin. Litho Cambec Press, Melbourne)

1986 (14 Oct–16 Dec). *Bicentenary of Norfolk Island Settlement* (1988) (*1st issue*). *Governor Phillip's Commission. T* **135** *and similar vert designs. Multicoloured. P* 14 × 13½.
396 36 c. Type **135** 60 35
397 55 c. Judge passing sentence of transportation 90 55
398 90 c. Governor Phillip meeting Home Secretary (inscr "Home Society") .. .. 1·40 85
399 90 c. As No. 398, but correctly inscr "Home Secretary" (16.12) .. .. 1·40 85
400 $1 Captain Arthur Phillip .. .. .. 1·60 95
396/400 .. .. *Set of* 5 5·50 3·25

See also Nos. 401/4, 421/4, 433/5, 436/7 and 438/43.

(Des B. Clinton. Litho Cambec Press, Melbourne)

1986 (16 Dec). *Bicentenary of Norfolk Island Settlement* (1988) (*2nd issue*). *Pre-European Occupation. T* **136** *and similar horiz designs. Multicoloured. P* 13½.
401 36 c. Type **136** 65 35
402 36 c. Bananas and taro 65 35
403 36 c. Polynesian outrigger canoe 65 35
404 36 c. Maori chief 65 35
401/4 .. .. *Set of* 4 2·40 1·25

137 Philip Island from Point Ross **138** Male Red-fronted Parakeet

(Des C. Abbott. Litho CPE Australia Ltd, Melbourne)

1987 (17 Feb)–**88**. *Norfolk Island Scenes. T* **137** *and similar square designs. Multicoloured. P* 13½.
405 1 c. Cockpit Creek Bridge (17.5.88) .. 10 10
406 2 c. Cemetery Bay Beach (17.5.88) .. 10 10
407 3 c. Island guesthouse (17.5.88) 10 10
408 5 c. Type **137** 10 10
409 15 c. Cattle in pasture (27.7.87) 10 15
410 30 c. Rock fishing (7.4.87) 25 30
411 37 c. Old Pitcairner-style house (27.7.87) .. 30 35
412 40 c. Shopping centre (7.4.87) 35 40
413 50 c. Emily Bay 40 45
414 60 c. Bloody Bridge (27.7.87) 50 55
415 80 c. Pitcairner-style shop (7.4.87) 65 70
416 90 c. Government House 75 80
417 $1 Melanesian Memorial Chapel 85 90
418 $2 Convict Settlement, Kingston (7.4.87) .. 1·60 1·75
419 $3 Ball Bay (27.7.87) .. .. .. 2·50 2·75
420 $5 Northern cliffs (17.5.88) .. .. 4·25 4·50
405/20 .. .. *Set of* 16 11·50 12·50

(Des Josephine Martin. Litho CPE Australia Ltd, Melbourne)

1987 (13 May). *Bicentenary of Norfolk Island Settlement* (1988) (*3rd issue*). *The First Fleet. Vert designs as T* **135**. *Multicoloured. P* 14 × 13½.
421 5 c. Loading supplies, Deptford 15 15
422 55 c. Fleet leaving Spithead 90 75
a. Horiz pair. Nos. 422/3 .. .. .. 1·75 1·50
423 55 c. H.M.S. *Sirius* leaving Spithead 90 75
424 $1 Female convicts below decks .. .. 1·50 1·25
421/4 .. .. *Set of* 4 3·00 2·75

Nos. 422/3 were printed together, *se-tenant*, in horizontal pairs throughout the sheet, forming a composite design.

(Des P. Slater. Litho CPE Australia Ltd, Melbourne)

1987 (16 Sept). *Red-fronted Parakeet* (*"Green Parrot"*). *T* **138** *and similar vert designs. Multicoloured. P* 14 × 13½.
425 5 c. Type **138** 25 25
a. Horiz strip of 4. Nos. 425/8 .. .. 1·60
426 15 c. Adult with fledgeling and egg 35 35
427 36 c. Young parakeets 50 50
428 55 c. Female parakeet 70 70
425/8 .. .. *Set of* 4 1·60 1·60

Nos. 425/8 were printed together, *se-tenant*, in horizontal strips of four throughout the sheet.

139 Christmas Tree and Restored Garrison Barracks **140** Airliner, Container Ship and Sydney Harbour Bridge

(Des T. Bland and Alison Ryves. Litho CPE Australia Ltd, Melbourne)

1987 (13 Oct). *Christmas. T* **139** *and similar horiz designs. Multicoloured. P* 13½ × 14.
429 30 c. Type **139** 25 30
430 42 c. Children opening presents 35 40
431 58 c. Father Christmas with children .. 50 55
432 63 c. Children's party 55 60
429/32 .. .. *Set of* 4 1·50 1·60

(Des Josephine Martin. Litho CPE Australia Ltd, Melbourne)

1987 (8 Dec). *Bicentenary of Norfolk Island Settlement* (1988) (*4th issue*). *Visit of La Perouse* (*navigator*). *Vert designs as T* **135**. *Multicoloured. P* 14 × 13½.
433 37 c. La Perouse with King Louis XVI .. 45 45
434 90 c. *L'Astrolabe* and *La Boussole* off Norfolk Island .. .. 1·00 1·00
435 $1 *L'Astrolabe* wrecked in Solomon Islands 1·25 1·25
433/5 .. .. *Set of* 3 2·40 2·40

(Des Josephine Martin. Litho CPE Australia Ltd, Melbourne)

1988 (25 Jan). *Bicentenary of Norfolk Island Settlement* (*5th issue*). *Arrival of First Fleet at Sydney. Vert designs as T* **135**. *Multicoloured. P* 14 × 13½.
436 37 c. Ship's cutter approaching Port Jackson 50 50
437 $1 Landing at Sydney Cove .. .. 1·40 1·40

(Des Josephine Martin. Litho CPE Australia Ltd, Melbourne)

1988 (4 Mar). *Bicentenary of Norfolk Island Settlement* (*6th issue*). *Foundation of First Settlement. Vert designs as T* **135**. *Multicoloured. P* 14 × 13½.
438 5 c. Lt. Philip Gidley King 10 10
439 37 c. Raising the flag, March 1788 .. .. 45 45
440 55 c. King exploring 60 60
441 70 c. Landing at Sydney Bay, Norfolk Island 75 75
442 90 c. H.M.S. *Supply* (brig) .. .. .. 1·00 1·00
443 $1 Sydney Bay settlement, 1788 .. .. 1·25 1·25
438/43 .. .. *Set of* 6 3·75 3·75

(Des Janet Boschen. Litho CPE Australia Ltd, Melbourne)

1988 (30 July). *"Sydpex '88" National Stamp Exhibition, Sydney. T* **140** *and similar multicoloured designs. P* 14 × 13½ (*vert*) *or* 13½ × 14 (*horiz*).
444 37 c. Type **140** 35 40
445 37 c. Exhibition label under magnifying glass (*horiz*) 35 40
446 37 c. Telephone and dish aerial 35 40
444/6 .. .. *Set of* 6 95 1·10
MS447 118 × 84 mm. Nos. 444/6 .. .. 1·00 1·25

In No. **MS**447 the horizontal design is perforated 14 at foot and 13½ on the other three sides.

141 Flowers and Decorations **142** Pier Store and Boat Shed

(Des Sue Pearson. Litho CPE Australia Ltd, Melbourne)

1988 (27 Sept). *Christmas. T* **141** *and similar vert designs. Multicoloured. P* 14 × 13½.
448 30 c. Type **141** 30 35
449 42 c. Flowers 40 45
450 58 c. Fishes and beach 55 60
451 63 c. Norfolk Island 60 65
448/51 .. .. *Set of* 4 1·60 1·90

(Des R. Murphy. Litho CPE Australia Ltd, Melbourne)

1988 (6 Dec). *Restored Buildings from the Convict Era. T* **142** *and similar horiz designs. Multicoloured. P* 13½ × 14.
452 39 c. Type **142** 35 40
453 55 c. Royal Engineers Building 50 55
454 90 c. Old Military Barracks 85 90
455 $1 Commissariat Store and New Military Barracks .. .. 95 1·00
452/5 .. .. *Set of* 4 2·40 2·50

143 *Lamprima aenea* **144** H.M.S. *Bounty* off Tasmania

(Des T. Nolan. Litho CPE Australia Ltd, Melbourne)

1989 (14 Feb). *Endemic Insects. T* **143** *and similar horiz designs. Multicoloured. P* 13½ × 14.

456	39 c. Type **143**	35	40
457	55 c. *Insulascirtus nythos*	50	55
458	90 c. *Caedicia araucariae*	85	90
459	$1 *Thrincophora aridela*	95	1·00
456/9	*Set of* 4	2·40	2·50

(Des C. Abbott. Litho CPE Australia Ltd, Melbourne (Nos. 460/3), B.D.T. (No. **MS**464))

1989 (28 Apr). *Bicentenary of the Mutiny on the* Bounty. *T* **144** *and similar horiz designs. Multicoloured. P* 13½.

460	5 c. Type **144**	15	15
461	39 c. Mutineers and Polynesian women, Pitcairn Island	50	50
462	55 c. Lake Windermere, Cumbria (Christian's home county)	70	70
463	$1.10, "Mutineers casting Bligh adrift" (Robert Dodd)	1·40	1·40
460/3	*Set of* 4	2·50	2·50
MS464	110×85 mm. 39 c. No. 461; 90 c. Isle of Man 1989 35p. Mutiny stamp; $1 Pitcairn Islands 1989 Settlement Bicent 90 c., No. 345. P 14	2·50	2·50

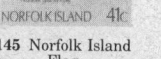

145 Norfolk Island Flag

146 Red Cross

(Des R. Fletcher. Litho CPE Australia Ltd, Melbourne)

1989 (10 Aug). *10th Anniv of Internal Self-Government. T* **145** *and similar vert designs. Multicoloured. P* 14×13½.

465	41 c. Type **145**	55	55
466	55 c. Old ballot box	65	65
467	$1 Norfolk Island Act, 1979	1·25	1·25
468	$1.10, Island crest	1·40	1·40
465/8	*Set of* 4	3·50	3·50

(Des E. Lenthall. Litho CPE Australia Ltd, Melbourne)

1989 (25 Sept). *75th Anniv of Red Cross on Norfolk Island. P* 13½.

469	**146** $1 bright rose-red and ultramarine	1·25	1·25

147 "Gethsemane"

148 John Royle (first announcer)

(Des Sue Pearson. Litho CPE Australia Ltd, Melbourne)

1989 (9 Oct). *Christmas. T* **147** *and similar horiz designs showing opening lines of hymns and local scenes. Multicoloured. P* 13½×14.

470	36 c. Type **147**	35	40
471	60 c. "In the Sweet Bye and Bye"	55	60
472	75 c. "Let the Lower Lights Be Burning"	70	75
473	80 c. "The Beautiful Stream"	75	80
470/3	*Set of* 4	2·10	2·25

(Des Philatelic Studios. Litho Leigh-Mardon Ltd, Melbourne)

1989 (21 Nov). *50th Anniv of Radio Australia. T* **148** *and similar vert designs each showing Kingston buildings. Multicoloured. P* 14×13½.

474	41 c. Type **148**	40	45
475	65 c. Radio waves linking Australia and Norfolk Island	60	65
476	$1.10, Anniversary kookaburra logo	1·00	1·10
474/6	*Set of* 3	1·75	2·00

149 H.M.S. *Bounty* on fire, Pitcairn Island, 1790

150 H.M.S. *Sirius* striking Reef

(Des G. Hitch. Litho Leigh-Mardon Ltd, Melbourne)

1990 (23 Jan). *History of the Norfolk Islanders (1st series). Settlement on Pitcairn Island. T* **149** *and similar vert design. Multicoloured. P* 14½.

477	70 c. Type **149**	65	70
478	$1.10, Arms of Norfolk Island	1·00	1·10

(Des Maree Edmiston. Litho Leigh-Mardon Ltd, Melbourne)

1990 (19 Mar). *Bicentenary of Wreck of H.M.S.* Sirius. *T* **150** *and similar horiz designs. Multicoloured. P* 13½.

479	41 c. Type **150**	40	45
	a. Horiz pair. Nos. 479/80	80	90
480	41 c. H.M.S. *Sirius* failing to clear bay	40	45
481	65 c. Divers at work on wreck	60	65
482	$1 Recovered artifacts and chart of site	95	1·00
479/82	*Set of* 4	2·10	2·25

Nos. 479/80 were printed together, *se-tenant*, in horizontal pairs throughout the sheet, each pair forming a composite design.

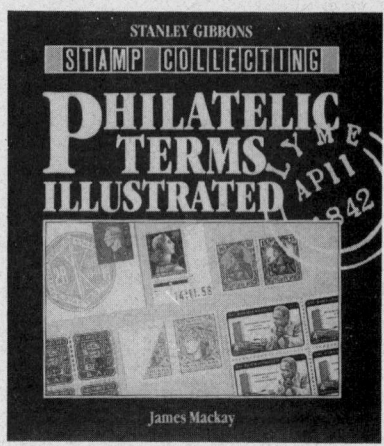

North Borneo

PRICES FOR STAMPS ON COVER TO 1945	
No. 1	from × 100
Nos. 2/3	from × 10
Nos. 4/5	—
Nos. 6/19	from × 10
Nos. 19b/21b	—
Nos. 22/8	from × 50
Nos. 29/35	—
Nos. 36/44	from × 100
Nos. 45/50	—
Nos. 51/2	from × 10
No. 54	—
Nos. 55/65	from × 10
Nos. 66/79	from × 4
Nos. 81/6	—
Nos. 87/91	from × 12
Nos. 92/111	from × 4
Nos. 112/26	from × 10
Nos. 127/40	from × 6
Nos. 141/5	—
Nos. 146/57	from × 5
Nos. 158/79	from × 8
Nos. 181/5	—
Nos. 186/8	from × 10
Nos. 189/230	from × 4
Nos. 231/4	—
Nos. 235/49	from × 3
Nos. 250/2	—
Nos. 253/75	from × 12
Nos. 276/92	from × 7
Nos. 293/4	—
Nos. 295/300	from × 6
Nos. 301/2	—
Nos. 303/17	from × 3
Nos. 318/19	from × 20
Nos. 320/34	from × 3
Nos. D1/26	from × 20
Nos. D27/8	—
Nos. D29/35	from × 7
No. D35a	—
Nos. D36/65	from × 20
Nos. D66/70	from × 5

BRITISH NORTH BORNEO COMPANY ADMINISTRATION

PRINTERS. The stamps of this country up to 1894 were designed by T. Macdonald and printed in lithography by Blades, East and Blades, London.

1

8 Cents.

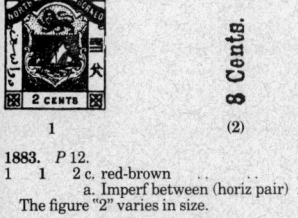

(2)

EIGHT CENTS

(3)

1883. *P* 12.
1 **1** 2 c. red-brown .. .. 15·00 27·00
a. Imperf between (horiz pair) .. ..

The figure "2" varies in size.

1883. *No.* 1 *surch as T* **2** *or* **3**.
2 **2** 8 c. on 2 c. red-brown £800 £650
3 **3** 8 c. on 2 c. red-brown £350 £150
a. Surch double .. .. .. — £3000

Type **2** was handstamped and stamps without stop are generally forgeries. Type **3** was a setting of 50 (10 × 5) providing ten varieties; it normally has a stop which sometimes failed to print.

CANCELLED-TO-ORDER—Prices are separately indicated in a third price column, for stamps showing the recognisable black bars remainder cancellation. The issues since 1916 have not been thus cancelled.

It should be noted, however, that a postmark of this form was in use for postal purposes up to this period, and was used at one or two of the smaller post-offices until 1949. A small oval with five bars was used to mark railway mail during 1945/55 and also as a paquebot mark at Jesselton *c.* 1950.

4

5

and Revenue

(6)

1883. *P* 14.
4 **4** 50 c. violet .. .. .. 60·00 — 10·00
a. "ΓIFTY" (R.5/2) .. .. £375 — £100
5 **5** $1 scarlet .. .. .. 45·00 — 7·50

1883. *P* 12.
6 **1** 4 c. pink .. .. 16·00 28·00
a. Imperf (horiz pair) .. .. .. † —
7 8 c. green .. .. 29·00 35·00

1886. *P* 14.
8 **1** ½ c. magenta .. .. 38·00 85·00
9 1 c. orange £130 £170
a. Imperf (pair) £225
b. Imperf horiz (vert pair) .. ..
10 2 c. brown .. .. 11·00 12·00
a. Imperf between (pair) £450
11 4 c. pink .. .. 11·00 28·00
12 8 c. green .. .. 11·00 28·00
a. Imperf between (horiz pair) £700
13 10 c. blue .. .. 11·00 26·00
a. Imperf (pair) £225
8/13 .. .. *Set of* 6 £190 £300

Imperforate examples of the 4 c. pink are listed under No. 6a.

1886. *Nos.* 8 *and* 13 *optd with T* **6**.
14 ½ c. magenta .. .. 45·00 £100
15 10 c. blue .. .. 80·00 £130

3 CENTS (7)

5 CENTS (8)

3 CENTS Small "3" variety (R.3/1, 3/4, 3/7)

(Surchd by *North Borneo Herald*, Sandakan)

1886. *T* **1** *surch as T* **7/8**. (*a*) *P* 12.
16 **7** 3 c. on 4 c. pink .. .. 75·00 £150
a. Small "3" £3250
17 **8** 5 c. on 8 c. green £110 £160

(*b*) *P* 14
18 **7** 3 c. on 4 c. pink .. .. 42·00 85·00
a. Small "3" £950
19 **8** 5 c. on 8 c. green .. .. 60·00 85·00
a. Surch inverted £1400

9

10

11

12

13

1886–87. (*a*) *P* 14.
21*b* **9** ½ c. magenta .. .. 10·00 22·00
22 ½ c. rose .. .. 1·75 6·50
a. Imperf (pair) .. .. 10·00
23 1 c. orange-yellow .. .. 3·75 9·50
a. Imperf between (vert pair) £300
b. Imperf (pair) .. .. 9·00
24 1 c. orange .. .. 95 4·00
a. Imperf (pair) .. .. 6·00
25 2 c. brown .. .. 1·25 4·50
a. Imperf (pair) .. .. 6·00
26 4 c. pink .. .. 1·00 4·50
a. Imperf (pair) .. .. 6·00
b. Imperf between (horiz or vert pair) £190
c. Imperf vert (horiz pair) £225
d. Error. 1 c. pink (centre stamp of strip of 3) £110 £200
da. Imperf between (pair) .. ..
db. Imperf (pair) £2000
27 8 c. green .. .. 2·00 8·50
a. Imperf (pair) .. .. 8·50
28 10 c. blue .. .. 4·00 13·00
a. Imperf between (vert pair) £300
b. Imperf (pair) .. .. 8·50
29 **10** 25 c. indigo .. .. 75·00 6·00
a. Imperf between (vert pair) .. ..
b. Imperf (pair) .. .. .. 55·00 10·00
30 **11** 50 c. violet .. .. 80·00 7·50
a. Imperf (pair) .. .. .. 45·00 6·00
31 **12** $1 scarlet .. .. £120 6·00
a. Imperf (pair) .. .. .. 60·00 6·00
32 **13** $2 sage-green .. .. £150 15·00
a. Imperf (pair) .. .. .. 70·00 13·00
21*b*/32 .. .. *Set of* 10 £400 65·00

(*b*) *P* 12
34 **9** ½ c. magenta .. .. 80·00 £170
35 1 c. orange .. .. 60·00 90·00

Nos. 21*b*/32 are known to have been sold as cancelled remainders, but these are difficult to distinguish from postally used. Values above 10 c. are infrequently found postally used so that the used prices quoted are for the remainders.

14

15

16

17

18

1887–92. *T* **14** (*as T* **9** *but inscr* "POSTAGE & REVENUE") *and T* **15/18** (*T* **10/13** *redrawn*). *P* 14.
36 **14** ½ c. magenta (1889) .. .. 2·25 6·50 —
a. Imperf vert (horiz pair) . † † £200
b. Rose .. .. 30 1·75 30
ba. Imperf between (horiz pair) .. £350
37 1 c. orange (1892) .. .. 40 1·75 30
a. Imperf vert (horiz pair) .. £300
38 2 c. brown (1889) .. .. .. 4·50 5·00 30
a. Imperf between (horiz pair) ..
b. Lake-brown .. .. .. 75 4·00 30
39 3 c. violet .. .. 1·25 7·00 30
a. Printed triple, one inverted ..
40 4 c. rose-pink (1889) .. . 2·00 8·00 30
a. Imperf between (pair) .. — £120 —
41 5 c. slate .. .. 1·75 7·00 30
a. Imperf between (pair) ..
42 6 c. lake (1892) .. .. .. 4·00 8·50 45
43 8 c. blue-green (1891) .. .. 5·00 7·50 45
a. Yellow-green .. .. .. 6·00 9·50 45
b. Printed triple, one inverted ..
44 10 c. blue (1891) .. .. .. 3·50 9·00 50
a. Imperf between (vert pair) .. † † —
b. Dull blue .. .. .. 3·50 8·00 50
ba. Imperf between (horiz pair) ..
c. Printed double .. ..
45 **15** 25 c. indigo (1888) .. .. .. 16·00 60·00 50
a. Imperf (pair) .. .. .. 70·00 — 3·00
b. Imperf vert (horiz pair) .. † † £250
46 **16** 50 c. violet (1888) .. .. .. 27·00 85·00 50
a. Imperf (pair) .. .. .. 75·00 — 3·00
b. Chalky blue .. .. .. † 90·00 †
47 **17** $1 scarlet (1888) .. .. .. 20·00 80·00 50
a. Imperf (pair) .. .. .. 70·00 — 3·00
48 **18** $2 dull green (1888) .. .. 60·00 £110 1·10
a. Imperf (pair) .. .. .. 90·00 — 3·50
36*b*/48 .. .. *Set of* 13 £130 £325 4·75

Nos. 36/44 also exist imperf (*Price* £6 *per pair unused*; £4 *cancelled*).

Nos. 39a, 43b and 44c are from waste sheets subsequently sold by the British North Borneo Company to collectors.

These stamps to the 10 c. value were forged on several occasions. Most forgeries of the ½ c. value can be identified by the presence of a diagonal line joining the top two horizontal strokes of the uppermost Chinese character.

The new 25 c. has the inscription "BRITISH NORTH BORNEO" in taller capitals. In the 50 c. the "0" of the numerals "50" in the two upper corners is square-shaped at the top and bottom instead of being oval. The 1 dollar has 14 pearls instead of 13 at each side, and on the 2 dollars the word "BRITISH" measures 10½ to 11 mm in length in place of 12 mm.

19

20

1889. *P* 14.
49 **19** $5 bright purple .. .. .. 70·00 90·00 6·00
a. Imperf (pair) .. .. .. 50·00 — 16·00
50 **20** $10 brown .. .. £100 £160 9·00
a. Imperf (pair) .. .. .. £120 — 20·00
b. "DOLLAPS" for "DOLLARS" (R.2/1) £900 £1100 £325
ba. Ditto. Imperf (pair) .. .. £1300 — £800

Two Cents. (21) **6 cents.** (22) **1 cent.** (23)

1890. *Surch as T* **21**, *in red.*

No.	Type	Description			
51	15	2 c. on 25 c. indigo	35·00	60·00	
		a. Surch inverted	£250	£275	
52		8 c. on 25 c. indigo	50·00	75·00	

The first printing of Nos. 51/2 had the two lines of the surcharge 3.5 mm apart. On a second printing of both values this gap widened to 5 mm.

1891–92. *Surch with T* **22**.

No.	Type	Description			
54	9	6 c. on 8 c. green (1892)	£5000	£3500	
		a. Large "s" in "cents"	£10000		
55	14	6 c. on 8 c. yellow-green	7·00	8·50	
		a. Surch inverted	£175	£250	
		b. "ɔents" for "cents"	£250	£300	
		c. "cetns." for "cents"	£275	£325	
		d. Large "s" in "cents"	95·00	95·00	
56	9	6 c. on 10 c. blue	25·00	15·00	
		a. Surch inverted	£130	£130	
		b. Surch double	£800		
		c. Surch treble	£250		
		d. Large "s" in "cents."	£110	£110	
57	14	6 c. on 10 c. blue	60·00	24·00	
		a. Large "s" in "cents."	£150	£120	

1892. *Surch as T* **23** ("Cents." *with capital* "C" *as in T* **21** *on No.* 65), *in red.*

No.	Type	Description			
63	14	1 c. on 4 c. rose-pink	10·00	14·00	
		a. Surch double	£500		
		b. Surch on back and on front	—	£500	
		ba. As b, but with surch double on front			
64		1 c. on 5 c. slate	6·00	6·00	
65	15	8 c. on 25 c. indigo	£110	£130	

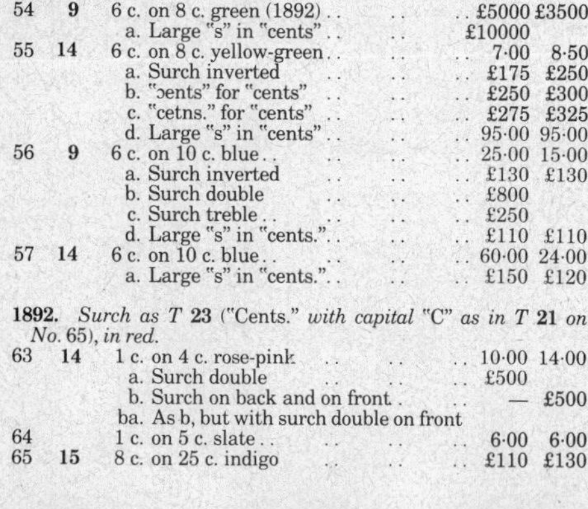

24 Dyak Chief

25 Sambar Stag (*Cervus unicolor*)

26 Sago Palm

27 Great Argus Pheasant

28 Arms of the Company

29 Malay Dhow

30 Estuarine Crocodile

31 Mount Kinabalu

32 Arms of the Company with Supporters

PERFORATION. There are a number of small variations in the perforation of the Waterlow issues of 1894 to 1922 which we believe were due to irregularity of the pins rather than different perforators.

In the following lists, stamps perf 12, 12½, 13 or compound are described as perf 12–13, stamps perf 13½, 14 or compound are described as perf 13½–14 and those perf 14½, 15 or compound are listed as perf 14½–15. In addition the 13½–14 perforation exists compound with 14½–15 and with 12–13, whilst perf 15½–16 comes from a separate perforator.

(Recess Waterlow)

1894. *P* 14½–15.

No.	Type	Description			
66	24	1 c. black and olive-bistre	1·25	4·50	20
		a. Imperf between (horiz or vert pair)	£400		
		b. Perf 13½–14	1·25	4·50	20
		c. Perf 13½–14, comp 14½–15	16·00	25·00	—
		d. Perf 13½–14, comp 12–13	9·00	20·00	—
		e. Perf 12–13			
67		1 c. black and bistre-brown	1·00	4·50	20
		a. Perf 13½–14	1·25	4·50	20
		b. Perf 13½–14, comp 12–13	10·00	22·00	—
		c. Perf 12–13			
68	25	2 c. black and rose-lake	3·50	4·50	30
		a. Imperf between (horiz or vert pair)	£275	£375	—
		b. Perf 13½–14	18·00	23·00	—
69	25	2 c. black and lake	3·25	4·00	30
		a. Perf 13½–14	20·00	28·00	—
		b. Perf 13½–14, comp 12–13	13·00	14·00	—
		c. Imperf between (horiz pair)			
70	26	3 c. olive-green and mauve	2·10	6·00	30
		a. Imperf between (horiz pair)	£300	£300	—
		b. Bronze-green and mauve			
		c. Perf 13½–14			
71		3 c. olive-green & violet (*p* 13½–14)	8·00	22·00	—
		a. Imperf between (horiz pair)			
72	27	5 c. black and vermilion	6·00	10·00	40
		a. Imperf between (horiz or vert pair)	£300		
		b. Perf 13½–14	25·00	42·00	—
		c. Perf 13½–14, comp 12–13	—	48·00	—
		d. Perf 13½–14, comp 14½–15			
		e. Perf 12–13			
73	28	6 c. black and bistre-brown	27·00	48·00	—
		a. Perf 13½–14	3·50	11·00	40
		b. Perf 13½–14, comp 12–13	—	40·00	—
		c. Perf 13½–14, comp 14½–15	32·00		
		d. Imperf between (horiz pair)			
74	29	8 c. black and dull purple	2·50	7·50	50
		a. Imperf between (vert pair)	£300	£300	£200
		b. Perf 13½–14	7·00	16·00	50
		ba. Imperf between (vert pair)	£325		
		d. Perf 13½–14, comp 12–13			
75	30	12 c. black and blue	24·00	48·00	2·00
		a. Perf 13½–14	24·00	48·00	2·00
		b. Imperf between (horiz pair)	†	†	£350
76		12 c. black and ultramarine	27·00	55·00	2·00
		a. Perf 13½–14	26·00	55·00	2·00
		b. Imperf between (pair)			
78	31	18 c. black and deep green	15·00	35·00	2·00
		a. Perf 13½–14	17·00	35·00	2·00
79	32	24 c. blue and rose-lake	16·00	38·00	2·00
		a. Imperf between (vert pair)	£350	£350	£250
		b. Perf 13½–14	16·00	38·00	2·00
		c. Perf 13½–14, comp 14½–15			
66/79		*Set of* 9	65·00	£150	7·50

32*a*

32*b*

32*c*

32*d*

(Litho Blades, East & Blades, London)

1894. *T* **32***a to* **32***d*, *and T* **19** *and* **20**, *but inscribed* "THE STATE OF NORTH BORNEO". *P* 14.

No.	Description			
81	25 c. indigo	8·00	26·00	70
	a. Imperf (pair)	16·00	—	2·75
	b. Imperf between (horiz or vert pair)	£500	—	75·00
	c. Printed double, one inverted	†	†	55·00
82	50 c. deep slate-purple	9·00	30·00	70
	a. Imperf (pair)	—	—	2·50
	b. Imperf between (horiz pair)			
	c. Printed double			
	d. Chalky blue	—	45·00	—
83	$1 scarlet	9·00	18·00	90
	a. Perf 14 × 11	£130		
	b. Imperf (pair)	14·00	—	5·00
	c. Printed both sides	25·00	—	—
84	$2 dull green	13·00	45·00	90
	a. Imperf (pair)	—	—	4·50
	b. Printed double			
85	$5 bright purple	£130	£180	9·50
	a. Imperf (pair)	80·00	—	14·00
	b. Dull purple	65·00	£100	3·50
86	$10 brown	£130	£190	5·00
	a. Imperf (pair)	80·00	—	11·00
81/6	*Set of* 6	£210	£350	10·50
81/6 Optd "Specimen"	*Set of* 6	£120		

For Nos. 81 to 83 in other colours, see Labuan 80*a*, 81*a* and 82*a*.

Nos. 81c, 82c, 83c and 84b are from waste sheets subsequently sold by the British North Borneo Company to collectors.

4

CENTS

(**33** (3½ mm between lines of surcharge))

(Surcharged by Waterlow)

1895 (June). *No.* 83 *surch as T* **33**.

No.	Description			
87	4 cents on $1 scarlet	2·50	1·50	30
	a. Surch double	£450		
88	10 cents on $1 scarlet	4·50	1·75	30
89	20 cents on $1 scarlet	10·00	8·50	30
90	30 cents on $1 scarlet	9·00	9·50	30
91	40 cents on $1 scarlet	14·00	18·00	30
87/91	*Set of* 5	35·00	35·00	1·40
87/91 Optd "Specimen"	*Set of* 5	85·00		

For 4 c. on $1 with wider spacing see No. 121.

No. 88 exists with the figures of the surcharge 2½ mm away from "CENTS". The normal setting has a space of 4 mm. Examples of the narrow setting have, so far, only been seen on cancelled-to-order stamps.

34

35

36

37 Orang-Utan

38

39

40

41 Sun Bear

42

43 Borneo Railway Train

44

45

(Recess Waterlow)

1897 (Mar)–**1902.** *T* **34** *to* **45.** *New frames. P* 13½–14.

No.	Description			
92	1 c. black and bistre-brown	3·50	2·50	20
	aa. Perf 16			
	a. Perf 14½–15	3·50	2·00	20
	b. Perf 13½–14, comp 12–13	27·00	28·00	—
	c. Imperf between (horiz pair)	†	†	£150
93	1 c. black and ochre	16·00	12·00	—
	a. Perf 14½–15	9·00	8·00	20
	b. Perf 13½–14, comp 12–13			
	c. Imperf between (horiz pair)			
94	2 c. black and lake	7·00	2·75	20
	a. Perf 14½–15	5·50	2·75	20
	b. Perf 13½–14, comp 12–13	—	11·00	—
	c. Perf 12–13			
	d. Imperf between (horiz pair)	†	†	£200
95	2 c. black and green (1900)	16·00	1·50	20
	a. Perf 14½–15	26·00	10·00	—
	b. Perf 13½–14, comp 12–13	55·00	18·00	—
	c. Perf 12–13			
	d. Imperf between (pair)	—	£350	—
96	3 c. green and rosy mauve	12·00	7·00	30
	a. Perf 14½–15	25·00	30·00	—
	b. Perf 13½–14, comp 12–13	45·00	50·00	—
97	3 c. green & dull mauve (*p* 14½–15)	3·50	3·00	30
98	4 c. black and green (1900)	6·00	—	40
	a. Perf 13½–14, comp 12–13			
99	4 c. black and carmine (1900)	8·00	4·75	30
	a. Perf 16	32·00	25·00	—
	b. Perf 14½–15	18·00	2·00	30
	c. Perf 13½–14, comp 12–13	16·00	17·00	—
	d. Perf 12–13			
100	5 c. black and orange-vermilion	25·00	3·50	30
	a. Perf 14½–15	30·00	2·75	30
	b. Perf 13½–14, comp 12–13	35·00	11·00	—
	c. Perf 12–13			
101	6 c. black and bistre-brown	13·00	7·50	30
	a. Perf 14½–15	7·00	3·00	30
102	8 c. black and brown-purple	25·00	25·00	—
	a. Perf 16	60·00	11·00	40
	b. Perf 14½–15	12·00	2·75	40
	c. Imperf between (vert pair)	£300	£250	—
103	8 c. black and brown	7·00	14·00	40
	a. Perf 14½–15	22·00	24·00	—
	b. Perf 16			
104	10 c. brown and slate-lilac (1902)	32·00	26·00	1·00
	a. Imperf between (vert pair)			
105	10 c. brown and slate-blue (1902)	60·00	45·00	1·00
106	12 c. black and dull blue	60·00	35·00	1·00
	a. Imperf between (pair)	†	†	£150
	b. Perf 14½–15	48·00	28·00	1·00
	c. Perf 13½–14, comp 12–13	85·00	55·00	—
	d. Perf 12–13			
107	16 c. green and chestnut (1902)	60·00	60·00	1·50
	a. Perf 14½–15	60·00	90·00	—
108	18 c. black and green (*p* 16)	9·00	20·00	50
	a. Imperf vert (horiz pair)	†	†	60·00
	b. Imperf between (vert pair)	†	†	£125
	c. Imperf (pair)	†	†	—

109 24 c. blue and lake .. .. .. 8·50 38·00 1·00
a. Perf 13½–14, comp 12–13 .. 23·00 55·00 —
b. Perf 12–13 .. .. .. 65·00
92/109 *(one of each value)* .. *Set of* 12 £190 £170 6·75
92/109 *(excl* 93, 97, 103) Optd "Specimen"
Set of 14 £170

In the above the 18 c. has "POSTAL REVENUE" instead of "POSTAGE AND REVENUE" and the 24 c. has those words omitted. These stamps were replaced by others with corrected inscriptions; see Nos. 110 and 111.

46

47

1897. *Corrected inscriptions. P* 13½–14.
110 **46** 18 c. black and green .. .. 35·00 12·00 75
a. Imperf between (horiz pair) † † £250
b. Perf 14½–15 .. .. 38·00 12·00 75
c. Perf 13½–14, comp 12–13 ..
111 **47** 24 c. blue and lake .. .. 28·00 28·00 1·00
a. Perf 16 .. .. .. 60·00 60·00 —
b. Perf 14½–15 .. .. 27·00 35·00 1·00
c. Perf 13½–14, comp 12–13 ..
d. Perf 12–13 ..
110/11 Optd "Specimen" .. *Set of* 2 45·00

BRITISH

4 CENTS (48) (4½ mm between lines of surcharge)

PROTECTORATE. (49)

4 cents (50)

1899. *Surch with T* **48**. *(a) P* 14½–15.
112 4 c. on 5 c. (No. 100a).. .. .. .. 25·00
a. Perf 13½–14 .. .. .. 10·00 10·00
b. Perf 13½–14, comp 12–13 .. .. 28·00 32·00
113 4 c. on 6 c. (No. 101a).. .. .. .. 16·00 20·00
a. Perf 13½–14 .. .. .. 9·00 22·00
114 4 c. on 8 c. (No. 102b).. .. .. .. 11·00 10·00
115 4 c. on 12 c. (No. 106b) .. .. .. 11·00 13·00
a. Imperf between (pair) £375 £400
b. Perf 13½–14 .. .. ..
c. Perf 12–13 .. .. ..
d. Perf 13½–14, comp 12–13 .. ..
116 4 c. on 18 c. (No. 110a) .. .. .. 9·50 13·00
a. Perf 13½–14 .. .. ..
117 4 c. on 24 c. (No. 111b) .. .. .. 11·00 12·00
a. Perf 16 .. .. .. 35·00 45·00
b. Perf 13½–14 .. .. .. 12·00 27·00
c. Perf 13½–14, comp 12–13 .. .. 22·00 30·00
d. Perf 12–13 .. .. .. 20·00 25·00

(b) P 14
118 4 c. on 25 c. indigo (No. 81) .. .. 5·00 8·50
a. Imperf between (horiz strip of 3) .. £800
119 4 c. on 50 c. deep slate-purple (No. 82) 6·00 12·00
a. Chalky blue .. .. .. 24·00 30·00
121 4 c. on $1 scarlet (No. 83) .. .. 5·00 8·50
122 4 c. on $2 dull green (No. 84).. .. 5·00 12·00
123 4 c. on $5 bright purple (No. 85) .. 85·00 £130
a. Dull purple .. .. .. 50·00 90·00
124 4 c. on $10 brown (No. 86) .. .. 50·00 90·00
112/24 .. .. .. *Set of* 12 £160 £275
112/24 Optd "Specimen" .. *Set of* 12 £150

No. 121 differs only from No. 87 in having the "4" and "cents" wider apart.

Examples of the Kudat postmark dated "AU 15 1899" struck on Nos. 112/24 are generally considered to be faked.

A new setting of the surcharge, with 5 mm between "4" and "CENTS", was used for the Specimen overprints, including unissued surcharges on the 1 c., 2 c. and 3 c. values *(price £90 the set of three)*.

1899. *Surch as T* **48** *but* 8½ *mm between lines of surcharge. P* 14.
125 4 c. on $5 (No. 85) .. .. .. 5·50 11·00
126 4 c. on $10 (No. 86) .. .. .. 5·50 11·00

(Surcharged by Waterlow)

1901 (8 Oct)–**05**. *Optd as T* **49**. *(a) P* 13½–14.
127 1 c. (No. 92) (R.) .. .. .. 2·00 1·50 10
a. Perf 14½–15 .. .. .. 1·50 1·60 10
128 2 c. (No. 95) (R.) .. .. .. 2·25 1·75 10
a. Perf 16 .. .. .. 3·50 4·00 15
b. Perf 14½–15 .. .. .. 4·00 5·50 15
129 3 c. (No. 96) .. .. .. 1·10 2·25 10
a. Imperf between (vert pair) ..
b. Perf 14½–15 .. .. .. 5·50 2·00 10
c. Perf 13½–14, comp 14½–15 .. 26·00
130 4 c. (No. 99) (G.) .. .. .. 4·25 1·50 10
a. Perf 14½–15 .. .. .. 7·00 1·50 10
131 5 c. (No. 100) (G.) .. .. .. 12·00 2·50 15
a. Perf 14½–15 .. .. .. 4·75 2·25 15
132 6 c. (No. 101) (R.) .. .. .. 22·00 32·00 —
a. No stop after "Protectorate" .. 65·00 65·00 —
b. Perf 16 .. .. .. 2·50 5·00 20
133 8 c. (No. 103) (B.) .. .. .. 2·75 3·00 20
a. No stop after "Protectorate" .. 3·00 14·00 —
b. Perf 13½–14, comp 12–13 .. 30·00 8·50 —
c. Imperf between (vert pair) ..
134 10 c. (No. 104) (R.) (7.02) .. .. 10·00 4·50 30
a. Perf 14½–15 .. .. .. 35·00 15·00 —
c. Perf 13½–14. No stop after "Protectorate" .. .. 95·00
d. Overprint double .. .. £350 — £225
e. On 10 c. (No. 105) .. ..
f. Imperf between (horiz pair) .. † † —
135 12 c. (No. 106) (R.) .. .. .. 23·00 12·00 1·00
136 16 c. (No. 107) (7.02) .. .. 38·00 18·00 1·50
a. Perf 14½–15 .. .. .. 40·00 24·00 1·50
b. Perf 13½–14, comp 12–13 .. 70·00 38·00 —
137 18 c. (No. 110) (R.) .. .. .. 8·00 15·00 60
a. No stop after "Protectorate" ..
b. Perf 13½–14, comp 12–13 ..
138 24 c. (No. 111).. .. .. .. 14·00 23·00 1·00
a. Perf 14½–15 .. .. .. 35·00 45·00 1·25
b. Imperf between (horiz pair) ..

(b) P 14
139 25 c. (No. 81) (R.) .. .. .. 2·00 10·00 30
a. No stop after "Protectorate" .. 90·00 £110 —
b. Overprints *tête-bêche* (pair) ..
c. Overprint inverted £350
140 50 c. (No. 82) (R.) .. .. .. 2·75 11·00 40
a. No stop after "Protectorate" .. 45·00 75·00 —
b. Chalky blue .. .. ..
141 $1 (No. 83) (R.) (1.04) .. .. 10·00 40·00 —
142 $1 (No. 83) .. .. .. 6·50 24·00 2·50
a. Imperf between (vert pair) .. £400
b. Opt double .. .. .. † † £250
c. Opt triple .. .. ..
143 $2 (No. 84) (R.) (1903) .. .. 23·00 60·00 3·50
a. Opt double .. .. .. £900 — £325
144 $5 (No. 85*b*) (R.) (2.05) .. .. £110 £190 4·00
145 $10 (No. 86) (R.) (2.05) .. .. £150 £250 7·00
a. Opt inverted .. .. ..£1100 † £350
127/45.. .. .. *Set of* 18 £350 £550 23·00
127/40 Optd "Specimen" .. *Set of* 14 £250

There was more than one setting of the overprint for some of the values. Full sheets of the 6 c. and 8 c. are known, without stop throughout.

1904–5. *Surch locally with T* **50**. *(a) P* 14½–15.
146 4 c. on 5 c. (No. 100a) .. .. 11·00 24·00 1·50
a. Surch omitted (in pair with normal) .. .. ..
147 4 c. on 6 c. (No. 101a) .. .. 4·25 13·00 1·00
a. Surch inverted £180
148 4 c. on 8 c. (No. 102b) .. .. 11·00 23·00 1·50
a. Surch inverted £225
149 4 c. on 12 c. (No. 106b) .. .. 15·00 27·00 1·50
a. Perf 13½–14 .. .. .. 28·00 38·00 1·50
b. Perf 13½–14, comp 12–13 .. 24·00 42·00 —
c. Surch omitted (in pair with normal) .. .. ..
150 4 c. on 18 c. (No. 110a) .. .. 14·00 25·00 2·00
a. Perf 13½–14 .. ..
151 4 c. on 24 c. (No. 111b) .. .. 16·00 30·00 2·00
a. Perf 16 .. .. .. 14·00 30·00 2·00
b. Perf 13½–14 .. .. .. 16·00 30·00 2·00
c. Perf 12–13 .. .. ..

(b) P 14
152 4 c. on 25 c. (No. 81).. .. .. 3·50 20·00 1·50
153 4 c. on 50 c. (No. 82).. .. .. 3·50 24·00 1·50
154 4 c. on $1 (No. 83) .. .. .. 4·25 30·00 2·00
155 4 c. on $2 (No. 84) .. .. .. 5·50 35·00 2·25
156 4 c. on $5 (No. 85) .. .. .. 11·00 40·00 2·50
a. Surch on No. 85*b* .. .. 80·00
157 4 c. on $10 (No. 86) .. .. .. 11·00 40·00 2·50
a. Surch inverted £1200
b. Surch omitted (in pair with normal) .. .. ..
146/57.. .. .. .. *Set of* 12 95·00 £300 19·00

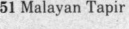

51 Malayan Tapir

52 Travellers' Tree

53 Railway at Jesselton

54 The Sultan of Sulu, his staff and W. C. Cowie, Managing Director of the Company

55 Indian Elephant

56 Sumatran Rhinoceros

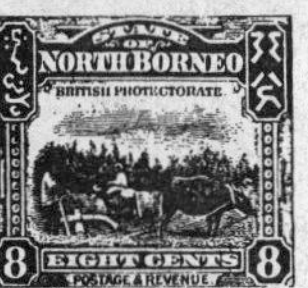
57 Ploughing with Buffalo

58 Wild Boar

59 Palm Cockatoo

60 Rhinoceros Hornbill

61 Banteng

62 Dwarf Cassowary

(Recess Waterlow)

1909 (1 July)–**24**. *Centres in black. P* 13½–14.
158 **51** 1 c. chocolate-brown 2·75 60 10
a. Perf 14½–15 9·50 6·00 —
159 1 c. brown 5·00 90 —
a. Perf 14½–15 9·50 2·00 20
b. Imperf between (vert pair) £550
160 **52** 2 c. green 75 30 10
a. Imperf between (pair)
b. Perf 14½–15 2·00 60 10
161 **53** 3 c. lake 2·00 90 10
162 3 c. rose-lake 2·50 60 10
a. Perf 14½–15 24·00 — 40
163 3 c. green (1924) 5·50 80 —
164 **54** 4 c. scarlet 1·25 15 10
a. Imperf between (vert pair)
b. Perf 14½–15 6·00 1·60 30
165 **55** 5 c. yellow-brown 6·00 2·00 10
a. Perf 14½–15
166 5 c. dark brown 7·00 2·00 —
167 **56** 6 c. olive-green 5·00 90 10
a. Perf 14½–15 35·00 4·50 60
168 6 c. apple-green 13·00 1·60 —
169 **57** 8 c. lake 2·00 90 10
a. Perf 14½–15
170 **58** 10 c. greyish blue 17·00 5·00 20
a. Perf 14½–15 28·00 11·00 —
171 10 c. blue 22·00 1·75 —
172 10 c. turquoise-blue 13·00 1·75 —
a. Perf 14½–15 27·00 4·50 —
173 **59** 12 c. deep blue 16·00 1·60 20
a. Perf 14½–15
b. Imperf vert (horiz pair) † † —
173*c* 12 c. deep bright blue
174 **60** 16 c. brown-lake 14·00 4·75 40
175 **61** 18 c. blue-green 42·00 27·00 50
176 **62** 24 c. deep rose-lilac 16·00 2·00 30
a. Deep lilac
158/76 *Set of* 13 £110 38·00 —
158/76 Optd "Specimen" *Set of* 13 £275
For this issue perf 12½ see Nos. 277, etc.

(63)

64

65

1909 (7 Sept). *No.* 175 *surch with T* **63** *by Waterlow. P* 13½–14.
177 20 c. on 18 c. blue-green (R.) (Optd S. £35) 3·50 35 10
a. Perf 14½–15 £130 55·00 —

(Recess Waterlow)

1911 (7 Mar). *P* 13½–14.
178 **64** 25 c. black and yellow-green 4·00 3·25 1·00
a. Perf 14½–15 8·50 23·00
b. Imperf (pair) 35·00
178*c* 25 c. black and blue-green 30·00
179 50 c. black and steel-blue 5·50 3·25 1·25
a. Perf 14½–15 15·00 18·00 —
ab. Imperf between (horiz pair)
c. Imperf (pair) 50·00
180 $1 black and chestnut 11·00 3·25 1·25
a. Perf 14½–15 26·00 13·00 —
b. Imperf (pair) 65·00
181 $2 black and lilac 27·00 11·00 3·00
182 **65** $5 black and lake 55·00 60·00 20·00
a. Imperf (pair) £120
183 $10 black and brick-red £140 £170 40·00
a. Imperf (pair) £160
178/83 *Set of* 6 £225 £225 60·00
178/83 Optd "Specimen" *Set of* 6 £225

BRITISH

PROTECTORATE
(66)

2
cents
(67)

(68)

1912 (July). *Nos.* 85 *and* 86 *optd with T* **66**.
184 $5 dull purple (R.) £750 — 6·00
185 $10 brown (R.) £900 — 6·00
a. Opt inverted † † —

1916 (Feb). *Stamps of* 1909–22 *surch as T* **67** *by Govt Printing Office, Sandakan. P* 13½–14.
186 2 c. on 3 c. black and rose-lake 9·00 7·00
a. "s" inverted (R. 2/5) 85·00 85·00
b. Surch double
187 4 c. on 6 c. black and olive-green (R.) 9·00 9·00
a. "s" inverted (R. 2/5) 85·00 85·00
b. "s" inserted by hand — £550
c. Perf 14½–15
ca. "s" inverted
188 10 c. on 12 c. black and deep blue (R.) 18·00 28·00
a. "s" inverted (R. 2/5) 90·00 90·00
186/8 *Set of* 3 32·00 40·00
186/8 Optd "Specimen" *Set of* 3 £100
Nos. 186/8 were surcharged from a setting of 25 (5×5) on which the required face values were inserted.

1916 (May). *Stamps of* 1909–11 *optd with T* **68** *by Waterlow. P* 13½–14. *Centres in black. (a) Cross in vermilion.*
189 **51** 1 c. brown 6·50 25·00
190 **52** 2 c. green 27·00 65·00
a. Perf 14½–15 32·00 70·00
191 **53** 3 c. rose-lake 18·00 30·00
192 **54** 4 c. scarlet 5·50 22·00
a. Perf 14½–15 £120 £110
193 **55** 5 c. yellow-brown 18·00 45·00
a. Perf 14½–15
194 **56** 6 c. apple-green 38·00 60·00
a. Perf 14½–15 £120
195 **57** 8 c. lake 17·00 48·00
196 **58** 10 c. blue 35·00 65·00
197 **59** 12 c. deep blue 48·00 70·00
198 **60** 16 c. brown-lake 48·00 70·00
199 **61** 20 c. on 18 c. blue-green 25·00 70·00
200 **62** 24 c. dull mauve 55·00 70·00
a. Imperf between (vert pair)
201 **64** 25 c. green (*p* 14½–15) £250 £350
189/201 *Set of* 13 £500 £900

(b) Cross in carmine
202 **51** 1 c. brown 18·00 45·00
a. Perf 14½–15 £130
203 **52** 2 c. green 26·00 32·00
b. Perf 14½–15 £130
ba. Opt double † —
204 **53** 3 c. rose-lake 23·00 55·00
205 **55** 5 c. yellow-brown 28·00 65·00
206 **56** 6 c. apple-green 26·00 65·00
a. Perf 14½–15
207 **57** 8 c. lake 18·00 55·00
208 **58** 10 c. blue 28·00 60·00
209 **59** 12 c. deep blue 48·00 90·00
210 **60** 16 c. brown-lake 50·00 90·00
211 **61** 20 c. on 18 c. blue-green 55·00 90·00
212 **62** 24 c. dull mauve 55·00 £120
213 **64** 25 c. green £600
a. Perf 14½–15 £375 £475
202/13 *Set of* 12 £650 £1100
The British North Borneo Company donated a proportion of the above issue to be sold by the National Philatelic War Fund for the benefit of the Red Cross and St. John's Ambulance Brigade.

RED CROSS 

TWO CENTS
(69)

FOUR CENTS
(70)

1918 (Aug). *Stamps of* 1909–11 *surch as T* **69**. *P* 13½–14.

(a) Lines of surcharge 9 mm apart
214 **51** 1 c. + 2 c. brown 1·75 6·50
a. Imperf between (horiz pair) £700
215 **52** 2 c. + 2 c. green 70 5·50
a. Imperf between (horiz or vert pair) £700
b. Imperf (pair)
c. Perf 14½–15
216 **53** 3 c. + 2 c. rose-red 3·50 9·00
a. Imperf between (horiz pair) £700
b. Perf 14½–15 22·00 55·00
217 3 c. + 2 c. dull rose-carmine £130
a. Perf 14½–15 £160
218 **54** 4 c. + 2 c. scarlet 55 3·75
a. Surch inverted £325
219 **55** 5 c. + 2 c. deep brown 4·00 11·00
220 5 c. + 2 c. pale brown 4·75 16·00
221 **56** 6 c. + 2 c. olive-green 3·25 17·00
a. Perf 14½–15 £130
221*b* 6 c. + 2 c. apple-green
c. Perf 14½–15 £225
222 **57** 8 c. + 2 c. lake 3·50 7·00
a. Inverted figure "3" for "C" in "CENTS"
223 **58** 10 c. + 2 c. blue 5·50 20·00
224 **59** 12 c. + 2 c. deep bright blue 8·00 25·00
a. Surch inverted £500
225 **60** 16 c. + 2 c. brown-lake 8·00 26·00
226 **62** 24 c. + 2 c. mauve 9·50 26·00

(b) Lines of surch 13–14 mm apart
227 **52** 2 c. + 2 c. green 50·00 £100
228 **56** 6 c. + 2 c. olive-green £200 £500
229 **64** 25 c. + 2 c. green 10·00 38·00
230 50 c. + 2 c. steel-blue 12·00 38·00
231 $1 + 2 c. chestnut 38·00 48·00
232 $2 + 2 c. lilac 55·00 90·00
233 **65** $5 + 2 c. lake £250 £400
234 $10 + 2 c. brick-red £250 £400
214/34 *Set of* 17 £600 £1000
The above stamps were dispatched from London in three consignments, of which two were lost through enemy action at sea.
Only one sheet was found of No. 228.
These stamps were sold at a premium of 2 c. per stamp, which went to the Red Cross Society.

1918 (Oct). *Stamps of* 1909–11 *surch with T* **70**, *in red. P* 13½–14.
235 **51** 1 c. + 4 c. chocolate 50 3·50
a. Imperf between (horiz pair)
236 **52** 2 c. + 4 c. green 65 5·50
237 **53** 3 c. + 4 c. rose-lake 75 3·25
238 **54** 4 c. + 4 c. scarlet 40 4·50
239 **55** 5 c. + 4 c. brown 1·75 15·00
240 **56** 6 c. + 4 c. apple-green 1·75 9·50
a. Imperf between (vert pair) £750
241 **57** 8 c. + 4 c. lake 1·10 8·50
242 **58** 10 c. + 4 c. turquoise-blue 2·00 12·00
242*a* 10 c. + 4 c. greenish blue 5·50 28·00
243 **59** 12 c. + 4 c. deep blue 5·50 11·00
a. Surch double £550
244 **60** 16 c. + 4 c. brown-lake 5·00 16·00
245 **62** 24 c. + 4 c. mauve 5·00 20·00
246 **64** 25 c. + 4 c. yellow-green 3·25 35·00
247 25 c. + 4 c. blue-green 23·00 65·00
248 50 c. + 4 c. steel-blue 14·00 35·00
a. Perf 14½–15 55·00
249 **64** $1 + 4 c. chestnut 14·00 50·00
a. Perf 14½–15 60·00
250 $2 + 4 c. lilac 40·00 75·00
251 **65** $5 + 4 c. lake £200 £400
252 $10 + 4 c. brick-red £200 £400
235/52 *Set of* 17 £450 £1000
Nos. 235/52 were sold at face, plus 4 c. on each stamp for Red Cross Funds.

MALAYA-BORNEO
EXHIBITION
1922.
(71)

THREE
CENTS
(72)

1922 (31 Mar). *Malaya-Borneo Exhibition, Singapore. Stamps of* 1909–22 *optd as T* **71** *by Govt Printing Office, Sandakan. P* 13½–14.
253 **51** 1 c. brown (R.) 4·50 35·00
a. "BORHEO" £275 £300
b. "BORNEQ" £400 £425
c. Stop after "EXHIBITION." 42·00
d. Raised stop after "1922" £275
e. "EXHIBITICN." with stop £400
f. Perf 14½–15 14·00 50·00
fa. "BORHEO" £375
fb. "BORNEQ" £550
fc. Raised stop after "1922" £375
fd. "EXHIBITICN." with stop £550
fe. "MHLAYA" and stop after "EXHIBITION"
ff. Stop after "EXHIBITION." 50·00
253*g* 1 c. brown (B.)(*p* 14½–15) £700
ga. Vert pair, with and without opt £2000
gb. Raised stop after "1922." £1300
gc. "BORHEO" £1300
gd. "BORNEQ" £1700
gf. "EXHIBITICN." with stop £1700
gg. "MHLAYA" and stop after EXHIBITION"
254 1 c. orange-brown (R.) 11·00 40·00
255 **52** 2 c. green (R.) 1·40 13·00
a. Stop after "EXHIBITION." 20·00
256 **53** 3 c. rose-lake (B.) 4·25 27·00
a. Stop after "EXHIBITION." 38·00
b. "EXHIBITICN." with stop £1100
c. Raised stop after "1922" £750
257 **54** 4 c. scarlet (B.) 1·40 22·00
a. Stop after "EXHIBITION." 19·00
b. Perf 14½–15
ba. Stop after "EXHIBITION."
258 **55** 5 c. orange-brown (B.) 5·50 38·00
a. Imperf between (vert pair) £900 £800
b. Stop after "EXHIBITION." 38·00
c. Opt double £2250
d. Opt double (with stop)
259 5 c. chestnut (B.) 14·00 48·00
a. Stop after "EXHIBITION." 55·00
260 **56** 6 c. apple-green (R.) 2·75 35·00
a. Stop after "EXHIBITION." 30·00
b. Opt double £2000
c. Opt double (with stop)
261 **57** 8 c. dull rose (B.) 3·75 35·00
a. Stop after "EXHIBITION." 38·00
262 8 c. deep rose-lake (B.) 3·75 35·00
a. Stop after "EXHIBITION." 38·00
263 **58** 10 c. turquoise-blue (R.) 4·50 35·00
a. Stop after "EXHIBITION." 38·00
b. Perf 14½–15 23·00
ba. Stop after "EXHIBITION."
264 10 c. greenish blue (R.) 4·50 38·00
a. Stop after "EXHIBITION." 38·00
265 **59** 12 c. deep blue (R.) 3·75 20·00
a. Stop after "EXHIBITION." 42·00
266 12 c. deep bright blue (R.) 25·00
a. Stop after "EXHIBITION." £130
267 **60** 16 c. brown-lake (B.) 5·50 40·00
a. Stop after "EXHIBITION." 42·00
b. Opt in red £2250
268 **61** 20 c. on 18 c. blue-green (B.) 7·00 40·00
a. Stop after "EXHIBITION." 80·00
269 20 c. on 18 c. blue-green (R.) 25·00 £130
a. Stop after "EXHIBITION." £200 £275
270 **62** 24 c. mauve (R.) 13·00 45·00
a. Stop after "EXHIBITION." 50·00
271 24 c. lilac (R.) 13·00 45·00
a. Stop after "EXHIBITION." 50·00
272 24 c. reddish lilac (R.) 22·00 55·00
a. Stop after "EXHIBITION." 75·00
273 **64** 25 c. blue-green (R.) 7·50 45·00
a. Stop after "EXHIBITION." 45·00
274 25 c. yellow-green (R.) 3·75 40·00
a. Stop after "EXHIBITION." 40·00
b. Opt double £1100
c. Perf 14½–15 13·00 55·00
ca. Stop after "EXHIBITION." £200
cb. Opt double £900
275 50 c. steel-blue (R.) 6·00 35·00
a. Stop after "EXHIBITION." 55·00
b. Perf 14½–15 20·00
ba. Stop after "EXHIBITION." £100
253/75 *Set of* 14 60·00 £400
253/75 Optd "Specimen" *Set of* 14 £400
These overprints were applied from a number of settings covering 10, 20, 25 or 30 stamps at a time.
Of the ten settings known for the horizontal stamps the earliest were only used for the 1 c. on which most of the varieties occur. Of the others the vast majority come from settings of 20 (10 × 2) with the stop after "EXHIBITION" variety on R. 2/7, or 25 (5 × 5) on which the same variety can be found on R. 5/4. In addition the 3 c. comes from a different setting of 20 (10 × 2) on which there is a raised stop after "1922" on R. 2/8 and "EXHIBITICN." on R. 2/9.
The 1 c. sequence is complicated, but additionally includes a setting of 10 with "BORHEO" on stamps 3 and 10, "BORNEQ" on stamp 4, raised stop on stamp 8 and "EXHIBITICN." on stamp 9. A setting of 20 repeats this sequence on its bottom line

as does one of 30, although in this instance "MHLAYA" replaces "EXHIBITICN" as the variety on stamp 9.

For the vertical stamps (2, 6, 10, 12, 16 and 20 c. on 18 c.) the settings were of 20 (10×2) or 25 (5×5). The stop after "EXHIBITION" occurs on R. 2/7 of the former and R. 5/4 of the latter.

The 25 c. and 50 c. high values were overprinted from a setting of 20 (10×2), with the stop after "EXHIBITION" on R. 2/7, or 25 (5×5).

1923 (Oct). *T* **54** *surch with T* **72**.
276 3 c. on 4 c. black and scarlet (Optd S. £50) .. 1·00 3·50
a. Surch double £500

1925–28. *As* 1909–22. *Centres in black, and some frame colours changed. P* 12½.
277 **51** 1 c. chocolate-brown 75 70
a. Imperf between (horiz pair) .. £400
278 **52** 2 c. claret 35 50
a. Imperf between (horiz or vert pair) † —
279 **53** 3 c. green (1925) .. .. .. 2·00 1·25
a. Imperf between (horiz pair) ..
280 **54** 4 c. scarlet 45 10
a. Imperf between (vert pair) .. £350
b. Imperf between (horiz pair) .. £550
281 **55** 5 c. yellow-brown .. .. .. 3·00 2·00
a. Imperf between (vert pair) ..
282 **56** 6 c. olive-green .. .. 2·50 40
283 **57** 8 c. carmine .. .. 1·50 10
a. Imperf between (horiz or vert pair) £350
284 **58** 10 c. turquoise-blue .. .. .. 1·75 40
a. Imperf between (horiz or vert pair) £450
285 **59** 12 c. deep blue .. .. 4·50 40
286 **60** 16 c. red-brown .. .. 13·00 45·00
287 **61** 20 c. on 18 c. blue-green (R.) .. .. 2·75 3·00
288 **62** 24 c. violet .. .. 30·00 45·00
289 **64** 25 c. green .. .. 4·00 4·25
290 50 c. steel-blue .. .. 6·50 11·00
291 $1 chestnut .. .. 15·00 50·00
292 $2 mauve .. .. 40·00 85·00
293 **65** $5 lake (1928) .. .. 90·00 £200
294 $10 orange-red (1928) £180 £275
277/94 .. .. .. *Set of* 18 £350 £650

Examples of No. 278 were supplied for U.P.U. distribution punched with a 3½ mm diameter hole.

73 Head of a Murut **76** Mount Kinabalu

(Eng J. A. C. Harrison. Recess Waterlow)

1931 (1 Jan). *50th Anniv of British North Borneo Company. T* **73, 76** *and similar designs. P* 12½.
295 3 c. black and blue-green 80 50
296 6 c. black and orange .. .. 10·00 2·75
297 10 c. black and scarlet .. .. 2·75 9·00
298 12 c. black and ultramarine .. .. .. 3·75 7·00
299 25 c. black and violet .. .. 25·00 25·00
300 $1 black and yellow-green .. .. .. 15·00 48·00
301 $2 black and chestnut .. .. 35·00 65·00
302 $5 black and purple .. .. 95·00 £180
295/302 .. .. .. *Set of* 8 £170 £300
295/302 Optd "Specimen" .. .. *Set of* 8 £275

Designs: *Vert*—6 c. Orang-Utan; 10 c. Dyak warrior; $1 Badge of the Company; $5 Arms of the Company. *Horiz*—25 c. Clouded Leopard; $2 Arms of the Company.

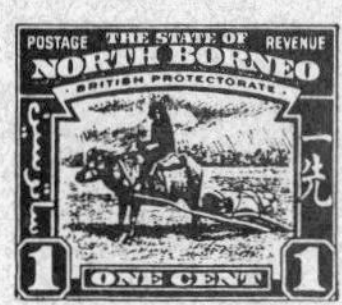

81 Buffalo Transport **82** Palm Cockatoo

(Eng J. A. C. Harrison. Recess Waterlow)

1939 (1 Jan). *T* **81/2** *and similar designs. P* 12½.
303 1 c. green and red-brown 25 20
304 2 c. purple and greenish blue 90 25
305 3 c. slate-blue and green 35 50
306 4 c. bronze-green and violet 65 25
307 6 c. deep blue and claret 45 75
308 8 c. scarlet .. .. 2·50 45
309 10 c. violet and bronze-green .. .. .. 20·00 3·75
310 12 c. green and royal blue .. .. .. 4·00 1·90
a. Green and blue .. .. .. 5·50 3·25
311 15 c. blue-green and brown .. .. .. 7·50 3·50
312 20 c. violet and slate-blue .. .. .. 5·00 3·00
313 25 c. green and chocolate .. .. .. 5·50 3·50
314 50 c. chocolate and violet .. .. .. 8·00 3·50
315 $1 brown and carmine .. .. .. 35·00 15·00
316 $2 violet and olive-green .. .. .. 55·00 60·00
317 $5 indigo and pale blue £200 £160
303/17 .. .. .. *Set of* 15 £300 £225
303/17 Perf "Specimen" .. .. *Set of* 15 £250

Designs: *Vert*—3 c. Native; 4 c. Proboscis Monkey; 6 c. Mounted Bajaus; 10 c. Orang-Utan; 15 c. Dyak; $1, $2 Badge of the Company. *Horiz*—8 c. Eastern Archipelago; 12 c. Murut with blow-pipe; 20 c. River scene; 25 c. Native boat; 50 c. Mt Kinabalu; $5 Arms of the Company.

WAR TAX (96) WAR TAX (97)

1941 (24 Feb). *Nos.* 303/4 *optd with T* **96/7**.
318 1 c. green and red-brown 10 30
319 2 c. purple and greenish blue .. .. .. 45 1·60

BRITISH MILITARY ADMINISTRATION

North Borneo, including Labuan, was occupied by the Japanese in January 1942. Following the defeat of Japan Allied troops landed in September 1945 and the territory was placed under British Military Administration on 5 January 1946.

(98) (99)

1945 (17 Dec). *Nos.* 303/17 *optd with T* **98**.
320 1 c. green and red-brown .. .. .. 1·25 40
321 2 c. purple and greenish blue .. .. .. 2·50 40
a. Opt double £2500
322 3 c. slate-blue and green 40 40
323 4 c. bronze-green and violet .. .. .. 12·00 7·00
324 6 c. deep blue and claret 50 30
325 8 c. scarlet 60 45
326 10 c. violet and bronze-green .. .. .. 1·75 30
327 12 c. green and blue .. .. .. 1·25 80
a. Green and royal blue .. ..
328 15 c. blue-green and brown 60 80
329 20 c. violet and slate-blue .. .. .. 1·00 70
330 25 c. green and chocolate .. .. .. 2·00 65
331 50 c. chocolate and violet .. .. .. 2·00 1·00
332 $1 brown and carmine .. .. .. 15·00 12·00
333 $2 violet and olive-green .. .. .. 15·00 12·00
a. Opt double £1500
334 $5 indigo and pale blue .. .. .. 8·00 6·50
320/34 .. .. .. *Set of* 15 55·00 40·00

These stamps and the similarly overprinted stamps of Sarawak were obtainable at all post offices throughout British Borneo (Brunei, Labuan, North Borneo and Sarawak), for use on local and overseas mail.

CROWN COLONY

North Borneo became a Crown Colony on 15 July 1946.

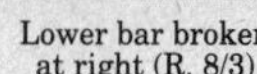

Lower bar broken at right (R. 8/3)

Lower bar broken at left (R. 8/4)

1947 (1 Sept–22 Dec). *Nos.* 303 *to* 317 *optd with T* **99** *and bars obliterating words* "THE STATE OF" *and* "BRITISH PROTECTORATE".
335 1 c. green and red-brown (15.12) 15 30
b. Lower bar broken at right .. .. 8·00
c. Lower bar broken at left .. .. 8·00
336 2 c. purple and greenish blue (22.12) 45 50
337 3 c. slate-blue and green (R.)(22.12) 15 15
338 4 c. bronze-green and violet 20 10
339 6 c. deep blue and claret (R.)(22.12) 15 20
340 8 c. scarlet 20 15
b. Lower bar broken at right .. .. 10·00
341 10 c. violet and bronze-green (15.12) 40 15
342 12 c. green and royal blue (22.12) 50 50
a. Green and blue .. ..
343 15 c. blue-green and brown (22.12) 50 25
344 20 c. violet and slate-blue (22.12) 35 25
345 25 c. green and chocolate (22.12) 35 25
b. Lower bar broken at right .. .. 15·00
346 50 c. chocolate and violet (22.12) 70 35
b. Lower bar broken at right .. .. 25·00
c. Lower bar broken at left .. .. 25·00
347 $1 brown and carmine (22.12) 60 75
348 $2 violet and olive-green (22.12) .. .. 2·00 3·50
349 $5 indigo and pale blue (R.) (22.12) .. .. 7·00 7·00
b. Lower bar broken at right .. .. 55·00
335/49 .. .. .. *Set of* 15 12·00 13·00
335/49 Perf "Specimen" .. .. *Set of* 15 £250

1948 (1 Nov). *Royal Silver Wedding. As Nos.* 30/1 *of Aden.*
350 8 c. scarlet 30 40
351 $10 mauve .. .. 11·00 24·00

1949 (10 Oct). *75th Anniv of Universal Postal Union. As Nos.* 114/17 *of Antigua.*
352 8 c. carmine 30 20
353 10 c. brown 60 20
354 30 c. orange-brown 70 80
355 55 c. blue 75 80
352/5 .. .. .. *Set of* 4 2·10 1·75

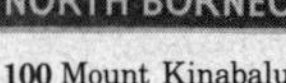

100 Mount Kinabalu

102 Coconut Grove

(Photo Harrison)

1950 (1 July)–**52**. *T* **100, 102** *and similar designs. Wmk Mult Script CA. Chalk-surfaced paper. P* 13½ × 14½ (*horiz*), 14½ × 13½ (*vert*).
356 1 c. red-brown 15 30
357 2 c. blue 15 15
358 3 c. green 15 10
359 4 c. bright purple 15 10
360 5 c. violet 15 10
361 8 c. scarlet 25 25
362 10 c. maroon 25 10
363 15 c. ultramarine 25 15
364 20 c. brown 20 10
365 30 c. olive-brown 45 10
366 50 c. rose-carmine ("JESSLETON") .. .. 45 1·40
366*a* 50 c. rose-carmine ("JESSELTON") (1.5.52) .. 85 50
367 $1 red-orange .. .. 1·25 55
368 $2 grey-green .. .. 2·00 4·50
369 $5 emerald-green .. .. 7·50 8·50
370 $10 dull blue .. .. 22·00 32·00
356/70 .. .. .. *Set of* 16 32·00 45·00

Designs: *Horiz*—2 c. Native musical instrument; 8 c. Map; 10 c. Log pond; 15 c. Malay prau, Sandakan; 20 c. Bajau Chief; $2 Murut with blowpipe; $5 Net-fishing; $10 Arms of North Borneo. *Vert*—4 c. Hemp drying; 5 c. Cattle at Kota Belud; 30 c. Suluk river canoe, Lahad Datu; 50 c. Clock tower, Jesselton; $1 Bajau horsemen.

1953 (3 June). *Coronation. As No.* 47 *of Aden.*
371 10 c. black and bright scarlet 30 20

115 Log Pond

(Photo Harrison)

1954 (1 Mar)–**59**. *Designs previously used for King George VI issue, but with portrait of Queen Elizabeth II as in T* **115**. *Chalk-surfaced paper. Wmk Mult Script CA. P* 14½×13½ (*vert*) *or* 13½×14½ (*horiz*).
372 1 c. red-brown (1.10.54) 10 20
373 2 c. blue (1.6.56) 20 10
374 3 c. green (1.2.57) 25 80
a. Deep green (14.1.59) 40 80
375 4 c. bright purple (16.5.55) 20 10
376 5 c. reddish violet (1.7.54) 25 10
377 8 c. scarlet (1.10.54) 20 10
378 10 c. maroon 15 10
379 15 c. bright blue (16.5.55) 25 10
380 20 c. brown (3.8.54) 15 10
381 30 c. olive-brown (3.8.54) 35 10
382 50 c. rose-carm ("JESSELTON") (10.2.56) .. 1·25 10
a. Rose (9.12.59) .. .. .. 2·25 30
383 $1 red-orange (1.4.55) .. .. .. 1·50 20
384 $2 deep green (1.10.55) .. .. .. 4·50 40
a. Grey-green (22.1.58) .. .. .. 5·50 3·50
385 $5 emerald-green (1.2.57) .. .. .. 8·00 13·00
386 $10 deep blue (1.2.57) .. .. .. 17·00 25·00
372/86 .. .. .. *Set of* 15 30·00 35·00

Designs: *Horiz*—1 c. Mount Kinabalu; 2 c. Native musical instrument; 8 c. Map; 15 c. Native prahu, Sandakan; 20 c. Bajau chief; $2 Murut with blowpipe; $5 Net-fishing; $10 Arms of North Borneo. *Vert*—3 c. Coconut grove; 4 c. Hemp drying; 5 c. Cattle at Kota Belud; 30 c. Suluk boat, Lahad Datu; 50 c. Clock Tower, Jesselton; $1 Bajau horseman.

Plate 2 of the 30 c., released 10 August 1960, had a finer, 250 screen, instead of the previous 200 (*price* £1.75 *mint*).

116 Borneo Railway, 1902

119 Arms of Chartered Company

(Recess Waterlow)

1956 (1 Nov). *75th Anniv of British North Borneo Co. T* **116, 119** *and similar designs. Wmk Mult Script CA. P* 13 × 13½ (*horiz*) *or* 13½ × 13 (*vert*).
387 10 c. black and rose-carmine .. .. .. 1·00 15
388 15 c. black and red-brown 25 15
389 35 c. black and bluish green 30 45
390 $1 black and slate 65 70
387/90 .. .. .. *Set of* 4 2·00 1·25

Designs: *Horiz*—15 c. Malay prau; 35 c. Mount Kinabalu.

120 Sambar Stag

121 Orang-Utan

(Des Chong Yun Fatt. Recess Waterlow (until 1962), then D.L.R.)

1961 (1 Feb). *W* w **12.** *Horiz designs as T* **120** *or vert designs as T* **121.** *P* 13.
391 1 c. emerald and brown-red 10 10
392 4 c. bronze-green and orange 15 40
393 5 c. sepia and violet 15 10
394 6 c. black and blue-green 10 10
395 10 c. green and red 15 10
396 12 c. brown and grey-green 15 10
397 20 c. blue-green and ultramarine .. .. 1·25 10
398 25 c. grey-black and scarlet 45 30
399 30 c. sepia and olive 20 10
400 35 c. slate-blue and red-brown 25 10
401 50 c. emerald and yellow-brown 30 10
402 75 c. grey-blue and bright purple .. .. 2·00 40
403 $1 brown and yellow-green .. .. .. 5·50 30
404 $2 brown and slate .. .. 6·50 1·50
405 $5 emerald and maroon .. .. .. 16·00 9·00
406 $10 carmine and blue .. .. .. 16·00 14·00
391/406 .. .. *Set of* 16 45·00 23·00

Designs: *Horiz*—4 c. Sun Bear; 5 c. Clouded Leopard; 6 c. Dusun woman with gong; 10 c. Map of Borneo; 12 c. Banteng; 20 c. Butterfly orchid; 25 c. Sumatran Rhinoceros; 30 c. Murut with blow-pipe; 35 c. Mount Kinabalu; 50 c. Dusun and buffalo transport; 75 c. Bajau horsemen. *Vert*—$2 Rhinoceros Hornbill; $5 Crested Wood Partridge; $10 Arms of North Borneo.

1963 (4 June). *Freedom from Hunger. As No.* 76 *of Aden.*
407 12 c. ultramarine 50 15

POSTAL FISCALS

Three Cents. Revenue
(F 1)
(Raised stop)

Ten Cents. Revenue
(F 2)

1886. *Regular issues surch as Type* F **1** *or* F **2.**
F1 **1** 3 c. on 4 c. pink (No. 6) .. .. .. 50·00 70·00
a. Raised stop after "Cents" .. .. 50·00
F2 5 c. on 8 c. green (No. 7).. .. .. 50·00 70·00
a. Raised stop after "Cents" £100
F3 **4** 10 c. on 50 c. violet (No. 4) .. .. 75·00 £100
a. Surch double .. .. .. — £550
b. No stop after "Cents" and stop after "Revenue." £225 £300

No. F1a occurs on every stamp in the first, second, third, sixth and seventh vertical columns in the sheet of 50 (10 × 5).

POSTAGE DUE STAMPS

POSTAGE DUE
(D 1)

1895 (1 Aug). *Stamps of* 1894 *optd with Type* D **1.** *P* 14½–15.

A. *Vertically* (*reading upwards*)
D 1 **25** 2 c. black and rose-lake .. .. 12·00 22·00 1·50
a. Opt double .. .. .. † † £200
b. Opt reading downwards .. † † £250
D 2 2 c. black and lake .. .. 7·50 13·00 60
a. Perf 13½–14 .. ..
b. Opt omitted (in vert pair with normal) .. .. .. † † £350
D 3 **26** 3 c. olive-green and mauve .. 3·50 8·00 75
a. Bronze-green and mauve ..
b. Opt reading downwards ..
D 3*c* 3 c. olive-green and violet ..
ca. Opt double .. .. † † £350
cb. Perf 13½–14 .. .. ..
D 4 **27** 5 c. black and vermilion .. .. 15·00 17·00 1·50
a. Printed double .. .. † — —
b. Stop after "DUE" .. .. 45·00
c. Perf 13½–14 .. .. — 40·00 —
ca. Opt double .. .. ..
d. Perf 13½–14, comp 12–13 .. — 45·00 —
D 5 **28** 6 c. black and bistre-brown .. 13·00 30·00 1·50
a. Perf 13½–14 .. .. 6·00 24·00 1·50
b. Perf 12–13 .. .. ..
c. Perf 13½–14, comp 12–13 ..
d. Opt reading downwards ..
D 6 **31** 18 c. black and deep green .. 27·00 45·00 3·00
a. Opt reading downwards .. £300 £170 —
D3/4 & D6 Optd "Specimen" *Set of* 3 90·00

B. *Horizontally*
D 7 **29** 8 c. black and dull purple .. 13·00 28·00 1·50
a. Opt double .. .. .. — † —
b. Perf 13½–14 .. .. ..
ba. Opt inverted .. .. .. † † 95·00
c. Perf 13½–14, comp 12–13 .. 22·00
D 8 **30** 12 c. black and blue .. .. — 27·00 1·50
a. Opt double .. .. .. † † £300
b. Perf 13½–14 .. .. 18·00 26·00 1·50
D 9 12 c. black & ultram (*p* 13½–14) 42·00 42·00 —
D10 **31** 18 c. black and deep green .. 24·00 38·00 3·00
a. Opt inverted .. .. £170 £350 —
b. Perf 13½–14 .. .. 32·00 42·00 3·00
ba. Opt double .. .. .. † † £200
D11 **32** 24 c. blue and rose-lake .. .. 26·00 42·00 3·00
a. Opt double .. .. .. † † —
b. Perf 13½–14 .. .. 14·00 38·00 —
c. Perf 13½–14, comp 14½–15 ..
D8 & D11 Optd "Specimen" .. *Set of* 2 50·00

1897. *Stamps of* 1897 *optd with Type* D **1.** *P* 14½–15.

A. *Vertically*
D12 2 c. black and lake .. .. .. 3·25 6·50 50
a. Perf 13½–14 .. .. .. 13·00

B. *Horizontally*
D13 2 c. black and lake .. .. .. 18·00 40·00
D14 8 c. black and brown-purple .. .. 16·00 30·00
a. Stop after "DUE." .. .. .. 17·00 42·00
D12 & D14 Optd "Specimen" .. *Set of* 2 45·00

1901. *Issue of* 1897–1902 *optd with Type* D **1.** *P* 13½–14.

A. *Vertically* (*reading upwards*)
D15 2 c. black and green .. .. .. 10·00 15·00 60
a. Perf 13½–14, comp 12–13 .. — 40·00 —
b. Perf 16 .. ..
c. Perf 12–13 .. ..
d. Opt reading downwards ..
D16 3 c. green and rosy mauve .. .. 8·00 10·00 60
a. Stop after "DUE" .. .. 27·00 45·00 —
b. Perf 14½–15 .. .. .. 3·25 8·00 40
c. Perf 13½–14, comp 14½–15 ..
d. Opt double .. ..
e. Opt double. Stop after "DUE" .. £130
D17 3 c. green & dull mauve (*p* 14½–15) 7·00 13·00 75
a. Stop after "DUE" .. .. 27·00 45·00 —
b. Opt double. Stop after "DUE" .. £200
D18 4 c. black and carmine .. .. 8·50 11·00 50
a. Perf 14½–15 .. .. ..
D19 5 c. black and orange-vermilion .. 9·00 15·00 75
a. Perf 14½–15 .. .. .. 17·00 19·00 —
b. Stop after "DUE" .. .. 25·00
D20 6 c. black and bistre-brown (Optd "Specimen" £25) .. .. — 12·00 40
a. Perf 14½–15 .. .. .. 2·75 10·00 40
b. Perf 13½–14, comp 12–13 ..
D20*c* 8 c. black and brown-purple (*p* 16) ..
D21 8 c. black and brown .. .. ..
a. Perf 14½–15 .. .. .. 3·00 8·50 40
ab. Opt reading downwards ..
D22 12 c. black and dull blue .. .. 26·00 65·00 2·00
a. Perf 14½–15 .. .. ..
D23 18 c. black and green (No. 108) ..
a. Perf 16 .. ..
D24 18 c. black and green (No. 110) .. 20·00 65·00 2·00
a. Perf 13½–14, comp 12–13 .. 27·00 65·00 2·00
D25 24 c. blue and lake (No. 109) .. — 22·00 60
D26 24 c. blue and lake (No. 111) ..
a. Perf 14½–15 .. .. .. 12·00 50·00 1·00

B. *Horizontally*
D27 2 c. black and green .. .. 38·00 50·00 3·00
D28 8 c. black and brown (*p* 14½–15) .. 50·00 60·00 4·00
a. Stop after "DUE".. .. .. 65·00 80·00 —

An example of the 5 c. value, No. D19a, has been seen clearly postmarked 1899.

1902–5. *Stamps of* 1901–5 *optd* "British Protectorate," *further optd with Type* D **1.** *P* 13½–14. A. *Vertically* (1902).
D29 2 c. black and green (*p* 16) .. .. .. — £140
D30 3 c. green and rosy mauve .. .. 70·00 85·00
D31 5 c. black and orange-vermilion (*p* 14½–15) £100 85·00
D32 8 c. black and brown .. .. .. 90·00 75·00
D33 24 c. blue and lake .. .. .. — 70·00

B. *Horizontally, at top of stamp* (1904–5)
D34 2 c. black and green (*p* 14½–15) .. .. 80·00 50·00
a. Perf 16 .. .. 60·00 70·00
D35 4 c. black and carmine .. .. .. 70·00 19·00

C. *Horizontally, at centre of stamp* (1904–5)
D35*a* 1 c. black and bistre-brown.. .. — — 23·00
b. Perf 14½–15 .. .. £250 — 23·00
D36 2 c. black and green.. .. .. 2·50 1·25 10
a. Perf 14½–15 .. .. .. 45·00 45·00 —
D37 3 c. green and rosy mauve .. .. 1·75 1·00 10
a. Perf 14½–15 .. .. .. 45·00 25·00 —
ab. "POSTAGE DUE" double ..
D38 4 c. black and carmine .. .. 4·50 4·00 20
a. "POSTAGE DUE" double .. 65·00 — 60·00
b. Perf 14½–15 .. .. .. 3·00 6·00 20
D39 5 c. black and orange-vermilion .. 5·00 3·00 20
a. Perf 14½–15 .. .. .. 17·00 16·00 —
D40 6 c. black and bistre-brown.. .. 6·50 5·50 25
a. "POSTAGE DUE" inverted .. † † 90·00
b. "POSTAGE DUE" double .. † — —
c. No stop after "PROTECTORATE" .. ..
d. Perf 16 .. .. 20·00 20·00 —
D41 8 c. black and brown .. .. 13·00 4·00 40
a. No stop after "PROTECTORATE" .. .. 38·00 35·00 —
D42 10 c. brown and slate-lilac .. .. 50·00 22·00 1·00
a. No stop after "PROTECTORATE" .. ..
D42*b* 10 c. brown and slate-blue .. .. 26·00 12·00 1·00
D43 12 c. black and blue .. .. 6·50 11·00 1·00
D44 16 c. green and chestnut .. .. 12·50 14·00 1·00
D45 18 c. black and green.. .. .. 4·00 10·00 1·00
a. "POSTAGE DUE" double .. £400 † 45·00
b. Imperf between (vert pair) .. — — £300
D46 24 c. blue and lake .. .. .. 6·50 17·00 1·00
a. Perf 14½–15 .. .. ..
b. "POSTAGE DUE" double .. £200 † 75·00

D. *Horizontally. Optd locally, with stop after* "DUE." (1904–5)
D47 1 c. black and bistre-brown .. .. 3·25 35·00 —
a. With raised stop after "DUE." .. 4·75 35·00 —

No. D35*a*/*b* are usually found cancelled-to-order suggesting that they came from remainder stocks which were not issued, but we have also seen one unused example of No. D35*a* and two of No. D35b.

1919–24. *Stamps of* 1909–22, *optd with Type* D **1.** *P* 13½–14.

A. *Horizontally at top of stamp*
D48 4 c. black and scarlet (1919) .. .. 45·00 11·00

B. *Horizontally towards foot of stamp*
D49 2 c. black and green (2.24) .. .. 5·50 32·00
a. Perf 14½–15 .. .. .. 7·00 32·00
D50 3 c. black and green .. .. .. 3·25 12·00
D51 4 c. black and scarlet .. .. .. 70 1·00
D52 5 c. black and yellow-brown .. .. 4·00 8·00
D53 6 c. black and olive-green .. .. 3·75 7·00
D53*a* 6 c. black and apple-green .. ..
D54 8 c. black and rose-lake .. .. 1·25 1·25
D55 10 c. black and turquoise-blue (7.24) .. 7·00 11·00
a. Perf 14½–15 .. .. .. 42·00 60·00
D56 12 c. black and deep blue (7.24) .. 16·00 22·00
D56*a* 16 c. black and red-brown .. .. 16·00 48·00
b. Black and brown-lake .. .. 6·00 32·00
D49/56a .. .. .. *Set of* 9 42·00 £110
D49 & D56*a* Optd "Specimen" .. *Set of* 2 45·00

Nos. D51/3 also exist with the overprint towards the centre of the stamp.

1926–31. *As* 1920–31, *but perf* 12½.
D57 2 c. black and claret .. .. 40 1·7
D58 3 c. black and green .. .. 1·75 7·0
D59 4 c. black and scarlet.. .. .. .. 50 1·2
D60 5 c. black and yellow-brown .. .. .. 3·50 25·0
D61 6 c. black and olive-green .. .. .. 2·75 1·7
D62 8 c. black and carmine .. .. .. 2·00 6·5
D63 10 c. black and turquoise-blue .. .. 4·00 35·0
D64 12 c. black and deep blue .. .. .. 9·00 45·0
D65 16 c. black and red-brown (1931) .. .. 23·00 75·0
D57/65 .. .. *Set of* 9 42·00 £18

Nos. D49/65 exist with two types of opt; A. Thick letters; pointed beard to "G". B. Thinner letters; "G" with square end to beard and "D" more open. No. D56*a* is Type B. and D56*b*, Type A.

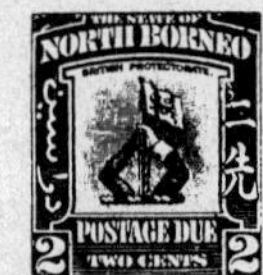

D **2** Crest of the Company

(Recess Waterlow)

1939 (1 Jan). *P* 12½.
D66 D **2** 2 c. brown .. .. 4·50 50·0
D67 4 c. scarlet .. .. 5·50 50·0
D68 6 c. violet .. .. 12·00 65·0
D69 8 c. green .. .. 12·00 £10
D70 10 c. blue .. .. 25·00 £14
D66/70 .. .. *Set of* 5 55·00 £35
D66/70 Perf "Specimen" .. .. *Set of* 5 £140

The stamps of North Borneo were withdrawn on 30 June 1964. For later issues see SABAH.

JAPANESE OCCUPATION OF NORTH BORNEO

Japanese forces landed in Northern Borneo on 16 December 1941 and the whole of North Borneo had been occupied by 1[9] January 1942.

Brunei, North Borneo, Sarawak and, after a short period, Labuan, were administered as a single territory by the Japanese. Until September–October 1942, previous stamp issues, without overprint, continued to be used in conjunction with existing postmarks. From the Autumn of 1942 onwards unoverprinted stamps of Japan were made available and examples can be found used from the area for much of the remainder of the War. Japanese Occupation issues for Brunei, North Borneo and Sarawak were equally valid throughout the combined territory but not, in practice, equally available.

PRICES FOR STAMPS ON COVER	
Nos. J1/17	*from* × 4
Nos. J18/19	*from* × 5
Nos. J20/32	*from* × 25
Nos. J33/4	*from* × 2
Nos. J35/48	*from* × 6

1942 (Sept). *Stamps of North Borneo optd in one line as T* **1** *o[f] Japanese Occupation of Brunei.* (*a*) *Nos.* 303/17.
J 1 1 c. green and red-brown .. .. .. 80·00 £10
J 2 2 c. purple and greenish blue .. .. 75·00 90·0
J 3 3 c. slate-blue and green .. .. .. 70·00 90·0
J 4 4 c. bronze-green and violet .. .. 35·00 70·0
J 5 6 c. deep blue and claret .. .. .. 70·00 90·0
J 6 8 c. scarlet .. .. 70·00 90·0
J 7 10 c. violet and bronze-green .. .. 70·00 90·0
J 8 12 c. green and bright blue .. .. .. 90·00 £15
J 9 15 c. blue-green and brown .. .. .. 90·00 £15
J10 20 c. violet and slate-blue £120 £17
J11 25 c. green and chocolate £120 £17
J12 50 c. chocolate and violet £170 £20
J13 $1 brown and carmine £150 £25
J14 $2 violet and olive-green £250 £35
J15 $5 indigo and pale blue £325 £45

(*b*) *Nos.* 318 *and* 319 ("WAR TAX")
J16 1 c. green and red-brown £140 £12
J17 2 c. purple and greenish blue £225 £15

1 Mt Kinabalu

2 Borneo Scene

(Litho G. Kolff, Batavia)

1943 (29 Apr). *P* 12½.
J18 **1** 4 c. red .. .. 10·00 15·0
J19 **2** 8 c. blue.. .. .. 10·00 15·0

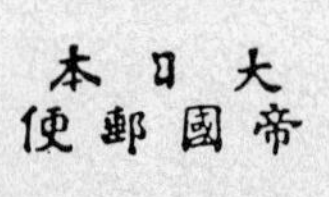
北ボルネオ
(3)

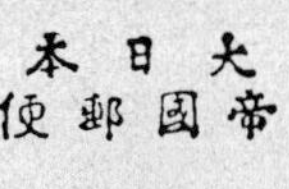

(3*a*)

("Imperial Japanese Postal Service North Borneo")

1944 (30 Sept). *Nos. 303/15 of North Borneo optd as T* **3**.

J20 1 c. green and red-brown . . . . . . 2·00 3·25
J21 2 c. purple and greenish blue . . . . . . 2·50 3·25
J22 3 c. slate-blue and green . . . . . . 2·00 3·00
J23 4 c. bronze-green and violet . . . . . . 2·50 3·50
J24 6 c. deep blue and claret . . . . . . 2·25 3·00
J25 8 c. scarlet . . . . 3·75 5·50
J26 10 c. violet and bronze-green . . . . . . 2·50 4·50
J27 12 c. green and bright blue . . . . . . 2·75 4·50
J28 15 c. blue-green and brown . . . . . . 3·25 6·50
J29 20 c. violet and slate-blue . . . . . . 9·50 15·00
J30 25 c. green and chocolate . . . . . . 9·50 17·00
J31 50 c. chocolate and violet . . . . . . 24·00 35·00
J32 $1 brown and carmine . . . . . . 42·00 55·00
J20/32 . . . . *Set of* 13 £100 £140

The spacing between the second and third lines of the overprint is 12 mm on the horizontal stamps, and 15 mm on the upright.

1944. *No.* J7 *with T* **3** *opt in addition.*

J32*a* 10 c. violet and bronze-green £150 £275

The 2 c., 3 c., 8 c., 12 c. and 15 c. stamps of the 1942 issue are also known with Type **3** opt.

1945. *No.* J1 *surch with T* **3***a*.

J33 **81** $2 on 1 c. green and red-brown . . £2500 £1800

本月大

オネルボ北

(4) 5 Girl War-worker 6 ("North Borneo")

1945 (?). *North Borneo No.* 315 *surch with T* **4**.

J34 $5 on $1 brown and carmine £2500 £1900

1945. *Contemporary stamps of Japan as T* **5** (*various subjects*) *optd with T* **6** *at Chinese Press, Kuching.*

J35 1 s. red-brown (No. 391) . . . . . . 1·60 3·50
J36 2 s. scarlet (No. 318) . . . . . . 1·60 3·50
J37 3 s. emerald-green (No. 319) . . . . . . 1·40 3·50
J38 4 s. yellow-green (No. 395) . . . . . . 1·75 3·50
J39 5 s. claret (No. 396) . . . . . . 1·75 3·75
J40 6 s. orange (No. 322) . . . . . . 2·00 4·50
J41 8 s. violet (No. 324) . . . . . . 1·75 4·50
J42 10 s. carmine and pink (No. 399) . . . . 2·00 4·50
J43 15 s. blue (No. 401) . . . . . . 2·00 4·00
J44 20 s. blue-slate (No. 328) . . . . . . 55·00 70·00
J45 25 s. brown and chocolate (No. 329) . . . . 42·00 50·00
J46 30 s. turquoise-blue (No. 330) . . . . £130 85·00
J47 50 s. olive and bistre (No. 331) . . . . 38·00 48·00
J48 1 y. red-brown and chocolate (No. 332) . . 38·00 50·00
J35/48 . . . . . . *Set of* 14 £275 £300

Designs:—2 s. General Nogi; 3 s. Hydro-electric Works; 4 s. Hyuga Monument and Mt Fuji; 5 s. Admiral Togo; 6 s. Garambi Lighthouse, Formosa; 8 s. Meiji Shrine; 10 s. Palms and map of S.E. Asia; 15 s. Airman; 20 s. Mt Fuji and cherry blossoms; 25 s. Horyu Temple; 30 s. Torii, Itsukushima Shrine at Miyajima; 50 s. Kinkaku Temple; 1 y. Great Buddha, Kamakura.

Examples of some values have been found with hand-painted forged overprints.

Northern Nigeria

The Protectorate of Northern Nigeria was formed on 1 January 1900 from the northern part of the Niger Company Territories. Only one post office existed in this area, at Lokoja, and this continued to use unoverprinted stamps of GREAT BRITAIN until the arrival of Nos. 1/9 during March 1900.

PRICES FOR STAMPS ON COVER

Nos. 1/7	*from* × 6
Nos. 8/9	—
Nos. 10/16	*from* × 5
Nos. 17/19	—
Nos. 20/6	*from* × 5
No. 27	—
Nos. 28/37	*from* × 5
Nos. 38/9	—
Nos. 40/9	*from* × 5
Nos. 50/2	—

PRINTERS. All issues were typographed by De La Rue & Co.

1

2

1900 (Mar). *Wmk Crown CA. P* 14.

1 **1** ½d. dull mauve and green . . . . 75 4·00
2 1d. dull mauve and carmine . . . . 1·25 1·75
3 2d. dull mauve and yellow . . . . 2·50 13·00
4 2½d. dull mauve and ultramarine . . 5·50 13·00
5 **2** 5d. dull mauve and chestnut . . . . 10·00 22·00
6 6d. dull mauve and violet . . . . 11·00 14·00
7 **1** 1s. green and black . . . . 12·00 27·00
8 2s. 6d. green and ultramarine . . . . 55·00 95·00
9 10s. green and brown £160 £300
1/9 . . . . . . *Set of* 9 £225 £425
1/9 Optd "Specimen" . . *Set of* 9 £200

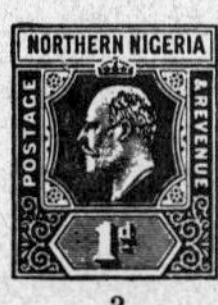
3

4

1902 (1 July). *Wmk Crown CA. P* 14.

10 **3** ½d. dull purple and green 50 60
11 1d. dull purple and carmine 60 20
12 2d. dull purple and yellow . . . . 50 1·40
13 2½d. dull purple and ultramarine . . . . 40 2·25
14 **4** 5d. dull purple and chestnut . . . . 1·50 4·50
15 6d. dull purple and violet . . . . 3·00 4·50
16 **3** 1s. green and black . . . . 2·50 3·25
17 2s. 6d. green and ultramarine . . . . 7·50 18·00
18 10s. green and brown . . . . 45·00 48·00
10/18 . . . . . . *Set of* 9 55·00 75·00
10/18 Optd "Specimen" . . . . *Set of* 9 £150

1904 (April). *Wmk Mult Crown CA. P* 14.

19 **4** £25 green and carmine, **O** . . £24000

1905 (Aug–Oct). *Wmk Mult Crown CA. P* 14.

20 **3** ½d. dull purple and green, **OC** (Oct) . . 1·25 1·00
21 1d. dull purple and carmine, **OC** . . 1·25 20
22 2d. dull purple and yellow, **OC** (Oct) . . 2·25 4·50
23 2½d. dull purple and ultramarine, **O** (Oct) 4·25 3·75
24 **4** 5d. dull purple and chestnut, **OC** (Oct) . . 8·50 12·00
25 6d. dull purple and violet, **OC** (Oct) . . 9·00 9·50
26 **3** 1s. green and black, **OC** (Oct) . . 13·00 18·00
27 2s. 6d. green and ultramarine, **OC** (Oct) 16·00 18·00
20/7 . . . . . . *Set of* 8 50·00 60·00

1910 (Jan)–**11.** *Wmk Mult Crown CA. P* 14.

28 **3** ½d. green, **O** (4.10) 40 15
29 1d. carmine, **O** (1.10) 30 15
30 2d. grey, **O** (10.11) . . . . 70 2·00
31 2½d. blue, **O** (10.10) . . . . 60 2·50
32 **4** 3d. purple/*yellow*, **C** (9.11) 70 30
34 5d. dull purple and olive-green, **C** (2.11) 1·75 3·25
35 6d. dull purple and purple, **C** (11.10) . . 4·00 7·50
a. Dull and bright purple (1911) . . 1·25 3·50
36 **3** 1s. black/*green*, **C** (11.10) 90 55
37 2s. 6d. black and red/*blue*, **C** (3.11) . . 6·50 12·00
38 **4** 5s. green and red/*yellow*, **C** (9.11) . . 17·00 40·00
39 **3** 10s. green and red/*green*, **C** (3.11) . . 40·00 45·00
28/39 . . . . . . *Set of* 11 60·00 £100
28/39 Optd "Specimen" . . . . *Set of* 11 £175

5

6

1912. *Wmk Mult Crown CA. P* 14.

40 **5** ½d. deep green, **O** 25 20
41 1d. red, **O** 25 15
42 2d. grey, **O** . . . . 90 2·25
43 **6** 3d. purple/*yellow*, **C** 40 60
44 4d. black and red/*yellow*, **C** 40 40
45 5d. dull purple and olive-green, **C** . . 1·00 3·25
46 6d. dull and bright purple, **C** . . 1·00 2·25
47 9d. dull purple and carmine, **C** . . 1·00 4·00
48 **5** 1s. black/*green*, **C** . . . . 1·50 50
49 2s. 6d. black and red/*blue*, **C** . . 7·00 18·00
50 **6** 5s. green and red/*yellow*, **C** . . 16·00 42·00
51 **5** 10s. green and red/*green*, **C** . . 30·00 45·00
52 **6** £1 purple and black/*red*, **C** . . £160 £150
40/52 . . . . . . *Set of* 13 £190 £240
40/52 Optd "Specimen" . . . . *Set of* 13 £225

Since 1 January 1914, Northern Nigeria has formed part of NIGERIA.

PRICES OF SETS

Set prices are given for many issues, generally those containing three stamps or more. Definitive sets include one of each value or major colour change, but do not cover different perforations, die types or minor shades. Where a choice is possible the set prices are based on the cheapest versions of the stamps included in the listings.

Northern Rhodesia

PRICES FOR STAMPS ON COVER TO 1945

Nos. 1/21	*from* × 2
Nos. 22/4	*from* × 5
Nos. 25/45	*from* × 2
Nos. D1/4	*from* × 15

1

2

(Eng W. G. Fairweather. Recess Waterlow)

1925 (1 April)–**29.** *Wmk Mult Script CA. P* 12½.

1 **1** ½d. green 20 10
2 1d. brown 20 10
3 1½d. carmine-red 20 20
4 2d. yellow-brown 30 10
5 3d. ultramarine 75 25
6 4d. violet 90 35
7 6d. slate-grey 90 15
8 8d. rose-purple . . . . . . 3·75 13·00
9 10d. olive-green . . . . . . 3·75 12·00
10 **2** 1s. yellow-brown and black . . . . 1·00 65
11 2s. brown and ultramarine . . . . 5·50 10·00
12 2s. 6d. black and green . . . . 6·00 4·25
13 3s. violet and blue (1929) . . . . 15·00 9·00
14 5s. slate-grey and violet . . . . 10·00 7·50
15 7s. 6d. rose-purple and black . . . . 85·00 £110
16 10s. green and black . . . . 40·00 45·00
17 20s. carmine-red and rose-purple . . £150 £160
1/17 . . . . . . *Set of* 17 £300 £350
1/17 Optd/Perf "Specimen" . . *Set of* 17 £1000

1935 (6 May). *Silver Jubilee. As Nos.* 91/4 *of Antigua.*

18 1d. light blue and olive-green 50 20
f. Diagonal line by turret . . . . 22·00
h. Dot by flagstaff . . . . 22·00
i. Dash by turret . . . . 22·00
19 2d. green and indigo 50 30
f. Diagonal line by turret . . . . 22·00
g. Dot to left of chapel . . . . 22·00
20 3d. brown and deep blue . . . . 1·75 2·50
g. Dot to left of chapel . . . . 45·00
21 6d. slate and purple . . . . 1·75 1·00
a. Frame printed double, one albino . . £1400
h. Dot by flagstaff . . . . 45·00
18/21 . . . . . . *Set of* 4 4·00 3·50
18/21 Perf "Specimen" . . . . *Set of* 4 70·00

For illustrations of plate varieties see Omnibus section following Zululand.

THERN-RHODE

Hyphen between "NORTHERN" AND "RHODESIA" (R. 9/6)

1937 (12 May). *Coronation. As Nos.* 13/15 *of Aden, but ptd by* B.W. *P* 11 × 11½.

22 1½d. carmine 40 35
23 2d. buff 70 35
24 3d. blue . . . . . . 1·25 1·75
a. Hyphen flaw . . . . 55·00
22/4 . . . . . . *Set of* 3 2·10 2·25
22/4 Perf "Specimen" . . . . *Set of* 3 50·00

3

4

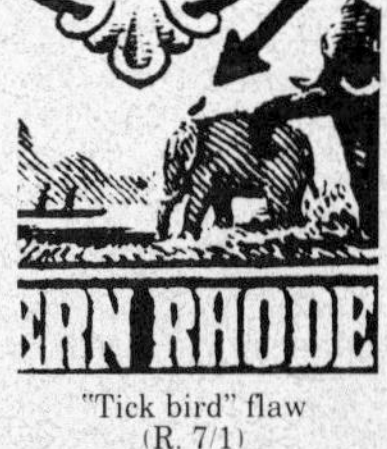

"Tick bird" flaw (R. 7/1)

(Recess Waterlow)

1938 (1 Mar)–**52.** *Wmk Mult Script CA. P* 12½.

25	3	½d. green	10	10
26		½d. chocolate (15.11.51)	10	70
		a. Perf 12½ × 14 (22.10.52)	50	2·50
27		1d. brown	10	10
		a. Chocolate (1948)	35	30
28		1d. green (15.11.51)	60	60
29		1½d. carmine-red	18·00	25
		a. Imperf between (horiz pair)	£8000	
		b. "Tick bird" flaw	£250	25·00
30		1½d. yellow-brown (10.1.41)	10	10
		b. "Tick bird" flaw	15·00	10·00
31		2d. yellow-brown	55·00	70
32		2d. carmine-red (10.1.41)	10	10
33		2d. purple (1.12.51)	45	30
34		3d. ultramarine	10	10
35		3d. scarlet (1.12.51)	50	50
36		4d. dull violet	10	10
37		4½d. blue (5.5.52)	40	2·25
38		6d. grey	15	10
39		9d. violet (5.5.52)	40	2·00
40	4	1s. yellow-brown and black	25	10
41		2s. 6d. black and green	4·50	1·25
42		3s. violet and blue	7·50	4·00
43		5s. grey and dull violet	6·00	3·00
44		10s. green and black	5·00	7·50
45		20s. carmine-red and rose-purple	23·00	35·00
25/45		*Set of* 21	£110	50·00
25/45 Perf "Specimen"		*Set of* 15	£250	

Nos. 26a and 28 exist in coils, constructed from normal sheets.

1946 (26 Nov). *Victory. As Nos.* 28/9 *of Aden. P* 13½ × 14.

46	1½d. red-orange	10	10
	a. Perf 14 × 13½	1·25	1·00
47	2d. carmine	10	10
46/7 Perf "Specimen"	*Set of* 2	45·00	

1948 (1 Dec). *Royal Silver Wedding. As Nos.* 30/1 *of Aden, but inscr* "NORTHERN RHODESIA" (*recess* 20s.).

48	1½d. orange	25	10
49	20s. brown-lake	35·00	38·00

1949 (10 Oct). *75th Anniv of U.P.U. As Nos.* 114/17 *of Antigua.*

50	2d. carmine	20	30
51	3d. deep blue	75	1·00
52	6d. grey	75	1·00
53	1s. red-orange	75	1·00
50/3	*Set of* 4	2·25	3·00

5 Cecil Rhodes and Victoria Falls

(Recess D.L.R.)

1953 (30 May). *Birth Centenary of Cecil Rhodes. Wmk Mult Script CA. P* 12 × 11½.

54	5	½d. brown	15	30
55		1d. green	15	40
56		2d. mauve	15	15
57		4½d. blue	40	3·25
58		1s. orange and black	45	1·50
54/8		*Set of* 5	1·10	5·00

6 Arms of the Rhodesias and Nyasaland

(Recess Waterlow)

1953 (30 May). *Rhodes Centenary Exhibition. Wmk Mult Script CA. P* 14 × 13½.

59	6	6d. violet	15	15

1953 (2 June). *Coronation. As No.* 47 *of Aden.*

60	1½d. black and yellow-orange	15	10

7 8

(Recess Waterlow)

1953 (15 Sept). *Wmk Mult Script CA. P* 12½ × 14 (*pence values*) *or* 12½ × 13½ (*shilling values*).

61	7	½d. deep brown	45	10
62		1d. bluish green	45	10
63		1½d. orange-brown	40	10
64		2d. reddish purple	50	10
65		3d. scarlet	40	10
66		4d. slate-lilac	75	30
67		4½d. deep blue	40	60
68		6d. grey-black	70	10
69		9d. violet	40	40
70	8	1s. orange-brown and black	40	10
71		2s. 6d. black and green	3·50	2·75
72		5s. grey and dull purple	5·00	12·00
73		10s. green and black	5·50	14·00
74		20s. rose-red and rose-purple	13·00	22·00
61/74		*Set of* 14	29·00	45·00

For issues from 1954 to 1963, see RHODESIA AND NYASALAND.

9 Arms 10

(Photo Harrison)

1963 (10 Dec). *Arms black, orange and blue; portrait and inscriptions black; background colours below. P* 14½ (*T* **9**) *or* 13½ × 13 (*T* **10**).

75	9	½d. bright violet	10	25
		a. Value omitted	£300	
76		1d. light blue	15	10
		a. Value omitted	6·00	
77		2d. brown	15	10
78		3d. yellow	15	10
		a. Value omitted	48·00	
		b. Value and orange (eagle) omitted	70·00	
		c. Eagle printed double	95·00	
79		4d. green	20	10
		a. Value omitted	60·00	
80		6d. light olive-green	20	10
		a. Value omitted	£160	
81		9d. yellow-brown	20	10
		a. Value omitted	£110	
		b. Value and orange (eagle) omitted	£170	
82		1s. slate-purple	20	10
83		1s. 3d. bright purple	70	10
84	10	2s. orange	70	60
85		2s. 6d. lake-brown	80	80
86		5s. magenta	2·50	3·50
87		10s. mauve	2·50	4·50
88		20s. blue	5·00	14·00
		a. Value omitted	£850	
75/88		*Set of* 14	12·00	21·00

Nos. 75/6 exist in coils, constructed from normal sheets.

A used example of the 3d. has been seen on which only the orange (eagle) has been omitted.

POSTAGE DUE STAMPS

D 1 D 2

(Typo D.L.R.)

1929–52. *Wmk Mult Script CA. P* 14.

D1	D 1	1d. grey-black	2·50	2·50
		a. *Black.* Chalky paper (22.1.52)	4·00	7·00
		b. Error. St. Edward's Crown W9*b*, C	£250	
D2		2d. grey-black	3·00	3·00
D3		3d. grey-black	3·00	20·00
		aa. *Black,* Chalky paper (22.1.52)	7·00	26·00
		a. Error. Crown missing, W9*a*, C	£120	
		b. Error. St. Edward's Crown, W9*b*, C	£100	
D4		4d. grey-black	5·00	22·00
D1/4		*Set of* 4	12·00	42·00
D1/4 Perf "Specimen"		*Set of* 4	80·00	

The 2d. is known bisected and used as a 1d. on understamped letters from South Africa at Chingola in May 1950.

Following the increase in the internal letter rate from 1½d. to 2d. on 1 July 1953 stocks of postage due stamps at Mkushi became exhausted. As an emergency measure the sub-postmaster was authorised to surcharge examples of Nos. 28 and 55 "POSTAGE DUE 1d." in red by typewriter. Examples properly used on cover between 6 July and 12 September 1953 are of considerable scarcity.

(Des D. Smith. Litho Govt Ptr, Lusaka)

1963 (10 Dec). *P* 12½.

D 5	D 2	1d. orange	25	1·25
D 6		2d. deep blue	25	1·50
D 7		3d. lake	35	2·00
D 8		4d. ultramarine	50	2·75
D 9		6d. purple	1·00	3·25
D10		1s. light emerald	3·00	8·50
		a. Imperf (vert pair)	£160	
		b. Block of four imperf horiz and imp between vert	£475	
D5/10		*Set of* 6	4·75	17·00

In all values the stamps in the right-hand vertical row of the sheet are imperforate on the right.

The stamps of Northern Rhodesia were withdrawn on 23 October 1964 when the territory attained independence. For later issues see ZAMBIA.

North-West Pacific Islands

(*see* New Guinea)

Nova Scotia

Organised postal services in Nova Scotia date from April 1754 when the first of a series of Deputy Postmasters was appointed, under the authority of the British G.P.O. This arrangement continued until 6 July 1851 when the colony assumed responsibility for its postal affairs.

For illustrations of the handstamp types see BRITISH POST OFFICES ABROAD notes, following GREAT BRITAIN.

AMHERST

CROWNED-CIRCLE HANDSTAMPS

CC1 CC 1 AMHERST. N.S.(R) (March 1845)
Price on cover £1000

ST. MARGARETS BAY

CROWNED-CIRCLE HANDSTAMPS

CC2 CC 1 ST. MARGARETS BAY. N.S.(R) (5.6.1845)
Price on cover £2250

Nos. CC1/2 were later used during temporary shortages of stamps, struck in red or black.

PRICES FOR STAMPS ON COVER	
Nos. 1/8	*from* × 2
Nos. 9/29	*from* × 5

1 2

Crown and Heraldic Flowers of United Kingdom and Mayflower of Nova Scotia.

(Recess P.B.)

1851 (1 Sept)–**57.** *Bluish paper. Imperf.*

1	1	1d. red-brown (12.5.53)	£2500	£400
		a. Bisected (½d.) (on cover)	†	£50000
2	2	3d. deep blue	£1500	£350
		a. Bisected (1½d.) (on cover)	†	£2750
3		3d. bright blue	£900	£150
		a. Bisected (1½d.) (on cover)	†	£2750
4		3d. pale blue (1857)	£700	£180
		a. Bisected (1½d.) (on cover)	†	£2750
5		6d. yellow-green	£4750	£400
		a. Bisected (3d.) (on cover)	†	£3500
6		6d. deep green (1857)	£12000	£750
		a. Bisected (3d.) (on cover)	†	£6000
		b. Quartered (1½d.) (on cover)	†	£38000
7		1s. cold violet	£19000	£7000
		a. Bisected (6d.) (on cover)	†	£42000
		b. Quartered (3d.) (on cover)	†	£55000
7*c*		1s. deep purple (1851)	£15000	£5000
		d. Watermarked	£20000	£7000
8		1s. purple (1857)	£14000	£3000
		a. Bisected (6d.) (on cover)	†	£32000

The watermark on No. 7d consists of the whole or part of a letter from the name "P. H. SAUNDERS" (the papermakers).

The stamps formerly catalogued on almost white paper are probably some from which the bluish paper has been discharged.

Reprints of all four values were made in 1890 on thin, hard, white paper. The 1d. is brown, the 3d. blue, the 6d. deep green, and the 1s. violet-black.

The 3d. bisects are only found used on cover to make up the 7½d. rate.

3 4 5

(Recess American Bank Note Co, New York)

1860–63. *P* 12. (*a*) *Yellowish paper.*

9	3	1 c. jet black	3·00	12·00
		a. Bisected (½ c.) (on cover)	†	£10000
10		1 c. grey-black	3·00	12·00
11		2 c. grey-purple	11·00	15·00
11*a*		2 c. purple	17·00	14·00
12		5 c. blue	£200	16·00
13		5 c. deep blue	£200	16·00
14	4	8½ c. deep green	2·50	
15		8½ c. yellow-green	2·50	
16		10 c. scarlet	12·00	18·00
17	5	12½ c. black	24·00	16·00
17*a*		12½ c. greyish black	—	16·00
		(*b*) *White paper*		
18	3	1 c. black	3·00	12·00
		a. Imperf between (horiz pair)	£150	
19		1 c. grey	3·00	12·00
20		2 c. dull purple	3·25	14·00
21		2 c. purple	3·25	14·00
22		2 c. grey-purple	3·25	14·00
		a. Bisected (1 c.) (on cover)	†	£4500
23		2 c. slate-purple	3·25	12·00
24		5 c. blue	£200	16·00
25		5 c. deep blue	£200	16·00

26	4	8½ c. deep green	16·00	35·00
27		10 c. scarlet	3·50	18·00
28		10 c. vermilion	4·00	18·00
		a. Bisected (5 c.) (on cover) ..	†	£1200
29	5	12½ c. black	19·00	22·00

Since 1868 Nova Scotia has used stamps of the Dominion of Canada.

Nyasaland Protectorate

PRICES FOR STAMPS ON COVER TO 1945

Nos. 1/9a	*from* × 15
Nos. 10/19	—
No. 20	*from* × 10
Nos. 21/6	*from* × 5
Nos. 27/31	—
Nos. 32/7	*from* × 6
Nos. 38/42	—
Nos. 43/7	*from* × 12
Nos. 48/52	—
No. 53	*from* × 15
No. 54	*from* × 2
No. 55	*from* × 4
Nos. 55b/7a	*from* × 7
Nos. 57d/63	*from* × 6
Nos. 64/71	—
Nos. 72/9	*from* × 5
Nos. 80/2	—
Nos. 83/95	*from* × 4
Nos. 96/9	—
Nos. 100/57	*from* × 2

By 1891 the territory west of Lake Nyasa was recognised as being under British protection and the southern, eastern and northern borders had been delineated with the Portuguese and German governments.

I. BRITISH CENTRAL AFRICA

A protectorate under the name "Nyassaland Districts" was declared on 14 May 1891, the title being changed to the "British Central Africa Protectorate" on 22 February 1893. Such a description had been in use for some time previously and the handwritten notice of 20 July 1891, announcing the introduction of postal services, described the area as "British Central Africa".

Until 1895 the British South Africa Company contributed to the revenues of the protectorate administration which, in return governed North Eastern Rhodesia. Stamps of the British South Africa Company overprinted "B.C.A." were used in both areas until 1895 and were retained for use in North Eastern Rhodesia until supplies were exhausted, probably in 1899.

B.C.A. (1) **B.C.A. FOUR SHILLINGS.** (2) **ONE PENNY.** (3)

1891 (April)–**1895.** *Stamps of Rhodesia optd as T* **1.** *P* 14, 14½.

1	1	1d. black	1·50	2·00
2	4	2d. sea-green and vermilion	1·50	2·50
		a. Bisected (1d.) (on cover) (1895) ..	†	£1800
3		4d. reddish chestnut and black ..	1·50	3·75
4	1	6d. ultramarine	40·00	20·00
5		6d. deep blue	5·00	8·00
6	4	8d. rose-lake and ultramarine	12·00	28·00
6a		8d. red and ultramarine	23·00	42·00
7	1	1s. grey-brown	9·50	11·00
8		2s. vermilion	20·00	32·00
9		2s. 6d. grey-purple	38·00	48·00
9a		2s. 6d. lilac	42·00	48·00
10	4	3s. brown and green (1895)	45·00	48·00
11		4s. grey-black and vermilion (2.93) ..	45·00	60·00
12	1	5s. orange-yellow	45·00	48·00
13		10s. deep green	85·00	£100
14	2	£1 deep blue	£350	£375
15		£2 rose-red	£550	
16		£5 sage-green	£1100	
17		£10 brown	£2500	
1/14		.. .. *Set of* 13	£575	£675

The overprint varies on values up to 10s. Sets may be made with *thin* or *thick* letters.

The bisected 2d, No. 2a, was authorised for use at Blantyre, Chiromo and Zomba in July and October 1895.

1892 (Aug)–**93.** *Stamps of Rhodesia surch as T* **2.**

18	4	3s. on 4s. grey-black and vermilion (10.93)	£275	£275
19	1	4s. on 5s. orange-yellow	65·00	75·00

1895. *No.* 2 *surch at Cape Town with T* **3.**

20	4	1d. on 2d. sea-green and vermilion ..	6·00	25·00
		a. Surch double	£2750	£2000

Specimens are known with double surcharge, without stop after "PENNY". These are from a trial printing made at Blantyre, but it is believed that they were not issued to the public (*Price* £600 *un.*).

5 Arms of the Protectorate **6**

(Des Sir Harry Johnston. Litho D.L.R.)

1895. *No wmk. P* 14.

21	5	1d. black	5·50	5·00
22		2d. black and green	13·00	11·00
23		4d. black and reddish buff	25·00	26·00
24		6d. black and blue	28·00	6·00
25		1s. black and rose	40·00	20·00
26	6	2s. 6d. black and bright magenta ..	£110	£100
27		3s. black and yellow	70·00	26·00
28		5s. black and olive	90·00	80·00
29		£1 black and yellow-orange	£650	£350
30		£10 black and orange-vermilion ..	£2500	£2500
31		£25 black and blue-green	£4500	
21/8		.. .. *Set of* 8	£350	£250
21/9 Optd "Specimen"		.. .. *Set of* 9	£375	

Cancellations inscribed "BRITISH CENTRAL AFRICA" within a double-circle and with the name of a town across the centre or at foot were intended for use on stamps presented for the payment of the hut tax. Such marks can be found in black, violet or blue and are without date.

1896 (Feb). *Wmk Crown CA* (*T* **5**) *or CC* (*sideways*) (*T* **6**), *P* 14.

32	5	1d. black	3·00	4·50
33		2d. black and green	13·00	5·00
34		4d. black and orange-brown	15·00	17·00
35		6d. black and blue	12·00	9·00
36		1s. black and rose	17·00	10·00
37	6	2s. 6d. black and magenta	80·00	80·00
38		3s. black and yellow	60·00	28·00
39		5s. black and olive	80·00	90·00
40		£1 black and blue	£625	£350
41		£10 black and orange (Optd S. £175) ..	£3500	£2250
42		£25 black and green (Optd S. £325) ..	£6500	
32/9		.. .. *Set of* 8	£250	£210
32/40 Optd "Specimen"		.. .. *Set of* 9	£375	

7 **8**

(Typo D.L.R.)

1897 (Aug). *T* **7** (*wmk Crown CA*) *and* **8** (*wmk Crown CC*). *P* 14.

43	7	1d. black and ultramarine	1·00	50
44		2d. black and yellow	1·00	80
45		4d. black and carmine	5·00	1·50
46		6d. black and green	22·00	4·25
47		1s. black and dull purple	6·00	7·00
48	8	2s. 6d. black and ultramarine	32·00	35·00
49		3s. black and sea-green	£160	£180
50		4s. black and carmine	45·00	55·00
50a		10s. black and olive-green	80·00	90·00
51		£1 black and dull purple	£200	£140
52		£10 black and yellow (Optd S. £175) ..	£2750	£1400
43/51		.. .. *Set of* 10	£500	£450
43/51 Optd "Specimen"		.. .. *Set of* 10	£225	

ONE PENNY (9)

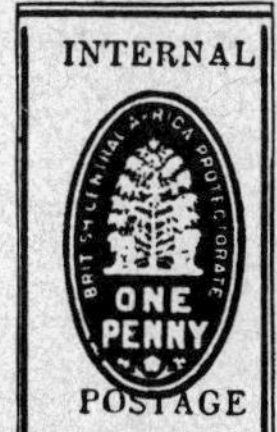

10

1897 (31 Dec). *No.* 49 *surch with T* **9**, *in red.*

53	8	1d. on 3s. black and sea-green	5·00	8·50
		a. "PNNEY" (R. 4/2)	£1100	£1200
		b. "PENN"	£650	£650
		c. Surch double	£450	

1898 (11 Mar). *Imperf.*

(*a*) *Setting I. The vertical frame lines of the stamps cross the space between the two rows of the sheet*

(i) *With the initials "J.G." or "J.T.G." on the back in black ink*

54	10	1d. vermilion and grey-blue	—	£450
		a. Without the initials	£1300	
		b. Without the initials and centre inverted	£6000	

(ii) *With a control number and letter or letters, printed in plain relief at the back*

55	10	1d. vermilion and grey-blue	—	£140

(*b*) *Setting II. The vertical frame lines do not cross the space between the rows except at the extreme ends of the sheet. Control as No.* 55.

55b	10	1d. vermilion and pale ultramarine	—	32·00
		c. Control on face	—	£3000
		d. Centre omitted (vert pair with normal)	£5500	
56		1d. vermilion and deep ultramarine	—	32·00
		a. Without Control at back ..	£850	65·00
		b. Control doubly impressed ..	—	£200

1898 (June). *Setting II. Control as No.* 55. *P* 12.

57	10	1d. vermilion and pale ultramarine ..	£800	12·00
57a		1d. vermilion and deep ultramarine ..	—	12·00
		ab. Without Control at back	£850	40·00
		ac. Two different Controls on back ..	—	£400
		ad. Control printed in black	£1000	

The two different settings of these stamps are each in 30 types, issued without gum.

1901. *Wmk Crown CA. P* 14.

57d	7	1d. dull purple and carmine-rose ..	85	40
57e		4d. dull purple and olive-green	4·00	4·50
58		6d. dull purple and brown	3·50	3·00
57d/8		.. .. *Set of* 3	7·50	7·00
57d/58 Optd "Specimen"		.. .. *Set of* 3	60·00	

11 **12**

(Typo D.L.R.)

1903–4. *T* **11** (*Wmk Crown CA*) *and* **12** (*Wmk Crown CC*). *P* 14.

59	11	1d. grey and carmine	2·25	25
60		2d. dull and bright purple	3·25	1·00
61		4d. grey-green and black	2·50	5·00
62		6d. grey and reddish buff	2·50	2·00
62a		1s. grey and blue	2·50	6·50
63	12	2s. 6d. grey-green and green	22·00	30·00
64		4s. dull and bright purple	45·00	60·00
65		10s. grey-green and black	60·00	95·00
66		£1 grey and carmine	£180	£150
67		£10 grey and blue (Optd S. £200) ..	£3500	£3250
59/66		.. .. *Set of* 9	£275	£300
59/66 Optd "Specimen"		.. .. *Set of* 9	£275	

1907. *T* **11.** *Wmk Mult Crown CA. P* 14.

68	1d. grey and carmine, **C**	1·25	90
69	2d. dull and bright purple, **C**	£8000	
70	4d. grey-green and black, **C**	£8000	
71	6d. grey and reddish buff, **C**	26·00	35·00

Nos. 69/70 were not issued in Nyasaland.

II. NYASALAND PROTECTORATE

The title of the Protectorate was changed again from 6 July 1907.

13 **14**

(Typo D.L.R.)

1908 (22 July). *P* 14. (*a*) *Wmk Crown CA.*

72	13	1s. black/*green*, **C**	1·40	4·50

(*b*) *Wmk Mult Crown CA*

73	13	½d. green, **O**	30	50
74		1d. carmine, **O**	60	15
75		3d. purple/*yellow*, **C**	1·00	2·00
76		4d. black and red/*yellow*, **C**	1·00	1·50
77		6d. dull purple and bright purple, **C** ..	3·75	6·00
78	14	2s. 6d. black and red/*blue*, **C**	30·00	45·00
79		4s. carmine and black, **C**	45·00	60·00
80		10s. green and red/*green*, **C**	70·00	£110
81		£1 purple and black/*red*, **C**	£375	£425
82		£10 purple & ultram, **C** (Optd S. £450) ..	£7000	£4000
72/81		.. .. *Set of* 10	£475	£575
72/81 Optd "Specimen"		.. .. *Set of* 10	£400	

15 **16**

(Typo D.L.R.)

1913 (1 Apr)–**19**. *T* **15** *and* **16** (*2s. 6d., etc.*). *Wmk Mult Crown CA. P* 14.

83 ½d. green, **O** 40 50
84 ½d. blue-green **O** (1918) 45 50
85 1d. carmine-red, **O** 75 55
86 1d. scarlet, **O** (1916) 45 45
87 2d. grey, **O** (1916) .. .. 1·25 50
88 2d. slate, **O** .. .. 1·75 70
89 2½d. bright blue, **O** .. .. 60 1·25
90 3d. purple/*yellow*, **C** (1914) .. .. 2·00 2·25
a. On pale yellow .. .. 2·50 5·50
91 4d. black and red/*yellow*, **C** (*shades*) .. .. 2·00 2·00
a. On pale yellow .. .. 3·25 6·00
92 6d. dull and bright purple, **C** .. .. .. 2·50 4·00
92*a* 6d. dull purple and bright violet, **C** .. .. 6·50 10·00
93 1s. black/*green*, **C** .. .. 1·75 4·50
a. On blue-green, olive back .. .. .. 2·00 1·50
b. On emerald back (Optd S. £35) .. .. .. 1·00 4·00
94 2s. 6d. black and red/*blue*, **C** .. .. .. 9·50 10·00
a. Break in scroll .. .. 60·00
b. Broken crown and scroll .. .. .. 60·00
95 4s. carmine and black, **C** .. .. 10·00 25·00
a. Break in scroll .. .. 85·00
b. Broken crown and scroll .. .. .. 85·00
96 10s. pale green and deep scarlet/*green*, **C** .. 48·00 65·00
a. Break in scroll £140
b. Broken crown and scroll £140
c. Green and deep scarlet/green, **C** (1919) 48·00 65·00
98 £1 purple and black/*red*, **C** £150 £140
a. Break in scroll £350
b. Broken crown and scroll £350
99 £10 purple & dull ultram, **C** (Optd S. £300) £3500
a. Purple and royal blue, **C** (1919) £2750 £1500
ab. Break in scroll .. ..
ac. Broken crown and scroll .. .. ..
83/98 .. .. *Set of* 12 **£175** **£210**
83/98 Optd "Specimen" .. .. *Set of* 12 **£350**

For illustrations of the varieties on Nos. 94/9 see above Bermuda No. 44.

For stamps overprinted "N.F." see TANZANIA.

1921–30. *T* **15** *and* **16** (*2s. to 10s.*). *Wmk Mult Script CA. P* 14.

100 ½d. green, **O** 60 20
101 1d. carmine, **O** 50 25
102 1½d. orange, **O** .. .. 3·25 13·00
103 2d. grey, **O** 50 20
105 3d. purple/*pale yellow*, **C** .. .. 4·00 2·25
106 4d. black and red/*yellow*, **C** .. .. 2·25 3·50
107 6d. dull and bright purple, **C** .. .. .. 3·00 3·25
108 1s. black/*emerald*, **C** (1930) .. .. 5·50 6·50
109 2s. purple and blue/*blue*, **C** .. .. 9·00 10·00
a. Break in scroll .. .. 60·00
b. Broken crown and scroll .. .. .. 60·00
110 2s. 6d. black and red/*blue*, **C** (1924) .. .. 12·00 15·00
a. Break in scroll .. .. 60·00
b. Broken crown and scroll .. .. .. 60·00
111 4s. carmine and black, **C** .. .. 9·00 12·00
a. Break in scroll .. .. 75·00
b. Broken crown and scroll .. .. .. 75·00
112 5s. green and red/*yellow*, **C** (1929) .. .. 26·00 40·00
a. Break in scroll £100
b. Broken crown and scroll £100
113 10s. green and red/*pale emerald*, **C** (1926) .. 65·00 85·00
a. Break in scroll £170
b. Broken crown and scroll £170
c. Green and scarlet/emerald, **C** (1927) .. £200 £400
ca. Break in scroll £500
cb. Broken crown and scroll £500
100/13 .. .. *Set of* 13 £130 £160
100/13 Optd/Perf "Specimen" .. *Set of* 13 £325

For illustrations of the varieties on Nos. 109/13 see above Bermuda No. 44.

17 King George V and Symbol of the Protectorate

(Des Major H. E. Green. Recess Waterlow)

1934 (June)–**35**. *Wmk Mult Script CA. P* 12½.

114 **17** ½d. green 55 30
115 1d. brown 60 30
116 1½d. carmine .. .. 60 1·25
117 2d. pale grey 80 80
118 3d. blue .. .. 1·50 85
119 4d. bright magenta (20.5.35) .. .. .. 2·00 1·50
120 6d. violet .. .. 1·25 40
121 9d. olive-bistre (20.5.35) .. .. .. 2·50 8·50
122 1s. black and orange .. .. 2·50 5·50
114/22 .. .. *Set of* 9 11·00 17·00
114/22 Perf "Specimen" .. .. *Set of* 9 £120

1935 (6 May). *Silver Jubilee. As Nos.* 91/4 *of Antigua but ptd by Waterlow. P* 11 × 12.

123 1d. ultramarine and grey 50 25
j. Kite and vertical log .. .. 20·00
124 2d. green and indigo 70 45
125 3d. brown and deep blue .. .. 5·00 9·50
j. Kite and vertical log .. .. 50·00
126 1s. slate and purple .. .. 12·00 15·00
j. Kite and vertical log .. .. 90·00
123/6 .. .. *Set of* 4 16·00 23·00
123/6 Perf "Specimen" .. .. *Set of* 4 70·00

For illustration of plate variety see Omnibus section following Zululand.

1937 (12 May). *Coronation. As Nos.* 13/15 *of Aden, but ptd by B.W. P* 11 × 11½.

127 ½d. green 20 15
128 1d. brown 45 15
129 2d. grey-black 50 40
127/9 .. .. *Set of* 3 1·00 60
127/9 Perf "Specimen" .. .. *Set of* 3 50·00

18 Symbol of the Protectorate

19

(T **18** recess Waterlow; T **19** typo D.L.R.)

1938 (1 Jan)–**44**. *P* 12½ (*T* **18**) *or* 14 (*T* **19**).

(*a*) *Wmk Mult Script CA*

130 **18** ½d. green 25 10
130*a* ½d. brown (12.12.42) 10 20
131 1d. brown 25 10
131*a* 1d. green (12.12.42) 10 10
132 1½d. carmine .. .. 45 1·75
132*a* 1½d. grey (12.12.42) 10 80
133 2d. grey 60 15
133*a* 2d. carmine (12.12.42) 10 10
134 3d. blue 10 10
135 4d. bright magenta 25 15
136 6d. violet 60 10
137 9d. olive-bistre .. .. 80 1·75
138 1s. black and orange 60 20
139 **19** 2s. purple and blue/*blue*, **C** .. .. .. 8·50 4·00
140 2s. 6d. black and red/*blue*, **C** .. .. .. 8·50 4·50
141 5s. pale green and red/*yellow*, **C** .. .. 35·00 12·00
a. Green and red/pale yellow, **O** (3.44) 65·00 40·00
142 10s. emerald and deep red/*pale green*, **C** .. 25·00 15·00
a. Bluish green and brown-red/pale green, **O** (1.38) .. .. .. £160 50·00

(*b*) *Wmk Mult Crown CA*

143 **19** £1 purple and black/*red*, **C** .. .. .. 24·00 18·00
130/43 .. .. *Set of* 18 95·00 50·00
130/43 Perf "Specimen" .. .. *Set of* 18 £500

No. 141*a* has a yellow surfacing often applied in horizontal lines giving the appearance of laid paper.

The printer's archives record the despatch of No. 142*a* to Nyasaland in January 1938, but no used examples have been reported before 1945.

20 Lake Nyasa

21 King's African Rifles

(Recess B.W.)

1945 (1 Sept). *T* **20**/**1** *and similar designs. Wmk Mult Script CA* (*sideways on horiz designs*). *P* 12.

144 ½d. black and chocolate 10 10
145 1d. black and emerald 10 20
146 1½d. black and grey-green 10 15
147 2d. black and scarlet 10 10
148 3d. black and light blue 10 10
149 4d. black and claret 25 25
150 6d. black and violet 50 10
151 9d. black and olive .. .. 45 1·75
152 1s. indigo and deep green 40 10
153 2s. emerald and maroon .. .. 2·50 2·75
154 2s. 6d. emerald and blue .. .. 3·00 2·50
155 5s. purple and blue .. .. 3·50 3·50
156 10s. claret and emerald .. .. 6·00 6·00
157 20s. scarlet and black .. .. 12·00 13·00
144/57 .. .. *Set of* 14 26·00 26·00
144/57 Perf "Specimen" .. .. *Set of* 14 £250

Designs: *Horiz*—1½d., 6d. Tea estate; 2d., 1s., 10s. Map of Nyasaland; 4d., 2s. 6d. Tobacco; 9d. Type **20** ; 5s., 20s. Badge of Nyasaland. *Vert*—3d., 2s. Fishing Village.

1946 (16 Dec). *Victory. As Nos.* 28/9 *of Aden.*

158 1d. green 10 10
159 2d. red-orange 10 10
158/9 Perf "Specimen" .. .. *Set of* 2 45·00

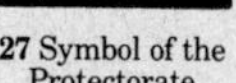

27 Symbol of the Protectorate

28 Arms in 1891 and 1951

(Recess B.W.)

1947 (20 Oct). *Wmk Mult Script CA. P* 12.

160 **27** 1d. red-brown and yellow-green 15 10
160 Perf "Specimen" .. .. 45·00

1948 (15 Dec). *Royal Silver Wedding. As Nos.* 30/1 *of Aden.*

161 1d. green 15 10
162 10s. mauve .. .. 11·00 14·00

1949 (21 Nov). *75th Anniv of U.P.U. As Nos.* 114/17 *of Antigua.*

163 1d. blue-green 30 15
164 3d. greenish blue .. .. 1·00 50
165 6d. purple .. .. 1·00 50
166 1s. ultramarine .. .. 1·00 50
163/6 .. .. *Set of* 4 3·00 1·50

(Des C. Twynam. Recess B.W.)

1951 (15 May). *Diamond Jubilee of Protectorate. Wmk Mult Scrip CA. P* 11 × 12.

167 **28** 2d. black and scarlet 25 30
168 3d. black and turquoise-blue 25 50
169 6d. black and violet 30 65
170 5s. black and indigo .. .. 90 4·50
167/70 .. .. *Set of* 4 1·50 5·50

1953 (30 May). *Rhodes Centenary Exhibition. As No.* 59 *o Northern Rhodesia.*

171 6d. violet 10 15

1953 (2 June). *Coronation. As No.* 47 *of Aden, but ptd by B.W.*

172 2d. black and brown-orange 10 10

29 Grading Cotton

(Recess B.W.)

1953 (1 Sept)–**54**. *Designs previously used for King George VI issue, but with portrait of Queen Elizabeth II as in T* **29**. *Wmk Mult Script CA. P* 12.

173 ½d. black and chocolate 10 40
a. Perf 12 × 12½ (8.3.54) 10 15
174 1d. brown and bright green 15 10
175 1½d. black and deep grey-green 15 70
176 2d. black and yellow-orange 15 10
a. Perf 12 × 12½ (8.3.54) 15 10
177 2½d. green and black 10 10
178 3d. black and scarlet 25 10
179 4½d. black and light blue 25 40
180 6d. black and violet 15 10
a. Perf 12 × 12½ (8.3.54) 15 10
181 9d. black and deep olive .. .. 70 2·00
182 1s. deep blue and slate-green 35 10
183 2s. deep green and brown-red .. .. .. **2·00** **2·75**
184 2s. 6d. deep emerald and deep blue .. .. **2·25** **3·75**
185 5s. purple and Prussian blue .. .. .. **3·50** **4·50**
186 10s. carmine and deep emerald .. .. .. **4·00** **5·00**
187 20s. red and black .. .. **8·50** **9·50**
173a/87 .. .. *Set of* 15 20·00 26·00

Designs: *Horiz*—½d., 9d. Lake Nyasa; 1½d., 6d. Tea estate; 2d., 1s., 10s. Map of Nyasaland; 3d., 2s. 6d. Tobacco; 5s., 20s. Badge of Nyasaland. *Vert*—1d. Symbol of the protectorate; 4½d., 2s. Fishing village.

Stamps perf 12 × 12½ come from sheets comb-perforated 11.8 × 12.25. They were also issued in coils of 480 stamps made up from sheets.

For issues between 1954 and 1963, see RHODESIA AND NYASALAND.

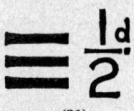

30

(31)

(Recess B.W.)

1963 (1 Nov). *T* **30**, *Revenue stamps optd* "POSTAGE", *or additionally surch as T* **31**. *P* 12.

188 ½d. on 1d. greenish blue 10 15
189 1d. green 10 10
190 2d. scarlet 10 20
191 3d. blue 10 10
192 6d. brown-purple 20 10
193 9d. on 1s. cerise 25 25
194 1s. purple 25 10
195 2s. 6d. black .. .. 40 1·50
196 5s. chocolate .. .. 65 1·25
197 10s. yellow-olive .. .. 1·25 3·50
a. Greenish olive .. .. 6·00 8·50
198 £1 deep violet .. .. 2·50 3·50
188/98 .. .. *Set of* 11 5·00 9·50

32 Mother and Child

33 Chambo (fish)

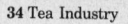

34 Tea Industry

35 Nyala

(Des V. Whiteley. Photo Harrison)

964 (1 Jan). *Designs as T 32/5. P 14½.*

99	½d. reddish violet	10	10
00	1d. black and green	10	10
01	2d. light red-brown	10	10
02	3d. red-brown, yellow-green & bistre-brown	10	10
03	4d. indigo and orange-yellow	20	20
04	6d. purple, yellow-green and light blue	20	10
05	1s. brown, turquoise-blue and pale yellow	15	10
06	1s. 3d. bronze-green and chestnut	65	10
07	2s. 6d. brown and blue	75	50
08	5s. blue, green, yellow and black	80	1·25
09	10s. green, orange-brown and black	1·50	3·00
10	£1 deep reddish purple and yellow	5·50	4·00
99/210	*Set of* 12	9·00	8·00

Designs: *As T 32/3*—2d. Zebu Bull; 3d. Groundnuts; 4d. Fishing. *As T 34*—1s. Timber; 1s. 3d. Turkish tobacco industry; 2s. 6d. Cotton industry; 5s. Monkey Bay, Lake Nyasa; 10s. Forestry, Afzelia.

POSTAGE DUE STAMPS

(Typo D.L.R.)

1950 (1 July). *As Type* D 1 *of Gold Coast, but inscr* "NYASALAND". *Wmk Mult Script CA. P* 14.

D1	1d. scarlet	2·00	5·50
D2	2d. ultramarine	5·00	11·00
D3	3d. green	7·50	4·75
D4	4d. purple	12·00	28·00
D5	6d. yellow-orange	20·00	48·00
D1/D5	*Set of* 5	42·00	90·00

The stamps of Nyasaland were withdrawn on 5 July 1964 when the territory attained independence. For later issues see MALAWI.

Orange Free State

PRICES FOR STAMPS ON COVER

Nos. 1/9	*from* × 12
Nos. 10/13	*from* × 10
Nos. 18/19	*from* × 12
No. 20	—
Nos. 21/42	*from* × 10
Nos. 48/51	*from* × 20
Nos. 52/138	*from* × 10
Nos. 139/51	*from* × 7
Nos. F1/17	—

INDEPENDENT REPUBLIC

1

(Typo D.L.R.)

1868 (1 Jan)–94. *P* 14.

1	1	1d. pale brown	2·25	45
2		1d. red-brown	2·25	35
3		1d. deep brown	3·00	40
4		6d. pale rose (1868)	10·00	3·50
5		6d. rose (1871)	3·50	3·00
6		6d. rose-carmine (1891)	10·00	12·00
7		6d. bright carmine (1894)	3·25	2·00
8		1s. orange-buff	50·00	5·00
9		1s. orange-yellow	8·00	1·50
		a. Double print	—	£2500

4 (2) *(a)* — 4 *(b)* — 4 *(c)* — 4 *(d)*

1877. *No. 6 surcharged T 2 (a) to (d).*

10	1	4d. on 6d. rose-carmine *(a)*	£170	40·00
		a. Surch inverted	—	£550
		b. Surch double *(a + c)*		
		c. Surch double, one inverted *(a + c inverted)*	—	£1100
		d. Surch double, one inverted *(a inverted + c)*		
11		4d. on 6d. rose-carmine *(b)*	£1000	£120
		a. Surch inverted	—	£750
		b. Surch double *(b + d)*		
12		4d. on 6d. rose-carmine *(c)*	75·00	25·00
		a. Surch inverted	—	£325
		b. Surch double		
13		4d. on 6d. rose-carmine *(d)*	95·00	32·00
		a. Surch inverted	£1000	£375

1878 (July). *P* 14.

18	1	4d. pale blue	7·00	2·25
19		4d. ultramarine	4·00	2·50
20		5s. green	8·50	8·00

1d. (3) *(a)* — 1d. *(b)* — 1d. *(c)* — 1d. *(d)* — 1d. *(e)* — 1d. *(f)*

Type 3: *(a)* Small "1" and "d." *(b)* Sloping serif. *(c)* Same size as *(b)*, but "1" with straighter horizontal serif. *(d)* Taller "1" with horizontal serif and antique "d". *(e)* Same size as *(d)* but with sloping serif and thin line at foot. *(f)* as *(d)* but with Roman "d".

1881 (19 May). *No. 20 surch T 3 (a) to (f) with heavy black bar cancelling the old value.*

21	1	1d. on 5s. green *(a)*	30·00	8·00
22		1d. on 5s. green *(b)*	18·00	8·00
		a. Surch inverted	—	£500
		b. Surch double	—	£500
23		1d. on 5s. green *(c)*	60·00	35·00
		a. Surch inverted	—	£550
		b. Surch double	—	£650
24		1d. on 5s. green *(d)*	27·00	10·00
		a. Surch inverted	£550	£500
		b. Surch double	—	£550
25		1d. on 5s. green *(e)*	£180	£200
		a. Surch inverted	—	£1300
		b. Surch double	—	£1100
26		1d. on 5s. green *(f)*	27·00	10·00
		a. Surch inverted	—	£450
		b. Surch double	—	£500

No. 21 was the first printing in one type only. Nos. 22 to 25 constitute the second printing about a year later, and are all found on the same sheet; and No. 26 the third printing of which about half have the stop raised.

Owing to defective printing, specimens may be found with the obliterating bar at the top of the stamps and others without the bar.

½d

(4)

1882 (Aug). *No. 20 surch with T 4 and with a thin black line cancelling old value.*

36	1	½d. on 5s. green	2·25	2·75
		a. Surch double	£350	£300
		b. Surch inverted		

3d (5) *(a)* — 3d *(b)* — 3d *(c)* — 3d *(d)* — 3d *(e)*

1882. *No. 19 surch with T 5 (a) to (e) with thin black line cancelling value.*

38	1	3d. on 4d. ultramarine *(a)*	38·00	22·00
		a. Surch double	—	£650
39		3d. on 4d. ultramarine *(b)*	30·00	16·00
		a. Surch double	—	£650
40		3d. on 4d. ultramarine *(c)*	24·00	16·00
		a. Surch double	—	£650
41		3d. on 4d. ultramarine *(d)*	35·00	16·00
		a. Surch double	—	£650
42		3d. on 4d. ultramarine *(e)*	£110	60·00
		a. Surch double	—	£750

1883–84. *P* 14.

48	1	½d. chestnut	60	50
49		2d. pale mauve	2·00	40
50		2d. bright mauve	2·00	30
51		3d. ultramarine	1·75	2·00

For 1d. purple, see No. 68.

2d (6) *(a)* — 2d *(b)* — 2d *(c)*

1888 (Sept–Oct). *No. 51 surch with T 6(a), (b) or (c).*

(a) Wide "2". (b) Narrow "2"

52	1	2d. on 3d. ultramarine *(a)* (Sept)	20·00	9·00
		a. Surch inverted	—	£700
53		2d. on 3d. ultramarine *(b)*	7·50	2·00
		a. Surch inverted	—	£300
		b. "2" with curved foot *(c)*		

1d (7) *(a)* — 1d *(b)* — Id *(c)*

1890 (Dec)–91. *Nos. 51 and 19 surch with T 7 (a) to (c).*

54	1	1d. on 3d. ultramarine *(a)*	1·10	60
		a. Surch double	75·00	
		c. "1" and "d" wide apart	£140	£110
55		1d. on 3d. ultramarine *(b)*	4·50	2·50
		a. Surch double	95·00	
57		1d. on 4d. ultramarine *(a)*	12·00	3·00
		a. Surch double	£110	£100
		b. Surch double *(a + b)*	£125	
		c. Surch triple		
58		1d. on 4d. ultramarine *(b)*	55·00	48·00
		a. Surch double	£175	
59		1d. on 4d. ultramarine *(c)*	£400	£300
		a. Surch double		

The settings of the 1d. on 3d. and on 4d. are not identical. The variety *(c)* does not exist on the 3d.

2½d.

(8)

1892 (Oct). *No 51 surch with T 8.*

67	1	2½d. on 3d. ultramarine	2·25	70
		a. No stop after "d"	40·00	

1894 (Sept). *Colour changed. P* 14.

68	1	1d. purple	45	30

½d (9) *(a)* — ½d *(b)* — ½d *(c)*

½d *(d)* — ½d *(e)* — ½d *(f)* — ½d *(g)*

Types *(a)* and *(e)* differ from types *(b)* and *(f)* respectively, in the serifs of the "1", but owing to faulty overprinting this distinction is not always clearly to be seen.

1896 (Sept). *No. 51 surch with T 9 (a) to (g).*

69	1	½d. on 3d. ultramarine *(a)*	1·60	2·50
70		½d. on 3d. ultramarine *(b)*	4·00	3·25
71		½d. on 3d. ultramarine *(c)*	4·00	2·50
72		½d. on 3d. ultramarine *(d)*	4·00	2·25
73		½d. on 3d. ultramarine *(e)*	3·25	2·25
74		½d. on 3d. ultramarine *(f)*	3·25	3·00
75		½d. on 3d. ultramarine *(g)*	1·75	2·25
		a. Surch double	11·00	10·00
		b. Surch triple		

The double and triple surcharges are often different types, but are always type *(g)*, or in combination with type *(g)*.

Double surcharges in the same type, but without the "d" and bar, also exist, probably from a trial sheet prepared by the printer. Both mint and used examples are known.

Halve Penny. — (10)

2½ — (11)

1896. *No. 51 surch with T 10.*

77	1	½d. on 3d. ultramarine	35	50
		(i) Errors in setting		
78	1	½d. on 3d. (no stop)	8·00	10·00
79		½d. on 3d. ("Peuny")	8·50	10·00
80		½d. on 3d. (no bar)	4·00	5·00
80*a*		½d. on 3d. (no bar or stop)	£400	£400
80*b*		½d. on 3d. (no bar and "Peuny")		
		(ii) Surch inverted		
81	1	½d. on 3d.	50·00	
81*a*		½d. on 3d. (no stop)		
81*b*		½d. on 3d. ("Peuny")		
		(iii) Surch double, one inverted		
81*c*	1	½d. on 3d. (Nos. 77 and 81)	£175	£200
81*d*		½d. on 3d. (Nos. 77 and 81*a*)	£450	
81*e*		½d. on 3d. (Nos. 77 and 81*b*)	£500	
81*f*		½d. on 3d. (Nos. 81 and 78)		
82		½d. on 3d. (Nos. 81 and 79)	—	£425

Nos. 69 to 75 also exist surcharged as last but they are considered not to have been issued with authority.

1897 (1 Jan). *No. 51 surch with T 11. (a) As in illustration. (b) With Roman "1" and antique "2" in fraction.*

83	1	2½d. on 3d. ultramarine *(a)*	1·25	80
83*a*		2½d. on 3d. ultramarine *(b)*	£125	90·00

1897. *P* 14.

84	1	½d. yellow (March)	45	35
85		½d. orange	45	35
87		1s. brown (Aug)	5·00	1·50

The 6d. blue was prepared for use in the Orange Free State, but had not been brought into use when the stamps were seized in Bloemfontein. A few have been seen without the "V.R.I." overprint, but they were not authorized or available for postage. *(Price £45.)*

BRITISH OCCUPATION

V. R. I. — V. R. I. — V. R. I.

4d — 31 (Level stops)

½d — (32) Thin "V" — (Raised stops) — ½d — (33) Thick "V"

V. R. I.

Inserted "R"

(Surch by Messrs Curling, Bloemfontein)

1900. *T 1 surch as T 31/33 (2½d. on 3d. optd "V.R.I." only).*

(a) First printings surch as T 31 with stops level (March)

101	½d. on ½d. orange	80	80
	a. No stop after "V"	14·00	14·00
	b. No stop after "I"	£150	£150
	c. "½" omitted	£150	£150
	d. "I" omitted		
	e. "V.R.I." omitted	£170	
	f. Value omitted	£110	
	g. Small "½"	45·00	45·00
	h. Surch double	£125	

102 1d. on 1d. purple 65 45
a. Error. Brown £500 £350
b. No stop after "V" .. .. 10·00 10·00
c. No stop after "R" £150 £160
d. No stop after "I" .. ..
e. "1" omitted £150
f. "I" omitted .. .. 55·00 55·00
g. "I" and stop after "R" omitted .. .. 55·00 55·00
h. "V.R.I." omitted £170
i. "d" omitted £300
j. Value omitted .. .. 90·00
k. Inverted stop after "R" £160
l. Wider space between "1" and "d" .. £100 £100
m. "V" and "R" close £150
n. Pair, one without surch £350
o. "V" omitted £450
103 2d. on 2d. bright mauve 45 60
a. No stop after "V" .. .. 9·00 9·00
b. No stop after "R" £300
c. No stop after "I" £300
d. "V.R.I." omitted £300
e. Value omitted .. ..
104 2½d. on 3d. ultramarine (*a*) .. .. .. 4·00 3·00
a. No stop after "V" .. .. 55·00 55·00
105 2½d. on 3d. ultramarine (*b*) £160 £160
106 3d. on 3d. ultramarine 75 65
a. No stop after "V" .. .. 10·00 10·00
b. Pair, one without surch £300
c. "V.R.I." omitted .. ..
d. Value omitted .. ..
107 4d. on 4d. ultramarine .. .. 3·25 4·00
a. No stop after "V" .. .. 40·00 40·00
108 6d. on 6d. bright carmine .. .. .. 35·00 35·00
a. No stop after "V" £250 £275
b. "6" omitted £300 £300
109 6d. on 6d. blue .. .. 2·25 2·75
a. No stop after "V" .. .. 24·00 24·00
b. "6" omitted .. .. 45·00 45·00
c. "V.R.I." omitted .. ..
110 1s. on 1s. brown .. .. 2·50 3·00
a. Error. Orange-yellow £2750 £2250
b. No stop after "V" .. .. 26·00 26·00
c. "1" omitted £100 £100
d. "1" omitted and spaced stop after "s" .. £110
e. "V.R.I." omitted £150 £110
f. Value omitted .. .. — £140
g. Raised stop after "s" .. .. .. 9·00 9·50
h. Wider space between "1" and "s" .. £150 £150
111 5s. on 5s. green .. .. 17·00 23·00
a. No stop after "V" £180 £180
b. "5" omitted £750 £750
c. Inverted stop after "R" £450 £450
d. Wider space between "5" and "s" .. £120 £120
e. Value omitted .. ..

All values are found with a rectangular, instead of an oval, stop after "R". Misplaced surcharges (upwards or sideways) occur.

(*b*) *Subsequent printings.* (i) *Surch as T* **32**

112 ½d. on ½d. orange 20 20
a. Raised and level stops mixed .. .. 1·40 1·60
b. Pair, one with level stops .. .. 7·50 10·00
c. No stop after "V" .. .. 2·00 2·00
d. No stop after "I" .. .. 22·00 22·00
e. "V" omitted £550
f. Small "½" .. .. 10·00 11·00
g. As a, and small "½" .. .. .. 10·00 11·00
i. Space between "V" and "R" .. ..
j. Value omitted .. ..
113 1d. on 1d. purple 20 20
a. Raised and level stops mixed .. .. 1·25 1·40
b. Pair, one with level stops .. .. 15·00 15·00
c. No stop after "V" .. .. 3·25 4·50
d. No stop after "R" .. .. 12·00 12·00
e. No stop after "I" .. .. 11·00 12·00
f. No stops after "V" and "I" £425
g. Surch inverted £300
h. Surch double .. .. 90·00 80·00
i. Pair, one without surch £150
j. Short figure "1" £100 £100
k. Space between "V" and "R" .. .. 70·00 75·00
l. Space between "R" and "I" .. .. 90·00
m. Space between "1" and "d" £160
n. Inserted "R" £300
114 2d. on 2d. bright mauve 35 30
a. Raised and level stops mixed .. .. 4·00 4·00
b. Pair, one with level stops .. .. 6·00 6·00
c. Surch inverted £350
d. "I" raised .. ..
e. Pair, one without surch .. .. ..
f. No stop after "V" £1000
115 2½d. on 3d. ultramarine (*a*) £180 £160
a. Raised and level stops mixed .. ..
116 2½d. on 3d. ultramarine (*b*) £1200
117 3d. on 3d. ultramarine 30 30
a. Raised and level stops mixed .. .. 5·50 5·50
b. Pair, one with level stops .. .. 13·00 13·00
c. No stop after "V" £140 £140
d. No stop after "R" .. .. — £500
e. "I" omitted £400
f. Surch double £400
g. Surch double, one diagonal £350
h. Ditto, diagonal surch, with mixed stops
n. Inserted "R" .. ..
118 4d. on 4d. ultramarine .. .. 1·10 1·50
a. Raised and level stops mixed .. .. 5·50
b. Pair, one with level stops .. .. 13·00 13·00
119 6d. on 6d. bright carmine .. .. .. 35·00 45·00
a. Raised and level stops mixed £140 £140
b. Pair, one with level stops £200
120 6d. on 6d. blue 70 40
a. Raised and level stops mixed .. .. 5·50 5·50
b. Pair, one with level stops .. .. 13·00 13·00
c. No stop after "V" £500
d. No stop after "R" .. ..
121 1s. on 1s. brown 70 45
a. Error. Orange-yellow £1200 £1200
b. Raised and level stops mixed .. .. 8·50
c. Pair, one with level stops .. .. 18·00 20·00
f. "s" omitted .. ..
g. "V.R.I." omitted .. ..
122 5s. on 5s. green (H/S S. £50) .. .. 4·00 4·25
a. Raised and level stops mixed £300 £300
b. Pair, one with level stops £900
c. Short top to "5" .. .. 55·00 55·00

(ii) *Surch as T* **33**

123 ½d. on ½d. orange 70 50
124 1d. on 1d. purple 60 35
a. Inverted "1" for "I" .. .. .. 11·00 13·00
b. No stops after "R" and "I" .. .. 85·00 65·00
c. No stop after "R" .. .. 32·00 32·00
d. Surch double £300 £300
n. Inserted "R" .. ..
125 2d. on 2d. bright mauve .. .. 1·25 1·50
a. Inverted "1" for "I" .. .. .. 13·00 13·00
126 2½d. on 3d. ultramarine (*a*) £550 £650
127 2½d. on 3d. ultramarine (*b*) .. .. ..
128 3d. on 3d. ultramarine .. .. 2·00 2·25
a. Inverted "1" for "I" .. .. .. 70·00 45·00
b. Surch double .. ..
ba. Surch double, one diagonal £400
129 6d. on 6d. bright carmine £375
130 6d. on 6d. blue .. .. 3·50 6·00
131 1s. on 1s. brown .. .. 5·50 5·50
132 5s. on 5s. green .. .. 18·00 23·00

Stamps with thick "V" occur in certain positions in *later* settings of the type with stops above the line (T **32**). *Earlier* settings with stops above the line have all stamps with thin "V".

Some confusion has previously been caused by the listing of certain varieties as though they occurred on stamps with thick "V", in fact they occur on stamps showing the normal thin "V", included in the settings which also contained the thick "V".

As small blocks of unsurcharged Free State stamps could be handed in for surcharging, varieties thus occur which are not found in the complete settings.

The inserted "R" variety occurs on positions 6 (T **32**) and 12 (T **33**) of the forme. The "R." of the original surcharge failed to print and the "R", but not the full stop, was added by the use of a handstamp. Traces of the original letter are often visible. The broken "V" flaw, also shown in the illustration, does not appear on No. 124n.

ORANGE RIVER COLONY

CROWN COLONY

ORANGE RIVER COLONY. (34)

4d (35)

E. R. I. 6d (36)

1900 (10 Aug)–**02.** *Nos.* 58*a*, 61*a and* 67 *of Cape of Good Hope (wmk Cabled Anchor. P* 14) *optd with T* **34** *by W. A. Richards and Sons, Cape Town.*

133 ½d. green (13.10.00) 20 10
a. No stop .. .. 7·00 8·50
b. Opt double £550
134 1d. carmine (May 1902) 25 10
a. No stop .. .. 9·00 11·00
135 2½d. ultramarine 30 35
a. No stop .. .. 35·00 40·00
133/5 .. .. *Set of* 3 65 45

In the ½d. and 2½d., the "no stop" after "COLONY" variety was the first stamp in the left lower pane. In the 1d. it is the twelfth stamp in the right lower pane on which the stop was present at the beginning of the printing but became damaged and soon failed to print.

1902 (14 Feb). *Surch with T* **35** *by "Bloemfontein Express".*

136 4d. on 6d. blue (No. 120) (R.) 50 60
a. No stop after "R" .. .. 30·00 30·00
c. Thick "V" .. .. 1·75 3·50
d. Thick "V" and inverted "1" for "I" .. 4·50 6·00

1902 (Aug). *Surch with T* **36.**

137 **1** 6d. on 6d. blue .. .. 1·75 3·00
a. Surch double, one inverted .. ..
b. Wide space between "6" and "d" (R.4/2) .. .. 60·00 75·00

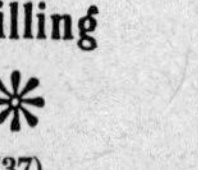

(37)

38 King Edward VII, Springbok and Gnu

1902 (Sept). *Surch with T* **37.**

138 **1** 1s. on 5s. green (O.) .. .. 3·00 4·50
a. Thick "V" .. .. 9·00 12·00
b. Short top to "5" .. .. 65·00 65·00
c. Surch double .. .. ..

(Typo D.L.R.)

1903 (3 Feb)–**04.** *Wmk Crown CA. P* 14.

139 **38** ½d. yellow-green (6.7.03) .. .. .. 2·50 55
140 1d. scarlet 60 10
141 2d. brown (6.7.03) .. .. 1·75 70
142 2½d. bright blue (6.7.03) 75 50
143 3d. mauve (6.7.03) .. .. 2·50 80
144 4d. scarlet and sage-green (6.7.03) .. 8·00 2·00
a. "IOSTAGE" for "POSTAGE" £800 £600
145 6d. scarlet and mauve (6.7.03) .. .. 3·75 70
146 1s. scarlet and bistre (6.7.03) .. .. 9·00 1·75
147 5s. blue and brown (31.10.04) .. .. 60·00 20·00
139/47 .. .. *Set of* 9 80·00 24·00
139/47 Optd "Specimen" .. .. *Set of* 9 £180

No. 144a occurs on R.10/2 of the upper left pane.

Several of the above values are found with the overprint "C.S.A.R.", in black, for use by the Central South African Railways.

1905 (Nov)–**09.** *Wmk Mult Crown CA. P* 14.

148 **38** ½d. yellow-green (28.7.07) .. .. 2·50 2
149 1d. scarlet .. .. 1·00 2
150 4d. scarlet and sage-green (8.11.07) .. 3·50 1·7
a. "IOSTAGE" for "POSTAGE" .. £180 £15
151 1s. scarlet and bistre (2.09) .. .. 22·00 5·5
148/51 .. .. *Set of* 4 26·00 7·0

POSTCARD STAMPS

From 1889 onwards the Orange Free State Post Office sold postcards franked with adhesives as Type 1, some subsequently surcharged, over which the State Arms had been overprinted.

There are five known dies of the Arms overprint which can be identified as follows:

(a) Shield without flags. Three cows (two lying down, one standing) at left. Point of shield complete.
(b) Shield with flags. Four cows (two lying down, two standing) at left (*illustrated*).
(c) Shield with flags. Three cows (one lying down, two standing) at left.
(d) Shield without flags. Three cows (one lying down, two standing) at left.
(e) Shield without flags. Three cows (two lying down, one standing) at left. Point of shield broken.

There are also other differences between the dies.

PRICES. Those in the left-hand column are for unused examples on complete postcard; those on the right for used examples off card. Examples used on postcard are worth more.

1889 (Feb). *No.* 2 (*placed sideways on card*) *optd Shield Type* (a).

P1 **1** 1d. red-brown .. .. 60·00 30·0
a. Optd Shield Type (b) .. .. .. 20·00 5·0

1891 (Aug). *No.* 48 *optd Shield Type* (b).

P2 **1** ½d. chestnut .. .. 2·00 1·0
a. Optd Shield Type (c) .. .. .. 6·00 3·0
b. Optd Shield Type (d) .. .. .. 3·00 1·5
c. Optd Shield Type (e) .. .. .. 7·00 3·5

1892 (June). *No.* 54 *optd Shield Type* (b).

P3 **1** 1d. on 3d. ultramarine .. .. .. 60·00 35·0
a. Optd Shield Type (c) .. .. .. 7·00 2·0

1½d. (P 1) 1½d. (P 2) 1½d. (P 3)

1892 (Sept)–**95.** *Nos.* 50/1 *optd Shield Type* (b) *or* (d) (*No.* P6) *and surch with Types* P **1/3.**

P4 **1** 1½d. on 2d. bright mauve (Type P **1**) (11.92) 5·00 2·50
P5 1½d. on 2d. bright mauve (Type P **2**) (9.93) .. 2·00 1·00
P6 1½d. on 2d. brt mauve (Type P **3**) (R.) (6.95) 7·00 3·00
P7 1½d. on 3d. ultramarine (Type P **1**) .. 5·00 1·50

½d. (P 4)

1895 (Aug). *No.* 48 *optd Shield Type* (e) *and surch with Type* P **4.**

P8 **1** ½d. on ½d. chestnut .. .. 6·00 2·0

1897 (Mar). *No.* 85 *optd Shield Type* (d).

P9 **1** ½d. orange .. .. 6·00 1·0
a. Optd Shield Type (e) .. .. .. 7·00 2·0

1½d. (P 5) 1½d. (P 6)

1897. *No.* 50 *optd Shield Type* (e) *and surch with Types* P **5/6.**

P10 **1** 1½d. on 2d. bright mauve (Type P **5**) (Mar) 3·00 2·0
P11 1½d. on 2d. bright mauve (Type P **6**) (Dec) 3·50 2·5
P12 1½d. on 2d. bright mauve (as Type P **6**, but without stop (Dec) .. .. .. 3·50 2·5

V.R.I. (P 7)

1900. *Nos.* P11/12 *optd as T* **31/2** *or with Type* P **7.**

P13 **1** 1½d. on 2d. bright mauve (No. P11) (T **31**) .. 15·00 4·00
P14 1½d. on 2d. bright mauve (No. P12) (T **31**) .. 15·00 4·00
P15 1½d. on 2d. bright mauve (No. P11) (T **32**) .. 15·00 4·00
P16 1½d. on 2d. bright mauve (No. P12) (T **32**) .. 15·00 4·00
P17 1½d. on 2d. brt mve (No. P11) (Type P **7**) 25·00 7·50
P18 1½d. on 2d. brt mve (No. P12) (Type P **7**) 25·00 7·50

FISCAL STAMPS USED FOR POSTAGE

The following were issued in 1878 (Nos. F1 and F3 in 1882) and were authorised for postal use between 1882 and 1886.

F 1

F 2

(Typo D.L.R.)

1882–86. *P* 14.

No.	Type	Description	Unused	Used
F 1	F 1	6d. pearl-grey	2·50	7·00
F 2		6d. purple-brown	—	8·00
F 3	F 2	1s. purple-brown	3·75	10·00
F 4		1s. pearl-grey	—	25·00
F 5		1s. 6d. blue	6·50	5·00
F 6		2s. magenta	6·50	4·50
F 7		3s. chestnut	8·50	25·00
F 8		4s. grey		
F 9		5s. rose	10·00	
F10		6s. green	—	25·00
F11		7s. violet		
F12		10s. orange	20·00	15·00
F13		£1 purple	28·00	18·00
F14		£2 red-brown	30·00	
F14*a*		£4 carmine		
F15		£5 green	45·00	22·00

The 8s. yellow was prepared but we have no evidence of its use postally without surcharge Type **F 3**.

ZES PENCE.

(F 3)

1886. *Surch with Type* F **3**.

No.	Type	Description	Unused	Used
F16	F 2	6d. on 4s. grey		
F17		6d. on 8s. yellow	£100	

Postage stamps overprinted for use as Telegraph stamps and used postally are omitted as it is impossible to say with certainty which stamps were genuinely used for postal purposes.

Stamps of SOUTH AFRICA are now in use.

Pakistan

DOMINION

PAKISTAN (1) PAKISTAN (2)

1947 (1 Oct). *Stamps of India, optd by litho at Nasik, as T* **1** (*3 p. to 12 a.*) *or* **2** (*14 a. and rupee values*).

No.	Type	Description	Unused	Used
1	**100*a***	3 p. slate	10	10
2		½ a. purple	10	10
3		9 p. green	10	10
4		1 a. carmine	10	10
5	**101**	1½ a. dull violet	10	10
6		2 a. vermilion	10	10
7		3 a. bright violet	10	10
8		3½ a. bright blue	25	1·40
9	**102**	4 a. brown	10	10
10		6 a. turquoise-green	20	10
11		8 a. slate-violet	20	10
12		12 a. lake	70	10
13	**103**	14 a. purple	70	25
14	**93**	1 r. grey and red-brown	70	10
		a. Overprint omitted in pair with normal	£600	
		b. Overprint inverted	£150	
15		2 r. purple and brown	1·50	35
16		5 r. green and blue	2·75	80
17		10 r. purple and claret	3·75	90
18		15 r. brown and green	30·00	55·00
19		25 r. slate-violet and purple	30·00	27·00
1/19		*Set of* 19	65·00	75·00

Numerous provisional "PAKISTAN" overprints, both hand-stamped and machine-printed, in various sizes and colours, on Postage and Official stamps, also exist.

These were made under authority of Provincial Governments, District Head Postmasters or Local Postmasters and are of considerable philatelic interest.

The 1 a. 3 p. (India No. 269) exists only as a local issue (*price*, Karachi opt, *70p. unused; £1.25 used*).

The 12 a., as No. 12, but overprinted at Karachi exists with over-print inverted (*Price £60 unused*).

3 Constituent Assembly Building, Karachi

6 Crescent and Stars

(Des A. R. Chughtai (1 r.). Recess D.L.R.)

1948 (9 July). *Independence. T* **3**, **6** *and similar horiz designs. P* 13½ × 14 *or* 11½ (*1 r.*).

No.	Type	Description	Unused	Used
20		1½ a. ultramarine	10	10
21		2½ a. green	10	10
22		3 a. purple-brown	10	10
23		1 r. scarlet	35	10
		a. Perf 14 × 13½	3·25	7·00
20/3		*Set of* 4	60	20

Designs:—2½ a. Karachi Airport entrance; 3 a. Gateway to Lahore Fort.

7 Scales of Justice

8 Star and Crescent

9 Lloyds Barrage

10 Karachi Airport

13 Khyber Pass

(Recess Pakistan Security Ptg Corp Ltd, Karachi (P 13 and 13½), D.L.R. (others))

1948 (14 Aug)–**56**?. *T* **7/10**, **13** *and similar designs.*

No.	Type	Description	Unused	Used
24	**7**	3 p. red (*p* 12½)	10	10
		a. Perf 13½ (1954?)	10	10
25		6 p. violet (*p* 12½)	15	10
		a. Perf 13½ (1954?)	35	15
26		9 p. green (*p* 12½)	10	10
		a. Perf 13½ (1954?)	10	10
27	**8**	1 a. blue (*p* 12½)	10	10
28		1½ a. grey-green (*p* 12½)	10	10
29		2 a. red (*p* 12½)	20	10
30	**9**	2½ a. green (*p* 14×13½)	60	1·75
31	**10**	3 a. green (*p* 14)	25	10
32	**9**	3½ a. bright blue (*p* 14×13½)	50	1·50
33		4 a. reddish brown (*p* 12½)	25	10
34	–	6 a. blue (*p* 14×13½)	30	30
35	–	8 a. black (*p* 12½)	30	20
36	**10**	10 a. scarlet (*p* 14)	50	1·50
37	–	12 a. scarlet (*p* 14×13½)	1·00	25
38	–	1 r. ultramarine (*p* 14)	75	10
		a. Perf 13½ (1954?)	4·50	50
39	–	2 r. chocolate (*p* 14)	14·00	10
		a. Perf 13½ (1954?)	14·00	55
40	–	5 r. carmine (*p* 14)	9·00	20
		a. Perf 13½ (7.53)	7·00	15
41	**13**	10 r. magenta (*p* 14)	4·50	6·50
		a. Perf 12	22·00	2·50
		b. Perf 13 (1951)	7·50	30
42		15 r. blue-green (*p* 12)	10·00	8·50
		a. Perf 14	9·00	18·00
		b. Perf 13 (1956?)	11·00	11·00
43		25 r. violet (*p* 14)	22·00	27·00
		a. Perf 12	15·00	22·00
		b. Perf 13 (1954)	22·00	12·00
24/43		*Set of* 20	50·00	24·00

Designs: *Vert* (*as T* 7)—6 a., 8 a., 12 a. Karachi Port Trust. (*As T* 10)—1 r., 2 r., 5 r. Salimullah Hostel, Dacca.

For 25 r. with W **98**, see No. 210.

14

(Recess D.L.R.)

1949 (11 Sept). *First Death Anniv of Mohammed Ali Jinnah. T* **14** *and similar type. P* 14.

No.	Type	Description	Unused	Used
44	**14**	1½ a. brown	1·00	40
45		3 a. green	1·00	40
46	–	10 a. black	2·50	4·00
44/6		*Set of* 3	4·00	4·25

Design:—10 a. Inscription reads "QUAID-I-AZAM/ MOHAMMAD ALI JINNAH" etc.

15 Star and Crescent

16 Karachi Airport

(Recess Pakistan Security Ptg Corp (P 13½), D.L.R. (others))

1949–53? *Redrawn. Crescent moon with points to left as T* **15/16**.

No.	Type	Description	Unused	Used
47	**15**	1 a. blue (*p* 12½)	90	10
		a. Perf 13½ (1953?)	90	10
48		1½ a. grey-green (*p* 12½)	90	10
		a. Perf 13½ (1952?)	1·25	10
49		2 a. red (*p* 12½)	90	10
		a. Perf 13½ (1953?)	90	10
50	**16**	3 a. green (*p* 14)	1·25	65
51	–	6 a. blue (as No. 34) (*p* 14×13½)	3·50	15
52	–	8 a. black (as No. 35) (*p* 12½)	2·50	10
53	**16**	10 a. scarlet (*p* 14)	3·00	40
54	–	12 a. scarlet (as No. 37) (*p* 14×13½)	6·00	15
47/54		*Set of* 8	17·00	1·40

17 Pottery

18 Aeroplane and Hour-glass

Two Types of 3½ a.:

I

II

19 Saracenic Leaf Pattern

20 Archway and Lamp

(Des A. R. Chughtai. Recess D.L.R., later printings, Pakistan Security Ptg Corp)

1951 (14 Aug)–**56**. *Fourth Anniv of Independence. P* 13.

No.	Type	Description	Unused	Used
55	**17**	2½ a. carmine	70	35
56	**18**	3 a. purple	40	10
57	**17**	3½ a. blue (I)	60	70
57*a*		3½ a. blue (II)(12.56)	1·25	60
58	**19**	4 a. green	35	10
59		6 a. brown-orange	45	10
60	**20**	8 a. sepia	3·50	10
61		10 a. violet	80	10
62	**18**	12 a. slate	80	10
55/62		*Set of* 9	8·00	1·40

The above and the stamps issued on the 14 August 1954, 1955 and 1956, are basically definitive issues, although issued on the Anniversary date of Independence.

21 "Scinde Dawk" stamp and Ancient and Modern Transport

(Recess D.L.R.)

1952 (14 Aug). *Centenary of "Scinde Dawk" Issue of India. P* 13.

No.	Type	Description	Unused	Used
63	**21**	3 a. deep olive/*yellow-olive*	60	35
64		12 a. deep brown/*salmon*	1·00	15

PRINTERS. All issues up to No. 219 were recess-printed by the Pakistan Security Printing Corporation, *unless otherwise stated.*

22 Kaghan Valley

23 Mountains, Gilgit

24 Tea Plantation, East Pakistan

1954 (14 Aug). *Seventh Anniv of Independence. T* **22/4** *and similar designs. P* 13½ (*14 a., 1 r., 2 r.*) *or* 13 (*others*).

No.	Description	Unused	Used
65	6 p. reddish violet	10	10
66	9 p. blue	60	40
67	1 a. carmine	10	10
68	1½ a. red	10	10
69	14 a. deep green	45	10
70	1 r. green	4·75	10
71	2 r. red-orange	1·75	10
65/71	*Set of* 7	7·00	45

Designs: *As T* **22**—1½ a. Mausoleum of Emperor Jehangir, Lahore. *As T* **23**—1 a. Badshahi Mosque, Lahore. *As T* **24**—1 r. Cotton plants, West Pakistan; 2 r. Jute fields and river, East Pakistan.

29 View of K 2

1954 (25 Dec). *Conquest of K 2 (Mount Godwin-Austen). P* 13.
72 **29** 2 a. deep violet 15 10

30 Karnaphuli Paper Mill, Type I (Arabic fraction on left)
Type II (Arabic fraction on right)

1955 (14 Aug)–**56**. *Eighth Anniv of Independence. similar horiz designs. P* 13.
73 2½ a. scarlet (I) 30 25
73*a* 2½ a. scarlet (II) (12.56) 30 30
74 6 a. deep ultramarine 40 10
75 8 a. deep reddish violet .. .. .. 1·25 10
76 12 a. carmine and orange .. .. .. 1·00 10
73/6 .. .. *Set of* 5 3·00 50
Designs:—6 a. Textile mill, West Pakistan; 8 a. Jute mill, East Pakistan; 12 a. Main Sui gas plant.

TENTH
ANNIVERSARY
UNITED NATIONS

24.10.55.

(34)

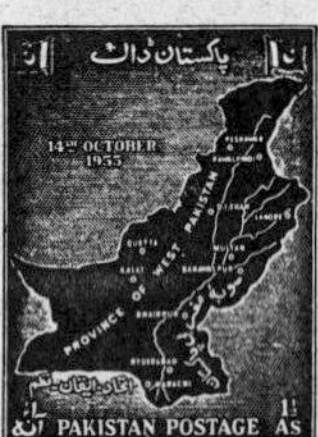

35 Map of West Pakistan

TENTH
ANNIVERSARY
UNITED NATIONS

24.10.55.

"UNITED NATIONS" shifted 1 mm to left (1½ a. R. 7/10; 12 a. R. 3/8, 5/8, 7/8, 9/8)

1955 (24 Oct). *Tenth Anniv of United Nations. Nos.* 68 *and* 76 *optd as T* **34**.
77 1½ a. red (B.) .. .. 1·75 5·00
a. "UNITED NATIONS" 1 mm to left 3·50 6·00
78 12 a. carmine and orange (B.) .. .. 75 4·25
a. "UNITED NATIONS" 1 mm to left 3·50 6·00
Forgeries exist of the overprints on Nos. 77/8. These are in very uneven thin type and measure 20 × 18 mm instead of the genuine 19½×19 mm.

1955 (7 Dec). *West Pakistan Unity. P* 13½.
79 **35** 1½ a. myrtle-green 15 10
80 2 a. sepia 15 10
81 12 a. deep rose-red 40 15
79/81 .. .. *Set of* 3 60 20

REPUBLIC

36 Constituent Assembly Building, Karachi

(Litho D.L.R.)

1956 (23 Mar). *Republic Day. P* 13.
82 **36** 2 a. myrtle-green 10 10

MINIMUM PRICE

The minimum price quote is 10p which represents a handling charge rather than a basis for valuing common stamps. For further notes about prices see introductory pages.

37

38 Map of East Pakistan

1956 (14 Aug). *Ninth Anniv of Independence. P* 13½.
83 **37** 2 a. scarlet 10 10

1956 (15 Oct). *First Session of National Assembly of Pakistan at Dacca. P* 13½.
84 **38** 1½ a. myrtle-green 15 30
85 2 a. sepia 15 10
86 12 a. deep rose-red 20 20
84/6 .. .. *Set of* 3 45 55

39 Karnaphuli Paper Mill, East Bengal

40 Pottery

41 Orange Tree

1957 (23 Mar). *First Anniv of Republic. P* 13.
87 **39** 2½ a. scarlet 20 10
88 **40** 3½ a. blue 30 10
89 **41** 10 r. myrtle-green and yellow-orange .. 80 20
87/9 .. .. *Set of* 3 1·10 20
The above and No. 95 are primarily definitive issues, although issued on the Anniversary of Republic Day.
For 10 r. with W **98**, see No. 208.

42 Pakistani Flag

43 Pakistani Industries

(Litho D.L.R.)

1957 (10 May). *Centenary of Struggle for Independence (Indian Mutiny). P* 13.
90 **42** 1½ a. bronze-green 10 10
91 12 a. light blue 20 10

(Litho D.L.R.)

1957 (14 Aug). *Tenth Anniv of Independence. P* 14.
92 **43** 1½ a. ultramarine 15 10
93 4 a. orange-red 25 25
94 12 a. mauve 30 40
92/4 .. .. *Set of* 3 65 65

44 Coconut Tree

45

1958 (23 Mar). *Second Anniv of Republic. P* 13.
95 **44** 15 r. red and deep reddish purple .. 3·75 3·00
This is a definitive issue, see note below No. 89.
See No. 209 for this stamp with W **98**.

(Photo Harrison)

1958 (21 Apr). *20th Death Anniv of Mohammed Iqbal (poet). P* 14½ × 14.
96 **45** 1½ a. yellow-olive and black 10 10
97 2 a. orange-brown and black 10 10
98 14 a. turquoise-blue and black 25 10
96/8 .. .. *Set of* 3 40 15

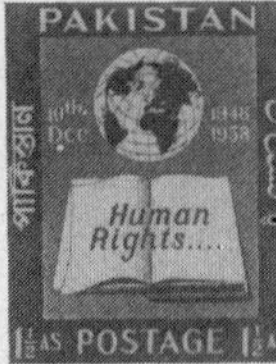

46 U.N. Charter and Globe

PAKISTAN
BOY SCOUT
2nd NATIONAL
JAMBOREE

CHITTAGONG
Dec. 58—Jan. 59

(47)

1958 (10 Dec). *Tenth Anniv of Declaration of Human Rights. P* 13.
99 **46** 1½ a. turquoise-blue 10 10
100 14 a. sepia 15 10

1958 (28 Dec). *Second Pakistan Boy Scouts National Jamboree, Chittagong. Nos.* 65 *and* 75 *optd with T* **47**.
101 6 p. reddish violet 10 10
102 8 a. deep reddish violet 15 10

REVOLUTION
DAY
Oct. 27, 1959

(48)

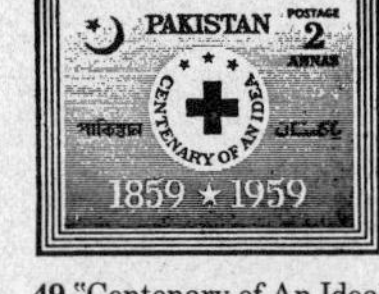

49 "Centenary of An Idea"

1959 (27 Oct). *Revolution Day. No.* 74 *optd with T* **48** *in red.*
103 6 a. deep ultramarine 15 10

1959 (19 Nov). *Red Cross Commemoration. Recess; cross typo. P* 13.
104 **49** 2 a. red and green 15 10
105 10 a. red and deep blue 55 10

50 Armed Forces Badge

51 Map of Pakistan

(Litho D.L.R.)

1960 (10 Jan). *Armed Forces Day. P* 13½ × 13.
106 **50** 2 a. red, ultramarine and blue-green .. 10 10
107 14 a. red and bright blue 30 10

1960 (23 Mar). *P* 13 × 13½.
108 **51** 6 p. deep purple 10 10
109 2 a. brown-red 10 10
110 8 a. deep green 25 10
111 1 r. blue 25 10
108/11 .. .. *Set of* 4 55 15

52 Uprooted Tree

53 Punjab Agricultural College

1960 (7 Apr). *World Refugee Year. P* 13.
112 **52** 2 a. rose-carmine 10 10
113 10 a. green 10 10

1960 (10 Oct). *Golden Jubilee of Punjab Agricultural College, Lyallpur. T* **53** *and similar horiz design. P* 12½ × 14.
114 2 a. slate-blue and carmine-red 10 10
115 8 a. bluish green and reddish violet 10 10
Design:—8 a. College arms.

55 "Land Reforms, Rehabilitation and Reconstruction"

56 Caduceus

(Des M. H. Hanjra. Photo D.L.R.)

1960 (27 Oct). *Revolution Day. P* 13 × 13½.
116 **55** 2 a. green, pink and brown 10 10
a. Green and pink omitted .. .. 9·00
b. Pink omitted .. .. .. 5·00
117 14 a. green, yellow and ultramarine .. 10 10

(Photo D.L.R.)

1960 (16 Nov). *Centenary of King Edward Medical College, Lahore. P* 13.
118 **56** 2 a. yellow, black and blue 15 10
119 14 a. emerald, black and carmine .. 30 10

57 "Economic Co-operation" 58 Zam-Zama Gun, Lahore ("Kim's Gun," after Rudyard Kipling)

1960 (5 Dec). *International Chamber of Commerce C.A.F.E.A. Meeting, Karachi. P* 13.
120 **57** 14 a. orange-red 15 10

(Centre typo, background recess Pakistan Security Ptg Corp)

1960 (24 Dec). *Third Pakistan Boy Scouts National Jamboree, Lahore. P* 12½ × 14.
121 **58** 2 a. carmine, yellow & dp bluish green 15 10

(New Currency. 100 paisa=1 rupee)

1 PAISA
(59)

1961 (1 Jan–14 Feb). *Nos.* 24a, 67/8, 83 *and* 108/9, *surch as T* **59.** *Nos.* 123/4 *and* 126 *surch by Pakistan Security Ptg Corp and others by the Times Press, Karachi.*
122 1 p. on 1½ a. red (10.1) 10 10
123 2 p. on 3 p. red 10 10
124 3 p. on 6 p. deep purple 10 10
a. "PASIA" for "PAISA" .. .. .. 2·50
125 7 p. on 1 a. carmine (14.2) 10 10
126 13 p. on 2 a. brown-red (14.2) 10 10
a. "PAIS" for "PAISA" .. .. .. 2·50
127 13 p. on 2 a. scarlet (14.2) 10 10
122/7 .. .. *Set of* 6 25 20

No. 122. Two settings were used, the first with figure "1" 2½ mm tall and the second 3 mm.

On the 1 p. with tall "1" and the 13 p. (No. 127), the space between the figures of value and "P" of "PAISA" varies between 1½ mm and 3 mm.

See also Nos. 262/4.

ERRORS. In the above issue and the corresponding official stamps we have listed errors in the stamps surcharged by the Pakistan Security Printing Corp but have not included the very large number of errors which occurred in the stamps surcharged by the less experienced Times Press. This was a very hurried job and there was no time to carry out the usual checks. It is also known that some errors were not issued to the public but came on the market by other means.

NOTE. Stamps in the old currency were also *handstamped* with new currency equivalents and issued in various districts but these local issues are outside the scope of this catalogue.

60 Khyber Pass 61 Shalimar Gardens, Lahore

62 Chota Sona Masjid (gateway)

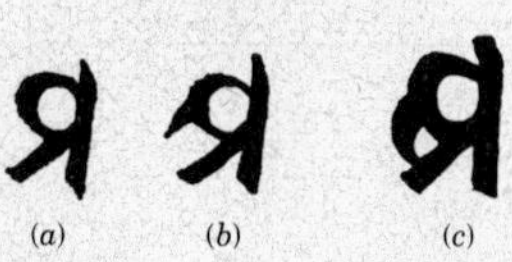

(*a*) (*b*) (*c*)

Types (*a*) and (*b*) show the first letter in the top right-hand inscription; (*a*) wrongly engraved, "SH" (*b*) corrected to "P".

On Nos. 131/2 and 134 the corrections were made individually on the plate, so that each stamp in the sheet may be slightly different.

Type (*c*) refers to No. 133a only.

1961–63. *No wmk. P* 13 (*T* **62**) *or* 14 (*others*).

(*a*) *Inscribed* "SHAKISTAN" *in Bengali*
128 **60** 1 p. violet (1.1.61) 25 10
129 2 p. rose-red (1.1.61) 25 10
130 5 p. ultramarine (23.3.61) 25 10

(*b*) *Inscribed* "PAKISTAN" *in Bengali*
131 **60** 1 p. violet 10 10
132 2 p. rose-red 10 10
133 3 p. reddish purple (27.10.61) 10 10
a. Re-engraved. First letter of Bengali inscription as Type (*c*) (1963) .. 60 85
134 5 p. ultramarine 15 10
135 7 p. emerald (23.3.61) 25 10
136 **61** 10 p. brown (14.8.61) 20 10
137 13 p. slate-violet (14.8.61) 10 10
138 25 p. deep blue (1.1.62) .. .. 2·50 10
139 40 p. deep purple (1.1.62) 40 10
140 50 p. deep bluish green (1.1.62) 35 10
141 75 p. carmine-red (23.3.62) 40 10
142 90 p. yellow-green (1.1.62) 40 10
143 **62** 1 r. vermilion (7.1.63) .. .. .. 1·75 10
a. Imperf (pair) .. ..
144 1 r. 25, reddish violet (27.10.61) 75 10
144*a* 2 r. orange (7.1.63) .. .. 3·50 15
144*b* 5 r. green (7.1.63) .. .. 6·00 65
128/44*b* .. .. *Set of* 19 16·00 1·50

See also Nos. 170/81 and 204/7.

(63) 64 Warsak Dam and Power Station

1961 (12 Feb). *Lahore Stamp Exhibition. No.* 110 *optd with T* **63**.
145 **51** 8 a. deep green (R.) 10 40

1961 (1 July). *Completion of Warsak Hydro-Electric Project. P* 12½ × 14.
146 **64** 40 p. black and blue 25 10

65 Narcissus 66 Ten Roses

1961 (2 Oct). *Child Welfare Week. P* 14.
147 **65** 13 p. turquoise-blue 10 10
148 90 p. bright purple 20 10

1961 (4 Nov). *Co-operative Day. P* 13.
149 **66** 13 p. rose-red and deep green 25 10
150 90 p. rose-red and blue 40 10

67 Police Crest and "Traffic Control" 68 Locomotive *Eagle* of 1861

(Photo D.L.R.)

1961 (30 Nov). *Police Centenary. P* 13.
151 **67** 13 p. silver, black and blue 15 10
152 40 p. silver, black and red 45 10

(Des M. Thoma. Photo D.L.R.)

1961 (31 Dec). *Railway Centenary. T* **68** *and similar horiz design. P* 14.
153 13 p. green, black and yellow 50 15
154 50 p. yellow, black and green 75 15

Design:—50 p. Diesel locomotive and tracks forming "1961".

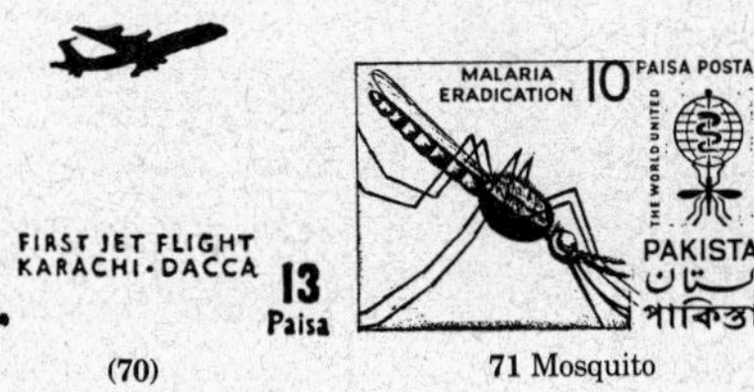

(70) 71 Mosquito

1962 (6 Feb). *First Karachi–Dacca Jet Flight. No.* 87 *surch with T* **70**.
155 **39** 13 p. on 2½ a. scarlet (R.) 10 10

(Photo D.L.R.)

1962 (7 Apr). *Malaria Eradication. T* **71** *and similar horiz design. P* 14.
156 10 p. black, yellow and red 10 10
157 13 p. black, greenish yellow and red 10 10

Design:—13 p. Mosquito pierced by blade.

73 Pakistan Map and Jasmine

(Photo Courvoisier)

1962 (8 June). *New Constitution. P* 12.
158 **73** 40 p. yellow-green, bluish green and grey 25 10

74 Football 78 Marble Fruit Dish and Bahawalpuri Clay Flask

1962 (14 Aug). *Sports. T* **74** *and similar horiz designs. P* 12½ × 14.
159 7 p. black and blue 10 10
160 13 p. black and green 10 10
161 25 p. black and purple 10 10
162 40 p. black and orange-brown .. .. .. 1·40 60
159/62 .. .. *Set of* 4 1·50 65

Designs:—13 p. Hockey; 25 p. Squash; 40 p. Cricket.

1962 (10 Nov). *Small Industries. T* **78** *and similar vert designs. P* 13.
163 7 p. brown-lake 10 10
164 13 p. deep green .. .. 1·50 35
165 25 p. reddish violet 10 10
166 40 p. yellow-green 10 10
167 50 p. deep red 10 10
163/7 .. .. *Set of* 5 1·50 50

Designs:—13 p. Sports equipment; 25 p. Camel-skin lamp and brassware; 40 p. Wooden powderbowl and basket-work; 50 p. Inlaid cigarette-box and brassware.

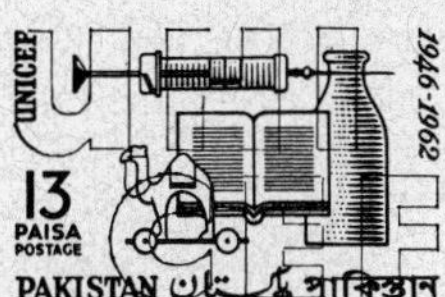

83 "Child Welfare"

(Des M. Thoma. Photo D.L.R.)

1962 (11 Dec). *16th Anniv of U.N.I.C.E.F. P* 14.
168 **83** 13 p. black, light blue and maroon .. 10 10
169 40 p. black, yellow and turquoise-blue .. 10 10

Nos. 170, etc. Nos. 131/42

1962–70. *As T* **60/1** *but with redrawn Bengali inscription at top right. No wmk.*
170 **60** 1 p. violet (1963) 10 10
171 2 p. rose-red (1964) 25 10
a. Imperf (pair) .. .. 2·75
172 3 p. reddish purple (1970) .. .. .. 1·00 35
173 5 p. ultramarine (1963) 10 10
174 7 p. emerald (1964) .. .. 2·25 35
175 **61** 10 p. brown (1963) 10 10
176 13 p. slate-violet 10 10
176*a* 15 p. bright purple (31.12.64) 15 10
ab. Imperf (pair) .. .. .. 3·75
176*b* 20 p. myrtle-green (26.1.70) 30 10
ba. Imperf (pair) .. .. .. 2·75
177 25 p. deep blue (1963) 90 10
a. Imperf (pair) .. .. .. 5·00
178 40 p. deep purple (1964) 15 10
a. Imperf (pair) .. .. .. 6·00
179 50 p. deep bluish green (1964) 15 10
180 75 p. carmine-red (1964) 20 10
181 90 p. yellow-green (1964) 20 20
170/81 .. .. *Set of* 14 5·50 1·50

Other values in this series and the high values (Nos. 204/10) are known imperforate but we are not satisfied as to their status.

U.N. FORCE W. IRIAN

(84) 85 "Dancing" Horse, Camel and Bull

1963 (15 Feb). *Pakistan U.N. Force in West Irian. No.* 176 *optd with T* **84**.
182 **61** 13 p. slate-violet (R.) 10 10

(Des S. Jahangir. Photo Courvoisier)

1963 (13 Mar). *National Horse and Cattle Show. P* 11½.
183 **85** 13 p. blue, sepia and cerise 10 10

86 Wheat and Tractor

1963 (21 Mar). *Freedom from Hunger. T* **86** *and similar horiz design. P* 12½ × 14.
184 13 p. orange-brown 50 10
185 50 p. bistre-brown .. .. 1·25 40
Design:—50 p. Rice.

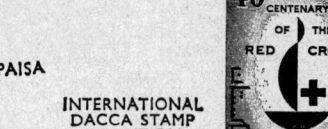

(**88**) **89** Centenary Emblem

1963 (23 Mar). *2nd International Stamp Exhibition, Dacca. No.* 109 *surch with T* **88**.
186 **51** 13 p. on 2 a. brown-red 10 10

1963 (25 June). *Centenary of Red Cross. Recess; cross typo. P* 13.
187 **89** 40 p. red and deep olive 50 15

100 YEARS OF P.W.D.
OCTOBER, 1963
13
=

90 Paharpur (**94**)

1963 (16 Sept). *Archaeological Series. T* **90** *and similar designs. P* 14 × 12½ (13 *p.*) *or* 12½ × 15 (*others*).
188 7 p. ultramarine 10 10
189 13 p. sepia 10 10
190 40 p. carmine 10 10
191 50 p. deep reddish violet 15 10
188/91 .. .. *Set of* 4 30 15
Designs: *Vert*—13 p. Moenjodaro; *Horiz*—40 p. Taxila; 50 p. Mainamati.

1963 (7 Oct). *Centenary of Public Works Department. No.* 133 *surch with T* **94** *by typography.*
192 **60** 13 p. on 3 p. reddish purple 10 10
Forged surcharges applied in *lithography* exist.

95 Ataturk's Mausoleum

1963 (10 Nov). *25th Death Anniv of Kemal Atatürk. P* 13½.
193 **95** 50 p. red 15 10

96 Globe and U.N.E.S.C.O. Emblem

(Photo D.L.R.)

1963 (10 Dec). *15th Anniv of Declaration of Human Rights. P* 14.
194 **96** 50 p. brown, red and ultramarine 10 10

97 Thermal Power Installations

1963 (25 Dec). *Completion of Multan Thermal Power Station. P* 12½ × 14.
195 **97** 13 p. ultramarine 10 10

PAKISTAN POSTAGE
PAISA 13
SAVE THE MONUMENTS OF NUBIA

98 Multiple Star and Crescent **99** Temple of Thot, Queen Nefertari and Maids

1963–79. *As Nos.* 43*b*, 89, 95 *and* 143/44*b*, *but W* **98**.
204 **62** 1 r. vermilion 20 10
b. Imperf (pair) .. .. 7·00
205 1 r. 25, reddish violet (1964) .. .. .. 1·00 10
a. *Purple* (1975?) .. .. 1·00 10
ab. Imperf (pair) .. .. 6·00
206 2 r. orange (1964) 55 10
a. Imperf (pair) .. .. 8·00
207 5 r. green (1964) .. .. 3·50 35
a. Imperf (pair) .. .. 14·00
208 **41** 10 r. myrtle-green & yellow-orge (1968) 3·50 3·25
a. Imperf (pair) .. ..
b. Wmk sideways 50 55
209 **44** 15 r. red and deep reddish purple (*wmk sideways*) (20.3.79) 80 85
a. Imperf (pair) .. .. 18·00
210 **13** 25 r. violet (1968) .. .. 12·00 14·00
a. Wmk sideways .. .. 1·25 1·40
ab. Imperf (pair) .. .. 15·00
204/10a .. .. *Set of* 7 6·00 3·00

1964 (30 Mar). *Nubian Monuments Preservation. T* **99** *and similar horiz design. P* 13 × 13½.
211 13 p. turquoise-blue and red 15 10
212 50 p. bright purple and black 35 10
Design:—50 p. Temple of Abu Simbel.

101 "Unisphere" and Pakistan Pavilion **103** Shah Abdul Latif's Mausoleum

1964 (22 Apr). *New York World's Fair. T* **101** *and similar design. P* 12½ × 14 (13 *p.*) *or* 14 × 12½ (1 *r.* 25).
213 13 p. ultramarine 10 10
214 1 r. 25, ultramarine and red-orange 20 20
Design: *Vert*—1 r. 25, Pakistan Pavilion on "Unisphere".

1964 (25 June). *Death Bicentenary of Shah Abdul Latif of Bhit. P* 13½ × 13.
215 **103** 50 p. bright blue and carmine-lake .. 30 10

104 Mausoleum of Quaid-i-Azam **105** Mausoleum

1964 (11 Sept). *16th Death Anniv of Mohammed Ali Jinnah (Quaid-i-Azam). P* 13½ (15 *p.*) *or* 13 (50 *p.*).
216 **104** 15 p. emerald-green 10 10
217 **105** 50 p. bronze-green 25 10

106 Bengali and Urdu Alphabets **107** University Building

1964 (5 Oct). *Universal Children's Day. P* 13.
218 **106** 15 p. brown 10 10

1964 (21 Dec). *First Convocation of the West Pakistan University of Engineering and Technology, Lahore. P* 12½ × 14.
219 **107** 15 p. chestnut 10 10

PROCESS. All the following issues were lithographed by the Pakistan Security Printing Corporation, *unless otherwise stated.*

108 "Help the Blind" **109** "I.T.U. Emblem and Symbols

(Des A. Chughtai)

1965 (28 Feb). *Blind Welfare. P* 13.
220 **108** 15 p. ultramarine and yellow 10 10

1965 (17 May). *I.T.U. Centenary. Recess. P* 12½ × 14.
221 **109** 15 p. reddish purple 80 15

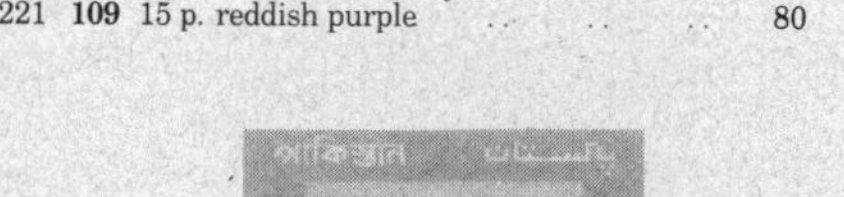

110 I.C.Y. Emblem

1965 (26 June). *International Co-operation Year. P* 13 × 13½.
222 **110** 15 p. black and light blue 30 10
223 50 p. green and yellow 55 30

111 "Co-operation"

112 Globe and Flags of Turkey, Iran and Pakistan

1965 (21 July). *First Anniv of Regional Development Co-operation Pact. P* 13½ × 13 (15 *p.*) *or* 13 (50 *p.*).
224 **111** 15 p. multicoloured 10 10
225 **112** 50 p. multicoloured 15 10

113 Soldier and Tanks

1965 (25 Dec). *Pakistan Armed Forces. T* **113** *and similar horiz designs. Multicoloured. P* 13½ × 13.
226 7 p. Type **113** 20 10
227 15 p. Naval officer and *Tughril* (destroyer) .. 20 10
228 50 p. Pilot and "F-104" Starfighters 45 10
226/8 .. .. *Set of* 3 75 15

116 Army, Navy and Air Force Crests **117** Atomic Reactor, Islamabad

1966 (13 Feb). *Armed Forces Day. P* 13½ × 13.
229 **116** 15 p. royal blue, dull grn, brt blue & buff 10 10

1966 (30 Apr). *Inauguration of Pakistan's First Atomic Reactor. Recess. P* 13.
230 **117** 15 p. black 10 10

118 Bank Crest

119 Children

1966 (25 Aug). *Silver Jubilee of Habib Bank. P* 12½ × 14.
231 **118** 15 p. blue-green, yellow-orange & sepia 10 10

1966 (3 Oct). *Universal Children's Day. P* 13½.
232 **119** 15 p. black, red and pale yellow 10 10

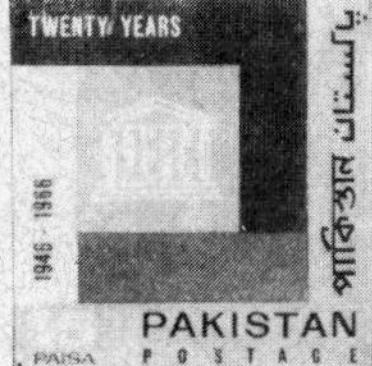

120 U.N.E.S.C.O. Emblem

1966 (24 Nov). *20th Anniv of U.N.E.S.C.O. P* 14.
233 **120** 15 p. multicoloured .. .. .. 1·50 25

121 Flag, Secretariat Building and President Ayub

1966 (29 Nov). *Islamabad (new capital). P* 13.
234 **121** 15 p. deep bluish green, chestnut, light blue and bistre-brown 10 10
235 50 p. deep bluish green, chestnut, light blue and black 15 10

122 Avicenna

123 Mohammed Ali Jinnah

1966 (3 Dec). *Foundation of Health and Tibbi Research Institute. P* 13 × 13½.
236 **122** 15 p. dull green and salmon 10 10
a. Imperf (pair) .. .. .. 55·00

1966 (25 Dec). *90th Birth Anniv of Mohammed Ali Jinnah. T* **123** *and similar design bearing same portrait but in different frame. Litho and recess. P* 13.
237 **123** 15 p. black, orange and greenish blue .. 10 10
238 – 50 p. black, purple and ultramarine .. 10 10

124 Tourist Year Emblem

125 Emblem of Pakistan T.B. Association

1967 (1 Jan). *International Tourist Year. P* 13½ × 13.
239 **124** 15 p. black, light blue and yellow-brown 10 10

1967 (10 Jan). *Tuberculosis Eradication Campaign. P* 13½ × 13.
240 **125** 15 p. red, sepia and chestnut 10 10

126 Scout Salute and Badge

127 "Justice"

1967 (29 Jan). *4th National Scout Jamboree. Photo. P* 12½ × 14.
241 **126** 15 p. light orange-brown and maroon .. 15 10

1967 (17 Feb). *Centenary of West Pakistan High Court. P* 13.
242 **127** 15 p. black, slate, light red and slate-blue 10 10

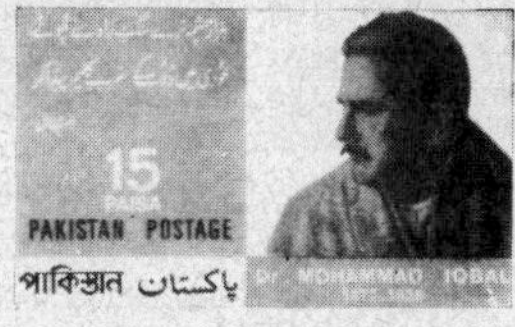

128 Dr. Mohammed Iqbal (philosopher)

1967 (21 Apr). *Iqbal Commemoration. P* 13.
243 **128** 15 p. sepia and light red 10 10
244 1 r. sepia and deep green 10 10

129 Hilal-i-Isteqlal Flag

1967 (15 May). *Award of Hilal-i-Isteqlal (for Valour) to Lahore, Sialkot, and Sargodha. P* 13.
245 **129** 15 p. multicoloured 10 10

130 "20th Anniversary"

1967 (14 Aug). *20th Anniv of Independence. Photo. P* 13.
246 **130** 15 p. red and deep bluish green 10 10

131 "Rice Exports"

132 Cotton Plant, Yarn and Textiles

1967 (26 Sept). *Pakistan Exports. T* **131/2** *and similar design. Photo. P* 13 × 13½.
247 10 p. yellow, deep bluish green and deep blue 10 10
248 15 p. multicoloured 10 10
a. Pale orange (top panel) omitted .. .. 10·00
249 50 p. multicoloured 10 10
247/9 .. .. *Set of* 3 15 10
Design: *Vert as T* **132**—50 p. Raw jute, bale and bags.

134 Clay Toys

1967 (2 Oct). *Universal Children's Day. P* 13.
250 **134** 15 p. multicoloured 10 10

135 Shah and Empress of Iran and Gulistan Palace, Teheran

1967 (26 Oct). *Coronation of Shah Mohammed Riza Pahlavi and Empress Farah of Iran. Recess and litho. P* 13.
251 **135** 50 p. purple, blue and light yellow-ochre 10 10

136 "Each For All–All For Each"

1967 (4 Nov). *Co-operative Day. P* 13.
252 **136** 15 p. multicoloured 10 10

137 Mangla Dam

1967 (23 Nov). *Indus Basin Project. P* 13.
253 **137** 15 p. multicoloured 10 10

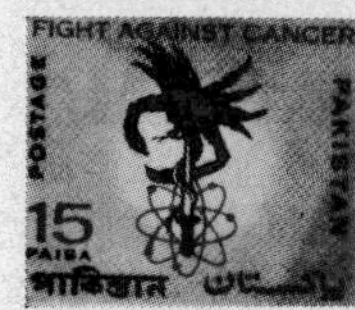

138 Crab pierced by Sword

139 Human Rights Emblem

1967 (26 Dec). *The Fight Against Cancer. P* 13.
254 **138** 15 p. red and black 15 10

1968 (31 Jan). *Human Rights Year. Photo. P* 14 × 13.
255 **139** 15 p. red and deep turquoise-blue .. 10 10
256 50 p. red, yellow and silver-grey 10 10

140 Agricultural University, Mymensingh

141 W.H.O. Emblem

1968 (28 Mar). *First Convocation of East Pakistan Agricultural University. Photo. P* 13½ × 13.
257 **140** 15 p. multicoloured 10 10

1968 (7 Apr). *20th Anniv of World Health Organization. Photo. P* 14 × 13.
258 **141** 15 p. green and orange-red 10 10
259 50 p. red-orange and indigo 10 15

142 Kazi Nazrul Islam (poet, composer and patriot)

1968 (25 June). *Nazrul Islam Commemoration. Recess and litho. P* 13.
260 **142** 15 p. sepia and pale yellow 10 10
261 50 p. sepia and pale rose-red 15 10
Nos. 260/1 with a two-line inscription giving the wrong date of birth ("1889") were prepared but not issued. Some are known to have been released in error.

4 PAISA

(143)

1968 (18 July–Aug). *Nos.* 56, 74 *and* 61 *surch as T* **143**.

262	4 p. on 3 a. purple	10	30
263	4 p. on 6 a. deep ultramarine (R.) (Aug)	15	30
264	60 p. on 10 a. violet (R.)	30	35
	a. Surch in black	30	55
	b. Surch triple	30·00	
262/4	*Set of* 3	45	85

144 Children running with Hoops

1968 (7 Oct). *Universal Children's Day. P* 13.
265 **144** 15 p. multicoloured .. 10 10

145 "National Assembly"

1968 (27 Oct). *"A Decade of Development". T* **145** *and similar horiz designs. P* 13.

266	10 p. multicoloured	10	10
267	15 p. multicoloured	15	10
268	50 p. multicoloured	40	15
269	60 p. light blue, dull purple and vermilion	40	15
266/9	*Set of* 4	95	45

Designs:—15 p. Industry and agriculture; 50 p. Army, Navy and Air Force; 60 p. Minaret and atomic reactor plant.

149 Chittagong Steel Mill

1969 (7 Jan). *Pakistan's First Steel Mill, Chittagong. P* 13.
270 **149** 15 p. grey, light blue & pale yellow-olive 10 10

150 "Family" **151** Olympic Gold Medal and Hockey Player

1969 (14 Jan). *Family Planning. P* 13½ × 13.
271 **150** 15 p. bright purple & pale greenish blue 10 10

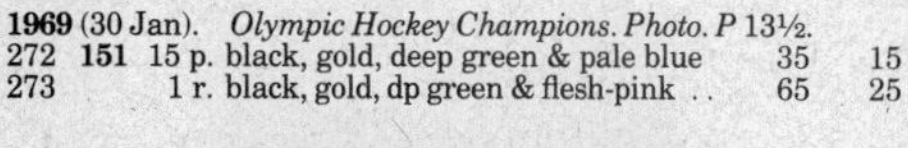

1969 (30 Jan). *Olympic Hockey Champions. Photo. P* 13½.

272	**151**	15 p. black, gold, deep green & pale blue	35	15
273		1 r. black, gold, dp green & flesh-pink	65	25

152 Mirza Ghalib and Lines of Verse

1969 (15 Feb). *Death Centenary of Mirza Ghalib (poet). P* 13.

274	**152**	15 p. multicoloured	10	10
275		50 p. multicoloured	10	10

The lines of verse on No. 275 are different from those in T **152**.

153 Dacca Railway Station

1969 (27 Apr). *First Anniv of New Dacca Railway Station. P* 13.
276 **153** 15 p. multicoloured .. 30 10

154 I.L.O. Emblem and "1919–1969" **155** Mughal Miniature (Pakistan)

1969 (15 May). *50th Anniv of International Labour Organisation. P* 13½.

277	**154**	15 p. buff and bluish green	10	10
278		50 p. cinnamon and cerise	10	10

1969 (21 July). *Fifth Anniv of Regional Co-operation for Development. T* **155** *and similar vert designs. Multicoloured. P* 13.

279	20 p. Type **155**	15	10
280	50 p. Safav miniature (Iran)	15	10
281	1 r. Ottoman miniature (Turkey)	20	10
279/81	*Set of* 3	45	25

158 Eastern Refinery, Chittagong

1969 (14 Sept). *First Oil Refinery in East Pakistan. Photo. P* 13½ × 13.
282 **158** 20 p. multicoloured .. 10 10

159 Children playing Outside "School"

1969 (6 Oct). *Universal Children's Day. Photo. P* 13.
283 **159** 20 p. multicoloured .. 10 10

160 Japanese Doll and P.I.A. Air Routes

1969 (1 Nov). *Inauguration of P.I.A. Pearl Route, Dacca–Tokyo. P* 13½ × 13.

284	**160**	20 p. multicoloured	10	10
		a. Yellow and pink omitted	7·00	
285		50 p. multicoloured	20	35
		a. Yellow and pink omitted	7·00	

161 "Reflection of Light" Diagram

1969 (4 Nov). *Millenary Commemorative of Ibn-al-Haitham (physicist). Photo. P* 13.
286 **161** 20 p. black, lemon and light blue .. 10 10

162 Vickers "Vimy" and Karachi Airport **163** Flags, Sun Tower and Expo Site Plan

1969 (2 Dec). *50th Anniv of First England–Australia Flight. Photo. P* 13½ × 13.
287 **162** 50 p. multicoloured .. 40 35

1970 (15 Mar). *World Fair, Osaka. P* 13.
288 **163** 50 p. multicoloured .. 15 25

164 New U.P.U. H.Q. Building

1970 (20 May). *New U.P.U. Headquarters Building. P* 13½ × 13.

289	**164**	20 p. multicoloured	10	10
290		50 p. multicoloured	20	25

The above, in a miniature sheet, additionally inscr "U.P.U. Day 9th Oct, 1971", were put on sale on that date in very limited numbers.

165 U.N. H.Q. Building

1970 (26 June). *25th Anniv of United Nations. T* **165** *and similar horiz design. Multicoloured. P* 13 × 13½.

291	20 p. Type **165**	10	10
292	50 p. U.N. emblem	15	20

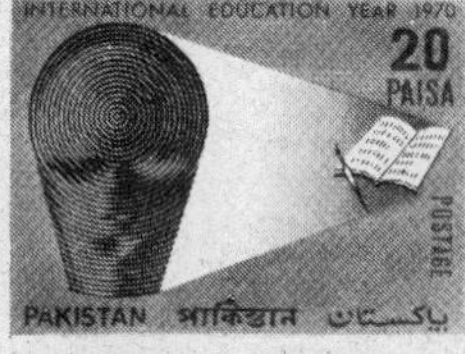

167 I.E.Y. Emblem, Book and Pen

1970 (6 July). *International Education Year. P* 13.

293	**167**	20 p. multicoloured	10	10
294		50 p. multicoloured	10	20

168 Saiful Malook Lake (Pakistan)

1970 (21 July). *Sixth Anniv of Regional Co-operation for Development. T* **168** *and similar square designs. Multicoloured. P* 13.

295	20 p. Type **168**	15	10
296	50 p. Seeyo-Se-Pol Bridge, Esfahan (Iran)	20	10
297	1 r. View from Fethiye (Turkey)	20	15
295/7	*Set of* 3	50	30

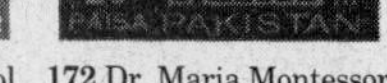

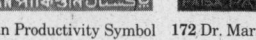

171 Asian Productivity Symbol **172** Dr. Maria Montessori

1970 (18 Aug). *Asian Productivity Year. Photo. P* 12½ × 14.
298 **171** 50 p. multicoloured 10 15

1970 (31 Aug). *Birth Centenary of Dr. Maria Montessori (educationist). P* 13.
299 **172** 20 p. multicoloured 10 10
300 50 p. multicoloured 10 15

173 Tractor and Fertilizer Factory

1970 (12 Sept). *Tenth Near East F.A.O. Regional Conference, Islamabad. P* 13.
301 **173** 20 p. bright green, and orange-brown 10 10

174 Children and Open Book

175 Pakistan Flag and Text

1970 (5 Oct). *Universal Children's Day. Photo. P* 13.
302 **174** 20 p. multicoloured 10 10

1970 (7 Dec). *General Elections for National Assembly. P* 13½ × 13.
303 **175** 20 p. green and bluish violet 10 10

1970 (17 Dec). *General Elections for Provincial Assemblies. As No.* 303, *but inscr* "PROVINCIAL ASSEMBLIES 17TH DEC., 1970".
304 **175** 20 p. green and pale magenta 10 10

176 Conference Crest and burning Al-Aqsa Mosque

1970 (26 Dec). *Conference of Islamic Foreign Ministers. Karachi. P* 13.
305 **176** 20 p. multicoloured 10 10

177 Coastal Embankments

1971 (25 Feb). *Coastal Embankments in East Pakistan Project. P* 13.
306 **177** 20 p. multicoloured 10 10

178 Emblem and United Peoples of the World

180 Chaharbagh School (Iran)

179 Maple Leaf Cement Factory, Daudkhel

1971 (21 Mar). *Racial Equality Year. P* 13.
307 **178** 20 p. multicoloured 10 10
308 50 p. multicoloured 10 20

1971 (1 July). *20th Anniv of Colombo Plan. P* 13.
309 **179** 20 p. brown, black and reddish violet .. 10 10

1971 (21 July). *Seventh Anniv of Regional Co-operation for Development. T* **180** *and similar horiz designs. Multicoloured. P* 13.
310 10 p. Selimiye Mosque (Turkey) 10 15
311 20 p. Badshahi Mosque (Lahore) 20 25
312 50 p. Type **180** 30 35
310/12 .. .. *Set of* 3 55 65

181 Electric Locomotive and Boy with Toy Train

1971 (4 Oct). *Universal Children's Day. P* 13.
313 **181** 20 p. multicoloured 50 25

182 Horseman and Symbols

1971 (15 Oct). *2500th Anniv of Persian Monarchy. P* 13.
314 **182** 10 p. multicoloured 15 15
315 20 p. multicoloured 25 25
316 50 p. multicoloured 35 40
314/16 .. .. *Set of* 3 65 70

The above exist in a miniature sheet, but only a very limited quantity was placed on sale.

183 Hockey-player and Trophy

1971 (24 Oct). *World Cup Hockey Tournament, Barcelona. P* 13.
317 **183** 20 p. multicoloured 45 25

184 Great Bath, Moenjodaro

1971 (4 Nov). *25th Anniv of U.N.E.S.C.O. and Campaign to save the Moenjodaro Excavations. P* 13.
318 **184** 20 p. multicoloured 10 15

185 U.N.I.C.E.F. Symbol

1971 (11 Dec). *25th Anniv of U.N.I.C.E.F. P* 13.
319 **185** 50 p. multicoloured 25 25

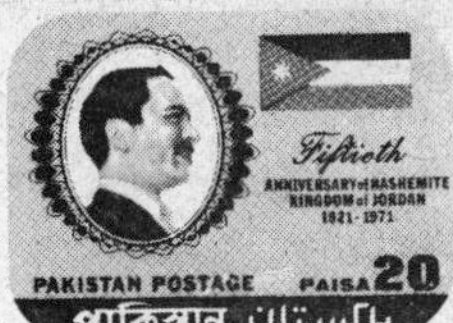

186 King Hussein and Jordanian Flag

1971 (25 Dec). *50th Anniv of Hashemite Kingdom of Jordan. P* 13.
320 **186** 20 p. multicoloured 15 15

187 Badge of Hockey Federation and Trophy

188 Reading Class

1971 (31 Dec). *Hockey Championships Victory. P* 13.
321 **187** 20 p. multicoloured 90 60

1972 (15 Jan). *International Book Year. P* 13½.
322 **188** 20 p. multicoloured 15 15

INDEPENDENT OF THE BRITISH COMMONWEALTH

On 30 January 1972 Pakistan left the Commonwealth.

For the convenience of collectors we continue to list later issues in this volume.

189 View of Venice

1972 (7 Feb). *U.N.E.S.C.O. Campaign to Save Venice. P* 13.
323 **189** 20 p. multicoloured 20 20

190 E.C.A.F.E. Emblem and Discs

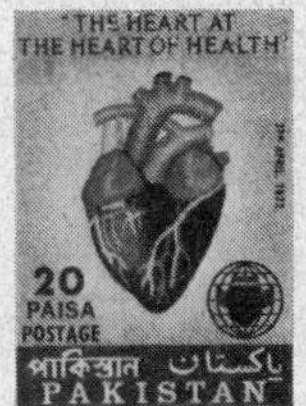

191 Human Heart

1972 (28 Mar). *25th Anniv of E.C.A.F.E. (Economic Commission for Asia and the Far East). P* 13.
324 **190** 20 p. multicoloured 10 20

1972 (7 Apr). *World Health Day. P* 13 × 13½.
325 **191** 20 p. multicoloured 20 20

192 "Only One Earth"

193 "Fisherman" (Cevat Dereli)

1972 (5 June). *U.N. Conference on the Human Environment, Stockholm. P* 13 × 13½.
326 **192** 20 p. multicoloured 20 20

1972 (21 July). *Eighth Anniv of Regional Co-operation for Development. T* **193** *and similar vert designs. Multicoloured. P* 13.
327 10 p. Type **193** 10 20
328 20 p. "Iranian Woman" (Behzad) 15 25
329 50 p. "Will and Power" (A. R. Chughtai) .. 35 45
a. Brown-ochre (border) omitted .. .. 15·00
327/9 .. .. *Set of* 3 55 80

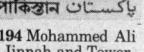

194 Mohammed Ali Jinnah and Tower

195 Donating Blood

1972 (14 Aug). *25th Anniv of Independence. T* **194** *and similar horiz designs. Multicoloured. P* 13 (*10 and 60 p.*) *or* 14 × 12½ (*20 p.*).

330 10 p. Type **194** 10 10
331 20 p. "Land Reform" (74 × 23½ *mm*) 15 20
 a. Horiz strip of 4. Nos. 331/4 55
332 20 p. "Labour Reform" (74 × 23½ *mm*) .. 15 20
333 20 p. "Education Policy" (74 × 23½ *mm*) .. 15 20
334 20 p. "Health Policy" (74 × 23½ *mm*) .. 15 20
335 60 p. National Assembly Building (46 × 28 *mm*) 25 25
330/5 .. .. *Set of* 6 80 1·00

Nos. 331/4 were printed horizontally *se-tenant* throughout the sheet.

1972 (6 Sept). *National Blood Transfusion Service. P* 13½×12½.
336 **195** 20 p. multicoloured 15 20

196 People and Squares

1972 (16 Sept). *Centenary of Population Census. P* 13½.
337 **196** 20 p. multicoloured 15 20

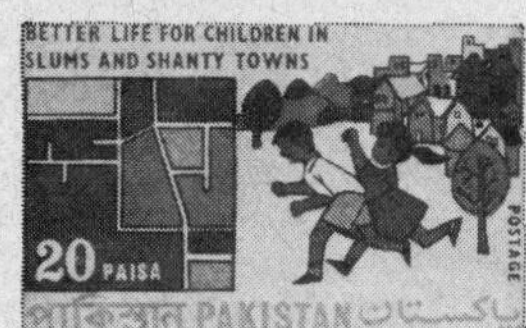

197 Children from Slums

1972 (2 Oct). *Universal Children's Day. P* 13.
338 **197** 20 p. multicoloured 15 20

198 People and Open Book

1972 (23 Oct). *Education Week. P* 13.
339 **198** 20 p. multicoloured 20 20

199 Nuclear Power Plant

1972 (28 Nov). *Inauguration of Karachi Nuclear Power Plant. P* 13.
340 **199** 20 p. multicoloured 15 20

200 Copernicus in Observatory

1973 (19 Feb). *500th Birth Anniv of Nicholas Copernicus (astronomer). P* 13.
341 **200** 20 p. multicoloured 20 25

201 Moenjodaro Excavations

202 Elements of Meteorology

1973 (23 Feb). *50th Anniv of Moenjodaro Excavations. P* 13 × 13½.
342 **201** 20 p. multicoloured 20 25

1973 (23 Mar). *I.M.O./W.M.O. Centenary. P* 13.
343 **202** 20 p. multicoloured 20 30

203 Prisoners-of-war

1973 (18 Apr). *Prisoners-of-war in India. P* 13.
344 **203** 1 r. 25, multicoloured .. .. .. 1·00 1·00

204 National Assembly Building and Constitution Book

1973 (21 Apr). *Constitution Week. P* 12½ × 13½.
345 **204** 20 p. multicoloured 25 30

205 Badge and State Bank Building

1973 (1 July). *25th Anniv of Pakistan State Bank. P* 13.
346 **205** 20 p. multicoloured 15 20
347 1 r. multicoloured 30 40

206 Lut Desert Excavations (Iran)

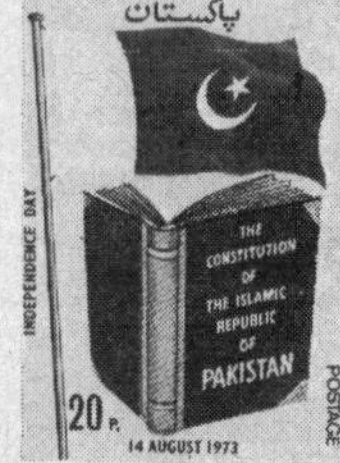

207 Constitution Book and Flag

1973 (21 July). *9th Anniv of Regional Co-operation for Development. T* **206** *and similar vert designs. Multicoloured. P* 13 × 13½.
348 20 p. Type **206** 20 20
349 60 p. Main Street, Moenjodaro (Pakistan) .. 35 35
350 1 r. 25, Mausoleum of Antiochus I (Turkey) .. 60 85
348/50 .. .. *Set of* 3 1·10 1·25

1973 (14 Aug). *Independence Day and Enforcement of the Constitution. P* 13.
351 **207** 20 p. multicoloured 15 20

208 Mohammed Ali Jinnah (Quaid-i-Azam)

209 *Wallago attu*

1973 (11 Sept). *25th Death Anniv of Mohammed Ali Jinnah. P* 13.
352 **208** 20 p. light emerald, pale yellow and black 15 20

1973 (24 Sept). *Fishes. T* **209** *and similar horiz designs. Multicoloured. P* 13½.
353 10 p. Type **209** 60 60
 a. Horiz strip of 4. Nos. 353/6 .. .. 2·50
354 20 p. *Labeo rohita* 65 65
355 60 p. *Tilapia mossambica* 70 70
356 1 r. *Catla catla* 80 80
353/6 .. .. *Set of* 4 2·50 2·50

Nos. 353/6 were printed within one sheet, horizontally *se-tenant*.

210 Children's Education

1973 (1 Oct). *Universal Children's Day. P* 13.
357 **210** 20 p. multicoloured 15 20

211 Harvesting

1973 (15 Oct). *Tenth Anniv of World Food Programme. P* 13.
358 **211** 20 p. multicoloured 30 30

212 Ankara and Kemal Atatürk

1973 (29 Oct). *50th Anniv of Turkish Republic. P* 13.
359 **212** 50 p. multicoloured 35 35

213 Boy Scout

214 "Basic Necessities"

1973 (11 Nov). *National Silver Jubilee Scout Jamboree. P* 13.
360 **213** 20 p. multicoloured 55 40

1973 (16 Nov). *25th Anniv of Declaration of Human Rights. P* 13.
361 **214** 20 p. multicoloured 30 30

215 Al-Biruni and Nandana Hill

216 Dr. Hansen, Microscope and Bacillus

1973 (26 Nov). *Al-Biruni Millennium Congress. P* 13.
362 **215** 20 p. multicoloured 25 20
363 1 r. 25, multicoloured 60 75

1973 (29 Dec). *Centenary of Hansen's Discovery of Leprosy Bacillus. P* 13.
364 **216** 20 p. multicoloured 50 30

217 Family and Emblem

218 Conference Emblem

1974 (1 Jan). *World Population Year. P* 13.
365 **217** 20 p. multicoloured 10 10
366 1 r. 25, multicoloured 30 40

1974 (22 Feb). *Islamic Summit Conference, Lahore. T* **218** *and similar design. P* 14 × 12½ (20 *p.*) *or* 13 (65 *p.*).

367 20 p. Type **218** 10 10
368 65 p. Emblem on "Sun" (42 × 30 *mm*) 25 45
MS369 102 × 102 mm. Nos. 367/8. Imperf .. 2·50 4·25

219 Units of Weight and Measurement **220** "Chand Chauthai" Carpet, Pakistan

1974 (1 July). *Adoption of International Weights and Measures System. P* 13.

370 **219** 20 p. multicoloured 15 25

1974 (21 July). *Tenth Anniv of Regional Co-operation for Development. Vert designs as T* **220** *showing carpets from member countries. Multicoloured. P* 13.

371 20 p. Type **220** 15 15
372 60 p. Persian carpet, 16th-century 45 50
373 1 r. 25, Anatolian carpet, 15th-century .. 65 1·00
371/3 .. .. *Set of* 3 1·10 1·50

221 Hands protecting Sapling **222** Torch and Map

1974 (9 Aug). *Tree Planting Day. P* 13.

374 **221** 20 p. multicoloured 40 30

1974 (26 Aug). *Namibia Day. P* 13.

375 **222** 60 p. multicoloured 35 60

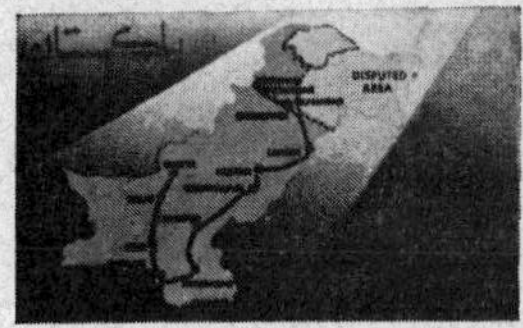

223 Highway Map

1974 (23 Sept). *Shahrah-e-Pakistan (Pakistan Highway). P* 13.

376 **223** 20 p. multicoloured 30 30

224 Boy at Desk **225** U.P.U. Emblem

1974 (7 Oct). *Universal Children's Day. P* 13.

377 **224** 20 p. multicoloured 30 30

1974 (9 Oct). *Centenary of Universal Postal Union. T* **225** *and similar vert design. Multicoloured. P* 13 × 13½ (20 *p.*) *or* 13 (2 *r.* 25).

378 20 p. Type **225** 20 20
379 2 r. 25, U.P.U. emblem, aeroplane and mail-wagon (30 × 41 *mm*) .. .. .. 55 1·40
MS380 100 × 101 mm. Nos. 378/9. Imperf .. 4·00 8·50

226 Liaquat Ali Khan **227** Dr. Mohammed Iqbal (poet and philosopher)

1974 (16 Oct). *Liaquat Ali Khan (First Prime Minister of Pakistan). P* 13 × 13½.

381 **226** 20 p. black and light vermilion 25 30

1974 (9 Nov). *Birth Centenary of Dr. Iqbal* (1977) (1*st issue*). *P* 13.

382 **227** 20 p. multicoloured 25 30

See also Nos. 399, 433 and 445/9.

228 Dr. Schweitzer and River Scene

1975 (14 Jan). *Birth Centenary of Dr. Albert Schweitzer. P* 13.

383 **228** 2 r. 25, multicoloured .. .. .. 1·25 1·50

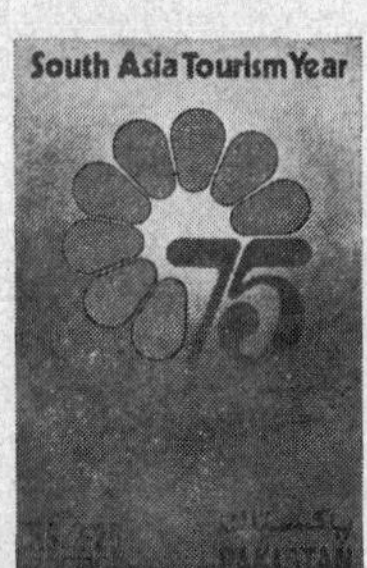

229 Tourism Year Symbol

1975 (15 Jan). *South East Asia Tourism Year. P* 13.

384 **229** 2 r. 25, multicoloured 55 80

230 Assembly Hall, Flags and Prime Minister Bhutto

(Des A. Salahuddin)

1975 (22 Feb). *First Anniv of Islamic Summit Conference, Lahore. P* 13.

385 **230** 20 p. multicoloured 20 20
386 1 r. multicoloured 45 70

231 "Scientific Research" **232** "Globe" and Algebraic Symbol

(Des A. Salahuddin (20 p.), M. Ahmed (2 r. 25))

1975 (15 June). *International Women's Year. T* **231** *and similar horiz design. Multicoloured. P* 13.

387 20 p. Type **231** 20 25
388 2 r. 25, Girl teaching woman ("Adult Education") .. .. 1·10 1·75

1975 (14 July). *International Congress of Mathematical Sciences, Karachi. P* 13.

389 **232** 20 p. multicoloured 30 30

233 Pakistani Camel-skin Vase **234** Sapling and Dead Trees

(Des I. Gilani)

1975 (21 July). *Eleventh Anniv of Regional Co-operation for Development. T* **233** *and similar multicoloured designs. P* 13.

390 20 p. Type **233** 25 25
391 60 p. Iranian tile (*horiz*) 50 50
392 1 r. 25, Turkish porcelain vase 75 85
390/2 .. .. *Set of* 3 1·40 1·40

1975 (9 Aug). *Tree Planting Day. P* 13 × 13½.

393 **234** 20 p. multicoloured 30 30

235 Black Partridge **236** "Today's Girls"

(Des A. Salahuddin)

1975 (30 Sept). *Wildlife Protection* (1*st series*). *P* 13.

394 **235** 20 p. multicoloured 80 35
395 2 r. 25, multicoloured .. .. .. 3·75 3·00

See also Nos. 400/1, 411/12, 417/18, 493/6, 560, 572/3, 581/2, 599, 600, 605, 621/2, 691 and 702.

1975 (6 Oct). *Universal Children's Day. P* 13.

396 **236** 20 p. multicoloured 25 30

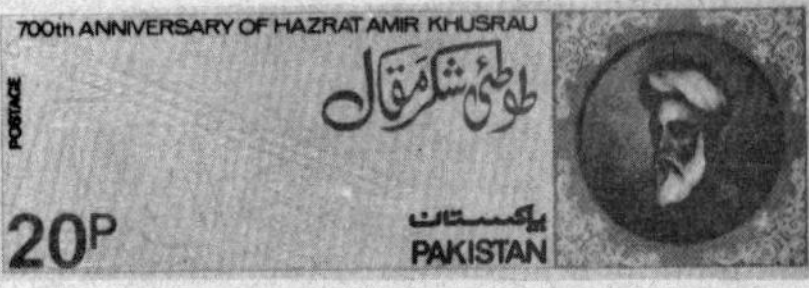

237 Hazrat Amir Khusrau, Sitar and Tabla

(Des A. Salahuddin)

1975 (24 Oct). *700th Birth Anniv of Hazrat Amir Khusrau (poet and musician). P* 13½ × 12½.

397 **237** 20 p. multicoloured 20 45
398 2 r. 25, multicoloured .. .. .. 75 1·60

238 Dr. Mohammed Iqbal **239** Urial (wild sheep)

(Des A. Salahuddin)

1975 (9 Nov). *Birth Centenary of Dr. Iqbal* (1977) (2*nd issue*). *P* 13.

399 **238** 20 p. multicoloured 25 30

(Des M. Ahmed)

1975 (31 Dec). *Wildlife Protection* (2*nd series*). *P* 13.

400 **239** 20 p. multicoloured 40 30
401 3 r. multicoloured .. .. .. 2·50 3·00

240 Moenjodaro Remains **241** Dome and Minaret of Rauza-e-Mubarak

(Des A. Salahuddin)

1976 (29 Feb). *"Save Moenjodaro"* (1*st series*). *T* **240** *and similar vert designs. Multicoloured. P* 13.

402 10 p. Type **240** 55 65
a. Horiz strip of 5. Nos. 402/6 .. .. 3·00
403 20 p. Remains (*different*) 65 75
404 65 p. The Citadel 65 75
405 3 r. Well inside a house 65 75
406 4 r. The "Great Bath" 75 85
402/6 .. .. *Set of* 5 3·00 3·25

Nos. 402/6 were printed horizontally *se-tenant* within the sheet, the five stamps forming a composite design of the excavations.

See also Nos. 414 and 430.

(Des A. Ghani. Photo)

1976 (3 Mar). *International Congress on Seerat. P* 13 × 13½.
407 **241** 20 p. multicoloured 20 20
408 3 r. multicoloured 70 90

242 Alexander Graham Bell and Telephone Dial

(Des M. M. Saeed. Photo)

1976 (10 Mar). *Telephone Centenary. P* 13.
409 **242** 3 r. multicoloured .. .. 1·25 2·00

243 College Arms within "Sun"

(Des A. Salahuddin)

1976 (15 Mar). *Centenary of National College of Arts, Lahore. P* 13.
410 **243** 20 p. multicoloured 25 35

244 Common Peafowl

(Des A. Salahuddin)

1976 (31 Mar). *Wildlife Protection* (*3rd series*). *P* 13.
411 **244** 20 p. multicoloured 75 35
412 3 r. multicoloured .. .. 3·00 3·50

245 Human Eye

(Des M. M. Saeed)

1976 (7 Apr). *Prevention of Blindness. P* 13.
413 **245** 20 p. multicoloured 30 35

246 Unicorn and Ruins

(Des I. Gilani)

1976 (31 May). *"Save Moenjodaro" (2nd series). P* 13.
414 **246** 20 p. multicoloured 25 30

247 Jefferson Memorial

248 Ibex

(Des I. Gilani (90 p.), A. Salahuddin (4 r.))

1976 (4 July). *Bicentenary of American Revolution. T* **247** *and similar horiz design. Multicoloured. P* 13 (90 *p.*) *or* 13½ (4 *r.*).
415 90 p. Type **247** .. .. 1·00 60
416 4 r. "Declaration of Independence" (47 × 36 *mm*) .. .. 3·75 4·50

(Des M. Ahmed)

1976 (12 July). *Wildlife Protection* (*4th series*). *P* 13.
417 **248** 20 p. multicoloured 30 35
418 3 r. multicoloured .. .. 1·75 2·50

249 Mohammed Ali Jinnah

(Des A. Salahuddin)

1976 (21 July). *Twelfth Anniv of Regional Co-operation for Development. T* **249** *and similar diamond-shaped designs. Multicoloured. P* 14.
419 20 p. Type **249** 25 35
a. Vert strip of 3. Nos. 419/21 65
420 65 p. Reza Shah the Great (Iran) 25 35
421 90 p. Kemal Atatürk (Turkey) 25 35
419/21 .. .. *Set of* 3 65 95

Nos. 419/21 were printed vertically *se-tenant* throughout the sheet.

250 Urdu Text

251 Mohammed Ali Jinnah and Wazir Mansion

1976 (14 Aug). *Birth Centenary of Mohammed Ali Jinnah* (*1st issue*). *P* 13. (*a*) *Type* **250**.
422 5 p. black, new blue and yellow 20 25
a. Block of 8. Nos. 422/9 .. .. .. 1·75
423 10 p. black, yellow and magenta 20 25
424 15 p. black and violet-blue 20 25
425 1 r. black, yellow and new blue 30 30

(*b*) *Multicoloured designs as T* **251**, *different buildings in the background*
426 20 p. Type **251** 20 25
427 40 p. Sind Madressah 20 25
428 50 p. Minar Qarardad-e-Pakistan 20 25
429 3 r. Mausoleum 45 50
422/9 .. .. *Set of* 8 1·75 2·10

Nos. 422/9 were printed in *se-tenant* blocks of 8 throughout the sheet.
See also No. 436.

252 Dancing-girl, Ruins and King Priest

(Des A. Salahuddin)

1976 (31 Aug). *"Save Moenjodaro" (3rd series). P* 14.
430 **252** 65 p. multicoloured 35 35

253 U.N. Racial Discrimination Emblem

(Des A. Salahuddin)

1976 (15 Sept). *U.N. Decade to Combat Racial Discrimination. P* 12½ × 13½.
431 **253** 65 p. multicoloured 25 40

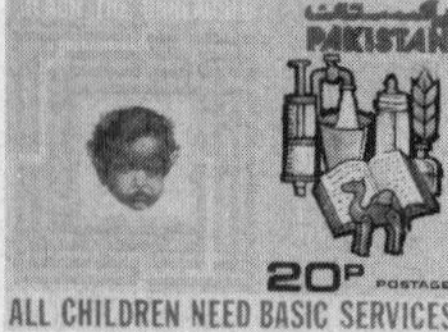

254 Child in Maze and Basic Services

(Des M. Ahmed)

1976 (4 Oct). *Universal Children's Day. P* 13.
432 **254** 20 p. multicoloured 15 20

Stamps commemorating the visit of King Khalid of Saudi Arabia and showing the Islamabad Mosque were prepared for release on 11 October 1976, but withdrawn before issue. Some are known to have been released in error.

255 Verse from "Allama Iqbal"

256 Mohammed Ali Jinnah giving Scout Salute

(Des M. A. Javed)

1976 (9 Nov). *Birth Centenary of Dr. Iqbal* (1977) (*3rd issue*). *P* 13.
433 **255** 20 p. multicoloured 15 20

(Des I. Gilani)

1976 (20 Nov). *Quaid-i-Azam Centenary Jamboree. P* 13½.
434 **256** 20 p. multicoloured 30 25

257 Children Reading

258 Mohammed Ali Jinnah

(Des M. Ahmed)

1976 (15 Dec). *Children's Literature. P* 13.
435 **257** 20 p. multicoloured 15 20

(Litho and embossed Cartor S.A., France)

1976 (25 Dec). *Birth Centenary of Mohammed Ali Jinnah* (*2nd issue*). *P* 12½.
436 **258** 10 r. emerald and gold .. .. 2·50 3·25

259 Rural Family

260 Turkish Vase, 1800 B.C.

(Des M. Ahmed)

1977 (14 Apr). *Social Welfare and Rural Development Year. P* 13.
437 **259** 20 p. multicoloured 15 10

(Des A. Salahuddin)

1977 (21 July). *13th Anniv of Regional Co-operation for Development. T* **260** *and similar horiz designs. P* 13.
438 20 p. red-orange, violet-blue and black .. 15 10
439 65 p. multicoloured 20 15
440 90 p. multicoloured 30 30
438/40 .. .. *Set of* 3 60 45

Designs:—60 p. Pakistani toy bullock cart, Moenjodaro; 90 p. Pitcher with spout, Sialk Hill, Iran.

261 Forest

262 Desert Scene

(Des A. Ahmed)

1977 (9 Aug). *National Tree Plantation Campaign. P* 13.

441 **261** 20 p. multicoloured 10 10

(Des M. A. Javed)

1977 (5 Sept). *U.N. Conference on Desertification, Nairobi. P* 13.

442 **262** 65 p. multicoloured 20 10

263 "Water for the Children of the World"

264 Aga Khan III

(Des A. Salahuddin)

1977 (3 Oct). *Universal Children's Day. P* 13½ × 12½.

443 **263** 50 p. multicoloured 30 15

(Des A. Rauf)

1977 (2 Nov). *Birth Centenary of Aga Khan III. P* 13.

444 **264** 2 r. multicoloured 55 85

265 Iqbal and Spirit of the Poet Roomi (from painting by Behzad)

266 The Holy "Khana-Kaaba" (House of God, Mecca)

(Des A. Ahmed)

1977 (9 Nov). *Birth Centenary of Dr. Mohammed Iqbal* (4*th issue*). *T* **265** *and similar vert designs. Multicoloured. P* 13.

445 20 p. Type **265** 25 35

a. Horiz strip of 5. Nos. 445/9 .. .. 1·40

446 65 p. Iqbal looking at Jamaluddin Afghani and Saeed Haleem Pasha at prayer (Behzad) 25 35

447 1 r. 25, Urdu verse 30 40

448 2 r. 25, Persian verse.. .. .. .. 35 45

449 3 r. Iqbal 40 50

445/9 .. .. *Set of* 5 1·40 1·90

Nos. 445, 448/9, 447 and 446 (in that order) were issued in horizontal *se-tenant* strips of 5.

(Des I. Gilani)

1977 (21 Nov). *Haj* (*pilgrimage to Mecca*). *P* 14.

450 **266** 65 p. multicoloured 30 30

267 Rheumatic Patient and Healthy Man

268 Woman in Costume of Rawalpindi-Islamabad

(Des T. Hameed)

1977 (19 Dec). *World Rheumatism Year. P* 13.

451 **267** 65 p. turquoise-blue, black and yellow .. 30 20

(Des A. Salahuddin)

1978 (5 Feb). *Indonesia–Pakistan Economic and Cultural Co-operation Organization. P* 12½ × 13½.

452 **268** 75 p. multicoloured 30 20

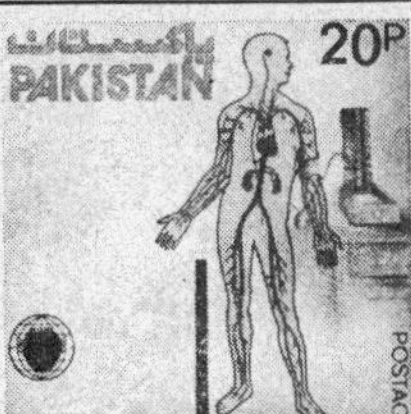

269 Human Body and Sphygmomanometer

270 Henri Dunant

(Des A. Salahuddin)

1978 (20 Apr). *World Hypertension Month. P* 13.

453 **269** 20 p. multicoloured 15 10

454 – 2 r. multicoloured 60 60

The 2 r. value is as T **269**, but has the words "Down with high blood pressure" instead of the Urdu inscription at bottom left.

(Des A. Salahuddin)

1978 (8 May). 150*th Birth Anniv of Henri Dunant* (*founder of Red Cross*). *P* 14.

455 **270** 1 r. black, new blue and vermilion .. 30 20

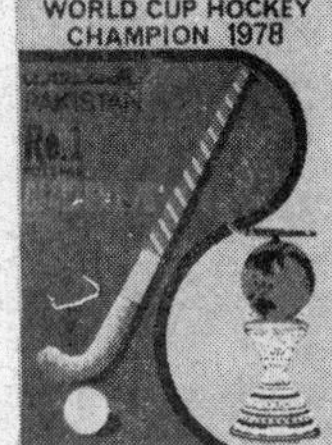

271 Red Roses (Pakistan)

272 "Pakistan, World Cup Hockey Champions"

(Des A. Salahuddin)

1978 (21 July). 14*th Anniv of Regional Co-operation for Development. T* **271** *and similar vert designs. Multicoloured. P* 13½.

456 20 p. Type **271** 10 10

a. Horiz strip of 3. Nos. 456/8 50

457 90 p. Pink roses (Iran).. .. .. .. 20 20

458 2 r. Yellow rose (Turkey) 25 25

456/8 .. .. *Set of* 3 50 50

Nos. 456/8 were printed together, *se-tenant*, in horizontal strips of 3 throughout the sheet.

(Des M. Munawar)

1978 (26 Aug). *"Riccione '78" International Stamp Fair. T* **272** *and similar vert designs. Multicoloured. P* 13.

459 1 r. Type **272** 50 15

460 2 r. Fountain at Piazza Turismo 75 30

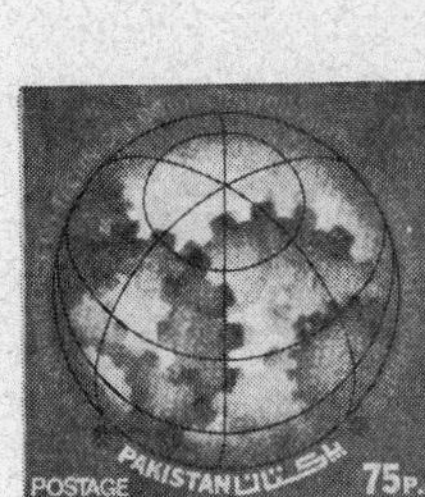

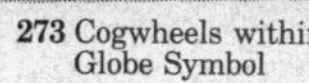

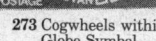

273 Cogwheels within Globe Symbol

274 St. Patrick's Cathedral

(Des A. Salahuddin)

1978 (3 Sept). *U.N. Technical Co-operation amongst Developing Countries Conference. P* 13.

461 **273** 75 p. multicoloured 15 10

(Des A. Salahuddin)

1978 (29 Sept). *Centenary of St. Patrick's Cathedral, Karachi. T* **274** *and similar vert design. Multicoloured. P* 13.

462 1 r. Type **274** 10 10

463 2 r. Stained glass window 25 25

275 Minar-i-Qarardad-e-Pakistan

276 Tractor

276a Mausoleum of Ibrahim Khan

Two Dies of 75 p. value:

Die I

Die II

Die I. Size of design 26½ × 21½ mm. Figures of value large; "p" small. Plough does not touch left-hand frame.

Die II. Size of design 25½ × 21 mm. Smaller figures; larger "p". Plough touches left-hand frame.

(Des A. Salahuddin. Litho (10, 25, 40, 50, 90 p.), recess (others))

1978 (7 Nov)–**81**. *No wmk* (2 *to* 90 *p.*) *or W* **98** (1 *to* 5 *r.*). *P* 14×13½ (2 *to* 5 *p.*), 13½×14 (10 *to* 90 *p.*) *or* 13 (1 *to* 5 *r.*).

464 **275** 2 p. deep grey-green 10 10

465 3 p. black 10 10

a. Imperf (pair) .. .. .. 5·00

466 5 p. deep ultramarine 10 10

467 **276** 10 p. new blue & greenish bl (7.10.79) .. 10 10

468 20 p. deep yellow-green (25.3.79) .. 30 10

469 25 p. dp green & dull magenta (19.3.79) 15 10

470 40 p. new blue and magenta (16.12.78) 10 10

471 50 p. slate-lilac & turq-green (19.3.79) .. 20 10

472 60 p. black (16.12.78) 10 10

a. Imperf (pair) .. .. .. 5·00

473 75 p. dull vermilion (I) (16.12.78) .. 60 10

a. Imperf (pair) .. .. .. 16·00

b. Die II (1980) 20 10

ba. Imperf (pair) .. .. .. 7·00

474 90 p. magenta and new blue (16.12.78) 15 10

475 **276a** 1 r. bronze-green (2.8.80) 10 10

a. Imperf (pair) .. .. .. 20·00

476 1 r. 50, red-orange (17.11.79) 10 10

a. Imperf (pair) .. .. .. 6·00

477 2 r. carmine-red (17.11.79) 10 10

a. Imperf (pair) .. .. .. 7·00

478 3 r. blue-black (4.6.80) 15 10

a. Imperf (pair) .. .. .. 9·00

479 4 r. black (1.1.81) 20 10

a. Imperf (pair) .. .. ..

480 5 r. sepia (1.1.81) 25 10

a. Imperf (pair) .. .. ..

464/80 .. .. *Set of* 17 1·75 75

The remaining values as Type **276** printed in recess, are from Die II.

Postal forgeries exist of the 2 r. and 3 r. values. These are poorly printed with perforations which do not match those of the genuine stamps.

GUM. Later printings of the 10 p., 20 p., 25 p., 4 r. and 5 r. values (Nos. 467/9 and 479/80) occur with matt, almost invisible gum of a PVA type, instead of the gum arabic used previously.

277 Emblem and "United Races" Symbol

278 Maulana Mohammad Ali Jauhar

(Des M. Munawar)

1978 (20 Nov). *International Anti-Apartheid Year. P* 13.

481 **277** 1 r. multicoloured 15 15

(Des A. Salahuddin)

1978 (10 Dec). *Birth Centenary of Maulana Mohammad Ali Jauhar* (*patriot*). *P* 13.

482 **278** 50 p. multicoloured 20 10

279 "Tornado", "Rapide" and Wright *Flyer*

(Des A. Salahuddin)

1978 (24 Dec). *75th Anniv of Powered Flight. T* **279** *and similar diamond-shaped designs. Multicoloured. P* 13.

483 65 p. Type **279** 50 50
a. Block of 4. Nos. 483/6 . . . . . . 2·40
484 1 r. "Phantom F4F", "Tri-star" and Wright *Flyer* 60 60
485 2 r. "X15", Tu. "104" and Wright *Flyer* . . 70 70
486 2 r. 25, Mig "15", "Concorde" and Wright *Flyer* 80 80
483/6 . . . . *Set of* 4 2·40 2·40

Nos. 483/6 were printed together, *se-tenant*, in blocks of 4 throughout the sheet.

280 "Holy Koran illuminating Globe" and Raudha-e-Mubarak (mausoleum)

281 "Aspects of A.P.W.A."

(Des A. Salahuddin)

1979 (10 Feb). *"12th Rabi-ul-Awwal" (Prophet Mohammed's birthday). P* 13.

487 **280** 20 p. multicoloured 15 10

(Des M. Saeed)

1979 (25 Feb). *30th Anniv of A.P.W.A. (All Pakistan Women's Association). P* 13.

488 **281** 50 p. multicoloured 20 10

282 Tippu Sultan Shaheed of Mysore

(Des A. Rauf)

1979 (23 Mar). *Pioneers of Freedom (1st series). T* **282** *and similar diamond-shaped designs. Multicoloured. W* **98.** *P* 14.

490 10 r. Type **282** 50 55
a. Horiz strip of 3. Nos. 490/2 . . . . 2·25
491 15 r. Sir Syed Ahmad Khan 80 85
492 25 r. Altaf Hussain Hali . . . . . . 1·25 1·40
490/2 . . . . *Set of* 3 2·25 2·50

Nos. 490/2 were printed together *se-tenant* in the same sheet: there being ten horizontal strips of 3 values and ten additional 10 r. stamps.

See also No. 757.

283 Himalayan Monal Pheasant

(Des M. Ahmed)

1979 (17 June). *Wildlife Protection (5th series). Pheasants. T* **283** *and similar horiz designs. Multicoloured. P* 13.

493 20 p. Type **283** 50 25
494 25 p. Kalij 50 30
495 40 p. Koklass 75 50
496 1 r. Cheer . . . . 1·50 95
493/6 . . . . *Set of* 4 3·00 1·75

284 "Pakistan Village Scene" (Ustad Bakhsh)

(Des A. Rauf)

1979 (21 July). *15th Anniv of Regional Co-operation for Development. Paintings. T* **284** *and similar horiz designs. Multicoloured. P* 14 × 12½.

497 40 p. Type **284** 20 25
a. Vert strip of 3. Nos. 497/9 60
498 75 p. "Iranian Goldsmith" (Kamal al Molk) . . 20 25
499 1 r. 60, "Turkish Harvest" (Namik Ismail) . . 25 30
497/9 . . . . *Set of* 3 60 70

Nos. 497/9 were printed together, *se-tenant*, in vertical strips of 3 throughout the sheet.

285 Guj Embroidered Shirt (detail)

1979 (23 Aug). *Handicrafts (1st series). T* **285** *and similar horiz designs. Multicoloured. P* 14 × 12½.

500 40 p. Type **285** 20 20
a. Block of 4. Nos. 500/3 . . . . . . 1·00
501 1 r. Enamel inlaid brass plate 25 25
502 1 r. 50, Baskets 30 30
503 2 r. Chain-stitch embroidered rug (detail) . . 40 40
500/3 . . . . *Set of* 4 1·00 1·00

Nos. 500/3 were printed together, *se-tenant*, in blocks of 4 throughout the sheet.

See also Nos. 578/9, 595/6 and 625/8.

286 Children playing on Climbing Frame

(Des A. Rauf)

1979 (10 Sept). *S.O.S. Children's Village, Lahore (orphanage). P* 13.

504 **286** 50 p. multicoloured 20 20

287 "Island" (Z. Maloof)

(Des A. Salahuddin)

1979 (22 Oct). *International Year of the Child. Children's Paintings. T* **287** *and similar horiz designs. Multicoloured. P* 14 × 12½.

505 40 p. Type **287** 15 15
a. Block of 4. Nos. 505/8 85
506 75 p. "Playground" (R. Akbar) 25 25
507 1 r. "Fairground" (M. Azam) 25 25
508 1 r. 50, "Hockey Match" (M. Tayyab) . . 30 30
505/8 . . . . *Set of* 4 85 85
MS509 79 × 64 mm. 2 r. "Child looking at Faces in the Sky" (M. Mumtaz) (*vert*). Imperf . . 3·25 3·25

Nos. 505/8 were printed together, *se-tenant*, in blocks of 4 throughout the sheet.

Examples of No. MS509 are known overprinted in gold for the "PHILEXFRANCE" International Stamp Exhibition in 1982. The Pakistan Post Office has declared such overprints to be bogus.

288 Warrior attacking Crab

289 Pakistan Customs Emblem

(Des A. Salahuddin)

1979 (12 Nov). *Fight Against Cancer. P* 14.

510 **288** 40 p. black, greenish yellow and magenta 20 20

(Des A. Salahuddin)

1979 (10 Dec). *Centenary of Pakistan Customs Service. P* 13 × 13½.

511 **289** 1 r. multicoloured 20 30

290 Boeing "747 (Jumbo)" and Douglas "DC-3" Airliners

291 Islamic Pattern

(Des A. Salahuddin)

1980 (10 Jan). *25th Anniv of Pakistan International Air Lines. P* 13.

512 **290** 1 r. multicoloured 35 40

(Des and litho Secura, Singapore)

1980 (15 Jan–10 Mar). *Matt, almost invisible PVA gum. P* 12.

513 **291** 10 p. slate-green and orange-yellow . . 10 10
514 15 p. slate-green and bright yellow-green 10 10
515 25 p. violet and brown-red (10.3) . . 10 10
516 35 p. carmine & brt yellow-green (10.3) . . 10 10
517 – 40 p. rosine and olive-sepia 15 10
518 – 50 p. violet and dull yellow-green (10.3) 10 10
519 – 80 p. brt yellow-green & black (10.3) . . 15 10
513/19 . . . . *Set of* 7 70 50

The 40 to 80 p. values also show different Islamic patterns, the 40 p. being horizontal and the remainder vertical.

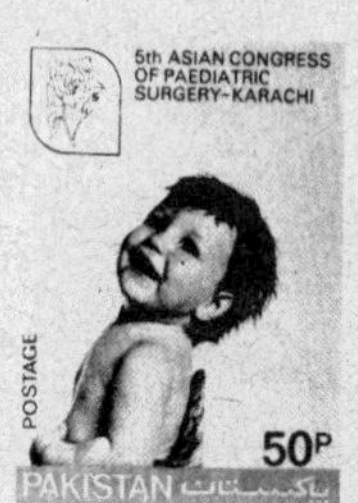

292 Young Child

293 Conference Emblem

(Des M. Saeed)

1980 (16 Feb). *5th Asian Congress of Paediatric Surgery, Karachi. P* 13.

530 **292** 50 p. multicoloured 20 30

(Des A. Salahuddin)

1980 (17 May). *11th Islamic Conference of Foreign Ministers, Islamabad. P* 13.

531 **293** 1 r. multicoloured 20 40

294 Karachi Port

(Des A. Salahuddin)

1980 (15 July). *Centenary of Karachi Port Authority. P* 13 × 13½.

532 **294** 1 r. multicoloured 40 40

RICCIONE 80

(295)

296 College Emblem with Old and New Buildings

1980 (30 Aug). *"Riccione 80" International Stamp Exhibition. Nos. 505/8 optd with T* **295** *in red.*

533 40 p. Type **287** 15 15
534 75 p. "Playground" (R. Akbar) 20 20
535 1 r. "Fairground" (M. Azam) 25 25
536 1 r. 50, "Hockey Match" (M. Tayyab) . . 30 30
533/6 . . . . *Set of* 4 80 80

(Des M. Munawar)

1980 (18 Sept). *75th Anniv of Command and Staff College, Quetta. P* 13.

537 **296** 1 r. multicoloured 10 15

WORLD TOURISM CONFERENCE
MANILA 80

(297)

1980 (27 Sept). *World Tourism Conference, Manila. No. 496 optd with T* **297**.

538 1 r. Cheer 10 15

298 Birth Centenary Emblem

(Des A. Salahuddin)

1980 (5 Oct). *Birth Centenary of Hafiz Mahmood Shairani. P* 13.
539 **298** 40 p. multicoloured 10 15

299 Shalimar Gardens, Lahore

(Des A. Salahuddin)

1980 (23 Oct). *Aga Khan Award for Architecture. P* 13.
540 **299** 2 r. multicoloured 25 50

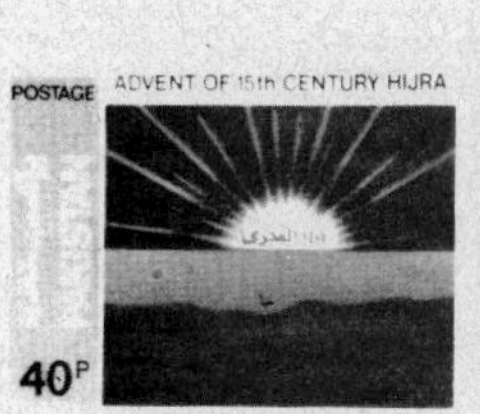

300 Rising Sun 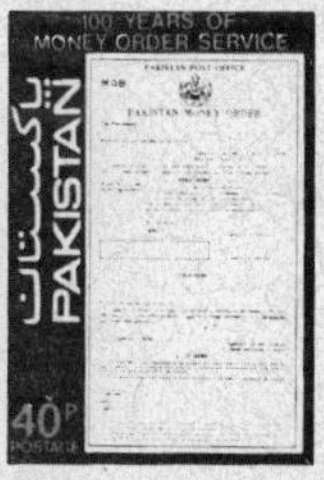 **301** Money Order Form

(Des S. Ahmed (40 p.), J. Sultana (2 r.), A. Salahuddin (others))

1980 (10 Nov). *1400th Anniv of Hegira* (*1st issue*). *T* **300** *and similar multicoloured designs. P* 14 (2 *r.*) *or* 13 (*others*).
541 40 p. Type **300** 10 10
542 2 r. Ka'aba and symbols of Moslem achievement (34 × 34 *mm*) 25 40
543 3 r. Holy Koran illuminating World (31 × 54 *mm*) 30 60
541/3 .. .. *Set of* 3 55 95
MS544 106 × 84 mm. 4 r. Candles. Imperf .. 45 1·00
See also No. 549.

(Des A. Ahmed)

1980 (20 Dec). *Centenary of Money Order Service. P* 13.
545 **301** 40 p. multicoloured 10 15

302 Postcards encircling Globe **303** Heinrich von Stephan and U.P.U. Emblem

(Des A. Ahmed)

1980 (27 Dec). *Centenary of Postcard Service. P* 13.
546 **302** 40 p. multicoloured 10 15

(Des J. Sultana)

1981 (7 Jan). *150th Birth Anniv of Heinrich von Stephan* (*founder of U.P.U.*). *P* 13.
547 **303** 1 r. multicoloured 15 15

304 Aircraft and Airmail Letters

(Des J. Sultana)

1981 (15 Feb). *50th Anniv of Airmail Service. P* 13.
548 **304** 1 r. multicoloured 15 15

305 Mecca  **306** Conference Emblem and Afghan Refugees

1981 (7 Mar). *1400th Anniv of Hegira* (*2nd issue*). *P* 13.
549 **305** 40 p. multicoloured 10 10

(Des Z. Akhlaq (Nos. 550 and 552), A. Ahmed (Nos. 551 and 553), M. Jafree (No. 554))

1981 (29 Mar). *Islamic Summit Conference* (*1st issue*). *T* **306** *and similar multicoloured designs. P* 13.
550 40 p. Type **306** 15 10
551 40 p. Conference emblem encircled by flags and Afghan refugees (28 × 58 *mm*) 15 10
552 1 r. Type **306** 25 10
553 1 r. As No. 551 .. .. 25 10
554 2 r. Conference emblem and map showing Afghanistan (48 × 32 *mm*) 30 35
550/4 .. .. *Set of* 5 1·00 60

307 Conference Emblem **308** Kemal Atatürk

(Des A. Salahuddin (Nos. 555, 557), A. Irani (Nos. 556, 558))

1981 (20 Apr). *Islamic Summit Conference* (*2nd issue*). *T* **307** *and similar multicoloured design. P* 13.
555 40 p. Type **307** 10 10
556 40 p. Conference emblem and flags (28 × 46 *mm*) 10 10
557 85 p. Type **307** 20 15
558 85 p. As No. 556 .. .. 20 15
555/8 .. .. *Set of* 4 55 30

(Des A. Salahuddin)

1981 (19 May). *Birth Centenary of Kemal Atatürk* (*Turkish statesman*). *P* 13.
559 **308** 1 r. multicoloured 15 15

309 Green Turtle **310** Dome of the Rock

(Des Jamal. Litho Secura, Singapore)

1981 (20 June). *Wildlife Protection* (*6th series*). *Matt, almost invisible PVA gum. P* 12 × 11½.
560 **309** 40 p. multicoloured 50 10

(Des A. Salahuddin)

1981 (25 July). *Palestinian Welfare. P* 13.
561 **310** 2 r. multicoloured 35 35

311 Malubiting West

(Litho Secura, Singapore)

1981 (20 Aug). *Mountain Peaks* (*1st series*). *Karakoram Range. T* **311** *and similar multicoloured designs. Matt, almost invisible PVA gum. P* 14 × 13½.
562 40 p. Type **311** 25 15
a. Horiz pair. Nos. 562/3 .. .. .. 50 30
563 40 p. Malubiting West (24 × 31 *mm*) 25 15
564 1 r. Haramosh 45 25
a. Horiz pair. Nos. 564/5 .. .. .. 90 50
565 1 r. Haramosh (24 × 31 *mm*) 45 25
566 1 r. 50, K6 .. .. 55 35
a. Horiz pair. Nos. 566/7 .. .. .. 1·10 70
567 1 r. 50, K6 (24 × 31 *mm*) 55 35
568 2 r. K2, Broad Peak, Gasherbrum 4 and Gasherbrum 2 .. .. 65 50
a. Horiz pair. Nos. 568/9 .. .. .. 1·25 1·00
569 2 r. K2 (24 × 31 *mm*) 65 50
562/9 .. .. *Set of* 8 3·25 2·25
The two designs of each value were printed together, *se-tenant*, in horizontal pairs throughout the sheet.
See also Nos. 674/5.

312 Pakistan Steel "Furnace No. 1"  **313** Western Tragopan

(Des A. Ahmed)

1981 (31 Aug). *First Firing of Pakistan Steel "Furnace No. 1", Karachi. P* 13.
570 **312** 40 p. multicoloured 10 10
571 2 r. multicoloured 15 20

(Litho Secura, Singapore)

1981 (15 Sept). *Wildlife Protection* (*7th series*). *Matt, almost invisible PVA gum. P* 14.
572 **313** 40 p. multicoloured 75 40
573 – 2 r. multicoloured .. .. 2·25 2·00
The 2 r. value is as Type **313** but the background design shows a winter view.

314 Disabled People and I.Y.D.P. Emblem  **315** World Hockey Cup below flags of participating Countries

(Des M. Saeed)

1981 (12 Dec). *International Year for Disabled Persons. P* 13.
574 **314** 40 p. multicoloured 10 10
575 2 r. multicoloured 30 55

(Des A. Salahuddin)

1982 (31 Jan). *Pakistan—World Cup Hockey Champions. T* **315** *and similar vert design. Multicoloured. P* 13.
576 1 r. Type **315** 65 50
577 1 r. World Hockey Cup above flags of participating countries 65 50

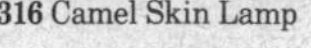

316 Camel Skin Lamp **317** Chest X-Ray of Infected Person

(Des A. Salahuddin. Litho Secura, Singapore)

1982 (20 Feb). *Handicrafts* (*2nd series*). *T* **316** *and similar vert design. Multicoloured. P* 14.
578 1 r. Type **316** 25 20
579 1 r. Hala pottery 25 20
See also Nos. 595/6.

(Des A. Ahmed)

1982 (24 Mar). *Centenary of Robert Koch's Discovery of Tubercle Bacillus. P* 13.

580 **317** 1 r. multicoloured 50 40

318 Indus Dolphin

(Des A. Salahuddin. Litho Secura, Singapore)

1982 (24 Apr). *Wildlife Protection* (8*th series*). *P* 12 × 11½.

581 **318** 40 p. multicoloured 75 50

582 – 1 r. multicoloured . . . . . . 1·25 1·50

The 1 r. value is as Type **318** but the design is reversed.

319 "Apollo–Soyuz" Link-up, 1975

(Des A. Salahuddin)

1982 (7 June). *Peaceful Uses of Outer Space. P* 13.

583 **319** 1 r. multicoloured 50 30

320 Sukkur Barrage

(Des A. Salahuddin)

1982 (17 July). *50th Anniv of Sukkur Barrage. P* 13.

584 **320** 1 r. multicoloured 25 10

RICCIONE – 82 –

321 Pakistan National Flag and Stylised Sun (322)

(Des A. Ahmed)

1982 (14 Aug). *Independence Day. T* **321** *and similar vert design. Multicoloured. P* 13.

585 40 p. Type **321** 10 20

586 85 p. Map of Pakistan and stylised torch . . 15 30

1982 (28 Aug). *"Riccione 82" International Stamp Exhibition. No.* 584 *optd with T* **322**.

587 **320** 1 r. multicoloured 10 10

323 Arabic Inscription and University Emblem

(Des Syed Tanwir Rizvi)

1982 (14 Oct). *Centenary of the Punjab University. P* 13½ × 13.

588 **323** 40 p. multicoloured 10 10

324 Scout Emblem and Tents **325** Laying Pipeline

(Des M. Saeed)

1982 (23 Dec). *75th Anniv of Boy Scout Movement. P* 13.

589 **324** 2 r. multicoloured 25 25

(Des A. Salahuddin)

1983 (6 Jan). *Inauguration of Quetta Natural Gas Pipeline Project. P* 13.

590 **325** 1 r. multicoloured 10 12

326 Common Peacock (*Papilio polyctor*)

(Litho Secura, Singapore)

1983 (15 Feb). *Butterflies. T* **326** *and similar horiz designs. Multicoloured. Matt, almost invisible PVA gum. P* 13½.

591 40 p. Type **326** 50 15

592 50 p. Common Rose (*Polydorus aristolchiae*) . . 50 15

593 60 p. Plain Tiger (*Danaus chrysippus*) . . 60 20

594 1 r. 50, Lemon Butterfly (*Papilio demoleus*) 80 55

591/4 . . . . . . *Set of* 4 2·25 95

(Litho Secura, Singapore)

1983 (9 Mar). *Handicrafts* (3*rd series*). *Vert designs as T* **316**. *Multicoloured. Matt, almost invisible PVA gum. P* 14.

595 1 r. Five flower motif needlework, Sind . . 10 15

596 1 r. Straw mats 10 15

327 School of Nursing and University Emblem

(Des A. Salahuddin)

1983 (16 Mar). *Presentation of Charter to Aga Khan University, Karachi. P* 13½ × 13.

597 **327** 2 r. multicoloured 25 25

No. 597 was issued in sheets of 8 (2 × 4), each horizontal pair being separated by a different *se-tenant* label showing views of the University.

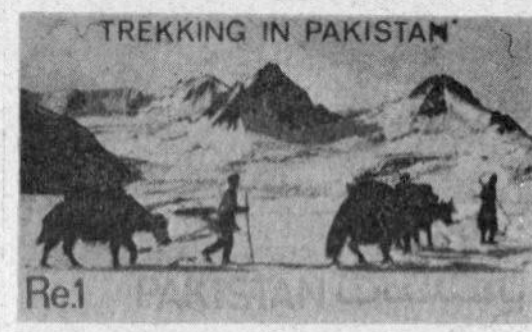

328 Yak Caravan crossing Zindiharam-Darkot Pass, Hindu Kush

(Des A. Salahuddin)

1983 (28 Apr). *Trekking in Pakistan. P* 13.

598 **328** 1 r. multicoloured 20 15

329 Marsh Crocodile

(Litho Secura, Singapore)

1983 (19 May). *Wildlife Protection* (9*th series*). *Matt, almost invisible PVA gum. P* 13½.

599 **329** 3 r. multicoloured . . . . . . 1·00 75

330 Goitred Gazelle **331** Floral Design

(Litho Secura, Singapore)

1983 (20 June). *Wildlife Protection* (10*th series*). *Matt, almost invisible PVA gum. P* 14 × 13½.

600 **330** 1 r. multicoloured 50 35

(Des A. Ahmed)

1983 (14 Aug). *36th Anniv of Independence. T* **331** *and similar vert design. Multicoloured. P* 13.

601 60 p. Type **331** 10 10

602 4 r. Hand holding flaming torch 40 45

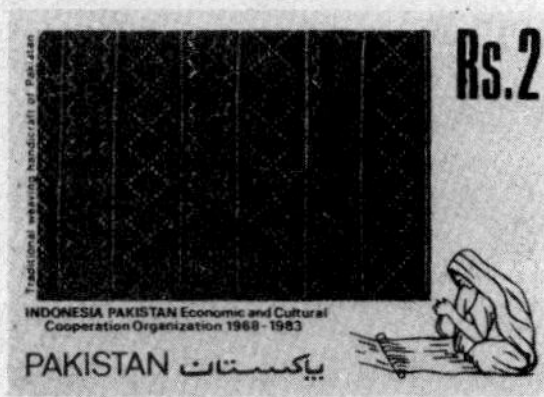

332 Traditional Weaving, Pakistan

(Des A. Salahuddin)

1983 (19 Aug). *Indonesian–Pakistan Economic and Cultural Co-operation Organization, 1969–1983. T* **332** *and similar horiz design. Multicoloured. P* 13.

603 2 r. Type **332** 20 25

604 2 r. Traditional weaving, Indonesia 20 25

333 "Siberian Cranes" (Great White Cranes) (Sir Peter Scott)

1983 (8 Sept). *Wildlife Protection* (11*th series*). *P* 13.

605 **333** 3 r. multicoloured 90 55

334 W.C.Y. Emblem

1983 (9 Oct). *World Communications Year. T* **334** *and similar multicoloured design. P* 13 (2 *r.*) *or* 14 (3 *r.*).

606 2 r. Type **334** 20 25

607 3 r. W.C.Y. emblem (*different*) (33 × 33 *mm*) 30 35

335 Farm Animals **336** Agricultural Produce and Fertiliser Factory

(Des A. Salahuddin)

1983 (24 Oct). *World Food Day. T* **335** *and similar horiz designs. Multicoloured. P* 13.

608 3 r. Type **335** 60 60

a. Horiz strip of 4. Nos. 608/11 . . . . 2·25

609 3 r. Fruit 60 60

610 3 r. Crops 60 60

611 3 r. Sea food 60 60

608/11 . . . . . . *Set of* 4 2·25 2·25

Nos. 608/11 were printed together, *se-tenant*, in horizontal strips of four throughout the sheet.

(Des J. Sultana)

1983 (24 Oct). *National Fertiliser Corporation. P* 13 × 13½.

612 **336** 60 p. multicoloured 10 10

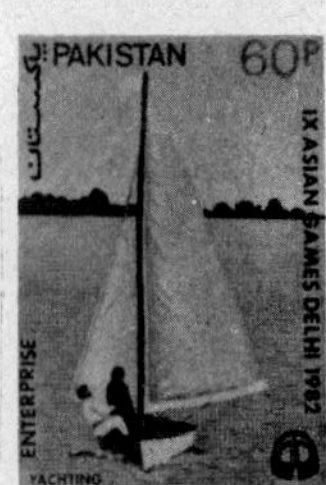

337 Lahore, 1852 **338** Winner of "Enterprise" Event

(Des A. Salahuddin)

1983 (13 Nov). *National Stamp Exhibition, Lahore. T* **337** *and similar vert designs showing panoramic view of Lahore in* 1852. *Multicoloured. P* 13 × 13½.

613	60 p. Musti Durwaza Dharmsala	10	10
	a. Horiz strip of 6. Nos. 613/18	45	
614	60 p. Khabgha	10	10
615	60 p. Type **337**	10	10
616	60 p. Summan Burj Hazuri	10	10
617	60 p. Flower Garden, Samadhi Northern Gate	10	10
618	60 p. Budda Darya, Badshahi Masjid	10	10
613/18	*Set of* 6	45	45

Nos. 613/18 were printed together, *se-tenant* in sheets of twelve, containing two horizontal strips of six.

(Des J. Sultana)

1983 (31 Dec). *Yachting Champions, Asian Games, Delhi. T* **338** *and similar vert design. Multicoloured. P* 13.

619	60 p. Type **338**	40	15
620	60 p. Winner of "OK" Dinghy event	40	15

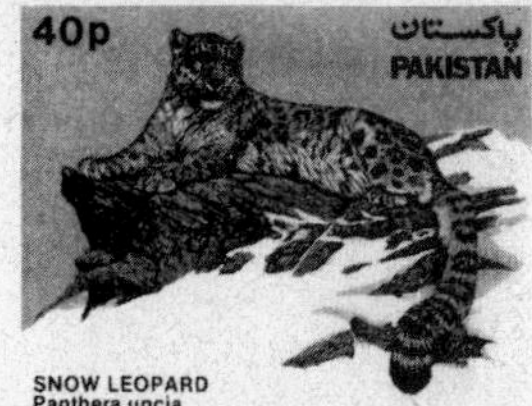

339 Snow Leopard

(Litho Secura, Singapore)

1984 (21 Jan). *Wildlife Protection* (12*th series*). *Matt, almost invisible PVA gum. P* 14.

621	**339**	40 p. multicoloured	50	15
622		1 r. 60, multicoloured	1·25	45

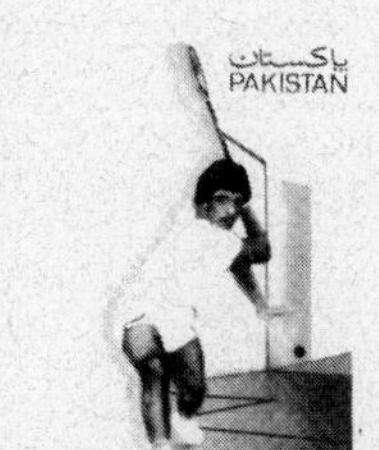

340 Jahangir Khan (World Squash Champion)

341 P.I.A. Airliner

1984 (17 Mar). *Squash. P* 13.

623	**340**	3 r. multicoloured	60	50

(Des A. Salahuddin)

1984 (29 Apr). 20*th Anniv of Pakistan International Airways' Service to China. P* 13.

624	**341**	3 r. multicoloured	1·50	1·25

342 Glass-work

343 Attock Fort

(Des A. Salahuddin. Litho Secura, Singapore)

1984 (31 May). *Handicrafts* (4*th series*). *T* **342** *and similar designs showing glass-work in Sheesh Mahal, Lahore Fort. P* 13½.

625	1 r. multicoloured (blue frame)	10	15
626	1 r. multicoloured (red frame)	10	15
627	1 r. multicoloured (green frame) (*horiz*)	10	15
628	1 r. multicoloured (violet frame) (*horiz*)	10	15
625/8	*Set of* 4	35	55

(Des J. Sultana)

1984 (16 June)–**87**. *Forts. T* **343** *and similar horiz designs. P* 11.

629	5 p. brownish black & brown-pur (1.11.84)	10	10
630	10 p. brownish black and rose-red (25.9.84)	10	10
631	15 p. reddish violet & bistre-brown (1.12.86)	10	10
632	20 p. black and bright reddish violet	10	10
633	50 p. sepia and Venetian red (10.4.86)	10	10
634	60 p. blackish brown and light brown	10	10
635	70 p. greenish blue (1987)	10	10
636	80 p. bistre-brown and dull scarlet (1.7.86)	10	10
629/36	*Set of* 8	40	40

Design:—5 p. Kot Diji Fort; 10 p. Rohtas Fort; 15 p. Bala Hisar Fort; 50 p. Hyderabad Fort; 60 p. Lahore Fort; 70 p. Sibi Fort; 80 p. Ranikot Fort.

Numbers have been reserved for future additions to this set.

344 Shah Rukn i Alam's Tomb, Multan

1984 (26 June). *Aga Khan Award for Architecture. P* 13.

647	**344**	60 p. multicoloured	30	30

345 Radio Mast and Map of World

1984 (1 July). 20*th Anniv of Asia–Pacific Broadcasting Union. P* 13.

648	**345**	3 r. multicoloured	50	40

346 Wrestling

(Des A. Salahuddin)

1984 (31 July). *Olympic Games, Los Angeles. T* **346** *and similar horiz designs. Multicoloured. P* 13.

649	3 r. Type **346**	60	40
650	3 r. Boxing	60	40
651	3 r. Athletics	60	40
652	3 r. Hockey	60	40
653	3 r. Yachting	60	40
649/53	*Set of* 5	2·75	1·75

347 Jasmine (National flower) and Inscription

348 Gearwheel Emblem and Flags of Participating Nations

(Des M. Munawar)

1984 (14 Aug). *Independence Day. T* **347** *and similar horiz design. Multicoloured. P* 13.

654	60 p. Type **347**	10	10
655	4 r. Symbolic torch	45	50

(Des A. Zafar)

1984 (1 Sept). *Pakistan International Trade Fair. P* 13.

656	**348**	60 p. multicoloured	15	10

349 Interior of Main Dome

1984 (5 Nov). *Tourism Convention. Shahjahan Mosque, Thatta. T* **349** *and similar horiz designs. Multicoloured. P* 13½.

657	1 r. Type **349**	15	15
	a. Horiz strip of 5. Nos. 657/61	65	
658	1 r. Brick and glazed tile work	15	15
659	1 r. Gateway	15	15
660	1 r. Symmetrical archways	15	15
661	1 r. Interior of a dome	15	15
657/61	*Set of* 5	65	65

Nos. 657/61 were printed together, *se-tenant*, in horizontal strips of 5 throughout the sheet

350 Bank Emblem in Floral Pattern

(Des A. Zafar)

1984 (7 Nov). 25*th Anniv of United Bank Ltd. P* 13½.

662	**350**	60 p. multicoloured	15	20

351 Conference Emblem

352 Postal Life Insurance Emblem within Hands

(Des A. Salahuddin)

1984 (24 Dec). 20*th United Nations Conference on Trade and Development. P* 14.

663	**351**	60 p. multicoloured	20	15

(Des A. Zafar and J. Sultana)

1984 (29 Dec). *Centenary of Postal Life Insurance. T* **352** *and similar vert design. Multicoloured. P* 13½.

664	60 p. Type **352**	15	10
665	1 r. "100" and Postal Life Insurance emblem	20	15

353 Bull (Wall painting)

354 International Youth Year Emblem and "75"

(Des A. Salahuddin and M. Munawar)

1984 (31 Dec). *U.N.E.S.C.O. Save Moenjadoro Campaign. T* **353** *and similar vert design. Multicoloured. P* 13½.

666	2 r. Type **353**	35	35
	a. Horiz pair. Nos. 666/7	70	70
667	2 r. Bull (seal)	35	35

Nos. 666/7 were printed together, *se-tenant*, in horizontal pairs throughout the sheet.

(Des A. Salahuddin)

1985 (6 Jan). 75*th Anniv of Girl Guide Movement. P* 13½.

668	**354**	60 p. multicoloured	40	10

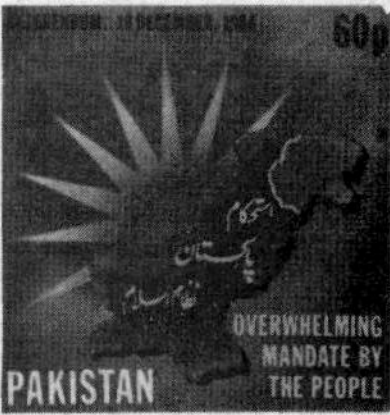

355 Smelting Ore

356 Map of Pakistan and Rays of Sun

1985 (15 Jan). *Inauguration of Pakistan Steel Corporation. T* **355** *and similar multicoloured design. P* 13.

669	60 p. Type **355**	15	10
670	1 r. Pouring molten steel from ladle (28 × 46 *mm*)	20	15

(Des A. Salahuddin)

1985 (20 Mar). *Presidential Referendum of* 19 *December* 1984. *P* 13.

671	**356**	60 p. multicoloured	15	10

357 Ballot Box and Voting Paper

(Des A. Salahuddin (No. 672), Sultana Shamim Haider (No. 673))

1985 (23 Mar). *March Elections. T* **357** *and similar multi-coloured design. P* 13.
672 1 r. Type **357** 15 15
673 1 r. Minar-e-Qarardad-e-Pakistan Tower, and word "Democracy" (31 × 43 *mm*) .. 15 15

(Des and litho Secura, Singapore)

1985 (27 May). *Mountain Peaks (2nd series). Horiz designs as T* **311**. *Multicoloured. Matt, almost invisible PVA gum.* P 14 × 13½.
674 40 p. Rakaposhi (Karakoram Range) .. 40 15
675 2 r. Nangaparbat (Western Himalayas) .. 85 45

358 Trophy and Medals from Olympic Games 1984, Asia Cup 1985 and World Cup 1982

(Des A. Salahuddin)

1985 (5 July). *Pakistan Hockey Team "Grand Slam" Success.* P 13.
676 **358** 1 r. multicoloured 50 45

359 King Edward Medical College

(Des Sultana Shamim Haider)

1985 (28 July). *125th Anniv of King Edward Medical College, Lahore. P* 13.
677 **359** 3 r. multicoloured 40 40

360 Illuminated Inscription in Urdu

(Des A. Salahuddin)

1985 (14 Aug). *Independence Day. T* **360** *and similar horiz design. Multicoloured. P* 13.
678 60 p. Type **360** 15 15
a. Sheetlet. Nos. 678/9 × 2 55
679 60 p. Illuminated "XXXVIII" (inscr in English) 15 15

Nos. 678/9 were issued *se-tenant*, both horizontally and vertically, in sheetlets of four stamps and four stamp-size labels inscribed in Urdu.

361 Sind Madressah-tul-Islam, Karachi

(Des A. Salahuddin)

1985 (1 Sept). *Centenary of Sind Madressah-tul-Islam (theological college), Karachi. P* 13.
680 **361** 2 r. multicoloured 35 35

362 Jamia Masjid Mosque by Day

(Des A. Salahuddin)

1985 (14 Sept). *Inauguration of New Jamia Masjid Mosque, Karachi. T* **362** *and similar horiz design. Multicoloured. P* 13.
681 1 r. Type **362** 20 15
682 1 r. Jamia Masjid illuminated at night .. 20 15

363 Lawrence College, Murree

(Des A. Salahuddin)

1985 (21 Sept). *125th Anniv of Lawrence College, Murree. P* 13.
683 **363** 3 r. multicoloured 45 35

364 United Nations Building, New York

(Des A. Salahuddin)

1985 (24 Oct). *40th Anniv of United Nations Organization. T* **364** *and similar diamond-shaped design. Multicoloured.* P 14.
684 1 r. Type **364** 10 15
685 2 r. U.N. Building and emblem 20 25

365 Tents and Jamboree Emblem

(Des A. Salahuddin)

1985 (8 Nov). *10th National Scout Jamboree. P* 13.
686 **365** 60 p. multicoloured 40 25

366 Islamabad

367 Map of S.A.A.R.C. Countries and National Flags

(Des H. Durrani)

1985 (30 Nov). *25th Anniv of Islamabad. P* 14½ × 14.
687 **366** 3 r. multicoloured 40 35

(Des A. Salahuddin)

1985 (8 Dec). *1st Summit Meeting of South Asian Association for Regional Cooperation, Dhaka, Bangladesh. T* **367** *and similar multicoloured design. P* 13½ × 13 (1 *r*.) *or* 13 (2 *r*.).
688 1 r. Type **367** .. .. 70 1·50
689 2 r. National flags (39 × 39 *mm*) 55 50

No. 688 is reported to have been withdrawn on 9 December 1985.

368 Globe and Peace Dove

369 Peregrine Falcon

(Des A. Salahuddin)

1985 (14 Dec). *25th Anniv of U.N. General Assembly's Declaration on Independence for Colonial Territories. P* 13.
690 **368** 60 p. multicoloured 20 15

(Des and litho Secura, Singapore)

1986 (20 Jan). *Wildlife Protection (13th series). Peregrine Falcon. Matt, almost invisible PVA gum. P* 13½.
691 **369** 1 r. 50, multicoloured .. .. .. 1·50 80

370 A.D.B.P. Building, Islamabad

(Des A. Salahuddin)

1986 (18 Feb). *25th Anniv of Agricultural Development Bank of Pakistan. P* 13.
692 **370** 60 p. multicoloured 15 10

371 Government S.E. College

372 Emblem and Bar Graph

(Des Sultana Shamim Haider)

1986 (25 Apr). *Centenary of Government Sadiq Egerton College, Bahawalpur. P* 13.
693 **371** 1 r. multicoloured 20 10

(Des Sultana Shamim Haider)

1986 (11 May). *25th Anniv of Asian Productivity Organization.* P 13½.
694 **372** 1 r. multicoloured 15 10

373 "1947 1986"

374 Open Air Class

(Des A. Salahuddin (80 p.), M. Munawar (1 r.))

1986 (14 Aug). *39th Anniv of Independence. T* **373** *and similar vert design. Multicoloured. P* 14.
695 80 p. Type **373** 15 10
696 1 r. Illuminated inscription in Urdu .. 15 10

(Des Sultana Shamim Haider)

1986 (8 Sept). *International Literacy Day. P* 13.
697 **374** 1 r. multicoloured 15 10

375 Mother and Child

376 Aitchison College

1986 (28 Oct). *U.N.I.C.E.F. Child Survival Campaign. P* 13½ × 13.
698 **375** 80 p. multicoloured 15 10

(Des A. Salahuddin)

1986 (3 Nov). *Centenary of Aitchison College, Lahore. P* 13½.
699 **376** 2 r. 50, multicoloured 30 30

377 Two Doves carrying Olive Branches

378 Table Tennis Players

(Des Sultana Shamim Haider)

1986 (20 Nov). *International Peace Year. P* 13.
700 **377** 4 r. multicoloured 40 40

(Des A. Salahuddin)

1986 (25 Nov). *4th Asian Cup Table Tennis Tournament, Karachi. P* 14.
701 **378** 2 r. multicoloured 20 20

379 Argali

(Des M. Jamal. Litho Secura, Singapore)

1986 (4 Dec). *Wildlife Protection* (14*th series*). *Argali. Matt, almost invisible PVA gum. P* 14.
702 **379** 2 r. multicoloured 45 30

380 Selimiye Mosque, Edirne, Turkey

(Des A. Salahuddin)

1986 (20 Dec). *"Ecophilex '86" International Stamp Exhibition, Islamabad. T* **380** *and similar vert designs. Multicoloured. P* 13.

703	3 r. Type **380**	40	40
	a. Horiz strip of 3. Nos. 703/5	1·10	
704	3 r. Gawhar Shad Mosque, Mashhad, Iran ..	40	40
705	3 r. Grand Mosque, Bhong, Pakistan ..	40	40
703/5	.. .. *Set of* 3	1·10	1·10

Nos. 703/5 were printed together, *se-tenant*, in horizontal strips of three, within sheetlets of 12.

381 St. Patrick's School

(Des A. Salahuddin)

1987 (29 Jan). *125th Anniv of St. Patrick's School, Karachi. P* 13.
706 **381** 5 r. multicoloured 50 50

MINIMUM PRICE

The minimum price quote is 10p which represents a handling charge rather than a basis for valuing common stamps. For further notes about prices see introductory pages.

382 Mistletoe Flowerpecker and Defence Symbols

(Des A. Salahuddin)

1987 (21 Feb). *Post Office Savings Bank Week. T* **382** *and similar vert designs, each showing a different bird. Multicoloured. P* 13.

707	5 r. Type **382**	45	45
	a. Block of 4. Nos. 707/10	1·60	
708	5 r. Spotted Pardalote and laboratory apparatus	45	45
709	5 r. Black-throated Blue Warbler and agriculture symbols	45	45
710	5 r. Red-capped Manakin and industrial skyline	45	45
707/10	.. .. .. *Set of* 4	1·60	1·60

Nos. 707/10 were printed together, *se-tenant*, in blocks of four throughout the sheet of 32 which contained six blocks of four and eight labels in the left and right-hand vertical columns.

383 New Parliament House, Islamabad

(Des A. Salahuddin)

1987 (23 Mar). *Inauguration of New Parliament House, Islamabad. P* 13.
711 **383** 3 r. multicoloured 20 25

384 Opium Poppies and Flames

(Des A. Salahuddin)

1987 (30 June). *Campaign against Drug Abuse. P* 13.
712 **384** 1 r. multicoloured 10 10

385 Flag and National Anthem Score

(Des A. Salahuddin)

1987 (14 Aug). *40th Anniv of Independence. T* **385** *and similar horiz design. Multicoloured. P* 13.

713	80 p. Type **385**	10	10
714	3 r. Text of speech by Mohammed Ali Jinnah, Minar-e-Qardad-e-Pakistan Tower and arms	20	25

386 "Tempest II"

(Des M. Hussaini and A. Salahuddin)

1987 (7 Sept). *Air Force Day. T* **386** *and similar horiz designs showing military aircraft. Multicoloured. P* 13½.

715	3 r. Type **386**	20	25
	a. Sheetlet. Nos. 715/24	1·75	
716	3 r. Hawker "Fury"	20	25
717	3 r. Supermarine "Attacker"	20	25
718	3 r. "F86 Sabre"	20	25
719	3 r. "F104 Star Fighter"	20	25
720	3 r. "C130 Hercules"	20	25
721	3 r. "F6"	20	25
722	3 r. "Mirage III"	20	25
723	3 r. "A5"	20	25
724	3 r. "F16 Fighting Falcon"	20	25
715/24	.. .. .. *Set of* 10	1·75	2·25

Nos. 715/24 were printed together, *se-tenant*, in sheetlets of 10.

387 Pasu Glacier

(Des A. Salahuddin)

1987 (1 Oct). *Pakistan Tourism Convention. T* 387 *and similar horiz designs showing views along Karakoram Highway. Multicoloured. P* 13.

725	1 r. 50, Type **387**	15	15
	a. Block of 4. Nos. 725/8	55	
726	1 r. 50, Apricot trees	15	15
727	1 r. 50, Karakoram Highway	15	15
728	1 r. 50, View from Khunjerab Pass ..	15	15
725/8	.. .. .. *Set of* 4	55	55

Nos. 725/8 were printed together, *se-tenant*, in blocks of four throughout the sheet of 24.

388 Shah Abdul Latif Bhitai Mausoleum

(Des A. Salahuddin)

1987 (8 Oct). *Shah Abdul Latif Bhitai (poet) Commemoration. P* 13.
729 **388** 80 p. multicoloured 10 10

389 D. J. Sind Science College, Karachi

(Des Sultana Shamim Haider)

1987 (7 Nov). *Centenary of D. J. Sind Science College, Karachi. P* 13.
730 **389** 80 p. multicoloured 10 10

390 College Building

391 Homeless People, Houses and Rising Sun

(Des Sultana Shamim Haider)

1987 (9 Dec). *25th Anniv of College of Physicians and Surgeons. P* 13.
731 **390** 1 r. multicoloured 10 10

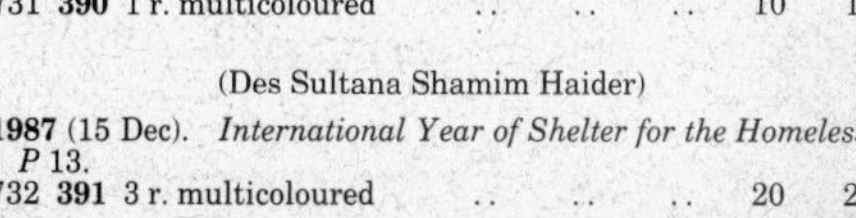

(Des Sultana Shamim Haider)

1987 (15 Dec). *International Year of Shelter for the Homeless. P* 13.
732 **391** 3 r. multicoloured 20 25

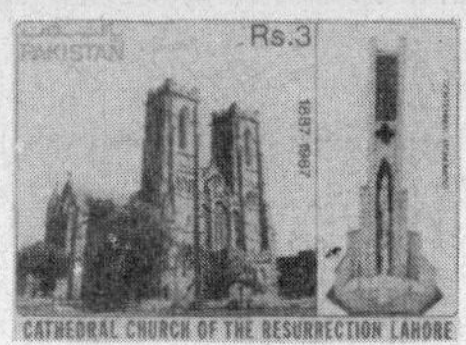

392 Cathedral Church of the Resurrection, Lahore

(Des A. Salahuddin)

1987 (20 Dec). *Centenary of Cathedral Church of the Resurrection, Lahore. P* 13.
733 **392** 3 r. multicoloured 20 25

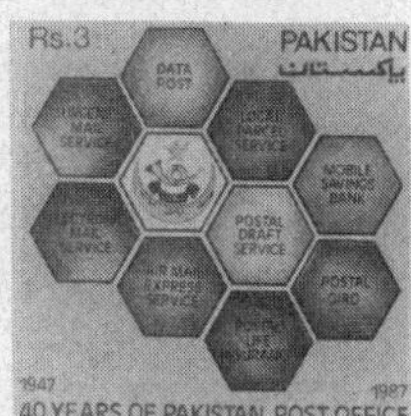

393 Honeycomb and Arms

(Des A. Salahuddin)

1987 (28 Dec). *40th Anniv of Pakistan Post Office. P* 13.
734 **393** 3 r. multicoloured 20 25

394 Corporation Emblem

(Des A. Salahuddin)

1987 (31 Dec). *Radio Pakistan's New Programme Schedules. P* 13.
735 **394** 80 p. multicoloured 10 10

395 Jamshed Nusserwanjee Mehta and Karachi Municipal Corporation Building

396 Leprosy Symbols within Flower

(Des A. Salahuddin)

1988 (7 Jan). *Birth Centenary* (1986) *of Jamshed Nusserwanjee Mehta (former President of Karachi Municipal Corporation). P* 13.
736 **395** 3 r. multicoloured 20 25

(Des Sultana Shamim Haider)

1988 (31 Jan). *World Leprosy Day. P* 13.
737 **396** 3 r. multicoloured 20 25

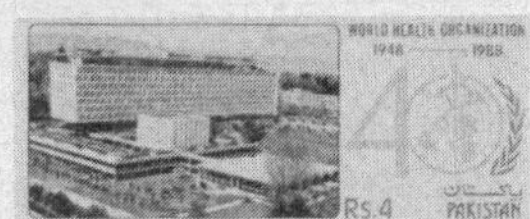

397 W.H.O. Building, Geneva

(Des A. Salahuddin)

1988 (7 Apr). *40th Anniv of World Health Organization. P* 13.
738 **397** 4 r. multicoloured 25 30

398 Globe

399 Crescent, Leaf Pattern and Archway

1988 (8 May). *125th Anniv of International Red Cross and Crescent. P* 13.
739 **398** 3 r. multicoloured 20 25

(Des A. Salahuddin)

1988 (14 Aug). *Independence Day. P* 13½.
740 **399** 80 p. multicoloured 10 10
741 4 r. multicoloured 25 30

400 Field Events

(Des A. Salahuddin)

1988 (17 Sept). *Olympic Games, Seoul. T* **400** *and similar horiz designs. Multicoloured. P* 13.
742 10 r. Type **400** 60 65
a. Sheetlet. Nos. 742/51 .. .. .. 5·50
743 10 r. Track events 60 65
744 10 r. Jumping and pole vaulting 60 65
745 10 r. Gymnastics 60 65
746 10 r. Table tennis, tennis, hockey and baseball 60 65
747 10 r. Volleyball, football, basketball and handball 60 65
748 10 r. Wrestling, judo, boxing and weightlifting 60 65
749 10 r. Shooting, fencing and archery .. 60 65
750 10 r. Water sports 60 65
751 10 r. Equestrian events and cycling .. 60 65
742/51 .. .. *Set of* 10 5·50 5·75
Nos. 742/51 were issued, *se-tenant*, in sheetlets of ten stamps and thirty-six half stamp-size labels.

401 Markhor

(Litho Secura, Singapore)

1988 (29 Oct). *Wildlife Protection (15th series). Markhor. Matt, almost invisible PVA gum. P* 14.
752 **401** 2 r. multicoloured 15 15

402 Islamia College, Peshawar

(Des A. Salahuddin)

1988 (22 Dec). *75th Anniv of Islamia College, Peshawar. P* 13½.
753 **402** 3 r. multicoloured 20 25

403 Symbols of Agriculture, Industry and Education with National Flags

(Des Sultana Shamim Haider (25 r.), G. M. Shaikh (50 r.), A. Salahuddin (75 r.))

1988 (29 Dec). *South Asian Association for Regional Co-operation, 4th Summit Meeting, Islamabad. T* **403** *and similar multicoloured designs. P* 13 *(25 r.),* 14 *(50 r.) or* 13½×13 *(75 r.).*
754 25 r. Type **403** .. .. 1·40 1·50
755 50 r. National flags on globe and symbols of communications (33×33 *mm*) .. 3·00 3·25
756 75 r. Stamps from member countries (52×29 *mm*) .. .. 4·25 4·50
754/6 .. .. *Set of* 3 7·75 8·25
No. 755 was printed in sheets of eight stamps and one stamp-size label, showing the S.A.A.R.C. emblem, in the central position.

(Des A. Salahuddin)

1989 (23 Jan). *Pioneers of Freedom (2nd series). Diamond-shaped design as T* **282**. *Multicoloured. W* **98**. *P* 14.
757 3 r. Maulana Hasrat Mohani 20 25

404 Logo

405 Zulfikar Ali Bhutto

(Des A. Salahuddin)

1989 (18 Feb). *"Adasia 89" 16th Asian Advertising Congress, Lahore. P* 13.
758 **404** 1 r. mult ("Pakistan" in yellow) .. 10 10
a. Sheetlet. Nos. 758/60, each × 3 70
759 1 r. mult ("Pakistan" in turquoise-bl) 10 10
760 1 r. mult ("Pakistan" in white) .. 10 10
758/60 .. .. *Set of* 3 25 25
Nos. 758/60 were printed together, *se-tenant*, in horizontal and vertical strips of three within the sheetlets of nine.

(Des A. Munir (1 r.), A. Salahuddin (2 r.))

1989 (4 Apr). *10th Death Anniv of Zulfikar Ali Bhutto (statesman). T* **405** *and similar vert design. Multicoloured. P* 13.
761 1 r. Type **405** 10 10
762 2 r. Zulfikar Ali Bhutto (*different*) .. 10 15

OFFICIAL STAMPS

PAKISTAN

(O 1)

1947. *Official stamps of India, Nos.* O143/50, *optd as Type* O **1** *and Nos.* O138/41 *optd as T* **2** *by litho, at Nasik.*
O 1 **O 20** 3 p. slate 15 10
O 2 ½ a. purple 15 10
O 3 9 p. green 30 95
O 4 1 a. carmine 15 10
O 5 1½ a. dull violet 15 10
O 6 2 a. vermilion 15 10
O 7 2½ a. bright violet .. .. 70 1·50
O 8 4 a. brown 20 10
O 9 8 a. slate-violet 30 30
O10 **93** 1 r. grey and red-brown 80 30
O11 2 r. purple and brown .. .. .. 2·75 95
O12 5 r. green and blue .. .. .. 10·00 15·00
O13 10 r. purple and claret .. .. .. 18·00 40·00
O1/13 .. .. *Set of* 13 30·00 55·00
See note after No. 19. The 1 a. 3 p. (India No. O146*a*) exists only as a local issue (*Price*, Karachi opt, £2 *mint*, £3.25 *used*).

SERVICE (O 2) **SERVICE** (O 3) **SERVICE** (O 4)

NOTE. Apart from a slight difference in size, Types O **2** and O **3** can easily be distinguished by the difference in the shape of the "c" Type O **4** is taller and thinner in appearance.

PRINTERS. Type O **2** was overprinted by De La Rue and Types O 3 and O **4** by the Pakistan Security Ptg Corp.

1948 (14 Aug)–**54**? *Optd with Type* O **2**.
O14 **7** 3 p. red (No. 24) 10 10
O15 6 p. violet (No. 25) (R.) 10 10
O16 9 p. green (No. 26) (R.) 10 10
O17 **8** 1 a. blue (No. 27) (R.) .. .. .. 2·50 10
O18 1½ a. grey-green (No. 28) (R.) .. .. 2·00 10
O19 2 a. red (No. 29) .. .. 1·25 10
O20 **10** 3 a. green (No. 31) .. .. .. 3·50 1·75
O21 **9** 4 a. reddish brown (No. 33) 80 10
O22 – 8 a. black (No. 35) (R.) .. .. .. 80 2·25
O23 – 1 r. ultramarine (No. 38) .. .. .. 1·00 10
O24 – 2 r. chocolate (No. 39) .. .. .. 6·00 2·00
O25 – 5 r. carmine (No. 40) .. .. .. 5·00 3·75
O26 **13** 10 r. magenta (No. 41) .. .. .. 8·00 18·00
a. Perf 12 (10.10.51) .. .. .. 7·50 18·00
b. Perf 13 (1954?) .. .. .. 9·50 24·00
O14/26 .. .. *Set of* 13 27·00 25·00

1949. *Optd with Type* O **2**.
O27 1 a. blue (No. 47) (R.) 50 10
O28 1½ a. grey-green (No. 48) (R.) 30 10
a. Opt inverted .. .. — 35·00
O29 2 a. red (No. 49) 80 10
a. Opt omitted (in pair with normal) £100
O30 3 a. green (No. 50) .. .. 3·75 2·25
O31 8 a. black (No. 52) (R.) .. .. .. 8·50 4·25
O27/31 .. .. *Set of* 5 12·50 6·00

1951 (14 Aug). *4th Anniv of Independence. As Nos.* 56, 58 *and* 60, *but inscr* "SERVICE" *instead of* "PAKISTAN POSTAGE".
O32 **18** 3 a. purple .. .. 55 1·50
O33 **19** 4 a. green 45 10
O34 **20** 8 a. sepia .. .. 2·50 80
O32/4 .. .. *Set of* 3 3·25 2·25

1953. *Optd with Type* O **3**.
O35 3 p. red (No. 24a) 10 10
O36 6 p. violet (No. 25a) (R.) 10 10
O37 9 p. green (No. 26a) (R.) 10 10
O38 1 a. blue (No. 47a) (R.) 10 10
O39 1½ a. grey-green (No. 48a) (R.) 10 10
O40 2 a. red (No. 49a) (1953?) 15 10
O41 1 r. ultramarine (No. 38a) .. .. .. 2·25 45
O42 2 r. chocolate (No. 39a) .. .. .. 2·00 10
O43 5 r. carmine (No. 40a) .. .. .. 6·50 1·50
O44 10 r. magenta (No. 41b) (date?) .. .. 10·00 22·00
O35/44 .. .. *Set of* 10 19·00 22·00

1954 (14 Aug). *Seventh Anniv of Independence. Nos.* 65/71 *optd with Type* O **3**.
O45 6 p. reddish violet (R.) 10 40
O46 9 p. blue (R.) .. .. 25 2·75
O47 1 a. carmine 15 35
O48 1½ a. red 15 35
O49 14 a. deep green (R.) .. .. .. 60 1·75
O50 1 r. green (R.) 75 10
O51 2 r. red-orange .. .. 1·25 15
O45/51 .. .. *Set of* 7 2·75 5·25

1955 (14 Aug). *Eighth Anniv of Independence. No.* 75 *optd with Type* O **3**.
O52 8 a. deep reddish violet (R.) 15 10

1957 (Jan)–**59**. *Nos.* 65/71 *optd with Type* O **4**.
O53 6 p. reddish violet (R.) 10 10
a. Opt inverted .. .. † —
O54 9 p. blue (R.) (1.59) 10 25
a. Opt inverted .. ..
O55 1 a. carmine 10 10
a. Opt inverted .. ..
O56 1½ a. red 10 10
a. Opt double .. ..
O57 14 a. deep green (R.) (2.59) .. .. .. 40 1·25
O58 1 r. green (R.) (4.58) 40 10
O59 2 r. red-orange (4.58) .. .. .. 2·25 10
O53/9 .. .. *Set of* 7 3·00 1·50

1958 (Jan)–**61**. *Optd with Type* O **4**.
O60 **7** 3 p. red (No. 24a) 10 10
O61 – 5 r. carmine (No. 40a) (7.59) .. .. 3·00 15
O62 **41** 10 r. myrtle-green and yellow-orange (No. 89) (R.) (1961) .. .. .. 6·00 4·00
a. Opt inverted .. .. 12·00
O60/2 .. .. *Set of* 3 8·00 4·00

1958 (Jan)–**61**. *Nos.* 74/5 *optd with Type* O **4**.
O63 6 a. deep ultramarine (R.) (4.61) 10 10
O64 8 a. deep reddish violet (R.) 10 10

1959 (Aug). *No.* 83 *optd with Type* O **4**.
O65 **37** 2 a. scarlet 10 10

1961 (Apr). *Nos.* 110/11 *optd with Type* O **4**.
O66 **51** 8 a. deep green 10 10
O67 1 r. blue 10 10
a. Opt inverted .. .. 6·50

NEW CURRENCY. In addition to the local *handstamped* surcharges mentioned in the note above No. 122, the following *typographed* surcharges were made at the Treasury at Mastung and issued in the Baluchi province of Kalat: 6 p. on 1 a. (No. O55), 9 p. on 1½ a. (No. O56) and 13 p. on 2 a. (No. O65). They differ in that the surcharges are smaller and "PAISA" is expressed as "Paisa". Being locals they are outside the scope of this catalogue.

1961. *Optd with Type* O **4**.
O68 1 p. on 1½ a. (No. 122) 10 10
a. Optd with Type O **3** 60 45
O69 2 p. on 3 p. (No. 123) (1.1.61) 10 10
a. Surch double .. ..
b. Optd with Type O **3** .. .. .. 1·50 1·50
O70 3 p. on 6 p. (No. 124) 10 10
O71 7 p. on 1 a. (No. 125) 10 10
a. Optd with Type O **3** .. .. .. 1·50 1·50
O72 13 p. on 2 a. (No. 126) 10 10
O73 13 p. on 2 a. (No. 127) 10 10
O68/73 .. .. *Set of* 6 25 25
No. O68 exists with small and large "1" (see note below Nos. 122/7, etc.).

ERRORS. See note after No. 127.

SERVICE

(O 5)

1961–63. *Nos.* 128/44*b optd with Type* O **4** (*rupee values*) *or* O **5** (*others*). (*a*) *Inscribed* "SHAKISTAN".
O74 1 p. violet (R.) (1.1.61) 10 10
O75 2 p. rose-red (R.) (12.1.61) 10 10
O76 5 p. ultramarine (R.) (23.3.61) 15 10

(*b*) *Inscribed* "PAKISTAN"
O77 1 p. violet (R.) 15 10
O78 2 p. rose-red (R.) 10 10
O79 3 p. reddish purple (R.) (27.10.61) 10 10
O80 5 p. ultramarine (R.) 45 10
O81 7 p. emerald (R.) (23.3.61) 10 10
O82 10 p. brown (R.) 10 10
a. Opt inverted .. ..
O83 13 p. slate-violet (R.) (14.2.61) 10 10
O85 40 p. deep purple (R.) (1.1.62) 10 10
O86 50 p. deep bluish green (R.) (1.1.62) 15 10
a. Opt double .. .. † —
O87 75 p. carmine-red (R.) (23.3.62) 20 10
a. Opt double .. ..
O88 1 r. vermilion (7.1.63) 35 10
a. Opt double .. .. 8·00
b. Opt as Type O 3 .. .. 5·50 5·50
c. Opt inverted .. .. 6·00
O89 2 r. orange (7.1.63) .. .. 1·25 20
O90 5 r. green (R.) (7.1.63) .. .. .. 3·50 3·25
O74/90 .. .. *Set of* 16 6·00 3·75

1963–78? *Nos.* 170, *etc., optd with Type* O **5**, *in red.*
O 91 1 p. violet 10 10
O 92 2 p. rose-red (1965) 10 10
a. Opt inverted .. .. 1·25
b. Albino opt .. ..
c. Opt double, one albino .. .. ..
O 93 3 p. reddish purple (1967) 55 30
a. Opt double .. .. 3·50
b. Opt inverted .. .. 1·25
O 94 5 p. ultramarine 10 10
a. Opt inverted .. .. 1·25
ab. Vert pair, top stamp without opt, lower with opt inverted .. ..
O 95 7 p. emerald (date?) .. .. 2·50 75
O 96 10 p. brown (1965) 10 10
a. Opt inverted .. .. 1·50
O 97 13 p. slate-violet 10 10
O 98 15 p. bright purple (31.12.64) 10 20
O 99 20 p. myrtle-green (26.1.70) 10 20
a. Opt double .. .. 20·00
O100 25 p. deep blue (1977) .. .. .. 1·25 25
O101 40 p. deep purple (1972?) .. .. .. 1·75 50
O102 50 p. deep bluish green (1965) 10 10
O103 75 p. carmine-red (date?) .. .. .. 1·50 1·25
O104 90 p. yellow-green (5.78?) .. .. .. 1·25 60
O91/104 .. .. *Set of* 14 8·00 4·00

1968–(?). *Nos.* 204, 206 *and* 207 *optd with Type* O **4**.
O105 **62** 1 r. vermilion 60 15
a. Opt inverted .. .. 6·00
O107 2 r. orange (date?) .. .. 2·25 50
a. Opt inverted .. .. 6·00
O108 5 r. green (R.) (date?) .. .. .. 4·50 1·25
a. Opt inverted .. .. 9·00
O105/8 .. .. *Set of* 3 6·50 1·75

1979–85. *Nos.* 464/72, 473b *and* 475/80 *optd as Type* O **5** *in black* (2 *r.*) *or in red* (*reading vertically downwards on* 2, 3 *and* 5 *p.*) (*others*).
O109 **275** 2 p. deep grey-green 10 10
a. Opt reading upwards .. ..
ab. Horiz pair, one with opt reading upwards, the other with opt omitted .. ..
O110 3 p. black 10 10
a. Opt reading upwards .. ..
O111 5 p. deep ultramarine 10 10
a. Opt reading upwards .. .. 1·50 1·50
b. Vert pair, top stamp without opt .. .. .. 3·00
O112 **276** 10 p. new blue and greenish blue .. 10 10
O113 20 p. deep yellow-green 10 10
O114 **276** 25 p. deep green and dull magenta .. 10 10
O115 40 p. new blue and magenta 20 10
a. Opt inverted .. ..
b. Albino opt .. .. 10·00
O116 50 p. slate-lilac and turquoise-green 10 10
O117 60 p. black 50 10
O118 75 p. dull vermilion (Die II) (1980) .. 20 10
O119 **276a** 1 r. bronze-green (1980) 10 10
O120 1 r. 50, red-orange (1979) 10 10
O121 2 r. carmine-red (1979) 10 10
O122 3 r. blue-black (1980) 15 20
O123 4 r. black (1985) 20 25
O124 5 r. sepia (1985) 25 30
O109/24 .. .. *Set of* 16 1·75 1·50

(Des and litho Secura, Singapore)

1980 (15 Jan–10 Mar). *As Nos.* 513/19 *but inscr* "SERVICE". *P* 12.
O125 **291** 10 p. slate-green and orange-yellow .. 20 10
O126 15 p. slate-green & brt yellow-green .. 10 10
O127 25 p. violet and brown-red (10 Mar) .. 10 10
O128 35 p. carmine & brt yell-grn (10 Mar) .. 10 10
O129 – 40 p. rosine and olive-sepia 10 10
O130 – 50 p. violet & dull yell-green (10 Mar) 10 10
O131 – 80 p. brt yellow-green & blk (10 Mar) .. 10 10
O125/31 .. .. *Set of* 7 45 35

SERVICE

(O 6)

1984 (25 Sept)–**85**. *Nos.* 630 *and* 632/3 *optd with Type* O **6** *in red.*
O132 10 p. brownish black and rose-red 10 10
O133 20 p. black & brt reddish violet (20.11.84) 10 10
O134 60 p. light brown & blackish brown (1985) 10 10

BAHAWALPUR

PRICES FOR STAMPS ON COVER TO 1945	
Nos. O1/6	*from* × 30
Nos. O7/8	*from* × 10
Nos. O11/18	*from* × 30

(1)

1947 (15 Aug). *Nos.* 265/8, 269*a*/77 *and* 259/62 *of India optd locally with T* **1**.

No.	Type	Description	Price
1	**100*a***	3 p. slate (R.)	4·00
2		½ a. purple	4·00
3		9 p. green (R.)	4·00
4		1 a. carmine	4·00
5	**101**	1½ a. dull violet (R.)	4·75
6		2 a. vermilion	4·75
7		3 a. bright violet (R.)	4·75
8		3½ a. bright blue (R.)	4·75
9	**102**	4 a. brown	5·50
10		6 a. turquoise-green (R.)	5·50
11		8 a. slate-violet (R.)	5·50
12		12 a. lake	5·50
13	**103**	14 a. purple	38·00
14	**93**	1 r. grey and red-brown	16·00
15		2 r. purple and brown (R.)	£300
16		5 r. green and blue (R.)	£325
17		10 r. purple and claret	£350
1/17		*Set of* 17	£1000

Nos. 1/17 were issued during the interim period, following the implementation of the Indian Independence Act, during which time Bahawalpur was part of neither of the two Dominions created. The Amir acceded to the Dominion of Pakistan on 3 October 1947 and these overprinted stamps of India were then withdrawn.

The stamps of Bahawalpur only had validity for use within the state. For external mail Pakistan stamps were used.

PRINTERS. All the following issues were recess-printed by De La Rue & Co, Ltd, London.

2 Amir Muhammad Bahawal Khan I Abbasi

3

1947 (1 Dec). *Bicentenary Commemoration. W* **3** (*sideways*). *P* 12½ × 11½.

No.	Type	Description	Unused	Used
18	**2**	½ a. black and carmine	30	1·25

4 H.H. the Amir of Bahawalpur

5 The Tombs of the Amirs

6 Mosque in Sadiq-Garh

7 Fort Derawar from the Lake

8 Nur-Mahal Palace

9 The Palace, Sadiq-Garh

10 H.H. the Amir of Bahawalpur

11 Three Generations of Rulers; H.H. the Amir in centre

1948 (1 Apr). *W* **3** (*sideways on vert designs*). *P* 12½ (*T* **4**), 11½ × 12½ (*T* **5**, **7**, **8** *and* **9**), 12½ × 11½ (*T* **6** *and* **10**) *or* 13½ × 14 (*T* **11**).

No.	Type	Description	Unused	Used
19	**4**	3 p. black and blue	20	5·00
20		½ a. black and claret	20	5·00
21		9 p. black and green	20	5·00
22		1 a. black and carmine	20	5·00
23		1½ a. black and violet	20	5·00
24	**5**	2 a. green and carmine	20	6·00
25	**6**	4 a. orange and brown	25	7·00
26	**7**	6 a. violet and blue	25	8·00
27	**8**	8 a. carmine and violet	25	8·00
28	**9**	12 a. green and carmine	35	9·00
29	**10**	1 r. violet and brown	1·50	10·00
30		2 r. green and claret	3·75	12·00
31		5 r. black and violet	5·50	20·00
32	**11**	10 r. scarlet and black	9·00	30·00
19/32		*Set of* 14	21·00	£120

12 H.H. The Amir of Bahawalpur and Mohammed Ali Jinnah

13 Soldiers of 1848 and 1948

1948 (3 Oct). *First Anniv of Union of Bahawalpur with Pakistan. W* **3**. *P* 13.

No.	Type	Description	Unused	Used
33	**12**	1½ a. carmine and blue-green	10	1·00

1948 (15 Oct). *Multan Campaign Centenary. W* **3**. *P* 11½.

No.	Type	Description	Unused	Used
34	**13**	1½ a. black and lake	20	4·00

1948. *As Nos.* 29/32, *but colours changed.*

No.	Type	Description	Unused	Used
35	**10**	1 r. deep green and orange	15	6·00
36		2 r. black and carmine	20	8·00
37		5 r. chocolate and ultramarine	20	14·00
38	**11**	10 r. red-brown and green	25	18·00
35/8		*Set of* 4	70	42·00

14 Irrigation

17 U.P.U. Monument, Berne

1949 (3 Mar). *Silver Jubilee of Accession of H.H. the Amir of Bahawalpur. T* **14** *and similar horiz designs. W* **3**. *P* 14.

No.	Description	Unused	Used
39	3 p. black and ultramarine	10	2·75
40	½ a. black and brown-orange	10	2·75
41	9 p. black and green	10	2·75
42	1 a. black and carmine	10	2·75
39/42	*Set of* 4	20	10·00

Designs:—½ a. Wheat; 9 p. Cotton; 1 a. Sahiwal bull.

1949 (10 Oct). *75th Anniv of Universal Postal Union. W* **3**. *P* 13.

No.	Type	Description	Unused	Used
43	**17**	9 p. black and green	20	2·00
		a. Perf 17½ × 17	1·60	8·00
44		1 a. black and magenta	20	2·00
		a. Perf 17½ × 17	1·60	8·00
45		1½ a. black and orange	20	2·00
		a. Perf 17½ × 17	1·60	8·00
46		2½ a. black and blue	20	2·00
		a. Perf 17½ × 17	1·60	8·00
43/6		*Set of* 4	70	7·00
43a/6a		*Set of* 4	5·75	29·00

OMNIBUS ISSUES

Details, together with prices for complete sets, of the various Omnibus issues from the 1935 Silver Jubilee series to date are included in a special section following Zululand at the end of the catalogue.

OFFICIAL STAMPS

O **1** Panjnad Weir

O **2** Dromedary and Calf

O **3** Blackbuck

O **4** Eastern White Pelicans

O **5** Juma Masjid Palace, Fort Derawar

O **6** Temple at Pattan Manara

1945 (1 Jan). *Various horizontal pictorial designs, with red Arabic opt. W* **3**. *P* 14.

No.	Type	Description	Unused	Used
O1	O **1**	½ a. black and green	1·25	3·75
O2	O **2**	1 a. black and carmine	1·75	2·25
O3	O **3**	2 a. black and violet	2·75	4·00
O4	O **4**	4 a. black and olive-green	6·00	10·00
O5	O **5**	8 a. black and brown	4·25	7·00
O6	O **6**	1 r. black and orange	4·25	7·00
O1/6		*Set of* 6	18·00	30·00

O **7** Baggage Camels

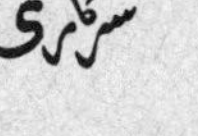

(O **8**)

1945 (10 Mar). *Red Arabic opt. No wmk. P* 14.

No.	Type	Description	Unused	Used
O7	O **7**	1 a. black and brown	18·00	30·00

1945 (Mar–June). *Surch as Type* O **8** (*at Security Printing Press, Nasik*) *instead of red Arabic opt. No wmk. P* 14.

No.	Type	Description	Unused	Used
O11	O **5**	½ a. on 8 a. black and purple	4·25	2·00
O12	O **6**	1½ a. on 1 r. black and orange	13·00	2·50
O13	O **1**	1½ a. on 2 r. black and blue (1 June)	50·00	2·75
O11/13		*Set of* 3	60·00	6·50

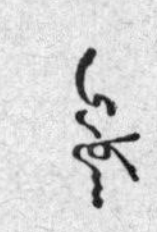

(O **9**)

O **10** H.H. the Amir of Bahawalpur

1945. *Optd with Type* O **9** (*by D.L.R.*) *instead of red Arabic opt. No wmk. P* 14.

No.	Type	Description	Unused	Used
O14	O **1**	½ a. black and carmine	1·00	5·50
O15	O **2**	1 a. black and carmine	1·25	5·50
O16	O **3**	2 a. black and orange	2·25	13·00
O14/16		*Set of* 3	4·00	22·00

1945. *P* 14.

No.	Type	Description	Unused	Used
O17	O **10**	3 p. black and blue	30	2·00
O18		1½ a. black and violet	2·50	4·75

O **11** Allied Banners

(Des E. Meronti. Recess, background litho)

1946 (1 May). *Victory. P* 14.

No.	Type	Description	Unused	Used
O19	O **11**	1½ a. green and grey	1·75	1·75

1948. *Nos.* 19, 22, 24/5 *and* 35/8 *optd as Nos.* O1/6.

No.	Type	Description	Unused	Used
O20	**4**	3 p. black and blue (R.)	10	4·00
O21		1 a. black and carmine (Blk.)	10	3·25

O22 5 2 a. green and carmine (Blk.) .. .. 10 4·50
O23 6 4 a. orange and brown (Blk.) .. .. 10 6·50
O24 10 1 r. deep green and orange (R.) .. .. 10 6·00
O25 2 r. black and carmine (R.) .. .. 10 8·00
O26 5 r. chocolate and ultramarine (R.) .. 20 14·00
O27 11 10 r. red-brown and green (R.) .. .. 25 18·00
O20/7 .. .. *Set of* 8 95 55·00

1949 (10 Oct). *75th Anniv of Universal Postal Union. Nos. 43/6 optd as Nos.* O1/6.
O28 17 9 p. black and green .. .. .. 15 4·50
a. Perf 17½ × 17 .. .. .. 2·25 13·00
O29 1 a. black and magenta .. .. .. 15 4·50
a. Perf 17½ × 17 .. .. .. 2·25 13·00
O30 1½ a. black and orange .. .. .. 15 4·50
a. Perf 17½ × 17 .. .. .. 2·25 13·00
O31 2½ a. black and blue .. .. .. 15 4·50
a. Perf 17½ × 17 .. .. .. 2·25 13·00
O28/31 .. .. *Set of* 4 55 16·00
O28a/31a .. .. *Set of* 4 8·00 45·00

Since 1949 only Pakistan stamps have been used in Bahawalpur for both internal and external mail.

Palestine

The stamps of TURKEY were used in Palestine from 1865.
In addition various European Powers, and Egypt, maintained post offices at Jerusalem (Austria, France, Germany, Italy, Russia), Jaffa (Austria, Egypt, France, Germany, Russia) and Haifa (Austria, France) using their own stamps or issues specially prepared for Levant post offices. All foreign post offices had closed by the time of the British Occupation.

PRICES FOR STAMPS ON COVER TO 1945	
No. 1	*from* × 6
No. 2	*from* × 4
Nos. 3/4	*from* × 5
Nos. 5/15	*from* × 4
Nos. 16/29	*from* × 3
Nos. 30/42	*from* × 2
No. 43	—
Nos. 44/57	*from* × 2
Nos. 58/9	—
Nos. 60/8	*from* × 3
Nos. 69/70	—
Nos. 71/89	*from* × 3
Nos. 90/103	*from* × 4
Nos. 104/11	*from* × 8
Nos. D1/5	*from* × 30
Nos. D6/20	*from* × 10

BRITISH MILITARY OCCUPATION

Valid also for use in Transjordan, Cilicia, Northern Egypt and Syria.

1

(2)

3

"E.E.F." = Egyptian Expeditionary Force

(Des G. Rowntree. Litho Typographical Dept, Survey of Egypt, Giza, Cairo)

1918 (10 Feb). *Wmk Royal Cypher in column (W* 100 *of Great Britain). Ungummed. Roul* 20.
1 1 1 p. indigo (Optd S. £550) £300 £225
a. Deep blue £275 £200
b. Blue £275 £200
Control: A 18 (*Prices, corner block of* 4; No. 1, £1250. No. 1*a*, £1125. No. 1*b*, £1250.)

1918 (16 Feb). *As last (ungummed), surch with T* 2.
2 1 5 m. on 1 p. cobalt-blue (Optd S. £550) .. £175 £800
a. "MILLILMES" (No. 10 in sheet) .. £2750 £3500
Control: B 18 A. (*Corner block*, £1300.)

1918 (5 Mar). *As No.* 1 *but colour changed. With gum.*
3 1 1 p. ultramarine .. .. 5·00 5·00
Control: C 18. (*Corner block*, £80.)

1918 (5 Mar *and* 13 May). *No.* 3 *surch with T* 2.
4 1 5 m. on 1 p. ultramarine .. .. .. 10·00 8·00
a. Arabic surch wholly or partly missing (No. 11 in sheet) £500
Controls: C 18 B (Mar). (*Corner block*, £750.)
D 18 C (May). (*Corner block*, £175.)

(Typo Stamping Dept, Board of Inland Revenue, Somerset House, London)

1918 (16 July–27 Dec). *Wmk Royal Cypher in column. P* 15 × 14.
5 3 1 m. sepia 50 50
a. Deep brown 55 55
6 2 m. blue-green 50 50
a. Deep green 60 60
7 3 m. yellow-brown (17 Dec) 60 60
a. Chestnut .. .. .. 15·00 10·00
8 4 m. scarlet 60 60
9 5 m. yellow-orange (25 Sept) 60 50
a. Orange 80 75
10 3 1 p. deep indigo (9 Nov) 60 25
11 2 p. pale olive .. .. 1·00 1·00
a. Olive .. .. 2·00 2·00
12 5 p. purple .. .. 3·00 4·00
13 9 p. ochre (17 Dec) .. .. .. 4·00 5·50
14 10 p. ultramarine (17 Dec) .. .. 4·00 5·50
15 20 p. pale grey (27 Dec) .. .. .. 10·00 20·00
a. Slate-grey .. .. .. 20·00 30·00
5/15 .. .. *Set of* 11 25·00 35·00

There are two sizes of the design of this issue:
19 × 23 mm. 1, 2, and 4 m., and 2 and 5 p.
18 × 21½ mm. 3 and 5 m., and 1, 9, 10 and 20 p.
There are numerous minor plate varieties in this issue, such as stops omitted in "E.E.F.", malformed Arabic characters, etc.

Originally issued by the Military Authorities for use of the civil population in occupied enemy territories (including at one time or another, a large part of Asia Minor), these stamps were used in Palestine until superseded by the following issue. They were demonetised on 1 May, 1922.

CIVIL ADMINISTRATION UNDER BRITISH HIGH COMMISSIONER

Palestine was placed under civil administration by a British High Commissioner on 1 July 1920.

فلسطين
PALESTINE
פלשתינה א״י
(4)

فلسطين
PALESTINE
פלשתינה א״י
(5)

فلسطين
PALESTINE
פלשתינה א״י
(6)

Differences:—
T 5. 20 mm vert and 7 mm between English and Hebrew.
T 6. 19 mm and 6 mm respectively.

(Optd at Greek Orthodox Convent, Jerusalem)

1920 (1 Sept). *Optd with T* 4 (*Arabic* 8 *mm long*). (*a*) *P* 15 × 14.
16 3 1 m. sepia .. .. 1·75 1·75
17 2 m. blue-green .. .. .. 8·50 5·00
18 3 m. chestnut .. .. 4·50 5·00
a. Opt inverted £750 £850
19 4 m. scarlet .. .. 1·60 1·90
20 5 m. yellow-orange .. .. .. 8·00 5·00
21 1 p. deep indigo (Sil.) .. .. 1·75 1·50
22 2 p. deep olive .. .. .. 1·75 2·25
23 5 p. deep purple .. .. .. 8·00 18·00
24 9 p. ochre .. .. 9·00 24·00
25 10 p. ultramarine .. .. .. 12·00 22·00
26 20 p. pale grey .. .. .. 17·00 35·00
(*b*) *P* 14
27 3 2 m. blue-green .. .. .. 1·75 2·00
28 3 m. chestnut .. .. 42·00 48·00
29 5 m. orange .. .. 2·00 1·25
16/29 .. .. *Set of* 14 £110 £150

Two settings of T 4 are known to specialists, the first being used for all values perf 15 × 14 except the 1 p. and the second for all values in both perfs.
Apart from minor varieties due to broken type, there are three major errors which are rare in some values. These are (*a*) two Hebrew characters at left transposed (all values of first setting only); (*b*) diamond-shaped dot over the Arabic "t" making the word read "Faleszin" for "Falestin" (2 p. to 20 p. of first setting and 1 m. and 3 m. perf 15 × 14, and 5 m. perf 14 of second setting); (*c*) "B" for final "E" of "PALESTINE" (2 p. to 20 p. of first setting and all values of second setting except 3 m. perf 14).
Faulty registration of the overprint in this issue has resulted in numerous misplaced overprints, either vertically or horizontally, which are not of great importance with the exception of Nos. 21 and 29 which exist with the overprint out of sequence, i.e. Hebrew/Arabic/English or English/Arabic/Hebrew or English/Hebrew only. Also all values are known with Arabic/English only.

1920 (22 Sept)–**21**. *Optd with T* 5* (*Arabic* 10 *mm long*).
(*a*) *P* 15 × 14
30 3 1 m. sepia (27.12.20) .. .. .. 75 1·00
a. Opt inverted .. .. .. £550 †
31 2 m. blue-green (27.12.20) .. .. 3·00 4·00
32 3 m. yellow-brown (27.12.20) .. .. 75 1·00
33 4 m. scarlet (27.12.20) .. .. .. 1·00 1·50
34 5 m. yellow-orange .. .. .. 3·25 1·00
35 1 p. deep indigo (Silver) (21.6.21) .. £750 20·00
36 2 p. olive (21.6.21) .. .. .. 60·00 26·00
37 5 p. deep purple (21.6.21) .. .. 27·00 10·00
(*b*) *P* 14
38 3 1 m. sepia £750 £850
39 2 m. blue-green .. .. .. 3·00 4·00
40 4 m. scarlet .. .. 75·00 £100
41 5 m. orange .. .. £120 14·00
a. Yellow-orange .. .. .. 2·00 1·75
42 1 p. deep indigo (Silver) .. .. 35·00 2·75
43 5 p. purple £300 £575

*In this setting the Arabic and Hebrew characters are badly worn and blunted, the Arabic "S" and "T" are joined (i.e. there is no break in the position indicated by the arrow in our illustration); the letters of "PALESTINE" are often irregular or broken; and the space between the two groups of Hebrew characters varies from 1 mm to over 1¾ mm. (*For clear, sharp overprint, see Nos.* 47/59.)
The dates of issue given are irrespective of the perforations, i.e. one or both perfs could have been issued on the dates shown.
Nos. 31 and 39 exist with any one line of the overprint partly missing.

1920 (6 Dec). *Optd with T* 6. (*a*) *P* 15 × 14.
44 3 3 m. yellow-brown .. .. .. 40·00 50·00
44*a* 5 m. yellow-orange £12000 £7500
(*b*) *P* 14
45 3 1 m. sepia .. .. 35·00 38·00
46 5 m. orange .. .. £750 40·00

1921 (29 May–4 Aug). *Optd as T* 5†. (*a*) *P* 15 × 14.
47 3 1 m. sepia (23.6) .. .. .. 5·00 4·00
48 2 m. blue-green (23.6) .. .. .. 10·00 7·00
49 3 m. yellow-brown (23.6) .. .. 30·00 5·00
a. "PALESTINE" omitted £1750
50 4 m. scarlet (23.6) .. .. .. 25·00 6·00
51 5 m. yellow-orange .. .. .. 30·00 2·25
52 1 p. deep indigo (Silver) (July) .. 25·00 1·00
53 2 p. olive (4.8) .. .. 35·00 8·50
54 5 p. purple (4.8) .. .. .. 30·00 17·00
55 9 p. ochre (4.8) .. .. .. 50·00 £120
56 10 p. ultramarine (4.8) .. .. 50·00 20·00
57 20 p. pale grey (4.8) .. .. .. £100 65·00
47/57 .. .. *Set of* 11 £350 £225
(*b*) *P* 14
58 3 1 m. sepia .. .. — £3000
59 20 p. pale grey £10000 £3500

†In this setting the Arabic and Hebrew characters are sharp and pointed as in T 6; there is usually a break between the Arabic "S" and "T" though this is sometimes filled with ink; and the whole overprint is much clearer. The space between the two groups of Hebrew characters is always 1¾ mm.

فلسطين
PALESTINE
פלשתינה א״י
(7)

فلسطين
PALESTINE
פלשתינה א״י
(8)

1921 (Sept–Oct). *Optd with T* 7 ("PALESTINE" *in sans-serif letters*) *by Stamping Dept, Board of Inland Revenue, Somerset House, London. Wmk Royal Cypher in column. P* 15 × 14.
60 3 1 m. sepia 40 25
61 2 m. blue-green 45 30
62 3 m. yellow-brown 45 10
63 4 m. scarlet 60 80
64 5 m. yellow-orange 75 25
65 1 p. bright turquoise-blue .. .. 1·25 30
66 2 p. olive .. .. 1·25 55
67 5 p. deep purple .. .. .. 4·75 6·00
68 9 p. ochre .. .. 11·00 13·00
69 10 p. ultramarine .. .. .. 13·00 £500
70 20 p. pale grey .. .. .. 60·00 £1000
60/70 .. .. *Set of* 11 85·00

(Printed and optd by Waterlow & Sons from new plates)

1922 (Sept–Nov). *T* 3 (*redrawn*), *optd with T* 8. *Wmk Mult Script CA.* (*a*) *P* 14.
71 3 1 m. sepia 30 15
a. Deep brown 45 15
b. Opt inverted .. .. .. — £9000
c. Opt double £500 £750
72 2 m. yellow 50 35
a. Orange-yellow .. .. .. 2·25 95
73 3 m. greenish blue 60 15
74 4 m. carmine-pink 35 30
75 5 m. orange 50 15
76 6 m. blue-green 90 70
77 7 m. yellow-brown .. .. .. 1·00 50
78 8 m. scarlet 90 35
79 1 p. grey .. .. 1·00 25
80 13 m. ultramarine 90 15
81 2 p. olive .. .. 2·50 60
a. Opt inverted £650 £650
b. Ochre .. .. £100 8·50
82 5 p. deep purple .. .. .. 6·00 2·00
82*a* 9 p. ochre £1000 £500
83 10 p. light blue .. .. .. 27·00 9·00
a. "E.F.F." for "E.E.F." in bottom panel £700 £600
84 20 p. bright violet .. .. .. £120 90·00
(*b*) *P* 15 × 14
86 3 5 p. deep purple .. .. .. 38·00 4·50
87 9 p. ochre .. .. 14·00 13·00
88 10 p. light blue .. .. .. 10·00 4·50
a. "E.F.F." for "E.E.F." in bottom panel £500 £400
89 20 p. bright violet .. .. .. 14·00 12·00
71/89 Optd "Specimen" .. .. *Set of* 15 £550

Most values can be found on thin paper.
In this issue the design of all denominations is the same size, 18 mm × 21½ mm. Varieties may be found with one or other of the stops between "E.E.F." missing.

BRITISH MANDATE TO THE LEAGUE OF NATIONS

The League of Nations granted a mandate to Great Britain for the administration of Palestine on 29 September 1923.

9 Rachel's Tomb

10 Dome of the Rock

11 Citadel, Jerusalem

12 Sea of Galilee

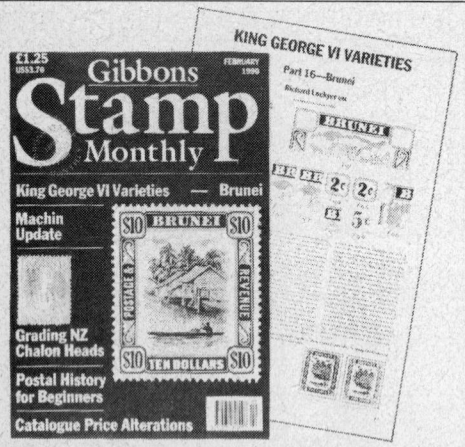

(Des F. Taylor. Typo Harrison)

1927 (1 June)–**45**. *Wmk Mult Script CA. P* 13½ × 14½ (2 *m. to* 20 *m.*) *or* 14.

90 **9** 2 m. greenish blue (14.8.27) 25 10
91 3 m. yellow-green 25 10
92 **10** 4 m. rose-pink (14.8.27) 2·50 70
93 **11** 5 m. orange (14.8.27) 25 10
a. From coils. Perf 14½×14 (1935) 10·00 15·00
b. Yellow (12.44) 50 15
c. Yellow. From coils. Perf 14½ × 14 (1945) 15·00 15·00
94 **10** 6 m. pale green (14.8.27) 1·75 1·00
a. Deep green 30 20
95 **11** 7 m. scarlet (14.8.27) 3·00 50
96 **10** 8 m. yellow-brown (14.8.27) 11·00 5·00
97 **9** 10 m. slate (14.8.27) 30 10
a. Grey. From coils. Perf 14½ × 14 (11.38) 15·00 20·00
b. Grey (1944) 30 10
98 **10** 13 m. ultramarine 3·75 30
99 **11** 20 m. dull olive-green (14.8.27) 70 15
a. Bright olive-green (12.44) 65 15
100 **12** 50 m. deep dull purple (14.8.27) 1·00 25
a. Bright purple (12.44) 1·00 20
101 90 m. bistre (14.8.27) 75·00 75·00
102 100 m. turquoise-blue (14.8.27) 2·00 35
103 200 m. deep violet (14.8.27) 8·00 4·00
a. Bright violet (1928) 25·00 15·00
b. Blackish violet (12.44) 4·00 2·00
90/103*b* *Set of* 14 90·00 75·00
90/103 H/S "Specimen" *Set of* 14 £425

Three sets may be made of the above issue; one on thin paper, one on thicker paper with a ribbed appearance, and another on thick white paper without ribbing.

2 m. stamps in the grey colour of the 10 m. exist as also 50 m. stamps in blue, but it has not been established whether they were issued.

Nos. 90/1 and 93 exist in coils, constructed from normal sheets.

1932 (1 June)–**44**. *New values and colours. Wmk Mult Script CA. P* 13½ × 14½ (4 *m. to* 15 *m.*) *or* 14.

104 **10** 4 m. purple (1.11.32) 15 10
105 **11** 7 m. deep violet 15 10
106 **10** 8 m. scarlet 15 10
107 13 m. bistre (1.8.32) 30 10
108 15 m. ultramarine (1.8.32) 55 10
a. Grey-blue (12.44) 30 10
b. Greenish blue 30 10
109 **12** 250 m. brown (15.1.42) 2·00 1·50
110 500 m. scarlet (15.1.42) 4·50 2·00
111 £P1 black (15.1.42) 5·00 2·50
104/11 *Set of* 8 11·00 6·00
104/11 Perf "Specimen" *Set of* 8 £525

No. 108 exists in coils, constructed from normal sheets.

POSTAL FISCALS

Type-set stamps inscribed "O.P.D.A." (= Ottoman Public Debt Administration) or "H.J.Z." (Hejaz Railway); British 1d. stamps (No. 336); and Palestine stamps overprinted with one or other of the above groups of letters, or with the word "Devair", with or without surcharge of new value, are fiscal stamps. They are known used as postage stamps, alone, or with other stamps to make up the correct rates, and were passed by the postal authorities, although they were not definitely authorised for postal use.

POSTAGE DUE STAMPS

D 1

D 2 (MILLIEME)

D 3 (MIL)

(Typo Greek Orthodox Convent, Jerusalem)

1923 (1 Apr). *P* 11.

D1 **D 1** 1 m. yellow-brown 25·00 40·00
a. Imperf (pair) £500
b. Imperf between (horiz pair) £1000
D2 2 m. blue-green 20·00 30·00
a. Imperf (pair) £550
D3 4 m. scarlet 20·00 35·00
D4 8 m. mauve 15·00 25·00
a. Imperf (pair) £200
b. Imperf between (horiz pair) — £1800
D5 13 m. steel blue 15·00 25·00
a. Imperf between (horiz pair) £850
D1/5 *Set of* 5 95·00 £140

Perfectly centred and perforated stamps of this issue are worth considerably more than the above prices, which are for average specimens.

(Types D **2**/**3**. Typo D.L.R.)

1924 (1 Dec). *Wmk Mult Script CA. P* 14.

D 6 **D 2** 1 m. deep brown 90 1·25
D 7 2 m. yellow 1·00 1·25
D 8 4 m. green 1·10 1·25
D 9 8 m. scarlet 2·00 80
D10 13 m. ultramarine 2·50 2·50
D11 5 p. violet 6·00 1·75
D6/11 *Set of* 6 12·50 8·00
D6/11 Optd "Specimen" *Set of* 6 £325

1928 (1 Feb)–**45**. *Wmk Mult Script CA. P* 14.

D12 **D 3** 1 m. brown 40 40
a. Perf 15 × 14 (1944) 20·00 30·00
D13 2 m. yellow 50 50
D14 4 m. green 65 55
a. Perf 15 × 14 (1945) 25·00 40·00
D15 6 m. orange-brown (10.33) 5·00 4·25
D16 8 m. carmine 1·00 50
D17 10 m. pale grey 1·00 60
D18 13 m. ultramarine 1·50 1·50
D19 20 m. pale olive-green 1·60 1·25
D20 50 m. violet 2·00 1·25
D12/20 *Set of* 9 12·50 9·50
D12/20 Perf (D15) or Optd (others) "Specimen" *Set of* 9 £350

The British Mandate terminated on 14 May 1948. Later issues of stamps and occupation issues will be found listed under Gaza, Israel and Jordan in Part 19 (*Middle East*) of this catalogue.

Papua (British New Guinea)

Stamps of QUEENSLAND were used in British New Guinea (Papua) from at least 1885 onwards. Post Offices were opened at Daru (1894), Kulumadau (Woodlarks) (1899), Nivani (1899), Port Moresby (1885), Samarai (1888), Sudest (1899) and Tamata (1899). Stamps were usually cancelled "N.G." (at Port Moresby from 1885) or "BNG" (without stops at Samarai or with stops at the other offices) from 1888. Queensland stamps were replaced in Papua by the issue of 1901.

PRICES FOR STAMPS ON COVER

Nos. 1/7	*from* × 12
No. 8	—
Nos. 9/14*a*	*from* × 15
Nos. 14*c*/21	*from* × 5
No. 22	—
Nos. 23/9*a*	*from* × 5
No. 29*b*	—
Nos. 30/2	*from* × 8
Nos. 34/8*b*	*from* × 5
No. 38*c*	—
Nos. 38*d*/71	*from* × 7
Nos. 72/4	—
Nos. 75/92*a*	*from* × 7
Nos. 93/8	*from* × 10
Nos. 99/109	*from* × 6
Nos. 110/11	—
Nos. 112/14	*from* × 6
No. 115	—
Nos. 116/28	*from* × 5
Nos. 130/53	*from* × 4
Nos. 154/7	*from* × 12
Nos. 158/67	*from* × 4
No. 168	*from* × 3
Nos. O1/12	*from* × 7

1 Lakatoi (trading canoe) with Hanuabada Village in Background

2 (Horizontal)

(Recess D.L.R.)

1901 (1 July)–**05**. *Wmk Mult Rosettes, W* **2**. *P* 14.

I. *Thick paper. Wmk horizontal*

1 **1** ½d. black and yellow-green 6·00 9·00
2 1d. black and carmine 5·00 7·00
3 2d. black and violet 7·00 7·00
4 2½d. black and ultramarine 13·00 11·00
5 4d. black and sepia 40·00 35·00
6 6d. black and myrtle-green 40·00 35·00
7 1s. black and orange 60·00 65·00
8 2s. 6d. black and brown (1905) £600 £550

II. *Thick paper. Wmk vertical*

9 **1** ½d. black and yellow-green 3·00 3·75
10 1d. black and carmine 3·00 2·00
11 2d. black and violet 4·00 4·00
12 2½d. black and ultramarine 8·00 12·00
13 4d. black and sepia 32·00 48·00
14 6d. black and myrtle-green 48·00 70·00
14*a* 1s. black and orange 55·00 70·00
14*b* 2s. 6d. black and brown £2000 £1600

III. *Thin paper. Wmk horizontal*

14*c* **1** ½d. black and yellow-green £140 £130
14*d* 2½d. black and ultramarine £180 £150
14*e* 2½d. black and dull blue £275 £200

IV. *Thin paper. Wmk vertical*

15 **1** ½d. black and yellow-green 8·00 14·00
16 1d. black and carmine
17 2d. black and violet 42·00 16·00
18 2½d. black and ultramarine
18*a* 2½d. black and dull blue
19 4d. black and sepia £160 £350
20 6d. black and myrtle-green £475 £750
21 1s. black and orange £450 £750
22 2s. 6d. black and brown £550 £950
1/22 *Set of* 8 £625 £625

The sheets of the ½d., 2d. and 2½d. show a variety known as "white leaves" on R. 4/5 while the 2d. and 2½d. (both R. 6/2) and the ½d. and 1s. (both R. 6/3) show what is known as the "unshaded leaves" variety.

Papua. (3)   **Papua.** (4)

1906–7. A. *Optd with T* **3** (*large opt*), *at Port Moresby* (8 Nov 1906).

I. *Thick paper. Wmk horizontal*

23 **1** 4d. black and sepia £200 £200
24 6d. black and myrtle-green 32·00 35·00
25 1s. black and orange 20·00 32·00
26 2s. 6d. black and brown £140 £150

II. *Thick paper. Wmk vertical*

27 **1** 2½d. black and ultramarine 3·75 13·00
28 4d. black and sepia £160 £160
29 6d. black and myrtle-green 18·00 32·00
29*a* 1s. black and orange £750 £650
29*b* 2s. 6d. black and brown £3000 £2500

III. *Thin paper. Wmk vertical*

30 **1** ½d. black and yellow-green 4·50 5·00
31 1d. black and carmine 7·50 13·00
32 2d. black and violet 4·50 3·00
23/32 (*cheapest*) *Set of* 8 £325 £350

B. *Optd with T* **4** (*small opt*), *at Brisbane* (May–June 1907)

I. *Thick paper. Wmk horizontal*

34 **1** ½d. black and yellow-green 35·00 48·00
35 2½d. black and ultramarine 65·00 85·00
36 1s. black and orange 60·00 £100
37 2s. 6d. black and brown 30·00 48·00
a. Opt reading downwards £1900
c. Opt double (horiz) — £1800
d. Opt triple (horiz) — £1500

II. *Thick paper. Wmk vertical*

38 **1** 2½d. black and ultramarine 6·00 17·00
a. Opt double
38*b* 1s. black and orange 60·00 70·00
38*c* 2s. 6d. black and brown £2250 £2250

III. *Thin paper. Wmk horizontal*

38*d* **1** ½d. black and yellow-green 75·00 75·00
39 2½d. black and ultramarine 18·00 40·00
a. Opt double
39*b* 2½d. black and dull blue 85·00 85·00

IV. *Thin paper. Wmk vertical*

40 **1** ½d. black and yellow-green 3·50 5·00
a. Opt double £1500
41 1d. black and carmine 3·75 6·00
a. Opt reading upwards £750 £625
42 2d. black and violet 4·50 2·25
42*a* 2½d. black and ultramarine
43 4d. black and sepia 25·00 40·00
44 6d. black and myrtle-green 21·00 35·00
a. Opt double £1800 £3000
45 1s. black and orange 27·00 40·00
a. Opt double, one diagonal — £1800
46 2s. 6d. black and brown 35·00 48·00
34/46 (*cheapest*) *Set of* 8 £110 £150

In the setting of this overprint Nos. 10, 16, and 21 have the "p" of "Papua" with a defective foot or inverted "d" for "p", and in No. 17 the "pua" of "Papua" is a shade lower than the first "a".

No. 37a comes from a single sheet on which the overprints were sideways. Examples exist showing one, two or four complete or partial overprints.

PRINTERS. All the following issues were printed at Melbourne. See notes at beginning of Australia.

5 Large "PAPUA"

B

C

Three types of the 2s. 6d.:—

A. Thin top to "2" and small ball. Thin "6" and small ball. Thick uneven stroke.
B. Thin top to "2" and large, well shaped ball. Thin "6" and large ball. Very thick uneven stroke.
C. Thick top to "2" and large, badly shaped ball. Thick "6" and uneven ball. Thin even line.

Type A is not illustrated as the stamp is distinguishable by perf and watermark.

The litho stones were prepared from the engraved plates of the 1901 issue, value for value except the 2s. 6d. for which the original plate was mislaid. No. 48 containing Type A was prepared from the original ½d. plate with the value inserted on the stone and later a fresh stone was prepared from the 1d. plate and this contained Type B. Finally, the original plate of the 2s. 6d. was found and a third stone was prepared from this, and issued in 1911. These stamps show Type C.

6 Small "PAPUA"

(Litho Government Printing Office, Melbourne, from transfers from original engraved plates)

1907–10. *Wmk Crown over A, W w* **11**.

A. *Large* "PAPUA". (*a*) *Wmk upright. P* 11

47 **5** ½d. black and yellow-green (11.07) 1·00 2·75

(*b*) *Wmk sideways. P* 11

48 **5** 2s. 6d. black and chocolate (A) (12.09) 48·00 60·00
a. "POSTAGIE" at right (R. 1/5) £250

B. *Small* "PAPUA"

I. *Wmk upright.* (*a*) *P* 11 (1907–8)

49 **6** 1d. black and rose (6.08) 4·75 2·00
50 2d. black and purple (10.08) 6·00 4·50
51 2½d. black and bright ultramarine (7.08) 12·00 20·00
a. Black and pale ultramarine 5·00 6·50

No.	Type	Description	Unused	Used
52	6	4d. black and sepia (20.1.07)	4·00	6·50
53		6d. black and myrtle-green (4.08)	11·00	15·00
54		1s. black and orange (10.08)	14·00	18·00
		(b) P 12½ (1907–9)		
55	6	2d. black and purple (10.08)	10·00	6·00
56		2½d. black and bright ultramarine (7.08)	45·00	55·00
		b. *Black and pale ultramarine*	32·00	42·00
57		4d. black and sepia (20.1.07)	7·00	7·00
58		1s. black and orange (1.09)	45·00	65·00
		II. *Wmk sideways.* (a) P 11 (1909–10)		
59	6	½d. black and yellow-green (12.09)	2·25	2·75
		a. *Black and deep green* (1910)	27·00	40·00
60		1d. black and carmine (1.10)	8·00	7·00
61		2d. black and purple (1.10)	4·50	2·75
62		2½d. black and dull blue (1.10)	4·25	14·00
63		4d. black and sepia (1.10)	3·50	6·00
64		6d. black and myrtle-green (11.09)	10·00	10·00
65		1s. black and orange (3.10)	40·00	48·00
		(b) P 12½ (1909–10)		
66	6	½d. black and yellow-green (12.09)	1·40	2·00
		a. *Black and deep green* (1910)	27·00	35·00
67		1d. black and carmine (12.09)	5·50	6·50
68		2d. black and purple (1.10)	3·00	2·50
69		2½d. black and dull blue (1.10)	7·50	22·00
70		6d. black and myrtle-green (11.09)	£1600	£2250
71		1s. black and orange (3.10)	12·00	25·00
		(c) *Perf compound of* 11 *and* 12½		
72	6	½d. black and yellow-green	£1800	£1800
73		2d. black and purple	£700	
		(d) *Mixed perfs* 11 *and* 12½		
74	6	4d. black and sepia	£2750	

(Litho Commonwealth Stamp Printing Office, Melbourne, by J. B. Cooke, from new stones made by fresh transfers)

1910 (Sept)–**11**. *Large* "PAPUA". *W* w **11** (*upright*). *P* 12½.

No.	Type	Description	Unused	Used
75	5	½d. black and green (12.10)	3·50	6·00
76		1d. black and carmine	8·00	3·00
77		2d. black and dull purple (*shades*) (12.10)	4·00	4·00
		a. "C" for "O" in "POSTAGE" (R.4/3)	60·00	60·00
78		2½d. black and blue-violet (10.10)	4·50	16·00
79		4d. black and sepia (10.10)	2·75	8·50
80		6d. black and myrtle-green	5·50	7·50
81		1s. black and deep orange (12.10)	5·50	15·00
82		2s. 6d. black and brown (B)	45·00	65·00
83		2s. 6d. black and brown (C) (1911)	45·00	65·00
75/83		*Set of* 8	70·00	£110

A variety showing a white line or "rift" in clouds occurs on R. 5/3 in Nos. 49/74 and the "white leaves" variety mentioned below No. 22 occurs on the 2d. and 2½d. values in both issues. They are worth about four times the normal price.

8

ONE PENNY

(9)

(Typo J. B. Cooke)

1911–15. *Printed in one colour. W* **8** (*sideways*).

No.	Type	Description	Unused	Used
		(a) P 12½ (1911–12)		
84	6	½d. yellow-green	60	3·00
		a. *Green*	30	1·75
85		1d. rose-pink	70	40
86		2d. bright mauve	70	75
87		2½d. bright ultramarine	4·75	8·50
		a. *Dull ultramarine*	5·50	8·50
88		4d. pale olive-green	2·00	10·00
89		6d. orange-brown	3·75	5·00
90		1s. yellow	8·50	13·00
91		2s. 6d. rose-carmine	28·00	38·00
		a. *Rose-red (aniline)*		
84/91		*Set of* 8	45·00	70·00

No. 91*a* always shows the watermark Crown to right of A, *as seen from the back of the stamp.*

No.	Type	Description	Unused	Used
		(b) P 14		
92	6	1d. rose-pink (6.15)	14·00	4·75
		a. *Pale scarlet*	5·00	2·00

1917. *Above issue surch with T* **9** *at Port Moresby.*

No.	Type	Description	Unused	Used
93	6	1d. on ½d. yellow-green	90	1·40
		a. *Green*	50	1·00
94		1d. on 2d. bright mauve	12·00	13·00
95		1d. on 2½d. ultramarine	1·25	3·75
96		1d. on 4d. pale olive-green	1·00	4·50
97		1d. on 6d. orange-brown	8·00	12·00
98		1d. on 2s. 6d. rose-carmine	1·50	8·00
93/98		*Set of* 6	22·00	38·00

(Typo J. B. Cooke (1916–18), T. S. Harrison (1918–26), A. J. Mullett (No. 101*a* only) (1926–27), or John Ash (1927–31))

1916–31. *Printed in two colours. W* **8** (*sideways*). *P* 14.

No.	Type	Description	Unused	Used
99	6	½d. myrtle and apple green (Harrison and Ash) (1919)	80	60
		a. *Myrtle and pale olive-green* (1927)	45	70
100		1d. black and carmine-red (1916)	1·40	60
		a. *Grey-black and red* (1918)	1·60	25
		b. *Intense black and red* (Harrison) (1926)	1·90	1·75
101		1½d. pale grey-blue (*shades*) and brown (1925)	80	30
		a. *Cobalt and light brown* (Mullett) (1927)	6·00	3·25
		b. *Bright blue and bright brown* (1929)	1·50	1·25
		c. "POSTACE" at right (R. 1/1) (all ptgs) *From*	35·00	38·00
102		2d. brown-purple and brown-lake (1919)	1·25	75
		a. *Deep brown-purple and lake* (1931)	17·00	1·25
		b. *Brown-purple and claret* (1931)	2·00	75
103		2½d. myrtle and ultramarine (1919)	4·00	8·00
104	6	3d. black and bright blue-green (1916)	1·25	1·75
		a. Error. Black and deep greenish Prussian blue*	£450	£450
		b. *Sepia-black and bright blue-green* (Harrison)	20·00	17·00
		c. *Black and blue-green* (1927)	3·25	4·75
105		4d. brown and orange (1919)	2·50	4·50
		a. *Light brown and orange* (1927)	4·75	12·00
106		5d. bluish slate and pale brown (1931)	4·25	13·00
107		6d. dull and pale purple (1919)	2·75	7·50
		a. *Dull purple and red-purple* (1927)	7·50	13·00
		b. "POSTACE" at left (R.6/2) (all ptgs) *From*	65·00	90·00
108		1s. sepia and olive (1919)	3·25	6·00
		a. *Brown and yellow-olive* (1927)	6·00	10·00
109		2s. 6d. maroon and pale pink (1919)	18·00	30·00
		a. *Maroon and bright pink* (*shades*) (1927)	18·00	35·00
110		5s. black and deep green (1916)	40·00	45·00
111		10s. green and pale ultramarine (1925)	£140	£180
99/111		*Set of* 13	£200	£250

*Beware of similar shades produced by removal of yellow pigment. No. 104a is a colour trial, prepared by Cooke, of which, it is believed, five sheets were sold in error.

The printers of the various shades can be determined by their dates of issue. The Ash printings are on whiter paper.

For 9d. and 1s 3d. values, see Nos. 127/8.

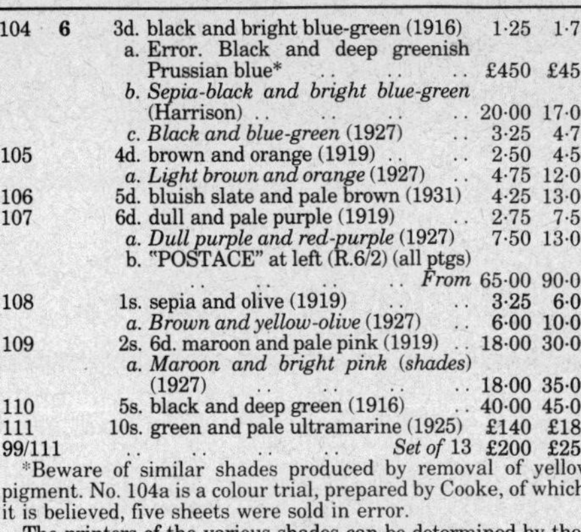

AIR MAIL

(10)

(11)

1929 (Oct)–**30**. *Air. Optd with T* **10** *by Govt Printer, Port Moresby.*

No.	Type	Description	Unused	Used
		(a) *Cooke printing. Yellowish paper*		
112	6	3d. black and bright blue-green	1·10	5·50
		a. Opt omitted in vert pair with normal	£2250	
		(b) *Harrison printing. Yellowish paper*		
113	6	3d. sepia-black and bright blue-green	50·00	60·00
		(c) *Ash printing. White paper*		
114	6	3d. black and blue-green	80	6·00
		a. Opt omitted in horiz pair with normal	£3250	
		b. Ditto, but vert pair	£2750	
		c. Opt vertical, on back	£2750	
		d. Opts *tête-bêche* (pair)	£1700	

1930 (15 Sept). *Air. Optd with T* **11**, *in carmine by Govt Printer, Port Moresby.* (a) *Harrison printings. Yellowish paper.*

No.	Type	Description	Unused	Used
115	6	3d. sepia-black and bright blue-green	£1100	£1800
116		6d. dull and pale purple	3·00	13·00
		a. "POSTACE" at left (R. 6/2)	65·00	£100
117		1s. sepia and olive	7·00	27·00
		a. Opt inverted	£2750	
		(b) *Ash printings. White paper*		
118	6	3d. black and blue-green	55	4·50
119		6d. dull purple and red-purple	5·50	10·00
		a. "POSTACE" at left (R. 6/2)	65·00	£100
120		1s. brown and yellow-olive	4·00	13·00
118/20		*Set of* 3	9·00	23·00

5d.

TWO PENCE

(12)

FIVE PENCE

(13)

1931 (1 Jan). *Surch with T* **12** *by Govt Printer, Port Moresby.*

No.	Type	Description	Unused	Used
		(a) *Mullett printing*		
121	6	2d. on 1½d. cobalt and light brown	16·00	40·00
		a. "POSTACE" at right (R. 1/1)	£150	£250
		(b) *Ash printing*		
122	6	2d. on 1½d. bright blue and bright brown	80	2·00
		a. "POSTACE" at right (R. 1/1)	32·00	48·00

1931. *Surch as T* **13** *by Govt Printer, Port Moresby.*

No.	Type	Description	Unused	Used
		(a) *Cooke printing*		
123	6	1s. 3d. on 5s. black and deep green	4·00	9·00
		(b) *Harrison printing. Yellowish paper*		
124	6	9d. on 2s. 6d. maroon and pale pink (Dec)	5·50	15·00
		(c) *Ash printings. White paper*		
125	6	5d. on 1s. brown and yellow-olive (26.7)	60	1·75
126		9d. on 2s. 6d. maroon and bright pink	5·00	8·50

(Typo J. Ash)

1932. *W* **15** *of Australia* (*Mult* "C of A"). *P* 11.

No.	Type	Description	Unused	Used
127	5	9d. lilac and violet	4·00	22·00
128		1s. 3d. lilac and pale greenish blue	7·00	27·00
127/8 Optd "Specimen"		*Set of* 2	£450	

15 Motuan Girl

18 Raggiana Bird of Paradise

20 Native Mother and Child　22 Papuan Motherhood

(Des F. E. Williams (2s., £1 and frames of other values), E. Whitehouse (2d., 4d., 6d., 1s., and 10s.); remaining centres from photos by Messrs F. E. Williams and Gibson. Recess J. Ash (all values) and W. C. G. McCracken (½d., 1d., 2d., 4d.))

1932 (14 Nov). *T* **15**, **18**, **20**, **22** *and similar designs. No wmk. P* 11.

No.	Description	Unused	Used
130	½d. black and orange	35	2·25
	a. *Black and buff* (McCracken)	12·00	20·00
131	1d. black and green	40	25
132	1½d. black and lake	60	4·50
133	2d. red	5·50	25
134	3d. black and blue	2·00	6·50
135	4d. olive-green	3·00	8·50
136	5d. black and slate-green	2·00	4·00
137	6d. bistre-brown	4·00	7·00
138	9d. black and violet	7·00	17·00
139	1s. dull blue-green	2·50	11·00
140	1s. 3d. black and dull purple	8·50	20·00
141	2s. black and slate-green	11·00	20·00
142	2s. 6d. black and rose-mauve	24·00	38·00
143	5s. black and olive-brown	48·00	50·00
144	10s. violet	75·00	75·00
145	£1 black and olive-grey	£170	£170
130/145	*Set of* 16	£325	£375

Designs: *Vert* (*as T* **15**)—1d. A Chieftain's son; 1½d. Tree-houses; 3d. Papuan dandy; 5d. Masked dancer; 9d. Papuan shooting fish; 1s. 3d. Lakatoi; 2s. Papuan art; 2s. 6d. Pottery making; 5s. Native policeman; £1 Delta house. (*As T* **18**)—1s. *Dubu*—or ceremonial platform. *Horiz* (*as T* **20**)—10s. Lighting a fire.

31 Hoisting the Union Jack

32 Scene on H.M.S. *Nelson*

(Recess J. Ash)

1934 (6 Nov). *50th Anniv of Declaration of British Protectorate. P* 11.

No.	Type	Description	Unused	Used
146	31	1d. green	80	2·25
147	32	2d. scarlet	1·75	2·25
148	31	3d. blue	1·50	3·00
149	32	5d. purple	4·75	7·00
146/9		*Set of* 4	8·00	13·00

HIS MAJESTY'S JUBILEE.

1910　1935

(33)

HIS MAJESTY'S JUBILEE. 1910 — 1935

(34)

MAJESTY'S　MAJESTY'S

Normal　"Accent" flaw (R. 5/4)

1935 (9 July). *Silver Jubilee. Nos.* 131, 133/4 *and* 136 *optd with T* **33** *or* **34** (*2d.*).

No.	Description	Unused	Used
150	1d. black and green	35	80
	a. "Accent" flaw	20·00	30·00
151	2d. scarlet	95	50
152	3d. black and blue	1·25	2·50
	a. "Accent" flaw	38·00	55·00
153	5d. black and slate-green	2·75	2·75
	a. "Accent" flaw	55·00	65·00
150/3	*Set of* 4	4·75	6·00

35

36 Port Moresby

(Recess J. Ash)

1937 (14 May). *Coronation. P* 11.

No.	Type	Description	Unused	Used
154	35	1d. green	40	15
155		2d. scarlet	40	15
156		3d. blue	40	20
157		5d. purple	40	35
154/7		*Set of* 4	1·40	75

(Recess J. Ash)

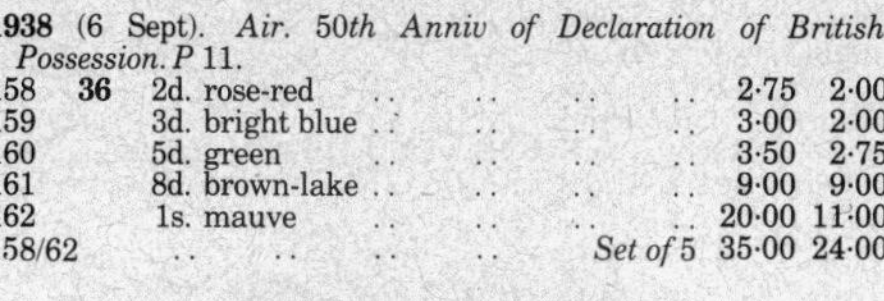

1938 (6 Sept). *Air. 50th Anniv of Declaration of British Possession. P* 11.
158 **36** 2d. rose-red .. 2·75 2·00
159 3d. bright blue .. 3·00 2·00
160 5d. green .. 3·50 2·75
161 8d. brown-lake .. 9·00 9·00
162 1s. mauve .. 20·00 11·00
158/62 *Set of* 5 35·00 24·00

37 Natives poling Rafts

(Recess J. Ash)

1939 (6 Sept). *Air. P* 11.
163 **37** 2d. rose-red .. 3·75 2·00
164 3d. bright blue .. 4·50 2·25
165 5d. green .. 5·50 1·50
166 8d. brown-lake .. 6·50 2·50
167 1s. mauve .. 8·50 5·00

(Recess W. C. G. McCracken)

1941 (2 Jan). *Air. P* 11½.
168 **37** 1s. 6d. olive-green .. 38·00 30·00
163/168 *Set of* 6 60·00 35·00

OFFICIAL STAMPS

1908 (Oct). *Punctured* "OS".
O1 **1** 2s. 6d. black and brown (No. 37) .. — 35·00
O2 2s. 6d. black and brown (No. 38c) .. £1100 £1100
O3 2s. 6d. black and brown (No. 46) .. — £200

1909–10. *Nos.* 49/71 *punctured* "OS". I. *Wmk upright. (a) P* 11.
O 4 **6** 1d. black and rose .. 5·00 1·50
O 5 2d. black and purple .. 6·50 3·00
O 6 2½d. black and bright ultramarine .. 13·00 10·00
a. Black and pale ultramarine .. 5·50 4·00
O 7 4d. black and sepia .. 5·50 4·00
O 8 6d. black and myrtle-green .. 12·00 9·00
O 9 1s. black and orange .. 15·00 12·00
O4/9 *Set of* 6 45·00 30·00

(*b*) *P* 12½
O10 **6** 2d. black and purple .. 8·00 4·00
O11 2½d. black and bright ultramarine .. 35·00 25·00
b. Black and pale ultramarine .. 22·00 18·00
O12 4d. black and sepia .. 8·00 5·00
O13 1s. black and orange .. 48·00 38·00
O10/13 *Set of* 4 75·00 60·00

II. *Wmk sideways. (a) P* 11
O14 **6** ½d. black and yellow-green .. 3·25 2·00
a. Black and deep green .. 28·00 25·00
O15 1d. black and carmine .. 9·00 5·00
O16 2d. black and purple .. 5·00 2·00
O17 2½d. black and dull blue .. 6·50 5·00
O18 4d. black and sepia .. 5·50 4·00
O19 6d. black and myrtle-green .. 15·00 6·00
O20 1s. black and orange .. 45·00 28·00
O14/20 *Set of* 7 80·00 48·00

(*b*) *P* 12½
O21 **6** ½d. black and yellow-green .. 2·00 1·50
a. Black and deep green .. 28·00 22·00
O22 1d. black and carmine .. 6·00 4·00
O23 2d. black and purple .. 3·50 1·50
O24 2½d. black and dull blue .. 10·00 7·00
O25 6d. black and myrtle-green .. — £400
O26 1s. black and orange .. 17·00 12·00

1910. *Nos.* 47/8 *punctured* "OS".
O27 **5** ½d. black & yellow-green (*wmk upright*) 2·75 2·00
O28 2s. 6d. black & chocolate (*wmk sideways*) 85·00 75·00

1910–11. *Nos.* 75/83 *punctured* "OS".
O29 **5** ½d. black and green .. 4·50 2·00
O30 1d. black and carmine .. 6·50 2·00
O31 2d. black and dull purple .. 4·75 2·00
a. "C" for "O" in "POSTAGE" .. 60·00 40·00
O32 2½d. black and blue-violet .. 6·50 6·00
O33 4d. black and sepia .. 6·50 5·00
O34 6d. black and myrtle-green .. 6·50 6·00
O35 1s. black and deep orange .. 11·00 9·00
O36 2s. 6d. black and brown (B) .. 48·00 35·00
O37 2s. 6d. black and brown (C) .. 48·00 35·00
O29/37 *Set of* 8 85·00 60·00

1911–12. *Nos.* 84/91 *punctured* "OS".
O38 **6** ½d. yellow-green .. 2·25 2·00
O39 1d. rose-pink .. 2·25 1·00
O40 2d. bright mauve .. 2·25 1·00
O41 2½d. bright ultramarine .. 6·50 6·00
O42 4d. pale olive-green .. 6·50 8·00
O43 6d. orange-brown .. 6·50 6·00
O44 1s. yellow .. 11·00 10·00
O45 2s. 6d. rose-carmine .. 35·00 32·00
O38/45 *Set of* 8 65·00 60·00

1930. *Nos.* 99/102*a and* 104*c*/9 *punctured* "OS".
O46 **6** ½d. myrtle and apple green .. 1·25 1·50
O47 1d. intense black and red .. 1·25 1·25
O48 1½d. bright blue and bright brown .. 1·50 1·50
a. "POSTACE" at right .. 38·00 42·00
O49 2d. deep brown-purple and lake .. 1·75 1·50
O50 3d. black and blue-green .. 2·75 2·75
O51 4d. light brown and orange .. 5·50 9·00
O52 6d. dull purple and pale purple .. 5·50 6·50
a. "POSTACE" at left .. 75·00 85·00
O53 1s. brown and yellow-olive .. 7·50 11·00
O54 2s. 6d. maroon and pale pink .. 27·00 35·00
O46/54 *Set of* 9 50·00 65·00

O S

(O 1)

(Typo T. S. Harrison (1d. and 2s. 6d.) and J. Ash)

1931 (29 July)–**32**. *Optd with Type* O **1**. *W* **8** *or W* **15** *of Australia* (9*d*., 1*s*. 3*d*.). *P* 14 *or* 11 (9*d*., 1*s*. 3*d*.).
O55 **6** ½d. myrtle and apple-green .. 80 3·50
O56 1d. grey-black and red .. 4·50 8·00
a. Intense black and red .. 2·50 3·25
O57 1½d. bright blue and bright brown .. 1·40 6·50
a. "POSTACE" at right .. 45·00 80·00
O58 2d. brown-purple and claret .. 2·00 7·00
O59 3d. black and blue-green .. 2·00 12·00
O60 4d. light brown and orange .. 2·00 11·00
O61 5d. bluish slate and pale brown .. 5·50 24·00
O62 6d. dull purple and red-purple .. 4·00 8·50
a. "POSTACE" at left .. 80·00 £130
O63 9d. lilac and violet (1932) .. 30·00 48·00
O64 1s. brown and yellow-olive .. 8·00 22·00
O65 1s. 3d. lilac & pale greenish blue (1932) 32·00 48·00
O66 2s. 6d. maroon and pale pink (Harrison) .. 32·00 60·00
a. Maroon and bright pink (Ash) .. 32·00 60·00
O55/66 *Set of* 12 £110 £225

Civil Administration, in Papua, was suspended in 1942; on resumption, after the Japanese defeat in 1945. Australian stamps were used until the appearance of the issue of the combined territories of Papua & New Guinea.

Papua New Guinea

AUSTRALIAN TRUST TERRITORY

The name of the combined territory was changed from "Papua and New Guinea" to "Papua New Guinea" at the beginning of 1972.

SPECIMEN OVERPRINTS. These come from specimen sets in which the lower values were cancelled-to-order, but stamps above the value of 10s. were overprinted "Specimen". These overprints are listed as they could be purchased from the Post Office.

1 Matschie's Tree Kangaroo

2 Buka Head-dresses

3 Native Youth

14 Map of Papua and New Guinea **15** Papuan shooting Fish

(Recess Note Printing Branch, Commonwealth Bank, Melbourne)

1952 (30 Oct)–**58**. *T* **1**/**3**, **14**/**15** *and similar designs. P* 14.
1 ½d. emerald .. 30 10
2 1d. deep brown .. 20 10
3 2d. blue .. 35 10
4 2½d. orange .. 1·75 40
5 3d. deep green .. 1·25 10
6 3½d. carmine-red .. 60 10
6*a* 3½d. black (2.6.58) .. 9·00 4·25
7 6½d. dull purple .. 2·25 10
a. Maroon (1956) .. 3·75 15
8 7½d. blue .. 10·00 4·50
9 9d. brown .. 6·00 60
10 1s. yellow-green .. 2·75 10
11 1s. 6d. deep green .. 12·00 80
12 2s. indigo .. 8·00 10
13 2s. 6d. brown-purple .. 7·00 40
14 10s. blue-black .. 60·00 11·00
15 £1 deep brown .. 75·00 11·00
1/15 *Set of* 16 £170 30·00
14/15 Optd "Specimen" *Set of* 2 £120

Designs: *Vert* (*as T* 1/3)—2½d. Greater Bird of Paradise; 3d. Native policeman; 3½d. Papuan head-dress. (*As T* 15)—6½d. Kiriwina Chief House; 7½d. Kiriwina yam house; 1s. 6d. Rubber tapping; 2s. Sepik dancing masks. *Horiz* (*as T* 14)—9d. Copra making; 1s. Lakatoi; 2s. 6d. Native shepherd and flock.

(**16**) (**17**)

1957 (29 Jan). *Nos.* 4 *and* 10 *surch with T* **16** *or T* **17**.
16 4d. on 2½d. orange .. 20 10
17 7d. on 1s. yellow-green .. 15 10

18 Cacao Plant

19 Klinki Plymill

20 Cattle

21 Coffee Beans

(Recess Note Ptg Branch, Commonwealth Bank, Melbourne)

1958 (2 June)–**60**. *New values. P* 14.
18 **18** 4d. vermilion .. 90 10
19 5d. green (10.11.60) .. 1·25 10
20 **19** 7d. bronze-green .. 8·50 10
21 8d. deep ultramarine (10.11.60) .. 1·50 2·00
22 **20** 1s. 7d. red-brown .. 30·00 20·00
23 2s. 5d. vermilion (10.11.60) .. 4·00 3·25
24 **21** 5s. crimson and olive-green .. 7·00 1·50
18/24 *Set of* 7 48·00 24·00

(**22**)

23 Council Chamber, Port Moresby

1959 (1 Dec). *No.* 1 *surch with T* **22**.
25 **1** 5d. on ½d. emerald .. 20 10

(Photo Harrison)

1961 (10 Apr). *Reconstitution of Legislative Council. P* 15 × 14.
26 **23** 5d. deep green and yellow .. 1·50 25
27 2s. 3d. deep green and light salmon .. 5·50 1·50

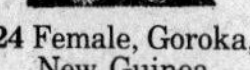

24 Female, Goroka, New Guinea

26 Female Dancer

28 Traffic Policeman

(Des Pamela M. Prescott, Recess Note Ptg Branch, Reserve Bank of Australia, Melbourne)

1961 (26 July)–**62**. *T* **24**, **26**, **28** *and similar designs. P* 14½ × 14 (1*d*., 3*d*., 3*s*.) *or* 14 × 14½ (*others*).
28 1d. lake .. 60 10
29 3d. indigo .. 30 10
30 1s. bronze-green .. 3·00 15
31 2s. maroon .. 45 15
32 3s. deep bluish green (5.9.62) .. 1·00 1·00
28/32 *Set of* 5 4·75 1·25

Designs:—*Vert* (*as T* **24**)—3d. Tribal Elder, Tari, Papua. (*As T* **26**)—2s. Male dancer.

29 Campaign Emblem

30 Map of South Pacific

(Recess Note Ptg Branch, Reserve Bank of Australia, Melbourne)

1962 (7 Apr). *Malaria Eradication. P* 14.
33 **29** 5d. carmine-red and light blue .. 45 15
34 1s. red and sepia .. 1·00 25
35 2s. black and yellow-green .. 1·40 70
33/5 *Set of* 3 2·50 1·00

(Des Pamela M. Prescott. Recess Note Ptg Branch, Reserve Bank of Australia, Melbourne)

1962 (9 July). *Fifth South Pacific Conference, Pago Pago. P* 14½ × 14.

No.	Type	Description	Unused	Used
36	30	5d. scarlet and light green	70	15
37		1s. 6d. deep violet and light yellow	2·00	60
38		2s. 6d. deep green and light blue	2·00	1·00
36/8		*Set of* 3	4·25	1·60

31 Throwing the Javelin **33** Runners

(Des G. Hamori. Photo Courvoisier)

1962 (24 Oct). *Seventh British Empire and Commonwealth Games, Perth. T* **31**, **33** *and similar design. P* 11½.

No.	Type	Description	Unused	Used
39		5d. brown and light blue	30	10
		a. Pair. Nos. 39/40	60	50
40		5d. brown and orange	30	10
41		2s. 3d. brown and light green	1·75	75
39/41		*Set of* 3	2·10	1·25

Design: (*As T* 31)—5d. High jump.

Nos. 39/40 are arranged together *se-tenant* in sheets of 100.

34 Raggiana Bird of Paradise **35** Common Phalanger

36 Rabaul **37** Queen Elizabeth II

(Des S. T. Cham (10s.), A. Buckley (photo) (£1). Photo Harrison (£1), Courvoisier (others)).

1963. *P* 14½ (£1) *or* 11½ (*others*).

No.	Type	Description	Unused	Used
42	34	5d. yellow, chestnut and sepia (27 Mar)	1·00	10
43	35	6d. red, yellow-brown and grey (27 Mar)	80	90
44	36	10s. multicoloured (13 Feb)	14·00	7·00
45	37	£1 sepia, gold and blue-green (3 July)	10·00	2·00
42/5		*Set of* 4	23·00	9·00
44/5 Optd "Specimen"		*Set of* 2	90·00	

1963 (1 May). *Red Cross Centenary. As No.* 351 *of Australia*.

No.	Type	Description	Unused	Used
46		5d. red, grey-brown and bluish green	60	10

38 Waterfront, Port Moresby

(Des J. McMahon (8d.), Pamela M. Prescott (2s. 3d.). Recess Note Ptg Branch, Reserve Bank of Australia, Melbourne)

1963 (8 May). *T* **38** *and similar horiz design. P* 14 × 13½.

No.	Type	Description	Unused	Used
47	38	8d. green	25	15
48	–	2s. 3d. ultramarine	25	15

Design:—2s. 3d. Piaggio "P-166" Aircraft landing at Tapini.

40 Games Emblem **41** Watam Head

(Des Pamela M. Prescott. Recess Note Ptg Branch, Reserve Bank of Australia, Melbourne)

1963 (14 Aug). *First South Pacific Games, Suva. P* 13½ × 14½.

No.	Type	Description	Unused	Used
49	40	5d. bistre	10	10
50		1s. deep green	20	20

(Des Pamela M. Prescott. Photo Courvoisier)

1964 (5 Feb). *Native Artefacts. T* **41** *and similar vert designs. Multicoloured. P* 11½.

No.	Type	Description	Unused	Used
51		11d. Type **41**	1·00	10
52		2s. 5d. Watam Head (*different*)	1·00	60
53		2s. 6d. Bosmun Head	1·00	10
54		5s. Medina Head	1·25	15
51/4		*Set of* 4	3·75	75

45 Casting Vote **46** "Health Centres"

(Photo Courvoisier)

1964 (4 Mar). *Common Roll Elections. P* 11½.

No.	Type	Description	Unused	Used
55	45	5d. brown and drab	10	10
56		2s. 3d. brown and pale blue	20	25

(Recess Note Ptg Branch, Reserve Bank of Australia, Melbourne)

1964 (5 Aug). *Health Services. T* **46** *and similar vert designs. P* 14.

No.	Type	Description	Unused	Used
57		5d. violet	10	10
58		8d. bronze-green	10	10
59		1s. blue	10	10
60		1s. 2d. brown-red	15	30
57/60		*Set of* 4	40	40

Designs:—8d. "School health"; 1s. "Infant, child and maternal health"; 1s. 2d. "Medical training".

50 Striped Gardener Bowerbird **51** Emperor of Germany Bird of Paradise

(Photo Courvoisier)

1964 (28 Oct)–**65**. *Vert designs as T* **50** (1*d. to* 8*d.*) *or* **51** (*others*). *Multicoloured; background colours given. P* 11½ (1*d. to* 8*d.*) *or* 12 × 11½ (1*s. to* 10*s.*).

No.	Type	Description	Unused	Used
61		1d. pale olive-yellow (20.1.65)	40	10
62		3d. light grey (20.1.65)	50	10
63		5d. pale red (20.1.65)	55	10
64		6d. pale green	75	10
65		8d. lilac	80	20
66		1s. salmon	90	10
67		2s. light blue (20.1.65)	85	20
68		2s. 3d. light green (20.1.65)	85	75
69		3s. pale yellow (20.1.65)	1·25	1·25
70		5s. cobalt (20.1.65)	12·00	1·75
71		10s. pale drab (Optd S. £120)	10·00	3·00
61/71		*Set of* 11	26·00	6·75

Designs:—3d. Adelbert Bowerbird; 5d. Blue Bird of Paradise; 6d. Lawes's Parotia; 8d. Black-billed Sicklebill; 2s. Brown Sicklebill; 2s. 3d. Lesser Bird of Paradise; 3s. Magnificent Bird of Paradise; 5s. Twelve-wired Bird of Paradise; 10s. Magnificent Riflebird.

61 Canoe Prow

(Des Pamela M. Prescott. Photo Courvoisier)

1965 (24 Mar). *Sepik Canoe Prows in Port Moresby Museum. T* **61** *and similar horiz designs showing carved prows. P* 11½.

No.	Type	Description	Unused	Used
72		4d. multicoloured	40	10
73		1s. 2d. multicoloured	1·75	85
74		1s. 6d. multicoloured	50	10
75		4s. multicoloured	1·50	25
72/5		*Set of* 4	3·50	1·10

1965 (14 Apr). *50th Anniv of Gallipoli Landing. As T* 184 *of Australia, but slightly larger* (22 × 34½ *mm*). *Photo*.

No.	Type	Description	Unused	Used
76		2s. 3d. sepia, black and emerald	20	10

65 Urban Plan and Native House

(Des G. Hamori. Photo Courvoisier)

1965 (7 July). *Sixth South Pacific Conference, Lae. T* **65** *and similar horiz design. P* 11½.

No.	Type	Description	Unused	Used
77		6d. multicoloured	10	10
78		1s. multicoloured	10	10

No. 78 is similar to T **65** but with the plan on the right and the house on the left. Also "URBANISATION" reads downwards.

66 Mother and Child **67** Globe and U.N. Emblem

(Photo Courvoisier)

1965 (13 Oct). *20th Anniv of U.N.O. T* **66/7** *and similar vert design. P* 11½.

No.	Type	Description	Unused	Used
79		6d. sepia, blue and pale turquoise-blue	10	10
80		1s. orange-brown, blue & dp reddish violet	10	10
81		2s. blue, blue-green and light yellow-olive	10	10
79/81		*Set of* 3	15	15

Design:—2s. U.N. Emblem and globes.

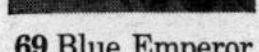

69 Blue Emperor **71** New Guinea Birdwing

(Photo Courvoisier)

1966 (14 Feb–12 Oct). *Decimal Currency. Butterflies. Vert designs as T* **69** (1 *to* 5 *c.*), *or horiz as T* **71** (*others*). *Multicoloured. P* 11½.

No.	Type	Description	Unused	Used
82		1 c. Type **69**	20	10
83		3 c. White-banded Map Butterfly	30	20
84		4 c. Mountain Swallowtail	35	15
85		5 c. Port Moresby Terinos	35	10
86		10 c. Type **71**	40	10
86*a*		12 c. Blue Crow (12.10)	2·00	2·00
87		15 c. Euchenor Butterfly	4·00	80
88		20 c. White-spotted Parthenos	2·50	25
89		25 c. Orange Jezebel	4·50	70
90		50 c. New Guinea Emperor	10·00	1·25
91		$1 Blue Spotted Leaf-wing	3·50	1·25
92		$2 Paradise Birdwing	5·50	3·00
82/92		*Set of* 12	30·00	8·50

80 "Molala Harai" **84** Throwing the Discus

(Des Rev. H. A. Brown. Photo Courvoisier)

1966 (8 June). *Folklore. Elema Art* (1*st series*). *T* **80** *and similar vert designs. P* 11½.

No.	Type	Description	Unused	Used
93		2 c. black and carmine	10	10
94		7 c. black, light yellow and light blue	10	10
95		30 c. black, carmine and apple-green	15	10
96		60 c. black, carmine and yellow	40	20
93/6		*Set of* 4	65	35

Designs:—7 c. "Marai"; 30 c. "Meavea Kivovia"; 60 c. "Toivita Tapaivita".

Nos. 93/6 were supplementary values to the decimal currency definitive issue.

See also Nos. 152/5 and 342/5.

(Photo Courvoisier)

1966 (31 Aug). *South Pacific Games, Nouméa. T* **84** *and similar vert designs. Multicoloured. P* 11½.

No.	Type	Description	Unused	Used
97		5 c. Type **84**	10	10
98		10 c. Football	10	10
99		20 c. Tennis	15	10
97/9		*Set of* 3	30	15

87 *Mucuna novoguineensis* 91 "Fine Arts"

(Des Mrs. D. Pearce. Photo Courvoisier)

1966 (7 Dec). *Flowers. T* **87** *and similar vert designs. Multi-coloured. P* 11½.

100 5 c. Type **87** 15 10
101 10 c. *Tecomanthe dentrophila* 15 10
102 20 c. *Rhododendron macgregoriae* 25 10
103 60 c. *Rhododendron konori* 40 25
100/3 .. .. *Set of* 4 85 40

(Des G. Hamori. Photo Courvoisier)

1967 (8 Feb). *Higher Education. T* **91** *and similar horiz designs. Multicoloured. P* 12½ × 12.

104 1 c. Type **91** 10 10
105 3 c. "Surveying" 10 10
106 4 c. "Civil Engineering" 10 10
107 5 c. "Science" 10 10
108 20 c. "Law" 10 10
104/8 .. .. *Set of* 5 20 20

96 *Sagra speciosa* 100 Laloki River

(Des Pamela M. Prescott. Photo Courvoisier)

1967 (12 Apr). *Fauna Conservation (Beetles). T* **96** *and similar vert designs. Multicoloured. P* 11½.

109 5 c. Type **96** 15 10
110 10 c. *Eupholus schoenherri* 20 10
111 20 c. *Sphingnotus albertisi* 30 10
112 25 c. *Cyphogastra albertisi* 30 10
109/12 .. .. *Set of* 4 85 25

(Des G. Wade. Photo Courvoisier)

1967 (28 June). *Laloki River Hydro-Electric Scheme, and "New Industries". T* **100** *and similar vert designs. Multicoloured. P* 12½.

113 5 c. Type **100** 10 10
114 10 c. Pyrethrum 10 10
115 20 c. Tea Plant 10 10
116 25 c. Type **100** 10 10
113/16 .. .. *Set of* 4 30 20

103 Air Attack at Milne Bay 107 Papuan Lory

(Des R. Hodgkinson (2 c.), F. Hodgkinson (5 c.), G. Wade (20 c., 50 c.). Photo Courvoisier)

1967 (30 Aug). *25th Anniv of the Pacific War. T* **103** *and similar multicoloured designs. P* 11½.

117 2 c. Type **103** 10 10
118 5 c. Kokoda Trail (*vert*) 10 10
119 20 c. The Coast Watchers 15 10
120 50 c. Battle of the Coral Sea 50 25
117/20 .. .. *Set of* 4 60 40

(Des T. Walcot. Photo Courvoisier)

1967 (29 Nov). *Christmas. Territory Parrots. T* **107** *and similar vert designs. Multicoloured. P* 12½.

121 5 c. Type **107** 20 10
122 7 c. Pesquet's Parrot 25 15
123 20 c. Dusky Lory 60 10
124 25 c. Edward's Fig Parrot 60 10
121/4 .. .. *Set of* 4 1·50 30

111 Chimbu Head-dresses 112

(Des P. Jones. Photo Courvoisier)

1968 (21 Feb). *"National Heritage". T* **111/12** *and similar multi-coloured designs. P* 12×12½ (5, 60 c.) *or* 12½×12 (10, 20 c.).

125 5 c. Type **111** 10 10
126 10 c. Southern Highlands Head-dress (*horiz*) 10 10
127 20 c. Western Highlands Head-dress (*horiz*) .. 15 10
128 60 c. Type **112** 40 20
125/8 .. .. *Set of* 4 60 40

115 *Hyla thesaurensis* 119 Human Rights Emblem and Papuan Head-dress (abstract)

(Des and photo Courvoisier)

1968 (24 Apr). *Fauna Conservation (Frogs). T* **115** *and similar horiz designs. Multicoloured. P* 11½.

129 5 c. Type **115** 15 15
130 10 c. *Hyla iris* 15 10
131 15 c. *Ceratobatrachas guentheri* 15 10
132 20 c. *Nyctimystes narinosa* 20 10
129/32 .. .. *Set of* 4 60 30

(Des G. Hamori. Litho Enschedé)

1968 (26 June). *Human Rights Year. T* **119** *and similar horiz design. Multicoloured. P* 13½ × 12½.

133 5 c. Type **119** 10 10
134 10 c. Human Rights in the World (abstract) .. 10 10

121 Leadership (abstract) 123 Egg Cowry

(Des G. Hamori. Litho Enschedé)

1968 (26 June). *Universal Suffrage. T* **121** *and similar horiz design. Multicoloured. P* 13½ × 12½.

135 20 c. Type **121** 10 10
136 25 c. Leadership of the Community (abstract) 10 10

(Des P. Jones. Photo Courvoisier)

1968–69. *Seashells. Multicoloured designs as T* **123**. *P* 12 × 12½ ($2), 12½ × 12 (1 c. *to* 20 c.) *or* 11½ (*others*).

137 1 c. Type **125** (29.1.69) 10 10
138 3 c. Laciniated Conch (30.10.68) 30 10
139 4 c. Lithograph Cone (29.1.69) 20 10
140 5 c. Marbled Cone (28.8.68) 25 10
141 7 c. Episcopal Mitre (29.1.69) 35 10
142 10 c. Red Volute (30.10.68) 45 10
143 12 c. Areola Bonnet (29.1.69) .. .. .. 1·50 55
144 15 c. Scorpion Conch (30.10.68) 80 25
145 20 c. Fluted Clam (28.8.68) 90 10
146 25 c. Chocolate Flamed Venus Shell (28.8.68) 90 30
147 30 c. Giant Murex (28.8.68) .. .. .. 1·25 35
148 40 c. Chambered Nautilus (30.10.68) .. .. 1·00 30
149 60 c. Pacific Triton (28.8.68) .. .. .. 1·25 20
150 $1 Emerald Snail (30.10.68) .. .. .. 3·00 50
151 $2 Glory of the Sea (*vert*) (29.1.69) .. .. 14·00 3·75
137/51 .. .. *Set of* 15 24·00 6·00

The 1, 5, 7, 15, 40, 60 c. and $1 exist with PVA gum as well as gum arabic.

138 Tito Myth 140 Luvuapo Myth

139 Iko Myth 141 Miro Myth

(Des from native motifs by Revd. H. A. Brown. Litho Enschedé)

1969 (9 Apr). *Folklore. Elema Art (2nd series). P* 12½ × 13½ × *Roul* 9 *between se-tenant pairs*.

152 **138** 5 c. black, yellow and red 10 10
a. Pair. Nos. 152/3 .. .. .. 20 20
153 **139** 5 c. black, yellow and red 10 10
154 **140** 10 c. black, grey and red 15 20
a. Pair. Nos. 154/5 .. .. .. 30 40
155 **141** 10 c. black, grey and red 15 20
152/5 .. .. *Set of* 4 50 60

Nos. 152/3 and 154/5 were issued in vertical *se-tenant* pairs, separated by a line of roulette.

142 "Fireball" Class Yacht 145 *Dendrobium ostinoglossum*

(Des J. Fallas. Recess Note Ptg Branch, Reserve Bank of Australia)

1969 (25 June). *Third South Pacific Games, Port Moresby. T* **142** *and similar designs. P* 14 × 14½ (5 c.) *or* 14½ × 14 (*others*).

156 5 c. black 10 10
157 10 c. deep bluish violet 10 10
158 20 c. myrtle-green 15 10
156/8 .. .. *Set of* 3 30 20

Designs: *Horiz*—10 c. Swimming pool, Boroko; 20 c. Games arena, Konedobu.

(Des P. Jones. Photo Courvoisier)

1969 (27 Aug). *Flora Conservation (Orchids). T* **145** *and similar vert designs. Multicoloured. P* 11½.

159 5 c. Type **145** 25 10
160 10 c. *Dendrobium lawesii* 35 30
161 20 c. *Dendrobium pseudofrigidum* 55 45
162 30 c. *Dendrobium conanthum* 70 30
159/62 .. .. *Set of* 4 1·75 1·00

149 Bird of Paradise 150 Native Potter

(Des G. Hamori. Photo Note Ptg Branch, Reserve Bank of Australia)

1969 (24 Sept)–**71**. *Coil stamps. P* 15 × *imperf*.

162*a* **149** 2 c. blue, black and red (1.4.71) .. 10 10
163 5 c. bright green, brown and red-orange 10 10

(Des G. Hamori. Photo Courvoisier)

1969 (24 Sept). *50th Anniv of International Labour Organization. P* 11½.

164 **150** 5 c. multicoloured 10 10

151 Tareko 155 Prehistoric Ambun Stone

(Des G. Hamori. Photo Courvoisier)

1969 (29 Oct). *Musical Instruments. T* **151** *and similar horiz designs. P* 12½ × 12.

165 5 c. multicoloured 10 10
166 10 c. black, olive-green and pale yellow .. 10 10
167 25 c. black, yellow and brown 15 10
168 30 c. multicoloured 25 10
165/8 .. .. *Set of* 4 55 30

Designs:—10 c. Garamut; 25 c. Iviliko; 30 c. Kundu.

(Des R. Bates. Photo Courvoisier)

1970 (11 Feb). *"National Heritage". T* **155** *and similar horiz designs. Multicoloured. P* 12½ × 12.

169 5 c. Type **155** 15 10
170 10 c. Masawa canoe of Kula Circuit 20 15
171 25 c. Torres' Map, 1606 .. .. .. 45 15
172 30 c. H.M.S. *Basilisk* (paddle-sloop), 1873 .. 60 20
169/72 .. .. *Set of* 4 1·25 50

159 King of Saxony Bird of Paradise

(Des T. Walcot. Photo Courvoisier)

1970 (13 May). *Fauna Conservation (Birds of Paradise). T* **159** *and similar vert designs. Multicoloured. P* 12 × 11½.

173 5 c. Type **159** .. .. 1·00 15
174 10 c. King Bird of Paradise .. .. .. 1·50 60
175 15 c. Raggiana Bird of Paradise .. .. 2·25 1·00
176 25 c. Sickle-crested Bird of Paradise .. .. 2·50 70
173/6 .. .. *Set of* 4 6·50 2·25

163 McDonnell Douglas "DC-6B" and Mt Wilhelm

164 Lockheed "Electra" and Mt Yule

165 Boeing "727" and Mt Giluwe

166 Fokker "Friendship" and Manam Island

(Des D. Gentleman. Photo Harrison)

1970 (8 July). *Australian and New Guinea Air Services. T* **163/6** *and similar horiz designs. Multicoloured. P* 14½ × 14.

177 5 c. Type **163** .. 25 10
a. Block of 4. Nos. 177/80 .. 90
178 5 c. Type **164** .. 25 10
179 5 c. Type **165** .. 25 10
180 5 c. Type **166** .. 25 10
181 25 c. McDonnell Douglas "DC-3" and Matupi Volcano .. 60 40
182 30 c. Boeing "707" and Hombrom's Bluff .. 70 60
177/82 .. *Set of* 6 2·00 1·25

Nos. 177/80 were issued together, *se-tenant*, in blocks of 4 throughout the sheet.

169 N. Miklouho-Maclay (scientist) and Effigy

170 Wogeo Island Food Bowl

(Des D. Gentleman. Photo Courvoisier)

1970 (19 Aug). *42nd ANZAAS (Australian-New Zealand Association for the Advancement of Science) Congress, Port Moresby. T* **169** *and similar horiz designs. P* 11½.

183 5 c. multicoloured .. 10 10
184 10 c. multicoloured .. 15 10
185 15 c. multicoloured .. 50 15
186 20 c. multicoloured .. 50 15
183/6 .. *Set of* 4 1·10 35

Designs:—10 c. B. Malinowski (anthropologist) and native hut; 15 c. T. Salvadori (ornithologist) and Dwarf Cassowary; 20 c. F. R. R. Schlechter (botanist) and flower.

(Des P. Jones. Photo Courvoisier)

1970 (28 Oct). *Native Artefacts. T* **170** *and similar multicoloured designs. P* 12½ × 12 (30 *c.*) *or* 12 × 12½ (*others*).

187 5 c. Type **170** .. 10 10
188 10 c. Lime Pot .. 20 10
189 15 c. Aibom Sago Storage Pot .. 20 10
190 30 c. Manus Island Bowl (*horiz*) .. 25 20
187/90 .. *Set of* 4 70 40

171 Eastern Highlands Dwelling

172 Spotted Phalanger

(Des G. Wade. Photo Courvoisier)

1971 (27 Jan). *Native Dwellings. T* **171** *and similar vert designs showing dwellings from the places given. Multicoloured. P* 11½.

191 5 c. Type **171** .. 15 10
192 7 c. Milne Bay .. 15 15
193 10 c. Purari Delta .. 15 10
194 40 c. Sepik .. 35 50
191/4 .. *Set of* 4 70 70

(Des R. Bates. Photo Courvoisier)

1971 (31 Mar). *Fauna Conservation. T* **172** *and similar multicoloured designs. P* 11½.

195 5 c. Type **172** .. 30 10
196 10 c. Long-fingered Possum .. 60 15
197 15 c. Feather-tailed Possum .. 1·25 1·00
198 25 c. Long-nosed Echidna (*horiz*) .. 1·75 1·00
199 30 c. Ornate Tree Kangaroo (*horiz*) .. 1·75 70
195/9 .. *Set of* 5 5·00 2·50

NEW INFORMATION

The editor is always interested to correspond with people who have new information that will improve or correct the Catalogue.

173 "Basketball"

174 Bartering Fish for Vegetables

(Des G. Hamori, Litho D.L.R.)

1971 (9 June). *Fourth South Pacific Games, Papeete, Tahiti. T* **173** *and similar horiz designs. Multicoloured. P* 13½ × 14.

200 7 c. Type **173** .. 10 10
201 14 c. "Sailing" .. 15 20
202 21 c. "Boxing" .. 15 25
203 28 c. "Athletics" .. 15 35
200/3 .. *Set of* 4 50 75

(Des G. Wade. Photo Courvoisier)

1971 (18 Aug). *Primary Industries. T* **174** *and similar vert designs. Multicoloured. P* 11½.

204 7 c. Type **174** .. 15 10
205 9 c. Man stacking yams .. 20 25
206 14 c. Vegetable market .. 30 10
207 30 c. Highlanders cultivating garden .. 50 50
204/7 .. *Set of* 4 1·00 80

175 Sia Dancer

176 Papuan Flag over Australian Flag

(Des Bette Hays. Photo Courvoisier)

1971 (27 Oct). *Native Dancers. T* **175** *and similar multicoloured designs. P* 11½.

208 7 c. Type **175** .. 20 10
209 9 c. Urasena dancer .. 30 20
210 20 c. Siassi Tubuan dancers (*horiz*) .. 80 90
211 28 c. Sia dancers (*horiz*) .. 1·00 1·10
208/11 .. *Set of* 4 2·10 2·00

(Des R. Bates. Photo Courvoisier)

1972 (26 Jan). *Constitutional Development. T* **176** *and similar horiz design. P* 12½ × 12.

212 **176** 7 c. multicoloured .. 30 10
a. Pair. Nos. 212/13 .. 60 90
213 – 7 c. multicoloured .. 30 10

Design:—No. 213, Crest of Papua New Guinea and Australian coat of arms.

Nos. 212/13 were printed vertically *se-tenant* within the sheet.

177 Map of Papua New Guinea and Flag of South Pacific Commission

178 Turtle

(Des R. Bates. Photo Courvoisier)

1972 (26 Jan). *25th Anniv of South Pacific Commission. T* **177** *and similar horiz design. P* 12½ × 12.

214 **177** 15 c. multicoloured .. 65 55
a. Pair. Nos. 214/15 .. 1·25 2·00
215 – 15 c. multicoloured .. 65 55

Design:—No. 215, Man's face and flag of the Commission.

Nos. 214/15 were printed vertically *se-tenant* within the sheet.

(Des R. Bates. Photo Courvoisier)

1972 (17 Mar). *Fauna Conservation (Reptiles). T* **178** *and similar horiz designs. Multicoloured. P* 11½.

216 7 c. Type **178** .. 40 10
217 14 c. Rainforest Dragon .. 1·00 1·25
218 21 c. Green Python .. 1·25 1·50
219 30 c. Salvador's Monitor .. 1·75 1·25
216/19 .. *Set of* 4 4·00 3·50

179 Curtiss "Seagull MF6" Aircraft and *Eureka* (schooner)

180 New National Flag

(Des Major L. G. Halls. Photo Courvoisier)

1972 (7 June). *50th Anniv of Aviation. T* **179** *and similar horiz designs. Multicoloured. P* 11½.

220 7 c. Type **179** .. 40 10
221 14 c. De Havilland "37" and native porters .. 1·00 1·25
222 20 c. Junkers "G-31" and gold dredger .. 1·10 1·25
223 25 c. Junkers "F-13" and mission church .. 1·10 1·25
220/3 .. *Set of* 4 3·25 3·50

(Des R. Bates. Photo Courvoisier)

1972 (16 Aug). *National Day. T* **180** *and similar vert designs. Multicoloured. P* 11½.

224 7 c. Type **180** .. 15 10
225 10 c. Native drum .. 20 25
226 30 c. Blowing conch-shell .. 35 50
224/6 .. *Set of* 3 60 70

181 Rev. Copland King

182 Mt Tomavatur Station

(Des G. Wade. Photo Courvoisier)

1972 (25 Oct). *Christmas (Missionaries). T* **181** *and similar horiz designs. Multicoloured. P* 11½.

227 7 c. Type **181** .. 25 40
228 7 c. Rev. Dr. Flierl .. 25 40
229 7 c. Bishop Verjus .. 25 40
230 7 c. Pastor Ruatoka .. 25 40
227/30 .. *Set of* 4 90 1·40

(Des R. Bates. Photo Courvoisier)

1973 (24 Jan). *Completion of Telecommunications Project 1968–72. T* **182** *and similar horiz designs. Multicoloured. P* 12½ (*Nos.* 231/4) *or* 11½ (*others*).

231 7 c. Type **182** .. 45 20
a. Block of 4. Nos. 231/4 .. 1·60
232 7 c. Mt Kerigomma Station .. 45 20
233 7 c. Sattelburg Station .. 45 20
234 7 c. Wideru Station .. 45 20
235 9 c. Teleprinter (36 × 26 *mm*) .. 45 55
236 30 c. Network Map (36 × 26 *mm*) .. 1·25 1·50
231/6 .. *Set of* 6 3·00 2·50

Nos. 231/4 were printed in *se-tenant* blocks of four within the sheet.

183 Queen Carola's Parotia

184 Wood Carver

(Des W. Cooper. Photo Courvoisier)

1973 (30 Mar). *Birds of Paradise. T* **183** *and similar vert designs. Multicoloured. P* 11½.

237 7 c. Type **183** .. 1·25 35
238 14 c. Goldie's Bird of Paradise .. 2·25 1·25
239 21 c. Ribbon-tailed Bird of Paradise (18 × 49 *mm*) .. 2·75 2·00
240 28 c. Princess Stephanie's Bird of Paradise (18 × 49 *mm*) .. 3·50 2·50
237/40 .. *Set of* 4 9·00 5·50

(Des R. Bates. Photo Courvoisier)

1973 (13 June)–**74**. *T* **184** *and similar horiz designs. Multicoloured. P* 11½.

241 1 c. Type **184** .. 10 10
242 3 c. Wig-makers (23.1.74) .. 20 10
243 5 c. Mt Bagana (22.8.73) .. 25 10
244 6 c. Pig Exchange (7.8.74) .. 50 50
245 7 c. Coastal village .. 20 10
246 8 c. Arawe mother (23.1.74) .. 35 15
247 9 c. Fire dancers .. 25 15
248 10 c. Tifalmin hunter (23.1.74) .. 45 10
249 14 c. Crocodile hunters (22.8.73) .. 45 30
250 15 c. Mt Elimbari .. 50 30
251 20 c. Canoe-racing, Manus (23.1.74) .. 1·00 40
252 21 c. Making sago (22.8.73) .. 65 45
253 25 c. Council House .. 70 45
254 28 c. Menyamya bowmen (22.8.73) .. 80 60
255 30 c. Shark-snaring (22.8.73) .. 1·00 75
256 40 c. Fishing canoes, Madang .. 1·50 80
257 60 c. Tapa cloth-making (23.1.74) .. 2·75 1·00
258 $1 Asaro Mudmen (23.1.74) .. 5·00 3·25
259 $2 Enga "Sing Sing" (7.8.74) .. 10·00 8·50
241/59 .. *Set of* 19 23·00 16·00

OMNIBUS ISSUES

Details, together with prices for complete sets, of the various Omnibus issues from the 1935 Silver Jubilee series to date are included in a special section following Zululand at the end of the catalogue.

185 Stamps of German New Guinea, 1897

Des R. Bates. Photo (1 c.), litho and recess (6 c.) or litho (7 c.) State Printing Works, Berlin. Photo and recess D.L.R. (9 c.). Recess and typo Reserve Bank of Australia (25 and 30 c.))

1973 (24 Oct). *75th Anniv of Papua New Guinea Stamps. T* **185** *and similar horiz designs. Chalky paper* (25, 30 c.). *P* 13½ (1, 6, 7 c.), 14 × 13½ (9 c.) *or* 14 × 14½ (25, 30 c.).

260 1 c. multicoloured 10 15
261 6 c. indigo, new blue and silver 20 35
262 7 c. multicoloured 25 35
263 9 c. multicoloured 30 45
264 25 c. orange and gold .. .. 55 1·00
265 30 c. plum and silver .. .. 65 1·25
260/65 .. .. *Set of* 6 1·75 3·25

Designs: *As T* **185**—6 c. 2 mark stamp of German New Guinea, 1900; 7 c. Surcharged registration label of New Guinea, 1914. 46 × 35 *mm*.—9 c. Papua 1s. stamp, 1901. 45 × 38 *mm*—25 c. ½d. stamp of New Guinea, 1925; 30 c. Papua 10s. stamp, 1932.

SELF-GOVERNMENT

186 Native Carved Heads

187 Queen Elizabeth II (from photograph by Karsh)

(Des G. Wade. Photo Courvoisier)

1973 (5 Dec). *Self-Government. P* 11½.

266 **186** 7 c. multicoloured 20 15
267 10 c. multicoloured 40 65

(Des and photo Harrison)

1974 (22 Feb). *Royal Visit. P* 14 × 14½.

268 **187** 7 c. multicoloured 25 15
269 30 c. multicoloured .. .. 1·00 1·75

188 Blyth's Hornbill

189 *Dendrobium bracteosum*

(Des T. Nolan. Photo Courvoisier)

1974 (12 June). *Birds' Heads. T* **188** *and similar multicoloured designs. P* 11½ (10 c.) *or* 12 (*others*).

270 7 c. Type **188** .. .. 1·50 70
271 10 c. Double-wattled Cassowary (33 × 49 *mm*) 2·50 2·75
272 30 c. New Guinea Harpy Eagle .. .. 6·00 7·50
270/2 .. .. *Set of* 3 9·00 10·00

(Des T. Nolan. Photo Courvoisier)

1974 (20 Nov). *Flora Conservation. T* **189** *and similar vert designs. Multicoloured. P* 11½.

273 7 c. Type **189** 50 10
274 10 c. *D. anosmum* .. .. 1·00 50
275 20 c. *D. smillieae* .. .. 1·40 1·25
276 30 c. *D. insigne* .. .. 1·75 1·75
273/6 .. .. *Set of* 4 4·25 3·25

190 Motu Lakatoi

191 1-toea Coin

(Des G. Wade. Photo Courvoisier)

1975 (26 Feb). *National Heritage—Canoes. T* **190** *and similar horiz designs. Multicoloured. P* 11½.

277 7 c. Type **190** 30 10
278 10 c. Tami two-master morobe 45 45
279 25 c. Aramia racing canoe .. .. .. 1·10 1·40
280 30 c. Buka Island canoe .. .. .. 1·10 1·10
277/80 .. .. *Set of* 4 2·75 2·75

(New Currency. 100 toea = 1 kina)

(Des G. Wade. Photo Courvoisier)

1975 (21 Apr). *New Coinage. T* **191** *and similar multicoloured designs. P* 11½.

281 1 t. Type **191** 10 10
282 7 t. New 2 t. and 5 t. coins (45 × 26 *mm*) .. 40 10
283 10 t. New 10 t. coin 60 30
284 20 t. New 20 t. coin .. .. 1·00 80
285 1 k. New 1 k. coin (45 × 26 *mm*) .. .. 3·50 4·00
281/5 .. .. *Set of* 5 5·00 4·50

192 *Ornithoptera alexandrae*

193 Boxing

(Des R. Bates. Photo Courvoisier)

1975 (11 June). *Fauna Conservation (Birdwing Butterflies). T* **192** *and similar vert designs. Multicoloured. P* 11½.

286 7 t. Type **192** 50 10
287 10 t. *O. victoriae regis* 80 45
288 30 t. *O. allottei* .. .. 1·75 1·50
289 40 t. *O. chimaera* .. .. 2·25 2·25
286/9 .. .. *Set of* 4 4·75 3·75

(Des R. Bates. Photo Courvoisier)

1975 (2 Aug). *Fifth South Pacific Games, Guam. T* **193** *and similar vert designs. Multicoloured. P* 11½.

290 7 t. Type **193** 15 10
291 20 t. Running 25 30
292 25 t. Basketball 30 45
293 30 t. Swimming 35 50
290/3 .. .. *Set of* 4 95 1·10

INDEPENDENT

194 Map and National Flag

(Des and photo Courvoisier)

1975 (10 Sept). *Independence. T* **194** *and similar horiz design. Multicoloured. P* 11½.

294 7 t. Type **194** 20 10
295 30 t. Map and National emblem 40 65
MS296 116 × 58 mm. Nos. 294/5 .. .. 1·50 1·50

195 M.V. *Bulolo*

196 Rorovana Carvings

(Des R. Bates. Photo Courvoisier)

1976 (21 Jan). *Ships of the* 1930s. *T* **195** *and similar horiz designs. Multicoloured. P* 11½.

297 7 t. Type **195** 30 10
298 15 t. M.V. *Macdhui* 45 30
299 25 t. M.V. *Malaita* 65 65
300 60 t. S.S. *Montoro* .. .. 1·75 2·50
297/300 .. .. *Set of* 4 2·75 3·25

(Des R. Bates. Photo Courvoisier)

1976 (17 Mar). *Bougainville Art. T* **196** *and similar horiz designs. Multicoloured. P* 11½.

301 7 t. Type **196** 20 10
302 20 t. Upe hats 40 75
303 25 t. Kapkaps 50 85
304 30 t. Canoe paddles 55 90
301/4 .. .. *Set of* 4 1·50 2·25

197 Rabaul House

198 Landscouts

(Des G. Wade. Photo Courvoisier)

1976 (9 June). *Native Dwellings. T* **197** *and similar horiz designs. Multicoloured. P* 11½.

305 7 t. Type **197** 20 10
306 15 t. Aramia house 35 25
307 30 t. Telefomin house 70 65
308 40 t. Tapini house 80 85
305/8 .. .. *Set of* 4 1·75 1·60

(Des R. Bates. Photo Courvoisier)

1976 (18 Aug). *50th Anniversaries of Survey Flight and Scouting in Papua New Guinea. T* **198** *and similar horiz designs. Multicoloured. P* 11½.

309 7 t. Type **198** 30 10
310 10 t. D. H. floatplane 40 20
311 15 t. Seascouts 50 65
312 60 t. Floatplane on water .. .. .. 1·25 2·00
309/12 .. .. *Set of* 4 2·25 2·50

199 Father Ross and New Guinea Highlands

(Des R. Bates. Photo Courvoisier)

1976 (28 Oct). *William Ross Commemoration. P* 11½.

313 **199** 7 t. multicoloured 40 15

200 Clouded Rainbow Fish

(Des P. Jones. Photo Courvoisier)

1976 (28 Oct). *Fauna Conservation (Tropical Fish). T* **200** *and similar horiz designs. Multicoloured. P* 11½.

314 5 t. Type **200** 30 10
315 15 t. Emperor or Imperial Angel Fish .. 60 45
316 30 t. Freckled Rock Cod .. .. .. 1·10 70
317 40 t. Threadfin Butterfly Fish .. .. 1·40 1·00
314/17 .. .. *Set of* 4 3·00 2·00

201 Man from Kundiawa

202 Headdress, Wasara Tribe

(Des R. Bates. Litho Questa (1, 2 k.) or photo Courvoisier (others))

1977 (12 Jan)–**78**. *T* **201/2** *and similar multicoloured designs showing headdresses. P* 14 (1, 2 *k.*) *or* 11½ (*others*).

318 1 t. Type **201** (29.3.78) 10 10
319 5 t. Masked dancer, Abelam area of Maprik (29.3.78) 10 10
320 10 t. Headdress from Koiari (7.6.78) 25 15
321 15 t. Woman with face paint, Hanuabada (29.3.78) 25 20
322 20 t. Orokaiva dancer (7.6.78) 50 30
323 25 t. Haus Tambaran dancer, Abelam area of Maprik (29.3.78) 40 30
324 30 t. Asaro Valley headdress (29.3.78) .. 45 35
325 35 t. Singsing costume, Garaina (7.6.68) .. 70 45
326 40 t. Waghi Valley headdress (29.3.78) .. 60 35
327 50 t. Trobriand Island dancer (7.6.78) .. 1·25 60
328 1 k. Type **202** .. .. 1·50 1·50
329 2 k. Headdress, Mekeo tribe .. .. .. 3·00 3·00
318/29 .. .. *Set of* 12 8·00 6·50

Sizes:—1, 5, 20 t. 25 × 31 *mm*; 35, 40 t. 23 × 38 *mm*; 1 k. 28 × 35 *mm*; 2 k. 33 × 23 *mm*; others 26 × 26 *mm*.

203 National Flag and Queen Elizabeth II

204 White-breasted Ground Pigeon

(Des and photo Harrison)

1977 (16 Mar). *Silver Jubilee. Horiz designs showing Queen Elizabeth as T* **203**. *Multicoloured. P* 14½ × 14.

330 7 t. Type **203** 25 10
a. Silver (face value and inscr) omitted .. £450
331 15 t. National emblem 35 35
332 35 t. Map of P.N.G. 65 70
330/2 .. .. *Set of* 3 1·10 1·00

(Des W. Cooper. Photo Courvoisier)

1977 (8 June). *Fauna Conservation (Birds). T* **204** *and similar horiz designs. Multicoloured. P* 11½.

333 5 t. Type **204** 25 10
334 7 t. Victoria Crowned Pigeon 25 10
335 15 t. Pheasant Pigeon 45 35
336 30 t. Orange-fronted Fruit Dove 75 65
337 50 t. Banded Imperial Pigeon .. .. .. 1·25 1·25
333/7 .. .. *Set of* 5 2·75 2·10

205 Guides and Gold Badge **206** Kari Marupi Myth

(Des R. Bates. Litho Questa)

1977 (10 Aug). *50th Anniv of Guiding in Papua New Guinea. Horiz designs showing badge as T* **205**. *Multicoloured. P* 14½.
338 7 t. Type **205** 20 10
339 15 t. Guides mapping 35 20
340 30 t. Guides washing 55 50
341 35 t. Guides cooking 60 60
338/41 .. .. *Set of* 4 1·50 1·25

(Des Revd. H. A. Brown. Litho Enschedé)

1977 (19 Oct). *Folklore. Elema Art* (3*rd series*). *T* **206** *and similar vert designs. P* 13½ × 13.
342 7 t. multicoloured 20 10
343 20 t. multicoloured 45 30
344 30 t. orange-red, light blue and black .. 50 65
345 35 t. orange-red, yellow and black .. 50 65
342/5 .. .. *Set of* 4 1·50 1·50
Designs:—20 t. Savoripi clan myth; 30 t. Oa-Laea myth; 35 t. Oa-Iriarapo myth.

207 Blue-tailed Skink **208** *Roboastra arika*

(Des T. Nolan. Photo Courvoisier)

1978 (25 Jan). *Fauna Conservation* (*Skinks*). *T* **207** *and similar horiz designs. Multicoloured. P* 11½.
346 10 t. Type **207** 30 10
347 15 t. Green Tree Skink 35 20
348 35 t. Crocodile Skink 55 55
349 40 t. New Guinea Blue-tongued Skink .. 75 70
346/9 .. .. *Set of* 4 1·75 1·40

(Des B. Twigden. Photo Courvoisier)

1978 (29 Aug). *Sea Slugs. T* **208** *and similar horiz designs. Multicoloured. P* 11½.
350 10 t. Type **208** 30 10
351 15 t. *Chromodoris fidelis* 35 25
352 35 t. *Flabellina macassarana* 70 80
353 40 t. *Chromodoris trimarginata* 75 85
350/3 .. .. *Set of* 4 1·90 1·75

209 Present Day Royal Papua New Guinea Constabulary **210** Ocarina

(Des R. Bates. Photo Harrison)

1978 (26 Oct). *History of Royal Papua New Guinea Constabulary. T* **209** *and similar horiz designs showing uniformed police and constabulary badges. Multicoloured. P* 14½.
354 10 t. Type **209** 30 10
355 15 t. Mandated New Guinea Constabulary, 1921–1941 .. .. 40 15
356 20 t. British New Guinea Armed Constabulary, 1890–1906 .. .. 45 40
357 25 t. German New Guinea Police, 1899–1914 50 45
358 30 t. Royal Papua and New Guinea Constabulary, 1906–1964 .. .. 60 60
354/8 .. .. *Set of* 5 2·00 1·50

(Des R. Bates. Litho Questa)

1979 (24 Jan). *Musical Instruments. T* **210** *and similar multicoloured designs. P* 14½ × 14 (7, 28 *t.*) *or* 14 × 14½ (*others*).
359 7 t. Type **210** 15 10
360 20 t. Musical bow (*horiz*) 25 20
361 28 t. Launut 30 30
362 35 t. Nose flute (*horiz*) 40 45
359/62 .. .. *Set of* 4 1·00 90

PRICES OF SETS

Set prices are given for many issues, generally those containing three stamps or more. Definitive sets include one of each value or major colour change, but do not cover different perforations, die types or minor shades. Where a choice is possible the set prices are based on the cheapest versions of the stamps included in the listings.

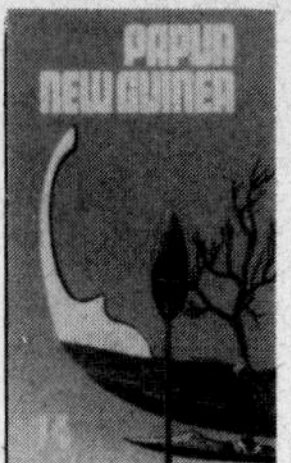

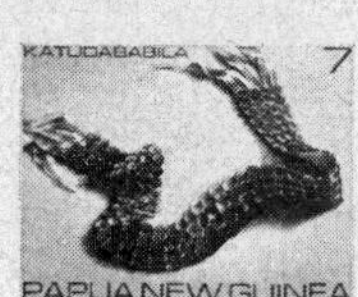

211 East New Britain Canoe **212** Katudababila (waist belt)

(Des G. Wade. Litho Questa)

1979 (28 Mar). *Traditional Canoe Prows and Paddles. T* **211** *and similar vert designs. Multicoloured. P* 14½.
363 14 t. Type **211** 15 15
364 21 t. Sepik war canoe 25 25
365 25 t. Trobriand Island canoe 25 30
366 40 t. Milne Bay canoe 40 60
363/6 .. .. *Set of* 4 95 1·10

(Des R. Bates. Photo Courvoisier)

1979 (6 June). *Traditional Currency. T* **212** *and similar horiz designs. Multicoloured. P* 12½ × 12.
367 7 t. Type **212** 10 10
368 15 t. Doga (chest ornament) 20 25
369 25 t. Mwali (armshell) 35 45
370 35 t. Soulava (necklace) 45 60
367/70 .. .. *Set of* 4 1·00 1·25

213 *Oenetus sp.* **214** "The Right to Affection and Love"

(Des T. Nolan. Photo Courvoisier)

1979 (29 Aug). *Fauna Conservation. Moths. T* **213** *and similar multicoloured designs. P* 11½.
371 7 t. Type **213** 20 10
372 15 t. *Celerina vulgaris* 30 30
373 20 t. *Alcidis aurora* (*vert*) 40 50
374 25 t. *Phyllodes conspicillator* 45 60
375 30 t. *Nyctalemon patroclus* (*vert*) .. 55 65
371/5 .. .. *Set of* 5 1·75 1·90

(Des G. Wade. Litho Enschedé)

1979 (24 Oct). *International Year of the Child. T* **214** *and similar vert designs. Multicoloured. P* 13½ × 13.
376 7 t. Type **214** 10 10
377 15 t. "The right to adequate nutrition and medical care" 15 15
378 30 t. "The right to play" 20 20
379 60 t. "The right to a free education" .. 45 60
376/9 .. .. *Set of* 4 80 90

215 "Post Office Service" **216** Detail from Betrothal Ceremony Mural, Minj District, Western Highlands Province

(Des G. Wade. Litho Enschedé)

1980 (23 Jan). *Admission to U.P.U.* (1979). *T* **215** *and similar horiz designs. Multicoloured. P* 13 × 13½.
380 7 t. Type **215** 10 10
381 25 t. "Wartime mail" 25 25
382 35 t. U.P.U. emblem 35 40
383 40 t. "Early postal services" 40 50
380/3 .. .. *Set of* 4 1·00 1·10

(Des W. Tubun. Photo Courvoisier)

1980 (26 Mar). *South Pacific Festival of Arts. T* **216** *and similar vert designs showing different details from mural of betrothal ceremony, Minj District, Western Highlands Province. P* 11½.
384 20 t. black, greenish yellow and pale orange .. 25 30
a. Strip of 5. Nos. 384/8 .. .. 1·10
385 20 t. multicoloured (two figures—left-hand black and yellow; right-hand black, yellow and red) 25 3
386 20 t. multicoloured (two figures—left-hand black and orange; right-hand black) .. 25 3
387 20 t. multicoloured (two figures, one behind the other) 25 3
388 20 t. multicoloured (one figure) 25 3
384/8 .. .. *Set of* 5 1·10 1·4
Nos. 384/8 were printed together, *se-tenant*, in horizontal strip of 5 throughout the sheet.

217 Family being Interviewed

(Des R. Bates. Litho Questa)

1980 (4 June). *National Census. T* **217** *and similar horiz designs. Multicoloured. P* 14 × 13½.
389 7 t. Type **217** 10 1
390 15 t. Population symbol 15 1
391 40 t. Figures and map of Papua New Guinea 30 4
392 50 t. Heads symbolising population growth .. 35 5
389/92 .. .. *Set of* 4 80 1·0

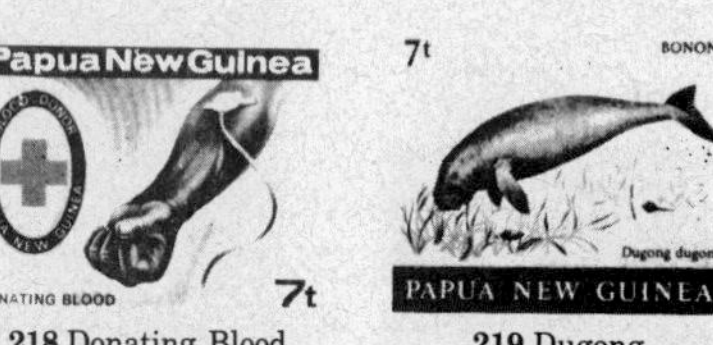

218 Donating Blood **219** Dugong

(Des R. Bates. Litho Questa)

1980 (27 Aug). *Red Cross Blood Bank. T* **218** *and similar horiz designs. Multicoloured. P* 14½.
393 7 t. Type **218** 15 1
394 15 t. Receiving transfusion 20 2
395 30 t. Map of Papua New Guinea showing blood transfusion centres 25 2
396 60 t. Blood and its components 40 6
393/6 .. .. *Set of* 4 90 1·0

(Des Dr. E. Lindgren (35 t.), T. Nolan (others). Photo Courvoisier)

1980 (29 Oct). *Mammals. T* **219** *and similar multicoloured designs. P* 11½.
397 7 t. Type **219** 10 1
398 30 t. New Guinea Marsupial Cat (*vert*) .. 40 4
399 35 t. Tube-nosed Bat (*vert*) 40 4
400 45 t. Rufescent Bandicoot ("Mumut") .. 50 5
397/400 .. .. *Set of* 4 1·25 1·2

220 White-headed Kingfisher **221** Native Mask

(Des W. Peckover. Photo Courvoisier)

1981 (21 Jan). *Kingfishers. T* **220** *and similar multicoloured designs. P* 11½.
401 3 t. Type **220** 10 1
402 7 t. Forest Kingfisher 15 1
403 20 t. Sacred Kingfisher 45 4
404 25 t. White-tailed Kingfisher (26 × 46 *mm*) .. 55 6
405 60 t. Blue-winged Kookaburra .. .. 1·25 1·4
401/5 .. .. *Set of* 5 2·25 2·2

(Des R. Bates. Photo Note Ptg Branch, Reserve Bank of Australia)

1981 (21 Jan). *Coil stamps. Vert designs as T* **221**. *P* 15 × *imperf.*
406 2 t. reddish violet and orange 10 10
407 5 t. cerise and blue-green 10 10
Design:—5 t. Hibiscus flower.

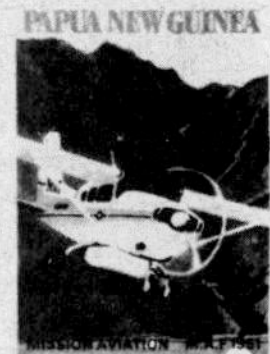

222 Mortar Team **223** M.A.F. (Missionary Aviation Fellowship) Aeroplane

(Des T. Reilly (15 t.), R. Bates (others). Litho Enschedé)

981 (25 Mar). *Defence Force. T* **222** *and similar horiz designs. Multicoloured. P* 13 × 13½.

08	7 t. Type **222**	15	10
09	15 t. Aeroplane and aircrew	30	25
10	40 t. *Aitape* (patrol boat) and seamen	70	65
11	50 t. Medical team examining children	75	75
08/11	*Set of* 4	1·75	1·50

(Des G. Wade. Litho Questa)

981 (17 June). *"Mission Aviation". T* **223** *and similar vert designs. Multicoloured. P* 14.

12	10 t. Type **223**	20	10
13	15 t. Catholic mission aeroplane	25	25
14	20 t. S.I.L. (Summer Institute of Linguistics) helicopter	35	35
15	30 t. Lutheran mission aeroplane	55	55
16	35 t. S.D.A. (Seventh Day Adventist Church) aeroplane	65	65
12/16	*Set of* 5	1·75	1·75

224 Scoop Net Fishing

225 *Forcartia buhleri*

(Des G. Wade. Litho Questa)

1981 (26 Aug). *Fishing. T* **224** *and similar horiz designs. Multicoloured. P* 14.

417	10 t. Type **224**	15	10
418	15 t. Kite fishing	30	30
419	30 t. Rod fishing	50	50
420	60 t. Scissor net fishing	95	85
417/20	*Set of* 4	1·75	1·60

(Des P. Jones. Photo Courvoisier)

1981 (28 Oct). *Land Snail Shells. T* **225** *and similar horiz designs. Multicoloured. P* 11½ × 12.

421	5 t. Type **225**	10	10
422	15 t. *Naninia citrina*	25	25
423	20 t. *Papuina adonis* and *papuina hermione*	35	35
424	30 t. *Papustyla hindei* and *papustyla novaepommeraniae*	50	50
425	40 t. *Rhynchotrochus strabo*	70	80
421/5	*Set of* 5	1·75	1·75

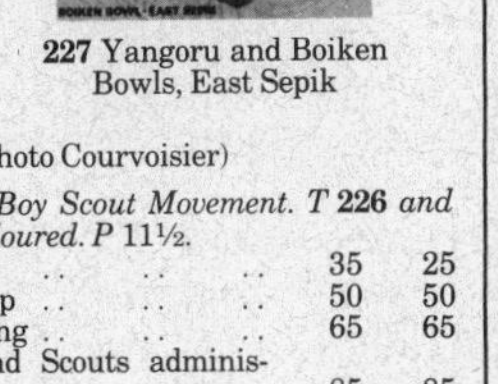

226 Lord Baden-Powell and Flag-raising Ceremony

227 Yangoru and Boiken Bowls, East Sepik

(Des G. Wade. Photo Courvoisier)

1982 (20 Jan). *75th Anniv of Boy Scout Movement. T* **226** *and similar horiz designs. Multicoloured. P* 11½.

426	15 t. Type **226**	35	25
427	25 t. Scout leader and camp	50	50
428	35 t. Scout, and hut building	65	65
429	50 t. Percy Chaterton, and Scouts administering first aid	85	85
426/9	*Set of* 4	2·10	2·00

(Des R. Bates. Litho Questa)

1982 (24 Mar). *Native Pottery. T* **227** *and similar multicoloured designs. P* 14 (10, 20 *t.*) *or* 14½ (*others*).

430	10 t. Type **227**	15	10
431	20 t. Utu cooking pot and small Gumalu pot, Madang	30	30
432	40 t. Wanigela pots, Northern District (37 × 23 *mm*)	55	55
433	50 t. Ramu Valley pots, Madang (37 × 23 *mm*)	70	80
430/3	*Set of* 4	1·50	1·60

228 "Eat Healthy Foods"

229 *Stylophora sp*

(Des G. Wade, Litho J.W.)

1982 (21 May). *Food and Nutrition. T* **228** *and similar horiz designs. Multicoloured. P* 14½ × 14.

434	10 t. Type **228**	15	10
435	15 t. Protein foods	30	30
436	30 t. Protective foods	55	55
437	40 t. Energy foods	65	70
434/7	*Set of* 4	1·50	1·50

(Des Courvoisier or W. Peckover (5 k.). Photo Courvoisier)

1982 (21 July)—**85**. *Granite paper.* (a) *Corals. Multicoloured designs as T* **229**. *P* 11½.

438	1 t. Type **229**	10	10
439	3 t. *Dendrophyllia sp.* (*vert*) (12.1.83)	15	10
440	5 t. *Acropora humilis*	15	10
441	10 t. *Dendronephthya sp.* (*vert*) (12.1.83)	25	10
442	12 t. As 10 t. (29.5.85)	75	60
443	15 t. *Distichopora sp*	20	20
444	20 t. *Isis sp.* (*vert*) (9.11.83)	30	25
445	25 t. *Acropora sp.* (*vert*) (9.11.83)	35	30
446	30 t. *Dendronephthya sp.* (*diff*) (*vert*) (12.1.83)	60	40
447	35 t. *Stylaster elegans* (*vert*) (9.11.83)	70	50
448	40 t. *Antipathes sp.* (*vert*) (12.1.83)	70	50
449	45 t. *Turbinarea sp.* (*vert*) (9.11.83)	80	60
450	1 k. *Xenia sp*	1·25	1·25
451	3 k. *Distichopora sp.* (*vert*) (12.1.83)	3·50	3·50

(*b*) *Bird of Paradise. Multicoloured square design,* 33 × 33 *mm*

452	5 k. Raggiana Bird of Paradise (15.8.84)	8·00	6·50
438/52	*Set of* 15	16·00	13·50

230 Missionaries landing on Beach

231 Athletics

(Des B. To Una. Photo Courvoisier)

1982 (15 Sept). *Centenary of Catholic Church in Papua New Guinea. Mural on wall of Nordup Catholic Church, East New Britain. T* **230** *and similar vert designs. Multicoloured. P* 11½.

457	10 t. Type **230**	15	10
	a. Horiz strip of 3. Nos. 457/9	40	
458	10 t. Missionaries talking to natives	15	10
459	10 t. Natives with slings and spears ready to attack	15	10
457/9	*Set of* 3	40	25

Nos. 457/9 come in *se-tenant* strips of 3 horizontally throughout the sheet, each strip forming a composite design.

(Des R. Bates. Litho Questa)

1982 (6 Oct). *Commonwealth Games and "Anpex 82" Stamp Exhibition, Brisbane. T* **231** *and similar horiz designs. Multicoloured. P* 14½.

460	10 t. Type **231**	15	10
461	15 t. Boxing	25	25
462	45 t. Rifle-shooting	55	70
463	50 t. Bowls	65	75
460/3	*Set of* 4	1·40	1·60

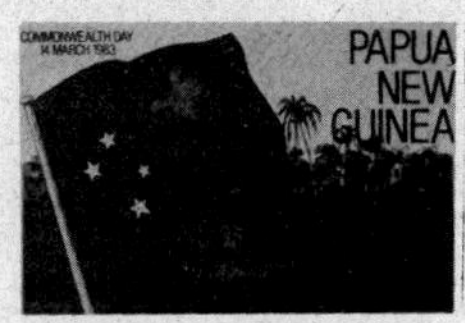

232 National Flag

(Des Walsall. Litho Harrison)

1983 (9 Mar). *Commonwealth Day. T* **232** *and similar horiz designs. Multicoloured. P* 14.

464	10 t. Type **232**	15	10
465	15 t. Basket-weaving and cabbage-picking	20	30
466	20 t. Crane hoisting roll of material	25	35
467	50 t. Lorries and ships	60	75
464/7	*Set of* 4	1·10	1·40

233 Transport Communications

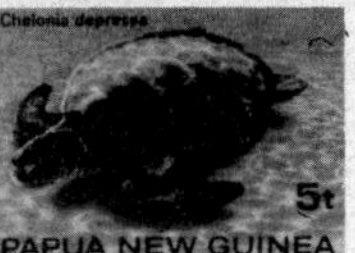

234 *Chelonia depressa*

(Des G. Wade. Litho J.W.)

1983 (7 Sept). *World Communications Year. T* **233** *and similar horiz designs. Multicoloured. P* 14.

468	10 t. Type **233**	20	10
469	25 t. "Postal service"	45	45
470	30 t. "Telephone service"	50	50
471	60 t. "Transport service"	85	90
468/71	*Set of* 4	1·75	1·75

(Des R. Bates. Photo Courvoisier)

1984 (8 Feb). *Turtles. T* **234** *and similar horiz designs. Multicoloured. P* 11½.

472	5 t. Type **234**	15	10
473	10 t. *Chelonia mydas*	25	10
474	15 t. *Eretmochelys imbricata*	35	30
475	20 t. *Lepidochelys olivacea*	40	35
476	25 t. *Caretta caretta*	50	50
477	40 t. *Dermochelys coriacea*	60	75
472/7	*Set of* 6	2·00	1·75

235 Avro "X VH-UXX" *Faith in Australia*

(Des T. Reilly. Litho Format)

1984 (9 May). *50th Anniv of First Airmail Australia-Papua New Guinea. T* **235** *and similar horiz designs. Multicoloured. P* 14½ × 14.

478	20 t. Type **235**	35	30
479	25 t. "DH86B VH-UYU" *Carmania*	45	45
480	40 t. Westland "Widgeon VH-UGI"	75	80
481	60 t. Consolidated "Catalina NC777" *Guba*	1·10	1·25
478/81	*Set of* 4	2·40	2·50

236 Parliament House

237 Ceremonial Shield and Club, Central Province

(Des A. Brennan, adapted G. Vasarhelyi. Litho Harrison)

1984 (7 Aug). *Opening of New Parliament House. P* 13½ × 14.

482	**236** 10 t. multicoloured	20	20

(Des Revd. A. H. Brown. Photo Courvoisier)

1984 (21 Sept). *Ceremonial Shields. T* **237** *and similar vert designs. Multicoloured. Granite paper. P* 11½.

483	10 t. Type **237**	20	10
484	20 t. Ceremonial shield, West New Britain	35	30
485	30 t. Ceremonial shield, Madang Province	55	60
486	50 t. Ceremonial shield, East Sepik	90	95
483/6	*Set of* 4	1·75	1·75

238 H.M.S. *Nelson* at Port Moresby, 1884

239 Fergusson Island

(Des R. Bates, Litho Format)

1984 (6 Nov). *Centenary of Protectorate Proclamations for British New Guinea and German New Guinea. T* **238** *and similar horiz designs. Multicoloured. P* 14½ × 14.

487	10 t. Type **238**	20	25
	a. Horiz pair. Nos. 487/8	40	50
488	10 t. Papua New Guinea flag and Port Moresby, 1984	20	25
489	45 t. Papua New Guinea flag and Rabaul, 1984	85	90
	a. Horiz pair. Nos. 489/90	1·75	1·75
490	45 t. German warship *Elisabeth* at Rabaul, 1884	85	90
487/90	*Set of* 4	2·00	2·00

The two designs for each value were issued together, *se-tenant*, as horizontal pairs throughout the sheets, each pair forming a composite picture.

(Des R. Bates. Photo Courvoisier)

1985 (6 Feb). *Tourist Scenes. T* **239** *and similar multicoloured designs. Granite paper. P* 11½.

491	10 t. Type **239**	20	10
492	25 t. Sepik River	45	45
493	40 t. Chimbu Gorge (*horiz*)	65	65
494	60 t. Dali Beach, Vanimo (*horiz*)	95	95
491/4	*Set of* 4	2·00	2·00

12t

(240)

241 Dubu Platform, Central Province

1985 (1 Apr). *No.* 408 *surch with T* **240**.

495	12 t. on 7 t. Type **222**	20	20
	a. Surch omitted (in horiz pair with normal)	£110	
	b. Surch inverted	†	—

At least one sheet of No. 495 exists with the surcharge completely omitted on five positions of the sheet and poorly printed on the remainder.

(Des G. Wade. Photo Heraclio Fournier)

1985 (1 May). *Ceremonial Structures. T* **241** *and similar vert designs. Multicoloured. P* 13.

496	15 t. Type **241**	35	15
497	20 t. Tamuniai house, West New Britain	45	35
498	30 t. Traditional yam tower, Trobriand Island	60	45
499	60 t. Huli grave, Tari	1·00	1·10
496/9	*Set of* 4	2·25	1·90

242 Head of New Britain Sparrow Hawk

243 National Flag and Parliament House

(Des P. Slater. Litho Format)

1985 (26 Aug). *Birds of Prey. T* **242** *and similar vert designs, Multicoloured. P* 14 × 14½.
500 12 t. Type **242** 30 30
a. Horiz pair. Nos. 500/1 . . . . 60 60
501 12 t. New Britain Sparrow Hawk in flight . . 30 30
502 30 t. Doria's Goshawk 55 55
a. Horiz pair. Nos. 502/3 . . . . 1·10 1·10
503 30 t. Doria's Goshawk in flight 55 55
504 60 t. Long-tailed Honey Buzzard . . . . 1·00 1·00
a. Horiz pair. Nos. 504/5 . . . . 2·00 2·00
505 60 t. Long-tailed Honey Buzzard in flight . . 1·00 1·00
500/5 . . . . *Set of* 6 3·25 3·25

Nos. 500/1, 502/3 and 504/5 were each printed together, *se-tenant*, in horizontal pairs throughout the sheets.

(Des R. Bates. Litho B.D.T.)

1985 (11 Sept). *10th Anniv of Independence. P* 14 × 15.
506 **243** 12 t. multicoloured 20 15

244 Early Postcard, Aerogramme, Inkwell and Spectacles

245 Figure with Eagle

(Des R. Bates. Litho Walsall)

1985 (9 Oct). *Centenary of the Papua New Guinea Post Office. T* **244** *and similar horiz designs. Multicoloured. P* 14½ × 14.
507 12 t. Type **244** 20 10
508 30 t. Queensland 1897 1d. die with proof and modern press printing stamps 50 45
509 40 t. Newspaper of 1885 announcing shipping service and loading mail into aircraft 70 60
510 60 t. Friedrich-Wilhelmshafen postmark of 1892 and Port Moresby F.D.C. postmark of 9 Oct 1985. . . . . 1·00 1·10
507/10 . . . . *Set of* 4 2·25 2·00
MS511 90 × 79 mm. Nos. 507/10 . . . . . . 2·25 2·75

(Des R. Bates. Photo Courvoisier)

1985 (13 Nov). *Nombowai Wood Carvings. T* **245** *and similar vert designs. Multicoloured. Granite paper. P* 11½.
512 12 t. Type **245** 30 10
513 30 t. Figure with clamshell 65 45
514 60 t. Figure with dolphin . . . . . . 1·25 1·00
515 80 t. Figure of woman with cockerel . . 1·50 1·50
512/15 . . . . *Set of* 4 3·25 2·75

246 *Cypraea valentia*

247 Rufous Fantail

(Des R. Bates. Photo Courvoisier)

1986 (12 Feb). *Seashells. T* **246** *and similar horiz designs. Multicoloured. Granite paper. P* 11½.
516 15 t. Type **246** 35 15
517 35 t. *Oliva buelowi* 75 65
518 45 t. *Oliva parkinsoni* . . . . . . 1·00 90
519 70 t. *Cypraea aurantium* . . . . . . 1·50 1·75
516/19 . . . . *Set of* 4 3·25 3·00

(Des A. Theobald. Litho Harrison)

1986 (21 Apr). *60th Birthday of Queen Elizabeth II. Vert designs as T* 110 *of Ascension. Multicoloured. P* 14½ × 14.
520 15 t. Princess Elizabeth in A.T.S. uniform, 1945 . . . . 20 15
521 35 t. Silver Wedding Anniversary photograph (by Patrick Lichfield), Balmoral, 1972 . . . . 50 55
522 50 t. Queen inspecting guard of honour, Port Moresby, 1982 . . . . 70 75
523 60 t. On board Royal Yacht *Britannia*, Papua New Guinea, 1982 . . . . . . 85 90
524 70 t. At Crown Agents' Head Office, London, 1983 . . . . 95 1·10
520/4 . . . . *Set of* 5 3·00 3·00

(Des W. Peckover. Photo Courvoisier)

1986 (22 May). *"Ameripex '86" International Stamp Exhibition, Chicago. Small Birds (1st series). T* **247** *and similar multicoloured designs. Granite paper. P* 12½.
525 15 t. Type **247** 40 15
526 35 t. Streaked Berrypecker 75 55
527 45 t. Red-breasted Pitta . . . . . . 1·00 70
528 70 t. Olive-yellow Robin (*vert*) . . . . 1·25 1·40
525/8 . . . . *Set of* 4 3·00 2·50

The scientific name on the 15 t. value refers to the 45 t. design, and vice versa.

See also Nos. 597/601.

248 Martin Luther nailing Theses to Cathedral Door, Wittenberg, and Modern Lutheran Pastor

249 *Dendrobium vexillarius*

(Des local artist. Litho Questa)

1986 (3 July). *Centenary of Lutheran Church in Papua New Guinea. T* **248** *and similar vert design. Multicoloured. P* 14 × 15.
529 15 t. Type **248** 35 15
530 70 t. Early church, Finschhafen, and modern Martin Luther Chapel, Lae Seminary . . 1·25 1·25

(Des Harrison. Litho B.D.T.)

1986 (4 Aug). *Orchids. T* **249** *and similar vert designs. Multicoloured. P* 13½.
531 15 t. Type **249** 40 15
532 35 t. *Dendrobium lineale* 80 55
533 45 t. *Dendrobium johnsoniae* . . . . 1·00 80
534 70 t. *Dendrobium cuthbertsonii* . . . . 1·60 1·25
531/4 . . . . *Set of* 4 3·50 2·50

250 Maprik Dancer

251 White Cap Anemonefish

(Des R. Bates. Litho B.D.T.)

1986 (12 Nov). *Papua New Guinea Dancers. T* **250** *and similar vert designs. Multicoloured. P* 14.
535 15 t. Type **250** 35 15
536 35 t. Kiriwina 75 55
537 45 t. Kundiawa 90 75
538 70 t. Fasu . . . . 1·50 1·40
535/8 . . . . *Set of* 4 3·25 2·50

(Des Harrison. Litho Format)

1987 (15 Apr). *Anemonefish. T* **251** *and similar horiz designs. Multicoloured. P* 15.
539 17 t. Type **251** 35 25
540 30 t. Black Anemonefish 55 40
541 35 t. Tomato Clownfish 60 50
542 70 t. Spine Cheek Anemonefish . . . . 1·25 90
539/42 . . . . *Set of* 4 2·50 1·90

15t =

252 *Roebuck* (Dampier), 1700

(**253**)

(Des R. Bates. Photo Courvoisier)

1987 (15 June)–**88**. *Ships. T* **252** *and similar square designs. Multicoloured. Granite paper. P* 11½.
543 1 t. *Boudeuse* (De Bougainville), 1768 (16.11.88) 10 10
544 5 t. Type **252** 10 10
545 10 t. H.M.S. *Swallow* (Philip Carteret), 1767 (16.11.88) 10 15
546 15 t. H.M.S. *Fly* (Blackwood), 1845 (17.2.88) 20 25
547 17 t. As 15 t. (16.3.88) 20 25
548 20 t. H.M.S. *Rattlesnake* (Owen Stanley), 1849 (17.2.88) 25 30
549 30 t. *Vitiaz* (Maclay), 1871 (16.11.88) . . 40 45
550 35 t. *San Pedrico* (Torres) and zabra, 1606 . . 45 50
551 40 t. *L'Astrolabe* (d'Urville), 1827 (17.2.88) . . 50 55
552 45 t. *Neva* (D'Albertis), 1876 . . . . 60 65
553 60 t. Spanish galleon (Jorge de Meneses), 1526 (17.2.88) 80 85
554 70 t. *Eendracht* (Schouten and Le Maire), 1616 . . . . 90 95
555 1 k. H.M.S. *Blanche* (Simpson), 1872 (16.3.88) . . . . 1·25 1·40
556 2 k. *Merrie England* (steamer), 1889 . . 2·50 2·75
557 3 k. *Samoa* (German colonial steamer), 1884 (16.11.88) . . . . 3·75 4·00
543/57 . . . . *Set of* 15 11·00 12·00

A printing by lithography of a 45 t. (as issued 70 t.), 70 t. (as 45 t.), 80 t. (as 35 t.) and 2 k. was originally produced, but such stamps were not issued for postal purposes. Examples in circulation are from a small quantity sold by the U.S.A. philatelic agent in error.

(Des Revd. A. H. Brown. Photo Courvoisier)

1987 (19 Aug). *War Shields. Vert designs as T* **237**. *Multicoloured. Granite paper. P* 11½.
558 15 t. Gulf Province 20 25
559 35 t. East Sepik 45 50
560 45 t. Madang Province 55 60
561 70 t. Telefomin 85 90
558/61 . . . . *Set of* 4 1·90 2·00

1987 (23 Sept). *No. 442 surch with T* **253**.
562 15 t. on 12 t. *Dendronephthya sp.* 25 25

For similar 20 t. surcharge see No. 602.

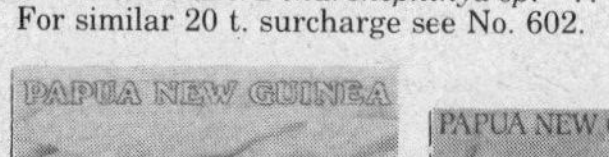

254 *Protoreaster nodosus*

255 Cessna "Stationair 6" taking off, Rabaraba

(Des Harrison. Litho B.D.T.)

1987 (30 Sept). *Starfish. T* **254** *and similar horiz designs. Multicoloured. P* 13½.
563 17 t. Type **254** 25 25
564 35 t. *Gomophia egeriae* 50 50
565 45 t. *Choriaster granulatus* 65 70
566 70 t. *Neoferdina ocellata* . . . . . . 95 1·00
563/6 . . . . *Set of* 4 2·10 2·25

(Des A. Theobald. Litho Questa)

1987 (11 Nov). *Aircraft in Papua New Guinea. T* **255** *and similar horiz designs. Multicoloured. P* 14.
567 15 t. Type **255** 35 25
568 35 t. Britten-Norman "Islander" over Hombrum Bluff 60 50
569 45 t. DHC "Twin Otter" over Highlands . . 75 70
570 70 t. Fokker "F28" over Madang . . . . 1·25 1·00
567/70 . . . . *Set of* 4 2·75 2·25

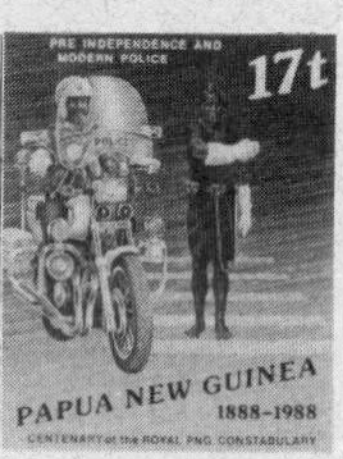

256 Pre-Independence Policeman on Traffic Duty and Present-day Motorcycle Patrol

(Des R. Bates. Litho Questa)

1988 (15 June). *Centenary of Royal Papua New Guinea Constabulary. T* **256** *and similar vert designs. Multicoloured. P* 14 × 15.
571 17 t. Type **256** 20 25
572 35 t. British New Guinea Armed Constabulary, 1890, and Governor W. MacGregor 45 50
573 45 t. Police badges 60 65
574 70 t. German New Guinea Police, 1888, and Dr. A. Hahl (founder) 90 95
571/4 . . . . *Set of* 4 1·90 2·10

257 Lakatoi (canoe) and Sydney Opera House

(Des R. Bates. Litho Harrison)

1988 (30 July). *"Sydpex '88" National Stamp Exhibition, Sydney. P* 14.
575 **257** 35 t. multicoloured 45 50

258 Papua New Guinea Flag on Globe and Fireworks

259 Male and Female Butterflies in Courtship

(Des R. Bates. Litho CPE Australia Ltd, Melbourne)

1988 (30 July). *Bicentenary of Australian Settlement. T* **258** *and similar horiz design. Multicoloured. P* 13½.

No.	Description		
576	35 t. Type **258**	45	50
	a. Horiz pair. Nos. 576/7	90	1·00
577	35 t. Australian flag on globe and fireworks	45	50
MS578	90 × 50 mm. Nos. 576/7	90	1·00

Nos. 576/7 were printed together, *se-tenant*, in horizontal pairs throughout the sheet, each pair forming a composite design.

(Des M. Parsons, adapted D. Miller. Litho Walsall)

1988 (19 Sept). *Queen Alexandra's Birdwing Butterfly. T* **259** *and similar multicoloured designs. P* 14½.

No.	Description		
579	5 t. Type **259**	15	10
580	17 t. Female laying eggs and mature larva (*vert*)	35	25
581	25 t. Male emerging from pupa (*vert*)	45	35
582	35 t. Male feeding	65	50
579/82	*Set of* 4	1·40	1·10

260 Athletics

(Des G. Wade. Litho CPE Australia Ltd, Melbourne)

1988 (19 Sept). *Olympic Games, Seoul. T* **260** *and similar horiz design. Multicoloured. P* 13½.

No.	Description		
583	17 t. Type **260**	20	25
584	45 t. Weightlifting	60	65

261 *Rhododendron zoelleri*

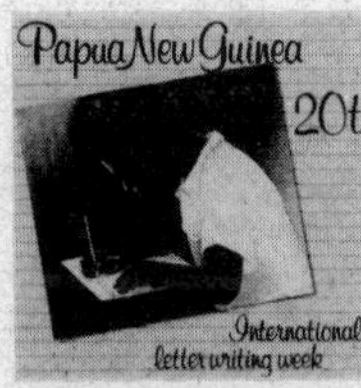

263 Writing Letter

262

(Des N. Cruttwell and I. Loe. Litho Leigh-Mardon Ltd, Melbourne)

1989 (25 Jan). *Rhododendrons. T* **261** *and similar vert designs. Multicoloured. W* **262**. *P* 14½.

No.	Description		
585	3 t. Type **261**	10	10
586	20 t. *Rhododendron cruttwellii*	25	30
587	60 t. *Rhododendron superbum*	80	85
588	70 t. *Rhododendron christianae*	90	95
585/8	*Set of* 4	1·75	2·00

(Des R. Bates. Litho Leigh-Mardon Ltd, Melbourne)

1989 (22 Mar). *International Letter Writing Week. T* **263** *and similar square designs. Multicoloured. W* **262**. *P* 14½.

No.	Description		
589	20 t. Type **263**	25	30
590	35 t. Stamping letter	45	50
591	60 t. Posting letter	80	85
592	70 t. Reading letter	90	95
589/92	*Set of* 4	2·10	2·40

264 Village House, Buka Island, North Solomons

265 Tit Berrypecker (female)

(Des G. Wade. Litho Leigh-Mardon Ltd, Melbourne)

1989 (17 May). *Traditional Dwellings. T* **264** *and similar horiz designs. Multicoloured. W* **262**. *P* 15.

No.	Description		
593	20 t. Type **264**	30	35
594	35 t. Koiari tree house, Central Province	50	55
595	60 t. Longhouse, Lauan, New Ireland	90	95
596	70 t. Decorated house, Basilaki, Milne Bay	1·00	1·10
593/6	*Set of* 4	2·40	2·75

(Des W. Peckover. Litho Questa)

1989 (12 July). *Small Birds (2nd issue). T* **265** *and similar vert designs. Multicoloured. P* 14½.

No.	Description		
597	20 t. Type **265**	30	35
	a. Horiz pair. Nos. 597/8	60	70
598	20 t. Tit Berrypecker (male)	30	35
599	35 t. Blue-capped Babbler	50	55
600	45 t. Black-throated Robin	65	70
601	70 t. Large Mountain Sericornis	1·00	1·10
597/601	*Set of* 5	2·50	2·75

Nos. 597/8 were printed together, *se-tenant*, in horizontal pairs throughout the sheet.

1989 (12 July). *No.* 539 *surch as T* **253**.

No.	Description		
602	20 t. on 17 t. Type **251**	35	35

266 Motu Motu Dancer, Gulf Province

267 Hibiscus, People going to Church and Gope Board

(Des G. Wade. Litho Leigh-Mardon Ltd, Melbourne)

1989 (6 Sept). *Traditional Dancers. T* **266** *and similar vert designs. Multicoloured. W* **262**. *P* 14×14½.

No.	Description		
603	20 t. Type **266**	30	35
604	35 t. Baining, East New Britain	50	55
605	60 t. Vailala River, Gulf Province	90	95
606	70 t. Timbunke, East Sepik Province	1·00	1·10
603/6	*Set of* 4	2·40	2·75

(Des R. Bates. Litho Leigh-Mardon Ltd, Melbourne)

1989 (8 Nov). *Christmas. T* **267** *and similar horiz designs showing flowers and carved panels. Multicoloured. P* 14×14½.

No.	Description		
607	20 t. Type **267**	30	35
608	35 t. Rhododendron, Virgin and Child and mask	50	55
609	60 t. D'Albertis Creeper, Christmas candle and warshield	90	95
610	70 t. Pacific Frangapani, peace dove and flute mask	1·00	1·10
607/10	*Set of* 4	2·40	2·75

268 Guni Falls

(Des A. Theobald. Litho Questa)

1990 (1 Feb). *Waterfalls. T* **268** *and similar vert designs. Multicoloured. P* 14.

No.	Description		
611	20 t. Type **268**	30	35
612	35 t. Rouna Falls	50	55
613	60 t. Ambua Falls	90	95
614	70 t. Wawoi Falls	1·00	1·10
611/14	*Set of* 4	2·40	2·75

POSTAGE DUE STAMPS

POSTAL CHARGES 6d.

IXIXIXIXIX

(D 1)

POSTAL CHARGES 3s.

(D 2)

1960 (1 Mar). *Postage stamps surcharged.* (*a*) *No.* 8 *with Type* D 1.

No.	Description		
D1	6d. on 7½d. blue (R.)	£650	£350
	a. Surch double	£2750	£1600

(*b*) *Nos.* 1, 4, 6*a*, 7/8 *as Type* D 2

No.	Description		
D2	1d. on 6½d. maroon	14·00	5·00
D3	3d. on ½d. emerald (B.)	16·00	5·00
	a. Surch double	£450	
D4	6d. on 7½d. blue (R.)	27·00	13·00
	a. Surch double	£450	
D5	1s. 3d. on 3½d. black (O.)	24·00	13·00
D6	3s. on 2½d. orange	40·00	26·00
D2/6	*Set of* 6	£110	55·00

Of No. D1a, only a few copies are known from a sheet used at Goroka.

D 3

(Typo Note Ptg Branch, Reserve Bank of Australia, Melbourne)

1960 (2 June). *W* **15** *of Australia. P* 14.

No.	Type	Description		
D 7	D 3	1d. orange	45	35
D 8		3d. yellow-brown	70	45
D 9		6d. blue	75	40
D10		9d. deep red	75	1·25
D11		1s. light emerald	75	50
D12		1s. 3d. violet	1·40	1·40
D13		1s. 6d. pale blue	5·50	5·00
D14		3s. yellow	6·00	1·00
D7/14		*Set of* 8	14·50	9·50

The use of Postal Charge stamps was discontinued on 12 February 1966, but they remained on sale at the Philatelic Bureau until 31 August 1966.

Pitcairn Islands

CROWN COLONY

Stamps of NEW ZEALAND were used by a Postal Agency operating on Pitcairn Islands from 7 June 1927 until October 1940.

PRICES FOR STAMPS ON COVER TO 1945
Nos. 1/8 *from* × 2

1 Cluster of Oranges

2 Christian on *Bounty* and Pitcairn Island

(Recess B.W. (1d., 3d., 4d., 8d. and 2s. 6d.), and Waterlow (others))

1940 (15 Oct)–**51**. *T* **1/2** *and similar horiz designs. Wmk Mult Script CA. P* 11½ × 11 (1d., 3d., 4d., 8d. *and* 2s. 6d.) *or* 12½ (*others*).

1 ½d. orange and green 40 45
2 1d. mauve and magenta 40 45
3 1½d. grey and carmine 45 50
4 2d. green and brown .. .. .. 1·60 1·00
5 3d. yellow-green and blue .. .. .. 1·25 1·40
5*a* 4d. black and emerald-green (1.9.51) .. 11·00 7·00
6 6d. brown and grey-blue .. .. .. 2·50 2·00
6*a* 8d. olive-green and magenta (1.9.51) .. 11·00 7·00
7 1s. violet and grey .. .. .. 1·75 2·00
8 2s. 6d. green and brown .. .. .. 6·00 3·50
1/8 .. .. *Set of* 10 32·00 23·00
1/8 (ex. *a* Nos.) Perf "Specimen" .. *Set of* 8 £600

Designs:—1½d. John Adams and his house; 2d. Lt. Bligh and H.M.S. *Bounty*; 3d. Pitcairn Islands and Pacific Ocean; 4d. *Bounty* Bible; 6d. H.M.S. *Bounty*; 8d. School, 1949; 1s. Fletcher Christian and Pitcairn Island; 2s. 6d. Christian on H.M.S. *Bounty* and Pitcairn Coast.

Flagstaff flaw
(R. 8/2)

1946 (2 Dec). *Victory. As Nos.* 28/9 *of Aden.*

9 2d. brown 25 10
10 3d. blue 25 15
a. Flagstaff flaw .. .. 10·00
9/10 Perf "Specimen" .. .. *Set of* 2 £110

1949 (1 Aug). *Royal Silver Wedding. As Nos.* 30/1 *of Aden.*

11 1½d. scarlet .. .. 1·00 1·00
12 10s. mauve .. .. 80·00 65·00

1949 (10 Oct). *75th Anniv of Universal Postal Union. As Nos.* 114/17 *of Antigua.*

13 2½d. red-brown .. .. 2·00 3·00
14 3d. deep blue .. .. 8·50 4·00
15 6d. deep blue-green .. .. .. 11·00 5·00
16 1s. purple .. .. 11·00 5·00
13/16 .. .. *Set of* 4 30·00 15·00

1953 (2 June). *Coronation. As No.* 47 *of Aden, but ptd by B.W.*

17 4d. black and deep bluish green .. .. 2·00 2·75

9 *Cordyline terminalis*

10 Pitcairn Island Map

(Recess D.L.R.)

1957 (2 July)–**63**. *T* **9/10** *and similar designs. Wmk Mult Script CA. P* 13×12½ (*horiz*) *or* 12½×13 (*vert*).

18 ½d. green and reddish lilac 50 30
a. Green and reddish purple (9.3.63) .. 75 1·40
19 1d. black and olive-green 60 30
a. Black and yellow-olive (19.2.59) .. 5·00 7·00
b. Black and light olive-green (24.2.60) 2·00 1·40
20 2d. brown and greenish blue 40 25
21 2½d. deep brown and red-orange 40 30
22 3d. emerald and deep ultramarine .. 50 30
23 4d. scarlet and deep ultramarine (I) .. 90 40
23*a* 4d. carmine-red & dp ultram (II) (5.11.58) 5·00 1·50
24 6d. pale buff and indigo 90 35
25 8d. deep olive-green and carmine-lake .. 45 30
26 1s. black and yellowish brown 50 30
27 2s. green and red-orange .. .. 30·00 10·00
28 2s. 6d. ultramarine and lake .. .. 12·00 5·50
a. Blue and deep lake (10.2.59) .. 17·00 10·00
18/28 .. .. *Set of* 12 48·00 18·00

Designs: *Vert*—2d. John Adams and *Bounty* Bible; 2s. Island wheelbarrow. *Horiz*—2½d. Handicrafts: Bird model; 3d. Bounty Bay; 4d. Pitcairn School; 6d. Pacific Ocean map; 8d. Inland scene; 1s. Handicrafts: Ship model; 2s. 6d. Launching new whaleboat.

Nos. 23/*a*. Type I is inscribed "PITCAIRN SCHOOL"; Type II "SCHOOLTEACHER'S HOUSE".

See also No. 33

20 Pitcairn Island and Simon Young

(Des H. E. Maud. Photo Harrison)

1961 (15 Nov). *Centenary of Return of Pitcairn Islanders from Norfolk Island. T* **20** *and similar horiz designs. W w* **12**. *P* 14½ × 13½.

29 3d. black and yellow 20 15
30 6d. red-brown and blue 50 20
31 1s. red-orange and blue-green 60 25
29/31 .. .. *Set of* 3 1·10 55

Designs:—6d. Norfolk Island and Pitcairn Islands; 1s. Migrant brigantine *Mary Ann*.

1963 (4 June). *Freedom from Hunger. As No.* 76 *of Aden.*

32 2s. 6d. ultramarine .. .. 22·00 3·00

1963 (4 Dec). *As No.* 18 *but wmk* w **12**.

33 **9** ½d. green and reddish purple 25 60

1963 (9 Dec). *Red Cross Centenary. As Nos.* 147/8 *of Antigua.*

34 2d. red and black .. .. 2·00 1·00
35 2s. 6d. red and blue .. .. 11·00 5·50

23 Pitcairn Is Longboat

24 Queen Elizabeth II (after Anthony Buckley)

(Des M. Farrar Bell. Photo Harrison)

1964 (5 Aug)–**65**. *T* **23/4** *and similar horiz designs. Multicoloured. W w* **12**. *P* 14 × 14½.

36 ½d. Type **23** 10 15
37 1d. H.M.S. *Bounty* 30 15
38 2d. "Out from Bounty Bay" 30 15
39 3d. Great Frigate Bird 30 15
40 4d. White Tern 30 15
41 6d. Pitcairn Warbler 30 15
42 8d. Red-footed Booby 30 15
a. Pale blue (beak) omitted £130
43 10d. Red-tailed Tropic Birds 30 15
44 1s. Henderson Island Crake 30 15
45 1s. 6d. Stephen's Lory .. .. .. 5·50 1·25
46 2s. 6d. Murphy's Petrel .. .. .. 5·00 1·50
47 4s. Henderson Island Fruit Dove .. .. 7·00 1·75
48 8s. Type **24** (5.4.65) .. .. .. 2·50 1·75
36/48 .. .. *Set of* 13 20·00 6·75

1965 (17 May). *I.T.U. Centenary. As Nos.* 166/7 *of Antigua.*

49 1d. mauve and orange-brown .. .. 1·00 40
50 2s. 6d. turquoise-green and bright blue .. 14·00 3·50

1965 (25 Oct). *International Co-operation Year. As Nos.* 168/9 *of Antigua.*

51 1d. reddish purple and turquoise-green .. 1·00 40
52 1s. 6d. deep bluish green and lavender .. 14·00 4·00

1966 (24 Jan). *Churchill Commemoration. As Nos.* 170/3 *of Antigua.*

53 2d. new blue .. .. 2·00 60
54 3d. deep green .. .. 4·50 80
55 6d. brown .. .. 7·50 1·50
56 1s. bluish violet .. .. 10·00 2·00
53/6 .. .. *Set of* 4 22·00 4·50

1966 (1 Aug). *World Cup Football Championships. As Nos.* 176/7 *of Antigua.*

57 4d. violet, yellow-green, lake & yell-brn 2·00 1·00
58 2s. 6d. chocolate, blue-green, lake & yell-brn 5·00 1·75

1966 (20 Sept). *Inauguration of W.H.O. Headquarters, Geneva. As Nos.* 178/9 *of Antigua.*

59 8d. black, yellow-green and light blue .. 4·50 1·25
60 1s. 6d. black, light purple and yellow-brown 7·50 1·50

1966 (1 Dec). *20th Anniv of U.N.E.S.CO. As Nos.* 196/8 *of Antigua.*

61 ½d. slate-violet, red, yellow and orange .. 20 30
62 10d. orange-yellow, violet and deep olive .. 5·00 1·75
63 2s. black, bright purple and orange .. .. 11·00 2·25
61/3 .. .. *Set of* 3 14·50 4·00

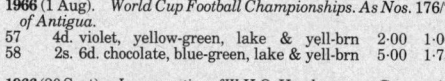

36 Mangarevan Canoe, *circa* 1325

(Des V. Whiteley. Photo Harrison)

1967 (1 Mar). *Bicentenary of Discovery of Pitcairn Islands. T* **36** *and similar horiz designs. Multicoloured. W w* **12**. *P* 14½.

64 ½d. Type **36** 10 10
65 1d. P. F. de Quiros and *San Pedro y Pablo*, 1606 .. .. 10 10
66 8d. *San Pedro y Pablo* and *Los Tres Reyes*, 1606 .. .. 15 10
67 1s. Carteret and H.M.S. *Swallow*, 1767 .. 15 10
68 1s. 6d. *Hercules*, 1819 .. .. .. 20 10
64/8 .. .. *Set of* 5 45 35

(New Currency. 100 cents = 1 New Zealand dollar)

½c

(**41** *Bounty* Anchor)

1967 (10 July). *Decimal currency. Nos.* 36/48 *surch in decimal currency by die-stamping in gold as T* **41**.

69 ½ c. on ½d. multicoloured 10 10
a. Deep brown omitted £300
b. Surch double, one albino .. ..
70 1 c. on 1d. multicoloured 25 15
71 2 c. on 2d. multicoloured 25 15
72 2½ c. on 3d. multicoloured 25 15
73 3 c. on 4d. multicoloured 25 15
74 5 c. on 6d. multicoloured 25 15
75 10 c. on 8d. multicoloured 30 15
a. "10 c." omitted £160
b. Pale blue (beak) omitted £130
76 15 c. on 10d. multicoloured 70 40
77 20 c. on 1s. multicoloured 80 55
78 25 c. on 1s. 6d. multicoloured .. .. 2·50 70
79 30 c. on 2s. 6d. multicoloured .. .. 2·75 1·00
80 40 c. on 4s. multicoloured .. .. .. 4·25 1·25
81 45 c. on 8s. multicoloured .. .. .. 4·25 1·50
69/81 .. .. *Set of* 13 15·00 5·75

On No. 75a the anchor emblem is still present. Several examples of this variety have been identified as coming from R. 9/1.

The ½ c. and 1 c. exist with PVA gum as well as gum arabic.

42 Bligh and *Bounty*'s Launch

(Des Jennifer Toombs. Litho D.L.R.)

1967 (7 Dec). *150th Death Anniv of Admiral Bligh. T* **42** *and similar horiz designs. P* 13½ × 13.

82 1 c. turq-blue, black and royal blue (*shades*) 10 10
83 8 c. black, yellow and magenta 15 10
84 20 c. black, brown and pale buff 15 10
82/4 .. .. *Set of* 3 35 20

Designs:—8 c. Bligh and followers cast adrift; 20 c. Bligh's tomb.

45 Human Rights Emblem

(Des G. Hamori. Litho D.L.R.)

1968 (4 Mar). *Human Rights Year. P* 13½ × 13.

85 **45** 1 c. multicoloured 10 10
86 2 c. multicoloured 10 10
87 25 c. multicoloured 15 10
85/7 .. .. *Set of* 3 20 15

46 Miro Wood and Flower

(Des Jennifer Toombs. Photo Harrison)

1968 (19 Aug). *Handicrafts* (1*st series*). *T* **46** *and similar designs. W w* **12** (*sideways on vert designs*). *P* 14 × 13½ (5, 10 c.) *or* 13½ × 14 (*others*).

88 5 c. multicoloured 15 10
89 10 c. bronze-green, brown and orange .. 20 20
90 15 c. deep bluish violet, chocolate and salmon 20 20
91 20 c. multicoloured 25 20
88/91 .. .. *Set of* 4 70 60

Designs: *Horiz*—10 c. Flying Fish model. *Vert*—15 c. "Hand" vases; 20 c. Woven baskets.

See also Nos. 207/10.

50 Microscope and Slides

(Des Jennifer Toombs. Litho D.L.R.)

1968 (25 Nov). *20th Anniv of World Health Organisation. T* **50** *and similar horiz design. W w* **12** *(sideways). P* 14.
92 2 c. black, turquoise-blue and ultramarine .. 10 10
93 20 c. black, orange and bright purple .. 25 15
Design:—20 c. Hypodermic syringe and jars of tablets.

52 Pitcairn Island

62 "Flying Fox" Cable System

(Des Jennifer Toombs. Litho Questa (50 c., $1), D.L.R. (others))

1969 (17 Sept)–**75**. *T* **52**, **62** *and similar designs. Chalk-surfaced paper. W w* **12** *(upright on* 3 c., 25 c., *sideways on* $1 *and horiz designs). P* 14½ × 14 (50 c.), 14 ($1) *or* 13 (*others*).
94 1 c. multicoloured 35 15
a. Glazed, ordinary paper (9.8.71) 75 65
95 2 c. multicoloured 25 15
96 3 c. multicoloured 25 15
97 4 c. multicoloured 25 15
98 5 c. multicoloured 25 15
99 6 c. multicoloured 25 15
100 8 c. multicoloured 35 15
101 10 c. multicoloured .. .. 2·00 85
a. Glazed, ordinary paper (9.8.71) .. .. 1·50 2·00
102 15 c. multicoloured 35 30
a. Queen's head omitted £425
103 20 c. multicoloured 35 30
104 25 c. multicoloured 40 30
105 30 c. multicoloured 55 45
106 40 c. multicoloured 75 60
106*a* 50 c. multicoloured (*glazed, ordinary paper*) (2.1.73) .. .. 9·00 7·00
106*b* $1 multicoloured (*glazed, ordinary paper*) (21.4.75) .. .. 16·00 14·00
94/106*b* .. .. .. *Set of* 15 28·00 22·00
Designs: *Horiz*—2 c. Captain Bligh and *Bounty* chronometer; 4 c. Plans and drawing of *Bounty*; 5 c. Breadfruit containers and plant; 6 c. Bounty Bay; 8 c. Pitcairn longboat; 10 c. Ship landing point; 15 c. Fletcher Christian's Cave; 20 c. Thursday October Christian's House; 30 c. Radio Station, Taro Ground; 40 c. *Bounty* Bible; 50 c. Pitcairn Coat of Arms. *Vert*—3 c. *Bounty* anchor; $1 Queen Elizabeth II.
See also No. 133.

65 Lantana

69 Auntie and Ann (grouper)

(Des Jennifer Toombs. Litho D.L.R.)

1970 (23 Mar). *Flowers. T* **65** *and similar vert designs. Multicoloured. W w* **12**. *P* 14.
107 1 c. Type **65** 20 15
108 2 c. "Indian Shot" 45 20
109 5 c. Pulau 85 35
110 25 c. Wild Gladiolus .. .. 2·00 1·00
107/10 .. .. *Set of* 4 3·25 1·50

(Des Jennifer Toombs. Photo Harrison)

1970 (12 Oct). *Fishes. T* **69** *and similar horiz designs. Multicoloured. W w* **12**. *P* 14.
111 5 c. Type **69** .. .. 2·50 70
112 10 c. Dream Fish (rudder fish) .. .. 2·50 85
113 15 c. Elwyn's Trousers (wrasse) .. .. 3·00 1·00
114 20 c. Whistling Daughter (wrasse) .. .. 3·25 1·25
111/14 .. .. *Set of* 4 10·00 3·50

ROYAL VISIT 1971

(70)

71 Polynesian Rock Carvings

1971 (22 Feb). *Royal Visit. No.* 101 *optd with T* **70**, *in silver*.
115 10 c. multicoloured .. .. 2·25 3·00

(Des Jennifer Toombs. Litho A & M)

1971 (3 May). *Polynesian Pitcairn. T* **71** *and similar multicoloured designs. W w* **12** *(sideways on* 10 *and* 15 c.*). P* 13½.
116 5 c. Type **71** .. .. 1·75 1·00
117 10 c. Polynesian artefacts (*horiz*) .. .. 2·25 1·25
118 15 c. Polynesian stone fish-hook (*horiz*) .. 2·50 1·25
119 20 c. Polynesian stone deity .. .. .. 2·50 1·50
116/19 .. .. *Set of* 4 8·00 4·50

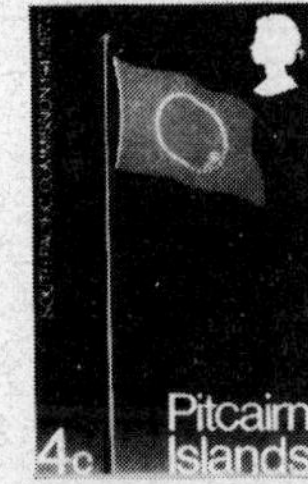

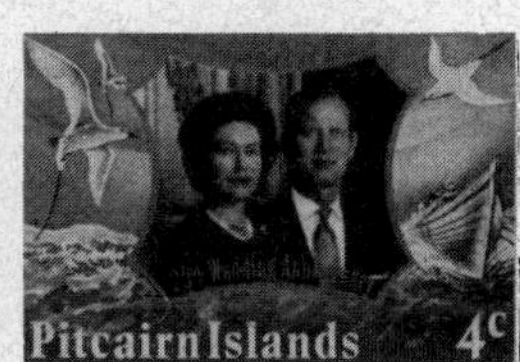

72 Commission Flag

73 Red-tailed Tropic Birds and Longboat

(Des Jennifer Toombs. Litho Questa)

1972 (4 Apr). *25th Anniv of South Pacific Commission. T* **72** *and similar horiz designs. Multicoloured (except* 4 c.*). W w* **12** *(sideways on* 4 c.*). P* 14.
120 4 c. dp blue, blue-violet & brt yellow (T **72**) .. 1·00 1·00
121 8 c. Young and Elderly (Health) .. .. 1·00 1·00
122 18 c. Junior School (Education) .. .. 1·50 1·50
123 20 c. Goods store (Economy) .. .. .. 2·00 2·00
120/3 .. .. *Set of* 4 5·00 5·00

(Des (from photographs by D. Groves) and photo Harrison)

1972 (20 Nov). *Royal Silver Wedding. Multicoloured; background colour given. W w* **12**. *P* 14 × 14½.
124 **73** 4 c. slate-green 40 60
125 20 c. bright blue 60 90

74 Rose-apple

75 Horn-shell and Mitres

(Des Jennifer Toombs. Litho J.W.)

1973 (25 June). *Flowers. T* **74** *and similar vert designs. Multicoloured. W w* **12** *(sideways). P* 14.
126 4 c. Type **74** .. .. 1·25 55
127 8 c. Mountain-apple .. .. 1·75 75
128 15 c. "Lata" .. .. 3·00 1·00
129 20 c. "Dorcas-flower" .. .. 3·25 1·25
130 35 c. Guava .. .. 4·00 1·75
126/30 .. .. *Set of* 5 12·00 4·75

1973 (14 Nov). *Royal Wedding. As Nos.* 165/6 *of Anguilla. Centre multicoloured. W w* **12** *(sideways). P* 13½.
131 10 c. bright mauve 30 15
132 25 c. emerald 35 30

1974 (4 Feb). *As No.* 94 *but wmk upright. Glazed, ordinary paper.*
133 **52** 1 c. multicoloured .. .. 1·75 3·00

134/46 Catalogue numbers vacant.

(Des Jennifer Toombs. Litho Questa)

1974 (15 Apr). *Shells. T* **75** *and similar horiz designs. Multicoloured. W w* **12**. *P* 14.
147 4 c. Type **75** .. .. 1·50 60
148 10 c. Dove-shell .. .. 1·75 80
149 18 c. Limpet and False Limpet .. .. 2·00 1·00
150 50 c. Lucine shell .. .. 2·75 1·25
147/50 .. .. *Set of* 4 7·00 3·25
MS151 130 × 121 mm. Nos. 147/50 .. .. 8·00 11·00

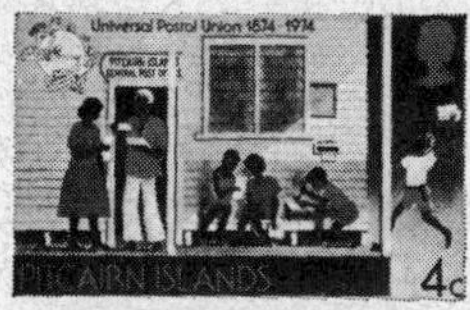

76 Island Post Office

(Des Jennifer Toombs. Litho Questa)

1974 (22 July). *Centenary of Universal Postal Union. T* **76** *and similar horiz designs. W w* **12** *(sideways). P* 14.
152 4 c. multicoloured 25 30
153 20 c. bright purple, light cinnamon and black 40 50
154 35 c. multicoloured 50 60
152/4 .. .. *Set of* 3 1·00 1·25
Designs:—20 c. Pre-stamp letter, 1922; 35 c. Mailship and Pitcairn longboat.

77 Churchill and Text "Lift up your Hearts . . ."

(Des Jennifer Toombs. Litho Questa)

1974 (30 Nov). *Birth Centenary of Sir Winston Churchill. T* **77** *and similar horiz design. W w* **14** *(sideways). P* 14½.
155 20 c. blackish olive, apple-green & dp slate .. 50 75
156 35 c. sepia, greenish yellow and deep slate .. 75 85
Design:—35 c. Text "Give us the tools . . .".

78 H.M.S. *Seringapatam*, 1830

(Des Jennifer Toombs. Litho Walsall)

1975 (22 July). *Mailboats. T* **78** *and similar horiz designs. Multicoloured. W w* **14** *(sideways). P* 14.
157 4 c. Type **78** 65 60
158 10 c. *Pitcairn* (missionary schooner), 1890 .. 70 85
159 18 c. R.M.S. *Athenic*, 1904 .. .. .. 80 1·40
160 50 c. S.S. *Gothic*, 1948 .. .. 2·00 2·75
157/60 .. .. *Set of* 4 3·50 5·00
MS161 145 × 110 mm. Nos. 157/60 .. .. 10·00 13·00

79 Pitcairn Wasp

80 Fletcher Christian

(Des Jennifer Toombs. Litho Questa)

1975 (9 Nov). *Pitcairn Insects. T* **79** *and similar horiz designs. Multicoloured. W w* **12** *(sideways). P* 14.
162 4 c. Type **79** 50 45
163 6 c. Grasshopper 70 55
164 10 c. Moths 80 70
165 15 c. Devil's Needle .. .. 1·25 1·25
166 20 c. Banana Moth .. .. 1·50 1·50
162/6 .. .. *Set of* 5 4·25 4·00

(Des Jennifer Toombs. Litho J.W.)

1976 (4 July). *Bicentenary of American Revolution. T* **80** *and similar vert designs. Multicoloured. W w* **14**. *P* 13½.
167 5 c. Type **80** 40 40
a. Horiz pair. Nos. 167 and 169 .. .. 1·10 1·10
168 10 c. H.M.S. *Bounty* 50 50
a. Horiz pair. Nos. 168 and 170 .. .. 1·50 1·75
169 30 c. George Washington 75 75
170 50 c. *Mayflower*, 1620 .. .. 1·00 1·25
167/70 .. .. *Set of* 4 2·50 2·75
The 5 and 30 c. and 10 and 50 c. values were each printed together, *se-tenant*, in horizontal pairs throughout the sheets.

81 Chair of Homage

82 The Island's Bell

(Des Jennifer Toombs. Litho J.W.)

1977 (6 Feb). *Silver Jubilee. T* **81** *and similar vert designs. Multicoloured.* W w **14**. *P* 13.

171	8 c. Prince Philip's visit, 1971	20	20
172	20 c. Type **81**	30	30
173	50 c. Enthronement	50	50
171/3	*Set of* 3	90	90

(Des Jennifer Toombs. Litho Walsall)

1977 (12 Sept)–**81**. *Various multicoloured designs as T* **82**. W w **14** (*upright on* 1 c., 9 c., 70 c. *and* $2; *sideways on others*). *P* 14.

174	1 c. Type **82**	10	15
175	2 c. Building a longboat	10	15
176	5 c. Landing cargo	15	15
177	6 c. Sorting supplies	10	15
178	9 c. Cleaning wahoo (fish)	10	15
179	10 c. Cultivation	10	15
179*a*	15 c. Sugar Mill (1.10.81)	80	80
180	20 c. Grating coconut and bananas	20	25
181	35 c. The Island church	35	45
182	50 c. Fetching miro logs, Henderson Is.	45	55
182*a*	70 c. Burning obsolete stamp issues (1.10.81)	1·25	1·25
183	$1 Prince Philip, Bounty Bay and Royal Yacht *Britannia*	65	95
184	$2 Queen Elizabeth II (photograph by Reginald Davis)	1·25	1·75
174/84	*Set of* 13	4·50	6·00

The 1 c., 9 c., 70 c. and $2 are vertical designs, the remainder horizontal.

83 Building a *Bounty* Model

84 Coronation Ceremony

(Des E. W. Roberts. Litho Questa)

1978 (9 Jan). *"Bounty Day". T* **83** *and similar horiz designs. Multicoloured.* W w **14** (*sideways*). *P* 14½.

185	6 c. Type **83**	40	35
186	20 c. The model at sea	70	60
187	35 c. Burning the model	85	70
185/7	*Set of* 3	1·75	1·50
MS188	166 × 122 mm. Nos. 185/7	6·50	7·50

(Des Jennifer Toombs. Litho Cartor S.A., France)

1978 (9 Oct). *25th Anniv of Coronation. Sheet* 94 × 78 *mm.* W w **14**. *P* 12.

MS189	**84** $1.20, multicoloured	1·75	2·25

85 Harbour before Development

(Des J.W. Litho Bruder Rosenbaum, Vienna)

1978 (18 Dec). *"Operation Pallium" (Harbour Development Project). T* **85** *and similar horiz designs. Multicoloured.* W w **14** (*sideways*). *P* 13½.

190	15 c. Type **85**	30	40
191	20 c. Unloading R.F.A. *Sir Geraint*	40	50
192	30 c. Work on the jetty	45	55
193	35 c. Harbour after development	50	60
190/3	*Set of* 4	1·50	1·90

86 John Adams and Diary Extract

(Des Jennifer Toombs. Litho Questa)

1979 (5 Mar). *150th Death Anniv of John Adams (mutineer from the "Bounty"). T* **86** *and similar horiz design. Multicoloured.* W w **14** (*sideways*). *P* 14.

194	35 c. Type **86**	40	60
195	70 c. John Adams' grave and diary extract	60	80

87 Pitcairn's Island sketched from H.M.S. *Amphitrite*

(Des Jennifer Toombs. Litho Questa)

1979 (12 Sept). *19th-century Engravings. T* **87** *and similar horiz designs.* W w **14** (*sideways*). *P* 14.

196	6 c. black, brown-ochre and stone	15	15
197	9 c. black, violet and pale violet	15	20
198	20 c. black, brt green & pale yellowish green	15	30
199	70 c. black, scarlet and pale rose	50	80
196/9	*Set of* 4	85	1·25

Designs:—9 c. Bounty Bay and Village of Pitcairn; 20 c. Lookout Ridge; 70 c. Church and School House.

88 Taking Presents to the Square

(Des and litho J.W.)

1979 (28 Nov). *Christmas and International Year of the Child. T* **88** *and similar horiz designs. Multicoloured.* W w **14** (*sideways*). *P* 13.

200	6 c. Type **88**	15	10
201	9 c. Decorating trees with the presents	15	10
202	20 c. Chosen men distribute the gifts	25	20
203	35 c. Carrying presents home	30	25
200/3	*Set of* 4	75	60
MS204	198 × 73 mm. Nos. 200/3. P 13½ × 14	2·00	2·00

89 Loading Mail from Supply Ship to Longboats

(Des Jennifer Toombs. Litho Format)

1980 (6 May). *"London 1980" International Stamp Exhibition. Sheet* 120 × 135 *mm containing T* **89** *and similar horiz designs. Multicoloured.* W w **14** (*sideways*). *P* 14½.

MS205 35 c. Type **89**; 35 c. Mail being conveyed by "Flying Fox" (hoisting mechanism) to the Edge; 35 c. Tractor transporting mail from the Edge to Adamstown; 35 c. Mail being off-loaded at Post Office .. 1·00 1·50

90 Queen Elizabeth the Queen Mother

(Des Harrison. Litho Questa)

1980 (4 Aug). *80th Birthday of Queen Elizabeth the Queen Mother.* W w **14** (*sideways*). *P* 14.

206	**90** 50 c. multicoloured	50	60

(Des Jennifer Toombs. Litho Questa)

1980 (29 Sept). *Handicrafts (2nd series). Multicoloured designs as T* **46**. W w **14** (*sideways on* 9 *and* 20 c.). *P* 14.

207	9 c. Turtles (wood carvings)	10	10
208	20 c. Pitcairn wheelbarrow (wood carving)	10	15
209	35 c. Gannet (wood carving) (*vert*)	15	25
210	40 c. Woven bonnet and fan (*vert*)	15	25
207/10	*Set of* 4	40	65

MINIMUM PRICE

The minimum price quote is 10p which represents a handling charge rather than a basis for valuing common stamps. For further notes about prices see introductory pages.

91 Part of Adamstown

(Des BG Studio. Litho Rosenbaum Bros, Vienna)

1981 (22 Jan). *Landscapes. T* **91** *and similar horiz designs. Multicoloured.* W w **14** (*sideways*). *P* 13½.

211	6 c. Type **91**	10	10
212	9 c. Big George	10	15
213	20 c. Christian's Cave, Gannets Ridge	15	20
214	35 c. Radio Station from Pawala Valley Ridge	20	30
215	70 c. Tatrimoa	30	45
211/15	*Set of* 5	75	1·10

92 Islanders preparing for Departure

93 Prince Charles as Colonel-in-Chief, Cheshire Regiment

(Des Jennifer Toombs. Litho Heraclio Fournier)

1981 (3 May). *125th Anniv of Pitcairn Islanders' Migration to Norfolk Island. T* **92** *and similar horiz designs. Multicoloured.* *P* 13 × 14.

216	9 c. Type **92**	15	20
217	35 c. View of Pitcairn Island from *Morayshire*	30	45
218	70 c. *Morayshire*	45	65
216/18	*Set of* 3	80	1·10

(Des J.W. Litho Format)

1981 (22 July). *Royal Wedding. T* **93** *and similar vert designs. Multicoloured.* W w **14**. *P* 14.

219	20 c. Wedding bouquet from Pitcairn Islands	25	25
220	35 c. Type **93**	40	40
221	$1.20, Prince Charles and Lady Diana Spencer	75	85
219/21	*Set of* 3	1·25	1·40

94 Lemon

95 Pitcairn Islands Coat of Arms

(Des Daphne Padden. Litho Harrison)

1982 (23 Feb). *Fruit. T* **94** *and similar horiz designs. Multicoloured.* W w **14** (*sideways*). *P* 14½.

222	9 c. Type **94**	10	10
223	20 c. Pomegranate	15	20
224	35 c. Avocado	25	30
225	70 c. Pawpaw	50	65
222/5	*Set of* 4	90	1·10

(Des Jennifer Toombs. Litho Harrison)

1982 (1 July). *21st Birthday of Princess of Wales. T* **95** *and similar vert designs. Multicoloured.* W w **14**. *P* 14½ × 14.

226	6 c. Type **95**	10	10
227	9 c. Princess at Royal Opera House, Covent Garden, December 1981	10	10
228	70 c. Balcony Kiss	50	55
229	$1.20, Formal portrait	80	1·00
226/9	*Set of* 4	1·25	1·50

96 Raphael's Angels

(Des Leslie McCombie. Litho Walsall)

1982 (19 Oct). *Christmas. T* **96** *and similar designs showing Raphael's Angels.* W w **14** (*sideways on* 15 c. *and* 20 c.). P 13½ × 14 (15 c., 20 c.) *or* 14 × 13½ (*others*).

230 15 c. black, silver and pink 15 15
231 20 c. black, silver and pale lemon 20 20
232 50 c. yellow-brown, silver and stone 45 45
233 $1 black, silver and cobalt 85 85
230/3 *Set of* 4 1·50 1·50

The 50 c. and $1 are vertical designs.

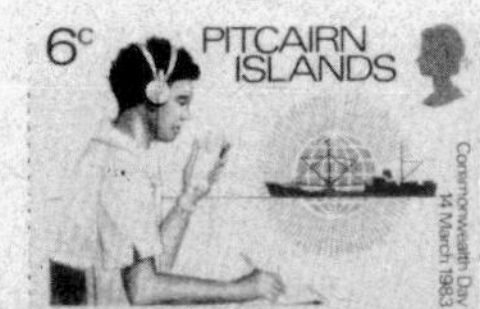

97 Radio Operator

(Des Jennifer Toombs. Litho Harrison)

1983 (14 Mar). *Commonwealth Day. T* **97** *and similar horiz designs. Multicoloured.* W w **14** (*sideways*). P 13½.

234 6 c. Type **97** 10 10
235 9 c. Postal clerk 10 10
236 70 c. Fisherman 50 65
237 $1.20, Artist 80 1·10
234/7 *Set of* 4 1·25 1·60

98 *Topaz* sights Smoke on Pitcairn

(Des Jennifer Toombs. Litho B.D.T.)

1983 (14 June). *175th Anniv of Folger's Discovery of the Settlers. T* **98** *and similar horiz designs.* W w **14** (*sideways*). P 14.

238 6 c. Type **98** 20 15
239 20 c. Three islanders approach the *Topaz* 30 30
240 70 c. Capt. Mayhew Folger welcomed by John Adams 75 75
241 $1.20, Folger presented with *Bounty* chronometer 1·10 1·10
238/41 *Set of* 4 2·10 2·10

99 Hattie-Tree

(Des Jennifer Toombs. Litho B.D.T.)

1983 (6 Oct). *Trees of Pitcairn Islands* (*1st series*). *T* **99** *and similar horiz designs. Multicoloured.* W w **14** (*sideways*). P 13½.

242 35 c. Type **99** 30 35
a. Pair. Nos. 242/3 60 70
243 35 c. Leaves from Hattie-Tree 30 35
244 70 c. Pandanus 65 70
a. Pair. Nos. 244/5 1·25 1·40
245 70 c. Pandanus and basket weaving 65 70
242/5 *Set of* 4 1·75 1·90

The two designs of each value were printed together, *se-tenant*, in horizontal and vertical pairs throughout the sheet.

See also Nos. 304/7.

100 *Pseudojuloides atavai*

(Des C. Abbott. Litho Format)

1984 (11 Jan). *Fishes* (*1st series*). *T* **100** *and similar horiz designs. Multicoloured.* W w **14** (*sideways*). P 14½.

246 1 c. Type **100** 10 15
247 4 c. *Halichoeres melasmapomus* 15 15
248 6 c. *Scarus longipinnis* 15 15
249 9 c. *Variola louti* 15 15
250 10 c. *Centropyge hotumatua* 15 15
251 15 c. *Stegastes emeryi* 20 20
252 20 c. *Chaetodon smithi* 30 30
253 35 c. *Xanthichthys mento* 40 40
254 50 c. *Chrysiptera galba* 50 50
255 70 c. *Genicanthus spinus* 70 70
256 $1 *Myripristis tiki* 90 90
257 $1.20, *Anthias ventralis* 1·25 1·25
258 $2 *Pseudocaranx dentex* 1·60 1·60
246/58 *Set of* 13 6·00 6·00

For 90 c. and $3 values see Nos. 312/13.

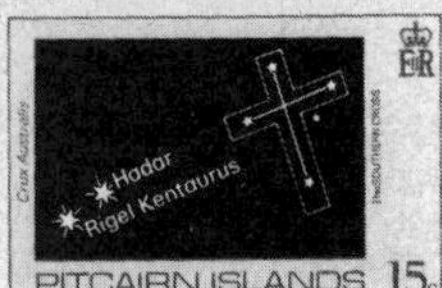

101 "Southern Cross"

(Des J. Cooter. Litho Walsall)

1984 (14 May). *Night Sky. T* **101** *and similar horiz designs.* W w **14** (*sideways*). P 14.

259 15 c. deep violet-blue, pale rose-lilac and gold 20 20
260 20 c. deep violet-blue, bright yell-grn & gold 30 30
261 70 c. deep violet-blue, yellow-ochre and gold 75 75
262 $1 deep violet-blue, pale blue and gold 1·00 1·00
259/62 *Set of* 4 2·00 2·00

Constellations:—20 c. "Southern Fish"; 70 c. "Lesser Dogs"; $1 "The Virgin".

102 Aluminium Longboat **103** "H.M.S. *Portland* standing off Bounty Bay" (J. Linton Palmer)

(Des C. Abbott. Litho Enschedé)

1984 (21 Sept). *"Ausipex" International Stamp Exhibition, Melbourne. Sheet* 134 × 86 *mm containing T* **102** *and similar horiz design. Multicoloured.* W w **14** (*sideways*). P 13½ × 14.

MS263 50 c. Type **102**; $2 Traditional-style wooden longboat 1·75 2·25

(Des Jennifer Toombs. Litho Questa)

1985 (16 Jan). *19th-Century Paintings* (*1st series*). *T* **103** *and similar horiz designs. Multicoloured.* W w **14** (*sideways*). P 13½ × 14 ($2) *or* 14 (*others*).

264 6 c. Type **103** 20 15
265 9 c. "Christian's Look Out" (J. Linton Palmer) 20 15
266 35 c. "The Golden Age" (J. Linton Palmer) 40 30
267 $2 "A View of the Village, 1825" (William Smyth) (48 × 31 *mm*) 1·40 1·40
264/7 *Set of* 4 2·00 1·75

The original printing of No. 267 was incorrectly dated "1835". The mistake was, however, spotted before issue and a replacement printing, correctly dated "1825", was provided. Those stamps dated "1835" were never issued for postal purposes, although isolated examples exist which may have been supplied by various philatelic agents in error.

See also Nos. 308/11.

104 The Queen Mother with the Queen and Princess Margaret, 1980 **105** *Act* 6 (container ship)

(Des A. Theobald ($2), C. Abbott (others). Litho Questa)

1985 (7 June). *Life and Times of Queen Elizabeth the Queen Mother. T* **104** *and similar vert designs. Multicoloured.* W w **16**. P 14½ × 14.

268 6 c. Receiving the Freedom of Dundee, 1964 10 10
269 35 c. Type **104** 30 35
270 70 c. The Queen Mother 55 60
271 $1.20, With Prince Henry at his christening (from photo by Lord Snowdon) 90 95
268/71 *Set of* 4 1·60 1·75

MS272 91 × 73 mm. $2 In coach at Ascot Races. Wmk sideways 1·50 1·75

(Des E. Nisbet. Litho Format)

1985 (28 Aug). *Ships* (*1st series*). *T* **105** *and similar multicoloured designs.* W w **14** (*sideways*). P 14 (*Nos.* 273/4) *or* 14 × 13½ (*others*).

273 50 c. Type **105** 75 85
274 50 c. *Columbus Louisiana* (container ship) 75 85
275 50 c. *Essi Gina* (tanker) (48 × 35 *mm*) 75 85
276 50 c. *Stolt Spirit* (tanker) (48 × 35 *mm*) 75 85
273/6 *Set of* 4 2·75 3·00

See also Nos. 296/9.

PRICES OF SETS

Set prices are given for many issues, generally those containing three stamps or more. Definitive sets include one of each value or major colour change, but do not cover different perforations, die types or minor shades. Where a choice is possible the set prices are based on the cheapest versions of the stamps included in the listings.

106 "Madonna and Child" (Raphael) **107** Green Turtle

(Des Jennifer Toombs. Litho Walsall)

1985 (26 Nov). *Christmas. T* **106** *and similar vert designs showing "Madonna and Child" paintings. Multicoloured.* W w **16**. P 14 × 13½.

277 6 c. Type **106** 15 15
278 9 c. Krause (after Raphael) 15 15
279 35 c. Andreas Mayer 35 35
280 $2 Unknown Austrian master 1·50 1·60
277/80 *Set of* 4 1·90 2·00

(Des J. Thatcher. Litho Questa)

1986 (12 Feb). *Turtles. T* **107** *and similar horiz designs. Multicoloured.* W w **16** (*sideways*). P 14½.

281 9 c. Type **107** 35 35
282 20 c. Green Turtle and Pitcairn Island 50 50
283 70 c. Hawksbill Turtle 1·25 1·25
284 $1.20, Hawksbill Turtle and Pitcairn Island 1·50 1·50
281/4 *Set of* 4 3·25 3·25

(Des A. Theobald. Litho Questa)

1986 (21 Apr). *60th Birthday of Queen Elizabeth II. Vert designs as T* **110** *of Ascension. Multicoloured.* W w **16**. P 14½ × 14.

285 6 c. Princess Elizabeth at Royal Lodge, Windsor, 1946 10 10
286 9 c. Wedding of Princess Anne, 1973 10 10
287 20 c. At Order of St. Michael and St. George service, St. Paul's Cathedral, 1961 20 20
288 $1.20, At Electrical Engineering Concert, Royal Festival Hall, 1971 85 90
289 $2 At Crown Agents Head Office, London, 1983 1·50 1·60
285/9 *Set of* 5 2·50 2·50

(Des D. Miller. Litho Questa)

1986 (23 July). *Royal Wedding. Square designs as T* **112** *of Ascension. Multicoloured.* W w **16**. P 14.

290 20 c. Prince Andrew and Miss Sarah Ferguson 20 20
291 $1.20, Prince Andrew aboard *Bluenose II* off Halifax, Canada, 1985 90 90

108 John I. Tay (pioneer missionary) and First Church **109** Pitcairn Island Home

(Des A. Theobald. Litho Walsall)

1986 (18 Oct). *Centenary of Seventh-Day Adventist Church on Pitcairn. T* **108** *and similar vert designs. Multicoloured.* W w **16**. P 14.

292 6 c. Type **108** 15 15
293 20 c. *Pitcairn* (mission schooner) and second church (1907) 35 35
294 35 c. Baptism at Down Isaac and third church (1945) 50 50
295 $2 Islanders singing farewell hymn and present church (1954) 2·00 2·00
292/5 *Set of* 4 2·75 2·75

(Des E. Nisbet. Litho Format)

1987 (20 Jan). *Ships* (*2nd series*). *Multicoloured designs as T* **105**. W w **16** (*sideways on Nos.* 298/9). P 14 (*Nos.* 296/7) *or* 14 × 13½ (*others*).

296 50 c. *Samoan Reefer* (freighter) 85 85
297 50 c. *Brussel* (container ship) 85 85
298 50 c. *Australian Exporter* (container ship) (48 × 35 *mm*) 85 85
299 50 c. *Taupo* (cargo liner) (48 × 35 *mm*) 85 85
296/9 *Set of* 4 3·00 3·00

(Des E. Roberts and D. Robertson. Litho Format)

1987 (21 Apr). *Pitcairn Island Homes. T* **109** *and similar horiz designs showing different houses.* W w **14** (*sideways*). P 13½ × 14.

300 **109** 70 c. black, brt reddish violet & brt violet 55 55
301 – 70 c. black, pale orange-yell & brn-ochre 55 55
302 – 70 c. black, dull blue and ultramarine 55 55
303 – 70 c. black, blue-green & deep blue-green 55 55
300/3 *Set of* 4 2·00 2·00

(Des Jennifer Toombs. Litho Format)

1987 (10 Aug). *Trees of Pitcairn Islands (2nd series). Horiz designs as T* **99**. *Multicoloured. W w* **16** *(sideways). P* 14½.
304 40 c. Leaves and flowers from *Erythrina variegata* 35 35
a. Pair. Nos. 304/5 .. .. 70 70
305 40 c. *Erythrina variegata* tree 35 35
306 $1.80, Leaves from *Aleurites moluccana* and nut torch .. .. 1·40 1·40
a. Pair. Nos. 306/7 .. .. 2·75 2·75
307 $1.80, *Aleurites moluccana* tree .. .. 1·40 1·40
304/7 .. .. *Set of* 4 3·25 3·25
The two designs of each value were printed together, *se-tenant*, in horizontal and vertical pairs throughout the sheet.

(Des Jennifer Toombs. Litho Questa)

1987 (7 Dec). *19th-Century Paintings (2nd series). Horiz designs as T* **103** *showing paintings by Lt. Conway Shipley in 1848. Multicoloured. W w* **16** *(sideways). P* 13½×14 ($1.80) *or* 14 *(others)*.
308 20 c. "House and Tomb of John Adams" .. 25 20
309 40 c. "Bounty Bay" 40 35
310 90 c. "School House and Chapel" 80 70
311 $1.80, "Pitcairn Island" (48×31 *mm*) .. 1·40 1·40
308/11 .. .. *Set of* 4 2·50 2·40

(Des C. Abbott. Litho Format)

1988 (14 Jan). *Fishes (2nd series). Horiz designs as T* **100**. *Multicoloured. W w* **16** *(sideways). P* 14½.
312 90 c. As No. 249 .. .. 75 80
313 $3 *Gymnothorax eurostus* .. .. .. 2·50 2·75

110 *Bounty* (replica)

111 H.M.S. *Swallow* (survey ship), 1767

(Des M. Bradbery. Litho Questa)

1988 (9 May). *Bicentenary of Australian Settlement. Sheet* 112 × 76 *mm. W w* **16**. *P* 14 × 13½.
MS314 **110** $3 multicoloured .. .. .. 2·10 2·25

(Des E. Nisbet. Litho B.D.T.)

1988 (14 Aug). *Ships. T* **111** *and similar horiz designs. Multicoloured. W w* **14** *(sideways). P* 13½.
315 5 c. Type **111** 10 10
316 10 c. H.M.S. *Pandora* (frigate), 1791 .. 10 10
317 15 c. H.M.S. *Briton* and H.M.S. *Tagus* (frigates), 1814 .. .. .. 10 15
318 20 c. H.M.S. *Blossom* (survey ship), 1825 .. 10 15
319 30 c. *Lucy Anne* (barque), 1831 .. .. 20 25
320 35 c. *Charles Doggett* (whaling ship), 1831 25 30
321 40 c. H.M.S. *Fly* (sloop), 1838 .. .. 25 30
322 60 c. *Camden* (missionary brig), 1840 .. 40 45
323 90 c. H.M.S. *Virago* (paddle-sloop), 1853 .. 60 65
324 $1.20, *Rakaia* (screw-steamer), 1867 .. 80 85
325 $1.80, H.M.S. *Sappho* (screw-sloop), 1882 1·25 1·40
326 $5 H.M.S. *Champion* (corvette), 1893 .. 3·25 3·50
315/26 .. .. *Set of* 12 6·75 7·25

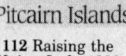

112 Raising the Union Jack, 1838

113 Angel

(Des Jennifer Toombs. Litho Walsall)

1988 (30 Nov). *150th Anniv of Pitcairn Island Constitution. T* **112** *and similar vert designs, each showing different extract from original Constitution. Multicoloured. W w* **14**. *P* 14.
327 20 c. Type **112** 15 20
328 40 c. Signing Constitution on board H.M.S. *Fly*, 1838 .. .. 30 35
329 $1.05, Voters at modern polling station .. 75 80
330 $1.80, Modern classroom .. .. 1·25 1·40
327/30 .. .. *Set of* 4 2·25 2·50

(Des M. Grimsdale. Litho Questa)

1988 (30 Nov). *Christmas. T* **113** *and similar vert designs. Multicoloured. W w* **16**. *P* 14 × 13½.
331 90 c. Type **113** 65 70
a. Horiz strip of 4. Nos. 331/4 .. .. 2·40
332 90 c. Holy Family 65 70
333 90 c. Two Polynesian Wise Men 65 70
334 90 c. Polynesian Wise Man and shepherd .. 65 70
331/4 .. .. *Set of* 4 2·40 2·50
Nos. 331/4 were printed together, *se-tenant*, in horizontal strips of four throughout the sheet.

114 Loading Stores, Deptford

115 R.N.Z.A.F. "Orion" making Mail Drop, 1985

(Des C. Abbott. Litho Questa)

1989 (22 Feb). *Bicentary of Pitcairn Island Settlement (1st issue). T* **114** *and similar horiz designs. Multicoloured. W w* **14** *(sideways). P* 14.
335 20 c. Type **114** 15 20
a. Sheetlet. Nos. 335/40 80
336 20 c. H.M.S. *Bounty* leaving Spithead .. 15 20
337 20 c. H.M.S. *Bounty* at Cape Horn 15 20
338 20 c. Anchored in Adventure Bay, Tasmania 15 20
339 20 c. Crew collecting breadfruit 15 20
340 20 c. Breadfruit in cabin 15 20
335/40 .. .. *Set of* 6 80 1·10
Nos. 335/40 were printed together, *se-tenant* in sheetlets of six, as two horizontal rows of three separated by a central gutter.
See also Nos. 341/7 and 356/61.

(Des C. Abbott. Litho Questa (Nos. 341/6), B.D.T. (No. **MS**347))

1989 (28 Apr). *Bicentenary of Pitcairn Island Settlement (2nd issue). Horiz designs as T* **114**. *Multicoloured. W w* **14** *(sideways). P* 14.
341 90 c. H.M.S. *Bounty* leaving Tahiti .. 65 70
a. Sheetlet. Nos. 341/6 .. .. .. 3·50
342 90 c. Bligh awoken by mutineers 65 70
343 90 c. Bligh before Fletcher Christian .. 65 70
344 90 c. Provisioning Bounty's launch .. 65 70
345 90 c. "Mutineers casting Bligh adrift" (Robert Dodd) 65 70
346 90 c. Mutineers discarding breadfruit plants 65 70
341/6 .. .. *Set of* 6 3·50 3·75
MS347 110 × 85 mm. 90 c. No. 345; 90 c. Isle of Man 1989 35p. Mutiny stamp; 90 c. Norfolk Island 39 c. Mutiny stamp. W w **16** (sideways) 2·40 2·75
Nos. 341/6 were printed in the same sheet format as Nos. 335/40

(Des A. Theobald. Litho Questa)

1989 (25 July). *Aircraft. T* **115** *and similar horiz designs. Multicoloured. W w* **16** *(sideways). P* 14×14½.
348 20 c. Type **115** 25 25
349 80 c. Beechcraft "Queen Air" on photo-mission, 1983 .. .. 80 80
350 $1.05, Helicopter landing diesel fuel from U.S.S. *Breton*, 1969 .. .. .. 1·10 1·10
351 $1.30, R.N.Z.A.F. "Hercules" dropping bulldozer, 1983 .. .. .. 1·25 1·25
348/51 .. .. *Set of* 4 3·00 3·00

116 Ducie Island

(Des A. Theobald. Litho Walsall)

1989 (23 Oct). *Islands of Pitcairn Group. T* **116** *and similar horiz designs. Multicoloured. W w* **14** *(sideways). P* 14.
352 15 c. Type **116** 15 15
353 90 c. Henderson Island 90 90
354 $1.05, Oeno Island .. .. .. 1·00 1·00
355 $1.30, Pitcairn Island .. .. .. 1·25 1·25
352/5 .. .. *Set of* 4 3·00 3·00

(Des C. Abbott. Litho Questa)

1990 (15 Jan). *Bicentenary of Pitcairn Island Settlement (3rd issue). Horiz designs as T* **114**. *Multicoloured. W w* **16** *(sideways). P* 14.
356 40 c. Mutineers sighting Pitcairn Island .. 30 35
a. Sheetlet. Nos. 356/61 .. .. .. 1·60
357 40 c. Ship's boat approaching landing .. 30 35
358 40 c. Exploring island 30 35
359 40 c. Ferrying goods ashore 30 35
360 40 c. Burning of H.M.S. *Bounty* 30 35
361 40 c. Pitcairn Island village 30 35
356/61 .. .. *Set of* 6 1·60 1·90
Nos. 356/61 were printed in the same sheet format as Nos. 335/40.

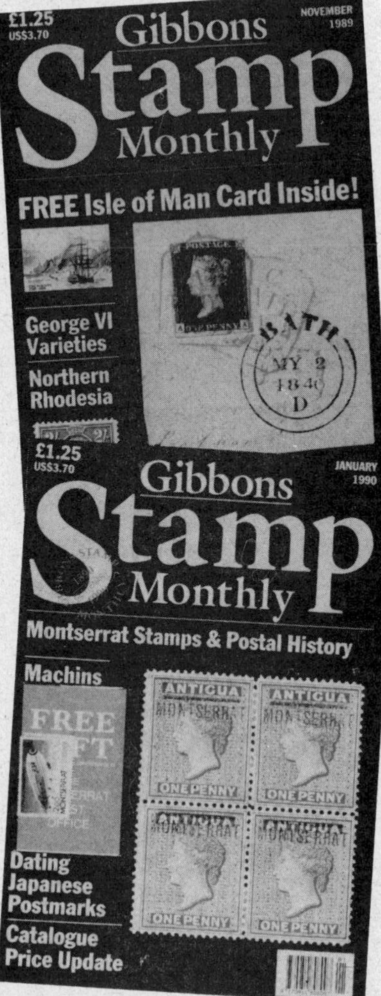

Prince Edward Island

PRICES FOR STAMPS ON COVER

Nos. 1/4	*from* × 2
Nos. 5/6	—
Nos. 7/8	*from* × 3
Nos. 9/20	*from* × 4
Nos. 21/6	*from* × 2
Nos. 27/31	*from* × 4
Nos. 32/3	*from* × 40
Nos. 34/45	*from* × 4
Nos. 46/7	*from* × 3

1 2 3

4 5 6

(Typo Charles Whiting, London)

1861 (1 Jan). *Yellowish toned paper.* (a) *P* 9.

No.	Type		Unused	Used
1	1	2d. rose	£160	£100
		a. Imperf between (horiz pair)	£3000	
		b. Imperf horiz (vert pair)		
		c. Bisected (1d.) (on cover)		
2		2d. rose-carmine	£160	£100
3	2	3d. blue	£350	£175
		a. Bisected (1½d.) (on cover)		
		b. Double print	£1000	
4	3	6d. yellow-green	£475	£250
		(b) Rouletted		
5	1	2d. rose	£1700	£1200

The 2d. and 3d., perf 9, were authorised to be bisected and used for half their normal value.

1862. *Yellowish toned paper. P* 11.

No.	Type		Unused	Used
6	4	1d. brown-orange	23·00	50·00
7	6	9d. bluish lilac (29.3.62)	40·00	16·00
8		9d. dull mauve	40·00	16·00

1863–68. *Yellowish toned paper.* (a) *P* 11½ × 12.

No.	Type		Unused	Used
9	4	1d. yellow-orange	8·50	13·00
		a. Bisected (½d.) (on cover)	†	£900
		b. Imperf between (horiz pair)	£200	
10		1d. orange-buff	11·00	12·00
11		1d. yellow	12·00	13·00
12	1	2d. rose	6·00	8·50
		a. Imperf vert (horiz pair)		
		b. Bisected (1d.) (on cover)	†	£1200
13		2d. deep rose	7·00	11·00
14	2	3d. blue	8·50	12·00
		a. Imperf horiz (vert pair)		
		b. Bisected (1½d.) (on cover)		
15		3d. deep blue	8·50	8·00
16	5	4d. black (1867)	12·00	15·00
		a. Imperf vert (horiz pair)		
		b. Bisected (2d.) (on cover)	†	£1000
17	3	6d. yellow-green (15.12.66)	17·00	17·00
		a. Bisected (3d.) (on cover)		
18		6d. blue-green (1868)	17·00	17·00
19	6	9d. lilac	16·00	16·00
20		9d. reddish mauve	16·00	16·00
		a. Imperf vert (horiz pair)	£300	
		b. Bisected (4½d.) (on cover)	†	£1100
		(b) Perf compound of 11 and 11–12½		
21	4	1d. yellow-orange	£150	60·00
22	1	2d. rose	£150	60·00
23	2	3d. blue	£170	60·00
24	5	4d. black	£190	£180
25	3	6d. yellow-green	£170	£180
26	6	9d. reddish mauve	£180	£180

1870. *Coarse, wove bluish white paper. P* 11½–12.

No.	Type		Unused	Used
27	1	2d. rose	7·00	8·50
28		2d. rose-pink	5·50	8·00
		a. "TWC"	65·00	
		b. Imperf between (horiz pair)	£110	
29	2	3d. pale blue	6·00	8·50
30		3d. blue	6·00	8·50
		a. Imperf between (horiz pair)	£250	
31	5	4d. black	3·00	26·00
		a. Imperf between (horiz pair)	£110	
		b. Bisected (2d.) (on cover)	†	£1300
		c. Perf compound 11 and 11½–12		

7

(Recess British-American Bank Note Co., Montreal and Ottawa)

1870 (1 June). *P* 12.

No.	Type		Unused	Used
32	7	4½d. (3d. stg), yellow-brown	13·00	26·00
33		4½d. (3d. stg), deep brown	13·00	26·00

8 9 10

11 12 13

(Typo Charles Whiting, London)

1872 (1 Jan). (a) *P* 11½–12.

No.	Type		Unused	Used
34	8	1 c. orange	1·60	8·50
35		1 c. yellow-orange	1·60	7·00
36		1 c. brown-orange	2·50	8·50
37	10	3 c. rose	3·25	7·00
		a. Stop between "PRINCE. EDWARD"	18·00	20·00
		b. Bisected (1½ c.) (on cover)		
		c. Imperf horiz (vert pair)	£300	
		(b) Perf 12 to 12¼, large holes		
38	9	2 c. blue	8·00	24·00
		a. Bisected (1 c.) (on cover)		
39	11	4 c. yellow-green	1·50	15·00
40		4 c. deep green	2·50	10·00
		a. Bisected (2 c.) (on cover)	†	£1900
41	12	6 c. black	1·60	10·00
		a. Bisected (3 c.) (on cover)	†	£700
		b. Imperf between (horiz pair)	£190	
		c. Imperf vert (horiz pair)		
42	13	12 c. reddish mauve	1·60	20·00
		(c) P 12½–13, smaller holes		
43	8	1 c. orange	12·00	
44		1 c. brown-orange	1·60	7·50
45	10	3 c. rose	8·50	8·50
		a. Stop between "PRINCE. EDWARD"	50·00	55·00
45*b*	12	6 c. black	—	£250
		(d) Perf compound of (a) and (c) 11½–12 × 12½–13		
46	8	1 c. orange	30·00	32·00
47	10	3 c. rose	32·00	32·00
		a. Stop between "PRINCE. EDWARD"	£170	£180

The stamps were withdrawn 1 July 1873, when the Colony became a Province of the Dominion of Canada.

Qatar

An independent Arab Shaikhdom, with a British postal administration until 23 May 1963.

There was no postal service from Qatar until 18 May 1950. Prior to this date the few foreign residents made their own arrangements for their mail to be carried to Bahrain for onward transmission through the postal services.

The first organised post from the capital, Doha, was an extension of the work in the state by the British Political Officer. From 18 May 1950 British residents were able to send mail via his office. The first three sendings had the Bahrain or British Postal Agencies in Eastern Arabia stamps cancelled by a circular office stamp, but later batches, up to the introduction of the first Doha postmark in July 1950, had the stamps cancelled on arrival at Bahrain.

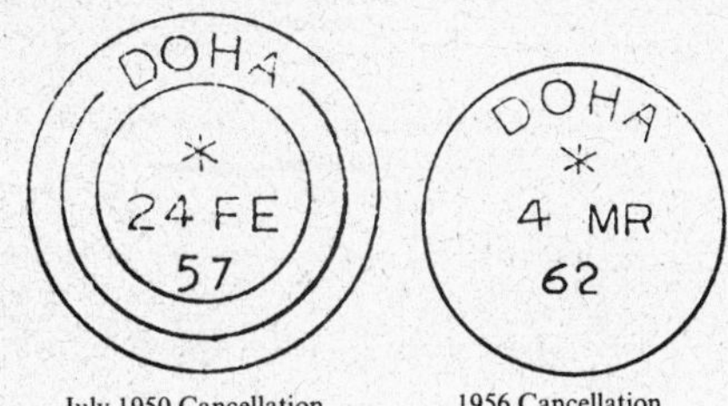

July 1950 Cancellation 1956 Cancellation

The Post Office became a separate entity in August 1950 when its services were made available to the general public. After initially using the Bahrain surcharges on Great Britain the supply of stamps for the Qatar office was switched to the British Postal Agencies in Eastern Arabia surcharges.

The circular cancellation, dating from July 1950, continued to be used until replaced by a slightly smaller version in early 1956.

A further post office was opened on 1 February 1956 at the Umm Said oil terminal, using its own cancellation.

Both offices were issued with standard oval Registered handstamps, Doha in 1950 and Umm Said in 1956.

1956 Umm Said Cancellation

All stamps to 1960 surcharged in issues of Great Britain

QATAR NP 1 NP (1) QATAR 3 NP NP (2) QATAR 75 NP (3)

1957 (1 Apr)–**59**. (a) *T* 154/60 (*St Edward's Crown wmk, W* 165) *surch as T* 1 *to* 3.

No.	Type		Unused	Used
1	1	1 n.p. on 5d. brown	10	10
2	2	3 n.p. on ½d. orange-red	15	15
3		6 n.p. on 1d. ultramarine	15	15
4		9 n.p. on 1½d. green	15	10
5		12 n.p. on 2d. light red-brown	20	30
6	1	15 n.p. on 2½d. carmine-red (I)	15	10
7	2	20 n.p. on 3d. deep lilac (B.)	15	10
8	1	25 n.p. on 4d. ultramarine	40	40
9		40 n.p. on 6d. reddish purple	15	10
		a. Deep claret (21.7.59)	30	10
10		50 n.p. on 9d. bronze-green	40	15
11	3	75 n.p. on 1s. 3d. green	50	50
12		1 r. on 1s. 6d. grey-blue	5·00	10
1/12		*Set of* 12	6·50	1·75

QATAR 2 RUPEES I
QATAR 2 RUPEES II
(4)

QATAR 5 RUPEES I
QATAR 5 RUPEES II
(5)

QATAR 10 RUPEES I
QATAR 10 RUPEES II
(6)

Type I (4/6). Type-set overprints. Bold thick letters with sharp corners and straight edges. Bars close together and usually slightly longer than in Type II.

Type II (4/6). Plate-printed overprints. Thinner letters, rounded corners and rough edges. Bars wider apart.

(*b*) *Nos.* 536/8 *surch with T* 4/6

No.	Type		I (1.4.57)		II (18.9.57)	
13	166	2 r. on 2s. 6d. black-brown	4·50	1·00	9·00	5·00
14	167	5 r. on 5s. rose-red	8·00	2·75	9·00	15·00
15	168	10 r. on 10s. ultramarine	10·00	8·50	45·00	90·00
13/15		*Set of* 3	20·00	11·00	55·00	£100

QATAR 15 NP

(7)

1957 (1 Aug). *World Scout Jubilee Jamboree. Nos.* 557/9 *surch in two lines as T* 7 (15 *n.p.*) *or in three lines (others).*

No.		Unused	Used
16	15 n.p. on 2½d. carmine-red	25	35
17	25 n.p. on 4d. ultramarine	25	35
18	75 n.p. on 1s. 3d. green	30	35
16/18	*Set of* 3	70	95

1960 (26 Apr–28 Sept). *Q.E.II (Mult Crowns wmk, W* 179) *surch as T* 1 *or* 2.

No.	Type		Unused	Used
20	2	3 n.p. on ½d. orange-red (28.9)	70	1·75
21		6 n.p. on 1d. ultramarine (21.6)	1·25	2·75
22		9 n.p. on 1½d. green (28.9)	75	1·50
23		12 n.p. on 2d. light red-brown (28.9)	3·75	6·50

24 1 15 n.p. on 2½d. carmine-red (II) 35 10
25 2 20 n.p. on 3d. deep lilac (B.) (28.9) .. 35 10
26 1 40 n.p. on 6d. deep claret (21.6) 60 25
20/6 .. .. *Set of* 7 7·00 11·50

8 Shaikh Ahmad bin Ali al Thani

9 Peregrine Falcon

10 Dhow

11 Oil Derrick

12 Mosque

(Des O. C. Meronti (T 8), M. Goaman (T 9), M. Farrar Bell (T 10), J. Constable and O. C. Meronti (T 11/12). Photo Harrison, (T 8/10). Recess D.L.R. (T 11/12))

1961 (2 Sept). *P* 14½ (5 *n.p. to* 75 *n.p.*) *or* 13 (1 *r. to* 10 *r.*).
27 8 5 n.p. carmine 10 10
28 15 n.p. black 10 10
29 20 n.p. reddish purple 10 10
30 30 n.p. deep green 10 10
31 9 40 n.p. red 85 10
32 50 n.p. sepia .. .. 1·25 10
33 10 75 n.p. ultramarine 60 30
34 11 1 r. scarlet 70 10
35 2 r. ultramarine .. .. .. 2·00 25
36 12 5 r. bronze-green .. .. .. 7·00 60
37 10 r. black .. .. 13·00 1·50
27/37 .. .. *Set of* 11 23·00 2·50

The Qatar Post Department took over the postal services on 23 May 1963. Later stamp issues will be found listed in Part 19 (*Middle East*) of this catalogue.

Queensland

The area which later became Queensland was previously part of New South Wales known as the Moreton Bay District. The first post office, at Brisbane, was opened in 1834 and the use of New South Wales stamps from the District became compulsory from 1 May 1854.

Queensland was proclaimed a separate colony on 10 December 1859, but continued to use New South Wales issues until 1 November 1860.

Post Offices opened in the Moreton Bay District before 10 December 1859, and using New South Wales stamps, were

Office	*Opened*	*Numeral Cancellation*
Brisbane	1834	95
Burnett's Inn (*became* Goodes Inn)	1850	108
Callandoon	1850	74
Condamine	1856	151
Dalby	1854	133
Drayton	1846	85
Gayndah	1850	86
Gladstone	1854	131
Goodes Inn	1858	108
Ipswich	1846	87
Maryborough	1849	96
Rockhampton	1858	201
Surat	1852	110
Taroom	1856	152
Toowoomba	1858	214
Warwick	1848	81

PRICES FOR STAMPS ON COVER

Nos. 1/3	*from* × 2
Nos. 4/56	*from* × 3
Nos. 57/8	—
Nos. 59/73	*from* × 4
Nos. 74/82	*from* × 2
Nos. 83/109	*from* × 3
Nos. 110/13	*from* × 2
Nos. 116/17	*from* × 3
Nos. 118/27	—
Nos. 128/50	*from* × 4
Nos. 151/65	—
Nos. 166/78	*from* × 10
Nos. 179/83	*from* × 4
Nos. 184/206	*from* × 15
No. 207	—
Nos. 208/54	*from* × 15
Nos. 256/64	*from* × 10
Nos. 264*a*/*b*	*from* × 2
Nos. 265/6	*from* × 20
Nos. 267/9	*from* × 5
Nos. 270/80*a*	—
Nos. 281/5	*from* × 10
Nos. 286/308	*from* × 12
No. 309	—
Nos. F1/37	—

1

2 Large Star

3 Small Star

(Dies eng W. Humphrys. Recess P.B.)

1860 (1 Nov). *W* **2**. *Imperf.*
1 1 1d. carmine-rose £2250 £800
2 2d. blue £5000 £1700
3 6d. green £3500 £800

1860 (Nov). *W* **2**. *Clean-cut perf* 14–15½.
4 1 1d. carmine-rose (1.11) £1000 £250
5 2d. blue (1.11) £400 £100
a. Imperf between (pair) .. ..
6 6d. green (15.11) .. .. .. £450 60·00

1860–61. *W* **3**. *Clean-cut perf* 14–15½.
7 1 2d. blue £450 £100
a. Imperf between (horiz pair) .. .. — £900
8 3d. brown (15.4.61) .. .. .. £250 50·00
a. Re-entry .. .. .. — £200
b. Retouch (R. 2/8) .. .. .. — £200
9 6d. green .. .. £500 50·00
10 1s. violet (15.11.60) .. .. .. £475 70·00
11 "REGISTERED" (6d.) olive-yellow (1.61) £325 70·00
a. Imperf between (pair) £2750

The perforation of the 3d. is that known as "intermediate between clean-cut and rough".

The 3d. re-entry shows doubling of the left-hand arabesque and the retouch has redrawn spandrel dots under "EN" of "PENCE", a single dot in the centre of the circle under "E" and the bottom outer frame liner closer to the spandrel's frame line.

1861 (July (?)). *W* **3**. *Clean-cut perf* 14.
12 1 1d. carmine-rose .. .. .. £100 35·00
13 2d. blue .. .. £275 50·00

1861 (Sept). *W* **3**. *Rough perf* 14–15½.
14 1 1d. carmine-rose .. .. .. 75·00 28·00
15 2d. blue .. .. 90·00 28·00
a. Imperf between (pair) .. ..
16 3d. brown .. .. 50·00 30·00
a. Imperf between (pair) £1400
b. Re-entry £200 £110
c. Retouch (R. 2/8) .. .. .. — £110
17 6d. deep green .. .. .. £100 27·00
18 6d. yellow-green .. .. .. £200 27·00
19 1s. violet .. .. £325 80·00
20 "REGISTERED" (6d.) orange-yellow .. 45·00 35·00

(Printed and perforated in Brisbane)

1862–67. *Thick toned paper. No wmk.* (*a*) *P* 13 (1862–63).
21 1 1d. Indian red (16.12.62) .. .. £250 60·00
22 1d. orange-vermilion (2.63) .. .. 60·00 12·00
a. Imperf (pair) .. .. .. — £500
b. Imperf between (pair) .. ..
23 2d. blue (16.12.62) .. .. .. 40·00 9·00
24 2d. pale blue .. .. .. 80·00 27·00
a. Imperf (pair) .. .. .. — £500
b. Imperf between (horiz pair) .. .. — £850
25 3d. brown .. .. 55·00 30·00
a. Re-entry .. .. .. — £110
b. Retouch (R. 2/8) .. .. .. — £110
26 6d. apple-green (17.4.63) .. .. 90·00 15·00
27 6d. yellow-green .. .. .. 80·00 12·00
a. Imperf between (horiz pair) .. .. — £950
28 6d. blue-green .. .. .. £130 27·00
a. Imperf (pair) .. .. .. — £500
29 1s. grey (14.7.63) (H/S S. £40) .. .. £130 22·00
a. Imperf between (horiz pair) .. .. — £850
b. Imperf between (vert pair) .. ..

The top or bottom row of perforation was sometimes omitted from the sheet, resulting in stamps perforated on three sides only.

(*b*) *P* 12½ × 13 (1867)
30 1 1d. orange-vermilion .. .. .. 60·00 27·00
31 2d. blue .. .. 48·00 20·00
32 3d. brown .. .. 65·00 25·00
a. Re-entry .. .. .. — 95·00
b. Retouch (R. 2/8) .. .. .. — 95·00
33 6d. apple-green .. .. .. 85·00 27·00
34 6d. yellow-green .. .. .. 85·00 27·00
35 1s. grey .. .. £170 32·00
a. Imperf between (horiz pair) .. ..

The previously listed stamps perforated 13 round holes come from the same perforating machine as Nos. 21/9 after the pins had been replaced. The holes vary from rough to clean-cut.

1864–65. *W* **3**. (*a*) *P* 13.
44 1 1d. orange-vermilion (1.65) .. .. 55·00 20·00
a. Imperf between (horiz pair) £375
45 2d. pale blue (1.65) .. .. .. 50·00 16·00
46 2d. deep blue .. .. .. 50·00 16·00
a. Imperf between (vert pair) £850
b. Bisected (1d.) (on cover) .. .. † £1800
47 6d. yellow-green (1.65) .. .. .. £120 22·00
48 6d. deep green .. .. .. £140 22·00
49 "REGISTERED" (6d.) orge-yell (21.6.64) 65·00 30·00
a. Double printed £750
b. Imperf .. .. ..

(*b*) *P* 12½ × 13
50 1 1d. orange-vermilion .. .. .. 95·00 40·00
50*a* 2d. deep blue .. .. ..

1866 (24 Jan). *Wmk* "QUEENSLAND/POSTAGE—POSTAGE/ STAMPS—STAMPS" *in three lines in script capitals with double wavy lines above and below the wmk and single wavy lines with projecting sprays between each line of words. There are ornaments ("fleurons") between* "POSTAGE" "POSTAGE" *and between* "STAMPS" "STAMPS". *Single stamps only show a portion of one or two letters of this wmk.* (*a*) *P* 13.
51 1 1d. orange-vermilion .. .. .. £130 25·00
52 2d. blue .. .. 45·00 17·00

(*b*) *P* 12½ × 13
52*a* 1 1d. orange-vermilion .. .. ..
52*b* 2d. blue .. ..

1866 (24 Sept). *Lithographed on thick paper. No wmk. P* 13.
53 1 4d. slate (H/S S. £40) .. .. .. £150 20·00
a. Re-entry .. .. .. — 85·00
b. Retouch (R. 2/8) .. .. .. — 85·00
55 4d. lilac .. .. 90·00 16·00
a. Re-entry .. .. .. — 75·00
b. Retouch (R. 2/8) .. .. .. — 75·00
56 4d. reddish lilac .. .. .. 90·00 16·00
a. Re-entry .. .. .. — 75·00
b. Retouch (R. 2/8) .. .. .. — 75·00
57 5s. bright rose (H/S S. £40) .. .. £275 80·00
58 5s. pale rose .. .. .. £200 55·00
a. Imperf between (vert pair) .. .. — £600

The 4d. is from a transfer taken from the 3d. die, and the 5s. was taken from the 1s. die, the final "s" being added. The alteration in the values was made by hand on the stone, and there are many varieties, such as tall and short letters in "FOUR PENCE", some of the letters of "FOUR" smudged out, and differences in the position of the two words.

4

1868–74. *Wmk small truncated Star,* W **4** *on each stamp, and the word* "QUEENSLAND" *in single-lined Roman capitals four times in each sheet.* (*a*) *P* 13.
59 1 1d. orange-vermilion (18.1.71) .. .. 45·00 4·50
60 2d. pale blue .. .. .. 45·00 4·50
61 2d. blue (3.4.68) .. .. .. 40·00 2·75
62 2d. bright blue .. .. .. 50·00 2·75
63 2d. greenish blue .. .. .. 85·00 2·50
64 2d. dark blue .. .. .. 45·00 2·50
a. Imperf .. .. ..
65 3d. olive-green (27.2.71) .. .. 80·00 5·00
a. Re-entry .. .. .. — 30·00
b. Retouch (R. 2/8) .. .. .. — 30·00
66 3d. greenish grey .. .. .. 95·00 5·50
a. Re-entry .. .. .. — 32·00
b. Retouch (R. 2/8) .. .. .. — 32·00
67 3d. brown .. .. 80·00 5·50
a. Re-entry .. .. .. — 32·00
b. Retouch (R. 2/8) .. .. .. — 32·00
68 6d. yellow-green (10.11.71) .. .. £130 7·00
69 6d. green .. .. £130 10·00
70 6d. deep green .. .. .. £170 17·00
71 1s. greenish grey (13.11.72) .. .. £325 32·00
72 1s. brownish grey .. .. .. £325 32·00
73 1s. mauve (19.2.74) .. .. .. £200 22·00
59/73 (*ex Nos.* 67, 71) H/S "Specimen" *Set of* 5 £175

(*b*) *P* 12 (about Feb 1874)
74 1 1d. orange-vermilion .. .. .. £250 24·00
75 2d. blue .. .. — 35·00
76 3d. greenish grey .. .. .. — £120
a. Re-entry .. .. ..
b. Retouch (R. 2/8) .. .. ..
77 3d. brown £250 £120
a. Re-entry .. .. ..
b. Retouch (R. 2/8) .. .. ..
78 6d. green .. .. £850 40·00
79 1s. mauve .. .. — 40·00

(*c*) *P* 13 × 12
80 1 1d. orange-vermilion .. .. .. — £150
81 2d. blue .. .. £850 40·00
82 3d. greenish grey .. .. ..

Reprints were made in 1895 of all five values on the paper of the regular issue, and perforated 13; the colours are:—1d. orange and orange-brown, 2d. dull blue and bright blue, 3d. deep brown, 6d. yellow-green, 1s. red-violet and dull violet. The "Registered" was also reprinted with these on the same paper, but perforated 12. One sheet of the 2d. reprint is known to have had the perforations missing between the fourth and fifth vertical rows.

5

6

(4d., litho. Other values recess)

1868–78. *Wmk Crown and Q,* W **5**. (*a*) *P* 13 (1868–75).
83 1 1d. orange-vermilion (10.11.68) .. .. 50·00 4·50
a. Imperf £150
84 1d. pale rose-red (4.11.74) .. .. 48·00 8·50
85 1d. deep rose-red .. .. .. 95·00 9·00
86 2d. pale blue (4.11.74) .. .. 48·00 1·75
87 2d. deep blue (20.11.68) .. .. 38·00 4·50
a. Imperf (pair) £275
b. Imperf between (vert pair) .. ..
88 3d. brown (11.6.75) .. .. .. 70·00 12·00
a. Re-entry .. .. .. — 55·00
b. Retouch (R. 2/8) .. .. .. — 55·00
89 4d. yellow (1.1.75) (H/S S. £60) .. £750 40·00
90 6d. deep green (9.4.69) .. .. £120 9·00
91 6d. yellow-green .. .. .. 95·00 6·50
92 6d. pale apple-green (1.1.75) .. .. £130 9·00
a. Imperf £160
93 1s. mauve .. .. £130 29·00

(b) P 12 (1876–78)

94 1 1d. deep orange-vermilion 38·00 5·00
95 1d. pale orange-vermilion 40·00 5·00
a. Imperf between (vert pair)
96 1d. rose-red 45·00 10·00
97 1d. flesh 60·00 10·00
98 2d. pale blue 80·00 15·00
99 2d. bright blue 22·00 1·00
100 2d. deep blue 25·00 1·50
101 3d. brown 60·00 9·00
a. Re-entry — 45·00
b. Retouch (R. 2/8) — 45·00
102 4d. yellow £600 25·00
103 4d. buff £600 20·00
104 6d. deep green £140 7·00
105 6d. green £130 4·25
106 6d. yellow-green £140 4·50
107 6d. apple-green £140 7·00
108 1s. mauve 40·00 9·00
109 1s. purple £140 5·00
a. Imperf between (pair)

(c) P 13 × 12 or 12 × 13

110 1 1d. orange-vermilion — 85·00
110*a* 1d. rose-red
111 2d. deep blue £1100 £130
112 4d. yellow
113 6d. deep green — £150

(d) P 12½ × 13

114 1 1d. orange-vermilion
115 2d. deep blue
115*a* 6d. yellow-green

(e) P 12½

115*b* 1 2d. deep blue

Reprints exist of the 1d., 2d., 3d., 6d. and 1s. on thicker paper, Wmk W **6**, and in different shades from the originals.

1879. *No wmk. P* 12.
116 1 6d. pale emerald-green £150 25·00
a. Imperf between (horiz pair) — £550
117 1s. mauve (*fiscal-cancel £5*) 95·00 48·00

No. 117 has a very indistinct lilac *burelé* band at back.

Nos. 116/17 can be found showing portions of a papermaker's watermark, either T. H. Saunders & Co or A. Pirie & Sons.

1881. *Lithographed from transfers from the* 1s. *die. Wmk Crown and Q,* W **6**. *P* 12.
118 1 2s. pale blue (6 Apr) 60·00 22·00
119 2s. blue (*fiscal-cancel £3*) 60·00 22·00
a. Imperf vert (horiz pair)
120 2s. deep blue (*fiscal-cancel £3*) 75·00 22·00
121 2s. 6d. dull scarlet (28 Aug) £110 40·00
122 2s. 6d. bright scarlet (*fiscal-cancel £3*) £130 40·00
123 5s. pale yellow-ochre (28 Aug) £150 60·00
124 5s. yellow-ochre (*fiscal-cancel £4*) £150 60·00
125 10s. reddish brown (Mar) £350 £110
a. Imperf £375
126 10s. bistre-brown £350 £110
127 20s. rose (*fiscal-cancel £6*) £700 £130

Of the 2s. and 20s. stamps there are five types of each, and of the other values ten types of each.

Beware of fiscally used copies that have been cleaned and provided with forged postmarks.

7

Die I

Die II

Dies I and II often occur in the same sheet.

Die I. The white horizontal inner line of the triangle in the upper right-hand corner merges into the outer white line of the oval above the "L".

Die II. The same line is short and does not touch the inner oval.

1879–80. *Typo. P* 12. *(a) Wmk Crown and Q,* W **5**.
128 7 1d. reddish brown (Die I) 65·00 15·00
a. Die II £100 15·00
ab. "QOEENSLAND" £850 £150
129 1d. orange-brown (Die I) £100 15·00
130 2d. blue (Die I) 55·00 10·00
a. "PENGE" (R. 12/6) £650 £110
b. "QUEENSbAND" (R. 5/6) — £110
c. "QU" joined
131 4d. orange-yellow £300 35·00

(b) No wmk, with lilac burelé band on back

132 7 1d. reddish brown (Die I) £275 35·00
a. Die II £300 65·00
ab. "QOEENSLAND" — £1400
133 2d. blue (Die I) £350 17·00
a. "PENGE" (R. 12/6) £3250 £600
b. "QUEENSbAND" (R. 5/6)

(c) Wmk Crown and Q, W **6**

134 7 1d. reddish brown (Die I) 32·00 5·00
a. Imperf between (pair) — £200
b. Die II 40·00 5·00
ba. "QOEENSLAND" £200 40·00
bb. Imperf between (pair) — £200
135 1d. dull orange (Die I) 9·00 3·00
a. Die II 9·00 3·00
ab. "QOEENSLAND" 55·00 20·00
136 1d. scarlet (Die I) 12·00 1·75
a. Die II 14·00 2·25
ab. "QOEENSLAND" 80·00 24·00
137 7 2d. blue (Die I) 25·00 1·00
a. "PENGE" £120 40·00
b. "QUEENSbAND" £120 40·00
c. Die II 27·00 3·00
138 2d. grey-blue (Die I) 25·00 1·00
a. "PENGE" £120 40·00
b. "QUEENSbAND" £120 40·00
c. Die II
139 2d. bright blue (Die I) 28·00 1·00
a. "PENGE" £130 40·00
b. "QUEENSbAND" £130 40·00
c. Imperf between (pair) £375
d. Die II
140 2d. deep blue (Die I) 30·00 1·00
a. "PENGE" £140 40·00
b. "QUEENSbAND" £140 40·00
c. Die II 24·00 4·50
141 4d. orange-yellow £100 10·00
a. Imperf between (pair)
142 6d. deep green 55·00 4·50
a. Imperf between (pair)
143 6d. yellow-green 60·00 4·50
144 1s. deep violet 50·00 4·50
145 1s. pale lilac 45·00 5·50

The variety "QO" is No. 48 in the first arrangement, and No. 44 in a later arrangement on the sheets.

All these values have been seen imperf and unused, but we have no evidence that any of them were used in this condition.

The above were printed in sheets of 120, from plates made up of 30 groups of four electrotypes. There are four different types in each group, and two such groups of four are known of the 1d. and 2d., thus giving eight varieties of these two values. There was some resetting of the first plate of the 1d., and there are several plates of the 2d.; the value in the first plate of the latter value is in thinner letters, and in the last plate three types in each group of four have the "TW" of "TWO" joined, the letters of "PENCE" are larger and therefore much closer together, and in one type the "O" of "TWO" is oval, that letter being circular in the other types.

Half-penny
(8)

9

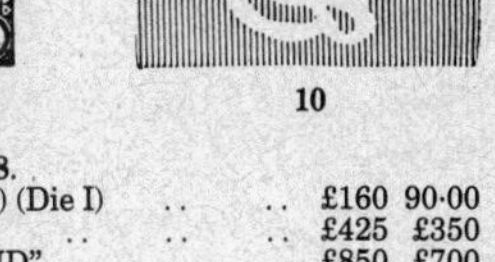
10

1880 (21 Feb). *Surch with T* **8**.
151 7 ½d. on 1d. (No. 134) (Die I) £160 90·00
a. Die II £425 £350
ab. "QOEENSLAND" £850 £700

Examples with "Half-penny" reading downwards are forged surcharges.

1882–86. *Recess. P* 12. *(a) Thin paper.* W **5** *twice sideways.*
152 9 2s. bright blue 60·00 17·00
153 2s. 6d. vermilion 50·00 20·00
154 5s. rose 45·00 22·00
155 10s. brown 95·00 40·00
156 £1 deep green £225 £120
a. Re-entry (R. 1/2) — £180
b. Retouch (R. 6/4) — £180
152, 154/6 H/S "Specimen" *Set of* 4 £150

(b) Thin paper. W **6** *twice sideways*

157 9 2s. 6d. vermilion 40·00 30·00
158 5s. rose 45·00 20·00
159 10s. brown £180 50·00
160 £1 deep green £180 60·00
a. Re-entry (R. 1/2) — £100
b. Retouch (R. 6/4) — £100

(c) Thick paper. W **10**

161 9 2s. bright blue 70·00 20·00
162 2s. 6d. vermilion 38·00 20·00
163 5s. rose 35·00 28·00
164 10s. brown 95·00 40·00
165 £1 deep green £170 60·00
a. Re-entry (R. 1/2) — £100
b. Retouch (R. 6/4) — £100

The re-entry on the £1 shows as a double bottom frame line and the retouch occurs alongside the bottom left numeral.

See also Nos. 270/1.

11

12

In T **12** the shading lines do not extend entirely across, as in T **11**, thus leaving a white line down the front of the throat and point of the bust.

1882–83. W **6**. *(a) P* 12.
166 11 1d. pale vermilion-red 3·00 30
a. Double impression
167 1d. deep vermilion-red 3·00 30
168 2d. blue 4·25 30
a. Imperf between (horiz pair)
169 4d. pale yellow 12·00 1·40
a. "PENGE" for "PENCE" (R. 8/1) £120 40·00
b. "EN" joined in "PENCE" (R. 4/6)
170 6d. green 9·00 70
171 1s. violet 16·00 1·90
172 1s. lilac 11·00 1·75
173 1s. deep mauve 11·00 1·40
174 1s. pale mauve 12·00 1·40
a. Imperf † —

(b) P 9½ × 12

176 11 1d. pale red 45·00 16·00
177 2d. blue £200 25·00
178 1s. mauve 90·00 19·00

The above were printed from plates made up of groups of four electrotypes as previously. In the 1d. the words of value are followed by a full stop. There are four types of the 4d., 6d., and 1s., eight types of the 1d., and twelve types of the 2d.

1887–89. W **6**. *(a) P* 12.
179 12 1d. vermilion-red 2·75 30
180 2d. blue 5·00 30
a. Oval white flaw on Queen's head behind diadem (R. 12/5)
181 2s. deep brown 55·00 23·00
182 2s. pale brown 50·00 20·00

(b) P 9½ × 12

183 12 2d. blue £150 22·00

These are from new plates; four types of each value grouped as before. The 1d. is without stop. In all values No. 2 in each group of four has the "L" and "A" of "QUEENSLAND" joined at the foot, and No. 3 of the 2d. has "P" of word "PENCE" with a long downstroke.

The 2d. is known bisected and used as a 1d. value.

13

14

1890–94. W **6** *(sideways on ½d.). P* 12½, 13 *(comb machine).*
184 13 ½d. pale green 2·75 50
185 ½d. deep green 2·75 50
186 ½d. deep blue-green 3·00 50
187 12 1d. vermilion-red 2·00 15
a. Imperf 23·00 23·00
b. Oval broken by tip of bust (R. 10/3)
188 2d. blue (old plate) 4·00 15
189 2d. pale blue (old plate) 3·75 15
190 2d. pale blue (retouched plate) 3·50 30
a. "FWO" for "TWO" (R. 8/7) — 20·00
191 14 2½d. carmine 10·00 55
192 12 3d. brown 8·50 1·40
193 11 4d. yellow 13·00 95
a. "PENGE" for "PENCE" (R. 8/1) 60·00
b. "EN" joined in "PENCE" (R. 4/6)
194 4d. orange 16·00 95
a. "PENGE" for "PENCE" (R. 8/1) 70·00 22·00
b. "EN" joined in "PENCE" (R. 4/6)
195 4d. lemon 20·00 1·25
a. "PENGE" for "PENCE" (R. 8/1) 80·00 28·00
b. "EN" joined in "PENCE" (R. 4/6)
196 6d. green 9·00 1·25
197 12 2s. red-brown 38·00 7·50
198 2s. pale brown 42·00 9·00

This issue is perforated by a new vertical comb machine, gauging about 12¾ × 12¾. The 3d. is from a plate similar to those of the last issue, No. 2 in each group of four types having "L" and "A" joined at the foot. The ½d. and 2½d. are likewise in groups of four types, but the differences are very minute. In the retouched plate of the 2d. the letters "L" and "A" no longer touch in No. 2 of each group and the "P" in No. 3 is normal.

1894–95. A. *Thick paper.* W **10**. *(a) P* 12½, 13.
202 12 1d. vermilion-red 2·50 15
a. Oval broken by tip of bust (R. 10/3)
203 1d. red-orange 2·50 15
a. Oval broken by tip of bust (R. 10/3)
204 2d. blue (retouched plate) 3·00 20
a. "FWO" for "TWO" (R. 8/7) — 20·00

(b) P 12

205 11 1s. mauve 12·00 2·75

B. *Unwmkd paper; with blue burelé band at back. P* 12½, 13
206 12 1d. deep vermilion-red 2·00 15
a. Oval broken by tip of bust (R. 10/3)
b. "PE" of "PENNY" omitted (R. 1/2) £100 75·00

C. *Thin paper. Crown and Q faintly impressed. P* 12½, 13
207 12 2d. blue (retouched plate) 6·00
a. "FWO" for "TWO" (R. 8/7)

15

16

17

18

1895–96. A. W **6** *(sideways on ½d.). (a) P* 12½, 13.
208 15 ½d. green 1·00 45
a. Double impression
209 ½d. deep green 1·00 45
a. Printed both sides 60·00
210 16 1d. orange-red 2·25 20
211 1d. pale red 2·00 20
212 2d. blue 3·25 35
213 17 2½d. carmine 8·00 3·00
214 2½d. rose 9·00 3·00
215 18 5d. purple-brown 10·00 2·75

(b) P 12

217 16 1d. red .. .. 20·00
218 2d. blue .. .. — 12·00

B. *Thick paper. W* **10** *(sideways) (part only on each stamp).*

(a) P 12½, 13

219 15 ½d. green .. .. 1·00 45
220 ½d. deep green .. .. 1·00 45

(b) P 12

221 15 ½d. green .. .. 12·00
222 ½d. deep green .. .. 12·00

C. *No wmk; with blue burelé band at back.* (a) *P* 12½, 13

223 15 ½d. green .. .. 1·00 50
a. Without *burelé* band .. .. 40·00
224 ½d. deep green .. .. 1·00

(b) P 12

225 15 ½d. green .. .. 15·00
a. Without *burelé* band .. .. 50·00

Nos. 223a and 225a are from the margins of the sheet.

D. *Thin paper, with Crown and Q faintly impressed. P* 12½, 13

227 15 ½d. green .. .. 1·40 50
228 16 1d. orange-red .. .. 3·00 30

19

1896. *W* **6**. *P* 12½, 13.

229 19 1d. vermilion .. .. 7·50 40

Used examples of a 6d. green as Type **19** (figures in lower corners only) are known, mostly with readable 1902 postmark dates. It is believed that this 6d. was prepared, but not officially issued (*Price* £1000 *used*).

20 21 22

23 24 25

Die I Die II

Two Dies of 4d.:

Die I. Serif of horizontal bar on lower right 4d. is clear of vertical frame line.
Die II. Serif joins vertical frame line.

1897–1907. *Figures in all corners. W* **6** *(sideways on* ½*d).* *P* 12½, 13.

231 20 ½d. deep green .. .. 3·50 2·00
a. Perf 12 .. .. — 90·00
232 21 1d. orange-vermilion .. .. .. 1·00 15
233 1d. vermilion .. .. 1·00 15
234 2d. blue .. .. 1·25 15
a. Cracked plate .. .. .. 50·00 20·00
235 2d. deep blue .. .. 1·25 15
a. Cracked plate .. .. .. 50·00 20·00
236 22 2½d. rose .. .. 15·00 6·00
237 2½d. purple/*blue* .. .. 8·50 85
238 2½d. brown-purple/*blue* .. .. .. 8·50 85
239 2½d. slate/*blue* .. .. 11·00 2·75
240 21 3d. brown .. .. 10·00 1·00
241 3d. deep brown .. .. 8·00 80
242 3d. reddish brown (1906) .. .. 8·00 80
243 3d. grey-brown (1907) .. .. .. 9·50 80
244 4d. yellow (Die I) .. .. .. 8·00 80
a. Die II .. .. 18·00 1·75
245 4d. yellow-buff (Die I) .. .. .. 8·00 80
a. Die II .. .. 18·00 1·75
246 23 5d. purple-brown .. .. .. 7·00 80
247 5d. dull brown (1906) .. .. .. 8·00 1·50
248 5d. black-brown (1907) .. .. .. 9·00 1·75
249 21 6d. green .. .. 7·00 1·25
250 6d. yellow-green .. .. 6·00 1·25
251 24 1s. pale mauve .. .. 13·00 1·00
252 1s. dull mauve .. .. 13·00 1·00
253 1s. bright mauve .. .. 15·00 2·00
254 25 2s. turquoise-green .. .. .. 30·00 7·00

The 1d. perf 12 × 9½ was not an authorised issue.

The cracked plate variety on the 2d. developed during 1901 and shows as a white break on the Queen's head and neck.

1897–8. *W* **6** *(a) Zigzag roulette in black. (b) The same but plain. (c) Roulette (a) and also (b). (d) Roulette (b) and perf* 12½, 13. *(e) Roulette (a) and perf* 12½, 13. *(f) Compound of (a), (b), and perf* 12½, 13.

256 21 1d. vermilion (*a*) .. .. 5·00 4·00
257 1d. vermilion (*b*) .. .. 2·50 1·50
258 1d. vermilion (*c*) .. .. 4·75
259 1d. vermilion (*d*) .. .. 3·00 2·50
260 1d. vermilion (*e*) .. .. 50·00
261 1d. vermilion (*f*) .. .. 60·00

26

27

1899–1906. *W* **6**. *P* 12½, 13.

262 26 ½d. deep green .. .. 1·00 20
263 ½d. grey-green .. .. 1·00 20
264 ½d. pale green (1906) .. .. .. 1·00 20

Stamps of T **26** without wmk, are proofs.

(Des F. Elliott)

1900 (19 June). *Charity. T* **27** *and horiz design showing Queen Victoria in medallion inscr* "PATRIOTIC FUND 1900". *W* **6**. *P* 12.

264*a* 1d. (6d.) claret .. .. 80·00 90·00
264*b* 2d. (1s.) violet £180 £200

These stamps, sold at 6d. and 1s. respectively, paid postage of 1d. and 2d. only, the difference being contributed to a Patriotic Fund.

28

QUEENSLAND QUEENSLAND
A B

TWO TYPES OF "QUEENSLAND". Three different duty plates, each 120 (12 × 10), were produced for Type **28**. The first contained country inscriptions as Type A and was only used for Nos. 265/6. The second duty plate used for Nos. 265/6 and 282/5 contained 117 examples as Type A and 3 as Type B occurring on R. 1/6, R. 2/6 and R. 3/6. The third plate, also used for Nos. 265/6 and 282/5, had all inscriptions as Type B.

(Typo Victoria Govt Printer, Melbourne)

1903 (4 July). *W* w **10**. *P* 12½.

265 28 9d. brown and ultramarine (A) .. 10·00 1·75
266 9d. brown and ultramarine (B) .. 10·00 1·75

1903. *W* **6**. *P* 12.

267 26 ½d. green .. .. 1·50 30
268 21 1d. vermilion .. .. 2·25 70
269 2d. blue .. .. — 5·00

Nos. 267/9 can be found with rough or clean cut holes from this comb machine. A perf 12½ line machine was also used, but stamps from it are difficult to distinguish.

1905. *Recess. W* **6**. *P* 12½, 13 *(irregular line).*

270 9 2s. 6d. vermilion .. .. 60·00 32·00
271 £1 deep green £450 £300
a. Re-entry (R. 1/2) .. .. .. — £400
b. Retouch (R. 6/4) .. .. .. — £400

29

1905–10. *Litho.* A. *W* **6**, *twice sideways.* (a) *P* 12 (1905–6).

272 9 5s. rose (7.06) .. .. 65·00 65·00
273 £1 deep green (7.11.05) .. .. .. £250 90·00
a. Re-entry (R. 1/2) .. .. .. — £150
b. Retouch (R. 6/4) .. .. .. — £150

(b) *P* 12½, 13 *(irregular line)*

274 9 £1 deep green (7.06) £350 £100
a. Re-entry (R. 1/2) .. .. .. — £160
b. Retouch (R. 6/4) .. .. .. — £160

B. *W* **29**, *twice sideways. P* 12½, 13 *(irregular line)* (1907–10)

275 9 2s. 6d. vermilion .. .. .. 40·00 26·00
276 2s. 6d. dull orange (1910) .. .. 55·00 32·00
277 5s. rose .. .. 45·00 26·00
278 5s. deep rose .. .. 55·00 38·00
279 10s. deep brown .. .. £100 35·00
280 £1 bluish green .. .. £170 80·00
a. Re-entry (R. 1/2) .. .. .. — £130
b. Retouch (R. 6/4) .. .. .. — £130
280c £1 deep green £325 £250
ca. Re-entry (R. 1/2) .. .. .. — £350
cb. Retouch (R. 6/4) .. .. .. — £350

The lithographic stone used for Nos. 272/80c took the full sheet of 30 so the varieties on the £1 recess-printed version also appear on the stamps printed by lithography.

30

32

Redrawn types of T **21**

T **30**. The head is redrawn, the top of the crown is higher and touches the frame, as do also the back of the chignon and the point of the bust. The forehead is filled in with lines of shading, and the figures in the corners appear to have been redrawn also.

T **32**. The forehead is plain (white instead of shaded), and though the top of the crown is made higher, it does not touch the frame; but the point of the bust and the chignon still touch The figure in the right lower corner does not touch the line below, and has not the battered appearance of that in the first redrawn type. The stamps are very clearly printed, the lines of shading being distinct.

1906 (Sept). *W* **6**. *P* 12½, 13 *(comb).*

281 30 2d. dull blue (*shades*) .. .. .. 5·00 1·50

(Typo Victoria Govt Printer, Melbourne)

1906 (Sept)–**10**. *Wmk Crown and double-lined A, W* w **11**.

(a) *P* 12 × 12½.

282 28 9d. brown and ultramarine (A) .. 22·00 2·50
283 9d. brown and ultramarine (B) .. 11·00 2·00
283*a* 9d. pale brown and blue (A) .. ..
284 9d. pale brown and blue (B) .. .. 11·00 2·25

(b) *P* 11 (1910)

285 28 9d. brown and blue (B) .. .. .. — £200

1907–09. *W* **29**. (a) *P* 12½, 13 *(comb).*

286 26 ½d. deep green .. .. 1·00 20
287 ½d. deep blue-green .. .. .. 1·00 20
288 21 1d. vermilion .. .. 1·00 15
a. Imperf (pair) £150
289 30 2d. dull blue .. .. 1·40 15
289*a* 2d. bright blue (3.08) .. .. .. 7·50 2·00
290 32 2d. bright blue (4.08) .. .. .. 1·50 15
291 21 3d. pale brown (8.08) .. .. .. 10·00 70
292 3d. bistre-brown .. .. 10·00 80
293 4d. yellow (Die I) .. .. .. 10·00 1·25
a. Die II .. .. 22·00 2·75
294 4d. grey-black (Die I) (4.09) .. .. 12·00 1·50
a. Die II .. .. 27·00 3·50
295 23 5d. dull brown .. .. 7·50 1·25
295*a* 5d. sepia (12.09) .. .. .. 11·00 2·00
296 21 6d. yellow-green .. .. 8·50 1·25
297 6d. bright green .. .. 10·00 1·50
298 24 1s. violet (1908) .. .. .. 11·00 1·60
299 1s. bright mauve .. .. 12·00 1·50
300 25 2s. turquoise-green (8.08) .. .. 30·00 6·50

Stamps of this issue also exist with the irregular line perforation 12½, 13. This was used when the comb perforation was under repair.

(b) *P* 13 × 11 *to* 12½

301 26 ½d. deep green .. ..
302 21 1d. vermilion .. .. 2·50 50
303 32 2d. blue .. .. 4·00 1·00
304 21 3d. bistre-brown .. .. .. 8·00 2·00
305 4d. grey-black .. .. 20·00
306 23 5d. dull brown .. .. 15·00
307 21 6d. yellow-green .. .. .. 16·00
308 23 1s. violet .. .. 25·00

The perforation (*b*) is from a machine introduced to help cope with the demands caused by the introduction of penny postage. The three rows at top (or bottom) of the sheet show varieties gauging 13 × 11½, 13 × 11, and 13 × 12 respectively, these are obtainable in strips of three showing the three variations.

Many values of the 1907–09 issue were subsequently produced by lithography.

1911. *W* **29**. *Perf irregular compound,* 10½ *to* 12½.

309 21 1d. vermilion .. .. — £120

This was from another converted machine, formerly used for perforating Railway stamps. The perforation was very unsatisfactory and only one or two sheets were sold.

POSTAL FISCALS

Authorised for use from 1 January 1880 until 1 July 1892

CANCELLATIONS. Beware of stamps which have had pen-cancellations cleaned off and then had faked postmarks applied. Used prices quoted are for postally used examples between the above dates.

F 1

F 2

1866–68. A. *No wmk. P* 13.

F 1 F1 1d. blue .. .. 25·00 5·00
F 2 6d. deep violet .. .. .. 25·00 30·00
F 3 1s. blue-green .. .. .. 30·00 9·00
F 4 2s. brown .. .. 85·00 42·00
F 5 2s. 6d. dull red .. .. .. 85·00 30·00
F 6 5s. yellow .. .. £200 60·00
F 7 10s. green £350 £100
F 8 20s. rose £425 £150

B. *Wmk F* **2**. *P* 13

F 9 F1 1d. blue .. .. 10·00 20·00
F10 6d. deep violet .. .. .. 25·00 30·00
F11 6d. blue .. .. 25·00 14·00
F12 1s. blue-green .. .. .. 30·00 14·00
F13 2s. brown .. .. 85·00 30·00
F13*a* 5s. yellow .. .. £200 65·00
F14 10s. green £350 £100
F15 20s. rose £425 £150

F 3

F 4

F 5

1871–2. *P* 12 *or* 13. A. *Wmk Large Crown and Q, as W* **10.**

F16	F 3	1d. mauve	10·00	5·00
F17		6d. red-brown	20·00	10·00
F18		1s. green	30·00	12·00
F19		2s. blue	40·00	10·00
F20		2s. 6d. brick-red	60·00	25·00
F21		5s. orange-brown	£100	25·00
F22		10s. brown	£200	75·00
F23		20s. rose	£350	£120

B. *No wmk. Blue burelé band at back*

F24	F 3	1d. mauve	14·00	6·50
F25		6d. red-brown	20·00	10·00
F26		6d. mauve	22·00	12·00
F27		1s. green	30·00	12·00
F28		2s. blue	45·00	50·00
F29		2s. 6d. vermilion	85·00	35·00
F30		5s. yellow-brown	£120	40·00
F31		10s. brown	£225	90·00
F32		20s. rose	£350	£110

1878–9. A. *No wmk. Lilac burelé band at back. P* 12.

F33	F 4	1d. violet	—	12·00

B. *Wmk Crown and Q, W* **5.** *P* 12

F34	F 4	1d. violet	15·00	8·00

Stamps as Type F 5 were not issued until 1 July 1892. The existence of postal cancellations on such issues was unauthorised.

The six former colonies of New South Wales, Queensland, South Australia, Tasmania, Victoria and Western Australia united to form the Commonwealth of Australia on 1 January 1901.

On 1 March 1901 control of the postal service passed to the federal administration. The first national postage due stamps appeared in July 1902, but it was not until January 1913 that postage stamps inscribed "AUSTRALIA" were issued.

Rhodesia

Stamps of BECHUANALAND were used in Matabeleland on the runner post between Gubulawayo and Mafeking (Bechuanaland) from 21 August 1888 until 5 May 1894. Such stamps were cancelled "GUBULAWAYO" or by the barred oval "678" obliteration.

Between 27 June 1890 and 13 May 1892 external mail from Mashonaland sent via Bechuanaland was franked with that territory's stamps. A similar arrangement, using the stamps of MOZAMBIQUE, existed for the route via Beira inaugurated on 2 January 1892. In both instances the stamps were cancelled by the post office receiving the mail from Mashonaland. After 14 May 1892 letters via Bechuanaland were franked with a combination of B.S.A. Company and Bechuanaland issues.

PRICES FOR STAMPS ON COVER TO 1945

Nos. 1/7	*from* × 5
Nos. 8/13	—
Nos. 14/17	*from* × 2
Nos. 18/24	*from* × 10
Nos. 25/6	—
Nos. 27/8	*from* × 7
Nos. 29/35	*from* × 10
Nos. 36/7	—
Nos. 41/6	*from* × 6
Nos. 47/50	—
Nos. 51/3	*from* × 2
Nos. 58/64	*from* × 3
Nos. 66/72	*from* × 8
Nos. 73/4	—
Nos. 75/87	*from* × 6
Nos. 88/93*a*	—
Nos. 94/9	*from* × 3
Nos. 100/10	*from* × 5
Nos. 111/13*e*	—
Nos. 114/18	*from* × 7
Nos. 119/60*a*	*from* × 2
Nos. 160*b*/6*b*	—
Nos. 167/78	*from* × 2
Nos. 179/81*a*	—
Nos. 182/5*a*	*from* × 2
Nos. 186/208	*from* × 3
Nos. 209/41	*from* × 2
Nos. 242/54*a*	—
Nos. 255/77	*from* × 2
Nos. 278/9*c*	—
Nos. 280/1	*from* × 7
Nos. 282/310	*from* × 2
Nos. 311/22	—

A. ISSUES FOR THE BRITISH SOUTH AFRICA COMPANY TERRITORY

1

2

½d.

(3)

(Recess B.W.)

1892 (2 Jan). *Thin wove paper. P* 14, 14½.

1	**1**	1d. black	9·00	1·25
2		6d. ultramarine	48·00	20·00
3		6d. deep blue	22·00	2·50
4		1s. grey-brown	27·00	7·50
5		2s. vermilion	40·00	25·00
6		2s. 6d. grey-purple	24·00	25·00
7		2s. 6d. lilac	24·00	25·00
8		5s. orange-yellow	42·00	48·00
9		10s. deep green	60·00	90·00
10	**2**	£1 deep blue	£160	£130
11		£2 rose-red*	£375	£150
12		£5 sage-green	£1500	£450
13		£10 brown	£2750	£700
1/10		*Set of* 10	£350	£350

*For later printing of the £2 see No. 74.

Nos. 3 and 7 came from later printings.

Great caution is needed in buying the high values in either used or unused condition, many stamps offered being revenue stamps cleaned and re-gummed or with forged postmarks.

The following sheet watermarks are known in the issues of 1892 and 1892–94. (1) William Collins, Sons & Co's paper watermarked with the firm's monogram, and "PURE LINEN WOVE BANK" in double-lined capitals. (2) As (1) with "EXTRA STRONG" and "139" added. (3) Paper by Wiggins, Teape & Co, watermarked "W T & Co" in script letters in double-lined wavy border. (4) The same firm's paper, watermarked "1011" in double-lined figures. (5) "WIGGINS TEAPE & CO LONDON" in double-lined block capitals. Many values can also be found on a slightly thicker paper without wmk, but single specimens are not easily distinguishable.

1892 (2 Jan).* *Nos.* 2 *and* 4 *surch as T* **3.**

14	**1**	½d. on 6d. ultramarine	60·00	95·00
15		2d. on 6d. ultramarine	55·00	£120
16		4d. on 6d. ultramarine	75·00	£160
17		8d. on 1s. grey-brown	85·00	£200

*This, being the date when postal services commenced, is the earliest date when these stamps could have been used, but it has not been established when supplies arrived.

Caution is needed in buying these surcharges as both forged surcharges and forged postmarks exist.

4

5 (ends of scrolls behind legs of springboks)

(T 4. Centre recess; value B.W.)

1892 (2 Jan)–**94.** *Thin wove paper* (*wmks as note after No.* 13). *P* 14, 14½.

18	**4**	½d. dull blue and vermilion	2·50	1·00
19		½d. deep blue and vermilion	2·50	2·25
20		2d. sea-green and vermilion	8·00	1·75
21		3d. grey-black and green (8.92)	8·00	1·75
22		4d. chestnut and black	8·00	1·75
23		8d. rose-lake and ultramarine	10·00	4·50
24		8d. red and ultramarine	10·00	4·50
25		3s. brown and green (1894)	85·00	60·00
26		4s. grey-black and vermilion (1893)	30·00	35·00
18/26		*Set of* 7	£140	95·00

(Recess P.B. from the Bradbury, Wilkinson plates)

1895? *Thick soft wove paper. P* 12½.

27	**4**	2d. green and red	20·00	5·00
28		4d. yellow-brown and black	22·00	9·00
		a. Imperf (pair)	£1200	

(Centre recess; value typo P.B.)

1896–97. *Wove paper. P* 14.

(*a*) *Die I. Plates* 1 *and* 2.

Small dot to the right of the tail of the right-hand supporter in the coat of arms. Body of lion only partly shaded.

29	**5**	1d. scarlet and emerald	10·00	2·75
		a. Carmine-red and emerald		
30		2d. brown and mauve	11·00	1·00
31		3d. chocolate and ultramarine	2·25	80
32		4d. ultramarine and mauve		
		a. Imperf between (pair)		
		b. Blue and mauve	9·50	6·00
33		6d. mauve and pink	55·00	5·00
34		8d. green and mauve/*buff*	4·50	45
		a. Imperf between (pair		
		b. Imperf (pair)	£1400	
35		1s. green and blue	15·00	1·75
36		3s. green and mauve/*blue*	48·00	27·00
		a. Imperf (pair)	£1700	
37		4s. orange-red and blue/*green*	40·00	2·00
29/37		*Set of* 9	£180	42·00

(*b*) *Die II. Plates* 3 *and* 4

No dot. Body of lion heavily shaded all over.

41	**5**	½d. slate and violet	1·00	1·50
42		1d. scarlet and emerald	1·50	2·25
43		2d. brown and mauve	3·75	3·50
44		4d. ultramarine and mauve	55·00	9·00
		a. Blue and mauve	6·00	40
46		6d. mauve and rose	4·50	45
47		2s. indigo and green/*buff*	20·00	2·00
48		2s. 6d. brown and purple/*yellow*	48·00	30·00
49		5s. chestnut and emerald	35·00	12·00
50		10s. slate and vermilion/*rose*	80·00	60·00
41/50		*Set of* 9	£170	£100

One Penny

(6)

THREE PENCE.

(7)

(Surchd by *Bulawayo Chronicle*)

1896 (April). *Matabele Rebellion provisionals. Surch with T* **6** *and* **7.**

51	**6**	1d. on 3d. (No. 21)	£300	£350
		a. "P" in "Penny" inverted	£6500	
		b. "y" in "Penny" inverted		
		c. Surch double		
52		1d. on 4s. (No. 26)	£300	£225
		a. "P" in "Penny" inverted	£6500	
		b. "y" in "Penny" inverted	£6500	
		c. Single bar through original value	£800	£1000
53	**7**	3d. on 5s. (No. 8)	£150	£200
		a. "R" in "THREE" inverted	£8500	
		b. "T" in "THREE" inverted	£8500	

Nos. 51 and 52 occur in two settings, one with 9¾ mm between value and upper bar, the other with 11 mm between value and upper bar.

BRITISH SOUTH AFRICA COMPANY.

(8)

9 (Ends of scrolls between legs of springboks)

1896 (22 May–Aug). *Cape of Good Hope stamps optd by Argus Printing Co, Cape Town, with T* **8.** *Wmk Anchor* (3*d. wmk Crown CA*). *P* 14.

58	**6**	½d. grey-black (No. 48*a*)	6·00	9·00
59	**17**	1d. rose-red (No. 58)	9·50	10·00
60	**6**	2d. deep bistre (No. 50*a*)	10·00	7·50
61		3d. pale claret (No. 40)	45·00	48·00
62		4d. blue (No. 51)	12·00	12·00
		a. "COMPANY," omitted	£7000	
63	**4**	6d. deep purple (No. 52*a*)	40·00	50·00
64	**6**	1s. yellow-ochre (No. 65) (Aug)	80·00	£110
58/64		*Set of* 7	£170	£200

(Eng J. A. C. Harrison (vignette), Bain or Rapkin (£1) (frames). Recess Waterlow)

1897. *P* 13½ *to* 16.

66	**9**	½d. grey-black and purple	1·60	2·50
67		1d. scarlet and emerald	3·00	3·25
68		2d. brown and mauve	2·75	60
69		3d. brown-red and slate-blue	2·50	30
		a. Imperf between (pair)	£1200	
70		4d. ultramarine and claret	5·00	1·25
		a. Imperf between (pair)	£3500	£3500
71		6d. dull purple and pink	5·50	3·50
72		8d. green and mauve/*buff*	8·50	40
		a. Imperf between (pair)	—	£900
73		£1 black and red-brown/*green*	£400	£225

(Recess Waterlow, from the Bradbury plate)

1897 (Jan). *P* 15.

74	**2**	£2 rosy red	£1600	£400

10

11

12

(Recess Waterlow)

1898–1908. *P* 13½ *to* 15½.

75	**10**	½d. dull bluish green	50	15
		a. Yellow-green (1904)	70	20
		aa. Imperf between (pair)	£600	
		ab. Imperf (pair)	£550	
76		½d. deep green (*shades*) (1908)	23·00	45
77		1d. rose (*shades*)	85	15
		a. Imperf (pair)	£550	£550
		b. Imperf between (pair)	£500	
78		1d. red (*shades*) (1905)	2·00	15
		a. Imperf between (pair)	£325	£375
		b. Imperf (pair)	£500	
79		2d. brown	1·25	10

International Fine Art
and Philatelic Auctioneers

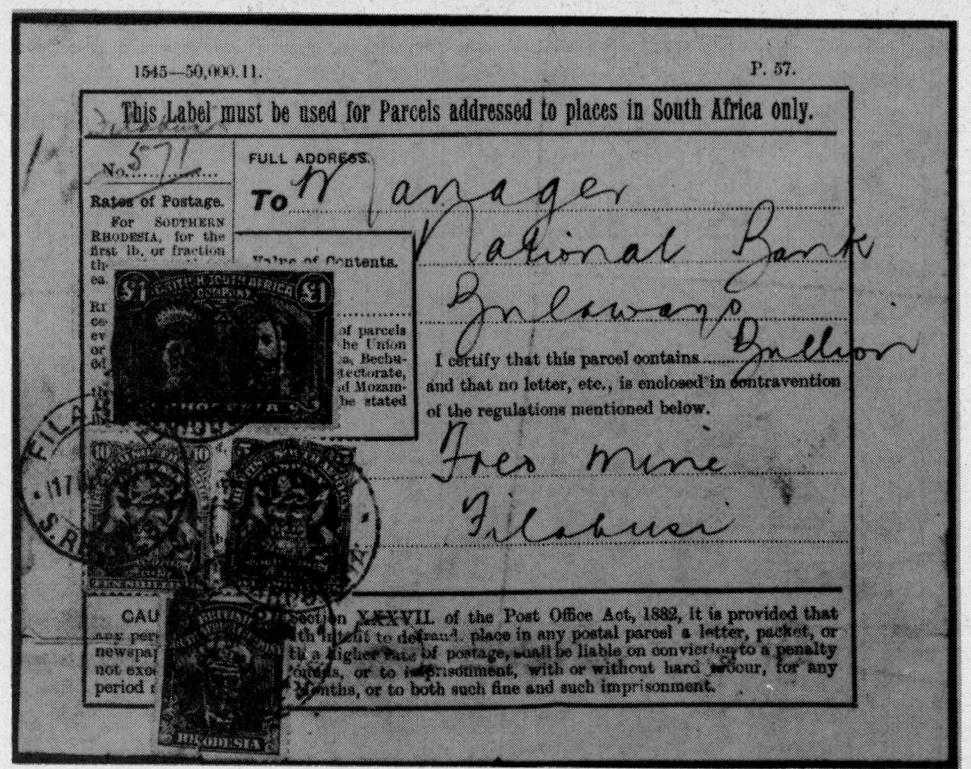

RARITIES OF RHODESIA

Auctioned by Christie's Robson Lowe on 10 June 1986

If you are thinking of buying or selling stamps at Christie's and would like further information, please contact one of the offices below:

Christie's New York
502 Park Avenue
New York, NY 10022
Tel: (1) 212 546 1000
Fax: (1) 212 980 8163

Christie's London
8 King Street, St. James's
London SW1Y 6QT
Tel: (071) 839 9060
Fax: (071) 839 1611

Christie's Zurich
Steinwiesplatz
8032 Zurich
Tel: (411) 69 05 05
Fax: (411) 251 04 71

Auctions also held in Hong Kong and Melbourne.

80	10	2½d. dull blue (*shades*)	3·75	20
		a. Imperf between (pair)	£600	£600
		b. Grey-blue (shades) (1903)	6·00	50
81		3d. claret	3·75	40
		a. Imperf between (pair)	£700	
82		4d. olive	3·50	15
		a. Imperf between (pair)	£800	
83		6d. reddish purple	6·50	1·75
		a. Reddish mauve (1902)	12·00	5·00
84	11	1s. bistre	7·00	1·25
		a. Imperf between (pair)	£2000	
		b. Deep olive-bistre (1907)	£275	
		bc. Imperf (pair)	£2250	
		bd. Imperf between (horiz pair)	£2500	
		c. Bistre brown (1908)	32·00	8·00
		d. Brownish yellow (1908)	14·00	3·75
85		2s. 6d. bluish grey (11.06)	25·00	55
		a. Imperf between (pair)	£900	£600
		b. Imperf (vert pair)	—	£5000
86		3s. deep violet (1902)	9·00	50
		a. Deep bluish violet (1908)	35·00	9·00
87		5s. brown-orange	24·00	7·00
88		7s. 6d. black (11.01)	40·00	14·00
89		10s. grey-green	15·00	1·50
90	12	£1 greyish red-purple (*p* 15½) (7.01)	£150	50·00
		a. Perf 14. *Blackish purple* (1902)	£170	50·00
91		£2 brown (5.08)	65·00	6·50
92		£5 deep blue (7.01)	£3000	£2250
93		£10 lilac (7.01)	£3000	£2250
93*a*		£20 yellow-bistre (1901?)	£7500	
75/90		*Set of* 14	£250	70·00
80/1, 85/6, 88/93 Perf "Specimen"		*Set of* 10	£900	

A £100 cherry-red, perf 13½, was ordered in June 1901, a number of mint, together with three examples showing fiscal cancellations, being known.

RHODESIA.

13 Victoria Falls (14)

(Recess Waterlow)

1905 (13 July). *Visit of British Association and Opening of Victoria Falls Bridge. P* 13½ *to* 15.

94	13	1d. red	2·50	2·50
95		2½d. deep blue	7·50	3·75
96		5d. claret (Optd S. £100)	17·00	30·00
97		1s. blue-green	18·00	22·00
		a. Imperf (pair)	£7500	
		b. Imperf vert (horiz pair)	£8000	
		c. Imperf horiz (vert pair)	£10000	
98		2s. 6d. black	£100	£140
99		5s. violet	85·00	40·00
94/99		*Set of* 6	£200	£210
94/9 Perf (5d.) or Optd (others) "Specimen"		*Set of* 6	£250	

1909 (15 Apr)–**12**. *Optd as T* 14. *P* 13½ *to* 15.

100	10	½d. green *to* deep green	1·25	15
		a. No stop	35·00	24·00
		b. Yellow-green (1911)	35·00	27·00
101		1d. carmine-rose	1·25	15
		a. No stop	50·00	24·00
		b. Imperf between (pair)	£300	
		c. Deep carmine-rose	1·25	15
		cd. Imperf between (pair)	£350	
102		2d. brown	1·60	1·75
		a. No stop	65·00	45·00
103		2½d. pale dull blue	1·00	20
		a. No stop	26·00	21·00
104		3d. claret	1·60	20
		a. No stop	80·00	50·00
105		4d. olive	2·75	35
		a. No stop	55·00	50·00
106		6d. dull purple	11·00	2·25
		a. No stop	70·00	40·00
		b. Reddish purple	5·00	1·25
107	11	1s. deep brownish bistre	8·50	1·00
		a. No stop	75·00	32·00
108		2s. 6d. bluish grey	15·00	4·00
		a. No stop	70·00	50·00
109		3s. deep violet	15·00	4·00
110		5s. orange	25·00	11·00
		a. No stop	75·00	55·00
111		7s. 6d. black	45·00	11·00
112		10s. dull green	25·00	8·50
		a. No stop	£200	£180
113	12	£1 grey-purple	£100	55·00
		a. Vertical pair, one without opt	£11000	
		b. Overprint in violet	£250	£225
113*c*		£2 brown (*bluish paper*)	£3000	£275
113*d*		£2 rosy brown (*p* 14½×15) (1912)	£3000	£275
113*e*		£5 deep blue (*bluish paper*)	£5000	£2000
100/113		*Set of* 14	£225	85·00
100/13 Perf "Specimen"		*Set of* 14	£300	

In some values the no stop variety occurs in every stamp in a vertical row of a sheet, in other values only once in a sheet. Other varieties, such as no serif to the right of apex of "A", no serif to top of "E", etc., exist in some values.

RHODESIA. 5d

RHODESIA. TWO SHILLINGS.

(15) (16)

1909 (April)–**11**. *Surch as T* 15 *and* 16 (2s.), *in black.*

114	10	5d. on 6d. reddish purple	6·50	6·50
		a. Surcharge in violet	65·00	
115		5d. on 6d. dull purple	9·00	6·50
116	11	7½d. on 2s. 6d. bluish grey	3·50	2·25
		a. Surcharge in violet	13·00	4·00
		ab. Surch double	†	—
117		10d. on 3s. deep violet	13·00	13·00
		a. Surcharge in violet	4·00	2·50
118		2s. on 5s. orange	12·00	7·00
114/18 Perf "Specimen"		*Set of* 4	£170	

In the 7½d. and 10d. surcharges, the bars are spaced as in T 16.

17

18

(Recess Waterlow)

1910 (11 Nov)–**13**. (*a*) *P* 14.

119	17	½d. yellow-green	5·00	75
120		½d. bluish green	9·50	75
		a. Imperf (pair)	£5500	£4000
121		½d. olive-green	20·00	1·25
122		½d. dull green	55·00	50·00
123		1d. bright carmine	8·00	20
		a. Imperf between (pair)	£15000	£10000
124		1d. carmine-lake	23·00	30
125		1d. rose-red	9·00	20
126		2d. black and grey	22·00	4·50
127		2d. black-purple and slate-grey	£160	
128		2d. black and slate-grey	24·00	3·75
129		2d. black and slate	24·00	4·50
130		2d. black and grey-black	29·00	7·00
131		2½d. ultramarine	14·00	5·00
131*a*		2½d. bright ultramarine	12·00	5·00
132		2½d. dull blue	14·00	5·00
133		2½d. chalky blue	14·00	8·00
134		3d. purple and ochre	17·00	20·00
135		3d. purple and yellow-ochre	18·00	5·50
136		3d. magenta and yellow-ochre	55·00	45·00
137		3d. violet and ochre	70·00	70·00
138		4d. greenish black and orange	70·00	70·00
139		4d. brown-purple and orange	50·00	35·00
140		4d. black and orange	18·00	10·00
141		5d. purple-brown and olive-green	20·00	30·00
141*a*		5d. purple-brown and olive-yellow	18·00	35·00
		ab. Error. Purple-brown and ochre	£550	£150
143		5d. lake-brown and olive	£170	60·00
143*a*		5d. lake-brown and green	£18000	£1500
144		6d. red-brown and mauve	17·00	18·00
145		6d. brown and purple	17·00	7·00
145*a*		6d. bright chestnut and mauve	£600	60·00
146		8d. black and purple	£3500	
147		8d. dull purple and purple	£100	60·00
148		8d. greenish black and purple	£110	50·00
149		10d. scarlet and reddish mauve	26·00	48·00
150		10d. carmine and deep purple	£500	65·00
151		1s. grey-black and deep blue-green	24·00	15·00
151*a*		1s. black and deep blue-green	75·00	20·00
152		1s. black and pale blue-green	20·00	8·00
152*a*		1s. purple-black and blue-green	£200	35·00
153		2s. black and ultramarine	45·00	42·00
154		2s. black and dull blue	£600	48·00
154*a*		2s. purple-black and ultramarine	£2000	£180
155		2s. 6d. black and lake	£300	£275
155*a*		2s. 6d. black and crimson	£300	£275
156		2s. 6d. sepia and deep crimson	£350	£325
156*a*		2s. 6d. bistre-brown and crimson	£650	£500
157		2s. 6d. black and rose-carmine	£275	£275
158		3s. green and violet (*shades*)	£120	£130
158*a*		3s. bright green and magenta	£900	£550
159		5s. vermilion and deep green	£200	£200
160		5s. scarlet and pale yellow-green	£275	£200
160*a*		5s. crimson and yellow-green	£225	£200
160*b*		7s. 6d. carmine and pale blue	£600	£500
161		7s. 6d. carmine and light blue	£650	£550
162		7s. 6d. carmine and bright blue	£1100	£700
163		10s. deep myrtle and orange	£550	£250
164		10s. blue-green and orange	£475	£250
165		£1 carmine-red and bluish black	£900	£375
166		£1 rose-scarlet and bluish black	£1000	£375
166*a*		£1 crimson and slate-black	£1100	£600
		b. Error. Scarlet and reddish mauve	£8500	

(*b*) *P* 15

167	17	½d. blue-green	£250	13·00
168		½d. yellow-green	£250	10·00
169		½d. apple-green	£500	22·00
170		1d. carmine	£250	7·00
170*a*		1d. carmine-lake	£400	12·00
170*b*		1d. rose-carmine	£250	8·50
171		2d. black and grey-black	£600	25·00
171*a*		2d. black and grey	£600	25·00
171*b*		2d. black and slate	£600	25·00
172		2½d. ultramarine (*shades*)	70·00	35·00
173		3d. purple and yellow-ochre	£2000	50·00
173*a*		3d. claret and pale yellow-ochre	£1500	50·00
174		4d. black and orange (*shades*)	35·00	60·00
175		5d. lake-brown and olive-green	£700	75·00
176		6d. brown and mauve	£800	60·00
177		1s. black and blue-green (*shades*)	£750	55·00
178		2s. black and dull blue	£950	£300
179		£1 red and black	£12000	£4000

(*c*) *P* 15 × 14 *or* 14 × 15

179*a*	17	½d. yellow-green	†	£2000
179*b*		1d. carmine	†	£3000
180		3d. purple and ochre	£3000	£250
181		4d. black and orange	£425	
181*a*		1s. black and blue-green	£16000	£3000

(*d*) *P* 13½

182	17	½d. yellow-green	£250	35·00
182*a*		½d. green	£250	35·00
183		1d. bright carmine	£1500	48·00
184		2½d. ultramarine (*shades*)	32·00	45·00
185		8d. black and purple (*shades*)	60·00	£200
185*a*		8d. grey-purple and dull purple	£350	£350
119/185 Optd "Specimen" perf 14 except 2½d. and 8d. perf 13½		*Set of* 18	£2750	

Plate varieties in T 17 are:—½d., double dot below "D" in right-hand value tablet (*from* £500 *un.* £350 *used*); 2d. to £1 excluding 2½d., straight stroke in Queen's right ear known as the "gash in ear" variety (*from* 3 *to* 8 *times normal*).

Stamps from the above and the next issue are known compound perf with 14 or 15 on one side only or on adjoining sides but we no longer list them.

(Recess Waterlow)

1913 (1 Sept)–**22**. *No wmk.* (i) *From single working plates.*

(*a*) *P* 14.

186	18	½d. blue-green	3·75	25
187		½d. deep green	1·50	20
		a. Imperf horiz (vert pair)	£500	
188		½d. yellow-green	3·50	20
188*b*		½d. dull green	2·00	20
		ba. Imperf vert (horiz pair)	£600	
189		½d. bright green	4·00	25
		a. Imperf between (vert pair)	£900	
190		1d. rose-carmine	2·50	20
		a. Imperf between (pair)	£425	£400
191		1d. carmine-red (*shades*)	4·00	20
		a. Imperf between (pair)	£800	
192		1d. brown-red	1·75	15
193		1d. red	2·00	15
		a. Imperf between (horiz pair)	£600	
194		1d. scarlet	7·00	30
		a. Imperf between (horiz pair)	£700	
195		1d. rose-red	2·50	15
		a. Imperf between (horiz pair)	£425	
		b. Imperf between (vert pair)	£1300	
196		1d. rosine	£500	19·00
197		1½d. brown-ochre (1919)	1·75	15
		a. Imperf between (horiz pair)	£400	£400
198		1½d. bistre-brown (1917)	1·75	15
		a. Imperf between (horiz pair)	£425	£400
199		1½d. drab-brown (1917)	1·75	15
		a. Imperf between (horiz pair)	£400	
		b. Imperf between (vert pair)	£1200	
200		2½d. deep blue	2·50	8·00
201		2½d. bright blue	2·50	8·00

(*b*) *P* 15

202	18	½d. blue-green	8·50	5·00
203		½d. green	11·00	5·00
204		1d. rose-red	£475	85·00
		a. Imperf between (horiz pair)	£8000	
205		1d. brown-red	1·25	2·25
206		1½d. bistre-brown (1919)	12·00	6·50
206*a*		1½d. brown-ochre (1917)	22·00	6·50
207		2½d. deep blue	15·00	20·00
208		2½d. bright blue	13·00	19·00

(*c*) *P* 14 × 15

208*a*	18	½d. green	£2250	£190

(*d*) *P* 15 × 14

208*b*	18	½d. green	£2250	£190

(*e*) *P* 13½

208*d*	18	1d. red (*shades*)	—	£500

Die I

Die II

Die III

The remaining values were printed from double, i.e. head and duty, plates. There are at least four different head plates made from three different dies, which may be distinguished as follows:—

Die I. The King's left ear is neither shaded nor outlined; no outline to top of cap. Shank of anchor in cap badge is complete.

Die II. The ear is shaded all over, but has no outline. The top of the cap has a faint outline. Anchor as Die I.

Die III. The ear is shaded and outlined; a heavy continuous outline round the cap. Shank of anchor is broken just below the lowest line which crosses it.

(ii) *Printed from double plates. Head Die* I. (*a*) *P* 14.

209	18	2d. black and grey	4·50	3·25
210		3d. black and yellow	38·00	3·75
211		4d. black and orange-red	3·75	15·00
212		5d. black and green	3·50	5·00
213		6d. black and mauve	£125	23·00
213*a*		8d. violet and green	£3750	
214		2s. black and brown	55·00	35·00

(*b*) *P* 15

215	18	3d. black and yellow	4·00	7·50
216		4d. black and orange-red	90·00	11·00
217		6d. black and mauve	3·25	3·25
217*a*		8d. violet and green	£11000	
218		2s. black and brown	10·00	18·00

(iii) *Head Die* II. (*a*) *P* 14

219	18	2d. black and grey	6·00	1·25
220		2d. black and brownish grey	15·00	2·50
221		3d. black and deep yellow	15·00	2·75
222		3d. black and yellow	26·00	2·50
223		3d. black and buff	4·25	2·50

224	18	4d. black and orange-red	8·00	3·00
225		4d. black and deep orange-red ..	4·75	3·00
226		5d. black and grey-green	7·50	13·00
227		5d. black and bright green	5·50	13·00
228		6d. black and mauve	12·00	1·50
229		6d. black and purple	27·00	2·50
230		8d. violet and green	9·50	20·00
231		10d. blue and carmine-red	9·00	13·00
232		1s. black and greenish blue	12·00	12·00
233		1s. black and turquoise-blue	4·00	5·50
234		2s. black and brown	32·00	6·50
235		2s. black and yellow-brown	£110	16·00
236		2s. 6d. indigo and grey-brown ..	28·00	10·00
236*a*		2s. 6d. pale blue and brown	60·00	16·00
236*b*		3s. brown and blue	50·00	60·00
237		3s. chestnut and bright blue	50·00	65·00
238		5s. blue and yellow-green	85·00	42·00
239		5s. blue and blue-green	40·00	42·00
240		7s. 6d. blackish purple and slate-black	£170	£170
241		10s. crimson and yellow-green	£170	£170
242		£1 black and purple	£475	£500
243		£1 black and violet	£600	£650

(*b*) *P* 15

244	18	2d. black and grey	2·75	3·50
245		4d. black and deep orange-vermilion ..	£750	£225
246		8d. violet and green	£170	£130
247		10d. blue and red	3·75	15·00
248		1s. black and greenish blue	13·00	3·75
249		2s. 6d. indigo and grey-brown ..	28·00	48·00
250		3s. chocolate and blue..	£850	£250
251		5s. blue and yellow-green	90·00	90·00
251*a*		5s. blue and blue-green	£1300	
252		7s. 6d. blackish purple and slate-black	65·00	£120
253		10s. red and green	£160	£250
254		£1 black and purple	£1000	£1000
254*a*		£1 black and deep purple	£2000	£2000
186/254*a*		Optd "Specimen" (various Dies and Perfs) .. .. *Set of* 19	£1900	

(iv) *Head Die* III. *Toned paper, yellowish gum.* (*a*) *P* 14

255	18	2d. black and brownish grey	5·50	3·00
256		2d. black and grey-black	2·75	1·40
		a. Imperf between (horiz pair) ..	£3500	
		b. Imperf between (horiz strip of 3)	£5000	
		c. Imperf vert (horiz pair)	£3000	£3000
257		2d. black and grey	3·25	1·90
258		2d. black and sepia	13·00	3·00
259		3d. black and yellow	2·50	1·40
260		3d. black and ochre	2·50	1·40
261		4d. black and orange-red	7·00	2·75
262		4d. black and dull red	6·00	3·25
263		5d. black and pale green	4·00	8·00
		a. Imperf between (horiz strip of 3)	£8000	
264		5d. black and green	4·00	8·00
265		6d. black and reddish mauve	3·25	2·25
		a. Imperf between (horiz pair) ..	£6000	
266		6d. black and dull mauve	2·75	2·25
267		8d. mauve and dull blue-green ..	14·00	25·00
268		8d. mauve and greenish blue ..	14·00	25·00
		a. Imperf vert (horiz pair)	£6000	
269		10d. indigo and carmine	8·00	18·00
270		10d. blue and red	6·50	17·00
271		1s. black and greenish blue	3·50	2·75
272		1s. black and pale blue-green ..	3·50	2·75
272*a*		1s. black and light blue	8·00	4·50
272*b*		1s. black and green	40·00	16·00
273		2s. black and brown	11·00	12·00
		aa. Imperf between (vert pair) ..	—	£12000
273*a*		2s. black and yellow-brown	£1000	80·00
274		2s. 6d. dp ultramarine & grey-brn	20·00	23·00
274*a*		2s. 6d. pale blue and pale bistre-brown (*shades*)	55·00	28·00
274*b*		3s. chestnut and light blue	£140	60·00
275		5s. deep blue and blue-green (*shades*)	55·00	40·00
276		5s. blue & pale yell-grn (*shades*) ..	55·00	40·00
276*a*		7s. 6d. maroon and slate-black ..	£750	£850
277		10s. carmine-lake and yellow-green ..	£300	£160
278		£1 black and bright purple	£500	£500
279		£1 black and deep purple	£500	£500
279*a*		£1 black and violet-indigo	£500	£500
279*b*		£1 black and deep violet	£500	£500

(*b*) *P* 15

279*c*	18	2d. black and brownish grey	£4500	£550

Half Penny
(19)

Half- Penny.
(20)

1917 (15 Aug). *No.* 190 *surch at the Northern Rhodesian Administrative Press, Livingstone, with T* 19, *in violet or violet-black.*

280	18	½d. on 1d. rose-carmine (*shades*) ..	1·75	4·00
		a. Surch inverted	£1700	£1700
		b. Letters "n n" spaced wider ..	7·50	11·00
		c. Letters "n y" spaced wider.. ..	4·00	7·50

The setting was in two rows of 10 repeated three times in the sheet.

The two colours of the surcharge occur on the same sheet.

1917 (22 Sept). *No.* 190 *surch as T* 20 (*new setting with hyphen, and full stop after* "Penny"), *in deep violet.*

281	18	½d. on 1d. rose-carmine (*shades*) ..	95	2·50

1922–24. *New printings on white paper with clear white gum.*

(i) *Single working plates.* (*a*) *P* 14

282	18	½d. dull green (1922)	4·75	45
		a. Imperf between (vert pair) ..	£1600	£1000
283		½d. deep blue-green (1922)	4·25	90
284		1d. bright rose (1922)	4·00	1·50
285		1d. bright rose-scarlet (1923)	3·75	1·25
		a. Imperf between (horiz pair) ..	£1600	
286		1d. aniline red (8.24)	20·00	2·75
287		1½d. brown-ochre (1923)	4·50	75
		a. Imperf between (vert pair) ..	£1600	£1000

(*b*) *P* 15

288	18	½d. dull green (1923)	25·00	22·00
289		1d. bright rose-scarlet (1923)	25·00	30·00
290		1½d. brown-ochre (1923)	30·00	28·00

(ii) *Double plates. Head Die* III. (*a*) *P* 14

291	18	2d. black and grey-purple (1922) ..	1·40	90
292		2d. black and slate-purple (1923) ..	2·25	1·25
293		3d. black and yellow (1922)	8·00	11·00
294		4d. black & orange-vermilion (1922–3)	7·00	14·00
295		6d. jet-black and lilac (1922–3) ..	4·50	2·50
296		8d. mauve and pale blue-green (1922)	25·00	42·00
297		8d. violet and grey-green (1923) ..	25·00	42·00
298		10d. bright ultramarine and red (1922)	7·00	22·00
299		10d. brt ultramarine & carm-red (1923)	7·00	22·00
300		1s. black and dull blue (1922–3) ..	2·00	2·50
		a. Imperf between (horiz pair) ..	£6000	
		b. Imperf between (vert pair) ..	£8000	
301		2s. black and brown (1922–3).. ..	13·00	17·00
302		2s. 6d. ultramarine and sepia (1922) ..	27·00	40·00
303		2s. 6d. violet-blue & grey-brown (1923)	25·00	38·00
304		3s. red-brown & turquoise-bl (1922) ..	38·00	50·00
305		3s. red-brown and grey-blue (1923) ..	60·00	60·00
306		5s. brt ultramarine and emerald (1922)	60·00	60·00
307		5s. deep blue and bright green (1923)	60·00	60·00
308		7s. 6d. brown-purple and slate (1922)	£140	£180
309		10s. crimson and brt yellow-green (1922)	£130	£150
310		10s. carmine and yellow-green (1923) ..	£140	£180
311		£1 black and deep magenta (1922) ..	£450	£500
311*a*		£1 black and magenta (1923).. ..	£450	£500

(*b*) *P* 15 (1923)

312	18	2d. black and slate-purple	32·00	
313		4d. black and orange-vermilion ..	35·00	
314		6d. jet-black and lilac	38·00	
315		8d. violet and grey-green	38·00	
316		10d. bright ultramarine & carmine-red	50·00	
317		1s. black and dull blue	50·00	
318		2s. black and brown	90·00	
319		2s. 6d. violet-blue and grey-brown ..	95·00	
320		3s. red-brown and grey-blue	£120	
321		5s. deep blue and bright green ..	£140	
322		£1 black and magenta	£600	

The 1922 printing shows the mesh of the paper very clearly through the gum. In the 1923 printing the gum is very smooth and the mesh of the paper is not so clearly seen. Where date is given as "(1922–23)" two printings were made, which do not differ sufficiently in colour to be listed separately.

Nos. 312/22 were never sent out to Rhodesia but only issued in London. Any used copies could, therefore, only have been obtained by favour.

In 1924 Rhodesia was divided into NORTHERN and SOUTHERN RHODESIA and between 1954 and 1964 these were merged in the Central African Federation (*see* RHODESIA AND NYASALAND). In 1964 there were again separate issues for Northern and Southern Rhodesia but after Northern Rhodesia became independent and was renamed Zambia, Southern Rhodesia was renamed RHODESIA in October 1964.

B. ISSUES FOR THE FORMER SOUTHERN RHODESIA

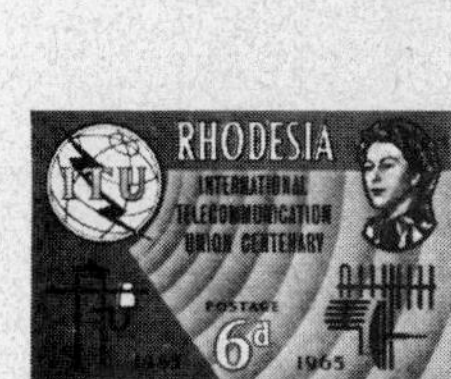

59 "Telecommunications"

60 Bangala Dam

(Des V. Whiteley. Photo Harrison)

1965 (17 May). *I.T.U. Centenary. P* 14½.

351	59	6d. violet and light yellow-olive ..	1·00	25
352		1s. 3d. violet and lilac	1·00	35
353		2s. 6d. violet and light brown ..	2·00	3·00
351/3		.. .. *Set of* 3	3·50	3·25

(Des V. Whiteley. Photo Harrison)

1965 (19 July). *Water Conservation. T* 60 *and similar vert designs. Multicoloured. P* 14.

354	3d. Type 60	20	10
355	4d. Irrigation canal	50	45
356	2s. 6d. Cutting sugar cane	80	1·25
354/6	.. .. *Set of* 3	1·40	1·60

63 Sir Winston Churchill, Quill, Sword and Houses of Parliament

(Des H. Baxter. Photo Harrison)

1965 (16 Aug). *Churchill Commemoration. P* 14½.

357	63	1s. 3d. black and bright blue	50	35

UNILATERAL DECLARATION OF INDEPENDENCE

Independence was declared by Rhodesia on 11 November 1965 but this was not recognised by the British Government. Following a conference in London during 1979 it was agreed that the British Government should resume control, pending elections to be held in February 1980.

After the elections Rhodesia became an independent republic within the Commonwealth on 18 April 1980, as ZIMBABWE.

64 Coat of Arms

(Des Col. C. R. Dickenson. Litho Mardon Printers, Salisbury)

1965 (8 Dec). *"Independence". P* 11.

358	64	2s. 6d. multicoloured	10	15
		a. Imperf (pair)	£450	

INDEPENDENCE
11th November
1965

INDEPENDENCE 11th November 1965 (65)

= 5/- (66)

1966 (17 Jan). (*a*) *Nos.* 92/105 *of Southern Rhodesia optd with T* 65 *or larger* (5s. *to* £1).

359	½d. yellow, yellow-green and light blue ..	10	10
	a. Pair, one stamp without opt. ..	£1400	
360	1d. reddish violet and yellow-ochre ..	10	10
361	2d. yellow and deep violet	10	10
362	3d. chocolate and pale blue.. ..	10	10
363	4d. yellow-orange and deep green ..	15	10
364	6d. carmine-red, yellow & dp dull green ..	15	10
365	9d. red-brown, yellow and olive-green ..	20	10
	a. Opt double	£130	
366	1s. blue-green and ochre	25	10
	a. Opt double	£130	
367	1s. 3d. red, violet and yellow-green ..	80	10
368	2s. blue and ochre	90	2·25
369	2s. 6d. ultramarine and vermilion ..	60	25
370	5s. light brown, bistre-yellow & lt blue ..	10·00	7·00
	a. Opt double	£200	
371	10s. black, yellow-ochre, lt bl & carm-red ..	3·25	1·25
372	£1 brown, yell-green, buff & salmon-pink	1·50	1·50

(*b*) *No.* 357 *surch with T* 66

373	5s. on 1s. 3d. black and bright blue (R.)	28·00	38·00
	a. "5/-" omitted		
359/73	.. .. *Set of* 15	42·00	45·00

Owing to the existence of forgeries, No. 370a should only be purchased when accompanied by a certificate of genuineness.

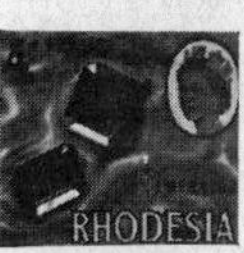

67 Emeralds

68 Zeederberg Coach, *circa* 1895

(Des V. Whiteley. Photo Harrison)

1966 (9 Feb). *As Nos.* 92/105 *of Southern Rhodesia, but inscr* "RHODESIA" *as T* 67. *Some designs and colours changed. P* 14½ (1*d. to* 4*d.*), 13½ × 13 (6*d. to* 2*s.* 6*d.*) *or* 14½ × 14 (5*s. to* £1).

374	–	1d. reddish violet and yellow-ochre ..	10	10
375	–	2d. yell-orge and dp grn (as No. 96)	10	10
		a. Yellow-orange omitted	£425	
376	–	3d. chocolate and pale blue ..	10	10
		a. Chocolate omitted	£550	
		b. Pale blue omitted	£475	
377	67	4d. emerald and sepia	30	10
378	50	6d. carmine-red, yellow & dp dull grn ..	15	10
379	–	9d. yellow and deep violet (as No. 94) ..	15	20
380	45	1s. yellow, yellow-green and light blue	15	10
381	–	1s. 3d. blue and ochre (as No. 101)	25	15
382	–	1s. 6d. red-brn, yell & olive-grn (as No. 98)	75	25
383	–	2s. red, violet and yell-grn (as No. 100)	40	80
384	–	2s. 6d. blue, vermilion & turquoise-bl	40	20
385	56	5s. light brown, bistre-yellow & lt blue	40	90
386	–	10s. black, yell-ochre, lt bl & carm-red ..	2·50	4·00
387	58	£1 brown, yell-green, buff & salmon-pk	17·00	10·00
374/87		.. .. *Set of* 14	20·00	15·00

Nos. 379/80 are in larger format, as T 50.

No. 374 exists in coils constructed from normal sheets. Coil-vending machines were withdrawn from service in 1967.

No. 376a occurred in the bottom row of a sheet and No. 376b in the top two rows of a sheet.

For stamps printed by lithography, see Nos. 397/407.

PRINTERS. All the following stamps were printed by lithography by Mardon Printers, Salisbury.

(Des V. Whiteley (Nos. 388/90))

1966 (2 May). *28th Congress of Southern Africa Philatelic Federation ("Rhopex"). T* 68 *and similar horiz designs. P* 14½.

388	3d. multicoloured	30	10
389	9d. grey-buff, sepia and grey-green ..	40	35
390	1s. 6d. pale blue and black	60	50
391	2s. 6d. salmon-pink, pale dull grn & blk	70	80
388/91	.. .. *Set of* 4	1·75	1·50
MS392	126×84 mm. Nos. 388/91 (*toned paper*)	22·00	30·00
	a. White paper	30·00	32·00

Designs:—9d. Sir Rowland Hill; 1s. 6d. The Penny Black; 2s. 6d. Rhodesian stamp of 1892 (No. 12).

69 De Havilland "Rapide" (1946)

70 Kudu

1966 (1 June). *20th Anniv of Central African Airways. T* **69** *and similar horiz designs. P* 14½ × 14.
393 6d. black, blue, yellow and green .. .. 1·00 35
394 1s. 3d. blue, yellow-orange, black and green 1·25 55
395 2s. 6d. black, blue, yellow and green .. 3·50 1·75
396 5s. black and blue .. .. 6·00 3·50
393/6 .. .. *Set of* 4 10·50 5·50
Aircraft:—1s. 3d. Douglas "DC3." (1953); 2s. 6d. Vickers "Viscount" (1956); 5s. Modern jet.

1966–69. *As Nos.* 374/87 *but litho. P* 14½ (1*d. to* 2*s.*) *or* 14½ × 14 (*others*).
397 1d. reddish violet and yellow-ochre (*shades*) (2.6.66) 15 10
398 2d. orange and green (1.11.67) 75 40
399 3d. chocolate-brn & pale grnsh bl (29.1.68) .. 65 10
400 4d. emerald, bistre-brown & drab (21.9.66) 55 10
401 6d. carmine-red, yell & ol-grey (1.11.66) .. 60 40
402 9d. yellow and light violet (20.11.67) .. 30 10
403 1s. 3d. blue and ochre (1.11.66) .. .. 3·75 30
404 2s. dull red, violet & sage-green (18.7.66) .. 3·75 5·00
405 5s. yellow-brown, deep bistre-yellow and light blue (25.6.66) .. .. .. 10·00 4·50
406 10s. black, buff, lt bl & carm-red (10.8.66) .. 40·00 48·00
407 £1 pale brown, yellow-green, brown-ochre and salmon (10.8.66) .. .. .. 45·00 55·00
397/407 .. .. *Set of* 11 90·00 £100
In addition to the change in printing process from photogravure to lithography and the difference in perforation in the 6d. to 2s. values (14½ instead of 13½ × 13) and shade variations, the oval portrait frame is larger (and in some values thicker) in the 1d. to 2s., and in the 1s. 3d. the Queen's head is also larger.
Trial printings exist of the 5s., 10s., and £1 values on a slightly thinner paper. These are rare.

1967–68. *Dual Currency Issue. As Nos.* 376, 380 *and* 382/4 *but value in decimal currency in addition as in T* **70**. *P* 14½. *White gum* (*No.* 408) *or cream gum* (*others*).
408 3d./2½ c. chocolate-brown and pale greenish blue (15.3.67) 60 20
409 1s./10 c. yell, grn & greenish bl (1.11.67) .. 70 45
410 1s. 6d./15 c. red-brown, yellow and yellow-green (11.3.68) .. .. 3·75 90
411 2s./20 c. dull red, viol and sage-grn (11.3.68) 10·00 9·00
412 2s. 6d./25 c. ultramarine-blue, vermilion and bright turquoise-blue (9.12.68) .. .. 50·00 60·00
408/12 .. .. *Set of* 5 60·00 65·00

71 Dr. Jameson (administrator)

(Des from painting by F. M. Bennett)

1967 (17 May). *Famous Rhodesians* (1*st issue*) *and* 50*th Death Anniv of Dr. Jameson. P* 14½.
413 **71** 1s. 6d. multicoloured 30 35
See also Nos. 426, 430, 457, 458, 469, 480, 488 and 513.

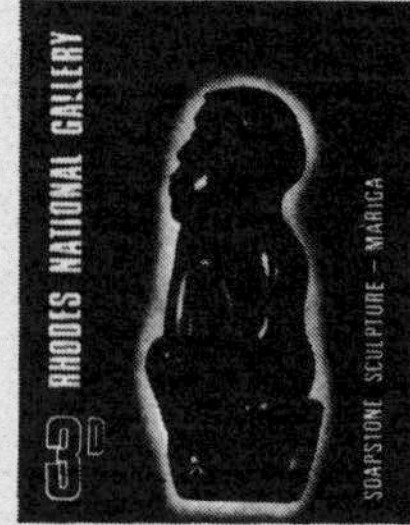

72 Soapstone Sculpture (Joram Mariga)

1967 (12 July). *Tenth Anniv of Opening of Rhodes National Gallery. T* **72** *and similar vert designs. P* 14½ × 14 (3*d.*, 9*d.*) *or* 14 (*others*).
414 3d. reddish chestnut, yellow-olive and black 10 10
415 9d. lt greenish blue, dp olive-brown & black 20 20
a. Perf 13½ .. .. 7·50 18·00
416 1s. 3d. multicoloured 20 25
417 2s. 6d. multicoloured 25 35
414/17 .. .. *Set of* 4 65 75
Designs:—9d. "The Burgher of Calais" (detail, Rodin); 1s. 3d. "The Knight" (stamp design wrongly inscr) (Roberto Crippa); 2s. 6d. "John the Baptist" (M. Tossini).

73 Baobab Tree

1967 (6 Sept). *Nature Conservation. T* **73** *and similar designs. P* 14½.
418 4d. light brown and black 20 25
419 4d. yellow-olive and black 20 25
420 4d. deep grey and black 20 25
421 4d. yellow-orange and black 20 25
418/21 .. .. *Set of* 4 70 90
Designs: *Horiz*—No. 418, Type **73**; No. 419, White Rhinoceros; No. 420, African Elephants. *Vert*—No. 421, Wild Gladiolus.

74 Wooden Hand Plough

(Des Rose Martin)

1968 (26 Apr). *15th World Ploughing Contest, Norton, Rhodesia. T* **74** *and similar horiz designs. P* 14½.
422 3d. pale orange, orange-verm & lake-brown 10 10
423 9d. multicoloured 20 20
424 1s. 6d. multicoloured 30 45
425 2s. 6d. multicoloured 35 70
422/5 .. .. *Set of* 4 85 1·40
Designs:—9d. Early wheel plough; 1s. 6d. Steam powered tractor, and ploughs; 2s. 6d. Modern tractor, and plough.

75 Alfred Beit (national benefactor) **76** Raising the Flag, Bulawayo, 1893

(Des from painting by A. Haywood)

1968 (15 July). *Famous Rhodesians* (2*nd issue*). *P* 14½.
426 **75** 1s. 6d. pale orange, black and brown .. 25 30

(Des Rose Martin)

1968 (4 Nov). *75th Anniv of Matabeleland. T* **76** *and similar vert designs. P* 14½.
427 3d. pale orange, red-orange and black .. 10 10
428 9d. multicoloured 15 20
429 1s. 6d. pale turquoise-green, deep emerald and blackish green 20 35
427/9 .. .. *Set of* 3 40 55
Designs:—9d. View and coat of arms of Bulawayo; 1s. 6d. Allan Wilson (combatant in the Matabele War).

77 Sir William Henry Milton (administrator)

(Des from painting by S. Kendrick)

1969 (15 Jan). *Famous Rhodesians* (3*rd issue*). *P* 14½.
430 **77** 1s. 6d. multicoloured 20 45

78 2 ft Gauge Steam Locomotive, Beira-Salisbury Line, 1899

(Des Rose Martin)

1969 (22 May). *70th Anniv of Opening of Beira-Salisbury Railway. T* **78** *and similar horiz designs showing locomotives. Multicoloured. P* 14½.
431 3d. Type **78** .. .. 1·00 10
432 9d. Steam locomotive, 1904 .. .. .. 2·00 75
433 1s. 6d. Articulated steam locomotive, 1950 .. 6·50 3·25
434 2s. 6d. Diesel locomotive, 1955 .. .. 8·50 6·50
431/4 .. .. *Set of* 4 16·00 9·50

79 Low Level Bridge

(Des Rose Martin)

1969 (18 Sept). *Bridges of Rhodesia. T* **79** *and similar horiz designs. Multicoloured. P* 14½.
435 3d. Type **79** 75 10
436 9d. Mpudzi bridge .. .. 1·25 25
437 1s. 6d. Umniati bridge .. .. .. 3·50 1·00
438 2s. 6d. Birchenough bridge .. .. .. 4·50 1·50
435/8 .. .. *Set of* 4 9·00 2·50

(New Currency. 100 cents = 1 dollar)

80 Harvesting Wheat **81** Devil's Cataract, Victoria Falls

(Des from colour-transparencies (3, 6 c.), Rose Martin (others))

1970 (17 Feb)–**73.** *Decimal Currency. T* **80/1** *and similar horiz designs. P* 14½.
439 1 c. multicoloured 10 10
a. Booklet pane of 4 20
440 2 c. multicoloured 10 10
441 2½ c. multicoloured 10 10
a. Booklet pane of 4 20
441*c* 3 c. multicoloured (1.1.73) .. .. 1·25 10
ca. Booklet pane of 4 .. .. 4·50
442 3½ c. multicoloured 10 10
a. Booklet pane of 4 40
442*b* 4 c. multicoloured (1.1.73) .. .. 1·25 30
ba. Booklet pane of 4 .. .. 4·50
443 5 c. multicoloured 15 10
443*b* 6 c. multicoloured (1.1.73) .. .. 4·00 2·00
443*c* 7½ c. multicoloured (1.1.73) .. .. 8·00 1·25
444 8 c. multicoloured .. .. 1·75 20
445 10 c. multicoloured 60 10
446 12½ c. multicoloured .. .. 1·25 10
446*a* 14 c. multicoloured (1.1.73) .. .. 15·00 1·50
447 15 c. multicoloured .. .. 3·50 15
448 20 c. multicoloured .. .. 2·50 15
449 25 c. multicoloured .. .. 3·50 65
450 50 c. turquoise and ultramarine .. .. 2·75 70
451 $1 multicoloured .. .. 5·00 4·00
452 $2 multicoloured .. .. 17·00 25·00
439/52 .. .. *Set of* 19 55·00 32·00
Designs: *Size as T* **80**—2 c. Pouring molten metal; 2½ c. Zimbabwe Ruins; 3 c. Articulated lorry; 3½ c. and 4 c. Statute of Cecil Rhodes; 5 c. Mine headgear. *Size as T* **81**—6 c. Hydrofoil *Seaflight*; 7½ c. As 8 c.; 10 c. Yachting on Lake McIlwaine; 12½ c. Hippopotamus in river; 14 c. and 15 c. Kariba Dam; 20 c. Irrigation canal. *As T* **80/1** *but larger* (31 × 26 *mm*)—25 c. Bateleur Eagles; 50 c. Radar antenna and Vickers "Viscount"; $1 "Air Rescue"; $2 Rhodesian flag.

82 Despatch Rider, *circa* 1890

(Des Rose Martin)

1970 (1 July). *Inauguration of Posts and Telecommunications Corporation. T* **82** *and similar horiz designs. Multicoloured. P* 14½.
453 2½ c. Type **82** 25 10
454 3½ c. Loading mail at Salisbury airport .. 40 25
455 15 c. Constructing telegraph line, *circa* 1890 1·25 2·00
456 25 c. Telephone and modern telecommunications equipment .. .. .. 2·00 3·50
453/6 .. .. *Set of* 4 3·50 5·25

83 Mother Patrick (Dominican nurse and teacher)

(Des Rose Martin from photograph)

1970 (16 Nov). *Famous Rhodesians* (4*th issue*). *P* 14½.
457 **83** 15 c. multicoloured 40 40

84 Frederick Courteney Selous (big-game hunter, explorer and pioneer)

(Des from painting by L. C. Dickinson)

1971 (1 Mar). *Famous Rhodesians* (5*th issue*). *P* 14½.
458 **84** 15 c. multicoloured 40 40

85 Hoopoe **86** Porphyritic Granite

(Des from photographs by Peter Ginn)

1971 (1 June). *Birds of Rhodesia (1st series). T* **85** *and similar multicoloured designs. P* 14½.

459 2 c. Type **85** . . 1·25 20
460 2½ c. Half-collared Kingfisher (*horiz*) . . 1·25 20
461 5 c. Golden-breasted Bunting . . 3·50 60
462 7½ c. Carmine Bee Eater . . 4·00 1·00
463 8 c. Red-eyed Bulbul . . 4·00 1·25
464 25 c. Senegal Wattled Plover (*horiz*) . . 8·50 2·75
459/64 . . *Set of* 6 20·00 5·50
See also Nos. 537/42.

(Des from photographs by University of Rhodesia and Dept of Geological Survey)

1971 (30 Aug). *"Granite 71" Geological Symposium. T* **86** *and similar vert designs. Multicoloured. P* 14.

465 2½ c. Type **86** . . 50 10
466 7½ c. Muscovite mica seen through microscope . . 1·25 80
467 15 c. Granite seen through microscope . . 2·00 2·75
468 25 c. Geological map of Rhodesia . . 2·75 4·00
465/8 . . *Set of* 4 6·00 7·00

87 Dr. Robert Moffat (missionary)

1972 (14 Feb). *Famous Rhodesians (6th issue). P* 14½.

469 **87** 13 c. multicoloured . . 1·00 90

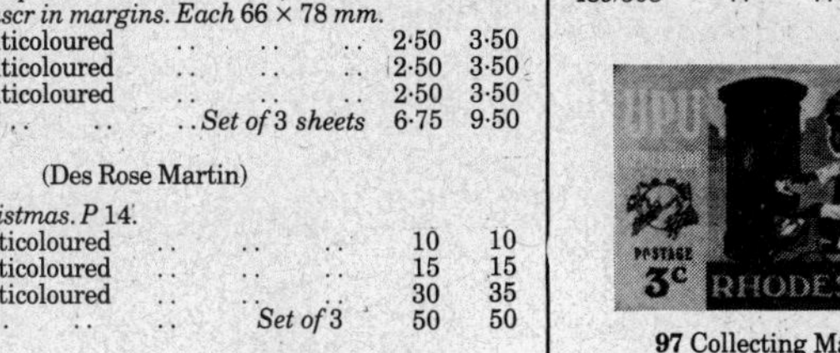

88 Bird ("Be Airwise") 89 "The Three Kings"

(Des C. Lawton)

1972 (17 July). *"Prevent Pollution". T* **88** *and similar horiz designs. Multicoloured. P* 14½.

470 2½ c. Type **88** . . 20 10
471 3½ c. Antelope ("Be Countrywise") . . 20 10
472 7 c. Fish ("Be Waterwise") . . 30 45
473 13 c. City ("Be Citywise") . . 45 70
470/3 . . *Set of* 4 1·00 1·25

1972 (28 Aug). *"Rhophil '72". As Nos.* 439a, 441a *and* 442a *with commemorative inscr in margins. Each* 66 × 78 *mm.*

MS474 1 c. multicoloured . . 2·50 3·50
MS475 2½ c. multicoloured . . 2·50 3·50
MS476 3½ c. multicoloured . . 2·50 3·50
MS474/6 . . *Set of* 3 *sheets* 6·75 9·50

(Des Rose Martin)

1972 (18 Oct). *Christmas. P* 14.

477 **89** 2 c. multicoloured . . 10 10
478 5 c. multicoloured . . 15 15
479 13 c. multicoloured . . 30 35
477/9 . . *Set of* 3 50 50

90 Dr. David Livingstone

91 W.M.O. Emblem

1973 (2 Apr). *Famous Rhodesians (7th issue). P* 14.

480 **90** 14 c. multicoloured . . 70 75

(Des S. J. Ivey)

1973 (2 July). *I.M.O./W.M.O. Centenary. P* 14.

481 **91** 3 c. multicoloured . . 15 10
482 14 c. multicoloured . . 50 60
483 25 c. multicoloured . . 1·00 1·50
481/3 . . *Set of* 3 1·50 2·00

92 Arms of Rhodesia

1973 (10 Oct). *50th Anniv of Responsible Government. P* 14.

484 **92** 2½ c. multicoloured . . 15 10
485 4 c. multicoloured . . 20 20
486 7½ c. multicoloured . . 35 70
487 14 c. multicoloured . . 60 1·75
484/7 . . *Set of* 4 1·10 2·40

93 George Pauling (construction engineer)

(Des P. Birch)

1974 (15 May). *Famous Rhodesians (8th issue). P* 14.

488 **93** 14 c. multicoloured . . 1·00 1·50

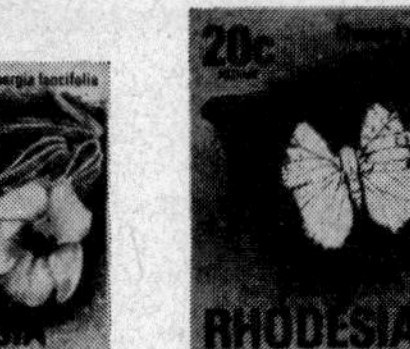

94 Greater Kudu 95 Thunbergia 96 Pearl Charaxes

(Des J. Huntly)

1974 (14 Aug)–**76**. *Various vert designs as T* **94/6**. *Multicoloured. P* 14½ (1 *to* 14 *c.*) *or* 14 (*others*). (*a*) *Antelopes. Size as T* **94**.

489 1 c. Type **94** . . 10 10
490 2½ c. Eland . . 75 10
a. Booklet pane of 4 . . 2·75
491 3 c. Roan Antelope . . 10 10
a. Booklet pane of 4 . . 70
492 4 c. Reedbuck . . 10 10
a. Booklet pane of 4 . . 70
493 5 c. Bushbuck . . 20 10

(*b*) *Wild Flowers. Size as T* **95**

494 6 c. Type **95** . . 40 10
495 7½ c. Flame Lily . . 3·00 35
496 8 c. As 7½ c. (1.7.76) . . 40 10
497 10 c. Devil Thorn . . 25 10
498 12 c. Hibiscus (1.7.76) . . 70 60
499 12½ c. Pink Sabi Star . . 4·50 50
500 14 c. Wild Pimpernel . . 7·00 70
501 15 c. As 12½ c. (1.7.76) . . 70 60
502 16 c. As 14 c. (1.7.76) . . 70 45

(*c*) *Butterflies. Size as T* **96**

503 20 c. Type **96** . . 1·25 35
504 24 c. Yellow Pansy (1.7.76) . . 1·50 40
505 25 c. As 24 c. . . 7·50 3·00
506 50 c. Queen Purple Tip . . 70 90
507 $1 Large Striped Swordtail . . 70 1·25
508 $2 Guinea Fowl Butterfly . . 80 1·50
489/508 . . *Set of* 20 27·00 11·00

97 Collecting Mail

98 Thomas Baines (artist)

(Des M. Chase)

1974 (20 Nov). *Centenary of Universal Postal Union. T* **97** *and similar horiz designs. Multicoloured. P* 14.

509 3 c. Type **97** . . 15 10
510 4 c. Sorting mail . . 20 10
511 7½ c. Mail delivery . . 50 65
512 14 c. Weighing parcel . . 1·00 1·75
509/12 . . *Set of* 4 1·75 2·25

(Des from self-portrait)

1975 (12 Feb). *Famous Rhodesians (9th issue). P* 14.

513 **98** 14 c. multicoloured . . 80 1·00

99 *Euphorbia confinalis*

100 Prevention of Head Injuries

(Des Nancy Abrey)

1975 (16 July). *International Succulent Congress, Salisbury ("Aloe '75"). T* **99** *and similar vert designs. Multicoloured. P* 14½.

514 2½ c. Type **99** . . 20 10
515 3 c. *Aloe excelsa* . . 20 10
516 4 c. *Hoodia lugardii* . . 30 15
517 7½ c. *Aloe ortholopha* . . 55 55
518 14 c. *Aloe musapana* . . 1·50 1·25
519 25 c. *Aloe saponaria* . . 2·00 2·00
514/19 . . *Set of* 6 4·25 3·50

(Des Val Bond)

1975 (15 Oct). *Occupational Safety. T* **100** *and similar horiz designs. Multicoloured. P* 14.

520 2½ c. Type **100** . . 15 10
521 4 c. Bandaged hand and gloved hand . . 20 10
522 7½ c. Broken glass and eye . . 35 20
523 14 c. Blind man and welder with protective mask . . 50 60
520/3 . . *Set of* 4 1·10 80

101 Telephones, 1876 and 1976 (102)

(Des M. Chase)

1976 (10 Mar). *Telephone Centenary. T* **101** *and similar vert design. P* 14.

524 3 c. grey-black and pale blue . . 10 10
525 14 c. brownish black and light stone . . 20 35
Design:—14 c. Alexander Graham Bell.

1976 (1 July). *Nos.* 495, 500 *and* 505 *surch as T* **102**.

526 8 c. on 7½ c. Flame Lily . . 15 15
a. Surch double, one albino . .
527 16 c. on 14 c. Wild Pimpernel . . 20 25
528 24 c. on 25 c. Yellow Pansy . . 30 50
526/8 . . *Set of* 3 60 80

103 Roan Antelope

104 Msasa

(Des N. Pedersen)

1976 (21 July). *Vulnerable Wildlife. T* **103** *and similar horiz designs. Multicoloured. P* 14.

529 4 c. Type **103** . . 20 10
530 6 c. Brown Hyena . . 25 10
531 8 c. Hunting Dog . . 35 25
532 16 c. Cheetah . . 45 45
529/32 . . *Set of* 4 1·10 75

(Des Nancy Abrey)

1976 (17 Nov). *Trees of Rhodesia. T* **104** *and similar vert designs. Multicoloured. P* 14.

533 4 c. Type **104** . . 15 10
534 6 c. Red Mahogany . . 15 10
535 8 c. Mukwa . . 20 30
536 16 c. Rhodesian Teak . . 25 50
533/6 . . *Set of* 4 65 75

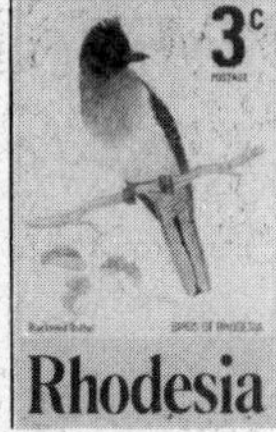

105 Common Bulbul

106 "Lake Kyle" (Joan Evans)

(Des B. Finch)

1977 (16 Mar). *Birds of Rhodesia (2nd series). T* **105** *and similar vert designs. Multicoloured. P* 14.

537 3 c. Type **105** . . 20 10
538 4 c. Yellow-mantled Whydah . . 20 10
539 6 c. Cape Longclaw . . 25 20
540 8 c. Eastern Long-tailed Shrike . . 45 30
541 16 c. Lesser Blue-eared Glossy Starling . . 75 70
542 24 c. Green Wood Hoopoe . . 95 90
537/42 . . *Set of* 6 2·50 2·00

1977 (20 July). *Landscape Paintings. T* **106** *and similar horiz designs. Multicoloured. P* 14.

543 3 c. Type **106** . . 15 10
544 4 c. "Chimanimani Mountains" (Joan Evans) 15 10
545 6 c. "Rocks near Bonsor Reef", (Alice Balfour) 15 10
546 8 c. "A Dwala near Devil's Pass" (Alice Balfour) . . 25 10
547 16 c. "Zimbabwe" (Alice Balfour) . . 35 40
548 24 c. "Victoria Falls" (Thomas Baines) . . 40 45
543/8 . . *Set of* 6 1·25 1·00

107 Virgin and Child

108 Fair Spire

(Des Dianne Deudney)

1977 (16 Nov). *Christmas. P* 14.
549 **107** 3 c. multicoloured 10 10
550 6 c. multicoloured 10 10
551 8 c. multicoloured 20 10
552 16 c. multicoloured 20 35
549/52 .. .. *Set of* 4 50 55

1978 (15 Mar). *Trade Fair Rhodesia, Bulawayo. T* **108** *and similar vert design. Multicoloured. P* 14.
553 4 c. Type **108** 15 10
554 8 c. Fair Spire (*different*) 20 25

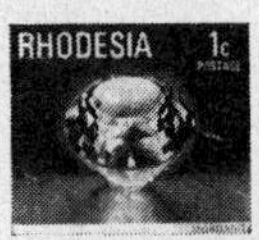

109 Morganite

110 White Rhinoceros

111 Odzani Falls

(Des N. Pedersen (1 to 17 c.), D. Myles (21 c. to $2))

1978 (16 Aug). *Multicoloured.*

(*a*) *Horiz designs as T* **109** *showing gemstones. P* 14½
555 1 c. Type **109** 10 10
556 3 c. Amethyst 15 10
557 4 c. Garnet 15 10
558 5 c. Citrine 15 10
559 7 c. Blue Topaz 20 10

(*b*) *Horiz designs as T* **110** *showing wild animals. P* 14½
560 9 c. Type **110** 20 10
561 11 c. Lion 20 15
562 13 c. Warthog 20 15
563 15 c. Giraffe 20 15
564 17 c. Common Zebra 20 10

(*c*) *Horiz designs as T* **111** *showing waterfalls. P* 14
565 21 c. Type **111** 20 30
566 25 c. Goba Falls 20 40
567 30 c. Inyangombi Falls 25 30
568 $1 Bridal Veil Falls 50 80
569 $2 Victoria Falls .. .. 75 1·00
555/69 .. .. *Set of* 15 3·00 3·00

112 Wright *Flyer*

(Des C. Herbert)

1978 (18 Oct). *75th Anniv of Powered Flight. T* **112** *and similar horiz designs. Multicoloured. P* 14.
570 4 c. Type **112** 10 10
571 5 c. Blériot "XI" 10 10
572 7 c. Vickers "Vimy" *Silver Queen* II 10 10
573 9 c. "A.W. 15 Atalanta" 10 10
574 17 c. Vickers "Viking 1B" 15 15
575 25 c. Boeing "720B" 20 30
570/5 .. .. *Set of* 6 65 65

POSTAGE DUE STAMPS

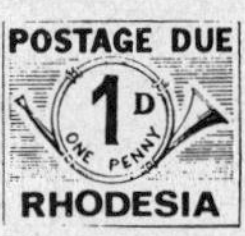

D **2**

D **3** Zimbabwe Bird (soapstone sculpture)

(Typo Printing and Stationery Dept, Salisbury)

1965 (17 June). *Roul* 9.
D1 D **2** 1d. orange-red (*roul* 5) .. .. .. 70 9·00
a. Roul 9 .. .. 1·00 3·75
D2 2d. deep blue .. .. 50 7·00
D3 4d. green .. .. 60 7·00
D4 6d. plum .. .. 60 6·00
D1a/4.. .. .. *Set of* 4 2·25 21·00
The 2d. has a stop below the "D".

(Litho Mardon Printers, Salisbury)

1966 (15 Dec). *P* 14½.
D 5 D **3** 1d. red .. .. 1·60 2·00
D 6 2d. bluish violet .. .. .. 2·00 2·25
D 7 4d. pale green .. .. 2·50 3·75
D 8 6d. reddish violet .. .. .. 2·50 2·75
D 9 1s. red-brown .. .. 3·00 3·00
D10 2s. black .. .. 4·00 6·50
D5/10 .. .. *Set of* 6 14·00 18·00

1970 (17 Feb)–**73.** *Decimal Currency. As Type* D **3**, *but larger* (26 × 22½ *mm*). *P* 14½.
D11 D **3** 1 c. bright green .. .. .. 90 1·25
D12 2 c. ultramarine 90 80
D13 5 c. bright reddish violet .. .. 2·25 1·75
D14 6 c. pale lemon (7.5.73) .. .. .. 3·25 2·50
D15 10 c. cerise .. .. 2·25 3·00
D11/15 .. .. *Set of* 5 8·50 8·50

For later issues see ZIMBABWE.

Rhodesia & Nyasaland

Stamps for the Central African Federation of Northern and Southern Rhodesia and Nyasaland Protectorate.

1

2

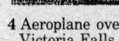

3 Queen Elizabeth II

(Recess Waterlow)

1954 (1 July)–**56.** *P* 13½ × 14 (*T* **1**), 13½ × 13 (*T* **2**) *or* 14 × 13½ (*T* **3**).
1 **1** ½d. red-orange 15 10
a. Coil stamp. Perf 12½×14 (6.2.56) .. 25 1·50
2 1d. ultramarine 15 10
a. Coil stamp. Perf 12½×14. *Deep blue* (9.55) .. .. 30 2·75
ab. Ultramarine (1.10.55) .. .. 35 2·50
3 2d. bright green 15 10
3*a* 2½d. ochre (15.2.56) .. .. .. 1·50 10
4 3d. carmine-red 20 10
5 4d. red-brown 50 15
6 4½d. blue-green 15 25
7 6d. bright reddish purple 40 10
a. Bright purple (5.5.56) 50 10
8 9d. violet 65 70
9 1s. grey-black 65 10
10 **2** 1s. 3d. red-orange and ultramarine .. 2·00 10
11 2s. deep blue and yellow-brown .. 4·50 65
12 2s. 6d. black and rose-red .. .. 5·50 65
13 5s. violet and olive-green .. .. 9·00 2·00
14 **3** 10s. dull blue-green and orange .. 13·00 7·00
15 £1 olive-green and lake .. .. 20·00 18·00
1/15 .. .. *Set of* 16 48·00 27·00
Nos. 1a and 2a printed on rotary machines by subsidiary company, Imprimerie Belge de Securité, in Belgium.

4 Aeroplane over Victoria Falls

5 Livingstone and Victoria Falls

(Des J. E. Hughes (3d.), V. E. Horne (1s.). Recess Waterlow)

1955 (15 June). *Centenary of Discovery of Victoria Falls. P* 13½ (*3d.*) *or* 13 (*1s.*).
16 **4** 3d. ultramarine & dp turquoise-grn .. 20 20
17 **5** 1s. purple and deep blue 30 25

6 Tea Picking

10 Rhodes's Grave

11 Lake Bangweulu

12*a* Rhodesian Railway Trains

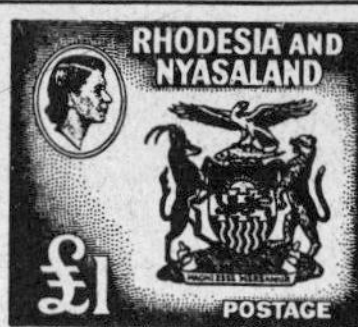

19 Federal Coat of Arms

(Des M. Kinsella (9d.). Recess Waterlow (½d., 1d., 2d., 1s.) until 1962, then D.L.R., D.L.R. (2½d., 4d., 6d., 9d., 2s., 2s. 6d.) and B.W. (others))

1959 (12 Aug)–**62.** *T* **6**, **10/11**, **12*a***, **19** *and similar designs. P* 13½ × 14 (*½d., 1d., 2d.*), 14½ (*2½d., 4d., 6d., 9d., 2s., 2s. 6d.*), 14 × 13½ (*3d.*), 13½ × 13 (*1s.*), 14 (*1s. 3d.*) *or* 11 (*others*).
18 ½d. black and light emerald 15 20
a. Coil stamp. Perf 12½×14 .. .. 70 2·00
19 1d. carmine-red and black 15 10
a. Coil stamp. Perf 12½×14 .. .. 70 2·00
ab. Carmine-red and grey-black .. 70 2·00
ac. Carmine-red (centre) omitted .. £200
20 2d. violet and yellow-brown 25 10
21 2½d. purple and grey-blue 25 40
22 3d. black and blue 15 10
a. Centre omitted £600
23 4d. maroon and olive 50 10
24 6d. ultramarine and deep myrtle-green .. 35 10
24*a* 9d. orge-brown & reddish violet (15.5.62) 3·25 1·75
25 1s. light green and ultramarine .. 60 10
26 1s. 3d. emerald and deep chocolate .. 1·75 10
27 2s. grey-green and carmine .. .. 3·25 45
28 2s. 6d. light blue and yellow-brown .. 3·75 25
29 5s. deep chocolate and yellow-green .. 5·50 2·25
30 10s. olive-brown and rose-red .. .. 23·00 12·00
31 £1 black and deep violet .. .. 30·00 25·00
18/31 .. .. *Set of* 16 60·00 38·00
Designs: *Vert* (*as T* **6**)—1d. V.H.F. mast; 2d. Copper mining; 2½d. Fairbridge Memorial. (*As T* **11**)—6d. Eastern Cataract, Victoria Falls. *Horiz* (*as T* **12*a***)—1s. Tobacco; 1s. 3d. Lake Nyasa; 2s. Chirundu Bridge; 2s. 6d. Salisbury Airport. (*As T* **19**)—5s. Rhodes Statue; 10s. Mlanje.

20 Kariba Gorge, 1955

(Photo Harrison (3d., 6d.), D.L.R. (others))

1960 (17 May). *Opening of Kariba Hydro-Electric Scheme. T* **20** *and similar horiz designs. P* 14½ × 14 (*3d., 6d.*) *or* 14 (*others*).
32 3d. blackish green and red-orange .. 25 10
a. Red-orange omitted £800
33 6d. brown and yellow-brown 70 20
34 1s. slate-blue and green .. .. .. 1·75 90
35 1s. 3d. light blue and orange-brown .. 2·50 80
a. Blue and deep orange-brown .. .. 4·25 4·25
36 2s. 6d. deep slate-purple and orange-red .. 3·00 4·50
37 5s. reddish violet and turquoise-blue .. 5·00 11·00
32/7 .. .. *Set of* 6 12·00 16·00
Designs:—6d. 330 kV power lines; 1s. Barrage wall; 1s. 3d. Barrage and lake; 2s. 6d. Interior of power station; 5s. Barrage wall and Queen Mother (top left).

26 Miner Drilling

(Des V. Whiteley. Photo Harrison)

1961 (8 May). *Seventh Commonwealth Mining and Metallurgical Congress. T* **26** *and similar horiz design. P* 15 × 14.
38 6d. olive-green and orange-brown 25 15
39 1s. 3d. black and light blue 40 60
Design:—1s. 3d. Surface installations, Nchanga Mine.

28 D.H. "Hercules" on Rhodesian Airstrip

31 Tobacco Plant

1962 (6 Feb). *30th Anniv of First London-Rhodesia Airmail Service. T* **28** *and similar horiz designs. P* 14½ × 14.
40 6d. bronze-green and vermilion 35 25
41 1s. 3d. light blue, black and yellow 90 50
42 2s. 6d. rose-red and deep violet .. .. 5·50 4·25
40/2 .. .. *Set of* 3 6·00 4·50
Designs:—1s. 3d. Empire "C" class flying-boat taking off from Zambesi; 2s. 6d. "Comet" at Salisbury airport.

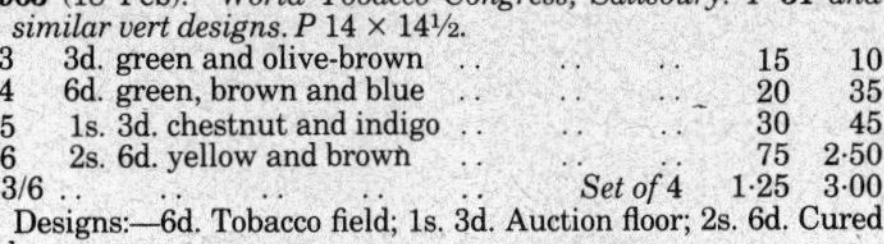

(Des V. Whiteley. Photo Harrison)

1963 (18 Feb). *World Tobacco Congress, Salisbury. T* **31** *and similar vert designs. P* 14 × 14½.

No.	Description		
43	3d. green and olive-brown	15	10
44	6d. green, brown and blue	20	35
45	1s. 3d. chestnut and indigo	30	45
46	2s. 6d. yellow and brown	75	2·50
43/6	*Set of* 4	1·25	3·00

Designs:—6d. Tobacco field; 1s. 3d. Auction floor; 2s. 6d. Cured tobacco.

35 Red Cross Emblem

(Photo Harrison)

1963 (6 Aug). *Red Cross Centenary. P* 14½ × 14.

No.	Type	Description		
47	**35**	3d. red	30	10

36 African "Round Table" Emblem

(Des V. Whiteley. Photo Harrison)

1963 (11 Sept). *World Council of Young Men's Service Clubs, Salisbury. P* 14½ × 14.

No.	Type	Description		
48	**36**	6d. black, gold and yellow-green	15	25
49		1s. 3d. black, gold, yell-grn & lilac	25	40

POSTAGE DUE STAMPS

The 1d. and 2d. (Nos. 2/3) exist with a rubber-stamped "POSTAGE DUE" cancellation. In the absence of proper labels these values were used as postage dues at the Salisbury G.P.O. but according to the G.P.O. the handstamp was intended as a cancellation and not as an overprint (although "unused" examples of the 1d. are known). Its use was discontinued at the end of August 1959.

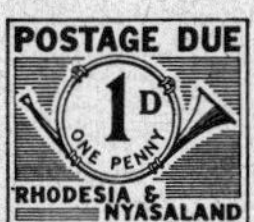

D 1

(Typo Federal Printing and Stationery Dept, Salisbury)

1961 (19 Apr). *P* 12½.

No.	Type	Description		
D1	D 1	1d. vermilion	1·00	2·50
		a. Imperf between (horiz pair)	£250	£300
D2		2d. deep violet-blue	1·25	3·00
D3		4d. green	1·75	4·00
D4		6d. purple	2·00	7·00
		a. Imperf between (horiz pair)	£400	
D1/4		*Set of* 4	5·50	15·00

The 2d. has a stop below the "D".

The stamps of the Federation were withdrawn on 19 February 1964 when all three constituent territories had resumed issuing their own stamps.

Sabah

(*formerly* North Borneo)

SABAH (136) **SABAH** (137)

1964 (1 July)–**65**. *Nos.* 391/406 *of North Borneo* (*D.L.R. printings*), *optd with T* **136** (*Nos.* 408/19) *or T* **137** (*Nos.* 420/3).

No.	Description		
408	1 c. emerald and brown-red	10	10
409	4 c. bronze-green and orange	15	30
410	5 c. sepia and violet	15	10
	a. Light sepia and deep violet (17.8.65)	30	30
411	6 c. black and blue-green	10	10
412	10 c. green and red	15	10
413	12 c. brown and grey-green	15	10
414	20 c. blue-green and ultramarine	1·25	10
415	25 c. grey-black and scarlet	45	60
416	30 c. sepia and olive	25	10
417	35 c. slate-blue and red-brown	30	20
418	50 c. emerald and yellow-brown	30	10
419	75 c. grey-blue and bright purple	2·00	55
420	$1 brown and yellow-green	3·25	50
421	$2 brown and slate	5·00	2·75
422	$5 emerald and maroon	7·50	7·00
423	$10 carmine and blue	12·00	13·00
408/23	*Set of* 16	29·00	23·00

Old stocks bearing Waterlow imprints of the 4 c., 5 c., 20 c. and 35 c. to $10 were used for overprinting, but in addition new printings of all values by De La Rue using the original plates with the De La Rue imprint replacing the Waterlow imprint were specially made for overprinting.

138 *Vanda hookeriana*

139 Great Orange Tip

1965 (15 Nov)–**68**. *As Nos.* 166/72 *of Johore, but with Arms of Sabah inset as in T* **138**. *W* w **13** (*upright*).

No.	Description		
424	1 c. multicoloured	10	20
425	2 c. multicoloured	10	20
426	5 c. multicoloured	10	10
427	6 c. multicoloured	20	15
428	10 c. multicoloured	20	10
429	15 c. multicoloured (pale black panel)	60	10
	a. Brown-black panel (20.2.68)	75	10
430	20 c. multicoloured	80	20
424/30	*Set of* 7	1·75	85

The 5 c. to 15 c. exist with PVA gum as well as gum arabic.

The higher values used with this issue were Nos. 20/27 of Malaysia (National Issues).

1970 (20 Nov). *As No.* 428, *but W* w **13** (*sideways*).

No.	Description		
431	10 c. multicoloured	1·75	2·00

1971 (1 Feb)–**78**. *As Nos.* 175/87 *of Johore but with Arms of Sabah, as in T* **139**. (*a*) *Litho by Bradbury, Wilkinson.*

No.	Description		
432	1 c. multicoloured	10	30
433	2 c. multicoloured	20	30
434	5 c. multicoloured	35	10
435	6 c. multicoloured	35	15
436	10 c. multicoloured	35	10
437	15 c. multicoloured	50	10
438	20 c. multicoloured	60	20
432/8	*Set of* 7	2·25	1·00
	(*b*) *Photo by Harrison* (1977–78)		
439	1 c. multicoloured	75	1·25
440	2 c. multicoloured	1·00	1·50
441	5 c. multicoloured	4·75	1·00
442	10 c. multicoloured	1·25	25
443	15 c. multicoloured	1·75	45
444	20 c. multicoloured	4·00	1·25
439/44	*Set of* 6	12·50	5·25

For differences between litho and photo printings, see after Johore No. 187.

The higher values used with this issue were Nos. 64/71 of Malaysia (National Issues).

140 *Hibiscus rosa-sinensis*

141 Coffee

1979 (30 Apr). *As Nos.* 188/94 *of Johore but with Arms of Sabah as in T* **140**.

No.	Description		
445	1 c. *Rafflesia hasseltii*	10	10
446	2 c. *Pterocarpus indicus*	10	10
447	5 c. *Lagerstroemia speciosa*	10	10
448	10 c. *Durio zibethinus*	10	10
449	15 c. Type **140**	15	10
450	20 c. *Rhododendron scortechinii*	20	10
451	25 c. *Phaeomeria speciosa*	20	10
445/51	*Set of* 7	75	30

For higher values used in conjunction with this series see Nos. 190/7 of Malaysia (National Issues).

1983–85.* *As Nos.* 447/8 *and* 450 *but without wmk.*

No.	Description		
454	5 c. *Lagerstroemia speciosa* (1.85)		
455	10 c. *Durio zibethinus* (1.85)	3·25	2·50
456	15 c. Type **140** (5.85)	6·00	5·00
457	20 c. *Rhododendron scortechinii* (blackish brown background) (1983)	4·50	3·50
457*a*	20 c. *Rhododendron scortechinii* (bronze-green background) (29.11.83)	8·50	80

*There was no official release date for these stamps. Dates shown are the earliest recorded from postmarks and may be revised if earlier examples are reported.

For details of the shade differences between watermarked and unwatermarked printings see after Malaysia–Johore, No. 200*a*.

On Nos. 454/6 and 457*a* the state crest is redrawn larger.

1986 (25 Oct). *As Nos.* 202/8 *of Johore but with Arms of Sabah as in T* **141**.

No.	Description		
459	1 c. Type **141**	10	10
460	2 c. Coconuts	10	10
461	5 c. Cocoa	10	10
462	10 c. Black pepper	10	10
463	15 c. Rubber	10	10
464	20 c. Oil palm	10	10
465	30 c. Rice	10	15
459/65	*Set of* 7	40	50

St. Helena

CROWN COLONY

PRICES FOR STAMPS ON COVER TO 1945

Nos. 1/2a	*from* × 12
Nos. 3/5	*from* × 6
Nos. 6/45	*from* × 10
Nos. 46/52	*from* × 4
Nos. 53/67	*from* × 3
No. 71	—
Nos. 72/86	*from* × 3
Nos. 87/8	*from* × 10
Nos. 89/95	*from* × 3
No. 96	—
Nos. 97/110	*from* × 3
Nos. 111/13	—
Nos. 114/40	*from* × 2

1

ONE PENNY (2)

FOUR PENCE (3)

(Recess P.B.)

Wmk Large Star, W w 1

1856 (1 Jan). *Imperf.*
1 1 6d. blue .. £500 £180

1861 (April (?)). (*a*) *Clean-cut perf* 14 *to* 16.
2 1 6d. blue .. £1250 £250

(*b*) *Rough perf* 14 *to* 16
2*a* 1 6d. blue .. £400 £130

NOTE: The issues which follow consist of 6d. stamps, T 1, printed in various colours and (except in the case of the 6d. values) surcharged with a new value, as T **2** to **10**, *e.g.* stamps described as "1d." are, in fact, 1d. on 6d stamps, and so on.
The numbers in the Type column below refer to the *types of the lettering* of the surcharged value.

(Printed by D.L.R. from P.B. plate)

Two Types of Bar on 1d. value:
A. Bar 16–17 mm long.
B. Bar 18½–19 mm long.

1863 (July). *Wmk Crown CC. Surch as T* **2/3** *with thin bar approximately the same length as the words. Imperf.*
3 2 1d. lake (Type A) .. £110 £140
a. Surch double .. £3500 £2250
b. Surch omitted .. £9500
4 1d. lake (Type B) .. £110 £140
a. Vert pair. Nos. 3/4 .. £1600
5 3 4d. carmine (*bar* 15½–16½ *mm*) .. £500 £250
a. Surch double .. £6500 £6500

ONE PENNY (4 (A)) ONE PENNY (4 (B)) ONE PENNY (4 (C))

TWO PENCE (5) THREE PENCE (6) FOUR PENCE (7)

ONE SHILLING (8) FIVE SHILLINGS (9)

Three Types of Bar:
A. Thin bar (16½ to 17 mm) nearly the same length as the words.
B. Thick bar (14 to 14½ mm) much shorter than the words, except on the 2d. (Nos. 9, 22, 28) where it is nearly the same length.
C. Long bar (17 to 18 mm) same length as the words.

1864–80. *Wmk Crown CC. 6d. as T* **1**, *without surcharge.*

(*a*) *P* 12½ (1864–73)
6 4 1d. lake (Type A) (1864) .. 24·00 24·00
a. Surch double
7 1d. lake (Type B) (1868) .. 75·00 50·00
a. Surch double
b. Imperf .. £2000
8 1d. lake (Type C) (1871) .. 30·00 16·00
a. Surch in blue-black .. £800 £550
9 5 2d. yellow (Type B) (1868) .. 75·00 60·00
a. Imperf .. £7000
10 2d. yellow (Type C) (1873) .. 65·00 35·00
a. Surch in blue-black .. £4500 £2750
11 6 3d. deep dull purple (Type B) (1868) .. 48·00 48·00
a. Surch double .. — £5000
b. Imperf .. £700
c. *Light purple* .. £2750 £750
12 3d. deep dull purple (Type A) (1873) .. 70·00 48·00
13 7 4d. carmine (Type A) (1864) .. 75·00 40·00
a. Surch double .. — £5000
14 7 4d. carmine (Type B) (*words* 18 *mm long*) (1868) .. 65·00 45·00
a. Surch double .. — £4250
b. Surch double (18 + 19 *mm widths*) £9000 £9000
c. Imperf .. £6000
15 4d. carmine-rose (Type B) (*words* 19 *mm long*) (1868) .. £160 £110
a. Surch omitted .. † —
16 – 6d. dull blue (1871) .. £475 85·00
a. Ultramarine (1873) .. £250 75·00
17 8 1s. deep yellow-green (Type A) (1864) 90·00 25·00
a. Surch double .. — £18000
18 1s. deep yellow-green (Type B) (1868) £300 £110
a. Surch double .. £9000
b. Imperf .. £10000
c. Surch omitted* .. £9000
19 1s. deep green (Type C) (1871) .. £160 16·00
a. Surch in blue-black
20 9 5s. orange (Type B) (1868) .. 35·00 45·00
a. Yellow .. £300 £250

(*b*) *P* 14 × 12½ (1876)
21 4 1d. lake (Type B) .. 45·00 15·00
22 5 2d. yellow (Type B) .. 55·00 45·00
23 3d. purple (Type B) .. £160 60·00
24 4d. carmine (Type B) (*words* 16½ *mm long*) .. 70·00 50·00
25 – 6d. milky blue .. £225 27·00
26 8 1s. deep green (Type C) .. £250 20·00

(*c*) *P* 14 (1880)
27 4 1d. lake (Type B) .. 45·00 14·00
28 5 2d. yellow (Type B) .. 60·00 18·00
29 – 6d. milky blue .. £225 40·00
30 8 1s. yellow-green (Type B) .. 20·00 12·00

The only known copy of No. 15a is in the Royal Collection, although a second badly damaged example may exist.
*No. 18c is from a sheet of the 1s. with surcharge misplaced, the fifth row of 12 stamps being thus doubly surcharged and the tenth row without surcharge.

2½d (10)

11

12

1884–94. *Wmk Crown CA. T* **1** *surch. Bars similar to Type B above (except 2½d., T* **10**, *and the 1s., in which the bar is nearly the same length as the words). The 6d. as before without surcharge. P* 14.
34 – ½d. green (*words* 17 *mm*) (1884) .. 2·00 3·50
a. "N" and "Y" spaced .. £350
35 – ½d. emerald (*words* 17 *mm*) (1885) .. 6·00 7·00
a. "N" and "Y" spaced .. £700
b. Surch double .. £1000
ba. Ditto. "N" and "Y" spaced* ..
36 – ½d. deep green (*words* 14½ *mm*) (1893) 90 1·10
37 4 1d. red (1887) .. 2·75 2·00
38 1d. pale red (1890) .. 2·25 2·00
39 5 2d. yellow (1894) .. 1·25 3·50
40 10 2½d. ultramarine (1893) .. 2·00 5·00
a. Surch double .. £9000
b. Stamp doubly printed .. £5000
41 6 3d. deep mauve (1887) .. 2·00 2·75
a. Surch double .. — £9000
42 3d. deep reddish lilac (1887) .. 4·50 7·00
a. Surch double .. £5000 £6000
43 7 4d. pale brown (*words* 16½ *mm*) (1890) 8·00 16·00
a. Additional thin bar in surch (R. 7/4) £350
43*b* 4d. sepia (*words* 17 *mm*) (1894) .. 13·00 8·00
44 – 6d. grey (1887) .. 10·00 3·50
45 8 1s. yellow-green (1894) .. 22·00 14·00
a. Surch double .. £4000
40/1, 43, 44 Optd "Specimen" .. *Set of* 4 £175

Examples of the above are sometimes found showing no watermark; these are from the bottom row of the sheet, which had escaped the watermark, the paper being intended for stamps of a different size to Type 1.
Some are found without bar and others with bar at top of stamp, due to careless overprinting.
Of the 2½d. with double surcharge only six copies exist, and of the 2½d. double printed, one row of 12 stamps existed on one sheet only.
*No. 35ba. No. 35a occurs on stamp No. 216 in the sheet. In No. 35ba only one of the two surcharges shows the variety.

CANCELLATIONS. Nos. 36/45 and No. 20, have been sold cancelled with a violet diamond-shaped grill with four interior bars extending over two stamps. These cannot be considered as *used* stamps, and they are consequently not priced in the list.
This violet obliteration is easily removed and many of these remainders have been cleaned and offered as unused; some are repostmarked with a date and name in thin type rather larger than the original, a usual date being "Ap. 4.01."

(Typo D.L.R.)

1890–97. *Wmk Crown CA. Plate I for the 1½d. Plate II for the other values (for differences see Seychelles). P* 14.
46 11 ½d. green (1897) .. 2·75 4·50
47 1d. carmine (1896) .. 6·00 1·00
48 1½d. red-brown and green (1890) .. 4·25 5·50
49 2d. orange-yellow (1896) .. 4·00 8·50
50 2½d. ultramarine (1896) .. 5·00 8·50
51 5d. mauve (1896) .. 11·00 23·00
52 10d. brown (1896) .. 15·00 35·00
46/52 .. *Set of* 7 42·00 75·00
46/52 Optd "Specimen" .. *Set of* 7 £275

The note below No. 45a *re* violet diamond-shaped grill cancellation also applies to Nos. 46/52.

1902. *Wmk Crown CA. P* 14.
53 12 ½d. green (Mar) .. 1·25 90
54 1d. carmine (24 Feb) .. 3·25 70
53/4 Optd "Specimen" .. *Set of* 2 70·00

13 Government House

14 The Wharf

(Typo D.L.R.)

1903 (May). *Wmk Crown CC. P* 14.
55 13 ½d. brown and grey-green .. 1·75 2·25
56 14 1d. black and carmine .. 1·50 35
57 13 2d. black and sage-green .. 6·00 1·25
58 14 8d. black and brown .. 13·00 32·00
59 13 1s. brown and brown-orange .. 13·00 26·00
60 14 2s. black and violet .. 38·00 48·00
55/60 .. *Set of* 6 65·00 £100
55/60 Optd "Specimen" .. *Set of* 6 £200

A printing of the 1d. value in Type 14 in red only on Mult Crown CA paper was made in 1911, but not sold to the public. Examples are known overprinted "SPECIMEN" (*Price* £400).

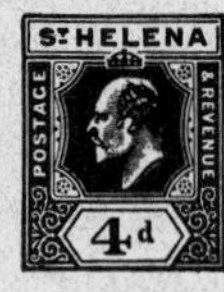

15

(Typo D.L.R.)

1908 (May). *P* 14. (*a*) *Wmk Mult Crown CA.*
64 15 2½d. blue, O .. 1·00 1·40
66 4d. black and red/*yellow*, OC .. 1·00 3·50
67 6d. dull and deep purple, OC .. 2·50 9·50

(*b*) *Wmk Crown CA*
71 15 10s. green and red/*green*, C .. £175 £275
64/71 .. *Set of* 4 £175 £275
64/71 Optd "Specimen" .. *Set of* 4 £225

16

17

(Typo D.L.R.)

1912–16. *Wmk Mult Crown CA. P* 14.
72 16 ½d. black and green .. 85 4·00
73 17 1d. black and carmine-red .. 1·25 1·00
a. Black and scarlet (1916) .. 24·00 27·00
74 1½d. black and dull orange (1913) .. 2·00 4·25
75 16 2d. black and greyish slate .. 2·00 1·75
76 17 2½d. black and bright blue .. 1·75 5·00
77 16 3d. black and purple/*yellow* (1913) .. 2·00 5·00
78 17 8d. black and dull purple .. 5·50 35·00
79 16 1s. black and black/*green* .. 8·00 18·00
80 17 2s. black and blue/*blue* .. 27·00 48·00
81 3s. black and violet (1913) .. 42·00 70·00
72/81 .. *Set of* 10 85·00 £170
72/81 Optd "Specimen" .. *Set of* 10 £250

No. 73*a* is on thicker paper than 73.

18

19

(Typo D.L.R.)

1912. *Wmk Mult Crown CA. P* 14.
83 18 4d. black and red/*yellow*, C .. 3·50 12·00
84 6d. dull and deep purple, C .. 2·50 5·00
83/4 Optd "Specimen" .. *Set of* 2 60·00

1913. *Wmk Mult Crown CA. P* 14.
85 19 4d. black and red/*yellow*, O .. 4·50 3·50
86 6d. dull and deep purple, O .. 9·50 20·00
85/6 Optd "Specimen" .. *Set of* 2 70·00

The split "A" variety illustrated above No. 86 of Gambia also occurs on Nos. 85/6 (*Prices*: 4d. £65, 6d. £120 *un*).

WAR TAX ONE PENNY (20)

WAR TAX 1d. (21)

1916 (Sept). *As No.* 73*a*, *on thin paper, surch with T* **20**.
87 17 1d. + 1d. black and scarlet (Optd S. £50) 50 2·00
a. Surch double .. — £6000

1919. *No. 73 on thicker paper, surch with T* **21**.

No.	Type	Description	Unused	Used
88	**17**	1d. + 1d. black and carmine-red (*shades*) (Optd S. £50)	40	3·00

1922 (Jan). *Printed in one colour. Wmk Mult Script CA. P* 14.

No.	Type	Description	Unused	Used
89	**17**	1d. green	50	10·00
90		1½d. rose-scarlet	6·00	25·00
91	**16**	3d. bright blue	12·00	30·00
89/91		*Set of* 3	17·00	60·00
89/91 Optd "Specimen"		*Set of* 3	75·00	

22 Badge of St. Helena

PLATE FLAWS ON THE 1922–37 ISSUE. Many constant plate varieties exist on both the vignette and duty plates of this issue.

The three major varieties are illustrated and listed below with prices for mint examples. Fine used stamps showing these flaws are worth a considerable premium over the mint prices quoted.

a. Broken mainmast. Occurs on R.2/1 of all sheets from the second printing onwards. It does not appear on Nos. 93/6 and 112/13 as these stamps only exist from the initial printing invoiced in May 1922.

b. Torn flag. Occurs on R.4/6 of all sheets from printings up to and including that invoiced in December 1922. The flaw was retouched for the printing invoiced in December 1926 and so does not occur on Nos. 99*e*, 103 and 107/10.

c. Cleft rock. Occurs on R.5/1 of all sheets from the second printing onwards. It does not appear on Nos. 93/6 and 112/13 as these stamps only exist from the initial printing invoiced in May 1922.

(Des T. Bruce. Typo D.L.R.)

1922 (June)–**37.** *P* 14. (*a*) *Wmk Mult Crown CA.*

No.	Type	Description	Unused	Used
92	**22**	4d. grey and black/*yellow*, **C** (2.23)	4·00	6·50
		a. Broken mainmast	90·00	
		b. Torn flag	90·00	
		c. Cleft rock	80·00	
93		1s. 6d. grey and green/*blue-green*, **C**	20·00	42·00
		b. Torn flag	£350	
94		2s. 6d. grey and red/*yellow*, **C**	22·00	48·00
		b. Torn flag	£400	
95		5s. grey and green/*yellow*, **C**	35·00	65·00
		b. Torn flag	£450	
96		£1 grey and purple/*red*, **C**	£400	£475
		b. Torn flag	£1500	
92/6 Optd "Specimen"		*Set of* 5	£500	

The paper of No. 93 is bluish on the surface with a full green back.

(*b*) *Wmk Mult Script CA*

No.	Type	Description	Unused	Used
97	**22**	½d. grey and black, **C** (2.23)	70	1·00
		a. Broken mainmast	28·00	
		b. Torn flag	50·00	
		c. Cleft rock	25·00	
98		1d. grey and green, **C**	1·25	80
		a. Broken mainmast	32·00	
		b. Torn flag	32·00	
		c. Cleft rock	28·00	
99	**22**	1½d. rose-red, **C** (2.23)	2·50	7·00
		a. Broken mainmast	80·00	
		b. Torn flag	80·00	
		c. Cleft rock	80·00	
		d. Carmine-rose	17·00	21·00
		da. Broken mainmast	£200	
		db. Torn flag	£200	
		dc. Cleft rock	£200	
		e. Deep carmine-red (1937)	80·00	£100
		ea. Broken mainmast	£500	
		ec. Cleft rock	£500	
100		2d. grey and slate, **C** (2.23)	1·50	1·50
		a. Broken mainmast	60·00	
		b. Torn flag	60·00	
		c. Cleft rock	50·00	
101		3d. bright blue, **C** (2.23)	1·50	4·00
		a. Broken mainmast	60·00	
		b. Torn flag	60·00	
		c. Cleft rock	50·00	
103		5d. green and carmine/*green*, **C** (1927)	2·50	5·50
		a. Broken mainmast	£110	
		c. Cleft rock	£100	
104		6d. grey and bright purple, **C**	3·25	8·00
		a. Broken mainmast	£120	
		b. Torn flag	£110	
		c. Cleft rock	£100	
105		8d. grey and bright violet, **C** (2.23)	3·25	6·50
		a. Broken mainmast	£150	
		b. Torn flag	£150	
		c. Cleft rock	£130	
106		1s. grey and brown, **C**	4·00	8·00
		a. Broken mainmast	£160	
		b. Torn flag	£120	
		c. Cleft rock	£110	
107		1s. 6d. grey and green/*green* (1927)	10·00	27·00
		a. Broken mainmast	£200	
		c. Cleft rock	£200	
108		2s. purple and blue/*blue*, **C** (1927)	10·00	27·00
		a. Broken mainmast	£200	
		c. Cleft rock	£200	
109		2s. 6d. grey and red/*yellow* (1927)	12·00	35·00
		a. Broken mainmast	£200	
		c. Cleft rock	£200	
110		5s. grey and green/*yellow* (1927)	30·00	55·00
		a. Broken mainmast	£350	
		c. Cleft rock	£350	
111		7s. 6d. grey and yellow-orange, **C**	70·00	£110
		a. Broken mainmast	£575	
		b. Torn flag	£525	
		c. Cleft rock	£575	
112		10s grey and olive-green, **C**	£110	£150
		b. Torn flag	£700	
113		15s. grey and purple/*blue*, **C**	£1000	£1500
		b. Torn flag	£2750	
97/112		*Set of* 15	£250	£350
97/113 Optd "Specimen"		*Set of* 16	£1000	

23 Lot and Lot's Wife

24 The "Plantation"

30 St. Helena

32 Badge of St. Helena

(Recess B.W.)

1934 (23 April). *Centenary of British Colonisation. T* **23/4, 30, 32** *and similar horiz designs. Wmk Mult Script CA. P* 12.

No.	Description	Unused	Used
114	½d. black and purple	35	80
115	1d. black and green	50	85
116	1½d. black and scarlet	1·75	2·50
117	2d. black and orange	1·40	1·25
118	3d. black and blue	1·40	4·50
119	6d. black and light blue	3·25	3·00
120	1s. black and chocolate	6·00	18·00
121	2s. 6d. black and lake	27·00	48·00
122	5s. black and chocolate	65·00	80·00
123	10s. black and purple	£200	£250
114/123	*Set of* 10	£275	£350
114/23 Perf "Specimen"	*Set of* 10	£350	

Design:—1½d. Map of St. Helena; 2d. Quay at Jamestown; 3d. James Valley; 6d. Jamestown; 1s. Munden's Promontory; 5s. High Knoll.

1935 (6 May). *Silver Jubilee. As Nos. 91/4 of Antigua.*

No.	Description	Unused	Used
124	1½d. deep blue and carmine	75	1·60
	f. Diagonal line by turret	30·00	
125	2d. ultramarine and grey	1·25	90
	f. Diagonal line by turret	40·00	
126	6d. green and indigo	5·50	1·75
	h. Dot by flagstaff	70·00	
127	1s. slate and purple	6·50	10·00
	h. Dot by flagstaff	85·00	
124/7	*Set of* 4	12·50	13·00
124/7 Perf "Specimen"	*Set of* 4	90·00	

For illustrations of plate varieties see Omnibus section following Zululand.

1937 (19 May). *Coronation. As Nos. 13/15 of Aden.*

No.	Description	Unused	Used
128	1d. green	30	15
129	2d. orange	75	15
130	3d. bright blue	1·00	25
128/30	*Set of* 3	1·90	50
128/30 Perf "Specimen"	*Set of* 3	55·00	

33 Badge of St. Helena

(Recess Waterlow)

1938 (12 May)–**44.** *Wmk Mult Script CA. P* 12½.

No.	Type	Description	Unused	Used
131	**33**	½d. violet	10	15
132		1d. green	20·00	4·00
132*a*		1d. yellow-orange (8.7.40)	15	15
133		1½d. scarlet	15	15
134		2d. red-orange	15	10
135		3d. ultramarine	90·00	30·00
135*a*		3d. grey (8.7.40)	20	15
135*b*		4d. ultramarine (8.7.40)	30	15
136		6d. light blue	45	15
136*a*		8d. sage-green (8.7.40)	1·75	75
		b. Olive-green (24.5.44)	4·00	3·00
137		1s. sepia	35	25
138		2s. 6d. maroon	4·50	2·25
139		5s. chocolate	7·00	7·50
140		10s. purple	8·00	15·00
131/140		*Set of* 14	£120	55·00
131/40 Perf "Specimen"		*Set of* 14	£300	

See also Nos. 149/51.

1946 (21 Oct). *Victory. As Nos. 28/9 of Aden.*

No.	Description	Unused	Used
141	2d. red-orange	10	10
142	4d. blue	10	10
141/2 Perf "Specimen"	*Set of* 2	60·00	

1948 (20 Oct). *Royal Silver Wedding. As Nos. 30/1 of Aden.*

No.	Description	Unused	Used
143	3d. black	30	20
144	10s. violet-blue	15·00	23·00

1949 (10 Oct). *75th Anniv of Universal Postal Union. As Nos. 114/17 of Antigua.*

No.	Description	Unused	Used
145	3d. carmine	60	30
146	4d. deep blue	1·50	90
147	6d. olive	1·75	90
148	1s. blue-black	1·75	1·10
145/8	*Set of* 4	5·00	3·00

1949 (1 Nov). *Wmk Mult Script CA. P* 12½.

No.	Type	Description	Unused	Used
149	**33**	1d. black and green	35	80
150		1½d. black and carmine	35	80
151		2d. black and scarlet	35	80
149/51		*Set of* 3	95	2·25

1953 (2 June). *Coronation. As No. 47 of Aden.*

No.	Description	Unused	Used
152	3d. black and deep reddish violet	50	65

34 Badge of St. Helena

35 Heart-shaped Waterfall

(Recess D.L.R.)

1953 (4 Aug)–**59**. *Horiz designs as T* **34**, *and T* **35**. *Wmk Mult Script CA. P* 14.

No.	Description	Unused	Used
153	½d. black and bright green	25	20
154	1d. black and deep green	15	15
155	1½d. black and reddish purple	1·00	40
	a. Black & deep reddish purple (14.1.59)	2·00	90
156	2d. black and claret	50	20
157	2½d. black and red	40	20
158	3d. black and brown	2·25	15
159	4d. black and deep blue	40	25
160	6d. black and deep lilac	40	20
161	7d. black and grey-black	65	75
162	1s. black and carmine	40	25
163	2s. 6d. black and violet	6·00	4·50
164	5s. black and deep brown	11·00	9·00
165	10s. black and yellow-orange	40·00	20·00
153/65	*Set of* 13	55·00	32·00

Designs:—1d. Flax plantation; 2d. Lace-making; 2½d. Drying flax; 3d. St. Helena Sand Plover; 4d. Flagstaff and The Barn; 6d. Donkeys carrying flax; 7d. Island map; 1s. The Castle; 2s. 6d. Cutting flax; 5s. Jamestown; 10s. Longwood House.

45 Stamp of 1856

(Recess D.L.R.)

1956 (3 Jan). *St. Helena Stamp Centenary. Wmk Mult Script CA. P* 11½.

166	**45**	3d. Prussian blue and carmine ..	10	10
167		4d. Prussian blue and reddish brown ..	10	10
168		6d. Prussian blue & dp reddish purple	15	15
166/8 ..		.. .. *Set of* 3	30	25

46 Arms of East India Company

(Recess Waterlow)

1959 (5 May). *Tercentenary of Settlement. T* **46** *and similar horiz designs. W* w **12**. *P* 12½ × 13.

169	3d. black and scarlet	10	10
170	6d. light emerald and slate-blue	30	15
171	1s. black and orange	30	20
169/71	.. .. *Set of* 3	65	40

Designs:—6d. East Indiaman *London* off James Bay; 1s. Commemoration Stone.

ST. HELENA
Tristan Relief
9d +

(49)

1961 (12 Oct). *Tristan Relief Fund. Nos.* 46 *and* 49/51 *of Tristan da Cunha surch as T* **49** *by Govt Printer, Jamestown.*

172	2½ c. + 3d. black and brown-red	—	£400
173	5 c. + 6d. black and blue	—	£400
174	7½ c. + 9d. black and rose-carmine	—	£475
175	10 c. + 1s. black and light brown	—	£550
172/5 ..	.. .. .. *Set of* 4	£4000	£1600

The above stamps were withdrawn from sale on 19 October, 434 complete sets having been sold.

50 Cunning Fish

51 Yellow Canary

53 Queen Elizabeth II

63 Queen Elizabeth II with Prince Andrew (after Cecil Beaton)

(Des V. Whiteley. Photo Harrison)

1961 (12 Dec)–**65**. *T* 50/1, 53, 63 *and similar designs. W* w **12**. *P* 11½ × 12 (*horiz*), 12 × 11½ (*vert*) *or* 14½ × 14 (£1).

176	1d. brt blue, dull violet, yellow & carmine ..	10	10
	a. Chalky paper (4.5.65)	65	10
177	1½d. yellow, green, black and light drab ..	30	10
178	2d. scarlet and grey	15	10
179	3d. light blue, black, pink and deep blue ..	35	10
	a. Chalky paper (30.11.65)	80	20
180	4½d. yellow-green, green, brown and grey ..	60	20
181	6d. red, sepia and light yellow-olive ..	1·50	25
	a. Chalky paper (30.11.65)	1·75	25
182	7d. red-brown, black and violet	35	30
183	10d. brown-purple and light blue	35	30
184	1s. greenish yellow, bluish green & brown	35	30
185	1s. 6d. grey, black and slate-blue	6·00	2·50
186	2s. 6d. red, pale yellow and turquoise, C ..	2·50	1·50
187	5s. yellow, brown and green	7·50	2·50
188	10s. orange-red, black and blue	15·00	8·50
189	£1 chocolate and light blue	22·00	17·00
	a. Chalky paper (30.11.65)	30·00	32·00
176/89 (*cheapest*)	.. .. *Set of* 14	50·00	30·00

Designs: *Horiz* (*as T* **50**)—2d. Brittle Starfish; 7d. Trumpet Fish; 10d. Feather Starfish; 2s. 6d. Orange Starfish; 10s. Deep-water Bull's-eye. *Vert* (*as T* **51**)—4½d. Red-wood Flower; 6d. Madagascar Red Fody; 1s. Gum-wood Flower; 1s. 6d. White Tern; 5s. Night-blooming Cereus.

1963 (4 June). *Freedom from Hunger. As No.* 76 *of Aden.*

190	1s. 6d. ultramarine	2·50	40

1963 (2 Sept). *Red Cross Centenary. As Nos.* 147/8 *of Antigua.*

191	3d. red and black	75	25
192	1s. 6d. red and blue	3·00	75

FIRST LOCAL POST
4th JANUARY 1965

(64)

65 Badge of St. Helena

1965 (4 Jan). *First Local Post. Nos.* 176, 179, 181 *and* 185 *optd with T* **64**.

193	1d. bright blue, dull violet, yellow & carmine	10	10
194	3d. light blue, black, pink and deep blue ..	10	10
195	6d. red, sepia and light yellow-olive ..	10	10
196	1s. 6d. grey, black and slate-blue ..	15	10
193/6 ..	.. .. .. *Set of* 4	35	20

1965 (17 May). *I.T.U. Centenary. As Nos.* 166/7 *of Antigua.*

197	3d. blue and grey-brown	35	10
198	6d. bright purple and bluish green	55	10

1965 (15 Oct). *International Co-operation Year. As Nos.* 168/9 *of Antigua.*

199	1d. reddish purple and turquoise-green ..	20	10
200	6d. deep bluish green and lavender	55	10

1966 (24 Jan). *Churchill Commemoration. As Nos.* 170/3 *of Antigua.*

201	1d. new blue	15	10
202	3d. deep green	35	10
203	6d. brown	50	10
204	1s. 6d. bluish violet	70	30
201/4 ..	.. .. .. *Set of* 4	1·50	55

1966 (1 July). *World Cup Football Championships. As Nos.* 176/7 *of Antigua.*

205	3d. violet, yellow-green, lake & yellow-brn ..	50	10
206	6d. chocolate, blue-green, lake & yellow-brn	75	15

1966 (20 Sept). *Inauguration of W.H.O. Headquarters, Geneva. As Nos.* 178/9 *of Antigua.*

207	3d. black, yellow-green and light blue ..	50	15
208	1s. 6d. black, light purple and yellow-brown	2·75	40

1966 (1 Dec). *20th Anniv of U.N.E.S.C.O. As Nos.* 196/8 *of Antigua.*

209	3d. slate-violet, red, yellow and orange ..	1·50	20
210	6d. orange-yellow, violet and deep olive ..	2·50	30
211	1s. 6d. black, bright purple and orange ..	4·00	1·00
209/11	.. .. .. *Set of* 3	7·00	1·40

(Des W. H. Brown. Photo Harrison)

1967 (5 May). *New Constitution. W* w **12** (*sideways*). *P* 14½ × 14.

212	**65**	1s. multicoloured	10	10
213		2s. 6d. multicoloured	20	10
		a. Red (ribbon, etc.) omitted	£375	

66 Fire of London

(Des M. Goaman. Recess D.L.R.)

1967 (4 Sept). *300th Anniv of Arrival of Settlers after Great Fire of London. T* **66** *and similar horiz designs. W* w **12**. *P* 13.

214	1d. carmine-red and black	10	10
	a. Carmine and black	15	15
215	3d. ultramarine and black	10	10
216	6d. slate-violet and black	10	10
217	1s 6d. olive-green and black	10	10
214/17	.. .. .. *Set of* 4	35	25

Designs:—3d. East Indiaman *Charles*; 6d. Settlers landing at Jamestown; 1s. 6d. Settlers clearing scrub.

70 Interlocking Maps of Tristan and St. Helena

(Des Jennifer Toombs. Photo Harrison)

1968 (4 June). *30th Anniv of Tristan da Cunha as a Dependency of St. Helena. T* **70** *and similar horiz design. W* w **12**. *P* 14 × 14½.

218	**70**	4d. purple and chocolate	10	10
219	–	8d. olive and brown	10	10
220	**70**	1s. 9d. ultramarine and chocolate ..	10	10
221	–	2s. 3d. greenish blue and brown ..	15	10
218/21		.. .. .. *Set of* 4	35	25

Design:—8d., 2s. 3d. Interlocking maps of St. Helena and Tristan.

72 Queen Elizabeth and Sir Hudson Lowe

(Des M. Farrar Bell. Litho D.L.R.)

1968 (4 Sept). *150th Anniv of the Abolition of Slavery in St. Helena. T* **72** *and similar horiz design. Multicoloured. W* w 12 *(sideways). P* 13 × 12½.

222	3d. Type **72**	10	1
223	9d. Type **72**	10	1
224	1s. 6d. Queen Elizabeth and Sir George Bingham	15	1
225	2s. 6d. As 1s. 6d.	25	1
222/5 ..	.. .. .. *Set of* 4	55	3

74 Blue Gum Eucalyptus and Road Construction

(Des Sylvia Goaman. Litho P.B.)

1968 (4 Nov). *Horiz designs as T* **74**. *Multicoloured. W* w **12** (*sideways*). *P* 13½.

226	½d. Type **74**	10	1
227	1d. Cabbage-tree and electricity development	10	1
228	1½d. St. Helena Redwood and dental unit ..	10	1
229	2d. Scrubweed and pest control	10	1
230	3d. Tree-fern and flats in Jamestown ..	12	1
231	4d. Blue gum Eucalyptus, pasture and livestock improvement	20	1
232	6d. Cabbage-tree and schools broadcasting	20	1
233	8d. St. Helena Redwood and country cottages	20	1
234	10d. Scrubweeed and new school buildings ..	20	1
235	1s. Tree-fern and reafforestation	20	1
236	1s. 6d. Blue gum Eucalyptus and heavy lift crane	70	1·2
237	2s. 6d. Cabbage-tree and Lady Field Children's Home	80	1·4
238	5s. St. Helena Redwood and agricultural training	90	1·7
239	10s. Scrubweed and New General Hospital	2·25	3·0
240	£1 Tree-fern and lifeboat *John Dutton* ..	10·00	15·0
226/40	.. .. .. *Set of* 15	14·00	21·0

See also No. 274 for distinct shade of £1 value.

89 Brig *Perseverance*

93 W.O. and Drummer of the 53rd Foot, 1815

(Des J.W. Litho P.B.)

1969 (19 Apr). *Mail Communications. T* **89** *and similar horiz designs. Multicoloured. W* w **12** (*sideways*). *P* 13½.

241	4d. Type **89**	20	10
242	8d. R.M.S. *Dane*	30	10
243	1s. 9d. S.S. *Llandovery Castle*	40	15
244	2s. 3d. R.M.S. *Good Hope Castle*	45	20
241/4 ..	.. .. .. *Set of* 4	1·25	50

(Des R. North. Litho Format)

1969 (3 Sept). *Military Uniforms. T* **93** *and similar vert designs. Multicoloured. W* w **12**. *P* 14.

245	6d. Type **93**	30	15
246	8d. Officer and Surgeon, 20th Foot, 1816 ..	40	15
247	1s. 8d. Drum Major, 66th Foot, 1816, and Royal Artillery Officer, 1820	50	15
248	2s. 6d. Private, 91st Foot, and 2nd Corporal, Royal Sappers and Miners, 1832 ..	60	20
245/8 ..	.. .. .. *Set of* 4	1·50	60

97 Dickens, Mr. Pickwick and Job Trotter (*Pickwick Papers*)

(Des Jennifer Toombs. Litho P.B.)

1970 (9 June). *Death Centenary of Charles Dickens. T* **97** *and similar horiz designs each incorporating a portrait of Dickens. Multicoloured. Chalk-surfaced paper. W* w **12** (*sideways*). *P* 13½ × 13.

249	4d. Type **97**	15	10
	a. Shiny unsurfaced paper	15	30
	b. Yellow omitted	£225	
250	8d. Mr. Bumble and Oliver (*Oliver Twist*) ..	20	10
	a. Shiny unsurfaced paper	20	50
251	1s. 6d. Sairey Gamp and Mark Tapley (*Martin Chuzzlewit*)	35	15
	a. Shiny unsurfaced paper	35	90

252 2s. 6d. Jo and Mr. Turveydrop (*Bleak House*) .. 45 30
a. Shiny unsurfaced paper .. .. 45 1·40
249/52 .. .. *Set of* 4 1·00 60
249a/52a .. .. *Set of* 4 1·00 2·75

Supplies sent to St. Helena were on paper with a dull surface which reacts to the chalky test and with PVA gum. Crown Agents supplies were from a later printing on shiny paper which does not respond to the chalky test and with gum arabic.

98 "Kiss of Life" **99** Officer's Shako Plate (20th Foot)

(Des Jennifer Toombs. Litho J.W.)

1970 (15 Sept). *Centenary of British Red Cross. T* **98** *and similar horiz designs. W* w **12** *(sideways). P* 14.
253 6d. bistre, vermilion and black 10 10
254 9d. turquoise-green, vermilion and black 10 10
255 1s. 9d. pale grey, vermilion and black 15 10
256 2s. 3d. pale lavender, vermilion and black .. 20 20
253/6 .. .. *Set of* 4 50 45

Designs:—9d. Nurse with girl in wheelchair; 1s. 9d. Nurse bandaging child's knee; 2s. 3d. Red Cross emblem.

(Des J.W. Litho Questa)

1970 (2 Nov). *Military Equipment* (1*st issue*). *T* **99** *and similar vert designs. Multicoloured. W* w **12**. *P* 12.
257 4d. Type **99** 80 20
258 9d. Officer's Breast-plate (66th Foot) .. .. 1·25 30
259 1s. 3d. Officer's Full Dress Shako (91st Foot) 1·50 40
260 2s. 11d. Ensign's Shako (53rd Foot).. .. 2·00 60
257/60 .. .. *Set of* 4 5·00 1·40

See also Nos. 281/4, 285/8 and 291/4.

100 Electricity Development **101** St. Helena holding the "True Cross"

(Litho P.B.)

1971 (15 Feb). *Decimal Currency. Designs as Nos.* 227/40, *but with values inscr in decimal currency as in T* **100**. *W* w **12** *(sideways). P* 13½.
261 ½p. multicoloured 10 10
262 1p. multicoloured (as 1½d.) 10 10
263 1½p. multicoloured (as 2d.) 10 10
264 2p. multicoloured (as 3d.) .. .. .. 1·50 90
265 2½p. multicoloured (as 4d.) 10 10
266 3½p. multicoloured (as 6d.) 15 10
267 4½p. multicoloured (as 8d.) 10 10
268 5p. multicoloured (as 10d.).. .. .. 10 10
269 7½p. multicoloured (as 1s.) 25 35
270 10p. multicoloured (as 1s. 6d.) 25 35
271 12½p. multicoloured (as 2s. 6d.) 25 50
272 25p. multicoloured (as 5s.) .. .. .. 60 1·25
273 50p. multicoloured (as 10s.).. .. .. 1·25 2·00
274 £1 multicoloured† .. .. 18·00 18·00
261/74 .. .. *Set of* 14 20·00 22·00

†Although the design of No. 274 in no way differs from that of No. 240, it was reprinted specially for decimalisation, and differs considerably in shade from No. 240, as do others from their counterparts in the 1968 set.

The main differences in No. 274 are in the mountain which is blue rather than pinkish blue and in the sea which is light blue instead of greenish blue.

See also No. 309.

(Des R. Granger Barrett. Litho Questa)

1971 (5 Apr). *Easter. W* w **12**. *P* 14 × 14½.
275 **101** 2p. multicoloured 10 10
276 5p. multicoloured 10 10
277 7½p. multicoloured 15 15
278 12½p. multicoloured 20 20
275/8 .. .. *Set of* 4 50 50

PRICES OF SETS

Set prices are given for many issues, generally those containing three stamps or more. Definitive sets include one of each value or major colour change, but do not cover different perforations, die types or minor shades. Where a choice is possible the set prices are based on the cheapest versions of the stamps included in the listings.

102 Napoleon (after painting by J.-L. David) and Tomb on St. Helena

(Des J.W. Litho Questa)

1971 (5 May). *150th Death Anniv of Napoleon, T* **102** *and similar vert design. Multicoloured. W* w **12**. *P* 13½.
279 2p. Type **102** 50 40
280 34p. "Napoleon at St. Helena" (H. Delaroche) 2·00 85

(Des J.W. Litho Questa)

1971 (10 Nov). *Military Equipment* (2*nd issue*). *Multicoloured designs as T* **99**. *W* w **12**. *P* 14.
281 1½p. Artillery Private's hanger .. .. 1·25 30
282 4p. Baker rifle and socket bayonet .. 2·00 60
283 6p. Infantry Officer's sword .. .. 2·00 80
284 22½p. Baker rifle and sword bayonet.. .. 2·50 1·25
281/4 .. .. *Set of* 4 7·00 2·75

(Des and litho J.W.)

1972 (19 June). *Military Equipment* (3*rd issue*). *Multicoloured designs as T* **99**. *W* w **12**. *P* 14.
285 2p. multicoloured 60 20
286 5p. reddish lilac, new blue and black .. 1·25 50
287 7½p. multicoloured .. .. 1·50 60
288 12½p. pale olive-sepia, brown and black .. 2·00 75
285/8 .. .. *Set of* 4 4·75 1·90

Designs:—2p. Royal Sappers and Miners breast-plate, post 1823; 5p. Infantry sergeant's spontoon, *circa* 1830; 7½p. Royal Artillery officer's breast-plate, *circa* 1830; 12½p. English military pistol, *circa* 1800.

103 St. Helena Sand Plover and White Tern

(Des (from photograph by D. Groves) and photo Harrison)

1972 (20 Nov). *Royal Silver Wedding. Multicoloured; background colour given. W* w **12**. *P* 14 × 14½.
289 **103** 2p. slate-green 25 25
290 16p. lake-brown 50 50

(Des J.W. Litho Questa)

1973 (20 Sept). *Military Equipment* (4*th issue*). *Multicoloured designs as T* **99**. *W* w **12** *(sideways). P* 14.
291 2p. Other Rank's shako, 53rd Foot, 1815 .. 1·00 55
292 5p. Band and Drums sword, 1830 .. .. 2·00 1·00
293 7½p. Royal Sappers and Miners Officer's hat, 1830 .. .. 2·25 1·25
294 12½p. General's sword, 1831 .. .. .. 3·50 1·50
291/4 .. .. *Set of* 4 8·00 4·00

1973 (14 Nov). *Royal Wedding. As Nos.* 165/6 *of Anguilla.*
295 2p. violet-blue 15 10
296 18p. light emerald 25 20

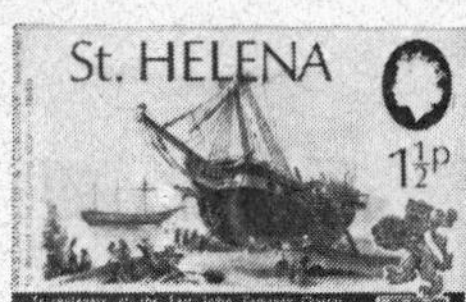

104 *Westminster* and *Claudine* beached, 1849

(Des J.W. Litho Questa)

1973 (17 Dec). *Tercentenary of East India Company Charter. T* **104** *and similar horiz designs. Multicoloured. W* w **12**. *P* 14.
297 1½p. Type **104** 50 35
298 4p. *True Briton*, 1790 .. .. 60 65
299 6p. *General Goddard* in action, 1795 .. .. 60 65
300 22½p. *Kent* burning in the Bay of Biscay, 1825 1·50 2·00
297/300 .. .. *Set of* 4 3·00 3·25

105 U.P.U. Emblem and Ships

(Des J.W. Litho Questa)

1974 (15 Oct). *Centenary of Universal Postal Union. T* **105** *and similar horiz design. Multicoloured. W* w **12** *(sideways on* **MS**303). *P* 14.
301 5p. Type **105** 25 25
302 25p. U.P.U. emblem and letters 55 55
MS303 89 × 84 mm. Nos. 301/2 .. .. .. 1·00 1·50

106 Churchill in Sailor Suit, and Blenheim Palace **107** Capt. Cook and H.M.S. *Resolution*

(Des Jennifer Toombs. Litho Questa)

1974 (30 Nov). *Birth Centenary of Sir Winston Churchill. T* **106** *and similar horiz design. W* w **14** *sideways (Nos.* 304/5) *or W* w **12** *sideways* (**MS**306). *P* 14.
304 5p. multicoloured 25 25
305 25p. black, flesh and reddish purple 55 75
MS306 108 × 93 mm. Nos. 304/5 .. .. .. 1·00 1·75

Design:—25p. Churchill and River Thames.

(Des J. Cooter. Litho Questa)

1975 (14 July). *Bicentenary of Capt. Cook's Return to St. Helena. T* **107** *and similar horiz design. Multicoloured. W* w **14** *(sideways on* 25p.). *P* 13½.
307 5p. Type **107** 50 50
308 25p. Capt. Cook and Jamestown .. .. 1·00 1·50

(Litho Questa)

1975 (13 Aug). *As No.* 264 *but whiter paper. P* 14.
309 2p. multicoloured .. .. 80 3·00

108 *Mellissia begonifolia* (tree) **109** £1 Note

(Des Jennifer Toombs. Litho J.W.)

1975 (20 Oct). *Centenary of Publication of "St. Helena" by J. C. Melliss. T* **108** *and similar multicoloured designs. W* w **14** *(sideways on* 12 *and* 25p.). *P* 13.
310 2p. Type **108** 25 20
311 5p. *Mellissius adumbratus* (beetle) 35 40
312 12p. St. Helena Sand Plover (*horiz*) .. .. 90 1·25
313 25p. *Scorpaenia mellissii* (fish) (*horiz*) .. 1·00 1·50
310/13 .. .. *Set of* 4 2·25 3·00

(Des V. Whiteley Studio. Litho J.W.)

1976 (15 Mar). *First Issue of Currency Notes. T* **109** *and similar horiz design. Multicoloured. W* w **12** *(sideways). P* 13½.
314 8p. Type **109** 40 30
315 33p. £5 Note .. .. 85 1·10

110 1d. Stamp of 1863

(Des C. Abbott. Litho J.W.)

1976 (4 May). *Festival of Stamps, London. T* **110** *and similar designs. W* w **14** *(sideways on* 5 *and* 25p.). *P* 13½.
316 5p. light red-brown, black and light flesh .. 15 15
317 8p. black, green and pale dull green 25 30
318 25p. multicoloured 40 45
316/18 .. .. *Set of* 3 70 80

Designs: *Vert*—8p. 1d. stamp of 1922. *Horiz*—25p. Mail carrier *Good Hope Castle*.

For miniature sheet containing No. 318 see Ascension No. **MS**218.

NEW INFORMATION

The editor is always interested to correspond with people who have new information that will improve or correct the Catalogue.

111 "High Knoll, 1806" (Capt. Barnett)

(Des C. Abbott. Litho Questa)

1976 (14 Sept)–**82.** *Aquatints and Lithographs of St. Helena.* *T* **111** *and similar horiz designs. Multicoloured.* W w **14** (*sideways*). *P* 13½ (£1, £2) or 14 (*others*).

A. *On white paper. Without imprint date.*

319A 1p. Type **111** 20 20
a. Cream paper (13.6.80) 20 20
320A 3p. "The Friar Rock, 1815" (G. Bellasis) 20 20
a. Cream paper (13.6.80) 15 15
321A 5p. "The Column Lot, 1815" (G. Bellasis) 15 20
322A 6p. "Sandy Bay Valley, 1809" (H. Salt) (23.11.76) 15 20
323A 8p. "Scene from Castle Terrace, 1815" (G. Bellasis) 20 25
324A 9p. "The Briars, 1815" (23.11.76) .. 20 25
325A 10p. "Plantation House, 1821" (J. Wathen) 50 60
326A 15p. "Longwood House, 1821" (J. Wathen) (23.11.76) 35 45
327A 18p. "St. Paul's Church" (V. Brooks) .. 35 45
328A 26p. "St. James's Valley, 1815" (Capt. Hastings) 45 65
329A 40p. "St. Matthew's Church, 1860" (V. Brooks) 70 95
330A £1 "St. Helena, 1815" (G. Bellasis) .. 1·50 2·25
a. Gold omitted £750
331A £2 "Sugar Loaf Hill, 1821" (J. Wathen) (23.11.76) .. .. .. 3·50 5·50
319A/31A .. .. .. *Set of* 13 7·50 11·00

B. *On cream paper with imprint date* ("1982") (10.5.82)

319B 1p. Type **111** 20 20
325B 10p. "Plantation House, 1821" (J. Wathen) 50 60
331B £2 "Sugar Loaf Hill, 1821" (J. Wathen) 3·75 5·00

The £1 and £2 are larger, 47 × 34 mm.

112 Duke of Edinburgh paying Homage

(Des M. Shamir. Litho J.W.)

1977 (7 Feb). *Silver Jubilee. T* **112** *and similar horiz designs. Multicoloured.* W w **14** (*sideways*). *P* 13.

332 8p. Royal visit, 1947 .. .. .. 20 35
333 15p. Queen's sceptre with dove 25 45
334 26p. Type **112** 35 50
332/4 .. .. *Set of* 3 70 1·10

113 Halley's Comet (from Bayeux Tapestry) 114 Sea Lion

(Des C. Abbott. Litho Questa)

1977 (23 Aug). *Tercentenary of Halley's Visit. T* **113** *and similar horiz designs. Multicoloured.* W w **14** (*sideways*). *P* 14.

335 5p. Type **113** 35 20
336 8p. Late 17th-century sextant 50 20
337 27p. Halley and Halley's Mount, St. Helena .. 1·00 60
335/7 .. .. *Set of* 3 1·75 90

(Des Jennifer Toombs. Litho Questa)

1978 (2 June). *25th Anniv of Coronation. T* **114** *and similar vert designs. P* 15.

338 25p. agate, cerise and silver 40 50
a. Sheetlet. Nos. 338/40 × 2 .. .. 2·00
339 25p. multicoloured 40 50
340 25p. agate, cerise and silver 40 50
338/40 .. .. *Set of* 3 1·10 1·40

Designs:—No. 338, Black Dragon of Ulster; No. 339, Queen Elizabeth II; No. 340, Type **114**.

Nos. 338/40 were printed together in small sheets of 6, containing two *se-tenant* strips of 3, with horizontal gutter margin between.

115 Period Engraving of St. Helena

(Des J.W. Litho Questa)

1978 (14 Aug). *Wreck of the "Witte Leeuw". T* **115** *and similar horiz designs. Multicoloured.* W w **14** (*sideways*). *P* 14½.

341 3p. Type **115** 15 15
342 5p. Chinese porcelain 20 20
343 8p. Bronze cannon 25 30
344 9p. Chinese porcelain (*different*) 30 35
345 15p. Pewter mug and ceramic flasks 50 55
346 20p. Dutch East Indiaman 60 70
341/6 .. .. *Set of* 6 1·75 2·00

116 H.M.S. *Discovery* 117 Sir Rowland Hill

(Des and litho (25p. also embossed) Walsall)

1979 (19 Feb). *Bicentenary of Captain Cook's Voyages,* 1768–79. *T* **116** *and similar vert designs. Multicoloured. P* 11.

347 3p. Type **116** 20 15
348 8p. Cook's portable observatory 30 25
349 12p. *Pharnaceum acidum* (based on sketch by Joseph Banks) 35 35
350 25p. Flaxman/Wedgwood medallion of Captain Cook 55 90
347/50 .. .. *Set of* 4 1·25 1·50

(Des J.W. Litho Questa)

1979 (20 Aug). *Death Centenary of Sir Rowland Hill. T* **117** *and similar designs.* W w **14** (*sideways on* 8 *to* 32p.). *P* 14.

351 5p. multicoloured 15 15
352 8p. multicoloured 20 20
353 20p. multicoloured 40 40
354 32p. black, magenta and deep mauve .. 55 55
351/4 .. .. *Set of* 4 1·10 1·10

Designs: *Horiz*—8p. 1965 1d. 1st Local Post stamp; 20p. 1863 1d. on 6d. stamp; 32p. 1902 1d. stamp.

118 R. F. Seal's Chart of 1823 showing the Elevation of the Coastline

(Des G. Vasarhelyi. Litho Questa)

1979 (10 Dec). *150th Anniv of the Inclined Plane. T* **118** *and similar designs.* W w **14** (*sideways on* 5 *and* 8p.). *P* 14.

355 5p. black, brownish grey and stone 20 15
356 8p. black, brownish grey and stone 20 20
357 50p. multicoloured 70 75
355/7 .. .. *Set of* 3 1·00 1·00

Designs: *Horiz*—8p. The Inclined Plane in 1829. *Vert*—50p. The Inclined Plane in 1979.

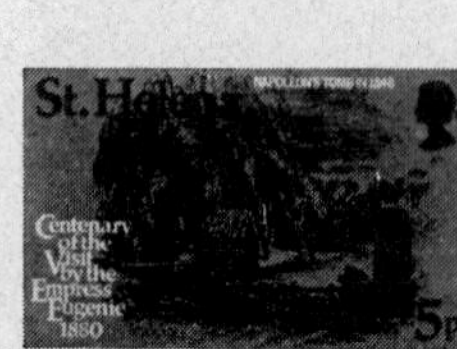

119 Napoleon's Tomb, 1848 120 East Indiaman

(Des J.W. Litho Questa)

1980 (23 Feb). *Centenary of Empress Eugenie's Visit. T* **119** *and similar horiz designs.* W w **14** (*sideways*). *P* 14.

358 5p. gold, reddish brown and pale red-brown 20 20
359 8p. gold, reddish brown and pale bistre .. 25 25
360 62p. gold, reddish brown & pale orange-brn .. 95 1·10
358/60 .. .. *Set of* 3 1·25 1·40
MS361 180 × 110 mm. Nos. 358/60 .. .. 1·50 2·00

Designs:—8p. Landing at St. Helena; 62p. At the tomb of Napoleon.

(Des C. Abbott. Litho Format)

1980 (6 May). *"London 1980" International Stamp Exhibition. T* **120** *and similar vert designs. Multicoloured.* W w **14**. *P* 14½.

362 5p. Type **120** 15 15
363 8p. *Dolphin* postal stone 15 20
364 47p. Postal stone outside Castle entrance, Jamestown 60 80
362/4 .. .. *Set of* 3 80 1·00
MS365 111 × 120 mm. Nos. 362/4 .. .. 85 1·50

121 Queen Elizabeth the Queen Mother

(Des and litho Harrison)

1980 (18 Aug*). *80th Birthday of Queen Elizabeth the Queen Mother.* W w **14** (*sideways*). *P* 14.

366 **121** 24p. multicoloured 50 50

*This is the local date of issue; the Crown Agents released the stamp on 4 August.

122 The Briars, 1815

(Des C. Abbott. Litho Questa)

1980 (17 Nov). *175th Anniv of Wellington's Visit. T* **122** *and similar multicoloured design.* W w **14** (*sideways on* 9p.). *P* 14.

367 9p. Type **122** 15 15
368 30p. "Wellington" (Goya) (*vert*) 45 45

Nos. 367/8 were each printed in small sheets of 10 stamps.

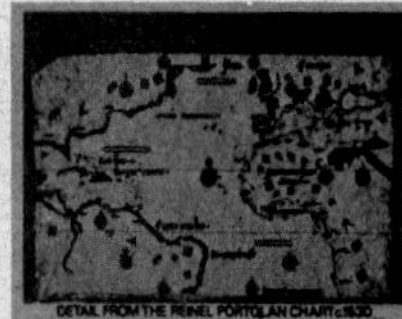

123 Redwood 124 Detail from Reinel Portolan Chart, *circa* 1530

(Des Daphne Padden. Litho Enschedé)

1981 (5 Jan). *Endemic Plants. T* **123** *and similar horiz designs. Multicoloured.* W w **14** (*sideways*). *P* 13½.

369 5p. Type **123** 15 15
370 8p. Old Father Live Forever 20 20
371 15p. Gumwood 25 25
372 27p. Black Cabbage 45 45
369/72 .. .. *Set of* 4 95 95

(Des Harrison. Litho Walsall)

1981 (22 May). *Early Maps. T* **124** *and similar horiz designs.* W w **14** (*sideways*). *P* 14 × 14½.

373 5p. multicoloured 15 15
374 8p. black, brown-lake and grey 20 20
375 20p. multicoloured 35 35
376 30p. multicoloured 50 50
373/6 .. .. *Set of* 4 1·10 1·10
MS377 114 × 83 mm. 24p. black and grey .. 40 65

Designs:—8p. John Thornton's Map of St. Helena, *circa* 1700; 20p. Map of St. Helena, 1815; 30p. Map of St. Helena, 1817; miniature sheet, Part of Gastaldi's map of Africa, 16th-century.

125 Prince Charles as Royal Navy Commander 126 *Charonia Variegata*

(Des J.W. Litho Questa)

1981 (22 July). *Royal Wedding. T* **125** *and similar vert designs. Multicoloured.* W w **14**. *P* 14.

378 14p. Wedding bouquet from St. Helena .. 25 25
379 29p. Type **125** 35 35
380 32p. Prince Charles and Lady Diana Spencer 50 50
378/80 .. .. *Set of* 3 1·00 1·00

(Des J.W. Litho Walsall)

1981 (10 Sept). *Seashells. T* **126** *and similar vert designs. Multicoloured.* W w **14**. *P* 14.

381 7p. Type **126** 35 20
382 10p. *Cypraea spurca sanctaehelenae* .. 40 25
383 25p. *Janthina janthina* 70 60
384 53p. *Pinna rudis* .. .. .. 1·25 1·25
381/4 .. .. *Set of* 4 2·40 2·10

127 Traffic Duty

128 St. Helena Dragonfly

(Des BG Studio. Litho Questa)

1981 (5 Nov). *25th Anniv of Duke of Edinburgh Award Scheme. T* **127** *and similar vert designs. Multicoloured.* W w **14**. *P* 14.

385 7p. Type **127** 15 15
386 11p. Signposting 15 15
387 25p. Animal care 35 35
388 50p. Duke of Edinburgh, in Guards' uniform, on horse-back 70 70
385/8 .. .. *Set of* 4 1·25 1·25

(Des C. Abbott. Litho Questa)

1982 (4 Jan). *Insects* (1*st series*). *T* **128** *and similar horiz designs. Multicoloured.* W w **14** (*sideways on* 7, 10 *and* 25*p., inverted on* 32*p.*). *P* 14½.

389 7p. Type **128** 30 25
390 10p. Burchell's Beetle 40 35
391 25p. Cockroach Wasp 70 60
392 32p. World's largest earwig (45 × 27 *mm*) .. 80 75
389/92 .. .. *Set of* 4 2·00 1·75

See also Nos. 411/14.

129 Charles Darwin

130 Prince and Princess of Wales at Balmoral, Autumn 1981

(Des L. Curtis. Litho Questa)

1982 (19 Apr). *150th Anniv of Charles Darwin's Voyage. T* **129** *and similar horiz designs. Multicoloured.* W w **14** (*sideways*). *P* 14.

393 7p. Type **129** 30 25
394 14p. Flagstaff Hill and Darwin's hammer .. 45 40
395 25p. Ring-necked Pheasant and Chukar Partridge 75 75
396 29p. H.M.S. *Beagle* off St. Helena 95 95
393/6 .. .. *Set of* 4 2·25 2·10

(Des C. Abbott. Litho Format)

1982 (1 July). *21st Birthday of Princess of Wales. T* **130** *and similar vert designs. Multicoloured.* W w **14**. *P* 13½ × 14 (7, 55*p.*) *or* 13½ (*others*).

397 7p. St. Helena coat of arms 15 12
398 11p. Type **130** 25 20
399 29p. Bride on Palace Balcony 55 60
a. Perf 13½ × 14 .. .. 30·00 10·00
b. Imperf (pair) £500
400 55p. Formal portrait .. .. 1·00 1·25
397/400 .. .. *Set of* 4 1·75 2·00

1st PARTICIPATION COMMONWEALTH GAMES 1982

(131)

132 Lord Baden-Powell

1982 (25 Oct). *Commonwealth Games, Brisbane. Nos.* 326 *and* 328 *optd with T* **131**.

401 15p. "Longwood House, 1821" (G. Wathen) .. 25 25
402 26p. "St. James's Valley, 1815" (Capt. Hastings) 45 45

(Des L. McCombie. Litho Walsall)

1982 (29 Nov). *75th Anniv of Boy Scout Movement. T* **132** *and similar designs.* W w **14** (*inverted on* 3*p.,* 29*p.; sideways on* 11*p.,* 59*p.*). *P* 14.

403 3p. lake-brown, grey and orange-yellow .. 15 15
404 11p. lake-brown, grey & bright yellow-green 35 25
405 29p. lake-brown, grey and reddish orange .. 70 60
406 59p. lake-brown, grey & bright yellow-green 1·25 1·25
403/6 .. .. *Set of* 4 2·25 2·00

Designs: *Horiz*—11p. Boy Scout (drawing by Lord Baden-Powell); 59p. Camping at Thompsons Wood. *Vert*—29p. Canon Walcott.

133 King and Queen Rocks

134 *Coriolus versicolor*

(Des C. Abbott. Litho B.D.T.)

1983 (14 Jan). *Views of St. Helena by Roland Svensson. T* **133** *and similar multicoloured designs.* W w **14** (*sideways on* 29*p.,* 59*p.*). *P* 14.

407 7p. Type **133** 20 20
408 11p. Turk's Cap 25 25
409 29p. Coastline from Jamestown (*horiz*) .. 65 65
410 59p. Mundens Point (*horiz*) .. .. .. 1·40 1·40
407/10 .. .. *Set of* 4 2·25 2·25

(Des C. Abbott. Litho Questa)

1983 (22 Apr). *Insects* (2*nd series*). *Horiz designs as T* **128**. *Multicoloured.* W w **14** (*sideways*). *P* 14½.

411 11p. Death's-head Hawk-moth 35 30
412 15p. Saldid-shore bug 40 35
413 29p. Click beetle 65 55
414 59p. Weevil .. .. 1·40 1·25
411/14 .. .. *Set of* 4 2·50 2·25

(Des Garden Studio. Litho Format)

1983 (16 June). *Fungi. T* **134** *and similar multicoloured designs.* W w **14** (*sideways on* 29*p.*). *P* 14.

415 11p. Type **134** 20 20
416 15p. *Pluteus brunneisucus* 30 30
417 29p. *Polyporus induratus* (*horiz*) 55 55
418 59p. *Coprinus angulatus* .. .. .. 1·25 1·25
415/18 .. .. *Set of* 4 2·10 2·10

135 Java Sparrow

136 Birth of St. Helena

(Des J.W. Litho Questa)

1983 (12 Sept). *Birds. T* **135** *and similar vert designs. Multicoloured.* W w **14**. *P* 14.

419 7p. Type **135** 30 20
420 15p. Madagascar Red Fody 45 35
421 33p. Common Waxbill 80 70
422 59p. Yellow Canary .. .. 1·50 1·40
419/22 .. .. *Set of* 4 2·75 2·50

(Des Jennifer Toombs. Litho Questa)

1983 (17 Oct). *Christmas. Life of St. Helena* (1*st series*). *T* **136** *and similar vert design. Multicoloured.* W w **14**. *P* 14 × 13½.

423 10p. Type **136** 25 25
a. Sheetlet Nos. 423/4, each ×5 .. .. 3·00
424 15p. St. Helena being taken to convent .. 30 30

Nos. 423/4 were printed together in small sheets of 10, containing horizontal strips of 5 for each value separated by a horizontal gutter margin.

See also Nos. 450/3 and 468/71.

137 1934 ½d. Stamp

138 Prince Andrew and H.M.S. *Invincible* (aircraft carrier)

(Des C. Abbott. Litho Questa)

1984 (3 Jan). *150th Anniv of St. Helena as a British Colony. T* **137** *and similar square designs showing values of the* 1934 *Centenary of British Colonisation issue or Colony Arms. Multicoloured.* W w **14** (*sideways*). *P* 13½.

425 1p. Type **137** 10 15
426 3p. 1934 1d. stamp 10 15
427 6p. 1934 1½d. stamp 10 20
428 7p. 1934 2d. stamp 15 20
429 11p. 1934 3d. stamp 20 30
430 15p. 1934 6d. stamp 25 35
431 29p. 1934 1s. stamp 50 75
432 33p. 1934 5s. stamp 55 85
433 59p. 1934 10s. stamp .. .. 1·10 1·60
434 £1 1934 2s. 6d. stamp .. .. 1·75 2·50
435 £2 St. Helena Coat of Arms .. .. .. 3·50 4·25
425/35 .. .. *Set of* 11 7·50 10·00

(Des D. Bowen. Litho Format)

1984 (4 Apr). *Visit of Prince Andrew. T* **138** *and similar horiz design. Multicoloured.* W w **14** (*sideways*). *P* 14.

436 11p. Type **138** 25 25
437 60p. Prince Andrew and H.M.S. *Herald* (survey ship) .. .. 1·25 1·40

139 *St. Helena* (schooner)

140 Twopenny Coin and Donkey

(Des A. Theobald. Litho Questa)

1984 (14 May). *250th Anniv of "Lloyd's List" (newspaper). T* **139** *and similar vert designs. Multicoloured.* W w **14**. *P* 14½ × 14.

438 10p. Type **139** 20 20
439 18p. Solomons Facade (local agent) 35 35
440 25p. Lloyd's Coffee House, London 50 55
441 50p. *Papanui* (freighter) .. .. .. 1·00 1·00
438/41 .. .. *Set of* 4 1·90 1·90

(Des G. Drummond. Litho Format)

1984 (23 July). *New Coinage. T* **140** *and similar horiz designs. Multicoloured.* W w **14** (*sideways*). *P* 14.

442 10p. Type **140** 35 35
443 15p. Five pence coin and St. Helena Sand Plover 45 45
444 29p. Penny coin and Yellowfin Tuna 75 75
445 50p. Ten pence coin and Arum Lily .. .. 1·25 1·25
442/5 .. .. *Set of* 4 2·50 2·50

141 Mrs. Rebecca Fuller (former Corps Secretary)

142 Queen Elizabeth the Queen Mother aged Two

(Des L. Curtis. Litho Walsall)

1984 (12 Oct). *Centenary of Salvation Army on St. Helena. T* **141** *and similar multicoloured designs.* W w **14** (*sideways on* 11*p.,* 25*p.*). *P* 14.

446 7p. Type **141** 35 25
447 11p. Meals-on-wheels service (*horiz*) 45 30
448 25p. Salvation Army Citadel, Jamestown (*horiz*) 80 60
449 60p. Salvation Army band at Jamestown Clock Tower .. .. 1·75 1·60
446/9 .. .. *Set of* 4 3·00 2·50

(Des Jennifer Toombs. Litho Questa)

1984 (9 Nov). *Christmas. Life of St. Helena* (2*nd series*). *Vert designs as T* **136**. *Multicoloured.* W w **14**. *P* 14.

450 6p. St. Helena visits prisoners 20 20
451 10p. Betrothal of St. Helena 30 30
452 15p. Marriage of St. Helena to Constantius .. 40 40
453 33p. Birth of Constantine 70 70
450/3 .. .. *Set of* 4 1·40 1·40

(Des A. Theobald (70p.), C. Abbott (others). Litho Questa)

1985 (7 June). *Life and Times of Queen Elizabeth the Queen Mother. T* **142** *and similar vert designs. Multicoloured.* W w **16**. *P* 14½ × 14.

454 11p. Type **142** 20 25
455 15p. At Ascot with the Queen 30 35
456 29p. Attending Gala Ballet at Covent Garden 60 65
457 55p. With Prince Henry at his christening .. 1·10 1·25
454/7 .. .. *Set of* 4 2·00 2·25
MS458 91 × 73 mm. 70p. The Queen Mother with Ford "V8 Pilot". Wmk sideways .. .. .. 1·40 1·60

143 Rock Bullseye

144 John J. Audubon

(Des L. Curtis. Litho Walsall)

1985 (12 July). *Marine Life. T* **143** *and similar horiz designs. Multicoloured. W* w **14** *(sideways). P* 13×13½.

459 7p. Type **143** .. 25 25
460 11p. Mackerel .. 30 30
461 15p. Skipjack Tuna .. 40 40
462 33p. Yellowfin Tuna .. 75 75
463 50p. Stump .. 1·25 1·25
459/63 .. *Set of* 5 2·75 2·75

(Des Josephine Martin (11p.). Litho Format)

1985 (2 Sept). *Birth Bicentenary of John J. Audubon (ornithologist). T* **144** *and similar designs. W* w **14** *(inverted on 11p., sideways on others). P* 14.

464 11p. black and blackish brown .. 35 25
465 15p. multicoloured .. 45 35
466 25p. multicoloured .. 65 55
467 60p. multicoloured .. 1·40 1·40
464/7 .. *Set of* 4 2·50 2·25

Designs: *Horiz* (from original Audubon paintings)—15p. Moorhen ("Common Gallinule"); 25p. White-tailed Tropic Bird; 60p. Common Noddy.

(Des Jennifer Toombs. Litho Questa)

1985 (14 Oct). *Christmas. Life of St. Helena (3rd series). Vert designs as T* **136**. *Multicoloured. W* w **14**. *P* 14×13½.

468 7p. St. Helena journeys to the Holy Land .. 25 25
469 10p. Zambres slays the bull .. 30 30
470 15p. The bull restored to life: conversion of St. Helena .. 40 40
471 60p. Resurrection of the corpse: the true Cross identified .. 1·50 1·50
468/71 .. *Set of* 4 2·25 2·25

145 Church Provident Society for Women Banner

146 Plaque at Site of Halley's Observatory on St. Helena

(Des A. Theobald. Litho J.W.)

1986 (7 Jan). *Friendly Societies' Banners. T* **145** *and similar horiz designs. Multicoloured. W* w **16** *(sideways). P* 13×13½.

472 10p. Type **145** .. 25 25
473 11p. Working Men's Christian Association .. 25 25
474 25p. Church Benefit Society for Children .. 55 55
475 29p. Mechanics and Friendly Benefit Society 65 65
476 33p. Ancient Order of Foresters .. 70 70
472/6 .. *Set of* 5 2·10 2·10

(Des A. Theobald. Litho Questa)

1986 (21 Apr). *60th Birthday of Queen Elizabeth II. Vert designs as T* **110** *of Ascension. Multicoloured. W* w **16**. *P* 14½×14.

477 10p. Princess Elizabeth making 21st birthday broadcast, South Africa, 1947 .. 20 25
478 15p. Silver Jubilee photograph, 1977 .. 30 35
479 20p. Princess Elizabeth on board H.M.S. *Implacable*, 1947 .. 40 45
480 50p. In the U.S.A., 1976 .. 1·00 1·10
481 65p. At Crown Agents Head Office, London, 1983 .. 1·25 1·40
477/81 .. *Set of* 5 2·75 3·25

(Des L. Curtis. Litho Walsall)

1986 (15 May). *Appearance of Halley's Comet. T* **146** *and similar vert designs. Multicoloured. W* w **14**. *P* 14½×14.

482 9p. Type **146** .. 25 25
483 12p. Edmond Halley .. 30 30
484 20p. Halley's planisphere of the southern stars .. 45 45
485 65p. *Unity* on passage to St. Helena, 1676 .. 1·40 1·40
482/5 .. *Set of* 4 2·10 2·10

(Des D. Miller. Litho Questa)

1986 (23 July). *Royal Wedding. Square designs as T* **112** *of Ascension. Multicoloured. W* w **16**. *P* 14.

486 10p. Prince Andrew and Miss Sarah Ferguson .. 20 25
487 40p. Prince Andrew with Governor J. Massingham on St. Helena .. 80 85

147 James Ross and H.M.S. *Erebus*

(Des C. Abbott. Litho Questa)

1986 (22 Sept). *Explorers. T* **147** *and similar horiz designs. W* w **16** *(sideways). P* 14½.

488 1p. deep brown and pink .. 10 10
489 3p. royal blue and grey-blue .. 10 10
490 5p. bronze-green and deep yellow-green .. 10 10
491 9p. purple-brown and claret .. 15 20
492 10p. deep brown and light brown .. 20 25
493 12p. myrtle-green and light green .. 20 25
494 15p. red-brown and brown-rose .. 25 30
495 20p. deep dull blue and light blue .. 35 40
496 25p. sepia and salmon-pink .. 45 50
497 40p. bottle-green and dull blue-green .. 70 75
498 60p. reddish brown and pale orange-brown .. 1·10 1·25
499 £1 deep turquoise-blue and turquoise-blue 1·75 1·90
500 £2 deep lilac and reddish lilac .. 3·50 3·75
488/500 .. *Set of* 13 8·00 8·75

Designs:—3p. Robert FitzRoy and H.M.S. *Beagle*; 5p. Adam Johann von Krusenstern and *Nadezhda*; 9p. William Bligh and H.M.S. *Resolution*; 10p. Otto von Kotzebue and *Rurik*; 12p. Philip Carteret and H.M.S. *Swallow*; 15p. Thomas Cavendish and *Desire*; 20p. Louis-Antoine de Bougainville and *La Boudeuse*; 25p. Fyedor Petrovich Lütke and *Senyavin*; 40p. Louis Isidore Duperrey and *La Coquille*; 60p. John Byron and H.M.S. *Dolphin*; £1 James Cook and H.M.S. *Endeavour*; £2 Jules Dumont d'Urville and *L'Astrolabe*.

148 Prince Edward and H.M.S. *Repulse* (battle cruiser), 1925

149 St. Helena Tea Plant

(Des E. Nisbet. Litho Questa)

1987 (16 Feb). *Royal Visits to St. Helena. T* **148** *and similar horiz designs. Multicoloured. W* w **16** *(sideways). P* 14.

501 9p. Type **148** .. 35 25
502 13p. King George VI and H.M.S. *Vanguard* (battleship), 1947 .. 40 30
503 38p. Prince Philip and Royal Yacht *Britannia*, 1957 .. 90 80
504 45p. Prince Andrew and H.M.S. *Herald* (survey ship), 1984 .. 1·10 95
501/4 .. *Set of* 4 2·50 2·10

(Des Annette Robinson. Litho Questa)

1987 (3 Aug). *Rare Plants (1st series). T* **149** *and similar vert designs. Multicoloured. W* w **16**. *P* 14½×14.

505 9p. Type **149** .. 40 30
506 13p. Baby's Toes .. 45 35
507 38p. Salad Plant .. 90 80
508 45p. Scrubwood .. 1·10 95
505/8 .. *Set of* 4 2·50 2·25

See also Nos. 527/30.

150 Lesser Rorqual

151 *Defence* and Dampier's Signature, 1691

(Des A. Riley. Litho Questa)

1987 (24 Oct). *Marine Mammals. T* **150** *and similar horiz designs. Multicoloured. W* w **16** *(sideways). P* 14.

509 9p. Type **150** .. 30 30
510 13p. Risso's Dolphin .. 40 40
511 45p. Sperm Whale .. 1·25 1·25
512 60p. Euphrosyne Dolphin .. 1·40 1·40
509/12 .. *Set of* 4 3·00 3·00
MS513 102×72 mm. 75p. Humpback Whale (48×31 *mm*). P 13½×14 .. 1·75 2·00

1987 (9 Dec). *Royal Ruby Wedding. Nos. 477/81 optd with T* **119** *of Ascension in silver.*

514 10p. Princess Elizabeth making 21st birthday broadcast, South Africa, 1947 .. 20 25
515 15p. Silver Jubilee photograph, 1977 .. 30 35
a. Opt omitted (vert pair with normal) .. £150
516 20p. Princess Elizabeth on board H.M.S. *Implacable*, 1947 .. 40 45
517 50p. In the U.S.A., 1976 .. 1·00 1·10
518 65p. At Crown Agents Head Office, London, 1983 .. 1·25 1·40
514/18 .. *Set of* 5 2·75 3·25

No. 515a occurred on the top row of several sheets.

(Des A. Theobald. Litho Walsall)

1988 (1 Mar). *Bicentenary of Australian Settlement. T* **151** *and similar horiz designs showing ships and signatures. Multicoloured. W* w **16** *(sideways). P* 14×14½.

519 9p. Type **151** .. 40 30
520 13p. H.M.S. *Resolution* (Cook), 1775 .. 60 40
521 45p. H.M.S. *Providence* (Bligh), 1792 .. 1·40 1·25
522 60p. H.M.S. *Beagle* (Darwin), 1836 .. 1·60 1·40
519/22 .. *Set of* 4 3·50 3·00

ALTERED CATALOGUE NUMBERS

Any Catalogue numbers altered from the last edition are shown as a list in the introductory pages.

152 "The Holy Virgin with the Child"

153 Ebony

(Des N. Harvey. Litho Questa)

1988 (11 Oct). *Christmas. T* **152** *and similar vert designs showing religious paintings. Multicoloured. W* w **14**. *P* 14.

523 5p. Type **152** .. 10 15
524 20p. "Madonna" .. 40 45
525 38p. "The Holy Family with St. John" .. 75 80
526 60p. "The Holy Virgin with the Child" .. 1·25 1·40
523/6 .. *Set of* 4 2·25 2·50

(Des D. Miller (8p.), E. Nisbet and D. Miller (others). Litho Questa)

1988 (1 Nov). *300th Anniv of Lloyd's of London. Designs as T* **123** *of Ascension. W* w **16** *(sideways on 20, 45p.). P* 14.

527 9p. agate and brown .. 20 25
528 20p. multicoloured .. 40 45
529 45p. multicoloured .. 90 95
530 60p. multicoloured .. 1·25 1·40
527/30 .. *Set of* 4 2·50 2·75

Designs: *Vert*—9p. Lloyd's Underwriting Room, 1886; 60p. *Spangereid* (full-rigged ship) on fire, St. Helena, 1920. *Horiz*—20p. *Edinburgh Castle* (liner); 45p. *Bosun Bird* (freighter).

(Des L. Ninnes. Litho Questa)

1989 (6 Jan). *Rare Plants (2nd series). T* **153** *and similar vert designs. Multicoloured. W* w **16**. *P* 14.

531 9p. Type **153** .. 20 25
532 20p. St. Helena Lobelia .. 40 45
533 45p. Large Bellflower .. 90 95
534 60p. She Cabbage Tree .. 1·25 1·40
531/4 .. *Set of* 4 2·50 2·75

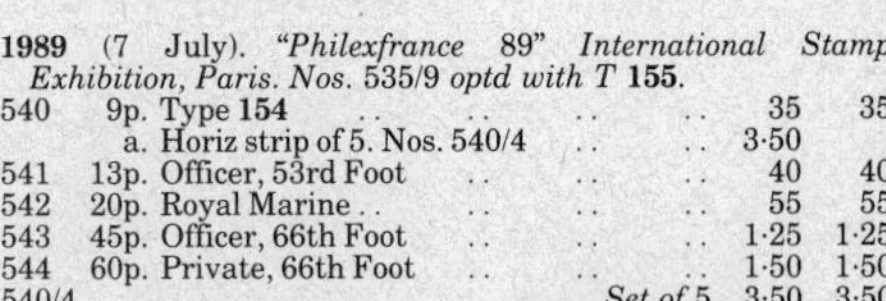

154 Private, 53rd Foot

(**155**)

(Des C. Collins. Litho Format)

1989 (5 June). *Military Uniforms of* 1815. *T* **154** *and similar vert designs. Multicoloured. W* w **16**. *P* 14.

535 9p. Type **154** .. 35 35
a. Horiz strip of 5. Nos. 535/9 .. 3·50
536 13p. Officer, 53rd Foot .. 40 40
537 20p. Royal Marine .. 55 55
538 45p. Officer, 66th Foot .. 1·25 1·25
539 60p. Private, 66th Foot .. 1·50 1·50
535/9 .. *Set of* 5 3·50 3·50

Nos. 535/9 were printed together, *se-tenant*, in horizontal strips of five throughout the sheet.

1989 (7 July). *"Philexfrance 89" International Stamp Exhibition, Paris. Nos. 535/9 optd with T* **155**.

540 9p. Type **154** .. 35 35
a. Horiz strip of 5. Nos. 540/4 .. 3·50
541 13p. Officer, 53rd Foot .. 40 40
542 20p. Royal Marine .. 55 55
543 45p. Officer, 66th Foot .. 1·25 1·25
544 60p. Private, 66th Foot .. 1·50 1·50
540/4 .. *Set of* 5 3·50 3·50

156 Agricultural Studies

157 "The Madonna with the Pear" (Dürer)

(Des A. Edmonston. Litho Questa)

1989 (24 Aug). *New Prince Andrew Central School. T* **156** *and similar horiz designs. Multicoloured. W* w **16** *(sideways). P* 14×14½.

545 13p. Type **156** .. 35 35
546 20p. Geography lesson .. 55 55
547 25p. Walkway and classroom block .. 65 65
548 60p. Aerial view of School .. 1·50 1·50
545/8 .. *Set of* 4 2·75 2·75

(Des D. Miller. Litho Questa)

1989 (23 Oct). *Christmas. Religious Paintings. T* **157** *and similar vert designs. Multicoloured. W* w **14**. *P* 14.

549 10p. Type **157** 30 30
550 20p. "The Holy Family under the Appletree" (Rubens) 55 55
551 45p. "The Virgin in the Meadow" (Raphael) 1·25 1·25
552 60p. "The Holy Family with St. John" (Raphael) .. .. 1·60 1·60
549/52 .. .. *Set of* 4 3·25 3·25

158 Chevrolet "6" 30 cwt Lorry, 1930

159 Sheep

(Des E. Nesbit. Litho Questa)

1989 (1 Dec). *Early Vehicles. T* **158** *and similar horiz designs. Multicoloured. W* w **16** *(sideways). P* 14½.

553 9p. Type **158** 20 25
554 20p. Austin "Seven", 1929 .. .. .. 40 45
555 45p. Morris "Cowley" 11.9 h.p., 1929 .. 90 95
556 60p. Sunbeam 25 h.p., 1932 .. .. 1·25 1·40
553/6 .. .. *Set of* 4 2·50 2·75
MS557 93×74 mm. £1 Ford "Model A Fordor" .. 2·00 2·25

(Des Doreen McGuiness. Litho Questa)

1990 (1 Feb). *Farm Animals. T* **159** *and similar vert designs. Multicoloured. W* w **16**. *P* 14.

558 9p. Type **159** 20 25
559 13p. Pigs 25 30
560 45p. Cow and calf 90 95
561 60p. Geese .. .. 1·25 1·40
558/61 .. .. *Set of* 4 2·40 2·50

POSTAGE DUE STAMPS

D 1 Outline Map of St. Helena

(Des L. Curtis. Litho Questa)

1986 (9 June). *W* w **16**. *P* 14½×14.

D1 **D 1** 1p. deep brown and cinnamon 10 10
D2 2p. deep brown and bright orange .. 10 10
D3 5p. deep brown and orange-vermilion .. 10 10
D4 7p. black and bright reddish violet .. 10 15
D5 10p. black and violet-blue 20 25
D6 25p. black and pale emerald 45 50
D1/6 .. .. *Set of* 6 85 1·00

St. Kitts-Nevis

ST. CHRISTOPHER

The first recorded postal marking for St. Christopher dates from 1746, although it is probable that a branch of the British G.P.O. operated on the island before that date.

Stamps of Great Britain were used between May 1858 and the end of March 1860 when control of the postal services passed to the local authorities. In the years which followed, prior to the introduction of St. Christopher stamps in April 1870, a circular "PAID" handstamp was used on overseas mail.

For illustrations of the postmark types see BRITISH POST OFFICES ABROAD notes, following GREAT BRITAIN.

BASSETERRE

Stamps of GREAT BRITAIN *cancelled* "A 12" *as Type* 2.

1858 *to* **1860.**

No.	Description	Price
Z1	1d. rose-red (1857), *perf* 14	
Z2	2d. blue (1858) (Plate No. 7)	£900
Z3	4d. rose (1857)	£300
Z4	6d. lilac (1856)	£180
Z5	1s. green (1856)	£900

PRICES FOR STAMPS ON COVER

Nos. 1/5	*from* × 10
Nos. 6/8	*from* × 15
Nos. 9/10	*from* × 7
Nos. 11/21	*from* × 6
Nos. 22/3	*from* × 8
Nos. 24/8	—
Nos. R1/6	—

1

Halfpenny

(2)

FOUR PENCE

(3)

(Typo D.L.R.)

1870 (1 April)–**76.** *Wmk Crown CC. (a) P* 12½.

No.	Type	Description	Unused	Used
1	1	1d. dull rose	55·00	40·00
		a. Wmk sideways	£225	£180
2		1d. magenta	35·00	26·00
3		1d. pale magenta	40·00	28·00
4		6d. green	80·00	7·50
5		6d. yellow-green	80·00	17·00
		(b) P 14 (1875–6)		
6	1	1d. magenta	80·00	11·00
		a. Bisected diag or vert (½d.) (on cover)	†	£1000
7		1d. pale magenta	55·00	7·00
8		6d. green	45·00	5·00
		a. Imperf between (pair)		
		b. Wmk sideways	£275	

1879 (Nov). *New values. Wmk Crown CC. P* 14.

No.	Type	Description	Unused	Used
9	1	2½d. red-brown	£170	£200
10		4d. blue	£150	15·00
		a. Wmk sideways		

1882–90. *Wmk Crown CA. P* 14.

No.	Type	Description	Unused	Used
11	1	½d. dull green	50	80
		a. Wmk sideways	£200	
12		1d. dull magenta	£350	60·00
		a. Bisected diagonally (½d.) (on cover)		
13		1d. carmine-rose	60	60
		a. Bisected (½d.) (on cover)		
14		2½d. pale red-brown	£170	55·00
15		2½d. deep red-brown	£180	60·00
16		2½d. ultramarine (1884)	1·50	1·50
17		4d. blue	£400	20·00
18		4d. grey (1884)	1·25	80
19		6d. olive-brown (1890)	80·00	£180
20		1s. mauve (1887)	90·00	65·00
21		1s. bright mauve	80·00	£100
19/20 Optd "Specimen"		*Set of* 2	£120	

1885 (March). *No.* 13 *bisected and No.* 8 *surch with T* 2 *(diag) and T* 3 *respectively.*

No.	Description	Unused	Used
22	½d. on half of 1d. carmine-rose	24·00	32·00
	a. Unsevered pair	£110	£120
	ab. Ditto, one surch inverted		
	b. Surch inverted	£400	£325
	c. Surch double		
23	4d. on 6d. green	48·00	48·00
	a. Full stop after "PENCE"	85·00	95·00
	b. Surch double	£1600	

ONE PENNY.

(4)

4d.

(5)

On Types 4, 5 and 7 the cancelling bar at foot was applied by hand, using a pen and ruler.

1886 (June). *No.* 8 *surch with T* 4 *or* 5.

No.	Type	Description	Unused	Used
24	1	1d. on 6d. green	16·00	28·00
		a. Surch inverted	£5000	
		b. Surch double	—	£1300
25		4d. on 6d. green	48·00	90·00
		a. No stop after "d"	£180	£200
		b. Surch double	£1400	£1600

No. 24b is only known penmarked or with violet handstamp.

1887 (May). *Surch with T* 4.

No.	Type	Description	Unused	Used
26	1	1d. on ½d. dull green	28·00	38·00

ONE PENNY.

(7)

1888 (May). *No.* 16 *surch.*

No.	Type	Description	Unused	Used
		(a) As T 4 but without bar through old value		
27	1	1d. on 2½d. ultramarine	£8000	£8000
		(b) With T 7		
28	1	1d. on 2½d. ultramarine	35·00	42·00
		a. Surch inverted	£6500	£4500

The 1d. of Antigua was used provisionally in St. Christopher in 1890, and can be distinguished by the postmark, which is "A 12" in place of "A02" (*price from £160 used*).

REVENUE STAMPS USED FOR POSTAGE

Saint Christopher

(R 1)

SAINT KITTS NEVIS REVENUE

(R 2)

1883. *Nos.* F6 *and* F8 *of Nevis optd with Type* R 1, *in violet. Wmk Crown CA. P* 14.

No.	Description	Unused	Used
R1	1d. lilac-mauve	£225	
R2	6d. green	55·00	75·00

1885. *Optd with Type* R 2. *Wmk Crown CA. P* 14.

No.	Type	Description	Unused	Used
R3	1	1d. rose	1·25	6·50
R4		3d. mauve	7·00	40·00
R5		6d. orange-brown	3·00	27·00
R6		1s. olive	1·50	27·00

Other fiscal stamps with overprints as above also exist, but none of these was ever available for postal purposes.

The stamps for St. Christopher were superseded by the general issue for Leeward Islands on 31 October 1890.

Stamps for St. Kitts, issued from 1980 onwards will be found listed after those for the combined colony.

NEVIS

Little is known concerning the early postal affairs of Nevis, but it is recorded that the British G.P.O. was to establish a branch office on the island under an Act of Parliament, passed in 1710, although arrangements may not have been finalised for a number of years afterwards. Nevis appears as "a new office" in the P.O. Accounts of 1787.

Stamps of Great Britain were used on the island from May 1858 until the colonial authorities assumed control of the postal service on 1 May 1860. Between this date and the introduction of Nevis stamps in 1861 No. CC1 was again used on overseas mail.

For illustrations of the handstamp and postmark types see BRITISH POST OFFICES ABROAD notes, following GREAT BRITAIN.

CHARLESTOWN

CROWNED-CIRCLE HANDSTAMPS

CC1 CC 5 NEVIS (R.) (9.1852) . . *Price on cover* £1600

No. CC1, but struck in black, was later used in the 1880's on several occasions when there were shortages of adhesive stamps.

Stamps of GREAT BRITAIN *cancelled* "A 09" *as Type* 2.

1858 *to* **1860.**

No.	Description	Price
Z1	1d. rose-red (1857), *perf* 14	£375
Z2	2d. blue (1858) (Plate Nos. 7, 8)	
Z3	4d. rose (1857)	£300
Z4	6d. lilac (1856)	£275
Z5	1s. green (1856)	

PRICES FOR STAMPS ON COVER

Nos. 1/22	*from* × 8
Nos. 23/4	*from* × 4
Nos. 25/34	*from* × 6
Nos. 35/6	*from* × 7
Nos. F1/8	*from* × 12

1

2

3

4

The designs on the stamps refer to a medicinal spring on the island

(Recess Nissen & Parker, London)

1861. *P* 13. *(a) Blued paper.*

No.	Type	Description	Unused	Used
1	1	1d. dull rose	£180	95·00
2	2	4d. rose	£600	£140
3	3	6d. grey-lilac	£500	£180
4	4	1s. green	£750	£150
		(b) Greyish paper		
5	1	1d. dull lake	35·00	35·00
6	2	4d. rose	70·00	50·00
7	3	6d. grey	65·00	40·00
8	4	1s. green	£140	50·00

1866. *White paper. P* 15.

No.	Type	Description	Unused	Used
9	1	1d. pale red	25·00	22·00
10		1d. deep red	25·00	22·00
11	2	4d. orange	95·00	19·00
12		4d. deep orange	95·00	19·00
13	4	1s. blue-green	£150	26·00
14		1s. yellow-green	£800	£100
		a. Laid paper	£10000	£3500
		b. No. 9 on sheet with crossed lines on hill	£3500	£500
		c. Ditto. On laid paper	†	£6500

(Lithographed by transfer from the engraved plates Nissen and Parker, London)

1876. *P* 15.

No.	Type	Description	Unused	Used
15	1	1d. pale rose-red	14·00	12·00
		a. Imperf (pair)	£225	
16		1d. deep rose-red	20·00	17·00
17		1d. vermilion-red	20·00	17·00
		a. Bisected (on cover)	†	£1000
18	2	4d. orange-yellow	£140	27·00
		a. Imperf between (vert pair)	£3000	
19	3	6d. grey	£180	£170
20	4	1s. pale green	50·00	80·00
		a. Imperf		
		b. Imperf between (horiz strip of three)	£3500	
		c. No. 9 on sheet with crossed lines on hill	£225	
21		1s. deep green	50·00	90·00

With one exception, resulting from a stone which was not retouched, No. 9 on the sheet of the 1s. *deep* green, has not the distinct "crossed lines on hill" of Nos. 14b, 20c and F5a, but traces of the lines are visible.

RETOUCHES. 1d. Lithograph.

	Description	Unused	Used
i.	No. 1 on sheet. Top of hill over kneeling figure redrawn by five thick lines and eight small slanting lines	£140	£150
ii.	No. 1 on sheet. Another retouch. Three series of short vertical strokes behind the kneeling figure	£140	£150
iii.	No. 3 on sheet. Right upper corner star and border below star retouched	£140	£150
iv.	No. 9 on sheet. Retouch in same position as on No. 3 but differing in detail	£160	£170
v.	No. 12 on sheet. Dress of standing figure retouched by a number of horizontal and vertical lines	£140	£150

1878. *Litho. P* 11½.

No.	Type	Description	Unused	Used
22	1	1d. vermilion-red	35·00	45·00
		a. Bisected (on cover)	†	£1000
		b. Imperf (pair)	£200	
		c. Imperf between (horiz pair)		

5 (Die I)

NEVIS. ½d.

(6)

(Typo D.L.R.)

1879–80. *Wmk Crown CC. P* 14.

No.	Type	Description	Unused	Used
23	5	1d. lilac-mauve (1880)	30·00	25·00
		a. Bisected (½d.) (on cover)	†	£700
24		2½d. red-brown	85·00	75·00

1882–90. *Wmk Crown CA. P* 14.

No.	Type	Description	Unused	Used
25	5	½d. dull green (1883)	2·50	3·75
26		1d. lilac-mauve	80·00	20·00
		a. Bisected (½d.) on cover	†	£700
27		1d. carmine (1884)	3·00	3·25
		a. Dull rose	14·00	10·00
28		2½d. red-brown	85·00	45·00
29		2½d. ultramarine (1884)	7·00	5·50
30		4d. blue	£275	45·00
31		4d. grey (1884)	3·25	2·50
32		6d. green (1883)	£350	£350
33		6d. chestnut (1888)	17·00	35·00
34		1s. pale violet (1890)	85·00	£140
33/4 Optd "Specimen"		*Set of* 2	£110	

1883. *No.* 26 *bisected vertically and surch with T* 6, *reading upwards or downwards.*

No.	Description	Unused	Used
35	½d. on half 1d. lilac-mauve (V.)	£275	26·00
	a. Surch double	—	£275
	b. Surch on half "REVENUE" stamp No. F6	—	£500
36	½d. on half 1d. lilac-mauve	£250	25·00
	a. Surch double	—	£275
	b. Unsevered pair	£800	
	ba. Surch on right half only		
	c. Surch on half "REVENUE" stamp No. F6	—	£500

FISCALS USED FOR POSTAGE

Revenue (F 1) REVENUE (F 2)

1882. *(a) Stamps of 1876 optd with Type F 1.*
F1 1d. bright red .. .. 20·00
F2 1d. rose .. .. 20·00 12·00
F3 4d. orange .. .. 45·00
F4 6d. grey .. .. 70·00
F5 1s. green .. .. 90·00
a. No. 9 on sheet with crossed lines on hill

(b) Nos. 26, 30 and 32 optd with Type F 2
F6 1d. lilac-mauve .. .. 16·00 17·00
F7 4d. blue .. .. 11·00 22·00
F8 6d. green .. .. 11·00 24·00

The retouches listed for the 1d. *lithograph* also occur on No. F1 (*Price from* £130).

The stamps of Nevis were superseded by the general issue for Leeward Islands on 31 October 1890. Stamps for Nevis were again issued in 1980 and will be found listed after those for the combined colony.

ST. KITTS-NEVIS

CROWN COLONY

Stamps for the combined colony were introduced in 1903, and were used concurrently with the general issues of Leeward Islands.

PRICES FOR STAMPS ON COVER TO 1945	
Nos. 1/9	from × 3
No. 10	—
Nos. 11/20	from × 3
No. 21	—
Nos. 22/3	from × 15
Nos. 24/34	from × 3
Nos. 35/6	—
Nos. 37/47	from × 2
Nos. 47a/b	—
Nos. 48/57	from × 2
Nos. 58/60	—
Nos. 61/4	from × 2
Nos. 65/7	from × 5
Nos. 68/77c	from × 2

1 Christopher Columbus

2 Medicinal Spring

(Typo D.L.R.)

1903. *Wmk Crown CA. P 14.*
1 1 ½d. dull purple and deep green .. 1·50 70
2 2 1d. grey-black and carmine .. 2·50 20
3 1 2d. dull purple and brown .. 2·25 8·00
4 2½d. grey-black and blue .. 9·00 3·50
5 2 3d. deep green and orange .. 2·75 12·00
6 1 6d. grey-black and bright purple .. 3·25 13·00
7 1s. grey-green and orange .. 6·00 10·00
8 2 2s. deep green and grey-black .. 8·50 14·00
9 1 2s. 6d. grey-black and violet .. 15·00 30·00
10 2 5s. dull purple and sage-green .. 30·00 48·00
1/10 .. .. .. *Set of* 10 70·00 £120
1/10 Optd "Specimen" .. .. *Set of* 10 £130

1905–18. *Wmk Mult Crown CA. P 14.*
11 1 ½d. dull purple and deep green, O .. 4·00 5·50
12 ½d. grey-green, O (1907) .. 30 35
a. Dull blue-green, O .. .. 25 1·25
13 2 1d. grey-black and carmine, C .. 1·00 25
14 1d. carmine, O (1907) 80 15
a. Scarlet, O 35 20
15 1 2d. dull purple and brown, OC .. 60 1·50
16 2½d. grey-black and blue, O .. 14·00 2·75
17 2½d. bright blue, O (1907) .. 60 40
18 2 3d. deep green and orange, OC .. 80 1·50
19 1 6d. grey-black and deep violet, O .. 8·50 20·00
a. Grey-black & dp purple, C (1908) .. 8·00 15·00
b. Grey-black & brt purple, C (1916) .. 4·25 15·00
20 1s. grey-green and orange, OC (1909) .. 1·75 12·00
21 2 5s. dull purple & sage-grn, C (11.18) .. 23·00 55·00
11/21 .. .. .. *Set of* 11 45·00 85·00
12, 14, 17 Optd "Specimen" .. .. *Set of* 3 60·00

WAR TAX (3) WAR STAMP (3a)

1916 (Oct). *Optd with T 3. Wmk Mult Crown CA. P 14.*
22 1 ½d. green (Optd S. £40) 10 30
a. Grey-green 15 30

1918 (Aug). *Special printing, optd with T 3a. Wmk Mult Crown CA. P 14.*
23 1 1½d. orange (Optd S. £45) 15 25

4

5

(Typo D.L.R.)

1920–22. *Wmk Mult Crown CA (sideways). P 14.*
24 4 ½d. blue-green, O .. .. .. 2·75 3·25
25 5 1d. carmine, O .. .. .. 1·50 1·50
26 4 1½d. orange-yellow, O 90 80
27 5 2d. slate-grey, O .. .. .. 2·00 3·00
28 4 2½d. ultramarine, O .. .. .. 95 4·00
29 5 3d. purple/*yellow*, C .. .. .. 80 6·50
30 4 6d. dull purple and bright mauve, C .. 2·50 7·50
31 5 1s. grey and black/*green*, C .. .. 1·25 3·00
32 4 2s. dull purple and blue/*blue*, C .. 5·00 15·00
33 5 2s. 6d. grey and red/*blue*, C .. .. 5·00 25·00
34 4 5s. green and red/*pale yellow*, C .. 5·00 35·00
35 5 10s. green and red/*green*, C .. .. 12·00 45·00
36 4 £1 purple and black/*red*, C (1922) .. £190 £275
24/36 .. .. .. *Set of* 13 £210 £375
24/36 Optd "Specimen" .. .. *Set of* 13 £325

1921–9. *Wmk Mult Script CA (sideways). P 14.*
37 4 ½d. blue-green, O 25 65
a. Yellow-green, O .. .. .. 1·00 70
38 5 1d. rose-carmine, O 20 15
39 1d. deep violet, O (1922) 90 35
a. Pale violet, O (1929) 90 35
40 4 1½d. red, O (1925) .. .. .. 60 2·50
40a 1½d. red-brown, O (1929) 30 15
41 5 2d. slate-grey, O (1922) 30 60
42 4 2½d. pale bright blue, O (1922) .. 1·25 2·25
43 2½d. brown, O (1922) .. .. 75 4·50
44 2½d. ultramarine, C (1927) .. .. 90 3·50
a. Ultramarine, O (1927) .. .. 1·75 50
45 5 3d. dull ultramarine, O (1922) .. 40 2·50
45a 3d. purple/*yellow*, C (1926) .. .. 50 2·50
46 4 6d. dull and bright purple, C (1924) .. 1·75 4·50
46a 5 1s. black/*green*, C (1929) .. .. 3·75 6·00
47 4 2s. purple and blue/*blue*, C (1922) .. 3·00 12·00
47a 5 2s. 6d. black and red/*blue*, C (1927) .. 12·00 24·00
47b 4 5s. green and red/*yellow*, C (1929) .. 20·00 42·00
37/47b .. .. .. *Set of* 16 42·00 95·00
37/47b Optd/Perf "Specimen" .. *Set of* 16 £375

No. 38 is overprinted "Specimen". A later printing exists perforated "Specimen" (*Price* £70).

6 Old Road Bay and Mount Misery

(Typo D.L.R.)

1923. *Tercentenary of Colony. Chalk-surfaced paper. P 14.*

(a) Wmk Mult Script CA (sideways)
48 6 ½d. black and green .. .. .. 1·50 5·50
49 1d. black and bright violet .. .. 1·50 1·50
50 1½d. black and scarlet .. .. .. 3·00 7·00
51 2d. black and slate-grey .. .. 1·75 1·50
52 2½d. black and brown .. .. .. 2·75 16·00
53 3d. black and ultramarine .. .. 3·25 12·00
54 6d. black and bright purple .. .. 8·00 20·00
55 1s. black and sage-green .. .. 12·00 27·00
56 2s. black and blue/*blue* .. .. 20·00 45·00
57 2s. 6d. black and red/*blue* .. .. 35·00 65·00
58 10s. black and red/*emerald* £190 £275

(b) Wmk Mult Crown CA (sideways)
59 6 5s. black and red/*pale yellow* .. .. 55·00 £150
60 £1 black and purple/*red* £1100 £1600
48/60 .. .. .. *Set of* 13 £1250 £2000
48/60 Optd "Specimen" .. .. *Set of* 13 £900

1935 (6 May). *Silver Jubilee. As Nos. 91/4 of Antigua, but ptd by Waterlow. P 11 × 12.*
61 1d. deep blue and scarlet 40 20
j. Kite and vertical log .. .. .. 15·00
k. Kite and horizontal log .. .. .. 15·00
62 1½d. ultramarine and grey 60 75
j. Kite and vertical log .. .. .. 20·00
63 2½d. brown and deep blue .. .. .. 1·00 80
64 1s. slate and purple .. .. .. 4·00 8·50
j. Kite and vertical log .. .. .. 50·00
k. Kite and horizontal log .. .. .. 50·00
61/4 .. .. .. *Set of* 4 5·50 9·25
61/4 Perf "Specimen" .. .. *Set of* 4 75·00

For illustrations of plate varieties see Omnibus section following Zululand.

1937 (12 May). *Coronation. As Nos. 13/15 of Aden.*
65 1d. scarlet 30 15
66 1½d. buff 35 10
67 2½d. bright blue 40 35
65/7 .. .. .. *Set of* 3 95 55
65/7 Perf "Specimen" .. .. *Set of* 3 50·00

Nos. 61/7 are inscribed "ST. CHRISTOPHER AND NEVIS".

7 King George VI

8 King George VI and Medicinal Spring

9 King George VI and Christopher Columbus

10 King George VI and Anguilla Island

(Typo; centre litho (T 10). D.L.R.)

1938 (15 Aug)–**48.** *Wmk Mult Script CA (sideways on T 8 and 9). P 14 (T 7 and 10) or 13 × 12 (T 8/9).*
68 7 ½d. green .. .. 1·00 10
a. Blue-green (5.4.43) 10 10
69 1d. scarlet .. .. 1·50 30
a. Carmine (5.43) 30 10
b. Rose-red (1947) 40 10
70 1½d. orange 15 10
71 8 2d. scarlet and grey, O .. .. .. 9·00 2·25
aa. Carmine and deep grey, C (1940) .. 24·00 9·00
a. Perf 14. *Scar & pale grey,* OC (1941) 60 30
ab. Perf 14. *Scarlet & deep grey* O (5.43) 16·00 5·00
72 7 2½d. ultramarine .. .. .. 1·50 20
a. Bright ultramarine (5.4.43) 15 10
73 8 3d. dull reddish purple and scarlet, O .. 4·75 90
a. Brown-purple & carmine-vermilion, C (1940) .. .. .. 7·50 2·50
b. Perf 14. *Reddish purple and scarlet,* CO (1942) 60 60
ba. Purple and scarlet, O (1943) .. .. 10·00 15·00
bb. Reddish mauve and scarlet, C (1946) 27·00 15·00
74 9 6d. green and bright purple, O .. .. 4·50 1·00
a. Perf 14. *Green & dp claret,* C (1942) 25·00 10·00
ab. Perf 14. *Green and purple,* OC .. 85 80
75 8 1s. black and green, O .. .. .. 8·00 1·00
a. Perf 14, OC (1943) 60 25
76 2s. 6d. black and scarlet, O .. .. 12·00 8·00
a. Perf 14, CO (1942) .. .. .. 4·50 2·50
77 9 5s. green and scarlet, O .. .. 40·00 10·00
a. Perf 14, CO (1942) .. .. .. 8·00 4·50
77b 10 10s. black and ultramarine (1.9.48) .. 12·00 18·00
77c £1 black and brown (1.9.48) .. .. 15·00 22·00
68/77c .. .. .. *Set of* 12 38·00 42·00
68/77 Perf "Specimen" .. .. *Set of* 10 £180

1946 (1 Nov). *Victory. As Nos. 28/9 of Aden.*
78 1½d. red-orange 10 10
79 3d. carmine 10 10
78/9 Perf "Specimen" .. .. *Set of* 2 60·00

1949 (3 Jan). *Royal Silver Wedding. As Nos. 30/1 of Aden.*
80 2½d. ultramarine 10 10
81 5s. carmine .. .. 3·25 2·50

1949 (10 Oct). *75th Anniv of Universal Postal Union. As Nos. 114/17 of Antigua.*
82 2½d. ultramarine 15 10
83 3d. carmine-red 30 25
84 6d. magenta 30 25
85 1s. blue-green 30 25
82/5 .. .. .. *Set of* 4 95 75

ANGUILLA ANGUILLA

TERCENTENARY 1650-1950 (11) TERCENTENARY 1650—1950 (12)

1950 (10 Nov). *Tercentenary of British Settlement in Anguilla. T 7 optd as T 11 and T 8/9, perf 13 × 1 , optd as T 12.*
86 7 1d. bright rose-red 10 10
87 1½d. orange 10 10
a. Error. Crown missing, W 9*a* .. £800
b. Error. St. Edward's Crown, W 9*b* .. £550
88 2½d. bright ultramarine 10 10
89 8 3d. dull purple and scarlet 10 10
90 9 6d. green and bright purple 10 10
91 8 1s. black and green (R.) 10 10
86/91 .. .. .. *Set of* 6 25 40

Nos. 87*a/b* occur on a row in the watermark, in which the crowns and letters "CA" alternate.

(New Currency. 100 cents = 1 West Indian dollar)

1951 (16 Feb). *Inauguration of B.W.I. University College. As Nos. 118/19 of Antigua.*
92 3c. black and yellow-orange 15 10
93 12c. turquoise-green and magenta 15 20

ST. CHRISTOPHER, NEVIS AND ANGUILLA

LEGISLATIVE COUNCIL

13 Bath House and Spa

14 Map of the Islands

1952 (14 June). *Vert designs as T 14 (3, 12 c.) or horiz as 13 (others). Wmk Mult Script CA. P 12½.*
94 1 c. deep green and ochre 15 25
95 2 c. green 20 25
96 3 c. carmine-red and violet 25 25
97 4 c. scarlet 20 20
98 5 c. bright blue and grey 20 10
99 6 c. ultramarine 20 15
100 12 c. deep blue and reddish brown 20 10
101 24 c. black and carmine-red 20 10
102 48 c. olive and chocolate .. .. .. 1·50 1·50
103 60 c. ochre and deep green .. .. 1·50 1·50
104 $1.20, deep green and ultramarine .. 4·00 1·75
105 $4.80, green and carmine .. .. 9·00 15·00
94/105 .. .. .. *Set of* 12 15·00 19·00

Designs:—2 c. Warner Park; 4 c. Brimstone Hill; 5 c. Nevis from the sea, North; 6 c. Pinney's Beach; 12 c. Sir Thomas Warner's Tomb; 24 c. Old Road Bay; 48 c. Sea Island cotton; 60 c. The Treasury; $1.20, Salt pond; $4.80, Sugar factory.

1953 (2 June). *Coronation. As No.* 47 *of Aden.*
106   2 c. black and bright green 10 10

25 Sombrero Lighthouse   **26** Map of Anguilla and Dependencies

(Recess Waterlow (until 1961), then D.L.R.)

1954 (1 Mar)–**63**. *Designs previously used for King George VI issue, but with portrait of Queen Elizabeth II as in T* **25/6** *or new values and designs* (½ *c.,* 8 *c.,* $2.40). *Wmk Mult Script CA. P* 12½.
106*a*   ½ c. deep olive (3.7.56) 10 10
107   1 c. deep green and ochre 10 10
   a. Deep green and orange-ochre (13.2.62) 20 15
   b. Imperf vert (horiz strip of three) . . † —
108   2 c. green 10 10
   a. Yellow-green (31.7.63) . . . . 80 1·00
109   3 c. carmine-red and violet 25 10
   a. Carmine and deep violet (31.7.63) . . 1·25 1·50
110   4 c. scarlet 10 10
111   5 c. bright blue and grey 10 10
112   6 c. ultramarine 10 10
   a. Blue (19.2.63) 50 20
112*b*   8 c. grey-black (1.2.57) 90 10
113   12 c. deep blue and red-brown 10 10
114   24 c. black and carmine-red (1.12.54) . . 10 10
115   48 c. olive-bistre and chocolate (1.12.54) . . 40 50
116   60 c. ochre and deep green (1.12.54) . . 1·00 85
117   $1.20, dp green & ultramarine (1.12.54) 4·00 90
   a. Deep green and violet-blue (19.2.63) . . 8·50 3·75
117*b* $2.40, black and red-orange (1.2.57) . . 7·50 11·00
118   $4.80, green and carmine (1.12.54) . . 11·00 11·00
106*a*/18 . . . . *Set of* 15 22·00 22·00

Design: *Horiz*—½ c., $1.20 Salt Pond; 1 c. Bath House and Spa; 2 c. Warner Park; 4 c. Brimstone Hill; 5 c. Nevis from the sea, North; 6 c. Pinney's Beach; 24 c. Old Road Bay; 48 c. Sea Island cotton; 60 c. The Treasury; $4.80, Sugar factory. *Vert*—3 c. Map of the islands; 12 c. Sir Thomas Warner's Tomb.

Stamps of St. Christopher, Nevis and Anguilla were in concurrent use with the stamps inscribed "LEEWARD ISLANDS" until 1 July 1956, when the general Leeward Islands stamps were withdrawn.

27 Alexander Hamilton and View of Nevis

(Des Eva Wilkin. Recess Waterlow)

1957 (11 Jan). *Birth Bicentenary of Alexander Hamilton. Wmk Mult Script CA. P* 12½.
119 **27** 24 c. green and deep blue 10 10

1958 (22 Apr). *Inauguration of British Caribbean Federation. As Nos.* 135/7 *of Antigua.*
120   3 c. deep green 25 10
121   6 c. blue 35 40
122   12 c. scarlet 45 15
120/2 . . . . *Set of* 3 95 60

MINISTERIAL GOVERNMENT

28 One Penny Stamp of 1861

(Recess Waterlow)

1961 (15 July). *Nevis Stamp Centenary. T* **28** *and similar horiz designs. W w* **12**. *P* 14.
123   2 c. red-brown and green 10 10
124   8 c. red-brown and deep blue 10 10
125   12 c. black and carmine-red 10 10
126   24 c. deep bluish green and red-orange . . 15 10
123/6 . . . . *Set of* 4 40 20

Designs:—8 c. Fourpence stamp of 1861; 12 c. Sixpence stamp of 1861; 24 c. One shilling stamp of 1861.

1963 (2 Sept). *Red Cross Centenary. As Nos.* 147/8 *of Antigua.*
127   3 c. red and black 10 10
128   12 c. red and blue 20 40

NEW INFORMATION

The editor is always interested to correspond with people who have new information that will improve or correct the Catalogue.

32 New Lighthouse, Sombrero   **33** Loading Sugar Cane, St. Kitts

(Des V. Whiteley. Photo Harrison)

1963 (20 Nov)–**65**. *Vert designs as T* **32** (2, 3, 15, 25, 60 *c.*, $1, $5) *or horiz as* **33** (*others*) *in sepia and light blue* (½ *c.*), *greenish yellow and blue* ($1) *or multicoloured* (*others*). *W w* **12** (*upright*). *P* 14.
129   ½ c. Type **32** 10 10
130   1 c. Type **33** 10 10
131   2 c. Pall Mall Square, Basseterre 10 10
   a. White fountain and Church . . . . 90·00
132   3 c. Gateway, Brimstone Hill Fort, St. Kitts 10 10
133   4 c. Nelson's Spring, Nevis 10 10
134   5 c. Grammar School, St. Kitts 10 10
135   6 c. Crater, Mt Misery, St. Kitts 10 10
136   10 c. Hibiscus 15 10
137   15 c. Sea Island cotton, Nevis 35 10
138   20 c. Boat building, Anguilla 20 10
139   25 c. White-crowned Pigeon (turquoise-blue background) 65 10
   a. Turquoise-green background (13.4.65) 1·25 40
140   50 c. St. George's Church Tower, Basseterre 40 25
141   60 c. Alexander Hamilton . . . . . . 1·00 25
142   $1 Map of St. Kitts-Nevis . . . . 2·25 40
143   $2.50, Map of Anguilla . . . . . . 2·25 2·00
144   $5 Arms of St. Christopher, Nevis and Anguilla . . . . 3·00 3·00
129/44 . . . . *Set of* 16 9·00 6·00

The 1, 4, 5, 6, 10 and 20 c. values exist with PVA gum as well as gum arabic.
See also Nos. 166/71.

ARTS
FESTIVAL
ST KITTS
1964

(48)

49 Festival Emblem

1964 (14 Sept). *Arts Festival. Nos.* 132 *and* 139 *optd as T* **48**.
145   3 c. Gateway, Brimstone Hill Fort, St. Kitts 10 10
   a. Opt double £150
146   25 c. White-crowned Pigeon 10 10
   a. "FESTIVAI" (R. 1/10) . . . . 55·00

1965 (17 May). *I.T.U. Centenary. As Nos.* 166/7 *of Antigua.*
147   2 c. bistre-yellow and rose-carmine 10 10
148   50 c. turquoise-blue and yellow-olive 40 35

1965 (15 Oct). *International Co-operation Year. As Nos.* 168/9 *of Antigua.*
149   2 c. reddish purple and turquoise-green . . 10 10
150   25 c. deep bluish green and lavender 15 10

1966 (24 Jan). *Churchill Commemoration. As Nos.* 170/3 *of Antigua.*
151   ½ c. new blue 10 10
   a. Value omitted £130
   b. Value at left instead of right . . . .
152   3 c. deep green 15 10
153   15 c. brown 30 15
154   25 c. bluish violet 35 15
151/4 . . . . *Set of* 4 75 35

1966 (4 Feb). *Royal Visit. As Nos.* 174/5 *of Antigua.*
155   3 c. black and ultramarine 10 10
156   25 c. black and magenta 30 10

1966 (1 July). *World Cup Football Championships. As Nos.* 176/7 *of Antigua.*
157   6 c. violet, yellow-green, lake & yellow-brn . . 10 10
158   25 c. chocolate, blue-green, lake & yell-brn . . 15 10

(Photo Harrison)

1966 (15 Aug). *Arts Festival. P* 14 × 14½.
159 **49** 3 c. black, buff, emerald-green and gold 10 10
160   25 c. black, buff, emerald-green and silver 10 10

1966 (20 Sept). *Inauguration of W.H.O. Headquarters, Geneva. As Nos.* 178/9 *of Antigua.*
161   3 c. black, yellow-green, and light blue . . 10 10
162   40 c. black, light purple, and yellow-brown . . 15 15

1966 (1 Dec). *20th Anniv of U.N.E.S.C.O. As Nos.* 196/8 *of Antigua.*
163   3 c. slate-violet, red, yellow and orange . . 10 10
164   6 c. orange-yellow, violet and deep olive . . 10 10
165   40 c. black, bright purple and orange . . 20 35
163/5 . . . . *Set of* 3 30 45

ASSOCIATED STATEHOOD

1967–69. *As Nos.* 129, 131/2, 137, 139 *and* 142 *but wmk sideways.*
166 **20**   ½ c. sepia and light blue (9.1.69) . . 15 40
167 –   2 c. multicoloured (27.6.67) 40 10
168 –   3 c. multicoloured (16.7.68) 15 10
169 –   15 c. multicoloured (16.7.68) 70 20
170 –   25 c. multicoloured (16.7.68) . . . . 1·50 20
171 – $1 greenish yellow and blue (16.7.68) . . 3·50 3·50
   a. Greenish yellow & ultramarine-blue (19.12.69) . . . . 6·00 4·75
166/71 . . . . *Set of* 6 5·75 4·00

The 2 c. and $1 values exist with PVA gum as well as gum arabic.
Nos. 172/81 vacant.

50 Government Headquarters, Basseterre   **53** John Wesley and Cross

(Des V. Whiteley. Photo Harrison)

1967 (1 July). *Statehood. T* **50** *and similar horiz designs. Multicoloured. W w* **12**. *P* 14½ × 14.
182   3 c. Type **50** 10 10
183   10 c. National Flag 10 10
184   25 c. Coat of Arms 10 10
182/4 . . . . *Set of* 3 15 10

(Litho D.L.R.)

1967 (1 Dec). *West Indies Methodist Conference. T* **53** *and similar vert designs. P* 13 × 13½.
185   3 c. black, cerise and reddish violet 10 10
186   25 c. black, light greenish blue and blue . . 10 10
187   40 c. black, yellow and orange 10 10
185/7 . . . . *Set of* 3 15 15

Designs:—25 c. Charles Wesley and Cross; 40 c. Thomas Coke and Cross.

56 "Herald" Aircraft over *Jamaica Producer* (freighter)   **57** Dr. Martin Luther King

(Des and litho D.L.R.)

1968 (30 July). *Caribbean Free Trade Area. W w* **12** (*sideways*). *P* 13.
188 **56**   25 c. multicoloured 15 10
189   50 c. multicoloured 15 10

(Des G. Vasarhelyi. Litho Enschedé)

1968 (30 Sept). *Martin Luther King Commemoration. W w* **12**. *P* 12 × 12½.
190 **57**   50 c. multicoloured 10 10

58 "Mystic Nativity" (Botticelli)   **60** Tarpon

(Des and photo Harrison)

1968 (27 Nov). *Christmas. Paintings. T* **58** *and similar vert design. Multicoloured. W w* **12** (*sideways*). *P* 14½ × 14.
191   12 c. Type **58** 10 10
192   25 c. "The Adoration of the Magi" (Rubens) . . 10 10
193   40 c. Type **58** 10 10
194   50 c. As 25 c. 10 10
191/4 . . . . *Set of* 4 20 15

(Des G. Drummond. Photo Harrison)

1969 (25 Feb). *Fishes. T* **60** *and similar horiz designs. W w* **12**. *P* 14 × 14½.
195   6 c. multicoloured 10 10
196   12 c. black, turquoise-green & greenish blue 15 10
197   40 c. multicoloured 20 10
198   50 c. multicoloured 25 15
195/8 . . . . *Set of* 4 60 20

Designs:—12 c. Garfish; 40 c. Horse-eye Jack; 50 c. Redsnapper.

64 The Warner Badge and Islands

67 "The Adoration of the Kings" (Mostaert)

(Des V. Whiteley. Litho Format)

1969 (1 Sept). *Sir Thomas Warner Commemoration. T* **64** *and similar horiz designs. Multicoloured. W* w **12** *(sideways). P* 13½ × 14.
199 20 c. Type **64** . . 10 10
200 25 c. Sir Thomas Warner's tomb . . 10 10
201 40 c. Charles I's commission . . 10 10
199/201 . . *Set of* 3 15 10

(Des Enschedé. Litho B.W.)

1969 (17 Nov). *Christmas. Paintings. T* **67** *and similar vert design. Multicoloured. W* w **12** *(sideways). P* 13½.
202 10 c. Type **67** . . 10 10
203 25 c. Type **67** . . 10 10
204 40 c. "The Adoration of the Kings" (Geertgen) 10 10
205 50 c. As 40 c. . . 10 10
202/5 . . *Set of* 4 20 15

73 Portuguese Caravels (16th-cent)

(Des and litho J.W.)

1970 (2 Feb–8 Sept). *Designs as T* **73** *in black, pale orange and emerald* (½ *c.) or multicoloured (others). W* w **12** *(upright on vert designs, sideways on horiz designs). P* 14.
206 ½ c. Pirates and treasure at Frigate Bay (*vert*) 10 10
207 1 c. English two-decker warship, 1650 (*vert*) 15 10
208 2 c. Naval flags of colonizing nations (*vert*) . . 15 10
209 3 c. Rapier hilt (17th-century) (*vert*) . . 15 10
210 4 c. Type **73** . . 15 10
211 5 c. Sir Henry Morgan and fireships, 1669 . . 20 10
212 6 c. L'Ollonois and pirate carrack (16th-century) . . 20 10
213 10 c. 17th-century smugglers' ship . . 25 10
214 15 c. "Piece-of-eight" (*vert*) (I) . . 1·25 40
214*a* 15 c. "Piece-of-eight" (*vert*) (II) (8.9.70) . . 40 10
215 20 c. Cannon (17th-century) . . 35 10
216 25 c. Humphrey Cole's Astrolabe, 1574 (*vert*) 40 10
217 50 c. Flintlock pistol (17th-century) . . 85 70
218 60 c. Dutch flute (17th-century) (*vert*) . . 2·25 70
219 $1 Captain Bartholomew Roberts and his crew's death warrant (*vert*) . . 2·50 75
220 $2.50, Railing piece (16th-century) . . 2·00 3·00
221 $5 Drake, Hawkins and sea battle . . 2·50 4·25
206/221 . . *Set of* 17 12·00 9·00

Nos. 214/*a*. Type I, coin inscribed "HISPANIANUM"; Type II, corrected to "HISPANIARUM". No. 214*a* also differs considerably in shade from No. 214.

See also Nos. 269/80 and 322/31.

85 Graveyard Scene (*Great Expectations*)

(Des Jennifer Toombs. Litho B.W.)

1970 (1 May). *Death Centenary of Charles Dickens. T* **85** *and similar designs. W* w **12** *(sideways on horiz designs). P* 13.
222 4 c. bistre-brown, gold and deep blue-green . . 10 10
223 20 c. bistre-brown, gold and reddish purple . . 10 10
224 25 c. bistre-brown, gold and olive-green . . 10 10
225 40 c. bistre-brown, gold and ultramarine . . 10 15
222/5 . . *Set of* 4 25 25

Designs: *Horiz*—20 c. Miss Havisham and Pip (*Great Expectations*). *Vert*—25 c. Dickens's Birthplace; 40 c. Charles Dickens.

86 Local Steel Band

(Des V. Whiteley. Litho Enschedé)

1970 (1 Aug). *Festival of Arts. T* **86** *and similar horiz designs. Multicoloured. W* w **12** *(sideways). P* 13½.
226 20 c. Type **86** . . 10 10
227 25 c. Local String Band . . 10 10
228 40 c. Scene from *A Midsummer Night's Dream* 10 10
226/8 . . *Set of* 3 15 15

87 1d. Stamp of 1870 and Post Office, 1970

88 "Adoration of the Shepherds" (detail) (Frans van Floris)

(Des J. Cooter. Litho J.W.)

1970 (14 Sept). *Stamp Centenary. T* **87** *and similar horiz designs. W* w **12** *(sideways). P* 14½.
229 ½ c. green and rose . . 10 10
230 20 c. deep blue, green and rose . . 10 10
231 25 c. brown-purple, green and rose . . 10 10
232 50 c. scarlet, green and black . . 30 45
229/32 . . *Set of* 4 50 50

Designs:—20 c., 25 c. 1d. and 6d. Stamps of 1870; 50 c. 6d. Stamp of 1870 and early postmark.

(Des Enschedé. Litho Format)

1970 (16 Nov). *Christmas. T* **88** *and similar vert design. Multicoloured. W* w **12**. *P* 14.
233 3 c. Type **88** . . 10 10
234 20 c. "The Holy Family" (Van Dyck) . . 10 10
235 25 c. As 20 c. . . 10 10
236 40 c. Type **88** . . 15 10
233/6 . . *Set of* 4 25 25

89 Monkey Fiddle

(Des Sylvia Goaman. Litho Format)

1971 (1 Mar). *Flowers. T* **89** *and similar horiz designs. Multicoloured. W* w **12** *(sideways). P* 14½.
237 ½ c. Type **89** . . 10 10
238 20 c. Tropical Mountain Violet . . 15 10
239 30 c. Trailing Morning Glory . . 15 10
240 50 c. Fringed Epidendrum . . 20 30
237/40 . . *Set of* 4 50 45

90 Royal Poinciana

(Des Enschedé. Litho J.W.)

1971 (1 June). *Phillipe de Poincy Commemoration. T* **90** *and similar multicoloured designs. W* w **12** *(sideways on 20 and 30 c.). P* 13½.
241 20 c. Type **90** . . 10 10
242 30 c. Château de Poincy . . 10 10
243 50 c. De Poincy's badge (*vert*) . . 20 15
241/3 . . *Set of* 3 35 20

91 The East Yorks

92 "Crucifixion" (Massys)

(Des V. Whiteley. Litho Walsall)

1971 (1 Sept). *Siege of Brimstone Hill, 1782. T* **91** *and similar horiz designs. Multicoloured. W* w **12** *(sideways). P* 14½.
244 ½ c. Type **91** . . 10 10
245 20 c. Royal Artillery . . 40 10
246 30 c. French infantry . . 50 10
247 50 c. The Royal Scots . . 65 20
244/7 . . *Set of* 4 1·40 35

(Des J. Cooter. Litho J.W.)

1972 (1 Apr). *Easter. W* w **12**. *P* 14 × 13½.
248 **92** 4 c. multicoloured . . 10 10
249 20 c. multicoloured . . 10 10
250 30 c. multicoloured . . 10 10
251 40 c. multicoloured . . 10 10
248/51 . . *Set of* 4 20 20

93 "Virgin and Child" (Borgognone)

94 Brown Pelicans

(Des J. Cooter. Litho J.W.)

1972 (2 Oct). *Christmas. T* **93** *and similar multicoloured designs. W* w **12** *(sideways on vert designs). P* 14.
252 3 c. Type **93** . . 10 10
253 20 c. "Adoration of the Kings" (J. Bassano) (*horiz*) . . 10 10
254 25 c. "Adoration of the Shepherds" (Domenichino) . . 10 10
255 40 c. "Virgin and Child" (Fiorenzo di Lorenzo) 10 10
252/5 . . *Set of* 4 25 15

(Des (from photograph by D. Groves) and photo Harrison)

1972 (20 Nov). *Royal Silver Wedding. Multicoloured; background colour given. W* w **12**. *P* 14 × 14½.
256 **94** 20 c. carmine . . 10 15
257 25 c. bright blue . . 15 15

95 Landing on St. Christopher, 1623

96 "The Last Supper" (Titian)

(Des J.W. Litho Questa)

1973 (28 Jan). *350th Anniv of Sir Thomas Warner's landing on St. Christopher. T* **95** *and similar horiz designs. Multicoloured. W* w **12**. *P* 13½.
258 4 c. Type **95** . . 15 10
259 25 c. Growing tobacco . . 15 10
260 40 c. Building fort at Old Road . . 20 10
261 $2.50, *Concepcion* . . 80 1·10
258/61 . . *Set of* 4 1·10 1·25

(Des J. Cooter. Litho Walsall)

1973 (16 Apr). *Easter. T* **96** *and similar multicoloured designs showing paintings of "The Last Supper" by the artists listed. W* w **12** *(sideways on* $2.50). *P* 13½ × 14 ($2.50) *or* 14 × 13½ *(others).*
262 4 c. Type **96** . . 10 10
263 25 c. Ascr to Roberti . . 10 10
264 $2.50, Juan de Juanes (*horiz*) . . 60 60
262/4 . . *Set of* 3 65 60

VISIT OF
H. R. H. THE PRINCE OF WALES 1973
(97)

1973 (31 May). *Royal Visit. Nos.* 258/61 *optd with T* **97** *by Questa.*
265 4 c. Type **95** . . 10 15
266 25 c. Growing tobacco . . 10 15
267 40 c. Building fort at Old Road . . 15 15
268 $2.50 *Concepcion* . . 45 50
265/8 . . *Set of* 4 65 85

(Des J.W. Litho Harrison ($10), J.W. (others))

1973 (12 Sept)–**74**. *As Nos.* 206, 208/9, 211/13, 214*a*/17, 219 *and new horiz design* ($10), *but W* w **12** *(sideways on vert designs, upright on horiz designs).*
269 ½ c. Pirates and treasure at Frigate Bay . . 10 40
270 2 c. Naval flags of colonizing nations . . 20 45
271 3 c. Rapier hilt . . 20 45
272 5 c. Sir Henry Morgan and fireships, 1669 . . 35 45
273 6 c. L'Ollonois and pirate carrack (16th-century) . . 35 40
274 10 c. 17th-century smugglers' ship . . 40 60
275 15 c. "Piece-of-eight" (II) . . 65 85
276 20 c. Cannon (17th-century) . . 75 95
277 25 c. Humphrey Cole's Astrolabe, 1574 . . 80 1·75
278 50 c. Flintlock pistol (17th-century) . . 1·10 1·50
279 $1 Captain Bartholomew Roberts and his crew's death warrant . . 2·75 3·50
280 $10 "The Apprehension of Blackbeard" (Edward Teach) (16.11.74) . . 20·00 13·00
269/80 . . *Set of* 12 25·00 22·00

Nos. 281/4 vacant.

99 Harbour Scene and 2d. Stamp of 1903

(Des V. Whiteley Studio. Litho Enschedé)

1973 (1 Oct). *70th Anniv of First St. Kitts-Nevis Stamps. T* **99** *and similar horiz designs. Multicoloured. W* w **12** *(sideways). P* 13 × 13½.

285	4 c. Type **99**	10	10
286	25 c. Sugar-mill and 1d. stamp of 1903	15	10
287	40 c. Unloading boat and ½d. stamp of 1903	35	10
288	$2.50, Rock-carvings and 3d. stamp of 1903	2·00	1·00
285/8	*Set of* 4	2·25	1·10
MS289	144 × 95 mm. Nos. 285/8	2·75	5·50

1973 (14 Nov). *Royal Wedding. As Nos. 165/6 of Anguilla.*

290	25 c. light emerald	15	10
291	40 c. brown-ochre	15	10

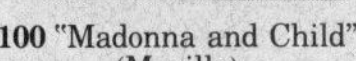

100 "Madonna and Child" (Murillo) **101** "Christ carrying the Cross" (S. del Piombo)

(Des J. Cooter. Litho Format)

1973 (1 Dec). *Christmas. T* **100** *and similar multicoloured designs showing "The Holy Family" by the artists listed. W* w **12** *(sideways on* $1*). P* 13½.

292	4 c. Type **100**	10	10
293	40 c. Mengs	15	10
294	60 c. Sassoferrato	25	15
295	$1 Filippino Lippi (*horiz*)	30	30
292/5	*Set of* 4	65	50

(Des J. Cooter. Litho D.L.R.)

1974 (8 Apr). *Easter. T* **101** *and similar multicoloured designs. W* w **12** *(sideways on* $2.50*). P* 13½.

296	4 c. Type **101**	10	10
297	25 c. "The Crucifixion" (Goya)	15	10
298	40 c. "The Trinity" (Ribera)	15	10
299	$2.50, "The Deposition" (Fra Bartolomeo) (*horiz*)	1·00	75
296/9	*Set of* 4	1·25	75

102 University Centre, St. Kitts **103** Hands reaching for Globe

(Des G. Drummond. Litho Questa)

1974 (1 June). *25th Anniv of University of West Indies. T* **102** *and similar horiz design. Multicoloured. W* w **12** *(sideways). P* 13½.

300	10 c. Type **102**	10	10
301	$1 As Type **102** but showing different buildings	15	25
MS302	99 × 95 mm. Nos. 300/1	35	65

(Des Jennifer Toombs. Litho Questa)

1974 (5 Aug). *Family Planning. T* **103** *and similar designs. W* w **12** *(sideways on* 25 c. *and* $2.50*). P* 14.

303	4 c. orange-brown, new blue and black	10	10
304	25 c. multicoloured	10	10
305	40 c. multicoloured	10	10
306	$2.50, multicoloured	35	55
303/6	*Set of* 4	50	65

Designs: *Horiz*—25 c. Instruction by nurse; $2.50, Emblem and globe on scales. *Vert*—40 c. Family group.

104 Churchill as Army Lieutenant **105** Aeroplane and Map

(Des PAD Studio. Litho Questa)

1974 (30 Nov). *Birth Centenary of Sir Winston Churchill. T* **104** *and similar vert designs. Multicoloured. W* w **12**. *P* 13½.

307	4 c. Type **104**	10	10
308	25 c. Churchill as Prime Minister	15	10
309	40 c. Churchill as Knight of the Garter	25	10
310	60 c. Churchill's statue, London	35	15
307/10	*Set of* 4	70	25
MS311	99 × 148 mm. Nos. 307/10	1·00	1·50

(Des J.W. Litho Questa)

1974 (16 Dec). *Opening of Golden Rock Airport, St. Kitts. Sheets* 98 × 148 *mm. W* w **12**. *P* 13½.

MS312	**105** 40 c. mult'coloured	20	40
MS313	45 c. multicoloured	20	40

106 "The Last Supper" (Doré) **107** E.C.C.A. H.Q. Buildings, Basseterre

(Des PAD Studio. Litho Questa)

1975 (24 Mar). *Easter. T* **106** *and similar vert designs showing paintings by Doré. Multicoloured. W* w **12**. *P* 14½.

314	4 c. Type **106**	10	10
315	25 c. "Christ Mocked"	10	10
316	40 c. "Jesus falling beneath the Cross"	10	10
317	$1 "The Erection of the Cross"	25	30
314/17	*Set of* 4	40	40

(Des J. Cooter. Litho Enschedé)

1975 (2 June*). *Opening of East Caribbean Currency Authority's Headquarters. T* **107** *and similar horiz designs. W* w **14** *(sideways). P* 13 × 13½.

318	12 c. multicoloured	10	10
319	25 c. multicoloured	10	10
320	40 c. light vermilion, silver and grey-black	15	10
321	45 c. multicoloured	15	15
	a. Silver omitted†	85·00	
318/21	*Set of* 4	30	25

Designs:—25 c. Specimen one-dollar banknote; 40 c. Half-dollar of 1801 and current 4-dollar coin; 45 c. Coins of 1801 and 1960.

*This is the local date of issue; the Crown Agents released the stamps on 28 April.

†This affects the dull silver coin on the left which on No. 321a appears in tones of the black plate.

1975–77. *As Nos.* 207, 209/13, 214*a*/15 *and* 218/19 *but W* w **14** *(sideways on* 4, 5, 6, 10, 20 *and* 60 *c.).*

A. *White, ordinary paper.*
B. *Cream, chalk-surfaced paper.*

		A		B	
322	1 c. English two-decker warship, 1650	†		30	20
323	3 c. Rapier hilt (17th-century)	20	10	1·25	1·50
324	4 c. Type **73**	20	10	1·25	1·50
325	5 c. Sir Henry Morgan and fireships, 1669	30	40	2·25	2·25
326	6 c. L'Ollonois and pirate carrack (16th-century)	60	10	80	1·50
327	10 c. 17th-century smugglers' ship	45	15	1·00	1·50
328	15 c. "Piece-of-eight" (II)	55	15	3·00	3·00
329	20 c. Cannon (17th-century)	1·40	2·00	1·75	3·50
330	60 c. Dutch flute (17th-century)	5·00	1·75	†	
331	$1 Captain Bartholomew Roberts and his crew's death warrant	†		6·50	3·00
323A/30A	*Set of* 8	8·00	4·25		
322B/31B	*Set of* 9			16·00	16·00

Dates of issue: Ordinary paper–5, 6 and 20 c. 11.6.75; others 11.6.76. Chalk-surfaced paper–5, 15 c. and $1 16.8.77; others 17.5.77

Nos. 332/7 vacant.

MINIMUM PRICE

The minimum price quote is 10p which represents a handling charge rather than a basis for valuing common stamps. For further notes about prices see introductory pages.

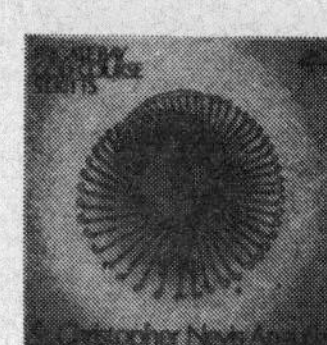

108 Evangeline Booth (Salvation Army General) **109** Golfer

(Des Jennifer Toombs. Litho Questa)

1975 (15 Sept). *International Women's Year. T* **108** *and similar vert designs. Multicoloured. W* w **12**. *P* 14.

338	4 c. Type **108**	10	10
339	25 c. Sylvia Pankhurst	20	10
340	40 c. Marie Curie	30	15
341	$2.50, Lady Annie Allen (teacher and guider)	1·60	2·25
338/41	*Set of* 4	2·00	2·25

(Des Sue Lawes. Litho Questa)

1975 (1 Nov). *Opening of Frigate Bay Golf Course. W* w **14** *(sideways). P* 13½.

342	**109** 4 c. black and rose-red	10	10
343	25 c. black and greenish yellow	20	10
344	40 c. black and light emerald	30	10
345	$1 black and new blue	80	50
342/5	*Set of* 4	1·25	55

110 "St. Paul" (Pier Francesco Sacchi) **111** "Crucifixion" (detail)

(Des J.W. Litho Questa)

1975 (1 Dec). *Christmas. T* **110** *and similar vert designs showing details from paintings in the National Gallery, London. Multicoloured. W* w **14**. *P* 13½.

346	25 c. Type **110**	10	10
347	40 c. "St James" (Bonifazio di Pitati)	20	10
348	45 c. "St. John the Baptist" (Mola)	20	10
349	$1 "St. Mary" (Raphael)	45	40
346/9	*Set of* 4	85	50

(Des J. Cooter. Litho Questa)

1976 (14 Apr). *Easter. Stained-glass Windows. T* **111** *and similar vert designs. Multicoloured. W* w **14**. *P* 14 × 13½ (4 *c.*) *or* 14 *(others).*

350	4 c. Type **111**	10	10
	a. Strip of 3. Nos. 350/2	15	
351	4 c. } "Crucifixion"	10	10
352	4 c. }	10	10
353	25 c. "Last Supper"	15	10
354	40 c. "Last Supper" (*different*)	20	10
355	$1 "Baptism of Christ"	45	40
350/5	*Set of* 6	85	65

Nos. 350/2 were printed horizontally *se-tenant*, together forming a composite design, No. 350 being the left-hand stamp.

Nos. 353/5 are smaller, 27 × 35 mm.

1976 (8 July). *West Indian Victory in World Cricket Cup. As Nos. 559/60 of Barbados.*

356	12 c. Map of the Caribbean	60	20
357	40 c. Prudential Cup	1·40	50
MS358	95 × 80 mm. Nos. 356/7	3·50	3·75

112 Crispus Attucks and the Boston Massacre **113** "The Nativity" (Sforza Book of Hours)

(Des J.W. Litho Questa)

1976 (26 July). *Bicentenary of American Revolution. T* **112** *and similar horiz designs. Multicoloured.* W w **14** (*sideways*). *P* 13½.

359 20 c. Type **112** 15 10
360 40 c. Alexander Hamilton and Battle of Yorktown 25 10
361 45 c. Jefferson and Declaration of Independence 25 10
362 $1 Washington and the Crossing of the Delaware 60 80
359/62 .. .. *Set of* 4 1·10 95

(Des Jennifer Toombs. Litho Questa)

1976 (1 Nov). *Christmas. T* **113** *and similar vert designs. Multicoloured.* W w **14**. *P* 14.

363 20 c. Type **113** 10 10
364 40 c. "Virgin and Child with St. John" (Pintoricchio) 15 10
365 45 c. "Our Lady of Good Children" (Ford Maddox-Brown) 15 10
366 $1 "Little Hands Outstretched to Bless" (Margaret Tarrant) 35 50
363/6 .. .. *Set of* 4 65 60

114 Royal Visit, 1966

115 "Christ on the Cross" (Niccolo di Liberatore)

(Des J.W. Litho Questa)

1977 (7 Feb). *Silver Jubilee. T* **114** *and similar vert designs. Multicoloured.* W w **14**. *P* 13½.

367 50 c. Type **114** 15 10
368 55 c. The Sceptre 15 10
369 $1.50, Bishops paying homage 30 50
367/9 .. .. *Set of* 3 55 60

(Des G. Hutchins. Litho Questa)

1977 (14 Apr*). *Easter. T* **115** *and similar designs showing paintings from the National Gallery, London. Multicoloured.* W w **14** (*sideways on* 50 c.). *P* 14.

370 25 c. Type **115** 10 10
371 30 c. "The Resurrection" (imitator of Mantegna) 10 10
372 50 c. "The Resurrection" (Ugolino da Siena) (*horiz*) 15 10
373 $1 "Christ Rising from the Tomb" (Gaudenzio Ferrari) 25 30
370/3 .. .. *Set of* 4 55 45

*This is the local release date; the Crown Agents released the stamps ten days earlier.

116 Estridge Mission

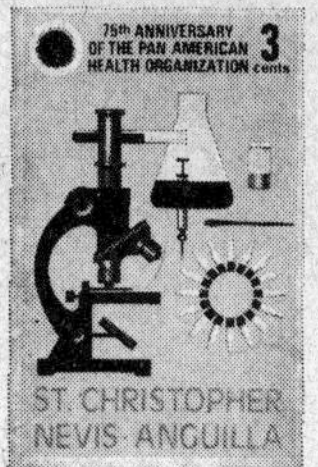

117 Laboratory Instruments

(Des Jennifer Toombs. Litho Cartor S.A., France)

1977 (27 June). *Bicentenary of Moravian Mission. T* **116** *and similar horiz designs.* W w **14** (*sideways*). *P* 12½.

374 4 c. black, greenish blue and new blue 10 10
375 20 c. black, brt mauve & brt reddish violet .. 10 10
376 40 c. black, yellow and yellow-orange 15 10
374/6 .. .. *Set of* 3 25 20

Designs:—20 c. Mission symbol; 40 c. Basseterre Mission.

(Des G. Hutchins. Litho Questa)

1977 (11 Oct). *75th Anniv of Pan-American Health Organization. T* **117** *and similar vert designs.* W w **14**. *P* 14.

377 3 c. multicoloured 10 10
378 12 c. multicoloured 10 10
379 20 c. multicoloured 15 10
380 $1 red-brown, bright orange and black .. 55 40
377/80 .. .. *Set of* 4 75 50

Designs:—12 c. Fat cells, blood cells and nerve cells; 20 c. "Community participation in health"; $1 Inoculation.

ALTERED CATALOGUE NUMBERS

Any Catalogue numbers altered from the last edition are shown as a list in the introductory pages.

118 "Nativity" (West Window)

119 Savanna Monkey with Vervet

(Des Jennifer Toombs. Litho Rosenbaum Bros, Vienna)

1977 (15 Nov). *Christmas. Vert designs as T* **118** *showing stained-glass windows from Chartres Cathedral. Multicoloured.* W w **14** (*inverted*). *P* 13½.

381 4 c. Type **118** 10 10
382 6 c. "Three Magi" (West window) 10 10
383 40 c. "La Belle Verriere" 15 10
384 $1 "Virgin and Child" (Rose window) 30 25
381/4 .. .. *Set of* 4 50 35

(Des BG Studio. Litho Questa)

1978 (15 Apr). *The Savanna ("Green") Monkey. T* **119** *and similar vert design.* W w **14**. *P* 14½.

385 **119** 4 c. yellow-brown, rosine and black .. 10 10
386 – 5 c. multicoloured 10 10
387 **119** 55 c. yellow-brown, apple-green & black 30 10
388 – $1.50, multicoloured 75 60
385/8 .. .. *Set of* 4 1·10 65

Design:—5 c., $1.50 Savanna Monkeys on branch.

120 Falcon of Edward III

121 Tomatoes

(Des C. Abbott. Litho Questa)

1978 (2 June). *25th Anniv of Coronation. T* **120** *and similar vert designs. P* 15.

389 $1 olive-brown and vermilion 20 20
a. Sheetlet. Nos. 389/91 × 2 .. .. .. 1·10
390 $1 multicoloured 20 20
391 $1 olive-brown and vermilion 20 20
389/91 .. .. *Set of* 3 55 55

Designs:—No. 389, Type **120**; No. 390, Queen Elizabeth II; No. 391, Brown Pelican.

(Des BG Studio. Litho D.L.R.)

1978 (8 Sept). *Horiz designs as T* **121**. *Multicoloured.* W w **14** (*sideways*). *P* 14½ × 14.

392 1 c. Type **121** 10 10
393 2 c. Defence Force band 10 10
394 5 c. Radio and T.V. station 10 10
395 10 c. Technical college 10 10
396 12 c. T.V. assembly plant 10 10
397 15 c. Sugar cane harvesting 15 10
398 25 c. Crafthouse (craft centre) 15 10
399 30 c. *Europa* (liner) 30 10
400 40 c. Lobster and sea crab 25 10
401 45 c. Royal St. Kitts Hotel and golf course .. 55 10
402 50 c. Pinney's Beach, Nevis 30 10
403 55 c. New runway at Golden Rock 30 10
404 $1 Cotton picking 35 30
405 $5 Brewery .. .. 1·00 1·25
406 $10 Pineapples and peanuts .. .. .. 2·25 2·50
392/406 .. .. *Set of* 15 4·75 4·25

122 Investiture

123 Wise Man with Gift of Gold

(Des L. Curtis. Litho Rosenbaum Bros, Vienna)

1978 (9 Oct). *50th Anniv of Boy Scout Movement on St. Christopher and Nevis. T* **122** *and similar vert designs. Multicoloured.* W w **14**. *P* 13½.

407 5 c. Type **122** 10 10
408 10 c. Map reading 10 10
409 25 c. Pitching tent 20 15
410 40 c. Cooking 35 25
411 50 c. First aid 40 35
412 55 c. Rev. W. A. Beckett (founder of scouting in St. Kitts) 45 45
407/12 .. .. *Set of* 6 1·40 1·10

(Des Jennifer Toombs. Litho Walsall)

1978 (1 Dec). *Christmas. T* **123** *and similar vert designs. Multicoloured.* W w **14**. *P* 13½.

413 5 c. Type **123** 10 10
414 15 c. Wise Man with gift of Frankincense 10 10
415 30 c. Wise Man with gift of Myrrh 10 10
416 $2.25, Wise Men paying homage to the infant Jesus 35 50
413/16 .. .. *Set of* 4 50 55

124 *Canna coccinea*

125 St. Christopher 1870–76 1d. Stamp and Sir Rowland Hill

(Des Daphne Padden. Litho Questa)

1979 (19 Mar). *Flowers (1st series). T* **124** *and similar vert designs. Multicoloured.* W w **14**. *P* 14.

417 5 c. Type **124** 10 10
418 30 c. *Heliconia bihai* 25 15
419 55 c. *Ruellia tuberosa* 40 20
420 $1.50, *Gesneria ventricosa* 90 70
417/20 .. .. *Set of* 4 1·40 1·00

See also Nos. 430/3.

(Des J.W. Litho Walsall)

1979 (2 July). *Death Centenary of Sir Rowland Hill. T* **125** *and similar horiz designs showing stamps and portrait. Multicoloured.* W w **14** (*sideways*). *P* 14½ × 14.

421 5 c. Type **125** 10 10
422 15 c. 1970 Stamp Centenary 50 c. commemorative 10 10
423 50 c. Great Britain 1841 2d. 30 30
424 $2.50, St. Kitts-Nevis 1923 300th Anniversary of Colony £1 commemorative .. 70 1·00
421/4 .. .. *Set of* 4 1·00 1·25

126 "The Woodman's Daughter"

127 Nevis Lagoon

(Des BG Studio. Litho Format)

1979 (12 Nov). *Christmas and International Year of the Child. Paintings by Sir John Millais. T* **126** *and similar vert designs. Multicoloured.* W w **14**. *P* 13½.

425 5 c. Type **126** 10 10
426 25 c. "Cherry Ripe" 15 15
427 30 c. "The Rescue" 15 15
428 55 c. "Bubbles" 20 20
425/8 .. .. *Set of* 4 50 50

MS429 100 × 68 mm. $1 "Christ in the House of His Parents" 45 50

(Des J. Cooter. Litho Questa)

1980 (4 Feb). *Flowers (2nd series). Vert designs as T* **124**. *Multicoloured.* W w **14** (*inverted*). *P* 14.

430 4 c. *Clerodendrum aculeatum* 10 10
431 55 c. *Inga laurina* 25 20
432 $1.50, *Epidendrum difforme* 60 50
433 $2 *Salvia serotina* 75 90
430/3 .. .. *Set of* 4 1·50 1·50

(Des and litho Secura, Singapore)

1980 (6 May). *"London 1980" International Stamp Exhibition. T* **127** *and similar multicoloured designs.* W w **14** (*sideways, on* 5 *and* 55 c., *inverted on* 30 c.). *P* 13.

434 5 c. Type **127** 10 10
435 30 c. Fig Tree Church (*vert*) 15 10
436 55 c. Nisbet Plantation 35 25
437 $3 "Nelson" (Fuger) (*vert*) .. .. .. 80 1·00
434/7 .. .. *Set of* 4 1·25 1·25

MS438 107 × 77 mm 75 c. Detail of "Nelson Falling" (D. Dighton). P 13½ × 13 .. .. 55 70
a. Wmk sideways .. .. 40·00

OFFICIAL STAMPS

OFFICIAL

(O 1)

1980 (3 Mar). *Nos.* 396, 398 *and* 400/6 *optd with Type* O **1**.

O1 12 c. T.V. assembly plant .. .. .. 1·25 75
O2 25 c. Crafthouse (craft centre) 15 15
O3 40 c. Lobster and sea crab 50 40
O4 45 c. Royal St. Kitts Hotel and golf course .. 45 30
O5 50 c. Pinney's Beach, Nevis 30 30
O6 55 c. New runway at Golden Rock 30 30
O7 $1 Cotton picking .. .. 1·25 2·00
O8 $5 Brewery .. .. 1·00 2·25
O9 $10 Pineapples and Peanuts .. .. .. 2·50 3·50
O1/9 .. .. *Set of* 9 7·00 9·50

From 23 June 1980 St. Kitts and Nevis had separate postal authorities, each with their own issues.

ST. KITTS

St. Kitts

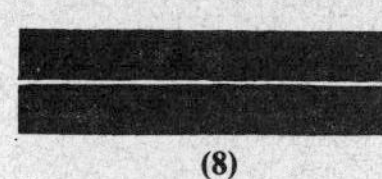

(8)

1980 (23 June). *As Nos.* 394/406 *of St. Christopher, Nevis and Anguilla optd with T* **8**. A. W w **14** (*sideways*). B. *No wmk.*

No.	Description	A		B	
29	5 c. Radio and T.V. station	15	15	10	10
30	10 c. Technical college	15	15	10	10
31	12 c. T.V. assembly plant	80	80	†	
32	15 c. Sugar cane harvesting	15	15	10	10
33	25 c. Crafthouse (craft centre)	15	15	10	10
34	30 c. *Europa* (liner)	15	15	10	10
35	40 c. Lobster and sea crab	20	20	10	15
36	45 c. Royal St. Kitts Hotel and golf course	15	15	†	
37	50 c. Pinney's Beach, Nevis	15	15	†	
38	55 c. New runway at Golden Rock	15	15	15	15
39	$1 Cotton picking	25	25	25	25
40	$5 Brewery	1·00	1·00	1·25	1·50
41	$10 Pineapples and peanuts	1·75	1·75	2·00	2·50
29A/41A	*Set of* 13	4·75	4·75		
29B/41B	*Set of* 10			3·75	4·50

9 H.M.S. *Vanguard*, 1762

10 Queen Elizabeth the Queen Mother

(Litho Secura, Singapore)

1980 (8 Aug). *Ships. T* **9** *and similar horiz designs. Multicoloured.* W w **14** (*sideways*). *P* 13 × 13½.

No.	Description		
42	4 c. Type **9**	10	10
	a. Opt omitted	60·00	
	c. No stop after "ST"	1·00	
43	10 c. H.M.S. *Boreas*, 1787	10	10
	a. Opt omitted	£100	
	c. No stop after "ST"	1·00	
44	30 c. H.M.S. *Druid*, 1827	15	10
	a. Opt omitted	£100	
	c. No stop after "ST"	1·25	
45	55 c. H.M.S. *Winchester*, 1831	20	15
	a. Opt inverted	£120	
	b. Opt omitted	£100	
	c. No stop after "ST"	1·50	
46	$1.50, Harrison Line *Philosopher*, 1857	40	30
	a. Opt omitted	£100	
	c. No stop after "ST"	2·00	
47	$2 Harrison Line *Contractor*, 1930	50	40
	a. Opt double	£100	
	b. Opt omitted	£150	
	c. No stop after "ST"	2·00	
42/7	*Set of* 6	1·25	90

Nos. 42/7 are overprinted "ST. KITTS" and have the previous combined inscription obliterated.

The "no stop" variety occurs on R.3/4 of the lower pane.

(Des and litho Format)

1980 (4 Sept). 80*th Birthday of Queen Elizabeth the Queen Mother.* W w **14**. *P* 13½.

No.		Description		
48	**10**	$2 multicoloured	60	60

No. 48 was printed in sheets containing two *se-tenant* stamp-size labels.

11 The Three Wise Men

(Des Walsall. Litho Questa)

1980 (10 Nov). *Christmas. T* **11** *and similar horiz designs. Multicoloured.* W w **14** (*sideways*). *P* 14½ × 14.

No.	Description		
49	5 c. Type **11**	10	10
50	15 c. The Shepherds	10	10
51	30 c. Bethlehem	10	10
52	$4 Nativity scene	60	60
49/52	*Set of* 4	70	65

12 Purple-throated Carib

13 Bananaquit

(Des Jennifer Toombs. Litho Questa)

1981 (5 Feb)–**82**. *Birds. Vert designs as T* **12** (1 *to* 10 *c.*) *or horiz as T* **13** (15 *c. to* $10). *Multicoloured.* W w **14** (*sideways on* 1 *to* 10 *c.*). *P* 13½ × 14 (1 *to* 10 *c.*) *or* 14 (15 *c. to* $10).
A. *Without imprint date*
B. *With imprint date at foot of design*

No.	Description	A		B	
53	1 c. Magnificent Frigate Bird	5	5	15	10
54	4 c. Wied's Crested Flycatcher	10	5	20	10
55	5 c. Type **12**	15	10	25	10
56	6 c. Burrowing Owl	15	10	25	10
57	8 c. Caribbean Martin	15	10	25	10
58	10 c. Yellow-crowned Night Heron	15	10	25	10
59	15 c. Type **13**	15	10	25	10
60	20 c. Scaly-breasted Thrasher	20	15	35	15
61	25 c. Grey Kingbird	20	15	35	15
62	30 c. Green-throated Carib	20	15	35	15
63	40 c. Turnstone	30	20	45	20
64	45 c. Black-faced Grassquit	35	25	55	25
65	50 c. Cattle Egret	40	30	60	30
66	55 c. Brown Pelican	40	30	70	30
67	$1 Lesser Antillean Bullfinch	60	50	90	50
68	$2.50, Zenaida Dove	1·25	1·25	1·75	1·50
69	$5 American Kestrel	2·25	2·50	3·00	2·75
70	$10 Antillean Crested Hummingbird	4·50	4·75	5·00	5·50
53/70	*Set of* 18	10·50	10·00	14·00	11·00

Dates of issue: Without imprint—5.2.81, 5 c. and 10 c. to $10; 30.5.81, 1, 4, 6, 8 c. With imprint—8.6.82, 1 c. to $10.

Nos. 59B/64B and 67B/8B exist with different imprint dates.

14 Battalion Company Sergeant, 3rd Regt of Foot ("The Buffs"), *circa* 1801

15 Miriam Pickard (first Guide Commissioner)

(Des G. Vasarhelyi. Litho Format)

1981 (5 Mar). *Military Uniforms* (1*st series*). *T* **14** *and similar vert designs. Multicoloured.* W w **14**. *P* 14½.

No.	Description		
71	5 c. Type **14**	10	10
72	30 c. Battalion Company Officer, 45th Regt of Foot, 1796–97	10	10
73	55 c. Battalion Company Officer, 9th Regt of Foot, 1790	20	10
74	$2.50, Grenadier, 38th Regt of Foot, 1751	55	35
71/4	*Set of* 4	80	45

See also Nos. 110/13 and 220/6.

(Des D. Shults. Litho Questa)

1981 (23 June–14 Dec). *Royal Wedding. Horiz designs as T* **26/27** *of Kiribati. Multicoloured.* (*a*) W w **14**. *P* 14.

No.	Description		
75	55 c. *Saudadoes*	15	15
	a. Sheetlet. No 75 × 6 and No. 76	1·10	
76	55 c. Prince Charles and Lady Diana Spencer	40	40
77	$2.50, *Royal George*	35	35
	a. Sheetlet No. 77 × 6 and No. 78	2·75	
78	$2.50, As No. 76	70	70
79	$4 *Britannia*	50	50
	a. Sheetlet. No. 79 × 6 and No. 80	3·50	
80	$4 As No. 76	1·00	1·00
75/80	*Set of* 6	2·75	2·75
MS81	120 × 109 mm. $5 As No. 76. Wmk sideways. P 12 (14 Dec)	3·00	1·50
	(*b*) *Booklet stamps. No wmk. P* 12 (19 Nov)		
82	55 c. As No. 76	30	30
	a. Booklet pane. No. 82 × 4	1·00	
83	$2.50, As No. 78	1·10	1·25
	a. Booklet pane. No. 83 × 2	2·25	

Nos. 75/80 were printed in sheetlets of seven stamps of the same face value, each containing six of the "Royal Yacht" design and one of the larger design showing Prince Charles and Lady Diana.

Nos. 82/3 come from $9.40 stamp booklets.

(Des Jennifer Toombs. Litho Walsall)

1981 (21 Sept). 50*th Anniv of St. Kitts Girl Guide Movement. T* **15** *and similar vert designs. Multicoloured.* W w **14**. *P* 14.

No.	Description		
84	5 c. Type **15**	10	10
85	30 c. Lady Baden-Powell's visit, 1964	15	10
86	55 c. Visit of Princess Alice, 1960	30	10
87	$2 Thinking-Day parade, 1980's	60	35
84/7	*Set of* 4	1·00	45

16 Stained-glass Windows

17 Admiral Samuel Hood

(Des Jennifer Toombs. Litho Format)

1981 (30 Nov). *Christmas. T* **16** *and similar vert designs showing stained-glass windows.* W w **14**. *P* 13 × 14.

No.	Description		
88	5 c. multicoloured	10	10
89	30 c. multicoloured	15	10
90	55 c. multicoloured	25	10
91	$3 multicoloured	80	50
88/91	*Set of* 4	1·10	60

(Des D. Shults. Litho Format)

1982 (15 Mar). *Bicentenary of Brimstone Hill Siege. T* **17** *and similar horiz designs.* W w **14** (*sideways*). *P* 14.

No.	Description		
92	15 c. multicoloured	10	10
93	55 c. multicoloured	20	10
MS94	96 × 71 mm. $5 black, red-orange & yell-brn	1·75	1·50

Designs:—55 c. Marquis De Bouillé; $5 Battle scene.

18 Alexandra, Princess of Wales, 1863

ROYAL BABY

(19)

(Des D. Shults and J. Cooter. Litho Format)

1982 (22 June). 21*st Birthday of Princess of Wales. T* **18** *and similar vert designs. Multicoloured.* W w **14**. *P* 13½ × 14.

No.	Description		
95	15 c. Type **18**	10	10
96	55 c. Coat of arms of Alexandra of Denmark	40	35
97	$6 Diana, Princess of Wales	1·50	1·50
95/7	*Set of* 3	1·75	1·75

1982 (12 July). *Birth of Prince William of Wales. Nos.* 95/7 *optd with T* **19**

No.	Description		
98	15 c. Type **18**	10	10
	a. Opt inverted	20·00	
99	55 c. Coat of arms of Alexandra of Denmark	40	35
100	$6 Diana, Princess of Wales	1·50	1·50
98/100	*Set of* 3	1·75	1·75

20 Naturalist Badge

21 Santa with Christmas Tree and Gifts

(Des Philatelists (1980) Ltd. Litho Questa)

1982 (18 Aug). 75*th Anniv of Boy Scout Movement. T* **20** *and similar vert designs. Multicoloured.* W w **14**. *P* 14 × 13½.

No.	Description		
101	5 c. Type **20**	10	10
102	55 c. Rescuer badge	30	15
103	$2 First Aid badge	65	80
101/3	*Set of* 3	90	90

(Des Marcel Frazer (5 c.), Sinclair Herbert (55 c.), Marijka Grey ($1.10), Gary Bowrin ($3). Litho Format)

1982 (20 Oct). *Christmas. Children's Paintings. T* **21** *and similar horiz designs. Multicoloured.* W w **14** (*sideways*). *P* 14 × 13½.

No.	Description		
104	5 c. Type **21**	10	10
105	55 c. The Inn	10	10
106	$1.10, Three Kings	20	15
107	$3 Annunciation	65	40
104/7	*Set of* 4	90	60

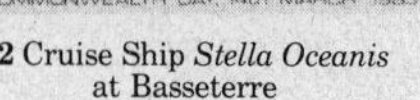

22 Cruise Ship *Stella Oceanis* at Basseterre

23 Sir William Smith (founder)

(Des G. Drummond. Litho Format)

1983 (14 Mar). *Commonwealth Day. T* **22** *and similar horiz design. Multicoloured.* W w **14** (*sideways*). *P* 14.

No.	Description		
108	55 c. Type **22**	20	10
109	$2 *Queen Elizabeth 2* at Basseterre	50	40

(Des G. Vasarhelyi. Litho Format)

1983 (25 May). *Military Uniforms* (2nd *series*). *Vert designs as* T **14**. *Multicoloured*. W w **14**. *P* 14½.

110 15 c. Light Company Private, 15th Regt of Foot, *circa* 1814 .. .. 15 10
111 30 c. Battalion Company Officer, 15th Regt of Foot, *circa* 1780 .. .. 25 10
112 55 c. Light Company Officer, 5th Regt of Foot, *circa* 1822 .. .. 45 15
113 $2.50, Battalion Company Officer, 11th Regt of Foot, *circa* 1804 .. .. 80 80
110/13 .. .. *Set of* 4 1·50 95

(Des J. Cooter. Litho Format)

1983 (27 July). *Centenary of the Boys' Brigade*. T **23** *and similar vert designs. Multicoloured*. W w **14**. *P* 13½.

114 10 c. Type **23** 15 10
115 45 c. B.B. members on steps of Sandy Point Methodist Church 35 15
116 50 c. Brigade drummers 45 20
117 $3 Boys' Brigade badge .. .. 1·75 1·50
114/17 .. .. *Set of* 4 2·40 1·75

INDEPENDENCE 1983 **(24)**

INDEPENDENCE 1983 **(24*a*)**

200 YEARS of MANNED FLIGHT 10c ST.KITTS

25 Montgolfier Balloon, 1783

1983 (19 Sept). *Nos.* 55, 59/63 *and* 66/70 *optd as* T **24** (*horiz* 20 *mm long on Nos.* 119/28)
A. No imprint date
B. With imprint date

		A		B	
118	5 c. Type **12** ..	10	10	10	10
	a. Opt inverted ..	†		48·00	—
	b. Pair one without opt ..	†		80·00	—
	c. Opt with T **24a** (local opt)	12·00	12·00	2·25	2·00
	ca. Opt inverted (reading upwards) ..	35·00	—	11·00	—
119	15 c. Type **13** ..	1·00	1·00	10	10
	a. Opt double ..	†		12·00	—
120	20 c. Scaly-breasted Thrasher ..	†		15	10
121	25 c. Grey Kingbird ..	†		20	10
	a. Opt inverted ..	†		14·00	—
122	30 c. Green-throated Carib ..	20·00	20·00	25	15
123	40 c. Turnstone ..	†		30	20
124	55 c. Brown Pelican ..	50	50	35	30
	a. Opt inverted ..	†		11·00	—
125	$1 Lesser Antillean Bullfinch	7·50	7·50	60	50
126	$2.50, Zenaida Dove ..	2·00	2·00	1·25	1·25
127	$5 American Kestrel ..	2·75	2·75	2·25	2·50
128	$10 Antillean Crested Hummingbird ..	6·00	6·00	4·50	5·00
118A/28A	.. *Set of* 8	35·00	35·00		
118B/28B	.. *Set of* 11			9·00	9·00

(Des A. Theobald. Litho Format)

1983 (28 Sept). *Bicentenary of Manned Flight*. T **25** *and similar multicoloured designs*. W w **15** (*sideways on Nos.* 130/3). *P* 14.

129 10 c. Type **25** 10 10
130 45 c. Sikorsky *Russian Knight* biplane (*horiz*) 15 10
131 50 c. Lockheed "Tristar" (*horiz*) 20 15
132 $2.50, Bell "XS-1" (*horiz*) 60 75
129/32 .. .. *Set of* 4 90 95
MS133 108 × 145 mm. Nos. 129/32 .. .. 95 1·25

26 Star over West Indian Town

27 Parrot in Tree

(Des Jennifer Toombs. Litho Format)

1983 (7 Nov). *Christmas*. T **26** *and similar horiz designs. Multicoloured*. W w **15** (*sideways*). *P* 14.

134 15 c. Type **26** 10 10
135 30 c. Shepherds watching Star 10 10
136 55 c. Mary and Joseph 15 10
137 $2.50, The Nativity 40 40
134/7 .. .. *Set of* 4 60 55
MS138 130 × 130 mm. Nos. 134/7. Wmk upright .. 75 1·10

(Des Court House Studio. Litho Format)

1984 (30 Jan). *Batik Designs* (1st *series*). T **27** *and similar vert designs*. W w **15**. *P* 14 × 13½.

139 45 c. multicoloured 10 10
140 50 c. multicoloured 10 10
141 $1.50, new blue, bistre-yellow & brt mag .. 30 40
142 $3 multicoloured 50 70
139/42 .. .. *Set of* 4 90 1·10

Designs:—50 c. Man under coconut tree; $1.50, Women with fruit; $3 Butterflies.

See also Nos. 169/72.

28 Cushion Star

(Des G. Drummond. Litho J.W.)

1984 (4 July). *Marine Wildlife*. T **28** *and similar multicoloured designs*. W w **15** (*sideways on* 5 c. *to* 75 c.). *P* 14.

143 5 c. Type **28** 10 10
144 10 c. Rough File Shell 20 10
145 15 c. Red-lined Cleaning Shrimp 15 10
146 20 c. Bristleworm 15 10
147 25 c. Flamingo Tongue 10 10
148 30 c. Christmas Tree Worm 10 15
149 40 c. Pink-tipped Anemone 25 20
150 50 c. Smallmouth Grunt 20 25
151 60 c. Glasseye Snapper 60 30
152 75 c. Reef Squirrelfish 30 35
153 $1 Sea Fans and Flamefish (*vert*) .. 40 45
154 $2.50, Reef Butterflyfish (*vert*) .. 1·00 1·10
155 $5 Blackbar Soldierfish (*vert*) .. 3·50 3·50
156 $10 Cocoa Damselfish (*vert*) .. 6·50 7·00
143/56 .. .. *Set of* 14 12·00 12·00

For 10 c., 60 c., $5 and $10 with watermark w **16** see Nos. 194/206.

29 Agriculture

(Des G. Vasarhelyi. Litho Questa)

1984 (15 Aug). *25th Anniv of 4-H Organisation*. T **29** *and similar horiz designs. Multicoloured*. W w **15** (*sideways*). *P*. 14.

157 30 c. Type **29** 20 10
158 55 c. Animal husbandry 30 15
159 $1.10, The 4-H Pledge 50 60
160 $3 On parade .. .. 1·00 1·25
157/60 .. .. *Set of* 4 1·75 1·90

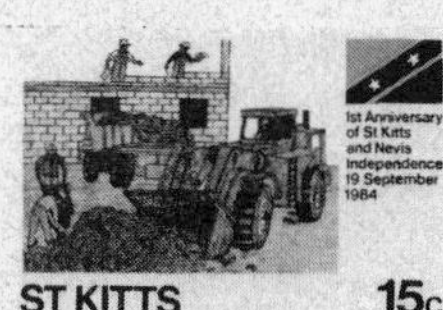

30 Construction of Royal St. Kitts Hotel

(Des K. Tatem (15 c.), Tessa Wattley (30 c.), Myrna Elcock and L. Freeman ($1.10), A. Williams ($3), adapted Jennifer Toombs. Litho Format)

1984 (18 Sept). *First Anniv of Independence of St. Kitts-Nevis*. T **30** *and similar multicoloured designs*. W w **15** (*sideways on* 15, 30 *c.*). *P* 14.

161 15 c. Type **30** 15 10
162 30 c. Independence celebrations 20 15
163 $1.10, National Anthem and aerial view (*vert*) 45 60
164 $3 "Dawn of a New Day" (*vert*) .. .. 1·00 1·25
161/4 .. .. *Set of* 4 1·50 1·90

31 Opening Presents

(Des Jennifer Toombs. Litho Questa)

1984 (1 Nov). *Christmas*. T **31** *and similar horiz designs. Multicoloured*. W w **15** (*sideways*). *P* 14.

165 15 c. Type **31** 15 10
166 60 c. Singing carols 30 25
167 $1 Nativity play 50 55
168 $2 Leaving church on Christmas Day .. 85 90
165/8 .. .. *Set of* 4 1·60 1·60

IMPERFORATES. Issues between Nos. 169 and 184 exist imperforate. Such items are not listed as there is no evidence that they fulfil the criteria outlined on page xi of this catalogue.

(Des Court House Studio. Litho Format)

1985 (6 Feb). *Batik Designs* (2nd *series*). *Horiz designs as* T **27**. W w **15** (*sideways*). *P* 13½ × 14.

169 15 c. black, bright green and light green .. 10 10
170 40 c. black, bright greenish blue and bright new blue 15 10
171 60 c. black, orange-vermilion and vermilion .. 25 15
172 $3 black, lake-brown and orange-brown .. 1·25 1·60
169/72 .. .. *Set of* 4 1·50 1·75

Designs:—15 c. Country bus; 40 c. Donkey cart; 60 c. Rum shop, and man on bicycle; $3 S.V. *Polynesia* (tourist yacht).

32 Container Ship *Tropic Jade*

33 James Derrick Cardin (leading Freemason)

(Des J. Cooter. Litho Format)

1985 (27 Mar). *Ships*. T **32** *and similar horiz designs. Multicoloured*. W w **15** (*sideways*). *P* 13½ × 14.

173 40 c. Type **32** 50 25
174 $1.20, *Atlantic Clipper* (schooner) .. 1·10 80
175 $2 *Mandalay* (schooner) .. .. 1·75 1·40
176 $2 *Cunard Countess* (liner) .. .. 1·75 1·40
173/6 .. .. *Set of* 4 4·50 3·50

(Des G. Vasarhelyi. Litho Format)

1985 (9 Nov). *150th Anniv of Mount Olive S.C. Masonic Lodge*. T **33** *and similar multicoloured designs*. W w **15** (*sideways on* 15, 75 *c., and* $3). *P* 15.

177 15 c. Type **33** 30 10
178 75 c. Banner of Mount Olive Lodge 85 55
179 $1.20, Masonic symbols (*horiz*) .. 1·40 1·40
180 $3 Lodge Charter (1835) .. .. 2·50 2·75
177/80 .. .. *Set of* 4 4·50 4·25

34 Map of St. Kitts

35 Queen Elizabeth and Prince Philip on St. Kitts

(Des. J. Cooter. Litho Format)

1985 (27 Nov). *Christmas. 400th Anniv of Sir Francis Drake's Visit*. T **34** *and similar vert designs. Multicoloured*. *P* 15.

181 10 c. Type **34** 15 10
182 40 c. *Golden Hind* 40 30
183 60 c. Sir Francis Drake 55 40
184 $3 Drake's heraldic shield .. .. 2·00 1·75
181/4 .. .. *Set of* 4 2·75 2·25

(Des D. Miller. Litho B.D.T.)

1986 (9 July). *60th Birthday of Queen Elizabeth II*. T **35** *and similar vert designs. Multicoloured*. *P* 13½.

185 10 c. Type **35** 10 10
186 20 c. Queen Elizabeth on St. Kitts 15 15
187 40 c. At Trooping the Colour 30 30
188 $3 In Sweden .. .. 1·75 2·00
185/8 .. .. *Set of* 4 2·10 2·25

(Des D. Miller. Litho Walsall)

1986 (23 July). *Royal Wedding. Square designs as* T **112** *of Ascension. Multicoloured*. W w **16**. *P* 14½ × 14.

189 15 c. Prince Andrew and Miss Sarah Ferguson 15 10
190 $2.50, Prince Andrew .. .. 1·50 1·75

36 Family on Smallholding

40th ANNIVERSARY U.N. WEEK 19-26 OCT.

(37)

(Des K. Tatem (15 c.), A. Williams ($1.20), adapted G. Vasarhelyi. Litho Questa)

1986 (18 Sept). *Agriculture Exhibition*. T **36** *and similar horiz design. Multicoloured*. W w **16** (*sideways*). *P* 13½ × 14.

191 15 c. Type **36** 10 10
192 $1.20, Hands holding people, computers and crops 60 65

(Litho Questa)

1986 (5 Nov)–**88**. *As Nos.* 144, 151 *and* 155/6 *but* W w **16** (*sideways on* 10, 60 *c.*). *With imprint date*. *P* 14.

194 10 c. Rough File Shell 20 15
201 60 c. Glasseye Snapper (17.8.88) 55 55
205 $5 Blackbar Soldierfish (*vert*) (17.8.88) .. 2·10 2·25
206 $10 Cocoa Damselfish (*vert* (17.8.88) .. 4·00 4·25
194/206 .. .. *Set of* 4 6·25 6·50

No. 194 exists with different imprint dates below the design.

1986 (12 Nov). *40th Anniv of United Nations Week. Nos.* 185/8 *optd with T* **37** *in gold.*
207 10 c. Type **35** 10 10
208 20 c. Queen Elizabeth on St. Kitts 15 15
209 40 c. At Trooping the Colour 20 25
210 $3 In Sweden .. .. 1·50 1·60
a. Opt triple .. .. 75·00
207/10 .. .. *Set of* 4 1·75 1·90

38 Adult Green Monkey with Young **39** Frederic Bartholdi (sculptor)

(Des Doreen McGuinness. Litho Walsall)

1986 (1 Dec). *Green Monkeys on St. Kitts. T* **38** *and similar vert designs. Multicoloured.* W w **16**. *P* 14×13½.
211 15 c. Type **38** 15 10
212 20 c. Adult on ground 20 15
213 60 c. Young monkey in tree 50 40
214 $1 Adult grooming young monkey 85 85
211/14 .. .. *Set of* 4 1·50 1·40

(Des D. Miller. Litho Format)

1986 (17 Dec). *Centenary of Statue of Liberty. T* **39** *and similar multicoloured designs.* W w **16** (*sideways on* 60 c., $1.50). *P* 14.
215 40 c. Type **39** 25 25
216 60 c. Torch (1876) and head (1878) on exhibition (*horiz*) 35 30
217 $1.50, French ship *Isere* carrying Statue (*horiz*) 75 75
218 $3 Statue of Liberty, Paris, 1884 .. .. 1·50 1·50
215/18 .. .. *Set of* 4 2·50 2·50
MS219 70×85 mm. $3.50, Head of Statue of Liberty .. .. 1·60 1·75

40 Officer, 9th Regt (East Norfolk), 1792 **41** Sugar Cane Warehouse

(Des C. Collins. Litho Format)

1987 (25 Feb). *Military Uniforms* (*3rd series*). *T* **40** *and similar vert designs. Multicoloured.* W w **16**. *P* 14½.
220 15 c. Type **40** 20 15
221 15 c. Officer, Regt de Neustrie, 1779 .. .. 20 15
222 40 c. Sergeant, 3rd Regt ("The Buffs"), 1801 40 30
223 40 c. Officer, French Artillery, 1812 .. .. 40 30
224 $2 Light Company Private, 5th Regt, 1778 1·40 1·50
225 $2 Grenadier of the Line, 1796 .. .. 1·40 1·50
220/5 .. .. *Set of* 6 3·50 3·50
MS226 121×145 mm. Nos. 220/5 .. .. 3·50 3·75

The two designs for each value were printed in sheets of 50 containing two panes 5×5 with the British uniform depicted on the left-hand pane and the French on the right.

(Des G. Vasarhelyi. Litho Format)

1987 (15 Apr). *Sugar Cane Industry. T* **41** *and similar vert designs. Multicoloured* (*colour of panel behind* "ST. KITTS" *given*). W w **16**. *P* 14.
227 15 c. greenish yellow (Type **41**) 10 10
a. Horiz strip of 5. Nos. 227/31 45
228 15 c. cinnamon 10 10
229 15 c. lilac 10 10
230 15 c. azure 10 10
231 15 c. pale greenish blue 10 10
232 75 c. bright green 55 55
a. Horiz strip of 5. Nos. 232/6 .. .. 2·50
233 75 c. lilac 55 55
234 75 c. dull green 55 55
235 75 c. orange-yellow 55 55
236 75 c. greenish blue 55 55
227/36 .. .. *Set of* 10 2·75 2·75

Designs:—Nos. 227/31, Sugar cane factory; Nos. 232/6, Loading sugar train.

Nos. 227/31 and 232/6 were each printed together, *se-tenant*, in horizontal strips of five throughout the sheets, each strip forming a composite design.

OMNIBUS ISSUES

Details, together with prices for complete sets, of the various Omnibus issues from the 1935 Silver Jubilee series to date are included in a special section following Zululand at the end of the catalogue.

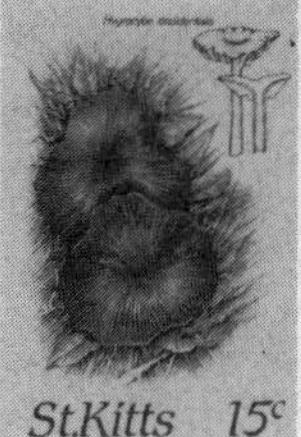

42 B.W.I.A. "L-1011-500 TriStar" **43** *Hygrocybe occidentalis*

(Des T. Hadler. Litho Format)

1987 (24 June). *Aircraft visiting St. Kitts. T* **42** *and similar horiz designs. Multicoloured.* W w **14** (*sideways*). *P* 14.
237 40 c. Type **42** 40 30
238 60 c. L.I.A.T. BAe "Super 748" 55 40
239 $1.20, W.I.A. "DHC-6 Twin Otter" 95 85
240 $3 American Eagle Aérospatiale "ATR-42" 2·00 2·25
237/40 .. .. *Set of* 4 3·50 3·50

(Des I. Loe. Litho Questa)

1987 (26 Aug). *Fungi. T* **43** *and similar vert designs. Multicoloured.* W w **16**. *P* 14.
241 15 c. Type **43** 20 10
242 40 c. *Marasmius haematocephalus* 35 25
243 $1.20, *Psilocybe cubensis* 80 80
244 $2 *Hygrocybe acutoconica* .. .. .. 1·25 1·25
245 $3 *Boletellus cubensis* .. .. .. 1·75 2·00
241/5 .. .. *Set of* 5 4·00 4·00

44 Carnival Clown **45** Ixora

(Des Rose Cameron-Smith. Litho Format)

1987 (28 Oct). *Christmas. T* **44** *and similar square designs showing different clowns. Multicoloured.* W w **16** (*sideways*). *P* 14½.
246 15 c. multicoloured 15 10
247 40 c. multicoloured 30 25
248 $1 multicoloured 60 50
249 $3 multicoloured .. .. 1·75 2·00
246/9 .. .. *Set of* 4 2·50 2·50

See also Nos. 266/9.

(Des Josephine Martin. Litho Questa)

1988 (20 Jan). *Flowers. T* **45** *and similar vert designs. Multicoloured.* W w **16**. *P* 14½×14.
250 15 c. Type **45** 20 10
251 40 c. Shrimp Plant 30 25
252 $1 Poinsettia 65 60
253 $3 Honolulu Rose .. .. 1·75 2·00
250/3 .. .. *Set of* 4 2·75 2·75

46 Fort Thomas Hotel **47** Ball, Wicket and Leeward Islands Cricket Association Emblem

(Des L. Curtis. Litho Walsall)

1988 (20 Apr). *Tourism* (*1st series*). *Hotels. T* **46** *and similar horiz designs. Multicoloured.* W w **14** (*sideways*). *P* 14 × 14½.
254 60 c. Type **46** 25 30
255 60 c. Fairview Inn 25 30
256 60 c. Frigate Bay Beach Hotel 25 30
257 60 c. Ocean Terrace Inn 25 30
258 $3 The Golden Lemon .. .. 1·25 1·40
259 $3 Royal St. Kitts Casino and Jack Tar Village .. .. 1·25 1·40
260 $3 Rawlins Plantation Hotel and Restaurant .. .. 1·25 1·40
254/60 .. .. *Set of* 7 4·25 2·75

See also Nos. 270/5.

(Des Joan Thompson. Litho Walsall)

1988 (13 July). *75th Anniv of Leeward Islands Cricket Tournament. T* **47** *and similar vert design. Multicoloured.* W w **14**. *P* 13 × 13½.
261 40 c. Type **47** 35 25
262 $3 Cricket match at Warner Park .. .. 1·75 2·00

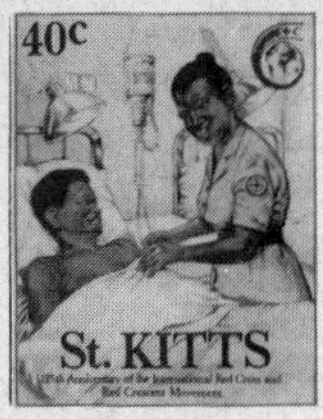

48 Flag of St. Kitts-Nevis **49** Red Cross Nurse with Hospital Patient

(Des L. Curtis. Litho Questa)

1988 (19 Sept). *5th Anniv of Independence. T* **48** *and similar vert designs. Multicoloured.* W w **16**. *P* 14½ × 14.
263 15 c. Type **48** 10 10
264 60 c. Arms of St. Kitts 30 30
MS265 61 × 53 mm. $5 Princess Margaret presenting Constitutional Instrument to Prime Minister Kennedy Simmonds, 1983. W w **14** .. 2·10 2·25

(Des Rose Cameron-Smith. Litho Format)

1988 (2 Nov). *Christmas. Square designs as T* **44** *showing carnival masqueraders.* W w **14** (*sideways*). *P* 14½.
266 15 c. multicoloured 10 10
267 40 c. multicoloured 20 25
268 80 c. multicoloured 40 45
269 $3 multicoloured .. .. 1·25 1·40
266/9 .. .. *Set of* 4 1·75 2·00

(Des L. Curtis. Litho Format)

1989 (25 Jan). *Tourism* (*2nd series*). *Colonial Architecture. Horiz designs as T* **46**. *Multicoloured.* W w **16** (*sideways*). *P* 14.
270 20 c. Georgian house 15 10
271 20 c. Colonial-style house 15 10
272 $1 Romney Manor 55 60
273 $1 Lavington Great House 55 60
274 $2 Government House .. .. 90 1·00
275 $2 Treasury Building .. .. 90 1·00
270/5 .. .. *Set of* 6 2·75 3·00

(Des C. Collins. Litho Format)

1989 (8 May). *125th Anniv of International Red Cross. T* **49** *and similar vert designs.* W w **16**. *P* 14×14½.
276 40 c. multicoloured 30 30
277 $1 multicoloured 65 65
278 $3 orange-vermilion and black .. .. 1·75 1·75
276/8 .. .. *Set of* 3 2·40 2·40

Designs:—$1 Loading patient into ambulance; $3 125th anniversary logo.

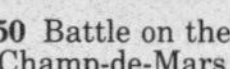

50 Battle on the Champ-de-Mars **51** Outline Map of St. Kitts

(Des D. Miller. Litho B.D.T.)

1989 (7 July). *"Philexfrance 89" International Stamp Exhibition, Paris. Sheet* 115×99 *mm.* W w **16**. *P* 14.
MS279 **50** $5 multicoloured .. .. .. 2·40 2·50

(Des A. Theobald ($5), D. Miller (others). Litho Questa)

1989 (20 July). *20th Anniv of First Manned Landing on Moon. Multicoloured designs as T* **126** *of Ascension.* W w **16** (*sideways on* 20 c., $1). *P* 14×13½ (10 c., $2) *or* 14 (*others*).
280 10 c. Lunar rover on Moon 10 10
281 20 c. Crew of "Apollo 13" (30×30 *mm*) 10 10
282 $1 "Apollo 13" emblem (30×30 *mm*) 45 50
283 $2 "Apollo 13" splashdown, South Pacific 95 1·00
280/3 .. .. *Set of* 4 1·40 1·50
MS284 100×83 mm. $5 Aldrin leaving "Apollo 11" lunar module. Wmk inverted. P 14×13½ .. 2·40 2·50

(Des D. Miller. Litho B.D.T.)

1989 (25 Oct). W w **16**. *P* 15×14.
285 **51** 10 c. deep mauve and black 10 10
286 15 c. bright carmine and black 10 10
287 20 c. yellow-orange and black 10 10
288 40 c. yellow and black 15 20
289 60 c. bright blue and black 25 30
290 $1 yellow-green and black 40 45
285/90 .. .. *Set of* 6 85 1·00

52 *Santa Mariagalante* passing St. Kitts, 1493

(Des L. Curtis. Litho Questa)

1989 (8 Nov). *500th Anniv of Discovery of America* (1992) *by Columbus. T* **52** *and similar horiz designs. Multicoloured. W* w **16** (*sideways*). *P* 14.

291	15 c. Type **52**	15	15
292	80 c. Arms of Columbus and map of fourth voyage, 1502-04	60	60
293	$1 Navigation instruments, *c.* 1500 ..	65	65
294	$5 Columbus and map of second voyage, 1493-96	2·75	2·75
291/4	.. .. *Set of* 4	3·75	3·75

53 Poinciana Tree

(Des G. Vasarhelyi. Litho Walsall)

1989 (17 Nov). *"World Stamp Expo '89" International Stamp Exhibition, Washington. T* **53** *and similar horiz designs. Multicoloured. W* w **14** (*sideways*). *P* 14.

295	15 c. Type **53**	10	10
296	40 c. Fort George Citadel, Brimstone Hill ..	20	25
297	$1 Private, Light Company, 5th Foot, 1778	45	50
298	$3 St. George's Anglican Church ..	1·50	1·75
295/8	.. .. *Set of* 4	2·00	2·25

OFFICIAL STAMPS

1980 (23 June). *Nos.* 32/41 *additionally optd with Type* O **1** *of St. Christopher, Nevis and Anguilla. A. W* w **14** (*sideways*). B. *No wmk.*

		A		B	
O 1	15 c. Sugar cane harvesting ..	10	10	†	
O 2	25 c. Crafthouse (craft centre) ..	10	10	10	10
O 3	30 c. *Europa* (liner)	10	10	15	15
O 4	40 c. Lobster and sea crab ..	10	15	15·00	27·00
O 5	45 c. Royal St. Kitts Hotel and golf course	15	15	†	
O 6	50 c. Pinney's Beach, Nevis ..	15	15	†	
O 7	55 c. New runway at Golden Rock	15	15	25	25
	a. Opt inverted	42·00	—	†	
O 8	$1 Cotton picking	25	25	40	40
O 9	$5 Brewery	1·00	1·50	2·25	3·00
O10	$10 Pineapples and peanuts ..	1·75	2·50	4·50	6·00
	a. Opt inverted	£100	—	†	
O1/10	.. .. .. *Set of* 10	3·50	4·50		
O2/10	.. .. .. *Set of* 7			20·00	35·00

OFFICIAL

(O 1)

1981 (5 Feb). *Nos.* 59A/70A *optd with Type* O 1.

O11	15 c. Type **13**	10	10
O12	20 c. Scaly-breasted Thrasher	10	10
O13	25 c. Grey Kingbird	15	10
O14	30 c. Green-throated Carib	15	10
O15	40 c. Turnstone	20	15
O16	45 c. Black-faced Grassquit	25	20
O17	50 c. Cattle Egret	25	20
O18	55 c. Brown Pelican	35	25
O19	$1 Lesser Antillean Bullfinch	55	45
O20	$2.50, Zenaida Dove	1·25	1·00
O21	$5 American Kestrel	2·25	2·00
O22	$10 Antillean Crested Hummingbird ..	4·25	4·25
O11/22	.. .. *Set of* 12	9·00	8·00

1983 (2 Feb). *Nos.* 75/80 *optd with Type* O 1 (55 c.) *or surch also* (*others*).

O23	45 c. on $2.50, *Royal George* (New Blue)	25	25
	a. Sheetlet No. O23 × 6 and No. O24	1·40	
	b. Surch double	18·00	
	c. Albino surch	10·00	
	f. Deep ultramarine surch	50	
	fd. Surch inverted	7·50	
	fe. Surch inverted (horiz pair)	25·00	
	g. Black opt		
O24	45 c. on $2.50, Prince Charles and Lady Diana Spencer (New Blue)	25	25
	b. Surch double	60·00	
	c. Albino surch	30·00	
	f. Deep ultramarine surch	75	
	fd. Surch inverted	30·00	
	g. Black opt		
O25	55 c. *Saudadoes* (New Blue)	30	30
	a. Sheetlet No. O25 × 6 and No. O26 ..	1·75	
	b. Opt double	22·00	
	c. Albino opt	12·00	
	d. Opt inverted	8·00	
	e. Opt inverted (horiz pair)	22·00	
	f. Deep ultramarine opt	60	
	fd. Opt inverted	7·00	
	fe. Opt inverted (horiz pair)	26·00	
O26	55 c. Prince Charles and Lady Diana Spencer (New Blue)	30	30
	b. Opt double	60·00	
	c. Albino opt	35·00	
	d. Opt inverted	27·00	
	f. Deep ultramarine opt	90	
	fd. Opt inverted	27·00	
O27	$1.10 on $4 *Britannia* (Blk.)	60	70
	a. Sheetlet. No. O27 × 6 and No. O28 ..	3·50	
	b. Surch double	17·00	
	f. Deep ultramarine surch	4·00	
O28	$1.10 on $4 Prince Charles and Lady Diana Spencer (Blk.)	60	70
	b. Surch double	45·00	
	f. Deep ultramarine surch	30·00	
O23/8	.. .. *Set of* 6	2·10	2·25

Nos. O23fe, O25e and O25fe show the surcharge or overprint intended for the large design, inverted and struck across a horizontal pair of the smaller. Nos. O24fd, O26d and O26fd each show two inverted surcharges or overprints intended for a horizontal pair of the smaller design.

1984 (4 July). *Nos.* 145/56 *optd with Type* O **1**.

O29	15 c. Red-lined Cleaning Shrimp	15	15
O30	20 c. Bristleworm	20	20
O31	25 c. Flamingo Tongue	25	25
O32	30 c. Christmas Tree Worm	30	30
O33	40 c. Pink-tipped Anemone	35	35
O34	50 c. Smallmouth Grunt	40	40
O35	60 c. Glasseye Snapper	45	45
O36	75 c. Reef Squirrelfish	55	55
O37	$1 Sea Fans and Flamefish (*vert*) ..	70	70
O38	$2.50, Reef Butterflyfish (*vert*)	1·75	1·75
O39	$5 Blackbar Soldierfish (*vert*)	2·75	3·00
O40	$10 Cocoa Damselfish (*vert*)	5·50	6·00
O29/40	.. .. *Set of* 12	12·00	13·00

NEVIS

(7) 8 Nevis Lighter

1980 (23 June). *Nos.* 394/406 *of St. Christopher, Nevis and Anguilla optd with T* **7**.

No.	Description	Unused	Used
37	5 c. Radio and T.V. Station	10	10
38	10 c. Technical college	10	10
39	12 c. T.V. assembly plant	40	40
40	15 c. Sugar cane harvesting	10	10
41	25 c. Crafthouse (craft centre)	15	10
	a. No wmk	1·75	3·00
42	30 c. *Europa* (liner)	20	15
43	40 c. Lobster and sea crab	70	70
44	45 c. Royal St. Kitts Hotel and golf course	70	70
45	50 c. Pinney's Beach, Nevis	50	50
46	55 c. New runway at Golden Rock	15	15
47	$1 Picking cotton	45	45
	a. No wmk	6·00	10·00
48	$5 Brewery	75	75
49	$10 Pineapples and peanuts	1·25	1·25
37/49	*Set of* 13	4·25	4·25

1980 (4 Sept). 80*th Birthday of Queen Elizabeth the Queen Mother. As T* **10** *of St. Kitts, but inscr* "NEVIS".

No.	Description	Unused	Used
50	$2 multicoloured	50	50

No. 50 was printed in sheets including two *se-tenant* stamp-size labels.

(Des Jennifer Toombs. Litho Questa)

1980 (8 Oct). *Boats. T* **8** *and similar multicoloured designs. W* w **14** (*sideways on* 5, 30 *and* 55 *c.*). *P* 14.

No.	Description	Unused	Used
51	5 c. Type **8**	10	10
52	30 c. Local fishing boat	15	10
53	55 c. *Caona* (catamaran)	25	10
54	$3 *Polynesia* (cruise schooner) (39 × 53 *mm*)	75	55
	a. Perf 12 (booklets)	75	1·10
	ab. Booklet pane of 3	2·25	
51/4	*Set of* 4	1·00	70

No. 54a comes from $12.30 stamp booklets containing No. 53 × 6 and one pane as No. 54ab. In this pane each stamp is surrounded by white margins, the pane being divided in three by vertical roulettes.

9 Virgin and Child

(Des Jennifer Toombs. Litho Format)

1980 (20 Nov). *Christmas. T* **9** *and similar vert designs. Multicoloured. W* w **14**. *P* 14.

No.	Description	Unused	Used
55	5 c. Type **9**	10	10
56	30 c. Angel	10	10
57	$2.50, The Three Wise Men	30	30
55/7	*Set of* 3	35	35

10 Charlestown Pier 11 New River Mill

(Des Jennifer Toombs. Litho Questa)

1981 (5 Feb)–**82**. *Horiz designs as T* **10** (5, 10 *c.*) *or T* **11** (15 *c. to* $10). *Multicoloured. W* w **14**. *P* 14 × 13½ (5, 10 *c.*) *or* 14 (*others*).
A. *No imprint date*
B. *With imprint date at foot of design* (9.6.82.)

No.	Description	A Unused	A Used	B Unused	B Used
58	5 c. Type **10**	10	10	10	10
59	10 c. Court House and Library	10	10	10	10
60	15 c. Type **11**	10	10	10	10
61	20 c. Nelson Museum	10	10	10	10
62	25 c. St. James' Parish Church	15	15	15	15
63	30 c. Nevis Lane	15	15	15	15
64	40 c. Zetland Plantation	20	20	20	20
65	45 c. Nisbet Plantation	20	25	20	25
66	50 c. Pinney's Beach	25	25	25	25
67	55 c. Eva Wilkin's Studio	25	30	25	30
68	$1 Nevis at dawn	50	45	50	45
69	$2.50, Ruins of Fort Charles	90	1·10	90	1·10
70	$5 Old Bath House	1·50	1·75	1·50	1·75
71	$10 Beach at Nisbet's	2·75	3·50	2·75	3·50
58/71	*Set of* 14	6·00	7·50	6·00	7·50

Nos. 61B/7B and 69B exist with different imprint dates.

(Des D. Shults. Litho Questa)

1981 (23 June–14 Dec). *Royal Wedding. Horiz designs as T* **26/27** *of Kiribati. Multicoloured.* (*a*) *W* w **14**. *P* 14.

No.	Description	Unused	Used
72	55 c. *Royal Caroline*	20	20
	a. Sheetlet. No. 72 × 6 and No. 73	1·60	
73	55 c. Prince Charles and Lady Diana Spencer	40	40
74	$2 *Royal Sovereign*	40	40
	a. Sheetlet. No. 74 × 6 and No. 75	2·75	
75	$2 As No. 73	80	80
76	$5 *Britannia*	80	80
	a. Sheetlet. No. 76 × 6 and No. 77	5·75	
77	$5 As No. 73	1·50	1·50
72/7	*Set of* 6	3·75	3·75
MS78	120 × 109 mm. $4.50, As No. 73, Wmk sideways. P 12 (14 Dec)	3·00	1·50

(*b*) *Booklet stamps. No wmk. P* 12 (19 Nov).

No.	Description	Unused	Used
79	55 c. As No. 72	25	30
	a. Booklet pane. No. 79 × 4	1·00	
80	$2 As No. 75	1·00	1·25
	a. Booklet pane. No. 80 × 2	2·00	

Nos. 72/7 were printed in sheetlets of seven stamps of the same face value, each containing six of the "Royal Yacht" design and one of the larger design showing Prince Charles and Lady Diana.

Nos. 79/80 come from $8.40 stamp booklets.

12 Zebra 13 Caroline of Brunswick, Princess of Wales, 1793

(Des Jennifer Toombs. Litho Questa)

1982 (16 Feb). *Butterflies* (1st *series*). *T* **12** *and similar horiz designs. Multicoloured. W* w **14** (*sideways*). *P* 14.

No.	Description	Unused	Used
81	5 c. Type **12**	10	10
82	30 c. Malachite	15	10
83	55 c. Southern Dagger Tail	20	15
84	$2 Large Orange Sulphur	60	70
81/4	*Set of* 4	90	90

See also Nos. 105/8.

(Des D. Shults and J. Cooter. Litho Format)

1982 (22 June). 21*st Birthday of Princess of Wales. T* **13** *and similar vert designs. Multicoloured. W* w **14**. *P* 13½ × 14.

No.	Description	Unused	Used
85	30 c. Type **13**	30	20
86	55 c. Coat of arms of Caroline of Brunswick	45	30
87	$5 Diana, Princess of Wales	1·50	1·60
85/7	*Set of* 3	2·00	1·90

1982 (12 July). *Birth of Prince William of Wales. Nos.* 85/7 *optd with T* **19** *of St. Kitts.*

No.	Description	Unused	Used
88	30 c. Type **13**	30	20
89	55 c. Coat of arms of Caroline of Brunswick	45	30
	a. Opt triple	35·00	
90	$5 Diana, Princess of Wales	1·50	1·60
88/90	*Set of* 3	2·00	1·90

14 Cyclist

(Des Philatelists (1980) Ltd. Litho Questa)

1982 (18 Aug). 75*th Anniv of Boy Scout Movement. T* **14** *and similar horiz designs. Multicoloured. W* w **14** (*sideways*). *P* 13½ × 14.

No.	Description	Unused	Used
91	5 c. Type **14**	15	10
92	30 c. Athlete	35	10
93	$2.50, Camp cook	90	80
91/3	*Set of* 3	1·25	85

15 Santa Claus 16 Tube Sponge

(Des Eugene Seabrookes (15 c.), Kharenzabeth Glasgow (30 c.), Davia Grant (£1.50), Leonard Huggins ($2.50); adapted Jennifer Toombs. Litho Format)

1982 (20 Oct). *Christmas. Children's Paintings. T* **15** *and similar multicoloured designs. W* w **14** (*sideways on* $1.50 *and* $2.50). *P* 13½ × 14 (15 *c.*, 30 *c.*) *or* 14 × 13½ (*others*).

No.	Description	Unused	Used
94	15 c. Type **15**	10	10
95	30 c. Carollers	10	10
96	$1.50, Decorated house and local band (*horiz*)	25	25
97	$2.50, Adoration of the Shepherds (*horiz*)	50	50
94/7	*Set of* 4	75	75

(Des G. Drummond. Litho Format)

1983 (12 Jan). *Corals* (1*st series*). *T* **16** *and similar vert designs. Multicoloured. W* w **14**. *P* 14.

No.	Description	Unused	Used
98	15 c. Type **16**	10	10
99	30 c. Stinging coral	15	10
100	55 c. Flower coral	25	10
101	$3 Sea Rod and Red Fire Sponge	70	80
98/101	*Set of* 4	1·00	90
MS102	82 × 115 mm. Nos. 98/101	1·10	1·40

See also Nos. 423/6.

17 H.M.S. *Boreas* off Nevis

(Des G. Drummond. Litho Format)

1983 (14 Mar). *Commonwealth Day. T* **17** *and similar horiz design. Multicoloured. W* w **14** (*sideways*). *P* 14.

No.	Description	Unused	Used
103	55 c. Type **17**	20	10
104	$2 Capt. Horatio Nelson and H.M.S. *Boreas* at anchor	65	75

(Des Jennifer Toombs. Litho Format)

1983 (8 June). *Butterflies* (2*nd series*). *Multicoloured designs as T* **12**. *W* w **14** (*sideways on* 30 *c. and* $2). *P* 14.

No.	Description	Unused	Used
105	30 c. Tropical Chequered Skipper	20	15
106	55 c. Caribbean Buckeye (*vert*)	25	20
107	$1.10, Common Long-tailed Skipper (*vert*)	50	55
108	$2 The "Mimic"	95	1·00
105/8	*Set of* 4	1·75	1·75

INDEPENDENCE 1983

(18)

INDEPENDENCE 1983

(18*a*)

19 Montgolfier Balloon, 1783

1983 (19 Sept). *Nos.* 58 *and* 60/71 *optd as T* **18** (20 *mm long on Nos.* 110/21).
A. *No imprint date*
B. *With imprint date.*

No.	Description	A Unused	A Used	B Unused	B Used
109	5 c. Type **10**	†		10	10
	a. Vert pair, lower stamp without opt.	†		65·00	—
	b. Optd with T **18***a* (local opt)	18·00	20·00	2·50	2·00
	ba. Opt T **18***a* inverted	†		45·00	—
110	15 c. Type **11**	35·00	35·00	10	10
111	20 c. Nelson Museum	10·00	10·00	10	10
112	25 c. St. James' Parish Church	10·00	10·00	10	15
113	30 c. Nevis Lane	1·50	1·50	15	15
	a. Opt inverted	†		11·00	—
114	40 c. Zetland Plantation	75	75	15	20
115	45 c. Nisbet Plantation	†		20	25
116	50 c. Pinney's Beach	†		20	25
117	55 c. Eva Wilkin's Studio	75	75	25	30
	a. Opt double	†		12·00	—
118	$1 Nevis at dawn	1·00	1·00	40	45
119	$2.50, Ruins of Fort Charles	1·50	1·50	90	1·10
120	$5 Old Bath House	2·50	3·00	1·50	1·75
121	$10 Beach at Nisbet's	5·00	6·00	2·75	3·00
	a. Opt inverted	60·00	—	†	
109bA/121A	*Set of* 11	75·00	80·00		
109B/121B	*Set of* 13			6·00	7·00

(Des A. Theobald. Litho Format)

1983 (28 Sept). *Bicentenary of Manned Flight. T* **19** *and similar multicoloured designs. W* w **15** (*sideways on* 45 *c. to* $2.50). *P* 14.

No.	Description	Unused	Used
122	10 c. Type **19**	10	10
123	45 c. Sikorsky "S-38", flying boat (*horiz*)	15	10
124	50 c. Beechcraft "Twin Bonanza" (*horiz*)	15	10
125	$2.50, B. Ae. "Sea Harrier" (*horiz*)	50	60
122/5	*Set of* 4	70	70
MS126	118 × 145 mm. Nos. 109/12. Wmk sideways	80	1·00

20 Mary praying over Holy Child

(Des Jennifer Toombs. Litho Format)

1983 (7 Nov). *Christmas. T* **20** *and similar horiz designs. Multicoloured. W* w **15** (*sideways*). *P* 14.

No.	Description	Unused	Used
127	5 c. Type **20**	10	10
128	30 c. Shepherds with flock	10	10
129	55 c. Three Angels	15	10
130	$3 Boy with two girls	55	60
127/30	*Set of* 4	70	70
MS131	135 × 149 mm. Nos. 127/30	70	1·00

21 *County of Oxford* (1945)

22 Boer War

(Des J. W. Litho Format)

1983 (10 Nov). *Leaders of the World. Railway Locomotives* (1st *series*). *T* **21** *and similar horiz designs, the first in each pair showing technical drawings and the second the locomotive at work. P* 12½.

132	55 c. multicoloured	25	30
	a. Vert pair. Nos. 132/3	50	60
133	55 c. multicoloured	25	30
134	$1 bright crimson, new blue and black	45	50
	a. Vert pair. Nos. 134/5	90	1·00
135	$1 multicoloured	45	50
136	$1 magenta, new blue and black	45	50
	a. Vert pair. Nos. 136/7	90	1·00
137	$1 multicoloured	45	50
138	$1 bright crimson, black and greenish yellow	45	50
	a. Vert pair. Nos. 138/9	90	1·00
139	$1 multicoloured	45	50
140	$1 multicoloured	45	50
	a. Vert pair. Nos. 140/1	90	1·00
141	$1 multicoloured	45	50
142	$1 greenish yellow, black and new blue	45	50
	a. Vert pair. Nos. 142/3	90	1·00
143	$1 multicoloured	45	50
144	$1 greenish yellow, black & brt magenta	45	50
	a. Vert pair. Nos. 144/5	90	1·00
145	$1 multicoloured	45	50
146	$1 multicoloured	45	50
	a. Vert pair. Nos. 146/7	90	1·00
147	$1 multicoloured	45	50
132/47	*Set of* 16	6·25	6·75

Designs:—Nos. 132/3, *County of Oxford*, Great Britain (1945), 134/5, *Evening Star*, Great Britain (1960); 136/7, Stanier "Class 5", Great Britain (1934); 138/9, *Pendennis Castle*, Great Britain (1924); 140/1, *Winston Churchill*, Great Britain (1946); 142/3, *Mallard*, Great Britain (1935); 144/5, *Britannia*, Great Britain (1951); 146/7, *King George V*, Great Britain (1927).

Nos. 132/3, 134/5, 136/7, 138/9, 140/1, 142/3, 144/5 and 146/7 were printed together, *se-tenant* in vertical pairs throughout the sheets.

See also Nos. 219/26, 277/84, 297/308, 352/9 and 427/42.

(Des Court House Studio. Litho Format)

1984 (11 Apr). *Leaders of the World. British Monarchs* (1st *series*). *T* **22** *and similar vert designs. Multicoloured. P* 12½.

148	5 c. Type **22**	10	10
	a. Horiz pair. Nos. 148/9	10	10
149	5 c. Queen Victoria	10	10
150	50 c. Queen Victoria at Osborne House	35	35
	a. Horiz pair. Nos. 150/1	70	70
151	50 c. Osborne House	35	35
152	60 c. Battle of Dettingen	40	40
	a. Horiz pair. Nos. 152/3	80	80
153	60 c. George II	40	40
154	75 c. George II at the Bank of England	50	50
	a. Horiz pair. Nos. 154/5	1·00	1·00
155	75 c. Bank of England	50	50
156	$1 Coat of Arms of George II	60	60
	a. Horiz pair. Nos. 156/7	1·10	1·10
157	$1 George II (*different*)	60	60
158	$3 Coat of Arms of Queen Victoria	1·50	1·60
	a. Horiz pair. Nos. 158/9	3·00	3·00
159	$3 Queen Victoria (*different*)	1·50	1·60
148/59	*Set of* 12	6·00	6·00

Nos. 148/9, 150/1, 152/3, 154/5, 156/7 and 158/9 were printed together, *se-tenant* in horizontal pairs throughout the sheet.

See also Nos. 231/6.

23 Golden Rock Inn

(Des Jennifer Toombs. Litho J.W.)

1984 (16 May). *Tourism.* (1st *series*). *T* **23** *and similar horiz designs. Multicoloured.* W w **15** (*sideways*). *P* 14.

160	55 c. Type **23**	20	20
161	55 c. Rest Haven Inn	20	20
162	55 c. Cliffdwellers Hotel	20	20
163	55 c. Pinney's Beach Hotel	20	20
160/3	*Set of* 4	70	70

See also Nos. 245/8.

24 Early Seal of Colony

(Des G. Drummond. Litho Format)

1984 (8 June). *W* w **15** (*sideways*). *P* 14.

164	**24**	$15 dull scarlet	5·00	6·50

25 Cadillac

(Des J. W. Litho Format)

1984 (25 July). *Leaders of the World. Automobiles* (1st *series*). *T* **25** *and similar horiz designs, the first in each pair showing technical drawings and the second paintings. P* 12½.

165	1 c. greenish yellow, black and magenta	10	10
	a. Vert pair. Nos. 165/6	10	10
166	1 c. multicoloured	10	10
167	5 c. new blue, magenta and black	10	10
	a. Vert pair. Nos. 167/8	10	10
168	5 c. multicoloured	10	10
169	15 c. multicoloured	15	15
	a. Vert pair. Nos. 169/70	30	30
170	15 c. multicoloured	15	15
171	35 c. magenta, greenish yellow and black	25	25
	a. Vert pair. Nos. 171/2	50	50
172	35 c. multicoloured	25	25
173	45 c. new blue, magenta and black	30	30
	a. Vert pair. Nos. 173/4	60	60
174	45 c. multicoloured	30	30
175	55 c. multicoloured	40	40
	a. Vert pair. Nos. 175/6	80	80
176	55 c. multicoloured	40	40
177	$2.50, magenta, black and greenish yellow	1·00	75
	a. Vert pair. Nos. 177/8	2·00	1·50
178	$2.50, multicoloured	1·00	75
179	$3 new blue, greenish yellow and black	1·10	80
	a. Vert pair. Nos. 179/80	2·10	1·60
180	$3 multicoloured	1·10	80
165/80	*Set of* 16	5·75	5·00

Designs:—Nos. 165/6, Cadillac "V16 Fleetwood Convertible" (1932); 167/8, Packard "Twin Six Touring Car" (1916); 169/70, Daimler, "2 Cylinder" (1886); 171/2, Porsche "911 S Targa" (1970); 173/4, Benz "Three Wheeler" (1885); 175/6, M.G. "TC" (1947); 177/8, Cobra "Roadster 289" (1966), 179/80, Aston Martin "DB6 Hardtop" (1966).

Nos. 165/6, 167/8, 169/70, 171/2, 173/4, 175/6, 177/8 and 179/80 were printed together, *se-tenant* in vertical pairs throughout the sheet.

See also Nos. 203/10, 249/64, 326/37, 360/71 and 411/22.

26 Carpentry

27 Yellow Bell

(Des Jennifer Toombs. Litho Questa)

1984 (1 Aug). *10th Anniv of Culturama Celebrations. T* **26** *and similar horiz designs. Multicoloured. W* w **15** (*sideways*). *P* 14.

181	30 c. Type **26**	10	10
182	55 c. Grass mat and basket-making	15	10
183	$1 Pottery-firing	25	25
184	$3 Culturama Queen and dancers	55	55
181/4	*Set of* 4	95	85

(Des Jennifer Toombs. Litho Format)

1984 (8 Aug)–**86**. *Flowers. T* **27** *and similar vert designs. Multicoloured. W* w **15**. *P* 14. *A. Without imprint date. B. With imprint date at foot of design* (23.7.86).

		A		B	
185	5 c. Type **27**	10	10	†	
186	10 c. Plumbago	10	10	†	
187	15 c. Flamboyant	10	10	†	
188	20 c. Eyelash Orchid	60	15	10	10
189	30 c. Bougainvillea	10	15	†	
190	40 c. Hibiscus *sp.*	70	25	15	20
191	50 c. Night-blooming Cereus	20	25	†	
192	55 c. Yellow Mahoe	20	25	†	
193	60 c. Spider-lily	25	30	†	
194	75 c. Scarlet Cordia	30	35	†	
195	$1 Shell-ginger	40	45	†	
196	$3 Blue Petrea	1·25	1·40	†	
197	$5 Coral Hibiscus	2·10	2·25	†	
198	$10 Passion Flower	4·00	4·25	†	
185/98	*Set of* 14	9·00	9·25	†	

28 Cotton-picking and Map

29 C.P. Mead

(Des A. Grant (15 c.), Tracy Watkins (55 c.), C. Manners ($1.10), D. Grant ($3), adapted Court House Advertising. Litho Format)

1984 (18 Sept). *First Anniv of Independence of St. Kitts-Nevis. T* **28** *and similar horiz designs. Multicoloured. W* w **15** (*sideways*). *P* 14.

199	15 c. Type **28**	15	10
200	55 c. Alexander Hamilton's birthplace	20	10
201	$1.10, Local agricultural produce	35	40
202	$3 Nevis Peak and Pinneys Beach	75	1·00
199/202	*Set of* 4	1·25	1·40

(Des J. W. Litho Format)

1984 (23 Oct). *Leaders of the World. Automobiles* (2*nd series*). *Horiz designs as T* **25**, *the first in each pair showing technical drawings and the second paintings. P* 12½.

203	5 c. black, pale new blue and yellow-brown	10	10
	a. Vert pair. Nos. 203/4	10	10
204	5 c. multicoloured	10	10
205	30 c. black, pale turquoise-green & lake-brn	20	20
	a. Vert pair. Nos. 205/6	40	40
206	30 c. multicoloured	20	20
207	50 c. black, pale drab and red-brown	30	25
	a. Vert pair. Nos. 207/8	60	50
208	50 c. multicoloured	30	25
209	$3 black, grey-brown and dull green	1·00	60
	a. Vert pair. Nos. 209/10	2·00	1·10
210	$3 multicoloured	1·00	60
203/10	*Set of* 8	2·75	1·75

Designs:—Nos. 203/4, Lagonda "Speed Model" touring car (1929); 205/6, Jaguar "E-Type" 4.2 litre (1967); 207/8, Volkswagen "Beetle" (1947); 209/10, Pierce Arrow "V12" (1932).

Nos. 203/10 were issued in a similar sheet format to Nos. 165/80.

(Des Court House Studio. Litho Format)

1984 (23 Oct). *Leaders of the World. Cricketers* (1*st series*). *T* **29** *and similar vert designs, the first in each pair showing a head portrait and the second the cricketer in action. P* 12½.

211	5 c. multicoloured	10	10
	a. Horiz pair. Nos. 211/12	15	15
212	5 c. multicoloured	10	10
213	25 c. multicoloured	30	30
	a. Horiz pair. Nos. 213/14	60	60
214	25 c. multicoloured	30	30
215	55 c. multicoloured	65	65
	a. Horiz pair. Nos. 215/16	1·25	1·25
216	55 c. multicoloured	65	65
217	$2.50, multicoloured	1·90	1·90
	a. Horiz pair. Nos. 217/18	3·75	3·75
218	$2.50, multicoloured	1·90	1·90
211/18	*Set of* 8	5·25	5·25

Designs:—Nos. 211/12, C. P. Mead; 213/14, J. B. Statham; 215/16, Sir Learie Constantine; 217/18, Sir Leonard Hutton.

Nos. 211/12, 213/14, 215/16 and 217/18 were printed together, *se-tenant*, in horizontal pairs throughout the sheets.

See also Nos. 237/44.

(Des J. W. Litho Format)

1984 (29 Oct). *Leaders of the World. Railway Locomotives* (2*nd series*). *Horiz designs as T* **21** *the first in each pair showing technical drawings and the second the locomotive at work. P* 12½.

219	5 c. multicoloured	10	10
	a. Vert pair. Nos. 219/20	10	10
220	5 c. multicoloured	10	10
221	10 c. multicoloured	10	10
	a. Vert pair. Nos. 221/2	15	15
222	10 c. multicoloured	10	10
223	60 c. multicoloured	40	40
	a. Vert pair. Nos. 223/4	80	80
224	60 c. multicoloured	40	40
225	$2.50, multicoloured	1·75	1·75
	a. Vert pair. Nos. 225/6	3·50	3·50
226	$2.50, multicoloured	1·75	1·75
219/26	*Set of* 8	4·00	4·00

Designs:—Nos. 219/20, Class "EF81", Japan (1968); 221/2, Class "5500", France (1927); 223/4, Class "240P", France (1940); 225/6, Shinkansen train, Japan (1964).

Nos. 219/26 were issued in a similar sheet format to Nos. 132/47.

30 Fifer and Drummer from Honeybees Band

(Des Jennifer Toombs. Litho Questa)

1984 (2 Nov). *Christmas. Local Music. T* **30** *and similar horiz designs. Multicoloured. W* w **15** (*sideways*). *P* 14.

227	15 c. Type **30**	15	10
228	40 c. Guitar and "barhow" players from Canary Birds Band	25	10
229	60 c. Shell All Stars steel band	30	10
230	$3 Organ and choir, St. John's Church, Fig Tree	1·25	1·00
227/30	*Set of* 4	1·75	1·10

(Des Court House Studio. Litho Format)

1984 (20 Nov). *Leaders of the World. British Monarchs* (2*nd series*). *Vert designs as T* **22**. *Multicoloured. P* 12½.

231	5 c. King John and Magna Carta	10	10
	a. Horiz pair. Nos. 231/2	10	10
232	5 c. Barons and King John	10	10
233	55 c. King John	30	30
	a. Horiz pair Nos. 233/4	60	60
234	55 c. Newark Castle	30	30
235	$2 Coat of arms	1·00	1·00
	a. Horiz pair. Nos. 235/6	2·00	2·00
236	$2 King John (*different*)	1·00	1·00
231/6	*Set of* 6	2·40	2·40

Nos. 231/6 were issued in a similar sheet format to Nos. 148/59.

(Des Court House Studio. Litho Format)

1984 (20 Nov). *Leaders of the World. Cricketers (2nd series). Vert designs as T* **29**, *the first in each pair listed showing a head portrait and the second the cricketer in action. P* 12½.

237 5 c. multicoloured 10 10
a. Horiz pair. Nos. 237/8 . . . . 15 15
238 5 c. multicoloured 10 10
239 15 c. multicoloured 15 15
a. Horiz pair. Nos. 239/40 . . . . 30 30
240 15 c. multicoloured 15 15
241 55 c. multicoloured 35 35
a. Horiz pair. Nos. 241/2 . . . . 70 70
242 55 c. multicoloured 35 35
243 $2,50, multicoloured . . . . 1·75 1·75
a. Horiz pair. Nos. 243/4 . . . . 3·50 3·50
244 $2.50, multicoloured . . . . 1·75 1·75
237/44 . . . . *Set of* 8 4·25 4·25

Designs:—Nos. 237/8, J. D. Love; 239/40, S. J. Dennis; 241/2, B. W. Luckhurst; 243/4, B. L. D'Oliveira.

Nos. 237/44 were issued in a similar sheet format to Nos. 211/18.

IMPERFORATES AND MISSING COLOURS. Various issues between Nos. 245 and 410 exist either imperforate or with colours omitted. Such items are not listed as there is no evidence that they fulfil the criteria outlined on page xi of this catalogue.

(Des Jennifer Toombs. Litho Format)

1985 (12 Feb). *Tourism (2nd series). Horiz designs as T* **23.** *Multicoloured. W* w **15** *(sideways). P* 14.

245 $1.20, Croney's Old Manor Hotel . . 45 45
246 $1.20, Montpelier Plantation Inn . . 45 45
247 $1.20, Nisbet's Plantation Inn . . 45 45
248 $1.20, Zetland Plantation Inn . . 45 45
245/8 . . *Set of* 4 1·60 1·60

(Des G. Turner (10 c.), J.W. (others). Litho Format)

1985 (20 Feb). *Leaders of the World. Automobiles (3rd series). Horiz designs as T* **25**, *the first in each pair showing technical drawings and the second paintings. P* 12½.

249 1 c. black, light green and pale green . . 10 10
a. Vert pair. Nos. 249/50 . . 10 10
250 1 c. multicoloured . . 10 10
251 5 c. black, cobalt and pale violet-blue . . 10 10
a. Vert pair. Nos. 251/2 . . 10 10
252 5 c. multicoloured . . 10 10
253 10 c. black, grey-olive and pale green . . 10 10
a. Vert pair. Nos. 253/4 . . 10 10
254 10 c. multicoloured . . 10 10
255 50 c. black, sage-green and pale cinnamon . . 30 30
a. Vert pair. Nos. 255/6 . . 60 60
256 50 c. multicoloured . . 30 30
257 60 c. black, dull yellowish green and pale blue 30 30
a. Vert pair. Nos. 257/8 . . 60 60
258 60 c. multicoloured . . 30 30
259 75 c. black, dull vermilion and pale orange . . 35 35
a. Vert pair. Nos. 259/60 . . 70 70
260 75 c. multicoloured . . 35 35
261 $2.50, black, light green and azure . . 45 45
a. Vert pair. Nos. 261/2 . . 90 90
262 $2.50, multicoloured . . 45 45
263 $3 black, bright yellow-green and pale green 50 50
a. Vert pair. Nos. 263/4 . . 1·00 1·00
264 $3 multicoloured . . 50 50
249/64 . . *Set of* 16 3·50 3·50

Designs:—Nos. 249/50, Delahaye "Type 35 Cabriolet" (1935); 251/2, Ferrari "Testa Rossa" (1958); 253/4, Voisin "Aerodyne" (1934); 255/6, Buick "Riviera" (1963); 257/8, Cooper "Climax" (1960); 259/60, Ford "999" (1904); 261/2, MG "M-Type Midget" (1930); 263/4, Rolls-Royce "Corniche" (1971).

Nos. 249/64 were issued in a similar sheet format to Nos. 165/80.

31 Broad-winged Hawk

32 Eastern Bluebird

(Des Jennifer Toombs. Litho Format)

1985 (19 Mar). *Local Hawks and Herons. T* **31** *and similar horiz designs. Multicoloured. W* w **15** *(sideways). P* 14.

265 20 c. Type **31** . . 50 15
266 40 c. Red-tailed Hawk . . 65 25
267 60 c. Little Blue Heron . . 80 40
268 $3 Great Blue Heron (white phase) . . 2·00 1·75
265/8 . . *Set of* 4 3·50 2·25

(Des R. Vigurs. Litho Format)

1985 (25 Mar). *Leaders of the World. Birth Bicentenary of John J. Audubon (ornithologist) (1st issue). T* **32** *and similar vert designs. Multicoloured. P* 12½.

269 5 c. Type **32** . . 15 10
a. Horiz pair. Nos. 269/70 . . 30 20
270 5 c. Common Cardinal . . 15 10
271 55 c. Belted Kingfisher . . 65 65
a. Horiz pair. Nos. 271/2 . . 1·25 1·25
272 55 c. Mangrove Cuckoo . . 65 65
273 60 c. Yellow Warbler . . 65 65
a. Horiz pair. Nos. 273/4 . . 1·25 1·25
274 60 c. Cerulean Warbler . . 65 65
275 $2 Burrowing Owl . . 1·40 1·40
a. Horiz pair. Nos. 275/6 . . 2·75 2·75
276 $2 Long-eared Owl . . 1·40 1·40
269/76 . . *Set of* 8 5·00 5·00

Nos. 269/70, 271/2, 273/4 and 275/6 were printed together, *se-tenant*, in horizontal pairs throughout the sheets.

See also Nos. 285/92.

(Des J.W. Litho Format)

1985 (26 Apr). *Leaders of the World. Railway Locomotives (3rd series). Horiz designs as T* **21**, *the first in each pair showing technical drawings and the second the locomotive at work. P* 12½.

277 1 c. multicoloured . . 10 10
a. Vert pair. Nos. 277/8 . . 10 10
278 1 c. multicoloured . . 10 10
279 60 c. multicoloured . . 45 45
a. Vert pair. Nos. 279/80 . . 90 90
280 60 c. multicoloured . . 45 45
281 90 c. multicoloured . . 55 55
a. Vert pair. Nos. 281/2 . . 1·10 1·10
282 90 c. multicoloured . . 55 55
283 $2 multicoloured . . 1·25 1·25
a. Vert pair. Nos. 283/4 . . 2·50 2·50
284 $2 multicoloured . . 1·25 1·25
277/84 . . *Set of* 8 4·00 4·00

Designs:—Nos. 277/8, Class "Wee Bogie", Great Britain (1882); 279/80, *Comet*, Great Britain (1851); 281/2, Class "8H", Great Britain (1908); 283/4, Class "A" No. 23, Great Britain (1866).

Nos. 277/84 were issued in a similar sheet format to Nos. 132/47.

(Des R. Vigurs. Litho Format)

1985 (3 June). *Leaders of the World. Birth Bicentenary of John J. Audubon (ornithologist) (2nd issue). Vert designs as T* **32** *showing original paintings. Multicoloured. P* 12½.

285 1 c. Painted Bunting . . 10 10
a. Horiz pair. Nos. 285/6 . . 10 10
286 1 c. Golden-crowned Kinglet . . 10 10
287 40 c. Common Flicker . . 50 50
a. Horiz pair. Nos. 287/8 . . 1·00 1·00
288 40 c. Western Tanager . . 50 50
289 60 c. Varied Thrush ("Sage Thrasher") . . 70 70
a. Horiz pair. Nos. 289/90 . . 1·40 1·40
290 60 c. Evening Grosbeak . . 70 70
291 $2.50, Blackburnian Warbler . . 1·75 1·75
a. Horiz pair. Nos. 291/2 . . 3·50 3·50
292 $2.50, Northern Oriole . . 1·75 1·75
285/92 . . *Set of* 8 5·50 5·50

Nos. 285/92 were issued in a similar sheet format to Nos. 269/76.

33 Guides and Guide Headquarters

34 The Queen Mother at Garter Ceremony

(Des G. Vasarhelyi. Litho Format)

1985 (17 June). *75th Anniv of Girl Guide Movement. T* **33** *and similar multicoloured designs. W* w **15** *(inverted on 60 c., sideways on 15 c.). P* 14.

293 15 c. Type **33** . . 10 10
294 60 c. Girl Guide uniforms of 1910 and 1985 (*vert*) . . 30 30
295 $1 Lord and Lady Baden-Powell (*vert*) . . 50 50
296 $3 Princess Margaret in Guide uniform (*vert*) . . 1·25 1·50
293/6 . . *Set of* 4 1·90 2·25

(Des T. Hadler (75 c., $1, $2.50), J.W. (others). Litho Format)

1985 (26 July). *Leaders of the World. Railway Locomotives (4th series). Horiz designs as T* **21**, *the first in each pair showing technical drawings and the second the locomotive at work. P* 12½.

297 5 c. multicoloured . . 10 10
a. Vert pair. Nos. 297/8 . . 10 10
298 5 c. multicoloured . . 10 10
299 30 c. multicoloured . . 15 20
a. Vert pair. Nos. 299/300 . . 30 40
300 30 c. multicoloured . . 15 20
301 60 c. multicoloured . . 35 40
a. Vert pair. Nos. 301/2 . . 70 80
302 60 c. multicoloured . . 35 40
303 75 c. multicoloured . . 40 45
a. Vert pair. Nos. 303/4 . . 80 90
304 75 c. multicoloured . . 40 45
305 $1 multicoloured . . 55 60
a. Vert pair. Nos. 305/6 . . 1·10 1·10
306 $1 multicoloured . . 55 60
307 $2.50, multicoloured . . 1·25 1·40
a. Vert pair. Nos. 307/8 . . 2·50 2·75
308 $2.50, multicoloured . . 1·25 1·40
297/308 . . *Set of* 12 5·00 5·50

Designs:—Nos. 297/8, *Snowdon Ranger*, Great Britain (1878); 299/300, Large Belpaire passenger locomotive, Great Britain (1904); 301/2, Great Western Railway "County" Class, Great Britain (1904); 303/4, *Nord L'Outrance*, France (1877); 305/6, Q.R. "Class PB-15", Australia (1899); 307/8, D.R.G. "Class 64", Germany (1928).

Nos. 297/308 were issued in a similar sheet format to Nos. 132/47.

(Des Court House Studio. Litho Format)

1985 (31 July). *Leaders of the World. Life and Times of Queen Elizabeth the Queen Mother. Various vertical portraits as T* **34**. *P* 12½.

309 45 c. multicoloured . . 25 30
a. Horiz pair. Nos. 309/10 . . 50 60
310 45 c. multicoloured . . 25 30
311 75 c. multicoloured . . 40 45
a. Horiz pair. Nos. 311/12 . . 80 90
312 75 c. multicoloured . . 40 45
313 $1.20, multicoloured . . 70 75
a. Horiz pair. Nos. 313/14 . . 1·40 1·50
314 $1.20, multicoloured . . 70 75
315 $1.50, multicoloured . . 80 85
a. Horiz pair. Nos. 315/16 . . 1·60 1·60
316 $1.50, multicoloured . . 80 85
309/16 . . *Set of* 8 3·75 4·25
MS317 85 × 114 mm. $2 multicoloured; $2 multicoloured . . 2·40 2·50

The two designs of each value were issued, *se-tenant*, in horizontal pairs within the sheets.

Each *se-tenant* pair shows a floral pattern across the bottom of the portraits which stops short of the left-hand edge on the left-hand stamp and of the right-hand edge on the right-hand stamp.

Designs as Nos. 309/10 and 315/16, but with face values of $3.50 × 2 and $6 × 2, also exist in additional miniature sheets from a restricted printing issued 27 December 1985.

35 Isambard Kingdom Brunel

36 St. Pauls Anglican Church, Charlestown

(Des Tudor Art Agency. Litho Format)

1985 (31 Aug). *150th Anniv of the Great Western Railway. T* **35** *and similar vert designs showing railway engineers and their achievements. Multicoloured. P* 12½.

318 25 c. Type **35** . . 35 35
a. Horiz pair. Nos. 318/19 . . 70 70
319 25 c. Royal Albert Bridge, 1859 . . 35 35
320 50 c. William Dean . . 45 45
a. Horiz pair. Nos. 320/1 . . 90 90
321 50 c. Locomotive *Lord of the Isles*, 1895 . . 45 45
322 $1 Locomotive *Lode Star*, 1907 . . 1·00 1·00
a. Horiz pair. Nos. 322/3 . . 2·00 2·00
323 $1 G. J. Churchward . . 1·00 1·00
324 $2.50, Locomotive *Pendennis Castle*, 1924 1·75 1·75
a. Horiz pair. Nos. 324/5 . . 3·50 3·50
325 $2.50, C. B. Collett . . 1·75 1·75
318/25 . . *Set of* 8 6·50 6·50

Nos. 318/19, 320/1, 322/3 and 324/5 were printed together, *se-tenant*, in horizontal pairs throughout the sheets, each pair forming a composite design.

(Des J.W. Litho Format)

1985 (4 Oct). *Leaders of the World. Automobiles (4th series). Horiz designs as T* **25**, *the first in each pair showing technical drawings and the second paintings. P* 12½.

326 10 c. black, azure and brown-red . . 10 10
a. Vert pair. Nos. 326/7 . . 10 15
327 10 c. multicoloured . . 10 10
328 35 c. black, pale turquoise-grn & greenish bl 20 25
a. Vert pair. Nos. 328/9 . . 40 50
329 35 c. multicoloured . . 20 25
330 75 c. black, bright green & lt purple-brown 40 45
a. Vert pair. Nos. 330/1 . . 80 90
331 75 c. multicoloured . . 40 45
332 $1.15, black, pale cinnamon & olive-green 65 70
a. Vert pair. Nos. 332/3 . . 1·25 1·40
333 $1.15, multicoloured . . 65 70
334 $1.50, black, pale blue and carmine . . 80 85
a. Vert pair. Nos. 334/5 . . 1·60 1·60
335 $1.50, multicoloured . . 80 85
336 $2 black, rose-lilac and reddish violet . . 1·10 1·25
a. Vert pair. Nos. 336/7 . . 2·25 2·50
337 $2 multicoloured . . 1·10 1·25
326/37 . . *Set of* 12 5·75 6·50

Designs:—Nos. 326/7, Sunbeam "Coupe de l'Auto" (1912); 328/9, Cisitalia "Pininfarina Coupe" (1948); 330/1, Porsche "928 S" (1980); 332/3, MG "K3 Magnette" (1933); 334/5, Lincoln "Zephyr" (1937); 336/7, Pontiac 2 Door (1926).

Nos. 326/37 were issued in a similar sheet format to Nos. 165/80.

1985 (23 Oct). *Royal Visit. Nos.* 76/7, 83, 86, 92/3, 98/9 *and* 309/10 *optd as T* **114** *of Montserrat or surch also.*

338 **16** 15 c. multicoloured . . 1·00 1·00
339 – 30 c. multicoloured (No. 92) . . 2·00 1·50
340 – 30 c. multicoloured (No. 99) . . 1·00 1·00
341 – 40 c. on 55 c. multicoloured (No. 86) . . 2·00 1·75
342 **34** 45 c. multicoloured . . 2·25 2·00
a. Horiz pair. Nos. 342/3 . . 4·50 4·00
343 – 45 c. multicoloured (No. 310) . . 2·25 2·00
344 – 55 c. multicoloured (No. 83) . . 1·25 1·25
345 – $1.50 on $5 multicoloured (No. 76) . . 2·25 2·25
a. Sheetlet. No. 345 × 6 and No. 346 . . 20·00
b. Error. Surch $1.60 . . 2·75 2·75
ba. Sheetlet. No. 345b × 6 and No. 346b 18·00
346 – $1.50 on $5 multicoloured (No. 77) . . 4·50 4·50
b. Error. Surch $1.60 . . 4·75 4·75
347 – $2.50, multicoloured (No. 93) . . 2·75 2·50
338/47 . . *Set of* 10 18·00 17·00

Nos. 345b/ba and 346b had the surcharge intended for similar St. Vincent sheetlets applied by mistake.

(Des G. Drummond. Litho Format)

1985 (5 Nov). *Christmas. Churches of Nevis (1st series). T* **36** *and similar horiz designs. Multicoloured. W* w **15**. *P* 15.

348 10 c. Type **36** . . 10 10
349 40 c. St. Theresa Catholic Church, Charlestown . . 20 25
350 60 c. Methodist Church, Gingerland . . 35 40
351 $3 St. Thomas Anglican Church, Lowland 1·60 1·75
348/51 . . *Set of* 4 2·00 2·25

See also Nos. 462/5.

(Des T. Hadler. Litho Format)

1986 (30 Jan). *Leaders of the World. Railway Locomotives* (5*th series*). *Horiz designs as T* **21**, *the first in each pair showing technical drawings and the second the locomotive at work. P* 12½.

352 30 c. multicoloured 25 25
a. Vert pair. Nos. 352/3 .. .. 50 50
353 30 c. multicoloured 25 25
354 75 c. multicoloured 65 65
a. Vert pair. Nos. 354/5 .. .. .. 1·25 1·25
355 75 c. multicoloured 65 65
356 $1.50, multicoloured .. .. .. 1·10 1·10
a. Vert pair. Nos. 356/7 .. .. .. 2·10 2·10
357 $1.50, multicoloured .. .. .. 1·10 1·10
358 $2 multicoloured .. .. 1·50 1·50
a. Vert pair. Nos. 358/9 .. .. .. 3·00 3·00
359 $2 multicoloured .. .. 1·50 1·50
352/9 .. .. *Set of* 8 6·25 6·25

Designs:—Nos. 342/3, *Stourbridge Lion*, U.S.A. (1829); 354/5, "EP-2 Bi-Polar", U.S.A. (1919); 356/7, U.P. "BO×4" gas turbine, U.S.A. (1953); 358/9, N.Y., N.H. and H.R. "FL9", U.S.A (1955).

Nos. 352/9 were issued in a similar sheet format to Nos. 132/47.

(Des G. Turner (60 c.), J.W. (others). Litho Format)

1986 (30 Jan). *Leaders of the World. Automobiles* (5*th series*). *Horiz designs as T* **25**, *the first in each pair showing technical drawings and the second paintings. P* 12½.

360 10 c. black, pale cinnamon and yellow-olive.. 10 10
a. Vert pair. Nos. 360/1 .. .. .. 10 15
361 10 c. multicoloured 10 10
362 60 c. black, salmon and bright scarlet .. 30 35
a. Vert pair. Nos. 362/3 .. .. .. 60 70
363 60 c. multicoloured 30 35
364 75 c. black, pale cinnamon and cinnamon .. 35 40
a. Vert pair. Nos. 364/5 .. .. .. 70 80
365 75 c. multicoloured 35 40
366 $1 black, lavender-grey and violet-grey .. 50 55
a. Vert pair. Nos. 366/7 .. .. .. 1·00 1·10
367 $1 multicoloured 50 55
368 $1.50, black, pale olive-yellow & olive-grn 75 80
a. Vert pair. Nos. 368/9 .. .. .. 1·50 1·60
369 $1.50, multicoloured 75 80
370 $3 black, azure and cobalt.. .. .. 1·50 1·60
a. Vert pair. Nos. 370/1 .. .. .. 3·00 3·25
371 $3 multicoloured .. .. 1·50 1·60
360/71 .. .. *Set of* 12 6·25 6·75

Designs:—No. 360/1, Adler "Trumpf" (1936); 362/3, Maserati "Tipo 250F" (1957); 364/5, Oldsmobile "Limited" (1910); 366/7, Jaguar "C-Type" (1951); 368/9, ERA "1.5L B Type" (1937); 370/1 Chevrolet "Corvette" (1953).

Nos. 360/71 were issued in a similar sheet format to Nos. 165/80.

37 "Spitfire" Prototype "K.5054", 1936

(Des J. Batchelor. Litho Format)

1986 (5 Mar). 50*th Anniv of the "Spitfire"* (*fighter aircraft*). *T* **37** *and similar horiz designs. Multicoloured. P* 12½.

372 $1 Type **37** .. .. 1·25 85
373 $2.50, Mark "1A" in Battle of Britain, 1940 .. 2·25 2·00
374 $3 Mark "XII" over convoy, 1944 .. .. 2·75 2·25
375 $4 Mark "XXIV", 1948 .. .. .. 3·25 2·75
372/5 .. .. *Set of* 4 8·50 7·00
MS376 114×86 mm. $6 "Seafire" Mark "III" on escort carrier H.M.S. *Hunter* .. .. .. 6·00 6·00

38 Head of Amerindian

39 Brazilian Player

(Litho Format)

1986 (11 Apr). 500*th Anniv of Discovery of America* (1992). *T* **38** *and similar vert designs. Multicoloured. P* 12½.

377 75 c. Type **38** 55 55
a. Horiz pair. Nos. 377/8 .. .. .. 1·10 1·10
378 75 c. Exchanging gifts for food from Amerindians 55 55
379 $1.75, Columbus's coat of arms .. .. 1·40 1·40
a. Horiz pair. Nos. 379/80.. .. .. 2·75 2·75
380 $1.75, Breadfruit plant .. .. .. 1·40 1·40
381 $2.50, Columbus's fleet .. .. .. 1·75 1·75
a. Horiz pair. Nos. 381/2 .. .. .. 3·50 3·50
382 $2.50, Christopher Columbus .. .. 1·75 1·75
377/82 .. .. *Set of* 6 6·50 6·50
MS383 95×84 mm. $6 Christopher Columbus (*different*) .. .. 4·75 5·00

The two designs of each value were printed together, *se-tenant*, in horizontal pairs throughout the sheets. Each pair forms a composite design showing charts of Columbus's route in the background.

(Des Court House Studio. Litho Format)

1986 (21 Apr). 60*th Birthday of Queen Elizabeth II. Multicoloured designs as T* **167** *of British Virgin Islands. P* 12½.

384 5 c. Queen Elizabeth in 1976 .. .. 10 10
385 75 c. Queen Elizabeth in 1953 .. .. 45 45
386 $2 In Australia .. .. 1·25 1·25
387 $8 In Canberra, 1982 (*vert*) .. .. 4·50 4·50
a. Wmk w **15** (inverted) .. .. 5·00
384/7 .. .. *Set of* 4 5·75 5·75
MS388 85×115 mm. $10 Queen Elizabeth II .. 6·00 6·00

The 5 c., 75 c. and $2 values exist with PVA gum as well as gum arabic.

(Des Court House Studio. Litho Format)

1986 (16 May). *World Cup Football Championship, Mexico. T* **39** *and similar multicoloured designs. P* 12½ (75 *c*., $1, $1.75, $6) *or* 15 (*others*).

389 1 c. Official World Cup mascot (*horiz*) .. 10 10
390 2 c. Type **39** 10 10
391 5 c. Danish player 10 10
392 10 c. Brazilian player (*different*) 10 10
393 20 c. Denmark v Spain 15 15
394 30 c. Paraguay v Chile 20 20
395 60 c. Italy v West Germany 40 40
396 75 c. Danish team (56×36 *mm*) 50 50
397 $1 Paraguayan team (56×36 *mm*) .. 65 65
398 $1.75, Brazilian team (56×36 *mm*) .. 1·25 1·25
399 $3 Italy v England.. .. .. .. 1·75 1·75
400 $6 Italian team (56×36 *mm*) .. .. 3·25 3·25
389/400 .. .. *Set of* 12 7·50 7·50
MS401 Five sheets, each 85×115 mm. (a) $1.50, As No. 398. (b) $2 As No. 393. (c) $2 As No. 400. (d) $2.50, As No. 395. (e) $4 As No. 394 .. .. .. *Set of* 5 *sheets* 6·50 7·50

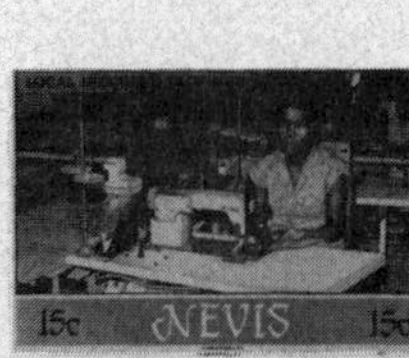

40 Clothing Machinist

41 Gorgonia

(Des G. Vasarhelyi. Litho Questa)

1986 (18 July). *Local Industries. T* **40** *and similar horiz designs. Multicoloured. W w* **15**. *P* 14.

402 15 c. Type **40** 15 10
403 40 c. Carpentry/joinery workshop 30 25
404 $1.20, Agricultural produce market .. 75 75
405 $3 Fishing boats landing catch .. .. 1·75 2·00
402/5 .. .. *Set of* 4 2·75 2·75

(Des Court House Studio. Litho Format)

1986 (23 July–15 Oct). *Royal Wedding* (1*st issue*). *Multicoloured designs at T* **168** *of British Virgin Islands. P* 12½.

406 60 c. Prince Andrew in midshipman's uniform 40 40
a. Pair. Nos. 406/7.. .. .. .. 80 80
407 60 c. Miss Sarah Ferguson 40 40
408 $2 Prince Andrew on safari in Africa (*horiz*) .. .. 1·25 1·25
a. Pair. Nos. 408/9.. .. .. .. 2·50 2·50
409 $2 Prince Andrew at the races (*horiz*) .. 1·25 1·25
406/9 .. .. *Set of* 4 3·00 3·00
MS410 115×85 mm. $10 Duke and Duchess of York on Palace balcony after wedding (*horiz*) (15.10.86) .. .. 4·50 5·00

Nos. 406/7 and 408/9 were each printed together, *se-tenant*, in horizontal and vertical pairs throughout the sheets.

See also Nos. 454/7.

(Litho Format)

1986 (15 Aug). *Automobiles* (6*th series*). *Horiz designs as T* **25**, *the first in each pair showing technical drawings and the second paintings. P* 12½.

411 15 c. multicoloured 10 10
a. Vert pair. Nos. 411/12 .. .. .. 20 20
412 15 c. multicoloured 10 10
413 45 c. black, light blue and grey-blue .. 30 30
a. Vert pair. Nos. 413/14 .. .. .. 60 60
414 45 c. multicoloured 30 30
415 60 c. multicoloured 35 35
a. Vert pair. Nos. 415/16 .. .. .. 70 70
416 60 c. multicoloured 35 35
417 $1 black, yellow-green and dull green .. 55 55
a. Vert pair. Nos. 417/18 .. .. .. 1·10 1·10
418 $1 multicoloured 55 55
419 $1.75, black, pale reddish lilac & deep lilac 95 95
a. Vert pair. Nos. 419/20 .. .. .. 1·90 1·90
420 $1.75, multicoloured 95 95
421 $3 multicoloured .. .. 1·60 1·60
a. Vert pair. Nos. 421/2 .. .. .. 3·25 3·25
422 $3 multicoloured .. .. 1·60 1·60
411/22 .. .. *Set of* 12 7·00 7·00

Designs:—Nos. 411/12, Riley "Brooklands Nine" (1930); 413/14, Alfa Romeo "GTA" (1966); 415/16, Pierce Arrow "Type 66" (1913); 417/18, Willys-Knight "66 A" (1928); 419/20, Studebaker "Starliner" (1953); 421/2, Cunningham "V-8" (1919).

Nos. 411/22 were issued in a similar sheet format to Nos. 165/80.

(Des G. Drummond. Litho Format)

1986 (8 Sept). *Corals* (2*nd series*). *T* **41** *and similar vert designs. Multicoloured. W w* **15** (*sideways*). *P* 15.

423 15 c. Type **41** 35 15
424 60 c. Fire Coral 70 40
425 $2 Elkhorn Coral .. .. 1·75 1·75
426 $3 Vase Sponge and Feather Star .. .. 2·40 2·75
423/6 .. .. *Set of* 4 4·75 4·50

(Des Court House Studio. Litho Format)

1986 (1 Oct). *Railway Locomotives* (6*th series*). *Horiz designs as T* **21**, *the first in each pair showing technical drawings and the second the locomotive at work. P* 12½.

427 15 c. multicoloured 10 10
a. Vert pair. Nos. 427/8 .. .. .. 20 20
428 15 c. multicoloured 10 10
429 45 c. multicoloured 25 25
a. Vert pair. Nos. 429/30 .. .. .. 50 50
430 45 c. multicoloured 25 25
431 60 c. multicoloured 30 30
a. Vert pair. Nos. 431/2 .. .. .. 60 60
432 60 c. multicoloured 30 30
433 75 c. multicoloured 40 40
a. Vert pair. Nos. 433/4 .. .. .. 80 80
434 75 c. multicoloured 40 40
435 $1 multicoloured 45 50
a. Vert pair. Nos. 435/6 .. .. .. 90 1·00
436 $1 multicoloured 45 50
437 $1.50, multicoloured 70 75
a. Vert pair. Nos. 437/8 .. .. .. 1·40 1·50
438 $1.50, multicoloured 70 75
439 $2 multicoloured 90 95
a. Vert pair. Nos. 439/40 .. .. .. 1·75 1·90
440 $2 multicoloured 90 95
441 $3 multicoloured .. .. 1·40 1·50
a. Vert pair. Nos. 441/2 .. .. .. 2·75 3·00
442 $3 multicoloured .. .. 1·40 1·50
427/42 .. .. *Set of* 16 8·00 8·50

Designs:—Nos. 427/8, Connor Single Class, Great Britain (1859); 429/30, Class "P2" *Cock o' the North*, Great Britain (1934); 431/2, Class "7000", Japan (1926); 433/4, Palatinate Railway Class "P3", Germany (1897); 435/6, *Dorchester*, Canada (1836); 437/8, "Centennial" Class diesel, U.S.A. (1969); 439/40, *Lafayette*, U.S.A. (1837); 441/2, Class "C-16", U.S.A. (1882).

Nos. 427/42 were issued in a similar sheet format to Nos. 132/47.

(Des Court House Studio. Litho Format)

1986 (28 Oct). *Centenary of Statue of Liberty. Multicoloured designs as T* **171** *of British Virgin Islands. P* 13½×14 ($1, $2) *or* 14×13½ (*others*).

443 15 c. Statue of Liberty and World Trade Centre, Manhattan 10 10
444 25 c. Sailing ship passing Statue 15 15
445 40 c. Statue in scaffolding 20 25
446 60 c. Statue (side view) and scaffolding .. 25 30
447 75 c. Statue and regatta 35 40
448 $1 Tall Ships parade passing Statue (*horiz*) 45 50
449 $1.50, Head and arm of Statue above scaffolding 70 75
450 $2 Ships with souvenir flags (*horiz*) .. 90 95
451 $2.50, Statue and New York waterfront .. 1·10 1·25
452 $3 Restoring Statue .. .. .. 1·40 1·50
443/52 .. .. *Set of* 4 5·00 5·50
MS453 Four sheets, each 85×115 mm. (a) $3.50, Statue at dusk. (b) $4 Head of Statue. (c) $4.50, Statue and lightning. (d) $5 Head and torch at sunset .. .. .. *Set of* 4 *sheets* 8·50 9·50

1986 (17 Nov). *Royal Wedding* (2*nd issue*). *Nos.* 406/9 *optd as T* **121** *of Montserrat in silver.*

454 60 c. Prince Andrew in midshipman's uniform 25 30
a. Pair. Nos. 454/5.. .. .. .. 60 70
455 60 c. Miss Sarah Ferguson 25 30
456 $2 Prince Andrew on safari in Africa (*horiz*) 90 95
a. Pair. Nos. 456/7.. .. .. .. 1·75 1·90
457 $2 Prince Andrew at the races (*horiz*) .. 90 95
454/7 .. .. *Set of* 4 2·10 2·25

42 Dinghy sailing

(Des G. Vasarhelyi. Litho Questa)

1986 (21 Nov). *Sports. T* **42** *and similar horiz designs. Multicoloured. P* 14.

458 10 c. Type **42** 10 10
459 25 c. Netball 30 15
460 $2 Cricket .. .. 1·75 1·75
461 $3 Basketball .. .. 2·00 2·00
458/61 .. .. *Set of* 4 3·75 3·75

43 St. George's Anglican Church, Gingerland

44 Constitution Document, Quill and Inkwell

(Des J. Cooter. Litho Questa)

1986 (8 Dec). *Christmas. Churches of Nevis* (2*nd series*). *T* **43** *and similar horiz designs. Multicoloured. P* 14.

462 10 c. Type **43** 10 10
463 40 c. Trinity Methodist Church, Fountain .. 20 25
464 $1 Charlestown Methodist Church 45 50
465 $5 Wesleyan Holiness Church, Brown Hill .. .. 2·25 2·40
462/5 .. .. *Set of* 4 2·75 3·00

(Des Maxine Marsh. Litho Questa)

1987 (11 Jan). *Bicentenary of U.S. Constitution and 230th Birth Anniv of Alexander Hamilton (U.S. statesman). T* **44** *and similar vert designs. Multicoloured. P* 14.
466 15 c. Type **44** 10 10
467 40 c. Alexander Hamilton and Hamilton House 20 25
468 60 c. Alexander Hamilton 25 30
469 $2 Washington and his Cabinet 90 95
466/9 .. .. *Set of* 4 1·25 1·40
MS470 70 × 82 mm. $5 Model ship *Hamilton* on float, 1788 .. .. 3·00 3·50

America's Cup
1987 Winners
'Stars & Stripes'

(45)

1987 (20 Feb). *Victory of* Stars and Stripes *in America's Cup Yachting Championship. No.* 54 *optd with T* **45**.
471 $3 Windjammer's S.V. *Polynesia* .. .. 1·40 1·50

46 Fig Tree Church

(Des Maxine Marsh. Litho Questa)

1987 (11 Mar). *Bicentenary of Marriage of Horatio Nelson and Frances Nisbet. T* **46** *and similar horiz designs. Multicoloured. W w* **15**. *P* 14.
472 15 c. Type **46** 10 10
473 60 c. Frances Nisbet 25 30
474 $1 H.M.S. *Boreas* 45 50
475 $3 Captain Horatio Nelson .. .. .. 1·40 1·50
472/5 .. .. *Set of* 4 2·00 2·10
MS476 102 × 82 mm. $3 As No. 473; $3 No. 475 .. 3·00 3·50

47 Queen Angelfish

(Des C. Abbott. Litho Format)

1987 (6 July). *Coral Reef Fishes. T* **47** *and similar triangular designs. Multicoloured. P* 14½.
477 60 c. Type **47** 40 40
a. Vert pair. Nos. 477/8 .. .. 80 80
478 60 c. Blue Angelfish 40 40
479 $1 Stoplight Parrotfish (male) 65 65
a. Vert pair. Nos. 479/80 .. .. 1·25 1·25
480 $1 Stoplight Parrotfish (female) 65 65
481 $1.50, Red Hind 90 90
a. Vert pair. Nos. 481/2 .. .. 1·75 1·75
482 $1.50, Rock Hind 90 90
483 $2.50, Coney (bicoloured phase) .. .. 1·40 1·40
a. Vert pair. Nos. 483/4 .. .. 2·75 2·75
484 $2.50, Coney (red-brown phase) .. .. 1·40 1·40
477/84 .. .. *Set of* 8 6·00 6·00
Nos. 477/8, 479/80, 481/2 and 483/4 were each printed together, *se-tenant*, in pairs throughout the sheets. The second design for each value is in the form of an inverted triangle.

48 *Panaeolus antillarum*

49 Rag Doll

(Des J. Cooter. Litho Format)

1987 (16 Oct). *Fungi. T* **48** *and similar vert designs. Multicoloured. W w* **16**. *P* 14.
485 15 c. Type **48** 15 10
486 50 c. *Pycnoporus sanguineus* 35 30
487 $2 *Gymnopilus chrysopellus* .. .. .. 1·00 95
488 $3 *Cantharellus cinnabarinus* .. .. .. 1·50 1·50
485/8 .. .. *Set of* 4 2·75 2·50

(Des J.W. Litho Walsall)

1987 (4 Dec). *Christmas. Toys. T* **49** *and similar horiz designs. Multicoloured. W w* **16** *(sideways). P* 14½.
489 10 c. Type **49** 10 10
490 40 c. Coconut boat 20 25
491 $1.20, Sandbox cart 55 60
492 $5 Two-wheeled cart .. .. 2·25 2·40
489/92 .. .. *Set of* 4 2·75 3·00

50 Hawk-wing Conch

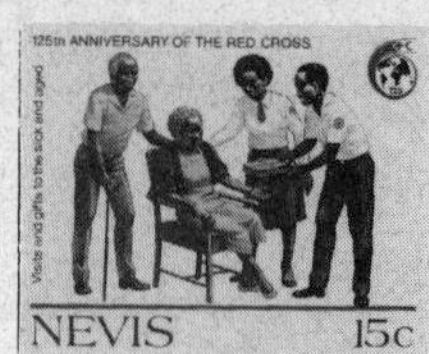

51 Visiting Pensioners at Christmas

(Des Josephine Martin. Litho Questa)

1988 (15 Feb). *Seashells and Pearls. T* **50** *and similar vert designs. Multicoloured. W w* **16**. *P* 14½ × 14.
493 15 c. Type **50** 15 10
494 40 c. Roostertail Conch 30 25
495 60 c. Emperor Helmet 40 30
496 $2 Queen Conch .. .. 1·25 1·25
497 $3 King Helmet .. .. 1·60 1·75
493/7 .. .. *Set of* 5 3·25 3·25

(Des L. Curtis. Litho Walsall)

1988 (20 June). *125th Anniv of International Red Cross. T* **51** *and similar horiz designs. Multicoloured. W w* **16** *(sideways). P* 14 × 14½.
498 15 c. Type **51** 10 10
499 40 c. Teaching children first aid 20 25
500 60 c. Providing wheelchairs for the disabled 25 30
501 $5 Helping cyclone victim .. .. .. 2·10 2·25
498/501 .. .. *Set of* 4 2·40 2·50

52 Athlete on Starting Blocks

53 Outline Map and Arms of St. Kitts–Nevis

(Des G. Vasarhelyi. Litho Format)

1988 (26 Aug). *Olympic Games, Seoul. T* **52** *and similar vert designs. Multicoloured. W w* **16**. *P* 14.
502 10 c. Type **52** 10 10
a. Horiz strip of 4. Nos. 502/5 .. .. 2·40
503 $1.20, At start 50 55
504 $2 During race 80 85
505 $3 At finish .. .. 1·25 1·40
502/5 .. .. *Set of* 4 2·40 2·50
MS506 137 × 80 mm. As Nos. 502/5, but each size 24 × 36 mm. Wmk sideways .. .. 2·50 3·00
Nos. 502/5 were printed together, *se-tenant*, in horizontal strips of 4 throughout the sheet, each strip forming a composite design showing an athlete from start to finish of race.

(Des L. Curtis. Litho Questa)

1988 (19 Sept). *5th Anniv of Independence. W w* **14**. *P* 14½ × 14.
507 **53** $5 multicoloured .. .. 2·10 2·25

(Des D. Miller (15 c., $2.50), E. Nisbet and D. Miller (60 c., $3). Litho Questa)

1988 (31 Oct). *300th Anniv of Lloyd's of London. Multicoloured designs as T* **123** *of Ascension. W w* **16** *(sideways on 60 c., $2.50). P* 14.
508 15 c. House of Commons passing Lloyd's Bill, 1871 .. .. 15 10
509 60 c. *Cunard Countess* (liner) (*horiz*) .. 35 35
510 $2.50, Space shuttle deploying satellite (*horiz*) .. .. 1·25 1·25
511 $3 *Viking Princess* on fire, 1966 .. .. 1·50 1·50
508/11 .. .. *Set of* 4 3·00 3·00

54 Poinsettia

55 British Fleet off St. Kitts

(Des I. Loe. Litho Questa)

1988 (7 Nov). *Christmas. Flowers. T* **54** *and similar vert designs. Multicoloured. W w* **16**. *P* 14½ × 14.
512 15 c. Type **54** 10 10
513 40 c. Tiger Claws 20 25
514 60 c. Sorrel Flower 25 30
515 $1 Christmas Candle 45 50
516 $5 Snow Bush .. .. 2·10 2·25
512/16 .. .. *Set of* 5 2·75 3·00

(Des Jane Hartley. Litho Format)

1989 (17 Apr). *"Philexfrance 89" International Stamp Exhibition, Paris. Battle of Frigate Bay, 1782. T* **55** *and similar vert designs. Multicoloured. W w* **16**. *P* 13½ × 14 ($3) *or* 14 (*others*).
517 50 c. Type **55** 25 30
a. Horiz strip of 3. Nos. 517/19 .. .. 1·75
518 $1.20, Battle off Nevis 55 60
519 $2 British and French fleets exchanging broadsides .. .. 95 1·00
520 $3 French map of Nevis, 1764 .. .. 1·50 1·60
517/20 .. .. *Set of* 4 3·00 3·25
Nos. 517/19 were printed together, *se-tenant*, in horizontal strips of 3 throughout the sheet, each strip forming a composite design.

56 Cicada

(Des I. Loe. Litho Questa)

1989 (15 May). *"Sounds of the Night". T* **56** *and similar vert designs. Multicoloured. W w* **16**. *P* 14.
521 10 c. Type **56** 10 10
522 40 c. Grasshopper 30 30
523 60 c. Cricket 45 45
524 $5 Tree frog .. .. 3·00 3·00
521/4 .. .. *Set of* 4 3·50 3·50
MS525 135 × 81 mm. Nos. 521/4 .. .. 3·75 4·00

(Des A. Theobald ($6), D. Miller (others). Litho Questa)

1989 (20 July). *20th Anniv of First Manned Landing on Moon. Multicoloured designs as T* **126** *of Ascension. W w* **16** *(sideways on 40 c., $2). P* 14 × 13½ (15 c., $3) *or* 14 (*others*).
526 15 c. Vehicle Assembly Building, Kennedy Space Centre 10 10
527 40 c. Crew of "Apollo 12" (30 × 30 *mm*) .. 20 25
528 $2 "Apollo 12" emblem (30 × 30 *mm*) .. 95 1·00
529 $3 "Apollo 12" astronaut on Moon .. 1·50 1·60
526/9 .. .. *Set of* 4 2·50 2·75
MS530 100 × 83 mm. $6 Aldrin undertaking lunar seismic experiment. P 14 × 13½ .. .. 2·75 3·00

OFFICIAL STAMPS

1980 (30 July). *Nos.* 40/9 *additionally optd with Type* O **1** *of St. Christopher, Nevis and Anguilla.*
O 1 15 c. Sugar cane harvesting 10 10
O 2 25 c. Crafthouse (craft centre) 10 10
a. "OFFICIAL" opt double .. .. 55·00
b. "OFFICIAL" opt omitted (in horiz pair with normal) .. .. 85·00
c. Optd on No. 41a .. .. .. 5·50 8·00
O 3 30 c. *Europa* (liner) 10 10
O 4 40 c. Lobster and sea crab 15 15
O 5 45 c. Royal St. Kitts Hotel and golf course .. 20 25
a. Opt inverted .. .. 13·00
O 6 50 c. Pinney's Beach, Nevis 20 25
a. Opt inverted .. .. 75·00
O 7 55 c. New runway at Golden Rock 20 25
a. Opt double .. .. 15·00
O 8 $1 Picking cotton 30 35
O 9 $5 Brewery .. .. 1·00 1·00
a. Opt inverted .. .. 80·00
O10 $10 Pineapples and peanuts .. .. 2·25 2·25
O1/10 .. .. *Set of* 10 4·00 4·50

1981 (Mar). *Nos.* 60A/71A *optd with Type* O **1** *of St. Kitts.*
O11 15 c. New River Mill 10 10
O12 20 c. Nelson Museum 10 10
O13 25 c. St. James' Parish Church 10 15
O14 30 c. Nevis Lane 15 15
O15 40 c. Zetland Plantation 15 20
O16 45 c. Nisbet Plantation 20 25
O17 50 c. Pinney's Beach 20 25
O18 55 c. Eva Wilkin's Studio 25 30
O19 $1 Nevis at dawn 40 45
O20 $2.50, Ruins of Fort Charles 85 90
O21 $5 Old Bath House .. .. 1·25 1·75
O22 $10 Beach at Nisbet's .. .. 2·25 2·75
O11/22 .. .. *Set of* 12 5·00 6·50

1983 (2 Feb). *Nos.* 72/7 *optd with Type* O **1** *of St. Kitts* (55 c.) *or surch also* (*others*).
O23 45 c. on $2 *Royal Sovereign* (New Blue) .. 20 25
a. Sheetlet. No. O23 × 6 and No. O24 .. 1·40
b. Surch inverted .. .. 10·00
c. Surch inverted (horiz pair) .. .. 38·00
d. Albino surch .. .. 9·00
da. Albino surch inverted .. .. ..
e. Horiz pair, one without surch .. ..
f. Deep ultramarine surch 40 50
fb. Surch inverted .. .. 7·00
fc. Surch inverted (horiz pair) .. .. 18·00
g. Black surch .. .. 60·00
O24 45 c. on $2 Prince Charles and Lady Diana Spencer (New Blue) 20 25
b. Surch inverted .. .. 30·00
d. Albino surch .. .. 23·00
f. Deep ultramarine surch 40 50
fb. Surch inverted .. .. 18·00
g. Black surch £150

O25	55 c. *Royal Caroline* (New Blue)	20	25
	a. Sheetlet No. O25 × 6 and No. O26	1·40	
	d. Albino opt	9·00	
	db. Albino opt inverted	11·00	
	dc. Albino opt inverted (horiz pair)	13·00	
	f. Deep ultramarine opt	75	
	fb. Opt inverted	7·00	
	fc. Opt inverted (horiz pair)	25·00	
	ff. Opt double	16·00	
	g. Black opt	60·00	
O26	55 c. Prince Charles and Lady Diana Spencer (New Blue)	25	25
	d. Albino opt	20·00	
	db. Albino opt inverted	25·00	
	f. Deep ultramarine opt	1·00	
	fb. Opt inverted	25·00	
	ff. Opt double	32·00	
	g. Black opt	£150	
O27	$1.10 on $5 *Britannia* (Blk.)	45	50
	a. Sheetlet. No. O27 × 6 and No. O28	3·00	
	d. Albino surch	9·00	
	f. Deep ultramarine surch.	6·00	
	fb. Surch inverted	8·00	
	fc. Surch inverted (horiz pair)	32·00	
O28	$1.10 on $5 Prince Charles and Lady Diana Spencer (Blk.)	55	60
	d. Albino surch	27·00	
	f. Deep ultramarine surch	40·00	
	fb. Surch inverted	50·00	
O23/28	*Set of* 6	1·75	1·75

Nos. O23c, O23fc, O25dc, O25fc and O27fc show the surcharge or overprint intended for the large design inverted and struck across a horizontal pair of the smaller. Nos. O24b, O24fb, O26db, O26fb and O28fb each show two inverted surcharges intended for a horizontal pair of the smaller design.

1985 (2 Jan). *Nos.* 187/98 *optd with Type* O 1 *of St. Kitts.*

O29	15 c. Flamboyant	10	10
O30	20 c. Eyelash Orchid	10	10
O31	30 c. Bougainvillea	15	15
O32	40 c. Hibiscus sp.	20	20
O33	50 c. Night-blooming Cereus	25	25
O34	55 c. Yellow Mahoe	25	25
O35	60 c. Spider-lily	30	30
O36	75 c. Scarlet Cordia	40	40
O37	$1 Shell-ginger	50	50
O38	$3 Blue Petrea	1·25	1·50
O39	$5 Coral Hibiscus	2·25	2·75
O40	$10 Passion Flower	4·00	4·50
O29/40	*Set of* 12	8·75	10·00

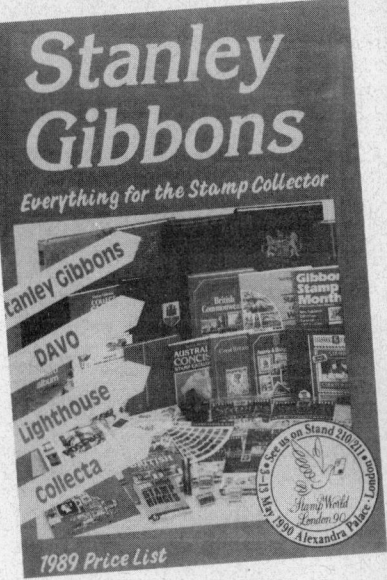

St. Lucia

Although a branch office of the British G.P.O. was not opened at Castries, the island capital, until 1844 some form of postal arrangements for overseas mails existed from at least 1841 when the issue of a Ship Letter handstamp is recorded.

The stamps of Great Britain were used on the island from May 1858 until the end of April 1860 when the local authorities assumed responsibility for the postal service. No. CC1 was again used on overseas mail between 1 May and the introduction of St. Lucia stamps in December 1860.

For illustrations of the handstamp and postmark types see BRITISH POST OFFICES ABROAD notes, following GREAT BRITAIN.

CASTRIES

CROWN-CIRCLE HANDSTAMPS

CC1 CC1 ST. LUCIA (R.) (1.5.1844) *Price on cover* £900

No. CC1 was utilised, struck in black, during a shortage of 1d. stamps in 1904. *Price on cover* £275.

Stamps of GREAT BRITAIN *cancelled* "A 11" *as Type* **2**.

1858 *to* **1860**

Z1	1d. rose-red (1857), *perf* 14	£1400
Z2	2d. blue (1855)	
Z3	4d. rose (1857)	£325
Z4	6d. lilac (1856)	£200
Z5	1s. green (1856)	£750

PRICES FOR STAMPS ON COVER TO 1945

Nos. 1/8	*from* × 5
Nos. 9/10	†
Nos. 11/24	*from* × 6
Nos. 25/30	*from* × 3
Nos. 31/6	*from* × 2
Nos. 39/42	*from* × 3
Nos. 43/50	*from* × 5
Nos. 51/2	—
Nos. 53/62	*from* × 3
No. 63	*from* × 4
Nos. 64/75	*from* × 3
Nos. 76/7	—
Nos. 78/88	*from* × 3
No. 89	*from* × 4
No. 90	*from* × 20
Nos. 91/112	*from* × 3
Nos. 113/24	*from* × 2
Nos. 125/7	*from* × 10
Nos. 128/41	*from* × 2
Nos. D1/6	*from* × 20
Nos. F1/28	—

CROWN COLONY

1

Half penny

(2)

(Recess P.B.)

1860 (18 Dec). *Wmk Small Star, W w* **2**. *P* 14 *to* 16.

1	1	(1d.) rose-red	£100	75·00
		a. Imperf vert (horiz pair)		
		b. Double impression	£1300	
2		(4d.) blue	£300	£225
		a. Deep blue		
		b. Imperf vert (horiz pair)		
3		(6d.) green	£350	£300
		a. Imperf vert (horiz pair)		
		b. Deep green	£350	£300

(Recess D.L.R.)

1863. *Wmk Crown CC. P* 12½.

5	1	(1d.) lake	55·00	80·00
		b. Brownish lake	75·00	75·00
7		(4d.) indigo	£125	£125
8		(6d.) emerald-green	£250	£250

Prepared for use, but not issued. Surch as T **2**

9	1	½d. on (6d.) emerald-green	40·00	
10		6d. on (4d.) indigo	£1200	

1864 (19 Nov)–**76**. *Wmk Crown CC.* (*a*) *P* 12½.

11	1	(1d.) black	16·00	12·00
		a. Intense black	15·00	11·00
12		(4d.) yellow	£120	30·00
		b. Lemon-yellow	£1500	
		c. Chrome-yellow	£130	30·00
		d. Olive-yellow	£250	70·00
13		(6d.) violet	70·00	28·00
		a. Mauve	£150	28·00
		b. Deep lilac	90·00	32·00
14		(1s.) brown-orange	£275	25·00
		b. Orange	£200	25·00
		c. Pale orange	£150	25·00
		ca. Imperf between (horiz pair)		

(*b*) *P* 14

15	1	(1d.) black (6.76)	16·00	15·00
		a. Imperf between (horiz pair)		
16		(4d.) yellow (6.76)	60·00	18·00
		a. Olive-yellow	£130	80·00
17		(6d.) mauve (6.76)	60·00	30·00
		a. Pale lilac	60·00	18·00
		b. Violet	£170	60·00
18		(1s.) orange (10.76)	£225	22·00
		a. Deep orange	£180	16·00

HALFPENNY

(3)

2½ PENCE

(4)

5

1881 (Sept). *Surch with T* **3** *or* **4**. *Wmk Crown CC. P* 14

23	1	½d. green	42·00	55·00
24		2½d. brown-red	18·00	18·00

The 1d. black is known surcharged "1d." in violet ink by hand, but there is no evidence that this was done officially.

1882–84. *Surch as T* **3**. *Wmk Crown CA.* (*a*) *P* 14

25	1	½d. green (1882)	12·00	22·00
26		1d. black (C.)	17·00	8·00
		a. Bisected (on cover)	†	—
27		4d. yellow	£170	17·00
28		6d. violet	22·00	25·00
29		1s. orange	£225	£160

(*b*) *P* 12

30	1	4d. yellow	£350	28·00

Deep blue stamps, wmk Crown CA, perf 14 or 12, are fiscals from which the overprint "THREE PENCE—REVENUE", or "REVENUE", has been fraudulently removed.

(Typo D.L.R.)

1883 (6 July)–**86**. *Wmk Crown CA. Die* I. *P* 14.

31	5	½d. dull green	2·75	2·75
32		1d. carmine-rose	22·00	7·50
33		2½d. blue	13·00	1·25
34		4d. brown (1885)	14·00	70
35		6d. lilac (1886)	£250	£200
36		1s. orange-brown (1885)	£400	£140

We no longer list imperforate examples of stamps appearing between 1863 and 1887 as there is no evidence that these were ever issued.

1886–87. *Wmk Crown CA. Die* I. *P* 14.

39	5	1d. dull mauve	2·50	5·00
40		3d. dull mauve and green	50·00	12·00
41		6d. dull mauve and blue (1887)	3·25	7·00
42		1s. dull mauve and red (1887)	50·00	15·00
39/42		*Set of* 4	95·00	35·00
39/42 Optd "Specimen"		*Set of* 4	£160	

1891–98. *Wmk Crown CA. Die* II. *P* 14.

43	5	½d. dull green	50	25
44		1d. dull mauve	90	15
45		2d. ultramarine and orange (1898)	70	1·00
46		2½d. ultramarine	1·75	30
47		3d. dull mauve and green	3·25	5·50
48		4d. brown	1·40	2·25
49		6d. dull mauve and blue	9·50	12·00
50		1s. dull mauve and red	2·75	5·00
51		5s. dull mauve and orange	25·00	55·00
52		10s. dull mauve and black	45·00	60·00
43/52		*Set of* 10	80·00	£130
45, 51, 52 Optd "Specimen"		*Set of* 3	£125	

For description and illustration of differences between Die I and Die II see Introduction.

ONE HALF PENNY

(6)

½d

(7)

ONE PENNY

(8)

N

Normal "N"

N

Thick "N"

Three types of T **8**

I. All letters "N" normal.
II. Thick diagonal stroke in first "N".
III. Thick diagonal stroke in second "N".

1891–92 (*a*) *Stamps of Die* I *surch.*

53	6	½d. on 3d. dull mauve and green	50·00	55·00
		a. Small "A" in "HALF"	80·00	80·00
		b. Small "O" in "ONE"	80·00	80·00
54	7	½d. on half 6d. dull mauve and blue	12·00	3·25
		a. No fraction bar	£140	£140
		b. Surch sideways	£325	
		c. Surch double	£350	£400
		d. "2" in fraction omitted	£325	£450
		e. Thick "1" with sloping serif	£130	£130
		f. Surch triple	£550	
		g. Figure "1" used as fraction bar	£375	£250
55	8	1d. on 4d. brown (I) (12.91)	3·00	3·00
		a. Surch double	£150	
		b. Surch inverted	£700	£600
		c. Type II	18·00	18·00
		ca. Surch double	£150	
		cb. Surch inverted	—	£600
		d. Type III	18·00	18·00

(*b*) *Stamp of Die* II *surch*

56	6	½d. on 3d. dull mauve and green	27·00	14·00
		a. Surch double	£650	£600
		b. Surch inverted	£1600	£650
		c. Small "O" in "ONE"	£130	£130
		d. Small "A" in "HALF"	£130	£130
		e. "ONE" misplaced ("O" over "H")	£130	£130

9

10

(Typo D.L.R.)

1902–3. *Wmk Crown CA. P* 14.

58	9	½d. dull purple and green	1·50	80
59		1d. dull purple and carmine	1·75	45
60		2½d. dull purple and ultramarine	7·50	5·50
61	10	3d. dull purple and yellow	4·00	8·50
62		1s. green and black	6·50	10·00
58/62		*Set of* 5	19·00	23·00
58/62 Optd "Specimen"		*Set of* 5	£100	

11 The Pitons

(Recess D.L.R.)

1902 (15 Dec). *400th Anniv of Discovery by Columbus. Wmk Crown CC, sideways. P* 14

63	11	2d. green and brown	6·50	1·75
63 Optd "Specimen"			60·00	

This stamp was formerly thought to have been issued on 16 December but it has been seen on a postcard clearly postmarked 15 December.

1904–10. *Wmk Mult Crown CA. P* 14.

64	9	½d. dull purple and green, CO	70	20
65		½d. green, O (1907)	80	20
66		1d. dull purple and carmine, CO	90	15
67		1d. carmine, O (1907)	80	10
68		2½d. dull purple and ultramarine, CO	2·75	1·25
69		2½d. blue, O (1907)	2·75	1·25
70	10	3d. dull purple and yellow, O	3·50	3·00
71		3d. purple/*yellow*, C (1909)	1·75	6·50
72		6d. dull purple and violet, CO (1905)	4·00	4·75
		a. Dull and bright purple, C (1907)	3·50	9·00
73		6d. dull purple, C (1910)	10·00	17·00
74		1s. green and black, C (1905)	12·00	11·00
75		1s. black/*green*, C (1909)	2·75	4·50
76		5s. green and carmine, O (1905)	27·00	55·00
77		5s. green and red/*yellow*, C (1907)	27·00	40·00
64/77		*Set of* 14	80·00	£130
65, 67, 69, 71/2*a*, 75/7 Optd "Specimen"		*Set of* 9	£170	

12

13

14

15

16

(Typo D.L.R.)

1912–20. *Wmk Mult Crown CA. P* 14.

78	12	½d. deep green, O	60	40
		a. Yellow-green, O (1916)	55	25
79		1d. carmine-red, O	1·90	10
		a. Scarlet, O (1916)	2·25	10
		b. Rose-red, O	2·25	40
80	13	2d. grey, O	1·50	4·00
		a. Slate-grey, O (1916)	7·50	10·00
81	12	2½d. ultramarine, O	2·00	2·75
		a. Bright blue, O (1918)	1·40	2·75
		b. Deep bright blue, O	6·00	7·50
82	15	3d. purple/*yellow*, C	60	2·00
		a. On pale yellow (Die I)	5·00	8·50
		b. On pale yellow (Die II)	4·50	15·00
83	14	4d. black and red/*yellow*, C	90	1·75
		a. White back (Optd S £25)	60	1·50
84	15	6d. dull and bright purple, C	2·00	6·50
		a. Grey-purple and purple, C (1918)	9·00	13·00
85		1s. black/*green*, C	2·50	4·25
		a. On blue-green, olive back	3·75	6·00
86		1s. orange-brown, C (1920)	4·25	20·00
87	16	2s. 6d. black and red/*blue*, C	12·00	20·00
88	15	5s. green and red/*yellow*, C	18·00	48·00
78/88		*Set of* 11	40·00	95·00
78/88 Optd "Specimen"		*Set of* 11	£170	

WAR TAX

(17)

WAR TAX

(18)

1916 (June). *No. 79a optd locally with T* **17**.

89	12	1d. scarlet	2·75	3·25
		a. Opt double	£350	£375
		b. Carmine	25·00	25·00

For the overprinting with Type **17** the top margin of the sheet was folded beneath the top row of stamps so that marginal examples from this row show an inverted albino impression of the overprint in the top margin.

1916 (Sept). *No. 79a optd in London with T* **18**.

90	12	1d. scarlet (Optd S. £40)	15	15

1921–26. *Wmk Mult Script CA. P* 14.
91 **12** ½d. green, O 20 15
92 1d. rose-carmine, O .. .. .. 1·75 6·00
93 1d. deep brown, O (1922) 20 15
94 **14** 1½d. dull carmine, O (1922) 30 75
95 **13** 2d. slate-grey, O 20 15
96 **12** 2½d. bright blue, O .. .. .. 1·25 2·00
97 2½d. orange, O (1925) .. .. .. 4·50 20·00
98 2½d. dull blue, O (1926).. .. .. 90 2·50
99 **15** 3d. bright blue, O (1922) .. .. 3·75 12·00
a. Dull blue, O (1926) .. .. 80 7·00
100 3d. purple/*yellow,* C (1926) .. .. 55 2·75
a. Deep purple/yellow, C .. .. 2·75 7·50
101 **14** 4d. black and red/*yellow,* C (1924) .. 80 2·50
102 **15** 6d. grey-purple and purple, C.. .. 1·00 4·75
103 1s. orange-brown, C .. .. .. 1·50 4·00
104 **16** 2s. 6d. black and red/*blue,* C(1924) .. 12·00 25·00
105 **15** 5s. green and red/*pale yellow,* C (1923) 24·00 42·00
91/105 .. .. *Set of* 15 42·00 £110
91/105 Optd "Specimen" .. *Set of* 15 £200

1935 (6 May). *Silver Jubilee. As Nos.* 91/4 *of Antigua.*
109 ½d. black and green 15 25
f. Diagonal line by turret .. .. 12·00
110 2d. ultramarine and grey 45 25
111 2½d. brown and deep blue 90 65
f. Diagonal line by turret .. .. 25·00
g. Dot to left of chapel .. .. 25·00
112 1s. slate and purple .. .. .. 3·00 3·75
h. Dot by flagstaff.. .. .. 50·00
109/12 .. .. .. *Set of* 4 4·00 4·50
109/12 Perf "Specimen" .. *Set of* 4 75·00

For illustrations of plate varieties see Omnibus section following Zululand.

19 Port Castries

20 Columbus Square, Castries

21 Ventine Falls

25 The Badge of the Colony

(Recess D.L.R.)

1936 (1 Mar-Apr). *T* **19/21, 25** *and similar designs. Wmk Mult Script CA. P* 14 *or* 13 × 12 (1s. *and* 10s.).
113 **19** ½d. black and bright green 20 45
a. Perf 13 × 12 (8.4.36) .. .. 35 2·50
114 **20** 1d. black and brown 25 10
a. Perf 13 × 12 (8.4.36) .. .. 1·40 2·50
115 **21** 1½d. black and scarlet 55 30
a. Perf 12 × 13 .. .. .. 5·00 1·75
116 **19** 2d. black and grey 25 15
117 **20** 2½d. black and blue 20 15
118 **21** 3d. black and dull green .. .. 1·25 70
119 **19** 4d. black and red-brown .. .. 30 1·00
120 **20** 6d. black and orange .. .. .. 55 1·00
121 – 1s. black and light blue .. .. 70 2·00
122 – 2s. 6d. black and ultramarine .. 3·50 13·00
123 – 5s. black and violet .. .. .. 8·00 20·00
124 **25** 10s. black and carmine.. .. .. 35·00 45·00
113/124 .. .. .. *Set of* 12 45·00 75·00
113/24 Perf "Specimen" .. *Set of* 12 £180

Designs: *Vert (as T* **21**) 2s. 6d. Inniskilling monument. *Horiz (as T* **19**) 1s. Fort Rodney, Pigeon Island; 5s. Government House.

1937 (12 May). *Coronation. As Nos.* 13/15 *of Aden, but ptd by B. W. P* 11 × 11½.
125 1d. violet 20 15
126 1½d. carmine 30 15
127 2½d. blue 30 15
125/7 .. .. *Set of* 3 70 40
125/7 Perf "Specimen" .. *Set of* 3 55·00

26 King George VI

27 Columbus Square

28 Government House

31 Device of St. Lucia

(Des E. Crafer (T **26**), H. Fleury (5s.). Recess Waterlow (½d. to 3½d., 8d., 3s., 5s., £1), D.L.R. (6d., 1s.) and B.W. (2s., 10s.))

1938 (22 Sept)–**48**. *T* **26/8, 31** *and similar designs. Wmk Mult Script CA (sideways on 2s.).*
128 **26** ½d. green (*p* 14½ × 14) 30 10
a. Perf 12½ (1943) 10 10
129 1d. violet (*p* 14½ × 14) 80 20
a. Perf 12½ (1938) 10 15
129*b* 1d. scarlet (*p* 12½) (1947) 10 10
c. Perf 14½ × 14 (1948) 10 10
130 1½d. scarlet (*p* 14½ × 14) 35 10
a. Perf 12½ (1943) 10 20
131 2d. grey (*p* 14½ × 14) 15 25
a. Perf 12½ (1943) 10 10
132 2½d. ultramarine (*p* 14½ × 14) .. 20 10
a. Perf 12½ (1943) 10 10
132*b* 2½d. violet (*p* 12½) (1947) 10 10
133 3d. orange (*p* 14½ × 14) 10 10
a. Perf 12½ (1943) 10 10
133*b* 3½d. ultramarine (*p* 12½) (1947) .. 20 15
134 **27** 6d. claret (*p* 13½) 35 40
a. Carmine-lake (*p* 13½) (1945) .. 1·25 35
b. Perf 12. *Claret* (1948) 40 45
134*c* **26** 8d. brown (*p* 12½) (1946) 80 25
135 **28** 1s. brown (*p* 13½) 15 25
a. Perf 12 (1948) 30 20
136 – 2s. blue and purple (*p* 12) .. .. 3·00 90
136*a* **26** 3s. bright purple (*p* 12½) (1946) .. 7·50 2·75
137 – 5s. black and mauve (*p* 12½) .. 5·00 3·50
138 **31** 10s. black/*yellow* (*p* 12) .. .. 3·50 8·00
141 **26** £1 sepia (*p* 12½) (1946) .. .. 11·00 8·00
128a/141 .. .. .. *Set of* 17 28·00 22·00
128/41 Perf "Specimen" .. *Set of* 17 £300

Designs: *Horiz (as T* **28**): 2s. The Pitons; 5s. Loading bananas.

1946 (8 Oct). *Victory. As Nos.* 28/9 *of Aden.*
142 1d. lilac 10 10
143 3½d. blue 10 10
142/3 Perf "Specimen" .. .. *Set of* 2 50·00

1948 (26 Nov). *Royal Silver Wedding. As Nos.* 30/1 *of Aden.*
144 1d. scarlet 15 10
145 £1 purple-brown .. .. 11·00 28·00

(New Currency. 100 cents=1 West Indian dollar)

32 King George VI

33 Device of St. Lucia

(Recess Waterlow (**32**), B.W. (**33**))

1949 (1 Oct)–**50**. *Value in cents or dollars. Wmk Mult Script CA. P* 12½ (1 *c. to* 16 *c.*), 11 × 11½ (*others*).
146 **32** 1 c. green 10 10
a. Perf 14 (1949) 75 40
147 2 c. magenta 10 10
a. Perf 14½ × 14 (1949) .. .. 1·50 1·00
148 3 c. scarlet 10 10
149 4 c. grey 10 10
a. Perf 14½ × 14 .. .. .. — £3750
150 5 c. violet 10 10
151 6 c. orange 10 10
152 7 c. ultramarine 25 15
153 12 c. claret 50 15
a. Perf 14½ × 14 (1950) £275 £180
154 16 c. brown 50 15
155 **33** 24 c. light blue 20 10
156 48 c. olive-green.. .. .. .. 1·50 50
157 $1.20, purple .. .. 2·25 4·00
158 $2.40, blue-green .. .. .. 3·00 12·00
159 $4.80, rose-carmine .. .. .. 7·00 18·00
146/159 .. .. .. *Set of* 14 14·00 32·00

1949 (10 Oct). *75th Anniv of Universal Postal Union. As Nos.* 114/17 *of Antigua.*
160 5 c. violet 15 15
161 6 c. orange 25 25
162 12 c. magenta 20 20
163 24 c. blue-green 40 20
160/3 .. .. *Set of* 4 90 70

1951 (16 Feb). *Inauguration of B.W.I. University College. As Nos.* 118/19 *of Antigua.*
164 3 c. black and scarlet.. .. .. .. 15 10
165 12 c. black and deep carmine 15 10

34 Phoenix rising from Burning Buildings

NEW 1951
CONSTITUTION
(35)

(Flames typo, rest recess B.W.)

1951 (19 June). *Reconstruction of Castries. Wmk Mult Script CA. P* 13½ × 13.
166 **34** 12 c. red and blue 10 20

1951 (25 Sept). *New Constitution. Optd with T* **35** *by Waterlow. P* 12½.
167 **32** 2 c. magenta 10 15
168 4 c. grey 10 15
169 5 c. violet 10 15
170 12 c. claret 10 25
167/70 .. .. *Set of* 4 30 60

1953 (2 June). *Coronation. As No.* 47 *of Aden.*
171 3 c. black and scarlet.. .. .. .. 10 10

36 Queen Elizabeth II

37 Device of St. Lucia

(Recess Waterlow (T **36**), until 1960, then D.L.R. B.W. (T **37**))

1953 (28 Oct)–**63**. *Wmk Mult Script CA. P* 14½×14 (*T* **36**) *or* 11×11½ (*T* **37**)
172 **36** 1 c. green (1.4.54) 10 10
173 2 c. magenta 10 10
174 3 c. red (2.9.54) 10 10
175 4 c. slate (7.1.54) 10 10
176 5 c. violet (1.4.54) 10 10
a. Slate-violet (19.2.63) 75 40
177 6 c. orange (2.9.54) 15 10
a. Brown-orange (26.9.61) 50 10
178 8 c. lake (2.9.54) 10 10
179 10 c. ultramarine (2.9.54) 10 10
a. Blue (14.8.62) 20 10
180 15 c. red-brown (2.9.54) 20 10
a. Brown (30.10.57) 30 10
181 **37** 25 c. deep turquoise-blue (2.9.54) .. 20 10
182 50 c. deep olive-green (2.9.54) .. .. 2·00 35
183 $1 bluish green (2.9.54) .. .. 2·50 60
184 $2.50, carmine (2.9.54) .. .. 4·50 3·00
172/84 .. .. *Set of* 13 9·00 3·75

1958 (22 Apr). *Inauguration of British Caribbean Federation. As Nos.* 135/7 *of Antigua.*
185 3 c. deep green 15 10
186 6 c. blue 20 25
187 12 c. scarlet 20 30
185/7 .. .. *Set of* 3 50 60

MINISTERIAL GOVERNMENT

38 Columbus's *Santa Maria* off the Pitons

39 Stamp of 1860

(Recess Waterlow)

1960 (1 Jan). *New Constitution for the Windward and Leeward Islands.* W w **12.** *P* 13.
188 **38** 8 c. carmine-red 20 10
189 10 c. red-orange 20 10
190 25 c. deep blue 25 15
188/90 .. .. *Set of* 3 60 30

(Eng H. Bard. Recess Waterlow)

1960 (18 Dec). *Stamp Centenary.* W w **12.** *P* 13½.
191 **39** 5 c. rose-red and ultramarine 10 10
192 16 c. deep blue and yellow-green.. .. 10 10
193 25 c. green and carmine-red 10 10
191/3 .. .. *Set of* 3 20 20

1963 (4 June). *Freedom from Hunger. As No.* 76 *of Aden.*
194 25 c. bluish green 30 10

1963 (2 Sept). *Red Cross Centenary. As Nos.* 147/8 *of Antigua.*
195 4 c. red and black 15 10
196 25 c. red and blue 40 45

40 Queen Elizabeth II **41**
(after A. C. Davidson-Houston)

42 Fishing Boats

43 Castries Harbour

44 Vigie Beach

45 Queen Elizabeth II

(Des V. Whiteley. Photo Harrison)

1964 (1 Mar)–**69**. *Designs as T* **40/5**, *W w* **12**. *P* 14½ (*T* **40**), *others* 14½×14 (*vert*) *or* 14×14½ (*horiz*).

No.	Description	Mint	Used
197	1 c. crimson	10	10
198	2 c. bluish violet	10	10
199	4 c. turquoise-green	15	10
	a. *Deep turquoise* (5.8.69)	20	15
200	5 c. Prussian blue	10	10
201	6 c. yellow-brown	15	10
202	8 c. multicoloured	10	10
203	10 c. multicoloured	20	10
204	12 c. multicoloured	15	10
205	15 c. multicoloured	20	10
206	25 c. multicoloured	20	10
207	35 c. blue and buff	1·25	10
208	50 c. multicoloured	1·10	10
209	$1 multicoloured	1·25	25
210	$2.50, multicoloured	2·00	1·50
197/210	*Set of* 14	6·00	2·00

Designs:—1 to 6 c. Type **40**; 8, 10 c. Type **41**. *Horiz as T* **42/3**—15 c. Pigeon Island; 25 c. Reduit Beach; 50 c. The Pitons.

See also No. 249.

1964 (23 April). *400th Birth Anniv of William Shakespeare. As No.* 164 *of Antigua.*

No.	Description	Mint	Used
211	10 c. blue-green	10	10

1965 (17 May). *I.T.U. Centenary. As Nos.* 166/7 *of Antigua.*

No.	Description	Mint	Used
212	2 c. mauve and magenta	10	10
213	50 c. lilac and light olive-green	90	35

1965 (25 Oct). *International Co-operation Year. As Nos.* 168/9 *of Antigua.*

No.	Description	Mint	Used
214	1 c. reddish purple and turquoise-green	10	10
215	25 c. deep bluish green and lavender	15	15

1966 (24 Jan). *Churchill Commemoration. As Nos.* 170/3 *of Antigua.*

No.	Description	Mint	Used
216	4 c. new blue	10	10
217	6 c. deep green	15	10
218	25 c. brown	20	15
219	35 c. bluish violet	30	20
216/19	*Set of* 4	65	45

1966 (4 Feb). *Royal Visit. As Nos.* 174/5 *of Antigua.*

No.	Description	Mint	Used
220	4 c. black and ultramarine	10	10
221	25 c. black and magenta	40	25

1966 (1 July). *World Cup Football Championships, England. As Nos.* 176/7 *of Antigua.*

No.	Description	Mint	Used
222	4 c. violet, yellow-green, lake & yellow-brn	10	10
223	25 c. chocolate, blue-green, lake & yellow-brn	20	20

1966 (20 Sept). *Inauguration of W.H.O. Headquarters, Geneva. As Nos.* 178/9 *of Antigua.*

No.	Description	Mint	Used
224	4 c. black, yellow-green and light blue	10	10
225	25 c. black, light purple and yellow-brown	25	20

1966 (1 Dec). *20th Anniv of U.N.E.S.C.O. As Nos.* 196/8 *of Antigua.*

No.	Description	Mint	Used
226	4 c. slate-violet, red, yellow and orange	10	10
227	12 c. orange-yellow, violet and deep olive	20	15
228	25 c. black, bright purple and orange	35	30
226/8	*Set of* 3	60	45

ASSOCIATED STATEHOOD

STATEHOOD
1st MARCH 1967

(49)

STATEHOOD
1st MARCH 1967

(50)

51 Map of St. Lucia

(Optd by Art Printery, Castries from dies supplied by Harrison. Photo Harrison (No. 240))

1967 (7 Mar). *Statehood.* (*a*) *Postage. Nos.* 198 *and* 200/9 *optd with T* **49** (2, 5, 6 *c.*) *or T* **50** (*others*) *in red.*

No.	Description	Mint	Used
229	2 c. bluish violet	20	15
	a. Horiz pair, one without opt		
230	5 c. Prussian blue	10	10
	a. Opt inverted	45·00	
231	6 c. yellow-brown	10	10
232	8 c. multicoloured	20	10
233	10 c. multicoloured	25	10
234	12 c. multicoloured	20	10
235	15 c. multicoloured	25	30
236	25 c. multicoloured	30	30
237	35 c. blue and buff	50	35
238	50 c. multicoloured	50	55
239	$1 multicoloured	50	55
229/39	*Set of* 11	2·75	2·25

(*b*) *Air. P* 14½ × 14.

No.	Description	Mint	Used
240	**51** 15 c. new blue	10	10

Overprinted 1 c. and $2.50 stamps were prepared for issue but were not put on sale over the post office counter. Later, however, they were accepted for franking (*Price for set of* 2 *£6 mint, £11 used*).

52 "Madonna and Child with the Infant Baptist" (Raphael)

53 Batsman and Sir Frederick Clarke (Governor)

(Des and photo Harrison)

1967 (16 Oct). *Christmas. W w* **12** (*sideways*). *P* 14½.

No.	Description	Mint	Used
241	**52** 4 c. multicoloured	10	10
242	25 c. multicoloured	10	10

(Des V. Whiteley. Photo Harrison)

1968 (8 Mar). *M.C.C.'s West Indies Tour. W w* **12** (*sideways*). *P* 14½ × 14.

No.	Description	Mint	Used
243	**53** 10 c. multicoloured	20	15
244	35 c. multicoloured	45	40

54 "The Crucified Christ with the Virgin Mary, Saints and Angels" (Raphael)

55 "Noli me tangere" (detail by Titian)

(Des and photo Harrison)

1968 (25 Mar). *Easter. W w* **12** (*sideways*). *P* 14 × 14½.

No.	Description	Mint	Used
245	**54** 10 c. multicoloured	10	10
246	**55** 15 c. multicoloured	10	10
247	**54** 25 c. multicoloured	10	10
248	**55** 35 c. multicoloured	10	10
	a. Yellow (sunset) omitted	£140	
245/8	*Set of* 4	20	10

1968 (14 May)*. *As No.* 205 *but W w* **12** (*sideways*).

No.	Description	Mint	Used
249	15 c. multicoloured	15	15

*This is the London release date. Stamps from this printing were available some months earlier on St. Lucia.

56 Dr. Martin Luther King

57 "Virgin and Child in Glory" (Murillo)

(Des V. Whiteley. Litho D.L.R.)

1968 (4 July). *Martin Luther King Commemoration. W w* **12**. *P* 13½ × 14.

No.	Description	Mint	Used
250	**56** 25 c. blue, black and flesh	10	10
251	35 c. violet-black, black and flesh	10	10

(Des and photo Harrison)

1968 (17 Oct). *Christmas. Paintings. T* **57** *and similar vert design. Multicoloured. W w* **12** (*sideways*). *P* 14½ × 14.

No.	Description	Mint	Used
252	5 c. Type **57**	10	10
253	10 c. "Madonna with Child" (Murillo)	10	10
254	25 c. Type **57**	10	10
255	35 c. As 10 c.	10	10
252/5	*Set of* 4	15	10

59 Purple-throated Carib

(Des V. Whiteley. Litho Format)

1969 (10 Jan). *Birds. T* **59** *and similar horiz design. Multicoloured. W w* **12** (*sideways*). *P* 14.

No.	Description	Mint	Used
256	10 c. Type **59**	25	10
257	15 c. St. Lucia Amazon	35	15
258	25 c. Type **59**	45	20
259	35 c. As 15 c.	55	20
256/9	*Set of* 4	1·40	60

61 "Head of Christ Crowned with Thorns" (Reni)

62 "Resurrection of Christ" (Sodoma)

(Des and photo Harrison)

1969 (20 Mar). *Easter. W w* **12** (*sideways*). *P* 14½ × 14.

No.	Description	Mint	Used
260	**61** 10 c. multicoloured	10	10
261	**62** 15 c. multicoloured	10	10
262	**61** 25 c. multicoloured	10	10
263	**62** 35 c. multicoloured	10	10
260/3	*Set of* 4	15	15

63 Map showing "CARIFTA" Countries

(Des J. Cooter. Photo Harrison)

1969 (29 May). *First Anniv of CARIFTA (Caribbean Free Trade Area). T* **63** *and similar horiz designs. Multicoloured. W w* **12**. *P* 14.

No.	Description	Mint	Used
264	5 c. Type **63**	10	10
265	10 c. Type **63**	10	10
266	25 c. Handclasp and names of CARIFTA countries	10	10
267	35 c. As 25 c.	10	10
264/7	*Set of* 4	15	10

65 Emperor Napoleon and Empress Josephine

66 "Virgin and Child" (P. Delaroche)

(Des and litho Enschedé)

1969 (22 Sept). *Birth Bicentenary of Napoleon Bonaparte. P* 14 × 13.

No.	Description	Mint	Used
268	**65** 15 c. multicoloured	10	10
269	25 c. multicoloured	10	10
270	35 c. multicoloured	10	10
271	50 c. multicoloured	15	15
268/71	*Set of* 4	25	20

(Des J. W. Photo Harrison)

1969 (27 Oct). *Christmas. Paintings. T* **66** *and similar vert design. Multicoloured. W w* **12** (*sideways*). *P* 14½ × 14.

No.	Description	Mint	Used
272	5 c. Type **66**	10	10
273	10 c. "Holy Family" (Rubens)	10	10
274	25 c. Type **66**	10	10
275	35 c. As 10 c.	10	10
272/5	*Set of* 4	15	10

MINIMUM PRICE

The minimum price quote is 10p which represents a handling charge rather than a basis for valuing common stamps. For further notes about prices see introductory pages.

68 House of Assembly

69 "The Sealing of the Tomb" (Hogarth)

(Des J. Cooter ($10), Sylvia and M. Goaman (others). Litho Questa ($10), Format (others))

1970 (2 Feb)–**73**. *T* **68** *and similar designs. Multicoloured. W* w **12** *(sideways on* 1 c. *to* 35 c. *and* $10). *P* 14.

276	1 c. Type **68**	10	10
277	2 c. Roman Catholic Cathedral	10	10
278	4 c. The Boulevard, Castries	15	10
279	5 c. Castries Harbour	15	10
280	6 c. Sulphur springs	15	10
281	10 c. Vigie Airport	20	10
282	12 c. Reduit Beach	20	10
283	15 c. Pigeon Island	25	10
284	25 c. The Pitons and yacht	40	10
285	35 c. Marigot Bay	40	10
286	50 c. Diamond Waterfall (*vert*)	70	60
287	$1 Flag of St. Lucia (*vert*)	75	70
288	$2.50, St. Lucia Coat of Arms (*vert*)	1·50	1·75
289	$5 Queen Elizabeth II (*vert*)	3·25	4·75
289*a*	$10 Map of St. Lucia (*vert*) (3.12.73)	9·00	11·00
276/89*a*	*Set of* 15	15·00	17·00

See also Nos. 367/8 and 395/8.

(Des V. Whiteley. Litho Enschedé)

1970 (7 Mar). *Easter. Triptych by Hogarth. T* **69** *and similar multicoloured designs. W* w **12** *(sideways). Roul.* 9 × *P* 12½.

290	25 c. Type **69**	15	20
	a. Strip of 3. Nos. 290/2	55	
291	35 c. "The Three Marys at the Tomb"	15	20
292	$1 "The Ascension" (39 × 55 *mm*)	30	40
290/2	*Set of* 3	55	70

Nos. 290/2 were issued in sheets of 30 (6 × 5) containing the Hogarth Triptych spread over all three values of the set. This necessitated a peculiar arrangement with the $1 value (which depicts the centre portion of the triptych) 10 mm higher than the other values in the *se-tenant* strip.

72 Charles Dickens and Dickensian Characters

(Des V. Whiteley. Litho B.W.)

1970 (8 June). *Death Centenary of Charles Dickens. W* w **12** *(sideways). P* 14.

293	**72**	1 c. multicoloured	10	10
294		25 c. multicoloured	10	10
295		35 c. multicoloured	15	10
296		50 c. multicoloured	20	20
293/6		*Set of* 4	40	30

73 Nurse and Emblem

(Des R. Granger Barrett. Litho J.W.)

1970 (18 Aug). *Centenary of British Red Cross. T* **73** *and similar horiz design. Multicoloured. W* w **12** *(sideways). P* 14.

297	10 c. Type **73**	10	10
298	15 c. Flags of Great Britain, Red Cross and St. Lucia	10	10
299	25 c. Type **73**	15	10
300	35 c. As 15 c.	20	10
297/300	*Set of* 4	45	20

PRICES OF SETS

Set prices are given for many issues, generally those containing three stamps or more. Definitive sets include one of each value or major colour change, but do not cover different perforations, die types or minor shades. Where a choice is possible the set prices are based on the cheapest versions of the stamps included in the listings.

74 "Madonna with the Lilies" (Luca della Robbia)

75 "Christ on the Cross" (Rubens)

(Des P. B. Litho and embossed Walsall)

1970 (16 Nov). *Christmas. P* 11.

301	**74**	5 c. multicoloured	10	10
302		10 c. multicoloured	10	10
303		35 c. multicoloured	10	10
304		40 c. multicoloured	10	15
301/4		*Set of* 4	20	20

(Des and litho Enschedé)

1971 (29 Mar). *Easter. T* **75** *and similar vert design. Multicoloured. W* w **12**. *P* 13½ × 13.

305	10 c. Type **75**	10	10
306	15 c. "Descent from the Cross" (Rubens)	10	10
307	35 c. Type **75**	10	10
308	40 c. As 15 c.	15	15
305/8	*Set of* 4	25	20

76 Moule à Chique Lighthouse

(Des J. W. Litho Questa)

1971 (1 May). *Opening of Beane Field Airport. T* **76** *and similar horiz design. Multicoloured. W* w **12** *(sideways). P* 14½ × 14.

309	5 c. Type **76**	10	10
310	25 c. Aircraft landing at Beane Field	15	10

77 Morne Fortune

78 Morne Fortune, Modern View

(Des V. Whiteley. Litho Questa)

1971 (10 Aug.). *Old and New Views of St. Lucia. T* **77/8** *and similar horiz designs. Multicoloured. W* w **12** *(sideways). P* 13½ × 13.

311	5 c. Type **77**	10	10
312	5 c. Type **78**	10	10
313	10 c. } Castries city	10	10
314	10 c. }	10	10
315	25 c. } Pigeon Island	10	10
316	25 c. }	10	10
317	50 c. } View from grounds of Govt House	20	30
318	50 c. }	20	30
311/18	*Set of* 8	60	90

Each value of this issue was printed horizontally and vertically *se-tenant* in two designs showing respectively old and new views of St. Lucia.

The old views are taken from paintings by J. H. Caddy.

79 "Virgin and Child with Two Angels" (Verrocchio)

80 "St. Lucia" (Dolci School) and Coat of Arms

(Des J. Cooter. Litho J.W.)

1971 (15 Oct). *Christmas. T* **79** *and similar vert designs. Multicoloured. W* w **12**. *P* 14.

319	5 c. Type **79**	10	10
320	10 c. "Virgin and Child, St. John the Baptist and an Angel" (Morando)	10	10
321	35 c. "Madonna and Child" (Battista)	15	10
322	40 c. Type **79**	20	25
319/22	*Set of* 4	40	40

(Des and litho Harrison)

1971 (13 Dec). *National Day. W* w **12**. *P* 14 × 14½.

323	**80**	5 c. multicoloured	10	10
324		10 c. multicoloured	10	10
325		25 c. multicoloured	15	10
326		50 c. multicoloured	25	30
323/6		*Set of* 4	40	40

81 "The Dead Christ Mourned" (Carracci)

(Des G. Drummond. Litho Questa)

1972 (15 Feb). *Easter. T* **81** *and similar horiz design. Multicoloured. W* w **12**. *P* 14.

327	10 c. Type **81**	10	10
328	25 c. "Angels weeping over the dead Christ" (Guercino)	10	10
329	35 c. Type **81**	15	10
330	50 c. As 25 c.	20	30
327/30	*Set of* 4	45	35

82 Science Block and Teachers' College

(Des P. Powell. Litho Questa)

1972 (18 Apr). *Morne Educational Complex. T* **82** *and similar horiz designs. Multicoloured. W* w **12**. *P* 14.

331	5 c. Type **82**	10	10
332	15 c. University Centre	10	10
333	25 c. Secondary School	10	10
334	35 c. Technical College	15	10
331/4	*Set of* 4	30	25

83 Steamship Stamp and Map

Des J. Cooter. Litho Questa)

1972 (22 June). *Centenary of First Postal Service by St. Lucia Steam Conveyance Co Ltd. T* **83** *and similar horiz designs. W* w **12**. *P* 14.

335	5 c. multicoloured	10	10
336	10 c. ultramarine, mauve and black	15	10
337	35 c. light rose-carmine, pale greenish blue and black	35	10
338	50 c. multicoloured	90	1·00
335/8	*Set of* 4	1·40	1·00

Designs:—10 c. Steamship stamp and Castries Harbour; 35 c. Steamship stamp and Soufrière; 50 c. Steamship stamps.

84 "The Holy Family" (Sebastiano Ricci)

(Des J. Cooter. Litho J.W.)

1972 (18 Oct). *Christmas. W* w **12** *(sideways). P* 14½.

339	**84**	5 c. multicoloured	10	10
340		10 c. multicoloured	10	10
341		35 c. multicoloured	10	10
342		40 c. multicoloured	15	15
339/42		*Set of* 4	25	20

ALTERED CATALOGUE NUMBERS

Any Catalogue numbers altered from the last edition are shown as a list in the introductory pages.

85 Arms and St. Lucia Amazon

86 Week-day Headdress

(Des (from photograph by D. Groves) and photo Harrison)

1972 (20 Nov). *Royal Silver Wedding. Multicoloured; background colour given.* W w **12**. *P* 14 × 14½.

343	**85**	15 c. carmine	20	10
344		35 c. yellow-olive	20	10

(Des Sylvia Goaman. Litho A. & M.)

1973 (1 Feb). *Local Headdresses. T* **86** *and similar vert designs. Multicoloured.* W w **12**. *P* 13.

345	5 c. Type **86**	10	10
346	10 c. Formal style	10	10
347	25 c. Unmarried girl's style	10	10
348	50 c. Ceremonial style	20	20
345/8	*Set of* 4	30	25

87 Coat of Arms

88 H.M.S. *St. Lucia*, 1803

(Des and litho Harrison)

1973–76. *Coil Stamps. P* 14½ × 14.
A. W w **12** *upright* (19.4.73). B. W w **12** *sideways* (1976).

			A		B	
349	**87**	5 c. olive-green	10	15	15	30
350		10 c. new blue	15	15	20	35
351		25 c. lake-brown	15	20	†	
349/51		*Set of* 3	35	45		

For 10 c. value watermarked w **16** see No. 953.

(Des R. Granger Barrett. Litho Questa)

1973 (24 May). *Historic Ships. T* **88** *and similar horiz designs. Multicoloured.* W w **12**. *P* 13½ × 14.

352	15 c. Type **88**	15	10
353	35 c. H.M.S. *Prince of Wales*, 1765	20	10
354	50 c. *Oliph Blossom*, 1605	30	15
355	$1 H.M.S. *Rose*, 1757	45	55
352/5	*Set of* 4	1·00	70
MS356	122 × 74 mm. Nos. 352/5	1·00	2·75

89 Plantation and Flower

90 "The Virgin with Child" (Maratta)

(Des PAD Studio. Litho Walsall)

1973 (26 July). *Banana Industry. T* **89** *and similar horiz designs. Multicoloured.* W w **12**. *P* 14.

357	5 c. Type **89**	10	10
358	15 c. Aerial spraying	15	10
359	35 c. Boxing plant	20	10
360	50 c. Loading a boat	40	40
357/60	*Set of* 4	75	45

(Des J. Cooter. Litho Walsall)

1973 (17 Oct). *Christmas. T* **90** *and similar vert designs. Multicoloured.* W w **12** *(sideways). P* 13½.

361	5 c. Type **90**	10	10
362	15 c. "Madonna in the Meadow" (Raphael)	10	10
363	35 c. "The Holy Family" (Bronzino)	15	10
364	50 c. "Madonna of the Pear" (Dürer)	20	25
361/4	*Set of* 4	45	30

1973 (14 Nov). *Royal Wedding. As Nos.* 165/6 *of Anguilla.*

365	40 c. grey-green	10	10
366	50 c. rosy lilac	10	10

1974 (15 Mar). *As Nos.* 277/8 *but wmk upright.*

367	2 c. Roman Catholic Cathedral	60	70
368	4 c. The Boulevard, Castries	80	90

91 "The Betrayal"

92 3-Escalins Coins, 1798

(Des J. Cooter. Litho D.L.R.)

1974 (1 Apr). *Easter. T* **91** *and similar horiz designs showing paintings by Ugolino da Siena. Multicoloured.* W w **12** *(sideways on Nos. 369/72, upright on* **MS**373). *P* 13.

369	5 c. Type **91**	10	10
370	35 c. "The Way to Calvary"	15	10
371	80 c. "The Deposition"	15	15
372	$1 "The Resurrection"	20	25
369/72	*Set of* 4	50	40
MS373	180 × 140 mm. Nos. 369/72	1·25	2·00

(Des J. Cooter. Litho Format)

1974 (20 May). *Coins of Old St. Lucie. T* **92** *and similar vert designs. Multicoloured.* W w **12** *(sideways). P* 14 × 13½.

374	15 c. Type **92**	15	10
375	35 c. 6-escalins coins, 1798	20	10
376	40 c. 2-livres 5-sols coins, 1813	20	10
377	$1 6-livres 15-sols coins, 1813	55	65
374/7	*Set of* 4	1·00	75
MS378	151 × 115 mm. Nos. 374/7	1·60	2·50

93 Baron de Laborie

94 "Virgin and Child" (Andrea del Verrocchio)

(Des J. W. Litho Questa)

1974 (29 Aug). *Past Governors of St. Lucia. T* **93** *and similar vert designs. Multicoloured.* W w **12** *(sideways on Nos. 379/82, upright on* **MS**383). *P* 14.

379	5 c. Type **93**	10	10
380	35 c. Sir John Moore	10	10
381	80 c. Sir Dudley Hill	15	10
382	$1 Sir Frederick Clarke	25	35
379/82	*Set of* 4	50	50
MS383	153 × 117 mm. Nos. 379/82	50	2·00

(Des PAD Studio. Litho D.L.R.)

1974 (18 Nov). *Christmas. T* **94** *and similar vert designs. Multicoloured.* W w **12**. *P* 13 × 13½.

384	5 c. Type **94**	10	10
385	35 c. "Virgin and Child" (Andrea della Robbia)	10	10
386	80 c. "Madonna and Child" (Luca della Robbia)	15	15
387	$1 "Virgin and Child" (Rossellino)	20	25
384/7	*Set of* 4	40	40
MS388	92 × 140 mm. Nos. 384/7	90	1·75

95 Churchill and Montgomery

96 "Christ on the Cross" (School of Van der Weyden)

(Des PAD Studio. Litho Format)

1974 (30 Nov). *Birth Centenary of Sir Winston Churchill. T* **95** *and similar horiz design. Multicoloured.* W w **12** *(sideways). P* 14.

389	5 c. Type **95**	10	10
390	$1 Churchill and Truman	30	35

(Des J. Cooter. Litho Questa)

1975 (27 Mar). *Easter. T* **96** *and similar vert designs. Multicoloured.* W w **12**. *P* 13½.

391	5 c. Type **96**	10	10
392	35 c. "Noli me tangere" (Romano)	10	10
393	80 c. "Calvary" (Gallego)	15	15
394	$1 "Noli me tangere" (Correggio)	20	25
391/4	*Set of* 4	40	40

1975 (28 July). *As Nos.* 278 *etc. but* W w **14** *(sideways).*

395	4 c. The Boulevard, Castries	90	90
396	5 c. Castries Harbour	1·00	1·00
397	10 c. Vigie Airport	1·40	1·40
398	15 c. Pigeon Island	2·00	2·00
395/8	*Set of* 4	4·75	4·75

97 "Nativity" (French Book of Hours)

98 American Schooner *Hanna*

1975 (12 Dec). *Christmas. T* **97** *and similar vert designs. Multicoloured.* W w **12**. *P* 14½.

399	5 c. Type **97**	10	10
400	10 c. } Epiphany scene	10	10
401	10 c. } (stained-glass window)	10	10
402	10 c. }	10	10
403	40 c. "Nativity" (Hastings Book of Hours)	20	20
404	$1 "Virgin and Child with Saints" (Borgognone)	35	50
399/404	*Set of* 6	75	90
MS405	105 × 109 mm. Nos. 399 and 403/4	75	1·00

Nos. 400/2 were printed horizontally *se-tenant* within the sheet to form the composite design listed.

(Des J. W. Litho Format)

1976 (26 Jan). *Bicentenary of American Revolution. T* **98** *and similar horiz designs showing ships. Multicoloured. P* 14½.

406	½ c. Type **98**	10	10
407	1 c. Mail Packet *Prince of Orange*	10	10
408	2 c. H.M.S. *Edward*	10	10
409	5 c. Merchantman *Millern*	30	10
410	15 c. American lugger *Surprise*	60	10
411	35 c. H.M.S. *Serapis*	1·10	20
412	50 c. American frigate *Randolph*	1·25	40
413	$1 American frigate *Alliance*	2·25	1·00
406/13	*Set of* 8	5·00	1·75
MS414	142 × 116 mm. Nos. 410/13. P 13	3·50	4·50

99 Laughing Gull

100 H.M.S. *Ceres*

(Des J.W. Litho Questa)

1976 (17 May)–**79**. *T* **99** *and similar vert designs. Multicoloured. Ordinary paper.* W w **12** (1 c.), W w **14** *(others). P* 14.

415	1 c. Type **99**	15	20
416	2 c. Little Blue Heron	25	20
417	4 c. Belted Kingfisher	35	20
418	5 c. St. Lucia Amazon	85	20
419	6 c. St. Lucia Oriole	85	30
420	8 c. Brown Trembler	85	30
421	10 c. American Kestrel	85	30
422	12 c. Red-billed Tropic Bird	85	30
423	15 c. Moorhen	85	15
424	25 c. Common Noddy	70	25
	a. Chalk-surfaced paper (7.79)	1·00	25
425	35 c. Sooty Tern	1·25	40
	a. Chalk-surfaced paper (1979)	2·25	2·50
426	50 c. Osprey	1·75	50
427	$1 White-breasted Trembler	2·00	65
428	$2.50, St. Lucia Black Finch	2·50	2·50
429	$5 Red-necked Pigeon	3·50	3·50
430	$10 Caribbean Elaenia	5·50	6·50
	a. Chalk-surfaced paper (7.79)	6·00	7·50
415/30	*Set of* 16	20·00	15·00

1976 (19 July). *West Indian Victory in World Cricket Cup. As Nos.* 559/60 *of Barbados.*

431	50 c. Caribbean map	1·00	75
432	$1 Prudential Cup	1·50	2·00
MS433	92 × 79 mm. Nos. 431/2	3·25	4·00

(Des J. Cooter. Litho Walsall)

1976 (4 Sept). *Royal Navy Crests. T* **100** *and similar vert designs. Multicoloured.* W w **14** *(inverted). P* 14.

434	10 c. Type **100**	20	10
435	20 c. H.M.S. *Pelican*	30	10
436	40 c. H.M.S. *Ganges*	55	10
437	$2 H.M.S. *Ariadne*	1·50	1·75
434/7	*Set of* 4	2·40	1·75

101 "Madonna and Child" (Murillo)
102 Queen Elizabeth II

(Des J. Cooter. Litho Questa)

1976 (15 Nov). *Christmas. T* **101** *and similar vert designs. Multicoloured. W w* **14**. *P* 13½.
438 10 c. Type **101** 10 10
439 20 c. "Madonna and Child with Angels" (Costa) 10 10
440 50 c. "Madonna and Child Enthroned" (Isenbrandt) 15 10
441 $2 "Madonna and Child with St. John" (Murillo) 50 65
438/41 .. .. *Set of* 4 70 75
MS442 105 × 93 mm. $2.50, As Type **101** .. .. 70 1·25

(Des Daphne Padden. Litho Questa)

1977 (7 Feb). *Silver Jubilee. W w* **14** (*sideways*). *P* 14.
443 **102** 10 c. multicoloured 10 10
444 20 c. multicoloured 15 15
445 40 c. multicoloured 20 25
446 $2 multicoloured 60 90
443/6 .. .. *Set of* 4 95 1·25
MS447 128 × 95 mm. **102** $2.50 multicoloured .. 60 1·00

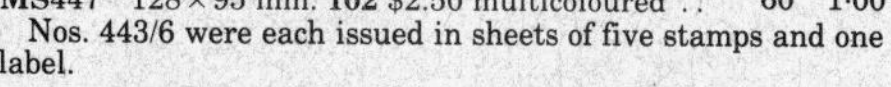
Nos. 443/6 were each issued in sheets of five stamps and one label.

103 Scouts from Tapion School
104 "Nativity" (Giotto)

(Des J. W. Litho Format)

1977 (17 Oct). *Caribbean Boy Scout Jamboree. T* **103** *and similar vert designs. Multicoloured. P* 14½.
448 ½ c. Type **103** 10 10
449 1 c. Sea scouts 10 10
450 2 c. Scout from Micoud 10 10
451 10 c. Two scouts from Tapion School 15 10
452 20 c. Venture scouts 20 15
453 50 c. Scout from Gros Islet 45 35
454 $1 Sea scouts in motor boat 75 90
448/54 .. .. *Set of* 7 1·50 1·50
MS455 75 × 85 mm. $2.50, As $1 .. .. 1·50 2·50

(Des J. W. Litho Questa)

1977 (31 Oct). *Christmas. T* **104** *and similar vert designs. Multicoloured. P* 14.
456 ½ c. Type **104** 10 10
457 1 c. "Perugia triptych" (Fra Angelico) .. 10 10
458 2 c. "Virgin and Child" (El Greco) 10 10
459 20 c. "Madonna of the Rosary" (Caravaggio) .. 10 10
460 50 c. "Adoration of the Magi" (Velazquez) .. 20 10
461 $1 "Madonna of Carmel" (Tiepolo) 30 40
462 $2.50, "Adoration of the Magi" (Tiepolo) .. 55 80
456/62 .. .. *Set of* 7 1·10 1·25

105 "Susan Lunden"
106 Yeoman of the Guard and Life Guard

(Des C. Abbott. Litho Harrison)

1977 (28 Nov). *400th Birth Anniv of Rubens. T* **105** *and similar vert designs. Multicoloured. W w* **14** (*sideways*). *P* 14 × 15.
463 10 c. Type **105** 10 10
464 35 c. "The Rape of the Sabine Women" (detail) 15 10
465 50 c. "Ludovicus Nonnius" 25 10
466 $2.50, "Minerva protects Pax from Mars" (detail) 65 80
463/6 .. .. *Set of* 4 1·00 90
MS467 145 × 120 mm. Nos. 463/6 .. .. 1·00 1·75

(Des J. W. Litho Questa)

1978 (2 June). *25th Anniv of Coronation. T* **106** *and similar horiz designs. Multicoloured. P* 14.
468 15 c. Type **106** 10 10
469 20 c. Groom and postillion 10 10
470 50 c. Footman and coachman 15 10
471 $3 State trumpeter and herald 60 80
468/71 .. .. *Set of* 4 85 90
MS472 114 × 88 mm. $5 Master of the Horse and Gentleman-at-Arms .. .. 1·00 1·25
Nos. 468/71 also exist perf 12 (*Price for set of* 4 95*p mint or used*) from additional sheetlets of 3 stamps and one label. Stamps perforated 14 are from normal sheets of 50.

107 Queen Angelfish

(Des G. Vasarhelyi. Litho Format)

1978 (19 June). *Fishes. T* **107** *and similar horiz designs. Multicoloured. P* 15.
473 10 c. Type **107** 10 10
474 20 c. Foureye Butterflyfish 20 10
475 50 c. French Angelfish 40 20
476 $2 Yellowtail Damselfish .. .. .. 1·00 1·25
473/6 .. .. *Set of* 4 1·40 1·40
MS477 155 × 89 mm. $2.50, Rock Beauty .. 1·40 1·90

108 French Grenadier and Map of the Battle
109 The Annunciation

(Des J. W. Litho Questa)

1978 (29 Nov). *Bicentenary of Battle of Cul-de-Sac. T* **108** *and similar horiz designs. Multicoloured. P* 14
478 10 c. Type **108** 10 10
479 30 c. British Grenadier officer and map of St. Lucia (Bellin), 1762 .. .. .. 25 10
480 50 c. Coastline from Gros Islet to Cul-de-Sac and British fleet opposing French landings 30 10
481 $2.50, General James Grant, 1798, and Light Infantrymen of 46th Regiment .. .. 1·25 85
478/81 .. .. *Set of* 4 1·75 95

(Des Jennifer Toombs. Litho Questa)

1978 (4 Dec). *Christmas. T* **109** *and similar horiz design. Multicoloured. W w* **14**. *P* 14.
482 30 c. Type **109** 10 10
483 50 c. Type **109** 15 10
484 55 c. The Nativity 15 10
485 80 c. As 55 c. 20 20
482/5 .. .. *Set of* 4 55 40

INDEPENDENT

110 Hewanorra International Air Terminal

(Des J. W. Litho Questa)

1979 (22 Feb). *Independence. T* **110** *and similar horiz designs. Multicoloured. W w* **14** (*sideways*). *P* 14.
486 10 c. Type **110** 10 10
487 30 c. New coat of arms 10 10
488 50 c. Government House and Sir Allen Lewis (first Governor-General) 15 10
489 $2 French, St. Lucia and Union flags on map of St. Lucia 30 45
486/9 .. .. *Set of* 4 50 55
MS490 127 × 80 mm. Nos. 486/9 .. .. 50 1·00

111 Popes Paul VI and John Paul I

(Des J.W. Litho Harrison)

1979 (28 May). *Pope Paul VI Commemoration. T* **111** *and similar horiz designs. Multicoloured. W w* **14** (sideways). *P* 14½ × 14.
491 10 c. Type **111** 10 10
492 30 c. President Sadat of Egypt with Pope Paul 20 10
493 50 c. Pope Paul with Secretary-General U Thant 35 20
494 55 c. Pope Paul and Prime Minister Golda Meir of Israel 40 25
495 $2 Martin Luther King received in audience by Pope Paul .. .. 1·00 80
491/5 .. .. *Set of* 5 1·75 1·25

112 Dairy Farming

(Des G. Drummond. Litho Format)

1979 (2 July). *Agriculture Diversification. T* **112** *and similar horiz designs. Multicoloured. W w* **14** (*sideways*). *P* 14.
496 10 c. Type **112** 10 10
497 35 c. Fruit and vegetables 10 10
498 50 c. Water conservation 10 10
499 $3 Copra industry 35 50
496/9 .. .. *Set of* 4 50 60

113 Lindbergh and Flying-boat
114 "A Prince of Saxony" (Cranach the Elder)

(Des L. Curtis. Litho Walsall)

1979 (2 Oct). *50th Anniv of Lindbergh's Inaugural Airmail Flight via St. Lucia. T* **113** *and similar horiz designs. W w* **14** (*sideways*). *P* 14.
500 10 c. black, Indian red and pale orange .. 10 10
501 30 c. multicoloured 10 10
502 50 c. multicoloured 10 10
503 $2 multicoloured 30 40
500/3 .. .. *Set of* 4 50 50
Designs:—30 c. Flying boat and route map; 50 c. Arrival at La Toc, September, 1929; $2 Letters on first flight.

(Litho Questa)

1979 (6 Dec). *International Year of the Child. Paintings. T* **114** *and similar vert designs. Multicoloured. P*. 14.
504 10 c. Type **114** 10 10
505 50 c. "The Infanta Margarita" (Velazquez) .. 15 10
506 $2 "Girl playing Badminton" (Chardin) .. 30 40
507 $2.50, "Mary and Francis Wilcox" (Stock) .. 35 45
504/7 .. .. *Set of* 4 70 80
MS508 113 × 94 mm. $5 "Two Children" (Picasso) 1·10 1·60

115 Notice of Introduction of Penny Post
116 "Madonna and Child" (Bernardino Fungai)

(Des J.W. Litho Questa)

1979 (10 Dec). *Death Centenary of Sir Rowland Hill. T* **115** *and similar vert designs. Multicoloured. P* 14.
509 10 c. Type **115** 10 10
510 50 c. Original stamp sketch 20 10
511 $2 1860 1d. stamp 45 50
512 $2.50, Penny Black stamp 55 60
509/12 .. .. *Set of* 4 1·10 1·10
MS513 111 × 85 mm. $5 Sir Rowland Hill .. 90 1·10
Nos. 509/12 also exist perf 12 (*Price for set of* 4 £1·10 *mint or used*) from additional sheetlets of 5 stamps and one label. Stamps perforated 14 are from normal sheets of 40.

(Des R. Vigurs. Litho Walsall)

1980 (14 Jan). *Christmas* (1979) *and International Year of the Child. T* **116** *and similar vert designs showing "Madonna and Child" paintings by various artists. Multicoloured. W w* **14**. *P* 14.
514 10 c. Type **116** 10 10
515 50 c. Carlo Dolci 15 10
516 $2 Titian 30 30
517 $2.50, Giovanni Bellini 40 40
514/17 .. .. *Set of* 4 80 70
MS518 94 × 120 mm. Nos. 514/17 .. .. 1·10 1·25

OMNIBUS ISSUES

Details, together with prices for complete sets, of the various Omnibus issues from the 1935 Silver Jubilee series to date are included in a special section following Zululand at the end of the catalogue.

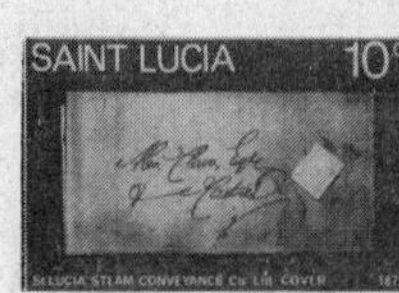

117 St. Lucia Steam Conveyance Company Cover, 1873

118 Mickey Mouse astride Rocket

(Des G. Drummond. Litho Questa)

1980 (6 May). *"London 1980" International Stamp Exhibition. T* **117** *and similar horiz designs. Multicoloured. W* w **14** (*sideways*). *P* 14.

519 10 c. Type **117** 10 10
520 30 c. S.S. *Assistance* 1d. postmark of 1879 .. 10 10
521 50 c. Postage due handstamp of 1929 .. .. 15 10
522 $2 Crowned-circle paid stamp of 1844 .. 40 55
519/22 .. .. *Set of* 4 60 65
MS523 85 × 76 mm. Nos. 519/22 .. .. .. 65 90

(Litho Format)

1980 (29 May). *10th Anniv of Moon Landing* (1979). *Walt Disney Cartoon Characters. T* **118** *and similar multicoloured designs showing characters in space scenes. P* 11.

524 ½ c. Type **118** 10 10
525 1 c. Donald Duck being towed by rocket (*horiz*) 10 10
526 2 c. Minnie Mouse on Moon 10 10
527 3 c. Goofy hitching lift to Mars 10 10
528 4 c. Goofy and moondog (*horiz*) 10 10
529 5 c. Pluto burying bone on Moon (*horiz*) .. 10 10
530 10 c. Donald Duck and love-sick martian (*horiz*) 10 10
531 $2 Donald Duck paddling spaceship (*horiz*) 1·40 1·00
532 $2.50, Mickey Mouse driving moonbuggy (*horiz*) .. .. 1·60 1·10
524/32 .. .. *Set of* 9 3·00 2·00
MS533 102 × 127 mm. $5 Goofy leaping from space-ship on to Moon. P 13½ .. .. 2·00 2·25

119 Queen Elizabeth the Queen Mother

(Litho Questa)

1980 (4 Aug). *80th Birthday of Queen Elizabeth the Queen Mother. P* 14.

534 **119** 10 c. multicoloured 20 10
535 $2.50, multicoloured .. .. .. 1·75 1·50
MS536 85 × 65 mm. **119** $3 multicoloured .. 1·50 2·10

120 Hawker Siddeley "HS 748"

(Des A. Theobald. Litho Harrison)

1980 (11 Aug). *Transport. Horiz designs as T* **120**. *Multicoloured. W* w 14 (*sideways on* 5 c. *to* $1). *P* 14½ × 14.

537 5 c. Type **120** 25 10
538 10 c. McDonnell Douglas "DC-10" airliner .. 35 10
539 15 c. Local bus 35 10
540 20 c. Refrigerated freighter 35 10
541 25 c. "Islander" aeroplane 50 10
542 30 c. Pilot boat 40 10
543 50 c. Boeing "727" airliner 65 25
544 75 c. *Cunard Countess* (liner) 65 60
545 $1 Lockheed "Tristar" airliner 85 65
546 $2 Cargo liner .. .. 1·25 1·25
547 $5 Boeing "707" airliner .. .. 4·50 3·50
548 $10 *Queen Elizabeth 2* (liner) .. .. 5·50 5·50
537/48 .. .. *Set of* 12 14·00 11·00

For stamps with watermark W w **15** see Nos. 690/8.

121 Shot-putting

122 Coastal Landscape within Cogwheel

(Des M. Diamond. Litho Questa)

1980 (22 Sept). *Olympic Games, Moscow. T* **121** *and similar horiz designs. Multicoloured. P* 14.

549 10 c. Type **121** 10 10
550 50 c. Swimming 10 10
551 $2 Gymnastics 40 50
552 $2.50, Weight-lifting 45 60
549/52 .. .. *Set of* 4 90 1·10
MS553 108 × 83 mm. $5 Athletes with Olympic Torch .. .. 1·25 1·40

(Des BG Studio. Litho Questa)

1980 (30 Sept). *75th Anniv of Rotary International. T* **122** *and similar vert designs showing different coastal landscapes within cogwheels. P* 14.

554 10 c. multicoloured 10 10
555 50 c. multicoloured 15 10
556 $2 greenish black, carmine & greenish yell 40 40
557 $2.50, multicoloured 50 55
554/7 .. .. *Set of* 4 1·00 1·00
MS558 103 × 106 mm. $5 multicoloured .. .. 1·50 1·75

123 Sir Arthur Lewis

(Des J. W. Litho Questa)

1980 (23 Oct). *Nobel Prize Winners. T* **123** *and similar vert designs. Multicoloured. P* 14.

559 10 c. Type **123** 10 10
560 50 c. Martin Luther King Jnr 20 15
561 $2 Ralph Bunche 50 60
562 $2.50, Albert Schweitzer 70 80
559/62 .. .. *Set of* 4 1·25 1·40
MS563 115 × 91 mm. $5 Albert Einstein .. 1·50 1·75

1980
HURRICANE

$1.50 RELIEF

(124)

1980 (3 Nov). *Hurricane Relief. Nos.* 539/40 *and* 543 *surch with T* **124**.

564 $1.50 on 15 c. Local bus 30 40
565 $1.50 on 20 c. Refrigerated freighter 30 40
566 $1.50 on 50 c. Boeing "727" airliner 30 40
564/6 .. .. *Set of* 3 80 1·10

125 "The Nativity" (Giovanni Battista)

126 Brazilian Agouti

(Des J. Cooter. Litho Questa)

1980 (1 Dec). *Christmas. Paintings. T* **125** *and similar vert designs. Multicoloured. W* w **14**. *P* 14 × 13½.

567 10 c. Type **125** 10 10
568 30 c. "Adoration of the Kings" (Pieter the Elder) 10 10
569 $2 "Adoration of the Shepherds" (ascribed to Murillo) 40 60
567/9 .. .. *Set of* 3 50 60
MS570 102 × 88 mm. $1 × 3, Angel with people of St. Lucia (*composite design*) (*each* 30 × 75 *mm*). P 14½ × 14 .. .. 65 90

(Des G. Drummond. Litho Questa)

1981 (19 Jan). *Wildlife. T* **126** *and similar vert designs. Multicoloured. P* 14.

571 10 c. Type **126** 15 10
572 50 c. St. Lucia Amazon 45 10
573 $2 Purple-throated Carib 90 80
574 $2.50, Fiddler Crab .. .. .. 1·00 1·00
571/4 .. .. *Set of* 4 2·25 1·75
MS575 103 × 87 mm. $5 Monarch Butterfly .. 2·40 2·50

127 Prince Charles at Balmoral

128 Lady Diana Spencer

(Des J. W. Litho Questa)

1981 (23 June). *Royal Wedding. T* **127** *and similar vert designs. Multicoloured. P* 14.

576 25 c. Prince Charles and Lady Diana Spencer 15 10
577 50 c. Clarence House 20 10
578 $4 Type **127** 75 80
576/8 .. .. *Set of* 3 1·00 90
MS579 96 × 82 mm. $5 Glass Coach and coachman 1·50 1·50

Nos. 576/8 also exist perforated 12 (*price for set of* 3 £1 *mint or used*) from additional sheetlets of five stamps and one label. These stamps have changed background colours.

(Manufactured by Walsall)

1981 (23 June). *Royal Wedding. Booklet stamps. T* **128** *and similar vert designs. Multicoloured. Roul* 5 × *imperf* Self-adhesive.*

580 50 c. Type **128** 15 30
a. Booklet pane. Nos. 580/1 each × 3 .. 1·75
581 $2 Prince Charles 50 80
582 $5 Prince Charles and Lady Diana Spencer 1·75 2·50
a. Booklet pane of 1 .. .. .. 1·75
580/2 .. .. *Set of* 3 2·25 3·25

*The 50 c. and $2 values were each separated by various combinations of rotary knife (giving a straight edge) and roulette. The $5 value exists only with straight edges.

129 "The Cock"

130 "Industry"

(Des J.W. Litho Questa)

1981 (20 July). *Birth Centenary of Picasso. T* **129** *and similar vert designs. Multicoloured. P* 13½ × 14.

583 30 c. Type **129** 15 10
584 50 c. "Man with an Ice-Cream" 20 10
585 55 c. "Woman dressing her Hair" 20 10
586 $3 "Seated Woman" 80 85
583/6 .. .. *Set of* 4 1·25 1·00
MS587 128 × 102 mm. $5 "Night Fishing at Antibes" .. .. 1·75 2·50

(Des Walsall. Litho Format)

1981 (28 Sept). *25th Anniv of Duke of Edinburgh Award Scheme. T* **130** *and similar vert designs. Multicoloured. W* w **14**. *P* 14½.

588 10 c. Type **130** 10 10
589 35 c. "Community service" 10 10
590 50 c. "Physical recreation" 15 10
591 $2.50, Duke of Edinburgh speaking at Caribbean Conference, 1975 .. 55 70
588/91 .. .. *Set of* 4 70 75

131 Louis Braille

132 "Portrait of Fanny Travis Cochran" (Cecilia Beaux)

(Des J.W. Litho Questa)

1981 (10 Nov). *International Year for Disabled Persons. Famous Disabled People. T* **131** *and similar horiz designs. Multicoloured. P* 14.

592 10 c. Type **131** 10 10
593 50 c. Sarah Bernhardt 25 15
594 $2 Joseph Pulitzer 80 90
595 $2.50, Henri de Toulouse-Lautrec .. .. 90 1·00
592/5 .. .. *Set of* 4 1·75 1·90
MS596 115 × 90 mm. $5 Franklin Delano Roosevelt .. .. 1·90 2·25

(Des BG Studio. Litho Questa)

1981 (1 Dec). *Decade for Women. Paintings. T* **132** *and similar vert designs. Multicoloured. P* 14.

597 10 c. Type **132** 10 10
598 50 c. "Women with Dove" (Marie Laurencin) .. 30 15
599 $2 "Portrait of a Young Pupil of David" (Aimee Duvivier) 90 90
600 $2.50, "Self-portrait" (Rosalba Carriera) .. 1·00 1·00
597/600 .. .. *Set of* 4 2·00 1·90
MS601 104 × 78 mm. $5 "Self-portrait" (Elizabeth Vigee-le-Brun) .. .. 2·50 2·50

133 "The Adoration of the Magi" (Sfoza) **134** 1860 1d. Stamp

(Des BG Studio. Litho Format)

1981 (15 Dec). *Christmas Paintings. T* **133** *and similar vert designs. Multicoloured. W w* **14.** *P* 14.

602 10 c. Type **133** 10 10
603 30 c. "The Adoration of the Kings" (Orcanga) 20 10
604 $1.50, "The Adoration of the Kings" (Gerard) 70 60
605 $2.50, "The Adoration of the Kings" (Foppa) 1·00 1·25
602/5 .. .. *Set of* 4 1·75 1·75

(Des J.W. Litho Questa)

1981 (29 Dec). *First Anniv of U.P.U. Membership. T* **134** *and similar horiz designs. Multicoloured. P* 14.

606 10 c. Type **134** 10 10
607 30 c. 1969 First anniversary of Caribbean Free Trade Area 25 c. commemorative .. 25 10
608 50 c. 1979 Independence $2 commemorative 40 20
609 $2 U.P.U. emblem with U.P.U. and St. Lucia flags .. .. 1·25 1·40
606/9 .. .. *Set of* 4 1·75 1·60
MS610 128 × 109 mm. $5 U.P.U. Headquarters, Berne, and G.P.O. Building, Castries .. .. 2·25 2·50

135 Scene from Football Match

(Des Clover Mill. Litho Format)

1982 (15 Feb). *World Cup Football Championship, Spain. T* **135** *and similar horiz designs showing scenes from different matches. P* 15.

611 10 c. multicoloured 15 10
612 50 c. multicoloured 40 15
613 $2 multicoloured 90 90
614 $2.50, multicoloured .. .. 1·00 1·00
611/14 .. .. *Set of* 4 2·25 1·90
MS615 104 × 84 mm. $5 multicoloured .. .. 2·00 2·25

136 Pigeon Island National Park **137** Map-reading

(Des J. Cooter. Litho Format)

1982 (13 Apr). *Bicentenary of Battle of the Saints. T* **136** *and similar horiz designs. Multicoloured. W w* **14.** *P* 14.

616 10 c. Type **136** 20 10
617 35 c. Battle scene 60 10
618 50 c. Rodney (English admiral) and De Grasse (French admiral) 75 20
619 $2.50, Map of the Saints, Martinique and St. Lucia .. .. 2·25 2·25
616/19 .. .. *Set of* 4 3·50 2·25
MS620 125 × 75 mm. Nos. 616/19 .. .. .. 3·75 4·00

(Litho Questa)

1982 (4 Aug). *75th Anniv of Boy Scout Movement. T* **137** *and similar vert designs. Multicoloured. W w* **14.** *P* 14.

621 10 c. Type **137** 10 10
622 50 c. First Aid practice 30 15
623 $1.50, Camping 75 80
624 $2.50, Campfire singsong .. .. 1·25 1·50
621/4 .. .. *Set of* 4 2·25 2·25

138 Leeds Castle **139** "Adoration of the Kings" (detail, Jan Brueghel)

(Des PAD Studio. Litho Questa)

1982 (1 Sept). *21st Birthday of Princess of Wales. T* **138** *and similar vert designs. Multicoloured. P* 14½ × 14.

625 50 c. Type **138** 30 20
626 $2 Princess Diana boarding aircraft 75 75
627 $4 Wedding .. .. 1·40 1·40
625/7 .. .. *Set of* 3 2·25 2·10
MS628 102 × 75 mm. $5 Princess of Wales .. 1·75 2·00

(Des PAD Studio. Litho Harrison)

1982 (10 Nov). *Christmas. T* **139** *and similar vert designs depicting details from paintings. Multicoloured. W w* **14.** *P* 14.

629 10 c. Type **139** 10 10
630 30 c. "Nativity" (Lorenzo Costa) 15 10
631 50 c. "Virgin and Child" (Fra Filippo Lippi) .. 25 15
632 80 c. "Adoration of the Shepherds" (Nicolas Poussin) 40 55
629/32 .. .. *Set of* 4 75 75

140 The Pitons **141** Crown Agents Headquarters, Millbank, London

(Des D. Bowen. Litho Questa)

1983 (14 Mar). *Commonwealth Day. T* **140** *and similar horiz designs. Multicoloured. W w* **14** *(sideways). P* 14.

633 10 c. Type **140** 10 10
634 30 c. Tourist beach 15 10
635 50 c. Banana harvesting 20 15
636 $2 Flag of St. Lucia .. .. 60 1·00
633/6 .. .. *Set of* 4 85 1·10

(Des L. Curtis. Litho Questa)

1983 (1 Apr). *150th Anniv of Crown Agents. T* **141** *and similar vert designs. Multicoloured. W w* **14.** *P* 14.

637 10 c. Type **141** 10 10
638 15 c. Road construction 10 10
639 50 c. Road network map 20 25
640 $2 First St. Lucia stamp .. .. 60 1·00
637/40 .. .. *Set of* 4 80 1·25

142 Communications at Sea

(Des J.W. Litho Format)

1983 (12 July). *World Communications Year. T* **142** *and similar horiz designs. Multicoloured. P* 14½.

641 10 c. Type **142** 10 10
642 50 c. Communications in the air 20 15
643 $1.50, T.V. transmission via satellite 70 75
644 $2.50, Computer communications .. .. 1·10 1·25
641/4 .. .. *Set of* 4 1·90 2·00
MS645 107 × 88 mm. $5 Weather satellite .. .. 2·50 2·75

143 Longspine Squirrelfish

(Des G. Drummond. Litho Format)

1983 (23 Aug). *Coral Reef Fishes. T* **143** *and similar horiz designs. Multicoloured. P* 14½.

646 10 c. Type **143** 10 10
647 50 c. Banded Butterflyfish 20 15
648 $1.50, Blackbar Soldierfish 70 75
649 $2.50, Yellowtail Snapper .. .. 1·10 1·25
646/9 .. .. *Set of* 4 1·90 2·00
MS650 122 × 97 mm. $5 Red Hind .. .. .. 2·50 3·00

144 *Duke of Sutherland* (1930) **145** "The Niccolini-Cowper Madonna"

(Des J.W. Litho Format)

1983 (14 Oct). *Leaders of the World. Railway Locomotives (1st series). T* **144** *and similar horiz designs, the first in each pair showing technical drawings and the second the locomotive at work. P* 12½.

651 35 c. multicoloured 25 20
a. Vert pair. Nos. 651/2 .. .. 50 40
652 35 c. multicoloured 25 20
653 35 c. multicoloured 25 20
a. Vert pair. Nos. 653/4 .. .. 50 40
654 35 c. multicoloured 25 20
655 50 c. multicoloured 35 30
a. Vert pair. Nos. 655/6 .. .. 70 60
656 50 c. multicoloured 35 30
657 50 c. multicoloured 35 30
a. Vert pair. Nos. 657/8 .. .. 70 60
658 50 c. multicoloured 35 30
659 $1 multicoloured 55 50
a. Vert pair. Nos. 659/60 .. .. 1·10 1·00
660 $1 multicoloured 55 50
661 $1 multicoloured 55 50
a. Vert pair. Nos. 661/2 .. .. 1·10 1·00
662 $1 multicoloured 55 50
663 $2 multicoloured .. .. 1·00 1·00
a. Vert pair. Nos. 663/4 .. .. 2·00 2·00
664 $2 multicoloured .. .. 1·00 1·00
665 $2 multicoloured .. .. 1·00 1·00
a. Vert pair. Nos. 665/6 .. .. 2·00 2·00
666 $2 multicoloured .. .. 1·00 1·00
651/66 .. .. *Set of* 16 7·75 7·00

Designs:—Nos. 651/2, *Duke of Sutherland*, Great Britain (1930); 653/4, *City of Glasgow*, Great Britain (1940); 655/6, *Lord Nelson*, Great Britain (1926); 657/8, *Leeds United*, Great Britain (1928); 659/60, *Bodmin*, Great Britain (1945); 661/2, *Eton*, Great Britain (1930); 663/4, *Flying Scotsman*, Great Britain (1923); 665/6, *Rocket*, Great Britain (1829).

Nos. 651/2, 653/4, 655/6, 657/8, 659/60, 661/2, 663/4 and 665/6 were printed together, *se-tenant*, in vertical pairs throughout the sheets.

See also Nos. 715/26, 761/76, 824/31 and 858/73.

(Litho Format)

1983 (21 Nov). *Christmas. 500th Birth Anniv of Raphael. T* **145** *and similar vert designs showing details of Raphael paintings. Multicoloured. W w* **14.** *P* 14.

667 10 c. Type **145** 10 10
668 30 c. "The Holy Family with a Palm Tree" .. 15 10
669 50 c. "The Sistine Madonna" 25 20
670 $5 "The Alba Madonna" .. .. 2·00 2·25
667/70 .. .. *Set of* 4 2·25 2·25

146 George III **147** Clarke & Co's Drug Store

(Des Court House Studio. Litho Format)

1984 (13 Mar). *Leaders of the World. British Monarchs. T* **146** *and similar vert designs. Multicoloured. P* 12½.

671 5 c. Battle of Waterloo 10 10
a. Horiz pair. Nos. 671/2 .. .. 10 10
672 5 c. Type **146** 10 10
673 10 c. George III at Kew 10 10
a. Horiz pair. Nos. 673/4 .. .. 15 15
674 10 c. Kew Palace 10 10
675 35 c. Coat of Arms of Elizabeth I 25 25
a. Horiz pair. Nos. 675/6 .. .. 50 50
676 35 c. Elizabeth I 25 25
677 60 c. Coat of Arms of George III 40 40
a. Horiz pair. Nos. 677/8 .. .. 80 80
678 60 c. George III (*different*) 40 40
679 $1 Elizabeth I at Hatfield 60 60
a. Horiz pair. Nos. 679/80 .. .. 1·10 1·10
680 $1 Hatfield Palace 60 60
681 $2.50, Spanish Armada .. .. 1·40 1·40
a. Horiz pair. Nos. 681/2 .. .. 2·75 2·75
682 $2.50, Elizabeth I (*different*) .. .. .. 1·40 1·40
671/82 .. .. *Set of* 12 4·75 4·75

Nos. 671/2, 673/4, 675/6, 677/8, 679/80 and 681/2 were printed together in *se-tenant* horizontal pairs throughout the sheets.

(Des J. Cooter. Litho Questa)

1984 (6 Apr). *Historic Buildings. T* **147** *and similar multi-coloured designs. W w* **15** *(sideways on 45 c. to $2.50). P* 14 × 13½ *(10 c.) or* 13½ × 14 *(others).*

683 10 c. Type **147** 10 10
684 45 c. Colonial architecture (*horiz*) 25 25
685 65 c. Colonial "chattel" house (*horiz*) 35 35
686 $2.50, Treasury after 1906 earthquake (*horiz*) 1·40 1·60
683/6 .. .. *Set of* 4 1·90 2·00

1984 (15 May). *As Nos.* 540/42, 545/6 *and* 548, *but W* w **15** (*sideways on* 20 *c. to* $1). *P* 14½ × 14.

No.	Description		
690	20 c. Refrigerator ship	65	20
691	25 c. "Islander" aeroplane	75	25
692	30 c. Pilot boat	85	30
695	$1 Lockheed "Tristar" airliner	2·00	80
696	$2 Cargo liner	3·00	2·50
698	$10 *Queen Elizabeth 2* (liner)	8·50	11·00
690/8	*Set of* 6	14·00	13·50

148 Logwood

(Des J. Cooter. Litho Format)

1984 (12 June). *Forestry Resources. T* **148** *and similar multicoloured designs. W* w **15** (*inverted on* 65 *c., sideways on others*). *P* 14 × 13½ (65 *c.*) *or* 13½ × 14 (*others*).

No.	Description		
699	10 c. Type **148**	15	10
700	45 c. Calabash	40	25
701	65 c. Gommier (*vert*)	55	40
702	$2.50, Raintree	1·75	2·00
699/702	*Set of* 4	2·50	2·50

149 Bugatti Type "57SC Atlantic Coupe"

(Des J.W. Litho Format)

1984 (25 June). *Leaders of the World. Automobiles* (1*st series*). *T* **149** *and similar horiz designs, the first in each pair showing technical drawings and the second paintings. P* 12½.

No.	Description		
703	5 c. black, reddish lavender and lemon	10	10
	a. Vert pair. Nos. 703/4	10	10
704	5 c. multicoloured	10	10
705	10 c. black, azure and rose-carmine	10	10
	a. Vert pair. Nos. 705/6	15	15
706	10 c. multicoloured	10	10
707	$1 black, pale green and orange-brown	45	45
	a. Vert pair. Nos. 707/8	90	90
708	$1 multicoloured	45	45
709	$2.50, black, pale flesh and slate-blue	75	75
	a. Vert pair. Nos. 709/10	1·50	1·50
710	$2.50, multicoloured	75	75
703/10	*Set of* 8	2·25	2·25

Designs:—Nos. 703/4, Bugatti Type "57SC Atlantic Coupe"; 705/6, Chevrolet "Bel Air Convertible"; 707/8, Alfa Romeo "1750 GS (Zagato)"; 709/10, Duesenberg "S J Roadster".

Nos. 703/4, 705/6, 707/8 and 709/10 were printed together, *se-tenant*, in vertical pairs throughout the sheets.

See also Nos. 745/60, 789/96 and 902/13.

150 Pygmy Gecko

151 Men's Volleyball

(Des Jennifer Toombs. Litho Format)

1984 (8 Aug). *Endangered Wildlife. T* **150** *and similar horiz designs. Multicoloured. W* w **15** (*sideways*). *P* 14.

No.	Description		
711	10 c. Type **150**	20	10
712	45 c. Maria Island Ground Lizard	50	30
713	65 c. Green Iguana	70	60
714	$2.50, Couresse Snake	2·00	2·25
711/14	*Set of* 4	3·00	3·00

(Des J.W. Litho Format)

1984 (21 Sept). *Leaders of the World. Railway Locomotives* (2*nd series*). *Horiz designs as T* **144**, *the first in each pair showing technical drawings and the second the locomotive at work. P* 12½.

No.	Description		
715	1 c. multicoloured	10	10
	a. Vert pair. Nos. 715/16	10	10
716	1 c. multicoloured	10	10
717	15 c. multicoloured	20	15
	a. Vert pair. Nos. 717/18	40	30
718	15 c. multicoloured	20	15
719	50 c. multicoloured	45	40
	a. Vert pair. Nos. 719/20	90	80
720	50 c. multicoloured	45	40
721	75 c. multicoloured	65	55
	a. Vert pair. Nos. 721/2	1·25	1·10
722	75 c. multicoloured	65	55
723	$1 multicoloured	80	75
	a. Vert pair. Nos. 723/4	1·60	1·50
724	$1 multicoloured	80	75
725	$2 multicoloured	1·50	1·50
	a. Vert pair. Nos. 725/6	3·00	3·00
726	$2 multicoloured	1·50	1·50
715/26	*Set of* 12	6·50	6·00

Designs:—Nos. 715/16, *Taw*, Great Britain (1897); 717/18, "Crocodile 1.C.C.1." type, Switzerland (1920); 719/20, *The Countess*, Great Britain (1903); 721/2, Class "GE6/6 C.C.", Switzerland (1921); 723/4, Class "P8", Germany (1906); 725/6, *Der Adler*, Germany (1835).

Nos. 715/26 were issued in a similar sheet format to Nos. 651/66.

IMPERFORATES AND MISSING COLOURS. Various issues between Nos. 727 and 893 exist either imperforate or with colours omitted. Such items are not listed as there is no evidence that they fulfil the criteria outlined on page xi of this catalogue.

(Des Court House Studio. Litho Format)

1984 (21 Sept). *Leaders of the World. Olympic Games, Los Angeles. T* **151** *and similar vert designs. Multicoloured. P* 12½.

No.	Description		
727	5 c. Type **151**	10	10
	a. Horiz pair. Nos. 727/8	10	10
728	5 c. Women's volleyball	10	10
729	10 c. Women's hurdles	10	10
	a. Horiz pair. Nos. 729/30	15	15
730	10 c. Men's hurdles	10	10
731	65 c. Show jumping	25	25
	a. Horiz pair. Nos. 731/2	50	50
732	65 c. Dressage	25	25
733	$2.50, Women's gymnastics	70	70
	a. Horiz pair. Nos. 733/4	1·40	1·40
734	$2.50, Men's gymnastics	70	70
727/34	*Set of* 8	1·90	1·90

Nos. 727/8, 729/30, 731/2, 733/4 were printed together, *se-tenant*, in horizontal pairs throughout the sheets.

Examples of No. 537 exist overprinted "RUMBRIDGE PACK R.F.C./1984 TOUR". This was a private souvenir, connected with a tour to St. Lucia by an English rugby club in October 1984. It was not sold by the St. Lucia Post Office or Philatelic Bureau.

152 Glass of Wine and Flowers

153 Slaves preparing Manioc

(Des G. L. Vasarhelyi. Litho Format)

1984 (31 Oct). *Christmas. T* **152** *and similar vert designs. Multicoloured. W* w **15**. *P* 14.

No.	Description		
735	10 c. Type **152**	10	10
736	35 c. Priest and decorated altar	20	15
737	65 c. Nativity scene	35	35
738	$3 Holy Family	1·50	1·60
735/8	*Set of* 4	1·90	1·90
MS739	147 × 77 mm. Nos. 735/8	2·75	3·25

(Des J. Cooter. Litho Format)

1984 (12 Dec). 150*th Anniv of Abolition of Slavery. T* **153** *and similar vert designs. Each black and yellow-ochre. W* w **15**. *P* 14 × 13½.

No.	Description		
740	10 c. Type **153**	10	10
741	35 c. Sifting and cooking cassava flour	15	20
742	55 c. Cooking pot, and preparing tobacco	25	30
743	$5 Stripping tobacco leaves for twist tobacco	2·25	2·50
740/3	*Set of* 4	2·40	2·75
MS744	154 × 110 mm. As Nos. 740/3, but without dates and side inscription and with the face values in different positions	3·25	4·25

(Des Artists International (65 c.), J.W. (others). Litho Format)

1984 (19 Dec). *Leaders of the World. Automobiles* (2*nd series*). *Horiz designs as T* **149**, *the first in each pair showing technical drawings and the second paintings. P* 12½.

No.	Description		
745	10 c. black, pale green and lake-brown	10	10
	a. Vert pair. Nos. 745/6	15	15
746	10 c. multicoloured	10	10
747	30 c. black, azure and bright yellow-green	20	20
	a. Vert pair. Nos. 747/8	40	40
748	30 c. multicoloured	20	20
749	55 c. black, greenish yellow and orange-brown	35	35
	a. Vert pair. Nos. 749/50	70	70
750	55 c. multicoloured	35	35
751	65 c. black, grey and brown-lilac	40	40
	a. Vert pair. Nos. 751/2	80	80
752	65 c. multicoloured	40	40
753	75 c. black, pale cinnamon, & orange-verm	40	40
	a. Vert pair. Nos. 753/4	80	80
754	75 c. multicoloured	40	40
755	$1 black, pale cinnamon and dull violet-blue	45	45
	a. Vert pair. Nos. 755/6	90	90
756	$1 multicoloured	45	45
757	$2 black, pale green and orange-red	60	60
	a. Vert pair. Nos. 757/8	1·10	1·10
758	$2 multicoloured	60	60
759	$3 black, pale cinnamon & orange-verm	75	75
	a. Vert pair. Nos. 759/60	1·50	1·50
760	$3 multicoloured	75	75
745/60	*Set of* 16	5·75	5·75

Designs:—Nos. 745/6, Panhard and Levassor; 747/8, N.S.U. "RO-80" Saloon; 749/50, Abarth "Bialbero"; 751/2, TVR "Vixen 2500M"; 753/4, Ford "Mustang" Convertible; 755/6, Ford "Model T"; 757/8, Aston Martin" DB3S"; 759/60, Chrysler "Imperial CG Dual Cowl" Phaeton.

Nos. 745/60 were issued in a similar sheet format to Nos. 703/10.

(Des T. Hadler (5, 15, 35 c.), J.W. (others). Litho Format)

1985 (4 Feb). *Leaders of the World. Railway Locomotives* (3*rd series*). *Horiz designs as T* **144**, *the first in each pair showing technical drawings and the second the locomotive at work. P* 12½.

No.	Description		
761	5 c. multicoloured	10	10
	a. Vert pair. Nos. 761/2	20	10
762	5 c. multicoloured	10	10
763	15 c. multicoloured	15	10
	a. Vert pair. Nos. 763/4	30	20
764	15 c. multicoloured	15	10
765	35 c. multicoloured	30	25
	a. Vert pair. Nos. 765/6	60	50
766	35 c. multicoloured	20	25
767	60 c. multicoloured	45	40
	a. Vert pair. Nos. 767/8	90	80
768	60 c. multicoloured	45	40
769	75 c. multicoloured	65	50
	a. Vert pair. Nos. 769/70	1·25	1·00
770	75 c. multicoloured	65	50
771	$1 multicoloured	75	65
	a. Vert pair. Nos. 771/2	1·50	1·25
772	$1 multicoloured	75	65
773	$2 multicoloured	1·50	1·40
	a. Vert pair. Nos. 773/4	3·00	2·75
774	$2 multicoloured	1·50	1·40
775	$2.50, multicoloured	1·75	1·60
	a. Vert pair. Nos. 775/6	3·50	3·00
776	$2.50, multicoloured	1·75	1·60
761/76	*Set of* 16	10·00	8·50

Designs:—Nos. 761/2, Class "C53", Japan (1928); 763/4, Class "Heavy L", India (1885); 765/6, Class "B18¼", Australia (1926); 767/8, *Owain Glyndwr*, Great Britain (1923); 769/70, *Lion*, Great Britain (1838); 771/2, Coal type locomotive, Great Britain (1873); 773/4, No. 2238, Class "Q6", Great Britain (1921); 775/6, Class "H", Great Britain (1920).

Nos. 761/76 were issued in a similar sheet format to Nos. 651/66.

154 Girl Guide Badge in Shield and Crest of St. Lucia

155 *Clossiana selene*

(Des Court House Studio. Litho Questa)

1985 (21 Feb). 75*th Anniv of Girl Guide Movement and* 60*th Anniv of Guiding in St. Lucia. W* w **15**. *P* 14.

No.	Description		
777	**154** 10 c. multicoloured	20	10
778	35 c. multicoloured	50	15
779	65 c. multicoloured	70	35
780	$3 multicoloured	2·50	1·90
777/80	*Set of* 4	3·50	2·25

(Des Jennifer Toombs. Litho Format)

1985 (28 Feb). *Leaders of the World. Butterflies. T* **155** *and similar vert designs. Multicoloured. P* 12½.

No.	Description		
781	15 c. Type **155**	15	10
	a. Horiz pair. Nos. 781/2	30	20
782	15 c. *Inachis io*	15	10
783	40 c. *Philaethria werneckei*	35	30
	a. Horiz pair. Nos. 783/4	70	60
784	40 c. *Catagramma sorana*	35	30
785	60 c. *Kallima inachus*	45	40
	a. Horiz pair. Nos. 785/6	90	80
786	60 c. *Hypanartia paullus*	45	40
787	$2.25, *Morpho rhetenor helena*	1·75	1·50
	a. Horiz pair. Nos. 787/8	3·50	3·00
788	$2.25, *Ornithoptera meridionalis*	1·75	1·50
781/8	*Set of* 8	4·75	4·00

Nos. 781/2, 783/4, 785/6 and 787/8 were printed together, *se-tenant*, in horizontal pairs throughout the sheets.

(Des J.W. Litho Format)

1985 (29 Mar). *Leaders of the World. Automobiles* (3*rd series*). *Horiz designs as T* **149**, *the first in each pair showing technical drawings and the second paintings. P* 12½.

No.	Description		
789	15 c. black, cobalt and Indian red	10	10
	a. Vert pair. Nos. 789/90	15	20
790	15 c. multicoloured	10	10
791	50 c. black, pale orange and deep rose-red	25	30
	a. Vert pair. Nos. 791/2	50	60
792	50 c. multicoloured	25	30
793	$1 black, pale green and reddish orange	45	50
	a. Vert pair. Nos. 793/4	90	1·00
794	$1 multicoloured	45	50
795	$1.50, black, pale green & pale red-brown	60	70
	a. Vert pair. Nos. 795/6	1·10	1·40
796	$1.50, multicoloured	60	70
789/96	*Set of* 8	2·40	3·00

Designs:—Nos. 789/90, Hudson "Eight" (1940); 791/2, KdF (1937); 793/4, Kissel "Goldbug" (1925); 795/6, Ferrari "246 GTS" (1973).

Nos. 789/96 were issued in a similar sheet format to Nos. 703/10.

156 Grenadier, 70th Regiment, c 1775

157 Messerschmitt "109-E"

(Des J. Cooter. Litho Format)

1985 (7 May). *Military Uniforms. T* **156** *and similar vert designs. Multicoloured.* W w **15** (*sideways*). *P* 15.

797	5 c. Type **156**. .	20	15
798	10 c. Officer, Grenadier Company, 14th Regiment, 1780 . .	20	15
799	20 c. Officer, Battalion Company, 46th Regiment, 1781	20	15
800	25 c. Officer, Royal Artillery, *c.* 1782	20	15
801	30 c. Officer, Royal Engineers, 1782	35	15
802	35 c. Officer, Battalion Company, 54th Regiment, 1782	15	20
803	45 c. Private, Grenadier Company, 14th Regiment, 1782 . .	55	35
804	50 c. Gunner, Royal Artillery, 1796. .	55	35
805	65 c. Private, Battalion Company, 85th Regiment, *c.* 1796	25	30
806	75 c. Private, Battalion Company, 76th Regiment, 1796	30	35
807	90 c. Private, Battalion Company, 81st Regiment, *c.* 1796	35	40
808	$1 Sergeant, 74th (Highland) Regiment, 1796	40	45
809	$2.50, Private, Light Company, 93rd Regiment, 1803	2·25	2·25
810	$5 Private, Battalion Company, 1st West India Regiment, 1803 . .	4·00	4·00
811	$15 Officer, Royal Artillery, 1850 . .	6·25	6·50
797/811	*Set of* 15	14·50	14·50

The 25 c. exists with different imprint dates below the design.

For 5, 10, 30, 45, 50 c., $2.50, $5, and additional values, all without watermark see Nos. 928/46.

For 5, 10, 20, 25 c. and additional values, all watermarked w **16** (sideways) see Nos. 993/1003.

(Des J.W. Litho Format)

1985 (30 May). *Leaders of the World. Military Aircraft. T* **157** *and similar horiz designs, the first in each pair showing paintings and the second technical drawings. P* 12½.

812	5 c. multicoloured	10	10
	a. Vert pair. Nos. 812/13 . .	10	10
813	5 c. black, pale new blue and pale yellow . .	10	10
814	55 c. multicoloured	40	35
	a. Vert pair. Nos. 814/15 . .	80	70
815	55 c. black, pale new blue and pale yellow . .	40	35
816	60 c. multicoloured	40	40
	a. Vert pair. Nos. 816/17 . .	80	80
817	60 c. black, pale new blue and pale yellow . .	40	40
818	$2 multicoloured	1·25	1·25
	a. Vert pair. Nos. 818/19 . .	2·50	2·50
819	$2 black, pale new blue and pale yellow . .	1·25	1·25
812/19	*Set of* 8	3·75	3·75

Designs:—Nos. 812/13, Messerschmitt "109-E"; 814/15, Avro "683 Lancaster Mark I"; 816/17, North American "P.51-D Mustang"; 818/19, Supermarine "Spitfire Mark II".

Nos. 812/13, 814/15, 816/17 and 818/19 were printed together, *se-tenant*, in vertical pairs throughout the sheets.

158 Magnificent Frigate Birds, Frigate Island Bird Sanctuary

159 Queen Elizabeth the Queen Mother

(Des G. Drummond. Litho Format)

1985 (20 June). *Nature Reserves. T* **158** *and similar horiz designs. Multicoloured.* W w **15**. *P* 15.

820	10 c. Type **158**. .	35	15
821	35 c. Mangrove Cuckoo, Scorpion Island, Savannes Bay	1·00	30
822	65 c. Lesser Yellowlegs, Maria Island Reserve . .	1·40	55
823	$3 Audubon's Shearwaters, Lapins Island Reserve . .	3·25	3·75
820/3 . .	*Set of* 4	5·50	4·25

(Des Tudor Art Agency ($2.50), J.W. (others). Litho Format)

1985 (26 June). *Leaders of the World. Railway Locomotives* (4*th series*). *Horiz designs as T* **144**, *the first in each pair showing technical drawings and second the locomotive at work. P* 12½.

824	10 c. multicoloured	15	10
	a. Vert pair. Nos. 824/5	30	20
825	10 c. multicoloured	15	10
826	30 c. multicoloured	30	20
	a. Vert pair. Nos. 826/7	60	40
827	30 c. multicoloured	30	20
828	75 c. multicoloured	65	45
	a. Vert pair. Nos. 828/9	1·25	90
829	75 c. multicoloured	65	45
830	$2.50, multicoloured	1·75	1·40
	a. Vert pair. Nos. 830/1	3·50	2·75
831	$2.50, multicoloured	1·75	1·40
824/31	*Set of* 8	5·00	3·75

Designs:—Nos. 824/5, No. 28 tank locomotive, Great Britain (1897); 826/7, No. 1621 Class "M", Great Britain (1893); 828/9, Class "Dunalastair", Great Britain (1896); 830/1, No. 2290 "Big Bertha" type, Great Britain (1919).

Nos. 824/31 were issued in a similar sheet format to Nos. 651/66.

(Des Court House Studio. Litho Format)

1985 (16 Aug). *Leaders of the World. Life and Times of Queen Elizabeth the Queen Mother. Various vertical portraits as T* **159**. *P* 12.

832	40 c. multicoloured	25	30
	a. Horiz pair. Nos. 832/3 . .	50	60
833	40 c. multicoloured	25	30
834	75 c. multicoloured	35	45
	a. Horiz pair. Nos. 834/5 . .	70	90
835	75 c. multicoloured	35	45
836	$1.10, multicoloured	50	65
	a. Horiz pair. Nos. 836/7 . .	1·00	1·25
837	$1.10, multicoloured	50	65
838	$1.75, multicoloured	80	1·00
	a. Horiz pair. Nos. 838/9 . .	1·60	2·00
839	$1.75, multicoloured	80	1·00
832/9 . .	*Set of* 8	3·50	4·25
MS840	84×114 mm. 42 multicoloured; $2 multicoloured	2·10	2·25

The two designs of each value were issued, *se-tenant*, in horizontal pairs within the sheets.

Each *se-tenant* pair shows a floral pattern across the bottom of the portraits which stops short of the left-hand edge on the left-hand stamp and of the right-hand edge on the right-hand stamp.

Designs as Nos. 832/3 and 836/7, but with face values of $3 × 2 and $6 × 2, also exist in additional miniature sheets from a restricted printing issued 31 December 1985.

160 "Youth playing Banjo" (Wayne Whitfield)

161 "Papa Jab"

(Litho Format)

1985 (5 Sept). *International Youth Year. Paintings by Young St. Lucians. T* **160** *and similar designs.* W w **15** (*sideways*). *P* 15.

841	10 c. black, new blue and bright magenta . .	10	10
842	45 c. multicoloured	20	25
843	75 c. multicoloured	35	40
844	$3.50, multicoloured	1·60	1·75
841/4 . .	*Set of* 4	2·00	2·25
MS845	123×86 mm. $5 multicoloured . .	2·25	2·75

Designs: *Vert* (*as T* **160**)—45 c. "Motorcyclist" (Mark Maragh); 75 c. "Boy and Girl at Pitons" (Bartholomew Eugene); $3.50, "Abstract" (Lyndon Samuel). *Horiz* (80 × 55 *mm*)—$5 Young people and St. Lucia landscapes.

1985 (26 Oct). *Royal Visit. Nos.* 649, 685/6, 702, 713, 778 *and* 836/7 *optd as T* **114** *of Montserrat.*

846	**154**	35 c. multicoloured	3·50	2·50
847	–	65 c. multicoloured (No. 685) . .	3·00	3·00
848	–	65 c. multicoloured (No. 713) . .	3·00	3·00
849	–	$1.10, multicoloured (No. 836)	4·00	4·00
		a. Horiz pair. Nos. 849/50 . .	8·00	8·00
850	–	$1.10, multicoloured (No. 837)	4·00	4·00
851	–	$2.50, multicoloured (No. 649)	4·00	4·00
852	–	$2.50, multicoloured (No. 686)	3·50	3·50
853	–	$2.50, multicoloured (No. 702)	3·50	3·50
846/53		*Set of* 8	26·00	25·00

(Litho Format)

1985 (24 Dec). *Christmas. Masqueraders. T* **161** *and similar vert designs. Multicoloured. P* 15.

854	10 c. Type **161**. .	10	10
855	45 c. "Paille Banane"	20	25
856	65 c. "Cheval Bois"	30	35
854/6 . .	*Set of* 3	50	60
MS857	70×83 mm. $4 "Madonna and Child" (Dunstan St. Omer)	1·75	1·90

(Des T. Hadler. Litho Format)

1986 (27 Jan). *Leaders of the World. Railway Locomotives* (5*th series*). *Horiz designs as T* **144**, *the first in each pair showing technical drawings and the second the locomotive at work. P* 12½.

858	5 c. multicoloured	15	15
	a. Vert pair. Nos. 858/9	30	30
859	5 c. multicoloured	15	15
860	15 c. multicoloured	15	15
	a. Vert pair. Nos. 860/1	30	30
861	15 c. multicoloured	15	15
862	30 c. multicoloured	30	30
	a. Vert pair. Nos. 862/3	60	60
863	30 c. multicoloured	30	30
864	60 c. multicoloured	55	55
	a. Vert pair. Nos. 864/5	1·10	1·10
865	60 c. multicoloured	55	55
866	75 c. multicoloured	70	70
	a. Vert pair. Nos. 866/7	1·40	1·40
867	75 c. multicoloured	70	70
868	$1 multicoloured	80	80
	a. Vert pair. Nos. 868/9	1·60	1·60
869	$1 multicoloured	80	80
870	$2.25, multicoloured	1·75	1·75
	a. Vert pair. Nos. 870/1	3·50	3·50
871	$2.25, multicoloured	1·75	1·75
872	$3 multicoloured	2·25	2·25
	a. Vert pair. Nos. 872/3	4·50	4·50
873	$3 multicoloured	2·25	2·25
858/73	*Set of* 16	12·00	12·00

Designs:—Nos. 858/9, Rack loco *Tip Top*, U.S.A (1983); 860/1, *Stephenson*, Great Britain (1975); 862/3, No. 737 Class "D", Great Britain (1901); 864/5, No. 13 Class "2-CO-2", Great Britain (1922); 866/7, *Electra*, Great Britain (1954); 868/9, *City of Newcastle*, Great Britain (1922); 870/1, Von Kruckenburg propeller-driven rail car, Germany (1930); 872/3, No. 860, Japan (1893).

Nos. 858/73 were issued in a similar sheet format to Nos. 651/66.

162 Campfire Cooking Utensils

(Des Court House Studio. Litho Format)

1986 (3 Mar). 75*th Annivs of Girl Guide Movement and Boy Scouts of America. Two sheets, each* 85×113 *mm, containing vert designs as T* **162**. *Multicoloured. P* 12½.

MS874	$4 Type **162**: $4 Scout salute	5·50	6·50
MS875	$6 Wickerwork: $6 Lady Baden-Powell . .	7·50	8·50

The two stamps in each sheet were printed together, *se-tenant*, in horizontal pairs, each forming a composite design.

Nos. **MS**874/5 exist with plain or decorative margins.

Overprints on these miniature sheets commemorating "Capex '87" International Stamp Exhibition, Toronto, were not authorised by the St. Lucia administration.

(Des Court House Studio. Litho Format)

1986 (21 Apr). 60*th Birthday of Queen Elizabeth II* (1*st issue*). *Multicoloured designs as T* **167** *of British Virgin Islands. P* 12½.

876	5 c. Queen Elizabeth II	10	10
877	$1 Princess Elizabeth	60	55
878	$3.50, Queen Elizabeth II (*different*)	2·00	2·25
879	$6 In Canberra, 1982 (*vert*) . .	3·25	3·50
876/9 . .	*Set of* 4	5·50	5·75
MS880	85×115 mm. $8 Queen Elizabeth II (*different*)	4·50	4·75

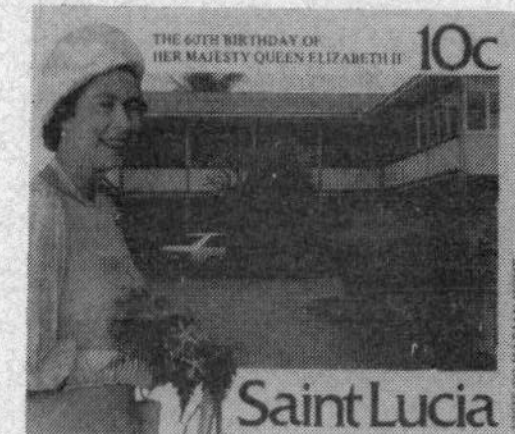

163 Queen Elizabeth and Marian Home

(Des Court House Studio. Litho Questa)

1986 (14 June). 60*th Birthday of Queen Elizabeth II* (2*nd issue*). *T* **163** *and similar horiz designs. Multicoloured.* W w **15** (*sideways*). *P* 14×15.

881	10 c. Type **163**. .	15	15
882	45 c. Queen addressing rally, Mindoo Phillip Park, 1985	35	35
883	50 c. Queen opening Leon Hess Comprehensive School, 1985	40	40
884	$5 Queen Elizabeth and Government House, Castries . .	2·50	2·75
881/4 . .	*Set of* 4	3·00	3·25
MS885	121×85 mm. $7 Queen Elizabeth and Royal Yacht *Britannia*, Castries. .	3·50	4·00

164 Pope John Paul II kissing Ground, Castries Airport

(Des Court House Studio. Litho Questa)

1986 (7 July). *Visit of Pope John Paul II. T* **164** *and similar multicoloured designs.* W w **15** (*sideways on* 55, 60 *c.*). *P* 14½×14 (80 *c.*) *or* 14×14½ (*others*).

886	55 c. Type **164**. .	60	45
887	60 c. Pope and St. Joseph's Convent	60	45
888	80 c. Pope and Castries Catholic Cathedral (*vert*)	90	70
886/8 . .	*Set of* 3	1·90	1·40
MS889	85×123 mm. $6 Pope John Paul II (*vert*). P 14½×14	4·00	4·50

(Litho Format)

1986 (12 Aug). *Royal Wedding* (1st *issue*). *Multicoloured designs as T* **168** *of British Virgin Islands. P* 12½.

890 80 c. Miss Sarah Ferguson 45 50
a. Pair. Nos. 890/1 .. .. 90 1·00
891 80 c. Prince Andrew 45 50
892 $2 Prince Andrew and Miss Sarah Ferguson (*horiz*) .. .. 1·25 1·40
a. Pair. Nos. 892/3 .. .. 2·50 2·75
893 $2 Prince Andrew with Mrs Nancy Reagan (*horiz*) .. .. 1·25 1·40
890/3 .. .. *Set of* 4 3·00 3·25

Nos. 890/1 and 892/3 were each printed together, *se-tenant*, in horizontal and vertical pairs throughout the sheets.

165 Peace Corps Teacher with Students

166 Prince Andrew in Carriage

(Des J. Cooter. Litho Questa)

1986 (25 Sept). *25th Anniv of United States Peace Corps. T* **165** *and similar multicoloured designs. W w* **15** (*sideways on* $2). *P* 14.

894 80 c. Type **165** 35 40
895 $2 President John Kennedy (*vert*) .. 1·10 1·25
896 $3.50, Peace Corps emblem between arms of St. Lucia and U.S.A. .. .. .. 1·60 2·00
894/6 .. .. *Set of* 3 2·75 3·25

(Des Court House Studio. Litho Format)

1986 (15 Oct). *Royal Wedding* (2*nd issue*). *T* **166** *and similar vert designs. Multicoloured. P* 15.

897 50 c. Type **166** 35 35
898 80 c. Miss Sarah Ferguson in coach 50 50
899 $1 Duke and Duchess of York at altar .. 60 60
900 $3 Duke and Duchess of York in carriage .. 1·75 2·00
897/900 .. .. *Set of* 4 3·00 3·00
MS901 115 × 85 mm. $7 Duke and Duchess of York on Palace balcony after wedding (*horiz*) .. 3·25 3·50

(Des Court House Studio. Litho Format)

1986 (23 Oct). *Automobiles* (4*th series*). *Horiz designs as T* **149**, *the first in each pair showing technical drawings and the second paintings. P* 12½.

902 20 c. multicoloured 10 15
a. Vert pair. Nos. 902/3 .. .. .. 20 30
903 20 c. multicoloured 10 15
904 50 c. multicoloured 25 30
a. Vert pair. Nos. 904/5 .. .. .. 50 60
905 50 c. multicoloured 25 30
906 60 c. multicoloured 30 35
a. Vert pair. Nos. 906/7 .. .. .. 60 70
907 60 c. multicoloured 30 35
908 $1 multicoloured 40 55
a. Vert pair. Nos. 908/9 .. .. .. 80 1·10
909 $1 multicoloured 40 55
910 $1.50, multicoloured 60 70
a. Vert pair. Nos. 910/11 .. .. .. 1·10 1·40
911 $1.50, multicoloured 60 70
912 $3 multicoloured .. .. 1·25 1·40
a. Vert pair. Nos. 912/13 .. .. .. 2·50 2·75
913 $3 multicoloured .. .. 1·25 1·40
902/13 .. .. *Set of* 12 5·00 6·00

Designs:—Nos. 902/3, AMC "AMX" (1969); 904/5, Russo-Baltique (1912); 906/7, Lincoln "K.B." (1932); 908/9, Rolls Royce "Phantom II Continental" (1933); 910/11, Buick "Century" (1939); 912/13, Chrysler "300 C" (1957).

Nos. 902/13 were issued in a similar sheet format to Nos. 703/10.

167 Chak-Chak Band

(Des Jennifer Toombs. Litho Format)

1986 (7 Nov). *Tourism. T* **167** *and similar horiz designs. Multicoloured. W w* **15**. *P* 15.

914 15 c. Type **167** 10 10
915 45 c. Folk dancing 25 25
916 80 c. Steel band 50 50
917 $5 Limbo dancing .. .. 2·10 2·50
914/17 .. .. *Set of* 4 2·75 3·00
MS918 157 × 109 mm. $10 Fire-eating. Wmk sideways .. .. 4·75 5·50

168 St. Ann Catholic Church, Mon Repos

169 Outline Map of St. Lucia

(Litho Format)

1986 (3 Dec). *Christmas. T* **168** *and similar multicoloured designs. P* 15.

919 10 c. Type **168** 10 10
920 40 c. St. Joseph the Worker Catholic Church, Gros Islet 30 25
921 80 c. Holy Trinity Anglican Church, Castries 50 40
922 $4 Our Lady of the Assumption Catholic Church, Soufriere (*vert*) .. .. 2·00 2·50
919/22 .. .. *Set of* 4 2·50 3·00
MS923 120 × 101 mm $7 St. Lucy Catholic Church, Micoud .. .. 3·75 4·50

(Des L. Curtis. Litho Walsall)

1987 (24 Feb)–**89**. *W w* **14** (*sideways*). *P* 14. A. *No imprint at foot.* B. *With imprint date.*

			A		B	
924	**169**	5 c. black and cinnamon ..	10	10	10	10
925		10 c. black and pale emerald	10	10	10	10
926		45 c. black & bright orange	35	35	†	
927		50 c. black and violet-blue	35	35	20	25
927c		$1 black and bright rose	40	45	†	
924/7c ..		.. .. *Set of* 5	1·00	1·00	†	

Dates of issue:—24.2.87, Nos. 924A/7A; 9.88, Nos. 924B/5B; 17.3.89, Nos. 927B, 927cA.

For 5 c. and 10 c. watermarked w **16** (sideways) see Nos. 1018/19.

(Des J. Cooter. Litho Format)

1987 (16 Mar). *As Nos.* 797/8, 801, 803/4, 809/10 *and new values* (15, 60, 80 *c. and* $20), *all without wmk. P* 15.

928 5 c. Type **156** 15 15
929 10 c. Officer, Grenadier Company, 14th Regiment, 1780 .. .. 15 15
930 15 c. Private, Battalion Company, 2nd West India Regiment, 1803 .. .. .. 15 15
933 30 c. Officer, Royal Engineers, 1782 .. 10 15
935 45 c. Private, Grenadier Company, 14th Regiment, 1782 .. .. 20 25
936 50 c. Gunner, Royal Artillery, 1796 .. .. 35 35
937 60 c. Officer, Battalion Company, 5th Regiment, 1778 .. .. 40 40
940 80 c. Officer, Battalion Company, 27th Regiment, *c.* 1780 .. .. 50 50
943 $2.50, Private, Light Company, 93rd Regiment, 1803 .. .. 1·00 1·10
944 $5 Private, Battalion Company, 1st West India Regiment, 1803 .. .. .. 2·10 2·25
946 $20 Private, Grenadier Company, 46th Regiment, 1778 .. .. 10·00 12·00
928/46 .. .. *Set of* 11 13·50 15·00

For various values watermarked w **16** (sideways) see Nos. 993/1003.

170 Statue of Liberty and Flags of France and U.S.A.

171 First Cadastral Survey Map and Surveying Instruments, 1775

(Des A. Theobald. Litho Format)

1987 (29 Apr). *Centenary of Statue of Liberty* (1986). *T* **170** *and similar vert designs. Multicoloured. W w* **16**. *P* 14½.

947 15 c. Type **170** 10 10
948 80 c. Statue and *Mauretania* (liner) 50 45
949 $1 Statue and "Concorde" 60 50
950 $5 Statue and flying boat at sunset .. 2·25 2·50
947/50 .. .. *Set of* 4 3·00 3·25
MS951 107 × 88 mm. $6 Statue and Manhattan at night. Wmk sideways .. .. .. 2·75 3·25

1987 (July). *Coil stamp. As No.* 350, *but W w* **16**. *P* 14½ × 14.

953 **87** 10 c. turquoise-green 10 10

(Des N. Shewring. Litho Walsall)

1987 (31 Aug). *New Cadastral Survey of St. Lucia. T* **171** *and similar vert designs. Multicoloured. W w* **16**. *P* 14.

955 15 c. Type **171** 15 10
956 60 c. Map and surveying instruments, 1814 35 30
957 $1 Map and surveying instruments, 1888 55 55
958 $2.50, Cadastral survey map and surveying instruments, 1987 .. .. .. 1·25 1·50
955/8 .. .. *Set of* 4 2·10 2·25

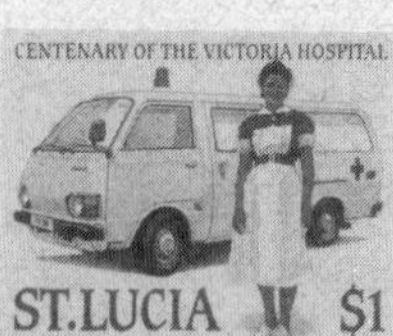

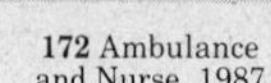

172 Ambulance and Nurse, 1987

173 "The Holy Family"

(Des C. Abbott. Litho Questa)

1987 (4 Nov). *Centenary of Victoria Hospital, Castries. T* **172** *and similar horiz designs. Multicoloured. W w* **16** (*sideways*). *P* 14 × 14½.

959 **172** $1 multicoloured 65 65
a. Pair. Nos. 959/60 .. .. .. 1·25 1·25
960 – $1 indigo 65 65
961 – $2 multicoloured .. .. 1·00 1·00
a. Pair. Nos. 961/2 .. .. .. 2·00 2·00
962 – $2 indigo .. .. 1·00 1·00
959/62 .. .. *Set of* 4 3·00 3·00
MS963 86 × 68 mm. $4.50, multicoloured .. 3·00 3·50

Designs:—No. 960, Nurse and carrying hammock, 1913; No. 961, $2 Victoria Hospital, 1987; No. 962, Victoria Hospital, 1887; No. **MS**963, Hospital gates, 1987.

Nos. 959/60 and 961/2 were each printed together, *se-tenant*, in horizontal and vertical pairs throughout the sheets.

(Des D. Miller. Litho Format)

1987 (30 Nov). *Christmas. T* **173** *and similar square designs showing paintings. Multicoloured. W w* **16** (*sideways*). *P* 14½.

964 15 c. Type **173** 15 10
965 50 c. "Adoration of the Shepherds" 30 25
966 60 c. "Adoration of the Magi" 35 35
967 90 c. "Madonna and Child" 60 60
964/7 .. .. *Set of* 4 1·25 1·10
MS968 82 × 67 mm. $6 Type **173** .. .. 2·75 3·25

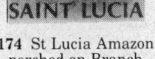

174 St Lucia Amazon perched on Branch

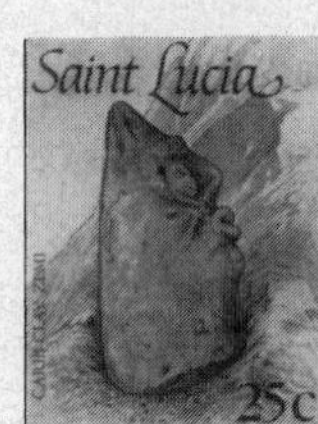

175 Carib Clay Zemi

(Des W. Oliver. Litho Walsall)

1987 (18 Dec). *St. Lucia Amazon. T* **174** *and similar vert designs. Multicoloured. W w* **16**. *P* 14.

969 15 c. Type **174** 15 10
970 35 c. Pair in flight 30 20
971 50 c. Perched on branch (rear view) 40 35
972 $1 Emerging from tree 75 75
969/72 .. .. *Set of* 4 1·40 1·25

(Des C. Collins. Litho Walsall)

1988 (24 Feb). *Amerindian Artifacts. T* **175** *and similar vert designs. Multicoloured. W w* **16**. *P* 14½ × 14.

973 25 c. Type **175** 10 10
974 30 c. Troumassee cylinder 15 15
975 80 c. Three pointer stone 40 45
976 $3.50, Dauphine petroglyph .. .. 1·50 1·60
973/6 .. .. *Set of* 4 1·90 2·10

176 East Caribbean Currency

177 Rural Telephone Exchange

(Des D. Miller (10 c.), S. Conlin (others). Litho B.D.T.)

1988 (29 Apr). *50th Anniv of St. Lucia Co-operative Bank. T* **176** *and similar horiz designs. Multicoloured. W w* **14** (*sideways*). *P* 15 × 14.

977 10 c. Type **176** 10 10
978 45 c. Castries branch 30 30
979 60 c. As 45 c. 40 40
980 80 c. Vieux Fort branch 60 60
977/80 .. .. *Set of* 4 1·25 1·25

(Des A. Theobald. Litho Walsall)

1988 (10 June). *50th Anniv of Cable and Wireless* (*West Indies*) *Ltd. T* **177** *and similar horiz designs. Multicoloured. W w* **16** (*sideways*). *P* 14.

981 15 c. Type **177** 10 10
982 25 c. Early and modern telephones 15 15
983 80 c. St. Lucia Teleport dish aerial 40 45
984 $2.50, Map showing Eastern Caribbean Microwave System .. .. .. 1·00 1·10
981/4 .. .. *Set of* 4 1·40 1·60

178 Stained Glass Window

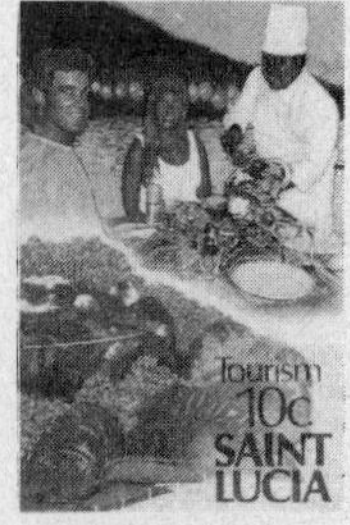

179 Garnished Lobsters

(Des O. Bell. Litho Format)

1988 (15 Aug). *Centenary of Methodist Church in St. Lucia. T* **178** *and similar diamond-shaped designs. Multicoloured. W w* **16** *(sideways). P* 14½.

985 15 c. Type **178** 10 10
986 80 c. Church interior 40 45
987 $3.50, Methodist Church, Castries .. 1·50 1·60
985/7 .. .. *Set of* 3 1·75 1·90

(Des D. Miller. Litho Harrison)

1988 (15 Sept). *Tourism (2nd series). T* **179** *and similar vert designs showing local delicacies. Multicoloured. W w* **16**. *P* 14 × 13½.

988 10 c. Type **179** 15 15
a. Horiz strip of 4. Nos. 988/91 .. .. 2·00
989 30 c. Cocktail and tourists at buffet .. 20 20
990 80 c. Fresh fruits and roasted breadfruit .. 55 55
991 $2.50, Barbecued Red Snappers (fish) .. 1·25 1·25
988/91 .. .. *Set of* 4 2·00 2·00
MS992 88 × 104 mm. $5.50, Fruit stall, Castries market. P 14½ × 14 .. .. .. 2·25 2·50

Nos. 988/91 were printed together, *se-tenant*, in horizontal strips of four throughout the sheet, forming a composite design of tourists at beach barbecue.

(Des J. Cooter. Litho Format)

1988 (Sept)–**89**. *As Nos.* 797/800, 930, 937, 940 *and* 946, *but W w* **16** *(sideways). P* 15.

993 5 c. Type **156** (6.89) 10 10
994 10 c. Officer, Grenadier Company, 14th Regiment, 1780 (6.89) 10 10
995 15 c. Private, Battalion Company, 2nd West India Regiment, 1803 .. 10 10
996 20 c. Officer, Battalion Company, 46th Regiment, 1781 (6.89) 10 10
997 25 c. Officer, Royal Artillery, *c*. 1782 .. 10 10
999 60 c. Officer, Battalion Company, 5th Regiment, 1778 .. .. .. 25 30
1000 80 c. Officer, Battalion Company, 27th Regiment, *c*. 1780 .. .. .. 30 35
1003 $20 Private, Grenadier Company, 46th Regiment, 1778 (6.89) .. .. 8·25 8·50
993/1003 .. .. .. *Set of* 8 8·25 8·50

The 15 c. and 25 c. exist with different imprint dates below the designs.

(Des D. Miller (10 c.), L. Curtis and D. Miller (60 c.), E. Nisbet and D. Miller (80 c.), S. Noon and D. Miller ($2.50). Litho Questa)

1988 (17 Oct). *300th Anniv of Lloyd's of London. Designs as T* **123** *of Ascension. W w* **14** *(sideways on* 60, 80 *c.). P* 14.

1004 10 c. black, grey-lilac and brown 10 10
1005 60 c. multicoloured 35 35
1006 80 c. multicoloured 55 55
1007 $2.50, multicoloured .. .. .. 1·25 1·25
1004/7 .. .. *Set of* 4 2·00 2·00

Designs: *Vert*—10 c. San Francisco earthquake, 1906; $2.50, Castries fire, 1948. *Horiz*—60 c. Castries Harbour; 80 c. *Lady Nelson* (liner) 1942.

180 Snow on the Mountain

181 Princess Alexandra presenting Constitution

(Des R. Gorringe. Litho Format)

1988 (22 Nov). *Christmas. Flowers. T* **180** *and similar vert designs. Multicoloured. W w* **16**. *P* 14.

1008 15 c. Type **180** 15 10
1009 45 c. Christmas Candle 30 30
1010 60 c. Balisier 40 40
1011 80 c. Poinsettia 55 55
1008/11 .. .. *Set of* 4 1·25 1·25
MS1012 79 × 75 mm. $5.50, Christmas flower arrangement. Wmk sideways .. .. .. 2·50 3·00

(Des S. Noon. Litho Walsall)

1989 (22 Feb). *10th Anniv of Independence. T* **181** *and similar vert designs. Multicoloured. W w* **14**. *P* 13½ × 13.

1013 15 c. Type **181** 10 10
1014 80 c. Geothermal well 40 45
1015 $1 Sir Arthur Lewis Community College 45 50
1016 $2.50, Pointe Seraphine shopping centre 1·00 1·10
1013/16 .. .. *Set of* 4 1·75 1·90
MS1017 47 × 62 mm. $5 Man with national flag. W w **16**. .. .. 2·10 2·25

1989 (12 Apr). *As Nos.* 924B/5B, *but W w* **16** *(sideways). With imprint date. P* 14.

1018 **169** 5 c. black and cinnamon 10 10
1019 10 c. black and pale emerald 10 10

182 *Gerronema citrinum*

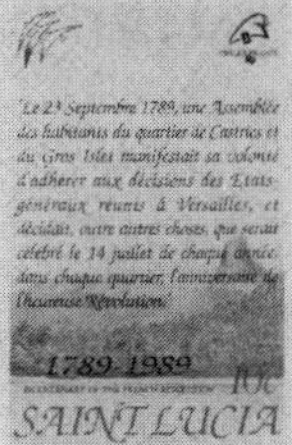

183 Local Revolutionary Declaration, 1789 and View of St. Lucia

(Des Josephine Martin. Litho Questa)

1989 (31 May). *Fungi. T* **182** *and similar vert designs. Multicoloured. W w* **16**. *P* 14½×14.

1022 15 c. Type **182** 15 15
1023 25 c. *Lepiota spiculata* 20 15
1024 50 c. *Calocybe cyanocephala* 40 35
1025 $5 *Russula puiggarii* .. .. .. 3·25 3·25
1022/5 .. .. *Set of* 4 3·50 3·50

(Litho Questa)

1989 (14 July). *Bicentenary of the French Revolution. T* **183** *and similar multicoloured designs each including the "Philexfrance" International Stamp Exhibition logo. W w* **14** *(sideways on* 60 *c.*, $3.50*). P* 14.

1026 10 c. Type **183** 15 15
1027 60 c. Hoisting Revolutionary flag, Morne Fortune, 1791 (*horiz*) 45 45
1028 $1 Declaration of Rights of Man and view of St. Lucia 65 65
1029 $3.50, Arrival of Capt. La Crosse, Gros Islet, 1792 (*horiz*) .. .. .. 2·00 2·00
1026/9 .. .. *Set of* 4 3·00 3·00

184 Red Cross Headquarters, St. Lucia

185 Christmas Lantern

(Des A. Theobald. Litho Questa)

1989 (10 Oct). *125th Anniv of International Red Cross. T* **184** *and similar horiz designs. Multicoloured. W w* **16** *(sideways). P* 14×14½.

1030 50 c. Type **184** 35 35
1031 80 c. Red Cross seminar, Castries, 1987 .. 50 50
1032 $1 Red Cross ambulance 60 60
1030/2 .. .. *Set of* 3 1·25 1·25

(Des Jennifer Toombs. Litho Questa)

1989 (17 Nov). *Christmas. T* **185** *and similar horiz designs showing decorative "building" lanterns. W w* **16** *(sideways). P* 14×14½.

1033 10 c. multicoloured 10 10
1034 50 c. multicoloured 25 30
1035 90 c. multicoloured 40 45
1036 $1 multicoloured 45 50
1033/6 .. .. *Set of* 4 1·00 1·10

186 Gwi Gwi

(Des R. Gorringe. Litho B.D.T.)

1990 (21 Feb–9 Apr). *Endangered Trees. T* **186** *and similar vert designs. Multicoloured. W w* **16**. *P* 14.

1037 10 c. Chinna (9.4) 10 10
1038 15 c. Latanier (9.4) 10 10
1039 20 c. Type **186** 10 10
1040 25 c. L'Encens 10 10
1041 50 c. Bois Lélé 20 25
1042 80 c. Bois D'Amande (9.4) 30 35
1045 $1.50, Pencil Cedar (9.4) 60 65
1048 $25 Chalantier Grand Bois .. .. .. 10·50 11·00
1037/48 .. .. *Set of* 8 10·50 11·00

MINIMUM PRICE

The minimum price quote is 10p which represents a handling charge rather than a basis for valuing common stamps. For further notes about prices see introductory pages.

POSTAGE DUE STAMPS

D 1

No. **No.**

Normal — Wide fount

(Type-set Government Printing Office)

1930. *Each stamp individually handstamped with different number. No wmk. No gum. Rough perf* 12. (*a*) *Horizontally laid paper.*

D1	D 1	1d. black/*blue*	1·75	5·50
		a. Wide, wrong fount "No."	7·00	14·00
		b. Missing stop after "ST"	23·00	38·00
		c. Missing stop after "LUCIA"	23·00	38·00
		d. Handstamped number double	£110	
		(*b*) *Wove paper*		
D2	D 1	2d. black/*yellow*	4·00	15·00
		a. Wide, wrong fount "No."	12·00	30·00
		b. Imperf between (vert pair)	£3500	
		c. Missing stop after "ST"	40·00	65·00
		d. Incorrect number with correction above	£170	

It is believed that there were three settings of the 1d. and two of the 2d., the same type being used for both values.

For the initial setting of the 1d. the wide "No." variety occurs on the last four stamps in the bottom row of the sheet of 60 (6 × 10). In later settings first the second and then later the first stamps in the same row were changed to show the variety. Nos. D1b and D2c occur on R.5/3 and No. D1c on R.9/2.

Some sheets from the initial printing of the 1d. show a paper-maker's watermark, "KINGSCLERE" in double-lined capitals above a crown, across a number of stamps.

The sheets had all outer edges, except that at the left, imperforate. It would appear that they were bound into books from which they could be detached, using the perforations at the left-hand edge.

The handstamped numbers were applied at the Post Office, using numbering machines. Each value had its own sequence of numbers and it is possible to recognise, by minor differences in fount, the use of two such machines. This is especially noticeable on examples of Nos. D1d and D2d where the corrections are often applied using a second machine. No. D2d shows the incorrect number partly erased and a correction struck across it.

D 2

D 3

D 4 St. Lucia Coat of Arms

(Typo D.L.R.)

1933–47. *Wmk Mult Script CA. P* 14.

D3	D 2	1d. black	3·50	3·50
D4		2d. black	6·00	6·00
D5		4d. black (28.6.47)	3·50	15·00
D6		8d. black (28.6.47)	3·50	17·00
D3/6		*Set of* 4	15·00	38·00
D3/6 Perf "Specimen"		*Set of* 4	£130	

1949 (1 Oct)–**52.** *Value in cents. Wmk Mult Script CA. Typo. P* 14.

D 7	D 3	2 c. black	1·75	9·50
		a. Chalky paper (27.11.52)	10	3·00
		ab. Error. Crown missing, W **9***a*	55·00	
		ac. Error. St. Edward's Crown, W **9***b*	24·00	
D 8		4 c. black	3·25	8·50
		a. Chalky paper (27.11.52)	30	4·25
		ab. Error. Crown missing, W **9***a*	70·00	
		ac. Error. St. Edward's Crown, W **9***b*	30·00	
D 9		8 c. black	2·75	13·00
		a. Chalky paper (27.11.52)	90	10·00
		ac. Error. St. Edward's Crown, W **9***b*	£110	
D10		16 c. black	12·00	28·00
		a. Chalky paper (27.11.52)	1·50	14·00
		ac. Error. St. Edward's Crown, W **9***b*	£130	
D7/10		*Set of* 4	18·00	55·00
D7a/10a		*Set of* 4	2·50	28·00

1965 (9 Mar). *As Nos.* D7/8 *but wmk* w **12**. *Unsurfaced paper. P* 14.

D11	D 3	2 c. black	35	4·00
D12		4 c. black	45	4·00

Nos. D9a, D10a and D11/12 exist overprinted as T **49** in red (*Price for set of* 4 £150 *mint*).

(Des L. Curtis. Litho Format)

1981 (4 Aug). *W* w **14**. *P* 14.

D13	D 4	5 c. brown-purple	10	10
D14		15 c. emerald	10	10
D15		25 c. red-orange	10	10
D16		$1 deep ultramarine	40	45
D13/16		*Set of* 4	50	55

OFFICIAL STAMPS

OFFICIAL (O 1) — **OFFICIAL** (O 2)

1983 (13 Oct). *Nos.* 537/48 *optd with Type* O **1**.

O 1	5 c. Type **120**	15	10
O 2	10 c. McDonnell Douglas "DC-10" airliner	15	10
O 3	15 c. Local bus	20	15
O 4	20 c. Refrigerated freighter	30	20
O 5	25 c. "Islander" aeroplane	35	20
O 6	30 c. Pilot boat	40	25
O 7	50 c. Boeing "727" airliner	55	35
O 8	75 c. *Cunard Countess* (liner)	75	50
O 9	$1 Lockheed "Tristar" airliner	95	75
O10	$2 Cargo liner	1·75	1·75
O11	$5 Boeing "707" airliner	3·50	3·50
O12	$10 *Queen Elizabeth 2* (liner)	6·50	7·50
O1/12	*Set of* 12	14·00	14·00

1985 (7 May). *Nos.* 797/811 *optd with Type* O **2**.

O13	5 c. Type **156**	10	10
O14	10 c. Officer, Grenadier Company, 14th Regiment, 1780	10	10
O15	20 c. Officer, Battalion Company, 46th Regiment, 1781	10	10
O16	25 c. Officer, Royal Artillery, *c* 1782	10	10
O17	30 c. Officer, Royal Engineers, 1782	10	15
O18	35 c. Officer, Battalion Company, 54th Regiment, 1782	15	20
O19	45 c. Private, Grenadier Company, 14th Regiment, 1782	20	25
O20	50 c. Gunner, Royal Artillery, 1796	20	25
O21	65 c. Private, Battalion Company, 85th Regiment, *c* 1796	25	30
O22	75 c. Private, Battalion Company, 76th Regiment, 1796	30	35
O23	90 c. Private, Battalion Company, 81st Regiment, *c* 1796	35	40
O24	$1 Sergeant, 74th (Highland) Regiment, 1796	40	45
O25	$2.50, Private, Light Company, 93rd Regiment, 1803	1·00	1·10
O26	$5 Private, Battalion Company, 1st West India Regiment, 1803	2·10	2·25
O27	$15 Officer, Royal Artillery, 1850	6·25	6·50
O13/27	*Set of* 15	10·50	11·00

POSTAL FISCAL STAMPS

Nos. F1/28 were authorised for postal use from 14 April 1885.

CANCELLATIONS. Many used examples of the Postal Fiscal stamps have had previous pen cancellations removed before being used postally.

SHILLING STAMP (F 1) — One Penny Stamp (F 2) — HALFPENNY Stamp (F 3)

1881. *Wmk Crown CC. P* 14. (*a*) *Surch as Type* F **1**.

F1	1	ONE PENNY STAMP, black (C.)	28·00	35·00
		a. Surch inverted	£700	£700
		b. Surch double	£650	£700
F2		FOUR PENNY STAMP, yellow	50·00	60·00
		a. Bisected (2d.) (on cover)		
F3		SIX PENCE STAMP, mauve	90·00	£100
F4		SHILLING STAMP, orange	50·00	60·00
		a. "SHILEING"	£650	
		b. "SHILDING"	£650	£700
		(*b*) *Surch as Type* F **2**		
F 7	1	One Penny Stamp, black (R.)	28·00	35·00
		a. Surch double	£700	
F 8		Four Pence Stamp, yellow	45·00	50·00
F 9		Six Pence Stamp, mauve	45·00	50·00
F10		Shilling Stamp, orange	48·00	70·00
		(*c*) *Surch as Type* F **3**		
F11	1	Halfpenny Stamp, green	28·00	35·00
		a. "Stamp" double	£450	£450
F12		One Shilling Stamp, orange (*wmk Crown CA*)	50·00	55·00
		a. "Stamp" double	£450	£500

FOUR PENCE REVENUE (F 4) — Revenue (F 5) — REVENUE (F 6)

1882. *Wmk Crown CA. Surch as Type* F **4**. (*a*) *P* 14.

F13	1	1d. black (C.)	19·00	20·00
		a. Imperf. (pair)	£1100	
F14		2d. pale blue	9·00	9·50
		a. Imperf (pair)		
F15		3d. deep blue (C.)	32·00	35·00
F16		4d. yellow	10·00	4·00
F17		6d. mauve	19·00	20·00
		(*b*) *P* 12		
F18	1	1d. black (C.)	19·00	20·00
F19		3d. deep blue (C.)	26·00	20·00
F20		1s. orange	26·00	13·00

1883. *Nos.* 25, 26, 30 *and* 32 *optd locally as Type* F **5**.

	(*a*) *Word* 11 *mm long*		
F21	1d. black (C.)	17·00	28·00
	a. Opt inverted		
	b. Opt double	£250	£350
	(*b*) *Word* 13 *mm*		
F22	1d. black (C.)	—	40·00
	(*c*) *Word* 15½ *mm*		
F23	½d. green	—	32·00
	a. "Revenue" double	—	£225
F24	1d. black (C.)	15·00	10·00
	a. "Revenue" double	£130	
	b. "Revenue" triple	£250	
	c. "Revenue" double, one inverted	£250	£300
F25	1d. rose (No. 30)	—	38·00
F26	4d. yellow	—	45·00

1884–85. *Optd with Type* F **6**. *Wmk Crown CA. P* 14.

F27	5	1d. slate (C.)	10·00	10·00
		a. Imperf (pair)		
F28		1d. dull mauve (Die I) (1885)	10·00	7·50

St. Vincent

Although postal markings for St. Vincent are recorded as early as 1793 it was not until 1852 that the British G.P.O. opened a branch office at Kingstown, the island's capital.

The stamps of Great Britain were used between May 1858 and the end of April 1860. From 1 May in that year the local authorities assumed responsibility for the postal services and fell back on the use of No. CC1 until the introduction of St. Vincent stamps in 1861.

For illustration of the handstamp and postmark types see BRITISH POST OFFICES ABROAD notes, following GREAT BRITAIN.

KINGSTOWN

CROWNED-CIRCLE HANDSTAMPS

CC1 CC 1 ST. VINCENT (R.) (30.1.1852) *Price on cover* £750

Stamps of GREAT BRITAIN *cancelled* "A 10" *as Type* **2**.

1858 *to* **1860**.
Z1 1d. rose-red (1857), *perf* 14 .. .. £550
Z2 2d. blue (1855) .. ..
Z3 4d. rose (1857) £350
Z4 6d. lilac (1856) £250
Z5 1s. green (1856) £950

PRICES FOR STAMPS ON COVER TO 1945	
Nos. 1/2	*from* × 3
Nos. 3/7	*from* × 5
No. 8	—
No. 9	*from* × 5
No. 10	—
Nos. 11/19	*from* × 4
Nos. 20/1	*from* × 3
Nos. 22/5	*from* × 4
Nos. 26/8	—
Nos. 29/31	*from* × 5
No. 32	—
Nos. 33/5	*from* × 2
Nos. 36/8	*from* × 4
Nos. 39/41	*from* × 6
Nos. 42/5	*from* × 4
No. 46	*from* × 12
Nos. 47/54	*from* × 4
Nos. 55/8	*from* × 8
No. 59	*from* × 10
No. 60	*from* × 6
Nos. 61/3	*from* × 8
Nos. 67/75	*from* × 3
Nos. 76/84	*from* × 2
Nos. 85/92	*from* × 3
No. 93	—
Nos. 94/8	*from* × 3
Nos. 99/107	*from* × 2
Nos. 108/19	*from* × 3
No. 120	—
No. 121	*from* × 3
No. 122	*from* × 5
No. 123	—
No. 124	*from* × 5
Nos. 126/9	*from* × 10
Nos. 131/45	*from* × 3
Nos. 146/8	*from* × 6
Nos. 149/59	*from* × 2

CROWN COLONY

1

(2)

3

(T **1**, **3** and **7** recess P.B.)

1861 (8 May). *No wmk.* (a) *Intermediate perf* 14 *to* 16.
1 1 1d. rose-red £7000 £450
a. Imperf vert (horiz pair) .. ..
2 6d. deep yellow-green £5500 £200
(b) *Rough perf* 14 *to* 16
3 1 1d. rose-red .. .. 30·00 14·00
a. Imperf vert (horiz pair) £350
b. Imperf (pair) £250

1862 (Sept). *No wmk. Rough perf* 14 *to* 16.
4 1 6d. deep green .. .. 50·00 18·00
a. Imperf between (horiz pair) .. £1200
b. Imperf (pair) £400

1863–68. *No wmk.* (a) *P* 11 *to* 12½.
5 1 1d. rose-red (3.63) .. .. .. 32·00 15·00
6 4d. deep blue (*shades*) (1866) £275 £110
a. Imperf between (horiz pair) ..
7 6d. deep green (7.68) .. .. .. £200 60·00
8 1s. slate-grey (8.66) £1750 £900
(b) *P* 14 *to* 16
9 1 1s. slate-grey (*shades*) £300 £125
(c) *P* 11 *to* 12½ × 14 *to* 16
10 1 1d. rose-red £2750 £1300
11 1s. slate-grey (*shades*) £225 £120

1869. *Colours changed. No wmk. P* 11 *to* 12½.
12 1 4d. yellow £350 £150
13 1s. indigo .. .. £325 90·00
14 1s. brown £425 £160

1871 (Apr). *Wmk Small Star, Type* w **2**. *Rough perf* 14 *to* 16.
15 1 1d. black .. .. 35·00 10·00
a. Imperf between (vert pair) £4500
16 6d. deep green .. .. £250 70·00

1872. *Colour changed.* W w **2**. *P* 11 *to* 12½.
17 1 1s. deep rose-red.. .. .. .. £750 £140

1872–75. W w **2**. (a) *Perf about* 15.
18 1 1d. black (*shades*) (1872) .. .. 32·00 7·50
19 6d. dull blue-green (*shades*) (1873) .. £600 30·00
a. *Deep blue-green* (1875) .. .. £600 38·00
(b) *P* 11 *to* 12½ × 15
20 1 1s. lilac-rose (1873) £5000 £400

No. 19*a* always has the watermark sideways and Nos. 16 and 19 normally have it upright but are known with it sideways.

1875. *Colour changed.* W w **2**. *P* 11 *to* 12½.
21 1 1s. claret.. .. .. £600 £250

1876–78. W w **2**. (a) *P* 11 *to* 12½ × 15.
22 1 1d. black (*shades*) (1876) .. .. 50·00 6·00
a. Imperf between (horiz pair) .. — £3250
23 6d. pale green (1877) .. .. .. £500 45·00
24 1s. vermilion (2.77) .. .. .. £700 85·00
a. Imperf vert (horiz pair) .. ..
(b) *P* 11 *to* 12½
25 1 4d. deep blue (7.77) .. .. .. £450 90·00
(c) *Perf about* 15
26 1 6d. pale green (3.77) £1500 £450
a. *Light yellow-green* (1878) .. .. £550 25·00
27 1s. vermilion (1878?) .. .. .. — £6500
a. Imperf .. .. — £2000

Nos. 23 and 26 always have the watermark sideways but No. 26*a* always has the watermark upright.

1880 (May). *No.* 19*a divided vertically by a line of perforation gauging* 12, *and surch locally as T* **2**.
28 1 1d. on half 6d. bright blue-green (R.) .. £350 £225
a. Unsevered pair £1200 £900

1880 (June). *W* w **2**. *P* 11 *to* 12½.
29 1 1d. olive-green .. .. 85·00 3·25
30 6d. bright green .. .. £275 60·00
31 1s. bright vermilion .. .. .. £650 50·00
a. Imperf between (horiz pair) ..
32 3 5s. rose-red £1000 £1200
a. Imperf £3250

d
1
2
(4)

d
1
2
Straight serif to "1" (R. 6/20)

ONE PENNY
(5)

4d
(6)

1881. *Nos.* 30/31 *surch locally. No.* 33 *is divided vertically like No.* 28.
33 4 ½d. on half 6d. bright green (R.) (1.9) .. £160 £160
a. Unsevered pair £375 £375
b. Fraction bar omitted (pair with and without bar) £3250 £4000
c. Straight serif to "1" .. ..
34 5 1d. on 6d. bright green (30.11) £375 £250
35 6 4d. on 1s. bright vermilion (28.11) .. £1200 £700

It is believed that Type 4 was applied as a setting of 36 (6 × 6) surcharges repeated three times on each sheet across rows 1 to 9. The missing fraction bar occurs on R. 6/3 of the setting.

The tenth vertical row of stamps appears to have been surcharged from a separate setting of 12 (2 × 6) on which the "straight serif" flaw occurs on the bottom right half-stamp.

Three unused single copies of No. 33 are known with the surcharge omitted.

7

2½ PENCE
(8)

1d
2½ PENCE
(9)

1881 (Dec). W w **2**. *P* 11 *to* 12½.
36 7 ½d. orange (*shades*) .. .. .. 7·00 2·50
37 1 1d. drab (*shades*) .. .. .. £700 4·75
38 4d. bright blue £1200 £100
a. Imperf between (horiz pair)..

(Recess D.L.R. from Perkins, Bacon plates)

1882 (Nov)–**83.** *No.* 40 *is surch with T* **8**. *Wmk Crown CA. P* 14.
39 1 1d. drab .. .. 28·00 90
40 2½d. on 1d. lake (1883).. .. .. 7·00 40
41 4d. ultramarine .. .. .. £300 28·00
a. *Dull ultramarine* £950 £350

1883–84. *Wmk Crown CA. P* 12.
42 7 ½d. green (1884) .. .. 45·00 25·00
43 1 4d. ultramarine-blue .. .. .. £250 18·00
a. *Grey-blue* £1000 £300
44 6d. bright green £400 £300
45 1s. orange-vermilion .. .. .. 80·00 42·00

The ½d. orange, 1d. rose-red, 1d. milky blue (without surcharge) and 5s. carmine-lake which were formerly listed are now considered to be colour trials. They are, however, of great interest. (*Prices un.* ½d. £900, 1d. red £900, 1d. blue £1200, 5s. £1500.)

1885 (Mar). *No.* 40 *surch locally as in T* **9**.
46 1 1d. on 2½d. on 1d. lake .. .. .. 9·00 10·00

Stamps with three cancelling bars instead of two are considered to be proofs.

1885–93. *No.* 49 *is surch with T* **8**. *Wmk Crown CA. P* 14.
47 7 ½d. green 60 20
a. *Deep green* .. .. 2·25 50
48 1 1d. rose-red .. .. 1·90 80
a. *Rose* (1886) .. .. 4·25 1·50
b. *Red* (1887) .. .. 1·40 35
c. *Carmine-red* (1889) .. .. .. 23·00 3·00
49 2½d. on 1d. milky blue (1889) .. .. 23·00 4·00
50 4d. red-brown .. .. £850 22·00
51 4d. purple-brown (1886) .. .. .. 35·00 75
a. *Chocolate* (1887) .. .. .. 35·00 1·25
52 6d. violet (1888) .. .. 85·00 95·00
53 3 5s. lake (1888) .. .. 27·00 48·00
a. Printed both sides £3500
b. *Brown-lake* (1893).. .. .. 29·00 48·00
49, 51, 52 Optd "Specimen" .. *Set of* 3 £160

2½d.
(10)

5
PENCE
(11)

1890 (Aug). *No.* 51*a surch with T* **10**.
54 1 2½d. on 4d. chocolate .. .. .. 48·00 60·00
a. No fraction bar (R. 1/7, 2/4) .. £200 £225

1890–93. *No.* 55 *is surch with T* **8**. *Colours changed. Wmk Crown CA. P* 14.
55 1 2½d. on 1d. grey-blue (1890) .. .. 11·00 55
a. *Blue* (1893).. .. .. .. 75 30
56 4d. yellow (1893) (Optd S. £30) .. 1·60 4·25
57 6d. dull purple (1891) .. .. .. 2·00 4·25
58 1s. orange (1891) .. .. .. 5·50 9·00
a. *Red-orange* (1892).. .. .. 8·50 16·00

1892 (Nov). *No.* 51*a surch with T* **11**, *in purple*.
59 1 5d. on 4d. chocolate (Optd S. £30) .. 9·00 16·00

Some letters are known double due to loose type, the best known being the first "E", but they are not constant.

FIVE PENCE
(12)

13

14

1893–94. *Surch with T* **12**. *Wmk Crown CA. P* 14.
60 1 5d. on 6d. carmine-lake (Optd S. £45) .. 10·00 20·00
a. *Deep lake* (1893) .. .. .. 80 1·75
b. *Lake* (1894) .. .. 1·75 4·25
c. Surch double.. .. .. .. £4000 £2750

(Recess D.L.R.)

1897 (13 July). *New values. Wmk Crown CA. P* 14.
61 1 2½d. blue .. .. 2·50 2·25
62 5d. sepia .. .. 5·50 17·00
61/2 Optd "Specimen" .. .. *Set of* 2 60·00

1897 (6 Oct). *Surch as T* **12**. *Wmk Crown CA. P* 14.
63 1 3d. on 1d. mauve (Optd S. £40) .. .. 7·50 15·00
a. *Red-mauve* .. .. 9·50 22·00

(Typo D.L.R.)

1899. *Wmk Crown CA. P* 14.
67 13 ½d. dull mauve and green 85 75
68 1d. dull mauve and carmine .. .. 3·25 45
69 2½d. dull mauve and blue .. .. .. 4·00 2·00
70 3d. dull mauve and olive .. .. .. 4·00 8·50
71 4d. dull mauve and orange .. .. .. 4·00 13·00
72 5d. dull mauve and black .. .. .. 7·00 13·00
73 6d. dull mauve and brown .. .. .. 13·00 25·00
74 14 1s. green and carmine .. .. .. 13·00 32·00
75 5s. green and blue .. .. 60·00 £110
67/75 .. .. *Set of* 9 £100 £180
67/75 Optd "Specimen" .. .. *Set of* 9 £175

15

16

(Typo D.L.R.)

1902. *Wmk Crown CA. P* 14.
76 **15** ½d. dull purple and green 85 55
77 1d. dull purple and carmine 85 20
78 **16** 2d. dull purple and black .. .. 1·75 2·25
79 **15** 2½d. dull purple and blue .. .. 2·00 3·25
80 3d. dull purple and olive .. .. 2·00 2·00
81 6d. dull purple and brown .. .. 9·00 18·00
82 **16** 1s. green and carmine .. .. .. 11·00 32·00
83 **15** 2s. green and violet .. .. .. 22·00 38·00
84 **16** 5s. green and blue .. .. .. 45·00 80·00
76/84 .. .. *Set of* 9 85·00 £160
76/84 Optd "Specimen" .. .. *Set of* 9 £120

1904–11. *Wmk Mult Crown CA. P* 14.
85 **15** ½d. dull purple and green, **OC** (1905) .. 75 80
86 1d. dull purple and carmine, **OC** .. 5·50 40
88 2½d. dull purple and blue, **C** (1906) .. 9·50 22·00
89 6d. dull purple and brown, **C** (1905) .. 10·00 22·00
90 **16** 1s. green and carmine, **OC** (1906) .. 8·00 22·00
91 **15** 2s. purple and bright blue/*blue*, **C** (3.09?) .. 22·00 42·00
92 **16** 5s. green and red/*yellow*, **C** (3.09?) .. 17·00 42·00
93 £1 purple and black/*red*, **C** (22.7.11) .. £300 £350
85/93 .. .. *Set of* 8 £350 £450
91/3 Optd "Specimen" .. .. *Set of* 3 £225

17 18

(Recess D.L.R.)

1907–08. *Wmk Mult Crown CA. P* 14.
94 **17** ½d. green (2.7.07) .. .. 1·00 65
95 1d. carmine (26.4.07) .. .. 2·50 15
96 2d. orange (5.08) .. .. 1·00 5·50
97 2½d. blue (8.07) .. .. 9·00 8·50
98 3d. violet (1.6.07) .. .. 4·25 14·00
94/8 .. .. *Set of* 5 16·00 26·00
94/8 Optd "Specimen" .. .. *Set of* 5 £100

1909. *No dot below* "d". *Wmk Mult Crown CA. P* 14.
99 **18** 1d. carmine (3.09) .. .. 1·25 25
100 6d. dull purple (16.1.09) .. .. .. 5·50 23·00
101 1s. black/*green* (16.1.09) .. .. .. 3·75 7·00
99/101 .. .. *Set of* 3 9·50 27·00
99/101 Optd "Specimen" .. .. *Set of* 3 60·00

1909 (Nov)–**11.** *T* **18**, *redrawn* (*dot below* "d", *as in T* **17**). *Wmk Mult Crown CA. P* 14.
102 ½d. green (31.10.10) .. .. 1·00 40
103 1d. carmine .. .. 1·00 15
104 2d. grey (3.8.11) .. .. 1·75 8·00
105 2½d. ultramarine (25.7.10) .. .. .. 3·00 2·00
106 3d. purple/*yellow* .. .. 2·00 3·00
107 6d. dull purple .. .. 2·00 5·00
102/7 .. .. *Set of* 6 9·50 17·00
102 and 104/6 Optd "Specimen" .. *Set of* 4 80·00

ONE

PENNY.

19 (20)

(Recess D.L.R.)

1913 (1 Jan)–**17.** *Wmk Mult Crown CA. P* 14.
108 **19** ½d. green 35 20
109 1d. red 60 25
a. Rose-red 75 35
b. Scarlet (1.17) .. .. 5·50 2·50
110 2d. grey .. .. 5·00 16·00
a. Slate .. .. 2·50 14·00
111 2½d. ultramarine 35 40
112 3d. purple/*yellow* .. .. 80 5·00
a. On lemon .. .. 2·50 11·00
b. On pale yellow .. .. 1·90 8·00
113 4d. red/*yellow* .. .. 80 2·00
114 5d. olive-green (7.11.13) .. .. .. 2·25 12·00
115 6d. claret .. .. 2·00 4·50
116 1s. black/*green* .. .. 1·50 3·25
117 1s. bistre (1.5.14) .. .. 3·50 9·00
118 **18** 2s. blue and purple .. .. .. 4·75 16·00
119 5s. carmine and myrtle .. .. .. 13·00 32·00
120 £1 mauve and black .. .. .. 70·00 £130
108/20 .. .. *Set of* 13 90·00 £190
108/20 Optd "Specimen" .. .. *Set of* 13 £250

Nos. 118/20 are from new centre and frame dies, the motto "PAX ET JUSTITIA" being slightly over 7 mm long, as against just over 8 mm in Nos. 99 to 107. Nos. 139/41 are also from the new dies.

1915. *Surch with T* **20**.
121 **19** 1d. on 1s. black/*green* (R.) .. .. 2·75 13·00
a. "ONE" omitted £850
b. "ONE" double £750
c. "PENNY" and bar double £700

The spacing between the two words varies from 7¾ mm to 10 mm.

WAR STAMP. WAR STAMP. WAR STAMP

(21) (22) (24)

1916 (June). *No.* 109 *optd locally with T* **21**. (*a*) *First and second settings; words* 2 *to* 2½ *mm apart.*
122 **19** 1d. red .. .. 1·50 2·75
a. Opt double £140 £140
b. Comma for stop .. .. .. 7·00 11·00

In the first printing every second stamp has the comma for stop. The second printing of this setting has full stops only. These two printings can therefore only be distinguished in blocks or pairs.

(*b*) *Third setting; words only* 1½ *mm apart*
123 **19** 1d. red .. .. 45·00
a. Opt double £1100

Stamps of the first setting are offered as this rare one. Care must be taken to see that the distance between the lines is not over 1½ mm.

(*c*) *Fourth setting; optd with T* **22**. *Words* 3½ *mm apart*
124 **19** 1d. carmine-red .. .. 1·25 4·00
a. Opt double £200

1916 (Aug)–**18.** *T* **19**, *new printing, optd with T* **24**.
126 1d. carmine-red (Optd S. £60) 25 50
127 1d. pale rose-red 20 50
128 1d. deep rose-red 15 50
129 1d. pale scarlet (1918) 15 50

1921–32. *Wmk Mult Script CA. P* 14.
131 **19** ½d. green (3.21) 25 15
132 1d. carmine (6.21) 20 25
a. Red 25 15
132*b* 1½d. brown (1.12.32) 60 15
133 2d. grey (3.22) 25 25
133*a* 2½d. bright blue (12.25) 60 25
134 3d. bright blue (3.22) .. .. .. 90 6·00
135 3d. purple/*yellow* (1.12.26) .. .. 45 1·50
135*a* 4d. red/*yellow* (9.30) .. .. .. 1·75 6·00
136 5d. sage-green (8.3.24) .. .. .. 70 5·00
137 6d. claret (1.11.27) .. .. .. 80 3·50
138 1s. bistre-brown (9.21) .. .. .. 2·00 7·00
a. Ochre (1927) .. .. .. 1·50 10·00
139 **18** 2s. blue and purple (8.3.24) .. .. 4·00 13·00
140 5s. carmine and myrtle (8.3.24) .. 10·00 30·00
141 £1 mauve and black (9.28) .. .. 70·00 £110
131/41 .. .. *Set of* 14 80·00 £160
131/41 Optd/Perf "Specimen" .. *Set of* 14 £250

1935 (6 May). *Silver Jubilee. As Nos.* 91/4 *of Antigua but ptd by Waterlow. P* 11 × 12.
142 1d. deep blue and scarlet 40 45
143 1½d. ultramarine and grey 75 55
144 2½d. brown and deep blue .. .. .. 1·25 55
145 1s. slate and purple .. .. 2·00 3·50
k. Kite and horizontal log .. .. 50·00
142/5 .. .. *Set of* 4 4·00 4·50
142/5 Perf "Specimen" .. .. *Set of* 4 75·00

For illustration of plate variety see Omnibus section following Zululand.

1937 (12 May). *Coronation. As Nos.* 13/15 *of Aden but ptd by B.W. P* 11 × 11½.
146 1d. violet 35 15
147 1½d. carmine 55 10
148 2½d. blue 65 45
146/8 .. .. *Set of* 3 1·40 60
146/8 Perf "Specimen" .. .. *Set of* 3 50·00

25

26 Young's Island and Fort Duvernette

27 Kingstown and Fort Charlotte

28 Bathing Beach at Villa

29 Victoria Park, Kingstown

(Recess B.W.)

1938 (11 Mar)–**47.** *Wmk Mult Script CA. P* 12.
149 **25** ½d. blue and green 10 10
150 **26** 1d. blue and lake-brown 10 10
151 **27** 1½d. green and scarlet 15 10
152 **25** 2d. green and black 40 35
153 **28** 2½d. blue-black and blue-green 10 40
153*a* **29** 2½d. green and purple-brown (1947) .. 10 10
154 **25** 3d. orange and purple 15 10
154*a* **28** 3½d. blue-black and blue-green (1947) .. 40 60
155 **25** 6d. black and lake 40 35
156 **29** 1s. purple and green 40 40
157 **25** 2s. blue and purple .. .. .. 3·50 55
157*a* 2s. 6d. red-brown and blue (1947) .. 1·00 3·50
158 5s. scarlet and deep green .. .. 7·00 2·50
158*a* 10s. violet and brown (1947) .. .. 3·50 7·50
159 £1 purple and black .. .. .. 13·00 15·00
149/59 .. .. *Set of* 15 26·00 28·00
149/59 Perf "Specimen" .. .. *Set of* 15 £250

1946 (15 Oct). *Victory. As Nos.* 28/9 *of Aden.*
160 1½d. carmine 10 10
161 3½d. blue 10 10
160/1 Perf "Specimen" .. .. *Set of* 2 50·00

1948 (30 Nov). *Royal Silver Wedding. As Nos.* 30/1 *of Aden.*
162 1½d. scarlet 10 10
163 £1 bright purple .. .. 15·00 12·00

No. 163 was originally printed in black, but the supply of these was stolen in transit. A few archive examples exist, some perforated "Specimen".

(New Currency. 100 cents=1 West Indian dollar)

1949 (26 Mar)–**52.** *Value in cents and dollars. Wmk Mult Script CA. P* 12.
164 **25** 1 c. blue and green 20 15
164*a* 1 c. green and black (10.6.52) 25 25
165 **26** 2 c. blue and lake-brown 15 15
166 **27** 3 c. green and scarlet 40 15
166*a* **25** 3 c. orange and purple (10.6.52) 25 25
167 4 c. green and black 35 20
167*a* 4 c. blue and green (10.6.52) 25 15
168 **29** 5 c. green and purple-brown 15 10
169 **25** 6 c. orange and purple 40 25
169*a* **27** 6 c. green and scarlet (10.6.52) 25 15
170 **28** 7 c. blue-black and blue-green .. .. 1·25 30
170*a* 10 c. blue-black and blue-green (10.6.52) 50 20
171 **25** 12 c. black and lake 35 15
172 **29** 24 c. purple and green 35 30
173 **25** 48 c. blue and purple .. .. .. 1·50 1·50
174 60 c. red-brown and blue .. .. .. 1·75 1·75
175 $1.20, scarlet and deep green .. .. 3·75 4·00
176 $2.40, violet and brown .. .. .. 5·50 9·00
177 $4.80, purple and black .. .. .. 10·00 17·00
164/77 .. .. *Set of* 19 24·00 32·00

1949 (10 Oct). *75th Anniv of Universal Postal Union. As Nos.* 114/17 *of Antigua.*
178 5 c. blue 15 15
179 6 c. purple 25 25
180 12 c. magenta 30 30
181 24 c. blue-green 40 25
178/81 .. .. *Set of* 4 1·00 85

1951 (16 Feb). *Inauguration of B.W.I. University College. As Nos.* 118/19 *of Antigua.*
182 3 c. deep green and scarlet 20 15
183 12 c. black and purple 25 15

1951 (21 Sept). *New Constitution. Optd with T* **34** *of Dominica, by B.W.*
184 **27** 3 c. green and scarlet 10 15
185 **25** 4 c. green and black 10 15
186 **29** 5 c. green and purple-brown 10 15
187 **25** 12 c. black and lake 10 15
184/7 .. .. *Set of* 4 30 55

1953 (2 June). *Coronation. As No.* 47 *of Aden.*
188 4 c. black and green 30 15

30 31

(Recess Waterlow (until 1961), then D.L.R.)

1955 (16 Sept)–**63.** *Wmk Mult Script CA. P* 13½×14 (*T* **30**) *or* 14 (*T* **31**).
189 **30** 1 c. orange 10 10
a. Deep orange (11.12.62) 45 60
190 2 c. ultramarine 10 10
a. Blue (26.9.61) 15 10
191 3 c. slate 25 10
192 4 c. brown 15 10
193 5 c. scarlet 25 10
194 10 c. reddish violet 20 10
a. Deep lilac (12.2.58) 20 10
195 15 c. deep blue 55 20
196 20 c. green 60 10
197 25 c. black-brown 50 10
198 **31** 50 c. red-brown .. .. 2·25 90
a. Chocolate (11.6.58) .. .. .. 2·25 75
199 $1 myrtle-green .. .. 3·50 1·00
a. Deep myrtle-green (11.6.58) .. .. 8·00 4·00
b. Deep yellowish green (15.1.63) .. 12·00 8·00
200 $2.50, deep blue .. .. 12·00 6·50
a. Indigo-blue (30.7.62) .. .. .. 25·00 12·00
189/200 .. .. *Set of* 12 18·00 8·00

See also Nos. 207/20 and **MS**633.

1958 (22 Apr). *Inauguration of British Caribbean Federation. As Nos.* 135/7 *of Antigua.*
201 3 c. deep green 40 20
202 6 c. blue 55 35
203 12 c. scarlet 80 35
201/3 .. .. *Set of* 3 1·60 80

MINISTERIAL GOVERNMENT

1963 (4 June). *Freedom from Hunger. As No.* 76 *of Aden.*
204 8 c. reddish violet 60 50

1963 (2 Sept). *Red Cross Centenary. As Nos.* 147/8 *of Antigua.*
205 4 c. red and black 15 20
206 8 c. red and blue 35 50

(Recess D.L.R.)

1964–65. *As* 1955 *but wmk* w **12.** (*a*) *P* 12½ (14 Jan–Feb 1964).
207 **30** 10 c. deep lilac 40 45
208 15 c. deep blue 70 50
209 20 c. green (24.2.64*) .. .. 5·50 2·00
210 25 c. black-brown .. .. 1·00 50
211 **31** 50 c. chocolate .. .. 4·00 8·00
207/11 .. .. *Set of* 5 10·50 10·00
(*b*) *P* 13 × 14 (*T* **30**) *or* 14 (*T* **31**)
212 **30** 1 c. orange (15.12.64) 15 10
213 2 c. blue (15.12.64) 15 10
214 3 c. slate (15.12.64) 50 10
215 5 c. scarlet (15.12.64) 15 10
216 10 c. deep lilac (15.12.64) 15 10
217 15 c. deep blue (9.11.64).. .. .. 80 30
218 20 c. green (1964) 45 10
219 25 c. black-brown (20.10.64) .. .. 1·25 25
220 **31** 50 c. chocolate (18.1.65).. .. .. 4·00 6·50
212/20 .. .. *Set of* 9 6·75 6·50
*This is the earliest known date recorded in St. Vincent although it may have been put on sale on 14.1.64.

32 Scout Badge and Proficiency Badges

33 Tropical Fruits

(Des V. Whiteley. Litho Harrison)

1964 (23 Nov). *50th Anniv of St. Vincent Boy Scouts Association.* W w **12.** *P* 14½.
221 **32** 1 c. yellow-green and chocolate 10 10
222 4 c. blue and brown-purple 10 10
223 20 c. yellow and black-violet 20 10
224 50 c. red and bronze-green 40 15
221/4 .. .. *Set of* 4 60 20

(Des V. Whiteley. Photo Harrison)

1965 (23 Mar). *Botanic Gardens Bicentenary. T* **33** *and similar multicoloured designs.* W w **12.** *P* 14½ × 13½ (*horiz*) *or* 13½ × 14½ (*vert*).
225 1 c. Type **33** 10 10
226 4 c. Breadfruit and H.M.S. *Providence*, 1791 10 10
227 25 c. Doric Temple and pond (*vert*) 15 10
228 40 c. Talipot Palm and Doric Temple (*vert*) .. 30 35
225/8 .. .. *Set of* 4 50 45

1965 (17 May). *I.T.U. Centenary. As Nos.* 166/7 *of Antigua.*
229 4 c. light blue and light olive-green 25 10
230 48 c. ochre-yellow and orange.. .. .. 1·00 45

37 Boat-building, Bequia (inscr "BEOUIA")

(Des M. Goaman. Photo Harrison)

1965 (16 Aug)–**67.** *T* **37** *and similar multicoloured designs.* W w **12.** *P* 14½ × 13½ (*horiz designs*) *or* 13½ × 14½ (*vert*).
231 1 c. Type **37** ("BEOUIA") 10 20
231*a* 1 c. Type **37** ("BEQUIA") (27.6.67) 10 10
232 2 c. Friendship Beach, Bequia 10 10
233 3 c. Terminal Building, Arnos Vale Airport 15 10
234 4 c. Woman with bananas (*vert*) .. .. 1·00 30
235 5 c. Crater Lake 15 10
236 6 c. Carib Stone (*vert*) 15 10
237 8 c. Arrowroot (*vert*).. .. .. .. 20 10
238 10 c. Owia Salt Pond 20 10
239 12 c. Deep water wharf 30 10
240 20 c. Sea Island cotton (*vert*) 30 10
241 25 c. Map of St. Vincent and islands (*vert*) .. 35 10
242 50 c. Breadfruit (*vert*).. .. .. .. 50 25
243 $1 Baleine Falls (*vert*) .. .. .. 4·00 30
244 $2.50, St. Vincent Amazon (*vert*) .. .. 12·00 4·00
245 $5 Arms of St. Vincent (*vert*) .. .. 7·00 5·50
231/45 .. .. *Set of* 16 22·00 10·00
The 1 c. (No. 231*a*), 2 c., 3 c., 5 c. and 10 c. exist with PVA gum as well as gum arabic.
See also No. 261.

1966 (24 Jan). *Churchill Commemoration. As Nos.* 170/3 *of Antigua.*
246 1 c. new blue 10 10
247 4 c. deep green 35 10
248 20 c. brown 75 45
249 40 c. bluish violet .. .. 1·50 1·25
246/9 .. .. *Set of* 4 2·40 1·60

1966 (4 Feb). *Royal Visit. As Nos.* 174/5 *of Antigua.*
250 4 c. black and ultramarine .. .. .. 1·50 25
251 25 c. black and magenta .. .. .. 4·00 1·25

1966 (20 Sept). *Inauguration of W.H.O. Headquarters, Geneva. As Nos.* 178/9 *of Antigua.*
252 4 c. black, yellow-green and light blue .. 30 10
253 25 c. black, light purple and yellow-brown .. 95 80

1966 (1 Dec). *20th Anniv of U.N.E.S.C.O. As Nos.* 196/8 *of Antigua.*
254 4 c. slate-violet, red, yellow and orange .. 40 10
255 8 c. orange-yellow, violet and deep olive .. 75 10
256 25 c. black, bright purple and orange.. .. 1·50 60
254/6 .. .. *Set of* 3 2·40 70

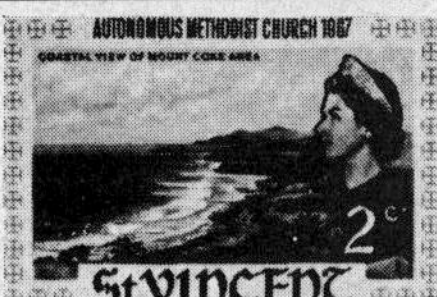

38 Coastal View of Mount Coke Area

(Des and photo Harrison)

1967 (1 Dec). *Autonomous Methodist Church. T* **38** *and similar horiz designs. Multicoloured.* W w **12.** *P* 14 × 14½.
257 2 c. Type **38** 10 10
258 8 c. Kingstown Methodist Church 10 10
259 25 c. First Licence to perform marriages .. 15 10
260 35 c. Conference Arms 15 10
257/60 .. .. *Set of* 4 35 15

1968 (20 Feb). *As No.* 234, *but W* w **12** *sideways.*
261 4 c. Woman with bananas 30 20
The above exists with PVA gum as well as gum arabic.

39 Meteorological Institute

(Des G. Vasarhelyi. Photo Harrison)

1968 (28 May). *World Meteorological Day.* W w **12.** *P* 14 × 14½.
262 **39** 4 c. multicoloured 10 10
263 25 c. multicoloured 10 10
264 35 c. multicoloured 15 10
262/4 .. .. *Set of* 3 25 15

40 Dr. Martin Luther King and Cotton Pickers

(Des V. Whiteley. Litho D.L.R.)

1968 (28 Aug). *Martin Luther King Commemoration.* W w **12** (*sideways*). *P* 13.
265 **40** 5 c. multicoloured 10 10
266 25 c. multicoloured 10 10
267 35 c. multicoloured 10 10
265/7 .. .. *Set of* 3 15 15

41 Speaker addressing Demonstrators

42 Scales of Justice and Human Rights Emblem

(Des V. Whiteley. Photo Enschedé)

1968 (1 Nov). *Human Rights Year. P* 13 × 14 (3 *c.*) *or* 14 × 13 (35 *c.*).
268 **41** 3 c. multicoloured 10 10
269 **42** 35 c. royal blue and turquoise-blue 10 10

43 Male Masquerader

44 Steel Bandsman

(Des V. Whiteley. Litho Format)

1969 (17 Feb). *St. Vincent Carnival. T* **43/4** *and similar designs. P* 14.
270 1 c. multicoloured 10 10
271 5 c. red and deep chocolate 10 10
272 8 c. multicoloured 10 10
273 25 c. multicoloured 15 15
270/3 .. .. *Set of* 4 30 20
Designs: *Horiz*—8 c. Carnival Revellers. *Vert*—25 c. Queen of Bands.

METHODIST CONFERENCE MAY 1969
(47)

1969 (14 May). *Methodist Conference. Nos.* 257/8, 241 *and* 260 *optd with T* **47**.
274 2 c. multicoloured 10 15
275 8 c. multicoloured 30 40
276 25 c. multicoloured 35 40
277 35 c. multicoloured .. .. 1·50 3·00
274/7 .. .. *Set of* 4 2·00 3·50

48 "Strength in Unity"

49 Map of "CARIFTA" Countries

(Des J. Cooter. Litho D.L.R.)

1969 (1 July). *First Anniv of CARIFTA (Caribbean Free Trade Area).* W w **12** (*sideways on T* **48**). *P* 13.
278 **48** 2 c. black, pale buff and red 10 10
279 **49** 5 c. multicoloured 10 10
280 **48** 8 c. black, pale buff and pale green 10 10
281 **49** 25 c. multicoloured 15 15
278/81 .. .. *Set of* 4 25 25

ASSOCIATED STATEHOOD

50 Flag of St. Vincent

(Des V. Whiteley, based on local designs. Photo Harrison)

1969 (27 Oct). *Statehood. T* **50** *and similar horiz designs.* W w **12.** *P* 14 × 14½.
282 4 c. multicoloured 10 10
283 10 c. multicoloured 10 10
284 50 c. grey, black and orange 15 10
282/4 .. .. *Set of* 3 25 15
Designs:—10 c. Battle scene with insets of Petroglyph and Carib chief Chatoyer; 50 c. Carib House with maces and scales.

51 Green Heron

(Des J.W. Photo Harrison)

1970 (12 Jan)–**71.** *T* **51** *and similar multicoloured designs. Chalk-surfaced paper.* W w **12** (*sideways on* 1, 2, 3, 6, 8, 20, 25 *c.*, $1, $2.50 *and upright on others*). *P* 14.
285 ½ c. House Wren (*vert*) 10 30
286 1 c. Type **51** 35 50
a. Glazed, ordinary paper (9.8.71).. .. 15 40
287 2 c. Lesser Antillean Bullfinches 15 20
288 3 c. St. Vincent Amazons 15 20
289 4 c. Rufous-throated Solitaire (*vert*) 20 20
290 5 c. Red-necked Pigeon (*vert*) .. .. .. 2·75 30
a. Glazed, ordinary paper (9.8.71).. .. 1·00 30
291 6 c. Bananaquits 25 10
292 8 c. Purple-throated Carib 25 10
293 10 c. Mangrove Cuckoo (*vert*) 30 10
294 12 c. Common Black Hawk (*vert*) 40 10
295 20 c. Bare-eyed Thrush 60 15
296 25 c. Hooded Tanager 70 20
297 50 c. Blue Hooded Euphonia .. .. .. 1·25 75
298 $1 Barn Owl (*vert*) .. .. 5·50 3·00
299 $2.50, Yellow-bellied Elaenia (*vert*) .. .. 6·50 3·50
300 $5 Ruddy Quail Dove .. .. 11·00 5·00
285/300 .. .. *Set of* 16 25·00 13·00
See also Nos. 361/8 and 396/8.

ALTERED CATALOGUE NUMBERS

Any Catalogue numbers altered from the last edition are shown as a list in the introductory pages.

52 "DHC-6" Twin Otter

(Des R. Granger Barrett. Litho Enschedé)

1970 (13 Mar). *20th Anniv of Regular Air Services. T* **52** *and similar horiz designs. Multicoloured. W w* **12** *(sideways). P* 14 × 13.

No.	Description	Unused	Used
301	5 c. Type **52**	10	10
302	8 c. Grumman "Goose"	15	10
303	10 c. Hawker Siddeley "HS-748"	20	10
304	25 c. Douglas "DC-3"	65	30
301/4	*Set of* 4	1·00	40

53 "Children's Nursery"

54 "Angel and the Two Marys at the Tomb" (stained-glass window)

(Des R. Granger Barrett. Photo Harrison)

1970 (1 June). *Centenary of British Red Cross. T* **53** *and similar horiz designs. Multicoloured. W w* **12**. *P* 14.

No.	Description	Unused	Used
305	3 c. Type **53**	10	10
306	5 c. "First Aid"	10	10
307	12 c. "Voluntary Aid Detachment"	10	10
308	25 c. "Blood Transfusion"	25	15
305/8	*Set of* 4	40	15

(Des L. Curtis. Litho J.W.)

1970 (7 Sept). *150th Anniv of St. George's Cathedral, Kingstown. T* **54** *and similar multicoloured designs. W w* **12** *(sideways on horiz designs). P* 14.

No.	Description	Unused	Used
309	½ c. Type **54**	10	10
310	5 c. St. George's Cathedral (*horiz*)	10	10
311	25 c. Tower, St. George's Cathedral	10	10
312	35 c. Interior, St. George's Cathedral (*horiz*)	15	10
313	50 c. Type **54**	20	30
309/13	*Set of* 5	45	35

55 "The Adoration of the Shepherds" (Le Nain)

(Des J. Cooter. Litho Questa)

1970 (23 Nov). *Christmas. T* **55** *and similar vert design. Multicoloured. W w* **12** *(sideways on 25 c., 50 c.). P* 14.

No.	Description	Unused	Used
314	8 c. "The Virgin and Child" (Bellini)	10	10
315	25 c. Type **55**	10	10
316	35 c. As 8 c.	10	10
317	50 c. Type **55**	15	20
314/17	*Set of* 4	35	25

56 New Post Office and 6d. Stamp of 1861

(Des J. Cooter. Litho Questa)

1971 (29 Mar). *110th Anniv of First St. Vincent Stamps. T* **56** *and similar horiz design. Multicoloured. W w* **12** *(sideways). P* 14.

No.	Description	Unused	Used
318	2 c. Type **56**	10	10
319	4 c. 1d. Stamp of 1861 and New Post Office	10	10
320	25 c. Type **56**	10	10
321	$1 As 4 c.	35	45
318/21	*Set of* 4	45	50

57 Trust Seal and Wildlife

58 "Madonna appearing to St. Anthony" (Tiepolo)

(Des G. Drummond. Litho J.W.)

1971 (4 Aug). *St. Vincent's National Trust. T* **57** *and similar horiz design. Multicoloured. W w* **12** *(sideways). P* 13½ × 14.

No.	Description	Unused	Used
322	12 c. Type **57**	25	10
323	30 c. Old Cannon, Fort Charlotte	40	15
324	40 c. Type **57**	55	25
325	45 c. As 30 c.	55	30
322/5	*Set of* 4	1·60	70

(Des J. Cooter. Litho Questa)

1971 (6 Oct). *Christmas. T* **58** *and similar horiz design. Multicoloured. W w* **12** *(sideways on 10 c. and $1). P* 14½ × 14 *(10 c., $1) or* 14 × 14½ *(5 c., 25 c.).*

No.	Description	Unused	Used
326	5 c. Type **58**	10	10
327	10 c. "The Holy Family on the Flight into Egypt" (detail, Pietro da Cortona)	10	10
328	25 c. Type **58**	10	10
329	$1 As 10 c.	30	35
326/9	*Set of* 4	40	40

59 Careening

60 Private, Grenadier Company, 32nd Foot (1764)

(Des J. Cooter. Litho J.W.)

1971 (25 Nov). *The Grenadines of St. Vincent. T* **59** *and similar vert designs. Multicoloured. W w* **12**. *P* 13½.

No.	Description	Unused	Used
330	1 c. Type **59**	10	10
331	5 c. Seine fishermen	10	10
332	6 c. Map of the Grenadines	10	10
333	15 c. Type **59**	10	10
334	20 c. As 5 c.	15	10
335	50 c. As 6 c.	30	60
330/5	*Set of* 6	50	80
MS336	177 × 140 mm. Nos. 330/5	7·00	11·00

(Des and litho J.W.)

1972 (14 Feb). *Military Uniforms. T* **60** *and similar vert designs. Multicoloured. W w* **12**. *P* 14 × 13½.

No.	Description	Unused	Used
337	12 c. Type **60**	90	15
338	30 c. Officer, Battalion Company, 31st Foot (1772)	1·75	65
339	50 c. Private, Grenadier Company, 6th Foot (1772)	2·50	1·00
337/9	*Set of* 3	4·50	1·60

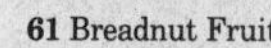

61 Breadnut Fruit

62 Candlestick Cassia

(Des P. Powell. Litho Questa)

1972 (16 May). *Fruit. T* **61** *and similar vert designs. Multicoloured. W w* **12** *(sideways). P* 13½.

No.	Description	Unused	Used
340	3 c. Type **61**	10	10
341	5 c. Pawpaw	10	10
342	12 c. Plumrose or Roseapple	30	30
343	25 c. Mango	70	70
340/3	*Set of* 4	1·00	1·00

(Des Sylvia Goaman. Litho B.W.)

1972 (31 July). *Flowers. T* **62** *and similar vert designs. Multicoloured. P* 13 *($1) or* 13½ × 14 *(others).*

No.	Description	Unused	Used
344	1 c. Type **62**	10	10
345	30 c. Lobster Claw	20	10
346	40 c. White Trumpet	25	15
347	$1 Soufriere tree	70	80
344/7	*Set of* 4	1·10	1·00

63 Sir Charles Brisbane and Coat of Arms

(Des Jennifer Toombs. Litho J.W.)

1972 (29 Sept). *Birth Bicentenary of Sir Charles Brisbane. T* **63** *and similar horiz designs. W w* **12** *(sideways). P* 13½.

No.	Description	Unused	Used
348	20 c. yellow-ochre, gold and red-brown	15	10
349	30 c. light yellow, light mauve and black	40	10
350	$1 multicoloured	1·40	70
348/50	*Set of* 3	1·75	75
MS351	171 × 111 mm. Nos. 348/50 (*sold at* $2)	4·50	6·50

Designs:—30 c. H.M.S. *Arethusa*, 1807; $1 H.M.S. *Blake*, 1808.

64 Arrowroot and Breadfruit

(Des (from photograph by D. Groves) and photo Harrison)

1972 (20 Nov). *Royal Silver Wedding. Multicoloured; background colour given. W w* **12**. *P* 14 × 14½.

No.	Type	Description	Unused	Used
352	**64**	30 c. red-brown	10	10
353		$1 myrtle-green	40	20

65 Sighting St. Vincent

66 "The Last Supper" (French Stained-glass Window)

(Des J. Cooter. Litho Enschedé)

1973 (31 Jan). *475th Anniv of Columbus's Third Voyage to the West Indies. T* **65** *and similar triangular designs. Multicoloured. W w* **12**. *P* 13½.

No.	Description	Unused	Used
354	5 c. Type **65**	25	10
355	12 c. Caribs watching Columbus's fleet	45	15
356	30 c. Christopher Columbus	1·00	60
357	50 c. *Santa Maria*	1·50	1·00
354/7	*Set of* 4	3·00	1·75

(Des J. Cooter. Litho Questa)

1973 (19 Apr). *Easter. T* **66** *and similar vert designs. Multicoloured. W w* **12** *(sideways). P* 14 × 13½.

No.	Type	Description	Unused	Used
358	**66**	15 c. multicoloured	10	10
		a. Horiz strip of 3. Nos. 358/60	45	
359	–	60 c. multicoloured	20	20
360	–	$1 multicoloured	20	20
358/60		*Set of* 3	45	45

Nos. 358, 360 and 359 were printed, in that order, horizontally *se-tenant* throughout a sheet of 45 stamps, and form a composite design of "The Last Supper".

1973 (13 June–23 Nov). *As Nos. 285 etc, but W w* **12** *upright on 2, 3, 6, 20 c. and sideways on others. Glazed paper.*

No.	Description	Unused	Used
361	2 c. Lesser Antillean Bullfinches (23.11)	20	15
362	3 c. St. Vincent Amazons (23.11)	20	15
363	4 c. Rufous-throated Solitaire (*vert*) (23.11)	25	15
364	5 c. Red-necked Pigeon (*vert*)	50	20
365	6 c. Bananaquits (23.11)	40	25
366	10 c. Mangrove Cuckoo (*vert*) (23.11)	55	15
367	12 c. Common Black Hawk (*vert*) (23.11)	85	55
368	20 c. Bare-eyed Thrush (23.11)	1·25	40
361/8	*Set of* 8	3·75	1·75

For the 1 c. value with watermark upright see Grenadines of St. Vincent No. 3a.

67 William Wilberforce and Poster   **68** P.P.F. Symbol

(Des Jennifer Toombs. Litho D.L.R.)

1973 (11 July). *140th Death Anniv of William Wilberforce. T* **67** *and similar horiz designs. Multicoloured. W w* **12**. *P* 14 × 13½.
369 30 c. Type **67** 10 10
370 40 c. Slaves cutting cane 15 15
371 50 c. Wilberforce and medallion 15 15
369/71 .. .. *Set of* 3 35 35

(Des PAD Studio. Litho Walsall)

1973 (3 Oct). *21st Anniv of International Planned Parenthood Federation. T* **68** *and similar vert design. Multicoloured. W w* **12** *(sideways). P* 14.
372 12 c. Type **68** 10 10
373 40 c. "IPPF" and symbol 20 20

1973 (14 Nov). *Royal Wedding. As Nos.* 165/6 *of Anguilla.*
374 50 c. deep blue 15 10
375 70 c. grey-green 20 10

69 Administrative Block, Mona

(Des PAD Studio. Litho Questa)

1973 (13 Dec). *25th Anniv of West Indies University. T* **69** *and similar multicoloured designs. W w* **12** *(sideways on* $1). *P* 14.
376 5 c. Type **69** 10 10
377 10 c. University Centre, Kingstown 10 10
378 30 c. Aerial view, Mona University 15 10
379 $1 University coat of arms *(vert)* 50 60
376/9 .. .. *Set of* 4 65 65

30c

(70)   **71** "The Descent from the Cross" (Sansovino)

1973 (15 Dec). *Nos.* 297, 292 *and* 298 *surch in half sheets with T* **70**, *by the Govt Printer, St. Vincent.*
380 30 c. on 50 c. multicoloured 50 30
a. Surch double .. .. 30·00
b. Surch double (on front) and single inverted (on reverse) .. .. .. 75·00
c. Surch double, one inverted .. .. 75·00
d. Surch inverted .. ..
381 40 c. on 8 c. multicoloured 60 40
a. Surch double .. .. 35·00
b. Surch inverted £125
382 $10 on $1 multicoloured .. .. .. 10·00 6·50
a. Surch double .. .. 95·00
b. Surch inverted £110
c. Surch double, one inverted £110
380/2 .. .. *Set of* 3 10·00 6·50

SPECIMEN STAMPS. From No. 383 onwards the stamps of St. Vincent exist overprinted "SPECIMEN", these being produced for publicity purposes.

(Des PAD Studio. Litho Enschedé)

1974 (10 Apr). *Easter. T* **71** *and similar vert designs showing sculptures. Multicoloured. W w* **12** *(sideways). P* 14 × 13½.
383 5 c. Type **71** 10 10
384 30 c. "The Deposition" (English, 14th-century) 10 10
385 40 c. "Pieta" (Fernandez) 10 10
386 $1 "The Resurrection" (French, 16th-century) 20 25
383/6 .. .. *Set of* 4 30 30

72 *Istra*

(Des J.W. Litho Questa)

1974 (28 June). *Cruise Ships. T* **72** *and similar horiz designs. Multicoloured. W w* **12** *(sideways). P* 14.
387 15 c. Type **72** 15 10
388 20 c. *Oceanic* 20 10
389 30 c. *Aleksandr Pushkin* 20 10
390 $1 *Europa* 50 30
387/90 .. .. *Set of* 4 95 40
MS391 134 × 83 mm. Nos. 387/90 .. .. 1·00 2·00

73 U.P.U. Emblem

(Des J.W. Litho Questa)

1974 (25 July). *Centenary of Universal Postal Union. T* **73** *and similar horiz designs. Multicoloured. W w* **12**. *P* 14.
392 5 c. Type **73** 10 10
393 12 c. Globe within posthorn 10 10
394 60 c. Map of St. Vincent and hand-cancelling 20 10
395 90 c. Map of the World 25 30
392/5 .. .. *Set of* 4 50 40

74 Royal Tern   **75** Scout Badge and Emblems

(Des J.W. Litho Questa)

1974 (29 Aug). *T* **74** *and similar vert designs. Multicoloured. Glazed paper. W w* **12** *(sideways on* 40 *c. and* $10). *P* 14.
396 30 c. Type **74** 90 45
397 40 c. Brown Pelican .. .. 1·00 60
398 $10 Magnificent Frigate Bird .. .. 17·00 9·00
396/8 .. .. *Set of* 3 17·00 9·00

(Des Sylvia Goaman. Litho Enschedé)

1974 (9 Oct). *Diamond Jubilee of Scout Movement in St. Vincent. W w* **12**. *P* 13 × 13½.
399 **75** 10 c. multicoloured 10 10
400 25 c. multicoloured 20 10
401 45 c. multicoloured 35 25
402 $1 multicoloured 75 50
399/402 .. .. *Set of* 4 1·25 75

76 Sir Winston Churchill   **77** The Shepherds

(Des C. Abbott. Litho Questa)

1974 (28 Nov). *Birth Centenary of Sir Winston Churchill. T* **76** *and similar vert designs. Multicoloured. W w* **12**. *P* 14.
403 25 c. Type **76** 10 10
404 35 c. Churchill in military uniform 15 10
405 45 c. Churchill in naval uniform 20 10
406 $1 Churchill in air-force uniform 35 40
403/6 .. .. *Set of* 4 70 50

(Des Jennifer Toombs. Litho Enschedé)

1974 (5 Dec). *Christmas. T* **77** *and similar vert designs. W w* **12**. *P* 12 × 12½.
407 **77** 3 c. violet-blue and black 10 10
a. Horiz strip of 4. Nos. 407/10 .. 20
408 – 3 c. violet-blue and black 10 10
409 – 3 c. violet-blue and black 10 10
410 – 3 c. violet-blue and black 10 10
411 **77** 8 c. apple-green and black 10 10
412 – 35 c. rose and deep maroon 20 10
413 – 45 c. olive-bistre and brown-black .. 20 10
414 – $1 lavender and slate-black 40 50
407/14 .. .. *Set of* 8 1·00 85

Designs:—Nos. 408, 412 Mary and crib; Nos. 409, 413 Joseph, ox and ass; Nos. 410, 414 The Magi.

Nos. 407/10 were issued horizontally *se-tenant* within the sheet, together forming a composite design of the Nativity.

MINIMUM PRICE

The minimum price quote is 10p which represents a handling charge rather than a basis for valuing common stamps. For further notes about prices see introductory pages.

78 Faces

(Des G. Drummond. Litho D.L.R.)

1975 (7–27 Feb). *Kingstown Carnival. T* **78** *and similar horiz designs. Multicoloured. W w* **12**. *P* 14 × 13½.
415 1 c. Type **78** 10 10
a. Booklet pane. No. 415 × 2 plus printed label (27.2) 35
b. Booklet pane. Nos. 415, 417 and 419 (27.2) 45
416 15 c. Pineapple women 20 15
a. Booklet pane. Nos. 416, 418 and 420 (27.2) 70
417 25 c. King of the Bands 20 20
418 35 c. Carnival dancers.. .. .. .. 25 15
419 45 c. Queen of the Bands 25 20
420 $1.25, "African Splendour" 35 55
415/20 .. .. *Set of* 6 1·10 1·10
MS421 146 × 128 mm. Nos. 415/20 .. .. 1·25 3·00

79 French Angelfish

Two types of $2.50:

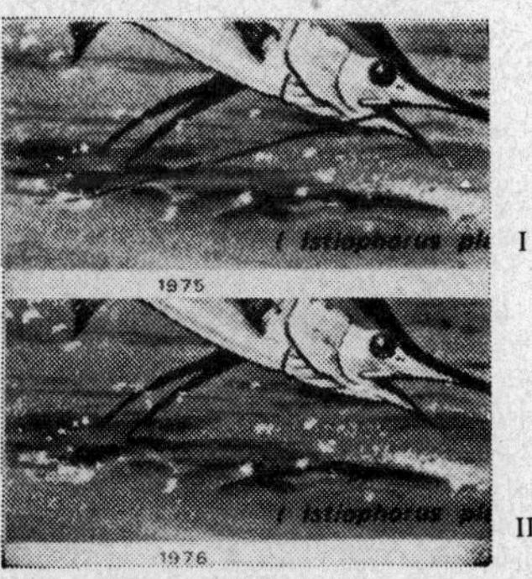

Type I. Fishing-line attached to fish's mouth. Imprint "1975".
Type II. Fishing-line omitted. Imprint "1976".

(Des G. Drummond. Litho Questa)

1975 (10 Apr)–**76**. *T* **79** *and similar horiz designs. Multicoloured. W w* **14** *(sideways). P* 14½.
422 1 c. Type **79** 15 25
423 2 c. Spotfin Butterfly-fish 15 25
424 3 c. Horse-eyed Jack 15 15
425 4 c. Mackerel 20 10
426 5 c. French Grunt 20 10
427 6 c. Spotted Goatfish 20 15
428 8 c. Ballyhoo 20 15
429 10 c. Sperm Whale 30 10
430 12 c. Humpback Whale 40 30
431 15 c. Cowfish 70 35
432 15 c. Skipjack (14.10.76) .. .. .. 2·75 35
433 20 c. Queen Angelfish 40 10
434 25 c. Princess Parrotfish 45 10
435 35 c. Red Hind 50 10
436 45 c. Atlantic Flying Fish 65 10
437 50 c. Porkfish 65 10
438 70 c. "Albacore" or Yellowfin Tuna (14.10.76) 3·75 70
439 90 c. Pompano (14.10.76) .. .. .. 3·75 70
440 $1 Queen Triggerfish 90 20
441 $2.50, Sailfish (I) .. .. 4·00 4·00
a. Type II (12.7.76) .. .. .. 3·50 1·50
442 $5 Dolphin Fish .. .. 5·00 2·50
443 $10 Blue Marlin .. .. 5·00 8·00
422/43 .. .. *Set of* 22 26·00 14·50

With the exception of Nos. 431, 435/6, 438/9 and 442 the above exist with different dates in the imprint at the foot of each stamp.

80 Cutting Bananas

(Des G. Drummond. Litho Questa)

1975 (26 June). *Banana Industry. T* **80** *and similar horiz designs. Multicoloured. W w* **12** *(sideways). P* 13½.
447 25 c. Type **80** 15 10
448 35 c. Packaging Station, La Croix 15 10
449 45 c. Cleaning and boxing 20 15
450 70 c. Shipping bananas aboard *Geest Tide* .. 40 30
447/50 .. .. *Set of* 4 80 50

81 Snorkel Diving

(Des G. Drummond. Litho Questa)

1975 (31 July). *Tourism. T* **81** *and similar horiz designs. Multicoloured. W w* **14** *(sideways). P* 13½.

451 15 c. Type **81** 15 10
452 20 c. Aquaduct Golf Course 20 10
453 35 c. Steel Band at Mariner's Inn 35 15
454 45 c. Sunbathing at Young Island 45 25
455 $1.25, Yachting marina .. .. .. 1·25 1·50
451/5 .. .. *Set of* 5 2·10 1·90

82 George Washington, John Adams, Thomas Jefferson and James Madison

(Des G. Drummond. Litho Questa)

1975 (11 Sept). *Bicentenary of American Revolution. T* **82** *and similar horiz designs. P* 14.

456 ½ c. black and lavender 10 10
457 1 c. black and light emerald 10 10
458 1½ c. black and light magenta 10 10
459 5 c. black and bright yellow-green 10 10
460 10 c. black and light violet-blue 15 10
461 25 c. black and dull orange-yellow 25 10
462 35 c. black and light greenish blue 40 15
463 45 c. black and bright rose 50 15
464 $1 black and light orange 85 40
465 $2 black and light yellow-olive .. .. 1·50 75
456/65 .. .. *Set of* 10 3·50 1·50
MS466 179 × 156 mm. Nos. 456/65 .. .. 5·00 4·00

Presidents:—1 c. Monroe, Quincy Adams, Jackson, van Buren; 1½ c. W. Harrison, Tyler, Polk, Taylor; 5 c. Fillmore, Pierce, Buchanan, Lincoln; 10 c. Andrew Johnson, Grant, Hayes, Garfield; 25 c. Arthur, Cleveland, B. Harrison, McKinley; 35 c. Theodore Roosevelt, Taft, Wilson, Harding; 45 c. Coolidge, Hoover, Franklin Roosevelt, Truman; $1 Eisenhower, Kennedy, Lyndon Johnson, Nixon; $2 Pres. Ford and White House.

Nos. 456/65 were each issued in sheets of ten stamps and two *se-tenant* labels.

83/4 "Shepherds"

(Des Jennifer Toombs. Litho Harrison)

1975 (4 Dec). *Christmas. T* **83/4** *and similar triangular designs. P* 13½ × 14. A. *W w* **12** *(upright)*. B. *W w* **12** *(sideways)*.

		A		B	
467	3 c. black and magenta ..	10	10	10	10
	a. Block of 4. Nos. 467/70 ..	20	20	20	20
468	3 c. black and magenta ..	10	10	10	10
469	3 c. black and magenta ..	10	10	10	10
470	3 c. black and magenta ..	10	10	10	10
471	8 c. black & lt greenish blue ..	10	10	10	10
	a. Pair. Nos. 471/2 ..	15	15	15	15
472	8 c. black & lt greenish blue ..	10	10	10	10
473	35 c. black and yellow ..	20	20	20	20
	a. Pair. Nos. 473/4 ..	40	40	40	40
474	35 c. black and yellow ..	20	20	20	20
475	45 c. black and yellow-green ..	25	25	25	25
	a. Pair. Nos. 475/6 ..	50	50	50	50
476	45 c. black and yellow-green ..	25	25	25	25
477	$1 black and bright lilac ..	50	50	50	50
	a. Pair. Nos. 477/8 ..	1·00	1·00	1·00	1·00
478	$1 black and bright lilac ..	50	50	50	50
467/78	.. *Set of* 12	2·00	2·00	2·00	2·00

Designs:—No. 467, "Star of Bethlehem"; 468, "Holy Trinity"; 469, As T **83**; 470, "Three Kings"; 471/2, As 467; 473/4, As 468; 475/6, T **83/4**; 477/8 As 470. The two designs of each denomination (Nos. 471/8) differ in that the longest side is at the foot or at the top as shown in T **83/4**.

Each denomination was printed in sheets of 16, the designs being *se-tenant* and so arranged that the watermark comes upright, inverted, sideways right and sideways left.

85 Carnival Dancers

(Des G. Drummond. Litho Questa)

1976 (19 Feb). *Kingstown Carnival. T* **85** *and similar horiz designs. Multicoloured. W w* **14** *(sideways). P* 13½.

479 1 c. Type **85** 10 10
a. Booklet pane. Nos. 479 and 480 plus printed label 20
480 2 c. Humpty-Dumpty people 10 10
a. Booklet pane. Nos. 480/2 35
481 5 c. Smiling faces 10 10
482 35 c. Dragon worshippers 20 10
a. Booklet pane. Nos. 482/4 80
483 45 c. Carnival tableaux 25 15
484 $1.25, Bumble-Bee dancers 45 45
479/84 .. .. *Set of* 6 90 80

70¢

(86)

87 Blue-headed Hummingbird and Yellow Hibiscus

1976 (8 Apr). *Nos.* 424 *and* 437 *surch as T* **86**.

485 70 c. on 3 c. Horse-eyed Jack .. .. .. 1·25 1·25
a. Surch inverted .. .. 40·00
486 90 c. on 50 c. Porkfish .. .. .. 1·40 1·40
a. Surch inverted .. .. 45·00

(Des G. Drummond. Litho Walsall)

1976 (20 May). *Hummingbirds and Hibiscuses. T* **87** *and similar vert designs. Multicoloured. W w* **14** *(inverted). P* 13½.

487 5 c. Type **87** 35 10
488 10 c. Antillean Crested Hummingbird and Pink Hibiscus 60 15
489 35 c. Purple-throated Carib and White Hibiscus .. .. 1·40 55
a. No wmk .. .. 35·00
490 45 c. Blue-headed Hummingbird and Red Hibiscus .. .. 1·50 65
491 $1.25, Green-throated Carib and Peach Hibiscus .. .. 9·50 5·50
487/91 .. .. *Set of* 5 12·00 6·25

1976 (16 Sept). *West Indian Victory in World Cricket Cup. As Nos.* 559/60 *of Barbados.*

492 15 c. Map of the Caribbean 75 25
493 45 c. Prudential Cup .. .. 1·75 1·00

88 St Mary's Church, Kingstown

(Des G. Drummond. Litho Questa)

1976 (18 Nov). *Christmas. T* **88** *and similar horiz designs. Multicoloured. W w* **14** *(sideways). P* 14.

494 35 c. Type **88** 15 10
495 45 c. Anglican Church, Georgetown 15 10
496 50 c. Methodist Church, Georgetown 20 10
497 $1.25, St. George's Cathedral, Kingstown .. 40 60
494/7 .. .. *Set of* 4 80 70

89 Barrancoid Pot-stand

(Des G. Vasarhelyi. Litho J.W.)

1976 (16 Dec). *National Trust. T* **89** *and similar horiz designs. Multicoloured. W w* **14** *(sideways). P* 13½.

498 5 c. Type **89** 10 10
499 45 c. National Museum 15 10
500 70 c. Carib sculpture 25 20
501 $1 Ciboney petroglyph 45 50
498/501 .. .. *Set of* 4 80 75

90 William I, William II, Henry I and Stephen

(Des G. Vasarhelyi. Litho J.W.)

1977 (7 Feb). *Silver Jubilee. T* **90** *and similar horiz designs. Multicoloured. P* 13½. (a) *W w* **14** *(sideways). From sheets.*

502 ½ c. Type **90** 10 10
503 1 c. Henry II, Richard I, John, Henry III .. 10 10
504 1½ c. Edward I, Edward II, Edward III, Richard II 10 10
505 2 c. Henry IV, Henry V, Henry VI, Edward IV 10 10
506 5 c. Edward V, Richard III, Henry VII, Henry VIII 10 10
507 10 c. Edward VI, Lady Jane Grey, Mary I, Elizabeth I 10 10
508 25 c. James I, Charles I, Charles II, James II 20 15
509 35 c. William III, Mary II, Anne, George I .. 30 20
510 45 c. George II, George III, George IV .. 35 25
511 75 c. William IV, Victoria, Edward VII .. 45 35
512 $1 George V, Edward VIII, George VI .. 55 45
513 $2 Elizabeth II leaving Westminster Abbey 95 70
502/13 .. .. *Set of* 12 2·75 2·40
MS514 170 × 146 mm. Nos. 502/13. P 14½ × 14 4·00 4·00

(*b*) *No wmk. From booklets*

515 ½ c. Type **90** .. .. 2·00 2·50
a. Booklet pane. Nos. 515/18 *se-tenant* .. 7·50
516 1 c. As No. 503 .. .. 2·00 2·50
517 1½ c. As No. 504 .. .. 2·00 2·50
518 2 c. As No. 505 .. .. 2·00 2·50
519 5 c. As No. 506 .. .. 2·00 2·50
a. Booklet pane. Nos. 519/22 *se-tenant* .. 7·50
520 10 c. As No. 507 .. .. 2·00 2·50
521 25 c. As No. 508 .. .. 2·00 2·50
522 35 c. As No. 509 .. .. 2·00 2·50
523 45 c. As No. 510 .. .. 2·00 2·50
a. Booklet pane. Nos. 523/6 *se-tenant* .. 7·50
524 75 c. As No. 511 .. .. 2·00 2·50
525 $1 As No. 512 .. .. 2·00 2·50
526 $2 As No. 513 .. .. 2·00 2·50
515/26 .. .. *Set of* 12 22·00 26·00

Nos. 502/13 were each issued in sheets of ten stamps and two *se-tenant* labels.

91 Grant of Arms

(Des G. Drummond. Litho Questa)

1977 (12 May). *Centenary of Windward Is Diocese. T* **91** *and similar horiz designs. Multicoloured. W w* **14** *(sideways). P* 13½.

527 15 c. Type **91** 10 10
528 35 c. Bishop Berkeley and mitres 10 10
529 45 c. Map and arms of diocese 10 10
530 $1.25, St. George's Cathedral and Bishop Woodroffe 30 45
527/30 .. .. *Set of* 4 45 50

CARNIVAL 1977
JUNE 25TH-JULY 5TH

(92)

1977 (2 June). *Kingstown Carnival. Nos.* 426, 429, 432/3 *and* 440 *optd with T* **92**.

531 5 c. French Grunt 10 10
a. Red opt .. .. 60·00
532 10 c. Sperm Whale (R.) 10 10
a. Optd double (R. and Blk.) .. .. 60·00
533 15 c. Skipjack (R.) 10 10
a. Black opt .. .. 50·00
534 20 c. Queen Angel Fish (R.) 10 10
a. Opt inverted .. .. 22·00
b. Black opt .. .. 55·00
535 $1 Queen Triggerfish 40 40
a. Red opt .. .. 60·00
531/5 .. .. *Set of* 5 70 70

93 Guide and Emblem

CARIBBEAN
VISIT 1977

(94)

(Des PAD Studio. Litho J.W.)

1977 (1 Sept). *50th Anniv of St. Vincent Girl Guides. T* **93** *and similar vert designs. The $2 value is additionally optd. "1930–1977". Multicoloured.* W w **14.** *P* 13½.

536 5 c. Type **93** 10 10
537 15 c. Early uniform, ranger, guide and brownie 15 10
538 20 c. Early uniform and guide 15 10
539 $2 Lady Baden-Powell 70 60
a. Optd dates omitted .. .. 25·00
536/9 .. .. *Set of 4* 95 65

1977 (27 Oct). *Royal Visit. No.* 513 *optd with T* **94.**

540 $2 Queen Elizabeth leaving Westminster Abbey 40 30
a. Opt inverted .. .. 50·00

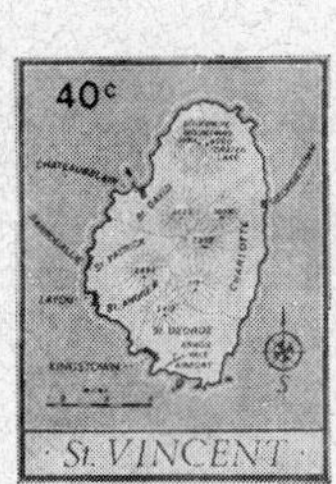

95 Map of St. Vincent

96 Opening Verse and Scene

(Des G. Drummond. Litho Questa)

1977–78. *Provisionals.* W w **12.** *P* 14½ × 14.

541 **95** 20 c. blk, dull violet-bl & pale bl (31.1.78) 15 15
542 40 c. black, dull orange & flesh (30.11.77) 25 20
a. Black (value) omitted .. .. 50·00
543 40 c. black, magenta and salmon (31.1.78) 20 15
541/3 .. .. *Set of 3* 55 45

Nos. 541/3 were printed in 1974, without value, for provisional use; they were locally surcharged before going on sale.

(Des Jennifer Toombs. Litho Enschedé)

1977 (1 Dec). *Christmas. Scenes and Verses from the carol "While Shepherds Watched their Flocks by Night". T* **96** *and similar vert designs. Multicoloured.* W w **14.** *P* 13 × 11.

544 5 c. Type **96** 10 10
545 10 c. Angel consoling shepherds 10 10
546 15 c. View of Bethlehem 10 10
547 25 c. Nativity scene 10 10
548 50 c. Throng of Angels.. .. .. 10 10
549 $1.25, Praising God 30 25
544/9 .. .. *Set of 6* 50 40
MS550 150 × 170 mm. Nos. 544/9. P 13½ .. 90 1·50

97 Painted Lady and *Bougainvillea glabra var. alba*

(Des Daphne Padden. Litho Walsall)

1978 (6 Apr). *Butterflies and Bougainvilleas. T* **97** *and similar horiz designs. Multicoloured.* W w **14** *(sideways). P* 14.

551 5 c. Type **97** 10 10
552 25 c. Silver Spot and "Golden Glow" 15 10
553 40 c. Red Anartia and "Mrs. McLean" .. 25 10
554 50 c. The Mimic and "Cyphen" 30 10
555 $1.25, Giant Hairstreak and "Thomasii" .. 65 55
551/5 .. .. *Set of 5* 1·25 75

(Des G. Drummond. Litho J.W.)

1978 (2 June). *25th Anniv of Coronation. Horiz designs as Nos. 422/5 of Montserrat. Multicoloured.* W w **14** *(sideways). P* 13.

556 40 c. Westminster Abbey 10 10
557 50 c. Gloucester Cathedral 10 10
558 $1.25, Durham Cathedral 20 15
559 $2.50, Exeter Cathedral 30 25
556/9 .. .. *Set of 4* 55 45
MS560 130 × 102 mm. Nos. 556/9. P 13½ × 14 .. 60 80

Nos. 556/9 were each printed in sheets of ten stamps and two *se-tenant* labels.

98 Rotary International Emblem and Motto

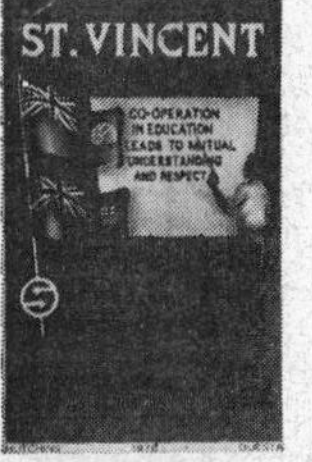

99 "Co-operation in Education Leads to Mutual Understanding and Respect"

(Des G. Hutchins. Litho Questa)

1978 (13 July). *International Service Clubs. T* **98** *and similar horiz designs showing club emblems and mottoes. Multicoloured.* W w **14** *(sideways). P* 14½.

561 40 c. Type **98** 20 10
562 50 c. Lions International 20 10
563 $1 Jaycees 45 35
561/3 .. .. *Set of 3* 75 40

(Des G. Hutchins. Litho Questa)

1978 (7 Sept). *10th Anniv of Project School to School (St. Vincent-Canada school twinning project). T* **99** *and similar multicoloured design showing flags and blackboard.* W w **14** *(sideways on $2). P* 14.

564 40 c. Type **99** 10 10
565 $2 "Co-operation in Education Leads to the Elimination of Racial Intolerance" *(horiz)* 40 50

100 Arnos Vale Airport

101 Young Child

(Des G. Drummond. Litho Questa)

1978 (19 Oct). *75th Anniv of Powered Flight. T* **100** *and similar horiz designs. Multicoloured.* W w **14** *(sideways). P* 14½ × 14.

566 10 c. Type **100** 10 10
567 40 c. Wilbur Wright landing *Flyer* 15 10
568 50 c. Orville Wright in *Flyer* 15 10
569 $1.25, Orville Wright and *Flyer* airborne .. 45 35
566/9 .. .. *Set of 4* 70 45

(Des A. Paish. Litho Questa)

1979 (14 Feb). *International Year of the Child. T* **101** *and similar vert designs showing portraits of young children.* W w **14.** *P* 14 × 13½.

570 8 c. black, gold and pale yellow-green .. 10 10
571 20 c. black, gold and pale rose-lilac 15 10
572 50 c. black, gold and pale violet-blue 25 10
573 $2 black, gold and flesh 75 50
570/3 .. .. *Set of 4* 1·10 55

10c+5c

SOUFRIERE
RELIEF
FUND 1979

(102)

103 Sir Rowland Hill

(Des G. Drummond. Litho Questa)

1979 (17 Apr). *Soufrière Eruption Relief Fund. Designs as T* **95** *but surchd as T* **102** *by Reliance Printery, Kingstown.* W w **12.** *P* 14½ × 14.

574 10 c. + 5 c. violet-blue and pale rose-lilac .. 10 15
575 50 c. + 25 c. yellow-brown and buff 20 20
576 $1 + 50 c. reddish brown and brownish grey 30 30
577 $2 + $1 deep green and apple-green .. 50 50
574/7 .. .. *Set of 4* 1·00 1·00

(Des J.W. Litho Harrison)

1979 (31 May). *Death Centenary of Sir Rowland Hill. T* **103** *and similar horiz designs. Multicoloured.* W w **14** *(sideways). P* 14.

578 40 c. Type **103** 15 10
579 50 c. Penny Black and Twopenny Blue stamps 20 15
580 $3 1861 1d. and 6d. stamps .. .. 1·00 1·10
578/80 .. .. *Set of 3* 1·25 1·25
MS581 170 × 123 mm. Nos. 578/80, 594/5 and 599 (see footnote after No. 601) .. .. .. 1·75 3·00

Nos. 578/80 were each printed in sheets including two *se-tenant* stamp-size labels.

104 First and Latest Buccament Postmarks and Map of St. Vincent

ST VINCENT AND
THE GRENADINES
AIR SERVICE 1979

(105)

(Des J.W. Litho Harrison)

1979 (31 May–1 Sept). *St. Vincent Post Offices. Horiz designs as T* **104** *showing first and latest postmarks and map of St. Vincent. Multicoloured.* W w **14** *(sideways). P* 14.

582 1 c. Type **104** 10 10
583 2 c. Sion Hill 10 10
584 3 c. Cumberland 10 10
585 4 c. Questelles 10 10
586 5 c. Layou 10 10
587 6 c. New Ground 10 10
588 8 c. Mesopotamia 10 10
589 10 c. Troumaca 10 10
590 12 c. Arnos Vale 15 10
591 15 c. Stubbs 15 10
592 20 c. Orange Hill 15 10
593 25 c. Calliaqua 15 10
594 40 c. Edinboro 25 20
595 50 c. Colonarie 30 25
596 80 c. Biabou 40 35
597 $1 Chateaubelair 50 50
598 $2 Head P.O., Kingstown 60 80
599 $3 Barrouallie .. .. 75 1·25
600 $5 Georgetown .. .. 1·25 2·00
601 $10 Kingstown .. .. 2·25 4·00
582/601 .. .. *Set of 20* 6·50 9·00

Dates of issue:—40, 50 c., $3 (from No. **MS**581 and booklets only) 31.5.79; others, and 40, 50 c., $3 from sheets, 1.9.79.

The 5, 10, 25 c. and $1 values exist with different imprint dates below the design.

See also Nos. **MS**581 and **MS**637.

1979 (6 Aug). *Opening of St. Vincent and the Grenadines Air Service. No.* 566 *optd with T* **105,** *in red, by Reliance Printery, Kingstown.*

602 10 c. Type **100** 10 10

INDEPENDENT

106 National Flag and *Ixora coccinea* (flower)

(Des J.W. Litho Enschedé)

1979 (27 Oct). *Independence. T* **106** *and similar horiz designs. Multicoloured.* W w **14** *(sideways). P* 12½ × 12.

603 20 c. Type **106** 10 10
604 50 c. House of Assembly and *Ixora stricta* (flower) 10 10
605 80 c. Prime Minister R. Milton Cato and *Ixora williamsii* (flower) 20 20
603/5 .. .. *Set of 3* 30 30

INDEPENDENCE 1979

(107)

1979 (27 Oct). *Independence. Nos.* 422, 425/30, 432, 434, 437/40, 441a *and* 443 *optd with T* **107,** *by Letchworth Press, Barbados.*

606 1 c. Type **79** 10 10
607 4 c. Mackerel 10 10
608 5 c. French Grunt 10 10
609 6 c. Spotted Goatfish 10 10
610 8 c. Ballyhoo 10 10
611 10 c. Sperm Whale 15 15
612 12 c. Humpback Whale 15 15
613 15 c. Skipjack 15 15
614 25 c. Princess Parrotfish 20 20
615 50 c. Porkfish 35 35
616 70 c. "Albacore" or Yellowfin Tuna 45 45
617 90 c. Pompano 50 50
618 $1 Queen Triggerfish 50 50
619 $2.50, Sailfish (II) .. .. .. 1·25 1·00
a. Opt inverted £100
b. Optd on Type I (No. 441) .. .. 9·00 9·00
620 $10 Blue Marlin .. .. 4·75 4·25
606/20 .. .. *Set of 15* 8·00 7·00

108 Virgin and Child

109 Jack Spaniard and Oleander

(Des Jennifer Toombs. Litho Questa)

1979 (1 Nov). *Christmas. Scenes and Verses from the carol "Silent Night". T* **108** *and similar horiz designs. Multicoloured.* W w **14** *(sideways). P* 13½.

621 10 c. Type **108** 10 10
622 20 c. Jesus in manger 10 10
623 25 c. Shepherds 10 10
624 40 c. Angel 10 10
625 50 c. Angels with infant Jesus 10 10
626 $2 Nativity scene 30 30
621/6 .. .. *Set of 6* 45 45
MS627 151 × 170 mm. Nos. 621/6 .. .. 50 1·00

(Des J.W. Litho Walsall)

1979 (13 Dec). *Flowers and Insects. T* **109** *and similar vert designs showing insects and different varieties of Oleander flower. Multicoloured.* W w **14.** *P* 14.

628 5 c. Type **109** 10 10
629 10 c. Labelle 10 10
630 25 c. Praying Mantis 10 10
631 50 c. Green Guava Beetle 10 10
632 $2 Citrus Weevil 30 30
628/32 .. .. *Set of 5* 50 40

(Des and litho D.L.R.)

1980 (28 Feb). *Centenary of St. Vincent "Arms" Stamps. Sheet 116 × 72 mm containing designs as T* **31**. *W w* **14** *(sideways). P 14 × 13½.*
MS633 116 × 72 mm. 50 c. reddish brown; $1 deep grey-green; $2.50 deep blue 50 75

110 Queen Elizabeth II

(Des J.W. Litho Harrison)

1980 (24 Apr). *"London 1980" International Stamp Exhibition. T* **110** *and similar horiz designs. Multicoloured. W w* **14** *(sideways). P 14.*
634 80 c. Type **110** 20 20
635 $1 Great Britain 1954 3d. and St. Vincent 1954 5 c. definitive stamps 30 30
636 $2 Unadopted postage stamp design of 1971 60 60
634/6 .. .. *Set of* 3 1·00 1·00
MS637 165 × 115 mm. Nos. 596/8 and 634/6 .. 1·25 1·50
Nos. 634/6 were each printed in sheets containing 2 *se-tenant* stamp-size labels.

111 Steel Band **112** Football

(Des G. Drummond. Litho Questa)

1980 (12 June). *Kingstown Carnival. T* **111** *and similar horiz design. Multicoloured. W w* **14** *(sideways). P 13½ × 14.*
638 20 c. Type **111** 10 10
a. Pair. Nos. 638/9 .. .. 20 20
639 20 c. Steel band *(different)* 10 10
Nos. 638/9 were printed together, *se-tenant*, in horizontal and vertical pairs throughout the sheet.

(Des Polygraphic. Litho Rosenbaum Bros, Vienna)

1980 (7 Aug). *"Sport for All". T* **112** *and similar vert designs. Multicoloured. W w* **14** *(inverted). P 13½.*
640 10 c. Type **112** 10 10
641 60 c. Cycling 15 10
642 80 c. Basketball 15 10
643 $2.50, Boxing 35 40
640/3 .. .. *Set of* 4 60 55

(**113**) **114** Brazilian Agouti

1980 (7 Aug). *Hurricane Relief. Nos. 640/3 surch with T* **113**. *W w* **14** *(upright).*
644 10 c. + 50 c. Type **112** 15 15
645 60 c. + 50 c. Cycling 25 25
646 80 c. + 50 c. Basketball 25 25
647 $2.50 + 50 c. Boxing 45 45
644/7 .. .. *Set of* 4 1·00 1·00

(Des L. Curtis. Litho Questa)

1980 (2 Oct). *Wildlife. T* **114** *and similar horiz designs. Multicoloured. W w* **14** *(sideways). P 14 × 14½.*
648 25 c. Type **114** 10 10
649 50 c. Giant Toad 15 10
650 $2 Small Indian Mongoose 40 55
648/50 .. .. *Set of* 3 60 60

115 Map of World showing St. Vincent **116** *Ville de Paris*, 1782

(Des G. Drummond. Litho Questa)

1980 (4 Dec). *St. Vincent "On the Map". T* **115** *and similar designs depicting maps showing St. Vincent. Multicoloured. W w* **14** *(sideways). P 13½ × 14.*
651 10 c. Type **115** 10 10
652 50 c. Western hemisphere 10 10
653 $1 Central America 25 15
654 $2 St. Vincent 40 30
651/4 .. .. *Set of* 4 70 50
MS655 143 × 95 mm. No. 654. P 12 .. .. .. 50 75

(Des J.W. Litho Rosenbaum Bros, Vienna)

1981 (19 Feb). *Sailing Ships. T* **116** *and similar vert designs. Multicoloured. W w* **14**. *P 13½.*
656 50 c. Type **116** 25 20
657 60 c. H.M.S. *Ramillies*, 1782 .. .. 30 30
658 $1.50, H.M.S. *Providence*, 1793 .. .. .. 70 75
659 $2 *Dee* (paddle-steamer packet) .. .. .. 95 1·00
656/9 .. .. *Set of* 4 2·00 2·00

117 Arrowroot Cultivation

(Des G. Drummond. Litho Format)

1981 (21 May). *Agriculture. T* **117** *and similar horiz designs. Multicoloured. W w* **14** *(sideways). P 14.*
660 25 c. Type **117** 10 15
a. Pair. Nos. 660/1 .. .. 20 30
661 25 c. Arrowroot processing 10 15
662 50 c. Banana cultivation 20 25
a. Pair. Nos. 662/3 .. .. 40 50
663 50 c. Banana export packaging station 20 25
664 60 c. Coconut plantation 25 30
a. Pair. Nos. 664/5 .. .. 50 60
665 60 c. Copra drying frames 25 30
666 $1 Cocoa cultivation 50 45
a. Pair. Nos. 666/7 .. .. 1·00 90
667 $1 Cocoa beans and sun drying frames .. 50 45
660/7 .. .. *Set of* 8 1·90 2·00
The two designs of each value were printed together, *se-tenant*, in horizontal and vertical pairs throughout the sheet.

(Des D. Shults. Litho Questa)

1981 (17 July–26 Nov). *Royal Wedding. Horiz designs as T* **26/27** *of Kiribati. Multicoloured. (a) W w* **15**. *P 14.*
668 60 c. *Isabella* 15 15
a. Sheetlet. No. 668 × 6 and No. 669 .. 1·10
669 60 c. Prince Charles and Lady Diana Spencer 40 40
670 $2.50, *Alberta* (tender) 40 40
a. Sheetlet. No. 670 × 6 and No. 671 .. 3·00
671 $2.50, As No. 669 .. .. 1·00 1·00
672 $4 *Britannia* 55 55
a. Sheetlet. No. 672 × 6 and No. 673 .. 4·50
673 $4 As No. 669 .. .. 1·75 1·75
668/73 .. .. *Set of* 6 3·75 3·75
MS674 120 × 109 mm. $5 As No. 669. Wmk sideways. P 12 (26 Nov) .. .. 1·25 1·00
(b) Booklet stamps. No wmk. P 12 (26 Nov)
675 60 c. As No. 668 .. .. 25 25
a. Booklet pane. No. 675 × 4 .. .. .. 1·00
676 $2.50, As No. 671 .. .. 1·25 1·25
a. Booklet pane. No. 676 × 2 .. .. .. 2·50
Nos. 668/73 were printed in sheetlets of seven stamps of the same face value, each containing six of the "Royal Yacht" design and one of the larger design showing Prince Charles and Lady Diana.
Nos. 675/6 come from $9.80 stamp booklets.

118 Kingstown General Post Office **119**

(Des G. Drummond. Litho Questa)

1981 (1 Sept). *U.P.U. Membership. W w* **14** *(sideways). P 14.*
677 **118** $2 multicoloured 70 90
a. Horiz pair. Nos. 677/8 .. .. .. 1·40 1·75
678 **119** $2 multicoloured 70 90
Nos. 677/8 were printed together, *se-tenant*, in horizontal pairs throughout the sheet, forming a composite design.

120 St. Vincent Flag with Flags of other U.N. Member Nations

(Des L. Curtis. Litho Format)

1981 (11 Sept). *First Anniv of U.N. Membership. T* **120** *and similar horiz design. Multicoloured. W w* **14** *(sideways). P 13½ × 14.*
679 $1.50, Type **120** 40 25
680 $2.50, Prime Minister Robert Milton Cato .. 70 50
Nos. 679/80 are inscribed "ST. VINCENT and the GRENADINES" and were each printed in small sheets of 6 including one *se-tenant* stamp-size label.

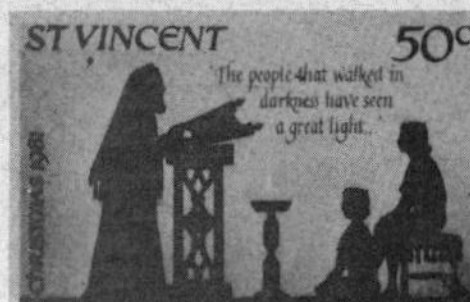

121 Silhouettes of Figures at Old Testament Reading, and Bible Extract

(Des Jennifer Toombs. Litho Security Printers (M), Malaysia)

1981 (19 Nov). *Christmas. T* **121** *and similar horiz designs showing silhouettes of figures. Multicoloured. W w* **14** *(sideways). P 12.*
681 50 c. Type **121** 15 10
682 60 c. Madonna, and angel 15 10
683 $1 Madonna, and Bible extract 25 25
684 $2 Joseph and Mary travelling to Bethlehem 50 50
681/4 .. .. *Set of* 4 95 85
MS685 129 × 127 mm. Nos. 681/4. P 13½ .. 95 1·40

122 Sugar Boilers

(Des L. Curtis. Litho Format)

1982 (5 Apr). *First Anniv of Re-introduction of Sugar Industry. T* **122** *and similar horiz designs. Multicoloured. W w* **14** *(sideways). P 14.*
686 50 c. Type **122** 25 15
687 60 c. Sugar drying plant 25 20
688 $1.50, Sugar mill machinery 70 75
689 $2 Crane loading sugar cane .. .. .. 95 1·00
686/9 .. .. *Set of* 4 1·90 1·90

123 Butterfly Float **124** Augusta of Saxe-Gotha, Princess of Wales, 1736

(Des G. Vasarhelyi. Photo Heraclio Fournier)

1982 (10 June). *Carnival* 1982. *T* **123** *and similar multicoloured designs. P 13½.*
690 50 c. Type **123** 20 15
691 60 c. Angel dancer *(vert)* 20 15
692 $1.50, Winged dancer *(vert)* 50 70
693 $2 Eagle float .. .. 70 1·00
690/3 .. .. *Set of* 4 1·50 1·75

(Des D. Shults and J. Cooter. Litho Format)

1982 (1 July). *21st Birthday of Princess of Wales. T* **124** *and similar vert designs. Multicoloured. W* **24** *of Kiribati. P 13½ × 14.*
694 50 c. Type **124** 30 20
695 60 c. Coat of arms of Augusta of Saxe-Gotha 30 25
696 $6 Diana, Princess of Wales .. .. .. 2·00 2·00
694/6 .. .. *Set of* 3 2·25 2·25

125 Scout Emblem **126** De Havilland "Moth", 1932

(Des L. Curtis. Litho Questa)

1982 (15 July). *75th Anniv of Boy Scout Movement. T* **125** *and similar vert design. Multicoloured. W w* **14**. *P 14.*
697 $1.50, Type **125** 70 75
698 $2.50, 75th anniv emblem .. .. 90 1·00

1982 (19 July). *Birth of Prince William of Wales. Nos. 694/6 optd with T* **19** *of St. Kitts.*
699 50 c. Type **124** 20 20
700 60 c. Coat of arms of Augusta of Saxe-Gotha 25 25
a. Opt inverted .. .. 50·00
701 $6 Diana, Princess of Wales .. .. .. 1·75 2·00
a. Opt double .. .. 20·00
699/701 .. .. *Set of* 3 2·00 2·25

(Des A. Theobald. Litho Questa)

1982 (29 July). *50th Anniv of Airmail Service. T* **126** *and similar horiz designs. Multicoloured.* W w **14** *(sideways). P* 14.
702 50 c. Type **126** . . 35 25
703 60 c. Grumman "Goose", 1952 . . 40 30
704 $1.50, Hawker-Siddeley "748", 1968 . . 85 75
705 $2 Britten-Norman "Trislander", 1982 . . 1·00 1·00
702/5 . . *Set of* 4 2·40 2·10

127 *Geestport* (freighter)

(Des G. Drummond. Litho Format)

1982 (27 Dec). *Ships. T* **127** *and similar horiz designs. Multicoloured.* W w **14** *(sideways). P* 14.
706 45 c. Type **127** . . 25 25
707 60 c. *Stella Oceanic* (liner) . . 30 35
708 $1.50, *Victoria* (liner) . . 70 75
709 $2 *Queen Elizabeth 2* (liner) . . 95 1·00
706/9 . . *Set of* 4 2·00 2·00

128 *Pseudocorynactis caribbeorum*

(Des McCombie-De Bay. Litho Security Printers (M), Malaysia)

1983 (10 Feb). *Marine Life. T* **128** *and similar multicoloured designs.* W w **14** *(sideways on 60 c., $1.50, $2). P* 12.
710 50 c. Type **128** . . 45 25
711 60 c. *Actinoporus elegans* (*vert*) . . 50 35
712 $1.50, *Arachnanthus nocturnus* (*vert*) . . 1·00 75
713 $2 *Hippocampus reidi* (*vert*) . . 1·25 1·00
710/13 . . *Set of* 4 3·00 2·00

129 Satellite View of St. Vincent

45¢ ■

(**130**)

(Des R. Vigurs. Litho Questa)

1983 (14 Mar). *Commonwealth Day. T* **129** *and similar horiz designs. Multicoloured.* W w **14** *(sideways). P* 14.
714 45 c. Type **129** . . 20 20
715 60 c. Flag of St. Vincent . . 25 25
716 $1.50, Prime Minister R. Milton Cato . . 50 65
717 $2 Harvesting bananas . . 75 90
714/17 . . *Set of* 4 1·50 1·75
Nos. 714/17 are inscribed "St. Vincent & The Grenadines".

1983 (26 Apr). *No. 681 surch with T* **130** *by Reliance Printery, Kingstown.*
718 45 c. on 50 c. Type **121** . . 25 25

131 Symbolic Handshake

132 Sir William Smith (founder)

(Des J.W. Litho Security Printers (M), Malaysia)

1983 (6 July). *10th Anniv of Treaty of Chaguaramas. T* **131** *and similar vert designs. Multicoloured.* W w **14** *(sideways). P* 11½ × 12.
719 45 c. Type **131** . . 25 20
720 60 c. Commerce emblem . . 30 25
721 $1.50, Caribbean map . . 60 65
722 $2 Flags of member countries and map of St. Vincent . . 85 90
719/22 . . *Set of* 4 1·75 1·75

(Des L. Curtis. Litho Security Printers (M), Malaysia)

1983 (6 Oct). *Centenary of Boys' Brigade. T* **132** *and similar vert designs. Multicoloured.* W w **14**. *P* 12 × 11½.
723 45 c. Type **132** . . 25 25
724 60 c. On parade . . 30 35
725 $1.50, Craftwork . . 70 85
726 $2 Community service . . 95 1·10
723/6 . . *Set of* 4 2·00 2·25

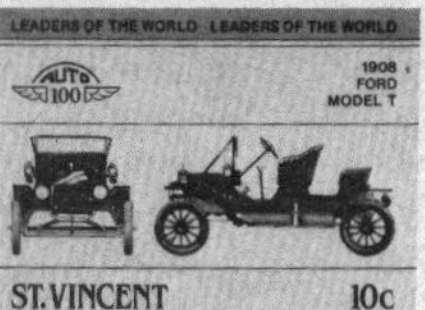

133 Ford "Model T" (1908)

(Des J.W. Litho Format)

1983 (25 Oct). *Leaders of the World. Automobiles (1st series). T* **133** *and similar horiz designs, the first in each pair showing technical drawings and the second paintings. P* 12½.
727 10 c. multicoloured . . 10 10
a. Vert pair. Nos. 727/8 . . 10 10
728 10 c. multicoloured . . 10 10
729 60 c. multicoloured . . 25 25
a. Vert pair. Nos. 729/30 . . 50 50
730 60 c. multicoloured . . 25 25
731 $1.50, multicoloured . . 30 30
a. Vert pair. Nos. 731/2 . . 60 60
732 $1.50, multicoloured . . 30 30
733 $1.50, multicoloured . . 30 30
a. Vert pair. Nos. 733/4 . . 60 60
734 $1.50, multicoloured . . 30 30
735 $2 multicoloured . . 45 45
a. Vert pair. Nos. 735/6 . . 90 90
736 $2 multicoloured . . 45 45
737 $2 multicoloured . . 45 45
a. Vert pair. Nos. 737/8 . . 90 90
738 $2 multicoloured . . 45 45
727/38 . . *Set of* 12 3·25 3·25
Designs:—Nos. 727/8, Ford "Model T" (1908); 729/30, Supercharged Cord "812" (1937); 731/2, Citroen "Open Tourer" (1937); 733/4, Mercedes Benz "300SL Gull-Wing" (1954); 735/6, Rolls-Royce "Phantom I" (1925); 737/8, Ferrari "Boxer 512BB" (1976).
Nos. 727/8, 729/30, 731/2, 733/4, 735/6 and 737/8 were printed together, *se-tenant*, in vertical pairs throughout the sheets.
See also Nos. 820/9, 862/7, 884/92 and 959/70.

134 Appearance of the Nativity Star

(Des Jennifer Toombs. Litho Security Printers (M), Malaysia)

1983 (15 Nov). *Christmas. T* **134** *and similar horiz designs showing the Shepherds.* W w **14**. *P* 12.
739 10 c. Type **134** . . 10 10
740 50 c. Message of the Angel . . 20 10
741 $1.50, The Heavenly Host . . 45 45
742 $2.40, Worshipping Jesus . . 65 75
739/42 . . *Set of* 4 1·25 1·25
MS743 130 × 130 mm. Nos. 739/42. Wmk sideways 1·25 1·75

135 *King Henry VIII*

(Des J.W. Litho Format)

1983 (8 Dec). *Leaders of the World. Railway Locomotives (1st series). T* **135** *and similar horiz designs, the first in each pair showing technical drawings and the second the locomotive at work. P* 12½.
744 10 c. multicoloured . . 10 10
a. Vert pair. Nos. 744/5 . . 10 10
745 10 c. multicoloured . . 10 10
746 10 c. multicoloured . . 10 10
a. Vert pair. Nos. 746/7 . . 10 10
747 10 c. multicoloured . . 10 10
748 25 c. multicoloured . . 10 10
a. Vert pair. Nos. 748/9 . . 20 20
749 25 c. multicoloured . . 10 10
750 50 c. multicoloured . . 20 20
a. Vert pair. Nos. 750/1 . . 40 40
751 50 c. multicoloured . . 20 20
752 60 c. multicoloured . . 25 25
a. Vert pair Nos. 752/3 . . 50 50
753 60 c. multicoloured . . 25 25
754 75 c. multicoloured . . 35 35
a. Vert pair. Nos. 754/5 . . 70 70
755 75 c. multicoloured . . 35 35
756 $2.50, multicoloured . . 75 75
a. Vert pair. Nos. 756/7 . . 1·50 1·50
757 $2.50, multicoloured . . 75 75
758 $3 multicoloured . . 90 90
a. Vert pair. Nos. 758/9 . . 1·75 1·75
759 $3 multicoloured . . 90 90
744/59 . . *Set of* 16 4·75 4·75
Designs:—Nos. 744/5, *King Henry VIII*, Great Britain (1927); 746/7, *Royal Scots Greys*, Great Britain (1961); 748/9, *Hagley Hall*, Great Britain (1928); 750/1, *Sir Lancelot*, Great Britain (1926); 752/3 Class "B12", Great Britain (1912); 754/5, Deeley "Compound" type, Great Britain (1902); 756/7, *Cheshire*, Great Britain (1927); 758/9, Bullied "Austerity" Class Q1, Great Britain (1942).
Nos. 744/59 were issued in a similar sheet format to Nos. 727/38.
See also Nos. 792/807, 834/41, 872/83, 893/904 and 1001/8.

136 Fort Duvernette

(Des Walsall. Litho Questa)

1984 (13 Feb). *Fort Duvernette. T* **136** *and similar horiz designs. Multicoloured.* W w **15** *(sideways). P* 14 × 14½.
760 35 c. Type **136** . . 20 25
761 45 c. Soldiers on fortifications . . 25 30
762 $1 Cannon facing bay . . 40 50
763 $3 Map of St. Vincent and mortar . . 1·25 1·60
760/3 . . *Set of* 4 1·90 2·40

137 White Frangipani

(Des J. Cooter. Litho Harrison)

1984 (2 Apr). *Flowering Trees and Shrubs. T* **137** *and similar horiz designs. Multicoloured.* W w **14** *(sideways). P* 13½ × 14.
764 5 c. Type **137** . . 10 10
765 10 c. Genip . . 10 10
766 15 c. Immortelle . . 15 10
767 20 c. Pink Poui . . 20 10
768 25 c. Buttercup . . 25 10
769 35 c. Sandbox . . 30 20
770 45 c. Locust . . 40 25
771 60 c. Colville's Glory . . 50 30
772 75 c. Lignum Vitae . . 60 35
773 $1 Golden Shower . . 80 50
774 $5 Angelin . . 2·75 2·50
775 $10 Roucou . . 5·00 4·75
764/75 . . *Set of* 12 10·00 8·50

138 Trench Warfare, First World War

139 Musical Fantasy Costume

(Des Court House Studio. Litho Format)

1984 (25 Apr). *Leaders of the World. British Monarchs. T* **138** *and similar vert designs. Multicoloured. P* 12½.
776 1 c. Type **138** . . 10 10
a. Horiz pair. Nos. 776/7 . . 10 10
777 1 c. George V and trenches . . 10 10
778 5 c. Battle of Bannockburn . . 10 10
a. Horiz pair. Nos. 778/9 . . 10 10
779 5 c. Edward II and battle . . 10 10
780 60 c. George V . . 30 30
a. Horiz pair. Nos. 780/1 . . 60 60
781 60 c. York Cottage, Sandringham . . 30 30
782 75 c. Edward II . . 40 40
a. Horiz pair. Nos. 782/3 . . 80 80
783 75 c. Berkeley Castle . . 40 40
784 $1 Coat of arms of Edward II . . 45 45
a. Horiz pair. Nos. 784/5 . . 90 90
785 $1 Edward II (*different*) . . 45 45
786 $4 Coat of arms of George V . . 1·40 1·40
a. Horiz pair. Nos. 786/7 . . 2·75 2·75
787 $4 George V and Battle of Jutland . . 1·40 1·40
776/87 . . *Set of* 12 4·50 4·50
Nos. 776/7, 778/9, 780/1, 782/3, 784/5 and 786/7 were printed together, *se-tenant*, in horizontal pairs throughout the sheets, each pair forming a composite design.

(Des G. Vasarhelyi. Litho Questa)

1984 (25 June). *Carnival 1984. T* **139** *and similar horiz designs showing Carnival costumes. Multicoloured.* W w **15** *(sideways). P* 14.
788 35 c. Type **139** . . 15 15
789 45 c. African princess . . 20 20
790 $1 Market woman . . 40 40
791 $3 Carib hieroglyph . . 1·25 1·40
788/91 . . *Set of* 4 1·75 2·00

(Des J.W. Litho Format)

1984 (27 July). *Leaders of the World. Railway Locomotives (2nd series). Horiz designs as T* **135**, *the first in each pair showing technical drawings and the second the locomotive at work. P* 12½.
792 1 c. multicoloured . . 10 10
a. Vert pair. Nos. 792/3 . . 10 10
793 1 c. multicoloured . . 10 10
794 2 c. multicoloured . . 10 10
a. Vert pair. Nos. 794/5 . . 10 10
795 2 c. multicoloured . . 10 10
796 3 c. multicoloured . . 10 10
a. Vert pair. Nos. 796/7 . . 10 10
797 3 c. multicoloured . . 10 10

798 50 c. multicoloured 30 30
a. Vert pair. Nos. 798/9 .. .. 60 60
799 50 c. multicoloured 30 30
800 75 c. multicoloured 40 40
a. Vert pair. Nos. 800/1 .. .. 80 80
801 75 c. multicoloured 40 40
802 $1 multicoloured 50 50
a. Vert pair. Nos. 802/3 .. .. 1·00 1·00
803 $1 multicoloured 50 50
804 $2 multicoloured 70 70
a. Vert pair. Nos. 804/5 .. .. 1·40 1·40
805 $2 multicoloured 70 70
806 $3 multicoloured 80 80
a. Vert pair. Nos. 806/7 .. .. 1·60 1·60
807 $3 multicoloured 80 80
792/807 .. .. *Set of* 16 5·00 5·00

Designs:—Nos. 792/3, Liberation Class, France (1945); 794/5, *Dreadnought*, Great Britain (1767); 796/7, No. 242A1, France (1946); 798/9, Class "Dean Goods", Great Britain (1883); 800/1, Hetton Colliery No. 1, Great Britain (1822); 802/3, *Penydarren*, Great Britain (1804); 804/5, *Novelty*, Great Britain (1829); 806/7, Class "44", Germany (1925).

Nos. 792/807 were issued in a similar sheet format to Nos. 727/38.

140 Slaves tilling Field

141 Weightlifting

(Des G. Vasarhelyi. Litho Questa)

1984 (1 Aug). *150th Anniv of Emancipation of Slaves on St. Vincent. T* **140** *and similar horiz designs. Multicoloured. W* w **15** *(sideways). P* 14.

808 35 c. Type **140** 20 20
809 45 c. Sugar-cane harvesting 25 25
810 $1 Cutting sugar-cane 45 45
811 $3 William Wilberforce and African slave caravan .. .. 1·25 1·40
808/11 .. .. *Set of* 4 2·00 2·10

(Des Court House Studio. Litho Format)

1984 (30 Aug). *Leaders of the World. Olympic Games, Los Angeles. T* **141** *and similar vert designs. Multicoloured. P* 12½.

812 1 c. Judo 10 10
a. Horiz pair. Nos. 812/13 .. .. 10 10
813 1 c. Type **141** 10 10
814 3 c. Pursuit cycling 10 10
a. Horiz pair. Nos. 814/15 .. .. 10 10
815 3 c. Cycle road-racing 10 10
816 60 c. Women's backstroke swimming 25 25
a. Horiz pair. Nos. 816/17 .. .. 50 50
817 60 c. Men's butterfly swimming 25 25
818 $3 Sprint start .. .. 1·00 1·00
a. Horiz pair. Nos. 818/19 .. .. 2·00 2·00
819 $3 Finish of long distance race .. .. 1·00 1·00
812/19 .. .. *Set of* 8 2·25 2·25

Nos. 812/13, 814/15, 816/17 and 818/19 were printed together, *se-tenant*, in horizontal pairs throughout the sheets.

(Des J.W. Litho Format)

1984 (22 Oct). *Leaders of the World. Automobiles* (2*nd series*). *Horiz designs as T* **133**, *the first in each pair showing technical drawings and the second paintings. P* 12½.

820 5 c. black, drab and bright green 10 10
a. Vert pair. Nos. 820/1 .. .. 10 10
821 5 c. multicoloured 10 10
822 20 c. black, pink and pale new blue 15 15
a. Vert pair. Nos. 822/3 .. .. 30 30
823 20 c. multicoloured 15 15
824 55 c. black, pale green and lake-brown 25 25
a. Vert pair. Nos. 824/5 .. .. 50 50
825 55 c. multicoloured 25 25
826 $1.50, black, pale turq-grn & turq-grn 45 45
a. Vert pair. Nos. 826/7 .. .. 90 90
827 $1.50, multicoloured 45 45
828 $2.50, black, turquoise-green and lilac 60 60
a. Vert pair. Nos. 828/9 .. .. 1·10 1·10
829 $2.50, multicoloured 60 60
820/9 .. .. *Set of* 10 2·50 2·50

Designs:—Nos. 820/1, Austin-Healey "Sprite" (1958); 822/3, Maserati "Ghibli Coupe" (1971); 824/5, Pontiac "GTO" (1964); 826/7, Jaguar "D-Type" (1957); 828/9, Ferrari "365 GTB4 Daytona" (1970).

Nos. 820/9 were issued in a similar sheet format to Nos. 727/38.

142 Grenadier, 70th Regt of Foot, 1773

143 N. S. Taylor

(Des J. Cooter. Litho Questa)

1984 (12 Nov). *Military Uniforms. T* **142** *and similar vert designs. Multicoloured. W* w **15**. *P* 14.

830 45 c. Type **142** 25 30
831 60 c. Grenadier, 6th Regt of Foot, 1775 .. .. 30 35
832 $1.50, Grenadier, 3rd Regt of Foot, 1768 .. 75 80
833 $2 Battalion Company officer, 14th Regt of Foot, 1780 .. .. 1·00 1·10
830/3 .. .. *Set of* 4 2·10 2·25

(Des J.W. Litho Format)

1984 (21 Nov). *Leaders of the World. Railway Locomotives* (3*rd series*). *Horiz designs as T* **135**, *the first in each pair showing technical drawings and the second the locomotive at work. Multicoloured. P* 12½.

834 5 c. multicoloured 10 10
a. Vert pair. Nos. 834/5 .. .. 10 15
835 5 c. multicoloured 10 10
836 40 c. multicoloured 30 35
a. Vert pair. Nos. 836/7 .. .. 60 70
837 40 c. multicoloured 30 35
838 75 c. multicoloured 50 55
a. Vert pair. Nos. 838/9 .. .. 1·00 1·10
839 75 c. multicoloured 50 55
840 $2.50, multicoloured .. .. 1·75 1·90
a. Vert pair. Nos. 840/1 .. .. 3·50 3·75
841 $2.50, multicoloured .. .. 1·75 1·90
834/41 .. .. *Set of* 8 4·50 5·25

Designs:—Nos. 834/5 Class "20", Rhodesia (1954); 836/7, *Southern Maid*, Great Britain (1928); 838/9, *Prince of Wales*, Great Britain (1911); 840/1, Class "05", Germany (1935).

Nos. 834/41 were issued in a similar sheet format to Nos. 727/38.

(Des Court House Studio. Litho Format)

1985 (7 Jan). *Leaders of the World. Cricketers. T* **143** *and similar vert designs, the first in each pair showing a head portrait and the second the cricketer in action. P* 12½.

842 5 c. multicoloured 10 10
a. Horiz pair. Nos. 842/3 .. .. 10 10
843 5 c. multicoloured 10 10
844 35 c. multicoloured 20 25
a. Horiz pair. Nos. 844/5 .. .. 40 50
845 35 c. multicoloured 20 25
846 50 c. multicoloured 30 35
a. Horiz pair. Nos. 846/7 .. .. 60 70
847 50 c. multicoloured 30 35
848 $3 multicoloured .. .. 1·75 1·90
a. Horiz pair. Nos. 848/9 .. .. 3·50 3·75
849 $3 multicoloured .. .. 1·75 1·90
842/9 .. .. *Set of* 8 4·25 4·75

Designs:—Nos. 842/3, N. S. Taylor; 844/5, T. W. Graveney; 846/7, R. G. D. Willis; 848/9, S. D. Fletcher.

Nos. 842/3, 844/5, 846/7, and 848/9 were printed together, *se-tenant*, in vertical pairs throughout the sheets.

IMPERFORATES AND MISSING COLOURS. Various issues between Nos. 850 and 1084 exist either imperforate or with colours omitted. Such items are not listed as there is no evidence that they fulfil the criteria outlined on page xi of this catalogue.

144 Eye Lash Orchid

145 Brown Pelican

(Des G. Drummond. Litho Format)

1985 (31 Jan). *Orchids. T* **144** *and similar vert designs. Multicoloured. W* w **15**. *P* 14.

850 35 c. Type **144** 30 25
851 45 c. *Ionopsis utricularioides* 40 30
852 $1 *Epidendrum secundum* 65 55
853 $3 *Oncidium altissimum* .. .. 1·50 1·60
850/3 .. .. *Set of* 4 2·50 2·40

(Des R. Vigurs. Litho Format)

1985 (7 Feb). *Leaders of the World. Birth Bicentenary of John J. Audubon (ornithologist). T* **145** *and similar vert designs. Multicoloured. P* 12½.

854 15 c. Type **145** 15 10
a. Horiz pair. Nos. 854/5 .. .. 30 20
855 15 c. Green Heron 15 10
856 40 c. Pileated Woodpecker 40 30
a. Horiz pair. Nos. 856/7 .. .. 80 60
857 40 c. Common Flicker 40 30
858 60 c. Painted Bunting 50 40
a. Horiz pair. Nos. 858/9 .. .. 1·00 80
859 60 c. White-winged Crossbill 50 40
860 $2.25, Red-shouldered Hawk .. .. 1·75 1·50
a. Horiz pair. Nos. 860/1 .. .. 3·50 3·00
861 $2.25, Common Caracara .. .. 1·75 1·50
854/61 .. .. *Set of* 8 5·00 4·25

Nos. 854/5, 856/7, 858/9 and 860/1 were printed together, *se-tenant*, in horizontal pairs throughout the sheets.

(Des Artists International. Litho Format)

1985 (11 Mar). *Leaders of the World. Automobiles* (3*rd series*). *Horiz designs as T* **133**, *the first in each pair showing technical drawings and the second paintings. P* 12½.

862 1 c. black, pale lemon and blue-green 10 10
a. Vert pair. Nos. 862/3 .. .. 10 10
863 1 c. multicoloured 10 10
864 55 c. black, pale new blue and violet-grey .. 20 20
a. Vert pair. Nos. 864/5 .. .. 40 40
865 55 c. multicoloured 20 20
866 $2 black, pale lemon & dull reddish purple 55 55
a. Vert pair. Nos. 866/7 .. .. 1·10 1·10
867 $2 multicoloured 55 55
862/7 .. .. *Set of* 6 1·40 1·40

Designs:—Nos. 862/3, Lancia "Aprilia" (1937); 864/5, Pontiac "Firebird Trans Am" (1973); 866/7, Cunningham "C-5R" (1953).

Nos. 862/7 were issued in a similar sheet format to Nos. 727/38.

146 Pepper

147 Bamboo Flute

(Des G. Drummond. Litho Format)

1985 (22 Apr). *Herbs and Spices. T* **146** *and similar vert designs. Multicoloured. W* w **15**. *P* 14.

868 25 c. Type **146** 15 15
869 35 c. Sweet Marjoram 20 25
870 $1 Nutmeg 50 55
871 $3 Ginger .. .. 1·50 1·60
868/71 .. .. *Set of* 4 2·10 2·25

(Des. T. Hadler ($2.50), J.W. (others). Litho Format)

1985 (26 Apr). *Leaders of the World. Railway Locomotives* (4*th series*). *Horiz designs as T* **135**, *the first in each pair showing technical drawings and the second the locomotive at work. P* 12½.

872 1 c. multicoloured 10 10
a. Vert pair. Nos. 872/3 .. .. 10 10
873 1 c. multicoloured 10 10
874 10 c. multicoloured 10 10
a. Vert pair. Nos. 874/5 .. .. 10 15
875 10 c. multicoloured 10 10
876 40 c. multicoloured 25 30
a. Vert pair. Nos. 876/7 .. .. 50 60
877 40 c. multicoloured 25 30
878 60 c. multicoloured 35 40
a. Vert pair. Nos. 878/9 .. .. 70 80
879 60 c. multicoloured 35 40
880 $1 multicoloured 55 60
a. Vert pair. Nos. 880/1 .. .. 1·10 1·10
881 $1 multicoloured 55 60
882 $2.50, multicoloured .. .. 1·25 1·40
a. Vert pair. Nos. 882/3 .. .. 2·50 2·75
883 $2.50, multicoloured .. .. 1·25 1·40
872/83 .. .. *Set of* 12 4·50 5·00

Designs:—Nos. 872/3, *Glen Douglas*, Great Britain (1913); 874/5, *Fenchurch*, Great Britain (1872); 876/7, No. 1 "Stirling Single", Great Britain (1870); 878/9, No. 158A, Great Britain (1866); 880/1, No. 103 Class "Jones Goods", Great Britain (1893); 882/3, *The Great Bear*, Great Britain (1908).

Nos. 872/83 were issued in a similar sheet format to Nos. 727/38.

(Des J.W. (25 c.), G. Turner ($1), Artists International (others). Litho Format)

1985 (7 June). *Leaders of the World. Automobiles* (4*th series*). *Horiz designs as T* **133**, *the first in each pair showing technical drawings and the second paintings. P* 12½.

884 25 c. black, greenish grey and brown-red .. 15 15
a. Vert pair. Nos. 884/5 .. .. 30 30
885 25 c. multicoloured 15 15
886 60 c. black, pale flesh and red-orange 25 25
a. Vert pair. Nos. 886/7 .. .. 50 50
887 60 c. multicoloured 25 25
888 $1 black, azure and dull lavender 30 30
a. Vert pair. Nos. 888/9 .. .. 60 60
889 $1 multicoloured 30 30
890 $1.50, black, pale blue and scarlet 40 40
a. Vert pair. Nos. 890/1 .. .. 80 80
891 $1.50, multicoloured 40 40
884/91 .. .. *Set of* 8 2·00 2·00
MS892 180×121 mm. $4×2 As Nos. 890/1; $5×2 As Nos. 888/9. P 14 .. .. 5·00 9·00

Designs:—Nos. 884/5, Essex "Coach" (1922); 886/7, Nash "Rambler" (1950); 888/9, Ferrari "Tipo 156" (1961); 890/1, Eagle-Weslake "Type 58" (1967).

Nos. 884/91 were issued in a similar sheet format to Nos. 727/38.

(Des J.W. (5 c., 30 c., $1), T. Hadler (others). Litho Format)

1985 (27 June). *Leaders of the World. Railway Locomotives* (5*th series*). *Horiz designs as T* **135**, *the first in each pair showing technical drawings and the second the locomotive at work. P* 12½.

893 5 c. multicoloured 10 10
a. Vert pair. Nos. 893/4 .. .. 10 10
894 5 c. multicoloured 10 10
895 30 c. multicoloured 15 20
a. Vert pair. Nos. 895/6 .. .. 30 40
896 30 c. multicoloured 15 20
897 60 c. multicoloured 35 40
a. Vert pair. Nos. 897/8 .. .. 70 80
898 60 c. multicoloured 35 40
899 75 c. multicoloured 40 45
a. Vert pair. Nos. 899/900 .. .. 80 90
900 75 c. multicoloured 40 45
901 $1 multicoloured 55 60
a. Vert pair. Nos. 901/2 .. .. 1·10 1·10
902 $1 multicoloured 55 60

903 $2.50, multicoloured .. .. 1·25 1·40
a. Vert pair. Nos. 903/4 .. .. .. 2·50 2·75
904 $2.50, multicoloured .. .. 1·25 1·40
893/904 .. .. *Set of* 12 5·00 5·50

Designs:—Nos. 893/4, Tank locomotive *Loch*, Great Britain (1874); 895/6, Class "47XX", Great Britain (1919); 897/8, Class "121", France (1876); 899/900, Class "24", Germany (1927); 901/2 Tank locomotive No. 1008, Great Britain (1889); 903/4, Class "PS-4", U.S.A. (1926).

Nos. 893/904 were issued in a similar sheet format to Nos. 727/38.

(Des Jennifer Toombs. Litho Format)

1985 (10 July). *Traditional Musical Instruments. T* **147** *and similar multicoloured designs. W w* **15** (*sideways on* $1, $2). *P* 15.
905 25 c. Type **147** 15 15
906 35 c. Quatro (four-stringed guitar) 20 25
907 $1 Ba-ha (bamboo pipe) (*vert*) 50 55
908 $2 Goat-skin drum (*vert*) .. .. .. 1·00 1·10
905/8 .. .. *Set of* 4 1·60 1·90
MS909 141 × 100 mm. Nos. 905/8 .. .. 2·25 2·75

148 Queen Elizabeth the Queen Mother

149 Elvis Presley

(Des Court House Studio. Litho Format)

1985 (9 Aug). *Leaders of the World. Life and Times of Queen Elizabeth the Queen Mother. Various vertical portraits as T* **148**. *P* 12½.
910 35 c. multicoloured 15 20
a. Horiz pair. Nos. 910/11 .. .. .. 30 40
911 35 c. multicoloured 15 20
912 85 c. multicoloured 35 45
a. Horiz pair. Nos. 912/13 .. .. .. 70 90
913 85 c. multicoloured 35 45
914 $1.20, multicoloured 45 60
a. Horiz pair. Nos. 914/15 .. .. .. 90 1·10
915 $1.20, multicoloured 45 60
916 $1.60, multicoloured 60 80
a. Horiz pair. Nos. 916/17 .. .. .. 1·10 1·60
917 $1.60, multicoloured 60 80
910/17 .. .. *Set of* 8 2·75 3·50
MS918 85 × 114 mm. $2.10, multicoloured; $2.10, multicoloured .. .. 1·75 2·50

The two designs of each value were issued, *se-tenant*, in horizontal pairs within the sheets.

Each *se-tenant* pair shows a floral pattern across the bottom of the portraits which stops short of the left-hand edge on the left-hand stamp and of the right-hand edge on the right-hand stamp.

Designs as Nos. 910/11 and 912/13, but with face values of $3.50 × 2 and $6 × 2, also exist in additional miniature sheets from a restricted printing issued 19 December 1985.

(Des Court House Studio. Litho Format)

1985 (16 Aug). *Leaders of the World. Elvis Presley (entertainer). Various vertical portraits as T* **149**. *Multicoloured, background colours given. P* 12½.
919 10 c. multicoloured (T **149**) 15 10
a. Horiz pair. Nos. 919/20 .. .. .. 30 20
920 10 c. multicoloured (bright blue) 15 10
921 60 c. multicoloured (brown) 45 35
a. Horiz pair. Nos. 921/2 .. .. .. 90 70
922 60 c. multicoloured (pale grey) 45 35
923 $1 multicoloured (brown) 70 55
a. Horiz pair. Nos. 923/4 .. .. .. 1·40 1·10
924 $1 multicoloured (bright blue) 70 55
925 $5 multicoloured (azure) .. .. .. 3·00 2·75
a. Horiz pair. Nos. 925/6 .. .. .. 6·00 5·50
926 $5 multicoloured (bright blue) .. .. 3·00 2·75
919/26 .. .. *Set of* 8 7·75 6·75
MS927 Four sheets each 145 × 107 mm. (a) 30 c. As Nos. 919/20 each × 2; (b) 50 c. As Nos. 921/2 each × 2; (c) $1.50 As Nos. 923/4 each × 2; (d) $4.50 As Nos. 925/6 each × 2 *Set of 4 sheets* 16·00 16·00

The two designs of each value were printed together, *se-tenant*, in horizontal pairs throughout the sheets.

150 Silos and Conveyor Belt

151 Michael Jackson

(Des G. Vasarhelyi. Litho Format)

1985 (17 Oct). *St. Vincent Flour Milling Industry. T* **150** *and similar horiz designs. Multicoloured. W w* **15**. *P* 15.
928 20 c. Type **150** 15 15
929 30 c. Roller mills 15 20
930 75 c. Administration building 40 45
931 $3 Bran finishers .. .. 1·60 1·75
928/31 .. .. *Set of* 4 2·00 2·25

1985 (27 Oct). *Royal Visit. Nos.* 672/3, 697/8, 711, 724 *and* 912/13 *optd as T* **114** *of Montserrat or surch also.*
932 – 60 c. multicoloured (No. 711) .. .. 2·50 2·00
933 – 60 c. multicoloured (No. 724) .. .. 3·00 2·50
934 – 85 c. multicoloured (No. 912) .. .. 4·00 3·50
a. Horiz pair. Nos. 934/5 .. .. 8·00 7·00
935 – 85 c. multicoloured (No. 913) .. .. 4·00 3·50
936 **125** $1.50, multicoloured .. .. .. 4·00 4·00
937 – $1.60 on $4 multicoloured (No. 672) .. 2·00 2·50
a. Sheetlet. No. 937 × 6 and No. 938 .. 19·00
ab. Sheetlet. No. 937 × 6 and No. 938a .. 19·00
938 – $1.60 on $4 multicoloured (No. 673) (surch $1.60 only) .. .. .. 9·00 9·00
a. Additionally optd "CARIBBEAN ROYAL VISIT—1985" .. .. 9·00
939 – $2.50, multicoloured (No. 698) .. .. 5·50 4·50
932/9 .. .. *Set of* 8 30·00 29·00

No. 938 shows a new face value only. "CARIBBEAN ROYAL VISIT—1985" being omitted from the surcharge. No. 938a is the corrected version issued subsequently.

(Des Court House Studio. Litho Format)

1985 (2 Dec). *Leaders of the World. Michael Jackson (entertainer). Various vertical portraits as T* **151**. *Multicoloured. P* 12½.
940 60 c. multicoloured 30 35
a. Horiz pair. Nos. 940/1 .. .. .. 60 70
941 60 c. multicoloured 30 35
942 $1 multicoloured 50 55
a. Horiz pair. Nos. 942/3 .. .. .. 1·00 1·10
943 $1 multicoloured 50 55
944 $2 multicoloured .. .. 1·00 1·10
a. Horiz pair. Nos. 944/5 .. .. .. 2·00 2·25
945 $2 multicoloured .. .. 1·00 1·10
946 $5 multicoloured .. .. 2·50 2·75
a. Horiz pair. Nos. 946/7 .. .. .. 5·00 5·50
947 $5 multicoloured .. .. 2·50 2·75
940/7 .. .. *Set of* 8 7·75 9·50
MS948 Four sheets, each 144 × 109 mm. (a) 45 c. As Nos. 940/1 each × 2; (b) 90 c. As Nos. 942/3 each × 2; (c) $1.50 As Nos. 944/5 each × 2; (d) $4 As Nos. 946/7 each × 2. *Set of 4 sheets* 15·00 16·00

The two designs for each value were printed together, *se-tenant*, in horizontal pairs throughout the sheets. The left-hand design shows the face value at top left (as on Type **151**) and the right-hand design at top right.

152 "The Serenaders" (Kim de Freitas)

153 *Santa Maria*

(Litho Format)

1985 (9 Dec). *Christmas. Children's Paintings. T* **152** *and similar vert designs. Multicoloured. W w* **15**. *P* 13½ × 14.
949 25 c. Type **152** 15 15
950 75 c. "Poinsettia" (Jackie Douglas) 35 40
951 $2.50, "Jesus our Master" (Bernadette Payne) .. .. 1·25 1·40
949/51 .. .. *Set of* 3 1·50 1·75

(Litho Format)

1986 (23 Jan). *500th Anniv of Discovery of America (1992) by Columbus (1st issue). T* **153** *and similar vert designs. Multicoloured. P* 12½.
952 60 c. Type **153** 30 35
a. Horiz pair. Nos. 952/3 .. .. .. 60 70
953 60 c. Christopher Columbus 30 35
954 $1.50, Columbus at Spanish Court 75 80
a. Horiz pair. Nos. 954/5 .. .. .. 1·50 1·60
955 $1.50, King Ferdinand and Queen Isabella of Spain 75 80
956 $2.75, *Santa Maria* and fruits .. .. 1·40 1·50
a. Horiz pair. Nos. 956/7 .. .. .. 2·75 3·00
957 $2.75, Maize and fruits .. .. .. 1·40 1·50
952/7 .. .. *Set of* 6 4·50 4·75
MS958 95 × 85 mm. $6 Christopher Columbus (*different*) .. .. 3·25 3·75

The two designs of each value were printed together, *se-tenant*, in horizontal pairs within the sheets.

See also Nos. 1125/31.

(Des Artists International. Litho Format)

1986 (27 Jan). *Leaders of the World. Automobiles (5th series). Horiz designs as T* **133**, *the first in each pair showing technical drawings and the second paintings. P* 12½.
959 30 c. black, cobalt and dull orange 15 15
a. Vert pair. Nos. 959/60 .. .. .. 30 30
960 30 c. multicoloured 15 15
961 45 c. black, lavender-grey and blue 25 25
a. Vert pair. Nos. 961/2 .. .. .. 50 50
962 45 c. multicoloured 25 25
963 60 c. black, bright blue and vermilion .. 35 35
a. Vert pair. Nos. 963/4 .. .. .. 70 70
964 60 c. multicoloured 35 35
965 90 c. black, greenish yellow and bright blue 40 40
a. Vert pair. Nos. 965/6 .. .. .. 80 80
966 90 c. multicoloured 40 40
967 $1.50, black, pale rose-lilac & brt magenta 55 55
a. Vert pair. Nos. 967/8 .. .. .. 1·10 1·10
968 $1.50, multicoloured 55 55
969 $2.50, black, blue and bright blue 70 70
a. Vert pair. Nos. 969/70 .. .. .. 1·40 1·40
970 $2.50, multicoloured 70 70
959/70 .. .. *Set of* 12 4·25 4·25

Designs:—Nos. 959/60, Cadillac "Type 53" (1916); 961/2, Triumph "Dolomite" (1939); 963/4, Panther "J-72" (1972); 965/6, Ferrari "275 GTB/4" (1967); 967/8, Packard "Caribbean" (1953); 969/70, Bugatti "Type 41 Royale" (1931).

Nos. 959/70 were issued in a similar sheet format to Nos. 727/38.

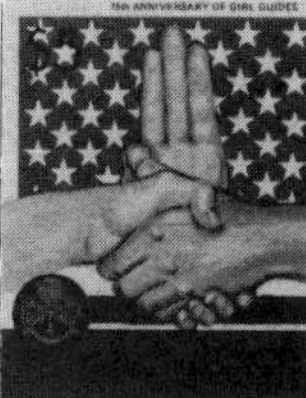

154 Guide Salute and Handclasp

155 Halley's Comet

(Des Court House Studio. Litho Format)

1986 (25 Feb). *75th Annivs of Girl Guide Movement and Boy Scouts of America. Two sheets, each* 85 × 113 *mm, containing vert designs as T* **154**. *Multicoloured. P* 12½.
MS971 $5 Type **154**: $5 Palette and paintbrushes 7·00 8·00
MS972 $6 Cross-tied logs: $6 Lord Baden-Powell 8·00 9·00

The two stamps in each sheet were printed together, *se-tenant*, in horizontal pairs, each forming a composite design.

Nos. **MS**971/2 exist with plain or decorative margins.

Overprints on these miniature sheets commemorating "Capex '87" International Stamp Exhibition, Toronto, were not authorised by the St. Vincent administration.

(Des G. Vasarhelyi. Litho Format)

1986 (14 Apr). *Appearance of Halley's Comet. T* **155** *and similar horiz designs. Multicoloured. W w* **15**. *P* 15.
973 45 c. Type **155** 40 30
974 60 c. Edmond Halley 45 35
975 75 c. Newton's telescope and astronomers .. 50 40
976 $3 Amateur astronomer on St. Vincent .. 1·75 1·60
973/6 .. .. *Set of* 4 2·75 2·40
MS977 155 × 104 mm. Nos. 973/6 .. .. 3·00 3·75

(Des Court House Studio. Litho Format)

1986 (21 Apr). *60th Birthday of Queen Elizabeth II (1st issue). Multicoloured designs as T* **167** *of British Virgin Islands. P* 12½.
978 10 c. Queen Elizabeth II 10 10
979 90 c. Princess Elizabeth 50 50
980 $2.50, Queen gathering bouquets from crowd .. .. 1·40 1·40
981 $8 In Canberra, 1982 (*vert*) .. .. 4·00 4·25
978/81 .. .. *Set of* 4 5·50 5·50
MS982 85 × 115 mm. $10 Queen Elizabeth II (*different*) .. .. 6·00 6·50

156 Mexican Player

157 Queen Elizabeth at Victoria Park, Kingstown

(Des Court House Studio. Litho Format)

1986 (7 May). *World Cup Football Championship, Mexico. T* **156** *and similar multicoloured designs. P* 12½ (75 c., $2, $4, $5) *or* 15 (*others*).
983 1 c. Football and world map (*horiz*) 10 10
984 2 c. Type **156** 10 10
985 5 c. Mexican player (*different*) 10 10
986 5 c. Hungary v Scotland 10 10
987 10 c. Spain v Scotland 10 10
988 30 c. England v U.S.S.R. (*horiz*) 15 20
989 45 c. Spain v France 25 30
990 75 c. Mexican team (56 × 36 *mm*) 35 40
991 $1 England v Italy 50 55
992 $2 Scottish team (56 × 36 *mm*) .. .. 1·00 1·10
993 $4 Spanish team (56 × 36 *mm*) .. .. 2·00 2·10
994 $5 English team (56 × 36 *mm*) .. .. 2·50 2·75
983/94 .. .. *Set of* 12 6·25 7·00
MS995 Four sheets, each 84 × 114 mm. (a) $1.50, As No. 993; (b) $2.25, As No. 992; (c) $2.50, As No. 990; (d) $5.50, As No. 994. P 12½ *Set of 4 sheets* 7·50 8·50

(Des Court House Studio. Litho Questa)

1986 (14 June). *60th Birthday of Queen Elizabeth II (2nd issue). T* **157** *and similar vert designs showing scenes from 1985 Royal Visit. Multicoloured. W w* **15**. *P* 15 × 14.
996 45 c. Type **157** 25 30
997 60 c. Queen and Prime Minister James Mitchell, Bequia 30 35
998 75 c. Queen, Prince Phillip and Mr. Mitchell, Port Elizabeth, Bequia 35 40
999 $2.50, Queen, Prince Phillip and Mr. Mitchell watching Independence Day parade, Victoria Park .. .. .. 1·25 1·40
996/9 .. .. *Set of* 4 1·90 2·25
MS1000 121 × 85 mm. $3 Queen at Victoria Park 2·00 2·40

(Des T. Hadler. Litho Format)

1986 (15 July). *Leaders of the World. Railway Locomotives* (*6th series*). *Horiz designs as T* **135**. *Multicoloured. P* 12½.
1001 30 c. multicoloured 20 20
a. Vert pair. Nos. 1001/2 . . . . 40 40
1002 30 c. multicoloured 20 20
1003 50 c. multicoloured 30 30
a. Vert pair. Nos. 1003/4 . . . . 60 60
1004 50 c. multicoloured 30 30
1005 $1 multicoloured 55 55
a. Vert pair. Nos. 1005/6 . . . . 1·10 1·10
1006 $1 multicoloured 55 55
1007 $3 multicoloured . . . . 1·60 1·60
a. Vert pair. Nos. 1007/8 . . . . 3·25 3·25
1008 $3 multicoloured . . . . 1·60 1·60
1001/8 . . . . *Set of* 8 4·75 4·75

Designs:—Nos. 1001/2, Class "ED41 BZZB" rack and adhesion locomotive, Japan (1926); 1003/4, Locomotive *The Judge*, Chicago Railroad Exposition, U.S.A. (1883); 1005/6, Class "E60C" electric locomotive, U.S.A. (1973); 1007/8, Class "SD40-2" diesel locomotive, U.S.A. (1972).

Nos. 1001/8 were issued in a similar sheet format to Nos. 727/38.

(Des Court House Studio. Litho Format)

1986 (18 July–15 Oct). *Royal Wedding* (*1st issue*). *Multicoloured designs as T* **168** *of British Virgin Islands. P* 12½.
1009 60 c. Profile of Prince Andrew 30 35
a. Pair. Nos. 1009/10 . . . . . . 60 70
1010 60 c. Miss Sarah Ferguson 30 35
1011 $2 Prince Andrew with Mrs. Nancy Reagan (*horiz*) . . . . 1·00 1·10
a. Pair. Nos. 1011/12 . . . . . . 2·00 2·25
1012 $2 Prince Andrew in naval uniform (*horiz*) . . . . 1·00 1·10
1009/12 . . . . *Set of* 4 2·40 2·50
MS1013 115×85 mm. $10 Duke and Duchess of York in carriage after wedding (*horiz*) (15.10) . . 5·50 6·50

Nos. 1009/10 and 1011/12 were each printed together, *se-tenant*, in horizontal and vertical pairs throughout the sheets.

158 *Acrocomia aculeata*

159 Cadet Force Emblem and Cadets of 1936 and 1986

(Des J. Cooter. Litho Questa)

1986 (30 Sept). *Timber Resources of St. Vincent. T* **158** *and similar vert designs. Multicoloured. W* w **15** (*sideways*). *P* 14.
1014 10 c. Type **158** 15 10
1015 60 c. *Pithecellobium saman* 45 35
1016 75 c. White Cedar 50 40
1017 $3 *Andira inermis* . . . . 1·75 2·00
1014/17 . . . . *Set of* 4 2·50 2·50

(Des G. Vasarhelyi. Litho Questa)

1986 (30 Sept). *50th Anniv of St. Vincent Cadet Force* (45 c., $2) *and 75th Anniv of St. Vincent Girls' High School* (*others*). *T* **159** *and similar multicoloured designs. W* w **15** (*sideways on* 45 c.). *P* 14.
1018 45 c. Type **159** 25 30
1019 60 c. Grimble Building, Girls' High School (*horiz*) 30 35
1020 $1.50, High School pupils (*horiz*) . . 75 80
1021 $2 Cadets on parade (*horiz*) . . . . 1·00 1·10
1018/21 . . . . *Set of* 4 2·10 2·25

1986 (15 Oct). *Royal Wedding* (*2nd issue*). *Nos.* 1009/12 *optd as T* **121** *of Montserrat in silver.*
1022 60 c. Profile of Prince Andrew 30 35
a. Pair. Nos. 1022/3 . . . . . . 60 70
1023 60 c. Miss Sarah Ferguson 30 35
1024 $2 Prince Andrew with Mrs. Nancy Reagan (*horiz*) . . . . 1·00 1·10
a. Pair. Nos. 1024/5 . . . . . . 2·00 2·25
1025 $2 Prince Andrew in naval uniform (*horiz*) . . . . 1·00 1·10
1022/5 . . . . *Set of* 4 2·40 2·50

160 King Arthur

(Des G. Vasarhelyi. Litho Format)

1986 (3 Nov). *The Legend of King Arthur. T* **160** *and similar horiz designs. Multicoloured. P* 14×13½.
1026 30 c. Type **160** 30 30
1027 45 c. Merlin taking baby Arthur 40 40
1028 60 c. Arthur pulling sword from stone . . 45 45
1029 75 c. Camelot 50 50
1030 $1 Arthur receiving Excalibur from the Lady of the Lake 70 70
1031 $1.50, Knights at the Round Table . . 1·00 1·00
1032 $2 The Holy Grail . . . . 1·40 1·40
1033 $5 Sir Lancelot jousting . . . . . . 3·00 3·00
1026/33 . . . . *Set of* 8 7·00 7·00

161 Statue of Liberty Floodlit

162 Fishing for Tri Tri

(Des Court House Studio. Litho Format)

1986 (26 Nov). *Centenary of Statue of Liberty. T* **161** *and similar vert designs showing aspects of the Statue. P* 14×13½.
1034 15 c. multicoloured 10 10
1035 25 c. multicoloured 15 15
1036 40 c. multicoloured 20 25
1037 55 c. multicoloured 25 30
1038 75 c. multicoloured 35 40
1039 90 c. multicoloured 45 50
1040 $1.75, multicoloured 90 95
1041 $2 multicoloured . . . . 1·00 1·10
1042 $2.50, multicoloured . . . . . . 1·25 1·40
1043 $3 multicoloured . . . . 1·50 1·60
1034/43 . . . . *Set of* 10 5·50 6·00
MS1044 Three sheets, each 85×115 mm. $3.50; $4; $5 . . . . . . *Set of* 3 *sheets* 7·00 8·50

(Des T. Hadler. Litho Format)

1986 (10 Dec). *Freshwater Fishing. T* **162** *and similar horiz designs. Multicoloured. P* 15.
1045 75 c. Type **162** 35 40
a. Pair. Nos. 1045/6 . . . . . . 70 80
1046 75 c. Tri Tri 35 40
1047 $1.50, Crayfishing 75 80
a. Pair. Nos. 1047/8 . . . . . . 1·50 1·60
1048 $1.50, Crayfish 75 80
1045/8 . . . . *Set of* 4 2·00 2·10

Nos. 1045/6 and 1047/8 were each printed together, *se-tenant*, in horizontal and vertical pairs throughout the sheets.

163 Baby on Scales

WORLD POPULATION
5 BILLION
11TH JULY 1987

(**164**)

(Litho Format)

1987 (10 June). *Child Health Campaign. T* **163** *and similar vert designs. Multicoloured. P* 14.
1049 10 c. Type **163** 10 10
1050 50 c. Oral rehydration therapy 25 30
1051 75 c. Breast feeding 35 40
1052 $1 Nurse giving injection 45 50
1049/52 . . . . *Set of* 4 1·00 1·10

1987 (10 June). *World Population Control. Nos.* 1049/52 *optd with T* **164**.
1053 10 c. Type **163** 10 10
1054 50 c. Oral rehydration therapy 35 35
1055 75 c. Breast feeding 45 45
1056 $1 Nurse giving injection 55 55
1053/6 . . . . *Set of* 4 1·25 1·25

165 Hanna Mandlikova

166 Miss Prima Donna, Queen of the Bands, 1986

(Litho Format)

1987 (22 June). *International Lawn Tennis Players. T* **165** *and similar vert designs. Multicoloured. P* 12½.
1057 40 c. Type **165** 20 25
1058 60 c. Yannick Noah 25 35
1059 80 c. Ivan Lendl 35 40
1060 $1 Chris Evert 45 50
1061 $1.25, Steffi Graf 55 60
1062 $1.50, John McEnroe 70 75
1063 $1.75, Martina Navratilova with Wimbledon trophy 80 85
1064 $2 Boris Becker with Wimbledon trophy 90 95
1057/64 . . . . *Set of* 8 3·50 4·25
MS1065 115×85 mm. $2.25 As No. 1063; $2.25 As No. 1064 . . . . 2·75 3·25

Designs as Nos. 1063/4, but each with a face value of $10, also exist embossed on gold foil from a restricted printing.

(Des Young Phillips. Litho Format)

1987 (29 June). *10th Anniv of Carnival. T* **166** *and similar vert designs. Multicoloured. P* 12½.
1066 20 c. Type **166** 10 15
1067 45 c. Donna Young, Miss Carnival, 1985 . . 20 25
1068 55 c. Miss St. Vincent and the Grenadines, 1986 . . . . 25 30
1069 $3.70, "Spirit of Hope" costume, 1986 . . 1·60 1·75
1066/9 . . . . *Set of* 4 1·90 2·25

The 45 c. value is inscribed "Miss Carival" in error.

THE KING OF ROCK AND ROLL LIVES FOREVER · AUGUST 16TH
1977–1987

(**167**)

168 Queen Victoria, 1841

1987 (26 Aug). *10th Death Anniv of Elvis Presley* (*entertainer*). *Nos.* 919/27 *optd with T* **167** *in silver.*
1070 10 c. multicoloured (T **149**) 15 15
a. Horiz pair. Nos. 1070/1 . . . . 30 30
1071 10 c. multicoloured (bright blue) 15 15
1072 60 c. multicoloured (brown) 40 40
a. Horiz pair. Nos. 1072/3 . . . . 80 80
1073 60 c. multicoloured (pale grey) 40 40
1074 $1 multicoloured (brown) 65 65
a. Horiz pair. Nos. 1074/5 . . . . 1·25 1·25
1075 $1 multicoloured (bright blue) 65 65
1076 $5 multicoloured (azure) . . . . 2·75 2·75
a. Horiz pair. Nos. 1076/7 . . . . 5·50 5·50
1077 $5 multicoloured (bright blue) . . . . 2·75 2·75
1070/7 . . . . *Set of* 8 7·00 7·00
MS1078 Four sheets, each 145 × 107 mm. (a) 30 c. As Nos. 1070/1 each × 2; (b) 50 c. As Nos. 1072/3 each × 2; (c) $1.50, As Nos. 1074/5 each × 2; (d) $4.50, As Nos. 1076/7 each × 2 . . . . 17·00 18·00

(Litho Format)

1987 (15 Oct). *Royal Ruby Wedding and 150th Anniv of Queen Victoria's Accession. T* **168** *and similar vert designs. Multicoloured. P* 12½.
1079 15 c. Type **168** 15 10
1080 75 c. Queen Elizabeth and Prince Andrew, 1960 . . . . 45 40
1081 $1 Coronation, 1953 . . . . . . 60 50
1082 $2.50, Duke of Edinburgh, 1948 . . . . 1·40 1·50
1083 $5 Queen Elizabeth II, *c.* 1980 . . . . 2·50 2·75
1079/83 . . . . *Set of* 5 4·50 4·75
MS1084 85×115 mm. $6 Princess Elizabeth with Prince Charles at his Christening, 1948 . . 3·75 4·00

169 Karl Benz and Benz Three-wheeler (1886)

(Litho Format)

1987 (4 Dec). *Century of Motoring. T* **169** *and similar horiz designs. Multicoloured. P* 12½.
1085 $1 Type **169** 60 60
1086 $2 Enzo Ferrari and Ferrari "Dino 206SP" (1966) . . . . 1·25 1·25
1087 $4 Charles Rolls and Sir Henry Royce and Rolls-Royce "Silver Ghost" (1907) . . 2·00 2·00
1088 $5 Henry Ford and Ford "Model T" (1908) . . 2·50 2·50
1085/8 . . . . *Set of* 4 5·75 5·75
MS1089 Four sheets, each 144×75 mm. (a) $3 As Type **169**. (b) $5 As No. 1086. (c) $6 As No. 1087. (d) $8 As No. 1088 . . . . *Set of* 4 *sheets* 15·00 16·00

170 Everton Football Team

(Litho Format)

1987 (4 Dec). *English Football Teams. T* **170** *and similar horiz designs. Multicoloured. P* 12½.

1090 $2 Type **170** .. .. 1·25 1·25
1091 $2 Manchester United .. .. 1·25 1·25
1092 $2 Tottenham Hotspur .. .. 1·25 1·25
1093 $2 Arsenal .. .. 1·25 1·25
1094 $2 Liverpool .. .. 1·25 1·25
1095 $2 Derby County .. .. 1·25 1·25
1096 $2 Portsmouth .. .. 1·25 1·25
1097 $2 Leeds United .. .. 1·25 1·25
1090/7 .. .. *Set of* 8 9·00 9·00

171 Five Cent Coins 172 Charles Dickens

(Des Young Phillips. Litho Format)

1987 (11 Dec). *East Caribbean Currency. T* **171** *and similar multicoloured designs. P* 15.

1098 5 c. Type **171** 10 10
1099 6 c. Two cent coins 10 10
1100 10 c. Ten cent coins 10 10
1101 12 c. Two and ten cent coins 10 10
1102 15 c. Five cent coins 10 10
1103 20 c. Ten cent coins 10 10
1104 25 c. Twenty-five cent coins 10 10
1105 30 c. Five and twenty-five cent coins 10 15
1106 35 c. Twenty-five and ten cent coins 15 20
1107 45 c. Twenty-five and two ten cent coins .. 20 25
1108 50 c. Fifty cent coins 20 25
1109 65 c. Fifty, ten and five cent coins 25 30
1110 75 c. Fifty and twenty-five cent coins 30 35
1111 $1 One dollar note (*horiz*) 40 45
1112 $2 Two one dollar notes (*horiz*) 80 85
1113 $3 Three one dollar notes (*horiz*) .. .. 1·25 1·40
1114 $5 Five dollar note (*horiz*) .. .. .. 2·10 2·25
1115 $10 Ten dollar note (*horiz*) .. .. .. 4·00 4·25
1098/115 .. .. *Set of* 18 9·00 10·00

(Des Jennifer Toombs. Litho Format)

1987 (17 Dec). *Christmas. 175th Birth Anniv of Charles Dickens. T* **172** *and similar vert designs. Multicoloured. P* 14 × 14½.

1116 6 c. Type **172** 10 10
a. Horiz pair. Nos. 1116/17 .. .. .. 15 15
1117 6 c. "Mr. Fezziwig's Ball" 10 10
1118 25 c. Type **172** 15 15
a. Horiz pair. Nos. 1118/19 .. .. .. 30 30
1119 25 c. "Scrooge's Third Visitor" 15 15
1120 50 c. Type **172** 30 30
a. Horiz pair. Nos. 1120/1 .. .. .. 60 60
1121 50 c. "The Cratchits' Christmas" 30 30
1122 75 c. Type **172** 45 45
a. Horiz pair. Nos. 1122/3 .. .. .. 90 90
1123 75 c. "A Christmas Carol" 45 45
1116/23 .. .. *Set of* 8 1·75 1·75
MS1124 141 × 101 mm. $5 Teacher reading to class .. .. 2·40 3·00

Nos. 1116/17, 1118/19, 1120/1 and 1122/3 were printed together, *se-tenant*, in horizontal pairs throughout the sheets, each pair forming a composite design showing an open book. The first design in each pair shows Type **172** and the second a scene from *A Christmas Carol*.

173 *Santa Maria* 174 Brown Pelican

(Des M. Pollard. Litho Format)

1988 (11 Jan). *500th Anniv of Discovery of America* (1992) *by Columbus (2nd issue). T* **173** *and similar square designs. Multicoloured. P* 14.

1125 15 c. Type **173** 15 15
1126 75 c. *Nina* and *Pinta* 50 50
1127 $1 Compass and hourglass 70 70
1128 $1.50, Claiming the New World for Spain 90 90
1129 $3 Arawak village .. .. 1·50 1·50
1130 $4 Parrot, hummingbird, pineapple and maize .. .. 2·00 2·00
1125/30 .. .. *Set of* 6 5·25 5·25
MS1131 114 × 86 mm. $5 Columbus, Arms and *Santa Maria*. P 13½ × 14 .. .. .. 3·50 3·75

(Des Maxine Marsh. Litho Format)

1988 (15 Feb). *P* 14.

1132 **174** 45 c. multicoloured 20 25

175 Windsurfing

(Litho Format)

1988 (26 Feb). *Tourism. T* **175** *and similar multicoloured designs. P* 15.

1133 10 c. Type **175** 10 10
1134 45 c. Scuba diving 20 25
1135 65 c. Aerial view of Young Island (*horiz*) .. 30 35
1136 $5 Charter yacht (*horiz*) .. .. .. 2·10 2·25
1133/6 .. .. *Set of* 4 2·40 2·50

176 *Nuestra Sénora del Rosario* (galleon) and Spanish Knight's Cross

(Litho Format)

1988 (29 July). *400th Anniv of Spanish Armada. T* **176** *and similar horiz designs. Multicoloured. P* 12½.

1137 15 c. Type **176** 15 10
1138 75 c. *Ark Royal* and English Armada medal 30 35
1139 $1.50, English fleet and Drake's dial .. 60 65
1140 $2 Dismasted Spanish ship and 16th-century shot 80 85
1141 $3.50, Attack of English fireships at Calais and 16th-century grenade .. 1·50 1·60
1142 $5 *Revenge* and Drake's Drum .. .. 2·10 2·25
1137/42 .. .. *Set of* 6 4·75 5·25
MS1143 123 × 92 mm. $8 Sighting the Armada 3·25 3·50

177 D. K. Lillee 178 Athletics

(Litho Format)

1988 (29 July). *Cricketers of* 1988 *International Season. T* **177** *and similar square designs. Multicoloured. P* 14.

1144 15 c. Type **177** 15 15
1145 50 c. G. A. Gooch 35 35
1146 75 c. R. N. Kapil Dev 45 45
1147 $1 S. M. Gavaskar 60 60
1148 $1.50, M. W. Gatting 80 80
1149 $2.50, Imran Khan .. .. 1·40 1·40
1150 $3 I. T. Botham .. .. 1·60 1·60
1151 $4 I. V. A. Richards .. .. 1·90 1·90
1144/51 .. .. *Set of* 8 6·50 6·50
MS1152 130 × 80 mm. $2 As $4; $3.50, As $3 2·75 3·25

(Des and litho Questa)

1988 (7 Dec). *Olympic Games, Seoul. T* **178** *and similar multicoloured designs. P* 14.

1153 10 c. Type **178** 10 10
1154 50 c. Long jumping (*vert*) 20 25
1155 $1 Triple jumping 45 50
1156 $5 Boxing (*vert*) .. .. 2·10 2·25
1153/6 .. .. *Set of* 4 2·50 2·75
MS1157 85 × 63 mm. $10 Olympic flame .. 4·25 4·75

NEW INFORMATION

The editor is always interested to correspond with people who have new information that will improve or correct the Catalogue.

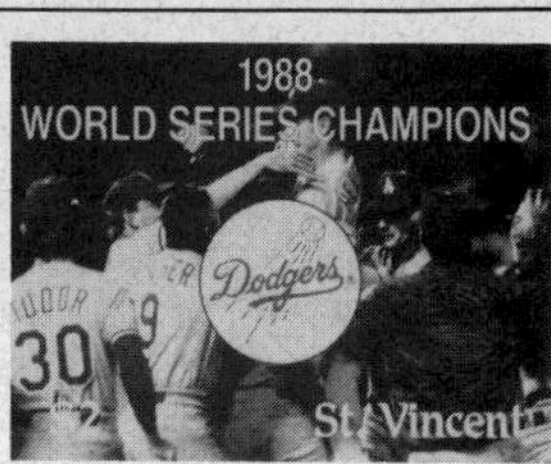

179 Babe Ruth 180 Los Angeles Dodgers (National League Champions)

(Litho Questa)

1988 (15 Dec). *Famous Baseball Players (1st series). P* 14.

1158 **179** $2 multicoloured 80 85

(Des W. Storozuk. Litho Questa)

1988 (15 Dec). 1988 *Baseball World Series. Sheet* 115×85 *mm containing T* **180** *and similar horiz design. Multicoloured. P* 14×13½.

MS1159 $2 Type **180**; $2 Team logos of Dodgers and Oakland Athletics .. .. .. 1·90 2·00

(Des Walt Disney Co. Litho Questa)

1988 (23 Dec). *Christmas. "Mickey's Christmas Train". Multicoloured designs as T* **246** *of Antigua. P* 14×13½.

1160 1 c. Minnie Mouse in parcels van (*horiz*) 10 10
1161 2 c. Mordie and Ferdie on low-loader wagon (*horiz*) 10 10
1162 3 c. Chip n'Dale in wagon with Christmas trees (*horiz*) 10 10
1163 4 c. Donald Duck's nephews riding with reindeer (*horiz*) 10 10
1164 5 c. Donald and Daisy Duck in restaurant car (*horiz*) 10 10
1165 10 c. Grandma Duck, Uncle Scrooge McDuck, Goofy and Clarabelle carol singing in carriage (*horiz*) 10 10
1166 $5 Mickey Mouse driving locomotive (*horiz*) .. .. 2·10 2·25
1167 $6 Father Christmas in guard's van (*horiz*) .. .. 2·50 2·75
1160/7 .. .. *Set of* 8 4·50 4·75
MS1168 Two sheets, each 127 × 102 mm, (a) $5 Mickey Mouse and nephews at railway station. (b) $5 Mickey and Minnie Mouse on carousel. P 13½×14 .. .. .. *Set of* 2 *sheets* 4·25 4·50

181 Mickey Mouse as Snake Charmer

(Des Walt Disney Co. Litho Questa)

1989 (7 Feb). *"India-89" International Stamp Exhibition, New Delhi. T* **181** *and similar multicoloured designs showing Walt Disney cartoon characters in India. P* 14×13½.

1169 1 c. Type **181** 10 10
1170 2 c. Goofy with Chowsingha Antelope .. 10 10
1171 3 c. Mickey and Minnie Mouse with Blue Peacock 10 10
1172 5 c. Goofy with Briolette Diamond and Mickey Mouse pushing mine truck .. 10 10
1173 10 c. Clarabelle with Orloff Diamond .. 10 10
1174 25 c. Mickey Mouse as tourist and Regent Diamond, Louvre, Paris 15 15
1175 $4 Minnie and Mickey Mouse with Kohinoor Diamond .. .. .. 2·00 2·00
1176 $5 Mickey Mouse and Goofy with Indian Rhinoceros .. .. 2·40 2·40
1169/76 .. .. *Set of* 8 4·25 4·25
MS1177 Two sheets, each 127 × 102 mm. (a) $6 Mickey Mouse riding Indian elephant. P 14×13½. (b) $6 Mickey Mouse as postman delivering Hope Diamond to Smithsonian Museum, U.S.A. (*vert*). P 13½×14. .. *Set of* 2 *sheets* 5·00 5·25

182 Harry James

(Des A. Nahigian. Litho Questa)

1989 (3 Apr). *Jazz Musicians. T* **182** *and similar horiz designs. Multicoloured. P* 14.

1178 10 c. Type **182** 10 10
1179 15 c. Sidney Bechet 10 10
1180 25 c. Benny Goodman 10 15
1181 35 c. Django Reinhardt 15 20
1182 50 c. Lester Young 25 30
1183 90 c. Gene Krupa 40 45
1184 $3 Louis Armstrong .. .. 1·50 1·60
1185 $4 Duke Ellington .. .. 1·90 2·00
1178/85 .. .. *Set of* 8 4·00 4·25
MS1186 Two sheets, each 107×92 mm. (a) $5 Charlie Parker. (b) $5 Billie Holliday *Set of* 2 *sheets* 6·00 6·50

183 Head of St. Vincent Amazon

(Des L. McQueen. Litho Questa)

1989 (5 Apr). *Wildlife Conservation. St. Vincent Amazon ("St. Vincent Parrot"). T* **183** *and similar multicoloured designs. P* 14.

1187 10 c. Type **183** 15 10
1188 20 c. St. Vincent Amazon in flight 20 10
1189 40 c. Feeding (*vert*) 35 25
1190 70 c. At entrance to nest (*vert*) 50 55
1187/90 *Set of* 4 1·10 90

184 Blue-hooded Euphonia ("Mistletoe Bird") **185** Birds in Flight

(Des Tracy Pedersen. Litho Questa)

1989 (5 Apr). *Birds of St. Vincent. T* **184** *and similar multicoloured designs. P* 14.

1191 25 c. Type **184** 20 15
1192 75 c. Common Black Hawk ("Crab Hawk") 55 50
1193 $2 Mangrove Cuckoo ("Coucou") 1·40 1·40
1194 $3 Hooded Tanager ("Prince Bird") 1·75 1·75
1191/4 *Set of* 4 3·50 3·50
MS1195 (a) 75×105 mm. $5 Rufous-throated Solitaire ("Soufriere Bird") (*vert*). (b) 105×75 mm. $5 Purple-throated Carib ("Doctor Bird") *Set of* 2 *sheets* 6·00 7·00

(Des N. Waldman. Litho B.D.T.)

1989 (10 Apr). *Wildlife Conservation. Noah's Ark. T* **185** *and similar square designs. Multicoloured. P* 14.

1196 40 c. Type **185** 20 25
a. Sheetlet. Nos. 1196/220 4·50
1197 40 c. Rainbow (left side) 20 25
1198 40 c. Noah's Ark on mountain 20 25
1199 40 c. Rainbow (right side) 20 25
1200 40 c. Birds in flight (*different*) 20 25
1201 40 c. Cow elephant 20 25
1202 40 c. Bull elephant 20 25
1203 40 c. Top of eucalyptus tree 20 25
1204 40 c. Kangaroos 20 25
1205 40 c. Hummingbird 20 25
1206 40 c. Lions 20 25
1207 40 c. White-tailed Deer 20 25
1208 40 c. Koala in fork of tree 20 25
1209 40 c. Koala on branch 20 25
1210 40 c. Hummingbird approaching flower 20 25
1211 40 c. Toucan and flower 20 25
1212 40 c. Toucan facing right 20 25
1213 40 c. Camels 20 25
1214 40 c. Giraffes 20 25
1215 40 c. Mountain Sheep 20 25
1216 40 c. Ladybirds on leaf 20 25
1217 40 c. Swallowtail butterfly 20 25
1218 40 c. Swallowtail butterfly behind leaves 20 25
1219 40 c. Pythons 20 25
1220 40 c. Dragonflies 20 25
1196/220 *Set of* 25 4·50 5·50

Nos. 1196/220 were printed together, *se-tenant*, in a sheetlet of 25, forming a composite design showing Noah's Ark and animals released after the Flood.

(Litho Questa)

1989 (17 Apr). *Easter. 500th Birth Anniv of Titian (artist). Vert designs as T* **238** *of Antigua. Multicoloured. P* 13½×14.

1221 5 c. "Baptism of Christ" (detail) 10 10
1222 30 c. "Temptation of Christ" 15 20
1223 45 c. "Ecce Homo" 20 25
1224 65 c. "Noli Me Tangere" (fragment) 30 35
1225 75 c. "Christ carrying the Cross" (detail) 35 40
1226 $1 "Christ crowned with Thorns" (detail) 45 50
1227 $4 "Lamentation over Christ" (detail) 1·90 2·00
1228 $5 "The Entombment" (detail) 2·40 2·50
1221/8 *Set of* 8 5·25 5·75
MS1229 (a) 98×111 mm. $6 "Pietà "(detail). (b) 114×95 mm. $6 "The Deposition" (detail) *Set of* 2 *sheets* 5·50 5·75

PRICES OF SETS

Set prices are given for many issues, generally those containing three stamps or more. Definitive sets include one of each value or major colour change, but do not cover different perforations, die types or minor shades. Where a choice is possible the set prices are based on the cheapest versions of the stamps included in the listings.

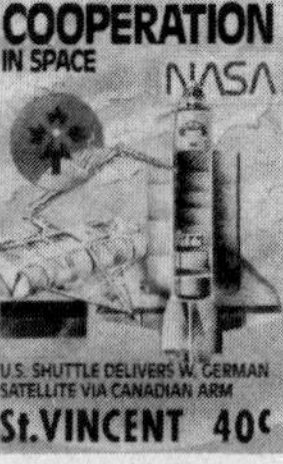

186 *Ile de France* **187** Space Shuttle deploying West German Satellite, 1983

(Des W. Wright. Litho Questa)

1989 (21 Apr). *Ocean Liners. T* **186** *and similar horiz designs. Multicoloured. P* 14.

1230 10 c. Type **186** 10 10
1231 40 c. *Liberté* 20 25
1232 50 c. *Mauretania* (launched 1906) 25 30
1233 75 c. *France* 35 40
1234 $1 *Aquitania* 45 50
1235 $2 *United States* 95 1·00
1236 $3 *Olympic* 1·50 1·60
1237 $4 *Queen Elizabeth* 1·90 2·00
1230/7 *Set of* 8 5·00 5·50
MS1238 Two sheets, each 141×108 mm. (a) $6 *Queen Mary* (85×28 *mm*). (b) $6 *Queen Elizabeth* 2 (85×28 *mm*) *Set of* 2 *sheets* 5·50 5·75

(Des M. Dorfman. Litho Questa)

1989 (26 Apr). *International Co-operation in Space. T* **187** *and similar vert designs. Multicoloured. P* 14.

1239 40 c. Type **187** 20 25
1240 60 c. Vladimir Remeck (Czech cosmonaut) and "Soyuz 28", 1978 30 35
1241 $1 Projected "Hermes" space plane and "Columbus" Space Station 45 50
1242 $4 Ulf Merbold (West German astronaut), 1983, and proposed European Spacelab 1·90 2·00
1239/42 *Set of* 4 2·50 2·75
MS1243 93×67 mm. $5 Meeting in space of "Apollo/Soyuz" mission crews, 1975 2·40 2·50

188 "Mercury 9" Capsule and Astronaut Cooper

(Des M. Dorfman. Litho Questa)

1989 (26 Apr). *25th Anniv of Launching of "Telstar II" Communications Satellite* (1988). *T* **188** *and similar vert designs, each showing satellite and T.V. screen. Multicoloured. P* 14.

1244 15 c. Type **188** 10 10
1245 35 c. Martin Luther King addressing crowd, 1963 15 20
1246 50 c. Speedskater, Winter Olympic Games, Innsbruck, 1964 25 30
1247 $3 Pope John XXIII blessing crowd 1·50 1·60
1244/7 *Set of* 4 1·75 2·00
MS1248 107×77 mm. $5 Launch of "Telstar II", 1963 2·40 2·50

(Litho Questa)

1989 (6 July). *Japanese Art. Multicoloured designs as T* **250** *of Antigua. P* 14×13½.

1249 10 c. "Autumn Flowers in Front of the Full Moon" (Hiroshige) 10 10
1250 40 c. "Hibiscus" (Hiroshige) 20 25
1251 50 c. "Iris" (Hiroshige) 25 30
1252 75 c. "Morning Glories" (Hiroshige) 35 40
1253 $1 "Dancing Swallows" (Hiroshige) 45 50
1254 $2 "Sparrow and Bamboo" (Hiroshige) 95 1·00
1255 $3 "Yellow Bird and Cotton Rose" (Hiroshige) 1·50 1·60
1256 $4 "Judos Chrysanthemums in a Deep Ravine in China" (Hiroshige) 1·90 2·00
1249/56 *Set of* 8 5·00 5·50
MS1257 Two sheets, each 102×76 mm. (a) $6 "Rural Cottages in Spring" (Sotatsu). P 14×13½. (b) $6 "The Six Immortal Poets portrayed as Cats" (Kuniyoshi) (*vert*). P 13½×14 *Set of* 2 *sheets* 5·50 5·75

Nos. 1249/56 were each printed in sheetlets of 10 containing two horizontal strips of 5 stamps separated by printed labels commemorating Emperor Hirohito.

OFFICIAL STAMPS

OFFICIAL

(O 1)

1982 (11 Oct). *Nos. 668/73 optd with Type* O 1.

O1 60 c. *Isabella* 25 30
a. Sheetlet. No. O1 × 6 and No. O2 2·00
b. Opt double
c. Albino opt 12·00
O2 60 c. Prince Charles and Lady Diana Spencer 50 50
b. Opt double
c. Albino opt 35·00
O3 $2.50, *Alberta* (tender) 80 90
a. Sheetlet. No. O3 × 6 and No. O4 5·50
b. Opt inverted 30·00
c. Opt inverted (horiz pair) 80·00
d. Albino opt 25·00
O4 $2.50, Prince Charles and Lady Diana Spencer 1·25 1·40
b. Opt inverted 95·00
c. Albino opt 65·00
O5 $4 *Britannia* 1·25 1·60
a. Sheetlet. No. O5 × 6 and No. O6 9·00
b. Opt double
c. Albino opt 20·00
d. Opt inverted
e. Opt inverted (horiz pair)
O6 $4 Prince Charles and Lady Diana Spencer 2·00 2·25
b. Opt double
c. Albino opt 55·00
d. Opt inverted
O1/6 *Set of* 6 5·50 6·25

Nos. O3c and O5e show the long overprint, intended for Nos. O4 or O6, inverted and struck across a horizontal pair of Nos. O3 or O5. Nos. O4b and O6d show two examples of Type O **1** inverted on the same stamp.

POSTAL FISCAL STAMPS

The following were primarily intended for the payment of passport fees, but were also valid for postal purposes and are frequently found used on parcels.

$5

STAMP DUTY

(F 1)

F **2** St. Vincent Coat of Arms

1980 (Feb). *Stamps as T* **95**, *without value, surch as Type* **F 1**. *W w* **12**. *P* 14½ × 14.

F1 $5 deep lavender and azure 3·00 2·50
F2 $10 light green and apple green 6·50 5·50
F3 $20 reddish purple and pale rose-lilac 12·50 12·00
F1/3 *Set of* 3 20·00 18·00

(Des Harrison. Recess D.L.R.)

1980 (19 May). W w **14**. *P* 14 × 13.

F4 F **2** $5 chalky blue 2·10 2·25
F5 $10 deep green 4·00 4·25
F6 $20 brown-red 9·50 9·75
F4/6 *Set of* 3 14·00 14·50

1984 (22 May). *As No.* F6, *but W w* **15**. *P* 12.

F9 F **2** $20 brown-red 8·25 8·50

GRENADINES OF ST. VINCENT

A group of islands south of St. Vincent which includes Bequia, Mustique, Canouan and Union.

For stamps inscribed "The Grenadines of St. VINCENT" issued by St. Vincent in 1971, see under St. Vincent Nos. 330/6.

Stamps of the Grenadines of St. Vincent exist overprinted "SPECIMEN", these being produced for publicity purposes.

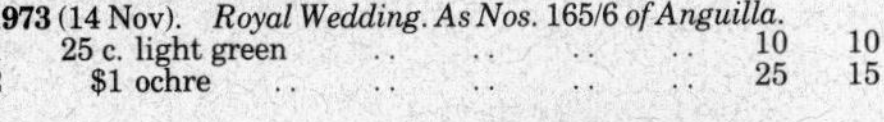

1973 (14 Nov). *Royal Wedding. As Nos.* 165/6 *of Anguilla.*

1	25 c. light green	10	10
2	$1 ochre	25	15

GRENADINES OF

(1)

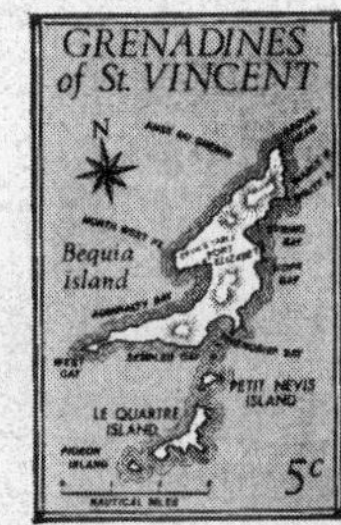

2 Map of Bequia

1974 (24 Apr). *Stamps of St. Vincent. T* **51** *etc. optd in litho with T* **1** *by Harrison & Sons. Glazed paper. W* w **12** (*sideways on* 4, 5, 10, 12, 50 *c. and* $5).

3	1 c. Green Heron	10	10
	a. Opt omitted	50·00	
	b. Albino opt	45·00	
4	2 c. Lesser Antillean Bullfinches	15	15
5	3 c. St. Vincent Amazons	75	75
6	4 c. Rufous-throated Solitaire	15	10
7	5 c. Red-necked Pigeon	15	10
8	6 c. Bananaquits	15	10
9	8 c. Purple-throated Carib	15	10
10	10 c. Mangrove Cuckoo	15	10
11	12 c. Common Black Hawk	20	15
	a. Opt double	£125	
12	20 c. Bare-eyed Thrush	35	20
13	25 c. Hooded Tanager	40	20
14	50 c. Blue-hooded Euphonia	70	40
	a. Albino opt	80·00	
15	$1 Barn Owl	1·50	75
16	$2.50, Yellow-bellied Elaenia	2·00	1·25
17	$5 Ruddy Quail Dove	3·50	2·25
3/17	.. .. *Set of* 15	9·25	6·00

(Des G. Drummond. Litho Enschedé)

1974 (9 May). *Maps* (1*st series*). *T* **2** *and similar vert designs. W* w **12** (*sideways*). *P* 13 × 12½.

18	5 c. black, light dull green and deep dull green	10	10
19	15 c. multicoloured	10	10
20	20 c. multicoloured	10	10
21	30 c. black, light rose-lilac and lake	10	10
22	40 c. black, lavender and deep ultramarine ..	10	10
23	$1 black, cobalt and bright ultramarine ..	25	20
18/23	.. .. *Set of* 6	60	35

Maps:—15 c. The Grenadines and Prune Island (inset); 20 c. Mayreau Island and Tobago Cays; 30 c. Mustique Island; 40 c. Union Island; $1 Canouan Island.

Nos. 18/23 were each issued in sheets of ten stamps and two *se-tenant* labels.

See also Nos. 85/8.

GRENADINES OF

(3)

4 Boat-building

1974 (7 June). *Nos.* 361/2 *of St. Vincent optd in typo with T* **3** *by Govt Printer, St. Vincent. Glazed paper. W* w **12**.

24	2 c. Lesser Antillean Bullfinches	40	30
25	3 c. St. Vincent Amazons	40	30
	a. Opt double	45·00	
	b. Albino opt	11·00	
	c. Chalky paper. Wmk sideways (No. 288)	30·00	30·00

1974 (25 July). *Centenary of Universal Postal Union. As Nos.* 392/5 *of St. Vincent but colours and face-values changed and inscr* "Grenadines of St. Vincent".

26	2 c. U.P.U. emblem	10	10
	a. Red (U.P.U. emblem) omitted	£650	
27	15 c. Globe within posthorn	10	10
28	40 c. Map of St. Vincent and hand-cancelling	10	10
29	$1 Map of the world	25	15
26/9	.. .. *Set of* 4	40	25

No. 26a was caused by a paper fold.

(Des G. Drummond. Litho Questa)

1974. *Bequia Island* (1*st series*). *T* **4** *and similar horiz designs. Multicoloured. P* 14. (*a*) *W* w **12** (*sideways*) (26.9.74).

30	5 c. Type **4**	90	1·50
31	30 c. Careening at Port Elizabeth	10	15
32	35 c. Admiralty Bay	10	15
33	$1 Fishing boat race	20	25

(*b*) *W* w **14** (*sideways*) (12.74)

34	5 c. Type **4**	15	10
30/4	.. .. *Set of* 5	1·25	2·00

No. 34 differs in shade from No. 30, notably in the shirt of the man at right, which is red on No. 34 instead of purple.

Nos. 30/4 were each issued in sheets of ten stamps and two *se-tenant* labels.

See also Nos. 185/8.

5 Music Volute (imprint at foot showing designer, date and printer)

(Des R. Granger Barrett. Litho Questa)

1974 (27 Nov)–**77.** *Shells and Molluscs. Horiz designs as T* **5.** *Multicoloured. W* w **14** (*sideways*). *P* 14.

A. *No imprint.* B. *Imprint at foot*

		A		B	
35	1 c. Atlantic Thorny Oyster	10	10	†	
36	2 c. Zigzag Scallop	10	10	†	
37	3 c. Reticulated Helmet ..	10	10	†	
38	4 c. Type **5**	10	10	10	10
39	5 c. Amber Pen Shell	10	10	10	10
40	6 c. Angular Triton	10	10	10	10
41	8 c. Flame Helmet	10	10	10	10
42	10 c. Caribbean Olive	10	10	10	10
	a. Corrected imprint	†		40	10
43	12 c. Common Sundial	10	10	†	
44	15 c. Glory of the Atlantic Cone	25	20	50	15
45	20 c. Flame Auger	30	35	30	20
	a. Corrected imprint	†		75	15
46	25 c. King Venus	25	20	50	15
47	35 c. Long-spined Star-shell ..	35	30	35	25
	a. Corrected imprint	†		1·00	25
48	45 c. Speckled Tellin	35	30	†	
49	50 c. Rooster Tail Conch ..	40	25	45	30
50	$1 Green Star Shell	1·00	75	1·00	60
51	$2.50, Incomparable Cone ..	2·25	1·25	4·00	1·25
52	$5 Rough File Clam	4·00	2·75	7·00	3·00
52*a*	$10 Measled Cowrie	10·00	4·00	†	
35A/52*a*A	.. .. *Set of* 19	18·00	10·00		
38B/52B	.. .. *Set of* 13			13·00	5·50

Dates of issue: 27.11.74, Nos. 35A/52A; 12.7.76, Nos. 52aA, 38B/42B, 45B, 47B and 49B/50B; 2.6.77, Nos. 42a, 44B, 45a, 46B, 47a, 51B, 52B.

On Nos. 42a, 44B, 45a, 46B, 47a, 51B and 52B the designer's name is correctly spelt as "R. Granger Barrett". Previously the last name had been spelt "Barratt".

1974 (28 Nov). *Birth Centenary of Sir Winston Churchill. As Nos.* 403/6 *of St. Vincent but colours and face-values changed and inscr* "GRENADINES OF ST. VINCENT".

53	5 c. Type **75**	10	10
54	40 c. As 35 c.	10	10
55	50 c. As 45 c.	15	10
56	$1 As $1	25	20
53/6	.. .. *Set of* 4	50	40

6 Cotton House, Mustique

(Des G. Drummond. Litho Questa)

1975 (27 Feb). *Mustique Island. T* **6** *and similar horiz designs. Multicoloured. W* w **14** (*sideways*). *P* 14.

57	5 c. Type **6**	10	10
58	35 c. "Blue Waters", Endeavour Bay ..	10	10
59	45 c. Endeavour Bay	10	10
60	$1 "Les Jolies Eaux", Gelliceaux Bay	25	20
57/60	.. .. *Set of* 4	40	30

Nos. 57/60 were each issued in sheets of ten stamps and two *se-tenant* labels.

7 Soldier Martinique

(Des G. Drummond. Litho Questa)

1975 (15 May). *Butterflies. T* **7** *and similar horiz designs. Multicoloured. W* w **14** (*sideways*). *P* 14.

61	3 c. Type **7**	20	10
62	5 c. Silver-spotted Flambeau	25	10
63	35 c. Gold Rim	80	10
64	45 c. Bright Blue and Donkey's Eye ..	1·00	10
65	$1 Biscuit	1·75	35
61/5	.. .. *Set of* 5	3·50	65

8 Resort Pavilion

(Des G. Drummond. Litho Harrison)

1975 (24 July). *Petit St. Vincent. T* **8** *and similar horiz designs. Multicoloured. W* w **14** (*sideways*). *P* 14.

66	5 c. Type **8**	10	10
67	35 c. The Harbour	10	10
68	45 c. The Jetty	15	10
69	$1 Sailing in coral lagoon	50	30
66/9	.. .. *Set of* 4	70	45

Nos. 66/9 were each issued in sheets of ten stamps and two *se-tenant* labels.

9 Ecumenical Church, Mustique

(Des G. Drummond. Litho Questa)

1975 (20 Nov). *Christmas. T* **9** *and similar horiz designs. Multicoloured. W* w **12** (*sideways*). *P* 14.

70	5 c. Type **9**	10	10
71	25 c. Catholic Church, Union Island ..	10	10
72	50 c. Catholic Church, Bequia	10	10
73	$1 Anglican Church, Bequia	25	15
70/3	.. .. *Set of* 4	40	25

10 Sunset Scene

(Des G. Drummond. Litho J.W.)

1976 (26 Feb). *Union Island* (1*st series*). *T* **10** *and similar horiz designs. Multicoloured. W* w **14** (*sideways*). *P* 13½.

74	5 c. Type **10**	10	10
75	35 c. Customs and Post Office, Clifton ..	10	10
76	45 c. Anglican Church, Ashton	10	10
77	$1 Mail schooner, Clifton Harbour ..	25	20
74/7	.. .. *Set of* 4	45	30

Nos. 74/7 were each issued in sheets of ten stamps and two *se-tenant* labels.

See also Nos. 242/5.

11 Staghorn Coral

(Des G. Drummond. Litho Questa)

1976 (13 May). *Corals. T* **11** *and similar horiz designs. Multicoloured. W* w **14** (*sideways*). *P* 14.

78	5 c. Type **11**	10	10
79	35 c. Elkhorn coral	25	10
80	45 c. Pillar coral	30	10
81	$1 Brain coral	80	20
78/81	.. .. *Set of* 4	1·25	30

12 25 c. Bicentennial Coin

(Des J. Cooter. Litho Questa)

1976 (15 July). *Bicentenary of American Revolution. T* **12** *and similar horiz designs. W* w **14** (*sideways*). *P* 13½.

82	25 c. silver, black and light violet-blue ..	10	10
83	50 c. silver, black and light rose-red	20	10
84	$1 silver, black and mauve	25	20
82/4	.. .. *Set of* 3	50	30

Designs:—50 c. Half-dollar coin; $1 One dollar coin.

Nos. 82/4 were each issued in sheets of ten stamps and two *se-tenant* labels.

(Des G. Drummond. Litho Questa)

1976 (23 Sept). *Maps* (2*nd series*). *Vert designs as T* **2**, *showing various islands as detailed below. W* w **14**. *P* 13½.

A. Bequia	D. Mustique	F. Prune
B. Canouan	E. Petit St. Vincent	G. Union
C. Mayreau		

To indicate individual islands, use the above letters as a suffix to the following catalogue numbers.

85	5 c. black, myrtle-green and pale emerald ..	10	10
	a. Booklet pane. Nos. 85/6 and 88 plus printed label	45	
	b. Booklet pane. Nos. 85 × 2 and 86 plus printed label	30	

86 10 c. black, ultramarine and greenish blue .. 10 10
a. Booklet pane. Nos. 86 × 2 and 87 plus printed label 40
87 35 c. black, red-brown and bright rose .. 20 20
a. Booklet pane. Nos. 87 × 2 and 88 plus printed label 65
88 45 c. black, scarlet and yellow-orange .. 25 25
85/8 .. .. *Set of 4 (one island)* 60 60
85/8 .. .. .. *Set of 28 (seven islands)* 4·00 4·00
Nos. 85/8 were only issued in $2.50 stamp booklets.

13 Station Hill School and Post Office

(Des G. Drummond. Litho Questa)

1976 (2 Dec). *Mayreau Island. T* **13** *and similar horiz designs. Multicoloured. W* w **14** *(sideways). P* 14.

89 5 c. Type **13** 10 10
90 35 c. Church at Old Wall 10 10
91 45 c. La Sourciere Anchorage 10 10
92 $1 Saline Bay 25 15
89/92 .. .. *Set of* 4 40 25
Nos. 89/92 were each issued in sheets of ten stamps and two *se-tenant* labels.

14 Coronation Crown Coin

(Des G. Vasarhelyi. Litho Questa)

1977 (3 Mar). *Silver Jubilee. T* **14** *and similar horiz designs. Multicoloured. W* w **14** *(sideways). P* 14.

93 25 c. Type **14** 20 10
94 50 c. Silver Wedding Crown 25 10
95 $1 Silver Jubilee Crown 30 15
93/5 .. .. *Set of* 3 65 30
Nos. 93/5 were each issued in sheets of ten stamps and two *se-tenant* labels.

15 Fiddler Crab

(Des BG Studio. Litho Questa)

1977 (19 May). *Crustaceans. T* **15** *and similar horiz designs. Multicoloured. W* w **14** *(sideways). P* 14.

96 5 c. Type **15** 10 10
97 35 c. Ghost crab 20 10
98 50 c. Blue crab 25 10
99 $1.25, Spiny lobster 55 40
96/9 .. .. *Set of* 4 95 55

16 Snorkel Diving

(Des G. Drummond. Litho Questa)

1977 (25 Aug). *Prune Island. T* **16** *and similar horiz designs. Multicoloured. W* w **14** *(sideways). P* 14½.

100 5 c. Type **16** 10 10
101 35 c. Palm Island Resort 10 10
102 45 c. Casuarina Beach 10 10
103 $1 Palm Island Beach Club 30 30
100/3 .. .. *Set of* 4 50 40
Nos. 100/3 were each issued in sheets of ten stamps and two *se-tenant* labels.

17 Mustique Island

(Des G. Drummond. Litho Questa)

1977 (31 Oct). *Royal Visit. Previously unissued stamps without face values, locally surch with new inscription. W* w **12**. *P* 14½ × 14.

104 **17** 40 c. turquoise-green and blue-green (Blk. (value) and R.) 15 10
105 $2 yellow-ochre and yellow-brown (R. (value) and B.) 55 25

18 The Clinic, Charlestown

(Des G. Drummond. Litho Harrison)

1977 (8 Dec). *Canouan Island* (*1st series*). T **18** *and similar horiz designs. Multicoloured. W* w **14**. *P* 14½.

106 5 c. Type **18** 10 10
107 35 c. Town jetty, Charlestown 10 10
108 45 c. Mail schooner arriving at Charlestown 10 10
109 $1 Grand Bay 30 20
106/9 .. .. *Set of* 4 50 30
Nos. 106/9 were each issued in sheets of ten stamps and two *se-tenant* labels.
See also Nos. 307/10.

19 Tropical Mockingbird

(Des J.W. Litho Enschedé)

1978 (11 May). *Birds and their Eggs. Horiz designs as T* **19**. *Multicoloured. W* w **14** *(sideways). P* 12½ × 12.

110 1 c. Type **19** 10 10
111 2 c. Mangrove Cuckoo 15 10
112 3 c. Osprey 20 10
113 4 c. Smooth-billed Ani 20 10
114 5 c. House Wren 20 10
115 6 c. Bananaquit 20 10
116 8 c. Carib Grackle 20 10
117 10 c. Yellow-bellied Elaenia 20 10
118 12 c. Collared Plover 30 10
119 15 c. Cattle Egret 30 10
120 20 c. Red-footed Booby 30 10
121 25 c. Red-billed Tropic Bird 30 10
122 40 c. Royal Tern 45 15
123 50 c. Grenada Flycatcher 45 20
124 80 c. Purple Gallinule 70 30
125 $1 Broad-winged Hawk 75 50
126 $2 Scaly-breasted Ground Dove 90 75
127 $3 Laughing Gull .. .. 1·25 1·00
128 $5 Common Noddy .. .. 2·25 1·25
129 $10 Grey Kingbird .. .. 4·50 2·25
110/29 .. .. *Set of* 20 12·50 6·00
See also Nos. **MS**155 and **MS**170.

(Des G. Drummond. Litho J.W.)

1978 (2 June). *25th Anniv of Coronation. Horiz designs as Nos. 422/5 of Montserrat. Multicoloured. W* w **14** *(sideways). P* 13.

130 5 c. Worcester Cathedral 10 10
131 40 c. Coventry Cathedral 10 10
132 $1 Winchester Cathedral 15 10
133 $3 Chester Cathedral 25 35
130/3 .. .. *Set of* 4 45 50
MS134 130 × 102 mm. Nos. 130/3. P 13½ × 14 .. 60 80
a. Top horiz pair imperf three sides .. £350
Nos. 130/3 were each issued in sheets of ten stamps and two *se-tenant* labels.
No. **MS**134a shows the 5 c. and 40 c. stamps in the sheet perforated along the top, but imperforate on the other three sides.

20 Green Turtle

21 Three Kings following Star

(Des R. Granger Barrett. Litho Walsall)

1978 (20 July). *Turtles. T* **20** *and similar horiz designs. Multicoloured. W* w **14** *(sideways). P* 14.

135 5 c. Type **20** 10 10
136 40 c. Hawksbill turtle 15 10
137 50 c. Leatherback turtle 15 10
138 $1.25, Loggerhead turtle 40 40
135/8 .. .. *Set of* 4 65 60

(Des Jennifer Toombs. Litho Questa)

1978 (2 Nov). *Christmas. Scenes and Verses from the Carol "We Three Kings of Orient Are". T* **21** *and similar vert designs. Multicoloured. W* w **14**. *P* 14 × 13½.

139 5 c. Type **21** 10 10
140 10 c. King with gift of Gold 10 10
141 25 c. King with gift of Frankincense 10 10
142 50 c. King with gift of Myrrh 10 10
143 $2 Three Kings paying homage to infant Jesus 30 20
139/43 .. .. *Set of* 5 45 30
MS144 154 × 175 mm. Nos. 139/43 .. .. 70 1·25

22 Sailing Yachts

23 False Killer Whale

(Des G. Drummond. Litho Questa)

1979 (25 Jan). *National Regatta. T* **22** *and similar vert designs showing sailing yachts. W* w **14**. *P* 14.

145 5 c. multicoloured 10 10
146 40 c. multicoloured 20 10
147 50 c. multicoloured 25 10
148 $2 multicoloured 75 60
145/8 .. .. *Set of* 4 1·10 75

(Des L. Curtis. Litho Questa)

1979 (8 Mar). *Wildlife. Horiz designs as T* **114** *of St. Vincent. Multicoloured. W* w **14** *(sideways). P* 14 × 14½.

149 20 c. Green Iguana 10 10
150 40 c. Common Opossum ("Manicou") .. 15 10
151 $2 Red-legged Tortoise 60 65
149/51 .. .. *Set of* 3 75 75
Nos. 149/51 were each printed in four panes of 12 throughout the sheet, each pane including two *se-tenant* labels.

(Des J.W. Litho. Enschedé)

1979 (21 May). *Death Centenary of Sir Rowland Hill. Horiz designs as T* **103** *of St. Vincent. Multicoloured. W* w **14** *(sideways). P* 12½ × 12.

152 80 c. Sir Rowland Hill 25 15
153 $1 Great Britain 1d. and 4d. stamps of 1858 with "A10" (Kingstown, St. Vincent) postmark 30 25
154 $2 St. Vincent ½d. and 1d. stamps of 1894 with Bequia postmark 50 40
152/4 .. .. *Set of* 3 95 70
MS155 165 × 115 mm. Nos. 124/6 and 152/4 .. 2·00 2·50
Nos. 152/4 were each printed in sheets including two *se-tenant* stamp-size labels.

1979 (24 Oct). *International Year of the Child. As Nos. 570/3 of St. Vincent.*

156 6 c. black, silver and pale blue 10 10
157 40 c. black, silver and salmon 10 10
158 $1 black, silver and buff 20 10
159 $3 black, silver and lilac 45 30
156/9 .. .. *Set of* 4 65 45

(Des J.W. Litho Enschedé)

1979 (27 Oct). *Independence. Horiz designs as T* **106** *of St. Vincent. Multicoloured. W* w **14** *(sideways). P* 12½ × 12.

160 5 c. National flag and *Ixora salici-folia* (flower) 10 10
161 40 c. House of Assembly and *Ixora odorata* (flower) 10 10
162 $1 Prime Minister R. Milton Cato and *Ixora javanica* (flower) 20 20
160/2 .. .. *Set of* 3 30 20

(Des R. Granger Barrett. Litho Walsall)

1980 (31 Jan). *Whales and Dolphins. T* **23** *and similar horiz designs. Multicoloured. W* w **14** *(sideways). P* 14.

163 10 c. Type **23** 10 10
164 50 c. Spinner Dolphin 30 20
165 90 c. Bottle-nosed Dolphin 55 40
166 $2 Short-finned Pilot Whale ("Blackfish") 90 65
163/6 .. .. *Set of* 4 1·75 1·10

(Des J.W. Litho Enschedé)

1980 (24 Apr). *"London 1980" International Stamp Exhibition. Horiz designs as T* **110** *of St. Vincent. Multicoloured. W* w **14** *(sideways). P* 12½ × 12.

167 40 c. Queen Elizabeth II 20 10
168 50 c. St. Vincent 1965 2 c. definitive 20 10
169 $3 1973 25 c. and Royal Wedding commemoratives 60 80
167/9 .. .. *Set of* 3 90 90
MS170 165 × 115 mm. Nos. 122/3, 127 and 167/9 2·25 2·50
Nos. 167/9 were printed in sheets including 2 *se-tenant* stamp-size labels.

(Des Polygraphic. Litho Rosenbaum Bros, Vienna)

1980 (7 Aug). *"Sport for All". Vert designs as T* **112** *of St. Vincent. Multicoloured. W* w **14**. *P* 13½.

171 25 c. Running 10 10
172 50 c. Sailing 10 10
173 $1 Long jumping 20 20
174 $2 Swimming 30 30
171/4 .. .. *Set of* 4 60 60

1980 (7 Aug). *Hurricane Relief. Nos.* 171/4 *surch with T* **113** *of St. Vincent.*
175 25 c.+50 c. Running . . 10 15
176 50 c.+50 c. Sailing . . 20 25
177 $1+50 c. Long jumping . . 25 35
178 $2+50 c. Swimming . . 40 55
175/8 . . *Set of* 4 85 1·10

24 Scene and Verse from the Carol "De Borning Day" **25** Post Office, Port Elizabeth

(Des Jennifer Toombs. Litho Questa)

1980 (13 Nov). *Christmas. T* **24** *and similar vert designs showing scenes and verses from the carol "De Borning Day". W w* **14**. *P* 14 × 13½.
179 5 c. multicoloured . . 10 10
180 50 c. multicoloured . . 10 10
181 60 c. multicoloured . . 10 10
182 $1 multicoloured . . 15 15
183 $2 multicoloured . . 25 25
179/83 . . *Set of* 5 50 50
MS184 159 × 178 mm. Nos. 179/83 . . 75 1·40

(Des G. Drummond. Litho Questa)

1981 (19 Feb). *Bequia Island (2nd series). T* **25** *and similar horiz designs. Multicoloured. W w* **14** *(sideways). P* 14½ × 14.
185 50 c. Type **25** . . 15 15
186 60 c. Moonhole . . 20 20
187 $1.50, Fishing boats, Admiralty Bay . . 40 40
188 $2 *Friendship Rose* (yacht) at jetty . . 55 55
185/8 . . *Set of* 4 1·10 1·10

The $2 value was originally printed with the country name in black and the face value in white. A quantity of these were stolen in transit before issue and the remainder were not placed on sale, the stamp being reprinted with the inscriptions in red.

Nos. 185/8 were each printed in sheets including two *se-tenant* stamp-size labels.

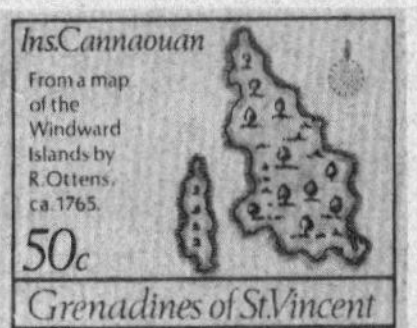

26 Ins. Cannaouan (map of Windward Islands by R. Ottens, *circa* 1765) **27** Bar Jack

(Des J. Cooter. Litho Format)

1981 (2 Apr). *Details from Early Maps. T* **26** *and similar horiz designs. Multicoloured. W w* **14** *(sideways). P* 13½.
189 50 c. Type **26** . . 30 30
a. Pair. Nos. 189/90 . . 60 60
190 50 c. Cannouan Is. (chart by J. Parsons, 1861) 30 30
191 60 c. Ins. Moustiques (map of Windward Islands by R. Ottens, *circa* 1765) . . 35 35
a. Pair. Nos. 191/2 . . 70 70
192 60 c. Mustique Is. (chart by J. Parsons, 1861) 35 35
193 $2 Ins. Bequia (map of Windward Islands by R. Ottens, *circa* 1765) . . 75 75
a. Pair. Nos. 193/4 . . 1·50 1·50
194 $2 Bequia Is. (map surveyed in 1763 by T. Jefferys) . . 75 75
189/94 . . *Set of* 6 2·50 2·50

The two designs of each value were printed together, *se-tenant*, in horizontal and vertical pairs throughout the sheet.

(Des D. Shults. Litho Questa)

1981 (17 July–26 Nov). *Royal Wedding. Horiz designs as T* **26/27** *of Kiribati. Multicoloured.* (a) *W w* **15**. *P* 14.
195 50 c. *Mary* . . 15 15
a. Sheetlet. No. 195 × 6 and No. 196 . . 1·10
196 50 c. Prince Charles and Lady Diana Spencer 40 40
197 $3 *Alexandra* . . 40 40
a. Sheetlet. No. 197 × 6 and No. 198 . . 3·25
198 $3 As No. 196 . . 1·25 1·25
199 $3.50, *Britannia* . . 45 45
a. Sheetlet. No. 199 × 6 and No. 200 . . 3·50
200 $3.50, As No. 196 . . 1·25 1·25
195/200 . . *Set of* 6 3·50 3·50
MS201 120 × 109 mm. $5 As No. 196. Wmk sideways. P 12 (26 Nov) . . 1·25 1·00

(*b*) *Booklet stamps. No wmk. P* 12 (26 Nov)
202 50 c. As No. 195 . . 20 30
a. Booklet pane. No. 202 × 4 . . 80
203 $3 As No. 198 . . 1·50 1·60
a. Booklet pane. No. 203 × 2 . . 3·00

Nos. 195/200 were printed in sheetlets of seven stamps of the same face value, each containing six of the "Royal Yacht" design and one of the larger design showing Prince Charles and Lady Diana.

Nos. 202/3 came from $10 stamp booklets.

(Des N. Weaver. Litho Questa)

1981 (9 Oct). *Game Fish. T* **27** *and similar horiz designs. Multicoloured. W w* **14** *(sideways). P* 14.
204 10 c. Type **27** . . 15 10
205 50 c. Tarpon . . 25 10
206 60 c. Cobia . . 30 10
207 $2 Blue Marlin . . 90 70
204/7 . . *Set of* 4 1·40 85

28 H.M.S. *Experiment* **29** Prickly Pear Fruit

(Des J. Cooter. Litho Security Printers (M), Malaysia)

1982 (28 Jan). *Ships. Horiz designs as T* **28**. *Multicoloured. W w* **14**. *P* 13½ × 13.
208 1 c. Type **28** . . 10 10
209 3 c. *Lady Nelson* (cargo liner) . . 10 10
210 5 c. *Daisy* (brig) . . 10 10
211 6 c. Carib canoe . . 10 10
212 10 c. *Hairoun Star* (freighter) . . 10 10
213 15 c. *Jupiter* (liner) . . 10 10
214 20 c. *Christina* (steam yacht) . . 10 10
215 25 c. *Orinoco* (paddle-steamer) . . 10 10
216 30 c. H.M.S. *Lively* . . 10 15
217 50 c. *Alabama* (Confederate warship) . . 20 25
218 60 c. *Denmark* (freighter) . . 25 30
219 75 c. *Santa Maria* . . 30 35
220 $1 *Baffin* (cable ship) . . 40 45
221 $2 *Queen Elizabeth 2* (liner) . . 80 85
222 $3 R.Y. *Britannia* . . 1·25 1·40
223 $5 *Geeststar* (cargo liner) . . 2·10 2·25
224 $10 *Grenadines Star* (ferry) . . 4·00 4·25
208/24 . . *Set of* 17 8·75 10·00

(Des G. Drummond. Litho Harrison)

1982 (5 Apr). *Prickly Pear Cactus. T* **29** *and similar vert designs. Multicoloured. W w* **14**. *P* 14.
225 10 c. Type **29** . . 10 10
226 50 c. Prickly Pear flower buds . . 25 25
227 $1 Flower of Prickly Pear Cactus . . 45 50
228 $2 Prickly Pear Cactus . . 95 1·00
225/8 . . *Set of* 4 1·50 1·60

30 Anne Neville, Princess of Wales, 1470 **31** Old and New Uniforms

(Des D. Shults and J. Cooter. Litho Format)

1982 (1 July). *21st Birthday of Princess of Wales. T* **30** *and similar vert designs. Multicoloured. W w* **15**. *P* 13½ × 14.
229 50 c. Type **30** . . 20 20
230 60 c. Coat of arms of Anne Neville . . 20 20
231 $6 Diana, Princess of Wales . . 1·25 1·25
229/31 . . *Set of* 3 1·50 1·50

(Des L. Curtis. Litho W.S. Cowell Ltd)

1982 (15 July). *75th Anniv of Boy Scout Movement. T* **31** *and similar vert design. Multicoloured. W w* **14** *(inverted). P* 14½.
232 $1.50, Type **31** . . 60 60
233 $2.50, Lord Baden-Powell . . 90 90

ROYAL BABY

BEQUIA

(32) **33** Silhouette Figures of Mary and Joseph

1982 (19 July). *Birth of Prince William of Wales. Nos.* 229/31 *optd with various island names as T* **32**.
A. Bequia B. Canouan C. Mayreau
D. Mustique E. Union Island

To indicate individual islands, use the above letters as a suffix to the following catalogue numbers.
234 50 c. Type **30** . . 20 20
a. Opt A (Bequia) double . . 40·00
b. Opt C (Mayreau) inverted . . 35·00
c. Opt D (Mustique) inverted . . 35·00
235 60 c. Coat of arms of Anne Neville . . 20 20
a. Opt D (Mustique) inverted . . 40·00
b. Opt E (Union Island) inverted . . 60·00
c. Opt E (Union Island) double . . £110
236 $6 Diana, Princess of Wales . . 1·25 1·25
234/6 . . *Set of* 3 1·50 1·50

(Des Jennifer Toombs. Litho Security Printers (M), Malaysia)

1982 (18 Nov). *Christmas. T* **33** *and similar horiz designs showing silhouettes of figures. Multicoloured. W w* **14**. *P* 13½.
237 10 c. Type **33** . . 10 10
238 $1.50, Animals in stable . . 45 45
239 $2.50, Mary and Joseph with baby Jesus . . 60 60
237/9 . . *Set of* 3 1·00 1·00
MS240 168 × 99 mm. Nos. 237/9 . . 1·00 1·75

45¢

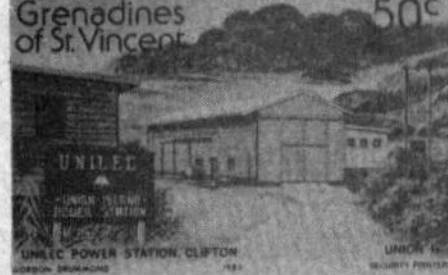

(34) **35** Power Station, Clifton

1983 (26 Apr). *No.* 123 *surch with T* **34** *by Reliance Printery, Kingstown.*
241 45 c. on 50 c. Grenada Flycatcher . . 20 25

(Des G. Drummond. Litho Security Printers (M), Malaysia)

1983 (12 May). *Union Island (2nd series). T* **35** *and similar horiz designs. Multicoloured. W w* **14**. *P* 13½.
242 50 c. Type **35** . . 15 15
243 60 c. Sunrise, Clifton harbour . . 15 15
244 $1.50, Junior Secondary School, Ashton . . 40 40
245 $2 Frigate Rock and Conch Shell Beach . . 55 55
242/5 . . *Set of* 4 1·10 1·10

Nos. 242/5 were each printed in sheets including two *se-tenant* stamp-size labels.

36 British Man-of-war **37** Montgolfier Balloon, 1783

(Des and litho J.W.)

1983 (15 Sept). *Bicentenary of Treaty of Versailles. T* **36** *and similar vert designs. Multicoloured. W w* **14**. *P* 14½.
246 45 c. Type **36** . . 15 15
247 60 c. American man-of-war . . 15 15
248 $1.50, Soldiers carrying U.S. flags . . 45 45
249 $2 British troops in battle . . 55 55
246/9 . . *Set of* 4 1·10 1·10

(Des A. Theobald. Litho Format)

1983 (15 Sept). *Bicentenary of Manned Flight. T* **37** *and similar multicoloured designs. W w* **14** *(sideways on Nos.* 251/53*). P* 14.
250 45 c. Type **37** . . 15 15
251 60 c. Ayres "Turbo-thrush Commander" (*horiz*) 15 15
252 $1.50, Lebaudy "1" dirigible (*horiz*) . . 45 45
253 $2 Space shuttle *Columbia* (*horiz*) . . 55 55
250/3 . . *Set of* 4 1·10 1·10
MS254 110 × 145 mm. Nos. 250/3. Wmk sideways 1·50 2·00

38 Coat of Arms of Henry VIII **39** Quarter Dollar and Half Dollar, 1797

(Des Court House Studio. Litho Format)

1983 (25 Oct). *Leaders of the World. British Monarchs. T* **38** *and similar vert designs. Multicoloured. P* 12½.
255 60 c. Type **38** . . 30 30
a. Horiz pair. Nos. 255/6 . . 60 60
256 60 c. Henry VIII . . 30 30
257 60 c. Coat of Arms of James I . . 30 30
a. Horiz pair. Nos. 257/8 . . 60 60
258 60 c. James I . . 30 30
259 75 c. Henry VIII . . 30 30
a. Horiz pair. Nos. 259/60 . . 60 60
260 75 c. Hampton Court . . 30 30
261 75 c. James I . . 30 30
a. Horiz pair. Nos. 261/2 . . 60 60
262 75 c. Edinburgh Castle . . 30 30
263 $2.50, The *Mary Rose* . . 50 40
a. Horiz pair. Nos. 263/4 . . 1·00 80
264 $2.50, Henry VIII and Portsmouth harbour 50 40
265 $2.50, Gunpowder Plot . . 50 40
a. Horiz pair. Nos. 265/6 . . 1·00 80
266 $2.50, James I and the Gunpowder Plot . . 50 40
255/66 . . *Set of* 12 4·00 3·50

Nos. 255/6, 257/8, 259/60, 261/2, 263/4 and 265/6 were printed together, *se-tenant*, in horizontal pairs throughout the sheets.

(Des J. Cooter. Litho Walsall)

1983 (1 Dec). *Old Coinage. T* **39** *and similar vert designs. Multicoloured.* W w **14.** *P* 14.
267 20 c. Type **39** 10 10
268 45 c. Nine Bitts, 1811–14 .. .. 15 15
269 75 c. Twelve Bitts and Six Bitts, 1811–14 .. 25 25
270 $3 Sixty-six Shillings, 1798 .. .. .. 80 80
267/70 .. .. *Set of* 4 1·10 1·10

40 Class "D 13"

(Des J.W. Litho Format)

1984 (15 Mar). *Leaders of the World. Railway Locomotives* (1st *series*). *T* **40** *and similar horiz designs, the first in each pair showing technical drawings and the second the locomotive at work. P* 12½.
271 5 c. multicoloured 10 10
a. Vert pair. Nos. 271/2 .. .. 10 10
272 5 c. multicoloured 10 10
273 10 c. multicoloured 10 10
a. Vert pair. Nos. 273/4 .. .. 15 15
274 10 c. multicoloured 10 10
275 15 c. multicoloured 15 15
a. Vert pair. Nos. 275/6 .. .. 30 30
276 15 c. multicoloured 15 15
277 35 c. multicoloured 25 25
a. Vert pair. Nos. 277/8 .. .. 50 50
278 35 c. multicoloured 25 25
279 45 c. multicoloured 30 30
a. Vert pair. Nos. 279/80 .. .. 60 60
280 45 c. multicoloured 30 30
281 60 c. multicoloured 40 40
a. Vert pair. Nos. 281/2 .. .. 80 80
282 60 c. multicoloured 40 40
283 $1 multicoloured 50 50
a. Vert pair. Nos. 283/4 .. .. 1·00 1·00
284 $1 multicoloured 50 50
285 $2.50, multicoloured 80 80
a. Vert pair. Nos. 285/6 .. .. 1·60 1·60
286 $2.50, multicoloured 80 80
271/86 .. .. *Set of* 16 4·50 4·50

Designs:—Nos. 271/2, Class "D 13", U.S.A. (1892); 273/4, High Speed Train "125", Great Britain (1980); 275/6, Class "T 9", Great Britain (1899); 277/8, *Claud Hamilton*, Great Britain (1900); 279/80, Class "J", U.S.A. (1941); 281/2, Class "D 16", U.S.A. (1895); 283/4, *Lode Star*, Great Britain (1907); 285/6, *Blue Peter*, Great Britain (1948).

Nos. 271/2, 273/4, 275/6, 277/8, 279/80, 281/2, 283/4 and 285/6 were printed together, *se-tenant* in vertical pairs throughout the sheet.

See also Nos. 311/26, 351/9, 390/7, 412/19, 443/58, 504/19 and 520/35.

41 Spotted Eagle Ray

(Des G. Drummond. Litho Format)

1984 (26 Apr). *Reef Fishes. T* **41** *and similar horiz designs. Multicoloured.* W w **15.** *P* 14.
287 45 c. Type **41** 25 30
288 60 c. Queen Trigger Fish 30 35
289 $1.50, White Spotted File Fish 75 80
290 $2 Schoolmaster .. .. 1·00 1·10
287/90 .. .. *Set of* 4 2·10 2·25

42 R. A. Woolmer 43 Junior Secondary School

(Des Court House Studio. Litho Format)

1984 (16 Aug). *Leaders of the World. Cricketers* (1st *series*). *T* **42** *and similar vert designs, the first in each pair showing a portrait and the second the cricketer in action. P* 12½.
291 1 c. multicoloured 10 10
a. Horiz pair. Nos. 291/2 .. .. 10 10
292 1 c. multicoloured 10 10
293 3 c. multicoloured 10 10
a. Horiz pair. Nos. 293/4 .. .. 10 10
294 3 c. multicoloured 10 10
295 5 c. multicoloured 10 10
a. Horiz pair. Nos. 295/6 .. .. 10 10
296 5 c. multicoloured 10 10
297 30 c. multicoloured 20 20
a. Horiz pair. Nos. 297/8 .. .. 40 40
298 30 c. multicoloured 20 20
299 60 c. multicoloured 40 40
a. Horiz pair. Nos. 299/300 .. .. .. 80 80
300 60 c. multicoloured 40 40
301 $1 multicoloured 60 60
a. Horiz pair. Nos. 301/2 .. .. 1·10 1·10
302 $1 multicoloured 60 60
303 $2 multicoloured .. .. 1·10 1·10
a. Horiz pair. Nos. 303/4 .. .. 2·10 2·10
304 $2 multicoloured .. .. 1·10 1·10
305 $3 multicoloured .. .. 1·40 1·40
a. Horiz pair. Nos. 305/6 .. .. 2·75 2·75
306 $3 multicoloured .. .. 1·40 1·40
291/306 .. .. *Set of* 16 6·50 6·50

Designs:—Nos. 293/4, K. S. Ranjitsinhji; 295/6, W. R. Hammond; 297/8, D. L. Underwood; 299/300, W. G. Grace; 301/2, E. A. E. Baptiste; 303/4, A. P. E. Knott; 305/6, L. E. G. Ames.

See also Nos. 331/8 and 364/9.

(Des G. Drummond. Litho Questa)

1984 (3 Sept). *Canouan Island* (2*nd series*). *T* **43** *and similar horiz designs. Multicoloured.* W w **15** (*sideways*). *P* 14.
307 35 c. Type **43** 20 20
308 45 c. Police Station 25 25
309 $1 Post Office 50 50
310 $3 Anglican Church .. .. 1·25 1·50
307/10 .. .. *Set of* 4 2·00 2·25

(Des J.W. Litho Format)

1984 (9 Oct). *Leaders of the World. Railway Locomotives* (2nd *series*). *Horiz designs as T* **40**, *the first in each pair showing technical drawings and the second the locomotive at work. P* 12½.
311 1 c. multicoloured 10 10
a. Vert pair. Nos. 311/12 .. .. 10 10
312 1 c. multicoloured 10 10
313 5 c. multicoloured 10 10
a. Vert pair. Nos. 313/14 .. .. 10 10
314 5 c. multicoloured 10 10
315 20 c. multicoloured 15 15
a. Vert pair. Nos. 315/16 .. .. 30 30
316 20 c. multicoloured 15 15
317 35 c. multicoloured 25 25
a. Vert pair. Nos. 317/18 .. .. 50 50
318 35 c. multicoloured 25 25
319 60 c. multicoloured 40 40
a. Vert pair. Nos. 319/20 .. .. 80 80
320 60 c. multicoloured 40 40
321 $1 multicoloured 50 50
a. Vert pair. Nos. 321/2 .. .. 1·00 1·00
322 $1 multicoloured 50 50
323 $1.50, multicoloured 65 65
a. Vert pair. Nos. 323/4 .. .. 1·25 1·25
324 $1.50, multicoloured 65 65
325 $3 multicoloured .. .. 1·00 1·00
a. Vert pair. Nos. 325/6 .. .. 2·00 2·00
326 $3 multicoloured .. .. 1·00 1·00
311/26 .. .. *Set of* 16 5·50 5·50

Designs:—Nos. 311/12, Class "C62", Japan (1948); 313/14, Class "V", Great Britain (1903); 315/16, *Catch-Me-Who-Can*, Great Britain (1808), 317/18, Class "E10", Japan (1948); 319/20, *J. B. Earle*, Great Britain (1904); 321/2, *Lyn*, Great Britain (1898); 323/4, *Talyllyn*, Great Britain (1865); 325/6, *Cardean*, Great Britain (1906).

Nos. 311/26 were issued in a similar sheet format to Nos. 271/86.

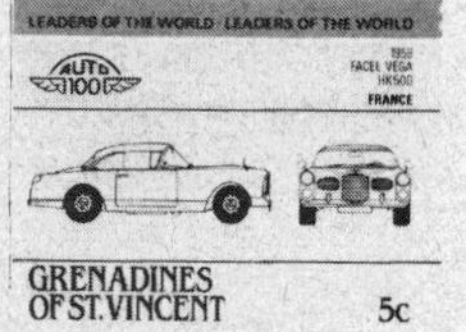

44 Lady of the Night 45 Facel "Vega HK500"

(Des Jennifer Toombs. Litho Questa)

1984 (15 Oct). *Night-blooming Flowers. T* **44** *and similar vert designs. Multicoloured.* W w **15.** *P* 14.
327 35 c. Type **44** 25 25
328 45 c. Four o'clock 30 30
329 75 c. Mother-in-Law's Tongue 40 40
330 $3 Queen of the Night .. .. .. 1·50 1·60
327/30 .. .. *Set of* 4 2·25 2·25

(Des Court House Studio. Litho Format)

1984 (28 Nov). *Leaders of the World. Cricketers* (2*nd series*). *Vert designs as T* **42**, *the first in each pair listed showing a head portrait and the second the cricketer in action. P* 12½.
331 5 c. multicoloured 10 10
a. Horiz pair. Nos. 331/2 .. .. 10 10
332 5 c. multicoloured 10 10
333 30 c. multicoloured 20 20
a. Horiz pair. Nos. 333/4 .. .. 40 40
334 30 c. multicoloured 20 20
335 $1 multicoloured 70 70
a. Horiz pair. Nos. 335/6 .. .. 1·40 1·40
336 $1 multicoloured 70 70
337 $2.50, multicoloured .. .. 1·50 1·50
a. Horiz pair. Nos. 337/8 .. .. 3·00 3·00
338 $2.50, multicoloured .. .. 1·50 1·50
331/8 .. .. *Set of* 8 4·25 4·25

Designs:—Nos. 331/2, S. F. Barnes; 333/4, R. Peel; 335/6, H. Larwood; 337/8, Sir John Hobbs.

Nos. 331/8 were issued in a similar sheet format to Nos. 291/306.

(Des J.W. Litho Format)

1984 (28 Nov). *Leaders of the World. Automobiles* (1*st series*). *T* **45** *and similar horiz designs, the first in each pair showing technical drawings and the second paintings. P* 12½.
339 5 c. black, azure and dull yellow-green .. 10 10
a. Vert pair. Nos. 339/40 .. .. 10 10
340 5 c. multicoloured 10 10
341 25 c. black, pale lilac and pink 15 15
a. Vert pair. Nos. 341/2 .. .. 30 30
342 25 c. multicoloured 15 15
343 50 c. black, pale blue and pale orange .. 20 20
a. Vert pair. Nos. 343/4 .. .. 40 40
344 50 c. multicoloured 20 20
345 $3 black, stone and brown lake 60 60
a. Vert pair. Nos. 345/6 .. .. 1·10 1·10
346 $3 multicoloured 60 60
339/46 .. .. *Set of* 8 1·60 1·60

Designs:—Nos. 339/40, Facel "Vega HK500"; 341/2, B.M.W. "328"; 343/4, Frazer-Nash "TT Replica 1.5L"; 345/6, Buick "Roadmaster Riviera".

Nos. 339/40, 341/2, 343/4 and 345/6 were printed together, *se-tenant*, in vertical pairs throughout the sheets.

See also Nos. 378/85 and 431/42.

46 The Three Wise Men and Star

(Des Jennifer Toombs. Litho Format)

1984 (3 Dec). *Christmas. T* **46** *and similar horiz designs. Multicoloured.* W w **15** (*sideways*). *P* 14½.
347 20 c. Type **46** 10 10
348 45 c. Journeying to Bethlehem 20 25
349 $3 Presenting gifts .. .. 1·00 1·40
347/9 .. .. *Set of* 3 1·10 1·60
MS350 177 × 107 mm. Nos. 347/9. Wmk inverted 1·25 2·00

IMPERFORATES AND MISSING COLOURS. Various issues between Nos. 351 and 672 exist either imperforate or with colours omitted. Such items are not listed as there is no evidence that they fulfil the criteria outlined on page xi of this catalogue.

(Des J.W. Litho Format)

1985 (31 Jan). *Leaders of the World. Railway Locomotives* (3rd *series*). *Horiz designs as T* **40**, *the first in each pair showing technical drawings and the second the locomotive at work. P* 12½.
351 1 c. multicoloured 10 10
a. Vert pair. Nos. 351/2 .. .. 10 10
352 1 c. multicoloured 10 10
353 15 c. multicoloured 10 10
a. Vert pair Nos. 353/4 .. .. 15 15
354 15 c. multicoloured 10 10
355 75 c. multicoloured 35 35
a. Vert pair. Nos. 355/6 .. .. 70 70
356 75 c. multicoloured 35 35
357 $3 multicoloured .. .. 1·00 1·00
a. Vert pair. Nos. 357/8 .. .. 2·00 2·00
358 $3 multicoloured .. .. 1·00 1·00
351/8 .. .. *Set of* 8 2·50 2·50
MS359 142 × 122 mm. Nos. 355/8. W w **15.** .. 11·00 11·00

Designs:—Nos. 351/2, P.L.M. "Grosse C", France (1898); 353/4, Class "C12", Japan (1932); 355/6, Class "D50", Japan (1923); 357/8, *Fire Fly*, Great Britain (1840).

Nos. 351/8 were issued in a similar sheet format to Nos. 271/86.

47 Caribbean King Crab 48 *Cypripedium calceolus*

(Des G. Drummond. Litho Format)

1985 (11 Feb). *Shell Fish. T* **47** *and similar horiz designs. Multicoloured.* W w **15** (*sideways*). *P* 14.
360 25 c. Type **47** 40 15
361 60 c. Queen Conch 55 35
362 $1 White Sea Urchin 80 60
363 $3 West Indian Top Shell .. .. .. 1·75 1·90
360/3 .. .. *Set of* 4 3·25 2·75

(Des Court House Studio. Litho Format)

1985 (22 Feb). *Leaders of the World. Cricketers* (3*rd series*). *Vert designs as T* **42** (55 c., 60 c.), *the first in each pair showing a head portrait and the second the cricketer in action, or horiz designs showing teams* ($2). *P* 12½.
364 55 c. multicoloured 30 35
a. Horiz pair. Nos. 364/5 .. .. 60 70
365 55 c. multicoloured 30 35
366 60 c. multicoloured 35 40
a. Horiz pair. Nos. 366/7 .. .. 70 80
367 60 c. multicoloured 35 40
368 $2 multicoloured .. .. 1·10 1·25
369 $2 multicoloured .. .. 1·10 1·25
364/9 .. .. *Set of* 6 3·25 3·50

Designs: *Vert* (*as T* **42**)—Nos. 364/5, M. D. Moxon; 366/7, L. Potter. *Horiz* (59 × 42 *mm*)—No. 368, Kent team; 369, Yorkshire team.

Nos. 364/5 and 366/7 were issued in a similar sheet format to Nos. 291/306.

(Des Jennifer Toombs. Litho Format)

1985 (13 Mar). *Leaders of the World. Flowers. T* **48** *and similar vert designs. Multicoloured. P* 12½.
370 5 c. Type **48** 10 10
a. Horiz pair. Nos. 370/1 .. .. 10 10
371 5 c. *Gentiana asclepiadea* 10 10
372 55 c. *Clianthus formosus* 30 35
a. Horiz pair. Nos. 372/3 .. .. 60 70
373 55 c. *Clemisia coriacea* 30 35
374 60 c. *Erythronium americanum* 35 40
a. Horiz pair. Nos. 374/5 .. .. 70 80

375 60 c. *Laelia anceps* 35 40
376 $2 *Leucadendron discolor* 90 90
a. Horiz pair. Nos. 376/7 .. .. .. 1·75 1·75
377 $2 *Meconopsis horridula* 90 90
370/7 .. .. *Set of* 8 2·75 3·00
Nos. 370/1, 372/3, 374/5 and 376/7 were printed together, *se-tenant*, in horizontal pairs throughout the sheets.

(Des J.W. (5 c.), G. Turner (others). Litho Format)

1985 (9 Apr). *Leaders of the World. Automobiles* (2*nd series*). *Horiz designs as T* **45**, *the first in each pair showing technical drawings and the second the paintings. P* 12½.
378 5 c. black, pale lemon and turquoise-blue .. 10 10
a. Vert pair. Nos. 378/9 .. .. .. 10 10
379 5 c. multicoloured 10 10
380 60 c. black, pale yellow and pale orange .. 25 25
a. Vert pair. Nos. 380/1 .. .. .. 50 50
381 60 c. multicoloured 25 25
382 $1 black, pale green and azure 30 30
a. Vert pair. Nos. 382/3 .. .. .. 60 60
383 $1 multicoloured 30 30
384 $1.50, black, pale cobalt and light green .. 35 35
a. Vert pair. Nos. 384/5 .. .. .. 70 70
385 $1.50, multicoloured 35 35
378/85 .. .. *Set of* 8 1·60 1·60
Designs:—Nos. 378/9, Winton (1903); 380/1, Invicta 4½ litre (1931); 382/3, Daimler "SP250 Dart" (1959); 384/5, Brabham "Repco BT19" (1966).
Nos. 378/85 were issued in a similar sheet format to Nos. 339/46.

49 Windsurfing

(Des G. Vasarhelyi. Litho Format)

1985 (9 May). *Tourism. Watersports. T* **49** *and similar horiz designs. Multicoloured. W w* **15** (*sideways*). *P* 14.
386 35 c. Type **49** 20 25
387 45 c. Water-skiing 25 30
388 75 c. Scuba-diving 35 40
389 $3 Deep-sea game fishing .. .. .. 1·50 1·60
386/9 .. .. *Set of* 4 2·10 2·25

(Des J.W. (50 c.), T. Hadler (others). Litho Format)

1985 (17 May). *Leaders of the World. Railway Locomotives* (4*th series*). *Horiz designs as T* **40**, *the first in each pair showing technical drawings and the second the locomotive at work. P* 12½.
390 10 c. multicoloured 10 10
a. Vert pair. Nos. 390/1 .. .. .. 10 15
391 10 c. multicoloured 10 10
392 40 c. multicoloured 25 30
a. Vert pair. Nos. 392/3 .. .. .. 50 60
393 40 c. multicoloured 25 30
394 50 c. multicoloured 25 30
a. Vert pair. Nos. 394/5 .. .. .. 50 60
395 50 c. multicoloured 25 30
396 $2.50, multicoloured .. .. .. 1·00 1·10
a. Vert pair. Nos. 396/7 .. .. .. 2·00 2·10
397 $2.50, multicoloured .. .. .. 1·00 1·10
390/7 .. .. *Set of* 8 2·75 3·00
Designs:—Nos. 390/1, Class "581" 12-car train, Japan (1968); 392/3, Class "231-132BT", Algeria (1936); 394/5, *Slieve Gullion*, Great Britain (1913); 396/7, Class "Beattie" well tank, Great Britain (1874).
Nos. 390/7 were issued in a similar sheet format to Nos. 271/86.

50 Passion Fruits and Blossom

51 Queen Elizabeth the Queen Mother

(Des G. Drummond. Litho Format)

1985 (24 June). *Fruits and Blossoms. T* **50** *and similar horiz designs. Multicoloured. W w* **15**. *P* 15.
398 30 c. Type **50** 15 20
399 75 c. Guava 35 40
400 $1 Sapodilla 50 55
401 $2 Mango .. .. 1·00 1·10
398/401 .. .. *Set of* 4 1·75 2·00
MS402 145×120 mm. Nos. 398/401. Wmk sideways. P 14½×15. .. .. 2·00 2·25

(Des Court House Studio. Litho Format)

1985 (31 July). *Leaders of the World. Life and Times of Queen Elizabeth the Queen Mother. Various vertical portraits as T* **51**. *P* 12½.
403 40 c. multicoloured 25 30
a. Horiz pair. Nos. 403/4 .. .. .. 50 60
404 40 c. multicoloured 25 30
405 75 c. multicoloured 40 45
a. Horiz pair. Nos. 405/6 .. .. .. 80 90
406 75 c. multicoloured 40 45
407 $1.10, multicoloured 60 65
a. Horiz pair. Nos. 407/8 .. .. .. 1·25 1·25
408 $1.10, multicoloured 60 65
409 $1.75, multicoloured .. .. .. 95 1·00
a. Horiz pair. Nos. 409/10.. .. .. 1·90 2·00
410 $1.75, multicoloured .. .. .. 95 1·00
403/10 .. .. *Set of* 8 4·00 4·25
MS411 85×114 mm. $2 multicoloured; $2 multicoloured .. .. 2·10 2·25
The two designs of each value were issued, *se-tenant*, in horizontal pairs within the sheets.
Each *se-tenant* pair shows a floral pattern across the bottom of the portraits which stops short of the left-hand edge on the left-hand stamp and of the right-hand edge on the right-hand stamp.
Designs as Nos. 403/4 and 407/8, but with face values of $4×2 and $5×2, also exist in additional miniature sheets from a restricted printing issued 19 December 1985.

(Des J.W. (35 c.), T. Hadler (others). Litho Format)

1985 (16 Sept). *Leaders of the World. Railway Locomotives* (5*th series*). *Horiz designs as T* **40**, *the first in each pair showing technical drawings and the second the locomotive at work. P* 12½.
412 35 c. multicoloured 20 25
a. Vert pair. Nos. 412/13 .. .. .. 40 50
413 35 c. multicoloured 20 25
414 70 c. multicoloured 35 40
a. Vert pair. Nos. 414/15 .. .. .. 70 80
415 70 c. multicoloured 35 40
416 $1.20, multicoloured 70 75
a. Vert pair. Nos. 416/17 .. .. .. 1·40 1·50
417 $1.20, multicoloured 70 75
418 $2 multicoloured .. .. 1·10 1·25
a. Vert pair. Nos. 418/19 .. .. .. 2·25 2·50
419 $2 multicoloured .. .. 1·10 1·25
412/19 .. .. *Set of* 8 4·25 4·75
Designs:—Nos. 412/13, *Coronation*, Great Britain (1937); 414/15, Class "E18", Germany (1935); 416/17, "Hayes" type, U.S.A. (1854), 418/19, Class "2120", Japan (1890).
Nos. 412/19 were issued in a similar sheet format to Nos. 271/86.

1985 (27 Oct). *Royal Visit. Nos.* 199/200, 222, 287, 398 *and* 407/8 *optd as T* **114** *of Montserrat or surch also.*
420 **50** 30 c. multicoloured .. .. 2·50 2·00
421 **41** 45 c. multicoloured .. .. 3·00 2·50
422 – $1.10, multicoloured (No. 407) .. 4·50 4·00
a. Horiz pair. Nos. 422/3 .. .. .. 9·00 8·00
423 – $1.10, multicoloured (No. 408) .. 4·50 4·00
424 – $1.50 on $3.50, mult (No. 199) 3·00 3·00
a. Sheetlet. No. 424×6 and No. 425.. 25·00
425 – $1.50 on $3.50, mult (No. 200) 9·00 9·00
426 – $3 multicoloured (No. 222) .. .. 5·50 5·00
420/6 .. .. *Set of* 7 28·00 26·00

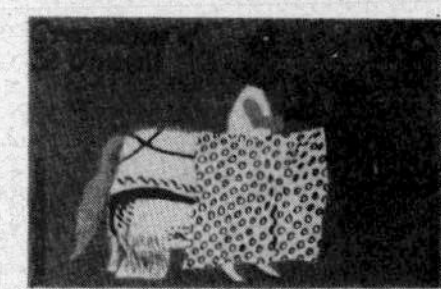

52 Donkey Man

(Des Jennifer Toombs. Litho Format)

1985 (16 Dec). *Traditional Dances. T* **52** *and similar multicoloured designs. P* 15.
427 45 c. Type **52** 25 30
428 75 c. Cake Dance (*vert*) 35 40
429 $1 Bois-Bois Man (*vert*) 50 55
430 $2 Maypole Dance .. .. 1·00 1·10
427/30 .. .. *Set of* 4 1·90 2·10

(Des Artists International (15 c.), J.W. ($3), G. Turner (others). Litho Format)

1986 (20 Feb). *Leaders of the World. Automobiles* (3*rd series*). *Horiz designs as T* **45**, *the first in each pair showing technical drawings and the second paintings. P* 12½.
431 15 c. black, pale rose-lilac and dull mauve .. 10 10
a. Vert pair. Nos. 431/2 .. .. .. 20 20
432 15 c. multicoloured 10 10
433 45 c. black, pale yellow and light brown .. 25 30
a. Vert pair. Nos. 433/4 .. .. .. 50 60
434 45 c. multicoloured 25 30
435 60 c. black, pale green and turquoise-blue .. 25 30
a. Vert pair. Nos. 435/6 .. .. .. 50 60
436 60 c. multicoloured 25 30
437 $1 black, pale cinnamon and sage-green .. 40 45
a. Vert pair. Nos. 437/8 .. .. .. 80 90
438 $1 multicoloured 40 45
439 $1.75, black, pale yellow and pale orange .. 65 70
a. Vert pair. Nos. 439/40 .. .. .. 1·25 1·40
440 $1.75, multicoloured 65 70
441 $3 multicoloured .. .. 1·00 1·10
a. Vert pair. Nos. 441/2 .. .. .. 2·00 2·00
442 $3 multicoloured .. .. 1·00 1·10
431/42 .. .. *Set of* 12 4·75 5·00
Designs:—Nos. 431/2, Mercedes-Benz 4.5 litre (1914); 433/4, Rolls Royce "Silver Wraith" (1954); 435/6, Lamborghini "Countach" (1974); 437/8, Marmon "V-16" (1932): 439/40, Lotus-Ford "49 B" (1968); 441/2, Delage 1.5 litre (1927).
Nos. 431/42 were issued in a similar sheet format to Nos. 339/46.

(Des T. Hadler (15 c., $3), J.W. (others). Litho Format)

1986 (14 Mar). *Leaders of the World. Railway Locomotives* (6*th series*). *Horiz designs as T* **40**, *the first in each pair showing technical drawings and the second the locomotive at work. P* 12½.
443 15 c. multicoloured 10 10
a. Vert pair. Nos. 443/4 .. .. .. 15 20
444 15 c. multicoloured 10 10
445 45 c. multicoloured 25 30
a. Vert pair. Nos. 445/6 .. .. .. 50 60
446 45 c. multicoloured 25 30
447 60 c. multicoloured 30 35
a. Vert pair. Nos. 447/8 .. .. .. 60 70
448 60 c. multicoloured 30 35
449 75 c. multicoloured 35 40
a. Vert pair. Nos. 449/50 .. .. .. 70 80
450 75 c. multicoloured 35 40
451 $1 multicoloured 40 50
a. Vert pair. Nos. 451/2 .. .. .. 80 1·00
452 $1 multicoloured 40 50
453 $1.50, multicoloured 55 70
a. Vert pair. Nos. 453/4 .. .. .. 1·10 1·40
454 $1.50, multicoloured 55 70
455 $2 multicoloured 80 85
a. Vert pair. Nos. 455/6 .. .. .. 1·60 1·60
456 $2 multicoloured 80 85
457 $3 multicoloured .. .. 1·25 1·40
a. Vert pair. Nos. 457/8 .. .. .. 2·50 2·75
458 $3 multicoloured .. .. 1·25 1·40
443/58 .. .. *Set of* 16 7·00 8·00
Designs:—Nos. 443/4, Class "T15", Germany (1897); 445/6, Class "13", Great Britain (1900); 447/8, *Halesworth*, Great Britain (1879); 449/50, Class "Problem", Great Britain (1859); 451/2, Class "Western" diesel, Great Britain (1961); 453/4, Drummond's "Bug", Great Britain (1899); 455/6, Class "Clan", Great Britain (1951); 457/8, Class "1800", Japan (1884).
Nos. 443/58 were issued in a similar sheet format to Nos. 271/86.

(Des Court House Studio. Litho Format)

1986 (21 Apr). 60*th Birthday of Queen Elizabeth II. Multicoloured designs as T* **167** *of British Virgin Islands. P* 12½.
459 5 c. Queen Elizabeth II 10 10
460 $1 At Princess Anne's christening, 1950 .. 50 55
461 $4 Princess Elizabeth .. .. .. 2·00 2·10
462 $6 In Canberra, 1982 (*vert*) .. .. .. 3·00 3·25
459/62 .. .. *Set of* 4 5·00 5·25
MS463 85×115 mm. $8 Queen Elizabeth II (*different*) .. .. 4·50 5·00

53 Handmade Dolls

(Des G. Drummond. Litho Format)

1986 (22 Apr). *Handicrafts. T* **53** *and similar horiz designs. Multicoloured. W w* **15**. *P* 15.
464 10 c. Type **53** 10 10
465 60 c. Basketwork 30 35
466 $1 Scrimshaw work 50 55
467 $3 Model boat .. .. 1·50 1·60
464/7 .. .. *Set of* 4 2·10 2·40

54 Uruguayan Team

(Des Court House Studio. Litho Format)

1986 (7 May). *World Cup Football Championship, Mexico. T* **54** *and similar multicoloured designs. P* 12½ (1 c., 10 c., $4, $5) *or* 15 (*others*).
468 1 c. Type **54** 10 10
469 10 c. Polish team 10 10
470 45 c. Bulgarian player (28×42 *mm*) 25 30
471 75 c. Iraqi player (28×42 *mm*) 35 40
472 $1.50, South Korean player (28×42 *mm*) .. 75 80
473 $2 Northern Irish player (28×42 *mm*) .. 1·00 1·10
474 $4 Portuguese team .. .. 2·00 2·10
475 $5 Canadian team .. .. 2·50 2·75
468/75 .. .. *Set of* 8 6·25 6·75
MS476 Two sheets, 85×114 mm. (a) $1 As No. 474: (b) $3 Type **54**. P 12½ *Set of* 2 *sheets* 2·00 2·50

55 *Marasmius pallescens*

56 *Brachymesia furcata*

(Des G. Drummond. Litho Questa)

1986 (23 May). *Fungi. T* **55** *and similar vert designs. Multicoloured. W w* **15** (*sideways*). *P* 14.
477 45 c. Type **55** 60 40
478 60 c. *Leucocoprinus fragilissimus* 70 50
479 75 c. *Hygrocybe occidentalis* 85 70
480 $3 *Xerocomus hypoxanthus* .. .. 2·25 2·50
477/80 .. .. *Set of* 4 4·00 3·75

(Des Court House Studio. Litho Format)

1986 (18 July–15 Oct). *Royal Wedding* (1st *issue*). *Multicoloured designs as T* **168** *of British Virgin Islands. P* 12½.

481 60 c. Miss Sarah Ferguson and Princess Diana applauding 30 35
a. Pair. Nos. 481/2.. .. .. 60 70
482 60 c. Prince Andrew at shooting match .. 30 35
483 $2 Prince Andrew and Miss Sarah Ferguson (*horiz*) 1.00 1.10
a. Pair. Nos. 483/4.. .. .. 2.00 2.25
484 $2 Prince Charles, Prince Andrew, Princess Anne and Princess Margaret on balcony (*horiz*) .. .. 1·00 1·10
481/4 .. .. *Set of* 4 2·40 2·50
MS485 115×85 mm. $8 Duke and Duchess of York in carriage after wedding (*horiz*) (15.10.86) 4·00 4·25

Nos. 481/2 and 483/4 were each printed together, *se-tenant*, in horizontal and vertical pairs throughout the sheets.

1986 (15 Oct). *Royal Wedding* (2*nd issue*). *Nos.* 481/4 *optd as T* **121** *of Montserrat in silver.*

486 60 c. Miss Sarah Ferguson and Princess Diana applauding 30 35
a. Pair. Nos. 486/7.. .. .. 60 70
487 60 c. Prince Andrew at shooting match .. 30 35
488 $2 Prince Andrew and Miss Sarah Ferguson (*horiz*) .. .. 1·00 1·10
a. Pair. Nos. 488/9.. .. .. 2·00 2·25
489 $2 Prince Charles, Prince Andrew, Princess Anne and Princess Margaret on balcony (*horiz*) .. .. 1·00 1·10
486/9 .. .. *Set of* 4 2·40 2·50

(Des M. Hillier. Litho Format)

1986 (19 Nov). *Dragonflies. T* **56** *and similar multicoloured designs. P* 15.

490 45 c. Type **56** 30 30
491 60 c. *Lepthemis vesiculosa* 35 35
492 75 c. *Perithemis domitta* 40 40
493 $2.50, *Tramea abdominalis* (*vert*).. .. 1·40 1·40
490/3 .. .. *Set of* 4 2·25 2·25

(Des Court House Studio. Litho Format)

1986 (26 Nov). *Centenary of Statue of Liberty. Vert views of Statue as T* **171** *of British Virgin Islands in separate miniature sheets. Multicoloured. P* 14×13½.

MS494 Nine sheets, each 85×115 mm. $1.50; $1.75; $2; $2.50; $3; $3.50; $5; $6; $8 *Set of* 9 *sheets* 17·00 18·00

57 American Kestrel

58 Santa playing Steel Band Drums

(Des Toni Lance. Litho Questa)

1986 (26 Nov). *Birds of Prey. T* **57** *and similar vert designs. Multicoloured. P* 14.

495 10 c. Type **57** 25 15
496 45 c. Common Black Hawk 65 45
497 60 c. Peregrine Falcon 85 55
498 $4 Osprey .. .. 3·50 3·75
495/8 .. .. *Set of* 4 4·75 4·50

(Des Court House Studio. Litho Questa)

1986 (26 Nov). *Christmas. T* **58** *and similar vert designs. Multicoloured. P* 14.

499 45 c. Type **58** 25 30
500 60 c. Santa windsurfing 30 35
501 $1.25, Santa skiing 60 65
502 $2 Santa limbo dancing .. .. 1·00 1·10
499/502 .. .. *Set of* 4 1·90 2·10
MS503 166×128 mm. Nos. 499/502 .. .. 3·50 3·75

(Litho Format)

1987 (5 May). *Railway Locomotives* (7*th series*). *Horiz designs, as T* **40**, *the first in each pair showing technical drawings and the second the locomotive at work. Multicoloured. P* 12½.

504 10 c. multicoloured 10 10
a. Vert pair. Nos. 504/5 .. .. 10 10
505 10 c. multicoloured 10 10
506 40 c. multicoloured 20 25
a. Vert pair. Nos. 506/7 .. .. 40 50
507 40 c. multicoloured 20 25
508 50 c. multicoloured 25 30
a. Vert pair. Nos. 508/9 .. .. 50 60
509 50 c. multicoloured 25 30
510 60 c. multicoloured 25 30
a. Vert pair. Nos. 510/11 .. .. 50 60
511 60 c. multicoloured 25 30
512 75 c. multicoloured 35 40
a. Vert pair. Nos. 512/13 .. .. 70 80
513 75 c. multicoloured 35 40
514 $1 multicoloured 45 50
a. Vert pair. Nos. 514/15 .. .. 90 1·00
515 $1 multicoloured 45 50
516 $1.25, multicoloured 55 60
a. Vert pair. Nos. 516/17 .. .. 1·10 1·25
517 $1.25, multicoloured 55 60
518 $1.50, multicoloured 70 75
a. Vert pair. Nos. 518/19 .. .. 1·40 1·50
519 $1.50, multicoloured 70 75
504/19 .. .. *Set of* 16 5·00 5·75

Designs:—Nos. 504/5, Class "1001", No. 1275, Great Britain (1874); 506/7, Class "4P Garratt", Great Britain (1927); 508/9, *Papyrus*, Great Britain (1929); 510/11, Class "V1", Great Britain (1930); 512/13, Class "40" diesel, No. D200, Great Britain (1958); 514/15, Class "42 Warship" diesel, Great Britain (1958); 516/17, Class "P-69", U.S.A. (1902); 518/19, Class "60-3 Shay", No. 15, U.S.A. (1913).

Nos. 504/19 were issued in a similar sheet format to Nos. 271/86.

(Litho Format)

1987 (26 Aug). *Railway Locomotives* (8*th series*). *Horiz designs as T* **40**, *the first in each pair showing technical drawings and the second the locomotive at work. P* 12½.

520 10 c. multicoloured 10 10
a. Vert pair. Nos. 520/1 .. .. 10 15
521 10 c. multicoloured 10 10
522 40 c. multicoloured 20 25
a. Vert pair. Nos. 522/3 .. .. 40 50
523 40 c. multicoloured 20 25
524 50 c. multicoloured 25 30
a. Vert pair. Nos. 524/5 .. .. 50 60
525 50 c. multicoloured 25 30
526 60 c. multicoloured 25 30
a. Vert pair. Nos. 526/7 .. .. 50 60
527 60 c. multicoloured 25 30
528 75 c. multicoloured 35 40
a. Vert pair. Nos. 528/9 .. .. 70 80
529 75 c. multicoloured 35 40
530 $1 multicoloured 45 50
a. Vert pair. Nos. 530/1 .. .. 90 1·00
531 $1 multicoloured 45 50
532 $1.50, multicoloured 70 75
a. Vert pair. Nos. 532/3 .. .. 1·40 1·50
533 $1.50, multicoloured 70 75
534 $2 multicoloured 90 95
a. Vert pair. Nos. 534/5 .. .. 1·75 1·90
535 $2 multicoloured 90 95
520/35 .. .. *Set of* 16 5·75 6·25

Designs:—Nos. 520/1, Class "142", East Germany (1977); 522/3, Class "120", West Germany (1979); 524/5, Class "X", Australia (1954); 526/7, Class "59", Great Britain (1986); 528/9, New York Elevated Railroad *Spuyten Duyvel*, U.S.A. (1875); 530/1, Camden & Amboy Railroad *Stevens* (later *John Bull*), U.S.A. (1831); 532/3, "Royal Hudson" Class "H1-d", No. 2850, Canada (1938), 534/5, "Pioneer Zephyr" 3-car set, U.S.A. (1934).

Nos. 520/35 were issued in a similar sheet format to Nos. 271/86.

59 Queen Elizabeth with Prince Andrew

60 Banded Coral Shrimp

(Litho Format)

1987 (15 Oct). *Royal Ruby Wedding and 150th Anniv of Queen Victoria's Accession. T* **59** *and similar vert designs. P* 12½.

536 15 c. multicoloured 15 15
537 45 c. deep chocolate, black & greenish yellow 30 30
538 $1.50, multicoloured 90 90
539 $3 multicoloured .. .. 1·75 1·75
540 $4 multicoloured .. .. 2·00 2·00
536/40 .. .. *Set of* 5 4·50 4·50
MS541 85×115 mm. $6 multicoloured .. .. 2·75 3·00

Designs:—45 c. Queen Victoria and Prince Albert, *c* 1855; $1.50, Queen and Prince Philip after Trooping the Colour, 1977; $3 Queen and Duke of Edinburgh, 1953; $4 Queen in her study, *c* 1980; $6 Princess Elizabeth, 1947.

(Litho Format)

1987 (17 Dec). *Marine Life. T* **60** *and similar horiz designs. Multicoloured. P* 15.

542 45 c. Type **60** 35 35
543 50 c. Arrow Crab and Flamingo Tongue .. 40 40
544 65 c. Cardinal Fish 50 50
545 $5 Moray Eel .. .. 3·00 3·00
542/5 .. .. *Set of* 4 3·75 3·75
MS546 85×115 mm. $5 Puffer Fish .. .. 3·00 3·50

61 *Australia IV*

62 Seine-fishing Boats racing

(Litho Format)

1988 (31 Mar). *Ocean Racing Yachts. T* **61** *and similar vert designs. Multicoloured. P* 12½.

547 50 c. Type **61** 30 30
548 65 c. *Crusader II* 40 40
549 75 c. *New Zealand K27* 45 45
550 $2 *Italia* .. .. 1·00 1·00
551 $4 *White Crusader* .. .. 1·75 1·75
552 $5 *Stars and Stripes* .. .. 2·25 2·25
547/52 .. .. *Set of* 6 5·50 5·50
MS553 100 × 140 mm. $1 *Champosa V* .. 45 50

(Litho Format)

1988 (31 Mar). *Bequia Regatta. T* **62** *and similar horiz designs. Multicoloured. P* 15.

554 5 c. Type **62** 10 10
555 50 c. *Friendship Rose* (motor fishing boat) .. 20 25
556 75 c. Fishing boats racing 30 35
557 $3.50, Yachts racing .. .. 1·50 1·60
554/7 .. .. *Set of* 4 1·90 2·00
MS558 115 × 85 mm. $8 Port Elizabeth, Bequia (60 × 40 *mm*). P 12½ .. .. 3·50 4·00

63 "Twin-Otter" making Night Approach

(Litho Format)

1988 (26 May). *Mustique Airways. T* **63** *and similar multicoloured designs. P* 14 × 13½.

559 15 c. Type **63** 10 10
560 65 c. Beech "Baron" aircraft in flight .. 30 35
561 75 c. "Twin-Otter" over forest 30 35
562 $5 Beech "Baron" on airstrip .. .. 2·10 2·25
559/62 .. .. *Set of* 4 2·50 2·75
MS563 115 × 85 mm. $10 Baleine Falls (36 × 56 *mm*). P 12½ .. .. 4·75 5·50

64 *Sv. Petr* in Arctic (Bering)

65 Asif Iqbal Razvi

(Litho Format)

1988 (29 July). *Explorers. T* **64** *and similar square designs. Multicoloured. P* 14 × 13½.

564 15 c. Type **64** 10 10
565 75 c. Bering's ships in pack ice 30 35
566 $1 Livingstone's steam launch *Ma-Robert* on Zambesi 45 50
567 $2 Meeting of Livingstone and H. M. Stanley at Ujiji 80 85
568 $3 Speke and Burton at Tabori .. .. 1·25 1·40
569 $3.50, Speke and Burton in canoe on Lake Victoria .. .. 1·50 1·60
570 $4 Sighting the New World, 1492 .. 1·60 1·75
571 $4.50, Columbus trading with Indians .. 2·00 2·10
563/71 .. .. *Set of* 8 7·25 7·75
MS572 Two sheets, each 115 × 85 mm. (a) $5 Sextant and coastal scene. (b) $5 *Santa Maria* at anchor. P 13½ × 14 .. .. *Set of* 2 *sheets* 4·25 4·50

(Litho Format)

1988 (29 July). *Cricketers of* 1988 *International Season. T* **65** *and similar multicoloured designs. P* 15.

573 20 c. Type **65** 15 15
574 45 c. R. J. Hadlee 30 30
575 75 c. M. D. Crowe 45 45
576 $1.25, C. H. Lloyd 70 70
577 $1.50, A. R. Boarder 80 80
578 $2 M. D. Marshall .. .. 1·00 1·00
579 $2.50, G. A. Hick .. .. 1·25 1·25
580 $3.50, C. G. Greenidge (*horiz*) .. .. 1·75 1·75
573/80 .. .. *Set of* 8 5·75 5·75
MS581 115 × 85 mm. $3 As $2 .. .. .. 1·75 2·00

66 Pam Shriver

(Litho Format)

1988 (29 July). *International Tennis Players. T* **66** *and similar multicoloured designs. P* 12½.

582 15 c. Type **66** . . 10 10
583 50 c. Kevin Curran (*vert*) . . 20 25
584 75 c. Wendy Turnbull (*vert*) . . 30 35
585 $1 Evonne Cawley (*vert*) . . 45 50
586 $1.50, Ilie Nastase . . 60 65
587 $2 Billie Jean King (*vert*) . . 80 85
588 $3 Bjorn Borg (*vert*) . . 1·25 1·40
589 $3.50, Virginia Wade with Wimbledon trophy (*vert*) . . 1·50 1·60
582/9 . . *Set of* 8 4·75 5·25
MS590 115 × 85 mm. $2.25, Stefan Edberg with Wimbledon cup; $2.25, Steffi Graf with Wimbledon trophy . . 2·00 2·25

No. 584 is inscribed "WENDY TURNBALL" in error.

67 Mickey and Minnie Mouse visiting Fatehpur Sikri

(Des Walt Disney Co. Litho Questa)

1989 (7 Feb). *"India-89" International Stamp Exhibition, New Delhi. T* **67** *and similar multicoloured designs showing Walt Disney cartoon characters in India. P* 14×13½.

591 1 c. Type **67** . . 10 10
592 2 c. Mickey and Minnie Mouse aboard "Palace on Wheels" train . . 10 10
593 3 c. Mickey and Minnie Mouse passing Old Fort, Delhi . . 10 10
594 5 c. Mickey and Minnie Mouse on camel, Pinjore Gardens, Haryana . . 10 10
595 10 c. Mickey and Minnie Mouse at Taj Mahal, Agra . . 10 10
596 25 c. Mickey and Minnie Mouse in Chandni Chowk, Old Delhi . . 10 10
597 $4 Goofy on elephant with Mickey and Minnie Mouse at Agra Fort, Jaipur . . 1·60 1·75
598 $5 Goofy, Mickey and Minnie Mouse at Gandhi Memorial, Cape Comorin . . 2·10 2·25
591/8 . . *Set of* 8 3·75 4·00
MS599 Two sheets, each 127 × 102 mm. (a) $6 Mickey and Minnie Mouse in vegetable cart, Jaipur. P 14 × 13½. (b) $6 Mickey and Minnie Mouse leaving carriage, Qutab Minar, New Delhi (*vert*). P 13½ × 14 . . *Set of* 2 *sheets* 5·00 5·25

(Litho Questa)

1989 (6 July). *Japanese Art. Horiz designs as T* **250** *of Antigua. Multicoloured. P* 14×13½.

600 5 c. "The View at Yotsuya" (Hokusai) . . 10 10
601 30 c. "Landscape at Ochanomizu" (Hokuju) 15 20
602 45 c. "Itabashi" (Eisen) . . 20 25
603 65 c. "Early Summer Rain" (Kunisada) . . 30 35
604 75 c. "High Noon at Kasumigaseki" (Kuniyoshi) . . 35 40
605 $1 "The Yoshiwara Embankment by Moonlight" (Kuniyoshi) . . 45 50
606 $4 "The Bridge of Boats at Sano" (Hokusai) . . 1·90 2·00
607 $5 "Lingering Snow on Mount Hira" (Kunitora) . . 2·40 2·50
600/7 . . *Set of* 8 5·25 5·75
MS608 Two sheets, each 103×76 mm. (a) $6 "Colossus of Rhodes" (Kunitora). (b) $6 "Shinobazu Pond" (Kokan) . . *Set of* 2 *sheets* 5·50 5·75

Nos. 600/7 were each printed in sheetlets of 10 containing two horizontal strips of 5 stamps separated by printed labels commemorating Emperor Hirohito.

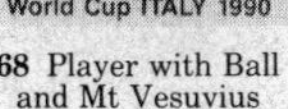

68 Player with Ball and Mt Vesuvius

69 Command Module *Columbia*

(Des J. Genzo. Litho B.D.T.)

1989 (10 July). *World Cup Football Championship, Italy. T* **68** *and similar vert designs each showing players and Italian landmarks. Multicoloured. P* 14.

609 $1.50, Type **68** . . 70 75
a. Sheetlet. Nos. 609/16 . . 5·00
610 $1.50, Fallen player, opponent kicking ball and Coliseum . . 70 75
611 $1.50, Player blocking ball and Venice . . 70 75
612 $1.50, Player tackling and Forum, Rome 70 75
613 $1.50, Two players competing for ball and Leaning Tower, Pisa . . 70 75
614 $1.50, Goalkeeper and Florence . . 70 75
615 $1.50, Two players competing for ball and St. Peter's, Vatican . . 70 75
616 $1.50, Player kicking ball and Pantheon 70 75
609/16 . . *Set of* 8 5·00 5·50

Nos. 609/16 were printed together, *se-tenant*, in a sheetlet of 8.

Des D. Miller. Litho B.D.T.)

1989 (2 Oct). *500th Anniv of Discovery of America* (1992) *by Columbus. Pre-Columbian Arawak Society. Vert designs as T* **247** *of Antigua. Multicoloured. P* 14.

617 25 c. Arawak smoking tobacco . . 10 15
618 75 c. Arawak rolling cigar . . 35 40
619 $1 Applying body paint . . 45 50
620 $1.50, Making fire . . 70 75
a. Horiz strip of 4. Nos. 620/3 . . 2·75
621 $1.50, Cassava production . . 70 75
622 $1.50, Woman baking bread . . 70 75
623 $1.50, Using stone implement . . 70 75
624 $4 Arawak priest . . 1·90 2·00
617/24 . . *Set of* 8 5·00 5·50
MS625 Two sheets, each 70×84 mm. (a) $6 Arawak chief. (b) $6 Men returning from fishing expedition . . *Set of* 2 *sheets* 5·75 6·00

Nos. 620/4 were printed together, *se-tenant*, in horizontal strips of 4 throughout the sheet of 20, each strip forming a composite design.

(Des D. Bruckner. Litho Questa)

1989 (2 Oct). *10th Anniv of First Manned Landing on Moon. T* **69** *and similar multicoloured designs. P* 14.

626 5 c. Type **69** . . 10 10
627 40 c. Astronaut Neil Armstrong saluting U.S. flag . . 20 25
628 55 c. *Columbia* above lunar surface . . 25 30
629 65 c. Lunar module *Eagle* leaving Moon . . 30 35
630 70 c. *Eagle* on Moon . . 35 40
631 $1 *Columbia* re-entering Earth's atmosphere . . 45 50
632 $3 "Apollo 11" emblem . . 1·50 1·60
633 $5 Armstrong and Aldrin on Moon . . 2·40 2·50
626/33 . . *Set of* 8 5·00 5·50
MS634 Two sheets, each 110×82 mm. (a) $6 Launch of "Apollo 11" (*vert*). (b) $6 "Apollo 11" splashdown . . *Set of* 2 *sheets* 5·75 6·00

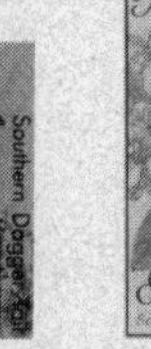

70 Southern Dagger Tail

71 *Solanum urens*

(Des D. Bruckner. Litho Questa)

1989 (16 Oct). *Butterflies. T* **70** *and similar horiz designs. Multicoloured. P* 14½.

635 5 c. Type **70** . . 10 10
636 30 c. Androgeus Swallowtail . . 15 20
637 45 c. Clench's Hairstreak . . 20 25
638 65 c. Buckeye . . 30 35
639 75 c. Venezuelan Sulphur . . 35 40
640 $1 Mimic . . 45 50
641 $4 Common Longtail Skipper . . 1·90 2·00
642 $5 Caribbean Buckeye . . 2·40 2·50
635/42 . . *Set of* 8 5·25 5·50
MS643 Two sheets. (a) 76×104 mm. $6 Large Orange Sulphur. (b) 104×76 mm. $6 Flambeau *Set of* 2 *sheets* 5·75 6·00

(Des Mary Walters. Litho Questa)

1989 (1 Nov). *Flowers from St. Vincent Botanical Gardens. T* **71** *and similar vert designs. Multicoloured. P* 14.

644 80 c. Type **71** . . 40 45
645 $1.25, *Passiflora andersonii* . . 60 65
646 $1.65, *Miconia andersonii* . . 80 85
647 $1.85, *Pitcairnia sulphurea* . . 90 95
644/7 . . *Set of* 4 2·40 2·50

OFFICIAL STAMPS

1982 (11 Oct). *Nos.* 195/200 *optd with Type* O **1** *of St. Vincent.*

O1 50 c. *Mary* . . 15 20
a. Sheetlet. No. O1 × 6 and No. O2 . . 1·10
b. Opt double
c. Albino opt . . 4·00
d. Horiz pair, one without opt
O2 50 c. Prince Charles and Lady Diana Spencer 40 45
b. Opt double
c. Albino opt . . 13·00
O3 $3 *Alexandra* . . 55 75
a. Sheetlet. No. O3 × 6 and No. O4 . . 4·00
b. Opt double . . 40·00
c. Albino opt . . 7·00
O4 $3 Prince Charles and Lady Diana Spencer 1·25 1·25
b. Opt double . . £125
c. Albino opt . . 30·00
O5 $3.50, *Britannia* . . 75 1·00
a. Sheetlet. No. O5 × 6 and No. O6 . . 5·50
c. Albino opt . . 9·00
O6 $3.50, Prince Charles and Lady Diana Spencer . . 1·50 1·75
c. Albino opt . . 25·00
O1/6 . . *Set of* 6 4·25 4·75

Appendix

The following issues for individual islands in the Grenadines group fall outside the criteria for full listing as detailed on page xi of the General Catalogue Information in this edition.

BEQUIA

1984

Leaders of the World. Railway Locomotives (1st series). *Two designs for each value, the first showing technical drawings and the second the locomotive at work.* 1, 5, 10, 25, 35, 45 c., $1.50, $2, *each* × 2
Grenadines of St. Vincent 1982 *Ships definitives* (Nos. 208/24) *optd* "BEQUIA". 1, 3, 5, 6, 10, 15, 20, 25, 30, 50, 60, 75 *c.*, $1, $2, $3, $5, $10
Leaders of the World. Automobiles (1st series). *Two designs for each value, the first showing technical drawings and the second the car in action.* 5, 40 c., $1, $1.50, *each* × 2
Leaders of the World. Olympic Games, Los Angeles. 1, 10, 60 c., $3, *each* × 2
Leaders of the World. Railway Locomotives (2nd series). *Two designs for each value, the first showing technical drawings and the second the locomotive at work.* 1, 5, 10, 35, 75 *c.*, $1, $2.50, $3, *each* × 2
Leaders of the World. Automobiles (2nd series). *Two designs for each value, the first showing technical drawings and the second the car in action.* 5, 10, 20, 25, 75 c., $1, $2.50, $3, *each* × 2

1985

Leaders of the World. Railway Locomotives (3rd series). *Two designs for each value, the first showing technical drawings and the second the locomotive at work.* 25, 55, 60 c., $2, *each* × 2
Leaders of the World. Dogs. 25, 35, 55 c., $2, *each* × 2
Leaders of the World, Warships of the Second World War. Two designs for each value, the first showing technical drawings and the second the ship at sea. 15, 50 c., $1, $1.50, *each* × 2
Leaders of the World. Flowers. 10, 20, 70 c., $2.50, *each* × 2
Leaders of the World. Automobiles (3rd series). *Two designs for each value, the first showing technical drawings and the second the car in action.* 5, 25, 50 c., $1, $1.25, $2, *each* × 2
Leaders of the World. Railway Locomotives (4th series). *Two designs for each value, the first showing technical drawings and the second the locomotive at work.* 25, 55, 60, 75 c., $1, $2.50, *each* × 2
Leaders of the World. Life and Times of Queen Elizabeth the Queen Mother. Two designs for each value, showing different portraits. 20, 65 c., $1.35, $1.80, *each* × 2
Leaders of the World. Automobiles (4th series). *Two designs for each value, the first showing technical drawings and the second the car in action.* 10, 35, 75 c., $1.15, $1.50, $2, *each* × 2

1986

Leaders of the World. Automobiles (5th series). *Two designs for each value, the first showing technical drawings and the second the car in action.* 25, 50, 65, 75 c., $1, $3, *each* × 2
60*th Birthday of Queen Elizabeth II.* 5, 75 c., $2, $8
World Cup Football Championship, Mexico. 1, 2, 5, 10, 45, 60, 75 c., $1.50, $1.50, $2, $3.50, $6
Royal Wedding (1st issue). 60 c., $2, *each* × 2
Railway Engineers and Locomotives. $1, $2.50, $3, $4
Royal Wedding (2nd issue). *Previous issue optd* "Congratulations T.R.H. The Duke & Duchess of York". 60 *c.*, $2, *each* × 2.
Automobiles (6th series). *Two designs for each value, the first showing technical drawings and the second the car in action.* 20, 60, 75, 90 *c.*, $1, $3, *each* × 2

1987

Automobiles (7th series). *Two designs for each value, the first showing technical drawings and the second the car in action.* 5, 20, 35, 60, 75, 80 c., $1.25, $1.75, *each* × 2
Royal Ruby Wedding. 15, 75 c., $1, $2.50, $5
Railway Locomotives (5th series). *Two designs for each value, the first showing technical drawings and the second the locomotive at work.* 15, 25, 40, 50, 60, 75 c., $1, $2, *each* × 2

1988

Explorers. 15, 50 c., $1.75, $2, $2.50, $3, $3.50, $4
International Lawn Tennis Players. 15, 45, 80 c., $1.25, $1.75, $2, $2.50, $3

1989

"Philexfrance 89" International Stamp Exhibition, Paris. Walt Disney Cartoon Characters. 1, 2, 3, 4, 5, 10 c., $5, $6

UNION ISLAND

1984

Leaders of the World. British Monarchs. Two designs for each value, forming a composite picture. 1, 5, 10, 20, 60 c., $3, *each* × 2
Leaders of the World. Railway Locomotives (1st series). *Two designs for each value, the first showing technical drawings and the second the locomotive at work.* 5, 60 c., $1, $2
Grenadines of St. Vincent 1982 *Ships definitives* (Nos. 208/24) *optd* "UNION ISLAND". 1, 3, 5, 6, 10, 15, 20, 25, 30, 50, 60, 75 *c.*, $1, $2, $3, $5, $10
Leaders of the World. Cricketers. Two designs for each value, the first showing a portrait and the second the cricketer in action. 1, 10, 15, 55, 60, 75 c., $1.50, $3, *each* × 2
Leaders of the World. Railway Locomotives (2nd series). *Two designs for each value, the first showing technical drawings and the second the locomotive at work.* 5, 10, 20, 25, 75 c., $1, $2.50, $3, *each* × 2

1985

Leaders of the World. Automobiles (1st series). *Two designs for each value, the first showing technical drawings and the second the car in action.* 1, 50, 75 c., $2.50, *each* × 2
Leaders of the World. Birth Bicent of John J. Audubon (ornithologist). Birds. 15, 50 c., $1, $1.50, *each* × 2
Leaders of the World. Railway Locomotives (3rd series). *Two designs for each value, the first showing technical drawings and the second the locomotive at work.* 5, 50, 60 c., $2, *each* × 2
Leaders of the World. Butterflies. 15, 25, 75 c., $2, *each* × 2
Leaders of the World. Automobiles (2nd series). *Two designs for each value, the first showing technical drawings and the second the car in action.* 5, 60 *c.*, $1, $1.50, *each* × 2
Leaders of the World. Automobiles (3rd series). *Two designs for each value, the first showing technical drawings and the second the car in action.* 10, 55, 60, 75, 90 *c.*, $1, $1.50, $2, *each* × 2
Leaders of the World. Life and Times of Queen Elizabeth the Queen Mother. Two designs for each value, showing different portraits. 55, 70 *c.*, $1.05, $1.70, *each* × 2

1986

Leaders of the World. Railway Locomotives (4th series). *Two designs for each value, the first showing technical drawings and the second the locomotive at work.* 15, 30, 45, 60, 75 c., $1.50, $2.50, $3, *each* × 2
60*th Birthday of Queen Elizabeth II.* 10, 60 c., $2, $8
World Cup Football Championship, Mexico. 1, 10, 30, 75 c., $1, $2.50, $3, $6
Royal Wedding (1st issue). 60 c., $2, *each* × 2
Automobiles (4th series). *Two designs for each value, the first showing technical drawings and the second the car in action.* 10, 60, 75 c., $1, $1.50, $3, *each* × 2
Royal Wedding (2nd issue). *Previous issue optd as Bequia.* 60 c., $2, *each* × 2
Railway Locomotives (5th series). *Two designs for each value, the first showing technical drawings and the second the locomotive at work.* 15, 45, 60, 75 *c.*, $1, $1.50, $2, $3, *each* × 2

1987

Railway Locomotives (6th series). *Two designs for each value, the first showing technical drawings and the second the locomotive at work.* 15, 25, 40, 50, 60, 75 *c.*, $1, $2, *each* × 2
Royal Ruby Wedding. 15, 45 c., $1.50, $3, $4
Railway Locomotives (7th series). *Two designs for each value, the first showing technical drawings and the second the locomotive at work.* 15, 20, 30, 45, 50, 75 *c.*, $1, $1.50, *each* × 2

Samoa

PRICES FOR STAMPS ON COVER TO 1945

Nos. 1/20 are very rare used on cover.

Nos. 21/40	*from* × 20
Nos. 41/8	*from* × 100
Nos. 49/56	*from* × 4
Nos. 57/64	*from* × 12
Nos. 65/8	*from* × 2
Nos. 69/97	*from* × 20
Nos. 101/9	*from* × 3
Nos. 110/14	—
Nos. 115/21	*from* × 3
Nos. 122/32	—
Nos. 134/64	*from* × 3
Nos. 165/76	—
Nos. 177/214	*from* × 2

INDEPENDENT KINGDOM OF SAMOA

The first postal service in Samoa was organised by C. L. Griffiths, who had earlier run the *Fiji Times* Express post in Suva. In both instances the principal purpose of the service was the distribution of newspapers of which Griffiths was the proprietor. The first issue of the *Samoa Times* (later the *Samoa Times and South Sea Gazette*) appeared on 6 October 1877 and the newspaper continued in weekly publication until 27 August 1881.

Mail from the Samoa Express post to addresses overseas was routed via New South Wales, New Zealand or U.S.A. and received additional franking with stamps of the receiving country on landing.

Cancellations, inscribed "APIA SAMOA", did not arrive until March 1878 so that examples of Nos. 1/9 used before that date were cancelled in manuscript.

1

(Des H. H. Glover. Litho S. T. Leigh & Co, Sydney, N.S.W.)

1877 (1 Oct)–**80.**

A. 1*st state: line above* "X" *in* "EXPRESS" *not broken. P* 12½

1 1 1d. ultramarine .. £225 95·00
2 3d. deep scarlet .. £250 £100
3 6d. bright violet .. £250 95·00
a. Pale lilac .. £275 95·00

B. 2*nd state: line above* "X" *broken, and dot between top of* "M" *and* "O" *of* "SAMOA". *P* 12½ (1878–79)

4 1 1d. ultramarine .. 85·00 90·00
5 3d. bright scarlet .. £250 £100
6 6d. bright violet .. £150 80·00
7 1s. dull yellow .. £130 80·00
a. Line above "X" not broken .. £130 90·00
b. Perf 12 (1879) .. 70·00 85·00
c. Orange-yellow .. 85·00 90·00
8 2s. red-brown .. £225 £160
a. Chocolate .. £250 £300
9 5s. green .. £800 £1000

C. 3*rd state: line above* "X" *repaired, dot merged with upper right serif of* "M" (1879). *(a) P* 12½

10 1 1d. ultramarine .. 80·00 80·00
11 3d. vermilion .. 95·00 95·00
12 6d. lilac .. £100 80·00
13 2s. brown .. £180 £180
a. Chocolate .. £180 £180
14 5s. green .. £500 £500
a. Line above "X" not repaired .. £600

(b) P 12

15 1 1d. blue .. 22·00 38·00
a. Deep blue .. 30·00 70·00
b. Ultramarine .. 26·00 38·00
16 3d. vermilion .. 40·00 60·00
a. Carmine-vermilion .. 40·00 70·00
17 6d. bright violet .. 38·00 42·00
a. Deep violet .. 38·00 75·00
18 2s. deep brown .. £120 £180
19 5s. yellow-green .. £400 £550
a. Deep green .. £375 £500
b. Line above "X" not repaired .. £475

D. 4*th state: spot of colour under middle stroke of* "M". *P* 12 (1880)

20 1 9d. orange-brown .. 50·00 £100

Originals exist imperf, but are not known used in this state.

On sheets of the 1d., 1st state, at least eight stamps have a stop after "PENNY". In the 2nd state, three stamps have the stop, and in the 3rd state, only one.

In the 1st state, all the stamps, 1d., 3d. and 6d., were in sheets of 20 (5 × 4) and also the 1d. in the 3rd state.

All values in the 2nd state, all values except the 1d. in the 3rd state and No. 20 were in sheets of 10 (5 × 2).

As all sheets of all printings of the originals were imperf at the outer edges, the only stamps which can have perforations on all four sides are Nos. 1 to 3*a*, 10 and 15 to 15*b*, all other originals being imperf on one or two sides.

The perf 12 stamps, which gauge 11.8, are generally very rough but later the machine was repaired and the 1d., 3d. and 6d. are known with clean-cut perforations.

Remainders of the 1d., unissued 2d. rose, 6d. (in sheets of 21 (7 × 3), 3d., 9d., 1s. (in sheets of 12 (4 × 3)) and of the 2s. and 5s. (sheet format unknown) were found in the Samoan post office when the service closed down in 1881. The remainders are rare in complete sheets, but of very little value as singles, compared with the originals.

Reprints of all values, in sheets of 40 (8 × 5), were made after the originals had been withdrawn from sale. These are practically worthless.

The majority of both reprints and remainders are in the 4th state as the 9d. with the spot of colour under the middle stroke of the "M", but a few stamps (both remainders and reprints) do not show this, while on some it is very faint.

There are three known types of forgery, one of which is rather dangerous, the others being crude.

The last mail despatch organised by the proprietors of the Samoa Express took place on 31 August 1881, although one cover is recorded postmarked 24 September 1881.

After the withdrawal of the Samoa Express service it would appear that the Apia municipality appointed a postmaster to continue the overseas post. Covers are known franked with U.S.A. or New Zealand stamps in Samoa, or routed via Fiji.

In December 1886 the municipal postmaster, John Davis, was appointed Postmaster of the Kingdom of Samoa by King Malietoa. Overseas mail sent via New Zealand was subsequently accepted without the addition of New Zealand stamps, although letters to the U.S.A. continued to require such franking until August 1891.

2 Palm Trees

3 King Malietoa Laupepa

4*a* 6 mm

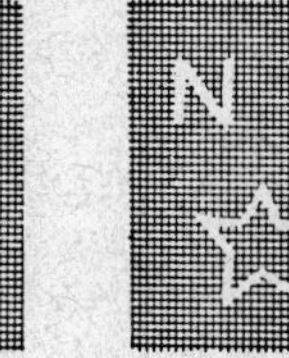

4*b* 7 mm

4*c* 4 mm

Description of Watermarks

(These are the same as W **12***a*/*c* of New Zealand)

W 4*a*. 6 mm between "N Z" and star; broad irregular star; comparatively wide "N"; "N Z" 11½ mm wide.

W 4*b*. 7 mm between "N Z" and star; narrower star; narrow "N"; "N Z" 10 mm wide.

W 4*c*. 4 mm between "N Z" and star; narrow star; wide "N"; "N Z" 11 mm wide.

(Des A. E. Cousins (T **3**). Dies eng W. R. Bock and A. E. Cousins (T **2**) or A. E. Cousins (T **3**). Typo Govt Ptg Office, Wellington)

1886–1900. (i) *W* **4***a*. *(a) P* 12½ (Oct–Nov 1886).

21 2 ½d. purple-brown .. 15·00 22·00
22 1d. yellow-green .. 5·50 12·00
23 2d. dull orange .. 8·00 7·50
24 4d. blue .. 14·00 8·50
25 1s. rose-carmine .. 45·00 7·50
a. Bisected (2½d.) (on cover)* .. † £250
26 2s. 6d. reddish lilac .. 48·00 38·00

(b) P 12 × 11½ (July–Nov 1887)

27 2 ½d. purple-brown .. 80·00 80·00
28 1d. yellow-green .. £100 29·00
29 2d. yellow .. 85·00 £140
30 4d. blue .. £250 £200
31 6d. brown-lake .. 18·00 8·00
32 1s. rose-carmine .. — £150
33 2s. 6d. reddish lilac .. £250

(ii) *W* **4***c*. *P* 12 × 11½ (May 1890)

34 2 ½d. purple-brown .. 70·00 30·00
35 1d. green .. 40·00 27·00
36 2d. brown-orange .. 65·00 28·00
37 4d. blue .. £120 5·00
38 6d. brown-lake .. £200 11·00
39 1s. rose-carmine .. £300 13·00
40 2s. 6d. reddish lilac .. £350 8·50

(iii) *W* **4***b*. *(a) P* 12 × 11½ (1890–92)

41 2 ½d. pale purple-brown .. 1·25 2·50
a. Blackish purple .. 1·25 2·50
42 1d. myrtle-green (5.90) .. 8·50 1·40
a. Green .. 8·50 1·40
b. Yellow-green .. 8·50 1·40
43 2d. dull orange (5.90) .. 10·00 1·75
44 3 2½d. rose (11.92) .. 75·00 3·50
a. Pale rose .. 75·00 3·50
45 2 4d. blue .. £200 10·00
46 6d. brown-lake .. £100 8·00
47 1s. rose-carmine .. £200 4·00
48 2s. 6d. slate-lilac .. — 5·00

(b) P 12½ (Mar 1891–92)

49 2 ½d. purple-brown ..
50 1d. green ..
51 2d. orange-yellow .. — £120
52 3 2½d. rose (1.92) .. 18·00 4·50
53 2 4d. blue .. — £450
54 6d. brown-purple .. £2000 £750
55 1s. rose-carmine .. — £400
56 2s. 6d. slate-lilac ..

(c) P 11 (May 1895–1900)

57 2 ½d. purple-brown .. 75 1·75
a. Deep purple-brown .. 65 1·75
b. Blackish purple (1900) .. 65 35·00
58 2 1d. green .. 1·25 1·75
a. Bluish green (1897) .. 1·25 1·75
b. Deep green (1900) .. 1·25 22·00
59 2d. pale yellow .. 32·00 35·00
a. Orange (1896) .. 32·00 35·00
b. Bright yellow (1.97) .. 5·50 4·00
c. Pale ochre (10.97) .. 4·50 1·00
d. Dull orange (1900) .. 5·50
60 3 2½d. rose .. 70 4·50
a. Deep rose-carmine (1900) .. 1·10 42·00
61 2 4d. blue .. 5·75 2·00
a. Deep blue (1900) .. 60 50·00
62 6d. brown-lake .. 5·50 4·00
a. Brown-purple (1900) .. 1·75 60·00
63 1s. rose .. 5·50 4·50
a. Dull rose-carmine/toned (5.98) .. 2·00 35·00
b. Carmine (1900) .. 1·25
64 2s. 6d. purple .. 55·00 9·50
a. Reddish lilac (wmk inverted) (1897) 7·50 7·50
b. Deep purple/toned (wmk reversed) (5.98) .. 4·75 9·50
ba. Imperf between (vert pair) .. £500
c. Slate-violet .. £120

*Following a fire on 1 April 1895 which destroyed stocks of all stamps except the 1s. value perf 12½, this was bisected diagonally and used as a 2½d. stamp for overseas letters between 24 April and May 1895, and was cancelled in blue. Fresh supplies of the 2½d. did not arrive until July 1895, although other values were available from 23 May.

Examples of the 1s. rose perforated 11, No. 63, were subsequently bisected and supplied cancelled-to-order by the post office to collectors, often with backdated cancellations. Most of these examples were bisected vertically and all were cancelled in black (*Price* £7).

The dates given relate to the earliest dates of printing in the various watermarks and perforations and not to issue dates.

The perf 11 issues (including those later surcharged or overprinted), are very unevenly perforated owing to the large size of the pins. Evenly perforated copies are extremely hard to find.

For the 2½d. black, see Nos. 81/2 and for the ½d. green and 1d. red-brown, see Nos. 88/9.

FIVE PENCE (5) FIVE PENCE (6) 5d (7)

1893 (Nov–Dec). *Handstamped singly, at Apia.*

(a) In two operations

65 5 5d. on 4d. blue (37) .. 40·00 38·00
a. Bars omitted .. — £375
66 5d. on 4d. blue (45) .. 60·00 £100
67 6 5d. on 4d. blue (37) .. 85·00 £110
68 5d. on 4d. blue (45) .. 90·00

(b) In three operations (Dec)

69 7 5d. on 4d. blue (37) (R.) .. 14·00 20·00
a. Stop after "d" .. £250 60·00
b. Bars omitted ..
70 5d. on 4d. blue (45) (R.) .. 14·00 45·00

In Types **5** and **6** the bars obliterating the original value vary in length from 13½ to 16½ mm and can occur with either the thick bar over the thin one or vice versa.

Double handstamps exist but we do not list them.

No. 69a came from a separate handstamp which applied the "5d." at one operation. Where the "d" was applied separately its position in relation to the "5" naturally varies.

SAMOA POST FIVE 5 PENCE — 8

Surcharged 1½d. — (9)

R 3d. — (10)

The "R" in Type **10** indicates use for registration fee.

(Des and die eng A. E. Cousins. Typo New Zealand Govt Ptg Office)

1894–1900. *W* **4***b* (*sideways*). *(a) P* 11½ × 12.

71 8 5d. dull vermilion (3.94) .. 12·00 2·75
a. Dull red .. 12·00 3·50

(b) P 11

72 8 5d. dull red (1895) .. 10·00 6·50
a. Deep red (1900) .. 1·25 13·00

1895–1900. *W* **4***b*.

(i) *Handstamped with T* **9** *or* **10**. *(a) P* 12 × 11½ (26.1.95)

73 2 1½d. on 2d. dull orange (B.) .. 5·00 5·00
74 3d. on 2d. dull orange .. 15·00 8·00

(b) P 11 (6.95)

75 2 1½d. on 2d. orange (B.) .. 1·50 2·50
a. Pair, one without handstamp ..
b. On 2d. yellow .. 75·00 60·00
76 3d. on 2d. orange .. 5·00 7·50
a. On 2d. yellow .. 75·00 60·00

(ii) *Surch printed**. *P* 11

77 2 1½d. on 2d. orange-yellow (B.) ..

(iii) *Handstamped as T* **9** *or* **10**.† *P* 11 (1896)

78 2 1½d. on 2d. orange-yellow (B.) .. 2·50 20·00
79 3d. on 2d. orange-yellow .. 3·00 45·00
a. Imperf between (vert pair) .. £400
b. Pair, one without handstamp ..

(iv) *Surch typo as T* **10**. *P* 11 (Feb 1900)

80 2 3d. on 2d. deep red-orange (G.) .. 1·50 £130

*It is believed that this was type-set from which clichés were made and set up in a forme and then printed on a hand press. This would account for the clear indentation on the back of the stamp and the variation in the position on the stamps which probably resulted from the clichés becoming loose in the forme.

†In No. 78 the "2" has a serif and the handstamp is in pale greenish blue instead of deep blue. In No. 79 the "R" is slightly narrower. In both instances the stamp is in a different shade.

A special printing in a distinctly different colour was made for No. 80 and the surcharge is in green.

Most of the handstamps exist double.

1896 (Aug). *Printed in the wrong colour.* W **4b**. (a) P 10 × 11.
81 3 2½d. black .. .. 90 3·00
(b) P 11
82 3 2½d. black .. .. 75·00 75·00
a. Mixed perfs 10 and 11 .. .. £350

Surcharged
2½d.
(11)

PROVISIONAL
GOVT.
(12)

1898–99. W **4b**. P 11. (a) *Handstamped as T* **11** (10.98).
83 2 2½d. on 1s. dull rose-carmine/*toned* .. 18·00 27·00
(b) *Surch as T* **11** (1899)
84 2 2½d. on 1d. bluish green (R.) .. .. 55 2·00
a. Surch inverted .. .. .. — £350
85 2½d. on 1s. dull rose-carmine/*toned* (R.) 3·50 8·00
a. Surch double £350
86 2½d. on 1s. dull rose-carmine/*toned* (Blk.) 3·50 8·00
a. Surch double £450
87 2½d. on 2s. 6d. deep purple/*toned* .. 4·75 11·00

The typographed surcharge was applied in a setting of nine, giving seven types differing in the angle and length of the fractional line, the type of stop, etc.

1899. *Colours changed.* W **4b**. P 11.
88 2 ½d. dull blue-green .. .. 65 1·40
a. Deep green .. .. 65 1·40
89 1d. deep red-brown .. .. 55 1·25

1899–1900. *Provisional Government. New printings optd with T* **12** *(longer words and shorter letters on 5d.).* W **4b**. P 11.
90 2 ½d. dull blue-green (R.) .. .. .. 25 1·00
a. Yellowish green (1900) .. .. 25 1·25
91 1d. chestnut (B.) .. .. 60 1·75
92 2d. dull orange (R.) .. .. .. 40 1·75
a. Orange-yellow (1900) .. .. 40 2·50
93 4d. deep dull blue (R.) .. .. .. 45 1·50
94 8 5d. dull vermilion (B.) .. .. .. 90 4·50
a. Red (1900) .. .. 90 4·50
95 2 6d. brown-lake (B.) .. .. .. 1·10 3·50
96 1s. rose-carmine (B.) .. .. .. 1·50 7·00
97 2s. 6d. reddish purple (R.) .. .. 4·75 16·00

The Samoan group of islands was partitioned on 1 March 1900: Western Samoa (Upolu, Savaii, Apolima and Manono) to Germany and Eastern Samoa (Tutuila, the Manu'a Is and Rose Is) to the United States. German issues of 1900–14 will be found listed in Part 7 (*Germany*) of this catalogue, there were no U.S. issues.

The Samoan Kingdom post office run by John Davis was suspended in March 1900.

WESTERN SAMOA

NEW ZEALAND OCCUPATION

The German Islands of Samoa surrendered to the New Zealand Expeditionary Force on 30 August 1914 and were administered by New Zealand until 1962.

G.R.I.
1d.
(13)

G.R.I.
1 Shillings.
(14)

SETTINGS. Nos. 101/9 were surcharged by a vertical setting of ten, repeated ten times across the sheet. Nos. 110/14 were from a horizontal setting of four repeated five times in the sheet.

Nos. 101b, 102a and 104a occurred on position 6. The error was corrected during the printing of No. 102.

Nos. 101c, 102c, 104d and 105b are from position 10.

Nos. 101d, 102e and 104b are from position 1.

No. 108b is from position 9.

(Surch by *Samoanische Zeitung*, Apia)

1914 (3 Sept). *German Colonial issue (ship) (no wmk) inscr "SAMOA" surch as T* **13** *or* **14** *(mark values).*
101 ½d. on 3 pf. brown .. .. .. 11·00 8·50
a. Surch double £600 £400
b. No fraction bar .. .. .. 40·00 30·00
c. Comma after "I" £600 £500
d. "1" to left of "2" in "½" .. .. 35·00 23·00
102 ½d. on 5 pf. green .. .. .. 30·00 10·00
a. No fraction bar .. .. .. 90·00 50·00
c. Comma after "I" £350 £170
d. Surch double £600 £400
e. "1" to left of "2" in "½" .. .. 55·00 40·00
103 1d. on 10 pf. carmine .. .. .. 95·00 40·00
a. Surch double £450 £400
104 2½d. on 20 pf. ultramarine .. .. 30·00 10·00
a. No fraction bar .. .. .. 60·00 38·00
b. "1" to left of "2" in "½" .. .. 60·00 40·00
c. Surch inverted £800 £750
d. Comma after "I" £450 £325
e. Surch double £650 £550
105 3d. on 25 pf. black and red/*yellow* .. 50·00 35·00
a. Surch double £500 £400
b. Comma after "I" £3500 £1750
106 4d. on 30 pf. black and orange/*buff* .. £100 60·00
107 5d. on 40 pf. black and carmine .. .. £110 70·00
108 6d. on 50 pf. black and purple/*buff* .. 55·00 35·00
a. Surch double £650 £700
b. Inverted "9" for "6" £140 £100
109 9d. on 80 pf. black and carmine/*rose* .. £190 95·00
110 "1 shillings" on 1 m. carmine £3000 £2750
111 "1 shilling" on 1 m. carmine £9500 £7000
112 2s. on 2 m. blue £3000 £2750
113 3s. on 3 m. violet-black £1400 £1200
a. Surch double £7000 £8000
114 5s. on 5 m. carmine and black £1000 £950
a. Surch double £11000 £11000

No. 108b is distinguishable from 108, as the "d" and the "9" are not in a line, and the upper loop of the "9" turns downwards to the left.

UNAUTHORISED SURCHARGES. Examples of the 2d. on 20 pf., 3d. on 30 pf., 3d. on 40 pf., 4d. on 40 pf., 6d. on 80 pf., 2s. on 3 m. and 2s. on Marshall Islands 2 m., together with a number of errors not listed above, were produced by the printer on stamps supplied by local collectors. These were not authorised by the New Zealand Military Administration.

SAMOA.
(15)

1914 (29 Sept)–**15**. *Stamps of New Zealand. T* **50**, **51**, **52** *and* **27**, *optd as T* **15**, *but opt only 14 mm long on all except 2½d. Wmk "N Z" and Star,* W **43** *of New Zealand.*
115 ½d. yellow-green (R.) (*p* 14×15) 25 30
116 1d. carmine (B.) (*p* 14×15) 25 10
117 2d. mauve (R.) (*p* 14×14½) (10.14) .. 60 95
118 2½d. deep blue (R.) (*p* 14) (10.14) .. 1·50 1·75
119 6d. carmine (B.) (*p* 14×14½) (10.14) .. 1·50 1·75
a. Perf 14×13½ .. .. .. 16·00 18·00
b. Vert pair. Nos. 119/a (1915) .. 35·00 50·00
120 6d. pale carmine (B.) (*p* 14×14½) (10.14) 10·00 9·50
121 1s. vermilion (B.) (*p* 14×14½) (10.14) .. 3·50 9·00

1914–24. *Postal Fiscal stamps as Type* F **4** *of New Zealand optd with T* **15**. W **43** *of New Zealand (sideways). Chalk-surfaced "De La Rue" paper.*
(a) P 14 (Nov 1914–17)
122 2s. blue (R.) (9.17) .. .. .. 80·00 £100
123 2s. 6d. grey-brown (B.) (9.17) .. .. 4·50 8·50
124 5s. yellow-green (R.) .. .. .. 9·00 12·00
125 10s. maroon (B.) .. .. .. 20·00 28·00
126 £1 rose-carmine (B.) .. .. .. 60·00 80·00
(b) P 14½ × 14, *comb* (1917–24)
127 2s. deep blue (R.) (3.18) .. .. 4·00 5·50
128 2s. 6d. grey-brown (B.) (10.24) .. .. 90·00 90·00
129 3s. purple (R.) (6.23) .. .. .. 9·00 22·00
130 5s. yellow-green (R.) (9.17) .. .. 13·00 15·00
131 10s. maroon (B.) (3.18) .. .. .. 40·00 40·00
132 £1 rose-carmine (B.) (3.18) .. .. 60·00 70·00

We no longer list the £2 value as it is doubtful if this was used for postal purposes.

See also Nos. 165/6e.

1916–19. *King George V stamps of New Zealand optd as T* **15**, *but 14 mm long.* (a) *T* **61**. *Typo.* P 14×15.
134 ½d. yellow-green (R.) 20 25
135 1½d. slate (R.) (1917) 25 25
136 1½d. orange-brown (R.) (1919) 15 40
137 2d. yellow (R.) (14.2.18) 40 15
138 3d. chocolate (B.) (1919) .. .. .. 75 10·00
(b) *T* **60**. *Recess.* P 14 × 14½, *etc.*
139 2½d. blue (R.) 65 60
a. Perf 14 × 13½ 35 35
b. Vert pair. Nos. 139/9a .. .. 11·00 16·00
140 3d. chocolate (B.) (1917) 35 90
a. Perf 14 × 13½ .. .. .. 45 1·60
b. Vert pair. Nos. 140/40a .. .. 11·00 17·00
141 6d. carmine (B.) (5.5.17) .. .. 1·25 90
a. Perf 14 × 13½ .. .. .. 1·50 3·25
b. Vert pair. Nos. 141/1a .. .. 12·00 18·00
142 1s. vermilion (B.) .. .. .. 3·50 9·00
a. Perf 14 × 13½ .. .. .. 1·25 1·25
b. Vert pair. Nos. 142/2a .. .. 16·00 30·00
134/42a .. .. *Set of* 9 4·50 13·00

LEAGUE OF NATIONS MANDATE

Administered by New Zealand.

1920 (July). *Victory. Nos. 453/8 of New Zealand optd as T* **15**, *but 14 mm long.*
143 ½d. green (R.) .. .. 1·25 1·75
144 1d. carmine (B.) .. .. 1·25 85
145 1½d. brown-orange (R.) .. .. .. 1·25 3·50
146 3d. chocolate (B.) .. .. 3·00 6·50
147 6d. violet (R.) .. .. 4·00 6·50
148 1s. orange-red (B.) .. .. .. 11·00 11·00
143/8 .. .. *Set of* 6 20·00 27·00

16 Native Hut

SILVER JUBILEE
OF
KING GEORGE V
1910 - 1935.
(17)

(Eng B.W. Recess-printed at Wellington, N.Z.)

1921 (23 Dec). W **43** *of New Zealand.* (a) P 14 × 14½.
149 16 ½d. green .. .. 40 2·75
150 1d. lake 35 20
151 1½d. chestnut .. .. 40 4·00
152 2d. yellow .. .. 40 1·90
149/52 .. .. *Set of* 4 1·40 8·00
(b) P 14 × 13½
153 16 ½d. green .. .. 65 1·75
154 1d. lake 70 20
155 1½d. chestnut .. .. 6·00 7·50
156 2d. yellow .. .. 5·50 35
157 16 2½d. grey-blue .. .. 70 3·00
158 3d. sepia .. .. 75 3·00
159 4d. violet .. .. 80 3·00
160 5d. light blue .. .. 75 5·00
161 6d. bright carmine .. .. .. 80 3·50
162 8d. red-brown .. .. 1·25 9·00
163 9d. olive-green .. .. 1·25 9·00
164 1s. vermilion .. .. 1·25 11·00
153/64 .. .. *Set of* 12 18·00 50·00

1925–28. *Postal Fiscal stamps as Type* F **4** *of New Zealand optd with T* **15**. W **43** *of New Zealand (sideways).* P 14½×14.
(a) *Thick, opaque, white chalk-surfaced "Cowan" paper*
165 2s. blue (R.) (12.25) .. .. .. 90·00 95·00
166 2s. 6d. deep grey-brown (B.) (10.28) .. 60·00 80·00
166*a* 3s. mauve (R.) (9.25) .. .. .. 45·00 50·00
166*b* 5s. yellow-green (R.) (11.26) .. .. 12·00 20·00
ba. Opt at top of stamp £1100
166*c* 10s. brown-red (B.) (12.25) .. .. 45·00 48·00
166*d* £1 rose-pink (B.) (11.26) .. .. 50·00 75·00
165/6*d* .. .. *Set of* 6 £250 £300
(b) *Thin, hard, chalk-surfaced "Wiggins Teape" paper*
166*e* £1 rose-pink (B.) (1928) .. .. — £600

1926–27. *T* **72** *of New Zealand, optd with T* **15**, *in red.*
(a) *"Jones" paper*
167 2s. deep blue (11.26) .. .. .. 4·50 12·00
168 3s. mauve (10.26) .. .. .. 7·00 22·00
(b) *"Cowan" paper*
169 2s. light blue (10.11.27) .. .. 5·00 26·00
170 3s. pale mauve (10.11.27) .. .. 42·00 65·00

1932 (Aug). *Postal Fiscal stamps as Type* F **6** *of New Zealand optd with T* **15**. W **43** *of New Zealand. Thick, opaque, white chalk-surfaced "Cowan" paper.* P 14.
171 2s. 6d. deep brown (B.) .. .. 13·00 25·00
172 5s. green (R.) .. .. 20·00 35·00
173 10s. carmine-lake (B.) .. .. .. 45·00 65·00
174 £1 pink (B.) .. .. 60·00 80·00
175 £2 bright purple (R.) £650
176 £5 indigo-blue (R.) £1700

The £2 and £5 values were primarily for fiscal use.

1935 (7 May). *Silver Jubilee. Optd with T* **17**. P 14 × 13½.
177 16 1d. lake 30 30
a. Perf 14 × 14½ .. .. .. 75·00 £100
178 2½d. grey-blue 60 65
179 6d. bright carmine .. .. .. 1·75 2·50
177/9 .. .. *Set of* 3 2·40 3·00

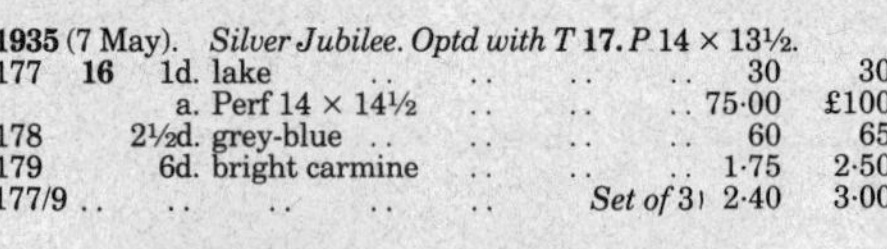

18 Samoan Girl
19 Apia

21 Chief and Wife
25 Lake Lanuto'o

(Recess D.L.R.)

1935 (7 Aug). *T* **18/19**, **21**, **25** *and similar designs.* W **43** *of New Zealand ("N Z" and Star).*
(a) P 14 × 13½, (b) P 13½ × 14 *or* (c) P 14
180 ½d. green (*a*) 10 35
181 1d. black and carmine (*b*) 10 10
182 2d. black and orange (*c*) .. .. .. 1·25 75
a. Perf 13½ × 14 .. .. .. 2·75 3·00
183 2½d. black and blue (*a*) 10 10
184 4d. slate and sepia (*b*) 40 15
185 6d. bright magenta (*b*) 30 10
186 1s. violet and brown (*b*) 25 10
187 2s. green and purple-brown (*a*) 50 50
188 3s. blue and brown-orange (*a*) .. .. 1·50 3·50
180/8 .. .. *Set of* 9 4·00 5·00

Designs: *Horiz*—2d. River scene; 4d. Canoe and house; 6d. R. L. Stevenson's home "Vailima"; 1s. Stevenson's Tomb. *Vert (as T* **25**)—3s. Falefa Falls.

See also Nos. 200/3.

WESTERN
SAMOA.
(27)

1935–42. *Postal Fiscal stamps as Type* F **6** *of New Zealand optd with T* **27**. W **43** *of New Zealand.* P 14.
(a) *Thick, opaque chalk-surfaced "Cowan" paper* (7.8.35)
189 2s. 6d. deep brown (B.) .. .. .. 6·00 13·00
190 5s. green (B.) .. .. 10·00 15·00
191 10s. carmine-lake (B.) .. .. .. 32·00 45·00
192 £1 pink (B.) .. .. 60·00 85·00
193 £2 bright purple (R.) £170 £225
194 £5 indigo-blue (R.) £450 £475
(b) *Thin, hard chalk-surfaced "Wiggins, Teape" paper* (1941–42)
194*a* 5s. green (B.) (6.42) .. .. .. 65·00 60·00
194*b* 10s. pale carmine-lake (B.) (6.41) .. 90·00 90·00
194*c* £2 bright purple (R.) (2.42) £400 £450
194*d* £5 indigo-blue (R.) (2.42) £600 £650

The £2 and £5 values were primarily for fiscal use.

See Nos. 207/14.

28 Coastal Scene

31 Robert Louis Stevenson

(Des J. Berry (1d. and 1½d.). L. C. Mitchell (2½d. and 7d.). Recess B.W.)

1939 (29 Aug). *25th Anniv of New Zealand Control. T* **28, 31** *and similar horiz designs. W* **98** *of New Zealand. P* 13½ × 14 *or* 14 × 13½ *(7d.).*

No.	Description		
195	1d. olive-green and scarlet	30	10
196	1½d. light blue and red-brown	35	30
197	2½d. red-brown and blue	90	65
198	7d. violet and slate-green	2·50	1·25
195/8	*Set of* 4	3·75	2·00

Designs:—1½d. Western Samoa; 2½d. Samoan dancing party.

32 Samoan Chief

33 Apia Post Office

(Recess B.W.)

1940 (2 Sept). *W* **98** *of New Zealand (Mult "N Z" and Star). P* 14 × 13½.

No.	Type	Description		
199	**32**	3d. on 1½d. brown	10	10

T **32** was not issued without surcharge.

(T **33**. Des L. C. Mitchell. Recess B.W.)

1944–49. *As Nos.* 180, 182/3 *and T* **33**. *W* **98** *of New Zealand (Mult "N Z" and Star) (sideways on* 2½d.*). P* 14 *or* 13½ × 14 *(5d.).*

No.	Description		
200	½d. green	25	3·75
202	2d. black and orange	1·25	4·00
203	2½d. black and blue (1948)	2·75	10·00
205	5d. sepia and blue (8.6.49)	20	50
200/5	*Set of* 4	4·00	16·00

1945–48. *Postal Fiscal stamps as Type* F **6** *of New Zealand optd with T* **27**. *W* **98** *of New Zealand. Thin hard, chalk-surfaced "Wiggins Teape" paper. P* 14.

No.	Description		
207	2s. 6d. deep brown (B.) (6.45)	2·00	5·50
208	5s. green (B.) (5.45)	5·00	7·50
209	10s. carmine-lake (B.) (4.46)	16·00	17·00
210	£1 pink (B.) (6.48)	80·00	£140
211	30s. brown (8.48)	£140	£200
212	£2 bright purple (R.) (11.47)	£140	£200
213	£3 green (8.48)	£170	£275
214	£5 indigo-blue (R.) (1946)	£250	£325
207/10	*Set of* 4	85·00	£140

The £2 to £5 values were mainly used for "fiscal purposes".

See also Nos. 232/5.

WESTERN
SAMOA
(**34**)

1946 (1 June). *Peace Issue. Nos.* 668, 670 *and* 674/5 *of New Zealand optd with T* **34** *(reading up and down at sides on 2d.).*

No.	Description		
215	1d. green	10	10
216	2d. purple (B.)	10	10
217	6d. chocolate and vermilion	10	10
218	8d. black and carmine (B.)	10	10
215/18	*Set of* 4	35	20

UNITED NATIONS TRUST TERRITORY

Administered by New Zealand.

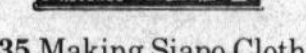

35 Making Siapo Cloth

42 Thatching a Native Hut

43 Preparing Copra

44 Samoan Chieftainess

(Recess B.W.)

1952 (10 Mar). *T* **35, 42/4** *and similar designs. W* **98** *of New Zealand (sideways on 1s. and 3s.). P* 13 *(½d., 2d., 5d. and 1s.) or* 13½ *(others).*

No.	Description		
219	½d. claret and orange-brown	10	20
220	1d. olive-green and green	10	10
221	2d. carmine-red	10	10
222	3d. pale ultramarine and indigo	30	10
223	5d. brown and deep green	2·50	70
224	6d. pale ultramarine and rose-magenta	30	10
225	8d. carmine	25	30
226	1s. sepia and blue	15	10
227	2s. yellow-brown	1·40	60
228	3s. chocolate and brown-olive	3·00	1·75
219/28	*Set of* 10	7·00	3·50

Designs: *Horiz (as T* **43***)*—1d. Native houses and flags; 3d. Malifa Falls (wrongly inscribed "Aleisa Falls"); 6d. Bonito fishing canoe; 8d. Cacao harvesting. *Vert (as T* **35***)*—2d. Seal of Samoa; 5d. Tooth-billed Pigeon.

1953 (25 May). *Coronation. Designs as Nos.* 715 *and* 717 *of New Zealand, but inscr* "WESTERN SAMOA".

No.	Description		
229	2d. brown	75	15
230	6d. slate-grey	1·00	35

WESTERN

SAMOA

(**45**)

1955 (14 Nov). *Postal Fiscal stamps as Type* F **6** *of New Zealand optd with T* **45**. *W* **98**. *Chalk-surfaced "Wiggins, Teape" paper. P* 14.

No.	Description		
232	5s. green (B.)	13·00	15·00
233	10s. carmine-lake (B.)	16·00	22·00
234	£1 pink (B.)	27·00	35·00
235	£2 bright purple (R.)	70·00	£130
232/5	*Set of* 4	£110	£170

The £2 value was mainly used for fiscal purposes.

46 Native Houses and Flags

47 Seal of Samoa

(Recess B.W.)

1958 (21 Mar). *Inauguration of Samoan Parliament. T* **46/7** *and similar horiz design. W* **98** *of New Zealand (sideways). P* 13½ × 13 *(6d.) or* 13½ *(others).*

No.	Description		
236	4d. cerise	10	10
237	6d. deep reddish violet	10	10
238	1s. deep ultramarine	10	10
236/8	*Set of* 3	20	15

Design:—1s. Map of Samoa, and the Mace.

INDEPENDENT

Samoa became independent on 1 January 1962.

49 Samoan Fine Mat

50 Samoa College

(Litho B.W.)

1962 (2 July). *Independence. T* **49/50** *and similar designs. W* **98** *of New Zealand (sideways on horiz stamps). P* 13½.

No.	Description		
239	1d. brown and rose-carmine	10	10
240	2d. brown, green, yellow and red	10	10
241	3d. brown, blue-green and blue	10	10
242	4d. magenta, yellow, blue and black	15	10
243	6d. yellow and blue	20	10
244	8d. bluish green, yellow-green and blue	20	10
245	1s. brown and bluish green	20	10
246	1s. 3d. yellow-green and blue	75	35
247	2s. 6d. red and ultramarine	1·50	1·25
248	5s. ultramarine, yellow, red and drab	3·25	2·50
239/48	*Set of* 10	5·75	4·25

Designs: *Horiz*—3d. Public library; 4d. Fono House; 6d. Map of Samoa; 8d. Airport; 1s. 3d. "Vailima"; 2s. 6d. Samoan flag; 5s. Samoan seal. *Vert*—1s. Samoan orator.

See Nos. 257/62.

59 Seal and Joint Heads of State

60 Signing the Treaty

(Des L. C. Mitchell. Photo Harrison)

1963 (1 Oct). *First Anniv of Independence. W* **98** *of New Zealand. P* 14.

No.	Type	Description		
249	**59**	1d. deep sepia and green	10	10
250		4d. deep sepia and blue	10	10
251		8d. deep sepia and rose-pink	10	10
252		2s. deep sepia and orange	20	10
249/52		*Set of* 4	35	15

(Des L. C. Mitchell. Photo Enschedé)

1964 (1 Sept). *2nd Anniv of New Zealand–Samoa Treaty of Friendship. P* 13½.

No.	Type	Description		
253	**60**	1d. multicoloured	10	10
254		8d. multicoloured	10	10
255		2s. multicoloured	15	10
256		3s. multicoloured	20	20
253/6		*Set of* 4	35	35

61 Kava Bowl

1965 (4 Oct)–**66?** *As Nos.* 239, 241/5, *but W* **61** *(sideways on horiz designs).*

No.	Description		
257	1d. brown and rose-carmine	20	20
258	3d. brown, blue-green and blue (1966?)	27·00	3·75
259	4d. magenta, yellow, blue and black	25	20
260	6d. yellow and blue	35	10
261	8d. bluish green, yellow-green and blue	20	10
262	1s. brown and bluish green	25	20
257/62	*Set of* 6	27·00	4·00

62 Red-tailed Tropic Bird

63 Flying Fish

(Des L. C. Mitchell. Photo Harrison)

1965 (29 Dec). *Air. W* **61** *(sideways). P* 14½.

No.	Type	Description		
263	**62**	8d. black, red-orange and blue	40	10
264	**63**	2s. black and blue	55	10

64 Aerial View of Deep Sea Wharf

(Des Tecon Co (U.S.A.). Photo Enschedé)

1966 (2 Mar). *Opening of First Deep Sea Wharf, Apia. T* **64** *and similar horiz design. Multicoloured. W* **61** *(sideways). P* 13½.

No.	Description		
265	1d. Type **64**	10	10
266	8d. Aerial view of wharf and bay	15	10
267	2s. As 8d.	25	15
268	3s. Type **64**	30	15
265/8	*Set of* 4	70	35

66 W.H.O. Building

(Des M. Goaman. Photo D.L.R.)

1966 (4 July). *Inauguration of W.H.O. Headquarters, Geneva. T* **66** *and similar horiz design. W* **61** *(sideways). P* 14.

No.	Description		
269	3d. yellow-ochre, blue and light slate-lilac	30	10
270	4d. blue, yellow, green & light orange-brown	35	10
271	6d. reddish lilac, emerald and yellow-olive	40	15
272	1s. blue, yellow, green and turquoise-green	60	20
269/72	*Set of* 4	1·50	50

Designs:—3d., 6d. Type **66**; 4d., 1s. W.H.O. Building on flag.

HURRICANE RELIEF
6d
(**68**)

1966 (1 Sept). *Hurricane Relief Fund. No.* 261 *surch with T* **68** *by Bradbury, Wilkinson.*

No.	Description		
273	8d. + 6d. bluish green, yellow-green and blue	10	10

69 Hon. Tuatagaloa L. S. (Minister of Justice)

(Des and photo Harrison)

1967 (16 Jan). *Fifth Anniv of Independence. T* **69** *and similar horiz designs. W* **61** *(sideways). P* 14½ × 14.

274	3d. sepia and bluish violet	10	10
275	8d. sepia and light new blue	10	10
276	2s. sepia and olive	10	10
277	3s. sepia and magenta	15	15
274/7	*Set of* 4	25	30

Designs:—8d. Hon. F. C. F. Nelson (minister of Works, Marine and Civil Aviation); 2s. Hon. To'omata T. L. (minister of Lands); Hon. Fa'alava'au G. (minister of Post Office, Radio and Broadcasting).

73 Samoan Fales (houses), 1890

(Des V. Whiteley. Photo Harrison)

1967 (16 May). *Centenary of Mulinu'u as Seat of Government. T* **73** *and similar horiz design. Multicoloured. W* **61**. *P* 14½ × 14.

278	8d. Type **73**	10	10
279	1s. Fono (Parliament) House, 1967	10	10

(New Currency. 100 sene or cents=1 tala or dollar)

75 Carunculated Honeyeater

76 Black-breasted Honeyeater

(Des V. Whiteley. Litho Format ($2, $4). Photo Harrison (others))

1967 (10 July)–**69**. *Decimal currency. Multicoloured designs as T* **75** *(1 s. to $1) or* **76** *($2, $4). W* **61** *(sideways). P* 13½ ($2, $4) *or* 14 × 14½ *(others).*

280	1 s. Type **75**	10	10
281	2 s. Pacific Pigeon	10	10
282	3 s. Samoan Starling	10	10
283	5 s. White-vented Flycatcher	15	10
284	7 s. Red-headed Parrot Finch	15	10
285	10 s. Purple Swamphen	20	10
286	20 s. Barn Owl	1·75	40
287	25 s. Tooth-billed Pigeon	1·50	15
288	50 s. Island Thrush	1·50	25
289	$1 Samoan Fantail	1·75	1·50
289*a*	$2 Type **76** (14.7.69)	5·50	7·00
289*b*	$4 Savaii White Eye (6.10.69)	38·00	40·00
280/9*b*	*Set of* 12	45·00	45·00

85 Nurse and Child

(Des G. Vasarhelyi. Photo D.L.R.)

1967 (27 Nov). *South Pacific Health Service. T* **85** *and similar horiz designs. Multicoloured. P* 14.

290	3 s. Type **85**	10	10
291	7 s. Leprosarium	10	10
292	20 s. Mobile X-ray Unit	20	10
293	25 s. Apia Hospital	25	15
290/3	*Set of* 4	50	30

89 Thomas Trood

93 Cocoa

(Des M. Farrar-Bell. Litho B.W.)

1968 (15 Jan). *6th Anniv of Independence. T* **89** *and similar horiz designs. Multicoloured. P* 13½.

294	2 s. Type **89**	10	10
295	7 s. Dr. Wilhelm Solf	10	10
296	20 s. J. C. Williams	10	10
297	25 s. Fritz Marquardt	15	10
294/7	*Set of* 4	25	20

(Des Jennifer Toombs. Photo Enschedé)

1968 (15 Feb). *Agricultural Development. T* **93** *and similar vert designs. W* **61**. *P* 13 × 12½.

298	3 s. deep red-brown, yellow-green and black	10	10
299	5 s. myrtle-green, greenish yellow & lt brn	10	10
300	10 s. scarlet, blackish brown and olive-yellow	10	10
301	20 s. yellow-bistre, yellow and blackish olive	15	10
298/301	*Set of* 4	25	15

Designs:—5 s. Breadfruit; 10 s. Copra; 20 s. Bananas.

97 Women weaving Mats

(Des G. Vasarhelyi. Photo Harrison)

1968 (22 Apr). *21st Anniv of the South Pacific Commission. T* **97** *and similar horiz designs. Multicoloured. W* **61**. *P* 14½ × 14.

302	7 s. Type **97**	10	10
303	20 s. Palm trees and bay	15	10
304	25 s. Sheltered cove	15	15
302/4	*Set of* 3	30	25

1928-1968
KINGSFORD-SMITH
TRANSPACIFIC FLIGHT
20
SENE

(100)

1968 (13 June). *40th Anniv of Kingsford Smith's Trans-Pacific Flight. No.* 285 *surch with T* **100**.

305	20 s. on 10 s. Purple Swamphen	10	10

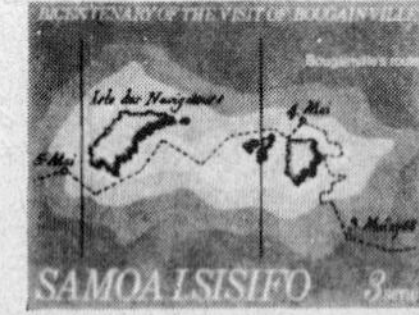

101 Bougainville's Route

(Des Jennifer Toombs. Litho B.W.)

1968 (17 June). *Bicentenary of Bougainville's Visit to Samoa. T* **101** *and similar horiz designs. W* **61** *(sideways). P* 14.

306	3 s. new blue and black	10	10
307	7 s. light ochre and black	15	10
308	20 s. multicoloured	45	15
309	25 s. multicoloured	60	25
306/9	*Set of* 4	1·10	45

Designs:—7 s. Louis de Bougainville; 20 s. Bougainvillea flower; 25 s. Ships *La Boudeuse* and *L'Etoile.*

105 Globe and Human Rights Emblem

106 Dr. Martin Luther King

(Des G. Vasarhelyi. Photo Harrison)

1968 (26 Aug). *Human Rights Year. W* **61**. *P* 14.

310	**105**	7 s. greenish blue, brown and gold	10	10
311		20 s. orange, green and gold	10	10
312		25 s. violet, green and gold	10	10
310/12		*Set of* 3	20	15

(Des and litho D.L.R.)

1968 (23 Sept). *Martin Luther King Commemoration. W* **61**. *P* 14½ × 14.

313	**106**	7 s. black and olive-green	10	10
314		20 s. black and bright purple	10	10

107 Polynesian Version of Madonna and Child

108 Frangipani—*Plumeria acuminata*

(Des and litho D.L.R.)

1968 (14 Oct). *Christmas. W* **61**. *P* 14.

315	**107**	1 s. multicoloured	10	10
316		3 s. multicoloured	10	10
317		20 s. multicoloured	10	10
318		30 s. multicoloured	10	10
315/18		*Set of* 4	20	15

(Des J.W. Litho Format)

1969 (20 Jan). *Seventh Anniv of Independence. T* **108** *and similar multicoloured designs. P* 14½.

319	2 s. Type **108**	10	10
320	7 s. Hibiscus *(vert)*	25	10
321	20 s. Red-Ginger *(vert)*	65	10
322	30 s. "Moso'oi"	80	25
319/22	*Set of* 4	1·60	40

109 R. L. Stevenson and *Treasure Island*

110 Weightlifting

(Des Jennifer Toombs. Litho D.L.R.)

1969 (21 Apr). *75th Death Anniv of Robert Louis Stevenson. Horiz designs, each showing portrait as in T* **109**. *Multicoloured. W* **61** *(sideways). P* 14.

323	3 s. Type **109**	15	10
324	7 s. *Kidnapped*	20	10
325	20 s. *Dr. Jekyll and Mr. Hyde*	45	10
326	22 s. *Weir of Hermiston*	55	15
323/6	*Set of* 4	1·25	30

(Des J. Mason. Photo Note Ptg Branch, Reserve Bank of Australia)

1969 (21 July). *Third South Pacific Games, Port Moresby. T* **110** *and similar vert designs. P* 13½.

327	3 s. black and sage-green	10	10
328	20 s. black and light blue	10	10
329	22 s. black and dull orange	10	10
327/9	*Set of* 3	15	15

Designs:—20 s. Yachting; 22 s. Boxing.

113 U.S. Astronaut on the Moon and the Splashdown near Samoan Islands

(Des J. Mason. Photo Note Ptg Branch, Reserve Bank of Australia)

1969 (24 July). *First Man on the Moon. P* 13½.

330	**113**	7 s. multicoloured	15	10
331		20 s. multicoloured	15	10

OMNIBUS ISSUES

Details, together with prices for complete sets, of the various Omnibus issues from the 1935 Silver Jubilee series to date are included in a special section following Zululand at the end of the catalogue.

114 "Virgin with Child" (Murillo)

(Des and photo Heraclio Fournier)

1969 (6 Oct). *Christmas. T* **114** *and similar vert designs. Multi-coloured. P* 14.

332 1 s. Type **114** 10 10
333 3 s. "The Holy Family" (El Greco) 10 10
334 20 s. "The Nativity" (El Greco) 15 10
335 30 s. "The Adoration of the Magi" (detail, Velazquez) 15 15
332/5 .. .. *Set of* 4 30 20
MS336 116 × 126 mm. Nos. 332/5 .. .. 60 1·25

115 Seventh Day Adventists' Sanatorium, Apia

(Des V. Whiteley. Litho Format)

1970 (19 Jan). *Eighth Anniv of Independence. T* **115** *and similar designs. W* **61** (*sideways on* 2, 7 *and* 22 *s.*). *P* 14.

337 2 s. yellow-brown, pale slate and black .. 10 10
338 7 s. violet, buff and black 10 10
339 20 s. rose, lilac and black 15 10
340 22 s. olive-green, cinnamon and black .. 15 15
337/40 .. .. *Set of* 4 30 20

Designs: *Horiz*—7 s. Rev. Father Violette and Roman Catholic Cathedral, Apia; 22 s. John Williams, 1797–1839, and London Missionary Society Church, Sapali'i. *Vert*—20 s. Mormon Church of Latter Day Saints, Tuasivi-on-Safotulafai.

119 Wreck of S.M.S. *Adler*

(Des J.W. Litho Questa)

1970 (27 Apr). *Great Apia Hurricane of* 1889. *T* **119** *and similar horiz designs. Multicoloured. W* **61** (*sideways*). *P* 13½.

341 5 s. Type **119** 45 10
342 7 s. U.S.S. *Nipsic* 50 10
343 10 s. H.M.S. *Calliope* 65 25
344 20 s. Apia after the hurricane .. .. .. 2·00 1·25
341/4 .. .. *Set of* 4 3·25 1·50

120 Sir Gordon Taylor's *Frigate Bird III*

(Des R. Honisett. Photo. Note Ptg Branch, Reserve Bank of Australia)

1970 (27 July). *Air. Aircraft. T* **120** *and similar horiz designs. Multicoloured. P* 13½ × 13.

345 3 s. Type **120** 30 10
346 7 s. Polynesian Airlines "DC-3" 60 10
347 20 s. Pan-American "Samoan Clipper" .. 1·50 60
348 30 s. Air Samoa Britten-Norman "Islander" 1·75 1·25
a. Pale purple omitted £250
345/8 .. .. *Set of* 4 3·75 1·75

121 Kendal's Chronometer and Cook's Sextant   122 "Peace for the World" (F. B. Eccles)

(Des J. Berry, adapted J. Cooter. Litho Questa)

1970 (14 Sept). *Cook's Exploration of the Pacific. T* **121** *and similar designs. W* **61** (*sideways on* 30 *s.*). *P* 14.

349 1 s. carmine, silver and black 20 15
350 2 s. multicoloured 35 25
351 20 s. black, bright blue and gold .. .. 1·75 1·00
352 30 s. multicoloured .. .. 2·75 1·75
349/52 .. .. *Set of* 4 4·50 2·75

Designs: *Vert*—2 s. Cook's statue, Whitby; 20 s. Cook's head. *Horiz* (83 × 25 *mm*)—30 s. Cook, H.M.S. *Endeavour* and island.

(Des from paintings. Photo Heraclio Fournier)

1970 (26 Oct). *Christmas. T* **122** *and similar vert designs. Multi-coloured. P* 13.

353 2 s. Type **122** 10 10
354 3 s. "The Holy Family" (W. E. Jahnke) .. 10 10
355 20 s. "Mother and Child" (F. B. Eccles) .. 15 10
356 30 s. "Prince of Peace" (Meleane Fe'ao) .. 20 15
353/6 .. .. *Set of* 4 35 25
MS357 111 × 158 mm. Nos. 353/6 .. .. .. 60 1·25

123 Pope Paul VI   124 Native and Tree

(Des J. Cooter. Litho Format)

1970 (29 Nov). *Visit of Pope Paul to Samoa. W* **61**. *P* 14 × 14½.

358 **123** 8 s. black and grey-blue 15 10
359 20 s. black and plum 35 10

(Des G. Drummond from sketches by the American Timber Co. Litho Questa)

1971 (1 Feb). *Timber Industry. T* **124** *and similar multicoloured designs. P* 13½.

360 3 s. Type **124** 10 10
361 8 s. Bulldozer in clearing (*horiz*) 10 10
362 20 s. Log in sawmill (*horiz*) 25 10
363 22 s. Floating logs and harbour 25 15
360/3 .. .. *Set of* 4 55 25

125 Fautasi (canoe) in Apia Harbour and first stamps of Samoa and U.S.A.

(*Half-sized illustration. Actual size* 84 × 26 *mm*)

(Des E. Roberts. Photo Courvoisier)

1971 (12 Mar). *"Interpex" Stamp Exhibition, New York. Sheet* 138 × 80 *mm. P* 11½.

MS364 **125** 70 s. multicoloured .. .. 85 1·40

126 Siva Dance   127 "Queen Salamasina"

(Des and litho J.W.)

1971 (9 Aug). *Tourism. T* **126** *and similar horiz designs. Multi-coloured. W* **61** (*sideways*). *P* 14.

365 5 s. Type **126** 40 10
366 7 s. Samoan cricket .. .. 1·00 60
367 8 s. Hideaway Hotel .. .. 1·00 35
368 10 s. Aggie Grey and her hotel .. .. 1·00 60
365/8 .. .. *Set of* 4 3·00 1·40

(Des Jennifer Toombs. Litho J.W.)

1971 (20 Sept). *Myths and Legends of Old Samoa* (1*st series*). *T* **127** *and similar vert designs from carvings by S. Ortquist. Multicoloured. W* **61** (*sideways*). *P* 14 × 13½.

369 3 s. Type **127** 10 10
370 8 s. "Lu and his Sacred Hens" 15 10
371 10 s. "God Tagaloa fishes Samoa from the sea" 20 10
372 22 s. "Mount Vaea and the Pool of Tears" .. 35 20
369/72 .. .. *Set of* 4 70 30

See also Nos. 426/9.

128 "The Virgin and Child" (Bellini)   129 Map and Scales of Justice

(Des J. Cooter. Litho J.W.)

1971 (4 Oct). *Christmas. T* **128** *and similar design. W* **61**. *P* 14 × 13½.

373 **128** 2 s. multicoloured 10 10
374 3 s. multicoloured 10 10
375 – 20 s. multicoloured 20 10
376 – 30 s. multicoloured 30 20
373/6 .. .. *Set of* 4 55 35

Design: *Vert*—20 s., 30 s. "The Virgin and Child with St. Anne and John the Baptist" (Leonardo da Vinci).

(Des E. Roberts. Photo Courvoisier)

1972 (10 Jan). *First South Pacific Judicial Conference. P* 11½ × 11.

377 **129** 10 s. multicoloured 15 15

Issued on matt, almost invisible gum.

130 Asau Wharf, Savaii   131 Flags of Member Countries

(Des V. Whiteley. Litho A. & M.)

1972 (10 Jan). *Tenth Anniv of Independence. T* **130** *and similar horiz designs. Multicoloured. W* **61** (*sideways*). *P* 13.

378 1 s. Type **130** 10 10
379 8 s. Parliament Building 10 10
380 10 s. Mothers' Centre 10 10
381 22 s. "Vailima" Residence and rulers 20 25
378/81 .. .. *Set of* 4 40 30

(Des V. Whiteley. Litho Questa)

1972 (17 Mar). *25th Anniv of South Pacific Commission. T* **131** *and similar multicoloured designs. W* **61** (*sideways on* 8 *s. and* 10 *s.*). *P* 14 × 13½ (3 *and* 7 *s.*) *or* 13½ × 14 (*others*).

382 3 s. Type **131** 10 10
383 7 s. Flag and Afoafouvale Misimoa (Gen Sec) 10 10
384 8 s. H.Q. building, Nouméa (*horiz*) 10 10
385 10 s. Flags and area map (*horiz*) 10 10
382/5 .. .. *Set of* 4 30 30

132 Expedition Ships   133 Bull Conch

(Des J. Berry; adapted J. Cooter. Litho Questa)

1972 (14 June). *250th Anniv of sighting of Western Samoa by Jacob Roggeveen. T* **132** *and similar horiz designs. Multicoloured. W* **61** *(sideways, except 2 s.). P* 14½.

386 2 s. Type **132** 15 10
387 8 s. Ships in storm 45 10
388 10 s. Ships passing island 50 10
389 30 s. Route of Voyage (85 × 25 *mm*) .. .. .. 1·75 1·50
386/9 .. .. *Set of* 4 2·50 1·60

(Des Format ($5) or J.W. (others). Litho Format ($5), Questa (others))

1972 (18 Oct)–**76**. *T* **133** *and similar multicoloured designs. W* **61** *(sideways, on 1 s. to 50 s.). White, ordinary paper. P* 13½ *($1 to $5) or* 14½ *(others).*

390 1 s. Type **133** 20 10
a. Cream, chalk-surfaced paper (30.11.76) 1·00 1·00
391 2 s. Rhinoceros Beetle 20 10
a. Cream, chalk-surfaced paper (30.11.76) 1·00 1·00
392 3 s. Skipjack (fish) 30 10
393 4 s. Painted Crab 30 10
a. Cream, chalk-surfaced paper (30.11.76) 1·00 1·00
394 5 s. Butterfly Fish 35 10
a. Cream, chalk-surfaced paper (30.11.76) 1·00 1·00
395 7 s. Samoan Monarch (butterfly) 85 10
396 10 s. Triton Shell 60 15
397 20 s. Jewel Beetle .. .. 1·25 30
398 50 s. Spiny Lobster .. .. 2·00 75
399 $1 Hawkmoth (29 × 45 *mm*) .. .. .. 4·50 1·75
399*a* $2 Green Turtle (29 × 45 *mm*) (18.6.73) .. 6·00 4·00
399*b* $4 Black Marlin (29 × 45 *mm*) (27.3.74) .. 5·00 7·00
399*c* $5 Green Tree Lizard (29 × 45 *mm*) (30.6.75) 5·50 7·50
390/9*c* .. .. *Set of* 13 24·00 20·00

134 "The Ascension"

135 Erecting a Tent

(Des PAD Studio. Litho Harrison)

1972 (1 Nov). *Christmas. Stained-glass Windows in Apia. T* **134** *and similar vert designs. Multicoloured. W* **61**. *P* 14 × 14½.

400 1 s. Type **134** 10 10
401 4 s. "The Blessed Virgin and Infant Christ" 10 10
402 10 s. "St. Andrew blessing Samoan canoe" .. 10 10
403 30 s. "The Good Shepherd" 40 30
400/3 .. .. *Set of* 4 50 40
MS404 70 × 159 mm. Nos. 400/3 .. .. .. 90 1·25

(Des G. Drummond. Litho Format)

1973 (29 Jan). *Boy Scout Movement. T* **135** *and similar horiz designs. Multicoloured. W* **61** *(sideways). P* 14.

405 2 s. Saluting the flag 10 10
406 3 s. First-aid 10 10
407 8 s. Type **135** 25 10
408 20 s. Samoan action-song 90 85
405/8 .. .. *Set of* 4 1·10 95

136 Hawker Siddeley "748"

(Des E. Roberts. Photo Courvoisier)

1973 (9 Mar). *Air. T* **136** *and similar horiz designs showing aircraft at Faleolo Airport. Multicoloured. P* 11½.

409 8 s. Type **136** 45 15
410 10 s. H.S. "748" in flight 55 15
411 12 s. H.S. "748" on runway 65 35
412 22 s. B.A.C. 1-11 .. .. 1·00 60
409/12 .. .. *Set of* 4 2·40 1·10

Issued on matt, almost invisible gum.

137 Apia General Hospital

138 Mother and Child, and Map

(Des C. Abbott. Litho Questa)

1973 (20 Aug). *25th Anniv of W.H.O. T* **137** *and similar vert designs. Multicoloured. W* **61**. *P* 14.

413 2 s. Type **137** 10 10
414 8 s. Baby clinic 20 10
415 20 s. Filariasis research 45 20
416 22 s. Family welfare 45 30
413/16 .. .. *Set of* 4 1·10 55

(Des W. E. Jahnke (3 s.), Fiasili Keil (4 s.), E. Cooter (others); adapted Jennifer Toombs. Litho J.W.)

1973 (15 Oct). *Christmas. T* **138** *and similar vert designs. Multicoloured. W* **61**. *P* 14.

417 3 s. Type **138** 10 10
418 4 s. Mother and child, and village 10 10
419 10 s. Mother and child, and beach 10 10
420 30 s. Samoan stable 45 50
417/20 .. .. *Set of* 4 55 55
MS421 144 × 103 mm. Nos. 417/20 .. .. 60 75

139 Boxing

(Des G. Drummond. Litho Questa)

1974 (24 Jan). *Commonwealth Games, Christchurch. T* **139** *and similar horiz designs. Multicoloured. W* **61** *(sideways). P* 14.

422 8 s. Type **139** 10 10
423 10 s. Weightlifting 10 10
424 20 s. Bowls 20 10
425 30 s. Athletics stadium 35 45
422/5 .. .. *Set of* 4 70 60

(Des Jennifer Toombs. Litho Questa)

1974 (13 Aug). *Myths and Legends of Old Samoa (2nd series). Vert designs as T* **127** *from carvings by S. Ortquist. Multicoloured. W* **61**. *P* 14 × 13½.

426 2 s. Tigilau and sacred dove 10 10
427 8 s. Pili, his sons and fishing net 10 10
428 20 s. Sina and the origin of the coconut .. 30 10
429 30 s. The warrior, Nafanua 45 45
426/9 .. .. *Set of* 4 80 55

140 Mail-van at Faleolo Airport

(Des E. Roberts. Photo Heraclio Fournier)

1974 (4 Sept). *Centenary of Universal Postal Union. T* **140** *and similar horiz designs. Multicoloured. P* 13 × 12½ *(50 s.) or* 13 *(others).*

430 8 s. Type **140** 15 10
431 20 s. Cargo liner at Apia Wharf 35 15
432 22 s. Early Post Office, Apia and letter .. 40 25
433 50 s. William Willis and *Age Unlimited* (sailing-raft) (87 × 29 *mm*) .. .. .. 80 1·00
430/3 .. .. *Set of* 4 1·50 1·40
MS434 140 × 82 mm. No. 433 .. .. .. 1·25 2·25

141 "Holy Family" (Sebastiano)

(Des PAD Studio. Litho Enschedé)

1974 (18 Nov). *Christmas. T* **141** *and similar horiz designs. Multicoloured. W* **61** *(sideways). P* 13 × 13½.

435 3 s. Type **141** 10 10
436 4 s. "Virgin and Child with Saints" (Lotto) .. 10 10
437 10 s. "Madonna and Child with St. John" (Titian) 10 10
438 30 s. "Adoration of the Shepherds" (Rubens) .. 35 45
435/8 .. .. *Set of* 4 45 50
MS439 128 × 87 mm. Nos. 435/8 .. .. .. 70 1·40

142 Winged Passion Flower

(Des J.W. Litho Questa)

1975 (15 Jan). *Tropical Flowers. T* **142** *and similar multicoloured designs. W* **61** *(sideways on 8 and 30 s.). P* 14.

440 8 s. Type **142** 20 10
441 20 s. Gardenia (*vert*) 50 45
442 22 s. *Barringtonia samoensis* (*vert*) 55 50
443 30 s. Malay apple 85 85
440/3 .. .. *Set of* 4 1·90 1·75

143 *Joyita* loading at Apia

144 "Pate" Drum

(Des E. Roberts. Photo Heraclio Fournier)

1975 (14 Mar). *"Interpex 1975" Stamp Exhibition, New York, and "Joyita Mystery". T* **143** *and similar horiz designs. Multicoloured. P* 13½.

444 1 s. Type **143** 10 10
445 8 s. *Joyita* sails for Tokelau Islands 15 10
446 20 s. Taking to rafts 35 25
447 22 s. *Joyita* abandoned 40 30
448 50 s. Discovery of *Joyita* north of Fiji .. .. 1·00 1·25
444/8 .. .. *Set of* 5 1·75 1·75
MS449 150 × 100 mm. Nos. 444/8. Imperf .. 2·50 3·50

(Des Iosua To'afa; adapted L. Curtis. Litho Harrison)

1975 (30 Sept). *Musical Instruments. T* **144** *and similar vert designs. Multicoloured. W* **61** *(sideways). P* 14.

450 8 s. Type **144** 10 10
451 20 s. "Lali" drum 20 10
452 22 s. "Logo" drum 20 10
453 30 s. "Pu" shell horn 35 30
450/3 .. .. *Set of* 4 75 50

145 "Mother and Child" (Meleane Fe'ao)

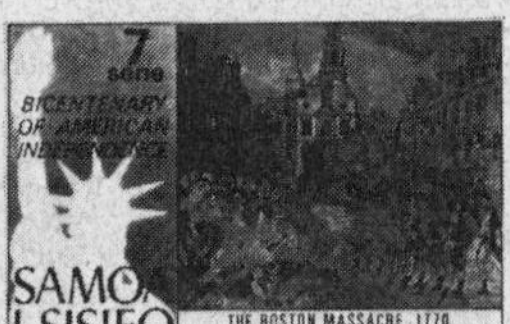

146 "The Boston Massacre, 1770" (Paul Revere)

(Des local artists; adapted G. Vasarhelyi. Litho Walsall)

1975 (25 Nov). *Christmas. T* **145** *and similar vert designs. Multicoloured. W* **61** *(inverted). P* 14.

454 3 s. Type **145** 10 10
455 4 s. "The Saviour" (Polataia Tuigamala) .. 10 10
456 10 s. "A Star is Born" (Iosua To'afa) 10 10
457 30 s. "Madonna and Child" (Ernesto Coter) .. 30 45
454/7 .. .. *Set of* 4 45 50
MS458 101 × 134 mm. Nos. 454/7 .. .. .. 60 1·25

(Des J. Cooter. Litho Walsall)

1976 (20 Jan). *Bicentenary of American Revolution. T* **146** *and similar horiz designs. Multicoloured. W* **61** *(sideways). P* 13½.

459 7 s. Type **146** 20 15
460 8 s. "The Declaration of Independence" (Trumbull) 20 15
461 20 s. "The Ship that Sank in Victory, 1779" (Ferris) 60 35
462 22 s. "Pitt addressing the Commons, 1782" (R. A. Hickel) 60 35
463 50 s. "The Battle of Princetown" (Mercer) .. 1·50 1·75
459/63 .. .. *Set of* 5 2·75 2·50
MS464 160 × 125 mm. Nos. 459/63 .. .. .. 5·00 6·00

147 Mullet Fishing

(Des V. Whiteley Studio. Litho Harrison)

1976 (27 Apr). *Fishing. T* **147** *and similar horiz designs. Multicoloured. W* **61**. *P* 14.

465 10 s. Type **147** 10 10
466 12 s. Fish traps 15 10
467 22 s. Samoan fishermen 30 10
468 50 s. Net fishing 85 70
465/8 .. .. *Set of* 4 1·25 90

ALTERED CATALOGUE NUMBERS

Any Catalogue numbers altered from the last edition are shown as a list in the introductory pages.

148 Paul Revere's Ride

(Des J. Berry. Photo Heraclio Fournier)

1976 (29 May). *"Interphil" Stamp Exhibition. Sheet* 120 × 80 *mm. P* 13.
MS469 **148** $1 gold, black and emerald .. .. 2·50 2·50

149 Boxing **150** Mary and Joseph going to Bethlehem

(Des C. Abbott. Litho Questa)

1976 (21 June). *Olympic Games, Montreal. T* **149** *and similar horiz designs. Multicoloured. W* **61** *(sideways). P* 14.
470 10 s. Type **149** 10 10
471 12 s. Wrestling 10 10
472 22 s. Javelin 15 10
473 50 s. Weightlifting 45 50
470/3 .. .. *Set of* 4 70 60

(Des C. Abbott. Litho Questa)

1976 (18 Oct). *Christmas. T* **150** *and similar vert designs. Multicoloured. W* **61**. *P* 13½.
474 3 s. Type **150** 10 10
475 5 s. The Shepherds 10 10
476 22 s. The Holy Family 15 10
477 50 s. The Magi 55 65
474/7 .. .. *Set of* 4 70 75
MS478 124 × 115 mm. Nos. 474/7 .. .. .. 80 1·75

151 Queen Elizabeth and View of Apia

(Des BG Studio. Litho Questa)

1977 (11 Feb). *Silver Jubilee and Royal Visit. T* **151** *and similar horiz designs. Multicoloured. W* **61** *(sideways). P* 13½.
479 12 s. Type **151** 20 10
480 26 s. Presentation of Spurs of Chivalry .. 35 20
481 32 s. Queen and Royal Yacht *Britannia* .. 50 25
482 50 s. Queen leaving Abbey 55 60
479/82 .. .. *Set of* 4 1·40 1·00

152 Map of Flight Route

(Des C. Abbott. Litho Walsall)

1977 (20 May). *50th Anniv of Lindbergh's Transatlantic Flight. Horiz designs showing the "Spirit of St. Louis". Multicoloured. W* **61** *(sideways). P* 14.
483 22 s. Type **152** 25 10
484 24 s. In flight 35 15
485 26 s. Landing 35 15
486 50 s. Col. Lindbergh 80 75
483/6 .. .. *Set of* 4 1·60 1·00
MS487 194 × 93 mm. Nos. 483/6 .. .. .. 2·40 2·75

153 3d. Express Stamp and First Mail Notice **154** "Samoan Nativity" (P. Feata)

(Des J. Cooter. Litho Questa)

1977 (29 Aug). *Stamp Centenary. T* **153** *and similar horiz designs. W* **61** *(sideways). P* 13½.
488 12 s. lemon, red and sepia 20 10
489 13 s. multicoloured 20 15
490 26 s. multicoloured 45 30
491 50 s. multicoloured .. .. 80 1·00
488/91 .. .. *Set of* 4 1·50 1·40

Designs:—13 s. Early cover and 6d. Express; 26 s. Apia Post Office and 1d. Express; 50 s. Schooner *Energy*, 1877, and 6d. Express.

(Designs adapted by J.W. Litho Questa)

1977 (11 Oct). *Christmas. T* **154** *and similar vert designs. Multicoloured. W* **61**. *P* 14.
492 4 s. Type **154** 10 10
493 6 s. "The Offering" (E. Saofaiga) 10 10
494 26 s. "Madonna and Child" (F. Tupou) 20 10
495 50 s. "Emmanuel" (M. Sapa'u) 35 40
492/5 .. .. *Set of* 4 55 50
MS496 117 × 159 mm. Nos. 492/5 .. .. .. 55 85

155 Apia Automatic Telephone Exchange

(Des J.W. Litho Questa)

1977 (28 Oct*). *Telecommunications Project. T* **155** *and similar horiz designs. Multicoloured. W* **61** *(sideways). P* 14.
497 12 s. Type **155** 15 10
498 13 s. Mulinuu Radio Terminal 15 10
499 26 s. Old and new telephones 30 20
500 50 s. "Global communication" 50 70
497/500 .. .. *Set of* 4 1·00 1·00

*The above were originally scheduled for release on 11 July and were put on sale by the Crown Agents in England on that date.

156 Polynesian Airlines Boeing "737"

(Des E. Roberts. Litho Heraclio Fournier)

1978 (21 Mar). *Aviation Progress. T* **156** *and similar horiz designs. Multicoloured. P* 14.
501 12 s. Type **156** 20 10
502 24 s. Wright brothers' *Flyer* 40 20
503 26 s. Kingsford Smith's *Southern Cross* .. 40 20
504 50 s. "Concorde" .. .. 1·10 85
501/4 .. .. *Set of* 4 1·90 1·25
MS505 150 × 120 mm. Nos. 501/4 .. .. .. 2·25 2·75

157 Hatchery, Aleipata **158** Pacific Pigeon

(Des J.W. Litho Questa)

1978 (14 Apr). *Hawksbill Turtle Conservation Project. T* **157** *and similar horiz design. Multicoloured. W* **61** *(sideways). P* 14½ × 14.
506 24 s. Type **157** 35 30
507 $1 Turtle .. .. 1·60 1·60

(Des Jennifer Toombs. Litho Questa)

1978 (21 Apr). *25th Anniv of Coronation. T* **158** *and similar vert designs. P* 15.
508 26 s. black, brown and deep magenta 25 30
a. Sheetlet. Nos. 508/10 × 2 .. .. 1·50
509 26 s. multicoloured 25 30
510 26 s. black, brown and deep magenta 25 30
508/10 .. .. *Set of* 3 70 80

Designs:—No. 508, King's Lion; No. 509, Queen Elizabeth II; No. 510, Type **158**.

Nos. 508/10 were printed together in small sheets of 6, containing two *se-tenant* strips of 3, with horizontal gutter margin between.

159 Flags of Western Samoa and Canada with Canadian National Tower **160** Captain Cook

(Des BG Studio. Litho Walsall)

1978 (9 June). *"Capex '78" International Stamp Exhibition, Toronto. Sheet* 119 × 79 *mm. W* **61**. *P* 14½.
MS511 **159** $1 blue, red and black .. .. .. 1·25 1·75

(Des J. Berry. Litho Harrison)

1978 (28 Aug). *250th Birth Anniv of Captain Cook. T* **160** *and similar vert designs. Multicoloured. W* **61**. *P* 14½ × 14.
512 12 s. Type **160** 30 15
513 24 s. Cook's cottage, Gt Ayton, Yorkshire .. 60 35
514 26 s. Old drawbridge over the river Esk, Whitby 70 35
515 50 s. H.M.S. *Resolution* .. .. 1·25 1·50
512/15 .. .. *Set of* 4 2·50 2·10

161 Thick-edged Cowry **162** "Madonna on the Crescent"

(Photo Courvoisier)

1978 (15 Sept)–**80**. *Shells. Horiz designs as T* **161**. *Multicoloured. P* 12½.
516 1 s. Type **161** 10 10
517 2 s. Isabella cowry 10 10
518 3 s. Money cowry 15 10
519 4 s. Eroded cowry 20 10
520 6 s. Honey cowry 20 10
521 7 s. Banded cowry 25 10
522 10 s. Globe cowry 30 10
523 11 s. Mole cowry 30 10
524 12 s. Children's cowry 30 10
525 13 s. Flag cone (20.11.78) 30 10
526 14 s. Soldier cone (20.11.78) 30 10
527 24 s. Cloth-of-gold cone (20.11.78) 30 10
528 26 s. Lettered cone (20.11.78) 35 10
529 50 s. Tiled cone (20.11.78) 50 15
530 $1 Black Marble cone (20.11.78) 95 60
530*a* $2 Marlin-spike auger (18.7.79) .. .. 1·50 90
530*b* $3 Scorpion Spider Conch (18.7.79) .. .. 2·25 1·50
530*c* $5 Common Harp (26.8.80) .. .. .. 3·75 3·00
516/30*c* .. .. *Set of* 18 11·00 6·00

Nos. 530*a/c* are larger, size 36 × 26 mm.
Issued on matt, almost invisible gum.

(Des C. Abbott. Litho Questa)

1978 (6 Nov). *Christmas. Woodcuts by Dürer. T* **162** *and similar vert designs. W* **61**. *P* 14.
531 4 s. black and yellow-brown 10 10
532 6 s. black and turquoise-blue 10 10
533 26 s. black and bright blue 15 10
534 50 s. black and bright violet 35 50
531/4 .. .. *Set of* 4 50 55
MS535 103 × 154 mm. Nos. 531/4 .. .. .. 70 1·00

Designs:—6 s. "Nativity"; 26 s. "Adoration of the Magi"; 50 s. "Annunciation".

163 Boy with Coconuts **164** *Charles W. Morgan*

(Des G. Drummond. Litho Questa)

1979 (10 Apr). *International Year of the Child. T* **163** *and similar horiz designs. Multicoloured. W* **61** *(sideways). P* 14.
536 12 s. Type **163** 15 10
537 24 s. White Sunday 30 15
538 26 s. Children at pump 35 15
539 50 s. Young girl with ukulele 70 80
536/9 .. .. *Set of* 4 1·40 1·10

(Des J. Cooter. Litho Format)

1979 (29 May). *Sailing Ships (1st series). Whaling Ships. T* **164** *and similar horiz designs. Multicoloured. W* **61** *(sideways). P* 13½.
540 12 s. Type **164** 25 10
541 14 s. *Lagoda* 30 10
542 24 s. *James T. Arnold* 45 20
543 50 s. *Splendid* 85 85
540/3 .. .. *Set of* 4 1·75 1·10

See also Nos. 561/4 and 584/7.

165 Launch of "Apollo 11"

166 Sir Rowland Hill (statue) and Penny Black

(Des J.W. Litho Questa)

1979 (20 June). *10th Anniv of Moon Landing. T* **165** *and similar designs in chocolate and dull vermilion* (12 s.) *or multicoloured* (*others*). *W* **61** (*sideways on* 14, 26 *s. and* $1). *P* 14½ × 14 (12, 24, 50 *s.*) *or* 14 × 14½ (*others*).

544	12 s. Type **165**	20	10
545	14 s. Lunar module and astronaut on Moon (*horiz*)	25	10
546	24 s. View of Earth from Moon	30	15
547	26 s. Astronaut on Moon (*horiz*)	30	15
548	50 s. Lunar and Command modules in Space	55	55
549	$1 Command module after splash-down (*horiz*)	1·25	1·50
544/9	*Set of* 6	2·50	2·25
MS550	90 × 130 mm. No. 549	1·00	1·60

No. **MS**550 is inscribed "Spashdown" in error.

(Des and litho J.W.)

1979 (27 Aug). *Death Centenary of Sir Rowland Hill. T* **166** *and similar vert designs. Multicoloured. W* **61**. *P* 14.

551	12 s. Type **166**	15	10
552	24 s. Two-penny Blue with "Maltese Cross" postmark	20	15
553	26 s. Sir Rowland Hill and Penny Black	20	15
554	$1 Two-penny Blue and Sir Rowland Hill (statue)	60	75
551/4	*Set of* 4	1·00	1·00
MS555	128 × 95 mm. Nos. 551/4	1·00	1·60

167 Anglican Church, Apia

(Des A. Peake. Photo Courvoisier)

1979 (22 Oct). *Christmas. Churches. T* **167** *and similar horiz designs. P* 11½.

556	4 s. black and pale blue	10	10
557	6 s. black and bright yellow-green	10	10
558	26 s. black and yellow-ochre	15	10
559	50 s. black and reddish lilac	30	30
556/9	*Set of* 4	45	35
MS560	150 × 124 mm. Nos. 556/9	50	75

Designs:—6 s. Congregational Christian, Leulumoega; 26 s. Methodist, Piula; 50 s. Protestant, Apia.

Issued on matt, almost invisible gum.

(Des J. Cooter. Litho Format)

1980 (22 Jan). *Sailing Ships (2nd series). Whaling Ships. Horiz designs as T* **164**. *Multicoloured. W* **61** (*sideways*) *P* 13½.

561	12 s. *William Hamilton*	25	10
562	14 s. *California*	30	15
563	24 s. *Liverpool II*	45	25
564	50 s. *Two Brothers*	95	70
561/4	*Set of* 4	1·75	1·10

168 "Equipment for a Hospital"

(Des M. Goaman (12, 50 s.), E. Roberts (others). Photo Heraclio Fournier)

1980 (26 Mar). *Anniversaries. T* **168** *and similar horiz designs. Multicoloured. P* 13½ × 14.

565	12 s. Type **168**	20	10
566	13 s. John Williams, dove with olive twig and commemorative inscription	20	15
567	14 s. Dr. Wilhelm Solf (instigator), flag and commemorative inscription	25	15
568	24 s. Cairn Monument	35	25
569	26 s. Williams Memorial, Savai'i	35	25
570	50 s. Paul P. Harris (founder)	60	60
565/70	*Set of* 6	1·75	1·40

Commemorations:—12, 50 s. 75th anniversary of Rotary International; 13, 26 s. 150th anniversary of John Williams' (missionary) arrival in Samoa; 14, 24 s. 80th anniversary of raising of German flag.

NEW INFORMATION

The editor is always interested to correspond with people who have new information that will improve or correct the Catalogue.

169 Samoan Village Scene

(Des J.W. Litho Walsall)

1980 (6 May). *"London 1980" International Stamp Exhibition. Sheet* 140 × 81 *mm. W* **61** (*sideways*). *P* 14.

MS571	**169** $1 multicoloured	80	1·25

170 Queen Elizabeth the Queen Mother

(Des Harrison. Litho Questa)

1980 (4 Aug). *80th Birthday of Queen Elizabeth the Queen Mother. P* 14.

572	**170** 50 s. multicoloured	50	35

171 1964 2nd Anniversary of New Zealand–Samoa Treaty of Friendship 2 s. Commemorative and "Zeapex '80" Emblem

(Des E. Roberts. Photo Heraclio Fournier)

1980 (23 Aug). *"Zeapex '80" International Stamp Exhibition, Auckland. Sheet* 130 × 80 *mm. P* 14.

MS573	**171** $1 multicoloured	1·25	1·40

172 Afiamalu Satellite Earth Station

(Des and photo Courvoisier)

1980 (1 Sept). *Afiamalu Satellite Earth Station. T* **172** *and similar horiz designs. Multicoloured. P* 11½.

574	12 s. Type **172**	15	10
575	14 s. Satellite station (*different*)	20	10
576	24 s. Satellite station and map of Savai'i and Upolu	30	15
577	50 s. Satellite and globe	60	60
574/7	*Set of* 4	1·10	85

173 Afiamalu Satellite Earth Station 24 s. Commemorative Stamp and "Sydpex 80" Emblem

(Des E. Roberts. Litho Sprintpak, Mayne Nickless Ltd, Australia)

1980 (29 Sept). *"Sydpex 80" International Stamp Exhibition, Sydney. Sheet* 130 × 80 *mm. Imperf.*

MS578	**173** $2 multicoloured	1·75	2·00

174 "The Saviour" (J. Poynton)

175 President Franklin D. Roosevelt and Hyde Park (family home)

(Des G. Vasarhelyi. Litho Format)

1980 (28 Oct). *Christmas. Paintings. T* **174** *and similar vert designs. Multicoloured. W* **61**. *P* 13½.

579	8 s. Type **174**	10	10
580	14 s. "Madonna and Child" (Lealofi F. Siaopo)	10	10
581	27 s. "Nativity" (Pasila Feata)	15	10
582	50 s. "Yuletide" (R. P. Aiono)	25	40
579/82	*Set of* 4	55	55
MS583	90 × 105 mm. Nos. 579/82	70	1·00

(Des J. Cooter. Litho Format)

1981 (26 Jan). *Sailing Ships (3rd series). Horiz designs as T* **164**. *Multicoloured. P* 13½.

584	12 s. *Ocean* (whaling ship)	20	10
585	18 s. *Horatio* (whaling ship)	30	15
586	27 s. H.M.S. *Calliope*	45	25
587	32 s. H.M.S. *Calypso*	50	50
584/7	*Set of* 4	1·25	90

(Des J.W. Litho Format)

1981 (29 Apr). *International Year for Disabled Persons. President Franklin D. Roosevelt Commemoration. T* **175** *and similar horiz designs. Multicoloured. P* 14.

588	12 s. Type **175**	15	10
589	18 s. Roosevelt's inauguration, 4 March 1933	25	15
590	27 s. Franklin and Eleanor Roosevelt	35	20
591	32 s. Roosevelt's Lend-lease Bill (Atlantic convoy, 1941)	40	30
592	38 s. Roosevelt the philatelist	45	35
593	$1 Campobello House (summer home)	1·00	1·00
588/93	*Set of* 6	2·40	1·90

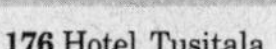

176 Hotel Tusitala

177 Wedding Bouquet from Samoa

(Des and litho Walsall)

1981 (29 June). *Tourism. T* **176** *and similar horiz designs. Multicoloured. W* **61** (*sideways*). *P* 14½ × 14.

594	12 s. Type **176**	15	10
595	18 s. Apia Harbour	25	15
596	27 s. Aggie Grey's Hotel	25	20
597	32 s. Preparation for Ceremonial Kava	30	30
598	54 s. Piula water pool	55	55
594/8	*Set of* 5	1·40	1·10

(Des J.W. Litho Walsall)

1981 (22 July). *Royal Wedding. T* **177** *and similar vert designs. Multicoloured. W* **61**. *P* 14.

599	18 s. Type **177**	25	10
600	32 s. Prince Charles as Colonel-in-Chief, Gordon Highlanders	35	20
601	$1 Prince Charles and Lady Diana Spencer	70	90
599/601	*Set of* 3	1·10	1·10

178 Tattooing Instruments

179 Black Marlin

(Des E. Roberts. Litho Cambec Press, Melbourne)

1981 (29 Sept). *Tattooing. T* **178** *and similar horiz designs. Multicoloured. P* 13½.

602	12 s. Type **178**	20	20
	a. Horiz strip of 4. Nos. 602/5	1·25	
603	18 s. First stage of tattooing	25	25
604	27 s. Progressive stage	30	30
605	$1 Completed tattoo	70	70
602/5	*Set of* 4	1·25	1·25

Nos. 602/5 were printed together, *se-tenant*, in horizontal strips of 4 throughout the sheet.

(Des E. Roberts. Litho Cambec Press, Melbourne)

1981 (9 Oct). *"Philatokyo '81" International Stamp Exhibition, Tokyo. Sheet* 130 × 80 *mm. P* 14 × 13½.

MS606	**179** $2 multicoloured	1·25	1·50

180 *Thespesia populnea*

181 George Washington's Pistol

(Des and litho J.W.)

1981 (30 Nov). *Christmas. Flowers. T* **180** *and similar vert designs. Multicoloured. W* **61**. *P* 13½.

607	11 s. Type **180**	15	10
608	15 s. Copper Leaf	20	15
609	23 s. *Allamanda cathartica*	30	25
610	$1 Mango	1·00	1·00
607/10	*Set of* 4	1·50	1·40
MS611	86 × 120 mm. Nos. 607/10	1·60	2·00

(Des J.W. Litho Format)

1982 (26 Feb). *250th Birth Anniv of George Washington. T* **181** *and similar horiz designs, each in black, ochre and stone. P* 13½.
612 23 s. Type **181** 30 30
613 25 s. Mount Vernon (Washington's house) . . 30 30
614 34 s. George Washington 40 40
612/14 . . . . *Set of* 3 90 90
MS615 104 × 103 mm. $1 Washington taking Oath of Office as President . . . . 95 1·00

182 *Forum Samoa* (container ship)

(Des E. Roberts. Litho Cambec Press, Melbourne)

1982 (24 May). *20th Anniv of Independence. T* **182** *and similar horiz designs. Multicoloured. P* 13½ × 14.
616 18 s. Type **182** 30 20
617 23 s. "Air services" 40 30
618 25 s. N.P.F. (National Provident Fund) Building, Apia 40 30
619 $1 "Telecommunications" . . . . 1·10 1·00
616/19 . . . . *Set of* 4 2·00 1·60

183 Scouts map-reading and "75" **184** Boxing

(Des J.W. Litho Walsall)

1982 (20 July). *75th Anniv of Boy Scout Movement. T* **183** *and similar horiz designs. Multicoloured. W* **61** *(sideways). P* 14½.
620 5 s. Type **183** 10 10
621 38 s. Scout salute and "75" 40 40
622 44 s. Scout crossing river by rope, and "75" . . 50 50
623 $1 "Tower" of Scouts and "75" . . . . 1·00 1·00
620/23 . . . . *Set of* 4 1·75 1·75
MS624 93 × 81 mm. $1 As No. 623 but with portrait of Lord Baden-Powell replacing emblem (47 × 35 *mm*). P 11 . . . . 1·00 1·10

(Des Garden Studio. Litho Walsall)

1982 (20 Sept). *Commonwealth Games, Brisbane. T* **184** *and similar vert designs. Multicoloured. W* w **14**. *P* 14½.
625 23 s. Type **184** 25 20
626 25 s. Hurdling 25 20
627 34 s. Weightlifting 35 30
628 $1 Bowling . . . . 95 1·10
625/8 . . . . *Set of* 4 1·60 1·60

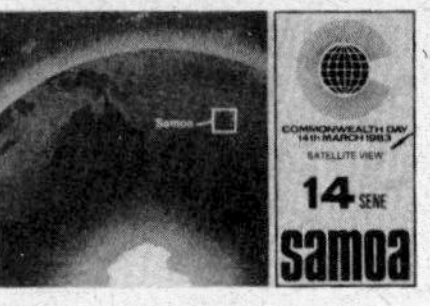

185 "Mary and Joseph" (Emma Dunlop) **186** Satellite View of Australasia

(Des J.W. Litho Questa)

1982 (15 Nov). *Christmas. Children's Pictures. T* **185** *and similar horiz designs. Multicoloured. W* **61** *(sideways). P* 14 × 14½.
629 11 s. Type **185** 15 10
630 15 s. "Mary, Joseph and baby Jesus" (Marie Tofaeono) 15 15
631 38 s. "Madonna and Child" (Ralph Laban and Fetalaiga Fareni) 40 30
632 $1 "Mother and Child" (Panapa Pouesi) . . 90 1·10
629/32 . . . . *Set of* 4 1·40 1·50
MS633 130 × 119 mm. Nos. 629/32 . . . . 1·60 2·00

(Des Walsall. Litho Enschedé)

1983 (23 Feb). *Commonwealth Day. T* **186** *and similar horiz designs. Multicoloured. W* w **14** *(sideways). P* 13 × 13½.
634 14 s. Type **186** 10 10
635 29 s. Flag of Samoa 15 20
636 43 s. Harvesting copra 25 25
637 $1 Head of State Malietoa Tanumafili II . . 50 80
634/7 . . . . *Set of* 4 90 1·25

187 Douglas "DC-1"

(Des J.W. Litho Questa)

1983 (7 June). *Bicentenary of Manned Flight and 50th Anniv of Douglas Commercial Aircraft. Sheet, 215 × 113 mm, containing horiz designs as T* **187**. *Multicoloured. W* w **14** *(sideways). P* 14.
MS638 32 s. × 10, each design showing a different Douglas aircraft from the "DC-1" to the "DC-10" . . 2·50 2·75

188 Pole-vaulting **189** Lime

(Des McCombie Skinner Studio. Litho Format)

1983 (31 Aug). *South Pacific Games. T* **188** *and similar vert designs. Multicoloured. W* w **14**. *P* 14 × 14½.
639 8 s. Type **188** 20 10
640 15 s. Netball 25 15
641 25 s. Tennis 40 30
642 32 s. Weight-lifting 45 40
643 35 s. Boxing 45 40
644 46 s. Football 60 50
645 48 s. Golf 70 65
646 56 s. Rugby 70 65
639/46 . . . . *Set of* 8 3·25 2·75

(Des E. Roberts. Litho Enschedé)

1983 (28 Sept)–**84**. *Fruit. T* **189** *and similar vert designs. Multicoloured. W* w **14** *(inverted on* 1 *s.). P* 13½ *($2 to $5) or* 14 × 13½ *(others).*
647 1 s. Type **189** 10 10
648 2 s. Star fruit 10 10
649 3 s. Mangosteen 10 10
650 4 s. Lychee 10 10
651 7 s. Passion fruit 10 10
652 8 s. Mango 10 10
653 11 s. Pawpaw 10 10
654 13 s. Pineapple 15 10
655 14 s. Breadfruit 15 10
656 15 s. Banana 20 10
657 21 s. Cashew Nut (30.11.83) 20 10
658 25 s. Guava (30.11.83) 50 15
659 32 s. Water Melon (30.11.83) 25 20
660 48 s. Sasalapa (30.11.83) 40 30
661 56 s. Avocado (30.11.83) 40 30
662 $1 Coconut (30.11.83) 70 50
663 $2 Vi Apple (11.4.84) . . . . 1·00 95
664 $4 Grapefruit (11.4.84) . . . . 2·00 1·90
665 $5 Orange (11.4.84) . . . . 2·50 2·40
647/65 . . . . *Set of* 19 8·00 6·75
Nos. 663/5 are larger, size 25 × 35½ mm.

190 On Parade **191** Togitogiga Falls, Upolu

(Des Brian Melton Studio. Litho Format)

1983 (10 Oct). *Centenary of Boys' Brigade. Sheet* 120 × 83 *mm. W* w **14**. *P* 14.
MS668 **190** $1 multicoloured . . . . 1·50 1·50

(Litho Format)

1984 (15 Feb). *Scenic Views. T* **191** *and similar horiz designs. Multicoloured. W* w **14** *(sideways). P* 14.
669 25 s. Type **191** 30 15
670 32 s. Lano Beach, Savai'i 50 35
671 48 s. Mulinu'u Point, Upolu 75 60
672 56 s. Nu'utele Island 80 65
669/72 . . . . *Set of* 4 2·10 1·50

19th U.P.U. CONGRESS HAMBURG 1984

192 Apia Harbour **(193)**

(Des Jennifer Toombs. Litho Questa)

1984 (24 May). *250th Anniv of "Lloyd's List" (newspaper). T* **192** *and similar vert designs. Multicoloured. W* w **14**. *P* 14 × 14½.
673 32 s. Type **192** 25 20
674 48 s. Apia hurricane, 1889 . . . . 40 45
675 60 s. *Forum Samoa* (container ship) 45 50
676 $1 *Matua* (cargo liner) 75 80
673/6 . . . . *Set of* 4 1·75 1·75

1984 (7 June). *Universal Postal Union Congress, Hamburg. No.* 662 *optd with T* **193**.
677 $1 Coconut 90 80

194 Olympic Stadium

(Des Garden Studio. Litho Format)

1984 (26 June). *Olympic Games, Los Angeles. T* **194** *and similar horiz designs. Multicoloured. W* w **14** *(sideways). P* 14½.
678 25 s. Type **194** 20 20
679 32 s. Weightlifting 25 25
680 48 s. Boxing 40 45
681 $1 Running 75 80
678/81 . . . . *Set of* 4 1·40 1·50
MS682 170 × 120 mm. Nos. 678/81 . . . . 1·40 1·60

195 Nomad "N24" Aircraft

(Des E. Roberts. Litho Walsall)

1984 (21 Sept). *"Ausipex" International Stamp Exhibition, Melbourne. Sheet* 131 × 80 mm. *W* w **14** *(sideways). P* 14.
MS683 **195** $2.50, multicoloured . . . . 2·50 2·75

196 "Faith"

(Litho Walsall)

1984 (7 Nov). *Christmas. "The Three Virtues" (Raphael). T* **196** *and similar horiz designs. Multicoloured. W* w **14** *(sideways). P* 14.
684 25 s. Type **196** 20 15
685 35 s. "Hope" 25 20
686 $1 "Charity" 75 90
684/6 . . . . *Set of* 3 1·10 1·10
MS687 63 × 76 mm. Nos. 684/6 . . . . 1·25 1·60

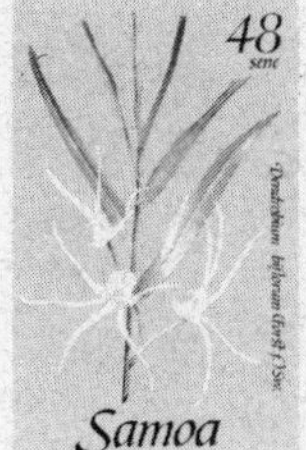

197 *Dendrobium biflorum* **198** Ford "Model A", 1903

(Des Jennifer Toombs. Litho Format)

1985 (23 Jan). *Orchids (1st series). T* **197** *and similar vert designs. Multicoloured. P* 14.
688 48 s. Type **197** 55 35
689 56 s. *Dendrobium vaupelianum Kraenzl* . . 65 45
690 67 s. *Glomera montana* 80 60
691 $1 *Spathoglottis plicata* . . . . 1·10 1·10
688/91 . . . . *Set of* 4 2·75 2·25
See also Nos. 818/21.

(Des A. Theobald. Litho Walsall)

1985 (26 Mar). *Veteran and Vintage Cars. T* **198** *and similar horiz designs. Multicoloured. P* 14.
692 48 s. Type **198** 60 35
693 56 s. Chevrolet "Tourer", 1912 . . . . 70 40
694 67 s. Morris "Oxford", 1913 . . . . 80 45
695 $1 Austin "Seven", 1923 . . . . 1·00 70
692/5 . . . . *Set of* 4 2·75 1·75

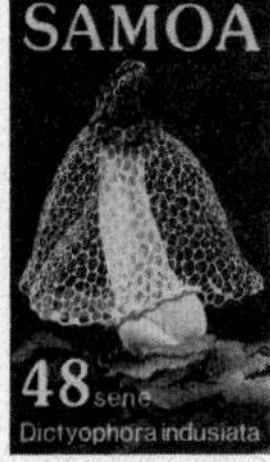

199 *Dictyophora indusiata* **200** The Queen Mother at Liverpool Street Station

(Des Doreen McGuinness. Litho Walsall)

1985 (17 Apr). *Fungi. T* **199** *and similar vert designs. Multicoloured. P* 14½.

696	48 s. Type **199**	35	35
697	56 s. *Ganoderma tornatum*	40	40
698	67 s. *Mycena chlorophos*	45	45
699	$1 *Mycobonia flava*	70	70
696/9	*Set of* 4	1·75	1·75

(Des A. Theobald ($2), C. Abbott (others). Litho Questa)

1985 (7 June). *Life and Times of Queen Elizabeth the Queen Mother. T* **200** *and similar vert designs. Multicoloured.* W w **16**. *P* 14½ × 14.

700	32 s. At Glamis Castle, aged 9	20	25
701	48 s. At Prince Henry's Christening with other members of the Royal family	30	35
702	56 s. Type **200**	35	40
703	$1 With Prince Henry at his christening (from photo by Lord Snowdon)	65	70
700/3	*Set of* 4	1·40	1·50
MS704	91 × 73 mm. $2 Arriving at Tattenham Corner Station with the Queen. Wmk sideways	1·25	1·50

201 Map of Pacific and Exhibition Logo

202 I.Y.Y. Emblem and Map (Alaska—Arabian Gulf)

(Des D. Hartley. Litho Enschedé)

1985 (26 Aug). *"Expo '85" World Fair, Japan. Sheet* 70 × 45 *mm. P* 14.

MS705	**201** $2 multicoloured	1·25	1·40

(Des Garden Studio. Litho B.D.T.)

1985 (18 Sept) *International Youth Year. T* **202** *and similar vert designs, showing background map and emblem* (*Nos.* 706 *and* 710) *or raised arms* (*others*). *Multicoloured. P* 14.

706	60 s. Type **202**	40	45
	a. Horiz strip of 5. Nos. 706/10	1·75	
707	60 s. Raised arms (Pakistan–Mexico)	40	45
708	60 s. Raised arms (Central America–China)	40	45
709	60 s. Raised arms (Japan–Greenland)	40	45
710	60 s. As Type **202** (Iceland–Siberia)	40	45
706/10	*Set of* 5	1·75	2·00

Nos. 706/10 were printed together, *se-tenant*, in horizontal strips of 5, throughout the sheet, the background forming a composite design of three continuous world maps.

203 "System"

204 *Hypolimnas bolina inconstans*

(Des L. Curtis. Litho Format)

1985 (5 Nov). *Christmas. T* **203** *and similar vert designs showing illustrations by Millicent Sowerby for R. L. Stevenson's "A Child's Garden of Verses". Multicoloured. P* 14 × 14½.

711	32 s. Type **203**	20	25
712	48 s. "Time to Rise"	30	35
713	56 s. "Auntie's Skirts"	35	40
714	$1 "Good Children"	65	70
711/14	*Set of* 4	1·40	1·50
MS715	87 × 109 mm. Nos. 711/14	1·50	2·00

(Des Annette Robinson. Litho Walsall)

1986 (13 Feb). *Butterflies. T* **204** *and similar vert designs. Multicoloured.* W w **16**. *P* 14½ × 14.

716	25 s. Type **204**	25	15
717	32 s. *Anapheis java sparrman*	30	20
718	48 s. *Deudorix epijarbas doris*	50	35
719	56 s. *Badamia exclamationis*	55	40
720	60 s. *Tirumala hamata mellitula*	55	40
721	$1 *Catochrysops taitensis*	80	65
716/21	*Set of* 6	2·75	1·90

205 Halley's Comet over Apia

206 U.S.S. *Vincennes*

(Des N. Shewring. Litho Walsall)

1986 (24 Mar). *Appearance of Halley's Comet. T* **205** *and similar horiz designs. Multicoloured.* W w **16** (*sideways*). *P* 14 × 14½.

722	32 s. Type **205**	15	20
723	48 s. Edmond Halley	30	35
724	60 s. Comet passing Earth	35	40
725	$2 Preparing *Giotto* spacecraft	1·10	1·25
722/5	*Set of* 4	1·75	2·00

(Des A. Theobald. Litho Questa)

1986 (21 Apr). *60th Birthday of Queen Elizabeth II. Vert designs as T* **110** *of Ascension. Multicoloured.* W w **16**. *P* 14½ × 14.

726	32 s. Engagement photograph, 1947	15	20
727	48 s. Queen with Liberty Bell, U.S.A., 1976	30	35
728	56 s. At Apia, 1977	35	40
729	67 s. At Badminton Horse Trials, 1978	40	45
730	$2 At Crown Agents Head Office, London, 1983	1·10	1·25
726/30	*Set of* 5	2·10	2·40

(Des E. Nisbet. Litho Questa)

1986 (22 May). *"Ameripex '86" International Stamp Exhibition, Chicago. T* **206** *and similar horiz designs. Multicoloured. P* 14 × 14½.

731	48 s. Type **206**	30	35
732	56 s. Sikorsky "S-42" flying boat	35	40
733	60 s. U.S.S. *Swan*	35	40
734	$2 "Apollo 10" descending	1·10	1·25
731/4	*Set of* 4	1·90	2·10

207 Vailima

(Des E. Roberts. Litho Cambec Press, Melbourne)

1986 (4 Aug). *"Stampex '86" Stamp Exhibition, Adelaide. Sheet* 158 × 97 *mm. P* 13½.

MS735	**207** $3 multicoloured	2·00	2·25

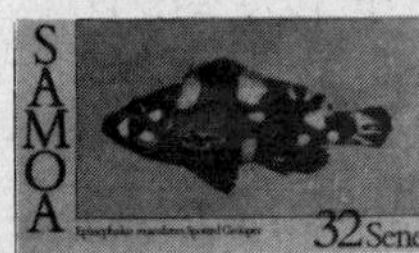

208 Spotted Grouper

(Des P. Rymers. Litho Walsall)

1986 (13 Aug). *Fishes. T* **208** *and similar horiz designs. Multicoloured. P* 14.

736	32 s. Type **208**	25	20
737	48 s. Sabel Squirrelfish	40	35
738	60 s. Lunartail Grouper	45	40
739	67 s. Longtail Snapper	50	45
740	$1 Berndt's Soldierfish	75	65
736/40	*Set of* 5	2·10	1·90

209 Samoan Prime Ministers, American Presidents and Parliament House

210 *Hibiscus rosa-sinensis* and Map of Samoa

(Des N. Shewring. Litho Format)

1986 (1 Dec). *Christmas. 25th Anniv of United States Peace Corps. T* **209** *and similar horiz design. Multicoloured. P* 14½.

741	45 s. Type **209**	25	30
742	60 s. French and American Presidents, Samoan Prime Minister and Statue of Liberty	35	40
MS743	131 × 72 mm. Nos. 741/2	1·25	1·50

No. **MS**743 also commemorates the Centenary of the Statue of Liberty.

(Des local artist, adapted G. Vasarhelyi. Litho Format)

1987 (16 Feb). *25th Anniv of Independence. T* **210** *and similar multicoloured designs. P* 14½ × 14 ($2) *or* 14 × 14½ (*others*).

744	15 s. Type **210**	15	10
745	45 s. Parliament Building, Apia	35	30
746	60 s. Boat race at Independence celebration	45	40
747	70 s. Peace dove and laurel wreath	50	50
748	$2 Head of State Malietoa Tanumafili II and national flag (*horiz*)	1·25	1·40
744/8	*Set of* 5	2·40	2·40

NEW INFORMATION

The editor is always interested to correspond with people who have new information that will improve or correct the Catalogue.

211 Gulper (*Eurypharynx*)

(Des J. Walker. Litho Format)

1987 (31 Mar). *Deep Ocean Fishes. T* **211** *and similar horiz designs. Multicoloured. P* 14.

749	45 s. Type **211**	45	30
750	60 s. Hatchet Fish	50	35
751	70 s. Angler Fish	60	45
752	$2 Gulper (*Saccopharynx*)	1·40	1·40
749/52	*Set of* 4	2·75	2·25

212 Workmen trimming Logs and building Fale (traditional house)

(Des Jennifer Toombs. Litho Questa)

1987 (13 June). *"Capex 87" International Stamp Exhibition, Toronto. Sheet* 122 × 66 *mm. P* 14½.

MS753	**212** $3 multicoloured	1·60	1·75

213 Lefaga Beach, Upolu

214 Abel Tasman

(Des D. Miller. Litho Questa)

1987 (29 July). *Coastal Scenery. T* **213** *and similar horiz designs. Multicoloured. P* 14.

754	45 s. Type **213**	25	30
755	60 s. Vaisala Beach, Savaii	30	35
756	70 s. Solosolo Beach, Upolu	40	45
757	$2 Neiafu Beach, Savaii	1·10	1·25
754/7	*Set of* 4	1·90	2·10

(Des M. Bradbery. Litho Questa)

1987 (30 Sept). *Bicentenary of Australian Settlement* (1988) (*1st issue*). *Explorers of the Pacific. T* **214** *and similar horiz designs. Multicoloured. P* 14 × 14½.

758	40 s. Type **214**	30	25
759	45 s. Capt. James Cook	45	30
760	80 s. Comte Louis-Antoine de Bougainville	50	50
761	$2 Comte Jean de la Perouse	1·10	1·25
758/61	*Set of* 4	2·10	2·10
MS762	90 × 73 mm. No. 761	1·10	1·25

See also Nos. 768/72.

(215)

216 Christmas Tree

1987 (16 Oct). *"Hafnia" International Stamp Exhibition, Copenhagen. No.* **MS**762 *optd with T* **215** *in red.*

MS763	90 × 73 mm. $2 Comte Jean de la Perouse	1·10	1·25

(Des Josephine Martin. Litho Questa)

1987 (30 Nov). *Christmas. T* **216** *and similar square designs. Multicoloured. P* 14.

764	40 s. Type **216**	20	25
765	45 s. Family going to church	25	30
766	50 s. Bamboo fire-gun	25	30
767	80 s. Inter-island transport	45	50
764/7	*Set of* 4	1·00	1·25

217 Samoa Coat of Arms and Australia Post Logo

218 Airport Terminal and Airliner taking off

(Des A. Theobald. Litho Questa)

1988 (27 Jan). *Bicentenary of Australian Settlement (2nd issue). Postal Services. T* **217** *and similar vert designs. Multicoloured. P* 14½×14.

768 45 s. Type **217** 40 40
a. Horiz strip of 5. Nos. 768/72 . . 1·75
769 45 s. Samoan mail van and aircraft . . 40 40
770 45 s. Loading mail plane . . 40 40
771 45 s. Australian mail van and aircraft . . 40 40
772 45 s. "Congratulations Australia" message on airmail letter . . 40 40
768/72 . . *Set of* 5 1·75 1·75

Nos. 768/72 were printed together, *se-tenant*, in horizontal strips of 5 throughout the sheet, Nos. 769/71 forming a composite design.

(Des E. Nisbet. Litho Walsall)

1988 (24 Mar). *Opening of Faleolo Airport. T* **218** *and similar horiz designs. Multicoloured. P* 13×13½.

773 40 s. Type **218** 35 25
774 45 s. Boeing "727" . . 40 30
775 60 s. DHC "Twin Otter" . . 45 35
776 70 s. Boeing "737" . . 55 50
777 80 s. Boeing "727" and control tower . . 70 60
778 $1 "DC9" over "fale" (house) . . 80 70
773/8 . . *Set of* 6 3·00 2·40

219 "Expo '88" Pacific Islands Village

220 Mormon Temple, Apia

(Des C. Abbott. Litho Walsall)

1988 (30 Apr). *"Expo '88" World Fair, Brisbane. T* **219** *and similar horiz designs. Multicoloured. P* 14 × 14½.

779 45 s. Type **219** . . 25 30
780 70 s. Expo Complex and monorail . . 35 40
781 $2 Map of Australia showing Brisbane . . 1·00 1·10
779/81 . . *Set of* 3 1·40 1·60

(Des Jennifer Toombs. Litho CPE Australia Ltd, Melbourne)

1988 (9 June). *Centenary of Arrival of the Latter-Day Saints in Samoa. Sheet* 86 × 77 *mm. P* 13½.

MS782 **220** $3 multicoloured . . 1·50 1·60

221 Athletics

222 Spotted Triller

(Des D. Miller. Litho Format)

1988 (10 Aug). *Olympic Games, Seoul. T* **221** *and similar vert designs. Multicoloured. P* 14.

783 15 s. Type **221** . . 10 10
784 60 s. Weightlifting . . 30 35
785 80 s. Boxing . . 40 45
786 $2 Olympic stadium . . 1·00 1·10
783/6 . . *Set of* 4 1·60 1·75
MS787 85 × 100 mm. Nos. 783/6 . . 1·75 2·00

(Des D. Johnston. Litho CPE Australia Ltd, Melbourne (Nos. 788/97), Questa (Nos. 798/803))

1988 (17 Aug)–**89**. *Birds. Multicoloured.*

(*a*) *Vert designs as T* **222**. *P* 13½

788 10 s. Type **222** . . 10 10
789 15 s. Samoan Wood Rail . . 10 10
790 20 s. Flat-billed Kingfisher . . 10 10
791 25 s. Samoan Fantail . . 10 15
792 35 s. Scarlet Robin . . 15 20
793 40 s. Black-breasted Honeyeater ("Mao") . . 20 25
794 50 s. Cardinal Honeyeater . . 25 30
795 65 s. Yellow-fronted Whistler . . 30 35
796 75 s. Many-coloured Fruit Dove . . 35 40
797 85 s. White-throated Pigeon . . 40 45

(*b*) *Horiz designs, each* 45 × 28 *mm. P* 13½ × 14.

798 75 s. Silver Gull (28.2.89) . . 35 40
799 85 s. Great Frigate Bird (28.2.89) . . 40 45
800 90 s. Eastern Reef Heron (28.2.89) . . 40 45
801 $3 Short-tailed Albatross (28.2.89) . . 1·40 1·50
802 $10 White Tern (31.7.89) . . 4·50 4·75
803 $20 Shy Albatross (31.7.89) . . 9·00 9·25
788/803 . . *Set of* 16 16·00 17·00

223 Forest

224 Congregational Church of Jesus, Apia

(Des G. Vasarhelyi. Litho Questa)

1988 (25 Oct). *National Conservation Campaign. T* **223** *and similar multicoloured designs. P* 14 × 13½ (15, 40, 45 *s.*) *or* 13½ × 14 (*others*).

807 15 s. Type **223** . . 10 10
808 40 s. Samoan handicrafts . . 20 25
809 45 s. Forest wildlife . . 25 30
810 50 s. Careful use of water (*horiz*) . . 25 30
811 60 s. Fishing (*horiz*) . . 30 35
812 $1 Coconut plantation (*horiz*) . . 55 60
807/12 . . *Set of* 6 1·50 1·75

(Des N. Shewring. Litho Format)

1988 (14 Nov). *Christmas. Samoan Churches. T* **224** *and similar vert designs. Multicoloured. P* 14.

813 15 s. Type **224** . . 10 10
814 40 s. Roman Catholic Church, Leauva'a . . 20 25
815 45 s. Congregational Christian Church, Moataa . . 25 30
816 $2 Baha'i Temple, Vailima . . 1·00 1·25
813/16 . . *Set of* 4 1·40 1·75
MS817 143 × 64 mm. Nos. 813/16 . . 1·50 1·90

225 *Phaius flavus*

226 *Eber* (German warship)

(Des H. Bevan. Litho Questa)

1989 (31 Jan). *Orchids (2nd series). T* **225** *and similar vert designs. Multicoloured. P* 14 × 13½.

818 15 s. Type **225** . . 15 10
819 45 s. *Calanthe triplicata* . . 35 30
820 60 s. *Luisia teretifolia* . . 40 35
821 $3 *Dendrobium mohlianum* . . 1·50 1·75
818/21 . . *Set of* 4 2·25 2·25

(Des E. Nisbet. Litho Walsall)

1989 (16 Mar). *Centenary of Great Apia Hurricane. T* **226** *and similar horiz designs. Multicoloured. P* 14.

822 50 s. Type **226** . . 25 30
a. Horiz strip of 4. Nos. 822/5 . . 1·90
823 65 s. *Olga* (German warship) . . 35 40
824 85 s. H.M.S. *Calliope* (screw corvette) . . 45 50
825 $2 U.S.S. *Vandalia* . . 1·00 1·10
822/5 . . *Set of* 4 1·90 2·10

Nos. 822/5 were printed together, *se-tenant*, in horizontal strips of 4 throughout the sheet.

See also No. **MS**839.

227 Samoan Red Cross Youth Group on Parade

228 Virgin Mary and Joseph

(Des L. Curtis. Litho Questa)

1989 (15 May). *125th Anniv of International Red Cross. T* **227** *and similar vert designs. Multicoloured. P* 14½×14.

826 50 s. Type **227** . . 25 30
827 65 s. Blood donors . . 35 40
828 75 s. Practising first aid . . 40 45
829 $3 Red Cross volunteers carrying patient 1·50 1·60
826/9 . . *Set of* 4 2·25 2·50

(Des A. Theobald ($3), D. Miller (others). Litho Questa)

1989 (20 July). *20th Anniv of First Manned Landing on Moon. Multicoloured designs as T* **126** *of Ascension. W* w **16** (*sideways on* 50, 65 *c.*). *P* 14×13½ (18 *s.*, $2) *or* 14 (*others*).

830 18 s. Saturn rocket on mobile launcher . . 10 10
831 50 s. Crew of "Apollo 14" (30×30 *mm*) . . 25 30
832 65 s. "Apollo 14" emblem (30×30 *mm*) . . 35 40
833 $2 Tracks of lunar transporter . . 1·00 1·10
830/3 . . *Set of* 4 1·50 1·75
MS834 100×83 mm. $3 Aldrin with U.S. flag on Moon. P 14×13½ . . 1·50 1·60

(Des T. Chance. Litho Cartor, France)

1989 (1 Nov). *Christmas. T* **228** *and similar horiz designs. Multicoloured. P* 13½.

835 18 s. Type **228** . . 10 10
836 50 s. Shepherds . . 25 30
837 55 s. Donkey and ox . . 30 35
838 $2 Three Wise Men . . 1·00 1·10
835/8 . . *Set of* 4 1·50 1·60

(Litho Walsall)

1989 (17 Nov). *"World Stamp Expo '89" International Stamp Exhibition, Washington. Sheet* 91×105 *mm containing designs as Nos.* 824/5. *Multicoloured. W* **61**. *Imperf.*

MS839 85 s. H.M.S. *Calliope*; $2 U.S.S. *Vandalia* 1·50 1·60

229 Pao Pao Outrigger

(Des R. Roberts. Litho Note Ptg Branch, Reserve Bank of Australia)

1990 (31 Jan). *Local Transport. T* **229** *and similar horiz designs. Multicoloured. P* 14×15.

840 18 s. Type **229** . . 10 10
841 55 s. Fautasi (large canoe) . . 30 35
842 60 s. Polynesian Airlines aircraft . . 30 35
843 $3 *Lady Samoa* (ferry) . . 1·50 1·60
840/3 . . *Set of* 4 1·90 2·10

Sarawak

Sarawak was placed under British protection in 1888. It was eded to Great Britain on 1 July 1946 and was administered as a Crown Colony until 16 September 1963 when it became a state of he Federation of Malaysia.

Stamps of INDIA were used in Sarawak from *circa* 1859. They were replaced by Sarawak issues from 1869, although these were only valid for "local" postage as far as Singapore. Mail for further afield needed a combination of Sarawak and STRAITS SETTLEMENTS stamps, a stock of the latter being kept by the Sarawak Post Office. This arrangement continued until 1 July 1897 when Sarawak joined the U.P.U.

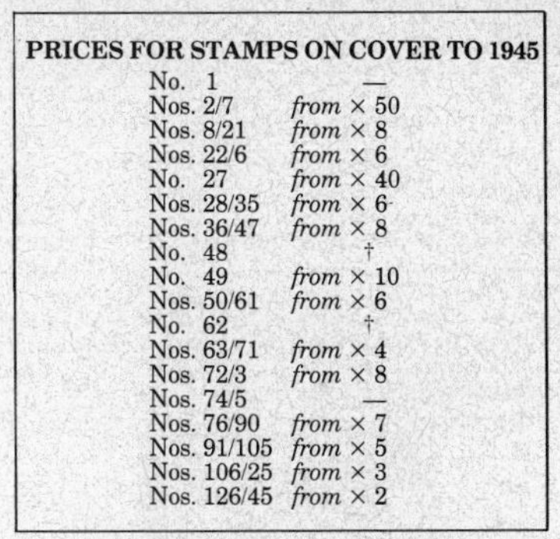

PRICES FOR STAMPS ON COVER TO 1945	
No. 1	—
Nos. 2/7	*from* × 50
Nos. 8/21	*from* × 8
Nos. 22/6	*from* × 6
No. 27	*from* × 40
Nos. 28/35	*from* × 6
Nos. 36/47	*from* × 8
No. 48	†
No. 49	*from* × 10
Nos. 50/61	*from* × 6
No. 62	†
Nos. 63/71	*from* × 4
Nos. 72/3	*from* × 8
Nos. 74/5	—
Nos. 76/90	*from* × 7
Nos. 91/105	*from* × 5
Nos. 106/25	*from* × 3
Nos. 126/45	*from* × 2

BROOKE FAMILY ADMINISTRATION

Sir James Brooke. 1842–11 June 1868
Sir Charles Brooke. 11 June 1868–17 May 1917

UNUSED PRICES. Nos. 1/7, 27 and 32/5 in unused condition are normally found to be without gum. Prices in the unused column are for stamps in this state. Examples of these issues with original gum are worth considerably more.

1 Sir James Brooke

2 Sir Charles Brooke

The initials in the corners of T 1 and 2 stand for "James (Charles) Brooke, Rajah (of) Sarawak".

T 1 and 2. Die eng Wm. Ridgway. Litho Maclure, Macdonald & Co, Glasgow)

1869 (1 Mar). *P* 11.
1 **1** 3 c. brown/*yellow* .. 40·00 £200

Specimens are known printed from the engraved die in orange-brown on orange surface-coloured paper, and perf 12. These were submitted to the Sarawak authorities as examples of the stamps and exist both with and without obliterations.

1871 (1 Jan). *P* 11 (*irregular*).
2 **2** 3 c. brown/*yellow* .. 1·25 3·00
a. Stop after "THREE" .. 35·00 48·00
b. Imperf between (vert pair) .. £325
c. Imperf between (horiz pair) .. £425

The "stop" variety, No. 2a, which occurs on stamp No. 97 in the sheet, is of no more philatelic importance than any of the numerous other variations, such as narrow first "A" in "SARAWAK" (No. 17) and "R" with long tail in left lower corner (No. 90), but it has been accepted by collectors for many years, and we therefore retain it. The papermaker's wmk "L N L" appears once or twice in sheets of No. 2.

Specimens are known, recess-printed, similar to those mentioned in the note after No. 1.

TWO CENTS

Copies of No. 2 surcharged as above were first reported in 1876 but following the discovery of dies for forgeries and faked postmarks in 1892 it was concluded that the issue was bogus, especially as the availability of the 2 c. of 1875 made it unnecessary to issue a provisional. It has now been established that a 2 c. postal rate was introduced from 1 August 1874 for the carriage of newspapers. Moreover two examples are known with a stop after "CENTS." and showing other minor differences from the forgery illustrated. This version could be genuine and if others come to light we will reconsider listing it.

1875 (1 Jan). *P* 11½–12.
3 **2** 2 c. mauve/*lilac* (*shades*) .. 2·50 9·00
4 4 c. red-brown/*yellow* .. 2·75 3·00
a. Imperf between (vert pair) .. £475
5 6 c. green/*green* .. 2·75 3·50
6 8 c. bright blue/*blue* .. 2·50 3·50
7 12 c. red/*pale rose* .. 6·50 6·50
3/7 .. *Set of* 5 15·00 23·00

Nos. 3, 4, 6 and 7 have the watermark "L N L" in the sheet, as No. 2. No. 5 is watermarked "L N T".

All values exist imperf and can be distinguished from the proofs by shade and impression. Stamps rouletted, pin-perf, or roughly perf 6½ to 7 are proofs clandestinely perforated.

The 12 c. "laid" paper, formerly listed, is not on a true laid paper, the "laid" effect being accidental and not consistent.

The lithographic stones for Nos. 3 to 7 were made up from strips of five distinct impressions hence there are five types of each value differing mainly in the lettering of the tablets of value. There are flaws on nearly every individual stamp, from which they can be plated.

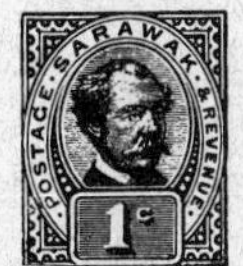

4 Sir Charles Brooke

(Typo D.L.R.)

1888 (10 Nov)–**1897**. *No wmk. P* 14.
8 **4** 1 c. purple and black (6.6.92) .. 80 45
9 2 c. purple and carmine (11.11.88) .. 85 65
a. Purple and rosine (1897) .. 4·00 1·25
10 3 c. purple and blue (11.11.88) .. 1·25 90
11 4 c. purple and yellow .. 9·50 24·00
12 5 c. purple and green (12.6.91) .. 8·00 1·50
13 6 c. purple and brown (11.11.88) .. 7·00 25·00
14 8 c. green and carmine (11.11.88) .. 4·50 2·50
a. Green and rosine (1897) .. 12·00 7·50
15 10 c. green and purple (12.6.91) .. 20·00 12·00
16 12 c. green and blue (11.11.88) .. 4·00 6·50
17 16 c. green and orange (28.12.97) .. 27·00 42·00
18 25 c. green and brown (19.11.88) .. 27·00 32·00
19 32 c. green and black (28.12.97) .. 24·00 35·00
20 50 c. green (26.7.97) .. 25·00 48·00
21 $1 green and black (2.11.97) .. 35·00 48·00
8/21 .. *Set of* 14 £170 £250

Prepared for use but not issued
21*a* $2 green and blue .. £350
21*b* $5 green and violet .. £350
21*c* $10 green and carmine .. £350

On No. 21 the value is in black on an uncoloured ground.

The tablet of value in this and later similar issues is in the second colour given.

One Cent. (5)

one cent. (6)

2c. (7)

5c (8)

5c. (9)

1889 (3 Aug)–**92**. *T* 4 *surch. P* 14.
22 **5** 1 c. on 3 c. (12.1.92) .. 20·00 22·00
a. Surch double .. £400 £300
23 **6** 1 c. on 3 c. (2.92) .. 2·75 2·75
a. No stop after "cent" (R. 2/6) .. 80·00
24 **7** 2 c. on 8 c. (3.8.89) .. 2·25 5·00
a. Surch double .. £275
b. Surch inverted .. £1800
c. Surch omitted (in pair with normal) .. £2000
25 **8** 5 c. on 12 c. (with stop after "C") (17.2.91) 17·00 25·00
a. No stop after "C" .. 17·00 24·00
b. "C" omitted .. £250
c. Surch double .. £900
d. Surch double, one vertical .. £1700
e. Surch omitted (in pair with normal) .. £5500
26 **9** 5 c. on 12 c. (17.2.91) .. 65·00 90·00
a. No stop after "C" .. 60·00 75·00
b. "C" omitted .. £325 £275
c. Surch double .. £800

ONE CENT (10)

1892 (23 May). *No.* 2 *surch with T* 10.
27 **2** 1 c. on 3 c. brown/*yellow* .. 50 90
a. Stop after "THREE." .. 16·00 24·00
b. Imperf between (vert pair) .. £400
c. Bar omitted (1st ptg) .. £130
d. Bar at top and bottom (1st ptg) .. £180
e. Surch double (2nd ptg) .. £300 £325

No. 27 was surcharged with a setting of 100 (10 × 10). It was originally intended that there should be no bar at foot, but this was then added at a second operation before the stamps were issued. Subsequent supplies were surcharged with "ONE CENT" and bar at one operation.

Varieties with part of the surcharge missing are due to gum on the face of the unsurcharged stamps receiving part of the surcharge, which was afterwards washed off.

11

12

13 Sir Charles Brooke 14

(Die eng Wm. Ridgway. Recess P.B.)

1895 (1 Jan–Sept). *No wmk. P* 11½–12.
28 **11** 2 c. brown-red .. 3·75 5·50
a. Imperf between (vert pair) .. £250
b. Imperf between (horiz pair) .. £225
c. Second ptg. Perf 12½ (Sept) .. 3·50 4·50
ca. Perf 12½. Imperf between (horiz pair) £250
29 **12** 4 c. black .. 3·50 2·50
a. Imperf between (horiz pair) .. £250
30 **13** 6 c. violet .. 3·00 7·00
31 **14** 8 c. green .. 10·00 6·00
28/31 .. *Set of* 4 18·00 18·00

Stamps of these types, printed in wrong colours, are trials and these, when surcharged with values in "pence", are from waste sheets that were used by Perkins, Bacon & Co as trial paper when preparing an issue of stamps for British South Africa.

4 CENTS. (15)

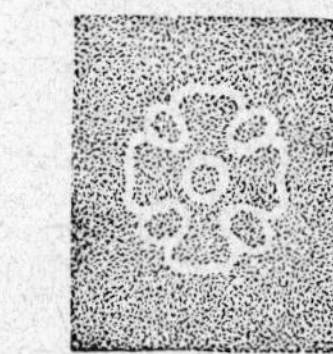

16

1899. *Surch as T* 15.
32 **2** 2 c. on 3 c. brown/*yellow* (19.9.99) .. 80 90
a. Stop after "THREE" .. 35·00
b. Imperf between (vert pair) .. £650
33 2 c. on 12 c. red/*pale rose* (29.6.99) .. 2·50 3·00
a. Surch inverted .. £700 £900
34 4 c. on 6 c. green/*green* (R.) (16.11.99) .. 15·00 35·00
35 4 c. on 8 c. bright blue/*blue* (R.) (29.6.99) 2·50 4·50
32/5 .. *Set of* 4 19·00 38·00

A variety of surcharge with small "S" in "CENTS" may be found in the 2 c. on 12 c. and 4 c. on 8 c. and a raised stop after "CENTS" on the 4 c. on 6 c.

The omission of parts of the surcharge is due to gum on the surface of the stamps (see note after No. 27).

(Typo D.L.R.)

1899 (10 Nov)–**1908**. *Inscribed* "POSTAGE POSTAGE." *No wmk. P* 14.
36 **4** 1 c. grey-blue and rosine (1.1.01) .. 30 45
a. Grey-blue and red .. 75 20
b. Ultramarine and rosine .. 2·50 40
c. Dull blue and carmine .. 4·50 3·75
37 2 c. green (16.12.99) .. 30 15
38 3 c. dull purple (1.2.08) .. 2·25 10
39 4 c. rose-carmine (10.11.99) .. 3·50 1·40
a. Aniline carmine .. 1·75 15
40 8 c. yellow and black (6.12.99) .. 1·75 70
41 10 c. ultramarine (10.11.99) .. 1·75 50
42 12 c. mauve (16.12.99) .. 2·00 1·50
a. Bright mauve (1905) .. 9·50 5·50
43 16 c. chestnut and green (16.12.99) .. 1·75 1·50
44 20 c. bistre and bright mauve (4.00) .. 4·00 2·25
45 25 c. brown and blue (16.12.99) .. 2·75 3·50
46 50 c. sage-green and carmine (16.12.99) .. 10·00 18·00
47 $1 rose-carmine and green (16.12.99) .. 24·00 35·00
a. Rosine and pale green .. 38·00 48·00
36/47 .. *Set of* 12 48·00 55·00

Prepared for use but not issued
48 **4** 5 c. olive-grey and green .. 12·00

The figures of value in the $1 are in colour on an uncoloured ground.

1902. *Inscribed* "POSTAGE POSTAGE". *W* **16**. *P* 14.
49 **4** 2 c. green .. 11·00 11·00

Sir Charles Vyner Brooke. 17 May 1917–1 June 1946

17 Sir Charles Vyner Brooke

ONE cent (18)

(Typo D.L.R.)

1918 (26 Mar). *No wmk. Chalky paper. P* 14.
50 **17** 1 c. slate-blue and red .. 20 25
a. Dull blue and carmine .. 35 50
51 2 c. green .. 60 35
52 3 c. brown-purple .. 1·40 1·10
53 4 c. rose-carmine .. 1·40 1·25
a. Rose-red .. 1·25 1·40
54 8 c. yellow and black .. 4·50 18·00
55 10 c. blue (*shades*) .. 2·00 2·25
56 12 c. purple .. 5·00 5·50
57 16 c. chestnut and green .. 5·00 4·25
58 20 c. olive and violet (*shades*) .. 3·50 4·00
59 25 c. brown and bright blue .. 4·00 7·00
60 50 c. olive-green and carmine .. 4·75 8·00
61 $1 bright rose and green .. 10·00 16·00
50/61 .. *Set of* 12 35·00 55·00
50/61 Optd "Specimen" .. *Set of* 12 £190

Prepared for use but not issued
62 17 1 c. slate-blue and slate .. .. 20·00
On the $1 the figures of value are in colour on an uncoloured ground.

1922–23. *New colours and values. No wmk. Chalk-surfaced paper. P* 14.
63 17 2 c. purple (5.3.23) .. .. 50 1·00
64 3 c. dull green (23.3.22) 40 60
65 4 c. brown-purple (10.4.23) 60 15
66 5 c. yellow-orange 40 90
67 6 c. claret (1.22) .. .. 75 1·00
68 8 c. bright rose-red .. .. 1·75 10·00
69 10 c. black (1923) .. .. 1·75 2·25
70 12 c. bright blue (12.22) .. .. 7·00 15·00
a. *Pale dull blue* .. .. 7·00 13·00
71 30 c. ochre-brown and slate .. .. 3·50 3·75
63/71 .. .. *Set of* 9 15·00 29·00

1923 (Jan). *Surch as T* **18**. (*a*) *First printing. Bars* 1¼ *mm apart.*
72 17 1 c. on 10 c. dull blue .. .. 12·00 35·00
a. "cnet" for "cent" (R. 9/5) £300 £600
73 2 c. on 12 c. purple .. .. 5·00 20·00
a. Thick, narrower "W" in "TWO" .. 17·00 40·00
(*b*) *Second printing. Bars* ¾ *mm apart*
74 17 1 c. on 10 c. dull blue .. .. 80·00 £130
b. "cnet" for "cent" (R.9/5) £8000
c. "en" of "cent" scratched out and "ne" overprinted (R.9/5) £3000
75 2 c. on 12 c. purple .. .. 45·00 75·00
a. Thick, narrower "W" in "TWO" .. £100

In the 2 c. on 12 c. the words of the surcharge are about 7½ mm from the bars.

The "cnet" error occurred on R.9/5 of all sheets from the first printing of the 1 c. on 10 c. A single example of the error, No. 74b, is known from the second printing, but the error was then corrected, as shown by the evidence of a surviving plate block, only to have the correct spelling scratched out, by a local employee, and "ne" substituted (No. 74c).

The thick "W" variety occurs on all stamps of the last two horizontal rows of the first printing (12 stamps per sheet), and in the last two vertical rows of the second (20 stamps per sheet).

1928 (Apr)–**29.** *W* **16** (*Multiple*). *Chalk-surfaced paper. P* 14.
76 17 1 c. slate-blue and carmine 45 35
77 2 c. bright purple 50 40
78 3 c. green .. .. 50 1·75
79 4 c. brown-purple .. .. 1·25 10
80 5 c. yellow-orange (5.8.29) .. .. 2·75 3·00
81 6 c. claret 70 30
82 8 c. bright rose-red .. .. 1·75 5·00
83 10 c. black .. .. 1·00 1·75
84 12 c. bright blue .. .. 1·75 4·75
85 16 c. chestnut and green .. .. 1·75 2·50
86 20 c. olive-bistre and violet .. .. 1·75 2·25
87 25 c. brown and bright blue .. .. 2·50 6·00
88 30 c. bistre-brown and slate .. .. 3·00 6·50
89 50 c. olive-green and carmine .. .. 3·50 5·50
90 $1 bright rose and green .. .. 7·50 17·00
76/90 .. .. *Set of* 15 27·00 50·00
76/90 Optd/Perf "Specimen" .. *Set of* 15 £200
In the $1 the value is as before.

19 Sir Charles Vyner Brooke

20

(Recess Waterlow)

1932 (1 Jan). *W* **20**. *P* 12½.
91 19 1 c. indigo 70 35
92 2 c. green 70 25
93 3 c. violet .. .. 2·25 60
94 4 c. red-orange 80 15
95 5 c. deep lake .. .. 2·25 60
96 6 c. scarlet .. .. 3·00 5·00
97 8 c. orange-yellow .. .. 3·00 4·50
98 10 c. black .. .. 2·25 2·50
99 12 c. deep ultramarine .. .. 2·75 4·50
100 15 c. chestnut .. .. 3·00 6·00
101 20 c. red-orange and violet .. .. 3·00 6·00
102 25 c. orange-yellow and chestnut .. 4·00 6·50
103 30 c. sepia and vermilion .. .. 4·00 10·00
104 50 c. carmine-red and olive-green .. 4·00 6·00
105 $1 green and carmine .. .. 5·50 15·00
91/105 .. .. *Set of* 15 35·00 60·00
91/105 Perf "Specimen" .. *Set of* 15 £200

21 Sir Charles Vyner Brooke

BMA
(22)

(Recess B.W.)

1934 (1 May)–**41.** *No wmk. P* 12.
106 21 1 c. purple 15 10
107 2 c. green 15 10
107*a* 2 c. black (1.3.41) .. .. 80 1·40
108 3 c. black 15 10
108*a* 3 c. green (1.3.41) 70 85
109 4 c. bright purple 15 15
110 5 c. violet 20 10
111 6 c. carmine 15 40
111*a* 21 6 c. lake-brown (1.3.41) .. .. 80 3·00
112 8 c. red-brown 15 10
112*a* 8 c. carmine (1.3.41) 75 10
113 10 c. scarlet 75 40
114 12 c. blue 30 25
114*a* 12 c. orange (1.3.41) .. .. 80 3·50
115 15 c. orange .. .. 40 2·50
115*a* 15 c. blue (1.3.41) .. .. 75 4·00
116 20 c. olive-green and carmine 90 40
117 25 c. violet and orange .. .. 40 1·00
118 30 c. red-brown and violet .. .. 60 1·25
119 50 c. violet and scarlet 60 60
120 $1 scarlet and sepia 60 50
121 $2 bright purple and violet .. .. 3·50 6·00
122 $3 carmine and green .. .. 10·00 11·00
123 $4 blue and scarlet .. .. 10·00 15·00
124 $5 scarlet and red-brown .. .. 13·00 20·00
125 $10 black and yellow .. .. 16·00 27·00
106/25 .. .. *Set of* 26 55·00 90·00
106/25 Perf "Specimen" .. *Set of* 26 £450
For the 3 c. green, wmkd Mult Script CA, see No. 152a.

BRITISH MILITARY ADMINISTRATION

Following the Japanese surrender elements of the British Military Administration reached Kuching on 11 September 1945. From October 1945 Australian stamps were made available until replaced by Nos. 126/45.

1945 (17 Dec). *Optd with T* **22**.
126 21 1 c. purple 20 40
127 2 c. black (R.) 20 30
a. Opt double .. .. † —
128 3 c. green 20 25
129 4 c. bright purple 20 25
130 5 c. violet (R.) 30 50
131 6 c. lake-brown 50 75
132 8 c. carmine .. .. 9·00 9·00
133 10 c. scarlet 50 60
134 12 c. orange .. .. 60 3·75
135 15 c. blue 85 40
136 20 c. olive-green and carmine .. .. 90 1·40
137 25 c. violet and orange (R.) .. .. 1·25 1·75
138 30 c. red-brown and violet .. .. 1·25 2·75
139 50 c. violet and scarlet .. .. 1·25 35
140 $1 scarlet and sepia .. .. 2·50 1·25
141 $2 bright purple and violet .. .. 9·00 4·50
142 $3 carmine and green .. .. 17·00 22·00
143 $4 blue and scarlet .. .. 25·00 25·00
144 $5 scarlet and red-brown .. .. 70·00 80·00
145 $10 black and yellow (R.) .. .. 85·00 £100
126/45 .. .. *Set of* 20 £200 £225

These stamps, and the similarly overprinted stamps of North Borneo, were obtainable at all post offices throughout British Borneo (Brunei, Labuan, North Borneo and Sarawak), for use on local and overseas mail.

The administration of Sarawak was returned to the Brooke family on 15 April 1946, but the Rajah, after consulting the inhabitants ceded the territory to Great Britain on 1 June 1946.

23 Sir James Brooke, Sir Charles Vyner Brooke and Sir Charles Brooke

(24)

(Recess B.W.)

1946 (18 May). *Centenary Issue. P* 12.
146 23 8 c. lake 20 15
147 15 c. blue 20 70
148 50 c. black and scarlet 35 80
149 $1 black and sepia .. .. 50 6·00
146/9 .. .. *Set of* 4 1·10 7·00
146/9 Perf "Specimen" .. *Set of* 4 90·00

CROWN COLONY

1947 (16 Apr). *Optd with T* **24**, *typo by B.W. in blue-black or red. Wmk Mult Script CA. P* 12.
150 21 1 c. purple 15 15
151 2 c. black (R.) 15 10
152 3 c. green (R.) 15 15
a. Albino opt £2250
153 4 c. bright purple 15 15
154 6 c. lake-brown 20 45
155 8 c. carmine 15 10
156 10 c. scarlet 20 20
157 12 c. orange 15 55
158 15 c. blue (R.) 15 40
159 20 c. olive-green and carmine (R.) .. 25 50
160 25 c. violet and orange (R.) 30 30
161 50 c. violet and scarlet (R.) 20 30
162 $1 scarlet and sepia 60 80
163 $2 bright purple and violet .. .. 90 3·00
164 $5 scarlet and red-brown .. .. 1·75 3·00
150/64 .. .. *Set of* 15 5·00 9·00
150/64 Perf "Specimen" .. *Set of* 15 £250
No. 152a shows an uninked impression of T 24.

1948 (25 Oct). *Royal Silver Wedding. As Nos.* 30/1 *of Aden.*
165 8 c. scarlet 30 20
166 $5 brown .. .. 21·00 24·00

1949 (19 Oct). *75th Anniv of Universal Postal Union. As Nos.* 114/17 *of Antigua.*
167 8 c. carmine 50 50
168 15 c. deep blue .. .. 1·25 2·00
169 25 c. deep blue-green .. .. 1·40 1·50
170 50 c. violet .. .. 2·00 2·50
167/70 .. .. *Set of* 4 4·50 6·00

25 *Troides Brookiana*

26 Western Tarsier

(Recess; Arms typo B.W.)

1950 (3 Jan). *T* **25/6** *and similar designs. Wmk Mult Script CA. P* 11½ × 11 (*horiz*) *or* 11 × 11½ (*vert*).
171 1 c. black 20 25
172 2 c. red-orange 20 30
173 3 c. green 10 25
174 4 c. chocolate 10 10
175 6 c. turquoise-blue 10 10
176 8 c. scarlet 10 15
177 10 c. orange .. .. 50 2·00
178 12 c. violet 85 60
179 15 c. blue 50 10
180 20 c. purple-brown and red-orange .. 50 15
181 25 c. green and scarlet 50 15
182 50 c. brown and violet 55 10
183 $1 green and chocolate .. .. 3·00 75
184 $2 blue and carmine .. .. 9·00 3·25
185 $5 black, yellow, red and purple .. 12·00 5·50
171/85 .. .. *Set of* 15 25·00 12·00

Designs: *Horiz*—8 c. Dayak dancer; 10 c. Malayan Pangolin; 12 c. Kenyah boys; 15 c. Fire-making; 20 c. Kelemantan rice barn; 25 c. Pepper vines; $1 Kelabit smithy; $2 Map of Sarawak; $5 Arms of Sarawak. *Vert*—3 c. Kayan tomb; 4 c. Kayan girl and boy; 6 c. Bead work; 50 c. Iban woman.

40 Map of Sarawak

(Recess B.W.)

1952 (1 Feb). *Wmk Mult Script CA. P* 11½ × 11.
186 40 10 c. orange 15 15

1953 (3 June). *Coronation. As No.* 47 *of Aden.*
187 10 c. black and deep violet-blue 70 55

41 Logging

44 Malabar Pied Hornbill

51 Queen Elizabeth II

52 Queen Elizabeth II (after Annigoni)

(Des M. Thoma (1, 2 c.), R. Turrell (4 c.), J. D. Hughes (6, 12 c.), A. Hakim bin Moliti (8 c.), J. Woodcock (10 c.), J. Browning (15 c.), G. Gundersen (20 c.), K. Munich (25 c.). Recess, Arms typo ($5). B.W.)

1955 (1 June)–**59.** *T* **41**, **44**, **51/2** *and similar designs. Wmk Mult Script CA. P* 11×11½ (1 c., 2 c., 4 c.), 12×13 (30 c., 50 c., $1, $2) *or* 11½×11 (*others*).
188 41 1 c. green (1.10.57) 10 20
189 – 2 c. red-orange (1.10.57) 20 20
190 – 4 c. lake-brown (1.10.57) 25 10
a. *Brown-purple* (18.3.59) .. .. 1·25 75
191 44 6 c. greenish blue (1.10.57) .. .. 1·75 10
192 – 8 c. rose-red (1.10.57) 15 10
193 – 10 c. deep green (1.10.57) 15 10
194 – 12 c. plum (1.10.57) .. .. 2·00 25
195 – 15 c. ultramarine (1.10.57) 80 10
196 – 20 c. olive and brown (1.10.57) 80 10
197 – 25 c. sepia and green (1.10.57) .. .. 2·00 10
198 51 30 c. red-brown and deep lilac .. .. 1·50 10
199 50 c. black and carmine (1.10.57) .. .. 1·25 10
200 52 $1 myrtle-green & orange-brn (1.10.57) 1·75 30
201 $2 violet and bronze-green (1.10.57) .. 2·75 1·00
202 – $5 multicoloured (1.10.57) .. .. 11·00 3·75
188/202 .. .. *Set of* 15 23·00 5·50

Designs: *Horiz*—8 c. Shield with spears; 10 c. Kenyah ceremonial carving; 12 c. Barong panau (sailing prau); 15 c. Turtles; 20 c. Melanan basket-making; 25 c. Astana, Kuching; $5 Arms of Sarawak. *Vert* (*as T* **41**)—2 c. Young Orang-Utan; 4 c. Kayan dancing; 50 c. Queen Elizabeth II; $2 Queen Elizabeth II (after Annigoni).

1963 (4 June). *Freedom from Hunger. As No.* 76 *of Aden.*
203 12 c. sepia .. .. 1·00 35

STATE OF MALAYSIA

1964–65. *As 1955–57 but wmk w* **12.** *Perfs as before.*

No.	Type	Description	Unused	Used
204	41	1 c. green (8.9.64)	10	25
205	–	2 c. red-orange (17.8.65)	40	2·00
206	44	6 c. greenish blue (8.9.64)	1·75	1·50
207	–	10 c. deep green (8.9.64)	25	15
208	–	12 c. plum (8.9.64)	80	3·00
209	–	15 c. ultramarine (17.8.65)	1·25	4·75
210	–	20 c. olive and brown (9.6.64)	50	40
211	–	25 c. deep sepia and bluish green (8.9.64)	1·00	2·50
204/11		*Set of* 8	5·50	13·00

53 *Vanda hookeriana*

54 Blue Pansy Butterfly

1965 (15 Nov). *As Nos.* 166/72 *of Johore but with Arms of Sarawak inset as in T* **53**.

No.	Description	Unused	Used
212	1 c. multicoloured	10	30
	c. Grey omitted	27·00	
213	2 c. multicoloured	10	30
	a. Black (country name and shield) omitted	65·00	
	c. Yellow-olive (stems) omitted	30·00	
214	5 c. multicoloured	20	10
215	6 c. multicoloured	30	20
	a. Black (country name and shield) omitted	65·00	
216	10 c. multicoloured	35	10
	a. Red omitted	32·00	
217	15 c. multicoloured	80	10
218	20 c. multicoloured	1·25	20
212/18	*Set of* 7	2·75	1·00

The 1 c., 6 c., 10 c. and 15 c. exist with PVA gum as well as gum arabic.

No. 213a was formerly listed with Trengganu No. 101 but there is evidence that it was issued in Sarawak.

A used example of No. 218 is known with the bright purple (blooms) omitted.

The higher values used with this issue were Nos. 20/7 of Malaysia (National Issues).

(Litho B.W.)

1971 (1 Feb). *As Nos.* 175/81 *of Johore but with Arms of Sarawak inset as in T* **54**.

No.	Description	Unused	Used
219	1 c. multicoloured	10	30
220	2 c. multicoloured	20	35
221	5 c. multicoloured	35	10
222	6 c. multicoloured	40	15
223	10 c. multicoloured	40	10
224	15 c. multicoloured	60	10
225	20 c. multicoloured	70	25
219/25	*Set of* 7	2·50	1·25

The higher values used with this issue were Nos. 64/71 of Malaysia (National Issues).

55 Blue Pansy Butterfly (different crest at right) **56** *Rhododendron scortechinii*

(Photo Harrison)

1977 (12 Feb)–**78.** *As Nos.* 219/21 *and* 223/5 *but ptd in photogravure showing new State Crest as T* **55**.

No.	Description	Unused	Used
226	1 c. multicoloured (1978)	3·50	3·50
227	2 c. multicoloured (1978)	2·75	3·00
228	5 c. multicoloured	55	25
230	10 c. multicoloured (4.4.77)	55	15
231	15 c. multicoloured (19.4.77)	90	20
232	20 c. multicoloured (1978)	4·00	2·50
226/32	*Set of* 6	11·00	8·50

1979 (30 Apr). *As Nos.* 188/94 *of Johore but with Arms of Sarawak as in T* **56**.

No.	Description	Unused	Used
233	1 c. *Rafflesia hasseltii*	10	10
234	2 c. *Pterocarpus indicus*	10	10
235	5 c. *Lagerstroemia speciosa*	10	10
236	10 c. *Durio zibethinus*	10	10
237	15 c. *Hibiscus rosa-sinensis*	10	10
238	20 c. Type **56**	15	10
239	25 c. *Phaeomeria speciosa*	15	10
233/9	*Set of* 7	65	30

For higher values used in conjunction with this series see Nos. 190/7 of Malaysia (National Issues).

1983 (11 Oct)–**86.*** *As Nos.* 235/6 *and* 238 *but without wmk.*

No.	Description	Unused	Used
242	5 c. *Lagerstroemia speciosa* (4.4.86)	3·25	2·00
243	10 c. *Durio zibethinus* (9.9.85)	2·25	1·50
245	20 c. Type **56** (blackish brown background)		
245*a*	20 c. Type **56** (bronze-green background) (2.8.84)	1·00	75

* There was no official release date for these stamps. Dates shown are the earliest recorded from postmarks and may be revised if earlier examples are reported.

For details of the shade differences between watermarked and unwatermarked printings see after Malaysia–Johore No. 200*a*.

On Nos. 242/3 and 245*a* the crest is closer to the face value than on Nos. 235/6, 238 and 245.

57 Coffee

1986 (25 Oct). *As Nos.* 202/8 *of Johore but with Arms of Sarawak as in T* **57**.

No.	Description	Unused	Used
247	1 c. Type **57**	10	10
248	2 c. Coconuts	10	10
249	5 c. Cocoa	10	10
250	10 c. Black pepper	10	10
251	15 c. Rubber	10	10
252	20 c. Oil palm	10	10
253	30 c. Rice	10	15
247/53	*Set of* 7	40	50

JAPANESE OCCUPATION OF SARAWAK

Japanese forces landed in North Borneo in 16 December 1941 and Sarawak was attacked on 23 December 1941.

Brunei, North Borneo, Sarawak and, after a short period, Labuan, were administered as a single territory by the Japanese. Until September–October 1942, previous stamp issues, without overprint, continued to be used in conjunction with existing postmarks. From the Autumn of 1942 onwards unoverprinted stamps of Japan were made available and examples can be found used from the area for much of the remainder of the War. Japanese Occupation issues for Brunei, North Borneo and Sarawak were equally valid throughout the combined territory but not, in practice, equally available.

PRICES FOR STAMPS ON COVER	
Nos. J1/21	*from* × 8
Nos. J22/6	—

府政国帝本日大

(1)

("Imperial Japanese Government")

1942. *Stamps of Sarawak optd with T* **1** *in violet.*

No.	Type	Description	Unused	Used
J 1	21	1 c. purple	18·00	22·00
J 2		2 c. green	42·00	55·00
J 3		2 c. black	35·00	45·00
J 4		3 c. black	80·00	£100
J 5		3 c. green	27·00	35·00
J 6		4 c. bright purple	20·00	25·00
J 7		5 c. violet	20·00	25·00
J 8		6 c. carmine	30·00	38·00
J 9		6 c. lake-brown	25·00	32·00
J10		8 c. red-brown	85·00	£110
J11		8 c. carmine	85·00	£100
J12		10 c. scarlet	25·00	30·00
J13		12 c. blue	45·00	55·00
J14		12 c. orange	80·00	£100
J15		15 c. orange	80·00	£100
J16		15 c. blue	32·00	42·00
J17		20 c. olive-green and carmine	22·00	32·00
J18		25 c. violet and orange	25·00	32·00
J19		30 c. red-brown and violet	25·00	35·00
J20		50 c. violet and scarlet	28·00	35·00
J21		$1 scarlet and sepia	30·00	45·00
J22		$2 bright purple and violet	75·00	95·00
J23		$3 carmine and green	£450	£550
J24		$4 blue and scarlet	85·00	£110
J25		$5 scarlet and red-brown	80·00	£110
J26		$10 black and yellow	95·00	£130

The overprint, being handstamped, exists inverted on all values.

Stamps of T **21** optd with Japanese symbols within an oval frame are revenue stamps, while the same stamps overprinted with three Japanese characters between two vertical double rules, were used as seals.

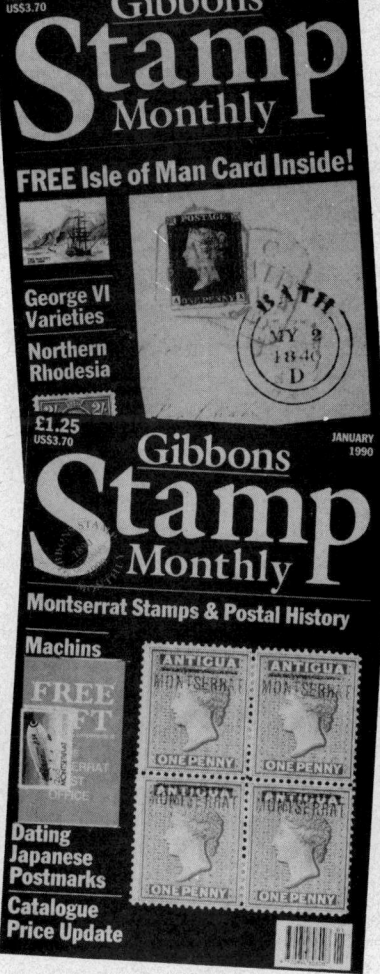

Seychelles

We no longer list the 6d. lilac (1862) (Plate No. 3) with obliteration "B 64" as there is no evidence that British stamps were sold in the Seychelles.

Stamps of MAURITIUS were used at Victoria on Mahé Island from 11 December 1861 until 1890, being cancelled "B 64". No further post offices were opened until 1901.

PRICES FOR STAMPS ON COVER TO 1945

Nos. 1/8	*from* × 8
Nos. 9/21	*from* × 20
Nos. 22/5	*from* × 5
Nos. 26/7	*from* × 7
Nos. 28/36	*from* × 4
Nos. 37/40	*from* × 20
Nos. 41/5	*from* × 5
Nos. 46/81	*from* × 4
Nos. 82/131	*from* × 3
Nos. 132/4	*from* × 10
Nos. 135/49	*from* × 3

DEPENDENCY OF MAURITIUS

PRINTERS. Nos. 1 to 123 were typographed by De La Rue & Co.

1

Die I

Die II

In Die I there are lines of shading in the middle compartment of the diadem which are absent from Die II.

1890 (5 April)–**92.** *Wmk Crown CA. P* 14. (i) *Die* I.

No.	Type	Description	Unused	Used
1	1	2 c. green and carmine	65	7·00
2		4 c. carmine and green	7·50	9·00
3		8 c. brown-purple and blue	3·25	3·50
4		10 c. ultramarine and brown	3·75	8·00
5		13 c. grey and black	4·50	9·00
6		16 c. chestnut and blue	2·00	2·75
7		48 c. ochre and green	16·00	16·00
8		96 c. mauve and carmine	38·00	45·00
1/8		*Set of* 8	65·00	90·00
1/8 Optd "Specimen"		*Set of* 8	£160	

(ii) *Die* II (1892)

No.	Type	Description	Unused	Used
9	1	2 c. green and rosine	50	90
10		4 c. carmine and green	75	85
11		8 c. brown-purple and ultramarine	2·25	1·40
12		10 c. bright ultramarine and brown	2·75	2·00
13		13 c. grey and black	85	1·50
14		16 c. chestnut and ultramarine	23·00	7·00
9/14		*Set of* 6	27·00	12·50

3 cents

(2)

18 CENTS

(3)

4

1893 (1 Jan). *Surch locally as T* **2**.

No.	Description	Unused	Used
15	3 c. on 4 c. (No. 10)	75	1·10
	a. Surch inverted	£300	£375
	b. Surch double	£450	
	c. Surch omitted (in pair with normal)	£3750	
16	12 c. on 16 c. (No. 6)	1·00	2·75
	a. Surch inverted	£450	
	b. Surch double	£3000	£4000
17	12 c. on 16 c. (No. 14)	2·50	1·25
	a. Surch double	£3500	£3500
	b. Surch omitted (in pair with normal)		
18	15 c. on 16 c. (No. 6)	8·00	11·00
	a. Surch inverted	£300	£350
	b. Surch double	£550	£550
19	15 c. on 16 c. (No. 14)	7·00	1·50
	a. Surch inverted	£650	£650
	b. Surch double	£800	£800
	c. Surch treble	£2000	
20	45 c. on 48 c. (No. 7)	7·50	4·00
21	90 c. on 96 c. (No. 8)	22·00	25·00
15/21	*Set of* 7	42·00	42·00

Nos. 15, 16, 18, 19 and 20 exist with "cents" omitted and with "cents" above value and are due to misplacement of the surcharge.

1893 (Nov). *New values. Die* II. *Wmk Crown CA. P* 14.

No.	Type	Description	Unused	Used
22	1	3 c. dull purple and orange	40	30
23		12 c. sepia and green	55	40
24		15 c. sage-green and lilac	3·25	2·00
25		45 c. brown and carmine	22·00	23·00
22/5		*Set of* 4	24·00	23·00
22/5 Optd "Specimen"		*Set of* 4	70·00	

1896 (1 Aug). *No.* 25 *surch as T* **3**.

No.	Type	Description	Unused	Used
26	1	18 c. on 45 c. brown and carmine	6·50	2·50
		a. Surch double	£1200	£1200
		b. Surch treble	£1400	
27		36 c. on 45 c. brown and carmine	10·00	26·00
		a. Surch double	£1100	
26/27 H/S "Specimen"		*Set of* 2	70·00	

1897–1900. *Colours changed and new values. Die* II. *Wmk Crown CA. P* 14.

No.	Type	Description	Unused	Used
28	1	2 c. orange-brown and green (1900)	20	45
29		6 c. carmine (1900)	2·00	40
30		15 c. ultramarine (1900)	2·50	2·50
31		18 c. ultramarine	1·40	90
32		36 c. brown and carmine	15·00	4·00
33	4	75 c. yellow and violet (1900)	35·00	50·00
34		1 r. bright mauve and deep red	8·50	3·50
35		1 r. 50, grey and carmine (1900)	48·00	70·00
36		2 r. 25, bright mauve and green (1900)	48·00	70·00
28/36		*Set of* 9	£150	£180
28/36 Optd "Specimen"		*Set of* 9	£160	

3 cents

6 cents

(5) (5a)

1901. *Nos.* 12, 14, 32 *and* 11 *surch locally with T* **5** *or* **5a**.

No.	Description	Unused	Used
37	3 c. on 10 c. (10.01)	30	60
	a. Surch double	£650	
38	3 c. on 16 c. (8.01)	30	85
	a. Surch inverted	£600	£600
	b. Surch double	£500	
	c. "3 cents" omitted	£550	£550
39	3 c. on 36 c. (21.6.01)	25	50
	a. Surch double	£750	£900
	b. "3 cents" omitted	£600	£650
40	6 c. on 8 c. (8.01)	30	1·50
	a. Surch inverted	£750	£800
37/40	*Set of* 4	1·00	3·00
37/40 H/S "Specimen"	*Set of* 4	£100	

1902 (June). *Surch locally as T* **5**.

No.	Type	Description	Unused	Used
41	1	2 c. on 4 c. (No. 10)	90	2·75
42	4	30 c. on 75 c. (No. 33)	80	4·00
		a. Narrow "0" in "30"	10·00	40·00
43		30 c. on 1 r. (No. 34)	3·25	15·00
		a. Narrow "0" in "30"	20·00	65·00
		b. Surch double	£750	
44		45 c. on 1 r. (No. 34)	3·25	15·00
45		45 c. on 2 r. 25, (No. 36)	19·00	30·00
		a. Narrow "5" in "45"	£100	£140
41/5		*Set of* 5	24·00	60·00
41/5 H/S "Specimen"		*Set of* 5	£110	

6

7

3 cents

(8)

1903 (26 May). *Wmk Crown CA. P* 14.

No.	Type	Description	Unused	Used
46	6	2 c. chestnut and green	25	40
47		3 c. dull green	1·00	1·25
48		6 c. carmine	1·00	15
49		12 c. olive-sepia and dull green	1·50	75
50		15 c. ultramarine	2·25	1·25
51		18 c. sage-green and carmine	3·00	6·00
52		30 c. violet and dull green	5·50	8·00
53		45 c. brown and carmine	7·00	11·00
54	7	75 c. yellow and violet	9·00	16·00
55		1 r. 50, black and carmine	32·00	48·00
56		2 r. 25, purple and green	24·00	48·00
46/56		*Set of* 11	80·00	£120
46/56 Optd "Specimen"		*Set of* 11	£180	

1903. *Surch locally with T* **8**.

No.	Type	Description	Unused	Used
57	6	3 c. on 15 c. ultramarine (3.7)	55	1·00
58		3 c. on 18 c. sage-green and carmine (2.9)	1·75	16·00
59		3 c. on 45 c. brown and carmine (21.7)	55	1·50
57/9		*Set of* 3	2·50	17·00
57/9 H/S "Specimen"		*Set of* 3	80·00	

CROWN COLONY

The Seychelles became a Separate Crown Colony by Letters Patent dated 31 August 1903.

1906. *Wmk Mult Crown CA. P* 14.

No.	Type	Description	Unused	Used
60	6	2 c. chestnut and green	30	1·00
61		3 c. dull green	70	30
62		6 c. carmine	80	10
63		12 c. olive-sepia and dull green	3·00	70
64		15 c. ultramarine	1·60	2·00
65		18 c. sage-green and carmine	3·00	5·50
66		30 c. violet and dull green	6·00	7·50
67		45 c. brown and carmine	3·00	5·00
68	7	75 c. yellow and violet	8·50	30·00
69		1 r. 50, black and carmine	28·00	30·00
70		2 r. 25, purple and green	30·00	35·00
60/70		*Set of* 11	75·00	£100

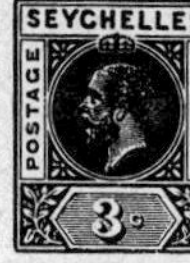

9

10

1912–13. *Wmk Mult Crown CA. P* 14.

No.	Type	Description	Unused	Used
71	9	2 c. chestnut and green	20	90
72		3 c. green	35	30
73		6 c. aniline carmine	8·00	4·50
		a. Carmine-red	2·25	25
74		12 c. olive-sepia and dull green	80	3·50
75		15 c. ultramarine	1·25	40
76		18 c. sage-green and carmine	1·25	3·50
77		30 c. violet and green	5·00	90
78		45 c. brown and carmine	2·50	16·00
79	10	75 c. yellow and violet	2·50	5·50
80		1 r. 50, black and carmine	5·50	85
81		2 r. 25, rose-purple and green	45·00	45·00
		a. Bright purple and green	30·00	2·50
71/81*a*		*Set of* 11	45·00	32·00
71/81 Optd "Specimen"		*Set of* 11	£180	

The split "A" variety illustrated above No. 86 of Gambia also occurs on Nos. 71/81 (*Prices about six to ten times normal*).

The 2 c., 3 c. and 15 c. were issued in April 1912, the 6 c. in June 1913 and the remainder in January 1913.

11

12

13

1917–22. *Wmk Mult Crown CA. P* 14.

No.	Type	Description	Unused	Used
82	11	2 c. chestnut and green, **O**	15	90
83		3 c. green, **O**	35	15
84	12	5 c. deep brown, **O** (1920)	35	2·25
85	11	6 c. carmine, **O**	55	20
		a. Rose, **O** (1919)	3·25	30
86		12 c. grey, **O** (1919)	25	1·00
87		15 c. ultramarine, **O**	30	85
88		18 c. purple/*yellow,* **C** (1919)	1·75	10·00
		a. On orange-buff (1920)	12·00	35·00
		b. On pale yellow (Die II) (1922)	75	12·00
89	13	25 c. black and red/*yellow,* **C**	1·50	12·00
		a. On orange-buff (1920)	32·00	55·00
		b. On pale yellow (Die II) (1922)	1·00	5·00
90	11	30 c. dull purple and olive, **C**	1·50	5·50
91		45 c. dull purple and orange, **C** (1919)	3·00	16·00
92	13	50 c. dull purple and black, **C** (1920)	3·00	9·00
93		75 c. black/*blue-green* (*olive back*), **C**	1·25	7·00
		a. On emerald back (Die II) (1922)	1·40	11·00
94		1 r. dull purple and red, **C** (1920)	7·00	22·00
95		1 r. 50, reddish purple and blue/*blue,* **C**	9·00	28·00
		a. Blue-pur & bl/blue, **C** (Die II) (1922)	8·50	26·00
96		2 r. 25, yellow-green and violet, **C**	27·00	75·00
97		5 r. green and blue, **C** (1920)	40·00	£120
82/97		*Set of* 16	85·00	£275
82/97 Optd "Specimen"		*Set of* 16	£250	

1921–32. *Wmk Mult Script CA. P* 14.

No.	Type	Description	Unused	Used
98	11	2 c. chestnut and green, **O**	10	15
99		3 c. green, **O**	20	15
100		3 c. black, **O** (1922)	50	25
101		4 c. green, **O** (1922)	60	25
102		4 c. sage-green and carmine, **O** (1928)	3·50	8·50
103	12	5 c. deep brown, **O**	75	3·00
104	11	6 c. carmine, **O**	80	4·00
105		6 c. deep mauve, **O** (1922)	30	10
106	13	9 c. red, **O** (1927)	1·25	2·75
107	11	12 c. grey (Die II), **O**	50	15
108		12 c. carmine-red, **O** (1922)	45	15
109		12 c. grey (Die I), **O** (1932)	3·75	65
110		15 c. bright blue, **O**	2·00	32·00
111		15 c. yellow, **O** (1922)	50	2·50
112		18 c. purple/*pale yellow,* **C** (1925)	2·00	6·50
113	13	20 c. bright blue, **O** (1922)	1·25	35
		a. Dull blue, **O** (1926)	4·00	55
114	11	25 c. black and red/*pale yellow,* **C** (1925)	2·50	5·50
115		30 c. dull purple and olive, **C**	80	8·00
116		45 c. dull purple and orange, **C**	80	5·00
117	13	50 c. dull purple and black, **C**	90	2·25
118		75 c. black/*emerald,* **C** (1924)	7·50	15·00
119		1 r. dull purple and red (Die II), **C**	7·00	17·00
120		1 r. dull purple and red (Die I), **C** (1932)	12·00	26·00
121		1 r. 50, purple and blue/*blue,* **C** (1924)	8·00	15·00
122		2 r. 25, yellow-green and violet, **C**	8·00	14·00
123		5 r. yellow-green and blue, **C**	48·00	75·00
98/123		*Set of* 24	80·00	£200
98/123 Optd "Specimen"		*Set of* 24	£350	

The 3 c. green and 12 c. grey (Die II) were reissued in 1927. "Specimens" of these also exist.

1935 (6 May). *Silver Jubilee. As Nos.* 91/4 *of Antigua but ptd by B.W. P* 11 × 12.

No.	Description	Unused	Used
128	6 c. ultramarine and grey-black	55	30
	a. Extra flagstaff	£160	
	b. Short extra flagstaff	80·00	
	d. Flagstaff on right-hand turret	80·00	
	e. Double flagstaff	80·00	
129	12 c. green and indigo	1·75	30
	a. Extra flagstaff	£2250	£2250
	b. Short extra flagstaff	£100	
	d. Flagstaff on right-hand turret	£100	
	e. Double flagstaff	£100	
130	20 c. brown and deep blue	1·90	40
	a. Extra flagstaff	£160	
	b. Short extra flagstaff	80·00	
	d. Flagstaff on right-hand turret	80·00	
	e. Double flagstaff	80·00	

31 1 r. slate and purple 3·00 7·50
a. Extra flagstaff £150
b. Short extra flagstaff £100
c. Lightning conductor £100
d. Flagstaff on right-hand turret £100
28/31 *Set of* 4 6·50 7·50
28/31 Perf "Specimen" *Set of* 4 80·00
For illustrations of plate varieties see Omnibus section following ululand.

937 (12 May). *Coronation. As Nos.* 13/15 *of Aden, but ptd by B.W. P* 11 × 11½.
32 6 c. sage-green 30 15
33 12 c. orange 45 15
34 20 c. blue 70 35
32/4 *Set of* 3 1·25 60
32/4 Perf "Specimen" *Set of* 3 55·00

14 Coco-de-mer Palm **15** Giant Tortoise

16 Fishing Pirogue

(Photo Harrison)

1938 (1 Jan)–**49**. *Wmk Mult Script CA. P* 14½ × 13½ (*vert*) *or* 13½ × 14½ (*horiz*).
135 **14** 2 c. purple-brown, **CO** (10.2.38) 10 15
136 **15** 3 c. green, **C** 2·00 70
136*a* 3 c. orange, **CO** (8.8.41) 15 20
137 **16** 6 c. orange, **C** 1·50 1·50
137*a* 6 c. greyish green, **C** (8.8.41) 1·25 40
b. Green, **OC** (11.42) 30 20
138 **14** 9 c. scarlet, **C** (10.2.38) 4·50 1·75
138*a* 9 c. grey-blue, **CO** (8.8.41) 15 20
b. Dull blue, **OC** (19.11.45) 1·00 50
139 **15** 12 c. reddish violet, **C** 16·00 55
139*a* 15 c. brown-carmine, **C** (8.8.41) 85 50
b. Brown-red, **O** (11.42) 30 15
139c **14** 18 c. carmine-lake, **CO** (8.8.41) 80 40
d. Rose-carmine, **C** (5.4.49) 45 40
140 **16** 20 c. blue, **C** 24·00 5·00
140*a* 20 c. brown-ochre, **CO** (8.8.41) 40 15
141 **14** 25 c. brown-ochre, **C** 32·00 9·00
142 **15** 30 c. carmine, **C** (10.2.38) 42·00 6·50
142*a* 30 c. blue, **CO** (8.8.41) 25 40
143 **16** 45 c. chocolate, **C** (10.2.38) 70 25
a. Purple-brown, **OC** (11.42) 70 25
144 **14** 50 c. deep reddish violet, **CO** (10.2.38) 15 10
144*a* 50 c. bright lilac, **C** (13.6.49) 15 35
145 **15** 75 c. slate-blue, **C** (10.2.38) 60·00 38·00
145*a* 75 c. deep slate-lilac, **CO** (8.8.41) 25 30
146 **16** 1 r. yellow-green, **C** (10.2.38) 90·00 48·00
146*a* 1 r. grey-black, **CO** (8.8.41) 30 30
147 **14** 1 r. 50, ultramarine, **CO** (10.2.38) 80 90
148 **15** 2 r. 25, olive, **CO** (10.2.38) 1·00 2·00
149 **16** 5 r. red, **CO** (10.2.38) 2·00 2·75
135/49 *Set of* 25 £250 £100
135/49 (*excl* 144*a*) Perf "Specimen" *Set of* 24 £350
The stamps on ordinary paper appeared in 1942–43.

Lamp on mast flaw (R. 1/5)

1946 (23 Sept). *Victory. As Nos.* 28/9 *of Aden.*
150 9 c. light blue 10 10
151 30 c. deep blue 10 10
a. Lamp on mast flaw 8·00
150/1 Perf "Specimen" *Set of* 2 48·00

1948 (5 Nov). *Royal Silver Wedding. As Nos.* 30/1 *of Aden.*
152 9 c. ultramarine 15 25
153 5 r. carmine 6·00 9·50

1949 (10 Oct). *75th Anniv of Universal Postal Union. As Nos.* 114/17 *of Antigua, but inscr* "SEYCHELLES" (*recess*).
154 18 c. bright reddish purple 15 15
155 50 c. purple 35 40
156 1 r. grey 30 15
157 2 r. 25, olive 50 40
154/7 *Set of* 4 1·10 1·00

MINIMUM PRICE

The minimum price quote is 10p which represents a handling charge rather than a basis for valuing common stamps. For further notes about prices see introductory pages.

17 Sail-fish **18** Map of Indian Ocean

(Photo Harrison)

1952 (3 Mar). *Various designs as T* **14/16** *but with new portrait and crown as in T* **17/18**. *Chalk-surfaced paper. Wmk Mult Script CA. P* 14½ × 13½ (*vert*) *or* 13½ × 14½ (*horiz*).
158 **17** 2 c. lilac 25 30
a. Error. Crown missing, W **9***a* £170
b. Error. St. Edward's Crown, W **9***b* 75·00
159 **15** 3 c. orange 25 30
a. Error. Crown missing, W **9***a* £150
b. Error. St. Edward's Crown, W **9***b* 70·00
160 **14** 9 c. chalky blue 20 35
a. Error. Crown missing, W **9***a* £225
b. Error. St. Edward's Crown, W **9***b* £100
161 **16** 15 c. deep yellow-green 25 45
a. Error. Crown missing, W **9***a* £225
b. Error. St. Edward's Crown, W **9***b* £110
162 **18** 18 c. carmine-lake 40 20
a. Error. Crown missing, W **9***a* £250
b. Error. St. Edward's Crown, W **9***b* £120
163 **16** 20 c. orange-yellow 55 60
a. Error. Crown missing, W **9***a* £275
b. Error. St. Edward's Crown, W **9***b* £160
164 **15** 25 c. vermilion 50 70
a. Error. Crown missing, W **9***a* £250
b. Error. St. Edward's Crown, W **9***b* £150
165 **17** 40 c. ultramarine 50 60
a. Error. Crown missing, W **9***a* £275
b. Error. St. Edward's Crown, W **9***b* £170
166 **16** 45 c. purple-brown 50 30
a. Error. Crown missing, W **9***a* £325
b. Error. St. Edward's Crown, W **9***b* £225
167 **14** 50 c. reddish violet 60 60
a. Error. Crown missing, W **9***a* £350
b. Error. St. Edward's Crown, W **9***b* £200
168 **18** 1 r. grey-black 90 75
b. Error. St. Edward's Crown, W **9***b* £375
169 **14** 1 r. 50, blue 2·25 4·50
b. Error. St. Edward's Crown, W **9***b* £500
170 **15** 2 r. 25, brown-olive 2·50 5·50
b. Error. St. Edward's Crown, W **9***b* £500
171 **18** 5 r. red 3·25 7·50
b. Error. St. Edward's Crown, W **9***b* £500
172 **17** 10 r. green 6·00 14·00
158/72 *Set of* 15 17·00 32·00
See *Introduction* re the watermark errors.

1953 (2 June). *Coronation. As No.* 47 *of Aden.*
173 9 c. black and deep bright blue 10 20

19 Sail-fish **20** Seychelles Flying Fox

(Photo Harrison)

1954 (1 Feb)–**61**. *Designs previously used for King George VI issue, but with portrait of Queen Elizabeth II, as in T* **19** *and T* **20**. *Chalk-surfaced paper. Wmk Mult Script CA. P* 14½ × 13½ (*vert*) *or* 13½ × 14½ (*horiz*).
174 **19** 2 c. lilac 10 10
175 – 3 c. orange 10 10
175*a* **20** 5 c. violet (25.10.57) 15 15
176 – 9 c. chalky blue 10 10
176*a* – 10 c. chalky blue (15.9.56) 25 15
ab. Blue (11.7.61) 60 30
177 – 15 c. deep yellow-green 15 15
178 – 18 c. crimson 10 10
179 – 20 c. orange-yellow 20 20
180 – 25 c. vermilion 20 25
180*a* – 35 c. crimson (15.9.56) 70 85
181 **19** 40 c. ultramarine 25 25
182 – 45 c. purple-brown 20 15
183 – 50 c. reddish violet 20 20
183*a* – 70 c. purple-brown (15.9.56) 1·50 1·25
184 – 1 r. grey-black 50 40
185 – 1 r. 50, blue 2·50 2·50
186 – 2 r. 25, brown-olive 3·00 5·00
187 – 5 r. red 8·50 6·50
188 **19** 10 r. green 18·00 15·00
174/88 *Set of* 19 32·00 30·00
Designs: *Horiz*—15 c., 20 c., 45 c., 70 c. Fishing pirogue; 18 c., 35 c., 1 r., 5 r. Map of Indian Ocean. *Vert*—3 c., 25 c., 2 r. 25, Giant Tortoise; 9 c., 50 c., 1 r. 50, Coco de Mer Palm.

21 "La Pierre de Possession"

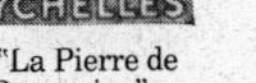

(**22**)

(Photo Harrison)

1956 (15 Nov). *Bicentenary of "La Pierre de Possession". Wmk Mult Script CA. P* 14½ × 13½.
189 **21** 40 c. ultramarine 10 10
190 1 r. black 10 10

191 191a 191 191b 191 191c

1957 (16 Sept). *No.* 182 *surch with T* **22**.
191 5 c. on 45 c. purple-brown 10 10
a. Italic "e" 2·50
b. Italic "s" 2·50
c. Italic "c" 2·00
d. Thick bars omitted £300
e. Surch double £160

23 Mauritius 6d. Stamp with Seychelles "B 64" Cancellation

(Recess: cancellation typo B.W.)

1961 (11 Dec). *Centenary of First Seychelles Post Office.* W w **12**. *P* 11½.
193 **23** 10 c. blue, black and purple 10 10
194 35 c. blue, black and myrtle-green 15 10
195 2 r. 25, blue, black and orange-brown 20 20
193/5 *Set of* 3 35 30

24 Black Parrot **29** Anse Royale Bay

40 Colony's Badge

(Des V. Whiteley. Photo Harrison)

1962 (21 Feb)–**68**. *T* **24, 29, 40** *and similar designs.* W w **12** (*upright*). *P* 13½ × 14½ (*horiz designs and* 10 *r.*) *or* 14½ × 13½ (*others*).
196 5 c. multicoloured 10 10
197 10 c. multicoloured 30 10
198 15 c. multicoloured 10 10
199 20 c. multicoloured 10 10
200 25 c. multicoloured 10 10
200*a* 30 c. multicoloured (15.7.68) 2·00 90
201 35 c. multicoloured 1·25 2·00
202 40 c. multicoloured 20 25
203 45 c. multicoloured (1.8.66) 3·00 2·00
204 50 c. multicoloured 25 25
205 70 c. ultramarine and light blue 4·00 3·00
206 75 c. multicoloured (1.8.66) 1·25 2·25
207 1 r. multicoloured 30 10
208 1 r. 50, multicoloured 2·25 3·50
209 2 r. 25, multicoloured 2·25 2·50
210 3 r. 50, multicoloured 2·00 4·50
211 5 r. multicoloured 3·25 2·50
212 10 r. multicoloured 11·00 4·50
196/212 *Set of* 18 30·00 25·00
Designs: *Vert* (*as T* **24**)—10 c. Vanilla vine; 15 c. Fisherman; 20 c. Denis Island lighthouse; 25 c. Clock Tower, Victoria; 50 c. Cascade Church; 70 c. Sail-fish; 75 c. Coco-de-Mer palm. *Horiz* (*as T* **29**)—30 c., 35 c. Anse Royale Bay; 40 c. Government House; 45 c. Fishing pirogue; 1 r. Cinnamon; 1r. 50, Copra; 2r. 25 Map; 3r. 50, Land settlement; 5 r. Regina Mundi convent.
The 1 r. exists with PVA gum as well as gum arabic, but the 30 c. exists with PVA gum only.
See also Nos. 233/7.
For stamps of the above issue overprinted "B.I.O.T" see under British Indian Ocean Territory.

1963 (4 June). *Freedom from Hunger. As No.* 76 *of Aden.*
213 70 c. reddish violet 60 25

1963 (16 Sept). *Red Cross Centenary. As Nos.* 147/8 *of Antigua.*
214 10 c. red and black 25 10
215 75 c. red and blue 75 40

(41)

42 Seychelles Flying Fox

1965 (15 Apr). *Nos.* 201 *and* 205 *surch as T* **41**.
216 45 c. on 35 c. multicoloured 10 10
217 75 c. on 70 c. ultramarine and light blue .. 15 10

1965 (1 June). *I.T.U. Centenary. As Nos.* 166/7 *of Antigua.*
218 5 c. orange and ultramarine 15 10
219 1 r. 50, mauve and apple-green 65 25

1965 (25 Oct). *International Co-operation Year. As Nos.* 168/9 *of Antigua.*
220 5 c. reddish purple and turquoise-green .. 10 10
221 40 c. deep bluish green and lavender 20 10

1966 (24 Jan). *Churchill Commemoration. As Nos.* 170/3 *of Antigua.*
222 5 c. new blue 15 10
223 15 c. deep green 40 10
224 75 c. brown 80 10
225 1 r. 50, bluish violet .. .. .. 1·25 45
222/5 .. .. *Set of* 4 2·25 65

1966 (1 July). *World Cup Football Championships. As Nos.* 176/7 *of Antigua.*
226 15 c. violet, yellow-green, lake & yellow-brn .. 10 10
227 1 r. chocolate, blue-green, lake & yellow-brn 20 10

1966 (20 Sept). *Inauguration of W.H.O. Headquarters, Geneva. As Nos.* 178/9 *of Antigua.*
228 20 c. black, yellow-green and light blue .. 15 10
229 50 c. black, light purple and yellow-brown .. 25 15

1966 (1 Dec). *20th Anniv of U.N.E.S.C.O. As Nos.* 196/8 *of Antigua.*
230 15 c. slate-violet, red, yellow and orange .. 25 10
231 1 r. orange-yellow, violet and deep olive .. 45 10
232 5 r. black, bright purple and orange .. .. 1·25 1·00
230/2 .. .. *Set of* 3 1·75 1·00

1967–69. *As Nos.* 196/7, 204 *and new values as T* **42** *but wmk* w **12** *(sideways).*
233 5 c. multicoloured (7.2.67) 35 15
234 10 c. multicoloured (4.6.68) 25 10
235 50 c. multicoloured (13.5.69) .. .. 1·75 1·50
236 60 c. red, blue and blackish brown (15.7.68) 1·25 45
237 85 c. ultramarine and light blue (as No. 205) (15.7.68) 90 40
233/7 .. .. *Set of* 5 4·00 2·40
The 10 c. exists with PVA gum as well as gum arabic, but the 50 c. to 85 c. exist with PVA gum only.

UNIVERSAL
ADULT
SUFFRAGE
1967

(43)

44 Cowrie Shells

1967 (18 Sept). *Universal Adult Suffrage. As Nos.* 198 *and* 206, *but W* w **12** *(sideways), and Nos.* 203 *and* 210 *(wmk upright), optd with T* **43**.
238 15 c. multicoloured 10 10
239 45 c. multicoloured 10 10
240 75 c. multicoloured 10 10
241 3 r. 50, multicoloured 20 15
238/41 .. .. *Set of* 4 30 25

(Des V. Whiteley. Photo Harrison)

1967 (4 Dec). *International Tourist Year. T* **44** *and similar horiz designs. Multicoloured. W* w **12**. *P* 14 × 13.
242 15 c. Type **44** 15 10
243 40 c. Cone Shells 20 10
244 1 r. Arthritic Spider Conch 25 10
245 2 r. 25, Subulate Auger and Triton Shells .. 55 40
242/5 .. .. *Set of* 4 1·00 45

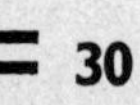

(48)

49 Farmer with Wife and Children at Sunset

1968 (16 Apr). *Nos.* 202/3 *and as No.* 206 *surch as T* **48** *(30 c.) or with "CENTS" added, and three bars (others). W* w **12** *(sideways on No.* 248).
246 30 c. on 40 c. multicoloured 10 10
247 60 c. on 45 c. multicoloured 10 10
248 85 c. on 75 c. multicoloured 10 10
246/8 .. .. *Set of* 3 25 25

(Des Mary Hayward. Litho Harrison)

1968 (2 Sept). *Human Rights Year. W* w **12**. *P* 14½ × 13½.
249 **49** 20 c. multicoloured 10 10
250 50 c. multicoloured 10 10
251 85 c. multicoloured 10 10
252 2 r. 25, multicoloured 20 30
249/52 .. .. *Set of* 4 30 40

50 Expedition landing at Anse Possession

54 Apollo Launch

(Des Mary Hayward. Litho and die-stamped Harrison)

1968 (30 Dec). *Bicentenary of First Landing on Praslin. T* **50** *and similar multicoloured designs. W* w **12** *(sideways on* 50 *c.,* 85 *c.). P* 14.
253 20 c. Type **50** 10 10
254 50 c. French warships at anchor (*vert*) .. 15 15
255 85 c. Coco-de-Mer and Black Parrot (*vert*) .. 35 20
256 2 r. 25, French warships under sail .. 50 50
253/6 .. .. *Set of* 4 1·00 80

(Des V. Whiteley. Litho Format)

1969 (9 Sept). *First Man on the Moon. T* **54** *and similar horiz designs. Multicoloured. W* w **12** *(sideways on horiz designs). P* 13½.
257 5 c. Type **54** 10 10
258 20 c. Module leaving Mother-ship for Moon .. 15 10
259 50 c. Astronauts and Space Module on Moon 20 15
260 85 c. Tracking station 25 15
261 2 r. 25, Moon craters with Earth on the "Horizon" 45 65
257/61 .. .. *Set of* 5 1·00 95

59 Picault's Landing, 1742

60 Badge of Seychelles

(Des Mary Hayward. Litho Enschedé)

1969 (3 Nov)–**75.** *Horiz designs as T* **59/60**. *Multicoloured. W* w **12** *(sideways). Slightly toned paper. P* 13 × 12½.
262 5 c. Type **59** 10 10
263 10 c. U.S. satellite-tracking station .. 10 10
a. Whiter paper (8.3.73) 40 30
264 15 c. *Königsberg I* at Aldabra, 1914† .. 40 15
a. Whiter paper (8.3.73) .. .. .. 2·50 65
265 20 c. Fleet re-fuelling off St. Anne, 1939–45 25 10
a. Whiter paper (13.6.74) .. .. 1·25 1·25
266 25 c. Exiled Ashanti King Prempeh .. 20 10
a. Whiter paper (8.3.73) 65 70
267 30 c. Laying Stone of Possession, 1756 .. 1·00 2·00
268 40 c. As 30 c. (11.12.72) .. .. .. 90 1·25
a. Whiter paper (13.6.74) .. .. 1·60 1·60
269 50 c. Pirates and treasure 30 15
a. Whiter paper (13.6.74) .. .. 1·25 1·25
270 60 c. Corsairs attacking merchantman .. 1·00 1·50
271 65 c. As 60 c. (11.12.72) .. .. .. 1·75 2·50
a. Whiter paper (13.8.75) .. .. 4·50 5·00
272 85 c. Impression of proposed airport .. 1·25 1·50
273 95 c. As 85 c. (11.12.72) .. .. .. 2·50 3·00
a. Whiter paper (13.6.74) .. .. 4·00 3·25
274 1 r. French Governor capitulating to British naval officer, 1794 .. .. 35 15
a. Whiter paper (8.3.73) .. .. .. 1·00 70
275 1 r. 50, H.M.S. *Sybille* and *Chiffone* in battle, 1801 .. .. 1·75 2·00
a. Whiter paper (8.3.73) .. .. .. 3·00 4·50
276 3 r. 50, Visit of the Duke of Edinburgh, 1956 .. .. 1·50 2·00
a. Whiter paper (13.8.75) .. .. 2·50 6·50
277 5 r. Chevalier Queau de Quincy .. .. 1·50 1·50
278 10 r. Indian Ocean chart, 1574 .. .. 2·75 3·25
279 15 r. Type **60** .. .. 4·00 7·50
262/79 .. .. *Set of* 18 18·00 24·00
263a/76a .. .. *Set of* 11 20·00 23·00
†The design is incorrect in that it shows *Königsberg II* and the wrong date ("1915").
The stamps on the whiter paper are highly glazed, producing shade variations and are easily distinguishable from the original printings on toned paper.

74 White Terns, French Warship and Island

(Des A. Smith; adapted V. Whiteley. Litho D.L.R.)

1970 (27 Apr). *Bicentenary of First Settlement, St. Anne Island. T* **74** *and similar horiz designs. Multicoloured. W* w **12** *(sideways). P* 14.
280 20 c. Type **74** 15 1
281 50 c. Flying Fish, ship and island 15 1
282 85 c. Compass and chart 15 1
283 3 r. 50, Anchor on sea-bed 30 4
280/3 .. .. *Set of* 4 65 5

78 Girl and Optician's Chart

79 Pitcher Plant

(Des A. Smith. Litho Questa)

1970 (4 Aug). *Centenary of British Red Cross. T* **78** *and similar multicoloured designs. W* w **12** *(sideways on horiz designs). P* 14.
284 20 c. Type **78** .. .. 10 1(
285 50 c. Baby, scales and milk bottles .. .. 15 1(
286 85 c. Woman with child and umbrella (*vert*) .. 15 1(
287 3 r. 50, Red Cross local H.Q. building .. 55 6(
284/7 .. .. *Set of* 4 85 6

(Des G. Drummond. Litho J.W.)

1970 (29 Dec). *Flowers. T* **79** *and similar vert designs. Multicoloured. W* w **12**. *P* 14.
288 20 c. Type **79** 45 15
289 50 c. Wild Vanilla 55 15
290 85 c. Tropic-Bird Orchid .. .. .. 1·40 30
291 3 r. 50, Vare Hibiscus .. .. .. 2·50 1·50
288/91 .. .. *Set of* 4 4·50 1·90
MS292 81 × 133 mm. Nos. 288/91. Wmk inverted 8·00 11·00

80 Seychelles "On the Map"

81 Piper "Navajo"

(Des and litho J.W.)

1971 (18 May). *"Putting Seychelles on the Map". Sheet* 152 × 101 *mm. W* w **12** *(sideways). P* 13½.
MS293 **80** 5 r. multicoloured .. .. .. 2·25 8·50

(Des and litho J.W.)

1971 (28 June). *Airport Completion. T* **81** *and similar multicoloured designs showing aircraft. W* w **12** *(sideways on horiz designs). P* 14 × 14½ (5, 20 *and* 60 *c.) or* 14½ *(others).*
294 5 c. Type **81** 10 10
295 20 c. Westland "Wessex" 20 10
296 50 c. "Catalina" flying-boat (*horiz*) 40 10
297 60 c. Grumman "Albatross" 45 10
298 85 c. Short "G" Class flying-boat (*horiz*) .. 65 10
299 3 r. 50, Vickers Supermarine "Walrus" (*horiz*) 3·50 3·00
294/9 .. .. *Set of* 6 4·75 3·25

82 Santa Claus delivering Gifts (Jean-Claude Waye Hive)

(83)

(Des Jennifer Toombs. Litho A. & M.)

1971 (12 Oct). *Christmas. Drawings by local children. T* **82** *and similar horiz designs. Multicoloured. W* w **12** *(sideways). P* 13½.
300 10 c. Type **82** 10 10
301 15 c. Santa Claus seated on turtle (Edison Thérésine) 10 10
302 3 r. 50, Santa Claus landing on island (Isabelle Tirant) 40 70
300/2 .. .. *Set of* 3 50 70

1971 (21 Dec). *Nos.* 267, 270 *and* 272 *surch in grey as T* **83**.
303 40 c. on 30 c. Laying Stone of Possession, 1756 30 55
304 65 c. on 60 c. Corsairs attacking merchantman 40 75
305 95 c. on 85 c. Impression of proposed airport .. 45 1·00
303/5 .. .. *Set of* 3 1·00 2·10

ROYAL VISIT 1972

(84) 85 Seychelles Brush Warbler

1972 (20 Mar). *Royal Visit. Nos.* 265 *and* 277 *optd with T* **84**.
306 20 c. Fleet re-fuelling off St. Anne, 1939–45 .. 15 20
307 5 r. Chevalier Queau de Quincy (Gold) .. 1·50 2·50

(Des R. Gillmor. Litho Questa)

1972 (24 July). *Rare Seychelles Birds. T* **85** *and similar vert designs. Multicoloured. W* w **12** (*sideways*). *P* 13½.
308 5 c. Type **85** 15 10
309 20 c. Bare-legged Scops Owl 40 20
310 50 c. Seychelles Blue Pigeon .. .. .. 1·00 65
311 65 c. Seychelles Magpie Robin .. .. .. 1·00 75
312 95 c. Seychelles Paradise Flycatcher .. .. 2·00 2·00
313 3 r. 50, Seychelles Kestrel .. .. .. 6·50 8·00
308/13 .. .. *Set of* 6 10·00 10·50
MS314 144 × 162 mm. Nos. 308/13 .. .. 16·00 20·00

86 Fireworks Display 87 Giant Tortoise and Sailfish

(Des V. Whiteley. Litho Questa)

1972 (18 Sept). *"Festival '72". T* **86** *and similar multicoloured designs. W* w **12** (*sideways on* 10 *and* 25 *c.*). *P* 14.
315 10 c. Type **86** 10 10
316 15 c. Pirogue race (*horiz*) 10 10
317 25 c. Floats and costumes 10 10
318 5 r. Water skiing (*horiz*) 60 80
315/18 .. .. *Set of* 4 65 80

(Des (from photograph by D. Groves) and photo Harrison)

1972 (20 Nov). *Royal Silver Wedding. Multicoloured; background colour given. W* w **12**. *P* 14 × 14½.
319 **87** 95 c. turquoise-blue 15 10
320 1 r. 50, red-brown 15 10

1973 (14 Nov). *Royal Wedding. As Nos.* 165/6 *of Anguilla.*
321 95 c. ochre 10 10
322 1 r. 50, dull deep blue 10 10

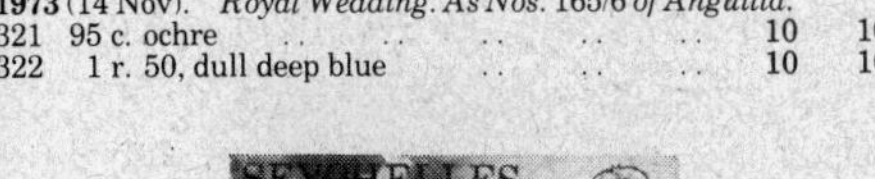

88 Soldier Fish

(Des G. Drummond. Litho Questa)

1974 (5 Mar). *Fishes. T* **88** *and similar horiz designs. Multicoloured. W* w **12**. *P* 14½ × 14.
323 20 c. Type **88** 15 10
324 50 c. File Fish 25 10
325 95 c. Butterfly Fish 30 20
326 1 r. 50, Gaterin .. .. 75 1·00
323/6 .. .. *Set of* 4 1·25 1·25

89 Globe and Letter

(Des Sylvia Goaman. Litho Enschedé)

1974 (9 Oct). *Centenary of Universal Postal Union. T* **89** *and similar horiz designs. Multicoloured. W* w **12** (*sideways*). *P* 12½ × 12.
327 20 c. Type **89** 10 10
328 50 c. Globe and radio beacon 20 10
329 95 c. Globe and postmark 35 40
330 1 r. 50, Emblems within "UPU" 50 70
327/30 .. .. *Set of* 4 1·00 1·10

90 Sir Winston Churchill (91)

(Des G. Vasarhelyi. Litho Questa)

1974 (30 Nov). *Birth Centenary of Sir Winston Churchill. T* **90** *and similar horiz design. Multicoloured. W* w **12**. *P* 14.
331 95 c. Type **90** 20 15
332 1 r. 50, Profile portrait 35 40
MS333 81 × 109 mm. Nos. 331/2 .. .. .. 60 1·50

1975 (8 Feb). *Visit of R.M.S. "Queen Elizabeth II". Nos.* 265a, 269a, 273a *and* 275a *optd with T* **91**.
334 20 c. Fleet re-fuelling off St. Anne, 1939–45 .. 10 15
335 50 c. Pirates and treasure 15 20
336 95 c. Impression of proposed airport (Sil.) .. 20 35
337 1 r. 50, H.M.S. *Sybille* and *Chiffone* in battle, 1801 .. .. 35 60
334/7 .. .. *Set of* 4 70 1·10

INTERNAL
SELF-GOVERNMENT
OCTOBER
1975

(92) **93** Queen Elizabeth I

1975 (1 Oct). *Internal Self-Government. Nos.* 265a, 271a, 274a *and* 276a *optd with T* **92** *in gold, by Enschedé.*
338 20 c. Fleet re-fuelling off St. Anne, 1939–45 .. 15 15
339 65 c. Corsairs attacking merchantman .. 25 30
340 1 r. French Governor capitulating to British naval officer, 1794 .. .. .. 30 35
341 3 r. 50, Visit of Duke of Edinburgh, 1956 .. 1·00 1·50
338/41 .. .. *Set of* 4 1·50 2·00

(Des C. Abbott. Litho Walsall)

1975 (15 Dec). *International Women's Year. T* **93** *and similar vert designs. Multicoloured. W* w **14** (*inverted*). *P* 13½.
342 10 c. Type **93** 10 10
343 15 c. Gladys Aylward 10 10
344 20 c. Elizabeth Fry 10 10
345 25 c. Emmeline Pankhurst 10 10
346 65 c. Florence Nightingale 25 20
347 1 r. Amy Johnson 40 35
348 1 r. 50, Joan of Arc 50 60
349 3 r. 50, Eleanor Roosevelt .. .. .. 1·50 2·25
342/9 .. .. *Set of* 8 2·50 3·25

94 Map of Praslin and Postmark **95** First Landing, 1609 (inset portrait of Premier James Mancham)

(Des J.W. Litho Questa)

1976 (30 Mar). *Rural Posts. T* **94** *and similar vert designs showing maps and postmarks. Multicoloured. W* w **14**. *P* 14.
350 20 c. Type **94** 15 10
351 65 c. La Digue 25 20
352 1 r. Mahé with Victoria postmark 30 25
353 1 r. 50, Mahé with Anse Royale postmark .. 45 70
350/3 .. .. *Set of* 4 1·00 1·10
MS354 166 × 127 mm. Nos. 350/3 .. .. 2·00 3·00

INDEPENDENT

(Des G. Drummond. Litho J.W.)

1976 (29 June). *Independence. T* **95** *and similar vert designs. Multicoloured. W* w **12** (*sideways*). *P* 13½.
355 20 c. Type **95** 10 10
356 25 c. The Possession Stone 10 10
357 40 c. First settlers, 1770 .. .. .. 15 15
358 75 c. Chevalier Queau de Quincy 20 20
359 1 r. Sir Bickham Sweet-Escott 25 20
360 1 r. 25, Legislative Building 40 50
361 1 r. 50, Seychelles badge 45 60
362 3 r. 50, Seychelles flag .. .. .. 90 1·40
355/62 .. .. *Set of* 8 2·25 2·75

96 Flags of Seychelles and U.S.A.

(Des and litho J.W.)

1976 (12 July). *Seychelles Independence and American Independence Bicentenary. T* **96** *and similar horiz design. Multicoloured. W* w **12** (*sideways*). *P* 13½.
363 1 r. Type **96** 25 15
364 10 r. Statehouses of Seychelles and Philadelphia .. .. 1·25 1·50

97 Swimming **98** Seychelles Paradise Flycatcher

(Des J.W. Litho Questa)

1976 (26 July). *Olympic Games, Montreal. T* **97** *and similar horiz designs. W* w **14** (*sideways*). *P* 14.
365 20 c. ultramarine, cobalt and sepia 10 10
366 65 c. bottle-green, apple-green and grey-black 10 10
367 1 r. chestnut, blue-green and grey-black .. 10 10
368 3 r. 50, crimson, rose and grey-black .. 35 40
365/8 .. .. *Set of* 4 55 60
Designs:—65 c. Hockey; 1 r. Basketball; 3 r. 50, Football.

(Des Mrs. R. Fennessy. Litho Questa)

1976–77. *Fourth Pan-African Ornithological Congress, Seychelles. T* **98** *and similar multicoloured designs. W* w **14** (*sideways on Nos.* 370/1). *P* 14. *A. Ordinary paper* (8.11.76). *B. Chalky paper* (7.3.77).

		A		B	
369	20 c. Type **98**	15	10	15	10
370	1 r. 25, Seychelles Sunbird (*horiz*)	65	65	65	65
371	1 r. 50, Seychelles Brown White Eye (*horiz*)	80	80	80	80
372	5 r. Black Parrot	2·00	2·00	2·00	2·00
369/72	.. .. *Set of* 4	3·25	3·25	3·25	3·25
MS373	161 × 109 mm. Nos. 369/72	4·25	4·75		
	a. 5 r. value in miniature sheet imperf	£850			

(99) **100** Inauguration of George Washington

1976 (22 Nov). *Independence. Nos.* 265a, 269, 271a, 273a, 274a, 276a *and* 277/9 *optd with T* **99** (*No.* 271 *additionally surch.*). *W* w **12** (*sideways*).
374 20 c. Fleet re-fuelling off St. Anne, 1939–45 .. 25 35
375 50 c. Pirates and treasure 40 50
376 95 c. Impression of proposed airport 55 70
a. Opt inverted .. .. 85·00
377 1 r. French Governor capitulating to British naval officer, 1794 .. .. .. 55 70
378 3 r. 50, Visit of Duke of Edinburgh, 1956 .. 2·75 3·50
a. Opt inverted .. .. 75·00
b. On No. 276 .. .. 3·25 3·50
379 5 r. Chevalier Queau de Quincy .. .. 3·00 3·50
380 10 r. Indian Ocean chart, 1574 .. .. 5·50 8·00
381 15 c. Type **60** .. .. 7·50 9·00
382 25 r. on 65 c. Corsairs attacking merchantman 11·00 16·00
374/82 .. .. *Set of* 9 28·00 38·00

(Des Jennifer Toombs. Litho Questa)

1976 (21 Dec). *Bicentenary of American Revolution. T* **100** *and similar horiz designs. P* 14 × 13½.
383 1 c. crimson and light rose 10 10
384 2 c. violet and light lilac 10 10
385 3 c. bright blue and azure 10 10
386 4 c. chestnut and light yellow 10 10
387 5 c. emerald and light yellow-green 10 10
388 1 r. 50, sepia and cinnamon 60 35
389 3 r. 50, dp turquoise-blue & pale blue-green .. 80 80
390 5 r. chestnut and light yellow .. .. 1·00 1·00
391 10 r. chalky blue and azure .. .. .. 1·75 1·75
383/91 .. .. *Set of* 9 4·00 3·75
MS392 141 × 141 mm. 25 r. plum and magenta 4·00 5·50
Designs:—2 c. Jefferson and Louisiana Purchase; 3 c. William Seward and Alaska Purchase; 4 c. Pony Express, 1860; 5 c. Lincoln's Emancipation Proclamation; 1 r. 50 Transcontinental Railroad, 1869; 3 r. 50 Wright Brothers flight, 1903; 5 r. Henry Ford's assembly-line, 1913; 10 r. J. F. Kennedy and 1969 Moon-landing; 25 r. Signing Independence Declaration, 1776.

101 Silhouette of the Islands

102 Cruiser *Aurora* and Flag

(Des G. Hutchins (Nos. 395/8), J.W. (others). Litho Questa)

1977 (5 Sept). *Silver Jubilee. T* **101** *and similar multicoloured designs. W* w **14** (*sideways on* 20 *and* 40 *c.,* 5 *and* 10 *r.*). *P* 14.

393	20 c. Type **101**	10	10
394	40 c. Silhouette (*different*)	10	10
395	50 c. The Orb (*vert*)	10	10
396	1 r. St. Edward's Crown (*vert*)	15	10
397	1 r. 25, Ampulla and Spoon (*vert*)	20	15
398	1 r. 50, Sceptre with Cross (*vert*)	20	20
399	5 r. Silhouette (*different*)	50	50
400	10 r. Silhouette (*different*)	90	90
393/400	.. .. *Set of* 8	1·75	1·75
MS401	133 × 135 mm. 20 c., 50 c., 1 r., 10 r. all wmk sideways	75	1·40

(Litho State Printing Works, Moscow)

1977 (7 Nov). 60*th Anniv of Russian October Revolution. P* 12 × 12½.

402 **102**	1 r. 50, multicoloured	30	20
MS403	101 × 129 mm. No. 402	30	35

103 Coral Scene

(Des G. Drummond. Litho Walsall (40 c., 1 r., 1 r. 25, 1 r. 50), J.W. or Questa (25 c. (No. 408B)), J.W. (others))

1977–84. *Multicoloured designs as T* **103**. *Rupee values show* "Re" *or* "Rs". *W* w **14** (*sideways on* 10, 20, 50 *and* 75 *c.*). *P* 14½ × 14 (40 *c.,* 1 *r.,* 1 *r.* 25, 1 *r.* 50), 13 (5, 10, 15, 20 *r.*) *or* 14 (*others*).

A. *No imprint*. B. *Imprint date at foot*

		A		B	
404	5 c. Reef Fish	10	10	†	
405	10 c. Hawksbill Turtle	10	10	10	10
406	15 c. Coco-de-Mer	10	10	10	10
407	20 c. Wild Vanilla Orchid ..	55	10	10	10
408	25 c. Tiger Butterfly	60	25	10	10
409	40 c. Type **103**	25	10	10	10
410	50 c. Giant Tortoise	20	10	10	10
411	75 c. Crayfish	20	10	15	20
412	1 r. Madagascar Red Fody ..	1·25	10	2·75	20
413	1 r. 25, White Tern	1·00	15	†	
414	1 r. 50, Seychelles Flying Fox	1·50	15	2·00	50
415	3 r. 50, Green Gecko	60	65	†	
416	5 r. Octopus	2·00	40	†	
417	10 r. Giant Tiger Cowrie ..	2·25	2·00	†	
418	15 r. Pitcher Plant	2·25	2·50	†	
419	20 r. Coat of arms	2·50	2·50	†	
404A/19A	.. .. *Set of* 16	13·50	8·00		
405B/14B	.. .. *Set of* 9			5·00	1·10

Dates of issue: Without imprint 10.11.77, 40 c., 1 r. to 1 r. 50; 6.2.78, 10, 20, 50, 75 c., 5 r., 20 r.; 10.4.78, others. With imprint 14.3.80, 10, 15, 25, 40, 50, 75, 1 r., 1 r. 50; 5.84, 20 c.

The 40 c., 1 r., 1 r. 25 and 1 r. 50 values are horizontal designs, 31 × 27 mm; the 5, 10, 15 and 20 r. are vertical, 28 × 36 mm; the others are horizontal, 29 × 25 mm.

The 10 c. and 25 c. (Nos. 405B and 408B) exist with different imprint dates.

For rupee values showing face value as "R" see Nos. 487/94.

For 10 c. and 50 c. with watermark w 14 (upright) and printed by Questa see Nos. 718 and 722. A printing of the 25 c. by Questa on the same date has the same perforation and watermark as J.W. printings of No. 408B.

104 St. Roch Roman Catholic Church, Bel Ombre

(Des G. Drummond. Litho Walsall)

1977 (5 Dec). *Christmas. T* **104** *and similar horiz designs. Multicoloured. W* w **14** (*sideways*). *P* 13½ × 14.

420	20 c. Type **104**	10	10
421	1 r. Anglican cathedral, Victoria	10	10
422	1 r. 50, Roman Catholic cathedral, Victoria	15	10
423	5 r. St. Mark's Anglican church, Praslin ..	30	45
420/3	.. .. *Set of* 4	50	55

105 Liberation Day ringed on Calendar

106 Stamp Portraits of Edward VII, George V and George VI

(Des local artists; adapted L. Curtis. Litho Questa)

1978 (5 June). *Liberation Day. T* **105** *and similar vert designs. Multicoloured. W* w **14**. *P* 14 × 13½.

424	40 c. Type **105**	10	10
425	1 r. 25, Hands holding bayonet, torch and flag	15	10
426	1 r. 50, Fisherman and farmer	15	15
427	5 r. Soldiers and rejoicing people	35	40
424/7	.. .. *Set of* 4	60	60

(Des G. Drummond. Litho Questa)

1978 (21 Aug). 25*th Anniv of Coronation. T* **106** *and similar vert designs. Multicoloured. W* w **14**. *P* 14.

428	40 c. Type **106**	10	10
429	1 r. 50, Victoria and Elizabeth II	10	10
430	3 r. Queen Victoria Monument	20	25
431	5 r. Queen's Building, Victoria	30	35
428/31	.. .. *Set of* 4	60	65
MS432	87 × 129 mm. Nos. 428/31	60	85

107 Gardenia

(Des G. Hutchins. Litho Questa)

1978 (16 Oct). *Wildlife. T* **107** *and similar horiz designs. Multicoloured. W* w **14** (*sideways*). *P* 13½ × 14.

433	40 c. Type **107**	10	10
434	1 r. 25, Seychelles Magpie Robin	40	25
435	1 r. 50, Seychelles Paradise Flycatcher ..	45	35
436	5 r. Green Turtle	70	85
433/6	.. .. *Set of* 4	1·50	1·40

108 Possession Stone

109 Seychelles Fody

(Des G. Hutchins. Litho Questa)

1978 (15 Dec). *Bicentenary of Victoria. T* **108** *and similar horiz designs. Multicoloured. W* w **14** (*sideways*). *P* 13½ × 14.

437	20 c. Type **108**	10	10
438	1 r. 25, Plan of 1782 "L'Etablissement" ..	15	15
439	1 r. 50, Clock Tower	15	15
440	5 r. Bust of Pierre Poivre	40	50
437/40	.. .. *Set of* 4	65	75

(Des G. Drummond. Litho Questa)

1979 (27 Feb). *Birds* (1*st series*). *T* **109** *and similar vert designs. Multicoloured. W* w **14**. *P* 14.

441	2 r. Type **109**	50	50
	a. Horiz strip of 5. Nos. 441/5	2·25	
442	2 r. Green Heron	50	50
443	2 r. Thick-billed Bulbul	50	50
444	2 r. Seychelles Cave Swiftlet	50	50
445	2 r. Grey-headed Lovebird	50	50
441/5	.. .. *Set of* 5	2·25	2·25

Nos. 441/5 were printed together, *se-tenant*, in horizontal strips of 5 throughout the sheet.

See also Nos. 463/7, 500/4 and 523/7.

COVER PRICES

Cover factors are quoted at the beginning of each country for most issues to 1945. An explanation of the system can be found on page x. The factors quoted do not, however, apply to philatelic covers.

110 Patrice Lumumba

111 1978 5 r. Liberation Day Commemorative and Sir Rowland Hill

(Des G. Vasarhelyi. Litho Questa)

1979 (5 June). *African Liberation Heroes. T* **110** *and similar ver[t] designs. W* w **14**. *P* 14 × 14½.

446	40 c. black, deep violet and lilac	10	1
447	2 r. black, blue and pale blue	25	2
448	2 r. 25, black, reddish brown & orange-brn ..	30	3
449	5 r. black, bronze-green and dull green ..	65	8
446/9	.. .. *Set of* 4	1·10	1·2

Designs:—2 r. Kwame Nkrumah; 2 r. 25, Dr. Eduardo Mondlane 5 r. Hamilcar Cabral.

(Des J.W. Litho Questa)

1979 (27 Aug). *Death Centenary of Sir Rowland Hill. T* **111** *an[d] similar vert designs showing stamps and Sir Rowland Hill Multicoloured. W* w **14**. *P* 14.

450	40 c. Type **111**	10	1
451	2 r. 25, 1972 50 c. Rare Birds commemorative	35	3
452	3 r. 1962 50 c. definitive	40	4
450/2	.. .. *Set of* 3	75	7
MS453	112 × 88 mm. 5 r. 1892 4 c. definitive. Wmk inverted	40	5

112 Child with Book

113 The Herald Angel

(Des BG Studio. Litho Questa)

1979 (26 Oct). *International Year of the Child. T* **112** *and similar multicoloured designs. W* w **14** (*sideways on* 40 *c. and* 2 *r.* 25). *P* 14½.

454	40 c. Type **112**	10	10
455	2 r. 25, Children of different races ..	20	30
456	3 r. Young child with ball (*vert*) ..	30	45
457	5 r. Girl with glove-puppet (*vert*) ..	40	65
454/7	.. .. *Set of* 4	85	1·25

Nos. 454/7 were each printed in sheets including two *se-tenant* stamp-size labels.

(Des J. Cooter. Litho Walsall)

1979 (3 Dec). *Christmas. T* **113** *and similar multicoloured designs. W* w **14** (*sideways on* 3 *r.*). *P* 14½ × 14 (3 *r.*) *or* 14 × 14½ (*others*).

458	20 c. Type **113**	10	10
459	2 r. 25, The Virgin and Child	25	30
460	3 r. The Three Kings (*horiz*)	35	45
458/60	.. .. *Set of* 3	60	70
MS461	87 × 75 mm. 5 r. The Flight into Egypt (*horiz*) (wmk sideways). P 14½ × 14 ..	50	70

R.1.10

(114)

115 Seychelles Kestrel

1979 (7 Dec). *As No.* 415 *but with imprint, surch with T* **114**.

462	1 r. 10 on 3 r. 50, Green Gecko	30	30

(Des G. Drummond. Litho Questa)

1980 (29 Feb). *Birds* (2*nd series*). *Seychelles Kestrel. T* **115** *and similar vert designs. Multicoloured. W* w **14** (*inverted*). *P* 14.

463	2 r. Type **115**	50	50
	a. Horiz strip of 5. Nos. 463/7	2·25	
464	2 r. Pair of Seychelles Kestrels	50	50
465	2 r. Seychelles Kestrel with eggs	50	50
466	2 r. Seychelles Kestrel on nest with chick ..	50	50
467	2 r. Seychelles Kestrel chicks in nest ..	50	50
463/7	.. .. *Set of* 5	2·25	2·25

Nos. 463/7 were printed together, *se-tenant*, in horizontal strips of 5 throughout the sheet.

116 10 Rupees Banknote   117 Sprinting

(Des B. Grout. Litho Questa)

1980 (18 Apr). *"London 1980" International Stamp Exhibition. New Currency.* *T* **116** *and similar multicoloured designs showing banknotes.* W w **14** (*sideways on* 40 c. *and* 1 r. 50). *P* 14.

468	40 c. Type **116**	10	10
469	1 r. 50, 25 rupees	15	15
470	2 r. 25, 50 rupees (*vert*)	25	25
471	5 r. 100 rupees (*vert*)	55	55
468/71	*Set of* 4	90	90
MS472	119 × 102 mm. Nos. 468/71 (wmk sideways)	90	1·40

(Des J.W. Litho Questa)

1980 (13 June). *Olympic Games, Moscow.* *T* **117** *and similar vert designs. Multicoloured.* W w **14**. *P* 14 × 14½.

473	40 c. Type **117**	10	10
474	2 r. 25, Weightlifting	20	20
475	3 r. Boxing	30	30
476	5 r. Yachting	40	40
473/6	*Set of* 4	80	80
MS477	90 × 121 mm. Nos. 473/6	1·00	1·90

118 "Jumbo Jet" Airliner   119 Female Palm

(Des A. Theobald. Litho Questa)

1980 (22 Aug). *International Tourism Conference, Manila.* *T* **118** *and similar horiz designs. Multicoloured.* W w **14** (*sideways*). *P* 14.

478	40 c. Type **118**	10	10
479	2 r. 25, Bus	35	35
480	3 r. Cruise liner	50	50
481	5 r. *La Belle Coralline* (tourist launch)	70	75
478/81	*Set of* 4	1·50	1·50

(Des L. Curtis. Litho Harrison)

1980 (14 Nov). *Coco-de-Mer (palms).* *T* **119** *and similar vert designs. Multicoloured.* W w **14**. *P* 14.

482	40 c. Type **119**	10	10
483	2 r. 25, Male Palm	25	20
484	3 r. Artefacts	40	35
485	5 r. Fisherman's gourd	55	55
482/5	*Set of* 4	1·10	1·00
MS486	82 × 140 mm. Nos. 482/5	1·75	2·00

1981 (9 Jan)–**86**. *As Nos.* 412/14, 415 (*but new value*), *and* 416/19 *all with face values redrawn to show* "R" *instead of* "Re" *or* "Rs" *and imprint date at foot. Chalk-surfaced paper.*

487	1 r. Madagascar Red Fody	55	25
	a. Ordinary paper (11.86)	20	25
488	1 r. 10, Green Gecko	20	25
489	1 r. 25, White Tern	60	30
490	1 r. 50, Seychelles Flying Fox	25	30
491	5 r. Octopus	90	95
492	10 r. Giant Tiger Cowrie	1·75	1·90
493	15 r. Pitcher Plant	2·75	3·00
494	20 r. Coat of arms	3·75	4·00
487/94	*Set of* 8	9·50	9·75

The 1 r., 1 r. 50 and 5 r. values exist with different imprint dates below the design.

For 1 r. 25 watermarked w **16** see No. 735.

120 Vasco da Gama's *Sao Gabriel*, 1497   121 Male White Tern

(Des J.W. Litho Format)

1981 (27 Feb). *Ships.* *T* **120** *and similar horiz designs. Multicoloured.* W w **14** (*sideways*). *P* 14½ × 14.

495	40 c. Type **120**	15	10
496	2 r. 25, Mascarenhas' caravel, 1505	60	55
497	3 r. 50, Darwin's H.M.S. *Beagle*, 1831	90	1·00
498	5 r. *Queen Elizabeth 2* (liner), 1968	1·10	1·40
495/8	*Set of* 4	2·50	2·75
MS499	141 × 91 mm. Nos. 495/98	2·50	3·25

(Des G. Drummond. Litho Questa)

1981 (10 Apr). *Birds* (3rd series). *White Tern.* *T* **121** *and similar vert designs. Multicoloured.* W w **14**. *P* 14.

500	2 r. Type **121**	80	65
	a. Horiz strip of 5. Nos. 500/4	3·50	
501	2 r. Pair of White Terns	80	65
502	2 r. Female White Tern	80	65
503	2 r. Female White Tern on nest, and egg	80	65
504	2 r. White Tern and chick	80	65
500/4	*Set of* 5	3·50	3·00

Nos. 500/4 were printed together, *se-tenant*, in horizontal strips of 5 throughout the sheet.

(Des D. Shults. Litho Questa)

1981 (23 June–16 Nov). *Royal Wedding. Horiz designs as T* **26/27** *of Kiribati. Multicoloured.* (*a*) W w **15**. *P* 14.

505	1 r. 50, *Victoria and Albert I*	20	25
	a. Sheetlet. No. 505 × 6 and No. 506	1·60	
506	1 r. 50, Prince Charles and Lady Diana Spencer	50	50
507	5 r. *Cleveland*	60	60
	a. Sheetlet. No. 507 × 6 and No. 508	4·50	
508	5 r. As No. 506	1·50	2·00
509	10 r. *Britannia*	1·00	1·50
	a. Sheetlet. No. 509 × 6 and No. 510	7·50	
510	10 r. As No. 506	2·25	2·25
505/10	*Set of* 6	5·50	6·50
MS511	120 × 109 mm. 7 r. 50, As No. 506. Wmk sideways. P 12 (16 Nov)	1·50	1·50

(*b*) *Booklet stamps. No wmk. P* 12 (16 Nov)

512	1 r. 50, As No. 505	25	40
	a. Booklet pane. No. 512 × 4	1·00	
513	5 r. As No. 508	1·00	1·40
	a. Booklet pane. No. 513 × 2	2·00	

Nos. 505/10 were printed in sheetlets of seven stamps of the same face value, each containing six of the "Royal Yacht" design and one of the larger design showing Prince Charles and Lady Diana.

Nos. 512/13 come from 22 r. stamp booklets.

122 Britten-Norman "Islander"   123 Seychelles Flying Foxes in Flight

(Litho Harrison)

1981 (27 July). *10th Anniv of Opening of Seychelles International Airport. Aircraft.* *T* **122** *and similar horiz designs. Multicoloured.* W w **14** (*sideways*). *P* 14½.

514	40 c. Type **122**	10	10
515	2 r. 25, Britten-Norman "Trislander"	45	45
516	3 r. 50, BAC (Vickers) "VC10" airliner	70	70
517	5 r. Boeing "747" airliner	1·00	1·00
514/17	*Set of* 4	2·00	2·00

(Litho Format)

1981 (9 Oct). *Seychelles Flying Fox (Roussette).* *T* **123** *and similar vert designs. Multicoloured.* W w **14**. *P* 14.

518	40 c. Type **123**	10	10
519	2 r. 25, Flying Fox eating	45	45
520	3 r. Flying Fox climbing across tree branch	70	70
521	5 r. Flying Fox hanging from tree branch	1·00	1·00
518/21	*Set of* 4	2·00	2·00
MS522	95 × 130 mm. Nos. 518/21	3·00	3·50

124 Chinese Little Bittern (male)   125 Silhouette Island and La Digue

(Des G. Drummond. Litho Questa)

1982 (4 Feb). *Birds* (4th series). *Chinese Little Bittern.* *T* **124** *and similar vert designs. Multicoloured.* W w **14**. *P* 14.

523	3 r. Type **124**	1·60	65
	a. Horiz strip of 5. Nos. 523/7	7·00	
524	3 r. Chinese Little Bittern (female)	1·60	65
525	3 r. Hen on nest	1·60	65
526	3 r. Nest and eggs	1·60	65
527	3 r. Hen with chicks	1·60	65
523/7	*Set of* 5	7·00	3·00

Nos. 523/7 were printed together, *se-tenant*, in horizontal strips of 5 throughout the sheet.

(Des J. Cooter. Litho Format)

1982 (22 Apr). *Modern Maps.* *T* **125** *and similar vert designs. Multicoloured.* W w **14**. *P* 14½.

528	40 c. Type **125**	10	10
529	1 r. 50, Denis and Bird Islands	30	25
530	2 r. 75, Praslin	55	65
531	7 r. Mahé	1·50	2·00
528/31	*Set of* 4	2·25	2·75
MS532	92 × 128 mm. Nos. 528/31	2·50	3·25

126 "Education"

(Des PAD Studio. Litho Harrison)

1982 (5 June). *5th Anniv of Liberation.* *T* **126** *and similar horiz designs. Multicoloured.* W w **14** (*sideways*). *P* 14.

533	40 c. Type **126**	10	10
534	1 r. 75, "Health"	25	25
535	2 r. 75, "Agriculture"	45	45
536	7 r. "Construction"	1·40	1·40
533/6	*Set of* 4	2·00	2·00
MS537	128 × 120 mm. Nos. 533/6. P 14½	3·00	4·00

127 Tourist Board Emblem   128 Tata Bus

(Des and litho Harrison)

1982 (1 Sept). *Tourism.* *T* **127** *and similar horiz designs. Multicoloured.* W w **14** (*sideways*). *P* 14.

538	1 r. 75, Type **127**	35	35
539	1 r. 75, Northolme Hotel	35	35
540	1 r. 75, Reef Hotel	35	35
541	1 r. 75, Barbarous Beach Hotel	35	35
542	1 r. 75, Coral Strand Hotel	35	35
543	1 r. 75, Beau Vallon Bay Hotel	35	35
544	1 r. 75, Fisherman's Cove Hotel	35	35
545	1 r. 75, Mahé Beach Hotel	35	35
538/45	*Set of* 8	2·50	2·50

(Des C. Abbott. Litho Harrison)

1982 (18 Nov). *Land Transport.* *T* **128** *and similar horiz designs. Multicoloured.* W w **14** (*sideways*). *P* 14.

546	20 c. Type **128**	10	10
547	1 r. 75, Mini-moke	30	25
548	2 r. 75, Ox-cart	50	55
549	7 r. Truck	1·40	1·75
546/9	*Set of* 4	2·10	2·40

129 Radio Seychelles Control Room

(Des A. Theobald. Litho Questa)

1983 (25 Feb). *World Communications Year.* *T* **129** *and similar horiz designs. Multicoloured.* W w **14** (*sideways*). *P* 14.

550	40 c. Type **129**	10	10
551	2 r. 75, Satellite Earth Station	45	50
552	3 r. 50, Radio Seychelles Television control room	70	75
553	5 r. Postal services sorting office	1·00	1·25
550/3	*Set of* 4	2·00	2·25

130 Agricultural Experimental Station

(Des L. Curtis. Litho Questa)

1983 (14 Mar). *Commonwealth Day.* *T* **130** *and similar horiz designs. Multicoloured.* W w **14** (*sideways*). *P* 14.

554	40 c. Type **130**	10	10
555	2 r. 75, Food processing plant	45	50
556	3 r. 50, Unloading fish catch	70	75
557	7 r. Seychelles flag	1·40	1·50
554/7	*Set of* 4	2·40	2·50

131 Denis Island Lighthouse

(Des Harrison. Litho Format)

1983 (14 July). *Famous Landmarks. T* **131** *and similar horiz designs. Multicoloured. W* w **14** (*sideways*). *P* 14 × 13½.

558 40 c. Type **131** 10 10
559 2 r. 75, Victoria Hospital 40 45
560 3 r. 50, Supreme Court 60 65
561 7 r. State House . . . . 1·25 1·40
558/61 . . . . *Set of* 4 2·10 2·25
MS562 110 × 98 mm. Nos. 558/61 . . . . 3·50 4·25

132 *Royal Vauxhall* Balloon, 1836

(Des A. Theobald. Litho Harrison)

1983 (15 Sept). *Bicentenary of Manned Flight. T* **132** *and similar horiz designs. Multicoloured. W* w **14** (*sideways*). *P* 14.

563 40 c. Type **132** 10 10
564 1 r. 75, De Havilland "D.H.50J" 40 30
565 2 r. 75, Grumman "Albatross" flying boat . . 55 55
566 7 r. Swearingen "Merlin" . . . . . . 1·40 1·75
563/6 . . . . *Set of* 4 2·25 2·25

133 "DC 10" Aircraft

134 Swamp Plant and Moorhen

(Des Park Advertising. Litho Walsall)

1983 (26 Oct). *1st International Flight of Air Seychelles. W* w **14** (*sideways*). *P* 14.

567 **133** 2 r. multicoloured 60 60

(Des L. Curtis. Litho Questa)

1983 (17 Nov). *Centenary of Visit to Seychelles by Marianne North (botanic artist). T* **134** *and similar vert designs. Multicoloured. W* w **14**. *P* 14.

568 40 c. Type **134** 15 10
569 1 r. 75, *Wormia flagellaria* 50 30
570 2 r. 75, Asiatic Pancratium 65 60
571 7 r. Pitcher Plant . . . . 1·50 1·60
568/71 . . . . *Set of* 4 2·50 2·25
MS572 90 × 121 mm. Nos. 568/71 . . . . 2·75 3·50

50c 

(**135**)

1983 (28 Dec). *Nos.* 505/10 *surch as T* **135**.

573 50 c. on 1 r. 50, *Victoria and Albert I* 15 15
a. Sheetlet. No. 573 × 6 and No. 574 . . 85
b. Albino surch . . . . 33·00
c. Surch double, one albino . . . . . . 35·00
d. Surch double, one inverted . . . . . 55·00
e. Surch double, one in 2 r. 25 value . . 45·00
574 50 c. on 1 r. 50, Prince Charles and Lady Diana Spencer 15 15
b. Albino surch . . . . 75·00
c. Surch double, one albino . . . . . . 85·00
d. Surch double, one inverted £125
e. Surch double, one in 2 r. 25 value . . £110
575 2 r. 25 on 5 r. *Cleveland* 45 50
a. Sheetlet. No. 575 × 6 and No. 576 . . 3·25
576 2 r. 25 on 5 r. As No. 574 . . . . . . 45 50
577 3 r. 75 on 10 r. *Britannia* 75 80
a. Sheetlet. No. 577 × 6 and No. 578 . . 5·00
b. Albino surch . . . . 30·00
c. Surch double . . . . 90·00
578 3 r. 75 on 10 r. As No. 574 . . . . . . 75 80
b. Albino surch . . . . 65·00
c. Surch double £225
573/8 . . . . *Set of* 6 2·50 2·50

MINIMUM PRICE

The minimum price quote is 10p which represents a handling charge rather than a basis for valuing common stamps. For further notes about prices see introductory pages.

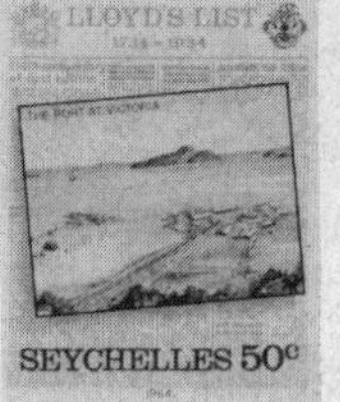

136 Coconut Vessel

137 Victoria Port

(Des Jennifer Toombs. Litho Format)

1984 (29 Feb). *Traditional Handicrafts. T* **136** *and similar horiz designs. Multicoloured. W* w **14** (*sideways*). *P* 14.

579 50 c. Type **136** 15 10
580 2 r. Scarf and doll 50 55
581 3 r. Coconut-fibre roses 70 75
582 10 r. Carved fishing boat and doll . . . . 2·00 2·75
579/82 . . . . *Set of* 4 3·00 3·75

(Des C. Collins. Litho Questa)

1984 (21 May). *25th Anniv of "Lloyd's List" (newspaper). T* **137** *and similar vert designs. Multicoloured. W* w **14**. *P* 14½ × 14.

583 50 c. Type **137** 15 10
584 2 r. Cargo liner 45 55
585 3 r. *Sun Viking* (liner) 70 80
586 10 r. Loss of R.F.A. *Ennerdale II* . . . . 2·25 2·75
583/6 . . . . *Set of* 4 3·25 3·75

138 Old S.P.U.P. Office

(Des D. Miller. Litho B.D.T.)

1984 (2 June). *20th Anniv of Seychelles People's United Party. T* **138** *and similar multicoloured designs. W* w **14** (*sideways on* 50 *c.*, 3 *r.*). *P* 14.

587 50 c. Type **138** 15 10
588 2 r. Liberation statue (*vert*) 40 50
589 3 r. New S.P.U.P. office 60 80
590 10 r. President René (*vert*) . . . . . . 2·00 2·75
587/90 . . . . *Set of* 4 2·75 3·75

139 1949 U.P.U. 2 r. 25 Stamp

(Des M. Joyce. Litho Harrison)

1984 (18 June). *Universal Postal Union Congress, Hamburg. Sheet* 70 × 85 *mm. W* w **14** (*sideways*). *P* 14½.

MS591 **139** 5 r. yellow-olive, flesh and black . . 1·40 1·90

140 Long Jumping

(Des L. Curtis. Litho Questa)

1984 (28 July). *Olympic Games, Los Angeles. T* **140** *and similar horiz designs. Multicoloured. W* w **14** (*sideways*). *P* 14.

592 50 c. Type **140** 10 10
593 2 r. Boxing 40 45
594 3 r. Swimming 60 75
595 10 r. Weightlifting . . . . 1·75 2·50
592/5 . . . . *Set of* 4 2·50 3·50
MS596 100 × 100 mm. Nos. 592/5 . . . . 2·50 3·75

141 Sub-aqua Diving

(Des A. Theobald. Litho Questa)

1984 (24 Sept). *Water Sports. T* **141** *and similar horiz designs. Multicoloured. W* w **14** (*sideways*). *P* 14.

597 50 c. Type **141** 20 10
598 2 r. Paragliding 60 45
599 3 r. Sailing 80 75
600 10 r. Water-skiing . . . . 2·25 2·50
597/600 . . . . *Set of* 4 3·50 3·50

142 Humpback Whale

143 Two Bare-legged Scops Owls in Tree

(Des A. Jardine. Litho Questa)

1984 (19 Nov). *Whale Conservation. T* **142** *and similar horiz designs. Multicoloured. W* w **14** (*sideways*). *P* 14.

601 50 c. Type **142** 55 15
602 2 r. Sperm Whale . . . . 1·40 55
603 3 r. Black Right Whale . . . . . . 1·60 85
604 10 r. Blue Whale . . . . 3·00 3·00
601/4 . . . . *Set of* 4 6·00 4·00

(Des I. Lewington. Litho Walsall)

1985 (11 Mar). *Birth Bicentenary of John J. Audubon (ornithologist). Bare-legged Scops Owl. T* **143** *and similar vert designs. Multicoloured. W* w **14**. *P* 14.

605 50 c. Type **143** 55 15
606 2 r. Owl on branch . . . . 1·25 70
607 3 r. Owl in flight . . . . 1·50 90
608 10 r. Owl on ground . . . . 3·00 3·00
605/8 . . . . *Set of* 4 5·50 4·25

144 Giant Tortoises

145 The Queen Mother with Princess Anne and Prince Andrew, 1970

(Des D. Miller. Litho Format)

1985 (15 Mar). *"Expo '85" World Fair, Japan. T* **144** *and similar vert designs. Multicoloured. W* w **14**. *P* 14.

609 50 c. Type **144** 20 10
610 2 r. White Terns 75 60
611 3 r. Windsurfing 85 75
612 5 r. Coco-de-Mer . . . . 1·25 1·40
609/12 . . . . *Set of* 4 2·75 2·50
MS613 130 × 80 mm. Nos. 609/12 . . . . 2·75 3·50

For these designs without "Expo '85" inscription see No. **MS**650.

(Des A. Theobald (10 r.), C. Abbott (others). Litho Questa)

1985 (7 June). *Life and Times of Queen Elizabeth the Queen Mother. T* **145** *and similar vert designs. Multicoloured. W* w **16**. *P* 14½ × 14.

614 50 c. The Queen Mother in 1930 . . . . 10 10
615 2 r. Type **145** 45 50
616 3 r. On her 75th Birthday 65 70
617 5 r. With Prince Henry at his christening (from photo by Lord Snowdon) . . . . 1·10 1·25
614/17 . . . . *Set of* 4 2·10 2·40
MS618 91 × 73 mm. 10 r. Arriving at Blenheim Palace by helicopter. Wmk sideways . . . . 2·50 2·50

146 Boxing

147 Agriculture Students

(Des O. Bell. Litho Questa)

1985 (24 Aug). *2nd Indian Ocean Islands Games. T* **146** *and similar horiz designs. Multicoloured. W* w **14** (*sideways*). *P* 14.

619 50 c. Type **146** 10 10
620 2 r. Football 45 50
621 3 r. Swimming 65 70
622 10 r. Windsurfing . . . . 2·25 2·40
619/22 . . . . *Set of* 4 3·00 3·25

1985 (1 Nov). *Acquisition of 1st Air Seychelles "Airbus". As No.* 735, *but additionally inscribed* "AIR SEYCHELLES FIRST AIRBUS".

623 1 r. 25, White Tern 60 60

(Des Joan Thompson. Litho Questa)

1985 (28 Nov). *International Youth Year. T* **147** *and similar vert designs. Multicoloured. W w* **16**. *P* 14.

624 50 c. Type **147** 10 10
625 2 r. Construction students building wall .. 45 50
626 3 r. Carpentry students 65 70
627 10 r. Science students .. .. .. 2·25 2·40
624/7 .. .. *Set of* 4 3·00 3·25

148 Ford "Model T" (1919)

149 Five Foot Transit Instrument

(Des J.W. Litho Questa)

1985 (18 Dec). *Vintage Cars. T* **148** *and similar horiz designs. Multicoloured. W w* **16** *(sideways). P* 14.

628 50 c. Type **148** 20 10
629 2 r. Austin "Seven" (1922) 70 50
630 3 r. Morris "Oxford" (1924) 85 70
631 10 r. Humber "Coupé" (1929) .. .. .. 2·25 2·40
628/31 .. .. *Set of* 4 3·50 3·25

(Des Harrison. Litho Format)

1986 (28 Feb). *Appearance of Halley's Comet. T* **149** *and similar vert designs. Multicoloured. W w* **16**. *P* 14.

632 50 c. Type **149** 25 10
633 2 r. Eight foot quadrant 70 50
634 3 r. Comet's orbit 90 75
635 10 r. Edmond Halley .. .. 2·40 2·40
632/5 .. .. *Set of* 4 3·75 3·50

150 Ballerina

151 Ferry to La Digue

(Des C. Abbott. Litho Format)

1986 (4 Apr). *Visit of Ballet du Louvre Company. "Giselle". T* **150** *and similar vert designs. Multicoloured. W w* **16**. *P* 13½.

636 2 r. Type **150** 75 60
637 3 r. Male dancer .. .. 1·00 90
MS638 80×90 mm. 10 r. Pas de deux .. .. 2·25 2·40

(Des A. Theobald. Litho Questa)

1986 (21 Apr). *60th Birthday of Queen Elizabeth II. Vert designs as T* **110** *of Ascension. Multicoloured. W w* **16**. *P* 14½×14.

639 50 c. Wedding photograph, 1947 .. .. 10 10
640 1 r. 25, At State Opening of Parliament, 1982 .. .. 30 35
641 2 r. Queen accepting bouquet, Seychelles, 1972 .. .. 45 50
642 3 r. On board Royal Yacht *Britannia*, Qatar, 1979 .. .. 70 75
643 5 r. At Crown Agents Head Office, London, 1983 .. .. 1·10 1·25
639/43 .. .. *Set of* 5 2·40 2·75

(Des G. Drummond. Litho Questa)

1986 (22 May). *"Ameripex '86" International Stamp Exhibition, Chicago. Inter-island Communications. T* **151** *and similar multicoloured designs. W w* **16** *(sideways on 50 c., 7 r.). P* 14.

644 50 c. Type **151** 20 10
645 2 r. Telephone kiosk (*vert*) 55 50
646 3 r. Post Office counter, Victoria (*vert*) .. 75 75
647 7 r. Air Seychelles Britten-Norman "Trislander" aircraft .. .. 1·75 1·75
644/7 .. .. *Set of* 4 3·00 2·75

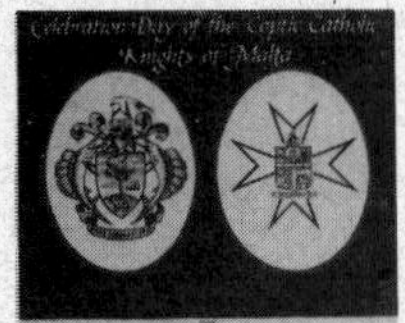

152 Crests of Seychelles and Knights of Malta

LAZOURNEN ENTERNASYONAL KREOL

(**153**)

(Des Jennifer Toombs. Litho Format)

1986 (7 June). *Seychelles Knights of Malta Day. W w* **16** *(sideways). P* 14.

648 **152** 5 r. multicoloured .. .. .. 1·10 1·25
MS649 101×81 mm. No. 648 .. .. .. 1·40 1·60

1986 (12 July). *Seychelles Philatelic Exhibition, Tokyo. Miniature sheet, 130×80 mm, containing stamps as Nos. 609/12, but without "Expo '85" inscription and emblem. W w* **16**. *P* 14.

MS650 As Nos. 609/12 .. .. 3·00 3·00

(Des D. Miller. Litho Questa)

1986 (23 July). *Royal Wedding. Vert designs as T* **112** *of Ascension. Multicoloured. W w* **16**. *P* 14.

651 2 r. Prince Andrew and Miss Sarah Ferguson 45 50
652 10 r. Prince Andrew boarding Wessex helicopter, 1983 .. .. 2·25 2·40

1986 (28 Oct). *International Creole Day. No. 487a optd with T* **153**.

653 1 r. Madagascar Red Fody 45 25

154 Pope John Paul at Seychelles Airport

155 *Melanitis leda*

(Des L. Curtis. Litho Questa)

1986 (1 Dec). *Visit of Pope John Paul II. T* **154** *and similar vert designs, each showing Pope and Seychelles scene. Multicoloured. W w* **16**. *P* 14½×14.

654 50 c. Type **154** 30 10
655 2 r. Catholic Cathedral, Victoria .. .. 1·00 60
656 3 r. Baie Lazare Parish Church .. .. 1·40 90
657 10 r. Aerial view of People's Stadium .. 2·75 2·75
654/7 .. .. *Set of* 4 5·00 4·00
MS658 95×106 mm. Nos. 654/7. Wmk inverted .. 6·00 6·50

(Des R. Lewington. Litho Questa)

1987 (18 Feb). *Butterflies. T* **155** *and similar horiz designs. Multicoloured. W w* **16** *(sideways). P* 14½.

659 1 r. Type **155** 40 25
660 2 r. *Phalanta philiberti* 70 60
661 3 r. *Danaus chrysippus* .. .. .. 1·00 1·00
662 10 r. *Euploea mitra* .. .. 3·00 3·50
659/62 .. .. *Set of* 4 4·50 4·75

156 *Gloripallium pallium*

157 Statue of Liberation

(Des Josephine Martin. Litho Walsall)

1987 (7 May). *Seashells. T* **156** *and similar vert designs. Multicoloured. W w* **14**. *P* 14½×14.

663 1 r. Type **156** 40 25
664 2 r. *Spondylus aurantius* 70 60
665 3 r. *Harpa ventricosa* and *Lioconcha ornata* .. .. 1·00 90
666 10 r. *Strombus lentiginosus* .. .. .. 2·75 2·75
663/6 .. .. *Set of* 4 4·25 4·00

(Des Harrison. Litho Format)

1987 (5 June). *10th Anniv of Liberation. T* **157** *and similar multicoloured designs. W w* **16** *(sideways on 2 r., 3 r.). P* 14.

667 1 r. Type **157** 20 25
668 2 r. Seychelles Hospital (*horiz*) 45 50
669 3 r. Orphanage Village (*horiz*) 70 75
670 10 r. Proposed Sail-fish Monument .. .. 2·25 2·50
667/70 .. .. *Set of* 4 3·25 3·50

158 Seychelles Savings Bank, Praslin

(Des A. Theobald. Litho Format)

1987 (25 June). *Centenary of Banking in Seychelles. T* **158** *and similar horiz designs. W w* **16** *(sideways). P* 14.

671 1 r. bronze-green and sage-green 20 25
672 2 r. bistre-brown and salmon 45 50
673 10 r. royal blue and cobalt .. .. .. 2·25 2·50
671/3 .. .. *Set of* 3 2·50 3·00

Designs:—2 r. Development Bank; 10 r. Central Bank.

1987 (9 Dec). *Royal Ruby Wedding. Nos. 639/43 optd with T* **119** *of Ascension in silver.*

674 50 c. Wedding photograph, 1947 .. .. 15 15
a. Opt inverted .. .. 75·00
675 1 r. 25, At State Opening of Parliament, 1982 .. .. 30 35
676 2 r. Queen accepting bouquet, Seychelles, 1972 .. .. 45 50
677 3 r. On board Royal Yacht *Britannia*, Qatar, 1979 .. .. 70 75
678 5 r. At Crown Agents Head Office, London, 1983 .. .. 1·10 1·25
674/8 .. .. *Set of* 5 2·40 2·75

159 Tuna-canning Factory

(Des O. Bell. Litho B.D.T.)

1987 (11 Dec). *Seychelles Fishing Industry. T* **159** *and similar diamond-shaped designs. Multicoloured. W w* **16**. *P* 14.

679 50 c. Type **159** 15 15
680 2 r. Trawler 45 50
681 3 r. Weighing catch 70 75
682 10 r. Unloading net .. .. 2·25 2·40
679/82 .. .. *Set of* 4 3·25 3·50

160 Water Sports

161 Young Turtles making for Sea

(Des Jennifer Toombs. Litho Questa)

1988 (9 Feb). *Tourism. T* **160** *and similar horiz designs, each showing beach hotel. Multicoloured. W w* **16** *(sideways). P* 14½.

683 1 r. Type **160** 20 25
684 2 r. Speedboat and yachts 45 50
685 3 r. Yacht at anchor 70 75
686 10 r. Hotel at night .. .. 2·25 2·40
683/6 .. .. *Set of* 4 3·25 3·50

(Des Doreen McGuinness. Litho Questa)

1988 (22 Apr). *The Green Turtle. T* **161** *and similar vert designs. Multicoloured. W w* **14**. *P* 14½ × 14.

687 2 r. Type **161** 45 45
a. Vert pair. Nos. 687/8 .. .. .. 90 90
688 2 r. Young turtles hatching 45 45
689 3 r. Female turtle leaving sea 70 70
a. Vert pair. Nos. 689/90 .. .. .. 1·40 1·40
690 3 r. Female laying eggs 70 70
687/90 .. .. *Set of* 4 2·10 2·10

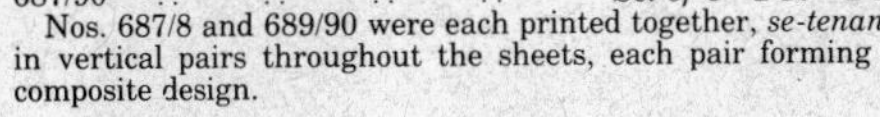

Nos. 687/8 and 689/90 were each printed together, *se-tenant*, in vertical pairs throughout the sheets, each pair forming a composite design.

162 Shot Put

163 Police Motorcyclists

(Des O. Bell. Litho Walsall)

1988 (29 July). *Olympic Games, Seoul. T* **162** *and similar vert designs. Multicoloured. W w* **16**. *P* 14½.

691 1 r. Type **162** 20 25
692 2 r. Type **162** 40 45
a. Horiz strip of 5. Nos. 692/6 .. .. 2·00
693 2 r. High jump 40 45
694 2 r. Gold medal winner on podium 40 45
695 2 r. Athletics 40 45
696 2 r. Javelin 40 45
697 3 r. As No. 694 .. .. 60 65
698 4 r. As No. 695 .. .. 80 85
699 5 r. As No. 696 .. .. 1·00 1·10
691/9 .. .. *Set of* 9 4·25 4·50
MS700 121 × 52 mm. 10 r. Tennis. W w **14** (sideways) .. .. 2·00 2·10

Nos. 691, 693 and 697/9 were each printed in sheets of 50 of one design. No. 693 also exists from sheets containing Nos. 692/6 printed together, *se-tenant*, in horizontal strips of five.

(Des D. Miller (1 r.), L. Curtis and D. Miller (2 r.), E. Nisbet and D. Miller (3 r.), S. Noon and D. Miller (10 r.). Litho Questa)

1988 (30 Sept). *300th Anniv of Lloyd's of London. Multicoloured designs as T* **123** *of Ascension.* W w **16** *(sideways on 2, 3 r.). P* 14.

701	1 r. Leadenhall Street, London, 1928	30	25
702	2 r. *Cinq Juin* (travelling post office) (*horiz*)	50	45
703	3 r. *Queen Elizabeth 2* (liner) (*horiz*)	80	65
704	10 r. Loss of *Hindenburg* (airship), 1937	2·25	2·10
701/4	*Set of* 4	3·50	3·00

(Des A. Theobald. Litho Questa)

1988 (25 Nov). *1st Anniv of Defence Forces Day. T* **163** *and similar horiz designs. Multicoloured.* W w **14** *(sideways). P* 14.

705	1 r. Type **163**	30	25
706	2 r. Air Wing helicopter	50	50
707	3 r. Patrol boat	80	90
708	10 r. BRDM armoured car	2·50	2·75
705/8	*Set of* 4	3·75	4·00

164 Father Christmas with Basket of Presents

165 *Dendrobium sp.*

(Des S. Hoareau (50 c.), R. Leste (2 r.), F. Anacoura (3 r.), A. McGaw (10 r.), adapted N. Harvey. Litho B.D.T.)

1988 (1 Dec). *Christmas. T* **164** *and similar vert designs. Multicoloured.* W w **14**. *P* $13\frac{1}{2}$.

709	50 c. Type **164**	10	10
710	2 r. Bird and gourd filled with presents	40	45
711	3 r. Father Christmas basket weaving	60	65
712	10 r. Christmas bauble and palm tree	2·00	2·10
709/12	*Set of* 4	2·75	3·00

(Des Annette Robinson. Litho Questa)

1988 (21 Dec). *Orchids (1st series). T* **165** *and similar multicoloured designs.* W w **16** *(sideways on 2, 10 r.). P* 14.

713	1 r. Type **165**	20	25
714	2 r. *Arachnis hybrid (horiz)*	40	45
715	3 r. *Vanda caerulea*	60	65
716	10 r. *Dendrobium phalaenopsis (horiz)*	2·00	2·10
713/16	*Set of* 4	3·00	3·00

See also Nos. 767/70.

(Litho Questa)

1988 (30 Dec). *As Nos.* 405B *and* 410B, *but* W w **14** *(upright). P* 14.

718	10 c. Hawksbill Turtle	10	10
722	50 c. Giant Tortoise	10	10

A Questa new printing of the 25 c. was issued on the same date. It has the same watermark and perforation as No. 408B.

166 India 1976 25 p. Nehru Stamp

167 Pres. Rene addressing Rally at Old Party Office

(Des O. Bell. Litho B.D.T.)

1989 (30 Mar). *Birth Centenary of Jawaharlal Nehru (Indian statesman). T* **166** *and similar horiz design, each showing flags of Seychelles and India. Multicoloured.* W w **16** *(sideways). P* $13\frac{1}{2}$.

724	2 r. Type **166**	40	45
725	10 r. Jawaharlal Nehru	2·00	2·25

1989 (May). *As No.* 489, *but* W w **16**. *Chalk-surfaced paper. Imprint date at foot. P* $14\frac{1}{2}\times14$.

735	1 r. 25, White Tern	25	30

(Des D. Miller. Litho Walsall)

1989 (5 June). *25th Anniv of Seychelles People's United Party. T* **167** *and similar vert designs. Multicoloured.* W w **16**. *P* 14.

742	1 r. Type **167**	20	25
743	2 r. Women with Party flags and Maison du Peuple	40	45
744	3 r. President Rene making speech and Torch of Freedom	60	65
745	10 r. President Rene, Party flag and Torch of Freedom	2·00	2·25
742/5	*Set of* 4	2·75	3·25

(Des A. Theobald (10 r.), D. Miller (others). Litho Questa)

1989 (20 July). *20th Anniv of First Manned Landing on Moon. Multicoloured designs as T* **126** *of Ascension.* W w **16** *(sideways on 2, 3 r.). P* $14\times13\frac{1}{2}$ *(1, 5 r.) or* 14 *(others).*

746	1 r. Lift off of "Saturn 5" rocket	20	25
747	2 r. Crew of "Apollo 15" (30×30 *mm*)	40	45
748	3 r. "Apollo 15" emblem (30×30 *mm*)	60	65
749	5 r. James Irwin saluting U.S. flag on Moon	1·00	1·10
746/9	*Set of* 4	2·00	2·25
MS750	100×83 mm. 10 r. Aldrin alighting from "Apollo 11" on Moon. P $14\times13\frac{1}{2}$	2·75	2·75

168 British Red Cross Ambulance, Franco-Prussian War, 1870

169 Black Parrot and Map of Praslin

(Des A. Theobald. Litho Questa)

1989 (12 Sept). *125th Anniv of International Red Cross. T* **168** *and similar horiz designs.* W w **16** *(sideways). P* $14\frac{1}{2}$.

751	1 r. black and orange-vermilion	20	25
752	2 r. black, light green and orange-vermilion	40	45
753	3 r. black and orange-vermilion	60	65
754	10 r. black and orange-vermilion	2·00	2·25
751/4	*Set of* 4	2·75	3·25

Designs:—2 r. H.M. Hospital Ship *Liberty*, 1914-18; 3 r. Sunbeam "Standard" army ambulance, 1914-18; 10 r. "White Train", South Africa, 1899-1902.

(Des I. Loe. Litho Questa)

1989 (16 Oct). *Island Birds. T* **169** *and similar vert designs. Multicoloured.* W w **16**. *P* $14\frac{1}{2}\times14$.

755	50 c. Type **169**	15	10
756	2 r. Sooty Tern and Ile aux Vaches	60	60
757	3 r. Magpie Robin and Frégate	80	80
758	5 r. Roseate Tern and Aride	1·40	1·40
755/8	*Set of* 4	2·75	2·75
MS759	83×109 mm. Nos. 755/8	2·75	2·75

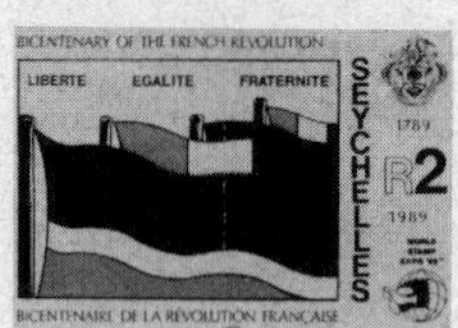

170 Flags of Seychelles and France

(Adapted D. Miller from local artwork. Litho B.D.T.)

1989 (17 Nov). *Bicentenary of French Revolution and "World Stamp Expo '89", International Stamp Exhibition, Washington. T* **170** *and similar horiz designs.* W w **16** *(sideways). P* 14.

760	2 r. multicoloured	40	45
761	5 r. black, new blue and scarlet	1·00	1·10
MS762	78×100 mm. 10 r. multicoloured	2·00	2·25

Designs:—5 r. Storming the Bastille, Paris, 1789; 10 r. Reading Revolutionary proclamation, Seychelles, 1791.

171 Beau Vallon School

172 *Disperis tripetaloides*

(Des L. Curtis. Litho B.D.T.)

1989 (29 Dec). *25th Anniv of African Development Bank. T* **171** *and similar multicoloured designs.* W w **16** *(sideways on 1, 2 r.). P* 14.

763	1 r. Type **171**	20	25
764	2 r. Seychelles Fishing Authority Headquarters	40	45
765	3 r. *Variola* (fishing boat) (*vert*)	60	65
766	10 r. *Deneb* (fishing boat) (*vert*)	2·00	2·25
763/6	*Set of* 4	3·00	3·25

(Des N. Shewring. Litho Questa)

1990 (26 Jan). *Orchids (2nd series). T* **172** *and similar vert designs. Multicoloured.* W w **16**. *P* 14.

767	1 r. Type **172**	20	25
768	2 r. *Vanilla phalaenopsis*	40	45
769	3 r. *Angraecum eburneum* subsp *superbum*	60	65
770	10 r. *Polystachya concreta*	2·00	2·10
767/70	*Set of* 4	2·75	3·00

POSTAGE DUE STAMPS

D 1

(Frame recess, value typo B.W.)

1951 (1 Mar). *Wmk Mult Script CA. P* $11\frac{1}{2}$.

D1	D 1	2 c. scarlet and carmine	80	1·50
D2		3 c. scarlet and green	1·25	1·50
D3		6 c. scarlet and bistre	1·25	1·25
D4		9 c. scarlet and orange	1·50	1·25
D5		15 c. scarlet and violet	1·75	6·00
D6		18 c. scarlet and blue	1·75	6·50
D7		20 c. scarlet and brown	1·75	6·50
D8		30 c. scarlet and claret	1·75	7·00
D1/8		*Set of* 8	10·50	28·00

1964 (7 July)–**65**. *As* 1951 *but* W w **12**.

D 9	D 1	2 c. scarlet and carmine	60	4·00
D10		3 c. scarlet and green (14.9.65)	1·00	5·50

(Litho Walsall)

1980 (29 Feb). *Design as Type* D 1 *but redrawn, size* 18 × 22 *mm.* W w **14** *(sideways). P* 14.

D11	5 c. rosine and magenta	10	15
D12	10 c. rosine and deep blue-green	10	15
D13	15 c. rosine and bistre	10	15
D14	20 c. rosine and orange-brown	10	20
D15	25 c. rosine and bright violet	10	20
D16	75 c. rosine and maroon	20	30
D17	80 c. rosine and deep grey-blue	20	30
D18	1 r. rosine and deep reddish purple	25	35
D11/18	*Set of* 8	1·00	1·60

ZIL ELWANNYEN SESEL

(SEYCHELLES OUTER ISLANDS)

For use from Aldabra, Coetivy, Farquhar and the Amirante Islands, served by the M.V. *Cinq-Juin* travelling post office.

I Inscr "ZIL ELOIGNE SESEL"

1 Reef Fish

2 *Cinq Juin*

1980 (20 June)–**81**. *Designs as Nos.* 404/11 (*with imprint*) *and* 487/94 *of Seychelles but inscr.* "ZIL ELOIGNE SESEL" *as in T* **1**. W w **14** (*sideways on* 10, 20, 50, 75 *c.*). *P* 14½ × 14 (40 *c.*, 1 *r.*, 1 *r.* 25, 1*r.* 50), 13½ (5, 10, 15, 20 *r.*) *or* 14 (*others*).

1	5 c. Type **1**	10	10
2	10 c. Hawksbill Turtle	10	10
3	15 c. Coco-de-Mer	10	10
4	20 c. Wild Vanilla	10	10
5	25 c. Butterfly on flower	30	10
6	40 c. Coral scene	20	10
7	50 c. Giant Tortoise	20	10
8	75 c. Crayfish	25	15
9	1 r. Madagascar Red Fody	50	20
10	1 r. 10, Green Gecko	30	25
11	1 r. 25, White Tern	60	35
12	1 r. 50, Seychelles Flying Fox	35	35
13	5 r. Octopus	70	90
	a. Perf 13 (1981)	65	80
14	10 r. Giant Tiger Cowrie	1·50	1·50
	a. Perf 13 (1981)	1·00	1·75
15	15 r. Pitcher Plant	2·00	2·50
	a. Perf 13 (1981)	1·75	2·50
16	20 r. Seychelles coat of arms	2·00	3·25
	a. Perf 13 (1981)	2·00	3·75
1/16	*Set of* 16	8·00	9·00

Nos. 1/12 exist with imprint dates of either "1980" or "1981", Nos. 13/16 with "1980" only and Nos. 13a/16a "1981" only.

(Des L. Curtis. Litho Walsall)

1980 (24 Oct). *Establishment of Travelling Post Office. T* **2** *and similar horiz designs. Multicoloured.* W w **14** (*sideways*). *P* 14.

17	1 r. 50, Type **2**	20	15
18	2 r. 10, Hand-stamping covers	30	20
19	5 r. Map of Zil Eloigne Sesel	60	40
17/19	*Set of* 3	1·00	65

Nos. 17/19 were printed in sheets including two *se-tenant* stamp-size labels.

The original version of No. 19 incorrectly showed the Agalega Islands as Seychelles territory. A corrected version was prepared prior to issue and stamps in the first type were intended for destruction. Mint examples and some used on first day covers are known, originating from supplies sent to some philatelic bureau standing order customers in error. Such stamps are not listed as they were not available from Seychelles post offices or valid for postage.

3 Yellowfin Tuna

(Des G. Drummond. Litho Rosenbaum Bros, Vienna)

1980 (28 Nov). *Marine Life. T* **3** *and similar horiz designs. Multicoloured.* W w **14**. *P* 14.

20	1 r. 50, Type **3**	20	15
21	2 r. 10, Blue Marlin (fish)	35	20
22	5 r. Sperm Whale	70	50
20/2	*Set of* 3	1·10	75

Nos. 20/2 were printed in sheets including two *se-tenant* stamp-size labels.

(Des D. Shults. Litho Questa)

1981 (23 June–16 Nov). *Royal Wedding. Horiz designs as T* **26/27** *of Kiribati. Multicoloured.* (*a*) W w **15**. *P* 14.

23	40 c. *Royal Escape*	10	10
	a. Sheetlet. No. 23 × 6 and No. 24	90	
24	40 c. Prince Charles and Lady Diana Spencer	40	40
25	5 r. *Victoria and Albert II*	40	40
	a. Sheetlet. No. 25 × 6 and No. 26	3·50	
26	5 r. As No. 24	1·40	1·40
27	10 r. *Britannia*	85	85
	a. Sheetlet. No. 27 × 6 and No. 28	7·00	
28	10 r. As No. 24	2·50	2·50
23/8	*Set of* 6	5·00	5·00
MS29	120 × 109 mm. 7 r. 50, As No. 24. Wmk sideways. P 12 (16 Nov)	2·00	2·00

(*b*) *Booklet stamps. No wmk. P* 12 (16 Nov)

30	40 c. As No. 23	25	35
	a. Booklet pane. No. 30 × 4	1·00	
31	5 r. As No. 26	75	1·00
	a. Booklet pane. No. 31 × 2	1·50	

Nos. 23/8 were printed in sheetlets of seven stamps of the same face value, each containing six of the "Royal Yacht" design and one of the larger design showing Prince Charles and Lady Diana.

Nos. 30/1 come from 13 r. 20 stamp booklets.

4 Wright's Skink

(Des and litho Walsall)

1981 (11 Dec). *Wildlife* (*1st series*). *T* **4** *and similar horiz designs. Multicoloured.* W w **14** (*sideways*). *P* 14.

32	1 r. 40, Type **4**	15	15
33	2 r. 25, Tree Frog	20	20
34	5 r. Robber Crab	40	40
32/4	*Set of* 3	65	65

See also Nos. 45/7.

5 *Cinq Juin* ("Communications")

(Des L. Curtis. Litho Harrison)

1982 (11 Mar). *Island Development. Ships. T* **5** *and similar horiz designs.* W w **14**. *P* 14 × 14½.

35	1 r. 75, black and orange	40	20
36	2 r. 10, black and turquoise-blue	50	30
37	5 r. black and bright scarlet	70	50
35/7	*Set of* 3	1·40	90

Designs:—2 r. 10, *Junon* ("fisheries protection"); 5 r. *Diamond M. Dragon* (drilling ship).

II Inscr "ZIL ELWAGNE SESEL"

6 *Paulette*

(Des L. Curtis. Litho Harrison)

1982 (22 July). *Local Mail Vessels. T* **6** *and similar horiz designs. Multicoloured.* W w **14** (*sideways*). *P* 14.

38	40 c. Type **6**	20	10
39	1 r. 75, *Janette*	40	30
40	2 r. 75, *Lady Esme*	50	40
41	3 r. 50, *Cinq Juin*	60	50
38/41	*Set of* 4	1·50	1·10

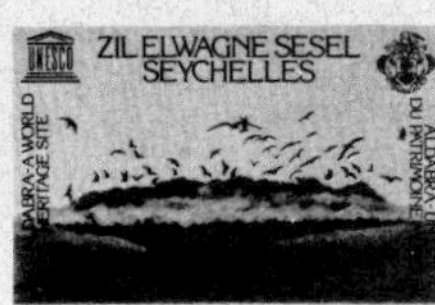

7 Birds flying over Island

8 Red Land Crab

(Des Harrison. Litho Format)

1982 (19 Nov). *Aldabra, World Heritage Site. T* **7** *and similar horiz designs. Multicoloured.* W w **14** (*sideways*). *P* 14.

42	40 c. Type **7**	30	15
43	2 r. 75, Map of the atoll	70	35
44	7 r. Giant Tortoises	1·25	75
42/4	*Set of* 3	2·00	1·10

(Des G. Drummond. Litho Questa)

1983 (25 Feb). *Wildlife* (*2nd series*). *T* **8** *and similar horiz designs. Multicoloured.* W w **14** (*sideways*). *P* 14 × 14½.

45	1 r. 75, Type **8**	25	25
46	2 r. 75, Black Terrapin	35	35
47	7 r. Madagascar Green Gecko	80	80
45/7	*Set of* 3	1·25	1·25

9 Map of Poivre Island and Île du Sud

10 Aldabra Warbler

(Des J. Cooter. Litho Format)

1983 (27 Apr). *Island Maps. T* **9** *and similar vert designs. Multicoloured.* W w **14**. *P* 14.

48	40 c. Type **9**	10	10
49	1 r. 50, Île des Roches	25	25
50	2 r. 75, Astove Island	40	40
51	7 r. Coëtivy Island	1·10	1·10
48/51	*Set of* 4	1·75	1·75
MS52	93 × 129 mm. Nos. 48/51	1·75	2·00

(Des G. Drummond. Litho Harrison)

1983 (13 July). *Birds. T* **10** *and similar multicoloured designs.* W w **14** (*sideways on* 5 *c. to* 2 *r.* 75). *P* 14.

53	5 c. Type **10**	10	10
54	10 c. Zebra Dove	35	10
55	15 c. Madagascar Nightjar	10	10
56	20 c. Madagascar Cisticola	10	10
57	25 c. Madagascar White Eye	50	10
58	40 c. Mascarene Fody	10	10
59	50 c. White-throated Rail	50	10
60	75 c. Black Bulbul	15	20
61	2 r. Western Reef Heron	1·25	55
62	2 r. 10, Souimanga Sunbird	40	45
63	2 r. 50, Madagascar Turtle Dove	45	50
64	2 r. 75, Sacred Ibis	50	55
65	3 r. 50, Black Coucal (*vert*)	60	65
66	7 r. Seychelles Kestrel (*vert*)	1·25	1·40
67	15 r. Comoro Blue Pigeon (*vert*)	2·75	3·00
68	20 r. Greater Flamingo (*vert*)	3·75	4·00
53/68	*Set of* 16	11·50	10·50

For 5 c., 10 c., 25 c. and 2 r. values in these designs, but inscribed "Zil Elwannyen Sesel", see Nos. 100/7 and 165/73.

11 Windsurfing

(Des G. Wilby. Litho Questa)

1983 (27 Sept). *Tourism. T* **11** *and similar horiz designs. Multicoloured.* W w **14** (*sideways*). *P* 14.

69	50 c. Type **11**	10	10
70	2 r. Hotel	25	25
71	3 r. View of beach	35	35
72	10 r. Islands at sunset	1·40	1·75
69/72	*Set of* 4	1·75	2·10

1983 (16–28 Dec). *Nos.* 23/8 *surch as T* **135** *of Seychelles.*

73	30 c. on 40 c. *Royal Escape*	20	20
	a. Sheetlet. No. 73 × 6 and No. 74	95	
	b. Surch double	50·00	
	c. Error. Surch 50 c. (as Seychelles No. 573)	60·00	
74	30 c. on 40 c. Prince Charles and Lady Diana Spencer	20	20
	b. Surch double	£125	
	c. Error. Surch 50 c. (as Seychelles No. 574)	£140	
75	2 r. on 5 r. *Victoria and Albert II* (28.12.83)	60	60
	a. Sheetlet. No. 75 × 6 and No. 76	3·75	
	b. Albino surch	40·00	
	c. Surch double	75·00	
76	2 r. on 5 r. As No. 74 (28.12.83)	60	60
	b. Albino surch	65·00	
	c. Surch double	£200	
77	3 r. on 10 r. *Britannia* (28.12.83)	75	75
	a. Sheetlet. No. 77 × 6 and No. 78	4·75	
78	3 r. on 10 r. As No. 74 (28.12.83)	75	75
73/8	*Set of* 6	2·75	2·75

12 Map of Aldabra and Commemorative Postmark

(Des L. Curtis. Litho Questa)

1984 (30 Mar). *Re-opening of Aldabra Post Office. T* **12** *and similar horiz designs. Multicoloured.* W w **14** (*sideways*). *P* 14.

79	50 c. Type **12**	15	15
80	2 r. 75, White-throated Rail	60	75
81	3 r. Giant Tortoise	60	80
82	10 r. Red-footed Booby	2·25	2·75
79/82	*Set of* 4	3·25	4·00

13 Fishing from Launch

(Des L. Curtis. Litho Walsall)

1984 (31 May). *Game Fishing. T* **13** *and similar multicoloured designs.* W w **14** (*sideways on* 50 *c.*, 10 *r.*). *P* 14.

83	50 c. Type **13**	15	15
84	2 r. Hooked fish (*vert*)	45	55
85	3 r. Weighing catch (*vert*)	60	75
86	10 r. Fishing from boat (*different*)	2·00	2·50
83/6	*Set of* 4	2·75	3·50

14 Giant Hermit Crab

15 Constellation of "Orion"

(Des G. Drummond. Litho Format)

1984 (24 Aug). *Crabs. T* **14** *and similar horiz designs. Multicoloured.* W w **14** *(sideways). P* 14½.

87	50 c. Type **14**	25	25
88	2 r. Fiddler Crabs	65	75
89	3 r. Sand Crab	80	1·00
90	10 r. Spotted Pebble Crab	2·50	3·00
87/90	*Set of* 4	3·75	4·50

(Des A. Theobald. Litho Format)

1984 (16 Oct). *The Night Sky. T* **15** *and similar vert designs. Multicoloured.* W w **14**. *P* 14.

91	50 c. Type **15**	15	15
92	2 r. "Cygnus"	50	55
93	3 r. "Virgo"	75	80
94	10 r. "Scorpio"	2·00	2·25
91/4	*Set of* 4	3·00	3·25

III Inscr "ZIL ELWANNYEN SESEL"

16 *Lenzites elegans*

17 The Queen Mother attending Royal Opera House, Covent Garden

(Des G. Drummond. Litho Walsall)

1985 (31 Jan). *Fungi. T* **16** *and similar vert designs. Multicoloured.* W w **14**. *P* 14.

95	50 c. Type **16**	15	15
96	2 r. *Xylaria telfairei*	45	50
97	3 r. *Lentinus sajor-caju*	65	70
98	10 r. *Hexagonia tenuis*	2·25	2·50
95/8	*Set of* 4	3·25	3·50

1985 (May)–**87**. *As Nos.* 54, 57, 59 *and* 61 *but inscr* "Zil Elwannyen Sesel". W w **14** *(sideways). P* 14.

100	10 c. Zebra Dove	15	10
103	25 c. Madagascar White Eye	10	10
105	50 c. White-throated Rail (1.7.87)	15	10
107	2 r. Western Reef Heron	70	50
100/7	*Set of* 4	1·00	65

The 10 c. exists with different imprint dates below the design.

For 10 c., 50 c. and 2 r. values watermarked w **16** (sideways) see Nos. 166/73.

(Des A. Theobald (10 r.), C. Abbott (others). Litho Questa)

1985 (7 June). *Life and Times of Queen Elizabeth the Queen Mother. T* **17** *and similar vert designs. Multicoloured.* W w **16**. *P* 14½×14.

115	1 r. The Queen Mother, 1936 (from photo by Dorothy Wilding)	20	25
116	2 r. With Princess Anne at Ascot, 1974	45	50
117	3 r. Type **17**	65	70
118	5 r. With Prince Henry at his christening (from photo by Lord Snowdon)	1·10	1·25
115/18	*Set of* 4	2·25	2·40
MS119	91×73 mm. 10 r. In a launch, Venice, 1985. Wmk sideways	2·25	2·50

18 Giant Tortoise

(Des. G. Vasarhelyi. Litho J.W.)

1985 (27 Sept). *Giant Tortoises of Aldabra (1st series). T* **18** *and similar horiz designs. Multicoloured.* W w **16** *(sideways). P* 14.

120	50 c. Type **18**	30	15
121	75 c. Giant Tortoises at stream	35	20
122	1 r. Giant Tortoises on grassland	45	25
123	2 r. Giant Tortoise (side view)	75	50
120/3	*Set of* 4	1·75	1·00
MS124	70×60 mm. 10 r. Two Giant Tortoises. P 13×13½	2·25	2·50

For stamps as Nos. 120/3, but without circular inscription around W.W.F. emblem, see Nos. 153/6.

19 Phoenician Trading Ship (600 B.C.)

(caption for 20, printed beside 19:) 20 *Acropora palifera* and *Tubastraea coccinea*

(Des N. Shewring. Litho Format)

1985 (25 Oct). *Famous Visitors. T* **19** *and similar horiz designs. Multicoloured.* W w **14** *(sideways). P* 14.

125	50 c. Type **19**	30	30
126	2 r. Sir Hugh Scott and H.M.S. *Sealark*, 1908	80	80
127	10 r. Vasco da Gama and *Sao Gabriel*, 1502	2·75	2·75
125/7	*Set of* 3	3·50	3·50

(Des A. Theobald. Litho Questa)

1986 (21 Apr). *60th Birthday of Queen Elizabeth II. Vert designs as T* **110** *of Ascension. Multicoloured.* W w **16**. *P* 14½×14.

128	75 c. Princess Elizabeth at Chester, 1951	20	25
129	1 r. Queen and Duke of Edinburgh at Falklands Service, St. Paul's Cathedral, 1985	20	25
130	1 r. 50, At Order of St. Michael and St. George service, St. Paul's Cathedral, 1968	35	40
131	3 r. 75, In Mexico, 1975	85	90
132	5 r. At Crown Agents Head Office, London, 1983	1·10	1·25
128/32	*Set of* 5	2·40	2·75

(Des D. Miller. Litho Questa)

1986 (23 July). *Royal Wedding. Square designs as T* **112** *of Ascension. Multicoloured.* W w **16**. *P* 14.

133	3 r. Prince Andrew and Miss Sarah Ferguson on Buckingham Palace balcony	70	75
134	7 r. Prince Andrew in naval uniform	1·60	1·75

(Des I. Loe. Litho Harrison)

1986 (17 Sept). *Coral Formations. T* **20** *and similar vert designs. Multicoloured.* W w **16**. *P* 14.

135	2 r. Type **20**	45	50
	a. Horiz strip of 5. Nos. 135/9	2·00	
136	2 r. *Echinopora lamellosa* and *Favia pallida*	45	50
137	2 r. *Sarcophyton sp.* and *Porites lutea*	45	50
138	2 r. *Goniopora sp.* and *Goniastrea retiformis*	45	50
139	2 r. *Tubipora musica* and *Fungia fungites*	45	50
135/9	*Set of* 5	2·00	2·25

Nos. 135/9 were printed together, *se-tenant*, in horizontal strips of 5 throughout the sheet, forming a composite design.

21 *Hibiscus tiliaceus* 22 *Chaetodon unimaculatus*

(Des Annette Robinson. Litho Walsall)

1986 (12 Nov). *Flora. T* **21** *and similar vert designs. Multicoloured.* W w **16**. *P* 14.

140	50 c. Type **21**	20	15
141	2 r. *Crinum angustum*	70	60
142	3 r. *Phaius tetragonus*	1·10	90
143	10 r. *Rothmannia annae*	2·50	2·40
140/3	*Set of* 4	4·00	3·50

(Des G. Drummond. Litho Questa)

1987 (26 Mar). *Coral Reef Fishes. T* **22** *and similar vert designs. Multicoloured.* W w **16**. *P* 14.

144	2 r. Type **22**	45	50
	a. Horiz strip of 5. Nos. 144/8	2·00	
145	2 r. *Ostorhincus fleurieu*	45	50
146	2 r. *Platax orbicularis*	45	50
147	2 r. *Abudefduf annulatus*	45	50
148	2 r. *Chaetodon lineolatus*	45	50
144/8	*Set of* 5	2·00	2·25

Nos. 144/8 were printed together, *se-tenant*, in horizontal strips of 5 throughout the sheet, forming a composite design.

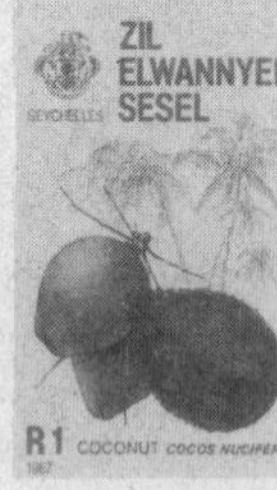

23 Coconut

24 "Vallee de Mai" (Christine Harter)

(Des R. Gorringe. Litho Walsall)

1987 (26 Aug). *Trees. T* **23** *and similar vert designs. Multicoloured.* W w **16**. *P* 14½.

149	1 r. Type **23**	25	30
150	2 r. Mangrove	55	60
151	3 r. Pandanus Palm	80	95
152	5 r. Indian Almond	1·25	1·60
149/52	*Set of* 4	2·50	3·00

(Des G. Vasarhelyi. Litho Questa)

1987 (9 Sept). *Giant Tortoises of Aldabra (2nd series). Designs as Nos.* 120/3, *but without circular inscr around W.W.F. emblem. Multicoloured.* W w **16** *(sideways). P* 14.

153	50 c. As Type **18**	35	35
154	75 c. Giant Tortoises at stream	45	45
155	1 r. Giant Tortoises on grassland	55	55
156	2 r. Giant Tortoise (side view)	90	90
153/6	*Set of* 4	2·00	2·00

1987 (9 Dec). *Royal Ruby Wedding. Nos.* 128/32 *optd with T* **119** *of Ascension in silver.*

157	75 c. Princess Elizabeth at Chester, 1951	15	20
158	1 r. Queen and Duke of Edinburgh at Falklands Service, St. Paul's Cathedral, 1985	20	25
159	1 r. 50, At Order of St. Michael and St. George service, St. Paul's Cathedral, 1968	35	40
160	3 r. 75, In Mexico, 1975	85	90
161	5 r. At Crown Agents Head Office, London, 1983	1·10	1·25
157/61	*Set of* 5	2·40	2·75

(Des D. Miller. Litho Questa)

1987 (16 Dec). *Tourism. T* **24** *and similar vert designs. Multicoloured.* W w **16**. *P* 14.

162	3 r. Type **24**	85	85
	a. Horiz strip of 3. Nos. 162/4	2·25	
163	3 r. Ferns	85	85
164	3 r. Bamboo	85	85
162/4	*Set of* 3	2·25	2·25

Nos. 162/4 were printed together, *se-tenant*, in horizontal strips of 3 throughout the sheet, forming the complete picture.

1988 (July–24 Nov). *As No.* 53, *but inscr* "Zil Elwannyen Sesel", *and Nos.* 100, 105 *and* 107, *all* W w **16** *(sideways). P* 14.

165	5 c. Type **10** (24.11)	10	10
166	10 c. Zebra Dove (24.11)	10	10
171	50 c. White-throated Rail (24.11)	10	10
173	2 r. Western Reef Heron	35	40
165/73	*Set of* 4	50	55

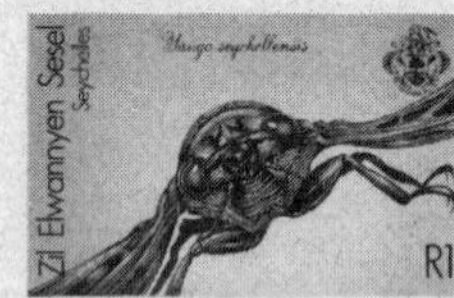

25 *Yanga seychellensis*

(Des I. Loe. Litho Walsall)

1988 (28 July). *Insects. T* **25** *and similar horiz designs. Multicoloured.* W w **14** *(sideways). P* 14.

180	1 r. Type **25**	25	25
181	2 r. *Belenois aldabraensis*	45	45
182	3 r. *Polyspilota seychelliana*	65	65
183	5 r. *Polposipus herculeanus*	1·10	1·10
180/3	*Set of* 4	2·25	2·25

26 Olympic Rings

(Des Joan Thompson. Litho Format)

1988 (31 Aug). *Olympic Games, Seoul. Sheet* 99 × 73 *mm.* W w **16** *(sideways). P* 14.

MS184	**26** 10 r. multicoloured	2·00	2·10

(Des D. Miller (1 r.), E. Nisbet and D. Miller (2 r.), O. Bell and D. Miller (3 r.), A. Theobald and D. Miller (5 r.). Litho Walsall)

1988 (28 Oct). *300th Anniv of Lloyd's of London. Multicoloured designs as T* **123** *of Ascension.* W w **14** *(sideways on* 2, 3 *r.). P* 14.

185	1 r. Modern Lloyd's Building, London	30	30
186	2 r. *Retriever* (cable ship) *(horiz)*	50	50
187	3 r. *Chantel* (fishing boat) *(horiz)*	75	75
188	5 r. Wreck of *Torrey Canyon* (tanker), Cornwall, 1967	1·25	1·25
185/8	*Set of* 4	2·50	2·50

OMNIBUS ISSUES

Details, together with prices for complete sets, of the various Omnibus issues from the 1935 Silver Jubilee series to date are included in a special section following Zululand at the end of the catalogue.

27 "Father Christmas landing with Presents" (Jean-Claude Boniface)

(Adapted G. Vasarhelyi. Litho Questa)

1988 (18 Nov). *Christmas. Children's Paintings. T* **27** *and similar multicoloured designs. W w* **16** *(sideways on* 1, 5 *r.). P* 13½ × 14 *(horiz) or* 14 × 13½ *(vert).*

189	1 r. Type **27**	25	25
190	2 r. "Church" (Francois Barra) *(vert)*	45	45
191	3 r. "Father Christmas flying on Bird" (Wizy Ernesta) *(vert)*	65	65
192	5 r. "Father Christmas in Sleigh over Island" (Federic Lang)	1·10	1·10
189/92	*Set of* 4	2·25	2·25

(Des A. Theobald (10 r.), D. Miller (others). Litho Questa)

1989 (20 July). *20th Anniv of First Manned Landing on Moon. Multicoloured designs as T* **126** *of Ascension. W w* **16** *(sideways on* 2, 3 *r.). P* 14×13½ *(*1, 5 *r.) or* 14 *(others).*

193	1 r. Firing Room, Launch Control Centre	30	30
194	2 r. Crews of "Apollo-Soyuz" mission (30×30 *mm*)	50	50
195	3 r. "Apollo-Soyuz" emblem (30×30 *mm*)	70	70
196	5 r. "Apollo" and "Soyuz" docking in space	1·25	1·25
193/6	*Set of* 4	2·50	2·50
MS197	82×100 mm. 10 r. Recovery of "Apollo 11". P 14×13½	2·00	2·10

28 Dumb Cane

29 Tec-Tec Broth

(Des Lynn Chadwick. Litho Questa)

1989 (9 Oct). *Poisonous Plants. T* **28** *and similar horiz designs. Multicoloured. W w* **16** *(sideways). P* 14.

198	1 r. Type **28**	30	30
199	2 r. Star of Bethlehem	55	55
200	3 r. Indian Liquorice	75	75
201	5 r. Black Nightshade	1·25	1·25
198/201	*Set of* 4	2·50	2·50

(Des O. Bell. Litho B.D.T.)

1989 (18 Dec). *Creole Cooking. T* **29** *and similar vert designs. Multicoloured. W w* **16**. *P* 14.

202	1 r. Type **29**	20	25
203	2 r. Pilaff á la Seychelloise	40	45
204	3 r. Mullet grilled in banana leaves	60	65
205	5 r. Daube	1·00	1·10
202/5	*Set of* 4	2·00	2·25
MS206	125×80 mm. Nos. 202/5	2·25	2·50

Stamps from No. **MS**206 have the white margin omitted on one or both vertical sides.

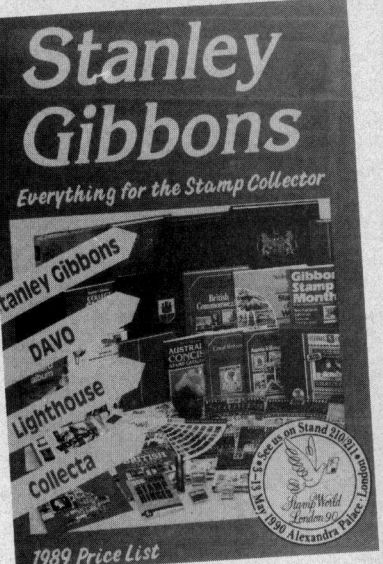

Sierra Leone

PRICES FOR STAMPS ON COVER TO 1945

Nos. 1/3	*from* × 10
Nos. 4/15	*from* × 6
Nos. 16/26	*from* × 8
Nos. 27/34	*from* × 12
Nos. 35/7	*from* × 6
No. 38	—
No. 39	*from* × 10
Nos. 41/52	*from* × 4
No. 53	—
No. 54	*from* × 25
Nos. 55/63	*from* × 3
Nos. 64/71	—
Nos. 73/84	*from* × 3
No. 85	—
Nos. 86/97	*from* × 3
No. 98	—
Nos. 99/110	*from* × 3
No. 111	—
Nos. 112/26	*from* × 2
Nos. 127/30	—
Nos. 131/45	*from* × 2
Nos. 146/8	—
Nos. 155/66	*from* × 2
No. 167	—
Nos. 168/78	*from* × 2
Nos. 179/80	—
Nos. 181/4	*from* × 6
Nos. 185/7	*from* × 5
Nos. 188/200	*from* × 2

CROWN COLONY AND PROTECTORATE

PRINTERS. All issues of Sierra Leone until 1932 were typographed by De La Rue & Co. Ltd, London.

1

2

HALF
PENNY

(3)

1859 (21 Sept)–**74.** *No wmk. P* 14.

No.	Type	Description	Unused	Used
1	1	6d. dull purple	£200	45·00
2		6d. grey-lilac (1865)	£225	40·00
3		6d. reddish violet (*p* 12½) (1872)	£300	55·00
4		6d. reddish lilac (1874)	35·00	25·00

Imperforate proofs exist.

The paper used for the 6d. value often shows varying degrees of blueing, caused by a chemical reaction.

1872–73. *Wmk Crown CC. P* 12½. (*a*) *Wmk sideways* (April 1872).

No.	Type	Description	Unused	Used
7	2	1d. rose-red	65·00	27·00
8		3d. buff	£110	35·00
9		4d. blue	£150	38·00
10		1s. green	£225	45·00
		(*b*) *Wmk upright* (Sept 1873)		
11	2	1d. rose-red	48·00	25·00
12		2d. magenta	95·00	48·00
13		3d. saffron-yellow	£475	85·00
14		4d. blue	£200	50·00
15		1s. green	£325	90·00

1876–77. *Wmk Crown CC. P* 14.

No.	Type	Description	Unused	Used
16	2	½d. brown	2·00	4·75
17		1d. rose-red	30·00	10·00
18		1½d. lilac (1877)	30·00	5·00
19		2d. magenta	35·00	3·75
20		3d. buff	35·00	4·00
21		4d. blue	80·00	6·00
22		1s. green	48·00	6·00
16/22		*Set of* 7	£225	35·00

1883 (June–26 Sept). *Wmk Crown CA. P* 14.

No.	Type	Description	Unused	Used
23	2	½d. brown	17·00	28·00
24		1d. rose-red (26.9.83)	£200	35·00
25		2d. magenta	35·00	6·50
26		4d. blue	£850	28·00

1884 SIERRA 5s. LEONE SURCHARGE. From 2 June 1884 the administration decided that, as a temporary measure, revenue and fiscal duties were to be paid with ordinary postage stamps. At that time there was no postage value higher than 1s., so a local surcharge, reading "SIERRA 5s. LEONE" was applied to No. 22. Until its withdrawal on 1 March 1885 this surcharge was valid for both fiscal and postal purposes, although no genuine postal cover or piece has yet been found. One mint example is known with overprint inverted.

Remainders of the surcharge were cancelled by a horizontal red brush stroke (*Price* £30).

1884 (July)–**91**. *Wmk Crown CA. P* 14.

No.	Type	Description	Unused	Used
27	2	½d. dull green	30	25
28		1d. carmine	1·40	35
		a. Rose-carmine (1885?)	28·00	8·50
29		1½d. pale violet (1889)	2·00	5·00
30		2d. grey	10·00	2·00
31		2½d. ultramarine (1891)	7·00	45
32		3d. yellow (1889)	1·75	3·50
33		4d. brown	1·50	1·00
34		1s. red-brown (1888)	12·00	9·00
27/34		*Set of* 8	32·00	20·00
27/8, 30/1, 33/4 (*perf* 14) Optd "Specimen"		*Set of* 6	£400	
27/8, 30, 33 (*perf* 12) Optd "Specimen"		*Set of* 4	£450	

1885–96. *Wmk Crown CC. P* 14.

No.	Type	Description	Unused	Used
35	1	6d. dull violet (1885)	55·00	22·00
		a. Bisected (3d.) (on cover)	†	£2250
36		6d. brown-purple (1890)	13·00	14·00
37		6d. purple-lake (1896)	2·00	6·50
36 Optd "Specimen"			60·00	

1893 (18 Jan). *Surch with T* **3**. *P* 14. (*a*) *Wmk Crown CC.*

No.	Type	Description	Unused	Used
38	2	½d. on 1½d. lilac	£350	£400
		a. "PFNNY" (R. 3/1)	£1800	£2250
		(*b*) *Wmk Crown CA*		
39	2	½d. on 1½d. pale violet	2·75	3·00
		a. Surch inverted	£100	£100
		b. "PFNNY" (R. 3/1)	70·00	70·00
		ba. Ditto. Surch inverted	£1400	

The 6d. fiscal, inscribed "STAMP DUTY" as Type **6,** surcharged "ONE-PENNY" is known used for postage between June and August 1894, but no official sanction for such usage has been found.

4

5

1896–97. *Wmk Crown CA. P* 14.

No.	Type	Description	Unused	Used
41	4	½d. dull mauve and green (1897)	65	75
42		1d. dull mauve and carmine	65	30
43		1½d. dull mauve and black (1897)	2·00	6·00
44		2d. dull mauve and orange	2·25	5·00
45		2½d. dull mauve and ultramarine	1·40	80
46	5	3d. dull mauve and slate	7·00	7·00
47		4d. dull mauve and carmine (1897)	6·50	13·00
48		5d. dull mauve and black (1897)	7·00	11·00
49		6d. dull mauve (1897)	7·00	12·00
50		1s. green and black	6·00	14·00
51		2s. green and ultramarine	20·00	26·00
52		5s. green and carmine	38·00	60·00
53		£1 purple/*red*	£140	£225
41/53		*Set of* 13	£200	£325
41/53 Optd "Specimen"		*Set of* 13	£250	

6

POSTAGE
AND
REVENUE

(7)

2½d. (8)

2½d. (9)

2½d. (10)

2½d. (11)

2½d. (12)

2½d. (13)

POSTAGE AND
REVENUE

(14)

1897 (Mar). *Fiscal stamps as T* **6**. *Wmk CA over Crown,* w **7.** *P* 14. (*a*) *Optd with T* **7**.

No.	Type	Description	Unused	Used
54		1d. dull purple and green	1·40	1·75
		a. Opt double	£950	£1000
		(*b*) *Optd with T* **7** *and surch T* **8**, **10**, **11** *or* **12** *with six thin bars across the original face value.*		
55	8	2½d. on 3d. dull purple and green	11·00	12·00
		a. Surch double		
		b. Surch double (Types **8** + **10**)	£5500	
		c. Surch double (Types **8** + **11**)		
56	10	2½d. on 3d. dull purple and green	50·00	65·00
57	11	2½d. on 3d. dull purple and green	£140	£160
58	12	2½d. on 3d. dull purple and green	£300	£350
59	8	2½d. on 6d. dull purple and green	8·50	11·00
60	10	2½d. on 6d. dull purple and green	40·00	50·00
61	11	2½d. on 6d. dull purple and green	£100	£110
62	12	2½d. on 6d. dull purple and green	£225	£250

Nos. 55/8 and 59/62 were surcharged from a setting of 30 (10 × 3) which contained twenty-two examples of Type **8**, five of Type **10**, two of Type **11** and one of Type **12**.

Two examples are known of No. 55a, five of No. 55b (of which two are in the Royal Collection) and two of No. 55c (one in the Royal Collection). A unique example of a double surcharge on No. 55 showing Types **8** + **12** is also in the Royal Collection.

(*c*) *Optd with T* **14** *and surch T* **8**, **9**, **10**, **11** *or* **13** *with five thin bars across the original face value.*

No.	Type	Description	Unused	Used
63	8	2½d. on 1s. dull lilac	80·00	60·00
64	9	2½d. on 1s. dull lilac	£1200	£1200
65	10	2½d. on 1s. dull lilac	£700	£700
66	11	2½d. on 1s. dull lilac	£400	£400
66*a*	13	2½d. on 1s. dull lilac	£1200	£1200
67	8	2½d. on 2s. dull lilac	£1200	£1400
68	9	2½d. on 2s. dull lilac	£24000	
69	10	2½d. on 2s. dull lilac	£10000	
70	11	2½d. on 2s. dull lilac	£6000	
71	13	2½d. on 2s. dull lilac	£24000	

The setting of 30 (10 × 3) used for both Nos. 63/6*a* and 67/71 contained twenty-two examples of Type **8**, one of Type **9**, two of Type **10**, four of Type **11** and one of Type **13**.

Most examples of Nos. 63/6*a* are water-stained. Stamps in this condition are worth about 40% of the prices quoted.

15

16

1903. *Wmk Crown CA. P* 14.

No.	Type	Description	Unused	Used
73	15	½d. dull purple and green	2·50	2·00
74		1d. dull purple and rosine	80	25
75		1½d. dull purple and black	1·25	3·75
76		2d. dull purple and brown-orange	3·75	8·00
77		2½d. dull purple and ultramarine	4·50	4·50
78	16	3d. dull purple and grey	5·00	7·00
79		4d. dull purple and rosine	6·00	7·50
80		5d. dull purple and black	6·00	9·50
81		6d. dull purple	9·00	8·50
82		1s. green and black	10·00	17·00
83		2s. green and ultramarine	25·00	30·00
84		5s. green and carmine	35·00	50·00
85		£1 purple/*red*	£200	£225
73/85		*Set of* 13	£250	£300
73/85 Optd "Specimen"		*Set of* 13	£250	

1904–5. *Wmk Mult Crown CA. P* 14.

No.	Type	Description	Unused	Used
86	15	½d. dull purple and green, **C** (1905)	5·00	2·00
87		1d. dull purple and rosine, **OC**	65	35
88		1½d. dull purple and black, **C** (1905)	2·50	7·50
89		2d. dull purple & brown-orange, **C** (1905)	4·00	3·50
90		2½d. dull purple and ultramarine, **C** (1905)	4·50	2·00
91	16	3d. dull purple and grey, **C** (1905)	9·00	3·00
92		4d. dull purple and rosine, **C** (1905)	4·00	4·00
93		5d. dull purple and black, **C** (1905)	7·50	14·00
94		6d. dull purple, **C** (1905)	2·75	3·25
95		1s. green and black, **C** (1905)	7·50	8·50
96		2s. green and ultramarine, **C** (1905)	14·00	16·00
97		5s. green and carmine, **C** (1905)	28·00	42·00
98		£1 purple/*red*, **C** (1905)	£225	£250
86/98		*Set of* 13	£275	£300

1907–11. *Wmk Mult Crown CA. P* 14.

No.	Type	Description	Unused	Used
99	15	½d. green, **O**	35	25
100		1d. carmine, **O**	4·50	20
		a. Red, **O**	1·00	15
101		1½d. orange, **O** (1910)	30	2·00
102		2d. greyish slate, **O** (1909)	80	1·50
103		2½d. blue, **O**	80	1·40
104	16	3d. purple/*yellow*, **OC** (1909)	2·75	2·75
105		4d. black and red/*yellow*, **C** (1908)	2·25	1·10
106		5d. purple and olive-green, **C** (1908)	4·50	4·25
107		6d. dull and bright purple, **C** (1908)	3·25	4·00
108		1s. black/*green*, **C** (1908)	5·00	4·50
109		2s. purple & bright blue/*blue*, **C** (1908)	15·00	10·00
110		5s. green and red/*yellow*, **C** (1908)	27·00	35·00
111		£1 purple and black/*red*, **C** (1911)	£170	£170
99/111		*Set of* 13	£200	£210
99/111 Optd "Specimen"		*Set of* 13	£300	

USED HIGH VALUES. The £2 and £5 values of the King George V series were intended for fiscal use only. Before the introduction of the airmail service at the end of 1926 there was no postal rate for which they could be used. Under the airmail rates used between 1926 and 1932 it is just possible that a very heavy letter may have required a £2 value. Postmarks on the £5 and on the £2 before December 1926 can only have been applied "by favour" or, in the case of the cds type, are on stamps removed from telegraph forms. Used prices quoted for Nos. 129 and 147 are for "by favour" cancellations.

17

18

19

20

1912–21. *Wmk Mult Crown CA. P* 14.

No.	Type	Description	Unused	Used
112	17	½d. blue-green, **O**	75	40
		a. Yellow-green	60	50
		b. Deep green	2·00	80
113		1d. carmine-red, **O**	75	10
		a. Scarlet (1916)	65	30
		b. Rose-red	1·00	20
114		1½d. orange, **O** (1913)	80	85
		a. Orange-yellow	1·75	95
115		2d. greyish slate, **O** (1913)	1·00	10
116		2½d. deep blue, **O** (1913)	6·00	2·00
		a. Ultramarine	60	65
116*b*	20	3d. purple/*yellow*, **C**	2·00	2·50
		ba. On pale yellow	2·50	3·25
117	18	4d. black & red/*yellow*, **O** (Die I) (1913)	80	3·50
		a. On lemon	3·75	5·50
		b. On pale yellow (Die II) (5.21)	1·50	2·50
118		5d. purple and olive-green, **O** (1913)	70	2·75
119		6d. dull and bright purple, **C** (1913)	3·25	3·25
120	19	7d. purple and orange, **C** (1913)	1·50	4·00
121		9d. purple and black, **C** (1913)	4·75	4·50
122	18	10d. purple and red, **C** (1913)	2·75	11·00
124	20	1s. black/*green*, **C**	2·50	3·25
		a. On blue-green, green back	1·75	2·50
125		2s. blue and purple/*blue*, **C**	6·50	3·25
126		5s. red and green/*yellow*, **C**	9·50	16·00

127 20 10s. red and green/*green*, C .. 40·00 60·00
a. Carmine and blue-green/green .. 48·00 65·00
b. Carmine and yellow-green/green 48·00 65·00
128 £1 black and purple/*red*, C .. £100 £140
129 £2 blue and dull purple, C (S. £100) £475 £600
130 £5 orange and green, C (S. £225) .. £1200
112/28 .. *Set of* 17 £150 £225
112/28 Optd "Specimen" .. *Set of* 17 £300

1921–28. *Wmk Mult Script CA. P* 14.
131 17 ½d. dull green, O .. 35 15
a. Bright green .. 90 35
132 1d. bright violet, O (Die I) (1924) .. 95 40
a. Die II (1926) .. 50 10
133 1½d. scarlet, O (1925) .. 50 30
134 2d. grey, O (1922) .. 40 10
135 2½d. ultramarine, O .. 45 1·25
136 18 3d. bright blue, O (1922) .. 40 25
137 4d. black and red/*pale yellow*, O (1925) 1·75 1·25
138 5d. purple and olive-green, O .. 50 55
139 6d. grey-purple and bright purple, C .. 1·25 1·50
140 19 7d. purple and orange, C (1928) .. 2·00 8·50
141 9d. purple and black, C (1922) .. 2·50 6·50
142 18 10d. purple and red, C (1926) .. 2·00 9·50
143 20 1s. black/*emerald*, C (1925) .. 2·25 3·75
144 2s. blue and dull purple/*blue*, C .. 6·50 6·50
145 5s. red and green/*yellow*, C (1927) .. 8·00 27·00
146 10s. red and green/*green*, C (1927) .. 45·00 75·00
147 £2 blue and dull purple, C (1923) (Optd S. £100) .. £425 £600
148 £5 orange and green, C (1923) (Optd S. £225) .. £1200
131/46 .. *Set of* 16 65·00 £130
131/46 Optd "Specimen" .. *Set of* 16 £250

21 Rice Field

22 Palms and Cola Tree

(Eng J.A.C. Harrison (T 21))

1932 (1 Mar). *Wmk Mult Script CA. (a) Recess Waterlow. P* 12½.
155 21 ½d. green .. 15 20
156 1d. violet .. 15 10
157 1½d. carmine .. 20 1·25
a. Imperf between (horiz pair) ..
158 2d. brown .. 20 10
159 3d. blue .. 25 75
160 4d. orange .. 40 1·40
161 5d. bronze-green .. 40 1·00
162 6d. light blue .. 35 1·25
163 1s. lake .. 70 2·25

(b) Recess B.W. P 12.
164 22 2s. chocolate .. 2·75 3·50
165 5s. deep blue .. 6·00 15·00
166 10s. green .. 35·00 60·00
167 £1 purple .. 65·00 £120
155/67 .. *Set of* 13 £100 £180
155/67 Perf "Specimen" .. *Set of* 13 £180

23 Arms of Sierra Leone

27 African Elephant

28 King George V

24 Old Slave Market, Freetown

(Des Father F. Welsh. Recess B.W.)

1933 (2 Oct). *Centenary of Abolition of Slavery and of Death of William Wilberforce. T* 23/4, 27/8 *and similar designs. Wmk Mult Script CA (sideways on horiz designs). P* 12.
168 ½d. green .. 35 60
169 1d. black and brown .. 25 10
170 1½d. chestnut .. 2·50 4·00
171 2d. purple .. 2·25 20
172 3d. blue .. 1·60 1·50
173 4d. brown .. 4·50 10·00
174 5d. green and chestnut .. 5·50 16·00
175 6d. black and brown-orange .. 6·00 8·00
176 1s. violet .. 4·00 11·00
177 2s. brown and light blue .. 18·00 24·00
178 5s. black and purple .. £120 £150
179 10s. black and sage-green .. £130 £180
180 £1 violet and orange .. £425 £500
168/180 .. *Set of* 13 £650 £800
168/80 Perf "Specimen" .. *Set of* 13 £650

Designs: *Vert*—1d. "Freedom"; 1½d. Map of Sierra Leone; 4d. Government sanatorium. *Horiz*—3d. Native fruit seller; 5d. Bullom canoe; 6d. Punting near Banana; 1s. Government buildings; 2s. Bunce Island; £1 Freetown harbour.

1935 (6 May). *Silver Jubilee. As Nos.* 91/4 *of Antigua, but ptd by B.W. P* 11×12.
181 1d. ultramarine and grey-black .. 25 15
a. Extra flagstaff .. 32·00
b. Short extra flagstaff .. 35·00
c. Lightning conductor .. 22·00
182 3d. brown and deep blue .. 90 2·00
a. Extra flagstaff .. 45·00
b. Short extra flagstaff .. 55·00
c. Lightning conductor .. 32·00
183 5d. green and indigo .. 1·40 4·00
a. Extra flagstaff .. 75·00
b. Short extra flagstaff .. 75·00
c. Lightning conductor .. 50·00
184 1s. slate and purple .. 4·50 2·75
a. Extra flagstaff .. £140
b. Short extra flagstaff .. £100
c. Lightning conductor .. 90·00
181/4 .. *Set of* 4 6·50 8·00
181/4 Perf "Specimen" .. *Set of* 4 70·00

For illustrations of plate varieties see Omnibus section following Zululand.

1937 (12 May). *Coronation. As Nos.* 13/15 *of Aden, but ptd by B.W. P* 11 × 11½.
185 1d. orange .. 70 25
186 2d. purple .. 70 30
187 3d. blue .. 80 95
185/7 .. *Set of* 3 2·00 1·40
185/7 Perf "Specimen" .. *Set of* 3 50·00

30 Freetown from the Harbour

31 Rice Harvesting

(Recess Waterlow)

1938 (1 May)–**44.** *Wmk Mult Script CA (sideways). P* 12½.
188 30 ½d. black and blue-green .. 10 10
189 1d. black and lake .. 10 10
a. Imperf between (vert pair) .. † —
190 31 1½d. scarlet .. 12·00 10
190*a* 1½d. mauve (1.2.41) .. 10 10
191 2d. mauve .. 22·00 80
191*a* 2d. scarlet (1.2.41) .. 10 10
192 30 3d. black and ultramarine .. 10 10
193 4d. black and red-brown (20.6.38) .. 25 35
194 31 5d. olive-green (20.6.38) .. 2·50 1·75
195 6d. grey (20.6.38) .. 30 10
196 30 1s. black and olive-green (20.6.38) .. 35 20
196*a* 31 1s. 3d. yellow-orange (1.7.44) .. 25 20
197 30 2s. black and sepia (20.6.38) .. 75 45
198 31 5s. red-brown (20.6.38) .. 3·50 1·50
199 10s. emerald-green (20.6.38) .. 5·00 4·00
200 30 £1 deep blue (20.6.38) .. 13·00 7·00
188/200 .. *Set of* 16 55·00 15·00
188/200 Perf "Specimen" .. *Set of* 16 £250

1946 (1 Oct). *Victory. As Nos.* 28/9 *of Aden.*
201 1½d. lilac .. 10 10
202 3d. ultramarine .. 15 10
201/2 Perf "Specimen" .. *Set of* 2 45·00

1948 (1 Dec). *Royal Silver Wedding. As Nos.* 30/1 *of Aden.*
203 1½d. bright purple .. 15 15
204 £1 indigo .. 14·00 11·00

1949 (10 Oct). *75th Anniv of U.P.U. As Nos.* 114/17 *of Antigua.*
205 1½d. purple .. 15 10
206 3d. deep blue .. 35 50
207 6d. grey .. 35 50
208 1s. olive .. 35 60
205/8 .. *Set of* 4 1·10 1·50

1953 (2 June). *Coronation. As No.* 47 *of Aden but ptd by B.W.*
209 1½d. black and purple .. 10 10

32 Cape Lighthouse

33 Cotton Tree, Freetown

(Recess Waterlow)

1956 (2 Jan)–**61.** *Designs as T* 32/3. *Wmk Mult Script CA. P* 13½ × 13 *(horiz) or* 14 *(vert).*
210 ½d. black and deep lilac .. 25 50
211 1d. black and olive .. 25 10
212 1½d. black and ultramarine .. 30 85
213 2d. black and brown .. 35 10
214 3d. black and bright blue .. 75 10
a. Perf 13 × 13½ .. 90 4·50
215 4d. black and slate-blue .. 1·50 35
216 6d. black and violet .. 70 10
217 1s. black and scarlet .. 50 10
218 1s. 3d. black and sepia .. 4·00 10
219 2s. 6d. black and chestnut .. 4·50 80
220 5s. black and deep green .. 1·00 50
221 10s. black and bright reddish purple .. 2·75 2·50
a. Black and purple (19.4.61) .. 8·00 20·00
222 £1 black and orange .. 9·00 14·00
210/22 .. *Set of* 13 23·00 18·00

Designs: *Horiz*—1d. Queen Elizabeth II Quay; 1½d. Piassava workers; 4d. Iron ore production, Marampa; 6d. Whale Bay, York Village; 1s. 3d. Aeroplane and map; 10s. Law Courts, Freetown; £1, Government House. *Vert*—3d. Rice harvesting; 1s. Bullom canoe; 2s.6d. Orugu Railway Bridge; 5s. Kuranko Chief.

Nos. 210/11 and 214 exist in coils, constructed from normal sheets.

INDEPENDENT

45 Palm Fruit Gathering

46 Licensed Diamond Miner

52

(Des K. Penny (½d., 1s.), Messrs Thoma, Turrell and Larkins (1d., 3d., 6d., 2s. 6d.), W. G. Rumley (1½d., 5s.), J. H. Vandi (2d., 10s.), R. A. Sweet (4d., 1s 3d.), J. White (£1). Recess B.W.)

1961 (27 Apr). *Independence. T* 45/6 *and similar designs. W* 52. *P* 13½.
223 ½d. chocolate and deep bluish green .. 10 10
224 1d. orange-brown and myrtle-green .. 30 10
225 1½d. black and emerald .. 10 10
226 2d. black and ultramarine .. 10 10
227 3d. orange-brown and blue .. 10 10
228 4d. turquoise-blue and scarlet .. 10 10
229 6d. black and purple .. 10 10
230 1s. chocolate and yellow-orange .. 10 10
231 1s. 3d. turquoise-blue and violet .. 15 10
232 2s. 6d. deep green and black .. 85 10
233 5s. black and red .. 90 90
234 10s. black and green .. 1·00 1·25
235 £1 carmine-red and yellow .. 5·00 4·00
223/235 .. *Set of* 13 7·50 6·50

Designs: *Vert*—1½d., 5s. Bundu mask; 2d., 10s. Bishop Crowther and Old Fourah Bay College; 1s. Palm fruit gathering; £1, Forces Bugler. *Horiz*—3d., 6d. Sir Milton Margai; 4d., 1s. 3d. Lumley Beach, Freetown; 2s. 6d. Licensed diamond miner.

53 Royal Charter, 1799

55 Old House of Representatives, Freetown, 1924

(Des C. P. Rang (3d., 4d.), F. H. Burgess (1s. 3d.). Recess B.W.)

1961 (25 Nov). *Royal Visit. T* 53, 55 *and similar designs. W* 52. *P* 13½.
236 3d. black and rose-red .. 10 10
237 4d. black and violet .. 10 15
238 6d. black and yellow-orange .. 10 10
239 1s. 3d. black and blue .. 80 10
236/9 .. *Set of* 4 95 25

Designs: *Vert*—4d. King's Yard Gate, Freetown, 1817. *Horiz*—1s. 3d. Royal Yacht *Britannia* at Freetown.

57 Campaign Emblem

(Recess B.W.)

1962 (7 Apr). *Malaria Eradication. W* 52. *P* 11 × 11½.
240 57 3d. carmine-red .. 10 10
241 1s. 3d. deep green .. 10 10

58 Fireball Lily

59 Jina-gbo

(Des M. Goaman. Photo Harrison)

1963 (1 Jan). *Flowers. Vert designs as T* **58** *(½d., 1½d., 3d., 4d., 1s., 2s. 6d., 5s., 10s.) or horiz as T* **59** *(others). Multicoloured. W* **52** *(sideways on vert designs). P* 14.

242	½d. Type **58**	10	10
243	1d. Type **59**	10	10
244	1½d. Stereospermum	10	10
245	2d. Black-eyed Susan	10	10
246	3d. Beniseed	10	10
247	4d. Blushing Hibiscus	10	10
248	6d. Climbing Lily	15	10
249	1s. Beautiful Crinum	20	10
250	1s. 3d. Blue Bells	40	20
251	2s. 6d. Broken Hearts	60	30
252	5s. Ra-ponthi	80	80
253	10s. Blue Plumbago	2·00	1·50
254	£1 African Tulip Tree	7·50	6·50
242/254	*Set of* 13	11·00	8·50

71 Threshing Machine and Corn Bins

(Des V. Whiteley. Recess B.W.)

1963 (21 Mar). *Freedom from Hunger. T* **71** *and similar horiz design. W* **52**. *P* 11½ × 11.

255	3d. black and yellow-ochre	15	10
256	1s. 3d. sepia and emerald-green	35	10

Design:—1s. 3d. Girl with onion crop.

2ND YEAR OF INDEPENDENCE 19 PROGRESS 63 DEVELOPMENT 3d. (73)

2nd Year Independence Progress Development 1963 10d. (74)

(Optd by Govt Printer, Freetown)

1963 (27 Apr). *Second Anniv of Independence. Surch or optd as T* **73/4**. *(a) Postage.*

257	3d. on ½d. black & deep lilac (No. 210) (R.)	10	10
	a. Small "c" in "INDEPENDENCE"	3·00	4·00
258	4d. on 1½d. black & ultram (No. 212) (Br.)	10	10
259	6d. on ½d. black & deep lilac (No. 210) (O.)	10	10
	a. Small "c" in "INDEPENDENCE"	3·50	4·50
260	10d. on 3d. black & bright blue (No. 214) (R.)	20	10
261	1s. 6d. on 3d. black & brt bl (No. 214) (V.)	20	10
262	3s. 6d. on 3d. black & brt bl (No. 214) (Ult.)	25	15
	(b) Air. Additionally optd "AIR MAIL"		
263	7d. on 1½d. black & ultram (No. 212) (C.)	10	10
264	1s. 3d. on 1½d. blk & ultram (No. 212) (R.)	10	10
265	2s. 6d. black and chestnut (No. 219) (V.)	40	15
266	3s. on 3d. black & bright blue (No. 214) (B.)	25	15
267	6s. on 3d. black & bright blue (No. 214) (R.)	50	20
268	11s. on 10s. black and bright reddish purple (No. 221) (C.)	75	75
269	11s. on £1 black and orange (No. 222) (C.)	£500	£170
257/268	*Set of* 12	2·50	1·60

75 Centenary Emblem

(Des M. Goaman. Recess B.W.)

1963 (1 Nov). *Centenary of Red Cross. T* **75** *and similar vert designs. W* **52**. *P* 11 × 11½.

270	3d. red and violet	20	10
271	6d. red and black	25	10
272	1s. 3d. red and deep bluish green	30	10
270/2	*Set of* 3	65	25

Designs:—6d. Red Cross emblem; 1s. 3d. Centenary emblem.

1853–1859–1963 Oldest Postal Service Newest G.P.O. in West Africa 1s. (78)

1853–1859–1963 Oldest Postage Stamp Newest G.P.O. in West Africa AIRMAIL (79)

1963 (4 Nov). *Postal Commemorations. Optd or surch by Govt Printer, Freetown. (a) Postage. As T* **78**.

273	3d. black and bright blue (No. 214)	10	10
	a. "1895" for "1859" (R. 3/3)	2·50	
274	4d. on 1½d. black & ultram (No. 212) (C.)	10	10
	a. "1895" for "1859" (R. 1/2)	3·50	
275	9d. on 1½d. black & ultram (No. 212) (V.)	10	10
276	1s. on 1s. 3d. turq-blue & vio (No. 231) (C.)	10	10
277	1s. 6d. on ½d. black & deep lilac (No. 210) (Mag.)	15	10
278	2s. on 3d. black & brt blue (No. 214) (Br.)	15	10
	a. "1895" for "1859" (R. 4/10)	8·00	
	(b) Air. As T **79**		
279	7d. on 3d. black & rose-red (No. 236) (Br.)	10	10
	a. "1895" for "1859" (R. 3/6, 4/4)	3·00	
280	1s. 3d. black and blue (No. 239) (C.)	40	20
	a. "1895" for "1859" (R. 7/3)	12·00	
281	2s. 6d. on 4d. turquoise-bl & scar (No. 228)	30	20
	a. "1895" for "1859" (R. 7/3)	35·00	
282	3s. on 3d. black and rose-red (No. 236) (V.)	45	60
	a. "1895" for "1859" (R. 3/3)	£180	
283	6s. on 6d. black & yell-orge (No. 238) (Ult.)	50	60
	a. "1895" for "1859" (R. 1/1)	40·00	
284	£1 black and orange (No. 222) (R.)	8·00	13·00
	a. "1895" for "1859" (R. 11/4)	£160	
273/84	*Set of* 12	9·00	13·50

The events commemorated are: 1853, "First Post Office"; 1859, "First Postage Stamps"; and 1963, "Newest G.P.O." in West Africa. Nos. 273, 278 have the opt. in five lines; Nos. 279, 282 in six lines (incl "AIRMAIL").

80 Lion Emblem and Map

81 Globe and Map

(Recess and litho Walsall Lithographic Co, Ltd)

1964 (10 Feb). *World's Fair, New York. Imperf. Self-Adhesive.*

	(a) Postage. T **80**		
285	1d. multicoloured	10	10
286	3d. multicoloured	10	10
	a. Lion omitted		
287	4d. multicoloured	10	10
288	6d. multicoloured	10	10
289	1s. multicoloured	10	10
	a. "POSTAGE 1/-" omitted	35·00	
290	2s. multicoloured	15	10
291	5s. multicoloured	25	20
	a. "POSTAGE 5/-" omitted	35·00	
	(b) Air. T **81**		
292	7d. multicoloured	10	10
293	9d. multicoloured	10	10
	a. "AIR MAIL 9d." omitted		
294	1s. 3d. multicoloured	10	10
	a. "AIR MAIL 1/3" omitted	35·00	
295	2s. 6d. multicoloured	15	10
296	3s. 6d. multicoloured	15	10
	a. "AIR MAIL 3/6" omitted		
297	6s. multicoloured	25	25
	a. "AIR MAIL 6/–" omitted	40·00	
298	11s. multicoloured	35	50
	a. "AIR MAIL 11/-" omitted	42·00	
285/298	*Set of* 14	1·40	1·40

Nos. 285/98 were issued in sheets of 30 (6 × 5) on green (postage) or yellow (airmail) backing paper with the emblems of Samuel Jones & Co. Ltd, self-adhesive paper-makers, on the back.

WARNING. These and later self-adhesive stamps should be kept on their backing paper except commercially used, which should be retained on cover or piece.

82 Inscription and Map

83 Pres. Kennedy and Map

(Recess and litho Walsall)

1964 (11 May). *President Kennedy Memorial Issue. Imperf. Self-adhesive. (a) Postage. Green backing paper.*

299	**82**	1d. multicoloured	10	10
300		3d. multicoloured	10	10
301		4d. multicoloured	10	10
302		6d. multicoloured	10	10
303		1s. multicoloured	10	10
304		2s. multicoloured	10	10
305		5s. multicoloured	25	20
		(b) Air. Yellow backing paper		
306	**83**	7d. multicoloured	10	10
307		9d. multicoloured	10	10
308		1s. 3d. multicoloured	10	10
309		2s. 6d. multicoloured	15	20
310		3s. 6d. multicoloured	15	20
311		6s. multicoloured	30	40
312		11s. multicoloured	45	60
299/312		*Set of* 14	1·50	1·75

(New Currency. 100 cents = 1 leone)

3c (84) AIRMAIL 7c (85) LE 1·00 (86)

1964–66. *Decimal currency. Various stamps surch locally.*

(i) *First issue* (4.8.64). *(a) Postage. Surch as T* **84**

313	1 c. on 6d. multicoloured (No. 248) (R.)	10	10
314	2 c. on 3d. black and rose-red (No. 236)	10	10
315	3 c. on 3d. multicoloured (No. 246)	10	10
	a. Surch inverted	£140	
316	5 c. on ½d. chocolate and deep bluish green (No. 223) (B.)	10	10
317	8 c. on 3d. black & yell-ochre (No. 255) (R.)	10	10
318	10 c. on 1s. 3d. multicoloured (No. 250) (R.)	10	10
319	15 c. on 1s. multicoloured (No. 249)	15	10
320	25 c. on 6d. black & yell-orge (No. 238) (V.)	25	25
321	50 c. on 2s. 6d. dp green & blk (No. 232) (O.)	50	50
	(b) Air. As T **85** *or* **86** *(Nos. 326/7)*		
322	7 c. on 1s. 3d. sepia and emerald-green (No. 256) (B.)	10	10
323	20 c. on 4d. turquoise-blue & scarlet (No. 228)	20	15
324	30 c. on 10s. black and green (No. 234) (R.)	30	30
325	40 c. on 5s. black and red (No. 233) (B.)	40	40
326	1 l. on 1s. 3d. multicoloured (No. 308) (R.)	60	80
327	2 l. on 11s. multicoloured (No. 312)	1·10	1·40
313/327	*Set of* 15	3·50	3·75

1c (87) TWO LEONES Le 2·00 (88)

(ii) *Second issue* (20.1.65). *Surch as T* **87** *or* **88** *(Nos. 332/3)*

	(a) Postage		
328	1 c. on 3d. orange-brown and blue (No. 227)	10	10
329	2 c. on 1d. multicoloured (No. 299)	10	10
330	4 c. on 3d. multicoloured (No. 300)	10	10
	a. Error. 4 c. on 1d. (No. 299)		
	b. Stamp omitted (in pair with normal)		
331	5 c. on 2d. multicoloured (No. 245)	10	10
332	1 l. on 5s. multicoloured (No. 252) (Gold)	1·25	1·25
333	2 l. on £1 carmine-red & yellow (No. 235) (B.)	2·25	2·25
	a. Surch double (B. + Blk.)	—	65·00
	(b) Air		
334	7 c. on 7d. multicoloured (No. 306) (R.)	10	10
335	60 c. on 9d. multicoloured (No. 307)	50	45
328/35	*Set of* 8	3·75	3·75

On No. 330b the stamp became detached before the surcharge was applied so that "4c" appears on the backing paper.

(iii) *Third issue* (4.65). *Surch in figures (various sizes). (a) Postage*

336	1 c. on 1½d. black & emerald (No. 225) (R.)	10	10
337	2 c. on 3d. multicoloured (No. 300)	10	10
338	2 c. on 4d. multicoloured (No. 287)	10	10
339	3 c. on 1d. multicoloured (No. 243)	10	10
340	3 c. on 2d. black and ultram (No. 226) (R.)	10	10
341	5 c. on 1s. 3d. turq-bl & violet (No. 231) (R.)	10	10
	a. Surch inverted		
342	15 c. on 6d. multicoloured (No. 302)	80	50
343	15 c. on 1s. multicoloured (No. 303) (R.)	1·25	90
344	20 c. on 6d. black and purple (No. 229) (R.)	30	15
345	25 c. on 6d. multicoloured (No. 248) (R.)	35	20
346	50 c. on 3d. orange-brn & blue (No. 227) (R.)	80	55
347	60 c. on 5s. multicoloured (No. 291) (V.)	2·50	1·75
348	1 l. on 4d. multicoloured (No. 301) (R.)	3·00	2·75
349	2 l. on £1 carmine-red & yell (No. 235) (B.)	4·50	3·75
	(b) Air		
350	7 c. on 9d. multicoloured (No. 293)	15	10
336/350	*Set of* 15	13·00	9·75

2c (89) TWO Leones (90)

(iv) *Fourth issue* (9.11.65). *Surch as T* **89**. *(a) Postage*

351	**80**	1 c. on 6d. multicoloured (V.)	2·75	7·00
352		1 c. on 2s. multicoloured (V.)	2·75	7·00
353	**82**	1 c. on 2s. multicoloured (V.)	2·75	7·00
354		1 c. on 5s. multicoloured (V.)	2·75	7·00
		(b) Air		
355	**81**	2 c. on 1s. 3d. multicoloured	2·75	7·00
356	**83**	2 c. on 1s. 3d. multicoloured	2·75	7·00
357		2 c. on 3s. 6d. multicoloured	2·75	7·00
358	**81**	3 c. on 7d. multicoloured	2·75	7·00
359	**83**	3 c. on 9d. multicoloured	2·75	7·00
360	**81**	5 c. on 2s. 6d. multicoloured	2·75	7·00
361	**83**	5 c. on 2s. 6d. multicoloured	2·75	7·00
362	**81**	5 c. on 3s. 6d. multicoloured	2·75	7·00
363		5 c. on 6s. multicoloured	2·75	7·00
364	**83**	5 c. on 6s. multicoloured	2·75	7·00
351/364		*Set of* 14	35·00	90·00

(v) *Fifth issue* (28.1.66). *Air. No. 374 further surch with T* **90**

365	2 l. on 30 c. on 6d. multicoloured	2·50	2·00

IN MEMORIAM 2c
TWO GREAT LEADERS

SIR MILTON MARGAI 1895-1964 SIR WINSTON CHURCHILL 1874-1965

(**91** Margai and Churchill)

1965 (19 May). *Sir Milton Margai and Sir Winston Churchill Commemoration. Nos. 242/3, 245/50 and 252/4 surch as T* **91** *on horiz designs or with individual portraits on vert designs as indicated.*

(a) Postage

No.	Description	Unused	Used
366	2 c. on 1d. Type **59**	10	10
367	3 c. on 3d. Beniseed (Margai)	10	10
368	10 c. on 1s. Beautiful Crinum (Churchill)	20	10
369	20 c. on 1s. 3d. Blue Bells	40	10
370	50 c. on 4d. Blushing Hibiscus (Margai)	90	35
371	75 c. on 5s. Ra-ponthi (Churchill)	2·25	1·25

(b) Air. Additionally optd "AIR MAIL"

No.	Description	Unused	Used
372	7 c. on 2d. Black-eyed Susan	20	10
373	15 c. on ½d. Type **58** (Margai)	35	10
374	30 c. on 6d. Climbing Lily (O. and W.)	1·25	25
375	1 l. on £1 African Tulip Tree	4·00	1·50
376	2 l. on 10s. Blue Plumbago (Churchill)	11·00	5·00
	a. Surch value omitted	£250	
366/376	*Set of* 11	18·00	8·00

92 Cola Plant and Nut

93 Arms of Sierra Leone

94 Inscription and Necklace

(Des M. Meers. Manufactured by Walsall Lithographic Co, Ltd)

1965 (Nov). *Imperf. Self-adhesive.*

A. *Embossed on silver foil, backed with paper bearing advertisements. Emerald, olive-yellow and carmine; denominations in colours given. Postage.*

No.	Type	Description	Unused	Used
377	**92**	1 c. emerald	25	10
378		2 c. carmine	25	10
379		3 c. olive-yellow	25	10
380		4 c. silver/*emerald*	30	10
381		5 c. silver/*carmine*	30	10

B. *Typo and embossed on cream paper backed with advertisements*

(a) Postage

No.	Type	Description	Unused	Used
382	**93**	20 c. multicoloured	1·00	35
383		50 c. multicoloured	2·50	1·40

(b) Air

No.	Type	Description	Unused	Used
384	**93**	40 c. multicoloured	2·25	1·40

C. *Foil-backed and litho, with advertisements on white paper backing (see footnote). Air*

No.	Type	Description	Unused	Used
385	**94**	7 c. multicoloured	55	15
386		15 c. multicoloured	85	50
377/386		*Set of* 10	7·50	4·00

The above stamps were issued in single form with attached tabs to remove the backing paper, with the exception of No. 385 which was in sheets of 25 bearing a single large advertisement on the back.

For other stamps in Type **92** see Nos. 421/31 and 435/42*a*. For 10 c. stamps in Type **93** see Nos. 433/*b*.

2c 15c
AIRMAIL
FIVE YEARS INDEPENDENCE 1961-1966 FIVE YEARS INDEPENDENCE 1961-1966

(**95**) (**96**)

1966 (27 Apr). *Fifth Anniv of Independence. Various stamps surch.*

(a) Postage. As T **95**

No.	Description	Unused	Used
387	1 c. on 6d. multicoloured (No. 248)	10	10
388	2 c. on 4d. multicoloured (No. 247)	10	10
389	3 c. on 1½d. black & ultram (No. 212) (B.)	10	10
390	8 c. on 1s. multicoloured (No. 249) (B.)	15	10
391	10 c. on 2s. 6d. multicoloured (No. 251) (B.)	15	10
392	20 c. on 2d. black and brown (No. 213) (B.)	20	10

(b) Air. As T **96**

No.	Description	Unused	Used
393	7 c. on 3d. red and violet (No. 270)	10	10
394	15 c. on 1s. multicoloured (No. 249)	20	10
395	25 c. on 2s. 6d. multicoloured (No. 251)	40	60
396	50 c. on 1½d. multicoloured (No. 244)	60	80
397	1 l. on 4d. multicoloured (No. 247)	1·00	1·60
387/397	*Set of* 11	2·50	3·00

The inscription on No. 387 is in larger type.

97 Lion's Head

98 Map of Sierra Leone

(Des and embossed Walsall)

1966 (12 Nov). *First Sierra Leone Gold Coinage Commemoration. Circular designs, embossed on gold foil, backed with paper bearing advertisements. Imperf. (a) Postage.*

No.	Type	Description	Unused	Used
		(i) ¼ golde coin. Diameter 1½ in.		
398	**97**	2 c. magenta and yellow-orange	10	10
399	**98**	3 c. emerald and bright purple	10	10
		(ii) ½ golde coin. Diameter 2⅛ in.		
400	**97**	5 c. vermilion and ultramarine	10	10
401	**98**	8 c. turquoise-blue and black	15	15
		(iii) 1 golde coin. Diameter 3¼ in.		
402	**97**	25 c. violet and emerald	35	35
403	**98**	1 l. orange and cerise	2·25	2·25
		(b) Air. (i) ¼ golde coin. Diameter 1½ in.		
404	**98**	7 c. red-orange and cerise	10	10
405	**97**	10 c. cerise and greenish blue	15	15
		(ii) ½ golde coin. Diameter 2⅛ in.		
406	**98**	15 c. orange and cerise	25	25
407	**97**	30 c. bright purple and black	40	45
		(iii) 1 golde coin. Diameter 3¼ in.		
408	**98**	50 c. bright green and purple	75	75
409	**97**	2 l. black and emerald	3·50	3·50
398/409		*Set of* 12	7·25	7·25

12½ 17½ =17½

(**99**) (**100**) (**101**)

1967 (2 Dec). *Decimal Currency Provisionals. Surch as T* **99** *(Nos. 410/13), T* **100** *(Nos. 415/17) or T* **101** *(others). (a) Postage.*

No.	Description	Unused	Used
410	6½ c. on 75 c. on 5s. mult (No. 371) (R.)	15	15
411	7½ c. on 75 c. on 5s. mult (No. 371) (S.)	15	15
412	9½ c. on 50 c. on 4d. mult (No. 370) (G.)	20	20
413	12½ c. on 20 c. on 1s. 3d. multicoloured (No. 369) (V.)	25	25
414	17½ c. on 50 c. multicoloured (No. 383)	1·40	1·40
415	17½ c. on 1 l. on 4d. mult (No. 348) (B.)	1·40	1·40
416	18½ c. on 1 l. on 4d. multicoloured (No. 348)	1·40	1·40
417	18½ c. on 60 c. on 5s. multicoloured (No. 347)	4·00	4·00
418	25 c. on 50 c. multicoloured (No. 383)	60	60

(b) Air

No.	Description	Unused	Used
419	11½ c. on 40 c. multicoloured (No. 384)	20	20
420	25 c. on 40 c. multicoloured (No. 384)	60	60
410/20	*Set of* 11	9·25	9·25

102 Eagle

(Manufactured by Walsall)

1967 (2 Dec)–**69**. *Decimal Currency. Imperf. Self-adhesive.*

(a) Postage. As T **92**, *but embossed on white paper, backed with paper bearing advertisements. Background colours given first, and value tablet colours in brackets*

No.	Type	Description	Unused	Used
421	**92**	½ c. carmine-red (carmine/*white*)	10	10
422		1 c. carmine (carmine/*white*)	15	10
423		1½ c. orange-yellow (green/*white*)	20	15
424		2 c. carmine-red (green/*white*)	35	10
425		2½ c. apple-green (yellow/*white*)	40	25
426		3 c. carmine-red (white/*carmine*)	30	10
427		3½ c. reddish purple (white/*green*)	40	30
428		4 c. carmine-red (white/*green*)	40	15
429		4½ c. dull green (green/*white*)	40	30
430		5 c. carmine (yellow/*white*)	40	15
431		5½ c. brown-red (green/*white*)	40	30

(b) Air. T **102** *embossed on black paper, backed with paper bearing advertisements; or, (No. 433), as T* **93**, *typo and embossed on cream paper, also with advertisements*

No.	Type	Description	Unused	Used
432	**102**	9½ c. red and gold/*black*	50	50
432*a*		9½ c. blue and gold/*black* (10.9.69)	2·50	2·00
433	**93**	10 c. multicoloured (red frame)	55	55
		a. Face value omitted		
433*b*		10 c. mult (black frame) (10.9.69)	2·75	2·25
434	**102**	15 c. green and gold/*black*	85	85
434*a*		15 c. red and gold/*black* (10.9.69)	3·00	3·00
421/34*a*		*Set of* 17	12·00	10·00

The ½, 1½, 2, 2½, 3, 3½ and 5 c. also exist without advertisements.

The footnote below Nos. 377/86 also applies here.

Although only released for collectors on 2 December, the 5 c. was known to be in use locally in February and the 3 c. in March. The 1 c. and 2 c. were also released locally some months earlier.

See also Nos. 538/44.

1968. *No advertisements on back, and colours in value tablet reversed. Background colours given first, and value tablet colours in brackets.*

No.	Type	Description	Unused	Used
435	**92**	½ c. carmine-red (white/*green*)	10	10
436		1 c. carmine (white/*carmine*)	15	10
437		2 c. carmine (white/*green*)	3·50	3·50
438		2½ c. apple-green (white/*yellow*)	4·00	4·00
439		3 c. carmine-red (carmine/*white*)	1·25	65

On Nos. 435 and 438, the figure "½" is larger than in Nos. 421 and 425.

It is believed that the ½ c. was released in February, the 2½ c. in April and the others in March.

The 1 c. also exists with advertisements on the backing paper.

The footnote below Nos. 377/86 also applies here.

1968–69. *No advertisements on back, colours changed and new value (7 c.). Background colours given first, and value tablet colours in brackets. (a) Postage.*

No.	Type	Description	Unused	Used
440	**92**	2 c. pink (white/*brown-lake*)	1·00	50
441		2½ c. deep bluish green (white/*orange*)	1·00	50
442		3½ c. olive-yellow (blue/*white*)	1·40	70

(b) Air

No.	Type	Description	Unused	Used
442*a*	**92**	7 c. yellow (carmine/*white*) (10.9.69)	4·50	2·25
435/42*a*		*Set of* 9	15·00	11·00

On Nos. 441/2 the fraction "½" is larger than in Nos. 425 and 427.

It is believed that the 3½ c. was released in March 1968 and the 2 and 2½ c. in May 1968.

The 2 c. also exists with advertisements on the backing paper.

The footnote below Nos. 377/86 also applies here.

103 Outline Map of Africa

(Litho Walsall)

1968 (25 Sept). *Human Rights Year. Each value comes in six types, showing different territories in yellow, as below. Imperf. Self-adhesive.*

A. Portuguese Guinea.
B. South Africa.
C. Mozambique.
D. Rhodesia.
E. South West Africa.
F. Angola.

To indicate yellow territory use above letters as suffix to the following catalogue numbers.

(a) Postage

No.	Type	Description	Each Territory	
443	**103**	½ c. multicoloured	10	10
444		2 c. multicoloured	10	10
445		2½ c. multicoloured	10	10
446		3½ c. multicoloured	10	10
447		10 c. multicoloured	15	15
448		11½ c. multicoloured	20	20
449		15 c. multicoloured	25	25

(b) *Air*

450 **103** 7½ c. multicoloured 15 15
451 9½ c. multicoloured 20 20
452 14½ c. multicoloured 25 25
453 18½ c. multicoloured 30 30
454 25 c. multicoloured 40 40
455 1 l. multicoloured .. .. 6·50 5·50
456 2 l. multicoloured .. .. 14·00 12·00
443/56 Each territory .. .. *Set of* 14 20·00 18·00
443/56 Six territories .. .. *Set of* 84 £120 £100

Nos. 443/56 were issued in sheets of 30 (6 × 5) on backing paper depicting diamonds or the coat of arms on the reverse. The six types occur once in each horizontal row.

1968 OLYMPIC PARTICIPATION

(104)

1968 (30 Nov). *Mexico Olympics Participation.*

(a) *Postage. No.* 383 *surch or optd* (*No.* 461) *as T* **104**

457 **93** 6½ c. on 50 c. multicoloured 10 10
458 17½ c. on 50 c. multicoloured 15 15
459 22½ c. on 50 c. multicoloured 25 25
a. Surch double £170
460 28½ c. on 50 c. multicoloured 35 35
461 50 c. multicoloured 50 50

(b) *Air. No.* 384 *surch or optd* (*No.* 466) *as T* **104**, *in red*

462 **93** 6½ c. on 50 c. multicoloured 10 10
a. Surch double £190
463 17½ c. on 40 c. multicoloured 15 15
464 22½ c. on 40 c. multicoloured 25 25
465 28½ c. on 40 c. multicoloured 35 35
466 40 c. multicoloured 50 50
457/66 .. .. *Set of* 10 2·50 2·50

105 1859 6d.

111 1965 15 c. Self-adhesive

(Litho Walsall)

1969 (1 Mar). *Fifth Anniv of World's First Self-adhesive Postage Stamps. Reproductions of earlier issues. Multicoloured. Imperf. Self-adhesive.* (a) *Postage. Vert designs.*

467 1 c. Type **105** 10 10
468 2 c. 1965 2 c. self-adhesive 10 10
469 3½ c. 1961 Independence 2 c. commemorative 10 10
470 5 c. 1965 20 c. self-adhesive 10 10
471 12½ c. 1948 Royal Silver Wedding £1 commemorative 30 15
472 1 l. 1923 £2 .. .. 3·50 2·75

(b) *Air. Horiz designs*

473 7½ c. Type **111** 20 10
474 9½ c. 1967 9½ c. self-adhesive 20 10
475 20 c. 1964 1s. 3d. self-adhesive 40 25
476 30 c. 1964 President Kennedy Memorial 6s. commemorative self-adhesive .. 55 35
477 50 c. 1933 Centenary of Abolition of Slavery £1 commemorative .. .. 1·75 1·00
478 2 l. 1963 2nd Anniversary of Independence 11s. commemorative .. .. 15·00 13·00
467/478 .. .. *Set of* 12 20·00 16·00

Nos. 467 and 473 were issued with tabs as note under Nos. 377/86 and No. 474 exists with tabs and also in the normal version on backing paper.

All values are on white backing paper with advertisements printed on the reverse.

117 Ore Carrier, Globe and Flags of Sierra Leone and Japan

118 Ore Carrier, Map of Europe and Africa and Flags of Sierra Leone and Netherlands

The 3½ c., 9½ c., 2 l. and 10 c., 50 c., 1 l. are as T **118** but show respectively the flags of Great Britain and West Germany instead of the Netherlands.

(Litho Walsall)

1969 (10 July). *Pepel Port Improvements. Imperf. Self-adhesive, backed with paper bearing advertisements.* (a) *Postage.*

479 **117** 1 c. multicoloured 10 10
480 **118** 2 c. multicoloured 10 10
481 – 3½ c. multicoloured 10 10
482 – 10 c. multicoloured 10 10
483 **118** 18½ c. multicoloured 20 25
484 – 50 c. multicoloured 70 85

(b) *Air*

485 **117** 7½ c. multicoloured 10 10
486 – 9½ c. multicoloured 15 10
487 **117** 15 c. multicoloured 20 25
488 **118** 25 c. multicoloured 30 35
489 – 1 l. multicoloured .. .. 1·25 1·50
490 – 2 l. multicoloured .. .. 2·50 3·75
479/90 .. .. *Set of* 12 5·00 6·50

119 African Development Bank Emblem

120 Boy Scouts Emblem in "Diamond"

(Litho and embossed Walsall)

1969 (10 Sept). *Fifth Anniv of African Development Bank. Self-adhesive, backed with paper bearing advertisements. Imperf.*

(a) *Postage*

491 **119** 3½ c. deep green, gold and blue .. 25 15

(b) *Air*

492 **119** 9½ c. bluish violet, gold and apple-green 30 40

(Litho Walsall)

1969 (6 Dec). *Boy Scouts Diamond Jubilee. T* **120** *and similar design. Imperf. Self-adhesive, backed with paper bearing advertisements.*

(a) *Postage*

493 **120** 1 c. multicoloured 10 10
494 2 c. multicoloured 10 10
495 3½ c. multicoloured 15 10
496 4½ c. multicoloured 15 15
497 5 c. multicoloured 15 15
498 75 c. multicoloured .. .. 9·00 5·00

(b) *Air*

499 – 7½ c. multicoloured 35 30
500 – 9½ c. multicoloured 45 35
501 – 15 c. multicoloured 70 50
502 – 22 c. multicoloured .. .. 1·25 70
503 – 55 c. multicoloured .. .. 7·50 4·00
504 – 3 l. multicoloured .. .. 85·00 60·00
493/504 .. .. *Set of* 12 95·00 65·00

Design: *Octagonal Shape* (65 × 51 *mm*)—Nos. 499/504 Scout saluting, Baden-Powell and badge.

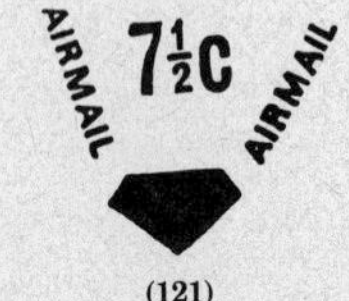

(121)

1970 (28 Mar). *Air. No.* 443 *surch as T* **121**.

Each Territory

505 **103** 7½ c. on ½ c. multicoloured (G.) .. 20 10
506 9½ c. on ½ c. multicoloured (P.) .. 20 10
507 15 c. on ½ c. multicoloured (B.) .. 40 25
508 28 c. on ½ c. multicoloured (G.) .. 70 55
509 40 c. on ½ c. multicoloured (B.) .. 1·25 1·40
510 2 l. on ½ c. multicoloured (Sil.) .. 6·00 6·50
505/10 Each Territory .. .. *Set of* 6 8·00 8·00
505/10 Six Territories .. .. *Set of* 36 45·00 45·00

122 Expo Symbol and Maps of Sierra Leone and Japan

(Litho Walsall)

1970 (22 June). *World Fair, Osaka. T* **122** *and similar design. Imperf. Self-adhesive, backed with paper bearing advertisements.*

(a) *Postage*

511 **122** 2 c. multicoloured 10 10
512 3½ c. multicoloured 10 10
513 10 c. multicoloured 15 10
514 12½ c. multicoloured 15 10
515 20 c. multicoloured 20 10
516 45 c. multicoloured 45 45

(b) *Air*

517 – 7½ c. multicoloured 10 10
518 – 9½ c. multicoloured 15 10
519 – 15 c. multicoloured 20 10
520 – 25 c. multicoloured 40 20
521 – 50 c. multicoloured 55 50
522 – 3 l. multicoloured .. .. 3·00 4·00
511/22 .. .. *Set of* 12 4·50 5·00

Design: *Chrysanthemum shape* (43 × 42 *mm*)—Nos. 517/22 Maps of Sierra Leone and Japan.

123 Diamond

124 Palm Nut

(Litho and embossed Walsall)

1970 (3 Oct). *Imperf. Self-adhesive, backed with paper bearing advertisements.*

523 **123** 1 c. multicoloured 10 10
524 1½ c. multicoloured 10 10
525 2 c. multicoloured 10 10
526 2½ c. multicoloured 10 10
527 3 c. multicoloured 15 10
528 3½ c. multicoloured 15 10
529 4 c. multicoloured 15 10
530 5 c. multicoloured 20 10
531 **124** 6 c. multicoloured 20 10
532 7 c. multicoloured 25 15
533 8½ c. multicoloured 30 15
534 9 c. multicoloured 30 15
535 10 c. multicoloured 35 15
536 11½ c. multicoloured 40 20
537 18½ c. multicoloured 60 45

1970 (3 Oct). *Air. As T* **102**, *but embossed on white paper. Backed with paper bearing advertisements.*

538 **102** 7½ c. gold and red 30 10
539 9½ c. rose and bright green 35 10
540 15 c. pink and greenish blue 45 20
541 25 c. gold and purple 75 50
542 50 c. bright green and orange .. .. 1·75 1·25
543 1 l. royal blue and silver .. .. 4·50 5·50
544 2 l. ultramarine and gold .. .. 9·00 13·00
523/44 .. .. *Set of* 22 18·00 20·00

126 "Jewellery Box" and Sewa Diadem

(Litho and embossed Walsall)

1970 (30 Dec). *Diamond Industry. T* **126** *and similar design. Imperf* (*backing paper roul* 20). *Self-adhesive, backed with paper bearing advertisements.* (*a*) *Postage.*

545	**126**	2 c. multicoloured	15	10
546		3½ c. multicoloured	15	10
547		10 c. multicoloured	35	15
548		12½ c. multicoloured	40	25
549		40 c. multicoloured	1·25	85
550		1 l. multicoloured	7·00	6·00
		(*b*) *Air*		
551	–	7½ c. multicoloured	30	10
552	–	9½ c. multicoloured	35	10
553	–	15 c. multicoloured	50	30
554	–	25 c. multicoloured	90	60
555	–	75 c. multicoloured	3·75	3·25
556	–	2 l. multicoloured	17·00	13·00
545/556		.. .. *Set of* 12	29·00	22·00

Design: *Horiz* (63 × 61 *mm*)—Nos. 551/6, Diamond and curtain.

10c AIRMAIL

127 "Traffic Changeover" (**128**)

1971 (1 Mar). *Changeover to Driving on the Right of the Road. Imperf* (*backing paper roul* 20). *Self-adhesive, backed with paper bearing advertisements.* (*a*) *Postage.*

557	**127**	3½ c. yellow-orange, ultram & blk	75	35
		(*b*) *Air*		
558	**127**	9½ c. ultramarine, yell-orge & blk	1·50	1·25

1971 (1 Mar). *Air. Surch as T* **128**, *in red* (*No.* 559), *blue* (*Nos.* 560 *and* 562) *or black* (*others*).

559	10 c. on 2d. black and ultramarine (No. 226) ..	40	20
560	20 c. on 1s. chocolate & yell-orge (No. 230) ..	70	45
561	50 c. on 1d. multicoloured (No. 243)	1·25	1·10
562	70 c. on 30 c. multicoloured (No. 476).. ..	2·00	2·50
563	1 l. on 30 c. multicoloured (No. 476).. ..	3·00	3·50
559/63	.. .. *Set of* 5	6·50	7·00

REPUBLIC

129 Flag and Lion's Head **130** Pres. Siaka Stevens

(Manufactured by Walsall)

1971 (27 Apr). *Tenth Anniv of Independence. T* **129** *and similar design. Imperf. Self-adhesive, backed with paper bearing advertisements.* (*a*) *Postage.*

564	**129**	2 c. multicoloured	10	10
565		3½ c. multicoloured	10	10
566		10 c. multicoloured	15	10
567		12½ c. multicoloured	20	10
568		40 c. multicoloured	70	35
569		1 l. multicoloured	1·50	2·00
		(*b*) *Air*		
570	–	7½ c. multicoloured	15	10
571	–	9½ c. multicoloured	15	10
572	–	15 c. multicoloured	25	10
573	–	25 c. multicoloured	35	35
574	–	75 c. multicoloured	1·25	1·25
575	–	2 l. multicoloured	4·00	5·50
564/75		.. .. .. *Set of* 12	8·00	9·00

Design: "*Map*" *shaped as T* **129**—Nos. 570/5, Bugles and lion's head.

(Litho D.L.R.)

1972 (5 Dec)–**78.** *Multicoloured; colour of background given. P* 13.
A. *Glazed ordinary paper.*
B. *Chalk-surfaced paper* (1975–78).

			A		B	
576	**130**	1 c. light rose-lilac ..	10	10	10	10
577		2 c. lavender (*shades*) ..	10	10	15	10
578		4 c. cobalt	10	10	20	10
579		5 c. light cinnamon ..	10	10	20	10
580		7 c. light rose	15	10	30	10
581		10 c. olive-bistre	15	10	30	10
582		15 c. pale yellow-green ..	25	15	55	20
583		18 c. yellow-ochre	25	15	55	35
584		20 c. pale greenish blue ..	30	15	65	40
585		25 c. orange-ochre.. ..	35	15	75	40
586		50 c. light turquoise-green	90	45	2·00	1·25
587		1 l. bright reddish mauve (*shades*)	1·50	1·00	3·50	2·50
588		2 l. orange-salmon ..	3·25	3·25	8·00	10·00
589		5 l. light stone	7·00	7·00	15·00	20·00
576/89		.. .. .. *Set of* 14	13·00	11·50	29·00	32·00

131 Guma Valley Dam and Bank Emblem

(Litho D.L.R.)

1975 (14 Jan). *Tenth Anniv of African Development Bank* (1974). *P* 13½ × 13. (*a*) *Postage.*

590	**131**	4 c. multicoloured	45·00	28·00
		(*b*) *Air*		
591	**131**	15 c. multicoloured	1·00	80

132 Opening Ceremony

(Litho D.L.R.)

1975 (25 Aug). *Opening of New Congo Bridge and President Stevens' 70th Birthday. P* 12½ × 13. (*a*) *Postage.*

592	**132**	5 c. multicoloured	5·00	1·75
		(*b*) *Air*		
593	**132**	20 c. multicoloured	70	25

133 Presidents Tolbert and Stevens, and Handclasp

(Litho D.L.R.)

1975 (3 Oct). *1st Anniv of Mano River Union. P* 12½ × 13. (*a*) *Postage.*

594	**133**	4 c. multicoloured	75	50
		(*b*) *Air*		
595	**133**	15 c. multicoloured	35	25

134 "Quaid-i-Azam" (Mohammed Ali Jinnah) **135** Queen Elizabeth II

(Litho Pakistan Security Printing Corporation)

1977 (28 Jan). *Birth Centenary of Mohammed Ali Jinnah* (*Quaid-i-Azam*). *P* 13.

596	**134**	30 c. multicoloured	75	30

(Des A. Larkins. Litho De La Rue, Colombia)

1977 (28 Nov). *Silver Jubilee. P* 12½ × 12.

597	**135**	5 c. multicoloured	10	10
598		1 l. multicoloured	90	80

136 College Buildings **137** St. Edward's Crown and Sceptres

(Des A. Larkins. Litho De La Rue, Colombia)

1977 (19 Dec). *150th Anniv of Fourah Bay College. T* **136** *and similar vert design. Multicoloured. P* 12 × 12½ (5 c.) *or* 12½ × 12 (20 c.).

599	5 c. Type **136**	10	10
600	20 c. The old college	35	30

(Des L. Curtis. Litho Harrison)

1978 (14 Sept). *25th Anniv of Coronation. T* **137** *and similar vert designs. Multicoloured. P* 14½ × 14.

601	5 c. Type **137**	10	10
602	50 c. Queen Elizabeth II in Coronation Coach	30	40
603	1 l. Queen Elizabeth II and Prince Philip ..	40	60
601/3	.. .. *Set of* 3	65	1·00

138 Fig Tree Blue **139** Young Child's Face

(Des J. Cooter. Litho Questa)

1979 (9 Apr). *Butterflies* (1*st series*). *T* **138** *and similar horiz designs. Multicoloured. P* 14½ × 14.

604	5 c. Type **138**	10	10
605	15 c. Narrow Blue-banded Swallowtail ..	25	15
606	25 c. Pirate	40	15
607	1 l. African Giant Swallowtail	2·00	1·50
604/7	.. .. *Set of* 4	2·50	1·60

See also Nos. 646/9.

(Des BG Studio. Litho Walsall)

1979 (13 Aug). *International Year of the Child and 30th Anniv of S.O.S. International* (*child distress organisation*). *T* **139** *and similar vert designs. Multicoloured. W w* **14**. *P* 14 × 13½.

608	5 c. Type **139**	10	10
609	27 c. Young child with baby	20	25
610	1 l. Mother with young child	50	1·10
608/10	.. .. *Set of* 3	65	1·25
MS611	114 × 84 mm. No. 610. Wmk sideways ..	1·00	1·75

140 Presidents Stevens (Sierra Leone) and Tolbert (Liberia), Dove with Letter and Bridge

(Des L. Curtis. Litho Questa)

1979 (3 Oct). *5th Anniv of Mano River Union and 1st Anniv of Postal Union. W w* **14** (*sideways*). *P* 13½ × 14.

612	**140**	5 c. sepia, orange and greenish yellow ..	10	10
613		22 c. sepia, orge-yell & brt reddish violet	10	15
614		27 c. sepia, light blue and orange ..	10	15
615		35 c. sepia, blue-green and orange-red ..	15	20
616		1 l. sepia, brt reddish violet & lt blue ..	50	1·00
612/16		.. .. *Set of* 5	75	1·40
MS617		144 × 73 mm. No. 616	55	1·00

141 Great Britain 1848 10d. Stamp **142** Knysna Touraco

(Des J.W. Litho Walsall)

1979 (19 Dec). *Death Centenary of Sir Rowland Hill. T* **141** *and similar vert designs showing stamps.* W w **14**. *P* 14 × 14½.

No.		Description	Mint	Used
618		10 c. black, orange-brown and new blue	15	10
619		15 c. black, brown-ochre and greenish blue	25	15
620		50 c. black, carmine and greenish yellow	60	70
618/20		*Set of* 3	90	85
MS621		90 × 99 mm. 1 l. black, carm-red & flesh	60	80

Designs:—15 c. 1872 4d.; 50 c. 1961 £1 Independence commemorative; 1 l. 1912 £1.

(Des J.W. Litho Format)

1980 (29 Jan)–**82**. *Birds. Multicoloured designs as T* **142**. W w **14** (*sideways on* 1, 2, 3, 5, 7 *c.*, 1, 2 *and* 5 *l.*). *P* 14.

A. *No imprint.* B. *Imprint date at foot*

No.	Description	A		B	
622	1 c. Type **142**	10	15	10	20
623	2 c. Olive-bellied Sunbird	10	15	10	20
624	3 c. Western Black-headed Oriole	20	15	10	20
625	5 c. Spur-winged Goose	20	10	10	10
626	7 c. Didric Cuckoo	20	10	60	20
627	10 c. Grey Parrot (*vert*)	25	15	15	15
628	15 c. Blue Quail (*vert*)	40	30	35	40
629	20 c. African Wood Owl (*vert*)	50	40	35	40
630	30 c. Great Blue Turaco (*vert*)	60	50	45	60
631	40 c. Blue-breasted Kingfisher (*vert*)	70	50	50	70
632	50 c. Black Crake (*vert*)	75	75	50	80
633	1 l. Hartlaub's Duck	1·10	1·50	50	90
634	2 l. Black Bee Eater	2·25	3·25	1·75	3·50
635	5 l. Barrow's Bustard	4·75	8·00	4·25	7·00
622/35	*Set of* 14	11·00	14·50	8·50	14·00

Dates of issue: No Imprint—29.1.80. With Imprint—21.12.81 5, 10, 15, 30, 40, 50 c., 1 l., 2 l., 5 l.; 15.3.82 1, 2, 3, 20 c.; 11.10.82 7 c.

For similar stamps, but without watermark, see Nos. 760/73.

143 Paul P. Harris (founder), President Stevens of Sierra Leone and Rotary Emblem

(Des BG Studio. Litho Walsall)

1980 (23 Feb). *75th Anniv of Rotary International.* W w **14** (*sideways*). *P* 13½.

No.	Type	Description	Mint	Used
636	**143**	5 c. multicoloured	10	10
637		27 c. multicoloured	10	10
638		50 c. multicoloured	20	25
639		1 l. multicoloured	40	55
636/9		*Set of* 4	65	85

144 *Maria*, 1884

145 Organisation for African Unity Emblem

(Des L. Dunn. Litho Walsall)

1980 (6 May). *"London 1980" International Stamp Exhibition. Mail Ships. T* **144** *and similar horiz designs. Multicoloured.* W w **14** (*sideways*). *P* 14.

No.	Description	Mint	Used
640	6 c. Type **144**	10	10
641	31 c. *Tarquah*, 1902	25	25
642	50 c. *Aureol*, 1951	40	50
643	1 l. *Africa Palm*, 1974	55	80
640/3	*Set of* 4	1·10	1·40

(Des L. Curtis. Litho Questa)

1980 (1 July). *African Summit Conference, Freetown.* W w **14**. *P* 14 × 14½.

No.	Type	Description	Mint	Used
644	**145**	20 c. black, light blue and bright purple	10	10
645		1 l. black, bright purple and light blue	45	45

146 Small Striped Swordtail

147 Arrival at Freetown Airport

(Des I. Loe. Litho Questa)

1980 (6 Oct). *Butterflies (2nd series). T* **146** *and similar vert designs. Multicoloured.* W w **14**. *P* 13½.

No.	Description	Mint	Used
646	5 c. Type **146**	10	10
647	27 c. Pearl Charaxes	30	15
648	35 c. White Barred Charaxes	35	25
649	1 l. Zaddach's Forester	1·10	1·40
646/9	*Set of* 4	1·75	1·75

(Des L. Curtis. Litho Format)

1980 (5 Dec). *Tourism. T* **147** *and similar vert designs. Multicoloured.* W w **14**. *P* 13½.

No.	Description	Mint	Used
650	6 c. Type **147**	10	10
651	26 c. Welcome to tourists	20	20
652	31 c. Freetown cotton tree	25	25
653	40 c. Beinkongo Falls	30	30
654	50 c. Sports facilities	40	40
655	1 l. African Elephant	95	95
650/5	*Set of* 6	2·00	2·00

148 Servals

149 Soldiers (Defence)

(Des P. Oxenham. Litho Questa)

1981 (28 Feb). *Wild Cats. T* **148** *and similar horiz designs. Multicoloured.* W w **14** (*sideways*). *P* 13½ × 14.

No.	Description	Mint	Used
656	6 c. Type **148**	10	10
	a. Horiz pair. Nos. 656/7	10	10
657	6 c. Serval cubs	10	10
658	31 c. African Golden Cats	30	30
	a. Horiz pair. Nos. 658/9	60	60
659	31 c. African Golden Cat cubs	30	30
660	50 c. Leopards	45	45
	a. Horiz pair. Nos. 660/1	90	90
661	50 c. Leopard cubs	45	45
662	1 l. Lions	80	80
	a. Horiz pair. Nos. 662/3	1·60	1·60
663	1 l. Lion cubs	80	80
656/63	*Set of* 8	2·75	2·75

The two designs of each value were printed together, *se-tenant*, in horizontal pairs throughout the sheet, forming composite designs.

(Des G. Hutchins. Litho Walsall)

1981 (18 Apr). *20th Anniv of Independence and 10th Anniv of Republic. National Services. T* **149** *and similar multicoloured designs.* W w **14** (*sideways on* 31 *c. and* 1 *l.*). *P* 14½.

No.	Description	Mint	Used
664	6 c. Type **149**	15	10
665	31 c. Nurses administering first aid, and ambulance (Health) (*horiz*)	50	15
666	40 c. Controlling traffic (Police Force)	65	20
667	1 l. Patrol boat (Coastguard) (*horiz*)	1·25	75
664/7	*Set of* 4	2·25	1·00

150 Wedding Bouquet from Sierra Leone

151 Sandringham

(Des J.W. Litho Harrison)

1981 (22 July). *Royal Wedding* (1*st issue*). *T* **150** *and similar vert designs. Multicoloured.* W w **14**. *P* 14.

No.	Description	Mint	Used
668	31 c. Type **150**	20	20
669	45 c. Prince Charles as helicopter pilot	25	25
670	1 l. Prince Charles and Lady Diana Spencer	45	85
668/70	*Set of* 3	80	1·10

(Des J.W. Litho Format)

1981 (9 Sept–30 Nov). *Royal Wedding* (2*nd issue*). *T* **151** *and similar vert designs. Multicoloured.* (a) *Sheet stamps. P* 12.

No.	Description	Mint	Used
671	35 c. Type **151**	30	35
672	60 c. Prince Charles in outdoor clothes	50	40
673	1 l. 50, Prince Charles and Lady Diana Spencer	1·00	1·40
671/3	*Set of* 3	1·60	1·90
MS674	96 × 83 mm. 3 l. Royal Landau. P 14	1·75	1·75

(*b*) *Booklet stamps. P* 14 (30 Nov)

No.	Description	Mint	Used
675	70 c. Type **151**	75	90
	a. Booklet pane. Nos. 675/6 × 2 plus two printed labels	3·00	
676	1 l. 30, As 60 c.	1·00	1·25
677	2 l. As 1 l. 50	3·25	3·50
	a. Booklet pane of 1	3·25	
675/7	*Set of* 3	4·50	5·00

Nos. 671/3 were each printed in small sheets of 6 including one *se-tenant* stamp-size label.

152 "Physical Recreation"

153 Pineapples

(Des BG Studio. Litho Questa)

1981 (30 Sept). *25th Anniv of Duke of Edinburgh Award Scheme and President's Award Scheme Publicity. T* **152** *and similar vert designs. Multicoloured.* W w **14**. *P* 14.

No.	Description	Mint	Used
678	6 c. Type **152**	10	10
679	31 c. "Community service"	15	10
680	1 l. Duke of Edinburgh	40	40
681	1 l. President Siaka Stevens	40	40
678/81	*Set of* 4	90	85

(Des BG Studio. Litho Questa)

1981 (16 Oct). *World Food Day* (1*st issue*). *T* **153** *and similar vert designs. Multicoloured.* W w **14**. *P* 14.

No.	Description	Mint	Used
682	6 c. Type **153**	10	10
683	31 c. Groundnuts	15	10
684	50 c. Cassava fruits	20	15
685	1 l. Rice plants	50	50
682/5	*Set of* 4	75	70

154 Groundnuts

(Litho Format)

1981 (2 Nov). *World Food Day* (2*nd issue*). *Agricultural Industry. T* **154** *and similar horiz designs. Multicoloured. P* 14½.

No.	Description	Mint	Used
686	6 c. Type **154**	10	10
687	31 c. Cassava	25	10
688	50 c. Rice	45	25
689	1 l. Pineapples	90	70
686/9	*Set of* 4	1·50	1·00

155 Scouts with Cattle

(**156**)

(Des M. Diamond. Litho Questa)

1982 (23 Aug). *75th Anniv of Boy Scout Movement. T* **155** *and similar horiz designs. Multicoloured. P* 14.

No.	Description	Mint	Used
690	20 c. Type **155**	25	10
691	50 c. Scouts picking flowers	50	40
692	1 l. Lord Baden-Powell	90	1·00
693	2 l. Scouts fishing	1·90	2·00
690/3	*Set of* 4	3·25	3·00
MS694	101 × 70 mm. 3 l. Scouts raising flag	2·75	3·25

1982 (30 Aug)–**85**. *Nos.* 668/74 *surch as T* **156**.

No.	Description	Mint	Used
695	50 c. on 31 c. Type **150**	40	40
696	50 c. on 35 c. Type **151**	40	40
697	50 c. on 45 c. Prince Charles as helicopter pilot	40	40
698	50 c. on 60 c. Prince Charles in outdoor clothes	40	40
699	90 c. on 1 l. Prince Charles and Lady Diana Spencer	75	75
699*a*	1 l. 30 on 60 c. Prince Charles in outdoor clothes (1985)	1·75	1·75
699*b*	2 l. on 35 c. Type **151** (1985)	2·75	2·75
	ba. Surch double	20·00	
700	2 l. on 1 l. 50, Prince Charles and Lady Diana Spencer	1·50	1·50
700*a*	8 l. on 1 l. 50, Prince Charles and Lady Diana Spencer (1985)	8·75	8·75
695/700*a*	*Set of* 9	15·00	15·00
MS701	95 × 83 mm. 3 l. 50 on 3 l. Royal Landau	1·75	1·75

Nos. 699*a*/*b* and 700*a* also exist surcharged in blue from a limited printing (*Price for set of* 3 £50 *mint*).

157 Heading

158 Prince and Princess of Wales

(Des PAD Studio. Litho Questa)

1982 (7 Sept). *World Cup Football Championship, Spain. T* **157** *and similar vert designs. Multicoloured. P* 14.
702 20 c. Type **157** .. 20 15
703 30 c. Dribbling .. 30 20
704 1 l. Tackling .. 95 1·00
705 2 l. Goalkeeping .. 1·90 2·00
702/5 .. *Set of* 4 3·00 3·00
MS706 92 × 75 mm. 3 l. Shooting .. 2·75 3·00
Nos. 702/5 were each printed in small sheets of 6 including one, *se-tenant*, stamp-sized label.

(Des PAD Studio. Litho Questa)

1982 (15 Sept). *21st Birthday of Princess of Wales. T* **158** *and similar vert designs. Multicoloured. P* 14½ × 14.
707 31 c. Caernarvon Castle .. 35 15
708 50 c. Type **158** .. 50 25
709 2 l. Princess of Wales .. 1·75 1·50
707/9 .. *Set of* 3 2·25 1·75
MS710 103 × 75 mm. 3 l. Princess of Wales (*different*) .. 2·50 2·50
Nos. 707/9 also exist in sheetlets of 5 stamps and 1 label.

1982 (15 Oct). *Birth of Prince William of Wales. Nos.* 707/10 *optd with T* **171** *of Antigua.*
711 31 c. Caernarvon Castle .. 35 15
712 50 c. Type **158** .. 50 25
713 2 l. Princess of Wales .. 1·75 1·50
711/13 .. *Set of* 3 2·25 1·75
MS714 103 × 75 mm. 3 l. Princess of Wales (*different*) .. 2·50 2·50
Nos. 711/13 also exist in sheetlets of 5 stamps and 1 label.

159 Washington with Troops

160 Temptation of Christ

(Des C. Mill. Litho Questa)

1982 (30 Oct). *250th Birth Anniv of George Washington. T* **159** *and similar multicoloured designs. P* 14.
715 6 c. Type **159** .. 10 10
716 31 c. Portrait of Washington (*vert*) .. 20 20
717 50 c. Washington with horse .. 35 35
718 1 l. Washington standing on battlefield (*vert*) 65 80
715/18 .. *Set of* 4 1·10 1·25
MS719 103 × 71 mm. 2 l. Washington at home .. 1·00 1·50

(Des N. Waldman Studio. Litho Questa)

1982 (18 Nov). *Christmas. Stained-glass Windows. T* **160** *and similar vert designs. Multicoloured. P* 13½ × 14.
720 6 c. Type **160** .. 10 10
721 31 c. Baptism of Christ .. 15 20
722 50 c. Annunciation .. 20 40
723 1 l. Nativity .. 55 90
720/3 .. *Set of* 4 85 1·40
MS724 74 × 104 mm. 2 l. Mary and Joseph .. 70 1·10

(**161**)   **162** Long Snouted Crocodile

1982 (2 Dec). *World Cup Football Championship Winners. Nos.* 702/6 *optd with T* **161**.
725 20 c. Type **157** .. 15 20
726 30 c. Dribbling .. 20 30
727 1 l. Tackling .. 55 55
728 2 l. Goalkeeping .. 1·00 1·75
725/8 .. *Set of* 4 1·75 2·75
MS729 91 × 75 mm. 3 l. Shooting .. 1·00 2·00

(Des G. Drummond. Litho Questa)

1982 (10 Dec). *Death Centenary of Charles Darwin. T* **162** *and similar horiz designs. Multicoloured. P* 14.
730 6 c. Type **162** .. 15 10
731 31 c. Rainbow Lizard .. 40 30
732 50 c. River Turtle .. 60 60
733 1 l. Chameleon .. 1·25 1·75
730/3 .. *Set of* 4 2·25 2·50
MS734 90 × 70 mm. 2 l. Royal Python (*vert*) .. 2·25 2·75

163 Diogenes

(Des Design Images. Litho Questa)

1983 (28 Jan). *500th Birth Anniv of Raphael. Details from painting "The School of Athens". T* **163** *and similar multicoloured designs. P* 13½.
735 6 c. Type **163** .. 10 10
736 31 c. Euclid, Ptolemy, Zoroaster, Raphael and Sodoma .. 20 30
737 50 c. Euclid and his pupils .. 35 45
738 2 l. Pythagoras, Francesco Maria della Rovere and Heraclitus .. 1·25 1·40
735/8 .. *Set of* 4 1·60 2·00
MS739 101 × 126 mm. 3 l. Plato and Aristotle (*vert*) 1·25 2·00

164 Agricultural Training

165 Map of Africa and Flag of Sierra Leone

(Litho Questa)

1983 (14 Mar). *Commonwealth Day. T* **164** *and similar horiz designs. Multicoloured. P* 14.
740 6 c. Type **164** .. 10 10
741 10 c. Tourism development .. 10 10
742 50 c. Broadcasting training .. 45 45
743 1 l. Airport services .. 90 90
740/3 .. *Set of* 4 1·40 1·40

(Des M. Diamond. Litho J.W.)

1983 (29 Apr). *25th Anniv of Economic Commission for Africa. P* 13.
744 **165** 1 l. multicoloured .. 80 1·10

166 Chimpanzees in Tree

(Des J. Iskowitz. Litho Questa)

1983 (19 May). *Endangered Species. T* **166** *and similar multicoloured designs. P* 14.
745 6 c. Type **166** .. 35 10
746 10 c. Three Chimpanzees (*vert*) .. 35 10
747 31 c. Chimpanzees swinging in tree (*vert*) .. 60 25
748 60 c. Group of Chimpanzees .. 1·10 1·75
745/8 .. *Set of* 4 2·25 2·00
MS749 115 × 80 mm. 3 l. African Elephant .. 1·50 2·25

167 Traditional Communications

168 Montgolfier Balloon, Paris, 1783

(Des R. Sauber. Litho Questa)

1983 (14 July). *World Communications Year. T* **167** *and similar horiz designs. Multicoloured. P* 14.
750 6 c. Type **167** .. 10 10
751 10 c. Mail via Mano River .. 10 10
752 20 c. Satellite ground station .. 10 10
753 1 l. British packet, *circa* 1805 .. 55 65
750/3 .. *Set of* 4 70 80
MS754 115 × 85 mm. 2 l. Telecommunications .. 80 1·25

(Des Artists International. Litho Questa)

1983 (31 Aug). *Bicentenary of Manned Flight. T* **168** *and similar multicoloured designs. P* 14.
755 6 c. Type **168** .. 15 10
756 20 c. *Deutschland* airship, Berlin, 1879 (*horiz*) 25 10
757 50 c. *Norge I*, North Pole, 1926 (*horiz*) .. 50 45
758 1 l. *Cape Sierra* sport balloon, Freetown, 1983 80 85
755/8 .. *Set of* 4 1·50 1·25
MS759 115 × 85 mm. 2 l. Airship of 21st century 1·00 1·75

1983 (Oct). *Birds. As Nos. 622B/35B but without wmk.*
760 1 c. Type **142** .. 40 50
761 2 c. Olive-bellied Sunbird .. 40 50
763 5 c. Spur-winged Goose .. 60 20
765 10 c. Grey Parrot (*vert*) .. 60 20
766 15 c. Blue Quail (*vert*) .. 70 20
767 20 c. African Wood Owl (*vert*) .. 1·25 40
768 30 c. Great Blue Turaco (*vert*) .. 1·00 70
769 40 c. Blue-breasted Kingfisher (*vert*) .. 1·75 1·00
770 50 c. Black Crake (*vert*) .. 1·75 1·25
772 2 l. Black Bee Eater .. 4·25 6·00
773 5 l. Barrow's Bustard .. 8·50 12·00
760/73 .. *Set of* 11 19·00 21·00

169 Mickey Mouse

(Litho Format)

1983 (18 Nov). *Space Ark Fantasy. T* **169** *and similar horiz designs featuring Disney cartoon characters. Multicoloured. P* 13½.
774 1 c. Type **169** .. 10 10
775 1 c. Huey, Dewey and Louie .. 10 10
776 3 c. Goofy in spaceship .. 10 10
777 3 c. Donald Duck .. 10 10
778 10 c. Ludwig von Drake .. 10 10
779 10 c. Goofy .. 10 10
780 2 l. Mickey Mouse and Giraffe in spaceship 1·10 1·25
781 3 l. Donald Duck floating in space .. 1·60 1·75
774/81 .. *Set of* 8 2·75 3·00
MS782 140 × 116 mm. 5 l. Mickey Mouse leaving spaceship .. 2·75 3·00

170 Graduates from Union Training Programme

(Des G. Vasarhelyi. Litho Format)

1984 (8 Feb). *10th Anniv of the Mano River Union. T* **170** *and similar horiz designs. Multicoloured. P* 15.
783 6 c. Type **170** .. 10 10
784 25 c. Intra-Union trade .. 10 10
785 31 c. Member Presidents on map .. 15 15
786 41 c. Signing ceremony marking Guinea's accession .. 20 20
783/6 .. *Set of* 4 45 45
MS787 75 × 113 mm. No. 786 .. 20 30

171 Gymnastics

172 "Apollo 11" Lift-off

(Des J. Iskowitz. Litho Questa)

1984 (27 Mar). *Olympic Games, Los Angeles. T* **171** *and similar horiz designs. Multicoloured. P* 14.
788 90 c. Type **171** .. 30 40
789 1 l. Hurdling .. 30 40
790 3 l. Javelin-throwing .. 75 1·25
788/90 .. *Set of* 3 1·25 1·90
MS791 104 × 71 mm. 7 l. Boxing .. 1·40 2·00

(Des J. Iskowitz. Litho Questa)

1984 (14 May). *15th Anniv of First Moonwalk. T* **172** *and similar multicoloured designs. P* 14.
792 50 c. Type **172** .. 20 20
793 75 c. Lunar module .. 30 30
794 1 l. 25, First Moonwalk .. 45 45
795 2 l. 50, Lunar exploration .. 85 85
792/5 .. *Set of* 4 1·60 1·60
MS796 99 × 69 mm. 5 l. Family watching Moonwalk on television (*horiz*) .. 1·60 2·25

173 "Concorde"

(Des Susan David. Litho Walsall)

1984 (19 June). *Universal Postal Union Congress, Hamburg. T* **173** *and similar horiz design. Multicoloured. P* 14.
797 4 l. Type **173** .. 2·00 1·40
MS798 100 × 70 mm. 4 l. Heinrich von Stephan (founder of U.P.U.) .. 2·00 2·50

SIERRA LEONE
12c
UNITED NATIONS DECADE FOR AFRICAN TRANSPORT

25c

174 Citroen "Traction Avante" (175)

(Des Susan David. Litho Format)

1984 (16 July). *United Nations Decade for African Transport. T* **174** *and similar horiz designs. Multicoloured. P* 14½ × 15.

799 12 c. Type **174** 10 10
800 60 c. Locomobile 20 25
801 90 c. A.C. "Ace" 30 35
802 1 l. Vauxhall "Prince Henry" 30 35
803 1 l. 50, Delahaye "135" 45 50
804 2 l. Mazda "1105" 60 65
799/804 . . . . *Set of* 6 1·75 1·90
MS805 107 × 75 mm. 6 l. Volkswagen "Beetle". P 15 . . . . 2·50 3·00

1984 (3 Aug). *Surch as T* **175**. (a) *On Nos.* 625, 627 *and* 634. A. *No imprint.* B. *Imprint date at foot.*

		A		B	
806	25 c. on 10 c. Grey Parrot (*vert*)	3·50	3·50	3·50	3·50
807	40 c. on 10 c. Grey Parrot (*vert*)	3·50	3·50	3·50	3·50
808	50 c. on 2 l. Black Bee Eater . .	3·50	3·50	3·50	3·50
809	70 c. on 5 c. Spur-winged Goose	3·50	3·50	3·50	3·50
810	10 l. on 5 c. Spur-winged Goose	7·00	7·00	7·00	7·00
806/10	. . *Set of* 5	19·00	19·00	19·00	19·00

(b) *On Nos.* 763, 765 *and* 772

811 25 c. on 10 c. Grey Parrot (*vert*) 75 75
812 40 c. on 10 c. Grey Parrot (*vert*) 50 50
813 50 c. on 2 l. Black Bee Eater 50 50
814 70 c. on 5 c. Spur-winged Goose 50 50
815 10 l. on 5 c. Spur-winged Goose . . . . 3·00 3·00
811/15 . . . . *Set of* 5 4·75 4·75

Nos. 806B/10B exist with either "1981" or "1982" imprint dates.

AUSIPEX 84

(176)

177 Portuguese Caravel

1984 (22 Aug). *"Ausipex" International Stamp Exhibition, Melbourne. Optd with T* **176**. (a) *On Nos.* 632 *and* 635. A. *No imprint.* B. *Imprint date at foot.*

		A		B	
816	50 c. Black Crake . .	5·00	5·00	5·00	5·00
817	5 l. Barrow's Bustard . .	15·00	15·00	15·00	15·00

(b) *On Nos.* 770 *and* 773

818 50 c. Black Crake 75 75
819 5 l. Barrow's Bustard . . . . 2·00 2·00

Nos. 816B/17B exist with either "1981" or "1982" imprint dates.

(Des G. Drummond. Litho Questa)

1984 (5 Sept)–**85**. *History of Shipping. T* **177** *and similar horiz designs. Multicoloured.* A. *Without imprint date below design.* P 14. B. *With imprint date below design.* P 12.

		A		B	
820	2 c. Type **177** . .	10	15	10	10
821	5 c. *Merlin* of Bristol . .	15	15	10	10
822	10 c. *Golden Hind*	15	15	10	10
823	15 c. *Mordaunt* . .	15	15	†	
824	20 c. *Atlantic* (transport)	20	15	10	10
825	25 c. H.M.S. *Lapwing* . .	20	15	10	10
826	30 c. *Traveller* (brig) . .	25	15	10	10
827	40 c. *Amistad* (schooner)	30	20	10	10
828	50 c. H.M.S. *Teazer* . .	30	20	10	10
829	70 c. *Scotia* (cable ship)	35	25	10	10
830	1 l. H.M.S. *Alecto* . .	45	30	10	10
831	2 l. H.M.S. *Blonde* . .	3·00	1·50	10	10
832	5 l. H.M.S. *Fox* . .	6·00	3·00	30	25
833	10 l. *Accra* (liner) . .	8·50	7·00	55	50
833*c*	15 l. H.M.S. *Favourite* . .	1·00	70	†	
833*d*	25 l. H.M.S. *Euryalus* . .	1·50	1·25	†	
820A/33*d*A	. . *Set of* 16	20·00	14·00		
820B/33B	. . *Set of* 13			1·60	1·50

Dates of issue:—Without imprint 5.9.84, 2 c., to 1 l.; 9.10.84, 2 l., 5 l.; 7.11.84, 10 l; 15.11.85, 15 l., 25 l. With imprint 7.85, 2 c. to 10 l.

178 Mail Runner approaching Mano River Depot, *c* 1843

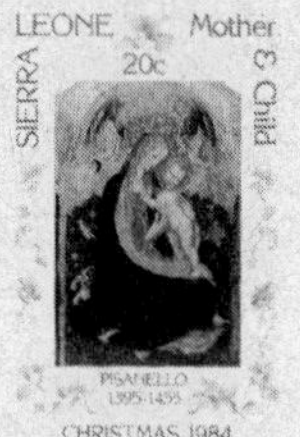

179 "Madonna and Child" (Pisanello)

(Des Susan David. Litho Walsall)

1984 (9 Oct). *125th Anniv of First Postage Stamps. T* **178** *and similar horiz designs. Multicoloured.* P 14.

834 50 c. Type **178** 20 15
835 2 l. Isaac Fitzjohn, First Postmaster, receiving letters, 1855 . . . . 65 65
836 3 l. 1859 packet franked with four 6d. stamps 1·00 1·00
834/6 . . . . *Set of* 3 1·75 1·75
MS837 100 × 70 mm. 5 l. Sierra Leone 1859 6d. purple and Great Britain 1840 Penny Black stamps . . . . 1·50 1·60

(Litho Walsall)

1984 (15 Nov). *Christmas. Madonna and Child paintings by artists named. T* **179** *and similar vert designs. Multicoloured.* P 14.

838 20 c. Type **179** 10 10
839 1 l. Memling 30 30
840 2 l. Raphael 55 55
841 3 l. Van der Werff 80 80
838/41 . . . . *Set of* 4 1·60 1·60
MS842 100 × 69 mm. 6 l. Picasso . . . . 1·60 1·90

180 Donald Duck in the "The Wise Little Hen"

(Litho Questa)

1984 (26 Nov). *50th Birthday of Donald Duck. Walt Disney Cartoon Characters. T* **180** *and similar horiz designs. Multicoloured.* P 12 (2 *l.*) *or* 14 × 13½ (*others*).

843 1 c. Type **180** 10 10
844 2 c. Mickey Mouse and Donald Duck in "Boat Builders" 10 10
845 3 c. Panchito, Donald Duck and Jose Carioca in "The Three Caballeros" . . 10 10
846 4 c. Donald Duck meeting Pythagoras in "Mathmagic Land" 10 10
847 5 c. Donald Duck and nephew in "The Mickey Mouse Club" 10 10
848 10 c. Mickey Mouse, Goofy and Donald Duck in "Donald on Parade" 10 10
849 1 l. Donald Duck riding donkey in "Don Donald" 50 40
850 2 l. Donald Duck in "Donald Gets Drafted" 90 75
851 4 l. Donald Duck meeting children in Tokyo Disneyland . . . . 1·75 1·50
843/51 . . . . *Set of* 9 3·00 2·50
MS852 126 × 102 mm. 5 l. Style sheet for Donald Duck . . . . 1·50 1·50

No. 850 was printed in sheetlets of 8.

181 Fischer's Whydah

(Des Susan David. Litho Walsall)

1985 (31 Jan). *Birth Bicentenary of John J. Audubon (ornithologist). Songbirds of Sierra Leone. T* **181** *and similar horiz designs. Multicoloured.* P 14.

853 40 c. Type **181** 65 20
854 90 c. Spotted Flycatcher . . . . 1·25 55
855 1 l. 30, Garden Warbler . . . . 1·50 1·25
856 3 l. Speke's Weaver . . . . 2·50 3·00
853/6 . . . . *Set of* 4 5·50 4·50
MS857 100 × 70 mm. 5 l. Great Grey Shrike . . 2·25 3·00

182 Fishing

(Des M. Zacharow. Litho Walsall)

1985 (14 Feb). *International Youth Year. T* **182** *and similar horiz designs. Multicoloured.* P 14.

858 1 l. 15, Type **182** 30 35
859 1 l. 50, Sawing timber 40 45
860 2 l. 15, Rice farming 55 60
858/60 . . . . *Set of* 3 1·10 1·25
MS861 100 × 70 mm. 5 l. Polishing diamonds . . 1·25 1·50

183 Eddie Rickenbacker and Spad "XIII", 1918

(Des K. Gromol. Litho Walsall)

1985 (28 Feb). *40th Anniv of International Civil Aviation Organization. T* **183** *and similar horiz designs. Multicoloured.* P 14.

862 70 c. Type **183** 60 30
863 1 l. 25, Samuel P. Langley and *Aerodrome No.* 5, 1903 . . . . 75 65
864 1 l. 30, Orville and Wilbur Wright with *Flyer No.* 1, 1903 . . . . 75 65
865 2 l. Charles Lindbergh and *Spirit of St. Louis*, 1927 . . . . 1·00 1·00
862/5 . . . . *Set of* 4 2·75 2·40
MS866 100 × 69 mm. 5 l. Sierra Leone Airlines Boeing "707-384C" . . . . 1·50 1·75

LE.1
SIERRA LEONE

184 "Temptation of Christ" (Botticelli) 185 The Queen Mother at St. Paul's Cathedral

(Des C. Walters. Litho Questa)

1985 (29 Apr). *Easter. Religious Paintings. T* **184** *and similar multicoloured designs.* P 14.

867 45 c. Type **184** 15 15
868 70 c. "Christ at the Column" (Velasquez) . . 25 25
869 1 l. 55, "Pietà" (Botticelli) (*vert*) . . 45 45
870 10 l. "Christ on the Cross" (Velasquez) (*vert*) 3·25 3·25
867/70 . . . . *Set of* 4 3·75 3·75
MS871 106 × 76 mm. 12 l. "Man of Sorrows" (Botticelli) . . . . 3·50 3·75

(Des J.W. Litho Questa)

1985 (8 July). *Life and Times of Queen Elizabeth the Queen Mother. T* **185** *and similar multicoloured designs.* P 14.

872 1 l. Type **185** 25 30
873 1 l. 70, With her racehorse, "Double Star", at Sandown (*horiz*) 45 50
874 10 l. At Covent Garden, 1971 . . . . 3·00 3·25
872/4 . . . . *Set of* 3 3·25 3·75
MS875 56 × 85 mm. 12 l. With Princess Anne at Ascot . . . . 3·00 3·75

75th ANNIVERSARY OF GIRL GUIDES

70c

(186)

1985 (25 July). *75th Anniv of Girl Guide Movement. Nos.* 690/4 *surch as T* **186**.

876 70 c. on 20 c. Type **155** 20 25
877 1 l. 30 on 50 c. Scouts picking flowers . . 35 40
878 5 l. on 1 l. Lord Baden-Powell . . . . 1·25 1·40
879 7 l. on 2 l. Scouts fishing . . . . 1·75 1·90
876/9 . . . . *Set of* 4 3·25 3·50
MS880 101 × 70 mm. 15 l. on 3 l. Scouts raising flag . . . . 3·75 4·00

MA YANHONJG CHINA GOLD MEDAL

Le2

(187)

1985 (25 July). *Olympic Gold Medal Winners, Los Angeles. Nos.* 788/91 *surch as T* **187**.

881 2 l. on 90 c. Type **171** (surch T **187**) . . 50 55
882 4 l. on 1 l. Hurdling (surch "E. MOSES U.S.A. GOLD MEDAL") . . . . 1·00 1·25
883 8 l. on 3 l. Javelin-throwing (surch "A. HAERKOENEN FINLAND GOLD MEDAL") . . . . 2·00 2·10
881/3 . . . . *Set of* 3 3·25 3·50
MS884 104 × 71 mm. 15 l. on 7 l. Boxing (surch "M. TAYLOR U.S.A. GOLD MEDAL") . . . . 3·75 4·00

70c

188 Chater-Lea (1905) at Hill Station House (189)

(Des A. DiLorenzo. Litho Questa)

1985 (15 Aug). *Centenary of the Motor Cycle and Decade for African Transport. T* **188** *and similar horiz designs. Multicoloured.* P 14.

885 1 l. 40, Type **188** 65 65
886 2 l. Honda "XR 350 R" at Queen Elizabeth II Quay, Freetown 85 85

887 4 l. Kawasaki "Vulcan" at Bo Clock Tower .. 1·50 1·50
888 5 l. Harley-Davidson "Electra-Glide" in Makeni village .. .. 1·75 1·75
885/8 .. .. *Set of* 4 4·25 4·25
MS889 104×71 mm. 12 l. Millet (1893).. .. 3·00 3·50

(Des Susan David. Litho Questa)

1985 (3 Sept). *300th Birth Anniv of Johann Sebastian Bach (composer). Vert designs as T* **206** *of Antigua. P* 14.
890 70 c. multicoloured 40 25
891 3 l. multicoloured .. .. 1·10 80
892 4 l. multicoloured .. .. 1·40 1·10
893 5 l. multicoloured .. .. 1·60 1·40
890/3 .. .. *Set of* 4 4·00 3·25
MS894 103×77 mm. 12 l. black .. .. .. 3·50 3·50
Designs:—70 c. Viola pomposa; 3 l. Spinet; 4 l. Lute; 5 l. Oboe; 12 l. "Johann Sebastian Bach" (Toby E. Rosenthal).

1985 (30 Sept). *Surch as T* **189**. (a) *On Nos.* 707/10
895 70 c. on 31 c. Caernarvon Castle 30 30
896 4 l. on 50 c. Type **158** .. .. .. 2·50 2·50
897 5 l. on 2 l. Princess of Wales .. .. 3·00 3·00
MS898 103×75 mm. 15 l. on 3 l. Princess of Wales (*different*) .. .. 6·00 6·00

(b) *On Nos.* 711/14
899 1 l. 30 on 31 c. Caernarvon Castle 80 80
900 5 l. on 50 c. Type **158** .. .. 3·00 3·00
901 7 l. on 2 l. Princess of Wales .. .. .. 4·00 4·00
895/901 .. .. *Set of* 6 12·00 12·00
MS902 103×75 mm. 15 l. on 3 l. Princess of Wales (*different*) .. .. 6·00 6·00

190 "Madonna and Child" (Crivelli)

191 Player kicking Ball

(Litho Questa)

1985 (18 Oct). *Christmas. "Madonna and Child" Paintings by artists named. T* **190** *and similar vert designs. Multicoloured. P* 14.
903 70 c. Type **190** 10 10
904 3 l. Bouts 35 40
905 4 l. Da Messina 50 55
906 5 l. Lochner 60 65
903/6 .. .. *Set of* 4 1·40 1·50
MS907 113×85 mm. 12 l. Miniature from Book of Kells .. .. 1·50 1·60

(Des Walt Disney Productions. Litho Questa)

1985 (30 Oct). *150th Birth Anniv of Mark Twain (author). Designs as T* **118** *of Anguilla, but vert, showing Walt Disney cartoon characters illustrating Mark Twain quotations. Multicoloured. P* 13½×14.
908 1 l. 50, Snow White and Bashful 20 25
909 3 l. Three Little Pigs 35 40
910 4 l. Donald Duck and nephew 50 55
911 5 l. Pinocchio and Figaro the cat 60 65
908/11 .. .. *Set of* 4 1·50 1·60
MS912 126×101 mm. 15 l. Winnie the Pooh .. 1·90 2·00

(Des Walt Disney Productions. Litho Questa)

1985 (30 Oct). *Birth Bicentenaries of Grimm Brothers (folklorists). Horiz designs as T* **119** *of Anguilla showing Walt Disney cartoon characters in scenes from "Rumpelstiltskin". Multicoloured. P* 14×13½.
913 70 c. The Miller (Donald Duck) and his daughter (Daisy Duck) meet the King (Uncle Scrooge) 20 25
914 1 l. 30, The King puts the Miller's daughter to work 35 40
915 2 l. Rumpelstiltskin demands payment .. 50 55
916 10 l. The King with gold spun from straw .. 2·75 3·00
913/16 .. .. *Set of* 4 3·50 3·75
MS917 126×100 mm. 15 l. The King and Queen with baby .. .. 4·00 4·25

(Litho Format)

1985 (28 Nov). *40th Anniv of United Nations Organization. Multicoloured designs as T* **208** *of Antigua showing United Nations (New York) stamps. P* 14½.
918 2 l. John Kennedy and 1954 Human Rights 8 c. 40 40
919 4 l. Albert Einstein (scientist) and 1958 Atomic Energy 3 c. 70 70
920 7 l. Maimonides (physician) and 1956 W.H.O. 8 c. .. .. 1·75 1·75
918/20 .. .. *Set of* 3 2·50 2·50
MS921 110×85 mm. 12 l. Martin Luther King (civil rights leader) (*vert*) .. .. .. 1·50 1·75

(Des M. Lemel. Litho Questa)

1986 (3 Mar). *World Cup Football Championship, Mexico. T* **191** *and similar vert designs. Multicoloured. P* 14.
922 70 c. Type **191** 15 10
923 3 l. Player controlling ball 40 40
924 4 l. Player chasing ball 55 60
925 5 l. Player kicking ball (*different*) 65 70
922/5 .. .. *Set of* 4 1·60 1·60
MS926 105×74 mm. 12 l. Player kicking ball (*different*) .. .. 1·50 1·75

(Des J. Iskowitz. Litho Questa)

1986 (11 Mar). *Centenary of Statue of Liberty (1st issue). Multicoloured designs as T* **211** *of Dominica. P* 14.
927 40 c. Times Square, 1905 (*vert*) 10 10
928 70 c. Times Square, 1986 (*vert*) 10 10
929 1 l. "Tally Ho" coach, *c* 1880 .. .. 15 15
930 10 l. Express bus, 1986 .. .. .. 1·25 1·40
927/30 .. .. *Set of* 4 1·40 1·60
MS931 105×75 mm. 12 l. Statue of Liberty (*vert*) 1·50 1·75
See also Nos. 1001/9.

(Des W. Hanson. Litho Questa)

1986 (1 Apr). *Appearance of Halley's Comet (1st issue). Horiz designs as T* **123** *of Anguilla. Multicoloured. P* 14.
932 15 c. Johannes Kepler (astronomer) and Paris Observatory 10 10
933 50 c. N.A.S.A. Space Shuttle landing, 1985 .. 10 10
934 70 c. Halley's Comet (from Bayeux Tapestry) 10 10
935 10 l. Comet of 530 A.D. and Merlin predicting coming of King Arthur .. .. 1·25 1·40
932/5 .. .. *Set of* 4 1·40 1·50
MS936 101×70 mm. 12 l. Halley's Comet .. 1·50 1·60

(Des and litho Questa)

1986 (23 Apr). *60th Birthday of Queen Elizabeth II. Vert designs as T* **125** *of Anguilla. P* 14.
937 10 c. black and yellow 10 10
938 1 l. 70, multicoloured 25 30
939 10 l. multicoloured .. .. 1·25 1·40
937/9 .. .. *Set of* 3 1·40 1·60
MS940 120×85 mm. 12 l. black and grey-brown 1·50 1·60
Designs:—10 c. Princess Elizabeth inspecting guard of honour, Cranwell, 1951; 1 l. 70, In Garter robes; 10 l. At Braemar Games, 1970; 12 l. Princess Elizabeth, Windsor Castle, 1943.

192 Chicago-Milwaukee "Hiawatha Express'

193 *Monodora myristica*

(Des P. Rhymer. Litho Questa)

1986 (22 May). *"Ameripex" International Stamp Exhibition, Chicago. American Trains. T* **192** *and similar horiz designs. Multicoloured. P* 14.
941 50 c. Type **192** 35 15
942 2 l. Rock Island Line "The Rocket" 55 45
943 4 l. Rio Grande "Prospector" 95 80
944 7 l. Southern Pacific "Daylight Express" .. 1·60 1·40
941/4 .. .. *Set of* 4 3·00 2·50
MS945 105×85 mm. 12 l. Pennsylvania "Broadway" .. .. 1·75 1·90

(Litho Questa)

1986 (1 July). *Royal Wedding. Vert designs as T* **213** *of Antigua. Multicoloured. P* 14.
946 10 c. Prince Andrew and Miss Sarah Ferguson 10 10
947 1 l. 70, Prince Andrew at clay pigeon shoot 30 30
948 10 l. Prince Andrew in naval uniform .. 1·40 1·40
946/8 .. .. *Set of* 3 1·60 1·60
MS949 88×88 mm. 12 l. Prince Andrew and Miss Sarah Ferguson (*different*) .. .. .. 1·50 1·60

(Des G. Drummond. Litho Format)

1986 (25 Aug). *Flowers of Sierra Leone. T* **193** *and similar vert designs. Multicoloured. P* 15.
950 70 c. Type **193** 10 10
951 1 l. 50, *Gloriosa simplex* 10 10
952 4 l. *Mussaenda erythrophylla* 20 20
953 6 l. *Crinum ornatum* 35 30
954 8 l. *Bauhinia purpurea* 50 40
955 10 l. *Bombax costatum* 60 45
956 20 l. *Hibiscus rosasinensis* .. .. .. 1·00 85
957 30 l. *Cassia fistula* .. .. 1·40 1·40
950/7 .. .. *Set of* 8 3·75 3·25
MS958 Two sheets, each 101×92 mm. (a) 40 l. *Clitoria ternatea*. (b) 40 l. *Plumbago auriculata* *Set of* 2 *sheets* 3·25 3·50

194 Handshake and Flags of Sierra Leone and U.S.A.

(Litho Questa)

1986 (26 Aug). *25th Anniv of United States Peace Corps. P* 14.
959 **194** 10 l. multicoloured 50 50

ALTERED CATALOGUE NUMBERS

Any Catalogue numbers altered from the last edition are shown as a list in the introductory pages.

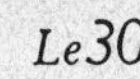

195 Transporting Goods by Canoe **(196)** **(197)**

(Des T. O'Toole. Litho Questa)

1986 (1 Sept). *International Peace Year. T* **195** *and similar horiz designs. Multicoloured. P* 14.
960 1 l. Type **195** 10 10
961 2 l. Teacher and class 10 10
962 5 l. Rural post office 20 25
963 10 l. Fishermen in longboat 40 45
960/3 .. .. *Set of* 4 65 75

1986 (15 Sept). *Various stamps surch.*

(a) *As T* **196** *on Nos.* 820A, 826/7A *and* 829A
964 30 l. on 2 c. Type **177** .. .. 1·50 1·60
965 40 l. on 30 c. *Traveller* (brig) .. .. .. 2·10 2·25
966 45 l. on 40 c. *Amistad* (schooner) .. .. 2·40 2·50
967 50 l. on 70 c. *Scotia* (cable ship) .. .. 2·60 2·75

(b) *As T* **197** *on Nos.* 937 *and* 939/40 (*in silver on Nos.* 968/9)
968 70 c. on 10 c. black and yellow 10 10
969 45 l. on 10 l. multicoloured .. .. .. 2·40 2·50
MS970 120×85 mm. 50 l. on 12 l. black and grey-brown .. .. 2·75 3·00

(c) *As T* **197** *on Nos.* 946 *and* 948/9, *in silver*
971 70 c. on 10 c. Prince Andrew and Miss Sarah Ferguson 10 10
972 45 l. on 10 l. Prince Andrew in naval uniform 2·40 2·50
964/72 .. .. *Set of* 8 12·00 12·50
MS973 88×88 mm. 50 l. on 12 l. Prince Andrew and Miss Sarah Ferguson (*different*) .. .. 2·75 3·00

1986 (15 Sept). *World Cup Football Championship Winners, Mexico. Nos.* 922/6 *optd with T* **216** *of Antigua or surch also, all in gold.*
974 70 c. Type **191** 10 10
975 3 l. Player controlling ball 15 20
976 4 l. Player chasing ball 20 25
977 40 l. on 5 l. Player kicking ball (*different*) .. 2·25 2·50
974/7 .. .. *Set of* 4 2·40 2·75
MS978 105×74 mm. 40 l. on 12 l. Player kicking ball (*different*) .. .. 2·25 2·50

198 Mickey and Minnie Mouse as Jack and Jill

(Des Walt Disney Co. Litho Format)

1986 (22 Sept). *"Stockholmia '86" International Stamp Exhibition, Sweden. T* **198** *and similar horiz designs showing Walt Disney cartoon characters in scenes from nursery rhymes. Multicoloured. P* 11.
979 70 c. Type **198** 10 10
980 1 l. Donald Duck as Wee Willie Winkie .. 10 10
981 2 l. Minnie Mouse as Little Miss Muffet .. 10 15
982 4 l. Goofy as Old King Cole 20 25
983 5 l. Clarabelle as Mary Quite Contrary .. 30 35
984 10 l. Daisy Duck as Little Bo Peep 55 60
985 25 l. Daisy Duck and Minnie Mouse in "Polly put the Kettle on" .. .. 1·40 1·50
986 35 l. Goofy, Mickey Mouse and Donald Duck as the Three Men in a Tub .. .. 1·90 2·00
979/86 .. .. *Set of* 8 4·00 4·50
MS987 Two sheets, each 127×102 mm. P 14×13½. (a) 40 l. Aunt Matilda as the Old Woman in the Shoe. (b) 40 l. Goofy as Simple Simon .. .. .. *Set of* 2 *sheets* 4·25 4·50

1986 (15 Oct). *Appearance of Halley's Comet (2nd issue). Nos.* 932/6 *optd as T* **218** *of Antigua (in silver on* 50 *l.) or surch also.*
988 50 c. N.A.S.A. Space Shuttle landing, 1985 .. 10 10
989 70 c. Halley's Comet (from Bayeux Tapestry) 10 10
990 1 l. 50 on 15 c. Johannes Kepler (astronomer) and Paris Observatory 10 10
991 45 l. on 10 l. Comet of 530 A.D. and Merlin predicting coming of King Arthur .. 3·00 3·25
988/91 .. .. *Set of* 4 2·75 3·00
MS992 101×70 mm. 50 l. on 12 l. Halley's Comet 3·25 3·50

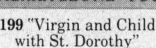

199 "Virgin and Child with St. Dorothy"

200 Nomoli (soapstone figure)

(Litho Questa)

1986 (17 Nov). *Christmas. Paintings by Titian. T* **199** *and similar multicoloured designs. P* 14.

993 70 c. Type **199** 10 10
994 1 l. 50, "The Gypsy Madonna" (*vert*) .. 10 10
995 20 l. "The Holy Family" .. .. .. 1·10 1·25
996 30 l. "Virgin and Child in an Evening Landscape" (*vert*) .. .. 1·60 1·75
993/6 .. .. *Set of* 4 2·50 2·75
MS997 76×102 mm. 40 l. "Madonna with the Pesaro Family" (*vert*) .. .. 2·50 3·25

(Des A. DiLorenzo. Litho Format)

1987 (2 Jan). *Bicentenary of Sierra Leone. T* **200** *and similar vert designs. Multicoloured. P* 15.

998 2 l. Type **200** 10 10
999 5 l. King's Yard Gate, Royal Hospital, 1817.. 20 25
MS1000 100×70 mm. 60 l. Early 19th-century British warship at Freetown .. .. .. 2·40 2·50

201 Removing Top of Statue's Torch

202 Emblem, Mother with Child and Syringe

(Litho Questa)

1987 (2 Jan). *Centenary of Statue of Liberty* (1986) (*2nd issue*). *T* **201** *and similar multicoloured designs. P* 14.

1001 70 c. Type **201** 10 10
1002 1 l. 50, View of Statue's torch and New York Harbour (*horiz*) 10 10
1003 2 l. Crane lifting torch 10 10
1004 3 l. Workman steadying torch 10 15
1005 4 l. Statue's crown (*horiz*) 15 20
1006 5 l. Statue of Liberty (side view) and fireworks 20 25
1007 10 l. Statue of Liberty and fireworks .. 40 45
1008 25 l. Bedloe Island, Statue and fireworks (*horiz*) .. .. 1·00 1·10
1009 30 l. Statue's face .. .. 1·25 1·40
1001/9 .. .. *Set of* 9 3·00 3·50

(Litho Questa)

1987 (18 Mar). *40th Anniv of U.N.I.C.E.F. P* 14.

1010 **202** 10 l. multicoloured 40 45

203 *U.S.A.*, 1987

(Des S. Heinmann. Litho Questa)

1987 (15 June). *America's Cup Yachting Championship. T* **203** *and similar multicoloured designs. P* 14.

1011 1 l. Type **203** 10 10
1012 1 l. 50, *New Zealand*, 1987 (*horiz*) .. 10 10
1013 2 l. 50, *French Kiss*, 1987 .. .. .. 10 10
1014 10 l. *Stars and Stripes*, 1987 (*horiz*) .. 40 45
1015 15 l. *Australia II*, 1983 .. .. .. 60 65
1016 25 l. *Freedom*, 1980 .. .. 1·00 1·10
1017 30 l. *Kookaburra III*, 1987 (*horiz*) .. 1·25 1·40
1011/17 .. .. *Set of* 7 3·00 3·50
MS1018 100×70 mm. 50 l. *Constellation*, 1964 .. 2·00 2·25

204 Mickey Mouse as Mountie and Parliament Building, Ottawa

(Des Walt Disney Co. Litho Format)

1987 (15 June). *"Capex '87" International Stamp Exhibition, Toronto. T* **204** *and similar horiz designs showing Walt Disney cartoon characters in Canada. Multicoloured. P* 11.

1019 2 l. Type **204** 10 10
1020 5 l. Goofy dressed as Mountie and totem poles 20 25
1021 10 l. Goofy windsurfing and Donald Duck fishing off Perce Rock 40 45
1022 20 l. Goofy with mountain goat in Rocky Mountains 80 85
1023 25 l. Donald Duck and Mickey Mouse in Old Quebec .. .. 1·00 1·10
1024 45 l. Goofy emerging from igloo and *Aurora Borealis* .. .. 1·75 1·90
1025 50 l. Goofy as gold prospector and post office, Yukon .. .. 2·00 2·10
1026 75 l. Dumbo flying over Niagara Falls .. 3·25 3·25
1019/26 .. .. *Set of* 8 8·25 9·00
MS1027 Two sheets, each 127×101 mm. (a) 100 l. Mickey Mouse driving chuckwagon in Calgary Stampede. (b) 100 l. Mickey Mouse and Goofy as Vikings in Newfoundland. P 14×13½ *Set of* 2 *sheets* 8·00 8·50

205 Blue Salamis

206 Cycling

(Des S. Heinmann. Litho Questa)

1987 (4 Aug)–**89**. *Butterflies. T* **205** *and similar vert designs. Multicoloured. A. Without imprint date. P* 14. *B. Without imprint date. P* 12.

		A		B	
1028	10 c. Type **205**	10	10	10	10
1029	20 c. Pale-tailed Blue ..	20	10	10	10
1030	40 c. Acraea Swallowtail ..	20	10	10	10
1031	1 l. Broad Blue-banded Swallowtail	20	10	10	10
1032	2 l. Giant Blue Swallowtail	25	25	10	10
1033	3 l. Blood Red Cymothoe ..	30	25	10	10
1034	5 l. Green-spotted Swallowtail	40	25	15	20
1035	10 l. Small Striped Swordtail	75	50	25	30
1036	20 l. Congo Long-tailed Blue	1·50	1·50	50	55
1037	25 l. Blue Monarch	1·75	1·75	65	70
1038	30 l. Black and Yellow Swallowtail	2·00	2·00	80	85
1039	45 l. Western Blue Charaxes	3·00	3·00	1·10	1·25
1040	60 l. Violet-washed Charaxes	1·75	2·00	1·50	1·60
1041	75 l. Orange Admiral ..	2·25	2·50	1·90	2·00
1042	100 l. Blue-patched Judy ..	3·00	3·50	2·50	2·75
1028/42	.. .. *Set of* 15	16·00	16·00	8·75	9·50

C. *With imprint date. P* 14

1028C 10 c. Type **205** 10 10
1029C 20 c. Pale-tailed Blue 10 10
1030C 40 c. Acraea Swallowtail 10 10
1031C 1 l. Broad Blue-banded Swallowtail .. 10 10
1032C 2 l. Giant Blue Swallowtail 10 10
1033C 3 l. Blood Red Cymothoe 10 10
1028C/33C .. .. .. *Set of* 6 30 30

Dates of issue:—4.8.87, Nos. 1028A/42A; 6.88, Nos. 1028B/37B; 8.88, Nos. 1038B/9B; 10.88, Nos. 1040B/1B; 3.89, No. 1042B; 1989, Nos. 1028C/33C.

(Des BG Studio. Litho Questa)

1987 (10 Aug). *Olympic Games, Seoul* (1988) (*1st issue*). *T* **206** *and similar vert designs. Multicoloured. P* 14.

1043 5 l. Type **206** 20 25
1044 10 l. Three Day Eventing 40 45
1045 45 l. Athletics .. .. 1·75 1·90
1046 50 l. Tennis .. .. 2·00 2·10
1043/6 .. .. *Set of* 4 4·00 4·25
MS1047 73×84 mm. 100 l. Olympic gold medal .. 4·00 4·25

See also Nos. 1137/41.

(Litho Questa)

1987 (17 Aug). *Birth Centenary of Marc Chagall* (*artist*). *Multicoloured designs as T* **225** *of Antigua. P* 13½×14.

1048 3 l. "The Quarrel" 10 15
1049 5 l. "Rebecca giving Abraham's Servant a Drink" 15 15
1050 10 l. "The Village" 20 25
1051 20 l. "Ida at the Window" 40 45
1052 25 l. "Promenade" 80 85
1053 45 l. "Peasants" .. .. 1·00 1·10
1054 50 l. "Turquoise Plate" (ceramic) .. .. 1·75 1·90
1055 75 l. "Cemetery Gate" .. .. .. 2·00 2·10
1048/55 .. .. *Set of* 8 3·00 3·25
MS1056 Two sheets, each 110 × 95 mm. (a) 100 l. "Wedding Feast" (stage design) (104 × 78 *mm*). (b) 100 l. "The Falling Angel" (104 × 78 *mm*). Imperf .. .. .. *Set of* 2 *sheets* 8·00 8·50

(Des W. Wright. Litho Format)

1987 (28 Aug). *Milestones of Transportation. Multicoloured designs as T* **226** *of Antigua. P* 15.

1057 3 l. "Apollo 8" spacecraft (first manned Moon orbit), 1968 (*vert*) 10 10
1058 5 l. Blanchard's balloon (first U.S. balloon flight), 1793 .. .. 15 20
1059 10 l. Amelia Earhart's Lockheed "Vega" (first solo transatlantic flight by woman), 1932 .. .. 30 35
1060 15 l. Vicker's "Vimy" (first non-stop transatlantic flight), 1919 .. .. .. 45 50
1061 20 l. British "Mk 1" tank (first combat tank), 1916 .. .. 60 65
1062 25 l. Sikorsky "VS-300" (first U.S. helicopter flight), 1939 .. .. .. 75 80
1063 30 l. Wright brothers' *Flyer 1* (first powered flight), 1903 .. .. .. 90 95
1064 35 l. Bleriot "XI" (first cross Channel flight), 1909 .. .. 1·00 1·10
1065 40 l. Paraplane (first flexible-wing ultralight), 1983 (*vert*) .. .. .. 1·25 1·40
1066 50 l. Daimler's first motorcycle, 1885 (*vert*) 1·50 1·60
1057/66 .. .. *Set of* 10 6·25 7·00
MS1067 114 × 83 mm. 100 l. "Rhinegold Express" (first electric railway) .. .. 3·00 3·25

207 Evonne Goolagong

(Des W. Storozuk. Litho Questa)

1987 (4 Sept). *Wimbledon Tennis Champions. T* **207** *and similar horiz designs. Multicoloured. P* 14.

1068 2 l. Type **207** 10 10
1069 5 l. Martina Navratilova 20 20
1070 10 l. Jimmy Connors 40 40
1071 15 l. Bjorn Borg 60 60
1072 30 l. Boris Becker .. .. 1·25 1·25
1073 40 l. John McEnroe .. .. 1·50 1·50
1074 50 l. Chris Evert Lloyd .. .. .. 1·75 1·75
1075 75 l. Virginia Wade .. .. .. 2·50 2·50
1068/75 .. .. *Set of* 8 7·50 7·50
MS1076 Two sheets, each 105 × 75 mm. (a) 100 l. Boris Becker (*different*). (b) 100 l. Steffi Graf *Set of* 2 *sheets* 6·50 7·00

208 Ducats, *Santa Maria* and Issac Abravanel (financier)

209 Cotton Tree

(Litho Questa)

1987 (11 Sept). *500th Anniv of Discovery of America by Columbus* (1992). *T* **208** *and similar horiz designs. Multicoloured. P* 14.

1077 5 l. Type **208** 15 20
1078 10 l. Astrolabe, *Pinta* and Abraham Zacuto (astronomer) 30 35
1079 45 l. Maravedis (coins), *Nina* and Luis de Santangel (financier) .. .. .. 1·25 1·40
1080 50 l. Carib and Spaniard with tobacco plant and Luis de Torres (translator) .. 1·50 1·60
1077/80 .. .. *Set of* 4 3·00 3·25
MS1081 101 × 70 mm. 100 l. Christopher Columbus and map .. .. 3·00 3·25

(Des Mary Walters. Litho Questa)

1987 (15 Sept). *Flora and Fauna. T* **209** *and similar horiz designs. Multicoloured. P* 14.

1082 3 l. Type **209** 10 10
1083 5 l. Dwarf Crocodile 15 20
1084 10 l. Kudu 30 35
1085 20 l. Yellowbells 60 65
1086 25 l. Hippopotamus and calf 75 80
1087 45 l. Comet Orchid .. .. .. 1·25 1·40
1088 50 l. Baobab Tree .. .. 1·50 1·60
1089 75 l. Elephant and calf .. .. .. 2·25 2·40
1082/9 .. .. *Set of* 8 6·25 6·75
MS1090 Two sheets, each 100 × 70 mm. (a) 100 l. Bananas, Coconut Palm, Papayas and Pineapple. (b) 100 l. Leopard .. *Set of* 2 *sheets* 5·75 6·00

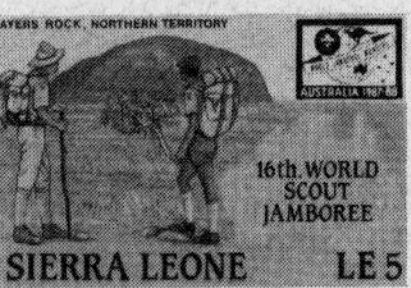

210 Scouts at Ayers Rock

(Des R. Vigurs. Litho Format)

1987 (5 Oct). *World Scout Jamboree, Australia. T* **210** *and similar horiz designs. Multicoloured. P* 15.

1091 5 l. Type **210** 15 20
1092 15 l. Scouts sailing yacht 45 50
1093 40 l. Scouts and Sydney skyline .. .. 1·25 1·40
1094 50 l. Scout, Sydney Harbour Bridge and Opera House .. .. 1·50 1·60
1091/4 .. .. *Set of* 4 3·00 3·25
MS1095 114 × 78 mm. 100 l. Flags of Sierra Leone, Australia and Boy Scouts .. .. 3·00 3·25

(Des and litho Questa)

1987 (9 Nov). *Bicentenary of U.S. Constitution. Multicoloured designs as T* **232** *of Antigua. P* 14.

No.	Description	Unused	Used
1096	5 l. White House	15	20
1097	10 l. George Washington (Virginia delegate) (*vert*)	30	35
1098	30 l. Patrick Henry (statesman) (*vert*)	90	95
1099	65 l. State Seal, New Hampshire	1·90	2·00
1096/9	*Set of* 4	3·00	3·25
MS1100	105 × 75 mm. 100 l. John Jay (jurist) (*vert*)	3·00	3·25

(Des Walt Disney Company. Litho Questa)

1987 (9 Dec). *60th Anniv of Mickey Mouse (Walt Disney cartoon character). Horiz designs as T* **220** *of Dominica showing cartoon characters at Tokyo Disneyland. Multicoloured. P* 14 × 13½.

No.	Description	Unused	Used
1101	20 c. Mickey and Minnie Mouse on Space Mountain	10	10
1102	40 c. Mickey Mouse at Country Bear Jamboree	10	10
1103	80 c. Mickey Mouse as bandleader and Minnie Mouse, Goofy and Pluto as musicians	10	10
1104	1 l. Goofy, Mickey Mouse and children in canoe and Mark Twain's river boat	10	10
1105	2 l. Mickey Mouse, Goofy and Chip n'Dale on Western River Railroad	10	10
1106	3 l. Goofy and Mickey Mouse as Pirates of the Caribbean	10	10
1107	10 l. Mickey Mouse, Goofy and children aboard Big Thunder Mountain train	30	35
1108	20 l. Mickey Mouse, Morty and Ferdie in boat and Goofy on flying carpet	60	65
1109	30 l. Mickey and Minnie Mouse in kimonos at Disneyland entrance	90	95
1101/9	*Set of* 9	1·90	2·10
MS1110	127 × 102 mm. 65 l. Mickey and Minnie Mouse in kimonos at Cinderella's Castle	1·90	2·00

211 "The Annunciation" (detail) (Titian)

212 *Russula cyanoxantha*

(Litho Questa)

1987 (21 Dec). *Christmas. Religious Paintings by Titian. T* **211** *and similar multicoloured designs. P* 14.

No.	Description	Unused	Used
1111	2 l. Type **211**	10	10
1112	10 l. "Madonna and Child with Saints"	30	35
1113	20 l. "Madonna and Child with Saints Ulfus and Brigid"	60	65
1114	35 l. "The Madonna of the Cherries"	1·00	1·10
1111/14	*Set of* 4	1·75	2·00
MS1115	70 × 100 mm. 65 l. "The Pesaro Altarpiece" (*vert*)	1·90	2·00

(Des and litho Questa)

1988 (15 Feb). *Royal Ruby Wedding. Vert designs as T* **234** *of Antigua. P* 14.

No.	Description	Unused	Used
1116	2 l. deep brown, black and grey	10	10
1117	3 l. multicoloured	10	10
1118	10 l. deep brown, black and orange	30	35
1119	50 l. multicoloured	1·50	1·60
1116/19	*Set of* 4	1·75	1·90
MS1120	76 × 100 mm. 65 l. multicoloured	1·90	2·00

Designs:—2 l. Wedding of Princess Elizabeth and Duke of Edinburgh, 1947; 3 l. Prince Charles' christening photograph, 1949; 10 l. Queen Elizabeth II with Prince Charles and Princess Anne, *c.* 1951; 50 l. Queen Elizabeth, *c.* 1960; 65 l. Wedding photograph, 1947.

(Des L. Nelson. Litho Questa)

1988 (29 Feb). *Fungi. T* **212** *and similar vert designs. Multicoloured. P* 14.

No.	Description	Unused	Used
1121	3 l. Type **212**	15	10
1122	10 l. *Lycoperdon perlatum*	40	35
1123	20 l. *Lactarius deliciosus*	75	80
1124	30 l. *Boletus edulis*	1·25	1·40
1121/4	*Set of* 4	2·25	2·40
MS1125	100 × 70 mm. 65 l. *Amanita muscaria*	1·90	2·00

213 Golden Pheasant Fish

(Des Mary Walters. Litho Format)

1988 (13 Apr). *Fishes of Sierra Leone. T* **213** *and similar horiz designs. Multicoloured. P* 15.

No.	Description	Unused	Used
1126	3 l. Type **213**	10	10
1127	10 l. Banded Toothcarp	30	35
1128	20 l. Jewel Fish	60	65
1129	35 l. Butterfly Fish	1·00	1·10
1126/9	*Set of* 4	1·75	1·90
MS1130	99 × 69 mm. 65 l. African Longfin	1·90	2·00

1988 (19 Apr). *Stamp Exhibitions. Nos.* 1016, 1072 *and* 1079 *optd as T* **241** *of Antigua with various emblems.*

No.	Description	Unused	Used
1131	25 l. *Freedom,* 1980 (optd "INDEPENDENCE 40", Israel)	75	80
1132	30 l. Boris Becker (optd "OLYMPHILEX '88", Seoul)	90	95
1133	45 l. Maravedis (coins), *Nina* and Luis de Santangel (financier) (optd "PRAGA 88", Prague)	1·25	1·40
1131/3	*Set of* 3	2·50	2·75

214 Hands holding Coffee Beans and Woman with Cocoa

215 Basketball

(Des L. Lamm. Litho Questa)

1988 (3 May). *International Fund for Agricultural Development. T* **214** *and similar horiz designs. Multicoloured. P* 14.

No.	Description	Unused	Used
1134	3 l. Type **214**	10	10
1135	15 l. Tropical fruits and man climbing palm tree	45	50
1136	25 l. Sheaf of rice and harvesters	75	80
1134/6	*Set of* 3	1·10	1·25

(Des L. Fried. Litho Questa)

1988 (15 June). *Olympic Games, Seoul (2nd issue). T* **215** *and similar vert designs. Multicoloured. P* 14.

No.	Description	Unused	Used
1137	3 l. Type **215**	10	10
1138	10 l. Judo	30	35
1139	15 l. Gymnastics	45	50
1140	40 l. Synchronized swimming	1·25	1·40
1137/40	*Set of* 4	2·00	2·10
MS1141	73 × 101 mm. 65 l. Sierra Leone athlete	1·90	2·00

216 Swallow-tailed Bee Eater

217 *Aureol* (cargo liner)

(Des L. Nelson. Litho Questa)

1988 (25 June). *Birds. T* **216** *and similar vert designs. Multicoloured. P* 14.

No.	Description	Unused	Used
1142	3 l. Type **216**	10	10
1143	5 l. Double-toothed Barbet	15	20
1144	8 l. African Golden Oriole	25	30
1145	10 l. Red Bishop	30	35
1146	12 l. Red-billed Shrike	35	40
1147	20 l. European Bee Eater	60	65
1148	35 l. Common Gonolek ("Barbary Shrike")	1·00	1·10
1149	40 l. Western Black-headed Oriole	1·25	1·40
1142/9	*Set of* 8	3·50	4·00
MS1150	Two sheets, each 111 × 82 mm. (a) 65 l. Purple Heron. (b) 65 l. Saddle-bill Stork *Set of* 2 *sheets*	3·75	4·00

(Des D. Miller. Litho Questa)

1988 (1 July). *Ships. T* **217** *and similar horiz designs. Multicoloured. P* 14.

No.	Description	Unused	Used
1151	3 l. Type **217**	15	15
1152	10 l. *Dunkwa* (freighter)	45	45
1153	15 l. *Melampus* (container ship)	65	65
1154	30 l. *Dumbaia* (freighter)	1·10	1·10
1151/4	*Set of* 4	2·10	2·10
MS1155	95 × 95 mm. 65 l. Loading container ship, Freetown	1·90	2·00

(Litho Questa)

1988 (22 Aug). *500th Birth Anniv of Titian (artist). Vert designs as T* **238** *of Antigua showing paintings. Multicoloured. P* 13½ × 14.

No.	Description	Unused	Used
1156	1 l. "The Concert" (detail)	10	10
1157	2 l. "Philip II of Spain"	10	10
1158	3 l. "Saint Sebastian" (detail)	10	10
1159	5 l. "Martyrdom of St. Peter Martyr"	15	20
1160	15 l. "St. Jerome"	45	50
1161	20 l. "St. Mark enthroned with Saints"	60	65
1162	25 l. "Portrait of a Young Man"	75	80
1163	30 l. "St. Jerome in Penitence"	90	95
1156/63	*Set of* 8	2·75	3·00
MS1164	Two sheets, each 110 × 95 mm. (a) 50 l. "Self Portrait". (b) 50 l. "Orpheus and Eurydice" *Set of* 2 *sheets*	3·00	3·25

218 Helicopter lowering "Mercury" Capsule to Flight Deck

219 Famine Relief Convoy crossing Desert

(Des W. Hanson. Litho B.D.T.)

1988 (26 Sept). *25th Death Anniv of John F. Kennedy (American statesman). U.S. Space Achievements. T* **218** *and similar horiz designs. Multicoloured. P* 14.

No.	Description	Unused	Used
1165	3 l. Type **218**	10	10
1166	5 l. *Liberty Bell 7* capsule descending (*vert*)	15	20
1167	15 l. Launch of first manned American capsule (*vert*)	45	50
1168	40 l. *Freedom 7* orbiting Earth	1·25	1·40
1165/8	*Set of* 4	1·75	2·00
MS1169	98 × 69 mm. 65 l. President Kennedy and quotation	1·90	2·00

(Des J. Genzo. Litho B.D.T.)

1988 (1 Nov). *125th Anniv of International Red Cross. T* **219** *and similar multicoloured designs. P* 14.

No.	Description	Unused	Used
1170	3 l. Type **219**	10	10
1171	10 l. Rifle and map of Battle of Solferino, 1859	30	35
1172	20 l. World War II hospital ship in Pacific	60	65
1173	40 l. Red Cross tent and World War I German biplanes	1·25	1·40
1170/3	*Set of* 4	2·00	2·25
MS1174	100 × 70 mm. 65 l. Henri Dunant (founder), Alfred Nobel and Peace Prize scroll (*horiz*)	1·90	2·00

(Des Walt Disney Company. Litho Questa)

1988 (1 Dec). *Christmas. "Mickey's Christmas Dance". Vert designs as T* **228** *of Dominica showing Walt Disney cartoon characters. Multicoloured. P* 13½ × 14.

No.	Description	Unused	Used
1175	10 l. Donald Duck's nephews playing as band	30	35
	a. Sheetlet. Nos. 1175/82	2·10	
1176	10 l. Clarabelle	30	35
1177	10 l. Goofy	30	35
1178	10 l. Scrooge McDuck and Grandma Duck	30	35
1179	10 l. Donald Duck	30	35
1180	10 l. Daisy Duck	30	35
1181	10 l. Minnie Mouse	30	35
1182	10 l. Mickey Mouse	30	35
1175/82	*Set of* 8	2·10	2·50
MS1183	Two sheets, each 127 × 102 mm. (a) 70 l. Mickey Mouse dancing the Charleston. (b) 70 l. Mickey Mouse jiving *Set of* 2 *sheets*	4·00	4·25

Nos. 1175/82 were printed together, *se-tenant* as a composite design, in sheetlets of eight.

220 "Adoration of the Magi" (detail)

GRAND SLAM WINNER

(**221**)

(Litho Questa)

1988 (15 Dec). *Christmas. Religious Paintings by Rubens. T* **220** *and similar vert designs. Multicoloured. P* 13½ × 14.

No.	Description	Unused	Used
1184	3 l. Type **220**	10	10
1185	3 l. 60, "Adoration of the Shepherds" (detail)	10	10
1186	5 l. "Adoration of the Magi" (detail)	15	20
1187	10 l. "Adoration of the Shepherds" (different detail)	30	35
1188	20 l. "Virgin and Child surrounded by Flowers"	60	65
1189	40 l. "St. Gregory the Great and Other Saints" (detail)	1·25	1·40
1190	60 l. "Adoration of the Magi" (detail)	1·75	1·90
1191	80 l. "Madonna and Child with Saints" (detail)	2·25	2·40
1184/91	*Set of* 8	5·75	6·50
MS1192	Two sheets, each 76 × 113 mm. (a) 100 l. "Virgin and Child enthroned with Saints". (b) 100 l. "St. Gregory the Great and Other Saints" *Set of* 2 *sheets*	5·75	6·00

1989 (16 Jan). *Steffi Graf's "Grand Slam" Tennis Victories. No.* **MS**1076b *optd* "GOLD MEDALIST" (*No.* **MS**1193e) *or with T* **221** (*others*), *each with different inscription on sheet margin, all in gold.*
MS1193 105×75 mm. 100 l. Steffi Graf. (a) Optd "AUSTRALIAN OPEN JANUARY 11–24, 1988 GRAF v EVERET". (b) Optd "FRENCH OPEN MAY 23–JUNE 5, 1988 GRAF v ZVEREVA". (c) Optd "WIMBLEDON JUNE 20–JULY 4, 1988 GRAF v NAVRATILOVA". (d) Optd "U.S. OPEN AUGUST 29–SEPTEMBER 11, 1988 GRAF v SABATINI". (e) Optd "SEOUL OLYMPICS 1988 GRAF v SABATINI" *Set of* 5 *sheets* 14·50 15·00
Each marginal overprint includes score of match involved.

222 Brazil v. Sweden, 1958   **223** Decathlon (Gold, C. Schenk, East Germany)

(Des J. McDaniel. Litho B.D.T.)

1989 (28 Apr). *World Cup Football Championship, Italy. T* **222** *and similar vert designs, each showing action from previous World Cup finals. Multicoloured. P* 14.
1194 3 l. Type **222** 10 10
1195 6 l. West Germany v. Hungary, 1954 .. 15 20
1196 8 l. England v. West Germany, 1966 .. 25 30
1197 10 l. Argentina v. Netherlands, 1978 .. 30 35
1198 12 l. Brazil v. Czechoslovakia, 1962 .. 35 40
1199 20 l. West Germany v. Netherlands, 1974 60 65
1200 30 l. Italy v. West Germany, 1982 .. 90 95
1201 40 l. Brazil v. Italy, 1970 .. .. .. 1·25 1·40
1194/201 .. .. *Set of* 8 3·50 4·00
MS1202 Two sheets, each 73×104 mm. (a) 100 l. Argentina v. West Germany, 1986. (b) 100 l. Uruguay v. Brazil, 1950 .. *Set of* 2 *sheets* 5·75 6·00

(Des L. Fried. Litho B.D.T.)

1989 (28 Apr). *Olympic Medal Winners, Seoul* (1988). *T* **223** *and similar horiz designs. Multicoloured. P* 14.
1203 3 l. Type **223** 10 10
1204 6 l. Men's heavyweight judo (Gold, H. Saito, Japan) 15 20
1205 10 l. Women's cycle road race (Silver, J. Niehaus, West Germany) 30 35
1206 15 l. Men's single sculls (Gold, T. Lange, East Germany) 45 50
1207 20 l. Men's 50 metres freestyle swimming (Gold, M. Biondi, U.S.A.) 60 65
1208 30 l. Men's 100 metres (Gold, C. Lewis, U.S.A.) 90 95
1209 40 l. Dressage (Gold, West Germany) .. 1·25 1·40
1210 50 l. Greco-Roman wrestling (57 kg) (Gold, A. Sike, Hungary) .. .. 1·50 1·60
1203/10 .. .. *Set of* 8 4·75 5·25
MS1211 Two sheets, each 70×100 mm. (a) 100 l. Olympic gold medal. (b) 100 l. Olympic torch and rings .. .. *Set of* 2 *sheets* 5·75 6·00

224 Map of Union States, Mail Lorry and Post Office

(Des J. Genzo. Litho B.D.T.)

1989 (19 May). *15th Anniv of Mano River Union. T* **224** *and similar horiz designs. Multicoloured. P* 14.
1212 1 l. Type **224** 10 10
1213 3 l. Map of West Africa and Presidents Momoh, Conte and Doe 10 10
1214 10 l. Construction of Freetown–Monrovia Highway 30 35
1212/14 .. .. *Set of* 3 35 40
MS1215 96×68 mm. 15 l. Presidents signing anniversary meeting communique 45 50

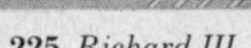

225 *Richard III*   **226** Centenary Logo

(Des G. Vasarhelyi. Litho B.D.T.)

1989 (30 May). *425th Birth Anniv of Shakespeare. T* **225** *and similar horiz designs. Multicoloured. P* 13.
1216 15 l. Type **225** 45 50
a. Sheetlet. Nos. 1216/23 .. .. 3·50
1217 15 l. *Othello* (Iago) 45 50
1218 15 l. *Two Gentlemen of Verona* 45 50
1219 15 l. *Macbeth* (Lady Macbeth) 45 50
1220 15 l. *Hamlet* 45 50
1221 15 l. *The Taming of the Shrew* 45 50
1222 15 l. *The Merry Wives of Windsor* .. 45 50
1223 15 l. *Henry IV* (Sir John Falstaff) .. 45 50
1224 15 l. *Macbeth* (The Witches) 45 50
a. Sheetlet. Nos. 1224/31 .. .. 3·50
1225 15 l. *Romeo and Juliet* 45 50
1226 15 l. *Merchant of Venice* 45 50
1227 15 l. *As You Like It* 45 50
1228 15 l. *The Taming of the Shrew* (banquet scene) 45 50
1229 15 l. *King Lear* 45 50
1230 15 l. *Othello* (Othello and Desdemona) .. 45 50
1231 15 l. *Henry IV* (Justice Shallow) 45 50
1216/31 .. .. *Set of* 16 6·50 7·25
MS1232 Two sheets, each 117×82 mm. (a) 100 l. Shakespeare and arms (49×36 *mm*). (b) 100 l. Shakespeare (49×36 *mm*) .. *Set of* 2 *sheets* 5·75 6·00
Nos. 1216/23 and 1224/31 were each printed together, *se-tenant*, in sheetlets of eight stamps and one central stamp-size label.

(Litho Questa)

1989 (8 June). *Centenary of Ahmadiyya Muslim Society. P* 14.
1233 **226** 3 l. brownish black and new blue .. 10 10

(Litho Questa)

1989 (3 July). *Japanese Art. Paintings by Seiho. Multicoloured designs as T* **250** *of Antigua. Multicoloured. P* 14×13½ (3, 10, 12, 40 *l.*) *or* 13½×14 (*others*).
1234 3 l. "Lapping Waves" 10 10
1235 6 l. "Hazy Moon" (*vert*) 15 20
1236 8 l. "Passing Spring" (*vert*) 25 30
1237 10 l. "Mackerels" 30 35
1238 12 l. "Calico Cat" 35 40
1239 30 l. "The First Time to be a Model" (*vert*) 90 95
1240 40 l. "Kingly Lion" .. .. 1·25 1·40
1241 75 l. "After a Shower" (*vert*) .. .. 2·25 2·50
1234/41 .. .. *Set of* 8 5·00 5·50
MS1242 Two sheets, each 102×77 mm. (a) 150 l. "Dozing in the midst of all the Chirping" (detail) (*vert*). P 13½×14. (b) 150 l. "Domesticated Monkeys and Rabbits" (detail). P 14×13½ *Set of* 2 *sheets* 8·50 8·75
Nos. 1234/41 were each printed in sheetlets of 10 containing two horizontal or vertical strips of 5 stamps separated by printed labels commemorating Emperor Hirohito.

227 Robespierre and Bastille

(Des The Design Element. Litho B.D.T.)

1989 (13 July). *"Philexfrance 89" International Stamp Exhibition, Paris, and Bicentenary of French Revolution. T* **227** *and similar multicoloured designs. P* 14.
1243 6 l. Type **227** 25 25
1244 20 l. Danton and Louvre 75 75
1245 45 l. Queen Marie Antoinette and Notre Dame .. .. 1·50 1·50
1246 80 l. Louis XVI and Palace of Versailles .. 2·50 2·50
1243/6 .. .. *Set of* 4 4·50 4·50
MS1247 77×107 mm. 150 l. Celebrating crowd, Paris (*vert*) .. .. 4·25 4·50

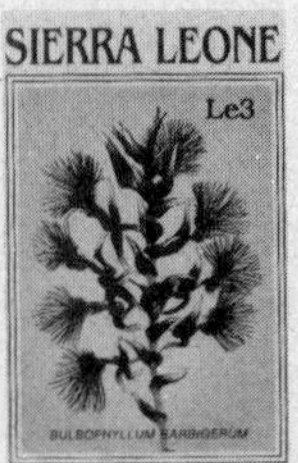

228 "Sputnik" Satellite in Orbit, 1957   **229** *Bulbophyllum barbigerum*

(Des G. Vasarhelyi. Litho B.D.T.)

1989 (20 July). *History of Space Exploration. T* **228** *and similar horiz designs. P* 14.
1248/301 10 l.×27, 15 l.×27 multicoloured *Set of* 54 17·00 17·50
MS1302 Three sheets, each 112×90 mm. 100 l. ×3 multicoloured .. .. *Set of* 3 *sheets* 9·00 9·50
Nos. 1248/301 were issued as six sheetlets, each of nine different designs.

(Des William Hanson Studio. Litho B.D.T.)

1989 (8 Sept). *Orchids of Sierra Leone. T* **229** *and similar vert designs. Multicoloured. P* 14.
1303 3 l. Type **229** 10 10
1304 6 l. *Bulbophyllum falcatum* 15 20
1305 12 l. *Habenaria macrara* 35 40
1306 20 l. *Eurychone rothchildiana* 60 65
1307 50 l. *Calyptrochilum christyanum* .. 1·50 1·60
1308 60 l. *Bulbophyllum distans* .. .. 1·75 1·90
1309 70 l. *Eulophia guineensis* .. .. .. 2·00 2·25
1310 80 l. *Diaphananthe pellucida* .. .. 2·25 2·50
1303/10 .. .. *Set of* 8 7·75 8·50
MS1311 Two sheets, each 112×80 mm. (a) 100 l. *Cyrtorchis arcuata* and Pagoda, Kew Gardens. (b) 100 l. *Eulophia cucullata* .. *Set of* 2 *sheets* 8·50 8·75

230 *Salamis temora*

(Des Mary Walters. Litho B.D.T.)

1989 (11 Sept). *Butterflies. T* **230** *and similar multicoloured designs. P* 14.
1312 6 l. Type **230** 15 20
1313 12 l. *Pseudacraea lucretia* 35 40
1314 18 l. *Charaxes boueti* (*vert*) 50 55
1315 30 l. *Graphium antheus* (*vert*) 90 95
1316 40 l. *Colotis protomedia* .. .. .. 1·25 1·40
1317 60 l. *Asterope pechueli* (*vert*) .. .. 1·75 1·90
1318 72 l. *Coenura aurantiaca* .. .. .. 2·00 2·25
1319 80 l. *Precis octavia* (*vert*) .. .. 2·25 2·50
1312/19 .. .. *Set of* 8 8·25 9·00
MS1320 Two sheets, each 100×70 mm. (a) 100 l. *Charaxes cithaeron* (*vert*). (b) 100 l. *Euphaedra themis* .. .. *Set of* 2 *sheets* 8·50 8·75

Singapore

A Crown Colony until the end of 1957. From 1 August 1958, an nternally self-governing territory designated the State of Singa- ore. From 16 September 1963, part of the Malaysian Federation ntil 9 August 1965, when it became an independent republic vithin the Commonwealth.

Stamps in the Crown Colony Victory design were prepared for ;ingapore in 1946, but not issued. Examples of the 8 c. carmine are nown to exist.

CROWN COLONY

(Typo D.L.R.)

948 (1 Sept)–**52.** *As T* **58** *of Straits Settlements, but inscr* "SINGAPORE" *at foot. Wmk Mult Script CA. Chalk-surfaced paper.* (*a*) *P* 14.

No.	Description	Unused	Used
1	1 c. black	15	10
2	2 c. orange	15	10
3	3 c. green	20	10
4	4 c. brown	20	15
5	6 c. grey	25	15
6	8 c. scarlet (1.10.48)	25	15
7	10 c. purple	20	10
8	15 c. ultramarine (1.10.48)	2·00	10
9	20 c. black and green (1.10.48)	2·50	20
0	25 c. purple and orange (1.10.48)	1·50	15
1	40 c. red and purple (1.10.48)	4·75	5·00
2	50 c. black and blue (1.10.48)	2·75	10
3	$1 blue and purple (1.10.48)	10·00	40
4	$2 green and scarlet (25.10.48)	48·00	2·25
5	$5 green and brown (1.10.48)	£100	2·25
/15	*Set of* 15	£150	10·00

(*b*) *P* 17½ × 18

No.	Description	Unused	Used
6	1 c. black (21.5.52)	50	1·50
7	2 c. orange (31.10.49)	70	80
9	4 c. brown (1.7.49)	70	10
9*a*	5 c. bright purple (1.9.52)	2·50	55
1	6 c. grey (10.12.52)	70	10
1*a*	8 c. green (1.9.52)	4·00	1·25
2	10 c. purple (9.2.50)	50	10
2*a*	12 c. scarlet (1.9.52)	4·00	3·50
3	15 c. ultramarine (9.2.50)	2·75	10
4	20 c. black and green (31.10.49)	2·50	90
4*a*	20 c. bright blue (1.9.52)	4·00	10
5	25 c. purple and orange (9.2.50)	80	10
5*a*	35 c. scarlet and purple (1.9.52)	4·00	90
6	40 c. red and purple (24.5.51)	16·00	8·50
7	50 c. black and blue (9.2.50)	4·50	10
8	$1 blue and purple (31.10.49)	11·00	20
	a. Error. St. Edward's Crown, W **9***b*	£2500	
9	$2 green and scarlet (24.5.51)	£100	1·75
	a. Error. St. Edward's Crown, W **9***b*	£2500	
0	$5 green and brown (19.12.51)	£120	1·75
6/30	*Set of* 18	£250	19·00

Nos. 28a and 29a occur on rows in the watermark in which the rowns and letters "CA" alternate.

948 (25 Oct). *Royal Silver Wedding. As Nos.* 30/1 *of Aden.*

No.	Description	Unused	Used
1	10 c. violet	75	10
2	$5 brown	95·00	27·00

949 (10 Oct). *75th Anniv of Universal Postal Union. As Nos.* 114/17 *of Antigua.*

No.	Description	Unused	Used
3	10 c. purple	75	10
4	15 c. deep blue	3·25	1·40
5	25 c. orange	3·75	1·25
6	50 c. blue-black	5·50	2·50
3/6	*Set of* 4	12·00	4·75

953 (2 June). *Coronation. As No.* 47 *of Aden.*

No.	Description	Unused	Used
7	10 c. black and reddish purple	85	10

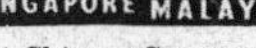

1 Chinese Sampan

2 Raffles Statue

3 Singapore River

4 Arms of Singapore

es Dr. C. A. Gibson-Hill, except 25 c., 30 c., 50 c. and $5 (from photographs, etc.). Photo Harrison (1 c. to 50 c.). Recess (centre typo on $5) B.W. (others))

55 (4 Sept)–**59**. *Designs as T* **1/4**. *Wmk Mult Script CA. P* 13½×14½ (*1 c. to* 50 *c.*) *or* 14 (*others*).

No.	Description	Unused	Used
	1 c. black	10	25
	2 c. yellow-orange	60	60
	4 c. brown	35	15
41	5 c. bright purple	35	15
42	6 c. deep grey-blue	35	15
43	8 c. turquoise-blue	55	55
44	10 c. deep lilac	2·00	10
45	12 c. rose-carmine	1·75	1·75
46	20 c. ultramarine	70	10
	a. Blue (13.3.58)	70	10
47	25 c. orange-red and bluish violet	75	10
	a. Orange-red and purple (21.1.59)	2·00	25
48	30 c. violet and brown-purple	2·00	10
49	50 c. blue and black	1·25	10
50	$1 blue and deep purple	16·00	10
51	$2 blue-green and scarlet	26·00	50
52	$5 yellow, red, brown and slate-black	35·00	2·75
38/52	*Set of* 15	75·00	6·00

Designs: *Horiz as T* **1**—2 c. Malay kolek; 4 c. Twa-kow lighter; 5 c. Lombok sloop; 6 c. Trengganu pinas; 8 c. Palari schooner; 10 c. Timber tongkong; 12 c. Hainan junk; 20 c. Cocos-Keeling schooner; 25 c. "Argonaut" aircraft; 30 c. Oil tanker; 50 c. *Chusan III* (liner).

Plate 2A and 2B of the 10 c. (12 April 1960) and the blue "3A" and "3B" plates of the 50 c. "3A–2A", "3B–2B" (part of the 24 January 1961 issue and later printings) were printed with a finer screen (250 dots per inch, instead of the normal 200) (*Price* 10 *c.*, £2.25 *un*, 20*p us*. 50 *c.*, £1.50 *un*, 10*p us*).

INTERNAL SELF-GOVERNMENT

16 The Singapore Lion

17 State Flag

(Photo Harrison)

1959 (1 June). *New Constitution. W* w **12**. *P* 11½ × 12.

No.	Type	Description	Unused	Used
53	**16**	4 c. yellow, sepia and rose-red	30	20
54		10 c. yellow, sepia and reddish purple	40	15
55		20 c. yellow, sepia and bright blue	1·10	1·75
56		25 c. yellow, sepia and green	1·10	1·10
57		30 c. yellow, sepia and violet	1·25	1·75
58		50 c. yellow, sepia and deep slate	1·50	1·75
53/8		*Set of* 6	5·00	6·00

(Litho Enschedé)

1960 (3 June). *National Day. W* w **12** (*sideways*). *P* 13½.

No.	Type	Description	Unused	Used
59	**17**	4 c. red, yellow and blue	20	20
60		10 c. red, yellow and grey	40	10

18 Clasped Hands

(Photo Enschedé)

1961 (3 June). *National Day. W* w **12**. *P* 13½.

No.	Type	Description	Unused	Used
61	**18**	4 c. black, brown and pale yellow	15	20
62		10 c. black, deep green and pale yellow	35	10

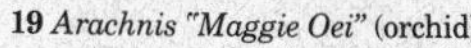

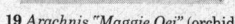

19 *Arachnis "Maggie Oei"* (orchid)

20 Sea-Horse

21 Six-banded Barb

24 *Vanda "Tan Chay Yan"* (orchid)

26*a* Black-naped Tern

30 White-rumped Shama

(Photo Harrison (orchids, fish and 15 c. bird) D.L.R. (birds, except 15 c.))

1962 (31 Mar)–**66.** *T* **19/21**, **24**, **26*a***, **30** *and similar designs. W* w **12**. *P* 12½ (i), 14½ × 13½ (ii), 13½ × 14½ (iii), 13½ × 13 (iv) *or* 13 × 13½ (v).

No.	Description	Unused	Used
63	1 c. multicoloured (i) (10.3.63)	10	50
64	2 c. brown and green (ii)	10	45
65	4 c. black and orange-red (iii)	10	10
	a. Black omitted	£120	
66	5 c. red and black (iii)	10	10
	a. Red omitted	£120	
67	6 c. black and greenish yellow (ii)	30	15
68	8 c. multicoloured (i) (10.3.63)	55	1·75
69	10 c. red-orange and black (iii)	15	10
	a. Red-orange omitted	90·00	
70	12 c. multicoloured (i) (10.3.63)	55	1·75
70*a*	15 c. multicoloured (i) (9.11.66)	80	10
	ab. Orange (eye) omitted	9·00	
71	20 c. orange and blue (ii)	30	10
	a. Orange omitted	£150	
72	25 c. black and orange (iii)	35	10
73	30 c. multicoloured (i) (10.3.63)	1·00	10
	a. Yellow (flowers) omitted	30·00	
74	50 c. multicoloured (iv) (10.3.63)	95	10
75	$1 multicoloured (iv) (10.3.63)	10·00	20
76	$2 multicoloured (iv) (10.3.63)	13·00	75
77	$5 multicoloured (v) (10.3.63)	27·00	2·75
63/77	*Set of* 16	48·00	7·50

Designs: *Horiz* (*as T* **21**)—5 c. Clown fish; 10 c. Harlequin; 25 c. Two-spot Gourami. (*As T* **30**)—$1 White-breasted Kingfisher. *Vert* (*as T* **20**)—6 c. Archer fish; 20 c. Butterfly fish. (*As T* **24**)—12 c. *Grammaphotyllum speciosum* (orchid); 30 c. *Vanda "Miss Joaquim"* (orchid). (*As T* **26*a***)—$2 Yellow-bellied Sunbird; $5 White-bellied Sea Eagle.

The 15 c., 30 c., $2 and $5 exist with PVA gum as well as gum arabic.

See also Nos. 83/88.

34 "The Role of Labour in Nation-Building"

35 Blocks of Flats, Singapore

(Photo Courvoisier)

1962 (3 June). *National Day. P* 11½ × 12.

No.	Type	Description	Unused	Used
78	**34**	4 c. yellow, rose-carmine and black	15	20
79		10 c. yellow, blue and black	35	10

(Photo Harrison)

1963 (3 June). *National Day. W* w **12**. *P* 12½.

No.	Type	Description	Unused	Used
80	**35**	4 c. orange-red, black, blue & turq-blue	15	20
81		10 c. orange-red, blk, yell-olive & turq–bl	35	10

36 Dancers in National Costume

37 Workers

(Photo Harrison)

1963 (8 Aug). *South East Asia Cultural Festival. W* w **12**. *P* 14 × 14½.

No.	Type	Description	Unused	Used
82	**36**	5 c. multicoloured	15	15

INDEPENDENT REPUBLIC

1966 (1 Mar)–**67**. *As Nos.* 63, 66, 69, 72, 74/5, *but W* w **12** (*sideways*).

No.	Description	Unused	Used
83	1 c. multicoloured (22.2.67)	10	85
84	5 c. red and black (30.5.67)	75	15
85	10 c. red-orange and black (30.5.67)	55	15
86	25 c. black and orange (9.66*)	50	20
87	50 c. multicoloured (29.1.66*)	1·50	1·00
	a. Imperf (pair)	£300	
88	$1 multicoloured (18.5.67)	7·00	4·00
83/8	*Set of* 6	9·50	5·75

*The 25 and 50 c. values were not released in London until 30.5.67 and 9.6.66. The 25 c. value, however, is known used in September 1966 and the 50 c. on 29.1.66.

The 1 c. and 25 c. exist with PVA gum as well as gum arabic.

(Photo D.L.R.)

1966 (9 Aug). *First Anniv of Republic. W* w **12** (*30 c.*) *or no wmk* (*others*). *P* 12½ × 13.

No.	Type	Description	Unused	Used
89	**37**	15 c. multicoloured	40	20
90		20 c. multicoloured	60	50
91		30 c. multicoloured	80	65
89/91		*Set of* 3	1·60	1·25

38 Flag Procession

(Photo D.L.R.)

1967 (9 Aug). *National Day. P* 14 × 14½.

No.	Type	Description		
92	38	6 c. rosine, brown and slate	20	20
93		15 c. reddish purple, brown and slate	40	10
94		50 c. bright blue, brown and slate	75	70
92/4		*Set of* 3	1·25	90

Nos. 92/4 are respectively inscribed "Build a Vigorous Singapore" in Chinese, Malay and Tamil in addition to the English inscription.

39 Skyscrapers and Afro-Asian Map

40 Symbolical Figure wielding Hammer, and Industrial Outline of Singapore

(Photo D.L.R.)

1967 (7 Oct). *2nd Afro-Asian Housing Congress. P* 14 × 13.

No.	Type	Description		
95	39	10 c. multicoloured	25	10
		a. Opt omitted	£170	£170
96		25 c. multicoloured	45	70
97		50 c. multicoloured	70	1·00
95/7		*Set of* 3	1·25	1·60

The above were originally scheduled for release in 1966, and when finally issued were overprinted with the new date and a black oblong obliterating the old date.

(Photo Harrison)

1968 (9 Aug). *National Day. Inscription at top in Chinese* (6 c.), *Malay* (15 c.) *or Tamil* (50 c.). *P* 13½ × 14.

No.	Type	Description		
98	40	6 c. orange-red, black and gold	20	15
99		15 c. apple-green, black and gold	25	15
100		50 c. greenish blue, black and gold	65	50
98/100		*Set of* 3	1·00	70

41 Half check Pattern

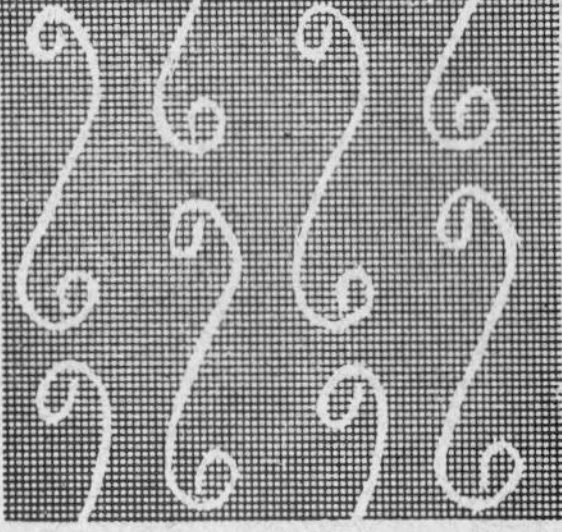

42 Scrolled "S" multiple

43 Mirudhangam

44 Pi Pa

45 Sword Dance

51 Dragon Dance

(Photo D.L.R. (5 c. to $1), Japanese Govt Printing Bureau, Tokyo (others))

1968–73. *T* 43/5, 51 *and similar designs.* 5 c. *to* $1: *Chalk-surfaced paper; W* 41; *P* 14. *Others: Ordinary paper; W* 42 *upright* (1 c., $5) *or sideways* (4 c., $2, $10); *P* 13½.

No.	Description		
101	1 c. multicoloured (10.11.69)	15	90
102	4 c. multicoloured (10.11.69)	30	1·25
103	5 c. multicoloured (29.12.68)	15	10
	a. Glazed unsurfaced paper (16.12.70)	2·75	3·00
	b. Chalky paper. Perf 13 (27.6.73)	2·75	2·75
104	6 c. black, lemon and orange (1.12.68)	15	30
105	10 c. multicoloured (29.12.68)	10	10
	a. Glazed unsurfaced paper (16.12.70)	3·00	2·50
	b. Chalky paper. Perf 13 (12.9.73)	2·75	2·25
106	15 c. multicoloured (29.12.68)	30	10
107	20 c. multicoloured (1.12.68)	15	15
	a. Perf 13 (12.9.73)	2·75	3·50
108	25 c. multicoloured (29.12.68)	40	30
	a. Perf 13 (27.6.73)	3·25	4·25
109	30 c. multicoloured (1.12.68)	30	20
	a. Perf 13 (12.9.73)	3·25	4·25
110	50 c. blk, orge-red & lt yell-brown (1.12.68)	50	30
	a. Perf 13 (12.9.73)	4·00	6·00
111	75 c. multicoloured (1.12.68)	80	45
112	$1 multicoloured (29.12.68)	1·50	45
	a. Perf 13 (12.9.73)	6·50	8·50
113	$2 multicoloured (10.11.69)	3·50	90
114	$5 multicoloured (10.11.69)	9·00	2·00
115	$10 multicoloured (6.12.69)	30·00	9·50
101/15	*Set of* 15	42·00	15·00
103b/12a	*Set of* 7	23·00	29·00

Designs: *Vert* (*as T* 45)—6 c. Lion dance; 10 c. Bharatha Natyam; 15 c. Tari Payong; 20 c. Kathak Kali; 25 c. Lu Chih Shen and Lin Chung; 50 c. Tari Lilin; 75 c. Tarian Kuda Kepang; $1 Yao Chi. (*As T* 44)—$2, Rebab; $10 Ta Ku. *Horiz* (*as T* 43)—$5 Vina.

58 E.C.A.F.E. Emblem

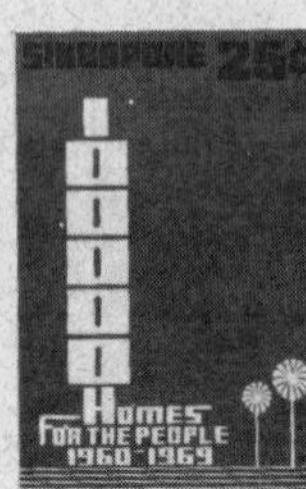

59 "100000" and Slogan as Block of Flats

(Des Eng Siak Loy. Photo Japanese Govt Ptg Bureau, Tokyo)

1969 (15 Apr). *25th Plenary Session of the U.N. Economic Commission for Asia and the Far East. P* 13.

No.	Type	Description		
116	58	15 c. black, silver and pale blue	35	15
117		30 c. black, silver and red	70	80
118		75 c. black, silver and violet-blue	1·25	1·50
116/18		*Set of* 3	2·00	2·25

(Des Tay Siew Chiah. Litho B.W.)

1969 (20 July). *Completion of "100,000 Homes for the People" Project. P* 13½.

No.	Type	Description		
119	59	25 c. black and emerald	70	50
120		50 c. black and deep blue	90	1·00

60 Aircraft over Silhouette of Singapore Docks

61 Sea Shells

(Des Eng Siak Loy and Han Kuan Cheng. Litho B.W.)

1969 (9 Aug). *150th Anniv of Founding of Singapore. T* 60 *and similar vert designs. P* 14 × 14½.

No.	Description		
121	15 c. black, vermilion and yellow	1·00	20
122	30 c. black, blue and new blue	1·50	60
123	75 c. multicoloured	3·00	2·00
124	$1 black and vermilion	3·50	3·00
125	$5 vermilion and black	35·00	45·00
126	$10 black and bright green	48·00	48·00
121/6	*Set of* 6	80·00	90·00
MS127	120 × 120 mm. Nos. 121/6. P 13½	£325	£350

Designs:—30 c. U.N. emblem and outline of Singapore; 75 c. Flags and outline of Malaysian Federation; $1 Uplifted hands holding crescent and stars; $5 Tail of Japanese aircraft and search-light beams; $10 Bust from statue of Sir Stamford Raffles.

(Des Tay Siew Chiah (15 c.), Eng Siak Loy (others). Litho Rosenbaum Bros, Vienna)

1970 (15 Mar). *World Fair, Osaka. T* 61 *and similar vert designs. Multicoloured. P* 13½.

No.	Description		
128	15 c. Type 61	90	15
129	30 c. Tropical fish	1·75	90
130	75 c. Greater Flamingo and Helmeted Hornbill	4·75	3·75
131	$1 Orchid	4·75	6·00
128/31	*Set of* 4	11·00	9·75
MS132	94 × 154 mm. Nos. 128/31	20·00	21·00

OMNIBUS ISSUES

Details, together with prices for complete sets, of the various Omnibus issues from the 1935 Silver Jubilee series to date are included in a special section following Zululand at the end of the catalogue.

62 "Kindergarten"

63 Soldier charging

(Des Choy Weng Yang. Litho B.W.)

1970 (1 July). *Tenth Anniv of People's Association. T* 62 *an[d] similar square designs. P* 13½.

No.	Description		
133	15 c. agate and bright orange	50	1
134	50 c. ultramarine and yellow-orange	1·40	1·4
135	75 c. bright purple and black	2·25	2·7
133/5	*Set of* 3	3·75	3·7

Designs:—50 c. "Sport"; 75 c. "Culture".

(Des Choy Weng Yang. Litho Rosenbaum Bros, Vienna)

1970 (9 Aug). *National Day. T* 63 *and similar vert designs. Mul[ti]coloured. P* 13½.

No.	Description		
136	15 c. Type 63	70	
137	50 c. Soldier on assault course	2·75	2·
138	$1 Soldier jumping	3·75	4·
136/8	*Set of* 3	6·50	6·

64 Sprinters

(Des Choy Weng Yang. Photo Japanese Govt Ptg Bureau, Toky[o])

1970 (23 Aug). *Festival of Sports. T* 64 *and similar horiz desig[ns]. P* 13 × 13½.

No.	Description		
139	10 c. magenta, black and ultramarine	90	
	a. Horiz strip of 4. Nos. 139/42	4·50	
140	15 c. black, ultramarine and red-orange	1·25	1·
141	25 c. black, red-orange and bright green	1·40	1·
142	50 c. black, bright green and magenta	1·50	1·
139/42	*Set of* 4	4·50	5·

Designs:—15 c. Swimmers; 25 c. Tennis-players; 50 c. Racin[g] cars.

Nos. 139/42 were issued together *se-tenant* in horizontal strips [of] four within the sheet.

65 *Neptune Aquamarine* (freighter)

(Des W. Lee. Litho Rosenbaum Bros, Vienna)

1970 (1 Nov). *Singapore Shipping. T* 65 *and similar horiz design[s]. P* 12.

No.	Description		
143	15 c. multicoloured	1·10	
144	30 c. yellow-ochre and ultramarine	3·25	3·
145	75 c. yellow-ochre and vermilion	5·00	6·
143/5	*Set of* 3	8·50	8·

Designs:—30 c. Container berth; 75 c. Ship-building.

66 Country Names forming Circle

(Des W. Lee. Litho D.L.R.)

1971 (1 Jan). *Commonwealth Heads of Government Meeti[ng], Singapore. T* 66 *and similar horiz designs. Multicoloured. P* ($1) *or* 15 × 14½ (*others*).

No.	Description		
146	15 c. Type 66	60	
147	30 c. Flags in circle	1·10	
148	75 c. Commonwealth flags	2·50	2·
149	$1 Commonwealth flags linked to Singapore (63 × 61 *mm*)	3·00	3·
146/9	*Set of* 4	6·50	6·

Imperforate examples of Nos. 146/7 overprinted "Specime[n]" are from printer's sample sheets.

67 Bicycle Rickshaws

68 Chinese New Year

(Des Eng Siak Loy (15, 20 and 30 c.), W. Lee (others). Litho B.W.)

971 (4 Apr). *Visit A.S.E.A.N. Year (A.S.E.A.N. = Association of South East Asian Nations). T* **67** *and similar designs. P* 13 × 13½ (50, 75 *c.*) *or* 11½ (*others*).
.50 15 c. black, deep bluish violet and orange .. 40 25
.51 20 c. indigo, orange and turquoise-blue .. 55 40
.52 30 c. vermilion and deep maroon .. .. 80 1·00
.53 50 c. multicoloured .. .. 2·75 4·00
.54 75 c. multicoloured .. .. 3·50 6·00
.50/4 .. .. *Set of* 5 7·00 10·50
Designs: *As T* **67**—20 c. Houseboat "village" and sampans; 0 c. Bazaar. *Horiz* (68 × 18 *mm*)—50 c. Modern harbour skyline; 5 c. Religious buildings.

(Des W. Lee. Litho Rosenbaum Bros, Vienna)

.971 (9 Aug). *Singapore Festivals. T* **68** *and similar vert designs. Multicoloured. P* 14.
.55 15 c. Type **68** 70 15
.56 30 c. Hari Raya .. .. 2·00 1·75
.57 50 c. Deepavali .. .. 2·75 3·25
.58 75 c. Christmas .. .. 3·25 4·00
.55/8 .. .. *Set of* 4 8·00 8·50
MS159 150 × 125 mm. Nos. 155/8 .. .. 35·00 30·00

69 "Dish" Aerial

(Des W. Lee. Litho B.W.)

971 (23 Oct). *Opening of Satellite Earth Station. P* 13½.
160 69 15 c. multicoloured .. .. .. 2·75 75
161 – 30 c. multicoloured .. .. .. 8·00 8·00
a. Block of 4. Nos. 161/4 .. .. 32·00
162 – 30 c. multicoloured .. .. .. 8·00 8·00
163 – 30 c. multicoloured .. .. .. 8·00 8·00
164 – 30 c. multicoloured .. .. .. 8·00 8·00
160/4 .. .. *Set of* 5 32·00 30·00
Designs:—Nos. 161/4 were printed in *se-tenant* blocks of four hroughout the sheet, the four stamps forming a composite design imilar to T **69**. They can be identified by the colour of the face value which is: yellow (No. 161), green (No. 162), magenta (No. 163) or orange (No. 164).

70 "Singapore River and Fort Canning, 1843–7" (Lieut. E. A. Porcher)

(Des W. Lee. Litho B.W.)

971 (5 Dec). *Art. T* **70** *and similar horiz designs. Multicoloured. P* 12½ × 13 (50 *c. and* $1) *or* 13 (*others*).
55 10 c. Type **70** .. .. 1·25 80
56 15 c. "The Padang, 1851" (J. T. Thomson) .. 2·00 1·50
57 20 c. "Singapore Waterfront, 1848–9" .. 2·50 1·90
58 35 c. "View from Fort Canning, 1846" (J. T. Thomson) .. .. 4·75 4·25
59 50 c. "View from Mt Wallich, 1857" (P. Carpenter) (69 × 47 *mm*) .. .. .. 7·00 7·00
70 $1 "Singapore Waterfront, 1861" (W. Gray) (69 × 47 *mm*) .. .. 10·00 13·00
55/70 .. .. *Set of* 6 25·00 25·00

ALTERED CATALOGUE NUMBERS

ny Catalogue numbers altered from the last dition are shown as a list in the introductory pages.

71 One Dollar of 1969

(Des W. Lee. Litho B.W.)

1972 (4 June). *Coins. T* **71** *and similar horiz designs. P* 13½.
171 15 c. orange, black and deep green 45 15
172 35 c. black and vermilion .. .. .. 1·00 1·25
173 $1 yellow, black and bright blue .. .. 3·25 4·25
171/3 .. .. *Set of* 3 4·25 5·00
Designs:—15 c. One-cent coin of George V; $1 One hundred and fifty dollar gold coin of 1969.

72 "Moon Festival" (Seah Kim Joo)

73 Lanterns and Fish

(Des W. Lee. Litho State Bank Note Printing Works, Helsinki)

1972 (9 July). *Contemporary Art. T* **72** *and similar multicoloured designs. P* 12½.
174 15 c. Type **72** 40 20
175 35 c. "Complimentary Forces" (Thomas Yeo) (36 × 54 *mm*) .. .. 1·25 1·50
176 50 c. "Rhythm in Blue" (Yusman Aman) (36 × 54 *mm*) .. .. 2·00 2·25
177 $1 "Gibbons" (Chen Wen Hsi) .. .. 3·75 4·75
174/7 .. .. *Set of* 4 6·75 8·00

(Des Eng Siak Loy. Litho State Bank Note Printing Works, Helsinki)

1972 (9 Aug). *National Day. T* **73** *and similar vert designs symbolising Festivals. Multicoloured. P* 12½.
178 15 c. Type **73** 45 15
179 35 c. Altar and candles .. .. .. 1·00 1·25
180 50 c. Jug, bowl and gifts .. .. .. 1·40 2·00
181 75 c. Candle .. .. 2·25 3·00
178/81 .. .. *Set of* 4 4·75 5·75

74 Student Welding

75 *Maria Rickmers*

(Des Eng Siak Loy. Photo Kultura, Budapest)

1972 (1 Oct). *Youth. T* **74** *and similar horiz designs. P* 12.
182 15 c. multicoloured 50 10
183 35 c. multicoloured .. .. 1·00 1·40
184 $1 red-orange, blue-violet & yellowish grn 3·00 4·50
182/4 .. .. *Set of* 3 4·00 5·50
Designs:—35 c. Sport; $1 Dancing.

(Des Choy Weng Yang (Nos. 185/7), Eng Siak Loy (**MS**188). Litho Harrison)

1972 (17 Dec). *Shipping. T* **75** *and similar multicoloured designs. P* 14 × 14½.
185 15 c. *Neptune Ruby* (container ship) (42 × 29 *mm*) 70 40
186 75 c. Type **75** .. .. 3·75 4·50
187 $1 Chinese junk .. .. 5·00 5·50
185/7 .. .. *Set of* 3 8·50 9·50
MS188 152 × 84 mm. Nos. 185/7 .. .. 16·00 22·00

76 P.Q.R. Slogan

77 Jurong Bird Park

(Des W. Lee. Litho B.W.)

1973 (25 Feb). *"Prosperity through Quality and Reliability" Campaign. T* **76** *and similar vert designs. P* 14.
189 **76** 15 c. multicoloured 40 15
190 – 35 c. multicoloured 85 75
191 – 75 c. multicoloured .. .. .. 1·40 2·00
192 – $1 multicoloured .. .. .. 1·75 2·75
189/92 .. .. *Set of* 4 4·00 5·00
Nos. 190/2 show various P.Q.R. emblems.

(Des Han Kuan Cheng. Litho Harrison)

1973 (29 Apr). *Singapore Landmarks. T* **77** *and similar vert designs. P* 12½.
193 15 c. black and red-orange 55 15
194 35 c. black and myrtle-green .. .. .. 1·00 1·00
195 50 c. black and red-brown .. .. .. 2·00 2·25
196 $1 black and purple .. .. 3·25 3·75
193/6 .. .. *Set of* 4 6·25 6·50
Designs:—35 c. National Theatre; 50 c. City Hall; $1 Fullerton Building and Singapore River.

78 Aircraft Tail-fins

79 "Culture"

(Des W. Lee. Litho B.W.)

1973 (24 June). *Aviation. T* **78** *and similar horiz designs. Multicoloured. P* 13½ × 13.
197 10 c. Type **78** 25 10
198 35 c. Emblem of Singapore Airlines and destinations 75 75
199 75 c. Emblem on tail-fin .. .. .. 1·40 1·60
200 $1 Emblems encircling the globe .. .. 2·00 2·25
197/200 .. .. *Set of* 4 4·00 4·25

(Des Eng Siak Loy. Litho Harrison)

1973 (9 Aug). *National Day. T* **79** *and similar vert designs. P* 13½.
201 **79** 10 c. orange and black .. .. .. 1·25 55
a. Block of 4. Nos. 201/4 .. .. 6·00
202 – 35 c. orange and black .. .. .. 1·50 1·25
203 – 50 c. orange and black .. .. .. 1·75 1·50
204 – 75 c. orange and black .. .. .. 2·00 1·75
201/4 .. .. *Set of* 4 6·00 4·50
Nos. 201/4 were printed in *se-tenant* blocks of four within the sheet, and form a composite design representing Singapore's culture.

80 Athletics, Judo and Boxing

81 Agave

82 Mangosteen

(Des C. Lim. Photo Heraclio Fournier)

1973 (1 Sept). *Seventh S.E.A.P.* Games. T* **80** *and similar designs. P* 14 (10 *to* 35 *c.*) *or* 13 × 14 (*others*).
205 10 c. gold, silver and indigo 25 20
206 15 c. gold and grey-black 50 30
207 25 c. gold, silver and black 65 65
208 35 c. gold, silver and deep blue .. .. 1·10 90
209 50 c. multicoloured .. .. 1·75 2·25
210 $1 silver, royal blue and yellow-green .. 3·25 5·00
205/10 .. .. *Set of* 6 7·00 8·50
MS211 130 × 111 mm. Nos. 205/10. P 13 × 14 .. 10·00 14·00
Designs: *As T* **80**—15 c. Cycling, weight-lifting, pistol-shooting and sailing; 25 c. Footballs; 35 c. Table-tennis bat, shuttlecock, tennis ball and hockey stick. *Horiz* (41 × 25 *mm*):—50 c. Swimmers; $1 Stadium.
*S.E.A.P. = South East Asian Peninsula.

(Des W. Lee (1 c. to 75 c.), Eng Siak Loy (others). Photo Heraclio Fournier)

1973. *Various multicoloured designs as T* **81/2**. *With fluorescent security markings.*

(*a*) *Stylized flowers and plants, size as T* **81**. *P* 13 (30.9.73)
212 1 c. Type **81** 20 30
213 5 c. *Coleus blumei* 10 15
a. Booklet pane. Nos. 213 × 4, 214 × 4, 216 × 2 *se-tenant* .. .. 2·50
214 10 c. *Vinca rosea* 15 10
215 15 c. *Helianthus angustifolius* 15 10
216 20 c. *Licuala grandis* 25 20
217 25 c. *Wedelia trilobata* 30 15
218 35 c. *Chrysanthemum frutescens* 50 40
219 50 c. *Costus malortieanus* 75 20
220 75 c. *Gerbera jamesonii* .. .. .. 1·75 45

(*b*) *Fruits, size as T* **82**. *P* 12½ × 13 (1.11.73)
221 $1 Type **82** .. .. 1·50 30
222 $2 Jackfruit .. .. 3·25 1·25
223 $5 Coconut .. .. 6·00 4·00
224 $10 Pineapple .. .. 12·00 14·00
212/24 .. .. *Set of* 13 24·00 19·00

83 Tiger and Orang-Utans

84 Multicolour Guppy

(Des Eng Siak Loy. Litho B.W.)

1973 (16 Dec). *Singapore Zoo. T* **83** *and similar vert designs. Multicoloured. P* 13.

No.	Description		
225	5 c. Type **83**	25	10
226	10 c. Leopard and Waterbuck	45	20
227	35 c. Leopard and Thamin	1·75	1·75
228	75 c. Horse and Lion	2·75	4·00
225/8	*Set of* 4	4·50	5·50

(Des Eng Siak Loy. Photo Heraclio Fournier)

1974 (21 Apr). *Tropical Fish. T* **84** *and similar vert designs. Multicoloured. P* 14.

No.	Description		
229	5 c. Type **84**	20	10
230	10 c. Half Black Guppy	40	15
231	35 c. Multicolour Guppy (*different*)	1·10	1·40
232	$1 Black Guppy	2·75	4·00
229/32	*Set of* 4	4·00	5·00

85 Scout Badge within "9"

86 U.P.U. Emblem and Multiple "Centenary"

(Des W. Lee. Litho Harrison)

1974 (9 June). *Ninth Asia-Pacific Scout Conference. P* 13½ × 14½.

No.	Description		
233 **85**	10 c. multicoloured	40	10
234	75 c. multicoloured	1·60	1·40

(Des W. Lee. Litho Harrison)

1974 (7 July). *Centenary of Universal Postal Union. T* **86** *and similar vert designs. P* 14 × 13½.

No.	Description		
235	10 c. orange-brown, purple-brown and gold	20	10
	a. Gold (U.P.U. symbol) omitted	£160	
236	35 c. new blue, deep blue and gold	55	75
237	75 c. multicoloured	1·25	2·25
235/7	*Set of* 3	1·75	2·75

Designs:—35 c. U.P.U. emblem and multiple U.N. symbols; 75 c. U.P.U. emblem and multiple peace doves.

87 Family Emblem

88 "Tree and Sun" (Chia Keng San)

(Des Eng Siak Loy. Litho B.W.)

1974 (9 Aug). *World Population Year. T* **87** *and similar horiz designs. Multicoloured. P* 12½ × 13½.

No.	Description		
238	10 c. Type **87**	20	10
239	35 c. Male and female symbols	80	90
	a. Emerald (male symbol) omitted	£250	
240	75 c. World population map	1·75	2·50
238/40	*Set of* 3	2·50	3·25

(Des Eng Siak Loy. Photo Heraclio Fournier)

1974 (1 Oct). *Universal Children's Day. T* **88** *and similar vert designs showing children's paintings. Multicoloured. P* 13½.

No.	Description		
241	5 c. Type **88**	20	10
242	10 c. "My Daddy and Mummy" (Angeline Ang)	35	10
243	35 c. "A Dump Truck" (Si-Hoe Yeen Joong)	1·75	2·00
244	50 c. "My Aunt" (Raymond Teo)	2·25	3·00
241/4	*Set of* 4	4·00	4·75
MS245	138 × 100 mm. Nos. 241/4. P 13	6·50	7·50

89 Street Scene

(Des Loy Chin. Litho Secura, Singapore)

1975 (26 Jan). *Singapore Views. T* **89** *and similar horiz designs. Multicoloured. P* 13½.

No.	Description		
246	15 c. Type **89**	45	10
247	20 c. Singapore River	60	70
248	$1 "Kelong" (fish-trap)	2·75	5·50
246/8	*Set of* 3	3·50	5·75

90 Emblem and Lighters' Prows

91 Satellite Earth Station, Sentosa

(Des Choy Weng Yang. Litho Secura, Singapore)

1975 (10 Mar). *Ninth Biennial Conference of International Association of Ports and Harbours, Singapore. T* **90** *and similar horiz designs. Multicoloured. P* 13½.

No.	Description		
249	5 c. Type **90**	15	10
250	25 c. Freighter and ship's wheel	70	70
251	50 c. Oil-tanker and flags	1·40	1·75
252	$1 Container-ship and propellers	2·25	4·00
249/52	*Set of* 4	4·00	6·00

(Des Sim Tong Khern. Photo Heraclio Fournier)

1975 (29 June). *"Science and Industry". T* **91** *and similar multicoloured designs. P* 13½.

No.	Description		
253	10 c. Type **91**	25	10
254	35 c. Oil refineries (*vert*)	75	1·00
255	75 c. "Medical Sciences"	1·50	2·50
253/5	*Set of* 3	2·25	3·25

92 "Homes and Gardens"

93 South African Crowned Cranes

(Des Tay Siew Chiah. Litho Secura, Singapore)

1975 (9 Aug). *Tenth National Day. T* **92** *and similar square designs. Multicoloured. P* 13½.

No.	Description		
256	10 c. Type **92**	20	10
257	35 c. "Shipping and Ship-building"	75	75
258	75 c. "Communications and Technology"	1·90	2·75
259	$1 "Trade, Commerce and Industry"	2·10	3·00
256/9	*Set of* 4	4·50	6·00

(Des Eng Siak Loy. Litho Harrison)

1975 (5 Oct). *Birds. T* **93** *and similar vert designs. Multicoloured. P* 14½ × 13½.

No.	Description		
260	5 c. Type **93**	70	15
261	10 c. Great Indian Hornbill	90	10
262	35 c. White-breasted Kingfisher and White-collared Kingfisher	3·50	2·75
263	$1 Sulphur-crested Cockatoo and Blue and Yellow Macaw	9·50	11·00
260/3	*Set of* 4	13·00	12·50

94 "Equality"

95 Yellow Flame

(Des Tay Siew Chiah. Litho Secura, Singapore)

1975 (7 Dec). *International Women's Year. T* **94** *and similar square designs. Multicoloured. P* 13½.

No.	Description		
264	10 c. Type **94**	25	10
265	35 c. "Development"	1·50	1·50
266	75 c. "Peace"	2·75	4·00
264/6	*Set of* 3	4·00	5·00
MS267	128 × 100 mm. Nos. 264/6	4·50	5·00

(Des Tay Siew Chiah. Litho Secura, Singapore)

1976 (18 Apr). *Wayside Trees. T* **95** *and similar vert designs. Multicoloured. P* 13½.

No.	Description		
268	10 c. Type **95**	40	10
269	35 c. Cabbage Tree	1·00	1·00
270	50 c. Rose of India	1·75	2·00
271	75 c. Variegated Coral Tree	2·00	3·50
268/71	*Set of* 4	4·50	6·00

96 *Arachnis hookeriana* × *Vanda* Hilo Blue

97 Festival Symbol and Band

(Des Eng Siak Loy. Litho Secura, Singapore)

1976 (20 June). *Singapore Orchids. T* **96** *and similar vert designs. Multicoloured. P* 13½.

No.	Description		
272	10 c. Type **96**	45	1
273	35 c. *Arachnis Maggie Oei* × *Vanda insignis*	1·25	1·0
274	50 c. *Arachnis Maggie Oei* × *Vandu* Rodman	2·25	2·5
275	75 c. *Arachnis hookeriana* × *Vanda* Dawn Nishimura	2·75	4·5
272/5	*Set of* 4	6·00	7·0

(Des Han Kuan Cheng. Litho Harrison)

1976 (9 Aug). *Tenth Anniv of Singapore Youth Festival. Hori designs showing festival symbol as T* **97**. *Multicoloured. P* 12½.

No.	Description		
276	10 c. Type **97**	20	1
277	35 c. Athletes	60	6
278	75 c. Dancers	1·40	1·4
276/8	*Set of* 3	2·00	1·9

98 "Queen Elizabeth Walk"

(Des H. Weepaul. Litho Secura, Singapore)

1976 (14 Nov). *Paintings of Old Singapore, circa* 1905–10, *b A. L. Watson. T* **98** *and similar horiz designs. Multicoloured With fluorescent security markings. P* 14.

No.	Description		
279	10 c. Type **98**	30	1
280	50 c. "The Padang"	1·75	1·7
281	$1 "Raffles Place"	3·25	3·5
279/81	*Set of* 3	4·75	4·7
MS282	164 × 91 mm. Nos. 279/81. P 13½	7·00	8·5

99 Chinese Costume

100 Radar, Missile and Soldiers

(Des Margaret Heng. Litho Harrison)

1976 (19 Dec). *Bridal Costumes. T* **99** *and similar vert designs Multicoloured. P* 14.

No.	Description		
283	10 c. Type **99**	25	1
284	35 c. Indian costume	1·00	1·0
285	75 c. Malay costume	1·75	2·0
283/5	*Set of* 3	2·75	2·7

(Des Eng Siak Loy. Litho Harrison)

1977 (12 Mar). *Tenth Anniv of National Service. T* **100** *an similar vert designs. Multicoloured. P* 14.

No.	Description		
286	10 c. Type **100**	30	1
287	50 c. Tank and soldiers	1·25	9
288	75 c. Soldiers, wireless operators, pilot and aircraft	2·00	1·7
286/9	*Set of* 3	3·25	2·4

101 Lyrate Cockle

102 Spotted Hermit Crab

(Des Tay Siew Chiah. Litho Secura, Singapore)

1977. *Multicoloured designs as T* **101/2**. *With fluorescent securi markings. P* 13. (*a*) *Shells as T* **101** (9.4.77).

No.	Description		
289	1 c. Type **101**	15	3
290	5 c. Folded Scallop	10	
	a. Booklet pane. Nos. 290 × 4 and 291 × 8 *se-tenant*	1·75	

291 10 c. Marble Cone 15 10
a. Imperf (pair) £300
292 15 c. Scorpion Conch 40 10
293 20 c. Amplustre Bubble 50 10
294 25 c. Spiral Babylon 60 10
295 35 c. Regal Thorny Oyster 80 40
296 50 c. Winged Frog Shell .. .. .. 1·00 10
297 75 c. Troschel's Murex .. .. 1·25 15

(b) *Fish and Crustaceans as T* **102** (4.6.77)

298 $1 Type **102** .. .. 1·50 15
299 $2 Stingray .. .. 1·75 50
300 $5 Cuttlefish .. .. 3·50 2·25
301 $10 Lionfish .. .. 7·50 5·50
289/301 .. .. *Set of* 13 17·00 8·50

103 Shipbuilding

104 Keyhole and Banknotes

(Des W. Lee. Litho Secura, Singapore)

1977 (1 May). *Labour Day. T* **103** *and similar horiz designs. Multicoloured. P* 13 × 12½.
302 10 c. Type **103** 15 10
303 50 c. Building construction 75 60
304 75 c. Road construction .. .. .. 1·00 1·00
302/4 .. .. *Set of* 3 1·75 1·75

(Des Tay Siew Chiah. Litho Secura, Singapore)

1977 (16 July). *Centenary of Post Office Savings Bank. T* **104** *and similar vert designs. Multicoloured. P* 13.
305 10 c. Type **104** 15 10
306 35 c. On-line banking service 60 50
307 75 c. GIRO service .. .. 1·25 1·25
305/7 .. .. *Set of* 3 1·75 1·60

105 Flags of Member Nations

106 "Chingay Procession" (Liang Yik Yin)

(Des Eng Siak Loy. Litho Secura, Singapore)

1977 (8 Aug). *Tenth Anniv of A.S.E.A.N. (Association of South-East Asian Nations). T* **105** *and similar vert designs. Multicoloured. P* 14.
308 10 c. Type **105** 15 10
309 35 c. "Agriculture" 60 50
310 75 c. "Industry" .. .. 1·25 1·10
308/10 .. .. *Set of* 3 1·75 1·50

(Des H. Weepaul. Litho Secura, Singapore)

1977 (1 Oct). *Children's Art. T* **106** *and similar horiz designs. Multicoloured. P* 12½.
311 10 c. Type **106** 20 10
312 35 c. "At the Bus Stop" (Chong Khing Ann) .. 75 50
313 75 c. "Playground" (Yap Li Hwa) .. .. 1·60 1·40
311/13 .. .. *Set of* 3 2·25 1·75
MS314 160 × 97 mm. Nos. 311/13 .. .. .. 3·25 3·50

107 "Life Sciences"

108 Botanical Gardens and Esplanade, Jurong Bird Park

(Des Tay Siew Chiah. Litho Format)

1977 (10 Dec). *Singapore Science Centre. T* **107** *and similar vert designs. Multicoloured. P* 14.
315 10 c. Type **107** 10 10
316 35 c. "Physical sciences" 45 30
a. Deep green and brown omitted .. £150
317 75 c. "Science and technology" .. .. 1·00 85
318 $1 Singapore Science Centre .. .. 1·25 1·00
315/18 .. .. *Set of* 4 2·50 2·00

(Des C. Kiat. Litho Harrison)

1978 (22 Apr). *Parks and Gardens. T* **108** *and similar multi-coloured designs. P* 14½.
319 10 c. Type **108** 15 10
320 35 c. Lagoon, East Coast Park (*vert*) 45 30
321 75 c. Botanical Gardens (*vert*) 75 50
319/21 .. .. *Set of* 3 1·25 75

109 Red-whiskered Bulbul

111 Map of South East Asia showing Cable Network

110 Thian Hock Keng Temple

(Des Eng Siak Loy. Litho Secura, Singapore)

1978 (1 July). *Singing Birds. T* **109** *and similar vert designs. Multicoloured. P* 13½.
322 10 c. Type **109** 35 10
323 35 c. Oriental White Eye 85 45
324 50 c. White-rumped Shama .. .. .. 1·10 75
325 75 c. White-crested Laughing Thrush and Huamei .. .. 1·50 1·40
322/5 .. .. *Set of* 4 3·50 2·40

(Des Eng Siak Loy. Litho Secura, Singapore)

1978 (9 Aug). *National Monuments. T* **110** *and similar horiz designs. Multicoloured. P* 13½.
326 10 c. Type **110** 15 15
327 10 c. Hajjah Fatimah Mosque 15 15
328 10 c. Armenian Church 15 15
329 10 c. Sri Mariamman Temple 15 15
326/9 .. .. *Set of* 4 55 55
MS330 173 × 86 mm. 35 c. × 4, as Nos. 326/9 .. 2·75 2·75
Stamps from No. **MS**330 are similar in design to Nos. 326/9 but have no borders and the inscriptions are slightly larger.

(Des J. Heng. Litho Secura, Singapore)

1978 (3 Oct). *A.S.E.A.N. (Association of South East Asian Nations) Submarine Cable Network (1st issue). Completion of Philippines–Singapore section. P* 13½ *(around design as well as stamp).*
331 **111** 10 c. multicoloured 10 10
332 35 c. multicoloured 40 40
333 50 c. multicoloured 50 50
334 75 c. multicoloured .. .. .. 80 1·00
331/4 .. .. *Set of* 4 1·60 1·75
See also Nos. 385/8 and 458/62.

112 *Neptune Spinel* (bulk carrier)

(Des Paul Wee Hui Hong. Litho Secura, Singapore)

1978 (18 Nov). *10th Anniv of Neptune Orient Shipping Lines. T* **112** *and similar horiz designs. Multicoloured. P* 13½.
335 10 c. Type **112** 15 10
336 35 c. *Neptune Aries* (tanker) 40 50
337 50 c. *Anro Temasek* (container ship) 45 75
338 75 c. *Neptune Pearl* (container ship) .. .. 80 1·40
335/8 .. .. *Set of* 4 1·60 2·50

113 "Concorde"

114 10 Kilometre Marker

(Des Paul Wee Hui Hong. Litho Secura, Singapore)

1978 (16 Dec). *Aviation. T* **113** *and similar horiz designs. Multicoloured. P* 13.
339 10 c. Type **113** 35 15
340 35 c. Boeing "747B" 50 30
341 50 c. Vickers "Vimy" 70 80
342 75 c. Wright Brothers' *Flyer* 1 .. .. .. 80 1·60
339/42 .. .. *Set of* 4 2·10 2·50

(Des W. Lee. Litho Secura, Singapore)

1979 (24 Feb). *Metrication. T* **114** *and similar vert designs. Multicoloured. P* 13½.
343 10 c. Type **114** 10 10
344 35 c. Tape measure 20 20
345 75 c. Weighing scales 45 45
343/5 .. .. *Set of* 3 65 65

115 Vanda Hybrid

116 Envelope with new Singapore Postcode

(Des Paul Wee Hui Hong. Litho Harrison)

1979 (14 Apr). *Orchids. T* **115** *and similar designs showing different varieties of Vanda Hybrid. P* 14½ × 14 *(10, 35 c.) or* 14 × 14½ *(others).*
346 10 c. multicoloured 15 10
347 35 c. multicoloured 35 20
348 50 c. multicoloured (*vert*) 50 30
349 75 c. multicoloured (*vert*) 70 45
346/9 .. .. *Set of* 4 1·50 90

(Des Paul Wee Hui Hong. Litho Secura, Singapore)

1979 (1 July). *Postal Code Publicity. P* 13.
350 **116** 10 c. multicoloured 10 10
351 – 50 c. multicoloured 30 35
The 50 c. design is as Type **116**, but the envelope is addressed to the Philatelic Bureau, General Post Office and has the postcode "Singapore 0104".

117 Early Telephone and Overhead Cables

118 "Lantern Festival" (Eng Chun-Ngan)

(Des Eng Siak Loy. Litho J.W.)

1979 (5 Oct). *Centenary of Telephone Service. T* **117** *and similar horiz designs. P* 13.
352 10 c. yellow-brown and new blue 10 10
353 35 c. bright orange, blue and reddish violet .. 20 25
354 50 c. blue, dp turquoise-grn & yellowish grn .. 35 35
355 75 c. yellowish green and bright orange .. 50 70
352/5 .. .. *Set of* 4 1·00 1·25
Designs:—35 c. Telephone dial and world map; 50 c. Modern telephone and city scene; 75 c. Latest computerised telephone and circuit diagram.

(Des Han Kuan Cheng. Litho Secura, Singapore)

1979 (10 Nov). *International Year of the Child. Children's Drawings. T* **118** *and similar horiz designs. Multicoloured. P* 12½ × 13.
356 10 c. Type **118** 10 10
357 35 c. "Singapore Harbour" (Wong Chien Chien) 30 30
358 50 c. "Use Your Hands" (Leong Choy Yeen) .. 40 45
359 75 c. "Soccer" (Tan Cheong Hin) 60 75
356/9 .. .. *Set of* 4 1·25 1·40
MS360 154 × 98 mm. Nos. 356/9 .. .. .. 1·60 1·75

119 View of Gardens

120 Hainan Junk

(Des Eng Siak Loy. Litho Secura, Singapore)

1979 (15 Dec). *120th Anniv of Botanic Gardens. T* **119** *and similar horiz designs showing different views of the gardens. P* 13 × 13½.
361 10 c. multicoloured 15 10
a. Imperf (pair) £375
362 50 c. multicoloured 60 75
363 $1 multicoloured .. .. 1·10 1·75
361/3 .. .. *Set of* 3 1·75 2·25

(Des Eng Siak Loy. Litho J.W.)

1980 (5 Apr)–**84**. *Ships. Multicoloured designs as T* **120**. *Ordinary paper (1 c., 10 c.), phosphorised paper ($1 to $10) and ordinary or phosphorised paper (others). P* 14 *(1 to 75 c.) or* 13½ *($1 to $10).*
364 1 c. Type **120** (26.4.80) 20 30
365 5 c. Clipper (26.4.80) 10 15
366 10 c. Fujian junk (26.4.80) 10 10
p. One narrow (4 mm) phosphor band (12.81) 45 10
pa. One wide (10 mm) phosphor band (2.84) 70 20
367 15 c. Golekkan (26.4.80) 15 10
368 20 c. Palari schooner (26.4.80) 20 15
369 25 c. East Indiaman (26.4.80) 25 15
370 35 c. Galleon (26.4.80) 30 15
371 50 c. Caravel (26.4.80) 50 25
372 75 c. Jiangsu trading junk (26.4.80) .. 55 45
373 $1 *Kedah* (coaster) (42 × 25 *mm*) 70 45
a. Imperf (pair) £275
374 $2 *Murex* (oil tanker) (42 × 25 *mm*) .. 1·25 90
375 $5 *Chusan* (screw steamer) (42 × 25 *mm*) .. 3·00 3·00
376 $10 *Braganza* (paddle-steamer) (42 × 25 *mm*) 6·00 6·00
364/76 .. .. *Set of* 13 12·00 11·00

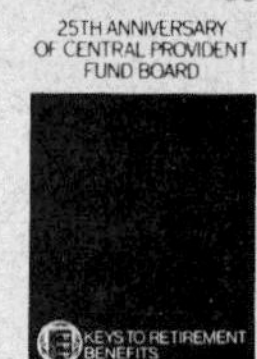

121 Straits Settlements 1867 1½ c. Stamp and Map of Singapore, 1843

122 C.P.F. Emblem and "Keys to Retirement Benefits"

(Des Paul Wee Hui Hong. Litho Secura, Singapore)

1980 (6 May). *"London 1980" International Stamp Exhibition. T* **121** *and similar vert designs. Multicoloured. P* 13.

377	10 c. Type **121** ..	..	20	10
378	35 c. Straits Settlements 1906 $500 stamp and treaty between Johore and British Colony of Singapore	..	35	25
379	$1 1948 $2 stamp and map of Malaysia	..	70	90
380	$2 1969 150th Anniversary of Singapore $10 commemorative and letter to Col. Addenbrooke from Sir Stamford Raffles	..	1·25	2·00
377/80	..	*Set of* 4	2·25	3·00
MS381	148 × 104 mm. Nos. 377/80	..	3·00	3·75

(Des Paul Wee Hui Hong. Litho Secura, Singapore)

1980 (1 July). *25th Anniv of Central Provident Fund Board. T* **122** *and similar vert designs showing C.P.F. emblem. Multicoloured. P* 13 × 12½.

382	10 c. Type **122** ..	..	10	10
383	50 c. "C.P.F. savings for home ownership"	..	40	25
384	$1 "C.P.F. savings for old-age"	..	75	70
382/4	..	*Set of* 3	1·10	90

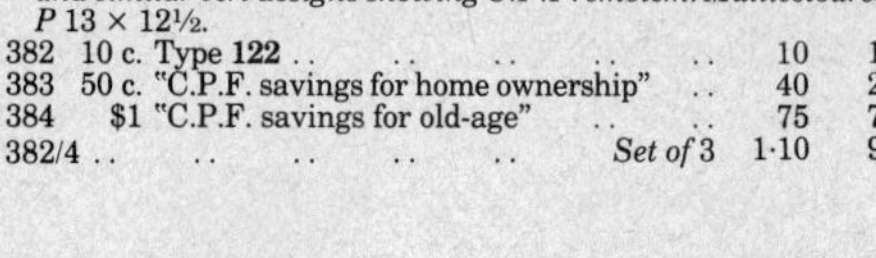

123 Map of South East Asia showing Cable Network

124 A.S.E.A.N. Trade Fair Emblem

(Des J. Heng. Litho Secura, Singapore)

1980 (8 Aug). *A.S.E.A.N. (Association of South East Asian Nations) Submarine Cable Network (2nd issue). Completion of Indonesia–Singapore Section. P* 13½ *(around design as well as stamp).*

385	**123**	10 c. multicoloured	..	10	10
386		35 c. multicoloured	..	40	20
387		50 c. multicoloured	..	50	30
388		75 c. multicoloured	..	65	75
385/8		..	*Set of* 4	1·50	1·10

(Des Paul Wee Hui Hong. Litho Secura, Singapore)

1980 (3 Oct). *A.S.E.A.N. (Association of South East Asian Nations) Trade Fair. P* 12½ × 13.

389	**124**	10 c. multicoloured	..	10	10
390		35 c. multicoloured	..	30	20
391		75 c. multicoloured	..	60	80
389/91		..	*Set of* 3	85	1·00

125 Ixora

126 International Currency Symbols

(Des S. Tan and Chua Ban Har. Litho J.W.)

1980 (8 Nov). *National Tree Planting Day. Flowers. T* **125** *and similar horiz designs. Multicoloured. P* 13½ × 13.

392	10 c. Type **125** ..	..	10	10
393	35 c. Allamanda	..	40	25
394	50 c. Sky Vine ..	..	50	35
395	75 c. Bougainvillea	..	60	65
392/5	..	*Set of* 4	1·40	1·10

(Des Paul Wee Hui Hong. Litho Secura, Singapore)

1981 (24 Jan). *10th Anniv of Monetary Authority of Singapore. P* 14.

396	**126**	10 c. black, vermilion & greenish yellow		10	10
397		35 c. multicoloured	..	30	20
398		75 c. multicoloured	..	55	60
396/8		..	*Set of* 3	80	75

(127)

128 Woodwork

1981 (4 Mar). *No. 65 surch with T* **127**.

399	**21**	10 c. on 4 c. black and orange-red	..	10	20

(Des Sng Tong Beng. Litho J.W.)

1981 (11 Apr). *Technical Training. T* **128** *and similar vert designs. Multicoloured. P* 13 × 13½.

400	10 c. Type **128** ..	..	10	10
401	35 c. Building construction	..	25	20
402	50 c. Electronics	..	40	30
403	75 c. Precision machining	..	50	60
400/3	..	*Set of* 4	1·10	1·00

129 Figures representing various Sports

130 "The Rights to Environmental Aids"

(Des Lim Ching San. Litho J.W.)

1981 (25 Aug). *"Sports for All". T* **129** *and similar vert designs showing figures representing various sports. P* 14.

404	10 c. multicoloured	..	10	10
405	75 c. multicoloured	..	90	90
406	$1 multicoloured	..	1·25	1·50
404/6	..	*Set of* 3	2·00	2·25

(Des Chua Ban Har. Litho Harrison)

1981 (24 Nov). *International Year for Disabled Persons. T* **130** *and similar vert designs. Multicoloured. One centre phosphor band (10 c.) or phosphorised paper (others). P* 14½.

407	10 c. Type **130** ..	..	10	10
408	35 c. "The right to social integration" ..	..	40	20
409	50 c. "The right to education" ..	..	60	35
410	75 c. "The right to work"	..	80	70
407/10	..	*Set of* 4	1·75	1·10

Nos. 407/10 were printed with phosphor bands or on phosphorised paper similar to that used on contemporary Great Britain issues.

131 Control Tower and Passenger Terminal Building, Changi Airport

132 Clipper

(Des J. Heng. Litho Secura, Singapore Ltd)

1981 (29 Dec). *Opening of Changi Airport. P* 14 × 13½.

411	**131**	10 c. multicoloured	..	10	10
412		35 c. multicoloured	..	35	20
413		50 c. multicoloured	..	45	30
414		75 c. multicoloured	..	70	50
415		$1 multicoloured	..	80	75
411/15		..	*Set of* 5	2·25	1·60
MS416		154 × 105 mm. Nos. 411/15	..	2·25	3·50

The five values show different background emblems representing the Parks and Recreation Dept, Public Works Dept, Telecommunications Authority, Port of Singapore and Dept of Civil Aviation.

(Des Eng Siak Loy. Litho J.W.)

1982 (3 Mar). *Butterflies. T* **132** *and similar horiz designs. Multicoloured. One centre phosphor band (10 c.) or phosphorised paper (others). P* 14½.

417	10 c. Type **132** ..	..	15	10
418	50 c. Blue Glassy Tiger	..	60	40
419	$1 Raja Brooke's Birdwing ..	..	90	1·25
417/19	..	*Set of* 3	1·50	1·50

133 A.S.E.A.N. Emblem

134 Football and Stylised Player

(Des Paul Wee Hui Hong. Litho Secura, Singapore)

1982 (14 June). *15th Anniv of A.S.E.A.N. (Association of Sou[th] East Asian Nations). One centre phosphor band (10 c.) or pho[s]phorised paper (others). P* 14½ × 14.

420	**133**	10 c. multicoloured	..	10	
421		35 c. multicoloured	..	25	
422	–	50 c. multicoloured	..	35	
423	–	75 c. multicoloured	..	50	
420/3		..	*Set of* 4	1·00	1·1

The 50 and 75 c. values are as Type **133**, but are inscribed "15[th] ASEAN Ministerial Meeting".

(Des Paul Wee Hui Hong. Litho Secura, Singapore)

1982 (9 July). *World Cup Football Championship, Spain. T* **13**[4] *and similar vert designs. One centre phosphor band (10 c.) [or] phosphorised paper (others). P* 12.

424	10 c. black, bright blue and greenish blue	..	15	
425	75 c. multicoloured	..	65	6
426	$1 multicoloured	..	85	9
424/6	..	*Set of* 3	1·50	1·4

Designs:—75 c. Football and World Cup, Asian Zone Fo[otball] emblem; $1 Football and globe.

135 Sultan Shoal Lighthouse, 1896

136 Yard Gantry Cranes

(Des Eng Siak Loy. Litho Secura, Singapore)

1982 (7 Aug). *Lighthouses of Singapore. T* **135** *and similar hor[iz] designs. Multicoloured. One centre phosphor band (10 c.) or pho[s]phorised paper (others). P* 12.

427	10 c. Type **135** ..	..	10	
428	75 c. Horsburgh Lighthouse, 1855	..	55	6
429	$1 Raffles Lighthouse, 1855	..	75	1·2
427/9	..	*Set of* 3	1·25	1·7
MS430	148 × 104 mm. Nos. 427/9	..	1·75	2·2

No. **MS**430 was printed on plain paper without phosphor.

(Des Goh Seng Lim. Litho Secura, Singapore)

1982 (15 Sept). *10th Anniv of Container Terminal. T* **136** *an[d] similar horiz designs. Multicoloured. One centre phosphor ban[d] (10 c.) or phosphorised paper (others). P* 13½.

431	10 c. Type **136** ..	..	10	
432	35 c. Computer	..	20	2
433	50 c. Freightlifter	..	30	3
434	75 c. Straddle carrier ..	..	45	5
431/4	..	*Set of* 4	90	1·(

137 Scouts on Parade

138 Productivity Movement Slogans

(Des Poh Siew Wah. Litho Secura, Singapore)

1982 (15 Oct). *75th Anniv of Boy Scout Movement. T* **137** *an[d] similar vert designs. Multicoloured. One centre phosphor ban[d] (10 c.) or phosphorised paper (others). P* 14 × 13.

435	10 c. Type **137** ..	..	15	
436	35 c. Scouts hiking	..	45	2
437	50 c. Scouts building tower	..	65	3
438	75 c. Scouts canoeing ..	..	95	8
435/8	..	*Set of* 4	2·00	1·2

(Des M. Gan. Litho Secura, Singapore)

1982 (17 Nov). *Productivity Movement. T* **138** *and simila[r] diamond-shaped designs. One centre phosphor band (10 c.) o[r] phosphorised paper (others). P* 13½.

439	10 c. orange and emerald	..	10	1
440	35 c. yellow-ochre and deep dull blue ..	..	35	3
441	50 c. maroon, bistre-yellow and brownish grey		55	4
442	75 c. maroon and lemon	..	75	6
439/42	..	*Set of* 4	1·60	1·2

Designs:—35 c. Family and housing ("Benefits of Productivity") 50 c. Works meeting ("Quality Control Circles"); 75 c. Aspects o[f] Singapore business ("Everybody's Business").

139 Commonwealth Logo and Country Names

140 Soccer

(Des Eng Siak Loy. Litho Secura, Singapore)

1983 (14 Mar). *Commonwealth Day. One centre phosphor band (10 c.) or phosphorised paper (others). P* 13 × 13½.
443 **139** 10 c. multicoloured 10 10
444 35 c. multicoloured 20 25
445 75 c. multicoloured 45 50
446 $1 multicoloured 65 70
443/6 .. .. *Set of* 4 1·25 1·40

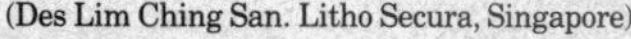

(Des Lim Ching San. Litho Secura, Singapore)

1983 (28 May). *12th South-East Asia Games. T* **140** *and similar vert designs. Multicoloured. One centre phosphor band (10 c.) or phosphorised paper (others). P* 13½ × 13.
447 10 c. Type **140** 10 10
448 35 c. Racket games 20 25
449 75 c. Athletics 45 50
450 $1 Swimming 65 70
447/50 .. .. *Set of* 4 1·25 1·40

141 Policeman and Family

142 1977 ASEAN Stamps and Statue of King Chulalongkorn

(Des Lim Ching San. Litho J.W.)

983 (24 June). *Neighbourhood Watch Scheme. T* **141** *and similar horiz designs. Multicoloured. One wide centre phosphor band (10 c.) or phosphorised paper (others). P* 13½ × 14.
51 10 c. Type **141** 15 10
52 35 c. Policeman and children 45 30
53 75 c. Policeman and inhabitants with linked arms 80 70
51/3 .. .. *Set of* 3 1·25 95

(Des Sylvia Tan and Ko Hui-Huy. Litho J.W.)

983 (4 Aug). *Bangkok International Stamp Exhibition. T* **142** *and similar vert designs. Multicoloured. One wide centre phosphor band (10 c.), phosphorised paper (35 c., $1) or ordinary paper (miniature sheet). P* 14.
54 10 c. Type **142** 10 10
55 35 c. 1980 ASEAN stamps and map of South-East Asia 25 25
56 $1 1982 ASEAN stamps and signatures of Heads of State 65 65
54/6 .. .. *Set of* 3 85 85
IS457 147 × 104 mm. Nos. 454/6 .. .. 1·75 2·25

143 Map of South-East Asia showing Cable Network

(Des J. Heng. Litho Secura, Singapore)

983 (27 Sept). *A.S.E.A.N. (Association of South-East Asian Nations) Submarine Cable Network (3rd issue). Completion of Malaysia-Singapore-Thailand section. One centre phosphor band (10 c.), phosphorised paper (35 c. to 75 c.) or ordinary paper (miniature sheet). P* 13½ *(around design as well as stamp).*
58 **143** 10 c. multicoloured 10 10
59 35 c. multicoloured 20 25
60 50 c. multicoloured 35 35
61 75 c. multicoloured 45 50
58/61 .. .. *Set of* 4 90 1·00
IS462 146 × 100 mm. Nos. 331, 388, 458/61 .. 1·60 2·25

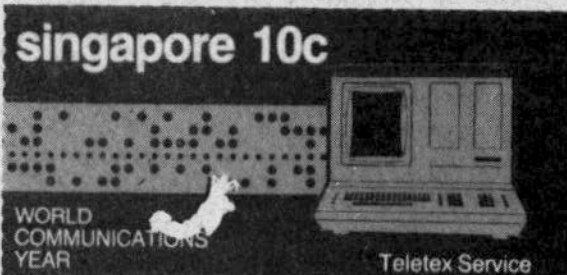

144 Teletex Service

(Des Sylvia Tan and Ko Hui-Huy. Litho Enschedé)

1983 (10 Nov). *World Communications Year. T* **144** *and similar horiz designs. Phosphorised paper. P* 12½ × 13.
463 10 c. greenish yellow, light emerald and black 10 10
464 35 c. greenish yellow, brt rose-red & chocolate 20 25
465 75 c. bright yellow-green, greenish blue and deep violet-blue 45 50
466 $1 greenish yell, olive-brn & brownish blk 50 55
463/6 .. .. *Set of* 4 1·10 1·25
Designs:—35 c. World telephone numbering plan; 75 c. Satellite transmission; $1 Sea communications.

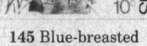

145 Blue-breasted Banded Rail

146 House of Tan Yeok Nee

(Des Poh Siew Wah. Litho Harrison)

1984 (15 Mar). *Coastal Birds. T* **145** *and similar horiz designs. Multicoloured. One wide centre phosphor band (10 c.) or phosphorised paper (others). P* 14½ × 13½.
467 10 c. Type **145** 25 10
468 35 c. Black Bittern 60 40
469 50 c. Brahminy Kite 75 50
470 75 c. Moorhen .. .. 1·00 85
467/70 .. .. *Set of* 4 2·40 1·60

(Des Poh Siew Wah. Litho Secura, Singapore)

1984 (7 June). *National Monuments. T* **146** *and similar vert designs. Multicoloured. One centre phosphor band (10 c.) or phosphorised paper (others). P* 12.
471 10 c. Type **146** 10 10
472 35 c. Thong Chai building 30 35
473 50 c. Telok Ayer market 40 45
474 $1 Nagore Durgha shrine .. .. .. 80 1·10
471/4 .. .. *Set of* 4 1·40 1·75

147 1970 $1 National Day Stamp

148 Schoolchildren

(Des P. Hong. Litho Secura, Singapore)

1984 (9 Aug–23 Nov). *"25 Years of Nation Building." T* **147** *and similar vert designs showing various Singapore stamps. Multicoloured. One centre phosphor band (10 c.) or phosphorised paper (others). P* 14 × 14½.
475 10 c. Type **147** 10 10
476 35 c. 1981 $1 "Sports for All" stamp 30 35
477 50 c. 1969 25 c. "100,000 Homes for the People" stamp 40 55
478 75 c. 1976 10 c. Wayside Trees stamp 60 75
479 $1 1981 $1 Opening of Changi Airport stamp 80 1·00
480 $2 1981 10 c. Monetary Authority stamp .. 1·75 2·25
475/80 .. .. *Set of* 6 3·50 4·50
MS481 132 × 106 mm. Nos. 475/80. P 12½ (23 Nov) 4·50 4·75
No. **MS**481 is on ordinary paper without a phosphor band on the 10 c. stamp.

(Des Lim Ching San. Litho Secura, Singapore)

1984 (26 Oct). *"Total Defence". T* **148** *and similar vert designs. One centre phosphor band. P* 12.
482 10 c. brown and orange-vermilion 10 15
a. Horiz strip of 5. Nos. 482/6 35
483 10 c. brown, yellow-olive and new blue .. 10 15
484 10 c. brown, bright violet and pale salmon .. 10 15
485 10 c. brown, orange-brown and mauve .. 10 15
486 10 c. brown, yellow and yellow-olive 10 15
482/6 .. .. *Set of* 5 35 65
Designs:—No. 482, Type **148**; 483, People of Singapore; 484, Industrial workers; 485, Civil Defence first aid worker; 486, Anti-aircraft gun crew.
Nos. 482/6 were printed together, *se-tenant*, in horizontal strips of five throughout the sheet.

149 Coleman Bridge

150 Damselfly

(Des Eng Siak Loy. Recess Harrison)

1985 (15 Mar). *Bridges of Singapore. T* **149** *and similar horiz designs. One phosphor band (10 c.) or phosphorised paper (others). P* 14½ × 14.
487 10 c. black (Type **149**) 15 10
488 35 c. black (Cavenagh Bridge) 30 30
489 75 c. black (Elgin Bridge) 55 55
490 $1 black (Benjamin Sheares Bridge) 70 70
487/90 .. .. *Set of* 4 1·50 1·50

(Des Eng Siak Loy. Recess and photo ($1 to $10) or litho (others) Japanese Govt Ptg Bureau, Tokyo)

1985 (24 Apr–5 June). *Insects. T* **150** *and similar horiz designs. Multicoloured. One narrow (5 mm) phosphor band (10 c.) or phosphorised paper (others). P* 13 × 13½.
491 5 c. Type **150** 10 10
492 10 c. Honey Bee 10 10
493 15 c. Potter Wasp 10 10
494 20 c. Carpenter Bee 10 10
495 25 c. Water Beetle 15 20
496 35 c. Ladybird Beetle 20 25
497 50 c. Shield Bug 30 35
498 75 c. Cicada 40 45
499 $1 Cricket (5 June) 55 60
500 $2 Grasshopper (5 June) .. .. .. 1·10 1·25
501 $5 Dragonfly (5 June) .. .. 2·75 3·00
502 $10 Longhorned Grasshopper (5 June) .. 5·75 6·00
491/502 .. .. *Set of* 12 10·00 11·00
Nos. 499/502 are larger, 35 × 30 mm.

151 Tennis, Canoeing, Judo and Children Playing

(Des M. Chiew. Litho Secura, Singapore)

1985 (1 July). *25th Anniv of the People's Association. T* **151** *and similar horiz designs. Multicoloured. One phosphor band (10 c.) or phosphorised paper (others). P* 13½ × 14.
503 10 c. Type **151** 15 10
504 35 c. Lion dance, martial arts and athletes with flags 30 30
505 50 c. Tae-kwon-do, Indian dance and Dragon dance 40 40
506 75 c. Boxing, table tennis, basketball and dancing 55 55
503/6 .. .. *Set of* 4 1·25 1·25

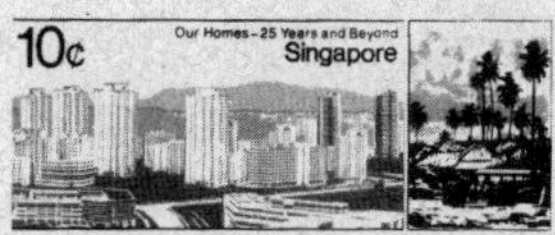

152 Modern Housing Estate and Squatter Settlement

(Des Eng Siak Loy. Litho Secura, Singapore)

1985 (9 Aug). *25th Anniv of Housing and Development Board. Horiz designs as T* **152** *with different aspects of housing shown at left. Multicoloured. One phosphor band (10 c.) or phosphorised paper (others). P* 13½ × 14.
507 10 c. Type **152** 15 10
508 35 c. Singapore family (Home-ownership) .. 30 30
509 50 c. Group of residents (Community development) 40 40
510 75 c. Construction workers (Building technology) 55 55
507/10 .. .. *Set of* 4 1·25 1·25
MS511 126 × 105 mm. Nos. 507/10 .. .. 1·25 1·75

153 Brownies

154 Badges and Emblems of Singapore Youth Organizations

(Des Foo Lye Lin. Litho J.W.)

1985 (6 Nov). *75th Anniv of Girl Guide Movement. T* **153** *and similar vert designs. One phosphor band (10 c.) or phosphorised paper (others). Multicoloured. P* 14.
512 10 c. Type **153** 10 10
513 35 c. Guides practising first aid 30 30
514 50 c. Senior Branch 40 40
515 75 c. Adult leaders and guides 55 55
512/15 .. .. *Set of* 4 1·25 1·25

(Des Eng Siak Loy. Litho Secura, Singapore)

1985 (18 Dec). *International Youth Year. T* **154** *and similar horiz designs. Multicoloured. One phosphor band (10 c.) or phosphorised paper (others). P* 12.
516 10 c. Type **154** 10 10
517 75 c. Hand protecting sapling 50 55
518 $1 Stylised figures and dove 65 70
516/18 .. .. *Set of* 3 1·10 1·25

155 Guava **156** Laboratory Technician and Salesmen with Bar Graph

(Des Poh Siew Wah. Litho J.W.)

1986 (26 Feb). *Singapore Fruits. T* **155** *and similar vert designs. Multicoloured. One centre phosphor band* (10 *c.*) *or phosphorised paper* (*others*). *P* 14.

519 10 c. Type **155** 10 10
520 35 c. Jambu Air 25 30
521 50 c. Rambutan 30 35
522 75 c. Ciku 50 55
519/22 . . . . *Set of* 4 1·00 1·10

(Des W. Lee. Litho Secura, Singapore)

1986 (1 May). *25th Anniv of National Trades Union Congress. T* **156** *and similar vert designs. Multicoloured. One phosphor band. P* 13½.

523 10 c. Type **156** 15 15
a. Horiz strip of 4. Nos. 523/6 55
524 10 c. Computer operator and welder . . 15 15
525 10 c. Draughtsmen and surveyors 15 15
526 10 c. Group of workers 15 15
523/6 . . . . *Set of* 4 55 55
MS527 148 × 100 mm. As Nos. 523/6, but each stamp with a face value of 35 c. Phosphorised paper 90 95

Nos. 523/6 were printed together, *se-tenant*, in horizontal strips of 4 throughout the sheet, forming a composite design.

157 Calligraphy **158** Industrial Automation

(Des Chua Ban Har. Litho (50 c. also die-stamped) Leigh-Mardon Ltd, Melbourne)

1986 (2 May). *"Expo '86" World Fair, Vancouver. T* **157** *and similar horiz designs. Multicoloured. "All-over" phosphor. P* 14 × 14½.

528 50 c. Type **157** 30 35
a. Horiz strip of 3. Nos. 528/30 . . . . 1·25
529 75 c. Garland maker 50 55
530 $1 Batik printer 65 70
528/30 . . . . *Set of* 3 1·25 1·40

Nos. 528/30 were printed together, *se-tenant*, in horizontal strips of 3 throughout the sheet.

(Des Eng Siak Loy. Litho J.W.)

1986 (1 Aug). *25th Anniv of Economic Development Board. T* **158** *and similar vert designs. Multicoloured. Phosphorised paper. P* 15 × 14½.

531 10 c. Type **158** 10 10
532 35 c. Manufacture of aircraft components . . 25 30
533 50 c. Electronics industry 30 35
534 75 c. Biotechnology industry 50 55
531/4 . . . . *Set of* 4 1·00 1·10

159 Map showing Route of Cable and *Vercors* (cable ship)

(Des J. Heng. Litho Secura, Singapore)

1986 (8 Sept). *SEA–ME–WE Submarine Cable Project. Phosphorised paper. P* 13½.

535 **159** 10 c. multicoloured 15 10
536 35 c. multicoloured 35 30
537 50 c. multicoloured 45 35
538 75 c. multicoloured 65 55
535/8 . . . . *Set of* 4 1·40 1·10

160 Stylized Citizens **161** Peace Doves and People of Different Races

(Des W. Lee. Litho Secura, Singapore)

1986 (15 Oct). *21st Anniv of Citizens' Consultative Committees. T* **160** *and similar vert designs showing citizens. Phosphorised paper. P* 12.

539 10 c. multicoloured 20 20
a. Block of 4. Nos. 539/42 . . . . 1·40
540 35 c. multicoloured 35 35
541 50 c. multicoloured 40 40
542 75 c. multicoloured 60 60
539/42 . . . . *Set of* 4 1·40 1·40

Nos. 539/42 were printed together, *se-tenant*, in blocks of 4 throughout the sheet, each block forming a composite design.

(Des Eng Siak Loy. Litho Secura, Singapore)

1986 (17 Dec). *International Peace Year. T* **161** *and similar horiz designs. Multicoloured. Phosphorised paper. P* 14 × 13½.

543 10 c. Type **161** 10 10
544 35 c. Doves and map of ASEAN countries . . 25 25
545 $1 Doves and globe 60 60
543/5 . . . . *Set of* 3 85 85

162 Orchard Road **163** Flags of Member Nations and Logo

(Des Chua Ban Har. Litho Secura, Singapore)

1987 (25 Feb). *Singapore Skyline. T* **162** *and similar horiz designs. Multicoloured. Phosphorised paper. P* 12.

546 10 c. Type **162** 15 10
547 50 c. Central Business District 40 30
548 75 c. Marina Centre and Raffles City . . 60 45
546/8 . . . . *Set of* 3 1·00 75

(Des Chua Ban Har. Litho Secura, Singapore)

1987 (15 June). *20th Anniv of Association of South-east Asian Nations. Phosphorised paper. P* 12.

549 **163** 10 c. multicoloured 10 10
550 35 c. multicoloured 25 25
551 50 c. multicoloured 30 30
552 75 c. multicoloured 45 45
549/52 . . . . *Set of* 4 1·00 95

164 Soldier with Rocket Launcher and Tank **165** Singapore River and Dragon Boats

(Des M. Ng. Litho Questa)

1987 (1 July). *20th Anniv of National Service. T* **164** *and similar vert designs. Multicoloured. Phosphorised paper. P* 15 × 14.

553 10 c. Type **164** 15 15
a. Horiz strip of 4. Nos. 553/6 55
554 10 c. Radar operator and patrol boat . . 15 15
555 10 c. Fighter pilot and aircraft 15 15
556 10 c. Servicemen pledging allegiance . . 15 15
553/6 . . . . *Set of* 4 55 55
MS557 148 × 100 mm. 35 c. × 5. As Nos. 553/6 and Singapore lion symbol (scarlet and black) . . 95 1·00

Nos. 553/6 were printed together, *se-tenant*, in horizontal strips of 4 throughout the sheet.

(Des Ng Keng Seng. Litho Secura, Singapore)

1987 (2 Sept). *River Conservation. T* **165** *and similar square designs. Multicoloured. Phosphorised paper. P* 13½.

558 10 c. Type **165** 10 10
559 50 c. Kallang Basin, canoe and fishing punt 35 30
560 $1 Kranji Reservoir, athletes and cyclist . . 70 60
558/60 . . . . *Set of* 3 1·00 90

166 Majapahit Gold Bracelet and Museum

(Des M. Ng. Litho Secura, Singapore)

1987 (12 Oct). *Centenary of National Museum. T* **166** *and similar horiz designs, each showing different drawings of Museum. Multicoloured. Phosphorised paper. P* 13½ × 14.

561 10 c. Type **166** 10 10
562 75 c. Ming fluted kendi (water vessel) . . 40 45
563 $1 Patani hulu pekakak keris (sword) . . 55 60
561/3 . . . . *Set of* 3 90 1·00

167 Omni-theatre

(Des Eng Siak Loy. Litho Leigh-Mardon Ltd, Melbourne)

1987 (10 Dec). *10th Anniv of Singapore Science Centre. T* **16** *and similar horiz designs. Multicoloured. Phosphorised pape P* 14½.

564 10 c. Type **167** 10 1
565 35 c. Omni-planetarium 30 2
566 75 c. Model of body cell 50 4
567 $1 Physical sciences exhibits 70 6
564/7 . . . . *Set of* 4 1·40 1·2

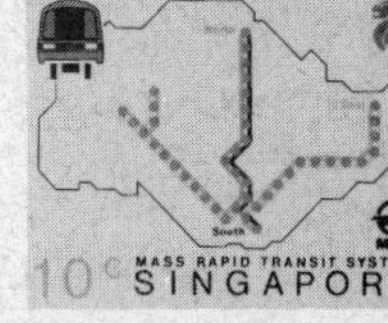

168 Modern Anti-aircraft Gun **169** Route Map

(Litho Secura, Singapore)

1988 (22 Feb). *Centenary of Singapore Artillery. T* **168** *an similar horiz designs. Multicoloured. Phosphorised pape P* 13½ × 14.

568 10 c. Type **168** 15 1
569 35 c. 25-pounder field gun firing salute . . 30 2
570 50 c. Gunner and 12-pounder gun, c. 1920 45 3
571 $1 Gunner and Maxim gun, 1889 . . 70 6
568/71 . . . . *Set of* 4 1·40 1·1

(Des Ng Keng Seng. Litho Secura, Singapore)

1988 (12 Mar). *Singapore Mass Rapid Transit System. T* **16** *and similar horiz designs. Multicoloured. Phosphorised pape P* 13½ × 14.

572 10 c. Type **169** 10 1
573 50 c. Train on elevated section 30 3
574 $1 Train in tunnel 55 6
572/4 . . . . *Set of* 3 80 9

170 Camera, Film and Outside Broadcast Van

(Des E. Soriano. Litho CPE Australia Ltd, Melbourne)

1988 (4 Apr). *25th Anniv of Television in Singapore. T* **170** *an similar horiz designs. Multicoloured. Phosphorised pape P* 13½ × 14.

575 10 c. Type **170** 10 1
576 35 c. Camera, studio lights and microphone 20 2
577 75 c. Television set and transmitter . . 40 4
578 $1 Globe on TV screen and dish aerial . . 55 6
575/8 . . . . *Set of* 4 1·10 1·2

MACHINE LABELS. From 19 April 1988 self-adhesive labe in the above design, with the background printed in orange ar grey, were available from machines situated outside a numb of Singapore post offices. Face values between 5 c. and $2 cou be selected and the location of individual machines is indicate by the code number, from 0001 to 0024, at bottom left.

171 Water Droplet and Blocks of Flats **172** Greeting Neighbours

(Des Ng Keng Song. Litho CPE Australia Ltd, Melbourne)

1988 (4 May). *25th Anniv of Public Utilities Board. T* **171** *an similar vert designs, each showing a different skyline. Mult coloured. Phosphorised paper. P* 13½.

579 10 c. Type **171** 10 1
580 50 c. Electric light bulb and city centre . . 30 3
581 $1 Gas flame and factories 55 6
579/81 . . . . *Set of* 3 80 1·0
MS582 116 × 75 mm. Nos. 579/81 . . . . 90 9

(Des M. Ng. Litho Leigh-Mardon Ltd, Melbourne)

88 (6 July). *10th Anniv of National Courtesy Campaign. T* **172** *and similar horiz designs, each showing campaign mascot "Singa". Multicoloured. Phosphorised paper. P* 14½.

3 10 c. Type **172** 10 10
4 30 c. Queueing at checkout 15 20
5 $1 Helping the elderly 55 60
3/5 .. .. *Set of* 3 70 80

173 Modern 30 Metre Turntable Fire Appliance

174 Container Ships and Warehouses

(Des Eng Siak Loy. Litho Secura, Singapore)

88 (1 Nov). *Centenary of Fire Service. T* **173** *and similar horiz design. Multicoloured. Phosphorised paper. P* 13½.

6 10 c. Type **173** 10 10
7 $1 Steam fire engine, c. 1890 .. .. .. 55 60

(Des Ng Keng Seng. Litho Secura, Singapore)

89 (3 Apr). *25th Anniv of Singapore Port Authority. T* **174** *and similar vert designs. Multicoloured. Phosphorised paper. P* 14×13½.

8 10 c. Type **174** 10 10
9 30 c. Shipping and oil storage depot 20 25
0 75 c. Container ships and Singapore skyline 50 55
1 $1 Container port at night 65 70
8/91 .. .. *Set of* 4 1·25 1·40

175 "Sago Street"

176 North-west Singapore City, 1920

(Litho Questa)

89 (17 May). *Paintings of Chinatown by Choo Keng Kwang. T* **175** *and similar square designs. Multicoloured. Phosphorised paper. P* 14½.

2 10 c. Type **175** 10 10
3 35 c. "Pagoda Street" 20 25
4 75 c. "Trengganu Street" 50 55
5 $1 "Temple Street" 65 70
2/5 .. .. *Set of* 4 1·25 1·40

(Des Leo Teck Chong. Litho Harrison)

89 (26 July). *Maps of Singapore. T* **176** *and similar multicoloured designs. Phosphorised paper. P* 14×14½ (15 c.) *or* 12½×13 (*others*).

6 15 c. Type **176** (top left) 10 10
a. Block of 4. Nos. 596/9 20
7 15 c. North-east Singapore (top right) .. 10 10
8 15 c. South-west Singapore (bottom left) .. 10 10
9 15 c. South-east Singapore (bottom right) .. 10 10
0 50 c. Singapore Island and Dependencies, 1860s 30 35
1 $1 British Settlement of Singapore, 1820s 65 70
6/601 .. .. *Set of* 6 1·00 1·10

Nos. 596/9 were printed together, *se-tenant*, in blocks of 4 roughout the sheet, each block forming a composite design. dividual stamps can be identified by the position of the lion nblem which is quoted in brackets.

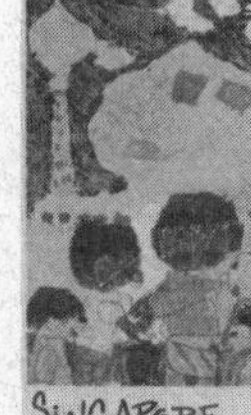

177 Clown Triggerfish

178 "Hari Raya Puasa" (Loke Yoke Yun)

(Des Eng Siak Loy. Litho Harrison)

89 (6 Sept). *Fishes. T* **177** *and similar horiz designs. Multicoloured. Phosphorised paper. P* 13½.

2 15 c. Type **177** 10 10
3 30 c. Majestic Angelfish 20 25
4 75 c. Emperor Angelfish 50 55
5 $1 Royal Empress Angelfish 65 70
2/5 .. .. *Set of* 4 1·25 1·40

(Adapted S. Ang Woon Beng. Litho Harrison)

1989 (25 Oct). *Festivals of Singapore. Children's Drawings. T* **178** *and similar vert designs. Multicoloured. Phosphorised paper. P* 14½.

606 15 c. Type **178** 10 10
607 35 c. "Chinese New Year" (Simon Koh) .. 20 25
608 75 c. "Thaipusam" (Henry Setiono) 50 55
609 $1 "Christmas" (Wendy Ang Lin Min) .. 65 70
606/9 .. .. *Set of* 4 1·25 1·40
MS610 126×75 mm. Nos. 606/9. P 14 .. .. 1·40 1·50

179 North Entrance of Stadium

180 "Singapore River, 1839" (Louis Le Breton)

(Des Lim Ching San. Litho Harrison)

1989 (27 Dec). *Opening of Singapore Indoor Stadium. T* **179** *and similar horiz designs. Multicoloured. Phosphorised paper. P* 14.

611 30 c. Type **179** 20 25
612 75 c. Arena 50 55
613 $1 East entrance 65 70
611/13 .. .. *Set of* 3 1·25 1·40
MS614 104×104 mm. Nos. 611/13 .. .. 1·25 1·40

(Des Choy Weng Yang. Litho Leigh-Mardon Ltd, Melbourne)

1990 (21 Mar). *Lithographs of 19th-century Singapore. T* **180** *and similar horiz designs. Multicoloured. Phosphorised paper. P* 13.

615 15 c. Type **180** 10 10
a. Booklet pane. No. 615×10 95
616 30 c. "Chinatown, 1837" (Barthelemy Lauvergne) 20 25
617 75 c. "Singapore Harbour, 1837" (Barthelemy Lauvergne) 50 55
618 $1 "View from Fort Canning, 1824" (Deroy) 65 70
615/18 .. .. *Set of* 4 1·25 1·40

The upper and lower edges of booklet pane No. 615a are imperforate.

POSTAGE DUE STAMPS

The postage due stamps of Malayan Postal Union were in use in Singapore until replaced by the following issues.

D 1

D 2

(Litho B.W.)

1968 (1 Feb)–**69**. *Toned paper. W* w **12**. *P* 9.

D1 D 1 1 c. green .. .. 20 1·00
D2 2 c. red .. .. 20 1·25
D3 4 c. yellow-orange .. .. 45 1·75
D4 8 c. chocolate 40 80
D5 10 c. magenta 50 90
a. White paper (16.12.69) .. .. 70 1·40
D6 12 c. slate-violet .. .. 90 1·50
a. White paper (16.12.69) .. .. 1·00 2·00
D7 20 c. new blue .. .. 2·00 3·00
a. White paper (16.12.69) .. .. 3·00 4·50
D8 50 c. drab .. .. 3·75 4·50
D1/8 .. .. *Set of* 8 7·50 13·50

1973. *White paper. W* w **12**. *P* 13 × 13½.

D 9 D 1 10 c. bright magenta (27.4) .. .. 70 3·50
D10 50 c. sage-green (24.8) .. .. .. 3·25 10·00

1977–78. *White paper. No wmk. P* 13×13½.

D11 D 1 1 c. green .. .. 25·00 32·00
D12 4 c. yellow-orange .. .. 25·00 32·00
D13 10 c. bright magenta .. .. 25·00 32·00
D14 20 c. new blue .. .. 38·00 42·00
D15 50 c. sage-green .. .. 45·00 48·00
D11/15 .. .. *Set of* 5 £140 £170

(Litho Secura, Singapore)

1978 (25 Sept)–**81**. *No wmk. P* 13×13½.

D16 D 2 1 c. blue-green .. .. 55 1·00
a. Perf 12 × 11½ (1981) 10 10
D17 4 c. pale orange .. .. 55 1·00
a. Perf 12 × 11½ (1981) 10 10
D18 10 c. cerise .. .. 60 1·10
a. Perf 12 × 11½ (1981) 10 10
D19 20 c. light blue .. .. 75 1·25
a. Perf 12 × 11½ (1981) 10 10
D20 50 c. yellow-green .. .. 1·25 1·75
a. Perf 12 × 11½ (1981) 30 35
D16/20 .. .. *Set of* 5 3·25 5·50
D16a/20a .. .. *Set of* 5 40 50

Solomon Islands

(*formerly* British Solomon Islands)

PRICES FOR STAMPS ON COVER TO 1945

Nos. 1/7	*from* × 12
Nos. 8/17	*from* × 25
Nos. 18/36	*from* × 6
Nos. 37/8	—
Nos. 39/51	*from* × 6
No. 52	—
Nos. 53/6	*from* × 2
Nos. 57/9	*from* × 6
Nos. 60/72	*from* × 2
Nos. D1/8	*from* × 5

BRITISH PROTECTORATE

1

2

(Des C. M. Woodford. Litho W. E. Smith & Co, Sydney)

1907 (14 Feb). *No wmk. P* 11.

1	1	½d. ultramarine	6·50	15·00
2		1d. rose-carmine	20·00	30·00
3		2d. indigo	23·00	30·00
		a. Imperf between (horiz pair)	£9000	
4		2½d. orange-yellow	30·00	35·00
		a. Imperf between (vert pair)	£4000	
		b. Imperf between (horiz pair)	£4000	£4000
5		5d. emerald-green	50·00	65·00
6		6d. chocolate	55·00	60·00
		a. Imperf between (vert pair)	£3250	
7		1s. bright purple	75·00	75·00
1/7		*Set of* 7	£225	£275

Three types exist of the ½d. and 2½d., and six each of the other values, differing in minor details.

Forgeries of Nos. 1/7 show different perforations and have the boat paddle touching the shore. Genuine stamps show a gap between the paddle and the shore.

(Recess D.L.R.)

1908 (1 Nov)–**11**. *Wmk Mult Crown CA (sideways). P* 14.

8	2	½d. green	50	80
9		1d. red	1·00	50
10		2d. greyish slate	1·25	1·00
11		2½d. ultramarine	2·00	2·50
11*a*		4d. red/*yellow* (3.11)	3·00	11·00
12		5d. olive	8·50	9·00
13		6d. claret	7·00	7·50
14		1s. black/*green*	9·50	12·00
15		2s. purple/*blue* (3.10)	27·00	48·00
16		2s. 6d. red/*blue* (3.10)	40·00	65·00
17		5s. green/*yellow* (3.10)	70·00	£100
8/17		*Set of* 11	£150	£225
8/17 Optd "Specimen"		*Set of* 11	£275	

The ½d. and 1d. were issued in 1913 on rather thinner paper and with brownish gum.

3

4

(T 3 and 4. Typo D.L.R.)

1913. *Inscribed* "POSTAGE POSTAGE". *Wmk Mult Crown CA. P* 14.

18	3	½d. green (1.4)	80	3·50
19		1d. red (1.4)	80	10·00
20		3d. purple/*yellow* (27.2)	80	4·00
		a. On orange-buff	3·00	20·00
21		11d. dull purple and scarlet (27.2)	3·00	14·00
18/21		*Set of* 4	4·75	28·00
18/21 Optd "Specimen"		*Set of* 4	70·00	

1914–23. *Inscribed* "POSTAGE REVENUE". *Wmk Mult Crown CA. P* 14.

22	4	½d. green, **O**	70	6·00
23		½d. yellow-green, **O** (1917)	2·00	9·00
24		1d. carmine-red, **O**	50	80
25		1d. scarlet, **O** (1917)	3·00	6·50
26		2d. grey, **O**	1·00	9·00
27		2½d. ultramarine, **O**	2·00	5·00
28		3d. purple/*pale yellow*, **C** (1.23)	15·00	50·00
29		4d. black and red/*yellow*, **C**	2·00	2·50
30		5d. dull purple and olive-green, **C**	13·00	23·00
31		5d. brown-purple and olive-green, **C**	13·00	25·00
32		6d. dull and bright purple, **C**	5·00	14·00
33		1s. black/*green*, **C**	3·00	7·00
		a. On blue-green, olive back	6·00	15·00
34		2s. purple and blue/*blue*, **C**	6·00	10·00
35		2s. 6d. black and red/*blue*, **C**	7·00	20·00
36		5s. green and red/*yellow*, **C**	23·00	30·00
		a. On orange-buff (1920)	38·00	55·00
37	4	10s. green and red/*green*, **C**	75·00	80·00
38		£1 purple and black/*red*, **C**	£210	£160
22/38		*Set of* 14	£325	£375
22/38 Optd "Specimen"		*Set of* 14	£400	

Variations in the coloured papers are mostly due to climate and do not indicate separate printings.

1922–31. *Wmk Mult Script CA. P* 14.

39	4	½d. green, **O** (10.22)	25	1·75
40		1d. scarlet, **O** (8.23)	8·50	8·50
41		1d. dull violet, **O** (1927)	1·00	4·50
42	3	1½d. bright scarlet, **O** (1924)	1·25	30
43	4	2d. slate-grey, **O** (4.23)	2·00	7·00
44		3d. pale ultramarine, **O** (11.23)	60	2·50
45		4d. black and red/*yellow*, **C** (1927)	3·25	12·00
45*a*		4½d. red-brown, **O** (1931)	3·00	13·00
46		5d. dull purple and olive-green, **C**	2·50	16·00
47		6d. dull and bright purple, **C**	3·50	12·00
48		1s. black/*emerald*, **C**	2·75	11·00
49		2s. purple and blue/*blue*, **C** (1927)	7·50	28·00
50		2s. 6d. black and red/*blue*, **C**	7·50	30·00
51		5s. green and red/*pale yellow*, **C**	23·00	42·00
52		10s. green and red/*emerald*, **C** (1925)	90·00	£120
39/52		*Set of* 15	£130	£225
39/52 Optd/Perf "Specimen"		*Set of* 15	£300	

1935 (6 May). *Silver Jubilee. As Nos.* 91/4 *of Antigua.*

53	1½d. deep blue and carmine	60	50
	f. Diagonal line by turret	25·00	
	h. Dot by flagstaff	25·00	
54	3d. brown and deep blue	2·75	4·00
	f. Diagonal line by turret	50·00	
	h. Dot by flagstaff	50·00	
55	6d. light blue and olive-green	5·00	8·50
	h. Dot by flagstaff	60·00	
56	1s. slate and purple	6·00	7·00
	f. Diagonal line by turret	80·00	
53/6	*Set of* 4	13·00	18·00
53/6 Perf "Specimen"	*Set of* 4	80·00	

For illustrations of plate varieties see Omnibus section following Zululand.

1937 (13 May). *Coronation Issue. As Nos.* 13/15 *of Aden but ptd by B.W. P* 11 × 11½.

57	1d. violet	25	40
58	1½d. carmine	30	50
59	3d. blue	40	40
57/9	*Set of* 3	85	1·10
57/9 Perf "Specimen"	*Set of* 3	55·00	

5 Spears and Shield

6 Native Constable and Chief

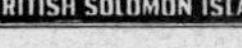

7 Canoe House

8 Roviana Canoe

(Recess D.L.R. (2d., 3d., 2s. and 2s. 6d.), Waterlow (others))

1939 (1 Feb)–**1951.** *T* **5/8** *and similar designs. Wmk Mult Script CA. P* 13½ *(2d., 3d., 2s. and 2s. 6d.) or* 12½ *(others).*

60	½d. blue and blue-green	15	50
61	1d. brown and deep violet	15	25
62	1½d. blue-green and carmine	35	70
63	2d. orange-brown and black	20	55
	a. Perf 12 (7.11.51)	30	1·25
64	2½d. magenta and sage-green	70	55
	a. Imperf between (vert pair)	£7000	
65	3d. black and ultramarine	25	60
	a. Perf 12 (29.11.51)	30	1·00
66	4½d. green and chocolate	8·00	13·00
67	6d. deep violet and reddish purple	35	50
68	1s. green and black	50	30
69	2s. black and orange	6·00	3·00
70	2s. 6d. black and violet	22·00	4·50
71	5s. emerald-green and scarlet	15·00	7·50
72	10s. sage-green and magenta (27.4.42)	7·00	8·50
60/72	*Set of* 13	50·00	35·00
60/72 Perf "Specimen"	*Set of* 13	£275	

Designs: *Horiz (as T* **8**)—1½d. Artificial Island, Malaita; 1s. Breadfruit; 5s. Malaita canoe. *(As T* **7**)—3d. Roviana canoes; 2s. Tinakula volcano; 2s. 6d. Common Scrub Hen. *Vert (as T* **6**)—4½d., 10s. Native house, Reef Islands; 6d. Coconut plantation.

1946 (15 Oct). *Victory. As Nos.* 28/9 *of Aden.*

73	1½d. carmine	15	15
74	3d. blue	15	10
73/4 Perf "Specimen"	*Set of* 2	50·00	

1949 (14 Mar). *Royal Silver Wedding. As Nos.* 30/1 *of Aden.*

75	2d. black	50	20
76	10s. magenta	10·00	8·00

1949 (10 Oct). *75th Anniv of Universal Postal Union. As Nos.* 114/17 *of Antigua.*

77	2d. red-brown	75	30
78	3d. deep blue	1·25	70
79	5d. deep blue-green	1·25	75
80	1s. blue-black	1·75	50
77/80	*Set of* 4	4·50	2·00

1953 (2 June). *Coronation. As No.* 47 *of Aden.*

81	2d. black and grey-black	30	4

17 Ysabel Canoe

18 Roviana Canoe

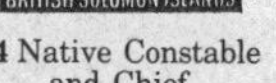

24 Native Constable and Chief

25 Arms of the Protectorate

(Des Miss I. R. Stinson (½d.), R. Bailey (2½d.), R. A. Sweet (5d 1s., 1s. 3d.), Capt. J. Brett Hilder (6d., 8d., 9d., 5s.). Recess B.W (½d., 2½d., 5d., 6d., 8d., 9d., 1s., 1s. 3d., 5s.), D.L.R. (1d., 2d., 2s. Waterlow (1½d., 3d., 2s. 6d., 10s., £1), until 1962, then D.L.R.)

1956 (1 Mar)–**63.** *T* **17/18, 24/5** *and similar horiz design Wmk Mult Script CA. P* 12 *(1d., 2d., 2s.),* 13 *(1½d., 3d., 2s 6d 10s., £1) or* 11½ *(others).*

82	½d. orange and purple	15	2
83	1d. yellow-green and red-brown	15	1
84	1½d. slate-green and carmine-red	15	2
	a. Slate-green and brown-red (31.7.63)	25	2
85	2d. deep brown and dull green	20	1
86	2½d. black and blue	25	4
87	3d. blue-green and red	25	1
88	5d. black and blue	25	5
89	6d. black and turquoise-green	50	2
90	8d. bright blue and black	25	1
90*a*	9d. emerald and black (28.1.60)	3·25	8
91	1s. slate and yellow-brown	50	4
	a. Slate and orange-brown (13.6.61)	2·50	2·0
91*b*	1s. 3d. black and blue (28.1.60)	5·00	1·7
	ba. Black and pale ultramarine (11.12.62)	7·50	2·5
92	2s. black and carmine	8·00	9
93	2s. 6d. emerald and bright purple	6·50	4
	a. Emerald and reddish purple (19.2.63)	8·50	1·7
94	5s. red-brown	8·00	1·7
95	10s. sepia	11·00	2·5
96	£1 black and blue (5.11.58)	42·00	35·0
82/96	*Set of* 17	75·00	40·0

Designs: *(As T* **17**)—5d., 1s. 3d. Map; 6d. *Miena* (schooner); 1 Voyage of H.M.S. *Swallow*, 1767; 2s. 6d. Native house, Re Islands; 5s. Mendaña and *Todos los Santos*. *(As T* **25**)—1 Roviana canoe; 1½d. Artificial Island, Malaita; 2d. Canoe hous 3d. Malaita Canoe; 8d., 9d. Henderson airfield, Guadalcanal; 2 Tinakula volcano.

LEGISLATIVE COUNCIL

32 Great Frigate Bird

(Litho Enschedé)

1961 (19 Jan). *New Constitution,* 1960. *W* w **12** *(sideway P* 13 × 12½.

97	**32**	2d. black and turquoise-green	10	1
98		3d. black and rose-carmine	10	1
99		9d. black and reddish purple	10	1
97/9		*Set of* 3	20	1

1963 (4 June). *Freedom from Hunger. As No.* 76 *of Aden.*

100	1s. 3d. ultramarine	2·50	3

1963 (2 Sept). *Red Cross Centenary. As Nos.* 147/8 *of Antigua.*

101	2d. red and black	60	2
102	9d. red and blue	1·40	7

1963–64. *As Nos.* 83/5, 87, 89, 90*a and* 91*a*/3, *but wmk* w **12**.

103	1d. yellow-green and red-brown (9.7.64)	25	3
104	1½d. slate-green and red (9.7.64)	25	5
105	2d. deep brown and dull green (9.7.64)	20	2
106	3d. light blue-green and scarlet (16.11.63)	40	1
	a. Yellowish green and red (9.7.64)	90	1·2
107	6d. black and turquoise (7.7.64)	60	4
108	9d. emerald and black (7.7.64)	20	3
109	1s. 3d. black and blue (7.7.64)	60	7
110	2s. black and carmine (9.7.64)	1·00	4·5
111	2s. 6d. emerald & reddish purple (9.7.64)	10·00	10·0
103/11	*Set of* 9	12·00	15·0

33 Makira Food Bowl

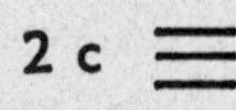

(48)

(Des M. Farrar-Bell. Litho D.L.R.)

65 (24 May). *Horiz designs as T* **33**. *W* w **12**. *P* 13 × 12½.

2	½d. black, deep slate-blue and light blue ..	10	30
3	1d. black, orange and yellow	50	20
4	1½d. black, blue and yellow-green	25	35
5	2d. black, ultramarine and light blue ..	40	25
6	2½d. black, light brown & pale yellow-brown	10	35
7	3d. black, green and light green	10	10
8	6d. black, magenta and yellow-orange ..	35	20
9	9d. brownish blk, dp bluish grn & pale yell	40	15
0	1s. black, chocolate and magenta	80	15
1	1s. 3d. black and rose-red	3·50	2·25
2	2s. black, bright purple and lilac	5·50	2·75
3	2s. 6d. black, olive-brown and light brown	1·00	70
4	5s. black, ultramarine and violet	10·00	4·25
5	10s. black, olive-green and yellow	11·00	4·00
6	£1 black, deep reddish violet and pink ..	11·00	5·00
2/126	.. .. *Set of* 15	40·00	18·00

Designs:—1d. *Dendrobium veratrifolium* (orchid); 1½d. Scor-
on Shell; 2d. Blyth's Hornbill; 2½d. Ysabel shield; 3d. Rennellese
ıb; 6d. Moorish Idol; 9d. Lesser Frigate Bird; 1s. *Dendrobium
ıcrophyllum* (orchid); 1s. 3d. *Dendrobium spectabilis* (orchid); 2s.
nford's Sea Eagle; 2s. 6d. Malaita belt; 5s. *Ornithoptera victoreae*
ıtterfly); 10s. Ducorp's Cockatoo; £1, Western canoe figurehead.

65 (28 June). *I.T.U. Centenary. As Nos.* 166/7 *of Antigua.*

7	2d. orange-red and turquoise-blue	20	10
8	3d. turquoise-blue and olive-brown	20	10

65 (25 Oct). *International Co-operation Year. As Nos.* 168/9 *of Antigua.*

9	1d. reddish purple and turquoise-green ..	15	10
0	2s. 6d. deep bluish green and lavender ..	60	15

66 (24 Jan). *Churchill Commemoration. As Nos.* 170/3 *of Antigua.*

1	2d. new blue	15	10
2	9d. deep green	25	10
3	1s. 3d. brown..	35	10
4	2s. 6d. bluish violet	40	15
1/4	.. .. *Set of* 4	1·00	30

(New Currency. 100 cents = 1 Australian dollar)

8 c. — Normal "8"

8 c. — Inverted "8" (No. 142a) (R. 9/2. Later corrected)

66–67. *Decimal Currency. Nos.* 112/26 *variously surch as T* **48** *by De La Rue.* A. *Wmk upright.* B. *Wmk sideways.*

		A		B	
5	1 c. on ½d.	10	10	10	10
6	2 c. on 1d.	10	10	10	10
7	3 c. on 1½d.	10	10	15	10
8	4 c. on 2d.	15	10	15	10
9	5 c. on 6d.	15	10	15	10
0	6 c. on 2½d.	15	10	10	10
1	7 c. on 3d.	15	10	10	10
2	8 c. on 9d.	25	10	15	10
	a. Inverted "8"	14·00	11·00	†	
3	10 c. on 1s.	30	10	40	10
4	12 c. on 1s. 3d.	†		65	10
5	13 c. on 1s. 3d.	75	15	2·50	75
6	14 c. on 3d.	†		40	10
7	20 c. on 2s.	75	25	2·50	30
8	25 c. on 2s. 6d.	60	40	2·00	35
9	35 c. on 2d.	†		1·75	25
	a. Surch omitted (horiz pair with normal)	†		—	—
	b. Surch value only omitted	†		—	—
	50 c. on 5s. (R.)	5·00	2·75	6·50	4·00
	$1 on 10s.	4·00	3·00	4·00	1·25
2	$2 on £1	3·25	6·50	5·00	3·00
A/152A	.. .. *Set of* 15	14·00	12·00		
B/152B	.. .. *Set of* 18			23·00	9·00

Dates of issue: 1967—1 March, 12 c., 14 c., 35 c. 1966—14
bruary. All watermark upright. 1966—All other watermark
eways.

The positions of the bars in the surcharge vary considerably from
mp to stamp within the sheets.

The stamps with sideways watermark are all from new printings
d in some instances there are marked shade variations from Nos.
2/26 which were used for making Nos. 135A/152A.

66 (1 July). *World Cup Football Championships. As Nos.* 176/7 *of Antigua.*

3	8 c. violet, yellow-green, lake & yellow-brn ..	15	10
4	35 c. chocolate, blue-green, lake & yellow-brn	30	10

66 (20 Sept). *Inauguration of W.H.O. Headquarters, Geneva. As Nos.* 178/9 *of Antigua.*

	3 c. black, yellow-green and light blue ..	25	10
	50 c. black, light purple and yellow-brown ..	1·00	20

6 (1 Dec). *20th Anniv of U.N.E.S.C.O. As Nos.* 196/8 *of Antigua.*

	3 c. slate-violet, red, yellow and orange ..	20	10
	25 c. orange-yellow, violet and deep olive ..	55	15
	$1 black, bright purple and orange ..	1·50	70
/9	.. .. *Set of* 3	2·00	85

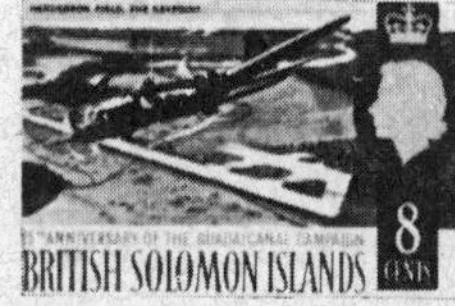

49 Henderson Field

(Des V. Whiteley. Photo Harrison)

1967 (28 Aug). *25th Anniv of Guadalcanal Campaign (Pacific War). T* **49** *and similar horiz design. Multicoloured. W* w **12**. *P* 14 × 14½.

160	8 c. Type **49**	10	10
161	35 c. Red Beach landings	10	10

51 Mendaña's *Todos los Santos* off Point Cruz

(Des V. Whiteley. Photo Harrison)

1968 (7 Feb). *Quatercentenary of the Discovery of Solomon Is. T* **51** *and similar horiz designs. Multicoloured. W* w **12**. *P* 14.

162	3 c. Type **51**	15	10
163	8 c. Arrival of missionaries	15	10
164	35 c. Pacific Campaign, World War II ..	30	10
165	$1 Proclamation of the Protectorate ..	50	60
162/5	.. .. *Set of* 4	1·00	75

55 Vine Fishing

(Des R. Granger Barrett. Photo Harrison)

1968 (20 May)–**71.** *Horiz designs as T* **55**. *Chalk-surfaced paper. W* w **12** (*inverted on No.* 167a). *P* 14½.

166	1 c. turquoise-blue, black and brown ..	10	10
	a. Glazed, ordinary paper (9.8.71).. ..	90	90
167	2 c. apple-green, black and brown	10	10
	a. Glazed, ordinary paper (9.8.71).. ..	90	90
168	3 c. green, myrtle-green and black	10	10
	a. Glazed, ordinary paper (9.8.71).. ..	90	90
169	4 c. bright purple, black and brown ..	15	10
	a. Glazed, ordinary paper (9.8.71).. ..	90	90
170	6 c. multicoloured	15	10
171	8 c. multicoloured	25	10
	a. Glazed, ordinary paper (9.8.71).. ..	1·50	1·60
172	12 c. yellow-ochre, brown-red and black ..	65	30
	a. Glazed, ordinary paper (9.8.71).. ..	2·25	2·50
173	14 c. orange-red, chocolate and black ..	80	60
174	15 c. multicoloured	80	45
	a. Glazed, ordinary paper (9.8.71).. ..	2·50	3·00
175	20 c. bright blue, red and black	2·00	80
	a. Glazed, ordinary paper (9.8.71).. ..	4·25	4·50
176	24 c. rose-red, black and yellow	1·40	85
177	35 c. multicoloured	1·50	70
178	45 c. multicoloured	1·50	75
179	$1 violet-blue, light green and black ..	2·50	2·00
180	$2 multicoloured	4·00	5·00
166/80	.. .. *Set of* 15	13·50	10·50
166a/75a	.. .. *Set of* 8	13·00	14·00

Designs:—2 c. Kite fishing; 3 c. Platform fishing; 4 c. Net fishing; 6 c. Gold Lip shell diving; 8 c. Night fishing; 12 c. Boat building; 14 c. Cocoa; 15 c. Road building; 20 c. Geological survey; 24 c. Hauling timber; 35 c. Copra; 45 c. Harvesting rice; $1, Honiara Port; $2, Internal air service.

The stamps on glazed, ordinary paper exist with PVA gum only. The 1 c. to 12 c. and 20 c. on chalk-surfaced paper exist with PVA gum as well as gum arabic, but the others exist with gum arabic only.

70 Map of Australasia and Diagram **71** Basketball Player

(Des R. Gates. Litho Enschedé)

1969 (10 Feb). *Inaugural Year of the South Pacific University. P* 12½ × 12.

181	**70**	3 c. multicoloured	10	10
182		12 c. multicoloured	10	10
183		35 c. multicoloured	15	10
181/3		.. .. *Set of* 3	20	15

(Des J. Cooter. Photo Harrison)

1969 (13 Aug). *Third South Pacific Games, Port Moresby. T* **71** *and similar vert designs. Multicoloured. W* w **12** (*sideways*). *P* 14½ × 14.

184	3 c. Type **71**	10	10
185	8 c. Footballer	10	10
186	14 c. Sprinter	10	10
187	45 c. Rugby player	20	15
184/7	.. .. *Set of* 4	40	20
MS188	126 × 120 mm. Nos. 184/7	3·50	8·00

Stamps from the miniature sheets differ slightly from those in the ordinary sheets, particularly the 14 c. value, which has a shadow below the feet on the runner. The footballer and rugby player on the 8 c. and 45 c. values also have shadows below their feet, but these are more pronounced than on the stamps from the ordinary sheets.

75 South Sea Island with Star of Bethlehem **76** Southern Cross, "PAX" and Frigatebird (stained glass window)

(Des L. Curtis. Photo Harrison)

1969 (21 Nov). *Christmas. W* w **12** (*sideways*). *P* 14½ × 14.

189	**75**	8 c. black, violet and turquoise-green ..	10	10
190	**76**	35 c. multicoloured	15	10

77 "Paid" Stamp, New South Wales 1896–1906 2d. Stamp and 1906–07 Tulagi Postmark

(Des G. Drummond. Litho B.W.)

1970 (15 Apr). *Inauguration of New G.P.O. Honiara. T* **77** *and similar horiz designs. W* w **12** (*sideways*). *P* 13.

191	7 c. light magenta, deep blue and black ..	20	15
192	14 c. sage-green, deep blue and black.. ..	25	15
193	18 c. multicoloured	25	15
194	23 c. multicoloured	30	20
191/4	.. .. *Set of* 4	90	60

Designs:—14 c. 1906–07 2d. stamp and C. M. Woodford; 18 c. 1910–14 5s. stamp and Tulagi postmark, 1913; 23 c. New G.P.O., Honiara.

81 Coat of Arms **83** British Red Cross H.Q., Honiara

(Des V. Whiteley. Photo Harrison)

1970 (15 June). *New Constitution. T* **81** *and similar design. W* w **12** (*sideways on* 18 *c.*). *P* 14½ × 14 (18 *c.*) *or* 14 × 14½ (35 *c.*).

195	18 c. multicoloured	15	10
196	35 c. pale apple-green, deep blue and ochre ..	30	15

Design: *Horiz*—35 c. Map.

(Des L. Curtis. Litho Questa)

1970 (17 Aug). *Centenary of British Red Cross. T* **83** *and similar horiz design. W* w **12** (*sideways*). *P* 14 × 14½.

197	3 c. multicoloured	10	10
198	35 c. blue, vermilion and black	25	15

Design:—35 c. Wheelchair and map.

86 Reredos (Altar Screen)

(Des L. Curtis. Litho J.W.)

1970 (19 Oct). *Christmas. T* **86** *and similar design. W* w **12** (*sideways on* 45 *c.*). *P* 14 × 13½ (8 *c.*) *or* 13½ × 14 (45 *c.*).

199	8 c. ochre and bluish violet	10	10
200	45 c. chestnut, yellow-orange & blackish brn	25	15

Design: *Vert*—8 c. Carved angel.

87 La Perouse and *La Boussole*

(Des J.W. Litho Questa)

1971 (28 Jan). *Ships and Navigators* (*1st series*). *T* **87** *and similar horiz designs. Multicoloured. W* w **12** (*sideways*). *P* 14.

201	3 c. Type **87**	55	20
202	4 c. Astrolabe and Polynesian Reed Map ..	65	20
203	12 c. Abel Tasman and *Heemskerk*	1·50	45
204	35 c. Te Puki canoe, Santa Cruz	3·00	75
201/4	.. .. *Set of* 4	5·00	1·40

See also Nos. 215/18, 236/9, 254/7 and 272/5.

88 J. Atkin, Bishop Patteson and S. Taroaniara

(Des J.W. Litho Questa)

1971 (5 April). *Death Centenary of Bishop Patteson. T* **88** *and similar multicoloured designs. W* w **12** (*sideways on* 2 *c*., 4 *c*.). *P* 14½ × 14 (2 *c*., 4 *c*.) *or* 14 × 14½ (*others*).

205	2 c. Type **88**	10	10
206	4 c. Last Landing at Nukapu	10	10
207	14 c. Memorial Cross and Nukapu (*vert*) ..	10	10
208	45 c. Knotted Leaf and canoe (*vert*)	20	10
205/8	.. .. *Set of* 4	30	15

89 Torch Emblem and Boxers **90** Melanesian Lectern

(Des C. Debenham. Litho Questa)

1971 (9 Aug). *Fourth South Pacific Games, Tahiti. T* **89** *and similar horiz designs. Multicoloured. W* w **12** (*sideways*). *P* 14.

209	3 c. Type **89**	10	10
210	8 c. Emblem and footballers	10	10
211	12 c. Emblem and runner	10	10
212	35 c. Emblem and skin-diver	10	10
209/12	.. .. *Set of* 4	20	15

(Des C. Abbott. Litho A. & M.)

1971 (15 Nov). *Christmas. T* **90** *and similar vert design. Multicoloured. W* w **12**. *P* 13½.

213	9 c. Type **90**	10	10
214	45 c. "United we Stand" (Margarita Bara) ..	15	15

(Des J.W. Litho Questa)

1972 (1 Feb). *Ships and Navigators* (*2nd series*). *Horiz designs as T* **87**. *Multicoloured. W* w **12** (*sideways*). *P* 14.

215	4 c. Bougainville and *La Boudeuse*	30	10
216	9 c. Horizontal planisphere and ivory backstaff	60	10
217	15 c. Philip Carteret and H.M.S. *Swallow* ..	85	15
218	45 c. Malaita canoe	3·75	1·25
215/18	.. .. *Set of* 4	5·00	1·40

91 *Cupha woodfordi*

(Des R. Granger Barrett. Litho Questa)

1972 (3 July)–**73**. *T* **91** *and similar horiz designs. Multicoloured. Cream paper. W* w **12** (*upright on* $5, *sideways on others*). *P* 14.

219	1 c. Type **91**	15	25
220	2 c. *Ornithoptera priamus urvillanus* ..	25	30
221	3 c. *Vindula sapor*	25	30
222	4 c. *Papilio ulysses orsippus*	25	30
223	5 c. Great Trevally	25	25
224	8 c. Little Bonito	40	50
225	9 c. Sapphire Demoiselle	50	55
226	12 c. *Costus speciosus*	1·25	80
227	15 c. Orange Anemone Fish	1·25	1·00
228	20 c. *Spathoglottis plicata*	3·25	1·75
229	25 c. *Ephemerantha comata*	3·25	1·50
230	35 c. *Dendrobium cuthbertsonii*	3·50	2·25
231	45 c. *Heliconia salomonica*	3·50	3·00
232	$1 Blue Finned Triggerfish	6·00	4·50
233	$2 *Ornithoptera allotti*	12·00	12·00
233*a*	$5 Great Frigate Bird (2.7.73)	10·00	10·00
219/33*a*	.. .. *Set of* 16	40·00	35·00

The 1 to 4 c. and $2 are butterflies; the 5 to 9 c., 15 c. and $1 are fishes; the 12 c. and 20 to 45 c. are flowers and the $5 a bird.

92 Greetings and Message Drum

(Des (from photograph by D. Groves) and photo Harrison)

1972 (20 Nov). *Royal Silver Wedding. Multicoloured; background colour given. W* w **12**. *P* 14 × 14½.

234	**92**	8 c. rose-carmine	10	10
235		45 c. deep yellow-olive	15	15

(Des J.W. Litho Questa)

1973 (9 Mar). *Ships and Navigators* (*3rd series*). *Horiz designs as T* **87**. *Multicoloured. W* w **12**. *P* 14.

236	4 c. D'Entrecasteaux and *Recherche* ..	30	15
237	9 c. Ship's hour-glass and chronometer ..	60	15
238	15 c. Lt. Shortland and H.M.S. *Alexander* ..	75	20
239	35 c. Tomoko (war canoe)	3·25	1·75
236/9	.. .. *Set of* 4	4·50	2·00

93 Pan Pipes

(Des and litho J.W.)

1973 (1 Oct). *Musical Instruments. T* **93** *and similar horiz designs. Multicoloured. W* w **12**. *P* 13½.

240	4 c. Type **93**	10	10
241	9 c. Castanets	10	10
242	15 c. Bamboo flute	15	10
243	35 c. Bauro gongs	30	25
244	45 c. Bamboo band	30	30
240/4	.. .. *Set of* 5	80	65

(Des PAD Studio. Litho Questa)

1973 (14 Nov). *Royal Wedding. As Nos.* 165/6 *of Anguilla.*

245	4 c. deep grey-blue	10	10
246	35 c. bright blue	15	10

94 "Adoration of the Kings" (Jan Brueghel)

(Des PAD Studio. Litho Questa)

1973 (26 Nov). *Christmas. T* **94** *and similar designs showing "Adoration of the Kings" by the artists listed. Multicoloured. W* w **12** (*sideways on* 22 *c*.). *P* 13½ (45 *c*.) *or* 14 (*others*).

247	8 c. Type **94**	10	10
248	22 c. Pieter Brueghel (*vert*)	25	25
249	45 c. Botticelli (48 × 35 *mm*)	50	50
247/9	.. .. *Set of* 3	70	70

95 Queen Elizabeth II and Map **96** "Postman"

(Des G. Drummond. Litho Questa)

1974 (18 Feb). *Royal Visit. W* w **12**. *P* 13½.

250	**95**	4 c. multicoloured	25	10
251		9 c. multicoloured	50	10
252		15 c. multicoloured	60	20
253		35 c. multicoloured	1·10	1·25
250/3		.. .. *Set of* 4	2·25	1·40

(Des and litho J.W.)

1974 (15 May). *Ships and Navigators* (*4th series*). *Horiz designs as T* **87**. *Multicoloured. W* w **12** (*sideways*). *P* 14.

254	4 c. Commissioner landing from S.S. *Titus* ..	20	10
255	9 c. Radar scanner	25	10
256	15 c. Natives being transported to a "Blackbirder" brig	40	15
257	45 c. Lieut. John F. Kennedy's *P.T. 109* ..	2·00	1·25
254/7	.. .. *Set of* 4	2·50	1·40

(Des Jennifer Toombs. Litho Questa)

1974 (29 Aug). *Centenary of Universal Postal Union. T* **96** *an[d] similar designs showing Origami figures. W* w **12** (*sideways on* [9] *and* 45 *c*.). *P* 14.

258	4 c. light yellow-green, deep green and black	10	1
259	9 c. light olive-bistre, lake-brown and black	10	1
260	15 c. mauve, purple and black	15	1
261	45 c. cobalt, dull ultramarine and black ..	35	6
258/61	.. .. *Set of* 4	65	7

Designs: *Horiz*—9 c. Carrier-pigeon; 45 c. Pegasus. *Vert*—15 c St. Gabriel.

97 "New Constitution" Stamp of 1970

(Des R. Granger Barrett. Litho Questa)

1974 (16 Dec). *New Constitution. T* **97** *and similar horiz design[s]. W* w **14** (*sideways*). *P* 14.

262	**97**	4 c. multicoloured	10	1
263	–	9 c. dull rose-red, black & lt yell-ochre	10	1
264	–	15 c. dull rose-red, blk & lt greenish yell	15	1
265	**97**	35 c. multicoloured	45	5
262/5		.. .. *Set of* 4	70	6
MS266		134 × 84 mm. Nos. 262/5	2·75	3·2

Design:—9 c., 15 c. "New Constitution" stamp of 1961 (insc "1960").

98 Golden Whistler

(Des G. Drummond. Litho Questa)

1975 (7 Apr). *Birds. T* **98** *and similar horiz designs. Multi-coloured. W* w **12**. *P* 14.

267	1 c. Type **98**	45	4
268	2 c. Common Kingfisher	50	5
269	3 c. Red-bibbed Fruit Dove	55	5
270	4 c. Little Button Quail	55	5
271	$2 Duchess Lorikeet	11·00	9·0
267/71	.. .. *Set of* 5	12·00	10·0

See also Nos. 305/20.

(Des and litho J.W.)

1975 (29 May). *Ships and Navigators* (*5th series*). *Horiz desig[ns] as T* **87**. *Multicoloured. W* w **12**. *P* 13½.

272	4 c. *Walande* (coaster)	25	
273	9 c. *Melanesian* (coaster)	30	
274	15 c. *Marsina* (container ship)	35	
275	45 c. *Himalaya* (liner)	1·00	1·5
272/5	.. .. *Set of* 4	1·75	1·6

99 800-Metres Race

(Des PAD Studio. Litho Walsall)

1975 (4 Aug). *Fifth South Pacific Games, Guam. T* **99** *and simil[ar] horiz designs. Multicoloured. W* w **14** (*sideways*). *P* 13½.

276	4 c. Type **99**	10	
277	9 c. Long-jump	10	
278	15 c. Javelin-throwing	15	
279	45 c. Football	45	
276/9	.. .. *Set of* 4	70	
MS280	130 × 95 mm. Nos. 276/9	3·50	4·

100 Christmas Scene and Candles **(101)**

(Des G. Vasarhelyi. Litho Questa)

1975 (13 Oct). *Christmas. T* **100** *and similar horiz designs. Mult[i]coloured. W* w **12** (*sideways*). *P* 14.

281	15 c. Type **100**	20	1
282	35 c. Shepherds, angels and candles	40	1
283	45 c. The Magi and candles	50	4
281/3	.. .. *Set of* 3	1·00	6
MS284	140 × 130 mm. Nos. 281/3	3·75	4·0

975 (12 Nov). *Nos. 267/70, 223/32, 271 and 233a with obliterating bar as T* **101** *over* "BRITISH".
85 1 c. Type **98** 20 30
86 2 c. Common Kingfisher 25 30
87 3 c. Red-bibbed Fruit Dove 25 30
88 4 c. Little Button Quail 35 30
89 5 c. Great Trevally 35 30
90 8 c. Little Bonito 50 45
91 9 c. Sapphire Demoiselle 50 45
92 12 c. *Costus speciosus* .. .. .. 1·50 75
93 15 c. Orange Anemone Fish .. .. .. 1·50 90
94 20 c. *Spathoglottis plicata* .. .. .. 2·75 1·25
95 25 c. *Ephemerantha comata* .. .. .. 2·75 1·50
96 35 c. *Dendrobium cuthbertsonii* .. .. 3·50 1·75
97 45 c. *Heliconia salomonica* .. .. .. 3·50 3·00
98 $1 Blue Finned Triggerfish (*cream paper*) 3·00 2·50
a. White paper .. .. 4·75 4·00
99 $2 Duchess Lorikeet .. .. 8·00 9·00
00 $5 Great Frigate Bird (*white paper*) .. 15·00 18·00
a. Cream paper .. .. 20·00 20·00
85/300 .. .. *Set of* 16 38·00 38·00

SELF-GOVERNMENT

102 Ceremonial Food-bowl

(Des J. Cooter. Litho Questa)

976 (12 Jan). *Artefacts* (1*st series*). *T* **102** *and similar multicoloured designs. W w* **12** (*upright on* 35 *c.; sideways on others*). *P* 14.
01 4 c. Type **102** 10 10
02 15 c. Chieftains' money 10 10
03 35 c. Nguzu-nguzu (canoe protector spirit) (*vert*) 25 20
04 45 c. Nguzu-nguzu canoe prow 30 25
01/4 .. .. *Set of* 4 65 55
See also Nos. 337/40, 353/6 and 376/9.

103 Golden Whistler

(Des G. Drummond. Litho Questa)

976 (8 Mar–6 Dec). *Nos. 267/71 with new country inscr* (*omitting* "BRITISH") *as T* **103**, *and new values. Multicoloured. W w* **14** (*sideways*). *P* 14.
05 1 c. Type **103** 20 30
06 2 c. Common Kingfisher 25 35
07 3 c. Red-bibbed Fruit Dove 25 30
08 4 c. Little Button Quail 30 30
09 5 c. Willie Wagtail 30 30
10 6 c. Golden Cowrie 40 40
11 10 c. Glory of the Sea Cone 50 40
12 12 c. Rainbow Lory 60 50
13 15 c. Pearly Nautilus 65 40
14 20 c. Venus Comb Murex 80 45
15 25 c. Commercial Trochus 85 50
16 35 c. Melon or Baler Shell .. .. .. 1·00 70
17 45 c. Orange Spider Conch .. .. .. 1·50 1·25
18 $1 Pacific Triton .. .. 2·75 2·50
19 $2 Duchess Lorikeet .. .. 6·50 4·75
20 $5 Great Frigate Bird (6.12) .. .. 6·50 6·00
05/20 .. .. *Set of* 16 21·00 17·00

104 Coastwatchers, 1942 **105** Alexander Graham Bell

(Des J. Cooter. Litho Walsall)

976 (24 May). *Bicentenary of American Revolution. T* **104** *and similar horiz designs. Multicoloured. W w* **14** (*sideways*). *P* 14.
21 6 c. Type **104** 20 10
22 20 c. *Amagiri* ramming *PT109* and Lt. J. F. Kennedy 60 30
23 35 c. Henderson Airfield .. .. .. 1·00 40
24 45 c. Map of Guadalcanal .. .. .. 1·10 70
21/4 .. .. *Set of* 4 2·75 1·40
S325 95 × 115 mm. Nos. 321/4 .. .. .. 4·50 6·50

ALTERED CATALOGUE NUMBERS

Any Catalogue numbers altered from the last edition are shown as a list in the introductory pages.

(Des P. Powell. Litho Harrison)

1976 (26 July). *Telephone Centenary. T* **105** *and similar vert designs. W w* **14** (*sideways*). *P* $14\frac{1}{2}$ × 14.
326 6 c. multicoloured 10 10
327 20 c. multicoloured 15 10
328 35 c. brown-orange, lt orange & lt vermilion .. 30 15
329 45 c. multicoloured 40 35
326/9 .. .. *Set of* 4 85 55
Designs:—20 c. Radio telephone via satellite; 35 c. Ericson's magneto telephone; 45 c. Stick telephone and first telephone.

106 B.A.C. "1–11" **107** The Communion Plate

(Des and litho Walsall)

1976 (13 Sept). *50th Anniv of First Flight to Solomon Islands. T* **106** *and similar horiz designs. Multicoloured. W w* **14** (*sideways*). *P* 14.
330 6 c. Type **106** 20 10
331 20 c. Britten-Norman "Islander" 35 10
332 35 c. "Dakota DC3" 65 15
333 45 c. De Havilland "DH50A" 75 45
330/3 .. .. *Set of* 4 1·75 65

(Des Jennifer Toombs. Litho Questa)

1977 (7 Feb). *Silver Jubilee. T* **107** *and similar vert designs. Multicoloured. W w* **14**. *P* $13\frac{1}{2}$.
334 6 c. Queen's visit, 1974 .. .. .. 10 10
335 35 c. Type **107** 15 20
336 45 c. The Communion 25 45
334/6 .. .. *Set of* 3 45 65

108 Carving from New Georgia **109** Spraying Roof and Mosquito

(Des J. Cooter. Litho Questa)

1977 (9 May). *Artefacts* (2*nd series*). *T* **108** *and similar vert designs showing carvings. W w* **14**. *P* 14.
337 6 c. multicoloured 10 10
338 20 c. multicoloured 10 10
339 35 c. slate-black, grey and rose-red 20 15
340 45 c. multicoloured 25 30
337/40 .. .. *Set of* 4 55 50
Designs:—20 c. Sea adaro (spirit); 35 c. Shark-headed man; 45 c. Man from Ulawa or Malaita.

(Des G. Vasarhelyi. Litho Questa)

1977 (27 July). *Malaria Eradication. T* **109** *and similar horiz designs. Multicoloured. W w* **14** (*sideways*). *P* 14.
341 6 c. Type **109** 10 10
342 20 c. Taking blood samples 20 10
343 35 c. Microscope and map 30 15
344 45 c. Delivering drugs 40 40
341/4 .. .. *Set of* 4 90 60

110 The Shepherds **111** Feather Money

(Des M. and G. Shamir. Litho Questa)

1977 (12 Sept). *Christmas. T* **110** *and similar vert designs. Multicoloured. W w* **14**. *P* 14.
345 6 c. Type **110** 10 10
346 20 c. Mary and Jesus in stable 10 10
347 35 c. The Three Kings 20 15
348 45 c. "The Flight into Egypt" 25 25
345/8 .. .. *Set of* 4 50 45

(Des D.L.R. Litho Harrison)

1977 (24 Oct). *Introduction of Solomon Islands Coins and Banknotes. T* **111** *and similar horiz designs. Multicoloured. W w* **14**. *P* 14 × $14\frac{1}{2}$.
349 6 c. Type **111** 10 10
a. Horiz pair. Nos. 349/50 .. .. .. 20 20
350 6 c. New currency coins 10 10
351 45 c. New currency notes 35 25
a. Horiz pair. Nos. 351/2 .. .. .. 70 50
352 45 c. Shell money 35 25
349/52 .. .. *Set of* 4 80 60
The two designs of each value were printed in horizontal *se-tenant* pairs throughout their sheets.

112 Figure from Shortland Island **113** Sandford's Sea Eagle

(Des J. Cooter. Litho Questa)

1978 (11 Jan). *Artefacts* (3*rd series*). *T* **112** *and similar vert designs. W w* **14**. *P* 14.
353 6 c. multicoloured 10 10
354 20 c. multicoloured 10 10
355 35 c. deep brown, black and orange 20 15
356 45 c. multicoloured 25 30
353/6 .. .. *Set of* 4 55 50
Designs:—20 c. Ceremonial shield; 35 c. Santa Cruz ritual figure; 45 c. Decorative combs.

(Des Jennifer Toombs. Litho Questa)

1978 (21 Apr). *25th Anniv of Coronation. T* **113** *and similar vert designs. Multicoloured. P* 15.
357 45 c. black, vermilion and silver 25 30
a. Sheetlet. Nos. 357/9 × 2 .. .. .. 1·25
358 45 c. multicoloured 25 30
359 45 c. black, vermilion and silver 25 30
357/9 .. .. *Set of* 3 65 80
Designs:—No. 357, King's Dragon; No. 358, Queen Elizabeth II; No. 359, Type **113**.
Nos. 357/9 were printed together in small sheets of 6, containing two *se-tenant* strips of 3, with horizontal gutter margin between.

INDEPENDENT

114 National Flag **115** John

(Des L. Curtis. Litho Questa)

1978 (7 July). *Independence. T* **114** *and similar vert designs. Multicoloured. W w* **14**. *P* 14.
360 6 c. Type **114** 10 10
361 15 c. Governor-General's flag 20 10
362 35 c. The Cenotaph, Honiara 35 30
363 45 c. National coat of arms 40 50
360/3 .. .. *Set of* 4 95 85

(Des J.W. Litho Questa)

1978 (4 Oct). *450th Death Anniv of Dürer. Details from his Painting "Four Apostles". T* **115** *and similar vert designs. Multicoloured. W w* **14**. *P* 14.
364 6 c. Type **115** 10 10
365 20 c. Peter 10 10
366 35 c. Paul 15 15
367 45 c. Mark 20 30
364/7 .. .. *Set of* 4 45 50

116 Firelighting **117** H.M.S. *Discovery*

(Des K. G. Watkinson; adapted J.W. Litho Questa)

1978 (15 Nov). *50th Anniv of Scouting in Solomon Islands. T* **116** *and similar horiz designs. Multicoloured. W* w **14** *(sideways). P* 14.
368 6 c. Type **116** 15 10
369 20 c. Camping 20 20
370 35 c. Solomon Islands Scouts 40 40
371 45 c. Canoeing 50 70
368/71 .. .. *Set of* 4 1·10 1·25

(Des and litho (45 c. also embossed) Walsall)

1979 (16 Jan). *Bicentenary of Captain Cook's Voyages,* 1768–79. *T* **117** *and similar vert designs. P* 11.
372 8 c. multicoloured 20 10
373 18 c. multicoloured 30 15
374 35 c. black, yellowish green and silver .. 40 25
375 45 c. multicoloured 55 40
372/5 .. .. *Set of* 4 1·25 80
Designs:—18 c. "Captain Cook" (Nathaniel Dance); 35 c. Sextant; 45 c. Flaxman/Wedgwood medallion of Captain Cook.

118 Fish Net Float

119 Running

(Des J. Cooter. Litho Questa)

1979 (21 Mar). *Artefacts (4th series). T* **118** *and similar designs. W* w **14** *(sideways on* 8 *and* 35 *c.). P* 14.
376 8 c. multicoloured 10 10
377 20 c. multicoloured 10 10
378 35 c. black, grey and rose 15 15
379 45 c. black, chestnut and apple-green.. .. 20 30
376/9 .. .. *Set of* 4 45 50
Designs: *Vert*—20 c. Armband of shell money; 45 c. Forehead ornament. *Horiz*—35 c. Ceremonial food bowl.

(Des L. Curtis. Litho Format)

1979 (4 June). *South Pacific Games, Fiji. T* **109** *and similar horiz designs. Multicoloured. W* w **14** *(sideways). P* 13½.
380 8 c. Type **119** 10 10
381 20 c. Hurdling 10 10
382 35 c. Football 15 15
383 45 c. Swimming 25 35
380/3 .. .. *Set of* 4 55 50

120 1908 6d. Stamp

121 Sea Snake

(Des J.W. Litho Format)

1979 (16 Aug). *Death Centenary of Sir Rowland Hill. T* **120** *and similar vert designs showing stamps. W* w 14. *P* 14.
384 8 c. carmine and pale rose 10 10
385 20 c. deep mauve and pale mauve 20 30
386 35 c. multicoloured 35 45
384/6 .. .. *Set of* 3 60 75
MS387 121 × 121 mm. 45 c. rosine, deep dull green and pink 45 65
Designs:—20 c. Great Britain 1856 6d.; 35 c. 1978 45 c. Independence commemorative; 45 c. 1922 10s.

(Des L. Curtis. Litho Enschedé)

1979 (18 Sept)–**83.** *Reptiles. Vert designs as T* **121**. *Multicoloured. W* w **14** *(inverted on Nos.* 394B *and* 397B). *P* 13½ × 13.
A. *No imprint.* B. *Imprint date at foot.*

			A		B	
388	1 c.	Type **121**	10	15	†	
389	3 c.	Red-banded Tree Snake ..	10	15	†	
390	4 c.	Whip Snake	10	15	†	
391	6 c.	Pacific Boa	10	15	†	
392	8 c.	Skink	10	10	†	
393	10 c.	Gecko (*Lepidodactylus lugubris*)	10	10	†	
394	12 c.	Monitor	40	25	15	20
395	15 c.	Anglehead	15	15	†	
396	20 c.	Giant Toad	15	20	†	
397	25 c.	Marsh Frog	60	40	20	30
398	30 c.	Horned Frog	80	50	60	60
399	35 c.	Tree Frog	25	35	†	
399*a*	40 c.	Burrowing Snake	†		35	50
400	45 c.	Guppy's Snake	30	40	†	
400*a*	50 c.	Tree Gecko	†		40	40
401	$1	Large Skink	1·25	1·25	85	70
402	$2	Guppy's Frog	1·25	1·40	†	
403	$5	Estuarine Crocodile ..	3·50	6·00	4·00	4·00
403*a*	$10	Hawksbill Turtle	†		6·50	6·75
388/403		.. .. *Set of* 16	8·00	10·50		
394/403*a*		.. .. *Set of* 8			12·00	12·00

Dates of issue:—18.9.79, Nos. 388A/403A; 25.1.82, Nos. 401B, 403B; 27.8.82, Nos. 394B, 397B; 20.9.82, No. 403*a*; 24.1.83, Nos. 399aB, 400aB; 31.8.83, No. 398B.

122 "Madonna and Child" (Morando)

123 H.M.S. *Curacao*, 1839

(Des BG Studio. Litho Questa)

1979 (15 Nov). *Christmas. International Year of the Child. T* **122** *and similar vert designs showing "Madonna and Child" paintings by various artists. Multicoloured. W* w **14**. *P* 14 × 14½.
404 4 c. Type **122** 10 10
405 20 c. Luini 15 10
406 35 c. Bellini 20 15
407 50 c. Raphael 25 30
404/7 .. .. *Set of* 4 60 55
MS408 92 × 133 mm. Nos. 404/7 .. .. .. 1·00 1·50

(Des L. Curtis. Litho Questa)

1980 (23 Jan). *Ships and Crests (1st series). T* **123** *and similar horiz designs. Multicoloured. W* w **14** *(sideways). P* 14.
409 8 c. Type **123** 15 10
410 20 c. H.M.S. *Herald*, 1854 .. .. .. 25 15
411 35 c. H.M.S. *Royalist*, 1889 .. .. .. 45 35
412 45 c. H.M.S. *Beagle*, 1878 .. .. .. 55 55
409/12 .. .. *Set of* 4 1·25 1·00
See also Nos. 430/3.

124 Steel Fishery Training Vessel

(Des G. Hutchins. Litho Secura, Singapore)

1980 (27 Mar). *Fishing. Ancillary Craft. T* **124** *and similar horiz designs. Multicoloured. W* w **14** *(sideways). P* 13½.
413 8 c. Type **124**.. .. .. 15 10
414 20 c. *Solomon Hunter* (fishery training vessel) 20 15
415 45 c. *Ufi Na Tasi* (refrigerated fish transport) 35 35
416 80 c. Research Vessel.. .. .. .. 60 75
413/16 .. .. *Set of* 4 1·10 1·25

125 *Comliebank* (cargo-liner) and 1935 Tulagi Registered Letter Postmark

(Des A. Theobald. Litho Questa)

1980 (6 May). *"London 1980" International Stamp Exhibition. Mail-carrying Transport. T* **125** *and similar horiz designs. Multicoloured. W* w **14** *(sideways). P* 14½ × 14.
417 45 c. Type **125**.. .. .. 35 50
a. Sheetlet. Nos. 417/20 .. .. .. 1·25
418 45 c. Douglas "C-47" aeroplane (U.S. Army Postal Service, 1943) 35 50
419 45 c. B.A.C. "1-11" airliner and 1979 Honiara postmark 35 50
420 45 c. *Corabank* (container ship) and 1979 Auki postmark 35 50
417/20 .. .. *Set of* 4 1·25 1·75
Nos. 417/20 were printed together as a sheetlet containing a *se-tenant* block of 4.

126 Queen Elizabeth the Queen Mother

127 Angel with Trumpet

(Des Harrison. Litho Questa)

1980 (4 Aug). *80th Birthday of Queen Elizabeth the Queen Mother. W* w **14** *(sideways). P* 14.
421 **126** 45 c. multicoloured 40 35

(Des C. Abbott. Litho Walsall)

1980 (2 Sept). *Christmas. T* **127** *and similar vert designs. Multicoloured. W* w **14**. *P* 14½ × 14.
422 8 c. Type **127** 10 10
423 20 c. Angel with fiddle.. .. .. .. 10 10
424 45 c. Angel with trumpet (*different*) 25 25
425 80 c. Angel with lute 40 45
422/5 .. .. *Set of* 4 70 75

128 *Parthenos sylvia*

129 Francisco Antonio Maurelle

(Des J. Cooter. Litho Secura, Singapore)

1980 (12 Nov). *Butterflies (1st series). T* **128** *and similar horiz designs. Multicoloured. W* w **14** *(sideways. P* 13½.
426 8 c. Type **128** 10 10
427 20 c. *Delias schoenbergi* 25 20
428 45 c. *Jamides cephion* 40 40
429 80 c. *Ornithoptera victoriae* .. .. .. 1·00 1·00
426/9 .. .. *Set of* 4 1·60 1·50
See also Nos. 456/9 and 610/13.

(Des L. Curtis. Litho Questa)

1981 (14 Jan). *Ships and Crests (2nd series). Horiz designs as T* **123**. *Multicoloured. W* w **14** *(sideways). P* 14.
430 8 c. H.M.S. *Mounts Bay* 15 10
431 20 c. H.M.S. *Charybdis* 25 15
432 45 c. H.M.S. *Hydra* 50 35
433 $1 Royal Yacht *Britannia* .. .. .. 1·25 1·00
430/3 .. .. *Set of* 4 1·90 1·40

(Des J. Cooter. Litho Questa)

1981 (23 Mar). *Bicentenary of Maurelle's Visit and Production of Bauche's Chart,* 1791 (*No.* **MS**438). *T* **129** *and similar designs. Wmk CA Diagonal (sideways on* 8 *c. and* $1). *P* 13½ × 14 (8 *c.,* $1) *or* 14 × 13½ *(others).*
434 8 c. black, deep brown and greenish yellow .. 15 10
435 10 c. black, vermilion and stone 20 10
436 45 c. multicoloured 60 65
437 $1 multicoloured .. .. 1·00 1·10
434/7 .. .. *Set of* 4 1·75 1·75
MS438 126 × 91 mm. 25 c. × 4, each black, vermilion and stone (wmk sideways). P 14½ .. .. 1·25 1·40
Designs: *Horiz*—10 c. Bellin's map of 1742 showing route of *La Princesa*; 45 c. *La Princesa. Vert*—$1 Spanish compass cards, 1745 and 1757. No. **MS**438, "Chart of a part of the South Sea" (*each stamp* 44 × 28 *mm*).
Stamps in No. **MS**438 were printed to form a composite design.

130 Netball

131 Prince Charles as Colonel-in-Chief, Royal Regiment of Wales

(Des R. Granger Barrett. Litho Security Printers (M), Malaysia)

1981 (7 July). *Mini South Pacific Games. T* **130** *and similar vert designs. Multicoloured. W* w **14**. *P* 12.
439 8 c. Type **130** 10 10
440 10 c. Tennis 15 15
441 25 c. Running 25 25
442 30 c. Football 25 25
443 45 c. Boxing 40 40
439/43 .. .. *Set of* 5 1·00 1·00
MS444 102 × 67 mm $1 Stylised athletes (wmk sideways) .. .. 1·00 1·10

(Des and litho J.W.)

1981 (22 July). *Royal Wedding. T* **131** *and similar vert designs. Multicoloured. W* w **14**. *P* 13½ × 13.
445 8 c. Wedding bouquet from Solomon Islands 10 10
446 45 c. Type **131** 30 40
447 $1 Prince Charles and Lady Diana Spencer 60 1·00
445/7 .. .. *Set of* 3 90 1·25

ALTERED CATALOGUE NUMBERS

Any Catalogue numbers altered from the last edition are shown as a list in the introductory pages.

132 "Music" 133 Primitive Church

(Des BG Studio. Litho Questa)

981 (28 Sept). *25th Anniv of Duke of Edinburgh Award Scheme. T* **132** *and similar vert designs. Multicoloured. W w* **14**. *P* 14.

48 8 c. Type **132** 10 10
49 25 c. "Handicrafts" 10 10
50 45 c. "Canoeing" 20 20
51 $1 Duke of Edinburgh 50 70
48/51 .. .. *Set of* 4 75 95

(Des BG Studio. Litho Format)

981 (12 Oct). *Christmas. Churches. T* **133** *and similar horiz designs. W w* **14** (*sideways*). *P* 14.

52 8 c. black, buff and cobalt 10 10
53 10 c. multicoloured 10 10
54 25 c. black, buff and dull green 15 10
55 $2 multicoloured .. .. 1·00 1·25
52/5 .. .. *Set of* 4 1·25 1·25

Designs:—10 c. St. Barnabas Anglican Cathedral, Honiara; 25 c. arly church; $2 Holy Cross Cathedral, Honiara.

(Des J. Cooter. Litho Secura, Singapore)

982 (5 Jan). *Butterflies* (*2nd series*). *Horiz designs as T* **128**. *Multicoloured. W w* **14** (*sideways*). *P* 13½ × 13.

56 10 c. Autumn Leaf or Leafwing (*Doleschallia bisaltide*) 15 10
57 25 c. Tailless Swallowtail (*Papilio bridgei hecataeus*) 35 25
58 35 c. *Taenaris phorcas* 40 30
a. Wmk inverted .. .. 50·00
59 $1 Blue Triangle or Common Bluebottle (*Graphium sarpedon*) .. .. 1·50 1·50
56/9 .. .. *Set of* 4 2·25 1·90

No. 458a shows a change of watermark position from sideways to nverted.

50 CENTS SURCHARGE
CYCLONE RELIEF FUND
1982

(134) 135 Pair of Sanford's Sea Eagles constructing Nest

5 CENTS SURCHARGE
CYCLONE RELIEF FUND
1982

"0" of "50" omitted from surcharge (R. 4/5)

982 (3 May). *Cyclone Relief Fund. No. 447 surch with T* **134** *in red.*

60 $1 + 50 c. Prince Charles and Lady Diana Spencer .. .. 2·50 2·75
a. "0" omitted .. .. 10·00

(Des N. Arlott. Litho Walsall)

982 (15 May). *Sanford's Sea Eagle. T* **135** *and similar vert designs. Multicoloured. W w* **14**. *P* 14.

61 12 c. Type **135** 30 30
a. Horiz strip of 5. Nos. 461/5 .. .. 1·60
62 12 c. Egg and chick 30 30
63 12 c. Hen feeding chicks 30 30
64 12 c. Fledgelings 30 30
65 12 c. Young bird in flight 30 30
66 12 c. Pair of birds and village dwellings .. 30 30
61/6 .. .. *Set of* 6 1·60 1·60

Nos. 461/6 were printed together, *se-tenant*, in various combiations throughout sheets also including one stamp-size label.

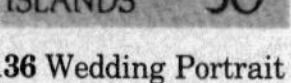

136 Wedding Portrait 137 Flags of Solomon Islands and United Kingdom

(Des Jennifer Toombs. Litho Walsall)

1982 (1 July). *21st Birthday of Princess of Wales. T* **136** *and similar vert designs. Multicoloured. W w* **14**. *P* 14½ × 14.

467 12 c. Solomon Islands coat of arms 15 10
468 40 c. Lady Diana Spencer at Broadlands, May 1981 .. .. 30 30
469 50 c. Type **136** 35 35
470 $1 Formal portrait 65 65
467/70 .. .. *Set of* 4 1·25 1·25

(Des Studio 53. Litho Questa)

1982 (11 Oct). *Royal Visit* (*Nos.* 471/2, **MS**475) *and Commonwealth Games, Brisbane* (*Nos.* 473/4, **MS**476). *T* **137** *and similar square designs. Multicoloured. W w* **14** (*sideways*). *P* 14.

471 12 c. Type **137** 15 15
a. Pair. Nos. 471/2 .. .. 30 30
472 12 c. Queen and Prince Philip 15 15
473 25 c. Running 30 35
a. Pair. Nos. 473/4 .. .. 60 70
474 25 c. Boxing 30 35
471/4 .. .. *Set of* 4 80 90
MS475 123 × 123 mm. Nos. 471/2 and $1 Royal Yacht *Britannia* .. .. 1·25 1·75
MS476 123 × 123 mm. Nos. 473/4 and $1 Royal Yacht *Britannia* .. .. 1·60 2·00

Nos. 471/2 and 473/4 were each printed in small sheets of 10, including 2 *se-tenant*, stamp-size, labels, the two stamp designs appearing *se-tenant*, both horizontally and vertically.

138 Boy Scouts

(Des McCombie Skinner. Litho Format)

1982 (4 Nov). *75th Anniv of Boy Scout Movement* (*Nos.* 477, 479, 481, 483) *and Centenary of Boys' Brigade* (*others*). *T* **138** *and similar horiz designs. Multicoloured. W w* **14** (*sideways*). *P* 14.

477 12 c. Type **138** 20 15
478 12 c. Boys' Brigade cadets 20 15
479 25 c. Lord Baden-Powell 35 35
480 25 c. Sir William Smith 35 35
481 35 c. Type **138** 40 40
482 35 c. As No. 478 .. .. 40 40
483 50 c. As No. 479 .. .. 60 65
484 50 c. As No. 480 .. .. 60 65
477/84 .. .. *Set of* 8 2·75 2·75

139 Leatherback Turtle

(Des L. Curtis. Litho Format)

1983 (5 Jan). *Turtles. T* **139** *and similar horiz designs. Multicoloured. W w* **14** (*sideways*). *P* 14½.

485 18 c. Type **139** 25 25
486 35 c. Loggerhead turtle 45 45
487 45 c. Pacific Ridley turtle 60 60
488 50 c. Green turtle 65 65
485/8 .. .. *Set of* 4 1·75 1·75

140 *Oliva vidum, Conus generalis* and *Murex tribulus*

(Des W. Fenton. Litho Questa)

1983 (14 Mar). *Commonwealth Day. Shells. T* **140** *and similar horiz designs. Multicoloured. W w* **14** (*sideways*). *P* 14.

489 12 c. Type **140** 15 15
490 35 c. Romu, Kurila, Kakadu and money belt .. 35 40
491 45 c. Shells from "Bride-price" necklaces .. 50 60
492 50 c. *Trochus niloticus* polished and in its natural state 55 65
489/92 .. .. *Set of* 4 1·40 1·60

141 Montgolfier Balloon

(Des A. Theobald. Litho Format)

1983 (30 June). *Bicentenary of Manned Flight. T* **141** *and similar horiz designs. Multicoloured. W w* **14** (*sideways*). *P* 14.

493 30 c. Type **141** 40 40
494 35 c. R.A.A.F. Lockheed "Hercules" 45 45
495 40 c. Wright brothers' *Flyer III* 55 55
496 45 c. Space shuttle *Columbia* 60 60
497 50 c. Beechcraft "Baron-Solair" 65 65
493/7 .. .. *Set of* 5 2·40 2·40

142 Weto Dancers

(Des J.W. Litho Format)

1983 (25 Aug). *Christmas. T* **142** *and similar horiz designs. Multicoloured. W w* **14** (*sideways*). *P* 14.

498 12 c. Type **142** 15 10
499 15 c. Custom wrestling 20 20
500 18 c. Girl dancers 20 20
501 20 c. Devil dancers 20 20
502 25 c. Bamboo band 30 35
503 35 c. Gilbertese dancers 40 45
504 40 c. Pan pipers 45 55
505 45 c. Girl dancers 50 65
506 50 c. Cross surrounded by flowers 55 70
498/506 .. .. *Set of* 9 2·50 3·00
MS507 153 × 112 mm. Nos. 498/506 .. .. 2·50 3·00

Stamps from No. **MS**507 are without the inscription, "Christmas 1983", shown on Nos. 498/506.

143 Earth Satellite Station 144 *Calvatia gardneri*

(Des Jennifer Toombs. Litho Format)

1983 (19 Dec). *World Communications Year. T* **143** *and similar horiz designs. Multicoloured. W w* **14** (*sideways*). *P* 14.

508 12 c. Type **143** 20 15
509 18 c. Ham radio operator 25 20
510 25 c. 1908 2½d. Canoe stamp 35 30
511 $1 1908 6d. Canoe stamp .. .. .. 1·25 1·40
508/11 .. .. *Set of* 4 1·90 1·90
MS512 131 × 103 mm. No. 511 .. .. .. 1·40 2·25

(Des Gillian Tomblin. Litho Enschedé)

1984 (30 Jan). *Fungi. T* **144** *and similar vert designs. Multicoloured. W w* 14. *P* 13½.

513 6 c. Type **144** 10 10
514 18 c. *Marasmiellus inoderma* 20 25
a. Booklet pane of 6 .. .. 1·25
515 35 c. *Pycnoporus sanguineus* 35 45
a. Booklet pane of 6 .. .. 2·10
516 $2 *Filoboletus manipularis* .. .. .. 2·25 2·50
513/16 .. .. *Set of* 4 2·50 3·00

Booklet panes Nos. 514a and 515a were from special sheets providing blocks of 6 (3 × 2) with vertical margins at both the left and right of each pane.

145 Cross surrounded by Flowers 146 *Olivebank*, 1892

(Des J.W. Litho Format)

1984 (16 Apr). *Visit of Pope John Paul II. W w* **14** (*sideways*). *P* 14.

517 **145** 12 c. multicoloured 20 10
518 50 c. multicoloured 65 80

(Des Studio 53. Litho Questa)

1984 (21 Apr). *250th Anniv of "Lloyd's List"* (*newspaper*). *T* **146** *and similar vert designs. Multicoloured. W w* **14**. *P* 14.

519 12 c. Type **146** 20 10
520 15 c. S.S. *Tinhow*, 1906 .. .. 25 20
521 18 c. *Oriana* at Point Cruz, Honiara 30 25
522 $1 Point Cruz, Honiara .. .. 1·25 1·40
519/22 .. .. *Set of* 4 1·75 1·75

(Des Jennifer Toombs. Litho Format)

1984 (18 June). *Universal Postal Union Congress, Hamburg. As No.* **MS**512 *but with changed sheet inscriptions and U.P.U. logo in margin. Multicoloured. W w* **14** (*sideways*). *P* 14.

MS523 $1 1908 6d. Canoe stamp .. .. .. 1·25 1·40

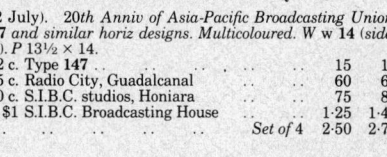

147 Village Drums — 148 Solomon Islands Flag and Torch-bearer

(Des McCombie Skinner Studio. Litho Questa)

1984 (2 July). *20th Anniv of Asia-Pacific Broadcasting Union. T* **147** *and similar horiz designs. Multicoloured.* W w **14** (*sideways*). *P* 13½ × 14.

524 12 c. Type **147** 15 15
525 45 c. Radio City, Guadalcanal 60 60
526 60 c. S.I.B.C. studios, Honiara 75 80
527 $1 S.I.B.C. Broadcasting House .. .. 1·25 1·40
524/7 .. .. *Set of* 4 2·50 2·75

(Des McCombie Skinner Studio. Litho Format)

1984 (4 Aug–22 Sept). *Olympic Games, Los Angeles. T* **148** *and similar multicoloured designs.* W w **14** (*sideways on* 25 *c. to* $1). *P* 14 × 13½ (12 *c.*) *or* 13½ × 14 (*others*).

528 12 c. Type **148** 15 20
529 25 c. Lawson Tama Stadium, Honiara (*horiz*) 30 35
a. Booklet pane Nos. 529/30, each × 2 (22.9.84) .. .. 1·90
530 50 c. Honiara Community Centre (*horiz*) .. 65 70
531 95 c. Alick Wickham inventing crawl stroke, Bronte Baths, New South Wales, 1898 (*horiz*) (22.9.84) .. .. 1·25 1·40
a. Booklet pane of 1 .. .. 1·25
532 $1 Olympic Stadium, Los Angeles (*horiz*) .. 1·25 1·40
528/32 .. .. *Set of* 5 3·25 3·50

No. 531 only exists from $3·95 stamp booklets.

149 Little Pied Cormorant

150 The Queen Mother with Princess Margaret at Badminton Horse Trials

(Des I. Loe. Litho Questa)

1984 (21 Sept). *"Ausipex" International Stamp Exhibition, Melbourne. Birds. T* **149** *and similar vert designs. Multicoloured.* W w **14**. *P* 14½.

533 12 c. Type **149** 20 15
534 18 c. Spotbill Duck 30 30
535 35 c. Rufous Night Heron 50 50
536 $1 Eastern Broad-billed Roller ("Dollar-bird") .. .. 1·25 1·40
533/6 .. .. *Set of* 4 2·00 2·10
MS537 130 × 96 mm. Nos. 533/6 .. .. .. 2·00 2·50

(Des A. Theobald ($1.50), C. Abbott (others). Litho Questa)

1985 (7 June). *Life and Times of Queen Elizabeth the Queen Mother. T* **150** *and similar vert designs. Multicoloured.* W w **16**. *P* 14½ × 14.

538 12 c. With Winston Churchill at Buckingham Palace, VE Day, 1945 .. .. 10 10
539 25 c. Type **150** 25 30
540 35 c. At a St. Patrick's Day parade 30 35
541 $1 With Prince Henry at his christening (from photo by Lord Snowdon) 90 95
538/41 .. .. *Set of* 4 1·40 1·50
MS542 91 × 73 mm. $1.50, In a gondola, Venice, 1985. Wmk sideways .. .. 1·40 1·50

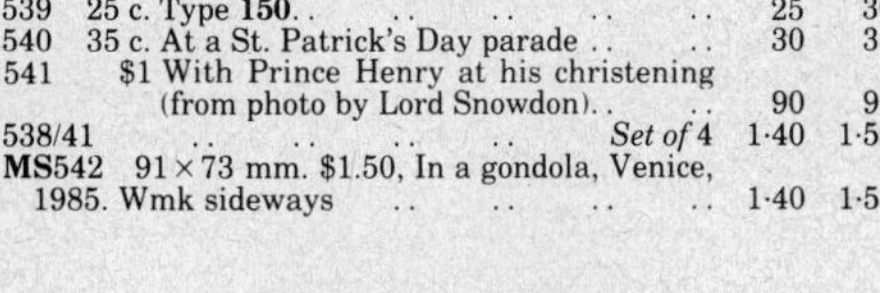

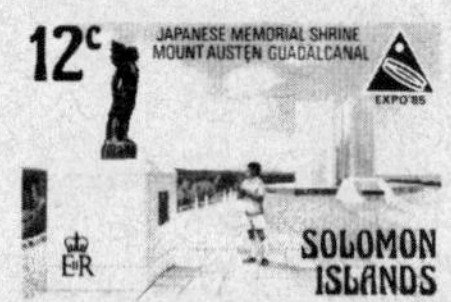

151 Japanese Memorial Shrine, Mount Austen, Guadalcanal

(Des D. Slater. Litho Questa)

1985 (28 June). *"Expo '85" World Fair, Japan. T* **151** *and similar horiz designs. Multicoloured.* W w **14** (*sideways*). *P* 14.

543 12 c. Type **151** 10 10
544 25 c. Digital telephone exchange equipment 25 30
545 45 c. Fishing vessel *Soltai No. 7* 40 45
546 85 c. Coastal village scene 75 80
543/6 .. .. *Set of* 4 1·40 1·50

152 Titiana Village

153 Girl Guide Activities

(Des O. Bell. Litho Walsall)

1985 (30 Aug). *Christmas. "Going Home for the Holiday". T* **152** *and similar horiz designs. Multicoloured.* W w **14** (*sideways*). *P* 14½.

547 12 c. Type **152** 10 10
548 25 c. Sigana, Santa Isabel 25 30
549 35 c. Artificial Island and Langa Lagoon .. 30 35
547/9 .. .. *Set of* 3 60 70

(Des D. Slater. Litho Walsall)

1985 (30 Sept). *75th Anniv of Girl Guide Movement* (12, 45 *c.*) *and International Youth Year* (*others*). *T* **153** *and similar vert designs. Multicoloured.* W w **16**. *P* 14.

550 12 c. Type **153** 20 10
551 15 c. Boys playing and child in wheelchair (Stop Polio) 25 20
552 25 c. Runners and Solomon Island scenes .. 35 30
553 35 c. Runners and Australian scenes ("Run Round Australia") 45 35
554 45 c. Guide colour party and badges .. 55 45
550/4 .. .. *Set of* 5 1·60 1·25
MS555 100 × 75 mm. Nos. 552/3 .. .. .. 55 60

154 Osprey

155 Water-powered Generator, Iriri

(Des Annette Robinson and C. Abbott. Litho Format)

1985 (25 Nov). *Birth Bicentenary of John J. Audubon (ornithologist). Sheet* 121 × 107 *mm containing T* **154** *and similar vert design.* W w **16**. *P* 14.

MS556 45 c. black, gold and deep blue; 50 c. (×2) multicoloured .. .. 2·00 2·25
Design:—45 c. John J. Audubon.

(Des B. Drake. Litho Walsall)

1986 (24 Jan). *Village Hydro-electric Schemes. Sheet* 109 × 135 *mm. containing T* **155** *and similar vert design. Multicoloured.* W w **16**. *P* 14.

MS557 30 c. Type **155**; 60 c. Domestic lighting .. 75 80

156 Building Red Cross Centre, Gizo

157 U.S. Memorial Obelisks, Henderson Airfield, Guadalcanal

(Des N. Shewring. Litho Walsall)

1986 (27 Mar). *Operation Raleigh (volunteer project). T* **156** *and similar diamond-shaped designs. Multicoloured.* W w **14**. *P* 14½ × 14.

558 18 c. Type **156** 35 20
559 30 c. Exploring rainforest 45 30
560 60 c. Observing Halley's Comet 75 60
561 $1 *Sir Walter Raleigh* and *Zebu* .. .. 1·10 1·10
558/61 .. .. *Set of* 4 2·40 2·00

Details of watermark and perforation for the stamps are given with the designs orientated so that the royal cypher appears in the top left corner.

(Des A. Theobald. Litho Questa)

1986 (21 Apr). *60th Birthday of Queen Elizabeth II. Vert designs as T* **110** *of Ascension. Multicoloured.* W w **16**. *P* 14½ × 14.

562 5 c. Princess Elizabeth and Duke of Edinburgh at Clydebank Town Hall, 1947 .. 10 10
563 18 c. At St. Paul's Cathedral for Queen Mother's 80th birthday service, 1980 .. 15 20
564 22 c. With children, Solomon Islands, 1982 .. 20 25
565 55 c. At Windsor Castle on her 50th birthday, 1976 .. .. 40 45
566 $2 At Crown Agents Head Office, London, 1983 .. .. 1·40 1·50
562/6 .. .. *Set of* 5 2·00 2·25

(Des D. Miller. Litho Cambec Press, Melbourne)

1986 (22 May). *"Ameripex '86" International Stamp Exhibition, Chicago. International Peace Year. Sheet* 100 × 75 *mm containing T* **157** *and similar horiz design. Multicoloured. P* 13½.

MS567 55 c. Type **157**; $1.65 Peace Corps emblem, President Kennedy and Statue of Liberty (25th anniv of Peace Corps) .. .. 1·50 1·60

(Des D. Miller. Litho Questa)

1986 (23 July). *Royal Wedding. Square designs as T* **112** *of Ascension. Multicoloured.* W w **16**. *P* 14.

568 55 c. Prince Andrew and Miss Sarah Ferguson 40 45
569 60 c. Prince Andrew at helm of Yacht *Bluenose II* off Nova Scotia, 1985 .. .. 45 50

+ 50c Cyclone Relief Fund 1986

158 *Freedom* (winner 1980) — (159)

(Des J. Dixon. Litho Leigh-Mardon Ltd, Melbourne)

1986 (22 Aug). *America's Cup Yachting Championship* (1987) (*1st issue*). *T* **158** *and similar vert designs. P* 14½.

570 18 c. multicoloured 15 20
a. Sheet of 50 .. .. 25·00
571 30 c. multicoloured 50 70
572 $1 multicoloured 75 80
570/2 .. .. *Set of* 3 1·25 1·50

Nos. 570/2 were issued as a sheet of 50, each horizontal strip of 5 being separated by gutter margins. The sheet contains 20 different designs at 18 c., 10 at 30 c. and 20 at $1. Individual stamps depict yachts, charts, the America's Cup or the emblem of the Royal Perth Yacht Club.

See also No. **MS**575.

1986 (23 Sept). *Cyclone Relief Fund. Nos.* 541 *and* **MS**567 *surch as T* **159** *in red.*

573 $1 + 50 c. Queen Mother with Prince Henry at his christening (from photo by Lord Snowdon) .. .. 1·10 1·25
MS574 100 × 75 mm. 55 c. + 25 c. Type **157**; $1.65 + 75 c. Peace Corps emblem, President Kennedy and Statue of Liberty (25th anniv of Peace Corps) .. .. 2·75 3·00

The surcharges on No. **MS**574 are vertical, in smaller type (length 16½ mm) and do not include "1986".

(Des J. Dixon. Litho Leigh-Mardon Ltd, Melbourne)

1987 (4 Feb). *America's Cup Yachting Championship* (*2nd issue*). *Sheet* 111 × 75 *mm, containing vert design as T* **158**. *Multicoloured. P* 14½.

MS575 $5 *Stars and Stripes* (1987 winner) .. 2·75 3·00

No. **MS**575 was also issued printed on gold foil and sold at a premium of $20 over the face value of the stamp.

160 *Dendrophyllia gracilis*

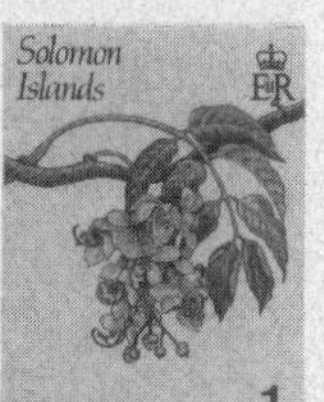

161 *Cassia fistula*

(Des D. Miller. Litho Format)

1987 (11 Feb). *Corals. T* **160** *and similar horiz designs. Multicoloured.* W w **16** (*sideways*). *P* 14.

576 18 c. Type **160** 15 15
577 45 c. *Dendronephthya sp* 40 40
578 60 c. *Clavularia sp* 55 55
579 $1.50, *Melithaea squamata* .. .. .. 1·10 1·10
576/9 .. .. *Set of* 4 2·00 2·00

(Des Gill Tomblin. Litho Walsall)

1987 (12 May)–**88**. *Flowers. T* **161** *and similar vert designs. Multicoloured.* W w **16**. *P* 14½ × 14.

580 1 c. Type **161** 10 10
581 5 c. *Allamanda cathartica* 10 10
582 10 c. *Catharanthus roseus* 10 10
583 18 c. *Mimosa pudica* 10 10
584 20 c. *Hibiscus rosa-sinensis* 10 10
585 22 c. *Clerodendrum thomsonae* 10 10
586 25 c. *Bauhinia variegata* 10 15
587 28 c. *Gloriosa rothschildiana* 15 20
588 30 c. *Heliconia solomonensis* 15 20
589 40 c. *Episcia* hybrid 20 25
590 45 c. *Bougainvillea* hybrid 20 25
591 50 c. *Alpinia purpurata* 25 30
592 55 c. *Plumeria rubra* 25 30
593 60 c. *Acacia farnesiana* 30 35
594 $1 *Ipomea purpurea* 45 50
595 $2 *Dianella ensifolia* .. .. 95 1·00
596 $5 *Passiflora foetida* .. .. 2·25 2·40
597 $10 *Hemigraphis sp* (1.3.88) .. .. 4·75 5·00
580/97 .. .. *Set of* 18 9·50 10·25

162 Mangrove Kingfisher on Branch **163** *Dendrobium conanthum*

(Des Josephine Martin. Litho Format)

1987 (15 July). *Mangrove Kingfisher. T* **162** *and similar vert designs. Multicoloured. W* w **14**. *P* 14.
598 60 c. Type **162**.. .. .. 55 55
a. Horiz strip of 4. Nos. 598/601 .. .. 2·00
599 60 c. Kingfisher diving 55 55
600 60 c. Entering water 55 55
601 60 c. Kingfisher with prey 55 55
598/601 .. .. *Set of* 4 2·00 2·00

Nos. 598/601 were printed together, *se-tenant*, in horizontal strips of 4 throughout the sheet, forming a composite design.

(Des Sue Wickison. Litho Walsall)

1987 (23 Sept). *Christmas. Orchids* (*1st series*). *T* **163** *and similar vert designs. Multicoloured. W* w **16**. *P* 13½×13.
602 18 c. Type **163**.. .. .. 20 10
603 30 c. *Spathoglottis plicata* 30 20
604 55 c. *Dendrobium gouldii* 45 35
605 $1.50, *Dendrobium goldfinchii* .. .. 1·25 1·40
602/5 .. .. *Set of* 4 2·00 1·90

See also Nos. 640/3.

164 Telecommunications Control Room and Satellite **165** Pupa of Queen Victoria's Birdwing

(Des D. Hartley. Litho CPE Australia Ltd, Melbourne)

1987 (16 Nov). *Asia-Pacific Transport and Communications Decade. T* **164** *and similar horiz designs. Multicoloured. P* 13½.
606 18 c. Type **164**.. .. .. 10 12
607 30 c. De Havilland "Twin Otter" mail plane 15 20
608 60 c. Guadalcanal road improvement project 35 40
609 $2 Beechcraft "Queen Air" and Henderson Control Tower .. .. 1·10 1·25
606/9 .. .. *Set of* 4 1·50 1·75

(Des R. Lewington. Litho Questa)

1987 (25 Nov). *Butterflies* (*3rd series*). *Queen Victoria's Birdwing. T* **165** *and similar vert designs. Multicoloured. W* w **16** (*sideways*). *P* 14½×14.
610 45 c. Type **165**.. .. .. 55 55
a. Strip of 4. Nos. 610/13 .. .. .. 2·00
611 45 c. Larva 55 55
612 45 c. Female butterfly 55 55
613 45 c. Male butterfly 55 55
610/13 .. .. *Set of* 4 2·00 2·00

Nos. 610/13 were printed together, *se-tenant*, in horizontal and vertical strips of 4 throughout the sheet of 16.

166 Student and National Agriculture Training Institute **167** Building a Fishing Boat

(Des D. Miller. Litho Format)

1988 (12 Feb). *10th Anniv of International Fund for Agricultural Development. T* **166** *and similar square designs. Multicoloured. W* w **16**. *P* 14½.
614 50 c. Type **166**.. .. .. 30 35
a. Horiz pair. Nos. 614/15.. .. .. 60 70
615 50 c. Students working in fields 30 35
616 $1 Transport by lorry 55 60
a. Horiz pair. Nos. 616/17.. .. .. 1·10 1·25
617 $1 Canoe transport.. .. .. .. 55 60
614/17 .. .. *Set of* 4 1·50 1·75

Nos. 614/15 and 616/17 were printed together, *se-tenant*, in horizontal pairs throughout the sheets, each pair forming a composite design.

(Des N. Shewring. Litho CPE Australia Ltd, Melbourne)

1988 (28 Apr). *"Expo '88" World Fair, Brisbane. T* **167** *and similar horiz designs. Multicoloured. P* 13½×14.
618 22 c. Type **167** 15 15
619 80 c. War canoe 40 45
620 $1.50, Traditional village 80 85
618/20 .. .. *Set of* 3 1·25 1·25
MS621 130 × 53 mm. Nos. 618/20 .. .. 1·25 1·40

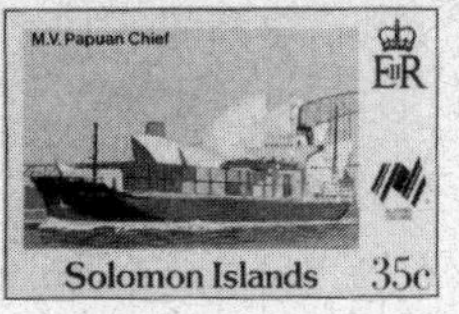

168 *Todos los Santos* in Estrella Bay, 1568 **169** *Papuan Chief* (container ship)

(Des M. Bradbury and J. Sayer. Litho Walsall)

1988 (6 July). *10th Anniv of Independence. T* **168** *and similar horiz designs. Multicoloured. W* w **14** (*sideways*). *P* 13×13½.
622 22 c. Type **168** 15 15
623 55 c. Raising the Union Jack, 1893 .. 30 35
624 80 c. High Court Building 40 45
625 $1 Dancers at traditional celebration .. 55 60
622/5 .. .. *Set of* 4 1·25 1·40

(Des E. Nisbet. Litho Walsall)

1988 (30 July). *Bicentenary of Australian Settlement and "Sydpex '88" National Stamp Exhibition, Sydney. T* **169** *and similar horiz designs. Multicoloured. W* w **16** (*sideways*). *P* 14.
626 35 c. Type **169** 20 25
627 60 c. *Nimos* (container ship) 30 35
628 70 c. *Malaita* (liner) 40 45
629 $1.30, *Makambo* (freighter) 70 75
626/9 .. .. *Set of* 4 1·40 1·60
MS630 140 × 76 mm. Nos. 626/9. W w **14** (sideways) .. .. 1·60 1·75

170 Archery **171** *Bulbophyllum dennisii*

(Des Joan Thompson. Litho Walsall)

1988 (5 Aug). *Olympic Games, Seoul. T* **170** *and similar multicoloured designs. W* w **16**. *P* 14½.
631 22 c. Type **170** 15 15
632 55 c. Weightlifting 35 40
633 70 c. Athletics 40 55
634 80 c. Boxing 45 60
631/4 .. .. *Set of* 4 1·25 1·50
MS635 100 × 80 mm. $2 Olympic Stadium (*horiz*). W w **14** (sideways) .. .. .. 1·10 1·25

(Des D. Miller (22, 65 c.), O. Bell and D. Miller (50 c.), E. Nisbet and D. Miller ($2). Litho Questa)

1988 (31 Oct). *300th Anniv of Lloyd's of London. Designs as T* **123** *of Ascension. W* w **16** (*sideways on* 50, 65 *c.*). *P* 14.
636 22 c. brownish black and brown 20 15
637 50 c. multicoloured 35 30
638 65 c. multicoloured 50 45
639 $2 multicoloured .. .. .. 1·40 1·50
636/9 .. .. *Set of* 4 2·25 2·25

Designs: *Vert*—22 c. King George V and Queen Mary laying foundation stone of Leadenhall Street Building, 1925; $2 *Empress of China*, 1911. *Horiz*—50 c. *Forthbank* (container ship); 65 c. Soltel satellite communications station.

(Des Sue Wickison. Litho Walsall)

1989 (20 Jan). *Orchids* (*2nd series*). *T* **171** *and similar vert designs. Multicoloured. W* w **14**. *P* 13½ × 13.
640 22 c. Type **171** 25 15
641 35 c. *Calanthe langei* 35 30
642 55 c. *Bulbophyllum blumei* 55 45
643 $2 *Grammatophyllum speciosum* .. 1·60 1·75
640/3 .. .. *Set of* 4 2·50 2·40

172 Red Cross Workers with Handicapped Children **173** *Phyllidia varicosa*

(Des A. Theobald. Litho Questa)

1989 (16 May). *125th Anniv of International Red Cross. T* **172** *and similar horiz designs. Multicoloured. W* w **16** (*sideways*). *P* 14½.
644 35 c. Type **172** 20 25
a. Horiz pair. Nos. 644/5 .. .. .. 40 50
645 35 c. Handicapped Children Centre minibus 20 25
646 $1.50, Blood donor 80 85
a. Horiz pair. Nos. 646/7 .. .. 1·60 1·75
647 $1.50, Balance test 80 85
644/7 .. .. *Set of* 4 1·75 2·00

Nos. 644/5 and 646/7 were each printed together, *se-tenant*, in horizontal pairs throughout the sheets, each pair forming a composite design.

(Des Sue Wickison. Litho Questa)

1989 (30 June). *Nudibranchs* (*Sea Slugs*). *T* **173** *and similar horiz designs. Multicoloured. W* w **14** (*sideways*). *P* 14×14½.
648 22 c. Type **173** 15 15
649 70 c. *Chromodoris bullocki* 55 55
650 80 c. *Chromodoris leopardus* 55 55
651 $1.50, *Phidiana indica* .. .. .. 1·00 1·00
648/51 .. .. *Set of* 4 2·25 2·25

(Des A. Theobald ($4), D. Miller (others). Litho Questa)

1989 (20 July). *20th Anniv of First Manned Landing on Moon. Multicoloured designs as T* **126** *of Ascension. W* w **16** (*sideways on* 35, 70 *c.*). *P* 14×13½ (22, 80 *c.*) *or* 14 (*others*).
652 22 c. "Apollo 16" descending by parachute .. 10 15
653 35 c. Launch of "Apollo 16" (30×30 *mm*) .. 20 25
654 70 c. "Apollo 16" emblem (30×30 *mm*) .. 40 45
655 80 c. Ultra-violet colour photograph of Earth 40 45
652/5 .. .. *Set of* 4 1·00 1·10
MS656 100×83 mm. $4 Moon's surface seen from Space. Wmk inverted. P 14×13½ .. .. 2·50 2·75

174 Five Stones Catch **175** Fishermen and Butterfly

(Des D. Miller ($3), R. Stewart (others). Litho B.D.T. ($3) or Walsall (others))

1989 (17 Nov). *"World Stamp Expo '89", International Stamp Exhibition, Washington. Children's Games. T* **174** *and similar multicoloured designs. W* w **16** (*sideways on* 67, 73 *c.*). *P* 14.
657 5 c. Type **174** 10 10
658 67 c. Blowing soap bubbles (*horiz*) 35 40
659 73 c. Coconut shell game (*horiz*) 40 45
660 $1 Seed wind sound 55 60
657/60 .. .. *Set of* 4 1·25 1·40
MS661 72×72 mm. $3 Softball. *W* w **14** .. 1·50 1·60

(Des N. Kohia and C. Vendi, adapted G. Vasarhelyi. Litho Questa)

1989 (30 Nov). *Christmas. T* **175** *and similar horiz designs. Multicoloured. W* w **16** (*sideways*). *P* 14.
662 18 c. Type **175** 10 10
663 25 c. The Nativity 15 20
664 45 c. Hospital ward at Christmas 25 30
665 $1.50, Village tug-of-war 80 90
662/5 .. .. *Set of* 4 1·10 1·25

176 Man wearing Headband, Necklace and Sash

(Des Sue Wickison. Litho Questa)

1990 (14 Mar). *Personal Ornaments. T* **176** *and similar vert designs. Multicoloured. W* w **14**. *P* 14.
666 5 c. Type **176** 10 10
667 12 c. Pendant 10 10
668 18 c. Man wearing medallion, nose ring and earrings 10 10
669 $2 Forehead ornament .. .. .. 1·10 1·25
666/9 .. .. *Set of* 4 1·10 1·25

POSTAGE DUE STAMPS

D 1

(Typo B.W.)

1940 (1 Sept). *Wmk Mult Script CA. P* 12.
D1 D 1 1d. emerald-green .. .. .. 3·25 6·50
D2 2d. scarlet .. .. 3·75 6·50
D3 3d. brown .. .. 4·25 10·00
D4 4d. blue .. .. 6·00 11·00
D5 5d. grey-green .. .. 7·00 14·00
D6 6d. purple .. .. 7·50 15·00
D7 1s. violet .. .. 11·00 26·00
D8 1s. 6d. turquoise-green.. .. .. 20·00 45·00
D1/8 .. .. *Set of* 8 55·00 £120
D1/8 Perf "Specimen" .. .. *Set of* 8 £150

Somaliland Protectorate

Egyptian post offices were opened in Somaliland during 1876 and the stamps of Egypt were used there until the garrisons were withdrawn in 1884.

Cancellations for these offices have been identified as follows (for illustrations of postmark types see after EGYPT):

BARBARA (Berbera). *Open* 1876? *to* 1884. Postmark type D.

ZEILA *Open* 1876 *to* 1884. Postmark types D, or as E without "V. R." (spelt ZEJLA). One example with seal type cancellation is also known.

Stamps of India were used at the two post offices from 1884 until 1903, Berbera usually using a circular datestamp and Zaila a squared circle postmark.

The Protectorate Post Office was established on 1 June 1903, when control of British Somaliland was transferred from the Indian Government to the British Foreign Office.

PRICES FOR STAMPS ON COVER TO 1945

Nos. 1/11	*from* × 25
Nos. 12/13	—
Nos. 18/22	*from* × 12
Nos. 23/4	—
Nos. 25/30	*from* × 30
Nos. 32/59	*from* × 12
Nos. 60/92	*from* × 6
Nos. 93/104	*from* × 3
Nos. 105/16	*from* × 4
Nos. O1/13	*from* × 6
Nos. O14/15	—

BRITISH SOMALILAND

(1)

2

3

SETTINGS OF TYPE 1

In all printings the ½, 1, 2, 2½, 3, 4, 8, 12 a. and 1 r. values were overprinted from a setting of 240 (2 panes 12 × 10, one above the other), covering the entire sheet at one operation.

The 6 a., which was in sheets of 320 (4 panes, each 8 × 10), had a modified setting of 160, applied twice to each sheet.

The high values were overprinted in sheets of 96 (8 panes, each 4 × 3).

The settings for the low value stamps contained two slightly different styles of overprint, identified by the position of "B" of "BRITISH". Type A shows this letter over the "M" of "SOMALILAND" and Type B over the "OM".

For the first printing with the overprint at the top of the design the 240 position setting showed all the stamps in the upper pane and 63 in the lower as Type A, with the remaining 57 as Type B. When the setting was used for the printing with overprint at foot it was amended slightly so that one of the Type A examples in the upper pane became a Type B.

The 6 a. value with overprint at top shows 250 examples of Type A and 70 as Type B in each sheet. This proportion altered in the printing with overprint at foot to 256 as Type A and 64 as Type B.

OVERPRINT VARIETIES

Missing second "I" in "BRITISH"—Occurs on the stamps with overprint at top from R.2/6 of the upper pane and R.5/1 of the lower, although it is believed that the example on the 2½ a. (No. 4a) only occurs from the second position. On the later printing with overprint at foot a similar error can be found on R.7/12 of the upper pane. Some examples of both these errors show traces of the letter remaining, but the prices quoted are for stamps with it completely omitted.

Figure "1" for first "I" in "BRITISH"—Occurs on R.6/4 of the upper pane for all printings of the 240 impression setting. In addition it has been reported from R.7/12 of the Queen Victoria 2½, 12 a. and 1 r. with overprint at foot. Both versions of the 6 a. show the variety on R.6/4 of the upper left and upper right panes.

Curved overprint—Occurs on R.3/4 of the top right-hand pane of the high values.

"SUMALILAND"—Occurs on R.2/9 of the upper pane for all low values with the overprint at foot, except the 6 a. A similar variety occurs on the high values from the same series on R.1/3 of the top left pane.

"SOMAL.LAND"—Occurs on R.7/5 of the lower pane from the 240 impression setting with the overprint at foot. In addition the Edwardian values of this series also have an example on R.6/7. The 6 a. has examples of the flaw on R.6/9 and R.7/5 of both the lower right and left panes. A similar variety occurs on the high values from the same series at R.3/4 of the third pane in the left-hand column.

1903 (1 June). *Stamps of India optd with T* 1, *at top of stamp, in Calcutta.*

1 **23** ½ a. yellow-green .. 65 1·75
a. "BRIT SH" .. £130
2 **25** 1 a. carmine .. 65 1·50
a. "BRIT SH" .. £150 £225
b. "BR1TISH" .. £110
3 **27** 2 a. pale violet .. 50 40
a. "BRIT SH" .. £250
b. "BR1TISH" .. £200
c. Opt double .. £600
4 **36** 2½ a. ultramarine .. 2·00 1·75
a. "BRIT SH" .. £325
b. "BR1TISH" .. £225
5 **28** 3 a. brown-orange .. 1·10 1·75
a. "BRIT SH" .. £350
b. "BR1TISH" .. £250
6 **29** 4 a. slate-green .. 1·25 2·75
a. "BR1TISH" .. £250
7 **21** 6 a. olive-bistre .. 3·50 4·50
a. "BR1TISH" .. £180
8 **31** 8 a. dull mauve .. 1·50 5·00
a. "BR1TISH" .. £250
9 **32** 12 a. purple/*red* .. 1·75 7·00
a. "BR1TISH" .. £250
10 **37** 1 r. green and carmine .. 3·25 10·00
a. "BR1TISH" .. £275
11 **38** 2 r. carmine and yellow-brown .. 19·00 27·00
a. Curved opt .. £100
12 3 r. brown and green .. 17·00 32·00
a. Curved opt .. £125
13 5 r. ultramarine and violet .. 20·00 40·00
a. Curved opt .. £150
1/13 .. *Set of* 13 65·00 £120

1903 (1 Sept–2 Nov). *Stamps of India optd with T* 1, *at bottom of stamp, in Calcutta.* (a) *On issues of Queen Victoria.*

18 **36** 2½ a. ultramarine (2.11) .. 1·25 4·25
a. "BR1TISH" .. £140
b. "SUMALILAND" .. £180
c. "SOMAL.LAND" .. £180
19 **21** 6 a. olive-bistre (2.11) .. 1·75 4·25
a. "BR1TISH" .. £160
b. "SOMAL.LAND" .. £100
20 **32** 12 a. purple/*red* (2.11) .. 3·50 12·00
a. "BR1TISH" .. £160
b. "SUMALILAND" .. £250
c. "SOMAL.LAND" .. £250
21 **37** 1 r. green and carmine (2.11) .. 2·00 10·00
a. "BR1TISH" .. £180
b. "SUMALILAND" .. £300
c. "SOMAL.LAND" .. £300
22 **38** 2 r. carmine and yellow-brown (2.11) .. 48·00 60·00
a. Curved opt .. £250
b. "SUMALILAND" .. £250
c. "SOMAL.LAND" .. £250
23 3 r. brown and green (2.11) .. 48·00 70·00
a. Opt double (one albino), both inverted .. £450
b. Curved opt .. £250
c. "SUMALILAND" .. £250
d. "SOMAL.LAND" .. £250
24 5 r. ultramarine and violet (2.11) .. 38·00 60·00
a. Curved opt .. £200
b. "SUMALILAND" .. £200
c. "SOMAL.LAND" .. £200

(b) *On issues of King Edward VII*

25 **42** ½ a. green .. 65 55
a. "BRIT SH" .. £275
b. "BR1TISH" .. 60·00
c. "SUMALILAND" .. 60·00
d. "SOMAL.LAND" .. 20·00
26 **43** 1 a. carmine (8.10) .. 50 30
a. "BRIT SH" .. £175
b. "BR1TISH" .. 65·00 65·00
c. "SUMALILAND" .. 65·00
d. "SOMAL.LAND" .. 22·00 22·00
27 **44** 2 a. violet (2.11) .. 1·00 2·50
a. "BRIT SH" .. £750
b. "BR1TISH" .. £160
c. "SUMALILAND" .. £160
d. "SOMAL.LAND" .. 38·00
28 **46** 3 a. orange-brown (2.11) .. 1·00 2·50
a. "BR1TISH" .. £160
b. "SUMALILAND" .. £160
c. "SOMAL.LAND" .. 38·00
29 **47** 4 a. olive (2.11) .. 1·00 4·00
a. "BR1TISH" .. £180
b. "SUMALILAND" .. £180
c. "SOMAL.LAND" .. 45·00
30 **49** 8 a. mauve (2.11) .. 1·25 2·25
a. "BR1TISH" .. £200
b. "SUMALILAND" .. £200
c. "SOMAL.LAND" .. 55·00
18/30 .. *Set of* 13 £120 £200

(Typo D.L.R.)

1904 (15 Feb–3 Sept). (a) *Wmk Crown CA. P* 14.

32 **2** ½ a. dull green and green .. 30 2·50
33 1 a. grey-black and red (3.9) .. 90 1·75
34 2 a. dull and bright purple (3.9) .. 1·50 1·00
35 2½ a. bright blue (3.9) .. 1·75 3·00
36 3 a. chocolate and grey-green (3.9) .. 1·00 2·25
37 4 a. green and black (3.9) .. 1·50 2·75
38 6 a. green and violet (3.9) .. 3·00 8·50
39 8 a. grey-black and pale blue (3.9) .. 2·75 5·50
40 12 a. grey-black and orange-buff (3.9) .. 5·50 11·00

(b) *Wmk Crown CC. P* 14

41 **3** 1 r. green (3.9) .. 12·00 26·00
42 2 r. dull and bright purple (3.9) .. 28·00 48·00
43 3 r. green and black (3.9) .. 28·00 48·00
44 5 r. grey-black and red (3.9) .. 30·00 48·00
32/44 .. *Set of* 13 £100 £190
32/44 Optd "Specimen" .. *Set of* 13 £180

1905 (July)–**11**. *Wmk Mult Crown CA. P* 14.

45 **2** ½ a. dull green and green, **O** .. 60 3·25
46 1 a. grey-black and red, **OC** (10.7.05) .. 1·25 1·25
47 2 a. dull and bright purple, **OC** .. 3·50 7·00
48 2½ a. bright blue, **O** .. 3·00 10·00
49 3 a. chocolate and grey-green, **OC** .. 1·50 7·00
50 4 a. green and black, **OC** .. 2·00 10·00
51 6 a. green and violet, **OC** .. 2·00 10·00
52 8 a. grey-black and pale blue, **O** .. 2·50 6·50
a. Black and blue, **C** (27.1.11) .. 32·00 55·00
53 12 a. grey-black and orange-buff, **O** .. 2·75 10·00
a. Blk & orge-brn, **C** (9.11.11) .. 15·00 42·00

1909 (30 Apr–May). *Wmk Mult Crown CA. P* 14.

58 **2** ½ a. bluish green, **O** (May) .. 6·00 10·00
59 1 a. red, **O** (Optd S. £25) .. 2·50 75
45/59 .. *Set of* 11 25·00 70·00

4

5

(Typo D.L.R.)

1912 (Nov)–**19**. *Wmk Mult Crown CA. P* 14.

60 **4** ½ a. green, **O** (11.13) .. 20 1·75
61 1 a. red, **O** .. 90 50
a. Scarlet, **O** (1917) .. 3·00 1·25
62 2 a. dull and bright purple, **C** (12.13) .. 3·50 7·00
a. Dull purple and violet-purple, **C** (4.19) .. 8·00 14·00
63 2½ a. bright blue, **O** (10.13) .. 80 4·50
64 3 a. chocolate and grey-green, **C** (10.13) 80 3·75
65 4 a. green and black, **C** (12.12) .. 80 4·75
66 6 a. green and violet, **C** (4.13) .. 80 3·25
67 8 a. grey-black and pale blue, **C** (10.13) 1·25 7·00
68 12 a. grey-black and orange-buff, **C** (10.13) .. 1·25 11·00
69 **5** 1 r. green, **C** .. 4·25 8·00
70 2 r. dull purple and purple, **C** (4.19) .. 18·00 40·00
71 3 r. green and black, **C** (4.19) .. 42·00 65·00
72 5 r. black and scarlet, **C** (4.19) .. 45·00 85·00
60/72 .. *Set of* 13 £110 £225
60/72 Optd "Specimen" .. *Set of* 13 £150

1921. *Wmk Mult Script CA. P* 14.

73 **4** ½ a. blue-green, **O** .. 40 2·25
74 1 a. carmine-red, **O** .. 40 30
75 2 a. dull and bright purple, **C** .. 60 1·00
76 2½ a. bright blue, **O** .. 40 3·50
77 3 a. chocolate and green, **C** .. 2·50 6·50
78 4 a. green and black, **C** .. 2·50 3·75
79 6 a. green and violet, **C** .. 1·50 8·00
80 8 a. grey-black and pale blue, **C** .. 1·50 5·00
81 12 a. grey-black and orange-buff, **C** .. 5·50 15·00
82 **5** 1 r. dull green, **C** .. 5·50 23·00
83 2 r. dull purple and purple, **C** .. 14·00 32·00
84 3 r. dull green and black, **C** .. 26·00 65·00
85 5 r. black and scarlet, **C** .. 45·00 95·00
73/85 .. *Set of* 13 95·00 £225
73/85 Optd "Specimen" .. *Set of* 13 £150

1935 (6 May). *Silver Jubilee. As Nos.* 91/4 *of Antigua but ptd by Waterlow. P* 11 × 12.

86 1 a. deep blue and scarlet .. 80 1·25
87 2 a. ultramarine and grey .. 80 1·25
j. Kite and vertical log .. 25·00
88 3 a. brown and deep blue .. 1·75 3·50
j. Kite and vertical log .. 40·00
k. Kite and horizontal log .. 40·00
89 1 r. slate and purple .. 5·00 6·00
j. Kite and vertical log .. 70·00
k. Kite and horizontal log .. 60·00
86/9 .. *Set of* 4 7·50 11·00
86/9 Perf "Specimen" .. *Set of* 4 75·00

For illustrations of plate varieties see Omnibus section following Zululand.

1937 (13 May). *Coronation. As Nos.* 13/15 *of Aden.*

90 1 a. scarlet .. 10 10
91 2 a. grey-black .. 20 25
92 3 a. bright blue .. 45 50
90/2 .. *Set of* 3 65 70
90/2 Perf "Specimen" .. *Set of* 3 50·00

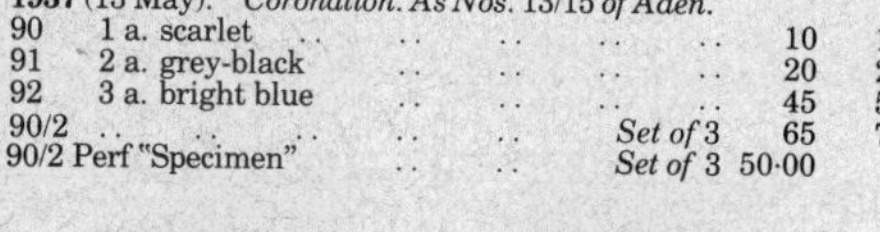

6 Berbera Blackhead Sheep

7 Lesser Kudu

8 Somaliland Protectorate

(Des H. W. Claxton. Recess Waterlow)

1938 (10 May). *Portrait to left. Wmk Mult Script CA. P* 12½.

93 **6** ½ a. green .. 15 60
94 1 a. scarlet .. 15 10
95 2 a. maroon .. 15 15
96 3 a. bright blue .. 1·50 1·75
97 **7** 4 a. sepia .. 80 1·75
98 6 a. violet .. 1·25 3·75
99 8 a. grey .. 65 3·75
100 12 a. red-orange .. 65 5·00

101 8 1 r. green .. 5·50 20·00
102 2 r. purple .. 6·50 16·00
103 3 r. bright blue .. 6·00 16·00
104 5 r. black .. 11·00 16·00
a. Imperf between (horiz pair) .. £5500
93/104 .. *Set of* 12 30·00 75·00
93/104 Perf "Specimen" .. *Set of* 12 £120

Following the Italian Occupation during 1940–41 the stamps of ADEN were used at Berbera from 1 July 1941 until 26 April 1942.

9 Berbera Blackhead Sheep

5 Cents
(10)

1 Shilling
(11)

(Recess Waterlow)

1942 (27 Apr). *As T* **6/8** *but with full-face portrait of King George VI, as in T* **9**. *Wmk Mult Script CA. P* 12½.
105 **9** ½ a. green .. 10 10
106 1 a. scarlet .. 10 10
107 2 a. maroon .. 30 10
108 3 a. bright blue .. 20 10
109 **7** 4 a. sepia .. 25 10
110 6 a. violet .. 25 10
111 8 a. grey .. 25 10
112 12 a. red-orange .. 70 10
113 **8** 1 r. green .. 45 25
114 2 r. purple .. 1·00 1·75
115 3 r. bright blue .. 1·10 4·50
116 5 r. black .. 3·00 3·75
105/16 .. *Set of* 12 7·00 10·00
105/16 Perf "Specimen" .. *Set of* 12 £130

1946 (15 Oct). *Victory. As Nos.* 28/9 *of Aden. P* 13½ × 14.
117 1 a. carmine .. 10 10
a. Perf 13½ .. 3·75 26·00
118 3 a. blue .. 10 10
117/18 Perf "Specimen" .. *Set of* 2 40·00

1949 (28 Jan). *Royal Silver Wedding. As Nos.* 30/1 *of Aden.*
119 1 a. scarlet .. 10 10
120 5 r. black .. 2·50 3·00

1949 (10 Oct). *75th Anniv of U.P.U. As Nos.* 114/17 *of Antigua and surch with new values.*
121 1 a. on 10 c. carmine .. 10 10
122 3 a. on 30 c. deep blue (R.) .. 25 20
123 6 a. on 50 c. purple .. 25 20
124 12 a. on 1s. red-orange .. 35 20
121/4 .. *Set of* 4 90 65

1951 (2 Apr). 1942 *issue surch as T* **10/11**.
125 5 c. on ½ a. green .. 10 10
126 10 c. on 2 a. maroon .. 10 10
127 15 c. on 3 a. bright blue .. 10 10
128 20 c. on 4 a. sepia .. 10 10
129 30 c. on 6 a. violet .. 25 10
130 50 c. on 8 a. grey .. 25 10
131 70 c. on 12 a. red-orange .. 25 40
132 1 s. on 1 r. green .. 20 10
133 2 s. on 2 r. purple .. 40 3·00
134 2 s. on 3 r. bright blue .. 85 2·50
135 5 s. on 5 r. black (R.) .. 2·00 4·00
125/35 .. *Set of* 11 4·00 9·00

At least one cover is known postmarked 1 April, in error, at Burao.

1953 (2 June). *Coronation. As No.* 47 *of Aden.*
136 15 c. black and green .. 10 15

12 Camel and Gurgi

13 Askari

(Recess B.W.)

1953 (15 Sept)–**58**. *T* **12/13** *and similar horiz designs. Wmk Mult Script CA. P* 12½.
137 **12** 5 c. slate-black .. 10 10
138 **13** 10 c. red-orange .. 60 10
a. Salmon (20.3.58) .. 1·50 45
139 **12** 15 c. blue-green .. 30 15
140 20 c. scarlet .. 30 15
141 **13** 30 c. reddish brown .. 60 10
142 – 35 c. blue .. 75 25
143 – 50 c. brown and rose-carmine .. 75 10
144 – 1 s. light blue .. 40 10
145 – 1 s. 30 c. ultramarine and black (1.9.58) 2·00 3·00
146 – 2 s. brown and bluish violet .. 6·00 2·00
147 – 5 s. red-brown and emerald .. 6·50 5·50
148 – 10 s. brown and reddish violet .. 4·00 10·00
137/48 .. *Set of* 12 20·00 19·00

Designs:—35 c., 2 s. Somali Stock Dove; 50 c., 5 s. Martial Eagle; 1 s. Berbera Blackhead Sheep; 1 s. 30, Sheikh Isaaq's Tomb; 10 s. Taleh Fort.

OPENING OF THE LEGISLATIVE COUNCIL 1957
(19)

LEGISLATIVE COUNCIL UNOFFICIAL MAJORITY, 1960
(20)

1957 (21 May). *Opening of Legislative Council. Nos.* 140 *and* 144 *optd with T* **19**.
149 20 c. scarlet .. 10 10
150 1 s. light blue .. 10 10

1960 (5 Apr). *Legislative Council's Unofficial Majority. Nos.* 140 *and* 145 *optd as T* **20**.
151 20 c. scarlet .. 10 10
152 1 s. 30, ultramarine and black .. 10 10

OFFICIAL STAMPS

BRITISH SOMALILAND
(O 1)

SERVICE BRITISH SOMALILAND
(O 2)

SERVICE O.H.M.S.
(O 3)

SETTING OF TYPE O 1

The 240 impression setting used for the Official stamps differs considerably from that on the contemporary postage issue with overprint at foot, although the "BR1TISH" error can still be found on R.6/4 of the upper pane. The Official setting is recorded as consisting of 217 overprints as Type A and 23 as Type B.

OVERPRINT VARIETIES

Figure "1" for first "I" in "BRITISH". Occurs on R.6/4 of the upper pane as for the postage issue.
"BRITIS H"—Occurs on R.8, stamps 4 and 10 of the lower pane.

1903 (1 June). *Official stamps of India,* 1883–1900, *optd with Type* O 1 *in Calcutta.*
O1 **23** ½ a. yellow-green .. 3·50 48·00
a. "BR1TISH" .. £250
b. "BRITIS H" .. £125
O2 **25** 1 a. carmine .. 9·00 7·50
a. "BR1TISH" .. £275 £225
b. "BRITIS H" .. £140
O3 **27** 2 a. pale violet .. 8·00 45·00
a. "BR1TISH" .. £300
b. "BRITIS H" .. £180
O4 **31** 8 a. dull mauve .. 10·00 £350
a. "BR1TISH" .. £600
b. "BRITIS H" .. £300
O5 **37** 1 r. green and carmine .. 10·00 £475
a. "BR1TISH" .. £600
b. "BRITIS H" .. £300
O1/5 .. *Set of* 5 35·00 £800

The 8 a. is known with the stop omitted after the "M" of "O.H.M.S.".

SETTING OF TYPE O 2

This 240 impression setting of "BRITISH SOMALILAND" also differs from that used to prepare the postage issue with overprint at foot, although many of the errors from the latter still occur in the same positions for the Official stamps. The setting used for Nos. O6/9*f* contained 180 overprints as Type A and 60 as Type B.

OVERPRINT VARIETIES

Missing second "I" in "BRITISH"—Occurs R.7/12 of upper pane as for the postage issue.
Figure "1" for first "I" in "BRITISH"—Occurs R.6/4 of upper pane as for the postage issue.
"SUMALILAND"—Occurs R.2/9 of the upper pane as for the postage issue.
"SOMAL.LAND"—Occurs R.6/7 of the lower pane as for the postage issue.

SERVICE
(O 2*a*)

"SERVICE" in wrong fount (Type O 2*a*)—Occurs R.1/7 of lower pane.

1903. *Prepared for use, but not issued. Postage stamps of India, Queen Victoria* 1892 *issue* (1 *r.*) *or King Edward VII* 1902 *issue (others), optd with Type* O **2** *in Calcutta.*
O6 **42** ½ a. green .. 40
a. "BRIT SH" .. 70·00
b. "BR1TISH" .. 50·00
c. "SUMALILAND" .. 50·00
d. "SOMAL.LAND" .. 30·00
e. "SERVICE" as Type O 2*a* .. 40·00
O7 **43** 1 a. carmine .. 40
a. "BRIT SH" .. 70·00
b. "BR1TISH" .. 50·00
c. "SUMALILAND" .. 50·00
d. "SOMAL.LAND" .. 30·00
e. "SERVICE" as Type O 2*a* .. 40·00
O8 **44** 2 a. violet .. 70
a. "BRIT SH" .. £100
b. "BR1TISH" .. 70·00
c. "SUMALILAND" .. 70·00
d. "SERVICE" as Type O 2*a* .. 45·00
O9 **49** 8 a. mauve .. 5·00
a. "BRIT SH" .. £1400
b. "BR1TISH" .. £400
c. "SUMALILAND" .. £400
d. "SERVICE" as Type O 2*a* .. £400
O9*f* **37** 1 r. green and carmine .. 20·00
fa. "BRIT SH" .. £1400
fb. "BR1TISH" .. £400
fc. "SUMALILAND" .. £400
fd. "SOMAL.LAND" .. £400
fe. "SERVICE" as Type O 2*a* .. £400
O6/9*f* .. *Set of* 5 24·00

Used examples of the four lower values are known, but there is no evidence that such stamps did postal duty.

SETTING OF TYPE O 3

The anna values were overprinted in sheets of 120 (2 panes 6 × 10) from a setting matching the pane size. The full stop after the "M" on the fifth vertical column was either very faint or completely omitted. The prices quoted are for stamps with the stop missing; examples with a partial stop are worth much less.

The 1 r. value was overprinted from a separate setting of 60 which did not show the "missing stop" varieties.

1904 (1 Sept)–**05.** *Stamps of Somaliland Protectorate optd with Type* O **3**. *P* 14. (*a*) *Wmk Crown CA.*
O10 **2** ½ a. dull green and green .. 3·25 48·00
a. No stop after "M" .. £400
O11 1 a. grey-black and carmine .. 3·25 7·00
a. No stop after "M" .. £300 £375
O12 2 a. dull and bright purple .. £120 48·00
a. No stop after "M" .. £1400 £650
O13 8 a. grey-black and pale blue .. 75·00 £130
a. No stop after "M" .. £550

(*b*) *Wmk Mult Crown CA*
O14 **2** 2 a. dull and bright purple, O (7.05?) 75·00 £500
a. No stop after "M" .. £1200

(*c*) *Wmk Crown CC*
O15 **3** 1 r. green .. £150 £450
O10/13, O15 .. *Set of* 5 £300 £600
O10/13, O15 Optd "Specimen" .. *Set of* 5 £140

All Somaliland Protectorate stamps were withdrawn from sale on 25 June 1960 and until the unification on 1 July, issues of Italian Somalia together with Nos. 353/5 of Somalia Republic were used. Later issues will be found listed in Part 14 (*Africa since Independence N–Z*) of this catalogue.

South Africa

The following territories combined on 31 May 1910 to form the Union of South Africa (of which they became provinces) and their issues are listed in alphabetical order in this Catalogue:—

CAPE OF GOOD HOPE (incl Griqualand West)
NATAL (incl New Republic and Zululand)
ORANGE FREE STATE
TRANSVAAL

The provinces continued to use their existing issues until the introduction of Nos. 3/17. From 19 August 1910 the issues of any province were valid for use throughout the Union.

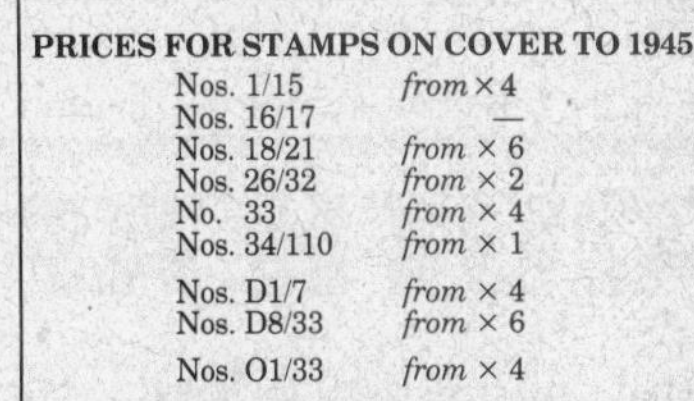

PRICES FOR STAMPS ON COVER TO 1945

Nos. 1/15	*from* × 4
Nos. 16/17	—
Nos. 18/21	*from* × 6
Nos. 26/32	*from* × 2
No. 33	*from* × 4
Nos. 34/110	*from* × 1
Nos. D1/7	*from* × 4
Nos. D8/33	*from* × 6
Nos. O1/33	*from* × 4

UNION OF SOUTH AFRICA

Although South Africa is now a republic, outside the British Commonwealth, all its stamp issues are listed together here purely as a matter of convenience to collectors.

1

(Des H. S. Wilkinson. Recess D.L.R.)

1910 (4 Nov). *Opening of Union Parliament. Inscribed bilingually. Wmk Multiple Rosettes. P* 14.
1 **1** 2½d. deep blue (H/S S. £325) .. 3·50 3·00
2 2½d. blue .. 2·00 1·25

The deep blue shade is generally accompanied by a blueing of the paper.

The price quoted for the "Specimen" handstamp is for the small italic type with capital and lower case letters.

2

3

4 Springbok's Head

(Typo D.L.R.)

1913 (1 Sept)–**24**. *Inscribed bilingually. W* **4**. (*a*) *P* 14.
3 **2** ½d. green .. 60 10
a. Stamp doubly printed .. £10000
b. Blue-green .. 1·75 10
c. Yellow-green .. 2·25 15
d. Booklet pane of 6 .. 24·00

No.	Type	Description	Un	Us
4	2	1d. rose-red (*shades*)	60	10
		a. Carmine-red	1·25	10
		b. Scarlet (*shades*)	85	15
		c. Booklet pane of 6	24·00	
5		1½d. chestnut (*shades*) (23.8.20)	30	10
		a. *Tête-bêche* (pair)	1·75	11·00
		b. Booklet pane of 6 (1921)	20·00	
6	3	2d. dull purple	1·25	10
		a. Deep purple	2·50	10
		b. Booklet pane of 6 (1922)	20·00	
7		2½d. bright blue	2·50	85
		a. Deep blue	5·00	3·00
8		3d. black and orange-red	5·50	25
		a. Black and dull orange-red	7·00	70
9		3d. ultramarine (*shades*) (4.10.22)	4·50	1·40
10		4d. orange-yellow and olive-green	9·00	45
		a. Orange-yellow and sage-green	7·50	40
11		6d. black and violet	5·50	15
		a. Black and bright violet	7·50	20
12		1s. orange	15·00	45
		a. Orange-yellow	25·00	55
13		1s. 3d. violet (*shades*) (1.9.20)	12·00	7·00
14		2s. 6d. purple and green	55·00	1·00
15		5s. purple and blue	£150	5·00
		a. Reddish purple and light blue	£150	8·00
16		10s. deep blue and olive-green	£250	5·50
17		£1 green and red (7.16)	£1000	£400
		a. Pale olive-green and red (1924)	£1300	£1600
3/17		*Set of* 15	£1400	£400
3/8, 10/17 Optd or H/S "Specimen"		*Set of* 14	£1700	

(*b*) *Coil stamps. P* 14 × *imperf*

No.	Type	Description	Un	Us
18	2	½d. green	4·50	1·00
19		1d. rose-red (13.2.14)	5·50	3·75
		a. Scarlet	7·00	4·00
20		1½d. chestnut (15.11.20)	5·00	4·25
21	3	2d. dull purple (7.10.21)	7·00	4·25
18/21		*Set of* 4	20·00	12·00

The 6d. exists with "Z" of "ZUID" wholly or partly missing due to wear of plate (*Price wholly missing, £75 un, £38 us*).

5

(Eng A. J. Cooper. Litho *Cape Times* Ltd)

1925 (26 Feb). *Air. Inscr bilingually. P* 12.

No.	Type	Description	Un	Us
26	5	1d. carmine	3·50	5·00
27		3d. ultramarine	7·00	7·00
28		6d. magenta	8·00	10·00
29		9d. green	17·00	45·00
26/9		*Set of* 4	32·00	60·00

Beware of forgeries of all values perforated 11, 11½ or 13.

INSCRIPTIONS. From 1926 until 1951 (also Nos. 167 and 262/5), most issues were inscribed in English and Afrikaans alternately throughout the sheets.

As we only stock these in *se-tenant* pairs, unused and used, we no longer quote for single used copies and they must be considered to be worth very much less than half the prices quoted for pairs. Prices are for horizontal pairs, vertical pairs being worth about 50% less.

Similarly, the War Effort bantam stamps (Nos. 96/103), and Nos. 124 and D30/3 are priced for units of two or three as the case may be.

PRICES for Nos. 30/135 are for horizontal pairs, *unless otherwise indicated.*

6 Springbok

7 *Dromedaris* (Van Riebeeck's ship)

8 Orange Tree

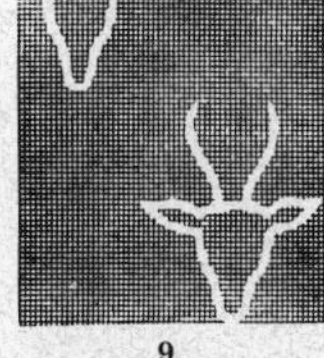

9

(Typo by Waterlow, from 1927 by Govt Printer, Pretoria)

1926 (1 Jan)–**27.** *W* **9.** *P* 14½ × 14.

No.	Type	Description	Un	Us
30	6	½d. black and green	2·25	1·75
		a. Missing "1" in "½"	£1500	
		b. Booklet pane of 6	25·00	
		c. Perf 13½ × 14 (1927)	£100	45·00
		ca. *Tête-bêche* (pair)	£1000	
		cb. Booklet pane of 6	£600	
31	7	1d. black and carmine	2·00	45
		a. Booklet pane of 6	25·00	
		b. Perf 13½ × 14 (1927)	£100	42·00
		ba. *Tête-bêche* (pair)	£1100	
		bb. Booklet pane of 6	£600	
32	8	6d. green and orange (1.5.26)	30·00	18·00
30/2		*Set of* 3	30·00	18·00

No. 30a exists in Afrikaans only. Nos. 30c and 31b were only issued in booklets.

Nos. 30/1 exist in coils, constructed from normal sheets.

For ½d. with pale grey centre, see No. 126.

For rotogravure printing see Nos. 42, etc.

10 "Hope"

(Recess B.W.)

1926 (1 Jan). *T* **10.** *Inscribed in English* (E) *or Afrikaans* (A). *W* **9.** *Imperf.*

No.	Description	E Un	E Us	A Un	A Us
		Single stamps			
33	4d. grey-blue (*shades*)	1·00	60	1·00	60

In this value the English and Afrikaans inscriptions are on separate sheets.

This stamp is known with private perforations or roulettes.

11 Union Buildings, Pretoria

12 Groot Schuur

12*a* A Native Kraal

13 Black and Blue Wildebeest

14 Ox-wagon inspanned

15 Ox-wagon outspanned

16 Cape Town and Table Bay

(Recess B.W.)

1927 (1 Mar)–**28.** *W* **9.** *P* 14 (*early ptgs*) *or* 14 × 13½ (*from* 1930 *onwards*).

No.	Type	Description	Un	Us
34	11	2d. grey and maroon	8·00	16·00
35	12	3d. black and red	18·00	25·00
35*a*	12*a*	4d. brown (23.3.28)	24·00	42·00
36	13	1s. brown and deep blue	30·00	40·00
37	14	2s. 6d. green and brown	£100	£200
38	15	5s. black and green	£225	£450
39	16	10s. bright blue and brown	£150	£125
		a. Centre inverted (*single stamp*)	£12000	
34/9		*Set of* 7	£500	£800
34/9 H/S "Specimen"		*Set of* 7	£1000	

17 D.H. "Moth"

(Typo Govt Ptg Wks, Pretoria)

1929 (16 Aug). *Air. Inscribed bilingually. No wmk. P* 14 × 13½.

No.	Type	Description	*Un single*	*Us single*
40	17	4d. green	5·00	2·50
41		1s. orange	8·00	10·00

PRINTER. All the following issues, except *where stated otherwise*, are printed by rotogravure (the design having either plain lines or a dotted screen) by the Government Printer, Pretoria.

I

II

The two types of the 1d. differ in the spacing of the horizontal lines in the side panels:—Type I close; Type II wide. The Afrikaans had the spacing of the words POSSEEL-INKOMSTE close in Type I and more widely spaced in Type II.

1930–45. *T* **6** *to* **8** *and* **11** *to* **14** *redrawn,* "SUIDAFRIKA" (*in one word*) *on Afrikaans stamps. W* **9.** *P* 15 × 14 (½*d.,* 1*d., and* 6*d.*) *or* 14.

No.	Description	Un	Us
42	½d. black and green (5.30)	1·75	1·50
	a. Two English or two Afrikaans stamps *se-tenant* (vert strip of 4)	40·00	
	b. *Tête-bêche*	£950	
	c. Booklet pane of 6	12·00	
43	1d. black and carmine (I) (4.30)	2·75	55
	a. *Tête-bêche*	£950	
	b. Frame omitted (*single stamp*)	£550	
	c. Booklet pane of 6	18·00	
43*d*	1d. black and carmine (II) (8.32)	25·00	2·25
44	2d. slate-grey and lilac (4.31)	14·00	4·00
	a. *Tête-bêche*	£1900	
	b. Frame omitted (*single stamp*)	£850	
	c. Booklet pane of 6	£110	
44*d*	2d. blue and violet (3.38)	£160	45·00
45	3d. black and red (11.31)	48·00	55·00
45*a*	3d. blue (10.33)	4·00	1·75
46	4d. brown (19.11.32)	75·00	50·00
46*a*	4d. brown (*shades*) (*again redrawn*) (1936)	2·50	1·50
47	6d. green and orange (5.31)	17·00	2·00
48	1s. brown and deep blue (14.9.32)	48·00	18·00
49	2s. 6d. green and brown (24.12.32)	90·00	75·00
49*a*	2s. 6d. blue and brown (1945)	14·00	8·00
42/9*a*	*Set of* 13	£450	£250

For similar designs with "SUID-AFRIKA" hyphenated, see Nos. 54 etc. and Nos. 114 etc.

Nos. 42/3, 43*d*/4 exist in coils.

No. 42a comes from the coil printing on the cylinder for which two horizontal rows were incorrectly etched so that two Afrikaans-inscribed stamps were followed by two English. This variety is normally without a coil join, although some examples do occur showing a repair join.

The 1d. (Type I) exists without watermark from a trial printing (*Price* £80 *un*).

The Rotogravure printings may be distinguished from the preceding Typographed and Recess printed issues by the following tests:—

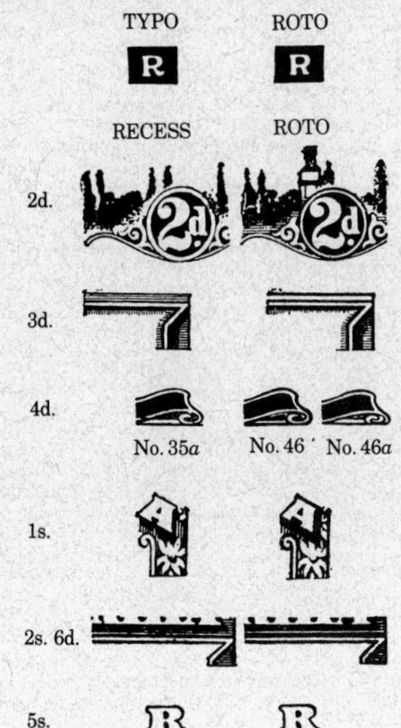

ROTOGRAVURE:

½d., 1d. and 6d. Leg of "R" in "AFR" ends squarely on the bottom line.

2d. The newly built War Memorial appears to the left of the value.

3d. Two fine lines have been removed from the top part of the frame.

4d. No. 46. The scroll is in solid colour.

No. 46*a*. The scroll is white with a crooked line running through it. (No. 35*a*. The scroll is shaded by the diagonal lines.)

1s. The shading of the last "A" partly covers the flower beneath.

2s. 6d. The top line of the centre frame is thick and leaves only one white line through it and the name.

5s. (Nos. 64/*a*). The leg of the "R" is straight.

Rotogravure impressions are generally coarser.

18 Church of the Vow

19 "The Great Trek"

20 A Voortrekker

21 Voortrekker Woman

1933 (3 May)–**36.** *Voortrekker Memorial Fund.* *W* **9.** *P* 14.

50	**18**	½d. +½d. black and green (16.1.36) ..	3·25	3·50
51	**19**	1d. +½d. grey-black and pink	3·25	1·50
52	**20**	2d. +1d. grey-green and purple ..	4·00	4·00
53	**21**	3d. +1½d. grey-green and blue ..	6·00	5·00
50/3		.. .. *Set of* 4	15·00	12·50

22 Gold Mine

22a Groot Schuur

I

II

III

Dies of 6d.

23 Groot Constantia

1933–49. "SUID-AFRIKA" (*hyphenated*) *on Afrikaans stamps.* *W* **9.** *P* 15 × 14 (½d., 1d. *and* 6d.) *or* 14 (*others*).

54	**6**	½d. grey and green (9.35)	2·50	80
		a. Coil stamp. Perf 13½ × 14 (1935) ..	24·00	30·00
		b. Booklet pane of 6 (with adverts on margins)	18·00	
56	**7**	1d. grey and carmine (*shades*) (19.4.34)	40	20
		a. Imperf (pair)	£150	
		b. Frame omitted (*single stamp*) ..	£250	
		c. Coil stamp. Perf 13½ × 14 (1935) ..	28·00	32·00
		d. Booklet pane of 6 (with adverts on margins) (1935)	6·00	
		e. Booklet pane of 6 (with blank margins) (1937)	7·00	
		f. Booklet pane of 2 (1937)	2·00	
		g. Booklet pane of 6 (without margins) (1938)	8·00	
		h. Booklet pane of 6 (with postal slogans on margins) (1948) ..	4·00	
		i. Grey and bright rose-carmine (7.48)	55	25
57	**22**	1½d. green and bright gold (12.11.36) ..	1·50	1·00
		a. Shading omitted from mine dump (in pair with normal) ..	75·00	
		b. Blue-green and dull gold (8.40) ..	5·00	1·40
		c. Booklet pane of 4 (1941) ..	15·00	
58	**11**	2d. blue and violet (11.38)	50·00	25·00
58*a*		2d. grey and dull purple (5.41) ..	20·00	30·00
59	**22*a***	3d. ultramarine (2.40)	3·75	60
61	**8**	6d. green and vermilion (I) (10.37) ..	65·00	16·00
61*a*		6d. green and vermilion (II) (6.38) ..	15·00	1·00
61*b*		6d. green and red-orange (III) (11.46) ..	10·00	75
62	**13**	1s. brown and chalky blue (2.39) ..	25·00	4·25
		a. Frame omitted (*single stamp*) ..	£850	
64	**15**	5s. black and green (10.33)	48·00	35·00
		a. Black and blue-green (9.49) ..	30·00	13·00
64*b*	**23**	10s. blue and sepia (8.39)	60·00	14·00
		ba. Blue and blackish brown (8.39) ..	32·00	3·00
54/64*ba*		(*only one 6d.*) .. .. *Set of* 10	£160	70·00

The ½d. and 1d. coil stamps may be found in blocks emanating from the residue of the large rolls which were cut into sheets and distributed to Post Offices.

Nos. 54 and 56 also exist in coils.

1d. Is printed from Type II. Frames of different sizes exist due to reductions made from time to time for the purpose of providing more space for the perforations.

3d. In No. 59 the frame is unscreened and composed of solid lines. Centre is diagonally screened. Scrolls above "3d." are clear lined, light in the middle and dark at sides.

6d. Die I. Green background lines faint. "SUID-AFRIKA" 16¼ mm long.

Die II. Green background lines heavy. "SUID-AFRIKA" 17 mm long. "S" near end of tablet. Scroll open.

Die III. Scroll closed up and design smaller (18 × 22 mm).

Single specimens of the 1930 issue inscribed in English may be distinguished from those listed above as follows:—

½d. and 1d. Centres in varying intensities of black instead of grey.

2d. The letters of "SOUTH AFRICA" are wider and thicker.

3d. The trees are shorter and the sky is lined.

6d. The frame is pale orange.

1s. The frame is greenish blue.

For similar designs, but printed in screened rotogravure, see Nos. 114 to 122*a*.

BOOKLET PANES. Booklets issued in 1935 contained ½d. and 1d. stamps in panes with advertisements in the top and bottom margins and no margin at right (Nos. 54b and 56d). These were replaced in 1937 by editions showing blank margins on all four sides (Nos. 56e and 64ca). Following a period when the booklet panes were without margins, a further 3s. booklet was issued in 1948 which had four margins on the panes and postal slogans at top and bottom (Nos. 56h, 87b and 114a).

JIPEX

1936

24 (24*a*)

(Des J. Booysen)

1935 (1 May). *Silver Jubilee. Inscr bilingually.* *W* **9.** *P* 15 × 14.

65	**24**	½d. black and blue-green	2·50	10·00
66		1d. black and carmine	2·75	4·00
67		3d. blue	23·00	48·00
68		6d. green and orange	42·00	60·00
65/8		.. .. *Set of* 4	65·00	£110

In stamps with English at top the ½d., 3d. and 6d. have "SILWER JUBILEUM" to left of portrait, and "POSTAGE REVENUE" or "POSTAGE" (3d. and 6d.) in left value tablet. In the 1d., "SILVER JUBILEE" is to the left of portrait. In alternate stamps the positions of English and Afrikaans inscriptions are reversed.

1936 (2 Nov). *Johannesburg International Philatelic Exhibition. Optd with T* **24*a***.

			Un sheet	*Us sheet*
MS69	**6**	½d. grey and green (No. 54) ..	4·00	10·00
MS70	**7**	1d. grey and carmine (No. 56)	3·00	7·00

Issued each in miniature sheet of six stamps with marginal advertisements.

25

25*a*

(Des J. Prentice)

1937 (12 May). *Coronation.* *W* **9** (*sideways*). *P* 14.

71	**25**	½d. grey-black and blue-green	25	40
72		1d. grey-black and carmine	35	40
73		1½d. orange and greenish blue	50	50
74		3d. ultramarine	2·25	1·40
75		1s. red-brown and turquoise-blue ..	5·50	3·25
		a. Hyphen omitted on Afrikaans stamp (R.2/13)	40·00	
71/5		.. .. *Set of* 5	8·00	5·50

1937–40. *W* **9.** *P* 15 × 14.

75*b*	**25*a***	½d. grey and green	4·50	90
		ba. Booklet pane of 6 (with blank margins) (1937)	22·00	
		bb. Booklet pane of 2 (1937) ..	7·00	
		bc. Booklet pane of 6 (without margins) (1938)	22·00	
		bd. Grey and blue-green (1940) ..	1·50	20

The lines of shading in T **25*a*** are all horizontal and thicker than in T **6**. In Nos. 75*b* and 75*bd* the design is composed of solid lines. For stamps with designs composed of dotted lines, see No. 114. Later printings of No. 75*bd* have a smaller design.

26 Voortrekker Ploughing

27 Wagon crossing Drakensberg

28 Signing of Dingaan–Retief Treaty

29 Voortrekker Monument

(Des W. Coetzer and J. Prentice)

1938 (14 Dec). *Voortrekker Centenary Memorial Fund.* *W* **9.** *P* 14 (*Nos.* 76/7) *or* 15 × 14 (*others*).

76	**26**	½d. + ½d. blue and green	7·00	4·00
77	**27**	1d. + 1d. blue and carmine	8·00	5·00
78	**28**	1½d. + 1½d. chocolate and blue-green ..	10·00	8·50
79	**29**	3d. + 3d. bright blue	11·00	9·50
76/9		.. .. *Set of* 4	32·00	26·00

30 Wagon Wheel

31 Voortrekker Family

(Des W. Coetzer and J. Prentice)

1938 (14 Dec). *Voortrekker Commemoration.* *W* **9.** *P* 15 × 14.

80	**30**	1d. blue and carmine	2·75	1·25
81	**31**	1½d. greenish blue and brown	3·50	1·25

32 Old Vicarage, Paarl, now a museum

33 Symbol of the Reformation

34 Huguenot Dwelling, Drakenstein Mountain Valley

(Des J. Prentice)

1939 (17 July). *250th Anniv of Huguenot Landing in South Africa and Huguenot Commemoration Fund.* *W* **9.** *P* 14 (*Nos.* 82/3) *or* 15 × 14 (*No.* 84).

82	**32**	½d. +½d. brown and green	4·50	4·25
83	**33**	1d. +1d. green and carmine	7·50	4·50
84	**34**	1½d. +1½d. blue-green and purple ..	11·00	8·00
82/4		.. .. *Set of* 3	21·00	15·00

34*a* Gold Mine

1941 (Aug)–**48.** *W* **9** (*sideways*). *P* 14 × 15.

87	**34*a***	1½d. blue-green and yellow-buff (*shades*)	25	15
		a. Yellow-buff (centre) omitted ..	£850	
		b. Booklet pane of 6 (with postal slogans on margins) (1948) ..	3·50	

35 Infantry

36 Nurse and Ambulance

37 Airman

38 Sailor, Destroyer and Lifebelts

39 Women's Auxiliary Services

40 Artillery

41 Electric Welding

42 Tank Corps

42*a* Signaller

1941–46. *War Effort.* *W* **9** (*sideways on* 2d., 4d., 6d.). *P* 14 (2d., 4d., 6d.) *or* 15 × 14 (*others*). (*a*) *Inscr alternately.*

88	**35**	½d. green (19.11.41)	75	45
		a. Blue-green (7.42)	2·25	1·25
89	**36**	1d. carmine (3.10.41)	75	35

90 37 1½d. myrtle-green (12.1.42) 35 25
91 39 3d. blue (1.8.41) .. .. 7·00 7·00
92 40 4d. orange-brown (20.8.41) .. .. 8·50 5·50
a. *Red-brown* (6.42) .. .. .. 22·00 17·00
93 41 6d. red-orange (3.9.41) .. .. .. 6·50 4·50
94 42*a* 1s. 3d. olive-brown (2.1.43) .. .. 7·50 4·50
a. *Blackish brown* (5.46) .. .. 5·50 4·00

(*b*) *Inscr bilingually*

		Un single	*Us single*
95 38	2d. violet (15.9.41)	45	10
96 42	1s. brown (27.10.41)	2·50	50
88/96	.. .. .. *Set of 7 pairs and 2 singles*	28·00	20·00

43 Infantry **44** Nurse **45** Airman **46** Sailor

47 Women's Auxiliary Services **48** Electric Welding **49** Heavy Gun in Concrete Turret

50 Tank Corps

Unit (*pair*)

Unit (*triplet*)

1942–44. *War Effort. Reduced sizes. In pairs perf* 14 (P) *or strips of three, perf* 15 × 14 (T), *subdivided by roulette* 6½. *W* **9** (*sideways on* 3d., 4d. *and* 1s.). (*a*) *Inscr alternately.*

			Un unit	*Us unit*
97	43	½d. blue-green (T) (10.42)	70	35
		a. *Green* (3.43)	2·50	90
		b. *Greenish blue* (7.44)	2·00	80
		c. Roulette omitted	£350	
98	44	1d. carmine-red (T) (5.1.43) ..	70	35
		a. *Bright carmine* (3.44)	1·00	35
		b. Roulette omitted	£350	
99	45	1½d. red-brown (P) (9.42)	65	25
		a. Roulette 13 (8.42)	1·50	2·25
		b. Roulette omitted	£225	
100	46	2d. violet (P) (2.43)	90	50
		a. *Reddish violet* (6.43)	1·50	50
		b. Roulette omitted	£275	
101	47	3d. blue (T) (10.42)	6·50	6·00
102	48	6d. red-orange (P) (10.42)	2·00	1·40
		(*b*) *Inscr bilingually*		
103	49	4d. slate-green (T) (10.42)	6·00	4·00
104	50	1s. brown (P) (11.42)	5·50	1·50
97/104		.. .. *Set of 8 units*	21·00	12·50

52 **53**

1943. *Coil stamps. Redrawn. In single colours with plain background. W* **9**. *P* 15 × 14.

105	52	½d. blue-green (18.2.43)	60	85
106	53	1d. carmine (9.43)	75	85

NEW INFORMATION

The editor is always interested to correspond with people who have new information that will improve or correct the Catalogue.

54 Union Buildings, Pretoria

1945–46. *Redrawn. W* **9**. *P* 14.

107 **54** 2d. slate and violet (3.45) .. .. .. 7·00 2·25
a. *Slate and bright violet* (*shades*) (10.46) 2·00 5·00

In Nos. 107 and 107*a* the Union Buildings are shown at a different angle from Nos. 58 and 58*a*. Only the centre is screened i.e., composed of very small square dots of colour arranged in straight diagonal lines. For whole design screened and colours changed, see No. 116. No. 107*a* also shows "2" of "2d." clear of white circle at top.

55 "Victory" **56** "Peace"

57 "Hope"

1945 (3 Dec). *Victory. W* **9**. *P* 14.

108	55	1d. brown and carmine	20	50
109	56	2d. slate-blue and violet	20	55
110	57	3d. deep blue and blue	20	60
108/10		.. .. *Set of* 3	55	1·50

58 King George VI **59** King George VI and Queen Elizabeth

60 Queen Elizabeth II as Princess, and Princess Margaret

(Des J. Prentice)

1947 (17 Feb). *Royal Visit. W* **9**. *P* 15 × 14.

111	58	1d. black and carmine	10	10
112	59	2d. violet	15	15
113	60	3d. blue	15	15
111/13		.. .. *Set of* 3	35	35

I
II

5s.

1947–54. "SUID-AFRIKA" *hyphenated on Afrikaans stamps. Printed from new cylinders with design in screened rotogravure. W* **9**. *P* 15 × 14 (½d., 1d. *and* 6d.) *or* 14 (*others*).

114	25*a*	½d. grey and green (frame only screened) (1947)	30	60
		a. Booklet pane of 6 (with postal slogans on margins) (1948) ..	3·00	
		b. Entire design screened (2.49) ..	50	60
		ba. Booklet pane of 6 (with margin at right) (1951)	3·50	
115	7	1d. grey and carmine (1.9.50) ..	35	15
		a. Booklet pane of 6 (with margin at right) (1951)	5·00	
116	54	2d. slate-blue and purple (3.50) ..	30	2·50
117	22*a*	3d. dull blue (4.49)	1·25	2·00
117*a*		3d. blue (3.51)	80	1·25
		b. Deep blue (1954)	60·00	50·00
118	12*a*	4d. brown (22.8.52)	80	3·00
119	8	6d. green and red-orange (III) (1.50)	1·50	40
		a. Green & brown-orange (III) (1951)	1·50	40
120	13	1s. brown and chalky blue (1.50) ..	4·50	2·00
		a. Blackish brown & ultram (4.52)	15·00	6·50
121	14	2s. 6d. green and brown (8.49) ..	8·00	11·00
122	15	5s. black and pale blue-green (I) (9.49)	30·00	18·00
122*a*		5s. black & dp yellow-green (II) (1.54)	60·00	50·00
114/22		.. .. *Set of* 9	40·00	35·00

In screened rotogravure the design is composed of very small squares of colour arranged in straight diagonal lines.

½d. Size 17¾ × 21¾ mm. Early printings have only the frame screened.

1d. Size 18 × 22 mm. For smaller, redrawn design, see No. 135.

2d. For earlier issue with centre only screened, and in different colours, see Nos. 107/*a*.

3d. No. 117. Whole stamp screened with irregular grain. Scrolls above "3d." solid and toneless. Printed from two cylinders.

No. 117*a*/*b*. Whole stamp diagonally screened. Printed from one cylinder. Clouds more pronounced.

4d. Two groups of white leaves below name tablet and a clear white line down left and right sides of stamp.

61 Gold Mine **62** King George VI and Queen Elizabeth

1948 (1 Apr). *W* **9**. *In pair, perf* 14, *sub-divided by roulette* 6½.

			Un unit of 4	*Us unit*
124	61	1½d. blue-green and yellow-buff ..	40	70

(Des J. Booysen and J. Prentice)

1948 (26 Apr). *Silver Wedding. W* **9**. *P* 14.

125	62	3d. blue and silver	50	25

(Typo Government Printer, Pretoria)

1948 (July). *W* **9**. *P* 14½ × 14.

126	6	½d. pale grey and blue-green	25	1·00

This was an economy printing made from the old plates of the 1926 issue for the purpose of using up a stock of cut paper. For the original printing in black and green, see No. 30.

63 *Wanderer* entering Durban

(Des J. Prentice)

1949 (2 May). *Centenary of Arrival of British Settlers in Natal. W* **9**. *P* 15 × 14.

127	63	1½d. claret	15	15

64 Hermes **65** Wagons approaching Bingham's Berg

"Lake" in East Africa (R. 2/19)

(Des J. Booysen and J. Prentice)

1949 (1 Oct). *75th Anniv of Universal Postal Union. As T* **64** *inscr* "UNIVERSAL POSTAL UNION" *and* "WERELDPOSUNIE" *alternately. W* **9** (*sideways*). *P* 14 × 15.

128	64	½d. blue-green	50	50
129		1½d. brown-red	60	65
130		3d. bright blue	1·25	1·40
		a. "Lake" in East Africa	15·00	
128/30		.. .. .. *Set of* 3	2·10	2·25

(Des W. Coetzer and J. Prentice)

1949 (1 Dec). *Inauguration of Voortrekker Monument, Pretoria. T* **65** *and similar horiz designs. W* **9**. *P* 15 × 14.

		Un single	*Us single*
131	1d. magenta	10	10
132	1½d. blue-green	10	10
133	3d. blue	10	10
131/3	.. .. .. *Set of* 3	15	15

Designs:—1½d. Voortrekker Monument, Pretoria; 3d. Bible, candle and Voortrekkers.

68 Union Buildings, Pretoria

1950 (Apr)–**51.** *W* **9** (*sideways*). *P* 14 × 15.
134 **68** 2d. blue and violet 15 20
a. Booklet panes of 6 (with margin at right) (1951) .. .. 8·00

1951 (22 Feb). *As No.* 115, *but redrawn with the horizon clearly defined. Size reduced to* 17¼ × 21¼ *mm.*
135 **7** 1d. grey and carmine 25 20

PRICES. All later issues except Nos. 167 and 262/5 are inscribed bilingually and prices are for single copies, unused and used.

69 Seal and Monogram **70** "Maria de la Quellerie" (D. Craey)

(Des Miss R. Reeves and J. Prentice (1d., 4½d.), Mrs T. Campbell and J. Prentice (others))

1952 (14 Mar). *Tercentenary of Landing of Van Riebeeck. T* **69/70** *and similar designs. W* **9** (*sideways on* 1d. *and* 4½d.). *P* 14 × 15 (1d. *and* 4½d.) *or* 14 × 15 (*others*).
136 ½d. brown-purple and olive-grey 10 10
137 1d. deep blue-green 10 10
138 2d. deep violet 20 10
139 4½d. blue 10 10
140 1s. brown 15 10
136/40 .. .. *Set of* 5 40 20
Designs: *Horiz*—2d. Arrival of Van Riebeeck's ships; 1s. "Landing at the Cape" (C. Davidson Bell). *Vert*—4½d. "Jan van Riebeeck" (D. Craey).

SATISE SADIPU

(74) (75) **76** Queen Elizabeth II

1952 (26 Mar). *South African Tercentenary International Stamp Exhibition, Cape Town. No.* 137 *optd with T* **74** *and No.* 138 *with T* **75**.
141 1d. deep blue-green 15 30
142 2d. deep violet 15 10

(Des H. Kumst)

1953 (3 June). *Coronation. W* **9** (*sideways*). *P* 14 × 15.
143 **76** 2d. deep violet-blue 20 10
a. *Ultramarine* 20 10

77 1d. "Cape Triangular" Stamp

(Des H. Kumst)

1953 (1 Sept). *Centenary of First Cape of Good Hope Stamp. T* **77** *and similar horiz design. W* **9.** *P* 15 × 14.
144 1d. sepia and vermilion 10 10
145 4d. deep blue and light blue 10 10
Design:—4d. Four pence "Cape Triangular" stamp.

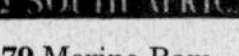

79 Merino Ram **80** Springbok

81 Aloes

(Des A. Hendriksz and J. Prentice (4½d.))

1953 (1 Oct). *W* **9.** *P* 14.
146 **79** 4½d. slate-purple and yellow 20 10
147 **80** 1s. 3d. chocolate 80 10
148 **81** 1s. 6d. vermilion and deep blue-green 70 25
146/8 .. .. *Set of* 3 1·50 35

82 Arms of Orange Free State and Scroll

(Des H. Kumst)

1954 (23 Feb). *Centenary of Orange Free State. W* **9.** *P* 15 × 14.
149 **82** 2d. sepia and pale vermilion 10 10
150 4½d. purple and slate 10 25

83 Warthog **92** Springbok **93** Gemsbok

(Des H. Kumst)

1954 (14 Oct). *T* **83, 92/3** *and similar designs. W* **9** (*sideways on large vert designs*). *P* 15 × 14 (½d. *to* 2d.), 14 (*others*).
151 ½d. deep blue-green 10 10
152 1d. brown-lake 10 10
153 1½d. sepia 10 10
154 2d. plum 10 10
155 3d. chocolate and turquoise-blue 15 10
156 4d. indigo and emerald 40 10
157 4½d. blue-black and grey-blue .. .. 60 1·25
158 6d. sepia and orange 50 10
159 1s. deep brown and pale chocolate 60 10
160 1s. 3d. brown and bluish green .. .. 1·00 10
161 1s. 6d. brown and rose .. .. .. 1·75 60
162 2s. 6d. brown-black and apple-green .. 3·50 20
163 5s. black-brown and yellow-orange .. 10·00 90
164 10s. black and cobalt .. .. .. 16·00 4·50
151/64 .. .. *Set of* 14 30·00 7·00
Designs: *Vert* (*as T* **83**)—1d. Black Wildebeest; 1½d. Leopard; 2d. Mountain Zebra. (*As T* **93**)—3d. White Rhinoceros; 4d. African Elephant; 4½d. Hippopotamus; 1s. Greater Kudu; 2s. 6d. Nyala; 5s. Giraffe; 10s. Sable Antelope. *Horiz* (*as T* **92**)—6d. Lion.
No. 152 exists in coils.
See also Nos. 170/7 and 185/97.

97 President Kruger **98** President M. Pretorius

(Des H. Kumst)

1955 (21 Oct). *Centenary of Pretoria. W* **9** (*sideways*). *P* 14 × 15.
165 **97** 3d. slate-green 10 10
166 **98** 6d. maroon 10 20

99 A. Pretorius, Church of the Vow and Flag **100** Settlers' Block-wagon and House

(Des H. Kumst)

1955 (1 Dec). *Voortrekker Covenant Celebrations, Pietermaritzburg. W* **9.** *P* 14.
Un pair *Us pair*
167 **99** 2d. blue and magenta .. .. .. 45 2·00

(Des H. Kumst)

1958 (1 July). *Centenary of Arrival of German Settlers in South Africa. W* **9.** *P* 14.
168 **100** 2d. chocolate and pale purple 10 10

101 Arms of the Academy

(Des H. Kumst)

1959 (1 May). *50th Anniv of the South African Academy of Science and Art, Pretoria. W* **9.** *P* 15 × 14.
169 **101** 3d. deep blue and turquoise-blue .. 10 10
a. Deep blue printing omitted .. £1000

1 S 1 S

102 Union Coat of Arms I II

1959–60. *As Nos.* 151/2, 155/6, 158/9 *and* 162/3, *but W* **102**.
170 ½d. deep greenish blue (12.60) .. .. 15 3·00
171 1d. brown-lake (I) (11.59) 10 10
a. Redrawn. Type II (10.60) 15 10
172 3d. chocolate and turquoise-blue (9.59) .. 15 10
173 4d. indigo and emerald (1.60) 50 20
174 6d. sepia and orange (2.60) 70 20
175 1s. deep brown and pale chocolate (11.59) .. 3·50 15
176 2s. 6d. brown-black & apple-green (12.59) .. 2·75 4·00
177 5s. black-brown & yellow-orange (10.60) .. 7·00 25·00
170/7 .. .. *Set of* 8 13·00 29·00
Nos. 171/a. In Type II "1d. Posgeld Postage" is more to the left in relation to "South Africa", with "1" almost central over "S" instead of to right as in Type I.
No. 171 exists in coils.

103 Globe and Antarctic Scene

(Des H. Kumst)

1959 (16 Nov). *South African National Antarctic Expedition. W* **102.** *P* 14 × 15.
178 **103** 3d. blue-green and orange 15 10

104 Union Flag **106** "Wheel of Progress"

(Des V. Ivanoff and H. Kumst (1s.), H. Kumst (others))

1960 (2 May). *50th Anniv of Union of South Africa. T* **104, 106** *and similar designs. W* **102** (*sideways on* 4d. *and* 6d.). *P* 14 × 15 (4d., 6d.) *or* 15 × 14 (*others*).
179 4d. orange-red and blue 25 10
180 6d. red, brown and light green 20 10
181 1s. deep blue and light yellow 20 10
182 1s. 6d. black and light blue .. .. 1·00 1·75
179/82 .. .. *Set of* 4 1·50 1·75
Designs: *Vert*—6d. Union Arms. *Horiz*—1s. 6d. Union Festival emblem.
See also No. 190, 192/3.

108 Locomotives of 1860 and 1960

(Des V. Ivanoff)

1960 (2 May). *Centenary of South African Railways. W* **102.** *P* 15 × 14.
183 **108** 1s. 3d. deep blue .. .. .. 1·25 30

109 Prime Ministers Botha, Smuts, Hertzog, Malan, Strijdom and Verwoerd

1960 (31 May). *Union Day. W* **102.** *P* 15 × 14.
184 **109** 3d. brown and pale brown 10 10
a. Pale brown omitted* £1500
*This is due to a rectangular piece of paper adhering to the background cylinder, resulting in R.2/1 missing the colour completely and six adjoining stamps having it partially omitted. The item in block of eight is probably unique.

(New Currency. 100 cents=1 rand)

1961 (14 Feb). *As previous issues but with values in cents and rand. W* **102** (*sideways on* 3½ *c.,* 7½ *c.,* 20 *c.,* 50 *c.,* 1 *r.*). *P* 15 × 14 (½ *c., to* 2½ *c.,* 10 *c.*), 14 × 15 (3½ *c.,* 7½ *c.*) *or* 14 (*others*).

No.	Value	Description	Unused	Used
185	½ c.	deep bluish green (as 151)	10	10
186	1 c.	brown-lake (as 152)	10	10
187	1½ c.	sepia (as 153)	10	10
188	2 c.	plum (as 154)	10	10
189	2½ c.	brown (as 184)	10	10
190	3½ c.	orange-red and blue (as 179)	15	60
191	5 c.	sepia and orange (as 158)	20	10
192	7½ c.	red, brown and light green (as 180)	20	80
193	10 c.	deep blue and light yellow (as 181)	20	15
194	12½ c.	brown and bluish green (as 160)	1·00	1·25
195	20 c.	brown and rose (as 161)	1·75	2·25
196	50 c.	black-brown & orange-yellow (as 163)	6·00	10·00
197	1 r.	black and cobalt (as 164)	14·00	19·00
185/97		*Set of* 13	21·00	30·00

REPUBLIC

110 African Pygmy Kingfisher

111 Kafferboom Flower

112 Afrikander Bull

113 Pouring Gold

114 Groot Constantia

115 Burchell's Gonolek

116 Baobab Tree

117 Maize

118 Cape Town Castle Entrance

119 Protea

120 Secretary Bird

121 Cape Town Harbour

122 Strelitzia

Two types of ½ c.:

I II

Type I from sheets. Spurs of branch indistinct.
Type II from coils. Spurs strengthened.

Three types of 1 c.:

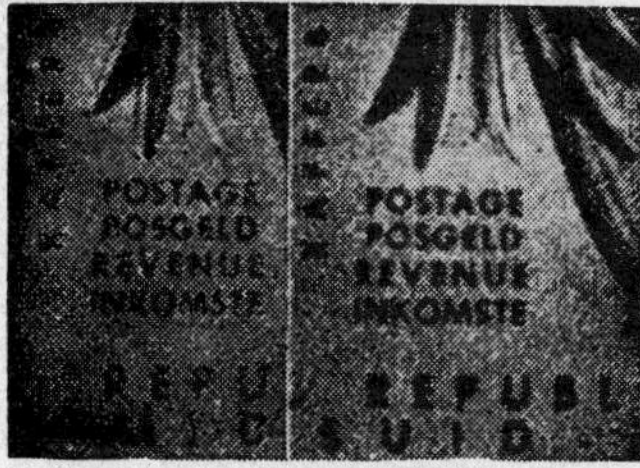

I II

III

Type I. Lowest point of flower between "OS" of "POSTAGE". Right-hand petal over "E".
Type II. Flower has moved fractionally to the right so that lowest point is over "S" of "POSTAGE". Right-hand petal over "E".
Type III. Lowest point directly over "O". Right-hand petal over "G".

Two types of 2½ c.

In Type I the lines of the building are quite faint. In Type II all lines of the building have been strengthened by re-engraving.

(Des Mrs. T. Campbell (½ c., 3 c., 1 r.); Miss N. Desmond (1 c.); De La Rue (2½ c., 5 c., 12½ c.); H. L. Prager (50 c.); Govt. Ptg Dept artist (others))

1961 (31 May)–**63.** *Unsurfaced paper. W* **102** (*sideways on* ½ *c.,* 1½ *c.,* 2½ *c.,* 5 *c. to* 20 *c.*). *P* 14 × 15 (½ *c.,* 1½ *c.*), 15 × 14 (1 *c.*), *or* 14 (*others*).

No.	Type	Value	Description	Unused	Used
198	**110**	½ c.	bright blue, carmine & brown (I)	10	10
			a. Perf 14 (3.63)	10	15
			b. Type II (coils) (18.5.63)	30	25
199	**111**	1 c.	red and olive-grey (I)	10	10
			a. Type II (1.62)	10	10
			b. Type III (coils) (5.63)	60	60
200	**112**	1½ c.	brown-lake and light purple	10	10
201	**113**	2 c.	ultramarine and yellow	20	10
202	**114**	2½ c.	violet and green (I)	15	10
			a. Type II. *Dp violet & green* (9.61)	20	10
203	**115**	3 c.	red and deep blue	80	10
204	**116**	5 c.	yellow and greenish blue	30	10
205	**117**	7½ c.	yellow-brown and light green	60	10
206	**118**	10 c.	sepia and green	75	10
207	**119**	12½ c.	red, yellow and black-green	2·00	10
			a. Yellow omitted	£180	
			b. Red omitted		
208	**120**	20 c.	turquoise-blue, carm & brn-orge	3·50	20
209	**121**	50 c.	black and bright blue	35·00	2·00
210	**122**	1 r.	orange, olive-green & light blue	20·00	2·00
198/210			*Set of* 13	55·00	4·00

1961–74 *Definitives*

Key to designs, perfs, watermarks, papers and phosphors

Value	*Type*	*Perf*	*W* **102.** *Ordinary*	*No wmk. Ordinary*	*W* **127.** *Chalky*
½ c. **110**	(I)	14×15	198	—	—
	(I)	14	198a	—	—
	(II)	14×15	198b	—	—
1 c. **111**	(I)	15×14	199	211	—
	(II)		199a	211a	227
	(III)		199b	—	—
1½ c. **112**		14×15	200	—	228
2 c. **113**		14	201	212	229
2½ c. **114**	(I)	14	202	—	—
	(II)		202a	213/*a*	230/*a*
3 c. **115**		14	203	214	—
5 c. **116**		14	204	215	231
7½ c. **117**		14	205	216	232
10 c. **118**		14	206	217/*b*	233/*a*
12½ c. **119**		14	207	—	—
20 c. **120**		14	208	218	234/*a*
50 c. **121**		14	209	219	235
1 r. **122**		14	210	—	236

Redrawn Designs

		W **127** *Upright or Tête-bêche. Plain or phosphorised*	W **127** *Tête-bêche. Phos frame*	*No wmk. Phosphorised Glossy*	*No wmk. Phosphorised Chalky*
½ c. **130***a*	14	238	—	—	—
	14×15	238*b*	—	—	—
	14	238*c*/*d*	—	—	—
1 c. **131**	15×14	239	—	—	—
	13½×14	239a	—	—	—
1½ c. **132**	14×15	240/*b*	284	—	—
	14×13½	240c	—	—	—
2 c. **133**	14	241/*a*	285/*a*	315a	—
	12½	—	—	315	315b
2½ c. **134**	14	242/*a*	286/*a*	—	—
3 c. **135**	14	243/*a*	287	—	—
	12½	—	—	316	316a
4 c. **134**	14	243*b*	288	—	—
5 c. **136**	14	244/*a*	289	318a	—
	12½	—	—	318	318b
6 c. **137**	14	—	290	—	—
	12½	—	—	—	319
7½ c. **137**	14	245	291	—	—
9 c. **139**	14	245*a*	292	—	—
	12½	—	—	320/*a*	—
10 c. **138**	14	246/a	293	321a	—
	12½	—	—	321	321b
12½ c. **139**	14	247/*a*	294	—	—
15 c. **140**	14	248	295	—	—
20 c. **141**	14	249/*a*	296/*a*	—	—
	12½	—	—	323	323a
50 c. **142**	14	250	—	—	—
	12½	—	—	324	324a
1 r. **143**	14	251	—	—	—
	12½	—	—	325	—

New Designs

		W **127** *Tête-bêche. Plain or phosphorised*	*W* **127** *Tête-bêche. Phos-frame*	*No wmk. Phosphorised Glossy*	*No wmk. Phosphorised Chalky*
½ c. **168**	14 × 13½	276	282	—	—
	14 × 14½	276a	—	313	—
	14 × 15	—	282a	—	—
1 c. **169**	13½ × 14	277	283	—	—
	14	—	—	314	—
4 c. **182**	14	310/*a*	—	—	—
	12½	—	—	317/*b*	317c
15 c. **182***a*	14	311	—	—	—
	12½	—	—	—	322

1961 (Aug)–**63.** *As Nos.* 199, 201/6 *and* 208/9 *but without wmk.*

No.	Type	Value	Description	Unused	Used
211	**111**	1 c.	red and olive-grey (I)	20	15
			a. Type II (9.62)	20	15
212	**113**	2 c.	ultramarine and yellow (8.63)	1·50	10
213	**114**	2½ c.	deep violet and green (II)	20	10
			a. Violet and green (12.61)	30	10
214	**115**	3 c.	red and deep blue (10.61)	45	10
215	**116**	5 c.	yellow & greenish blue (12.61)	50	10
216	**117**	7½ c.	yellow-brown & lt green (3.62)	80	10
217	**118**	10 c.	sepia and green (11.61)	1·00	15
			a. Sepia and emerald	35·00	10·00
			b. Sepia-brown & lt green (7.63)	1·50	15
218	**120**	20 c.	turq-bl, carm & brn-orge (4.63)	13·00	1·25
219	**121**	50 c.	black and bright blue (8.62)	13·00	3·00
211/19			*Set of* 9	28·00	4·25

123 Blériot Monoplane and Boeing 707 Airliner over Table Mountain

124 Folk-dancers

1961 (1 Dec). *50th Anniv of First South African Aerial Post. W* **102** (*sideways*). *P* 14 × 15.

No.	Type	Value	Description	Unused	Used
220	**123**	3 c.	blue and red	20	10

(Des K. Esterhuysen)

1962 (1 Mar). *50th Anniv of Volkspele (folk-dancing) in South Africa. W* **102** (*sideways*). *P* 14 × 15.

No.	Type	Value	Description	Unused	Used
221	**124**	2½ c.	orange-red and brown	15	10

125 The *Chapman*

1962 (20 Aug). *Unveiling of Precinct Stone, British Settlers Monument, Grahamstown. W* **102.** *P* 15 × 14.

No.	Type	Value	Description	Unused	Used
222	**125**	2½ c.	turquoise-green and purple	40	10
223		12½ c.	blue and deep chocolate	2·50	1·75

126 Red Disa (orchid), Castle Rock and Gardens

(Des M. F. Stern)

1963 (14 Mar). *50th Anniv of Kirstenbosch Botanic Gardens, Cape Town. P* 13½ × 14.

No.	Type	Value	Description	Unused	Used
224	**126**	2½ c.	multicoloured	20	10
			a. Red (orchid, etc) omitted	£900	

COVER PRICES

Cover factors are quoted at the beginning of each country for most issues to 1945. An explanation of the system can be found on page x. The factors quoted do not, however, apply to philatelic covers.

127 (normal version)

128 Centenary Emblem and Nurse   **129** Centenary Emblem and Globe

1963 (30 Aug). *Centenary of Red Cross. Chalk-surfaced paper. Wmk* **127** *(sideways on 2½ c.). P* 14 × 13½ *(2½ c.) or* 15 × 14 *(12½ c.).*

225	**128**	2½ c. red, black and reddish purple ..	20	10
226	**129**	12½ c. red and indigo	3·75	1·00
		a. Red cross omitted..	£1000	

1963–67. *As* 1961–3 *but chalk-surfaced paper and W* **127** *(sideways on* 1½ *c.,* 2½ *c.,* 5 *c.,* 7½ *c.,* 10 *c.,* 20 *c.). P* 15 × 14 *(1 c.),* 14 × 15 *(1½ c.), or* 14 *(others).*

227	**111**	1 c. red and olive-grey (II) (9.63) ..	10	10
228	**112**	1½ c. brown-lake & lt purple (1.67)	1·75	60
229	**113**	2 c. ultramarine and yellow (11.64)	15	10
230	**114**	2½ c. violet and green (II) (10.63) ..	10	10
		a. *Bright reddish violet and emerald* (II) (3.66)	35	20
231	**116**	5 c. yellow and greenish blue (9.66)	1·25	15
232	**117**	7½ c. yellow-brn & brt grn (23.2.66)	7·00	65
233	**118**	10 c. sepia-brown & lt emerald (9.64)	40	10
		a. *Sepia-brown and green* (1.67)	45	10
234	**120**	20 c. turq-bl, carm & brn-orge (7.64)	1·50	30
		a. *Deep turqoise-blue, carmine and flesh* (20.7.65)	1·75	30
235	**121**	50 c. black and ultramarine (4.66)	30·00	5·00
236	**122**	1 r. orange, lt green & pale bl (7.64)	55·00	24·00
227/36		.. .. *Set of* 10	90·00	27·00

In the 2½ c. (No. 230*a*), 5 c., 7½ c., 10 c. (Jan 1967 printing only) and 50 c. the watermark is indistinct but they can easily be distinguished from the stamps without watermark by their shades and the chalk-surfaced paper which is appreciably thicker and whiter.

130 Assembly Building, Umtata

1963 (11 Dec). *First Meeting of Transkei Legislative Assembly. Chalk-surfaced paper. W* **127.** *P* 15 × 14.

237	**130**	2½ c. sepia and light green	10	10
		a. Light green omitted	£1000	

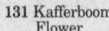

130a African Pygmy Kingfisher   **131** Kafferboom Flower   **132** Afrikander Bull

133 Pouring Gold   **134** Groot Constantia

135 Burchell's Gonolek   **136** Baobab Tree

137 Maize   **138** Cape Town Castle Entrance

139 Protea   **140** Industry   **141** Secretary Bird

142 Cape Town Harbour   **143** Strelitzia

(15 c. des C. E. F. Skotnes)

Redrawn types.

½ c. "½C" larger and "REPUBLIEK VAN REPUBLIC OF" smaller.

3 c. and 12½ c. Inscriptions and figures of value larger.

Others. "SOUTH AFRICA" and "SUID-AFRIKA" larger and bolder. The differences vary in each design but are easy to see by comparing the position of the letters of the country name with "REPUBLIC OF" and "REPUBLIEK VAN".

1964–72. *As* 1961–63 *but designs redrawn and new values (4 c., 9 c. and 15 c.). Chalk-surfaced paper. W* **127** *(sideways on* ½, 1½, 2½, 4, 5, 7½, 9, 10, 15 *and* 20 *c.). P* 14×15 *(1½ c.),* 15×14 *(1 c.) or* 14 *(others).*

238	**130a**	½ c. brt blue, carm & brn (21.5.64)	10	10
		a. Imperf (pair)	£250	
		b. Perf 14×15. *Brt blue, carmine and yellow-brown* (6.7.67) ..	15	15
		c. Perf 14. *Bright blue, lake and yellow-brown* (3.68)	10	10
		d. Perf 14. *Bright blue, carmine-lake and yellow-brown* (9.68)	15	10
239	**131**	1 c. red and olive-grey (9.3.67) ..	10	10
		a. Perf 13½×14 (7.68)	30	10
240	**132**	1½ c. dull red-brn & lt pur (21.9.67)	15	10
		a. *Purple-brown & lt pur* (1968)	15	10
		b. *Brt red-brown & lt pur* (5.68)	15	10
		c. Perf 14×13½. *Red-brown and light purple* (14.8.69) ..	35	25
241	**133**	2 c. ultramarine & yellow (8.1.68)	20	10
		a. *Blue and yellow* (10.71) ..	25	10
242	**134**	2½ c. violet and green (19.4.67) ..	20	10
		a. *Reddish violet and green* (8.67)	20	10
243	**135**	3 c. red and deep blue (11.64) ..	30	10
		a. *Brown-red & deep blue* (3.72)	35	10
243*b*	**134**	4 c. violet and green (10.71) ..	75	30
244	**136**	5 c. yellow & greenish bl (14.2.68)	40	10
		a. *Lemon & dp greenish bl* (10.71)	7·00	70
245	**137**	7½ c. yellow-brn & brt grn (26.7.67)	60	10
245*a*	**139**	9 c. red, yellow & slate-grn (2.72)	8·00	1·40
246	**138**	10 c. sepia and green (10.6.68) ..	1·25	10
		a. *Brown and pale green* (7.68)	4·00	3·00
247	**139**	12½ c. red, yellow & black-grn (3.64)	1·50	15
		a. *Red, pale yell & bl-grn* (2.2.66)	1·75	15
248	**140**	15 c. black, light olive-yellow and red-orange (1.3.67)	2·00	25
249	**141**	20 c. turquoise-blue, carmine and brown-orange (2.68)	4·00	15
		a. *Turquoise-blue, carmine and orange-buff* (12.71)	4·75	50
250	**142**	50 c. black and bright blue (17.6.68)	4·50	40
251	**143**	1 r. orange, lt green & lt bl (6.65)	6·00	1·00
238/51		.. .. *Set of* 16	25·00	3·50

WATERMARK. Two forms of the watermark Type **127** exist in the above issue: the normal Type **127** (sometimes indistinct), and a very faint *tête-bêche* watermark, i.e. alternately facing up and down, which was introduced in mid-1967. As it is extremely difficult to distinguish these on single stamps we do not list it.

The ½ (both perfs), 1, 2, 2½, 3, 15 c. and 1 r. are known in both forms, the 1½, 4, 5, 7½, 9, 10, 20 and 50 c. only in the *tête-bêche* form, and the 12½ c. Type **127** only.

GUM. The 2, 3, 5, 20, 50 c. and 1 r. exist with PVA gum as well as gum arabic.

PHOSPHORISED PAPER. From October 1971 onwards phosphor bands (see Nos. 282/96) gave way to phosphorised paper which cannot be distinguished from non-phosphor stamps without the aid of a lamp. For this reason we do not distinguish these printings in the above issue, but some are slightly different shades which are listed in the *Elizabethan Catalogue* and all have PVA gum.

The 4 c. and 9 c. are on phosphorised paper only and differ from Nos. 288 and 292 by the lack of phosphor bands.

NEW INFORMATION

The editor is always interested to correspond with people who have new information that will improve or correct the Catalogue.

145 "Springbok" Badge of Rugby Board   **147** Calvin

1964 (8 May). *75th Anniv of South African Rugby Board. Chalk-surfaced paper. T* **145** *and similar horiz design. W* **127** *(sideways on 2½ c.). P* 14 × 15 *(2½ c.) or* 15 × 14 *(12½ c.).*

252		2½ c. yellow-brown and deep green.. ..	15	10
253		12½ c. black and light yellow-green	5·50	4·25

Design:—12½ c. Rugby footballer.

1964 (10 July). *400th Death Anniv of Calvin (Protestant reformer). Chalk-surfaced paper. W* **127** *(sideways). P* 14 × 13½.

254	**147**	2½ c. cerise, violet and brown	10	10

148 Nurse's Lamp   **149** Nurse holding Lamp

I. Screened base to lamp   II. Clear base to lamp

1964 (12 Oct). *50th Anniv of South African Nursing Association. Chalk-surfaced paper. W* **127** *(sideways on 2½ c.). P* 14 × 15 *(2½ c.) or* 15 × 14 *(12½ c.).*

255	**148**	2½ c. ultramarine and dull gold (Type I)	10	10
256		2½ c. brt blue & yellow-gold (Type II) ..	30	10
		a. *Ultramarine and dull gold* ..	15	10
257	**149**	12½ c. bright blue and gold	3·00	2·00
		a. Gold omitted	£800	
255/7		.. .. *Set of* 3	3·00	2·00

150 I.T.U. Emblem and Satellites

1965 (17 May). *I.T.U. Centenary. T* **150** *and similar horiz design. Chalk-surfaced paper. W* **127.** *P* 15 × 14.

258	2½ c. orange and blue	25	10
259	12½ c. brown-purple and green	3·00	1·75

Design:—12½ c. I.T.U. emblem and symbols.

152 Pulpit in Groote Kerk, Cape Town   **153** Church Emblem

1965 (21 Oct). *Tercentenary of Nederduites Gereformeerde Kerk (Dutch Reformed Church) in South Africa. Chalk-surfaced paper. W* **127** *(sideways on 2½ c., inverted on 12½ c.). P* 14 × 15 *(2½ c.) or* 15 × 14 *(12½ c.).*

260	**152**	2½ c. brown and light yellow	15	10
261	**153**	12½ c. black, light orange and blue ..	1·75	1·25

154 Diamond   **155** Bird in flight

(Des C. E. F. Skotnes)

1966 (31 May). *Fifth Anniv of Republic. T* **154/5** *and similar designs. Chalk-surfaced paper. W* **127** *(sideways on* 1 c., 3 c.*). P* 14 × 13½ (1 c.), 13½ × 14 (2½ c.), 14 × 15 (3 c.) *or* 15 × 14 (7½ c.).

		Un pair	*Us pair*
262	1 c. black, bluish green and olive-yellow ..	35	35
263	2½ c. blue, deep blue and yellow-green ..	1·00	1·25
264	3 c. red, greenish yellow and red-brown ..	4·75	4·75
265	7½ c. blue, ultramarine and yellow.. ..	5·50	6·00
262/5	.. .. *Set of* 4	10·50	11·00

Designs: *Vert*—3 c. Maize plants. *Horiz*—7½ c. Mountain landscape.

Nos. 262/5 exist on Swiss-made paper with *tête-bêche* watermark from a special printing made for use in presentation albums for delegates to the U.P.U. Congress in Tokyo in 1969, as supplies of the original Harrison paper were by then exhausted (*Set of 4 pairs price* £140 *mint*).

158 Verwoerd and Union Buildings, Pretoria

(Des from portrait by Dr. Henkel)

1966 (6 Dec). *Verwoerd Commemoration. T* **158** *and similar designs. Chalk-surfaced paper. W* **127** *(sideways on* 3 c.*). P* 14 × 15 (3 c.) *or* 15 × 14 *(others).*

266	2½ c. blackish brown and turquoise ..	10	10
267	3 c. blackish brown and yellow-green ..	10	10
268	12½ c. blackish brown and greenish blue ..	70	50
266/8	.. .. *Set of* 3	80	50

Designs: *Vert*—3 c. "Dr. H. F. Verwoerd" (I. Henkel). *Horiz*—12½ c. Verwoerd and map of South Africa.

161 "Martin Luther" (Cranach the Elder)

162 Wittenberg Church Door

1967 (31 Oct). *450th Anniv of Reformation. W* **127** *((sideways), normal on* 2½ c., *tête-bêche on* 12½ c.*). P* 14 × 15.

269 **161**	2½ c. black and rose-red	10	10
270 **162**	12½ c. black and yellow-orange	1·75	1·75

163 "Profile of Pres. Fouché" (I. Henkel)

164 Portrait of Pres. Fouché

1968 (10 Apr). *Inauguration of President Fouché. W* **127** *(sideways). P* 14 × 15.

271 **163**	2½ c. chocolate and pale chocolate ..	10	10
272 **164**	12½ c. deep blue and light blue	80	1·25

No. 272 also exists with the watermark *tête-bêche* (*Price un* £1; *used* £1.50).

165 Hertzog in 1902

1968 (21 Sept). *Inauguration of General Hertzog Monument, Bloemfontein. T* **165** *and similar designs. W* **127** *(tête-bêche on* 2½ c., *inverted on* 3 c., *sideways on* 12½ c.*). P* 14 × 13½ (12½ c.) *or* 13½ × 14 *(others).*

273	2½ c. black, brown and olive-yellow ..	10	10
274	3 c. black, red-brown, red-orange and yellow	15	10
275	12½ c. black, red and yellow-orange ..	2·00	90
273/5	.. .. *Set of* 3	2·00	90

Designs: *Horiz*—3 c. Hertzog in 1924. *Vert*—12½ c. Hertzog Monument.

168 Natal Kingfisher

169 Kafferboom Flower

1969. *W* **127** *(tête-bêche, sideways on* ½ c.*). P* 14 × 13½ (½ c.) *or* 13½ × 14 (1 c.).

276 **168**	½ c. new bl, carm-red & yell-ochre (1.69)	10	15
	a. Coil. Perf 14 × 14½ (5.69).. ..	1·75	70
277 **169**	1 c. rose-red and olive-brown (1.69) ..	10	10

See also Nos. 282/3 and 313/14.

170 Springbok and Olympic Torch

171 Professor Barnard and Groote Schuur Hospital

1969 (15 Mar). *South African Games, Bloemfontein. W* **127** *(tête-bêche, sideways). P* 14 × 13½.

278 **170**	2½ c. black, blue-black, red & sage-grn	15	10
279	12½ c. black, blue-blk, red & cinnamon ..	1·00	1·25

1969 (7 July). *World's First Heart Transplant and 47th South African Medical Association Congress. T* **171** *and similar horiz design. W* **127** *(tête-bêche). P* 13½ × 14 (2½ c.) *or* 15 × 14 (12½ c.).

280	2½ c. plum and rose-red	15	10
281	12½ c. carmine-red and royal blue	1·75	2·25

Design:—12½ c. Hands holding heart.

1969–72. *As 1964–72 issue, Nos. 276/7, and new value (6 c.), but with phosphor bands printed horizontally and vertically between the stamp designs, over the perforations, producing a frame effect. W* **127** *arranged tête-bêche (upright on* 1, 2 *and* 3 c., *sideways on others). P* 14×13½ (½, 1½ c.), 13½×14 (1 c.), *or* 14 *(others).*

282 **168**	½ c. new blue, carmine-red and yellow-ochre (1.70)	15	30
	a. Coil. Perf 14×15 (2.71) ..	2·75	1·75
283 **169**	1 c. rose-red & olive-brown (12.69)	15	10
284 **132**	1½ c. red-brown & lt purple (12.69)	20	10
285 **133**	2 c. ultramarine and yellow (11.69)	25	10
	a. Deep ultramarine & yell (8.70)	35	15
286 **134**	2½ c. violet and green (1.70) ..	25	10
	a. Purple and green (24.7.70) ..	40	10
287 **135**	3 c. red and deep blue (30.9.69) ..	70	10
288 **134**	4 c. violet and green (1.3.71) ..	40	10
289 **136**	5 c. yellow & greenish bl (17.11.69)	75	10
290 **137**	6 c. yellow-brn & brt grn (3.5.71)	1·00	20
291	7½ c. yell-brn & brt grn (17.11.69)	3·50	25
292 **139**	9 c. red, yell & black-grn (17.5.71)	1·50	30
293 **138**	10 c. brown and pale green (1.70) ..	2·00	10
294 **139**	12½ c. red, yell & black-grn (2.5.70)	5·50	75
295 **140**	15 c. blk, lt ol-yell & red-orge (1.70)	2·75	90
296 **141**	20 c. turquoise-blue, carmine and brown-orange (18.2.70) ..	7·00	30
	a. Turquoise-blue, carmine and orange-buff (9.72)	7·00	30
282/96	.. .. *Set of* 15	24·00	3·25

No. 286 exists on normal RSA wmk as well as RSA *tête-bêche* wmk.

The 1, 2, 2½, 3, 10, 15 and 20 c. exist with PVA gum as well as gum arabic, but the 4, 6 and 9 c. exist with PVA gum only.

For stamps without wmk, see Nos. 313, etc.

173 Mail Coach

174 Transvaal Stamp of 1869

1969 (6 Oct). *Centenary of First Stamps of South African Republic (Transvaal). Phosphor bands on all four sides* (2½ c.). *W* **127** *(tête-bêche, sideways on* 12½ c.*). P* 13½ × 14 (2½ c.) *or* 14 × 13½ (12½ c.).

297 **173**	2½ c. yellow, indigo and yellow-brown	15	10
298 **174**	12½ c. emerald, gold and yellow-brown	3·25	2·00

PHOSPHOR FRAME. Nos. 299/306 have phosphor applied on all four sides as a frame.

175 "Water 70" Emblem

177 "The Sower"

1970 (14 Feb). *Water 70 Campaign. T* **175** *and similar design. W* **127** *(tête-bêche (sideways on* 2½ c.*)). P* 14 × 13½ (2½ c.) *or* 13½ × 14 (3 c.).

299	2½ c. green, bright blue and chocolate ..	15	10
300	3 c. Prussian blue, royal blue and buff ..	25	10

Design: *Horiz*—3 c. Symbolic waves.

1970 (24 Aug). *150th Anniv of Bible Society of South Africa. T* **177** *and similar horiz design (gold die-stamped on* 12½ c.*). W* **127** *(tête-bêche, sideways on* 2½ c.*). P* 14 × 13½ (2½ c.) *or* 13½ × 14 (12½ c.).

301	2½ c. multicoloured	15	10
302	12½ c. gold, black and blue	2·50	2·50

Design:—12½ c. "Biblia" and open book.

178 J. G. Strijdom and Strijdom Tower

179 Map and Antarctic Landscape

1971 (22 May). *"Interstex" Stamp Exhibition, Cape Town. P* 14 × 13½.

A. *W* **127** *(sideways tête-bêche)*. B. *W* **102** *(sideways).*

		A		B	
303 **178**	5 c. light greenish blue, black and pale yellow	20	10	1·75	4·00

1971 (22 May). *Tenth Anniv of Antarctic Treaty. W* **127** *(tête-bêche). P* 13½ × 14.

304 **179**	12½ c. blue-black, greenish bl & orge-red	5·00	4·50

180 "Landing of British Settlers, 1820" (T. Baines)

1971 (31 May). *Tenth Anniv of the Republic of South Africa. T* **180** *and similar design. W* **127** *(tête-bêche sideways on* 4 c.*). P* 13½ × 14 (2 c.) *or* 14 × 13½ (4 c.).

305	2 c. pale flesh and brown-red..	15	10
306	4 c. green and black	15	10

Design: *Vert*—4 c. Presidents Steyn and Kruger and Treaty of Vereeniging Monument.

No. 306 exists with PVA gum as well as gum arabic.

PHOSPHORISED PAPER. All issues from here are on phosphorised paper *unless otherwise stated.*

181 View of Dam

(Des C. Bridgeford (4 c.), C. Lindsay (others))

1972 (4 Mar). *Opening of Hendrik Verwoerd Dam. T* **181** *and similar horiz designs. Multicoloured. W* **127** *(tête-bêche). P* 13½ × 14.

307	4 c. Type **181**	20	10
308	5 c. Aerial view of Dam	25	10
309	10 c. Dam and surrounding country (58 × 21 *mm*)	1·50	1·75
307/9	.. .. *Set of* 3	1·75	1·75

182 Sheep

182*a* Lamb

(Des K. Esterhuysen (4 c.), H. Botha (15 c.))

1972 (15 May–Oct). *W* **127** *(tête-bêche). P* 14.
310 **182** 4 c. olive-brn, yell, pale bl & slate-bl .. 25 10
a. *Grey-olive, yellow, bright blue and slate-blue* (10.72) 25 10
311 **182a** 15 c. pale stone, deep blue and dull blue 1·75 20
Other shades exist of the 4 c.
See also Nos. 317 and 322.

183 Black and Siamese Cats — **184** Transport and Industry

1972 (19 Sept). *Centenary of Societies for the Prevention of Cruelty to Animals. W* **127** *(sideways tête-bêche). P* 14 × 13½.
312 **183** 5 c. multicoloured .. .. .. 1·25 10

1972–74. *As Nos.* 310/11 *and* 282 *etc. but no wmk. P* 14 × 14½ (½ c.), 14 (1 c.) *or* 12½ *(others). Phosphorised, glossy paper.*
313 **168** ½ c. bright blue, scarlet and yellow-ochre (coil) (6.73) .. .. 12·00 11·00
314 **169** 1 c. rose-red and olive-brown (1.74) 20 10
315 **133** 2 c. blue and orange-yellow (11.72) .. 15 10
a. Perf 14. *Deep ultramarine and orange-yellow* (coil) (7.73) .. 9·00 8·50
b. Chalky paper (17.7.74) 25 30
316 **135** 3 c. scarlet and deep blue (8.5.73) .. 50 10
a. Chalky paper (18.2.74) 60 70
317 **182** 4 c. grey-blue, yellow, blue and bluish slate* (1.10.73) 25 20
a. *Olive-sepia, yellow, azure and slate-blue* (18.2.74) .. 30 15
b. *Lavender-brown, pale yellow, blue and bluish slate** (26.7.74) .. 25 20
c. Chalky paper* (22.8.74) .. 60 45
318 **136** 5 c. orge-yell & greenish bl (4.10.73) 1·00 40
a. Perf 14. *Yellow and light greenish blue* (coil) (7.73) .. .. 9·50 9·00
b. Chalky paper (5.74) .. .. 1·50 60
319 **137** 6 c. yellow-brown and bright green (*chalky paper*) (22.7.74) .. 1·25 70
320 **139** 9 c. red, yellow-green & grn-blk (6.73) 1·75 1·25
a. *Red, deep yellowish green and green-black* (4.74) .. 2·00 75
321 **138** 10 c. reddish brown & brt grn (8.5.73) 75 15
a. Perf 14 (coil) (6.73) .. .. 11·00 11·00
b. Chalky paper (17.7.74) .. .. 1·25 70
322 **182a** 15 c. pale stone, deep blue and dull blue (*chalky paper*) (4.9.74) .. 2·25 2·50
323 **141** 20 c. turquoise-blue, rose-carmine and orange-buff (8.5.73) .. .. 3·25 35
a. Chalky paper (5.74) .. .. 4·25 70
324 **142** 50 c. black and bright blue (6.73) .. 4·00 1·00
a. Chalky paper (22.7.74) .. .. 8·00 4·25
325 **143** 1 r. orange, lt green & lt blue (8.10.73) 14·00 2·00
a. Orange omitted £900
313/25 .. .. *Set of* 13 38·00 17·00
*On these stamps the colours are known to vary within the sheet.
No. 314 also differs in that the central design has been moved down about 1 mm.
Nos. 317/c also differ from No. 310 by measuring 26¼ × 21 mm instead of 27¼ × 21¾ mm.

(Des J. Hoekstra (4 c.), M. Barnett (others))

1973 (1 Feb). *50th Anniv of ESCOM (Electricity Supply Commission). T* **184** *and similar vert designs. Multicoloured. P* 12 × 12½ (4 c.) *or* 12½ *(others).*
326 4 c. Type **184** 20 10
327 5 c. Pylon (21 × 28 *mm*) 30 10
328 15 c. Cooling Towers (21 × 28 *mm*) .. .. 3·00 2·75
326/8 .. .. *Set of* 3 3·25 2·75

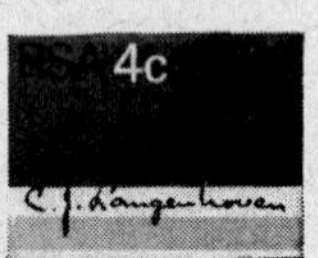

185 University Coat of arms — **187** C. J. Langenhoven

186 Rescuing Sailors

(Des P. de Wet (15 c.), H. Meiring (others))

1973 (2 Apr). *Centenary of University of South Africa. T* **185** *and similar designs. W* **127** *(tête-bêche)* (5 c.) *or no wmk (others). P* 12 × 12½ (5 c.) *or* 12½ *(others).*
329 4 c. multicoloured 20 10
330 5 c. multicoloured 30 15
331 15 c. black and gold .. .. .. 3·00 2·50
329/31 .. .. *Set of* 3 3·25 2·50
Designs: *Horiz* (37 × 21 *mm*)—5 c. University Complex, Pretoria. *Vert (As T* **185**)—15 c. Old University Building, Cape Town.

WATERMARK. All issues from this date are on unwatermarked paper, *unless otherwise stated.*

(Des M. Barnett)

1973 (2 June). *Bicentenary of Rescue by Wolraad Woltemade. T* **186** *and similar horiz designs. P* 11½ × 12½.
332 4 c. lt red-brown, lt yellow-green and black .. 25 10
333 5 c. yellow-olive, light yellow-green & black 40 10
334 15 c. red-brown, light yellow-green and black 5·00 4·25
332/4 .. .. *Set of* 3 5·00 4·25
Designs:—5 c. *De Jong Thomas* foundering; 15 c. *De Jong Thomas* breaking up and sailors drowning.

(Des J. Mostert)

1973 (1 Aug). *Birth Centenary of C. J. Langenhoven (politician and composer of national anthem). T* **187** *and similar designs. P* 12½ *(4 and 5 c.) or* 11½ × 12½ (15 c.).
335 **187** 4 c. multicoloured 25 10
336 – 5 c. multicoloured 35 10
337 – 15 c. multicoloured .. .. .. 5·00 4·25
335/7 .. .. *Set of* 3 5·00 4·25
Nos. 336/7 are as T **187** but with motifs rearranged. The 5 c. is vert, 21 × 38 mm, and the 15 c. is horiz, 38 × 21 mm.

188 Communications Map

(Des C. Webb)

1973 (1 Oct). *World Communications Day. P* 12½.

(a) No wmk. Glossy paper
338 **188** 15 c. multicoloured .. .. .. 80 1·40

(b) W **127** *(tête-bêche). Chalky paper*
339 **188** 15 c. multicoloured .. .. .. 1·50 4·00

189 Restored Buildings — **190** Burgerspond (obverse and reverse)

(Des W. Jordaan)

1974 (14 Mar). *Restoration of Tulbagh. T* **189** *and similar multi-coloured design. P* 12½.
340 4 c. Type **189** 15 10
341 5 c. Restored Church Street (58 × 21 *mm*) .. 25 35

(Des P. de Wet. Litho)

1974 (6 Apr). *Centenary of the Burgerspond (coin). P* 12½ × 12.
342 **190** 9 c. brown, orange-red & pale yell-olive 50 80

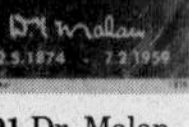

191 Dr. Malan — **192** Congress Emblem

(Des I. Henkel)

1974 (22 May). *Birth Centenary of Dr. D. F. Malan (Prime Minister). P* 12½ × 12.
343 **191** 4 c. blue and light blue 15 10

(Des Ingrid Paul)

1974 (13 June). *15th World Sugar Congress, Durban. P* 12 × 12½.
344 **192** 15 c. deep ultramarine and silver .. 80 1·25

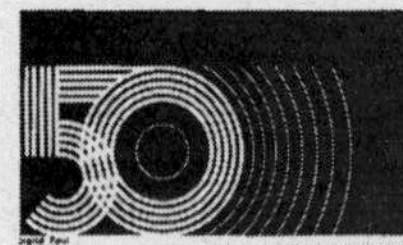

193 "50" and Radio Waves

(Des Ingrid Paul)

1974 (13 July). *50th Anniv of Broadcasting in South Africa. P* 12 × 12½.
345 **193** 4 c. red and black 10 10

194 Monument Building

(Des G. Cunningham)

1974 (13 July). *Inauguration of British Settlers' Monument, Grahamstown. P* 12 × 12½.
346 **194** 5 c. red and black 10 10

195 Stamps of the South African Provinces

(Des K. Esterhuysen)

1974 (9 Oct). *Centenary of Universal Postal Union. P* 12½.
347 **195** 15 c. multicoloured 80 80

196 Iris — **197** Bokmakierie Shrikes

(Des E. de Jong. Recess and photo)

1974 (20 Nov)–**76**. *Multicoloured. Glossy paper* (2, 3, 4, 6, 7, 30 *c. and* 1 *r.) or chalk-surfaced paper (others). P* 12½ *(1 to 25 c.) or* 12×12½ *(others).*

(a) Vert designs as T **196** *showing flowers, or horiz designs showing birds or fish.*
348 1 c. Type **196** 10 10
349 2 c. Wild Heath 15 10
a. Chalk-surfaced paper (2.75) 10 10
350 3 c. Geranium 20 10
a. Chalk-surfaced paper (*deep claret background*) (6.75) 10 10
ab. Imperf (pair) £250
ac. Brown-purple background (6.76) .. 10 10
351 4 c. Arum Lily 30 10
a. Chalk-surfaced paper (2.75) 10 10
ab. Imperf (pair) £160
352 5 c. Cape Gannet 20 10
353 6 c. Galjoen (fish) 25 10
354 7 c. Zebra Fish 25 10
355 9 c. Angel Fish 30 10
356 10 c. Moorish Idol 30 10
357 14 c. Roman (fish) 30 10
358 15 c. Greater Double-collared Sunbird .. 30 10
359 20 c. Yellow-billed Hornbill 45 10
360 25 c. Barberton Daisy 45 10

(b) Horiz designs as T **197**
361 30 c. Type **197** .. .. 6·50 35
362 50 c. Stanley Cranes .. .. .. 2·00 35
363 1 r. Bateleurs .. .. 7·00 2·50
348/63 .. .. *Set of* 16 17·00 3·50
A used block of 4 and a single on cover of No. 351 have been seen with the yellow omitted.

1974 (20 Nov)–**76.** *Coil stamps. As Nos.* 348/9, 352 *and* 356 *but photo, colours changed. Glossy paper. P* 12½.
370 1 c. reddish violet and pink 45 30
a. Perf 14. Chalk-surfaced paper (12.75) .. 45 30
371 2 c. bronze-green and yellow-ochre 70 30
a. Chalk-surfaced paper (7.75) 70 30
b. Perf 14. Chalk-surfaced paper (11.76?) .. 90 20
372 5 c. black and light slate-blue 85 30
373 10 c. deep violet-blue and light blue .. .. 3·75 3·75
a. Perf 14. Chalk-surfaced paper (4.76) .. 2·00 2·25
370/3 .. .. *Set of* 4 3·50 2·75

198 Voortrekker Monument and Encampment

(Des J. Hoekstra)

1974 (6 Dec). *25th Anniv of Voortrekker Monument, Pretoria. P* 12½.
374 **198** 4 c. multicoloured 20 20

199 SASOL Complex

200 President Diederichs

(Des C. Webb)

1975 (26 Feb). *25th Anniv of SASOL (South African Coal, Oil and Gas Corporation Ltd). P* 11½ × 12½.
375 **199** 15 c. multicoloured .. .. .. 1·25 1·50

(Des J. L. Booysen. Recess (4 c.) or photo (15 c.))

1975 (19 Apr). *Inauguration of the State President. P* 12½ × 11½.
376 **200** 4 c. agate and gold 10 10
377 15 c. royal blue and gold .. .. 70 1·25

201 Jan Smuts

202 "Dutch East Indiaman, Table Bay"

(Des J. Hoekstra. Recess and photo)

1975 (24 May). *Jan Smuts Commemoration. P* 12½ × 11½.
378 **201** 4 c. black and olive-black 10 10

(Des J. Hoekstra. Photo (Nos. 379/82) or litho (**MS**383))

1975 (18 June). *Death Centenary of Thomas Baines (painter). T* **202** *and similar horiz designs. Multicoloured. P* 11½ × 12½.
379 5 c. Type **202** 20 10
380 9 c. "Cradock, 1848" 30 20
381 15 c. "Thirsty Flat, 1848" 50 50
382 30 c. "Pretoria, 1874" .. .. 1·00 1·75
379/82 .. .. *Set of* 4 1·75 2·25
MS383 120 × 95 mm. Nos. 379/82 .. .. 1·90 4·00

203 Gideon Malherbe's House, Paarl

(Des P. de Wet. Recess and photo)

1975 (14 Aug). *Centenary of Genootskap van Regte Afrikaners (Afrikaner Language Movement). P* 12½.
384 **203** 4 c. multicoloured 10 10

204 "Automatic Sorting"

205 Title Page of *Die Afrikaanse Patriot*

(Des J. Sampson)

1975 (11 Sept). *Postal Mechanisation. P* 12½ × 11½.
385 **204** 4 c. multicoloured 10 10

(Des K. Esterhuysen. Recess and photo (4 c.). Des P. de Wet. Litho (5 c.))

1975 (10 Oct). *Inauguration of the Language Monument, Paarl. T* **205** *and similar vert design. P* 12½ × 11½.
386 4 c. black, pale stone and bright orange .. 10 10
387 5 c. multicoloured 10 10
Design:—5 c. "Afrikaanse Taalmonument".

206 Table Mountain

(Des P. Bosman and J. Hoekstra. Litho)

1975 (13 Nov). *Tourism. T* **206** *and similar horiz designs. Multicoloured. P* 12½.
388 15 c. Type **206** .. .. 2·75 2·75
a. Block of 4. Nos. 388/91 .. .. .. 10·00
389 15 c. Johannesburg .. .. 2·75 2·75
390 15 c. Cape Vineyards .. .. 2·75 2·75
391 15 c. Lions in Kruger National Park .. .. 2·75 2·75
388/91 .. .. *Set of* 4 10·00 10·00
Nos. 388/91 were printed together, *se-tenant*, in blocks of 4 throughout the sheet.

207 Globe and Satellites

(Des J. Hoekstra. Litho)

1975 (3 Dec). *Satellite Communication. P* 12½.
392 **207** 15 c. multicoloured 40 40

208 Bowls

(209)

(Des J. Maskew. Litho)

1976. *Sporting Commemorations. T* **208** *and similar vert designs. P* 12½ × 11½.
393 15 c. black and light sage-green (18.2) .. 30 60
394 15 c. black and bright yellow-green (15.3) .. 75 1·25
395 15 c. black and pale yellow-olive (16.8) .. 40 60
396 15 c. black and apple-green (2.12) 30 55
393/6 .. .. *Set of* 4 1·60 2·75
MS397 161 × 109 mm. Nos. 393/6 (2.12) .. .. 2·75 4·00
Designs:—No. 393, Type **208** (World Bowls Championships, Johannesburg); No. 394, Batsman (Centenary of Organised Cricket in South Africa); No. 395, Polo player; No. 396, Gary Player (golfer).

1976 (6 Apr). *South Africa's Victory in World Bowls Championships. No.* 393 *optd with T* **209** *in gold.*
398 **208** 15 c. black and light sage-green 25 65

210 "Picnic under a Baobab Tree"

(Des J. Hoekstra. Photo (4 c.) or litho (others and **MS**403))

1976 (20 Apr). *Birth Centenary of Erich Mayer (painter). T* **210** *and similar horiz designs. Multicoloured. P* 11½ × 12½.
399 4 c. Type **210** 15 10
a. Imperf (pair) £400
400 10 c. "Foot of the Blaawberg" 35 25
401 15 c. "Harbeespoort Dam" .. .. .. 60 1·00
402 20 c. "Street scene, Doornfontein" .. .. 80 1·50
399/402 .. .. *Set of* 4 1·75 2·50
MS403 121 × 95 mm. Nos. 399/402 .. .. 2·00 4·00

211 Cheetah

212 "Emily Hobhouse" (H. Naude)

(Des P. Bosman. Photo (3 c.) or litho (others))

1976 (5 June). *World Environmental Day. T* **211** *and similar horiz designs. Multicoloured. P* 11½ × 12½.
404 3 c. Type **211** 15 10
405 10 c. Black Rhinoceros 70 35
406 15 c. Blesbok .. .. 85 1·10
407 20 c. Mountain Zebra .. .. 1·25 1·75
404/7 .. .. *Set of* 4 2·75 3·00

(Des J. Hoekstra)

1976 (8 June). *50th Death Anniv of Emily Hobhouse (welfare worker). P* 12½ × 11½.
408 **212** 4 c. multicoloured 10 10

213 Steam Packet, 1876

214 Family with Globe

(Des K. Esterhuysen. Litho)

1976 (5 Oct). *Ocean Mail Service Centenary. P* 11½ × 12½.
409 **213** 10 c. multicoloured 60 85
a. Imperf (horiz pair) £300

(Des I. Ross)

1976 (6 Nov). *Family Planning and Child Welfare. P* 12½ × 11½.
410 **214** 4 c. chestnut and light salmon 10 10

215 Glasses of Wine

216 Dr. Jacob du Toit

First "die" of Afrikaans inscription at left omitted (R. 1/3 on every third sheet)

(Des H. Botha. Litho)

1977 (14 Feb). *International Wine Symposium, Cape Town. P* 12½ × 11½.
411 **215** 15 c. multicoloured 40 75
a. "die" omitted .. .. .. 13·00

(Des J. Hoekstra)

1977 (21 Feb). *Birth Centenary of J. D. du Toit (theologian and poet). P* 12½ × 11½.
412 **216** 4 c. multicoloured 10 10

217 Palace of Justice

218 *Protea repens*

(Des H. Meiring)

1977 (18 May). *Centenary of Transvaal Supreme Court. P* 11½ × 12½.
413 **217** 4 c. red-brown 10 10

(Des D. Findlay. Photo (1, 2, 3 c. (No. 416), 4, 5, 8, 10 to 20 c. (Nos. 425/a) and coil stamps) or litho (others))

1977 (27 May)–**82.** *Vert designs as T* **218** *showing Proteas or other Succulents. Multicoloured. (a) Sheet stamps. P* 12½.
414 1 c. Type **218** 10 10
415 2 c. *P punctata* 15 10
416 3 c. *P neriifolia* (photo) (p 12½) 10 10
416*a* 3 c. *P neriifolia* (litho) (p 14 × 13½) (1.10.79) 10 10
417 4 c. *P longifolia* 10 10
a. Imperf (pair) £100
418 5 c. *P cynaroides* 10 10
a. Perf 14 × 13½ (4.3.81) 10 10
b. Imperf (pair) £120
419 6 c. *P canaliculata* 35 15
a. Black (face value and inscr at foot) omitted £120
b. Perf 14 × 13½ (25.10.79*) 30 15
420 7 c. *P lorea* 25 15
a. Emerald ("RSA") omitted £150
b. Perf 14 × 13½ (19.9.80) 20 15
421 8 c. *P mundii* 20 10
a. Perf 14 × 13½ (10.7.81) 15 10
422 9 c. *P roupelliae* 20 15
a. Perf 14 × 13½ (22.12.78) .. .. 3·75 1·00
423 10 c. *P aristata* 30 10
a. Perf 14 × 13½ (12.1.82) 20 10
424 15 c. *P eximia* 25 10
425 20 c. *P magnifica* (photo) 30 10
a. Perf 14 × 13½ (16.2.78) 60 80
425*b* 20 c. *P magnifica* (litho) (p 14 × 13½) (24.5.82) 65 15

426 25 c. *P grandiceps* 60 15
a. Emerald ("RSA" and leaves) omitted .. £160
b. Perf 14 × 13½ (3.6.80) 40 10
427 30 c. *P amplexicaulis* 45 10
a. Perf 14 × 13½ (19.10.80) 40 15
428 50 c. *Leucospermum cordifolium* 65 15
a. Perf 14 × 13½ (9.10.80) 45 15
429 1 r. *Paranomus reflexus* .. .. .. 1·00 70
a. Perf 14 × 13½ (30.7.80) 80 50
430 2 r. *Orothamnus zeyheri* .. .. .. 3·00 2·50
a. Perf 14 × 13½ (22.5.81) .. .. .. 1·50 1·00

(*b*) *Coil stamps. Imperf × perf 14*

431 1 c. *Leucadendron argenteum* 25 30
432 2 c. *Mimetes cucullatus* 25 30
433 5 c. *Serruria florida* 25 30
434 10 c. *Leucadendron sessile* 25 40
414/34 .. .. *Set of* 21 6·00 3·75

*Sheets dated 15 August 1979.

There were two emerald plates used for the 7 c.; one for the design and background and a second, common with other values in the issue, used to apply "RSA". No. 420a shows this second emerald plate omitted.

Later printings of the coil stamps come with every fifth stamp numbered on the back.

219 Gymnast **220** Metrication Symbol on Globe

(Des D. Cowie. Litho)

1977 (15 Aug). *Eighth Congress of International Association of Physical Education and Sports for Girls and Women. P* 12½ × 11½.
435 **219** 15 c. black, salmon-red and yellow .. 25 30

(Des L. Wilsenach. Litho)

1977 (15 Sept). *Metrication. P* 12 × 12½.
436 **220** 15 c. multicoloured 25 30

221 Atomic Diagram

(Des R. Sargent. Litho)

1977 (8 Oct). *Uranium Development. P* 12 × 12½.
437 **221** 15 c. multicoloured 25 30

222 National Flag

(Des J. Hoekstra)

1977 (11 Nov). *50th Anniv of National Flag. P* 12 × 12½.
438 **222** 5 c. multicoloured 10 10

223 Walvis Bay, 1878

(Des A. H. Barrett. Litho)

1978 (10 Mar). *Centenary of Annexation of Walvis Bay. P* 12½.
439 **223** 15 c. multicoloured 50 40

224 Dr. Andrew Murray **225** Steel Rail

(Des J. Hoekstra. Litho)

1978 (9 May). *150th Birth Anniv of Dr. Andrew Murray (church statesman). P* 12½ × 12.
440 **224** 4 c. multicoloured 10 10

(Des H. Botha. Litho)

1978 (5 June). *50th Anniv of I.S.C.O.R. (South African Iron and Steel Industrial Corporation). P* 12½.
441 **225** 15 c. multicoloured 20 20

226 Richards Bay

(Des A. H. Barrett. Litho)

1978 (31 July). *Harbours. T* **226** *and similar horiz design. Multicoloured. P* 12½.
442 15 c. Type **226** 40 70
a. Pair. Nos. 442/3 .. .. 80 1·40
443 15 c. Saldanhabaai 40 70

Nos. 442/3 were printed together, *se-tenant*, in horizontal and vertical pairs throughout the sheet.

227 "Shepherd's Lonely Dwelling, Riversdale" **228** Pres. B. J. Vorster

(Des G. Mynhardt. Litho)

1978 (21 Aug). *125th Birth Anniv of J. E. A. Volschenk (painter). T* **227** *and similar horiz designs. Multicoloured. P* 12½.
444 10 c. Type **227** 20 20
445 15 c. "Clouds and Sunshine, Laneberg Range, Riversdale" 50 35
446 20 c. "At the Foot of the Mountain" 70 80
447 25 c. "Evening on the Veldt" .. .. 80 1·40
444/7 .. .. *Set of* 4 2·00 2·50
MS448 124 × 90 mm. Nos. 444/7 .. .. .. 2·75 3·75

(Des A. H. Barrett. Litho)

1978 (10 Oct). *Inauguration of President Vorster. P* 14 × 13½.
449 **228** 4 c. brown-purple and gold 50 15
a. Perf 12½ × 12 .. .. .. 10 10
450 15 c. dull violet and gold 25 30

229 Golden Gate

(Des A. H. Barrett. Litho)

1978 (13 Nov). *Tourism. T* **229** *and similar horiz designs. Multicoloured. P* 12½.
451 10 c. Type **229** 20 15
452 15 c. Blyde River Canyon 50 35
453 20 c. Amphitheatre, Drakensberg 70 80
454 25 c. Cango Caves .. .. 80 1·25
451/4 .. .. *Set of* 4 2·00 2·25

230 Dr. Wadley (inventor) and Tellurometer

(Des A. H. Barrett. Litho)

1979 (12 Feb). *25th Anniv of Tellurometer (radio distance measurer). P* 12½.
455 **230** 15 c. multicoloured 20 20

231 1929 4d. Airmail Stamp

(Des G. Mynhardt. Litho)

1979 (30 Mar). *50th Anniv of Stamp Production in South Africa. P* 14.
456 **231** 15 c. green, cream and slate 20 20

232 "Save Fuel"

(Des A. H. Barrett)

1979 (2 Apr). *Fuel Conservation. P* 12 × 12½.
457 **232** 4 c. black and vermilion 10 10
a. Pair. Nos. 457/8 .. .. 20 35
458 – 4 c. black and vermilion 10 10

No. 458 is as T **232** but has face value and country initials in bottom left-hand corner, and Afrikaans inscription above English.

Nos. 457/8 were printed together, *se-tenant*, in horizontal and vertical pairs throughout the sheet.

233 Isandlwana **234** "Health Care"

(Des A. H. Barrett. Litho)

1979 (25 May). *Centenary of Zulu War. T* **233** *and similar horiz designs in black and rose-red, showing drawings. P* 14.
459 4 c. Type **233** 15 10
460 15 c. Ulundi 35 40
461 20 c. Rorke's Drift 40 60
459/61 .. .. *Set of* 3 80 95
MS462 125 × 90 mm. Nos. 459/61. P 12½ .. 2·25 3·00

(Des J. Hoekstra. Litho)

1979 (19 June). *Health Year. P* 12½ × 12.
463 **234** 4 c. multicoloured 10 10
a. Perf 14 × 13½ 30 20

235 Children looking at Candle

(Des G. Mynhardt. Litho)

1979 (13 Sept). *50th Anniv of Christmas Stamp Fund. P* 14.
464 **235** 4 c. multicoloured 10 10

236 University of Cape Town **237** "Gary Player"

(Des G. Mynhardt. Litho)

1979 (1 Oct). *50th Anniv of University of Cape Town. P* 13½ × 14.
465 **236** 4 c. multicoloured 20 20
a. Perf 12 × 12½ 10 10

(Des H. de Klerk. Litho)

1979 (4 Oct). *"Rosafari 1979" World Rose Convention, Pretoria. T* **237** *and similar vert designs. Multicoloured. P* 14 × 13½.
466 4 c. Type **237** 15 10
467 15 c. "Prof. Chris Barnard" 30 40
468 20 c. "Southern Sun" 40 50
469 25 c. "Soaring Wings" 45 65
466/9 .. .. *Set of* 4 1·10 1·40
MS470 100 × 125 mm. Nos. 466/9 .. .. 1·50 2·00

238 University of Stellenbosch **239** F.A.K. Emblem

(Des A. H. Barrett. Litho)

1979 (8 Nov). *300th Anniv of Stellenbosch (oldest town in South Africa). T* **238** *and similar horiz design. Multicoloured. P* 14.

471 4 c. Type **238** 10 10
472 15 c. Rhenish Church on the Braak 20 35

(Des J. Hoekstra)

1979 (18 Dec). *50th Anniv of F.A.K. (Federation of Afrikaans Cultural Societies). P* 12½ × 12.

473 **239** 4 c. multicoloured 10 10

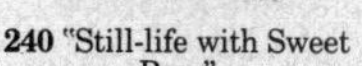

240 "Still-life with Sweet Peas" **241** "Cullinan II"

(Des G. Mynhardt. Litho)

1980 (6 May). *Paintings by Pieter Wenning. T* **240** *and similar multicoloured design. P* 14 × 13½.

474 5 c. Type **240** 10 10
475 25 c. "House in the Suburbs, Cape Town" (*44½ × 37 mm*) 30 55
MS476 94 × 121 mm. Nos. 474/5 .. .. .. 1·25 1·60

(Des A. H. Barrett. Litho)

1980 (12 May). *World Diamond Congresses, Johannesburg. T* **241** *and similar vert design. Multicoloured. P* 14.

477 15 c. Type **241** 45 45
478 20 c. "Cullinan I (Great Star of Africa)" .. 55 55

242 C. L. Leipoldt **243** University of Pretoria

(Des J. Hoekstra. Litho)

1980 (3 Sept). *Birth Centenary of C. L. Leipoldt (poet). P* 14 × 13½.

479 **242** 5 c. multicoloured 10 10

(Des P. de Wet. Litho)

1980 (9 Oct). *50th Anniv of University of Pretoria. P* 14 × 13½.

480 **243** 5 c. multicoloured 10 10

244 "Marine with Shipping" (Willem van de Velde)

(Des G. Mynhardt. Litho)

1980 (3 Nov). *Paintings from South African National Gallery, Cape Town. T* **244** *and similar multicoloured designs. P* 14.

481 5 c. Type **244** 10 10
482 10 c. "Firetail and his Trainer" (George Stubbs) 15 20
483 15 c. "Lavinia" (Thomas Gainsborough) (*vert*) 20 40
484 20 c. "Classical Landscape" (Pieter Post) .. 25 60
481/4 .. .. *Set of* 4 65 1·10
MS485 126 × 90 mm. Nos. 481/4 .. .. .. 1·00 1·75

245 Joubert, Kruger and M. Pretorius (Triumvirate Government) **246** Boers advancing up Amajuba Mountain

(Des A. H. Barrett. Litho)

1980 (15 Dec). *Centenary of Paardekraal Monument (cairn commemorating formation of Boer Triumvirate Government). T* **245** *and similar multicoloured design. P* 14 × 13½ (5 c.) *or* 13½ × 14 (10 c.).

486 5 c. Type **245** 10 10
487 10 c. Paardekraal Monument (*vert*) .. 10 15

(Des Diana Arbuthnot. Litho)

1981 (27 Feb). *Centenary of Battle of Amajuba. T* **246** *and similar multicoloured design. P* 13½ × 14 (5 c.) *or* 14 × 13½ (15 c.).

488 5 c. Type **246** 10 10
489 15 c. British troops defending hill (*horiz*) .. 20 25

247 Ballet *Raka*

(Des H. Botha. Litho)

1981 (23 May). *Opening of State Theatre, Pretoria. T* **247** *and similar horiz design. Multicoloured. P* 14.

490 20 c. Type **247** 25 30
491 25 c. Opera *Aida* 30 35
MS492 110 × 90 mm. Nos. 490/1 .. .. 60 70

248 Former Presidents C. R. Swart, J. J. Fouché, N. Diederichs and B. J. Vorster

(Des A. H. Barrett. Litho)

1981 (30 May). *20th Anniv of Republic. T* **248** *and similar design. P* 14.

493 5 c. black, grey-olive and bistre 10 10
494 15 c. multicoloured 20 20

Design: (28 × 22 *mm*)—15 c. President Marais Viljoen.

249 Girl with Hearing Aid **250** Microscope **251** *Calanthe natalensis*

(Des Mare Mouton. Litho)

1981 (12 June). *Centenary of Institutes for Deaf and Blind, Worcester. T* **249** *and similar vert design. Multicoloured. P* 13½ × 14.

495 5 c. Type **249** 10 10
496 15 c. Boy reading braille 20 25

(Des N. Hanna. Litho)

1981 (10 July). *50th Anniv of National Cancer Association. P* 13½ × 14.

497 **250** 5 c. multicoloured 10 10

(Des Jeanette Stead. Litho)

1981 (11 Sept). *Tenth World Orchid Conference, Durban. T* **251** *and similar vert designs. Multicoloured. P* 14.

498 5 c. Type **251** 10 10
499 15 c. *Eulophia speciosa* 25 25
500 20 c. *Disperis fanniniae* 30 35
501 25 c. *Disa uniflora* 40 40
498/501 .. .. *Set of* 4 90 95
MS502 120 × 91 mm. Nos. 498/501 .. .. 1·75 1·50

PRICES OF SETS

Set prices are given for many issues, generally those containing three stamps or more. Definitive sets include one of each value or major colour change, but do not cover different perforations, die types or minor shades. Where a choice is possible the set prices are based on the cheapest versions of the stamps included in the listings.

252 Voortrekkers in Uniform **253** Lord Baden-Powell **254** Dr. Robert Koch

(Des J. Hoekstra. Litho)

1981 (30 Sept). *50th Anniv of Voortrekker Movement (Afrikaans cultural youth organization). P* 14.

503 **252** 5 c. multicoloured 10 10

(Des J. Meyer. Litho)

1982 (22 Feb). *75th Anniv of Boy Scout Movement. P* 13½ × 14.

504 **253** 15 c. multicoloured 15 15

(Des J. Meyer. Litho)

1982 (24 Mar). *Centenary of Discovery of Tubercle Bacillus by Dr. Robert Koch. P* 13½ × 14.

505 **254** 20 c. multicoloured 15 20

255 *Maria van Riejbeck* (submarine) **256** Old Provost, Grahamstown

(Des A. H. Barrett. Litho)

1982 (2 Apr). *25th Anniv of Simonstown as South African Navy Base. T* **255** *and similar horiz designs. Multicoloured. P* 14.

506 8 c. Type **255** 10 10
507 15 c. Missile patrol vessel 15 25
508 20 c. Minesweeper 25 40
509 25 c. Harbour patrol boats 30 60
506/9 .. .. *Set of* 4 70 1·25
MS510 125 × 90 mm. Nos. 506/9 .. .. 1·40 1·40

(Des A. H. Barrett. Recess (Nos. 511, 512*b*, 513, 514, 515*a*, 516*a*, 521, 522*a*, 524, 525 and 526/7), photo (Nos. 528/31) or litho (others))

1982 (15 July)–**87**. *South African Architecture. Designs as T* **256**.

(*a*) *Sheet stamps. P* 14

511	1 c. reddish brown (*recess*)	10	10
511*a*	1 c. reddish brown (*litho*) (2.4.84)	10	10
512	2 c. yellow-olive (*litho*)	20	15
512*a*	2 c. deep green (*litho*) (9.5.83)	75	15
512*b*	2 c. bottle green (*recess*) (28.11.83)	10	10
512*c*	2 c. bottle green (*litho*) (21.11.85)	20	15
513	3 c. violet (*recess*)	20	10
513*a*	3 c. violet (*litho*) (28.11.85)	20	10
514	4 c. brown-olive (*recess*)	20	10
514*a*	4 c. brown-olive (*litho*) (25.3.85)	20	10
515	5 c. carmine (*litho*)	30	15
515*a*	5 c. brown-purple (*recess*) (11.11.83)	10	10
516	6 c. deep blue-green (*litho*)	40	10
516*a*	6 c. blackish green (*recess*) (9.8.84)	25	10
517	7 c. dull yellowish green (*litho*)	15	10
518	8 c. greenish blue (*litho*)	30	15
518*a*	8 c. indigo (*litho*) (3.1.83)	15	10
519	9 c. deep mauve (*litho*)	15	10
520	10 c. Venetian red (*litho*)	40	15
520*a*	10 c. purple-brown (*litho*) (26.1.83)	25	10
520*b*	11 c. cerise (*litho*) (2.4.84)	30	10
520*c*	12 c. deep violet-blue (*litho*) (1.4.85)	40	10
520*d*	14 c. lake-brown (*litho*) (1.4.86)	45	10
521	15 c. deep violet-blue (*recess*)	20	10
521*a*	16 c. rosine (*litho*) (1.4.87)	60	25
522	20 c. vermilion (*litho*)	60	25
522*a*	20 c. brownish black (*recess*) (15.6.83)	60	10
522*b*	20 c. brownish black (*litho*) (14.11.85)	55	15
523	25 c. bistre (*litho*)	40	20
523*a*	25 c. ochre (*litho*) (3.6.87)	45	15
524	30 c. agate (*recess*)	65	20
524*a*	30 c. reddish brown (*litho*) (12.3.86)	55	20
525	50 c. deep turquoise-blue (*recess*)	80	30
	a. Deep slate-blue (18.3.83)	1·00	65
525*b*	50 c. turquoise-blue (*litho*) (13.10.86)	75	20
526	1 r. deep violet (*recess*)	1·00	15
526*a*	1 r. deep violet (*litho*) (17.12.86)	1·00	30
527	2 r. deep carmine (*recess*)	2·00	30
527*a*	2 r. deep carmine (*litho*) (5.12.85)	2·00	50
511/27	*Set of* 21 (*one of each value*)	8·00	2·25

Designs: (28 × 20 *mm*)—2 c. Tuynhuys, Cape Town; 3 c. Appèlhof, Bloemfontein; 4 c. Raadsaal, Pretoria; 5 c. Cape Town Castle; 6 c. Goewermentsgebou, Bloemfontein; 7 c. Drostdy, Graaff-Reinet; 8 c. Leeuwenhof, Cape Town; 9 c. Libertas, Pretoria; 10 c. City Hall, Pietermaritzburg; 11 c. City Hall, Kimberley; 12 c. City Hall, Port Elizabeth; 14 c. City Hall, Johannesburg; 15 c. Matjesfontein; 16 c. City Hall, Durban; 20 c. Post Office, Durban; 25 c. Melrose House, Pretoria. (45 × 28 *mm*)—30 c. Old Legislative Assembly Building, Pietermaritzburg; 50 c. Raadsaal, Bloemfontein; 1 r. Houses of Parliament, Cape Town; 2 r. Uniegebou, Pretoria.

For certain printings of Nos. 511/27*a* the design width of each stamp was reduced by a millimetre. Of the original set of 17 all showed "wide" designs with the exception of the 1 r. Changes in design size occurred in subsequent printings so that Nos. 512*c*, 513, 521 and 524 can be found in both wide and narrow versions. Of the remainder Nos. 511*a*, 512*b*, 513*a*, 514*a*, 515*a*, 516*a*, 520*b*/*d*, 521*a*, 522*a*/*b*, 524*a*, 525*a*/*b*, 526 and 527*a* exist as "narrow" designs only.

(*b*) *Coil stamps. P* 14 × *imperf*

528	1 c. brown	10	20
529	2 c. yellow-green	10	20
530	5 c. lake-brown	10	20
531	10 c. light brown	15	25
528/31	*Set of* 4	40	75

Designs: (28 × 20 *mm*)—1 c. Drostdy, Swellendam; 2 c. City Hall, East London; 5 c. Head Post Office, Johannesburg; 10 c. Morgenster, Somerset West.

257 Bradysaurus

258 Gough Island Base

(Des Sheila Nowers. Litho)

1982 (1 Dec). *Karoo Fossils. T* **257** *and similar horiz designs. Multicoloured. P* 14.

532	8 c. Type **257**	25	10
533	15 c. Lystrosaurus	35	40
534	20 c. Euparkeria	40	60
535	25 c. Thrinaxodon	45	65
532/5	*Set of* 4	1·25	1·60
MS536	107 × 95 mm. Nos. 532/5	1·75	1·75

(Des D. Thorpe. Litho)

1983 (19 Jan). *Weather Stations. T* **258** *and similar horiz designs. Multicoloured. P* 13½ × 14.

537	8 c. Type **258**	20	10
538	20 c. Marion Island base	45	45
539	25 c. Taking meteorological readings	45	50
540	40 c. Launching weather balloon, Sanae	70	75
537/40	*Set of* 4	1·60	1·60

259 Class "S2" Light Shunting Locomotive

260 Rugby

(Des H. Botha. Litho)

1983 (27 Apr). *Steam Railway Locomotives. T* **259** *and similar horiz designs. Multicoloured. P* 14.

541	10 c. Type **259**	25	10
542	20 c. Class "16E" express locomotive	45	50
543	25 c. Class "6H" locomotive	50	60
544	40 c. Class "15F" main-line locomotive	80	90
541/4	*Set of* 4	1·75	1·90

(Des Sheila Nowers. Litho)

1983 (20 July). *Sport in South Africa. T* **260** *and similar multicoloured designs. P* 14.

545	10 c. Type **260**	10	10
546	20 c. Soccer (*horiz*)	25	30
547	25 c. Yachting	30	35
548	40 c. Horse-racing (*horiz*)	50	65
545/8	*Set of* 4	1·10	1·25

261 Plettenberg Bay

262 Thomas Pringle

(Des A. H. Barrett. Litho)

1983 (12 Oct). *Tourism. Beaches. T* **261** *and similar horiz designs. Multicoloured. P* 14.

549	10 c. Type **261**	10	10
550	20 c. Durban	25	30
551	25 c. West coast	30	35
552	40 c. Clifton	50	65
549/52	*Set of* 4	1·10	1·25
MS553	128×90 mm. Nos. 549/52	1·75	1·75

(Des J. van Ellinckhuijzen. Litho)

1984 (24 Feb). *South African English Authors. T* **262** *and similar vert designs. P* 14.

554	10 c. olive-brown, yellow-brown and grey	10	10
555	20 c. olive-brown, deep bluish green and grey	25	35
556	25 c. olive-brown, deep brown-rose and grey	30	45
557	40 c. olive-brown, olive-ochre and grey	50	75
554/7	*Set of* 4	1·10	1·50

Designs:—20 c. Pauline Smith; 25 c. Olive Schreiner; 40 c. Sir Percy Fitzpatrick.

263 Manganese

(Des H. Botha. Litho)

1984 (8 June). *Strategic Minerals. T* **263** *and similar horiz designs. Multicoloured. P* 14.

558	11 c. Type **263**	25	10
559	20 c. Chromium	45	30
560	25 c. Vanadium	55	40
561	30 c. Titanium	60	45
558/61	*Set of* 4	1·75	1·10

264 Bloukrans River Bridge

265 Preamble to the Constitution in Afrikaans

(Des D. Bagnall. Litho)

1984 (24 Aug). *South African Bridges. T* **264** *and similar horiz designs. Multicoloured. P* 14.

562	11 c. Type **264**	35	10
563	25 c. Durban four level interchange	70	50
564	30 c. Mfolozi rail bridge	75	60
565	45 c. Gouritz River bridge	95	1·00
562/5	*Set of* 4	2·50	2·00

(Des G. Mynhardt. Litho)

1984 (3 Sept). *New Constitution. T* **265** *and similar vert designs. P* 14.

566	11 c. stone, black and bistre	50	50
	a. Horiz pair. Nos. 566/7	1·00	1·00
567	11 c. stone, black and bistre	50	50
568	25 c. stone, deep claret and bistre	30	30
569	30 c. multicoloured	40	40
566/9	*Set of* 4	1·50	1·50

Designs:—No. 566, Preamble to the Constitution in English; 568, Last two lines of National Anthem; 569, South African coat of arms.

Nos. 566/7 were printed together, *se-tenant*, in horizontal pairs.

266 Pres. P. W. Botha

267 Pro Patria Medal

1984 (2 Nov). *Inauguration of President Botha. Litho. P* 14.

570	**266**	11 c. multicoloured	20	10
571		25 c. multicoloured	40	30

(Des B. Jackson. Litho)

1984 (9 Nov). *Military Decorations. T* **267** *and similar vert designs. Multicoloured. P* 14.

572	11 c. Type **267**	20	10
573	25 c. De Wet Decoration	45	40
574	30 c. John Chard Decoration	50	55
575	45 c. Honoris Crux (Diamond) Decoration	75	1·00
572/5	*Set of* 4	1·75	1·90
MS576	71 × 116 mm. Nos. 572/5	1·75	2·00

268 "Reflections" (Frans Oerder)

269 Cape Parliament Building

1985 (22 Feb). *Paintings by Frans Oerder. T* **268** *and similar horiz designs. Multicoloured. Litho. P* 14.

577	11 c. Type **268**	25	15
578	25 c. "Ladies in a Garden"	40	35
579	30 c. "Still-life with Lobster"	45	45
580	50 c. "Still-life with Marigolds"	70	70
577/80	*Set of* 4	1·60	1·50
MS581	129 × 74 mm. Nos. 577/80	1·75	2·00

(Des A. H. Barrett. Litho)

1985 (15 May). *Centenary of Cape Parliament Building. T* **269** *and similar horiz designs. Multicoloured. P* 14.

582	12 c. Type **269**	15	10
583	25 c. Speaker's Chair	20	20
584	30 c. "National Convention 1908–9" (Edward Roworth)	30	25
585	50 c. Republic Parliamentary emblem	40	35
	a. Black (inscr and outline) omitted	£160	
582/5	*Set of* 4	95	80

270 Freesia

271 Sugar Bowl

(Des Sheila Nowers. Litho)

1985 (23 Aug). *Floral Emigrants. T* **270** *and similar vert designs. Multicoloured. P* 14.

586	12 c. Type **270**	10	10
587	25 c. Nerine	20	20
588	30 c. Ixia	25	25
589	50 c. Gladiolus	35	35
586/9	*Set of* 4	80	80

(Des H. Botha. Litho)

1985 (5 Nov). *Cape Silverware. T* **271** *and similar multicoloured designs. P* 14.

590	12 c. Type **271**	10	10
591	25 c. Teapot	20	20
592	30 c. Loving cup (*vert*)	25	25
593	50 c. Coffee pot (*vert*)	35	35
590/3	*Set of* 4	80	80

272 Blood Donor Session

273 National Flag

(Des Sheila Nowers. Litho)

1986 (20 Feb). *Blood Donor Campaign. T* **272** *and similar horiz designs. Multicoloured. P* 14.

594	12 c. Type **272**	25	10
595	20 c. Baby receiving blood transfusion	40	15
596	25 c. Operation in progress	45	20
597	30 c. Ambulanceman and accident victim	50	25
594/7	*Set of* 4	1·40	60

(Des J. Hoekstra. Litho)

1986 (30 May). *25th Anniv of Republic of South Africa. T* **273** *and similar horiz design. Multicoloured. P* 14.

598	14 c. Type **273**	25	30
	a. Horiz pair. Nos. 598/9	50	60
599	14 c. As Type **273**, but inscr "UNITY IS STRENGTH"	25	30

Nos. 598/9 were printed together, *se-tenant*, in horizontal pairs throughout the sheet.

274 Drostdyhof, Graaff-Reinet

(Des A. H. Barrett. Litho)

1986 (14 Aug). *Restoration of Historic Buildings. T* **274** *and similar horiz designs. Multicoloured. P* 14.

600	14 c. Type **274**	20	10
601	20 c. Pilgrim's Rest mining village	35	20
602	25 c. Strapp's Store, Bethlehem	40	25
603	30 c. Palmdene, Pietermaritzburg	45	30
600/3	*Set of* 4	1·25	80

MACHINE LABELS. From 14 August 1986 gummed labels in the above design, ranging in value from 1 c. to 99 r. 99, were available from an experimental machine at Sunnyside Post Office in Pretoria. The machine was moved to the "Johannesburg 100" exhibition from 6 to 11 October 1986 and was then reinstalled at Sunnyside on 17 October 1986. Further machines were introduced subsequently and each can be identified by a code number, between P.001 and P.034, at right.

275 Von Brandis Square, Johannesburg, *c* 1900

(Des J. van Niekerk. Litho)

1986 (25 Sept). *Centenary of Johannesburg. T* **275** *and similar horiz designs. Multicoloured. P* 14.

604 14 c. Type **275** 25 10
605 20 c. Gold mine (26×20 *mm*) 50 25
606 25 c. Johannesburg skyline, 1986 . . . . 60 25
607 30 c. Gold bars (26×20 *mm*) 70 35
604/7 . . . . *Set of* 4 1·90 85

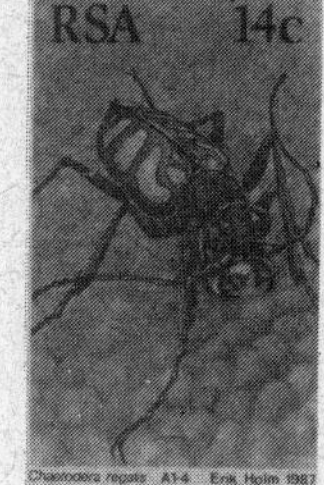

276 Gordon's Rock, Paarlberg

277 *Chaetodera regalis*

(Des A. H. Barrett. Litho)

1986 (20 Nov). *Rock Formations. T* **276** *and similar vert designs. Multicoloured. P* 14.

608 14 c. Type **276** 40 10
609 20 c. The Column, Drakensberg 55 30
610 25 c. Maltese Cross, Sederberge 65 40
611 30 c. Bourke's Luck Potholes, Blyde River Gorge 80 55
608/11 . . . . *Set of* 4 2·25 1·25

(Des E. Holm. Litho)

1987 (6 Mar). *South African Beetles. T* **277** *and similar vert designs. Multicoloured. P* 14.

612 14 c. Type **277** 30 10
613 20 c. *Trichostetha fascicularis* 40 35
614 25 c. *Julodis viridipes* 55 45
615 30 c. *Ceroplesis militaris* 65 55
612/15 . . . . *Set of* 4 1·75 1·25

278 Eland, Sebaaieni Cave

(Des H. Botha. Litho)

1987 (4 June). *Rock Paintings. T* **278** *and similar horiz designs. Multicoloured. P* 14.

616 16 c. Type **278** 25 10
617 20 c. Leaping lion, Clocolan 45 35
618 25 c. Black Wildebeest, uMhlwazini Valley 55 45
619 30 c. Bushman dance, Floukraal 60 55
616/19 . . . . *Set of* 4 1·75 1·25

279 Oude Pastorie, Paarl

(Des A. H. Barrett. Litho)

1987 (3 Sept). 300*th Anniv of Paarl. T* **279** *and similar horiz designs. Multicoloured. P* 14.

620 16 c. Type **279** 25 10
621 20 c. Grapevines 40 30
622 25 c. Wagon-building 45 40
623 30 c. KWV Cathedral Wine Cellar 50 40
620/3 . . . . *Set of* 4 1·40 1·10

VLOEDRAMP
NATAL

(280)

281 "Belshazzar's Feast" (Rembrandt)

1987 (16 Nov). *Natal Flood Relief Fund* (1*st issue*). *No.* 521*a surch as T* **280** *in Afrikaans or English.*

624 16 c. + 10 c. rosine (surch T **280**) 25 30
a. Pair. Nos. 624/5 . . . . 50 60
625 16 c. + 10 c. rosine (surch "NATAL FLOOD DISASTER") 25 30

Nos. 624/5 were surcharged together, *se-tenant*, in horizontal and vertical pairs throughout the sheet.

See also Nos. 629/30 and 635/6.

(Des Sheila Nowers. Litho)

1987 (19 Nov). *The Bible Society of South Africa. T* **281** *and similar multicoloured designs. P* 14.

626 16 c. "The Bible" in 75 languages (54×34 *mm*) 30 10
627 30 c. Type **281** 50 25
628 50 c. "St. Matthew and the Angel" (Rembrandt) (*vert*) 70 40
626/8 . . . . *Set of* 3 1·40 65

A 40 c. value, showing the inscription "The Word of God" in various languages, was prepared, but not issued.

1987 (1 Dec). *Natal Flood Relief Fund* (2*nd issue*). *No.* 626 *surch as T* **280**, *but larger* (*Afrikaans version* 32 *mm wide*).

629 16 c. + 10 c. multicoloured (surch "NATAL FLOOD DISASTER") 30 40
a. Pair. Nos. 629/30 . . . . . . 60 80
630 16 c. + 10 c. multicoloured (surch as T **280**) . . 30 40

Nos. 629/30 were surcharged together, *se-tenant*, in horizontal and vertical pairs throughout the sheet.

These stamps are known postmarked at Mooirivier on 25 November 1987.

282 Bartolomeu Dias and Cape of Good Hope

283 Huguenot Monument, Franschhoek

(Des Sheila Nowers. Litho)

1988 (3 Feb). 500*th Anniv of Discovery of Cape of Good Hope by Bartolomeu Dias. T* **282** *and similar horiz designs. Multicoloured. P* 14.

631 16 c. Type **282** 25 10
632 30 c. Kwaaihoek Monument 40 30
633 40 c. Caravels 55 45
634 50 c. Martellus map, *c*. 1489 . . . . . . 75 55
631/4 . . . . *Set of* 4 1·75 1·25

1988 (1 Mar). *Natal Flood Relief Fund* (3*rd issue*). *No.* 631 *surch as T* **280**, *but larger* (*Afrikaans version* 19 *mm wide*).

635 16 c. + 10 c. multicoloured (surch as T **280**) 25 35
a. Pair. Nos. 635/6 . . . . 50 70
636 16 c. + 10 c. multicoloured (surch "NATAL FLOOD DISASTER") 25 35

Nos. 635/6 were surcharged together, *se-tenant*, in horizontal and vertical pairs throughout the sheet.

(Des H. Botha. Litho)

1988 (13 Apr). 300*th Anniv of Arrival of First French Huguenots at the Cape. T* **283** *and similar vert designs. Multicoloured. P* 14.

637 16 c. Type **283** 15 10
638 30 c. Map of France showing Huguenot areas 25 25
639 40 c. Title page of French/Dutch New Testament of 1672 . . . . 35 30
640 50 c. St. Bartholomew's Day Massacre, Paris, 1572 . . . . 45 40
637/40 . . . . *Set of* 4 1·10 90

National
Flood Disaster
+10c

(284)

285 Pelican Point Lighthouse, Walvis Bay

1988 (13 Apr). *National Flood Relief Fund. Nos.* 637/40 *surch as T* **284** *in English* (E) *or in Afrikaans* (*"Nasionale Vloedramp"*) (A).

641 16 c. + 10 c. multicoloured (E) 25 30
a. Pair. Nos. 641/2 . . . . 50 60
642 16 c. + 10 c. multicoloured (A) 25 30
643 30 c. + 10 c. multicoloured (A) 35 40
a. Pair. Nos. 643/4 . . . . 70 80
644 30 c. + 10 c. multicoloured (E) 35 40
645 40 c. + 10 c. multicoloured (A) 40 50
a. Pair. Nos. 645/6 . . . . 80 1·00
646 40 c. + 10 c. multicoloured (E) 40 50
647 50 c. + 10 c. multicoloured (E) 50 65
a. Pair. Nos. 647/8 . . . . 1·00 1·25
648 50 c. + 10 c. multicoloured (A) 50 65
641/8 . . . . *Set of* 8 2·75 3·25

The two versions of each surcharge were printed together, *se-tenant*, both horizontally and vertically, throughout the sheets.

(Des Sheila Nowers. Litho)

1988 (9 June). *Lighthouses. T* **285** *and similar horiz designs. Multicoloured. P* 14.

649 16 c. Type **285** 25 10
650 30 c. Green Point, Cape Town 40 40
651 40 c. Cape Agulhas 50 50
652 50 c. Umhlanga Rocks, Durban 60 60
649/52 . . . . *Set of* 4 1·60 1·40
MS653 132 × 112 mm. Nos. 649/52 . . . . 1·60 1·60

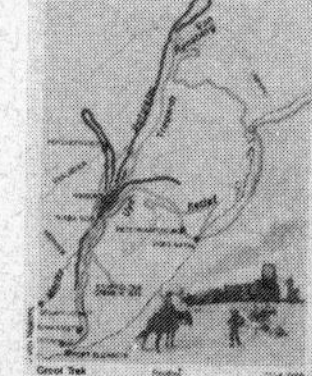

286 *Huernia zebrina*

287 Map of Great Trek Routes

(Des H. Botha)

1988 (1 Sept)–**89**. *Succulents. T* **286** *and similar horiz designs. Multicoloured.*

(*a*) *Sheet stamps. Litho. P* 14.

654 1 c. Type **286** 10 10
655 2 c. *Euphorbia symmetrica* 10 10
656 5 c. *Lithops dorotheae* 10 10
657 7 c. *Gibbaeum nebrownii* 10 10
658 10 c. *Didymaotus lapidiformis* 10 10
659 16 c. *Vanheerdea divergens* 10 10
659*a* 18 c. *Faucaria tigrina* (1.4.89) 10 10
660 20 c. *Conophytum mundum* 10 10
661 25 c. *Cheiridopsis peculiaris* 10 10
662 30 c. *Tavaresia barklyi* 15 20
663 35 c. *Dinteranthus wilmotianus* 15 20
664 40 c. *Frithia pulchra* 20 25
665 50 c. *Lapidaria margaretae* 20 25
666 90 c. *Dioscorea elephantipes* 40 45
667 1 r. *Trichocaulon cactiforme* 40 40
668 2 r. *Crassula columnaris* 85 90
654/68 . . . . *Set of* 16 2·40 2·75

(*b*) *Coil stamps. Photo. P* 14 × *imperf.*

669 1 c. *Adromischus marianiae* 10 10
670 2 c. *Titanopsis calcarea* 10 10
671 5 c. *Dactylopsis digitata* 10 10
672 10 c. *Pleiospilos bolusii* 10 10
669/72 . . . . *Set of* 4 10 10

(Des J. van Niekerk (16 c.). Litho)

1988 (21 Nov). 150*th Anniv of Great Trek. T* **287** *and similar multicoloured designs. P* 14.

673 16 c. Type **287** 20 10
674 30 c. "Exodus" (tapestry by W. Coetzer) (56 × 20 *mm*) 30 30
675 40 c. "Crossing the Drakensberg" (tapestry by W. Coetzer) (77 × 20 *mm*) 45 45
676 50 c. "After the Service, Church of the Vow" (J. H. Pierneef) (*horiz*) 55 55
673/6 . . . . *Set of* 4 1·40 1·25

288 Coelacanth

289 Man-made Desert

(Des A. McBride. Litho)

1989 (9 Feb). 50*th Anniv of Discovery of Coelacanth. T* **288** *and similar horiz designs. Multicoloured. P* 14.

677 16 c. Type **288** 15 10
678 30 c. Prof. J. L. B. Smith and Dr. M. Courtenay-Latimer examining Coelacanth 25 20
679 40 c. J. L. B. Smith Institute of Ichthyology, Grahamstown 35 30
680 50 c. Coelacanth and GEO midget submarine 45 40
677/80 . . . . *Set of* 4 1·10 90

(Des D. Murphy. Litho)

1989 (3 May). *National Grazing Strategy. T* **289** *and similar horiz designs. Multicoloured. P* 14.

681 18 c. Type **289** 15 10
682 30 c. Formation of erosion gully 25 25
683 40 c. Concrete barrage in gully 30 30
684 50 c. Reclaimed veldt 35 35
681/4 . . . . *Set of* 4 95 90

290 South Africa *v* France Match, 1980

291 "Composition in Blue"

(Des B. Jackson. Litho)

1989 (22 June). *Centenary of South African Rugby Board. T* **290** *and similar horiz designs. Multicoloured. P* 14.

685	18 c. Type **290**	15	10
686	30 c. South Africa *v* Australia, 1963	25	25
687	40 c. South Africa *v* New Zealand, 1937	30	30
688	50 c. South Africa *v* British Isles, 1896	35	35
685/8	*Set of* 4	95	90

1989 (3 Aug). *Paintings by Jacob Hendrik Pierneef. T* **291** *and similar horiz designs. Multicoloured. Litho. P* 14.

689	18 c. Type **291**	15	10
690	30 c. "Zanzibar"	25	25
691	40 c. "The Bushveld"	30	30
692	50 c. "Cape Homestead"	35	35
689/92	*Set of* 4	95	90
MS693	114×86 mm. Nos. 689/92	95	1·00

292 Pres. F. W. de Klerk

293 Gas-drilling Rig, Mossel Bay

1989 (20 Sept). *Inauguration of President F. W. de Klerk. T* **292** *and similar vert design. Multicoloured. Litho. P* 14.

694	18 c. Type **292**	15	10
695	45 c. F. W. de Klerk (*different*)	30	35

(Des H. Botha. Litho)

1989 (19 Oct). *Energy Sources. T* **293** *and similar horiz designs. Multicoloured. P* 14×14½.

696	18 c. Type **293**	15	10
697	30 c. Coal to oil conversion plant	25	25
698	40 c. Nuclear power station	30	30
699	50 c. Thermal electric power station	35	35
696/9	*Set of* 4	95	90

294 Electric Goods Train and Map of Railway Routes

(Des A. Barrett. Litho)

1990 (15 Feb). *Co-operation in Southern Africa. T* **294** *and similar horiz designs. Multicoloured. P* 14½×14.

700	18 c. Cahora Bassa Hydro-electric Scheme, Mozambique, and map of transmission lines (68×26 *mm*)	10	10
701	30 c. Type **294**	15	20
702	40 c. Projected dam on upper Orange River, Lesotho and map of Highlands Water Project (68×26 *mm*)	20	25
703	50 c. Cow, syringe, and outline map of Africa	25	30
700/3	*Set of* 4	60	70
MS704	136×78 mm. Nos. 700/3	65	80

POSTAGE DUE STAMPS

D 1

UNION OF SOUTH AFRICA (A)   UNION OF SOUTH AFRICA (B)

(Typo D.L.R.)

1914–22. *Inscribed bilingually. Lettering as* A. W **4**. P 14.

			Un single	Used single
D1	D 1	½d. black and green (19.3.15)	1·00	3·50
D2		1d. black and scarlet (19.3.15)	1·00	10
		a. Black ptd double	£1200	
D3		2d. black and reddish violet (12.12.14)	3·75	15
		a. Black and bright violet (1922)	4·50	25
D4		3d. black and bright blue (2.2.15)	1·75	35
D5		5d. black and sepia (19.3.15)	3·50	12·00
D6		6d. black and slate (19.3.15)	6·50	13·00
D7		1s. red and black (19.3.15)	60·00	£110
D1/7		*Set of* 7	70·00	£120

There are interesting minor varieties in some of the above values, e.g. ½d. to 3d., thick downstroke to "d"; 1d., short serif to "1"; raised "d"; 2d., forward point of "2" blunted; 3d., raised "d"; very thick "d".

(Litho Govt Printer, Pretoria)

1922. *Lettering as* A. *No wmk. Rouletted.*

D 8	D 1	½d. black and bright green (6.6.22)	75	4·50
D 9		1d. black and rose-red (3.10.22)	55	65
D10		1½d. black and yellow-brown (3.6.22)	1·00	1·75
D8/10		*Set of* 3	2·00	6·25

(Litho Govt Printer, Pretoria)

1922–26. *Type* D 1 *redrawn. Lettering as* B. P 14.

D11	½d. black and green (1.8.22)	30	1·75
D12	1d. black and rose (16.5.23)	35	15
D13	1½d. black and yellow-brown (12.1.24)	50	90
D14	2d. black and pale violet (16.5.23)	55	45
	a. Imperf (pair)	£175	£200
	b. Black and deep violet	4·75	2·50
D15	3d. black and blue (3.7.26)	6·50	11·00
D16	6d. black and slate (9.23)	8·50	6·00
D11/16	*Set of* 6	15·00	18·00

The locally printed stamps, perf 14, differ both in border design and in figures of value from the rouletted stamps. All values except the 3d. and 6d. are known with closed "G" in "POSTAGE" usually referred to as the "POSTADE" variety. This was corrected in later printings.

D 2

D 3

D 4

(Typo Pretoria)

1927–28. *Inscribed bilingually. No wmk.* P 13½ × 14.

D17	D 2	½d. black and green	35	1·25
D18		1d. black and carmine	35	30
D19		2d. black and mauve	1·25	30
		a. Black and purple	5·50	80
D20		3d. black and blue	5·50	12·00
D21		6d. black and slate	7·50	6·00
D17/21		*Set of* 5	13·00	18·00

1932–42. *Type* D 2 *redrawn.* W **9**. P 15 × 14.

(a) Frame roto, value typo

D22	½d. black and blue-green (1934)	1·00	1·25
D23	2d. black and deep purple (10.4.33)	3·25	75

(b) Whole stamp roto

D25	1d. black and carmine (3.34)	60	10
D26	2d. black and deep purple (1940)	6·00	10
	a. Thick (double) "2d." (R. 5/6, R. 18/2)	£110	15·00
D27	3d. black and Prussian blue (3.8.32)	9·00	10·00
D28	3d. deep blue and blue (1935)	4·00	15
	a. Indigo and milky blue (1942)	12·00	1·50
D29	6d. green and brown-ochre (7.6.33)	15·00	4·00
	a. Green and bright orange (1938)	7·00	1·25
D22/9a	*Set of* 7	28·00	12·00

In No. D26 the value, when magnified, has the meshed appearance of a photogravure screen, whereas in No. D23 the black of the value is solid.

1943–44. *Inscr bilingually. Roto.* W **9**. *In units of three, perf* 15 × 14 *subdivided by roulette* 6½.

			Un unit	Us unit
D30	D 3	½d. blue-green (1944)	4·00	18·00
D31		1d. carmine	4·00	3·00
D32		2d. dull violet	5·50	5·50
		a. Bright violet	13·00	24·00
D33		3d. indigo (1943)	26·00	50·00
D30/3		*Set of* 4	35·00	70·00

COVER PRICES

Cover factors are quoted at the beginning of each country for most issues to 1945. An explanation of the system can be found on page x. The factors quoted do not, however, apply to philatelic covers.

Split "D" (R. 7/5 on every fourth sheet)

1948–49. *New figure of value and capital "D". Whole stamp roto.* W **9**. P 15 × 14.

D34	D 4	½d. black and blue-green	3·75	4·25
D35		1d. black and carmine	4·00	2·00
D36		2d. black and violet (1949)	5·00	2·50
		a. Thick (double) "2D." (R. 15/5–6, R. 16/5–6)	42·00	19·00
D37		3d. deep blue and blue	14·00	9·50
		a. Split "D"	60·00	
D38		6d. green and bright orange (1949)	20·00	8·00
D34/8		*Set of* 5	42·00	24·00

1950–58. *As Type* D 4, *but "SUID-AFRIKA" hyphenated. Whole stamp roto.* W **9**. P 15 × 14.

D39	1d. black and carmine (5.50)	50	20
D40	2d. black and violet (4.51)	50	20
	a. Thick (double) "2D." (R. 15/5–6, R. 16/5–6)	7·00	6·00
	b. Black and reddish violet (12.52)	50	20
	ba. Thick (double) "2D."	7·00	6·00
D41	3d. deep blue and blue (5.50)	3·50	1·25
	a. Split "D"	30·00	
D42	4d. deep myrtle-green and emerald (2.58)	3·25	6·00
D43	6d. green and bright orange (3.50)	7·00	6·00
D44	1s. black-brown and purple-brown (2.58)	7·00	8·50
D39/44	*Set of* 6	19·00	20·00

D 5

D 6 Afrikaans at top

D 7 English at top

1961 (14 Feb). *Values in cents as Type* D **5**. *Whole stamp roto.* W **102**. P 15 × 14.

D45	1 c. black and carmine	20	1·75
D46	2 c. black and violet	35	1·75
D47	4 c. deep myrtle-green and emerald	80	4·50
D48	5 c. deep blue and blue	1·75	4·50
D49	6 c. green and orange-red	3·25	4·50
D50	10 c. sepia and brown-lake	4·75	7·50
D45/50	*Set of* 6	10·00	22·00

1961 (31 May)–**69.** *Roto.* W **102**. P 15 × 14.

D51	D 6	1 c. black and carmine	40	60
D52	D 7	1 c. black and carmine (6.62)	40	1·75
D53		2 c. black and deep reddish violet	40	55
D54	D 6	4 c. dp myrtle-green & light emerald	1·40	1·40
D54*a*	D 7	4 c. dp myrtle-grn & lt emerald (6.69)	4·00	6·50
D55		5 c. deep blue and grey-blue	2·00	3·00
D56		5 c. black and grey-blue (6.62)	1·75	4·50
D57	D 6	6 c. deep green and red-orange	4·50	4·00
D58	D 7	10 c. sepia and purple-brown	3·50	2·25
D51/8		*Set of* 9	16·00	22·00

1967 (Dec)–**71.** *Roto.* W **127** (*tête-bêche*). P 15 × 14.

D59	D 6	1 c. black and carmine	20	30
D60	D 7	1 c. black and carmine	20	30
D61	D 6	2 c. black and deep reddish violet	30	50
D62	D 7	2 c. black and deep reddish violet	30	50
D62*b*		4 c. dp myrtle-green & emerald (6.69)*	8·50	13·00
D62*c*	D 6	4 c. dp myrtle-green & emerald (6.69)*	£110	90·00
D63		4 c. black and pale green (4.71)	9·50	12·00
D64	D 7	4 c. black and pale green (4.71)	9·50	12·00
D65	D 6	5 c. black and deep blue	50	50
D66	D 7	5 c. black and deep blue	50	50
D67	D 6	6 c. green and orange-red (1968)	2·25	4·00
D68	D 7	6 c. green and orange-red (1968)	2·25	4·00
D69	D 6	10 c. black and purple-brown	1·00	2·50
		a. Black and brown-lake (12.69)	1·00	2·50
D70	D 7	10 c. black and purple-brown	1·00	2·50
		a. Black and brown-lake (12.69)	1·00	2·50
D59/70*a* except D62*b/c*		*Set of* 12	25·00	35·00

Nos. D59/70 were printed in two panes, one with inscriptions as Type D **6** and the other as Type D **7**.

*Nos. D62*b/c* were part of a printing of No. D54/*a*. Most were printed on paper with the Arms watermark, but some were printed on RSA paper with the watermark upright and faint. Most of these were spoiled but a few sheets were issued in Types D **7** and D **6**, the latter being very scarce.

1971 *Roto.* W **127** (*tête-bêche*). P 14.

D71	D 6	2 c. black and deep reddish violet	11·00	7·00
D72	D 7	2 c. black and deep reddish violet	11·00	7·00
D73	D 6	4 c. deep myrtle-green & lt emerald	35·00	32·00
D74	D 7	4 c. deep myrtle-green & lt emerald	26·00	25·00
D71/4		*Set of* 4	75·00	65·00

D 8

1972 (22 Mar). *English at right* (1, 4 *and* 8 c.) *or at left* (*others*). W **127** (*sideways tête-bêche*). *Chalk-surfaced paper* (4 c. *to* 10 c.). P 14×13½.

D75	D 8	1 c. deep yellowish green	50	1·25
D76		2 c. bright orange	70	1·60
D77		4 c. plum	1·50	2·00
D78		6 c. chrome-yellow	1·75	3·00
D79		8 c. ultramarine	2·00	3·75
D80		10 c. bright scarlet	3·00	4·75
D75/80		*Set of* 6	8·50	15·00

The 6 c. also exists on phosphorised paper.

The use of Postage Due stamps ceased in 1975.

OFFICIAL STAMPS

OFFICIAL. OFFISIEEL. (O 1)   OFFISIEEL OFFICIAL (O 2)

(Approximate measurements between lines of opt are shown in mm in brackets)

1926 (1 Dec). *Optd vertically upwards, with stops, as Type* O **1**.

(a) On 1913 issue (singles)

O1	3	2d. Nos. 6/6a (12½)	15·00	1·75

(b) On 1926 issue (pairs)

O2	6	½d. No. 30 (12½)	4·25	10·00
O3	7	1d. No. 31 (12½)	2·00	3·75
O4	8	6d. No. 32 (12½)	£550	75·00

This overprint is found on the ½d., 1d. and 6d. values of both the London and Pretoria printings. The London printings of the ½d. and 1d. stamps are considerably scarcer than the Pretoria, but the 6d. Pretoria printing is scarcer still.

1928–29. *Optd vertically upwards, as Type* O **1**, *but without stops.*

O5	11	2d. No. 34 (17½)	4·50	17·00
O6		2d. No. 34 (19) (1929)	3·25	8·00
O7	8	6d. No. 32 (11½)	15·00	22·00

1929. *Typographed stamps optd with Type* O **2**.

O 8	6	½d. No. 30 (13½)	1·50	2·00
		a. Stop after "OFFISIEEL" on English stamp	24·00	24·00
		b. Ditto. On Afrikaans stamp	24·00	24·00
O 9	7	1d. No. 31 (13½)	3·00	3·75
O10	8	6d. No. 32 (13½)	9·00	27·00
		a. Stop after "OFFISIEEL" on English stamp	55·00	75·00
		b. Ditto. On Afrikaans stamp	55·00	75·00
O8/10		*Set of* 3	12·00	29·00

1930–47. *Rotogravure stamps ("SUIDAFRIKA" in one word) optd with Type* O **2**.

O11	6	½d. No. 42 (9½–12) (1931)	2·00	3·00
		a. Stop after "OFFISIEEL" on English stamp	24·00	25·00
		b. Ditto. On Afrikaans stamp	24·00	25·00
O12		½d. No. 42 (12½) (1932)	3·25	4·00
O13	7	1d. No. 43 (12½ and 13½)	4·25	4·50
		a. Stop after "OFFISIEEL" on English stamp	24·00	25·00
		b. Ditto. On Afrikaans stamp	24·00	25·00
O14		1d. No. 43*d* (12½) (1932)	9·00	9·00
		a. Opt double	£250	£275
O15	11	2d. No. 44 (21) (1931)	6·00	11·00
O15*a*		2d. No. 44*d* (20½) (1938)	65·00	85·00
O16	8	6d. No. 47 (12½) (1931)	7·00	8·50
		a. Stop after "OFFISIEEL" on English stamp	40·00	42·00
		b. Ditto. On Afrikaans stamp	40·00	42·00
O17	13	1s. No. 48 (19) (1932)	35·00	50·00
O18		1s. No. 48 (21) (1933)	35·00	50·00
O19	14	2s. 6d. No. 49 (18) (1933)	50·00	75·00
O20		2s. 6d. No. 49 (21) (1934)	42·00	60·00
O20*a*		2s. 6d. No. 49*a* (19½–20) (1947)	24·00	50·00
		ab. Diaeresis on second "E"	£550	£600

Nos. O8a/b, O10a/b, O11a/b, O13a/b and O16a/b. The pairs include one stamp with variety and the other normal. Pairs of No. O20ab exist with the variety on either stamp (English or Afrikaans). Pairs with both stamps showing the variety are worth much more.

1931. *Recess-printed stamps opt with Type* O **2**.

O21	13	1s. No. 36 (17½, 18 and 20½)	28·00	60·00
		a. Stop after "OFFICIAL" on Afrikaans stamp	£100	£170
O22	14	2s. 6d. No. 37 (17½ and 18)	55·00	£100
		a. Stop after "OFFICIAL" on Afrikaans stamp	£250	£350

Nos. O21a and O22a. The pairs include one stamp with variety and the other normal.

OFFICIAL OFFISIEEL (O 3)   OFFICIAL OFFISIEEL (O 4)

1935–50. *Rotogravure stamps* ("SUID-AFRIKA" *hyphenated*).

(*a*) *Optd with Type* O **2** ("OFFICIAL" *at right*)

O23	**6**	½d. No. 54 (12½) (1936)	3·00	9·00
O24	**25*a***	½d. No. 75*b* (11 and 12½) (1938) ..	4·50	5·50
O24*a*		½d. No. 75*bd* (12) (1947)	90	4·00
O24*b*		½d. No. 114 (11) (1949)	1·00	3·50
O25	**7**	1d. No. 56 (11½–13)	65	80
O26	**22**	1½d. No. 57 (20) (1937)..	12·00	13·00
O26*a*		1½d. No. 57*b* (20) (1939)	16·00	8·50
O26*b*	**34*a***	1½d. No. 87 (14½) (1944)	2·50	6·00
		ba. Diaeresis on second "E" (1946?) ..	85·00	85·00
O26*c*		1½d. No. 87 (16) (1948)	2·00	3·50
O27	**11**	2d. No. 58 (20) (1939)	38·00	17·00
O27*a*	**54**	2d. No. 107 (20) (1947)	2·25	11·00
		ab. Diaeresis on second "E" (1947) ..	£200	£300
O27*b*		2d. No. 107*a* (20) (1949)	5·50	11·00
O28	**8**	6d. No. 61 (12 and 13) (1937) ..	48·00	25·00
O28*a*		6d. No. 61*a* (11½–13) (1939) ..	8·00	10·00
O28*b*		6d. No. 61*b* (12) (1947)	4·00	8·00
O29	**13**	1s. No. 62 (20) (1939)	26·00	17·00
		aa. Diaeresis on second "E" (1944?)..	£750	£700
O29*a*		1s. No. 120 (17½–18½) (1950) ..	8·00	17·00
O29*b*	**15**	5s. No. 64*a* (20) (1948) ..	30·00	60·00
O29*c*	**23**	10s. No. 64*b* (19½) (1948) ..	60·00	£110

(*b*) *Optd with Type* O **3** ("OFFICIAL" *at left*)

O30	**15**	5s. No. 64*a* (18) (1940)..	42·00	75·00
O31	**23**	10s. No. 64*b* (19) (1940)..	£110	£140

Prices for Nos. O26ba and O27ab are for horizontal pairs with the variety on both stamps. No. O29aa shows the variety on one stamp only, but pairs also exist with it on both.

1944. *Optd with Type* O **4** *reading up and down and with diaeresis over the second* "E" *of* "OFFISIEEL".

O32	**25*a***	½d. No. 75*bd* (10)	7·50	9·50

OFFISIEEL OFFICIAL (O 5)

OFFICIAL OFFISIEEL (O 6)

1944. *Optd with Type* O **5** *reading upwards* ("OFFICIAL" *at right*).

O33	**11**	2d. No. 58*a* (18½)	2·75	10·00

1949–50. *Optd with Type* O **6** *reading upwards* ("OFFICIAL" *at left*).

O34	**34*a***	1½d. No. 87 (16)..	10·00	17·00
O35	**68**	2d. No. 134 (16) (1950)	£950	£1100

OFFISIEEL OFFICIAL

(O 7)

1950–54. *Optd as Type* O **7**.

O35*a*	**25*a***	½d. No. 75*bd* (10) (1951)	1·00	5·50
O35*b*		½d. No. 114 (10) (1953)	70	1·50
O36	**7**	1d. No. 56*i* (10)	1·00	4·00
O36*a*		1d. No. 115 (10) (1951)	1·00	1·50
O36*b*		1d. No. 135 (10) (1952)	90	1·50
O37	**34*a***	1½d. No. 87 (14½) (1951)	1·40	2·25
O38	**68**	2d. No. 134 (14½)	1·00	2·00
		a. Opt inverted	£1000	
O39	**8**	6d. No. 119 (10)	1·00	3·00
O39*a*		6d. No. 119*a* (10) (1951)	1·50	3·00
O40	**13**	1s. No. 120 (19)	5·50	12·00
O40*a*		1s. No. 120*a* (19) (1953)	85·00	£110
O41	**14**	2s. 6d. No. 121 (19)	8·50	26·00
O41*a*	**15**	5s. No. 64*a* (19) (1951)	65·00	60·00
O41*b*		5s. No. 122 (19) (1953)	22·00	48·00
O41*c*		5s. No. 122*a* (19) (1954)	45·00	65·00
O42	**23**	10s. No. 64*ba* (19)	50·00	80·00

On No. O36*a* the overprint is thicker.

The use of official stamps ceased in January 1955.

South Arabia

The stamps of the Aden States surcharged in fils and dinars and with the word "ADEN" obliterated and replaced by "SOUTH ARABIA" (or commemorative inscription also) are listed under the Aden States.

PRICES OF SETS

Set prices are given for many issues, generally those containing three stamps or more. Definitive sets include one of each value or major colour change, but do not cover different perforations, die types or minor shades. Where a choice is possible the set prices are based on the cheapest versions of the stamps included in the listings.

South Arabian Federation

Comprising Aden and most of the territories of the former Western Aden Protectorate plus one from the Eastern Aden Protectorate.

(Currency. 100 cents=1 shilling)

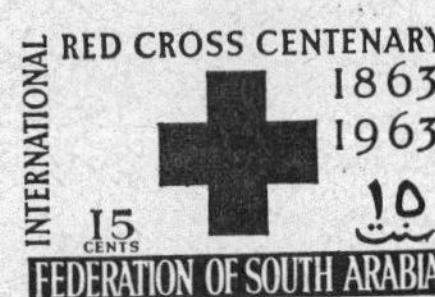

1 Red Cross Emblem

1963 (25 Nov). *Red Cross Centenary. W* w **12**. *P* 13½.

1	**1**	15 c. red and black	20	15
2		1 s. 25, red and blue	40	25

(New Currency. 1000 fils=1 dinar)

2 Federal Crest

3 Federal Flag

(Des V. Whiteley. Photo Harrison)

1965 (1 Apr). *P* 14½ × 14 (*T* **2**) *or* 14½ (*T* **3**).

3	**2**	5 f. blue	10	10
4		10 f. violet-blue	10	10
5		15 f. turquoise-green	10	10
6		20 f. green	10	10
7		25 f. yellow-brown	10	10
8		30 f. yellow-bistre	10	10
9		35 f. chestnut	10	10
10		50 f. red	10	10
11		65 f. yellow-green	25	20
12		75 f. crimson	25	10
13	**3**	100 f. multicoloured	30	10
14		250 f. multicoloured	65	25
15		500 f. multicoloured	1·75	50
16		1 d. multicoloured	3·25	2·25
3/16		.. .. *Set of* 14	6·50	3·25

4 I.C.Y. Emblem

(Des V. Whiteley. Litho Harrison)

1965 (24 Oct). *International Co-operation Year. W* w **12**. *P* 14½.

17	**4**	5 f. reddish purple and turquoise-green	20	10
18		65 f. deep bluish green and lavender ..	50	10

5 Sir Winston Churchill and St. Paul's Cathedral in Wartime

(Des Jennifer Toombs. Photo Harrison)

1966 (24 Jan). *Churchill Commemoration. No wmk. P* 14.

19	**5**	5 f. black, cerise, gold and new blue ..	10	10
20		10 f. black, cerise, gold and deep green	25	10
21		65 f. black, cerise, gold and brown ..	65	10
22		125 f. black, cerise, gold and bluish violet	90	75
19/22		.. .. *Set of* 4	1·75	85

6 Footballer's Legs, Ball and Jules Rimet Cup

(Des V. Whiteley. Litho Harrison)

1966 (1 July). *World Cup Football Championship, England. No wmk. P* 14.

23	**6**	10 f. violet, yellow-green, lake & yell-brn	15	10
24		50 f. chocolate, blue-grn, lake & yell-brn	45	10

7 W.H.O. Building

(Des M. Goaman. Litho Harrison)

1966 (20 Sept). *Inauguration of W.H.O. Headquarters, Geneva. No wmk. P* 14.

25	**7**	10 f. black, yellow-green and light blue	25	10
26		75 f. black, light purple and yellow-brown	45	15

8 "Education"

9 "Science"

10 "Culture"

(Des Jennifer Toombs. Litho Harrison)

1966 (15 Dec). *20th Anniv of U.N.E.S.C.O. No wmk. P* 14.

27	**8**	10 f. slate-violet, red, yellow and orange	15	10
28	**9**	65 f. orange-yellow, vio & dp olive ..	45	45
29	**10**	125 f. black, bright purple and orange ..	1·75	1·25
27/9		.. .. *Set of* 3	2·10	1·60

The South Arabian Federation became fully independent on 30 November 1967. Later issues for this area will be found listed in Part 19 (*Middle East*) of this catalogue under YEMEN, PEOPLE'S DEMOCRATIC REPUBLIC.

South Australia

PRICES FOR STAMPS ON COVER

Nos. 1/3	*from* × 3
No. 4	†
Nos. 5/12	*from* × 2
Nos. 13/18	*from* × 3
Nos. 19/43	*from* × 4
Nos. 44/9*b*	—
Nos. 50/110	*from* × 3
No. 111	—
Nos. 112/34	*from* × 6
Nos. 135/45	*from* × 3
Nos. 146/66	*from* × 5
Nos. 167/77	*from* × 10
Nos. 178/80	—
Nos. 181/94	*from* × 12
Nos. 195/208	—
Nos. 229/34	*from* × 12
No. 235	—
Nos. 236/44	*from* × 8
Nos. 245/60	*from* × 15
Nos. 262/7	*from* × 20
Nos. 268/75	*from* × 30
Nos. 276/9	—
Nos. 280/8	*from* × 30
Nos. 289/92	—
Nos. 293/304	*from* × 15
No. 305	—
Nos. O1/13	—
Nos. O14/36	*from* × 20
Nos. O37/42	*from* × 5
Nos. O43/6	*from* × 50
Nos. O47/9	—
Nos. O50/3	*from* × 30
No. O54	*from* × 15
Nos. O55/71	*from* × 50
Nos. O72/85	*from* × 75
Nos. O86/7	—

SPECIMEN OVERPRINTS. Those listed are from U.P.U. distributions between 1889 and 1895. Further "Specimen" overprints exist, but these were used for other purposes.

1

2 Large Star

(Eng Wm Humphrys. Recess P.B.)

1855. *Printed in London.* *W* **2.** *Imperf.*

No.	Type	Description	Unused	Used
1	1	1d. dark green (26.10.55)	£2500	£350
2		2d. rose-carmine (*shades*) (1.1.55) ..	£800	£125
3		6d. deep blue (26.10.55)	£2000	£150

Prepared and sent to the Colony, but not issued

No.	Type	Description	Unused	Used
4	1	1s. violet	£4500	

A printing of 500,000 of these 1s. stamps was made and delivered, but as the colour was liable to be confused with that of the 6d. stamp, the stock was destroyed on 5 June 1857.

NOTE. Proofs of the 1d. and 6d. without wmk exist, and these are found with forged star watermarks added, and are sometimes offered as originals.

For reprints of the above and later issues, see note after No. 194.

1856–58. *Printed by Govt Ptr, Adelaide, from Perkins, Bacon plates.* *W* **2.** *Imperf.*

No.	Type	Description	Unused	Used
5	1	1d. deep yellow-green (15.6.58) ..	£5000	£400
6		1d. yellow-green (11.10.58)	—	£475
7		2d. orange-red (23.4.56)	—	£110
8		2d. blood-red (14.11.56)	£1200	90·00
		a. Printed on both sides		
9		2d. red (*shades*) (29.10.57)	£650	55·00
		a. Printed on both sides	—	£600
10		6d. slate-blue (7.57)	£2000	£200
11		1s. red-orange (8.7.57)	—	£400
12		1s. orange (11.6.58)	£3750	£300

1858–59. *W* **2.** *Rouletted.* (*This first rouletted issue has the same colours as the local imperf issue*).

No.	Type	Description	Unused	Used
13	1	1d. yellow-green (8.1.59)	£475	45·00
14		1d. light yellow-green (18.3.59).. ..	£475	50·00
		a. Imperf between (pair)		
15		2d. red (17.2.59)	£110	18·00
		a. Printed on both sides		
17		6d. slate-blue (12.12.58)..	£375	25·00
18		1s. orange (18.3.59)	£800	35·00
		a. Printed on both sides	—	£1000

3

4

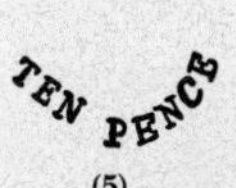

(5)

1860–69. *Second rouletted issue, printed in colours only found rouletted or perforated. Surch with T* **5** (*Nos.* 35/7). *W* **2.**

No.	Type	Description	Unused	Used
19	1	1d. bright yellow-green (22.4.61) ..	45·00	25·00
20		1d. dull blue-green (17.12.63)	40·00	23·00
21		1d. sage-green	50·00	27·00
22		1d. pale sage-green (27.5.65)	40·00	
23		1d. deep green (1864)	£225	65·00
24		1d. deep yellow-green (1869)	90·00	
24*a*		2d. pale red	60·00	4·00
		b. Printed on both sides	—	£375
25		2d. pale vermilion (3.2.63)	48·00	4·00
26		2d. bright vermilion (19.8.64)	38·00	2·75
		a. Imperf between (horiz pair)	£700	£300
27	3	4d. dull violet (24.1.67)	48·00	17·00
28	1	6d. violet-blue (19.3.60)	£140	6·00
29		6d. greenish blue (11.2.63)	65·00	4·00
30		6d. dull ultramarine (25.4.64)	60·00	4·00
		a. Imperf between (horiz pair)	—	£300
31		6d. violet-ultramarine (11.4.68).. ..	£150	6·00
32		6d. dull blue (26.8.65)	£100	6·50
		a. Imperf between (pair)	—	£600
33		6d. Prussian blue (7.9.69)	£550	50·00
33*a*		6d. indigo	—	55·00
34	4	9d. grey-lilac (24.12.60)	42·00	9·00
		a. Imperf between (horiz pair)		
35		10d. on 9d. orange-red (B.) (20.7.66) ..	90·00	24·00
36		10d. on 9d. yellow (B.) (29.7.67)	£140	20·00
37		10d. on 9d. yellow (Blk.) (14.8.69) ..	£1200	30·00
		a. Surch inverted at the top	—	£2500
		b. Printed on both sides	—	£800
		c. Roul × perf 10	†	—
38	1	1s. yellow (25.10.61)	£450	28·00
		a. Imperf between (vert pair)	—	£1200
39		1s. grey-brown (10.4.63)..	£150	16·00
40		1s. dark grey-brown (26.5.63)	£130	16·00
41		1s. chestnut (25.8.63)	£150	11·00
42		1s. lake-brown (27.3.65)..	£110	12·00
		a. Imperf between (horiz pair)	—	£400
43	3	2s. rose-carmine (24.1.67)	£160	25·00
		a. Imperf between (vert pair)	—	£750

1868–71. *Remainders of old stock subsequently perforated by the* 11½–12½ *machine.*

(*a*) *Imperf stamps. P* 11½–12½

No.	Type	Description	Unused	Used
44	1	2d. pale vermilion (Feb 1868)	—	£900
45		2d. vermilion (18.3.68)	—	£1000

(*b*) *Rouletted stamps. P* 11½–12½

No.	Type	Description	Unused	Used
46	1	1d. bright green (9.11.69)	—	£450
47		2d. pale vermilion (15.8.68)	—	£400
48		6d. Prussian blue (8.11.69)	—	£200
		aa. Horiz pair perf all round, roul between		
48*a*		6d. indigo		
49	4	9d. grey-lilac (29.3.71)	£1500	£160
		a. Perf × roulette	—	£150
49*b*	1	1s. lake-brown (23.5.70)..		

1867–70. *W* **2.** *P* 11½–12½ × *roulette.*

No.	Type	Description	Unused	Used
50	1	1d. pale bright green (2.11.67)	£140	18·00
51		1d. bright green (1868)	£100	18·00
52		1d. grey-green (26.1.70)	£140	20·00
		a. Imperf between (horiz pair)		
53		1d. blue-green (29.11.67)	£175	30·00
54	3	4d. dull violet (July 1868)	£1400	£130
55		4d. dull purple (1869)	—	90·00
56	1	6d. bright pale blue (29.5.67)	£450	19·00
57		6d. Prussian blue (30.7.67)	£400	19·00
		a. Printed on both sides		
58		6d. indigo (1.8.69)	£500	24·00
59	4	10d. on 9d. yellow (B.) (2.2.69)	£600	30·00
		a. Printed on both sides	—	£550
60	1	1s. chestnut (April 1868)	£250	15·00
61		1s. lake-brown (3.3.69)	£250	15·00

NOTE. The stamps perf 11½, 12½, or compound of the two, are here combined in one list, as both perforations are on the one machine, and all the varieties *may* be found in each sheet of stamps. This method of classifying the perforations by the machines is by far the most simple and convenient.

3-PENCE

(6)

7 (=Victoria *W* **20**)

1868–79. *Surch with T* **6** (*Nos.* 66/8). *W* **2.** *P* 11½–12½.

No.	Type	Description	Unused	Used
62	1	1d. pale bright green (8.2.68)	£150	18·00
63		1d. grey-green (18.2.68)	£120	40·00
64		1d. dark green (20.3.68)	50·00	17·00
		a. Printed on both sides		
65		1d. deep yellow-green (28.6.72) ..	45·00	18·00
66	3	3d. on 4d. Prussian blue (Blk.) (7.2.71)	—	£700
67		3d. on 4d. sky-blue (Blk.) (12.8.70) ..	£275	9·00
		a. Imperf		
		b. Rouletted	—	£500
68		3d. on 4d. deep ultramarine (Blk.) (9.72)	65·00	6·00
		a. Surch double (10.9.74)	—	£3250
		b. Additional surch on back	—	£2400
		c. Surch omitted (26.4.74)	£14000	£8000
70		4d. dull purple (1.2.68)	55·00	15·00
		a. Imperf between (horiz pair) ..		
71		4d. dull violet (1868)	50·00	8·00
72	1	6d. bright pale blue (23.2.68)	£300	11·00
73		6d. Prussian blue (29.9.69)	90·00	6·00
		a. Perf 11½ × imperf (horiz pair) ..		
74		6d. indigo (1869)	£120	17·00
75	4	9d. claret (7.72)..	90·00	8·00
76		9d. bright mauve (1.11.72)	90·00	8·00
		a. Printed on both sides	—	£300
77		9d. red-purple (15.1.74)	40·00	8·00
78		10d. on 9d. yellow (B.) (15.8.68).. ..	£1000	24·00
		a. Error. Wmk Crown and S A (1868)	—	£900
79		10d. on 9d. yellow (Blk.) (13.9.69) ..	£200	27·00
80	1	1s. lake-brown (9.68)	£150	11·00
81		1s. chestnut (8.10.72)	£110	16·00
82		1s. dark red-brown	90·00	11·00
83		1s. red-brown (6.1.69)	£100	11·00
84	3	2s. pale rose-pink (10.10.69)	£950	£150
85		2s. deep rose-pink (8.69)	—	£100
86		2s. crimson-carmine (16.10.69) ..	70·00	18·00
87		2s. carmine (1869)	60·00	10·00
		a. Printed on both sides	—	£300

1870–71. *W* **2.** *P* 10.

No.	Type	Description	Unused	Used
88	1	1d. grey-green (6.70)	£120	15·00
89		1d. pale bright green (9.8.70)	£120	15·00
90		1d. bright green (1871)	£100	15·00
91	3	3d. on 4d. dull ultramarine (R.) (6.8.70)	£325	50·00
92		3d. on 4d. pale ultram (Blk.) (14.2.71)	£250	12·00
93		3d. on 4d. ultramarine (Blk.) (14.8.71)	£100	16·00
93*a*		3d. on 4d. Prussian blue (Blk.) (16.12.71)		
94		4d. dull lilac (1870)	£110	10·00
95		4d. dull purple (1871)	£100	10·00
96	1	6d. bright blue (19.6.70)..	£180	17·00
97		6d. indigo (11.10.71)	£225	16·00
98		1s. chestnut (4.1.71)	£150	19·00

1870–73. *W* **2.** *P* 10 × 11½–12½, 11½–12½ × 10, *or compound.*

No.	Type	Description	Unused	Used
99	1	1d. pale bright green (11.10.70) ..	£140	14·00
		a. Printed on both sides		
100		1d. grey-green	£130	15·00
101		1d. deep green (19.6.71)	75·00	10·00
102	3	3d. on 4d. pale ultram (Blk.) (9.11.70) ..	£175	30·00
103		4d. dull lilac (11.5.72)	—	18·00
104		4d. slate-lilac (5.3.73)	£120	18·00
105	1	6d. Prussian blue (2.3.70)	£140	8·00
106		6d. bright Prussian blue (26.10.70) ..	£150	10·00
107	4	10d. on 9d. yellow (Blk.) (1.70)	£110	14·00
108	1	1s. chestnut (17.6.71)	—	32·00
109	3	2s. rose-pink (24.4.71)	—	£170
110		2s. carmine (2.3.72)	£120	25·00

1871 (17 July). *W* **7.** *P* 10.

No.	Type	Description	Unused	Used
111	3	4d. dull lilac	£1500	£250
		a. Printed on both sides		

8 Broad Star

8 PENCE

(9)

1876–1900. *W* **8.** *Surch with T* **9** (*Nos.* 118/21). (*a*) *P* 11½–12½.

No.	Type	Description	Unused	Used
112	3	3d. on 4d. ultramarine (1.6.79).. ..	50·00	14·00
		a. Surch double	—	£1000
113		4d. violet-slate (15.3.79)	90·00	11·00
114		4d. plum (16.4.80)	40·00	6·00
115		4d. deep mauve (8.6.82)	40·00	5·00
116	1	6d. indigo (2.12.76)	90·00	4·50
		a. Imperf between (horiz pair) ..		
117		6d. Prussian blue (7.78)	55·00	4·00
118	4	8d. on 9d. brown-orange (7.76).. ..	48·00	4·50
119		8d. on 9d. burnt umber (1880)	55·00	4·50
120		8d. on 9d. brown (9.3.80)	55·00	4·50
		a. Imperf between (vert pair)	£350	
121		8d. on 9d. grey-brown (10.5.81).. ..	48·00	6·00
		a. Surch double	—	£350
122		9d. purple (9.3.80)	30·00	6·00
		a. Printed on both sides	—	£200
123		9d. rose-lilac (21.8.80)	8·00	2·00
124		9d. rose-lilac (*large holes*) (26.5.00) ..	8·00	2·25
125	1	1s. red-brown (3.11.77)..	42·00	2·75
		a. Imperf between (horiz pair) ..	—	£250
126		1s. reddish lake-brown (1880)	40·00	3·00
127		1s. lake-brown (9.1.83)..	45·00	2·75
128		1s. Vandyke brown (1891)	60·00	8·00
129		1s. dull brown (1891)	38·00	2·75
130		1s. chocolate (*large holes*) (6.5.97) ..	24·00	3·00
		a. Imperf vert (horiz pair)	£200	
131		1s. sepia (*large holes*) (22.5.00).. ..	24·00	3·00
		a. Imperf between (vert pair)	£150	
132	3	2s. carmine (15.2.77)	25·00	4·00
		a. Imperf between (horiz pair) ..	—	£400
		b. Imperf (pair)		
133		2s. rose-carmine (1885)	32·00	6·00
134		2s. rose-carmine (*large holes*) (6.12.98)..	30·00	5·50

The perforation with larger, clean-cut holes resulted from the fitting of new pins to the machine.

(*b*) *P* 10

No.	Type	Description	Unused	Used
135	1	6d. Prussian blue (11.11.79)	80·00	12·00
136		6d. bright blue (1879)	£100	11·00
136*a*		1s. reddish lake-brown	£225	

(*c*) *P* 10 × 11½–12½, 11½–12½ × 10, *or compound*

No.	Type	Description	Unused	Used
137	3	4d. violet-slate (21.5.79)	£100	10·00
138		4d. dull purple (4.10.79)	22·00	2·00
139	1	6d. Prussian blue (29.12.77)	48·00	2·50
140		6d. bright blue	70·00	5·50
141		6d. bright ultramarine	35·00	1·75
142		1s. reddish lake-brown (9.2.85) ..	75·00	9·00
143		1s. dull brown (29.6.86)	90·00	10·00
144	3	2s. carmine (27.12.77)	40·00	5·00
145		2s. rose-carmine (1887)	35·00	4·50
		a. Imperf between (horiz pair) ..	—	£400

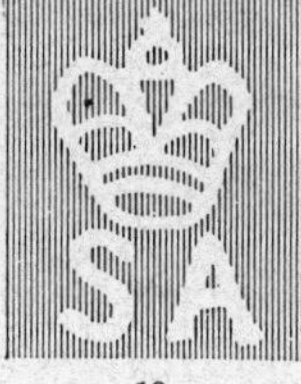

10

11

12

1901–2. *Wmk Crown SA* (*wide*), *W* **10.** *P* 11½–12½ (*large holes*).

No.	Type	Description	Unused	Used
146	4	9d. claret (1.2.02)	9·00	9·00
147	1	1s. dark brown (12.6.01)	20·00	9·00
148		1s. dark reddish brown (1902).. ..	20·00	10·00
		a. Imperf between (vert pair).. ..		
149		1s. red-brown (aniline) (18.7.02) ..	22·00	11·00
150	3	2s. crimson (29.8.01)	25·00	12·00
151		2s. carmine	19·00	8·00

(Plates and electrotypes by D.L.R. Printed in Adelaide)

1868–76. *W* **10.** (*a*) *Rouletted.*

No.	Type	Description	Unused	Used
152	12	2d. deep brick-red (8.68)	38·00	3·25
153		2d. pale orange-red (5.10.68)	35·00	2·75
		a. Printed on both sides	—	£200
		b. Imperf between (horiz pair) ..	—	£225

(*b*) *P* 11½–12½

No.	Type	Description	Unused	Used
154	11	1d. blue-green (10.1.75)	65·00	11·00
155	12	2d. pale orange-red (5.5.69)	£850	£190

(*c*) *P* 11½–12½ × *roulette*

No.	Type	Description	Unused	Used
156	12	2d. pale orange-red (20.8.69)	—	£120

(*d*) *P* 10 × *roulette*

No.	Type	Description	Unused	Used
157	12	2d. pale orange-red (7.5.70)	£200	20·00

(*e*) *P* 10

No.	Type	Description	Unused	Used
158	11	1d. blue-green (4.75)	18·00	3·50
159	12	2d. brick-red (4.70)	9·00	25
160		2d. orange-red (1.7.70)	8·00	20
		a. Printed on both sides	—	£160

(*f*) *P* 10 × 11½–12½, 11½–12½ × 10, *or compound*

No.	Type	Description	Unused	Used
161	11	1d. blue-green (27.8.75)	38·00	10·00
162	12	2d. brick-red (19.1.71)	£400	6·00
163		2d. orange-red (3.2.71)	£100	8·50
		a. Imperf (8.76)	£750	

.869. *Wmk Large Star, W* **2.** (*a*) *Rouletted.*
.64 **12** 2d. orange-red (13.3.69) .. .. 38·00 11·00

(*b*) *P* 11½–12½ × *roulette*
.65 **12** 2d. orange-red (1.8.69) .. .. .. — 90·00

(*c*) *P* 11½–12½
65*a* **12** 2d. orange-red (7.69) .. .. .. — £800

871 (15 July). *Wmk V and Crown, W* **7.** *P* 10.
66 **12** 2d. brick-red .. .. 40·00 12·00

13

HALF-

PENNY

(14)

1876–85. *Wmk Crown SA (close), W* **13.** (*a*) *P* 10.
167 **11** 1d. blue-green (9.2.76) .. .. .. 4·50 1·25
168 1d. yellowish green (11.78) .. .. 4·75 1·25
169 1d. deep green (11.79) .. .. .. 5·00 1·25
a. Imperf between (horiz pair) ..
170 **12** 2d. orange-red (8.76) .. .. .. 4·50 10
171 2d. dull brick-red (21.5.77) .. .. 4·50 10
172 2d. blood-red (31.10.79) .. .. £200 3·00
173 2d. pale red (4.85) .. .. .. 4·50 10

(*b*) *P* 10 × 11½–12½, *or* 11½–12½ × 10, *or compound*
174 **11** 1d. deep green (11.2.80) .. .. 18·00 2·25
175 1d. blue-green (2.3.80) .. .. .. 8·00 1·90
176 **12** 2d. orange-red (4.9.77) .. .. .. £120 3·00
177 2d. brick-red (6.80) .. .. .. £120 3·00

(*c*) *P* 11½–12½
178 **11** 1d. blue-green (2.84) .. .. .. — £110
179 **12** 2d. orange-red (14.9.77) .. .. — £110
180 2d. blood-red (1.4.80) .. .. .. — £110

For stamps perf 15, see Nos. 238/40.

1882 (1 Jan). *Surch with T* **14.** *W* **13.** *P* 10.
.81 **11** ½d. on 1d. green.. .. .. .. 7·00 2·50

15

16

17

18

1883–95. **W 13** (*sideways on ½d.*). (*a*) *P* 10.
182 **15** ½d. chocolate (1.3.83) .. .. .. 2·25 40
a. Imperf between (horiz pair) ..
183 ½d. Venetian red (4.4.89) .. .. 2·00 35
184 ½d. brown (1895) .. .. .. 2·25 35
185 **16** 3d. sage-green (12.86) (Optd S. £25) .. 8·00 1·10
186 3d. olive-green (6.6.90) .. .. .. 8·00 1·50
187 3d. deep green (12.4.93) .. .. 5·50 60
188 **17** 4d. pale violet (3.90) (Optd S. £30) .. 7·00 95
189 4d. aniline violet (3.1.93) .. .. 9·00 1·00
190 **18** 6d. pale blue (4.87) (Optd S. £25) .. 7·00 1·40
191 6d. blue (5.5.87) .. .. .. 8·50 60

(*b*) *P* 10 × 11½–12½, 11½–12½ × 10, *or compound*
192 **15** ½d. pale brown (25.9.91) .. .. 11·00 1·25
193 ½d. dark brown (9.9.92).. .. .. 4·00 95
a. Imperf between (horiz pair) .. 75·00

(*c*) *P* 11½–12½
194 **15** ½d. Venetian red (12.10.90) .. .. 5·50 75

For stamps perf 15, see Nos. 236/7 and 242/4 and for those perf 13 Nos. 247/8, 254/6 and 259/60.

REPRINTS. In 1884, and in later years, reprints on paper wmkd Crown SA, W **10**, were made of Nos. 1, 2, 3, 4, 12, 13, 14, 15, 19, 24, 27, 28, 32, 33, 34, 35, 36, 37, 38, 40, 43, 44, 49*a*, 53, 65, 67, 67 with surcharge in red, 70, 71, 72, 73, 78, 79, 81, 83, 86, 90, 118, 119, 120, 121, 122, 155, 158, 159, 164, 181, 182. They are overprinted "REPRINT".

In 1889 examples of the reprints for Nos. 1/3, 12, 15, 19, 27, 32/8, 44, 67, 67 surcharged in red, 70/1, 73, 83, 86, 118, 121/2, 158/9, 164 and 181/2, together with No. 141 overprinted "Specimen", were supplied to the U.P.U. for distribution

19

(20)

5D.

(21)

(Plates and electrotypes by D.L.R. Printed in Adelaide)

1886–96. *T* **19** (*inscr* "POSTAGE & REVENUE"). *W* **13.** *Parts of two or more wmks, on each stamp, sometimes sideways.* A. *Perf* 10. B. *Perf* 11½–12½ (*small or large holes*).

		A		B	
195	2s. 6d. mauve	25·00	8·00	†	
	a. Dull violet	†		24·00	6·00
	b. Bright aniline violet	†		25·00	7·00
196	5s. rose-pink	40·00	12·00	32·00	12·00
	a. Rose-carmine ..	†		35·00	14·00
197	10s. green	£110	35·00	80·00	35·00
198	15s. brownish yellow ..	£250	—	£275	£120
199	£1 blue	£200	90·00	£150	80·00
200	£2 Venetian red ..	£450	£200	£450	£200
201	50s. dull pink	£600	£250	£600	—
202	£3 sage green	£700	£200	£700	£200
203	£4 lemon	£900	—	£800	—
204	£5 grey	£1500	—	£1600	—
205	£5 brown (1896) ..	†		£1600	£1000
206	£10 bronze	£2250	£700	£1700	£700
207	£15 silver	£4500	—	£4500	—
208	£20 claret	£5000	—	£5000	—

195/208 (*all perf* 10 *ex No.* 205)
Optd "Specimen" | *Set of* 14 £500

Variations exist in the length of the words and shape of the letters of the value inscription.

The 2s. 6d. dull violet, 5s. rose-pink, 10s., £1 and £5 brown exist perf 11½–12½ with either large or small holes; the 2s. 6d. aniline, 5s. rose-carmine, 15s., £2 and 50s. with large holes only and the remainder only with small holes.

Stamps perforated 11½–12½ small holes, are, generally speaking, rather rarer than those with the 1895 (large holes) gauge.

Stamps perf 10 were issued on 20 Dec 1886. Stamps perf 11½–12½ (small holes) are known with earliest dates covering the period from June 1890 to Feb 1896. Earliest dates of stamps with large holes range from July 1896 to May 1902.

1891 (1 Jan). *Colours changed and surch with T* **20/21.** *W* **13.**

(*a*) *P* 10
229 **17** 2½d. on 4d. pale grn (Br.) (Optd S. £25) 4·50 2·50
a. Fraction bar omitted .. .. 90·00 75·00
230 2½d. on 4d. deep green (Br.) .. .. 5·00 1·75
a. "2" and "½" closer together .. 20·00 18·00
b. Fraction bar omitted .. ..
c. Imperf between (horiz pair) ..
d. Imperf between (vert pair) .. — £325
231 **18** 5d. on 6d. pale brn (C.) (Optd S. £25) 11·00 3·25
232 5d. on 6d. dark brown (C.) .. .. 11·00 3·00
a. No stop after "5D" £150

(*b*) *P* 10 × 11½–12½ *or* 11½–12½ × 10
233 **17** 2½d. on 4d. pale green (Br.) .. .. 6·00 3·00
234 2½d. on 4d. deep green (Br.) .. .. 6·00 3·00

(*c*) *P* 11½–12½
235 **17** 2½d. on 4d. green (Br.) .. .. 25·00 40·00

1893–4. *Surch with T* **20** (*No.* 241). *W* **13** (*sideways on ½d.*). *P* 15.
236 **15** ½d. pale brown (1.93) .. .. .. 2·50 30
237 ½d. dark brown .. .. 2·50 30
a. Perf 12½ between (pair) .. .. £120 28·00
b. Imperf between (horiz pair) .. 80·00
238 **11** 1d. green (8.5.93) .. .. .. 3·00 1·25
239 **12** 2d. pale orange (9.2.93) .. .. 5·50 10
240 2d. orange-red .. .. 6·00 10
a. Imperf between (vert pair).. .. £150
241 **17** 2½d. on 4d. green (14.10.93) .. .. 7·00 2·00
a. "2" and "½" closer .. .. .. 30·00 19·00
b. Fraction bar omitted .. ..
242 4d. purple (1.1.94) .. .. .. 10·00 2·00
243 4d. slate-violet .. .. 10·00 1·75
244 **18** 6d. blue (20.11.93) .. .. .. 19·00 3·50

22 Red Kangaroo

23

24 G.P.O., Adelaide

(Des Tannenberg, Melbourne; plates by D.L.R. Typo Sands and McDougall, Adelaide)

1894 (1 Mar). *W* **13.** *P* 15.
245 **22** 2½d. violet-blue .. .. 9·00 1·00
246 **23** 5d. brown-purple .. .. .. 10·00 1·25
245/6 Optd "Specimen" .. .. *Set of* 2 50·00

1895–99. *W* **13** (*sideways on ½d.*). *P* 13.
247 **15** ½d. pale brown (9.95) .. .. .. 2·50 30
248 ½d. deep brown (19.3.97) .. .. 2·50 30
249 **11** 1d. pale green (11.1.95) .. .. 4·00 1·25
250 1d. green .. .. 4·00 1·25
a. Imperf between (vert pair).. ..
251 **12** 2d. pale orange (19.1.95) .. .. 3·50 10
252 2d. orange-red (9.5.95) .. .. .. 3·50 10
253 **22** 2½d. violet-blue (11.2.95) .. .. 4·00 45
254 **16** 3d. pale olive-green (26.7.97) .. .. 5·00 55
255 3d. dark olive-green (27.11.99).. .. 5·00 50
256 **17** 4d. violet (21.1.96) .. .. .. 6·00 40
257 **23** 5d. brown-purple (1.96) .. .. 6·50 50
258 5d. purple .. .. 6·50 45
259 **18** 6d. pale blue (3.96) .. .. .. 7·00 40
260 6d. blue .. .. 7·00 40

The 1d. in pale green, formerly listed under No. 261 as redrawn with slightly thicker lettering, is now accepted as resulting from a printing from a worn plate.

(½d. Typo D.L.R.)

1898–1906. *W* **13.**

A. *Perf* 13 (1898–1903). B. *Perf* 12 × 11½ (*comb*) (1904–6)

			A		B	
262	**24**	½d. yellow-green	1·00	20	1·25	15
263	**11**	1d. rosine	2·00	10	5·00	10
264		1d. scarlet	2·75	10	3·00	10
		a. Deep red	2·50	10	†	
265	**12**	2d. bright violet	2·00	10	2·75	10
266	**22**	2½d. indigo	4·50	45	5·50	45
267	**23**	5d. dull purple	†		7·00	85

Earliest dates: Perf 13. ½d., 27 Dec 1899; 1d. rosine, 8 August 1899; 1d. scarlet, 23 December 1903; 2d. 10 October 1899; 2½d. 25 March 1898.

Perf 12 × 11½. ½d. July 1905; 1d. rosine, 2 February 1904; 1d. scarlet, 25 July 1904; 2d. 11 October 1904; 2½d. 4 July 1906; 5d. January 1905.

25

The measurements given indicate the length of the value inscription in the bottom label. The dates are those of the earliest known postmarks.

1902–4. *As T* **19**, *but top tablet as T* **25** (*thin* "POSTAGE"). *W* **13.**

(*a*) *P* 11½–12½
268 3d. olive-green (18½ mm) (1.8.02) .. 2·75 35
269 4d. red-orange (17 mm) (29.11.02) .. 4·50 70
270 6d. blue-green (16–16½ mm) (29.11.02).. 5·50 70
271 8d. ultramarine (19 mm) (25.4.02) .. 7·50 1·90
272 8d. ultramarine (16½ mm) (22.3.04) .. 7·50 1·90
a. "EIGNT" £1000 £1300
273 9d. rosy lake (19.9.02) .. .. .. 7·00 1·00
a. Imperf between (vert pair) £190
b. Imperf between (horiz pair) .. ..
274 10d. dull yellow (29.11.02) .. .. 8·50 2·00
275 1s. brown (18.8.02) .. .. .. 10·00 1·75
a. Imperf between (horiz pair) .. ..
b. Imperf between (vert pair) £450
c. "POSTAGE" and value in red-brown 45·00 20·00
276 2s. 6d. pale violet (19.9.02) .. .. 27·00 9·00
a. Bright violet (2.2.03) .. .. .. 20·00 7·00
277 5s. rose (17.10.02) .. .. .. 55·00 40·00
278 10s. green (1.11.02) .. .. .. £100 60·00
279 £1 blue (1.11.02).. .. .. .. £225 £120

(*b*) *P* 12
280 3d. olive-green (20 mm) (15.4.04) .. ... 3·50 70
a. "POSTAGE" omitted; value below "AUSTRALIA" £350
281 4d. orange-red (17½–18 mm) (18.2.03) .. 5·00 70
282 6d. blue-green (15 mm) (14.11.03) .. .. 14·00 2·25
283 9d. rosy lake (2.12.03) .. .. .. 15·00 3·00

26

V

TWO SHILLINGS AND SIXPENCE

X

In Type X the letters in the bottom line are slightly larger than in Type V, especially the "A", "S" and "P".

Y

FIVE SHILLINGS

Z

In Type Z the letters "S" and "G" are more open than in Type Y. Nos. 196/*a* and 277 are similar to Type Y with all letters thick and regular and the last "S" has the top curve rounded instead of being slightly flattened.

1904–11. *As T* **19**, *but top tablet as T* **26** (*thick* "POSTAGE"). *W* **13.** *P* 12.
284 6d. blue-green (27.4.04) .. .. .. 4·50 70
285 8d. bright ultramarine (4.7.05) .. .. 7·00 2·00
a. Value closer (15¼ mm) .. .. .. 15·00
b. Dull ultramarine (2.4.08) .. .. 8·00 2·25
ba. Ditto. Value closer (15¼ mm) .. .. 21·00
286 9d. rosy lake (17–17¼ mm) (18.7.04) .. 7·00 1·00
a. Value 16½–16¾ mm (2.06) .. .. 15·00 3·50
b. Brown-lake. Perf 12½ small holes (6.6.11) 10·00
287 10d. dull yellow (8.07).. .. .. .. 12·00 3·00
a. Imperf between (horiz pair) £225 £160
b. Imperf between (vert pair) £200
288 1s. brown (12.4.04) .. .. 9·00 1·75
a. Imperf between (vert pair) £130
b. Imperf between (horiz pair) £180
289 2s. 6d. bright violet (V.) (14.7.05) .. .. 32·00 6·00
a. Dull violet (X) (8.06) .. .. .. 32·00 6·00
290 5s. rose-scarlet (Y) (8.04) .. .. .. 40·00 20·00
a. Scarlet (Z) (8.06) .. .. 40·00 20·00
b. Pale rose. Perf 12½ (small holes) (Z) (7.10) 55·00 22·00
291 10s. green (26.8.08) £100 £125
292 £1 blue (29.12.04) £150 £100
a. Perf 12½ (small holes) (7.10) .. .. £130 80·00

The "value closer" variety on the 8d. occurs six times in the sheet of 60. The value normally measures 16½ mm but in the variety it is 15¼ mm.

The 9d., 5s. and £1, perf 12½ (small holes), are late printings made in 1910–11 to use up the Crown SA paper.

No. 286*b* has the value as Type C of the 9d. on Crown over A paper.

27

1905–11. *W* **27.** *P* 12 × 11½ (*new comb machine*).

No.	Type	Description	Unused	Used
293	24	½d. pale green (4.07)	1·00	20
		a. Yellow-green	1·10	15
294	11	1d. rosine (2.12.05)	1·90	10
		a. Scarlet (4.11)	1·75	10
295	12	2d. bright violet (2.2.06)	2·50	10
		aa. Imperf between (pair)		
		a. Mauve (4.08)	1·60	10
296	22	2½d. indigo-blue (14.9.10)	7·00	95
297	23	5d. brown-purple (11.3.08)	7·50	1·40

Three types of the 9d., perf 12½, distinguishable by the distance between "NINE" and "PENCE".

A. Distance 1¾ mm. B. Distance 2¼ mm. C. Distance 2½ mm.

1906–12. *T* **19** ("POSTAGE" *thick as T* **26**). *W* **27.** *P* 12 *or* 12½ (*small holes*).

No.	Description	Unused	Used
298	3d. sage-green (19 mm) (26.6.06)	4·00	70
	a. Imperf between (horiz pair)	—	£500
	b. Perf 12½. *Sage-green* (17 mm) (9.12.09)	4·50	70
	c. Perf 12½. *Deep olive* (20 mm) (7.10)	17·00	3·25
	d. Perf 12½. *Yellow-olive* (14 mm) (16.12.11)	8·00	80
	da. Perf 12½. *Bright olive-green* (19–19¾ mm) (5.12)	7·50	70
	e. Perf 11 (17 mm) (10.7.11)	£180	£180
299	4d. orange-red (10.9.06)	6·00	1·25
	a. Orange	7·50	1·10
	b. Perf 12½. *Orange* (27.10.09)	6·00	1·10
300	6d. blue-green (1.9.06)	7·00	75
	a. Perf 12½ (21.4.10)	5·50	55
	ab. Perf 12½. Imperf between (vert pair)	£275	£250
301	8d. bright ultramarine (*p* 12½) (8.09)	10·00	3·00
	a. Value closer (8.09)	28·00	24·00
302	9d. brown-lake (3.2.06)	10·00	1·50
	a. Imperf between (vert pair)	£190	
	aa. Imperf between (horiz pair)	£200	
	b. Deep lake (9.5.08)	24·00	3·00
	c. Perf 12½. *Lake* (A) (5.9.09)	11·00	3·00
	d. Perf 12½. *Lake* (B) (7.09)	12·00	3·00
	e. Perf 12½. *Brown-lake* (C)	17·00	5·00
	ea. Perf 12½. *Deep lake*. Thin paper (C)	14·00	3·00
	f. Perf 11 (1909)	—	£160
303	1s. brown (30.5.06)	11·00	2·50
	a. Imperf between (horiz pair)	£180	
	b. Perf 12½ (10.3.10)	8·00	1·00
304	2s. 6d. bright violet (X) (10.6.09)	30·00	6·00
	a. Perf 12½. *Pale violet* (X) (6.10)	30·00	7·00
	ab. Perf 12½. *Deep purple* (X) (5.11.12)	35·00	5·50
305	5s. bright rose (*p* 12½) (Z) (24.4.11)	55·00	

The "value closer" variety of the 8d. occurred 11 times in the sheet of 60 in the later printing only. On No. 301 the value measures 16½ mm while on No. 301a it is 15¼ mm.

The 1s. brown, perf compound of 11½ and 12½, formerly listed is now omitted, as it must have been perforated by the 12 machine, which in places varied from 11½ to 13.

OFFICIAL STAMPS

A. Departmentals

Following suspected abuses involving stamps supplied for official use it was decided by the South Australian authorities that such supplies were to be overprinted with a letter, or letters, indicating the department of the administration to which the stamps had been invoiced.

The system was introduced on 1 April 1868 using overprints struck in red. Later in the same year the colour of the overprints was amended to blue, and, during the latter months of 1869, to black.

In 1874 the Postmaster-General recommended that this somewhat cumbersome system be replaced by a general series of "O.S." overprints with the result that the separate accounting for the Departmentals ceased on 30 June of that year. Existing stocks continued to be used, however, and it is believed that much of the residue was passed to the Government Printer to pay postage on copies of the *Government Gazette*.

We are now able to provide a check list of these most interesting issues based on the definitive work, *The Departmental Stamps of South Australia* by A. R. Butler, FRPSL, RDP, published by the Royal Philatelic Society, London in 1978.

No attempt has been made to assign the various overprints to the catalogue numbers of the basic stamps, but each is clearly identified by both watermark and perforation. The colours are similar to those of the contemporary postage stamps, but there can be shade variations. Errors of overprint are recorded in footnotes, but not errors occurring on the basic stamps used.

Most departmental overprints are considered to be scarce to rare in used condition, with unused examples, used multiples and covers being regarded as considerable rarities.

Forgeries of a few items do exist, but most can be readily identified by comparison with genuine examples. A number of forged overprints on stamps not used for the genuine issues also occur.

A. (Architect)

Optd in red with stop. *W* **2.** 2d. (*roul*), 4d. (*p* 11½–12½), 6d. (*roul*), 1s. (*roul*)

Optd in red without stop. *W* **2.** *Roul*. 1d., 6d., 1s.

Optd in black. (*a*) *W* **2.** 4d. (*p* 11½–12½), 4d. (*p* 10), 4d. (*p* 10 × 11½–12½), 6d. (*p* 11½–12½), 2s. (*roul*)
(*b*) *W* **10.** 2d. D.L.R. (*roul*), 2d. D.L.R. (*p* 10)

A.G. (Attorney-General)

Optd in red. *W* **2.** *Roul*. 1d., 2d., 6d., 1s.

Optd in blue. (*a*) *W* **2.** *Roul*. 6d.
(*b*) *W* **10.** *Roul*. 2d. D.L.R.

Optd in black. (*a*) *W* **2.** 1d. (*p* 11½–12½ × *roul*), 4d. (*p* 11½–12½), 4d. (*p* 10), 6d. (*p* 11½–12½ × *roul*), 6d. (*p* 11½–12½), 1s. (*p* 11½–12½ × *roul*), 1s. (*p* 10)
(*b*) *W* **10.** 2d. D.L.R. (*roul*), 2d. D.L.R. (*p* 10)

A.O. (Audit Office)

Optd in red. *W* **2.** 2d. (*roul*), 4d. (*p* 11½–12½), 6d. (*roul*)

Optd in blue. (*a*) *W* **2.** *P* 11½–12½. 1d., 6d.
(*b*) *W* **10.** *Roul*. 2d. D.L.R.

Optd in black. (*a*) *W* **2.** 1d. (*p* 11½–12½), 1d. (*p* 10), 1d. (*p* 10 × 11½–12), 2d. D.L.R. (*roul*), 4d. (*p* 11½–12½), 4d. (*p* 10), 4d. (*p* 10 × 11½–12½), 6d. (*roul*), 6d. (*p* 11½–12½), 1s. (*p* 10), 1s. (*p* 11½–12½ × *roul*)
(*b*) *W* **7.** *P* 10. 4d.
(*c*) *W* **10.** 2d. D.L.R. (*roul*), 2d. D.L.R. (*p* 10)

B.D. (Barracks Department)

Optd in red. *W* **2.** *Roul*. 2d., 6d., 1s.

B.G. (Botanic Garden)

Optd in black. (*a*) *W* **2.** 1d. (*p* 11½–12½ × *roul*), 1d. (*p* 11½–12½), 1d. (*p* 10), 1d. (*p* 10 × 11½–12½), 2d. D.L.R. (*roul*), 6d. (*roul*), 6d. (*p* 11½–12½ × *roul*), 6d. (*p* 11½–12½), 6d. (*p* 10), 1s. (*p* 11½–12½ × *roul*), 1s. (*p* 11½–12½), 1s. (*p* 10 × 11½–12½)
(*b*) *W* **7.** *P* 10. 2d. D.L.R.
(*c*) *W* **10.** 2d. D.L.R. (*roul*), 2d. D.L.R. (*p* 10)

B.M. (Bench of Magistrates)

Optd in red. *W* **2.** *Roul*. 2d.

Optd in black. *W* **10.** *Roul*. 2d. D.L.R.

C. (Customs)

Optd in red. *W* **2.** 1d. (*roul*), 2d. (*roul*), 4d. (*p* 11½–12½), 6d. (*roul*), 1s. (*roul*)

Optd in blue. (*a*) *W* **2.** *Roul*. 1d., 4d., 6d., 1s., 2s.
(*b*) *W* **10.** *Roul*. 2d. D.L.R.

Optd in black. (*a*) *W* **2.** 1d. (*roul*), 1d. (*p* 10), 1d. (*p* 10 × 11½–12½), 2d. D.L.R. (*p* 10 × 11½–12½), 4d. (*p* 11½–12½), 4d. (*p* 10), 4d. (*p* 10 × 11½–12½), 6d. (*roul*), 6d. (*p* 11½–12½), 6d. (*p* 10), 1s. (*p* 11½–12½ × *roul*), 1s. (*p* 11½–12½), 2s. (*roul*)
(*b*) *W* **7.** *P* 10. 2d. D.L.R.
(*c*) *W* **10.** 2d. D.L.R. (*roul*), 2d. D.L.R. (*p* 10 × *roul*), 2d. D.L.R. (*p* 10), 2d. D.L.R. (*p* 10 × 11½–12½)

The 2d. (*W* **10.** *Roul*) with black overprint is known showing the error "G" for "C".

C.D. (Convict Department)

Optd in red. *W* **2.** 2d. (*roul*), 4d. (*p* 11½–12½), 6d. (*roul*), 1s. (*roul*)

Optd in black. (*a*) *W* **2.** 1d. (*p* 11½–12½ × *roul*), 2d. D.L.R. (*roul*), 2d. D.L.R. (*p* 11½–12½), 2d. D.L.R. (*p* 11½–12½ × *roul*), 4d. (*p* 11½–12½), 6d. (*p* 11½–12½ × *roul*), 1s. (*p* 11½–12½ × *roul*)
(*b*) *W* **10.** *Roul*. 2d. D.L.R.

C.L. (Crown Lands)

Optd in red. *W* **2.** 2d. (*roul*), 4d. (*p* 11½–12½), 6d. (*roul*), 1s. (*roul*)

Optd in blue. (*a*) *W* **2.** *Roul*. 4d., 6d.
(*b*) *W* **10.** *Roul*. 2d. D.L.R.

Optd in black. (*a*) *W* **2.** 2d. D.L.R. (*roul*), 4d. (*p* 11½–12½), 4d. (*p* 10), 4d. (*p* 10 × 11½–12½), 6d. (*roul*), 6d. (*p* 11½–12½), 1s. (*p* 11½–12½ × *roul*), 1s. (*p* 11½–12½), 2s. (*roul*), 2s. (*p* 11½–12½)
(*b*) *W* **7.** *P* 10. 2d. D.L.R., 4d.
(*c*) *W* **10.** 2d. D.L.R. (*roul*), 2d. D.L.R. (*p* 10), 2d. D.L.R. (*p* 10 × 11½–12½)

The 2s. (*W* **2.** *P* 11½–12½) with black overprint is known showing the stop omitted after "L".

C.O. (Commissariat Office)

Optd in red. *W* **2.** 2d. (*roul*), 4d. (*p* 11½–12½), 6d. (*roul*), 1s. (*roul*)

Optd in black. (*a*) *W* **2.** 4d. (*p* 11½–12½), 4d. (*p* 10), 4d. (*p* 10 × 11½–12½), 6d. (*p* 11½–12½), 1s. (*p* 11½–12½), 2s. (*p* 11½–12½)
(*b*) *W* **10.** 2d. D.L.R. (*roul*), 2d. D.L.R. (*p* 10)

The 2s. (*W* **2.** *P* 11½–12½) with black overprint is known showing the stop omitted after "O".

C.P. (Commissioner of Police)

Optd in red. *W* **2.** 2d. (*roul*), 4d. (*p* 11½–12½), 6d. (*roul*)

C.S. (Chief Secretary)

Optd in red. *W* **2.** 2d. (*roul*), 4d. (*p* 11½–12½), 6d. (*roul*), 1s. (*roul*)

Optd in blue. (*a*) *W* **2.** *Roul*. 4d., 6d.
(*b*) *W* **10.** *Roul*. 2d. D.L.R.

Optd in black. (*a*) *W* **2.** 2d. D.L.R. (*roul*), 4d. (*roul*), 4d. (*p* 11½–12½ × *roul*), 4d. (*p* 11½–12½), 4d. (*p* 10), 4d. (*p* 10 × 11½–12½), 6d. (*p* 11½–12½ × *roul*), 6d. (*p* 11½–12½), 6d. (*p* 10), 6d. (*p* 10 × 11½–12½), 1s. (*p* 11½–12½ × *roul*), 1s. (*p* 11½–12½), 1s. (*p* 10), 1s. (*p* 10 × 11½–12½), 2s. (*p* 10 × 11½–12½)
(*b*) *W* **7.** *P* 10. 4d.
(*c*) *W* **10.** 2d. D.L.R. (*roul*), 2d. D.L.R. (*p* 10)

C.Sgn. (Colonial Surgeon)

Optd in red. *W* **2.** 2d. (*roul*), 4d. (*p* 11½–12½), 6d. (*roul*)

Optd in black. (*a*) *W* **2.** 2d. D.L.R. (*roul*), 4d. (*p* 11½–12½), 4d. (*p* 10), 4d. (*p* 10 × 11½–12½), 6d. (*roul*), 6d. (*p* 11½–12½), 1s. (*p* 11½–12½ × *roul*)
(*b*) *W* **10.** 2d. D.L.R. (*roul*), 2d. D.L.R. (*p* 11½–12½ × *roul*), 2d. D.L.R. (*p* 10)

Two types of overprint exist on the 2d. D.L.R. (*W* **10.** *Roul*), the second type having block capitals instead of the serifed type used for the other values.

D.B. (Destitute Board)

Optd in red. *W* **2.** 1d. (*roul*), 2d. (*roul*), 4d. (*p* 11½–12½), 6d. (*roul*), 1s. (*roul*)

Optd in blue. (*a*) *W* **2.** *Roul*. 2d. D.L.R., 6d.
(*b*) *W* **10.** *Roul*. 2d. D.L.R.

Optd in black. (*a*) *W* **2.** 1d. (*p* 11½–12½), 4d. (*p* 11½–12½), 4d. (*p* 10), 6d. (*p* 10 × 11½–12½), 1s. (*p* 10)
(*b*) *W* **10.** 2d. D.L.R. (*roul*), 2d. D.L.R. (*p* 10), 2d. D.L.R. (*p* 10 × 11½–12½)

The 2d. D.L.R. (*W* **10.** *P* 10) with black overprint is known showing the stop omitted after "D".

D.R. (Deeds Registration)

Optd in red. *W* **2.** *Roul*, 2d., 6d.

E. (Engineer)

Optd in red. *W* **2.** 2d. (*roul*), 4d. (*p* 11½–12½), 6d. (*roul*), 1s. (*roul*)

Optd in blue. (*a*) *W* **2.** *Roul*. 1s.
(*b*) *W* **10.** *Roul*. 2d. D.L.R.

Optd in black. (*a*) *W* **2.** 4d. (*p* 11½–12½ × *roul*), 4d. (*p* 11½–12½), 4d. (*p* 10), 4d. (*p* 10 × 11½–12½), 6d. (*p* 11½–12½), 6d. (*p* 10 × 11½–12½), 1s. (*p* 11½–12½ × *roul*), 1s. (*p* 11½–12½), 1s. (*p* 10 × 11½–12½), 2s. (*p* 10 × 11½–12½)
(*b*) *W* **7.** *P* 10. 4d.
(*c*) *W* **10.** 2d. D.L.R. (*roul*), 2d. D.L.R. (*p* 10)

E.B. (Education Board)

Optd in red. *W* **2.** 2d. (*roul*), 4d. (*p* 11½–12½), 6d. (*roul*)

Optd in blue. (*a*) *W* **2.** *Roul*. 4d., 6d.
(*b*) *W* **10.** *Roul*. 2d. D.L.R.

Optd in black. (*a*) *W* **2.** 2d. D.L.R. (*roul*), 4d. (*roul*), 4d. (*p* 11½–12½), 4d. (*p* 10), 4d. (*p* 10 × 11½–12½), 6d. (*p* 11½–12½ × *roul*), 6d. (*p* 11½–12½)
(*b*) *W* **7.** *P* 10. 2d. D.L.R.
(*c*) *W* **10.** 2d. D.L.R. (*roul*), 2d. D.L.R. (*p* 10), 2d. D.L.R. (*p* 10 × 11½–12½)

G.F. (Gold Fields)

Optd in black. (*a*) *W* **2.** *Roul*. 6d.
(*b*) *W* **10.** 2d. D.L.R. (*p* 10 × *roul*), 2d. D.L.R. (*p* 10)

G.P. (Government Printer)

Optd in red. *W* **2.** *Roul*. 1d., 2d., 6d., 1s.

Optd in blue. (*a*) *W* **2.** *Roul*. 1d., 6d., 1s., 2s.
(*b*) *W* **10.** *Roul*. 2d. D.L.R.

Optd in black. (*a*) *W* **2.** 1d. (*roul*), 1d. (*p* 11½–12½ × *roul*), 1d. (*p* 11½–12½), 1d. (*p* 10), 1d. (*p* 10 × 11½–12½), 6d. (*p* 11½–12½ × *roul*), 1s. (*p* 10), 1s. (*p* 10 × 11½–12½), 2s. (*roul*), 2s. (*p* 11½–12½), 2s. (*p* 10 × 11½–12½)
(*b*) *W* **10.** 2d. D.L.R. (*roul*), 2d. D.L.R. (*p* 10)

The 1d. (*W* **2.** *Roul*) with red overprint is known showing "C.P." instead of "G.P.".

G.S. (Government Storekeeper)

Optd in red. *W* **2.** *Roul*. 2d., 6d., 1s.

G.T. (Goolwa Tramway)

Optd in red. *W* **2.** 1d. (*roul*), 2d. (*roul*), 4d. (*p* 11½–12½), 6d. (*roul*), 1s. (*roul*)

Optd in black. (*a*) *W* **2.** 2d. D.L.R. (*roul*), 4d. (*p* 11½–12½)
(*b*) *W* **10.** 2d. D.L.R. (*roul*), 2d. D.L.R. (*p* 10)

The 2d. and 6d. (both *W* **2.** *Roul*) with red overprint are known showing the stop omitted after "T". The 1s. (*W* **2.** *Roul*) with red overprint is known showing "C.T." instead of "G.T.".

H. (Hospitals)

Optd in black. (*a*) *W* **7.** *P* 10. 2d. D.L.R.
(*b*) *W* **10.** 2d. D.L.R. (*p* 10), 2d. D.L.R. (*p* 10 × 11½–12½)

H.A. (House of Assembly)

Optd in red. *W* **2.** 1d. (*roul*), 2d. (*roul*), 4d. (*p* 11½–12½), 6d. (*roul*), 1s. (*roul*)

Optd in black. (*a*) *W* **2.** 1d. (*p* 11½–12½), 1d. (*p* 10), 1d. (*p* 10 × 11½–12½), 4d. (*p* 11½–12½), 4d. (*p* 10), 6d. (*roul*), 6d. (*p* 11½–12½), 1s. (*p* 11½–12½ × *roul*), 1s. (*p* 11½–12½)
(*b*) *W* **10.** 2d. D.L.R. (*roul*), 2d. D.L.R. (*p* 10)

I.A. (Immigration Agent)

Optd in red. *W* **2.** 1d. (*roul*), 2d. (*roul*), 4d. (*p* 11½–12½), 6d. (*roul*)

I.E. (Intestate Estates)

Optd in black. W **10.** *P* 10. 2d. D.L.R.

I.S. (Inspector of Sheep)

Optd in red. *W* **2.** *Roul*. 2d., 6d.

Optd in blue. *W* **2.** *P* 11½–12½. 6d.

Optd in black. (*a*) *W* **2.** 2d. D.L.R. (*roul*), 6d. (*p* 11½–12½ × *roul*)
(*b*) *W* **10.** 2d. D.L.R. (*roul*), 2d. D.L.R. (*p* 10)

L.A. (Lunatic Asylum)

Optd in red. *W* **2.** 1d. (*roul*), 2d. (*roul*), 4d. (*p* 11½–12½), 6d. (*roul*), 1s. (*roul*)

Optd in black. (*a*) *W* **2.** 4d. (*p* 11½–12½), 4d. (*p* 10), 4d. (*p* 10 × 11½–12½), 6d. (*p* 11½–12½ × *roul*), 6d. (*p* 11½–12½), 1s. (*p* 11½–12½), 2s. (*roul*)
(*b*) *W* **10.** 2d. D.L.R. (*roul*), 2d. D.L.R. (*p* 10)

L.C. (Legislative Council)

Optd in red. *W* **2.** *Roul*. 2d., 6d.

Optd in black. (*a*) *W* **2.** *Roul*. 6d.
(*b*) *W* **10.** 2d. D.L.R. (*roul*), 2d. D.L.R. (*p* 10 × *roul*)

The 2d. and 6d. (both *W* **2.** *Roul*) with red overprint are known showing the stop omitted after "C".

L.L. (Legislative Librarian)

Optd in red. *W* **2.** 2d. (*roul*), 4d. (*p* 11½–12½), 6d. (*roul*)

Optd in black. (*a*) *W* **2.** *P* 11½–12½. 6d.
(*b*) *W* **10.** *P* 10. 2d. D.L.R.

The 2d. and 6d. (both *W* **2.** *Roul*) with red overprint are known showing the stop omitted from between the two letters.

L.T. (Land Titles)

Optd in red. *W* **2.** 2d. (*roul*), 4d. (*p* 11½–12½), 6d. (*roul*), 1s. (*roul*)

Optd in blue. *W* **10.** *Roul*. 2d. D.L.R.

Optd in black. (*a*) *W* **2.** 4d. (*p* 11½–12½), 4d. (*p* 10), 4d. (*p* 10 × 11½–12½), 6d. (*p* 11½–12½ × *roul*), 6d. (*p* 11½–12½), 6d. (*p* 10), 6d. (*p* 10 × 11½–12½)
(*b*) *W* **7.** *P* 10. 2d. D.L.R.
(*c*) *W* **10.** 2d. D.L.R. (*roul*), 2d. D.L.R. (*p* 10)

The 2d. and 6d. (both *W* **2.** *Roul*) with red overprint are known showing the stop omitted after "T".

M. (Military)

Optd in red. *W* **2.** *Roul.* 2d., 6d., 1s.
Optd in black. *W* **2.** 6d. (*p* 11½–12½ × *roul*), 1s. (*p* 11½–12½ × *roul*), 2s. (*roul*)

M.B. (Marine Board)

Optd in red. *W* **2.** 1d. (*roul*), 2d. (*roul*), 4d. (*roul*), 4d. (*p* 11½–12½), 6d. (*roul*), 1s. (*roul*)
Optd in black. (*a*) *W* **2.** 1d. (*roul*), 1d. (*p* 11½–12½), 2d. D.L.R. (*roul*), 4d. (*p* 11½–12½ × *roul*), 4d. (*p* 11½–12½), 4d. (*p* 10), 4d. (*p* 10 × 11½–12½), 6d. (*roul*), 6d. (*p* 11½–12½), 6d. (*p* 10), 6d. (*p* 10 × 11½–12½), 1s. (*p* 11½–12½ × *roul*), 1s. (*p* 11½–12½), 1s. (*p* 10), 1s. (*p* 10 × 11½–12½)
(*b*) *W* **7.** *P* 10. 2d. D.L.R., 4d.
(*c*) *W* **10.** 2d. D.L.R. (*roul*), 2d. D.L.R. (*p* 10)

M.R. (Manager of Railways)

Optd in red. *W* **2.** *Roul.* 2d., 6d.
Optd in black. (*a*) *W* **2.** 1d. (*p* 11½–12½), 1d. (*p* 10), 2d. D.L.R. (*roul*), 4d. (*roul*), 4d. (*p* 11½–12½), 6d. (*roul*), 6d. (*p* 11½–12½ × *roul*), 6d. (*p* 11½–12½), 10d. on 9d. (*roul*), 1s. (*roul*), 1s. (*p* 11½–12½ × *roul*), 2s. (*p* 11½–12½), 2s. (*p* 10 × 11½–12½)
(*b*) *W* **10.** 2d. D.L.R. (*roul*), 2d. D.L.R. (*p* 10), 2d. D.L.R. (*p* 10 × 11½–12½)

M.R.G. (Main Roads Gambierton)

Optd in red without stops. *W* **2.** *Roul.* 2d., 6d.
Optd in blue without stops. *W* **10.** *Roul.* 2d. D.L.R.
Optd in black without stops. *W* **10.** 2d. D.L.R. (*roul*), 2d. D.L.R. (*p* 10)
Optd in black with stops. *W* **10.** 2d. D.L.R. (*roul*), 2d. D.L.R. (*p* 10)

The 2d. D.L.R. (*W* **10.** *P* 10) with black overprint is known showing the stops omitted after "M" and "R".

N.T. (Northern Territory)

Optd in black. (*a*) *W* **2.** *P* 11½–12½. 1d., 3d. on 4d., 4d., 6d., 1s.
(*b*) *W* **10.** 2d. D.L.R. (*roul*), 2d. D.L.R. (*p* 10)

O.A. (Official Assignee)

Optd in red. *W* **2.** 2d. (*roul*), 4d. (*p* 11½–12½)
Optd in blue. *W* **10.** *Roul.* 2d. D.L.R.
Optd in black. (*a*) *W* **2.** 4d. (*p* 11½–12½), 4d. (*p* 10)
(*b*) *W* **7.** *P* 10. 2d. D.L.R.
(*c*) *W* **10.** 2d. D.L.R. (*roul*), 2d. D.L.R. (*p* 10 × *roul*), 2d. D.L.R. (*p* 10)

P. (Police)

Optd in blue. (*a*) *W* **2.** *Roul.* 6d.
(*b*) *W* **10.** *Roul.* 2d. D.L.R.
Optd in black. (*a*) *W* **2.** 6d. (*p* 11½–12½ × *roul*), 6d. (*p* 11½–12½), 6d. (*p* 10)
(*b*) *W* **7.** *P* 10. 2d. D.L.R.
(*c*) *W* **10.** 2d. D.L.R. (*roul*), 2d. D.L.R. (*p* 11½–12½), 2d. D.L.R. (*p* 11½–12½ × *roul*), 2d. D.L.R. (*p* 10 × *roul*), 2d. D.L.R. (*p* 10), 2d. D.L.R. (*p* 10 × 11½–12½)

P.A. (Protector of Aborigines)

Optd in red. *W* **2.** *Roul.* 2d., 6d.
Optd in black. (*a*) *W* **2.** *Roul.* 2d. D.L.R., 6d.
(*b*) *W* **10.** 2d. D.L.R. (*roul*), 2d. D.L.R. (*p* 10)

P.O. (Post Office)

Optd in red. *W* **2.** *Roul.* 1d., 2d., 6d., 1s.
Optd in blue. *W* **2.** *Roul.* 2d., 2d. D.L.R.
Optd in black. (*a*) *W* **2.** 1d. (*p* 10 × 11½–12½), 2d. D.L.R. (*roul*), 4d. (*p* 11½–12½), 6d. (*roul*), 6d. (*p* 11½–12½), 1s. (*p* 11½–12½ × *roul*), 1s. (*p* 11½–12½), 1s. (*p* 10), 1s. (*p* 10 × 11½–12½)
(*b*) *W* **10.** 2d. D.L.R. (*roul*), 2d. D.L.R. (*p* 10 × *roul*), 2d. D.L.R. (*p* 10)

The 6d. (*W* **2.** *Roul*) with red overprint is known showing the stop omitted after "O", but with two stops after "P".

P.S. (Private Secretary)

Optd in red. *W* **2.** 1d. (*roul*), 2d. (*roul*), 4d. (*p* 11½–12½), 6d. (*roul*), 1s. (*roul*)
Optd in black. (*a*) *W* **2.** 1d. (*p* 11½–12½ × *roul*), 1d. (*p* 11½–12½), 1d. (*p* 10), 3d. (*in black*) on 4d. (*p* 11½–12½), 3d. (*in red*) on 4d. (*p* 10), 3d. (*in black*) on 4d. (*p* 10), 4d. (*p* 11½–12½), 4d. (*p* 10), 4d. (*p* 10 × 11½–12½), 6d. (*roul*), 6d. (*p* 11½–12½ × *roul*), 6d. (*p* 11½–12½), 6d. (*p* 10), 9d. (*roul*), 9d. (*p* 11½–12½), 10d. on 9d. (*p* 10 × 11½–12½), 1s. (*p* 11½–12½ × *roul*), 2s. (*p* 11½–12½)
(*b*) *W* **7.** *P* 10. 2d. D.L.R.
(*c*) *W* **10.** 2d. D.L.R. (*roul*), 2d. D.L.R. (*p* 10)

P.W. (Public Works)

Optd in red without stop after "W". *W* **2.** *Roul.* 2d., 6d., 1s.
Optd in black. (*a*) *W* **2.** 2d. D.L.R. (*roul*), 4d. (*p* 10), 6d. (*roul*), 6d. (*p* 11½–12½), 1s. (*p* 11½–12½ × *roul*)
(*b*) *W* **10.** 2d. D.L.R. (*roul*), 2d. D.L.R. (*p* 10)

R.B. (Road Board)

Optd in red. *W* **2.** 1d. (*roul*), 2d. (*roul*), 4d. (*p* 11½–12½), 6d. (*roul*), 1s. (*roul*)
Optd in blue without stops. *W* **10.** *Roul.* 2d. D.L.R.
Optd in black. (*a*) *W* **2.** 1d. (*p* 11½–12½ × *roul*), 1d. (*p* 10), 4d. (*p* 10), 2s. (*roul*)
(*b*) *W* **7.** *P* 10. 2d. D.L.R.
(*c*) *W* **10.** 2d. D.L.R. (*roul*), 2d. D.L.R. (*p* 10)

The 6d. (*W* **2.** *Roul*) with red overprint is known showing the stop omitted after "B".

R.G. (Registrar-General)

Optd in red. *W* **2.** *Roul.* 2d., 6d., 1s.
Optd in blue. (*a*) *W* **2.** *P* 11½–12½ × *roul.* 6d.
(*b*) *W* **10.** 2d. D.L.R. (*roul*), 2d. D.L.R. (*p* 11½–12½ × *roul*)
Optd in black. (*a*) *W* **2.** 2d. D.L.R. (*roul*), 6d. (*p* 10), 6d. (*p* 10 × 11½–12½), 1s. (*p* 11½–12½ × *roul*), 1s. (*p* 10)
(*b*) *W* **7.** *P* 10. 2d. D.L.R.
(*c*) *W* **10.** 2d. D.L.R. (*roul*), 2d. D.L.R. (*p* 10 × *roul*), 2d. D.L.R. (*p* 10), 2d. D.L.R. (*p* 10 × 11½–12½)

S. (Sheriff)

Optd in red. *W* **2.** *Roul.* 2d., 6d.
Optd in blue. (*a*) *W* **2.** *P* 11½–12½ × *roul.* 6d.
(*b*) *W* **10.** *Roul.* 2d. D.L.R.
Optd in black. (*a*) *W* **2.** 4d. (*p* 11½–12½), 4d. (*p* 10), 6d. (*roul*), 6d. (*p* 11½–12½), 6d. (*p* 10)
(*b*) *W* **10.** 2d. D.L.R. (*roul*), 2d. D.L.R. (*p* 10 × *roul*), 2d. D.L.R. (*p* 10), 2d. D.L.R. (*p* 10 × 11½–12½)

S.C. (Supreme Court)

Optd in red. *W* **2.** *Roul.* 2d., 6d.
Optd in black. *W* **10.** *P* 10. 2d. D.L.R.

S.G. (Surveyor-General)

Optd in red. *W* **2.** 2d. (*roul*), 4d. (*p* 11½–12½), 6d. (*roul*)
Optd in blue. (*a*) *W* **2.** *Roul.* 4d.
(*b*) *W* **10.** *Roul.* 2d. D.L.R.
Optd in black. (*a*) *W* **2.** 2d. D.L.R. (*roul*), 4d. (*p* 11½–12½), 4d. (*p* 10), 4d. (*p* 10 × 11½–12½), 6d. (*p* 11½–12½ × *roul*), 6d. (*p* 11½–12½), 6d. (*p* 10), 6d. (*p* 10 × 11½–12½)
(*b*) *W* **7.** *P* 10. 2d. D.L.R.
(*c*) *W* **10.** 2d. D.L.R. (*roul*), 2d. D.L.R. (*p* 10 × *roul*), 2d. D.L.R. (*p* 10)

S.M. (Stipendiary Magistrate)

Optd in red. *W* **2.** 1d. (*roul*), 2d. (*roul*), 4d. (*roul*), 4d. (*p* 11½–12½), 6d. (*roul*), 1s. (*roul*)
Optd in blue. (*a*) *W* **2.** *Roul.* 2d., 4d., 6d.
(*b*) *W* **10.** *Roul.* 2d. D.L.R.
Optd in black. (*a*) *W* **2.** 1d. (*p* 11½–12½), 1d. (*p* 10), 2d. D.L.R. (*roul*), 4d. (*roul*), 4d. (*p* 11½–12½ × *roul*), 4d. (*p* 11½–12½), 4d. (*p* 10), 4d. (*p* 10 × 11½–12½), 6d. (*p* 11½–12½ × *roul*), 6d. (*p* 11½–12½), 6d. (*p* 10), 6d. (*p* 10 × 11½–12½), 1s. (*p* 11½–12½ × *roul*)
(*b*) *W* **7.** *P* 10. 2d. D.L.R.
(*c*) *W* **10.** 2d. D.L.R. (*roul*), 2d. D.L.R. (*p* 10 × *roul*), 2d. D.L.R. (*p* 10), 2d. D.L.R. (*p* 10 × 11½–12½)

The 2d. and 4d. (both *W* **2.** *Roul*) with red overprint are known showing the stop omitted after "M".

S.T. (Superintendent of Telegraphs)

Optd in red. *W* **2.** *Roul.* 2d., 6d.
Optd in blue. *W* **10.** 2d. D.L.R. (*roul*), 2d. D.L.R. (*p* 11½–12½)
Optd in black. (*a*) *W* **2.** *Roul.* 2d. D.L.R., 6d.
(*b*) *W* **7.** *P* 10. 2d. D.L.R.
(*c*) *W* **10.** 2d. D.L.R. (*roul*), 2d. D.L.R. (*p* 10 × *roul*), 2d. D.L.R. (*p* 10)

The 2d. and 6d. (both *W* **2.** *Roul*) with red overprint (2d., 6d.) or black overprint (6d.) are known showing the stop omitted after "T".

T. (Treasury)

Optd in red. *W* **2.** 1d. (*roul*), 2d. (*roul*), 4d. (*p* 11½–12½ × *roul*), 6d. (*roul*), 1s. (*roul*)
Optd in blue. (*a*) *W* **2.** *Roul.* 1d., 4d., 6d., 2s.
(*b*) *W* **10.** *Roul.* 2d. D.L.R.
Optd in black. (*a*) *W* **2.** 1d. (*p* 10), 2d. D.L.R. (*roul*), 4d. (*roul*), 4d. (*p* 11½–12½), 6d. (*roul*), 6d. (*p* 11½–12½), 1s. (*p* 11½–12½ × *roul*), 1s. (*p* 10 × 11½–12½), 2s. (*roul*), 2s. (*p* 11½–12½), 2s. (*p* 10 × 11½–12½)
(*b*) *W* **7.** *P* 10. 2d. D.L.R.
(*c*) *W* **10.** 2d. D.L.R. (*roul*), 2d. D.L.R. (*p* 10)

T.R. (Titles Registration)

Optd in black. (*a*) *W* **2.** 4d. (*p* 11½–12½), 4d. (*p* 10 × 11½–12½), 6d. (*p* 11½–12½), 6d. (*p* 10 × 11½–12½), 1s. (*p* 11½–12½)
(*b*) *W* **10.** *P* 10. 2d. D.L.R.

V. (Volunteers)

Optd in red. *W* **2.** *Roul.* 2d., 6d., 1s.
Optd in black. (*a*) *W* **2.** *Roul.* 6d.
(*b*) *W* **7.** *P* 10. 2d. D.L.R.
(*c*) *W* **10.** 2d. D.L.R. (*roul*), 2d. D.L.R. (*p* 10 × *roul*), 2d. D.L.R. (*p* 10)

The 2d. (*W* **10.** *P* 10 × *roul*) overprinted in black is only known showing the stop omitted after "V".

VA. (Valuator of Runs)

Optd in black without stop after "V". (*a*) *W* **2.** *P* 10. 4d.
(*b*) *W* **10.** *P* 10. 2d. D.L.R.

VN. (Vaccination)

Optd in black without stop after "V". *W* **2.** *P* 10. 4d.

W. (Waterworks)

Optd in red. *W* **2.** *Roul.* 2d.
Optd in black. (*a*) *W* **2.** *P* 11½–12½. 6d., 2s.
(*b*) *W* **10.** 2d. D.L.R. (*roul*), 2d. D.L.R. (*p* 10)

The 2d. (*W* **2.** *Roul*) with red overprint is known showing the stop omitted after "W".

B. General

O.S. (O 1) **O.S.** (O **2**)

1874–77. *Optd with Type* O **1.** *W* **2.** (*a*) *P* 10.

O 1	**3**	4d. dull purple (18.2.74)	£950	£250
		(*b*) *P* 11½–12½ × 10.		
O 2	**1**	1d. green (2.1.74)	—	75·00
O 3	**3**	4d. dull violet (12.2.75)	32·00	4·50
O 4	**1**	6d. Prussian blue (20.10.75)	—	8·00
O 4*a*	**3**	2s. rose-pink		
O 5		2s. carmine (3.12.76)	—	75·00
		(*c*) *P* 11½–12½		
O 6	**1**	1d. deep yellow-green (30.1.74)	—	16·00
		a. Printed on both sides	—	£250
O 7	**3**	3d. on 4d. ultramarine (26.6.77)	£700	£200
		a. No stop after "S"	—	£300
O 8		4d. dull violet (13.7.74)	23·00	5·00
		a. No stop after "S"	—	25·00
O 9	**1**	6d. bright blue (31.8.75)	45·00	11·00
		a. "O.S." double	—	40·00
O10		6d. Prussian blue (27.3.74)	35·00	4·50
		a. No stop after "S"	—	28·00
O11	**4**	9d. red-purple (22.3.76)	£180	50·00
		a. No stop after "S"	£275	
O12	**1**	1s. red-brown (5.8.74)	32·00	5·00
		a. "O.S." double	—	50·00
		b. No stop after "S"	60·00	25·00
O13	**3**	2s. crimson-carmine (13.7.75)	48·00	8·50
		a. No stop after "S"		
		b. No stops	—	50·00
		c. Stops at top of letters		

1876–85. *Optd with Type* O **1.** *W* **8.** (*a*) *P* 10.

O14	**1**	6d. bright blue (1879)	50·00	8·00
		(*b*) *P* 10 × 11½–12½, 11½–12½ × 10, *or compound*		
O15	**3**	4d. violet-slate (24.1.78)	50·00	6·00
O16		4d. plum (29.11.81)	24·00	2·25
O17		4d. deep mauve	16·00	2·00
		a. No stop after "S"	—	20·00
		b. No stop after "O"		
		c. "O.S." double		
		d. "O.S." inverted	—	85·00
O18	**1**	6d. bright blue (1877)	22·00	2·50
		a. "O.S." inverted		
		b. No stop after "O"		
O19		6d. bright ultramarine (27.3.85)	20·00	2·00
		a. "O.S." inverted		
		b. "O.S." double		
		c. "O.S." double, one inverted	—	£180
		d. No stop after "S"		
		e. No stops after "O" & "S"		
O20		1s. red-brown (27.3.83)	22·00	4·00
		a. "O.S." inverted		
		b. No stop after "O"		
		c. No stop after "S"		
O21	**3**	2s. carmine (16.3.81)	25·00	4·25
		a. "O.S." inverted	—	90·00
		b. No stop after "S"		
		(*c*) *P* 11½–12½		
O22	**3**	3d. on 4d. ultramarine	£400	
O23		4d. violet-slate (14.3.76)	£120	6·00
O24		4d. deep mauve (19.8.79)	32·00	2·00
		a. "O.S." inverted		
		b. "O.S." double, one inverted		
		c. No stop after "S"		
O25	**1**	6d. Prussian blue (6.77)	25·00	3·00
		a. "O.S." double	—	30·00
		b. "O.S." inverted		
O26	**4**	8d. on 9d. brown (9.11.76)	£275	75·00
		a. "O.S." double	£500	
		b. "O" only	—	£200
O26*c*		9d. purple	£700	
O27	**1**	1s. red-brown (12.2.78)	15·00	3·00
		a. "O.S." inverted	£150	75·00
		b. No stop after "S"	£150	
O28		1s. lake-brown (8.11.83)	13·00	2·50
O29	**3**	2s. rose-carmine (12.8.85)	30·00	4·25
		a. "O.S." double	—	60·00
		b. "O.S." inverted	—	65·00
		c. No stop after "S"	—	30·00

1891–1903. *Optd with Type* O **2.** (*a*) *W* **8.** *P* 11½–12½.

O30	**1**	1s. lake-brown (18.4.91)	15·00	8·00
O31		1s. Vandyke brown	18·00	5·00
O32		1s. dull brown (2.7.96)	15·00	3·50
		a. No stop after "S"		
O33		1s. sepia (*large holes*) (4.1.02)	11·00	2·50
		a. "O.S." double		
		b. No stop after "S"		
O34	**3**	2s. carmine (26.6.00)	32·00	6·00
		a. No stop after "S"		
		(*b*) *W* **8.** *P* 10 × 11½–12½		
O35	**3**	2s. rose-carmine (9.11.95)	23·00	4·00
		a. No stop after "S"	60·00	
		b. "O.S." double		
		(*c*) *W* **10.** *P* 11½–12½		
O36	**1**	1s. dull brown (7.3.03)	15·00	2·50

1874–76. *Optd with Type* O **1.** *W* **10.** (*a*) *P* 10.

O37	**11**	1d. blue-green (30.9.75)	55·00	15·00
		a. "O.S." inverted		
		b. No stop after "S"		
O38	**12**	2d. orange-red (18.2.74)	8·00	30
		a. No stop after "S"		
		b. "O.S." double		
		(*b*) *P* 10 × 11½–12½, 11½–12½ × 10, *or compound*		
O39	**11**	1d. blue-green (16.9.75)		
		a. No stop after "S"		
O40	**12**	2d. orange-red (27.9.76)	—	3·75
		(*c*) *P* 11½–12½		
O41	**11**	1d. blue-green (13.8.75)	—	12·00
		a. "O.S." inverted		
		b. No stop after "S"		
O42	**12**	2d. orange-red (20.5.74)	—	80·00

1876–80. *Optd with Type* O **1.** *W* **13.** (*a*) *P* 10.

O43	**11**	1d. blue-green (2.10.76)	3·50	15
		a. "O.S." inverted	—	30·00
		b. "O.S." double	32·00	25·00
		c. "O.S." double, one inverted		
		d. No stops	—	12·00
		e. No stop after "S"	—	7·00
		f. No stop after "O"		
O44		1d. deep green	4·50	15
		a. "O.S." double	—	28·00
O45	**12**	2d. orange-red (21.9.77)	4·00	15
		a. "O.S." double	35·00	22·00
		b. "O.S." inverted	—	14·00
		c. "O.S." double, both inverted	—	70·00
		d. "O.S." double, one inverted		
		e. No stop after "O"	—	12·00
		f. No stop after "S"		
		g. No stops after "O" & "S"		
O46		2d. brick-red	23·00	65

(*b*) *P* 10 × 11½–12½, 11½–12½ × 10, *or compound*
O47 11 1d. deep green (14.8.80) .. .. .. — 18·00
a. "O.S." double .. .. ..
O48 12 2d. orange-red (6.4.78) .. .. .. 35·00 6·00
a. "O.S." inverted .. .. ..
b. No stop after "S" .. .. ..

(*c*) *P* 11½–12½
O49 12 2d. orange-red (15.7.80) .. .. — 60·00

1882 (20 Feb). *No.* O43 *surch with T* **14**. *W* **13**. *P* 10.
O50 11 ½d. on 1d. blue-green .. .. .. 12·00 3·00
a. "O.S." inverted .. .. ..

1888–91. *Optd with Type* O **1**. *W* **13**. *P* 10.
O51 17 4d. violet (24.1.91) .. .. .. 7·00 70
O52 18 6d. blue (15.11.88) .. .. .. 4·50 50
a. "O.S." double .. .. ..
b. No stop after "S" .. .. ..

1891. *As No.* O51 *surch with T* **20**. *W* **13**. (*a*) *P* 10.
O53 17 2½d. on 4d. green (1.8.91) .. .. 24·00 3·25
a. "2" and "½" closer .. .. .. — 35·00
b. No stop after "S" .. .. ..
c. "O.S." omitted (in pair with normal)
d. "O.S." inverted .. .. ..
e. "O.S." double .. .. ..

(*b*) *P* 10 × 11½–12½, 11½–12½ × 10, *or compound*
O54 17 2½d. on 4d. green (1.10.91) .. .. 27·00 7·00

(*c*) *P* 11½–12½
O54*a* 17 2½d. on 4d. green (1.6.91) .. ..

1891–95. *Optd with Type* O **2**. *W* **13**. (*a*) *P* 10.
O55 15 ½d. brown (2.5.94) .. .. .. 5·50 2·00
a. No stop after "S" .. .. ..
O56 11 1d. green (22.4.91) .. .. .. 4·50 15
a. "O.S." double .. .. .. 35·00
b. No stop after "S" .. .. .. — 7·00
c. "O.S." in blackish blue .. .. £200 2·75
d. "O.S." double, one inverted
O57 12 2d. orange-red (22.4.91) .. .. 4·00 15
a. No stop after "S" .. .. .. — 8·00
b. "O.S." double .. .. ..
O58 17 2½d. on 4d. green (18.8.94) .. .. 16·00 1·60
a. No stop after "S" .. .. .. — 15·00
b. "O.S." inverted £110
c. "2" and "½" closer .. .. .. 45·00 15·00
d. Fraction bar omitted .. ..
O59 4d. pale violet (13.2.91) .. .. 5·50 60
a. "O" only .. .. .. — 40·00
b. "O.S." double .. .. ..
c. No stop after "S" .. .. ..
O60 4d. aniline violet (31.8.93) .. .. 7·00 50
a. No stop after "S" .. .. ..
b. "O.S." double .. .. ..
O61 18 5d. on 6d. brown (2.12.91) .. .. 25·00 4·00
a. No stop after "S" .. .. .. 65·00 20·00
b. No stop after "5D" £150
O62 6d. blue (4.4.93) .. .. .. 3·50 50
a. No stop after "S" .. .. ..
b. "O.S." in blackish blue .. ..

(*b*) *P* 10 × 11½–12½
O63 15 ½d. pale brown (26.3.95) .. .. 6·00 1·90
O64 17 2½d. on 4d. green (17.9.95) .. .. — 30·00
a. "O.S." double .. .. ..

(*c*) *P* 11½–12½
O65 15 ½d. Venetian red (13.6.91) .. .. 13·00 2·50

1893–1901. *Optd with Type* O **2**. *W* **13**. *P* 15.
O66 15 ½d. pale brown (8.6.95) .. .. 4·00 1·25
O67 11 1d. green (8.9.94) .. .. .. 3·00 15
a. No stop after "S" .. .. ..
b. "O.S." double .. .. ..
O68 12 2d. orange-red (16.6.94) .. .. 4·00 15
a. "O.S." double .. .. .. — 18·00
b. "O.S." inverted .. .. .. — 12·00
O68*c* 22 2½d. violet-blue .. .. .. 7·00 75
O69 17 4d. slate-violet (4.4.95) .. .. 8·00 75
a. "O.S." double .. .. .. — 20·00
O70 23 5d. purple (29.3.01) .. .. .. 12·00 1·75
O71 18 6d. blue (20.9.93) .. .. .. 4·50 50

1895–1901. *Optd with Type* O **2**. *W* **13**. *P* 13.
O72 15 ½d. brown (17.5.98) .. .. .. 5·50 1·50
a. Opt triple, twice sideways £150
O73 11 1d. green (20.5.95) .. .. .. 5·00 15
a. No stop after "S" .. .. .. 25·00 7·00
O74 12 2d. orange (11.2.96) .. .. .. 3·75 15
a. No stop after "S" .. .. .. — 7·00
b. "O.S." double .. .. ..
O75 22 2½d. violet-blue (5.7.97) .. .. 5·50 45
a. No stop after "S" .. .. ..
O76 17 4d. violet (12.96) .. .. .. 5·00 45
a. No stop after "S" .. .. .. 25·00 10·00
b. "O.S." double .. .. .. 25·00 15·00
O77 23 5d. purple (29.9.01) .. .. .. 8·00 1·90
a. No stop after "S" .. .. ..
O78 18 6d. blue (13.9.99) .. .. .. 5·50 60
a. No stop after "S" .. .. .. 25·00

O. S.

(O 3)

1899–1901. *Optd with Type* O **3**. *W* **13**. *P* 13.
O80 24 ½d. yellow-green (12.2.00) .. .. 4·00 30
a. No stop after "S" .. .. ..
b. "O.S." inverted .. .. .. 35·00
O81 11 1d. rosine (22.9.99) .. .. .. 2·75 30
a. "O.S." inverted .. .. .. — 25·00
b. "O.S." double .. .. ..
c. No stop after "S" .. .. .. — 12·00
O82 12 2d. bright violet (1.6.00) .. .. 4·50 35
a. "O.S." inverted .. .. .. 26·00 26·00
b. "O.S." double .. .. ..
c. No stop after "S" .. .. .. 22·00
O83 22 2½d. indigo (2.10.01) .. .. .. 5·00 70
a. "O.S." inverted .. .. .. — 25·00
b. No stop after "S" .. .. .. 30·00
O84 17 4d. violet (18.11.00) .. .. .. 4·00 15
a. "O.S." inverted .. .. .. 55·00
b. No stop after "S" .. .. .. 20·00
O85 18 6d. blue (8.10.00) .. .. .. 4·50 45
a. No stop after "S" .. .. .. 22·00

1891 (May). *Optd as Type* O **3** *but wider. W* **13**. *P* 10.
O86 19 2s. 6d. pale violet £2000 £1600
O87 5s. pale rose £2000 £1600
Only one sheet (60) of each of these stamps was printed.

Stamps overprinted for Official use were withdrawn on 30 September 1903.

The six former colonies of New South Wales, Queensland, South Australia, Tasmania, Victoria and Western Australia united to form the Commonwealth of Australia on 1 January 1901.

On 1 March 1901 control of the postal service passed to the federal administration. The first national postage due stamps appeared in July 1902, but it was not until January 1913 that postage stamps inscribed "AUSTRALIA" were issued.

South Georgia

As South Georgia remained a dependency of the Falkland Islands between 1963 and 1980 stamps so inscribed are listed under FALKLAND ISLANDS DEPENDENCIES.

South Georgia and the South Sandwich Islands

(*formerly* Falkland Islands Dependencies)

Under the new constitution, effective 3 October 1985, South Georgia and South Sandwich Islands ceased to be dependencies of the Falkland Islands.

(Des A. Theobald. Litho Questa)

1986 (21 Apr). *60th Birthday of Queen Elizabeth II. Vert designs as T* **110** *of Ascension. Multicoloured. W* w **16**. *P* 14½ × 14.
153 10p. Four generations of Royal Family at Prince Charles' christening, 1948 .. 25 25
154 24p. With Prince Charles and Lady Diana Spencer, Buckingham Palace, 1981 .. 55 55
155 29p. In robes of Order of the British Empire, St. Paul's Cathedral, London 60 60
156 45p. At banquet, Canada, 1976 .. .. 95 95
157 58p. At Crown Agents Head Office, London, 1983 .. .. 1·25 1·25
153/7 .. .. *Set of* 5 3·25 3·25

(Des D. Miller. Litho Questa)

1986 (10 Nov). *Royal Wedding. Vert designs as T* **153** *of Falkland Islands. Multicoloured. W* w **16**. *P* 14½ × 14.
158 17p. Prince Andrew and Miss Sarah Ferguson at Ascot 40 40
159 22p. Wedding photograph 50 50
160 29p. Prince Andrew with Lynx helicopter on board H.M.S. *Brazen* 60 60
158/60 .. .. *Set of* 3 1·40 1·40

26 Southern Black-backed Gull

(Des T. Chater. Litho Walsall)

1987 (24 Apr). *Birds. T* **26** *and similar multicoloured designs. W* w **16** (*sideways on horiz designs*). *P* 14½.
161 1p. Type **26** 10 10
162 2p. Blue-eyed Cormorant 10 10
163 3p. Snowy Sheathbill (*vert*) 10 10
164 4p. Great Skua (*vert*) 10 10
165 5p. Pintado Petrel ("Cape Pigeon") 10 10
166 6p. Georgian Diving Petrel 10 10
167 7p. South Georgia Pipit (*vert*) 10 15
168 8p. Georgian Teal ("South Georgian Pintail") (*vert*) 15 20
169 9p. Fairy Prion 15 20
170 10p. Chinstrap Penguin 20 25
171 20p. Macaroni Penguin (*vert*) 35 40
172 25p. Light-mantled Sooty Albatross (*vert*) .. 45 50
173 50p. Giant Petrel (*vert*) 90 95
174 £1 Wandering Albatross .. .. .. 1·75 1·90
175 £3 King Penguin (*vert*) .. .. .. 5·00 5·25
161/75 .. .. *Set of* 15 8·50 9·25

(Des L. Curtis. Litho Questa)

1987 (5 Dec). *30th Anniv of International Geophysical Year. Vert designs as T* **39** *of British Antarctic Territory. W* w **16**. *P* 14½ × 14.
176 24p. black and pale turquoise-blue 50 55
177 29p. multicoloured 55 60
178 58p. multicoloured .. .. 1·10 1·25
176/8 .. .. *Set of* 3 1·90 2·10
Designs:—24p. I.G.Y. logo; 29p. Grytviken; 58p. Glaciologist using hand-drill to take core sample.

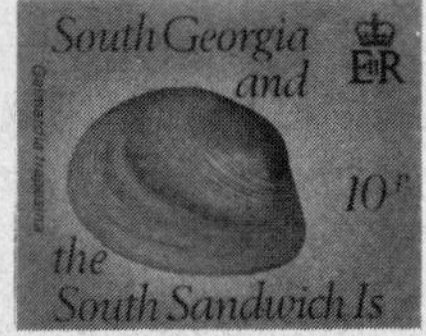

27 *Gaimardia trapesina*

(Des I. Strange. Litho Questa)

1988 (26 Feb). *Sea Shells. T* **27** *and similar horiz designs. Multicoloured. W* w **16** (*sideways*). *P* 14 × 14½.
179 10p. Type **27** 20 25
180 24p. *Margarella tropidophoroides* 50 55
181 29p. *Trophon scotianus* 55 60
182 58p. *Chlanidota densesculpta* .. .. 1·10 1·25
179/82 .. .. *Set of* 4 2·10 2·40

(Des E. Nisbet and D. Miller (24p.), D. Miller (others). Litho Questa)

1988 (17 Sept). *300th Anniv of Lloyd's of London. Designs as T* **123** *of Ascension. W* w **16** (*sideways on* 24, 29*p*.). *P* 14.
183 10p. brownish black and brown 20 25
184 24p. multicoloured 50 55
185 29p. brownish black and emerald 60 65
186 58p. brownish black and carmine-red .. .. 1·10 1·25
183/6 .. .. *Set of* 4 2·10 2·40
Designs: *Vert*—10p. Queen Mother at opening of new Lloyd's building, 1957; 58p. *Horatio* (tanker) on fire, 1916. *Horiz*—24p. *Lindblad Explorer* (cruise liner); 29p. Whaling station, Leith Harbour.

28 Glacier Headwall

29 Retracing Shackleton's Trek

(Des I. Loe. Litho Questa)

1989 (31 July). *Glacier Formations. T* **28** *and similar horiz designs. Multicoloured. W* w **16** (*sideways*). *P* 14.
187 10p. Type **28** 30 30
188 24p. Accumulation area 60 60
189 29p. Ablation area 70 70
190 58p. Calving front .. .. 1·40 1·40
187/90 .. .. *Set of* 4 2·75 2·75

(Des O. Bell. Litho Questa)

1989 (28 Nov). *25th Anniv of Combined Services Expedition to South Georgia. T* **29** *and similar horiz designs. Multicoloured. W* w **16** (*sideways*). *P* 14 × 14½.
191 10p. Type **29** 20 25
192 24p. Surveying at Royal Bay 50 55
193 29p. H.M.S. *Protector* (ice patrol ship) .. 55 60
194 58p. Raising Union Jack on Mount Paget .. 1·10 1·25
191/4 .. .. *Set of* 4 2·10 2·40

South West Africa

(*formerly* German S. W. Africa)

The stamps of Germany were used in the colony from July 1886 until the introduction of issues for GERMAN SOUTH-WEST AFRICA in May 1897. Following occupation by South African forces in 1914–15 the issues of SOUTH AFRICA were used, being replaced by the overprinted issues in 1923.

Walvis (or Walfish) Bay, the major anchorage on the South West Africa coast, was claimed by Great Britain as early as 1796. In 1878 the 430 sq mile area around the port, together with a number of offshore islands, was annexed to Cape Province, passing to the Union of South Africa in 1910.

Stamps of the Cape of Good Hope and South Africa were used at Walfish Bay, often cancelled with numeral obliterator 300, until the enclave was transferred to the South West Africa administration on 1 October 1922.

The Walfish Bay territory reverted to South Africa on 30 August 1977 and from that date the stamps of South Africa were, once again, in use.

PRICES FOR STAMPS ON COVER TO 1945

Nos. 1/40*a*	*from* × 6
Nos. 41/133	*from* × 2
Nos. D1/5	*from* × 10
Nos. D6/51	*from* × 20
Nos. O1/4	*from* × 3
Nos. O5/20	*from* × 15
No. O21	—
No. O22	*from* × 15

INSCRIPTIONS. Most of the postage stamps up to No. 140 are inscribed alternately in English and Afrikaans throughout the sheets and the same applies to all the Official stamps and to Nos. D30/33.

PRICES for Nos. 1/140 are for horizontal pairs, *unless otherwise indicated.*

South West / **Africa.** (1)   **Zuid-West** / **Afrika.** (2)

1923. *Stamps of South Africa, T* **2** *and* **3**, *typo with T* **1** *and* **2** *alternately.* I. 14 *mm between lines of typo overprint.* (2 Jan).

1 ½d. green .. 1·00 3·75
 a. "Wes" for "West" .. 90·00 £100
 b. "Afr ica" (R.20/2) .. £150
2 1d. rose-red .. 1·25 3·75
 a. Opt inverted .. £550
 b. "Wes" for "West" .. £180
 c. "Af.rica" for "Africa" .. £140 £160
 d. Opt double .. £750
 e. "Afr ica" (R.20/2) .. £160
3 2d. dull purple .. 1·75 5·50
 a. Opt inverted .. £550 £600
4 3d. ultramarine .. 7·50 15·00
5 4d. orange-yellow and sage-green .. 12·00 29·00
6 6d. black and violet .. 8·00 29·00
7 1s. orange-yellow .. 23·00 45·00
8 1s. 3d. pale violet .. 35·00 55·00
 a. Opt inverted .. £250
9 2s. 6d. purple and green .. 80·00 £125
10 5s. purple and blue .. £200 £325
11 10s. blue and olive-green .. £2250 £2750
12 £1 green and red .. £1400 £1800
1/12 .. *Set of* 12 £3500 £4500
1/12 Optd "Specimen" .. *Set of* 12 *singles* £1750

Minor varieties, due to wear of type including broken "t" in West," may be found. Varieties showing one line of overprint only, or lower line above upper line, due to misplacement, may also be found. All values may be found with faint stop after "Afrika," and the ½d., 1d., 2d. and 3d. occasionally without stop.

14 mm between lines, but opt lithographed in shiny ink

12*a* ½d. green .. 7·50 25·00
12*b* 4d. orange-yellow and sage-green .. 45·00 70·00
12*c* 6d. black and violet .. 40·00 65·00
12*d* 1s. orange-yellow .. 85·00 £120
12*e* 1s. 3d. pale violet .. £120 £140
12*f* 2s. 6d. purple and green .. £275 £350
12*a*/12*f* .. *Set of* 6 £500 £650

II. *10 mm between lines of typo overprint* (May 1923)

13 5s. purple and blue .. £225 £350
 a. "Afrika" without stop .. £2250
14 10s. blue and olive-green .. £850 £1200
 a. "Afrika" without stop .. £3250 £3500
15 £1 green and red .. £1600 £2000
 a. "Afrika" without stop .. £6000
13/15 .. *Set of* 3 £2400 £3250

MINIMUM PRICE

The minimum price quote is 10p which represents a handling charge rather than a basis for valuing common stamps. For further notes about prices see introductory pages.

Zuidwest / **Afrika.** (3)   **South West** / **Africa.** (4)

1923–24. *Stamps of South Africa, T* **2** *and* **3**, *optd as T* **3** *("Zuidwest" in one word, without hyphen) and* **4** *alternately.*

III. "South West" 14 *mm long;* "Zuidwest" 11 *mm long;* 14 *mm between lines of opt* (Aug-Sept, 1923)

16 ½d. green (9.24) .. 3·00 10·00
 a. "outh" for "South" .. £1300
17 1d. rose-red .. 3·00 6·50
 a. "outh" for "South" .. £1300
18 2d. dull purple .. 3·00 3·25
 a. Opt double .. £850
19 3d. ultramarine .. 3·50 6·00
20 4d. orange-yellow and sage-green .. 4·75 11·00
21 6d. black and violet .. 11·00 26·00
22 1s. orange-yellow .. 14·00 35·00
23 1s. 3d. pale violet .. 28·00 45·00
24 2s. 6d. purple and green .. 50·00 90·00
25 5s. purple and blue .. 80·00 £150
26 10s. blue and olive-green .. £250 £350
27 £1 green and red .. £450 £550
16/27 .. *Set of* 12 £800 £1050

Two sets may be made with this overprint, one with bold lettering, and the other with thinner lettering and smaller stops.

IV. "South West" 16 *mm long;* "Zuidwest" 12 *mm long;* 14 *mm between lines of opt* (July 1924)

28 2s. 6d purple and green .. 80·00 £150

VI. "South West" 16 *mm long**; "Zuidwest" 12 *mm long;* 9½ *mm between lines of opt* (Dec. 1924)

29 ½d. green .. 3·25 18·00
30 1d. rose-red .. 1·50 6·00
31 2d. dull purple .. 3·00 9·00
32 3d. ultramarine .. 3·50 15·00
 a. Deep bright blue .. 50·00 80·00
33 4d. orange-yellow and sage-green .. 5·00 19·00
34 6d. black and violet .. 6·50 24·00
35 1s. orange-yellow .. 11·00 32·00
36 1s. 3d. pale violet .. 14·00 35·00
37 2s. 6d. purple and green .. 45·00 70·00
38 5s. purple and blue .. 70·00 £125
39 10s. blue and olive-green .. £110 £140
40 £1 green and red .. £450 £550
40*a* £1 pale olive-green and red .. £375 £550
29/40*a* .. *Set of* 12 £575 £850
35, 39/40 H/S "Specimen" .. *Set of* 3 £600

*Two sets with this overprint may be made one with "South West" 16 mm long, and the other 16½ mm the difference occurring in the spacing between the words. No. 40*a* only exists with the latter spacing.

Suidwes / **Afrika.** (5)   **South West** / **Africa.** (6)

1926. *Pictorial types of South Africa optd with T* **5** *(on stamps inscr in Afrikaans) and* **6** *(on stamps inscr in English) sideways, alternately in black.*

41 ½d. black and green .. 1·75 8·50
42 1d. black and carmine .. 1·60 7·00
43 6d. green and orange .. 25·00 48·00
41/3 .. *Set of* 3 26·00 55·00

SOUTH WEST AFRICA (7)   **SUIDWES-AFRIKA** (8)

1926. *Triangular stamps of South Africa, imperf, optd with T* **7** (E.) *or T* **8** (A.).

Single stamps E A

44 10 4d. grey-blue .. 65 2·00 65 2·00

1927. *As Nos. 41/3, but Afrikaans opt on stamp inscr in English and vice versa.*

45 ½d. black and green .. 1·40 4·25
 a. "Africa" without stop .. £150
46 1d. black and carmine .. 1·40 2·50
 a. "Africa" without stop .. £200
47 6d. green and orange .. 12·00 25·00
 a. "Africa" without stop .. £170
45/7 .. *Set of* 3 13·50 28·00

SOUTH WEST AFRICA (9)   **S.W.A.** (10)   **S.W.A.** (11)

1927. *As No. 44E, but overprint T* **9**.

Single stamps

48 4d. grey-blue (Optd S. £80) .. 7·50 19·00

1927. *Pictorial stamps of South Africa optd alternately as T* **5** *and* **6**, *in blue, but with lines of overprint spaced 16 mm.*

49 2d. grey and purple .. 3·50 14·00
50 3d. black and red .. 3·75 20·00
51 1s. brown and blue .. 13·00 32·00
52 2s. 6d. green and brown .. 45·00 65·00
53 5s. black and green .. 75·00 £110
54 10s. blue and bistre-brown .. £110 £160
49/54 .. *Set of* 6 £225 £325
49/51, 54 H/S "Specimen" .. *Set of* 4 £400

A variety of Nos. 49, 50, 51 and 54, with spacing 16½ mm between lines of overprint, occurs in one vertical row of each sheet.

1927. *As No. 44, but perf* 11½ *by John Meinert, Ltd, Windhoek.*

Single stamps E A

55 4d. grey-blue .. 70 3·50 70 3·50
 a. Imperf between (pair) .. 30·00 55·00 30·00 55·00
55 Optd "Specimen" .. 80·00 80·00

1927–30. *Optd with T* **10**. (*a*) *T* **3** *of South Africa.*

Single stamps

56 1s. 3d. pale violet (H/S S.£70) .. 1·25 6·00
 a. Without stop after "A" .. £110
57 £1 pale olive-green and red .. £175 £225
 a. Without stop after "A" .. £2750 £3000

(*b*) *Pictorial stamps of South Africa*

Un pair *Us pair*

58 ½d. black and green .. 1·50 3·50
 a. Without stop after "A" .. 50·00 75·00
 b. "S.W.A." opt above value .. 2·50 11·00
 c. As b, in vert pair, top stamp without opt £450
59 1d. black and carmine .. 1·25 3·25
 a. Without stop after "A" .. 50·00 75·00
 b. "S.W.A." opt at top (30.4.30) .. 1·50 8·00
 c. As b, in vert pair, top stamp without opt £375
60 2d. grey and purple .. 4·50 6·50
 a. Without stop after "A" .. 75·00 £110
 b. Opt double, one inverted .. £750 £850
61 3d. black and red .. 6·00 23·00
 a. Without stop after "A" .. 75·00 £120
62 4d. brown (1928) .. 18·00 45·00
 a. Without stop after "A" .. 85·00 £130
63 6d. green and orange .. 13·00 22·00
 a. Without stop after "A" .. £110
64 1s. brown and blue .. 24·00 38·00
 a. Without stop after "A" .. £1700
65 2s. 6d. green and brown .. 48·00 75·00
 a. Without stop after "A" .. £180 £250
66 5s. black and green .. 75·00 £100
 a. Without stop after "A" .. £250 £350
67 10s. blue and bistre-brown .. £140 £180
 a. Without stop after "A" .. £400 £500
58/67 .. *Set of* 10 £275 £425
58/61, 63/7 H/S "Specimen" .. *Set of* 9 £650

The overprint is normally found at the base of the ½d., 1d., 6d., 1s. 3d. and £1 values and at the top of the remainder.

1930. *Nos. 42 and 43 of South Africa (rotogravure printing), optd with T* **10**.

68 ½d. black and green .. 5·50 14·00
69 1d. black and carmine .. 5·50 14·00

1930 (27 Nov–Dec). *Air. T* **17** *of South Africa optd.* (*a*) *As T* **10**.

Un single *Us single*

70 4d. green (*first printing*) .. 12·00 22·00
 a. No stop after "A" of "S.W.A." .. 80·00 £110
 b. Later printings .. 7·00 24·00
71 1s. orange (*first printing*) .. 70·00 £110
 a. No stop after "A" of "S.W.A." .. £400 £500
 b. Later printings .. 15·00 48·00

First printing: Thick letters, blurred impression. Stops with rounded corners.

Later printings: Thinner letters, clear impression. Clean cut, square stops.

(*b*) *As T* **11** (12.30)

72 4d. green .. 1·25 4·25
 a. Opt double .. £130
 b. Opt inverted .. £120
73 1s. orange .. 1·50 12·00
 a. Opt double

12 Kori Bustard

13 Cape Cross

14 Bogenfels

15 Windhoek

16 Waterberg

17 Luderitz Bay

18 Bush Scene

19 Elands

20 Mountain Zebra and Blue Wildebeests

21 Herero Huts

22 Welwitschia Plant

23 Okuwahaken Falls

24 Monoplane over Windhoek

25 Biplane over Windhoek

(Recess B.W.)

1931 (5 Mar). *T* **12** *to* **25** *(inscr alternately in English and Afrikaans).* *W* **9** *of South Africa. P* 14 × 13½. *(a) Postage.*

74	½d. black and emerald	85	90
75	1d. indigo and scarlet	70	1·50
76	2d. blue and brown	50	1·75
77	3d. grey-blue and blue	50	2·50
78	4d. green and purple	65	3·75
79	6d. blue and brown	60	5·00
80	1s. chocolate and blue	1·00	6·50
81	1s. 3d. violet and yellow	8·00	11·00
82	2s. 6d. carmine and grey	19·00	22·00
83	5s. sage-green and red-brown	20·00	40·00
84	10s. red-brown and emerald	55·00	60·00
85	20s. lake and blue-green	£110	£110
	(b) Air		
86	3d. brown and blue	32·00	40·00
87	10d. black and purple-brown	55·00	80·00
74/87	*Set of* 14	£275	£350

26

(Recess B.W.)

1935 (1 May). *Silver Jubilee. Inscr bilingually. W* **9** *of South Africa. P* 14 × 13½.

			Un single	*Us single*
88	**26**	1d. black and scarlet	40	25
89		2d. black and sepia	90	25
90		3d. black and blue	9·00	13·00
91		6d. black and purple	4·50	3·50
88/91		*Set of* 4	13·50	15·00

1935–36. *Voortrekker Memorial Fund. T* **18** *to* **21** *of South Africa optd with T* **10**.

92	½d. + ½d. olive-green and green	1·00	4·50
	a. Opt inverted	£200	
93	1d. + ½d. grey-black and pink	1·50	3·25
94	2d. + 1d. grey-green and purple	5·00	6·00
	a. Without stop after "A"	£180	
	b. Opt double	£160	
95	3d. + 1½d. grey-green and blue	15·00	22·00
	a. Without stop after "A"	£180	£200
92/5	*Set of* 4	20·00	32·00

27 Mail Train

28

(Recess B.W.)

1937 (1 Mar). *W* **9** *of South Africa. P* 14 × 13½.

96	**27**	1½d. purple-brown	4·50	1·40

(Recess B.W.)

1937 (12 May). *Coronation. W* **9** *of South Africa (sideways). P* 13½ × 14.

97	**28**	½d. black and emerald	45	15
98		1d. black and scarlet	45	15
99		1½d. black and orange	55	15
100		2d. black and brown	60	15
101		3d. black and blue	65	15
102		4d. black and purple	70	20
103		6d. black and yellow	80	1·25
104		1s. black and grey-black	1·25	1·25
97/104		*Set of* 8	5·00	3·00

1938 (14 Dec). *Voortrekker Centenary Memorial. Nos.* 76 *to* 79 *of South Africa optd as T* **11**.

105	½d. + ½d. blue and green	5·00	5·50
106	1d. + 1d. blue and carmine	8·50	3·50
107	1½d. + 1½d. chocolate and blue-green	8·50	12·00
108	3d. + 3d. bright blue	23·00	19·00
105/8	*Set of* 4	40·00	35·00

1938 (14 Dec). *Voortrekker Commemoration. Nos.* 80/1 *of South Africa optd as T* **11**.

109	1d. blue and carmine	4·00	4·00
110	1½d. greenish blue and brown	6·50	7·00

1939 (17 July). *250th Anniv of Landing of Huguenots in South Africa and Huguenot Commemoration Fund. Nos.* 82/4 *of South Africa optd as T* **11**.

111	½d. + ½d. brown and green	4·00	5·00
112	1d. + 1d. green and carmine	4·50	5·50
113	1½d. + 1½d. blue-green and purple	7·00	9·00
111/13	*Set of* 3	14·00	18·00

SWA (29) **SWA** (30) **SWA** (31) **S W A** (32)

1941–43. *War Effort. Nos.* 88/96 *of South Africa optd with T* **29** *or* **30** *(3d. and 1s.). (a) Inscr alternately.*

114	½d. green	75	1·25
	a. Blue-green (1942)	65	90
115	1d. carmine	55	90
116	1½d. myrtle-green (1942)	55	90
117	3d. blue	3·25	3·50
118	4d. orange-brown	6·50	3·50
	a. Red-brown	7·50	11·00
119	6d. red-orange	2·50	3·00
120	1s. 3d. olive-brown (15.1.43)	6·00	4·00
	(b) Inscr bilingually	*Un single*	*Us single*
121	2d. violet	40	25
122	1s. brown	60	25
114/22	*Set of* 7 *pairs and* 2 *singles*	19·00	15·00

1943–44. *War Effort (reduced sizes). Nos.* 97/104 *of South Africa, optd with T* **29** *(1½d. and 1s., No.* 130*), or T* **31** *(others).*

	(a) Inscr alternately	*Un unit*	*Us unit*
123	½d. blue-green (T)	40	75
	a. Green	1·50	1·75
	b. Greenish blue	75	75
124	1d. carmine-red (T)	70	70
	a. Bright carmine	70	70
125	1½. red-brown (P)	45	40
126	2d. violet (P)	1·25	65
	a. Reddish violet	1·75	75
127	3d. blue (T)	2·50	4·00
128	6d. red-orange (P)	2·00	2·25
	a. Opt inverted	£375	
	(b) Inscr bilingually		
129	4d. slate-green (T)	2·00	4·50
	a. Opt inverted	£350	
130	1s. brown (opt T **29**) (P)	6·00	8·50
	a. Opt inverted	£375	
	b. Opt T **31** (1944)	2·50	2·50
	c. Opt T **31** inverted	£350	£275
123/30b	*Set of* 8 *units*	10·50	13·50

The "units" referred to above consist of pairs (P) or triplets (T).

No. 128 exists with another type of opt as Type **31**, but with broader "s", narrower "w" and more space between the letters.

1945. *Victory. Nos.* 108/10 *of South Africa optd with T* **30**.

131	1d. brown and carmine	25	30
	a. Opt inverted	£200	
132	2d. slate-blue and violet	30	35
133	3d. deep blue and blue	65	55
131/3	*Set of* 3	1·10	1·10

1947 (17 Feb). *Royal Visit. Nos.* 111/13 *of South Africa optd as T* **31**, *but* 8½ × 2 *mm.*

134	1d. black and carmine	10	10
135	2d. violet	10	15
136	3d. blue	15	15
134/6	*Set of* 3	30	35

1948 (26 Apr). *Royal Silver Wedding. No.* 125 *of South Africa, optd as T* **31**, *but* 4 × 2 *mm.*

137	3d. blue and silver	80	35

1949 (1 Oct). *75th Anniv of U.P.U. Nos.* 128/30 *of South Africa optd as T* **30**, *but* 13 × 4 *mm.*

138	½d. blue-green	90	80
139	1½d. brown-red	90	80
140	3d. bright blue	1·50	1·00
	a. "Lake" in East Africa	18·00	
138/40	*Set of* 3	3·00	2·40

1949 (1 Dec). *Inauguration of Voortrekker Monument, Pretoria. Nos.* 131/3 *of South Africa optd with T* **32**.

141	1d. magenta	10	10
142	1½d. blue-green	10	10
143	3d. blue	10	20
141/3	*Set of* 3	20	25

1952 (14 Mar). *Tercentenary of Landing of Van Riebeeck. Nos.* 136/40 *of South Africa optd as T* **30**, *but* 8 × 3½ *mm (1d., 4½d.) or* 11 × 4 *mm (others).*

144	½d. brown-purple and olive-grey	10	15
145	1d. deep blue-green	10	10
146	2d. deep violet	40	10
147	4½d. blue	25	60
148	1s. brown	80	10
144/8	*Set of* 5	1·40	80

PRINTERS. The following stamps were printed by the Government Printer, Pretoria, in photogravure (Nos. 149/234) or lithography (subsequent issues), *unless stated otherwise.*

33 Queen Elizabeth II and *Catophracties Alexandri*

1953 (2 June). *Coronation. T* **33** *and similar horiz designs. W* **9** *of South Africa. P* 14.

149	1d. bright carmine	75	10
150	2d. deep bluish green	75	10
151	4d. magenta	1·60	55
152	6d. dull ultramarine	1·75	1·00
153	1s. deep orange-brown	1·75	40
149/53	*Set of* 5	6·00	1·90

Designs:—2d. *Bauhinia macrantha*, 4d. *Caralluma nebrownii*, 6d. *Gloriosa virescens*, 1s. *Rhigozum tricholotum*.

34 "Two Bucks" (rock painting)

36 "Rhinoceros Hunt" (rock painting)

38 Karakul Lamb

39 Ovambo Woman blowing Horn

(Des O. Schroeder (1d, to 4d.), M. Vandenschen (4½d. to 10s.))

1954 (15 Nov). *T* **34, 36, 38/9** *and similar designs. W* **9** *of South Africa (sideways on vert designs). P* 14.

154	1d. brown-red	20	10
155	2d. deep brown	35	10
156	3d. dull purple	1·75	10
157	4d. blackish olive	1·25	10
158	4½d. deep blue	1·25	15
159	6d. myrtle-green	1·25	10
160	1s. deep mauve	1·25	15
161	1s. 3d. cerise	4·50	30
162	1s. 6d. purple	4·50	35
163	2s. 6d. bistre-brown	6·00	60
164	5s. deep bright blue	13·00	2·75
165	10s. deep myrtle-green	38·00	15·00
154/65	*Set of* 12	65·00	18·00

Designs: *Vert (as T* **34**)–2d. "White Lady" (rock painting). *(As T* **38**)—2s. 6d. Lioness; 5s. Gemsbok; 10s. African Elephant. *(As T* **39**)—1s. Ovambo woman; 1s. 3d. Herero woman; 1s. 6d. Ovambo girl. *Horiz (as T* **36**)—4d. "White Elephant and Giraffe" (rock painting).

1960 *As Nos.* 154/7, 162, *but W* **102** *of South Africa (sideways on vert designs). P* 14.

166	1d. brown-red	55	45
167	2d. deep brown	70	50
168	3d. dull purple	1·40	1·25
169	4d. blackish olive	4·25	4·50
170	1s. 6d. purple	15·00	15·00
166/70	*Set of* 5	19·00	19·00

(New Currency. 100 cents=1 rand)

46 G.P.O. Windhoek

47 Finger Rock

48 Mounted Soldier Monument

49 Quivertree

50 S.W.A. House, Windhoek

50*a* Greater Flamingoes and Swakopmund Lighthouse

51 Fishing Industry

52 Greater Flamingo

53 German Lutheran Church, Windhoek

54 Diamond

55 Fort Namutoni

55*a* Hardap Dam

56 Topaz

57 Tourmaline

58 Heliodor

1961 (14 Feb)–**63**. *Unsurfaced paper. W* **102** *of South Africa (sideways on vert designs). P* 14.
171 **46** ½ c. brown and pale blue 50 10
172 **47** 1 c. sepia and reddish lilac 15 10
173 **48** 1½ c. slate-violet and salmon 20 10
174 **49** 2 c. deep green and yellow 40 10
175 **50** 2½ c. red-brown and light blue .. 35 10
176 **50*a*** 3 c. ultramarine and rose-red (1.10.62) 3·00 10
177 **51** 3½ c. indigo and blue-green 70 15
178 **52** 5 c. scarlet and grey-blue .. .. 2·75 10
179 **53** 7½ c. sepia and pale lemon 70 15
180 **54** 10 c. blue and greenish yellow .. 1·75 15
181 **55** 12½ c. indigo and lemon 85 20
182 **55*a*** 15 c. chocolate and light blue (16.3.63) 10·00 2·75
183 **56** 20 c. brown and red-orange .. .. 4·50 25
184 **57** 50 c. deep bluish green & yellow-orge 8·00 1·25
185 **58** 1 r. yellow, maroon and blue .. 12·00 8·50
171/185 .. .. *Set of* 15 40·00 12·00
See also Nos. 186/91, 202/16, 224/6 and 240.

1962–66. *As No.* 171, *etc., but without watermark.*
186 **46** ½ c. brown and pale blue (8.62) .. 40 70
187 **48** 1½ c. slate-violet and salmon (9.62) .. 2·50 35
188 **49** 2 c. deep green and yellow (5.62) .. 1·50 55
189 **50** 2½ c. red-brown and light blue (1964) .. 2·25 60
190 **51** 3½ c. indigo and blue-green (1966) .. 7·50 3·75
191 **52** 5 c. scarlet and grey-blue (9.62) .. 3·50 35
186/91 .. .. *Set of* 6 16·00 5·75

59 "Agricultural Development"

60 Centenary Emblem and Map

61 Centenary Emblem and part of Globe

1963 (16 Mar). *Opening of Hardap Dam. W* **102** *of South Africa (sideways). P* 14.
192 **59** 3 c. chocolate and light green 25 15

1963 (30 Aug). *Centenary of Red Cross. P* 14.
193 **60** 7½ c. red, black and light blue .. .. 6·00 3·00
194 **61** 15 c. red, black and orange-brown .. 9·00 5·00

62 Interior of Assembly Hall

63 Calvin

1964 (14 May). *Opening of Legislative Assembly Hall, Windhoek. W* **102** *of South Africa. P* 14.
195 **62** 3 c. ultramarine and salmon 40 10

1964 (1 Oct). 400*th Death Anniv of Calvin (Protestant reformer). P* 14.
196 **63** 2½ c. brown-purple and gold 30 5
197 15 c. deep bluish green and gold .. .. 1·75 75

64 Mail Runner of 1890

65 Kurt von François (founder)

66 Dr. H. Vedder

(Des D. Aschenborn)

1965 (18 Oct). 75*th Anniv of Windhoek. Chalk-surfaced paper. W* **127** *of South Africa (sideways). P* 14.
198 **64** 3 c. sepia and scarlet 40 10
199 **65** 15 c. red-brown and blue-green .. .. 1·00 65

1966 (4 July). 90*th Birth Anniv of Dr. H. Vedder (philosopher and writer). Chalk-surfaced paper. W* **127** *of South Africa (sideways). P* 14.
200 **66** 3 c. blackish green and salmon .. 35 10
201 15 c. deep sepia and light blue 75 50
Nos. 200/1 exist on Swiss-made paper with *tête-bêche* watermark from a special printing made for use in presentation albums for delegates to the U.P.U. Congress in Tokyo in 1969, as supplies of the original Harrison paper were by then exhausted (*Set of 2 price £17 mint*).

1966–72. *As* 1961–66 *but chalk-surfaced paper and W* **127** *of South Africa* (sideways on vert designs).*
202 **46** ½ c. brown and pale blue (1967) .. 90 10
203 **47** 1 c. sepia and light reddish lilac (1967) 50 10
a. Grey-brown and lilac (9.72) .. 85 10
204 **48** 1½ c. slate-violet and salmon (1968) .. 5·00 25
205 **49** 2 c. deep bluish green and yellow .. 1·00 10
206 **50** 2½ c. dp red-brown & lt turquoise-blue 75 10
a. Dp red-brown & pale blue (1967) 40 10
207 **50*a*** 3 c. ultramarine and rose-red (1970) 4·50 30
208 **51** 3½ c. indigo and blue-green (1967) .. 3·50 1·75
209 **50** 4 c. dp red-brown & lt turq-bl (1.4.71) 1·50 1·00
210 **52** 5 c. scarlet and grey-blue (1968) .. 2·50 10
211 **53** 6 c. sepia & greenish yellow (31.8.71) 6·50 5·00
212 7½ c. sepia and pale lemon (1967) .. 1·75 20
213 **55** 9 c. indigo & greenish yellow (1.7.71) 6·50 4·75
214 **54** 10 c. brt blue & greenish yellow (6.70) 9·00 90
a. Whiter background† (9.72) .. 9·50 75
215 **55*a*** 15 c. chocolate and light blue (1.72) .. 10·00 4·00
216 **56** 20 c. brown and red-orange (1968) .. 8·00 65
202/16 .. .. *Set of* 15 55·00 17·00
*The watermark in this issue is indistinct but the stamps can be distinguished from the stamps without watermark by their shades and the chalk-surfaced paper which is appreciably thicker and whiter. The 1, 1½, 3, 4, 5, 6, 9, 10, 15 and 20 c. are known only with the watermark *tête-bêche* but the ½ c. and 2½ c. exist with both forms, the remainder being as illustrated.
† No. 214a, printed from sheets, has a much whiter background around the value and behind "SOUTH WEST AFRICA" compared with No. 214, which was issued in coils only.
See also Nos. 224/6 and 240.

67 Camelthorn Tree

(Des D. Aschenborn (2½ c., 3 c.), Govt Printer, Pretoria (15 c.))

1967 (6 Jan). *Verwoerd Commemoration. Chalk-surfaced paper. T* **67** *and similar designs. W* **127** *of South Africa (sideways on vert designs). P* 14.
217 2½ c. black and emerald-green 20 10
218 3 c. brown and new blue 25 10
219 15 c. blackish brown and reddish purple .. 70 45
217/19 .. .. *Set of* 3 1·00 60
Designs: *Vert.*—3 c. Waves breaking against rock; 15 c. Dr. H. F. Verwoerd.

70 President Swart

71 President and Mrs. Swart

1968 (2 Jan). *Swart Commemoration. Chalk-surfaced paper. W* **127** *of South Africa (tête-bêche, sideways). P* 14 × 15.
220 **70** 3 c. orange-red, black & turquoise-blue
G. Inscribed in German 45 15
A. Inscribed in Afrikaans 45 15
E. Inscribed in English 45 15
221 **71** 15 c. red, blackish olive and dull green
G. Inscribed in German .. .. 1·50 1·75
A. Inscribed in Afrikaans .. .. 1·50 1·75
E. Inscribed in English .. .. 1·50 1·75
a. Red, brownish olive & bronze-green
G. Inscribed in German .. .. 3·00 2·25
A. Inscribed in Afrikaans .. .. 3·00 2·25
E. Inscribed in English .. .. 3·00 2·25
220/1 .. .. *Set of* 2 *values in strips of three* 10·00
Set of 6 *singles* 5·00 5·00
The three languages appear, *se-tenant*, both horizontally and vertically, throughout the sheet.

1970 (14 Feb). *Water 70 Campaign. As Nos.* 299/300 *of South Africa, but without phosphor band and inscr* "SWA".
222 2½ c. green, bright blue and chocolate .. 50 15
223 3 c. Prussian blue, royal blue and buff .. 50 15

72 G.P.O., Windhoek

73 "Red Sand-dunes, Eastern South West Africa"

1970–71. *As Nos.* 202 *and* 204/5 *but* "POSGELD INKOMSTE" *omitted and larger figure of value as in T* **72**. *W* **127** *of South Africa (tête-bêche, sideways on* 1½ *and* 2 *c.).*
224 **72** ½ c. brown and pale blue (6.70) .. .. 1·25 20
225 – 1½ c. slate-violet and salmon (1.6.71) .. 11·00 8·50
226 – 2 c. deep bluish green and lemon (11.70) 1·25 20
224/6 .. .. *Set of* 3 12·00 8·50

1970 (24 Aug). 150*th Anniv of Bible Society of South Africa. As Nos.* 301/2 *of South Africa, but inscr* "SWA".
228 2½ c. multicoloured .. .. .. 1·50 10
229 12½ c. gold, black and blue .. .. 8·00 6·50
No. 228 has a phosphor frame, probably added in error.
A mint example of No. 229 exists with a second, blind, impression of the die-stamped features.

1971 (31 May). *"Interstex" Stamp Exhibition, Cape Town. As No.* 303A *of South Africa, but without phosphor frame and inscr* "SWA".
230 5 c. light greenish blue, black and pale yellow 4·50 1·50

1971 (31 May). *Tenth Anniv of Antarctic Treaty. As No.* 304 *of South Africa, but without phosphor frame, and inscr* "SWA".
231 12½ c. blue-black, greenish blue & orge-red 45·00 25·00

1971 (31 May). *Tenth Anniv of the South African Republic. As Nos.* 305/6 *of South Africa, but without phosphor frame, and inscr* "SWA".
232 2 c. pale flesh and brown-red .. .. 3·00 50
233 4 c. green and black .. .. .. 3·00 50

1972 (19 Sept). *Centenary of S.P.C.A. As No.* 312 *of South Africa, but inscr* "SWA".
234 5 c. multicoloured .. .. .. 3·00 35

WATERMARK. All issues from this date are on unwatermarked paper.

(Lettering by E. de Jong)

1973 (1 May). *Scenery. T* **73** *and similar multicoloured designs showing paintings by Adolph Jentsch. P* 11½ × 12½ (10 *and* 15 *c.*) *or* 12½ × 11½ (*others*).
235 2 c. Type **73** 75 75
236 4 c. "After the Rain" .. .. .. 1·25 1·25
237 5 c. "Barren Country" .. .. .. 1·50 1·50
238 10 c. "Schaap River" (*vert*) .. .. 2·75 2·75
239 15 c. "Namib Desert" (*vert*) .. .. 4·00 4·00
235/9 .. .. *Set of* 5 9·00 9·00

1973 (28 May). *As Nos.* 207 *but without wmk. Phosphorised paper.*
240 **50*a*** 3 c. ultramarine and rose-red .. .. 2·00 1·25
No. 240 is also distinguishable in that the lettering of "SOUTH WEST AFRICA" is whiter.

74 *Sarcocaulon rigidum*

75 *Euphorbia virosa*

(Des D. Findlay)

1973 (1 Sept)–**79**. *Succulents. Various multicoloured designs as T* **74/5**. *Phosphorised glossy paper (original printing of all values) or ordinary paper* (1, 2, 3, 4, 5, 9, 10, 15, 20, 30, 50 *c.*).

(*a*) *As T* **74**. *P* 12½.
241 1 c. Type **74** 15 10
a. Black (face value, etc.) omitted £120
242 2 c. *Lapidaria margaretae* 50 15
a. Perf 14 × 13½ (4.8.79) 20 10
243 3 c. *Titanopsis schwantesii* 20 10
a. Black (face value, etc.) omitted £120
b. Perf 14 × 13½ (8.8.79) 25 15
244 4 c. *Lithops karasmontana* 25 10
245 5 c. *Caralluma lugardii* 40 15
a. Black (face value, etc.) omitted £120
b. Perf 14 × 13½ (12.12.79) 40 20
246 6 c. *Dinteranthus microspermus* 35 15

247 7 c. *Conophytum gratum* 35 25
248 9 c. *Huernia oculata* 50 20
249 10 c. *Gasteria pillansii* 50 25
a. Black (face value, etc.) omitted £200
b. Perf 14 × 13½ (13.8.79) 40 30
250 14 c. *Stapelia pedunculata* 70 45
251 15 c. *Fenestraria aurantiaca* 65 25
252 20 c. *Decabelone grandiflora* .. .. .. 3·00 30
253 25 c. *Hoodia bainii* .. .. 1·75 70

(*b*) *As T* **75**. *P* 11½ × 12½ (30 *c*., 1 *r*.) *or* 12½ × 11½ (50 *c*.)
254 30 c. Type **75** 85 50
a. Perf 13½ × 14 (27.12.79) 90 90
255 50 c. *Pachypodium namaquanum* (*vert*) .. 1·25 2·00
a. Perf 14 × 13½ (18.12.79) .. .. 1·50 1·50
256 1 r. *Welwitschia bainesii* .. .. 2·00 3·00
241/56 .. .. *Set of* 16 11·50 7·00

1973 (1 Sept)–**80**. *Coil stamps. As Nos.* 241/2 *and* 245 *but photo, colours changed. P* 14.
257 1 c. black and light mauve 40 20
a. Chalk-surfaced paper (7.76?) 30 15
b. Imperf × perf 14. Chalk-surfaced paper (1980) .. .. 1·75 1·75
258 2 c. black and yellow 30 15
a. Chalk-surfaced paper (7.76?) 40 15
b. Imperf × perf 14. Chalk-surfaced paper (1.79) 55 20
259 5 c. black and light rose-red 70 25
a. Imperf × perf 14. Chalk-surfaced paper (8.2.78) 75 30
257/9 .. .. *Set of* 3 1·10 55

Coils of Nos. 257b, 258b and 259a come with every fifth stamp numbered on the reverse.

76 Chat-shrike

77 Giraffe, Antelope and Spoor

(Des D. Findlay)

1974 (13 Feb). *Rare Birds. T* **76** *and similar vert designs. Multicoloured. P* 12½ × 11½.
260 4 c. Type **76** .. .. 2·50 65
261 5 c. Peach-faced Lovebirds .. .. .. 2·75 95
262 10 c. Damaraland Rock Jumper .. .. 7·00 3·00
263 15 c. Rüppell's Parrots .. .. .. 11·00 7·50
260/3 .. .. *Set of* 4 21·00 11·00

(Des O. Schröder)

1974 (10 Apr). *Twyfelfontein Rock-engravings. T* **77** *and similar multicoloured designs. P* 11½ × 12½ (15 *c*.) *or* 12½ (*others*).
264 4 c. Type **77** .. .. 1·25 50
265 5 c. Elephant, hyena, antelope and spoor .. 1·50 80
a. Black (value and "SWA") omitted .. £550
266 15 c. Kudu Cow (38 × 21 *mm*) .. .. 6·00 4·75
264/6 .. .. *Set of* 3 8·00 5·50

78 Cut Diamond

79 Wagons and Map of the Trek

(Des M. Barnett)

1974 (30 Sept). *Diamond Mining. T* **78** *and similar vert design. Multicoloured. P* 12½ × 11½.
267 10 c. Type **78** .. .. 4·00 2·25
268 15 c. Diagram of shore workings .. .. 4·50 3·25

(Des K. Esterhuysen)

1974 (13 Nov). *Centenary of Thirstland Trek. P* 11½ × 12½.
269 **79** 4 c. multicoloured 85 50

80 Peregrine Falcon

81 Kolmannskop (ghost town)

(Des D. Findlay)

1975 (19 Mar). *Protected Birds of Prey. T* **80** *and similar vert designs. Multicoloured. P* 12½ × 11½.
270 4 c. Type **80** .. .. 1·50 55
271 5 c. Verreaux's Eagle .. .. .. 1·75 70
272 10 c. Martial Eagle .. .. 5·00 3·25
273 15 c. Egyptian Vulture .. .. .. 6·50 5·00
270/3 .. .. *Set of* 4 13·00 8·50

(Des A. H. Barrett)

1975 (23 July). *Historic Monuments. T* **81** *and similar horiz designs. Multicoloured. P* 11½ × 12½.
274 5 c. Type **81** 20 10
275 9 c. "Martin Luther" (steam tractor) 40 40
276 15 c. Kurt von Francois and Old Fort, Windhoek 80 60
274/6 .. .. *Set of* 3 1·25 1·00

82 "View of Lüderitz"

(Des J. Hoekstra)

1975 (15 Oct). *Otto Schröder. T* **82** *and similar horiz designs showing his paintings. Multicoloured. P* 11½ × 12½.
277 15 c. Type **82** 55 45
a. Block of 4. Nos. 277/80 .. .. 2·00
278 15 c. "View of Swakopmund" 55 45
279 15 c. "Harbour Scene" 55 45
280 15 c. "Quayside, Walvis Bay" 55 45
277/80 .. .. *Set of* 4 2·00 1·60
MS281 122 × 96 mm. Nos. 277/80 .. .. 2·25 4·50

Nos. 277/80 were printed together, in *se-tenant* blocks of four within the sheet.

83 Elephants

(Des H. Pager)

1976 (31 Mar). *Prehistoric Rock Paintings. T* **83** *and similar horiz designs. Multicoloured. P* 11½ × 12½.
282 4 c. Type **83** 40 10
283 10 c. Rhinoceros 65 30
284 15 c. Antelope 80 50
285 20 c. Man with bow and arrow .. .. 1·10 70
282/5 .. .. *Set of* 4 2·75 1·40
MS286 121 × 95 mm. Nos. 282/5 .. .. 2·75 3·75

84 Schwerinsburg

(Des H. Pager)

1976 (14 May). *Castles. T* **84** *and similar horiz designs. Multicoloured. P* 11½ × 12½.
287 10 c. Type **84** 50 25
288 15 c. Schloss Duwisib 70 40
289 20 c. Heynitzburg .. .. .. 1·00 60
287/9 .. .. *Set of* 3 2·00 1·10

85 Large-toothed Rock Hyrax

(Des D. Findlay)

1976 (16 July). *Fauna Conservation. T* **85** *and similar horiz designs. Multicoloured. P* 11½ × 12½.
290 4 c. Type **85** 50 20
291 10 c. Kirk's Dik-Dik .. .. .. 1·50 60
292 15 c. Kuhl's Tree Squirrel .. .. .. 2·25 1·10
290/2 .. .. *Set of* 3 3·75 1·75

86 The Augustineum, Windhoek

(Des H. Pager)

1976 (17 Sept). *Modern Buildings. T* **86** *and similar horiz design. P* 11½ × 12½.
293 15 c. black and yellow 30 30
294 20 c. black and light yellow 40 35

Design:—20 c. Katutura Hospital, Windhoek.

87 Ovambo Water Canal System

(Des A. H. Barrett)

1976 (19 Nov). *Water and Electricity Supply. T* **87** *and similar horiz design. Multicoloured. P* 11½ × 12½.
295 15 c. Type **87** 30 30
296 20 c. Ruacana Falls Power Station 40 40

88 Coastline near Pomona

(Des A. H. Barrett)

1977 (29 Mar). *Namib Desert. T* **88** *and similar horiz designs. Multicoloured. P* 12½.
297 4 c. Type **88** 20 15
298 10 c. Bush and dunes, Sossusvlei 30 30
299 15 c. Plain near Brandberg 50 40
300 20 c. Dunes, Sperr Gebiet 60 45
297/300 .. .. *Set of* 4 1·40 1·10

89 Kraal

(Des A. H. Barrett)

1977 (15 July). *The Ovambo People. T* **89** *and similar horiz designs. P* 11½ × 12½.
301 4 c. multicoloured 10 10
302 10 c. black, dull orange and cinnamon .. 30 10
303 15 c. multicoloured 30 15
304 20 c. multicoloured 35 30
301/4 .. .. *Set of* 4 95 60

Designs—10 c. Grain baskets; 15 c. Pounding grain; 20 c. Women in tribal dress.

90 Terminal Buildings

(Des H. Pager and A. H. Barrett)

1977 (22 Aug). *J. G. Strijdom Airport, Windhoek. P* 12½.
305 **90** 20 c. multicoloured 30 30

91 Drostdy, Lüderitz

92 Side-winding Adder

(Des A. H. Barrett)

1977 (4 Nov). *Historic Houses. T* **91** *and similar horiz designs. Multicoloured. P* 12 × 12½.
306 5 c. Type **91** 15 10
307 10 c. Woermannhaus, Swakopmund 40 25
308 15 c. Neu-Heusis, Windhoek 45 25
309 20 c. Schmelenhaus, Bethanie 65 30
306/9 .. .. *Set of* 4 1·50 80
MS310 122 × 96 mm. Nos. 306/9 .. .. 1·50 2·25

(Des D. Findlay)

1978 (6 Feb). *Small Animals. T* **92** *and similar horiz designs. Multicoloured. P* 12½.
311 4 c. Type **92** 15 10
312 10 c. Grant's Desert Golden Mole 30 20
313 15 c. Palmato Gecko 50 20
314 20 c. Namaqua Chameleon 65 25
311/14 .. .. *Set of* 4 1·40 60

93 Ostrich Hunting

(Des A. H. Barrett)

1978 (14 Apr). *The Bushmen. T* **93** *and similar horiz designs in light grey-brown, stone and black. P* 12 × 12½.
315 4 c. Type **93** 15 10
316 10 c. Woman carrying fruit 25 10
317 15 c. Hunters kindling fire 35 15
318 20 c. Woman with musical instrument 40 30
315/18 .. .. *Set of* 4 1·00 55

ALGEMENE
STEMREG

94 Lutheran Church, Windhoek (**95**)

(Des A. H. Barrett)

1978 (16 June). *Historic Churches. T* **94** *and similar horiz designs. P* 12½.

319 4 c. grey-black and cinnamon 10 10
320 10 c. grey-black and ochre 15 10
321 15 c. grey-black and light brown-rose .. 20 15
322 20 c. grey-black and light grey-blue .. 30 20
319/22 .. .. *Set of* 4 65 50
MS323 125 × 90 mm. Nos. 319/22 .. .. 1·00 1·75

Designs:—10 c. Lutheran Church, Swakopmund; 15 c. Rhenish Mission Church, Otjimbingwe; 20 c. Rhenish Missionary Church Keetmanshoop.

1978 (1 Nov). *Universal Suffrage. Designs as Nos.* 244/5, 249 *and* 251/3 *optd with T* **95** *(or similar inscr in English or German).*

324 4 c. *Lithops karasmontana* .. .. ..
A. Opt in Afrikaans 10 10
E. Opt in English 10 10
G. Opt in German 10 10
325 5 c. *Caralluma lugardii* .. .. ..
A. Opt in Afrikaans 10 10
E. Opt in English 10 10
G. Opt in German 10 10
326 10 c. *Gasteria pillansii* .. .. ..
A. Opt in Afrikaans 10 10
E. Opt in English 10 10
G. Opt in German 10 10
327 15 c. *Fenestraria aurantiaca* .. ..
A. Opt in Afrikaans 15 15
E. Opt in English 15 15
G. Opt in German 15 15
328 20 c. *Decabelone grandiflora* .. ..
A. Opt in Afrikaans 20 20
E. Opt in English 20 20
G. Opt in German 20 20
329 25 c. *Hoodia bainni* .. .. ..
A. Opt in Afrikaans 25 25
E. Opt in English 25 25
G. Opt in German 25 25
324/9 .. .. *Set of* 18 (6 *strips of* 3) 2·40 2·40

Nos. 324A/G, 325A/G, 326A/G, 327A/G, 328A/G and 329A/G were each printed together, *se-tenant*, in horizontal and vertical strips of 3 throughout the sheets.

96 Greater Flamingo **97** Silver Topaz

(Des D. Findlay)

1979 (5 Apr). *Water Birds. T* **96** *and similar vert designs. Multicoloured. P* 14.

330 4 c. Type **96** 20 10
331 15 c. White-breasted Cormorant 45 20
332 20 c. Chestnut-banded Sand Plover 50 25
333 25 c. Eastern White Pelican 55 30
330/3 .. .. *Set of* 4 1·50 75

(Des H. Botha)

1979 (26 Nov). *Gemstones. T* **97** *and similar horiz designs. Multicoloured. P* 14.

334 4 c. Type **97** 25 10
335 15 c. Aquamarine 55 20
336 20 c. Malachite 60 25
337 25 c. Amethyst 60 30
334/7 .. .. *Set of* 4 1·75 75

98 Killer Whale **99** Impala

(Des A. H. Barrett)

1980 (25 Mar). *Whales. T* **98** *and similar multicoloured designs. P* 14.

338 4 c. Type **98** 35 10
339 5 c. Humpback Whale (38 × 22 *mm*) .. 40 10
340 10 c. Black Right Whale (38 × 22 *mm*) .. 55 30
341 15 c. Sperm Whale (58 × 22 *mm*) .. 1·00 60
342 20 c. Fin Whale (58 × 22 *mm*) .. .. 1·25 80
343 25 c. Blue Whale (88 × 22 *mm*) .. .. 1·60 1·10
338/43 .. .. *Set of* 6 4·50 2·75
MS344 202 × 95 mm. Nos. 338/43 .. .. 5·50 6·00

(Des P. Bosman)

1980 (25 June). *25th Anniv of Division of Nature Conservation and Tourism. Antelopes. T* **99** *and similar horiz designs. Multicoloured. P* 14.

345 5 c. Type **99** 15 5
346 10 c. Topi 20 10
347 15 c. Roan Antelope 40 15
348 20 c. Sable Antelope 50 20
345/8 .. .. *Set of* 4 1·10 45

100 Black-backed Jackal **101** Meerkat

(Des Sheila Nowers (11, 12, 14, 16 c.), P. Bosman (others))

1980 (1 Oct)–**88**. *Wildlife. Multicoloured designs as T* **100**. *Chalk-surfaced paper* (14 c., 16 c.) *or ordinary paper (others). P* 14.

349 1 c. Type **100** 10 10
a. Chalk-surfaced paper (11.6.85) .. 20 20
350 2 c. Hunting Dog 15 10
a. Chalk-surfaced paper (4.6.86) .. 25 25
351 3 c. Brown Hyena 10 10
a. Chalk-surfaced paper (10.2.88) .. 20 25
352 4 c. Springbok 10 10
a. Chalk-surfaced paper (29.7.87) .. 20 25
353 5 c. Gemsbok 10 10
a. Chalk-surfaced paper (11.6.85) .. 30 30
354 6 c. Greater Kudu 10 10
a. Chalk-surfaced paper (8.8.88) .. 20 25
355 7 c. Mountain Zebra (*horiz*) 20 20
a. Chalk-surfaced paper (19.3.86) .. 20 25
356 8 c. Cape Porcupine (*horiz*) 10 10
a. Chalk-surfaced paper (11.6.85) .. 25 25
357 9 c. Ratel (*horiz*) 15 10
a. Chalk-surfaced paper (10.2.88) .. 20 20
358 10 c. Cheetah (*horiz*) 15 10
358*a* 11 c. Blue Wildebeest (2.4.84) 15 20
358*b* 12 c. African Buffalo (*horiz*) (1.4.85) .. 25 25
ba. Booklet pane of 10 with margins all round (1.8.85) .. .. .. 2·25
358*c* 14 c. Caracal (*horiz*) (1.4.86) 35 35
359 15 c. Hippopotamus (*horiz*) 15 10
a. Chalk-surfaced paper (10.2.88) .. 15 20
359*b* 16 c. Warthog (*horiz*) (1.4.87) 30 30
360 20 c. Eland (*horiz*) 15 10
a. Chalk-surfaced paper (11.6.85) .. 15 15
361 25 c. Black Rhinoceros (*horiz*) 20 20
a. Chalk-surfaced paper (11.6.85) .. 20 25
362 30 c. Lion (*horiz*) 25 20
a. Chalk-surfaced paper (4.6.86) .. 25 30
363 50 c. Giraffe 30 30
a. Chalk-surfaced paper (21.4.88) .. 40 45
364 1 r. Leopard 70 55
a. Chalk-surfaced paper (4.6.86) .. 60 65
365 2 r. African Elephant 85 90
a. Chalk-surfaced paper (10.2.88) .. 1·00 1·25
349/65 .. .. *Set of* 21 4·25 4·00

(Des P. Bosman. Photo)

1980 (1 Oct). *Coil stamps. Wildlife. Vert designs as T* **101**. *Imperf × perf* 14.

366 1 c. yellow-brown 10 10
367 2 c. deep dull blue 10 10
368 5 c. yellow-olive 10 10
366/8 .. .. *Set of* 3 20 20

Designs:—2 c. Savanna Monkey; 5 c. Chacma Baboon.

102 Von Bach

(Des A. H. Barrett)

1980 (25 Nov). *Water Conservation. Dams. T* **102** *and similar horiz designs. Multicoloured. P* 14.

369 5 c. Type **102** 10 10
370 10 c. Swakoppoort 15 10
371 15 c. Naute 20 20
372 20 c. Hardap 25 25
369/72 .. .. *Set of* 4 60 60

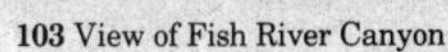

103 View of Fish River Canyon **104** *Aloe erinacea*

(Des A. H. Barrett)

1981 (20 Mar). *Fish River Canyon. T* **103** *and similar horiz designs showing various views of canyon. P* 14.

373 5 c. multicoloured 10 10
374 15 c. multicoloured 20 20
375 20 c. multicoloured 25 25
376 25 c. multicoloured 30 30
373/6 .. .. *Set of* 4 75 70

(Des D. Findlay)

1981 (14 Aug). *Aloes. T* **104** *and similar vert designs. Multicoloured. P* 14 × 13½.

377 5 c. Type **104** 10 10
378 15 c. *Aloe viridiflora* 25 20
379 20 c. *Aloe pearsonii* 30 25
380 25 c. *Aloe littoralis* 30 25
377/80 .. .. *Set of* 4 85 65

105 Paul Weiss-Haus

(Des A. H. Barrett)

1981 (16 Oct). *Historic Buildings of Lüderitz. T* **105** *and similar horiz designs. Multicoloured. P* 14.

381 5 c. Type **105** 10 10
382 15 c. Deutsche Afrika Bank 20 20
383 20 c. Schroederhaus 30 30
384 25 c. Altes Postamt 30 35
381/4 .. .. *Set of* 4 75 80
MS385 125 × 90 mm. Nos. 381/4 .. .. 85 90

106 Salt Pan **107** Kalahari Starred Tortoise (*Psammobates oculifer*)

(Des A. H. Barrett)

1981 (4 Dec). *Salt Industry. T* **106** *and similar horiz designs. Multicoloured. P* 14.

386 5 c. Type **106** 10 10
387 15 c. Dumping and washing 20 20
388 20 c. Loading by conveyor 25 30
389 25 c. Dispatch to refinery 30 35
386/9 .. .. *Set of* 4 70 80

(Des A. H. Barrett)

1982 (12 Mar). *Tortoises. T* **107** *and similar horiz designs. Multicoloured. P* 14.

390 5 c. Type **107** 10 10
391 15 c. Leopard Tortoise (*Geochelone pardalis*) .. 20 20
392 20 c. Angulate Tortoise (*Chersina angulata*) .. 25 30
393 25 c. Speckled Padloper (*Homopus signatus*) .. 30 35
390/3 .. .. *Set of* 4 70 80

108 Mythical Sea-monster

(Des Sheila Nowers)

1982 (28 May). *Discoverers of South West Africa. (1st series). Bartolomeu Dias. T* **108** *and similar horiz designs. Multicoloured. P* 14.

394 15 c. Type **108** 20 20
395 20 c. Bartolomeu Dias and map of Africa showing voyage 30 30
396 25 c. Dias' caravel 45 40
397 30 c. Dias erecting commemorative cross, Angra das Voltas, 25 July 1488 .. 45 45
394/7 .. .. *Set of* 4 1·25 1·25

See also Nos. 455/8.

109 Brandberg **110** Otjikaeva Head-dress of Herero Woman

(Des A. H. Barrett)

1982 (3 Aug). *Mountains of South West Africa. T* **109** *and similar horiz designs. Multicoloured. P* 13½ × 14.
398 6 c. Type **109** 10 10
399 15 c. Omatako 20 20
400 20 c. Die Nadel 25 30
401 25 c. Spitzkuppe 30 35
398/401 .. .. *Set of* 4 75 85

(Des A. H. Barrett)

1982 (15 Oct). *Traditional Head-dresses of South West Africa. (1st series). T* **110** *and similar vert designs. Multicoloured. P* 14.
402 6 c. Type **110** 10 10
403 15 c. Ekori head-dress of Himba 25 20
404 20 c. Oshikoma hair-piece and iipando plaits of Ngandjera 35 30
405 25 c. Omhatela head-dress of Kwanyama .. 35 35
402/5 .. .. *Set of* 4 95 85
See also Nos. 427/30.

111 Fort Vogelsang

112 Searching for Diamonds, Kolmanskop, 1908

(Des J. van Ellinckhuijzen)

1983 (16 Mar). *Centenary of Lüderitz. T* **111** *and similar designs. P* 14.
406 6 c. brownish black and deep carmine-red .. 10 10
407 20 c. brownish black and yellow-brown .. 25 30
408 25 c. brownish black and chestnut 30 35
409 30 c. brownish black and brown-purple .. 35 40
410 40 c. brownish black and bright green .. 50 55
406/10 .. .. *Set of* 5 1·40 1·50
Designs: *Vert* (23 × 29 *mm*)—20 c. Chief Joseph Fredericks; 30 c. Heinrich Vogelsang (founder); 40 c. Adolf Lüderitz (colonial promoter). *Horiz* (*As T* **111**)—25 c. Angra Pequena.

(Des J. van Ellinckhuijzen)

1983 (8 June). *75th Anniv of Discovery of Diamonds. T* **112** *and similar designs. P* 13½ × 14 (10, 20 *c.*) *or* 14 × 13½ (*others*).
411 10 c. deep brown and pale stone 15 15
412 20 c. maroon and pale stone 30 30
413 25 c. Prussian blue and pale stone 35 35
414 40 c. brownish black and pale stone 55 55
411/14 .. .. *Set of* 4 1·25 1·25
Designs: *Horiz* (34 × 19 *mm*)—20 c. Digging for diamonds, Kolmanskop, 1908. *Vert* (19 × 26 *mm*)—25 c. Sir Ernest Oppenheimer (industrialist); 40 c. August Stauch (prospector).

113 "Common Zebras drinking" (J. van Ellinckhuijzen)

114 The Rock Lobster

1983 (1 Sept). *Painters of South West Africa. T* **113** *and similar horiz designs. Multicoloured. P* 13½ × 14.
415 10 c. Type **113** 15 15
416 20 c. "Rossing Mountain" (H. Henckert) .. 25 30
417 25 c. "Stampeding African Buffalo" (F. Krampe) 30 35
418 40 c. "Erongo Mountains" (J. Blatt) 50 55
415/18 .. .. *Set of* 4 1·10 1·25

(Des J. van Ellinckhuijzen)

1983 (23 Nov). *Lobster Industry. T* **114** *and similar horiz designs. Multicoloured. P* 13½ × 14.
419 10 c. Type **114** 15 15
420 20 c. Mother ship and fishing dinghies .. 25 30
421 25 c. Netting lobsters from dinghy 30 35
422 40 c. Packing lobsters 50 55
419/22 .. .. *Set of* 4 1·10 1·25

115 Hohenzollern House

(Des A. H. Barrett)

1984 (8 Mar). *Historic Buildings of Swakopmund. T* **115** *and similar horiz designs. P* 14.
423 10 c. grey-black and orange-brown 15 15
424 20 c. grey-black and new blue 30 25
425 25 c. grey-black and yellow-green 30 30
426 30 c. grey-black and ochre 35 30
423/6 .. .. *Set of* 4 1·00 90
Designs:—20 c. Railway Station; 25 c. Imperial District Bureau; 30 c. Ritterburg.

(Des A. H. Barrett)

1984 (25 May). *Traditional Head-dresses of South West Africa (2nd series). Multicoloured designs as T* **110**. *P* 14.
427 11 c. Eendjushi head-dress of Kwambi .. 25 15
428 20 c. Bushman woman 40 25
429 25 c. Omulenda head-dress of Kwaluudhi .. 45 30
430 30 c. Mbukushu women 45 30
427/30 .. .. *Set of* 4 1·40 90

116 Map and German Flag

117 Sweet Thorn

(Des J. van Ellinckhuijzen)

1984 (7 Aug). *Centenary of German Colonisation. T* **116** *and similar horiz designs. Multicoloured. P* 14 × 14½.
431 11 c. Type **116** 25 15
432 25 c. Raising the German flag, 1884 .. 50 35
433 30 c. German Protectorate boundary marker 50 40
434 45 c. *Elizabeth* and *Leipzig* (German corvettes) .. .. 1·25 1·00
431/4 .. .. *Set of* 4 2·25 1·75

(Des Eva-Maria Linsmayer)

1984 (22 Nov). *Spring in South West Africa. T* **117** *and similar vert designs. Multicoloured. P* 14.
435 11 c. Type **117** 15 15
436 25 c. Camel Thorn 30 30
437 30 c. Hook Thorn 30 30
438 45 c. Candle-pod Acacia 45 45
435/8 .. .. *Set of* 4 1·10 1·10

118 Head of Ostrich

(Des J. van Ellinckhuijzen)

1985 (15 Mar). *Ostriches. T* **118** *and similar horiz designs. Multicoloured. P* 14.
439 11 c. Type **118** 20 10
440 25 c. Ostrich on eggs 40 20
441 30 c. Newly-hatched chick and eggs .. 50 35
442 50 c. Mating dance 70 55
439/42 .. .. *Set of* 4 1·60 1·10

119 Kaiserstrasse

(Des A. H. Barrett)

1985 (6 June). *Historic Buildings of Windhoek. T* **119** *and similar horiz designs. P* 14.
443 12 c. black and brown-ochre 10 10
444 25 c. black and grey-olive 20 20
445 30 c. black and brown 20 25
446 50 c. black and yellow-brown 50 55
443/6 .. .. *Set of* 4 90 1·00
Designs:—25 c. Turnhalle; 30 c. Old Supreme Court Building; 50 c. Railway Station.

120 Zwilling Locomotive

121 Lidumu-dumu (keyboard instrument)

(Des J. van Ellinckhuijzen)

1985 (2 Aug). *Narrow-gauge Railway Locomotives. T* **120** *and similar horiz designs. Multicoloured. P* 14.
447 12 c. Type **120** 25 10
448 25 c. Feldspur side-tank locomotive 40 20
449 30 c. Jung and Henschel side-tank locomotive 50 30
450 50 c. Henschel Hd locomotive 65 45
447/50 .. .. *Set of* 4 1·60 95

NEW INFORMATION

The editor is always interested to correspond with people who have new information that will improve or correct the Catalogue.

(Des J. van Ellinckhuijzen)

1985 (17 Oct). *Traditional Musical Instruments. T* **121** *and similar horiz designs. Multicoloured. P* 14.
451 12 c. Type **121** 10 10
452 25 c. Ngoma (drum) 15 20
453 30 c. Okambulumbumbwa (stringed instrument) 20 25
454 50 c. // Gwashi (stringed instrument) .. 30 35
451/4 .. .. *Set of* 4 65 80

122 Erecting Commemorative Pillar at Cape Cross, 1486

123 Ameib, Erongo Mountains

(Des J. van Ellinckhuijzen)

1986 (24 Jan). *Discoverers of South West Africa (2nd series). Diogo Cao. T* **122** *and similar horiz designs. P* 14.
455 12 c. black, brownish grey & deep dull green 15 10
456 20 c. black, brownish grey & pale red-brown 20 15
457 25 c. black, brownish grey and dull blue .. 25 20
458 30 c. black, brownish grey & dull reddish pur 35 25
455/8 .. .. *Set of* 4 85 60
Designs:—20 c. Diogo Cao's coat of arms; 25 c. Caravel; 30 c. Diogo Cao.

(Des J. van Niekerk)

1986 (24 Apr). *Rock Formations. T* **123** *and similar horiz designs. Multicoloured. P* 14.
459 14 c. Type **123** 30 15
460 20 c. Vingerklip, near Outjo 40 15
461 25 c. Petrified sand dunes, Kuiseb River .. 45 20
462 30 c. Orgelpfeifen, Twyfelfontein 50 25
459/62 .. .. *Set of* 4 1·50 65

124 Model wearing Swakara Coat

125 Pirogue, Lake Liambezi

(Des J. van Ellinckhuijzen)

1986 (10 July). *Karakul Industry. T* **124** *and similar vert designs. Multicoloured. P* 14.
463 14 c. Type **124** 20 15
464 20 c. Weaving karakul wool carpet 30 15
465 25 c. Flock of karakul ewes on veld 30 20
466 30 c. Karakul rams 35 25
463/6 .. .. *Set of* 4 1·10 65

1986 (6 Nov). *Life in the Caprivi Strip. T* **125** *and similar horiz designs. Multicoloured. P* 14.
467 14 c. Type **125** 30 15
468 20 c. Ploughing with oxen 45 20
469 25 c. Settlement in Eastern Caprivi 55 35
470 30 c. Map of Caprivi Strip 65 45
467/70 .. .. *Set of* 4 1·75 1·10

126 "Gobabis Mission Station", 1863

127 *Garreta nitens*

1987 (19 Feb). *Paintings by Thomas Baines. T* **126** *and similar horiz designs. Multicoloured. P* 14.
471 14 c. Type **126** 30 15
472 20 c. "Outspan at Koobie", 1861 .. .. 50 30
473 25 c. "Outspan under Oomahaama Tree", 1862 .. .. 55 45
474 30 c. "Swakop River", 1861 .. .. .. 65 60
471/4 .. .. *Set of* 4 1·75 1·40

(Des E. Holm)

1987 (7 May). *Useful Insects. T* **127** *and similar horiz designs. Multicoloured. P* 14.
475 16 c. Type **127** 30 15
476 20 c. *Alcimus stenurus* 45 30
477 25 c. *Anthophora caerulea* 55 45
478 30 c. *Hemiempusa capensis* 65 60
475/8 .. .. *Set of* 4 1·75 1·40

128 Okaukuejo

(Des J. van Niekerk)

1987 (23 July). *Tourist Camps. T* **128** *and similar horiz designs. Multicoloured. P* 14½×14.
479 16 c. Type **128** 20 10
480 20 c. Daan Viljoen 25 20
481 25 c. Ai-Ais 30 30
482 30 c. Hardap 30 30
479/82 . . . . *Set of* 4 95 80

129 Wreck of *Hope* (whaling schooner), 1804

130 Bartolomeu Dias

(Des Sheila Nowers)

1987 (15 Oct). *Shipwrecks. T* **129** *and similar horiz designs. Multicoloured. P* 14.
483 16 c. Type **129** 30 15
484 30 c. *Tilly*, 1885 . . . . . . 50 35
485 40 c. *Eduard Bohlen*, 1909 . . . . 60 45
486 50 c. *Dunedin Star*, 1942 . . . . 80 60
483/6 . . . . *Set of* 4 2·00 1·40

(Des Sheila Nowers)

1988 (7 Jan). *500th Anniv of Discovery of Cape of Good Hope by Bartolomeu Dias. T* **130** *and similar vert designs. Multicoloured. P* 14.
487 16 c. Type **130** 15 15
488 30 c. Caravel 30 25
489 40 c. Map of South West Africa, c. 1502 . . 40 30
490 50 c. King João II of Portugal 50 40
487/90 . . . . *Set of* 4 1·25 1·00

131 Sossusvlei

(Des J. van Niekerk)

1988 (3 Mar). *Landmarks of South West Africa. T* **131** *and similar horiz designs. Multicoloured. P* 14.
491 16 c. Type **131** 15 15
492 30 c. Sesriem Canyon 30 25
493 40 c. Hoaruseb "clay castles" 40 30
494 50 c. Hoba meteorite 50 40
491/4 . . . . *Set of* 4 1·25 1·00

MACHINE LABELS. From 3 March 1988 gummed labels in the above design numbered "PT01", ranging in value from 1 c. to 99 r. 99, were available from a machine located at the Windhoek Post Office. During March 1989 three further machines at Ausspanplatz (PT02), Swakopmund (PT03) and Keetmanshoop (PT04) were added.

132 First Postal Agency, Otyimbingue, 1888

133 Herero Chat

(Des H. Pulon)

1988 (7 July). *Centenary of Postal Service in South West Africa. T* **132** *and similar horiz designs. Multicoloured. P* 14.
495 16 c. Type **132** 15 10
496 30 c. Post Office, Windhoek, 1904 . . . . 25 20
497 40 c. Mail-runner and map 30 25
498 50 c. Camel mail, 1904 . . . . 35 30
495/8 . . . . *Set of* 4 95 70

(Des G. Arnott)

1988 (3 Nov). *Birds of South West Africa. T* **133** *and similar vert designs. Multicoloured. P* 14.
499 16 c. Type **133** 15 10
500 30 c. Gray's Lark 20 20
501 40 c. Rüppell's Bustard 25 25
502 50 c. Monteiro's Hornbill 25 30
499/502 . . . . *Set of* 4 75 75

134 Dr. C. H. Hahn and Gross-Barmen Mission

135 Beechcraft "1900"

(Des H. Pulon)

1989 (16 Feb). *Missionaries. T* **134** *and similar horiz designs. Multicoloured. P* 14.
503 16 c. Type **134** 15 10
504 30 c. Revd. J. G. Krönlein and Berseba Mission 20 20
505 40 c. Revd. F. H. Kleinschmidt and Rehoboth Mission 25 25
506 50 c. Revd. J. H. Schmelen and Bethanien Mission 30 30
503/6 . . . . *Set of* 4 80 75

(Des M. Botha)

1989 (18 May). *75th Anniv of Aviation in South West Africa. T* **135** *and similar horiz designs. Multicoloured. P* 14.
507 18 c. Type **135** 15 15
508 30 c. Ryan "Navion" 25 25
509 40 c. Junkers "F13" 30 30
510 50 c. Pfalz "Otto" biplane 40 40
507/10 . . . . *Set of* 4 1·00 1·00

136 Barchan Dunes

(Des A. H. Barrett)

1989 (14 Aug). *Namib Desert Sand Dunes. T* **136** *and similar horiz designs. Multicoloured. P* 14.
511 18 c. Barchan dunes 15 15
512 30 c. Star dunes (36×20 *mm*) 25 25
513 40 c. Transverse dunes 30 30
514 50 c. Crescentic dunes (36×20 *mm*) . . 40 40
511/14 . . . . *Set of* 4 1·00 1·00

137 Ballot Box and Outline Map of South West Africa

1989 (24 Aug). *South West Africa Constitutional Election. P* 14.
515 **137** 18 c. purple-brown and salmon . . 15 15
516 35 c. deep grey-blue and pale emerald 25 25
517 45 c. plum and lemon 30 30
518 60 c. dull green and deep yellow-ochre 40 40
515/18 . . . . *Set of* 4 1·00 1·00

138 Gypsum

139 Oranjemund Alluvial Diamond Field

(Des J. van Niekerk)

1989 (16 Nov). *Minerals. T* **138/9** *and similar multicoloured designs. P* 14.
519 1 c. Type **138** 10 10
520 2 c. Fluorite 10 10
521 5 c. Mimetite 10 10
522 7 c. Cuprite 10 10
523 10 c. Azurite 10 10
524 18 c. Boltwoodite 10 10
525 20 c. Dioptase 10 10
526 25 c. Type **139** 10 15
527 30 c. Tsumeb lead and copper complex . . 15 20
528 35 c. Rosh Pinah zinc mine 15 20
529 40 c. Diamonds 20 25
530 45 c. Wulfenite 20 25
531 50 c. Uis tin mine 20 25
532 1 r. Rössing uranium mine 40 50
533 2 r. Gold 85 90
519/33 . . . . *Set of* 15 2·50 2·75

The 1, 2, 5, 7, 10, 18, 20, 40, 45 c. and 2 r. are vertical as T **138**, and the 25, 30, 35, 50 c. and 1 r. horizontal as T **139**.

140 Arrow Poison

(Des Eva-Maria Linsmayer)

1990 (1 Feb). *Flora. T* **140** *and similar vert designs. Multicoloured. P* 14.
534 18 c. Type **140** 10 10
535 35 c. Baobab flower 20 25
536 45 c. Sausage Tree flowers 20 25
537 60 c. Devil's Claw 30 35
534/7 . . . . *Set of* 4 65 75

POSTAGE DUE STAMPS

Postage Due stamps of Transvaal or South Africa overprinted

1923. *Optd with T 1 and 2 alternately.*

I. *14 mm between lines of overprint. (a) On stamps of Transvaal*

		Un pair	Us pair
D1	5d. black and violet	4·00	22·00
	a. "Wes" for "West"	£100	
	b. "Afrika" (no stop)	55·00	
D2	6d. black and red-brown	13·00	25·00
	a. "Wes" for "West"	£140	
	b. "Afrika" (no stop)	90·00	

(b) On South Africa stamps (De La Rue printing)

D3	2d. black and violet	10·00	18·00
	a. "Wes" for "West"	£100	£120
	b. "Afrika" (no stop)	£100	
D4	3d. black and blue	6·00	18·00
	a. "Wes" for "West"	80·00	
D5	6d. black and slate	17·00	26·00
	a. "Wes" for "West"	70·00	

(c) On South Africa stamps (Pretoria printing)

(i) *Type* D 1 (A). *Rouletted*

D6	1d. black and rose	4·00	11·00
	a. "Wes" for "West"	55·00	
	b. "Afrika" (no stop)	55·00	
	c. Unrouletted between (pair)	£900	
D7	1½d. black and yellow-brown	75	6·50
	a. "Wes" for "West"	50·00	
	b. "Afrika" (no stop)	45·00	

(ii) *Type* D 1 (B). *P* 14

D8	½d. black and green	2·00	11·00
	a. Opt inverted	£250	
	b. Opt double	£400	£400
	c. "Wes" for "West"	45·00	
	d. "Afrika" (no stop)	45·00	
D9	2d. black and violet	1·40	11·00
	a. "Wes" for "West"	60·00	
	b. "Afrika" (no stop)	60·00	

The "Wes" variety occurs in the English overprint only, in some printings.

A variety of Nos. D1, D4, D5 and D9 with spacing 15 mm between lines of overprint occurs on four stamps in each pane of certain printings of this setting.

Nos. D1, D4, D6, D7 and D9 exist with 2 mm spacing between "South" and "West", and also with 2½ mm; Nos. D2, D3 and D8 only with 2 mm spacing; and No. D5 only with 2½ mm.

II. *10 mm between lines of overprint. (a) On stamp of Transvaal*

D10	5d. black and violet	40·00	75·00

(b) On South Africa stamps (De La Rue printing)

D11	2d. black and violet	7·00	18·00
	a. "Afrika" (no stop)	80·00	
D12	3d. black and blue	6·00	17·00
	a. "Afrika" (no stop)	55·00	

(c) On South Africa stamp (Pretoria printing). Type D 1 (A), *rouletted*

D13	1d. black and rose (July 1923)	£4000	

1923–27. *Optd as T* 3 ("Zuidwest" *in one word without hyphen) and* 4.

III. "South West" *14 mm long;* "Zuidwest" *11 mm long; 14 mm between lines of overprint* (Sept 1923). *(a) On stamp of Transvaal*

D14	6d. black and red-brown	14·00	45·00

(b) On South Africa stamps (Pretoria printing) Type D 1 (A)

(i) *Rouletted*

D15	1d. black and rose	1·75	10·00

(ii) *P* 14

D16	½d. black and green	3·75	11·00
D17	1d. black and rose	3·75	11·00

IV. "South West" *16 mm long;* "Zuidwest" *12 mm long; 14 mm between lines of overprint. (a) On stamp of Transvaal*

D17*a*	5d. black and violet	£350	£550

(b) On South Africa stamps (Pretoria printing). Type D 1 (B). *P* 14

D18	½d. black and green	2·25	12·00
D19	1d. black and rose	3·00	13·00
D20	6d. black and slate	2·25	20·00
	a. "Afrika" (no stop)	£100	
D18/20	*Set of* 3	6·75	40·00

V. *As* IV, *but 12 mm between lines of overprint*

(a) On stamp of Transvaal

D21	5d. black and violet	2·25	16·00

(b) On South Africa stamp (De La Rue printing)

D22	3d. black and blue	8·00	20·00

(c) On South Africa stamps (Pretoria printing). Type D 1 (B). *P* 14

D23	½d. black and green	1·75	12·00
D24	1½d. black and yellow-brown	2·50	12·00

VI. *As* IV, *but 9½ mm between lines of overprint*

(a) On stamp of Transvaal

D25	5d. black and violet	1·75	8·50
	a. "Africa" (no stop)	45·00	

(b) On South Africa stamp (De La Rue printing)

D26	3d. black and blue	3·25	17·00

(c) On South Africa stamps (Pretoria printing). Type D 1 (B). *P* 14

D27	½d. black and green	2·25	12·00
D28	1d. black and rose	1·10	5·50
	a. "Africa" (no stop)	55·00	
D29	1½d. black and yellow-brown	1·50	11·00
	a. "Africa" (no stop)	45·00	
D30	2d. black and violet	2·00	8·50
	a. "Africa" (no stop)	45·00	
D31	3d. black and blue	2·00	8·50
	a. "Africa" (no stop)	45·00	
D32	6d. black and slate	6·50	25·00
	a. "Africa" (no stop)	75·00	
D27/32	*Set of* 6	14·00	65·00

In Nos. D18/25, D29, D31 and D32, "South West" is 16 mm long, and in Nos. D26 and D27, 16½ mm long. Nos. D28 and D30 exist in both 16 mm and 16½ mm varieties. (*See note after* No. 40*a*.) In Nos. D20, D29, D31 and D32 a variety with "South West" 16½ mm long occurs once only in each sheet of 120 stamps (in certain printings only, in the case of D20), and similarly Nos. D28 and D30 occur with the two measurements on the same sheet from certain printings.

Suidwes — Afrika. (D 1)

South West — Africa. (D 2)

1927. *Optd as Types* D 1 *and* D 2, *alternately. 12 mm between lines of overprint. (a) On stamp of Transvaal.*

D33	5d. black and violet	13·00	40·00

(b) On South Africa stamps (Pretoria printing). Type D 1, *redrawn. P* 14

D34	1½d. black and yellow-brown	55	7·00
	a. "Africa" (no stop)	32·00	
D35	2d. black and pale violet	1·75	7·00
	a. "Africa" (no stop)	35·00	
D36	2d. black and deep violet	1·90	7·50
	a. "Africa" (no stop)	38·00	
D37	3d. black and blue	6·00	20·00
	a. "Africa" (no stop)	50·00	
D38	6d. black and slate	4·75	16·00
	a. "Africa" (no stop)	85·00	
D34/8	*Set of* 5	13·50	50·00

(c) On South Africa stamp (Pretoria printing). Type D 2. *P* 14

D39	1d. black and carmine	70	6·00
	a. "Africa" (no stop)	10·00	

1928–29. *Optd with T* **10**. *On South Africa stamps (Pretoria printing). P* 14. *(a) Type* D 1, *redrawn.*

		Un single	Us single
D40	3d. black and blue	40	8·50
	a. Without stop after "A"	22·00	
D41	6d. black and slate	5·50	14·00

(b) Type D 2

D42	½d. black and green	40	5·00
D43	1d. black and carmine	40	2·75
	a. Without stop after "A"	35·00	
D44	2d. black and mauve	40	3·00
D45	3d. black and blue	1·50	13·00
D46	6d. black and slate	1·00	14·00
	a. Without stop after "A"	25·00	
D42/6	*Set of* 5	3·25	35·00

D 3 — D 4 — D 5

(Litho B.W.)

1931 (23 Feb). *Inscribed bilingually. W* **9** *of South Africa. P* 12.

D47	D **3**	½d. black and green	60	3·25
D48		1d. black and scarlet	60	1·25
D49		2d. black and violet	70	2·25
D50		3d. black and blue	1·50	12·00
D51		6d. black and slate	5·50	18·00
D47/51		*Set of* 5	8·00	32·00

PRINTER. The following issues have been printed by the South African Government Printer, Pretoria.

1959 (18 May). *Centre typo; frame roto. W* **9** *of South Africa. P* 15 × 14.

D52	D **4**	1d. black and scarlet	90	7·00
D53		2d. black and reddish violet	90	8·00
D54		3d. black and blue	1·00	9·00
D52/4		*Set of* 3	2·50	22·00

1960 (Dec). *As Nos.* D52 *and* D54 *but W* **102** *of South Africa.*

D55	1d. black and scarlet	2·25	4·50
D56	3d. black and blue	2·25	5·50

1961 (14 Feb). *As Nos.* D52 *etc, but whole stamp roto, and value in cents. W* **102** *of South Africa.*

D57	1 c. black and blue-green	20	1·50
D58	2 c. black and scarlet	20	1·50
D59	4 c. black and reddish violet	30	1·50
D60	5 c. black and light blue	40	2·50
D61	6 c. black and green	45	3·50
D62	10 c. black and yellow	75	4·00
D57/62	*Set of* 6	2·10	13·00

1972 (22 Mar). *W* **127** *(sideways tête-bêche). Phosphorised chalk-surfaced paper. P* 14 × 13½.

D63	D **5**	1 c. emerald	45	2·50
D64		8 c. ultramarine	2·00	4·50

The use of Postage Due stamps ceased in April 1975.

OFFICIAL STAMPS

OFFICIAL South West — Africa. (O 1)

OFFISIEEL Suidwes — Afrika. (O 2)

1926 (Dec). *Nos.* 30, 31, 6 *and* 32 *of South Africa optd with Typ O* 1 *on English stamp and* O 2 *on Afrikaans stamp alternately.*

		Un pair	U pai
O1	½d. black and green	65·00	£11
O2	1d. black and carmine	65·00	£11
O3	2d. dull purple	£140	£17
O4	6d. green and orange	85·00	£11
O1/4	*Set of* 4	£325	£45

OFFICIAL S.W.A. (O 3)

OFFISIEEL S.W.A. (O 4)

1929 (May). *Nos.* 30, 31, 32 *and* 34 *of South Africa optd with Type O* 3 *on English stamp and* O 4 *on Afrikaans stamp.*

O5	½d. black and green	1·00	8·00
O6	1d. black and carmine	1·00	8·00
O7	2d. grey and purple	1·50	8·50
	a. Pair, stamp without stop after "OFFICIAL"	5·00	28·00
	b. Pair, stamp without stop after "OFFISIEEL"	5·00	28·00
	c. Pair comprising a and b	16·00	60·00
O8	6d. green and orange	3·00	11·00
O5/8	*Set of* 4	6·00	32·00

Types O 3 and O 4 are normally spaced 17 mm between lines on all except the 2d. value, which is spaced 13 mm.

Except on No. O7, the words "OFFICIAL" or "OFFISIEEL" normally have no stops after them.

OFFICIAL S.W.A. (O 5)

OFFISIEEL S.W.A. (O 6)

OFFICIAL. S.W.A. (O 7)

OFFISIEEL. S.W.A. (O 8)

1929 (Aug). *Nos.* 30, 31 *and* 32 *of South Africa optd with Types* O 5 *and* O 6, *and No.* 34 *with Types* O 7 *and* O 8, *languages to correspond.*

O 9	½d. black and green	65	7·50
O10	1d. black and carmine	75	7·50
O11	2d. grey and purple	90	10·00
	a. Pair, one stamp without stop after "OFFICIAL"	3·75	30·00
	b. Pair, one stamp without stop after "OFFISIEEL"	3·75	30·00
	c. Pair consisting of a and b	18·00	65·00
O12	6d. green and orange	3·00	26·00
O9/12	*Set of* 4	4·75	45·00

OFFICIAL (O 9)

OFFISIEEL (O 10)

1931. *English stamp optd with Type* O **9** *and Afrikaans stamp with Type* O **10** *in red.*

			Un pair	Us pair
O13	**12**	½d. black and emerald	3·50	11·00
O14	**13**	1d. indigo and scarlet	75	11·00
O15	**14**	2d. blue and brown	70	9·00
O16	**17**	6d. blue and brown	2·00	11·00
O13/16		*Set of* 4	6·25	38·00

OFFICIAL (O 11)

OFFISIEEL (O 12)

1938 (1 July). *English stamp optd with Type* O 11 *and Afrikaans with Type* O 12 *in red.*

O17	**27**	1½d. purple-brown	11·00	20·00

OFFICIAL (O 13)

OFFISIEEL (O 14)

1945–50. *English stamp optd with Type* O **13**, *and Afrikaans stamp with Type* O 14 *in red.*

O18	**12**	½d. black and emerald	3·50	13·00
O19	**13**	1d. indigo and scarlet (1950)	1·50	10·00
		a. Opt double	£400	
O20	**27**	1½d. purple-brown	12·00	17·00
O21	**14**	2d. blue and brown (1947?)	£400	£550
O22	**17**	6d. blue and brown	5·00	17·00
O18/20, O22		*Set of* 4	20·00	50·00

OFFICIAL (O 15)

OFFISIEEL (O 16)

1951 (16 Nov)–**52**. *English stamp optd with Type* O **15** *and Afrikaans stamp with Type* O **16**, *in red.*

O23	**12**	½d. black and emerald (1952)	4·00	8·00
O24	**13**	1d. indigo and scarlet	1·00	8·00
		a. Opts transposed	35·00	65·00
O25	**27**	1½d. purple-brown	11·00	14·00
		a. Opts transposed	45·00	75·00
O26	**14**	2d. blue and brown	80	8·50
		a. Opts transposed	25·00	65·00
O27	**17**	6d. blue and brown	2·75	20·00
		a. Opts transposed	20·00	65·00
O23/7		*Set of* 5	18·00	55·00

The above errors refer to stamps with the English overprint on Afrikaans stamp and *vice versa.*

The use of official stamps ceased in January 1955.

Southern Cameroons

The following issue, although ordered by the Southern Cameroons authorities, was also on sale in Northern Cameroons, until the latter joined Nigeria. The stamps therefore can be found with Nigerian postmarks.

CAMEROONS
U.K.T.T.
(1)

1960 (1 Oct)–**61**. *Nos.* 69/71, 72 *ca/cc and* 73/80 *of Nigeria optd with T* **1**, *in red.*

1	**18**	½d. black and orange	10	20
2	–	1d. black and bronze-green	10	10
		a. Grey-blk & dull bronze-grn (19.9.61)	10	20
3	–	1½d. blue-green	10	15
4	**21**	2d. grey (Type B)	10	15
		a. Slate-blue (Type A)	†	—
		b. Bluish grey (Type B)	22·00	10·00
		c. Pale grey (Type B) (19.9.61)	10	20
5	–	3d. black and deep lilac	15	10
6	–	4d. black and blue	10	40
7	**24**	6d. orange-brown and black (*p* 14)	15	10
		a. Perf 13×13½ (19.9.61)	10	35
8	–	1s. black and maroon	15	10
9	**26**	2s. 6d. black and green	80	80
10	–	5s. black and red-orange	90	2·75
11	–	10s. black and red-brown	2·25	3·00
12	**29**	£1 black and violet	6·50	11·00
1/12		*Set of* 12	10·00	17·00

Nos. 2 and 4/*b* were overprinted on stamps printed by Waterlows' subsidiary, Imprimerie Belge de Securité.

Nos. 2*a*, 4*c* and 7*a* were from new printings produced by De La Rue instead of Waterlow.

The above stamps were withdrawn on 30 September 1961, when Southern Cameroons became part of the independent republic of Cameroun.

Southern Nigeria

The Colony and Protectorate of Southern Nigeria was formed on 1 January 1900 by the amalgamation of Niger Coast Protectorate with the southern part of the Niger Territories. Lagos was incorporated into the territory on 16 February 1906.

The stamps of NIGER COAST PROTECTORATE were used in Southern Nigeria until the introduction of Nos. 1/9, and also during a shortage of these values in mid-1902. The issues of LAGOS were utilized throughout Southern Nigeria after 16 February 1906 until supplies were exhausted.

PRICES FOR STAMPS ON COVER

Nos. 1/7	*from* × 6
Nos. 8/9	—
Nos. 10/18	*from* × 4
Nos. 19/20	—
Nos. 21/30	*from* × 4
Nos. 31/2	—
Nos. 33/42	*from* × 4
Nos. 43/4	—
Nos. 45/53	*from* × 4
Nos. 55/6	—

PRINTERS. All issues of Southern Nigeria were typographed by De La Rue & Co, Ltd, London.

1

2

3

1901 (Mar)–**02**. *Wmk Crown CA. P* 14.

1	**1**	½d. black and pale green	50	75
		a. Black and green (1902)	35	50
2		1d. black and carmine	40	50
3		2d. black and red-brown	1·75	3·50
4		4d. black and sage-green	1·75	5·00
5		6d. black and purple	1·75	3·50
6		1s. green and black	7·00	10·00
7		2s. 6d. black and brown	26·00	42·00
8	**1**	5s. black and orange-yellow	35·00	60·00
9		10s. black and purple/*yellow*	60·00	£110
1/9		*Set of* 9	£110	£200
1/9 Optd "Specimen"		*Set of* 9	£120	

1903 (Mar)–**04**. *Wmk Crown CA. P* 14.

10	**2**	½d. grey-black and pale green	50	15
11		1d. grey-black and carmine	1·25	15
12		2d. grey-black and chestnut	2·00	90
13		2½d. grey-black and blue (1904)	2·00	75
14		4d. grey-black and olive-green	1·75	3·25
15		6d. grey-black and purple	3·25	8·00
16		1s. green and black	11·00	7·00
17		2s. 6d. grey-black and brown	9·00	24·00
		a. Grey and yellow-brown	50·00	65·00
18		5s. grey-black and yellow	32·00	60·00
19		10s. grey-black and purple/*yellow*	25·00	48·00
20		£1 green and violet	£200	£275
10/20		*Set of* 11	£250	£375
10/20 Optd "Specimen"		*Set of* 11	£160	

1904 (June)–**08**. *Wmk Mult Crown CA. P* 14.

21	**2**	½d. grey-black and pale green, **OC**	30	10
22		1d. grey-black and carmine, **OC**	1·75	10
23		2d. grey-black and chestnut, **O**	1·75	45
		a. Pale grey and chestnut (1907)	2·50	45
24		2½d. grey-black and bright blue, **O** (1905)	80	95
25		3d. orange-brown and bright purple, **C** (1907) (Optd S. £20)	8·50	1·25
26		4d. grey-black & olive-green, **OC** (1905)	12·00	11·00
		a. Grey-black & pale olive-grn, **C** (1907)	11·00	12·00
27		6d. grey-black and bright purple, **OC**	4·00	70
28		1s. grey-green and black, **OC**	2·25	80
29		2s. 6d. grey-black and brown, **OC** (1905)	13·00	7·50
30		5s. grey-black and yellow, **OC** (1905)	26·00	35·00
31		10s. grey-black & purple/*yellow*, **C** (1908)	60·00	90·00
32		£1 green and violet, **OC** (1905)	85·00	£120
21/32		*Set of* 12	£190	£240

I

II

Die I. Thick "1"; small "d".
Die II. Thinner "1"; larger "d".

1907–11. *Colours changed. Ordinary paper* (½*d. to* 2½*d.*) *or chalk-surfaced paper* (*others*). *Wmk Mult Crown CA. P* 14.

33	**2**	½d. pale green	45	20
		a. Blue-green (1910)	20	20
34		1d. carmine (I)	60	15
		a. Die II. *Carmine-red* (1910)	25	10
35		2d. greyish slate (1909)	70	70
36		2½d. blue (1909)	1·00	3·25
37		3d. purple/*yellow* (1909)	90	30
38		4d. black and red/*yellow* (1909)	60	80
39		6d. dull purple and purple (1909)	7·00	3·00
		a. Dull purple and bright purple (1911)	9·00	2·25
40		1s. black/*green* (1909)	4·75	40
41		2s. 6d. black and red/*blue* (1909)	4·00	90
42		5s. green and red/*yellow* (1909)	23·00	35·00
43		10s. green and red/*green* (1909)	48·00	65·00
44		£1 purple and black/*red* (1909)	£130	£140
33/44		*Set of* 12	£190	£210
33/44 Optd "Specimen"		*Set of* 12	£225	

It was formerly believed that the plate used for printing the head was retouched in 1907 but the fact that the 1d. Die II, which did not appear until 1910, only exists in the first state of the head threw some doubts on this theory. Specialists now recognise that two dies of the head existed and that plates from both were used in Southern Nigeria.

The differences are very small and we refrain from listing them until more research is done, both in this country and in others where they may have been used. The differences are illustrated below:

A

B

In Head A the fifth line of shading on the king's cheek shows as a line of dots and the lines of shading up to the king's hair are broken in places. In Head B the lines of shading are more regular, especially the fifth line.

The following stamps are known:

Ordinary colours: 21 ordinary and chalky, A; 22 ordinary and chalky, A; 23, A; 23*a*, B; 24, A; 25, B; 26 ordinary and chalky, A; 27 ordinary, A; 27 chalky, B; 28 ordinary, A; 28 chalky, B; 29 ordinary, A; 29 chalky, A and B; 30 ordinary, A; 30 chalky, B; 31, B; 32 ordinary, A; 32 chalky, B.

New colours: 33, A and B; 33*a*, B; 34, A and B; 34*a*, A; 35/44, B.

1912. *Wmk Mult Crown CA. P* 14.

45	**3**	½d. green	30	10
46		1d. red	50	10
47		2d. grey	50	85
48		2½d. bright blue	1·75	2·75
49		3d. purple/*yellow*	75	30
50		4d. black and red/*yellow*	70	2·00
51		6d. dull and bright purple	75	90
52		1s. black/*green*	1·75	60
53		2s. 6d. black and red/*blue*	4·50	11·00
54		5s. green and red/*yellow*	8·00	30·00
55		10s. green and red/*green*	32·00	60·00
56		£1 purple and black/*red*	£130	£140
45/56		*Set of* 12	£160	£225
45/56 Optd "Specimen"		*Set of* 12	£225	

On 1 January 1914 Southern Nigeria became part of NIGERIA.

Southern Rhodesia

PRICES FOR STAMPS ON COVER TO 1945
Nos. 1/61 *from* × 2

SELF-GOVERNMENT

1

2 King George V

3 Victoria Falls

(Recess Waterlow)

1924 (1 Apr)–**29**. *P* 14.

1	**1**	½d. blue-green	55	10
		a. Imperf between (horiz pair)	£500	£500
		b. Imperf between (vert pair)	£550	£550
		c. Imperf vert (horiz pair)	£600	
2		1d. bright rose	70	10
		a. Imperf between (horiz pair)	£600	£500
		b. Imperf between (vert pair)	£600	
		c. Perf 12½ (coil) (1929)	2·75	50·00
3		1½d. bistre-brown	70	25
		a. Imperf between (horiz pair)	£7000	
		b. Imperf between (vert pair)	£2500	
		c. Printed double, once albino	80·00	
4		2d. black and purple-grey	55	25
		a. Imperf between (horiz pair)	£4500	
5		3d. blue	1·10	2·00
6		4d. black and orange-red	1·10	2·75
7		6d. black and mauve	1·10	2·00
		a. Imperf between (horiz pair)	£7000	
8		8d. purple and pale green	10·00	32·00
9		10d. blue and rose	10·00	30·00
10		1s. black and light blue	2·50	3·00
11		1s. 6d. black and yellow	15·00	27·00
12		2s. black and brown	17·00	17·00
13		2s. 6d. blue and sepia	30·00	48·00
14		5s. blue and blue-green	55·00	80·00
1/14		*Set of* 14	£130	£225

Prices for "imperf between" varieties are for adjacent stamps from the same pane and not for those separated by wide gutter margins between vertical or horizontal pairs, which come from the junction of two panes.

(T **2** recess by B.W.; T **3** typo by Waterlow)

1931 (1 April)–**37**. *T* **2** (*line perf* 12 *unless otherwise stated*) *and* **3** (*comb perf* 15 × 14). (*The* 11½ *perf is comb.*).

15	**2**	½d. green	20	20
		a. Perf 11½ (1933)	20	10
		b. Perf 14 (1935)	50	10
16		1d. scarlet	20	10
		a. Perf 11½ (1933)	40	10
		b. Perf 14 (1935)	35	10
16*c*		1½d. chocolate (1933)	45·00	35·00
		d. Perf 11½ (1.4.32)	1·25	45
17	**3**	2d. black and sepia	3·25	70
18		3d. deep ultramarine	8·00	11·00
19	**2**	4d. black and vermilion	1·10	70
		a. Perf 11½ (1935)	15·00	5·00
		b. Perf 14 (10.37)	32·00	38·00
20		6d. black and magenta	2·00	50
		a. Perf 11½ (1933)	12·00	55
		b. Perf 14 (1936)	20·00	60
21		8d. violet and olive-green	1·75	3·25
		a. Perf 11½ (1934)	15·00	25·00
21*b*		9d. vermilion and olive-green (1.9.34)	6·00	7·50
22		10d. blue and scarlet	6·00	3·00
		a. Perf 11½ (1933)	6·00	13·00
23		1s. black and greenish blue	1·75	1·75
		a. Perf 11½ (1935)	45·00	25·00
		b. Perf 14 (10.37)	£160	£120
24		1s. 6d. black and orange-yellow	10·00	16·00
		a. Perf 11½ (1936)	48·00	55·00
25		2s. black and brown	13·00	4·50
		a. Perf 11½ (1933)	40·00	30·00
26		2s. 6d. blue and drab	26·00	35·00
		a. Perf 11½ (1933)	30·00	30·00
27		5s. blue and blue-green	48·00	48·00
		a. Printed on gummed side	£3000	
15/27		*Set of* 15	£120	£110

No. 16*c* was issued in booklets only.

PRINTERS. All stamps from Types 4 to 29 were recess-printed by Waterlow and Sons, Ltd, London, except where otherwise stated.

4

1932 (1 May). *P* 12½.

29	**4**	2d. green and chocolate	2·25	30
30		3d. deep ultramarine	3·25	1·75
		a. Imperf horiz (vert pair)	£6000	£6500
		b. Imperf between (vert pair)	£8000	

5 Victoria Falls

1935 (6 May). *Silver Jubilee. P* 11 × 12.

31	**5**	1d. olive and rose-carmine	75	30
32		2d. emerald and sepia	2·00	1·75
33		3d. violet and deep blue	5·00	10·00
34		6d. black and purple	7·00	8·50
31/4		*Set of* 4	13·50	18·00

1935–41. *Inscr* "POSTAGE AND REVENUE".

35	**4**	2d. green and chocolate (*p* 12½)	1·40	3·50
		a. Perf 14 (1941)	30	10
35*b*		3d. deep blue (*p* 14) (1938)	55	10

6 Victoria Falls and Railway Bridge

7 King George VI

1937 (12 May). *Coronation. P* 12½.

36	**6**	1d. olive and rose-carmine	55	25
37		2d. emerald and sepia	55	60
38		3d. violet and blue	3·00	4·00
39		6d. black and purple	2·25	1·50
36/9		*Set of* 4	5·50	5·75

1937 (25 Nov). *P* 14.

40	**7**	½d. green	15	10
41		1d. scarlet	15	10
42		1½d. red-brown	15	10
43		4d. red-orange	35	10
44		6d. grey-black	45	10
45		8d. emerald-green	1·25	80
46		9d. pale blue	1·00	20
47		10d. purple	1·10	1·75
48		1s. black and blue-green	60	10
		a. Double print of frame	£375	
49		1s. 6d. black and orange-yellow	4·50	1·25
50		2s. black and brown	6·00	55
51		2s. 6d. ultramarine and purple	5·00	2·00
52		5s. blue and blue-green	18·00	2·00
40/52		*Set of* 13	35·00	8·00

Nos. 40/1 exist in coils, constructed from normal sheets.

8 British South Africa Co's Arms

9 Fort Salisbury, 1890

10 Cecil John Rhodes (after S. P. Kendrick)

15 Lobengula's Kraal and Govt House, Salisbury

Recut shirt collar (R. 6/1)

(Des Mrs. L. E. Curtis (½d., 1d., 1½d., 3d.), Mrs I. Mount (others))

1940 (3 June). *British South Africa Company's Golden Jubilee. T* **8/10, 15** *and similar designs. P* 14.

53		½d. slate-violet and green	10	10
54		1d. violet-blue and scarlet	10	10
55		1½d. black and red-brown	10	10
		a. Recut shirt collar	5·00	
56		2d. green and bright violet	25	20
57		3d. black and blue	30	30
58		4d. green and brown	70	70
59		6d. chocolate and green	30	70
60		1s. blue and green	35	90
53/60		*Set of* 8	1·75	2·50

Designs: *Horiz* (*as T* 8)—2d. Fort Victoria; 3d. Rhodes makes peace. *Vert* (*as T* 10)—4d. Victoria Falls Bridge; 6d. Statue of Sir Charles Coghlan.

16 Mounted Pioneer

17 Queen Elizabeth II when Princess and Princess Margaret

(Roto South African Govt Printer, Pretoria)

1943 (1 Nov). *50th Anniv of Occupation of Matabeleland. W* **9** *of South Africa* (*Mult Springbok*) *sideways. P* 14.

61	**16**	2d. brown and green	10	10

1947 (1 Apr). *Royal Visit. T* **17** *and similar horiz design. P* 14.

62		½d. black and green	10	10
63		1d. black and scarlet	10	10

Design:—1d. King George VI and Queen Elizabeth.

19 Queen Elizabeth

20 King George VI

21 Queen Elizabeth II when Princess

22 Princess Margaret

1947 (8 May). *Victory. P* 14.

64	**19**	1d. carmine	10	10
65	**20**	2d. slate	10	10
66	**21**	3d. blue	10	10
67	**22**	6d. orange	10	10
64/7		*Set of* 4	25	25

(Recess B.W.)

1949 (10 Oct). *75th Anniv of Universal Postal Union. As Nos.* 115/16 *of Antigua.*

68		2d. slate-green	65	20
69		3d. blue	1·10	2·50

23 Queen Victoria, Arms and King George VI

1950 (12 Sept). *Diamond Jubilee of Southern Rhodesia. P* 14.

70	**23**	2d. green and brown	10	10

24 "Medical Services"

(Des A. R. Winter (2d.), Mrs. J. M. Enalim (others))

1953 (15 Apr). *Birth Centenary of Cecil Rhodes. T* **24** *and similar horiz designs. P* 14.

71		½d. pale blue and sepia	15	40
72		1d. chestnut and blue-green	15	10
73		2d. grey-green and violet	15	10
74		4½d. deep blue-green & deep ultramarine	75	1·75
75		1s. black and red-brown	2·50	60
71/5		*Set of* 5	3·25	2·50

Designs:—1d. "Agriculture"; 2d. "Building"; 4½d. "Water Supplies"; 1s. "Transport".

No. 74 also commemorates the Diamond Jubilee of Matabeleland.

1953 (30 May). *Rhodes Centenary Exhibition, Bulawayo. As No.* 59 *of Northern Rhodesia but without watermark.*

76		6d. violet	15	15

30 Queen Elizabeth II

(Recess D.L.R.)

1953 (1 June). *Coronation. P* 12 × 12½.

77	**30**	2s. 6d. carmine	5·50	5·00

31 Sable Antelope

33 Rhodes's Grave

34 Farm Worker

42 Basket Maker

43 Balancing Rocks

44 Coat of Arms

(Recess, centre typo (4d.), B.W.)

1953 (31 Aug). *T* **31, 33/4, 42/4** *and similar designs. P* 13½ × 14 (*2d., 6d., 5s.*), 14 (*10s., £1*) *or* 14 × 13½ (*others*).

78		½d. grey-green and claret	15	25
79		1d. green and brown	15	10
80		2d. deep chestnut and reddish violet	15	10
81		3d. chocolate and rose-red	30	35
82		4d. red, green and indigo	1·00	10
83		4½d. black and deep bright blue	70	1·00
84		6d. brown-olive & deep turquoise-green	1·25	15
85		9d. deep blue and reddish brown	2·50	1·50
86		1s. reddish violet and light blue	75	10
87		2s. purple and scarlet	5·00	3·25
88		2s. 6d. yellow-olive and orange-brown	5·50	3·75
89		5s. yellow-brown and deep green	14·00	7·50
90		10s. red-brown and olive	15·00	35·00
91		£1 rose-red and black	23·00	35·00
78/91		*Set of* 14	60·00	80·00

Designs: *Vert* (*as T* 31)—1d. Tobacco planter. (*As T* 33)—6d. Baobab tree. *Horiz* (*as T* 34)—4d. Flame Lily; 4½d. Victoria Falls; 9d. Lion; 1s. Zimbabwe Ruins; 2s. Birchenough Bridge; 2s. 6d. Kariba Gorge.

For issues from 1954 to 1963 see under RHODESIA AND NYASALAND.

45 Maize

50 Flame Lily

56 Cattle

58 Coat of Arms

(Des V. Whiteley. Photo Harrison)

1964 (19 Feb). *T* **45, 50, 56, 58** *and similar horiz designs. P* 14½ (*½d. to 4d.*), 13½ × 13 (*6d. to 2s. 6d.*) *or* 14½ × 14 (*others*).

92		½d. yellow, yellow-green and light blue	15	30
93		1d. reddish violet and yellow-ochre	15	10
		a. Reddish violet omitted	£550	
94		2d. yellow and deep violet	15	10
95		3d. chocolate and pale blue	15	10
96		4d. yellow-orange and deep green	25	10
97		6d. carmine-red, yellow and deep dull green	40	10
98		9d. red-brown, yellow and olive-green	1·50	80
99		1s. blue-green and ochre	1·50	10
		a. blue-green (Queen and emeralds) omitted	£850	
100		1s. 3d. red, violet and yellow-green	3·00	10
101		2s. blue and ochre	2·25	85
102		2s. 6d. ultramarine and vermilion	2·25	70
		a. Vermilion omitted	£375	
103		5s. light brown, bistre-yellow & light blue	4·50	2·00
104		10s. black, yell-ochre, lt blue & carmine-red	10·00	6·50
105		£1 brown, yellow-green, buff & salmon-pink	7·00	13·00
92/105		*Set of* 14	30·00	21·00

Designs: (*As T* 45)—1d. African Buffalo; 2d. Tobacco; 3d. Greater Kudu; 4d. Citrus. (*As T* 50)—9d. Ansellia Orchid; 1s. Emeralds; 1s. 3d. Aloe; 2s. Lake Kyle; 2s. 6d. Tiger Fish. (*As T* 56)—10s. Helmet Guineafowl.

Nos. 92 and 93 exist in coils constructed from normal sheets.

See also Nos. 359/72 of Rhodesia.

POSTAGE DUE STAMPS

SOUTHERN

RHODESIA

(D 1)

1951 (1 Oct). *Postage Due stamps of Great Britain optd with Type* D 1.

D1	D 1	½d. emerald (No. D27)	3·25	7·00
D2		1d. violet-blue (No. D36)	1·75	65
D3		2d. agate (No. D29)	4·00	1·75
D4		3d. violet (No. D30)	2·75	1·25
D5		4d. blue (No. D38)	1·50	2·25
D6		4d. dull grey-green (No. D31)	£130	£225
D7		1s. deep blue (No. D33)	3·00	1·75
D1/5, 7		.. .. *Set of* 6	14·50	13·00

In October 1964 Southern Rhodesia was renamed Rhodesia. Issues after this date will be found listed under RHODESIA.

Sri Lanka

(*formerly* Ceylon)

REPUBLIC

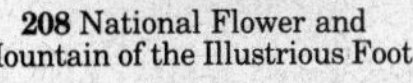

208 National Flower and Mountain of the Illustrious Foot

209 Map of World with Buddhist Flag

(Des L. D. P. Jayawardena. Litho D.L.R.)

1972 (22 May). *Inauguration of the Republic of Sri Lanka. P* 13.

591	**208**	15 c. multicoloured	15	10

(Des L. D. P. Jayawardena. Litho Harrison)

1972 (26 May). *Tenth Conference of the World Fellowship of Buddhists. P* 14 × 13.

592	**209**	5 c. multicoloured	10	15
		a. "1972" ptd double		
		b. "1972" ptd double, one inverted ..		

This stamp was scheduled for release in May 1971, and when finally released had the year "1972" additionally overprinted in red. Sheets are known without this overprint but their status has not been established.

210 Book Year Emblem

211 Imperial Angelfish

(Des L. D. P. Jayawardena. Photo Pakistan Security Printing Corp)

1972 (8 Sept). *International Book Year. P* 13.

593	**210**	20 c. light yellow-orange and lake-brown	20	25

(Des G. D. Kariyawasam. Litho Rosenbaum Bros, Vienna)

1972 (12 Oct). *T* **211** *and similar horiz designs showing fish. Multicoloured. P* 13 × 13½.

594	2 c. Type **211**	10	20
	a. Plum colour omitted	3·00	
595	3 c. Green Chromide	10	20
596	30 c. Skipjack	45	10
597	2 r. Black Ruby Barb	85	1·25
594/7	.. .. .. *Set of* 4	1·25	1·50

On No. 594a the stripes of the fish are in green instead of plum.

212 Memorial Hall

(Des R. B. Mawilmada. Litho D.L.R.)

1973 (17 May). *Opening of Bandaranaike Memorial Hall. P* 14.

598	**212**	15 c. light cobalt and deep grey-blue ..	10	10

213 King Vessantara giving away his Children

214 Bandaranaike Memorial Conference Hall

(Des P. Wanigatunga. Litho D.L.R.)

1973 (3 Sept). *Rock and Temple Paintings. T* **213** *and similar vert designs. Multicoloured. P* 13½ × 14.

599	35 c. Type **213**	20	10
600	50 c. The Prince and the Grave-digger ..	25	10
601	90 c. Bearded old man	40	45
602	1 r. 55, Two female figures	55	80
599/602	.. .. .. *Set of* 4	1·25	1·25
MS603	115 × 141 mm. Nos. 599/602	1·25	1·75

(Des and litho Harrison)

1974 (6 Sept). *20th Commonwealth Parliamentary Conference, Colombo. P* 14½.

604	**214**	85 c. multicoloured	20	20

215 Prime Minister Bandaranaike

216 "UPU" and "100"

(Des and photo Harrison)

1974 (25 Sept). *P* 14½.

605	**215**	15 c. multicoloured	15	10
		a. Red (face value) omitted	3·00	
		b. Pale blue (background) omitted ..	3·00	

(Des P. Jayatillake. Litho German Bank Note Ptg Co, Leipzig)

1974 (9 Oct). *Centenary of Universal Postal Union. P* 13½ × 13.

606	**216**	50 c. multicoloured	50	55

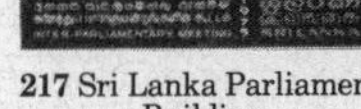

217 Sri Lanka Parliament Building

218 Sir Ponnambalam Ramanathan (politician)

(Litho Toppan Printing Co, Japan)

1975 (1 Apr). *Inter-Parliamentary Meeting. P* 13.

607	**217**	1 r. multicoloured	30	40

(Des A. Rasiah. Litho Toppan Ptg Co, Japan)

1975 (4 Sep). *Ramanathan Commemoration. P* 13.

608	**218**	75 c. multicoloured	30	40

219 D. J. Wimalasurendra (engineer)

220 Mrs. Bandaranaike, Map and Dove

(Des A. Dharmasiri. Litho Toppan Ptg Co, Japan)

1975 (17 Sept). *Wimalasurendra Commemoration. P* 13.

609	**219**	75 c. blue-black and new blue	30	40

(Des B. U. Ananda Somatilaka. Litho Toppan Ptg Co, Japan)

1975 (22 Dec). *International Women's Year. P* 13.

610	**220**	1 r. 15, multicoloured	1·25	80

OMNIBUS ISSUES

Details, together with prices for complete sets, of the various Omnibus issues from the 1935 Silver Jubilee series to date are included in a special section following Zululand at the end of the catalogue.

221 Ma-ratmal

222 Mahaweli Dam

(Des and litho Toppan Ptg Co, Japan)

1976 (1 Jan). *Indigenous Flora. T* **221** *and similar vert designs. Multicoloured. P* 13.

611	25 c. Type **221**	10	10
	a. Imperf (pair)	55·00	
612	50 c. Binara	10	10
613	75 c. Daffodil orchid	15	15
614	10 r. Diyapara	3·00	3·75
611/14	.. .. .. *Set of* 4	3·00	3·75
MS615	153 × 153 mm. Nos. 611/14	4·25	5·00

A used example of No. 613 has been seen with the yellow printing apparently omitted. This results in the leaves appearing blue instead of green.

(Des R. B. Mawilmada. Litho German Bank Note Ptg Co, Leipzig)

1976 (8 Jan). *Diversion of the Mahaweli River. P* 13 × 12½.

616	**222**	85 c. turquoise, violet-blue and azure ..	30	40

223 Dish Aerial

224 Conception of the Buddha

(Des P. A. Miththapala. Litho German Bank Note Ptg Co, Leipzig)

1976 (6 May). *Opening of Satellite Earth Station, Padukka. P* 14 × 13½.

617	**223**	1 r. multicoloured	65	65

(Des P. Wanigatunga. Litho Toppan Ptg Co, Japan)

1976 (7 May). *Vesak. T* **224** *and similar horiz designs showing paintings from the Dambava Temple. Multicoloured. P* 13.

618	5 c. Type **224**	10	10
619	10 c. King Suddhodana and the astrologers ..	10	10
620	1 r. 50, The astrologers being entertained ..	20	30
621	2 r. The Queen in a palanquin	25	35
622	2 r. 25, Royal procession	30	70
623	5 r. Birth of the Buddha	70	1·40
618/23	.. .. .. *Set of* 6	1·40	2·50
MS624	161 × 95 mm. Nos. 618/23	4·25	5·50

225 Blue Sapphire

226 Prime Minister Mrs. S. Bandaranaike

(Des State Gem Corporation. Litho Toppan Ptg Co, Japan)

1976 (16 June). *Gems of Sri Lanka. T* **225** *and similar horiz designs. Multicoloured. P* 12 × 12½.

625	60 c. Type **225**	1·00	25
626	1 r. 15, Cat's Eye	1·40	85
627	2 r. Star sapphire	2·00	2·00
628	5 r. Ruby	3·25	4·00
625/8	.. .. .. *Set of* 4	7·00	6·50
MS629	152 × 152 mm. Nos. 625/8	7·50	8·00

(Photo Harrison)

1976 (3 Aug). *Non-aligned Summit Conference, Colombo. P* 14×14½.

630	**226**	1 r. 15, multicoloured	25	20
631		2 r. multicoloured	40	35

227 Statue of Liberty

228 Bell, Early Telephone and Telephone Lines

(Des A. Harischandra. Litho German Bank Note Ptg Co, Leipzig)

1976 (29 Nov). *Bicentenary of American Revolution. P* 13½.

632	**227**	2 r. 25, cobalt and indigo	65	65

(Des A. Harischandra. Litho German Bank Note Ptg Co, Leipzig)

1976 (21 Dec). *Telephone Centenary. P* 13.
633 **228** 1 r. multicoloured 30 20

229 Maitreya (pre-carnate Buddha)

230 Kandyan Crown

(Des P. Wanigatunga. Litho German Bank Note Ptg Co, Leipzig)

1977 (1 Jan). *Centenary of Colombo Museum. T* **229** *and similar vert designs showing statues. Multicoloured. P* 12½.
634 50 c. Type **229** 15 10
635 1 r. Sundara Murti Swami (Tamil psalmist) 30 20
636 5 r. Tara (goddess) .. .. 1·10 1·75
634/6 .. .. *Set of* 3 1·40 1·90

(Des R. B. Mawilmada. Litho Toppan Ptg Co, Japan)

1977 (18 Jan). *Regalia of the Kings of Kandy. T* **230** *and similar vert design. Multicoloured. P* 13.
637 1 r. Type **230** 35 40
638 2 r. Throne and footstool .. .. .. 75 1·75

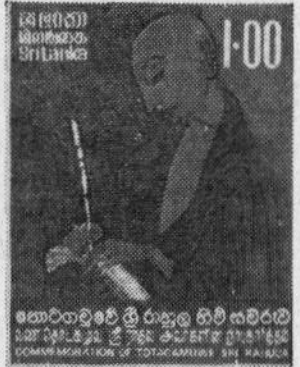

231 Sri Rahula Thero (poet)

232 Sir Ponnambalam Arunachalam (social reformer)

(Des S. Dissanayaka. Litho Toppan Ptg Co, Japan)

1977 (23 Feb). *Sri Rahula Commemoration. P* 13.
639 **231** 1 r. multicoloured 40 45

(Litho Toppan Ptg Co, Japan)

1977 (10 Mar). *Ponnambalam Arunachalam Commemoration. P* 13.
640 **232** 1 r. multicoloured 30 45

233 Brass Lamps

234 Siddi Lebbe (author and educationalist

(Des A. Harischandra. Litho Toppan Ptg Co, Japan)

1977 (7 Apr). *Handicrafts. T* **233** *and similar vert designs. Multicoloured. P* 13.
641 20 c. Type **233** 15 10
642 25 c. Jewellery box 15 10
643 50 c. Caparisoned elephant 30 10
644 5 r. Mask .. .. 1·60 2·50
641/4 .. .. *Set of* 4 2·00 2·50
MS645 205 × 89 mm. Nos. 641/4 .. .. .. 3·00 3·50

(Des Sarasvati Rockwood. Litho Toppan Ptg Co, Japan)

1977 (11 June). *Siddi Lebbe Commemoration. P* 13½.
646 **234** 1 r. multicoloured 30 50

235 Girl Guide

236 Parliament Building and "Wheel of Life"

(Des and litho Asher & Co, Melbourne)

1977 (13 Dec). *60th Anniv of Sri Lanka Girl Guides Association. P* 14½ × 15.
647 **235** 75 c. multicoloured 85 30

(Des R. B. Mawilmada. Photo Enschedé)

1978 (4 Feb). *Election of New President. P* 12 × 12½.
648 **236** 15 c. gold, brt yellow-green & emerald .. 20 10

No. 648 was re-issued on 7 September 1978, additionally dated "1978.09.07" to mark the Promulgation of the Constitution for the Democratic Socialist Republic of Sri Lanka. This re-issue was only available on First Day Covers (*Price on F.D.C.* £2).

See also Nos. 680/c.

237 Youths Running

238 Prince Siddhartha's Renunciation

(Des M. Dissanayake. Litho Asher & Co, Melbourne)

1978 (27 Apr). *National Youth Service Council. P* 15 × 14½.
649 **237** 15 c. multicoloured 15 10

(Des P. Wanigatunga. Litho Metal Box Singapore Ltd)

1978 (16 May). *Vesak. Rock Carvings from Borobudur Temple. T* **238** *and similar horiz design in buff, brown and ultramarine. P* 13.
650 15 c. Type **238** 15 10
651 50 c. Prince Siddhartha shaving his hair .. 30 35

•05

(239)

240 Veera Puran Appu

1978 (18 May–20 Nov). *Nos.* 559, 601/2, 605 *and* 648/9 *surch as T* **239**.
652 5 c. on 90 c. Bearded old man (26.6.) .. 15 15
a. Surch inverted .. .. 12·00
653 10 c. on 35 c. Type **213**.. .. .. .. 15 15
a. Surch inverted .. .. 12·00
654 25 c. on 15 c. Type **215** (20.11) .. .. 1·75 1·00
a. Dot after "25" (R. 3/4) .. .. 11·00
655 25 c. on 15 c. Type **236** (20.11) .. .. 1·75 1·00
a. Surch inverted .. .. 10·00
656 25 c. on 15 c. Type **237** (Blk. and Pink) (20.11) 1·75 1·00
a. Surch and obliterating square inverted .. 9·00
ab. Surch only inverted .. .. .. 8·50
657 1 r. on 1 r. 55, Two female figures (17.11) .. 60 40
a. Surch inverted .. ..
652/7 .. .. *Set of* 6 5·50 3·25

No. 656 has the surcharge applied in black on a pink square, previously printed over the original face value.

(Des A. Dharmasiri. Litho Metal Box Singapore Ltd)

1978 (8 Aug). *130th Death Anniv of Veera Puran Appu (revolutionary). P* 13.
658 **240** 15 c. multicoloured 15 15

241 *Troides helena darsius*

SRI LANKA

15

(242)

(Des G. Ratnavira. Litho J.W.)

1978 (28 Nov). *Butterflies. T* **241** *and similar vert designs. Multicoloured. P* 14 × 13½.
659 25 c. Type **241** 20 10
660 50 c. *Cethosia nietneri nietneri* 30 10
661 5 r. *Kallima philarchus philarchus* .. 70 1·00
662 10 r. *Papilio polymnestor parinda* .. .. 1·10 1·50
659/62 .. .. *Set of* 4 2·10 2·40
MS663 203 × 147 mm. Nos. 659/62 .. .. 3·50 4·00

1979 (22 Mar). *No.* 486 *of Ceylon surch with T* **242** *in black and turquoise-blue.*
664 15 c. on 10 c. myrtle-green 80 55
a. Surch double .. .. 12·00
b. Turq-blue surch omitted.. .. .. 20·00

Type **242** shows only part of the turquoise-blue section of the overprint ("SRI LANKA"), which also includes a rectangle obliterating the original face value. The new value is printed on this rectangle in black.

243 Prince Danta and Princess Hema Mala bringing the Sacred Tooth Relic from Kalinga

244 Piyadasa Sirisena

(Des A. Dharmasiri. Litho J.W.)

1979 (3 May). *Vesak. Kelaniya Temple Paintings. T* **243** *and similar vert designs. Multicoloured. P* 13 × 13½.
665 25 c. Type **243** 10 10
666 1 r. Theri Sanghamitta bringing the Bodhi Tree branch to Sri Lanka 15 15
667 10 r. King Kirti Sri Rajasinghe offering fan of authority to the Sangha Raja .. .. 95 1·10
665/7 .. .. *Set of* 3 1·00 1·10
MS668 120 × 80 mm. Nos. 665/7 .. .. .. 1·40 2·00

(Des P. Jayatillake. Litho Toppan Ptg Co, Japan)

1979 (22 May). *Piyadasa Sirisena (writer) Commemoration. P* 13.
669 **244** 1 r. 25, multicoloured 20 20

245 Wrestlers

246 Dudley Senanayake

(Des R. B. Mawilmada. Litho Metal Box Singapore Ltd)

1979 (28 May). *Wood Carvings from Embekke Temple. T* **245** *and similar vert design. P* 14.
670 20 r. chocolate, ochre and deep green .. 95 1·50
671 50 r. agate, bistre-yellow and deep green .. 2·25 3·00
Design:—50 r. Dancer.

(Photo Heraclio Fournier)

1979 (19 June). *Dudley Senanayake (former Prime Minister) Commemoration. P* 14.
672 **246** 1 r. 25, bottle green 15 20

247 Mother with Child

248 Ceylon 1857 6d. Stamp and Sir Rowland Hill

(Des A. Dharmasiri and R. Mawilmada. Litho Metal Box Singapore Ltd)

1979 (31 July). *International Year of the Child. T* **247** *and similar horiz designs. Multicoloured. P* 12½.
673 5 c. Type **247** 10 10
674 3 r. Superimposed heads of children of different races 30 60
675 5 r. Children playing.. .. .. .. 40 70
673/5 .. .. *Set of* 3 65 1·25

(Des A. Dharmasiri. Litho Toppan Ptg Co, Japan)

1979 (27 Aug). *Death Centenary of Sir Rowland Hill. P* 13.
676 **248** 3 r. multicoloured 25 40

249 Conference Emblem and Parliament Building

250 Airline Emblem on Aircraft Tail-fin

(Des A. Harischandra. Litho Toppan Ptg Co, Japan)

1979 (28 Aug). *International Conference of Parliamentarians on Population and Development, Colombo. P* 13.
677 **249** 2 r. multicoloured 15 40

(Des S. Saparamadu. Litho Metal Box Singapore Ltd)

1979 (1 Sept). *Inauguration of "Airlanka" Airline. P* 12½.
678 **250** 3 r. black, deep blue-green & vermilion 15 40

251 Coconut Tree

252 Swami Vipulananda

(Des G. Wathuwalagedara. Litho Metal Box Singapore Ltd)

1979 (10 Sept). *10th Anniv of Asian and Pacific Coconut Community. P* 14.
679 **251** 2 r. multicoloured 15 40

1979 (10 Oct)–**87**. *Design as No.* 648 *but smaller,* 20 × 24 *mm. P* 12½ × 13.
680 **236** 25 c. gold, brt yellow-green & emerald 15 15
680*a* 50 c. gold, brt yell-grn & emer (6.6.81) 40 10
680*b* 60 c. gold, bright yellow-green and emerald (30.12.83) 60 30
680*c* 75 c. gold, bright yellow-green and emerald (1.7.87) 10 10
680/*c* .. .. *Set of* 4 1·10 55

(Des R. B. Mawilmada. Litho Metal Box Singapore Ltd)

1979 (18 Nov). *Swami Vipulananda (philosopher) Commemoration. P* 12½.
681 **252** 1 r. 25, multicoloured 20 25

253 Inscription and Crescent

254 "The Great Teacher" (Institute emblem)

(Des Q. V. Saldin. Litho Metal Box Singapore Ltd)

1979 (22 Nov). *1500th Anniv of the Hegira (Mohammedan religion). P* 12½.
682 **253** 3 r. 75, black, deep green and blue-green 35 70

(Des H. P. Rupasinghe. Litho Metal Box Singapore Ltd)

1979 (29 Nov). *50th Anniv of Institute of Ayurveda (school of medicine). P* 13 × 12½.
683 **254** 15 c. multicoloured 15 25

255 Ceylon Blue Magpie

256 Rotary International Emblem and Map of Sri Lanka

(Des G. Ratnavira. Litho German Bank Note Ptg Co, Leipzig)

1979 (13 Dec). *Birds. T* **255** *and similar vert designs. Multicoloured. P* 13½ × 14.
684 10 c. Type **255** 10 15
685 15 c. Ceylon Hanging Parrot ("Ceylon Lorikeet") 10 10
686 75 c. Ceylon Whistling Thrush ("Ceylon Arrenga") 15 15
687 1 r. Ceylon Spurfowl 15 15
688 5 r. Yellow-fronted Barbet 60 85
689 10 r. Yellow-tufted Bulbul .. .. .. 75 1·40
684/9 .. .. *Set of* 6 1·75 2·50
MS690 15 × 15 mm. Nos. 684/9 .. .. .. 2·50 3·25

(Des A. Harischandra. Litho Metal Box Singapore Ltd)

1979 (27 Dec). *50th Anniv of Sri Lanka Rotary Movement and 75th Anniv of Rotary International. P* 14.
691 **256** 1 r. 50, multicoloured 30 40

257 A. Ratnayake

.35

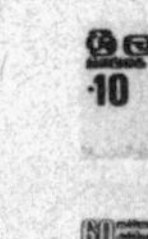
(258)

259 Tank and Stupa (symbols of Buddhist culture)

(Photo Govt Ptg Works, Rome)

1980 (7 Jan). *80th Birth Anniv of A. Ratnayake (politician). P* 13½.
692 **257** 1 r. 25, deep grey-green 20 20

1980 (17 Mar). *No.* 680 *surch with T* **258**.
693 **236** 35 c. on 25 c. gold, brt yell-grn & emer .. 15 15
a. Surch ".33" (R. 6/1) .. .. .. 15·00
b. Dot omitted (R. 7/6) .. .. .. 3·00

(Des R. B. Mawilmada. Photo Govt Ptg Works, Rome)

1980 (25 Mar). *60th Anniv of All Ceylon Buddhist Congress. T* **259** *and similar horiz design showing symbols of Buddhist culture. Multicoloured. P* 13½.
694 10 c. Type **259** 10 10
695 35 c. Bo-leaf wheel and fan 10 15

260 Colonel Olcott

261 Patachara's Journey through Forest

(Des S. Senevirante. Litho J.W.)

1980 (17 May). *Centenary of Arrival of Colonel Olcott (campaigner for Buddhism). P* 14.
696 **260** 2 r. multicoloured 25 35

(Des A. Dharmasiri. Litho Metal Box Singapore Ltd)

1980 (23 May). *Vesak. Details from Temple Paintings, Purvaramaya, Kataluwa. T* **261** *and similar horiz design. Multicoloured. P* 13½.
697 35 c. Type **261** 10 10
698 1 r. 60, Patachara crossing river 25 35

262 George E. de Silva

263 Dalada Maligawa

(Des A. Rasiah. Litho German Bank Note Ptg Co, Leipzig)

1980 (8 June). *George E. de Silva (politician) Commemoration. P* 13.
699 **262** 1 r. 60, multicoloured 15 10

(Des A. Dharmasiri and R. B. Mawilmada. Litho Metal Box Singapore Ltd)

1980 (25 Aug). *U.N.E.S.C.O.—Sri Lanka Cultural Triangle Project. T* **263** *and similar horiz designs. P* 13.
700 35 c. claret 10 10
701 35 c. grey 10 10
702 35 c. rose-carmine 10 10
703 1 r. 60, olive-green 20 30
704 1 r. 60, slate-green 20 30
705 1 r. 60, sepia 20 30
700/5 .. .. *Set of* 6 70 1·10
MS706 215 × 115 mm. Nos. 700/5 .. .. 70 1·25
Designs:—No. 701, Dambulla; No. 702, Alahana Pirivena; No. 703, Jetavanarama; No. 704, Abhayagiri; No. 705, Sigiri.

264 Co-operation Symbols

265 Lanka Mahila Samiti Emblem

(Des R. B. Mawilmada. Litho Metal Box Singapore Ltd)

1980 (1 Oct). *50th Anniv of Co-operative Department. P* 13.
707 **264** 20 c. multicoloured 10 10

(Des R. B. Mawilmada. Photo Govt Ptg Works, Rome)

1980 (7 Nov). *50th Anniv of Lanka Mahila Samiti (Rural Women's Movement). P* 14 × 13.
708 **265** 35 c. violet, rosine and yellow 10 10

266 The Holy Family

267 Colombo Public Library

(Des L. Priyantha Silva. Litho Metal Box Singapore Ltd)

1980 (20 Nov). *Christmas. T* **266** *and similar vert design. Multicoloured. P* 12 × 11½.
709 35 c. Type **266** 10 10
710 3 r. 75, The Three Wise Men 25 35
MS711 125 × 75 mm. Nos. 709/10. P 13½ .. 40 60

(Des P. Jayatillake. Litho Toppan Ptg Co, Japan)

1980 (17 Dec). *Opening of Colombo Public Library. P* 12 × 12½.
712 **267** 35 c. multicoloured 10 10

268 Flag of Walapane Disawa

269 Fishing Cat

(Des Mrs. J. L. M. Fernando. Litho Toppan Ptg Co, Japan)

1980 (18 Dec). *Ancient Flags. T* **268** *and similar horiz designs. P* 13.
713 10 c. black, green and brown-purple 10 10
714 25 c. black, greenish yellow and brown-purple 10 10
715 1 r. 60, black, greenish yellow & brn-purple 15 20
716 20 r. black, greenish yellow and brown-purple 1·25 2·00
713/16 .. .. *Set of* 4 1·40 2·00
MS717 215 × 140 mm. Nos. 713/16 .. .. 1·60 2·25
Designs:—25 c. Flag of the Gajanayaka, Huduhumpola, Kandy; 1 r. 60, Sinhala royal flag; 20 r. Sinhala royal flag, Ratnapura.

(Des L. Ranasinghe. Litho J.W.)

1981 (10 Feb). *Animals. T* **269** *and similar horiz designs. Multicoloured. P* 13½ × 14.
718 2 r. 50 on 1 r. 60, Type **269** 15 15
719 3 r. on 1 r. 50, Golden Palm Civet 15 20
720 4 r. on 2 r. Indian Spotted Chevrotain .. 25 30
721 5 r. on 3 r. 75, Rusty-spotted Cat 35 45
718/21 .. .. *Set of* 4 80 1·00
MS722 165 × 89 mm. Nos. 718/21 .. .. 1·00 1·75
Nos. 718/21 are previously unissued stamps surcharged as in T **269**.
For redrawn designs with revised face values see Nos. 780/2.

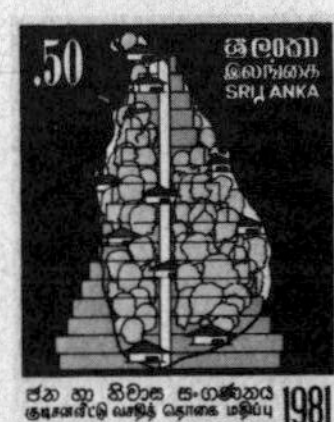
270 Heads and Houses on Map of Sri Lanka

271 Sri Lanka Light Infantry Regimental Badge

(Des D. Hemaratna. Litho Toppan Ptg Co, Japan)

1981 (2 Mar). *Population and Housing Census. P* 12½ × 12.
723 **270** 50 c. multicoloured 15 10

(Des D. Karunaratne. Litho Metal Box Singapore Ltd)

1981 (1 Apr). *Centenary of Sri Lanka Light Infantry. P* 12 × 11½.
724 **271** 2 r. multicoloured 30 30

272 Panel from "The Great Stupa" in Honour of the Buddha, Sanci, India, 1st-century A.D.

273 St. John Baptist de la Salle

(Des P. Jayatillake. Litho German Bank Note Ptg Co, Leipzig)

1981 (5 May). *Vesak. T* **272** *and similar vert designs. P* 13 × 13½.
725 35 c. black, blackish green and sage-green .. 10 10
726 50 c. multicoloured 10 10
727 7 r. black and flesh 40 45
725/7 .. .. *Set of* 3 45 50
MS728 147 × 108 mm. Nos. 725/7. P 13 × 14. .. 1·50 1·50
Designs:—50 c. Silk banner representing a Bodhisattva from "Thousand Buddhas", Tun-Huang, Central Asia; 7 r. Bodhisattva from Fondukistan, Afghanistan.

(Des Grant Kenyon and Eckhardt Ltd. Litho State Printing Works, Moscow)

1981 (15 May). *300th Anniv of De La Salle Brothers (Religious Order of the Brothers of the Christian Schools). P* 12½ × 12.
729 **273** 2 r. brt rose, deep violet-blue & new blue 40 40

274 Rev. Polwatte Sri Buddadatta **275** Dr. Al-Haj T. B. Jayah

(Des G. Fernando. Litho Metal Box Singapore Ltd)

1981 (22 May). *National Heroes. T* **274** *and similar vert designs, each showing scholar, writer and Buddhist campaigner. P* 12.
730 50 c. bistre 15 25
731 50 c. brown-rose 15 25
732 50 c. deep mauve 15 25
730/2 .. .. *Set of* 3 40 65
Designs:—No. 731, Rev. Mohottiwatte Gunananda; No. 732, Dr. Gnanaprakasar.

(Des P. Jayatillake. Litho Metal Box Singapore Ltd)

1981 (31 May). *Dr. Al-Haj T. B. Jayah (statesman) Commemoration. P* 12.
733 **275** 50 c. grey-green 15 20

276 Dr. N. M. Perera **277** Stylised Disabled Person and Globe

(Des P. Jayatillake. Litho Metal Box Singapore Ltd)

1981 (6 June). *Dr. N. M. Perera (campaigner for social reform) Commemoration. P* 12.
734 **276** 50 c. rose-red 20 20

(Des A. Adhikari. Litho State Printing Works, Moscow)

1981 (19 June). *International Year for Disabled Persons. P* 12 × 12½.
735 **277** 2 r. vermilion, black and grey 15 30

278 Hand placing Vote into Ballot Box

(Des J. Vincent (50 c.), R. Mawilmada (7 r.). Litho State Printing Works, Moscow)

1981 (7 July). *50th Anniv of Universal Franchise. T* **278** *and similar multicoloured design. P* 12½ × 12 (50 c.) *or* 12 × 12½ (7 r.)
736 50 c. Type **278** 15 10
737 7 r. Ballot box, and people forming map of Sri Lanka (*vert*) 70 40

279 T. W. Rhys Davids (founder) **280** Federation Emblem and "25"

(Des P. Jayatillake. Litho State Printing Works, Moscow)

1981 (14 July). *Centenary of Pali Text Society. P* 12½ × 12.
738 **279** 35 c. stone, dp brown & orange-brown .. 20 10

(Des R. Mawilmada. Litho Secura, Singapore)

1981 (21 July). *25th Anniv of All Ceylon Buddhist Students' Federation. P* 13½.
739 **280** 2 r. black, greenish yellow & dull verm 35 20

MINIMUM PRICE

The minimum price quote is 10p which represents a handling charge rather than a basis for valuing common stamps. For further notes about prices see introductory pages.

281 "Plan for Happiness" **282** Dove Symbol with Acupuncture Needle and "Yin-Yang" (Chinese universe duality emblem)

(Des D. Wijesinghe. Litho Secura, Singapore)

1981 (25 Sept). *Population and Family Planning. P* 13½ × 13.
740 **281** 50 c. multicoloured 25 10

(Des F. Perera. Litho State Printing Works, Moscow)

1981 (20 Oct). *World Acupuncture Congress. P* 12 × 12½.
741 **282** 2 r. black, yellow and red-orange .. 85 85

283 Union and Sri Lanka Flags **284** "Conserve our Forests"

(Des and litho J.W.)

1981 (21 Oct). *Royal Visit. P* 14.
742 **283** 50 c. multicoloured 15 10
743 5 r. multicoloured 65 75
MS744 165 × 90 mm. Nos. 742/3 .. .. .. 95 1·40

(Des Ravi Advertising. Litho German Bank Note Co, Leipzig)

1981 (27 Nov). *Forest Conservation. T* **284** *and similar horiz designs. P* 13.
745 35 c. multicoloured 10 10
746 50 c. olive-brown and stone 10 10
747 5 r. multicoloured .. .. 75 1·00
745/7 .. .. *Set of* 3 80 1·00
MS748 180 × 90 mm. Nos. 745/7. P 14 × 13 .. 95 1·40
Designs:—50 c. "Plant a tree"; 5 r. Jak (tree).

285 Sir James Peiris **286** F. R. Senanayaka

(Des P. Jayatillake. Litho Metal Box Singapore Ltd)

1981 (20 Dec). *Birth Centenary of Sir James Peiris (politician). P* 12.
749 **285** 50 c. light brown 25 15

(Des M. Katugampola. Litho J.W.)

1982 (1 Jan). *Birth Centenary of F. R. Senanayaka (national hero). P* 14.
750 **286** 50 c. olive-brown 25 25

287 Philip Gunawardhane **288** Department of Inland Revenue Building, Colombo

(Des P. Jayatillake. Litho J.W.)

1982 (11 Jan). *10th Death Anniv of Philip Gunawardhane (politician). P* 14.
751 **287** 50 c. cerise 25 25

(Des S. Mallikerachchi. Litho J.W.)

1982 (9 Feb). *50th Anniv of Department of Inland Revenue. P* 14.
752 **288** 50 c. black, blue-black & reddish orange 25 25

289 Rupavahini Emblem **290** Cricketer and Ball

(Des G. Arthasad. Litho J.W.)

1982 (15 Feb). *Inauguration of Rupavahini (national television service). P* 14.
753 **289** 2 r. 50, lemon, purple-brown and grey 80 1·00

(Des R. Mawilmada. Litho J.W.)

1982 (17 Feb). *First Sri Lanka–England Cricket Test Match, Colombo. P* 14.
754 **290** 2 r. 50, multicoloured .. .. .. 1·75 1·75

291 *Obsbeckia wightiana* **292** Mother breast-feeding Child

(Des P. Jayatillake. Litho Security Printers (M), Malaysia)

1982 (1 Apr). *Flowers. T* **291** *and similar horiz designs. Multicoloured. P* 12.
755 35 c. Type **291** 10 10
756 2 r. *Mesua nagassarium* 20 20
757 7 r. *Rhodomyrtus tomentosa* 50 90
758 20 r. *Phaius tancarvilleae* .. .. .. 1·40 2·00
755/8 .. .. *Set of* 4 2·00 2·75
MS759 180 × 110 mm. Nos. 755/8 .. .. 3·00 3·50

(Des A. Ratnapala. Litho Pakistan Security Printing Corp)

1982 (6 Apr). *Food and Nutrition Policy Planning. P* 13.
760 **292** 50 c. multicoloured 30 30

293 Conference Emblem **294** King Vessantara giving away magical, rain-making White Elephant

(Des M. Hussain. Litho J.W.)

1982 (21 Apr). *World Hindu Conference. P* 14.
761 **293** 50 c. multicoloured 30 30

(Des A. Dharmasiri. Litho J.W.)

1982 (23 Apr). *Vesak. Legend of Vessantara Jataka. Details of Cloth Painting from Arattana Rajamaha Vihara (temple), Hanguranketa, District of Nuwara Eliya. T* **294** *and similar horiz designs. Multicoloured. P* 14.
762 35 c. Type **294** 20 10
763 50 c. King Vessantara with family in Vankagiri Forest 20 10
764 2 r. 50, Vessantara giving away his children as slaves 75 85
765 5 r. Vessantara and family returning to Jetuttara in royal chariot .. .. .. 1·40 2·00
762/5 .. .. *Set of* 4 2·25 2·75
MS766 160 × 115 mm. Nos. 762/5 .. .. 2·50 3·00

295 Parliament Buildings, Sri Jayawardanapura **296** Dr. C. W. W. Kannangara

(Des M. Katugampola. Litho J.W.)

1982 (29 Apr). *Opening of Parliament Building Complex, Sri Jayawardanapura, Kotte. P* 14.
767 **295** 50 c. multicoloured 30 30

(Des M. Katugampola. Litho State Printing Works, Moscow)

1982 (22 May). *Dr. C. W. W. Kannangara ("Father of Free Education") Commemoration. P* 12 × 12½.
768 **296** 50 c. yellow-olive 30 30

297 Lord Baden-Powell **298** Dr. G. P. Malalasekara

(Des W. Rohana. Litho State Printing Works, Moscow)

1982 (24 May). *125th Birth Anniv of Lord Baden-Powell. P* 12½ × 12.
769 **297** 50 c. multicoloured 50 30

(Des A. Rasiah. Litho State Printing Works, Moscow)

1982 (26 May). *Dr. G. P. Malalasekara (founder of World Fellowship of Buddhists) Commemoration. P* 12 × 12½.
770 **298** 50 c. deep bluish green 30 30

299 Wheel encircling Globe **300** Wildlife

(Des A. Ratnapala. Litho State Printing Works, Moscow)

1982 (1 June). *World Buddhist Leaders Conference. P* 12½ × 12.
771 **299** 50 c. multicoloured 30 30

(Des U. Karunaratna. Litho State Printing Works, Moscow)

1982 (5 June). *World Environment Day. P* 12½ × 12.
772 **300** 50 c. multicoloured 55 35

301 Sir Waitialingam Duraiswamy

(Des A. Rasiah. Litho State Printing Works, Moscow)

1982 (14 June). *Sir Waitialingam Duraiswamy (statesman and educationalist) Commemoration. P* 12 × 12½.
773 **301** 50 c. blackish brown and brown 25 25

302 Y.M.C.A. Emblem

(Des R. Mawilmada. Litho State Printing Works, Moscow)

1982 (24 June). *Centenary of Colombo Y.M.C.A. P* 11½ × 11.
774 **302** 2 r. 50, multicoloured .. .. 1·00 1·40

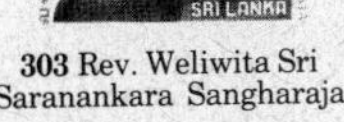

303 Rev. Weliwita Sri Saranankara Sangharaja **304** Maharagama Sasana Sevaka Samithiya Emblem

(Des M. Katugampola. Litho State Printing Works, Moscow)

1982 (5 July). *Rev. Weliwita Sri Saranankara Sangharaja (Buddhist leader) Commemoration. P* 12 × 12½.
775 **303** 50 c. brown and yellow-orange 30 30

(Des A. Ratnapala. Litho Toppan Ptg Co, Japan)

1982 (4 Aug). *Silver Jubilee of Maharagama Sasana Sevaka Samithiya (Buddhist Social Reform Movement). P* 12 × 12½.
776 **304** 50 c. multicoloured 30 30

305 Dr. Robert Koch **306** Sir John Kotelawala

(Des W. Rohana. Litho Toppan Ptg Co, Japan)

1982 (21 Sept). *Centenary of Robert Koch's Discovery of Tubercle Bacillus. P* 12 × 12½.
777 **305** 50 c. multicoloured 50 35

(Des A. Rasiah. Litho State Printing Works, Moscow)

1982 (2 Oct). *2nd Death Anniv of Sir John Kotelawala. P* 12 × 12½.
778 **306** 50 c. deep olive 30 30

307 Eye Donation Society and Lions Club Emblems **308** 1859 4d. Dull Rose and 1948 15 c. Independence Commemorative

(Des Grant Kenyon and Eckhardt Ltd. Litho State Printing Works, Moscow)

1982 (16 Nov). *World-Wide Sight Conservation Project. P* 12 × 12½.
779 **307** 2 r. 50, multicoloured 55 75

(Des L. Ranasinghe. Litho J.W.)

1982 (16 Nov)–**83**. *As Nos.* 718/20, *but without surcharges and showing revised face values. P* 14.
780 2 r. 50, Type **269** (1.6.83) 10 10
781 3 r. Golden Palm Civet (21.6.83) 10 10
782 4 r. Indian Spotted Chevrotain 15 10
780/2 .. .. *Set of* 3 20 25

A 5 r. value as No. 721 was scheduled for release on 28.5.86, but was withdrawn before issue due to objections to the design.

(Des D. Karunaratne. Litho Security Printers (M), Malaysia)

1982 (2 Dec). *125th Anniv of First Postage Stamps. T* **308** *and similar horiz design. Multicoloured. P* 13 × 13½.
784 50 c. Type **308** 10 15
785 2 r. 50, 1859 1s. 9d. green and 1981 50 c. "Just Society" stamp 25 50
MS786 59 × 84 mm. Nos. 784/5 (*sold at* 5 *r.*) .. 45 85

309 Sir Oliver Goonetilleke **310** Sarvodaya Emblem

(Des A. Ratnapala. Litho State Printing Works, Moscow)

1982 (17 Dec). *4th Death Anniv of Sir Oliver Goonetilleke (statesman). P* 12 × 12½.
787 **309** 50 c. olive-grey, bistre-brown and black 15 25

(Des P. Gunasinghe. Litho Secura, Singapore)

1983 (1 Jan). *25th Anniv of Sarvodaya Movement. P* 13 × 13½.
788 **310** 50 c. multicoloured 30 30

311 Morse Key, Radio Aerial and Radio Amateur Society Emblem **312** Customs Co-operation Council Emblem and Sri Lanka Flag

(Des W. Rohana. Litho Secura, Singapore)

1983 (17 Jan). *Amateur Radio Society. P* 13 × 13½.
789 **311** 2 r. 50, multicoloured .. .. 75 1·00

(Des W. Rohana. Litho Secura, Singapore)

1983 (26 Jan). *30th Anniv of International Customs Day. P* 12 × 11½.
790 **312** 50 c. multicoloured 15 20
791 5 r. multicoloured 55 90

313 Bottle-nosed Dolphin **314** *Lanka Athula* (container ship)

(Des G. Ratnavira. Litho Harrison)

1983 (22 Feb). *Marine Mammals. T* **313** *and similar horiz designs. P* 14½ × 14.
792 50 c. black, new blue and grey-green .. 15 15
793 2 r. multicoloured 25 30
794 2 r. 50, black, dp grey-blue & dp bluish grey 25 30
795 10 r. multicoloured 70 80
792/5 .. .. *Set of* 4 1·25 1·40

Designs:—2 r. Dugongs; 2 r. 50, Humpback Whale; 10 r. Sperm Whale.

(Des Vision Ltd. Litho Security Printers (M), Malaysia)

1983 (1 Mar). *Ships of the Ceylon Shipping Corporation. T* **314** *and similar horiz designs. Multicoloured. P* 11½ × 12.
796 50 c. Type **314** 10 10
797 2 r. 50, Map of routes 15 30
798 5 r. *Lanka Kalyani* (freighter) 25 55
799 20 r. *Tammanna* (tanker) .. .. .. 1·10 2·00
796/9 .. .. *Set of* 4 1·40 2·75

315 Woman with I.W.D. Emblem and Sri Lanka Flag **316** Waterfall

(Des R. Mawilmada. Litho Secura, Singapore)

1983 (8 Mar). *International Women's Day. T* **315** *and similar vert design. Multicoloured. P* 13.
800 50 c. Type **315** 10 15
801 5 r. Woman, emblem, map and symbols of progress 25 60

(Des S. Lankatilake. Litho Secura, Singapore)

1983 (14 Mar). *Commonwealth Day. T* **316** *and similar horiz designs. Multicoloured. P* 13.
802 50 c. Type **316** 10 10
803 2 r. 50, Tea plucking 15 20
804 5 r. Harvesting rice 25 35
805 20 r. Decorated elephants .. .. .. 80 1·75
802/5 .. .. *Set of* 4 1·10 2·10

317 Lions Club International Badge **318** "The Dream of Queen Mahamaya"

(Des U. Karunaratna. Litho J.W.)

1983 (7 May). *25th Anniv of Lions Club International in Sri Lanka. P* 14.
806 **317** 2 r. 50, multicoloured 45 60

(Des G. Keyt and A. Dharmasiri. Litho Toppan Ptg Co, Japan)

1983 (13 May). *Vesak. Life of Prince Siddhartha from temple murals at Gotami Vihara. T* **318** *and similar vert designs. Multicoloured. P* 12½ × 12.

807 35 c. Type **318** 10 10
808 50 c. "Prince Siddhartha given to Maha Brahma" 10 10
809 5 r. "Prince Siddhartha and the Sleeping Dancers" 25 60
810 10 r. "The Meeting with Mara" . . . . . . 55 1·25
807/10 . . . . *Set of* 4 80 1·75
MS811 150 × 90 mm. Nos. 807/10 . . . . 90 1·75

319 First Telegraph Transmission Colombo to Galle, 1858 **320** Henry Woodward Amarasuriya (philanthropist)

(Des W. Rohana. Litho Toppan Ptg Co, Japan)

1983 (17 May). *125th Anniv of Telecommunications in Sri Lanka* (2 *r.*) *and World Communications Year* (10 *r.*). *T* **319** *and similar horiz design. Multicoloured. P* 12 × 12½.

812 2 r. Type **319** 10 35
813 10 r. World Communications Year emblem . . 55 1·25

(Litho Security Printers (M), Malaysia (No. 810), Pakistan Security Printing Corp (others))

1983 (22 May). *National Heroes. T* **320** *and similar vert designs. P* 12 × 11½ (*No.* 814) *or* 13 (*others*).

814 50 c. bright emerald 15 30
815 50 c. new blue 15 30
816 50 c. magenta 15 30
817 50 c. turquoise-green 15 30
814/17 . . . . *Set of* 4 55 1·10

Designs:—No. 815, Father Simon Perera (historian); No. 816, Charles Lorenz (lawyer and newspaper editor); No. 817, Noordeen Abdul Cader (first President of All-Ceylon Muslim League).

A fifth design to commemorate C. W. Thamotheram Pillai was prepared for this set, but was withdrawn at the last moment when it was realised that the wrong portrait had been used. It is understood, however, that supplies were sold at some rural post offices where the instruction was not received in time. A corrected version was later issued, see No. 825.

321 Family and Village **322** Caravan of Bulls

(Des K. Gunasiri and U. Karunaratna. Litho Toppan Ptg Co, Japan)

1983 (23 June). *Gam Udawa* (*Village Re-awakening Movement*). *T* **321** *and similar horiz design. Multicoloured. P* 12 × 12½.

818 50 c. Type **321** 10 15
819 5 r. Village view 25 65

(Des A. Rasiah (35 c., 2 r.), D. Hemaratna (2 r. 50), U. Karunaratna (5 r.). Litho State Printing Office, Budapest)

1983 (22 Aug). *Transport. T* **322** *and similar horiz designs. Multicoloured. P* 12

820 35 c. Type **322** 10 10
821 2 r. Steam train 30 35
822 2 r. 50, Ox and cart 30 50
823 5 r. Ford motor car . . . . 45 1·00
820/3 . . . . *Set of* 4 1·10 1·75

323 Sir Tikiri Banda Panabokke **324** C. W. Thamotheram Pillai

(Des and litho Harrison)

1983 (2 Sept). *20th Death Anniv of Adigar Sir Tikiri Banda Panabokke. P* 14 × 14½.

824 **323** 50 c. Indian red 30 30

(Des and litho Pakistan Security Printing Corp)

1983 (1 Oct). *C. W. Thamotheram Pillai (Tamil scholar) Commemoration. P* 13.

825 **324** 50 c. orange-brown 30 30

See note below No. 817.

325 Arabi Pasha **326** Sri Lanka Wood Pigeon

(Des and litho Pakistan Security Printing Corp)

1983 (13 Nov). *Centenary of the Exile to Ceylon of Arabi Pasha (Egyptian nationalist). P* 13 × 13½.

826 **325** 50 c. green 30 30

(Des G. Ratnavira. Litho Format)

1983 (22 Nov)–**88**. *Birds. T* **326** *and similar horiz designs. Multicoloured. P* 14½.

827 25 c. Type **326** 40 10
828 35 c. Large Sri Lanka White Eye 40 10
829 2 r. Sri Lanka Dusky Blue Flycatcher . . 10 10
829*a* 7 r. As 35 c. (28.9.88) 20 25
830 20 r. Ceylon Coucal 60 65
827/30 . . . . *Set of* 5 1·50 1·10
MS831 183 × 93 mm. Nos. 827/9 and 830 . . 2·75 3·25

327 Pelene Siri Vajiragnana **328** Mary praying over Jesus and St. Joseph welcoming Shepherds

(Des and litho Harrison)

1983 (25 Nov). *Pelene Siri Vajiragnana (scholar) Commemoration. P* 14 × 14½.

832 **327** 50 c. red-brown 30 30

(Des P. de Silva. Litho German Bank Note Co, Leipzig)

1983 (30 Nov). *Christmas. P* 12½ × 13.

833 **328** 50 c. multicoloured 10 15
834 5 r. multicoloured 25 60
MS835 85 × 141 mm. Nos. 833/4 . . . . 35 80

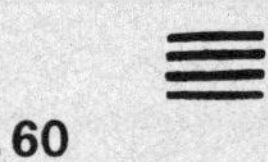

.60 .60

(**329**) (**330**)

1983 (1 Dec). *No. 680a surch with T* **329/30**.

836 **236** 60 c. on 50 c. gold, bright yellow-green and emerald (surch T **329**) . . 25 25
a. Surch inverted . . . .
837 60 c. on 50 c. gold, bright yellow-green and emerald (surch T **330**) . . 65 65

331 Paddy Field, Globe and F.A.O. Emblem

(Des R. Mawilmada. Litho State Ptg Works, Moscow)

1984 (2 Jan). *World Food Day. P* 12½ × 12.

838 **331** 3 r. multicoloured 15 40

332 Modern Tea Factory **333** Students and University

(Des M. Ratnapala. Litho State Ptg Works, Moscow)

1984 (31 Jan). *Centenary of the Colombo Tea Auctions. T* **332** *and similar horiz designs. Multicoloured. P* 12½ × 12.

839 1 r. Type **332** 10 15
840 2 r. Logo 15 30
841 5 r. Girl picking tea 30 75
842 10 r. Auction in progress . . . . . . 65 1·40
839/42 . . . . *Set of* 4 1·00 2·40

(Des R. Mawilmada. Litho Security Printers (M), Malaysia)

1984 (10 Feb). *4th Anniv of Mahapola Scheme for Development and Education. T* **333** *and similar vert designs. Multicoloured. P* 12.

843 60 c. Type **333** 10 15
844 1 r. Teacher with Gnana Darsana class . . 10 15
845 5 r. 50, Student with books and microscope 35 1·00
846 6 r. Mahapola lamp symbol . . . . . . 40 1·25
843/6 . . . . *Set of* 4 75 2·25

334 King Daham Sonda instructing Angels **335** Development Programme Logo

(Des A. Dharmasiri. Litho D.L.R)

1984 (27 Apr). *Vesak. The Story of King Daham Sonda from ancient casket paintings. T* **334** *and similar horiz designs. Multicoloured. A. P* 14. *B. P* 13 × 13½.

		A		B	
847	35 c. Type **334**	10	10	25	20
848	60 c. Elephant paraded with gift of gold	10	20	20	25
849	5 r. King Daham Sonda leaps into mouth of God Sakra . .	30	75	45	1·00
850	10 r. God Sakra carrying King Daham Sonda . .	65	1·25	65	1·50
847/50	. . . . *Set of* 4	95	2·00	1·40	2·75
MS851	154 × 109 mm. Nos. 847/50. P 13			1·00	2·00

(Des R. Mawilmada. Litho Harrison)

1984 (5 May). *Sri Lanka Lions Clubs' Development Programme. P* 14 × 14½.

852 **335** 60 c. multicoloured 20 25

336 Dodanduwe Siri Piyaratana Tissa Mahanayake Thero (Buddhist scholar) **337** Association Emblem

(Litho State Ptg Works, Moscow)

1984 (22 May). *National Heroes. T* **336** *and similar vert designs. P* 12 × 12½.

853 60 c. yellow-bistre 10 15
854 60 c. yellow-green 10 15
855 60 c. emerald-green 10 15
856 60 c. red 10 15
857 60 c. deep yellow-brown 10 15
853/7 . . . . *Set of* 5 20 65

Designs:—No. 853, Type **336**; 854, G. P. Wickremarachchi (physician); 855, Sir Mohamed Macan Markar (politician); 856, Dr. W. Arthur de Silva (philanthropist), 857, K. Balasingham (lawyer).

(Des A. Harischandra. Litho Govt Printing Bureau, Tokyo)

1984 (16 June). *Centenary of Public Service Mutual Provident Association. P* 13 × 13½.

858 **337** 4 r. 60, multicoloured 25 70

338 Sri Lanka Village **339** World Map showing A.P.B.U. Countries

(Des S. Herath. Litho State Ptg Wks, Moscow)

1984 (23 June). *6th Anniv of "Gam Udawa" (Village Reawakening Movement). P* 12 × 12½.

859 **338** 60 c. multicoloured 10 15

(Des G. Arthasad. Litho State Ptg Wks, Moscow)

1984 (30 June). *20th Anniv of Asia-Pacific Broadcasting Union. P* 12½ × 12.

860 **339** 7 r. multicoloured 50 85

340 Drummers and Elephant carrying Royal Instructions — **341** *Vanda memoria* Ernest Soysa (orchid)

(Des R. Mawilmada. Litho State Ptg Wks, Moscow)

1984 (11 Aug). *Esala Perahera (Procession of the Tooth), Kandy. T* **340** *and similar horiz designs. Multicoloured. P* 12½×12.

861 4 r. 60, Type **340** 35 50
a. Horiz strip of 4. Nos. 861/4 .. .. 1·25
862 4 r. 60, Dancers and elephants 35 50
863 4 r. 60, Elephant carrying Tooth Relic .. 35 50
864 4 r. 60, Custodian of the Sacred Tooth and attendants 35 50
861/4 .. .. *Set of* 4 1·25 1·75
MS865 223×108 mm. Nos. 861/4 .. .. 1·25 2·00

Nos. 861/4 were printed together, *se-tenant*, in horizontal strips of 4 throughout the sheet, forming a composite design.

(Des G. Ratnavira. Litho D.L.R.)

1984 (22 Aug). *50th Anniv of Ceylon Orchid Circle. T* **341** *and similar vert designs, showing orchids. Multicoloured. A. P* 14. *B. P* 13½×13.

		A		B	
866	60 c. Type **341**	30	15	15	15
867	4 r. 60, *Acanthephippium bicolor*	80	1·00	65	1·00
868	5 r. *Vanda tessellata var. rufescens*	1·00	1·25	45	90
869	10 r. *Anoectochilus setaceus* ..	1·00	1·50	†	
866/9	.. .. .. *Set of* 4	2·75	3·50	†	
MS870	155×110 mm. Nos. 866/9. P 13			3·00	4·00

342 Symbolic Athletes and Stadium — **343** D. S. Senanayake, Temple and Fields

(Des M. Heenkenda. Litho Govt Printing Bureau, Tokyo)

1984 (5 Oct). *National School Games. P* 13½×13.

871 **342** 60 c. black, grey and bright new blue .. 25 25

(Des L. Jayawardena (35 c.), G. Fernando (60 c.), N. Lasantha (4 r. 60), R. Mawilmada (6 r.). Litho J.W.)

1984 (20 Oct). *Birth Centenary of D. S. Senanayake (former Prime Minister). T* **343** *and similar horiz designs. Multicoloured. P* 14.

872 35 c. Type **343** 10 10
873 60 c. Senanayake and statue 10 10
874 4 r. 60, Senanayake and irrigation project .. 25 50
875 6 r. Senanayake and House of Representatives 30 60
872/5 .. .. *Set of* 4 55 1·10

344 Lake House — **345** Agricultural Workers and Globe

(Des Grant Kenyon and Eckhardt Ltd. Litho State Printing Office, Budapest)

1984 (19 Nov). *150th Anniv of the "Observer" Newspaper. P* 13×13½.

876 **344** 4 r. 60, multicoloured 30 60

(Des M. Ratnapala. Litho German Bank Note Ptg Co, Leipzig)

1984 (10 Dec). *20th Anniv of World Food Programme. P* 13×13½.

877 **345** 7 r. multicoloured 50 60

346 College Emblem — **347** Dove and Stylized Figures

(Des S. Herath. Litho J.W.)

1984 (24 Dec). *Centenary of Baari Arabic College, Weligama. P* 13×12½.

878 **346** 4 r. 60, blackish olive, turquoise-green and turquoise-blue 45 65

(Des S. Chandrajeewa (4 r. 60), O. Weerakkody (20 r.). Litho J.W.)

1985 (1 Jan). *International Youth Year. T* **347** *and similar horiz design. Multicoloured. P* 12½×13.

879 4 r. 60, Type **347** 25 30
880 20 r. Dove, stylized figures and flower .. 1·10 1·25

348 Religious Symbols — **349** College Crest

(Des R. Mawilmada. Litho Security Printers (M), Malaysia)

1985 (20 Jan). *World Religion Day. P* 12.

881 **348** 4 r. 60, multicoloured 25 50

(Des G. Arthasad. Litho J.W.)

1985 (29 Jan). *150th Anniv of Royal College, Colombo. T* **349** *and similar vert design. P* 13×12½.

882 60 c. bright yellow and deep ultramarine .. 10 10
883 7 r. multicoloured .. .. 40 1·00

Design:—7 r. Royal College.

350 Banknotes, Buildings, Ship and "Wheel of Life" — **351** Wariyapola Sri Sumangala Thero

(Des R. Mawilmada. Litho J.W.)

1985 (7 Feb). *5th Anniv of Mahapola Scheme. P* 14.

884 **350** 60 c. multicoloured 15 20

(Des G. Fernando. Litho State Printing Office, Budapest)

1985 (2 Mar). *Wariyapola Sri Sumangala Thero (Buddhist priest and patriot) Commemoration. P* 13×13½.

885 **351** 60 c. blk, reddish brn & greenish yell 15 20

352 Victoria Dam — **353** Cover of 50th Edition of International Buddhist Annual, *Vesak Sirisara*

(Des G. Arthasad. Litho State Ptg Wks, Moscow)

1985 (12 Apr). *Inauguration of Victoria Hydro-electric Project. T* **352** *and similar multicoloured design. P* 12½×12 *(60 c.) or* 12×12½ *(7 r.).*

886 60 c. Type **352** 15 15
887 7 r. Map of Sri Lanka enclosing dam and power station (*vert*) 65 95

(Des B. Harischandra (35 c.), R. Mawilmada (others). Litho J.W.)

1985 (26 Apr). *Centenary of Vesak Poya Holiday. T* **353** *and similar vert designs. Multicoloured. P* 13×12½.

888 35 c. Type **353** 10 10
889 60 c. Buddhists worshipping at temple .. 10 10
890 6 r. Buddhist Theosophical Society Headquarters, Colombo 30 35
891 9 r. Buddhist flag 50 55
888/91 .. .. *Set of* 4 80 90
MS892 180×110 mm. Nos. 888/91 .. .. 2·00 2·50

354 Ven. Waskaduwe Sri Subhuthi (priest and scholar) — **355** Stylised Village and People

(Des S. Silva. Litho J.W.)

1985 (22 May). *Personalities. T* **354** *and similar vert designs. P* 13×12½.

893 60 c. black, yellow-orange and lake-brown .. 10 15
894 60 c. black, yellow-orange and deep mauve .. 10 15
895 60 c. black, yellow-orange and light brown .. 10 15
896 60 c. black, yellow-orange and emerald .. 10 15
893/6 .. .. *Set of* 4 35 55

Designs:— No. 893, Type **354**; 894, Revd. Fr. Peter A. Pillai (educationist and social reformer); 895, Dr. Senarath Paranavitane (scholar); 896, A. M. Wapche Marikar (architect and educationist).

(Des S. Herath. Litho German Bank Note Co, Leipzig)

1985 (23 June). *Gam Udawa '85 (Village Re-awakening Movement). P* 13½×13.

897 **355** 60 c. multicoloured 20 25

356 Emblem — **357** Kothmale Dam and Reservoir

(Des B. Harischandra. Litho German Bank Note Co, Leipzig)

1985 (25 June). *50th Anniv of Colombo Young Poets' Association. P* 14.

898 **356** 60 c. multicoloured 15 20

(Des R. Mawilmada. Litho J.W.)

1985 (24 Aug). *Inauguration of Kothmale Hydro-electric Project. T* **357** *and similar horiz design. Multicoloured. P* 14.

899 60 c. Type **357** 10 15
900 6 r. Kothmale Power Station 35 60

358 Federation Logo — **359** Breast Feeding

(Des R. Mawilmada. Litho J.W.)

1985 (2 Sept). *10th Asian and Oceanic Congress of Obstetrics and Gynaecology. P* 14.

901 **358** 7 r. multicoloured .. .. .. 1·00 1·00

(Des B. Harischandra. Litho Cartor, France)

1985 (5 Sept). *U.N.I.C.E.F. Child Survival and Development Programme. T* **359** *and similar vert designs. Multicoloured. W w* **17**. *P* 13½.

902 35 c. Type **359** 10 10
903 60 c. Child and oral rehydration salts .. 10 10
904 6 r. Weighing child (growth monitoring) .. 50 50
905 9 r. Immunization 80 80
902/5 .. .. *Set of* 4 1·40 1·40
MS906 99×180 mm. Nos. 902/5. P 12½ .. 1·40 1·60

360 Blowing Conch Shell — **361** Casket containing Land Grant Deed

(Des G. Malaviachi. Litho Heraclio Fournier, Spain)

1985 (27 Sept). *10th Anniv of World Tourism Organization. T* **360** *and similar horiz designs. Multicoloured. P* 14.

907 1 r. Type **360** 10 10
908 6 r. Parliamentary Complex, Jayawardhanapura, Kotte 30 50
909 7 r. Tea plantation 40 65
910 10 r. Ruwanveliseya (Buddhist shrine), Anuradhapura 60 85
907/10 .. .. *Set of* 4 1·25 1·90
MS911 179×89 mm. Nos. 907/10. P 13½ .. 1·40 2·00

(Des B. Harischandra. Litho Harrison)

1985 (15 Oct). *50th Anniv of Land Development Ordinance. P* 14×15.

912 **361** 4 r. 60, multicoloured 30 60

PRICES OF SETS

Set prices are given for many issues, generally those containing three stamps or more. Definitive sets include one of each value or major colour change, but do not cover different perforations, die types or minor shades. Where a choice is possible the set prices are based on the cheapest versions of the stamps included in the listings.

362 Koran and Map of Sri Lanka **363** "Our Lady of Matara" Statue

(Des R. Mawilmada. Litho Cartor, France)

1985 (17 Oct). *Translation of The Koran into Sinhala. W* w **17**. *P* 13½.
913 **362** 60 c. gold and bright violet 15 25

(Des S. Silva. Litho Security Printers (M), Malaysia)

1985 (5 Nov). *Christmas. T* **363** *and similar vert design. Multicoloured. P* 12.
914 60 c. Type **363**.. .. .. 10 10
915 9 r. "Our Lady of Madhu" statue 50 60
MS916 180×100 mm. Nos. 914/15 .. .. 1·25 1·50

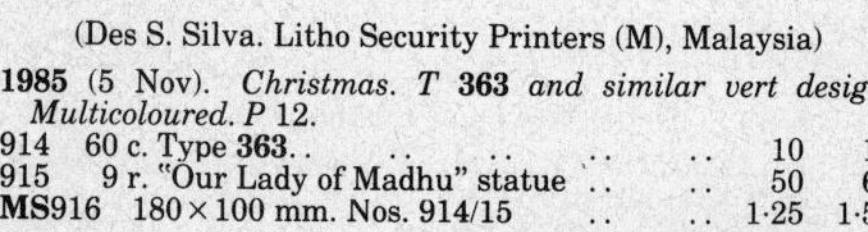

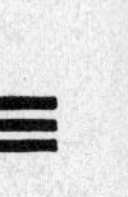

.75

(364) **365** Linked Arms and Map of S.A.A.R.C. Countries

1985 (1 Dec)–**86**. *Nos.* 680*b*, 780, 828, 860 *and* 879 *surch as T* **364**.
917 **236** 75 c. on 60 c. gold, bright yellow-green and emerald (G.) 10 10
a. Surch double .. .. .. † —
918 **347** 1 r. on 4 r. 60, mult (29.4.86) 20 15
919 **339** 1 r. on 7 r. multicoloured (20.1.86) .. 35 15
920 **269** 5 r. 75 on 2 r. 50, multicoloured (Br) .. 50 35
a. Surch double
921 – 7 r. on 35 c. mult (No. 828) (10.3.86) .. 65 45
a. Surch inverted .. .. ..
917/21 .. .. *Set of* 5 1·50 1·10

(Des B. Harischandra. Litho J.W.)

1985 (8 Dec). *1st Summit Meeting of South Asian Association for Regional Co-operation, Dhaka, Bangladesh. T* **365** *and similar horiz design. Multicoloured. P* 14.
922 60 c. Type **365**.. .. .. 40 75
923 5 r. 50, Logo and flags of member countries 40 50

No 922 was, reportedly, withdrawn on 11 December after Pakistan objected to the boundaries shown on the map.

366 "Viceroy Special" Train

(Des G. Malaviachi. Litho Format)

1986 (2 Feb). *Inaugural Run of "Viceroy Special" Train from Colombo to Kandy. P* 12½.
924 **366** 1 r. multicoloured 50 45

367 Girl and Boy Students **368** D. R. Wijewardena

(Des S. Silva. Litho Heraclio Fournier, Spain)

1986 (14 Feb). *6th Anniv of Mahapola Scheme. P* 14.
925 **367** 75 c. multicoloured 10 20

(Des S. Silva. Litho J.W.)

1986 (23 Feb). *Birth Centenary of D. R. Wijewardena (newspaper publisher). P* 14×14½.
926 **368** 75 c. orange-brown and deep olive .. 10 20

369 Ven Welitara Gnanatillake Maha Nayake Thero **370** Red Cross Flag and Personnel

(Des S. Silva. Litho Cartor, France)

1986 (26 Feb). *Ven. Welitara Gnanatillake Maha Nayake Thero (scholar) Commemoration. W* w **17**. *P* 13½.
927 **369** 75 c. multicoloured 25 25

(Des W. Rohana. Litho Format)

1986 (31 Mar). *50th Anniv of Sri Lanka Red Cross Society. P* 12½.
928 **370** 75 c. multicoloured 35 25

371 Comet depicted as Goddess visiting Sun-god **372** Woman lighting Lamp

(Des W. Rohana. Litho Format)

1986 (5 Apr). *Appearance of Halley's Comet. T* **371** *and similar horiz designs. Multicoloured. P* 12½.
929 50 c. Type **371**.. .. .. 10 10
930 75 c. Comet and constellations of Scorpius and Sagittarius 10 10
931 6 r. 50, Comet's orbit 35 60
932 8 r. 50, Edmond Halley 50 85
929/32 .. .. *Set of* 4 90 1·40
MS933 180×115 mm. Nos. 929/32 .. .. 1·75 2·25

(Des B. Harischandra. Litho Format)

1986 (10 Apr). *Sinhalese and Tamil New Year. T* **372** *and similar vert designs. Multicoloured. P* 12½.
934 50 c. Type **372**.. .. .. 10 10
935 75 c. Woman and festive foods 10 15
936 6 r. 50, Women playing drum 35 75
937 8 r. 50, Anointing and making offerings at temple .. .. 50 1·00
934/7 .. .. *Set of* 4 85 1·75
MS938 178×108 mm. Nos. 934/7 .. .. 1·75 2·00

373 The King donating Elephant to the Brahmin **374** Ven. Kalukondayave Sri Prajnasekhara Maha Nayake Thero (Buddhist leader and social reformer)

(Des N. Bulathsinhala. Litho Format)

1986 (16 May). *Vesak. Wall paintings from Samudragiri Temple, Mirissa. T* **373** *and similar horiz designs. Multicoloured. P* 12½.
939 50 c. Type **373**.. .. .. 10 10
940 75 c. The Bodhisattva in the Vasavarthi heaven 10 15
941 5 r. The offering of milk rice by Sujatha .. 35 75
942 10 r. The offering of parched corn and honey by Thapassu and Bhalluka .. .. 60 1·25
939/42 .. .. *Set of* 4 90 2·00

(Des S. Silva. Litho Format)

1986 (22 May). *National Heroes. T* **374** *and similar vert designs. Multicoloured. P* 12½.
943 75 c. Type **374**.. .. .. 10 15
944 75 c. Brahmachari Walisinghe Harischandra (social reformer) (birth centenary) 10 15
945 75 c. Martin Wickramasinghe (author and scholar) 10 15
946 75 c. G. G. Ponnambalam (politician) .. 10 15
947 75 c. A. M. A. Azeez (Islamic scholar) (75th birth anniv) 10 15
943/7 .. .. *Set of* 5 20 65

375 Stylised Village and People **376** Co-op Flag and Emblem

(Des S. Herath. Litho German Bank Note Co, Leipzig)

1986 (23 June). *Gam Udawa '86 (Village Re-awakening Movement). P* 13½×13.
948 **375** 75 c. multicoloured 25 25

(Des A. Harischandra. Litho Format)

1986 (5 July). *75th Anniv of Sri Lanka Co-operative Movement. P* 12½.
949 **376** 1 r. multicoloured 40 40

377 Arthur V. Dias **378** Bull Elephant

(Des S. Silva. Litho Harrison)

1986 (31 July). *Birth Centenary of Arthur V. Dias (philanthropist). P* 14×15.
950 **377** 1 r. chestnut and dull violet-blue .. 25 25

(Des G. Ratnavira. Litho Harrison)

1986 (5 Aug). *Sri Lanka Wild Elephants. T* **378** *and similar horiz designs. Multicoloured. P* 15×14.
951 5 r. Type **378** 50 75
a. Horiz strip of 4. Nos. 951/4 .. .. 1·75
952 5 r. Cow elephant and calf 50 75
953 5 r. Cow elephant 50 75
954 5 r. Elephants bathing 50 75
951/4 .. .. *Set of* 4 1·75 2·75

Nos. 951/4 were printed, together, *se-tenant*, in horizontal strips of four throughout the sheet.

379 Congress Logo **380** Map showing Route of Cable and Telephone Receiver

(Des S. Silva. Litho Govt Printing Bureau, Tokyo)

1986 (14 Aug). *2nd Indo-Pacific Congress on Legal Medicine and Forensic Sciences. P* 13½×13.
955 **379** 8 r. 50, multicoloured 50 75

(Des R. Mawilmada. Litho Security Printers (M), Malaysia)

1986 (8 Sept). *SEA-ME-WE Submarine Cable Project. P* 13½×14.
956 **380** 5 r. 75, multicoloured 35 60

381 Anniversary Logo **382** Logo on Flag

(Des R. Mawilmada. Litho Format)

1986 (20 Sept). *25th Anniv of Dag Hammarskjöld Award. P* 12½.
957 **381** 2 r. multicoloured 25 20

(Des A. Harischandra. Litho Security Printers (M), Malaysia)

1986 (22 Sept). *2nd National School Games. P* 12.
958 **382** 1 r. multicoloured 25 20

383 Logo　**384** College Building and Crest

(Des W. Rohana. Litho Govt Printing Bureau, Tokyo)

1986 (27 Sept). *60th Anniv of Surveyors' Institute of Sri Lanka. P* 13½ × 13.
959 **383** 75 c. red-brown and cinnamon .. 10 20

(Des W. Rohana. Litho Security Printers (M), Malaysia)

1986 (1 Nov). *Centenary of Ananda College, Colombo. T* **384** *and similar horiz designs. P* 12.
960 75 c. multicoloured 10 10
961 5 r. multicoloured 20 25
962 5 r. 75, multicoloured 20 25
963 6 r. carmine-red, gold and rose-lilac .. 20 25
960/3 .. .. *Set of* 4 60 70
Designs:—5 r. Sports field and college crest; 5 r. 75, Col. H. S. Olcott (founder), Ven. Migettuwatte Gunananda, Ven. Hikkaduwe Sri Sumangala (Buddhist leaders) and Buddhist flag; 6 r. College flag.

385 Mangrove Swamp　**386** Family and Housing Estate

(Des G. Ratnavira. Litho Security Printers (M), Malaysia)

1986 (11 Nov). *Mangrove Conservation. T* **385** *and similar horiz designs. Multicoloured. P* 12.
964 35 c. Type **385** 10 10
965 50 c. Mangrove tree 10 10
966 75 c. Germinating mangrove flower .. 10 10
967 6 r. Fiddler Crab 45 55
964/7 .. .. *Set of* 4 60 70

(Des R. Mawilmada. Litho Govt Printing Bureau, Tokyo)

1987 (1 Jan). *International Year of Shelter for the Homeless. P* 13 × 13½.
968 **386** 75 c. multicoloured 25 10

387 Ven. Ambagahawatte Indasabhawaragnanasamy Thero　**388** Proctor John de Silva

(Des S. Silva. Litho Security Printers (M), Malaysia)

1987 (29 Jan). *Ven. Ambagahawatte Indasabhawaragnanasamy Thero (Buddhist monk) Commemoration. P* 12.
969 **387** 5 r. 75, multicoloured 20 25

(Des S. Silva. Litho Security Printers (M), Malaysia)

1987 (31 Jan). *Proctor John de Silva (playwright) Commemoration. P* 12.
970 **388** 5 r. 75, multicoloured 20 25

389 Mahapola Logo and Aspects of Communication　**390** Dr. R. L. Brohier

(Des R. Mawilmada. Litho Security Printers (M), Malaysia)

1987 (6 Feb). *7th Anniv of Mahapola Scheme. P* 12.
971 **389** 75 c. multicoloured 10 10

(Des S. Silva. Litho Security Printers (M), Malaysia)

1987 (10 Feb). *Dr. Richard L. Brohier (historian and surveyor) Commemoration. P* 12.
972 **390** 5 r. 75, multicoloured 20 25

391 Tyre Corporation Building, Kelaniya, and Logo

(Des A. Harischandra. Litho Questa)

1987 (23 Mar). *25th Anniv of Sri Lanka Tyre Corporation. P* 14.
973 **391** 5 r. 75, black, lake and bright orange .. 20 25

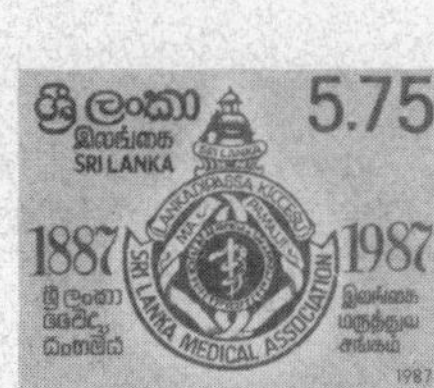

392 Logo　**393** Clasped Hands, Farmer and Paddy Field

(Des A. Harischandra. Litho Govt Printing Bureau, Tokyo)

1987 (24 Mar). *Centenary of Sri Lanka Medical Association. P* 13 × 13½.
974 **392** 5 r. 75, lake-brown, greenish yellow & blk 20 25

(Des B. Harischandra. Litho Questa)

1987 (29 Mar). *Inauguration of Farmers' Pension and Social Security Benefit Scheme. P* 14.
975 **393** 75 c. multicoloured 10 10

394 Exhibition Logo　**395** Young Children with W.H.O. and Immunization Logos

(Des W. Rohana. Litho Security Printers (M), Malaysia)

1987 (2 Apr). *Mahaweli Maha Goviya Contest and Agro Mahaweli Exhibition. P* 12.
976 **394** 75 c. multicoloured 10 10

(Des B. Harischandra. Litho Questa)

1987 (7 Apr). *World Health Day. P* 14.
977 **395** 1 r. multicoloured 20 10

396 Girls playing on Swing　**397** Lotus Lanterns

(Des G. Fernando. Litho Security Printers (M), Malaysia)

1987 (9 Apr). *Sinhalese and Tamil New Year. T* **396** *and similar vert design. Multicoloured. P* 12.
978 75 c. Type **396** 10 10
979 5 r. Girls with oil lamp and sun symbol .. 20 25

(Des W. Rohana. Litho Security Printers (M), Malaysia)

1987 (4 May). *Vesak. T* **397** *and similar horiz designs. Multicoloured. P* 12.
980 50 c. Type **397** 10 10
981 75 c. Octagonal lanterns 10 10
982 5 r. Star lanterns 20 25
983 10 r. Gok lanterns 35 40
980/3 .. .. *Set of* 4 60 70
MS984 150 × 90 mm. Nos. 980/3 .. .. .. 65 75

398 Emerald-collared Parakeet　**399** Ven. Heenatiyana Sri Dhammaloka Maha Nayake Thero (Buddhist monk)

(Des G. Ratnavira. Litho Questa)

1987 (18 May). *Birds. T* **398** *and similar horiz designs. Multicoloured. P* 14.
985 50 c. Type **398** 10 10
986 1 r. Legge's Flowerpecker 15 10
987 5 r. Ceylon White-headed Starling .. 15 20
988 10 r. Ceylon Jungle Babbler (*Turdoides rufescens*) 30 35
985/8 .. .. *Set of* 4 50 60
MS989 140 × 80 mm. Nos. 985/8 .. .. .. 1·00 1·25
No. 986 exists with different imprint dates beneath the design.

(Des S. Silva. Litho Security Printers (M), Malaysia)

1987 (22 May). *National Heroes. T* **399** *and similar vert designs. Multicoloured. P* 12.
990 75 c. Type **399** 10 10
991 75 c. P. de S. Kularatne (educationist) .. 10 10
992 75 c. M. C. Abdul Rahuman (legislator) .. 10 10
990/2 .. .. *Set of* 3 15 15

400 Peasant Family and Village　**401** *Mesua nagassarium*

(Des J. Semage. Litho Security Printers (M), Malaysia)

1987 (23 June). *Gam Udawa '87 (Village Re-awakening Movement). P* 12.
993 **400** 75 c. multicoloured 10 10

(Des P. Hewabettage (75 c.), B. Harischandra (5 r.). Litho Security Printers (M), Malaysia)

1987 (25 June). *Forest Conservation. T* **401** *and similar horiz design. Multicoloured. P* 12.
994 75 c. Type **401** 10 10
995 5 r. Elephants in forest 20 25

402 Dharmaraja College, Crest and Col. H. Olcott (founder)　**403** Youth Services Logo

(Des C. Kandewela. Litho Security Printers (M), Malaysia)

1987 (30 June). *Centenary of Dharmaraja College, Kandy. P* 12.
996 **402** 75 c. multicoloured 25 10

(Des H. Dayaratne. Litho Security Printers (M), Malaysia)

1987 (15 July). *20th Anniv of National Youth Services. P* 12.
997 **403** 75 c. multicoloured 10 10

404 Arm holding Torch and Mahaweli Logo　**405** Open Bible and Logo

(Des W. Rohana. Litho Security Printers (M), Malaysia)

1987 (5 Sept). *Mahaweli Games. P* 12.
998 **404** 75 c. multicoloured 25 25

(Des C. Beling. Litho Security Printers (M), Malaysia)

1987 (2 Oct). *175th Anniv of Ceylon Bible Society. P* 12.
999 **405** 5 r. 75, multicoloured 20 25

406 Hurdler and Committee Symbol

407 Madonna and Child, Flowers and Oil Lamp

(Des R. Mawilmada. Litho Heraclio Fournier, Spain)

1987 (8 Oct). *50th Anniv of National Olympic Committee. P* 13.
1000 **406** 10 r. multicoloured 35 40

(Des B. Mendis. Litho Security Printers (M), Malaysia)

1987 (17 Nov). *Christmas. T* **407** *and similar vert design. Multicoloured. P* 12 (75 *c.*) *or* 12½ × 13 (10 *r.*).
1001 75 c. Type **407** 10 10
1002 10 r. Christ Child in manger, star and dove 35 40
MS1003 145 × 82 mm. Nos. 1001/2. P 12 .. 40 45

408 Sir Ernest de Silva

409 Society Logo

(Des P. Gunasinghe. Litho German Bank Note Co, Leipzig)

1987 (25 Nov). *Birth Centenary of Sir Ernest de Silva (philanthropist and philatelist). P* 13 × 13½.
1004 **408** 75 c. multicoloured 10 10

(Des W. Rohana. Litho German Bank Note Co, Leipzig)

1987 (28 Nov). *150th Anniv of Kandy Friend-in-Need Society. P* 13½ × 13.
1005 **409** 75 c. multicoloured 10 10

410 University Flag and Graduates

411 Father Joseph Vaz

(Des R. Samarasinghe. Litho Security Printers (M), Malaysia)

1987 (14 Dec). *First Convocation of Buddhist and Pali University. P* 12.
1006 **410** 75 c. multicoloured 10 10

(Des S. Silva. Litho Security Printers (M), Malaysia)

1987 (15 Dec). *300th Anniv of Arrival of Father Joseph Vaz in Kandy. P* 12.
1007 **411** 75 c. multicoloured 10 10

412 Wheel of Dhamma, Dagaba and Bo Leaf

413 Dharmayatra Lorry

(Des W. Rohana. Litho Security Printers (M), Malaysia)

1988 (1 Jan). *30th Anniv of Buddhist Publication Society, Kandy. P* 12.
1008 **412** 75 c. multicoloured 10 10

(Des B. Harischandra. Litho German Bank Note Co, Leipzig)

1988 (4 Jan). *5th Anniv of Mahapola Dharmayatra Service. P* 13½ × 13.
1009 **413** 75 c. multicoloured 10 10

NEW INFORMATION

The editor is always interested to correspond with people who have new information that will improve or correct the Catalogue.

414 Society Logo

415 National Youth Centre, Maharagama

(Des R. Samarasinghe. Litho Security Printers (M), Malaysia)

1988 (8 Jan). *Centenary of Ceylon Society of Arts. P* 12.
1010 **414** 75 c. multicoloured 10 10

(Des R. Chandrajeewa. Litho Security Printers (M), Malaysia)

1988 (31 Jan). *Opening of National Youth Centre, Maharagama. P* 13½ × 13.
1011 **415** 1 r. multicoloured 25 10

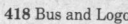

416 Citizens with National Flag and Map of Sri Lanka

417 Graduates, Clay Lamp and Open Book

(Des R. Samarasinghe. Litho Security Printers (M), Malaysia)

1988 (4 Feb). *40th Anniv of Independence. T* **416** *and similar vert design. Multicoloured. P* 12.
1012 75 c. Type **416** 10 10
1013 8 r. 50, "40" in figures and lion emblem .. 30 35

(Des R. Samarasinghe. Litho Security Printers (M), Malaysia)

1988 (11 Feb). *8th Anniv of Mahapola Scheme. P* 12.
1014 **417** 75 c. multicoloured 10 10

418 Bus and Logo

419 Ven. Weligama Sri Sumangala Maha Nayake Thero

(Des W. Rohana. Litho Security Printers (M), Malaysia)

1988 (19 Feb). *30th Anniv of Sri Lanka Transport Board. P* 12.
1015 **418** 5 r. 75, multicoloured 20 25

(Des S. Silva. Litho Security Printers (M), Malaysia)

1988 (13 Mar). *Ven. Weligama Sri Sumangala Maha Nayake Thero (Buddhist monk) Commemoration. P* 12.
1016 **419** 75 c. multicoloured 10 10

420 Regimental Colour

421 Chevalier I. X. Pereira

(Des W. Rohana. Litho Security Printers (M), Malaysia)

1988 (20 Apr). *Centenary of Regiment of Artillery. P* 12.
1017 **420** 5 r. 75, multicoloured 20 25

(Des S. Silva. Litho Security Printers (M), Malaysia)

1988 (26 Apr). *Birth Centenary of Chevalier I. X. Pereira (politician). P* 12.
1018 **421** 5 r. 75, multicoloured 20 25

422 Invitation to the Deities and Brahmas

423 Father Ferdinand Bonnel (educationist)

(Des N. Bulathsinhala. Litho State Ptg Wks, Moscow)

1988 (13 May). *Vesak. Paintings from Narendrarama Rajamaha Temple, Suriyagoda. T* **422** *and similar horiz design. Multicoloured. P* 12½ × 12.
1019 50 c. Type **422** 10 10
1020 75 c. Bodhisathva at the Seventh Step .. 10 10
MS1021 150 × 92 mm. Nos. 1019/20 .. .. 15 15

(Des S. Silva. Litho State Ptg Wks, Moscow)

1988 (22 May). *National Heroes. T* **423** *and similar vert designs. Multicoloured. P* 12 × 12½.
1022 75 c. Type **423** 10 10
1023 75 c. Sir Razik Fareed (politician) .. 10 10
1024 75 c. W. F. Gunawardhana (scholar) .. 10 10
1025 75 c. Edward Nugawela (politician) .. 10 10
1026 75 c. Chief Justice Sir Arthur Wijeyewardene 10 10
1022/6 .. .. *Set of* 5 15 15

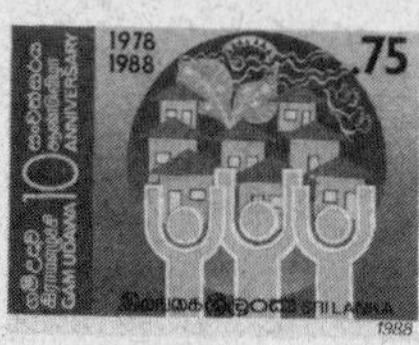

424 Stylized Figures and Reawakened Village

425 Maliyadeva College, Kurunegala, and Crest

(Des P. Gunasinghe. Litho Security Printers (M), Malaysia)

1988 (23 June). *10th Anniv of Gam Udawa (Village Re-awakening Movement). P* 12.
1027 **424** 75 c. multicoloured 10 10

(Des W. Rohana. Litho German Bank Note Co, Leipzig)

1988 (30 June). *Centenary of Maliyadeva College, Kurunegala. P* 13½ × 13.
1028 **425** 75 c. multicoloured 10 10

426 M.J.M. Lafir, Billiard Game and Trophy

427 Flags of Australia and Sri Lanka, Handclasp and Map of Australia

(Des S. Silva. Litho State Ptg Wks, Moscow)

1988 (5 July). *Mohamed Junaid Mohamed Lafir (World Amateur Billiards Champion, 1973) Commemoration. P* 12½ × 12.
1029 **426** 5 r. 75, multicoloured 20 25

(Des R. Samarasinghe. Litho Security Printers (M), Malaysia)

1988 (19 July). *Bicentenary of Australian Settlement. P* 12.
1030 **427** 8 r. 50, multicoloured 30 35

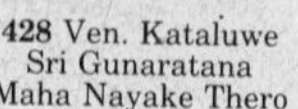

428 Ven. Kataluwe Sri Gunaratana Maha Nayake Thero

429 Athlete, Rice and Hydro-electric Dam

(Des S. Silva. Litho State Ptg Wks, Moscow)

1988 (11 Aug). *Ven. Kataluwe Sri Gunaratana Maha Nayake Thero (Buddhist monk) Commemoration. P* 12 × 12½.
1031 **428** 75 c. multicoloured 10 10

(Des P. Gunasinghe. Litho Security Printers (M), Malaysia)

1988 (3 Sept). *Mahaweli Games. P* 12.
1032 **429** 75 c. multicoloured 10 10

430 Athletics

431 Outline Map of Sri Lanka and Anniversary Logo

(Des P. Gunasinghe. Litho State Ptg Wks, Moscow)

1988 (6 Sept). *Olympic Games, Seoul. T* **430** *and similar vert designs. Multicoloured. P* 12 × 12½.

1033	75 c. Type **430**	10	10
1034	1 r. Swimming	10	10
1035	5 r. 75, Boxing	20	25
1036	8 r. 50, Map of Sri Lanka and logos of Olympic Committee and Seoul Games	30	35
1033/6	.. .. *Set of* 4	55	65
MS1037	181 × 101 mm. Nos. 1033/6	60	70

(Des S. Silva. Litho Security Printers (M), Malaysia)

1988 (12 Sept). *40th Anniv of World Health Organization. P* 12.

1038	**431** 75 c. multicoloured	10	10

432 Games Logo

433 Mahatma Gandhi

(Des A. Harischandra. Litho Security Printers (M), Malaysia)

1988 (20 Sept). *3rd National School Games. P* 12.

1039	**432** 1 r. black, gold and mauve	20	10

(Des S. Silva. Litho Security Printers (M), Malaysia)

1988 (2 Oct). *40th Death Anniv of Mahatma Gandhi. P* 12.

1040	**433** 75 c. multicoloured	15	10

434 Globe with Forms of Transport and Communications

435 Woman with Rice Sheaf and Hydro-electric Project

(Des R. Samarasinghe. Litho State Ptg Wks, Moscow)

1988 (28 Oct). *Asia–Pacific Transport and Communications Decade. T* **434** *and similar horiz design. P* 12½ × 12.

1041	75 c. multicoloured	10	10
1042	5 r. 75, magenta, royal blue and black ..	20	25

Design:—5 r. 75, Antenna tower with dish aerials and forms of transport.

(Des B. Harischandra. Litho Security Printers (M), Malaysia)

1988 (31 Oct). *Commissioning of Randenigala Project. T* **435** *and similar horiz design. Multicoloured. P* 12.

1043	75 c. Type **435**	10	10
1044	5 r. 75, Randenigala Dam and reservoir	20	25

436 Handicrafts and Centre Logo in Cupped Hands

437 Angel, Dove, Olive Branch and Globe

(Des R. Samarasinghe. Litho Secura, Singapore)

1988 (17 Nov). *Opening of Gramodaya Folk Art Centre, Colombo. P* 13½.

1045	**436** 75 c. multicoloured	15	15

(Des B. Mendis. Litho State Ptg Wks, Moscow)

1988 (21 Nov). *Christmas. T* **437** *and similar vert design. Multicoloured. P* 12×12½.

1046	75 c. Type **437**	10	10
1047	8 r. 50, Shepherds and Star of Bethlehem	30	35
MS1048	175×100 mm. Nos. 1046/7	40	45

438 Dr. E. W. Adikaram

439 Open Book in Tree and Children reading

(Des S. Silva. Litho Security Printers (M), Malaysia)

1988 (28 Dec). *Dr. E. W. Adikaram (educationist) Commemoration. P* 12.

1049	**438** 75 c. multicoloured	15	15

(Des Lakmini Amararatne. Litho German Bank Note Co, Leipzig)

1989 (23 Jan). *10th Anniv of Free Distribution of School Text Books. P* 13½×13.

1050	**439** 75 c. multicoloured	15	15

440 Wimalaratne Kumaragama

441 Logo and New Chamber of Commerce Building

(Des S. Silva. Litho German Bank Note Co, Leipzig)

1989 (27 Jan). *Poets of Sri Lanka. T* **440** *and similar vert designs. Multicoloured. P* 13×13½.

1051	75 c. Type **440**	10	10
1052	75 c. G. H. Perera	10	10
1053	75 c. Sagara Palansuriya	10	10
1054	75 c. P. B. Alwis Perera	10	10
1051/4	.. .. *Set of* 4	20	20

(Des Mel Ads Ltd. Litho Security Printers (M), Malaysia)

1989 (25 Mar). *150th Anniv of Ceylon Chamber of Commerce. P* 12.

1055	**441** 75 c. multicoloured	15	15

442 Bodhisatva at Lunch and Funeral Pyre

443 Parawahera Vajiragnana Thero (Buddhist monk)

(Des N. Bulathsinhala. Litho State Ptg Wks, Moscow)

1989 (15 May). *Vesak. Wall Paintings from Medawala Monastery, Harispattuwa. T* **442** *and similar horiz designs. Multicoloured. P* 12½×12.

1056	50 c. Type **442**	10	10
1057	75 c. Rescue of King Vessantara's children by god Sakra	10	10
1058	5 r. Bodhisatva ploughing and his son attacked by snake	20	25
1059	5 r. 75, King Vessantara giving away his children	20	25
1056/9	.. .. *Set of* 4	55	65
MS1060	150×90 mm. Nos. 1056/9	60	70

(Des S. Silva. Litho Security Printers (M), Malaysia)

1989 (22 May). *National Heroes. T* **443** *and similar multicoloured designs. P* 12.

1061	75 c. Type **443**	10	10
1062	75 c. Father Maurice Jacques Le Goc (educationist)	10	10
1063	75 c. Hemapala Munidasa (author) ..	10	10
1064	75 c. Ananda Samarakoon (composer) ..	10	10
1065	75 c. Simon Casie Chitty (scholar) (*horiz*)	10	10
1061/5	.. .. *Set of* 5	25	30

444 College Crest

445 Dramachakra, Lamp, Buddhist Flag and Map

(Des K. Wickramanayake. Litho Security Printers (M), Malaysia)

1989 (5 June). *150th Anniv of Hartley College, Point-Pedro (1988). P* 12.

1066	**444** 75 c. multicoloured	15	15

(Des P. Gunasinghe. Litho State Ptg Wks, Moscow)

1989 (18 June). *Establishment of Ministry of Buddha Sasana. P* 12½×12.

1067	**445** 75 c. multicoloured	15	15

446 Hands holding Brick and Trowel, House and Family

(Des P. Gunasinghe. Litho State Ptg Wks, Moscow)

1989 (23 June). *Gam Udawa '89 (Village Re-awakening Movement). P* 12½×12.

1068	**446** 75 c. multicoloured	15	15

POSTAL FISCALS

F 1 Republic Crest

(Recess Harrison)

1979 (28 May)—**83.** *W* **4** *of Maldive Islands. P* 13 × 12.

F2	F 1	20 r. blackish green	4·00	2·50
F3		50 r. deep slate-violet	8·50	5·50
F4		100 r. deep carmine-red (14.10.83) ..	17·00	16·00

The above, together with 500 and 1000 r. values, were originally released for fiscal purposes on 24 June 1974. The dates quoted are those on which they were validated for postal use. All three were withdrawn on 6 August 1984.

(Litho Harrison)

1984 (15 Aug). *W* **77** *of Brunei. P* 14½ × 14.

F5	F 1	50 r. orange	15·00	10·00
F6		100 r. dull chocolate	30·00	30·00

A 500 r. value also exists, but was not valid for postal purposes.

(Recess Harrison)

1984 (21 Sept). *W* **77** *of Brunei. P* 14½ × 14.

F7	F 1	50 r. orange-vermilion	1·40	1·50
F8		100 r. deep reddish purple	3·00	3·25

Stamps in this series with face values of 500 or 1000 r. were not valid for postal purposes.

Stellaland

PRICES FOR STAMPS ON COVER
The issues of Stellaland are very rare on cover.

1 Arms of the Republic

(Litho by Van der Sandt, de Villiers & Co, Cape Town)

1884 (Feb). *P* 12.

1	1	1d. red	£170	£250
		a. Imperf between (pair)	£1400	
2		3d. orange	12·00	£250
		a. Imperf between (pair)	£350	
3		4d. blue	12·00	£275
		a. Imperf between (pair)	£350	
4		6d. lilac-mauve	12·00	£275
		a. Imperf between (pair)	£650	
5		1s. green	28·00	

1885 (Oct). *Surch "Twee" in violet-lake.*

6	1	2d. on 4d. blue	£3000	

No date stamps were employed in Stellaland, the stamps being pen-cancelled with the initials of the postal official and date, but a date stamp was used on arrival at Barkly West or Kimberley.

Stellaland, with surrounding territory, was proclaimed the British Bechuanaland Colony on 30 September 1885. Its stamps were withdrawn and superseded by British Bechuanaland stamps on 2 December 1885. It is now part of South Africa.

Sudan

ANGLO-EGYPTIAN CONDOMINIUM

An Egyptian post office was opened at Suakin in 1867 and the stamps of Egypt, including postage dues and the official (No. O64), were used in the Sudan until replaced by the overprinted "SOUDAN" issue of 1897.

Cancellations have been identified from eleven post offices, using the following postmark types:

A

B

C

D

E

F

G

H

I

J

K

L

BERBER (*spelt* BARBAR). *Open* 1873 *to* 1884. *Postmark type* G.
DABROUSSA. *Open* 1889? *onwards. Postmark as type* J *but with* 11 *bars in arcs.*
DONGOLA. *Open* 1873 *to* 1885 *and* 1896 *onwards. Postmark types* F, G, K, L.
GEDAREF. *Open* ? *Postmark type* H.
KASSALA. *Open* 1875 *to* 1885. *Postmark type* G.
KHARTOUM. *Open* 1873 *to* 1884. *Postmark types* E (*spelt* KARTUM), G (*spelt* HARTUM), I (*with or without line of Arabic above date*).
KORTI. *Open* 1884/5 *and* 1897. *Postmark type* K.
SUAKIN. *Open* 1867 *onwards. Postmark types* A, B, C (*spelt* SUAKIM), D (*spelt* SUAKIM *and also with year replaced by concentric arcs*), I (*spelt* SOUAKIN), J (*spelt* SAWAKIN, *number of bars differs*).
TANI. *Open* 1885. *Postmark type* K.
TOKAR. *Open* 1891 *onwards. Postmark type* J (7 *bars in arcs*).
WADI HALFA. *Open* 1873 *onwards. Postmark types* F (*spelt* WADI HALFE), G (*spelt* WADI HALFE), I, J (*number of bars differs*).
WADI HALFA CAMP. *Open* 1896 *onwards. Postmark type* I.

Official records also list post offices at the following locations, but no genuine postal markings from them have yet been reported: Chaka, Dara, Debeira, El Abiad, El Fasher, El Kalabat, Faras, Fashoda, Fazogl, Ishkeit, Kalkal, Karkok, Mesellemia, Sara, Sennar and Taoufikia (not to be confused with the town of the same name in Egypt.

M

The post office at Kassala was operated by Italy from 1894 until 1896, using stamps of Eritrea cancelled with postmark type M.

From the last years of the nineteenth century that part of Sudan lying south of the 5 degree North latitude line was administered by Uganda (the area to the east of the Nile) (until 1912) or by Belgium (the area to the west of the Nile, known as the Lado Enclave) (until 1910).

Stamps of Uganda or East Africa and Uganda were used at Gondokoro and Nimuli between 1901 and 1911, usually cancelled with circular date stamps or, probably in transit at Khartoum, by a lozenge-shaped grid of 18 × 17 dots.

Stamps of Belgian Congo were used from the Lado Enclave between 1897 and 1910, as were those of Uganda (1901–10) and Sudan (1902–10), although no local postmarks were supplied, examples being initially cancelled in manuscript.

PRICES FOR STAMPS ON COVER TO 1945

Nos. 1/9	*from* × 12
Nos. 10/17	*from* × 6
Nos. 18/29	*from* × 5
Nos. 30/95	*from* × 2
Nos. D1/11	*from* × 30
Nos. O1/3	—
Nos. O4/22	*from* × 15
Nos. A1/16	*from* × 6

(1)

1897 (1 Mar). *Nos.* 54*b*, 55*a*, 57/*a*, 58*a*, 59, 60, 62*a and* 63 *of Egypt optd as T* 1 *by Govt Ptg Wks, Bûlâq, Cairo.*

1	1 m. pale brown	1·25	2·00
	a. Opt inverted	£250	
	b. Opt omitted (in vert pair with normal)	£800	
	c. *Deep brown*	1·50	2·25
3	2 m. green	1·25	1·75
4	3 m. orange-yellow	1·40	1·50
5	5 m. rose-carmine	2·00	70
	a. Opt inverted	£300	
	b. Opt omitted (in vert pair with normal)	£800	
6	1 p. ultramarine	7·00	2·00
7	2 p. orange-brown	35·00	12·00
8	5 p. slate	40·00	12·00
	a. Opt double	£1750	
	b. Opt omitted (in vert pair with normal)	£2500	
9	10 p. mauve	30·00	40·00
1/9	*Set of* 8	£110	65·00

Numerous forgeries exist including some which show the characteristics of the varieties mentioned below.

There are six varieties of the overprint on each value most of which can be supplied in vertical strips at double the catalogue price.

In some printings the large dot is omitted from the left-hand Arabic character on one stamp in the pane of 60.

Only two examples, one unused and the other used (in the Royal Collection), are known of No. 8a. In both instances one impression is partially albino.

PRINTERS. All stamps of Sudan were printed by De La Rue & Co, Ltd, London, *except where otherwise stated.*

2 Arab Postman

3

(Des E. A. Stanton. Typo)

1898 (1 Mar). *W* **3**. *P* 14.

10	**2**	1 m. brown and pink	30	30
11		2 m. green and brown	1·00	1·00
12		3 m. mauve and green	1·50	2·00
13		5 m. carmine and black	75	25
14		1 p. blue and brown	4·00	3·00
15		2 p. black and blue	11·00	6·00
16		5 p. brown and green	19·00	7·50
17		10 p. black and mauve	19·00	2·25
10/17		*Set of* 8	50·00	20·00

4

5 Milliemes

(5)

1902–21. *W 4. P 14.*

No.	Type	Description	Unused	Used
18	2	1 m. brown and carmine (5.05)	30	10
19		2 m. green and brown (11.02)	80	10
20		3 m. mauve and green (7.03)	1·10	25
21		4 m. blue and bistre (20.1.07)	1·50	2·50
22		4 m. vermilion and brown (10.07)	1·50	75
23		5 m. scarlet and black (12.03)	2·00	10
24		1 p. blue and brown (12.03)	1·60	15
25		2 p. black and blue (2.08)	20·00	1·75
26		2 p. purple and orange-yell, C (22.12.21)	3·00	4·75
27		5 p. brown and green, OC (2.08)	16·00	30
28		10 p. black and mauve, OC (2.11)	16·00	1·25
18/28		*Set of* 11	55·00	11·00

1903 (Sept). *No. 16 surch at Khartoum with T 5, in blocks of 30.*

No.	Type	Description	Unused	Used
29		5 m. on 5 pi. brown and green	6·50	9·00
		a. Surch inverted	£300	£275

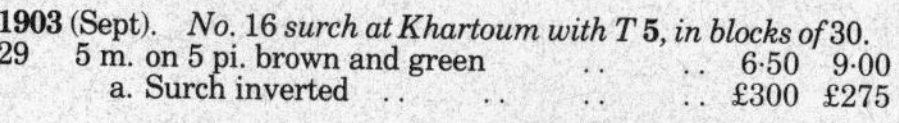

6

7

1921–23. *Chalk-surfaced paper. Typo. W 4. P 14.*

No.	Type	Description	Unused	Used
30	6	1 m. black and orange (4.2.22)	80	1·75
31		2 m. yellow-orange and chocolate (1922)	5·50	5·50
		a. Yellow and chocolate (1923)	5·50	6·00
32		3 m. mauve and green (25.1.22)	2·50	3·50
33		4 m. green and chocolate (21.3.22)	3·25	1·25
34		5 m. olive-brown and black (4.2.22)	1·75	10
35		10 m. carmine and black (1922)	1·50	10
36		15 m. bright blue and chestnut (14.12.21)	2·75	1·00
30/36		*Set of* 7	16·00	11·50

1927–41. *W 7. P 14.*

No.	Type	Description	Unused	Used
37	6	1 m. black and orange, **CO**	10	10
38		2 m. orange and chocolate, **CO**	15	10
39		3 m. mauve and green, **CO**	15	10
40		4 m. green and chocolate, **CO**	25	10
41		5 m. olive-brown and black, **CO**	25	10
42		10 m. carmine and black, **CO**	25	10
43		15 m. bright blue and chestnut, **CO**	25	10
44	2	2 p. purple and orange-yellow, **CO**	25	10
44*a*		3 p. red-brown and blue, **CO** (1.1.40)	1·50	10
44*b*		4 p. ultramarine and black, **C** (2.11.36)	1·50	10
45		5 p. chestnut and green, **CO**	80	10
45*a*		6 p. greenish blue and black, **CO** (2.11.36)	1·75	20
45*b*		8 p. emerald and black, **CO** (2.11.36)	1·75	45
46		10 p. black and reddish purple, **C**	90	10
		a. Black and bright mauve, **O** (1941)	6·50	60
46*b*		20 p. pale blue and blue, **CO** (17.10.35)	1·75	10
37/46*b*		*Set of* 15	10·50	1·25

The ordinary paper of this issue is thick, smooth and opaque and is a wartime substitute for chalk-surface paper.

For similar stamps, but with different Arabic inscriptions, see Nos. 96/111.

AIR MAIL (8) **AIR MAIL** (9) **AIR** Extended foot to "R" (R.5/12)

1931 (15 Feb–Mar). *Air. Stamps of 1927 optd with T 8 or 9 (2 p.).*

No.	Type	Description	Unused	Used
47		5 m. olive-brown and black (Mar)	35	70
48		10 m. carmine and black	85	3·25
49		2 p. purple and orange-yellow	85	3·25
		a. Extended foot to "R"	16·00	
47/9		*Set of* 3	1·90	6·50

2½ 2½

10 Statue of Gen. Gordon

AIR MAIL (11)

1931 (1 Sept)–**37.** *Air. Recess. W 7 (sideways). P 14.*

No.	Type	Description	Unused	Used
49*b*	10	3 m. green and sepia (1.1.33)	2·50	5·50
50		5 m. black and green	1·00	20
51		10 m. black and carmine	1·00	35
52		15 m. red-brown and sepia	40	10
		a. Perf 11½ × 12½ (1937)	1·75	10
53		2 p. black and orange	30	10
		a. Perf 11½ × 12½ (1937)	4·50	13·00
53*b*	10	2½ p. magenta and blue (1.1.33)	2·50	10
		c. Perf 11½ × 12½ (1936)	1·25	15
		ca. Aniline magenta and blue	3·75	3·25
54		3 p. black and grey	60	15
		a. Perf 11½ × 12½ (1937)	85	55
55		3½ p. black and violet	1·25	80
		a. Perf 11½ × 12½ (1937)	2·50	10·00
56		4½ p. red-brown and grey	9·00	15·00
57		5 p. black and ultramarine	1·00	40
		a. Perf 11½ × 12½ (1937)	1·50	35
57*b*		7½ p. green and emerald (17.10.35)	4·00	3·50
		c. Perf 11½ × 12½ (1937)	2·25	5·50
57*d*		10 p. brown and greenish blue (17.10.35)	8·00	40
		e. Perf 11½ × 12½ (1937)	2·25	9·00
49*b*/57*d*		*Set of* 12 (*p* 14)	27·00	24·00
52a/7e		*Set of* 8 (*p* 11½×12½)	15·00	35·00

1932 (18 July). *Air. No. 44 surch with T 11.*

No.	Type	Description	Unused	Used
58		2½ p. on 2 p. purple and orange-yellow	2·00	3·50

12 Gen. Gordon (after C. Ouless)

13 Gordon Memorial College, Khartoum

14 Gordon Memorial Service, Khartoum (after R. C. Woodville)

1935 (1 Jan). *50th Death Anniv of General Gordon. Recess. W 7. P 14.*

No.	Type	Description	Unused	Used
59	12	5 m. green	35	10
60		10 m. yellow-brown	55	25
61		13 m. ultramarine	85	5·00
62		15 m. scarlet	1·25	25
63	13	2 p. blue	1·25	20
64		5 p. orange-vermilion	1·25	40
65		10 p. purple	6·50	6·00
66	14	20 p. black	22·00	38·00
67		50 p. red-brown	55·00	70·00
59/67		*Set of* 9	80·00	£110

7½ PIASTRES ٧ ١/٢ قروش (15)

5 MILLIEMES ٥ مليمات (16)

1935. *Air. Surch as T 15.*

No.	Type	Description	Unused	Used
68	10	15 m. on 10 m. black and carmine (Apr)	40	10
		a. Surch double	£600	£650
69		2½ p. on 3 m. green and sepia (Apr)	85	4·50
		a. Second arabic letter from left missing	65·00	£100
		b. Small "½"	2·75	15·00
70		2½ p. on 5 m. black and green (Apr)	40	2·00
		a. Second Arabic letter from left missing	35·00	55·00
		b. Small "½"	1·75	9·00
		c. Surch inverted	£600	£650
		d. Ditto with variety a.	£1000	
		e. Ditto with variety b.	£2250	
71		3 p. on 4½ p. red-brown and grey (Apr)	1·75	9·00
72		7½ p. on 4½ p. red-brown and grey (Mar)	6·00	26·00
73		10 p. on 4½ p. red-brown and grey (Mar)	5·00	26·00
68/73		*Set of* 6	13·00	60·00

Nos. 69a and 70a occur in position 49 of the sheet of 50; the small "½" variety occurs in positions 17, 27, 32, 36, 41, 42 and 46.

The 15 m. on 10 m. and the 7½ p. on 4½ p. surcharged in red and the 2½ p. on 3 m. and 2½ p. on 5 m. in green are from proof sheets; the latter two items being known cancelled. A 7¼ p. on 4½ p. also exists from a proof sheet.

1938 (1 July). *Air. Surch as T 16.*

No.	Type	Description	Unused	Used
74	10	5 m. on 2½ p. (*p* 11½ × 12½)	1·25	10
75		3 p. on 3½ p. (*p* 14)	17·00	19·00
		a. Perf 11½ × 12½	£350	£450
76		3 p. on 7½ p. (*p* 14)	2·75	5·00
		a. Perf 11½ × 12½	£350	£450
77		5 p. on 10 p. (*p* 14)	1·50	4·25
		a. Perf 11½ × 12½	£350	£450
74/7		*Set of* 4	20·00	25·00

A 5 p. on 2½ p., perf 11½ × 12½, exists either mint or cancelled from a trial printing.

5 Mills. ٥ مليم

(17) Normal ("Malime")

"Malmime" (Left-hand pane R. 5/1) Short "mim" (Right-hand pane R. 3/1) Broken "lam" (Right-hand pane R. 6/2)

5 M

Inserted "5" (Bottom right-hand pane R. 4/5)

1940 (25 Feb). *Surch with T 17 by McCorquodale (Sudan) Ltd, Khartoum.*

No.	Type	Description	Unused	Used
78	6	5 m. on 10 m. carmine and black	20	30
		a. "Malmime"	20·00	24·00
		b. Two dots omitted (Right-hand pane R. 8/6)	20·00	24·00
		c. Short "mim"	20·00	24·00
		d. Broken "lam"	20·00	24·00
		e. Inserted "5"	75·00	

4½ PIASTRES (18)

4½ Piastres ٤١/٢ قرش (19)

1940–1. *Surch as T 18 or 19 at Khartoum.*

No.	Type	Description	Unused	Used
79	6	4½ p. on 5 m. olive-brown & blk (9.2.41)	27·00	2·00
80	2	4½ p. on 8 p. emerald and black (12.12.40)	18·00	4·50

20 Tuti Island, R. Nile, near Khartoum

21 Tuti Island, R. Nile near Khartoum

(Des Miss H. M. Hebbert. Litho Security Printing Press, Nasik, India)

1941 (25 Mar–10 Aug). *P 14 × 13½ (T 20) or P 13½ × 14 (T 21).*

No.	Type	Description	Unused	Used
81	20	1 m. slate and orange (10.8)	10	70
82		2 m. orange and chocolate (10.8)	25	70
83		3 m. mauve and green (10.8)	25	10
84		4 m. green and chocolate (10.8)	15	20
85		5 m. olive-brown and black (10.8)	15	10
86		10 m. carmine and black (10.8)	6·00	1·75
87		15 m. bright blue and chestnut	15	10
88	21	2 p. purple and orange-yellow (10.8)	3·00	60
89		3 p. red-brown and blue	70	10
90		4 p. ultramarine and black	60	10
91		5 p. chestnut and green (10.8)	3·75	4·50
92		6 p. greenish blue and black (10.8)	12·00	40
93		8 p. emerald and black (10.8)	8·50	45
94		10 p. slate and purple (10.8)	30·00	75
95		20 p. pale blue and blue (10.8)	30·00	22·00
81/95		*Set of* 15	85·00	29·00

22

23

1948 (1 Jan). *Arabic inscriptions below camel altered. Typo. W 7. P 14*

No.	Type	Description	Unused	Used
96	22	1 m. black and orange, **C**	30	75
97		2 m. orange and chocolate, **C**	65	75
98		3 m. mauve and green, **C**	30	25
99		4 m. deep green and chocolate, **C**	30	10
100		5 m. olive-brown and black, **C**	40	15
101		10 m. rose-red and black, **C**	80	10
		a. Centre inverted	†	—
102		15 m. ultramarine and chestnut, **C**	40	10
103	23	2 p. purple and orange-yellow, **C**	1·75	10
104		3 p. red-brown and deep blue, **C**	1·50	10
105		4 p. ultramarine and black, **C**	1·50	55
106		5 p. brown-orange and deep green, **C**	1·75	35
107		6 p. greenish blue and black, **C**	1·50	80
108		8 p. bluish green and black, **O**	2·00	1·25
109		10 p. black and mauve, **OC**	2·25	50
110		20 p. pale blue and deep blue, **O**	2·50	10
		a. Perf 13, **C**	26·00	50·00
111		50 p. carmine and ultramarine, **C**	5·00	40
96/111		*Set of* 16	21·00	5·50

A single used example is known of No. 101a.

For similar stamps, but with different Arabic inscriptions, see Nos. 37/46*b*.

24

25

1948 (1 Oct). *Golden Jubilee of "Camel Postman" design. Chalk-surfaced paper. Typo. W* **7**. *P* 13.
112 **24** 2 p. black and light blue 10 10

1948 (23 Dec). *Opening of Legislative Assembly, Chalk-surfaced paper. Typo. W* **7**. *P* 13.
113 **25** 10 m. rose-red and black 10 10
114 5 p. brown-orange and deep green .. 10 15

26 Blue Nile Bridge, Khartoum

(Des Col. W. L. Atkinson (2½ p., 6 p.), G. R. Wilson (3 p.), others from photographs. Recess)

1950 (1 July). *Air. T* **26** *and similar horiz designs. W* **7**. *P* 12.
115 2 p. black and blue-green .. .. .. 2·25 10
116 2½ p. light blue and red-orange 50 20
117 3 p. reddish purple and blue .. .. 1·50 10
118 3½ p. purple-brown and yellow-brown .. 75 1·50
119 4 p. brown and light blue 70 75
120 4½ p. black and ultramarine .. .. .. 2·00 2·50
a. Black and steel-blue .. .. .. 2·25 2·75
121 6 p. black and carmine 60 40
122 20 p. black and purple .. .. .. 1·75 1·75
115/122 .. .. *Set of* 8 9·00 6·50
Designs:—2½ p. Kassala Jebel; 3 p. Sagia (water wheel); 3½ p. Port Sudan; 4 p. Gordon Memorial College; 4½ p. *Gordon Pasha* (Nile mail boat); 6 p. Suakin; 20 p. G.P.O., Khartoum.

34 Ibex

35 Cotton Picking

(Des Col. W. L. Atkinson (1 m., 2 m., 4 m., 5 m., 10 m., 3 p., 3½ p., 20 p.), Col. E. A. Stanton (50 p.) others from photographs. Typo)

1951 (1 Sept)–**62**? *Designs as T* **34/5**. *Chalk-surfaced paper. W* **7**. *P* 14 (*millieme values*) *or* 13 (*piastre values*).
123 1 m. black and orange 10 60
124 2 m. black and bright blue 25 10
125 3 m. black and green .. .. .. 60 1·50
126 4 m. black and yellow-green 10 40
127 5 m. black and purple 10 10
a. Black and reddish purple (1962?) .. 25 10
128 10 m. black and pale blue 10 10
129 15 m. black and chestnut 10 10
a. Black and brown-orange (1962?) .. 15 10
130 2 p. deep blue and pale blue 15 10
a. Deep blue and very pale blue (1962?) 30 10
131 3 p. brown and pale ultramarine 45 10
a. Brown and deep blue (1962?) .. 65 10
132 3½ p. bright green and red-brown 25 10
133 4 p. ultramarine and black 25 10
a. Deep blue and black (1962?) .. 55 10
134 5 p. orange-brown and yellow-green .. 25 10
135 6 p. blue and black .. .. .. 1·25 30
a. Deep blue and black (1962?) .. 1·75 40
136 8 p. blue and brown .. .. .. 2·50 50
a. Deep blue and brown (1962?) .. 2·25 25
137 10 p. black and green .. .. .. 1·00 10
138 20 p. blue-green and black .. .. .. 3·00 35
139 50 p. carmine and black .. .. .. 6·50 55
123/139 .. .. *Set of* 17 15·00 3·75
Designs: *Vert as T* **34**—2 m. Whale-headed Stork; 3 m. Giraffe; 4 m. Baggara girl; 5 m. Shilluk warrior; 10 m. Hadendowa; 15 m. Policeman. *Horiz as T* **35**—3 p. Ambatch reed canoe; 3½ p. Nuba wrestlers; 4 p. Weaving; 5 p. Saluka farming; 6 p. Gum tapping; 8 p. Darfur chief; 10 p. Stack Laboratory; 20 p. Nile Lechwe. *Vert as T* **35**—50 p. Camel postman.

SELF-GOVERNMENT

51 Camel Postman

1954 (9 Jan). *Self-Government. Chalk-surfaced paper. Typo. W* **7**. *P* 13.
140 **51** 15 m. orange-brown and bright green .. 25 20
141 3 p. blue and indigo 25 30
142 5 p. black and reddish purple 25 20
140/2 .. .. *Set of* 3 65 65
Stamps as Type **51**, but dated "1953" were released in error at the Sudan Agency in London. They had no postal validity (*Price per set £14 un*).

Later issues of Sudan as an independent republic will be found in Part 14 (*Africa since Independence N–Z*) of this catalogue.

POSTAGE DUE STAMPS

1897 (1 Mar). *Type D* **3** *of Egypt, optd with T* **1** *at Bûlâq*.
D1 2 m. green .. .. 1·75 8·00
a. Opt omitted (in horiz pair with normal) £1900
D2 4 m. maroon .. .. 1·75 8·00
a. Bisected (2 m.) (on cover) .. .. † —
D3 1 p. ultramarine .. .. 4·50 5·00
D4 2 p. orange .. .. 7·50 11·00
a. Bisected (1 p.) (on cover) .. .. † —
D1/4 .. .. *Set of* 4 14·00 29·00
In some printings the large dot is omitted from the left-hand Arabic character on one stamp in the pane.
No. D1 has been recorded used as a bisect.

D 1 Gunboat *Zafir* D 2

1901 (1 Jan). *Typo. W* **4**. *P* 14.
D5 **D 1** 2 m. black and brown, **OC** 45 60
a. Wmk sideways .. .. ..
D6 4 m. brown and green, **OC** .. .. 1·50 90
D7 10 m. green and mauve, **OC** .. .. 3·75 3·50
a. Wmk sideways .. .. .. † —
D8 20 m. ultramarine and carmine, **CO** .. 3·00 3·25
D5/8 .. .. *Set of* 4 8·00 7·50
Nos. D6 and D8 exist used as bisects.

1927–30. *W* **7**. *P* 14.
D 9 **D 1** 2 m. black and brown, **C** (1930) .. 1·25 1·75
D10 4 m. brown and green, **C** 90 80
D11 10 m. green and mauve, **CO** .. .. 1·25 1·60
D9/11 .. .. *Set of* 3 3·00 3·50

1948 (1 Jan). *Arabic inscriptions at foot altered. Chalk-surfaced paper. Typo. W* **7**. *P* 14.
D12 **D 2** 2 m. black and brown-orange .. .. 80 7·50
D13 4 m. brown and green .. .. .. 2·00 11·00
D14 10 m. green and mauve .. .. .. 4·50 6·00
D15 20 m. ultramarine and carmine .. .. 8·00 13·00
D12/15 .. .. *Set of* 4 14·00 35·00
The 10 and 20 m. were reissued in 1980 on Sudan arms watermarked paper.

OFFICIAL STAMPS

1900 (8 Feb). *5 mils of* 1897 *punctured* "S G" *by hand. The* "S" *has* 14 *and the* "G" 12 *holes*.
O1 5 m. rose-carmine .. .. 45·00 20·00

1901 (Jan). *1 m. wmk Quatrefoil, punctured as No.* O1.
O2 1 m. brown and pink .. .. 42·00 30·00
Nos. O1/2 are found with the punctured "SG" inverted, reversed or inverted and reversed.

O.S.G.S. O.S.G.S.

(O 1) ("On Sudan Government Service") (O 2)

1902. *No.* 10 *optd at Khartoum as Type* O **1** *in groups of* 30 *stamps*.
O3 **2** 1 m. brown and pink .. .. .. 2·00 6·50
a. Oval "O" (No. 19) .. .. .. 65·00 95·00
b. Round stops. (Nos. 25 to 30) .. 7·50 24·00
c. Opt inverted £275 £350
d. Ditto and oval "O" £2000
e. Ditto and round stops £600 £750
f. Opt double £350
g. Ditto and round stops £800
h. Ditto and oval "O" .. .. ..

1903–12. *T* **2** *optd as Type* O **2**, *by D.L.R. in sheets of* 120 *stamps*.
(i) *Wmk Quatrefoil* (3.06)
O 4 10 p. black and mauve .. .. .. 11·00 13·00
a. Malformed "O" £100
(ii) *Wmk Mult Star and Crescent*
O 5 1 m. brown and carmine (9.04) 40 10
a. Opt double .. ..
b. Malformed "O" .. .. .. 18·00
O 6 3 m. mauve and green (2.04) .. .. 1·50 15
a. Opt double £800 £800
b. Malformed "O" .. .. .. 32·00
O 7 5 m. scarlet and black (1.1.03) .. .. 1·75 10
a. Malformed "O" .. .. .. 38·00
O 8 1 p. blue and brown (1.1.03) .. .. 1·75 10
a. Malformed "O" .. .. .. 38·00
O 9 2 p. black and blue (1.1.03) .. .. 11·00 20
a. Malformed "O" £100
O10 5 p. brown and green (1.1.03) .. .. 2·00 30
a. Malformed "O" .. .. .. 42·00
O11 10 p. black and mauve (9.12) .. .. 4·00 25·00
a. Malformed "O" .. .. .. 60·00
O4/11 .. .. *Set of* 8 30·00 35·00
The malformed "O" is slightly flattened on the left-hand side and occurs on position 7 of the lower pane.

1913 (Jan)–**22.** *Nos.* 18/20 *and* 23/8 *punctured* "SG" *by machine. The* "S" *has* 12 *holes and the* "G" 13.
O12 **2** 1 m. brown and carmine .. .. 1·50 25
O13 2 m. green and brown (1915) .. .. 2·50 1·25
O14 3 m. mauve and green .. .. .. 2·00 65
O15 5 m. scarlet and black 70 15
O16 1 p. blue and brown .. .. .. 1·25 35
O17 2 p. black and blue .. .. .. 1·75 55
O18 2 p. purple and orange-yellow, **C** (1922) 3·00 1·50
O19 5 p. brown and green, **OC** .. .. 3·25 1·00
O20 10 p. black and mauve, **OC** (1914) .. 6·50 7·50
O12/20 .. .. *Set of* 9 20·00 12·00

1922. *Nos.* 32/5 *punctured* "SG" *by machine. The* "S" *has* 9 *holes and the* "G" 10.
O21 **6** 3 m. mauve and green .. .. .. 7·50 3·50
O22 4 m. green and chocolate .. .. 7·50 3·50
O23 5 m. olive-brown and black 80 50
O24 10 m. carmine and black .. .. .. 1·75 55
O21/4 .. .. *Set of* 4 16·00 7·25

1927–30. *Nos.* 39/42, 44, 45 *and* 46 *punctured* "SG" *by machine. Nos.* O25/8 *have* 9 *holes in the* "S" *and* 10 *in the* "G"; *Nos.* O29/31 12 *holes in the* "S" *and* 13 *in the* "G".
O25 **6** 3 m. mauve and green, **C** (1928) .. 5·00 2·00
O26 4 m. green and chocolate, **C** (1930) .. 40·00 23·00
O27 5 m. olive-brown and black, **C** 60 10
O28 10 m. carmine and black, **C** .. .. 1·50 25
O29 **2** 2 p. purple and orange-yellow, **C** .. 3·50 70
O30 5 p. chestnut and green, **C** .. .. 6·50 3·25
O31 10 p. black and reddish purple, **C** .. 13·00 9·00
O25/31 .. .. *Set of* 7 65·00 35·00
The use of Nos. O25/31 on internal official mail ceased in 1932, but they continued to be required for official mail to foreign destinations until replaced by Nos. O32/46 in 1936.

S.G. S.G. S.G.

(O 3) (O 4) (O 4*a*)

1936 (19 Sept)–**46.** *Nos.* 37/43 *optd with Type* O **3**, *and* 44/46*a with Type* O **4**. *W* **7**. *P* 14.
O32 **6** 1 m. black and orange, **O** (22.11.46) .. 35 3·75
a. Opt double .. .. † —
O33 2 m. orange and chocolate, **O** (4.45) .. 25 1·50
O34 3 m. mauve and green, **C** (1.37) 80 10
O35 4 m. green and chocolate, **C** .. .. 80 1·25
O36 5 m. olive-brown and black, **CO** (3.40) .. 25 10
O37 10 m. carmine and black, **C** (6.46) .. 35 10
O38 15 m. bright blue and chestnut, **CO** (21.5.37) 85 10
O39 **2** 2 p. purple and orange-yellow, **CO** (4.37) 1·00 10
O39*a* 3 p. red-brown and blue, **O** (4.46) .. 75 40
O39*b* 4 p. ultramarine and black, **CO** (4.46) .. 80 15
O40 5 p. chestnut and green, **CO** .. .. 1·75 10
O40*a* 6 p. greenish blue and black, **O** (4.46) .. 2·00 60
O40*b* 8 p. emerald and black, **O** (4.46) .. 2·50 6·00
O41 10 p. black and reddish purple, **C** (10.37) 5·00 2·50
a. Black and bright mauve, **O** (1941) .. 8·50 2·00
O42 20 p. pale blue and blue, **O** (6.46) .. 7·00 9·50
O32/42 .. .. *Set of* 15 22·00 23·00

1948 (1 Jan). *Nos.* 96/102 *optd with Type* O **3**, *and* 103/111 *with Type* O **4**.
O43 **22** 1 m. black and orange 10 75
O44 2 m. orange and chocolate 20 10
O45 3 m. mauve and green .. .. .. 25 1·25
O46 4 m. deep green and chocolate 25 10
O47 5 m. olive-brown and black 25 10
O48 10 m. rose-red and black 25 15
O49 15 m. ultramarine and chestnut 25 10
O50 **23** 2 p. purple and orange-yellow 35 10
O51 3 p. red-brown and deep blue 35 10
O52 4 p. ultramarine and black 50 10
a. Perf 13 (optd Type O **4***a*) .. .. 10·00 12·00
O53 5 p. brown-orange and deep green .. 50 10
O54 6 p. greenish blue and black 50 10
O55 8 p. bluish green and black 50 30
O56 10 p. black and mauve 60 20
O57 20 p. pale blue and deep blue .. .. 2·25 25
O58 50 p. carmine and ultramarine .. .. 19·00 8·50
O43/58 .. .. *Set of* 16 23·00 11·00

1950 (1 July). *Air. Optd with Type* O **4***a*.
O59 2 p. black and blue-green (R.) .. .. 4·50 90
O60 2½ p. light blue and red-orange .. .. 1·25 80
O61 3 p. reddish purple and blue 80 70
O62 3½ p. purple-brown and yellow-brown .. 80 2·75
O63 4 p. brown and light blue .. .. .. 80 2·25
O64 4½ p. black and ultramarine (R.) .. .. 2·50 5·00
a. Black and steel-blue .. .. .. 3·50 7·00
O65 6 p. black and carmine (R.) .. .. 1·00 2·50
O66 20 p. black and purple (R.) .. .. .. 5·00 8·50
O59/66 .. .. *Set of* 8 15·00 21·00

1951 (1 Sept)–**62**? *Nos.* 123/9 *optd with Type* O **3**, *and* 130/9 *with Type* O **4***a*.
O67 1 m. black and orange (R.) .. .. 20 1·25
O68 2 m. black and bright blue (R.) 20 10
O69 3 m. black and green (R.) .. .. .. 1·00 5·50
O70 4 m. black and yellow-green (R.) 10 60
O71 5 m. black and purple (R.) 10 10
O72 10 m. black and pale blue (R.) 10 10
O73 15 m. black and chestnut (R.) 10 10
O74 2 p. deep blue and pale blue 10 10
a. Opt inverted £375
b. Deep blue and very pale blue (1962?) 20 10
O75 3 p. brown and deep ultramarine 75 10
a. Brown and deep blue (1962?) .. .. 1·00 10
O76 3½ p. bright green and red-brown 25 10
a. Light emerald & red-brown (1962?) 75 15
O77 4 p. ultramarine and black 25 10
a. Deep blue and black (1962?) 25 10
O78 5 p. orange-brown and yellow-green .. 25 10
O79 6 p. blue and black 25 40
a. Deep blue and black (1962?) 75 75
O80 8 p. blue and brown 45 10
a. Deep blue and brown (1962?) 80 25
O81 10 p. black and green (R.) 50 10
O81*a* 10 p. black and green (Blk.) (1958) .. 5·00 15
O82 20 p. blue-green and black .. .. .. 1·25 25
a. Opt inverted .. .. — £500
O83 50 p. carmine and black .. .. .. 3·50 1·25
O67/83 .. .. *Set of* 18 12·50 9·50
The 5, 10 and 15 m. values were later reissued with a thinner overprint.

COVER PRICES

Cover factors are quoted at the beginning of each country for most issues to 1945. An explanation of the system can be found on page x. The factors quoted do not, however, apply to philatelic covers.

ARMY SERVICE STAMPS

ARMY OFFICIAL ARMY OFFICIAL Army Service

(A 1) (A 2) (A 3)

1905 (Jan). *T* **2** *optd at Khartoum as Types* A **1** *or* A **2**. *Wmk Mult Star and Crescent.* (i) "ARMY" *reading up.*

A1 1 m. brown and carmine (A **1**) .. .. 2·25 1·75
 a. "!" for "I" .. .. 35·00 20·00
 b. Opt Type A **2** .. .. 27·00 12·00

(ii) *Overprint horizontal*

A2 1 m. brown and carmine (A **1**) £275
 a. "!" for "I" £3000
 b. Opt Type A 2 .. .. £1800

The horizontal overprint exists with either "ARMY" or "OFFICIAL" reading the right way up. It did not fit the stamps, resulting in misplacements where more than one whole overprint appears, or when the two words are transposed.

(iii) "ARMY" *reading down*

A3 1 m. brown and carmine (A **1**) .. .. 55·00 48·00
 a. "!" for "I" £600 £600
 b. Opt Type A **2** £500 £350

1905 (Nov). *As No* A 1, *but wmk Quatrefoil,* W **3**.

A4 1 m. brown and pink (A **1**) .. .. 90·00 95·00
 a. "!" for "I" £2500 £1600
 b. Opt Type A **2** £1100 £1100

The 29th stamp in each setting of 30 (Nos. A1–A4) has an exclamation mark for first "I" in "OFFICIAL" while the 6th and 12th stamps are Type A **2**.

Two varieties of the 1 millieme

A. 1st Ptg. 14 mm between lines of opt.
B. Later Ptgs. 12 mm between lines.
All other values are Type B.

1906 (Jan)–**11**. *T* **2** *optd as Type* A **3**.

(i) *Wmk Mult Star and Crescent,* W **4**

A 5 1 m. brown and carmine (Type A) £160 £140
A 6 1 m. brown and carmine (Type B) .. .. 1·50 20
 a. Opt double, one diagonal .. .. — £600
 b. Opt inverted £325 £325
 c. Pair, one without opt .. .. ..
 d. "Service" omitted .. .. .. — £3250
 e. "A" for "A" in "Army" £150 £150
A 7 2 m. green and brown .. .. .. 5·00 1·00
 a. Pair, one without opt £1600
 b. "Army" omitted £2250
A 8 3 m. mauve and green .. .. .. 14·00 40
 a. Opt inverted £1700
A 9 5 m. scarlet and black .. .. .. 1·25 10
 a. Opt. double £190 £190
 ab. Opt double, one diagonal £200
 b. Opt inverted .. .. — £200
 c. "Amry" .. .. — £2250
 d. "Λ" for "A" in "Army" .. .. .. — £250
 e. Opt double, one inverted £650 £325
A10 1 p. blue and brown .. .. .. 7·50 15
 a. "Army" omitted .. .. .. — £1800
A11 2 p. black and blue (1.09) .. .. 20·00 10·00
 a. Opt double .. .. — £2250
A12 5 p. brown and green (5.08) .. .. 75·00 35·00
A13 10 p. black and mauve (5.11) £450 £525
A6/10 Optd "Specimen" .. .. *Set of* 5 £200

There were a number of printings of these Army Service stamps; the earlier are as Type A 3; the 1908 printing has a narrower "A" in "Army" and the 1910–11 printings have the tail of the "y" in "Army" much shorter.

(ii) *Wmk Quatrefoil,* W 3

A14 2 p. black and blue .. .. 32·00 9·00
A15 5 p. brown and green .. .. .. 90·00 £100
A16 10 p. black and mauve £120 £130
A14/16 .. .. *Set of* 3 £210 £210
A14/16 Optd "Specimen" .. .. *Set of* 3 £175

1912 (1 Jan)–**22**. *Nos.* 18/20 *and* 23/8 *punctured* "AS" *by machine. The* "A" *has* 12 *holes and the* "S" 11.

A17 **2** 1 m. brown and carmine .. .. 8·50 1·50
A18 2 m. green and brown .. .. .. 1·50 65
A19 3 m. mauve and green .. .. .. 10·00 1·50
A20 5 m. scarlet and black 90 25
 a. On No. 13 .. ..
A21 1 p. blue and brown .. .. .. 3·75 50
A22 2 p. black and blue .. .. .. 8·00 2·25
A23 2 p. purple and orange-yellow, **C** (1922) 17·00 8·50
A24 5 p. brown and green, **OC** .. .. 11·00 7·00
A25 10 p. black and mauve, **O** (1914) .. £350 £190
A17/25 .. .. *Set of* 9 £375 £200

1922–24. *Nos.* 31*a and* 34/5 *punctured* "AS" *by machine. The* "A" *has* 8 *holes and the* "S" 9.

A26 **6** 2 m. yellow and chocolate (1924) .. 20·00 11·00
A27 5 m. olive-brown and black (4.2.22) .. 1·75 60
A28 10 m. carmine and black .. .. 2·75 90
A26/8 .. .. *Set of* 3 22·00 11·50

The use of Nos. A17/28 on internal Army mail ceased when the Egyptian units were withdrawn at the end of 1924, but existing stocks continued to be used on Army mail to foreign destinations until supplies were exhausted.

Swaziland

PRICES FOR STAMPS ON COVER TO 1945	
Nos. 1/10	*from* × 40
Nos. 11/20	*from* × 4
Nos. 21/4	*from* × 5
Nos. 25/7	*from* × 10
Nos. 28/38	*from* × 4
Nos. 39/41	*from* × 5
Nos. D1/2	*from* × 30

TRIPARTITE GOVERNMENT

Following internal unrest and problems caused by the multitude of commercial concessions granted by the Swazi king the British and Transvaal governments intervened during 1889 to establish a tripartite administration under which the country was controlled by their representatives, acting with the agent of the Swazi king.

The Pretoria government had previously purchased the concession to run the postal service and, on the establishment of the tripartite administration, provided overprinted Transvaal stamps for use from the post offices opened at Bremersdorp, Darkton and Embekelweni.

Swazieland
(1)

1889 (18–20 Oct). *Stamps of Transvaal* (*South African Republic*) *optd with T* **1**, *in black.* (*a*) *P* 12½ × 12.

1 **18** 1d. carmine .. .. 14·00 15·00
 a. Opt inverted £425 £500
2 2d. olive-bistre .. .. 70·00 14·00
 a. Opt inverted .. .. — £900
 b. "Swazielan" £900 £650
3 1s. green .. .. 10·00 13·00
 a. Opt inverted £450 £450

(*b*) *P* 12½

4 **18** ½d. grey .. .. 8·50 14·00
 a. Opt inverted £425 £475
 b. "Swazielan" £750 £650
 c. "Swazielan" inverted .. .. .. — £2000
5 2d. olive-bistre .. .. 12·00 14·00
 a. Opt inverted £425 £450
 b. "Swazielan" £425 £450
 c. "Swazielan" inverted £1400 £1400
 d. Opt double £1750
6 6d. blue .. .. 15·00 30·00
7 2s. 6d. buff (20 Oct) £110 £140
8 5s. slate-blue (20 Oct) £110 £140
 a. Opt inverted £1600 £1600
 b. "Swazielan" £4000
 c. "Swazielan" inverted .. .. ..
9 10s. fawn (20 Oct) £4000 £2500

The variety without "d" occurs on the left-hand bottom corner stamp in each sheet of certain printings.

1892 (Aug). *Optd in carmine. P* 12½.

10 **18** ½d. grey .. .. 7·00 13·00
 a. Opt inverted £475
 b. Opt double £400 £400
 c. Pair, one without opt .. .. .. — £500

A printing of the above with stop after "Swazieland" was made in July 1894 but these were not issued.

After further negotiations in 1894 the British and Transvaal governments agreed that Swaziland would become a protectorate of the Transvaal in February 1895. The overprinted stamps were withdrawn on 7 November 1894 and replaced by ordinary issues of the Transvaal.

Shortly after the outbreak of the Boer War in 1899 the Transvaal administration withdrew from Swaziland and there was no postal service from the area until the country became a British Protectorate in March 1902. From that date, until the introduction of the 1933 definitives, the post offices listed below used Transvaal or South Africa stamps.

The following post offices or postal agencies existed in Swaziland before 1933. Dates given are those on which it is generally accepted that the offices were first opened. Some were subsequently closed before the end of the period.

Bremersdorp (1889)	Mankaiana (1913)
Darkton (1889)	Mbabane (*previously* Embabaan) (1905)
Dwaleni (1918)	M'dimba (1898)
Embabaan (1895)	Mhlotsheni (1910)
Embekelweni (1889)	Mooihoek (1918)
Ezulweni (1910)	Motshane (1929)
Forbes Reef (1906)	Nomahasha (1904)
Goedgegun (1925)	Nsoko (1927)
Hlatikulu (1903)	Piggs Peak (1899)
Hluti (1912)	Sandhlan (1903)
Ivy (1912)	Sicunusa (1913)
Kubuta (1926)	Stegi (1910)
Mahamba (1899)	Umkwakweni (1898)
Malkerns (1914)	White Umbuluzi (1925)
Malomba (1928)	

BRITISH PROTECTORATE

2 King George V

3 King George VI

(Des Rev. C. C. Tugman. Recess D.L.R.)

1933 (2 Jan). *Wmk Mult Script CA. P* 14.

11 **2** ½d. green 25 30
12 1d. carmine 25 10
13 2d. brown 30 45
14 3d. blue 45 50
15 4d. orange .. .. 1·00 1·40
16 6d. bright purple .. .. .. 1·00 80
17 1s. olive .. .. 1·50 2·75
18 2s. 6d. bright violet .. .. .. 15·00 28·00
19 5s. grey .. .. 35·00 50·00
20 10s. sepia £100 £120
11/20 .. .. *Set of* 10 £140 £180
11/20 Perf "Specimen" .. .. *Set of* 10 £250

The ½d., 1d., 2d. and 6d. values exist overprinted "OFFICIAL", but authority for their use was withdrawn before any were actually used. However, some stamps had already been issued to the Secretariat staff before instructions were received to invalidate their use (*Price £6500 per set un*).

1935 (4 May). *Silver Jubilee. As Nos.* 91/4 *of Antigua, but ptd by B.W. P* 11 × 12.

21 1d. deep blue and scarlet 25 15
 a. Extra flagstaff .. .. 60·00
 b. Short extra flagstaff .. .. .. 40·00
 c. Lightning conductor .. .. .. 40·00
 d. Flagstaff on right-hand turret .. .. 40·00
 e. Double flagstaff .. .. .. 40·00
22 2d. ultramarine and grey-black 30 25
 a. Extra flagstaff .. .. 75·00
 b. Short extra flagstaff .. .. .. 50·00
 c. Lightning conductor .. .. .. 45·00
23 3d. brown and deep blue .. .. .. 45 1·00
 a. Extra flagstaff .. .. 60·00
 b. Short extra flagstaff .. .. .. 45·00
 c. Lightning conductor .. .. .. 40·00
24 6d. slate and purple .. .. .. 60 1·00
 a. Extra flagstaff .. .. 70·00
 b. Short extra flagstaff .. .. .. 50·00
 c. Lightning conductor .. .. .. 50·00
21/4 .. .. *Set of* 4 1·40 2·25
21/4 Perf "Specimen" .. .. *Set of* 4 70·00

For illustrations of plate varieties see Omnibus section following Zululand.

1937 (12 May). *Coronation. As Nos.* 13/15 *of Aden, but ptd by B.W. P* 11 × 11½.

25 1d. carmine 40 15
26 2d. yellow-brown 60 10
27 3d. blue 65 20
25/7 .. .. *Set of* 3 1·50 40
25/7 Perf "Specimen" .. .. *Set of* 3 50·00

(Recess D.L.R.)

1938 (1 Apr)–**54**. *Wmk Mult Script CA. P* 13½ × 13.

28 **3** ½d. green 20 30
 a. Perf 13½ × 14 (1.43) 10 40
 b. Perf 13½ × 14. *Bronze-green* (2.50) 25 70
29 1d. rose-red 40 15
 a. Perf 13½ × 14 (1.43) 10 15
30 1½d. light blue .. .. 1·75 35
 a. Perf 14 (1941) 40 60
 b. Perf 13½ × 14 (1.43) 10 20
31 2d. yellow-brown 85 35
 a. Perf 13½ × 14 (1.43) 10 10
32 3d. ultramarine .. .. 1·75 50
 a. Deep blue (10.38) .. .. .. 1·75 50
 b. Perf 13½ × 14. *Ultramarine* (1.43) 40 70
 c. Perf 13½ × 14. *Light ultram* (10.46) 1·50 1·50
 d. Perf 13½ × 14. *Deep blue* (10.47) .. 1·00 1·25
33 4d. orange .. .. 1·00 65
 a. Perf 13½ × 14 (1.43) 20 40
34 6d. deep magenta .. .. 1·75 60
 a. Perf 13½ × 14 (1.43) .. .. .. 45 1·50
 b. Perf 13½ × 14. *Reddish purple* (*shades*) (7.44) 70 35
 c. Perf 13½ × 14. *Claret* (13.10.54) .. 75 45
35 1s. brown-olive .. .. 2·50 40
 a. Perf 13½ × 14 (1.43) 20 10
36 2s. 6d. bright violet .. .. .. 8·00 2·75
 a. Perf 13½ × 14. *Violet* (1.43) .. .. 2·00 1·25
 b. Perf 13½ × 14. *Reddish violet* (10.47) .. .. 2·75 2·00
37 5s. grey .. .. 15·00 3·00
 a. Perf 13½ × 14. *Slate* (1.43) .. .. 38·00 30·00
 b. Perf 13½ × 14. *Grey* (5.44) .. .. 7·00 4·00
38 10s. sepia .. .. 22·00 4·75
 a. Perf 13½ × 14 (1.43) .. .. .. 4·00 3·00
28/38a .. .. *Set of* 11 13·00 8·50
28/38 Perf "Specimen" .. .. *Set of* 11 £180

The above perforations vary slightly from stamp to stamp, but the average measurements are respectively: 13.3 × 13.2 comb (13½ × 13), 14.2 line (14) and 13.3 × 13.8 comb (13½ × 14).

Swaziland
(4)

1945 (3 Dec). *Victory. Nos.* 108/10 *of South Africa optd with T* **4**.

		Un pair	*Us pair*
39	1d. brown and carmine	20	20
40	2d. slate-blue and violet	30	20
41	3d. deep blue and blue	35	50
39/41	.. .. .. *Set of 3 pairs*	75	80

1947 (17 Feb). *Royal Visit. As Nos.* 32/5 *of Basutoland.*

		Un	*Us*
42	1d. scarlet	10	10
43	2d. green	10	10
44	3d. ultramarine	10	10
45	1s. mauve	10	10
42/5	.. .. .. *Set of* 4	15	20
42/5 Perf "Specimen"	.. .. *Set of* 4	80·00	

1948 (1 Dec). *Royal Silver Wedding. As Nos.* 30/1 *of Aden.*

46 1½d. ultramarine 10 10
47 10s. purple-brown .. .. 16·00 12·00

1949 (10 Oct). *75th Anniv of Universal Postal Union. As Nos. 114/17 of Antigua.*

No.		Description	Un	Used
48		1½d. blue	10	10
49		3d. deep blue	30	15
50		6d. magenta	35	30
51		1s. olive	35	30
48/51		*Set of* 4	1·00	70

1953 (3 June). *Coronation. As No. 47 of Aden.*

No.		Description	Un	Used
52		2d. black and yellow-brown	10	15

5 Havelock Asbestos Mine

7 Swazi Married Woman

(Recess B.W.)

1956 (2 July). *T* **5, 7** *and similar designs. Wmk Mult Script CA. P 13 × 13½ (horiz) or 13½ × 13 (vert).*

No.	Type	Description	Un	Used
53	**5**	½d. black and orange	10	10
54	–	1d. black and emerald	10	10
55	**7**	2d. black and brown	10	10
56	–	3d. black and rose-red	10	10
57	–	4½d. black and deep bright blue	30	10
58	–	6d. black and magenta	20	10
59	**5**	1s. black and deep olive	15	10
60	–	1s. 3d. black and sepia	80	35
61	–	2s. 6d. emerald and carmine-red	1·00	60
62	–	5s. deep lilac and slate-black	2·50	70
63	**7**	10s. black and deep lilac	7·50	4·00
64	–	£1 black and turquoise-blue	18·00	22·00
53/64		*Set of* 12	27·00	26·00

Designs: *Horiz*—1d., 2s. 6d. A Highveld view; *Vert*—3d., 1s. 3d. Swazi courting couple; 4½d., 5s. Swazi warrior; 6d., £1. Greater Kudu.

(New Currency. 100 cents = 1 rand)

½c (11) 1c (12) 2c (13) 3½c (14)

2½c (I) 2½c (II) 4c (I) 4c (II)

5c (I) 5c (II) 25c (I) 25c (II)

50c (I) 50c (II) 50c (III)

R1 (I) R1 (II) R1 (III) R2 (I) R2 (II)

1961 (14 Feb–May). *Nos. 53/64 surch as T* **11** *to* **14**.

No.		Description	Un	Used
65		½ c. on ½d.	1·00	1·25
		a. Surch inverted	£170	
66		1 c. on 1d.	10	10
		a. Surch double	£250	
67		2 c. on 2d.	10	10
68		2½ c. on 2d.	10	10
69		2½ c. on 3d. (Type I)	10	10
		a. Type II	10	15
70		3½ c. on 2d. (May)	10	10
71		4 c. on 4½d. (Type I)	10	10
		a. Type II	20	10
72		5 c. on 6d. (Type I)	10	10
		a. Type II	10	10
73		10 c. on 1s.	6·00	3·00
		a. Surch double (vert pair)*	£300	
74		25 c. on 2s. 6d. (Type I)	30	65
		a. Type II (central)	75	60
		b. Type II (bottom left)	£110	£140
75		50 c. on 5s. (Type I)	30	60
		a. Type II	4·00	2·25
		b. Type III	£250	£350
76		1 r. on 10s. (Type I)	1·25	60
		a. Type II	2·75	2·75
		b. Type III	30·00	42·00
77		2 r. on £1 (Type I)	9·00	9·00
		a. Type II (middle left)	4·50	5·50
		b. Type II (bottom)	27·00	60·00
65/77a		*Set of* 13	12·00	11·00

*No. 73a is best collected as a vertical pair, due to the fall of the second surcharge.

No. 74b has the thin Type II surcharge at bottom left, in similar position to the thicker Type I, No. 74, with which it should not be confused.

No. 77b has the surcharge centrally placed at bottom. No. 77a has it at middle left, above "KUDU".

No. 66 with surcharge central (instead of bottom left) and No. 75a bottom left (instead of middle left) are believed to be from trial sheets released with the normal stocks. They do not represent separate printings. (No. 66 *price* £35 *un*).

(Recess B.W.)

1961. *As 1956 issue, but with values in cents and rands. Wmk Mult Script CA. P 13 × 13½ (horiz) or 13½ × 13 (vert).*

No.		Description	Un	Used
78		½ c. black and orange (as ½d.) (14.2)	10	15
79		1 c. black and emerald (as 1d.) (14.2)	10	10
80		2 c. black and brown (as 2d.) (10.9)	10	25
81		2½ c. black and rose-red (as 3d.) (14.2)	15	10
82		4 c. black & dp bright bl (as 4½d) (10.9)	15	25
83		5 c. black and magenta (as 6d.) (10.9)	25	10
84		10 c. black and deep olive (as 1s.) (14.2)	15	10
85		12½ c. black and sepia (as 1s 3d.) (14.2)	90	40
86		25 c. emerald and carmine-red (as 2s 6d.) (1.8)	1·25	80
87		50 c. deep lilac & slate-blk (as 5s.) (10.9)	2·00	1·40
88		1 r. black and deep lilac (as 10s.) (10.9)	3·00	3·50
89		2 r. black and turquoise-blue (as £1) (1.8)	9·00	11·00
78/89		*Set of* 12	16·00	16·00

15 Swazi Shields

16 Battle Axe

(Des Mrs. C. Hughes. Photo Enschedé)

1962 (24 Apr)–**66**. *Various designs as T* **15/16**. *W w* **12**. *P 14×13 (horiz) or 13×14 (vert).*

No.		Description	Un	Used
90		½ c. black, brown and yellow-brown	10	10
91		1 c. yellow-orange and black	10	10
92		2 c. dp bluish green, black & yellow-olive	10	10
93		2½ c. black and vermilion	10	10
		a. Black and dull red (5.66)	10	10
94		3½ c. yellow-green and deep grey	10	10
95		4 c. black and turquoise-green	10	10
		a. Black & deep turquoise-green (5.66)	10	10
96		5 c. black, red and orange-red	25	10
97		7½ c. deep brown and buff	25	15
		a. Blackish brn & yellowish buff (5.66)	30	20
98		10 c. black and light blue	50	10
99		12½ c. carmine and grey-olive	45	70
100		15 c. black and bright purple	40	50
101		20 c. black and green	30	60
102		25 c. black and bright blue	35	60
103		50 c. black and rose-red	4·25	2·25
104		1 r. emerald and ochre	2·50	2·25
105		2 r. carmine-red and ultramarine	6·50	4·50
90/105		*Set of* 16	14·00	10·50

Designs: *Vert*—2 c. Forestry; 2½ c. Ceremonial headdress; 3½ c. Musical instrument; 4 c. Irrigation; 5 c. Long-tailed Whydah; 7½ c. Rock paintings; 10 c. Secretary Bird; 12½ c. Pink Arum; 15 c. Swazi married woman; 20 c. Malaria control; 25 c. Swazi warrior; 1 r. Aloes. *Horiz*—50 c. Southern Ground Hornbill; 2 r. Msinsi in flower.

1963 (4 June). *Freedom from Hunger. As No. 76 of Aden.*

No.		Description	Un	Used
106		15 c. reddish violet	40	15

1963 (2 Sept). *Red Cross Centenary. As Nos. 147/8 of Antigua.*

No.		Description	Un	Used
107		2½ c. red and black	10	10
108		15 c. red and blue	40	20

31 Train and Map

(Des R. A. H. Street. Recess B.W.)

1964 (5 Nov). *Opening of Swaziland Railway. W w* **12**. *P* 11½.

No.	Type	Description	Un	Used
109	**31**	2½ c. emerald-green and purple	15	10
110		3½ c. turquoise-blue & deep yellow-ol	15	10
111		15 c. red-orange and deep chocolate	20	10
112		25 c. olive-yellow and deep ultram	35	15
109/12		*Set of* 4	75	25

1965 (17 May). *I.T.U. Centenary. As Nos. 166/7 of Antigua.*

No.		Description	Un	Used
113		2½ c. light blue and bistre	10	10
114		15 c. bright purple and rose	25	15

1965 (25 Oct). *International Co-operation Year. As Nos. 168/9 of Antigua.*

No.		Description	Un	Used
115		½ c. reddish purple and turquoise-green	10	10
116		15 c. deep bluish green and lavender	40	15

1966 (24 Jan). *Churchill Commemoration. As Nos. 170/3 of Antigua.*

No.		Description	Un	Used
117		½ c. new blue	10	10
118		2½ c. deep green	20	10
119		15 c. brown	35	15
120		25 c. bluish violet	50	35
117/20		*Set of* 4	1·00	55

1966 (1 Dec). *20th Anniv of U.N.E.S.C.O. As Nos. 196/8 of Antigua.*

No.		Description	Un	Used
121		2½ c. slate-violet, red, yellow and orange	10	10
122		7½ c. orange-yellow, violet and deep olive	20	10
123		15 c. black, bright purple and orange	35	20
121/3		*Set of* 3	60	30

PROTECTED STATE

32 King Sobhuza II and Map

33 King Sobhuza II

(Des and photo Harrison)

1967 (25 Apr). *Protected State. W w* **12** *(sideways on horiz designs). P* 14½.

No.	Type	Description	Un	Used
124	**32**	2½ c. multicoloured	10	10
125	**33**	7½ c. multicoloured	10	10
126	**32**	15 c. multicoloured	10	10
127	**33**	25 c. multicoloured	10	10
124/7		*Set of* 4	25	20

34 Students and University

(Des V. Whiteley. Photo Harrison)

1967 (7 Sept). *First Conferment of University Degrees. P 14 × 14½.*

No.	Type	Description	Un	Used
128	**34**	2½ c. sepia, ultramarine & lt yellow-orge	10	10
129		7½ c. sepia, ultramarine & lt greenish bl	10	10
130		15 c. sepia, ultramarine and rose	10	10
131		25 c. sepia, ultramarine and light violet	10	10
128/31		*Set of* 4	25	15

35 Inclawa Ceremony

36 Reed Dance

(Des Mrs. G. Ellison. Photo Harrison)

1968 (5 Jan). *Traditional Customs. P* 14.

No.	Type	Description	Un	Used
132	**35**	3 c. silver, vermilion and black	10	10
133	**36**	10 c. silver, light brown, orange and black	10	10
134	**35**	15 c. gold, vermilion and black	10	10
135	**36**	25 c. gold, light brown, orange and black	10	10
132/5		*Set of* 4	30	15

(37)

38 Cattle Ploughing

1968 (1 May). *No. 96 surch with T* **37**.

No.		Description	Un	Used
136		3 c. on 5 c. black, red and orange-red	10	10

INDEPENDENT

(Des Mrs. G. Ellison. Photo Enschedé)

1968 (6 Sept). *Independence. T* **38** *and similar horiz designs. W w* **12** *(sideways). P 14 × 12½.*

No.		Description	Un	Used
137		3 c. multicoloured	10	10
		a. Imperf (pair)	£120	
138		4½ c. multicoloured	10	10
		a. Imperf (pair)	£120	
139		17½ c. yellow, green, black and gold	15	10
140		25 c. slate, black and gold	45	30
137/40		*Set of* 4	65	45
MS141		180 × 162 mm. Nos. 137/40 each × 5	14·00	16·00
		a. Error. Imperf	£1200	

Designs:—4½ c. Overhead cable carrying asbestos; 17½ c. Cutting sugar cane; 25 c. Iron ore mining and railway map.

Nos. 137/40 were printed in sheets of 50, but also in miniature sheets of 20 (4 × 5) containing *se-tenant* strips of each value.

INDEPENDENCE
1968

(42)

43 Cape Porcupine

1968 (6 Sept). *Nos.* 90/105 *optd as* T **42**, *and No.* 93 *additionally surch* 3 c., *by Enschedé. (a) Wmk upright.*

No.		Description		
142	½ c.	black, brown and yellow-brown	10	10
		a. Brown omitted	£160	
		b. Albino opt	40·00	
143	1 c.	yellow-orange and black	10	10
144	2 c.	dp bluish green, black & yellow-olive	10	10
145	2½ c.	black and vermilion	10	10
		a. Black and dull red	10	10
146	3 c.	on 2½ c. black and vermilion	10	10
		a. Black and dull red	10	10
147	3½ c.	yellow-green and deep grey	15	10
148	4 c.	black and turquoise-green	10	10
		a. Black and deep turquoise-green	25	15
		b. Black and pale turquoise-green	20	15
149	5 c.	black, red and orange-red	60	10
150	7½ c.	deep brown and buff	20	10
151	10 c.	black and light blue	60	10
152	12½ c.	carmine and grey-olive	25	30
153	15 c.	black and bright purple	25	30
154	20 c.	black and green	55	70
155	25 c.	black and bright blue	35	40
156	50 c.	black and rose-red	2·50	1·75
157	1 r.	emerald and ochre	2·50	3·00
158	2 r.	carmine-red and ultramarine	5·50	7·00
		(b) Wmk sideways		
159	50 c.	black and rose-red	2·25	1·75
160	2 r.	carmine-red and ultramarine	5·50	5·00
142/60		*Set of* 19	19·00	18·00

The 2½ c., 3½ c., 5 c., 12½ c., 50 c. (No. 156) and 2 r. (No. 158) exist with gum arabic only, the 1 c., 2 c., 3 c., 4 c., and 15 c. with both gum arabic and PVA gum and the remainder with PVA gum only.

(Des and litho D.L.R.)

1969 (1 Aug)–**75**. *T* **43** *and similar designs showing animals. Multicoloured.* W w **12** (*sideways on* 3 c., 3½ c., 1 r., 2 r.). *P* 13 × 13½ (3 c., 3½ c.), 12½ × 13 (1 r., 2 r.) *or* 13 × 12½ (*others*).

No.		Description		
161	½ c.	Caracal	10	10
162	1 c.	Type **43**	10	10
163	2 c.	Crocodile	20	10
		a. Perf 12½ × 12 (29.9.75)	2·25	1·00
164	3 c.	Lion	50	10
165	3½ c.	African Elephant	50	10
166	5 c.	Bush Pig	30	10
167	7½ c.	Impala	35	10
168	10 c.	Chacma Baboon	45	10
169	12½ c.	Ratel	70	1·00
170	15 c.	Leopard	1·25	70
171	20 c.	Blue Wildebeest	95	60
172	25 c.	White Rhinoceros	1·40	1·00
173	50 c.	Common Zebra	1·50	2·00
174	1 r.	Waterbuck (*vert*)	3·00	4·00
175	2 r.	Giraffe (*vert*)	6·00	8·50
161/75		*Set of* 15	15·00	16·00

Nos. 161/73 are horizontal as Type **43** but the 3 c. and 3½ c. are larger, 35 × 24½ mm.

No. 163a was printed by the D.L.R. works in Bogotá, Colombia.

See also Nos. 219/20 and 229.

44 King Sobhuza II and Flags

45 King Sobhuza II, U.N. Building and Emblem

(Des D.L.R. Litho P.B.)

1969 (24 Sept). *Admission of Swaziland to the United Nations.* W w **12** (*sideways*). *P* 13½.

No.	Type	Description		
176	**44**	3 c. multicoloured	10	10
177	**45**	7½ c. multicoloured	10	10
178	**44**	12½ c. multicoloured	10	10
179	**45**	25 c. multicoloured	20	20
176/9		*Set of* 4	35	35

46 Athlete, Shield and Spears

47 *Bauhinia galpinii*

(Des L. Curtis. Litho Format)

1970 (16 July). *Ninth Commonwealth Games, Edinburgh.* T **46** *and similar vert designs. Multicoloured.* W w **12**. *P* 14.

No.		Description		
180	3 c.	Type **46**	10	10
181	7½ c.	Runner	10	10
182	12½ c.	Hurdler	10	10
183	25 c.	Procession of Swaziland competitors	20	20
180/3		*Set of* 4	35	35

(Des L. Curtis from "Wild Flowers of Natal" by Dr. W. G. Wright. Litho Questa)

1971 (1 Feb). *Flowers.* T **47** *and similar vert designs. Multicoloured.* W w **12**. *P* 14½.

No.		Description		
184	3 c.	Type **47**	20	10
185	10 c.	*Crocosmia aurea*	35	10
186	15 c.	*Gloriosa superba*	50	15
187	25 c.	*Watsonia densiflora*	70	35
184/7		*Set of* 4	1·60	60

48 King Sobhuza II in Ceremonial Dress

49 UNICEF emblem

(Des L. Curtis. Litho Format)

1971 (22 Dec). *Golden Jubilee of Accession of King Sobhuza II.* T **48** *and similar vert designs. Multicoloured.* W w **12**. *P* 14.

No.		Description		
188	3 c.	Type **48**	10	10
189	3½ c.	Sobhuza II in medallion	10	10
190	7½ c.	Sobhuza II attending Incwala ceremony	10	10
191	25 c.	Sobhuza II and aides at opening of Parliament	20	35
188/91		*Set of* 4	30	40

(Des Sylvia Goaman. Litho J.W.)

1972 (17 Apr). *25th Anniv of UNICEF.* W w **12** (*sideways*). *P* 13½.

No.	Type	Description		
192	**49**	15 c. black and bright lilac	15	10
193	–	25 c. black and yellow-olive	20	20

The 25 c. value is as T **49**, but the inscription is rearranged.

50 Local Dancers

(Des G. Drummond. Litho Questa)

1972 (11 Sept). *Tourism.* T **50** *and similar horiz designs. Multicoloured.* W w **12**. *P* 13½ × 14.

No.		Description		
194	3½ c.	Type **50**	10	10
195	7½ c.	Swazi beehive hut	15	10
196	15 c.	Ezulwini Valley	25	20
197	25 c.	Fishing, Usutu River	60	40
194/7		*Set of* 4	1·00	65

51 Spraying Mosquitoes

(Des PAD Studio. Litho Questa)

1973 (21 May). *25th Anniv of W.H.O.* T **51** *and similar horiz design. Multicoloured.* W w **12**. *P* 14.

No.		Description		
198	3½ c.	Type **51**	10	10
199	7½ c.	Anti-malaria vaccination	15	10

52 Mining

(Des G. Drummond. Litho Questa)

1973 (21 June). *Natural Resources.* T **52** *and similar horiz designs. Multicoloured.* W w **12**. *P* 13½.

No.		Description		
200	3½ c.	Type **52**	15	10
201	7½ c.	Cattle	20	10
202	15 c.	Water	25	15
203	25 c.	Rice	30	30
200/3		*Set of* 4	80	55

53 Coat of Arms

54 Flags and Mortar-board

(Des J.W. Litho Walsall)

1973 (7 Sept). *Fifth Anniv of Independence.* T **53** *and similar horiz designs. Multicoloured (except* 3 c.). W w **12**. *P* 14.

No.		Description		
204	3 c.	Type **53** (salmon and black)	10	10
205	10 c.	King Sobhuza II saluting	15	10
206	15 c.	Parliament Buildings	25	30
207	25 c.	National Somhlolo Stadium	35	40
204/7		*Set of* 4	80	75

(Des P. Powell. Litho Format)

1974 (29 Mar). *Tenth Anniv of University of Botswana, Lesotho and Swaziland.* T **54** *and similar vert designs. Multicoloured.* W w **12** (*sideways*). *P* 14.

No.		Description		
208	7½ c.	Type **54**	10	10
209	12½ c.	University campus	15	10
210	15 c.	Map of Southern Africa	20	20
211	25 c.	University badge	30	35
208/11		*Set of* 4	65	60

55 King Sobhuza as College Student

56 New Post Office, Lobamba

(Des Mary Nelson; adapted PAD Studio. Litho Enschedé)

1974 (22 July). *75th Birthday of King Sobhuza II.* T **55** *and similar vert designs. Multicoloured.* W w **12**. *P* 13 × 10½.

No.		Description		
212	3 c.	Type **55**	10	10
213	9 c.	King Sobhuza in middle-age	10	10
214	50 c.	King Sobhuza at 75 years of age	40	60
212/14		*Set of* 3	50	60

(Des R. Granger Barrett. Litho Questa)

1974 (9 Oct). *Centenary of Universal Postal Union.* T **56** *and similar horiz designs. Multicoloured.* W w **12** (*sideways*). *P* 14.

No.		Description		
215	4 c.	Type **56**	10	10
216	10 c.	Mbabane Temporary Post Office, 1902	25	15
217	15 c.	Carrying mail by cableway	45	50
218	25 c.	Mule-drawn mail-coach	55	70
215/18		*Set of* 4	1·25	1·25

(New Currency. 100 cents = 1 lilangeni (*plural* emalangeni))

1975 (2 Jan). *New currency. As Nos.* 174/5 *but inscr in emalangeni.* W w **12** (*upright*). *P* 12½ × 13.

No.		Description		
219	1 e.	Waterbuck	2·00	2·50
220	2 e.	Giraffe	4·00	4·50

57 Umcwasho Ceremony

58 Control Tower, Matsapa Airport

(Des PAD Studio. Litho Kynoch Press)

1975 (20 Mar). *Swazi Youth.* T **57** *and similar multicoloured designs.* W w **12** (*sideways on* 3, 10 *and* 25 c.). *P* 14.

No.		Description		
221	3 c.	Type **57**	10	10
222	10 c.	Butimba (hunting party)	15	10
223	15 c.	Lusekwane (sacred shrub) (*horiz*)	20	15
224	25 c.	Goina Regiment	25	30
221/4		*Set of* 4	60	45

(Des V. Whiteley Studio. Litho Questa)

1975 (18 Aug). *Tenth Anniv of Internal Air Service.* T **58** *and similar horiz designs. Multicoloured.* W w **14** (*sideways*). *P* 14.

No.		Description		
225	4 c.	Type **58**	30	10
226	5 c.	Fire engine	30	10
227	15 c.	Douglas "Dakota"	1·40	80
228	25 c.	Hawker Siddeley "748"	1·90	1·25
225/8		*Set of* 4	3·50	2·[illegible]

(Litho De La Rue, Bogotá, Colombia)

1975 (29 Sept). *As No.* 164 *but* W w **12** *upright.*

No.		Description		
229	3 c.	Lion	2·00	2·00

NEW INFORMATION

The editor is always interested to correspond with people who have new information that will improve or correct the Catalogue.

(59)

1975 (15 Nov). *Nos.* 167 *and* 169 *surch as T* **59**.
230 3 c. on 7½ c. Impala 80 50
231 6 c. on 12½ c. Ratel 95 75

60 Elephant Symbol

(Des Mary-Jane Rostami. Litho Questa)

1975 (22 Dec). *International Women's Year. T* **60** *and similar designs.* W w **14** (*sideways on* 4 *and* 5 *c.*). *P* 14.
232 4 c. light bluish grey, black & light brt blue 10 10
233 5 c. multicoloured 10 10
234 15 c. multicoloured 35 30
235 25 c. multicoloured 50 40
232/5 .. .. *Set of* 4 95 70
Designs: *Horiz*—5 c. Queen Labotsibeni. *Vert*—15 c. Craftswoman; 25 c. "Women in Service".

61 African Black-headed Oriole

(Des C. Abbott. Litho Questa)

1976 (2 Jan)–**78**. *Birds. T* **61** *and similar multicoloured designs.* W w **14** (*sideways on* 1 *c.*, 3 *c.*, 2 *e.*). *Chalk-surfaced paper. P* 14.
236 1 c. Type **61** 35 25
237 2 c. African Green Pigeon (*vert*) 35 20
238 3 c. Green-winged Pytilia 50 30
239 4 c. Violet Starling (*vert*) 50 15
a. Ordinary paper (31.7.78) 55 40
240 5 c. Black-headed Heron (*vert*) 50 20
241 6 c. Stonechat (*vert*) 60 20
242 7 c. Chorister Robin Chat (*vert*) 50 30
243 10 c. Four-coloured Bush-shrike (*vert*) .. 60 30
244 15 c. Black-collared Barbet (*vert*) 80 55
245 20 c. Grey Heron (*vert*) .. .. .. 1·50 75
246 25 c. Giant Kingfisher (*vert*) .. .. .. 1·50 75
247 30 c. Verreaux's Eagle (*vert*) .. .. .. 1·50 85
248 50 c. Red Bishop (*vert*) .. .. .. 1·50 1·25
a. Ordinary paper (31.7.78) .. .. 90 1·00
249 1 e. Pin-tailed Whydah (*vert*) .. .. 2·25 2·75
a. Ordinary paper (31.7.78) .. .. 1·75 2·50
250 2 e. Lilac-breasted Roller .. .. .. 4·00 5·00
a. Ordinary paper (31.7.78) .. .. 3·00 4·50
236/50a .. .. *Set of* 15 13·00 11·50

62 Blindness from Malnutrition **63** Marathon

(Des Jennifer Toombs. Litho Questa)

1976 (15 June). *Prevention of Blindness. T* **62** *and similar horiz designs. Multicoloured.* W w **14** (*sideways*). *P* 14.
251 5 c. Type **62** 10 10
252 10 c. Infected retina 20 10
253 20 c. Blindness from trachoma 35 35
254 25 c. Medicines 40 40
251/4 .. .. *Set of* 4 95 80

(Des PAD Studio. Litho Walsall)

1976 (17 July). *Olympic Games, Montreal. T* **63** *and similar vert designs. Multicoloured.* W w **14** (*inverted*). *P* 14.
255 5 c. Type **63** 10 10
256 6 c. Boxing 10 10
257 20 c. Football 25 25
258 25 c. Olympic torch and flame 30 35
255/8 .. .. *Set of* 4 65 65

MINIMUM PRICE

The minimum price quote is 10p which represents a handling charge rather than a basis for valuing common stamps. For further notes about prices see introductory pages.

64 Footballer Shooting **65** Alexander Graham Bell and Telephone

(Des J.W. Litho Questa)

1976 (13 Sept). *F.I.F.A. Membership. T* **64** *and similar vert designs. Multicoloured.* W w **14**. *P* 14.
259 4 c. Type **64** 10 10
260 6 c. Heading 10 10
261 20 c. Goalkeeping 25 25
262 25 c. Player about to shoot 30 30
259/62 .. .. *Set of* 4 65 60

(Des J.W. Litho Walsall)

1976 (22 Nov). *Telephone Centenary. T* **65** *and similar horiz designs.* W w **14** (*sideways*). *P* 14.
263 4 c. multicoloured 10 10
264 5 c. multicoloured 10 10
265 10 c. multicoloured 15 10
266 15 c. multicoloured 20 20
267 20 c. multicoloured 30 30
263/7 .. .. *Set of* 5 75 55
Nos. 264/7 are as T **65**, but show different telephones.

66 Queen Elizabeth II and King Sobhuza II

(Des Walsall. Litho Questa)

1977 (7 Feb). *Silver Jubilee. T* **66** *and similar horiz designs. Multicoloured.* W w **14** (*sideways*). *P* 13½.
268 20 c. Type **66** 20 20
269 25 c. Coronation Coach at Admiralty Arch .. 20 20
270 50 c. Queen in coach 30 45
268/70 .. .. *Set of* 3 65 75

67 Matsapa College

(Des J. Cooter. Litho Questa)

1977 (2 May). *50th Anniv of Police Training. T* **67** *and similar multicoloured designs.* W w **14** (*upright on* 20 *c.*, *sideways on others*). *P* 14.
271 5 c. Type **67** 10 10
272 10 c. Uniformed police and land rover 20 10
273 20 c. Police badge (*vert*) 35 25
274 25 c. Dog handling 40 35
271/4 .. .. *Set of* 4 95 65

68 Animals and Hunters

(Des BG Studio. Litho Questa)

1977 (8 Aug). *Rock Paintings. T* **68** *and similar horiz designs. Multicoloured.* W w **14** (*sideways*). *P* 14.
275 5 c. Type **68** 25 10
276 10 c. Four dancers in a procession 30 10
277 15 c. Man with cattle 40 20
278 20 c. Four dancers 45 30
275/8 .. .. *Set of* 4 1·25 55
MS279 103 × 124 mm. Nos. 275/8 .. .. 1·50 1·75

69 Timber, Highveld Region

70 Timber, Highveld Region

(Des L. Curtis. Litho D.L.R.)

1977 (17 Oct). *Maps of the Regions. T* **69** *and similar horiz designs. Multicoloured.* W w **14** (*sideways*). *P* 13½.
280 5 c. Type **69** 10 10
281 10 c. Pineapple, Middleveld 20 10
282 15 c. Orange and Lemon, Lowveld 30 20
283 20 c. Cattle, Lubombo region 40 30
280/3 .. .. *Set of* 4 90 55
MS284 87 × 103 mm. Four 25 c. designs as T **70**, together forming a composite map of Swaziland .. 1·40 1·60

71 Cabbage Tree

(Des Jennifer Toombs. Litho Walsall)

1978 (12 Jan). *Trees of Swaziland. T* **71** *and similar horiz designs. Multicoloured* (*except* 5 *c.*). W w **14** (*sideways*). *P* 13½.
285 5 c. Type **71** (apple-green, ochre and black) .. 15 10
286 10 c. Marula 35 10
287 20 c. Kiaat 55 40
288 25 c. Lucky bean-tree 60 50
285/8 .. .. *Set of* 4 1·50 90

72 Rural Electrification at Lobamba **73** Elephant

(Des G. Drummond. Litho Questa)

1978 (6 Mar). *Hydro-electric Power. T* **72** *and similar horiz designs.* W w **14** (*sideways*). *P* 13½.
289 5 c. black and buff 10 10
290 10 c. black and light green 15 10
291 20 c. black and pale blue 25 30
292 25 c. black and magenta 30 35
289/92 .. .. *Set of* 4 70 65
Designs:—10 c. Edwaleni Power Station; 20 c. Switchgear, Magudza Power Station; 25 c. Turbine Hall, Edwaleni.

(Des C. Abbott. Litho Questa)

1978 (2 June). *25th Anniv of Coronation. T* **73** *and similar vert designs. P* 15.
293 25 c. chalky blue, black and sage-green .. 20 30
a. Sheetlet. Nos. 293/5 × 2 .. .. .. 1·10
294 25 c. multicoloured 20 30
295 25 c. chalky blue, black and sage-green .. 20 30
293/5 .. .. *Set of* 3 55 80
Designs:—No. 293, Queen's Lion; No. 294, Queen Elizabeth II; No. 295, Type **73**.
Nos. 293/5 were printed together in small sheets of 6, containing two *se-tenant* strips of 3, with horizontal gutter margin between.

74 Clay Pots

(Des C. Abbott. Litho Questa)

1978 (24 July). *Handicrafts* (1*st series*). *T* **74** *and similar horiz designs. Multicoloured.* W w **14** (*sideways*). *P* 13½ × 14.
296 5 c. Type **74** 10 10
297 10 c. Basketwork 10 10
298 20 c. Wooden utensils 15 15
299 30 c. Wooden pot 25 30
296/9 .. .. *Set of* 4 50 50
See also Nos. 310/13.

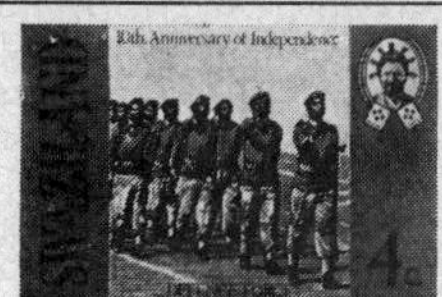

75 Defence Force

(Des BG Studio. Litho Questa)

1978 (6 Sept). *10th Anniv of Independence. T* **75** *and similar horiz designs. Multicoloured. W* w **14** *(sideways). P* 14.

No.	Description		
300	4 c. Type **75**	10	10
301	6 c. The King's Regiment	10	10
302	10 c. Tinkabi tractor (agricultural development)	15	10
303	15 c. Water-pipe laying (self-help scheme)	20	10
304	25 c. Sebenta adult literacy scheme	25	25
305	50 c. Fire emergency service	40	50
300/5	*Set of* 6	1·00	85

76 Archangel Gabriel appearing before Shepherds

77 Prospecting at Phophonyane

(Des V. Whiteley Studio. Litho Harrison)

1978 (12 Dec). *Christmas. T* **76** *and similar horiz designs. Multicoloured. W* w **14**. *P* 14½ × 14.

No.	Description		
306	5 c. Type **76**	10	10
307	10 c. Three Wise Men paying homage to infant Jesus	10	10
308	15 c. Archangel Gabriel warning Joseph	10	10
309	25 c. Flight into Egypt	20	20
306/9	*Set of* 4	30	35

(Des C. Abbott. Litho Walsall)

1979 (10 Jan). *Handicrafts (2nd series). Horiz designs as T* **74**. *Multicoloured. W* w **14** *(sideways). P* 13½.

No.	Description		
310	5 c. Sisal bowls	10	10
311	15 c. Pottery	10	10
312	20 c. Basket work	15	15
313	30 c. Hide shield	20	20
310/13	*Set of* 4	45	45

(Des L. Curtis. Litho Questa)

1979 (27 Mar). *Centenary of Discovery of Gold in Swaziland. T* **77** *and similar vert designs. W* w **14**. *P* 14.

No.	Description		
314	5 c. gold and deep ultramarine	15	10
315	15 c. gold and deep brown	30	20
316	25 c. gold and deep green	45	30
317	50 c. gold and carmine-red	70	90
314/17	*Set of* 4	1·40	1·25

Designs:—15 c. Early 3-stamp battery mill; 25 c. Cyanide tanks at Piggs Peak; 50 c. Pouring off molten gold.

78 "Girls at the Piano"

(Des BG Studio. Litho Questa)

1979 (8 May). *International Year of the Child. Paintings by Renoir. T* **78** *and similar horiz designs. Multicoloured. W* w **14** *(sideways). P* 13½.

No.	Description		
318	5 c. Type **78**	10	10
319	15 c. "Madame Charpentier and her Children"	15	10
320	25 c. "Girls picking Flowers"	20	15
321	50 c. "Girl with Watering Can"	40	55
318/21	*Set of* 4	70	70
MS322	123 × 135 mm. Nos. 318/21	85	1·25

79 1933 1d. Carmine Stamp and Sir Rowland Hill

(Des J.W. Litho Walsall)

1979 (17 July). *Death Centenary of Sir Rowland Hill. T* **79** *and similar horiz designs showing stamps and portrait of Sir Rowland Hill. Multicoloured. W* w **14** *(sideways). P* 14½ × 14.

No.	Description		
323	10 c. 1945 3d. Victory commemorative	15	10
324	20 c. Type **79**	25	25
325	25 c. 1968 25 c. Independence commemorative	25	30
323/5	*Set of* 3	60	60
MS326	115 × 90 mm. 50 c. 1956 6d. Great Kudu Antelope definitive	65	85

80 Obverse and Reverse of 5 Cents

(Des G. Hutchins. Litho Walsall)

1979 (6 Sept). *Coins. T* **80** *and similar horiz designs. W* w **14** *(sideways). P* 13½.

No.	Description		
327	5 c. black and light brown	10	10
328	10 c. black and new blue	15	10
329	20 c. black and yellowish green	25	20
330	50 c. black and yellow-orange	45	45
331	1 e. black and cerise	75	80
327/31	*Set of* 5	1·50	1·50

Designs:—10 c. Obverse and reverse of 10 cents; 20 c. Obverse and reverse of 20 cents; 50 c. Reverse of 50 cents; 1 e. Reverse of 1 lilangeni.

81 Big Bend Post Office

(Des J. Cooter. Litho Questa)

1979 (22 Nov). *Post Office Anniversaries. T* **81** *and similar designs. W* w **14** *(sideways on* 5, 20 *and* 50 *c.). P* 13½.

No.	Description		
332	5 c. multicoloured	10	10
333	15 c. multicoloured	15	10
334	20 c. black, sage-green and magenta	**20**	**15**
335	50 c. multicoloured	40	60
332/5	*Set of* 4	70	80

Designs and commemorations: *Horiz*—5 c. Type **81** (25th anniversary of Posts and Telecommunications Services); 20 c. 1949 75th anniversary of U.P.U. 1s. commemorative stamp (10th anniversary of U.P.U. membership); 50 c. 1974 centenary of U.P.U. 25 c. commemorative stamp (10th anniversary of U.P.U. membership). *Vert*—15 c. Microwave antenna. Mount Ntondozi (25th anniversary of Posts and Telecommunications Services).

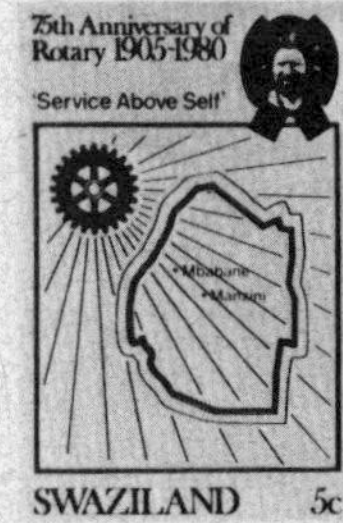

82 Map of Swaziland

83 *Brunsvigia radulosa*

(Des BG Studio. Litho Walsall)

1980 (23 Feb). *75th Anniv of Rotary International. T* **82** *and similar vert designs in gold and bright blue. W* w **14**. *P* 13½.

No.	Description		
336	5 c. Type **82**	10	10
337	15 c. Vitreous cutter and optical illuminator	15	10
338	50 c. Scroll	40	55
339	1 e. Rotary Headquarters, Evanston, U.S.A.	80	1·25
336/9	*Set of* 4	1·40	1·75

(Des BG Studio. Litho Secura, Singapore)

1980 (28 Apr)–**83**. *Flowers. Multicoloured designs as T* **83**.

A. *Without imprint date below design. P* 13½.

No.	Description		
340A	1 c. Type **83**	15	10
341A	2 c. *Aloe suprafoliata*	15	10
342A	3 c. *Haemanthus magnificus*	15	10
	c. Perf 12	75	60
343A	4 c. *Aloe marlothii*	20	10
	c. Perf 12	1·50	1·25
344A	5 c. *Dicoma zeyheri*	15	10
	c. Perf 12	1·00	90
345A	6 c. *Aloe kniphofioides*	20	20
346A	7 c. *Cyrtanthus bicolor*	15	10
347A	10 c. *Eucomis autumnalis*	25	10
348A	15 c. *Leucospermum gerrardii*	15	10
	c. Perf 12		
349A	20 c. *Haemanthus multiflorus*	40	25
350A	30 c. *Acridocarpus natalitius*	20	20
351A	50 c. *Adenium swazicum*	30	30
352A	1 e. *Protea simplex*	55	60
353A	2 e. *Calodendrum capense*	1·10	1·25
354A	5 e. *Gladiolus ecklonii*	2·75	3·00
340A/54A	*Set of* 15	6·00	5·50

B. *With imprint date. P* 12 (12.83)

No.	Description		
340B	1 c. Type **83**	15	15
341B	2 c. *Aloe suprafoliata*	15	15
343B	4 c. *Aloe marlothii*	20	15
345B	6 c. *Aloe kniphofioides*	20	20
347B	10 c. *Eucomis autumnalis*	25	15
349B	20 c. *Haemanthus multiflorus*	40	40
340B/9B	*Set of* 6	1·25	1·10

Nos. 347/51 are horizontal, 42 × 25 mm, and Nos. 352/4 vertical, 28 × 38 mm.

84 Mail Runner

(Des A. Theobald. Litho Walsall)

1980 (6 May). *"London 1980" International Stamp Exhibition. T* **84** *and similar horiz designs. Multicoloured. W* w **14** *(sideways). P* 14.

No.	Description		
355	10 c. Type **84**	10	10
356	20 c. Post Office mail truck	20	15
357	25 c. Mail sorting office	25	20
358	50 c. Ropeway conveying mail at Bulembu	50	70
355/8	*Set of* 4	95	1·00

85 Yellow Fish

(Des and litho Walsall)

1980 (25 Aug). *River Fishes. T* **85** *and similar horiz designs. Multicoloured. W* w **14** *(sideways). P* 13½.

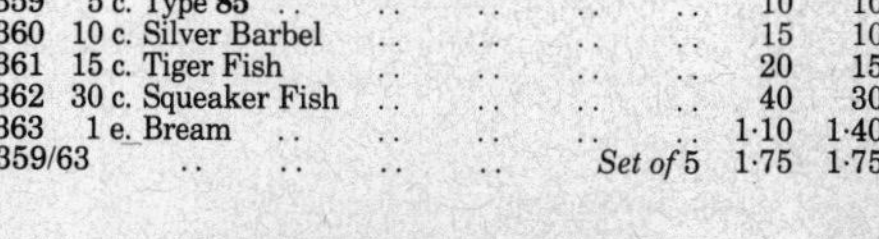

No.	Description		
359	5 c. Type **85**	10	10
360	10 c. Silver Barbel	15	10
361	15 c. Tiger Fish	20	15
362	30 c. Squeaker Fish	40	30
363	1 e. Bream	1·10	1·40
359/63	*Set of* 5	1·75	1·75

86 Oribi

(Des G. Drummond. Litho Harrison)

1980 (1 Oct). *Wildlife Conservation. T* **86** *and similar multicoloured designs. W* w **14** *(sideways on* 5 *and* 50 *c.). P* 14.

No.	Description		
364	5 c. Type **86**	10	10
365	10 c. Nile Crocodile (*vert*)	15	10
366	50 c. Temminck's Ground Pangolin	70	70
367	1 e. Leopard (*vert*)	1·25	1·50
364/7	*Set of* 4	1·90	2·00

87 Public Bus Service

(Des G. Hutchins. Litho Format)

1981 (5 Jan). *Transport. T* **87** *and similar horiz designs. Multicoloured. W* w **14** *(sideways). P* 14½.

No.	Description		
368	5 c. Type **87**	10	10
369	25 c. Royal Swazi National Airways	25	15
370	30 c. Swaziland United Transport	30	20
371	1 e. Swaziland Railway	1·75	1·75
368/71	*Set of* 4	2·10	2·00

88 Mantenga Falls

89 Prince Charles on Hike

(Des L. Curtis. Litho Format)

1981 (16 Mar). *Tourism. T* **88** *and similar horiz designs. Multicoloured. W* w **14** *(sideways). P* 14.

No.	Description		
372	5 c. Type **88**	10	10
373	15 c. Mananga Yacht Club	15	10
374	30 c. White Rhinoceros in Mlilwane Game Sanctuary	40	30
375	1 e. Roulette wheel, playing cards and dice ("casinos")	1·40	1·60
372/5	*Set of* 4	1·75	1·90

(Des J.W. Litho Walsall)

1981 (21 July). *Royal Wedding. T* **89** *and similar vert designs. Multicoloured.* W w **14**. *P* 14.

376 10 c. Wedding bouquet from Swaziland .. 15 10
377 25 c. Type **89** 15 10
378 1 e. Prince Charles and Lady Diana Spencer 60 70
376/8 .. .. *Set of* 3 80 75

90 Installation of King Sobhuza II, 22 December 1921

91 "Physical Recreation"

(Des J.W. Litho Harrison)

1981 (24 Aug). *Diamond Jubilee of King Sobhuza II. T* **90** *and similar horiz designs. Multicoloured.* W w **14** (*sideways*). *P* 14½.

379 5 c. Type **90** 10 10
380 10 c. Royal visit, 1947 .. .. 15 10
381 15 c. King Sobhuza II and Coronation of Queen Elizabeth II, 1953 .. .. 20 15
382 25 c. King Sobhuza taking Royal Salute, Independence, 1968 .. .. 25 25
383 30 c. King Sobhuza in youth 30 30
384 1 e. King Sobhuza and Parliament Buildings 90 1·25
379/84 .. .. *Set of* 6 1·60 1·90

(Des BG Studio. Litho Questa)

1981 (5 Nov). *25th Anniv of Duke of Edinburgh Award Scheme. T* **91** *and similar vert designs. Multicoloured.* W w **14**. *P* 14.

385 5 c. Type **91** 10 10
386 20 c. "Expeditions" 15 10
387 50 c. "Skills" 40 25
388 1 e. Duke of Edinburgh in ceremonial dress 80 80
385/8 .. .. *Set of* 4 1·25 1·00

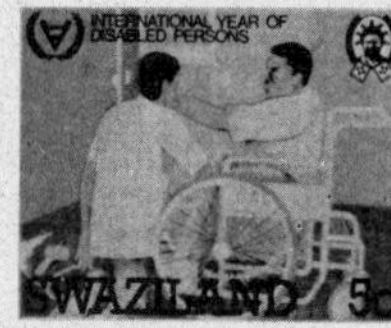

92 Disabled Person in Wheelchair

(Des and litho Walsall)

1981 (16 Dec). *International Year for the Disabled. T* **92** *and similar multicoloured designs.* W w **14** (*sideways on* 5 *c. and* 1 *e.*). *P* 14 × 14½ (5 *c.*, 1 *e.*) *or* 14½ × 14 (*others*).

389 5 c. Type **92** 10 10
390 15 c. Teacher with disabled child (*vert*) .. 20 15
391 25 c. Disabled craftsman (*vert*) 30 20
392 1 e. Disabled driver in invalid carriage .. 1·40 1·40
389/92 .. .. *Set of* 4 1·75 1·60

93 Esper Citrus Swallowtail (*Papilio demodocus*)

94 Man holding a Flower, after discarding Cigarettes

(Des I. Loe. Litho Rosenbaum Bros, Vienna)

1982 (6 Jan). *Butterflies (1st series). T* **93** *and similar horiz designs. Multicoloured.* W w **14** (*sideways*). *P* 14.

393 5 c. Type **93** 20 10
394 10 c. Godart Green-veined Charaxes (*Charaxes candiope*) 40 10
395 50 c. Linnaeus Narrow Green or Blue-banded Swallowtail (*Papilio nireus*) .. .. 1·25 75
396 1 e. Bois Duval Angled Grass Yellow (*Eurema desjardinsii*) .. .. 1·75 1·75
393/6 .. .. *Set of* 4 3·25 2·40

(Des PAD Studio. Litho Format)

1982 (27 Apr). *Pan-African Conference on Smoking and Health. T* **94** *and similar vert design. Multicoloured.* W w **14**. *P* 14.

397 5 c. Type **94** 15 10
398 10 c. Smoker and non-smoker climbing stairs 20 15

ALTERED CATALOGUE NUMBERS

Any Catalogue numbers altered from the last edition are shown as a list in the introductory pages.

95 Male Fishing Owl

96 Swaziland Coat of Arms

(Des G. Drummond. Litho J.W.)

1982 (16 June). *Wildlife Conservation (1st series). Pel's Fishing Owl. T* **95** *and similar vert designs. Multicoloured.* W w **14**. *P* 13½ × 13.

399 35 c. Type **95** 80 90
a. Horiz strip of 5. Nos. 399/403 .. .. 3·50
400 35 c. Female Fishing Owl at nest 80 90
401 35 c. Pair of Fishing Owls 80 90
402 35 c. Fishing Owl, nest and egg 80 90
403 35 c. Adult Fishing Owl with youngster .. 80 90
399/403 .. .. *Set of* 5 3·50 4·00

Nos. 399/403 were printed together, *se-tenant*, in horizontal and vertical strips of 5 throughout the sheet.

See also Nos. 425/9 and Nos. 448/52.

(Des C. Abbott. Litho W. S. Cowells Ltd)

1982 (1 July). *21st Birthday of Princess of Wales. T* **96** *and similar vert designs. Multicoloured.* W w **14**. *P* 14½.

404 5 c. Type **96** 10 10
405 20 c. Princess leaving Eastleigh Airport, Southampton, August 1981 .. .. 15 10
406 50 c. Bride at Buckingham Palace 35 35
407 1 e. Formal portrait 80 80
404/7 .. .. *Set of* 4 1·25 1·25

97 Irrigation

(Des G. Hutchins. Litho Walsall)

1982 (1 Sept). *Sugar Industry. T* **97** *and similar horiz designs. Multicoloured.* W w **14** (*sideways*). *P* 14 × 14½.

408 5 c. Type **97** 10 10
409 20 c. Harvesting 25 15
410 30 c. Mhlume mills 35 25
411 1 e. Sugar transportation by train .. .. 1·00 1·40
408/11 .. .. *Set of* 4 1·50 1·75

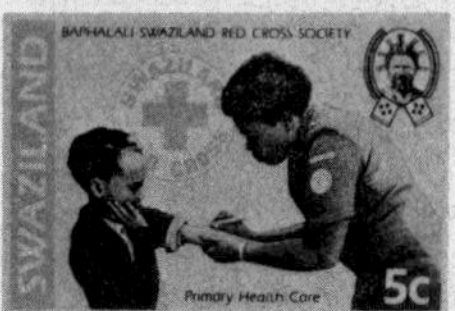

98 Nurse with Child

(Des L. Curtis. Litho Questa)

1982 (9 Nov). *Swaziland Red Cross Society (Baphalali). T* **98** *and similar horiz designs. Multicoloured.* W w **14** (*sideways*). *P* 14.

412 5 c. Type **98** 10 10
413 20 c. Juniors carrying stretcher 25 15
414 50 c. Disaster relief 55 60
415 1 e. Henri Dunant (founder of Red Cross) .. 1·25 1·40
412/15 .. .. *Set of* 4 1·90 2·00

99 Taking the Oath

100 Satellite View of Earth

(Des B. Melton. Litho Format)

1982 (6 Dec). *75th Anniv of Boy Scout Movement. T* **99** *and similar horiz designs. Multicoloured.* W w **14** (*sideways*). *P* 14 × 13½.

416 5 c. Type **99** 10 10
417 10 c. Hiking and exploration 15 10
418 25 c. Community development 30 20
419 75 c. Lord Baden-Powell .. .. .. 1·00 1·00
416/19 .. .. *Set of* 4 1·40 1·25
MS420 107 × 109 mm. 1 e. World Scout badge .. 1·25 1·40

(Des A. Theobald. Litho Harrison)

1983 (14 Mar). *Commonwealth Day. T* **100** *and similar multicoloured designs.* W w **14** (*sideways on* 50 *c.*, 1 *e.*). *P* 14.

421 6 c. Type **100** 10 10
422 10 c. King Sobhuza II 10 10
423 50 c. Swazi woman and beehive huts (*horiz*) .. 35 55
424 1 e. Spraying sugar crops (*horiz*) .. .. 70 1·00
421/4 .. .. *Set of* 4 1·10 1·50

(Des G. Drummond. Litho J.W.)

1983 (16 May). *Wildlife Conservation (2nd series). Lammergeier. Vert designs as T* **95**. *Multicoloured.* W w **14**. *P* 13½ × 13.

425 35 c. Adult male 80 80
a. Horiz strip of 5. Nos. 425/9 .. .. 3·50
426 35 c. Pair 80 80
427 35 c. Nest and egg 80 80
428 35 c. Female at nest 80 80
429 35 c. Adult bird with fledgling 80 80
425/9 .. .. *Set of* 5 3·50 3·50

Nos. 425/9 were printed together, *se-tenant*, in horizontal strips of 5 throughout the sheet.

101 Swaziland National Football Team

102 Montgolfier Balloon

(Des G. Vasarhelyi. Litho Format)

1983 (20 Aug). *Tour of Swaziland by English Football Clubs. Three sheets, 101 × 72 mm, each containing one 75 c. stamp as T* **101**. *Multicoloured.* W w **14** (*sideways*). *P* 13½.

MS430 75 c. Type **101**; 75 c. Tottenham Hotspur; 75 c. Manchester United .. *Set of 3 sheets* 2·25 2·75

(Des. D. Hartley-Marjoram. Litho Format)

1983 (22 Aug). *Bicentenary of Manned Flight. T* **102** *and similar multicoloured designs.* W w **14** (*sideways on* 10 *c. to* 50 *c.*). *P* 14.

431 5 c. Type **102** 10 10
432 10 c. Wright brothers' *Flyer* (*horiz*) 15 10
433 25 c. Fokker "Fellowship" (*horiz*) 30 35
434 50 c. Bell "X-1" (*horiz*) 60 65
431/4 .. .. *Set of* 4 95 1·00
MS435 73 × 73 mm. 1 e. Space shuttle *Columbia* 1·25 1·40

103 Dr. Albert Schweitzer (Peace Prize, 1952)

(Des G. Vasarhelyi. Litho Harrison)

1983 (21 Oct). *150th Birth Anniv of Alfred Nobel. T* **103** *and similar horiz designs. Multicoloured.* W w **14** (*sideways*). *P* 14.

436 6 c. Type **103** 15 10
437 10 c. Dag Hammarskjöld (Peace Prize, 1961) 15 10
438 50 c. Albert Einstein (Physics Prize, 1921) .. 85 70
439 1 e. Alfred Nobel .. .. 1·50 1·50
436/9 .. .. *Set of* 4 2·40 2·10

104 Maize

(Des Jennifer Toombs. Litho Harrison)

1983 (29 Nov). *World Food Day. T* **104** *and similar horiz designs. Multicoloured.* W w **14** (*sideways*). *P* 14.

440 6 c. Type **104** 10 10
441 10 c. Rice 10 10
442 50 c. Cattle herding 55 65
443 1 e. Ploughing .. .. 1·10 1·40
440/3 .. .. *Set of* 4 1·60 2·00

105 Women's College

106 Male on Ledge

(Des C. Abbott. Litho Format)

1984 (12 Mar). *Education. T* **105** *and similar horiz designs. Multicoloured.* W w **14** (*sideways*). *P* 14.

444	5 c. Type **105**	10	10
445	15 c. Technical Training School	15	15
446	50 c. University	45	60
447	1 e. Primary school	90	1·10
444/7	*Set of* 4	1·40	1·75

(Des G. Drummond. Litho J.W.)

1984 (18 May). *Wildlife Conservation.* (3rd series) *Bald Ibis. T* **106** *and similar vert designs. Multicoloured.* W w **14**. *P* 13½ × 13.

448	35 c. Type **106**	95	95
	a. Horiz strip of 5. Nos. 448/52	4·25	
449	35 c. Male and female	95	95
450	35 c. Bird and egg	95	95
451	35 c. Female on nest of eggs	95	95
452	35 c. Adult and fledgling	95	95
448/52	*Set of* 5	4·25	4·25

Nos. 448/52 were printed together, *se-tenant*, in horizontal strips of 5 throughout the sheet.

107 Mule-drawn Passenger Coach

(Des A. Theobald. Litho Walsall)

1984 (15 June). *Universal Postal Union Congress, Hamburg. T* **107** *and similar horiz designs. Multicoloured.* W w **14** (*sideways*). *P* 14½.

453	7 c. Type **107**	15	10
454	15 c. Ox-drawn post wagon	20	15
455	50 c. Mule-drawn mail coach	60	60
456	1 e. Bristol to London mail coach	1·10	1·10
453/6	*Set of* 4	1·90	1·75

108 Running

(Des Harrison. Litho Walsall)

1984 (27 July). *Olympic Games, Los Angeles. T* **108** *and similar horiz designs. Multicoloured.* W w **14** (*sideways*). *P* 14.

457	7 c. Type **108**	10	10
458	10 c. Swimming	10	10
459	50 c. Shooting	45	50
460	1 e. Boxing	90	95
457/60	*Set of* 4	1·40	1·40
MS461	100 × 70 mm. Nos. 457/60	1·50	1·60

109 *Suillus bovinus*

(Des J. Spencer. Litho Format)

1984 (19 Sept). *Fungi. T* **109** *and similar multicoloured designs.* W w **14** (*sideways on* 10 c., 1 e.). *P* 14.

462	10 c. Type **109**	20	10
463	15 c. *Langermannia gigantea* (*vert*)	30	10
464	50 c. *Coriolus versicolor* (*vert*)	65	40
465	1 e. *Boletus edulis*	1·00	90
462/5	*Set of* 4	2·00	1·40

110 King Sobhuza opening Railway, 1964 (**111**)

(Des W. Fenton. Litho Walsall)

1984 (5 Nov). *20th Anniv of Swaziland Railways. T* **110** *and similar horiz designs. Multicoloured.* W w **14** (*sideways*). *P* 14.

466	10 c. Type **110**	25	10
467	25 c. Type "15A" locomotive at Siweni Yard	55	30
468	30 c. Container loading, Matsapha Station	55	30
469	1 e. Locomotive No. 268 leaving Alto Tunnel	1·50	95
466/9	*Set of* 4	2·50	1·50
MS470	144 × 74 mm. Nos. 466/9	2·50	3·00

1984 (15 Dec). *Nos.* 340B, 341A, 342A, 343A, 345B *and* 346A *surch as T* **111**.

471	10 c. on 4 c. *Aloe marlothii*	15	10
	a. Surch on No. 343Ac	15	10
	b. Surch on No. 343B	1·50	1·50
472	15 c. on 7 c. *Cyrtanthus bicolor*	20	10
473	20 c. on 3 c. *Haemanthus magnificus*	30	15
	a. Surch on No. 342Ac	1·50	1·50
474	25 c. on 6 c. *Aloe kniphofioides*	30	20
	a. Surch triple	†	—
475	30 c. on 1 c. Type **83**	35	20
476	30 c. on 2 c. *Aloe suprafoliata*	40	60
	a. Surch on No. 341B	1·50	1·50
471a/6	*Set of* 6	1·50	1·25

112 Rotary International Logo and Map of World

113 Male Ground Hornbill

(Des G. Vasarhelyi. Litho Questa)

1985 (23 Feb). *80th Anniv of Rotary International. T* **112** *and similar horiz designs. Multicoloured.* W w **14** (*sideways*). *P* 14.

477	10 c. Type **112**	20	10
478	15 c. Teacher and handicapped children	25	20
479	50 c. Youth exchange	60	55
480	1 e. Nurse and children	1·00	1·10
477/80	*Set of* 4	1·90	1·75

(Des G. Drummond. Litho Harrison)

1985 (15 May). *Birth Bicentenary of John J. Audubon (ornithologist). Southern Ground Hornbills. T* **113** *and similar vert designs. Multicoloured.* W w **14**. *P* 14.

481	25 c. Type **113**	65	65
	a. Horiz strip of 5. Nos. 481/5	3·00	
482	25 c. Male and female Ground Hornbills	65	65
483	25 c. Female at nest	65	65
484	25 c. Ground Hornbill in nest, and egg	65	65
485	25 c. Adult and fledgeling	65	65
481/5	*Set of* 5	3·00	3·00

Nos. 481/5 were printed together, *se-tenant*, in horizontal strips of 5 throughout the sheet.

114 The Queen Mother in 1975

115 Buick "Tourer"

(Des A. Theobald (2 e.), C. Abbott (others). Litho Questa)

1985 (7 June). *Life and Times of Queen Elizabeth the Queen Mother. T* **114** *and similar vert designs. Multicoloured.* W w **16**. *P* 14½ × 14.

486	10 c. The Queen Mother in South Africa, 1947	10	10
487	15 c. With the Queen and Princess Margaret (from photo by Norman Parkinson)	10	10
488	50 c. Type **114**	30	35
489	1 e. With Prince Henry at his christening (from photo by Lord Snowdon)	65	70
486/9	*Set of* 4	1·00	1·10
MS490	91 × 73 mm. 2 e. Greeting Prince Andrew. Wmk sideways	1·25	1·40

(Des D. Hartley. Litho Walsall)

1985 (16 Sept). *Century of Motoring. T* **115** *and similar horiz designs. Multicoloured.* W w **14** (*sideways*). *P* 14.

491	10 c. Type **115**	20	10
492	15 c. Four cylinder Rover	25	15
493	50 c. De Dion Bouton	60	50
494	1 e. "Model T" Ford	85	1·00
491/4	*Set of* 4	1·75	1·60

116 Youths building Bridge over Ravine

(Des Vrein Barlocher. Litho Format)

1985 (2 Dec). *International Youth Year* (10, 50 c.), *and 75th Anniv of Girl Guide Movement* (*others*). *T* **116** *and similar horiz designs. Multicoloured.* W w **16** (*sideways*). *P* 14.

495	10 c. Type **116**	15	10
496	20 c. Girl Guides in camp	20	15
497	50 c. Youth making model from sticks	45	60
498	1 e. Guides collecting brushwood	80	1·25
495/8	*Set of* 4	1·40	1·90

117 Halley's Comet over Swaziland

118 King Mswati III

(Des Jennifer Toombs. Litho B.D.T.)

1986 (27 Feb). *Appearance of Halley's Comet.* W w **14** (*sideways*). *P* 14.

499	**117** 1 e. 50, multicoloured	1·50	1·50

(Des A. Theobald. Litho Format)

1986 (21 Apr). *60th Birthday of Queen Elizabeth II. Vert designs as T* **110** *of Ascension. Multicoloured.* W w **16**. *P* 14 × 14½.

500	10 c. Christening of Princess Anne, 1950	10	10
501	30 c. On Palace balcony after wedding of Prince and Princess of Wales, 1981	20	25
502	45 c. Royal visit to Swaziland, 1947	25	30
503	1 e. At Windsor Polo Ground, 1984	55	60
504	2 e. At Crown Agents Head Office, London, 1983	1·10	1·25
500/4	*Set of* 5	1·90	2·25

(Des L. Curtis. Litho Walsall)

1986 (25 Apr). *Coronation of King Mswati III. T* **118** *and similar designs.* W w **16** (*sideways on* 20 c. *to* 2 e.). *P* 14½×14 (10 c.) *or* 14×14½ (*others*).

505	10 c. black and gold	20	10
506	20 c. multicoloured	35	20
507	25 c. multicoloured	40	25
508	30 c. multicoloured	45	30
509	40 c. multicoloured	50	45
510	2 e. multicoloured	1·75	2·50
505/10	*Set of* 6	3·25	3·50

Designs: *Horiz*—20 c. Prince with King Sobhuza II at Incwala ceremony; 25 c. At primary school; 30 c. At school in England; 40 c. Inspecting guard of honour at Matsapha Airport; 2 e. Dancing the Simemo.

119 Emblems of Round Table and Project Orbis (eye disease campaign)

120 Yellow Pansy

(Des M. Kesson, adapted G. Vasarhelyi. Litho Walsall)

1986 (6 Oct). *50th Anniv of Round Table Organization. T* **119** *and similar vert designs showing branch emblems. Multicoloured.* W w **16**. *P* 14.

511	15 c. Type **119**	10	10
512	25 c. Ehlanzeni 51	15	20
513	55 c. Mbabane 30	35	40
514	70 c. Bulembu 54	45	50
515	2 e. Manzini 44	1·25	1·40
511/15	*Set of* 5	2·10	2·40

(Des I. Loe. Litho Questa)

1987 (17 Mar). *Butterflies. T* **120** *and similar horiz designs. Multicoloured. P* 14.

516	10 c. Type **120**	10	10
517	15 c. Guineafowl	10	10
518	20 c. Red Forest Charaxes	10	10
519	25 c. Paradise Skipper	10	10
520	30 c. Broad Bordered Acraea	15	20
521	35 c. Veined Swallowtail	15	20
522	45 c. Large Striped Swordtail	20	25
523	50 c. Eyed Pansy	20	25
524	55 c. Zebra White	25	30
525	70 c. Gaudy Commodore	30	35
526	1 e. Common Dotted Border	40	45
527	5 e. Queen Purple Tip	2·10	2·25
528	10 e. Natal Barred Blue	4·25	4·50
516/28	*Set of* 13	7·50	8·00

121 Two White Rhinoceroses

122 Hybrid Tea Rose "Blue Moon"

(Des Doreen McGuinness. Litho Questa)

1987 (1 July). *White Rhinoceros. T* **121** *and similar horiz designs. Multicoloured. W* w **16** (*sideways*). *P* 14½.
529 15 c. Type **121** 25 15
530 25 c. Female and calf 40 35
531 45 c. Rhinoceros charging 70 70
532 70 c. Rhinoceros wallowing . . . . . . 1·00 1·10
529/32 . . . . *Set of* 4 2·10 2·10

(Des Josephine Martin. Litho Questa)

1987 (19 Oct). *Garden Flowers. T* **122** *and similar vert designs. Multicoloured. W* w **16**. *P* 14½.
533 15 c. Type **122** 25 15
534 35 c. Rambler Rose "Danse du feu" 45 35
535 55 c. Pompon Dahlia "Odin" 60 50
536 2 e. *Lilium davidii var. willmottiae* . . 2·00 2·50
533/6 . . . . *Set of* 4 3·00 3·25

1987 (9 Dec). *Royal Ruby Wedding. Nos.* 501/4 *optd with T* **119** *of Ascension in silver.*
537 30 c. On Palace balcony after wedding of Prince and Princess of Wales, 1981 . . 15 20
538 45 c. Royal visit to Swaziland, 1947 . . 25 30
539 1 e. At Windsor Polo Ground, 1984 . . 55 70
540 2 e. At Crown Agents Head Office, London, 1983 . . . . 1·10 1·40
537/40 . . . . *Set of* 4 1·90 2·40

123 *Zabalius aridus*

(Des I. Loe. Litho Questa)

1988 (14 Mar). *Insects. T* **123** *and similar horiz designs. Multicoloured. W* w **16** (*sideways*). *P* 14.
541 15 c. Type **123** 25 15
542 55 c. *Callidea bohemani* 60 55
543 1 e. *Phymateus viridipes* . . . . . . 95 1·00
544 2 e. *Nomadacris septemfasciata* . . . . 1·90 2·25
541/4 . . . . *Set of* 4 3·25 3·50

124 Athlete with Swazi Flag and Olympic Stadium

(Des C. Abbott. Litho Format)

1988 (22 Aug). *Olympic Games, Seoul. T* **124** *and similar horiz designs. Multicoloured. W* w **16** (*sideways*). *P* 14.
545 15 c. Type **124** 20 10
546 35 c. Taekwondo 35 25
547 1 e. Boxing 80 80
548 2 e. Tennis . . . . 1·40 1·50
545/8 . . . . *Set of* 4 2·50 2·40

125 Savanna Monkey ("Green Monkey")

126 Dr. David Hynd (founder of Swazi Red Cross)

(Des I. Loe. Litho Questa)

1989 (16 Jan). *Small Mammals. T* **125** *and similar horiz designs. Multicoloured. W* w **16** (*sideways*). *P* 14.
549 35 c. Type **125** 30 25
550 55 c. Large-toothed Rock Hyrax ("Rock Dassie") 40 30
551 1 e. Zorilla 70 70
552 2 e. African Wild Cat . . . . 1·25 1·25
549/52 . . . . *Set of* 4 2·40 2·25

(Des T. Chance. Litho Security Printers (M), Malaysia)

1989 (21 Sept). *125th Anniv of International Red Cross. T* **126** *and similar horiz designs. Multicoloured. W* w **14** (*sideways*). *P* 12.
553 15 c. Type **126** 15 15
554 60 c. First aid training 40 40
555 1 e. Sigombeni Clinic 70 70
556 2 e. Refugee camp . . . . 1·10 1·10
553/6 . . . . *Set of* 4 2·10 2·10

OMNIBUS ISSUES

Details, together with prices for complete sets, of the various Omnibus issues from the 1935 Silver Jubilee series to date are included in a special section following Zululand at the end of the catalogue.

127 King Mswati III with Prince of Wales, 1987

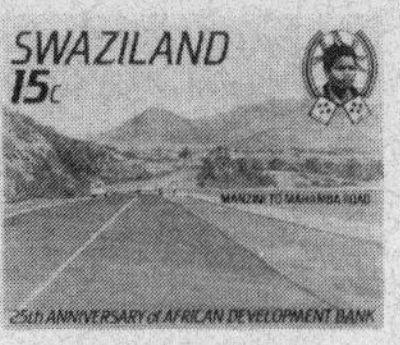

128 Manzini to Mahamba Road

(Des L. Curtis. Litho Harrison)

1989 (15 Nov). *21st Birthday of King Mswati III. T* **127** *and similar horiz designs. Multicoloured. P* 14×14½.
557 15 c. Type **127** 10 10
558 60 c. King with Pope John Paul II, 1988 . . 30 35
559 1 e. Introduction of Crown Prince to people, 1983 . . . . 50 55
560 2 e. King Mswati III and Queen Mother . . 95 1·00
557/60 . . . . *Set of* 4 1·60 1·75

(Des A. Theobald. Litho Questa)

1989 (18 Dec). *25th Anniv of African Development Bank. T* **128** *and similar horiz designs. Multicoloured. W* w **16** (*sideways*). *P* 14×14½.
561 15 c. Type **128** 10 10
562 60 c. Microwave Radio Receiver, Mbabane . . 30 35
563 1 e. Mbabane Government Hospital 50 55
564 2 e. Ezulwini Power Station switchyard . . 95 1·00
561/4 . . . . *Set of* 4 1·60 1·75

POSTAGE DUE STAMPS

D 1

Postage Due
2d

(D 2)

D 3

(Typo D.L.R.)

1933 (2 Jan)–**57**. *Wmk Mult Script CA. P* 14.
D1 D **1** 1 d. carmine, **O** . . . . 20 3·50
    a. Deep carmine, **C** (24.10.51) . . 20 4·00
    ac. Error. St Edward's Crown, W **9***b*, **C** 55·00
D2 2d. pale violet, **O** . . . . 1·00 10·00
    a. Chalky paper (22.2.57) . . . . 2·25 13·00
D1/2 Perf "Specimen" . . . . *Set of* 2 40·00

1961 (8 Feb). *No.* 55 *surch with Type* D **2**.
D3 **7** 2d. on 2d. . . . . 3·00 5·50

Another 2d. on 2d. Postage Due, with small surcharge as Type D **5**, was produced *after the currency change*, to meet the philatelic demand (*Price* 15*p unused*).

(Typo D.L.R.)

1961 (14 Feb). *Chalk-surfaced paper. Wmk Mult Script CA. P* 14.
D4 D **3** 1 c. carmine 15 55
D5 2 c. violet 15 75
D6 5 c. green . . . . 20 1·00
D4/6 . . . . *Set of* 3 45 2·10

Postage Due
1c

(D 4)

Postage Due
1c

(D 5)

1961. *No.* 55 *surcharged*. A. *As Type* D **4**. (14 Feb).
D 7 **7** 1 c. on 2d. . . . . 1·25 2·25
D 8 2 c. on 2d. . . . . 1·25 2·25
D 9 5 c. on 2d. . . . . 1·50 2·25
D7/9 . . . . *Set of* 3 3·50 6·00

B. *As Type* D **5**. (Date?)
D10 **7** 1 c. on 2d. . . . . 80 2·25
D11 2 c. on 2d. . . . . 55 1·50
D12 5 c. on 2d. . . . . 1·00 2·25
D10/12 . . . . *Set of* 3 2·10 5·50

D 6

(Des and litho B.W.)

1971 (1 Feb). *W* w **12**. *P* 11½.
D13 D **6** 1 c. bright rose-red . . . . . . 35 1·25
D14 2 c. purple . . . . 50 1·60
D15 5 c. dull green . . . . 80 2·00
D13/15 . . . . *Set of* 3 1·50 4·25

1977 (17 Jan). *W* w **14** (*sideways*). *P* 11½.
D16 D **6** 1 c. rose-red . . . . 45 1·50
D17 2 c. purple . . . . 65 1·75
D18 5 c. dull green . . . . 1·10 2·25
D16/18 . . . . *Set of* 3 2·00 5·00

(Litho Harrison)

1978 (20 Apr)–**85**. *W* w **14**. *P* 14½×14.
D19 D **6** 1 c. carmine 10 10
D19*a* 1 c. brown-red (13.3.85) 10 10
D20 2 c. purple 10 10
D21 5 c. blue-green 10 10
D19/21 . . . . *Set of* 4 20 20

Tanganyika

The stamps of GERMANY were used in the colony between October 1890 and July 1893 when issues for GERMAN EAST AFRICA were provided.

PRICES FOR STAMPS ON COVER TO 1945

The Mafia Island provisionals (No. M1/52) are very rare used on cover.

Nos. N1/5	*from* × 8
Nos. 45/59	*from* × 6
Nos. 60/2	—
Nos. 63/73	*from* × 6
Nos. 74/86	*from* × 8
Nos. 87/8	—
Nos. 89/92	*from* × 6
Nos. 93/106	*from* × 3
No. 107	—

MAFIA ISLAND

BRITISH OCCUPATION

Mafia Island was captured by the British from the Germans in January 1915. Letters were first sent out unstamped, then with stamps handstamped with Type M 1. Later the military were supplied with handstamps by the post office in Zanzibar. These were used to produce Nos. M11/52.

(M 1)

(M 3)

1915 (Jan). *German East Africa Yacht types, handstamped with Type* M 1. *Wmk Lozenges, or no wmk* (1 r., 2 r.). A. *In black* (2½ h. *in blackish lilac*). B. *In deep purple*. C. *In reddish violet*.

		A	B	C
M 1	2½ h. brown	£350	†	£200
	a. Pair, one without handstamp	†	†	£1000
M 2	4 h. green	£350	£300	£175
	a. Pair, one without handstamp	†	†	£950
M 3	7½ h. carmine	£350	£300	£100
	a. Pair, one without handstamp	£1600	†	£950
M 4	15 h. ultramarine	£475	£400	£125
	a. Pair, one without handstamp	†	†	£950
M 5	20 h. black and red/*yellow*	£475	£400	£225
	a. Pair, one without handstamp	†	£1600	£1000
M 6	30 h. black and carmine	£525	£450	£275
	a. Pair, one without handstamp	£1600	†	£1000
M 7	45 h. black and mauve	£600	£500	£325
	a. Pair, one without handstamp	£1600	†	£1100
M 8	1 r. carmine	£3000	†	£2750
M 9	2 r. green	£3500	†	£3250
M10	3 r. blue-black and red	£4250	†	£3500

Prices are for unused examples.

A few contemporary Zanzibar stamps (1, 3, 6 and 15 c.) are known with the above handstamp.

1915 (May). *German East Africa Yacht types with handstamped four-line surcharge* "G.R.—POST—6 CENTS—MAFIA" *in black, green or violet. Wmk Lozenges or no wmk* (1 r., 2 r.).

M11	6 c. on 2½ h. brown	£500	£700
	a. Pair, one without handstamp	†	—
M12	6 c. on 4 h. green	£500	£700
	a. Pair, one without handstamp		
M13	6 c. on 7½ h. carmine	£500	£700
	a. Pair, one without handstamp		
M14	6 c. on 15 h. ultramarine	£500	£700
M15	6 c. on 20 h. black and red/*yellow*	£500	£700
M16	6 c. on 30 h. black and carmine	£700	£800
M17	6 c. on 45 h. black and mauve	£700	£800
	a. Pair, one without handstamp		
M18	6 c. on 1 r. carmine	£4000	
M19	6 c. on 2 r. green	£5000	
M20	6 c. on 3 r. blue-black and red	£6000	

The 5, 20 and 40 pesa values of the 1901 Yacht issue are also known with the above surcharge as are the contemporary 1 c. and 6 c. Zanzibar stamps.

1915 (Sept). (a) *German East African fiscal stamps.* "Statistik des Waaren-Verkehrs" (*Trade Statistical Charge*) *handstamped in bluish green or violet,* "O.H.B.M.S. Mafia" *in a circle, as Type* M 3.

M21	24 pesa, vermilion/*buff*	£275	£375
M22	12½ heller, drab	£275	£375
	a. Pair, one without handstamp	£1100	
M23	25 heller, dull green	£275	£375
M24	50 heller, slate	£275	£375
	a. Pair, one without handstamp	£1100	
M25	1 rupee, lilac	£275	£375

(b) *German East African* "Ubersetzungs- Gebühren" (*Translation Fee*) *stamp, overprinted as before*

M26	25 heller, grey	£425	£500

G. R
POST
MAFIA

(M 4)

G. R.
Post
MAFIA.

(M 5)

(c) *Stamps as above, but with further opt as Type* M 4, *in bluish green or violet*

M27	24 pesa, vermilion/*buff*	£375
M28	12½ heller, drab	£375
M29	25 heller, dull green	£375
M30	50 heller, slate	£375
M31	1 rupee, lilac	£375
M32	25 heller, grey (No. M26)	£500
	a. Pair, one without handstamp Type M 4	£1700

Type M 3 is also known handstamped on the 7½ h., 20 h. and 30 h. values of German East Africa 1905 Yacht issue and also on contemporary 1, 3, 6 and 25 c. Zanzibar stamps.

1915 (Sept). *Stamps of Indian Expeditionary Forces* (*India optd* "I.E.F.") *with a further opt Type* M 4 *handstruck in green, greenish black or dull blue.*

M33	55	3 p. grey	15·00	28·00
		a. Pair, one stamp without opt	—	£300
M34	56	½ a. green	22·00	30·00
		a. Pair, one stamp without opt	—	£350
M35	57	1 a. carmine	25·00	30·00
M36	59	2 a. mauve	35·00	50·00
M37	61	2½ a. ultramarine	45·00	65·00
M38	62	3 a. orange-brown	45·00	65·00
		a. Pair, one stamp without opt	—	£400
M39	63	4 a. olive	60·00	85·00
M40	65	8 a. purple	£100	£150
		a. Pair, one stamp without opt	—	£500
M41	66	12 a. dull claret	£170	£225
M42	67	1 r. brown and green	£180	£250
M33/42		*Set of* 10	£600	£850

All values exist with the overprint inverted, and several are known with overprint double or sideways.

1916 (Oct). *Stamps of Indian Expeditionary Forces* (*India optd* "I.E.F.") *with further opt Type* M 5 *handstruck in green, greenish black or dull blue.*

M43	55	3 p. grey	65·00	80·00
M44	56	½ a. green	65·00	80·00
M45	57	1 a. carmine	60·00	70·00
M46	59	2 a. mauve	85·00	£100
M47	61	2½ a. ultramarine	90·00	£110
M48	62	3 a. orange-brown	90·00	£110
M49	63	4 a. olive	£100	£120
M50	65	8 a. purple	£130	£170
M51	66	12 a. dull claret	£180	£225
M52	67	1 r. brown and green	£180	£225
M43/52		*Set of* 10	£900	£1100

Stamps with handstamp inverted are known.

NYASALAND-RHODESIAN FORCE

This issue was sanctioned for use by the Nyasaland-Rhodesian Force during operations in German East Africa, Mozambique and Nyasaland. Unoverprinted Nyasaland stamps were used by the Force prior to the introduction of Nos. N1/5 and, again, in 1918.

N. F.

(N 1)

1916 (7 Aug–18 Sept*). *T* 15 *of Nyasaland optd with Type* N 1 *by Govt Printer, Zomba.*

N1	15	½d. green	80	4·00
N2		1d. scarlet	70	2·50
N3		3d. purple/*yellow* (15 Sept*)	5·00	14·00
		a. Opt double	—	£6000
N4		4d. black and red/*yellow* (13 Sept*)	19·00	30·00
N5		1s. black/*green* (18 Sept*)	20·00	32·00
N1/5		*Set of* 5	40·00	70·00
N1/5 Optd "Specimen"		*Set of* 5	£300	

* Earliest known dates of use.

Of No. N3a only six copies were printed, these being the bottom row on one pane issued at M'bamba Bay F.P.O., German East Africa in March 1918.

This overprint was applied in a setting of 60 (10 rows of 6) and the following minor varieties occur on all values: small stop after "N" (R. 1/1); broken "F" (R. 4/3); very small stop after "F" (R. 6/5); no serifs at top left and bottom of "N" (R. 10/1).

TANGANYIKA

BRITISH OCCUPATION OF GERMAN EAST AFRICA

G.E.A. (1) G. E. A. (2) G.E.A. (3)

1917–21. *Stamps of Kenya, Uganda and Tanganyika optd with T* 1 *and* 2. *Wmk Mult Crown CA. Ordinary paper* (1 c. *to* 15 c.) *or chalk-surfaced paper* (*others*).

45	3	1 c. black (R.)	15	70
46		1 c. black (Verm)	11·00	15·00
47		3 c. green	15	15
48		6 c. scarlet	15	10
49		10 c. orange	15	30
50		12 c. slate-grey	15	1·25
51		15 c. bright blue	15	1·75
52		25 c. black and red/*yellow*	30	2·25
		a. On pale-yellow (1921) (Optd S. £35)	1·40	6·00
53		50 c. black and lilac	50	2·75
54		75 c. black/*blue-green, olive-back* (R.)	65	3·00
		a. On emerald back (Optd S. £42)	1·75	14·00
55	4	1 r. black/*green* (R.)	1·00	5·50
		a. On emerald back	2·25	14·00
56		2 r. red and black/*blue*	4·50	15·00
57		3 r. violet and green	6·50	26·00
58		4 r. red and green/*yellow*	15·00	38·00
59		5 r. blue and dull purple	24·00	42·00
60		10 r. red and green/*green*	45·00	90·00
		a. On emerald back	50·00	£120
61		20 r. black and purple/*red*	£130	£170
62		50 r. carmine and green (S. £150)	£500	£625
45/61		*Set of* 16	£200	£350
45/61 Optd "Specimen"		*Set of* 16	£375	

Early printings of the rupee values exist with very large stop after the "E" in "G.E.A." (R. 5/3). There are round stops after "E" varieties, which in one position of later printings became a small stop.

1921. *As* 1917–21 *but wmk Mult Script CA.*

63	3	12 c. slate-grey, **O**	2·75	15·00
64		15 c. bright blue, **O**	30	2·50
65		50 c. black and dull purple, **C**	7·50	32·00
66	4	2 r. red and black/*blue*, **C**	32·00	70·00
67		3 r. violet and green, **C**	42·00	85·00
68		5 r. blue and dull purple, **C**	55·00	90·00
63/8		*Set of* 6	£130	£275
63/8 Optd "Specimen"		*Set of* 6	£200	

1922. *T* 3 *of Kenya optd by the Government printer at Dar-es-Salaam with T* 3. *Wmk Mult Script CA.*

72	1 c. black (R.)	30	7·00
73	10 c. orange-yellow	45	9·00

BRITISH MANDATED TERRITORY

4 Giraffe 5

(Recess B.W.)

1922. *Head in black. Wmk Mult Script CA.* (a) *P* 15 × 14.

74	4	5 c. slate-purple	55	20
75		10 c. green	30	20
76		15 c. carmine-red	55	10
77		20 c. orange	45	10
78		25 c. black	2·75	5·50
79		30 c. blue	2·25	2·50
80		40 c. yellow-brown	1·50	3·00
81		50 c. slate-grey	1·25	1·50
82		75 c. yellow-bistre	2·75	9·00

(b) *P* 14. A. *Wmk sideways.* B. *Wmk upright*

			A		B	
83	5	1 s. green	1·75	7·50	1·25	5·00
84		2 s. purple	4·25	9·00	2·50	11·00
85		3 s. black	6·50	18·00	†	
86		5 s. scarlet	11·00	38·00	7·50	35·00
87		10 s. deep blue	55·00	95·00	35·00	70·00
88		£1 yellow-orange	90·00	£160	85·00	£160
74/88		*Set of* 15 (*incl* 85A)			£130	£275
74/88 Optd "Specimen"		*Set of* 15			£425	

In the £1 stamp the words of value are on a curved scroll running across the stamp above the words "POSTAGE AND REVENUE".

1925. *As* 1922. *Frame colours changed.*

89	4	5 c. green	30	90
90		10 c. orange-yellow	1·75	1·00
91		25 c. blue	2·00	10·00
92		30 c. purple	75	5·50
89/92		*Set of* 4	4·25	16·00
89/92 Optd "Specimen"		*Set of* 4	70·00	

6 7

(Typo D.L.R.)

1927–31. *Head in black. Wmk Mult Script CA. P* 14.

93	6	5 c. green	20	10
94		10 c. yellow	25	10
95		15 c. carmine-red	20	10
96		20 c. orange-buff	50	10
97		25 c. bright blue	65	75
98		30 c. dull purple	90	2·50
98*a*		30 c. bright blue (1931)	11·00	30
99		40 c. yellow-brown	1·00	2·75
100		50 c. grey	75	25
101		75 c. olive-green	1·75	8·50
102	7	1 s. green, **O**	2·25	80
103		2 s. deep purple, **O**	4·50	2·00
104		3 s. black, **O**	8·00	23·00
105		5 s. carmine-red, **C**	9·00	13·00
106		10 s. deep blue, **C**	32·00	55·00
107		£1 brown-orange, **C**	85·00	£120
93/107		*Set of* 16	£140	£200
93/107 Optd/Perf "Specimen"		*Set of* 16	£250	

For issues between 1935 and 1961 see KENYA, UGANDA AND TANGANYIKA.

INDEPENDENT REPUBLIC

8 Teacher and Pupils

9 District Nurse and Child

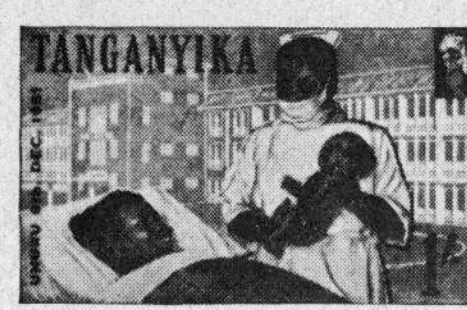

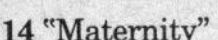

14 "Maternity"

15 Freedom Torch over Mt Kilimanjaro

(Des V. Whiteley. Photo Harrison)

1961 (9 Dec)–**64**. *Independence. T* **8/9**, **14/15** *and similar designs. P* 14×15 (5 *c.*, 30 *c.*), 15×14 (10 *c.*, 15 *c.*, 20 *c.*, 50 *c.*) *or* 14½ (*others*).

No.	Description		
108	5 c. sepia and light apple-green	10	10
109	10 c. deep bluish green	10	10
110	15 c. sepia and blue	10	10
	a. Blue omitted	£200	
111	20 c. orange-brown	10	10
112	30 c. black, emerald and yellow	10	10
	a. Inscr "UHURU 196"	£325	£130
	b. "1" inserted after "196"	10·00	
113	50 c. black and yellow	10	10
114	1 s. brown, blue and olive-yellow	15	10
115	1 s. 30, red, yellow, black, brown and blue	70	10
	a. Red, yellow, blk, brn & dp bl (10.3.64)	80	10
116	2 s. blue, yellow, green and brown	40	10
117	5 s. deep bluish green and orange-red	50	40
118	10 s. black, reddish purple and light blue	6·50	2·25
	a. Reddish purple (diamond) omitted	£150	
119	20 s. red, yellow, black, brown and green	3·00	7·00
108/19	*Set of* 12	10·00	9·00

Designs: *Vert* (*as T* **9**)—15 c. Coffee-picking; 20 c. Harvesting maize; 50 c. Serengeti lions. *Horiz* (*as T* **8**)—30 c. Tanganyikan flag. (*As T* **14**)—2 s. Dar-es-Salaam waterfront; 5 s. Land tillage; 10 s. Diamond and mine. *Vert*—20 s. Type **15**.

No. 112a. The missing "1" in "1961" occurs on emerald Plate 1C, R. 10/10. The "1" was later inserted but it is, however, very slightly shorter and the figure is more solid than normal.

19 Pres. Nyerere inaugurating Self-help Project

20 Hoisting Flag on Mt Kilimanjaro

(Photo Harrison)

1962 (9 Dec). *Inauguration of Republic. Vert designs as T* **19/20**. *P* 14½.

No.	Description		
120	30 c. emerald	10	10
121	50 c. yellow, black, green, red and blue	10	10
122	1 s. 30, multicoloured	10	10
123	2 s. 50, black, red and blue	15	30
120/3	*Set of* 4	25	35

Designs:—1 s. 30, Presidential emblem; 2 s. 50, Independence Monument.

23 Map of Republic

24 Torch and Spear Emblem

(Des M. Goaman. Photo Harrison)

1964 (7 July). *United Republic of Tanganyika and Zanzibar Commemoration. P* 14 × 14½.

No.	Type	Description		
124	**23**	20 c. yellow-green and light blue	10	10
125	**24**	30 c. blue and sepia	10	10
126		1 s. 30, orange-brown and ultramarine	10	10
127	**23**	2 s. 50, purple and ultramarine	20	30
124/7		*Set of* 4	25	35

Despite the inscription on the stamps the above issue was only on sale in Tanganyika and had no validity in Zanzibar.

The United Republic of Tanganyika and Zanzibar, formed 26 April 1964, was renamed the United Republic of Tanzania on 29 October 1964.

PRICES OF SETS

Set prices are given for many issues, generally those containing three stamps or more. Definitive sets include one of each value or major colour change, but do not cover different perforations, die types or minor shades. Where a choice is possible the set prices are based on the cheapest versions of the stamps included in the listings.

Tanzania
(*formerly* Tanganyika)

Issues to No. 176, except Nos. Z142/5, were also valid in Kenya and Uganda.

25 Hale Hydro-Electric Scheme

26 Tanzanian Flag

27 National Servicemen

33 Dar-es-Salaam Harbour

38 Arms of Tanzania

(Des V. Whiteley. Photo Harrison)

1965 (9 Dec). *T* **25/7**, **33**, **38** *and similar designs. P* 14 × 14½ (5 *c.*, 10 *c.*, 20 *c.*, 50 *c.*, 65 *c.*), 14½ × 14 (15 *c.*, 30 *c.*, 40 *c.*), *or* 14 (*others*).

No.	Description		
128	5 c. ultramarine and yellow-orange	10	10
129	10 c. black, greenish yellow, green & blue	10	10
130	15 c. multicoloured	10	10
131	20 c. sepia, grey-green and greenish blue	10	10
132	30 c. black and red-brown	10	10
133	40 c. multicoloured	25	20
134	50 c. multicoloured	25	10
135	65 c. green, red-brown and blue	1·25	1·25
136	1 s. multicoloured	40	10
137	1 s. 30, multicoloured	3·00	40
138	2 s. 50, blue and orange-brown	2·75	90
139	5 s. lake-brown, yellow-green and blue	80	20
140	10 s. olive-yellow, olive-green and blue	1·00	1·50
141	20 s. multicoloured	3·75	8·50
128/41	*Set of* 14	12·50	12·00

Designs: *Horiz* (*as T* **25**)—20 c. Road-building; 50 c. Common Zebras, Manyara National Park; 65 c. Mt Kilimanjaro. *Vert* (*as T* **27**)—30 c. Drum, spear, shield and stool; 40 c. Giraffes, Mikumi National Park. *Horiz* (*As T* **33**)—1 s. 30, Skull of *Zinjanthropus* and excavations, Olduvai Gorge, 2 s. 50, Fishing; 5 s. Sisal industry; 10 s. State House, Dar-es-Salaam.

Z **39** Pres. Nyerere and First Vice-Pres. Karume within Bowl of Flame

Z **40** Hands supporting Bowl of Flame

(Des J. Ahmed (Type Z **39**), G. Vasarhelyi (Type Z **40**). Photo Enschedé)

1966 (26 April). *2nd Anniv of United Republic. P* 14 × 13.

No.	Type	Description		
Z142	Z **39**	30 c. multicoloured	10	10
Z143	Z **40**	50 c. multicoloured	10	10
Z144		1 s. 30, multicoloured	10	15
Z145	Z **39**	2 s. 50, multicoloured	25	90
Z142/5		*Set of* 4	35	1·00

Nos. Z142/5 were on sale in Zanzibar only.

39 Cardinal

40 Mud Skipper

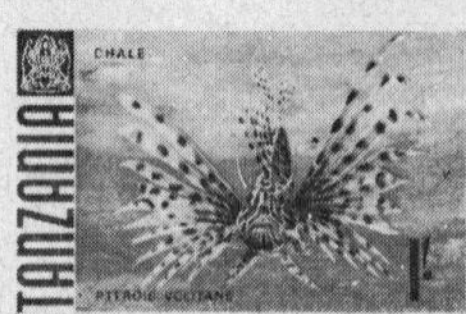

41 Scorpion Fish

(Des Rena Fennessy. Photo Harrison)

1967 (9 Dec)–**73**. *Designs as T* **39/41**. *Chalk-surfaced paper. P* 14 × 15 (5 *c. to* 70 *c.*) *or* 14½ (*others*).

No.	Description		
142	5 c. magenta, yellow-olive and black	10	15
	a. Glazed, ordinary paper (22.1.71)	15	35
143	10 c. brown and bistre	10	10
	a. Glazed, ordinary paper (27.9.72)	15	30
144	15 c. grey, turquoise-blue and black	10	15
	a. Glazed, ordinary paper (22.1.71)	15	40
145	20 c. brown and turquoise-green	10	10
	a. Glazed, ordinary paper (16.7.73)	15	35
146	30 c. sage-green and black	10	10
	a. Glazed, ordinary paper (3.5.71)	95	40
147	40 c. yellow, chocolate and bright green	15	10
	a. Glazed, ordinary paper (10.2.71)	35	30
148	50 c. multicoloured	15	10
	a. Glazed, ordinary paper (10.2.71)	25	35
149	65 c. orange-yellow, bronze-green and black	3·50	4·00
150	70 c. multicoloured (15.9.69)	1·00	2·50
	a. Glazed, ordinary paper (22.1.71)	4·00	4·75
151	1 s. orange-brown, slate-blue and maroon	30	10
	a. Glazed, ordinary paper (3.2.71)	40	10
152	1 s. 30, multicoloured	3·00	10
153	1 s. 50, multicoloured (15.9.69)	1·50	50
	a. Glazed, ordinary paper (27.9.72)	2·00	10
154	2 s. 50, multicoloured	1·75	45
	a. Glazed, ordinary paper (27.9.72)	4·50	10
155	5 s. greenish yellow, black & turquoise-grn	3·50	90
	a. Glazed, ordinary paper (3.2.71)	3·25	10
156	10 s. multicoloured	2·00	1·40
	a. Glazed, ordinary paper (*dull blue-green background*) (3.2.71)	2·50	10
	ab. Deep dull green background (12.9.73)	3·00	50
157	20 s. multicoloured	4·00	4·00
	a. Glazed, ordinary paper (3.2.71)	8·00	15
142/57	*Set of* 16	18·00	13·00
142a/57a	*Set of* 14	24·00	6·75

Designs: *Horiz as T* **39/40**—15 c. White Spotted Puffer; 20 c. Sea Horses; 30 c. Bat Fish; 40 c. Sweetlips; 50 c. Blue Club-nosed Wrasse; 65 c. Bennett's Butterfly; 70 c. Striped Grouper. *Horiz as T* **41**—1 s. 30, Powder Blue Surgeon; 1 s. 50, Fusilier; 2 s. 50, Red Snapper; 5 s. Moorish Idol; 10 s. Picasso Fish; 20 s. Squirrel Fish.

On chalk-surfaced paper all values except the 30 c., exist with PVA gum as well as gum arabic, but the 70 c. and 1 s. 50 exist with PVA gum only. Stamps on glazed, ordinary paper come only with PVA gum.

53 *Papilio hornimani*

54 *Euphaedra neophron*

80c

(**55**)

(Des Rena Fennessy. Photo Harrison)

1973 (10 Dec)–**78**. *Various vert designs as T* **53/4**.

(*a*) *Size as T* **53**. *P* 14½×14

No.	Description		
158	5 c. light yellow-olive, lt violet-blue & black	25	10
159	10 c. multicoloured	30	10
160	15 c. light violet-blue and black	30	10
161	20 c. reddish cinnamon, orange-yellow & blk	40	10
162	30 c. yellow, orange and black	40	10
	a. Bistre-yellow, orange & black (20.4.78)	40	10
163	40 c. multicoloured	50	10
164	50 c. multicoloured	50	10
165	60 c. lt grey-brown, lemon & reddish brown	75	10
166	70 c. turquoise-green, pale orange and black	70	10

(*b*) *Size as T* **54**. *P* 14

No.	Description		
167	1 s. multicoloured	70	15
168	1 s. 50, multicoloured	1·50	25
169	2 s. 50, multicoloured	1·75	45
170	5 s. multicoloured (*brt green background*)	2·25	70
	a. Apple-green background (20.4.78)	1·50	60
171	10 s. multicoloured	2·25	3·00
172	20 s. multicoloured	3·75	6·00
158/72	*Set of* 15	14·00	10·00

Butterflies:—10 c. *Colotis ione*; 15 c. *Amauris makuyuensis*; 20 c. *Libythea laius*; 30 c. *Danaus chrysippus*; 40 c. *Sallya rosa*; 50 c. *Axiocerses styx*; 60 c. *Eurema hecabe*; 70 c. *Acraea insignis*; 1 s. *Euphaedra neophron*; 1 s. 50, *Precis octavia*; 2 s. 50, *Charaxes eupale*; 5 s. *Charaxes pollux*; 10 s. *Salamis parhassus*; 20 s. *Papilio ophidicephalus*.

Nos. 159 and 164 exist in coils, constructed from normal sheets.

1975 (17 Nov). *Nos.* 165, 168/9 *and* 172 *surch as T* **55**.

No.	Description		
173	80 c. on 60 c. *Eurema hecabe*	1·25	65
174	2 s. on 1 s. 50, *Precis octavia*	2·50	2·50
175	3 s. on 2 s. 50, *Charaxes eupale*	11·00	16·00
176	40 s. on 20 s. *Papilio ophidicephalus*	6·00	7·50
173/6	*Set of* 4	19·00	24·00

1976 (15 Apr). *Telecommunications Development. As Nos.* 56/60 *of Kenya but inscr* "TANZANIA".

No.	Description		
177	50 c. Microwave Tower	10	10
178	1 s. Cordless switchboard	15	10
179	2 s. Telephones	25	30
180	3 s. Message Switching Centre	30	40
177/80	*Set of* 4	70	70
MS181	120 × 120 mm. Nos. 177/80	1·00	1·25

1976 (5 July). *Olympic Games, Montreal. As Nos* 61/5 *of Kenya but inscr* "TANZANIA".

No.	Description		
182	50 c. Akii Bua, Ugandan hurdler	15	10
183	1 s. Filbert Bayi, Tanzanian runner	20	10
184	2 s. Steve Muchoki, Kenyan boxer	45	35
185	3 s. Olympic flame and East Africa flags	55	50
182/5	*Set of* 4	1·25	85
MS186	129 × 154 mm. Nos. 182/5	4·50	4·00

1976 (4 Oct). *Railway Transport. As Nos. 66/70 of Kenya but inscr* "TANZANIA".
187 50 c. Tanzania-Zambia Railway 20 10
188 1 s. Nile Bridge, Uganda 30 10
189 2 s. Nakuru Station, Kenya 75 40
190 3 s. Class "A" locomotive, 1896 .. .. 90 65
187/90 .. .. *Set of 4* 1·90 1·00
MS191 154 × 103 mm. Nos. 187/90 .. .. 5·00 2·75

1977 (10 Jan). *Game Fish of East Africa. As Nos. 71/5 of Kenya but inscr* "TANZANIA".
192 50 c. Nile Perch 25 10
193 1 s. Tilapia 35 10
194 3 s. Sailfish .. .. 1·40 60
195 5 s. Black Marlin .. .. 1·60 80
192/5 .. .. *Set of 4* 3·25 1·40
MS196 153 × 129 mm. Nos. 192/5 .. .. 3·75 2·25

1977 (15 Jan). *Second World Black and African Festival of Arts and Culture, Nigeria. As Nos 76/80 of Kenya but inscr* "TANZANIA".
197 50 c. Maasai Manyatta (village), Kenya .. 15 10
198 1 s. "Heartbeat of Africa" (Ugandan dancers 20 10
199 2 s. Makonde sculpture 45 55
200 3 s. "Early Man and Technology" (skinning hippopotamus) 55 70
197/200 .. .. *Set of 4* 1·25 1·25
MS201 132 × 190 mm. Nos. 197/200 .. .. 2·50 3·00

1977 (5 Apr). *25th Anniv of Safari Rally. As Nos 81/5 of Kenya but inscr* "TANZANIA".
202 50 c. Rally-car and villagers 15 10
203 1 s. Pres. Kenyatta starting rally 20 10
204 2 s. Car fording river 50 60
205 5 s. Car and elephants .. .. .. 1·25 1·75
202/5 .. .. *Set of 4* 1·90 2·25
MS206 126 × 93 mm. Nos. 202/5 .. .. .. 3·50 3·25

1977 (30 June). *Centenary of Ugandan Church. As Nos. 86/90 of Kenya but inscr* "TANZANIA".
207 50 c. Canon Kivebulaya 10 10
208 1 s. Modern Namirembe Cathedral 15 10
209 2 s. The first Cathedral 35 40
210 5 s. Early congregation, Kigezi 90 90
207/10 .. .. *Set of 4* 1·25 1·25
MS211 126 × 89 mm. Nos. 207/10 .. .. 1·50 2·00

1977 (26 Sept). *Endangered Species. As Nos. 96/101 of Kenya but inscr* "TANZANIA".
212 50 c. Pancake Tortoise 20 10
213 1 s. Nile Crocodile 25 10
214 2 s. Hunter's Hartebeest .. .. .. 1·00 55
215 3 s. Red Colobus monkey .. .. .. 1·75 1·00
216 5 s. Dugong .. .. 2·00 2·00
212/16 .. .. *Set of 5* 4·75 3·25
MS217 127 × 101 mm. Nos. 213/16 .. .. 5·00 5·00

56 Prince Philip and President Nyerere

(Des G. Vasarhelyi. Litho Questa)

1977 (23 Nov). *Silver Jubilee. T* **56** *and similar horiz designs. Multicoloured. P* 14 × 13½.
218 50 c. Type **56** 15 10
219 5 s. Pres. Nyerere with Queen and Prince Philip 35 35
220 10 s. Jubilee emblem and Commonwealth flags 60 75
221 20 s. The Crowning .. .. 1·00 1·50
218/21 .. .. *Set of 4* 1·90 2·40
MS222 128 × 102 mm. Nos. 218/21 .. .. 1·90 2·75

57 Improvements in Rural Living Standards

(Des N. P. Ndembo. Litho B.W.)

1978 (5 Feb). *First Anniv of Chama Cha Mapinduzi (New Revolutionary Party). T* **57** *and similar horiz designs. P* 13½ × 14.
223 50 c. multicoloured 10 10
224 1 s. multicoloured 10 10
225 3 s. multicoloured 35 60
226 5 s. black, light green and greenish yellow 55 85
223/6 .. .. *Set of 4* 1·00 1·40
MS227 142 × 106 mm. Nos. 223/6 .. .. 1·00 1·40
Designs:—1 s. Flag raising ceremony, Zanzibar; 3 s. Handing over of TANU headquarters, Dodoma; 5 s. Chairman Julius Nyerere.

1978 (17 Apr). *World Cup Football Championship, Argentina. As Nos. 122/6 of Kenya but inscr* "TANZANIA".
228 50 c. Joe Kadenge and forwards 15 10
229 1 s. Mohamed Chuma and cup presentation 15 10
230 2 s. Omari Kidevu and goalmouth scene .. 40 60
231 3 s. Polly Ouma and forwards 50 75
228/31 .. .. *Set of 4* 1·10 1·25
MS232 136 × 81 mm. Nos. 228/31 .. .. 2·00 1·75

25th ANNIVERSARY CORONATION 2nd JUNE 1953 (58)

25th ANNIVERSARY CORONATION 2nd JUNE 1953 (59)

1978 (2 June). *25th Anniv of Coronation. Nos. 218/22. A. Optd as T* **58**. *P* 14 × 13½. B. *Optd as T* **59**. *P* 12 × 11½.

		A		B	
233	50 c. Type **56**	10	10	10	10
234	5 s. Pres. Nyerere with Queen and Prince Philip	35	45	35	50
235	10 s. Jubilee emblem and Commonwealth flags	50	65	50	65
236	20 s. The Crowning	80	1·25	80	1·25
233/6	.. .. .. *Set of 4*	1·60	2·25	1·60	2·25
MS237	128 × 102 mm. Nos. 233/6 ..	1·60	2·50	1·60	2·50

60 "Do not Drink and Drive"

61 Lake Manyara Hotel

(Des J.W. Litho B.W.)

1978 (1 July). *Road Safety. T* **60** *and similar vert designs. P* 13½ × 13.
238 50 c. multicoloured 15 10
239 1 s. multicoloured 20 10
240 3 s. orange-red, black and light brown .. 70 60
241 5 s. multicoloured .. .. 1·00 90
238/41 .. .. *Set of 4* 1·90 1·40
MS242 92 × 129 mm. Nos. 238/41. P 14 .. .. 2·00 2·00
Designs:—1 s. "Show courtesy to young, old and crippled"; 3 s. "Observe the Highway Code"; 5 s. "Do not drive a faulty vehicle"

(Des M. Raza. Litho B.W.)

1978 (11 Sept). *Game Lodges. T* **61** *and similar horiz designs. Multicoloured. P* 13½ × 13.
243 50 c. Type **61** 10 10
244 1 s. Lobo Wildlife Lodge 20 10
245 3 s. Ngorongoro Crater Lodge 40 35
246 5 s. Ngorongoro Wildlife Lodge 55 55
247 10 s. Mafia Island Lodge .. .. .. 1·25 1·60
248 20 s. Mikumi Wildlife Lodge .. .. .. 2·50 3·50
243/8 .. .. *Set of 6* 4·50 5·50
MS249 118 × 112 mm. Nos. 243/8 .. .. 6·00 7·50

62 "Racial Suppression"

63 Fokker "Friendship"

(Des local artist; adapted G. Hutchins. Litho Harrison)

1978 (24 Oct). *International Anti-Apartheid Year. T* **62** *and similar vert designs. P* 14½ × 14.
250 50 c. multicoloured 10 10
251 1 s. black, yellowish green and yellow .. 15 10
252 2 s. 50, multicoloured 40 40
253 5 s. multicoloured 70 85
250/3 .. .. *Set of 4* 1·25 1·25
MS254 127 × 132 mm. Nos. 250/3 .. .. 1·50 2·00
Designs:—1 s. "Racial division"; 2 s. 50, "Racial harmony"; 5 s. "Fall of suppression and rise of freedom".

(Des J. Mzinga; adapted J.W. Litho Walsall)

1978 (28 Dec). *75th Anniv of Powered Flight. T* **63** *and similar horiz designs. Multicoloured. P* 13½.
255 50 c. Type **63** 20 10
256 1 s. "Dragon" on Zanzibar Island, 1930's .. 25 10
257 2 s. "Concorde" .. .. 1·00 45
258 5 s. Wright brothers' *Flyer*, 1903 .. .. 1·25 85
255/8 .. .. *Set of 4* 2·40 1·25
MS259 133 × 97 mm. Nos. 255/8 .. .. 2·40 2·50

COVER PRICES

Cover factors are quoted at the beginning of each country for most issues to 1945. An explanation of the system can be found on page x. The factors quoted do not, however, apply to philatelic covers.

64 Corporation Emblem

(Des local artists; adapted BG Studio. Litho Harrison)

1979 (3 Feb). *1st Anniv of Tanzania Posts and Telecommunications Corporation. T* **64** *and similar horiz design. Multicoloured. P* 14½ × 14.
260 50 c. Type **64** 10 10
261 5 s. Headquarters buildings 50 70
MS262 82 × 97 mm. Nos. 260/1 .. .. .. 1·00 1·50

30c

65 Pres. Nyerere (patron of National I.Y.C. Committee) with Children

(66)

(Des J. Mzinga. Litho B.W.)

1979 (25 June). *International Year of the Child. T* **65** *and similar horiz designs. Multicoloured. P* 14½.
263 50 c. Type **65** 10 10
264 1 s. Day care centre 15 10
265 2 s. "Immunisation" (child being vaccinated) 25 45
266 5 s. National I.Y.C. Committee emblem .. 40 80
263/6 .. .. *Set of 4* 80 1·25
MS267 127 × 91 mm. Nos. 263/6 .. .. .. 1·50 1·50

1979 (Aug–Sept*). *Nos. 159 and 166 surch as T* **66** *(No. 269 has horiz bar through original value).*
268 10 c. + 30 c. multicoloured 15 20
a. Surch inverted .. .. † —
269 50 c. on 70 c. turquoise-green, pale orge & bl. 15 25
* The earliest known postmark date for No. 268 is 15 September and for No. 269 30 August.
The face value of No. 268 was 40 c.; the 30 c. surcharge being added to the original 10 c., which was not obliterated. This method was adopted because of difficulties during the actual surcharging. On No. 269 the 70 c. face value is obliterated by a bar.
Examples of No. 268a were used at Singida in December 1979.

67 Planting Young Trees

68 Mwenge Satellite Earth Station

(Des J. Mzinga. Litho J.W.)

1979 (24 Sept). *Forest Preservation. T* **67** *and similar vert designs. Multicoloured. P* 14 × 14½.
270 50 c. Type **67** 10 10
271 1 s. Replacing dead trees with saplings .. 20 10
272 2 s. Rainfall cycle 50 50
273 5 s. Forest fire warning .. .. .. 80 1·25
270/3 .. .. *Set of 4* 1·40 1·75

(Des and litho J.W.)

1979 (14 Dec). *Opening of Mwenge Satellite Earth Station. P* 13½.
274 **68** 10 c. multicoloured 10 10
275 40 c. multicoloured 10 10
276 50 c. multicoloured 10 10
277 1 s. multicoloured 20 20
274/7 .. .. *Set of 4* 40 40

69 Tabata Dispensary, Dar-es-Salaam

(Litho J.W.)

1980 (10 Apr). *75th Anniv of Rotary International. T* **69** *and similar horiz designs. Multicoloured. P* 13.
278 50 c. Type **69** 10 10
279 1 s. Ngomvu Village water project 15 10
280 5 s. Flying Doctor service (plane donation) 55 70
281 20 s. Torch and 75th Anniversary emblem .. 1·75 2·50
278/81 .. .. *Set of 4* 2·25 3·00
MS282 120 × 101 mm. Nos. 278/81. P 14 .. .. 2·50 3·00

'LONDON 1980'
PHILATELIC EXHIBITION

70 Zanzibar 1896 2 r. Stamp and 1964 25 c. Definitive

(71)

(Des J.W. Litho Questa)

1980 (21 Apr). *Death Centenary of Sir Rowland Hill* (1979). *T* **70** *and similar multicoloured designs. P* 14.
283 40 c. Type **70** 10 10
284 50 c. Tanganyika 1962 Independence 50 c. commemorative and man attaching stamp to letter (*vert*) 10 10
285 10 s. Tanganyika 1922 25 c. stamp and 1961 1 s. 30, definitive .. .. 1·00 1·25
286 20 s. Penny Black and Sir Rowland Hill (*vert*) 1·50 2·00
283/6 .. .. *Set of* 4 2·25 3·00
MS287 158 × 120 mm. Nos. 283/6 .. .. 2·25 3·50

1980 (5 May). *"London 1980" International Stamp Exhibition. Nos.* 283/7 *optd with T* **71**.
288 40 c. Type **71** 10 10
289 50 c. Tanganyika 1962 Independence 50 c. commemorative and man attaching stamp to letter 10 10
290 10 s. Tanganyika 1922 25 c. stamp and 1961 1 s. 30, definitive .. .. .. 1·00 1·50
291 20 s. Penny Black and Sir Rowland Hill .. 1·50 2·25
288/91 .. .. *Set of* 4 2·25 3·50
MS292 158 × 120 mm. Nos. 288/91 .. .. 2·75 3·50

District 920 - 55th Annual Conference. Arusha. Tanzania

(72)

1980 (23 June). *Annual Conference of District* 920, *Rotary International, Arusha. Nos.* 278/82 *optd as T* **72**.
293 50 c. Type **69** 20 10
294 1 s. Ngomvu Village water project 25 10
295 5 s. Flying Doctor service (plane donation) 70 70
296 20 s. Torch and 75th Anniversary of Rotary International Emblem .. .. 2·25 2·50
293/6 .. .. *Set of* 4 3·00 3·00
MS297 120 × 101 mm. Nos. 293/6 .. .. 3·00 3·50

73 Conference, Tanzanian Posts and Telecommunications Corporation and U.P.U. Emblems

(Des and litho J.W.)

1980 (1 July). *P.A.P.U. (Pan-African Postal Union) Plenipotentiary Conference, Arusha. P* 13.
298 **73** 50 c. black and bright violet 10 10
299 1 s. black and ultramarine 15 10
300 5 s. black and orange-red 65 65
301 10 s. black and blue-green .. .. 1·25 1·40
298/301 .. .. *Set of* 4 2·00 2·00

74 Gidamis Shahanga (marathon)

(Litho J.W.)

1980 (18 Aug). *Olympic Games, Moscow. T* **74** *and similar horiz designs. Multicoloured. P* 13.
302 50 c. Type **74** 10 15
a. Horiz strip of 4. Nos. 302/5 .. .. 2·25
303 1 s. Nzael Kyomo (sprints) 15 15
304 10 s. Zakayo Malekwa (javelin) .. .. 80 1·25
305 20 s. William Lyimo (boxing) .. .. 1·50 2·00
302/5 .. .. *Set of* 4 2·25 3·25
MS306 172 × 117 mm. Nos. 302/305. P 14 2·25 3·25
Nos. 302/305 were printed either in separate sheets or together, *se-tenant*, in horizontal strips of 4 throughout the sheet.

75 Spring Hare

76 Impala

(Des Rena Fennessy. Litho B.W.)

1980 (1 Oct). *Wildlife. Multicoloured designs. P* 14.

(*a*) *Horiz as T* **75**
307 10 c. Type **75** 10 10
308 20 c. Large-spotted Genet 10 10
309 40 c. Banded Mongoose 10 10
310 50 c. Ratel 10 10
311 75 c. Large-toothed Rock Hyrax 10 10
312 80 c. Leopard 10 10

(*b*) *Horiz as T* **76**
313 1 s. Type **76** 10 10
314 1 s. 50, Giraffe 10 10
315 2 s. Common Zebra 10 10
316 3 s. Buffalo 15 10
317 5 s. Lion 20 10
318 10 s. Black Rhinoceros 30 30
319 20 s. African Elephant 40 50
320 40 s. Cheetah 65 80
307/20 .. .. *Set of* 14 2·00 2·25

1980 (2 Dec)–**81**. *Nos.* O41 *and* O43 *with* "OFFICIAL" *opt Type* O 1 *obliterated by horizontal line*.
320*a* 10 c. multicoloured .. ..
320*b* 40 c. multicoloured (21.2.81) .. ..
Nos. 320*a*/*b* exist on commercial mail from Morogoro. The dates given are those of the earliest postmarks reported.

77 Ngorongoro Conservation Area Authority Emblem

ROYAL WEDDING
H.R.H. PRINCE CHARLES
29th JULY 1981

(78)

(Des D. Kyungu. Litho J.W.)

1981 (2 Feb). 60*th Anniv of Ngorongoro and Serengeti National Parks. T* **77** *and similar horiz designs. P* 13.
321 50 c. multicoloured 10 10
322 1 s. black, gold and deep blue-green .. 10 10
323 5 s. multicoloured 55 60
324 20 s. multicoloured .. .. 2·10 2·25
321/4 .. .. *Set of* 4 2·50 2·75
Designs:—1 s. Tanzania National Parks emblem; 5 s. Friends of the Serengeti emblem; 20 s. Friends of Ngorongoro emblem.
Nos. 321/4 exist overprinted "75th ANNIVERSARY GIRL GUIDES 1910 1985" or "CONGRATULATIONS TO THE DUKE & DUCHESS OF YORK ON THE OCCASION OF THEIR MARRIAGE", but there is no evidence that these overprints were available from post offices in Tanzania.

1981 (29 July). *Royal Wedding. Nos.* 220/1 *optd with T* **78**.
325 10 s. Jubilee emblem and Commonwealth flags .. .. 1·50 1·00
326 20 s. Crowning .. .. 2·25 1·75
MS327 88 × 97 mm. Nos. 325/6 .. .. .. 8·00 5·00

79 Mail Runner

(Des D. Kyungu. Litho State Printing Works, Moscow)

1981 (21 Oct). *Commonwealth Postal Administrations Conference, Arusha. T* **79** *and similar horiz designs. Multicoloured. P* 12½ × 12.
328 50 c. Type **79** 10 10
329 1 s. Letter sorting 15 15
330 5 s. Letter Post symbols .. .. .. 65 1·00
331 10 s. Flags of Commonwealth nations .. 1·25 2·00
328/31 .. .. *Set of* 4 1·90 3·00
MS332 130 × 100 mm. Nos. 328/31 .. .. 1·90 3·00

80 Morris Nyunyusa (blind drummer)

(Des and litho Harrison)

1981 (30 Nov). *International Year for Disabled Persons. T* **80** *and similar horiz designs. Multicoloured. P* 14.
333 50 c. Type **80** 15 10
334 1 s. Mgulani Rehabilitation Centre, Dar-es-Salaam 20 10
335 5 s. Aids for disabled persons .. .. 1·25 1·40
336 10 s. Disabled children cleaning school compound .. .. 2·00 2·50
333/6 .. .. *Set of* 4 3·25 3·50

81 President Mwalimu Julius K. Nyerere

82 Ostrich

(Litho J.W.)

1982 (13 Jan). 20*th Anniv of Independence. T* **81** *and similar horiz designs. Multicoloured. P* 13 × 13½.
337 50 c. Type **81** 10 10
338 1 s. Electricity plant, Mtoni 15 10
339 3 s. Sisal industry 45 80
340 10 s. "Universal primary education" .. 1·10 2·00
337/40 .. .. *Set of* 4 1·60 2·75
MS341 120 × 85 mm. Nos. 337/40 .. .. 1·60 2·75

(Des and litho J.W.)

1982 (25 Jan). *Birds. T* **82** *and similar vert designs. Multicoloured. P* 13½ × 13.
342 50 c. Type **82** 40 10
343 1 s. Secretary Bird 50 10
344 5 s. Kori Bustard .. .. 1·50 1·75
345 10 s. Saddle-bill Stork .. .. .. 2·00 2·50
342/5 .. .. *Set of* 4 4·00 4·00

83 Jella Mtaga

(Des P. Ndembo. Litho J.W.)

1982 (2 June). *World Cup Football Championship, Spain. T* **83** *and similar horiz designs. Multicoloured. P* 14.
346 50 c. Type **83** 15 10
347 1 s. Football stadium 20 10
348 10 s. Diego Maradona .. .. 1·50 2·00
349 20 s. FIFA emblem .. .. 2·50 3·25
346/9 .. .. *Set of* 4 4·00 4·75
MS350 130 × 100 mm. Nos. 346/9 .. .. 4·25 4·75
Nos. 346/9 exist overprinted "CONGRATULATIONS TO THE DUKE & DUCHESS OF YORK ON THE OCCASION OF THEIR MARRIAGE", but there is no evidence that these overprints were available from post offices in Tanzania.

84 "Jade" of Seronera (cheetah) with Cubs

(Des and litho Harrison)

1982 (15 July). *Animal Personalities. T* **84** *and similar horiz designs. Multicoloured. P* 14.
351 50 c. Type **84** 20 10
352 1 s. Female Golden Jackal and cubs (incorrectly inscr "Wild dog") 30 10
353 5 s. "Fifi" and two sons of "Gombe" (chimpanzees) .. .. 1·00 1·75
354 10 s. "Bahati" of Lake Manyara with twins, "Rashidi" and "Ramadhani" (elephants) 1·90 2·75
351/4 .. .. *Set of* 4 3·00 4·09
MS355 120 × 89 mm. Nos. 351/4. P 14½ .. 3·50 4·25

85 Brick-laying

86 Ploughing Field

(Des P. Ndembo. Litho J.W.)

1982 (25 Aug). 75*th Anniv of Boy Scout Movement. T* **85** *and similar horiz designs. Multicoloured. P* 14.
356 50 c. Type **85** 15 10
357 1 s. Camping 20 10
358 10 s. Tracing signs .. .. 1·50 2·00
359 20 s. Lord Baden-Powell .. .. .. 2·50 3·25
356/9 .. .. *Set of* 4 4·00 5·00
MS360 130 × 100 mm. Nos. 356/9 .. .. 4·25 5·00
No. **MS**360 exists overprinted "75th ANNIVERSARY GIRL GUIDES 1910–1985", but there is no evidence that this overprint was available from post offices in Tanzania.

(Des P. Ndembo. Litho J.W.)

1982 (16 Oct). *World Food Day. T* **86** *and similar horiz designs. Multicoloured. P* 14.
361 50 c. Type **86** 10 10
362 1 s. Dairy farming 15 10
363 5 s. Maize farming 60 75
364 10 s. Grain storage .. .. 1·00 1·60
361/4 .. .. *Set of* 4 1·60 2·25
MS365 129 × 99 mm. Nos. 361/4 .. .. 2·00 2·50

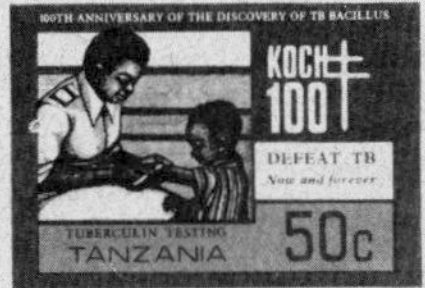

87 Immunization

(Des P. Ndembo. Litho State Printing Works, Moscow)

1982 (1 Dec). *Centenary of Robert Koch's Discovery of Tubercle Bacillus. T* **87** *and similar horiz designs. Multicoloured. P* 12½ × 12.

366	50 c. Type **87**	15	10
367	1 s. Dr. Robert Koch	20	10
368	5 s. International Union Against TB emblem	65	1·25
369	10 s. World Health Organization emblem	1·25	2·25
366/9	*Set of* 4	2·00	3·25

88 Letter Post

(Litho State Printing Works, Moscow)

1983 (3 Feb). *5th Anniv of Posts and Telecommunications Corporation. T* **88** *and similar horiz designs. Multicoloured. P* 12.

370	50 c. Type **88**	10	10
371	1 s. Training institute	10	10
372	5 s. Satellite communications	55	90
373	10 s. U.P.U., I.T.U. and T.P.T.C.C. (Tanzania Posts and Telecommunications Corporation) emblems	1·10	2·00
370/3	*Set of* 4	1·75	2·75
MS374	126×96 mm. Nos. 370/3	1·75	3·00

89 Pres. Mwalimu Julius Nyerere

(Litho J.W.)

1983 (14 Mar). *Commonwealth Day. T* **89** *and similar horiz designs. Multicoloured. P* 14.

375	50 c. Type **89**	10	10
376	1 s. Athletics and boxing	15	10
377	5 s. Flags of Commonwealth countries	60	80
378	10 s. Pres. Nyerere and members of British Royal Family	1·25	1·75
375/8	*Set of* 4	1·90	2·40
MS379	121×100 mm. Nos. 375/8	1·75	2·75

Nos. 375/8 exist overprinted "CONGRATULATIONS TO THE DUKE & DUCHESS OF YORK ON THE OCCASION OF THEIR MARRIAGE", but there is no evidence that these overprints were available from post offices in Tanzania.

90 Eastern and Southern African Management Institute, Arusha, Tanzania

(Des P. Ndembo. Litho State Ptg Wks, Moscow)

1983 (12 Sept). *25th Anniv of the Economic Commission for Africa. T* **90** *and similar horiz designs. Multicoloured. P* 12½ × 12.

380	50 c. Type **90**	15	10
381	1 s. 25th Anniversary inscription and U.N. logo	20	10
382	5 s. Mineral collections	1·25	1·50
383	10 s. E.C.A. Silver Jubilee logo and O.A.U. flag	1·50	2·25
380/3	*Set of* 4	2·75	3·50
MS384	132×102 mm. Nos. 380/3	2·75	3·50

91 Telephone Cables

(Des P. Ndembo. Litho J.W.)

1983 (17 Oct). *World Communications Year. T* **91** *and similar horiz designs. Multicoloured. P* 14.

385	50 c. Type **91**	15	10
386	1 s. W.C.Y. logo	20	10
387	5 s. Postal service	70	1·00
388	10 s. Microwave tower	1·25	2·00
385/8	*Set of* 4	2·10	2·75
MS389	102×92 mm. Nos. 385/88	2·10	3·00

92 Bagamoyo Boma

(Des J. de Silva and P. Ndembo. Litho State Ptg Wks, Moscow)

1983 (12 Dec). *Historical Buildings. T* **92** *and similar horiz designs. Multicoloured. P* 12½ × 12.

390	1 s. Type **92**	10	10
391	1 s. 50, Beit el Ajaib, Zanzibar	15	25
392	5 s. Anglican Cathedral, Zanzibar	55	1·00
393	10 s. Original German Government House and present State House, Dar-es-Salaam	1·10	2·00
390/3	*Set of* 4	1·75	3·00
MS394	130×100 mm. Nos. 390/3	1·90	3·00

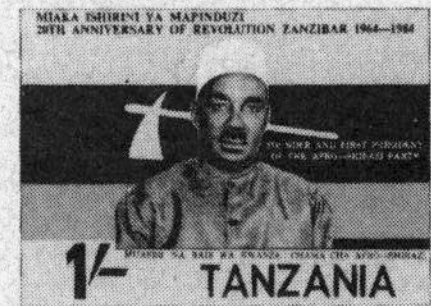

93 Sheikh Abeid Amani Karume (founder of Afro-Shirazi Party)

(Des P. Ndembo. Litho J.W.)

1984 (18 June). *20th Anniv of Zanzibar Revolution. T* **93** *and similar horiz designs. Multicoloured. P* 14.

395	1 s. Type **93**	10	10
396	1 s. 50, Clove farming	15	25
397	5 s. Symbol of Industrial Development	55	1·00
398	10 s. New housing schemes	1·10	2·00
395/8	*Set of* 4	1·75	3·00
MS399	130×100 mm. 15 s. *Mapinduzi* (ferry) and map	1·50	2·75

94 Boxing

(Des P. Ndembo. Litho State Ptg Wks, Moscow)

1984 (6 Aug). *Olympic Games, Los Angeles. T* **94** *and similar horiz designs. Multicoloured. P* 12½ × 12.

400	1 s. Type **94**	10	10
401	1 s. 50, Running	15	10
402	5 s. Basketball	45	60
403	20 s. Football	1·50	2·25
400/3	*Set of* 4	2·00	2·75
MS404	130×100 mm. Nos. 400/3	2·00	2·75

95 Icarus in Flight

(Des P. Ndembo. Litho J.W.)

1984 (15 Nov). *40th Anniv of International Civil Aviation Organization. T* **95** *and similar horiz designs. Multicoloured. P* 13 × 12½.

405	1 s. Type **95**	10	10
406	1 s. 50, Aircraft and air traffic controller	15	20
407	5 s. Aircraft undergoing maintenance	55	1·25
408	10 s. I.C.A.O. badge	1·10	2·00
405/8	*Set of* 4	1·75	3·25
MS409	130×100 mm. Nos. 405/8	1·90	3·00

96 Sochi – Conical House

(Des P. Ndembo. Litho State Ptg Wks, Moscow)

1984 (20 Dec). *Traditional Houses. T* **96** *and similar horiz designs. Multicoloured. P* 12½ × 12.

410	1 s. Type **96**	10	10
411	1 s. 50, Isyenga – circular type	15	20
412	5 s. Tembe – flatroofed type	45	1·25
413	10 s. Banda – coastal type	90	2·00
410/13	*Set of* 4	1·40	3·25
MS414	129×99 mm. Nos. 410/13	1·50	3·00

97 Production of Cotton Textiles

(Des P. Ndembo. Litho J.W.)

1985 (1 Apr). *5th Anniv of Southern African Development Co-ordination Conference. T* **97** *and similar horiz designs. Multicoloured. P* 14.

415	1 s. 50, Type **97**	20	15
416	4 s. Diamond mining	80	80
417	5 s. Map of member countries and means of communication	80	85
418	20 s. Flags and signatures of member countries	2·00	2·75
415/18	*Set of* 4	3·50	4·00
MS419	110×104 mm. Nos. 415/18	3·50	4·00

98 Tortoise

(Des P. Ndembo (15s., 20s.), J. de Silva (others). Litho J.W.)

1985 (8 May). *Rare Animals of Zanzibar. T* **98** *and similar multicoloured designs. P* 12½×13 (17 *s.* 50) *or* 13×12½ (*others*).

420	1 s. Type **98**	15	10
421	4 s. Leopard	60	70
422	10 s. Civet Cat	1·25	1·90
423	17 s. 50, Red Colobus Monkey (*vert*)	2·00	2·50
420/3	*Set of* 4	3·50	4·75
MS424	110×93 mm. 15 s. Black Rhinoceros; 20 s. Giant Ground Pangolin	1·75	2·50

99 The Queen Mother

(Litho Holders Press)

1985 (30 Sept). *Life and Times of Queen Elizabeth the Queen Mother. T* **99** *and similar horiz designs. Multicoloured. P* 14.

425	20 s. Type **99**	1·25	1·75
426	20 s. Queen Mother waving to crowd	1·25	1·75
427	100 s. Oval portrait with flowers	6·00	8·00
428	100 s. Head and shoulders portrait	6·00	8·00
425/8	*Set of* 4	13·00	18·00
MS429	Two sheets, each 125×63 mm. (a) Nos. 425 and 427; (b) Nos. 426 and 428. *Set of* 2 *sheets*	13·00	17·00

Nos. 425/9 exist imperforate from a restricted printing.

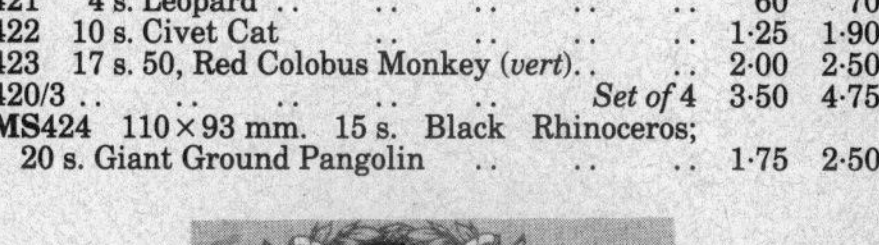

100 Locomotive No. 3022

GOLD MEDAL
HENRY TILLMAN
USA
(101)

(Litho Holders Press)

1985 (7 Oct). *Tanzanian Railway Locomotives* (1*st series*). *T* **100** *and similar horiz designs. Multicoloured. P* 14.

430	5 s. Type **100**	65	70
431	10 s. Locomotive No. 3107	1·00	1·25
432	20 s. Locomotive No. 6004	1·50	2·25
433	30 s. Locomotive No. 3129	2·25	3·00
430/3	*Set of* 4	4·75	6·50
MS434	125×93 mm. Nos. 430/3	7·50	8·50

See also Nos. 445/50.

1985 (22 Oct). *Olympic Games Gold Medal Winners, Los Angeles. Nos.* 400/4 *optd as T* **101**.

435	1 s. Type **94** (optd with T **101**)	10	10
436	1 s. 50, Running (optd "GOLD MEDAL USA")	15	20
437	5 s. Basketball (optd "GOLD MEDAL USA")	45	1·00
438	20 s. Football (optd "GOLD MEDAL FRANCE")	1·75	2·75
435/8	*Set of* 4	2·25	3·50
MS439	130×100 mm. Nos. 435/8	6·00	7·50

COVER PRICES

Cover factors are quoted at the beginning of each country for most issues to 1945. An explanation of the system can be found on page x. The factors quoted do not, however, apply to philatelic covers.

102 Cooking and Water Pots

103 Class "64" Locomotive

(Des J. Mzinga. Litho State Ptg Wks, Moscow)

1985 (4 Nov). *Pottery. T* **102** *and similar horiz designs. Multicoloured. P* 12½×12.

440	1 s. 50, Type **102**	10	10
441	2 s. Large pot and frying pot with cover	15	10
442	5 s. Trader selling pots	25	25
443	40 s. Beer pot	1·50	2·00
440/3	*Set of* 4	1·75	2·25
MS444	129×98 mm. 30 s. Water pots	1·50	2·00

(Des P. Ndembo. Litho State Ptg Wks, Moscow)

1985 (25 Nov). *Tanzanian Railway Locomotives (2nd series). T* **103** *and similar horiz designs. P* 12½×12.

445	1 s. 50, multicoloured	20	10
446	2 s. multicoloured	30	20
447	5 s. multicoloured	50	50
448	10 s. multicoloured	85	90
449	30 s. black, brownish black and red	2·25	2·50
445/9	*Set of* 5	3·75	3·75
MS450	130×100 mm. 15 s. black, blackish brown and rose-pink; 20 s. black, blackish brown and rose-pink	3·50	3·50

Designs:—2 s. Class "36" locomotive; 5 s. "DFH1013" shunting locomotive; 10 s. "DE 1001" diesel-electric locomotive; 15 s. Class "30" steam locomotive; 20 s. Class "11" steam locomotive; 30 s. Steam locomotive, Zanzibar, 1906.

Nos. 445/6 and 448/9 exist overprinted "CONGRATULATIONS TO THE DUKE & DUCHESS OF YORK ON THE OCCASION OF THEIR MARRIAGE", but there is no evidence that these overprints were available from post offices in Tanzania.

104 Young Pioneers

(Des P. Ndembo. Litho J.W.)

1986 (20 Jan). *International Youth Year. T* **104** *and similar horiz designs. P* 14.

451	1 s. 50, multicoloured	15	15
452	4 s. reddish brown, pale brown and black	30	45
453	10 s. multicoloured	70	1·10
454	20 s. reddish brown, pale brown and black	1·40	2·00
451/4	*Set of* 4	2·25	3·25
MS455	130×100 mm. 30 s. reddish brown, pale brown and black	2·25	3·00

Designs:—4 s. Child health care; 10 s. Uhuru Torch Race; 20 s. Young workers and globe; 30 s. Young people farming.

105 Rolls-Royce "20/25" (1936)

(Litho Holders Press)

1986 (10 Mar). *Centenary of Motoring. T* **105** *and similar horiz designs. Multicoloured. P* 14.

456	1 s. 50, Type **105**	15	10
457	5 s. Rolls-Royce "Phantom II" (1933)	25	30
458	10 s. Rolls-Royce "Phantom I" (1926)	55	75
459	30 s. Rolls-Royce "Silver Ghost" (1907)	1·40	1·60
456/9	*Set of* 4	2·10	2·50
MS460	125×93 mm. Nos. 456/9	2·25	2·75

106 Rotary Logo and Queen Chess Piece

(Litho Holders Press)

1986 (17 Mar). *World Chess Championships, Moscow. T* **106** *and similar horiz design. P* 14.

461	20 s. new blue and magenta	1·50	1·50
462	100 s. multicoloured	5·50	5·50
MS463	124×64 mm. Nos. 461/2	7·00	8·00

Design:—100 s. Hand moving chess piece.

No. 461 also commemorates Rotary International.

Slightly different versions of Nos. 461/2, incorporating the Tanzania emblem and with "TANZANIA" and face value at top on the 100 s., were not issued.

107 Mallard

(Litho Holders Press)

1986 (22 May). *Birth Bicentenary of John J. Audubon (ornithologist) (1985). T* **107** *and similar horiz designs. Multicoloured. P* 14.

464	5 s. Type **107**	30	25
465	10 s. Eider	55	50
466	20 s. Scarlet Ibis	1·00	1·25
467	30 s. Roseate Spoonbill	1·25	1·50
464/7	*Set of* 4	2·75	3·25
MS468	122×91 mm. Nos. 464/7	2·75	3·50

Nos. 464/8 exist imperforate from a restricted printing.

108 Pearls

109

(Litho J.W.)

1986 (27 May). *Tanzanian Minerals. T* **108** *and similar horiz designs. Multicoloured. Phosphorised paper (Nos. 469/72). P* 14.

469	1 s. 50, Type **108**	30	15
470	2 s. Sapphire	35	25
471	5 s. Tanzanite	60	60
472	40 s. Diamonds	3·50	3·75
469/72	*Set of* 4	4·25	4·25
MS473	130×100 mm. 30 s. Rubies. W **109**	3·50	3·75

110 *Hibiscus calyphyllus* 111 Oryx

(Litho Holders Press)

1986 (25 June). *Flowers of Tanzania. T* **110** *and similar vert designs. Multicoloured. P* 14.

474	1 s. 50, Type **110**	10	10
475	5 s. *Aloe graminicola*	15	15
476	10 s. *Nersium oleander*	25	25
477	30 s. *Nymphaea caerulea*	65	65
474/7	*Set of* 4	1·00	1·00
MS478	90×119 mm. Nos. 474/7	1·40	1·60

(Litho Holders Press)

1986 (30 June). *Endangered Animals of Tanzania. T* **111** *and similar vert designs. Multicoloured. P* 14.

479	5 s. Type **111**	20	15
480	10 s. Giraffe	40	40
481	20 s. Rhinoceros	85	85
482	30 s. Cheetah	1·25	1·40
479/82	*Set of* 4	2·40	2·50
MS483	91×121 mm. Nos. 479/82	2·75	3·00

112 Immunization 113 Butterfly Fish

(Des P. Ndembo. Litho State Ptg Wks, Moscow)

1986 (29 July). *U.N.I.C.E.F. Child Survival Campaign. T* **112** *and similar horiz designs. Multicoloured. P* 12½×12.

484	1 s. 50, Type **112**	10	10
485	2 s. Growth monitoring	10	10
486	5 s. Oral rehydration therapy	10	15
487	40 s. Breast feeding	50	85
484/7	*Set of* 4	60	1·00
MS488	110×101 mm. 30 s. Healthy baby	45	80

(Des P. Ndembo. Litho State Ptg Wks, Moscow)

1986 (28 Aug). *Marine Life. T* **113** *and similar horiz designs. Multicoloured. P* 12½×12

489	1 s. 50, Type **113**	10	10
490	4 s. Parrot Fish	15	15
491	10 s. Turtle	35	35
492	20 s. Octopus	65	65
489/92	*Set of* 4	1·10	1·10
MS493	131×101 mm. 30 s. Corals	75	1·00

114 Team Captains shaking Hands 115 Pres. Nyerere receiving Beyond War Award

(Litho Questa)

1986 (30 Oct). *World Cup Football Championship, Mexico. T* **114** *and similar horiz designs. Multicoloured. P* 14.

494	1 s. 50, Type **114**	10	10
495	2 s. Referee sending player off	10	10
496	10 s. Goalkeeper and ball in net	15	25
497	20 s. Goalkeeper saving ball	30	50
494/7	*Set of* 4	50	80
MS498	95×72 mm. 30 s. Winning Argentine team	45	70

(Des P. Ndembo. Litho Mardon Printers Ltd, Zimbabwe)

1986 (20 Dec). *International Peace Year. T* **115** *and similar horiz designs. Multicoloured. P* 14½.

499	1 s. 50, Type **115**	15	10
500	2 s. Children of many races	20	10
501	10 s. African cosmonaut and rocket launch	30	30
502	20 s. United Nations Headquarters, New York	45	45
499/502	*Set of* 4	1·00	85
MS503	109×86 mm. 30 s. International Peace Year symbols	70	80

116 Mobile Bank Service

(Des P. Ndembo. Litho Questa)

1987 (7 Feb). *20th Anniv of National Bank of Commerce. T* **116** *and similar horiz designs. Multicoloured. P* 14.

504	1 s. 50, Type **116**	15	10
505	2 s. National Bank of Commerce Head Office	20	10
506	5 s. Pres. Mwinyi laying foundation stone	30	25
507	20 s. Cotton harvesting	45	55
504/7	*Set of* 4	1·00	90

117 Parade of Young Party Members

(Litho Holders Press)

1987 (10 Mar). *10th Anniv of Chama Cha Mapinduzi Party and 20th Anniv of Arusha Declaration. T* **117** *and similar horiz designs. Multicoloured. P* 14.

508	2 s. Type **117**	15	10
509	3 s. Harvesting coffee	20	10
510	10 s. Pres. Nyerere addressing Second Peace Initiative Reunion	30	20
511	30 s. Presidents Julius Nyerere and Ali Hassan Mwinyi	50	60
508/11	*Set of* 4	1·10	90

ALTERED CATALOGUE NUMBERS

Any Catalogue numbers altered from the last edition are shown as a list in the introductory pages.

118 Nungu Nungu Hair Style   119

(Litho Leigh-Mardon Ltd, Melbourne)

1987 (16 Mar). *Traditional Hair Styles. T* **118** *and similar vert designs. Multicoloured. W* **119**. *P* 14½.

512 1 s. 50, Type **118** 15 10
513 2 s. Upanga wa jogoo style 20 15
514 10 s. Morani style 30 25
515 20 s. Twende kilioni style 45 60
512/15 .. .. *Set of* 4 1·00 1·00
MS516 110×99 mm. 30 s. Hair plaiting 70 80

120 Royal Family on Buckingham Palace Balcony after Trooping the Colour

(Litho Holders Press)

1987 (24 Mar). *60th Birthday of Queen Elizabeth II* (1986). *T* **120** *and similar horiz designs. Multicoloured. P* 14.

517 5 s. Type **120** 15 10
518 10 s. Queen and Prince Philip at Royal Ascot 25 20
519 40 s. Queen Elizabeth II 80 80
520 60 s. Queen Elizabeth with crowd .. 1·10 1·25
517/20 .. .. .. *Set of* 4 2·10 2·10
MS521 125×90 mm. Nos. 517/20 .. .. 2·25 2·40

121 Bees   122 Crocodile

(Litho State Ptg Wks, Moscow)

1987 (22 Apr). *Insects. T* **121** *and similar horiz designs. Multicoloured. P* 12½×12.

522 1 s. 50, Type **121** 15 10
523 2 s. Greater Grain-borer 20 15
524 10 s. Tse-tse Fly 35 25
525 20 s. Wasp 55 55
522/5 .. .. *Set of* 4 1·10 1·10
MS526 110×101 mm. 30 s. Mosquito 80 90

(Des J. Mzinga (3 s., 30 s.), P. Ndembo (others). Litho State Ptg Wks, Moscow)

1987 (2 July). *Reptiles. T* **122** *and similar horiz designs. Multicoloured. P* 12½×12.

527 2 s. Type **122** 15 10
528 3 s. Black-striped Grass-snake 20 15
529 10 s. Adder 35 30
530 20 s. Green Mamba 65 70
527/30 .. .. *Set of* 4 1·25 1·10
MS531 101×101 mm. 30 s. Tortoise 85 90

123 Emblems of Posts/ Telecommunications and Railways   124 Basketry

(Des and litho Questa)

1987 (27 July). *10th Anniv of Tanzania Communications and Transport Corporations. T* **123** *and similar horiz designs. Multicoloured. P* 14.

532 2 s. Type **123** 10 10
533 8 s. Emblems of Air Tanzania and Harbours Authority 15 15
MS534 100×66 mm. 20 s. Methods of transport and communication 30 35

(Des P. Ndembo. Litho State Ptg Wks, Moscow)

1987 (15 Dec). *Traditional Handicrafts. T* **124** *and similar horiz designs. Multicoloured. P* 12½×12.

535 2 s. Type **124** 15 10
536 3 s. Decorated gourds 15 15
537 10 s. Stools 25 20
538 20 s. Makonde carvings 40 45
535/8 .. .. *Set of* 4 85 80
MS539 89×89 mm. 40 s. Makonde carver at work 65 75

10th Anniversary of
TANZANIA ZAMBIA
RAILWAY
AUTHORITY
1976-1986

(125)

1987 (30 Dec). *10th Anniv of Tanzania–Zambia Railway* (1986). *Nos.* 445/9 *optd with T* **125**.

540 **103** 1 s. 50, multicoloured 10 10
541 – 2 s. multicoloured 15 15
542 – 5 s. multicoloured 20 20
543 – 10 s. multicoloured 30 30
544 – 30 s. black, brownish black and red .. 50 50
540/4 .. .. *Set of* 5 1·10 1·10

126 Mdako (pebble game)

(Des P. Ndembo. Litho State Ptg Wks, Moscow)

1988 (15 Feb). *Traditional Pastimes. T* **126** *and similar horiz designs. Multicoloured. P* 12½×12.

545 2 s. Type **126** 10 10
546 3 s. Wrestling 10 10
547 8 s. Bullfighting, Zanzibar 15 15
548 20 s. Bao (board game) 35 35
545/8 .. .. *Set of* 4 65 65
MS549 100×90 mm. 30 s. Archery 50 60

127 Plateosaurus

(Des G. Vasarhelyi. Litho Format)

1988 (22 Apr). *Prehistoric and Modern Animals. T* **127** *and similar trapezium-shaped designs. Multicoloured. P* 12½.

550 2 s. Type **127** 10 10
a. *Tête-bêche* (horiz pair) 20 20
551 3 s. Pteranodon 10 10
a. *Tête-bêche* (horiz pair) 20 20
552 5 s. Jurassic Brontosaurus 10 10
a. *Tête-bêche* (horiz pair) 20 20
553 7 s. Lion 15 15
a. *Tête-bêche* (horiz pair) 30 30
554 8 s. Tiger 15 15
a. *Tête-bêche* (horiz pair) 30 30
555 12 s. Orang-utan 15 15
a. *Tête-bêche* (horiz pair) 30 30
556 20 s. Elephant 35 35
a. *Tête-bêche* (horiz pair) 70 70
557 100 s. Stegosaurus .. .. 1·25 1·25
a. *Tête-bêche* (horiz pair) .. .. 2·50 2·50
550/7 .. .. *Set of* 8 2·00 2·00

Nos. 550/7 were issued in sheets which had the second and fourth stamps *tête-bêche* in each horizontal row of five.

128 Marchers with Party Flag   129 Population Symbols on Map

(Des P. Ndembo. Litho Questa)

1988 (1 July). *National Solidarity Walk. T* **128** *and similar horiz designs. Multicoloured. P* 14×14½.

558 2 s. + 1 s. Type **128** 15 15
559 3 s. + 1 s. Pres. Mwinyi leading Walk .. 15 15
MS560 121×121 mm. 50 s. + 1 s. Pres. Ali Hassan Mwinyi (35×25 *mm*). P 14½ 75 85

(Des P. Ndembo. Litho Questa)

1988 (8 Aug). *Third National Population Census. T* **129** *and similar horiz designs. Multicoloured. P* 14.

561 2 s. Type **129** 10 10
562 3 s. Census official at work 10 10
563 10 s. Community health care 15 15
564 20 s. Population growth 1967–1988 .. 30 30
561/4 .. .. *Set of* 4 55 55
MS565 96×91 mm. 40 s. Development of modern Tanzania 55 60

130 Javelin   131 Football

(Litho State Ptg Wks, Moscow)

1988 (5 Sept). *Olympic Games, Seoul* (1*st issue*). *T* **130** *and similar horiz designs. Multicoloured. P* 12½×12.

566 2 s. Type **130** 10 10
567 3 s. Hurdling 10 10
568 7 s. Long distance running 10 10
569 12 s. Relay racing 10 10
566/9 .. .. *Set of* 4 30 30
MS570 100×70 mm. 40 s. Badminton 50 50

(Des D. Miller. Litho Questa)

1988 (5 Sept). *Olympic Games, Seoul* (2*nd issue*). *T* **131** *and similar vert designs. Multicoloured. P* 14.

571 10 s. Type **131** 10 10
572 20 s. Cycling 20 25
573 70 s. Volleyball 45 50
574 50 s. Fencing 60 65
571/4 .. .. *Set of* 4 1·25 1·40
MS575 77×92 mm. 100 s. Gymnastics 90 95

(Des D. Miller. Litho Questa)

1988 (5 Sept). *Winter Olympic Games, Calgary. Vert designs as T* **131**. *Multicoloured. P* 14.

576 5 s. Cross-country skiing 10 10
577 25 s. Figure skating 20 25
578 50 s. Downhill skiing 45 50
579 75 s. Bobsleighing 65 70
576/9 .. .. *Set of* 4 1·25 1·40
MS580 77×92 mm. 100 s. Ice hockey sticks wrapped in Olympic and Canadian colours .. 90 95

132 Goat   133 "Love You, Dad" (Pinocchio)

(Litho Questa)

1988 (9 Sept). *Domestic Animals. T* **132** *and similar multicoloured designs. P* 14.

581 4 s. Type **132** 10 10
582 5 s. Rabbit (*horiz*) 10 10
583 8 s. Cows (*horiz*) 10 10
584 10 s. Kitten (*horiz*) 15 15
585 12 s. Pony 15 15
586 20 s. Puppy 30 30
581/6 .. .. *Set of* 6 75 75
MS587 102×73 mm. 100 s. Chicken (*horiz*) .. 1·50 1·50

(Des Walt Disney Company. Litho Questa)

1988 (9 Sept). *Greetings Stamps. T* **133** *and similar horiz designs showing Walt Disney cartoon characters. Multicoloured. P* 14×13½.

588 4 s. Type **133** 10 10
589 5 s. "Happy Birthday" (Brer Rabbit and Chip n'Dale) 10 10
590 10 s. "Trick or Treat" (Daisy and Donald Duck) 10 10
591 12 s. "Be kind to Animals" (Ferdie and Mordie with Pluto) 10 10
592 15 s. "Love" (Daisy and Donald Duck) .. 15 15
593 20 s. "Let's Celebrate" (Mickey Mouse and Goofy) 25 25
594 30 s. "Keep in Touch" (Daisy and Donald Duck) 35 35
595 50 s. "Love you, Mom" (Minnie Mouse with Ferdie and Mordie) 60 60
588/95 .. .. *Set of* 8 1·50 1·50
MS596 Two sheets, each 127×101 mm. (a) 150 s. "Let's work together" (Goofy dressed as a fireman). (b) 150 s. "Have a super Sunday" (Goofy dressed as American footballer) *Set of* 2 *sheets* 3·75 4·00

134 Pearl Charaxes   135 Independence Torch and Mt Kilimanjaro

(Des Jennifer Toombs. Litho Questa)

1988 (17 Oct). *Butterflies. T* **134** *and similar horiz designs. Multicoloured. P* 14½.

597	8 s. Type **134**	15	10
598	30 s. Brown Nymphalid	35	30
599	40 s. Dotted Border	45	40
600	50 s. Large Blue Charaxes	60	50
601	60 s. Figtree Blue	75	70
602	75 s. Greenpatch Swallowtail	90	90
603	90 s. African Map Butterfly	1·10	1·10
604	100 s. Blue Salamis	1·25	1·25
597/604	*Set of* 8	5·00	4·75
MS605	Two sheets, each 80×50 mm. (a) 200 s. Lilac Nymph. (b) 250 s. African Leaf Butterfly *Set of 2 sheets*	6·50	6·00

(Des R. Vigurs. Litho Questa)

1988 (1 Nov). *National Monuments. T* **135** *and similar vert designs. Multicoloured. P* 14.

606	5 s. Type **135**	10	10
607	12 s. Arusha Declaration Monument	10	10
608	30 s. Askari Monument	25	30
609	60 s. Independence Monument	55	60
606/9	*Set of* 4	80	90
MS610	100×89 mm. 100 s. Askari Monument statue	1·25	1·40

136 Eye Clinic

137 Loading Patient into Ambulance

(Des P. Ndembo. Litho National Printing & Packaging, Zimbabwe)

1988 (19 Dec). *25th Anniv of Dar-es-Salaam Lions Club. T* **136** *and similar horiz designs. Multicoloured. P* 14½.

611	2 s. Type **136**	10	10
612	3 s. Family at shallow water well	10	10
613	7 s. Rhinoceros and map of Tanzania	15	15
614	12 s. Club presenting school desks	15	15
611/14	*Set of* 4	35	35
MS615	100×65 mm. 40 s. Lions International logo	60	65

(Des P. Ndembo. Litho State Ptg Wks, Moscow)

1988 (30 Dec). *125th Anniv of International Red Cross and Red Crescent. T* **137** *and similar horiz designs. Multicoloured. P* 12½×12.

616	2 s. Type **137**	10	10
617	3 s. Mother and baby health clinic	10	10
618	7 s. Red Cross flag	10	10
619	12 s. Henri Dunant (founder)	15	15
616/19	*Set of* 4	30	30
MS620	90×90 mm. 40 s. Members of Red Cross International Committee, 1863	50	55

138 Paradise Whydah

139 Bushbaby

(Des S. Barlowe. Litho B.D.T.)

1989 (15 Mar). *Birds. T* **138** *and similar vert designs. Multicoloured. P* 13½.

621	20 s. Type **138**	35	35
	a. Sheetlet. Nos. 621/40	6·25	
622	20 s. Black-collared Barbet	35	35
623	20 s. Bateleur	35	35
624	20 s. Lilac-breasted Roller and Openbill Storks in flight	35	35
625	20 s. Red-tufted Malachite Sunbird and Openbill Stork in flight	35	35
626	20 s. Dark Chanting Goshawk	35	35
627	20 s. White-fronted Bee Eater, Carmine Bee Eater and Little Bee Eaters	35	35
628	20 s. Narina Trogon and Marabou Stork in flight	35	35
629	20 s. Grey Parrot	35	35
630	20 s. Hoopoe	35	35
631	20 s. Masked Lovebird ("Yellow-collared Lovebird")	35	35
632	20 s. Yellow-billed Hornbill	35	35
633	20 s. Hammerkop	35	35
634	20 s. Violet-crested Turaco and flamingos in flight	35	35
635	20 s. Malachite Kingfisher	35	35
636	20 s. Greater Flamingos	35	35
637	20 s. Yellow-billed Storks	35	35
638	20 s. Whale-headed Stork ("Shoebill Stork")	35	35
639	20 s. Saddle-bill Stork and Blacksmith Plover	35	35
640	20 s. Crowned Crane	35	35
621/40	*Set of* 20	6·25	6·25
MS641	Two sheets, each 105×75 mm. (a) 350 s. Helmet Guineafowl (28×42 *mm*). (b) 350 s. Ostrich (28×42 *mm*). P 14 .. *Set of 2 sheets*	7·50	7·50

Nos. 622/41 were printed together, *se-tenant*, in a sheetlet of 20 forming a composite design of birds at a waterhole.

(Des J. Barberis (Nos. 642/4, 648, **MS**650a), S. Barlowe (others). Litho Questa)

1989 (20 Mar). *Fauna and Flora. T* **139** *and similar multicoloured designs. P* 14.

642	5 s. Type **139**	10	10
643	10 s. Bushbaby holding insect (*horiz*)	15	15
644	20 s. Bushbaby on forked branch	30	30
645	30 s. Black Cobra on Umbrella Acacia	40	40
646	45 s. Bushbaby at night (*horiz*)	55	55
647	70 s. Red-billed Tropic Bird and Tree Ferns	85	85
648	100 s. African Tree Frog on Cocoa Tree	1·25	1·25
649	150 s. Black-headed Heron and Egyptian Papyrus	1·75	1·75
642/9	*Set of* 8	4·75	4·75
MS650	Two sheets. (a) 115×85 mm. 350 s. African Palm Civet (*horiz*). (b) 65×65 mm. 350 s. Pink-backed Pelican and Baobab Tree (*horiz*) *Set of 2 sheets*	7·50	7·50

Nos. 645, 647/9 and **MS**650 are without the World Wildlife Fund logo.

140 Juma Ikangaa (marathon runner)

141 Drums

(Des W. Storozuk. Litho Questa)

1989 (10 Apr). *International Sporting Personalities. T* **140** *and similar vert designs. Multicoloured. P* 14.

651	4 s. Type **140**	10	10
652	8 s. 50, Steffi Graf (tennis player)	15	15
653	12 s. Yannick Noah (tennis player)	15	15
654	40 s. Pelé (footballer)	50	50
655	100 s. Erhard Keller (speed skater)	1·25	1·25
656	125 s. Sadanoyama (sumo wrestler)	1·50	1·50
657	200 s. Taino (sumo wrestler)	2·00	2·00
658	250 s. I. Aoki (golfer)	2·50	2·50
651/8	*Set of* 8	7·50	7·50
MS659	Two sheets. (a) 100×71 mm. 350 s. Joe Louis (boxer). (b) 100×76 mm. 350 s. T. Nakajima (golfer) .. *Set of 2 sheets*	7·50	7·50

(Des P. Ndembo. Litho Harrison)

1989 (29 June). *Musical Instruments. T* **141** *and similar horiz designs. Multicoloured. P* 14.

660	2 s. Type **141**	10	10
661	3 s. Xylophones	10	10
662	10 s. Thumbpiano	15	15
663	20 s. Fiddles	30	30
660/3	*Set of* 4	50	50
MS664	91×80 mm. 40 s. Violins with calabash resonators	55	55

142 Chama Cha Mapinduzi Party Flag

143 Class "P36" Locomotive, U.S.S.R.

(Des P. Ndembo. Litho Questa)

1989 (1 July). *National Solidarity Walk. T* **142** *and similar multicoloured designs. P* 14½.

665	5 s. + 1 s. Type **142**	10	10
666	10 s. + 1 s. Marchers with party flag and President Mwinyi	15	15
MS667	122×122 mm. 50 s. + 1 s. President Mwinyi (*vert*)	65	70

(Des W. Wright. Litho B.D.T.)

1989 (22 Aug). *Steam Locomotives. T* **143** *and similar multicoloured designs. P* 14.

668	10 s. Type **143**	15	15
669	25 s. Class "12", Belgium	30	30
670	60 s. Class "C62", Japan	70	70
671	75 s. Pennsylvania Railroad Class "T1", U.S.A.	85	85
672	80 s. Class "WP", India	90	90
673	90 s. East African Railways Class "59"	95	95
674	150 s. Class "People", China	1·50	1·50
675	200 s. Southern Pacific "Daylight Express" U.S.A.	2·00	2·00
668/75	*Set of* 8	6·50	6·50
MS676	Two sheets, each 114×85 mm. (a) 350 s. Stephenson's *Planet*, Great Britain (*vert*). (b) 350 s. "Coronation Scot", Great Britain (*vert*) *Set of 2 sheets*	7·50	7·50

NEW INFORMATION

The editor is always interested to correspond with people who have new information that will improve or correct the Catalogue.

OFFICIAL STAMPS

OFFICIAL (O 1) **OFFICIAL** (O 2) (3½ mm tall)

1961 (9 Dec). *Nos.* 108/14 *and* 117 *optd with Type* O **1** (10, 15, 20, 50 *c. or larger* (17 *mm*) 5, 30 *c.*) *or with Type* O **2** (1 *s. or larger* (22 *mm*) 5 *s.*).

O1	5 c. sepia and light apple-green	10	1
O2	10 c. deep bluish green	10	1
O3	15 c. sepia and blue	10	1
O4	20 c. orange-brown	10	1
O5	30 c. black, emerald and yellow	10	1
O6	50 c. black and yellow	10	1
O7	1 s. brown, blue and olive-yellow	10	1
O8	5 s. deep bluish green and orange-red	65	7
O1/8	*Set of* 8	90	9

(Opt photo Harrison)

1965 (9 Dec). *Nos.* 128/132, 134, 136, 139 *optd as Types* O (15 *c.*, 30 *c. or larger* (17 *mm*) 5 *c.*, 10 *c.*, 20 *c.*, 50 *c.*), *or with* O (1 *s.*, 5 *s.*).

O 9	5 c. ultramarine and yellow-orange	10	1
O10	10 c. black, greenish yellow, green & blue	10	1
O11	15 c. multicoloured	10	1
O12	20 c. sepia, grey-green and greenish blue	10	1
O13	30 c. black and red-brown	10	1
O14	50 c. multicoloured	15	1
O15	1 s. multicoloured	30	1
O16	5 s. lake-brown, yellow-green and blue	1·50	2·0
O9/16	*Set of* 8	2·00	2·2

OFFICIAL

(O **3**) (3 mm tall)

(Opt litho Govt Printer, Dar-es-Salaam)

1967 (10–18 Nov). *Nos.* 134, 136 *and* 139 *optd as No.* O14 (50 *c.*) *or with Type* O **3** (*others*).

O17	50 c. multicoloured (18.11)		
O18	1 s. multicoloured (18.11)	11·00	3·0
O19	5 s. lake-brown, yellow-green and blue	9·00	5·5

The issue dates given are for the earliest known postmarked copies.

Nos. O9/16 were overprinted by Harrison in photogravure and Nos. O17/19 have litho overprints by the Government Printer Dar-es-Salaam. On No. O17 the overprint is the same size (17 mm long) as on No. O14.

1967 (9 Dec)–**71**. *Nos.* 142/6, 148, 151 *and* 155 *optd as Type* O 1, *but larger* (*measuring* 17 *mm*) (5 *c. to* 50 *c.*) *or as Type* O **2** (1 *s. and* 5 *s.*). *Chalk-surfaced paper.*

O20	5 c. magenta, yellow-olive and black	10	25
	a. Glazed, ordinary paper (22.1.71)	70	80
O21	10 c. brown and bistre	10	10
O22	15 c. grey, turquoise-blue and black	10	15
	a. Glazed, ordinary paper (22.1.71)	70	90
O23	20 c. brown and turquoise-green	10	10
O24	30 c. sage-green and black	10	10
O25	50 c. multicoloured	15	15
	a. Glazed, ordinary paper (22.1.71)	95	40
O26	1 s. orange-brown, slate-blue and maroon	25	25
	a. Glazed, ordinary paper (3.2.71)	1·40	40
O27	5 s. greenish yellow, black & turquoise-grn	2·25	3·00
	a. Glazed, ordinary paper (3.2.71)	3·50	4·50
O20/7	*Set of* 8	2·75	3·50

The chalk-surfaced paper exists with both PVA gum and gum arabic, but the glazed, ordinary paper exists PVA gum only.

OFFICIAL (O 4) **OFFICIAL** (O 5)

1970 (10 Dec)–**73**. *Nos.* 142/8, 151 *and* 155 *optd locally by letterpress as Type* O **4** (5 *to* 50 *c.*) *or as Type* O **2** *but measuring* 28 *mm* (1 *s. and* 5 *s.*). (*a*) *Chalk-surfaced paper.*

O28	5 c. magenta, yellow-olive and black	10	30
	a. "OFFCIAL" (R.7/6)		
O29	10 c. brown and bistre	10	10
	a. "OFFCIAL" (R.7/6)		
O30	20 c. brown and turquoise-green	20	25
O31	30 c. sage-green and black	25	25
O28/31	*Set of* 4	55	85
	(*b*) *Glazed, ordinary paper* (1973)		
O32	5 c. magenta, yellow-olive and black	—	1·00
	a. "OFFCIAL" (R.7/6)	—	20·00
	b. "OFFICIA" (R.10/9)	—	20·00
O33	10 c. brown and bistre		
	a. "OFFCIAL" (R.7/6)		
O34	15 c. grey, turquoise-blue and black		
	a. "OFFCIAL" (R.7/6)		
O35	20 c. brown and turquoise-green		
O36	40 c. yellow, chocolate and bright green	—	2·00
	a. Opt double		
	b. "OFFICIA" (R.10/9)	—	40·00
O37	50 c. multicoloured	—	1·50
	a. "OFFCIAL" (R.7/6)	—	30·00
O38	1 s. orange-brown, slate-blue and maroon		
	a. Opt double		
O39	5 s. greenish yellow, black & turquoise-grn		

The letterpress overprint can be distinguished from the photogravure by its absence of screening dots and the overprint showing through to the reverse, apart from the difference in length.

1973 (10 Dec). *Nos.* 158/9, 161, 163/4 *and* 166/70 *optd with Type* O **1** (5 *to* 70 *c.*) *or Type* O **5** (*others*).

O40	5 c. light yellow-olive, lt violet-blue & black	15	25
O41	10 c. multicoloured	25	10
O42	20 c. reddish cinnamon, orange-yellow & blk	30	10
O43	40 c. multicoloured	40	15
O44	50 c. multicoloured	45	15
O45	70 c. turquoise-green, pale orange and black	70	35
O46	1 s. multicoloured	70	15
O47	1 s. 50, multicoloured	1·25	70
	a. Pair, one without opt	†	—
O48	2 s. 50, multicoloured	1·50	1·50
O49	5 s. multicoloured	2·00	2·25
O40/9	*Set of* 10	7·00	5·25

No. O47a is due to a paper fold and comes from a sheet used at Kigoma in 1974.

1977 (Feb). *Nos.* 159, 161 *and* 163/4 *optd locally by letterpress as Type* O **4**.

No.	Description	Mint	Used
O50	10 c. multicoloured	—	1·50
	a. "OFFCIAL" (R. 7/6)	—	30·00
O51	20 c. multicoloured	—	1·50
	a. "OFFCIAL" (R. 7/6)	—	30·00
	b. Opt inverted		
	c. Opt double		
O52	40 c. multicoloured	—	2·00
	a. "OFFCIAL" (R. 7/6)	—	40·00
O53	50 c. multicoloured	—	2·00
	a. "OFFCIAL" (R. 7/6)	—	40·00
	b. Opt inverted		

OFFICIAL (O **6**)   OFFICIAL (O **7**)

1980 (Nov)–**85**. *Nos.* 307/12 *optd with Type* O **6**, *and Nos.* 313/17 *optd with Type* O **7**.

No.	Description	Mint	Used
O54	10 c. Type **75**	10	10
O55	20 c. Large-spotted Genet	10	10
O56	40 c. Banded Mongoose	10	10
O57	50 c. Ratel	10	10
O58	75 c. Large-toothed Rock Hyrax	10	10
O59	80 c. Leopard	15	15
O60	1 s. Type **76**	15	10
O61	1 s. 50, Giraffe (29.8.85)*	40	25
O62	2 s. Common Zebra	20	20
O63	3 s. African Buffalo	25	25
O64	5 s. Lion	35	35
O54/64	*Set of* 11	1·60	1·60

*Earliest known postmark date.

On the stamps overprinted with Types O **6** and O **7** the overprint reads downwards on the 10 c., 50 c., 2 s. and 5 s. and upwards on the others.

POSTAGE DUE STAMPS

Postage Due stamps of Kenya and Uganda were issued for provisional use as such in Tanganyika on 1 July 1933. The postmark is the only means of identification.

The Postage Due stamps of Kenya, Uganda and Tanganyika were used in Tanganyika until 2 January 1967.

D 1

(Litho D.L.R.)

1967 (3 Jan). *P* 14 × 13½.

No.	Type	Description	Mint	Used
D1	D 1	5 c. scarlet	35	2·50
D2		10 c. green	45	2·75
D3		20 c. deep blue	70	3·50
D4		30 c. red-brown	70	4·25
D5		40 c. bright purple	70	5·50
D6		1 s. orange	1·25	7·00
D1/6		*Set of* 6	3·75	23·00

1969–71. *As Nos.* D1/6, *but perf* 14 × 15.
A. *Chalk-surfaced paper* (19.12.69).
B. *Glazed, ordinary paper* (13.7.71).

No.	Type	Description	A Mint	A Used	B Mint	B Used
D 7	D 1	5 c. scarlet	25	2·25	1·50	3·50
D 8		10 c. green	40	2·25	75	2·50
D 9		20 c. deep blue	40	2·75	1·25	4·00
D10		30 c. red-brown	40	5·50	85	3·50
D11		40 c. bright purple	1·00	6·00	3·75	8·50
D12		1 s. orange	†		3·75	12·00
D7/11A		*Set of* 5	2·25	17·00		
D7B/12B		*Set of* 6			10·50	30·00

The stamps on chalk-surfaced paper exist only with gum arabic, but the stamps on glazed paper exist only with PVA gum.

1973 (12 Dec). *As Nos.* D1/6, *but glazed ordinary paper. P* 15.

No.	Type	Description	Mint	Used
D13	D 1	5 c. scarlet	50	2·75
D14		10 c. emerald	50	2·75
D15		20 c. deep blue	70	3·25
D16		30 c. red-brown	75	3·75
D17		40 c. bright mauve	75	4·75
D18		1 s. bright orange	1·25	6·50
D13/18		*Set of* 6	4·00	21·00

(Litho Questa)

1978 (31 July). *Chalky paper. P* 13½ × 14.

No.	Type	Description	Mint	Used
D19	D 1	5 c. brown-red	10	40
D20		10 c. emerald	10	40
D21		20 c. steel-blue	10	60
D22		30 c. red-brown	15	80
D23		40 c. bright purple	15	90
D24		1 s. bright orange	25	1·25
D19/24		*Set of* 6	70	4·00

Appendix

The following stamps have either been issued in excess of postal needs, or have not been made available to the public in reasonable quantities at face value. Miniature sheets, imperforate stamps, etc., are excluded from this section.

1986

Caribbean Royal Visit. Optd on previous issues. (*a*) *On Nos.* 425/8 20 *s.* × 2, 100 *s.* × 2. (*b*) *On Nos.* 430/3 5, 10, 20, 30 *s.*
"Ameripex" International Stamp Exhibition, Chicago. Optd on Nos. 425/8. 20 *s.* × 2, 100 *s.* × 2.

1988

Centenary of Statue of Liberty (1986). 1, 2, 3, 4, 5, 6, 7, 8, 10, 12, 15, 18, 20, 25, 30, 35, 40, 45, 50, 60 *s.*
Royal Ruby Wedding. Optd on No. 378. 10 *s.*
125th Anniv of Red Cross. Optd on Nos. 486/7. 5, 40 *s.*
63rd Anniv of Rotary International in Africa. Optd on Nos. 422/3. 10 *s.*, 17 *s.* 50.

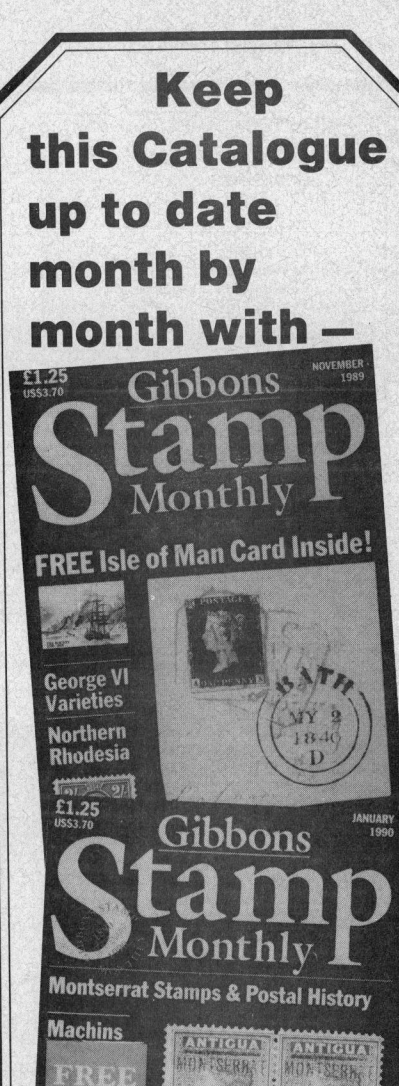

Tasmania

PRICES FOR STAMPS ON COVER

Nos. 1/4	*from* × 2
Nos. 5/12	*from* × 3
Nos. 14/23	*from* × 2
No. 24	—
Nos. 25/56	*from* × 3
Nos. 57/77	*from* × 6
Nos. 78/9	—
Nos. 80/90	*from* × 3
No. 91	—
Nos. 92/109	*from* × 3
No. 110	—
Nos. 111/23	*from* × 3
Nos. 124/6	—
Nos. 127/34	*from* × 4
Nos. 135/55	*from* × 3
Nos. 156/8	*from* × 20
Nos. 159/66	*from* × 10
Nos. 167/9	*from* × 15
Nos. 170/4	*from* × 6
Nos. 216/22	*from* × 15
Nos. 223/5	—
Nos. 226/7	*from* × 15
Nos. 229/36	*from* × 20
Nos. 237/57	*from* × 10
No. 258	—
Nos. 259/61	*from* × 10
Nos. F1/25	—
Nos. F26/9	*from* × 15
Nos. F30/9	—

SPECIMEN OVERPRINTS. Those listed are from U.P.U. distributions between 1892 and 1904. Further "Specimen" overprints exist, but these were used for other purposes.

1

2

3

(Eng C. W. Coard. Recess H. and C. Best at the *Courier* newspaper, Hobart)

1853 (1 Nov). *No wmk. Imperf. Twenty-four varieties in four rows of six each.*

(*a*) *Medium soft yellowish paper with all lines clear and distinct*

1 1 1d. pale blue £3250 £600
2 1d. blue £3250 £600

(*b*) *Thin hard white paper with lines of the engraving blurred and worn*

3 1 1d. pale blue £3000 £550
4 1d. blue £3000 £550

1853–55. *No wmk. Imperf. In each plate there are twenty-four varieties in four rows of six each.*

(*a*) *Plate I. Finely engraved. All lines in network and background thin, clear, and well defined.* (1853)

(i) *First state of the plate, brilliant colours*

5 2 4d. bright red-orange £2250 £500
a. Double impression .. .. ..
6 4d. bright brownish orange .. .. .. — £650

(ii) *Second state of plate, with blurred lines and worn condition of the central background*

7 2 4d. red-orange £2000 £350
8 4d. orange £1800 £325
9 4d. pale orange .. .. — £325

(*b*) *Plate II. Coarse engraving, lines in network and background thicker and blurred* (1855)

10 2 4d. orange £2000 £300
a. Double print, one albino .. ..
11 4d. dull orange £2000 £300
12 4d. yellowish orange £2000 £300

In the 4d. Plate I, the outer frame-line is thin all round. In Plate II it is, by comparison with other parts, thicker in the lower left angle.

The 4d. is known on vertically laid paper from proof sheets. Examples from Plate I have the lines close together and those from Plate II wide apart (*Price* £5000 *unused*).

In 1879 reprints were made of the 1d. in blue and the 4d., Plate I, in brownish yellow, on thin, tough, white wove paper, and perforated 11½. In 1887, a reprint from the other plate of the 4d. was made in reddish brown and in black, and in 1889 of the 1d. in blue and in black, and of the 4d. (both plates) in yellow and in black on white card, imperforate. As these three plates were defaced after the stamps had been superseded, all these reprints show two, or three thick strokes across the Queen's head.

All three plates were destroyed in July 1950.

(Eng. W. Humphrys, after water-colour sketch by E. Corbould. Recess P.B.)

1855 (17 Aug–16 Sept). *Wmk Large Star, W* w 1. *Imperf.*

14 3 1d. carmine (16.9) £4000 £750
15 2d. deep green (16.9) £1500 £550
16 2d. green (16.9) £1500 £500
17 4d. deep blue .. .. £1200 85·00
18 4d. blue .. .. £1200 95·00

Proofs of the 1d. and 4d. on thick paper, *without watermark*, are sometimes offered as the issued stamps.

(Recess H. and C. Best, Hobart, from P.B. plates)

1856 (Apr)–**57**. *No wmk. Imperf.* (*a*) *Thin white paper.*

19 3 1d. pale brick-red (4.56) £4000 £550
20 2d. dull emerald-green (1.57) £5000 £700
21 4d. deep blue (5.57) .. .. .. £600 85·00
22 4d. blue (5.57) .. .. £500 85·00
23 4d. pale blue (5.57) .. .. — £120

(*b*) *Pelure paper*

24 3 1d. deep red-brown (11.56) £3000 £600

4 7 8

(Recess H. Best (August 1857–May 1859), J. Davies (August 1859–March 1862), J. Birchall (March 1863), M. Hood (October 1863–April 1864), Govt Printer (from July 1864), all from P.B. plates)

1857 (Aug)–**69**. *Wmk double-lined numerals "1", "2" or "4" as W 4 on appropriate value. Imperf.*

25 3 1d. deep red-brown .. .. .. £400 21·00
26 1d. pale red-brown .. .. .. £275 16·00
27 1d. brick-red (1863) .. .. .. £140 15·00
28 1d. dull vermilion (1865).. .. .. 80·00 15·00
29 1d. carmine (1867) .. .. .. 80·00 15·00
a. Double print .. .. — £120
b. Error. Wmkd "2" (1869) .. ..
30 2d. dull emerald-green .. .. .. — 60·00
31 2d. green .. .. — 27·00
a. Double print .. .. — £150
32 2d. yellow-green .. .. £200 55·00
33 2d. deep green (1858) .. .. .. £170 30·00
34 2d. slate-green (1860) .. .. .. £120 45·00
35 4d. deep blue .. .. — 70·00
a. Double print .. .. — £150
36 4d. pale blue .. .. £100 11·00
37 4d. blue .. .. £100 15·00
a. Double print .. .. — £150
38 4d. bright blue .. .. £100 15·00
a. Printed on both sides.. .. .. † —
b. Double print .. .. — £120
39 4d. cobalt-blue .. .. — 55·00

Printings before July 1864 were all carried out at the *Courier* printing works which changed hands several times during this period.

CANCELLATIONS. Beware of early Tasmanian stamps with pen-cancellations cleaned off and faked postmarks applied.

(Recess P.B.)

1858 (Jan). *Wmk double-lined numerals "6" or "12" as W 4. Imperf.*

40 7 6d. dull lilac .. .. £600 65·00
41 8 1s. bright vermilion .. .. .. £500 70·00
42 1s. dull vermilion .. .. — 55·00

Examples of the 6d. lilac on paper watermarked Large Star exist from a proof sheet (*Price* £650 *unused*).

(Recess J. Davies (March 1860), J. Birchall (April 1863), Govt Printer (from February 1865), all from P.B. plates)

1860 (Mar)–**67**. *Wmk double-lined "6" as W 4. Imperf.*

44 7 6d. dull slate-grey .. .. .. £275 50·00
45 6d. grey .. .. — 55·00
46 6d. grey-violet (4.63) .. .. .. £130 50·00
a. Double print .. .. — £200
47 6d. dull bluish purple (2.65) .. .. £130 40·00
48 6d. bluish purple (2.65) .. .. .. £250 45·00
49 6d. reddish mauve (4.67).. .. .. £550 £150

In 1871 reprints were made of the 6d. (in mauve) and the 1s. on white wove paper, and perforated 11½. They are found with or without "REPRINT". In 1889 they were again reprinted on white card, imperforate. These later impressions are also found overprinted "REPRINT" and perforated 11½.

PERFORATED ISSUES. From 1 October 1857 the Tasmania Post Office only supplied purchasers requiring five or more complete sheets of stamps. The public obtained their requirements, at face value, from licensed stamp vendors, who obtained their stocks at a discount from the Post Office.

From 1863 onwards a number of the stamp vendors applied their own roulettes or perforations. The Hobart firm of J. Walch & Sons achieved this so successfully that they were given an official contract in July 1869 to perforate sheets for the Post Office. The Government did not obtain a perforating machine until late in 1871.

1863–71. *Double-lined numeral watermarks. Various unofficial roulettes and perforations.*

(*a*) *By. J. Walch & Sons, Hobart*

(i) *Roulette about* 8, *often imperf* × *roul* (1863–68)

50 3 1d. brick-red .. .. — £150
51 1d. carmine £300 £100
52 2d. yellow-green .. ..
53 2d. slate-green .. ..
54 4d. pale blue .. .. — £140
55 7 6d. dull lilac .. .. — £170
56 8 1s. vermilion .. .. — £500

(ii) *P* 10 (1864–69)

57 3 1d. brick-red .. .. 45·00 18·00
58 1d. dull vermilion.. .. .. .. 45·00 18·00
59 1d. carmine .. .. 42·00 18·00
60 2d. yellow-green .. .. £225 70·00
61 2d. slate-green £275 £120
62 4d. pale blue .. .. 90·00 9·50
63 4d. blue .. .. 90·00 9·50
a. Double print .. .. — £110
64 7 6d grey-violet .. .. £150 13·00
65 6d. dull bluish purple .. .. .. 80·00 16·00
66 6d. bluish purple .. .. — 18·00
67 6d. reddish mauve .. .. £300 60·00
68 8 1s. vermilion .. .. 90·00 19·00
a. Imperf vert (horiz pair) .. ..

(iii) *P* 12 (1865–71—*from July* 1869 *under contract to the Post Office*)

69 3 1d. dull vermilion.. .. .. .. 45·00
70 1d. carmine .. .. 35·00 6·50
a. Error. Wmkd "2" (*pen cancel* £75) .. — £1000
71 2d. yellow-green .. .. £100 38·00
72 4d. deep blue .. .. 70·00 11·00
73 4d. blue .. .. 70·00 13·00
74 4d. cobalt-blue .. .. — 28·00
75 7 6d. bluish purple .. .. £120 18·00
a. Imperf between (vert pair) .. ..
76 6d. reddish mauve .. .. 70·00 32·00
a. Imperf between (vert or horiz pair) ..
77 8 1s. vermilion .. .. 95·00 28·00
a. Double print .. .. — £150
b. Imperf between (horiz pair) .. ..

(iv) *Perf compound* 10 × 12 (1865–69)

78 3 1d. carmine £1300
79 4d. blue .. .. — £900

(*b*) *P* 12½ *by R. Harris, Launceston* (1864–68)

80 3 1d. brick-red .. .. 45·00 23·00
81 1d. dull vermilion.. .. .. .. 42·00 17·00
82 1d. carmine .. .. 25·00 6·50
83 2d. yellow-green .. .. £225 80·00
84 2d. sage-green £200 £100
85 4d. blue .. .. £130 35·00
86 4d. bright blue .. .. £130 35·00
87 7 6d. dull bluish purple .. .. .. £160 40·00
88 6d. bluish purple .. .. £170 40·00
89 6d. reddish mauve .. .. £350 90·00
90 8 1s. vermilion .. .. £180 65·00

(*c*) *Imperf* × *oblique roulette* 11½ *at Oatlands* (1866)

91 3 4d. blue .. ..

(*d*) *Oblique roulette* 10–10½, *possibly at Deloraine* (1867)

92 3 1d. brick-red .. .. — £325
93 1d. carmine £900 £275
94 2d. yellow-green .. .. — £425
95 4d. bright blue .. .. — £375
96 7 6d. grey-violet .. .. — £600

(*e*) *Oblique roulette* 14–15, *probably at Cleveland* (1867–69)

97 3 1d. brick-red .. .. — £375
98 1d. dull vermilion .. .. — £375
99 1d. carmine .. .. — £375
100 2d. yellow-green .. .. — £425
101 4d. pale blue .. .. — £325
102 7 6d. grey-violet .. .. — £600
103 8 1s. vermilion .. .. — £750

(*f*) *Pin-perf* 5½ *to* 9½ *at Longford* (1867)

104 3 1d. carmine .. .. £300 70·00
105 2d. yellow-green.. .. .. ..
106 4d. bright blue .. .. — £160
107 7 6d. grey-violet .. .. — £150
108 6d. reddish mauve .. .. .. — £425
109 8 1s. vermilion .. ..

(*g*) *Pin-perf* 12 *at Oatlands* (1867)

110 3 4d. blue .. ..

(*h*) *Pin-perf* 13½ *to* 14½ (1867)

111 3 1d. brick-red .. .. — £190
112 1d. dull vermilion .. .. — £190
113 1d. carmine .. ..
114 2d. yellow-green .. .. — £275
115 4d. pale blue .. .. — £160
116 7 6d. grey-violet .. .. — £375
117 8 1s. vermilion .. ..

(*j*) *Serrated perf* 19 *at Hobart* (1868–69)

118 3 1d. carmine (*pen-cancel* £9) £225 £100
119 2d. yellow-green .. .. — £200
120 4d. deep blue .. .. £550 95·00
121 4d. cobalt-blue .. .. — 95·00
122 7 6d. bluish purple .. .. — £375
123 8 1s. vermilion .. ..

(*k*) *Roul* 4½, *possibly at Macquarie River* (1868)

124 3 4d. blue .. ..
125 7 6d. reddish mauve .. ..
126 8 1s. vermilion .. ..

For stamps perforated 11½ or 12 by the Post Office see Nos. 135/43.

11

12

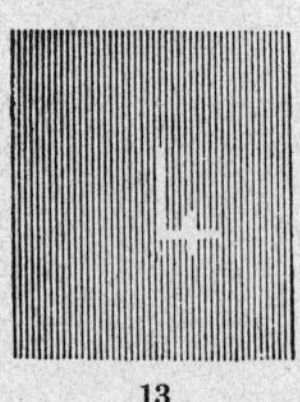
13

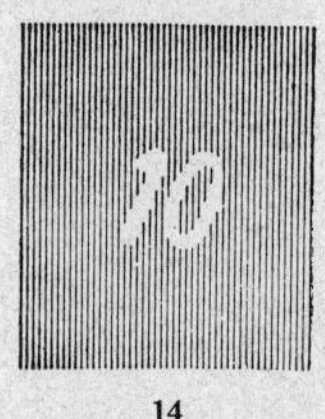
14

(Typo Govt Printer, Hobart, from plates made by D.L.R.)

1870 (1 Nov)–**71.** *Wmk single-lined numerals* **W 12** (*2d.*), **13** (*1d., 4d.*) *or* **14** (*1d., 10d.*). (*a*) *P* 12 *by J. Walch & Sons.*

127 **11** 1d. rose-red (*wmk* "10") .. .. .. 27·00 8·50
a. Imperf (pair) £190 £190
b. Deep rose-red .. .. .. 45·00 6·50
128 1d. rose-red (*wmk* "4") (3.71) .. .. 40·00 8·50
a. Imperf (pair) .. .. .. — £160
129 2d. yellow-green .. .. .. 38·00 4·50
a. Imperf (pair) .. .. ..
b. Blue-green .. .. .. 42·00 4·50
130 4d. blue £700 £400
131 10d. black .. .. 18·00 10·00
a. Imperf (pair) £110

(*b*) *P* 11½ *by the Post Office* (1871)

132 **11** 1d. rose-red (*wmk* "10") £900
133 2d. yellow-green .. .. .. 80·00 6·50
a. Blue-green .. .. .. 32·00 3·25
ab. Double print .. .. ..
134 10d. black .. .. 22·00 12·00

The above were printed on paper obtained from New South Wales.

See also Nos. 144/55, 156/8, 159/66, 170/4, 226/7, 242 and 255/6.

(Recess Govt Printer, Hobart)

1871–91. *Double-lined numeral watermarks as* **W 4.** *Perforated by the Post Office.* (*a*) *P* 11½.

135 **7** 6d. dull mauve .. .. .. 70·00 19·00
136 6d. bright mauve .. .. .. 65·00 19·00
a. Imperf between (pair) .. .. — £425
137 6d. dull purple (3.75) .. .. 65·00 19·00
a. Imperf (pair) .. .. .. — £400
138 6d. bright purple (5.78) .. .. 65·00 28·00
a. Double print .. .. .. — £110
b. Imperf between (horiz pair) £750
139 6d. lilac-purple (10.79) .. .. 70·00 38·00
140 **8** 1s. dull vermilion (1.73) .. .. 80·00 38·00
a. Imperf between (horiz pair) .. ..
141 1s. brownish vermilion (1.73) .. .. 70·00 38·00

(*b*) *P* 12

142 **7** 6d. bright purple (1884) .. .. 80·00 16·00
143 6d. dull claret (7.91) .. .. 24·00 11·00

15

16

(Typo Govt Printer, Hobart, from plates made by D.L.R.)

1871 (25 Mar)–**78.** **W 15.** (*a*) *P* 11½.

144 **11** 1d. rose (5.71) .. .. .. 3·25 50
a. Imperf (pair) (*pen cancel £25*) ..
b. Bright rose .. .. .. 3·25 50
c. Carmine .. .. .. 4·50 50
d. Pink .. .. .. 4·50 1·50
e. Vermilion (4.75) .. .. £200 65·00
145 2d. deep green (11.72) .. .. 12·00 50
a. Blue-green .. .. .. 20·00 50
b. Yellow-green (12.75) .. .. £110 1·50
146 3d. pale red-brown .. .. .. 30·00 3·25
a. Imperf (pair) £120
b. Deep red-brown .. .. .. 30·00 3·75
ba. Imperf between (pair) .. ..
c. Purple-brown (1.78) .. .. 30·00 3·25
ca. Imperf (pair) .. .. .. — £275
d. Brownish purple .. .. .. 30·00 3·25
147 4d. pale yellow (8.8.76) .. .. 35·00 9·50
a. Ochre (7.78) .. .. .. 42·00 5·50
b. Buff .. .. 35·00 6·50
148 9d. blue (2.10.71) .. .. .. 13·00 5·00
a. Imperf (pair) £120
b. Double print .. .. ..
149 5s. purple (*pen cancel £3.75*) .. .. £130 25·00
a. Imperf (pair) .. .. ..
b. Mauve .. .. £110 25·00

(*b*) *P* 12

150 **11** 1d. rose .. .. 60·00 5·50
a. Carmine .. .. .. 65·00 7·00
151 2d. green .. .. £400 95·00
a. Imperf (pair) .. .. .. — £150
152 3d. red-brown .. .. .. 60·00 14·00
a. Deep red-brown .. .. .. 60·00 14·00
153 4d. buff .. .. £225 15·00
154 9d. pale blue .. .. .. 28·00
155 5s. purple £225
a. Mauve £150

(Typo D.L.R.)

1878 (28 Oct). **W 16.** *P* 14.

156 **11** 1d. carmine .. .. .. 2·75 25
a. Rose-carmine .. .. .. 2·75 25
b. Scarlet .. .. .. 2·75 25
157 2d. pale green .. .. .. 3·00 25
a. Green .. .. 3·00 25
158 8d. dull purple-brown .. .. .. 12·00 2·75

(Typo Govt Printer, Hobart (some printings of 1d. in 1891 by *Mercury* Press) from plates made by Victoria Govt Printer, Melbourne (½d.) or D.L.R. (others))

1880 (Apr)–**91.** **W 16** (*sideways on 1d.*). (*a*) *P* 11½.

159 **11** ½d. orange (8.3.89) .. .. .. 1·90 90
a. Deep orange .. .. .. 1·90 1·10
160 1d. dull red (14.2.89) .. .. .. 3·50 1·10
a. Vermilion-red .. .. .. 2·75 1·10
161 3d. red-brown .. .. .. 8·00 2·50
a. Imperf (pair) .. .. .. 80·00
162 4d. deep yellow (1.83) .. .. 25·00 9·00
a. Chrome-yellow .. .. .. 25·00 10·00
b. Olive-yellow .. .. .. 90·00 20·00
c. Buff .. .. 26·00 6·50

(*b*) *P* 12

163 **11** ½d. orange .. .. 2·00 1·50
a. Deep orange .. .. .. 1·90 1·25
164 1d. pink (1891) .. .. .. 11·00 2·50
a. Imperf (pair) .. .. .. 90·00 £100
b. Rosine .. .. 4·00 1·25
c. Dull rosine .. .. .. 6·50 2·75
ca. Imperf (pair) .. .. .. 65·00
165 3d. red-brown .. .. .. 7·00 1·75
a. Imperf between (pair) £450
166 4d. deep yellow .. .. .. 50·00 12·00
a. Chrome-yellow .. .. .. 70·00 12·00
ab. Printed both sides £180

SPECIMEN AND PRESENTATION REPRINTS OF TYPE 11. In 1871 the 1d., 2d., 3d., 4d. blue, 9d., 10d. and 5s. were reprinted on soft white wove paper to be followed, in 1879, by the 4d. yellow and 8d. on rough white wove. Both these reprintings were perforated 11½. In 1886 it was decided to overprint remaining stocks with the word "REPRINT".

In 1889 Tasmania commenced sending sample stamps to the U.P.U. in Berne and a further printing of the 4d. blue was made, imperforate, on white card. This, together with the 5s. in mauve on white card, both perforated 11½ and overprinted "REPRINT", were included in presentation sets supplied to members of the states' legislatures in 1901.

Halfpenny
(**17**)

$2\frac{1}{2}$ d.
(**18**) (2¼ mm between "d", and "2")

$2\frac{1}{2}$ d.
(**19**) (3½ mm between "d" and "2")

1889 (1 Jan). *No. 156b surch locally with T* **17.**

167 **11** ½d. on 1d. scarlet .. .. .. 8·00 5·00
a. "al" in "Half" printed sideways (R. 1/2) £700 £450

No. 167a occurred in a second printing and was later corrected.

A reprint on white card, perforated 11½ or imperforate, overprinted "REPRINT" was produced in 1901.

1891 (1 Jan–June). *Surch locally.* **W 16.** (*a*) *With T* **18.** *P* 11½.

168 **11** 2½d. on 9d. pale blue .. .. .. 5·50 2·25
a. Surch double, one inverted £250 £250
b. Deep blue (May) .. .. .. 6·25 3·00

(*b*) *With T* **19.** *P* 12

169 **11** 2½d. on 9d. pale blue (June) .. .. 5·00 2·25
a. Blue surch. .. .. ..

A reprint, using a third setting, perforated 11½ and overprinted "REPRINT" was produced in 1901.

(Typo Govt Printer, Hobart)

1891 (Apr–Aug). **W 15.** (*a*) *P* 11½.

170 **11** ½d. orange .. .. 12·00 4·00
a. Brown-orange .. .. .. 10·00 3·75
171 1d. rosine .. .. 10·00 4·00

(*b*) *P* 12

172 **11** ½d. orange .. .. 12·00 6·00
a. Imperf (pair) .. .. .. 60·00
173 1d. dull rosine .. .. .. 14·00 6·00
a. Rosine .. .. 25·00 10·00
174 4d. bistre (Aug) .. .. .. 13·00 4·75

20

21

21a

1892 (12 Feb)–**99.** **W 16.** *P* 14.

216 **20** ½d. orange and mauve (11.92) .. 1·25 40
217 **21** 2½d. purple .. .. 2·50 1·00
218 **20** 5d. pale blue and brown .. .. 4·50 1·40
219 6d. violet and black (11.92) .. .. 5·50 1·75
220 **21a** 10d. purple-lake & deep green (30.1.99) 9·00 5·50
221 **20** 1s. rose and green (11.92) .. .. 6·00 1·75
222 2s. 6d. brown and blue (11.92) .. 20·00 7·50
223 5s. lilac and red (3.2.97) .. .. 35·00 18·00
224 10s. mauve and brown (11.92) .. 75·00 40·00
225 £1 green and yellow (2.97) £500 £150
216/25 .. .. *Set of* 10 £600 £200
216/25 Optd "Specimen" .. .. *Set of* 10 £250

See also Nos. 243 and 257/8.

(Typo Govt Printer, Hobart)

1896. **W 16.** *P* 12.

226 **11** 4d. pale bistre .. .. 12·00 5·50
227 9d. pale blue .. .. 7·50 2·00
a. Blue .. .. 8·00 3·00

22 Lake Marion

23 Mount Wellington

24 Hobart

25 Tasman's Arch

26 Spring River, Port Davey

27 Russell Falls

28 Mount Gould, Lake St. Clair

29 Dilston Falls

30

(Eng. L. Phillips. Recess D.L.R.)

1899 (Dec)–**1900.** **W 30.** *P* 14.

229 **22** ½d. deep green (31.3.00) .. .. 2·50 40
230 **23** 1d. bright lake .. .. .. 2·50 20
231 **24** 2d. deep violet .. .. .. 3·00 15
232 **25** 2½d. indigo (1900) .. .. .. 10·00 4·50
233 **26** 3d. sepia (1900) .. .. .. 7·50 1·00
234 **27** 4d. deep orange-buff (1900) .. .. 13·00 1·75
235 **28** 5d. bright blue (31.3.00) .. .. 14·00 4·00
236 **29** 6d. lake (31.3.00) .. .. .. 18·00 3·50
229/36 .. .. *Set of* 8 65·00 14·00
229/36 Optd "Specimen" .. .. *Set of* 8 £225

See also Nos. 237/9, 240/1, 245/8, 249/54 and 260/1.

DIFFERENCES BETWEEN LITHOGRAPHED AND TYPOGRAPHED PRINTINGS OF TYPES 22/9

	Lithographed	Typographed
	General appearance fine.	*Comparatively crude and coarse appearance.*
½d.	All "V over Crown" wmk.	All "Crown over A" wmk.
1d.	The shading on the path on the right bank of the river consists of very fine dots. In printings from worn stones the dots hardly show.	The shading on the path is coarser, consisting of large dots and small patches of colour.
	The shading on the white mountain is fine (or almost absent in many stamps).	The shading on the mountain is coarse, and clearly defined.
2d.	Three rows of windows in large building on shore, at extreme left, against inner frame.	Two rows of windows.
3d.	Clouds very white.	Clouds dark.
	Stars in corner ornaments have long points.	Stars have short points.
	Shading of corner ornaments is defined by a coloured outer line.	Shading of ornaments terminates against white background.
4d.	Lithographed only.	—
6d.	No coloured dots at base of waterfall.	Coloured dots at base of waterfall.
	Outer frame of value tablets is formed by outer line of design.	Thick line of colour between value tablets and outer line.
		Small break in inner frame below second "A" of "TASMANIA".

(Litho, using transfers from D.L.R. plates, Federal Government Printing Office, Melbourne)

1902 (Jan)–**03.** *Wmk V over Crown,* **W w 10** (*sideways on ½d., 2d.*). *P* 12½.

237 **22** ½d. green .. .. 1·25 25
a. Wmk upright
b. Perf 11 .. .. 3·25 45
c. Perf comp of 12½ and 11 .. .. 50·00 35·00

238 23 1d. carmine-red .. .. 3·00 25
239 24 2d. violet .. .. 1·50 10
a. Perf 11 .. .. 1·50 30
b. Perf comp of 12½ and 11 .. .. 55·00 35·00
c. *Purple* .. .. 1·50 10
ca. Perf 11 .. .. 3·25 15
d. Wmk upright .. .. ..
237/9 Optd "Specimen" .. .. *Set of* 3 £120

As the V and Crown paper was originally prepared for stamps of smaller size, portions of two or more watermarks appear on each stamp.

We only list the main groups of shades in this and the following issues. There are variations of shade in all values, particularly in the 2d. where there is a wide range, also in the 1d. in some issues.

(Typo, using electrotyped plates, Federal Govt Ptg Office, Melbourne)

1902 (Oct)–**03**. *Wmk V over Crown*, W w **10**. *P* 12½.
240 23 1d. pale red (*wmk sideways*) .. .. 2·50 20
a. Perf 11 .. .. 13·00 20
b. Perf comp of 12½ and 11 .. .. £160 35·00
c. Wmk upright (1.03) .. .. ..
241 1d. rose-red (*wmk upright*) (4.03) (Optd S. £40) .. .. ..
a. Perf 11 .. .. 2·00 15
b. Perf comp of 12½ and 11 .. .. 11·00 20
c. *Deep carmine-red* .. .. .. £150 35·00
ca. Perf 11 .. .. 50·00 75
cb. Perf comp of 12½ and 11 .. .. — 15·00

(Typo Federal Govt Ptg Office, Melbourne)

1903–05. *Wmk V over Crown*, W w **10**. *P* 12½.
242 11 9d. blue (1905) .. .. 7·00 2·50
a. Perf 11 .. .. 7·50 2·75
b. Perf comp of 12½ and 11 .. .. — £375
c. *Pale blue* .. .. 8·50 2·75
d. *Bright blue* .. .. 8·50 3·00
e. *Ultramarine* £350
f. *Indigo* £130
243 20 1s. rose and green .. .. .. 8·50 3·00
a. Perf 11 .. .. 22·00
242/3 Optd "Specimen" .. .. *Set of* 2 £100

1½d. (31) ONE PENNY (32)

1904 (29 Dec). *No.* 218 *surch with T* **31**.
244 20 1½d. on 5d. pale blue & brn (Optd S. £28) 1·25 90

Stamps with inverted surcharge or without surcharge *se-tenant* with stamps with normal surcharge were obtained irregularly and were not issued for postal use.

(Litho, using transfers from D.L.R. plates, Federal Govt Ptg Office, Melbourne)

1905 (Sept)–**12**. *Wmk Crown over A*, W w **11** (*sideways on horiz stamps*). *P* 12½.
245 24 2d. purple .. .. 3·25 15
a. Perf 11 .. .. 7·00 15
b. Perf comp of 12½ and 11 .. .. 14·00 2·75
c. Perf comp of 12½ and 12 .. .. — 42·00
d. Perf comp of 11 and 12 .. ..
e. *Dull purple* .. .. 2·25
ea. Perf 11 .. .. 11·00 25
246 26 3d. brown .. .. 7·50 85
a. Perf 11 .. .. 11·00 1·60
b. Perf comp of 12½ and 11 .. .. 48·00
247 27 4d. orange-buff (3.07) .. .. 12·00 1·75
a. Perf 11 .. .. 11·00 1·75
b. Perf comp of 12½ and 11 .. .. £160
c. *Brown-ochre* (wmk sideways). Perf 11 (6.11) .. .. .. 24·00 8·50
d. *Orange-yellow* (3.12) .. .. 15·00 3·75
da. Perf 11 .. .. 17·00
248 29 6d. lake (7.08) .. .. .. 23·00 3·50
a. Perf 11 .. .. 28·00 4·00
b. Perf comp of 12½ and 11 .. .. £130

Stamps with perf compound of 12½ and 12 or 11 and 12 are found on sheets which were sent from Melbourne incompletely perforated. The line of perforation gauging 12 was done at the Government Printing Office, Hobart.

(Typo, using electrotyped plates, Federal Govt Ptg Office, Melbourne)

1905 (Sept)–**11**. *Wmk Crown over A*, W w **11** (*sideways on horiz designs*). *P* 12½.
249 22 ½d. yellow-green (10.12.08) .. .. 1·25 20
a. Perf 11 .. .. 1·25 20
b. Perf comp of 12½ and 11 .. .. 35·00
c. Perf comp of 11 and 12 .. .. 55·00
d. Wmk upright (1909) .. ..
da. Perf 11 .. .. ..
250 23 1d. rose-red .. .. 1·50 10
a. Perf 11 .. .. 1·50 10
b. Perf comp of 12½ and 11 .. .. 2·00 70
c. Perf comp of 12½ and 12 .. .. 40·00 5·50
d. Perf comp of 11 and 12 .. .. 45·00
e. *Bright rose* .. .. — 15
ea. Perf 11 .. .. 3·50 15
f. Wmk sideways (1908) .. ..
g. *Crimson* (3.10) .. ..
ga. Perf 11 .. .. — 30
gb. Perf comp of 12½ and 12 .. ..
251 24 2d. purple (8.07) .. .. .. 3·00 10
a. Wmk upright .. ..
b. Perf 11 .. .. 2·50 10
ba. Wmk upright .. ..
c. Perf comp of 12½ and 11 .. .. 18·00 6·00
d. Perf comp of 12½ and 12 .. ..
e. Perf comp of 11 and 12 .. .. 70·00 38·00
252 2d. bright violet (new plate)* (1.11) .. 2·50 20
a. Wmk upright .. ..
b. Perf 11 .. .. 2·75 20
c. Perf comp of 12½ and 11 .. .. 70·00
253 26 3d. brown (3.09) .. .. .. 6·50 1·25
a. Perf 11 .. .. 8·00 1·50
b. Perf comp of 12½ and 11 .. .. £130
254 29 6d. dull lake (12.10) .. .. .. 15·00 4·75
a. Perf 11 .. .. 15·00 4·50
b. Perf comp of 12½ and 11 .. .. £130

*Stamps from this stereotyped plate differ from Nos. 251*c* and 251*ca* in the width of the design (33 to 33¾ mm, against just over 32 mm), in the taller, bolder letters of "TASMANIA", in the slope of the mountain in the left background, which is clearly outlined in white, and in the outer vertical frame-line at left, which appears "wavy". Compare Nos. 259, etc, which are always from this plate.

The note after No. 248 *re* perfs compound with perf 12 also applies here.

(Typo Federal Govt Printing Office, Melbourne)

1906–13. *Wmk Crown over A*, W w **11**. *P* 12½.
255 11 8d. purple-brown (1907) .. .. 17·00 4·00
a. Perf 11 .. .. 15·00 3·00
256 9d. blue (1907) .. .. 7·00 2·25
a. Perf 11 .. .. 7·00 2·25
b. Perf comp of 12½ and 11 (1909) .. 48·00
c. Perf comp of 12½ and 12 (1909) .. 90·00
d. Perf comp of 11 and 12 .. .. £180
257 20 1s. rose and green (1907) .. .. 9·00 1·50
a. Perf 11 (1907) .. .. .. 9·50 4·50
b. Perf comp of 12½ and 11 .. .. 14·00
c. Perf comp of 12½ and 12 .. .. 45·00
258 10s. mauve and brown (1906) .. .. £100 60·00
a. Perf 11 .. .. £150
b. Perf comp of 12½ and 12 .. .. £140

The note after No. 248 *re* perfs compound with perf 12, also applies here.

1912 (Oct). *No.* 252 *surch with T* **32**. *P* 12½.
259 24 1d. on 2d. bright violet (R.) 90 25
a. Perf 11 .. .. 1·50 35
b. Perf comp of 12½ and 11 .. .. 85·00 85·00

(Typo, using electrotyped plates, Federal Govt Ptg Office, Melbourne)

1912 (Dec). *Thin paper, white gum* (*as Victoria*, 1912). W w **11** (*sideways on* 3*d.*). *P* 12½.
260 23 1d. crimson .. .. 5·50 30
a. Perf 11 .. .. 6·00 30
b. Perf comp of 12½ and 11 .. ..
261 26 3d. brown .. .. 22·00 27·00

POSTAL FISCAL STAMPS

VALIDITY. Nos. F1/29 were authorised for postal purposes on 1 November 1882.

CLEANED STAMPS. Beware of postal fiscal stamps with pen-cancellations removed.

F 1

F 2

F 3

F 4

(Recess Alfred Bock, Hobart)

1863–80. *Wmk double-lined* "1", W **4**. (*a*) *Imperf.*
F 1 F 1 3d. green (1.65) .. .. .. 45·00 35·00
F 2 F 2 2s. 6d. carmine (11.63) .. .. 50·00 35·00
F 3 2s. 6d. lake (1880) .. .. ..
F 4 F 3 5s. brown (1.64) £130 £110
F 5 5s. sage-green (1880) .. .. 50·00 42·00
F 6 F 4 10s. orange (1.64) £170 £110
F 7 10s. salmon (1880) £120 £110

(*b*) *P* 10
F 8 F 1 3d. green .. .. 28·00 16·00
F 9 F 2 2s. 6d. carmine .. .. .. 30·00
F10 F 3 5s. brown .. .. 45·00
F11 F 4 10s. orange .. .. 30·00

(*c*) *P* 12
F12 F 1 3d. green .. .. 32·00 20·00
F13 F 2 2s. 6d. carmine .. .. .. 32·00 27·00
F14 F 3 5s. brown .. .. 55·00
F15 5s. sage-green .. .. .. 22·00 19·00
F16 F 4 10s. orange .. .. 30·00 27·00
F17 10s. salmon .. .. 22·00 20·00

(*d*) *P* 12½
F18 F 1 3d. green .. .. 55·00
F19 F 2 2s. 6d. carmine .. .. .. 55·00
F20 F 3 5s. brown .. .. 70·00
F21 F 4 10s. orange-brown .. .. .. 45·00

(*e*) *P* 11½
F22 F 1 3d. green .. ..
F23 F 2 2s. 6d. lake .. .. 28·00 25·00
F24 F 3 5s. sage-green .. .. .. 22·00 16·00
F25 F 4 10s. salmon .. .. 38·00 30·00

See also No. F30.

In 1879, the 3d., 2s. 6d., 5s. (brown), and 10s. (orange) were reprinted on thin, tough, white paper, and are found with or without "REPRINT". In 1889 another reprint was made on white card, imperforate and perforated 12. These are also found with or without "REPRINT".

F 5 Duck-billed Platypus

REVENUE (F 6)

(Typo D.L.R.)

1880 (19 Apr). W **16** (*sideways*). *P* 14.
F26 F 5 1d. slate .. .. 8·50 3·25
F27 3d. chestnut .. .. 9·00 2·25
F28 6d. mauve .. .. 38·00 2·00
F29 1s. rose-pink .. .. 45·00 3·75

All values are known imperf, but not used.

Reprints are known of the 1d. in *deep blue* and the 6d. in lilac. The former is on yellowish white, the latter on white card. Both values also exist on wove paper, perf 12, with the word "REPRINT".

1888. W **16**. *P* 12
F30 F 2 2s. 6d. lake .. .. 15·00 11·00
a. Imperf between (horiz pair) .. £450

1900 (Nov). *Optd with Type* F **6**. (*a*) *On Types* F **2** *and* F **4**. W **16**. *P* 12.
F31 F 2 2s. 6d. carmine £160
a. "REVFNUE" .. .. ..
b. Opt inverted .. .. ..
c. Imperf £170
ca. "REVFNUE" £250
F32 F 4 10s. salmon .. .. ..
a. "REVFNUE" .. .. ..
b. On No. F 17 (wmk W 4) .. ..
ba. "REVFNUE" .. .. ..

(*b*) *On No.* F27
F33 F 5 3d. chestnut .. .. .. 15·00
a. Double opt, one vertical .. .. 75·00 £100

(*c*) *On stamps as Nos.* F26/9, *but litho locally.* W **15** (*No.* F34) *or* W **16** (*others*). *P* 12
F34 F 5 1d. blue .. .. 65·00
F35 1d. blue .. .. 15·00
a. Imperf between (horiz pair) .. £300
b. "REVENUE" inverted £100
c. "REVENUE" double £160
d. *Pale blue* .. .. 15·00
F36 2d. chestnut .. .. 16·00
a. Value omitted £180 £150
b. Value double £225 £150
c. Imperf between (horiz pair) .. £200
F37 6d. mauve .. .. 50·00
a. Double print £200
F38 1s. pink .. .. 75·00

(*d*) *On No.* 225
F39 20 £1 green and yellow £150 £125
a. Opt double, one vertical £275

It was not intended that stamps overprinted with Type F **6** should be used for postal purposes, but an ambiguity in regulations permitted such usage until corrected on 1 December 1900. All postal fiscal stamps were invalidated for postal purposes after 30 June 1901.

The six former colonies of New South Wales, Queensland, South Australia, Tasmania, Victoria and Western Australia united to form the Commonwealth of Australia on 1 January 1901.

On 1 March 1901 control of the postal service passed to the federal administration. The first national postage due stamps appeared in July 1902, but it was not until January 1913 that postage stamps inscribed "AUSTRALIA" were issued.

Togo

The stamps of GERMANY were used in the colony from March 1888 until June 1897 when issues for TOGO were provided.

PRICES FOR STAMPS ON COVER

Nos. H1/22	*from* × 6
Nos. H23/33	—
Nos. H34/58	*from* × 6

ANGLO-FRENCH OCCUPATION

British and French forces invaded Togo on 12 August 1914 and the German administration surrendered on 26 August 1914.

***Stamps of German Colonial issue Types* A *and* B 1900 *and* 1909–14 (5 *pf. and* 10 *pf.*)**

TOGO
Anglo-French
Occupation
(1)

Half penny
(2)

SETTINGS. Nos. H1/33 were all overprinted or surcharged by the Catholic Mission, Lome.

The initial setting for the 3 pf. to 80 pf. was of 50 (10×5), repeated twice on each sheet of 100. Overprints from this setting, used for Nos. H1/9, had the lines of type 3 mm apart.

Nos. H1/2 were subsequently surcharged, also from a setting

of 50, to form Nos. H12/13. The surcharge setting showed a thin dropped "y" with small serifs on R. 1/1–2, 2/1, 3/1, 4/1 and 5/1–2.

The type from the overprint and surcharge was then amalgamated in a new setting of 50 on which the lines of the overprint were only 2 mm apart. On this amalgamated setting, used for Nos. H27/8, the thin "y" varieties were still present and R. 4/7 showed the second "O" of "TOGO" omitted.

The surcharge was subsequently removed from this "2 mm" setting which was then used to produce Nos. H17/19. The missing "O" was spotted and corrected before any of the 30 pf. stamps were overprinted.

The remaining low values of the second issue, Nos. H14/16 and H20/2, were overprinted from settings of 25 (5×5), either taken from the last setting of 50 or from an amended version on which there was no space either side of the hyphen. This slightly narrower overprint was subsequently used for Nos. H29/33. It shows the top of the second "O" broken so that it resembles a "U" on R. 1/5.

The mark values were overprinted from settings of 20 (5×4), showing the same differences in the spacing of the lines as on the low values.

It is believed that odd examples of some German colonial values were overprinted from individual settings in either spacing.

1914 (24 Sept). *Optd with T* **1** *by Catholic Mission, Lome. Wide setting. Lines 3 mm apart.*

H 1 3 pf. brown .. .. £110 85·00
H 2 5 pf. green .. .. £100 85·00
H 3 10 pf. carmine (Wmk Lozenges).. .. £120 £100
a. Opt inverted £7000 £4000
b. Opt *tête-bêche* in vert pair .. † £6500
c. No wmk .. .. .. † £5500
H 4 20 pf. ultramarine .. .. 28·00 23·00
H 5 25 pf. black and red/*yellow* .. .. 28·00 23·00
H 6 30 pf. black and orange/*buff* .. .. 28·00 28·00
H 7 40 pf. black and carmine £225 £250
H 8 50 pf. black and purple/*buff* £9000 £7000
H 9 80 pf. black and carmine/*rose* £250 £275
H10 1 m. carmine £5000 £2500
H11 2 m. blue.. .. .. .. £7500 £7000
a. "Occupation" double £11000 £10000
b. Opt inverted £9500

The *tête-bêche* overprint on the 10 pf. is due to the sheet being turned round after the upper 50 stamps had been overprinted so that vertical pairs from the two middle rows have the overprint *tête-bêche*.

1914 (1 Oct). *Nos.* H1 *and* H2 *surch as T* **2**.

H12 ½d. on 3 pf. brown £200 £200
a. Thin "y" in "penny".. .. .. £500 £400
H13 1d. on 5 pf. green £200 £200
a. Thin "y" in "penny".. .. .. £500 £400

TOGO
Anglo-French
Occupation
(3)

TOGO
Anglo-French
Occupation
Half penny
(4)

1914 (Oct). (*a*) *Optd with T* **3**. *Narrow Setting. Lines 2 mm apart.*

H14 3 pf. brown £3500 £600
H15 5 pf. green £750 £550
H16 10 pf. carmine .. .. † £1300
H17 20 pf. ultramarine .. .. .. 14·00 12·00
a. "TOG" £4000 £4000
b. Nos. H4 and H17 *se-tenant* (vert pair) £5500
H18 25 pf. black and red/*yellow* .. .. 19·00 25·00
a. "TOG" £12000
H19 30 pf. black and orange/*buff* .. .. 19·00 25·00
H20 40 pf. black and carmine £3500 £1100
H21 50 pf. black and purple/*buff* .. .. † £5500
H22 80 pf. black and carmine/*rose* £1600 £1600
H23 1 m. carmine £7000 £3750
H24 2 m. blue.. .. .. .. † £7500
H25 3 m. violet-black .. .. .. † £25000
H26 5 m. lake and black .. .. .. † £25000

(*b*) *Narrow setting, but including value, as T* **4**

H27 ½d. on 3 pf. brown .. .. .. 26·00 25·00
a. "TOG" £425 £275
b. Thin "y" in "penny" .. .. 55·00 42·00
H28 1d. on 5 pf. green .. .. .. 4·00 4·00
a. "TOG" £130 £100
b. Thin "y" in "penny" .. .. 12·00 15·00

In the 20 pf. one half of a sheet was overprinted with the wide setting (3 mm), and the other half with the narrow setting (2 mm), so that vertical pairs from the middle of the sheet show the two varieties of the overprint.

TOGO
Anglo-French
Occupation
(6)

TOGO
ANGLO-FRENCH
OCCUPATION
(7)

TOGO
ANGLO-FRENCH
OCCUPATION
(8)

1915 (7 Jan). *Optd as T* **6**. *The words* "Anglo-French" *measure* 15 *mm instead of* 16 *mm as in T* **3**.

H29 3 pf. brown £6000 £2500
H30 5 pf. green £200 £130
a. "Occupation" omitted £6000
H31 10 pf. carmine £200 £130
a. No wmk .. .. † £7000
H32 20 pf. ultramarine £1400 £475
H32*a* 40 pf. black and carmine .. .. † £7500
H33 50 pf. black and purple/*buff* £9000 £6000

This printing was made on another batch of German Togo stamps, found at Sansane-Mangu.

Stamps of Gold Coast overprinted

1915 (May). *Stamps of Gold Coast, optd locally with T* **7** ("OCCUPATION" 14½ *mm long*).

H34 9 ½d. green 25 60
g. Opt double £250 £300
H35 10 1d. red 25 30
g. Opt double £225 £275
h. Opt inverted £130 £150
ha. Ditto. "TOGO" omitted ..
H36 11 2d. greyish slate 30 40
H37 9 2½d. bright blue 40 55
H38 11 3d. purple/*yellow* 65 80
a. White back .. .. .. 3·50 6·00
H40 6d. dull and bright purple .. .. 65 1·75
H41 9 1s. black/*green* .. .. .. 1·25 2·50
g. Opt double £350
H42 2s. purple and blue/*blue* .. .. 4·75 7·00
H43 11 2s. 6d. black and red/*blue* .. .. 4·50 8·50
H44 9 5s. green and red/*yellow* (*white back*) 8·00 12·00
H45 10s. green and red/*green* .. .. 29·00 38·00
H46 20s. purple and black/*red* £110 £120
H34/46 .. .. .. *Set of* 12 £140 £170

Varieties (*Nos. indicate positions in pane*).
A. *Small* "F" *in* "FRENCH" (25, 58 *and* 59).
B. *Thin* "G" *in* "TOGO" (24).
C. *No hyphen after* "ANGLO" (5).
D. *Two hyphens after* "ANGLO" (5).
E. "CUPATION" *for* "OCCUPATION" (33).
F. "CCUPATION" *for* "OCCUPATION" (57).

Prices are for unused. Used are worth more

		A	B	C	D	E	F
H34	½d.	1·50	3·00	3·00	†	80·00	42·00
H35	1d.	1·75	4·25	4·25	†	†	£100
	h. Inverted ..	£550	£1000	£1000	†	†	†
H36	2d.	1·75	5·50	48·00	25·00	†	£100
H37	2½d.	2·50	6·00	24·00	30·00	†	90·00
H38	3d.	2·50	6·00	30·00	†	†	£100
	a. White back	14·00	40·00	†	†	†	†
H40	6d.	4·25	8·00	†	†	†	£150
H41	1s.	4·25	9·00	†	†	†	80·00
H42	2s.	16·00	25·00	70·00	†	†	£200
H43	2s. 6d.. ..	18·00	30·00	80·00	†	†	£375
H44	5s.	25·00	42·00	£100	†	†	£200
H45	10s.	70·00	£120	†	†	†	£350
H46	20s.	£200	£300	†	†	†	£475

1916 (Apr). *London opt T* **8** ("OCCUPATION" 15 *mm long*). *Heavy type and thicker letters showing through on back.*

H47 9 ½d. green 15 40
H48 10 1d. red 15 25
H49 11 2d. greyish slate 35 45
H50 9 2½d. bright blue 45 90
H51 11 3d. purple/*yellow* 55 70
H52 6d. dull and bright purple .. .. 55 1·00
H53 9 1s. black/*green* .. .. .. 1·25 1·50
a. On blue-green, olive back .. 3·25 4·25
b. On emerald back £160 £225
H54 2s. purple and blue/*blue* .. .. 4·50 5·00
H55 11 2s. 6d. black and red/*blue* .. .. 4·50 5·50
H56 9 5s. green and red/*yellow* .. .. 7·50 15·00
a. On orange-buff .. .. .. 7·50 18·00
H57 10s. green and red/*green* .. .. 24·00 42·00
a. On blue-green, olive back .. 16·00 30·00
H58 20s. purple and black/*red* £110 £120
H47/58 .. .. .. *Set of* 12 £130 £160
H47/58 Optd "Specimen" .. .. *Set of* 12 £350

Tokelau Islands
see after New Zealand

Tonga

The Tongan Post Office was established in 1885 and FIJI 2d. and 6d. stamps are recorded in use until the arrival of Nos. 1/4.

PRICES FOR STAMPS ON COVER TO 1945

Nos. 1/4	*from* × 20
Nos. 5/9	*from* × 10
Nos. 10/28	*from* × 5
Nos. 29/32	*from* × 4
Nos. 33/7	*from* × 5
Nos. 38/54	*from* × 4
Nos. 55/63	*from* × 6
Nos. 64/70	*from* × 3
Nos. 71/87	*from* × 2

The Official stamps, Nos. O1/10, are very rare used on cover.

PROTECTORATE KINGDOM

King George I, 1845–93

1 King George I

2

(Eng Bock and Cousins. Plates made and typo Govt Ptg Office, Wellington)

1886–88. *W* **2**. *P* 12½ (*line*) *or* 12 × 11½ (*comb*)*.

1 1 1d. carmine (*p* 12½) (27.8.86) .. .. £180 6·00
a. Perf 12½ × 10 .. .. ..
b. Perf 12 × 11½ (15.7.87) .. .. 10·00 3·25
ba. Pale carmine (*p* 12 × 11½) .. 16·00 8·00
2 2d. pale violet (*p* 12½) (27.8.86) .. 30·00 10·00
a. Bright violet .. .. .. 45·00 3·50
b. Perf 12 × 11½ (15.7.87) .. .. 23·00 2·75
ba. Bright violet (*p* 12 × 11½) .. 23·00 3·00
3 6d. blue (*p* 12½) (9.10.86) .. .. 32·00 2·25
a. Perf 12 × 11½ (15.10.88) .. .. 28·00 2·25
ab. Dull blue (*p* 12 × 11½) .. .. 15·00 2·25
4 1s. pale green (*p* 12½) (9.10.86) .. 65·00 4·00
a. Deep green (*p* 12½) .. .. .. 70·00 2·25
b. Perf 12 × 11½ (15.10.88) .. .. 35·00 6·00
ba. Deep green (*p* 12 × 11½) .. .. 35·00 3·25

*See note after New Zealand, No. 186.

FOUR
PENCE.
(3)

EIGHT
PENCE.
(4)

(Surch Messrs Wilson & Horton, Auckland, N.Z.)

1891 (10 Nov). *Nos.* 1b *and* 2b *surch.*

5 3 4d. on 1d. carmine .. .. .. 2·00 10·00
a. No stop after "PENCE" .. .. 38·00 70·00
6 4 8d. on 2d. violet .. .. .. 35·00 60·00
a. Short "T" in "EIGHT" .. .. 90·00 £130

No. 5a occurred on R. 6/8 and 9, R. 10/11, all from the righthand pane.

1891 (23 Nov). *Optd with stars in upper right and lower left corners. P* 12½.

7 1 1d. carmine .. .. 35·00 40·00
a. Three stars £160
b. Four stars £225
c. Five stars £375
d. Perf 12 × 11½ £150
da. Three stars £300
db. Four stars £350
dc. Five stars £550
8 2d. violet.. .. .. .. 42·00 38·00
a. Perf 12 × 11½ £150

1892 (15 Aug). *W* **2**. *P* 12 × 11½.

9 1 6d. yellow-orange .. .. .. 11·00 18·00

5 Arms of Tonga

6 King George I

(Dies eng A. E. Cousins. Typo at Govt Printing Office, Wellington, N.Z.)

1892 (10 Nov). *W* **2**. *P* 12 × 11½.

10 5 1d. pale rose .. .. 12·00 16·00
a. Bright rose .. .. 12·00 16·00
b. Bisected diag (½d.) (1893) (on cover) .. † £650
11 6 2d. olive .. .. 11·00 15·00
12 5 4d. chestnut .. .. 27·00 42·00
13 6 8d. bright mauve .. .. .. 48·00 70·00
14 1s. brown .. .. 55·00 70·00
10/14 .. .. *Set of* 5 £140 £190

No. 10b was used to provide a 2½d. rate before the introduction of No. 16.

½d.
(7)

2½d.
(8)

FIVE
PENCE.
(9)

7½d.
(10)

1893. *Printed in new colours and surch with T* **7/10** *by Govt Printing Office, Wellington.* (*a*) *In carmine. P* 12½ (21 Aug).

15 5 ½d. on 1d. bright ultramarine .. .. 23·00 23·00
a. Surch omitted .. .. ..
16 6 2½d. on 2d. green.. .. .. .. 14·00 12·00
17 5 5d. on 4d. orange .. .. .. 4·00 6·50
18 6 7½d. on 8d. carmine .. .. .. 24·00 60·00

(*b*) *In black. P* 12 × 11½ (Nov)

19 5 ½d. on 1d. dull blue .. .. .. 45·00 48·00
20 6 2½d. on 2d. green.. .. .. .. 17·00 17·00
a. Surch double .. .. .. — £800

SURCHARGE.
HALF-PENNY
(11)

SURCHARGE,
2½d.
(12)

(Surch at the *Star* Office, Auckland, N.Z.)

1894 (June). *Surch with T* **11** *or* **12**.

21 5 ½d. on 4d. chestnut (B.).. .. .. 1·50 7·00
a. "SURCHARCE" .. .. .. 7·50 16·00
22 6 ½d. on 1s. brown .. .. .. 1·50 11·00
a. "SURCHARCE" .. .. .. 10·00 35·00
b. Surch double £350
c. Surch double with "SURCHARCE" £850

23 **6** 2½d. on 8d. bright mauve .. .. 5·00 9·50
a. No stop after "SURCHARGE" .. 30·00 40·00
b. "2½d." omitted .. .. ..
24 2½d. on 1s. green (No. 4*a*) .. .. 23·00 20·00
a. No stop after "SURCHARGE" .. 60·00
b. Perf 12 × 11½ .. .. .. 15·00 27·00
ba. No stop after "SURCHARGE" .. 55·00

Nos. 21/4 were surcharged in panes of 60 (6 × 10) with Nos. 21a and 22a occurring on R. 1/6, 3/6, 5/6, 8/6, and 10/6, 23a on R. 3/1–3 and 24a and 24ba on R. 6/3 and R. 7/3 or R. 7/1–2.

(Design resembling No. 11 litho and surch at *Star* Office, Auckland, N.Z.)

1895 (May). *As T* **6** *surch as T* **11** *and* **12**. *No wmk. P* 12.
25 **11** 1d. on 2d. pale blue (C.) .. .. 27·00 22·00
26 **12** 1½d. on 2d. pale blue (C.) .. .. 38·00 27·00
a. Perf 12 × 11 .. .. .. 35·00 27·00
27 2½d. on 2d. pale blue (C.)* .. .. 40·00 45·00
a. No stop after "SURCHARGE" .. £225 £225
28 7½d. on 2d. pale blue (C.) £180
a. Perf 12 × 11 .. .. .. 55·00 45·00

*The 2½d. on 2d. is the only value which normally has a stop after the word "SURCHARGE".
No. 27a occurs on R. 1/3 of the right-hand pane.

King George II, 1893–1918

13 King George II

Half-
Penny-
VAEUA OE PENI
(14)

(Litho *Star* Office, Auckland, N.Z.)

1895 (16 Aug). *No wmk. P* 12.
29 **13** 1d. olive-green .. .. 15·00 18·00
a. Bisected diagonally (½d.) (on cover) † £600
b. Imperf between (pair) .. .. — £5500
30 2½d. rose .. .. 20·00 20·00
a. Stop (flaw) after "POSTAGE" .. 50·00 50·00
31 5d. blue .. .. 12·00 28·00
a. Perf 12 × 11 .. .. .. 15·00 28·00
b. Perf 11 .. .. £325
32 7½d. orange-yellow .. .. .. 17·00 30·00
a. Yellow .. .. 17·00 30·00

1895 (Sept). *T* **13** *redrawn and surch. No wmk. P* 12.
33 **11** ½d. on 2½d. vermilion .. .. .. 30·00 32·00
a. "SURCHARCE" .. .. .. 65·00
b. Stop after "POSTAGE" .. .. 75·00
34 1d. on 2½d. vermilion .. .. .. 30·00 28·00
a. Stop after "POSTAGE" .. .. 55·00
35 **12** 7½d. on 2½d. vermilion .. .. .. 48·00 48·00
a. Stop after "POSTAGE" .. .. 80·00

In the ½d. surcharge there is a stop after "SURCHARGE" and not after "PENNY". In the 1d. and 7½d. the stop is after the value only.

1896 (May). *Nos.* 26a *and* 28a *with typewritten surcharge* "Half-Penny-", *in violet, and Tongan surcharge, in black, as T* **14**.
(A) *Tongan surch reading downwards.*
(B) *Tongan surch reading upwards.*

			A		B	
36	**6**	½d. on 1½d. on 2d.	£170	—	£180	—
		a. Perf 12	£170	—	£180	£200
		ab. "Haalf" (*p* 12)	†		£700	—
		c. "H" double	†		—	—
		d. Tongan surch omitted ..	†		£2000	—
37		½d. on 7½d. on 2d.	35·00	50·00	35·00	50·00
		a. "Hafl" for "Half" ..	£550	£600	†	
		b. "Hafl" ("Penny" omitted)	£800	—	†	
		c. "PPenny"	£275	—	†	
		d. Stops instead of hyphens	£250	—	£350	—
		e. "Halyf"	—	—	†	
		f. "Half-Penny-" inverted	£950	—	£1300	—
		g. No hyphen after "Penny"	—	—	†	
		h. "Hwlf"	†		—	—
		j. "Penny" double.. ..	†		—	—
		k. "Penny" twice, with "Half" on top of upper "Penny"..	†		—	—
		l. Capital "P" over small "p"	—	—	†	
		m. Perf 12	—	—	£275	—
		ma. No hyphen after "Half" (*p* 12)	—	—	†	
		mb. Tongan surch double ..	†		£950	—

There are variations in the relative positions of the words "Half" and "Penny", both vertically and horizontally.

15 Arms

16 Ovava Tree, Kana-Kubolu

17 King George II

18 Prehistoric Trilith at Haamonga

19 Bread Fruit

20 Coral

21 View of Haapai

22 Red Shining Parrot

23 View of Vavau Harbour

I No sword hilt

II Top of hilt showing

24 Tortoises (*upright*)

WATERMARKS. Stamps with W **24** upright show all the tortoise heads pointing upwards, or downwards if inverted. On stamps with sideways watermark the heads point upwards or downwards alternately.

(Recess D.L.R.)

1897 (1 June). *W* **24**. *P* 14.
38 **15** ½d. indigo .. ..
a. Wmk sideways 70 80
39 **16** 1d. black and scarlet .. .. ..
a. Wmk sideways 70 40
40 **17** 2d. sepia and bistre (I) .. .. ..
a. Wmk sideways .. .. .. 5·50 2·00
41 2d. sepia and bistre (II) .. .. 32·00 5·00
a. Wmk sideways .. .. .. 30·00 5·00
42 2d. grey and bistre (II) .. .. ..
a. Wmk sideways .. .. .. 4·00 70
43 2½d. black and blue .. .. .. 2·50 70
a. Wmk sideways .. .. .. 2·00 65
ab. No fraction bar in "½" .. .. 60·00 60·00
44 **18** 3d. black and yellow-green .. .. 2·00 2·75
a. Wmk sideways .. .. ..
45 **19** 4d. green and purple .. .. ..
a. Wmk sideways .. .. .. 3·75 4·00
46 **17** 5d. black and orange .. .. .. 13·00 9·00
47 **20** 6d. red .. ..
a. Wmk sideways .. .. .. 6·00 2·50
48 **17** 7½d. black and green .. .. .. 7·00 15·00
a. Centre inverted £3250
49 10d. black and lake .. .. .. 16·00 22·00
50 1s. black and red-brown .. .. 8·50 6·00
a. No hyphen before "TAHA" .. £140 £140
51 **21** 2s. black and ultramarine .. ..
a. Wmk sideways .. .. .. 18·00 20·00
52 **22** 2s. 6d. deep purple .. .. .. 38·00 25·00
a. Wmk sideways .. .. .. 38·00 25·00
53 **23** 5s. black and brown-red .. .. 24·00 22·00
a. Wmk sideways .. .. ..
38/52 .. .. *Set of* 14 £130 £120

The 1d., 3d. and 4d. are known bisected and used for half their value.

T – L
1 June, 1899.
(25)

26 Queen Salote

1899 (1 June). *Royal Wedding. No.* 39a *optd with T* **25** *at* "Star" *Office, Auckland, N.Z.*
54 **16** 1d. black and scarlet .. .. .. 24·00 42·00
a. "1889" for "1899" (R. 8/1, 8/4) .. £200 £275
b. Wmk upright .. .. ..

The Letters "T L" stand for Taufa'ahau, the King's family name, and Lavinia, the bride.

Queen Salote, 1918–65

Die I

Die II

(Recess D.L.R.)

1920–37. *W* **24** (*sideways*). *P* 14.
55 **15** ½d. yellow-green (1934).. .. .. 20 80
56 **26** 1½d. grey-black (1935) .. .. .. 20 1·50
57 2d. slate-purple and violet .. .. 2·50 10·00
57*a* 2d. black and dull purple (Die I) (1924) 4·00 65
b. Die II (1937) .. .. .. 2·50 2·00
58 2½d. black and blue .. .. .. 2·50 14·00
59 2½d. bright ultramarine (1934) 35 40
60 5d. black and orange-vermilion .. 3·25 3·25
61 7½d. black and yellow-green .. .. 1·75 1·75
62 10d. black and lake .. .. .. 1·25 4·50
63 1s. black and red-brown .. .. 1·25 1·50
55/63 .. .. *Set of* 10 14·00 35·00
55/63 Optd/Perf "Specimen" .. *Set of* 9 £160

In Die II the ball of the "2" is larger and the word "PENI-E-UA" is re-engraved and slightly shorter; the "U" has a spur on the left side.

TWO PENCE

PENI-E-UA
(27)

TWO PENCE

PENI-E-UA
(28)

1923 (20 Oct)–**24**. *Nos.* 46, 48/9, 50, 51/2 *and* 53a *surch as T* **27** (*vert stamps*) *or* **28** (*horiz stamps*).
64 2d. on 5d. black and orange (B.) 65 85
65 2d. on 7½d. black and green (B.) .. .. 12·00 20·00
66 2d. on 10d. black and lake (B.) .. .. 4·75 20·00
67 2d. on 1s. black and red-brown (B.) .. 22·00 22·00
a. No hyphen before "TAHA" £275
68 2d. on 2s. black and ultramarine (R.) ..
a. Wmk sideways .. .. 3·00 4·50
69 2d. on 2s. 6d. deep purple (R.) .. .. 12·00 6·50
70 2d. on 5s. black and brown-red (R.) ..
a. Wmk sideways .. .. 2·00 2·50
64/70 .. .. *Set of* 7 50·00 70·00

29 Queen Salote

(Recess D.L.R.)

1938 (12 Oct). 20*th Anniv of Queen Salote's Accession. Tablet at foot dated* "1918–1938". *W* **24**. *P* 14.
71 **29** 1d. black and scarlet .. .. .. 55 1·75
72 2d. black and purple .. .. .. 3·50 1·50
73 2½d. black and ultramarine .. .. 3·75 2·00
71/3 .. .. *Set of* 3 7·00 4·75
71/3 Perf "Specimen" .. .. *Set of* 3 65·00

For Silver Jubilee issue in a similar design, see Nos. 83/87.

Die III

(Recess D.L.R.)

1942–49. *Wmk Mult Script CA (sideways on* 5s.). *P* 14.

No.	Type	Description	Unused	Used
74	**15**	½d. yellow-green	15	70
75	**16**	1d. black and scarlet	20	45
76	**26**	2d. black and purple (Die II)	15	35
		a. Die III (4.49)	3·50	5·00
77		2½d. bright ultramarine	15	25
78	**18**	3d. black and yellow-green	15	25
79	**20**	6d. red	25	50
80	**26**	1s. black and red-brown	15	70
81	**22**	2s. 6d. deep purple	10·00	14·00
82	**23**	5s. black and brown-red	11·00	22·00
74/82		*Set of* 9	20·00	35·00
74/82 Perf "Specimen"		*Set of* 9	£160	

In Die III the foot of the "2" is longer than in Die II and extends towards the right beyond the curve of the loop; the letters of "PENI-E-UA" are taller and differently shaped.

UANIMA TA'U 'OE PULE 'A 'ENE 'AFIO 1918-1943

30

(Recess D.L.R.)

1944 (25 Jan). *Silver Jubilee of Queen Salote's Accession. As T* **29**, *but inscr* "1918–1943" *at foot, as T* **30**. *Wmk Mult Script CA. P* 14.

No.	Description	Unused	Used
83	1d. black and carmine	10	15
84	2d. black and purple	10	15
85	3d. black and green	10	15
86	6d. black and orange	10	30
87	1s. black and brown	10	30
83/7	*Set of* 5	35	95
83/7 Perf "Specimen"	*Set of* 5	70·00	

1949 (10 Oct). *75th Anniv of Universal Postal Union. As Nos.* 114/17 *of Antigua.*

No.	Description	Unused	Used
88	2½d. ultramarine	20	10
89	3d. olive	40	55
90	6d. carmine-red	40	20
91	1s. red-brown	40	35
88/91	*Set of* 4	1·25	1·00

31 Queen Salote **33**

32 Queen Salote

(Photo Waterlow)

1950 (1 Nov). *Queen Salote's Fiftieth Birthday. Wmk Mult Script CA. P* 12½.

No.	Type	Description	Unused	Used
92	**31**	1d. carmine	15	20
93	**32**	5d. green	15	30
94	**33**	1s. violet	15	55
92/4		*Set of* 3	40	95

34 Map **35** Palace, Nuku'alofa

(Recess Waterlow)

1951 (2 July). *50th Anniv of Treaty of Friendship between Great Britain and Tonga. T* **34/5** *and similar designs. Wmk Mult Script CA. P* 12½ (3*d*.), 13 × 13½ (½*d*.), 13½ × 13 (*others*).

No.	Description	Unused	Used
95	½d. green	20	25
96	1d. black and carmine	10	20
97	2½d. green and brown	20	20
98	3d. yellow and bright blue	25	25
99	5d. carmine and green	25	25
100	1s. yellow-orange and violet	25	25
95/100	*Set of* 6	1·10	1·25

Designs: *Horiz*—2½d. Beach scene; 5d. Flag; 1s. Arms of Tonga and G.B. *Vert*—3d. H.M.N.Z.S. *Bellona*.

40 Royal Palace, Nuku'alofa **43** Swallows' Cave, Vava'u

52 Queen Salote **53** Arms of Tonga

(Des J. Berry. Centre litho, frame recess (£1), recess (others) B.W.)

1953 (1 July). *T* **40**, **43**, **52/3** *and similar designs. W* **24**. *P* 11 × 11½ (*vert*) *or* 11½ × 11 (*horiz*).

No.	Description	Unused	Used
101	1d. black and red-brown	10	10
102	1½d. blue and emerald	10	10
103	2d. deep turquoise-green and black	20	10
104	3d. blue and deep bluish green	20	10
105	3½d. yellow and carmine-red	20	20
106	4d. yellow and deep rose-carmine	35	10
107	5d. blue and red-brown	25	10
108	6d. black and deep blue	25	10
109	8d. emerald and deep reddish violet	30	15
110	1s. blue and black	30	10
111	2s. sage-green and brown	45	60
112	5s. orange-yellow and slate-lilac	7·50	2·75
113	10s. yellow and black	5·50	3·00
114	£1 yellow, scarlet, ultramarine & dp brt bl	8·00	6·50
101/14	*Set of* 14	21·00	12·00

Designs: *Horiz (as T* **40**)—1½d. Shore fishing with throw-net; 2d. *Hifofua* and *Aoniu* (ketches); 3½d. Map of Tongatapu; 4d. Vava'u Harbour; 5d. Post Office, Nuku'alofa; 6d. Aerodrome, Fua'amotu; 8d. Nuku'alofa wharf; 2s. Lifuka, Ha'apai; 5s. Mutiny of the *Bounty*. *Vert (as T* **43**)—1s. Map of Tonga Islands.

54 Stamp of 1886 **55** Whaling Ship and Whaleboat

(Des D. M. Bakeley. Photo Harrison)

1961 (1 Dec). *75th Anniv of Tongan Postal Service. T* **54/5** *and similar horiz designs. W* **24**. *P* 14½ × 13½.

No.	Description	Unused	Used
115	1d. carmine and brown-orange	10	10
116	2d. ultramarine	20	10
117	4d. blue-green	10	10
118	5d. violet	25	10
119	1s. red-brown	25	10
115/19	*Set of* 5	80	20

Designs:—4d. Queen Salote and Post Office, Nuku'alofa; 5d. *Aoniu II* (inter-island freighter); 1s. Mailplane over Tongatapu.

1862
TAU'ATĀINA
EMANCIPATION
1962

(59)

60 "Protein Foods"

1962 (7 Feb). *Centenary of Emancipation. Nos.* 101, 104, 107/10, 112, 117 *optd with T* **59** (*No.* 126 *surch also*), *in red, by R. S. Wallbank, Govt Printer.*

No.	Description	Unused	Used
120	1d. black and red-brown	10	10
121	4d. blue-green	10	15
122	5d. blue and red-brown	15	15
123	6d. black and deep blue	15	20
124	8d. emerald and deep reddish violet	30	25
125	1s. blue and black	15	20
	a. Opt inverted	£350	£190
126	2s. on 3d. blue and deep bluish green	40	55
	a. Missing fraction-bar in surch	10·00	
127	5s. orange-yellow and slate-lilac	50	85
	a. Opt inverted	£180	£250
120/127	*Set of* 8	1·75	2·25

(Des M. Goaman. Photo Harrison)

1963 (4 June). *Freedom from Hunger. W* **24**. *P* 14 × 14½.

No.	Type	Description	Unused	Used
128	**60**	11d. ultramarine	20	15

OMNIBUS ISSUES

Details, together with prices for complete sets, of the various Omnibus issues from the 1935 Silver Jubilee series to date are included in a special section following Zululand at the end of the catalogue.

61 Coat of Arms

62 Queen Salote

63 Queen Salote

(Des Ida West. Die-cut Walsall)

1963 (17 June). *First Polynesian Gold Coinage Commemoration. Circular designs. Embossed on gold foil, backed with paper, inscr overall* "TONGA THE FRIENDLY ISLANDS". *Imperf.*

No.	Type	Description	Unused	Used
		(a) Postage. ¼ *koula coin. Diameter* 1⅝ *in.*		
129	**61**	1d. carmine	10	10
130	**62**	2d. deep blue	10	10
131	**61**	6d. blue-green	15	15
132	**62**	9d. bright purple	15	15
133	**61**	1s. 6d. violet	20	25
134	**62**	2s. light emerald	25	30
		(b) Air. (i) ½ *koula coin. Diam* 2⅛ *in.*		
135	**63**	10d. carmine	20	20
136	**61**	11d. blue-green	20	20
137	**63**	1s. 1d. deep blue	20	20
		(ii) 1 *koula coin. Diam* 3⅛ *in.*		
138	**63**	2s. 1d. bright purple	30	30
139	**61**	2s. 4d. light emerald	35	35
140	**63**	2s. 9d. violet	35	40
129/140 *and* O17		*Set of* 13	5·00	6·00

Examples of a 9d. Postage value in the design of the 1s. 6d. exists, but these have been identified as proofs.

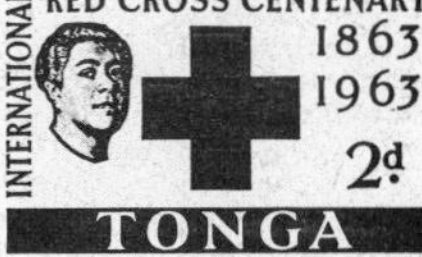

64 Red Cross Emblem

(Des V. Whiteley. Litho B.W.)

1963 (7 Oct). *Red Cross Centenary. W* **24**. *P* 13½.

No.	Type	Description	Unused	Used
141	**64**	2d. red and black	10	10
142		11d. red and blue	20	15

65 Queen Salote

66 Map of Tongatapu

(Des M. Meers. Die-cut Walsall)

1964 (19 Oct). *Pan-Pacific South-East Asia Woman's Association Meeting, Nuku'alofa. Embossed on gold foil, backed with paper inscr overall* "TONGA THE FRIENDLY ISLANDS". *Imperf.*

No.	Type	Description	Unused	Used
		(a) Postage		
143	**65**	3d. pink	10	10
144		9d. light blue	10	10
145		2s. yellow-green	15	20
146		5s. lilac	30	40
		(b) Air		
147	**66**	10d. blue-green	10	10
148		1s. 2d. black	15	15
149		3s. 6d. cerise	20	25
150		6s. 6d. violet	35	50
143/150		*Set of* 8	1·25	1·60

(67)

1965 (18 Mar). *"Gold Coin" stamps of* 1963 *surch as T* **67** *by Walsall Lithographic Co. New figures of value in gold; obliterating colours shown in brackets. (a) Postage.*

No.	Type	Description	Unused	Used
151	**61**	1s. 3d. on 1s. 6d. violet (R.)	15	15
152	**62**	1s. 9d. on 9d. bright purple (W.)	15	20
153	**61**	2s. 6d. on 6d. blue-green (R.)	20	35
154		5s. on 1d. carmine	14·00	16·00
155	**62**	5s. on 2d. deep blue	2·50	3·00
156		5s. on 2s. light emerald	60	75
		(b) Air		
157	**63**	2s. 3d. on 10d. carmine	15	25
158	**61**	2s. 9d. on 11d. blue-green (W.)	20	35
159	**63**	4s. 6d. on 2s. 1d. bright purple (R.)	10·00	12·00
160	**61**	4s. 6d. on 2s. 4d. light emerald (R.)	10·00	12·00
161	**63**	4s. 6d. on 2s. 9d. violet (R.)	7·00	7·00
151/161 *and* O18		*Set of* 12	42·00	48·00

King Taufa'ahau IV, 16 December 1965

1866-1966
TUPOU COLLEGE
& SECONDARY
EDUCATION

(68)

AIRMAIL
1866 CENTENARY 1966
TUPOU COLLEGE
&
SECONDARY EDUCATION
10d XX

(69)

1966 (18 June). *Centenary of Tupou College and Secondary Education. Nos.* 115/16 *and* 118/19 *optd or surch. (a) Postage. As T* **68**.

No.	Description	Unused	Used
162	1d. carmine and brown-orange (P.)	10	10
163	3d. on 1d. carmine and brown-orange (P.)	10	10
	a. Misplaced "3d" (R. 2/5)	1·50	
164	6d. on 2d. ultramarine (R.)	10	10
165	1s. 2d. on 2d. ultramarine (R.)	10	10
166	2s. on 2d. ultramarine (R.)	15	10
167	3s. on 2d. ultramarine (R.)	15	15
	(b) Air. As T **69**		
168	5d. violet	10	10
169	10d. on 1d. carmine and brown-orange	10	10
170	1s. red-brown	10	10
171	2s. 9d. on 2d. ultramarine	15	15
	a. Sideways second "X" (R. 3/4)	6·00	
172	3s. 6d. on 5d. violet	15	15
	a. Sideways second "X" (R. 3/4)	6·00	
173	4s. 6d. on 1s. red-brown	20	15
	a. Sideways second "X" (R. 3/4)	6·00	
162/173 and O19/20	*Set of* 14	2·00	1·75

On No. 163a the "d" is 20 mm from the "X" instead of the normal 22 mm.

(70)

(71)

1966 (16 Dec). *Queen Salote Commemoration. "Women's Association" stamps of* 1964 *optd as T* **70/1**, *or surch also, by Walsall Lithographic Co. Inscriptions and new figures of value in first colour and obliterating shapes in second colour given.*

No.	Type	Description	Unused	Used
		(a) Postage. Optd as T **70**		
174	**65**	3d. (silver and ultramarine)	10	10
175		5d. on 9d. (silver and black)	10	10
176		9d. (silver and black)	10	10
177		1s. 7d. on 3d. (silver and ultramarine)	15	15
178		3s. 6d. on 9d. (silver and black)	30	20
179		6s. 6d. on 3d. (silver and ultramarine)	50	30
		(b) Air. Optd as T **71**		
180	**66**	10d. (silver and black)	10	10
181		1s. 2d. (black and gold)	10	10
182		4s. on 10d. (silver and black)	35	20
183		5s. 6d. on 1s. 2d. (black and gold)	45	30
184		10s. 6d. on 1s. 2d. (gold and black)	65	45
174/184		*Set of* 11	2·50	1·75

(New Currency. 100 seniti = 1 pa'anga)

1 SENITI 1 (72)

10 Seniti 10 (73)

1967 (25 Mar). *Decimal currency. Various stamps surch as T* **72/3**.

No.	Description	Unused	Used
185	1 s. on 1d. (No. 101)	10	10
186	2 s. on 4d. (No. 106)	10	10
187	3 s. on 5d. (No. 107)	10	10
188	4 s. on 5d. (No. 107)	30	30
189	5 s. on 3½d. (No. 105)	10	10
190	6 s. on 8d. (No. 109)	10	10
191	7 s. on 1½d. (No. 102)	10	10
192	8 s. on 6d. (No. 108)	10	10
193	9 s. on 3d. (No. 104)	15	15
194	10 s. on 1s. (No. 110)	15	15
195	11 s. on 3d. on 1d. (No. 163)	15	20
	a. Misplaced "3d" (R. 2/5)	2·25	
196	21 s. on 3s. on 2d. (No. 167)	25	35
197	23 s. on 1d. (No. 101)	25	35
198	30 s. on 2s. (No. 111)* (R.)	1·25	1·75
199	30 s. on 2s. (No. 111)* (R.)	1·50	2·00
200	50 s. on 6d. (No. 108) (R.)	85	1·25
201	60 s. on 2d. (No. 103) (R.)	1·25	1·75
185/201 and O21	*Set of* 18	7·50	10·00

The above surcharges come in a variety of types and sizes. *No. 198 has the surcharged value expressed horizontally; No. 199 has the figures "30" above and below "SENITI".

74 Coat of Arms (reverse)

75 King Taufa'ahau IV (obverse)

(Die-cut Walsall)

1967 (4 July). *Coronation of King Taufa'ahau IV. Circular designs. Embossed on palladium foil, backed with paper inscr overall* "The Friendly Islands Tonga", *etc. Imperf.*

Sizes

(a) Diameter 1½ *in.* — *(d) Diameter* $2^3/_{10}$ *in.*
(b) Diameter $1^7/_{10}$ *in.* — *(e) Diameter* $2^7/_{10}$ *in.*
(c) Diameter 2 *in.* — *(f) Diameter* $2^9/_{10}$ *in.*

No.	Type	Description	Unused	Used
		(a) Postage		
202	**74**	1 s. orange and greenish blue *(b)*	10	10
203	**75**	2 s. greenish blue and deep magenta *(c)*	10	10
204	**74**	4 s. emerald and bright purple *(d)*	10	10
205	**75**	15 s. turquoise and violet *(e)*	25	25
206	**74**	28 s. black and bright purple *(a)*	50	40
207	**75**	50 s. carmine-red and ultramarine *(c)*	85	65
208	**74**	1 p. blue and carmine *(f)*	1·50	1·10
		(b) Air		
209	**75**	7 s. carmine-red and black *(b)*	10	10
210	**74**	9 s. brown-purple and emerald *(c)*	10	10
211	**75**	11 s. greenish blue and orange *(d)*	15	15
212	**74**	21 s. black and emerald *(e)*	30	30
213	**75**	23 s. bright purple and light emerald *(a)*	40	35
214	**74**	29 s. ultramarine and emerald *(c)*	50	40
215	**75**	2 p. bright purple and orange *(f)*	2·00	1·25
202/15		*Set of* 14	6·00	4·50

The commemorative coins depicted in reverse (Type **74**) are inscribed in various denominations as follows: 1 s.—"20 SENITI"; 4 s.—"PA'ANGA"; 9 s.—"50 SENITI"; 21 s.—"TWO PA'ANGA"; 28 s.—"QUARTER HAU"; 29 s.—"HALF HAU"; 1 p. "HAU".

The
Friendly Islands
welcome the
United States
Peace Corps
S

(76)

1967 (15 Dec). *Arrival of U.S. Peace Corps in Tonga. As Nos.* 101/14, *but imperf in different colours and surch as T* **76**.

No.	Description	Unused	Used
	(a) Postage.		
216	1 s. on 1d. black and orange-yellow	10	10
217	2 s. on 2d. ultramarine and carmine-red	10	10
218	3 s. on 3d. chestnut and yellow	10	10
219	4 s. on 4d. reddish violet and yellow	10	10
220	5 s. on 5d. green and yellow	10	10
221	10 s. on 1s. carmine-red and yellow	10	10
222	20 s. on 2s. claret and new blue	15	15
223	50 s. on 5s. sepia and orange-yellow	30	35
224	1 p. on 10s. orange-yellow	50	55
	(b) Air		
225	11 s. on 3½d. ultramarine (R.)	10	10
226	21 s. on 1½d. emerald	20	20
227	23 s. on 3½d. ultramarine	20	20
216/27 *and* O26/8	*Set of* 15	2·75	3·00

On Nos. 219 and 224 the opt is smaller, and in four lines instead of five. On Nos. 216/20 the surcharge takes the form of an alteration to the currency name as in T **76**.

2 SENITI 2 (77)

10 SENITI 10 (78)

1968 (6 Apr). *Various stamps surch as T* **77/8**.

No.	Description	Unused	Used
	(a) Postage		
228	1 s. on 1d. (No. 101) (R.)	10	10
229	2 s. on 4d. (No. 106)	10	10
230	3 s. on 3d. (No. 104) (B.)	10	10
231	4 s. on 5d. (No. 107) (R.)	10	10
232	5 s. on 2d. (No. 103) (R.)	10	10
233	6 s. on 6d. (No. 108) (R.)	10	10
234	7 s. on 1½d. (No. 102) (R.)	10	10
235	8 s. on 8d. (No. 109) (R.)	10	10
236	9 s. on 3½d. (No. 105)	20	20
237	10 s. on 1s. (No. 110) (R.)	20	20
238	20 s. on 5s. (No. 112) (R.)	40	40
239	2 p. on 2s. (No. 111) (R.)	1·50	1·50
	(b) Air. Surch as T **78** *with* "AIRMAIL" *added*		
240	11 s. on 10s. (No. 113) (R.)	25	25
241	21 s. on 10s. (No. 113) (R.)	40	40
242	23 s. on 10s. (No. 113) (R.)	40	40
228/42 *and* O22/5	*Set of* 19	6·50	6·50

H M'S BIRTHDAY 4 JULY 1968

(79)

Friendly Islands
Field & Track Trials
South Pacific Games
Port Moresby
1969
S

(80)

1968 (4 July). *50th Birthday of King Taufa'ahua IV. Nos.* 202/15 *optd as T* **79**. *(a) Postage.*

No.	Type	Description	Unused	Used
243	**74**	1 s. orange and greenish blue *(b)* (R.)	10	10
244	**75**	2 s. greenish blue & dp magenta *(b)* (B.)	10	10
245	**74**	4 s. emerald and bright purple *(d)* (R.)	10	10
246	**75**	15 s. turquoise and violet *(e)* (B.)	25	15
247	**74**	28 s. black and bright purple *(a)* (R.)	55	30
248	**75**	50 s. carmine-red and ultramarine *(c)* (B.)	1·00	60
249	**74**	1 p. blue and carmine *(f)* (R.)	2·25	1·25
		(b) Air		
250	**75**	7 s. carmine-red and black *(b)* (B.)	10	10
251	**74**	9 s. brown-purple and emerald *(c)* (R.)	15	10
252	**75**	11 s. greenish blue and orange *(d)* (B.)	15	10
253	**74**	21 s. black and emerald *(e)* (R.)	40	25
		a. Opt (gold only) double	£275	

254 **75** 23 s. bright purple & lt emerald (a) (B.) .. 40 25
255 **74** 29 s. ultramarine and emerald (c) (R.) .. 65 35
256 **75** 2 p. bright purple and orange (f) (B.) .. 4·50 2·00
243/56 *and* O29/32 .. .. *Set of* 18 17·00 9·00

The overprints vary in size, but are all crescent-shaped as Type **79** and inscribed "H.M'S BIRTHDAY 4 JULY 1968" (Type **79**) or "HIS MAJESTY'S 50th BIRTHDAY" (others).

1968 (19 Dec). *South Pacific Games Field and Track Trials, Port Moresby, New Guinea. Nos.* 101/14, *but imperf, in different colours and surch as T* **80**. (a) *Postage.*
257 5 s. on 5d. green and yellow (R.) 10 10
258 10 s. on 1s. carmine-red and yellow 10 10
259 15 s. on 2s. claret and new blue 15 15
260 25 s. on 2d. ultramarine and carmine-red .. 15 15
261 50 s. on 1d. black and orange-yellow 30 30
262 75 s. on 10s. orange-yellow (G.) 45 45

(b) *Air*
263 6 s. on 6d. black and yellow* 10 10
264 7 s. on 4d. reddish violet and yellow 10 10
265 8 s. on 8d. black and greenish yellow 10 10
a. Surch 11½ mm as on 6d. .. .. † 90·00
266 9 s. on 1½d. emerald 10 10
267 11 s. on 3d. chestnut and yellow 10 10
268 21 s. on 3½d. ultramarine 15 15
269 38 s. on 5s. sepia and orange-yellow 20 20
270 1 p. on 10s. orange-yellow 50 50
257/70 *and* O33/4 .. .. .. *Set of* 16 2·75 2·75

*On No. 263 the surcharge is smaller (11½ mm wide).

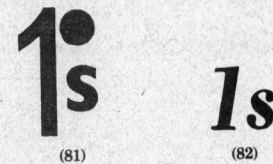

1s (81) 1s (82)

1969. *Emergency Provisionals. Various stamps (Nos. 273/6 are imperf and in different colours) surch as T* **81** *or* **82**. (a) *Postage.*
271 1 s. on 1s. 2d. on 2d. ultramarine (No. 165) .. 65 65
272 1 s. on 2s. on 2d. ultramarine (No. 166) .. 65 65
273 1 s. on 6d. black and yellow (as No. 108) .. 25 25
274 2 s. on 3½d. ultramarine (as No. 105) .. 30 30
275 3 s. on 1½d. emerald (as No. 102) .. 30 30
276 4 s. on 8d. black & greenish yell (as No. 109) 50 50

(b) *Air. Nos.* 171/3 *surch with T* **82**
277 1 s. on 2s. 9d. on 2d. ultramarine .. 65 65
a. Sideways second "X" (R. 3/4) .. 5·50
278 1 s. on 3s. 6d. on 5d. violet .. 65 65
a. Sideways second "X" (R. 3/4) .. 5·50
279 1 s. on 4s. 6d. on 1s. red-brown .. 65 65
a. Sideways second "X" (R. 3/4) .. 5·50
271/9 .. .. *Set of* 9 4·25 4·25

SELF-ADHESIVE ISSUES. From No. 280 until No. 922 all stamps were manufactured by Walsall Security Printers Ltd and are self-adhesive. The backing paper is separated by roulette or perforations (from No. 780 onwards), and shows on its reverse the words "*TONGA where time begins*", or, from No. 568 onwards, various texts or illustrations. This also applies to the Official stamps.

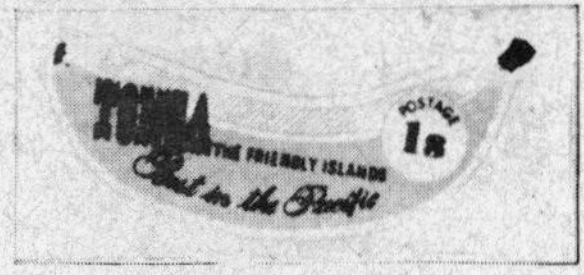

83 Banana

1969 (21 Apr). *Coil stamps.*
280 **83** 1 s. scarlet, black and greenish yellow .. 30 35
281 2 s. brt green, black & greenish yellow .. 40 45
282 3 s. violet, black and greenish yellow .. 45 50
283 4 s. ultramarine, black & greenish yell 55 60
284 5 s. bronze-green, black & greenish yell 75 80
280/4 .. .. *Set of* 5 2·25 2·40

Nos. 280/4 were produced in rolls of 200, each even stamp having a number applied to the front of the backing paper, with the usual inscription on the reverse.

See also Nos. 325/9, 413/17 and 675/89.

84 Putting the Shot **86** Oil Derrick and Map

1969 (13 Aug). *Third South Pacific Games, Port Moresby. T* **84** *and similar design.* (a) *Postage.*
285 **84** 1 s. black, red and buff 10 10
286 3 s. bright green, red and buff 10 10
287 6 s. blue, red and buff 10 10
288 10 s. bluish violet, red and buff 10 10
289 30 s. blue, red and buff 15 20

(b) *Air*
290 – 9 s. black, violet and orange 10 10
291 – 11 s. black, ultramarine and orange .. 10 10
292 – 20 s. black, bright green and orange .. 15 15
293 – 60 s. black, cerise and orange 45 55
294 – 1 p. black, blue-green and orange .. 70 80
285/94 *and* O35/6 .. .. .. *Set of* 12 2·75 3·25

Design:—9, 11, 20, 60 s., 1 p. Boxing.

1969 (23 Dec). *First Oil Search in Tonga. T* **86** *and similar vert design.*

(a) *Postage*
295 **86** 3 s. multicoloured 10 10
296 7 s. multicoloured 15 15
297 20 s. multicoloured 40 40
298 25 s. multicoloured 45 45
299 35 s. multicoloured 70 70

(b) *Air*
300 – 9 s. multicoloured 20 20
301 – 10 s. multicoloured 20 20
302 – 24 s. multicoloured 45 45
303 – 29 s. multicoloured 50 50
304 – 38 s. multicoloured 70 70
295/304 *and* O37/8 .. .. .. *Set of* 12 7·00 7·00

Design:—Nos. 300/4, Oil derrick and island of Tongatapu.

87 Members of the British and Tongan Royal Families

1970 (7 Mar). *Royal Visit. T* **87** *and similar design. Multicoloured.*

(a) *Postage*
305 **87** 3 s. multicoloured 20 10
306 5 s. multicoloured 25 10
307 10 s. multicoloured 40 20
308 25 s. multicoloured .. .. .. 1·00 55
309 50 s. multicoloured .. .. .. 1·75 90

(b) *Air*
310 – 7 s. multicoloured 35 15
311 – 9 s. multicoloured 40 20
312 – 24 s. multicoloured .. .. .. 1·00 55
313 – 29 s. multicoloured .. .. .. 1·25 60
314 – 38 s. multicoloured .. .. .. 1·50 80
305/14 *and* O39/41 .. .. .. *Set of* 13 17·00 9·00

Design:—Nos. 310/14, Queen Elizabeth II and King Taufu'ahau Tupou IV.

89 Book, Tongan Rulers and Flag

1970 (4 June). *Entry into British Commonwealth. T* **89** *and similar design.* (a) *Postage.*
315 **89** 3 s. multicoloured 10 10
316 7 s. multicoloured 15 15
317 15 s. multicoloured 25 20
318 25 s. multicoloured 35 25
319 50 s. multicoloured 60 50

(b) *Air*
320 – 9 s. turquoise-blue, gold and scarlet .. 15 15
321 – 10 s. bright purple, gold and greenish blue 15 15
322 – 24 s. olive-yellow, gold and green .. 35 30
323 – 29 s. new blue, gold and orange-red .. 40 30
324 – 38 s. deep orange-yellow, gold & brt emer 50 40
315/24 *and* O42/4 .. .. .. *Set of* 13 5·00 4·50

Design: *"Star" shaped* (44 × 51 *mm*)—Nos. 320/4, King Taufa'ahau Tupou IV.

90 Coconut

1970 (9 June). *Coil stamps.* (a) *As T* **83** *but colours changed.*
325 **83** 1 s. greenish yellow, bright purple & blk 15 20
326 2 s. greenish yellow, ultramarine & black 20 30
327 3 s. greenish yellow, chocolate and black 25 30
328 4 s. greenish yellow, emerald and black 25 30
329 5 s. greenish yellow, orge-red & bl .. 30 35

(b) *T* **90**. *Multicoloured; colour of face value given*
330 **90** 6 s. rose-carmine 35 40
331 7 s. bright purple 40 45
332 8 s. bluish violet 45 55
333 9 s. turquoise 55 65
334 10 s. pale orange 55 65
325/34 .. .. *Set of* 10 3·00 3·75

Nos. 325/34 and O45/54 were produced in rolls of 200, each even stamp having a number applied to the front of the backing paper, with the usual inscription on the reverse.

91 "Red Cross"

(Litho (postage) or litho and die-stamped (air))

1970 (17 Oct). *Centenary of British Red Cross. T* **91** *and similar "cross" shaped design.* (a) *Postage.*
335 **91** 3 s. vermilion, black and light green .. 10 10
336 7 s. vermilion, black and ultramarine .. 15 15
337 15 s. vermilion and bright purple .. 30 30
338 25 s. vermilion, black and turquoise-blue 50 50
339 75 s. vermilion and deep red-brown .. 2·25 2·25

(b) *Air*
340 – 9 s. vermilion and silver 20 20
341 – 10 s. vermilion and bright purple .. 20 20
342 – 18 s. vermilion and green 35 35
343 – 38 s. vermilion and ultramarine .. .. 1·00 1·00
344 – 1 p. vermilion and turquoise-blue .. 2·75 2·75
335/44 *and* O55/7 .. .. .. *Set of* 13 12·00 12·00

Design: *As T* **91**—Nos. 340/4 as Nos. 335/9 but with inscription rearranged and coat of arms omitted.

On Nos. 335/6 and 338 the black colour is produced as a composite of the other two colours used.

(92)

(93)

1971 (30 Jan). *Fifth Death Anniv of Queen Salote. Nos.* 174/84 *surch as T* **92/3**. *Obliterating shapes in black; inscriptions and figures of value in colour given.* (a) *Postage. Surch as T* **92**.
345 **65** 2 s. on 5d. on 9d. (silver) 10 10
346 3 s. on 9d. (orange-red) 10 10
347 5 s. on 3d. (bright green) 15 15
348 15 s. on 3s. 6d. on 9d. (orange-brown) .. 45 35
a. Surch double .. .. — 30·00
349 25 s. on 6s. 6d. on 3d. (purple) .. 80 65
350 50 s. on 1s. 7d. on 3d. (gold) .. .. 1·75 1·25

(b) *Air. Surch as T* **93**
351 **66** 9 s. on 10d. (silver) 30 20
352 24 s. on 4s. on 10d. (orange-brown) .. 80 60
353 29 s. on 5s. 6d. on 1s. 2d. (orange-red) .. 90 80
354 38 s. on 10s. 6d. on 1s. 2d. (bright green) 1·40 1·00
345/54 *and* O58/61 .. .. .. *Set of* 14 15·00 11·50

3s■

(94)

HONOURING
JAPANESE
POSTAL
CENTENARY
1871-1971
15s■
(95)

1971 (17 Apr). *"Philatokyo 1971" Stamp Exhibition. As Nos.* 101/2, 106 *and* 109/11, *but imperf, colours changed and surch as T* **94** *(Nos.* 355/6, 358/61 *and* 363), *as T* **95** *(Nos.* 357, 362) *or with similar surcharge in four lines (No.* 364). (a) *Postage.*
355 3 s. on 8d. blk & greenish yellow (Blk. & R.) 10 10
356 7 s. on 4d. reddish violet & yellow (Blk. & R.) 10 10
357 15 s. on 1s. carmine, red and yellow 20 20
358 25 s. on 1d. black & orange-yellow (Blk. & R.) 30 30
359 75 s. on 2s. claret & new blue (Blk. & R.) .. 85 85

(b) Air. Additionally surch "AIRMAIL"

No.	Type	Description	Unused	Used
360		9 s. on 1½d. emerald (Blk. and R.) ..	10	10
361		10 s. on 4d. reddish violet & yellow (Blk. & R.)	10	10
362		18 s. on 1s. carmine-red and yellow (V.) ..	20	20
363		38 s. on 1d. black & orange-yellow (Blk. & R.)	40	40
364		1 p. on 2s. claret and new blue	1·00	1·00
355/64 *and* O62/4		.. .. .. *Set of* 13	5·50	5·50

96 Wristwatch

97 Pole-vaulter

1971 (20 July)–**72**. *Air. Backed with paper bearing advertisements.*

No.	Type	Description	Unused	Used
365	**96**	14 s. multicoloured	55	55
365*a*		17 s. multicoloured (20.7.72)	65	65
366		21 s. multicoloured	75	75
366*a*		38 s. multicoloured (20.7.72)	1·10	1·10
365/6*a and* O65/6*a*		.. .. .. *Set of* 8	5·50	5·50

1971 (20 July). *Fourth South Pacific Games, Tahiti. T* **97** *and similar design. (a) Postage.*

No.	Type	Description	Unused	Used
367	**97**	3 s. multicoloured	10	10
368		7 s. multicoloured	10	10
369		15 s. multicoloured	15	15
370		25 s. multicoloured	25	30
371		50 s. multicoloured	40	60
		(b) Air		
372	–	9 s. multicoloured	10	10
373	–	10 s. multicoloured	10	10
374	–	24 s. multicoloured	25	30
375	–	29 s. multicoloured	30	40
376	–	38 s. multicoloured	35	50
367/76 *and* O67/9		.. .. *Set of* 13	3·50	5·00

Design: *Horiz*—Nos. 372/6, High-jumper.

98 Medal of Merit (reverse)

99 Child

1971 (30 Oct). *Investiture of Royal Tongan Medal of Merit. T* **98** *and similar "medal" shaped design. Multicoloured; colour of medal given.*

No.	Type	Description	Unused	Used
		(a) Postage		
377	**98**	3 s. gold	10	10
378		24 s. silver	20	20
379	–	38 s. brown	30	30
		(b) Air		
380	–	10 s. gold	15	15
381	–	75 s. silver	65	65
382	**98**	1 p. brown	75	75
377/82 *and* O70/2		.. .. *Set of* 9	3·75	3·75

Design: *As T* **98**—Nos. 379/81, Obverse of the Medal of Merit.

1971 (31 Dec). *25th Anniv of UNICEF. T* **99** *and similar design.*

No.	Type	Description	Unused	Used
		(a) Postage		
383	**99**	2 s. multicoloured	10	10
384		4 s. multicoloured	10	10
385		8 s. multicoloured	10	10
386		16 s. multicoloured	20	20
387		30 s. multicoloured	30	30
		(b) Air		
388	–	10 s. multicoloured	15	15
389	–	15 s. multicoloured	20	20
390	–	25 s. multicoloured	30	30
391	–	50 s. multicoloured	50	50
392	–	1 p. multicoloured	95	95
383/92 *and* O73/5		.. .. *Set of* 13	4·50	4·50

Design: *Vert* (21 x 42 *mm*)—Nos. 388/92, Woman.

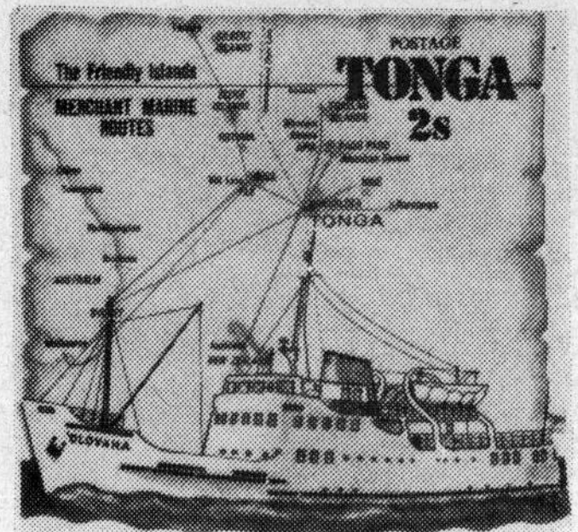

100 Map of South Pacific, and *Olovaha*

1972 (14 Apr). *Merchant Marine Routes. T* **100** *and similar design.*

No.	Type	Description	Unused	Used
		(a) Postage		
393	**100**	2 s. multicoloured	10	10
394		10 s. multicoloured	20	10
395		17 s. multicoloured	40	20
396		21 s. multicoloured	50	25
397		60 s. multicoloured	2·00	1·00
		(b) Air		
398	–	9 s. multicoloured	20	10
399	–	12 s. multicoloured	25	15
400	–	14 s. multicoloured	30	15
401	–	75 s. multicoloured	2·25	1·25
402	–	90 s. multicoloured	2·75	1·50
393/402 *and* O76/8		.. .. .. *Set of* 13	13·00	7·00

Design:—Nos. 398/402, Map of South Pacific and *Niuvakai*.

101 ¼ Hau Coronation Coin

1972 (15 July). *Fifth Anniv of Coronation. T* **101** *and similar design.*

No.	Type	Description	Unused	Used
		(a) Postage		
403	**101**	5 s. multicoloured	10	10
404		7 s. multicoloured	10	10
405		10 s. multicoloured	15	10
406		17 s. multicoloured	25	15
407		60 s. multicoloured	85	40
		(b) Air		
408	–	9 s. multicoloured	15	10
409	–	12 s. multicoloured	20	10
410	–	14 s. multicoloured	25	15
411	–	21 s. multicoloured	30	15
412	–	75 s. multicoloured	1·10	45
403/12 *and* O79/81		.. .. *Set of* 13	7·00	3·50

Design (47 × 41 *mm*):—Nos. 408/12, as T **101**, but with coins above inscription instead of beneath it.

102 Water Melon

1972 (30 Sept). *Coil stamps. (a) As T* **83**, *but inscription altered, omitting "Best in the Pacific", and colours changed.*

No.	Type	Description	Unused	Used
413	**83**	1 s. light yellow, scarlet and black ..	15	10
414		2 s. light yellow, ultramarine and black	20	15
415		3 s. light yellow, yellow-green and black	25	20
416		4 s. light yellow, royal blue and black ..	25	20
417		5 s. light yellow, reddish brn & bl	25	20
		(b) As T **90** *but colours changed. Colour of face value given*		
418	**90**	6 s. dull orange	25	20
419		7 s. ultramarine	30	25
420		8 s. bright magenta	30	25
421		9 s. brown-orange	30	25
422		10 s. bright new blue	35	30
		(c) T **102**. *Colour of face value given*		
423	**102**	15 s. new blue	55	45
424		20 s. reddish orange	70	60
425		25 s. chocolate	80	70
426		40 s. yellow-orange	1·75	1·50
427		50 s. lemon	2·00	1·75
413/27		.. .. .. *Set of* 15	7·50	6·50

Nos. 413/27 and O82/96 were produced in rolls, each even stamp having a number applied to the front of the backing paper, with the usual inscription on the reverse.

NOVEMBER 1972
INAUGURAL
Internal Airmail
Nuku'alofa — Vava'u

(**103**)

1972 (2 Nov). *Inaugural Internal Airmail. No. 398 surch with T* **103**.

No.	Type	Description	Unused	Used
428		7 s. on 9 s. multicoloured	1·10	1·50

104 Hoisting Tongan Flag

1972 (9 Dec). *Proclamation of Sovereignty over Minerva Reefs. T* **104** *and similar design. (a) Postage.*

No.	Type	Description	Unused	Used
429	**104**	5 s. multicoloured	10	10
430		7 s. multicoloured	10	10
431		10 s. multicoloured	15	10
432		15 s. multicoloured	25	15
433		40 s. multicoloured	80	40
		(b) Air		
434	–	9 s. multicoloured	15	10
435	–	12 s. multicoloured	20	10
436	–	14 s. multicoloured	25	15
437	–	38 s. multicoloured	75	35
438	–	1 p. multicoloured	2·00	1·00
429/38 *and* O97/9		.. .. *Set of* 13	8·00	4·25

Design: *Spherical* (52 *mm diameter*)—Nos. 434/8, Proclamation in Govt Gazette.

105 Coins around Bank

1973 (30 Mar). *Foundation of Bank of Tonga. T* **105** *and similar design. (a) Postage.*

No.	Type	Description	Unused	Used
439	**105**	5 s. multicoloured	10	10
440		7 s. multicoloured	10	10
441		10 s. multicoloured	15	10
442		20 s. multicoloured	25	15
443		30 s. multicoloured	35	25
		(b) Air		
444	–	9 s. multicoloured	20	10
445	–	12 s. multicoloured	20	10
446	–	17 s. multicoloured	25	15
447	–	50 s. multicoloured	80	40
448	–	90 s. multicoloured	1·50	90
439/48 *and* O100/2		.. .. *Set of* 13	7·50	4·25

Design: *Horiz* (64 × 52 *mm*)—Nos. 444/8, Bank and banknotes.

106 Handshake and Scout in Outrigger Canoe

1973 (29 June). *Silver Jubilee of Scouting in Tonga. T* **106** *and similar design. (a) Postage.*

No.	Type	Description	Unused	Used
449	**106**	5 s. multicoloured	20	10
450		7 s. multicoloured	30	15
451		15 s. multicoloured	85	40
452		21 s. multicoloured	1·00	50
453		50 s. multicoloured	3·75	1·75

(b) Air

454	–	9 s. multicoloured	50	25
455	–	12 s. multicoloured	60	30
456	–	14 s. multicoloured	85	50
457	–	17 s. multicoloured	95	60
458	–	1 p. multicoloured	13·00	5·50
449/58 *and* O103/5		*Set of* 13	£100	42·00

Design: *Square* (53 × 53 *mm*)—Nos. 454/8, Scout badge.

107 Excerpt from Cook's Log-book

1973 (2 Oct). *Bicentenary of Capt. Cook's Visit to Tonga. T* **107** *and similar design. (a) Postage.*

459	**107**	6 s. multicoloured	20	15
460		8 s. multicoloured	25	20
461		11 s. multicoloured	40	25
462		35 s. multicoloured	2·50	1·40
463		40 s. multicoloured	2·50	1·40

(b) Air

464	–	9 s. multicoloured	30	20
465	–	14 s. multicoloured	55	30
466	–	29 s. multicoloured	2·25	1·25
467	–	38 s. multicoloured	2·50	1·50
468	–	75 s. multicoloured	5·00	2·75
459/68 *and* O106/8		*Set of* 13	27·00	15·00

Design: *Vert*—Nos. 464/8, H.M.S. *Resolution*.

(108)

109 Red Shining Parrot

1973 (19 Dec). *Commonwealth Games, Christchurch, New Zealand. Various stamps optd as T* **108** *(No. 474 optd "AIRMAIL" in addition). (a) Postage.*

469	5 s. on 50 s. (No. 371) (Blk. and Gold)	15	10
470	12 s. on 38 s. (No. 379) (R. and Silver)	30	15
471	14 s. on 75 s. (No. 381) (R. and Gold)	30	15
472	20 s. on 1 p. (No. 382) (Blk. and Gold)	50	25
473	50 s. on 24 s. (No. 378) (Blk. and Silver)	1·25	65

(b) Air

474	7 s. on 25 s. (No. 370) (Blk. and Silver)	15	10
475	9 s. on 38 s. (No. 376) (V.)	20	10
476	24 s. (No. 374)	60	25
477	29 s. on 9 s. (No. 454) (B.)	70	35
478	40 s. on 14 s. (No. 456)	1·00	60
469/78 *and* O109/11	*Set of* 13	9·00	5·50

1974 (20 Mar). *Air.*

479	**109**	7 s. multicoloured	25	20
480		9 s. multicoloured	30	25
481		12 s. multicoloured	35	30
482		14 s. multicoloured	40	35
483		17 s. multicoloured	50	45
484		29 s. multicoloured	80	70
485		38 s. multicoloured	1·00	90
486		50 s. multicoloured	1·50	1·25
487		75 s. multicoloured	2·00	1·75
479/87		*Set of* 9	6·50	5·50

Nos. 479/87 and O112/20 were produced in rolls, each stamp having a number applied to the front of the backing paper, with the usual inscription on the reverse.

110 "Stamped Letter"

1974 (20 June). *Centenary of Universal Postal Union. T* **110** *and similar design. (a) Postage.*

488	**110**	5 s. multicoloured	10	10
489		10 s. multicoloured	15	10
490		15 s. multicoloured	25	15
491		20 s. multicoloured	30	25
492		50 s. multicoloured	1·25	75

(b) Air

493	–	14 s. multicoloured	25	15
494	–	21 s. multicoloured	35	30
495	–	60 s. multicoloured	1·40	75
496	–	75 s. multicoloured	1·60	85
497	–	1 p. multicoloured	1·90	1·10
488/97 *and* O121/3		*Set of* 13	9·50	5·75

Design: *Horiz*—Nos. 493/7, Carrier pigeon scattering letters over Tonga.

111 Girl Guide Badges

1974 (11 Sept). *Tongan Girl Guides. T* **111** *and similar design.*

(a) Postage

498	**111**	5 s. multicoloured	40	10
499		10 s. multicoloured	60	20
500		20 s. multicoloured	1·25	55
501		40 s. multicoloured	2·75	1·25
502		60 s. multicoloured	3·50	2·00

(b) Air

503	–	14 s. multicoloured	1·00	35
504	–	16 s. multicoloured	1·00	35
505	–	29 s. multicoloured	1·75	80
506	–	31 s. multicoloured	2·00	90
507	–	75 s. multicoloured	4·75	2·50
498/507 *and* O124/6		*Set of* 13	29·00	15·00

Design: *Vert*—Nos. 503/7, Girl Guide leaders.

112 H.M.S. *Resolution*

1974 (11 Dec). *Establishment of Royal Marine Institute. T* **112** *and similar design. (a) Postage.*

508	**112**	5 s. multicoloured	45	10
509		10 s. multicoloured	65	20
510		25 s. multicoloured	1·00	45
511		50 s. multicoloured	2·00	1·00
512		75 s. multicoloured	3·00	1·75

(b) Air

513	–	9 s. multicoloured	75	20
514	–	14 s. multicoloured	1·00	35
515	–	17 s. multicoloured	1·10	40
516	–	60 s. multicoloured	3·00	1·50
517	–	90 s. multicoloured	4·25	2·50
508/17 *and* O127/9		*Set of* 13	22·00	11·00

Design: *Horiz* (51 × 46 *mm*)—Nos. 513/17, *James Cook* (bulk carrier).

113 Dateline Hotel, Nuku'alofa

1975 (11 Mar). *South Pacific Forum and Tourism. T* **113** *and similar vert designs. (a) Postage.*

518	**113**	5 s. multicoloured	10	10
519		10 s. multicoloured	10	10
520		15 s. multicoloured	20	20
521		30 s. multicoloured	45	45
522		1 p. multicoloured	1·60	1·50

(b) Air

523	–	9 s. multicoloured	10	10
524	–	12 s. multicoloured	15	15
525	–	14 s. multicoloured	20	20
526	–	17 s. multicoloured	20	20
527	–	38 s. multicoloured	55	55
518/27 *and* O130/2		*Set of* 13	8·00	7·00

Designs (46 × 60 *mm*):—9, 12, 14 s. Beach; 17, 38 s. Surf and sea.

114 Boxing

1975 (11 June). *Fifth South Pacific Games, Guam. T* **114** *and similar "star"-shaped design. (a) Postage.*

528	**114**	5 s. multicoloured	10	10
529		10 s. multicoloured	15	10
530		20 s. multicoloured	25	20
531		25 s. multicoloured	30	25
532		65 s. multicoloured	70	55

(b) Air

533	–	9 s. multicoloured	15	10
534	–	12 s. multicoloured	20	15
535	–	14 s. multicoloured	20	15
536	–	17 s. multicoloured	25	20
537	–	90 s. multicoloured	90	80
528/37 *and* O133/5		*Set of* 13	5·25	4·00

Design (37 × 43 *mm*):—Nos. 533/7, Throwing the Discus.

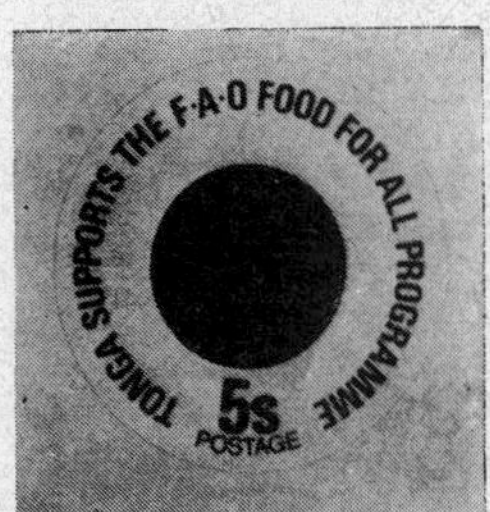

115 Commemorative Coin

1975 (3 Sept). *F.A.O. Commemoration. T* **115** *and similar designs.*

(a) Postage

538	5 s. multicoloured	10	10
539	20 s. multicoloured	30	15
540	50 s. new blue, black and silver	65	35
541	1 p. ultramarine, black and silver	1·25	75
542	2 p. black and silver	2·25	1·75

(b) Air

543	12 s. multicoloured	25	15
544	14 s. multicoloured	25	15
545	25 s. vermilion, black and silver	35	20
546	50 s. bright magenta, black and silver	60	40
547	1 p. black and silver	1·25	75
538/47	*Set of* 10	6·50	4·25

Nos. 539/47 are as T **115** but show different coins. Nos. 542 and 544 are horiz, size 75 × 42 mm.

116 Commemorative Coin

1975 (4 Nov). *Centenary of Tongan Constitution. T* **116** *and similar designs showing coinage. Multicoloured. (a) Postage.*

548		5 s. Type **116**	10	10
549		10 s. King George I	15	10
550		20 s. King Taufa'ahau IV	30	20
551		50 s. King George II	60	35
552		75 s. Tongan arms	1·00	70
		(b) Air		
553		9 s. King Taufa'ahau IV	15	10
554		12 s. Queen Salote	20	10
555		14 s. Tongan arms	20	10
556		38 s. King Taufa'ahau IV	40	25
557		1 p. Four monarchs	1·25	70
548/57 *and* O136/8		*Set of* 13	6·00	3·75

Sizes:—60 × 40 mm, Nos. 549 and 551; 76 × 76 mm, Nos. 552 and 557; 57 × 56 mm, others.

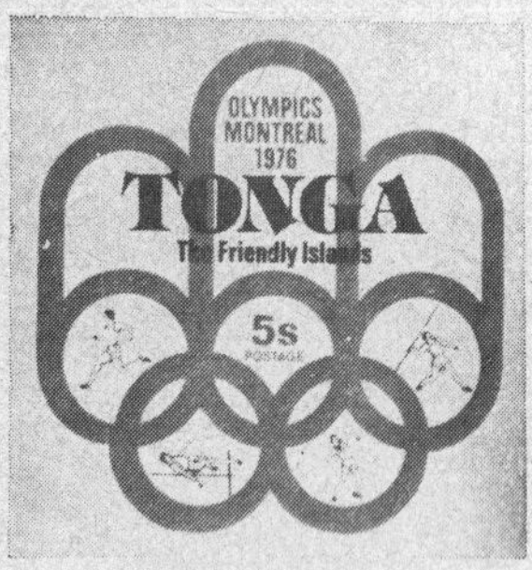

117 Montreal Logo

1976 (24 Feb). *First Participation in Olympic Games. (a) Postage.*

558	**117**	5 s. vermilion, black and blue	15	10
559		10 s. vermilion, black and emerald	25	10
560		25 s. vermilion, black and bistre	65	35
561		35 s. vermilion, black and mauve	75	40
562		70 s. vermilion, black and olive-yellow	2·00	90
		(b) Air. Montreal logo optd on Girl Guide stamps (Nos. 500 etc)		
563	**111**	12 s. on 20 s. multicoloured	30	15
564	–	14 s. on 16 s. multicoloured	30	15
565	–	16 s. multicoloured	35	15
566	**111**	38 s. on 40 s. multicoloured	1·00	45
567	–	75 s. multicoloured	2·25	95
558/67 *and* O139/41		*Set of* 13	13·00	6·50

118 Signatories of Declaration of Independence

1976 (26 May). *Bicentenary of American Revolution. T* **118** *and similar horiz designs showing signatories to the Declaration of Independence. (a) Postage.*

568	**118**	9 s. multicoloured	40	15
569	–	10 s. multicoloured	40	15
570	–	15 s. multicoloured	70	35
571	–	25 s. multicoloured	1·25	60
572	–	75 s. multicoloured	3·75	1·75
		(b) Air		
573	–	12 s. multicoloured	50	15
574	–	14 s. multicoloured	60	20
575	–	17 s. multicoloured	80	35
576	–	38 s. multicoloured	1·90	75
577	–	1 p. multicoloured	4·50	2·00
568/77 *and* O142/4		*Set of* 13	20·00	9·00

119 Nathaniel Turner and John Thomas (Methodist missionaries)

1976 (25 Aug). *150th Anniv of Christianity in Tonga. T* **119** *and similar design. (a) Postage.*

578	**119**	5 s. multicoloured	15	15
579		10 s. multicoloured	25	25
580		20 s. multicoloured	40	40
581		25 s. multicoloured	45	45
582		85 s. multicoloured	1·90	1·90
		(b) Air. Design showing Missionary Ship "Triton" (45 × 59 mm)		
583	–	9 s. multicoloured	25	25
584	–	12 s. multicoloured	30	30
585	–	14 s. multicoloured	35	35
586	–	17 s. multicoloured	40	40
587	–	38 s. multicoloured	1·00	1·00
578/87 *and* O145/7		*Set of* 13	10·00	10·00

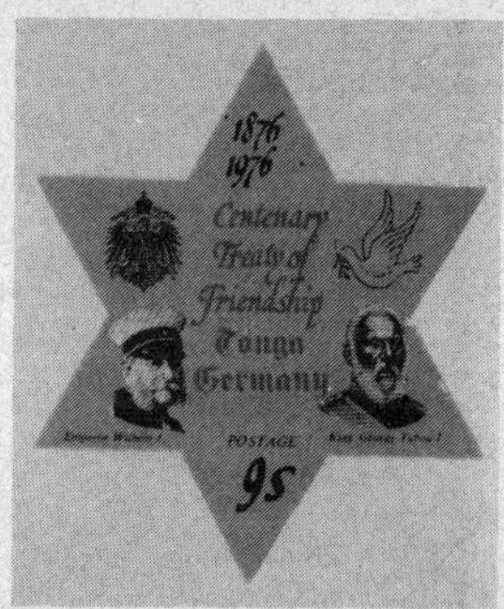

120 Emperor Wilhelm I and King George Tupou I

1976 (1 Nov). *Centenary of Treaty of Friendship with Germany.*

		(a) Postage		
588	**120**	9 s. multicoloured	20	20
589		15 s. multicoloured	30	30
590		22 s. multicoloured	40	40
591		50 s. multicoloured	90	90
592		73 s. multicoloured	1·40	1·40
		(b) Air. Circular design (52 mm diameter) showing Treaty Signing		
593	–	11 s. multicoloured	25	25
594	–	17 s. multicoloured	40	40
595	–	18 s. multicoloured	40	40
596	–	31 s. multicoloured	60	60
597	–	39 s. multicoloured	70	70
588/97 *and* O148/50		*Set of* 13	9·50	9·50

121 Queen Salote and Coronation Procession

1977 (7 Feb). *Silver Jubilee. (a) Postage.*

598	**121**	11 s. multicoloured	2·00	40
599		20 s. multicoloured	1·00	30
600		30 s. multicoloured	1·25	40
601		50 s. multicoloured	2·25	75
602		75 s. multicoloured	3·00	1·00
		(b) Air. Square design (59 × 59 mm) showing Queen Elizabeth and King Taufa'ahau		
603	–	15 s. multicoloured	80	25
604	–	17 s. multicoloured	1·00	30
605	–	22 s. multicoloured	18·00	3·00
		a. Horiz roul omitted (vert pair)		
606	–	31 s. multicoloured	1·00	40
607	–	39 s. multicoloured	1·25	50
598/607 *and* O151/3		*Set of* 13	35·00	8·00

122 Tongan Coins

1977 (4 July). *Tenth Anniv of King's Coronation. (a) Postage.*

608	**122**	10 s. multicoloured	20	20
609		15 s. multicoloured	25	25
610		25 s. multicoloured	35	35
611		50 s. multicoloured	75	75
612		75 s. multicoloured	1·00	1·00
		(b) Air. Oval design (64 × 46 mm) showing 1967 Coronation Coin		
613	–	11 s. multicoloured	25	20
614	–	17 s. multicoloured	30	30
615	–	18 s. multicoloured	30	30
616	–	39 s. multicoloured	45	45
617	–	1 p. multicoloured	1·50	1·50
608/17 *and* O154/6		*Set of* 13	7·50	7·50

123 H.M.S. *Resolution*

1977 (28 Sept). *Bicentenary of Capt. Cook's Last Voyage.*

		(a) Postage.		
618	**123**	10 s. multicoloured	1·00	60
619		17 s. multicoloured	1·50	95
620		25 s. multicoloured	2·50	1·75
621		30 s. multicoloured	2·75	2·00
622		40 s. multicoloured	3·25	2·50
		(b) Air. Horiz design (52 × 46 mm) showing coin and extract from Cook's journal		
623	–	15 s. multicoloured	1·40	90
624	–	22 s. multicoloured	2·25	1·60
625	–	31 s. multicoloured	2·75	2·00
626	–	50 s. multicoloured	4·00	3·00
627	–	1 p. multicoloured	7·50	6·00
618/27 *and* O157/9		*Set of* 13	40·00	29·00

124 Humpback Whale **(125)**

1977 (16 Dec). *Whale Conservation. (a) Postage.*

628	**124**	15 s. black, grey and bright blue	70	40
629		22 s. black, grey and dull green	90	55
630		31 s. black, grey and orange	1·10	70
631		38 s. black, grey and bright lilac	1·40	95
632		64 s. black, grey and red-brown	2·25	1·50
		(b) Air. Hexagonal design (66 × 51 mm) showing Sei and Fin Whales		
633	–	11 s. multicoloured	65	35
634	–	17 s. multicoloured	80	50
635	–	18 s. multicoloured	80	50
636	–	39 s. multicoloured	1·50	1·00
637	–	50 s. multicoloured	1·90	1·40
628/37 *and* O160/2		*Set of* 13	17·00	12·00

1978 (17 Feb). *Various stamps surch as T* **125**. *(a) Postage.*

638	**115**	15 s. on 5 s. multicoloured	80	1·00
639	**119**	15 s. on 5 s. multicoloured (Br.)	80	1·00
640	**117**	15 s. on 10 s. verm, blk & emerald (G.)	80	1·00
641	**119**	15 s. on 10 s. multicoloured	80	1·00
642	**121**	15 s. on 11 s. multicoloured (Blk. & Sil.)	2·00	2·25
643	**114**	15 s. on 20 s. multicoloured	80	1·00
644	–	15 s. on 38 s. mult (No. O133) (V.)	80	1·00
		(b) Air		
645	–	17 s. on 9 s. multicoloured (No. 533)	80	1·00
646	–	17 s. on 9 s. multicoloured (583) (V.)	80	1·00
647	–	17 s. on 12 s. multicoloured (534) (V.)	80	1·00
648	–	17 s. on 12 s. mult (573) (R. & Gold)	80	1·00
649	–	17 s. on 18 s. mult (595) (Olive & Br.)	80	1·00
650	–	17 s. on 38 s. multicoloured (527) (G.)	80	1·00
651	–	17 s. on 38 s. multicoloured (556)	80	1·00
652	–	1 p. on 35 s. mult (O151) (Silver & B.)	24·00	24·00
653	–	1 p. on 38 s. mult (576) (V. & Gold)	5·50	7·00
654	–	1 p. on 75 s. mult (572) (G. & Sil.)	5·50	7·00
638/54		*Set of* 17	42·00	48·00

The surcharges on Nos. 638/9 are formed by adding a figure "1" to the existing face value.

The surcharge on No. 644 includes the word "POSTAGE".

126 Flags of Canada and Tonga

978 (5 May). *Commonwealth Games, Edmonton. (a) Postage.*

55 **126** 10 s. blue, red and black 15 15
56 15 s. multicoloured 25 25
57 20 s. turquoise-green, black and red .. 35 35
58 25 s. red, blue and black 40 40
59 45 s. black and red 90 90

(b) Air. Leaf-shaped design (39 × 40 *mm*) *showing Maple Leaf*

60 – 17 s. black and red 30 30
61 – 35 s. black, red and blue 60 60
62 – 38 s. black, red and turquoise-green .. 75 75
63 – 40 s. black, red and green 80 80
64 – 65 s. black, red and chestnut .. .. 1·40 1·40
55/64 *and* O163/5 .. .. .. *Set of* 13 8·00 8·00

127 King Taufa'ahau Tupou IV

1978 (4 July). 60*th Birthday of King Taufa'ahau Tupou IV*.

(a) Postage

665 **127** 2 s. black, deep blue and cobalt .. 10 10
666 5 s. black, deep blue and rose-pink .. 10 10
667 10 s. black, deep blue and mauve .. 20 20
668 25 s. black, deep blue and brownish grey 45 35
669 75 s. black, deep blue and yellow-ochre .. 1·10 1·00

b) Air. Star-shaped design (44 × 51 *mm*) *showing portrait of King*

670 – 11 s. black, dp blue & greenish yellow .. 20 20
671 – 15 s. black, deep blue and cinnamon .. 30 25
672 – 17 s. black, deep blue and bright lilac .. 35 25
673 – 39 s. black, dp blue & turquoise-green .. 60 55
674 – 1 p. black, deep blue and pink .. .. 1·75 1·40
665/74 *and* O166/8 .. .. .. *Set of* 13 7·00 6·00

128 Banana

1978 (29 Sept)–**82**. *(a) Coil stamps. Designs as T* **128** *showing bananas (the number coinciding with the face value).*

675 1 s. black and greenish yellow 10 10
676 2 s. deep blue and greenish yellow 10 10
677 3 s. purple-brown, yellow and greenish yellow 10 10
678 4 s. deep blue, yellow and greenish yellow .. 10 10
679 5 s. vermilion, yellow and greenish yellow .. 10 10

(b) Coil stamps. Coconut-shaped design (18 × 26 *mm*)

680 6 s. purple, emerald and bistre-brown .. 15 15
681 7 s. greenish blue, emerald and light brown .. 20 20
682 8 s. vermilion, emerald and light brown .. 20 20
683 9 s. deep mauve, emerald and light brown .. 25 25
684 10 s. emerald and light brown 25 25

(c) Coil stamps. Pineapple-shaped design (17 × 30 *mm*)

684*a* 13 s. deep mauve, emerald and cinnamon (17.12.82) .. .. 1·25 1·25
685 15 s. blue-green, orange-brown and emerald .. 35 35
686 20 s. brown, orange-brown and emerald .. 40 40
687 30 s. magenta, orange-brown and emerald .. 50 50
688 50 s. black, orange-brown and emerald .. 90 90
689 1 p. purple, orange-brown and emerald .. 1·75 1·75

(d) Mixed fruit oval design (55 × 29 *mm*)

689*a* 2 p. multicoloured (17.12.82) .. .. .. 4·50 4·50
689*b* 3 p. multicoloured (17.12.82) .. .. .. 6·00 6·00
675/89*b* .. .. .. *Set of* 18 15·00 15·00

Nos. 675/89 and O169/83 were produced in rolls, each even stamp having a number applied to the backing paper, with the usual inscription on the reverse.

129 Humpback Whale

1978 (15 Dec). *Endangered Wildlife Conservation. T* **129** *and similarly shaped designs. Multicoloured. (a) Postage.*

690 15 s. Type **129** 55 20
691 18 s. Insular Flying Fox 55 25
692 25 s. Turtle 60 30
693 28 s. Red Shining Parrot 80 35
694 60 s. Type **129** .. .. 1·50 80

(b) Air

695 17 s. Type **129** 55 25
696 22 s. As 18 s. 55 30
697 31 s. As 25 s. 70 40
698 39 s. As 28 s. .. .. 1·00 50
699 45 s. Type **129** .. .. 1·25 65
690/9 *and* O184/6 .. .. .. *Set of* 13 11·50 6·00

130 Metrication Symbol

1979 (16 Feb). *Decade of Progress. T* **130** *and other multi-angular designs in ultramarine and gold (31 s.) or multicoloured (others).*

(a) Postage

700 5 s. Type **130** 10 10
701 11 s. Map of South Pacific Islands 15 15
702 18 s. "Building wall of progress" with the assistance of the United States Peace Corps 25 20
703 22 s. New churches 35 25
704 50 s. Map showing air routes 70 50

(b) Air

705 15 s. As 50 s. 20 20
706 17 s. As 11 s. 25 20
707 31 s. Rotary International emblem 40 35
708 39 s. Government offices 55 40
709 1 p. "Communications" .. .. .. 1·40 1·25
700/9 *and* O187/9 .. .. .. *Set of* 13 6·50 5·00

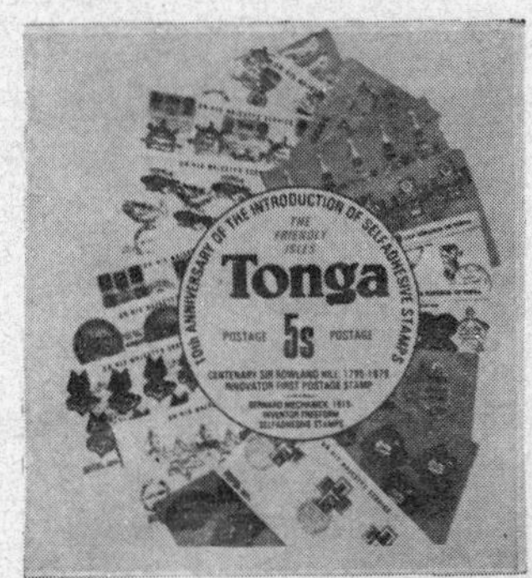

131 Various Envelopes bearing Self-adhesive Stamps

1979 (1 June). *Death Centenary of Sir Rowland Hill and* 10*th Anniv of Tongan Self-adhesive Stamps. (a) Postage.*

710 **131** 5 s. multicoloured 10 10
711 10 s. multicoloured 20 15
712 25 s. multicoloured 55 35
713 50 s. multicoloured .. .. .. 1·00 60
714 1 p. multicoloured .. .. .. 2·00 1·25

(b) Air. Multi-angular design (53 × 53 *mm*) *showing various self-adhesive stamps*

715 – 15 s. multicoloured 30 20
716 – 17 s. multicoloured 35 25
717 – 18 s. multicoloured 35 25
718 – 31 s. multicoloured 60 40
719 – 39 s. multicoloured 75 45
710/19 *and* O190/2 .. .. .. *Set of* 13 9·00 6·00

132

(Des R. Edge and K. Jones)

1979 (17 Aug)–**82**. *Air. Coil stamps.*

720 **132** 5 s. black and cobalt 15 15
721 11 s. black and bright blue 25 25
722 14 s. black and violet 25 25
723 15 s. black and mauve 30 30
724 17 s. black and bright magenta 30 30
725 18 s. black and bright rose-red 30 30
726 22 s. black and orange-vermilion 35 35
726*a* 29 s. black and rose (17.12.82) .. .. 2·00 2·50
727 31 s. black and orange-yellow 55 55
727*a* 32 s. black and yellow-ochre (17.12.82) .. 2·25 2·75
728 39 s. black and bright yellow-green .. 70 70
728*a* 47 s. black and light brown (17.12.82) .. 2·75 3·25
729 75 s. black and bright blue-green .. 1·25 1·50
730 1 p. black and emerald .. .. .. 1·75 2·00
720/30 .. .. .. *Set of* 14 12·00 13·50

Nos. 720/30 and O193/203 were produced in rolls, each even stamp having a number applied to the backing paper, with the usual inscription on the reverse.

133 Rain Forest, Island of 'Eua

1979 (23 Nov). *Views as seen through the Lens of a Camera.*

(a) Postage

731 **133** 10 s. multicoloured 20 15
732 18 s. multicoloured 25 25
733 31 s. multicoloured 35 35
734 50 s. multicoloured 60 45
735 60 s. multicoloured 70 60

(b) Air. Design as T **133** *but showing Isle of Kao*

736 – 5 s. multicoloured 10 10
737 – 15 s. multicoloured 25 20
738 – 17 s. multicoloured 25 25
739 – 39 s. multicoloured 50 40
740 – 75 s. multicoloured 80 75
731/40 *and* O204/6 .. .. .. *Set of* 13 5·50 4·50

134 King George Tupou I, Admiral Du Bouzet and Map of Tonga

(135)

1980 (9 Jan). 125*th Anniv of France–Tonga Treaty of Friendship.*

(a) Postage

741 **134** 7 s. multicoloured 10 15
742 10 s. multicoloured 15 20
743 14 s. multicoloured 20 25
744 50 s. multicoloured 70 75
745 75 s. multicoloured .. .. .. 1·00 1·10

(b) Air. Design as T **134** *but showing King George Tupou I, Napoleon III and "L'Aventure" (French warship)*

746 – 15 s. multicoloured 20 25
747 – 17 s. multicoloured 25 30
748 – 22 s. multicoloured 35 40
749 – 31 s. multicoloured 40 45
750 – 39 s. multicoloured 55 60
741/50 *and* O207/9 .. .. .. *Set of* 13 6·50 7·00

1980 (30 Apr). *Olympic Games, Moscow. Nos.* 710/19 *surch or optd only (No.* 755*) as T* **135** *in black on silver background.*

(a) Postage

751 **131** 13 s. on 5 s. multicoloured 20 25
752 20 s. on 10 s. multicoloured 30 35
753 25 s. multicoloured 35 40
754 33 s. on 50 s. multicoloured 45 50
755 1 p. multicoloured .. .. .. 1·40 1·50

(b) Air

756 – 9 s. on 15 s. multicoloured 15 20
757 – 16 s. on 17 s. multicoloured 25 30
758 – 29 s. on 18 s. multicoloured 40 45
759 – 32 s. on 31 s. multicoloured 45 50
760 – 47 s. on 39 s. multicoloured 65 70
751/60 *and* O210/12 .. .. .. *Set of* 13 6·50 7·00

136 Scout at Camp-fire

1980 (30 Sept). *South Pacific Scout Jamboree, Tonga and 75th Anniv of Rotary International. (a) Postage.*

761 **136** 9 s. multicoloured 30 15
762 13 s. multicoloured 40 20
763 15 s. multicoloured 40 20
764 30 s. multicoloured 75 40

(b) Air. Design as T **136** *showing Scout activities and Rotary emblem*

765 – 29 s. multicoloured 75 45
766 – 32 s. multicoloured 80 45
767 – 47 s. multicoloured .. .. 1·10 70
768 – 1 p. multicoloured .. .. 2·00 1·25
761/8 *and* O214/15 .. .. *Set of* 10 9·50 6·50

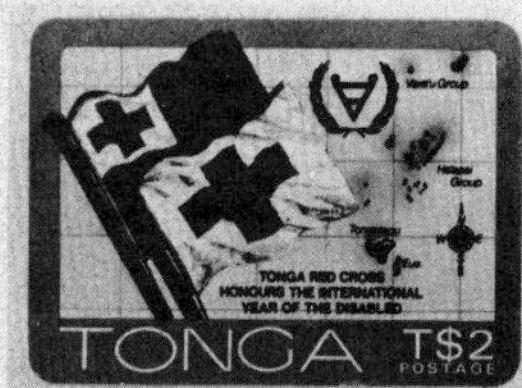

9

(137)

138 Red Cross and Tongan Flags, with Map of Tonga

1980 (3 Dec)–**82.** *Various stamps surch as T* **137**. *(a) Postage.*

769 **117** 9 s. on 35 s. vermilion, black and mauve 15 20
770 **119** 13 s. on 20 s. multicoloured 20 25
771 13 s. on 25 s. multicoloured 20 25
772 – 19 s. on 25 s. multicoloured (No. 571) .. 35 50
773 **114** 1 p. on 65 s. multicoloured .. .. 1·50 2·00
773*a* – 5 p. on 25 s. multicoloured (No. O214) (B.) (4.1.82) .. .. 8·50 7·50
773*b* – 5 p. on 2 p. multicoloured (No. O215) (B.) (4.1.82) .. .. 8·50 7·50
ba. Stamp omitted (centre stamp of strip of 3) .. ..

(b) Air

774 – 29 s. on 14 s. multicoloured (No. 585) .. 45 60
775 – 29 s. on 39 s. multicoloured (No. 597) .. 45 60
776 – 32 s. on 12 s. multicoloured (No. 554) .. 50 75
777 – 32 s. on 14 s. multicoloured (No. 574) .. 50 75
778 – 47 s. on 12 s. multicoloured (No. 524) .. 70 1·00
779 – 47 s. on 12 s. multicoloured (No. 584) .. 70 1·00
769/79 *and* O216 .. .. .. *Set of* 14 20·00 21·00

On No. 773ba the centre stamp in a vertical strip of 3 became detached so that the surcharge was applied to the white backing paper.

1981 (9 Sept). *International Year for Disabled Persons.*

(a) Postage. P 14½ × 14.

780 **138** 2 p. multicoloured .. .. .. 1·50 1·00
781 3 p. multicoloured .. .. .. 1·75 1·25

(b) Air. Vert design (25 × 33 mm) showing Red Cross flag and map depicting Tongatapu and Eua. P 13½

782 – 29 s. multicoloured 30 20
783 – 32 s. multicoloured 35 25
784 – 47 s. multicoloured 45 30
780/4 .. .. *Set of* 5 4·00 2·75

139 Prince Charles and King Taufa'ahau Tupou IV

1981 (21 Oct). *Royal Wedding and Centenary of Treaty of Friendship between Tonga and Great Britain. T* **139** *and similar vert designs. Multicoloured. P* 13½.

785 13 s. Type **139** 30 20
786 47 s. Prince Charles and Lady Diana Spencer 55 40
787 1 p. 50, Prince Charles and Lady Diana (*different*) .. .. 1·40 1·25
a. Imperf backing paper (pair) ..
788 3 p. Prince and Princess of Wales after wedding ceremony .. .. .. 2·50 2·00
785/8 .. .. *Set of* 4 4·25 3·50

140 Report of Printing in *Missionary Notices*

1981 (25 Nov). *Christmas. 150th Anniv of first Books Printed in Tonga. T* **140** *and similar horiz designs. Multicoloured. P* 13½.

789 9 s. Type **140** 20 15
790 13 s. *Missionary Notices* report (*different*) .. 25 20
791 32 s. Type in chase 60 40
792 47 s. Bible class 90 70
789/92 .. .. *Set of* 4 1·75 1·25

141 Landing Scene

1981 (25 Nov). *Bicentenary of Maurelle's Discovery of Vava'u. T* **141** *and similar horiz designs. Multicoloured. P* 14 × 14½.

793 9 s. Type **141** 25 20
794 13 s. Map of Vava'u 40 25
795 47 s. *La Princesa* .. .. 1·75 1·25
796 1 p. *La Princesa* (*different*) .. .. .. 4·00 3·00
793/6 .. .. *Set of* 4 5·75 4·25
MS797 100 × 78 mm. As No. 796. Imperf .. 4·00 4·00

The stamp from No. **MS**797 is as No. 796 but without inscription at foot of design.

142 Battle Scene

1981 (16 Dec). *175th Anniv of Capture of "Port au Prince" (ship). T* **142** *and similar horiz designs in black and new blue. P* 13½.

798 29 s. Type **142** 35 25
799 32 s. Battle scene (*different*) 40 30
800 47 s. Map of Ha'apai Group 50 50
801 47 s. Native canoes preparing to attack .. 50 50
802 1 p. *Port au Prince* 85 75
798/802 .. .. *Set of* 5 2·40 2·10

The 47 s. values were printed together, *se-tenant*, in horizontal and vertical pairs throughout the sheet.

143 Baden-Powell at Brownsea Island, 1907

CYCLONE RELIEF
T$1+50s
POSTAGE & RELIEF

(144)

1982 (22 Feb). *75th Anniv of Boy Scout Movement and 125th Birth Anniv of Lord Baden-Powell. T* **143** *and similar vert designs. P* 13½.

803 29 s. Type **143** 35 30
804 32 s. Baden-Powell on his charger "Black Prince" 40 35
805 47 s. Baden-Powell at Imperial Jamboree, 1924 55 45
806 1 p. 50, Cover of first *Scouting for Boys* journal 1·60 1·25
807 2 p. 50, Newsboy, 1900 and Mafeking Siege 3d. stamp .. .. 3·50 2·75
803/7 .. .. *Set of* 5 5·75 4·50

1982 (14 Apr). *Cyclone Relief. No. 788 optd with T* **144** *in silver.*

808 1 p. + 50 s. on 3 p. Prince and Princess of Wales after wedding ceremony .. .. 2·00 2·25
a. Imperf backing paper (pair) £200

145 Ball Control

146 M.V. *Olovaha II*

1982 (7 July). *World Cup Football Championship, Spain. T* **145** *and similar vert designs. Multicoloured. P* 13½.

809 32 s. Type **145** 40 45
810 47 s. Goalkeeping 55 60
811 75 s. Heading 90 95
812 1 p. 50, Shooting .. .. 1·75 1·75
809/12 .. .. *Set of* 4 3·25 3·25

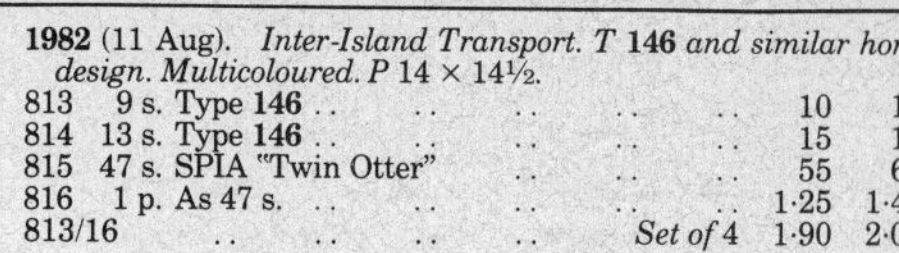

1982 (11 Aug). *Inter-Island Transport. T* **146** *and similar hor design. Multicoloured. P* 14 × 14½.

813 9 s. Type **146** 10 1
814 13 s. Type **146** 15 1
815 47 s. SPIA "Twin Otter" 55 6
816 1 p. As 47 s. .. .. 1·25 1·4
813/16 .. .. *Set of* 4 1·90 2·0

147 Mail Canoe

148 Decathlon

1982 (29 Sept). *Tin Can Mail Centenary. T* **147** *and similar ver designs. P* 13½ × 14.

817 13 s. multicoloured 15 15
818 32 s. multicoloured 25 25
819 47 s. multicoloured 35 35
820 2 p. black and pale turquoise-green .. .. 1·40 1·40
817/20 .. .. *Set of* 4 2·00 2·00
MS821 135 × 90 mm. Nos. 817/19. Imperf .. 1·25 1·40
MS822 135 × 89 mm. As No. 820 but with gold inscriptions. Imperf .. .. 2·50 2·75

Designs:—32 s. Mail canoe and ship; 47 s. Collecting Tin Can mail; 2 p. Map of Niuafo'ou.

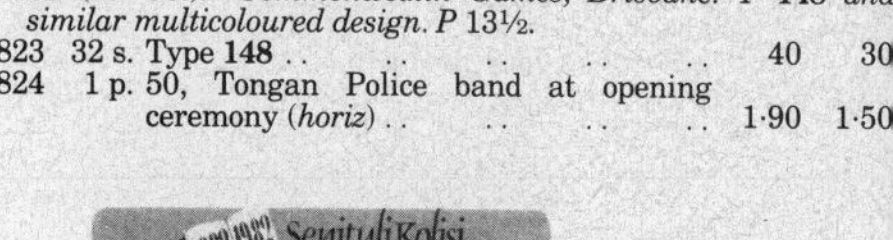

1982 (25 Oct). *Commonwealth Games, Brisbane. T* **148** *and similar multicoloured design. P* 13½.

823 32 s. Type **148** 40 30
824 1 p. 50, Tongan Police band at opening ceremony (*horiz*) .. .. 1·90 1·50

149 Pupils

Christmas
Greetings
1982

(150)

1982 (25 Oct). *Tonga College Centenary. T* **149** *and similar multicoloured designs. P* 13½ *(Nos. 825/6) or* 14 × 14½ *(others).*

825 5 s. Type **149** (Tongan inscription) 15 10
826 5 s. Type **149** (English inscription) 15 10
827 29 s. School crest and monument (Tongan inscr) (29 × 22 *mm*) 65 65
828 29 s. As No. 827, but inscr in English 65 65
829 29 s. King George Tupou I (founder) and school (Tongan inscr) (29 × 22 *mm*) .. 65 65
830 29 s. As No. 829, but inscr in English .. 65 65
825/30 .. .. *Set of* 6 2·50 2·50

Nos. 825/6 were printed together, *se-tenant*, in pairs and Nos. 827/30 in blocks of four throughout the sheets.

1982 (17 Nov). *Christmas. Nos. 817/19 optd as T* **150** *in bright carmine (13 s.) or silver (others).*

831 13 s. Type **147**.. .. .. 15 15
a. Bright purple opt .. .. ..
832 32 s. Mail boat and ship 35 35
833 47 s. Collecting Tin Can mail 40 50
831/3 .. .. *Set of* 3 80 90

151 H.M.S. *Resolution*, and S. S. *Canberra*

1983 (22 Feb). *Sea and Air Transport. T* **151** *and similar horiz designs. Multicoloured. P* 14.

834 29 s. Type **151** (sage-green background) .. 45 45
835 32 s. Type **151** (buff background) 55 55
836 47 s. Montgolfier's balloon and "Concorde" (pale blue background) 75 75
837 1 p. 50, As No. 836 (lilac background) .. 2·00 2·00
834/7 .. .. *Set of* 4 3·25 3·25
MS838 120 × 165 mm. 2 p. 50, S.S. *Canberra* and "Concorde" .. .. 3·50 3·50

152 Globe and Inset of Tonga

TONGA 32s

153 SPIA DH "Twin Otter"

1983 (14 Mar). *Commonwealth Day. T* **152** *and similar horiz designs. Multicoloured. P* 14.
839 29 s. Type **152** 35 30
840 32 s. Tongan dancers . . . . 6·00 2·00
841 47 s. Trawler 50 50
842 1 p. 50, King Taufa'ahau Tupou IV and flag 1·75 1·75
839/42 . . . . *Set of* 4 7·75 4·00

1983 (11 May). *Inauguration of Niuafo'ou Airport. T* **153** *and similar horiz design. Multicoloured. P* 14 × 14½.
843 32 s. Type **153** 20 20
844 47 s. Type **153** 25 25
845 1 p. SPIA Boeing "707" 60 70
846 1 p. 50, As 1 p. . . . . 80 1·25
843/6 . . . . *Set of* 4 1·75 2·25

154 "Intelsat IV" Satellite **155** Obverse and Reverse of Pa'anga Banknote

1983 (22 June). *World Communications Year. T* **154** *and similar multicoloured designs. P* 11 (2 *p.*) *or* 14 × 14½ (*others*).
847 29 s. Type **154** 20 20
848 32 s. "Intelsat IVA" satellite 25 25
849 75 s. "Intelsat V" satellite 50 50
850 2 p. Moon post cover (45 × 32 *mm*) . . 1·10 1·40
847/50 . . . . *Set of* 4 1·90 2·10

1983 (3 Aug). *10th Anniv of Bank of Tonga. P* 14.
851 **155** 1 p. multicoloured 60 65
852 2 p. multicoloured . . . . 1·10 1·25

156 Early Printing Press **157** Yacht off Coast

(Des A. Benjamin and R. Edge)

1983 (22 Sept). *Printing in Tonga. T* **156** *and similar vert designs. Multicoloured. P* 14.
853 13 s. Type **156** 15 15
854 32 s. Arrival of W. Woon 25 25
855 1 p. Early Tongan print 50 60
856 2 p. *The Tonga Chronicle* . . . . 90 1·25
853/6 . . . . *Set of* 4 1·60 2·00

1983 (17 Nov). *Christmas. Yachting off Vava'u. T* **157** *and similar vert designs. Multicoloured. P* 11.
857 29 s. Type **157** 25 25
858 32 s. View of yacht from cave 25 25
859 1 p. 50, Anchored yacht . . . . 80 1·00
860 2 p. 50, Yacht off coast (*different*) . . 1·25 1·50
857/60 . . . . *Set of* 4 2·25 2·75

158 Abel Tasman and *Zeehan* **159** *Swainsonia casta*

(Des R. Edge)

1984 (12 Mar). *Navigators and Explorers of the Pacific* (1*st series*). *T* **158** *and similar horiz designs. P* 14.
861 32 s. deep dull green and black 45 45
862 47 s. reddish violet and black 65 65
863 90 s. light brown and black . . . . 1·25 1·25
864 1 p. 50, royal blue and black . . . . 2·10 2·10
861/4 . . . . *Set of* 4 4·00 4·00

Designs:—47 s. Samuel Wallis and H.M.S. *Dolphin*; 90 s. William Bligh and H.M.S. *Bounty*; 1 p. 50, James Cook and H.M.S. *Resolution*.

See also Nos. 896/9.

STAMPS DIE-CUT OR PERFORATED. During 1985 developments took place in the production of Tonga and Niuafo'ou self-adhesive stamps. Since 1981 these had been produced in traditional formats on backing paper perforated in the usual way. The individual stamps were, however, separated by the removal of the margins between them by the die-cutting process.

As an experiment some supplies of Tonga Nos. 870, 896, **MS**904, 905/9, 915/18, O225 and Niuafo'ou Nos. 56/60, together with the entire printing of Tonga Nos. 910/14, were produced with the margins intact so that both stamps and backing paper were perforated through.

Such issues are usually inscribed "Bend forward and peel off backing paper" on the reverse.

1984 (10 Apr)–**85**. *Marine Life. T* **159** *and similar multi-coloured designs. Stamps die-cut and backing paper perf* 14 (1, 2, 3, 5 *p.*) *or* 14½ (*others*).
865 1 s. Type **159** 10 10
866 2 s. *Porites sp* (26.6.84) 20 20
867 3 s. *Holocentrus ruber* (18.5.84) 20 20
868 5 s. *Cyprae mappa viridis* 20 20
869 6 s. *Dardanus megistos* (crab) (17.9.84) . . 25 25
870 9 s. *Stegostoma fasciatum* (18.5.84) . . 25 25
b. Stamp perforated (28.5.85) . . 25 25
871 10 s. *Conus bullatus* 35 35
872 13 s. *Pterois volitans* (18.5.84) 35 35
873 15 s. *Conus textile* 40 40
874 20 s. *Dascyllus aruanus* (18.5.84) . . 45 45
875 29 s. *Conus aulicus* 50 50
876 32 s. *Acanthurus leucosternon* (18.5.84) . . 65 65
877 47 s. *Lambis truncata* 70 70
878 1 p. *Millepora dichotama* (26.6.84) . . 1·50 1·50
879 2 p. *Birgus latro* (crab) (17.9.84) . . 2·50 2·50
880 3 p. *Chicoreus palma-rosae* . . . . 3·50 3·50
881 5 p. *Thunnus albacares* (18.5.84) . . 5·50 5·50
865/81 . . . . *Set of* 17 16·00 16·00

Nos. 878/81 are horizontal, 38 × 23 mm.

For 1, 2, 5, 6, 10, 15, 20, 32 s. and 3 p. with normal gum and perforations see Nos. 976*a*/*b* and 999/1017.

160 Printer checking Newspaper **161** U.S.A. Flag and Running

1984 (26 June). *20th Anniv of* Tonga Chronicle (*newspaper*). *Die-cut.*
882 **160** 3 s. grey-brown and bright blue . . 10 10
a. Sheetlet of 12 50
883 32 s. grey-brown and vermilion . . 40 45
a. Sheetlet of 12 . . . . 4·75

Nos. 882/3 were each printed in sheetlets of 12, the designs being superimposed on a reproduction of the front page from the first edition. This was printed in grey and is in Tongan for the 3 s. and English for the 32 s.

(Des R. Edge)

1984 (23 July). *Olympic Games, Los Angeles. T* **161** *and similar horiz designs, each showing U.S. flag. Each printed in black, scarlet-vermilion and bright new blue. P* 14 × 14½.
884 29 s. Type **161** 25 25
885 47 s. Javelin-throwing 30 30
886 1 p. 50, Shot-putting 85 85
887 3 p. Olympic torch . . . . 1·60 1·60
884/7 . . . . *Set of* 4 2·75 2·75

162 Sir George Airy and Dateline on World Map **163** Australia 1914 Kookaburra 6d. Stamp

(Des R. Edge)

1984 (20 Aug). *Centenary of International Dateline. T* **162** *and similar horiz design. Multicoloured. P* 14.
888 47 s. Type **162** 50 50
889 2 p. Sir Sandford Fleming and Map of Pacific time zones . . . . 2·00 2·25

1984 (17 Sept). *"Ausipex" International Stamp Exhibition, Melbourne. T* **163** *and similar vert design. Multicoloured. P* 14.
890 32 s. Type **163** 35 35
891 1 p. 50, Tonga 1897 Parrot 2s. 6d. stamp . . 1·50 1·50
MS892 90 × 100 mm. As Nos. 890/1, but without exhibition logo and with "TONGA" and face values in gold. Die-cut . . . . 1·90 2·25

Examples of No. **MS**892 without face values are Exhibition Banquet souvenirs without postal validity.

MINIMUM PRICE

The minimum price quote is 10p which represents a handling charge rather than a basis for valuing common stamps. For further notes about prices see introductory pages.

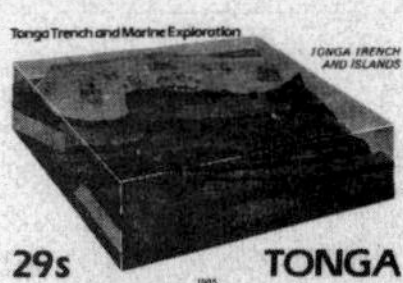

164 Beach at Sunset ("Silent Night") **165** Section of Tonga Trench

(Des R. Edge)

1984 (12 Nov). *Christmas. Carols. T* **164** *and similar vert designs. Multicoloured. P* 14.
893 32 s. Type **164** 40 45
894 47 s. Hut and palm trees ("Away in a Manger") 60 65
895 1 p. Sailing boats ("I Saw Three Ships") . . 1·25 1·40
893/5 . . . . *Set of* 3 1·90 2·25

Nos. 893/5 were each issued in sheets of 20 stamps with 5 labels, in the central vertical row, showing progressive stages of the design.

(Des R. Edge)

1985 (27 Feb). *Navigators and Explorers of the Pacific* (2*nd series*). *Horiz designs as T* **158**. *Stamps die-cut and backing paper perf* 14.
896 32 s. black and turquoise-blue 50 35
b. Stamp perforated . . . . 25·00 25·00
897 47 s. black and blue-green 65 50
898 90 s. black and scarlet . . . . 1·25 90
899 1 p. 50, black and buff . . . . 1·75 1·50
896/9 . . . . *Set of* 4 3·75 3·00

Designs:—32 s. Willem Schouten and *Eendracht*; 47 s. Jacob Le Maire and *Hoorn*; 90 s. Fletcher Christian and *Bounty*; 1 p. 50, Francisco Maurelle and *La Princessa*.

No. 896b has no inscription on the reverse.

1985 (10 Apr). *Geological Survey of the Tonga Trench. T* **165** *and similar multicoloured designs. Stamps die-cut and backing paper perf* 14.
900 29 s. Type **165** 50 50
901 32 s. Diagram of marine seismic survey . . 50 50
902 47 s. Diagram of aerial oil survey (*vert*) . . 70 70
903 1 p. 50, Diagram of sea bed survey (*vert*) . . 2·00 2·00
900/3 . . . . *Set of* 4 3·25 3·25
MS904 100×100 mm. 1 p. 50, Angler Fish. Die-cut . . . . 1·75 2·00
b. Stamp perforated . . . . 5·00

166 *Port au Prince* at Gravesend, 1805 **167** Quintal (Byron Russell) and Capt. Bligh (Charles Laughton)

1985 (18 June). *175th Anniv of Will Mariner's Departure for England. T* **166** *and similar horiz designs. Multicoloured.* A. *Stamp die-cut and backing paper perf* 14. B. *Both stamp and backing paper perf* 14.

		A		B	
905	29 s. Type **166**	30	35	30	35
906	32 s. Capture of *Port au Prince*, Tonga, 1806 . .	30	35	30	35
907	47 s. Will Mariner on Tongan canoe, 1807 . .	45	50	45	50
908	1 p. 50, Mariner boarding brig *Favourite*, 1810 . .	1·40	1·50	1·40	1·50
909	2 p. 50, *Cuffnells* in English Channel, 1811 . .	2·40	2·50	2·40	2·50
905/9	. . . . *Set of* 5	4·25	4·50	4·25	4·50

1985 (16 July). *50th Anniv of Film "Mutiny on the Bounty". T* **167** *and similar horiz designs showing film stills. Multicoloured. Both stamp and backing paper perf* 14.
910 47 s. Type **167** 80 80
a. Horiz strip of 5. Nos. 910/14 . . 3·50
911 47 s. Captain Bligh and prisoners . . 80 80
912 47 s. Fletcher Christian (Clark Gable) . . 80 80
913 47 s. Mutineers threatening Bligh . . 80 80
914 47 s. Bligh and Roger Byam (Franchot Tone) in boat 80 80
910/14 . . . . *Set of* 5 3·50 3·50

Nos. 910/14 were printed together, *se-tenant*, in horizontal strips of 5 throughout the sheet.

168 Lady Elizabeth Bowes-Lyon, 1910 **169** Mary and Joseph arriving at Inn

1985 (20 Aug). *Life and Times of Queen Elizabeth the Queen Mother and 75th Anniv of Girl Guide Movement. T* **168** *and similar horiz designs. A. Stamp die-cut and backing paper perf* 14. *B. Both stamp and backing paper perf* 14.

		A		B	
915	32 s. black, salmon-pink and reddish brown	30	35	60	65
916	47 s. black, pale rose-lilac and reddish brown	45	50	90	1·00
917	1 p. 50, black, olive-yellow and reddish brown	1·40	1·50	2·75	3·00
918	2 p. 50, multicoloured	2·40	2·50	4·75	5·00
915/18	.. .. *Set of* 4	4·00	4·25	8·00	8·50

Designs:—47 s. Duchess of York at Hadfield Girl Guides' Rally, 1931; 1 p. 50, Duchess of York in Girl Guide uniform; 2 p. 50, Queen Mother in 1985 (from photo by Norman Parkinson).

1985 (12 Nov). *Christmas. T* **169** *and similar vert designs. Multicoloured. P* 14.
919 32 s. Type **169**.. .. .. 25 30
920 42 s. The shepherds 35 40
921 1 p. 50, The Three Wise Men .. .. .. 1·25 1·40
922 2 p. 50, The Holy Family .. .. .. 2·10 2·25
919/22 .. .. *Set of* 4 3·50 4·00

NOTE. Unless stated otherwise Tonga issues from No. 922 had the normal form of gum and were not self-adhesive.

170 Comet and Slogan "Maybe Twice in a Lifetime"

4s 4s
(**171**)

(Litho Walsall)

1986 (26 Mar). *Appearance of Halley's Comet. T* **170** *and similar horiz designs. Multicoloured. P* 14.
923 42 s. Type **170**.. .. .. 60 60
a. Horiz strip of 5. Nos. 923/7 .. .. 2·75
924 42 s. Edmond Halley 60 60
925 42 s. Solar System 60 60
926 42 s. Telescope 60 60
927 42 s. *Giotto* spacecraft 60 60
928 57 s. Type **170**.. .. .. 75 75
a. Horiz strip of 5. Nos. 928/32 .. .. 3·25
929 57 s. As No. 924 .. .. 75 75
930 57 s. As No. 925 .. .. 75 75
931 57 s. As No. 926 .. .. 75 75
932 57 s. As No. 927 .. .. 75 75
923/32 .. .. *Set of* 10 5·50 5·50
Nos. 923/7 and 928/32 were each printed together, *se-tenant*, in horizontal strips of five, forming composite designs, throughout the sheets.

1986 (16 Apr). *Nos.* 866/7, 869/70, 872, 874, 879 *and* 881 *surch as T* **171**.
933 4 s. on 2 s. *Porites sp.* 10 10
934 4 s. on 13 s. *Pterois volitans* 10 10
935 42 s. on 3 s. *Holocentrus ruber* 30 35
936 42 s. on 9 s. *Stegostoma fasciatum* 30 35
937 57 s. on 6 s. *Dardanus megistos* 40 45
938 57 s. on 20 s. *Dascyllus aruanus* 40 45
939 2 p. 50 on 2 p. *Birgus latro* .. .. .. 2·10 2·25
940 2 p. 50 on 5 p. *Thunnus albacares* .. .. 2·10 2·25
933/40 .. .. *Set of* 8 5·00 5·50

172 King Taufa'ahau Tupou IV of Tonga

(Litho Walsall)

1986 (22 May). *Royal Links with Great Britain and 60th Birthday of Queen Elizabeth II. T* **172** *and similar designs. P* 14.
941 **172** 57 s. multicoloured 65 65
a. Horiz pair. Nos. 941/2 .. .. 1·25 1·25
942 – 57 s. multicoloured 65 65
943 – 2 p. 50, reddish brown, blk & pale new bl 2·25 2·50
941/3 .. .. *Set of* 3 3·50 3·75
Designs: *Horiz* (*as T* **172**)—No. 942, Queen Elizabeth II. *Square* (40×40 *mm*)—No. 943, Queen Elizabeth II and King Taufa'ahau Tupou IV, Tonga, 1970.
Nos. 941/2 were printed together, *se-tenant*, in horizontal pairs throughout the sheet, and No. 943 in sheetlets of five stamps and one stamp-size label.

173 Peace Corps Nurse giving Injection

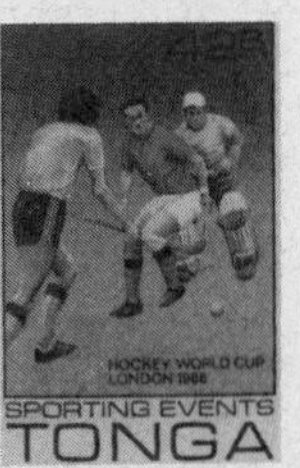

174 Hockey (World Hockey Cup for Men, London)

(Litho Walsall)

1986 (22 May). *"Ameripex '86" International Stamp Exhibition, Chicago. 25th Anniv of United States Peace Corps. T* **173** *and similar horiz design. Multicoloured. P* 14.
944 57 s. Type **173**.. .. .. 45 50
945 1 p. 50, Peace Corps teacher and pupil .. 1·25 1·40
MS946 90×90 mm. Nos. 944/5, magnifying glass and tweezers. Imperf .. .. 1·75 1·90

(Litho Walsall)

1986 (23 July). *Sporting Events. T* **174** *and similar vert designs. Multicoloured. P* 14.
947 42 s. Type **174**.. .. .. 55 55
948 57 s. Handball (13th Commonwealth Games, Edinburgh) 65 65
949 1 p. Boxing (13th Commonwealth Games, Edinburgh) .. .. 1·10 1·10
950 2 p. 50, Football (World Cup Football Championship, Mexico) .. .. 2·75 2·75
947/50 .. .. *Set of* 4 4·50 4·50

175 1886 1d. King George I Definitive

(Des A. Benjamin. Litho Walsall)

1986 (27 Aug). *Centenary of First Tonga Stamps. T* **175** *and similar multicoloured designs. P* 14.
951 32 s. Type **175**.. .. .. 45 45
952 42 s. 1895 7½d. King George II inverted centre error 60 60
953 57 s. 1950 Queen Salote's 50th Birthday 1d. 75 75
954 2 p. 50, 1986 Royal Links with Great Britain 2 p. 50 .. .. 2·75 2·75
951/4 .. .. *Set of* 4 4·00 4·00
MS955 132×104 mm. 50 s.×8 Vert designs forming montage of Tonga stamps .. .. 4·50 5·00
Nos. 951/5 were printed with an overall pattern similar to watermark W **24**.

176 Girls wearing Shell Jewellery

BOY SCOUT
JAMBOREE
5th-10th DEC'86
(**177**)

(Litho Walsall)

1986 (12 Nov). *Christmas. T* **176** *and similar multicoloured designs. P* 14.
956 32 s. Type **176**.. .. .. 30 30
957 42 s. Boy with wood carvings (*vert*) 40 40
958 57 s. Children performing traditional dance (*vert*) 50 50
959 2 p. Children in dugout canoe .. .. 1·90 1·90
956/9 .. .. *Set of* 4 2·75 2·75

1986 (2 Dec). *Scout Jamboree, Tongatapu. Nos.* 957/8 *optd with T* **177** *in silver.*
960 42 s. Boy with wood carvings (*vert*) 45 45
961 57 s. Children performing traditional dance (*vert*) 55 55

178 Dumont D'Urville and *L'Astrolabe*

179 Noah's Ark

(Litho Walsall)

1987 (24 Feb). *150th Anniv of Dumont D'Urville's Second Voyage. T* **178** *and similar horiz designs. Multicoloured. P* 14.
962 32 s. Type **178**.. .. .. 60 60
963 42 s. Tongan girls (from *Voyage au Pole et dans l'Oceanie*) 75 75
964 1 p. Contemporary chart .. .. .. 1·75 1·75
965 2 p. 50, Wreck of *L'Astrolabe* .. .. 3·00 3·00
962/5 .. .. *Set of* 4 5·50 5·50

(Des and litho Walsall)

1987 (6 May). *World Wildlife Fund. Sheet* 115×110 *mm containing T* **179** *and similar vert designs. Multicoloured. P* 13½.
MS966 42 s. Type **179**; 42 s. Eagles; 42 s. Giraffes and birds; 42 s. Gulls; 42 s. Ostriches and elephants; 42 s. Elephant; 42 s. Lions, zebras, antelopes and giraffes; 42 s. Chimpanzees; 42 s. Frogs and antelopes; 42 s. Lizard and tigers; 42 s. Snake and tiger; 42 s. Butterfly .. .. 4·50 4·75
The stamps within No. **MS**966 show a composite design of animals entering Noah's Ark.

180 Two Paddlers in Canoe

181 King Taufa'ahau Tupou IV

(Des C. Abbott. Litho Questa)

1987 (1 July). *"Siv'a'alo" (Tonga-Fiji-Samoa) Canoe Race. T* **180** *and similar square designs. Multicoloured. P* 14.
967 32 s. Type **180**.. .. .. 25 30
968 42 s. Five paddlers 35 40
969 57 s. Paddlers and canoe bow 45 50
a. Value omitted (R. 3/2) .. .. ..
970 1 p. 50, Two paddlers (different) .. .. 1·10 1·25
967/70 .. .. *Set of* 4 1·90 2·25
MS971 153×59 mm. Nos. 967/70 .. .. 2·10 2·50
The stamps within No. **MS**971 show a composite design of two canoes racing.
No. 969a occurred on a batch of fifty sheets distributed to local post offices in Tonga. The remainder of the first printing was withdrawn and replaced, later in the month, by sheets showing the error corrected.

(Des and litho Walsall)

1987 (1 July)–**88**. *20th Anniv of Coronation of King Taufa'ahau Tupou IV. Self-adhesive. Stamps die-cut.*
972 **181** 1 s. black and olive-green 10 1
a. Booklet pane. Nos. 972×2, 974×4, 975×2 and 976×4 .. .. 1·60
b. Booklet pane. Nos. 972, 972*d*×2, 973×2, 974×4 and 975×3 (4.7.88) 95
c. Booklet pane. Nos. 972×4, 972*d*×2 and 976×6 (4.7.88) .. .. 1·90
972*d* 2 s. black and pale orange (4.7.88) .. 10 1
973 5 s. black and pale magenta 10 1
a. Booklet pane. Nos. 973×7, 974×2 and 975×3.. 80
974 10 s. black and reddish lilac 10 1
975 15 s. black and rose-red.. .. .. 15 2
976 32 s. black and turquoise-blue 30 3
972/6 .. .. *Set of* 6 55 7
Nos. 972/6 were only available from stamp booklets. These are self-adhesive stamps and the backing card forms the booklet cover.

(Litho Walsall)

1987 (Sept). *As Nos.* 871 *and* 876 (*previously self-adhesive*), *but printed with normal gum and perforations. Multicoloured. P* 14½.
976*a* 10 s. *Conus bullatus* .. .. .. 4·00 4·00
976*b* 32 s. *Acanthurus leucosternon* .. .. 11·00 11·00
Nos. 976*a*/*b* were printed from the same plates as the self-adhesive issue. They are without imprint date at foot and show a space of 23 mm between the two horizontal lines across each design.
For redrawn versions of these stamps with imprint date see Nos. 1005 and 1008.

182 Arms and Tongan Citizens

183 Father Christmas Octopus and Rat with Sack of Presents

(Des and litho Walsall)

1987 (23 Sept). *125th Anniv of First Parliament. P* 14½×14.
977 **182** 32 s. multicoloured 25 3
978 42 s. multicoloured 35 4
979 75 s. multicoloured 60 6
980 2 p. multicoloured .. .. .. 1·60 1·7
977/80 .. .. *Set of* 4 2·50 2·7

(Des and litho Walsall)

1987 (25 Nov). *Christmas. T* **183** *and similar horiz design showing cartoons. Multicoloured. P* 13½ × 14.
981 42 s. Type **183** 40 4
982 57 s. Delivering presents by outrigger canoe 60 6
983 1 p. Delivering presents by motorised tricycle .. .. 95 1·0
984 3 p. Drinking cocktails .. .. .. 2·75 3·0
981/4 .. .. *Set of* 4 4·00 4·5

184 King Taufa'ahau Tupou IV, *Olovaha* (inter-island ferry), Oil Rig and Pole Vaulting

(Des and litho Walsall)

1988 (4 July). *70th Birthday of King Taufa'ahau Tupou IV. T* **184** *and similar horiz designs, each showing portrait. Multicoloured. P* 11½.

985 32 s. Type **184** 30 35
986 42 s. Banknote, coins, Ha'amonga Trilithon and woodcarver 40 45
987 57 s. Rowing, communications satellite and Red Cross worker 60 65
988 2 p. 50, Scout emblem, 1982 47 s. Scout stamp and Friendly Island Airways aircraft .. .. 2·40 2·50
985/8 .. .. *Set of* 4 3·25 3·50

185 Capt. Cook and Journal — 186 Athletics

(Des and litho Walsall)

1988 (11 July). *Bicentenary of Australian Settlement. Sheet* 115 × 110 *mm containing T* **185** *and similar vert designs. Multicoloured. P* 13½.

MS989 42 s. Type **185**; 42 s. Ships in Sydney Harbour and Governor Philip; 42 s. Australia 1952 2s. 6d. aborigine definitive and early settlement; 42 s. Burke and Wills (explorers); 42 s. Emu, opals and gold prospector's licence; 42 s. ANZAC cap badge and soldier; 42 s. Cover from first overland mail by Trans Continental; 42 s. Ross Smith, England–Australia flown cover and G.B. 1969 1s. 9d. commemorative stamp; 42 s. Don Bradman and Harold Larwood (cricketers); 42 s. World War II campaign medals; 42 s. Australia 1978 18 c. Flying Doctor Service stamp and sheep station; 42 s. Sydney Opera House .. .. 4·75 5·00

(Des and litho Walsall)

1988 (11 Aug). *Olympic Games, Seoul. T* **186** *and similar vert designs. Multicoloured. P* 14.

990 57 s. Type **186** 60 65
991 75 s. Yachting 70 75
992 2 p. Cycling .. .. 1·90 2·00
993 3 p. Tennis .. .. 2·75 3·00
990/3 .. .. *Set of* 4 5·25 5·75

187 Traditional Tongan Fale

(Des and litho Walsall)

1988 (9 Sept). *Music in Tonga. T* **187** *and similar horiz designs. Multicoloured. P* 14.

994 32 s. Type **187** 30 35
995 42 s. Church choir 40 45
996 57 s. Tonga Police Band outside Royal Palace 55 60
997 2 p. 50, "The Jets" pop group .. .. .. 2·40 2·50
994/7 .. .. *Set of* 4 3·25 3·50

188 Olympic Flame

(Des and litho Walsall)

1988 (9 Sept). *"Sport Aid '88". Sheet* 105 × 75 *mm, containing T* **188** *and design as No.* 997. *Multicoloured. P* 14.

MS998 57 s. Type **188**; 57 s. As No. 997 .. 1·10 1·25

(Litho Walsall)

1988 (4 Oct)–**89**. *Redrawn designs as Nos.* 865/6, 868/9, 871/6, 879/81 *(previously self-adhesive) and new values* (7, 35, 42, 57 *s.,* 1 *p.,* 1 *p.* 50), *all with normal gum, perforations and imprint date at foot. Multicoloured. P* 14 (1 *p. to* 5 *p.*) *or* 14½×14 *(others).*

999 1 s. Type **159** 10 10
1000 2 s. *Porites* sp (18.10.88) 10 10
1001 4 s. *Pterois volitans* (2.3.89) 10 10
1002 5 s. *Cypraea mappa viridis* 10 10
1003 6 s. *Dardanus megistos* (crab) (18.10.88) .. 10 10
1004 7 s. Wandering Albatross (2.3.89) 10 10
1005 10 s. *Conus bullatus* 10 10
1006 15 s. *Conus textile* (18.10.88) 10 15
1007 20 s. *Dascyllus aruanus* 20 25
1008 32 s. *Acanthurus leucosternon* 25 30
1009 35 s. Sea Horse (2.3.89) 30 35
1010 42 s. Lesser Frigate Bird (18.10.88) 35 40
1011 50 s. *Conus aulicus* (2.3.89) 45 50
1012 57 s. Brown Booby (18.10.88) 45 50
1013 1 p. *Chelonia mydas* (turtle) (2.3.89) 85 90
1014 1 p. 50, Humpback Whale (2.3.89) .. .. 1·25 1·40
1015 2 p. *Birgus latro* (crab) (19.1.89) .. .. 1·75 1·90
1016 3 p. *Chicoreus palma-rosae* (18.10.88) .. 2·50 2·75
1017 5 p. *Thunnus albacares* (19.1.89) .. .. 4·25 4·50
999/1017 .. .. *Set of* 19 11·50 13·00

Nos. 1013/17 are horizontal, 41×26 mm.

On the redrawn designs there is a larger gap between the two horizontal lines on each design. For Nos. 1005 and 1008 this measures 25 mm. For these two values with a gap of 23 mm and no imprint date see Nos. 916*a*/*b*.

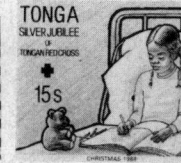

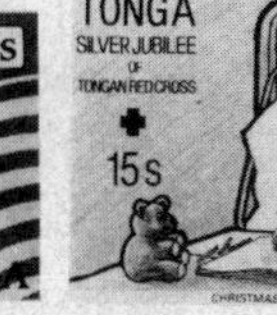

189 Capt. Cook's H.M.S. *Resolution* — 190 Girl in Hospital Bed

(Des and litho Walsall)

1988 (20 Oct). *Centenary of Tonga–U.S.A. Treaty of Friendship. T* **189** *and similar horiz designs. Multicoloured. P* 14.

1018 42 s. Type **189** 40 45
1019 57 s. *Santa Maria* 55 60
1020 2 p. Cook and Christopher Columbus .. 1·90 2·00
1018/20 .. .. *Set of* 3 2·50 2·75
MS1021 140 × 115 mm. Nos. 1018/20 .. .. 2·75 3·00

(Des and litho Walsall)

1988 (17 Nov). *Christmas. 125th Anniv of International Red Cross and 25th Anniv of Tongan Red Cross. T* **123** *and similar horiz designs. Multicoloured. P* 14½.

1022 15 s. Type **190** (A) 15 20
 a. Horiz pair. Nos. 1022/3 .. .. 30 40
1023 15 s. Type **190** (B) 15 20
1024 32 s. Red Cross nurse reading to boy (A) .. 30 35
 a. Horiz pair. Nos. 1024/5 .. .. 60 70
1025 32 s. Red Cross nurse reading to boy (B) .. 30 35
1026 42 s. Red Cross nurse taking pulse (A) .. 40 45
 a. Horiz pair. Nos. 1026/7 .. .. 80 85
1027 42 s. Red Cross nurse taking pulse (B) .. 40 45
1028 57 s. Red Cross nurse with sleeping child (A) 55 60
 a. Horiz pair. Nos. 1028/9 .. .. 1·10 1·25
1029 57 s. Red Cross nurse with sleeping child (B) 55 60
1030 1 p. 50, Boy in wheelchair (A) .. .. 1·40 1·50
 a. Horiz pair. Nos. 1030/1 .. .. 2·75 3·00
1031 1 p. 50, Boy in wheelchair (B) .. .. 1·40 1·50
1022/31 .. .. *Set of* 10 5·00 5·50

Nos. 1022/3, 1024/5, 1026/7, 1028/9 and 1030/1 were printed together, *se-tenant*, in horizontal pairs throughout the sheets with the first stamp in each pair inscribed "INTERNATIONAL RED CROSS 125th ANNIVERSARY" (A) and the second "SILVER JUBILEE OF TONGAN RED CROSS" (B).

191 Map of Tofua Island and Breadfruit — 192 *Hypolimnas bolina*

(Des and litho Walsall)

1989 (28 Apr). *Bicentenary of Mutiny on the* Bounty. *T* **191** *and similar multicoloured designs. P* 13½×14.

1032 32 s. Type **191** 30 35
1033 42 s. H.M.S. *Bounty* and chronometer .. 40 45
1034 57 s. Captain Bligh and *Bounty*'s launch cast adrift 55 60
1032/4 .. .. *Set of* 3 1·10 1·25
MS1035 106×80 mm. 2 p. Fletcher Christian on H.M.S. *Bounty* (*vert*); 3 p. Bligh cast adrift. P 14×13½ (2 p.) or 13½×14×13½×13½ (3 p.) 4·75 5·00

(Litho Walsall)

1989 (18 May). *Butterflies. T* **192** *and similar vert designs. Multicoloured. P* 14½×14.

1036 42 s. Type **192** 40 45
1037 57 s. *Jamides bochus* 55 60
1038 1 p. 20, *Melanitis leda solandra* .. .. 1·10 1·25
1039 2 p. 50, *Danaus plexippus* .. .. 2·40 2·50
1036/9 .. .. *Set of* 4 4·00 4·25

NEW INFORMATION

The editor is always interested to correspond with people who have new information that will improve or correct the Catalogue.

193 Football at Rugby School, 1870 — 194 Short "S30" Flying Boat, 1939 (50th anniv of first flight)

(Litho Walsall)

1989 (22 Aug). *Inauguration of National Sports Stadium and South Pacific Mini Games, Tonga. T* **193** *and similar horiz designs showing development of rugby, tennis and cricket. Multicoloured. P* 14.

1040 32 s. Type **193** 30 35
 a. Sheetlet. Nos. 1040/4×2 .. .. 3·00
1041 32 s. D. Gallaher (All Black's captain, 1905) and Springboks rugby match, 1906 .. 30 35
1042 32 s. King George V with Cambridge team, 1922 and W. Wakefield (England captain, 1926) 30 35
1043 32 s. E. Crawford (Ireland captain, 1926) and players on cigarette cards 30 35
1044 32 s. S. Mafi (Tonga captain, 1970s) and modern rugby match 30 35
1045 42 s. Royal tennis, 1659 .. .. .. 40 45
 a. Sheetlet. Nos. 1045/9×2 .. .. 4·00
1046 42 s. Major Wingfield and lawn tennis, 1873 .. .. 40 45
1047 42 s. Oxford and Cambridge tennis teams, 1884 .. .. 40 45
1048 42 s. Bunny Ryan, 1910, and players on cigarette cards 40 45
1049 42 s. Boris Becker and modern tennis match 40 45
1050 57 s. Cricket match, 1743, and F. Pilch memorial 55 60
 a. Sheetlet. Nos. 1050/4×2 .. .. 5·50
1051 57 s. W. G. Grace (19th-century cricketer) 55 60
1052 57 s. *Boys Own Paper* cricket article, 1909 55 60
1053 57 s. Australian cricket team, 1909, and players on cigarette cards 55 60
1054 57 s. The Ashes urn, and modern cricket match 55 60
1040/54 .. .. *Set of* 15 5·50 6·25

Nos. 1040/4, 1045/9 and 1050/4 were each issued in sheetlets of ten containing two horizontal strips of five separated by a central inscribed gutter.

(Litho Walsall)

1989 (23 Oct). *Aviation in Tonga. T* **194** *and similar horiz designs. Multicoloured. P* 14½×14.

1055 42 s. Type **194** 40 45
1056 57 s. Vought "F4U Corsair", 1943 .. .. 55 60
1057 90 s. Boeing "737" at Fua'amotu Airport .. 85 90
1058 3 p. Montgolfier balloon, Wright biplane, "Concorde" and space shuttle (97×26 *mm*) .. .. 2·75 3·00
1055/8 .. .. *Set of* 4 4·00 4·50

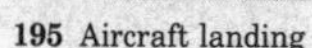

195 Aircraft landing — 196 Rowland Hill, Mulready Cover and Penny Blacks

(Litho Walsall)

1989 (9 Nov). *Christmas. "Flying Home". T* **195** *and similar vert designs. P* 14×13½.

1059 32 s. blue-green, deep brown & dull orange 30 35
1060 42 s. blue-green, deep brown and emerald 40 45
1061 57 s. blue-green, deep brown and vermilion 55 60
1062 3 p. blue-green, deep brown & deep mauve 2·75 3·00
1059/62 .. .. *Set of* 4 3·50 4·00

Designs:—42 s. Villagers waving to aircraft; 57 s. Outrigger canoe and aircraft; 3 p. Aircraft over headland.

(Litho Walsall)

1989 (17 Nov). *20th Universal Postal Union Congress, Washington. Sheet* 115×110 *mm containing T* **196** *and similar vert designs. Multicoloured. P* 13½.

MS1063 57 s. Type **196**; 57 s. Early train and steam ship; 57 s. Stage coach, Pony Express poster and rider; 57 s. French hot-air balloon and flown cover; 57 s. Samuel Morse and telegraph key; 57 s. Early British mail van and pillar box; 57 s. Unloading early mail plane; 57 s. *Queen Mary* and *Graf Zeppelin* flown cover; 57 s. Helicopter and mail van; 57 s. Computer and fax machine; 57 s. "Apollo 11" emblem and space cover; 57 s. U.P.U. Monument and space shuttle 6·25 6·50

OFFICIAL STAMPS

G.F.B. (O 1) ½ 1D (O 2)

(G.F.B. = Gaue Faka Buleaga = On Government Service)

1893 (13 Feb). *Optd with Type* O 1 *by Govt Printing Office, Wellington, N.Z. W* **2**. *P* 12 × 11½.
O1 **5** 1d. ultramarine (C.) .. .. .. 9·00 28·00
a. Bisected diagonally (½d.) (on cover)
O2 **6** 2d. ultramarine (C.) .. .. .. 20·00 35·00
O3 **5** 4d. ultramarine (C.) .. .. .. 38·00 70·00
O4 **6** 8d. ultramarine (C.) .. .. .. 80·00 £130
O5 1s. ultramarine (C.) .. .. .. 90·00 £150
O1/5 .. .. *Set of* 5 £210 £350

Above prices are for stamps in good condition and colour. Faded and stained stamps from the remainders are worth much less.

1893 (Dec). *Nos* O1 *to* O5 *variously surch with new value, sideways as Type* O **2**.
O 6 **5** ½d. on 1d. ultramarine .. .. 13·00 30·00
O 7 **6** 2½d. on 2d. ultramarine .. .. 15·00 28·00
O 8 **5** 5d. on 4d. ultramarine .. .. 15·00 28·00
O 9 **6** 7½d. on 8d. ultramarine .. .. 18·00 40·00
a. "D" of "7½D." omitted .. ..
b. Surch double £1000
O10 10d. on 1s. ultramarine .. .. 20·00 45·00
O6/10 .. .. *Set of* 5 75·00 £150

OFFICIAL AIR MAIL 1862 TAU'ATAINA EMANCIPATION 1962 (O 3)

OFFICIAL AIRMAIL 40 SENITI (O 4)

1962 (7 Feb). *Air. Centenary of Emancipation. Nos.* 112/14, 116 *and* 118/19 *optd with Type* O **3** *in red by* R. S. Wallbank, *Govt Printer.*
O11 – 2d. ultramarine .. .. .. 11·00 6·00
a. "OFFICIAI" .. .. .. 20·00 11·00
b. "MAIl" .. .. .. 20·00 11·00
O12 – 5d. violet .. .. .. 12·00 6·50
a. "OFFICIAI" .. .. .. 22·00 12·00
b. "MAIl" .. .. .. 22·00 12·00
O13 – 1s. red-brown .. .. .. 7·50 3·75
a. "OFFICIAI" .. .. .. 25·00 11·00
b. "MAIl" .. .. .. 25·00 11·00
c. Opt double ..
ca. "OFFICIAI" ..
cb. "MAIl" ..
O14 – 5s. orange-yellow and slate-lilac .. 90·00 55·00
a. "MAIl" .. .. .. £200 75·00
O15 **52** 10s. yellow and black .. .. 42·00 22·00
a. "MAIl" £100
O16 **53** £1 yellow, scar, ultram & dp brt blue .. 70·00 35·00
a. "MAIl" £150
O11/O16 .. .. .. *Set of* 6 £200 £120

SET PRICES. Official Stamps from here onwards are included in the complete set prices given with any corresponding Postage issues.

1963 (15 July). *Air. First Polynesian Gold Coinage Commemoration. As T* **63** *but inscr* "OFFICIAL AIRMAIL". 1 *koula coin (diam* 3⅛ *in.). Imperf.*
O17 **63** 15s. black .. .. 3·00 4·00

1965 (18 Mar). *No.* O17 *surch as T* **67**.
O18 **63** 30s. on 15s. black .. .. .. 3·00 3·50

1966 (18 June). *Air. Centenary of Tupou College and Secondary Education. No.* 117 *surch with* "OFFICIAL AIRMAIL" *and new value, with commemorative inscription as in T* **69** *but in italic capital letters.*
O19 10s. on 4d. blue-green 40 35
a. Surch inverted £350 £150
O20 20s. on 4d. blue-green 60 50

1967 (25 Mar). *Air. Decimal currency. No.* 112 *surch* "OFFICIAL AIRMAIL ONE PA'ANGA" *in three lines, in red.*
O21 1 p. on 5s. .. .. 1·75 2·25
a. "AIRMAIL" above "OFFICIAL" .. £130

No. O21a occurred once in a number of sheets until it was corrected.

1967 (4 July). *Air. No.* 114 *surch in various denominations as Type* O **4**.
O22 **53** 40 s. on £1 .. .. .. 50 50
O23 60 s. on £1 .. .. .. 70 70
O24 1 p. on £1 .. .. .. 90 90
O25 2 p. on £1 .. .. .. 1·50 1·50

Nos. O22/5 were first used on 4 July 1967, but supplies of unused stamps were not made available until April 1968.

The Friendly Islands welcome the United States Peace Corps Official Airmail 30s (O 5)

Friendly Islands Trials Field & Track South Pacific Games Port Moresby 1969 T$1·00 OFFICIAL AIRMAIL (O 6)

1967 (15 Dec). *Air. Arrival of U.S. Peace Corps in Tonga. As No.* 114, *but imperf, and background colour changed, and surch as Type* O **5**.
O26 **53** 30 s. on £1 yellow, scarlet, ultramarine and emerald-green 20 25
O27 70 s. on £1 yellow, scarlet, ultramarine and emerald-green 40 45
O28 1 p. 50, on £1 yellow, scarlet, ultramarine and emerald-green 70 85

1968 (4 July). *50th Birthday of King Taufa'ahua IV. No.* 207 *surch.* "HIS MAJESTY'S 50th BIRTHDAY" (*as T* **79**), "OFFICIAL AIRMAIL" *and new value.*
O29 **75** 40 s. on 50 s. (Turq.) .. .. .. 1·00 60
O30 60 s. on 50 s. (G.) .. .. .. 1·50 80
O31 1 p. on 50 s. (V.) .. .. .. 2·25 1·25
O32 2 p. on 50 s. (P.) .. .. .. 4·00 2·00

1968 (19 Dec). *Air. South Pacific Games Field and Track Trials, Port Moresby, New Guinea. As No.* 114, *but imperf, background colour changed and surch as Type* O **6**.
O33 **53** 20 s. on £1 yellow, scarlet, ultramarine and emerald-green 15 15
O34 1 p. on £1 yellow, scarlet, ultramarine and emerald-green 40 40

1969 (13 Aug). *Air. Third South Pacific Games, Port Moresby. Design as Nos.* 290/4.
O35 70 s. carmine-red, bright green and turquoise 45 60
O36 80 s. carmine-red, orange and turquoise .. 55 70

OFFICIAL AIRMAIL 1969 OIL SEARCH 90s (O 7)

Royal Visit MARCH 1970 OFFICIAL AIRMAIL T$1·25 (O 8)

1969 (23 Dec). *Air. First Oil Search in Tonga. As No.* 114 *but imperf, background colour changed to emerald-green, and surch as Type* O **7**.
O37 **53** 90 s. on £1 multicoloured .. .. 2·00 2·00
a. "1966" for "1969" .. ..
O38 1 p. 10 on £1 multicoloured (R.) .. 2·00 2·00
a. "1966" for "1969" .. ..

No. O38 is surch as Type O **7**, but without "OFFICIAL AIRMAIL".

1970 (7 Mar). *Royal Visit. As No.* 110 *but imperf, colours changed, and surch as Type* O **8**.
O39 75 s. on 1s. carmine-red and yellow .. 3·00 1·50
O40 1 p. on 1s. carmine-red and yellow (B.) .. 3·50 2·00
O41 1 p. 25 on 1s. carmine-red & yellow (G.) .. 4·25 2·50

(O 9)

1970 (4 June). *Entry into British Commonwealth. As No.* 112 *but imperf, background colour changed, and surch as Type* O **9**.
O42 50 s. on 5s. orange-yellow and sepia .. 60 50
O43 90 s. on 5s. orange-yellow and sepia (R.) .. 80 70
O44 1 p. 50 on 5s. orange-yellow & sepia (G.) .. 1·50 1·25

1970 (4 June). *As Nos.* 325/34, *but inscr.* "OFFICIAL POST". *Colour of* "TONGA" *given for* 6 *to* 10 *s.*
O45 **83** 1 s. greenish yellow, brt purple & blk .. 15 15
O46 2 s. greenish yellow, ultram & black .. 20 20
O47 3 s. greenish yellow, chocolate & blk .. 25 25
O48 4 s. greenish yellow, emerald and black 25 25
O49 5 s. greenish yellow, orange-red & blk .. 30 30
O50 **90** 6 s. ultramarine 35 35
O51 7 s. deep mauve 40 40
O52 8 s. gold 45 45
O53 9 s. bright carmine 55 55
O54 10 s. silver 55 55
O45/54 .. .. .. *Set of* 10 3·00 3·00

The note after No. 334 also applies here.

See also Nos. O82/91.

Centenary British Red Cross 1870-1970

OFFICIAL AIRMAIL 30s

(O 10)

1970 (17 Oct). *Centenary of British Red Cross. As Nos.* 102 *and* 112 *but imperf, colours changed and surch as Type* O **10**.
O55 30 s. on 1½d. emerald (Blk. and R.) .. 70 70
O56 80 s. on 5s. orange-yellow & sepia (B. & R.) .. 2·25 2·25
O57 90 s. on 5s. orange-yellow & sepia (B. & R.) .. 2·25 2·25

1965 IN MEMORIAM 1970 (O 11)

(O 12)

1971 (30 Jan). *Air. Fifth Death Anniv of Queen Salote. As No.* 113 *but imperf, colours changed and surch as Type* O **11**.
O58 **52** 20 s. on 10s. orange-yellow 70 60
O59 30 s. on 10s. orange-yellow (V.) .. 90 80
O60 50 s. on 10s. orange-yellow (B.) .. 1·75 1·25
O61 2 p. on 10s. orange-yellow (G.) .. 6·50 5·00

1971 (17 Apr). *Air.* "*Philatokyo 1971*" *Stamp Exhibition. Unissued Red Cross surcharges on No.* 107, *but imperf, colours changed and additionally surch as Type* O **12**.
O62 30 s. on 5d. green and yellow (B. & R.) .. 40 40
O63 80 s. on 5d. green and yellow (Blk. & R.) .. 1·00 1·00
O64 90 s. on 5d. green and yellow (P. & R.) .. 1·25 1·25

1971 (20 July)–**72**. *Air. As Nos.* 365/6a, *but inscr* "OFFICIAL AIRMAIL".
O65 **96** 14 s. multicoloured 55 55
O65*a* 17 s. multicoloured (20.7.72) 65 65
O66 21 s. multicoloured 75 75
O66*a* 38 s. multicoloured (20.7.72) .. .. 1·10 1·10

O **13** Football

1971 (20 July). *Air. Fourth South Pacific Games, Tahiti.*
O67 O **13** 50 s. multicoloured 40 5
O68 90 s. multicoloured 60 9
O69 1 p. 50, multicoloured .. .. .. 80 1·2

INVESTITURE 1971 OFFICIAL 60s AIRMAIL (O 14)

(*Illustration reduced. Actual size* 61 × 13 *mm*)

1971 (30 Oct). *Air. Investiture of Royal Tongan Medal of Merit. Nos.* 315, 318 *and* 316 *surch as Type* O **14**.
O70 **89** 60 s. on 3 s. multicoloured 50 5
O71 80 s. on 25 s. multicoloured 70 7
O72 1 p. 10 on 7 s. multicoloured 80 8

O **15** "UNICEF" and Emblem

1971 (31 Dec). *Air. 25th Anniv of UNICEF.*
O73 O **15** 70 s. multicoloured 70 7
O74 80 s. multicoloured 75 7
O75 90 s. multicoloured 85 8

1972 (14 Apr). *Air. Merchant Marine Routes. Design similar to T* **100**, *but inscr* "OFFICIAL AIRMAIL".
O76 20 s. multicoloured 50 3
O77 50 s. multicoloured .. .. 1·75 8
O78 1 p. 20, multicoloured .. .. .. 3·25 2·0

Design:—Nos. O76/8, Map of South Pacific, and *Aoniu.*

1972 (15 July). *Air. Fifth Anniv of Coronation. Design similar to T* **101**, *but inscr* "OFFICIAL AIRMAIL".
O79 50 s. multicoloured 80 4
O80 70 s. multicoloured .. .. 1·10 6
O81 1 p. 50, multicoloured .. .. .. 2·40 1·0

Design (47 × 57 *mm*):—Nos. O79/81, As T **101**, but with different background.

1972 (30 Sept). *As Nos.* 413/27, *but inscr* "OFFICIAL POST".

(*a*) *As Nos.* 413/17
O82 **83** 1 s. light yellow, scarlet and black .. 15 10
O83 2 s. light yellow, dp blue-green & black 20 15
O84 3 s. light yellow, yellow-green and black 25 20
O85 4 s. light yellow and black 25 20
O86 5 s. light yellow and black 25 20

(*b*) *As Nos.* O50/4, *but colours changed. Colour of* "TONGA" *given*
O87 **90** 6 s. light green 25 20
O88 7 s. light green 30 25
O89 8 s. light green 30 25
O90 9 s. light green 30 25
O91 10 s. light green 35 30

(*c*) *As Nos.* 423/7. *Colour of face value given*
O92 **102** 15 s. new blue 55 45
O93 20 s. reddish orange 70 60
O94 25 s. chocolate 80 70
O95 40 s. yellow-orange .. .. .. 1·75 1·50
O96 50 s. royal blue .. .. 2·00 1·75
O82/96 .. .. *Set of* 15 7·50 6·50
The note after No. 427 also applies here.

1972 (9 Dec). *Air. Proclamation of Sovereignty over Minerva Reefs. Design similar to T* **104**, *but inscr* "OFFICIAL AIRMAIL".
O97 25 s. multicoloured 40 25
O98 75 s. multicoloured .. .. 1·25 70
O99 1 p. 50, multicoloured .. .. .. 2·50 1·25
Design: *Horiz* (64 × 39 *mm*)—Nos. O97/9, Flags and map.

ESTABLISHMENT
BANK OF TONGA
40s
OFFICIAL AIRMAIL

(O 16)

1973 (30 Mar). *Air. Foundation of Bank of Tonga. No.* 396 *surch as Type* O **16**.
O100 **100** 40 s. on 21 s. mult (Blk. & G.) .. 85 50
O101 85 s. on 21 s. multicoloured (B. & G.) 1·75 90
O102 1 p. 25 on 21 s. multicoloured (Br.) .. 2·00 1·10

SILVER JUBILEE
TONGAN SCOUTING
1948 - 1973

(O 17)

1973 (29 June). *Silver Jubilee of Scouting in Tonga. Nos.* O76, O74 *and* 319 *variously optd or surch as Type* O **17** *in silver* (*Nos.* O103/4) *or silver and blue* (*No.* O105).
O103 – 30 s. on 20 s. multicoloured .. .. 14·00 3·50
O104 **O 15** 80 s. multicoloured .. .. 30·00 11·00
O105 **89** 1 p. 40 on 50 s. multicoloured .. 45·00 24·00

1973 (2 Oct). *Air. Bicentenary of Capt. Cook's Visit. Design similar to T* **107**, *but inscr* "OFFICIAL AIRMAIL".
O106 25 s. multicoloured .. .. .. 1·75 1·00
O107 80 s. multicoloured .. .. .. 5·00 2·75
O108 1 p. 30, multicoloured .. .. .. 6·50 4·00
Design: *Horiz* (52 × 45 *mm*)—Nos. O106/8, *James Cook* (bulk carrier).

1974

(O 18)

1973 (19 Dec). *Air. Commonwealth Games. Nos.* O67/9 *optd with Type* O **18**.
O109 **O 13** 50 s. multicoloured (B.) .. .. 1·00 60
O110 90 s. multicoloured (Blk.) .. .. 1·75 1·00
O111 1 p. 50, multicoloured (G.) .. .. 2·50 1·75
a. Opt double £150

O **19** Dove of Peace

1974 (20 Mar). *Air.*
O112 **O 19** 7 s. turq-grn, reddish vio & orge-red 25 20
O113 9 s. turq-grn, reddish vio & red-brn 30 25
O114 12 s. turq-grn, reddish vio & yell-orge 35 30
O115 14 s. turquoise-green, reddish violet and bistre-yellow 40 35
O116 17 s. multicoloured 50 45
O117 29 s. multicoloured 80 70
O118 38 s. multicoloured .. .. .. 1·00 90
O119 50 s. multicoloured .. .. .. 1·50 1·25
O120 75 s. multicoloured .. .. .. 2·00 1·75
O112/120 .. .. *Set of* 9 6·50 5·50

1974 (20 June). *Air. Centenary of Universal Postal Union. Design similar to T* **110**, *but inscr* "OFFICIAL AIRMAIL".
O121 25 s. dp red-orange, lt yellow-green & black 60 35
O122 35 s. lemon, magenta and black 75 45
O123 70 s. deep orange, bright blue and black .. 1·75 1·00
Design: *Square* (40 × 40 *mm*)—Letters "UPU".

1974 (11 Sept). *Air. Tongan Girl Guides. Design similar to T* **111**, *but inscr* "OFFICIAL AIRMAIL".
O124 45 s. multicoloured .. .. .. 3·50 1·75
O125 55 s. multicoloured .. .. .. 3·75 2·00
O126 1 p. multicoloured .. .. .. 6·50 3·75
Design: *Oval* (35 × 52 *mm*)—Lady Baden-Powell.

(O 20)

1974 (11 Dec). *Air. Establishment of Royal Marine Institute. Nos.* 446 *and* 451 *surch as Type* O **20**, *each obliterating the centre part of the original design.*
O127 30 s. on 15 s. multicoloured (Gold, B. & P.) 1·75 75
O128 35 s. on 15 s. multicoloured (Sil., B. & Blk.) 2·00 90
a. Black ("TONGA TONGA") omitted .. £200
O129 80 s. on 17 s. multicoloured (Blk. & R.) .. 3·50 2·25

1975 (11 Mar). *Air. South Pacific Forum and Tourism. Designs similar to T* **113** *but inscr* "OFFICIAL AIRMAIL".
O130 50 s. multicoloured .. .. .. 1·10 80
O131 75 s. multicoloured .. .. .. 1·75 1·25
O132 1 p. 25, multicoloured .. .. .. 2·50 1·75
Designs: (49 × 43 *mm*)—50 s. Jungle arch; others, Sunset scene.

1975 (11 June). *Air. Fifth South Pacific Games. Design similar to T* **114** *but inscr* "OFFICIAL AIRMAIL".
O133 38 s. multicoloured 45 30
O134 75 s. multicoloured 80 60
O135 1 p. 20, multicoloured .. .. .. 1·40 1·25
Design: *Oval* (51 × 27 *mm*):—Runners on track.

O **21** Tongan Monarchs

1975 (4 Nov). *Air. Centenary of Tongan Constitution.*
O136 **O 21** 17 s. multicoloured 30 25
O137 60 s. multicoloured 80 55
O138 90 s. multicoloured .. .. .. 1·25 75

1976 (24 Feb). *Air. First Participation in Olympic Games. Design similar to T* **117** *but inscr* "OFFICIAL AIRMAIL".
O139 45 s. multicoloured .. .. .. 1·75 85
O140 55 s. multicoloured .. .. .. 2·00 1·00
O141 1 p. multicoloured .. .. .. 3·25 1·90
Design: *Oval* (36 × 53 *mm*)—Montreal logo.

1976 (26 May). *Air. Bicentenary of American Revolution. Designs as T* **118** *showing signatories to the Declaration of Independence. Inscr* "OFFICIAL AIRMAIL".
O142 20 s. multicoloured .. .. .. 1·00 40
O143 50 s. multicoloured .. .. .. 2·25 1·00
O144 1 p. 15, multicoloured .. .. .. 4·75 2·50

1976 (25 Aug). *Air. 150th Anniv of Christianity in Tonga. Hexagonal design* (65 × 52 *mm*) *showing Lifuka Chapel.*
O145 65 s. multicoloured .. .. .. 1·40 1·40
O146 85 s. multicoloured .. .. .. 1·75 1·75
O147 1 p. 15, multicoloured .. .. .. 2·50 2·50

1976 (1 Nov). *Air. Centenary of Treaty of Friendship with Germany. Rectangular design* (51 × 47 *mm*) *showing text.*
O148 30 s. multicoloured 60 60
O149 60 s. multicoloured .. .. .. 1·40 1·40
O150 1 p. 25, multicoloured .. .. .. 2·75 2·75

1977 (7 Feb). *Air. Silver Jubilee. Vert design* (57 × 66 *mm*) *showing flags of Tonga and the U.K.*
O151 35 s. multicoloured .. .. .. 4·50 60
O152 45 s. multicoloured .. .. .. 1·00 40
O153 1 p. 10, multicoloured .. .. .. 1·50 60

1977 (4 July). *Air. Tenth Anniv of King's Coronation. Square design* (50 × 50 *mm*) *showing* 1967 *Coronation Coin.*
O154 20 s. multicoloured 40 40
O155 40 s. multicoloured 80 80
O156 80 s. multicoloured .. .. .. 1·75 1·75

1977 (28 Sept). *Air. Bicentenary of Capt. Cook's Last Voyage. Rectangular design* (52 × 46 *mm*) *showing text.*
O157 20 s. multicoloured .. .. .. 2·50 1·60
O158 55 s. on 20 s. multicoloured .. .. 5·50 3·50
O159 85 s. on 20 s. multicoloured (V. and Blk.) .. 8·00 5·50
The face values of Nos. O158/9 are surcharged on the stamps, the original face value being incorrect.

1977 (16 Dec). *Air. Whale Conservation. Hexagonal design* (66 × 51 *mm*) *showing Blue Whale.*
O160 45 s. multicoloured .. .. .. 1·75 1·25
O161 65 s. multicoloured .. .. .. 2·50 1·90
O162 85 s. multicoloured .. .. .. 3·00 2·25

1978 (5 May). *Air. Commonwealth Games, Edmonton. "Tear-drop" design* (35 × 52 *mm*) *showing Games Emblem.*
O163 30 s. black, blue and red 45 45
O164 60 s. black, red and blue .. .. 1·00 1·00
O165 1 p. black, red and blue .. .. 1·60 1·60

1978 (4 July). *Air. 60th Birthday of King Taufa'ahau Tupou IV. Medal-shaped design* (21 × 45 *mm*) *showing portrait of King.*
O166 26 s. black, vermilion and yellow .. 35 30
O167 85 s. black, light brown and yellow .. .. 1·10 1·00
O168 90 s. black, bright violet and yellow .. .. 1·25 1·10

1978 (29 Sept). *Coil stamps.* (*a*) *Designs similar to Nos.* 675/9 *but inscr* "OFFICIAL POST".
O169 1 s. purple and greenish yellow 10 10
O170 2 s. brown and greenish yellow 10 10
O171 3 s. carmine, yellow and greenish yellow .. 10 10
O172 4 s. brown, yellow and greenish yellow .. 10 10
O173 5 s. blue-green, yellow and greenish yellow 10 10

(*b*) *Designs similar to Nos.* 680/4 *but inscr* "OFFICIAL POST"
O174 6 s. yellow-brown, emerald and light brown 15 15
O175 7 s. blue-black, emerald and light brown .. 20 20
O176 8 s. magenta, emerald and light brown 20 20
O177 9 s. red-brown, emerald and light brown .. 25 25
O178 10 s. deep green, emerald and light brown .. 25 25

(*c*) *Designs similar to Nos.* 685/9 *but inscr* "OFFICIAL POST"
O179 15 s. grey-black, orange-brown and emerald 35 35
O180 20 s. vermilion, orange-brown and emerald 40 40
O181 30 s. emerald and orange-brown 50 50
O182 50 s. new blue, orange-brown and emerald .. 90 90
O183 1 p. reddish violet, orange-brown & emer .. 1·75 1·75
O169/83 .. .. *Set of* 15 4·75 4·75

1978 (15 Dec). *Air. Endangered Wildlife Conservation. Designs as Nos.* 690/2 *but inscr* "OFFICIAL AIRMAIL".
O184 40 s. Type **129** .. .. 1·25 55
O185 50 s. Insular Flying Fox .. .. .. 1·25 70
O186 1 p. 10, Turtle .. .. 2·25 1·50

1979 (16 Feb). *Air. Decade of Progress. Designs similar to Nos.* 700/9 *but inscr* "OFFICIAL AIRMAIL".
O187 38 s. Tonga Red Cross emblem 55 40
O188 74 s. As No. 702 .. .. 1·00 75
O189 80 s. As No. 701 .. .. 1·10 80

1979 (1 June). *Air. Death Centenary of Sir Rowland Hill and 10th Anniv of Tongan Self-adhesive Stamps. Hand-shaped design* (45 × 53 *mm*) *showing self-adhesive stamps being removed from backing paper.*
O190 45 s. multicoloured 90 60
O191 65 s. multicoloured .. .. .. 1·25 85
O192 80 s. multicoloured .. .. .. 1·60 1·10

O **22** Blue-crowned Lory with foliage
O **23** Blue-crowned Lory without foliage

1979 (17 Aug). *Air. Coil stamps.*
O193 **O 22** 5 s. mult (face value in black) .. 15 15
O194 11 s. multicoloured 25 25
O195 14 s. multicoloured 25 25
O196 15 s. multicoloured 30 30
O197 17 s. multicoloured 30 30
O198 18 s. multicoloured 30 30
O199 22 s. multicoloured 35 35
O200 31 s. multicoloured 55 55
O201 39 s. multicoloured 70 70
O202 75 s. multicoloured .. .. .. 1·25 1·50
O203 1 p. multicoloured .. .. .. 1·75 2·00
O193/203 .. .. *Set of* 11 5·50 6·00
See also No. O213.

1979 (23 Nov). *Air. Views as seen through the Lens of a Camera. Design as T* **133** *but showing Niuatoputapu and Tafahi.*
O204 35 s. multicoloured 45 35
O205 45 s. multicoloured 55 40
O206 1 p. multicoloured .. .. .. 1·10 1·00

1980 (9 Jan). *Air. 125th Anniv of France-Tonga Treaty of Friendship. Design as T* **134** *but showing the Establishment of the Principle of Religious Freedom in the Pacific Islands.*
O207 40 s. multicoloured 55 60
O208 55 s. multicoloured 80 85
O209 1 p. 25, multicoloured .. .. .. 1·75 1·90

1980 (30 Apr). *Air. Olympic Games, Moscow. Nos.* O190/2 *surch as T* **135** *in black on silver background.*
O210 26 s. on 45 s. multicoloured 35 40
O211 40 s. on 65 s. multicoloured 55 60
O212 1 p. 10, on 1 p. multicoloured .. .. 1·60 1·75

1980 (May). *No.* O193 *redrawn without foliage as Type* O **22**.

O213	O **23**	5 s. mult (face value in magenta) ..	£100	

1980 (30 Sept). *Air. South Pacific Scout Jamboree, Tonga and 75th Anniv of Rotary International. Design showing Scout camp and Rotary emblem.*

O214	25 s. multicoloured	70	40
O215	2 p. multicoloured	3·50	3·00

T$2 OFFICIAL OFFICIAL

(O **24**) (O **25**) (O **26**)

1980 (3 Dec). *Air. No.* O145 *surch with Type* O **24**.

O216	2 p. on 65 s. multicoloured	3·00	3·50

1983 (22 Feb–Mar). *Nos.* 834/6 *handstamped with Type* O **25** (29 *s.*, 32 *s.*) *or optd with Type* O **26** (47 *s.*).

O217	29 s. Type **151**	2·50	2·50
O218	32 s. Type **151**	3·25	3·25
O219	47 s. Montgolfier's balloon and "Concorde" (Mar)	4·50	4·50
O217/19	.. .. *Set of* 3	9·25	9·25

OFFICIAL ***OFFICIAL*** *OFFICIAL*

(O **27**) (O **28**) (O **29**)

1894 (10 Apr)–**85**. *Nos.* 865/79 *and* 881 *optd with Type* O **27** (1, 5, 10, 15, 29, 47 *s.*) *or with Type* O **28** (*others*).

O220	1 s. Type **159**	10	10
O221	2 s. *Porites sp* (26.6.84)	10	10
O222	3 s. *Holocentrus ruber* (18.5.84)	10	10
O223	5 s. *Cypraea mappa viridis*	10	10
O224	6 s. *Dardanus megistos* (17.9.84).. ..	10	10
O225	9 s. *Stegostoma fasciatum* (18.5.84) ..	35	35
	b. Optd on No. 870b (28.5.85)	10	10
O226	10 s. *Conus bullatus*	10	10
O227	13 s. *Pterois volitans* (18.5.84)	10	10
O228	15 s. *Conus textile*	10	15
O229	20 s. *Dascyllus aruanus* (18.5.84)	20	25
O230	29 s. *Conus aulicus*	25	30
O231	32 s. *Acanthurus leucosternon* (18.5.84) ..	25	30
O232	47 s. *Lambis truncata*	40	45
O233	1 p. *Millepora dichotama* (26.6.84) ..	85	90
O234	2 p. *Birgus latro* (17.9.84)..	1·75	1·90
O235	5 p. *Thunnus albacares* (28.5.85).. ..	4·25	4·50
O220/35	.. .. *Set of* 16	7·75	8·50

1986 (16 Apr). *Nos.* 933/9 *optd with Type* O **29**.

O236	4 s. on 2 s. *Porites sp.*	10	10
O237	4 s. on 13 s. *Pterois volitans*	10	10
O238	42 s. on 3 s. *Holocentrus ruber*	35	40
O239	42 s. on 9 s. *Stegostoma fasciatum* ..	35	40
O240	57 s. on 6 s. *Dardanus megistos*	45	50
O241	57 s. on 20 s. *Dascyllus aruanus*	45	50
O242	2 p. 50 on 2 p. *Birgus latro*	2·10	2·25
O236/42	.. .. *Set of* 7	3·50	3·75

NIUAFO'OU

The following stamps were provided for the remote island of Niuafo'ou and were not valid for postage in the remainder of Tonga.

SELF-ADHESIVE ISSUES. Nos. 1/63 were manufactured by Walsall Security Printers using the self-adhesive system as described above Tonga No. 280.

1 Map of Niuafo'ou

NIUAFO'OU
KINGDOM OF TONGA
(2)

1983 (11 May). (a) *P* 14.
1 1 1 s. pale stone, black and rosine .. 10 10
2 2 s. pale stone, black and light emerald 10 10
3 3 s. pale stone, black & dull ultram .. 10 10
4 3 s. pale stone, black and chestnut .. 10 10
5 5 s. pale stone, black and deep magenta 10 10
6 6 s. pale stone, black and greenish blue 10 10
7 9 s. pale stone, black & dull yell-grn .. 10 10
8 10 s. pale stone, black & dull ultram .. 15 15
9 13 s. pale stone, black and light emerald 20 20
10 15 s. pale stone, black and chestnut .. 20 20
11 20 s. pale stone, black and greenish blue 25 25
12 29 s. pale stone, black and deep magenta 40 40
13 32 s. pale stone, black & dull yellow-green 45 45
14 47 s. pale stone, black and rosine .. 55 55

(b) *No. 820 of Tonga surch (No. 15) with T 2 by lithography or optd only (No. 16) by typography. P* 13½
15 1 p. on 2 p. pale turquoise-green & black (V.) 1·50 1·50
a. Deep mauve surch in typography .. 10·00 10·00
16 2 p. pale turquoise-green (Gold) .. 2·25 2·50
1/16 .. .. *Set of* 16 6·00 6·25

Most examples of No. 15 have the surcharge printed by lithography. A small quantity did, however, receive a typography surcharge in a different shade to form No. 15a. In addition to the colour the typography printing can be identified by the white rims to the letters and figures. All examples of No. 16 were printed by typography.

1983 (11 May). *Inauguration of Niuafo'ou Airport. As T* **153** *of Tonga. P* 14 × 14½.
17 29 s. multicoloured .. .. 80 1·00
18 1 p. multicoloured .. .. 2·50 3·25

3s
(3)

4 Eruption of Niuafo'ou

1983 (30 May). *As T* 1, *but without value, surch with T* 3 *by Tonga Government Printer.*
19 3 s. pale stone, black and royal blue .. 10 10
20 5 s. pale stone, black and royal blue .. 10 10
21 32 s. pale stone, black and royal blue .. 55 55
a. Surch inverted £600
22 2 p. pale stone, black and royal blue .. 2·50 3·00
a. Surch inverted £125
b. Surch double
19/22 .. .. *Set of* 4 2·75 3·25

(Des R. Edge)

1983 (29 Sept). *25th Anniv of Re-settlement. T* 4 *and similar horiz designs. Multicoloured. P* 14.
23 5 s. Type 4 .. .. 15 10
24 29 s. Lava flow 45 40
25 32 s. Islanders fleeing to safety .. 55 40
26 1 p. 50, Evacuation by canoe .. 1·75 1·75
23/6 .. .. *Set of* 4 2·50 2·40

5 Purple Swamphen

6 Green Turtle

(Des N. Arlott)

1983 (15 Nov). *Birds of Niuafo'ou. T* 5 *and similar designs. P* 11 (1 *p.*, 2 *p.*), 14 (20 *s. to* 47 *s.*) *or* 14½ (*others*).
27 1 s. black and deep mauve 15 15
28 2 s. black and bright blue 15 15
29 3 s. black and blue-green 15 15
30 5 s. black and yellow 15 15
31 6 s. black and red-orange 15 15
32 9 s. multicoloured 15 15
33 10 s. multicoloured 20 20
34 13 s. multicoloured 20 20
35 15 s. multicoloured 25 25
36 20 s. multicoloured 35 35
37 29 s. multicoloured 55 55
38 32 s. multicoloured 60 60
39 47 s. multicoloured 90 90
40 1 p. multicoloured .. .. .. 2·00 2·00
41 2 p. multicoloured .. .. .. 3·75 3·75
27/41 .. .. *Set of* 15 8·75 8·75

Designs: *Vert* (22 × 29 *mm*)—2 s. White-collared Kingfisher; 3 s. Red-headed Parrot Finch; 5 s. Banded Rail; 6 s. Polynesian Scrub Hen ("Niuafo'ou Megapode"); 9 s. Green Honeyeater; 10 s. Purple Swamphen (*different*); (22 × 36 *mm*)—29 s. Red-headed Parrot Finch (*different*); 32 s. White-collared Kingfisher (*different*); (29 × 42 *mm*)—1 p. As 10 s. *Horiz* (29 × 22 *mm*)—13 s. Banded Rail (*different*); 15 s. Polynesian Scrub Hen ("Niuafo'ou Megapode") (*different*); (36 × 22 *mm*)—20 s. As 13 s.; 47 s. As 15 s.; (42 × 29 *mm*)—2 p. As 15 s.

(Des R. Edge)

1984 (7 Mar). *Wildlife and Nature Reserve. T* 6 *and similar multicoloured designs. P* 14.
42 29 s. Type 6 .. .. 30 35
43 32 s. Insular Flying Fox (*vert*) 30 35
44 47 s. Humpback Whale 45 50
45 1 p. 50, Polynesian Scrub Hen ("Niuafo'ou Megapode") (*vert*) .. .. 1·50 2·00
42/5 .. .. *Set of* 4 2·25 2·75

7 Diagram of Time Zones

8 Australia 1913 £2 Kangaroo Definitive

(Des R. Edge)

1984 (20 Aug). *Centenary of International Dateline. T* 7 *and similar horiz design. Multicoloured. P* 14.
46 47 s. Type 7 .. .. 40 50
47 2 p. Location map showing Niuafo'ou .. 1·50 1·75

1984 (17 Sept). *"Ausipex" International Stamp Exhibition, Melbourne. T* 8 *and similar vert design. Multicoloured. P* 14.
48 32 s. Type 8 .. .. 30 35
49 1 p. 50, Niuafo'ou 1983 10 s. map definitive .. 1·25 1·75
MS50 90 × 100 mm. As Nos. 48/9, but without exhibition logo and with face value at foot. Die cut. .. 1·75 2·25

Examples of No. **MS**50 without face values are Exhibition Banquet souvenirs without postal validity.

9 Dutch Brass Band entertaining Tongans

10 *Ysabel*, 1902

(Des R. Edge)

1985 (20 Feb). *400th Birth Anniv of Jacob Le Maire (discoverer of Niuafo'ou). T* 9 *and similar vert designs. P* 14.
51 13 s. purple-brown, pale cinnamon & brt orge 15 15
52 32 s. purple-brn, pale cinnamon & brt new bl 35 40
53 47 s. purple-brn, pale cinnamon & brt green 45 50
54 1 p. 50, purple-brn, pale cinnamon & lemon 1·50 1·60
51/4 .. .. *Set of* 4 2·25 2·40
MS55 90 × 90 mm. 1 p. 50, purple-brown, pale cinnamon and new blue. Imperf .. .. 1·50 1·75

Designs:—No. 52, Tongans preparing kava; No. 53, Tongan canoes and outriggers; Nos. 54/5, *Eendracht* at anchor off Tafahi Island.

1985 (22 May). *Mail Ships. T* 10 *and similar horiz designs. Multicoloured. A. Stamp die-cut and backing paper perf* 14. *B. Both stamp and backing paper perf* 14.

		A		B	
56	9 s. Type 10	10	10	15	15
57	13 s. *Tofua I*, 1908	15	15	20	20
58	47 s. *Mariposa*, 1934	45	50	60	60
59	1 p. *Matua*, 1936	1·40	1·50	1·75	1·75
56/9	.. .. *Set of* 4	1·90	2·00	2·40	2·40

For description of the two forms of perforation see after Tonga No. 864.

11 Preparing to fire Rocket

12 Halley's Comet, 684 A.D.

1985 (5 Nov). *Niuafo'ou Rocket Mails. T* 11 *and similar horiz designs. Multicoloured. P* 14.
60 32 s. Type 11 .. .. 35 35
61 42 s. Rocket in flight 45 45
62 57 s. Ship's crew watching rocket's descent .. 60 60
63 1 p. 50, Islanders reading mail .. .. 1·50 1·50
60/3 .. .. *Set of* 4 2·75 2·75

(Des and litho Walsall)

1986 (26 Mar). *Appearance of Halley's Comet. T* 12 *and similar vert designs. Multicoloured. P* 14.
64 42 s. Type 12 .. .. 60 60
a. Horiz strip of 5. Nos. 64/8 .. 2·75
65 42 s. Halley's Comet, 1066, from Bayeux Tapestry 60 60
66 42 s. Edmond Halley 60 60
67 42 s. Halley's Comet, 1910 .. .. 60 60
68 42 s. Halley's Comet, 1986 .. .. 60 60
69 57 s. Type 12 .. .. 75 75
a. Horiz strip of 5. Nos. 69/73 .. 3·25
70 57 s. As No. 65 .. .. 75 75
71 57 s. As No. 66 .. .. 75 75
72 57 s. As No. 67 .. .. 75 75
73 57 s. As No. 68 .. .. 75 75
64/73 .. .. *Set of* 10 6·00 6·00

Nos. 64/8 and 69/73 were each printed together, *se-tenant*, in horizontal strips of five, forming composite designs, throughout the sheets.

X X

4s
(13)

14 Swimmers with Mail

1986 (16 Apr). *Nos.* 32/9 *surch as T* 13 *in blue.*
74 4 s. on 9 s. Green Honeyeater 10 10
75 4 s. on 10 s. Purple Swamphen 10 10
76 42 s. on 13 s. Banded Rail 50 50
77 42 s. on 15 s. Polynesian Scrub Hen .. 50 50
78 57 s. on 29 s. Red-headed Parrot Finch .. 70 70
79 57 s. on 32 s. White-collared Kingfisher .. 70 70
80 2 p. 50 on 20 s. Banded Rail .. .. 2·50 2·50
81 2 p. 50 on 47 s. Polynesian Scrub Hen .. 2·50 2·50
74/81 .. .. *Set of* 8 7·00 7·00

(Des and litho Walsall)

1986 (22 May). *"Ameripex '86" International Stamp Exhibition, Chicago. 25th Anniv of United States Peace Corps. Horiz designs as T* **173** *of Tonga. Multicoloured. P* 14.
82 57 s. Peace Corps surveyor and pipeline .. 55 55
83 1 p. 50, Inspecting crops .. .. 1·50 1·50
MS84 90 × 90 mm. Nos. 82/3, magnifying glass and tweezers. Imperf .. .. .. 2·00 2·25

(Des Walsall. Litho Questa)

1986 (27 Aug). *Centenary of First Tonga Stamps. T* 14 *and similar horiz designs showing Niuafo'ou mail transport. Multicoloured. P* 14.
85 42 s. Type 13 .. .. 60 60
86 57 s. Collecting tin can mail 75 75
87 1 p. Ship firing mail rocket .. .. 1·25 1·25
88 2 p. 50, "Collecting the Mails" (detail) (C. Mayger) .. .. 2·75 2·75
85/8 .. .. *Set of* 4 4·75 4·75
MS89 135 × 80 mm. No. 88 .. .. 3·00 3·25

Nos. 85/8 were issued in sheets of twenty stamps and five *se-tenant* labels, in the central vertical column, showing the colour separations of the designs.

15 Woman with Nourishing Foods ("Eat a balanced diet")

16 Hammerhead Shark

(Des C. Abbott. Litho Walsall)

1987 (11 Mar). *Red Cross. Preventive Medicine. T* 15 *and similar horiz designs. Multicoloured. P* 14 × 14½.
90 15 s. Type 15 .. .. 30 30
91 42 s. Nurse with baby ("Give them post-natal care") 75 75
92 1 p. Man with insecticide ("Insects spread disease") .. .. 1·50 1·50
93 2 p. 50, Boxer ("Say no to alcohol, drugs, tobacco") .. .. 2·75 2·75
90/3 .. .. *Set of* 4 4·75 4·75

(Des and litho Walsall)

1987 (29 Apr). *Sharks. T* **16** *and similar horiz designs. Multicoloured. P* 14.

94	29 s. Type **16**	50	50
95	32 s. Tiger Shark	50	50
96	47 s. Grey Nurse Shark	70	70
97	1 p. Great White Shark	1·40	1·40
94/7	*Set of* 4	2·75	2·75
MS98	90×90 mm. 2 p. Shark and fishes	3·00	3·25

17 Capt. E. C. Musick and Sikorsky "S-42" Flying Boat

(Des and litho Walsall)

1987 (2 Sept). *Air Pioneers of the South Pacific. T* **17** *and similar horiz designs. Multicoloured. P* 14.

99	42 s. Type **17**	55	55
100	57 s. Capt. J. W. Burgess and Shorts "S-30" flying boat	70	70
101	1 p. 50, Sir Charles Kingsford Smith and Fokker "F.VIIb-3m" *Southern Cross*	1·50	1·50
102	2 p. Amelia Earhart and Lockheed "Electra 10A"	2·00	2·00
99/102	*Set of* 4	4·25	4·25

18 Polynesian Scrub Hen and 1983 1 s. Map Definitive

19 Sailing Ship and Ship's Boat

(Des and litho Walsall)

1988 (18 May). *5th Anniversaries of First Niuafo'ou Postage Stamp (42, 57 s.) or Niuafo'ou Airport Inauguration (1, 2 p.). T* **18** *and similar horiz designs. Multicoloured. P* 14.

103	42 s. Type **18**	40	45
104	57 s. As Type **18**, but with stamp at left	60	65
105	1 p. "Concorde" and 1983 Airport Inauguration 29 s. stamp	95	1·00
106	2 p. As 1 p., but with stamp at left	1·90	2·00
103/6	*Set of* 4	3·50	3·75

(Des and litho Walsall)

1988 (11 July). *Bicentenary of Australian Settlement. Sheet 115 × 110 mm containing T* **19** *and similar vert designs. Multicoloured. P* $13^1/_2$.

MS107 42 s. Type **19**; 42 s. Aborigines; 42 s. Early settlement; 42 s. Marine and convicts; 42 s. Sheep station; 42 s. Mounted stockman; 42 s. Kangaroos and early Trans Continental locomotive; 42 s. Kangaroos and train carriages; 42 s. Flying Doctor aircraft; 42 s. Cricket match; 42 s. Wicket and Sydney skyline; 42 s. Fielders and Sydney Harbour Bridge .. 6·00 6·50

Each horizontal strip of 4 within No. **MS**107 shows a composite design.

20 Audubon's Shearwaters and Blowholes, Houma, Tonga

21 Sextant

(Des and litho Walsall)

1988 (18 Aug). *Islands of Polynesia. T* **20** *and similar vert designs. Multicoloured. P* 14.

108	42 s. Type **20**	50	50
109	57 s. Kiwi at Akaroa Harbour, New Zealand	70	70
110	90 s. Red-tailed Tropic Birds at Rainmaker Mountain, Samoa	1·00	1·00
111	2 p. 50, Laysan Albatross at Kapoho Volcano, Hawaii	2·75	2·75
108/11	*Set of* 4	4·50	4·50

(Litho Walsall)

1989 (28 Apr). *Bicentenary of Mutiny on the* Bounty. *Sheet 115×110 mm containing T* **21** *and similar vert designs. Multicoloured. P* $13^1/_2$.

MS112 42 s. Type **21**; 42 s. Capt. Bligh; 42 s. Lieutenant, 1787; 42 s. Midshipman, 1787; 42 s. Tahitian woman and contemporary newspaper; 42 s. Breadfruit plant; 42 s. Pistol and extract from *Mutiny on the Bounty*; 42 s. Book illustration of Bligh cast adrift; 42 s. Profile of Tahitian woman and extract from contemporary newspaper; 42 s. Signatures of *Bounty* officers; 42 s. Fletcher Christian; 42 s. Tombstone of John Adams, Pitcairn Island .. 6·00 6·50

22 Hatchet Fish

23 Formation of Earth's Surface

(Des and litho Walsall)

1989 (2 June). *Fishes of the Deep. T* **22** *and similar horiz designs. Multicoloured. P* 14.

113	32 s. Type **22**	30	35
114	42 s. Snipe Eel	40	45
115	57 s. Viper Fish	55	60
116	1 p. 50, Football Fish	1·40	1·50
113/16	*Set of* 4	2·40	2·50

(Litho Walsall)

1989 (6 June–1 Aug). *The Evolution of the Earth. T* **23** *and similar vert designs. Multicoloured.*

(*a*) *Size* $27×35^1/_2$ *mm. P* $14^1/_2$

117	1 s. Type **23**	10	10
118	2 s. Cross-section of Earth's crust	10	10
119	5 s. Volcano	10	10
120	10 s. Cross-section of Earth during cooling	10	10
121	15 s. Sea	10	15
122	20 s. Mountains	20	25
123	32 s. River gorge	25	30
124	42 s. Early plant life, Silurian era	35	40
125	50 s. Fossils and Cambrian lifeforms	45	50
126	57 s. Carboniferous forest and coal seams	45	50

(*b*) *Size* $25^1/_2×40$ *mm. P* 14 (1 Aug)

127	1 p. Dragonfly and amphibians, Carboniferous era	85	90
128	1 p. 50, Dinosaurs, Jurassic era	1·25	1·40
129	2 p. Early bird and mammals, Jurassic era	1·75	1·90
130	5 p. Human family and domesticated dog, Pleistocene era	4·25	4·50
117/30	*Set of* 14	9·00	10·00

24 Astronaut on Moon and Newspaper Headline

1989 (17 Nov). *"World Stamp Expo '89" International Stamp Exhibition, Washington. P* 14.

131 **24**	57 s. multicoloured	55	60

(Litho Walsall)

1989 (17 Nov). *20th Universal Postal Union Congress, Washington. Miniature sheet, 185 × 150 mm, containing designs as Nos. 117/31, but with U.P.U. emblem at top right and some new values. P* $14^1/_2×14$ *(top two rows) or* 14 *(bottom row).*

MS132 32 s. × 5 (as Nos. 117/21); 42 s. × 5 (as Nos. 122/6); 57 s. × 5 (as Nos. 127/31) .. 5·50 5·75

On No. **MS**132 the row of five 57 s. values are at the foot of the sheet and are perforated in a different gauge from the top two rows.

Transjordan

PRICES FOR STAMPS ON COVER

Nos. 1/88a	from × 10
Nos. 89/142	from × 5
Nos. 143/243	from × 3
Nos. D112/24	from × 5
Nos. D159/248	from × 3
No. O117	from × 5

Transjordan was part of the Turkish Empire from 1516 to 1918. The area was overrun by British and Arab forces, organised by Colonel T. E. Lawrence, in September 1918, and as Occupied Enemy Territory (East), became part of the Syrian state under the Emir Faisal, who was king of Syria from 11 March to 24 July 1920. On 25 April 1920 the Supreme Council of the Allies assigned to the United Kingdom a mandate to administer both Palestine and Transjordan, as the area to the east of the Jordan was called. The mandate came into operation on 29 September 1923. During 1920 the stamps of the Arab Kingdom of Syria were in use.

BRITISH MANDATED TERRITORY

(1000 milliemes = 100 piastres = £1 Egyptian)

"EAST". Where the word "East" appears in the Arabic overprints it is not used in its widest sense but as implying the land or government "East of Jordan".

شرقي الاردن

("East of Jordan")
(1)

(1a)

(Optd at Greek Orthodox Convent, Jerusalem)

1920 (Nov). *T* 3 *of Palestine optd with T* 1. (a) *P* 15 × 14.

No.	Type	Description	Unused	Used
1	1	1 m. sepia	40	80
		a. Opt inverted	£170	
2		2 m. blue-green	4·00	6·00
		a. Silver opt	£180	£200
3		3 m. yellow-brown	50	80
		a. Opt Type 1a	£1000	
4		4 m. scarlet	60	80
5		5 m. yellow-orange	70	1·00
5a		1 p. deep indigo (Silver)		
6		2 p. olive	2·00	4·00
		a. Opt Type 1a	£1100	
7		5 p. deep purple	15·00	20·00
		a. Opt Type 1a	£1100	
8		9 p. ochre	£1300	£1400
1/7 (ex 5a)		Set of 7	20·00	30·00
		(b) P 14		
9	1	1 m. sepia	30	60
		a. Opt inverted	£200	
10		2 m. blue-green	30	60
		a. Silver opt	£200	
11		3 m. yellow-brown	5·00	7·50
12		4 m. scarlet	10·00	15·00
13		5 m. orange	70	80
14		1 p. deep indigo (Silver)	90	1·75
15		2 p. deep olive	1·25	2·50
16		5 p. purple	2·00	5·00
17		9 p. ochre	3·50	15·00
18		10 p. ultramarine	4·00	15·00
19		20 p. pale grey	8·00	24·00
9/19		Set of 11	32·00	80·00

Emir Abdullah, 1 April 1921–22 May 1946

Abdullah, a son of the King of the Hejaz, was made Emir of Transjordan in 1921. On 26 May 1923 Transjordan was recognised as an autonomous state and on 20 February 1928 it was accorded a degree of independence.

("Tenth of a piastre")
(2)

("Piastre")
(3)

1922 (Nov). *Nos.* 1/19 *additionally handstamped with steel dies at Amman as T* 2 *or* 3. (a) *P* 15 × 14.

No.	Type	Description	Unused	Used
20	2	1/10 p. on 1 m. sepia	25·00	45·00
		a. Red surch	70·00	70·00
		b. Violet surch	70·00	70·00
21		2/10 p. on 2 m. blue-green	28·00	28·00
		a. Error. Surch "3/10" for "2/10"	£110	£110
		b. Red surch	80·00	80·00
		c. Violet surch	£100	£100
22		3/10 p. on 3 m. yellow-brown	10·00	10·00
		a. Pair, one without surch	£750	
		b. Opt Type 1a	£1500	
		c. Violet surch	£150	£150
23		4/10 p. on 4 m. scarlet	50·00	50·00
24		5/10 p. on 5 m. yellow-orange	£180	£100
		a. Violet surch	£350	£300
25	3	2 p. on 2 p. olive	£250	75·00
		aa. Opt Type 1a	£1500	
		a. Red surch	£275	80·00
		b. Violet surch	£300	90·00
26		5 p. on 5 p. deep purple	50·00	70·00
		a. Opt Type 1a	£1500	
27		9 p. on 9 p. ochre	£300	£350
		a. Red surch	£130	£140
		(b) P 14		
28	2	1/10 p. on 1 m. sepia	20·00	25·00
		a. Red surch	60·00	60·00
		b. Violet surch	£300	£350
29		2/10 p. on 2 m. blue-green	25·00	25·00
		a. Error. Surch "3/10" for "2/10"	£100	£100
		b. Red surch	80·00	80·00
		c. Violet surch	80·00	80·00
30	2	5/10 p. on 5 m. orange	£250	£100
		a. Violet surch		
31	3	1 p. on 1 p. deep indigo (R.)	£200	60·00
		a. Violet surch	£400	
32		9 p. on 9 p. ochre (R.)	£500	£500
33		10 p. on 10 p. ultramarine	£950	£1000
34		20 p. on 20 p. pale grey	£800	£850
		a. Violet surch	£900	£950

T 3 *of Palestine* (*perf* 15×14) *similarly surch*

No.	Type	Description	Unused	Used
35	3	10 p. on 10 p. ultramarine	£2500	£3000
36		20 p. on 20 p. pale grey	£2500	£3000

T 2 reads "tenths of a piastre". T 3 reads "the piastre", both with Arabic figures below. These surcharges were supplied in order to translate the Egyptian face values of the stamps into terms intelligible to the local population, *i.e.* tenths of a piastre (= milliemes) and piastres of the Turkish gold pound; but the actual face value of the stamps remained unchanged.

Being handstamped the surcharge may be found either at the top or bottom of the stamp, and exists double on most values.

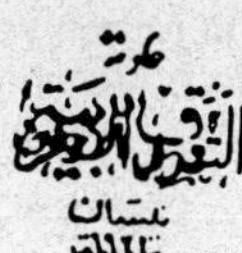

("Arab Government of the East, April 1921")
(4)

1922 (Dec). *Stamps of* 1920, *handstamped with a steel die as T* 4 *in red-purple, violet or black.** (a) *P* 15 × 14.

No.	Type	Description	Unused	Used
37	4	1 m. sepia (R.P.)	25·00	25·00
		a. Violet opt	28·00	28·00
		b. Black opt	22·00	22·00
38		2 m. blue-green (R.P.)	22·00	22·00
		a. Violet opt	20·00	20·00
		b. Black opt	18·00	18·00
39		3 m. yellow-brown (R.P.)	25·00	25·00
		a. Opt Type 1a	£1600	
		b. Violet opt	7·00	7·00
		c. Black opt	8·00	8·00
40		4 m. scarlet (R.P.)	45·00	50·00
		a. Violet opt	45·00	50·00
		b. Black opt	45·00	50·00
41		5 m. yellow-orange (R.P.)	35·00	10·00
		a. Violet opt	15·00	10·00
42		2 p. olive (No. 6) (R.P.)	55·00	40·00
		a. Violet opt	20·00	15·00
		b. Black opt	12·00	10·00
		c. On No. 6a (R.P.)	£1500	
		d. On No. 6a (V.)	£1500	£1300
43		5 p. deep purple (R.P.)	80·00	£100
		aa. Pair, one without opt	£1500	
		a. Violet opt	60·00	80·00
44		9 p. ochre (R.P.)	£400	£450
		a. Violet opt	£200	£250
		ab. Opt Type 1a	£2000	
		b. Black opt	65·00	80·00
		(b) P 14		
45	4	1 m. sepia (R.P.)	12·00	15·00
		a. Pair, one without opt	£1000	
		b. Violet opt	22·00	20·00
		c. Black opt	18·00	18·00
46		2 m. blue-green (R.P.)	25·00	25·00
		a. Violet opt	8·00	8·00
		b. Black opt	10·00	10·00
46c		3 m. yellow-brown (V.)	£750	£350
47		5 m. orange (R.P.)	£300	75·00
		a. Violet opt	25·00	20·00
48		1 p. deep indigo (R.P.)	25·00	15·00
		a. Violet opt	15·00	9·00
49		2 p. olive (V.)	75·00	80·00
50		5 p. purple (R.P.)	90·00	£100
		a. Violet opt	£100	£110
51		9 p. ochre (V.)	£900	£1000
52		10 p. ultramarine (R.P.)	£1800	£1900
		a. Violet opt	£1500	£1600
53		20 p. pale grey (R.P.)	£1900	£2000
		a. Violet opt	£1600	£1700

*The ink of the "black" overprint is not a true black, but is caused by a mixture of inks from different ink-pads. The colour is, however, very distinct from either of the others. Other values may exist with "black" overprint.

Most values are known with inverted and/or double overprints.

حكومة الشرق
العربية
نيسان سنة ٩٢١

("Arab Government of the East, April 1921")
(5)

1923 (1 Mar). *Stamps of* 1920, *with typographed overprint, T* 5.

(a) *P* 15 × 14

No.	Type	Description	Unused	Used
54	5	1 m. sepia (Gold)	£2500	£2500
55		2 m. blue-green (Gold)	20·00	22·00
56		3 m. yellow-brown (Gold)	12·00	15·00
		a. Opt double	£250	
		b. Opt inverted	£275	
		c. Black opt	75·00	85·00
57		4 m. scarlet	10·00	12·00
58		5 m. yellow-orange	50·00	45·00
59		2 p. olive (No. 6) (Gold)	15·00	15·00
		a. Black opt	£300	
		b. On No. 6a (Gold)	£1200	£1000
60		5 p. deep purple (No. 7) (Gold)	40·00	60·00
		a. Opt inverted	£400	
		b. On No. 7a	£1500	
		ba. Ditto. Gold opt inverted	£2000	
		(b) P 14		
62	5	1 m. sepia (Gold)	18·00	24·00
		a. Opt inverted	£300	
63	5	2 m. blue-green (Gold)	15·00	18·00
		a. Opt inverted	£350	
		b. Opt double	£350	
64		5 m. orange	12·00	12·00
65		1 p. deep indigo (Gold)	12·00	14·00
		a. Opt double	£450	£475
		b. Black opt	£800	£850
66		9 p. ochre	45·00	80·00
67		10 p. ultramarine (Gold)	75·00	£100
68		20 p. pale grey (Gold)	75·00	£100
		a. Opt inverted	£450	
		b. Opt double	£500	
		c. Opt double, one inverted	£500	
		e. Opt double, one gold, one black, latter inverted	£1000	
		f. Black opt	£800	
		fa. Black opt inverted	£1000	
		fb. Black opt double, one inverted	£1200	

There are numerous constant minor varieties in this overprint in all values.

The 20 p. exists with top line of overprint only or with the lines transposed, both due to misplacement.

Same overprint on stamp of Palestine, T 3

No.	Type	Description	Unused	Used
69	5	5 m. orange	£1800	£2000

In this variety the overprint, T 1 of Jordan, has been applied to the stamp, but is not inked, so that it is hardly perceptible.

(6) (7)

(8) (9)

1923 (April–Oct). *Stamps of the preceding issues further surch by means of handstamps.* (a) *Issue of Nov* 1920.

No.	Type	Description	Unused	Used
70	–	2½/10ths p. on 5 m. (13) (B.–Blk.)	£150	£150
		a. Black surch	£150	£150
		b. Violet surch	£150	£150
		(b) Stamp of Palestine		
71	6	5/10 p. on 3 m. (7)	£7500	
		(c) Issue of Nov 1922		
72	6	5/10 p. on 3 m. (22)	£7000	
73		5/10 p. on 5 p. (26) (V.)	70·00	80·00
73b		5/10 p. on 9 p. (27a)	£350	£375
74	7	1/2 p. on 5 p. (26)	70·00	80·00
75		1/2 p. on 9 p. (27)	£7500	
		a. On No. 27a	£350	£400
76		1/2 p. on 9 p. (32)	—	£8000
77	8	1 p. on 5 p. (26)	80·00	£100
		(d) Issue of Dec 1922		
78	6	5/10 p. on 3 m. (39)	85·00	£100
		a. On No. 39a	£750	
		ab. Pair, one without surch		
		b. On No. 39b	40·00	50·00
		c. Without numeral of value	£150	
79		5/10 p. on 5 p. (43a)	8·00	14·00
		c. Pair, one without surch	£500	
79d		5/10 p. on 9 p. (44b)	—	£1200
		e. Surch on No. 44a	—	£1300
80	7	1/2 p. on 2 p. (42)	£100	£120
		b. On No. 42a	80·00	£110
		c. On No. 42b	60·00	£110
		e. On No. 42b. Pair, one without surch	£1000	
		f. On No. 42c	£2000	
81		1/2 p. on 5 p. (43a)	£3000	
82		1/2 p. on 5 p. (50)	£2500	
83	8	1 p. on 5 p. (43)	£3000	
		b. On No. 43a	£2000	£2250
		(e) Issue of 1 March 1923		
84	6	5/10 p. on 3 m. (56)	25·00	30·00
85	7	1/2 p. on 9 p. (p 15×14)	90·00	£150
86		1/2 p. on 9 p. (66)	£150	
87	9	1 p. on 10 p. (67)	£2250	£2500
		a. Violet surch	£2750	
88		2 p. on 20 p. (68)	60·00	80·00
88a		2 p. on 20 p. (68f)	£2000	

The handstamp on No. 88 has an Arabic "2" in place of the "1" shown in the illustration of Type **9**.

Being handstamped many of the above exist inverted or double.

TYPES OF SAUDI ARABIA. The following illustrations are repeated here for convenience from Saudi Arabia.

11

20

21 22

حكومة

الشرق العربية

٩ شعبان ١٣٤١

("Arab Government of the East, 9 Sha'ban 1341")
(10)

("Arab Government of the East. Commemoration of Independence, 25 May 1923")
(11)

It should be noted that as Arabic is read from right to left, the overprint described as reading downwards appears to the English reader as though reading upwards. Our illustration of Type 11 shows the overprint reading downwards.

1923 (April). *Stamps of Saudi Arabia. T* 11, *with typographed opt, T* 10.

89 10 1/8 p. chestnut .. .. 2·00 1·75
a. Opt double £200
b. Opt inverted £150
90 1/2 p. scarlet .. .. 2·00 1·75
91 1 p. blue .. .. 1·25 80
a. Opt inverted £160 £180
92 1½ p. lilac .. .. 1·50 1·75
a. Opt double £225
b. Top line omitted .. .. .. — £225
c. Pair, one without opt £300
93 2 p. orange .. .. 2·00 5·00
94 3 p. brown .. .. 3·00 7·00
a. Opt inverted £300
b. Opt double £300
c. Pair, one without opt £500
95 5 p. olive .. .. 5·00 8·00
89/95 .. .. *Set of* 7 15·00 23·00

On same stamps, surcharged with new values (Saudi Arabia, Nos. 47 and 49)

96 10 1/4 p. on 1/8 p. chestnut .. .. 4·00 5·00
a. Ditto and surch inverted £200
b. Ditto. but 2nd and 3rd lines of opt omitted £250
97 10 p. on 5 p. olive .. .. 15·00 20·00

In this setting, the first line of the overprint measures 9 mm, the second 18½–19½ mm, and the third, 19–21 mm. On 35 stamps out of the setting of 36 the Arabic "9" (right-hand character in bottom line) is widely spaced from the rest of the inscription. Minor varieties of this setting exist on all values.

For later setting, varying from the above, see Nos. 121/4.

1923 (25 May). *T* 3 *of Palestine optd with T* 11, *reading up or down, in black or gold. A. Reading downwards. B. Reading upwards.*

				A		B	
98	11	1 m. (Blk.) ..	..	17·00	17·00	90·00	£100
		a. Opt double, one inverted (Blk.) ..	..	£750	£750	†	
		b. Gold opt	..	£150	£160	£150	£160
		c. Opt double, one inverted (Gold) ..	..	£900	—	†	
		d. Opt double (Blk. + Gold) ..	..	£900	£900	†	
99		2 m. (Blk.) ..	..	28·00	35·00	45·00	50·00
100		3 m. (Blk.) ..	..	10·00	12·00	90·00	£100
101		4 m. (Blk.) ..	..	10·00	12·00	25·00	32·00
102		5 m. (Blk.) ..	..	50·00	60·00	†	
103		1 p. (Gold)	..	£900	—	50·00	60·00
		a. Opt double	..	£1200	£1200	—	—
		b. Black opt	..	†		—	—
104		2 p. (Blk.) ..	..	50·00	70·00	—	—
105		5 p. (Gold)	..	60·00	70·00	£750	£550
		a. Opt double	..	£650	—	†	
106		9 p. (Blk.) ..	..	70·00	90·00	50·00	60·00
107		10 p. (Blk.) ..	..	60·00	80·00	£600	—
108		20 p. (Blk.) ..	..	£700	—	70·00	90·00

The 9 and 10 p. are perf 14, all the other values being perf 15 × 14.

An error reading "933" instead of "923" occurs as No. 2 in the setting of 24 on all values. As only 24 stamps were overprinted for each of Nos. 103A, 105B, 107B and 108A only one example of the error can exist for each. No such examples have so far been recorded.

No. 107A surch with T 9

109 9 1 p. on 10 p. ultramarine £8000

نصف قرش

(12)

1923 (Sept). *No.* 92 *surch with T* 12. *(a) Handstamped.*

110 12 1/2 p. on 1½ p. lilac .. .. 6·00 6·00
a. Surch and opt inverted .. .. 75·00
b. Opt double .. .. 75·00
c. Opt double, one inverted .. .. 90·00 £100
d. Pair, one without opt £180

This handstamp is known inverted, double and double, one inverted.

(b) Typographed

111 12 1/2 p. on 1½ p. lilac .. .. 50·00 50·00
a. Surch inverted £250
b. Surch double £300
c. Pair, one without surch £500

حكومة حكومة

الشرق العربية الشرق العربية

٩ شبان ١٣٤١ ٩ شعبان ١٣٤١

(13*a*) (13*b*)
("Arab Government of the East, 9 Sha'ban, 1341")

These two types differ in the spacing of the characters and in the position of the bottom line which is to the left of the middle line in T 13*a* and centrally placed in T 13*b*.

1923 (Oct). *T* 11 *of Saudi Arabia handstamped as T* 13*a or* 13*b*.

112 13*a* 1/2 p. scarlet .. .. 6·00 7·00
113 13*b* 1/2 p. scarlet .. .. 6·00 7·00

(15 "Arab Government of the East")

("Commemorating the coming of His Majesty the King of the Arabs" and date)
(16)

1924 (Jan). *T* 11 *of Saudi Arabia with typographed opt T* 15.

114 15 1/2 p. scarlet .. .. 6·00 8·00
a. Opt inverted £250
115 1 p. blue £300 £200
116 1½ p. lilac £350

The 1/2 p. exists with thick, brown gum, which tints the paper, and with white gum and paper.

1924 (18 Jan). *Visit of King Hussein of Hejaz. T* 11 *of Saudi Arabia optd with T* 15 *and with further typographed opt T* 16.

A. *In Black*. B. *In Gold*

				A		B	
117	16	1/2 p. scarlet	..	1·00	1·00	2·00	2·00
		a. Type 15 omitted	..	£150	—	†	
		b. Type 16 inverted	..	£200	—	†	
		c. Imperf between (pr)	..	£100	—	—	—
118		1 p. blue	..	1·25	1·25	2·00	2·00
		a. Type 15 omitted	..	£150	—	†	
		b. Both opts inverted	..	£200	—	£300	—
		d. Imperf between (pr)	..	†		—	—
119		1½ p. lilac	..	2·00	2·00	3·00	3·00
		a. Type 15 inverted	..	£125	—	£150	—
120		2 p. orange	..	4·00	4·00	6·00	6·00

The spacing of the lines of the overprint varies considerably, and a variety dated "432" for "342" occurs on the twelfth stamp in each sheet.

1924 (Mar–May). *T* 11 *of Saudi Arabia optd as T* 10 *(new setting).**

121 1/2 p. scarlet .. .. 3·00 3·00
a. Opt inverted £100
122 1/2 p. maroon .. .. 10·00 8·00
a. Opt inverted £120
123 1 p. blue .. .. 5·00 2·00
a. Opt double £150
124 1½ p. lilac .. .. 7·50 8·50

*This setting is from fresh type, the first line measuring 8¾ mm, the second nearly 20 mm and third 18¼ mm.

On all stamps in this setting (except Nos. 1, 9, 32 and 33) the Arabic "9" is close to the rest of the inscription.

The dots on the character "Y" (the second character from the left in the second line) are on many stamps vertical (:) instead of horizontal (..).

There are many errors. In the third line, No. 24 of the setting reads "Shabál", and No. 27 reads "Shabn" (instead of "Shab'an").

On some sheets of the 1/2 p. (both colours), the right hand character, "H", in the first line, was omitted from the second stamp in the first row of the sheet.

حكومة الشرق العربي ١٣٤٢

("Government of the Arab East, 1342")
(17)

حكومة الشرق العربي سنة ١٣٤٣

("Government of the Arab East, 1343")
(18)

1924 (Sept–Nov). *T* 11 *of Saudi Arabia with type-set opt as T* 17.

125 17 1/8 p. chestnut 35 25
a. Opt inverted £130
126 1/4 p. green 30 30
a. Tête-bêche (pair) .. .. .. 7·50 10·00
b. Opt inverted £100
127 1/2 p. scarlet 30 30
128 1/2 p. maroon .. .. 1·50 60
129 1 p. blue .. .. 2·50 1·50
a. Imperf between (horiz pair) .. £120
130 1½ p. lilac .. .. 2·50 2·50
131 2 p. orange .. .. 2·00 2·00
132 17 3 p. brown-red .. .. 1·50 1·50
a. Opt inverted £100
b. Opt double £100
133 5 p. olive .. .. 2·00 2·50
134 10 p. brown-purple and mauve (R.) .. 4·00 5·00
a. Centre inverted .. .. ..
b. Black opt £140
125/34 .. .. *Set of* 10 15·00 15·00

Varieties may be found with dates "1242" or "1343", with "1" or "2" inverted, and other errors exist.

1925 (Aug). *T* 20/22 *of Saudi Arabia with lithographed opt T* 18.

135 18 1/8 p. chocolate 30 60
a. Imperf between (horiz pair) .. £100 £120
136 1/4 p. ultramarine 30 60
137 1/2 p. carmine 40 35
138 1 p. green 40 35
139 1½ p. orange .. .. 75 1·50
140 2 p. blue .. .. 1·00 1·75
a. Opt treble £150 £200
141 3 p. sage-green (R.) .. .. .. 1·25 2·50
a. Imperf between (horiz pair) .. £100 £150
b. Black opt £120 £150
142 5 p. chestnut .. .. 2·00 5·00
135/42 .. .. *Set of* 8 5·75 11·50

The whole series exists imperforate and (except the 1 and 2 p.) with inverted overprint, both perf and imperf.

شرق الاردن

("East of the Jordan")
(19)

22 Emir Abdullah

23 Emir Abdullah

(Opt typo by Waterlow)

1925 (1 Nov). *Stamps of Palestine*, 1922 *(without the three-line Palestine opt), optd with T* 19. *Wmk Mult Script CA. (a) P* 14.

143 19 1 m. deep brown 10 15
144 2 m. yellow 10 15
145 3 m. greenish blue 10 15
146 4 m. carmine-pink 10 15
147 5 m. orange 10 15
a. Yellow-orange .. .. 35·00 20·00
148 6 m. blue-green 15 20
149 7 m. yellow-brown 15 20
150 8 m. scarlet 20 30
151 13 m. ultramarine 40 60
152 1 p. grey 40 40
153 2 p. olive 60 70
a. Olive-green .. .. £100 25·00
154 5 p. deep purple .. .. 2·50 3·00
155 9 p. ochre .. .. 4·00 4·50
156 10 p. light blue .. .. 7·00 8·00
a. Error. "E.F.F." in bottom panel .. £900 £800
157 20 p. bright violet .. .. 14·00 15·00
143/57 .. .. *Set of* 15 27·00 30·00
143/57 Optd "Specimen" .. .. *Set of* 15 £120

(b) P 15 × 14

157*a* 19 9 p. ochre £1300 £1400
158 10 p. blue .. .. 75·00 85·00
158*a* 20 p. bright violet £1300 £1000

(New Currency. 1000 millièmes = £1 Palestinian)

(Recess Perkins, Bacon & Co)

1927 (1 Nov)–**29**. *New Currency. Wmk Mult Script CA. P* 14.

159 22 2 m. greenish blue 15 15
160 3 m. carmine-pink 20 20
161 4 m. green 50 70
162 5 m. orange 25 15
163 10 m. scarlet 50 45
164 15 m. ultramarine 60 25
165 20 m. olive-green 80 85
166 23 50 m. purple .. .. 2·50 2·50
167 90 m. bistre .. .. 5·00 6·50
168 100 m. blue .. .. 6·50 5·50
169 200 m. violet .. .. 16·00 17·00
170 500 m. brown (1929) .. .. 60·00 70·00
171 1000 m. slate-grey (1929) £100 £120
159/71 .. .. *Set of* 13 £180 £200
159/71 Optd/perf "Specimen" .. *Set of* 13 £180

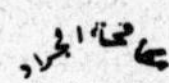

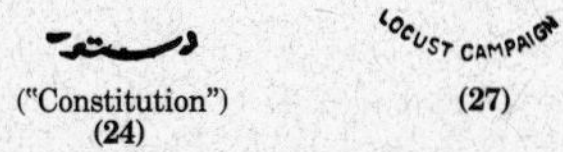

("Constitution")
(24)

(27)

(Optd at Cairo)

1928 (1 Sept). *New Constitution of* 20 *February* 1928. *Optd with T* 24.

172 22 2 m. greenish blue 50 80
173 3 m. carmine-pink .. .. 60 1·25
174 4 m. green .. .. 60 1·40
175 5 m. orange 60 60
176 10 m. scarlet .. .. 1·00 2·00
177 15 m. ultramarine .. .. 1·00 1·00
178 20 m. olive-green .. .. 3·00 4·50
179 23 50 m. purple .. .. 5·00 4·75
180 90 m. bistre .. .. 13·00 22·00
181 100 m. blue .. .. 22·00 27·00
182 200 m. violet .. .. 55·00 80·00
172/82 .. .. *Set of* 11 90·00 £130

(Optd at Alexandria by Whitehead, Morris & Co)

1930 (1 Apr). *Locust Campaign. Optd as T* 27.

183 22 2 m. greenish blue .. .. 75 1·50
a. Opt inverted £250

184	**22**	3 m. carmine-pink	80	1·50
185		4 m. green	60	1·75
186		5 m. orange	7·00	8·50
		a. Opt double	£400	£550
		b. Pair, one without bottom line	£500	
187		10 m. scarlet	55	1·50
188		15 m. ultramarine	80	1·50
		a. Opt inverted	£225	£350
189		20 m. olive-green	1·00	2·00
190	**23**	50 m. purple	5·00	7·50
191		90 m. bistre	10·00	22·00
192		100 m. blue	12·00	22·00
193		200 m. violet	30·00	55·00
194		500 m. brown	75·00	95·00
		a. "C" of "LOCUST" omitted	£700	£700
183/94		*Set of* 12	£125	£200

28

29

(Re-engraved with figures of value at left only. Recess Perkins, Bacon)

1930 (1 June)–**39.** *Wmk Mult Script CA. P* 14.

194*b*	**28**	1 m. red-brown (6.2.34)	15	15
		c. Perf 13½ × 13 (1939)	80	30
195		2 m. greenish blue	15	15
		a. Perf 13½ × 13. *Bluish green* (1939)	1·00	30
196		3 m. carmine-pink	15	15
196*a*		3 m. green (6.2.34)	25	25
		b. Perf 13½ × 13 (1939)	3·50	2·00
197		4 m. green	25	30
197*a*		4 m. carmine-pink (6.2.34)	1·00	25
		b. Perf 13½ × 13 (1939)	25·00	7·00
198		5 m. orange	25	10
		a. Coil stamp. P 13½ × 14 (1936)	9·00	1·50
		b. Perf 13½ × 13 (1939)	22·00	1·25
199		10 m. scarlet	40	15
		a. Perf 13½ × 13 (1939)	45·00	2·75
200		15 m. ultramarine	50	15
		a. Coil stamp. P 13½ × 14 (1936)	9·00	2·00
		b. Perf 13½ × 13 (1939)	10·00	2·25
201		20 m. olive-green	1·00	35
		a. Perf 13½ × 13 (1939)	25·00	7·50
202	**29**	50 m. purple	1·50	1·00
203		90 m. bistre	2·50	3·50
204		100 m. blue	3·50	3·50
205		200 m. violet	8·50	9·00
206		500 m. brown	20·00	27·00
207		£P1 slate-grey	45·00	60·00
194*b*/207		*Set of* 16	75·00	95·00
194*b*/207 Perf "Specimen"		*Set of* 16	£130	

For stamps perf 12 see Nos. 230/43, and for T **28** lithographed, perf 13½, see Nos. 222/9.

30 Mushetta

31 Threshing Scene

32 The Khazneh at Petra

33 Emir Abdullah

(Vignettes from photographs; frames des Yacoub Sukker. Recess Bradbury, Wilkinson)

1933 (1 Feb). *As T* **30** (*various designs*) *and T* **31/3**. *Wmk Mult Script CA. P* 12.

208	1 m. black and maroon	40	50
209	2 m. black and claret	40	40
210	3 m. blue-green	50	65
211	4 m. black and brown	75	1·25
212	5 m. black and orange	80	80
213	10 m. carmine	1·50	2·00
214	15 m. blue	2·50	1·25
215	20 m. black and sage-green	3·25	3·50
216	50 m. black and purple	6·00	7·50
217	90 m. black and yellow	10·00	15·00
218	100 m. black and blue	12·00	15·00
219	200 m. black and violet	40·00	48·00
220	500 m. scarlet and red-brown	£130	£170
221	£P1 black and yellow-green	£425	£625
208/21	*Set of* 14	£575	£800
208/21 Perf "Specimen"	*Set of* 14	£500	

Designs: *As T* **30**—2 m. Nymphaeum, Jerash; 3 m. Kasr Kharana; 4 m. Kerak Castle; 5 m. Temple of Artemis, Jerash; 10 m. Ajlun Castle; 20 m. Allenby Bridge over the Jordan.

The 90 m., 100 m. and 200 m. are similar to the 3 m., 5 m. and 10m. respectively, but are larger (33½ × 23½ mm). The 500 m. is similar to T **32**, but larger (23½ × 33½ mm).

34

(Litho Survey Dept, Cairo)

1942 (18 May). *T* **28**, *but with Arabic characters above portrait and in top left circle modified as in T* **34**. *No wmk. P* 13½.

222	**34**	1 m. red-brown	30	40
223		2 m. green	30	35
224		3 m. yellow-green	40	50
225		4 m. carmine-pink	60	40
226		5 m. yellow-orange	75	15
227		10 m. scarlet	1·00	60
228		15 m. blue	1·50	1·25
229		20 m. olive-green	3·25	2·00
222/9		*Set of* 8	7·50	5·00

(Recess Bradbury, Wilkinson)

1943 (1 Jan)–**44.** *Wmk Mult Script CA. P* 12.

230	**28**	1 m. red-brown	10	20
231		2 m. bluish green	10	20
232		3 m. green	10	20
233		4 m. carmine-pink	10	15
234		5 m. orange	10	10
235		10 m. red	20	15
236		15 m. blue	35	20
237		20 m. olive-green (5.44)	45	30
238	**29**	50 m. purple (5.44)	75	35
239		90 m. bistre (5.44)	2·00	1·50
240		100 m. blue (5.44)	2·75	70
241		200 m. violet (5.44)	5·00	2·50
242		500 m. brown (5.44)	11·00	7·50
243		£P1 slate-grey (5.44)	23·00	16·00
230/43		*Set of* 14	42·00	27·00

Nos. 237/43 were released in London by the Crown Agents about May 1944 but were not put on sale in Transjordan until 26 August 1946.

Printings of the 3, 4, 10, 12, 15 and 20 m. in changed colours were released on 12 May 1947.

POSTAGE DUE STAMPS

حكومة
مستحق
الشرق العربية
مستحق　　　　٩ شعبان ١٣٤١

(D 1 "Due")　　　　(D 2)

1923 (Sept). *Issue of April,* 1923, *with opt T* **10**, *with further typographed opt Type* D **1** (*the* 3 p. *with handstamped surch as T* **12** *at top*).

D112	½ p. on 3 p. brown	12·00	15·00
	a. "Due" inverted	50·00	55·00
	b. "Due" double	50·00	60·00
	ba. "Due" double, one inverted	£150	
	c. Arabic "t" & "h" transposed	£100	
	ca. As c, inverted	£250	
	d. Surch at foot of stamp	25·00	
	da. Ditto, but with var. c	£120	
	e. Surch omitted	£200	
D113	1 p. blue	8·00	9·00
	a. Type **10** inverted	80·00	
	b. "Due" inverted	45·00	40·00
	c. "Due" double	50·00	
	d. "Due" double, one inverted	£150	
	e. Arabic "t" & "h" transposed	70·00	
	f. "Due" omitted (in vertical pair)	£200	
D114	1½ p. lilac	8·00	9·00
	a. "Due" inverted	45·00	45·00
	b. "Due" double	50·00	
	ba. "Due" double, one diagonal	75·00	
	c. Arabic "t" & "h" transposed	70·00	
	ca. As c, inverted	£200	
	d. "Due" omitted (in pair)	£200	
D115	2 p. orange	9·00	10·00
	a. "Due" inverted	60·00	60·00
	b. "Due" double	65·00	
	ba. "Due" double, one diagonal	£100	
	c. "Due" treble	£150	
	d. Arabic "t" & "h" transposed	70·00	
	e. Arabic "h" omitted	90·00	

The variety, Arabic "t" and "h" transposed, occurred on No. 2 in the first row of all values in the first batch of sheets printed. The variety, Arabic "h" omitted, occurred on every stamp in the first three rows of at least three sheets of the 2 p.

Handstamped in four lines as Type D **2** *and surch as on No.* D112

D116	½ p. on 3 p. brown	40·00	50·00
	a. Opt and surch inverted	£200	
	b. Opt double	£200	
	c. Surch omitted	£225	
	d. Opt inverted. Surch normal, but at foot of stamp	£150	
	e. Opt omitted and opt inverted (pair)	£300	
	f. "Due" double, one inverted	£160	
	g. "Due" double, one larger	£180	
	h. Surch double	£250	

حكومة
الشرق العربية
مستحق
٩ شعبان ١٣٤١

(D 3)

مستحق
شرق الاردن

("Due. East of the Jordan")
(D 4)

1923 (Oct). *T* **11** *of Saudi Arabia handstamped with Type* D **3**.

D117	½ p. scarlet	1·00	1·7
D118	1 p. blue	1·50	2·0
D119	1½ p. lilac	1·75	2·7
D120	2 p. orange	2·25	3·2
D121	3 p. brown	3·75	6·5
	a. Pair, one without handstamp	£200	
D122	5 p. olive	6·50	9·0
D117/22	*Set of* 6	15·00	22·0

There are three types of this handstamp, differing in some of the Arabic characters. They occur inverted, double etc.

1923 (Nov). *T* **11** *of Saudi Arabia with opt similar to Type* D *but first three lines typo and fourth handstruck.*

D123	1 p. blue	50·00	
D124	5 p. olive	6·00	

(Opt typo by Waterlow)

1925 (Nov). *Stamps of Palestine* 1922 (*without the three-lin Palestine opt*), *optd with Type* D **4**. *P* 14.

D159	1 m. deep brown	1·40	2·0
D160	2 m. yellow	1·50	1·5
D161	4 m. carmine-pink	2·25	2·5
D162	8 m. scarlet	3·25	4·0
D163	13 m. ultramarine	3·75	4·0
D164	5 p. deep purple	4·50	6·0
	a. Perf 15 × 14	40·00	50·0
D159/64	*Set of* 6	15·00	18·0
D159/64 Optd "Specimen"	*Set of* 6	60·00	

مستحق

١ مليم (1 m.) (D 5)　　٢ مليم (2 m.)　　٤ مليم (4 m.)

٨ مليم (8 m.)　　١٣ مليم (13 m.)　　٥ قروش (5 p.)

(Surch typo at Jerusalem)

1926. *Postage stamps of* 1 *November* 1925, *surch "Due" and new value as Type* D **5**. *Bottom line of surcharge differs for each value as illustrated.*

D165	1 m. on 1 m. deep brown	1·75	2·5
D166	2 m. on 1 m. deep brown	2·00	2·5
D167	4 m. on 3 m. greenish blue	2·25	3·2
D168	8 m. on 3 m. greenish blue	2·25	3·5
D169	13 m. on 13 m. ultramarine	2·25	3·7
D170	5 p. on 13 m. ultramarine	3·25	4·5
D165/70	*Set of* 6	12·50	18·0

١ مستحق ١

1　　1

(D 6 "Due")　　D 7　　D 8

(Surch at Cairo)

1929 (1 Jan). *Nos.* 159 *etc. optd only or surch in addition as Type* D **6**.

D183	**22**	1 m. on 3 m. carmine-pink	45	8
D184		2 m. greenish blue	60	8
		a. Pair, one without surch	£250	
D185		4 m. on 15 m. ultramarine	90	1·2
		a. Surch inverted	£100	£15
D186		10 m. scarlet	90	1·2
D187	**23**	20 m. on 100 m. blue	3·25	4·0
		a. Vert pair, one without surch	£250	
D188		50 m. purple	4·00	5·5
		a. Pair, one without surch	£300	
D183/8		*Set of* 6	9·00	12·5

(Recess Perkins, Bacon)

1929 (1 Apr)–**39.** *Wmk Mult Script CA. P* 14.

D189	D **7**	1 m. red-brown	20	4
		a. Perf 13½ × 13 (1939)	60·00	40·0
D190		2 m. orange-yellow	20	6
D191		4 m. green	20	7
D192		10 m. scarlet	50	1·0
D193		20 m. olive-green	1·50	3·0
D194		50 m. blue	2·00	4·0
D189/94		*Set of* 6	4·25	8·7
D189/94 Perf "Specimen"		*Set of* 6	50·00	

(Litho Survey Dept, Cairo)

1942 (22 Dec). *Redrawn. Top line of Arabic in taller lettering No wmk. P* 13½.

D230	D **8**	1 m. red-brown	40	1·7
D231		2 m. orange-yellow	1·25	1·7
D232		10 m. scarlet	1·25	1·2
D230/2		*Set of* 3	2·75	4·2

(Recess Bradbury, Wilkinson)

1944. *Wmk Mult Script CA. P* 12.

D244	D **7**	1 m. red-brown	10	4
D245		2 m. orange-yellow	10	5
D246		4 m. green	20	6
D247		10 m. carmine	45	7
D248		20 m. olive-green	4·75	7·0
D244/8		*Set of* 5	5·00	8·5

OFFICIAL STAMP

(حكومة)
الشرق العربي
١٣٤٢

("Arab Government of the East, 1342" = 1924)
(O 1)

1924. *T* 11 *of Saudi Arabia with typographed opt, Type* O 1.
O117 ½p. scarlet . . . . . . 25·00 £100

By treaty of 22 March 1946 with the United Kingdom, Transjordan was proclaimed an independent kingdom on 25 May 1946.

Later issues are listed under JORDAN in Part 19 (*Middle East*) of this catalogue.

Transvaal

(*formerly* South African Republic)

PRICES FOR STAMPS ON COVER

Nos. 1/6 are rare used on cover.

Nos. 7/80	*from* × 20
Nos. 86/155	*from* × 3
Nos. 156/62	*from* × 6
Nos. 163/9	*from* × 5
Nos. 170/225	*from* × 10
Nos. 226/34	*from* × 20
Nos. 235/7	—
Nos. 238/43	*from* × 12
Nos. 244/55	*from* × 4
Nos. 256/7	*from* × 6
Nos. 258/9	—
Nos. 260/76	*from* × 20
Nos. D1/7	*from* × 20

The issues for Pietersburg, Lydenburg, Rustenburg, Schweizer Renecke, Volksrust and Wolmaransstad are very rare when on cover.

1 (Eagle with spread wings)

2

3

(Typo Adolph Otto, Gustrow, Mecklenburg-Schwerin)

1869. *Thin paper, clear and distinct impressions.* (a) *Imperf.*
1 1 1d. brown-lake . . £350
 a. Orange-red . . £350
2 6d. bright ultramarine . . £130
 a. Pale ultramarine . . £110 £120
3 1s. deep green . . £500
 a. *Tête-bêche* (pair) . . £8000

(*b*) *Fine roulette, 15½ to 16*
4 1 1d. brown-lake . . 65·00
 a. Brick-red . . 55·00
 b. Orange-red . . 55·00
 c. Vermilion . . 55·00
5 6d. bright ultramarine . . 55·00
 a. Pale ultramarine . . 55·00
6 1s. deep green . . 90·00
 a. Yellow-green . . 70·00
 b. Emerald-green . . 70·00

A *tête-bêche* pair of the 6d. imperforate is also said to exist.

PLATES. The German printings of the 1d., 6d. and 1s. in Type 1 were from two pairs of plates, each pair printing sheets of 80 in two panes of five horizontal rows of eight.

One pair of plates, used for Nos. 4*a*, 4*c*, 5*a* and 6/*a*, produced stamps spaced 1¼ to 1½ mm apart with the rouletting close to the design on all four sides. The 1d. from these "narrow" plates shows a gap in the outer frame line at the bottom right-hand corner. The second pair, used for Nos. 1/3, 4, 4*b*, 5/*a* and 6*b*, had 2½ to 3½ mm between the stamps. These "wide" plates were sent to the Transvaal in 1869 and were used there to produce either single or double pane printings until 1883.

The 6d. and 1s. "wide" plates each had an inverted *cliché*. When printed these occurred on right-hand pane R. 4/1 of the 6d. and right-hand pane R.1/1 of the 1s. These were never corrected and resulted in *tête-bêche* pairs of these values as late as 1883.

REPRINTS AND IMITATIONS. A number of unauthorised printings were made of these stamps by the German printer. Many of these can be identified by differences in the central arms, unusual colours or, in the case of the 1d., by an extra frame around the numeral tablets at top.

Genuine stamps always show the "D" of "EENDRAGT" higher than the remainder of the word, have no break in the border above "DR" and depict the flagstaff at bottom right, behind "MAGT", stopping short of the central shield. They also show the eagle's eye as a clear white circle. On the forgeries the eye is often blurred.

The most difficult of the reprints to detect is the 1s. yellow-green which was once regarded as genuine, but was subsequently identified, by J. N. Luff in *The Philatelic Record* 1911–12, as coming from an unauthorised plate of four. Stamps from this plate show either a white dot between "EEN" and "SHILLING" or a white flaw below the wagon pole.

(Typo M. J. Viljoen, Pretoria)

1870 (4 Apr–4 July).

I. *Thin gummed paper from Germany. Impressions coarse and defective.* (a) *Imperf*
8 1 1d. dull rose-red . . 60·00
 a. Reddish pink . . 60·00
 b. Carmine-red . . 55·00
9 6d. dull ultramarine . . £170
 a. *Tête-bêche* (pair) . . £5500

(*b*) *Fine roulette, 15½ to 16*
10 1 1d. carmine-red . . £700 £200
11 6d. dull ultramarine . . £180 90·00

(*c*) *Wide roulette, 6½*
12 1 1d. carmine-red . . — £850

II. *Thick, hard paper with thin yellow smooth gum* (*No.* 15) *or yellow streaky gum* (*others*). (a) *Imperf* (26 Apr)
13 1 1d. pale rose-red . . 50·00
 a. Carmine-red . . 55·00 65·00
14 1s. yellow-green . . 65·00 65·00
 a. *Tête-bêche* (pair) . . £7500

(*b*) *Fine roulette, 15½ to 16*
15 1 1d. carmine-red (24 May) . . 80·00
16 6d. ultramarine (10 May) . . 65·00 65·00
 a. *Tête-bêche* (pair) . . £6500 £5500
17 1s. yellow-green (26 Apr) . . £525 £525

III. *Medium paper, blotchy heavy printing and whitish gum. Fine roulette* 15½ *to* 16 (4 July)
18 1 1d. rose-red . . 38·00 38·00
 a. Carmine-red . . 38·00 38·00
 b. Crimson. From over-inked plate . . £130
19 6d. ultramarine . . 65·00 65·00
 a. *Tête-bêche* (pair)
 b. Deep ultram. From over-inked plate . . £400 £150
20 1s. deep green . . 75·00 65·00
 a. From over-inked plate . . £400 £150

The rouletting machine producing the wide 6½ gauge was not introduced until 1875.

Nos. 18*b*, 19*b* and 20a were printed from badly over-inked plates giving heavy blobby impressions.

(Typo J. P. Borrius, Potchefstroom)

1870 (Sept)–**71**. *Stout paper, but with colour often showing through, whitish gum.* (a) *Imperf*
21 1 1d. black . . £120 £120

(*b*) *Fine roulette, 15½ to 16*
22 1 1d. black . . 14·00 16·00
 a. Grey-black . . 14·00 16·00
23 6d. blackish blue (7.71) . . 95·00 40·00
 a. Dull blue . . 65·00 38·00

(Typo Adolph Otto, Gustrow, Mecklenburg-Schwerin)

1871 (July). *Thin paper, clear and distinct impressions. Fine roulette,* 15½ *to* 16.
24 2 3d. pale reddish lilac . . 80·00 75·00
 a. Deep lilac . . 85·00 75·00

No. 24 and later printings in the Transvaal were produced from a pair of plates in the same format as the 1869 issue. All genuine stamps have a small dot on the left leg of the eagle.

Imperforate examples in the issued shade, without the dot on eagle's leg, had been previously supplied by the printer, probably as essays, but were not issued for postal purposes. They exist *tête-bêche* (*price for un pair* £3250).

Imperforate and rouletted stamps in other colours are reprints.

(Typo J. P. Borrius, Potchefstroom)

1872–74. *Fine roulette,* 15½ *to* 16. (a) *Thin transparent paper*
25 1 1d. black . . £150 £525
26 1d. bright carmine . . £140 50·00
27 6d. ultramarine . . 70·00 40·00
28 1s. green . . 70·00 40·00

(*b*) *Thinnish opaque paper, clear printing* (Dec 1872)
29 1 1d. reddish pink . . 55·00 35·00
 a. Carmine-red . . 55·00 35·00
30 2 3d. grey-lilac . . 75·00 35·00
31 1 6d. ultramarine . . 50·00 25·00
 a. Pale ultramarine . . 55·00 25·00
32 1s. yellow-green . . 55·00 25·00
 a. Green . . 55·00 25·00
 aa. Bisected (6d.) (on cover)

(*c*) *Thickish wove paper* (1873–74)
33 1 1d. dull rose . . £400 65·00
 a. Brownish rose . . £475 95·00
 b. Printed on both sides
34 6d. milky blue . . £140 32·00
 a. Deep dull blue . . 75·00 30·00
 aa. Imperf (pair) . . £525
 ab. Imperf between (horiz pair) . . £475
 ac. Wide roulette 6½

(*d*) *Very thick dense paper* (1873–74)
35 1d. dull rose . . £475 £110
 a. Brownish rose . . — 85·00
36 6d. dull ultramarine . . £170 55·00
 a. Bright ultramarine . . £180 55·00
37 1s. yellow-green . . £700 £550

(Typo P. Davis & Son, Pietermaritzburg)

1874 (Sept). P 12½. (a) *Thin transparent paper.*
38 1 1d. pale brick-red . . 70·00 35·00
 a. Brownish red . . 65·00 35·00
39 6d. deep blue . . 90·00 35·00

(*b*) *Thicker opaque paper*
40 1 1d. pale red . . £110 65·00
41 6d. blue . . 85·00 40·00
 a. Imperf between (pair)
 b. Deep blue . . 80·00 40·00

(Typo Adolph Otto, Gustrow, Mecklenburg-Schwerin)

1874 (Oct). *Thin smooth paper, clearly printed. Fine roulette* 15½ *to* 16.
42 3 6d. bright ultramarine . . 50·00 20·00
 a. Bisected (3d.) (on cover)

Stamps in other shades of blue, brown or red, often on other types of paper, are reprints.

(Typo J. F. Celliers on behalf of Stamp Commission, Pretoria)

1875 (29 Apr)–**77**.

I. *Very thin, soft opaque (semi-pelure) paper.* (a) *Imperf*
43 1 1d. orange-red . . £120 40·00
 a. Pin-perf
44 2 3d. lilac . . 80·00 40·00
45 1 6d. blue . . 75·00 38·00
 a. Milky blue . . £120 38·00
 aa. *Tête-bêche* (pair) . . £6000
 ab. Pin-perf

(*b*) *Fine roulette,* 15½ *to* 16
46 1 1d. orange-red . . £400 £130
47 2 3d. lilac . . £425 £140
48 1 6d. blue . . £400 £130

(*c*) *Wide roulette,* 6½
49 1 1d. orange-red . . — £150
50 2 3d. lilac . . £550 £200
51 1 6d. blue . . — £120
 a. Bright blue . . — £120
 b. Milky blue . . — £120

II. *Very thin, hard transparent (pelure) paper* (1875–76)
(*a*) *Imperf*
52 1 1d. brownish red . . 42·00 20·00
 a. Orange-red . . 38·00 20·00
 b. Dull red . . 38·00 38·00
 ba. Pin-perf . . £400 £225
53 2 3d. lilac . . 42·00 38·00
 a. Pin-perf . . — £225
 b. Deep lilac . . 55·00 38·00
54 1 6d. pale blue . . 38·00 38·00
 a. Blue . . 38·00 20·00
 ab. *Tête-bêche* (pair) . . — £4750
 ac. Pin-perf . . — £200
 b. Deep blue . . 38·00 20·00

(*b*) *Fine roulette* 15½ *to* 16
55 1 1d. orange-red . . £250 £120
 a. Brown-red . . £250 £120
56 2 3d. lilac . . £325 £110
57 1 6d. blue . . £150 95·00
 a. Deep blue . . £150 £110

(*c*) *Wide roulette,* 6½
58 1 1d. orange-red . . £700 £150
 a. Bright red . . — £130
59 2 3d. lilac . . — £180
60 1 6d. deep blue . . £700 85·00

III. *Stout hard-surfaced paper with smooth, nearly white, gum* (1876). (a) *Imperf*
61 1 1d. bright red . . 18·00 12·00
62 2 3d. lilac
63 1 6d. bright blue . . 75·00 17·00
 a. *Tête-bêche* (pair) . . — £4750
 b. Pale blue . . 75·00 18·00
 c. Deep blue (deep brown gum) . . 40·00 14·00
 ca. *Tête-bêche* (pair) . . — £3500

(*b*) *Fine roulette,* 15½ *to* 16
64 1 1d. bright red . . £400 £140
65 2 3d. lilac . . £225
66 1 6d. bright blue . . — £140
 a. Deep blue (deep brown gum) . . — £400

(*c*) *Wide roulette,* 6½
67 1 1d. bright red . . £400 £140
68 6d. pale blue . . — £200
 a. Deep blue (deep brown gum) . . £475 £225

IV. *Coarse, soft white paper* (1876–77). (a) *Imperf*
69 1 1d. brick-red . . 80·00 45·00
70 6d. deep blue . . £140 45·00
 a. Milky blue . . £250 75·00
71 1s. yellow-green . . £225 80·00
 a. Bisected (6d.) (on cover)

(*b*) *Fine roulette,* 15½ *to* 16
72 1 1d. brick-red . . — £250
73 6d. deep blue . . — £130
74 1s. yellow-green . . £550 £250

(*c*) *Wide roulette,* 6½
75 1 1d. brick-red . . — £300
76 6d. deep blue
77 1s. yellow-green . . — £800

(*d*) *Fine* × *wide roulette*
78 1 1d. brick-red . . £550 £250

V. *Hard, thick, coarse yellowish paper* (1876–77)
79 1 1d. brick-red (*imperf*)
80 1d. brick-red (*wide roulette*)

The pin-perforated stamps have various gauges and were probably produced privately or by one or more post offices other than Pretoria.

On Nos. 63*c*/*ca*, 66*a* and 68*a* the brown gum used was so intense that it caused staining of the paper which is still visible on used examples.

See also Nos. 171/4.

FIRST BRITISH OCCUPATION

By 1876 conditions in the Transvaal had deteriorated and the country was faced by economic collapse, native wars and internal dissension. In early 1877 Sir Theophilus Shepstone, appointed Special Commissioner to the South African Republic by the British Government, arrived in Pretoria and on 12 April annexed the Transvaal with the acquiescence of at least part of the European population.

V. R.

TRANSVAAL.

(4)

V. R.

TRANSVAAL.

(5)

T 4 is the normal overprint, but in some printings No. 11 (R.2/3) on the pane has a wider-spaced overprint, as T 5.

1877 (Apr). *Optd with T 4 in red. (a) Imperf.*
86 2 3d. lilac (*semi-pelure*) (No. 44) £1100 £225
a. Opt Type 5
87 3d. lilac (*pelure*) (No. 53) £1100 £150
a. Opt Type 5 £4750
b. Opt on back £3000
c. Opt double, in red and in black £4750
88 1 6d. milky blue (No. 70) £1300 £160
a. Opt inverted — £4250
b. Opt double £3500
c. Opt Type 5 £4250
d. Deep blue — £225
89 1s. yellow-green (No. 71) £450 £140
a. Bisected (6d.) (on cover) † £1200
b. Opt inverted — £3250
c. Opt Type 5 £3000

(b) Fine roulette, 15½ to 16
90 2 3d. lilac (*pelure*) (No. 56) — £1100
91 1 6d. deep blue (No. 73) — £1100
92 1s. yellow-green (No. 74) £1000 £450
a. Opt Type 5

(c) Wide roulette, 6½
93 2 3d. lilac (*pelure*) (No. 59) — £1100
a. Opt Type 5
94 1 6d. deep blue (No. 76) — £1100
a. Opt Type 5
95 1s. yellow-green (No. 77) £2750 £1000
a. Opt inverted — £3500

Nos. 88a, 89b and 95a occurred on the inverted *cliché* of the basic stamps.

1877 (June). *Optd with T 4 in black.*

I. Very thin, hard transparent (pelure) paper
96 1 1d. orange-red (*imperf*) (No. 52a) £170 95·00
97 1d. orange-red (*fine roulette*) (No. 55) — £1000

II. Stout hard-surfaced paper with smooth, nearly white, gum
98 1 1d. bright red (*imperf*) (No. 61) 16·00 16·00
a. Opt inverted £475 £400
b. Opt Type 5 £750 £800
99 1d. bright red (*fine roulette*) (No. 64) £140 45·00
a. Opt inverted
b. Opt double
100 1d. bright red (*wide roulette*) (No. 67) £475 £140

III. New ptgs on coarse, soft white paper. (a) Imperf
101 1 1d. brick-red (5.77) 16·00 16·00
a. Opt double — £900
b. Opt Type 5
102 2 3d. lilac 65·00 27·00
a. Opt inverted
b. Deep lilac £140 75·00
103 1 6d. dull blue 80·00 27·00
a. Opt double £2750
b. Opt inverted £1200 £150
c. *Tête-bêche* (pair) — £3000
d. Opt Type 5 — £1000
da. Opt Type 5 inverted
e. Blue (bright to deep) £150 22·00
ea. Bright blue, opt inverted — £475
f. Pin-perf — £450
104 1s. yellow-green 75·00 38·00
a. Opt inverted £850 £150
b. *Tête-bêche* (pair) — £3000
c. Opt Type 5 £2750 £900
d. Bisected (6d.) (on cover) † £900

(b) Fine roulette, 15½ to 16
105 1 1d. brick-red 65·00 65·00
106 2 3d. lilac £140 55·00
107 1 6d. dull blue £150 38·00
a. Opt inverted — £550
b. Opt Type 5 £3500
108 1s. yellow-green £150 80·00
a. Opt inverted £800 £375
b. Opt Type 5 — £2500

(c) Wide roulette, 6½
109 1 1d. brick-red £550 £140
a. Opt Type 5
110 2 3d. lilac — £475
111 1 6d. dull blue — £1100
a. Opt inverted — £3000
112 1s. yellow-green £325 £110
a. Opt inverted £1100 £475

1877 (31 Aug). *Optd with T 4 in black.*
113 1 6d. blue/*rose* (*imperf*) 55·00 38·00
a. Bisected (3d.) (on cover)
b. Opt inverted 55·00 38·00
c. *Tête-bêche* (pair) £2500
d. Opt omitted £2750
114 6d. blue/*rose* (*fine roulette*) £150 65·00
a. Opt inverted £425 55·00
b. *Tête-bêche* (pair)
c. Opt omitted
115 6d. blue/*rose* (*wide roulette*)
a. Opt inverted
b. Opt omitted

V. R. Transvaal (6) — *V. R.* Transvaal (7)

1877 (28 Sept)–79. *Optd with T 6 in black. (a) Imperf*
116 1 1d. red/*blue* 42·00 22·00
a. "Transvral" (Right pane R. 2/3) — £2500
b. Opt double £3000
c. Opt inverted £600 £300
d. Opt omitted
117 1d. red/*orange* (6.12.77) 10·00 11·00
a. Pin-perf
b. Printed both sides
c. Opt double £2500
d. Optd with Type 7 (15.4.78) 38·00 27·00
118 2 3d. mauve/*buff* (24.10.77) 22·00 22·00
a. Opt inverted — £550
b. Pin-perf
c. Optd with Type 7 (15.4.78) 38·00 26·00
ca. Pin-perf — £550
119 3d. mauve/*green* (18.4.79) £130 26·00
a. Pin-perf
b. Opt inverted — £1500
c. Opt double
d. Optd with Type 7 80·00 20·00
da. Opt inverted — £1500
db. Opt omitted — £2750
dc. Printed both sides
120 1 6d. blue/*green* (27.11.77) 65·00 28·00
a. Deep blue/green 80·00 32·00
b. Broken "Y" for "V" in "V. R." (Left pane R. 3/7)
c. Small "v" in "Transvaal" (Left pane R. 5/2)
d. "V..R" (Right pane R. 3/4) — £550
e. *Tête-bêche* (pair) — £3000
f. Opt inverted — £700
g. Pin-perf
121 6d. blue/*blue* (20.3.78) 42·00 22·00
a. *Tête-bêche* (pair) — £2750
b. Opt inverted — £700
c. Opt omitted — £1600
d. Opt double — £2500
e. Pin-perf
f. Bisected (3d.) (on cover) † £475
g. Optd with Type 7 80·00 22·00
ga. *Tête-bêche* (pair) £7500
gb. Opt inverted — £300

(b) Fine roulette, 15½ to 16
122 1 1d. red/*blue* 65·00 32·00
a. "Transvral" (Right pane R. 2/3) — £2750
123 1d. red/*orange* (6.12.77) 26·00 22·00
a. Imperf between (pair)
b. Optd with Type 7 (15.4.78) — £110
124 2 3d. mauve/*buff* (24.10.77) 80·00 22·00
a. Imperf between (pair)
b. Opt inverted — £2500
c. Optd with Type 7 (15.4.78) £130 95·00
ca. Imperf between (pair)
125 3d. mauve/*green* (18.4.79) £550 £150
a. Optd with Type 7 £500 £150
126 6d. blue/*green* (27.11.77) 65·00 18·00
a. "V..R" (Right pane R. 3/4) — £1000
b. *Tête-bêche* (pair)
c. Opt inverted — £475
d. Opt omitted — £3000
e. Bisected (3d.) (on cover) † £450
127 6d. blue/*blue* (20.3.78) £180 45·00
a. Opt inverted — £900
b. Opt omitted — £2500
c. Imperf between (pair)
d. Bisected (3d.) (on cover) † £450
e. Optd with Type 7 — 95·00
ea. Opt inverted — £800

(c) Wide roulette, 6¼
128 1 1d. red/*orange* (15.4.78) £225 95·00
a. Optd with Type 7 — £225
129 2 3d. mauve/*buff* (24.10.77) — 95·00
a. Optd with Type 7 (15.4.78) — £275
130 3d. mauve/*green* (18.4.79) — £250
a. Optd with Type 7 — £275
131 1 6d. blue/*green* (27.11.77) — £850
132 6d. blue/*blue* (20.3.78) — £225
a. Opt inverted
b. Optd with Type 7 — £275
ba. Opt inverted

Nos. 116/32 were overprinted from various settings covering sheets of 80 or panes of 40 (8 ×5). Initially these settings contained Type 6 only, but the type was reset in March 1878 to contain examples of Type 7 also.

V. R. Transvaal (8) — V. R. Transvaal (8a) — 9

1879 (Aug-Sept). *Optd with T 8 in black. (a) Imperf.*
145 1 1d. red/*yellow* 38·00 32·00
a. Small "T", Type 8a £225 £150
b. Red/orange 32·00 25·00
ba. Small "T", Type 8a £160 £150
146 2 3d. mauve/*green* £250 20·00
a. Small "T", Type 8a £275 £150
147 3d. mauve/*blue* 35·00 25·00
a. Small "T", Type 8a £170 75·00

(b) Fine roulette, 15½ to 16
148 1 1d. red/*yellow* — £200
a. Small "T", Type 8a £800 £525
b. Red/orange £1000 £375
ba. Small "T", Type 8a
149 2 3d. mauve/*green* £700 £225
a. Small "T", Type 8a
150 3d. mauve/*blue* — £150
a. Small "T", Type 8a — £600

(c) Wide roulette, 6½
151 1 1d. red/*yellow* — £800
a. Small "T", Type 8a
b. Red/orange
152 2 3d. mauve/*green*
a. Small "T", Type 8a
153 3d. mauve/*blue*

(d) Pin-perf, about 17
154 1 1d. red/*yellow* — £525
a. Small "T", Type 8a
155 2 3d. mauve/*blue*

The small "T" variety occurs on right pane R. 2/8, 3/8, 4/8 and 5/8 of the 1d. and on the same positions, but from the left pane, for the 3d.

(Recess B.W.)

1878 (26 Aug)–**80**. *P* 14, 14½.
156 9 ½d. vermilion (1880) 16·00 25·00
157 1d. pale red-brown 4·00 3·00
a. Brown-red 3·50 2·25
158 3d. dull rose 4·50 2·25
a. Claret 7·00 4·00
159 4d. sage-green 8·50 4·25
160 6d. olive-black 4·00 3·00
a. Black-brown 5·00 2·25
161 1s. green 85·00 30·00
162 2s. blue £110 65·00

The above prices are for specimens perforated on all four sides. Stamps from margins of sheets, with perforations absent on one or two sides, can be supplied for about 30% less.

1 Penny (10) — 1 Penny (11) — 1 Penny (12)

1 Penny (13) — 1 Penny (14)

1 PENNY (15) — *1 Penny* (16)

1879 (22 April). *No. 160a surch with T 10 to 16.*

A. In black. B. In red.

			A		B	
163	10	1d. on 6d.	£160	48·00	£450	£160
164	11	1d. on 6d.	65·00	35·00	£160	£110
165	12	1d. on 6d.	£140	48·00	£350	£160
166	13	1d. on 6d.	65·00	48·00	£160	£110
167	14	1d. on 6d.	£425	£130	—	£2000
168	15	1d. on 6d.	35·00	22·00	£100	55·00
169	16	1d. on 6d.	£150	70·00	£450	£170

Nos. 163/9 were surcharged from a setting of 60 containing eleven examples of Type **10**, four of Type **11**, four of Type **12**, nine of Type **13**, two of Type **14**, twenty-five of Type **15** and five of Type **16**.

The red surcharges may have been produced first.

SECOND REPUBLIC

Following the first Boer War the independence of the South African Republic was recognised by the Convention of Pretoria from 8 August 1881 .

Nos. 156/62 remained valid and some values were available for postage until 1885.

EEN PENNY
(17)

1882 (Aug). *No. 159 surch with T 17.*
170 9 1d. on 4d. sage-green 3·75 2·50
a. Surch inverted £300

Used examples of a similar, but larger, surcharge (width 19 mm) are known.

(Typo J. F. Celliers)

1883 (20 Feb). *Re-issue of T 1 and 2. P 12.*
171 1 1d. grey (*to black*) (Apr) 1·50 75
172 2 3d. grey-black (*to black*)/*rose* 7·50 2·25
a. Bisected (1d.) (on cover) † £475
173 3d. pale red (Mar) 3·50 1·00
a. Bisected (1d.) (on cover)
b. Chestnut 15·00 2·25
c. Vermilion 13·00 2·50
174 1 1s. green (*to deep*) (July) 8·50 1·50
a. Bisected (6d.) (on cover) † £250
b. *Tête-bêche* (pair) £400 80·00

Reprints are known of Nos. 172, 173, 173*b* and 173*c*. The paper of the first is *bright rose* in place of *dull rose*, and the impression is brownish black in place of grey-black to deep black. The reprints on white paper have the paper thinner than the originals, and the gum yellowish instead of white. The colour is a dull deep orange-red.

18

PERFORATIONS. Stamps perforated 11½×12 come from the first vertical row of sheets of the initial printing otherwise perforated 12½×12 .

REPRINTS. Reprints of the general issues 1885–93, 1894–95, 1895–96 and 1896–97 exist in large quantities. They cannot readily be distinguished from genuine originals except by comparison with used stamps, but the following general characteristics may be noted. The reprints are all perf 12½, large holes; the paper is whiter and thinner than that usually employed for the originals and their colours lack the lustre of those of the genuine stamps.

Forged surcharges have been made on these reprints.

(Des J. Vurtheim. Typo Enschedé)

1885 (13 Mar)–**1893**. *P* 12½.
175 **18** ½d. grey (30.3.85) 15 10
a. Perf 13½ .. .. 2·50 70
b. Perf 12½×12 .. .. 1·00 10
ba. Perf 11½×12 .. ..
176 1d. carmine 15 10
a. Perf 12½×12 .. .. 50 10
aa. Perf 11½×12 .. .. 5·00 2·00
b. Rose 15 10
ba. Perf 12½×12 .. .. 15 10
177 2d. brown-purple (*p* 12½×12) (9.85) .. 30 10
178 2d. olive-bistre (14.4.87) 30 10
a. Perf 12½×12 .. .. 2·50 10
179 2½d. mauve (*to* bright) (8.93) 75 10
180 3d. mauve (*to* bright) 75 25
a. Perf 12½×12 .. .. 4·25 55
aa. Perf 11½×12 .. .. 16·00 11·00
181 4d. bronze-green .. .. 1·40 25
a. Perf 13½ .. .. 3·25 55
b. Perf 12½×12 .. .. 8·50 55
ba. Perf 11½×12 .. .. £140 55·00
182 6d. pale dull blue 70 10
a. Perf 13½ .. .. 3·25 70
b. Perf 12½×12 .. .. 4·25 15
ba. Perf 11½×12 .. ..
183 **18** 1s. yellow-green .. .. .. 1·75 35
a. Perf 13½ .. .. 9·50 4·00
b. Perf 12½×12 .. .. 5·00 20
184 2s. 6d. orange-buff (*to* buff) (2.12.85) .. 3·25 1·40
a. Perf 12½×12 .. .. 6·00 3·25
185 5s. slate (2.12.85) .. .. .. 4·00 1·75
a. Perf 12½×12 .. .. 4·75 1·50
186 10s. fawn (2.12.85) .. .. .. 16·00 1·90
187 £5 dp grn (3.92)* (Optd "Monster" £150) £2000 £170

Singles of the 6d. pale dull blue imperforate have been reported used in 1893.

*Most examples of No. 187 on the market are either forgeries or reprints.

HALVE PENNY

(19)

1885 (22 May–Aug). *Surch with T* **19**. A. *Reading down*. B. *Reading up*.

		A		B	
188 **2**	½d. on 3d. (No. 173) ..	90	1·25	90	1·25
189 **1**	½d. on 1s. (No. 174) (Aug)	3·00	4·00	3·00	4·00
	a. *Tête-bêche* (pair) ..		†	—	£150

Nos. 188/9 were surcharged by a setting of 40. After the left pane had been surcharged reading down the sheets were turned so that the right pane had the surcharges reading up.

HALVE PENNY Z.A.R (20) TWEE PENCE Z. A. R. (21) HALVE PENNY (22)

1885 (1 Sept). *No.* 160*a surch with T* **20**/1 *in red*.
190 **9** ½d. on 6d. black-brown .. .. .. 5·50 7·00
191 2d. on 6d. black-brown 95 95

1885 (28 Sept). *No.* 180*a surch with T* **21**.
192 **18** ½d. on 3d. mauve 80 80
a. "PRNNY" (R. 6/6) .. .. .. 22·00
b. 2nd "N" inverted (R. 3/8) .. .. 50·00
c. Perf 11½×12 .. .. 3·00

2d (23) 2d (24)

1887 (15 Jan). *No.* 180*a surch with T* **23**/4.
193 **18** 2d. on 3d. mauve (Type **23**) .. .. 2·00 2·00
a. Surch double .. .. — £140
b. Perf 11½×12 .. .. 3·25 3·25
194 2d. on 3d. mauve (Type **24**) 55 55
a. Surch double .. .. — £160
b. Perf 11½×12 .. .. 2·00 2·00

Nos. 193/4 were surcharged from the same setting of 60 (10 × 6) which showed Type **24** on the top five horizontal rows and Type **23** on the sixth horizontal row.

COVER PRICES

Cover factors are quoted at the beginning of each country for most issues to 1945. An explanation of the system can be found on page x. The factors quoted do not, however, apply to philatelic covers.

Halve Penny (25) 1 Penny (26)

2½ Pence (27) 2½ Pence (28)

Two types of surcharge:
A. Vertical distance between bars 12½ mm.
B. Distance 13½ mm.

1893. *T* **18** *surch*. *P* 12½. (*a*) *In red*.
195 **25** ½d. on 2d. olive-bistre (A) (27 May) .. 50 55
a. Surch inverted .. .. 1·10 1·10
b. Surch Type B 90 90
ba. Surch inverted .. .. 3·75

(*b*) *In black*
196 **25** ½d. on 2d. olive-bistre (A) (2 July) .. 50 50
a. Surch inverted .. .. 3·00 3·00
b. Extra surch on back inverted .. £120
c. Surch Type B 70 70
ca. Surch inverted .. .. — 8·00
cb. Extra surch on back inverted ..
197 **26** 1d. on 6d. blue (A) (26 Jan) 10 10
a. Surch double .. .. 38·00 32·00
b. Surch inverted .. .. 90 1·00
c. Surch Type B 35 35
ca. Surch inverted .. .. 2·75 2·75
cb. Surch double .. .. — 50·00
d. Pair with and without surch .. £100
198 **27** 2½d. on 1s. green (A) (2 Jan) 40 35
a. "2/½" for "2½" (R. 1/10) .. .. 15·00 15·00
b. Surch inverted .. .. 1·00 1·10
ba. Surch inverted and "2/½" for "2½" £140
c. Extra surch on back inverted ..
d. Surch Type B 75 90
da. Surch inverted .. .. 4·50 5·25
199 **28** 2½d. on 1s. green (A) (24 June) .. 95 90
a. Surch double .. .. 23·00 23·00
b. Surch inverted .. .. 4·50 4·50
c. Surch Type B .. .. 3·50 3·50
ca. Surch double .. ..
cb. Surch inverted .. ..

Surcharge Types **25/8** all show a similar setting of the horizontal bars at top and bottom. On horizontal rows 1 to 4 and 6 the bars are 12½ mm apart and on row 5 the distance is 13½ mm.

29 (Wagon with shafts)

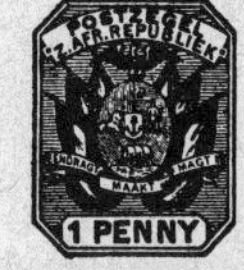

30 (Wagon with pole)

1894 (July). *P* 12½.
200 **29** ½d. grey 10 10
201 1d. carmine 10 10
202 2d. olive-bistre 10 10
203 6d. pale dull blue 60 40
204 1s. yellow-green .. .. .. 2·75 3·00

For note *re* reprints, see below T **18**.

1895 (16 Mar)–**96**. *P* 12½.
205 **30** ½d. pearl-grey (1895) 10 10
a. Lilac-grey 10 10
206 1d. rose-red 10 10
207 2d. olive-bistre (1895) 10 10
208 3d. mauve (1895) 15 10
209 4d. olive-black (1895) 65 55
210 6d. pale dull blue (1895) 40 20
211 1s. yellow-green (18.3.95) 70 65
212 5s. slate (1896) .. .. 2·75 3·25
212*a* 10s. pale chestnut (1896) .. .. 3·75 1·25
205/8, 211 Optd "Monster" .. *Set of* 5 £150

For note *re* reprints, see below T **18**.

Halve Penny

(31)

1d. (32—Round dot) 1d. (32*a*—Square dot)

1895 (July–August). *Nos.* 211 *and* 179 *surch with T* **31/2**.
213 **30** ½d. on 1s. green (R.) 10 10
a. Surch spaced 55 65
b. "Pennij" for "Penny" (R. 6/6) .. 35·00
c. Surch inverted .. .. 3·00 2·75
d. Surch double .. .. 42·00

214 **18** 1d. on 2½d. bright mauve (G.) 10 10
a. Surch inverted .. .. 14·00 11·00
b. Surch double .. ..
c. Surch on back only .. .. ..
d. Surch Type **32*a*** 95 95
da. Surch inverted .. .. .. 38·00

The normal space between "Penny" and the bars is 3 mm. On No. 213a, which comes from the fifth horizontal row of the setting, this is increased to 4 mm. Copies may be found in which one or both of the bars have failed to print.

Type **32*a*** with square stop occurred on R. 3/3-4, 3/6-8, 4/4-5, 4/7-8, 4/10, 6/3, 6/7-8 and 6/10 of the setting of 60.

33

34

1895 (July). *Fiscal stamp optd* "POSTZEGEL". *P* 11½.
215 **33** 6d. bright rose (G.) 50 65
a. Imperf between (pair) .. ..

(Litho The Press Printing and Publishing Works, Pretoria)

1895 (6 Sept). *Introduction of Penny Postage*. *P* 11.
215*b* **34** 1d. red (pale *to* deep) 35 15
ba. Imperf between (pair) .. .. 25·00 20·00

1896–97. *P* 12½.
216 **30** ½d. green (1896) 10 10
217 1d. rose-red and green (1896) 10 10
218 2d. brown and green (2.97) 10 10
219 2½d. dull blue and green (6.96) 10 10
220 3d. purple and green (3.97) 10 15
221 4d. sage-green and green (3.97) 10 15
222 6d. lilac and green (11.96) 10 15
223 1s. ochre and green (3.96) 20 10
224 2s. 6d. dull violet and green (6.96) .. 50 50

For note *re* reprints, see below T **18**.

SECOND BRITISH OCCUPATION

FORGERIES. The forgeries of the "V.R.I." and "E.R.I." overprints most often met with can be recognised by the fact that the type used is perfect and the three stops are always in alignment with the bottom of the letters. In the genuine overprints, which were made from old type, it is impossible to find all three letters perfect and all three stops perfect and in exact alignment with the bottom of the letters.

V. R. I. (35) E. R. I. (36) E. R. I. Half Penny (37)

1900 (18 June). *Optd with T* **35**.
226 **30** ½d. green 15 15
f. "V.I.R." £500
227 1d. rose-red and green 15 15
f. No stop after "R" and "I" .. .. 40·00 40·00
228 2d. brown and green 55 20
f. "V.I.R." £500
229 2½d. dull blue and green 15 20
230 3d. purple and green 15 20
231 4d. sage-green and green 50 20
f. "V.I.R." £500
232 6d. lilac and green 50 25
233 1s. ochre and green 65 50
234 2s. 6d. dull violet and green .. .. 1·25 1·40
235 5s. slate .. .. 2·25 2·50
236 10s. pale chestnut .. .. .. 4·00 4·00
237 **18** £5 deep green* .. .. .. — £750
234/7 Optd "Specimen" .. *Set of* 4 £200

The error "V.I.R." occurred on stamp No. 34 in the first batch of stamps to be overprinted—a few sheets of the ½d., 2d. and 4d. The error was then corrected and stamps showing it are very rare.

*Many examples of No. 237 on the market are forgeries and the stamp should only be purchased if accompanied by a recent expert committee certificate.

Varieties.
A. No stop after "V". B. No stop after "R".
C. No stop after "I". D. Overprint inverted.
E. Overprint double.

		A	B	C	D	E
226	½d.	8·00	5·50	4·00	5·00	—
227	1d.	8·00	5·50	2·75	5·00	38·00
228	2d.	14·00	†	17·00	8·00	—
229	2½d.	12·00	—	8·00	5·00	†
230	3d.	15·00	24·00	16·00	38·00	†
231	4d.	22·00	27·00	13·00	13·00	†
232	6d.	8·00	14·00	12·00	12·00	†
233	1s.	8·00	—	18·00	16·00	38·00
234	2s. 6d.	15·00	30·00	†	†	†
235	5s.	—	†	†	†	†
236	10s.	38·00	†	38·00	†	†
237	£5	—	†	†	†	†

The above prices are for unused. Used are worth the same, or rather more in some cases.

1901–2. *Optd with T* **36**.
238 **30** ½d. green (7.01) 10 10
239 1d. rose-red and green (20.3.01) .. 10 10
a. "E" of opt omitted .. .. .. 50·00
240 3d. purple and green (6.02) 65 65
241 4d. sage-green and green (6.02) .. 65 75
242 2s. 6d. dull violet and green (10.02) .. 3·25 4·00

1901 (July). *Surch with T* **37**.

No.	Type	Description	Unused	Used
243	**30**	½d. on 2d. brown and green	10	10
		a. No stop after "E"	38·00	

38 (POSTAGE REVENUE) **39** (POSTAGE POSTAGE)

(Typo D.L.R.)

1902 (1 April)–**1903**. *Wmk Crown CA. P* 14.

No.	Type	Description	Unused	Used
244	**38**	½d. black and bluish green	50	10
245		1d. black and carmine	55	10
246		2d. black and purple	80	10
247		2½d. black and blue	1·50	50
248		3d. black and sage-green (1903)	2·00	25
249		4d. black and brown (1903)	2·50	50
250		6d. black and orange-brown	1·00	45
251		1s. black and sage-green	6·00	2·00
252		2s. black and brown	12·00	11·00
253	**39**	2s. 6d. magenta and black	6·50	4·00
254		5s. black and purple/*yellow*	9·00	6·50
255		10s. black and purple/*red*	20·00	14·00
244/55		*Set of* 12	55·00	35·00
244/55 Optd "Specimen"		*Set of* 12	£160	

The colour of the "black" centres varies from brownish grey or grey to black.

1903. *Wmk Crown CA. P* 14.

No.	Type	Description	Unused	Used
256	**39**	1s. grey-black and red-brown	3·00	75
257		2s. grey-black and yellow	5·50	4·50
258		£1 green and violet	60·00	50·00
259		£5 orange-brown and violet	£1200	£400
256/9 Optd "Specimen"		*Set of* 4	£225	

1904–9. *Wmk Mult Crown CA. P* 14.

No.	Type	Description	Unused	Used
260	**38**	½d. black and bluish green, **O**	1·25	20
261		1d. black and carmine, **O**	1·50	10
262		2d. black and purple, **C** (1906)	1·75	25
263		2½d. black and blue, **CO** (1905)	1·50	80
264		3d. black and sage-green, **C** (1906)	1·50	15
265		4d. black and brown, **C** (1906)	1·75	30
266		6d. black and orange, **O** (1905)	1·25	20
		a. Black and brown-orange, **C**	1·25	20
267	**39**	1s. black and red-brown, **O** (1905)	1·50	25
268		2s. black and yellow, **O** (1906)	5·00	1·50
269		2s. 6d. magenta and black, **O** (1909)	11·00	2·00
270		5s. black and purple/*yellow*, **O**	7·50	1·50
271		10s. black and purple/*red*, **O** (1907)	17·00	2·00
272		£1 green and violet, **OC** (1908)	60·00	9·50
260/72		*Set of* 13	£100	17·00

There is considerable variation in the "black" centres as in the previous issue.

1905–9. *Wmk Mult Crown CA. P* 14.

No.	Type	Description	Unused	Used
273	**38**	½d. yellow-green	55	10
		a. Deep green (1908)	75	15
274		1d. scarlet	50	10
		a. Wmk Cabled Anchor, T **13** of Cape of Good Hope	—	£450
275		2d. purple (1909)	2·25	15
276		2½d. bright blue (1909)	5·00	5·00
273/6		*Set of* 4	7·50	1·75
273/6 Optd "Specimen"		*Set of* 4	60·00	

A 2d. grey, T **38**, was prepared for use but not issued. It exists overprinted "Specimen", *price* £125.

The monocoloured ½d. and 1d. are printed from new combined plates. These show a slight alteration in that the frame does not touch the crown.

Many of the King's Head stamps are found overprinted or perforated "C.S.A.R.", for use by the Central South African Railways.

FISCALS WITH POSTAL CANCELLATIONS

Various fiscal stamps are found apparently postally used, but these were used on telegrams not on postal matter.

POSTAGE DUE STAMPS

D 1

(Typo D.L.R.)

1907. *Wmk Mult Crown CA. P* 14.

No.	Type	Description	Unused	Used
D1	D **1**	½d. black and blue-green	1·25	1·25
D2		1d. black and scarlet	1·50	70
D3		2d. brown-orange	1·50	1·25
D4		3d. black and blue	2·50	2·00
D5		5d. black and violet	1·50	6·50
D6		6d. black and red-brown	3·75	6·00
D7		1s. scarlet and black	5·00	5·00
D1/7		*Set of* 7	15·00	20·00

Transvaal now uses the stamps of SOUTH AFRICA.

NEW INFORMATION

The editor is always interested to correspond with people who have new information that will improve or correct the Catalogue.

PIETERSBURG

Authorised by President Kruger and in use until 9 April 1901, when British troops entered the town.

PRICES. Genuinely used copies are very rare. Stamps cancelled by favour exist and are worth the same as the unused prices quoted.

The issued stamps are initialled by the Controller but three sheets of the ½d. were stuck together and this resulted in some being issued without initials. The 1d., 2d., 4d. and 1s. values without initials must be regarded as proofs and are worth about £5 each.

Sheets of the 6d. without initials are believed to be remainders, some being overprinted "PHILATELIC CONGRESS PRETORIA OCTOBER 1934" and affixed to menus for the Congress dinner.

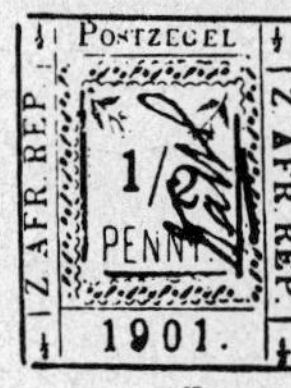

P 1

P 2

P 3

TYPES P 1/3. Each value was printed in sheets of 24 (6 × 4) of which the first two horizontal rows were as Type P **1**, the third row as Type P **2** and the fourth as Type P **3**.

(Type-set *De Zoutpansberg Wachter* Press, Pietersburg)

1901 (20 Mar (*1d.*)–3 Apr (*others*)). A. *Imperf.*

(a) Controller's initials in black

No.	Type	Description	Price
1	P **1**	½d. black/*green*	15·00
		e. Controller's initials omitted	95·00
2	P **2**	½d. black/*green*	45·00
		d. Controller's initials omitted	95·00
3	P **3**	½d. black/*green*	45·00
		d. Controller's initials omitted	95·00
4	P **1**	1d. black/*red*	3·50
5	P **2**	1d. black/*red*	5·50
6	P **3**	1d. black/*red*	7·00
7	P **1**	2d. black/*orange*	6·00
8	P **2**	2d. black/*orange*	14·00
9	P **3**	2d. black/*orange*	22·00
10	P **1**	4d. black/*blue*	5·50
11	P **2**	4d. black/*blue*	9·50
12	P **3**	4d. black/*blue*	32·00
13	P **1**	6d. black/*green*	9·50
14	P **2**	6d. black/*green*	15·00
15	P **3**	6d. black/*green*	40·00
16	P **1**	1s. black/*yellow*	8·00
17	P **2**	1s. black/*yellow*	14·00
18	P **3**	1s. black/*yellow*	25·00

(b) Controller's initials in red

No.	Type	Description	Price
19	P **1**	½d. black/*green*	15·00
20	P **2**	½d. black/*green*	35·00
21	P **3**	½d. black/*green*	40·00

B. *P* 11½. *(a) Controller's initials in red*

No.	Type	Description	Price
22	P **1**	½d. black/*green*	5·50
		c. Imperf vert (horiz pair)	95·00
23	P **2**	½d. black/*green*	17·00
		c. Imperf vert (horiz pair)	£120
24	P **3**	½d. black/*green*	12·00
		b. Imperf vert (horiz pair)	£120

(b) Controller's initials in black

No.	Type	Description	Price
25	P **1**	1d. black/*red*	2·00
		m. Imperf vert (horiz pair)	55·00
		n. Imperf between (vert pair: No. 25 + No. 26)	
		o. Imperf horiz (vert pair)	
26	P **2**	1d. black/*red*	2·75
		f. Imperf vert (horiz pair)	80·00
		g. Imperf horiz (vert pair: No. 26 + No. 27)	
27	P **3**	1d. black/*red*	4·00
		f. Imperf vert (horiz pair)	80·00
28	P **1**	2d. black/*orange*	5·50
29	P **2**	2d. black/*orange*	8·00
30	P **3**	2d. black/*orange*	14·00

CONSTANT VARIETIES

Rows 1 *and* 2 *are as Type* P **1**, *Row* 3 *as Type* P **2** *and Row* 4 *as Type* P **3**.

½d. *value*

First printing—Imperf

Position	Variety		No.	Price
R.1/2	No stop after left "AFR"		(No. 1a)	80·00
R.1/3	"½" at top left, no bar over lower right "½"		(No. 1b)	80·00
R.1/6	No stop after date		(No. 1c)	
R.2/5	"BEP" at left, no stop after date		(No. 1d)	80·00
R.3/3	"AFB" at left		(No. 2a)	80·00
R.3/4	"POSTZEGEI"		(No. 2b)	80·00
R.3/6	No bar over lower right "½"		(No. 2c)	80·00
R.4/1	No stop after right "AFR"		(No. 3a)	80·00
R.4/4	No stop after left "Z", no bar under top right "½"		(No. 3b)	80·00
R.4/5	"POSTZECEL AER" at left		(No. 3c)	80·00

Second printing

Position	Variety		No.	Price
R.1/4	No stop after right "AFR"	*Imperf*	(No. 19a)	95·00
		Perf	(No. 22a)	55·00
R.2/1	Left side of inner frame too high	*Imperf*	(No. 19b)	95·00
		Perf	(No. 22b)	55·00
R.3/5	Centre figures "½" level	*Imperf*	(No. 20a)	75·00
		Perf	(No. 23a)	55·00
R.3/6	No stop after right "AFR"	*Imperf*	(No. 20b)	75·00
		Perf	(No. 23b)	55·00
R.4/6	Hyphen between right "AFR" and "REP"	*Imperf*	(No. 21a)	75·00
		Perf	(No. 24a)	55·00

Third printing—Imperf

Position	Variety		No.	Price
R.1/1 & 4	Top left "½" inverted, no stop after right "AFR"		(No. 19c)	95·00
R.1/2	Top right "½" inverted		(No. 19d)	£120
R.1/3	"⅓" at lower right		(No. 19e)	£120
R.1/5	"POSTZFGEL"		(No. 19f)	£120
R.1/6	Left spray inverted, "AFB" at right		(No. 19g)	£120
R.2/1	"REB" at left, left side of inner frame too high		(No. 19h)	£120
R.2/2	"BEP" at left		(No. 19i)	£120
R.2/3	"POSTZEOEL"		(No. 19j)	£120
R.2/4	"AER" at right		(No. 19k)	£120
R.2/5	No stop after date		(No. 19l)	
R.3/1	"⅓" at top left, "PE" of "PENNY" spaced		(No. 20c)	£120
R.3/2	Right spray inverted		(No. 20d)	£120
R.3/3	Top left "½" inverted		(No. 20e)	£120
R.4/3	"⅓" at top right		(No. 21b)	£120
R.4/4	Lower left "½" inverted		(No. 21c)	£120
R.4/5	"¼" at top left		(No. 21d)	£120

1d. *value*

First printing

Position	Variety		No.	Price
R.1/2	Inverted "1" at lower left, first "1" of date dropped	*Imperf*	(No. 4a)	45·00
		Perf	(No. 25a)	29·00
R.1/3	No bar under top left "1"	*Imperf*	(No. 4b)	45·00
		Perf	(No. 25b)	29·00
R.1/4	No bar over lower right "1"	*Imperf*	(No. 4c)	45·00
		Perf	(No. 25c)	
R.1/5	"POSTZFGEL"	*Imperf*	(No. 4d)	45·00
		Perf	(No. 25d)	29·00
R.1/6	"AFB" at right	*Imperf*	(No. 4e)	45·00
		Perf	(No. 25e)	29·00
R.2/1	"REB" at left	*Imperf*	(No. 4f)	45·00
		Perf	(No. 25f)	29·00
R.2/2	"BEP" at left	*Imperf*	(No. 4g)	45·00
		Perf	(No. 25g)	29·00
R.2/3	"POSTZEOEL"	*Imperf*	(No. 4h)	45·00
		Perf	(No. 25h)	29·00
R.2/4	"AER" at right	*Imperf*	(No. 4i)	45·00
		Perf	(No. 25i)	29·00
R.2/5	No stop after date	*Imperf*	(No. 4j)	45·00
		Perf	(No. 25j)	29·00
R.2/6	No stop after "PENNY"	*Imperf*	(No. 4k)	45·00
		Perf	(No. 25k)	29·00
R.3/2	Right spray inverted	*Imperf*	(No. 5a)	45·00
		Perf	(No. 26a)	29·00
R.3/3	No bar over lower left "1"	*Imperf*	(No. 5b)	45·00
		Perf	(No. 26b)	29·00
R.3/4	No stop after left "Z"	*Imperf*	(No. 5c)	45·00
		Perf	(No. 26c)	29·00
R.3/6	"POSTZEGFL", no stop after right "AFR"	*Imperf*	(No. 5d)	45·00
		Perf	(No. 26d)	29·00
R.4/1	No stop after right "AFR"	*Imperf*	(No. 6a)	45·00
		Perf	(No. 27a)	29·00
R.4/2 & 6	Left spray inverted	*Imperf*	(No. 6b)	29·00
		Perf	(No. 27b)	17·00
R.4/3	"POSTZEGEI"	*Imperf*	(No. 6c)	45·00
		Perf	(No. 27c)	29·00
R.4/4	No bar under top right "1"	*Imperf*	(No. 6d)	45·00
		Perf	(No. 27d)	29·00

Second printing

Position	Variety		No.	Price
R.1/2	First "1" in date dropped	*Imperf*	(No. 4l)	45·00
		Perf	(No. 25l)	29·00
R.3/6	No stop after right "AFR"	*Imperf*	(No. 5e)	45·00
		Perf	(No. 26e)	29·00
R.4/5	Dropped "P" in "PENNY"	*Imperf*	(No. 6e)	45·00
		Perf	(No. 27e)	29·00

2d. *value*

First printing—Imperf

Position	Variety		No.	Price
R.1/1	"1" at lower right		(No. 7a)	60·00
R.1/2	No stop after left "AFR" (*on small part of printing*)		(No. 7b)	£120
R.1/3	No bar over lower right "2" (*on small part of printing*)		(No. 7c)	£120
R.1/3	"PENNY" for "PENCE"		(No. 7d)	60·00
R.1/5	"POSTZFGEL"		(No. 7e)	60·00
R.1/6	"AFB" at right		(No. 7f)	60·00
R.2/1	"REB" at left		(No. 7g)	60·00
R.2/2	"AFB" at left		(No. 7h)	60·00
R.2/3	"POSTZEOEL"		(No. 7i)	60·00
R.2/4	"AER" at right		(No. 7j)	60·00
R.2/5	No stop after date		(No. 7k)	60·00
R.2/6	No stop after date, vertical line after "POSTZEGEL"		(No. 7l)	60·00
R.3/2	Right spray inverted		(No. 8a)	60·00
R.3/3	No bar over lower left "2"		(No. 8b)	60·00
R.3/4	Centre "2" inverted, no stop after left "Z"		(No. 8c)	60·00
R.3/6	"POSTZEGFL", no stop after right "AFR"		(No. 8d)	60·00
R.4/1	Centre "2" wider, no stop after right "AFR" (*occurs on second printing also*)		(No. 9a)	60·00
R.4/2	Centre "2" wider, left spray inverted		(No. 9b)	60·00
R.4/3	"POSTZEGEI"		(No. 9c)	60·00
R.4/4	No bar under top right "2"		(No. 9d)	60·00
R.4/5	"1" at lower left, "P" in "PENCE" dropped		(No. 9e)	60·00
R.4/6	Left spray inverted		(No. 9f)	60·00

Second printing

Position	Variety		No.	Price
R.1/2	First "1" in date dropped	*Imperf*	(No. 7m)	60·00
		Perf	(No. 28a)	40·00
R.2/1	No stop after left "REP"	*Imperf*	(No. 7n)	60·00
		Perf	(No. 28b)	40·00
R.3/4	No stop after left "Z"	*Imperf*	(No. 8e)	60·00
R.3/6	No stop after right "AFR"	*Imperf*	(No. 8f)	60·00
		Perf	(No. 29a)	40·00
R.4/1	Centre 2 wider, no stop after right "AFR" (*occurs on first printing also*)	*Imperf*	(No. 9a)	60·00
		Perf	(No. 30a)	40·00

R.4/2	Centre "2" wider	*Imperf*	(No. 9g)	60·00
		Perf	(No. 30b)	40·00
R.4/5	"P" in "PENCE" dropped	*Imperf*	(No. 9h)	60·00
		Perf	(No. 30c)	40·00

4d. value

First printing

R.1/2	No stop after left "AFR'	(No. 10a)	60·00
R.1/3	No bar over lower right "4"	(No. 10b)	60·00
R.1/3	"PENNY" for "PENCE" (*on small part of printing*)	(No. 10c)	£120
R.1/5	"POSTZFGEL"	(No. 10d)	60·00
R.1/6	"AFB" at right	(No. 10e)	60·00
R.2/1	"REB" at left	(No. 10f)	60·00
R.2/2	"AFB" at left	(No. 10g)	60·00
R.2/3	"POSTZEOEL"	(No. 10h)	60·00
R.2/4	"AER" at right	(No. 10i)	60·00
R.2/5	No stop after date	(No. 10j)	60·00
R.3/2	Right spray inverted	(No. 11a)	60·00
R.3/3	No bar over lower left "4" (*on small part of printing*)	(No. 11b)	£120
R.3/4	No stop after left "Z"	(No. 11c)	60·00
R.3/6	"POSTZEGFL"	(No. 11d)	60·00
R.4/1	Centre "4" wider, no stop after right "AFR"	(No. 12a)	60·00
R.4/2	Centre "4" wider, left spray inverted	(No. 12b)	60·00
R.4/3	"POSTZEGEI"	(No. 12c)	60·00
R.4/4	No bar under top right "4"	(No. 12d)	60·00
R.4/5	"AER" at left, "P" in "PENCE" dropped	(No. 12e)	60·00
R.4/6	Left spray inverted	(No. 12f)	60·00

Second printing

R.2/1	Left inner frame too high	(No. 10k)	60·00
R.4/1–2	Centre "4" wider	(No. 12g)	40·00
R.4/5	"P" in "PENCE" dropped	(No. 12h)	60·00

6d. value

First printing

R.1/2	No stop after left "AFR"	(No. 13a)	75·00
R.1/3	No bar over lower right "6"	(No. 13b)	95·00
R.1/3	"PENNY" for "PENCE" (*on small part of printing*)	(No. 13c)	£120
R.1/5	"POSTZFGEL"	(No. 13d)	75·00
R.1/6	"AFB" at right	(No. 13e)	75·00
R.2/1	"REB" at left	(No. 13f)	75·00
R.2/2	"AFB" at left	(No. 13g)	75·00
R.2/3	"POSTZEOEL"	(No. 13h)	75·00
R.2/4	"AER" at right	(No. 13i)	75·00
R.2/5	No stop after date	(No. 13j)	75·00
R.3/2	Right spray inverted	(No. 14a)	75·00
R.3/4	Centre "6" inverted, no stop after left "Z" (*on small part of printing*)	(No. 14b)	£120
R.3/4	No stop after left "Z"	(No. 14c)	90·00
R.3/6	"POSTZEGFL"	(No. 14d)	75·00
R.4/1	Centre "6" wider, no stop after right "AFR"	(No. 15a)	75·00
R.4/2	Centre "6" wider, left spray inverted	(No. 15b)	75·00
R.4/3	"POSTZEGEI"	(No. 15c)	75·00
R.4/4	No bar under top right "6"	(No. 15d)	75·00
R.4/5	"AER" at left, "P" in "PENCE" dropped	(No. 15e)	75·00
R.4/6	Left spray inverted	(No. 15f)	75·00

Second printing

R.2/1	Left inner frame too high, no stop after left "REP"	(No. 13k)	75·00
R.4/1–2	Centre "6" wider	(No. 15g)	55·00
R.4/5	"P" in "PENCE" dropped	(No. 15h)	

1s. value

R.1/2	No stop after left "AFR"	(No. 16a)	55·00
R.1/3	No bar over lower right "1"	(No. 16b)	55·00
R.2/5	No stop after date	(No. 16c)	55·00
R.3/4	"POSTZEGEI", no stop after left "Z"	(No. 17a)	55·00
R.4/1	No stop after right "AFR"	(No. 18a)	55·00
R.4/4	No bar under top right "1"	(No. 18b)	55·00
R.4/5	"AER" at left	(No. 18c)	55·00

LOCAL BRITISH OCCUPATION ISSUES DURING THE SOUTH AFRICAN WAR 1900–2

Stamps of the Transvaal Republic, unless otherwise stated, variously overprinted or surcharged.

LYDENBURG

V.R.I.
3d.

(L 1)

1900 (Sept). *No. 217 surch with Type* L 1, *others optd* "V.R.I" *only*.

1	30	½d. green	85·00	65·00
2		1d. rose-red and green	70·00	65·00
3		2d. brown and green	£650	£500
4		2½d. blue and green	£1700	£550
5		3d. on 1d. rose-red and green	70·00	55·00
6		3d. purple and green		
7		4d. sage-green and green	£1400	£500
8		6d. lilac and green	£1400	£400
9		1s. ochre and green	£2750	

Only one genuine copy of No. 6 (unused) is known.

Type 34 surcharged "V.R.I. 1d." is now considered by experts to be bogus.

RUSTENBURG

1900 (23 June). *Handstamped* **V.R.** *in violet.*

1	30	½d. green	£100	70·00
2		1d. rose-red and green	80·00	55·00
3		2d. brown and green	£170	70·00
4		2½d. blue and green	£100	60·00
5		3d. purple and green	£150	70·00
6		6d. lilac and green	£500	£250
7		1s. ochre and green	£1000	£550
8		2s. 6d. dull violet and green	—	£3500

SCHWEIZER RENECKE

BESIEGED

(SR 1)

1900 (Aug). *Handstamped with Type* SR 1 *in black, reading vert up or down.* (*a*) *On stamps of Transvaal.*

1	30	½d. green	†	£225
2		1d. rose-red and green	†	£225
3		2d. brown and green	†	£300
4		6d. lilac and green	†	£750
		(*b*) *On stamps of Cape of Good Hope*		
5	17	½d. green	†	£400
6		1d. carmine	†	£400

This was a siege issue, authorised by the commander of the British troops in the town shortly after 19 August and exhausted by the end of September 1900. All stamps were cancelled with the dated circular town postmark ("Schweizer Reneke, Z.A.R."), usually after having been stuck on paper before use. Unused, without the postmark, do not exist.

VOLKSRUST

1902 (Mar). *Optd* "V.R.I.", *T* **35**. *P* 12.

1	33	1d. pale blue	—	40·00
2		6d. dull carmine	—	45·00
3		1s. olive-bistre	—	60·00
4		1s. 6d. brown	—	70·00
5		2s. 6d. dull purple	—	70·00

These are the normal Transvaal Revenue stamps of the period, authorised for postal use in Volksrust.

WOLMARANSSTAD

Cancelled V-R-I. (L 3)

Cancelled V-R-I. (L 4)

1900 (June). *Optd with Type* L **3**.

1	30	½d. green (B.)	£200	£300
		a. Opt inverted		
2		1d. rose-red and green (B.)	£140	£200
3		2d. brown and green (B.)	£1200	
4		2½d. blue and green (R.)	£1000	
		a. Opt in blue		
5		3d. purple and green (B.)	£1800	£2000
6		4d. sage-green and green (B.)	£2500	
7		6d. lilac and green (B.)	£2500	£3000
8		1s. ochre and green (B.)	—	£5000

1900 (July). *Optd with Type* L **4**.

9	34	1d. red (B.)	£150	£200

Trinidad and Tobago

TRINIDAD

CROWN COLONY

The first post office was established at Port of Spain in 1800 to deal with overseas mail. Before 1851 there was no post office inland service, although a privately-operated one along the coast did exist, for which rates were officially fixed (see No. 1). During 1851 the colonial authorities established an inland postal system which commenced operation on 14 August. Responsibility for the overseas mails passed to the local post authorities in 1858.

No. CC1 is recorded in the G.P.O. Record Book on 21 March 1852 and most examples are found used with the early Britannia 1d. stamps to indicate prepayment of the additional overseas rate in cash or, later, to show that letters were fully franked with adhesive stamps. This is the normal usage of the handstamp and commands little, if any premium over the cover price quoted below for the stamps involved. The use of the handstamp without an adhesive is rare.

For illustrations of the handstamp types see BRITISH POST OFFICES ABROAD notes, following GREAT BRITAIN.

PORT OF SPAIN

CROWNED-CIRCLE HANDSTAMPS

CC1 CC 6 TRINIDAD (R.) (*without additional adhesive stamp*) (21.3.52) .. *Price on cover* £500

PRICES FOR STAMPS ON COVER

No. 1	*from* × 2
Nos. 2/12	*from* × 5
No. 13	—
Nos. 14/20	*from* × 2
Nos. 25/30	—
Nos. 31/44	*from* × 3
No. 45	—
Nos. 46/59	*from* × 3
Nos. 60/3	*from* × 4
Nos. 64/8	*from* × 3
Nos. 69/85	*from* × 12
No. 87	—
Nos. 88/90	*from* × 15
Nos. 91/7	*from* × 10
Nos. 98/102	*from* × 5
No. 103	—
Nos. 104/5	*from* × 15
Nos. 106/12	*from* × 8
No. 113	—
Nos. 114/21	*from* × 4
Nos. 122/4	—
No. 125	*from* × 10
Nos. 126/30	*from* × 5
No. 131	—
Nos. 132/43	*from* × 3
Nos. 144/5	—
Nos. 146/8	*from* × 3
Nos. D1/17	*from* × 12

1

2 Britannia

1847 (24 Apr). *Litho. Imperf.*

1	1	(5 c.) blue	£13000	£7000

The "LADY McLEOD" stamps were issued in April 1847, by David Bryce, owner of the S.S. *Lady McLeod*, and sold at five cents each for the prepayment of the carriage of letters by his vessel between Port of Spain and San Fernando.

The price quoted for used examples of No. 1 is for pen-cancelled. Stamps cancelled by having a corner skimmed-off are worth less.

(Recess P.B.)

1851 (14 Aug)–**1856**. *No value expressed. Imperf. Blued paper.*

2	2	(1d.) purple-brown (1851)	4·75	50·00
3		(1d.) blue *to* deep blue (1851)	4·00	35·00
4		(1d.) deep blue (1853)*	£150	65·00
5		(1d.) grey (1851)	25·00	38·00
6		(1d.) brownish grey (1853)	22·00	45·00
7		(1d.) brownish red (1853)	£350	45·00
8		(1d.) brick-red (1856)	£120	50·00

*No. 4 shows the paper deeply and evenly blued, especially on the back. It has more the appearance of having been printed on blue paper rather than on white paper that has become blued.

1854–57. *Imperf. White paper.*

9	2	(1d.) deep purple (1854)	9·00	50·00
10		(1d.) dark grey (1854)	20·00	65·00
11		(1d.) blue (? date)		
12		(1d.) rose-red (1857)	£1500	50·00

PRICES. Prices quoted for the unused of most of the above issues and Nos. 25 and 29 are for "remainders" with original gum, found in London. Old colours that have been out to Trinidad are of much greater value.

3 Britannia 4

The following provisional issues were lithographed in the Colony (from die engraved by Charles Petit), and brought into use to meet shortages of the Perkins Bacon stamps during the following periods:

(1) Sept 1852–May 1853; (2) March 1855–June 1855; (3) Dec 1856–Jan 1857; (4) Oct 1858–Jan 1859; (5) March 1860–June 1860.

1852–60. *No value expressed. Imperf.*

A. *First Issue* (Sept 1852). *Fine impression; lines of background clear and distinct.* (i) *Yellowish paper*

13	3	(1d.) blue	£8500	£2000
		(ii) *Bluish cartridge paper* (Feb 1853)		
14	3	(1d.) blue	—	£2250

B. *Second issue* (March 1855). *Thinner paper. Impression less distinct than before*

15	3	(1d.) pale blue *to* greenish blue	—	£900

C. *Third issue* (December 1856). *Background often of solid colour, but with clear lines in places*

16	3	(1d.) bright blue *to* deep blue	£4500	£1200

D. *Fourth issue* (October 1858). *Impression less distinct, and rarely showing more than traces of background lines*

17	3	(1d.) very deep greenish blue	—	£650
18		(1d.) slate-blue	£4000	£650

E. *Fifth issue* (March 1860). *Impression shows no (or hardly any) background lines*

19	3	(1d.) grey *to* bluish grey	£4000	£450
20		(1d.) red (*shades*)	11·00	£450

In the worn impression of the fourth and fifth issues, the impression varies according to the position on the stone. Generally speaking, stamps of the fifth issue have a flatter appearance and cancellations are often less well defined. The paper of both these issues is thin or very thin. In all issues except 1853 (Feb) the gum tends to give the paper a toned appearance.

Stamps in the slate-blue shade (No. 18) also occur in the fifth issue, but are not readily distinguishable.

(Recess P.B.)

1859 (9 May). *Imperf.*

25	4	4d. grey-lilac	55·00	£275
28		6d. deep-green	—	£425
29		1s. indigo	60·00	£275
30		1s. purple-slate		

No. 30 may be of unissued status.

1859 (Sept). *(a) Pin-perf* 12½.

No.	Type	Description	Unused	Used
31	2	(1d.) rose-red	£500	42·00
32		(1d.) carmine-lake	£500	42·00
33	4	4d. dull lilac	—	£700
34		4d. dull purple	—	£700
35		6d. yellow-green	£1800	£150
36		6d. deep green	£1800	£130
37		1s. purple-slate	£2750	£850
		(b) Pin-perf 13½–14		
38	2	(1d.) rose-red	65·00	17·00
39		(1d.) carmine-lake	£110	15·00
40	4	4d. dull lilac	£650	65·00
40*a*		4d. brownish purple	60·00	85·00
41		4d. dull purple	£200	85·00
42		6d. yellow-green	£300	60·00
43		6d. deep green	£250	55·00
43*a*		6d. bright yellow-green	60·00	70·00
		b. Imperf between (vert pair)	£3500	
44		1s. purple-slate	—	£550
		(c) Compound pin-perf 13½–14 × 12½		
45	2	(1d.) carmine-lake		
45*a*	4	4d. dull purple	†	—

PRICES. The Pin-perf stamps are very scarce with perforations on all sides and the prices quoted above are for good average specimens.

The note after No. 12 also applies to Nos. 38, 40*a*, 43*a*, 46, 47 and 50.

1860 (Aug). *Clean-cut perf* 14–16½.

No.	Type	Description	Unused	Used
46	2	(1d.) rose-red	70·00	32·00
		a. Imperf vert (horiz pair)	£1100	
47	4	4d. brownish lilac	85·00	60·00
48		4d. lilac	—	£225
49		6d. bright yellow-green	£200	75·00
50		6d. deep green	£150	£120

1861 (June). *Rough perf* 14–16½.

No.	Type	Description	Unused	Used
52	2	(1d.) rose-red	65·00	20·00
53		(1d.) rose	65·00	17·00
54	4	4d. brownish lilac	£160	35·00
55		4d. lilac	£350	35·00
		a. Imperf		
56		6d. yellow-green	£150	55·00
57		6d. deep green	£350	55·00
58		1s. indigo	£600	£130
59		1s. deep bluish purple	£750	£225

(Recess D.L.R.)

1862–63. *Thick paper. (a) P* 11½, 12.

No.	Type	Description	Unused	Used
60	2	(1d.) crimson-lake	60·00	10·00
61	4	4d. deep purple	60·00	35·00
62		6d. deep green	£500	40·00
63		1s. bluish slate	£600	65·00
		(b) P 11½, 12, *compound with* 11		
63*a*	2	(1d.) crimson-lake	—	£350
63*b*	4	6d. deep green	—	£5000
		(c) P 13 (1863)		
64	2	(1d.) lake	24·00	15·00
65	4	6d. emerald-green	£275	45·00
67		1s. bright mauve	£2750	£225
		(d) P 12½ (1863)		
68	2	(1d.) lake	18·00	16·00

1863–75. *Wmk Crown CC. P* 12½.

No.	Type	Description	Unused	Used
69	2	(1d.) lake	24·00	3·25
		a. Wmk sideways	70·00	7·00
70		(1d.) rose	24·00	1·40
		a. Imperf (pair)		
71		(1d.) scarlet	24·00	90
72		(1d.) carmine	24·00	1·50
73	4	4d. bright violet	65·00	8·00
74		4d. pale mauve	£110	9·00
75		4d. dull lilac	55·00	9·50
77		6d. emerald-green	48·00	10·00
78		6d. deep green	£200	7·50
80		6d. yellow-green	35·00	3·00
81		6d. apple-green	35·00	4·50
82		6d. blue-green	55·00	4·75
83		1s. bright deep mauve	90·00	6·00
84		1s. lilac-rose	70·00	5·00
85		1s. mauve (aniline)	60·00	4·25

The 1s. in a purple-slate shade is a colour changeling.

5

(Typo D.L.R.)

1869. *Wmk Crown CC. P* 12½.

No.	Type	Description	Unused	Used
87	5	5s. rose-lake	95·00	55·00

1872. *Colours changed. Wmk Crown CC. P* 12½.

No.	Type	Description	Unused	Used
88	4	4d. grey	65·00	3·25
89		4d. bluish grey	65·00	4·00
90		1s. chrome-yellow	80·00	1·00

1876. *Wmk Crown CC. (a) P* 14.

No.	Type	Description	Unused	Used
91	2	(1d.) lake	8·00	50
		a. Bisected (½d.) (on cover)	†	£425
92		(1d.) rose-carmine	8·00	1·00
93		(1d.) scarlet	24·00	75
94	4	4d. bluish grey	55·00	70
95		6d. bright yellow-green	45·00	1·25
96		6d. deep yellow-green	50·00	1·00
97		1s. chrome-yellow	55·00	2·50
		(b) P 14 × 12½		
97*a*	4	6d. yellow-green	—	£4500

(6) (7)

1879–82. *Surch with T* **6** *or* **7**. *P* 14.

No.	Type	Description	Unused	Used
		(a) Wmk Crown CC (June 1879)		
98	2	½d. lilac	7·00	4·75
99		½d. mauve	7·00	4·75
		a. Wmk sideways	35·00	35·00
		(b) Wmk Crown CA (1882)		
100	2	½d. lilac	£200	60·00
101		1d. rosy carmine	13·00	30
		a. Bisected (½d.) (on cover)	†	£350

1882. *Wmk Crown CA. P* 14.

No.	Type	Description	Unused	Used
102	4	4d. bluish grey	95·00	5·00

(8) Various styles

1882 (9 May). *Surch by hand in various styles as T* **8** *in red or black ink and the original value obliterated by a thick or thin bar or bars, of the same colour.*

No.	Type	Description	Unused	Used
103		1d. on 6d. (No. 95) (Bk.)	—	£1500
104		1d. on 6d. (No. 95) (R.)	2·75	3·00
105		1d. on 6d. (No. 96) (R.)	3·00	3·00
		a. Bisected (½d.) (on cover)	†	£300

10

11 Britannia

12 Britannia

(Typo D.L.R.)

1883–94. *P* 14. *(a) Wmk Crown CA.*

No.	Type	Description	Unused	Used
106	10	½d. dull green	30	15
107		1d. carmine	1·50	10
		a. Bisected (½d.) (on cover)	†	£400
108		2½d. bright blue	3·75	15
110		4d. grey	2·25	20
111		6d. olive-black (1884)	2·00	1·50
112		1s. orange-brown (1884)	2·00	1·50
		(b) Wmk Crown CC		
113	5	5s. maroon (1894)	17·00	32·00
106/13		*Set of* 7	26·00	32·00
106/12 Optd "Specimen"		*Set of* 6	£400	

Two types of 1d. value:

ONE PENNY (I) (round "o") ONE PENNY (II) (oval "o")

(Typo D.L.R.)

1896 (17 Aug)–**1900**. *P* 14. *(a) Wmk Crown CA.*

No.	Type	Description	Unused	Used
114	11	½d. dull purple and green	30	15
115		1d. dull purple and rose (I)	2·00	10
116		1d. dull purple and rose (II) (1900)	70·00	1·50
117		2½d. dull purple and blue	1·50	15
118		4d. dull purple and orange	3·50	5·50
119		5d. dull purple and mauve	5·00	5·50
120		6d. dull purple and black	3·50	4·50
121		1s. green and brown	4·50	5·00
		(b) Wmk CA over Crown		
122	12	5s. green and brown, **O**	28·00	48·00
123		10s. green and ultramarine, **O**	95·00	£100
124		£1 green and carmine, **OC**	85·00	95·00
114/24		*Set of* 10	£200	£240
114/24 Optd "Specimen"		*Set of* 10	£150	

No. 119, surcharged "3d." was prepared for use but not issued (*Price £3500 unused*). It also exists overprinted "Specimen" (*Price £85*).

Collectors are warned against apparently postally used copies of this issue which bear "REGISTRAR-GENERAL" obliterations and are of very little value.

13 Landing of Columbus

(Recess D.L.R.)

1898. *Discovery of Trinidad Commemoration. Wmk Crown CC. P* 14.

No.	Type	Description	Unused	Used
125	13	2d. brown and dull violet	1·50	40
125 Optd "Specimen"			50·00	

1901–06. *Colours changed. Wmk Crown CA or CA over Crown* (5s.). *P* 14.

No.	Type	Description	Unused	Used
126	11	½d. grey-green, **O** (1902)	35	35
127		1d. black/*red*, **O** (II)	80	10
		a. Value omitted	£10000	
128		2½d. purple and blue/*blue*, **O** (1902)	3·75	25
129		4d. green and blue/*buff*, **OC** (1902)	1·50	4·25
130		1s. black and blue/*yellow*, **O** (1903)	12·00	4·00
131	12	5s. lilac and mauve, **O**	23·00	38·00
		a. Deep purple and mauve, **OC** (1906)	30·00	50·00
126/31		*Set of* 6	38·00	42·00
126/31 Optd "Specimen"		*Set of* 6	£100	

A pane of sixty of No. 127a was found in a post office in Trinidad but not more than nine copies are believed to have been sold, and the rest withdrawn.

1904–09. *Wmk Mult Crown CA. P* 14.

No.	Type	Description	Unused	Used
132	11	½d. grey-green, **OC**	75	15
133		½d. blue-green, **O** (1906)	2·50	80
134		1d. black/*red*, **OC** (II)	75	10
135		1d. rose-red, **O** (1907)	80	10
136		2½d. purple and blue/*blue*, **C**	7·50	90
137		2½d. blue, **O** (1906)	1·50	15
138		4d. grey and red/*yellow*, **C** (1906)	1·00	4·75
		a. Black and red/yellow, **C**	8·00	13·00
139		6d. dull purple and black, **C** (1905)	8·00	13·00
140		6d. dull and bright purple, **C** (1906)	3·50	5·50
141		1s. black and blue/*yellow*, **C**	9·00	7·50
142		1s. purple and blue/*golden yellow*, **C**	7·50	9·50
143		1s. black/*green*, **C** (1906)	1·00	1·25
144	12	5s. deep purple and mauve, **C** (1907)	32·00	50·00
145		£1 green and carmine, **C** (1907)	90·00	95·00
132/45		*Set of* 14	£140	£150
135, 137/8, 140, 142/3 Optd "Specimen"		*Set of* 6	£100	

No. 135 is from a new die, the letters of "ONE PENNY" being short and thick, while the point of Britannia's spear breaks the uppermost horizontal line of shading in the background.

14

15

16

(Typo D.L.R.)

1909. *Wmk Mult Crown CA. P* 14.

No.	Type	Description	Unused	Used
146	14	½d. green, **O**	70	10
147	15	1d. rose-red, **O**	35	10
148	16	2½d. blue, **O**	4·00	1·25
146/8		*Set of* 3	4·50	1·25
146/8 Optd "Specimen"		*Set of* 3	50·00	

TOBAGO

Although early postal markings are recorded from 1772 onwards it was not until 1841 that the British G.P.O. established a branch office at Scarborough, the island capital, to handle the overseas mail.

The stamps of Great Britain were in use from May 1858 to the end of March 1860 when the control of the postal service passed to the local authorities.

From 1 April 1860 Nos. CC1/2 were again used on overseas mail, pending the introduction of Tobago stamps in 1879.

For illustrations of the handstamp and postmark types see BRITISH POST OFFICES ABROAD notes, following GREAT BRITAIN.

SCARBOROUGH

CROWNED-CIRCLE HANDSTAMPS

No.	Type	Description		Price
CC1	CC 2	TOBAGO (R.) (31.10.1851)	*Price on cover*	£600
CC2	CC 6	TOBAGO (R.) (1875)	*Price on cover*	£800

Stamps of GREAT BRITAIN *cancelled* "A 14" *as Type* **2**.

1858 *to* **1860**.

No.	Description	Price
Z 1	1d. rose-red (1857), *perf* 14	£650
Z 2	4d. rose (1857)	£225
Z 3	6d. lilac (1856)	£200
Z 4	1s. green (1856)	£700

PRICES FOR STAMPS ON COVER

Nos. 1/4	*from* × 25
Nos. 5/7	—
Nos. 8/12	*from* × 10
Nos. 13/19	*from* × 6
Nos. 20/4	*from* × 30
Nos. 26/33	*from* × 25

CANCELLATIONS. Beware of early stamps of Tobago with fiscal endorsements removed and forged wide "A 14" postmarks added.

1

2

2½ PENCE

(3)

(T 1 and 2. Typo D.L.R.)

1879 (1 Aug). *Fiscal stamps issued provisionally pending the arrival of stamps inscr "POSTAGE". Wmk Crown CC. P 14.*
1 1 1d. rose .. 60·00 50·00
2 3d. blue .. 50·00 35·00
3 6d. orange .. 20·00 35·00
4 1s. green .. £350 60·00
a. Bisected (6d.) (on cover)
5 5s. slate .. £550 £500
6 £1 mauve .. £5000

The stamps were introduced for fiscal purposes on 1 July 1879.

Stamps of T 1, watermark Crown CA, are fiscals which were never admitted to postal use.

1880 (Nov). *No. 3 bisected vertically and surch with pen and ink.*
7 1 1d. on half of 6d. orange .. £4500 £500

1880 (20 Dec). *Wmk Crown CC. P 14.*
8 2 ½d. purple-brown .. 16·00 25·00
9 1d. Venetian red .. 48·00 28·00
a. Bisected (½d.) (on cover) .. † £1300
10 4d. yellow-green .. £180 23·00
a. Bisected (2d.) (on cover) .. † £1300
b. Malformed "CE" in "PENCE" .. £1100 £400
11 6d. stone .. £225 90·00
12 1s. yellow-ochre .. 45·00 35·00

For illustration of Nos. 10b, 18a, 22b, 30a, 31a and 33b see above No. 4 of Dominica.

1883 (Apr). *No. 11 surch with T 3.*
13 2 2½d. on 6d. stone .. 18·00 15·00
a. Surch double .. £2500 £1200
b. Large "2" with long tail .. £100 £110

"SLASH" FLAW. Stamps as Type 2 were produced from Key and Duty plates. On the Key plate used for consignments between 2 October 1892 and 16 December 1896, damage in the form of a large cut or "slash" shows after the "E" of "POSTAGE".

After 1896 an attempt was made to repair the "slash". This resulted in its disappearance, but left an incomplete edge to the circular frame at right.

1882–84. *Wmk Crown CA. P 14.*
14 2 ½d. purple-brown (1882) .. 1·00 10·00
15 1d. Venetian red (1882) .. 1·00 1·25
a. Bisected diag (½d.) (on cover)
16 2½d. dull blue (1883) .. 5·50 80
a. Bright blue .. 1·75 75
b. Ultramarine .. 1·75 75
c. "Slash" flaw .. 12·00 20·00
ca. "Slash" flaw repaired .. 60·00
18 4d. yellow-green (1882) .. £170 90·00
a. Malformed "CE" in "PENCE" .. £900 £400
19 6d. stone (1884) .. £550 £475

1885–96. *Colours changed and new value. Wmk Crown CA. P 14.*
20 2 ½d. dull green (1886) .. 20 35
a. "Slash" flaw .. 9·00 20·00
ab. "Slash" flaw repaired .. 18·00
21 1d. carmine (1889) .. 45 20
a. "Slash" flaw .. 7·00 10·00
ab. "Slash" flaw repaired .. 25·00
22 4d. grey (1885) .. 50 55
a. Imperf (pair) .. £1700
b. Malformed "CE" in "PENCE" .. 50·00 80·00
c. "Slash" flaw .. 50·00 85·00
ca. "Slash" flaw repaired .. 75·00
23 6d. orange-brown (1886) .. 60 2·50
a. "Slash" flaw .. 50·00 85·00
ab. "Slash" flaw repaired .. 75·00
24 1s. olive-yellow (1894) .. 70 5·50
a. Pale olive-yellow .. 6·50
b. "Slash" flaw .. 60·00 £120
ba. "Slash" flaw repaired .. 85·00
24c 1s. orange-brown (1896) .. 3·25
ca. "Slash" flaw .. 75·00
20, 21 and 23 Optd "Specimen" .. *Set of* 3 £170

No. 24c was printed in the colour of the 6d. by mistake.

½ PENNY (4) 2½ PENCE (5) ½d POSTAGE (6)

1886–89. *Nos. 16, 19 and 23 surch as T 4.*
26 ½d. on 2½d. dull blue (4.86) .. 2·25 6·00
a. Figure further from word .. 14·00 28·00
b. Surch double .. £1300 £1100
c. Surch omitted. Vert pair with No. 26 .. £8000
d. Ditto with No. 26a .. £15000
27 ½d. on 6d. stone (1.86) .. 1·50 12·00
a. Figure further from word .. 35·00 75·00
b. Surch inverted .. £1300
c. Surch double .. £1500
28 ½d. on 6d. orange-brown (8.87) .. 55·00 70·00
a. Figure further from word .. £225 £250
b. Surch double .. — £1000
29 1d. on 2½d. dull blue (7.89) .. 19·00 14·00
a. Figure further from word .. 70·00 75·00

The surcharge is in a setting of 12 (two rows of 6) repeated five times in the pane. Nos. 7, 9 and 10 in the setting have a raised "P" in "PENNY", and No. 10 also shows the wider spacing between figure and word.

1891–92. *No. 22 surch with T 4 or 5.*
30 ½d. on 4d. grey (3.92) .. 8·50 24·00
a. Malformed "CE" in "PENCE" .. £300 £400
b. Surch double .. £1800
31 2½d. on 4d. grey (8.91) .. 3·00 6·50
a. Malformed "CE" in "PENCE" .. £225 £300
b. Surch double .. £1800

1896. *Fiscal stamp (T 1, value in second colour, wmk Crown CA, P 14), surch with T 6.*
33 ½d. on 4d. lilac and carmine .. 14·00 18·00
a. Space between "½" and "d" .. 32·00 42·00
b. Malformed "CE" in "PENCE" .. £300 £350

From 1896 until 1913 Trinidad stamps were used in Tobago.

TRINIDAD AND TOBAGO

PRICES FOR STAMPS ON COVER	
Nos. 149/55	*from* × 3
Nos. 156/7	—
Nos. 174/89	*from* × 10
Nos. 206/56	*from* × 2
Nos. D18/25	*from* × 12

17

18

(Typo D.L.R.)

1913–23. *Wmk Mult Crown CA. P 14.*
149 17 ½d. green, O .. 45 10
a. Yellow-green (1915) .. 1·00 15
b. Blue-green (thick paper) (1917) .. 1·25 40
c. Blue-green/bluish (3.18) .. 9·00 9·00
150 1d. bright red, O .. 40 15
a. Red (thick paper) (1916) .. 25 10
b. Pink (1918) .. 5·50 80
c. Carmine-red (5.18) .. 25 10
151 2½d. ultramarine, O .. 3·25 30
a. Bright blue (thick paper) (1916) .. 1·50 30
b. Bright blue (thin paper) (1918) .. 3·50 40
152 4d. black and red/*yellow*, OC .. 50 2·50
a. White back (12.13) (Optd S. £16) .. 1·75 5·50
b. On lemon (1917) .. 10·00
c. On pale yellow (Optd S. £20) (1923) .. 2·75 6·50
153 6d. dull and reddish purple, C .. 3·25 3·25
a. Dull and deep purple (1918) .. 1·75 3·75
b. Dull purple and mauve (2.18) .. 4·50 5·50
154 1s. black/*green*, O .. 75 2·50
a. White back (Optd S. £16) .. 65 3·25
b. On blue-green, olive back .. 1·75 3·75
c. On emerald back (Optd S. £20) .. 1·00 2·50
155 18 5s. dull purple and mauve, C (1914) .. 27·00 48·00
a. Deep purple and mauve (1918) .. 27·00 48·00
b. Lilac and violet .. 45·00 55·00
c. Dull purple and violet .. 50·00 60·00
d. Brown-purple and violet .. 26·00 50·00
156 £1 grey-green and carmine, C (1914) .. 90·00 £110
a. Deep yellow-green and carmine (1918) .. 90·00 £110
149/56 .. *Set of* 8 £110 £140
149/56 Optd "Specimen" .. *Set of* 8 £140

No. 156*a* is from a plate showing background lines very worn.

18*a*

1914 (18 Sept). *Red Cross Label authorised for use as ½d. stamp. Typo. P 11–12.*
157 18*a* (½d.) Red .. 9·00 £180

The above was authorised for internal use on one day only, to raise funds for the Red Cross. The used price is for stamp on cover.

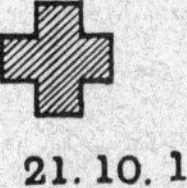
21. 10. 15.
(19)

19. 10. 16.

(19*a*)

1915 (21 Oct). *Optd with T 19. Cross in red with outline and date in black.*
174 17 1d. red .. 35 40
a. Cross 2 mm to right .. 12·00 12·00
b. "1" of "15" forked foot .. 5·00 7·50
c. Broken "0" in "10" .. 9·00 9·50

The varieties occur in the following positions on the *pane* of 60: a. No. 11. b. No. 42. c. No. 45. Variety a. is only found on the right-hand pane.

1916 (19 Oct). *Optd with T 19a. Cross in red with outline and date in black.*
175 17 1d. scarlet .. 10 30
a. No stop after "16" .. 6·50 12·00
b. "19.10.16" omitted

No. 175a appears on stamp No. 36 on the right-hand pane only.

FORGERIES. Beware of forgeries of the "War Tax" errors listed below. There are also other unlisted errors which are purely fakes.

WAR TAX (19*b*) WAR TAX (20) WAR TAX (21) WAR TAX (22)

1917 (2 Apr). *Optd with T 19b.*
176 17 1d. red .. 15 70
a. Opt inverted .. £140
b. Scarlet .. 15 80

1917 (May). *Optd with T 20.*
177 17 ½d. green .. 10 10
a. Pair, one without opt .. £170
178 1d. red .. 15 25
a. Pair, one without opt .. £170
b. Scarlet .. 40 15
ba. Opt double .. 80·00

The varieties without overprint were caused by the type being shifted over towards the left so that one stamp in the lowest row of each pane escaped.

1917 (21 June). *Optd with T 21.*
179 17 ½d. yellow-green .. 75 1·75
a. Pale green .. 10 1·25
b. Deep green .. 60 1·75
180 1d. red .. 10 10
a. Pair, one without opt

No. 180a was caused by a shifting of the type to the left-hand side, but only a few stamps on the right-hand vertical row escaped the overprint and such pairs are very rare.

1917 (21 July–Sept). *Optd with T 22.*
181 17 ½d. yellow-green .. 1·75 2·50
a. Deep green .. 10 70
182 1d. red (Sept) .. 15 15

WAR TAX (23) WAR TAX (24) WAR TAX (25)

1917 (1 Sept). *Optd with T 23 (closer spacing between lines of opt).*
183 17 ½d. deep green .. 10 65
a. Pale yellow-green
184 1d. red .. 7·50 13·00

1917 (31 Oct). *Optd with T 24.*
185 17 1d. scarlet .. 10 40
a. Opt inverted .. 70·00

1918 (7 Jan). *Optd with T 25.*
186 17 1d. scarlet .. 10 10
a. Opt double .. £130
b. Opt inverted .. 80·00

War Tax (26) War Tax (26a)

27

1918 (13 Feb–May). *Optd with T 26.*
187 17 ½d. bluish green .. 10 35
a. Pair, one without opt .. £400
b. "TAX" omitted
188 1d. scarlet .. 10 25
a. Opt double .. 80·00
b. Rose-red (1.5.18) .. 10 25

No. 187b occurs on R. 10/1 and was caused by a paper fold.

1918 (14 Sept). *New printing as T 26, but 19 stamps on each sheet have the letters of the word "Tax" wider spaced, the "x" being to the right of "r" of "War" as T 26a. Thick bluish paper.*
189 17 1d. scarlet ("Tax" spaced) .. 35 1·75
a. Opt double .. £140

1921–22. *Wmk Mult Script CA. P 14.*
206 17 ½d. green, O .. 35 60
207 1d. scarlet, O .. 20 20
208 1d. brown, O (17.2.22) .. 20 25
209 2d. grey, O (17.2.22) .. 1·00 1·25
210 2½d. bright blue, O .. 70 4·50
211 3d. bright blue, O (17.2.22) .. 1·75 1·75
212 6d. dull and bright purple, C .. 1·50 8·00
213 18 5s. dull purple and purple, C (1921) .. 28·00 65·00
214 5s. deep purple and purple, C (1922) .. 28·00 65·00
215 £1 green and carmine, C .. 75·00 £150
206/15 .. *Set of* 9 95·00 £200
206/15 Optd "Specimen" .. *Set of* 9 £200

(Typo D.L.R.)

1922–28. *P 14. (a) Wmk Mult Crown CA.*
216 **27** 4d. black and red/*pale yellow*, **C** 40 80
217 1s. black/*emerald*, **C** 1·50 4·00

(b) Wmk Mult Script CA
218 **27** ½d. green, **O** 10 10
219 1d. brown, **O** 15 10
220 1½d. bright rose, **O** 40 10
a. Scarlet 20 10
222 2d. grey, **O** 20 15
223 3d. blue, **O** 40 25
224 4d. black and red/*pale yellow*, **C** (1928) 2·50 2·00
225 6d. dull purple and bright magenta, **C** 2·00 10·00
226 6d. green and red/*emerald*, **C** (1924) 80 30
227 1s. black/*emerald*, **C** 80 90
228 5s. dull purple and mauve, **C** 10·00 16·00
229 £1 green and bright rose, **C** 80·00 £150
216/29 *Set of* 13 90·00 £170
216/29 Optd "Specimen" *Set of* 13 £225

(New Currency. 100 cents = 1 dollar)

28 First Boca **29** Imperial College of Tropical Agriculture

(Recess B.W.)

1935 (1 Feb)–**37**. *T* **28/9** *and similar horiz designs. Wmk Mult Script CA (sideways). P 12.*
230 1 c. blue and green 30 10
a. Perf 13×12½ (1936) 10 10
231 2 c. ultramarine and yellow-brown 30 10
a. Perf 13×12½ (1936) 35 10
232 3 c. black and scarlet 20 10
a. Perf 13×12½ (1936) 40 10
233 6 c. sepia and blue 70 30
a. Perf 13×12½ (1937) 60 80
234 8 c. sage-green and vermilion 30 65
235 12 c. black and violet 45 25
a. Perf 13×12½ (1937) 1·00 1·25
236 24 c. black and olive-green 25 35
a. Perf 13×12½ (1937) 4·00 2·50
237 48 c. deep green 4·00 9·00
238 72 c. myrtle-green and carmine 11·00 16·00
230/8 *Set of* 9 15·00 24·00
230/8 Perf "Specimen" *Set of* 9 90·00
Designs:—3 c. Mt Irvine Bay, Tobago; 6 c. Discovery of Lake Asphalt; 8 c. Queen's Park, Savannah; 12 c. Town Hall, San Fernando; 24 c. Government House; 48 c. Memorial Park; 72 c. Blue Basin.

1935 (6 May). *Silver Jubilee. As Nos. 91/4 of Antigua but ptd by B.W. P 11 × 12.*
239 2 c. ultramarine and grey-black 20 20
a. Extra flagstaff 30·00
b. Short extra flagstaff 20·00
c. Lightning conductor 20·00
d. Flagstaff on right-hand turret 25·00
240 3 c. deep blue and scarlet 20 30
a. Extra flagstaff 50·00
c. Lightning conductor 30·00
241 6 c. brown and deep blue 60 1·75
a. Extra flagstaff 80·00
b. Short extra flagstaff 50·00
c. Lightning conductor 50·00
242 24 c. slate and purple 3·50 3·25
a. Extra flagstaff £100
c. Lightning conductor 60·00
d. Flagstaff on right-hand turret 75·00
239/42 *Set of* 4 4·00 5·00
239/42 Perf "Specimen" *Set of* 4 65·00
For illustrations of plate varieties see Omnibus section following Zululand.

1937 (12 May). *Coronation. As Nos. 13/15 of Aden.*
243 1 c. green 15 10
244 2 c. yellow-brown 35 10
245 8 c. orange 65 20
243/5 *Set of* 3 1·00 35
243/5 Perf "Specimen" *Set of* 3 50·00

37 First Boca **47** King George VI

1938 (2 May)–**44**. *T* **37** *and similar horiz designs, and T* **47**. *Wmk Mult Script CA (sideways on 1 c. to 60 c.)*

(a) P 11½ × 11
246 1 c. blue and green 10 10
247 2 c. blue and yellow-brown 10 10
248 3 c. black and scarlet 10·00 50
248*a* 3 c. green and purple-brown (1941) 10 10
249 4 c. chocolate 15·00 1·00
249*a* 4 c. scarlet (1941) 40 30
249*b* 5 c. magenta (1.5.41) 10 10
250 6 c. sepia and blue 20 10
251 8 c. sage-green and vermilion 40 15
252 12 c. black and purple 5·00 95
a. Black and slate-purple (1944) 1·50 10
253 24 c. black and olive-green 35 10
254 60 c. myrtle-green and carmine 5·00 40

(b) T **47**. *P 12*
255 $1.20, blue-green (1.40) 3·25 25
256 $4.80, rose-carmine (1.40) 18·00 11·00
246/56 *Set of* 14 48·00 12·00
246/56 *exc* 249*b* Perf "Specimen" *Set of* 13 £190
Designs:—2 c. Imperial College of Tropical Agriculture; 3 c. Mt Irvine Bay, Tobago; 4 c. Memorial Park; 5 c. G.P.O. and Treasury; 6 c. Discovery of Lake Asphalt; 8 c. Queen's Park, Savannah; 12 c. Town Hall, San Fernando; 24 c. Government House; 60 c. Blue Basin.

1946 (1 Oct). *Victory. As Nos. 28/9 of Aden.*
257 3 c. chocolate 10 10
258 6 c. blue 10 15
257/8 Perf "Specimen" *Set of* 2 40·00

1948 (22 Nov). *Silver Wedding. As Nos. 30/1 of Aden (recess $4.80).*
259 3 c. red-brown 10 10
260 $4.80, carmine 13·00 12·00

1949 (10 Oct). *75th Anniv of Universal Postal Union. As Nos. 114/17 of Antigua.*
261 5 c. bright reddish purple 15 10
262 6 c. deep blue 25 20
263 12 c. violet 25 25
264 24 c. olive 25 20
261/4 *Set of* 4 80 65

1951 (16 Feb). *University College of B.W.I. As Nos. 118/19 of Antigua.*
265 3 c. green and red-brown 15 10
266 12 c. black and reddish violet 20 10

48 First Boca **49** Mt Irvine Bay, Tobago

(Recess B.W.)

1953 (20 Apr)–**59**. *Designs previously used for King George VI issue, but with portrait of Queen Elizabeth II as in T* **48** *(1 c., 2 c., 12 c.) or* **49** *(other values). Wmk Mult Script CA. P 12 (dollar values) or 11½×11 (others).*
267 1 c. blue and green 15 10
a. Blue and bluish green (10.6.59) 65 50
268 2 c. indigo and orange-brown 15 10
269 3 c. deep emerald and purple-brown 15 10
270 4 c. scarlet 20 10
271 5 c. magenta 30 10
272 6 c. brown and greenish blue 30 10
273 8 c. deep yellow-green and orange-red 50 10
274 12 c. black and purple 30 10
275 24 c. black and yellow-olive 30 10
a. Black and olive (16.11.55) 30 10
b. Black and greenish olive (12.12.56) 60 20
276 60 c. blackish green and carmine 5·00 30
277 $1.20, bluish green 80 75
a. Perf 11½ (19.1.55) 1·00 15
278 $4.80, cerise 5·00 12·00
a. Perf 11½ (16.11.55) 5·50 7·00
267/78a *Set of* 12 12·00 7·00
Designs: *Horiz*—2 c. Imperial College of Tropical Agriculture; 4 c. Memorial Park; 5 c. G.P.O. and Treasury; 6 c. Discovery of Lake Asphalt; 8 c. Queen's Park, Savannah; 12 c. Town Hall, San Fernando; 24 c. Government House; 60 c. Blue Basin. *Vert* (18 × 21 *mm*)—$1.20, $4.80, Queen Elizabeth II.

1953 (3 June). *Coronation. As No. 47 of Aden.*
279 3 c. black and green 10 10

ONE CENT
(50)

1956 (20 Dec). *No. 268 surch with T* **50**.
280 1 c. on 2 c. indigo and orange-brown 15 35

1958 (22 Apr). *Inauguration of British Caribbean Federation. As Nos. 135/7 of Antigua.*
281 5 c. deep green 15 10
282 6 c. blue 20 15
283 12 c. scarlet 20 10
281/3 *Set of* 3 50 25

PRINTERS. Nos. 284 to 354 were printed in photogravure by Harrison & Sons, *unless otherwise stated.*

51 Cipriani Memorial **52** Queen's Hall

53 Copper-rumped Hummingbird

54 Map of Trinidad and Tobago

(Des V. Whiteley (1, 2, 12, 35, 60 c., $4.80), J. Matthews (5 c.), H. Baxter (6, 8, 10, 15 c.), M. Goaman (25 c., 50 c., $1.20))

1960 (24 Sept)–**67**. *Designs as T* **51/4**. *W w* **12** *(upright). P 13½×14½ (1 c., 60 c., $1.20, $4.80) or 14½×13½ (others).*
284 1 c. stone and black 10 10
285 2 c. bright blue 10 10
a. Blue (23.6.64) 25 10
b. New blue (18.4.67) 25 10
286 5 c. chalky blue 10 10
287 6 c. red-brown 10 10
a. Pale chestnut (13.4.67) 25 10
288 8 c. yellow-green 10 10
289 10 c. deep lilac 10 10
290 12 c. vermilion 10 10
291 15 c. orange 90 45
291*a* 15 c. orange (15.9.64) 75 10
292 25 c. rose-carmine and deep blue 35 10
293 35 c. emerald and black 75 10
294 50 c. yellow, grey and blue 35 10
295 60 c. vermilion, yellow-green and indigo 45 20
a. Perf 14½ (1.10.65)* £100 40·00
296 $1.20, multicoloured 4·00 1·00
297 $4.80, apple-green and pale blue 4·50 4·25
284/97 *Set of* 15 11·00 6·00
Designs: *Vert as T* **51**—60 c. Anthurium Lilies. *Horiz as T* **52**—5 c. Whitehall; 6 c. Treasury Building; 8 c. Governor-General's House; 10 c. General Hospital, San Fernando; 12 c. Oil refinery; 15 c. (No. 291), Crest; 15 c. (No. 291*a*), Coat of arms; 25 c. Scarlet Ibis; 35 c. Pitch Lake; 50 c. Mohammed Jinnah Mosque.
*This is the earliest date reported to us. It comes from an unannounced printing which was despatched to Trinidad on 3 December 1964.
The 2, 5, 6, 12 and 25 c. exist with PVA gum as well as gum arabic.
See also No. 317.

65 Scouts and Gold Wolf Badge

1961 (4 Apr). *Second Caribbean Scout Jamboree. Design multicoloured; background colours below. W w* **12**. *P 13½ × 14½.*
298 **65** 8 c. light green 10 10
299 25 c. light blue 10 10

INDEPENDENT

66 "Buccoo Reef" (painting by Carlisle Chang) **71** "Protein Foods"

1962 (31 Aug). *Independence. T* **66** *and similar horiz designs. W w* **12**. *P 14½.*
300 5 c. bluish green 10 10
301 8 c. grey 10 10
302 25 c. reddish violet 10 10
303 35 c. brown, yellow, green and black 15 10
304 60 c. red, black and blue 25 20
300/4 *Set of* 5 60 35
Designs:—8 c. Piarco Air Terminal; 25 c. Hilton Hotel, Port-of-Spain; 35 c. Greater Bird of Paradise and map; 60 c. Scarlet Ibis and map.

(Des M. Goaman)

1963 (4 June). *Freedom from Hunger. W w* **12**. *P 14 × 13½.*
305 **71** 5 c. brown-red 10 10
306 8 c. yellow-bistre 10 10
307 25 c. violet-blue 20 10
305/7 *Set of* 3 35 15

72 Jubilee Emblem

1964 (15 Sept). *Golden Jubilee of Trinidad and Tobago Girl Guides' Association. W w* **12**. *P 14½ × 14.*
308 **72** 6 c. yellow, ultramarine and rose-red 10 10
309 25 c. yellow, ultramarine and bright blue 10 10
310 35 c. yellow, ultramarine & emerald-grn 10 10
308/10 *Set of* 3 20 15

73 I.C.Y. Emblem

(Litho State Ptg Wks, Vienna)

1965 (15 Nov). *International Co-operation Year. P* 12.

No.	Type	Description	Unused	Used
311	**73**	35 c. red-brown, dp green & ochre-yell ..	25	10

74 Eleanor Roosevelt, Flag and U.N. Emblem

1965 (10 Dec). *Eleanor Roosevelt Memorial Foundation. W* w **12**. *P* 13½ × 14.

No.	Type	Description	Unused	Used
312	**74**	25 c. black, red and ultramarine ..	10	10

75 Parliament Building

FIFTH YEAR OF
INDEPENDENCE
31st AUGUST 1967

(**79**)

1966 (8 Feb). *Royal Visit. T* **75** *and similar horiz designs. Multicoloured. W* w **12** (*sideways*). *P* 13½ × 14½.

No.	Description	Unused	Used
313	5 c. Type **75**	15	10
314	8 c. Map, Royal Yacht *Britannia* and Arms	80	70
315	25 c. Map and flag	85	55
316	35 c. Flag and panorama	90	70
313/16	.. .. *Set of* 4	2·40	1·75

1966 (15 Nov). *As No.* 284 *but W* w **12** (*sideways*).

No.	Description	Unused	Used
317	1 c. stone and black	10	10

No. 317 exists with PVA gum as well as gum arabic.

1967 (31 Aug). *Fifth Year of Independence. Nos.* 288/9, 291*a and* 295 *optd as T* **79**.

No.	Description	Unused	Used
318	8 c. yellow-green	10	10
319	10 c. deep lilac	10	10
320	15 c. orange	10	10
321	60 c. vermilion, yellow-green and indigo ..	15	10
318/21	.. .. *Set of* 4	15	15

On No. 321 the overprint is in five lines.

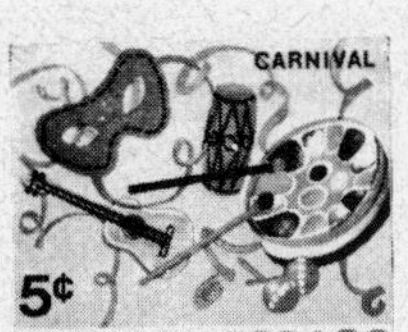

80 Musical Instruments

81 Calypso King

1968 (17 Feb). *Trinidad Carnival. Horiz designs as T* **80** (15 *and* 25 *c.*), *or vert designs as T* **81** (35 *and* 60 *c.*). *Multicoloured. P* 12.

No.	Description	Unused	Used
322	5 c. Type **80**	10	10
323	10 c. Type **81**	10	10
324	15 c. Steel band	10	10
325	25 c. Carnival procession	10	10
326	35 c. Carnival King	10	10
327	60 c. Carnival Queen	15	15
322/7	.. .. *Set of* 6	25	20

86 Doctor giving Eye-Test

87 Peoples of the World and Emblem

1968 (7 May). *20th Anniv of World Health Organization. W* w **12** (*sideways*). *P* 14.

No.	Type	Description	Unused	Used
328	**86**	5 c. red, blackish brown and gold ..	10	10
329		25 c. orange, blackish brown and gold ..	10	10
330		35 c. bright blue, black and gold ..	10	10
328/30		.. .. .. *Set of* 3	20	10

1968 (5 Aug). *Human Rights Year. W* w **12** (*sideways*). *P* 13½ × 14.

No.	Type	Description	Unused	Used
331	**87**	5 c. cerise, black and greenish yellow ..	10	10
332		10 c. new blue, black and greenish yellow	10	10
333		25 c. apple-green, black & greenish yell ..	10	10
331/3		.. .. *Set of* 3	15	15

88 Cycling

(Des G. Vasarhelyi. Islands additionally die-stamped in gold (5 c. to 35 c.))

1968 (14 Oct). *Olympic Games, Mexico. T* **88** *and similar horiz designs. Multicoloured. W* w **12**. *P* 14.

No.	Description	Unused	Used
334	5 c. Type **88**	10	10
335	15 c. Weightlifting	10	10
336	25 c. Relay-racing	10	10
337	35 c. Sprinting	10	10
338	$1.20, Maps of Mexico and Trinidad ..	25	20
334/8	.. .. *Set of* 5	40	25

93 Cocoa Beans

94 Green Hermit

(Des G. Vasarhelyi. Queen's profile die-stamped in gold (G.) or silver (S.), also the Islands on 20, 25 c.)

1969–72. *Designs as T* **93/4**. *W* w **12** (*sideways on* 1 *to* 8 *c.*, 40 *c.*, 50 *c.*). *P* 14 × 14½ ($2.50, $5) *or* 14 (*others*).

A. *Chalk-surfaced paper* (1.4.69)
B. *Glazed, ordinary paper* (24.3.72*)

No.	Description	A Unused	A Used	B Unused	B Used
339	1 c. multicoloured (S.) ..	10	10	10	10
	a. Queen's head omitted ..	75·00	—	†	
340	3 c. multicoloured (G.) ..	10	10	10	10
341	5 c. multicoloured (G.) ..	20	10	20	10
	a. Queen's head omitted ..	†		—	—
	b. Imperf (pair)	†		£200	—
	ba. Ditto and Queen's head omitted	†		£325	—
342	6 c. multicoloured (G.) ..	10	10	25	25
	a. Queen's head omitted ..	£100	—	†	
	b. Imperf (pair)	£250	—	†	
343	8 c. multicoloured (S.) ..	10	10	†	
344	10 c. multicoloured (G.) ..	25	10	30	10
345	12 c. mult (blue-grn leaves) (S.)	15	20	20	40
	a. Myrtle-green leaves ..	3·25	2·00	†	
346	15 c. multicoloured (S.) ..	10	10	20	10
	a. Queen's head omitted ..	£350	—	†	
347	20 c. scarlet, black & grey (G.)	15	10	30	20
348	25 c. scarlet, blk & new bl (S.)	15	15	85	25
	a. Silver (Queen's head and island) omitted	†		85·00	—
349	30 c. multicoloured (S.) ..	25	10	50	25
350	40 c. multicoloured (G.) ..	1·50	10	3·00	60
351	50 c. multicoloured (S.) ..	25	35	1·50	1·50
352	$1 multicoloured (G.) ..	60	15	1·50	1·75
	a. Gold (Queen's head) omitted	£100	—	—	—
353	$2.50, multicoloured (G.) ..	80	2·00	†	
	a. Perf 14 (1972)	15·00	15·00	†	
354	$5 multicoloured (G.) ..	1·50	3·00	†	
	a. Gold (Queen's head) omitted	£300	—	†	
	b. Perf 14 (1972)	35·00	35·00	†	
339A/54A	.. .. *Set of* 16	5·50	6·00	†	
339B/52B	.. .. *Set of* 13	†		8·00	5·00

Designs: *Horiz as T* **93**—3 c. Sugar refinery; 5 c. Rufous-vented Chachalaca; 6 c. Oil refinery; 8 c. Fertilizer plant; 40 c. Scarlet Ibis; 50 c. Maracas Bay; $2.50, Fishing; $5, Red House. *Vert as T* **94**—12 c. Citrus fruit; 15 c. Arms of Trinidad and Tobago; 20, 25 c. Flag and outline of Trinidad and Tobago; 30 c. Chaconia plant; $1, Poui tree.

*This was the date of receipt at the G.P.O.; the dates of issue are not known.

The listed missing die-stamped heads have the heads completely omitted and, except for No. 352a which results from a shift, show a blind impression of the die. They should not be confused with stamps from sheets containing a row of partially missing heads progressing down to mere specks of foil. The 20 c. value also exists with the gold omitted from the map only. We have also seen stamps with an additional "blind" profile cutting into the rear of the head but without a second die-stamped impression. Varieties of this nature are outside the scope of this catalogue.

See also Nos. 432/4 and 473.

108 Captain A. A. Cipriani (labour leader) and Entrance to Woodford Square

(Photo State Ptg Works, Vienna)

1969 (1 May). *50th Anniv of International Labour Organization. T* **108** *and similar horiz design. P* 12.

No.	Description	Unused	Used
355	6 c. black, gold and carmine-red	10	10
356	15 c. black, gold and new blue	10	10

Design:—15 c. Arms of Industrial Court and entrance to Woodford Square.

110 Cornucopia and Fruit

111 Map showing "CARIFTA" Countries

(Des and photo State Ptg Works, Vienna)

1969 (1 Aug). *First Anniv of CARIFTA (Caribbean Free Trade Area). T* **110/11** *and similar multicoloured designs. P* 13½.

No.	Description	Unused	Used
357	6 c. Type **110**	10	10
358	10 c. British and member nations' flags (*horiz*)	10	10
359	30 c. Type **111**	10	10
360	40 c. Boeing "727" in flight (*horiz*)	15	10
357/60	.. .. *Set of* 4	25	15

114 Space Module landing on Moon

(Des G. Vasarhelyi. Litho D.L.R.)

1969 (2 Sept). *First Man on the Moon. T* **114** *and similar multi-coloured designs. P* 14.

No.	Description	Unused	Used
361	6 c. Type **114**	10	10
362	40 c. Space module and astronauts on Moon (*vert*)	15	10
363	$1 Astronauts seen from inside space module	20	15
361/3	.. .. *Set of* 3	35	15

The above were released by the Philatelic Agency in the U.S.A. on 1 September, but not sold locally until 2 September.

117 Parliamentary Chamber, Flags and Emblems

(Photo Harrison)

1969 (23 Oct*). *15th Commonwealth Parliamentary Association Conference, Port-of-Spain. T* **117** *and similar horiz designs. Multicoloured. W* w **12**. *P* 14½ × 13½.

No.	Description	Unused	Used
364	10 c. Type **117**	10	10
365	15 c. J.F. Kennedy College	10	10
366	30 c. Parliamentary maces	10	10
367	40 c. Cannon and emblem	10	10
364/7	.. .. *Set of* 4	30	15

*This was the local release date; the Philatelic Agency in New York released the stamps ten days earlier.

121 Congress Emblem

122 Emblem and Islands at Daybreak

(Photo Rosenbaum Bros, Vienna)

1969 (3 Nov). *International Congress of the Junior Chamber of Commerce. T* **121/2** *and similar vert design. P* 13½.

No.	Description	Unused	Used
368	6 c. black, red and gold	10	10
369	30 c. gold, lake and light blue	10	10
370	40 c. black, gold and ultramarine	10	10
368/70	.. .. *Set of* 3	15	20

Design:—40 c. Emblem, palm-trees and ruin.

The above were released by the Philatelic Agency in the U.S.A. on 2 November, but not sold locally until 3 November.

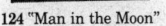

124 "Man in the Moon"

129 Statue of Gandhi

(Des V. Whiteley. Litho Questa)

1970 (6 Feb). *Carnival Winners. T* **124** *and similar multicoloured designs. W* w **12** *(sideways on 40 c.). P* 14.

371 5 c. Type **124** 10 10
372 6 c. "City beneath the Sea" 10 10
373 15 c. "Antelope" God Bamibara 10 10
374 30 c. "Chanticleer" Pheasant Queen of Malaya 10 10
375 40 c. Steel Band of the Year (*horiz*) 10 10
371/5 . . . . *Set of* 5 25 15

The above were released by the Philatelic Agency in the U.S.A. on 2 February, but not sold locally until 6 February.

(Photo State Printing Works, Vienna)

1970 (2 Mar). *Gandhi Centenary Year* (1969). *T* **129** *and similar multicoloured design. P* 12.

376 10 c. Type **129** 15 10
377 30 c. Head of Gandhi and Indian flag (*horiz*) . . 20 10

131 Symbols of Culture, Science, Arts and Technology

132 New U.P.U. H.Q. Building

(Des G. Lee. Photo State Printing Works, Vienna)

1970 (26 June). *25th Anniv of United Nations. T* **131/2** *and similar designs. Multicoloured. P* 12 (30 c.), 13½ × 14 (10 c.) *or* 13½ (*others*).

378 5 c. Type **131** 10 10
379 10 c. Children of different races, map and flag (34 × 25 *mm*) 10 10
380 20 c. Noah's Ark, rainbow and dove (35 × 24 *mm*) 15 10
381 30 c. Type **132** 15 15
378/81 . . . . *Set of* 4 25 20

NATIONAL
COMMERCIAL
BANK
ESTABLISHED
1.7.70

(133)

134 "East Indian Immigrants" (J. Cazabon)

1970 (1 July). *Inauguration of National Commercial Bank. No.* 341A *optd with T* **133**.

382 5 c. multicoloured 10 10

(Des from paintings by Cazabon. Litho Questa)

1970 (Oct). *125th Anniv of San Fernando. T* **134** *and similar designs. W* w **12** *(sideways on* 5 c. *and* 40 c.). *P* 13½.

383 3 c. multicoloured 10 10
384 5 c. black, blue and yellow-ochre 10 10
385 40 c. black, blue and yellow-ochre 35 10
383/5 . . . . *Set of* 3 40 15

Designs: *Horiz*—5 c. "San Fernando Town Hall"; 40 c. "San Fernando Harbour, 1860".

135 "The Adoration of the Shepherds" (detail, School of Seville)

(Des G. Drummond. Litho Format)

1970 (8 Dec). *Christmas. Paintings. T* **135** *and similar vert designs. Multicoloured. P* 13½.

386 3 c. Type **135** 10 10
387 5 c. "Madonna and Child with Saints" (detail, Titian) 10 10
388 30 c. "The Adoration of the Shepherds" (detail, Le Nain) 10 15
389 40 c. "The Virgin and Child, St. John and an Angel" (Morando) 10 10
390 $1 "The Adoration of the Kings" (detail, Veronese) 45 85
386/90 . . . . *Set of* 5 65 1·00
MS391 114 × 153 mm. Nos. 386/9 . . . . 1·60 2·00

136 Red Brocket

(Des State Printing Works, Vienna. Litho Questa)

1971 (9 Aug). *Trinidad Wildlife. T* **136** *and similar horiz designs. Multicoloured. W* w **12** *(sideways). P* 13½.

392 3 c. Type **136** 20 15
393 5 c. Collared Peccary ("Quenk") 25 15
394 6 c. Paca ("Lappe") 30 30
395 30 c. Brazilian Agouti . . . . 1·50 3·00
396 40 c. Ocelot . . . . 1·75 2·75
392/6 . . . . *Set of* 5 3·50 5·50

137 A. A. Cipriani

138 "Virgin and Child with St. John" (detail, Bartolommeo)

(Litho D.L.R.)

1971 (30 Aug*). *Ninth Anniv of Independence. T* **137** *and similar vert design. Multicoloured. W* w **12**. *P* 14.

397 5 c. Type **137** 10 10
398 30 c. Chaconia medal 15 20

*This was the local release date, but the New York agency issued the stamps on 25 August.

(Litho Harrison)

1971 (25 Oct). *Christmas. T* **138** *and similar vert designs. Multicoloured. W* w **12** *(sideways on* 10 *and* 15 c.). *P* 14 × 14½.

399 3 c. Type **138** 10 10
400 5 c. Local crèche 10 10
401 10 c. "Virgin and Child with Saints Jerome and Dominic" (detail, Lippi) 10 10
402 15 c. "Virgin and Child with St. Anne" (detail, Gerolamo dai Libri) 15 15
399/402 . . . . *Set of* 4 25 20

139 Satellite Earth Station, Matura

(Litho Harrison)

1971 (18 Nov). *Satellite Earth Station. T* **139** *and similar vert designs. Multicoloured. W* w **12** *(sideways on* 10 c.). *P* 14 (10 c.) *or* 14 × 13½ (*others*).

403 10 c. Type **139** 10 10
404 30 c. Dish antennae 15 20
405 40 c. Satellite and the earth 25 30
403/5 . . . . *Set of* 3 45 55
MS406 140 × 76 mm. Nos. 403/5 (wmk sideways). Imperf . . . . 1·25 2·00
a. Yellow and pale blue omitted . . . .

140 Morpho Hybrid

(Des G. Drummond. Photo Harrison)

1972 (18 Feb). *Butterflies. T* **140** *and similar horiz designs. Multicoloured. W* w **12** *(sideways on* 5 c.). *P* 14.

407 3 c. Type **140** 30 10
408 5 c. Purple Mort Bleu 35 10
409 6 c. Jaune d'Abricot 40 10
410 10 c. Purple King Shoemaker 60 15
411 20 c. Southern White Page . . . . . . 1·25 1·40
412 30 c. Little Jaune . . . . 1·75 2·25
407/12 . . . . *Set of* 6 4·25 3·50

141 *Lady McLeod* (paddle-steamer) and McLeod Stamp

142 Trinity Cross

(Des J. Cooter. Litho Harrison)

1972 (24 Apr*). *125th Anniv. of First Trinidad Postage Stamp. T* **141** *and similar horiz designs. W* w **12**. *P* 14.

413 5 c. multicoloured 15 10
414 10 c. multicoloured 25 10
415 30 c. greenish blue, reddish chestnut and black 50 45
413/15 . . . . *Set of* 3 80 55
MS416 83 × 140 mm. Nos. 413/15 . . . . 1·00 1·25
a. Wmk sideways . . . . 20·00 25·00

Designs:—10 c. Map and Lady McLeod stamp; 30 c. Lady McLeod stamp and inscription.

*This was the local release date, but the New York Agency issued the stamps on 12 April.

(Des G. Drummond. Photo Enschedé)

1972 (28 Aug). *Tenth Anniv of Independence. T* **142** *and similar vert designs. Multicoloured. W* w **12**. *P* 13½ × 13.

417 5 c. Type **142** 10 10
418 10 c. Chaconia Medal 10 10
419 20 c. Hummingbird Medal 15 15
420 30 c. Medal of Merit 15 20
417/20 . . . . *Set of* 4 40 40
MS421 93 × 121 mm. Nos. 417/20 . . . . 60 1·00

One example of MS421 has been seen with the blue (background and frame) omitted from the 10 c. Another example has been seen with carmine (background and frame) omitted from the 30 c.

See also Nos. 440/4.

143 Bronze Medal, 1964 Relay

(Des G. Drummond. Litho Questa)

1972 (7 Sept). *Olympic Games, Munich. T* **143** *and similar horiz designs. Multicoloured. W* w **12**. *P* 14.

422 10 c. Type **143** 10 10
423 20 c. Bronze, 1964 200 metres 20 10
424 30 c. Silver, 1952 weightlifting 25 15
425 40 c. Silver, 1964 400 metres 30 20
426 50 c. Silver, 1948 weightlifting 30 35
422/6 . . . . *Set of* 5 1·00 75
MS427 153 × 82 mm. Nos. 422/6 . . . . 1·00 1·75

144 "Adoration of the Kings" (detail, Dosso)

(Des G. Drummond. Photo J.W.)

1972 (9 Nov). *Christmas. T* **144** *and similar horiz design. Multicoloured. W* w **12**. *P* 14.

428 3 c. Type **144** 10 10
429 5 c. "The Holy Family and a Shepherd" (Titian) 10 10
430 30 c. As 5 c. 50 55
428/30 . . . . *Set of* 3 55 60
MS431 73 × 99 mm. Nos. 428/30 . . . . 85 1·50

1973–74. *Nos.* 340/2, *but W* w **12** *(upright). Glazed, ordinary paper.*

432 3 c. multicoloured (9.74?) . . . . . . 2·25 4·00
433 5 c. multicolourex (1973) . . . . . . 6·50 1·75
a. Yellow (background) omitted £125
434 6 c. multicoloured (1974) . . . . . . 1·50 1·50
432/4 . . . . *Set of* 3 9·00 6·50

COVER PRICES

Cover factors are quoted at the beginning of each country for most issues to 1945. An explanation of the system can be found on page x. The factors quoted do not, however, apply to philatelic covers.

145 E.C.L.A. Building, Chile

(Des G. Drummond. Litho Questa)

1973 (15 Aug). *Anniversaries. Events described on stamps. T* **145** *and similar horiz designs. Multicoloured. W* w **12**. *P* 14.

435	10 c. Type **145**	10	10
436	20 c. Interpol emblem	30	10
437	30 c. W.M.O. emblem	30	15
438	40 c. University of the West Indies	30	15
435/8	*Set of* 4	90	40
MS439	155 × 92 mm. Nos. 435/8	90	1·25

(Des J. Cooter. Litho Harrison)

1973 (30 Aug). *Eleventh Anniv of Independence. Vert designs as T* **142**. *Multicoloured. W* w **12**. *P* 14½ × 14.

440	10 c. Trinity Cross	10	10
441	20 c. Medal of Merit	15	10
442	30 c. Chaconia Medal	15	15
443	40 c. Hummingbird Medal	25	20
440/3	*Set of* 4	55	45
MS444	75 × 122 mm. Nos. 440/3. P 14	70	1·25

146 G.P.O., Port-of-Spain

147 "Madonna with Child" (Murillo)

(Des J. Cooter. Photo J.W.)

1973 (8 Oct). *Second Commonwealth Conference of Postal Administrations, Trinidad. T* **146** *and similar horiz design. Multicoloured. W* w **12** *(sideways). P* 14.

445	30 c. Type **146**	15	15
446	40 c. Conference Hall, Chaguaramas*	20	20
MS447	115 × 115 mm. Nos. 445/6	50	90

*Wrongly inscr "CHAGARAMAS" on stamp.

(Des PAD Studio. Photo Harrison)

1973 (22 Oct). *Christmas. W* w **12** *(sideways on* **MS**450). *P* 14½ × 14.

448 **147**	5 c. multicoloured	10	10
449	$1 multicoloured	35	45
MS450	94 × 88 mm. Nos. 448/9. P 14	60	1·40

148 Berne H.Q. within U.P.U. Emblem

(Des PAD Studio. Photo Harrison)

1974 (18 Nov). *Centenary of Universal Postal Union. T* **148** *and similar horiz design. Multicoloured. W* w **12** *(sideways). P* 13 × 14.

451	40 c. Type **148**	20	20
452	50 c. Map within emblem	20	30
MS453	117 × 104 mm. Nos. 451/2. P 13 × 14½	16·00	18·00

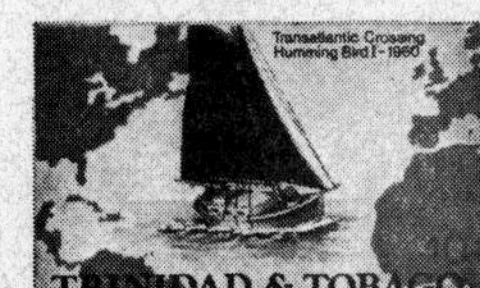

149 *Humming Bird I* crossing Atlantic Ocean (1960)

(Des and photo Harrison)

1974 (2 Dec). *First Anniv of World Voyage by H. and K. La Borde. T* **149** *and similar horiz design. Multicoloured. W* w **12** *(sideways). P* 14.

454	40 c. Type **149**	30	15
455	50 c. *Humming Bird II* crossing globe	35	25
MS456	109 × 84 mm. Nos. 454/5 (wmk upright)	2·00	4·00

150 "Sex Equality"

(Des Hetty J. Mejias de Grannes; adapted V. Whiteley. Litho Harrison)

1975 (23 June). *International Women's Year. W* w **14** *(sideways). P* 14.

457 **150**	15 c. multicoloured	10	10
458	30 c. multicoloured	20	25

151 Common Vampire Bat, Microscope and Syringe

(Des PAD Studio. Photo Harrison)

1975 (23 Sept). *Isolation of Rabies Virus. T* **151** *and similar horiz design. Multicoloured. W* w **14**. *P* 14 × 14½.

459	25 c. Type **151**	25	20
460	30 c. Dr. Pawan, instruments and book	30	25

152 Route-map and Tail of Boeing "707"

(Des C. Abbott. Litho Walsall)

1975 (27 Nov). *35th Anniv of British West Indian Airways. T* **152** *and similar horiz designs. W* w **14** *(sideways). P* 14.

461	20 c. Type **152**	15	10
462	30 c. "707" on ground	20	20
463	40 c. "707" in flight	30	30
461/3	*Set of* 4	60	55
MS464	119 × 110 mm. Nos. 461/3	80	1·25

153 "From the Land of the Humming Bird"

(Des and photo Harrison)

1976 (12 Jan). *Carnival. 1974 Prizewinning Costumes. T* **153** *and similar horiz design. Multicoloured. W* w **14** *(sideways). P* 14.

465	30 c. Type **153**	10	10
466	$1 "The Little Carib"	30	50
MS467	83 × 108 mm. Nos. 465/6	90	90

154 Angostura Building, Port-of-Spain

(Des Jennifer Toombs. Litho J.W.)

1976 (14 July). *150th Anniv. of Angostura Bitters. T* **154** *and similar horiz designs. Multicoloured. W* w **14** *(sideways). P* 13.

468	5 c. Type **154**	10	10
469	35 c. Medal, New Orleans 1885/6	15	20
470	45 c. Medal, Sydney 1879	20	35
471	50 c. Medal, Brussels 1897	20	35
468/71	*Set of* 4	50	85
MS472	119 × 112 mm. Nos. 468/71. P 14	90	1·25

REPUBLIC

1976 (2 Aug). *As No.* 344B *but W* w **14**.

473	10 c. multicoloured	55	45

1976 (4 Oct). *West Indian Victory in World Cricket Cup. As Nos.* 559/60 *of Barbados.*

474	35 c. Caribbean map	45	30
475	45 c. Prudential Cup	55	40
MS476	80 × 80 mm. Nos. 474/5	1·75	2·25

155 "Columbus sailing through the Bocas" (Campins)

(Des J.W. Litho Questa)

1976 (1 Nov)–**78**. *Paintings, Hotels and Orchids. Horiz designs as T* **155**. *Multicoloured. W* w **14**. *P* 14.

479	5 c. Type **155**	25	10
480	6 c. Robinson Crusoe Hotel, Tobago (17.1.78)	10	15
482	10 c. "San Fernando Hill" (J. Cazabon)	10	10
483	12 c. *Paphinia cristata* (7.6.78)	75	10
484	15 c. Turtle Beach Hotel (17.1.78)	20	15
485	20 c. "East Indians in a Landscape" (J. Cazabon)	25	10
486	25 c. Mt Irvine Hotel (17.1.78)	20	10
487	30 c. *Caularthon bicornutum* (7.6.78)	90	10
488	35 c. "Los Gallos Point" (J. Cazabon)	50	10
489	40 c. *Miltassia* (7.6.78)	1·00	10
490	45 c. "Corbeaux Town" (J. Cazabon)	60	10
491	50 c. *Oncidium ampliatum* (7.6.78)	1·25	15
492	70 c. Beach facilities, Mt Irvine Hotel (17.1.78)	40	70
494	$2.50, *Oncidium papilio* (7.6.78)	1·75	1·00
495	$5 Trinidad Holiday Inn (17.1.78)	1·75	3·50
479/95	*Set of* 15	8·75	5·75
MS497	171 × 100 mm. Nos. 479, 482, 485, 488 and 490. Wmk sideways	1·00	1·25
MS498	171 × 88 mm. Nos. 480, 484, 486, 492 and 495. Wmk sideways (17.1.78)	3·00	3·75
MS499	170 × 90 mm. Nos. 483, 487, 489, 491 and 494. Wmk sideways (7.6.78)	3·75	4·00

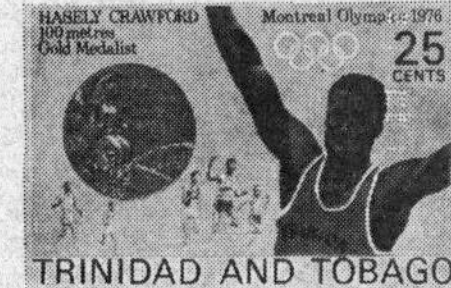

156 Hasely Crawford and Olympic Gold Medal

(Des J.W. Litho D. L. R.)

1977 (4 Jan). *Hasely Crawford Commemoration. W* w **14** *(sideways). P* 12 × 12½.

501 **156**	25 c. multicoloured	15	20
MS502	93 × 70 mm. No. 501	30	40

157 Lindbergh's Sikorsky "S-38", 1929

158 National Flag

(Des and litho J.W.)

1977 (4 Apr). *50th Anniv of Airmail Service. T* **157** *and similar horiz designs. Multicoloured. W* w **14** *(sideways). P* 13.

503	20 c. Type **157**	25	20
504	35 c. Arrival of Charles and Anne Lindbergh	35	25
505	45 c. Boeing "707", c. 1960	45	35
506	50 c. Boeing "747", 1969	1·10	1·60
503/6	*Set of* 4	1·90	2·25
MS507	130 × 100 mm. Nos. 503/6. P 14	3·50	3·50

(Des and litho J.W.)

1977 (26 July). *Inauguration of the Republic. T* **158** *and similar vert designs. Multicoloured. W* w **14**. *P* 13.

508	20 c. Type **158**	10	10
509	35 c. Coat of Arms	15	15
510	45 c. Government House	25	25
508/10	*Set of* 3	40	40
MS511	125 × 84 mm. Nos. 508/10. P 14	50	80

159 White Poinsettia

160 Miss Janelle (Penny) Commissiong with Trophy

(Des J.W. Litho Walsall)

1977 (11 Oct). *Christmas. T* **159** *and similar vert design. Multicoloured. W w* **14**. *P* 14 × 14½.
512 10 c. Type **159** 10 10
513 35 c. Type **159** 15 10
514 45 c. Red Poinsettia 20 20
515 50 c. As 45 c. 25 40
512/15 .. .. *Set of* 4 60 70
MS516 112 × 142 mm. Nos. 512/15 .. .. 80 1·25

(Des BG Studio. Litho Questa)

1978 (2 Aug). *Miss Janelle (Penny) Commissiong ("Miss Universe 1977") Commemoration. T* **160** *and similar vert designs showing Miss Commissiong. Multicoloured. W w* **14**. *P* 14½.
517 10 c. Type **160** 10 10
518 35 c. Portrait 25 25
519 45 c. In evening dress 30 45
517/19 .. .. *Set of* 3 60 70
MS520 186 × 120 mm. Nos. 517/19 .. .. 80 1·00
a. 45c. value imperf on three sides .. ..

161 Tayra

162 "Burst of Beauty"

(Des G. Drummond. Litho Walsall)

1978 (7 Nov). *Wildlife. T* **161** *and similar horiz designs. Multicoloured. W w* **14** *(sideways). P* 13½.
521 15 c. Type **161** 20 10
522 25 c. Ocelot 30 20
523 40 c. Brazilian Tree Porcupine 50 30
524 70 c. Tamandua 65 80
521/4 .. .. *Set of* 4 1·50 1·25
MS525 128 × 101 mm. Nos. 521/4 .. .. 1·50 2·00

(Des C. Abbott. Litho Format)

1979 (1 Feb). *Carnival* 1978. *T* **162** *and similar vert designs. P* 13½.
526 5 c. multicoloured 10 10
527 10 c. multicoloured 10 10
528 35 c. multicoloured 10 10
529 45 c. multicoloured 10 10
530 50 c. yellow-brown, rosine and deep lilac .. 10 10
531 $1 multicoloured 20 30
526/31 .. .. *Set of* 6 50 50
Designs:—10 c. Rain worshipper; 35 c. "Zodiac"; 45 c. Praying mantis; 50 c. "Eye of the Hurricane"; $1 Steel orchestra.

163 Day Care

164 Geothermal Exploration

(Des BG Studio. Litho J.W.)

1979 (5 June). *International Year of the Child. T* **163** *and similar vert designs. Multicoloured. P* 13.
532 5 c. Type **163** 10 10
533 10 c. School feeding programme 10 10
534 35 c. Dental care 15 15
535 45 c. Nursery school 15 20
536 50 c. Free bus transport 15 20
537 $1 Medical care 40 55
532/7 .. .. *Set of* 6 80 1·00
MS538 114 × 132 mm. Nos. 532/7. P 14 × 13½ .. 1·25 1·60

(Des local artist; adapted L. Curtis. Litho Format)

1979 (3 July). *4th Latin American Geological Congress. T* **164** *and similar horiz designs. Multicoloured. W w* **14** *(sideways). P* 13½.
539 10 c. Type **164** 10 10
540 35 c. Hydrogeology 20 20
541 45 c. Petroleum exploration 25 25
542 70 c. Environmental preservation 35 70
539/42 .. .. *Set of* 4 80 1·10
MS543 185 × 89 mm. Nos. 539/42 .. .. 1·25 1·60

165 1879 1d. rose and Map of Tobago

(Des J. Cooter. Litho Format)

1979 (1 Aug). *Tobago Stamp Centenary. T* **165** *and similar horiz designs in black, rose-lilac and dull orange* ($1) *or multicoloured (others). W w* **14** *(sideways). P* 13½ × 14.
544 10 c. Type **165** 10 10
545 15 c. 1879 3d. and 1880 ½d. surcharged on half of 6d. 10 10
546 35 c. 1879 6d. and 1886 ½d. surcharged on 6d. 25 25
547 45 c. 1879 1s. and 1886 ½d. surcharged on 2½d. 30 30
548 70 c. 1879 5s. and Great Britain 1856 1s. with "A14" (Scarborough, Tobago) postmark 45 80
549 $1 1879 £1 and General Post Office, Scarborough, Tobago .. .. 60 1·25
544/9 .. .. *Set of* 6 1·60 2·50
MS550 165 × 155 mm. Nos. 544/9 .. .. 1·90 2·50

166 1962 60 c. Independence Commemorative and Sir Rowland Hill

(Des and litho J.W.)

1979 (4 Oct). *Death Centenary of Sir Rowland Hill. T* **166** *and similar horiz designs showing stamps and Sir Rowland Hill. Multicoloured. W w* **14** *(sideways). P* 13.
551 25 c. Type **166** 25 10
552 45 c. 1977 35 c. Inauguration of Republic commemorative 35 20
553 $1 1879 Trinidad ½d. surcharge and Tobago 1880 4d. 40 60
551/3 .. .. *Set of* 3 90 80
MS554 115 × 125 mm. No. 551/3. P 13½ × 14 .. 90 1·00

167 Poui Tree in Churchyard

1844—
1980
POPULATION
CENSUS
12th MAY 1980
(**168**)

(Des G. Hutchins. Litho Format)

1980 (21 Jan). *Centenary of Princes Town. T* **167** *and similar horiz designs. Multicoloured. W w* **14** *(sideways). P* 14½ × 14.
555 5 c. Type **167** 10 10
556 10 c. Princes Town Court House 10 10
557 50 c. Locomotive of the Royal Train, 1880 .. 35 60
558 $1.50, H.M.S. *Bacchante* (corvette) .. 70 1·25
555/8 .. .. *Set of* 4 1·00 1·75
MS559 177 × 102 mm. Nos. 555/8 .. .. 1·60 2·00

1980 (8 Apr). *Population Census. Nos.* 479/80 *and* 482 *optd with T* **168**.
560 5 c. Type **155** 10 20
561 6 c. Robinson Crusoe Hotel, Tobago 10 30
562 10 c. "Old View" (Cazabon) 15 20
560/2 .. .. *Set of* 3 30 60

169 Scarlet Ibis (male)

170 Silver and Bronze Medals for Weightlifting, 1948 and 1952

(Des G. Drummond. Litho Questa)

1980 (6 May). *Scarlet Ibis. T* **169** *and similar vert designs. Multicoloured. W w* **14**. *P* 14.
563 50 c. Type **169** 65 65
a. Strip of 5. Nos. 563/7 .. .. .. 3·00
564 50 c. Male and female 65 65
565 50 c. Hen and nest 65 65
566 50 c. Nest and eggs 65 65
567 50 c. Chick in nest 65 65
563/7 .. .. *Set of* 5 3·00 3·00
Nos. 563/7 were printed together, *se-tenant*, in horizontal and vertical strips of 5 throughout.

(Des G. Hutchins. Litho Walsall)

1980 (22 July). *Olympic Games, Moscow. T* **170** *and similar designs. W w* **14** *(sideways). P* 14.
568 10 c. multicoloured 10 10
569 15 c. multicoloured 10 10
570 70 c. multicoloured 30 45
568/70 .. .. *Set of* 3 30 50
MS571 110 × 149 mm. $2.50, black, silver and orange-vermilion (wmk upright) .. .. 80 1·40
Designs: *Horiz*—15 c. Hasely Crawford (100 metres sprint winner, 1976) and gold medal; 70 c. Silver medal for 400 metres and bronze medals for 4 × 400 metres relay, 1964. *Vert*—$2.50, Olympic Games emblems for Moscow, 1980, Olympia, 776 B.C. and Athens, 1896.

171 Charcoal Production

(Des J. Cooter. Litho Walsall)

1980 (8 Sept). *11th Commonwealth Forestry Conference. T* **171** *and similar horiz designs. Multicoloured. W w* **14** *(sideways). P* 14.
572 10 c. Type **171** 10 10
573 55 c. Logging 35 25
574 70 c. Teak plantation 40 40
575 $2.50, Watershed management .. .. 1·25 1·50
572/5 .. .. *Set of* 4 1·90 2·00
MS576 135 × 87 mm. Nos. 572/5 .. .. 2·50 2·75

172 Beryl McBurnie (dance and culture) and Audrey Jeffers (social worker)

(Des BG Studio. Litho Questa)

1980 (29 Sept). *Decade for Women (1st issue). T* **172** *and similar horiz designs. Multicoloured. W w* **14** *(sideways). P* 14.
577 $1 Type **172** 45 55
578 $1 Elizabeth Bourne (judiciary) and Isabella Teshier (government) 45 55
579 $1 Dr. Stella Abidh (public health) and Louise Horne (nutrition) 45 55
577/9 .. .. *Set of* 3 1·25 1·50
See also Nos. 680/2.

173 Netball Stadium

(Des BG Studio. Litho Format)

1980 (21 Oct). *World Netball Tournament. W w* **14** *(sideways). P* 13½ × 14.
580 **173** 70 c. multicoloured 30 45

174 I.Y.D.P. Emblem, Athlete and Disabled Person

175 "Our Land Must Live"

(Des BG Studio. Litho Format)

1981 (23 Mar). *International Year for Disabled Persons. T* **174** *and similar horiz designs. W w* **14**. *P* 14½.
581 10 c. black, vermilion and dull yellowish green 15 10
582 70 c. black, vermilion and buff 50 70
583 $1.50, black, vermilion and cobalt .. .. 90 1·40
584 $2 black, vermilion and flesh .. .. 1·25 1·75
581/4 .. .. *Set of* 4 2·50 3·50
Designs:—70 c. I.Y.D.P. emblem and doctor with disabled person; $1.50, Emblem, and blind man and woman; $2 Emblem and inscription.

(Des Debbie Galt; adapted G. Vasarhelyi. Litho J.W.)

1981 (7 July). *Environmental Preservation. T* **175** *and similar horiz designs. Multicoloured. W w* **14** *(sideways). P* 13 × 13½.
585 10 c. Type **175** 10 10
586 55 c. "Our seas must live" 30 30
587 $3 "Our skies must live" .. .. .. 1·50 1·60
585/7 .. .. *Set of* 3 1·75 1·75
MS588 142 × 89 mm. Nos. 585/7 .. .. 2·50 2·75

176 "Food or Famine"

177 "First Aid Skills"

(Des and litho Harrison)

1981 (16 Oct). *World Food Day. T* **176** *and similar horiz designs. Multicoloured.* W w **14** (*sideways*). *P* 14½ × 14.

589 10 c. Type **176** 10 10
590 15 c. "Produce more" (threshing and milling rice) 10 10
591 45 c. "Fish for food" (Bigeye) 30 20
592 55 c. "Prevent hunger" 35 25
593 $1.50, "Fight malnutrition" 85 90
594 $2 "Fish for food" (Smallmouth Grunt) .. 1·10 1·25
589/94 .. .. *Set of* 6 2·40 2·40
MS595 164 × 98 mm. Nos. 589/94 .. .. .. 2·75 3·00

(Des L. Curtis. Litho Format)

1981 (17 Nov). *President's Award Scheme. T* **177** *and similar vert designs. Multicoloured.* W w **14**. *P* 14.

596 10 c. Type **177** 15 10
597 70 c. "Motor mechanics" 60 45
598 $1 "Expedition" 75 55
599 $2 Presenting an award .. .. 1·25 1·40
596/9 .. .. *Set of* 4 2·50 2·25

178 Pharmacist at Work **179** "Production"

(Des C. Abbott. Litho Questa)

1982 (12 Feb). *Commonwealth Pharmaceutical Conference. T* **178** *and similar vert designs.* W w **14**. *P* 14½ × 14.

600 10 c. Type **178** 10 10
601 $1 Gerritoute (plant) 65 65
602 $2 Rachette (plant) .. .. 1·25 1·25
600/2 .. .. *Set of* 3 1·75 1·75

(Des Debbie Galt; adapted G. Vasarhelyi. Litho Questa)

1982 (28 June). *75th Anniv of Boy Scout Movement. T* **179** *and similar vert designs. Multicoloured.* W w **14**. *P* 14.

603 15 c. Type **179** 35 10
604 55 c. "Tolerance" 75 25
605 $5 "Discipline" .. .. 4·00 3·75
603/5 .. .. *Set of* 3 4·50 3·75

180 Charlotteville **181** "Pa Pa Bois"

(Des Harrison. Litho Format)

1982 (18 Oct). *25th Anniv of Tourist Board. T* **180** *and similar vert designs. Multicoloured.* W w **14**. *P* 13½ × 14.

606 55 c. Type **180** 35 25
607 $1 Boating 55 55
608 $3 Fort George .. .. 1·75 1·90
606/8 .. .. *Set of* 3 2·40 2·40

(Des D. Louison. Litho Harrison)

1982 (8 Nov). *Folklore. Local Spirits and Demons. T* **181** *and similar horiz designs. Multicoloured.* W w **14** (*sideways*). *P* 14.

609 10 c. Type **181** 10 10
610 15 c. "La Diablesse" 10 10
611 65 c. "Lugarhoo", "Phantom" and "Soucouyant" 35 30
612 $5 "Bois de Soleil", "Davens" and "Mamma de l'Eau" .. .. 2·50 3·25
609/12 .. .. *Set of* 4 2·75 3·25
MS613 133 × 100 mm. Nos. 609/12 .. .. 3·50 4·00

182 Cane Harvesting

((Des W. Fenton. Litho Harrison)

1982 (13 Dec). *Canefarmers' Association Centenary. T* **182** *and similar horiz designs. Multicoloured.* W w **14** (*sideways*). *P* 14.

614 30 c. Type **182** 15 15
615 70 c. Farmers loading bullock cart 40 40
616 $1.50, Cane field in bloom 85 95
614/16 .. .. *Set of* 3 1·25 1·40
MS617 72 × 117 mm. Nos. 614/16. P 14½. .. 1·40 1·50

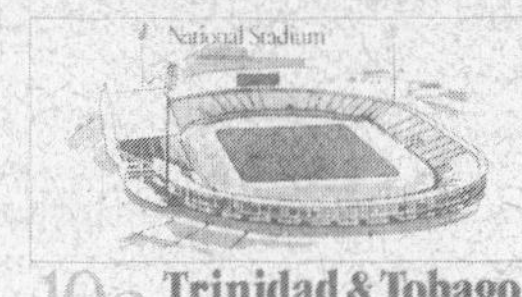

183 National Stadium

(Des McCombie Skinner. Litho Harrison)

1982 (28 Dec). *20th Anniv of Independence. T* **183** *and similar horiz designs. Multicoloured.* W w **14** (*sideways*). *P* 13 × 14.

618 10 c. Type **183** 10 10
619 35 c. Caroni water treatment plant 20 15
620 50 c. Mount Hope Maternity Hospital 30 25
621 $2 National Insurance Board Mall, Tobago .. 80 1·25
618/21 .. .. *Set of* 4 1·25 1·50

184 Commonwealth Flags

(Des C. Abbott. Litho Harrison)

1983 (14 Mar). *Commonwealth Day. T* **184** *and similar multicoloured designs.* W w **14** (*sideways on* 10, 55 *c.*). *P* 14.

622 10 c. Type **184** 10 10
623 55 c. Satellite view of Trinidad and Tobago .. 25 20
624 $1 "Nodding donkey" oil pump (*vert*) .. 40 50
625 $2 Map of Trinidad and Tobago (*vert*) .. 85 1·00
622/5 .. .. *Set of* 4 1·40 1·60

185 BW1A "Tristar"

(Des D. Miller. Litho Format)

1983 (11 July). *10th Anniv of CARICOM.* W w **14** (*sideways*). *P* 14.

626 **185** 35 c. multicoloured 50 25

186 V.D.U. Operator

(Des G. Vasarhelyi. Litho Harrison)

1983 (5 Aug). *World Communications Year. T* **186** *and similar horiz designs. Multicoloured.* W w **14** (*sideways*). *P* 14.

627 15 c. Type **186** 10 10
628 55 c. Scarborough Post Office, Tobago 35 20
629 $1 Textel building 65 60
630 $3 Morne Blue E.C.M.S. station .. .. 1·75 1·90
627/30 .. .. *Set of* 4 2·50 2·50

187 Financial Complex

(Des D. Miller. Litho Format)

1983 (19 Sept). *Conference of Commonwealth Finance Ministers.* W w **14** (*sideways*). *P* 14.

631 **187** $2 multicoloured .. .. 80 1·00

188 Kingfish **189** Bois Pois

(Des N. Weaver. Litho Format)

1983 (17 Oct). *World Food Day. T* **188** *and similar horiz designs. Multicoloured.* W w **14** (*sideways*). *P* 14 × 13½ (10 *c.*, 55 *c.*) *or* 13½ (*others*).

632 10 c. Type **188** 15 10
633 55 c. Flying Fish 70 35
634 70 c. Queen Conch 90 70
635 $4 Red Shrimp .. .. 3·75 4·50
632/5 .. .. *Set of* 4 5·00 5·00

(Des I. Loe. Litho Questa)

1983 (14 Dec)–**84**. *Flowers. T* **189** *and similar multicoloured designs.* W w **14** (*sideways on* 5 *c. to* $1.50). *P* 14. *A. Without imprint date. B. With imprint date* (10.84).

		A		B	
636	5 c. Type **189**	25	10	25	10
637	10 c. Maraval Lily	20	10	10	10
638	15 c. Star Grass	35	15	10	10
639	20 c. Bois Caco	10	10	†	
640	25 c. Strangling Fig	35	25	10	10
641	30 c. *Cassia moschata* ..	30	15	†	
642	50 c. Chalice Flower	15	20	†	
643	65 c. Black Stick	40	25	†	
644	80 c. *Columnea scandens* ..	50	35	†	
645	95 c. Cat's Claw	65	40	†	
646	$1 Bois L'agli	75	40	†	
647	$1.50, *Eustoma exaltatum* ..	1·00	65	†	
648	$2 Chaconia	1·25	85	†	
649	$2.50, *Chrysothemis pulchella*	75	60	†	
650	$5 *Centratherum punctatum* ..	3·00	3·00	†	
651	$10 Savanna Flower ..	4·25	4·25	†	
636A/51A	.. .. *Set of* 16	13·00	10·50	†	
636B/40B	.. .. *Set of* 4			35	30

Nos. 648/51 are horizontal, 39 × 29 mm.
No. 637B exists with different imprint dates at foot.
For these designs watermarked w **16** see Nos. 686/701.

190 Castle Chess Pieces in Staunton and 17th-century Styles **191** Swimming

(Des L. Curtis. Litho Questa)

1984 (14 Sept). *60th Anniv of World Chess Federation. T* **190** *and similar vert designs. Multicoloured.* W w **14**. *P* 14.

652 50 c. Type **190** .. .. 1·00 35
653 70 c. Staunton and 12th-century Bishops .. 1·25 65
654 $1.50, Staunton and 13th-century Queens .. 2·00 1·75
655 $2 Staunton and 19th-century Kings .. 2·50 2·25
652/5 .. .. *Set of* 4 6·00 4·50

(Des Garden Studio. Litho Harrison)

1984 (21 Sept). *Olympic Games, Los Angeles. T* **191** *and similar vert designs. Multicoloured.* W w **14**. *P* 14 × 14½.

656 15 c. Type **191** 10 10
657 55 c. Track and field events 30 20
658 $1.50, Sailing 70 80
659 $4 Cycling .. .. 2·00 2·50
656/9 .. .. *Set of* 4 2·75 3·25
MS660 132 × 85 mm. Nos. 656/9 .. .. .. 4·00 5·50

192 Slave Schooner and Shackles **193** Children's Band

(Des O. Bell. Litho Walsall)

1984 (22 Oct). *150th Anniv of Abolition of Slavery. T* **192** *and similar vert designs. Multicoloured.* W w **14**. *P* 13½ × 13.

661 35 c. Type **192** 55 20
662 55 c. Slave and "Slave Triangle" map 75 30
663 $1 *Capitalism and Slavery* (book by Dr. Eric Williams) .. .. 1·25 75
664 $2 Toussaint l'Ouverture (Haitian revolutionary) .. .. 1·75 1·90
661/4 .. .. *Set of* 4 3·75 2·75
MS665 95 × 100 mm. Nos. 661/4 .. .. .. 3·75 4·50

(Des G. Vasarhelyi. Litho J.W.)

1984 (13 Nov). *125th Anniv of St. Mary's Children's Home. T* **193** *and similar horiz designs. Multicoloured.* W w **14** (*sideways*). *P* 13½.

666 10 c. Type **193** 10 10
667 70 c. St. Mary's Children's Home 40 40
668 $3 Group of children .. .. 2·00 2·25
666/8 .. .. *Set of* 3 2·25 2·40

194 Parang Band

195 Capt. A. A. Cipriani and T. U. B. Butler

(Des D. Miller. Litho Questa)

1984 (26 Nov). *Parang Festival. T* **194** *and similar horiz designs. Multicoloured. W w* **14** *(sideways). P* 14 × 14½.

669 10 c. Type **194** 10 10
670 30 c. Music and poinsettia 20 15
671 $1 Bandola, bandolin and cuatro (musical instruments) 60 65
672 $3 Double bass, fiddle and guitar (musical instruments) .. .. 1·75 2·00
669/72 .. .. *Set of* 4 2·40 2·50

(Des G. Vasarhelyi. Litho Questa)

1985 (17 June). *Labour Day. Labour Leaders. T* **195** *and similar horiz designs. W w* **14**. *P* 14.

673 55 c. black and bright rose 25 30
674 55 c. black and orange-yellow 25 30
675 55 c. black and emerald 25 30
673/5 .. .. *Set of* 3 70 80

Designs:—No. 674, C. P. Alexander and Q. O'Connor; 675, A. Cola Rienzi and C. T. W. E. Worrell.

196 *Lady Nelson* (1928)

(Des E. Nisbet. Litho Format)

1985 (20 Aug). *Ships. T* **196** *and similar horiz designs. Multicoloured. W w* **14**. *P* 14½ × 14.

676 30 c. Type **196**.. .. .. 50 15
677 95 c. *Lady Drake* (1928) 85 50
678 $1.50, *Federal Palm* (1961) .. .. 1·50 1·25
679 $2 *Federal Maple* (1961) .. .. .. 2·00 1·75
676/9 .. .. *Set of* 4 4·25 3·25

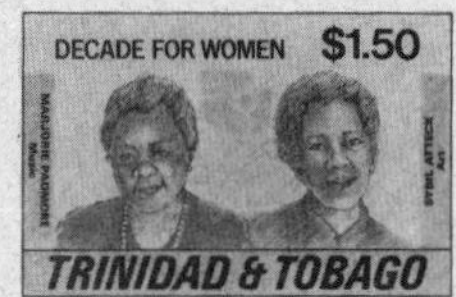

197 Marjorie Padmore (music) and Sybil Atteck (art)

(Des Julijana Zappin. Litho Walsall)

1985 (11 Nov). *Decade for Women (2nd issue). T* **197** *and similar horiz designs. Multicoloured. W w* **16** *(sideways). P* 14.

680 $1.50, Type **197** 70 80
681 $1.50, May Cherrie (medical social worker) and Evelyn Tracey (social worker) .. 70 80
682 $1.50, Umilta McShine (education) and Jessica Smith-Phillips (public service) .. 70 80
680/2 .. .. *Set of* 3 1·90 2·25

198 Badge of Trinidad and Tobago Cadet Force (75th Anniv)

199 Anne-Marie Javouhey (foundress)

(Des D. Slater. Litho Harrison)

1985 (9 Dec). *International Youth Year. T* **198** *and similar horiz designs. Multicoloured. W w* **16** *(sideways). P* 14 × 14½.

683 10 c. Type **198**.. .. .. 10 10
684 65 c. Guide badges (75th anniv of Girl Guide movement) 35 40
685 95 c. Young people of Trinidad 45 55
683/5 .. .. *Set of* 3 75 90

1985 (Dec)–**89**. *As Nos.* 636/7, 639/41 *and* 643/51, *but W w* **16** *(sideways on* 5, 10, 20, 25, 30, 65, 80, 95 *c.,* $1, $1.50). *With imprint date. P* 14.

686 5 c. Type **189** 10 10
687 10 c. Maraval Lily (4.8.86) 10 10
689 20 c. Bois Caco (8.88) 10 10
690 25 c. Strangling Fig (8.88) 10 10
691 30 c. *Cassia moschata* (5.87) 10 10
693 65 c. Black Stick (5.87) 15 20
694 80 c. *Columnea scandens* (5.87) 20 25
695 95 c. Cat's Claw 25 30
696 $1 Bois L'agli 25 30
697 $1.50, *Eustoma exaltatum* (5.87) 40 45
698 $2 Chaconia (39×29 *mm*) (5.87) 50 55
699 $2.50, *Chrysothemis pulchella* (39×29 *mm*) (5.89) 65 70
700 $5 *Centratherum punctatum* (39×29 *mm*) 1·25 1·40
701 $10 Savanna Flower (39×29 *mm*) .. 2·75 3·00
686/701 .. .. .. *Set of* 14 6·00 6·75

Nos. 687, 689/91, 693/8 and 700/1 exist with different imprint dates at foot.

(Des Joan Thompson. Litho Format)

1986 (19 Mar). *150th Anniv of Arrival of Sisters of St. Joseph de Cluny. T* **199** *and similar vert designs. Multicoloured. W w* **16** *(sideways). P* 14 × 14½.

702 10 c. Type **199** 10 10
703 65 c. St. Joseph's Convent, Port-of-Spain .. 25 40
704 95 c. Children and statue of Anne-Marie Javouhey 35 55
702/4 .. .. *Set of* 3 60 95

200 Tank Locomotive *Arima*

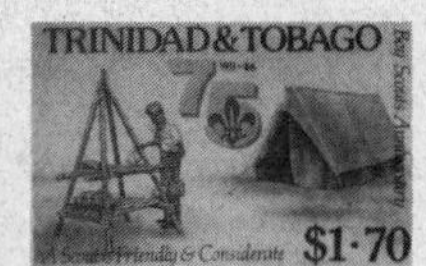

201 Scout Camp

(Des J.W. Litho Format)

1986 (26 May). *"Ameripex '86" International Stamp Exhibition, Chicago. Trinidad Railway Locomotives. T* **200** *and similar horiz designs. W w* **16**. *P* 14½ × 14.

705 65 c. Type **200**.. .. .. 25 30
706 95 c. Canadian-built locomotive No. 22 .. 35 40
707 $1.10, Tender engine 40 55
708 $1.50, Saddle tank 60 75
705/8 .. .. *Set of* 4 1·40 1·75
MS709 105 × 80 mm. Nos. 705/8 .. .. .. 1·75 2·50

(Des N. Shewring. Litho Questa)

1986 (21 July). *75th Anniv of Trinidad and Tobago Boy Scouts. T* **201** *and similar horiz design. Multicoloured. W w* **16** *(sideways). P* 14.

710 $1.70, Type **201** .. .. 1·00 1·00
711 $2 Scouts of 1911 and 1986 .. .. .. 1·25 1·50

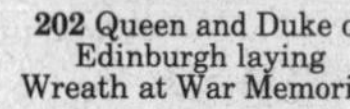

202 Queen and Duke of Edinburgh laying Wreath at War Memorial

203 Eric Williams at Graduation, 1935

(Des C. Abbott. Litho Walsall)

1986 (16 Sept). *60th Birthday of Queen Elizabeth II. T* **202** *and similar vert designs. Multicoloured. W w* **16**. *P* 14½ × 14.

712 10 c. Type **202**.. .. .. 10 10
713 15 c. Queen with Trinidadian dignitaries aboard *Britannia* 10 10
714 30 c. With President Ellis Clarke 15 15
715 $5 Receiving bouquet .. .. .. 1·90 2·00
712/15 .. .. *Set of* 4 1·90 2·10

(Des D. Miller. Litho Format)

1986 (25 Sept). *75th Birth Anniv of Dr. Eric Williams. T* **203** *and similar multicoloured designs. W w* **14** *(sideways on* 95 *c.,* $5). *P* 14.

716 10 c. Type **203**.. .. .. 10 10
717 30 c. Premier Eric Williams (wearing red tie) 15 15
718 30 c. As No. 717, but wearing black and orange tie 15 15
719 95 c. Arms of University of West Indies and Dr. Williams as Pro-Chancellor (*horiz*) 35 40
720 $5 Prime Minister Williams and Whitehall (*horiz*) .. .. 1·90 2·00
716/20 .. .. *Set of* 5 2·25 2·50
MS721 105 × 100 mm. Nos. 716/17 and 719/20. Wmk sideways .. .. 3·00 3·25

204 "PEACE" Slogan and Outline Map of Trinidad and Tobago

205 Miss Giselle La Ronde and BWIA Airliner

(Adapted L. Curtis. Litho Questa)

1986 (3 Nov). *International Peace Year. T* **204** *and similar horiz design. Multicoloured. W w* **16** *(sideways). P* 14.

722 95 c. Type **204**.. .. .. 30 35
723 $3 Peace dove with olive branch .. .. 95 1·40

(Des D. Miller. Litho Walsall)

1987 (27 July). *Miss World 1986. T* **205** *and similar vert designs. Multicoloured. W w* **16**. *P* 14.

724 10 c. Type **205**.. .. .. 15 10
725 30 c. In swimsuit on beach 25 15
726 95 c. Miss Giselle La Ronde 50 40
727 $1.65, Wearing Miss World sash 70 75
724/7 .. .. *Set of* 4 1·40 1·25

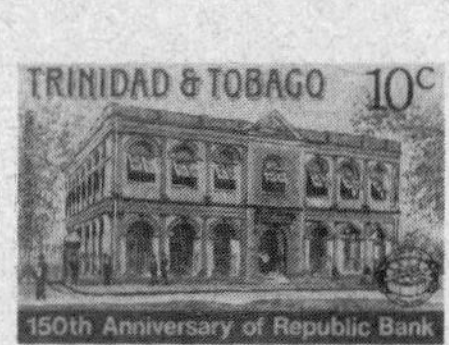

206 Colonial Bank, Port of Spain

207 Sergeant in Parade Order and Soldiers in Work Dress and Battle Dress

(Des J.W. Litho Walsall)

1987 (21 Dec). *150th Anniv of Republic Bank. T* **206** *and similar horiz designs. Multicoloured. W w* **14** *(sideways). P* 14.

728 10 c. Type **206**.. .. .. 10 10
729 65 c. Cocoa plantation 25 25
730 95 c. Oil field 35 40
731 $1.10, Belmont Tramway Company tramcar 40 50
728/31 .. .. *Set of* 4 95 1·10

(Des C. Abbott. Litho Questa)

1988 (29 Feb). *25th Anniv of Defence Force. T* **207** *and similar vert designs. Multicoloured. W w* **16** *(sideways). P* 14.

732 10 c. Type **207**.. .. .. 15 10
733 30 c. Women soldiers 30 15
734 $1.10, Defence Force officers 70 65
735 $1.50, Naval ratings and patrol boat .. 80 80
732/5 .. .. *Set of* 4 1·75 1·60

(Des D. Hartley and L. Curtis. Litho Walsall)

1988 (6 June). *West Indian Cricket. Horiz designs as T* **186** *of Barbados, each showing portrait, cricket equipment and early belt buckle. Multicoloured. W w* **14** *(sideways). P* 14.

736 30 c. George John 30 20
737 65 c. Learie Constantine 40 35
738 95 c. Sonny Ramadhin 55 55
739 $1.50, Gerry Gomez .. .. 95 1·00
740 $2.50, Jeffrey Stollmeyer .. .. .. 1·40 1·60
736/40 .. .. *Set of* 5 3·25 3·25

208 Uriah Butler (labour leader)

209 Mary Werges and Santa Rosa Church

(Des G. Vasarhelyi. Litho Walsall)

1988 (11 July). *50th Anniv of Oilfield Workers Trade Union* (1987). *T* **208** *and similar vert designs. Multicoloured. W w* **16**. *P* 14½ × 14.

741 10 c. Type **208** 10 10
742 30 c. Adrian Rienzi (O.W.T.U. president, 1937-42) 10 10
743 65 c. John Rojas (O.W.T.U. president, 1943-62) 15 20
744 $5 George Weekes (O.W.T.U. president, 1962-87) .. .. 1·25 1·40
741/4 .. .. *Set of* 4 1·40 1·60

(Des O. Bell. Litho Walsall)

1988 (22 Aug). *Centenary of Borough of Arima. T* **209** *and similar horiz designs. Multicoloured. W w* **16** *(sideways). P* 14 × 14½.

745 20 c. Type **209** 10 10
746 30 c. Governor W. Robinson and Royal Charter 10 10
747 $1.10, Arrival of Governor Robinson .. 30 35
748 $1.50, Mayor J. F. Wallen and Centenary logo 40 45
745/8 .. .. *Set of* 4 75 90

(Des D. Miller (30 c.), S. Noon and D. Miller (others). Litho Questa)

1988 (21 Nov). *300th Anniv of Lloyd's of London. Multicoloured designs as T* **123** *of Ascension. W w* **16** *(sideways on* $1.10, $1.55). *P* 14.

749 30 c. Queen Mother at Topping-out Ceremony of new building, 1984 .. .. 15 10
750 $1.10, BWIA Tristar "500" airliner (*horiz*) 40 35
751 $1.55, Steel works, Trinidad (*horiz*) .. 50 45
752 $2 *Atlantic Empress* on fire off Tobago, 1979 .. .. 65 55
749/52 .. .. *Set of* 4 1·50 1·25

210 Colonial Arms of Trinidad & Tobago and 1913 1d. Stamp

(Des W. Carr, adapted D. Miller. Litho Questa)

1989 (20 Mar). *Centenary of Union of Trinidad and Tobago. T* **210** *and similar horiz designs. Multicoloured.* W w **16** *(sideways). P* 14½.

753 40 c. Type **210** 15 10
754 $1 Pre-1889 Tobago emblem and Tobago 1896 ½d. on 4d. stamp 30 30
755 $1.50, Pre-1889 Trinidad emblem and Trinidad 1883 4d. stamp 45 45
756 $2.25, Current Arms of Trinidad and Tobago and 1977 45 c. Republic stamp 65 70
753/6 .. .. *Set of* 4 1·40 1·40

211 Common Piping Guan

212 Blind Welfare (75th Anniversary)

(Des Doreen McGuinness. Litho Walsall)

1989 (31 July). *Rare Fauna of Trinidad and Tobago. T* **211** *and similar horiz designs. Multicoloured. W* w **14** *(sideways). P* 14×14½.

757 $1 Type **211** 50 50
a. Vert strip of 5. Nos. 757/61 .. .. 2·25
758 $1 *Phyllodytes auratus* (frog) 50 50
759 $1 *Cebus albifrons trinitatis* (monkey) .. 50 50
760 $1 Tamandua 50 50
761 $1 *Lutra longicaudis* (otter) 50 50
757/61 .. .. *Set of* 5 2·25 2·25

Nos. 757/61 were printed together, *se-tenant*, in vertical strips of 5 throughout the sheet, forming a composite background design.

(Des S. Noon. Litho Walsall)

1989 (2 Oct). *Anniversaries. T* **212** *and similar vert designs. Multicoloured. W* w **14**. *P* 14½×14.

762 10 c. Type **212** 10 10
763 40 c. Port-of-Spain City Hall (75th anniv) .. 15 15
764 $1 Guides and Brownies (75th anniv) .. 40 40
765 $2.25, Red Cross members (50th anniv) .. 80 90
762/5 .. .. *Set of* 4 1·25 1·40

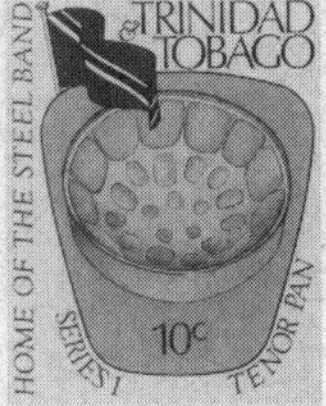

213 Tenor Pan

(Des T. Mussio, adapted D. Miller. Litho Questa)

1989 (30 Nov). *Steel Pans (1st series). T* **213** *and similar vert designs. Multicoloured. W* w **16**. *P* 14½×14.

766 10 c. Type **213** 10 10
767 40 c. Guitar pans 10 15
768 $1 Cello pans 30 35
769 $2.25, Bass pans 65 70
766/9 .. .. *Set of* 4 1·00 1·10

POSTAGE DUE STAMPS

D 1

D 2

(Typo D.L.R.)

1885 (1 Jan). *Wmk Crown CA. P* 14.

D1 D 1 ½d. slate-black .. .. 22·00 30·00
D2 1d. slate-black .. .. 1·40 15
D3 2d. slate-black .. .. 10·00 15
D4 3d. slate-black .. .. 26·00 40
D5 4d. slate-black .. .. 16·00 3·75
D6 5d. slate-black .. .. 16·00 60
D7 6d. slate-black .. .. 26·00 5·00
D8 8d. slate-black .. .. 28·00 3·75
D9 1s. slate-black .. .. 32·00 7·00
D1/9 .. .. *Set of* 9 £160 45·00

1905–6. *Wmk Mult Crown CA. P* 14.

D10 D 1 1d. slate-black 65 15
D11 2d. slate-black .. .. 3·25 15
D12 3d. slate-black .. .. 2·25 75
D13 4d. slate-black .. .. 6·00 6·50
D14 5d. slate-black .. .. 6·50 8·00
D15 6d. slate-black .. .. 6·00 9·50
D16 8d. slate-black .. .. 11·00 14·00
D17 1s. slate-black .. .. 12·00 20·00
D10/17 .. .. *Set of* 8 42·00 55·00

1923–45. *Wmk Mult Script CA. P* 14.

D18 D 1 1d. black (1923) 30 80
D19 2d. black (1923) 30 75
D20 3d. black (1925) .. .. 30 1·25
D21 4d. black (1929) .. .. 1·50 6·00
D22 5d. black (1944) .. .. 16·00 28·00
D23 6d. black (1945) .. .. 20·00 13·00
D24 8d. black (1945) .. .. 24·00 50·00
D25 1s. black (1945) .. .. 42·00 55·00
D18/25 .. .. *Set of* 8 95·00 £140
D18/25 Optd/Perf "Specimen" .. *Set of* 8 £140

1947 (1 Sept)–**61.** *Value in cents. Wmk Mult Script CA. P* 14.

D26 D 1 2 c. black, **O** .. .. 95 2·25
aa. Chalky paper (20.1.53) .. .. 20 1·50
a. Error. Crown missing. W **9a**, **C** .. 48·00
b. Error. St. Edward's Crown. W **9b**, **C** 22·00
D27 4 c. black, **O** .. .. 85 3·00
a. Chalky paper (10.8.55) .. .. 55 2·50
D28 6 c. black, **O** .. .. 85 6·00
aa. Chalky paper (20.1.53) .. .. 25 3·50
a. Error. Crown missing. W **9a**, **C** .. 85·00
b. Error. St. Edward's Crown. W **9b**, **C** 45·00
D29 8 c. black, **O** .. .. 90 8·50
a. Chalky paper (10.9.58) .. .. 35 3·75
D30 10 c. black, **O** .. .. 85 2·75
a. Chalky paper (10.8.55) .. .. 1·00 3·75
D31 12 c. black, **O** .. .. 90 8·00
aa. Chalky paper (20.1.53) .. .. 40 4·50
a. Error. Crown missing. W **9a**, **C** .. £120
b. Error. St. Edward's Crown, W **9b**, **C** 65·00
D32 16 c. black, **O** .. .. 2·00 15·00
a. Chalky paper (22.8.61) .. .. 3·00 12·00
D33 24 c. black, **O** .. .. 3·75 7·50
a. Chalky paper (10.8.55) .. .. 2·75 11·00
D26/33 .. .. *Set of* 8 9·75 48·00
D26/33a .. .. *Set of* 8 7·50 38·00
D26/33 Perf "Specimen" .. .. *Set of* 8 £140

(Litho B.W.)

1969 (25 Nov)–**70.** *Size* 19 × 24 *mm. P* 14 × 13½.

D34 D 2 2 c. pale blue-green .. .. .. 15 1·25
D35 4 c. magenta (1970) .. .. .. 25 1·75
D36 6 c. brown (1970) .. .. .. 50 2·50
D37 8 c. slate-lilac (1970) .. .. .. 65 3·25
D38 10 c. dull red (1970) .. .. .. 65 3·25
D39 12 c. pale orange (1970) .. .. .. 70 3·50
D40 16 c. bright apple-green (1970) 15 50
D41 24 c. grey (1970) 20 70
D42 50 c. grey-blue (1970) .. .. .. 35 1·00
D43 60 c. sage-green (1970) .. .. .. 45 1·00
D34/43 .. .. *Set of* 10 3·50 17·00

(Litho Questa)

1976 (3 May)*–**77.** *Redrawn in smaller size* (17 × 21 *mm*). *P* 13½ × 14.

D44 D 2 2 c. pale blue-green (31.3.77) 10 35
D45 4 c. light claret 10 35
D46 6 c. brown (31.3.77) 15 50
D47 8 c. bright lilac (31.3.77) 15 50
D48 10 c. dull red (31.3.77) 15 50
D49 12 c. pale orange 20 70
D44/9 .. .. *Set of* 6 75 2·75

*The date for the 4 and 12 c. is the local date; the Crown Agents released the stamps on 19 March.

"TOO LATE" STAMPS

A handstamp with the words "TOO LATE" was used upon letters on which a too-late fee had been paid, and was sometimes used for cancelling the stamps on such letters.

OFFICIAL STAMPS

O S (O 1) OFFICIAL (O 2) OFFICIAL (O 3)

1894. *Optd with Type* O **1** (*a*) *Wmk Crown CA. P* 14.

O1 **10** ½d. dull green .. .. 28·00 35·00
O2 1d. carmine .. .. 32·00 38·00
O3 2½d. ultramarine .. .. 40·00 55·00
O4 4d. grey .. .. 40·00 60·00
O5 6d. olive-black .. .. 40·00 60·00
O6 1s. orange-brown .. .. 50·00 75·00

(*b*) *Wmk Crown CC. P* 12½.

O7 **5** 5s. rose-lake £100 £160

1909. *Optd with Type* O **2**. *Wmk Mult Crown CA. P* 14.

O8 **11** ½d. green, **O** .. .. 30 2·00
O9 1d. rose-red, **O** .. .. 30 2·00
a. Opt double .. .. — £200
b. Opt vertical .. .. 38·00
c. Opt inverted .. .. — £150

1910. *Optd with Type* O **2**. *Wmk Mult Crown CA. P* 14.

O10 **14** ½d. green, **O** .. .. 60 1·50

1913. *Optd with Type* O **3**.

O11 **17** ½d. green, **O** 25 80
a. Overprint vertical .. ..

OFFICIAL (O 4) OFFICIAL (O 5) **OFFICIAL** (O 6)

1914. *Optd with Type* O **4**.

O12 **17** ½d. green, **O** .. .. 1·10 3·25

1914–17. *Optd with Type* O **5** (*without stop*).

O13 **17** ½d. green .. .. 55 3·00
a. Blue-green (thick paper) (1917) .. 40 3·00

1916. *Optd with Type* O **5** (*with stop*).

O14 **17** ½d. yellow-green, **O** 30 50
a. Overprint double .. .. .. 17·00

1917 (22 Aug). *Optd with Type* O **6**.

O15 **17** ½d. green, **O** .. .. 55 3·50
a. Yellow-green .. .. 85 5·00
b. Blue-green (thick paper) .. .. 30 3·50

Tristan Da Cunha

Although first settled in 1817 no surviving mail is known from Tristan da Cunha until two whaler's letters written in 1836 and 1843, these being carried home in other whaling ships. Then there is a long gap until the late 1800's when other letters are known—surprisingly only some seven in number, up to 1908 when the first of the island cachet handstamps came into use.

The collecting of postal history material from 1908 to 1952, when Tristan's first stamps were issued, revolves around the numerous cachets of origin which were struck on mail from the island during these 44 years. The handstamps producing these cachets were supplied over the years by various people particularly interested in the island and the islanders, and were mostly used by the clergymen who volunteered to go and serve as the community's ministers.

The postal cachets are illustrated below. The use of the different cachets on mail frequently overlapped, at one period in 1930 there were five different types of handstamp in use. As there was no official source for providing them they appeared on the island from various donors; then disappeared without trace once they became worn out. Only one of these early rubber handstamps has apparently survived, Cachet Va.

Covers bearing the cachets are recognised collector's items, but are difficult to value in general terms. As elsewhere the value is discounted by poor condition of the cover, and may be increased by use on a scarce date or with additional postal markings.

Cachet Types V and VII on cover are the commonest, Type Va, used only for three months, and Type IVa are the scarcest, equalling the scarcest use of Type I examples. All cacheted covers, particularly if non-philatelic, are desirable forerunner items. Even a philatelic cover of Type V is, at present, worth in the region of £35.

Dates given are of the first recorded use.

Cachet I — Cachet II

Cat. No.			*Value on cover*
C1	**1908** (May).	Cachet I	*..from* £4000
C2	**1919** (31 July).	Cachet II	*..from* £400

Cachet III

C3	**1921** (8 Feb).	Cachet III	*..from* £225

Cachet IVa

C4	**1928** (25 Feb).	Cachet IV (*as* IVa, *but without centre label*)	*..from* £800
C5	**1928** (28 Oct).	Cachet IVa	*..from* £5500

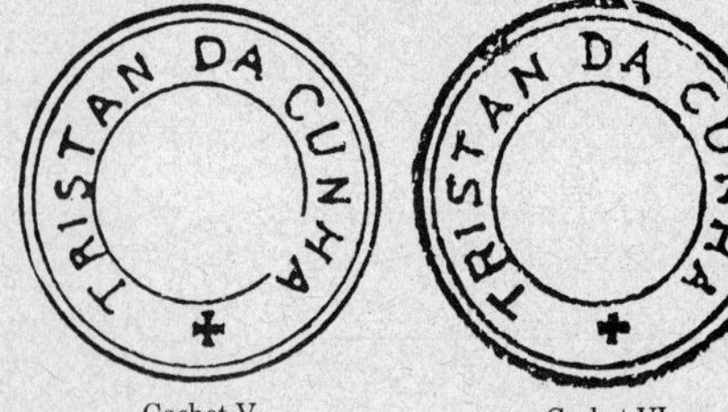

Cachet V — Cachet VI

C6	**1929** (24 Feb).	Cachet V	*..from* 35·00
C7	**1929** (15 May).	Cachet Va (*as* V, *but without break in inner ring. Shows "T" "C" and "N" damaged*)..	*..from* £6500
C8	**1936** (Aug).	Cachet VI	*..from* 55·00

Cachet VII

C9	**1936** (1 Feb).	Cachet VII	*..from* 20·00

During World War II there was little mail from the island as its function as a meteorological station was cloaked by security. Such covers as are known are generally struck with the "tombstone" naval censor mark and postmarked "maritime mail" or have South African postal markings. A few philatelic items from early in the war bearing cachets exist, but this usage was soon stopped by the military commander and the handstamps were put away until peace returned. Covers from the period would be worth from £75 to, at least, £350.

Cachet VIII

C10	**1946** (8 May).	Cachet VIII	*..from* 70·00

Cachet IX

C11	**1948** (29 Feb).	Cachet IX	*..from* 45·00

Cachet X

C12	**1949** (Jan).	Cachet X	*from* 35·00

Cachet XI

Cachet XII

RESETTLEMENT
SURVEY - 1962

Cachet XIII

Cachets XI to XIII from the 1961/63 "volcano eruption" and "return to the island" period vary in value from £30 to £120, due to philatelic usage on the one hand and scarce mailings from the small survey parties on shore during this period on the other.

TRISTAN DA CUNHA

(1)

1952 (1 Jan). *Stamps of St. Helena, optd with T* **1**.

1	**33**	½d. violet	15	85
2		1d. black and green	30	1·25
3		1½d. black and carmine	30	1·25
4		2d. black and scarlet	30	1·50
5		3d. grey	40	1·25
6		4d. ultramarine	65	2·00
7		6d. light blue	2·00	2·50
8		8d. sage-green	2·00	3·00
9		1s. sepia	2·00	2·00
10		2s. 6d. maroon	17·00	14·00
11		5s. chocolate	23·00	27·00
12		10s. purple	48·00	55·00
1/12		.. .. *Set of* 12	90·00	£100

1953 (2 June). *Coronation. As No.* 47 *of Aden.*

13	3d. black and grey-green	90	1·50

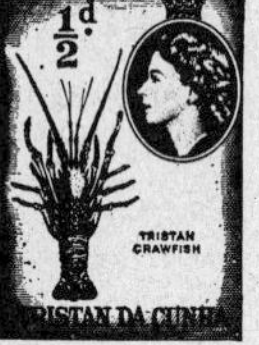

2 Tristan Crawfish

3 Carting Flax for Thatching

(Recess D.L.R.)

1954 (2 Jan). *T* **2/3** *and similar designs. Wmk Mult Script CA. P* 12½ × 13 (*horiz*) *or* 13 × 12½ (*vert*).

14	½d. red and deep brown	10	10
15	1d. sepia and bluish green	10	15
16	1½d. black and reddish purple	2·00	30
17	2d. grey-violet and brown-orange	30	15
18	2½d. black and carmine-red	1·75	50
19	3d. ultramarine and olive-green	80	20
20	4d. turquoise-blue and deep blue	1·25	40
21	5d. emerald and black	1·25	40
22	6d. deep green and violet	1·25	45
23	9d. reddish violet and Venetian red ..	1·25	45
24	1s. deep yellow-green and sepia	1·25	45
25	2s. 6d. deep brown and light blue	20·00	10·00
26	5s. black and red-orange	48·00	16·00
27	10s. brown-orange and purple	30·00	20·00
14/27	.. .. *Set of* 14	£100	45·00

Designs: *Vert*—1½d. Rockhopper Penguin; 3d. Island longboat. *Horiz*—2d. Big Beach factory; 2½d. Yellow-nosed Albatross; 4d. Tristan from the south-west; 5d. Girls on donkeys; 6d. Inaccessible Island from Tristan; 9d. Nightingale Island; 1s. St. Mary's Church; 2s. 6d. Southern Elephant-Seal at Gough Island; 5s. Inaccessible Island Rail; 10s. Island spinning wheel.

16 Starfish

17 Concha Fish

(Des Mr. and Mrs. G. F. Harris. Recess Waterlow)

1960 (1 Feb). *Marine Life. Vert designs as T* **16/17**. *W w* **12**. *P* 13.

28	½d. black and orange	15	30
29	1d. black and bright purple..	15	15
30	1½d. black and light turquoise-blue	15	15
31	2d. black and bluish green	20	15
32	2½d. black and sepia	25	15
33	3d. black and brown-red	25	15
34	4d. black and yellow-olive	30	20
35	5d. black and orange-yellow	45	25
36	6d. black and blue	50	25
37	9d. black and rose-carmine	55	30
38	1s. black and light brown	75	25
39	2s. 6d. black and ultramarine	11·00	15·00
40	5s. black and light emerald	28·00	22·00
41	10s. black and violet	45·00	40·00
28/41	.. .. *Set of* 14	80·00	70·00

Designs:—1½d. Klip Fish; 2d. Heron Fish; 2½d. Swordfish; 3d. Tristan Crawfish; 4d. Soldier Fish; 5d. "Five Finger" Fish; 6d. Mackerel; 9d. Stumpnose Fish; 1s. Blue Fish; 2s. 6d. Snoek; 5s. Shark; 10s. Black Right Whale.

NEW INFORMATION

The editor is always interested to correspond with people who have new information that will improve or correct the Catalogue.

1961 (15 Apr). *As Nos. 28/30 and 32/41 but values in South African decimal currency.*

42 ½ c. black and orange (as ½d.) 10 15
43 1 c. black and bright purple (as 1d.) .. 15 15
44 1½ c. black and light turquoise-blue (as 1½d.) 35 20
45 2 c. black and sepia (as 2½d.) 40 20
46 2½ c. black and brown-red (as 3d.) 50 20
47 3 c. black and yellow-olive (as 4d.) .. 65 20
48 4 c. black and orange-yellow (as 5d.) .. 80 20
49 5 c. black and blue (as 6d) 85 20
50 7½ c. black and rose-carmine (as 9d.) .. 90 20
51 10 c. black and light brown (as 1s.) .. 1·00 20
52 25 c. black and ultramarine (as 2s. 6d.) .. 6·00 11·00
53 50 c. black and light emerald (as 5s.) .. 20·00 22·00
54 1 r. black and violet (as 10s.) .. .. 40·00 42·00
42/54 .. .. *Set of* 13 65·00 70·00

Following a volcanic eruption the island was evacuated on 10 October 1961, but resettled in 1963.

TRISTAN DA CUNHA
RESETTLEMENT
1963

(30)

1963 (12 Apr). *Tristan Resettlement. As Nos. 176/88 of St. Helena, but Wmk Mult Script CA (sideways on 1d., 2d., 7d., 10d., 2s. 6d., 10s), optd with T* **30**.

55 1d. bright blue, dull violet, yellow & carmine 15 10
56 1½d. yellow, green, black and light drab .. 20 15
57 2d. scarlet and grey 25 15
58 3d. light blue, black, pink and deep blue .. 30 15
a. Black printed double* £350
59 4½d. yellow-green, green, brown and grey .. 50 20
60 6d. red, sepia and light yellow-olive.. .. 55 15
61 7d. red-brown, black and violet 50 15
62 10d. brown-purple and light blue 50 15
63 1s. greenish yellow, bluish green & brown .. 50 15
64 1s. 6d. grey, black and slate-blue .. .. 1·25 60
65 2s. 6d. red, pale yellow and turquoise .. 1·00 45
66 5s. yellow, brown and green.. .. .. 4·50 1·25
67 10s. orange-red, black and blue .. .. 6·50 1·25
55/67 .. .. *Set of* 13 13·00 4·25

*No. 58a shows the outline round the Queen's head printed double.

1963 (1 Oct). *Freedom from Hunger. As No. 76 of Aden.*

68 1s. 6d. carmine 90 20

1964 (1 Feb). *Red Cross Centenary. As Nos. 147/8 of Antigua.*

69 3d. red and black 35 15
70 1s. 6d. red and blue 65 20

31 South Atlantic Map

32 Queen Elizabeth II

(Queen's portrait by Anthony Buckley. Des, eng and recess B.W.)

1965 (17 Feb)–**67**. *Designs as T* **31/2**. *W w* **12** *(sideways on £1). P 11½ × 11 (vert) or 11 × 11½ (horiz).*

71 ½d. black and ultramarine.. .. .. 15 15
72 1d. black and emerald-green 25 15
73 1½d. black and blue 25 15
74 2d. black and purple 25 15
75 3d. black and turquoise-blue 25 15
75*a* 4d. black and orange (1.9.67) .. .. 3·50 3·50
76 4½d. black and brown 25 15
77 6d. black and green 25 15
78 7d. black and rose-red 25 15
79 10d. black and chocolate 25 15
80 1s. black and carmine 25 15
81 1s. 6d. black and yellow-olive .. .. 2·50 1·25
82 2s. 6d. black and orange-brown .. .. 2·75 1·75
83 5s. black and violet .. .. .. 5·50 3·25
84 10s. deep blue and carmine.. .. .. 1·75 1·25
84*a* 10s. black and deep turquoise-blue (1.9.67) 17·00 10·00
84*b* £1 deep blue and orange-brown (1.9.67) .. 17·00 10·00
71/84*b* .. .. *Set of* 17 45·00 28·00

Designs: *Horiz as T* **31**—1d. Flagship of Tristão da Cunha; 1½d. *Heemstede*; 2d. New England whaling ship; 3d. *Shenandoah*; 4d. H.M.S. *Challenger*; 4½d. H.M.S. *Galatea*; 6d. H.M.S. *Cilicia*; 7d. Royal Yacht *Britannia*; 10d. H.M.S. *Leopard*; 1s. M.V. *Tjisadane*; 1s. 6d. M.V. *Tristania*; 2s. 6d. M.V. *Boissevain*; 5s. M.S. *Bornholm*; 10s. (No. 84*a*), Research Vessel *R.S.A. Vert*—10s. (No. 84), £1, Type **32**.

1965 (11 May*). *I.T.U. Centenary. As Nos. 166/7 of Antigua.*

85 3d. orange-red and grey 50 10
86 6d. reddish violet and yellow-orange .. 60 10

*This is the local date of issue; the stamps were not released in London until 17 May.

1965 (25 Oct). *International Co-operation Year. As Nos. 168/9 of Antigua.*

87 1d. reddish purple and turquoise-green .. 40 15
88 6d. deep bluish green and lavender .. .. 1·50 25

1966 (24 Jan). *Churchill Commemoration. As Nos. 170/3 of Antigua.*

89 1d. new blue 50 25
a. Value omitted £350
90 3d. deep green .. .. 2·50 40
91 6d. brown .. .. 3·50 45
92 1s. 6d. bluish violet .. .. .. 4·00 60
89/92 .. .. *Set of* 4 9·50 1·50

No. 89a was caused by misplacement of the gold and also shows the country inscription moved to the right.

45 H.M.S. *Falmouth* at Tristan and Soldier of 1816

(Des V. Whiteley. Litho Harrison)

1966 (15 Aug). *150th Anniv of Tristan Garrison. W w* **12** *(sideways). P 14½.*

93 **45** 3d. multicoloured 20 10
94 6d. multicoloured 20 10
95 1s. 6d. multicoloured 20 10
96 2s. 6d. multicoloured 30 10
93/6 .. .. *Set of* 4 80 35

1966 (1 Oct*). *World Cup Football Championships. As Nos. 176/7 of Antigua.*

97 3d. violet, yellow-grn, lake & yell-brn .. 25 10
98 2s. 6d. chocolate, blue-grn, lake & yellow-brn 65 20

*Released in St. Helena on 1 July in error.

1966 (1 Oct). *Inauguration of W.H.O. Headquarters, Geneva. As Nos. 178/9 of Antigua.*

99 6d. black, yellow-green and light blue .. 1·00 30
100 5s. black, light purple and yellow-brown .. 1·25 70

1966 (1 Dec). *20th Anniv of U.N.E.S.C.O. As Nos. 196/8 of Antigua.*

101 10d. slate-violet, red, yellow and orange .. 60 15
102 1s. 6d. orange-yellow, violet and deep olive 65 15
103 2s. 6d. black, bright purple and orange .. 80 20
101/3 .. .. *Set of* 3 1·90 45

46 Calshot Harbour

(Des V. Whiteley. Litho D.L.R.)

1967 (2 Jan). *Opening of Calshot Harbour. P 14 × 14½.*

104 **46** 6d. multicoloured 10 10
105 10d. multicoloured 10 10
106 1s. 6d. multicoloured 10 10
107 2s. 6d. multicoloured 15 10
104/7 .. .. *Set of* 4 30 15

(47)

48 Prince Alfred, First Duke of Edinburgh

1967 (10 May). *No. 76 surch with T* **47**.

108 4d. on 4½d. black and brown 10 10

(Des M. Goaman. Litho Harrison)

1967 (10 July). *Centenary of First Duke of Edinburgh's Visit to Tristan. W w* **12**. *P 14½.*

109 **48** 3d. multicoloured 10 10
110 6d. multicoloured 10 10
111 1s. 6d. multicoloured 10 10
112 2s. 6d. multicoloured 15 10
109/12 .. .. *Set of* 4 25 15

49 Wandering Albatross

(Des V. Whiteley. Photo Harrison)

1968 (15 May). *Birds. T* **49** *and similar horiz designs. Multicoloured. W w* **12**. *P 14 × 14½.*

113 4d. Type **49** 40 10
114 1s. Wilkin's Finch 45 10
115 1s. 6d. Tristan Thrush 50 10
116 2s. 6d. Greater Shearwater 90 15
113/16 .. .. *Set of* 4 2·00 35

53 Union Jack and Dependency Flag

(Des Jennifer Toombs. Litho D.L.R.)

1968 (1 Nov). *30th Anniv of Tristan da Cunha as a Dependency of St. Helena. T* **53** *and similar horiz design. W w* **12** *(sideways). P 14.*

117 **53** 6d. multicoloured 10 10
118 – 9d. sepia, blue and turquoise-blue .. 10 10
119 **53** 1s. 6d. multicoloured 10 10
120 – 2s. 6d. carmine, blue and turquoise-blue 15 10
117/20 .. .. *Set of* 4 40 35

Design:—9d., 2s. 6d. St. Helena and Tristan on chart.

55 Frigate

(Des and recess B.W.)

1969 (1 June). *Clipper Ships. T* **55** *and similar horiz designs. W w* **12**. *P 11 × 11½.*

121 4d. new blue 40 10
122 1s. carmine (full-rigged ship) 40 10
123 1s. 6d. blue-green (barque) 45 15
124 2s. 6d. chocolate (full-rigged clipper) .. 50 20
121/4 .. .. *Set of* 4 1·60 50

59 Sailing Ship off Tristan da Cunha

(Des Jennifer Toombs. Litho Format)

1969 (1 Nov). *United Society for the Propagation of the Gospel. T* **59** *and similar horiz designs. Multicoloured. W w* **12** *(sideways). P 14½ × 14.*

125 4d. Type **59** 10 10
126 9d. Islanders going to first Gospel service .. 10 10
127 1s. 6d. Landing of the first minister .. 10 10
128 2s. 6d. Procession outside St. Mary's Church 15 15
125/8 .. .. *Set of* 4 40 40

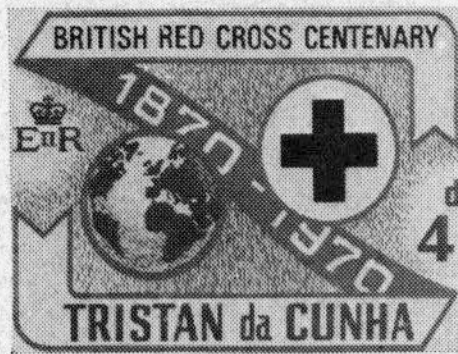

63 Globe and Red Cross Emblem

(Des and litho B.W.)

1970 (1 June). *Centenary of British Red Cross. T* **63** *and similar designs. W w* **12** *(sideways on vert designs). P 13.*

129 **63** 4d. lt emerald, scarlet & dp bluish green 10 10
130 9d. bistre, scarlet and deep bluish green 10 10
131 – 1s. 9d. light drab, scarlet & ultramarine 15 15
132 – 2s. 6d. reddish purple, scarlet & ultram 25 30
129/32 .. .. *Set of* 4 55 60

Design: *Vert*—1s. 9d., 2s. 6d., Union Jack and Red Cross Flag.

64 Crawfish and Longboat

(65)

(Des Harrison. Litho Enschedé)

1970 (1 Nov). *Crawfish Industry. T* **64** *and similar horiz design. Multicoloured. W w* **12**. *P 12½ × 13.*

133 4d. Type **64** 20 10
134 10d. Packing and storing Crawfish 25 10
135 1s. 6d. Type **64** 35 20
136 2s. 6d. As 10d. 40 25
133/6 .. .. *Set of* 4 1·10 60

1971 (14 Feb).* *Decimal Currency. As Nos. 71/84a surch as T* **65**, *by B. W. in typo. Glazed paper.*

137 ½p. on 1d. black and emerald-green .. 15 15
138 1p. on 2d. black and purple 15 15
139 1½p. on 4d. black and orange 25 15
140 2½p. on 6d. black and green 25 15
141 3p. on 7d. black and rose-red 25 15
142 4p. on 10d. black and chocolate 25 20
143 5p. on 1s. black and carmine 25 20
144 7½p. on 1s. 6d. black and yellow-olive .. 95 95
145 12½p. on 2s. 6d. black and orange-brown .. 2·00 2·50
146 15p. on 1½d. black and blue .. .. 2·75 3·00
147 25p. on 5s. black and violet .. .. 3·25 5·00
148 50p. on 10s. black and deep turquoise-blue 7·00 11·00
137/48 .. .. *Set of* 12 16·00 21·00

*This was the local release date, but the Crown Agents issued the stamps one day later.

66 *Quest*

(Des V. Whiteley. Litho J.W.)

1971 (1 June). *50th Anniv of Shackleton–Rowett Expedition. T* **66** *and similar horiz designs.* W w **12** *(sideways). P* 13½ × 14.

No.	Description	Unused	Used
149	1½p. multicoloured	90	30
150	4p. sepia, pale green and apple-green	1·00	40
151	7½p. black, bright purple and pale green	1·00	40
152	12½p. multicoloured	1·40	45
149/52	*Set of* 4	4·00	1·40

Designs:—4p. Presentation of Scout Troop flag; 7½p. Cachet on pair of 6d. G.B. stamps; 12½p. Shackleton, postmarks and longboat taking mail to the *Quest*.

67 H.M.S. *Victory* at Trafalgar and Thomas Swain catching Nelson

68 Cow Pudding

(Des R. Granger Barrett. Litho Questa)

1971 (1 Nov). *Island Families. T* **67** *and similar horiz designs showing ships and the names of families associated with them. Multicoloured.* W w **12** *(sideways). P* 13½.

No.	Description	Unused	Used
153	1½p. Type **67**	25	30
154	2½p. *Emily of Stonington* (P. W. Green)	35	40
155	4p. *Italia* (Lavarello and Repetto)	40	50
156	7½p. H.M.S. *Falmouth* (William Glass)	55	65
157	12½p. American whaling ship (Rogers and Hagan)	65	80
153/7	*Set of* 5	2·00	2·40

(Des M. and Sylvia Goaman. Recess and litho B.W. (50p., £1); Litho A. & M. (others))

1972 (29 Feb). *T* **68** *and similar multicoloured designs showing flowering plants.* W w **12** *(sideways on horiz designs). P* 13.

No.	Description	Unused	Used
158	½p. Type **68**	15	10
159	1p. Peak Berry	25	10
160	1½p. Sand Flower (*horiz*)	25	15
161	2½p. N.Z. Flax (*horiz*)	30	15
162	3p. Island Tree	30	15
163	4p. Bog Fern	35	15
164	5p. Dog Catcher	35	15
165	7½p. Celery	85	30
166	12½p. Pepper Tree	1·50	60
167	25p. Foul Berry (*horiz*)	1·75	1·50
168	50p. Tussock	3·50	1·75
169	£1 Tussac (*horiz*)	5·00	3·00
158/69	*Set of* 12	13·00	7·00

69 Launching

(Des R. Svensson. Litho Walsall)

1972 (1 June). *Tristan Longboats. T* **69** *and similar multicoloured designs.* W w **12** *(sideways on 2½p. and 4p.). P* 14.

No.	Description	Unused	Used
170	2½p. Type **69**	15	10
171	4p. Under oars	20	10
172	7½p. Coxswain Arthur Repetto (*vert*)	25	15
173	12½p. Under sail for Nightingale Island (*vert*)	30	20
170/73	*Set of* 4	80	50

70 Tristan Thrushes and Wandering Albatrosses

(Des (from photographs by D. Groves) and photo Harrison)

1972 (20 Nov). *Royal Silver Wedding. Multicoloured; background colours given.* W w **12**. *P* 14 × 14½.

No.	Description	Unused	Used
174 **70**	2½p. red-brown	35	40
175	7½p. dull ultramarine	15	40

71 Church Altar

(Des J. Cooter. Litho Questa)

1973 (8 July). *Golden Jubilee of St. Mary's Church.* W w **12**. *P* 13½.

No.	Description	Unused	Used
176 **71**	25p. multicoloured	60	50

72 H.M.S. *Challenger's* Laboratory

(Des V. Whiteley Studio. Litho Questa)

1973 (15 Oct). *Centenary of H.M.S. Challenger's Visit. T* **72** *and similar horiz designs. Multicoloured.* W w **12**. *P* 13½.

No.	Description	Unused	Used
177	4p. Type **72**	30	25
178	5p. H.M.S. *Challenger* off Tristan	30	25
179	7½p. *Challenger's* pinnace off Nightingale Is	30	30
180	12½p. Survey route	40	40
177/80	*Set of* 4	1·10	1·10
MS181	145 × 96 mm. Nos. 177/80	1·10	3·50

73 Approaching English Port

(Des Jennifer Toombs. Litho Questa)

1973 (10 Nov). *Tenth Anniv of Return to Tristan da Cunha. T* **73** *and similar horiz designs. Multicoloured (except 4p.).* W w **12**. *P* 14.

No.	Description	Unused	Used
182	4p. Type **73** (reddish brn, lemon & gold)	25	25
183	5p. Survey party	25	25
184	7½p. Embarking on *Bornholm*	35	35
185	12½p. Approaching Tristan	45	45
182/5	*Set of* 4	1·10	1·10

1973 (14 Nov). *Royal Wedding. As Nos.* 165/6 *of Anguilla.*

No.	Description	Unused	Used
186	7½p. bright blue	10	10
187	12½p. light turquoise-green	15	10

74 Rockhopper Penguin and Egg

(Des R. Granger Barrett. Litho Questa)

1974 (1 May). *Rockhopper Penguins. T* **74** *and similar horiz designs.* W w **12**. *P* 14.

No.	Description	Unused	Used
188	2½p. Type **74**	3·00	75
189	5p. Rockhopper Colony, Inaccessible Island	3·50	1·00
190	7½p. Penguin fishing	4·00	1·25
191	25p. Adult and fledgling	4·50	1·50
188/91	*Set of* 4	13·50	4·00

75 Map with Rockhopper Penguin and Wandering Albatross

(Des J.W. Litho Questa)

1974 (1 Oct). *"The Lonely Island". Sheet* 154 × 104 *mm.* W w **12** *(sideways). P* 13½.

No.	Description	Unused	Used
MS192 **75**	35p. multicoloured	1·90	2·75

76 Blenheim Palace

(Des Sylvia Goaman. Litho Questa)

1974 (30 Nov). *Birth Centenary of Sir Winston Churchill. T* **76** *and similar horiz design.* W w **14** *(sideways). P* 14.

No.	Description	Unused	Used
193	7½p. pale yellow and black	15	10
194	25p. black, sepia and grey	40	25
MS195	93 × 93 mm. Nos. 193/4. W w **12** (sideways)	75	1·60

Design:—25p. Churchill with Queen Elizabeth II.

77 *Plocamium fuscorubrum*

(Des Sylvia Goaman. Litho Harrison)

1975 (16 Apr). *Sea Plants. T* **77** *and similar horiz designs.* W w **12** *(sideways). P* 13 × 13½.

No.	Description	Unused	Used
196	4p. rose-carmine, light lilac and black	15	10
197	5p. apple-green, light violet-blue and deep bluish green	15	15
198	10p. red-orange, stone and brown-purple	20	15
199	20p. multicoloured	30	25
196/9	*Set of* 4	70	60

Designs:—5p. *Ulva lactua;* 10p. *Epymenia flabellata;* 20p. *Macrocystis pyrifera.*

78 Killer Whale

(Des G. Drummond. Litho Walsall)

1975 (1 Nov). *Whales. T* **78** *and similar horiz designs. Multicoloured.* W w **12** *(sideways). P* 13½.

No.	Description	Unused	Used
200	2p. Type **78**	40	25
201	3p. Rough-toothed Dolphin	40	25
202	5p. Black Right Whale	45	30
203	20p. Fin Whale	1·00	70
200/3	*Set of* 4	2·00	1·40

79 ½d. Stamp of 1952

80 Island Cottage

(Des C. Abbott. Litho J.W.)

1976 (27* May). *Festival of Stamps, London. T* **79** *and similar designs.* W w **14** *(sideways on 5 and 25p). P* 13½.

No.	Description	Unused	Used
204	5p. black, violet and light lilac	15	20
205	9p. black, deep green and turquoise	15	25
206	25p. multicoloured	40	50
204/6	*Set of* 3	65	85

Designs: *Vert*—9p. 1953 Coronation stamp. *Horiz*—25p. Mail carrier *Tristania II*.

*This is the local date of issue. The stamps were released by the Crown Agents on 4 May.

For miniature sheet containing No. 206 see No. **MS**218 of Ascension.

(Des C. Abbott. Litho Questa)

1976 (4 Oct). *Paintings by Roland Svensson (1st series). T* **80** *and similar multicoloured designs.* W w **14** *(sideways on 5p., 10p. and* **MS**211*). P* 14.

No.	Description	Unused	Used
207	3p. Type **80**	15	15
208	5p. The potato patches (*horiz*)	15	20
209	10p. Edinburgh from the sea (*horiz*)	20	25
210	20p. Huts, Nightingale Island	30	35
207/10	*Set of* 4	70	85
MS211	125 × 112 mm. Nos. 207/10	80	1·75

See also Nos. 234/8 and 272/6.

81 The Royal Standard

(Des and litho J.W.)

1977 (7 Feb). *Silver Jubilee. T* **81** *and similar horiz designs. Multicoloured. W* w **14** *(sideways). P* 13.
212 10p. Royal Yacht *Britannia* .. 25 30
213 15p. Type **81** .. 15 20
214 25p. Royal family .. 25 25
212/14 .. *Set of* 3 60 65
For Nos. 213/14 surcharged, see Nos. 232/3.

82 H.M.S. *Eskimo*

(Des L. Curtis. Litho Walsall)

1977 (1 Oct). *Ships' Crests. T* **82** *and similar horiz designs. Multicoloured. W* w **14** *(sideways). P* 14.
215 5p. Type **82** .. 20 15
216 10p. H.M.S. *Naiad* .. 30 15
217 15p. H.M.S. *Jaguar* .. 40 25
218 20p. H.M.S. *London* .. 45 30
215/18 .. *Set of* 4 1·25 75
MS219 142 × 140 mm. Nos. 215/18 .. 1·75 2·50

83 Great-winged Petrel

(Des BG Studio. Litho Walsall)

1977 (1 Dec). *Multicoloured designs as T* **83** *showing birds. W* w **14** *(sideways on 1 and 2p.). P* 13½.
220 1p. Type **83** .. 10 10
221 2p. White-faced Storm Petrel .. 15 15
222 3p. Hall's Giant Petrel .. 15 15
223 4p. Soft-plumaged Petrel .. 20 20
224 5p. Wandering Albatross .. 20 20
225 10p. Kerguelen Petrel .. 30 30
226 15p. Swallow-tailed Tern .. 50 50
227 20p. Greater Shearwater .. 55 55
228 25p. Broad-billed Prion .. 65 65
229 50p. Great Skua .. 1·25 1·00
230 £1 Common Diving Petrel .. 2·00 1·75
231 £2 Yellow-nosed Albatross .. 3·75 3·25
220/31 .. *Set of* 12 9·00 8·00
The 3p. to £2 are vertical designs.

4p

(84)	Normal	Straight top to serif in "½" (Pl 1C R. 5/1–5)
	½	½

1978 (19 Jan*). *Provisional definitives. Nos.* 213/14 *surch as T* **84**.
232 4p. on 15p. Type **81** .. 2·25 6·50
233 7½p. on 25p. Royal family .. 2·25 6·50
a. Straight top to serif .. 21·00
*This is the local date of issue. Covers dated 26 November 1977 are philatelic mail forwarded to the island for cancellation, the stamps having been released in London on 31 October 1977. Supplies for the island population did not arrive until 19 January.

(Des C. Abbott. Litho Questa)

1978 (1 Mar). *Paintings by Roland Svensson (2nd series). Horiz designs as T* **80**. *Multicoloured. W* w **14** *(sideways). P* 14.
234 5p. St. Mary's Church .. 15 15
235 10p. Longboats .. 20 25
236 15p. A Tristan home .. 25 30
237 20p. The harbour, 1970 .. 30 40
234/7 .. *Set of* 4 80 1·00
MS238 115 × 128 mm. Nos. 234/7 .. 1·50 2·25

ALTERED CATALOGUE NUMBERS

Any Catalogue numbers altered from the last edition are shown as a list in the introductory pages.

85 King's Bull **86** Sodalite

(Des Jennifer Toombs. Litho Questa)

1978 (21 Apr). *25th Anniv of Coronation. T* **85** *and similar vert designs. W* w **14**. *P* 15.
239 25p. bistre, bright violet and silver .. 35 35
a. Sheetlet Nos. 239/41 × 2 .. 1·90
240 25p. multicoloured .. 35 35
241 25p. bistre, bright violet and silver .. 35 35
239/41 .. *Set of* 3 95 95
Designs:—No. 239, Type **85**; No. 240, Queen Elizabeth II; No. 241, Tristan crawfish.
Nos. 239/41 were printed together in small sheets of 6, containing two *se-tenant* strips of 3, with horizontal gutter margin between.

(Des J.W. Litho Questa)

1978 (9 June). *Local Minerals. T* **86** *and similar horiz designs. Multicoloured. W* w **14** *(sideways). P* 13½.
242 3p. Type **86** .. 25 10
243 5p. Aragonite .. 30 10
244 10p. Sulphur .. 45 20
245 20p. Lava containing pyroxene crystal .. 65 35
242/5 .. *Set of* 4 1·50 65

87 Klipfish

(Des R. Granger Barrett. Litho Harrison)

1978 (29 Sept). *Fish. T* **87** *and similar horiz designs. W* w **14** *(sideways). P* 14.
246 5p. black, yellow-brown and yellow-green .. 10 10
247 10p. black, yellow-brown and emerald .. 15 15
248 15p. multicoloured .. 20 20
249 20p. multicoloured .. 30 25
246/9 .. *Set of* 4 65 60
Designs:—10p. Fivefinger; 15p. Concha; 20p. Soldier.

88 R.F.A. *Orangeleaf* **89** Southern Elephant Seal

(Des R. Granger Barrett. Litho Cartor S.A., France)

1978 (24 Nov). *Royal Fleet Auxiliary Vessels. T* **88** *and similar horiz designs. Multicoloured. W* w **14** *(sideways). P* 12½ × 12.
250 5p. Type **88** .. 15 10
251 10p. R.F.A. *Tarbatness* .. 20 10
252 20p. R.F.A. *Tidereach* .. 35 25
253 25p. R.F.A. *Reliant* .. 45 30
250/3 .. *Set of* 4 1·10 65
MS254 136 × 140 mm. Nos. 250/3 (Wmk inverted) 2·00 3·00

(Des J.W. Litho Questa)

1979 (3 Jan). *Wildlife Conservation. T* **89** *and similar vert designs. Multicoloured. W* w **14**. *P* 14.
255 5p. Type **89** .. 15 10
256 10p. Afro-Australian Fur Seal .. 25 15
257 15p. Tristan Thrush .. 40 20
258 20p. Nightingale Finch .. 50 25
255/8 .. *Set of* 4 1·10 60

90 Tristan Longboat

(Des R. Granger Barrett. Litho Questa)

1979 (8 Feb). *Visit of R.M.S. "Queen Elizabeth 2". T* **90** *and similar horiz designs. Multicoloured. W* w **14** *(sideways). P* 14½.
259 5p. Type **90** .. 20 20
260 10p. R.M.S. *Queen Mary* .. 25 30
261 15p. R.M.S. *Queen Elizabeth* .. 30 35
262 20p. R.M.S. *Queen Elizabeth 2* .. 30 40
259/62 .. *Set of* 4 95 1·10
MS263 148 × 96 mm. 25p. R.M.S. *Queen Elizabeth 2 (131 × 27 mm)* .. 1·00 2·25

91 1952 "TRISTAN DA CUNHA" overprinted St. Helena 10s. Definitive

(Des J.W. Litho Questa)

1979 (27 Aug). *Death Centenary of Sir Rowland Hill. T* **91** *and similar designs showing stamps. W* w **14** *(sideways on* 5 *and* 10*p.). P* 14.
264 5p. black, lilac and bistre-yellow .. 15 15
265 10p. black, red and apple-green .. 20 20
266 25p. multicoloured .. 30 30
264/6 .. *Set of* 3 60 60
MS267 83 × 103 mm. 50p. black and vermilion .. 60 70
Designs: *Horiz*—10p. 1954 5s. definitive. *Vert*—25p. 1963 3d. Tristan da Cunha Resettlement commemorative; 50p. 1946 1d. 4 Potatoes local label.

92 "The Padre's House" **93** *Tristania II* (mail ship)

(Des G. Hutchins. Litho Questa)

1979 (26 Nov). *International Year of the Child. Children's Drawings. T* **92** *and similar horiz designs. Multicoloured. W* w **14** *(sideways). P* 14.
268 5p. Type **92** .. 10 10
269 10p. "Houses in the Village" .. 15 15
270 15p. "St. Mary's Church" .. 15 15
271 20p. "Rockhopper Penguins" .. 25 25
268/71 .. *Set of* 4 60 60

(Des C. Abbott. Litho Questa)

1980 (29 Feb). *Paintings by Roland Svensson (3rd series). Landscapes. Multicoloured designs as T* **80**. *W* w **14** *(sideways on* 5 *and* 10*p.). P* 14.
272 5p. "Stoltenhoff Island" (*horiz*) .. 10 10
273 10p. "Nightingale from the East" (*horiz*) .. 15 20
274 15p. "The Administrator's Abode" .. 20 25
275 20p. "Ridge where the Goat jump off" .. 25 30
272/5 .. *Set of* 4 60 75
MS276 126 × 109 mm. Nos. 272/5 (wmk sideways) 70 1·00

(Des C. Abbott. Litho Walsall)

1980 (6 May). *"London 1980" International Stamp Exhibition. T* **93** *and similar vert designs. Multicoloured. W* w **14**. *P* 14.
277 5p. Type **93** .. 15 15
278 10p. Unloading mail at Calshot Harbour .. 15 15
279 15p. Tractor transporting mail to Post Office 25 25
280 20p. Ringing the "dong" to summons people to Post Office .. 30 30
281 25p. Distributing mail .. 30 30
277/81 .. *Set of* 5 1·00 1·00

94 Queen Elizabeth the Queen Mother **95** *Golden Hind*

(Des Harrison. Litho Questa)

1980 (11 Aug*). *80th Birthday of Queen Elizabeth the Queen Mother. W* w **14** *(sideways). P* 14.
282 **94** 14p. multicoloured .. 25 25
*This is the local date of issue. The Crown Agents released this stamp in London on 4 August.

(Des G. Vasarhelyi. Litho Walsall)

1980 (6 Sept). *400th Anniv of Sir Francis Drake's Circumnavigation of the World. T* **95** *and similar vert designs. Multicoloured. W* w **14**. *P* 14½ × 14.
283 5p. Type **95** .. 20 10
284 10p. Drake's route .. 25 15
285 20p. Sir Francis Drake .. 30 20
286 25p. Queen Elizabeth I .. 40 25
283/6 .. *Set of* 4 1·00 65

96 "Humpty Dumpty"

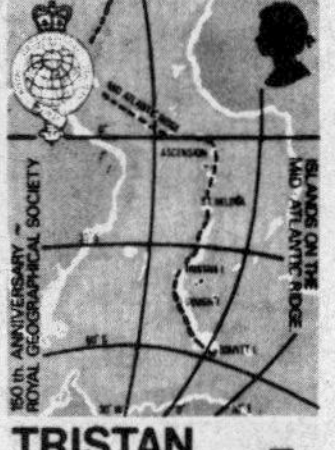

97 South Atlantic Ocean showing Islands on Mid-Atlantic Ridge

(Des G. Vasarhelyi. Litho J.W.)

1980 (31 Oct). *Christmas. Scenes from Nursery Rhymes. T* **96** *and similar horiz designs. Multicoloured. W* w **14** (*sideways*). *P* 13.

No.	Description	Unused	Used
287	15p. Type **96**	20	25
	a. Sheetlet Nos. 287/95	1·60	
288	15p. "Mary had a little Lamb"	20	25
289	15p. "Little Jack Horner"	20	25
290	15p. "Hey Diddle Diddle"	20	25
291	15p. "London Bridge"	20	25
292	15p. "Old King Cole"	20	25
293	15p. "Sing a Song of Sixpence"	20	25
294	15p. "Tom, Tom the Piper's Son"	20	25
295	15p. "The Owl and the Pussy Cat"	20	25
287/95	*Set of* 9	1·60	1·75

Nos. 287/95 were printed together, *se-tenant*, within a small sheet of 9 stamps.

(Des A. Crawford, adapted BG Studio. Litho Rosenbaum Bros, Vienna)

1980 (15 Dec). *150th Anniv of Royal Geographical Society. Maps. T* **97** *and similar vert designs. Multicoloured. W* w **14**. *P* 13½.

No.	Description	Unused	Used
296	5p. Type **97**	15	15
297	10p. Tristan da Cunha group (Beauforts Survey, 1806)	20	20
298	15p. Tristan Island (Crawford, 1937–38)	30	30
299	20p. Gough Island (1955–56)	35	40
296/9	*Set of* 4	90	95

98 Revd. Edwin Dodgson as Young Man

99 Detail from Captain Denham's Plan, 1853

(Des Jennifer Toombs. Litho Questa)

1981 (23 Mar). *Centenary of Revd. Edwin Dodgson's Arrival on Tristan da Cunha. T* **98** *and similar multicoloured designs. W* w **14** (*sideways on* 20p.). *P* 14.

No.	Description	Unused	Used
300	10p. Type **98**	20	15
301	20p. Dodgson and view of Tristan da Cunha (*horiz*)	30	30
302	30p. Dodgson with people of Tristan da Cunha	45	45
300/2	*Set of* 3	85	80
MS303	140 × 134 mm. Nos. 300/2 (wmk sideways)	1·00	1·50

(Des L. McCombie. Litho Questa)

1981 (22 May). *Early Maps. T* **99** *and similar horiz designs. Multicoloured. W* w **14** (*sideways*). *P* 13½ × 14.

No.	Description	Unused	Used
304	5p. Type **99**	15	10
305	14p. Detail from map by A. Dalrymple, 17 March 1781	25	20
306	21p. Detail from Captain Denham's plan, 1853 (*different*)	35	30
304/6	*Set of* 3	65	55
MS307	110 × 70 mm. 35p. Detail from map by J. van Keulen, *circa* 1700	50	60

100 Wedding Bouquet from Tristan da Cunha

101 Explorer with Rucksack

(Des J.W. Litho Walsall)

1981 (22 July). *Royal Wedding. T* **100** *and similar vert designs. Multicoloured. W* w **14**. *P* 14.

No.	Description	Unused	Used
308	5p. Type **100**	10	10
309	20p. Prince of Wales at Investiture	25	25
310	50p. Prince Charles and Lady Diana Spencer	65	65
308/10	*Set of* 3	90	90

(Des BG Studio. Litho Questa)

1981 (14 Sept). *25th Anniv of Duke of Edinburgh Award Scheme. T* **101** *and similar vert designs. Multicoloured. W* w **14**. *P* 14.

No.	Description	Unused	Used
311	5p. Type **101**	10	10
312	10p. Explorer at campsite	15	15
313	20p. Explorer map reading	25	25
314	25p. Duke of Edinburgh	30	30
311/14	*Set of* 4	70	70

102 Inaccessible Island Rail on Nest

(Des R. Granger Barrett. Litho Walsall)

1981 (1 Nov). *Inaccessible Island Rail. T* **102** *and similar horiz designs. Multicoloured. W* w **14** (*sideways*). *P* 13½ × 14.

No.	Description	Unused	Used
315	10p. Type **102**	30	30
	a. Strip of 4. Nos. 315/18	1·10	
316	10p. Inaccessible Island Rail eggs	30	30
317	10p. Rail chicks	30	30
318	10p. Adult Rail	30	30
315/18	*Set of* 4	1·10	1·10

Nos. 315/18 were printed together, *se-tenant*, in horizontal and vertical strips of 4 throughout the sheet.

103 Six-gilled Shark

(Des I. Loe. Litho Enschedé)

1982 (8 Feb). *Sharks. T* **103** *and similar horiz designs. Multicoloured. W* w **14** (*sideways*). *P* 13½.

No.	Description	Unused	Used
319	5p. Type **103**	20	10
320	14p. Porbeagle Shark	35	20
321	21p. Blue Shark	50	35
322	35p. Hammerhead Shark	60	50
319/22	*Set of* 4	1·50	1·00

104 *Marcella*

105 Lady Diana Spencer at Windsor, July 1981

(Des J. Cooter. Litho Questa)

1982 (5 Apr). *Sailing Ships* (*1st series*). *T* **104** *and similar horiz designs. Multicoloured. W* w **14** (*sideways*). *P* 13½.

No.	Description	Unused	Used
323	5p. Type **104**	20	20
324	15p. *Eliza Adams*	35	35
325	30p. *Corinthian*	60	60
326	50p. *Samuel and Thomas*	1·00	1·00
323/6	*Set of* 4	2·00	2·00

See also Nos. 341/4.

(Des Jennifer Toombs. Litho Walsall)

1982 (1 July). *21st Birthday of Princess of Wales. T* **105** *and similar vert designs. Multicoloured. W* w **14**. *P* 14½ × 14.

No.	Description	Unused	Used
327	5p. Tristan da Cunha coat of arms	15	15
328	15p. Type **105**	25	25
329	30p. Prince and Princess of Wales in wedding portrait	45	45
330	50p. Formal portrait	75	75
327/30	*Set of* 4	1·40	1·40

106 Lord Baden-Powell

1ST PARTICIPATION
COMMONWEALTH
GAMES 1982

(107)

(Des C. Abbott. Litho J.W.)

1982 (20 Sept). *75th Anniv of Boy Scout Movement. T* **106** *and similar multicoloured designs. W* w **14** (*sideways on No.* 333). *P* 13 × 13½ (50p.) *or* 13½ × 13 (*others*).

No.	Description	Unused	Used
331	5p. Type **106**	20	15
332	20p. First Scout camp, Brownsea, 1907	40	35
333	50p. Local Scouts on parade (*horiz*)	80	75
331/3	*Set of* 3	1·25	1·10
MS334	88 × 104 mm. 50p. Moral of the Acorn and the Oak. P 14	1·00	1·10

1982 (28 Sept). *Commonwealth Games, Brisbane. Nos.* 224 *and* 228 *optd with T* **107**.

No.	Description	Unused	Used
335	5p. Wandering Albatross	10	10
336	25p. Broad-billed Prion	35	30

108 Formation of Island

109 Tractor pulling Trailer

(Des J.W. Litho Questa)

1982 (1 Nov). *Volcanoes. T* **108** *and similar horiz designs. Multicoloured. W* w **14** (*sideways*). *P* 14 × 14½.

No.	Description	Unused	Used
337	5p. Type **108**	15	15
338	15p. Plan of surface cinder cones and cross-section of volcano showing feeders	30	35
339	25p. Eruption	45	50
340	35p. 1961 Tristan eruption	65	70
337/40	*Set of* 4	1·40	1·50

(Des J. Cooter. Litho Questa)

1983 (1 Feb). *Sailing Ships* (*2nd series*). *Multicoloured designs as T* **104**. *W* w **14** (*sideways on* 20p., 35p.). *P* 13½.

No.	Description	Unused	Used
341	5p. *Islander* (*vert*)	15	15
342	20p. *Roscoe*	35	35
343	35p. *Columbia*	55	55
344	50p. *Emeline* (*vert*)	80	80
341/4	*Set of* 4	1·75	1·75

(Des C. Abbott. Litho Format)

1983 (2 May). *Land Transport. T* **109** *and similar horiz designs. Multicoloured. W* w **14** (*sideways*). *P* 14.

No.	Description	Unused	Used
345	5p. Type **109**	15	15
346	15p. Pack donkeys	25	25
347	30p. Bullock cart	50	50
348	50p. Landrover	75	75
345/8	*Set of* 4	1·50	1·50

110 Early Chart of South Atlantic

111 "Christ's Charge to St. Peter" (detail) (Raphael)

(Des L. Curtis. Litho Questa)

1983 (1 Aug). *Island History. T* **110** *and similar horiz designs. Multicoloured* (*except 50p. black, bright scarlet and buff*). *W* w **14** (*sideways*). *P* 14.

No.	Description	Unused	Used
349	1p. Type **110**	15	10
350	3p. Tristao da Cunha's caravel	15	10
351	4p. Notice left by Dutch on first landing, 1643	15	10
352	5p. 17th-century views of the island	15	10
353	10p. British army landing party, 1815	25	25
354	15p. 19th-century view of the settlement	35	30
355	18p. Governor Glass's house	35	35
356	20p. The Revd. W. F. Taylor and Peter Green	40	40
357	25p. *John and Elizabeth* (American whaling ship)	60	50
358	50p. Letters Patent declaring Tristan da Cunha a dependency of St. Helena	1·10	95
359	£1 Commissioning H.M.S. *Atlantic Isle*, 1944	2·00	2·00
360	£2 Evacuation, 1961	3·50	3·75
349/60	*Set of* 12	8·00	8·00

(Des and litho Walsall)

1983 (27 Oct). *500th Birth Anniv of Raphael. T* **111** *and similar designs, showing different details of "Christ's Charge to St. Peter". W* w **14**. *P* 14½.

No.	Description	Unused	Used
361	10p. multicoloured	20	20
362	25p. multicoloured	35	35
363	40p. multicoloured	60	60
361/3	*Set of* 3	1·00	1·00
MS364	115 × 90 mm. 50p. multicoloured (*horiz*). Wmk sideways	70	80

On No. **MS**364 the Queen's head has been replaced by the Royal Cypher.

ALTERED CATALOGUE NUMBERS

Any Catalogue numbers altered from the last edition are shown as a list in the introductory pages.

112 1952 6d. Stamp

113 *Agrocybe praecox var. cutefracta*

(Des C. Abbott. Litho Questa)

1984 (3 Jan). *150th Anniv of St. Helena as a British Colony. T* **112** *and similar horiz designs showing 1952 overprints on St. Helena stamps. Multicoloured. W w* **14** *(sideways). P* 14.

365 10p. Type **112** 15 15
366 15p. 1952 1s. stamp 25 25
367 25p. 1952 2s. stamp 35 35
368 60p. 1952 10s. stamp 85 85
365/8 .. .. *Set of* 4 1·40 1·40

(Des McCombie Skinner Studio. Litho Questa)

1984 (25 Mar). *Fungi. T* **113** *and similar multicoloured designs. W w* **14** *(sideways on 30 p., 50 p.). P* 14.

369 10p. Type **113** 20 20
370 20p. *Laccaria tetraspora* 35 35
371 30p. *Agrocybe cylindracea (horiz)* 45 45
372 50p. *Sacoscypha coccinea (horiz)* 80 80
369/72 .. .. *Set of* 4 1·60 1·60

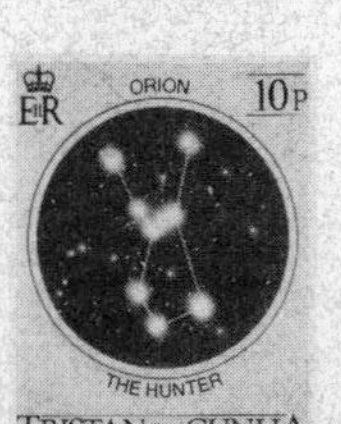

114 Constellation of "Orion"

115 Sheep-shearing

(Des Harrison. Litho Questa)

1984 (30 July). *The Night Sky. T* **114** *and similar vert designs. Multicoloured. W w* **14**. *P* 14½ × 14.

373 10p. Type **114** 25 25
374 20p. "Scorpius" 40 40
375 25p. "Canis Major" 50 50
376 50p. "Crux" 90 90
373/6 .. .. *Set of* 4 1·90 1·90

(Des G. Wilby. Litho Walsall)

1984 (1 Oct). *Tristan Woollens Industry. T* **115** *and similar vert designs. Multicoloured. W w* **14**. *P* 14½.

377 9p. Type **115** 20 20
378 17p. Carding wool 30 30
379 29p. Spinning 50 50
380 45p. Knitting 75 75
377/80 .. .. *Set of* 4 1·60 1·60
MS381 120 × 85 mm. As Nos. 377/80, but without white borders around the designs .. .. .. 1·60 2·00

116 "Christmas Dinner-table"

117 "H.M.S. *Julia* Ashore, 1817" (Midshipman C. W. Browne)

(Des G. Vasarhelyi. Litho Questa)

1984 (3 Dec). *Christmas. Children's Drawings. T* **116** *and similar horiz designs. Multicoloured. W w* **14** *(sideways). P* 14.

382 10p. Type **116** 20 20
383 20p. "Santa Claus in ox cart" 30 30
384 30p. "Santa Claus in longboat" 50 50
385 50p. "The Nativity" 85 85
382/5 .. .. *Set of* 4 1·75 1·75

(Des A. Crawford, adapted G. Vasarhelyi. Litho Questa)

1985 (4 Feb). *Shipwrecks (1st series). T* **117** *and similar designs. W w* **14** *(sideways on 35p.). P* 14 × 13½ *(10, 25p.) or* 13½ × 14 *(35, 60p.).*

386 10p. royal blue and light grey-blue 30 30
387 25p. red-brown and emerald 65 65
388 35p. yellow-brown and orange-yellow .. 85 85
386/8 .. .. *Set of* 3 1·60 1·60
MS389 142 × 101 mm. 60p. multicoloured. Wmk sideways .. .. 1·40 1·60

Designs: *Vert*—25p. *Mabel Clark's* Bell, St. Mary's Church. *Horiz*—35p. "Barque *Glenhuntley* foundering, 1898" (John Hagan); 60p. Map of Tristan da Cunha showing sites of shipwrecks.

See also Nos. 411/14 and 426/9.

118 The Queen Mother at Ascot with Princess Margaret

119 Jonathan Lambert and "Isles of Refreshment" Flag, 1811

(Des A. Theobald (80p.), C. Abbott (others). Litho Questa)

1985 (7 June). *Life and Times of Queen Elizabeth the Queen Mother. T* **118** *and similar vert designs. Multicoloured. W w* **16**. *P* 14½ × 14.

390 10p. The Queen Mother and Prince Charles, 1954 .. .. 20 25
391 20p. Type **118** 40 45
392 30p. Queen Elizabeth the Queen Mother .. 60 65
393 50p. With Prince Henry at his christening 1·00 1·10
390/3 .. .. *Set of* 4 2·00 2·25
MS394 91 × 73 mm. 80p. The Queen Mother and the young Princess Anne at Trooping the Colour. Wmk sideways .. .. 1·60 1·75

(Des D. Slater. Litho J.W.)

1985 (30 Sept). *Flags. T* **119** *and similar multicoloured designs. W w* **16** *(sideways on 10p., inverted on others). P* 14.

395 10p. Type **119** 25 30
396 15p. 21st Light Dragoons guidon and cannon from Fort Malcolm (1816–17) *(vert)* .. 35 40
397 25p. White Ensign and H.M.S. *Falmouth* offshore, 1816 *(vert)* 60 65
398 60p. Union Jack and Tristan da Cunha *(vert)* 1·40 1·60
395/8 .. .. *Set of* 4 2·40 2·75

120 Lifeboat heading for Barque *West Riding*

121 Halley's Comet, 1066, from Bayeux Tapestry

(Des D. Miller. Litho Format)

1985 (28 Nov). *Centenary of Loss of Island Lifeboat. T* **120** *and similar vert designs. Multicoloured. W w* **14**. *P* 14 × 13½.

399 10p. Type **120** 35 45
400 30p. Map of Tristan da Cunha .. .. .. 80 1·00
401 50p. Memorial plaque to lifeboat crew .. 1·25 1·40
399/401 .. .. *Set of* 3 2·25 2·50

(Des D. Miller. Litho Walsall)

1986 (3 Mar). *Appearance of Halley's Comet. T* **121** *and similar horiz designs. Multicoloured. W w* **16** *(sideways). P* 14.

402 10p. Type **121** 20 30
403 20p. Path of Comet 40 55
404 30p. Comet over Inaccessible Island .. 60 75
405 50p. H.M.S. *Paramour* and map of South Atlantic .. .. 1·00 1·25
402/5 .. .. *Set of* 4 2·00 2·50

(Des A. Theobald. Litho Questa)

1986 (21 Apr). *60th Birthday of Queen Elizabeth II. Vert designs as T* **110** *of Ascension. Multicoloured. W w* **16**. *P* 14½ × 14.

406 10p. With Prince Charles, 1950 .. .. 20 25
407 15p. Queen at Trooping the Colour 30 35
408 25p. In robes of Order of the Bath, Westminster Abbey, 1972 .. .. 50 55
a. Silver (cypher and logo) omitted £275
409 45p. In Canada, 1977 .. .. 90 95
410 65p. At Crown Agents Head Office, London, 1983 .. .. 1·25 1·40
406/10 .. .. *Set of* 5 2·75 3·25

122 "*Allanshaw* wrecked on East Beach, 1893" (drawing by John Hagan)

123 Wandering Albatross

(Des A. Crawford, adapted G. Vasarhelyi. Litho J.W.)

1986 (2 June). *Shipwrecks (2nd series). T* **122** *and similar designs. W w* **16** *(sideways on 9p.). P* 13½ × 13 *(9p.) or* 13 × 13½ *(others).*

411 9p. dp turquoise-blue, dp grey-blue & black 25 25
412 20p. grey-olive, olive-yellow and black .. 45 45
413 40p. bright blue, bright violet and black .. 85 85
411/13 .. .. *Set of* 3 1·75 1·75
MS414 142 × 80 mm. 65p. orange-brown and black. Wmk sideways. P 13½ × 13 .. .. 1·75 2·25

Designs: *Vert*—20p. Church font from wreck of *Edward Vittery*, 1881; 40p. Ship's figurehead. *Horiz*—65p. Gaetano Lavarello and Andrea Repetto, survivors from *Italia*, 1892.

(Des D. Miller. Litho Questa)

1986 (23 July). *Royal Wedding. Square designs as T* **112** *of Ascension. Multicoloured. W w* **16**. *P* 14.

415 10p. Prince Andrew and Miss Sarah Ferguson 20 25
416 40p. Prince Andrew piloting helicopter, Digby, Canada, 1985 .. .. 80 85

(Des A. Theobald. Litho Questa)

1986 (30 Sept). *Flora and Fauna of Inaccessible Island. T* **123** *and similar vert designs. Multicoloured. W w* **16**. *P* 14.

417 5p. Type **123** 20 20
418 10p. *Lagenophora nudicaulis* (daisy) 30 30
419 20p. Vanessa (butterfly) 65 65
420 25p. Wilkin's Finch 75 75
421 50p. White-chinned Petrel .. .. 1·25 1·25
417/21 .. .. *Set of* 5 2·75 2·75

124 Flightless Moth and Edinburgh

125 Castaways from *Blenden Hall* attacking Sea Elephant, 1821

(Des C. Abbott. Litho Walsall)

1987 (23 Jan). *Island Flightless Insects and Birds. T* **124** *and similar vert designs. Multicoloured. W w* **14**. *P* 14½.

422 10p. Type **124** 25 25
423 25p. Strap-winged Fly and Crater Lake .. 55 55
424 35p. Inaccessible Island Rail and Inaccessible Island .. .. 1·00 1·00
425 50p. Gough Island Coot and Gough Island .. 1·50 1·50
422/5 .. .. *Set of* 4 3·00 3·00

(Des A. Crawford, adapted G. Vasarhelyi. Litho Walsall)

1987 (2 Apr*). *Shipwrecks (3rd series). T* **125** *and similar designs. W w* **16** *(sideways on 17p.). P* 13½ × 14 *(17p.) or* 14 × 13½ *(others).*

426 11p. black and olive-brown 30 30
427 17p. black and bright lilac 45 45
428 45p. black and deep blue-green .. .. 1·00 1·00
426/8 .. .. *Set of* 3 1·60 1·60
MS429 131 × 70 mm. 70p. royal blue, bright green and pale blue. Wmk sideways. P 13½ × 14 .. .. 2·00 2·25

Designs: *Horiz*—17p. Barquentine *Henry A. Paull* stranded at Sandy Point, 1879; 70p. Map of Inaccessible Island showing sites of shipwrecks. *Vert*—45p. Gustav Stoltenhoff, 1871, and Stoltenhoff Island.

*This is the local date of issue. The Crown Agents placed the stamps on sale from 2 February 1987.

126 Rockhopper Penguin swimming

127 Microscope and Published Report

(Des I. Strange. Litho Questa)

1987 (22 June). *Rockhopper Penguins. T* **126** *and similar horiz designs. Multicoloured. W w* **16** *(sideways). P* 14½.

430 10p. Type **126** 35 30
431 20p. Adult with egg 55 50
432 30p. Adult with juvenile 75 70
433 50p. Head of Rockhopper Penguin .. .. 1·25 1·10
430/3 .. .. *Set of* 4 2·75 2·40

(Des N. Shewring. Litho Questa)

1987 (7 Dec). *50th Anniv of Norwegian Scientific Expedition. T* **127** *and similar square designs. Multicoloured. W w* **16** *(10p., 20p.) or w* **14** *(30p., 50p.) (all sideways). P* 14.

434 10p. Type **127** 30 35
435 20p. Scientists ringing Yellow-nosed Albatross 60 70
436 30p. Expedition hut, Little Beach Point .. 85 95
437 50p. S.S. *Thorshammer* (whale factory ship) 1·50 1·60
434/7 .. .. *Set of* 4 3·00 3·25

1988 (9 Mar). *Royal Ruby Wedding. Nos.* 406/10 *optd with* T **119** *of Ascension in silver.*

438	10p. Princess Elizabeth with Prince Charles, 1950	20	25
439	15p. Queen Elizabeth II at Trooping the Colour	30	35
440	25p. In robes of Order of the Bath, Westminster Abbey, 1972	50	55
441	45p. In Canada, 1977	90	95
442	65p. At Crown Agents Head Office, London, 1983	1·25	1·40
438/42	*Set of* 5	2·75	3·25

128 Nightingale Finch ("Tristan Bunting") **129** Painted Penguin Eggs

(Des A. Theobald. Litho Questa)

1988 (21 Mar). *Fauna of Nightingale Island. T* **128** *and similar vert designs. Multicoloured.* W w **16**. *P* 14.

443	5p. Type **128**	20	15
444	10p. Tristan Thrush (immature)	30	25
445	20p. Yellow-nosed Albatross (chick)	50	45
446	25p. Greater Shearwater	60	55
447	50p. Elephant Seal	1·10	1·10
443/7	*Set of* 5	2·40	2·25

(Des O. Bell. Litho Questa)

1988 (30 May). *Tristan da Cunha Handicrafts. T* **129** *and similar horiz designs. Multicoloured.* W w **16** *(sideways). P* 14 × 14½.

448	10p. Type **129**	25	25
449	15p. Moccasins	35	35
450	35p. Knitwear	75	75
451	50p. Model longboat	1·10	1·10
448/51	*Set of* 4	2·25	2·25

130 Processing Blubber

(Des N. Shewring. Litho Questa)

1988 (6 Oct). *19th-century Whaling. T* **130** *and similar horiz designs. Multicoloured.* W w **16** *(sideways). P* 14 × 14½.

452	10p. Type **130**	25	25
453	20p. Harpoon guns	45	45
454	30p. Scrimshaw (carved whale bone)	65	65
455	50p. Whaling ships	1·10	1·10
452/5	*Set of* 4	2·25	2·25
MS456	76 × 56 mm. £1 Right Whale	2·10	2·10

(Des E. Nisbet and D. Miller (25, 35p.), D. Miller (others). Litho Harrison)

1988 (7 Nov). *300th Anniv of Lloyd's of London. Designs as T* **123** *of Ascension.* W w **16** *(sideways on* 25, 35*p.). P* 14.

457	10p. multicoloured	25	25
458	25p. multicoloured	55	55
459	35p. brownish black and emerald	80	80
460	50p. brownish black and carmine-red	1·25	1·25
457/60	*Set of* 4	2·50	2·50

Designs: *Vert*—10p. New Lloyd's Building, 1988; 50p. *Kobenhavn* (barque), 1928. *Horiz*—25p. *Tristania II* (crawfish trawler); 35p. *St. Helena* (mail ship).

131 "Government House" **132** Giant Petrel

(Des N. Harvey. Litho Walsall)

1988 (10 Dec). *Augustus Earle's Paintings,* 1824. *T* **131** *and similar horiz designs. Multicoloured.* W w **16** *(sideways). P* 14.

461	1p. Type **131**	10	10
462	3p. "Squall off Tristan"	10	10
463	4p. "Rafting Blubber"	10	10
464	5p. "View near Little Beach"	10	10
465	10p. "Man killing Albatross"	20	25
466	15p. "View on The Summit"	25	30
467	20p. "Nightingale Island"	35	40
468	25p. "Earle on Tristan"	45	50
469	35p. "Solitude–Watching the Horizon"	60	65
470	50p. "Northeaster"	90	95
471	£1 "Tristan Village"	1·75	1·90
472	£2 "Governor Glass at Dinner"	3·50	3·75
461/72	*Set of* 12	7·50	8·00

Examples of Nos. 461/72 showing Earle's dates as "1793–1835" were sold by the U.S.A. agents, and by the authorities on Ascension, in error. Supplies sent to Tristan da Cunha show the correct dates "1793–1838".

(Des A. Theobald. Litho Walsall)

1989 (6 Feb). *Fauna of Gough Island. T* **132** *and similar vert designs. Multicoloured.* W w **16**. *P* 14.

473	5p. Type **132**	15	15
474	10p. Gough Island Coot ("Gough Moorhen")	20	25
475	20p. Gough Island Finch ("Gough Bunting")	40	45
476	25p. Sooty Albatross	50	55
477	50p. Amsterdam Fur Seal	1·00	1·10
473/7	*Set of* 5	2·00	2·25

133 *Eriosorus cheilanthoides* **134** Surgeon's Mortar

(Des Jane Fern. Litho Walsall)

1989 (22 May). *Ferns. T* **133** *and similar vert designs. Multicoloured.* W w **14**. *P* 14×13½.

478	10p. Type **133**	30	30
479	25p. *Asplenium alvarezense*	65	65
480	35p. *Elaphoglossum hybridum*	80	80
481	50p. *Ophioglossum opacum*	1·25	1·25
478/81	*Set of* 4	2·75	2·75

(Des Jennifer Toombs. Litho Questa)

1989 (25 Sept). *Nautical Museum Exhibits. T* **134** *and similar horiz designs. Multicoloured.* W w **16** *(sideways). P* 14.

482	10p. Type **134**	30	30
483	20p. Parts of darting-gun harpoon	55	55
484	30p. Ship's compass with binnacle-hood	70	70
485	60p. Rope-twisting device	1·40	1·40
482/5	*Set of* 4	2·75	2·75

135 Cattle Egret **136** *Peridroma saucia*

(Des Josephine Martin and Sally Hynard. Litho Questa)

1989 (20 Nov). *Vagrant Birds. T* **135** *and similar vert designs. Multicoloured.* W w **16**. *P* 14.

486	10p. Type **135**	20	25
487	25p. Spotted Sandpiper	50	55
488	35p. Purple Gallinule	70	75
489	50p. Barn Swallow	1·00	1·10
486/9	*Set of* 4	2·10	2·40

(Des I. Loe. Litho Questa)

1990 (1 Feb). *Moths. T* **136** *and similar horiz designs. Multicoloured.* W w **14** *(sideways). P* 14.

490	10p. Type **136**	20	25
491	15p. *Ascalapha odorata*	30	35
492	35p. *Agrius cingulata*	70	75
493	60p. *Eumorpha labruscae*	1·25	1·40
490/3	*Set of* 4	2·25	2·50

POSTAGE DUE STAMPS

D 1 D 2 D 3 Outline Map of Tristan da Cunha

(Typo D.L.R.)

1957 (1 Feb). *Chalk-surfaced paper. Wmk Mult Script CA. P* 14.

D1	D **1**	1d. scarlet	1·75	3·50
D2		2d. orange-yellow	2·25	4·50
D3		3d. green	3·50	5·50
D4		4d. ultramarine	5·00	7·00
D5		5d. lake	5·00	13·00
D1/5		*Set of* 5	16·00	30·00

(Des J.W. Litho Questa)

1976 (27 May*). W w **12** *(sideways). P* 13½ × 14.

D 6	D **2**	1p. magenta	25	50
D 7		2p. dull emerald	25	60
D 8		4p. bluish violet	25	70
D 9		5p. new blue	25	70
D10		10p. chestnut	40	1·10
D6/10		*Set of* 5	1·25	3·25

*This is the local date of issue; the Crown Agents released the stamps four days later.

1976 (3 Sept). W w **14** *(sideways). P* 13½ × 14.

D11	D **2**	1p. magenta	10	15
D12		2p. dull emerald	10	15
D13		4p. bluish violet	10	20
D14		5p. new blue	10	25
D15		10p. chestnut	15	35
D11/15		*Set of* 5	40	1·00

(Des L. Curtis. Litho Questa)

1986 (20 Nov). W w **16**. *P* 14½×14.

D16	D **3**	1p. deep brown and cinnamon	10	10
D17		2p. deep brown and bright orange	10	10
D18		5p. deep brown and orange-vermilion	10	10
D19		7p. black and bright reddish violet	10	15
D20		10p. black and violet-blue	20	25
D21		25p. black and pale emerald	45	50
D16/21		*Set of* 6	85	1·00

POSTAL FISCAL STAMPS

NATIONAL SAVINGS

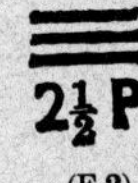

(F 1) (F 2)

1970 (15 May). *No.* 77 *optd with Type* **F 1** *in red.*

F1	6d. black and green	10	1

No. F1 was originally intended as a National Savings Stamp, bu also retained postal validity.

(Handstamped locally by rubber handstamp)

1971 (Feb). *Decimal currency. No.* F 1 *handstamped with Typ* **F 2**, *in violet.*

F2	2½p. on 6d. black and green	4·75	8·0
	a. Pair, one without handstamp	£350	£35

Beware of forgeries of this handstamp.

Trucial States

The Trucial States consisted of Abu Dhabi, Ajman (with Ianama), Dubai, Fujeira, Ras al Khaima, Sharjah and Umm al Qiwain. However the following issue of stamps was only put into se in Dubai, despite the inscription "TRUCIAL STATES".

The first organised postal service in Dubai commenced on 19 ugust 1909 when an Indian Branch Office, administered from arachi, was opened, using the unoverprinted stamps of India, rincipally the ½ a. and 1 a. values.

The initial cancellation was a single-ring type inscribed "DUBAI .O. PERSIAN GULF", which remained in use until 1933.

1909 Cancellation

Its replacement was of the Indian double-circle type showing a milar inscription.

Dubai was upgraded to Sub-Post Office status on 1 April 1942 nd this change was reflected in a new double-ring mark inscribed DUBAI" only. At the same time the office was provided with a ingle-ring handstamp which also incorporated a cancelling device f seven wavy lines.

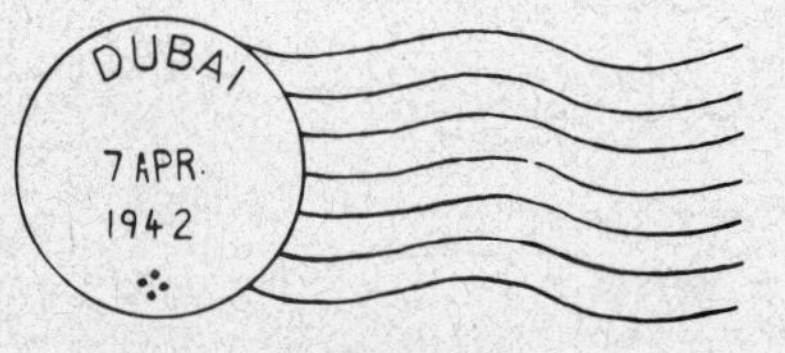

1942 Handstamp

(illustration reduced: actual size 65 × 27 mm)

A further version of the double-ring type appeared in 1946, howing the "PERSIAN GULF" inscription restored to the lower egment of the postmark.

In October 1947 control of the Dubai Post Office passed to akistan whose stamps were used there until the end of March 948.

On 1 April 1948 the post office was transferred, yet again, to ritish control and Great Britain stamps surcharged for use in the ritish Postal Agencies in Eastern Arabia were then sold in Dubai ntil 6 January 1961, being cancelled with British style single and ouble-ring postmarks.

1 Palms

2 Dhow

(Des M. Goaman. Photo Harrison (T 1). Des M. Farrar-Bell. Recess D.L.R. (T 2))

61 (7 Jan). *P* 15 × 14 (*T* **1**) *or* 13 × 12½ (*T* **2**).

No.	Type	Description	Unused	Used
	1	5 n.p. green	25	10
		15 n.p. red-brown	25	10
		20 n.p. bright blue	40	10
		30 n.p. orange-red	40	10
		40 n.p. reddish violet	40	10
		50 n.p. bistre	40	10
		75 n.p. grey	60	10
	2	1 r. green	3·00	30
		2 r. black	3·00	4·50
		5 r. carmine-red	4·50	9·50
		10 r. deep ultramarine	12·00	18·00
1		*Set of* 11	22·00	29·00

The Dubai Post Department took over the postal services on June 1963. Later issues for Dubai will be found in Part 19 (*Middle East*) of this catalogue.

Turks and Caicos Islands

TURKS ISLANDS

DEPENDENCY OF JAMAICA

A branch of the British Post Office opened at Grand Turk on December 1854 replacing an earlier arrangement under ich mail for the islands was sorted by local R.M.S.P. agents. No. CC1 is known used between 22 October 1857 and 20 April 32.

For illustrations of the handstamp types see BRITISH POST OFFICES ABROAD notes, following GREAT BRITAIN.

GRAND TURK

CROWNED-CIRCLE HANDSTAMPS

CC1 CC 4 TURKS-ISLANDS (1857) . .

PRICES FOR STAMPS ON COVER TO 1945	
Nos. 1/5	*from* × 12
No. 6	—
Nos. 7/20	*from* × 12
Nos. 20*a*/48	—
Nos. 49/52	*from* × 3
Nos. 53/7	*from* × 4
Nos. 58/65	*from* × 10
Nos. 66/9	*from* × 4
Nos. 70/2	*from* × 8
Nos. 101/9	*from* × 5
Nos. 110/26	*from* × 4
Nos. 129/39	*from* × 3
Nos. 140/53	*from* × 10
Nos. 154/90	*from* × 3
Nos. 191/3	*from* × 10
Nos. 194/205	*from* × 2

1

(Recess P.B.)

1867 (4 April). *No wmk. P* 11–12.

No.	Type	Description	Unused	Used
1	**1**	1d. dull rose	28·00	38·00
2		6d. black	65·00	70·00
3		1s. dull blue	60·00	55·00

1873–79. *Wmk Small Star.* W w **2** (*sideways on Nos.* 5 *and* 6). *P* 11–12 × 14½–15½.

No.	Type	Description	Unused	Used
4	**1**	1d. dull rose-lake (7.73)	35·00	38·00
		a. Wmk sideways		
5		1d. dull red (1.79)	45·00	48·00
		a. Imperf between (pair)	£8000	
		c. Wmk upright		
6		1s. lilac (1.79)	£5500	£2000

1881 (1 Jan). *Stamps of the preceding issues surcharged locally, in black.*

There are twelve different settings of the ½d., nine settings of the 2½d., and six settings of the 4d.

(2) (3)

Setting 1. *T* **2**. *Long fraction bar. Two varieties repeated fifteen times in the sheet.*

No.	Description	Unused	Used
7	½ on 6d. black	48·00	55·00

Setting 2. *T* **3**. *Short fraction bar. Three varieties in a vertical strip repeated ten times in sheet.*

Setting 3. *Similar to setting* 2, *but the middle stamp of the three varieties has a longer bar.*

No.	Description	Unused	Used
8	½ on 6d. black (*setting* 2 *only*)	50·00	
9	½ on 1s. dull blue	60·00	80·00
	a. Surch double	£3500	

(4) (5) (6)

Three varieties in a vertical strip repeated ten times in sheet.

Section 4. Types **4**, **5**, **6**.
Setting 5. Types **4** (*without bar*), **5**, **6**.
Setting 6. Types **4**, **5**, **6** (*without bar*).
Setting 7. Types **4** (*shorter thick bar*), **6**, **6**.

No.	Description	Unused	Used
10	½ on 1d. dull red (*setting* 7 *only*) (T **6**)	£1000	
	a. Type **4** (shorter thick bar)	£1700	
11	½ on 1s. dull blue (*setting* 6 *and* 7) (T **4**)	£450	
	a. Type **4** (shorter thick bar)	£450	
	b. Type **5**	£450	
	c. Type **6**	£275	
	d. Type **6** (without bar)	£450	
	e. Surch double (T **6** without bar)		
12	½ on 1s. lilac (T **4**)	£275	£300
	a. Without bar	£450	
	b. With short thick bar	£450	
	c. Surch double		
13	½ on 1s. lilac (T **5**)	£110	£120
	a. Surch double	£1200	
14	½ on 1s. lilac (T **6**)	90·00	
	a. Without bar	£450	

(7) (8) (9) (10)

Setting 8. *T* **7**. *Three varieties in a vertical strip. All have a very short bar.*

No.	Description	Unused	Used
15	½ on 1d. dull red	42·00	

Setting 9. *T* **8**. *Three varieties in a vertical strip. Bars long and thick and "1" leaning a little to left.*

No.	Description	Unused	Used
16	½ on 1d. dull red	£120	
	a. Surch double		

Setting 10. *T* **9** *and* **10**. *Fifteen varieties repeated twice on a sheet. Ten are of T* **9**, *five of T* **10**.

No.	Description	Unused	Used
17	½ on 1d. dull red (T **9**)	38·00	45·00
	a. Surch double		
18	½ on 1d. dull red (T **10**)	45·00	55·00
19	½ on 1s. lilac (T **9**)	65·00	75·00
20	½ on 1s. lilac (T **10**)	£130	£160
20*a*	½ on 1s. dull blue (T **9**)	£6000	

Types **9** *and* **11**. The difference is in the position of the "2" in relation to the "1". In setting 10 the "2" is to the left of the "1" except on No. 10 and in setting 11 it is to the right except on No. 2

(11) (12) (13) (14)

Setting 11. *T* **11** *to* **14**. *Fifteen varieties repeated twice in a sheet. Ten of T* **11**, *three of T* **12**, *and one each of T* **13** *and* **14**.

Setting 12. *Similar to last, but T* **13** *replaced by another T* **12**.

No.	Description	Unused	Used
21	½ on 1d. dull red (T **11**)	45·00	
22	½ on 1d. dull red (T **12**)	90·00	
23	½ on 1d. dull red (T **13**)	£1000	
24	½ on 1d. dull red (T **14**)	£275	
24*a*	½ on 1s. dull blue (T **11**)	£8000	

(15) (16)

Setting 1. *T* **15**. *Fraction in very small type.*

No.	Description	Unused	Used
25	2½ on 6d. black	£6500	

Setting 2. *T* **16**. *Two varieties repeated fifteen times in a sheet. Large "2" on level with top of the "1", long thin bar.*

No.	Description	Unused	Used
26	2½ on 6d. black	£225	
	a. Imperf between (pair)		
	b. Surch double	£4000	

(17) (18) (19)

Setting 3. *T* **17**. *As T* **16**, *but large "2" not so high up.*

No.	Description	Unused	Used
27	2½ on 1s. lilac	£1300	

Setting 4. *T* **18**. *Three varieties in a vertical strip repeated ten times in sheet. Large "2" placed lower and small bar.*

No.	Description	Unused	Used
28	2½ on 6d. black	£110	£120
	a. Surch double		

Setting 5. *T* **19**. *Three varieties in a vertical strip repeated ten times in sheet "2" further from "½", small fraction bar.*

No.	Description	Unused	Used
29	2½ on 1s. lilac	£600	£550

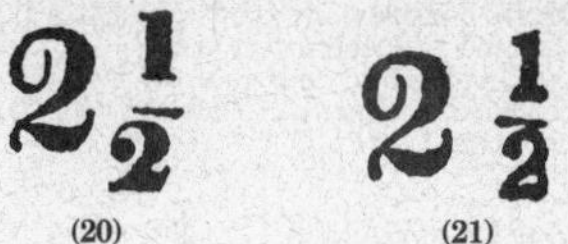

(20) (21)

Setting 6. *T* **20** *and* **21**. *Fifteen varieties. Ten of T* **20** *and five of T* **21**, *repeated twice in a sheet.*

No.	Description	Unused	Used
30	2½ on 1s. lilac (T **20**)	£5500	
31	2½ on 1s. lilac (T **21**)		

(22) (23) (24)

Setting 7. *T* **22**. *Three varieties in a vertical strip, repeated ten times in a sheet.*

No.	Description	Unused	Used
32	2½ on 6d. black	£7000	
33	2½ on 1s. dull blue	£7000	

Setting 8. *T* **23** *and* **24**. *Fifteen varieties. Ten of T* **23** *and five of T* **24**, *repeated twice in a sheet.*

No.	Description	Unused	Used
34	2½ on 1d. dull red (T **23**)	£250	
35	2½ on 1d. dull red (T **24**	£400	
36	2½ on 1s. lilac (T **23**)	£450	
	a. Surch "½" double	£2000	
37	2½ on 1s. lilac (T **24**)	£1200	
	a. Surch "½" double	£3500	

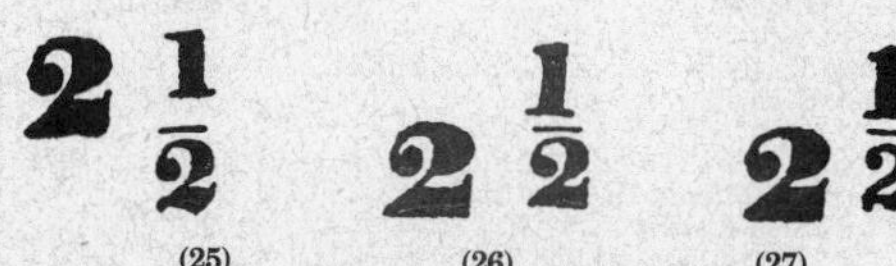

(25) (26) (27)

Setting 9. *T* **25, 26,** *and* **27**. *Fifteen varieties. Ten of T* **25**, *three of T* **26**, *one of T* **26** *without bar, and one of T* **27**, *repeated twice in a sheet.*
38 2½ on 1s. dull blue (T **25**) .. £375
39 2½ on 1s. dull blue (T **26**) .. £1200
40 2½ on 1s. dull blue (T **26**) (without bar) .. £6000
41 2½ on 1s. dull blue (T **27**) .. £6000

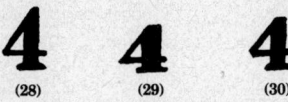

4 **4** **4**
(28) (29) (30)

Setting 1. *T* **28**. *"4" 8 mm high, pointed top.*
42 4 on 6d. black .. £160 £170

Settings 2–6. *T* **29** *and* **30**.
43 4 on 6d. black (T **29**) .. 38·00
44 4 on 6d. black (T **30**) .. £325 £350
45 4 on 1s. lilac (T **29**) .. £325
a. Surch double ..
46 4 on 1s. lilac (T **30**) .. £2000
a. Surch double ..
47 4 on 1d. dull red (T **29**) .. £400 £350
48 4 on 1d. dull red (T **28**) .. £400 £375

The components of these settings can only be distinguished when in blocks. Details are given in the handbook by John J. Challis.

31

One Penny
(32)

(Typo D.L.R.)

1881. *Wmk Crown CC (sideways; upright on 4d.). P* 14.
49 **1** 1d. brown-red (Oct) .. 38·00 42·00
50 **31** 4d. ultramarine (Die I) (Aug) .. 65·00 60·00
51 **1** 6d. olive-black (Oct) .. 65·00 75·00
52 1s. slate-green (Oct) .. 90·00 95·00

1882–85. *Wmk Crown CA. P* 14.
53 **31** ½d. blue-green (Die I) (2.82) .. 5·50 16·00
a. Pale green (12.85) .. 60 3·50
55 **1** 1d. orange-brown (10.83) .. 35·00 30·00
a. Bisected (½d.) (on cover) .. † £1200
56 **31** 2½d. red-brown (Die I) (2.82) .. 11·00 13·00
57 4d. grey (Die I) (10.84) .. 4·50 2·00
a. Bisected (2d.) (on cover) .. † £1000

1887 (July)–**89**. *Wmk Crown CA. (a) P* 12.
58 **1** 1d. crimson-lake .. 6·50 2·50
a. Imperf between (pair) ..
(b) P 14
59 **1** 6d. yellow-brown (2.89) (Optd S. £60) 2·00 2·75
60 1s. sepia .. 2·25 2·75

During a shortage of 1d. stamps a supply of JAMAICA No. 27 was sent to the Turks and Caicos Islands in April 1889 and used until replaced by No. 61.

1889 (May). *Surch at Grand Turk with T* **32**.
61 **31** 1d. on 2½d. red-brown .. 4·50 9·50
a. "ONE" omitted ..
b. Bisected (½d.) (on cover) .. † —

No. 61a was caused by misplacement of the surcharge. Stamps from the same sheet can be found with the surcharge reading "Penny One".

1889–93. *Wmk Crown CA. P* 14.
62 **1** 1d. crimson-lake (7.89) .. 2·00 3·50
a. Bisected (½d.) (on cover) .. † —
63 1d. lake .. 1·25 2·25
a. Bisected (½d.) (on cover) .. † —
64 1d. pale rosy lake .. 65 3·75
65 **31** 2½d. ultram (Die II) (4.93) (Optd S. £55) 1·00 75

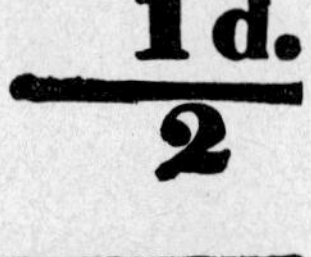

(33)

34

1893 (July). *No.* 57 *surch at Grand Turk with T* **33**.
Setting 1. *Bars between "1d." and "2" separate, instead of continuous across the rows of stamps.*
66 ½d. on 4d. grey .. £190 £120

Setting 2. *Continuous bars. Thin and thick bar* 10¾ *mm apart. "2" under the "1".*
67 ½d. on 4d. grey .. 90·00 90·00

Setting 3. *As last, but bars* 11¾ *mm apart.*
68 ½d. on 4d. grey .. 90·00 90·00

Setting 4. *Bars* 11 *mm apart. Five out of the six varieties in the strip have the "2" below the space between the "1" and "d".*
69 ½d. on 4d. grey .. 90·00

There is a fifth setting, but the variation is slight.

(Typo D.L.R.)

1894–95. *Wmk Crown CA. P* 14.
70 **31** ½d. dull green (Die II) (1894) .. 25 75
71 4d. dull purple & ultram (Die II) (5.95) 5·50 11·00
72 **34** 5d. olive-green and carmine (6.94) .. 2·25 10·00
a. Bisected (2½d.) (on cover) .. † £1800
70/2 .. *Set of* 3 7·25 20·00
71/2 Optd "Specimen" .. *Set of* 2 £100

TURKS AND CAICOS ISLANDS

35 Salt raking 36

The dates on the stamps have reference to the political separation from Bahamas.

(Recess D.L.R.)

1900 (10 Nov)–**04**. *Wmk Crown CA (½d. to 1s.) or Wmk Crown CC (2s., 3s.). P* 14.
101 **35** ½d. green .. 2·50 3·75
102 1d. red .. 2·75 75
103 2d. sepia .. 75 1·25
104 2½d. blue .. 3·00 6·00
a. Greyish blue (1904) .. 90 1·00
105 4d. orange .. 3·50 7·00
106 6d. dull mauve .. 1·25 5·50
107 1s. purple-brown .. 1·75 8·00
108 **36** 2s. purple .. 35·00 48·00
109 3s. lake .. 48·00 60·00
101/9 .. *Set of* 9 85·00 £130
101/9 Optd "Specimen" .. *Set of* 9 £225

1905–08. *Wmk Mult Crown CA. P* 14.
110 **35** ½d. green .. 40 15
111 1d. red .. 7·50 50
112 3d. purple/*yellow* (1908) (Optd S. £50) .. 90 5·00
110/12 .. *Set of* 3 8·00 5·00

37 Turk's-head Cactus

38

(Recess D.L.R.)

1909 (2 Sept)–**11**. *Wmk Mult Crown CA. P* 14.
115 **37** ¼d. rosy mauve (1910) .. 30 1·00
116 ¼d. red (1911) .. 20 25
117 **38** ½d. yellow-green .. 20 25
118 1d. red .. 20 30
119 2d. greyish slate .. 90 1·40
120 2½d. blue .. 1·25 3·75
121 3d. purple/*yellow* .. 1·75 2·00
122 4d. red/*yellow* .. 3·00 7·00
123 6d. purple .. 6·00 7·00
124 1s. black/*green* .. 2·50 8·50
125 2s. red/*green* .. 18·00 35·00
126 3s. black/*red* .. 20·00 35·00
115/26 .. *Set of* 12 48·00 90·00
115/26 Optd "Specimen" .. *Set of* 12 £225
See also Nos. 154 and 162.

39

WAR TAX
(40)

1913 (1 Apr)–**21**. *Wmk Mult Crown CA. P* 14.
129 **39** ½d. green .. 30 1·00
130 1d. red .. 60 1·10
a. Bright scarlet .. 1·10 1·60
b. Rose-carmine (1918) .. 1·00 1·60
131 2d. greyish slate .. 1·10 1·25
132 2½d. ultramarine .. 1·90 2·50
a. Bright blue (1918) .. 2·75 2·50
133 3d. purple/*yellow* .. 2·25 5·50
a. On lemon .. 12·00
b. On yellow-buff .. 2·50 5·50
c. On orange-buff .. 70
d. On pale yellow .. 1·50 4·00
134 4d. red/*yellow* .. 80 6·00
a. On orange-buff (Optd S. £48) .. 75 6·50
b. Carmine on pale yellow .. 3·00 7·50
135 5d. pale olive-green (18.5.16) .. 3·00 7·50
136 6d. dull purple .. 2·25 3·25
137 1s. brown-orange .. 1·50 4·00
138 2s. red/*blue-green* .. 6·00 14·00
a. On greenish white (1919) .. 16·00 45·00
b. On emerald (3.21) (Optd S. £48) .. 22·00 45·00
139 3s. black/*red* .. 15·00 25·00
129/39 .. *Set of* 11 30·00 60·00
129/39 Optd "Specimen" .. *Set of* 11 £180

1917 (3 Jan). *Optd with T* **40** *at bottom of stamp.*
140 **39** 1d. red .. 10 6
a. Overprint double .. £150
b. "TAX" omitted ..
c. "WAR TAX" omitted in vert pair with normal ..
d. Opt inverted at top .. £100
e. Opt double, one inverted* .. £100
f. Opt inverted only, in pair with No. 140e* .. £400
141 3d. purple/*yellow-buff* .. 45 2·0
a. Opt double .. 38·00
142 3d. purple/*lemon* .. 1·25 3·5
a. Opt double .. 35·00
b. Opt double, one inverted .. £250

*In Nos. 140e/f the inverted overprint is at foot and reads "TA WAR" owing to displacement. No. 140e also exists with "WAR omitted from the inverted overprint.

In both values of the first printings the stamp in the bottom left hand corner of the sheet has a long "T" in "TAX", and on the firs stamp of the sixth row the "X" is damaged and looks like a reverse "K".

1917 (Oct). *Second printing with overprint at top or in middle stamp.*
143 **39** 1d. red .. 10 5
a. Inverted opt at bottom or centre .. 23·00
c. Overprint omitted, in pair with normal .. £140
d. Double overprint, one at top, one at bottom .. 35·00
e. As d., but additional overprint in top margin .. 90·00
f. Vertical pair, one as d., the other normal .. £180
g. Pair, one overprint inverted, one normal .. £225
h. Double overprint at top (in pair with normal .. £180
i. Overprint double .. 35·00 35·
144 3d. purple/*yellow* .. 35 1·
a. Opt double .. 19·00
b. Opt double, one inverted ..
144c 3d. purple/*lemon*

1918. *Overprinted with T* **40**.
145 **39** 3d. purple/*yellow* (R.) .. 4·00 13·
a. Opt double ..

WAR TAX
(41)

WAR TAX
(42)

WAR TAX
(43)

1918. *Optd with T* **41** *in London by D.L.R.*
146 **39** 1d. rose-carmine .. 20 1·
a. Bright rose-scarlet .. 15
147 3d. purple/*yellow* .. 15
146/7 Optd. "Specimen" .. *Set of* 2 80·00

1919. *Optd with T* **41** *in London by D.L.R.*
148 **39** 3d. purple/*orange-buff* (R.) .. 10
148 Optd "Specimen" .. 40·00

1919. *Local overprint. T* **40**, *in violet.*
149 **39** 1d. bright rose-scarlet .. 10 1·0
a. "WAR" omitted .. 95·00
b. Opt double .. 16·00
c. Opt double in pair with normal .. 95·00
d. Opt double, one inverted ..
e. Rose-carmine .. 4·00 6·0
ea. Opt double ..

1919. *Optd with T* **42**.
150 **39** 1d. scarlet .. 10
a. Opt double .. 95·00 95·
b. Opt double, one albino and reversed ..
151 3d. purple/*orange-buff* .. 30 1·

1919 (17 Dec). *Optd with T* **43**.
152 **39** 1d. scarlet .. 10
a. Opt inverted ..
153 3d. purple/*orange-buff* .. 10

The two bottom rows of this setting have the words "WAR" ar "TAX" about 1 mm further apart.

1921 (23 April). *Wmk Mult Script CA. P* 14.
154 **37** ¼d. rose-red .. 35 4·
155 **39** ½d. green .. 65 4·
156 1d. carmine-red .. 45 2·
157 2d. slate-grey .. 80 9·
158 2½d. bright blue .. 1·40 5·
159 5d. sage-green .. 5·00 20·
160 6d. purple .. 5·50 22·
161 1s. brown-orange .. 6·00 20·
154/161 .. *Set of* 8 17·00 75·
154/61 Optd "Specimen" .. *Set of* 8 £140

44

45

(Recess D.L.R.)

1922 (20 Nov)–**26**. *P* 14. *(a) Wmk Mult Script CA.*
162 **37** ¼d. black (11.10.26) .. 15
163 **44** ½d. yellow-green .. 30
a. Bright green .. 35
b. Apple-green .. 2·00 4·
164 1d. brown .. 40 2·
165 1½d. scarlet (24.11.25) .. 2·00 4·
166 2d. slate .. 40 1·
167 2½d. purple/*pale yellow* .. 20

44 3d. bright blue .. .. 40 1·50
4d. red/*pale yellow* .. .. .. 75 2·75
a. Carmine/pale yellow .. .. 2·75 7·00
5d. sage-green .. .. 65 6·00
6d. purple .. .. 60 2·75
1s. brown-orange .. .. .. 70 4·50
2s. red/*emerald* .. .. 2·00 4·75

(b) Wmk Mult Crown CA

44 2s. red/*emerald* (24.11.25) .. .. 16·00 38·00
3s. black/*red* (24.11.25) .. .. 5·00 13·00
75 .. .. *Set of* 14 26·00 75·00
75 Optd "Specimen" .. .. *Set of* 14 £200

3 (1 Mar). *Inscr* "POSTAGE & REVENUE". *Wmk Mult Script A. P* 14.
45 ½d. green 35 40
1d. brown 35 70
1½d. scarlet .. .. 35 1·25
2d. grey 35 30
2½d. purple/*yellow* .. .. .. 35 1·00
3d. bright blue .. .. 35 1·40
6d. purple .. .. 40 2·50
1s. brown-orange .. .. .. 2·25 3·50
2s. red/*emerald* .. .. .. 3·25 15·00
5s. green/*yellow* .. .. .. 11·00 30·00
10s. purple/*blue* .. .. .. 38·00 70·00
86 .. .. *Set of* 11 50·00 £110
86 Optd "Specimen" .. .. *Set of* 11 £160

5 (6 May). *Silver Jubilee. As Nos.* 91/4 *of Antigua, but ptd by aterlow. P* 11 × 12.
½d. black and green 15 40
j. Kite and vertical log .. .. .. 14·00
k. Kite and horizontal log .. .. .. 14·00
3d. brown and deep blue .. .. .. 1·25 1·75
j. Kite and vertical log .. .. .. 35·00
6d. light blue and olive-green .. .. 1·25 2·00
j. Kite and vertical log .. .. .. 35·00
1s. slate and purple .. .. 1·25 3·25
j. Kite and vertical log .. .. .. 35·00
90 .. .. *Set of* 4 3·50 6·50
90 Perf "Specimen" .. .. *Set of* 4 65·00
or illustrations of plate varieties see Omnibus section owing Zululand.

7 (12 May). *Coronation. As Nos.* 13/15 *of Aden.*
½d. myrtle-green 10 10
a. Deep green .. ..
2d. grey-black 20 15
3d. bright blue 40 20
3 .. .. *Set of* 3 65 35
3 Perf "Specimen" .. .. *Set of* 3 50·00

46 Raking Salt

47 Salt Industry

(Recess Waterlow)

3 (18 June)–**45**. *Wmk Mult Script CA. P* 12½.
46 ¼d. black 10 10
½d. yellowish green 45 15
a. Deep green (6.11.44) 10 30
1d. red-brown 10 10
1½d. scarlet 20 10
2d. grey 30 15
2½d. yellow-orange 75 20
a. Orange (6.11.44) 75 40
3d. bright blue 20 10
6d. mauve .. .. 5·00 1·25
a 6d. sepia (9.2.45) 15 15
1s. yellow-bistre .. .. .. 2·00 4·50
a 1s. grey-olive (9.2.45) 15 15
47 2s. deep rose-carmine .. .. .. 11·00 5·00
a. Bright rose-carmine (6.11.44) .. 6·50 7·50
5s. yellowish green .. .. .. 18·00 9·00
a. Deep green (6.11.44) .. .. 12·00 10·00
10s. bright violet .. .. .. 4·00 4·50
205 .. .. *Set of* 14 26·00 23·00
205 Perf "Specimen" .. .. *Set of* 14 £200

(4 Nov). *Victory. As Nos.* 28/9 *of Aden.*
2d. black 10 10
3d. blue 15 10
7 Perf "Specimen" .. .. *Set of* 2 40·00

(13 Sept). *Royal Silver Wedding. As Nos.* 30/1 *of Aden.*
1d. red-brown 15 10
10s. mauve .. .. 5·00 5·00

) Badge of the Islands

53 Queen Victoria and King George VI

(Recess Waterlow)

1948 (14 Dec). *Centenary of Separation from Bahamas. T* **50**, **53** *and similar designs. Wmk Mult Script CA. P* 12½.
210 **50** ½d. blue-green 15 15
211 2d. carmine 30 15
212 – 3d. blue 35 15
213 – 6d. violet 30 20
214 **53** 2s. black and bright blue 35 35
215 5s. black and green 60 60
216 10s. black and brown .. .. .. 70 2·75
210/16 .. .. *Set of* 7 2·50 4·00
Designs: *Horiz*—3d. Flag of Turks and Caicos Islands; 6d. Map of islands.

1949 (10 Oct). *75th Anniv of Universal Postal Union. As Nos.* 114/17 *of Antigua.*
217 2½d. red-orange 10 15
218 3d. deep blue 25 25
219 6d. brown 25 25
220 1s. olive 25 25
217/20 .. .. *Set of* 4 75 80

65 Bulk Salt Loading

66 Dependency's Badge

(Recess Waterlow)

1950 (1 Aug). *T* **65** *and similar horiz designs, and T* **66**. *Wmk Mult Script CA. P* 12½.
221 ½d. green 15 40
222 1d. red-brown 15 50
223 1½d. deep carmine 20 50
224 2d. red-orange 15 40
225 2½d. grey-olive 20 50
226 3d. bright blue 20 40
227 4d. black and rose 80 70
228 6d. black and blue 80 50
229 1s. black and blue-green 55 40
230 1s. 6d. black and scarlet .. .. 1·25 3·25
231 2s. emerald and ultramarine .. .. 1·00 3·00
232 5s. blue and black .. .. .. 5·00 3·75
233 10s. black and violet .. .. .. 12·00 12·00
221/33 .. .. *Set of* 13 20·00 23·00
Designs:—1d. Salt Cay; 1½d. Caicos mail; 2d. Grand Turk; 2½d. Sponge diving; 3d. South Creek; 4d. Map; 6d. Grand Turk Light; 1s. Government House; 1s. 6d. Cockburn Harbour; 2s. Government Offices; 5s. Loading salt.

1953 (2 June). *Coronation. As No.* 47 *of Aden, but ptd by B.W. & Co.*
234 2d. black and orange-red 15 80

67 M.V. *Kirksons*

(Recess Waterlow)

1955 (1 Feb). *T* **67** *and similar horiz design. Wmk Mult Script CA. P* 12½.
235 5d. black and bright green 30 20
236 8d. black and brown 30 10
Design:—8d. Greater Flamingoes in flight.

69 Queen Elizabeth II (after Annigoni)

70 Bonefish

82 Dependency's Badge

(Recess B.W.)

1957 (25 Nov). *T* **69/70**, **82** *and similar horiz design as T* **70**. *W w* **12**. *P* 13½ × 14 (1*d*.), 14 (10*s*.) *or* 13½ (*others*).
237 1d. deep blue and carmine 15 20
238 1½d. grey-green and orange 15 30
239 2d. red-brown and olive 15 15
240 2½d. carmine and green 15 15
241 3d. turquoise-blue and purple 15 15
242 4d. lake and black 15 15
243 5d. slate-green and brown 15 40
244 6d. carmine-rose and blue 35 10
245 8d. vermilion and black 75 10
246 1s. deep blue and black 20 10
247 1s. 6d. sepia and deep ultramarine .. 60 50
248 2s. deep ultramarine and brown .. .. 1·75 2·25
249 5s. black and carmine .. .. .. 60 2·00
250 10s. black and purple .. .. .. 5·50 8·00
237/250 *and* 253 .. .. *Set of* 15 32·00 27·00
Designs:—2d. Red Grouper; 2½d. Spiny Lobster; 3d. Albacore; 4d. Muttonfish Snapper; 5d. Permit, 6d. Conch; 8d. Greater Flamingoes; 1s. Spanish Mackerel; 1s. 6d. Salt Cay; 2s. *Uakon* (Caicos sloop); 5s. Cable Office.

83 Map of the Turks and Caicos Islands

(Photo D.L.R.)

1959 (4 July). *New Constitution. Wmk Mult Script CA. P* 13½ × 14.
251 **83** 6d. deep olive and light orange 15 10
252 8d. violet and light orange 15 10

84 Brown Pelican

(Des Mrs. S. Hurd. Photo Harrison)

1960 (1 Nov). *W w* 12. *P* 14 × 14½.
253 **84** £1 sepia and deep red .. .. .. 27·00 16·00

CROWN COLONY

1963 (4 June). *Freedom from Hunger. As No.* 76 *of Aden.*
254 8d. carmine 20 10

1963 (2 Sept). *Red Cross Centenary. As Nos.* 147/8 *of Antigua.*
255 2d. red and black 15 10
256 8d. red and blue 30 25

1964 (23 April). *400th Birth Anniv of William Shakespeare. As No.* 164 *of Antigua.*
257 8d. green 10 10

1965 (17 May). *I.T.U. Centenary. As Nos.* 166/7 *of Antigua.*
258 1d. vermilion and brown 10 10
259 2s. light emerald and turquoise-blue .. 20 10

1965 (25 Oct). *International Co-operation Year. As Nos.* 168/9 *of Antigua.*
260 1d. reddish purple and turquoise-green .. 10 10
261 8d. deep bluish green and lavender 20 10

1966 (24 Jan). *Churchill Commemoration. As Nos.* 170/3 *of Antigua.*
262 1d. new blue 10 10
263 2d. deep green 15 10
264 8d. brown 15 10
a. Gold ptg double £125
265 1s. 6d. bluish violet 25 25
262/5 .. .. *Set of* 4 50 35

1966 (4 Feb). *Royal Visit. As Nos.* 174/5 *of Antigua.*
266 8d. black and ultramarine 25 10
267 1s. 6d. black and magenta 45 15

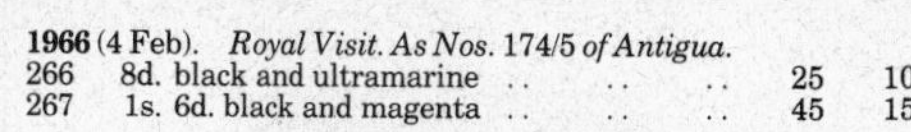

85 Andrew Symmer going ashore

(Des V. Whiteley. Photo D.L.R.)

1966 (1 Oct). *Bicentenary of "Ties with Britain" T* **85** *and similar horiz designs. P* 13½.
268 1d. deep blue and orange 10 10
269 8d. red, blue and orange-yellow 10 10
270 1s. 6d. multicoloured 10 10
268/70 .. .. *Set of* 3 15 10
Designs:—8d. Andrew Symmer and Royal Warrant; 1s. 6d. Arms and Royal Cypher.

1966 (1 Dec). *20th Anniv of U.N.E.S.C.O. As Nos.* 196/8 *of Antigua.*
271 1d. slate-violet, red, yellow and orange .. 10 10
272 8d. orange-yellow, violet and deep olive .. 15 10
273 1s. 6d. black, bright purple and orange .. 20 40
271/3 .. .. *Set of* 3 35 50

88 Turk's-head Cactus

89 Boat-building

90 Arms of Turks and Caicos Islands

91 Queen Elizabeth II

(Des V. Whiteley. Photo Harrison)

1967 (1 Feb). *Designs as T* **88/91**. *W* w **12**. *P* 14½ × 14 (*vert*) *or* 14 × 14½ (*horiz*).

274 1d. olive-yellow, vermilion & brt bluish vio .. 10 10
275 1½d. brown and orange-yellow 10 10
276 2d. deep slate and deep orange-yellow .. 10 10
277 3d. agate and dull green 10 10
278 4d. bright mauve, black and turquoise .. 10 10
279 6d. sepia and new blue 15 10
280 8d. yellow, turquoise-blue and deep blue .. 15 10
281 1s. maroon and turquoise 20 10
282 1s. 6d. orange-yellow, lake-brn & dp turq-bl 50 20
283 2s. multicoloured 50 70
284 3s. maroon and turquoise-blue 55 30
285 5s. ochre, blue and new blue .. .. 1·00 1·50
286 10s. multicoloured .. .. 1·50 2·00
287 £1 Prussian blue, silver and crimson .. 3·00 4·50
274/287 .. .. *Set of* 14 7·00 8·50

Designs: *Vert as T* **88**—2d. Donkey; 3d. Sisal industry; 6d. Salt industry; 8d. Skin-diving; 1s. 6d. Water-skiing. *Horiz as T* **89**—4d. Conch industry; 1s. Fishing; 2s. Crawfish industry; 3s. Maps of Turks and Caicos Islands and West Indies; 5s. Fishing industry.

102 Turks Islands 1d. Stamp of 1867

(Des R. Granger Barrett. Photo Harrison)

1967 (1 May). *Stamp Centenary. T* **102** *and similar horiz designs. W* w **12**. *P* 14½.

288 1d. black and light magenta.. .. .. 10 10
289 6d. black and bluish grey 10 10
290 1s. black and turquoise-blue 10 10
288/90 .. .. *Set of* 3 15 10

Designs:—6d. Queen Elizabeth "stamp" and Turks Islands 6d. stamp of 1867; 1s. Turks Islands 1s. stamp of 1867.

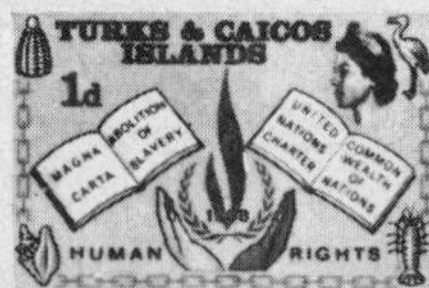

104 Human Rights Emblem and Charter

(Des R. Granger Barrett. Photo Harrison)

1968 (1 Apr). *Human Rights Year. W* w **12**. *P* 14 × 14½.

291 **104** 1d. multicoloured 10 10
292 8d. multicoloured 10 10
293 1s. 6d. multicoloured 10 10
291/3 .. .. *Set of* 3 10 10

105 Dr Martin Luther King and "Freedom March"

(Des V. Whiteley. Photo Harrison)

1968 (1 Oct). *Martin Luther King Commemoration. W* w **12**. *P* 14 × 14½.

294 **105** 2d. yellow-brown, blackish brn & dp bl 10 10
295 8d. yellow-brown, blackish brn & lake 10 10
296 1s. 6d. yellow-brn, blackish brn & vio .. 10 10
294/6 .. .. *Set of* 3 10 10

(New Currency. 100 cents=1 dollar)

1c

(106)

107 "The Nativity with John the Baptist"

1969 (8 Sept)–71. *Decimal currency. Nos.* 274/87 *surch as T* **106** *by Harrison & Sons, and new value* (¼ *c.*) *as T* **90**.

297 ¼ c. pale greenish grey and multicoloured 10 10
a. *Bronze-green & multicoloured* (2.2.71) 10 10
298 1 c. on 1d. olive-yell, verm & brt bluish vio 10 10
a. Wmk sideways 10 10
299 2 c. on 2d. deep slate & deep orange-yellow 10 10
a. Wmk sideways 10 10
300 3 c. on 3d. agate and dull green .. 10 10
a. Wmk sideways 10 10
301 4 c. on 4d. bright mauve, black & turquoise 10 10
302 5 c. on 6d. sepia and new blue 10 10
a. Wmk sideways 10 10
303 7 c. on 8d. yellow, turquoise-blue & dp blue 10 10
a. Wmk sideways 10 10
304 8 c. on 1½d. brown and orange-yellow .. 10 10
305 10 c. on 1s. maroon and turquoise .. 20 10
306 15 c. on 1s. 6d. orange-yellow, lake-brown and deep turquoise-blue 25 10
a. Wmk sideways 20 25
307 20 c. on 2s. multicoloured 30 25
308 30 c. on 3s. maroon and turquoise-blue .. 55 35
309 50 c. on 5s. ochre, blue and new blue .. 1·00 45
310 $1 on 10s. multicoloured .. .. 1·00 1·00
311 $2 on £1 Prussian blue, silver and crimson 4·00 10·00
a. Wmk sideways .. .. .. 1·50 3·00
297/311a .. .. *Set of* 15 4·50 4·75

The 4, 8, 10, 20, 30, 50 c., and $1 exist with PVA gum as well as gum arabic.

No. 311 was only on sale through the Crown Agents.

(Des adapted by V. Whiteley. Litho D.L.R.)

1969 (20 Oct). *Christmas. Scenes from 16th-cent Book of Hours. T* **107** *and similar vert design. Multicoloured. W* w **12**. *P* 13 × 12½.

312 1 c. Type **107** 10 10
313 3 c. "The Flight into Egypt" 10 10
314 15 c. Type **107** 10 10
315 30 c. As 3 c. 15 10
312/15 .. .. *Set of* 4 25 15

109 Coat of Arms

110 "Christ bearing the Cross"

(Des L. Curtis. Litho B.W.)

1970 (2 Feb). *New Constitution. Multicoloured; background colours given. W* w **12** (*sideways*). *P* 13 × 12½.

316 **109** 7 c. brown 10 10
317 35 c. deep violet-blue 20 15

(Des, recess and litho Enschedé)

1970 (17 Mar). *Easter. Details from the "Small Engraved Passion" by Dürer. T* **110** *and similar vert designs. W* w **12** (*sideways*). *P* 13 × 13½.

318 5 c. olive-grey and blue 10 10
319 7 c. olive-grey and vermilion.. .. .. 10 10
320 50 c. olive-grey and red-brown 20 20
318/20 .. .. *Set of* 3 25 25

Designs:—7 c. "Christ on the Cross"; 50 c. "The Lamentation of Christ".

113 Dickens and Scene from *Oliver Twist*

(Des Sylvia Goaman. Recess and litho D.L.R.)

1970 (17 June). *Death Centenary of Charles Dickens. T* **113** *a similar horiz designs. W* w **12** (*sideways*). *P* 13.

321 1 c. black and yellow-brown/*yellow* 10
322 3 c. black and Prussian blue/*flesh* 10
323 15 c. black and grey-blue/*flesh* 10
324 30 c. black and drab/*blue* 20
321/4 .. .. *Set of* 4 35

Designs (each incorporating portrait of Dickens as in T **113**, a a scene from one of his novels):—3 c. *A Christmas Carol*; 15 c. *Pi wick Papers*; 30 c. *The Old Curiosity Shop*.

114 Ambulance—1870

(Des Harrison. Litho B.W.)

1970 (4 Aug). *Centenary of British Red Cross. T* **114** *and sim horiz design. Multicoloured. W* w **12**. *P* 13½ × 14.

325 1 c. Type **114** 10
326 5 c. Ambulance—1970 10
a. Wmk sideways 15
ab. Grey omitted £250
327 15 c. Type **114** 15
a. Wmk sideways 25
328 30 c. As 5 c. 15
a. Wmk sideways 40
325/8 .. .. *Set of* 4 35

115 Duke of Albermarle and Coat of Arms

(Des V. Whiteley. Litho Enschedé)

1970 (1 Dec). *Tercentenary of Issue of Letters Patent. T* **115** *similar horiz design. Multicoloured. W* w **12**. *P* 12½ × 13½.

329 1 c. Type **115** 10
330 8 c. Arms of Charles II and Elizabeth II .. 20
331 10 c. Type **115** 20
332 35 c. As 8 c. 40
329/32 .. .. *Set of* 4 75

116 Boat-building

117 Seahorse

1971 (2 Feb). *Designs as T* **88/91** *etc., but inscr in dec currency as in T* **116**. *W* w **12** (*sideways on* 1 *c.*, 2 *c.*, 3 *c.*, 5 *c.*, 15 *c. and* $2).

333 1 c. olive-yell, verm & brt bluish vio (as 1d.) 10
334 2 c. deep slate & deep orange-yell (as 2d.) .. 10
335 3 c. agate and dull green (as 3d.) 15
336 4 c. bright mauve, black & turquoise (as 4d.) 20
337 5 c. sepia and new blue (as 6d.) 20
338 7 c. yellow, turquoise-blue & dp blue (as 8d.) 25
339 8 c. brown and orange-yellow 30
340 10 c. maroon and turquoise (as 1s.) 30
341 15 c. orange-yellow, lake-brown and deep turquoise-blue (as 1s. 6d.) 80
342 20 c. multicoloured (as 2s.) 85
343 30 c. maroon and turquoise-blue (as 3s.) .. 1·25
344 50 c. ochre, blue and new blue (as 5s.) .. 1·75
345 $1 multicoloured (as 10s.) .. .. .. 2·25
a. Green omitted .. ..
346 $2 Prussian blue, silver and crimson (as £1) 4·00
333/46 .. .. *Set of* 14 11·00 1

The ¼ c. value was also re-issued, but it can only distinguished from No. 297 by its revised sheet format of 25 ins of 60.

(Des G. Vasarhelyi. Litho J.W.)

1971 (4 May). *Tourist Development. T* **117** *and similar m coloured designs. W* w **12** (*sideways on Nos.* 348/50). *P* 14 × (1 *c.*) *or* 14½ × 14 (*others*).

347 1 c. Type **117** 10
348 3 c. Queen Conch Shell (*horiz*) 10
349 15 c. Oystercatcher (*horiz*) 30
350 30 c. Blue Marlin (*horiz*) 30
347/50 .. .. *Set of* 4 60

118 Pirate Sloop

119 The Wilton Diptych (Left Wing)

(Des and litho J.W.)

1 (27 July). *Pirates. T* **118** *and similar horiz designs. Multi-*
loured. W w **12** *(sideways). P* 14.
2 c. Type **118** 10 10
3 c. Pirate treasure 10 10
15 c. Marooned sailor 45 15
30 c. Buccaneers 70 45
/4 . . . . *Set of* 4 1·25 70

(Des J.W. Litho Questa)

1 (12 Oct). *Christmas. T* **119** *and similar vert design. Multi-*
loured. W w **12**. *P* 13½.
2 c. Type **119** 10 10
a. Horiz pair. Nos. 355/6 . . . . . . 10 10
2 c. The Wilton Diptych (Right Wing) . . 10 10
8 c. Type **119** 10 10
a. Horiz pair. Nos. 357/8 . . . . . . 20 10
8 c. As No. 356 . . . . 10 10
15 c. Type **119** 15 10
a. Horiz pair. Nos. 359/60 . . . . . . 30 20
15 c. As No. 356 . . . . 15 10
/60 . . . . *Set of* 6 55 35
he two stamps of each denomination were printed in horizontal
enant pairs throughout the sheet.

120 Cape Kennedy Launching Area

121 "Christ before Pilate" (Rembrandt)

(Des V. Whiteley. Litho A. & M.)

2 (21 Feb). *Tenth Anniv of Colonel Glenn's Splashdown.*
120 *and similar multicoloured designs.* W w **12** *(sideways on* 5,
0 and 15 *c.). P* 13½.
5 c. Type **120** 10 10
10 c. "Friendship 7" space capsule 10 10
15 c. Map of Islands and splashdown 15 10
20 c. N.A.S.A. Space Medal *(vert)* 15 10
/4 . . . . *Set of* 4 40 25

(Des and litho J.W.)

2 (21 Mar). *Easter. T* **121** *and similar designs.* W w **12** *(side-*
ways on 15 *c.). P* 13½.
2 c. black and lilac 10 10
15 c. black and rose-pink 15 10
30 c. black and greenish yellow 15 15
/7 . . . . *Set of* 3 30 20
esigns: *Horiz*—15 c. "The Three Crosses" (Rembrandt).
t—30 c. "The Descent from the Cross" (Rembrandt).

122 Christopher Columbus

123 Turk's-head Cactus and Spiny Lobster

(Des P. Powell. Litho J.W.)

2 (28 July*). *Discoverers and Explorers. T* **122** *and similar*
ulticoloured designs. W w **12** *(sideways on* 8 *and* 30 *c.). P* 13½.
¼ c. Type **122** 10 10
8 c. Sir Richard Grenville *(horiz)* 30 10
10 c. Capt. John Smith 35 10
30 c. Juan Ponce de Leon *(horiz)* 85 75
/71 . . . . *Set of* 4 1·40 75
This was the local date of issue; the Crown Agents released the
nps on 4 July.

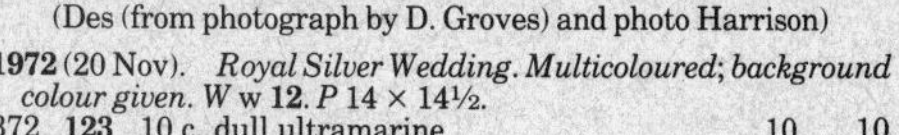

(Des (from photograph by D. Groves) and photo Harrison)

1972 (20 Nov). *Royal Silver Wedding. Multicoloured; background colour given.* W w **12**. *P* 14 × 14½.
372 **123** 10 c. dull ultramarine 10 10
373 20 c. myrtle-green 15 10

124 Treasure Hunting, *circa* 1700

125 Arms of Jamaica and Turks & Caicos Islands

(Des C. Abbott. Litho Questa)

1973 (18 Jan). *Treasure. T* **124** *and similar vert designs.* W w **12** *(sideways). P* 14 × 14½.
374 3 c. multicoloured 10 10
375 5 c. reddish purple, silver and black 10 10
376 10 c. magenta, silver and black 20 10
377 30 c. multicoloured 60 30
374/7 . . . . *Set of* 4 85 35
MS378 127 × 108 mm. Nos. 374/7 . . . . 1·50 2·00
Designs:—5 c. Silver Bank medallion (obverse); 10 c. Silver Bank medallion (reverse); 30 c. Treasure hunting, 1973.

(Des PAD Studio. Litho Walsall)

1973 (16 Apr). *Centenary of Annexation to Jamaica.* W w **12** *(sideways). P* 13½ × 14.
379 **125** 15 c. multicoloured 20 10
380 35 c. multicoloured 40 15

126 Sooty Tern

127 Bermuda Sloop

(Des R. Granger Barrett. Litho Questa)

1973 (1 Aug). *T* **126** *and similar vert designs.* W w **12** *(sideways). P* 14.
381 ¼ c. Type **126** 10 15
382 1 c. Magnificent Frigate Bird 20 25
383 2 c. Common Noddy 30 30
384 3 c. Blue-grey Gnatcatcher 85 40
385 4 c. Little Blue Heron 35 40
386 5 c. Catbird 30 20
387 7 c. Black-whiskered Vireo 80 20
388 8 c. Osprey . . . . 1·75 40
389 10 c. Greater Flamingo 70 35
390 15 c. Brown Pelican . . . . . . 1·25 50
391 20 c. Parula Warbler . . . . . . 3·00 1·25
392 30 c. Northern Mockingbird . . . . 1·75 90
393 50 c. Ruby-throated Hummingbird . . . . 3·00 2·75
394 $1 Bananaquit . . . . . . 3·50 4·00
395 $2 Cedar Waxwing . . . . . . 5·50 5·50
381/95 . . . . . . *Set of* 15 21·00 15·00
See also Nos. 411/14 and 451/64.

(Des R. Granger Barrett. Litho Questa)

1973 (14 Aug). *Vessels. T* **127** *and similar horiz designs. Multicoloured.* W w **12**. *P* 13½.
396 2 c. Type **127** 10 10
397 5 c. H.M.S. *Blanche* 20 10
398 8 c. U.S. privateer *Grand Turk* and P.O. packet *Hinchinbrooke* 25 15
399 10 c. H.M.S. *Endymion* 25 15
400 15 c. R.M.S. *Medina* 35 70
401 20 c. H.M.S. *Daring* 45 75
396/401 . . . . . . *Set of* 6 1·40 1·75
MS402 198 ×101 mm. Nos. 396/401 . . . . 1·40 2·50

1973 (14 Nov). *Royal Wedding. As Nos.* 165/6 *of Anguilla.*
403 12 c. light turquoise-blue 10 10
404 18 c. dull indigo 10 10

128 Duho (stool)

(Des Jennifer Toombs. Litho Questa)

1974 (17 July). *Lucayan Remains. T* **128** *and similar horiz designs. Multicoloured.* W w **12** *(sideways). P* 14½ × 14.
405 6 c. Type **128** 10 10
406 10 c. Broken wood bowl 10 10
407 12 c. Greenstone axe 10 10
408 18 c. Wood bowl 10 10
409 35 c. Fragment of duho 20 20
405/9 . . . . *Set of* 5 50 40
MS410 240 × 90 mm. Nos. 405/9 . . . . 75 1·25

1974–75. *As Nos.* 381 *etc, but* W w **12** *(upright).*
411 1 c. Magnificent Frigate Bird (11.6.75) . . 50 90
412 2 c. Common Noddy (27.9.74) 75 70
413 3 c. Blue-grey Gnatcatcher (19.3.75) . . 2·00 1·00
414 20 c. Parula Warbler (11.6.75) . . . . 2·75 3·50
411/14 . . . . *Set of* 4 5·50 5·50
Nos. 415/25 vacant.

129 G.P.O., Grand Turk

(Des G. Drummond. Litho Questa)

1974 (9 Oct). *Centenary of Universal Postal Union. T* **129** *and similar horiz designs. Multicoloured.* W w **12**. *P* 14.
426 4 c. Type **129** 10 10
427 12 c. Sloop and island map 20 10
428 18 c. "U.P.U." and globe 20 10
429 55 c. Posthorn and emblem 35 35
426/9 . . . . *Set of* 4 75 55

130 Churchill and Roosevelt

131 Spanish Captain, *circa* 1492

(Des V. Whiteley. Litho Questa)

1974 (30 Nov). *Birth Centenary of Sir Winston Churchill. T* **130** *and similar horiz design. Multicoloured.* W w **14** *(sideways). P* 14.
430 12 c. Type **130** 15 15
431 18 c. Churchill and vapour-trails 15 15
MS432 85 × 85 mm. Nos. 430/1 . . . . 40 55

(Des J.W. Litho Questa)

1975 (26 Mar). *Military Uniforms. T* **131** *and similar vert designs. Multicoloured.* W w **14**. *P* 14.
433 5 c. Type **131** 10 10
434 20 c. Officer, Royal Artillery, 1783 . . . . 30 15
435 25 c. Officer, 67th Foot, 1798 . . . . 35 15
436 35 c. Private, 1st West India Regt, 1833 . . 45 25
433/6 . . . . *Set of* 4 1·10 50
MS437 145 × 88 mm. Nos. 433/6 . . . . 1·25 2·00

132 Ancient Windmill, Salt Cay

133 Star Coral

(Des P. Powell. Litho Questa)

1975 (16 Oct). *Salt-raking Industry. T* **132** *and similar multicoloured designs.* W w **12** *(sideways on* 10 *and* 20 *c.). P* 14.
438 6 c. Type **132** 10 10
439 10 c. Salt pans drying in sun *(horiz)* . . 10 10
440 20 c. Salt-raking *(horiz)* 20 15
441 25 c. Unprocessed salt heaps 20 20
438/41 . . . . *Set of* 4 55 40

(Des C. Abbott. Litho Questa)

1975 (4 Dec). *Island Coral. T* **133** *and similar horiz designs. Multicoloured.* W w **14** *(sideways). P* 14.
442 6 c. Type **133** 15 10
443 10 c. Elkhorn Coral 20 10
444 20 c. Brain Coral 35 15
445 25 c. Staghorn Coral 40 20
442/5 . . . . *Set of* 4 1·00 40

134 American Schooner

135 1s. 6d. Royal Visit Stamp of 1966

(Des J.W. Litho Questa)

1976 (28 May). *Bicentenary of American Revolution. T* **134** *and similar vert designs. Multicoloured. W w* **14**. *P* 13½.

446	6 c. Type **134**	30	10
447	20 c. British ship of the line	70	15
448	25 c. American privateer *Grand Turk*	70	20
449	55 c. British ketch	1·25	60
446/9	*Set of* 4	2·75	95
MS450	95 × 151 mm. Nos. 446/9	2·75	4·50

Each value depicts, at the top, the engagement between the *Grand Turk* and the P.O. Packet *Hinchinbrooke*, as in T **134**.

1976–77. *As Nos.* 381/95, *and new value* ($5), *but W w* **14** (*upright*).

451	¼ c. Type **126** (12.77)	15	60
452	1 c. Magnificent Frigate Bird (12.77)	35	40
453	2 c. Common Noddy (12.77)	35	60
454	3 c. Blue-grey Gnatcatcher (14.6.76)	90	25
455	4 c. Little Blue Heron (12.77)	65	50
456	5 c. Catbird (12.77)	70	70
457	10 c. Greater Flamingo (12.77)	80	75
458	15 c. Brown Pelican (12.77)	1·25	1·25
459	20 c. Parula Warbler (30.11.76)	1·50	75
460	30 c. Northern Mockingbird (12.77)	1·25	1·75
461	50 c. Ruby-throated Hummingbird (12.77)	1·50	2·00
462	$1 Bananaquit (12.77)	2·25	2·75
463	$2 Cedar Waxwing (12.77)	3·75	4·50
464	$5 Painted Bunting (24.11.76)	3·50	4·00
451/64	*Set of* 14	17·00	19·00

No. 465 vacant.

(Des V. Whiteley Studio. Litho Walsall)

1976 (14 July). *Tenth Anniv of Royal Visit. T* **135** *and similar horiz design. Multicoloured. W w* **14** (*sideways*). *P* 14½ × 14.

466	20 c. Type **135**	50	30
467	25 c. 8d. Royal Visit stamp	60	30

136 "The Virgin and Child with Flowers" (C. Dolci)

137 Balcony Scene, Buckingham Palace

(Des G. Drummond. Litho Questa)

1976 (10 Nov). *Christmas. T* **136** *and similar vert designs. Multicoloured. W w* **14**. *P* 13½.

468	6 c. Type **136**	10	10
469	10 c. "Virgin and Child with St. John and an Angel" (Studio of Botticelli)	10	10
470	20 c. "Adoration of the Magi" (Master of Paraiso)	15	15
471	25 c. "Adoration of the Magi" (French miniature)	20	20
468/71	*Set of* 4	45	35

(Des J.W. (**MS**475), C. Abbott (others) Litho Questa)

1977 (7 Feb–6 Dec). *Silver Jubilee. T* **137** *and similar vert designs. Multicoloured. W w* **14**. *P* 14 × 13½ (**MS**475) *or* 13½ (*others*).

472	6 c. Queen presenting O.B.E. to E. T. Wood	10	10
473	25 c. The Queen with regalia	20	25
474	55 c. Type **137**	40	55
472/4	*Set of* 3	60	75
MS475	120 × 97 mm. $5 Queen Elizabeth II (6.12.77)	1·00	1·40

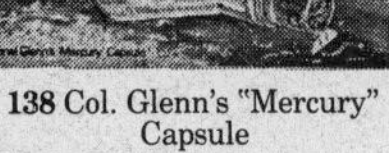

138 Col. Glenn's "Mercury" Capsule

139 "Flight of the Holy Family" (Rubens)

(Des and litho J.W.)

1977 (20 June). *25th Anniv of U.S. Tracking Station. T* **138** *and similar multicoloured designs. W w* **14** (*sideways on horiz designs*). *P* 13½.

476	1 c. Type **138**	10	10
477	3 c. Moon buggy "Rover" (*vert*)	10	10
478	6 c. Tracking Station, Grand Turk	10	10
479	20 c. Moon landing craft (*vert*)	15	15
480	25 c. Col. Glenn's rocket launch (*vert*)	20	20
481	50 c. "Telstar 1" satellite	30	40
476/81	*Set of* 6	70	80

(Des J.W. Litho Questa)

1977 (23 Dec). *Christmas and 400th Birth Anniv of Rubens. T* **139** *and similar vert designs. Multicoloured. P* 14.

482	½ c. Type **139**	10	10
483	½ c. "Adoration of the Magi" (1634)	10	10
484	1 c. "Adoration of the Magi" (1624)	10	10
485	6 c. "Virgin within Garland"	10	10
486	20 c. "Madonna and Child Adored by Angels"	15	10
487	$2 "Adoration of the Magi" (1618)	1·25	1·25
482/7	*Set of* 6	1·40	1·25
MS488	100 × 81 mm. $1 detail of 20 c.	60	1·00

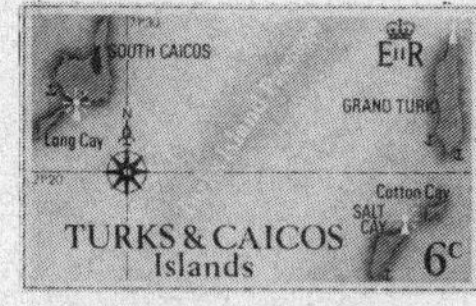

140 Map of Passage

(Des R. Granger Barrett. Litho J.W.)

1978 (2 Feb). *Turks Islands Passage. T* **140** *and similar horiz designs. Multicoloured. P* 13½. *A. No wmk. B. W w* **14** (*sideways*).

		A		B	
489	6 c. Type **140**	10	10	10	10
490	20 c. Caicos sloop passing Grand Turk Lighthouse	35	45	35	45
491	25 c. Motor cruiser	40	55	40	55
492	55 c. *Jamaica Planter* (freighter)	85	1·25	85	1·25
489/92	*Set of* 4	1·50	2·10	1·50	2·10
MS493	136 × 88 mm. Nos. 489/92. P 14½	1·50	2·25	55·00	—

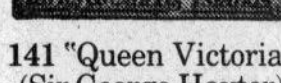

141 "Queen Victoria" (Sir George Hayter)

142 Ampulla and Anointing Spoon

(Manufactured by Walsall (Nos. 499/501). Des PAD Studio. Litho Questa (others))

1978 (2 June-July). *25th Anniv of Coronation. Multicoloured.*

(*a*) *Sheet stamps. Vert designs as T* **141** *showing British monarchs in coronation robes. P* 14

494	6 c. Type **141**	10	10
495	10 c. "King Edward VII" (Sir Samuel Fildes)	10	10
496	25 c. King George V	20	15
497	$2 King George VI	1·00	1·00
494/7	*Set of* 4	1·25	1·10
MS498	161 × 113 mm. $2.50, Queen Elizabeth II	1·00	1·00

(*b*) *Booklet stamps. Vert designs as T* **142**. *Imperf × roul* 5*. *Self-adhesive* (July)

499	15 c. Type **142**	15	30
	a. Booklet pane. Nos. 499/501	1·90	
	b. Booklet pane. Nos. 499/500, each × 3	1·25	
500	25 c. St. Edward's Crown	15	30
501	$2 Queen Elizabeth II in coronation robes	1·75	2·75
499/501	*Set of* 3	1·90	3·00

Nos. 494/7 also exist perf 12 (*Price for set of* 4 *£1.25 mint or used*) from additional sheetlets of 3 stamps and 1 label. Stamps perforated 14 are from normal sheets of 50.

*Nos. 499/501 are separated by various combinations of rotary-knife (giving a straight edge) and roulette.

143 Wilbur Wright and *Flyer III*

(Des Curtis Design. Litho Format)

1978 (July). *75th Anniv of Powered Flight. T* **143** *and similar horiz designs. Multicoloured. P* 14½.

502	1 c. Type **143**	10	10
503	6 c. Wright brothers and Cessna "337"	10	10
504	10 c. Orville Wright and "Electra"	10	10
505	15 c. Wilbur Wright and "C-47"	15	15
506	35 c. Wilbur Wright and "Islander"	35	35
507	$2 Wilbur Wright and Wright biplane	1·25	1·50
502/7	*Set of* 6	1·75	2·00
MS508	111 × 84 mm. $1 Orville Wright and Wright glider	75	1·40

144 Hurdling

(Des J.W. Litho Format)

1978 (3 Aug). *Commonwealth Games, Edmonton. T* **144** *similar horiz designs. Multicoloured. P* 14½.

509	6 c. Type **144**	10
510	20 c. Weightlifting	15
511	55 c. Boxing	30
512	$2 Cycling	1·00
509/12	*Set of* 4	1·25
MS513	105 × 79 mm. $1 Sprinting	75

145 Indigo Hamlet

146 "Madonna of the Siskin"

(Des G. Drummond. Litho Questa)

1978 (17 Nov)–**83**. *Fishes. Horiz designs as T* **145**. *Multicolou*

A. *No imprint date. P* 14

514A	1 c. Type **145**	10
515A	2 c. Tobacco fish (19.1.79)	20
516A	3 c. Passing Jack	10
517A	4 c. Porkfish (19.1.79)	25
518A	5 c. Spanish Grunt	10
519A	7 c. Yellowtail Snapper (19.1.79)	30
520A	8 c. Foureye Butterflyfish (19.1.79)	40
521A	10 c. Yellowfin Grouper	20
522A	15 c. Beau Gregory	20
523A	20 c. Queen Angelfish	30
524A	30 c. Hogfish (19.1.79)	85
525A	50 c. Fairy Basslet (19.1.79)	90
526A	$1 Clown Wrasse (19.1.79)	1·60
527A	$2 Stoplight Parrotfish (19.1.79)	3·00
528A	$5 Queen Triggerfish (19.1.79)	3·25
514A/28A	*Set of* 15	10·00 1

B. *With imprint date at foot of design. P* 14 (15 c.) *or* 12 (*ot*

514B	1 c. Type **145** (15.12.81)	25
518B	5 c. Spanish Grunt (15.12.81)	45
521B	10 c. Yellowfin Grouper (15.12.81)	55
522B	15 c. Beau Gregory (25.1.83)	90
523B	20 c. Queen Angelfish (15.12.81)	90
	a. Perf 14 (25.1.83)	85
525B	50 c. Fairy Basslet (15.12.81)	1·50
526B	$1 Clown Wrasse (15.12.81)	2·75
	a. Perf 14 (25.1.83)	2·00
527B	$2 Stoplight Parrotfish (15.12.81)	4·50
	a. Perf 14 (25.1.83)	3·00
528B	$5 Queen Triggerfish (15.12.81)	9·50 1
	a. Perf 14 (25.1.83)	7·50
514B/28B	*Set of* 9	15·00 1

(Des BG Studio. Litho Questa)

1978 (11 Dec). *Christmas. Paintings by Dürer. T* **146** *and sim multicoloured designs. P* 14.

529	6 c. Type **146**	10
530	20 c. "The Virgin and Child with St. Anne"	15
531	35 c. "Paumgärtner Nativity" (*horiz*)	20
532	$2 "Praying Hands"	85
529/32	*Set of* 4	1·10
MS533	137 × 124 mm. $1 "Adoration of the Magi" (*horiz*)	60

147 Osprey

(Des G. Drummond. Litho Questa)

1979 (29 May). *Endangered Wildlife. T* **147** *and similar h designs. Multicoloured. P* 14.

534	6 c. Type **147**	25
535	20 c. Green Turtle	35
536	25 c. Queen Conch	45
537	55 c. Rough-toothed Dolphin	80
538	$1 Humpback Whale	1·25
534/8	*Set of* 5	2·75
MS539	117 × 85 mm. $2 Iguana	2·25

148 "The Beloved" (painting by D. G. Rossetti)

(Des G. Vasarhelyi. Litho Questa)

9 (2 July). *International Year of the Child. T* **148** *and similar* *oriz designs showing paintings and I.Y.C. emblem. Multi-* *loured. P* 14.

6 c. Type **148** 10 10
25 c. "Tahitian Girl" (P. Gauguin) 15 10
55 c. "Calmady Children" (Sir Thomas Lawrence) 25 20
$1 "Mother and Daughter" (detail, P. Gauguin) 45 45
'3 .. .. *Set of* 4 80 70
544 112 × 85 mm. $2 "Marchesa Elena rimaldi" (A. van Dyck) .. .. 55 1·25

149 R.M.S.P. *Medina* and Handstamped Cover

150 Cuneiform Script

Des J.W. Litho Questa (Nos. 545/51). Des and litho Walsall (Nos. 552/64))

9 (27 Aug)–**80**. *Death Centenary of Sir Rowland Hill.*

Sheet stamps. Horiz designs as T **149**. *Multicoloured. P* 12 ($2) *or* 14 (*others*)

6 c. Type **149** 10 10
20 c. Sir Rowland Hill and map of Caribbean 15 15
45 c. R.M.S. *Orinoco* and cover bearing Penny Black stamp 25 25
75 c. R.M.S. *Shannon* and letter to Grand Turk 40 40
$1 R.M.S.P. *Trent* and map of Caribbean .. 55 55
$2 Turks Islands 1867 and Turks and Caicos Islands 1900 1d. stamps (6.5.80) .. 90 90
'50 .. .. *Set of* 6 2·10 2·10
551 170×113 mm. As No. 550. P 12 .. .. 1·00 1·75

os. 545/9 also exist perf 12 (*Price for set of* 5 £1.75 *mint or* *l*) from additional sheetlets of 5 stamps and 1 label. No. 550 exists in this format. Stamps perforated 14 are from normal ts of 40.

o. **MS**551 has the inscription "International Stamp Exhibi- Earls Court—London 6–14 May 1980. LONDON 1980" printed on the sheet margin. The individual stamps are not printed.

Booklet stamps. Designs as T **150**. *Imperf* × *roul* 5*. *Self-adhesive* (27.9.79)

5 c. black and bright emerald 10 10
a. Booklet pane. Nos. 552/7 80
5 c. black and bright emerald 10 10
5 c. black and bright emerald 10 10
15 c. black and light blue 20 20
15 c. black and light blue 20 20
15 c. black and light blue 20 20
25 c. black and light blue 30 30
a. Booklet pane. Nos. 558/63 .. .. 2·25
25 c. black and light blue 60 45
25 c. black and light blue 30 30
40 c. black and bright rosine 45 45
40 c. black and bright rosine 45 45
40 c. black and bright rosine 45 45
$1 black and lemon .. .. 1·10 1·25
a. Booklet pane of 1 .. .. 1·10

esigns: *Horiz*—No. 552. Type **150**; No. 553, Egyptian papyrus; 554, Chinese paper; No. 555, Greek runner; No. 556, Roman horse; No. 557, Roman post ship; No. 558, Pigeon post; No. 559, way post; No. 560, Packet paddle-steamer; No. 561, Balloon ; No. 562, First airmail; No. 563, Supersonic airmail. *Vert*—No. Original stamp press.

Nos. 552/63 are separated by various combinations of rotary e (giving a straight edge) and roulette. No. 564 exists only with ight edges.

PRICES OF SETS

t prices are given for many issues, generally se containing three stamps or more. Definitive s include one of each value or major colour ange, but do not cover different perforations, types or minor shades. Where a choice is ssible the set prices are based on the cheapest ersions of the stamps included in the listings.

BRASILIANA 79

(**151**)

152 "St. Nicholas", Prikra, Ukraine

1979 (10 Sept). *"Brasiliana 79" International Stamp Exhibition, Rio de Janeiro. No.* **MS**551 *optd with T* **151**.

MS565 170 × 113 mm. $2 Turks Islands 1867 and Turks and Caicos Islands 1900 1d. stamps .. 55 1·25

Stamps from Nos. **MS**551 and **MS**565 are identical as the overprint on **MS**565 appears on the margin of the sheet.

(Des M. Diamond. Litho Questa)

1979 (19 Oct). *Christmas. Art. T* **152** *and similar vert designs. Multicoloured. P* 13½ × 14.

566 1 c. Type **152** 10 10
567 3 c. "Emperor Otto II with Symbols of Empire" (Master of the Registrum Gregorii) .. 10 10
568 6 c. "Portrait of St. John" (Book of Lindisfarne) 10 10
569 15 c. "Adoration of the Majestas Domini" (Prayer Book of Otto II) 10 10
570 20 c. "Christ attended by Angels" (Book of Kells) 15 15
571 25 c. "St. John the Evangelist" (Gospels of St. Medard of Soissons), Charlemagne .. 20 15
572 65 c. "Christ Pantocrator", Trocany, Ukraine 30 25
573 $1 "Portrait of St. John" (Canterbury Codex Aureus) 45 45
566/73 .. .. *Set of* 8 1·10 1·10
MS574 106 × 133 mm. $2 "Portrait of St. Matthew" (Book of Lindisfarne) .. .. 70 1·50

153 Pluto and Starfish

(Litho Format)

1979 (2 Nov). *International Year of the Child. Walt Disney Cartoon Characters. T* **153** *and similar vert designs showing characters at the seaside. Multicoloured. P* 11.

575 ¼ c. Type **153** 10 10
576 ½ c. Minnie Mouse in summer outfit 10 10
577 1 c. Mickey Mouse underwater 10 10
578 2 c. Goofy and turtle 10 10
579 3 c. Donald Duck and dolphin 10 10
580 4 c. Mickey Mouse fishing 10 10
581 5 c. Goofy surfing 10 10
582 25 c. Pluto and crab 45 20
583 $1 Daisy water-skiing .. .. .. 2·00 1·10
575/83 .. .. *Set of* 9 2·50 1·25
MS584 126 × 96 mm. $1.50, Goofy after water-skiing accident. P 13½ .. .. 1·25 1·40
a. Error. Imperf £180

154 "Christina's World" (painting by Andrew Wyeth)

(Des J.W. Litho Format)

1979 (19 Dec). *Works of Art. T* **154** *and similar multicoloured designs. P* 13½.

585 6 c. Type **154** 10 10
586 10 c. Ivory Leopards, Benin (19th-cent) .. 10 10
587 20 c. "The Kiss" (painting by Gustav Klimt) (*vert*) 15 15
588 25 c. "Portrait of a Lady" (painting by R. van der Weyden) (*vert*) 15 15
589 80 c. Bull's head harp, Sumer, *c.* 2600 B.C. (*vert*) 30 30
590 $1 "The Wave" (painting by Hokusai) .. 45 45
585/90 .. .. *Set of* 6 95 95
MS591 110 × 140 mm. $2 "Holy Family" (painting by Rembrandt) (*vert*) .. .. 70 1·25

155 Pied-billed Grebe

156 Stamp, Magnifying Glass and Perforation Gauge

(Des G. Drummond. Litho Questa)

1980 (20 Feb). *Birds. T* **155** *and similar horiz designs. Multicoloured. P* 14.

592 20 c. Type **155** 55 15
593 25 c. Ovenbirds at nest 60 20
594 35 c. Hen Harrier 80 30
595 55 c. Yellow-bellied Sapsucker .. .. 1·00 35
596 $1 Blue-winged Teal .. .. 1·40 80
592/6 .. .. *Set of* 5 4·00 1·60
MS597 107 × 81 mm. $2 Glossy Ibis .. .. 2·75 2·50

(Des BG Studio. Litho Questa)

1980 (6 May). *"London 1980" International Stamp Exhibition. T* **156** *and similar horiz designs. P* 14.

598 25 c. black and chrome-yellow 15 15
599 40 c. black and bright green 25 25
MS600 76 × 97 mm. $2 vermilion, black and blue 70 1·10

Designs:—40 c. Stamp, tweezers and perforation gauge; $2, Earls Court Exhibition Centre.

157 Trumpet Triton

158 Queen Elizabeth the Queen Mother

(Des G. Drummond. Litho Questa)

1980 (26 June). *Shells. T* **157** *and similar horiz designs. Multicoloured. P* 14.

601 15 c. Type **157** 20 20
602 20 c. Measled Cowry 25 25
603 30 c. True Tulip 35 35
604 45 c. Lion's Paw 45 45
605 55 c. Sunrise Tellin 55 55
606 70 c. Crown Cone 70 70
601/6 .. .. *Set of* 6 2·25 2·25

(Des G. Vasarhelyi. Litho Questa)

1980 (4 Aug). *80th Birthday of Queen Elizabeth the Queen Mother. P* 14.

607 **158** 80 c. multicoloured .. .. .. 1·60 1·25
MS608 57 × 80 mm. **158** $1.50, multicoloured. P 12. 2·25 2·50

159 Doctor examining Child and Lions International Emblem

(Des Design Images. Litho Questa)

1980 (29 Aug). *"Serving the Community". T* **159** *and similar horiz designs. Multicoloured. P* 14.

609 10 c. Type **159** 10 10
610 15 c. Students receiving scholarships and Kiwanis International emblem 15 10
611 45 c. Teacher with students and Soroptimist emblem 35 35
612 $1 Lobster trawler and Rotary International emblem 80 80
609/12 .. .. *Set of* 4 1·25 1·25
MS613 101 × 74 mm. $2 School receiving funds and Rotary International emblem .. .. 1·50 2·00

No. **MS**613 also commemorates the 75th anniversary of Rotary International.

(Litho Walsall)

1980 (30 Sept). *Christmas. Scenes from Walt Disney's Cartoon Film "Pinocchio". Horiz designs as T* **153**. *Multicoloured. P* 11.

614 ¼ c. Scene from *Pinocchio* 10 10
615 ½ c. As puppet 10 10
616 1 c. Pinocchio changed into a boy 10 10
617 2 c. Captured by fox 10 10
618 3 c. Pinocchio and puppeteer 10 10
619 4 c. Pinocchio and bird's nest nose 10 10
620 5 c. Pinocchio eating 10 10
621 75 c. Pinocchio with ass ears 60 60
622 $1 Pinocchio underwater 80 80
614/22 .. .. *Set of* 9 1·50 1·50
MS623 127 × 102 mm. $2 Pinocchio dancing (*vert*) 1·75 2·00

160 Martin Luther King Jr

(Des Design Images. Litho Questa)

1980 (22 Dec). *Human Rights. Personalities. T* **160** *and similar horiz designs. Multicoloured. P* 14 × 13½.
624 20 c. Type **160** 15 10
625 30 c. John F. Kennedy 30 25
626 45 c. Roberto Clemente (baseball player) .. 45 35
627 70 c. Sir Frank Worrel (cricketer) 90 65
628 $1 Harriet Tubman.. .. .. 1·10 80
624/8 .. .. *Set of* 5 2·50 1·90
MS629 103 × 80 mm. $2 Marcus Garvey .. 1·10 1·25

161 Yachts **162** Night Queen Cactus

(Litho Questa)

1981 (29 Jan). *South Caicos Regatta. T* **161** *and similar horiz designs. Multicoloured. P* 14.
630 6 c. Type **161** 10 10
631 15 c. Trophy and yachts 15 15
632 35 c. Spectators watching speedboat race .. 25 20
633 $1 Caicos sloops 60 50
630/3 .. .. *Set of* 4 90 80
MS634 113 × 85 mm. $2 Queen Elizabeth II and map of South Caicos (*vert*) .. .. .. 1·10 1·75

(Des J. Cooter. Litho Questa)

1981 (10 Feb). *Flowering Cacti. T* **162** *and similar vert designs. Multicoloured. P* 13½ × 14.
635 25 c. Type **162** 25 25
636 35 c. Ripsaw Cactus 35 35
637 55 c. Royal Strawberry Cactus 40 50
638 80 c. Caicos Cactus 60 75
635/8 .. .. *Set of* 4 1·40 1·75
MS639 72 × 86 mm. $2 Turks Head Cactus. P 14½ 1·25 2·00

(Litho Format)

1981 (16 Feb). *50th Anniv of Walt Disney's Cartoon Character, Pluto. Vert designs as T* **153**. *Multicoloured. P* 13½.
640 10 c. Pluto playing on beach with shell .. 10 10
641 75 c. Pluto on raft, and porpoise 75 75
MS642 127 × 101 mm. $1.50 Pluto in scene from film *Simple Things* .. .. 1·60 1·75

(Litho Format)

1981 (20 Mar). *Easter. Walt Disney Cartoon Characters. Vert designs as T* **153**. *Multicoloured. P* 11.
643 10 c. Donald Duck and Louie 20 20
644 25 c. Goofy and Donald Duck 40 40
645 60 c. Chip and Dale 85 85
646 80 c. Scrooge McDuck and Huey .. .. 1·25 1·25
643/6 .. .. *Set of* 4 2·40 2·40
MS647 126 × 101 mm. $4 Chip (or Dale). P 13½ 4·00 3·00

163 "Woman with Fan" **164** Kensington Palace

(Des J.W. Litho Questa)

1981 (28 May). *Birth Centenary of Picasso. T* **163** *and similar vert designs. Multicoloured. P* 13½ × 14.
648 20 c. Type **163** 20 15
649 45 c. "Woman with Pears" 35 30
650 80 c. "The Accordionist" 60 50
651 $1 "The Aficionado" 80 80
648/51 .. .. *Set of* 4 1·75 1·60
MS652 102 × 127 mm. $2 "Girl with a Mandolin" 1·10 1·25

(Des J.W. Litho Questa)

1981 (23 June). *Royal Wedding. T* **164** *and similar vert designs. Multicoloured. P* 14.
653 35 c. Prince Charles and Lady Diana Spencer 20 15
654 65 c. Type **164** 35 30
655 90 c. Prince Charles as Colonel of the Welsh Guards 45 45
653/5 .. .. *Set of* 3 90 80
MS656 96 × 82 mm. $2 Glass Coach .. .. 90 1·00
Nos. 653/5 also exist perforated 12 (*price for set of* 3 £1 *mint or used*) from additional sheetlets of five stamps and one label. These stamps have changed background colours.

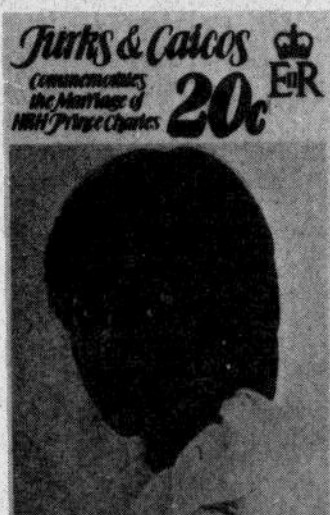

165 Lady Diana Spencer **166** Marine Biology Observation

(Manufactured by Walsall)

1981 (7 July). *Royal Wedding. Booklet stamps. T* **165** *and similar vert designs. Multicoloured. Roul* 5 × *imperf**. *Self-adhesive.*
657 20 c. Type **165** 25 30
a. Booklet pane. Nos. 657/8, each × 3 .. 3·00
658 $1 Prince Charles .. .. 75 1·00
659 $2 Prince Charles and Lady Diana Spencer 2·00 2·50
a. Booklet pane of 1 .. .. 2·00
657/9 .. .. *Set of* 3 2·75 3·50
*The 20 c. and $1 values were each separated by various combinations of rotary knife (giving a straight edge) and roulette. The $2 value exists only with straight edges.

(Des G. Drummond. Litho Questa)

1981 (21 Aug). *Diving. T* **166** *and similar horiz designs. Multicoloured. P* 14.
660 15 c. Type **166** 20 15
661 40 c. Underwater photography 50 35
662 75 c. Wreck diving 90 70
663 $1 Diving with dolphins .. .. .. 1·25 1·00
660/3 .. .. *Set of* 4 2·50 2·00
MS664 91 × 75 mm. $2 Diving flag .. .. 1·75 2·25

(Litho Questa)

1981 (2 Nov). *Christmas. Horiz designs as T* **153** *showing scenes from Walt Disney's cartoon film "Uncle Remus". P* 13½.
665 ¼ c. multicoloured 10 10
666 ½ c. multicoloured 10 10
667 1 c. multicoloured 10 10
668 2 c. multicoloured 10 10
669 3 c. multicoloured 10 10
670 4 c. multicoloured 10 10
671 5 c. multicoloured 10 10
672 75 c. multicoloured 60 60
673 $1 multicoloured 80 80
665/73 .. .. *Set of* 9 1·40 1·40
MS674 128 × 103 mm. $2 multicoloured .. .. 1·75 1·90

167 Map of Grand Turk, and Lighthouse **168** Caribbean Buckeye

(Des J.W. Litho Questa)

1981 (1 Dec). *Tourism. T* **167** *and similar horiz designs. Multicoloured. P* 14.
675 20 c. Type **167** 35 35
a. Vert strip of 10. Nos. 675/84 .. 1·25
676 20 c. Map of Salt Cay, and "industrial archaeology" 35 35
677 20 c. Map of South Caicos, and "island flying" 35 35
678 20 c. Map of East Caicos, and "beach combing" 35 35
679 20 c. Map of Grand Caicos (middle), and cave exploring 35 35
680 20 c. Map of North Caicos, and camping and hiking 35 35
681 20 c. Map of North Caicos, Parrot Cay, Dellis Cay, Fort George Cay, Pine Cay and Water Cay, and "environmental studies" 35 35
682 20 c. Map of Providenciales, and scuba diving 35 35
683 20 c. Map of West Caicos, and "cruising and bird sanctuary" 35 35
684 20 c. Turks and Caicos Islands flag 35 35
675/84 .. .. *Set of* 10 3·25 3·25
Nos. 675/84 were printed together, *se-tenant*, in vertical strips of 10 throughout the sheet of 40, the two panes (2 × 10), separated by a gutter margin, being *tête-bêche*.

(Des J. Cooter. Litho Questa)

1982 (21 Jan). *Butterflies. T* **168** *and similar vert designs. Multicoloured. P* 14.
685 20 c. Type **168** 30 30
686 35 c. Clench's Hairstreak 50 50
687 65 c. Gulf Fritillary 90 90
688 $1 Bush Sulphur .. .. 1·40 1·40
685/8 .. .. *Set of* 4 2·75 2·75
MS689 72 × 56 mm. $2 Turk Island Leaf Butterfly 2·75 3·50

OMNIBUS ISSUES

Details, together with prices for complete sets, of the various Omnibus issues from the 1935 Silver Jubilee series to date are included in a special section following Zululand at the end of the catalogue.

169 Flag Salute on Queen's Birthday **170** Footballer

(Litho Questa)

1982 (17 Feb). *75th Anniv of Boy Scout Movement. T* **169** *a[nd] similar vert designs. Multicoloured. P* 14.
690 40 c. Type **169** 50
691 50 c. Raft building 60
692 75 c. Sea scout cricket match .. .. .. 1·10 1
693 $1 Nature study .. .. 1·50 1
690/3 .. .. *Set of* 4 3·25 3
MS694 100 × 70 mm. $2 Lord Baden-Powell and scout salute .. .. 2·50 2

(Des G. Vasarhelyi. Litho Questa)

1982 (30 Apr). *World Cup Football Championship, Spain. T* [1]
and similar designs showing footballers. P 14.
695 10 c. multicoloured 15
696 25 c. multicoloured 20
697 45 c. multicoloured 25
698 $1 multicoloured 80
695/8 .. .. *Set of* 4 1·25 1
MS699 117 × 83 mm. $2 multicoloured (*horiz*) .. 1·25 2

171 Washington crossing the Delaware and Phillis Wheatley (poetess) **172** "Second Thoughts"

(Des Design Images. Litho Questa)

1982 (3 May). *250th Birth Anniv of George Washington* (20, 35 [c.]) *and Birth Centenary of Franklin D. Roosevelt* (65, 80 *c.*). *T* 1[71] *and similar horiz designs. Multicoloured. P* 14.
700 20 c. Type **171** 30
701 35 c. George Washington and Benjamin Banneker (surveyor) 45
702 65 c. Franklin D. Roosevelt meeting George Washington Carver (agricultural researcher) 80
703 80 c. Roosevelt as stamp collector .. .. 1·00 1·
700/3 .. .. *Set of* 4 2·25 2
MS704 100 × 70 mm. $2 Roosevelt with stamp showing profile of Washington .. .. .. 2·00 2

(Litho Questa)

1982 (23 June). *Norman Rockwell (painter) Commemoratio[n]. T* **172** *and similar vert designs. Multicoloured. P* 14 × 13½.
705 8 c. Type **172** 15
706 15 c. "The Proper Gratuity" 20
707 20 c. "Before the Shot" 25
708 25 c. "The Three Umpires" 25
705/8 .. .. *Set of* 4 75

173 Princess of Wales **174** "Skymaster" over Caicos Cays

(Des PAD Studio. Litho Questa)

1982 (1 July–18 Nov). *21st Birthday of Princess of Wales. T* [173] *and similar vert designs. Multicoloured. P* 14½ × 14.

(*a*) *Sheet stamps. Pale green frames*
709 55 c. Sandringham 70
710 70 c. Prince and Princess of Wales 85
711 $1 Type **173** .. .. 1·25 1·
709/11 .. .. *Set of* 3 2·50 2
MS712 102 × 76 mm. $2 Princess Diana (*different*) 2·00 2·

(*b*) *Booklet stamps. As Nos.* 709/11 *but printed with new values a[nd] blue frame* (18.11.82)
713 8 c. Sandringham 35
714 35 c. Prince and Princess of Wales 70 1
715 $1.10, Type **173** .. .. 1·75 1
713/15 .. .. *Set of* 3 2·50 3
Nos. 713/15 also exist from sheets printed in horizontal *tête-bê[che]* pairs throughout.

(Des MBI Studios. Litho Questa)

2 (23 Aug). *Aircraft. T* **174** *and similar horiz designs. Multi-ɔloured. P* 14.
8 c. Type **174** 15 15
15 c. "Jetstar" over Grand Turk 20 25
65 c. Helicopter over South Caicos 65 80
$1.10, Seaplane over Providenciales .. 1·10 1·25
/19 .. .. *Set of* 4 1·90 2·25
720 99 × 69 mm. $2 Boeing "727" over Turks nd Caicos Islands.. .. .. 2·00 2·50

(Litho Questa)

2 (1 Dec). *Christmas. Scenes from Walt Disney's Cartoon Film Mickey's Christmas Carol". Horiz designs as T* **153**. *Multi-ɔloured. P* 13½.
1 c. Donald Duck, Mickey Mouse and Scrooge 10 10
1 c. Goofy (Marley's ghost) and Scrooge .. 10 10
2 c. Jiminy Cricket and Scrooge 10 10
2 c. Huey, Dewey and Louie 10 10
3 c. Daisy Duck and youthful Scrooge .. 10 10
3 c. Giant and Scrooge 10 10
4 c. Two bad wolves, a wise pig and a reformed Scrooge 10 10
65 c. Donald Duck and Scrooge .. .. 1·00 65
$1.10, Mortie and Scrooge .. .. .. 1·60 1·10
/9 .. .. *Set of* 9 2·50 1·75
730 126 × 101 mm. $2 Mickey and Minnie louse with Mortie .. .. 2·75 2·00

175 West Caicos Trolley Tram

(Des N. Waldman. Litho Questa)

3 (18 Jan). *Trams and Locomotives. T* **175** *and similar horiz esigns. Multicoloured. P* 14
15 c. Type **175** 20 25
55 c. West Caicos steam locomotive 65 70
90 c. East Caicos sisal locomotive .. .. 90 1·00
$1.60, East Caicos steam locomotive .. 1·75 1·90
/4 .. .. *Set of* 4 3·25 3·50
735 99 × 69 mm. $2.50, Steam engine pulling ars of sisal .. .. 2·25 2·25

'6 Policewoman on Traffic Duty

177 "St. John and the Virgin Mary" (detail)

(Des N. Waldman. Litho Questa)

3 (14 Mar). *Commonwealth Day. T* **176** *and similar horiz esigns. Multicoloured. P* 14
1 c. Type **176** 15 20
a. Vert strip of 4. Nos. 736/9 .. .. 2·40
8 c. Stylised sun and weather vane 15 20
65 c. Yacht 85 90
$1 Cricket .. .. 1·50 1·60
9 .. .. *Set of* 4 2·40 2·50
ɔs. 736/9 were printed together, *se-tenant*, in vertical strips of throughout the sheet.

(Des Design Images. Litho Questa)

3 (7 Apr). *Easter. T* **177** *and similar vert designs showing etails from the "Mond Crucifixion" by Raphael. Multicoloured.* 13½ × 14.
35 c. Type **177** 20 25
50 c. "Two Women" 30 35
95 c. "Angel with two jars" 50 60
$1.10, "Angel with one jar" 60 80
3 .. .. *Set of* 4 1·40 2·00
744 100 × 130 mm. $2.50, "Christ on the Cross" 1·60 2·00

178 Minke Whale

179 First Hydrogen Balloon, 1783

(Des D. Hamilton. Litho Questa)

1983 (16 May–11 July). *Whales. T* **178** *and similar horiz designs. Multicoloured. P* 13½.
745 50 c. Type **178** 75 75
746 65 c. Black Right Whale (11.7.83) .. .. 1·00 1·00
747 70 c. Killer Whale (13.6.83) .. .. 1·25 1·25
748 95 c. Sperm Whale (13.6.83) .. .. 1·40 1·40
749 $1.10, Cuvier's Beaked Whale (11.7.83) .. 1·60 1·60
750 $2 Blue Whale (13.6.83) .. .. 3·00 3·00
751 $2.20, Humpback Whale .. .. 3·25 3·25
752 $3 Long-finned Pilot Whale .. .. 4·25 4·25
745/52 .. .. *Set of* 8 15·00 15·00
MS753 112 × 82 mm. $3 Fin Whale (11.7.83) .. 4·50 5·00
Nos. 745/52 were each issued in sheetlets of four.

(Des BG Studio. Litho Questa)

1983 (30 Aug). *Bicentenary of Manned Flight. T* **179** *and similar vert designs. Multicoloured. P* 14.
754 25 c. Type **179** 25 25
755 35 c. *Friendship 7* 35 35
756 70 c. First hot air balloon, 1783 .. .. 70 70
757 95 c. Space shuttle *Columbia* 90 90
754/7 .. .. *Set of* 4 2·00 2·00
MS758 112 × 76 mm. $2 Montgolfier balloon and Space shuttle .. .. 1·50 2·00

180 Fiddler Pig

181 Bermuda Sloop

(Litho Format)

1983 (4 Oct). *Christmas. Walt Disney Cartoon Characters. T* **180** *and similar vert designs. Multicoloured. P* 11.
759 1 c. Type **180** 10 10
760 1 c. Fifer Pig 10 10
761 2 c. Practical Pig 10 10
762 2 c. Pluto 10 10
763 3 c. Goofy 10 10
764 3 c. Mickey Mouse 10 10
765 35 c. Gyro Gearloose 35 35
766 50 c. Ludwig von Drake 50 50
767 $1.10, Huey, Dewey and Louie .. .. 1·00 1·00
759/67 .. .. *Set of* 9 1·75 1·75
MS768 127 × 102 mm. $2.50, Mickey and Minnie Mouse with Huey, Dewey and Louie. P 13½ .. 3·25 3·00

(Des G. Drummond. Litho Questa)

1983 (5 Oct)–**85**. *Ships. T* **181** *and similar horiz designs. Multicoloured.* A. *P* 14. B. *P* 12½ × 12.

No.	Description	A	A	B	B
769	4 c. Arawak dug-out canoe ..	15	15	10	10
770	5 c. *Santa Maria*	20	15	10	10
771	8 c. British and Spanish ships in battle	80	15	10	10
772	10 c. Type **181**	80	20	10	10
773	20 c. U.S. privateer *Grand Turk*	40	30	20	25
774	25 c. H.M.S. *Boreas*	1·50	35	25	30
775	30 c. H.M.S. *Endymion* attacking French ship, 1790s ..	1·50	50	30	35
776	35 c. *Caesar* (barque)	80	50	35	40
777	50 c. *Grapeshot* (schooner) ..	1·75	65	50	55
778	65 c. H.M.S. *Invincible* (battle cruiser)	3·00	1·50	70	75
779	95 c. H.M.S. *Magicienne* ..	3·00	1·40	1·00	1·10
780	$1.10, H.M.S. *Durban* ..	3·75	2·40	1·10	1·25
781	$2 *Sentinel* (cable ship) ..	4·50	2·75	2·10	2·25
782	$3 H.M.S. *Minerva*	6·00	4·00	3·00	3·25
783	$5 Caicos sloop	7·50	8·00	5·25	5·50
769/83	.. .. .. *Set of* 15	30·00	20·00	13·50	14·50

Dates of issue:—5.10.83, Nos. 772A, 775A, 778A, 780A/2A; 16.12.83, Nos. 771A, 774A, 777A, 779A; 9.1.84, Nos. 769A/70A, 773A, 776A, 783A; 3.85, Nos. 769B, 771B/2B, 775B, 778B, 780B, 783B; 12.8.85, Nos. 770B, 773B/4B, 776B/7B, 779B, 781B; 12.85, No. 782B.

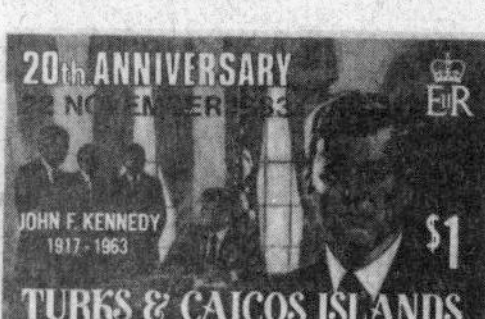

182 President Kennedy and Signing of Civil Rights Legislation

(Des Design Images. Litho Questa)

1983 (22 Dec). *20th Death Anniv of President J. F. Kennedy. P* 14.
784 **182** 20 c. multicoloured 20 15
785 $1 multicoloured .. .. 1·10 1·25

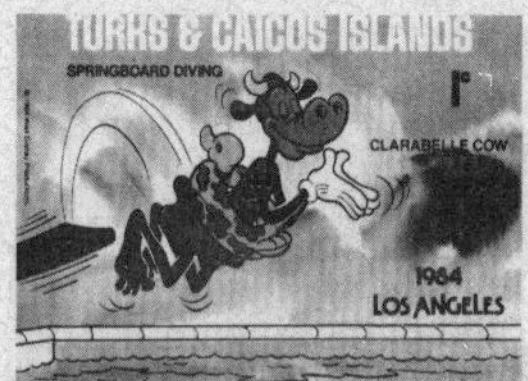

183 Clarabelle Cow Diving

(Litho Questa)

1984 (21 Feb–Apr). *Olympic Games, Los Angeles. T* **183** *and similar horiz designs showing Disney cartoon characters in Olympic events. Multicoloured.* A. *Inscr* "1984 LOS ANGELES". *P* 14 × 13½. B. *Inscr* "1984 OLYMPICS LOS ANGELES" *and Olympic emblem. P* 14 × 13½ (**MS** 795B) *or* 12 (*others*) (4.84).

No.	Description	A	A	B	B
786	1 c. Type **183**	10	10	10	10
787	1 c. Donald Duck in 500m kayak race	10	10	10	10
788	2 c. Huey, Dewey and Louie in 1000m kayak race..	10	10	10	10
789	2 c. Mickey Mouse in single kayak	10	10	10	10
790	3 c. Donald Duck highboard diving	10	10	10	10
791	3 c. Minnie Mouse in kayak slalom	10	10	10	10
792	25 c. Mickey Mouse freestyle swimming	40	45	40	45
793	75 c. Donald Duck playing water-polo	1·25	1·40	1·25	1·40
794	$1 Uncle Scrooge and Donald Duck yachting	1·60	1·75	1·60	1·75
786/94	.. .. .. *Set of* 9	3·25	3·50	3·25	3·50
MS795	117 × 90 mm. $2 Pluto platform diving	2·75	3·00	2·75	3·00

184 "Cadillac V–16", 1933

185 "Rest during the Flight to Egypt, with St. Francis"

(Des N. Waldman. Litho Questa)

1984 (15 Mar). *Classic Cars and 125th Anniv of first Commercial Oil Well. T* **184** *and similar horiz designs. Multicoloured. P* 14.
796 4 c. Type **184** 10 10
797 8 c. Rolls-Royce "Phantom III", 1937 .. 15 15
798 10 c. Saab "99", 1969 .. .. 15 15
799 25 c. Maserati "Bora", 1973 .. .. .. 40 40
800 40 c. Datsun "260Z", 1970 .. .. .. 65 65
801 55 c. Porsche "917", 1971 .. .. .. 80 80
802 80 c. Lincoln "Continental", 1939 .. .. 90 90
803 $1 Triumph "TR3A", 1957 .. .. .. 1·25 1·25
796/803 .. .. *Set of* 8 4·00 4·00
MS804 70 × 100 mm. $2 Daimler, 1886 .. .. 2·00 2·50

(Des S. Karp. Litho Walsall)

1984 (9 Apr). *Easter. 450th Death Anniv of Correggio (painter). T* **185** *and similar vert designs. Multicoloured. P* 14.
805 15 c. Type **185** 20 15
806 40 c. "St. Luke and St. Ambrose" 45 40
807 60 c. "Diana and her Chariot".. .. .. 65 65
808 95 c. "The Deposition of Christ" 80 80
805/8 .. .. *Set of* 4 1·90 1·75
MS809 100 × 79 mm. $2 "The Nativity with Saints Elizabeth and John the younger" (*horiz*) .. .. 1·50 2·25

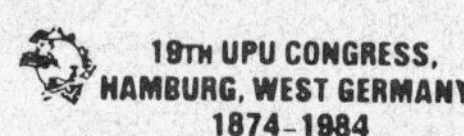

(**186**)

1984 (19 June). *Universal Postal Union Congress, Hamburg. Nos. 748/9 and* **MS**753 *optd with T* **186**.
810 95 c. Sperm Whale .. .. 1·60 1·50
811 $1.10, Cuvier's Beaked Whale .. .. 1·75 1·60
MS812 112 × 82 mm. $3 Fin Whale .. .. 4·00 4·25

187 "The Adventure of the Second Stain"

188 Clown-Fish

(Des S. Karp. Litho Walsall)

1984 (16 July). *125th Birth Anniv of Sir Arthur Conan Doyle (author). T* **187** *and similar horiz designs showing scenes from Sherlock Holmes stores. Multicoloured. P* 14.

813 25 c. Type **187** 90 70
814 45 c. "The Adventure of the Final Problem" .. 1·50 1·25
815 70 c. "The Adventure of the Empty House" .. 2·00 1·75
816 85 c. "The Adventure of the Greek Interpreter" 2·25 2·00
813/16 .. *Set of* 4 6·00 5·25
MS817 100 × 70 mm. $2 Sir Arthur Conan Doyle 4·75 3·75

(Des Susan David. Litho Walsall)

1984 (22 Aug). *"Ausipex" International Stamp Exhibition, Melbourne. 175th Birth Anniv of Charles Darwin. T* **188** *and similar vert designs. Multicoloured. P* 14 × 13½.

818 5 c. Type **188** 25 15
819 35 c. Monitor Lizard .. .. 1·25 1·25
820 50 c. Rainbow Lory .. .. 1·75 1·75
821 $1.10, Koalas .. .. 2·50 2·50
818/21 .. *Set of* 4 5·25 5·00
MS822 100×70 mm. $2 Eastern Grey Kangaroo .. .. 3·50 4·25

189 Donald Duck cutting down Christmas Tree

(Litho Questa)

1984 (8 Oct–26 Nov). *Christmas. Walt Disney Cartoon Characters. T* **189** *and similar horiz designs showing scenes from "Toy Tinkers". Multicoloured. P* 12 (75 *c.*) *or* 14 × 13½ (*others*).

823 20 c. Type **189** 65 45
824 35 c. Donald Duck and Chip n'Dale playing with train set 85 65
825 50 c. Donald Duck and Chip n'Dale playing with catapult .. .. 1·25 85
826 75 c. Donald Duck, Chip n'Dale and Christmas tree (26.11) .. .. 1·75 1·40
827 $1.10, Donald Duck, toy soldier and Chip n'Dale .. .. 2·25 1·90
823/7 .. *Set of* 5 6·00 4·75
MS828 126 × 102 mm. $2 Donald Duck as Father Christmas .. .. 3·00 3·25

No. 826 was printed in sheetlets of 8 stamps.

190 Magnolia Warbler

191 Leonardo da Vinci and Illustration of Glider Wing (15th century)

(Des Susan David. Litho Walsall)

1985 (28 Jan). *Birth Bicentenary of John J. Audubon (ornithologist). T* **190** *and similar vert designs. Multicoloured. P* 14.

829 25 c. Type **190** .. .. 1·00 45
830 45 c. Short-eared Owl .. .. 1·75 80
831 70 c. Mourning Dove and eggs .. .. 1·90 1·50
832 85 c. Caribbean Martin .. .. 2·00 1·75
829/32 .. *Set of* 4 6·00 4·00
MS833 100×70 mm. $2 Oystercatcher and chicks .. .. 3·75 4·00

(Des K. Gromol. Litho Walsall)

1985 (22 Feb). *40th Anniv of International Civil Aviation Organization. Aviation Pioneers. T* **191** *and similar horiz designs. Multicoloured. P* 14.

834 8 c. Type **191** 20 15
835 25 c. Sir Alliott Verdon Roe and "C.102" jetliner (1949) 50 40
836 65 c. Robert H. Goddard and first liquid fuel rocket (1926) .. .. 1·25 95
837 $1 Igor Sikorsky and Sikorsky "VS300" helicopter (1939) .. .. 1·75 1·50
834/7 .. *Set of* 4 3·25 2·75
MS838 100×70 mm. $2 Amelia Earhart's Lockheed "10E Electra" (1937) .. .. 2·75 3·00

192 Benjamin Franklin and Marquis de Lafayette

(Des Susan David. Litho Walsall)

1985 (28 Mar). *Centenary of the Statue of Liberty's Arrival in New York. T* **192** *and similar horiz designs. Multicoloured. P* 14.

839 20 c. Type **192** 60 50
840 30 c. Frederic Bartholdi (designer) and Gustave Eiffel (engineer) 70 60
841 65 c. Sailing ship *Isere* arriving in New York with statue, 1885 .. .. 1·75 1·50
842 $1.10, United States fund raisers Louis Agassiz, Charles Sumner, H. W. Longfellow and Joseph Pulitzer .. .. 2·00 1·75
839/42 .. *Set of* 4 4·50 4·00
MS843 99×69 mm. $2 Dedication ceremony, 1886 .. .. 3·00 3·50

193 Sir Edward Hawke and H.M.S. *Royal George*

(Des Susan David. Litho Walsall)

1985 (17 Apr). *Salute to the Royal Navy. T* **193** *and similar multicoloured designs. P* 14.

844 20 c. Type **193** 85 85
845 30 c. Lord Nelson and H.M.S. *Victory* .. 1·25 1·25
846 65 c. Admiral Sir George Cockburn and H.M.S. *Albion* .. .. 1·75 1·75
847 95 c. Admiral Sir David Beatty and H.M.S. *Indefatigable* .. .. 2·25 2·25
844/7 .. *Set of* 4 5·50 5·50
MS848 99×69 mm. $2 18th-century sailor and cannon (*vert*) .. .. 3·00 3·50

194 Mark Twain riding on Halley's Comet

195 The Queen Mother outside Clarence House

(Des J. Iskowitz. Litho Walsall)

1985 (17 May). *International Youth Year. Birth Annivs of Mark Twain (150th) and Jakob Grimm (Bicentenary). T* **194** *and similar multicoloured designs. P* 13½ × 14 (25, 35 *c.*, $2) *or* 14 × 13½ (50, 95 *c.*).

849 25 c. Type **194** 60 40
850 35 c. *Grand Turk* (Mississippi river steamer) 80 55
851 50 c. Hansel and Gretel and gingerbread house (*vert*) .. .. 1·00 75
852 95 c. Rumpelstiltskin (*vert*) .. .. 1·75 1·50
849/52 .. *Set of* 4 3·75 3·00
MS853 99×68 mm. $2 Mark Twain and the Brothers Grimm .. .. 2·75 3·00

(Des J.W. Litho Questa)

1985 (15 July). *Life and Times of Queen Elizabeth the Queen Mother. T* **195** *and similar multicoloured designs. P* 14.

854 30 c. Type **195** 45 45
855 50 c. Visiting Biggin Hill airfield (*horiz*) .. 75 75
856 $1.10, 80th birthday portrait .. .. 1·90 1·90
854/6 .. *Set of* 3 2·75 2·75
MS857 56×85 mm. $2 With Prince Charles at Garter ceremony, Windsor Castle, 1968 .. 2·75 3·00

196 King George II and Score of "Zadok the Priest" (1727)

197 Harley-Davidson Dual Cylinder (1915) on Middle Caicos

(Des Susan David. Litho Format)

1985 (17 July). *300th Birth Anniv of George Frederick Handel (composer). T* **196** *and similar vert designs. P* 15.

858 4 c. multicoloured 35 20
859 10 c. multicoloured 55 25
860 50 c. multicoloured .. .. 1·50 1·00
861 $1.10, multicoloured .. .. 2·50 2·50
858/61 .. *Set of* 4 4·50 3·50
MS862 101×76 mm. $2 black, deep dull purple and dull violet-blue .. .. 4·00 4·00

Designs:—10 c. Queen Caroline and score of "Funeral Anthem" (1737); 50 c. King George I and score of "Water Music" (1714); Queen Anne and score of "Or la Tromba" from *Rinaldo* (1711); $2 George Frederick Handel.

(Des Susan David. Litho Format)

1985 (17 July). *300th Birth Anniv of Johann Sebastian Ba (composer). Vert designs as T* **206** *of Antigua. Multicolour P* 15.

863 15 c. Bassoon 45
864 40 c. Natural Horn .. .. 1·00
865 60 c. Viola D'Amore .. .. 1·40
866 95 c. Clavichord .. .. 2·00 1
863/6 .. *Set of* 4 4·25 3
MS867 102×76 mm. $2 Johann Sebastian Bach .. .. 3·50 3

(Des Mary Walters. Litho Questa)

1985 (4 Sept). *Centenary of the Motor Cycle. T* **197** *and sim multicoloured designs. P* 14.

868 8 c. Type **197** 15
869 25 c. Triumph "Thunderbird" (1950) on Grand Turk 35
870 55 c. BMW "K100RS" (1985) on North Caicos 80
871 $1.20, Honda "1100 Shadow" (1985) on South Caicos .. .. 1·75 2
868/71 .. *Set of* 4 2·75 3
MS872 106×77 mm. $2 Daimler single track (1885) (*vert*) .. .. 2·75 3

198 Pirates in Prison

(Des Walt Disney Productions. Litho Questa)

1985 (4 Oct). *30th Anniv of Disneyland, U.S.A. T* **198** *c similar horiz designs showing scenes from "Pirates of Caribbean" exhibition. Multicoloured. P* 14 × 13½.

873 1 c. Type **198** 10
874 1 c. The fate of Captain William Kidd .. 10
875 2 c. Bartholomew Roberts 10
876 2 c. Two buccaneers 10
877 3 c. Privateers looting 10
878 3 c. Auction of captives 10
879 35 c. Singing pirates 80
880 75 c. Edward Teach—"Blackbeard" .. 1·60 1
881 $1.10, Sir Henry Morgan .. .. 1·90 1
873/81 .. *Set of* 9 4·00 3
MS882 123 × 86 mm. $2.50, Mary Read and Anne Bonney .. .. 3·50 3

199 Brownies from China, Turks and Caicos and Papua New Guinea

(Des Mary Walters. Litho Questa)

1985 (4 Nov). *75th Anniv of Girl Guide Movement and 3 Anniv of Grand Turk Company. T* **199** *and similar h designs. Multicoloured. P* 14.

883 10 c. Type **199** 45
884 40 c. Brownies from Surinam, Turks and Caicos and Korea .. .. 1·25
885 70 c. Guides from Australia, Turks and Caicos and Canada .. .. 1·75 1
886 80 c. Guides from West Germany, Turks and Caicos and Israel .. .. 1·90 1
883/6 .. *Set of* 4 4·75
MS887 107×76 mm. $2 75th anniversary emblem .. .. 3·00 3

200 Iguana and Log

201 Duke and Duchess of York after Wedding

(Des I. MacLaury. Litho Questa)

1986 (20 Nov). *Turks and Caicos Ground Iguana. T* **200** *c similar horiz designs. Multicoloured. P* 14.

888 8 c. Type **200** 45
889 10 c. Iguana on beach 55
890 20 c. Iguana at nest 80
891 35 c. Iguana eating flowers .. .. 1·40
888/91 .. *Set of* 4 3·00
MS892 105×76 mm. $2 Map showing habitat .. 4·50

(Litho Questa)

1986 (19 Dec). *Royal Wedding. T* **201** *and similar vert designs. Multicoloured. P* 14.
893 35 c. Type **201** 45 50
894 65 c. Miss Sarah Ferguson in wedding carriage 85 90
895 $1.10, Duke and Duchess of York on Palace balcony after wedding .. .. 1·40 1·50
893/5 .. .. *Set of* 3 2·40 2·50
MS896 85×85 mm. $2 Duke and Duchess of York leaving Westminster Abbey .. .. 2·50 3·00

202 "The Prophecy of the Birth of Christ to King Achaz"   **203** H.M.S. *Victoria*, 1859, and Victoria Cross

(Litho Questa)

987 (9 Dec). *Christmas. T* **202** *and similar vert designs, each showing illuminated illustration by Giorgio Clovio from "Farnese Book of Hours". Multicoloured. P* 14.
97 35 c. Type **202** 65 50
98 50 c. "The Annunciation" 80 65
99 65 c. "The Circumcision" .. .. 1·25 1·00
00 95 c. "Adoration of the Kings" .. .. .. 1·50 1·50
97/900 .. .. *Set of* 4 3·75 3·25
MS901 76×106 mm. $2 "The Nativity" .. .. 3·25 3·75

(Litho Questa)

987 (24 Dec). *150th Anniv of Accession of Queen Victoria. T* **203** *and similar horiz designs. Multicoloured. P* 14.
02 8 c. Type **203** 25 15
03 35 c. *Victoria* (paddle-steamer) and gold sovereign 75 60
04 55 c. Royal Yacht *Victoria and Albert I* and 1840 Penny Black stamp .. .. 1·25 1·25
05 95 c. Royal Yacht *Victoria and Albert II* and Victoria Public Library .. .. 1·75 2·00
02/5 .. .. *Set of* 4 3·50 3·50
MS906 129×76 mm. $2 *Victoria* (barque) .. 3·00 3·75

(Des and litho Questa)

987 (31 Dec). *Bicentenary of U.S. Constitution. Multicoloured designs as T* **232** *of Antigua. P* 14.
07 10 c. State Seal, New Jersey 15 15
08 35 c. 18th-century family going to church ("Freedom of Worship") (*vert*) .. 45 50
09 65 c. U.S. Supreme Court, Judicial Branch, Washington (*vert*) 80 85
10 80 c. John Adams (statesman) (*vert*) .. 1·00 1·10
07/10 .. .. *Set of* 4 2·10 2·40
MS911 105×75 mm. $2 George Mason (Virginia delegate) (*vert*) .. .. 2·40 2·75

Nos. 907/10 were each printed in sheetlets of five stamps and one stamp-size label, which appears in the centre of the bottom row.

204 *Santa Maria*   **205** Arawak Artifact and Scouts in Cave, Middle Caicos

(Litho Questa)

988 (20 Jan). *500th Anniv of Discovery of America by Columbus (1992) (1st issue). T* **204** *and similar horiz designs. Multicoloured. P* 14.
2 4 c. Type **204** 10 10
3 25 c. Columbus meeting Tainos Indians .. 45 45
4 70 c. *Santa Maria* anchored off Indian village .. .. 1·25 1·25
5 $1 Columbus in field of grain .. .. 1·50 1·50
2/15 .. .. *Set of* 4 3·00 3·00
S916 105 × 76 mm. $2 *Santa Maria, Pinta* and *Nina* .. .. 2·75 3·25

See also Nos. 947/51.

(Litho Questa)

88 (12 Feb). *World Scout Jamboree, Australia. T* **205** *and similar multicoloured designs. P* 14.
7 8 c. Type **205** 20 15
8 35 c. *Santa Maria*, scouts and Hawks Nest Island (*horiz*) 55 55
9 65 c. Scouts diving to wreck of galleon .. 95 95
0 95 c. Visiting ruins of 19th-century sisal plantation (*horiz*) .. .. .. 1·40 1·40
7/20 .. .. *Set of* 4 2·75 2·75
S921 118 × 82 mm. $2 Splashdown of John Glenn's "Mercury" capsule, 1962 .. .. 3·00 3·50

No. **MS921** is inscribed "Sight" in error.

40TH WEDDING ANNIVERSARY
H.M. QUEEN ELIZABETH II
H.R.H. THE DUKE OF EDINBURGH

(**206**)

207 Football

1988 (14 Mar). *Royal Ruby Wedding. Nos.* 772A, 774A *and* 781A *optd with T* **206**.
922 10 c. Type **181** 15 15
923 25 c. H.M.S. *Boreas* 30 35
924 $2 *Sentinel* (cable ship) .. .. .. 2·40 2·50
922/4 .. .. *Set of* 3 2·50 2·75

(Des L. Fried. Litho B.D.T.)

1988 (29 Aug). *Olympic Games, Seoul. T* **207** *and similar vert designs. Multicoloured. P* 14.
925 8 c. Type **207** 15 15
926 30 c. Yachting 35 40
927 70 c. Cycling 85 90
928 $1 Athletics .. .. 1·25 1·40
925/8 .. .. *Set of* 4 2·25 2·50
MS929 102 × 71 mm. $2 Swimming .. .. 2·40 2·50

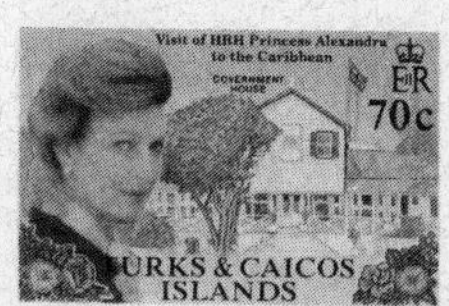

208 Game-fishing Launch and Swordfish   **209** Princess Alexandra and Government House

(Des L. Birmingham. Litho Questa)

1988 (5 Sept). *Billfish Tournament. T* **208** *and similar multicoloured designs. P* 14.
930 8 c. Type **208** 15 15
931 10 c. Competitors with swordfish catch .. 20 15
932 70 c. Game-fishing launch .. .. .. 1·10 1·10
933 $1 Blue Marlin .. .. 1·40 1·50
930/3 .. .. *Set of* 4 2·50 2·50
MS934 119 × 85 mm. $2 Stylized Sailfish (*horiz*) 3·00 3·25

(Litho Questa)

1988 (24 Oct). *Christmas. 500th Birth Anniv of Titian (artist). Vert designs as T* **238** *of Antigua inscr* "CHRISTMAS 1988" *and with royal cypher at top right. Multicoloured. P* $13^1/_2$ × 14.
935 15 c. "Madonna and Child with Saint Catherine" 20 25
936 25 c. "Madonna with a Rabbit" 30 35
937 35 c. "Virgin and Child with Saints" .. 40 45
938 40 c. "The Gypsy Madonna" 50 55
939 50 c. "The Holy Family and a Shepherd" .. 60 65
940 65 c. "Madonna and Child" 75 80
941 $3 "Madonna and Child with Saints" .. 3·50 3·75
935/41 .. .. *Set of* 7 5·75 6·00
MS942 Two sheets, each 110 × 95 mm. (a) $2 "Adoration of the Magi" (detail). (b) $2 "The Annunciation" (detail) .. .. *Set of* 2 *sheets* 4·75 5·00

(Des and litho Questa)

1988 (14 Nov). *Visit of Princess Alexandra. T* **209** *and similar multicoloured designs. P* 14.
943 70 c. Type **209** .. .. 1·10 1·10
944 $1.40, Princess Alexandra and map of islands .. .. 1·90 1·90
MS945 92 × 72 mm. $2 Princess Alexandra (*vert*) 2·75 3·00

210 Coat of Arms

(Des and litho Questa)

1988 (15 Dec). *P* $14^1/_2$ × 15.
946 **210** $10 multicoloured .. .. .. 10·50 11·00

(Des D. Miller. Litho Questa)

1989 (15 May). *500th Anniv of Discovery of America by Columbus (1992) (2nd issue). Pre-Columbian Carib Society. Multicoloured designs as T* **247** *of Antigua. P* 14.
947 10 c. Cutting tree bark for canoe 15 15
948 50 c. Body painting (*horiz*) 80 80
949 65 c. Religious ceremony (*horiz*) 95 95
950 $1 Canoeing .. .. 1·50 1·50
947/50 .. .. *Set of* 4 3·00 3·00
MS951 84×70 mm. $2 Cave pictograph (*horiz*) 3·50 3·50

(Des Design Element. Litho Questa)

1989 (17 Nov). *"World Stamp Expo '89" International Stamp Exhibition, Washington. Sheet* 77×62 mm *containing horiz design as T* **257** *of Antigua. Multicoloured. P* 14.
MS952 $1.50, Lincoln Memorial .. .. 1·75 1·90

(Des W. Hanson. Litho Questa)

1989 (19 Nov). *"World Stamp Expo '89" International Stamp Exhibition, Washington (2nd issue). Bicentenary of the U.S. Presidency. Horiz designs as T* **238** *of Dominica. Multicoloured. P* 14.
953 50 c. Andrew Jackson and DeWitt Clinton railway locomotive 60 65
a. Sheetlet. Nos. 953/8 .. .. 3·50
954 50 c. Martin van Buren, Moses Walker and early baseball game 60 65
955 50 c. William H. Harrison and campaign parade 60 65
956 50 c. John Tyler, Davy Crockett and the Alamo, Texas 60 65
957 50 c. James K. Polk, California gold miner and first U.S. postage stamp 60 65
958 50 c. Zachary Taylor and Battle of Buena Vista, 1846 .. .. 60 65
959 50 c. Rutherford B. Hayes and end of Confederate Reconstruction 60 65
a. Sheetlet. Nos. 959/64 .. .. .. 3·50
960 50 c. James A. Garfield and Battle of Shiloh 60 65
961 50 c. Chester A. Arthur and opening of Brooklyn Bridge, 1883 .. .. .. 60 65
962 50 c. Grover Cleveland, Columbian Exposition, Chicago, 1893, and commemorative stamp 60 65
963 50 c. Benjamin Harrison, Pan-American Union Building and map of Americas 60 65
964 50 c. William McKinley and Rough Rider Monument 60 65
965 50 c. Herbert Hoover, Sonya Heine (skater) and Ralph Metcalf (athlete) 60 65
a. Sheetlet. Nos. 965/70 .. .. .. 3·50
966 50 c. Franklin D. Roosevelt with dog and in wheelchair 60 65
967 50 c. Statue of Washington by Frazer and New York World's Fair, 1939 .. .. 60 65
968 50 c. Harry S. Truman, Veterans Memorial Building, San Francisco, and U.N. emblem 60 65
969 50 c. Dwight D. Eisenhower and U.S. troops landing in Normandy, 1944 .. .. 60 65
970 50 c. John F. Kennedy and "Apollo 11" astronauts on Moon, 1969 .. .. .. 60 65
953/70 .. .. *Set of* 18 9·75 10·50

Nos. 953/8, 959/64 and 965/70 were each printed together, *se-tenant*, in sheetlets of six stamps.

(Litho Questa)

1989 (18 Dec). *Christmas. Paintings by Bellini. Vert designs as T* **259** *of Antigua. Multicoloured. P* 14.
971 15 c. "Madonna and Child" 20 25
972 25 c. "The Madonna of the Shrubs" 30 35
973 35 c. "The Virgin and Child" 40 45
974 40 c. "The Virgin and Child with a Greek Inscription" 50 55
975 50 c. "The Madonna of the Meadow" 60 65
976 65 c. "The Madonna of the Pear" 75 80
977 70 c. "The Virgin and Child" (*different*) .. 85 90
978 $1 "Madonna and Child" (*different*) .. 1·25 1·40
971/8 .. .. *Set of* 8 4·25 4·75
MS979 Two sheets, each 96 × 72 mm. (a) $2 "The Virgin and Child enthroned". (b) $2 "The Madonna with John the Baptist and another Saint" .. .. *Set of* 2 *sheets* 4·75 5·00

CAICOS ISLANDS

CAICOS ISLANDS

(1)

1981 (24 July). *Nos.* 514A, 518A, 520A, 523A *and* 525A/7A *of Turks and Caicos Islands optd with T* 1.
1 1 c. Indigo Hamlet 10 10
2 5 c. Spanish Grunt 10 10
3 8 c. Foureye Butterflyfish 10 10
4 20 c. Queen Angelfish 25 30
5 50 c. Fairy Basslet 65 70
6 $1 Clown Wrasse .. .. 1·00 1·25
7 $2 Stoplight Parrotfish .. .. 2·50 2·75
1/7 .. .. *Set of* 7 4·25 4·75

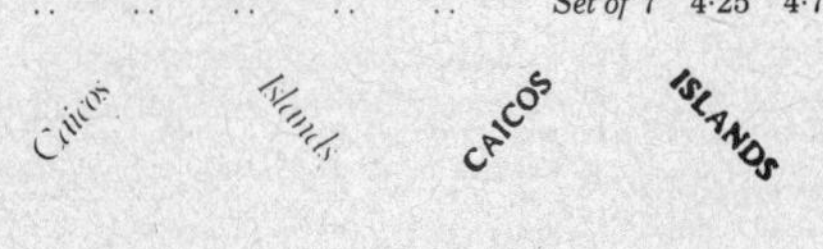

(2) (3)

1981 (24 July). *Royal Wedding. Nos.* 653/6 *of Turks and Caicos Islands optd. A. With T* 2 *in London. B. With T* 3 *in New York.*

		A		B	
8	35 c. Prince Charles and Lady Diana Spencer	25	25	1·25	1·25
	a. Opt inverted	†		£130	—
9	65 c. Kensington Palace ..	40	40	2·00	2·00
	a. Opt inverted	†		95·00	—
10	90 c. Prince Charles as Colonel of the Welsh Guards	50	50	2·25	2·25
	a. Opt inverted	†		£110	—
	b. Opt double	†		£110	—
8/10	.. .. *Set of* 3	1·00	1·00	5·00	5·00
MS11	96 × 82 mm. $2 Glass Coach	3·00	3·00	4·50	4·50
	a. Opt inverted	†		—	—

Nos. 8B/10 come either in sheets of 40 (2 panes 4 × 5) or in sheetlets of 5 stamps and one label. Examples of Nos. 8Ba, 9Ba and 10Ba are known from both formats, but No. 10Bb only exists from sheetlets.

Nos. 8/10 also exist perforated 12 (*Price for set of* 3 *with London opt £4 or with New York opt £9, mint or used*) from additional sheetlets of five stamps and one label. These stamps have changed background colours.

1981 (29 Oct). *Royal Wedding. Booklet stamps. As Nos.* 657/9 *of Turks and Caicos Islands, but each inscr* "Caicos Islands". *Multicoloured. Roul* 5 × *imperf*. Self-adhesive.*
12 20 c. Lady Diana Spencer 80 60
a. Booklet pane. Nos. 12/13, each × 3 .. 4·00
13 $1 Prince Charles .. .. 3·75 2·75
14 $2 Prince Charles and Lady Diana Spencer 10·00 6·00
a. Booklet pane of 1 .. .. .. 10·00
12/14 .. .. *Set of* 3 13·00 8·50

*The 20 c. and $1 values were each separated by various combinations of rotary knife (giving a straight edge) and roulette. The $2 value exists only with straight edges.

4 Conch and Lobster Fishing, South Caicos

(Des J. Cooter (8 c. to 21 c.). Litho)

1983 (6 June)–**84**. *T* 4 *and similar horiz designs. Multicoloured. P* 14.
15 8 c. Type **4** 10 10
16 10 c. Hawksbill Turtle, East Caicos 15 15
17 20 c. Arawak Indians and idol, Middle Caicos 25 30
18 35 c. Boat-building, North Caicos 45 50
19 50 c. Marine biologist at work, Pine Cay .. 60 65
20 95 c. Boeing "707" airliner at new airport, Providenciales .. .. 1·25 1·40
21 $1.10, Columbus' *Pinta*, West Caicos .. 1·40 1·50
22 $2 Fort George Cay (18.5.84) .. .. 2·75 3·00
23 $3 Pirates Anne Bonny and Calico Jack at Parrot Cay (18.5.84) .. .. .. 4·50 4·75
15/23 .. .. *Set of* 9 10·50 11·00

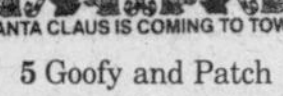

5 Goofy and Patch

6 "Leda and the Swan"

(Litho Walsall)

1983 (7 Nov). *Christmas. T* **5** *and similar vert designs showing Disney cartoon characters. Multicoloured. P* 11.
30 1 c. Type **5** 10 10
31 1 c. Chip and Dale 10 10
32 2 c. Morty 10 10
33 2 c. Morty and Ferdie 10 10
34 3 c. Goofy and Louie 10 10
35 3 c. Donald Duck, Huey, Dewey and Louie .. 10 10
36 50 c. Uncle Scrooge .. .. 1·00 90
37 70 c. Mickey Mouse and Ferdie .. .. 1·50 1·25
38 $1.10, Pinocchio, Jiminy Cricket and Figaro 2·00 1·90
30/8 .. .. *Set of* 9 4·00 3·75
MS39 126 × 101 mm. $2 Morty and Ferdie. P 13½ × 14 .. .. 3·25 3·50

(Des and litho Questa)

1983 (15 Dec). 500*th Birth Anniv of Raphael. T* **6** *and similar vert designs. Multicoloured. P* 14.
40 35 c. Type **6** 50 50
41 50 c. "Study of Apollo for Parnassus" 70 70
42 95 c. "Study of two figures for the battle of Ostia" .. .. 1·25 1·25
43 $1.10, "Study for the Madonna of the Goldfinch" .. .. 1·50 1·50
40/3 .. .. *Set of* 4 3·50 3·50
MS44 71 × 100 mm. $2.50, "The Garvagh Madonna" .. .. 3·00 3·25

7 High Jumping

8 Horace Horsecollar and Clarabelle Cow

(Litho Questa)

1984 (1 Mar). *Olympic Games, Los Angeles. T* **7** *and similar designs. P* 14.
45 4 c. multicoloured 10 10
46 25 c. multicoloured 20 20
47 65 c. black, deep grey-blue and new blue .. 50 50
48 $1.10, multicoloured 85 85
45/8 .. .. *Set of* 4 1·50 1·50
MS49 105 × 75 mm. $2 multicoloured .. .. 2·75 3·00

Designs: *Vert*—25 c. Archery; 65 c. Cycling; $1.10, Football. *Horiz*—$2 Show jumping.

(Des Walt Disney Productions. Litho Questa)

1984 (23 Apr). *Easter. Walt Disney Cartoon Characters. T* **8** *and similar horiz designs. Multicoloured. P* 14 × 13½.
50 35 c. Type **8** 60 60
51 45 c. Mickey and Minnie Mouse, and Chip .. 75 75
52 75 c. Gyro Gearloose, Chip 'n Dale .. .. 1·25 1·25
53 85 c. Mickey Mouse, Chip 'n Dale .. .. 1·40 1·40
50/3 .. .. *Set of* 4 3·50 3·50
MS54 127 × 101 mm. $2.20, Donald Duck .. 3·50 3·75

AUSIPEX 1984

(9) (10)

1984 (19 June). *Universal Postal Union Congress, Hamburg. Nos.* 20/1 *optd with T* **9**.
55 95 c. Boeing "707" airliner at new airport, Providenciales .. .. 1·00 1·25
56 $1.10, Columbus' *Pinta*, West Caicos .. 1·25 1·50

1984 (22 Aug). *"Ausipex" International Stamp Exhibition, Melbourne. No.* 22 *optd with T* **10**.
57 $2 Fort George Cay .. .. 2·40 2·50

11 Seamen sighting American Manatees

(Des L. Lightbourne. Litho Walsall)

1984 (12 Sept). 492*nd Anniv of Columbus' First Landfall. T* **11** *and similar horiz designs. Multicoloured. P* 14.
58 10 c. Type **11** 15 15
59 70 c. Fleet of Columbus .. .. 1·10 1·10
60 $1 First landing in West Indies .. .. 1·60 1·60
58/60 .. .. *Set of* 3 2·50 2·50
MS61 99 × 69 mm. $2 Fleet of Columbus (*different*) 2·75 3·00

NEW INFORMATION

The editor is always interested to correspond with people who have new information that will improve or correct the Catalogue.

12 Donald Duck and Mickey Mouse with Father Christmas

(Litho Questa)

1984 (26 Nov). *Christmas. Walt Disney Cartoon Characters. T* **12** *and similar vert designs. Multicoloured. P* 12 ($2) *or* 13½ × 14 (*others*).
62 20 c. Type **12** 40 40
63 35 c. Donald Duck opening refrigerator .. 65 65
64 50 c. Mickey Mouse, Donald Duck and toy train 90 90
65 75 c. Donald Duck and parcels .. .. 1·25 1·25
66 $1.10, Donald Duck and carol singers .. 1·75 1·75
62/6 .. .. *Set of* 5 4·50 4·50
MS67 127 × 102 mm. $2 Donald Duck as Christmas tree .. .. 3·00 3·50

No. 65 was printed in sheetlets of 8 stamps.

13 Thick-billed Vireo

14 Two Children learning to Read and Write (Education)

(Des Susan David. Litho Walsall)

1985 (12 Feb). *Birth Bicentenary of John J. Audubon (ornithologist). T* **13** *and similar horiz designs. Multicoloured. P* 14.
68 20 c. Type **13** 60 40
69 35 c. Black-faced Grassquit 85 65
70 50 c. Pearly-eyed Thrasher .. .. .. 1·25 90
71 $1 Greater Antillean Bullfinch .. .. 1·75 1·75
68/71 .. .. *Set of* 4 4·00 3·25
MS72 100 × 70 mm. $2 Stripe-headed Tanager .. 3·25 3·50

(Des C. Walters. Litho Walsall)

1985 (8 May). *International Youth Year and 40th Anniv of United Nations. T* **14** *and similar vert designs. Multicoloured. P* 14.
73 16 c. Type **14** 20 25
74 35 c. Two children on playground swings (Health) 50 55
75 70 c. Boy and girl (Love) .. .. 1·00 1·10
76 90 c. Three children (Peace) .. .. .. 1·25 1·40
73/6 .. .. *Set of* 4 2·75 3·00
MS77 101 × 71 mm. $2 Child, dove carrying ears of wheat and map of the Americas .. .. 2·75 3·00

15 Air Caicos "DC-3" on Ground

16 The Queen Mother visiting Foundation for the Disabled, Leatherhead

(Des K. Gromol. Litho Walsall)

1985 (23 May). 40*th Anniv of International Civil Aviation Organization. T* **15** *and similar horiz designs. Multicoloured. P* 14.
78 35 c. Type **15** 50 55
79 75 c. Air Caicos Convair "440" .. .. 1·10 1·25
80 90 c. TCNA "Islander" .. .. 1·25 1·40
78/80 .. .. *Set of* 3 2·50 3·00
MS81 100 × 70 mm. $2.20, Hang-gliding over the Caicos Islands .. .. 3·00 3·25

(Des J.W. Litho Questa)

1985 (8 July). *Life and Times of Queen Elizabeth the Queen Mother. T* **16** *and similar multicoloured designs. P* 14.
82 35 c. Type **16** 50 55
83 65 c. With Princess Anne (*horiz*) 90 95
84 95 c. At Epsom, 1961 .. .. 1·40 1·60
82/4 .. .. *Set of* 3 2·50 2·75
MS85 56 × 85 mm. $2 visiting Royal Hospital, Chelsea .. .. 2·75 3·00

(Des Walt Disney Productions. Litho Questa)

1985 (5 Dec). *150th Birth Anniv of Mark Twain (author). Horiz designs as T* **118** *of Anguilla, showing Walt Disney cartoon characters in scenes from "Tom Sawyer, Detective". Multicoloured. P* 14 × 13½.
86 8 c. Huckleberry Finn (Goofy) and Tom Sawyer (Mickey Mouse) reading reward notice 15 10
87 35 c. Huck and Tom meeting Jake Dunlap .. 60 55
88 95 c. Huck and Tom spying on Jubiter Dunlap .. .. 1·25 1·40
89 $1.10, Huck and Tom with hound (Pluto) .. 1·50 1·60
86/9 .. .. *Set of* 4 3·25 3·25
MS90 127 × 101 mm. $2 Tom unmasking Jubiter Dunlap .. .. 2·75 3·00

(Des Walt Disney Productions. Litho Questa)

1985 (5 Dec). ***Birth Bicentenaries of Grimm Brothers (folklorists). Horiz designs as T* 119 *of Anguilla, showing Walt Disney cartoon characters in scenes from "Six Soldiers of Fortune". Multicoloured. P*** 14 × 13½.
91 16 c. The Soldier (Donald Duck) with his meagre pay 20 25
92 25 c. The Soldier meeting the Strong Man (Horace Horsecollar) 30 35
93 65 c. The Soldier meeting the Marksman (Mickey Mouse) 85 90
94 $1.35, The Fast Runner (Goofy) winning the race against the Princess (Daisy Duck) .. 1·75 1·90
91/4 .. .. *Set of* 4 2·75 3·00
MS95 126 × 101 mm. $2 The Soldier and the Strong Man with sack of gold .. .. .. 2·50 2·75

Tuvalu

Formerly known as the Ellice Islands when they shared a joint administration with the Gilbert group. On 1 January 1976 the two island-groups separated and the Ellice Islands were renamed Tuvalu.

CROWN COLONY

1 Gilbertese and Tuvaluan

(Des Iakopo Nivatui; adapted J. Cooter. Litho Questa)

1976 (1 Jan). *Separation of the Islands. T* **1** *and similar multicoloured designs. W w* **14** *(sideways on 4 and 35 c.). P* 13½.
1 4 c. Type I 45 80
2 10 c. Map of the islands (*vert*) .. .. .. 55 1·00
3 35 c. Canoes .. .. 75 1·50
1/3 .. .. *Set of* 3 1·60 3·00

TUVALU

(2)

3 50 c. Coin and Octopus

1976 (1 Jan). *Nos. 173 etc. of Gilbert & Ellice Is optd as T* **2** *in silver (35 c.) or blue (others).* (*a*) W w **12** (upright).
4 2 c. Lagoon fishing £700 £140
5 5 c. Gilbertese canoe 80 60
6 8 c. Weaving pandanus fronds 95 60
7 10 c. Weaving a basket .. .. .. 1·50 80
8 50 c. Local handicrafts .. .. .. 27·00 18·00
9 $1 Weaving coconut screen .. .. 85·00 70·00

(*b*) W w **12** (*sideways*)
10 2 c. Lagoon fishing .. .. £130 30·00
11 3 c. Cleaning pandanus leaves 85 60
12 5 c. Gilbertese canoe .. .. .. 2·25 1·50
13 25 c. Loading copra .. .. 4·00 3·50

(*c*) W w **14** (*inverted*)
14 1 c. Cutting toddy 30 20
15 6 c. De-husking coconuts 90 40
16 15 c. Tiger shark .. .. 1·00 65
17 50 c. Local handicrafts .. .. .. 1·75 80
18 $1 Weaving coconut screen .. .. 3·00 1·25
19 $2 Coat of arms .. .. 3·00 1·25

(*d*) W w **14** (*sideways*)
20 2 c. Lagoon fishing 80 40
21 3 c. Cleaning pandanus leaves 90 30
22 4 c. Casting nets .. .. 1·00 45
23 20 c. Beating a rolled pandanus leaf .. .. 1·00 1·00
24 25 c. Loading copra .. .. 1·25 75
25 35 c. Fishing at night .. .. 2·25 1·75
4/7 and 14/25 .. .. .. *Set of* 15 17·00 9·50

(Des G. Drummond. Litho Walsall)

1976 (21 Apr). *New Coinage. Vert designs, each showing coin as in T* **3**. *Multicoloured. W w* **14** *(inverted). P* 13½.
26 5 c. Type 3 .. .. 25 15
27 10 c. Red-eyed Crab 35 20
28 15 c. Flying Fish 45 25
29 35 c. Green Turtle 60 45
26/9 .. .. *Set of* 4 1·50 95

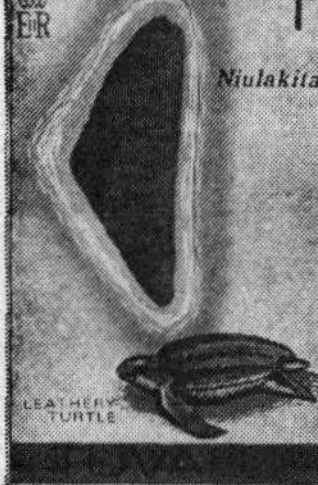

4 Niulakita and Seven-ridged Leathery Turtle

5 Title page of New Testament

(Des J. Cooter. Litho Questa)

1976 (1 July–1 Sept). *Vert designs showing maps (1 to 25 c.) or horiz designs showing scenes (others). Multicoloured. W w* **14** *(sideways on 35 c. to $5). P* 13½.
30 1 c. Type 4 .. .. 85 60
31 2 c. Nukulaelae and sleeping mat 40 35
32 4 c. Nui and talo (vegetable) 40 20
33 5 c. Nanumanga and grass skirt .. .. 1·25 20
34 6 c. Nukufetau and Coconut Crab 70 30
35 8 c. Funafuti and Banana tree 75 50
36 10 c. Map of Tuvalu 75 20
37 15 c. Niutao and Flying fish .. .. 1·00 20
38 20 c. Vaitupu and Maneapa (house) 70 20
39 25 c. Nanumea and fish-hook .. .. 4·00 90
40 35 c. Te Ano (game) 60 20
41 50 c. Canoe pole fishing 75 30
42 $1 Reef fishing by flare 80 40
43 $2 Living house .. .. 1·50 60
44 $5 M.V. *Nivanga* (1.9.76) .. .. .. 38·00 14·00
30/44 .. .. *Set of* 15 45·00 16·00
See also Nos. 58/72.

(Des G. Drummond. Litho Harrison)

1976 (6 Oct). *Christmas. T* **5** *and similar horiz designs. Multicoloured. W w* **14**. *P* 14 × 14½.
45 5 c. Type 5 .. .. 70 40
46 20 c. Lotolelei Church 70 40
47 25 c. Kelupi Church 70 40
48 30 c. Mataloa o Tuvalu Church 80 40
49 35 c. Palatasio o Keliso Church 80 40
45/9 .. .. *Set of* 5 3·25 1·75

6 Queen Elizabeth and Prince Philip

(Des G. Vasarhelyi. Litho Format)

1977 (9 Feb). *Silver Jubilee. T* **6** *and similar horiz designs. Multicoloured. P* 13½.
50 15 c. Type 6 .. .. 75 30
51 35 c. Prince Philip carried ashore at Vaitupu 1·25 40
52 50 c. Queen and attendants .. .. .. 1·25 50
50/2 .. .. *Set of* 3 3·00 1·10
MS53 98 × 144 mm. Nos. 50/2. P 15 .. .. 6·00 6·00

7 "Health"

(Des I. Oliver. Litho Format)

1977 (4 May). *30th Anniv of South Pacific Commission. T* **7** *and similar horiz designs. Multicoloured. P* 13½.
54 5 c. Type 7 .. .. 20 20
55 20 c. "Education" 25 20
56 30 c. "Fruit-growing" 25 20
57 35 c. Map of S.P.C. area 30 25
54/7 .. .. *Set of* 4 90 75

1977 (13 June)–**78**. *As Nos. 30/6, 38/9 and 44, but no wmk, or new values and designs.* (30, 40 c.).
58 1 c. Type 4 (9.77) 20 15
59 2 c. Nukulaelae and sleeping mat (3.78) .. 20 25
60 4 c. Nui and talo (vegetable) (3.78) 20 15
61 5 c. Nanumanga and grass skirt (9.77) .. 25 15
62 6 c. Nukufetau and Coconut Crab (3.78) .. 20 35
63 8 c. Funafuti and Banana tree (9.77) .. 20 25
64 10 c. Map of Tuvalu (9.77) 20 20
65 20 c. Vaitupu and Maneapa (house) (10.78) .. 90 1·50
66 25 c. Nanumea and fish-hook (9.77) .. .. 1·00 20
67 30 c. Fatele (local dancing) (19.4.78) 30 20
68 40 c. Screw Pine (19.4.78) 30 15
69 $5 M.V. *Nivanga* .. .. 8·00 5·00
58/69 .. .. *Set of* 12 11·00 7·00
No. 70/2 vacant.

8 Scout Promise

(Des I. Oliver. Litho Format)

1977 (10 Aug). *50th Anniv of Scouting in the Central Pacific. T* **8** *and similar horiz designs. Multicoloured. P* 13½.
73 5 c. Type 8 .. .. 30 25
74 20 c. Canoeing 30 25
75 30 c. Scout shelter 40 30
76 35 c. Lord Baden-Powell 40 30
73/6 .. .. *Set of* 4 1·25 1·00

9 Hurricane Beach (Expedition photo)

(Des I. Oliver. Litho Format)

1977 (2 Nov). *Royal Society Expeditions, 1896/7. T* **9** *and similar designs. P* 13½ × 14 *(5 and 35 c.) or* 14 × 13½ *(others).*
77 5 c. multicoloured 25 15
78 20 c. black and light blue 40 20
79 30 c. black and light blue 40 20
80 35 c. multicoloured 40 20
77/80 .. .. *Set of* 4 1·25 65
Designs: *Vert*—20 c. Boring apparatus on H.M.S. *Porpoise*; 30 c. Dredging chart. *Horiz*—35 c. Charles Darwin and H.M.S. *Beagle*.

10 Pacific Pigeon

11 *Lawedua* (coaster)

(Des G. Drummond. Litho Format)

1978 (25 Jan). *Wild Birds. T* **10** *and similar vert designs. Multicoloured. P* 14 × 13½.
81 8 c. Type 10 .. .. 1·00 35
82 20 c. Eastern Reef Heron .. .. .. 1·25 50
83 30 c. White Tern .. .. 1·75 60
84 40 c. Lesser Frigate Bird .. .. .. 1·75 65
81/4 .. .. *Set of* 4 5·25 1·90

(Des I. Oliver. Litho Format)

1978 (5 Apr). *Ships. T* **11** *and similar horiz designs. Multicoloured. P* 13½ × 14.
85 8 c. Type 11 .. .. 15 15
86 10 c. *Wallacia* (tug) 15 15
87 30 c. *Cenpac Rounder* (freighter) 20 20
88 40 c. *Pacific Explorer* (freighter) 25 20
85/8 .. .. *Set of* 4 65 65

(Des G. Drummond. Litho Format)

1978 (2 June). *25th Anniv of Coronation. Horiz designs as Nos. 422/5 of Montserrat. Multicoloured. P* 13½ × 14.
89 8 c. Canterbury Cathedral 10 10
90 30 c. Salisbury Cathedral 10 10
91 40 c. Wells Cathedral 15 10
92 $1 Hereford Cathedral 40 30
89/92 .. .. *Set of* 4 60 40
MS93 137 × 108 mm. Nos. 89/92. P 15 .. .. 80 90
Nos. 89/92 were each printed in sheets containing 2 *se-tenant* stamp-size labels.

INDEPENDENT

INDEPENDENCE
1ST OCTOBER
1978
(12)

13 White Frangipani

1978 (1 Oct). *Independence. Nos.* 63/4, 65, 67/8 *and as Nos.* 37 *and* 40, *but without wmk, optd as T* 12 *by Format.*

No.	Description		
94	8 c. Funafuti and Banana tree	10	10
95	10 c. Map of Tuvalu	10	10
96	15 c. Niutao and Flying fish	10	10
97	20 c. Vaitupu and Maneapa (house)	15	15
98	30 c. Fatele (local dancing)	15	15
99	35 c. Te Ano (game)	20	20
100	40 c. Screw Pine	20	20
94/100	*Set of* 7	75	75

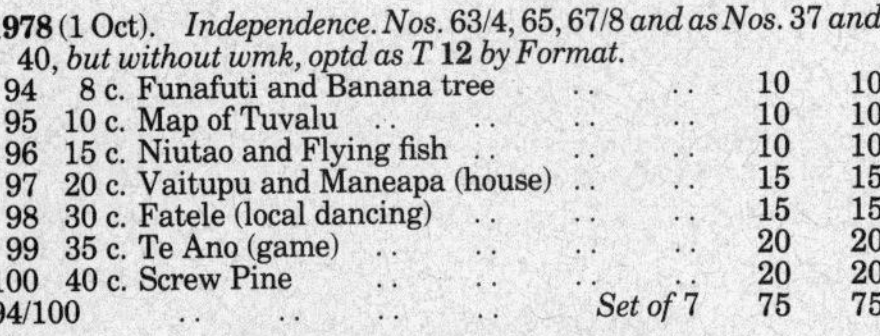

(Des J. Cooter. Litho Format)

1978 (4 Oct). *Wild Flowers. T* **13** *and similar vert designs. Multicoloured. P* 14.

No.	Description		
101	8 c. Type **13**	15	10
102	20 c. Susana	15	10
103	30 c. Tiale	20	15
104	40 c. Inato	25	25
101/4	*Set of* 4	65	55

14 Squirrelfish

(Des G. Drummond. Litho Format)

1979 (24 Jan)–**81**. *Fishes. Multicoloured designs as T* **14**. *P* 14.

No.	Description		
105	1 c. Type **14**	10	10
106	2 c. Yellow-banded Goatfish	10	10
107	4 c. Imperial Angelfish	10	10
108	5 c. Rainbow Butterfly	15	10
109	6 c. Blue Angelfish	15	10
110	8 c. Blue Striped Snapper	15	10
111	10 c. Orange Clownfish	25	10
112	15 c. Chevroned Coralfish	25	10
113	20 c. Fairy Cod	35	15
114	25 c. Clown Triggerfish	35	20
115	30 c. Long-nosed Butterfly	35	10
116	35 c. Yellowfin Tuna	40	20
117	40 c. Spotted Eagle Ray	40	10
117*b*	45 c. Black-tipped Rock Cod (16.6.81)	1·50	2·00
118	50 c. Hammerhead Shark	50	20
119	70 c. Lionfish (*vert*)	65	30
120	$1 White-barred Triggerfish (*vert*)	70	55
121	$2 Beaked Coralfish (*vert*)	1·50	60
122	$5 Tiger Shark (*vert*)	2·75	1·25
105/22	*Set of* 19	9·00	5·50

Nos. 105/22 were each printed in sheets containing 2 *se-tenant* stamp-size printed labels.

Both fine (300 lines of dots per linear inch) and coarse (175 lines of dots per linear inch) screens were used to produce plates for this issue. The 1, 5, 8, 10, 30 and 40 c. values can be found with either screen. The 15, 25, 35, 45 and 50 c. only exist with coarse screen and the remainder only with fine screen.

15 "Explorer of the Pacific"

(Des J. Cooter. Litho Format)

1979 (14 Feb). *Death Bicentenary of Captain Cook. T* **15** *and similar horiz designs. Multicoloured. P* 14 × 14½.

No.	Description		
123	8 c. Type **15**	30	20
	a. Horiz strip of 4. Nos. 123/6	1·40	
	ab. Imperf. Horiz strip of 4		
124	30 c. "A new island is discovered"	40	25
125	40 c. "Transit of Venus, Tahiti, 3 June, 1769"	40	25
126	$1 Death of Captain Cook, Hawaii, 14 February, 1779	50	35
123/6	*Set of* 4	1·40	95

Nos. 123/6 were printed together, *se-tenant*, in horizontal strips of 4 throughout the sheet.

MINIMUM PRICE

The minimum price quote is 10p which represents a handling charge rather than a basis for valuing common stamps. For further notes about prices see introductory pages.

16 Grumman "Goose G21A" and Nukulaelae Island

(Des J. Cooter. Litho Format)

1979 (16 May). *Internal Air Service. T* **16** *and similar horiz designs. Multicoloured. P* 13½.

No.	Description		
127	8 c. Type **16**	15	15
128	20 c. "Goose" and Vaitupu	20	20
129	30 c. "Goose" and Nui	30	30
130	40 c. "Goose" and Funafuti	35	35
127/30	*Set of* 4	90	90

17 Sir Rowland Hill, 1976 4 c. Separation Commemorative and London's First Pillar Box, 1855

18 Child's Face

(Des J. Cooter. Litho Format)

1979 (27 Aug). *Death Centenary of Sir Rowland Hill. T* **17** *and similar horiz designs. Multicoloured. P* 13½ × 14.

No.	Description		
131	30 c. Type **17**	25	15
132	40 c. Sir Rowland Hill, 1976 10 c. Separation commemorative and Penny Black	25	15
133	$1 Sir Rowland Hill, 1976 35 c. Separation commemorative and mail coach	50	30
131/3	*Set of* 3	90	55
MS134	148 × 140 mm. Nos. 131/3. P 15	1·00	1·25

(Des G. Vasarhelyi. Litho Format)

1979 (20 Oct). *International Year of the Child. T* **18** *and similar vert designs showing children's faces. P* 14 × 13½.

No.	Description		
135	8 c. multicoloured	10	10
136	20 c. multicoloured	15	10
137	30 c. multicoloured	15	15
138	40 c. multicoloured	20	25
135/8	*Set of* 4	55	55

19 *Cypraea argus*

(Des J. Cooter. Litho Format)

1980 (20 Feb). *Cowrie Shells. T* **19** *and similar horiz designs. Multicoloured. P* 13½ × 14.

No.	Description		
139	8 c. Type **19**	15	10
140	20 c. *Cypraea scurra*	15	10
141	30 c. *Cypraea carneola*	20	15
142	40 c. *Cypraea aurantium*	30	20
139/42	*Set of* 4	70	45

20 Philatelic Bureau, Funafuti, and 1976 8 c. Definitive

21 Queen Elizabeth the Queen Mother

(Des J. Cooter. Litho Questa)

1980 (30 Apr). *"London 1980" International Stamp Exhibition. T* **20** *and similar horiz designs. Multicoloured. P* 13½ × 14.

No.	Description		
143	10 c. Type **20**	15	15
144	20 c. Gilbert and Ellice Islands stamp with Nukulaelae postmark of 1946 and 1976 2 c. definitive	25	20
145	30 c. Fleet Post Office, U.S. Navy, airmail letter of 1943	25	25
146	$1 Tuvalu coat of arms and map	50	45
143/6	*Set of* 4	1·00	95
MS147	160 × 136 mm. Nos. 143/6	1·00	1·40

(Des G. Drummond. Litho Format)

1980 (14 Aug). *80th Birthday of Queen Elizabeth the Queen Mother. P* 13½.

No.	Description		
148 **21**	50 c. multicoloured	35	25

22 *Aethaloessa calidalis*

(Des J. Cooter. Litho Format)

1980 (20 Aug). *Moths. T* **22** *and similar horiz designs. Multicoloured. P* 14.

No.	Description		
149	8 c. Type **22**	10	10
150	20 c. *Parotis suralis*	15	10
151	30 c. *Dudua aprobola*	20	15
152	40 c. *Decadarchis simulans*	20	15
149/52	*Set of* 4	60	45

23 Air Pacific "Heron"

45 CENTS

(24)

(Des G. Drummond. Litho Format)

1980 (5 Nov). *Aviation Commemorations. T* **23** *and similar horiz designs. Multicoloured. P* 13½ × 14.

No.	Description		
153	8 c. Type **23**	10	10
154	20 c. Hawker Siddeley "748"	15	10
155	30 c. "Sunderland" flying boat	15	15
156	40 c. Orville Wright and *Flyer*	20	15
153/6	*Set of* 4	55	45

Commemorations:—8 c. 1st regular air service to Tuvalu, 1964; 20 c. Air service to Tuvalu; 30 c. War time R.N.Z.A.F. flying boat service to Funafuti, 1945; 40 c. Wright Brothers' 1st flight, 17 December 1903.

TWO TYPES OF SURCHARGE FOR NO. 157

Type I

Type II

Type I. Applied by lithography. Clean lines with an even distribution of the ink.

Type II. Applied by typography. Ragged lines with an uneven distribution of the ink, especially at the edges of the figures and bars. On some stamps the impression of the surcharge is visible on the back.

1981 (19 Jan). *No.* 118 *surch with T* **24**.

No.	Description		
157	45 c. on 50 c. Hammerhead Shark (I)	25	40
	a. Type II (typo) surch	3·25	2·00

25 *Hypolimnas bolina elliciana* (male)

26 Brig *Elizabeth*, 1809

(Des J. Cooter. Litho Questa)

1981 (3 Feb). *Butterflies.* T **25** *and similar horiz designs. Multicoloured. P* 14 × 14½.

158 8 c. Type **25** 15 10
159 20 c. *Hypolimnas bolina elliciana* (female) .. 20 15
160 30 c. *Hypolimnas bolina elliciana* (female) (*different*) 20 20
161 40 c. *Junonia vallida* 25 20
158/61 .. .. *Set of* 4 70 60

(Des R. Granger Barrett. Litho Format)

1981 (13 May). *Ships* (1*st series*). *T* **26** *and similar horiz designs. Multicoloured. W* w **15** (*sideways*). *P* 14.

162 10 c. Type **26** 20 15
163 25 c. Brigantine *Rebecca*, 1819 .. .. 25 25
164 35 c. Whaling ship *Independence II*, 1821 .. 30 30
165 40 c. H.M.S. *Basilisk*, 1872 .. .. .. 35 35
166 45 c. H.M.S. *Royalist*, 1890 .. .. .. 40 40
167 50 c. Barque *Olivebank*, 1920 .. .. .. 40 40
162/7 .. .. *Set of* 6 1·75 1·75

Nos. 162/7 were each produced in sheets of six stamps and two labels, these occurring in the second horizontal row.

See also Nos. 235/40 and 377/80.

(Des D. Shults. Litho Questa)

1981 (10 July–26 Nov). *Royal Wedding. Horiz designs as T* **26/27** *of Kiribati. Multicoloured.* (*a*) *W* w **15**. *P* 14.

168 10 c. *Carolina* 10 15
a. Sheetlet. No. 168 × 6 and No. 169 .. 90
169 10 c. Prince Charles and Lady Diana Spencer 35 35
170 45 c. *Victoria and Albert III* 20 20
a. Sheetlet. No. 170 × 6 and No. 171 .. 1·40
171 45 c. As No. 169 .. .. 30 30
172 $2 *Britannia* 50 50
a. Sheetlet No. 172 × 6 and No. 173 .. 4·25
173 $2 As No. 169 .. .. 1·75 1·75
168/73 .. .. *Set of* 6 2·75 2·75
MS174 120 × 109 mm. $1.50, As No. 169. Wmk sideways. P 12 (26 Nov) .. .. .. 1·50 1·00

(*b*) *Booklet stamps. No wmk. P* 12 (26 Nov)

175 10 c. As No. 168 .. .. 15 15
a. Booklet pane. No. 175 × 4 55
176 45 c. As No. 171 .. .. 75 80
a. Booklet pane. No. 176 × 2 .. .. 1·50

Nos. 168/73 were printed in sheetlets of seven stamps of the same face value, each containing six of the "Royal Yacht" design and one of the larger design showing Prince Charles and Lady Diana.

Nos. 175/6 come from $1.70 stamp booklets.

27 U.P.U. Emblem

28 Map of Funafuti and Anchor

(Des, eng and recess Harrison)

1981 (19 Nov). *U.P.U. Membership. W* **4** *of Maldive Islands. P* 14½ × 14.

177 **27** 70 c. deep ultramarine 30 30
178 $1 red-brown 50 60
MS179 86 × 71 mm. Nos. 177/8. No wmk .. 2·25 2·25

(Des J. Cooter. Litho Questa)

1982 (17 Feb). *Amatuku Maritime School. T* **28** *and similar horiz designs. Multicoloured. W* w **15** (*sideways*). *P* 13½ × 14.

180 10 c. Type **28** 10 10
181 25 c. Motor launch 25 25
182 35 c. School buildings and jetty 35 35
183 45 c. School flag and freighters 40 40
180/3 .. .. *Set of* 4 1·00 1·00

29 Caroline of Brandenburg–Ansbach, Princess of Wales, 1714

TONGA CYCLONE
RELIEF
1982
+20c
(30)

(Des D. Shults and J. Cooter. Litho Format)

1982 (19 May). *21st Birthday of Princess of Wales. T* **29** *and similar vert designs. Multicoloured. W* w **15**. *P* 13½ × 14.

184 10 c. Type **29** 10 10
185 45 c. Coat of arms of Caroline of Brandenburg-Ansbach 20 15
186 $1.50, Diana, Princess of Wales 60 60
184/6 .. .. *Set of* 3 75 75

1982 (20 May). *Tonga Cyclone Relief. Nos.* 170/1 *surch as T* **30** (*words in one line on No.* 188).

187 45 c. + 20 c. *Victoria and Albert III* 30 50
a. Sheetlet. No. 187 × 6 and No. 188 .. 3·75
b. Surch inverted .. .. 15·00
c. Surch inverted (horiz pair) .. .. 25·00
d. Surch double .. .. 8·00
188 45 c. + 20 c. Prince Charles and Lady Diana Spencer 50 75
a. Surch inverted .. .. 30·00
b. Surch double .. .. 28·00

No. 187c shows the long surcharge, intended for No. 188, inverted and struck across a horizontal pair of No. 187. No. 188a shows two examples of Type **30** inverted on the same stamp.

1982 (14 July). *Birth of Prince William of Wales. Nos.* 184/6 *optd with T* **19** *of St. Kitts.*

189 10 c. Type **29** 10 10
190 45 c. Coat of Arms of Caroline of Brandenburg-Ansbach 25 15
a. Opt inverted .. .. 32·00
191 $1.50, Diana, Princess of Wales 90 70
189/91 .. .. *Set of* 3 1·10 80

31 Tuvalu and World Scout Badges

32 Tuvalu Crest and Duke of Edinburgh's Standard

(Des J. Cooter. Litho Walsall)

1982 (18 Aug). *75th Anniv of Boy Scout Movement. T* **31** *and similar horiz designs. Multicoloured. W* w **15** (*sideways*). *P* 13½ × 14.

192 10 c. Type **31** 15 15
193 25 c. Camp-fire 40 40
194 35 c. Parade 45 45
195 45 c. Boy Scout 55 55
192/5 .. .. *Set of* 4 1·40 1·40

(Des J. Cooter. Litho Format)

1982 (26 Oct). *Royal Visit. T* **32** *and similar vert designs. Multicoloured. W* w **15**. *P* 14.

196 25 c. Type **32** 25 25
197 45 c. Tuvalu flag and Royal Standard 40 40
198 50 c. Portrait of Queen Elizabeth II 40 40
196/8 .. .. *Set of* 3 95 95
MS199 104 × 85 mm. Nos. 196/8. Wmk inverted .. .. 1·00 1·50

33 Fisherman's Hat and Equipment

(Des G. Drummond. Litho Walsall)

1983 (14 Mar)–**84**. *Handicrafts. T* **33** *and similar multicoloured designs. W* w **15** (*sideways on* 1 *c. to* 45 *c.*). *P* 14.

200 1 c. Type **33** 10 10
201 2 c. Cowrie shell handbags 10 10
202 5 c. Wedding and babyfood baskets 10 10
203 10 c. Model canoe 10 10
203*a* 15 c. Ladies' sun hats (30.4.84) 50 40
204 20 c. Palm climbing rope and platform with toddy pot 20 20
205 25 c. Pandanus baskets 20 20
205*a* 30 c. Basket tray and coconut stands (18.4.84) 70 50
206 35 c. Pandanus pillows and shell necklaces .. 25 30
207 40 c. Round baskets and fans 30 35
208 45 c. Reef sandals and fish trap 35 40
209 50 c. Rat trap (*vert*) 40 45
209*a* 60 c. Fisherman's waterproof boxes (*vert*) (18.4.84) .. .. 1·25 70
210 $1 Pump drill and adze (*vert*) 75 70
211 $2 Fisherman's hat and canoe bailers (*vert*) 1·50 1·25
212 $5 Fishing rod, lures and scoop nets (*vert*) . 3·50 2·50
200/12 .. .. *Set of* 16 9·00 7·50

34 *Te Tautai* (trawler)

(Des G. Drummond. Litho Format)

1983 (14 Mar). *Commonwealth Day. T* **34** *and similar horiz designs. Multicoloured. W* w **15** (*sideways*). *P* 14.

213 20 c. Type **34** 15 15
214 35 c. Traditional dancing, Motufoua School .. 25 25
215 45 c. Satellite view of Pacific 30 30
216 50 c. *Morning Star* (container ship) 40 40
213/16 .. .. *Set of* 4 1·00 1·00

No. 214 is incorrectly inscribed "MOTOFOUA SCHOOL".

35 *Pantala flavescens*

(Des J. Cooter. Litho Format)

1983 (25 May). *Dragonflies. T* **35** *and similar horiz designs. Multicoloured. W* w **15** (*sideways*). *P* 14.

217 10 c. Type **35** 15 10
218 35 c. *Anax guttatus* 45 40
219 40 c. *Tholymis tillarga* 50 45
220 50 c. *Diplacodes bipunctata* 70 60
217/20 .. .. *Set of* 4 1·60 1·40

36 Brigade Members Racing

60c
(37)

(Des J. Cooter. Litho Format)

1983 (10 Aug). *Centenary of Boys' Brigade. T* **36** *and similar multicoloured designs. W* w **15** (*sideways on* 10 *c.*, 35 *c.*). *P* 13½.

221 10 c. Type **36** 15 15
222 35 c. B. B. members in outrigger canoe .. 40 45
223 $1 On parade (*vert*) .. .. 1·25 1·40
221/3 .. .. *Set of* 3 1·60 1·75

1983 (26 Aug). *No.* 210 *surch with T* **37**.

224 60 c. on $1 Pump drill and adze 70 70

38 Montgolfier Balloon, 1783

39 Early Communications

(Des A. Theobald. Litho Format)

1983 (21 Sept). *Bicentenary of Manned Flight. T* **38** *and similar multicoloured designs. W* w **15** (*sideways on* 35 *c.*, 45 *c.*). *P* 14.

225 25 c. Type **38** 30 30
226 35 c. McKinnon (Grumman) "Turbo-goose" (*horiz*) 40 40
a. No wmk .. ..
227 45 c. Beechcraft "Super King Air 200" (*horiz*) 50 50
228 50 c. *Double Eagle II* balloon 60 60
225/8 .. .. *Set of* 4 1·60 1·60
MS229 114 × 145 mm. Nos. 225/8. Wmk sideways 1·75 1·90

(Des J.W. Litho Questa)

1983 (18 Nov). *World Communications Year. T* **39** *and similar horiz designs. Multicoloured. W* w **15**. *P* 14.

230 25 c. Type **39** 25 25
231 35 c. Radio operator 30 30
232 45 c. Modern telephone 35 35
233 50 c. Funafuti transmitting station 40 40
230/3 .. .. *Set of* 4 1·10 1·10

30c

(40)

1984 (1 Feb). *No.* 208 *surch with T* **40**.

234 30 c. on 45 c. Reef sandals and fish trap .. 35 40

(Des R. Granger Barrett. Litho Format)

1984 (16 Feb). *Ships* (2*nd series*). *Horiz designs as T* **26**. *Multicoloured. W* w **15** (*sideways*). *P* 14.

235 10 c. S.S. *Titus*, 1897 .. .. 15 15
236 20 c. S.S. *Malaita*, 1905 .. .. 20 20
237 25 c. S.S. *Aymeric*, 1906 .. .. 20 20
238 35 c. S.S. *Anshun*, 1965 .. .. 25 25
239 45 c. M.V. *Beaverbank*, 1970 .. .. .. 35 35
240 50 c. M.V. *Benjamin Bowring*, 1981 .. .. 35 35
235/40 .. .. *Set of* 6 1·40 1·40

Nos. 235/40 were each produced in sheets of six stamps and two labels, these occurring in the second horizontal row.

41 Class "GS-4"

(Des J.W. Litho Format)

1984 (29 Feb). *Leaders of the World. Railway Locomotives* (1*st series*). *T* **41** *and similar horiz designs, the first in each pair showing technical drawings and the second the locomotive at work. P* 12½.

241 1 c. multicoloured 10 10
a. Vert pair. Nos. 241/2 .. .. .. 10 10
242 1 c. multicoloured 10 10
243 15 c. multicoloured 20 25
a. Vert pair. Nos. 243/4 .. .. .. 40 50
244 15 c. multicoloured 20 25
245 40 c. multicoloured 25 35
a. Vert pair. Nos. 245/6 .. .. .. 50 70
246 40 c. multicoloured 25 35
247 60 c. multicoloured 35 45
a. Vert pair. Nos. 247/8 .. .. .. 70 90
248 60 c. multicoloured 35 45
241/8 .. .. *Set of* 8 1·40 2·00

Designs:—Nos. 241/2, Class "GS-4", U.S.A. (1941); 243/4, Class "AD 60", Australia (1952); 245/6, Class "C 38", Australia (1943); 247/8, *Lord of the Isles*, Great Britain (1892).

See also Nos. 253/68, 273/80, 313/20 and 348/55.

42 *Ipomoea pes-caprae*

(Des Michael and Sylvia Goaman. Litho Questa)

1984 (30 May). *Beach Flowers. T* **42** *and similar horiz designs. Multicoloured. W* w **15**. *P* 14.

249 25 c. Type **42** 25 25
250 45 c. *Ipomoea macrantha* 40 40
251 50 c. *Triumfetta procumbens* 45 45
252 60 c. *Portulaca quadrifida* 50 50
249/52 .. .. *Set of* 4 1·40 1·40

(Des J.W. Litho Format)

1984 (27 June). *Leaders of the World, Railway Locomotives* (2*nd series*). *Designs as T* **41**, *the first in each pair showing technical drawings and the second the locomotive at work. P* 12½.

253 10 c. multicoloured 15 15
a. Vert pair. Nos. 253/4 .. .. .. 25 30
254 10 c. multicoloured 15 15
255 15 c. multicoloured 15 20
a. Vert pair. Nos. 255/6 .. .. .. 30 40
256 15 c. multicoloured 15 20
257 20 c. multicoloured 25 30
a. Vert pair. Nos. 257/8 .. .. .. 50 60
258 20 c. multicoloured 25 30
259 25 c. multicoloured 25 35
a. Vert pair. Nos. 259/60 .. .. .. 50 70
260 25 c. multicoloured 25 35
261 40 c. multicoloured 30 40
a. Vert pair. Nos. 261/2 .. .. .. 60 80
262 40 c. multicoloured 30 40
263 50 c. multicoloured 30 50
a. Vert pair. Nos. 263/4 .. .. .. 60 1·00
264 50 c. multicoloured 30 50
265 60 c. multicoloured 40 60
a. Vert pair. Nos. 265/6 .. .. .. 80 1·10
266 60 c. multicoloured 40 60
267 $1 multicoloured 50 80
a. Vert pair. Nos. 267/8 .. .. .. 1·00 1·60
268 $1 multicoloured 50 80
253/68 .. .. *Set of* 16 4·00 5·50

Designs:—Nos. 253/4, "Casey Jones" type engine, U.S.A. (1896); 255/6, Triplex type, U.S.A. (1914); 257/8, Class "370" Advanced Passenger Train, Great Britain (1981); 259/60, Class "4F", Great Britain (1924); 261/2, Class "Tornado Rover", Great Britain (1888); 263/4, *Broadlands*, Great Britain (1967); 265/6, *Locomotion No.* 1, Great Britain (1825); 267/8, Class "C57", Japan, (1937).

Nos. 253/68 were issued in a similar sheet format to Nos. 241/8.

43 Exhibition Emblem

44 A. Shrewsbury

(Des G. Drummond. Litho Format)

1984 (21 Aug). *"Ausipex" International Stamp Exhibition, Melbourne* (*Nos.* 269/70) *and 15th South Pacific Forum* (*others*). *T* **43** *and similar horiz designs. Multicoloured, W* w **15** (*sideways*). *P* 14.

269 60 c. Type **43** 30 40
270 60 c. Royal Exhibition Building, Melbourne .. 30 40
271 60 c. Arms of Tuvalu 30 40
272 60 c. Tuvalu flag 30 40
269/72 .. .. *Set of* 4 1·10 1·40

(Des J.W. Litho Format)

1984 (4 Oct). *Leaders of the World. Railway Locomotives* (3*rd series*). *Horiz designs as T* **41**, *the first in each pair showing technical drawings and the second the locomotive at work. P* 12½.

273 1 c. multicoloured 10 10
a. Vert pair. Nos. 273/4 .. .. .. 10 10
b. Error. Wmk w **15** .. .. .. 6·00
ba. Vert pair. Nos. 273b/4b .. .. .. 12·00
274 1 c. multicoloured 10 10
b. Error. Wmk w **15** .. .. .. 6·00
275 15 c. multicoloured 15 20
a. Vert pair. Nos. 275/6 .. .. .. 30 40
276 15 c. multicoloured 15 20
277 30 c. multicoloured 35 40
a. Vert pair. Nos. 277/8 .. .. .. 70 80
b. Error. Wmk w **15** .. .. .. 6·00
ba. Vert pair. Nos. 277b/8b .. .. .. 12·00
278 30 c. multicoloured 35 40
b. Error. Wmk w **15** .. .. .. 6·00
279 $1 multicoloured .. .. 90 1·00
a. Vert pair. Nos. 279/80 .. .. .. 1·75 2·00
b. Error. Wmk w **15** .. .. .. 11·00
ba. Vert pair. Nos. 279b/80b .. .. .. 22·00
280 $1 multicoloured .. .. 90 1·00
b. Error. Wmk w **15** .. .. .. 11·00
273/80 .. .. *Set of* 8 2·50 3·00

Designs:—Nos. 273/4, Class "9700", Japan (1897); 275/6, Class "231" C/K, France (1909); 277/8, Class "640", Italy (1907); 279/80, Class "4500", France (1906).

Nos. 273/80 were issued in a similar sheet format to Nos. 241/8.

(Des Court House Studio. Litho Format)

1984 (5 Nov). *Leaders of the World. Cricketers. T* **44** *and similar vert designs, the first listed in each pair showing the cricketer in action and the second a head portrait. P* 12½.

281 5 c. multicoloured 10 10
a. Horiz pair. Nos. 281/2 .. .. .. 20 20
282 5 c. multicoloured 10 10
283 30 c. multicoloured 35 40
a. Horiz pair. Nos. 283/4 .. .. .. 70 80
284 30 c. multicoloured 35 40
285 50 c. multicoloured 55 60
a. Horiz pair. Nos. 285/6 .. .. .. 1·10 1·25
286 50 c. multicoloured 55 60
287 60 c. multicoloured 65 70
a. Horiz pair. Nos. 287/8 .. .. .. 1·25 1·40
288 60 c. multicoloured 65 70
281/8 .. .. *Set of* 8 3·00 3·25

Designs:—Nos. 281/2, A. Shrewsbury; 283/4, H. Verity; 285/6, E. H. Hendren; 287/8, J. Briggs.

Nos. 281/2, 283/4, 285/6 and 287/8 were printed together, *se-tenant*, in horizontal pairs throughout the sheets.

45 Trees and Stars

(Des Jennifer Toombs. Litho Format)

1984 (14 Nov). *Christmas. Children's Drawings. T* **45** *and similar horiz designs. Multicoloured. W* w **15** (*sideways*). *P* 14½ × 14.

289 15 c. Type **45** 10 10
290 40 c. Fishing from outrigger canoes 20 20
291 50 c. Three Wise Men bearing gifts 25 25
292 60 c. The Holy Family 35 35
289/92 .. .. *Set of* 4 75 75

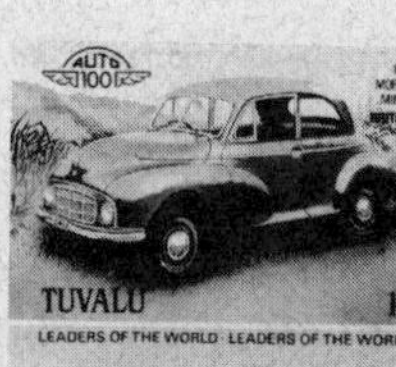

46 Morris Minor

47 Common Flicker

(Des J.W. ($1), Artists International (others). Litho Format)

1984 (7 Dec). *Leaders of the World. Automobiles* (1*st series*). *T* **46** *and similar horiz designs, the first in each pair showing technical drawings and the second paintings. P* 12½.

293 1 c. black, pale cinnamon and yellow-ochre .. 10 10
a. Vert pair. Nos. 293/4 .. .. .. 10 10
294 1 c. multicoloured 10 10
295 15 c. black, pale flesh and brown-lilac .. 15 20
a. Vert pair. Nos. 295/6 .. .. .. 30 40
296 15 c. multicoloured 15 20
297 50 c. black, pale cinnamon and dull mauve .. 40 45
a. Vert pair. Nos. 297/8 .. .. .. 80 90
298 50 c. multicoloured 40 45
299 $1 black, pale green and cobalt 70 80
a. Vert pair. Nos. 299/300 .. .. .. 1·40 1·60
300 $1 multicoloured 70 80
293/300 .. .. *Set of* 8 2·25 2·75

Designs:—Nos. 293/4, Morris "Minor"; 295/6, Studebaker "Avanti"; 297/8, Chevrolet "International Six"; 299/300, Allard "J2".

Nos. 293/4, 295/6, 297/8 and 299/300 were printed together, *se-tenant*, in vertical pairs throughout the sheets.

See also Nos. 321/8, 356/71, 421/32 and 446/70.

IMPERFORATES AND MISSING COLOURS. Various issues between Nos. 301 and 529 exist either imperforate or with colours omitted. Such items are not listed as there is no evidence that they fulfil the criteria outlined on page xi of this catalogue.

(Des R. Vigurs. Litho Format)

1985 (12 Feb). *Leaders of the World. Birth Bicentenary of John J. Audubon (ornithologist). T* **47** *and similar vert designs. Multicoloured. P* 12½.

301 1 c. Type **47** 10 10
a. Horiz pair. Nos. 301/2 .. .. .. 10 10
302 1 c. Say's Phoebe 10 10
303 25 c. Townsend's Warbler 30 35
a. Horiz pair. Nos. 303/4 .. .. .. 60 70
304 25 c. Bohemian Waxwing 30 35
305 50 c. Prothonotary Warbler 55 60
a. Horiz pair. Nos. 305/6 .. .. .. 1·10 1·25
306 50 c. Worm-eating Warbler 55 60
307 70 c. Broad-winged Hawk 80 85
a. Horiz pair. Nos. 307/8 .. .. .. 1·60 1·75
308 70 c. Hen Harrier 80 85
301/8 .. .. *Set of* 8 3·00 3·25

Nos. 301/2, 303/4, 305/6 and 307/8 were printed together, *se-tenant*, in horizontal pairs throughout the sheets.

48 Black-naped Tern

(Des G. Drummond. Litho Format)

1985 (27 Feb). *Birds and their Eggs. T* **48** *and similar horiz designs. Multicoloured. W* w **15** (*sideways*). *P* 14.

309 15 c. Type **48** 35 20
310 40 c. White-capped Noddy 75 50
311 50 c. White-tailed Tropicbird 85 60
312 60 c. Sooty Tern .. .. 1·00 70
309/12 .. .. *Set of* 4 2·75 1·75

(Des J.W. (5 c., $1), T. Hadler (others). Litho Format)

1985 (19 Mar). *Leaders of the World. Railway Locomotives* (4*th series*). *Horiz designs as T* **41** *the first in each pair showing technical drawings and the second the locomotive at work. P* 12½.

313 5 c. multicoloured 10 10
a. Vert pair. Nos. 313/14 .. .. .. 10 10
314 5 c. multicoloured 10 10
315 10 c. multicoloured 10 10
a. Vert pair. Nos. 315/16 .. .. .. 20 20
316 10 c. multicoloured 10 10
317 30 c. multicoloured 30 35
a. Vert pair. Nos. 317/18 .. .. .. 60 70
318 30 c. multicoloured 30 35
319 $1 multicoloured .. .. 75 1·00
a. Vert pair. Nos. 319/20 .. .. .. 1·50 2·00
ab. Imperf (vert pair) .. .. ..
320 $1 multicoloured .. .. 75 1·00
313/20 .. .. *Set of* 8 2·25 2·75

Designs:—Nos. 313/14, "Churchward 28XX", Great Britain (1905); 315/16, Class "KF", China (1935); 317/18, Class "99.77", East Germany (1952); 319/20, Pearson type, Great Britain (1853).

Nos. 313/20 were issued in a similar sheet format to Nos. 241/8.

(Des Artists International. Litho Format)

1985 (3 Apr). *Leaders of the World. Automobiles* (2*nd series*). *Horiz designs as T* **46**, *the first in each pair showing technical drawings and the second paintings. P* 12½.

321 1 c. black, apple green and deep dull green 10 10
a. Vert pair. Nos. 321/2 .. .. .. 10 10
322 1 c. multicoloured 10 10
323 20 c. black, pink and rose-red 15 20
a. Vert pair. Nos. 323/4 .. .. .. 30 40
324 20 c. multicoloured 15 20
325 50 c. black, dull violet-blue & brt reddish vio 30 45
a. Vert pair. Nos. 325/6 .. .. .. 60 90
326 50 c. multicoloured 30 45
327 70 c. black, dull pink and grey-brown .. 40 60
a. Vert pair. Nos. 327/8 .. .. .. 80 1·10
328 70 c. multicoloured 40 60
321/8 .. .. *Set of* 8 1·60 2·25

Designs:—Nos. 321/2, Rickenbacker (1923); 323/4, Detroit-Electric Two Door Brougham (1914); 325/6, Packard "Clipper" (1941); 327/8, Audi "Quattro" (1982).

Nos. 321/8 were issued in a similar sheet format to Nos. 293/300.

49 Curtiss "P-40N"

50 Queen Elizabeth the Queen Mother

(Des A. Theobald. Litho Questa)

1985 (29 May). *World War II Aircraft. T* **49** *and similar horiz designs. Multicoloured. W* w **15**. *P* 14.

329 15 c. Type **49** 40 20
330 40 c. Consolidated "B-24 Liberator" 70 45
331 50 c. Lockheed "PV-1 Ventura" 80 55
332 60 c. Douglas "C-54 Skymaster" 90 65
329/32 .. .. *Set of* 4 2·50 1·60
MS333 110×108 mm. Nos. 329/32. Wmk sideways .. .. 2·50 2·25

(Des D. Ewart ($1.20), Maxine Marsh (others). Litho Format)

1985 (4 July). *Leaders of the World. Life and Times of Queen Elizabeth the Queen Mother. Various vertical portraits as T* **50**. *P* 12½.

334 5 c. multicoloured 10 10
a. Horiz pair. Nos. 334/5 10 10
335 5 c. multicoloured 10 10
336 30 c. multicoloured 20 25
a. Horiz pair. Nos. 336/7 40 50
337 30 c. multicoloured 20 25
338 60 c. multicoloured 30 45
a. Horiz pair. Nos. 338/9 60 90
339 60 c. multicoloured 30 45
340 $1 multicoloured 50 65
a. Horiz pair. Nos. 340/1 1·00 1·25
341 $1 multicoloured 50 65
334/41 *Set of* 8 1·75 2·50
MS342 85×114 mm. $1.20, multicoloured; $1.20, multicoloured 1·10 2·00

The two designs of each value were issued, *se-tenant*, in horizontal pairs within the sheets.

Each *se-tenant* pair shows a floral pattern across the bottom of the portraits which stops short of the left-hand edge on the left-hand stamp and of the right-hand edge on the right-hand stamp.

Designs as Nos. 336/7 and 338/9, but with face values of $2×2 and $3×2, also exist in additional miniature sheets from a restricted printing issued 10 January 1986.

51 Guide playing Guitar **52** Stalk-eyed Ghost Crab

(Des Jennifer Toombs. Litho Format)

1985 (28 Aug). *75th Anniv of Girl Guide Movement. T* **51** *and similar vert designs. Multicoloured. W w* **15** *(sideways). P* 15.

343 15 c. Type **51** 15 20
344 40 c. Building camp-fire 40 45
345 50 c. Patrol Leader with Guide flag 50 55
346 60 c. Guide saluting 60 65
343/6 *Set of* 4 1·50 1·60
MS347 141×77 mm. Nos. 343/6. Wmk upright 1·75 2·00

(Des J.W. (10 c.), T. Hadler (others). Litho Format)

1985 (18 Sept). *Leaders of the World. Railway Locomotives (5th series). Horiz designs as T* **41**, *the first in each pair showing technical drawings and the second the locomotive at work. P* 12½.

348 10 c. multicoloured 10 15
a. Vert pair. Nos. 348/9 20 30
349 10 c. multicoloured 10 15
350 40 c. multicoloured 40 45
a. Vert pair. Nos. 350/1 80 90
351 40 c. multicoloured 40 45
352 65 c. multicoloured 70 75
a. Vert pair. Nos. 352/3 1·40 1·50
353 65 c. multicoloured 70 75
354 $1 multicoloured 1·10 1·25
a. Vert pair. Nos. 354/5 2·25 2·50
355 $1 multicoloured 1·10 1·25
348/55 *Set of* 8 4·00 4·50

Designs:—Nos. 348/9, *Green Arrow*, Great Britain (1936); 350/1, Class "SD-50" diesel, U.S.A. (1982); 352/3, D.R.G. *Flying Hamburger*, Germany (1932); 354/5, Class "1070", Japan (1908).

Nos. 348/55 were issued in a similar sheet format to Nos. 241/8.

(Des Artists International. Litho Format)

1985 (8 Oct). *Leaders of the World. Automobiles (3rd series). Horiz designs as T* **46**, *the first in each pair showing technical drawings and the second paintings. P* 12½.

356 5 c. black, grey and bright mauve 10 10
a. Vert pair. Nos. 356/7 10 15
357 5 c. multicoloured 10 10
358 10 c. black, pale salmon-pink and Indian red 10 15
a. Vert pair. Nos. 358/9 20 30
359 10 c. multicoloured 10 15
360 15 c. black, light brown and Indian red 15 20
a. Vert pair. Nos. 360/1 30 40
361 15 c. multicoloured 15 20
362 35 c. black, brown-red & light turq-blue 35 40
a. Vert pair. Nos. 362/3 70 80
363 35 c. multicoloured 35 40
364 40 c. black, dull yellow-grn & yellowish grn 35 40
a. Vert pair. Nos. 364/5 70 80
365 40 c. multicoloured 35 40
366 55 c. black, pale stone and brown-olive 45 50
a. Vert pair. Nos. 366/7 90 1·00
367 55 c. multicoloured 45 50
368 $1 black, brown and lake-brown 80 90
a. Vert pair. Nos. 368/9 1·60 1·75
369 $1 multicoloured 80 90
370 $1.50, black, flesh and dull scarlet 1·10 1·25
a. Vert pair. Nos. 370/1 2·10 2·50
371 $1.50, multicoloured 1·10 1·25
356/71 *Set of* 16 6·00 7·00

Designs:—Nos. 356/7, Cord "L-29" (1929); 358/9, Horch "670 V-12" (1932); 360/1, Lanchester (1901); 362/3, Citroen "2 CV" (1950); 364/5. MGA (1957); 366/7, Ferrari "250 GTO" (1962); 368/9, Ford "V-8" (1932); 370/1, Aston Martin "Lagonda" (1977).

Nos. 356/71 were issued in a similar sheet format to Nos. 293/300.

(Des G. Drummond. Litho Format)

1986 (7 Jan). *Crabs. T* **52** *and similar horiz designs. Multicoloured. P* 15.

372 15 c. Type **52** 20 20
373 40 c. Red and White Painted Crab 45 50
374 50 c. Red-spotted Crab 55 60
375 60 c. Red Hermit Crab 70 80
372/5 *Set of* 4 1·75 1·90

53 Chess Knight on Board and Flags of U.S. and U.S.S.R. (World Chess Championships) **54** Peace Dove carrying Wreath and Rainbow

(Des Court House Studio. Litho Format)

1986 (19 Mar). *International Events. Sheet* 148×127 *mm, containing T* **53** *and similar vert design. Multicoloured. P* 12½.

MS376 $3 Type **53**: $3 Emblem (80th anniv of Rotary 7·50 7·50

No. **MS**376 exists with plain or decorative margins.

Overprints on this miniature sheet commemorating "Capex 87" International Stamp Exhibition, Toronto, or the World Scout Jamboree, were not authorised by the Tuvalu administration.

(Des R. Granger Barrett. Litho Format)

1986 (14 Apr). *Ships (3rd series). Missionary Vessels. Horiz designs as T* **26**. *Multicoloured. W w* **15**. *P* 15.

377 15 c. *Messenger of Peace* 15 15
378 40 c. *John Wesley* 35 40
379 50 c. *Duff* 40 45
380 60 c. *Triton* 50 55
377/80 *Set of* 4 1·25 1·40

(Des Court House Studio. Litho Format)

1986 (21 Apr–14 June). *60th Birthday of Queen Elizabeth II. Multicoloured designs as T* **167** *of British Virgin Islands. P* 12½.

381 10 c. Queen wearing ceremonial cloak, New Zealand, 1977 15 10
382 90 c. Before visit to France, 1957 75 80
383 $1.50, Queen in 1982 1·25 1·40
384 $3 In Canberra, 1982 (*vert*) 2·50 2·75
381/4 *Set of* 4 4·25 4·50
MS385 85×115 mm. $4 Queen carrying bouquet (14.6) 3·25 3·50

The 10 c., 90 c. and $1.50 values exist with PVA gum as well as gum arabic.

(Des Gloria McConnaghy. Litho Questa)

1986 (22 May). *25th Anniv of United States Peace Corps. W w* **15**. *P* 14.

386 **54** 50 c. multicoloured 80 80

55 Island and Flags of Tuvalu and U.S.A. **56** South Korean Player

(Des Court House Studio. Litho Questa)

1986 (22 May). *"Ameripex" International Stamp Exhibition, Chicago. W w* **15**. *P* 14×13½.

387 **55** 60 c. multicoloured 85 85

(Des Court House Studio. Litho Format)

1986 (30 June). *World Cup Football Championship, Mexico. T* **56** *and similar multicoloured designs. P* 15 (1 c. *to* 40 c.) *or* 12½ *(others).*

388 1 c. Type **56** 10 10
389 5 c. French player 10 10
390 10 c. West German captain with World Cup trophy, 1974 10 10
391 40 c. Italian player 50 40
392 60 c. World Cup final, 1974 (59×39 *mm*) 65 55
393 $1 Canadian team (59×39 *mm*) 1·00 1·00
394 $2 Northern Irish team (59×39 *mm*) 2·00 2·00
395 $3 English team (59×39 *mm*) 3·00 3·00
388/95 *Set of* 8 6·50 6·50
MS396 Two sheets, each 85×114 mm. (a) $1.50, As No. 393; (b) $2·50, As No. 394 *Set of* 2 *sheets* 4·50 5·00

(Litho Format)

1986 (18 July–15 Oct). *Royal Wedding. Multicoloured designs as T* **168** *of British Virgin Islands. P* 12½.

397 60 c. Prince Andrew and Miss Sarah Ferguson 50 55
a. Pair. Nos. 397/8 1·00 1·10
398 60 c. Prince Andrew with prizewinning bull 50 55
399 $1 Prince Andrew at horse trials (*horiz*) 85 90
a. Pair. Nos. 399/400 1·75 1·75
400 $1 Miss Sarah Ferguson and Princess Diana (*horiz*) 85 90
397/400 *Set of* 4 2·40 2·50
MS401 85×115 mm. $6 Duke and Duchess of York after wedding (*horiz*) (15.10) 5·25 5·50

Nos. 397/8 and 399/400 were printed together, *se-tenant*, in horizontal and vertical pairs throughout the sheets.

57 Mourning Gecko **(58)**

(Des Jennifer Toombs. Litho Questa)

1986 (30 July). *Lizards. T* **57** *and similar horiz designs. Multicoloured. W w* **15**. *P* 14.

402 15 c. Type **57** 45 45
403 40 c. Oceanic Stump-toed Gecko 80 80
404 50 c. Azure-tailed Skink 1·00 1·00
405 60 c. Moth Skink 1·25 1·25
402/5 *Set of* 4 3·25 3·25

1986 (4 Aug). *"Stampex '86" Stamp Exhibition, Adelaide. No. 386 optd with T* **58**.

406 **54** 50 c. multicoloured 40 45

59 Map and Flag of Australia

(Des G. Drummond. Litho Format)

1986 (4 Aug). *15th Anniv of South Pacific Forum. T* **59** *and similar horiz designs showing maps and national flags. Multicoloured. W w* **15**. *P* 15.

407 40 c. Type **59** 45 45
a. Sheetlet. Nos. 407/20 5·50
408 40 c. Cook Islands 45 45
409 40 c. Micronesia 45 45
410 40 c. Fiji 45 45
411 40 c. Kiribati 45 45
412 40 c. Western Samoa 45 45
413 40 c. Nauru 45 45
414 40 c. Vanuatu 45 45
415 40 c. New Zealand 45 45
416 40 c. Tuvalu 45 45
417 40 c. Tonga 45 45
418 40 c. Solomon Islands 45 45
419 40 c. Papua New Guinea 45 45
420 40 c. Niue 45 45
407/20 *Set of* 14 5·50 5·50

Nos. 407/20 were printed together, *se-tenant*, as a sheetlet of fourteen stamps arranged round a central label.

(Des Court House Studio. Litho Format)

1986 (13 Oct). *Automobiles (4th series). Horiz designs as T* **46**, *the first in each pair showing technical drawings and the second paintings. P* 12½.

421 15 c. multicoloured 15 15
a. Vert pair. Nos. 421/2 30 30
422 15 c. multicoloured 15 15
423 40 c. multicoloured 35 40
a. Vert pair. Nos. 423/4 70 80
424 40 c. multicoloured 35 40
425 50 c. multicoloured 45 50
a. Vert pair. Nos. 425/6 90 1·00
426 50 c. multicoloured 45 50
427 60 c. multicoloured 55 60
a. Vert pair. Nos. 427/8 1·10 1·25
428 60 c. multicoloured 55 60
429 90 c. multicoloured 80 85
a. Vert pair. Nos. 429/30 1·60 1·75
430 90 c. multicoloured 80 85
431 $1.50, multicoloured 1·10 1·40
a. Vert pair. Nos. 431/2 2·10 2·75
432 $1.50, multicoloured 1·10 1·40
421/32 *Set of* 12 6·00 7·00

Designs:—Nos. 421/2, Cooper "500" (1953); 423/4, Rover "2000" (1964); 425/6, Ruxton (1930); 427/8, Jowett "Jupiter" (1950); 429/30, Cobra "Daytona Coupe" (1964); 431/2, Packard Model F "Old Pacific" (1903).

Nos. 421/32 were issued in a similar sheet format to Nos. 293/300.

OMNIBUS ISSUES

Details, together with prices for complete sets, of the various Omnibus issues from the 1935 Silver Jubilee series to date are included in a special section following Zululand at the end of the catalogue.

1986 (28 Oct). *Royal Wedding (2nd issue). Nos. 397/400 optd as T* **121** *of Montserrat in silver.*
433 60 c. Prince Andrew and Miss Sarah Ferguson 70 70
a. Pair. Nos. 433/4.. .. .. 1·40 1·40
434 60 c. Prince Andrew with prizewinning bull 70 70
435 $1 Prince Andrew at horse trials (*horiz*) .. 1·00 1·00
a. Pair. Nos. 435/6.. .. .. 2·00 2·00
436 $1 Miss Sarah Ferguson and Princess Diana (*horiz*) .. .. 1·00 1·00
433/6 .. .. *Set of* 4 3·00 3·00

60 Sea Star

61 *Nephrolepis saligna*

(Des G. Drummond. Litho Questa)

1986 (5 Nov). *Coral Reef Life (1st series). T* **60** *and similar horiz designs. Multicoloured. P* 14.
437 15 c. Type **60** 40 40
438 40 c. Pencil Urchin 90 90
439 50 c. Fragile Coral .. .. 1·00 1·00
440 60 c. Pink Coral .. .. 1·10 1·10
437/40 .. .. *Set of* 4 3·00 3·00
See also Nos. 498/501 and 558/62.

(Des Court House Studio. Litho Format)

1986 (24 Nov). *Centenary of Statue of Liberty. Vert views of Statue as T* **171** *of British Virgin Islands in separate miniature sheets. Multicoloured. P* 14 × 13½.
MS441 Nine sheets, each 85 × 115 mm. $1.25; $1.50; $1.80; $2; $2.25; $2.50; $3; $3.25; $3.50 .. .. .. *Set of* 9 *sheets* 19·00 22·00

(Des R. Granger Barrett. Litho Questa)

1987 (4 Feb). *Ships (4th series). Missionary Steamers. Horiz designs as T* **26**. *Multicoloured. P* 14.
442 15 c. *Southern Cross IV* 40 40
443 40 c. *John Williams VI* 90 90
444 50 c. *John Williams IV* .. .. 1·00 1·00
445 60 c. *M.S. Southern Cross* .. .. 1·10 1·10
442/5 .. .. *Set of* 4 3·00 3·00

(Litho Format)

1987 (7 May–6 June). *Automobiles (5th series). Horiz designs as T* **46**, *the first in each pair showing technical drawings and the second paintings. P* 12½.
446 1 c. multicoloured 10 10
a. Vert pair. Nos. 446/7 .. .. 10 10
447 1 c. multicoloured 10 10
448 2 c. multicoloured 10 10
a. Vert pair. Nos. 448/9 .. .. 10 10
449 2 c. multicoloured 10 10
450 5 c. multicoloured 10 10
a. Vert pair. Nos. 450/1 .. .. 10 15
451 5 c. multicoloured 10 10
452 10 c. multicoloured 10 15
a. Vert pair. Nos. 452/3 .. .. 20 30
453 10 c. multicoloured 10 15
454 20 c. multicoloured 20 25
a. Vert pair. Nos. 454/5 .. .. 40 50
455 20 c. multicoloured 20 25
456 30 c. multicoloured 25 30
a. Vert pair. Nos. 456/7 .. .. 50 60
457 30 c. multicoloured 25 30
458 40 c. multicoloured 35 40
a. Vert pair. Nos. 458/9 .. .. 70 80
459 40 c. multicoloured 35 40
460 50 c. multicoloured 45 50
a. Vert pair. Nos. 460/1 .. .. 90 1·00
461 50 c. multicoloured 45 50
462 60 c. multicoloured 55 60
a. Vert pair. Nos. 462/3 .. .. 1·10 1·25
463 60 c. multicoloured 55 60
464 70 c. multicoloured 60 65
a. Vert pair. Nos. 464/5 .. .. 1·25 1·25
465 70 c. multicoloured 60 65
466 75 c. multicoloured 65 70
a. Vert pair. Nos. 466/7 .. .. 1·25 1·40
467 75 c. multicoloured 65 70
468 $1 multicoloured 90 95
a. Vert pair. Nos. 468/9 .. .. 1·75 1·90
469 $1 multicoloured 90 95
446/9 .. .. *Set of* 24 7·50 8·25
MS470 100 × 85 mm. Nos. 468/9 (6.6) .. .. 1·75 2·25
Designs:—Nos. 446/7, Talbot-Lago (1938); 448/9, Du Pont "Model G" (1930); 450/1, Riley "RM" (1950); 452/3, Chevrolet "Baby Grand" (1915); 454/5, Shelby "Mustang GT 500 KR" (1968); 456/7, Ferrari "212 Export Barchetta" (1952); 458/9, Peerless "Model 48-Six" (1912); 460/1, Sunbeam "Alpine" (1954); 462/3, Matra-Ford "MS 80" (1969); 464/5, Squire 1½ Litre (1934); 466/7, Talbot "105" (1931); 468/9, Plymouth "Model Q" (1928).
Nos. 446/69 were issued in a similar sheet format to Nos. 293/300.

(Des J. Cooter. Litho Questa)

1987 (7 July). *Ferns. T* **61** *and similar vert designs. Multicoloured. W w* **15** *(sideways). P* 14.
471 15 c. Type **61** 35 35
472 40 c. *Asplenium nidus* 60 60
473 50 c. *Microsorum scolopendria* 75 75
474 60 c. *Pteris tripartita* 85 85
471/4 .. .. *Set of* 4 2·25 2·25
MS475 62 × 62 mm. $1.50, *Psilotum nudum*. Wmk upright .. .. 2·00 2·50

62 Floral Arrangement

63 Queen Victoria, 1897 (photo by Downey)

(Des Jennifer Toombs. Litho Questa)

1987 (12 Aug). *Flowers and "Fous". T* **62** *and similar vert designs showing either floral arrangements or "fous" (women's headdresses). Multicoloured. W w* **15** *(sideways). P* 14.
476 15 c. Type **62** 15 15
a. Horiz pair. Nos. 476/7 .. .. 30 30
477 15 c. "Fou" 15 15
478 40 c. "Fou" 35 40
a. Horiz pair. Nos. 478/9 .. .. 70 80
479 40 c. Floral arrangement 35 40
480 50 c. Floral arrangement 45 50
a. Horiz pair. Nos. 480/1 .. .. 90 1·00
481 50 c. "Fou" 45 50
482 60 c. "Fou" 55 60
a. Horiz pair. Nos. 482/3 .. .. 1·10 1·25
483 60 c. Floral arrangement 55 60
476/83 .. .. *Set of* 8 2·75 3·00
The two designs of each value were printed together, *se-tenant*, in horizontal pairs throughout the sheets.

(Litho Format)

1987 (15 Oct). *Royal Ruby Wedding and 150th Anniv of Queen Victoria's Accession. T* **63** *and similar square designs. P* 15.
484 40 c. brownish black, black and deep olive .. 35 40
485 60 c. purple-black, black and deep blue-green 55 60
486 80 c. brownish black, black and deep dull blue 70 75
487 $1 brownish black, black and deep claret .. 90 95
488 $2 multicoloured .. .. 1·75 1·90
484/8 .. .. *Set of* 5 3·75 4·25
MS489 86 × 101 mm. $3 brownish black .. .. 2·75 3·25
Designs:—60 c. Wedding of Princess Elizabeth and Duke of Edinburgh, 1947; 80 c. Queen, Duke of Edinburgh and Prince Charles, *c.* 1950; $1 Queen with Princess Anne, 1950; $2 Queen Elizabeth II, 1970; $3 Queen and Prince Charles at Princess Anne's christening, 1950.

64 Coconut Crab

(Des M. Pollard. Litho Questa)

1987 (11 Nov). *Crustaceans. T* **64** *and similar diamond-shaped designs. Multicoloured. W w* **15**. *P* 14.
490 40 c. Type **64** 45 45
491 50 c. Painted Crayfish 60 60
492 60 c. Ocean Crayfish 70 70
490/2 .. .. *Set of* 3 1·60 1·60

65 Aborigine and Ayers Rock

(Des Young Philips. Litho Format)

1987 (2 Dec). *World Scout Jamboree, Australia. T* **65** *and similar horiz designs. Multicoloured. P* 12½.
493 40 c. Type **65** 40 40
494 60 c. Capt. Cook and H.M.S. *Endeavour* .. 80 80
495 $1 Scout saluting and Scout Park entrance 1·10 1·10
496 $1.50, Koala and kangaroo .. .. .. 1·40 1·40
493/6 .. .. *Set of* 4 3·25 3·25
MS497 115 × 85 mm. $2.50, Lord and Lady Baden-Powell .. .. 2·50 3·00

(Des G. Drummond. Litho Format)

1988 (29 Feb). *Coral Reef Life (2nd series). Horiz designs as T* **60**. *Multicoloured. P* 15.
498 15 c. Spanish Dancer 35 35
499 40 c. Hard corals 70 70
500 50 c. Feather Stars 80 80
501 60 c. Staghorn corals 85 85
498/501 .. .. *Set of* 4 2·40 2·40

66 Red Junglefowl

67 Henri Dunant (founder)

(Des Jennifer Toombs. Litho Format)

1988 (2 Mar). *Birds. T* **66** *and similar horiz designs. Multicoloured. P* 15.
502 5 c. Type **66** 10 10
503 10 c. White Tern 10 10
504 15 c. Common Noddy 10 15
505 20 c. Phoenix Petrel 15 20
506 25 c. American Golden Plover 20 25
507 30 c. Crested Tern 25 30
508 35 c. Sooty Tern 30 35
509 40 c. Bristle-thighed Curlew 35 40
510 45 c. Bar-tailed Godwit 35 40
511 50 c. Eastern Reef Heron 40 45
512 55 c. Great Frigate Bird 45 50
513 60 c. Red-footed Booby 50 55
514 70 c. Rufous-necked Sandpiper ("Red-necked Stint") 60 65
515 $1 Long-tailed Koel ("Long-tailed Cuckoo") 85 90
516 $2 Red-tailed Tropic Bird .. .. .. 1·60 1·75
517 $5 Banded Rail .. .. 4·25 4·50
502/17 .. .. *Set of* 16 9·50 10·50

(Des M. Pollard. Litho Format)

1988 (9 May). *125th Anniv of International Red Cross. T* **67** *and similar horiz designs. P* 12½.
518 15 c. vermilion and pale reddish brown .. 15 20
519 40 c. vermilion and ultramarine 40 45
520 50 c. vermilion and turquoise-green .. 50 55
521 60 c. vermilion and purple 55 60
518/21 .. .. *Set of* 4 1·40 1·60
MS522 96 × 66 mm. $1.50, vermilion & emerald 1·40 1·50
Designs:—40 c. Junior Red Cross members on parade; 50 c. Red Cross worker with boy in wheelchair; 60 c. First aid training; $1.50, Lecture.

68 H.M.S. *Endeavour*

(Litho Format)

1988 (15 June). *Voyages of Captain Cook. T* **68** *and similar horiz designs. Multicoloured. P* 12½.
523 20 c. Type **68** 40 40
524 40 c. Stern of H.M.S. *Endeavour* 60 60
525 50 c. Cook preparing to land at Tahiti (*vert*) 70 70
526 60 c. Maori chief (*vert*) 75 75
527 80 c. H.M.S. *Resolution* and Hawaiian canoe 1·00 1·00
528 $1 "Captain Cook" (after Nathaniel Dance) (*vert*) .. .. 1·25 1·25
523/8 .. .. *Set of* 6 4·25 4·25
MS529 115 × 85 mm. $2.50, H.M.S. *Resolution* in Antarctica .. .. 3·00 3·50

69 *Ganoderma applanatum*

(Des J. Cooter. Litho Format)

1988 (25 July). *Fungi (1st series). T* **69** *and similar vert designs. Multicoloured. P* 15.
530 40 c. Type **69** 65 65
531 50 c. *Pseudoepicoccum cocos* (brown leaf spot) 70 70
532 60 c. *Rigidoporus zonalis* 80 80
533 90 c. *Rigidoporus microporus* .. .. .. 1·10 1·10
530/3 .. .. *Set of* 4 3·00 3·00
See also Nos. 554/7.

COVER PRICES

Cover factors are quoted at the beginning of each country for most issues to 1945. An explanation of the system can be found on page x. The factors quoted do not, however, apply to philatelic covers.

70 Rifle-shooting

(Litho Format)

1988 (19 Aug). *Olympic Games, Seoul. T* **70** *and similar horiz designs. Multicoloured. P* 12½.

No.	Description		Unused	Used
534	10 c. Type **70**		10	15
535	20 c. Judo		20	25
536	40 c. Canoeing		40	45
537	60 c. Swimming		55	60
538	80 c. Yachting		75	80
539	$1 Gymnastics		95	1·00
534/9		*Set of* 6	2·75	3·00

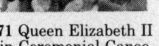

71 Queen Elizabeth II in Ceremonial Canoe

72 Virgin Mary

(Des and litho Questa)

1988 (28 Sept). *10th Anniv of Independence. T* **71** *and similar designs showing scenes from Royal Visit of* 1982. *W w* **15** *(sideways on* 60, 90 *c.,* $1.20). *P* 14.

No.	Description		Unused	Used
540	60 c. multicoloured		55	60
541	90 c. multicoloured		85	90
542	$1 multicoloured (*horiz*)		95	1·00
543	$1.20, multicoloured		1·10	1·25
540/3		*Set of* 4	3·00	3·50
MS544	Designs as Nos. 540/3 in separate miniature sheets, each 85 × 85 mm	*Set of* 4 *sheets*	3·50	3·75

(Des M. Pollard. Litho Questa)

1988 (5 Dec). *Christmas. T* **72** *and similar diamond-shaped designs. Multicoloured. P* 14.

No.	Description		Unused	Used
545	15 c. Type **72**		15	20
546	40 c. Christ Child		40	45
547	60 c. Joseph		55	60
545/7		*Set of* 3	1·00	2·00
MS548	73 × 99 mm. $1.50, Angel		1·40	1·50

73 Dancing Skirt and Dancer

(Des Jennifer Toombs. Litho Questa)

1989 (31 Mar). *Traditional Dancing Skirts. T* **73** *and similar designs showing skirts and dancer silhouettes. P* 14½.

No.	Description		Unused	Used
549	40 c. multicoloured		40	45
550	50 c. multicoloured		50	55
551	60 c. multicoloured		55	60
552	90 c. multicoloured		85	90
549/52		*Set of* 4	2·10	2·25
MS553	110×75 mm. $1.50, multicoloured (dancer) (*vert*)		1·40	1·50

(Litho Questa)

1989 (24 May). *Fungi (2nd series). Vert designs as T* **69**. *Multicoloured. P* 14.

No.	Description		Unused	Used
554	40 c. *Trametes muelleri*		60	60
555	50 c. *Pestalotiopsis palmarum* (grey leaf spot)		70	70
556	60 c. *Trametes cingulata*		75	75
557	90 c. *Schizophyllum commune*		1·10	1·10
554/7		*Set of* 4	2·75	2·75

(Des G. Drummond. Litho Questa)

1989 (31 July). *Coral Reef Life (3rd series). Horiz designs as T* **60**. *Multicoloured. P* 14.

No.	Description		Unused	Used
558	40 c. Pennant Coralfish		55	55
559	50 c. Anemone Fish		70	70
560	60 c. Batfish		75	75
561	90 c. Threadfin Coralfish		1·10	1·10
558/61		*Set of* 4	2·75	2·75
MS562	110×85 mm. Nos. 558/61		3·00	3·00

74 *Nivaga II*

75 Conch Shell

(Des M. Pollard. Litho Questa)

1989 (9 Oct). *Delivery of* Nivaga II *(new inter-island ship). Sheet* 116×85 *mm. P* 14.

No.	Description	Unused	Used
MS563 **74**	$1.50, multicoloured	1·40	1·50

(Des Jennifer Toombs. Litho Questa)

1989 (29 Nov). *Christmas. T* **75** *and similar vert designs. Multicoloured. P* 14.

No.	Description		Unused	Used
564	40 c. Type **75**		40	45
565	50 c. Posy of flowers		50	55
566	60 c. Germinating coconut		55	60
567	90 c. Jewellery		85	90
564/7		*Set of* 4	2·10	2·25

POSTAGE DUE STAMPS

D 1 Tuvalu Crest

(Des G. Drummond. Litho Questa)

1981 (3 May). *P* 13½ × 14.

No.	Type	Description		Unused	Used
D1	D 1	1 c. black and bright purple		10	10
D2		2 c. black and greenish blue		10	10
D3		5 c. black and ochre		10	10
D4		10 c. black and blue-green		20	20
D5		20 c. black and purple-brown		35	35
D6		30 c. black and bright orange		35	40
D7		40 c. black and blue		45	50
D8		50 c. black and yellow-green		55	60
D9		$1 black and deep mauve		1·00	1·10
D1/9			*Set of* 9	2·75	3·00

1982 (25 Nov)–**83**. *As Nos.* D1/9 *but P* 14½ × 15 *and with imprint date at foot.*

No.	Type	Description		Unused	Used
D10	D 1	1 c. black and bright purple		10	10
D11		2 c. black and greenish blue		10	10
D12		5 c. black and ochre		10	10
D13		10 c. black and blue-green		10	10
D14		20 c. black and purple-brown		15	20
D15		30 c. black and bright orange (25.5.83)		25	30
D16		40 c. black and blue (25.5.83)		35	40
D17		50 c. black and yellow-green (25.5.83)		40	45
D18		$1 black and deep mauve (25.5.83)		85	90
D10/18			*Set of* 9	2·00	2·25

The imprint date on Nos. D10/14 is "1982" and on Nos. D15/18 "1983".

OFFICIAL STAMPS

For the use of the Philatelic Bureau.

OFFICIAL (O 1) OFFICIAL (O 2)

TWO TYPES OF OVERPRINT FOR NOS. O1/19

This issue was overprinted using two different processes.

All values, except for the 35, 45 and 50 c., come with the overprint applied by typography. This process results in ragged lines, uneven distribution of the ink, especially at the edges of the letters, and often has the impression of the letters visible from the reverse.

In addition nine of these values have been found with overprints applied by lithography. These show clean lines and an even distribution of the ink.

The 35, 45 and 50 c. values have only been seen with overprints applied by lithography.

1981 (2 July). *Nos.* 105/22 *optd with Type* O 1.

No.	Description		Unused	Used
O 1	1 c. Type **14**		10	10
	a. Litho opt			
O 2	2 c. Yellow-banded Goatfish		10	10
O 3	4 c. Imperial Angelfish		10	10
O 4	5 c. Rainbow Butterfly		10	10
O 5	6 c. Blue Angelfish		10	10
	a. Litho opt		30	30
O 6	8 c. Blue Striped Snapper		10	10
O 7	10 c. Orange Clownfish		15	15
	a. Litho opt		30	25
O 8	15 c. Chevroned Coralfish		20	20
O 9	20 c. Fairy Cod		25	25
O10	25 c. Clown Triggerfish		25·00	
	a. Litho opt		30	30
O11	30 c. Long-nosed Butterfly		30	30
	a. Litho opt			
O12	35 c. Yellowfin Tuna (*litho opt*)		35	35
O13	40 c. Spotted Eagle Ray		40	40
O14	45 c. Black-tipped Rock Cod (*litho opt*)		45	45
O15	50 c. Hammerhead Shark (*litho opt*)		50	50
O16	70 c. Lionfish		75	75
	a. Litho opt		4·00	3·00
O17	$1 White-barred Triggerfish		1·10	1·10
	a. Litho opt		2·50	2·50
O18	$2 Beaked Coralfish		3·25	3·00
	a. Litho opt		2·25	2·25
O19	$5 Tiger Shark		5·50	6·00
	a. Litho opt		15·00	12·00
O1/19		*Set of* 19	11·00	11·00

1983 (26 Aug)–**85**. *Nos.* 202/3a, 205/12, 224 *and* 234 *optd as Type* O 1, *but* 20½ × 4 *mm.* (5 *c.*), *or as Type* O **2** *(others).*

No.	Description		Unused	Used
O20	5 c. Wedding and baby food baskets (1.2.84)		10	10
	a. Optd as Type O 2 (5.85)		15	15
O21	10 c. Hand-carved model of canoe (1.2.84)		10	10
O22	15 c. Ladies' sun hats (30.4.84)		15	15
O23	25 c. Pandanus baskets (1.2.84)		25	25
O24	30 c. on 45 c. Reef sandals and fish trap (1.2.84)		50	50
O25	30 c. Basket tray and coconut stand (30.4.84)		30	30
O26	35 c. Pandanus pillows and shell necklaces (1.2.84)		40	35
O27	40 c. Round baskets and fans (1.2.84)		45	40
O28	45 c. Reef sandals and fish trap (1.2.84)		45	40
O29	50 c. Rat trap (1.2.84)		50	45
O30	60 c. on $1 Pump drill and adze		75	75
O31	60 c. Fisherman's waterproof boxes (30.4.84)		60	60
O32	$1 Pump drill and adze (1.2.84)		1·00	1·00
O33	$2 Fisherman's hat and canoe bailers (1.2.84)		1·75	2·00
O34	$5 Fishing rod, lures and scoop nets (1.2.84)		4·25	4·75
O20/34		*Set of* 15	10·50	11·00

OFFICIAL

(O 3)

1989 (22 Feb). *Nos.* 502/17 *optd with Type* O 3.

O35	5 c. Type **66**	10	10
O36	10 c. White Tern	10	10
O37	15 c. Common Noddy	10	15
O38	20 c. Phoenix Petrel	15	20
O39	25 c. American Golden Plover	20	25
O40	30 c. Crested Tern	25	30
O41	35 c. Sooty Tern	30	35
O42	40 c. Bristle-thighed Curlew	35	40
O43	45 c. Bar-tailed Godwit	35	40
O44	50 c. Eastern Reef Heron	40	45
O45	55 c. Great Frigate Bird	45	50
O46	60 c. Red-footed Booby	50	55
O47	70 c. Rufous-necked Sandpiper ("Red-necked Stint")	60	65
O48	$1 Long-tailed Koel ("Long-tailed Cuckoo")	85	90
O49	$2 Red-tailed Tropic Bird	1·60	1·75
O50	$5 Banded Rail	4·25	4·50
O35/50	*Set of* 16	9·50	10·50

Appendix

The following issues for individual islands of Tuvalu fall outside the criteria for full listing as detailed on page xi of this edition.

FUNAFUTI

1984

Leaders of the World. Railway Locomotives (1st series). *Two designs for each value, the first showing technical drawings and the second the locomotive at work.* 15, 20, 30, 40, 50, 60 *c., each* × 2

Leaders of the World. Automobiles (1st series). *Two designs for each value, the first showing technical drawings and the second the car in action.* 1, 10, 40 c., $1, *each* × 2

Leaders of the World. Railway Locomotives (2nd series). *Two designs for each value, the first showing technical drawings and the second the locomotive at work.* 5, 15, 25, 35, 40, 55, 60 c., $1, *each* × 2

1985

Leaders of the World. Automobiles (2nd series). *Two designs for each value, the first showing technical drawings and the second the car in action.* 1, 30, 55, 60 c., *each* × 2

Leaders of the World. Railway Locomotives (3rd series). *Two designs for each value, the first showing technical drawings and the second the locomotive at work.* 5, 15, 35, 40, 50 c., $1, *each* × 2

Leaders of the World. Life and Times of Queen Elizabeth the Queen Mother. Two designs for each value, showing different portraits. 5, 25, 80 c., $1.05, *each* × 2

1986

60th Birthday of Queen Elizabeth II. 10, 50 c., $1.50, $3.50

Royal Wedding (1st issue). 60 c., $1, *each* × 2

Royal Wedding (2nd issue). *Previous Royal Wedding stamps optd* "Congratulations T.R.H. The Duke & Duchess of York". 60 c., $1, *each* × 2

Railway Locomotives (4th series). *Two designs for each value, the first showing technical drawings and the second the locomotive at work.* 20, 40, 60 c., $1.50, *each* × 2

1987

Automobiles (3rd series). *Two designs for each value, the first showing technical drawings and the second the car in action.* 10, 20, 40, 60, 75, 80 c., $1, $1.50, *each* × 2

Royal Ruby Wedding. 20, 50, 75 c., $1.20, $1.75

1988

Olympic Games, Seoul. 10, 20, 40, 50, 80, 90 c.

NANUMAGA

1984

Leaders of the World. Automobiles (1st series). *Two designs for each value, the first showing technical drawings and the second the car in action.* 5, 10, 25, 30, 40 c., $1, *each* × 2

Leaders of the World. British Monarchs. Two designs for each value, forming a composite picture. 10, 20, 30, 40, 50 c., $1, *each* × 2

Leaders of the World. Automobiles (2nd series). *Two designs for each value, the first showing technical drawings and the second the car in action.* 5, 10, 50 c., $1, *each* × 2

1985

Leaders of the World. Railway Locomotives. Two designs for each value, the first showing technical drawings and the second the locomotive at work. 10, 25, 50, 60 c., *each* × 2

Leaders of the World. Flowers. 25, 30, 40, 50 c., *each* × 2

Leaders of the World. Automobiles (3rd series). *Two designs for each value, the first showing technical drawings and the second the car in action.* 10, 25, 75 c., $1, *each* × 2

Leaders of the World. Life and Times of Queen Elizabeth the Queen Mother. Two designs for each value, showing different portraits. 15, 55, 65, 90 c., *each* × 2

1986

60th Birthday of Queen Elizabeth II. 5 c., $1, $1.75, $2.50

World Cup Football Championship, Mexico. 1, 5, 5, 10, 20, 35, 50, 60, 75 c., $1, $2, $4

Royal Wedding (1st issue). 60 c., $1, *each* × 2

Royal Wedding (2nd issue). *Previous Royal Wedding stamps optd as for Funafuti.* 60 c., $1, *each* × 2

1987

Automobiles (4th series). *Two designs for each value, the first showing technical drawings and the second the car in action.* 5, 10, 15, 20, 25, 40, 60 c., $1, *each* × 2

Royal Ruby Wedding. 15, 35, 60 c., $1.50, $1.75

NANUMEA

1984

Leaders of the World. Railway Locomotives (1st series). *Two designs for each value, the first showing technical drawings and the second the locomotive at work.* 15, 20, 30, 40, 50, 60 c., *each* × 2

Leaders of the World. Famous Cricketers. Two designs for each value, the first showing a portrait and the second the cricketer in action. 1, 10, 40 c., $1, *each* × 2

1985

Leaders of the World. Automobiles (1st series). *Two designs for each value, the first showing technical drawings and the second the car in action.* 5, 40, 50, 60 c., *each* × 2

Leaders of the World. Railway Locomotives (2nd series). *Two designs for each value, the first showing technical drawings and the second the locomotive at work.* 1, 35, 50, 60 c., *each* × 2

Leaders of the World. Automobiles (2nd series). *Two designs for each value, the first showing technical drawings and the second the car in action.* 15, 20, 50, 60 c., *each* × 2

Leaders of the World. Cats. 5, 30, 50 c., $1, *each* × 2

Leaders of the World. Life and Times of Queen Elizabeth the Queen Mother. Two designs for each value, showing different portraits. 5, 30, 75 c., $1.05, *each* × 2

1986

60th Birthday of Queen Elizabeth II. 10, 80 c., $1.75, $3

World Cup Football Championship, Mexico. 1, 2, 5, 10, 25, 40, 50, 75, 90 c., $1, $2.50, $4

Royal Wedding (1st issue). 60 c., $1, *each* × 2

Royal Wedding (2nd issue). *Previous Royal Wedding stamps optd as for Funafuti.* 60 c., $1, *each* × 2

Automobiles (3rd series). *Two designs for each value, the first showing technical drawings and the second the car in action.* 10, 20, 35, 50, 75 c., $2, *each* × 2

1987

Royal Ruby Wedding. 40, 60, 80 c., $1, $2

NIUTAO

1984

Leaders of the World. Automobiles (1st series). *Two designs for each value, the first showing technical drawings and the second the car in action.* 15, 30, 40, 50 c., *each* × 2

Leaders of the World. Railway Locomotives (1st series). *Two designs for each value, the first showing technical drawings and the second the locomotive at work.* 5, 10, 20, 40, 50 c., $1, *each* × 2

1985

Leaders of the World. Famous Cricketers. Two designs for each value, the first showing a portrait and the second the cricketer in action. 1, 15, 50 c., $1, *each* × 2

Leaders of the World. Birth Bicent of John J. Audubon (ornithologist). Birds. 5, 15, 25 c., $1, *each* × 2

Leaders of the World. Automobiles (2nd series). *Two designs for each value, the first showing technical drawings and the second the car in action.* 20, 25, 40, 60 c., *each* × 2

Leaders of the World. Railway Locomotives (2nd series). *Two designs for each value, the first showing technical drawings and the second the locomotive at work.* 10, 30, 45, 60, 75 c., $1.20, *each* × 2

Leaders of the World. Life and Times of Queen Elizabeth the Queen Mother. Two designs for each value, showing different portraits. 15, 35, 70, 95 c., *each* × 2

1986

60th Birthday of Queen Elizabeth II. 5, 60 c., $1.50, $3.50

Royal Wedding (1st issue). 60 c., $1, *each* × 2

Royal Wedding (2nd issue). *Previous Royal Wedding stamps optd as for Funafuti.* 60 c., $1, *each* × 2

1987

Royal Ruby Wedding. 60th Birthday of Queen Elizabeth II issue of 1986 *optd* "40th WEDDING ANNIVERSARY OF H.M. QUEEN ELIZABETH II". 5, 60 c., $1.50, $3.50

NUI

1984

Leaders of the World. Railway Locomotives (1st series). *Two designs for each value, the first showing technical drawings and the second the locomotive at work.* 15, 25, 30, 50 c., *each* × 2

Leaders of the World. British Monarchs. Two designs for each value, forming a composite picture. 1, 5, 15, 40, 50 c., $1, *each* × 2

1985

Leaders of the World. Railway Locomotives (2nd series). *Two designs for each value, the first showing technical drawings and the second the locomotive at work.* 5, 15, 25 c., $1, *each* × 2

Leaders of the World. Automobiles (1st series). *Two designs for each value, the first showing technical drawings and the second the car in action.* 25, 30, 40, 50 c., *each* × 2

Leaders of the World. Famous Cricketers. Two designs for each value, the first showing a portrait and the second the cricketer in action. 1, 40, 60, 70 c., *each* × 2

Leaders of the World. Life and Times of Queen Elizabeth the Queen Mother. Two designs for each value, showing different portraits. 5, 50, 75, 85 c., *each* × 2

Leaders of the World. Automobiles (2nd series). *Two designs for each value, the first showing technical drawings and the second the car in action.* 5, 15, 40, 60, 90 c., $1.10, *each* × 2

1986

60th Birthday of Queen Elizabeth II. 10, 80 c., $1.75, $3

Royal Wedding (1st issue). 60 c., $1, *each* × 2

Royal Wedding (2nd issue). *Previous Royal Wedding stamps optd as for Funafuti.* 60 c., $1, *each* × 2

1987

Railway Locomotives (3rd series). *Two designs for each value, the first showing technical drawings and the second the locomotive at work.* 10, 25, 35, 40, 60, 75 c., $1, $1.25, *each* × 2

Royal Ruby Wedding. 20, 50, 75 c., $1.20, $1.75

1988

Railway Locomotives (4*th series*). *Two designs for each value, the first showing technical drawings and the second the locomotive at work*. 5, 10, 20, 25, 40, 50, 60, 75 c., *each* × 2

NUKUFETAU

1984

Leaders of the World. Automobiles (1*st series*). *Two designs for each value, the first showing technical drawings and the second the car in action*. 10, 25, 30, 50, 60 c., *each* × 2

Leaders of the World. British Monarchs. Two designs for each value, forming a composite picture. 1, 10, 30, 50, 60 c., $1, *each* × 2

1985

Leaders of the World. Famous Cricketers. Two designs for each value, the first showing a portrait and the second the cricketer in action. 1, 10, 55 c., $1, *each* × 2

Leaders of the World. Railway Locomotives (1*st series*). *Two designs for each value, the first showing technical drawings and the second the locomotive at work*. 1, 10, 60, 70 c., *each* × 2

Leaders of the World. Automobiles (2*nd series*). *Two designs for each value, the first showing technical drawings and the second the car in action*. 5, 10, 15, 20, 50, 60, 75 c., $1.50, *each* × 2

Leaders of the World. Life and Times of Queen Elizabeth the Queen Mother. Two designs for each value, showing different portraits. 10, 45, 65 c., $1, *each* × 2

1986

Leaders of the World. Railway Locomotives (2*nd series*). *Two designs for each value, the first showing technical drawings and the second the locomotive at work*. 20, 40, 60 c., $1.50, *each* × 2

60*th Birthday of Queen Elizabeth II*. 5, 40 c., $2, $4

Royal Wedding (1*st issue*). 60 c., $1, *each* × 2

Royal Wedding (2*nd issue*). *Previous Royal Wedding stamps optd as for Funafuti*. 60 c., $1, *each* × 2

1987

Railway Locomotives (3*rd series*). *Two designs for each value, the first showing technical drawings and the second the locomotive at work*. 5, 10, 15, 25, 30, 50, 60 c., $1, *each* × 2

Royal Ruby Wedding. 60*th Birthday of Queen Elizabeth II issue of* 1986 *optd as for Niutao*. 5, 40 c., $2, $4

NUKULAELAE

1984

Leaders of the World. Railway Locomotives (1*st series*). *Two designs for each value, the first showing technical drawings and the second the locomotive at work*. 5, 15, 40 c., $1, *each* × 2

Leaders of the World. Famous Cricketers. Two designs for each value, the first showing a portrait and the second the cricketer in action. 5, 15, 30 c., $1, *each* × 2

Leaders of the World. Railway Locomotives (2*nd series*). *Two designs for each value, the first showing technical drawings and the second the locomotive at work*. 5, 20, 40 c., $1, *each* × 2

1985

Leaders of the World. Automobiles. Two designs for each value, the first showing technical drawings and the second the car in action. 5, 35, 50, 70 c., *each* × 2

Leaders of the World. Dogs. 5, 20, 50, 70 c., *each* × 2

Leaders of the World. Railway Locomotives (3*rd series*). *Two designs for each value, the first showing technical drawings and the second the locomotive at work*. 10, 25, 50 c., $1, *each* × 2

Leaders of the World. Automobiles (2*nd series*). *Two designs for each value, the first showing technical drawings and the second the car in action*. 10, 25, 35, 50, 75 c., $1, *each* × 2

Leaders of the World. Life and Times of Queen Elizabeth the Queen Mother. Two designs for each value, showing different portraits. 5, 25, 85 c., $1, *each* × 2

1986

60*th Birthday of Queen Elizabeth II*. 10 c., $1, $1.50, $3

Railway Locomotives (4*th series*). *Two designs for each value, the first showing technical drawings and the second the locomotive at work*. 10, 15, 25, 40, 50, 80 c., $1, $1.50, *each* × 2

Royal Wedding (1*st issue*). 60 c., $1, *each* × 2

Royal Wedding (2*nd issue*). *Previous Royal Wedding stamps optd as for Funafuti*. 60 c., $1, *each* × 2

1987

Royal Ruby Wedding. 15, 35, 60 c., $1.50, $1.75

VAITUPU

1984

Leaders of the World. Automobiles (1*st series*). *Two designs for each value, the first showing technical drawings and the second the car in action*. 15, 25, 30, 50 c., *each* × 2

Leaders of the World. British Monarchs. Two designs for each value, forming a composite picture. 1, 5, 15, 40, 50 c., $1, *each* × 2

Leaders of the World. Automobiles (2*nd series*). *Two designs for each value, the first showing technical drawings and the second the car in action*. 5, 15, 25, 30, 40, 50, 60 c., $1, *each* × 2

1985

Leaders of the World. Railway Locomotives (1*st series*). *Two designs for each value, the first showing technical drawings and the second the locomotive at work*. 10, 25, 50, 60 c., *each* × 2

Leaders of the World, Butterflies. 5, 15, 50, 75 c., *each* × 2

Leaders of the World. Automobiles (3*rd series*). *Two designs for each value, the first showing technical drawings and the second the car in action*. 15, 30, 40, 60 c., *each* × 2

Leaders of the World. Life and Times of Queen Elizabeth the Queen Mother. Two designs for each value, showing different portraits. 15, 40, 65, 95 c., *each* × 2

1986

Leaders of the World. Railway Locomotives (2*nd series*). *Two designs for each value, the first showing technical drawings and the second the locomotive at work*. 5, 25, 80 c., $1, *each* × 2

60*th Birthday of Queen Elizabeth II*. 5, 60 c., $2, $3.50

Royal Wedding (1*st issue*). 60 c., $1, *each* × 2

Royal Wedding (2*nd issue*). *Previous Royal Wedding stamps optd as for Funafuti*. 60 c., $1, *each* × 2

1987

Railway Locomotives (3*rd series*). *Two designs for each value, the first showing technical drawings and the second the locomotive at work*. 10, 15, 25, 35, 45, 65, 85 c., $1, *each* × 2

Royal Ruby Wedding. 60*th Birthday of Queen Elizabeth II issue of* 1986 *optd as for Niutao*. 5, 60 c., $2, $3.50

Uganda

PRICES FOR STAMPS ON COVER TO 1945

The type-written stamps of Uganda, Nos. 1/53, are very rare used on cover.

Nos. 54/60	*from* × 15
No. 61	—
Nos. 70/5	*from* × 12
No. 76	—
Nos. 84/90	*from* × 15
No. 91	—
Nos. 92/3	*from* × 30

PROTECTORATE

'U G'
50

1

'U G'
20

2

TYPE-WRITTEN STAMPS. Nos. 1/53 were type-written by the Revd. E. Millar at Mengo. For all "printings" a thin laid paper was used, and all issues were imperforate.

The original typewriter used had wide letters, but in late April, 1895 Millar obtained a new machine on which the type face was in a narrower fount.

Each sheet was made up of whatever values were required at the time, so that different values can be found *se-tenant* or *tête-bêche*. These last were caused by the paper being inverted in the machine so that space at the foot could be utilised.

For the first issue the sheets were of 117 (9 × 13), but with the introduction of the narrower width (Nos. 17 onwards) a larger number of stamps per sheet, 143 (11 × 13), was adopted.

The manuscript provisionals, Nos. 9*a*/16, come from the Mission at Ngogwe, most of the manuscript surcharges including the initials of the Revd. G. R. Blackledge stationed there.

1895 (20 Mar). *Wide letters. Wide stamps,* 20 *to* 26 *mm wide.*

1	**1**	5 (cowries), black	£2500	
2		10 (cowries), black	£1600	£1000
3		15 (cowries), black		
4		20 (cowries), black	£2000	£1000
5		25 (cowries), black		
6		30 (cowries), black	£1100	£1100
7		40 (cowries), black	£1700	£1100
8		50 (cowries), black	£1000	£950
9		60 (cowries), black	£1200	£1200

A strip of three of No. 2 is known on cover of which one copy has the value "10" altered to "5" in manuscript and initialled "E.M.".

1895 (May). *Wide stamps with pen-written surcharges, in black.*

9*a*	**1**	10 on 30 (c.) black	—	£24000
10		10 on 50 (c.) black	—	£18000
11		15 on 10 (c.) black	—	£18000
12		15 on 20 (c.) black	—	£22000
13		15 on 40 (c.) black	—	£18000
14		15 on 50 (c.) black	—	£24000
15		25 on 50 (c.) black	—	£24000
16		50 on 60 (c.) black	—	£24000

1895 (April). *Wide letters. Narrow stamps,* 16 *to* 18 *mm wide.*

17	**1**	5 (c.) black	£1000	£850
18		10 (c.) black	£1000	£950
19		15 (c.) black	£750	£750
20		20 (c.) black	£800	£600
21		25 (c.) black	£750	£750
22		30 (c.) black	£5000	£5000
23		40 (c.) black	£5000	£5000
24		50 (c.) black	£2500	
25		60 (c.) black	£3000	

1895 (May). *Narrow letters. Narrow stamps* 16 *to* 18 *mm wide.*

26	**2**	5 (c.) black	£400	
27		10 (c.) black	£400	
28		15 (c.) black	£400	
29	**2**	20 (c.) black	£300	
30		25 (c.) black	£400	
31		30 (c.) black	£425	
32		40 (c.) black	£450	
33		50 (c.) black	£400	
34		60 (c.) black	£1000	

1895 (Nov). *Narrow letters. Narrow stamps,* 16–18 *mm wide. Change of colour.*

35	**2**	5 (c.) violet	£300	£325
36		10 (c.) violet	£275	£275
37		15 (c.) violet	£275	£275
38		20 (c.) violet	£300	£275
		a. "G U" for "U G"		
39		25 (c.) violet	£375	£375
40		30 (c.) violet	£500	£400
41		40 (c.) violet	£400	£400
42		50 (c.) violet	£375	£400
43		100 (c.) violet	£2250	

Stamps of 35 (c.) and 45 (c.) have been chronicled in both colours. They were never prepared for postal use, and did not represent a postal rate, but were type-written to oblige a local official.

'V.96.R'
25
'Uganda'

3

1896 (June).

44	**3**	5 (c.) violet	£250	£275
45		10 (c.) violet	£250	£250
46		15 (c.) violet	£250	£275
47		20 (c.) violet	£225	£175
48		25 (c.) violet	£275	
49		30 (c.) violet	£275	
50		40 (c.) violet	£275	£375
51		50 (c.) violet	£325	£400
52		60 (c.) violet	£1200	
53		100 (c.) violet	£1200	£1200

UGANDA
POSTAGE
V†R
1 ANNA
PROTECTORATE

4 (Thin "1")

UGANDA
POSTAGE
V†R
1 ANNA
PROTECTORATE

5 (Thick "1")

UGANDA
POSTAGE
V†R
4 ANNAS
PROTECTORATE

6

UGANDA
POSTAGE
V†R
L
4 ANNAS
PROTECTORATE

7

In the 2 a. and 3 a. the dagger points upwards; the stars in the 2 a. are level with the top of "VR". The 8 a. is as T **6** but with left star at top and right star at foot. The 1 r. has three stars at foot. The 5 r. has central star raised and the others at foot.

(Type-set by the Revd. F. Rowling at Lubwa's, in Usoga)

1896 (7 Nov). (*a*) *Types* **4/6**.

A. *Normal.* B. *Small* "o" *in* "POSTAGE"

			A		B	
54	**4**	1 a. black	40·00	40·00	£120	£120
55	**5**	1 a. black	6·00	6·50	22·00	24·00
56	**6**	2 a. black	6·50	7·00	24·00	26·00
57		3 a. black	7·50	8·50	28·00	30·00
58		4 a. black	7·50	8·50	28·00	30·00
59		8 a. black	11·00	14·00	40·00	45·00
60		1 r. black	30·00	35·00	£140	£160
61		5 r. black	£110	£150	£275	£350

(*b*) *Optd* "L", *in black as in T* **7** *for local use, by a postal official, R. R. Racey, at Kampala*

			A		B	
70	**4**	1 a. black	60·00	55·00	£325	—
71	**6**	2 a. black	25·00	50·00	85·00	£130
72		3 a. black	70·00	70·00	£375	—
73		4 a. black	38·00	70·00	£130	—
74		8 a. black	70·00	90·00	£300	—
75		1 r. black	£140	£170	£400	—
76		5 r. black	£3250	£3250	—	—

Tête-bêche pairs of all values may be found owing to the settings of 16 (4 × 4) being printed side by side or above one another. They are worth a premium. The variety with small "O" occurs on R. 3/1.

8

9

UGANDA

(10)

(Recess D.L.R.)

1898–1902. *P* 14. (*a*) *Wmk Crown CA.*

84	**8**	1 a. scarlet	70	30
		a. Carmine-rose (1902)	25	30
86		2 a. red-brown	40	1·75
87		3 a. pale grey	3·25	4·50
		a. Bluish grey	3·25	4·00
88		4 a. deep green	1·75	4·00
89		8 a. pale olive	2·75	11·00
		a. Grey-green	3·25	11·00
		(*b*) *Wmk Crown CC*		
90	**9**	1 r. dull blue	15·00	12·00
		a. Bright blue	20·00	20·00
91		5 r. brown	48·00	55·00
84/91		*Set of* 7	65·00	80·00
84/91 Optd "Specimen"		*Set of* 7	£150	

1902. *T* **11** *of British East Africa optd with T* **10**.

92		½ a. yellow-green	35	35
		a. Opt omitted (in pair with normal)	£1000	
		b. Opt inverted (at foot)	£550	
		c. Opt double	£750	
93		2½ a. deep blue (R.)	50	95
		a. Opt double	£600	

For issues between 1903 and 1976 see KENYA, UGANDA AND TANGANYIKA.

SELF-GOVERNMENT

11 Ripon Falls and Speke Memorial

(Des S. Scott. Recess B.W.)

1962 (28 July). *Centenary of Speke's Discovery of Source of the Nile. W w* **12**. *P* 14.

95	**11**	30 c. black and red	10	10
96		50 c. black and slate-violet	10	10
97		1 s. 30, black and green	10	10
98		2 s. 50, black and blue	20	55
95/8		*Set of* 4	35	60

INDEPENDENT

12 Murchison Falls

13 Tobacco-growing

14 Mulago Hospital

(Des V. Whiteley. Photo Harrison)

1962 (9 Oct)–**64**. *Independence. Various designs as T* **12/14**. *P* 15×14 (5 *c. to* 50 *c.*) *or* 14½ (*others*).
99 5 c. deep bluish green .. 10 10
100 10 c. reddish brown .. 10 10
a. *Brown* (coil) .. 10 10
b. *Deep yellow-brown* (17.10.64) .. 10 10
101 15 c. black, red and green .. 10 10
102 20 c. plum and buff .. 10 10
103 30 c. blue .. 10 10
104 50 c. black and turquoise-green .. 10 10
105 1 s. sepia, red and turquoise-green .. 15 10
106 1 s. 30, yellow-orange and violet .. 20 10
107 2 s. black, carmine and light blue .. 40 15
108 5 s. vermilion and deep green .. 2·00 75
109 10 s. slate and chestnut .. 1·75 1·50
110 20 s. brown and blue .. 4·50 11·00
99/110 .. *Set of* 12 8·50 12·00

Designs: *As T* **12/13**—10 c. Tobacco growing; 15 c. Coffee growing; 20 c. Ankole cattle; 30 c. Cotton; 50 c. Mountains of the Moon. *As T* **14**—1 s. 30, Cathedrals and Mosque; 2 s. Makerere College; 5 s. Copper mining; 10 s. Cement industry; 20 s. Parliament Buildings.

15 South African Crowned Crane

(Photo Harrison)

1965 (20 Feb). *International Trade Fair, Kampala. P* 14½ × 14.
111 **15** 30 c. multicoloured .. 10 10
112 1 s. 30, multicoloured .. 15 10

16 Black Bee Eater

17 African Jacana

18 Ruwenzori Turaco

(Des Mrs. R. Fennessy. Photo Harrison)

1965 (9 Oct). *Birds. Various designs as T* **16/18**. *P* 15 × 14 (5 *c.*, 15 *c.*, 20 *c.*, 40 *c.*, 50 *c.*), 14 × 15 (10 *c.*, 30 *c.*, 65 *c.*) *or* 14½ (*others*).
113 5 c. multicoloured .. 10 10
114 10 c. chestnut, black and light blue .. 10 10
115 15 c. yellow and sepia .. 15 10
116 20 c. multicoloured .. 15 10
117 30 c. black and brown-red .. 70 10
118 40 c. multicoloured .. 60 25
119 50 c. grey-blue and reddish violet .. 25 10
a. White bird (grey-blue omitted) .. 80·00
120 65 c. orange-red, black and light grey .. 1·75 85
121 1 s. multicoloured .. 45 10
122 1 s. 30, chestnut, black and yellow .. 3·50 20
123 2 s. 50, multicoloured .. 3·75 65
124 5 s. multicoloured .. 5·50 2·00
125 10 s. multicoloured .. 7·50 5·50
126 20 s. multicoloured .. 14·00 22·00
113/26 .. *Set of* 14 35·00 28·00

Designs: *Vert as T* **16**—15 c. Orange Weaver; 20 c. Narina Trogon; 40 c. Blue-breasted Kingfisher; 50 c. Whale-headed Stork. *Horiz as T* **17**—30 c. Sacred Ibis; 65 c. Red-crowned Bishop. *As T* **18**. *Vert*—1 s. 30, African Fish Eagle; 5 s. Lilac-breasted Roller. *Horiz*—2 s. 50, Great Blue Turaco; 10 s. Black-collared Lovebird; 20 s. South African Crowned Crane.

The 15 c., 40 c., 65 c., and 1s. exist with PVA gum as well as gum arabic.

19 Carved Screen

(Des Mrs. R. Fennessy. Photo Harrison)

1967 (26 Oct). 13*th Commonwealth Parliamentary Association Conference. T* **19** *and similar horiz designs. Multicoloured. P* 14.
127 30 c. Type **19** .. 10 10
128 50 c. Arms of Uganda .. 10 10
129 1 s. 30, Parliamentary Building .. 10 10
130 2 s. 50, Conference Chamber .. 15 70
127/30 .. *Set of* 4 25 70

20 *Cordia abyssinica*

21 *Acacia drepanolobium*

(Des Mrs. R. Fennessy. Photo Harrison)

1969 (9 Oct)–**74**. *Flowers. Various designs as T* **20/1**. *Chalk-surfaced paper. P* 14½×14 (5 *c. to* 70 *c.*) *or* 14 (*others*).
131 5 c. brown, green and light olive-yellow .. 10 20
a. Glazed, ordinary paper (11.4.73) .. 25 10
132 10 c. multicoloured .. 10 10
a. Glazed, ordinary paper (27.9.72) .. 25 10
133 15 c. multicoloured .. 25 10
134 20 c. bluish violet, yellow-ol & pale sage-grn 15 10
a. Glazed, ordinary paper (27.9.72) .. 25 10
135 30 c. multicoloured .. 20 10
136 40 c. reddish violet, yell-grn & pale ol-grey 20 10
137 50 c. multicoloured .. 20 10
138 60 c. multicoloured .. 45 60
a. Glazed, ordinary paper (9.5.73) .. 1·50 40
139 70 c. multicoloured .. 35 25
a. Glazed, ordinary paper (27.9.72) .. 70 45
140 1 s. multicoloured .. 20 10
a. Glazed, ordinary paper (22.1.71) .. 70 10
141 1 s. 50, multicoloured (cobalt background) 35 10
a. Glazed, ordinary paper (3.2.71) .. 50 10
b. *Azure background* (chalk-surfaced paper) (21.1.74) .. 55 20
142 2 s. 50, multicoloured .. 70 35
a. Glazed, ordinary paper (3.2.71) .. 1·25 10
143 5 s. multicoloured .. 1·50 70
a. Glazed, ordinary paper (3.2.71) .. 1·75 10
144 10 s. multicoloured .. 3·50 2·00
a. Glazed, ordinary paper (3.2.71) .. 3·75 10
145 20 s. multicoloured .. 6·50 3·25
a. Glazed, ordinary paper (22.1.71) .. 11·00 15
131/45 .. *Set of* 15 13·00 7·00
131a/45a .. *Set of* 11 19·00 1·40

Designs: *As T* **20**—10 c. *Grewia similis*; 15 c. *Cassia didymobotrya*; 20 c. *Coleus barbatus*; 30 c. *Ockna ovata*; 40 c. *Ipomoea spathulata*; 50 c. *Spathodea nilotica*; 60 c. *Oncoba spinosa*; 70 c. *Carissa edulis*. *As T* **21**—1 s. 50, *Clerodendrum myricoides*; 2 s. 50, *Acanthus arboreus*; 5 s. *Kigelia aethiopium*; 10 s. *Erythrina abyssinica*; 20 s. *Monodora myristica*.

2/

(22)

1975 (29 Sept). *Nos.* 141/2 *and* 145a *surch as T* **22**.
146 2 s. on 1 s. 50, multicoloured .. 2·00 1·50
147 3 s. on 2 s. 50, multicoloured .. 20·00 30·00
148 40 s. on 20 s. multicoloured .. 5·50 3·50
a. Surch on No. 145 .. — 3·50
146/8 .. *Set of* 3 25·00 32·00

23 Millet

24 Maize

(Des Mrs. R. Fennessy. Photo Harrison)

1975 (9 Oct). *Ugandan Crops. T* **23/4** *and similar horiz designs. P* 14 × 14½ (10 *to* 80 *c.*) *or* 14 (*others*).
149 10 c. black, apple-green and yellow-brown .. 10 10
150 20 c. multicoloured .. 10 10
151 30 c. multicoloured .. 10 10
152 40 c. multicoloured .. 10 10
153 50 c. multicoloured .. 10 10
154 70 c. black, apple-green and light blue-green 15 10
155 80 c. multicoloured .. 15 10
156 1 s. multicoloured .. 15 10
157 2 s. multicoloured .. 30 25
158 3 s. multicoloured .. 50 35
159 5 s. multicoloured .. 90 60
160 10 s. multicoloured .. 1·50 1·25
161 20 s. apple-green, black and bright purple .. 2·50 2·40
162 40 s. apple-green, black and yellow-orange .. 5·00 4·75
149/62 .. *Set of* 14 10·00 9·00

Designs: *As T* **23**—20 c. Sugar; 30 c. Tobacco; 40 c. Onions; 50 c. Tomatoes; 70 c. Tea; 80 c. Bananas. *As T* **24**—2 s. Pineapples; 3 s. Coffee; 5 s. Oranges; 10 s. Groundnuts; 20 s. Cotton; 40 s. Runner Beans.

Face value colours: 5 s. green; 10 s. brown; 20 s. bright purple; 40 s. yellow-orange. For 5 s. to 40 s. with colours changed see Nos. 220/3.

Nos. 149 and 153 exist in coils constructed from normal sheets.

1976 (15 Apr). *Telecommunications Development. As Nos.* 56/60 *of Kenya, but inscr* "UGANDA".
163 50 c. Microwave tower .. 10 10
164 1 s. Cordless switchboard .. 10 10
165 2 s. Telephone .. 20 25
166 3 s. Message Switching Centre .. 30 45
163/6 .. *Set of* 4 60 70
MS167 120 × 120 mm. Nos. 163/6 .. 90 1·25

1976 (5 July). *Olympic Games, Montreal. As Nos.* 61/5 *of Kenya, but inscr* "UGANDA".
168 50 c. Akii Bua, hurdler .. 15 10
169 1 s. Filbert Bayi, runner .. 20 10
170 2 s. Steve Muchoki, boxer .. 40 30
171 3 s. East African flags .. 55 45
168/71 .. *Set of* 4 1·10 75
MS172 129 × 154 mm. Nos. 168/71 .. 4·50 4·50

1976 (4 Oct). *Railway Transport. As Nos.* 66/70 *of Kenya, but inscr* "UGANDA".
173 50 c. Tanzania–Zambia railway .. 20 10
174 1 s. Nile Bridge, Uganda .. 35 10
175 2 s. Nakuru Station, Kenya .. 75 45
176 3 s. Class A loco, 1896 .. 95 55
173/6 .. *Set of* 4 2·00 1·00
MS177 154 × 103 mm. Nos. 173/6 .. 3·25 2·25

1977 (10 Jan). *Game Fish of East Africa. As Nos.* 71/5 *of Kenya, but inscr* "UGANDA".
178 50 c. Nile Perch .. 15 10
179 1 s. Tilapia .. 20 10
180 3 s. Sailfish .. 70 40
181 5 s. Black Marlin .. 1·00 60
178/81 .. *Set of* 4 1·90 1·00
MS182 153 × 129 mm. Nos. 178/81 .. 3·50 2·00

1977 (15 Jan). *Second World Black and African Festival of Arts and Culture, Nigeria. As Nos.* 76/80 *of Kenya, but inscr* "UGANDA".
183 50 c. Maasai Manyatta (village) .. 15 10
184 1 s. "Heartbeat of Africa" (Ugandan dancers) 20 10
185 2 s. Makonde sculpture .. 45 40
186 3 s. "Early Man and Technology" (skinning hippopotamus) .. 60 70
183/6 .. *Set of* 4 1·25 1·10
MS187 132 × 109 mm. Nos. 183/6 .. 2·00 2·25

1977 (5 Apr). 25*th Anniv of Safari Rally. As Nos.* 81/5 *of Kenya, but inscr* "UGANDA".
188 50 c. Rally-car and villagers .. 15 10
189 1 s. Starting-line .. 15 10
190 2 s. Car fording river .. 35 35
191 5 s. Car and elephants .. 90 1·00
188/91 .. *Set of* 4 1·40 1·40
MS192 126 × 93 mm. Nos. 188/91 .. 1·75 2·50

1977 (30 June). *Centenary of Ugandan Church. As Nos.* 86/90 *of Kenya, but inscr* "UGANDA".
193 50 c. Canon Kivebulaya .. 10 10
194 1 s. Modern Namirembe Cathedral .. 15 10
195 2 s. Old Namirembe Cathedral .. 30 40
196 5 s. Early congregation, Kigezi .. 60 90
193/6 .. *Set of* 4 1·00 1·25
MS197 126 × 89 mm. Nos. 193/6 .. 1·00 1·75

80c ═

(25)

26 Shot Putting

1977 (22 Aug). *Design as No.* 155 *surch with T* **25** *in mauve by Harrison.*
198 80 c. on 60 c. multicoloured .. 25 20
a. Surch omitted .. £175

A 60 c. stamp was to have been added to Nos. 149/62 using the design of the 80 c. (bananas), but it was cancelled and those already printed were surcharged to make No. 198.

1977 (26 Sept). *Endangered Species. As Nos.* 96/101 *of Kenya, but inscr* "UGANDA".
199 50 c. Pancake Tortoise .. 30 10
200 1 s. Nile Crocodile .. 45 10
201 2 s. Hunter's Hartebeest .. 1·75 40
202 3 s. Red Colobus monkey .. 2·00 75
203 5 s. Dugong .. 2·25 1·40
199/203 .. *Set of* 5 6·00 2·50
MS204 127 × 101 mm. Nos. 200/3 .. 6·00 3·75

1978 (10 Apr). *World Cup Football Championship, Argentina* (1*st issue*). *As Nos.* 122/6 *of Kenya but inscr* "UGANDA".
205 50 c. Joe Kadenge and forwards .. 15 10
206 1 s. Mohamed Chuma and cup presentation 15 10
207 2 s. Omari Kidevu and goalmouth scene .. 40 35
208 5 s. Polly Ouma and forwards .. 70 85
205/8 .. *Set of* 4 1·25 1·10
MS209 136 × 81 mm. Nos. 205/8 .. 2·50 2·75

(Litho Questa)

1978 (28 Aug). *Commonwealth Games, Edmonton. T* **26** *and similar horiz designs. Multicoloured. P* 14.

210 50 c. Type **26** 15 10
211 1 s. Long jumping 15 10
212 2 s. Running 30 30
213 5 s. Boxing 55 70
210/13 *Set of* 4 1·00 1·00
MS214 114×85 mm. Nos. 210/13. P 12½×12 1·75 3·00

1978 (11 Sept). *World Cup Football Championship, Argentina (2nd issue). Designs as Nos.* 205/8 *but additionally inscr* "WORLD CUP 1978".

215 50 c. Polly Ouma and forwards 15 10
216 2 s. Omari Kidevu and goalmouth scene 45 40
217 5 s. Joe Kadenge and forwards 1·00 90
218 10 s. Mohamed Chuma and cup presentation 1·75 1·60
215/18 *Set of* 4 3·00 2·75
MS219 140×87 mm. Nos. 215/18. P 12×11½ 3·00 3·25

(Litho Questa)

1978. *As Nos.* 159/62 *but printing process and colours changed.*

220 5 s. multicoloured (face value in blue) 70 70
221 10 s. multicoloured (face value in magenta) 1·00 1·25
222 20 s. multicoloured (face value in brown) 1·50 2·00
223 40 s. multicoloured (face value in red) 2·75 3·50
220/3 *Set of* 4 5·50 6·50

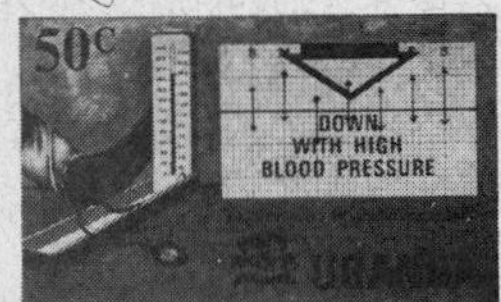

27 Measurements of High Blood Pressure

(Litho Questa)

1978 (25 Sept). *"Down with High Blood Pressure". T* **27** *and similar horiz designs. Multicoloured. P* 14 × 13½.

224 50 c. Type **27** 15 10
225 1 s. Hypertension and the heart 25 10
226 2 s. Fundus of the eye in hypertension 55 35
227 5 s. Kidney and high blood pressure 1·25 80
224/7 *Set of* 4 2·00 1·10
MS228 180 × 115 mm. Nos. 224/7 2·25 2·25

28 Off Loading Cattle

(Litho Questa)

1978 (16 Dec). *75th Anniv of Powered Flight. T* **28** *and similar horiz designs. Multicoloured. P* 14.

229 1 s. Type **28** 15 10
230 1 s. 50, "Domestic services" (passengers boarding "Islander" light aircraft) 20 15
231 2 s. 70, Export of Uganda coffee 40 35
232 10 s. "Time machines in the air" (Wright *Flyer* and "Concorde") 1·50 1·25
229/32 *Set of* 4 2·00 1·60
MS233 166 × 110 mm. Nos. 229/32 2·25 2·75

29 Queen Elizabeth II leaving Owen Falls Dam

(Des BG Studio. Litho Ashton-Potter)

1979 (15 Feb). *25th Anniv of Coronation* (1978). *T* **29** *and similar horiz designs. Multicoloured. P* 12½ × 12.

234 1 s. Type **29** 15 10
235 1 s. 50, Regalia 20 10
236 2 s. 70, Coronation ceremony 45 20
237 10 s. Royal family on balcony of Buckingham Palace 1·00 60
234/7 *Set of* 4 1·60 80
MS238 150 × 102 mm. Nos. 234/7 1·75 1·75

30 Dr. Joseph Kiwanuka (first Ugandan bishop)

(Des G. Vasarhelyi. Litho Questa)

1979 (15 Feb). *Centenary of Catholic Church in Uganda. T* **30** *and similar horiz designs. Multicoloured. P* 14.

239 1 s. Type **30** 15 10
240 1 s. 50, Lubaga Cathedral 15 10
241 2 s. 70, Ugandan pilgrimage to Rome, Holy Year, 1975 20 25
242 10 s. Friar Lourdel-Mapeera (early missionary) 60 80
239/42 *Set of* 4 1·00 1·10
MS243 128 × 91 mm. Nos. 239/42 1·40 1·75

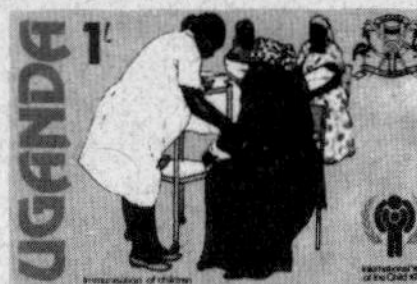

31 Immunisation of Children

(Des J.W. Litho Questa)

1979 (28 June). *International Year of the Child. T* **31** *and similar horiz designs. Multicoloured. P* 14.

244 1 s. Type **31** 15 10
245 1 s. 50, Handicapped children at play 20 20
246 2 s. 70, Ugandan I.Y.C. emblem 35 35
247 10 s. Children in class 80 90
244/7 *Set of* 4 1·40 1·40
MS248 136 × 113 mm. Nos. 244/7 1·40 2·00

UGANDA LIBERATED 1979 (**32**) — UGANDA LIBERATED 1979 (**33**) — UGANDA LIBERATED 1979 (**34**)

1979 (12 July–16 Aug?). *Liberation.*

(*a*) *Nos.* 149/55 *optd with T* **32** *and* 156/62 *with T* **33** (12 July)

249 10 c. black, apple-green and yellow-brown 10 10
250 20 c. multicoloured 10 10
251 30 c. multicoloured 10 10
252 40 c. multicoloured 10 10
253 50 c. multicoloured 10 10
254 70 c. black, apple-green and light blue-green 10 10
255 80 c. multicoloured 10 10
a. Opt double £110
256 1 s. multicoloured 15 15
257 2 s. multicoloured 20 25
258 3 s. multicoloured 35 40
259 5 s. multicoloured 55 60
260 10 s. multicoloured 1·10 1·25
261 20 s. apple-green, black and bright purple 2·25 2·40
262 40 s. apple-green, black and yellow-orange 4·50 4·75
a. Opt double £130

(*b*) *Nos.* 210/13 (*Commonwealth Games*) *optd with T* **34** (1 Aug)

263 50 c. Type **26** 10 10
264 1 s. Long jumping 15 20
265 2 s. Running 25 30
266 5 s. Boxing 60 65

(*c*) *Nos.* 207, 215 *and* 217/18 (*World Cup Football Championships*) *optd with T* **34** (1 Aug)

267 50 c. Polly Ouma and forwards 10 10
268 2 s. Omari Kidevu and goal-mouth scene 25 30
a. Optd on No. 216 14·00 23·00
269 5 s. Joe Kadenge and forwards 60 65
270 10 s. Mohamed Chuma and cup presentation 1·25 1·40

(*d*) *Nos.* 220/3 *optd with T* **33** (1979)

271 5 s. multicoloured 55 60
272 10 s. multicoloured 1·10 1·25
273 20 s. multicoloured 2·25 2·40
274 40 s. multicoloured 4·50 4·75

(*e*) *Nos.* 229/32 (*75th Anniv of Powered Flight*) *optd with T* **34** (1 Aug)

275 1 s. Type **28** 15 20
276 1 s. 50, "Domestic services" (passengers boarding "Islander" light aircraft) 20 25
277 2 s. 70, Export of Uganda coffee 40 45
278 10 s. "Time machines in the air" (Wright *Flyer* and "Concorde") 1·25 1·40

(*f*) *Nos.* 234/7 (*25th Anniv of Coronation*) *optd as T* **33** *or surch also and No.* **MS**238 *additionally inscr* "Diplomatic Relations Normalised" *with Ugandan and British flags replacing portrait of Amin* (12 July)

279 1 s. Type **29** 15 20
280 1 s. 50, Regalia 20 25
281 2 s. 70, Coronation ceremony 40 45
282 15 s. on 10 s. Royal family on balcony of Buckingham Palace 1·75 1·90
MS283 150×102 mm. Nos. 234/6 and 15 s. as No. 237*
* The sheet contains unoverprinted stamps; the additional inscriptions and changes in design appear only on the sheet margin.

(*g*) *Nos.* 239/42 (*Centenary of Catholic Church in Uganda*) *optd with T* **34** *and No.* **MS**243 *with additional inscr* "FREEDOM OF WORSHIP DECLARED" *replacing part of the margin decoration* (1 Aug)

284 1 s. Type **30** 15 20
285 1 s. 50, Lubaga Cathedral 20 25
286 2 s. 70, Ugandan pilgrimage to Rome, Holy Year, 1975 40 45
287 10 s. Friar Lourdel-Mapeera (early missionary) 1·25 1·40
MS288 128×91 mm. Nos. 239/42*. P 12½×12 (1979) 2·25 2·75
* The sheet contains the original unoverprinted stamps; the additional inscription appears on the sheet margin.

(*h*) *Nos.* 244/8 (*International Year of the Child*) *optd with T* **34** (16 Aug)

289 1 s. Type **31** 15 20
290 1 s. 50, Handicapped children at play 20 25
291 2 s. 70, Ugandan I.Y.C. emblem 40 45
292 10 s. Children in class 1·25 1·40
MS293 136 × 113 mm. Nos. 289/92 2·25 2·75
249/82, 284/7 *and* 289/92 *Set of* 42 26·00 29·00

35 Radio Wave Symbol

(Des G. Vasarhelyi. Litho Questa)

1979 (11 Sept). *50th Anniv of International Consultative Radio Committee and International Telecommunications Union. P* 14.

294 **35** 1 s. multicoloured 15 10
295 1 s. 50, multicoloured 20 10
296 2 s. 70, multicoloured 35 35
297 10 s. multicoloured 80 90
294/7 *Set of* 4 1·40 1·25

36 20s. Definitive Stamp of 1965 and Sir Rowland Hill

(Des BG Studio. Litho Questa)

1979 (Oct). *Death Centenary of Sir Rowland Hill. T* **36** *and similar horiz designs showing stamps and Sir Rowland Hill. Multicoloured. P* 14.

298 1 s. Type **36** 15 10
299 1 s. 50, 1967 13th Commonwealth Parliamentary Association Conference 50 c. commemorative 20 10
300 2 s. 70, 1962 Independence 20 s. commemorative 35 40
301 10 s. Uganda Protectorate 1898 1 a. 80 1·25
298/301 *Set of* 4 1·40 1·60
MS302 154×98 mm. Nos. 298/301 1·50 2·00

37 Impala — **38** Lions with Cub

(Des G. Drummond. Litho Questa)

1979 (3 Dec)–**82**. *Wildlife. Horiz designs as T* **37** (10 *to* 80 *c.*) *or T* **38** (1 *to* 40 *s.*). *Multicoloured. P* 14×13½ (10 *to* 80 *c.*) *or* 14 (1 *to* 40 *s.*). A. *No imprint date.* B. *With imprint date* ("1982") *at foot of design* (1982).

		A		B	
303	10 c. Type **37**	10	10	†	
304	20 c. Large-spotted Genet	10	10	†	
305	30 c. Thomson's Gazelle	15	10	†	
306	50 c. Lesser Bushbaby	15	10	†	
307	80 c. Hunting Dog	20	10	†	
308	1 s. Type **38**	30	10	15	10
309	1 s. 50, Gorilla	45	10	†	
310	2 s. Common Zebra	45	10	25	15
311	2 s. 70, Leopard with cub	50	10	†	
312	3 s. 50, Black Rhinoceros	55	15	†	
313	5 s. Waterbuck	55	25	40	35
314	10 s. African Buffalo	60	50	†	
315	20 s. Hippopotamus	80	1·00	†	
316	40 s. African Elephant	1·50	2·25	†	
303/16	*Set of* 14	5·75	4·00		

For designs as Nos. 308/12 and 315/16, but with face values in revalued currency, see Nos. 433/9.

LONDON 1980 (**39**)

40 Rotary Emblem

1980 (6 May). *"London 1980" International Stamp Exhibition. Nos.* 298/302 *optd as T* **39**.

317 1 s. Type **36** 15 10
318 1 s. 50, 1967 13th Commonwealth Parliamentary Association Conference 50 c. commemorative 20 10
319 2 s. 70, 1962 Independence 20s. commemorative 35 25
320 10 s. Uganda Protectorate 1898 1a. 80 80
317/20 *Set of* 4 1·40 1·10
MS321 154 × 99 mm. Nos. 317/20 1·40 1·75

(Des BG Studio. Litho Questa)

1980 (25 Aug). *75th Anniv of Rotary International. T* **40** *and similar multicoloured design. P* 14.

322 1 s. Type **40** 10 10
323 20 s. Paul Harris (founder) with wheel-barrow containing "Rotary projects" (*horiz*) 1·50 1·50
MS324 100 × 76 mm. Nos. 322/3. Imperf. 2·10 2·50

41 Football

FOOTBALL
GOLD MEDALISTS, C.S.S.R.

(42)

(Des G. Vasarhelyi. Litho Questa)

1980 (29 Dec). *Olympic Games, Moscow. T* **41** *and similar horiz designs. Multicoloured. P* 14.

325 1 s. Type **41** 10 10
326 2 s. Relay 10 10
327 10 s. Hurdles 40 60
328 20 s. Boxing .. .. 80 1·25
325/8 .. .. *Set of* 4 1·25 1·75
MS329 118×90 mm. 2 s. 70, 3 s., 5 s., 25 s. As Nos. 325/8 .. .. 1·75 2·75

1980 (29 Dec). *Olympic Games, Moscow. Medal Winners. Nos.* 325/9 *optd as T* **42**.

330 1 s. Type **41** 10 10
331 2 s. Relay 10 15
332 10 s. Hurdles 40 50
333 20 s. Boxing .. .. 80 1·00
330/3 .. .. *Set of* 4 1·25 1·50
MS334 118×90 mm. 2 s. 70, 3 s., 5 s., 25 s. As Nos. 330/3 .. .. 1·50 3·00

Overprints:—2s. "RELAY GOLD MEDALIST U.S.S.R."; 10s. "HURDLES 110 m. GOLD MEDALIST THOMAS MUNKLET, D.D.R."; 20s. "BOXING WELTERWEIGHT SILVER MEDALIST JOHN MUGABI, UGANDA".

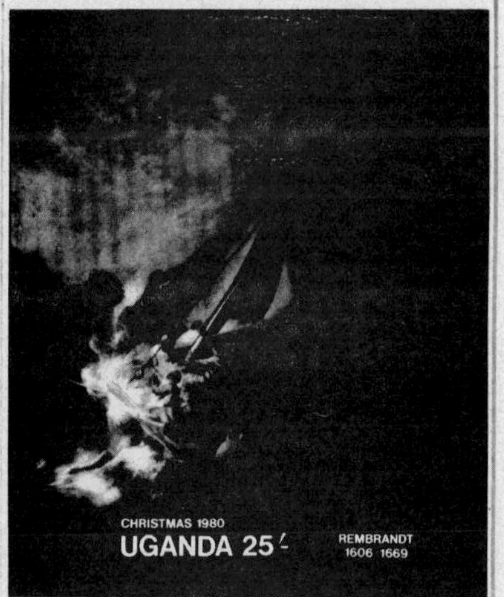

43 "Christ in the Storm on the Sea of Galilee" (painting, Rembrandt)

1980 (31 Dec). *Christmas. Sheet* 79 × 101 *mm. Litho. Imperf.*
MS335 **43** 25 s. multicoloured .. .. .. 2·75 3·50

44 Heinrich von Stephan and U.P.U. Emblem

45 Tower of London

(Des BG Studio. Litho Questa)

1981 (2 June). *150th Birth Anniv of Heinrich von Stephan (founder of U.P.U.). T* **44** *and similar horiz designs. Multicoloured. P* 14.

336 1 s. Type **44** 10 10
337 2 s. U.P.U. Headquarters 15 15
338 2 s. 70, Air mail, 1935 .. .. .. 20 20
339 10 s. Mail transport by train, 1927 .. .. 80 80
336/9 .. .. *Set of* 4 1·10 1·10
MS340 112 × 95 mm. Nos. 336/9 .. .. .. 1·90 1·90

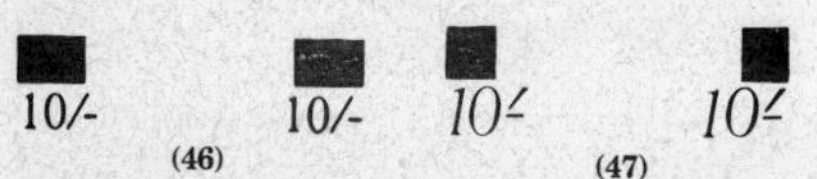

(46) (47)

(Des J.W. Litho Questa)

1981 (July). *Royal Wedding. T* **45** *and similar vert designs. Multicoloured. P* 14. (*a*) *Unissued stamps surcharged* (13 July). A. *As T* **46**. B. *As T* **47**.

		A		B	
341	10 s. on 1 s. Prince Charles and Lady Diana Spencer	65	65	25	20
	a. Surch on 5 s. value ..	50·00	—	†	
	b. Surch on 20 s. value ..	45·00	—	†	
	c. Surch omitted	90·00	—	†	
342	50 s. on 5 s. Type **45**	1·00	1·00	40	30
	a. Surch omitted	85·00	—	†	
343	200 s. on 20 s. Prince Charles at Balmoral	3·00	3·00	1·50	1·25
	a. Surch omitted	£130	—	†	
	b. Surch inverted	50·00	—	†	
	c. Surch inverted on 1 s. value	50·00	—	†	
	d. Surch inverted on 5 s. value	50·00	—	†	
341/3	.. .. .. *Set of* 3	4·25	4·25	2·00	1·60
MS344	95×80 mm. 250 s. on 25 s. Royal Mews	12·00	12·00	2·75	2·00
	a. Surch omitted	—	—	†	

(*b*) *Redrawn with new face values. Background colours changed* (29 July)

345 10 s. As No. 341 .. .. 15 15
346 50 s. Type **45** 30 30
347 200 s. As No. 343 .. .. 1·00 1·00
345/7 .. .. *Set of* 3 1·25 1·25
MS348 95×80 mm. 250 s. As No. **MS**344 .. 1·75 2·00

Nos. 345/7 also exist perforated 12 (*price for set of* 3 £1.25 *mint or used*) from additional sheetlets of 5 stamps and one label. These stamps have changed background colours.

The issue was originally printed with face values of 1, 5 and 20 s. and 25 s. for the miniature sheet. Before it could be placed on sale the Uganda currency was devalued and the stamps were surcharged, and later reprinted with corrected face values.

48 "Sleeping Woman before Green Shutters"

(Des J.W. Litho Questa)

1981 (21 Sept). *Birth Centenary of Picasso. T* **48** *and similar multicoloured designs. P* 14 × 13½.

349 10 s. Type **48** 10 10
350 20 s. "Bullfight" 20 20
351 30 s. "Detail of a Nude asleep in a Landscape" 25 25
352 200 s. "Interior with a Girl Drawing" .. .. 1·75 2·25
349/52 .. .. *Set of* 4 2·00 2·50
MS353 120 × 146 mm. 250 s. "Minotaure" (112 × 139 *mm*). Imperf .. .. 2·25 3·00

49 Deaf People using Sign Language

(Des Design Images. Litho Format)

1981 (28 Dec). *International Year for Disabled Persons. T* **49** *and similar horiz designs. Multicoloured. P* 15.

354 1 s. Type **49** 10 10
355 10 s. Disabled teacher in classroom 15 10
356 50 s. Teacher and disabled children 70 50
357 200 s. Blind person with guide dog .. .. 2·00 2·00
354/7 .. .. *Set of* 4 2·50 2·25
MS358 122 × 93 mm. Nos. 354/7 .. .. .. 3·75 4·00

50 Footballers

(Des G. Vasarhelyi. Litho Questa)

1982 (11 Jan). *World Cup Football Championship, Spain. T* **50** *and similar horiz designs showing World Cup* (250 *s.*) *or footballers* (*others*). *P* 14.

359 1 s. multicoloured 10 10
360 10 s. multicoloured 15 10
361 50 s. multicoloured 70 50
362 200 s. multicoloured .. .. 2·00 2·00
359/62 .. .. *Set of* 4 2·50 2·25
MS363 116×77 mm. 250 s. multicoloured .. 2·75 3·00

NEW INFORMATION

The editor is always interested to correspond with people who have new information that will improve or correct the Catalogue.

51 Mpoma Satellite Earth Station

(Des Artists International. Litho Format)

1982 (10 May). *"Peaceful Use of Outer Space". T* **51** *and similar horiz designs. Multicoloured. P* 15.

364 5 s. Type **51** 10 10
365 10 s. *Pioneer II* (satellite) 20 20
366 50 s. Space Shuttle 90 90
367 100 s. *Voyager* 2 (satellite) .. .. .. 1·75 1·75
364/7 .. .. *Set of* 4 2·75 2·75
MS368 118×89 mm. 150 s. Space Shuttle (*different*) .. .. 2·50 2·00

52 Dr. Robert Koch

21st BIRTHDAY
HRH Princess of Wales
JULY 1 1982

(**53**)

(Des R. Vigurs. Litho Questa)

1982 (14 June). *Centenary of Robert Koch's Discovery of Tubercle Bacillus. T* **52** *and similar multicoloured designs. P* 14.

369 1 s. Type **52** 25 10
370 10 s. Microscope 55 30
371 50 s. Ugandans receiving vaccinations .. .. 1·60 1·40
372 100 s. Tubercle virus .. .. 2·75 2·40
369/72 .. .. *Set of* 4 4·50 3·75
MS373 85×64 mm. 150 s. Medical College classroom scene (*horiz*) .. .. 4·00 3·25

1982 (7 July). *21st Birthday of Princess of Wales. Nos.* 345/8 *optd with T* **53**. *P* 14.

374 10 s. Prince Charles and Lady Diana Spencer 20 15
375 50 s. Type **45** 75 50
376 200 s. Prince Charles at Balmoral .. .. 2·50 2·00
374/6 .. .. *Set of* 3 3·00 2·40
MS377 95×82 mm. 250 s. Royal Mews .. .. 2·75 2·25

Nos. 374/6 also exist perforated 12 (*price for set of* 3 £2.25 *mint or used*) from additional sheetlets of 5 stamps and one label. These stamps have changed background colours.

Nos. 374/7, and the sheetlets, also exist with the top line of the overprint shown as "21st Birthday" instead of "21st BIRTHDAY" as in Type **53**. (*Price for set of* 3 *and miniature sheet £10 mint*).

54 Yellow-billed Hornbill

55 Scout Band

(Des Artists International. Litho Questa)

1982 (12 July). *Birds. T* **54** *and similar vert designs. Multicoloured. P* 14.

378 1 s. Type **54** 15 10
379 20 s. Superb Starling 60 35
380 50 s. Bateleur .. .. 1·25 1·50
381 100 s. Saddle-bill Stork .. .. .. 2·00 2·50
378/81 .. .. *Set of* 4 3·50 4·00
MS382 115×85 mm. 200 s. Laughing Dove .. 5·00 5·00

(Des G. Vasarhelyi. Litho Questa)

1982 (23 Aug). *75th Anniv of Boy Scout Movement. T* **55** *and similar horiz designs. Multicoloured. P* 14.

383 5 s. Type **55** 35 10
384 20 s. Scout receiving Bata Shoe trophy .. 80 35
385 50 s. Scouts with wheelchair patient .. .. 1·75 1·00
386 100 s. First aid instruction .. .. .. 2·50 2·25
383/6 .. .. *Set of* 4 4·75 3·25
MS387 112×85 mm. 150 s. Lord Baden-Powell .. .. 3·25 3·00

56 Swearing-in of Roosevelt

(Des Design Images. Litho Format)

1982 (8 Nov). *250th Birth Anniv of George Washington (Nos. 389/90) and Birth Centenary of Franklin D. Roosevelt (others). T* **56** *and similar horiz designs. Multicoloured. P* 15.

388 50 s. Type **56** 30 30
389 200 s. Swearing-in of Washington .. .. 1·25 1·25
MS390 100×69 mm. 150 s. Washington at Mt Vernon .. .. 1·40 1·60
MS391 100×70 mm. 150 s. Roosevelt at Hyde Park Mansion .. .. 1·40 1·60

57 Italy v West Germany

(Des D. Miller. Litho)

1982 (30 Dec). *World Cup Football Championship Winners. T* **57** *and similar horiz designs. Multicoloured. P* 14½.

392 10 s. Type **57** 25 10
393 200 s. Victorious Italian team .. .. 1·75 2·00
MS394 97×117 mm. 250 s. Espana '82 emblem with Spanish and Italian flags .. .. 1·90 2·40

58 Dancers

59 "St. George and the Dragon" (Raphael)

(Des and litho Questa)

1983 (14 Mar). *Commonwealth Day. Cultural Art. T* **58** *and similar horiz designs. Multicoloured. P* 14.

395 5 s. Type **58** 10 10
396 20 s. Traditional currency 15 20
397 50 s. Homestead 40 45
398 100 s. Drums 80 85
395/8 .. .. *Set of* 4 1·25 1·40

(Des Design Images. Litho Questa)

1983 (16 Apr). *500th Birth Anniv of Raphael (painter). T* **59** *and similar vert designs. Multicoloured. P* 13½.

399 5 s. Type **59** 10 10
400 20 s. "St. George and the Dragon" (*different*) 15 20
401 50 s. "Crossing the Red Sea" (*detail*) 40 45
402 200 s. "The Expulsion of Heliodorus" (*detail*) .. 1·50 1·60
399/402 .. .. *Set of* 4 1·90 2·10
MS403 126×101 mm. 250 s. "The Meeting of Pope Leo the Great and Attila the Hun" (*detail*) .. .. 1·50 1·75

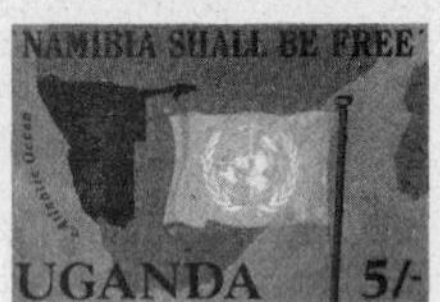

60 Map showing Namibia and U.N. Flag

(Des R. Vigurs. Litho Format)

1983 (15 Aug). *Commemorations. T* **60** *and similar horiz design. Multicoloured. P* 15.

404 5 s. Type **60** 10 10
405 200 s. 7th Non-aligned Summit Conference logo 1·25 1·60

BOYS BRIGADE CENTENARY 1883-1983

61 Elephants in Grassland

(62)

(Des J. Iskowitz. Litho Format)

1983 (22 Aug). *Wildlife. T* **61** *and similar multicoloured designs. P* 15.

406 5 s. Elephants in "Elephants' Graveyard" 40 10
407 10 s. Type **61** 65 20
408 30 s. Elephants at waterhole .. .. .. 1·40 80
409 70 s. Elephants having dust bath .. .. 1·90 1·75
406/9 .. .. *Set of* 4 4·00 2·50
MS410 87 × 64 mm. 300 s. Grevy's Zebra drinking (*vert*) .. .. 2·50 3·00
See also No. 642.

1983 (19 Sept). *Centenary of Boys' Brigade. Nos. 383/7 optd with T* **62** *or surch also.*

411 5 s. Type **55** 10 10
412 20 s. Scout receiving Bata Shoe trophy .. 15 15
413 50 s. Scouts with wheelchair patient .. 25 30
414 400 s. on 100 s. First aid instruction .. 2·40 2·75
411/14 .. .. *Set of* 4 2·50 3·00
MS415 112×85 mm. 150 s. Lord Baden-Powell .. 90 1·25

100/-

63 Mpoma Satellite Earth Station

(64)

(Des D. Dorfman. Litho Format)

1983 (3 Oct). *World Communications Year. T* **63** *and similar horiz designs. Multicoloured. P* 15.

416 20 s. Type **63** 15 15
417 50 s. Railroad computer and operator .. 45 50
418 70 s. Cameraman filming lions 45 65
419 100 s. Aircraft cockpit 60 80
416/19 .. .. *Set of* 4 1·50 1·90
MS420 128×103 mm. 300 s. Communications satellite .. .. 1·60 2·00
No. 416 has the "o" omitted from "Station".

1983 (7 Oct). *Nos.* 303, 305/7, 308A, 309 *and* 313A *surch as T* **64**.

421 100 s. on 10 c. Type **37** 45 45
422 135 s. on 1 s. Type **38** 60 60
423 175 s. on 30 c. Thomson's Gazelle 75 75
424 200 s. on 50 c. Lesser Bushbaby 85 85
425 400 s. on 80 c. Hunting Dog .. .. 1·60 1·60
426 700 s. on 5 s. Waterbuck .. .. .. 2·75 3·00
427 1000 s. on 1 s. 50, Gorilla .. .. .. 4·00 4·00
421/7 .. .. *Set of* 7 10·00 10·00

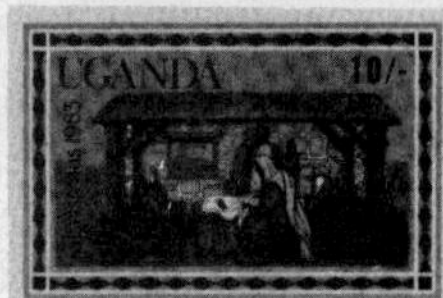

65 The Nativity

(Des PAD Studio. Litho Questa)

1983 (12 Dec). *Christmas. T* **65** *and similar horiz designs. Multicoloured. P* 14.

428 10 s. Type **65** 10 10
429 50 s. Shepherds and Angels 25 30
430 175 s. Flight into Egypt .. .. 80 1·00
431 400 s. Angels blowing trumpets .. .. 1·90 2·25
428/31 .. .. *Set of* 4 2·75 3·25
MS432 85×57 mm. 300 s. The Three Kings .. 1·40 1·50

1983 (19 Dec). *Designs as Nos. 308/12 and 315/16 but with face values in revalued currency.*

433 100 s. Type **38** 65 35
434 135 s. Gorilla 75 50
435 175 s. Common Zebra 95 70
436 200 s. Leopard with cub .. .. 1·25 80
437 400 s. Black Rhinoceros .. .. 2·00 2·00
438 700 s. African Elephant .. .. 3·50 3·75
439 1000 s. Hippopotamus .. .. 4·25 4·75
433/9 .. .. *Set of* 7 12·00 11·50

66 Ploughing with Oxen

(Des J.W. Litho Questa)

1984 (16 Jan). *World Food Day. T* **66** *and similar horiz design. Multicoloured. P* 14.

440 10 s. Type **66** 10 10
441 300 s. Harvesting bananas .. .. 2·25 2·25

67 Ruth Kyalisiima, Sportsman of the Year 1983

(Des J. Iskowitz. Litho Format)

1984 (1 Oct). *Olympic Games, Los Angeles. T* **67** *and similar multicoloured designs. P* 15.

442 5 s. Type **67** 10 10
443 115 s. Javelin-throwing 40 45
444 155 s. Wrestling 50 55
445 175 s. Rowing 60 65
442/5 .. .. *Set of* 4 1·40 1·50
MS446 108×79 mm. 500 s. Fund-raising walk (*vert*) .. .. 1·50 1·60

68 Entebbe Airport

(Des BG Studio. Litho Format)

1984 (29 Oct). *40th Anniv of International Civil Aviation Organization. T* **68** *and similar horiz designs. Multicoloured. P* 15.

447 5 s. Type **68** 10 10
448 115 s. Loading cargo plane .. .. .. 1·00 1·00
449 155 s. Uganda police helicopter .. .. 1·50 1·50
450 175 s. East African Civil Flying School, Soroti 1·75 1·75
447/50 .. .. *Set of* 4 3·75 3·75
MS451 100×70 mm. 250 s. Balloon race .. 1·50 1·75

69 Silver-barred Charaxes

(Des J. Johnson. Litho Questa)

1984 (19 Nov). *Butterflies. T* **69** *and similar horiz designs. Multicoloured. P* 14.

452 5 s. Type **69** 20 10
453 115 s. Western Emperor Swallowtail .. .. 1·10 90
454 155 s. African Giant Swallowtail .. .. 1·50 1·25
455 175 s. Blue Salamis .. .. 2·00 1·50
452/5 .. .. *Set of* 4 4·25 3·25
MS456 127×90 mm. 250 s. Veined Yellow .. 1·25 1·50

70 *Nothobranchius taeniopygus*

(Des Associated Creative Designers. Litho Format)

1985 (1 Apr–10 June). *Lake Fishes. T* **70** *and similar horiz designs. Multicoloured. P* 15.

457 5 s. Type **70** 10 10
458 10 s. *Bagrus dogmac* 10 10
459 50 s. *Polypterus senegalus* 20 10
460 100 s. *Clarias* 25 10
461 135 s. *Mormyrus kannume* (10 June) .. 25 15
462 175 s. *Synodontis victoriae* 30 20
463 205 s. *Haplochromis brownae* 30 25
464 400 s. *Lates niloticus* 40 30
465 700 s. *Protopterus aethiopicus* 60 60
466 1000 s. *Barbus radcliffii* 80 80
467 2500 s. *Malapterus electricus* (10 June) .. 1·25 1·25
457/67 .. .. *Set of* 11 4·00 4·00

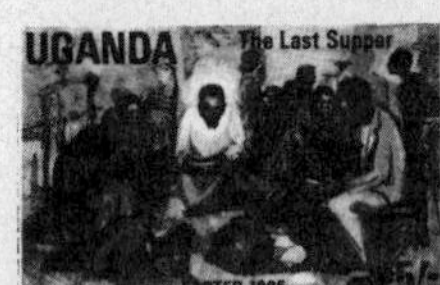

71 The Last Supper

(Des Associated Creative Designers. Litho Questa)

1985 (13 May). *Easter. T* **71** *and similar horiz designs. Multicoloured. P* 14.

468 5 s. Type **71** 10 10
469 115 s. Christ showing the nail marks to Thomas 50 40
470 155 s. The raising of the Cross 60 50
471 175 s. Pentecost 75 60
468/71 .. .. *Set of* 4 1·75 1·40
MS472 99×70 mm. 250 s. The last prayer in the Garden .. .. 80 1·00

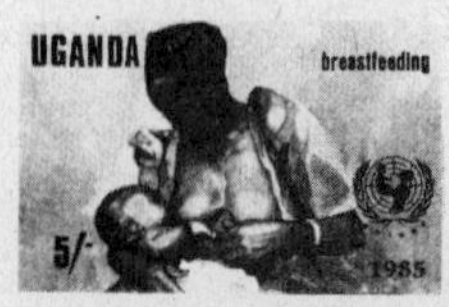

72 Breast Feeding

73 Queen Elizabeth the Queen Mother

(Des Associated Creative Designers. Litho Questa)

1985 (29 July). *U.N.I.C.E.F. Child Survival Campaign. T* **72** *and similar horiz designs. Multicoloured. P* 14.

473 5 s. Type **72** 10 10
474 115 s. Growth monitoring 70 70
475 155 s. Immunisation 90 90
476 175 s. Oral re-hydration therapy .. .. .. 1·00 1·00
473/6 .. .. *Set of* 4 2·40 2·40
MS477 75×55 mm. 500 s. Pregnant woman preparing nourishing food .. .. 1·75 2·00

(Des J.W. Litho Questa)

1985 (21 Aug). *Life and Times of Queen Elizabeth the Queen Mother and Decade for Women. T* **73** *and similar vert design. Multicoloured. P* 14.

478 1000 s. Type **73** .. .. 2·00 2·10
MS479 57×81 mm. 1500 s. The Queen Mother inspecting Kings African Rifles, Kampala .. 3·25 3·50

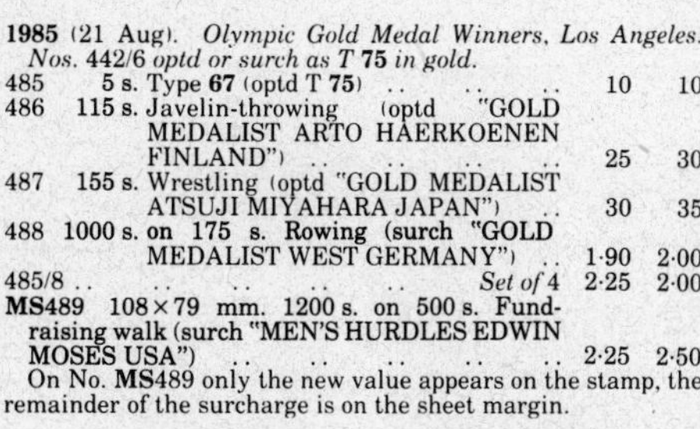

GOLD MEDALIST
BENITA BROWN-FITZGERALD
USA

74 Sedge Warbler (**75**)

(Des S. Heinmann. Litho Questa)

1985 (21 Aug). *Birth Bicentenary of John J. Audubon (ornithologist) (1st issue). T* **74** *and similar vert designs. Multicoloured. P* 14.

480 115 s. Type **74** 85 85
481 155 s. Cattle Egret .. .. 1·00 1·00
482 175 s. Crested Lark .. .. 1·25 1·25
483 500 s. Tufted Duck .. .. 1·75 1·75
480/3 .. .. *Set of* 4 4·25 4·25
MS484 99×69 mm. 1000 s. Tawny Owl .. .. 5·50 4·50
See also Nos. 494/8.

1985 (21 Aug). *Olympic Gold Medal Winners, Los Angeles. Nos.* 442/6 *optd or surch as T* **75** *in gold.*

485 5 s. Type **67** (optd T **75**) 10 10
486 115 s. Javelin-throwing (optd "GOLD MEDALIST ARTO HAERKOENEN FINLAND") 25 30
487 155 s. Wrestling (optd "GOLD MEDALIST ATSUJI MIYAHARA JAPAN") .. 30 35
488 1000 s. on 175 s. Rowing (surch "GOLD MEDALIST WEST GERMANY") .. 1·90 2·00
485/8 .. .. *Set of* 4 2·25 2·00
MS489 108×79 mm. 1200 s. on 500 s. Fund-raising walk (surch "MEN'S HURDLES EDWIN MOSES USA") .. .. 2·25 2·50
On No. **MS**489 only the new value appears on the stamp, the remainder of the surcharge is on the sheet margin.

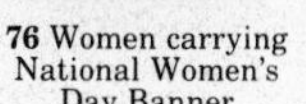

76 Women carrying National Women's Day Banner

77 Man beneath Tree laden with Produce (F.A.O.)

(Des and litho Questa)

1985 (1 Nov). *Decade for Women. T* **76** *and similar multicoloured designs. P* 14.

490 5 s. Type **76** 10 10
491 115 s. Girl Guides (*horiz*) 85 85
492 155 s. Mother Teresa (Nobel Peace Prize winner, 1979) .. .. 1·25 1·25
490/2 .. .. *Set of* 3 2·00 2·00
MS493 85×59 mm. 1500 s. As 115 s. .. .. 3·50 3·50
Nos. 491 and **MS**493 also commemorate the 75th anniversary of the Girl Guide movement.

(Litho Questa)

1985 (23 Dec). *Birth Bicentenary of John J. Audubon (ornithologist) (2nd issue). Horiz designs as T* **198** *of Antigua showing original paintings. Multicoloured. P* 12.

494 5 s. Rock Ptarmigan 35 10
495 155 s. Sage Grouse 90 80
496 175 s. Lesser Yellowlegs .. .. 1·25 1·25
497 500 s. Brown-headed Cowbird .. .. .. 2·25 2·25
494/7 .. .. *Set of* 4 4·25 4·00
MS498 72×102 mm. 1000 s. Whooping Crane. P 14 .. .. 5·50 5·00
Nos. 494/7 were each printed in sheetlets of 5 stamps and one stamp-size label which appears in the centre of the bottom row.

(Des BG Studio. Litho Format)

1986 (1 Apr). *40th Anniv of United Nations Organization. T* **77** *and similar designs. P* 15.

499 10 s. multicoloured 10 10
500 180 s. multicoloured 40 30
501 200 s. new blue, agate and bright green .. 40 30
502 250 s. new blue, brownish blk & scar-verm 45 35
503 2000 s. multicoloured .. .. 2·50 2·50
499/503 .. .. *Set of* 5 3·50 3·25
MS504 69×69 mm. 2500 s. multicoloured .. 2·50 2·75
Designs: *Horiz*—180 s. Soldier of U.N. Peace-Keeping Force; 250 s. Hands releasing peace dove. *Vert*—200 s. U.N. emblem; 2000 s. Flags of U.N. and Uganda; 2500 s. U.N. Building, New York, and flags of member nations.

NRA LIBERATION
1986

78 Goalkeeper catching Ball (**79**)

(Des Shelley Haas. Litho Questa)

1986 (17 Apr). *World Cup Football Championship, Mexico. T* **78** *and similar multicoloured designs. P* 14.

505 10 s. Type **78** 10 10
506 180 s. Player with ball 40 30
507 250 s. Two players competing for ball .. 45 35
508 2500 s. Player running with ball .. .. 3·00 3·25
505/8 .. .. *Set of* 4 3·50 3·50
MS509 87×66 mm. 3000 s. Player kicking ball (*vert*) .. .. 3·25 3·50

1986 (30 Apr). *Liberation by National Resistance Army. Nos.* 462, 465/7 *and* **MS**493 *optd with T* **79** *or larger* (22×8 *mm*) (*No.* **MS**493).

510 175 s. *Synodontis victoriae* (Sil.) 40 40
511 700 s. *Protopterus aethiopicus* (Sil.) .. 1·00 1·00
512 1000 s. *Barbus radcliffii* .. .. .. 1·50 1·75
513 2500 s. *Malapterus electricus* .. .. 3·00 3·25
510/13 .. .. *Set of* 4 5·50 5·75
MS514 85×59 mm. 1500 s. Girl Guides .. .. 2·50 2·50
Nos. 510/13 also exist with the overprint colours transposed.

(Des W. Hanson. Litho Questa)

1986 (30 Apr). *Appearance of Halley's Comet* (1st issue). *Horiz designs as T* **123** *of Anguilla. Multicoloured. P* 14.

515 50 s. Tycho Brahe and Arecibo Radio Telescope, Puerto Rico 10 10
516 100 s. Recovery of astronaut John Glenn from sea, 1962 .. .. 20 15
517 140 s. "The Star in the East" (painting by Giotto) 35 25
518 2500 s. Death of Davy Crockett at the Alamo, 1835 .. .. 3·00 3·25
515/18 .. .. *Set of* 4 3·25 3·25
MS519 102×70 mm. 3000 s. Halley's Comet over Uganda .. .. 4·00 4·00

UGANDA

80 Niagara Falls **81** *Gloria* (Colombia)

(Des Mary Walters. Litho Format)

1986 (22 May). *"Ameripex '86" International Stamp Exhibition, Chicago. American Landmarks. T* **80** *and similar horiz designs. Multicoloured. P* 15.

520 50 s. Type **80** 10 10
521 100 s. Jefferson Memorial, Washington D.C. 20 15
522 250 s. Liberty Bell, Philadelphia 45 35
523 1000 s. The Alamo, San Antonio, Texas .. 1·60 1·60
524 2500 s. George Washington Bridge, New York–New Jersey .. .. .. 3·00 3·25
520/4 .. .. *Set of* 5 4·75 4·75
MS525 87×64 mm. 3000 s. Grand Canyon .. 3·00 3·25

(Litho Questa)

1986 (24 May). *60th Birthday of Queen Elizabeth II. Vert designs as T* **125** *of Anguilla. P* 14.

526 100 s. black and yellow 20 15
527 140 s. multicoloured 25 20
528 2500 s. multicoloured .. .. 2·75 3·00
526/8 .. .. *Set of* 3 3·00 3·00
MS529 120×85 mm. 3000 s. black & grey-brown 3·25 3·50
Designs:—100 s. Princess Elizabeth at London Zoo; 140 s. Queen Elizabeth at race meeting, 1970; 2500 s. With Prince Philip at Sandringham, 1982; 3000 s. Engagement photograph, 1947.

(Des J. Iskowitz. Litho Questa)

1986 (2 July). *Centenary of Statue of Liberty. T* **81** *and similar multicoloured designs showing cadet sailing ships. P* 14.

530 50 s. Type **81** 15 10
531 100 s. *Mircea* (Rumania) 30 20
532 140 s. *Sagres II* (Portugal) (*horiz*) 40 40
533 2500 s. *Gazela Primiero* (U.S.A.) (*horiz*) .. 3·00 3·50
530/3 .. .. *Set of* 4 3·50 3·75
MS534 113×82 mm. 3000 s. Statue of Liberty .. 3·25 3·50

(Des and litho Questa)

1986 (23 July). *Royal Wedding. Multicoloured designs as T* **213** *of Antigua. P* 14.

535 50 s. Prince Andrew and Miss Sarah Ferguson (*horiz*) 10 10
536 140 s. Prince Andrew with Princess Anne at shooting match (*horiz*) 20 20
537 2500 s. Prince Andrew and Miss Sarah Ferguson at Ascot (*horiz*) .. .. 2·75 3·00
535/7 .. .. *Set of* 3 2·75 3·00
MS538 88×88 mm. 3000 s. Prince Andrew and Miss Sarah Ferguson (*different*) .. .. .. 3·25 3·25

WINNERS

Argentina 3 W.Germany 2

(**82**)

1986 (15 Sept). *World Cup Football Championship Winners, Mexico. Nos.* 505/9 *optd as T* **82**, *or surch also, in gold.*

539 50 s. on 10 s. Type **78** 10 10
540 180 s. Player with ball 25 25
541 250 s. Two players competing for ball .. 35 35
542 2500 s. Player running with ball .. .. 2·75 3·25
539/42 .. .. *Set of* 4 3·00 3·50
MS543 87×66 mm. 3000 s. Player kicking ball (*vert*) .. .. 3·00 3·25

1986 (15 Oct). *Appearance of Halley's Comet* (2nd issue). *Nos.* 515/19 *optd with T* **218** *of Antigua* (*in silver on* 3000 s.).

544 50 s. Tycho Brahe and Arecibo Radio Telescope, Puerto Rico 10 10
545 100 s. Recovery of astronaut John Glenn from sea, 1962 .. .. 20 15
546 140 s. "The Star in the East" (painting by Giotto) 35 25
547 2500 s. Death of Davy Crockett at the Alamo, 1835 .. .. 3·00 3·25
544/7 .. .. *Set of* 4 3·25 3·25
MS548 102×70 mm. 3000 s. Halley's Comet over Uganda .. .. 3·00 3·50

83 St. Kizito

(Des Associated Creative Designers. Litho Questa)

1986 (15 Oct). *Christian Martyrs of Uganda. T* **83** *and similar horiz designs. Multicoloured. P* 14.

549 50 s. Type **83** 10 10
550 150 s. St. Kizito instructing converts .. 15 20
551 200 s. Martyrdom of Bishop James Hannington, 1885 .. .. 20 25
552 1000 s. Burning of Bugandan Christians, 1886 .. .. 1·00 1·50
549/52 .. .. *Set of* 4 1·25 1·75
MS553 89×59 mm. 1500 s. King Mwanga of Buganda passing sentence on Christians .. 1·50 2·00

84 "Madonna of the Cherries" (Titian)

(Litho Questa)

1986 (26 Nov). *Christmas. Religious Paintings. T* **84** *and similar multicoloured designs. P* 14.

554 50 s. Type **84** 10 10
555 150 s. "Madonna and Child" (Dürer) (*vert*) .. 30 20
556 200 s. "Assumption of the Virgin" (Titian) (*vert*) 35 25
557 2500 s. "Praying Hands" (Dürer) (*vert*) .. 3·00 3·50
554/7 .. .. *Set of* 4 3·25 3·50
MS558 Two sheets, each 102×76 mm. (a) 3000 s. "Presentation of the Virgin in the Temple" (Titian). (b) 3000 s. "Adoration of the Magi" (Dürer) .. .. *Set of 2 sheets* 3·50 4·00

85 Red-billed Firefinch and Glory Lily

(Litho Format)

1987 (22 July). *Flora and Fauna. T* **85** *and similar horiz designs. Multicoloured. P* 15.

559 2 s. Type **85** 10 10
560 5 s. African Pygmy Kingfisher and Nandi Flame 15 15
561 10 s. Scarlet-chested Sunbird and Crown of Thorns 20 25
562 25 s. White Rhinoceros and Yellow-billed Oxpecker 50 55

563 35 s. Lion and Elephant Grass 70 75
564 45 s. Cheetahs and Doum Palm 90 95
565 50 s. Cordon Bleu and Desert Rose .. 1·00 1·10
566 100 s. Giant Eland and Acacia .. .. 2·00 2·10
559/66 .. .. *Set of* 8 5·00 5·25
MS567 98×67 mm. (a) 150 s. Carmine Bee Eaters and Sausage Tree. (b) 150 s. Cattle Egret and Zebras .. .. .. *Set of* 2 *sheets* 6·00 7·00

86 Tremml's *Eagle* (longest man-powered flight), 1987

(Des W. Hanson. Litho Format)

1987 (14 Aug). *Milestones of Transportation. T* **86** *and similar horiz designs. Multicoloured. P* 15.
568 2 s. Type **86** 10 10
569 3 s. Junkers "W-33L" *Bremen* (first east-west transatlantic flight), 1928 .. 10 10
570 5 s. Lockheed *Winnie Mae* (Post's first solo round-the-world flight), 1933 .. .. 20 20
571 10 s. *Voyager* (first non-stop round-the-world flight), 1986 .. .. .. 40 40
572 15 s. Chanute biplane glider, 1896 .. 50 50
573 25 s. Airship *Norge* and Polar Bear (first transpolar flight), 1926 .. .. 75 75
574 35 s. Curtis biplane and U.S.S. *Pennsylvania* (first take-off and landing from ship), 1911 .. .. 90 90
575 45 s. Shepard and "Freedom 7" spacecraft (first American in space), 1961 .. 1·10 1·10
576 100 s. "Concorde" (first supersonic passenger flight), 1976 .. .. 3·00 3·00
568/76 .. .. *Set of* 9 6·50 6·50

87 Olympic Torch-bearer

(Litho Questa)

1987 (5 Oct). *Olympic Games, Seoul* (1988) (1*st issue*). *T* **87** *and similar horiz designs. Multicoloured. P* 14.
577 5 s. Type **87** 10 10
578 10 s. Swimming 20 25
579 50 s. Cycling .. .. 1·00 1·10
580 100 s. Gymnastics .. .. 2·00 2·10
577/80 .. .. *Set of* 4 3·00 3·25
MS581 100×75 mm. 150 s. Boxing .. .. 3·00 3·50
See also Nos. 628/32.

88 Child Immunization **89** Golden-backed Weaver

(Des Associated Creative Designers. Litho Questa)

1987 (8 Oct) *25th Anniv of Independence. T* **88** *and similar horiz designs. P* 14.
582 5 s. multicoloured 10 10
583 10 s. multicoloured 20 25
584 25 s. multicoloured 50 55
585 50 s. multicoloured .. .. 1·00 1·10
582/5 .. .. *Set of* 4 1·60 1·75
MS586 90×70 mm. 100 s. black, bright scarlet and greenish yellow .. .. 2·00 2·40
Designs:—10 s. Mulago Hospital, Kampala; 25 s. Independence Monument, Kampala City Park; 50 s. High Court, Kampala; 100 s. Stylized head of Crested Crane, "25" and Ugandan flag.

(Des Jennifer Toombs. Litho Questa)

1987 (19 Oct). *Birds of Uganda. T* **89** *and similar multicoloured designs. P* 14.
587 5 s. Type **89** 15 15
588 10 s. Hoopoe 20 25
589 15 s. Red-throated Bee Eater 30 35
590 25 s. Lilac-breasted Roller 50 55
591 35 s. Pygmy Goose 70 75
592 45 s. Scarlet-chested Sunbird 90 95
593 50 s. Crowned Crane .. .. 1·00 1·10
594 100 s. Long-tailed Fiscal Shrike .. .. 2·00 2·10
587/94 .. .. *Set of* 8 5·25 5·50
MS595 80×60 mm. (a) 150 s. African Fish Eagle. (b) 150 s. African Barn Owl *Set of* 2 *sheets* 6·00 7·00

MINIMUM PRICE

The minimum price quote is 10p which represents a handling charge rather than a basis for valuing common stamps. For further notes about prices see introductory pages.

90 Hippocrates (physician) and Surgeons performing Operation

(Des L. Nelson. Litho Questa)

1987 (2 Nov). *Great Scientific Discoveries. T* **90** *and similar multicoloured designs. P* 14.
596 5 s. Type **90** 15 15
597 25 s. Einstein and Deep Space (Theory of Relativity) 75 75
598 35 s. Isaac Newton and diagram from *Opticks* (Theory of Colour and Light) .. 1·00 1·00
599 45 s. Karl Benz, early Benz and modern Mercedes cars .. .. 1·50 1·50
596/9 .. .. *Set of* 4 3·00 3·00
MS600 97×70 mm. 150 s. *Challenger* (space shuttle) (*vert*) .. .. 3·00 3·75

91 Scout with Album and Uganda Stamps

(Des Mary Walters. Litho Questa)

1987 (20 Nov). *World Scout Jamboree, Australia. T* **91** *and similar horiz designs. Multicoloured. P* 14.
601 5 s. Type **91** 10 10
602 25 s. Scouts planting tree 50 55
603 35 s. Canoeing on Lake Victoria 70 75
604 45 s. Hiking 90 95
601/4 .. .. *Set of* 4 2·00 2·25
MS605 95×65 mm. 150 s. Jamboree and Uganda scout emblems .. .. 3·00 3·75

92 "The Annunciation"

(Litho Questa)

1987 (18 Dec). *Christmas. T* **92** *and similar multicoloured designs showing scenes from French diptych, c.* 1250. *P* 14.
606 5 s. Type **92** 10 10
607 10 s. "The Nativity" 20 25
608 50 s. "Flight into Egypt" .. .. .. 1·00 1·10
609 100 s. "The Adoration of the Magi" .. .. 2·00 2·10
606/9 .. .. *Set of* 4 3·00 3·25
MS610 76×105 mm. 150 s. "Mystic Wine" (tapestry detail) (*vert*) .. .. .. 3·00 3·50

93 Class "12" Light Shunter Locomotive

94 Columbite-Tantalite

(Des BG Studio. Litho Questa)

1988 (18 Jan). *Locomotives of East Africa Railways. T* **93** *and similar horiz designs. Multicoloured. P* 14.
611 5 s. Type **93** 15 15
612 10 s. Class "92" diesel-electric 15 15
613 15 s. Locomotive No. 2506 .. .. .. 15 15
614 25 s. Tank locomotive No. 126 .. .. 30 30
615 35 s. Class "31" locomotive 35 35
616 45 s. Class "31" locomotive (*different*) .. 45 45
617 50 s. Class "59" Double Garratt locomotive 50 50
618 100 s. Class "87" diesel-electric shunter .. 90 90
611/18 .. .. *Set of* 8 2·75 2·75
MS619 Two sheets, each 100 × 74 mm. (a) 150 s. Class "31". (b) 150 s. Class "59" Double Garratt *Set of* 2 *sheets* 4·00 4·50

(Des Mary Walters. Litho Questa)

1988 (18 Jan). *Minerals. T* **94** *and similar vert designs. Multicoloured. P* 14.
620 1 s. Type **94** 10 10
621 2 s. Galena 10 10
622 5 s. Malachite 15 15
623 10 s. Cassiterite 15 15
624 35 s. Ferberite 40 40
625 50 s. Emerald 55 55
626 100 s. Monazite 90 90
627 150 s. Microcline .. .. 1·25 1·25
620/7 .. .. *Set of* 8 3·25 3·25

95 Hurdling

(Des BG Studio. Litho Questa)

1988 (16 May). *Olympic Games, Seoul* (*2nd issue*). *T* **95** *and similar horiz designs. Multicoloured. P* 14.
628 5 s. Type **95** 10 10
629 25 s. High jumping 20 25
630 35 s. Javelin throwing 25 30
631 45 s. Long jumping 30 35
628/31 .. .. *Set of* 4 70 90
MS632 85 × 114 mm. 150 s. Olympic medals .. 1·00 1·25

96 *Spathodea campanulata*

(Des L. Nelson. Litho Format)

1988 (29 July). *Flowers. T* **96** *and similar multicoloured designs. P* 15.
633 5 s. Type **96** 10 10
634 10 s. *Gloriosa simplex* 10 10
635 20 s. *Thevetica peruviana* (*vert*) 15 15
636 25 s. *Hibiscus schizopetalus* 20 25
637 35 s. *Aframomum sceptrum* 25 30
638 45 s. *Adenium obesum* 30 35
639 50 s. *Kigelia africana* (*vert*) 35 40
640 100 s. *Clappertonia ficifolia* 70 75
633/40 .. .. *Set of* 8 1·90 2·10
MS641 Two sheets, each 109 × 79 mm. (a) 150 s. *Costus spectabilis*. (b) 150 s. *Canarina abyssinica* (*vert*) .. .. *Set of* 2 *sheets* 2·00 2·25

97 Elephants in Grassland (Type **61** redrawn)

(Litho Questa)

1988 (29 July). *Wildlife. Endangered Species. P* 14.
642 **97** 10 s. multicoloured .. ..

98 Red Cross Worker vaccinating Baby **99** Giraffes, Kidepo Valley National Park

(Des Associated Creative Art Designers. Litho Questa)

1988 (28 Oct). *125th Anniv of International Red Cross. T* **98** *and similar designs. P* 14.
643 10 s. bright scarlet, pale yellow and black 10 10
644 40 s. multicoloured 25 30
645 70 s. multicoloured 45 50
646 90 s. multicoloured 60 65
643/6 .. .. *Set of* 4 1·25 1·40
MS647 110 × 78 mm. 150 s. multicoloured .. 1·00 1·10
Designs: *Horiz*—10 s. "AIDS" with test tube as "I"; 70 s. Distributing food to refugees; 90 s. Red Cross volunteers with accident victim. *Vert*—150 s. Henri Dunant (founder).

(Litho Questa)

1988 (31 Oct). *500th Birth Anniv of Titian (artist). Vert designs as T* **238** *of Antigua. Multicoloured. P* 13½ × 14.
648 10 s. "Portrait of a Lady" 10 10
649 20 s. "Portrait of a Man" 15 15
650 40 s. "Isabella d'Este" 25 30
651 50 s. "Vincenzo Mosti" 35 40
652 70 s. "Pope Paul III Farnese" 45 50
653 90 s. "Violante" 60 65
654 100 s. "Titian's Daughter Lavinia" 70 75
655 250 s. "Dr. Parma" .. .. 1·75 1·90
648/55 .. .. *Set of* 8 3·75 4·25
MS656 Two sheets, each 110 × 95 mm. (a) 350 s. "The Speech of Alfonso D'Avalos" (detail). (b) 350 s. "Cain and Abel" (detail) .. *Set of* 2 *sheets* 5·00 5·50

(Des Mary Walters. Litho Questa)

1988 (18 Nov). *National Parks of Uganda. T* **99** *and similar vert designs. Multicoloured. P* 14.

657 10 s. Type **99** 15 10
658 25 s. Zebras, Lake Mburo National Park 30 25
659 100 s. African Buffalo, Murchison Falls National Park 90 90
660 250 s. Pelicans, Queen Elizabeth National Park .. .. 2·00 2·25
657/60 .. .. *Set of* 4 3·00 3·25
MS661 97 × 68 mm. 350 s. Roan Antelopes, Lake Mburo National Park .. .. 2·50 2·75

100 Doctor examining Child's Eyes

110 M HURDLES
R. KINGDOM
USA

(**101**)

(Des L. Watkins. Litho Questa)

1988 (1 Dec). *40th Anniv of World Health Organization. T* **100** *and similar horiz designs. Multicoloured. P* 14.

662 10 s. Type **100** 10 10
663 25 s. Mental health therapist with patient 20 25
664 45 s. Surgeon performing operation .. 30 35
665 100 s. Dentist treating girl 70 75
666 200 s. Doctor examining child .. .. 1·40 1·50
662/6 .. .. *Set of* 5 2·40 2·75
MS667 107 × 88 mm. 350 s. Delegates approving Declaration of Alma-Ata, 1978 .. .. 2·50 2·75

(Des Walt Disney Co. Litho Questa)

1988 (2 Dec). *Christmas. "Santa's Helpers". Multicoloured designs as T* **228** *of Dominica showing Walt Disney cartoon characters. P* 13½ × 14.

668 50 c. Father Christmas with list .. 40 40
a. Sheetlet. Nos. 668/75 .. 3·00
669 50 c. Goofy carrying presents .. 40 40
670 50 c. Mickey Mouse on toy train .. 40 40
671 50 c. Reindeer at window 40 40
672 50 c. Donald Duck's nephew with building blocks 40 40
673 50 c. Donald Duck holding sack .. 40 40
674 50 c. Chip n'Dale on conveyor belt .. 40 40
675 50 c. Donald Duck's nephew operating conveyor belt 40 40
668/75 .. .. *Set of* 8 3·00 3·00
MS676 Two sheets, each 127×102 mm. (a) 350 s. Mickey Mouse loading sack of toys on sleigh (*horiz*). P 14×13½. (b) 350 s. Mickey Mouse and Chip n'Dale grooming reindeer. P 13½×14 *Set of* 2 *sheets* 5·00 5·50

Nos. 668/75 were printed together, *se-tenant* as a composite design, in sheetlets of eight.

1989 (30 Jan). *Olympic Gold Medal Winners, Seoul. Nos.* 628/32 *optd as T* 101 *or surch also.*

677 5 s. Type **95** (optd with T **101**) 10 10
678 25 s. High jumping (optd "HIGH JUMP G. AVDEENKO USSR") 20 25
679 35 s. Javelin throwing (optd "JAVELIN T. KORJUS FINLAND") 25 30
680 300 s. on 45 s. Long jumping (optd "LONG JUMP C. LEWIS USA") .. .. 2·25 2·40
677/80 .. .. *Set of* 4 2·50 2·75
MS681 85×114 mm. 350 s. on 150 s. Olympic medals with medal table optd on sheet margin 2·50 2·75

102 Goalkeeper with Ball

UGANDA 20/
1895 STAMP
PHILEXFRANCE
BICENTENNIAL

103 1895 5 Cowries Stamp

(Des J. Genzo. Litho Questa)

1989 (24 Apr). *World Cup Football Championship, Italy (1990). T* **102** *and similar multicoloured designs. P* 14.

682 10 s. Type **102** 10 10
683 25 s. Player kicking ball (*horiz*) .. 20 25
684 75 s. Heading ball towards net (*horiz*) 50 55
685 200 s. Tackling .. .. 1·40 1·50
682/5 .. .. *Set of* 4 1·90 2·10
MS686 118×87 mm. 300 s. Football and World Cup trophy (*horiz*) .. .. .. 2·25 2·40

(Litho Questa)

1989 (15 May). *Japanese Art. Paintings by Hokusai. Horiz designs as T* **250** *of Antigua. Multicoloured. P* 14×13½.

687 10 s. "Fuji and the Great Wave off Kanagawa" 10 10
688 15 s. "Fuji from Lake Suwa" 10 15
689 20 s. "Fuji from Kajikazawa" 15 20
690 60 s. "Fuji from Shichirigahama" .. 40 45
691 90 s. "Fuji from Ejiri in Sunshu" .. 60 65
692 120 s. "Fuji above Lightning" 80 85
693 200 s. "Fuji from Lower Meguro in Edo" 1·40 1·50
694 250 s. "Fuji from Edo" .. .. .. 1·75 1·90
687/94 .. .. *Set of* 8 4·75 5·25
MS695 Two sheets, each 102×76 mm. (a) 500 s. "The Red Fuji from the Foot". (b) 500 s. "Fuji from Umezawa" .. .. .. *Set of* 2 *sheets* 6·50 6·75

Nos. 687/94 were each printed in sheetlets of 10 containing two horizontal strips of 5 stamps separated by printed labels commemorating Emperor Hirohito.

(Des U. Purins. Litho B.D.T.)

1989 (7 July). *"Philexfrance 89" International Stamp Exhibition, Paris. T* **103** *and similar vert designs. P* 14.

696 20 s. black, brt scarlet & pale grey-brown 15 20
697 70 s. black, yellowish green and azure .. 45 50
698 100 s. black, dull violet and pale brown-rose 70 75
699 250 s. black, orange-yell & pale greenish yell 1·75 1·90
696/9 .. .. *Set of* 4 2·75 3·00
MS700 176×131 mm. Nos. 696/9 (*sold at* 500 *s.*) 3·25 3·50

Designs:—70 s. 1895 10 on 50 cowries stamp; 100 s. 1896 25 cowries stamp; 250 s. 1896 1 rupee stamp.

104 Scout advising on Immunization

105 *Suillus granulatus*

(Des Associated Creative Designers. Litho Questa)

1989 (3 Aug). *2nd All African Scout Jamboree, Uganda, and 75th Anniv of Ugandan Scout Movement. T* **104** *and similar multicoloured designs. P* 14.

701 10 s. Type **104** 10 10
702 70 s. Poultry keeping 45 50
703 90 s. Scout on crutches leading family to immunization centre 60 65
704 100 s. Scouts making bricks 70 75
701/4 .. .. *Set of* 4 1·60 1·75
MS705 99×67 mm. 500 s. Ugandan Scout logo (*vert*) .. .. 3·25 3·50

(Des Mary Walters. Litho B.D.T.)

1989 (14 Aug). *Fungi. T* **105** *and similar vert designs. Multicoloured. P* 14.

706 10 s. Type **105** 10 10
707 15 s. *Omphalotus olearius* 10 15
708 45 s. *Oudemansiella radicata* 30 35
709 50 s. *Clitocybe nebularis* 35 40
710 60 s. *Macrolepiota rhacodes* 40 45
711 75 s. *Lepista nuda* 50 55
712 150 s. *Suillus luteus* .. .. .. 1·00 1·10
713 200 s. *Agaricus campestris* .. .. 1·40 1·50
706/13 .. .. *Set of* 8 3·75 4·25
MS714 Two sheets, each 100×68 mm. (a) 350 s. *Bolbitius vitellinus*. (b) 350 s. *Schizophyllum commune* .. .. .. *Set of* 2 *sheets* 5·00 5·25

106 Saddle-bill Stork

107 Rocket on Launch Pad

(Des S. Barlowe. Litho Questa)

1989 (12 Sept). *Wildlife at Waterhole. T* **106** *and similar vert designs. Multicoloured. P* 14½×14.

715 30 s. Type **106** 20 25
a. Sheetlet. Nos. 715/34 .. .. 3·75
716 30 s. Eastern White Pelican 20 25
717 30 s. Marabou Stork 20 25
718 30 s. Egyptian Vulture 20 25
719 30 s. Bateleur 20 25
720 30 s. African Elephant 20 25
721 30 s. Giraffe 20 25
722 30 s. Goliath Heron 20 25
723 30 s. Black Rhinoceros 20 25
724 30 s. Common Zebra and Oribi 20 25
725 30 s. African Fish Eagle 20 25
726 30 s. Hippopotamus 20 25
727 30 s. Black-backed Jackal and Eastern White Pelican 20 25
728 30 s. African Buffalo 20 25
729 30 s. Olive Baboon 20 25
730 30 s. Bohar Reedbuck 20 25
731 30 s. Lesser Flamingo and Serval 20 25
732 30 s. Whale-headed Stork ("Shoebill Stork") 20 25
733 30 s. Crowned Crane 20 25
734 30 s. Impala 20 25
715/34 .. .. *Set of* 20 3·75 4·50
MS735 Two sheets, each 99×68 mm. (a) 500 s. Lion. (b) 500 s. Long-crested Eagle *Set of* 2 *sheets* 6·50 6·75

Nos. 715/34 were printed together, *se-tenant*, in a sheetlet of 20 stamps, forming a composite design showing wildlife at a waterhole.

(Des T. Agans. Litho Questa)

1989 (20 Oct). *20th Anniv of First Manned Landing on Moon. T* **107** *and similar multicoloured designs. P* 14.

736 10 s. Type **107** 10 10
737 20 s. Lunar module *Eagle* on Moon .. 15 20
738 30 s. "Apollo 11" command module .. 20 25
739 50 s. *Eagle* landing on Moon 35 40
740 70 s. Astronaut Aldrin on Moon 45 50
741 250 s. Neil Armstrong alighting from *Eagle* (*vert*) .. .. 1·75 1·90
742 300 s. *Eagle* over Moon .. .. .. 2·25 2·50
743 350 s. Astronaut Aldrin on Moon (*vert*) 2·50 2·75
736/43 .. .. *Set of* 8 7·00 7·50
MS744 Two sheets, each 77×104 mm. (a) 500 s. "Saturn" rocket (*vert*). (b) 500 s. "Apollo 11" capsule on parachutes (*vert*) .. *Set of* 2 *sheets* 6·50 6·75

POSTAGE DUE STAMPS

The Postage Due stamps of Kenya, Uganda and Tanganyika were used in Uganda until 2 January 1967.

D 1

LIBERATED
1979

(D **2**)

D **3** Lion

(Litho D.L.R.)

1967 (3 Jan). *Chalk-surfaced paper. P* 14 × 13½.

D1 D 1 5 c. scarlet .. .. 20 2·00
D2 10 c. green .. .. 20 2·00
D3 20 c. deep blue .. .. 35 2·50
D4 30 c. red-brown .. .. 40 3·25
D5 40 c. bright purple .. .. .. 60 4·75
D6 1 s. orange .. .. 1·50 8·00
D1/6 .. .. *Set of* 6 3·00 20·00

1970 (31 Mar). *As Nos.* D1/6, *but on glazed ordinary paper. P* 14 × 15.

D 7 D 1 5 c. scarlet .. .. 15 1·00
D 8 10 c. green .. .. 15 1·00
D 9 20 c. deep blue .. .. 25 1·50
D10 30 c. red-brown .. .. 35 2·00
D11 40 c. bright purple .. .. .. 55 2·25
D7/11 .. .. 1·25 7·00

1973 (12 Dec). *Glazed, ordinary paper. P* 15.

D12 D 1 5 c. scarlet .. .. 60 2·25
D13 10 c. emerald .. .. 60 2·25
D14 20 c. deep blue .. .. 85 2·75
D15 30 c. red-brown .. .. 1·00 3·25
D16 40 c. bright mauve .. .. .. 1·40 4·75
D17 1 s. bright orange .. .. .. 2·25 5·50
D12/17 .. .. *Set of* 6 6·00 19·00

"UGANDA LIBERATED" OVERPRINTS. Nos. D1/17 were overprinted "UGANDA LIBERATED 1979", in very limited quantities, using a style of overprint similar to Type **32** (*Prices: Nos.* D1/6 *set of* 6 £275; D7/11 *set of* 5 £125; D12, 14/17 *set of* 5 £100; D13 £90, *all mint*).

(Litho Questa)

1979 (Dec). *Liberation. As Nos.* D1/6 *optd with Type* D **2**. *Chalk-surfaced paper. P* 13½ × 14.

D18 D 1 5 c. scarlet 10 15
D19 10 c. green 10 15
D20 20 c. dull ultramarine 10 15
D21 30 c. red-brown 10 20
D22 40 c. bright purple 15 20
D23 1 s. orange 15 20
D18/23 .. .. *Set of* 6 60 95

(Litho Questa)

1985 (11 Mar). *Animals. Type* D **3** *and similar vert designs. P* 14½ × 14.

D24 5 s. black and bright turquoise-green .. 10 10
D25 10 s. black and dull rose-lilac 10 10
D26 20 s. black and dull orange 10 10
D27 40 s. black and bright lilac 15 20
D28 50 s. black and pale greenish blue .. 30 35
D29 100 s. black and mauve 60 65
D24/9 .. .. *Set of* 6 1·10 1·25

Designs:—10 s. African Buffalo; 20 s. Kob; 40 s. African Elephant; 50 s. Common Zebra; 100 s. Black Rhinoceros.

Vanuatu

(*formerly* New Hebrides)

The former Condominium of the New Hebrides became the Republic of Vanuatu on 30 July 1980 and was admitted as a member of the Commonwealth.

99 Island of Erromango and Kauri Pine　**100** Rotary International

(Des L. Curtis. Litho J.W. (15, 30, 40 f.), Walsall (10, 35, 70, 500 f.), Questa (others))

1980 (30 July). *As Nos.* 242/54 *of New Hebrides but inscr* "VANUATU" *and without cyphers as in T* **99.** *P* 13 (15, 30, 40 *f.*) *or* 14 (*others*).
E. *Inscr in English.* W w **14.** F. *Inscr in French. No wmk.*

		E		F	
287	5 f. Type **99**	15	15	15	15
288	10 f. Territory map and copra making	15	15	15	15
289	15 f. Espiritu Santo and cattle	25	25	25	25
290	20 f. Efate and Vila P.O.	30	30	30	30
291	25 f. Malakula and head-dresses	35	35	35	35
292	30 f. Aoba, Maewo and pigs' tusks	45	45	45	45
293	35 f. Pentecost and land diver	50	50	50	50
294	40 f. Tanna and John Frum cross	60	60	70	60
295	50 f. Shepherd Island and out-rigger canoe	65	70	75	70
296	70 f. Banks Island and custom dancers	1·00	1·00	1·25	1·00
297	100 f. Ambrym and idols	1·25	80	1·50	1·10
298	200 f. Aneityum and baskets	1·40	1·40	1·75	1·75
299	500 f. Torres Island and archer fisherman	2·50	3·00	4·00	3·50
287/99	*Set of* 13	8·50	8·50	11·00	9·50

(Des L. Curtis. Litho Walsall)

1980 (16 Sept). *75th Anniv of Rotary International. T* **100** *and similar multicoloured design. P* 14. E. *Inscr in English.* W w **14** (*sideways on* 10 *f.*). F. *Inscr in French. No wmk.*

		E		F	
300	10 f. Type **100**	10	10	10	10
301	40 f. Rotary emblem (*vert*)	30	20	30	20

101 Kiwanis Emblem and Globe　**102** "The Virgin and Child enthroned with Saints and Angels" (Umkreis Michael Pacher)

(Des L. Curtis. Litho Walsall)

1980 (16 Sept). *Kiwanis International (service club), New Zealand District Convention, Port Vila. T* **101** *and similar design. P* 14. E. *Inscr in English.* W w **14** (*sideways on* 40 *f.*). F. *Inscr in French. No wmk.*

		E		F	
302	10 f. gold, ultram & chestnut	10	10	15	10
303	40 f. gold, blue-grn & brt bl	30	20	40	25

Design: *Horiz*—40 f. Kiwanis and Convention emblems.

(Des BG Studio. Litho Questa)

1980 (12 Nov). *Christmas. Details from Paintings. T* **102** *and similar vert designs. Multicoloured.* W w **14.** *P* 14 × 13½.

304	10 f. Type **102**	10	10
305	15 f. "The Virgin and Child with Saints, Angels and Donors" (Hans Memling)	10	10
306	30 f. "The Rest on the Flight to Egypt" (Adriaen van der Werff)	20	20
304/6	*Set of* 3	35	35

NEW INFORMATION

The editor is always interested to correspond with people who have new information that will improve or correct the Catalogue.

103 Blue-faced Parrot Finch　**104** Tribesman with Portrait of Prince Philip

(Des G. Drummond. Litho Questa)

1981 (18 Feb). *Birds (1st series). T* **103** *and similar vert designs. Multicoloured.* W w **14.** *P* 14.

307	10 f. Type **103**	40	20
308	20 f. Emerald Dove	60	40
309	30 f. Golden Whistler	80	60
310	40 f. Silver-shouldered Fruit Dove	90	75
307/10	*Set of* 4	2·50	1·75

See also Nos. 327/30.

(New Currency. Vatus)

(Des A. Theobald. Litho Format)

1981 (10 June). *60th Birthday of Prince Philip, Duke of Edinburgh. T* **104** *and similar vert designs. Multicoloured.* W w **14.** *P* 14 × 14½.

311	15 v. Type **104**	20	15
312	25 v. Prince Philip in casual dress	30	20
313	35 v. Queen and Prince Philip with Princess Anne and Master Peter Phillips	40	25
314	45 v. Prince Philip in ceremonial dress	50	35
311/14	*Set of* 4	1·25	85

105 Prince Charles with his Dog, Harvey　**106** National Flag and Map of Vanuatu

(Des J.W. Litho Walsall)

1981 (22 July). *Royal Wedding. T* **105** *and similar vert designs. Multicoloured.* W w **14.** *P* 14.

315	15 v. Wedding bouquet from Vanuatu	15	15
316	45 v. Type **105**	25	25
317	75 v. Prince Charles and Lady Diana Spencer	45	45
315/17	*Set of* 3	75	75

(Des C. Abbott. Litho Format)

1981 (30 July). *First Anniv of Independence. T* **106** *and similar designs.* W w **14** (*sideways on* 25 *and* 45 *v.*). *P* 14.

318	15 v. multicoloured	15	15
319	25 v. multicoloured	20	20
320	45 v. greenish yellow and brown-lake	30	30
321	75 v. multicoloured	50	50
318/21	*Set of* 4	1·00	1·00

Designs: *Horiz*—25 v. Vanuatu emblem; 45 v. Vanuatu national anthem. *Vert*—75 v. Vanuatu coat of arms.

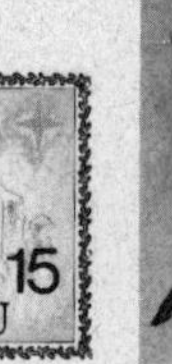

107 Three Shepherds　**108** New Caledonian Myiagra Flycatcher

(Adapted G. Vasarhelyi. Litho Questa)

1981 (11 Nov). *Christmas. Children's Paintings. T* **107** *and similar multicoloured designs.* W w **14** (*sideways on* 25 *and* 45 *v.*). *P* 14.

322	15 v. Type **107**	10	10
323	25 v. Vanuatu girl with lamb (*vert*)	15	15
324	35 v. Angel as butterfly	15	20
325	45 v. Boy carrying torch and gifts (*vert*)	25	30
322/5	*Set of* 4	60	65
MS326	133 × 94 mm. Nos. 322/5 (wmk sideways)	80	1·25

(Des G. Drummond. Litho Questa)

1982 (8 Feb). *Birds (2nd series). T* **108** *and similar vert designs. Multicoloured.* W w **14.** *P* 14½ × 14.

327	15 v. Type **108**	45	20
328	20 v. Rainbow Lorys	50	30
329	25 v. Buff-bellied Flycatchers	55	35
330	45 v. Collared Grey Fantails	80	65
327/30	*Set of* 4	2·10	1·40

109 *Flickingeria comata*　**110** Scouts round Camp-fire

(Des Jennifer Toombs. Litho Enschedé)

1982 (15 June). *Orchids. Multicoloured designs as T* **109.** W w **14** (*sideways on* 35, 45, 50 *and* 75 *v.*). *P* 13½.

331	1 v. Type **109**	10	15
332	2 v. *Calanthe triplicata*	10	15
333	10 v. *Dendrobium sladei*	15	15
334	15 v. *Dendrobium mohlianum*	20	20
335	20 v. *Dendrobium macrophyllum*	25	30
336	25 v. *Dendrobium purpureum*	30	35
337	30 v. *Robiquetia mimus*	35	40
338	35 v. *Dendrobium mooreanum* (*horiz*)	40	50
339	45 v. *Spathoglottis plicata* (*horiz*)	55	65
340	50 v. *Dendrobium seemannii* (*horiz*)	60	70
341	75 v. *Dendrobium conanthum* (*horiz*)	95	1·25
342	100 v. *Dendrobium macranthum*	1·25	1·25
343	200 v. *Coelogyne lamellata*	2·25	2·50
344	500 v. *Bulbophyllum longioscapum*	5·00	6·00
331/44	*Set of* 14	11·00	13·00

(Des L. Curtis. Litho Questa)

1982 (1 Sept). *75th Anniv of Boy Scout Movement. T* **110** *and similar horiz designs. Multicoloured.* W w **14** (*sideways*). *P* 14.

345	15 v. Type **110**	45	20
346	20 v. First aid	50	25
347	25 v. Constructing tower	55	40
348	45 v. Constructing raft	80	70
349	75 v. Scout saluting	1·25	1·25
345/9	*Set of* 5	3·25	2·50

111 Baby Jesus　**112** *Euploea sylvester*

(Des G. Vasarhelyi. Litho Questa)

1982 (1 Nov). *Christmas. Nativity Scenes. T* **111** *and similar multicoloured designs.* W w **14** (*sideways on* 15, 25 *v.*). *P* 14.

350	15 v. Type **111**	20	15
351	25 v. Mary and Joseph	30	30
352	35 v. Shepherds (*vert*)	40	40
353	45 v. Kings bearing gifts (*vert*)	55	60
350/3	*Set of* 4	1·25	1·25
MS354	132 × 92 mm. As Nos. 350/3 but without yellow borders	1·25	1·40

(Des J. Cooter. Litho Questa)

1983 (17 Jan). *Butterflies. T* **112** *and similar horiz designs. Multicoloured.* W w **14** (*sideways*). *P* 14 × 14½.

355	15 v. Type **112**	25	25
	a. Pair. Nos. 355/6	50	50
356	15 v. *Hypolimnas octocula*	25	25
357	20 v. *Papilio canopus hypsicles*	35	35
	a. Pair. Nos. 357/8	70	70
358	20 v. *Polyura sacco*	35	35
359	25 v. *Luthrodes cleotas*	40	40
	a. Pair. Nos. 359/60	80	80
360	25 v. *Parantica pumila*	40	40
355/60	*Set of* 6	1·75	1·75

Nos. 355/6, 357/8 and 359/60 were each printed in *se-tenant* pairs, horizontally and vertically throughout the sheets.

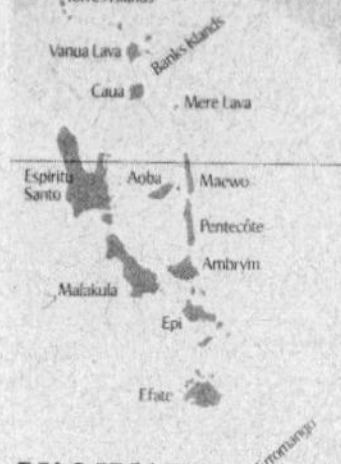

113 President Afi George Sokomanu　**114** Map of Northern Vanuatu

(Des L. Curtis. Litho Enschedé)

1983 (14 Mar). *Commonwealth Day. T* **113** *and similar horiz designs. Multicoloured.* W w **14** (*sideways*). *P* 13½ × 14.

361	15 v. Type **113**	15	10
362	20 v. Fisherman and liner *Oriana*	20	15
363	25 v. Herdsman and cattle	25	15
364	75 v. World map showing position of Vanuatu with Commonwealth and Vanuatu flags	50	70
361/4	*Set of* 4	1·00	1·00

(Des A. Theobald. Litho Harrison)

1983 (23 May). *Economic Zone. Sheet* 120 × 120 *mm containing T* **114** *and similar vert designs. Multicoloured.* W w **14**. *P* 13½ × 13.
MS365 25 v. × 6 Yellowfin Tuna; Type **114**; Map of Matthew Island; Map of Hunter Island; Grouper; Oceanic Bonito .. .. 1·75 1·90

115 Montgolfier Balloon of De Rozier and D'Arlandes, 1783

116 Mail at Bauerfield Airport

(Des A. Theobald. Litho Questa)

1983 (4 Aug). *Bicentenary of Manned Flight. T* **115** *and similar multicoloured designs, each with manned flight logo.* W w **14** (*sideways on* 35, 40 *and* 45 *v.*). *P* 13½.

366	15 v. Type **115**	15	15
367	20 v. J. A. C. Charles balloon (first use of hydrogen), 1783	25	25
368	25 v. Blanchard and Jeffries crossing English Channel, 1785	30	30
369	35 v. Giffard's airship, 1852 (*horiz*)	40	40
370	40 v. *La France* (airship of Renard and Krebs), 1884 (*horiz*)	45	45
371	45 v. *Graf Zeppelin* (first aerial circumnavigation), 1929 (*horiz*)	55	55
366/71	.. .. *Set of* 6	1·90	1·90

(Des L. McCombie. Litho Questa)

1983 (10 Sept). *World Communications Year. T* **116** *and similar horiz designs. Multicoloured.* W w **14** (*sideways*). *P* 14.

372	15 v. Type **116**	20	25
373	20 v. Switchboard operator	30	35
374	25 v. Telex operator	35	40
375	45 v. Satellite Earth station	65	70
372/5	.. .. *Set of* 4	1·40	1·50
MS376	138 × 95 mm. Nos. 372/5	1·50	1·60

117 *Cymatoderma elegans var. lamellatum*

118 Port Vila

(Des P. Cox. Litho Questa)

1984 (9 Jan). *Fungi. T* **117** *and similar multicoloured designs.* W w **14** (*sideways on* 35 *v.*, *inverted on* 45 *v.*). *P* 14.

377	15 v. Type **117**	20	25
378	25 v. *Lignosus rhinoceros*	35	40
379	35 v. *Stereum ostreu* (*horiz*)	45	50
380	45 v. *Ganoderma boninense*	65	70
377/80	.. .. *Set of* 4	1·50	1·75

(Des D. Miller. Litho Questa)

1984 (30 Apr). 250*th Anniv of "Lloyd's List" (newspaper). T* **118** *and similar vert designs. Multicoloured.* W w **14**. *P* 14½ × 14.

381	15 v. Type **118**	20	25
382	20 v. *Induna* (container ship)	30	35
383	25 v. Air Vanuatu aircraft	35	40
384	45 v. *Brahman Express* (container ship) ..	65	70
381/4	.. .. *Set of* 4	1·40	1·50

(Des A. Theobald. Litho Questa)

1984 (11 June). *Universal Postal Union Congress, Hamburg. As No.* 371 *but inscribed* "UPU CONGRESS HAMBURG" *and with U.P.U. logo.* W w **14** (*sideways*). *P* 13½ × 14.
385 45 v. multicoloured 65 70

119 Charolais

(Des Doreen McGuinness. Litho J.W.)

1984 (24 July). *Cattle. T* **119** *and similar horiz designs. Multicoloured.* W w **14** (*sideways*). *P* 14.

386	15 v. Type **119**	20	25
387	25 v. Charolais-afrikander	35	40
388	45 v. Friesian	65	70
389	75 v. Charolais-brahman	1·10	1·25
386/9	.. .. *Set of* 4	2·10	2·40

120 *Makambo*

(Des L. Dunn. Litho Walsall)

1984 (7 Sept). *"Ausipex" International Stamp Exhibition, Melbourne. T* **120** *and similar horiz designs showing ships. Multicoloured.* W w **14** (*sideways*). *P* 14.

390	25 v. Type **120**	40	40
391	45 v. *Rockton*	75	85
392	100 v. *Waroonga*	1·40	1·75
390/2	.. .. *Set of* 3	2·25	2·75
MS393	140 × 70 mm. Nos. 390/2	2·40	2·75

121 Father Christmas in Children's Ward

5
=
(**122**)

(Des D. Slater. Litho Questa)

1984 (19 Nov). *Christmas. T* **121** *and similar horiz designs. Multicoloured.* W w **14** (*sideways*). *P* 14.

394	25 v. Type **121**	35	40
395	45 v. Nativity play	65	70
396	75 v. Father Christmas distributing presents	1·10	1·25
394/6	.. .. *Set of* 3	1·90	2·10

1985 (16 Jan). *No.* 331 *surch with T* **122**.
397 5 v. on 1 v. Type **109** 15 15

123 Ambrym Island Ceremonial Dance

124 Peregrine Falcon diving

(Des D. Slater. Litho Questa)

1985 (22 Jan). *Traditional Costumes. T* **123** *and similar vert designs. Multicoloured.* W w **14**. *P* 14.

398	20 v. Type **123**	30	35
399	25 v. Pentecost Island marriage ceremony ..	35	40
400	45 v. Women's grade ceremony, South West Malakula	65	70
401	75 v. Ceremonial dance, South West Malakula	1·10	1·25
398/401	.. .. *Set of* 4	2·10	2·40

(Des N. Arlott. Litho Questa)

1985 (26 Mar). *Birth Bicentenary of John J. Audubon (ornithologist). Peregrine Falcon. T* **124** *and similar vert designs. Multicoloured.* W w **14**. *P* 14.

402	20 v. Type **124**	60	35
403	35 v. Peregrine Falcon in flight	75	50
404	45 v. Peregrine Falcon perched on branch	90	80
405	100 v. "Peregrine Falcon" (John J. Audubon)	1·60	1·75
402/5	.. .. *Set of* 4	3·50	3·00

OMNIBUS ISSUES

Details, together with prices for complete sets, of the various Omnibus issues from the 1935 Silver Jubilee series to date are included in a special section following Zululand at the end of the catalogue.

125 The Queen Mother on her 80th Birthday

126 *Mala* (patrol boat)

(Des A. Theobald (100 v.), C. Abbott (others). Litho Questa)

1985 (7 June). *Life and Times of Queen Elizabeth the Queen Mother. T* **125** *and similar vert designs. Multicoloured.* W w **16**. *P* 14½ × 14.

406	5 v. At her wedding to the Duke of York ..	10	10
407	20 v. Type **125**	30	35
408	35 v. At Ancona, Italy	45	50
409	55 v. With Prince Henry at his christening (from photo by Lord Snowdon)	75	80
406/9	.. .. *Set of* 4	1·40	1·50
MS410	91 × 73 mm. 100 v. At Covent Garden Opera House. Wmk sideways	1·40	1·50

(Des A. Theobald. Litho Format)

1985 (26 July). 5*th Anniv of Independence and "Expo '85" World Fair, Japan. T* **126** *and similar horiz designs. Multicoloured.* W w **16** (*sideways*). *P* 14.

411	35 v. Type **126**	45	50
412	45 v. Japanese fishing fleet	65	70
413	55 v. Vanuatu Mobile Force Band	75	80
414	100 v. Prime Minister Fr. Walter H. Lini ..	1·40	1·50
411/14	.. .. *Set of* 4	3·00	3·25
MS415	116 × 102 mm. Nos. 411/14	3·25	3·50

127 "Youth Activities" (Alain Lagaliu)

(Des D. Miller. Litho Questa)

1985 (16 Sept). *International Youth Year. Children's Paintings. T* **127** *and similar horiz designs. Multicoloured.* W w **14** (*sideways*). *P* 14.

416	20 v. Type **127**	30	35
417	30 v. "Village" (Peter Obed)	40	45
418	50 v. "Beach and "PEACE" Slogan" (Mary Estelle)	70	75
419	100 v. "Youth Activities" (*different*) (Abel Merani)	1·40	1·50
416/19	.. .. *Set of* 4	2·50	2·75

128 Map of Vanuatu with National and U.N. Flags

129 *Chromodoris elisabethina*

(Des D. Hartley. Litho Questa)

1985 (24 Sept). 4*th Anniv of United Nations Membership.* W w **14** (*sideways*). *P* 14.
420 **128** 45 v. multicoloured 65 70

(Des A. Riley. Litho Questa)

1985 (11 Nov). *Marine Life* (1*st series*). *Sea Slugs. T* **129** *and similar multicoloured designs.* W w **14** (*sideways on* 35, 55 *v.*). *P* 14½ × 14 (20, 100 *v.*) *or* 14 × 14½ (*others*).

421	20 v. Type **129**	30	35
422	35 v. *Halgerda aurantiomaculata* (*horiz*) ..	45	50
423	55 v. *Chromodoris kuniei* (*horiz*)	75	80
424	100 v. *Notodoris minor*	1·40	1·50
421/4	.. .. *Set of* 4	2·50	2·75

See also Nos. 442/5 and 519/22.

130 Scuba Diving

131 Liner S.S. *President Coolidge* leaving San Francisco

(Des O. Bell. Litho Walsall)

1986 (22 Jan). *Tourism. T* **130** *and similar vert designs. Multicoloured. W* w **16**. *P* 14.
425 30 v. Type **130** 60 40
426 35 v. Yasur volcano, Tanna 70 45
427 55 v. Land diving, Pentecost Island .. 90 70
428 100 v. Windsurfing .. .. 1·25 1·25
425/8 .. .. *Set of* 4 3·00 2·50

(Des A. Theobald. Litho Format)

1986 (21 Apr). *60th Birthday of Queen Elizabeth II. Vert designs as T* **110** *of Ascension. Multicoloured. W* w **16**. *P* 14×14½.
429 20 v. With Prince Charles and Princess Anne, 1951 .. .. 25 30
430 35 v. Prince William's Christening, 1982 .. 40 45
431 45 v. In New Hebrides, 1974 .. .. 55 60
432 55 v. On board Royal Yacht *Britannia*, Mexico, 1974 .. .. 65 70
433 100 v. At Crown Agents Head Office, London, 1983 .. .. 1·10 1·25
429/33 .. .. *Set of* 5 2·75 3·00

(Des L. Curtis. Litho Walsall)

1986 (19 May). *"Ameripex '86" International Stamp Exhibition, Chicago. Sinking of S.S.* President Coolidge. *T* **131** *and similar horiz designs. Multicoloured. W* w **16** *(sideways). P* 14.
434 45 v. Type **131** 55 60
435 55 v. S.S. *President Coolidge* as troopship, 1942 .. .. 65 70
436 135 v. Map of Espiritu Santo showing site of sinking, 1942 .. .. 1·50 1·60
434/6 .. .. *Set of* 3 2·40 2·50
MS437 80×105 mm. Nos. 434/6 .. .. .. 2·75 3·00

132 Halley's Comet and Vanuatu Statue

(Des Jennifer Toombs. Litho Questa)

1986 (23 June). *Appearance of Halley's Comet. T* **132** *and similar horiz designs. Multicoloured. W* w **16** *(sideways). P* 14½.
438 30 v. Type **132** 60 40
439 45 v. Family watching Comet 80 70
440 55 v. Comet passing Earth 90 90
441 100 v. Edmond Halley .. .. .. 1·40 1·60
438/41 .. .. *Set of* 4 3·25 3·25

133 Daisy Coral

(Des I. Loe. Litho Walsall)

1986 (27 Oct). *Marine Life (2nd series). Corals. T* **133** *and similar horiz designs. Multicoloured. W* w **16** *(sideways). P* 14.
442 20 v. Type **133** 50 30
443 45 v. Organ Pipe Coral 80 70
444 55 v. Sea Fan 90 90
445 135 v. Soft Coral .. .. 2·00 2·50
442/5 .. .. *Set of* 4 3·75 4·00

134 Children of Different Races
135 Datsun "240Z" (1969)

(Des C. Austin. Litho Harrison)

1986 (3 Nov). *Christmas. International Peace Year. T* **134** *and similar horiz designs. Multicoloured. W* w **14** *(sideways). P* 14.
446 30 v. Type **134** 60 40
447 45 v. Church and boy praying 80 75
448 55 v. U.N. discussion and Headquarters Building, New York 90 90
449 135 v. People of different races at work .. 2·00 2·50
446/9 .. .. *Set of* 4 4·00 4·00

(Des J.W. Litho Questa)

1987 (22 Jan). *Motor Vehicles. T* **135** *and similar horiz designs. Multicoloured. W* w **14** *(sideways). P* 14.
450 20 v. Type **135** 30 30
451 45 v. Ford "Model A" (1927) 60 60
452 55 v. Unic lorry (1924–5) 70 70
453 135 v. Citroen "DS19" (1975) .. .. 1·60 1·90
450/3 .. .. *Set of* 4 3·00 3·25

Hurricane Relief Fund +10

(**136**)
137 Young Coconut Plants

1987 (12 May). *Hurricane Relief Fund. No.* 332, *already surch as T* **122**, *and Nos.* 429/33, *all surch as T* **136**.
454 20 v. + 10 v. on 2 v. *Calanthe triplicata* .. 35 40
455 20 v. + 10 v. Princess Elizabeth with Prince Charles and Princess Anne, 1951 .. 35 40
456 35 v. + 15 v. Prince William's Christening, 1982 .. .. 60 65
457 45 v. + 20 v. Queen in New Hebrides, 1974 75 80
458 55 v. + 25 v. Queen on board Royal Yacht *Britannia*, Mexico, 1974 .. .. 95 1·00
459 100 v. + 50 v. Queen at Crown Agents Head Office, London, 1983 .. .. 1·75 1·90
454/9 .. .. *Set of* 6 4·25 4·75
The surcharge as T **136** on No. 454 includes the word "Surcharge" in addition to the inscription illustrated.

(Des R. Corringe. Litho Format)

1987 (13 May). *25th Anniv of I.R.H.O. Coconut Research Station. T* **137** *and similar horiz designs. Multicoloured. W* w **16** *(sideways). P* 14.
460 35 v. Type **137** 40 45
461 45 v. Coconut flower and fronds 55 60
462 100 v. Coconuts .. .. 1·10 1·25
463 135 v. Research Station .. .. .. 1·60 1·75
460/3 .. .. *Set of* 4 3·25 3·75
The inscriptions on Nos. 462/3 are in French.

138 Spotted Hawkfish
139 Elephant Beetle

(Des N. Harvey. Litho Questa)

1987 (15 July). *Fishes. T* **138** *and similar horiz designs. Multicoloured. W* w **16** *(sideways). P* 14×14½.
464 1 v. Type **138** 10 10
465 5 v. Moorish Idol 10 10
466 10 v. Black-saddled Puffer 10 10
467 15 v. Anemone Fish 15 20
468 20 v. Striped Surgeon 20 25
469 30 v. Six-barred Wrasse 30 35
470 35 v. Purple Queenfish 35 40
471 40 v. Long-jawed Squirrelfish 40 45
472 45 v. Clown Triggerfish 45 50
473 50 v. Scribed Wrasse 50 55
474 55 v. Regal Angelfish 55 60
475 65 v. Lionfish 65 70
476 100 v. Fosters Hawkfish .. .. .. 95 1·00
477 300 v. Vermiculated Triggerfish .. .. 3·00 3·25
478 500 v. Saddled Butterfly Fish .. .. 4·75 5·00
464/78 .. .. *Set of* 15 11·00 12·00

(Des I. Loe. Litho Questa)

1987 (22 Sept). *Insects. T* **139** *and similar horiz designs. Multicoloured. W* w **16** *(sideways). P* 14.
479 45 v. Type **139** 55 60
480 55 v. *Phyllodes imperialis* (moth) 65 70
481 65 v. Jewel Beetle 75 80
482 100 v. Fruit-piercing Moth .. .. .. 1·10 1·25
479/82 .. .. *Set of* 4 2·75 3·00

140 Away in a Manger"
141 Dugong Cow and Calf

(Des Josephine Martin. Litho Security Printers (M), Malaysia)

1987 (10 Nov). *Christmas. Christmas Carols. T* **140** *and similar vert designs. Multicoloured. W* w **14**. *P* 13½×14.
483 20 v. Type **140** 25 30
484 45 v. "Once in Royal David's City" 55 60
485 55 v. "While Shepherds watched their Flocks" 65 70
486 65 v. "We Three Kings of Orient Are" .. 75 80
483/6 .. .. *Set of* 4 2·00 2·10

1987 (9 Dec). *Royal Ruby Wedding. Nos.* 429/33 *optd with T* **119** *of Ascension in silver.*
487 20 v. Princess Elizabeth with Prince Charles and Princess Anne, 1951 .. 25 30
488 35 v. Prince William's Christening, 1982 .. 40 45
489 45 v. Queen in New Hebrides, 1974 .. 55 60
490 55 v. Queen on board Royal Yacht *Britannia*, Mexico, 1974 .. .. .. 65 70
491 100 v. Queen at Crown Agents Head Office, London, 1983 .. .. 1·10 1·25
487/91 .. .. *Set of* 5 2·75 3·00

(Des Doreen McGuinness. Litho Walsall)

1988 (29 Feb). *Dugong. T* **141** *and similar horiz designs. Multicoloured. W* w **16** *(sideways). P* 13×13½.
492 5 v. Type **141** 15 15
493 10 v. Dugong underwater 25 15
494 20 v. Two dugongs surfacing to breathe .. 40 30
495 45 v. Four dugongs swimming 75 75
492/5 .. .. *Set of* 4 1·40 1·25

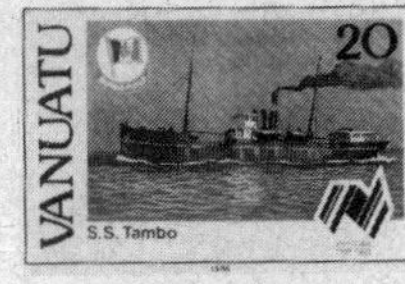

142 S.S. *Tambo*
143 Captain James Cook

(Des E. Nisbet. Litho Security Printers (M), Malaysia)

1988 (18 May). *Bicentenary of Australian Settlement. Ships. T* **142** *and similar horiz designs. Multicoloured. W* w **14** *(sideways). P* 12.
496 20 v. Type **142** 20 25
497 45 v. S.S. *Induna* 50 55
498 55 v. S.S. *Morinda* 60 65
499 65 v. S.S. *Marsina* 70 75
496/9 .. .. *Set of* 4 1·75 2·00

(Des A. Theobald. Litho Format)

1988 (29 July). *"Sydpex '88" National Stamp Exhibition, Sydney. W* w **16**. *P* 14.
500 **143** 45 v. black and rosine 50 55
No. 500 was printed in small sheets of 10 (5 × 2), the two strips separated by a horizontal gutter of five illustrated stamp-size labels. The outer edges of the sheet are imperforate so that the stamps have one or two adjacent sides imperforate.

(Des O. Bell, adapted D. Miller. Litho Walsall)

1988 (24 Aug). *"Expo '88" World Fair, Brisbane. Sheet* 100 × 80 *mm. containing designs as Nos.* 427/8, *but with addition of Australian Bicentenary symbol and imprint date. Multicoloured. W* w **14**. *P* 14.
MS501 55 v. Land diving, Pentecost Island; 100 v. Windsurfing .. .. 1·75 1·90

144 Boxer in training
145 Agricultural Crops

(Des S. Noon. Litho Security Printers (M), Malaysia)

1988 (19 Sept). *Olympic Games, Seoul. T* **144** *and similar vert designs. Multicoloured. W* w **14**. *P* 13½ × 14.
502 20 v. Type **144** 20 25
503 45 v. Athletics 50 55
504 55 v. Signing Olympic agreement 60 65
505 65 v. Soccer 70 75
502/5 .. .. *Set of* 4 1·75 2·00
MS506 54 × 66 mm. 150 v. Tennis. P 13½ .. 1·75 1·90

(Des O. Bell and D. Miller (55, 65 v.), D. Miller (20, 145 v.). Litho Questa)

1988 (25 Oct). *300th Anniv of Lloyd's of London. Multicoloured designs as T* **123** *of Ascension. W* w **16** *(sideways on 55, 65 v.). P* 14.
507 20 v. Interior of new Lloyd's Building, 1988 20 25
508 55 v. *Shirrabank* (freighter) (*horiz*) .. 60 65
509 65 v. *Adela* (ferry) (*horiz*) 70 75
510 145 v. *General Slocum* (excursion steamer) on fire, New York, 1904 .. .. 1·60 1·75
507/10 .. .. *Set of* 4 2·75 3·00

(Des A. Edmonston. Litho Format)

1988 (14 Nov). *Food and Agriculture Organization. T* **145** *and similar multicoloured designs. W* w **16** *(sideways on 45, 120 v.). P* 14½ × 14 *(horiz) or* 14 × 14½ *(vert).*
511 45 v. Type **145** 50 55
512 55 v. Fisherman with catch (*vert*) 60 65
513 65 v. Livestock on smallholding (*vert*) .. 70 75
514 120 v. Market women with produce .. 1·25 1·40
511/14 .. .. *Set of* 4 2·75 3·00

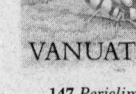

146 Virgin and Child ("Silent Night")
147 *Periclimenes brevicarpalis*

(Des Josephine Martin. Litho Format)

1988 (1 Dec). *Christmas. Carols. T* **146** *and similar horiz designs. Multicoloured. W* w **16** *(sideways). P* 14½ × 14.
515 20 v. Type **146** 20 25
516 45 v. Angels ("Angels from the Realms of Glory") 50 55
517 65 v. Shepherd boy with lamb ("O Come all ye Faithful") 70 75
518 155 v. Baby ("In that Poor Stable how Charming Jesus Lies") .. .. .. 1·75 1·90
515/18 .. .. *Set of* 4 2·75 3·00

(Des A. Riley. Litho Questa)

1989 (1 Feb). *Marine Life (3rd series). Shrimps. T* **147** *and similar horiz designs. Multicoloured. W* w **16** *(sideways). P* 14.
519 20 v. Type **147** 20 25
520 45 v. *Lysmata grabhami* 50 55
521 65 v. *Rhynchocinetes* sp 70 75
522 150 v. *Stenopus hispidus* .. .. 1·75 1·90
519/22 .. .. *Set of* 4 2·75 3·00

148 Consolidated "Catalina" Flying Boat

149 Porte de Versailles Hall No. 1

(Des A. Theobald. Litho Security Printers (M), Malaysia)

1989 (5 Apr). *Economic and Social Commission for Asia and the Pacific. Aircraft. T* **148** *and similar horiz designs. W* w **14** *(sideways). P* 12.
523 20 v. black and cobalt 30 30
524 45 v. black and turquoise-green 65 65
525 55 v. black and orange-yellow 80 80
526 200 v. black and orange-red .. .. .. 2·75 3·00
523/6 .. .. *Set of* 4 4·00 4·25
Designs:—45 v. Douglas "DC-3"; 55 v. Embraer "EMB110 Bandeirante"; 200 v. Boeing "737-300".

(Des O. Bell (Nos. 527/8), D. Miller (No. **MS**529). Litho Security Printers, Malaysia (Nos. 527/8), B.D.T. (No. **MS**529))

1989 (5 July). *"Philexfrance '89" International Stamp Exhibition, Paris. T* **149** *and similar horiz designs. W* w **14**. *P* 12.
527 **149** 100 v. multicoloured .. .. .. 1·40 1·40
a. Horiz pair. Nos. 527/8 .. .. 2·75 2·75
528 – 100 v. multicoloured (Eiffel Tower) .. 1·40 1·40
MS529 115×101 mm. 100 v. black, grey and scarlet (Revolt of French troops, Nancy, 1790 (42×28 *mm*)). W w **16** (sideways). P 14 .. 1·40 1·50
Nos. 527/8 were printed together, *se-tenant*, in horizontal pairs throughout the sheet, each pair forming a composite design.

(Des A. Theobald (100 v.), D. Miller (others). Litho Questa)

1989 (20 July). *20th Anniv of First Manned Landing on Moon. Multicoloured designs as T* **126** *of Ascension. W* w **16** *(sideways on 55, 65 v.). P* 14×13½ (45, 120 *v.*) *or* 14 (*others*).
530 45 v. Command module seen from lunar module 70 70
531 55 v. Crew of "Apollo 17" (30×30 *mm*) .. 80 80
532 65 v. "Apollo 17" emblem (30×30 *mm*) .. 90 90
533 120 v. Launch of "Apollo 17" .. .. .. 1·60 1·60
530/3 .. .. *Set of* 4 3·50 3·50
MS534 99×82 mm. 100 v. Recovery of "Apollo 11". Wmk inverted. P 14×13½ .. .. 1·40 1·50

(**150**)

151 New Hebrides 1978 "Concorde" 30 f. (French inscr) Stamp

1989 (18 Oct). *"Melbourne Stampshow '89". No.* 332 *surch with T* **150**.
535 100 v. on 2 v. *Calanthe triplicata* .. .. 1·50 1·60

(Des A. Theobald. Litho Leigh-Mardon Ltd, Melbourne)

1989 (6 Nov). *"World Stamp Expo '89", International Stamp Exhibition, Washington. T* **151** *and similar horiz designs. Multicoloured. W* w **16** *(inverted). P* 13½.
536 65 v. Type **151** 70 75
MS537 105×100 mm. 65 v. New Hebrides 1978 "Concorde" 10 f. (English inscr) stamp; 100 v. White House, Washington .. .. .. 1·75 1·90

NEW INFORMATION

The editor is always interested to correspond with people who have new information that will improve or correct the Catalogue.

152 *Alocasia macrorrhiza*

(Des Jennifer Toombs. Litho Security Printers (M), Malaysia)

1990 (5 Jan). *Flora. T* **152** *and similar vert designs. Multicoloured. W* w **14**. *P* 12.
538 45 v. Type **152** 50 55
539 55 v. *Acacia spirorbis* 60 65
540 65 v. *Metrosideros collina* 70 75
541 145 v. *Hoya australis* .. .. 1·60 1·75
538/41 .. .. *Set of* 4 3·00 3·25

Australasia

★ **For over 20 years, the source for Australasian scarce to rare stamps, postal history and cancellations, essays, proofs and specimens.**

★ **Leading specialists worldwide take advantage of our auction and private treaty facilities.**

If you would like to see either …

— OUR CURRENT AUCTION CATALOGUE

— DETAILS OF HOW WE CAN HELP YOU, THE PROSPECTIVE VENDOR

Then write, phone or fax us, giving details of your philatelic interests and we shall be delighted to help you in any way possible.

RODNEY A PERRY
Auction Galleries
TEL (03) 670 5455 FAX (03) 670 5601
422 COLLINS ST MELBOURNE 3000 AUSTRALIA

Victoria

PRICES FOR STAMPS ON COVER

Nos. 1/29	*from* × 2
Nos. 30/8	*from* × 4
Nos. 39/43	*from* × 3
Nos. 44/8	*from* × 2
Nos. 49/51	*from* × 4
No. 52	*from* × 8
No. 53	—
No. 54	*from* × 6
Nos. 55/90	*from* × 2
No. 91	—
Nos. 92/186	*from* × 3
Nos. 187/220	*from* × 4
Nos. 221/2	*from* × 10
Nos. 223/38	*from* × 5
Nos. 239/67	*from* × 10
Nos. 268/82	—
Nos. 283/91	*from* × 10
Nos. 292/6	—
Nos. 297/303	*from* × 12
Nos. 304/22	*from* × 8
Nos. 323/4	—
Nos. 325/6	*from* × 4
Nos. 327/9	*from* × 10
Nos. 330/45	*from* × 15
Nos. 346/7	*from* × 2
Nos. 348/75	*from* × 10
Nos. 376/7	—
Nos. 378/87	*from* × 10
Nos. 388/98	—
Nos. 399/409	*from* × 10
Nos. 410/12	—
Nos. 413/23	*from* × 4
Nos. 424/33	—
Nos. 434/43	*from* × 10
No. 444	—
No. 445	*from* × 10
Nos. 446/52	*from* × 6
No. 453	—
No. 454	*from* × 6
Nos. F1/6	—
Nos. F7/15	*from* × 20
Nos. F16/22	—
Nos. F23/5	*from* × 20
Nos. F26/40	—
Nos. F41/5	*from* × 20
Nos. F46/50	—
Nos. F51/2	*from* × 20
Nos. F53/9	—
Nos. D1/8	*from* × 30
Nos. D9/10	—
Nos. D11/67	*from* × 30

SPECIMEN OVERPRINTS. Those listed are from U.P.U. istributions in 1892 and 1897. Further "Specimen" overprints xist, but these were used for other purposes.

Unlike many British colonies, Victoria, with three exceptions nly, produced her own dies, plates and stamps. The exceptions vere the 1d. and 6d. "Queen-on-Throne" (the dies and plates for which were produced and the stamps printed by Perkins, Bacon) nd the 2d. of 1870 for which though it was printed throughout in Victoria, the die and plates were produced by De La Rue. Being the roducts of local endeavour in a remote country, the stamps of Victoria possess great technical interest for students although its ssues are too complicated for many collectors. The present list is n attempt alike to demonstrate their interest and to clarify their omplications, particularly by the inclusion of carefully written otes on various aspects of their production.

A. THE PRIVATE CONTRACT PERIOD, 1850–59 (Ham, ampbell & Co, Campbell and Fergusson, Calvert, Robinson)

1 Queen Victoria ("Half Length")

Des engraved on a single piece of steel by Thomas Ham, Melbourne)

I. Lithographed by Thomas Ham, Melbourne

850 (3 Jan). T **1**. *Imperf except groups (9) and (10).*

1d. Thin line at top

2d. Fine border and background

3d. White area to left of orb

(1) Original state of dies: 1*d.* (*tops of letters of* "VICTORIA" *reach to top of stamp*); 2*d.* (*fine border and background*); 3*d.* (*thicker white outline around left of orb, central band of orb does not protrude at left*). *No frame-lines on dies.*

1 1d. orange-vermilion — £1000
 a. Orange-brown — £550
 b. Dull chocolate-brown (shades) — £500
2 2d. lilac-mauve (*shades*) — £400
3 2d. brown-lilac (*shades*) £2250 £250
 a. Grey-lilac — £250
4 3d. bright blue (*shades*) — £275
 a. Blue (shades) — £170
 ab. Retouched (Nos. 10 and 11 in transfer-group only) — £275

Periods of use: 1d., 2d. and 3d. No. 4 (January 1850); 3d. No. 4*a* (March 1850 to October 1851).

Note on Group (1). With the exception of No. 4*a* all the above were printed from a small stone of 30 (5 × 6), laid down without the use of an Intermediate stone. The 3d. No. 4*a* was the first "Half Length" to appear in sheets of 120, which was the case for all subsequent Ham printings. It was produced from an Intermediate stone of 15 (5 × 3). The 2d. No. 2 was the first printing (from Stone "A") and Nos. 3 and 3*a* the second (from Stone "B"). Impressions clear and fine.

Note on margins found in the Ham printings: These stamps divide into two groups—Nos. 1 to 7—which were from 5-wide groups (or sheets) and Nos. 8 to 17—which were from 6-wide groups. The spacing between stamps horizontally is greater for Nos. 1 to 7 than Nos. 8 to 17 (and see later notes).

1d. Thick line at top

2d. Coarse background

3d. White area small and band protruding to left of orb

(2) Second state of dies: 1*d.* (*more colour over top of letters of* "VICTORIA"); 2*d.* (*fine border as* (1) *but with coarse background*); 3*d.* (*thinner white outline around left of orb, central band of orb protrudes at left*).

5 1d. red-brown (*shades*) £2750 £275
 a. Pale dull red-brown — £275
6 2d. grey-lilac (*shades*) £1000 80·00
 a. Dull grey — 80·00
7 3d. blue (*shades*) — £110
 a. Retouched (22 varieties) *from* — £225

Periods of use: 1d. (Feb–Sept 1850); 2d. (Jan–April 1850); 3d. (June 1851 to Dec 1852).

Note on Group (2). These were all printed in sheets of 120 (10 × 12), the Printing stones for the 1d. and 2d. being produced from an Intermediate stone of 30 (5 × 6), and that for the 3d. from one of 10 (5 × 2). Impressions are clear and fine.

Frame-lines added

(3) Third state of dies: *As in* (2) *but with frame-lines added, very close up, on all four sides.*

8 1d. dull orange-vermilion — £120
 a. Dull red (shades) — £120
9 1d. deep red-brown — £400
 a. Brownish red (shades) — £110
 b. Dull rose (shades) — £110
10 2d. grey (*shades*) — £120
 a. Olive-grey (shades) — £120
11 3d. blue (*shades*) — 50·00
 a. Deep blue (shades) — 50·00
 b. Pale greenish blue (shades) — £100

Periods of use: 1d. No. 8 (Oct 1850 to April 1851); 1d. No. 9 (April 1851 to March 1854): 2d. (Aug–Oct 1850); 3d. (Dec 1852 to April 1854).

Note on Group (3). Although the above were all printed in sheets of 120 the format was 12 × 10—and continued so—and not 10 × 12 as in Group (2). For No. 8 (i.e. third 1d. printing) an Intermediate stone of 30 (6 × 5) was used, but for all the others (i.e. fourth printings) one of 12 (6 × 2) was employed. These stamps (and those under Group (4) following) are very closely spaced as compared with the (1) and (2) groups. Group (3) represented the last state of the 1d. and 3d. dies but not of the 2d. Impressions vary from medium to fine.

White veil

(4) *As* (3) *but altered to give, for the* 1d. *and* 3d., *the so-called "white veils", and for the* 2d., *the effect of vertical drapes to the veil.*

12 1d. reddish brown — £100
 a. Bright pinky red (shades) £475 £100
13 2d. drab — £110
 a. Grey-drab — £110
 b. Lilac-drab — £110
 c. Red-lilac — £500
 d. Void S.W. corner — £1200
14 3d. blue (*shades*) — 45·00
 a. Deep blue (shades) — 45·00
 b. Greenish blue (shades) — 50·00
 c. Retouched (9 varieties) — £120

Periods of use: 1d. (April 1851–March 1854); 2d. (Aug–Oct 1850); 3d. (April–June 1854).

Note on Group (4): The alterations to the veils were made to each of the 12 impressions on the Intermediate Stones used for Group (3), and there are therefore 12 varieties of the veil in each value. Impressions are relatively coarse, particularly of the 2d. (save for No. 13*c*). Spacing of stamps is very close as in (3). In the 1d. and 2d. the shades found in Group (4) differ considerably from those met in (3).

2d. Coarse border and background

(5) Fourth state of die. 2d. value only: *Coarse border and background. Veil details as in original die.*

15 2d. red-lilac (*shades*) — £180
 a. Lilac — £180
 b. Grey — £275
 c. Dull brownish lilac — £100
 d. Retouched lower label—value omitted. (Nos. 15 to 15*c*) — £1800
 e. Other retouches (Nos. 15 to 15*c*) (17 varieties) *from* — £225

Period of use: May–August 1850.

Note on Group (5): This comprised the sixth printing of this value and was printed from Stone "A". For it (and also for Groups (6) and (7) below) Ham utilized an Intermediate Stone of 30 (6 × 5). This was the only printing of the 2d. value in which retouches were made to the printing stone. Impressions (save for No. 15*a*) are generally good, sometimes fine.

No. 15*b* can generally, and No. 15*c* can always be readily distinguished as they are on *thin* wove paper of good quality, not found elsewhere.

(6) 2d. only: *As* (5) *but with veils altered to give effect of vertical drapes.*

16 2d. lilac-grey — £110
 a. Deep grey — £110
 b. Brown-lilac (shades) — 60·00
17 2d. cinnamon (*shades*) £450 95·00
 a. Drab (shades) — 60·00
 b. Pale dull brown (shades) — 70·00
 c. Greenish grey — 60·00
 d. Olive-drab (shades) — £110
 e. Buff — £120

Periods of use: No. 16 etc. (Nov 1850–March 1851), No. 17 etc. (March 1851–Dec 1852).

Note on Group (6): The 2d. Stone "B" (No. 16, etc.) and Stone "C" (No. 17, etc.) constituted Ham's seventh and eighth printings respectively. Two shades in the Stone "B" printings do not differ greatly from shades in the Stone "A" printings, but all those listed under No. 17 are entirely and peculiarly distinctive. The veil alterations were again made to each of the impressions on the Intermediate Stones so that there are 30 varieties of these.

General note on Ham printings. Ham's contract was completed in May 1850 but his 1d. and 3d. stamps remained in use up till March and June 1854 respectively. The 2d. "Half Length" design was, however, as the result of an injury to the die, superseded by Ham's "Queen-on-Throne" design in December 1852. In all Ham made five printings of each of the 1d. and 3d. and eight of the 2d. The paper employed by the three contractors was distinctive. For instance, for the whole of the Campbell and Fergusson printings (1d. and 3d. only) a coarse wove paper of poor quality, easily thinned and with a marked "mesh" (horizontal or vertical) was used. This paper is nothing like any paper used for the Ham or Campbell printings, and affords the best preliminary test for all 1d. and 3d. "Half Lengths".

II. Lithographed by J. S. Campbell & Co, Melbourne

(7) *Wide settings. Stamps* 2½–3 *mm apart* (1*d.*) *or* 1½–2 *mm apart* (3*d.*).

18 1d. orange-red (*shades*) £425 £110
 a. Rose — £250
19 3d. blue (*shades*) £450 32·00
 a. Retouched (No. 17 in group) — £120

Periods of use: 1d. (Mar 1854–Jan 1855); 3d. (June 1854–April 1855, also 1858/9).

Note on Group (7): The Campbell 1d. was printed from a stone of 192 impressions (96 × 2), and the 3d. from a stone of 320 (160 × 2). For each value an intermediate stone of 24 (6 × 4) was used. Impressions are generally good.

III. Lithographed by Campbell and Fergusson, Melbourne

(8) *Wide settings as* (7). *Impressions medium to poor, depending on state of printing stones. Paper used is distinctive (see final note after Ham printings).*

(*a*) *Same intermediate stones as had been employed for Group* (7)

20 1d. brown (*shades*) £350 95·00
 a. Brick-red (shades) — 75·00
 b. Dull red (shades) — 75·00

21 1d. orange-brown (*shades*) .. .. — £100
a. Dull rose-red (shades) .. .. — 60·00
b. Bright rose-pink .. .. — £100
c. Retouched (4 varieties) .. .. — £400
22 1d. pink (*shades*) .. .. £325 32·00
a. Rose (shades) .. .. £325 32·00
b. Lilac-rose (shades) .. .. — 32·00
c. Dull brown-red (shades) .. .. .. — £100
d. Retouched (9 varieties) .. .. — £325
23 3d. bright blue (*shades*) .. .. £425 48·00
a. Greenish blue (shades) .. .. .. £375 40·00
b. Retouched (No. 17 in group) .. .. .. — 95·00
24 3d. Prussian blue (*shades*) .. .. — 70·00
a. Milky blue .. .. — £110
b. Retouched (No. 17 in group) .. .. .. — £225

Periods of use: 1d. No. 20, etc. (Stone 2, July 1854 and December 1855–May 1856): 1d. No. 21, etc. (Stone 3, Aug–Nov 1855); 1d. No. 22, etc. (Stones 4, 5, Feb–Aug 1855 and May–Oct 1856); 3d. No. 23, etc. (Stone "B", July 1857–Dec 1858); 3d. No. 24 etc. (Stone "C", Nov 1856–June 1857).

(*b*) *New intermediate stone of similar size* (6 × 4) *and spacing* 2½–3 *mm apart horizontally.* (*Stone* "D")

25 3d. steel-blue (*shades*) .. .. — 42·00
a. Greenish blue (shades) .. .. .. £350 30·00
b. Blue (shades) .. .. £350 30·00
c. Deep blue (shades) .. .. £350 30·00
d. Indigo (shades) .. .. — 38·00

Period of use: May 1855 to November 1856. Impressions generally heavier than previous 3d.

Note on Group (8): All printing stones were of 400 impressions, consisting of an upper and lower pane of 200 (20 × 10) save in two cases, viz.: the 3d. No. 23 which was of 320 (160 × 2) and No. 24 which was probably of 200 (20 × 10) impressions. The 3d. No. 24, etc., presents a considerably worn appearance. No. 25 (steel-blue) comprised the earlier part of the printing and is, comparatively, of good appearance and impression.

No. 21*b* is only found with barred oval cancellations and as these were not used after the end of 1855 they are of assistance in identification.

IV. 3d. stamps rouletted and perforated in 1857 and 1859 respectively

(9) *Rouletted* 7 *to* 8½ *at G.P.O., Melbourne (see later notes).*

(*a*) *Campbell printing* (*No.* 19)

26 3d. blue (shades) .. .. — £150
a. Retouched (No. 17 in group) .. .. ..

(*b*) *Campbell & Fergusson printing* (*No.* 23)

27 3d. bright blue (*shades*) .. .. — £160
a. Greenish blue (shades) .. .. .. — £140
b. Retouched (No. 17 in group) .. .. ..

Period of use: Sept–Dec 1858.

(10) *Perforated* 12 *by Robinson.* (*a*) *Campbell printing* (*No.* 19).

28 3d. blue (*shades*) .. .. — £110
a. Retouched (No. 17 in group) .. .. .. — £250

(*b*) *Campbell & Fergusson printing* (*No.* 23)

29 3d. greenish blue (*shades*) .. .. — £350
a. Retouched (No. 17 in group) .. .. ..

Period of use: Jan 1859 to Jan 1860.

Note on Groups (9) *and* (10): The roulettes are seldom found on all four sides. The great majority of the perforated stamps are badly off-centre.

Lithographic Reprints of the three values (the 2d. die then being in a defaced condition) were made in 1891, on paper wmk V over Crown (Type V2) W **23**, perf 12½. The 1891 Reprints of all issues were the direct result of Victoria, in that year, joining the Universal Postal Union. As a member she was expected to supply specimens of her old issues to other members. None of these being available and most of the old plates having been destroyed she was, in the majority of cases, compelled to make new plates for which, fortunately, all the original dies (save the "Emblems" (3) and the "Woodblocks" (4) were available.

FURTHER INFORMATION on these interesting issues, including the details of the numbers printed, the plating of the Transfer Groups, the papers used, the retouches, creased transfers, "abnormal" combinations, "stitch" watermarks, etc., etc., will be found in "The Half-Lengths of Victoria", the work by J. R. W. Purves, F.R.P.S.L., on which the above list is based.

2 Queen on Throne

1852–54. *T* **2.** *Imperf.*

Corner letters: Each of the fifty subjects of the original plate show different letter combinations of A to Z, except J.

I. Dec 1852. *Recess-printed by Thomas Ham from a steel plate of* 50 (10 × 5) *impressions, engraved by him by hand.*

30 2d. reddish brown .. .. £120 22·00
a. Chestnut .. .. — £110
b. Purple-brown .. .. £120 22·00

Reprints were made in 1891 (and later) using the original plate, on paper wmk V over Crown Type V2, both imperf and perf 12½.

II. Dec 1853–May 1854. *Lithographed by Campbell & Co, transfers for the stones being taken from Ham's steel plate. Period of issue: Dec 1853–April 1855 and May 1856–May 1857. On various types of good quality paper, hand-made and machine-wove.*

(i) *Early printings: full impression, detail around back of throne generally complete. Impressions fine and clear; colours rich*

31 2d. brownish purple .. .. £160 22·00
a. Grey-brown .. .. — 22·00
b. Purple-black .. .. — 22·00
c. Dull lilac-brown (spotty print on toned) .. — 40·00

Papers: The papers used for (i) and (ii) were, save in the two cases indicated, distinguished by their *whiteness*, as compared with the toned (yellowish) character of all that follow. This toning is due in part to the type of gum used but also to the larger proportion of wood pulp used in manufacture. The *hand-made* paper, which is always *white*, is found in (i) and (ii) only.

(ii) *Intermediate printings. Impressions not so full or sharp, background round top of throne not so fully defined*

32 2d. violet-black .. .. — 22·00
a. Grey-black .. .. — 24·00
b. Grey-lilac .. .. — 24·00
c. Dull brown (on toned) .. .. — 24·00
d. Substituted transfer (in pair) .. .. .. — £2000

(iii) *Later printings, on toned paper only. Background round top of throne generally whiter. Stamps lack the detail of* (i) *and* (ii) *although impression is reasonably good*

33 2d. grey-black .. .. £120 20·00
a. Purple-black .. .. £120 20·00

(iv) *Last printing; on toned paper only. Background generally full as* (i) *but impression is singularly flat, and lacking in fineness and sharpness. Normal colour is distinctive*

34 2d. grey-drab (*shades*) .. .. — 19·00
a. Black .. .. — £100

Notes on the Campbell & Co Printings

(*a*) *Stones*: In all, 2,000,000 stamps were printed (and issued) under this contract. They were not printed on the one occasion but on several. A total of 22 transfers were taken from the steel plate, *nine* printing stones being used. Of these the first eight were of 100 impressions (one "fifty" over another "fifty") and the ninth was of 300 impressions (three "fifties" over three "fifties"). Only three of these stones were used to a point where they showed wear and in those cases the wear was nothing like that found in the Campbell & Fergusson printings. Whiteness in the background around the throne, where it occurs, is more often the result of weak pressure in the taking of the transfers.

(*b*) *Shades*: These should be readily distinguishable from the C. & F. printings, with the possible exception of No. 32*b* which has a pinkish element.

(*c*) *Papers*: At least *six* varieties, all of good quality (comprising both hand and machine made papers) were used but they were all so different (and of so much better quality) to that employed for the C. & F. contract that, once a C. & F. stamp is acquired, no difficulty should be encountered in identifying a Campbell.

(*d*) *Vertical pairs* (they are rare) have been met from four of the Campbell stones, with *wide* distances (up to 19 mm) between the stamps. In such cases the top stamp is from the lower row of a top transfer of fifty and the bottom stamp from the top row of a similar lower transfer.

(*e*) *"Substituted Transfers"*. These (a block of four in the S.W. corner of a sheet) occurred on one out of the 22 transfers on printing stone 5. The horizontal pairs read WA–HN and GM–SX respectively and the vertical pairs VZ over VZ and WA over WA respectively. They are all of the greatest rarity.

(*f*) No *"Creased Transfer"* varieties are to be met in the Campbell printings where the method followed for laying down the printing stones differed from that employed for the Campbell & Fergussons. The same is true of the "Half-Lengths" printed by these two contractors.

Some instances of *retouching* (they are rare) may be met. One stone only was affected.

III. June 1854. *Lithographed by Campbell & Fergusson; transfers for the stones again being taken from Ham's steel plate. Period of issue: March 1855–May 1856. Printed, like the Campbell & Fergusson Half-Lengths, on a machine-wove paper of poor quality (easily thinned and torn). This factor alone provides an unfailing guide for distinguishing the products of the two contractors.*

(i) *Printings from stones which were not over-used; background around top of throne generally full and detail good*

35 2d. lilac (*shades*) .. .. £130 19·00
a. Purple (shades) .. .. — 19·00
b. Variety "TVO" .. .. — £550

(ii) *Early printings from stones which were over-used. Similar characteristics to* (i) *above, though detail is not quite so full. Distinctive shades*

36 2d. brown .. .. — 70·00
a. Brown-purple .. .. £160 22·00
b. Warm purple .. .. — 22·00
c. Rose-lilac .. .. — 22·00
d. Substituted transfer (pair) .. .. .. — £600

(iii) *Later printings from the same stones used for* (ii) *when in a worn condition. Impressions heavy, coarse and overcoloured; details blurred; generally white background around top of throne*

37 2d. dull lilac-mauve .. .. £110 22·00
a. Dull mauve .. .. £110 22·00
b. Grey-violet .. .. — 22·00
c. Red-lilac .. .. — 24·00
d. Substituted transfer (pair) .. .. .. — £600

(iv) *Printings from a stone giving* (*from the start*) *blotchy and unpleasing results, with poor definition. Mainly shows in extra colour patches found on most stamps*

38 2d. dull purple .. .. — 40·00
a. Dull grey-lilac .. .. £160 40·00
b. On thick card paper .. .. — £500

Notes on the Campbell & Fergusson Printings

(*a*) *Stones*: 3,000,000 stamps in all were printed under this contract, of which, however, 1,500,000 (deemed to be in excess of requirements) were destroyed. A total of four printing stones (comprising 16 transfers from the steel plate) were used. The greater size of the printing and the smaller number taken of transfers of fifty (and hence of printing impressions) explains the *overuse* of certain stones, and the badly-worn prints (with filled-in colour, finer details missing, etc.) that are often met.

(*b*) *Shades*: At least 95 per cent of these printings, whatever their actual shade names, have—by comparison with the Campbell stamps—a *pink* quality. Only about 2 per cent of the Campbells, a proportion of the stamps printed from one stone only, have such a quality, but in that case the paper used was wholly different.

(*c*) *Paper* is invariably of vertical mesh. *Both* horizontal and vertical meshes are found in the Campbells.

(*d*) *Vertical pairs* with *wide* spacing have been found. They are rare: See note above on similar Campbell pairs.

(*e*) *"Substituted Transfers"*: Here the entire *five* impressions comprising the left vertical row of a sheet were affected. The *horizontal* pairs (starting at the top and going down) are as follows: UY-BF, TX-MQ, DI-WA, SW-GM and CH-RW. The *vertical* pairs are UY over TX and DI over SW. They occur in various shades and stages of wear.

(*f*) *"Creased Transfer"* varieties. As in the C. & F. "Half-Length" printings, various major instances are met, including the "TVO" variety. At least two transfer groups of 50 were affected.

No retouching has been met in any printing.

3

4 Queen on Throne

(Die engraved and stamps lithographed by Campbell & Fergusson)

1854–65. *T* **3.** (*a*) *Imperf.*

39 1s. blue (*shades*) (6.7.54) .. .. £650 22·0
a. Greenish blue .. .. £750 22·0
b. Indigo-blue .. .. — £11

(*b*) *Rouletted* 7–7½ *at G.P.O., Melbourne (see later notes)*

40 1s. greenish blue (27.8.57) .. .. — 80·0
a. Blue .. .. — 80·0

(*c*) *Perf* 12 *by Robinson, early in* 1859

41 1s. blue (*shades*)(13.4.59) .. .. £120 15·0
a. Greenish blue .. .. £110 12·0
b. Indigo-blue .. .. — 22·0

For this stamp four printing stones, each of 400 impressions (i four panes of 100), were used. These were built up from an "inter mediate" stone of 40 (8 × 5) impressions. Retouches and "crease transfer" varieties also exist. At least two classes of paper were used.

This stamp was reprinted (by lithography) in 1891, wmk V ove Crown, Type V2, perf 12½. The transfers were taken from th original die.

(Recess P.B.)

1856–58. *T* **4.** *Wmk Large Star, W* w **1.** (*a*) *Imperf.*

42 1d. yellow-green (23.10.56) .. .. £110 19·0

(*b*) *Rouletted* 5½–6½ *by F. W. Robinson, in Melbourne*

43 6d. bright blue (1.11.58) .. .. 95·00 12·0
a. Light blue .. .. £160 24·0

The gumming for the 6d. was deemed unsatisfactory and it wa not used until the exhaustion of Nos. 44–48. The stock was imper and was rouletted by Robinson before issue. It only exists imperf obliterated "CANCELLED" in London, in 1861.

Re-entries and re-cuts occur in both values.

These two stamps were reprinted in 1891, Wmk V over Crowr Type V2, imperf, using the original steel plates. The 1d. is found i two colours—a dull yellow-green and a bright blue-green. The 6d has an indigo quality and can be found in two shades.

5

6

7

1854–59. *T* **5** *to* **7** (*the "Woodblocks"*). *Typo.*

I. *T* **5.** 6*d.*: *Printed in sheets of 100 stamps, representing tw impressions from a plate of 50 woodblocks (in two panes of 25— 5 × 5), engraved individually by S. Calvert. These all differ bu are of two main types:—*

A. *Small white mark after* "VICTORIA" *like an apostrophe.*
B. *No white mark after* "VICTORIA".

(*a*) *Imperf*

44 6d. reddish brown (13.9.54) .. .. 85·00 22·0
a. Dull orange .. .. 75·00 18·0
b. Orange-yellow .. .. 75·00 19·0

(*b*) *Rouletted* 7–9

45 6d. reddish brown (12.8.57) .. .. — 42·0
a. Dull orange (3.12.57) .. .. — 35·0
b. Orange-yellow .. .. — 42·0

These stamps may be met rouletted on two sides only, and als (with finer points) on all four sides. The first class emanates fron some "rouletters" used by the window-clerks at the G.P.O Melbourne (see note after No. 62). The latter class were "perfo ated" by Calvert, and this gauge was also used for the Roulette "Emblems" of early 1858.

(*c*) *Serpentine Roulette* 10½

46 6d. orange-yellow (5.12.57) .. .. — 55·0

(*d*) *Serrated* 18–19 × *serpentine* 10½; *also serrated compound o one side with serpentine*

47 6d. orange-yellow (19.10.57) .. .. — 55·0

(*e*) *Serrated* 18–19

48 6d. orange-yellow .. .. — 55·0

Part of (*b*) and all of (*c*), (*d*) and (*e*) were "perforated" by Calve under his contract of 14.10.57, a total of 163,000 stamps being s treated. The "pin-perf about 10" variety previously listed belong to 1856 and is clearly not of official origin.

II. *T* **5.** 2*s.*: *For this value Calvert employed a plate of* 25 (5 × 5 *separately engraved wood-blocks, two impressions of which mad up the sheet of* 50. (*a*) *Imperf.*

49 2s. dull bluish green (1.9.54) £900 £11

(*b*) *Rouletted* 7–7½

50 2s. dull bluish green .. .. — £35

(*c*) *Perf* 12 *by Robinson* (1859)

51 2s. dull bluish green .. .. £200 30·0
a. Pale bluish green .. .. £200 25·0

Nos. 49–51 were printed on a printed *yellow* background whic is usually faint. For the blue-on-green printings of 1864–81 se Nos. 127, 130, 140 and 147. These latter were printed in sheets o 30, in two panes of 15 (3 × 5). The plate comprised 18 of the origina woodblocks and 12 electros.

III. *T* **6.** REGISTRATION *stamp.* (*a*) *Imperf.*

52 1s. rose-pink and blue (1.12.54) .. .. .. £600 75·0

(*b*) *Rouletted* 7–7½

53 1s. rose-pink and blue £3000 £18

IV. *T* **7.** "TOO LATE" *stamp. Imperf.*

54 6d. lilac and green (1.1.55) £450 £12

The *same* main plate of 25 woodblock impressions (5 × 5 printed four times make up a sheet of 100) was originally used for both the "Registered" and "Too Late" stamps. For the portions printed in blue and green respectively separate stereotype plates were used of each stamp.

A second woodblock plate of 25 (5 × 5) impressions from a different model was used (with the first plate) for later printings of the "Registered" only. Die 2 is distinguished by the longer head "R" of "VICTORIA" and the absence of the small white letters "V" and "R" etc. The "Registered" stamp ceased to be so used from 5.1.58 although Postmasters were then instructed to use up remaining stocks for normal postal purposes. The "Too Late" stamp was withdrawn from issue as from 1.7.57. A very few used multiples of both these stamps are known. They all represent abnormal usage.

8

1857–60. T **8** (*"Emblems"*). *Typo.*

For these stamps the dies were "wood-blocks" engraved by Calvert, and the "plates" consisted of 120 individual electrotypes clamped together. In all, six settings were employed for the 4d. value and three each for the 1d. and 2d. values.

I. 1857: Printed by Calvert

(i) *Wmk Large Star, W* w **1**. (*a*) *Imperf*

65 1d. yellow-green (18.2.57) . . 95·00 13·00
a. Deep green . . £110 26·00
b. Printed on both sides . . — £700
66 4d. vermilion (26.1.57) . . £250 10·00
a. Brown-vermilion . . £225 9·00
b. Printed on both sides . . — £550
67 4d. dull red (20.7.57) . . £160 7·50
68 4d. dull rose (6.9.57) . . £180 7·50

(*b*) *Rouletted* 7–9 (*often on two sides only*)

59 1d. yellow-green . . £275 65·00
60 4d. vermilion . . — £100
61 4d. dull red (1.8.57) . . — 38·00
62 4d. dull rose . . — 26·00

Nos. 59–62 were not rouletted by Calvert, but by one or other of three "rouletters" used by the clerks at the selling windows of the G.P.O., Melbourne. One of these "rouletters" gauged 6½–7½ and another 7¾–9. The most effective of them was purchased from one Raymond early in August 1857.

(*c*) *P* 12

63 1d. yellow-green . . — £275

This stamp and Nos. 66, 66*a*, 72 and 77 were the result of the perforating (by Robinson), probably in 1860, of a few sheets of old stock.

(ii) *No wmk. On good quality medium-wove paper.* (*a*) *Imperf*

64 2d. pale lilac (25.5.57) . . £160 10·00
a. Grey-lilac . . £160 10·00

(*b*) *Rouletted* 7–9 (*often on two sides only*)

65 2d. pale lilac . . — 23·00
a. Grey-lilac . . £1500 23·00

See note following No. 62.

(*c*) *P* 12

66 2d. pale lilac . . — £225
a. Grey-lilac . . — £225

See note following No. 63.

(*d*) *Serrated* 18–19

67 2d. grey-lilac . . £500 £350

This variety is probably the result of an experiment by Calvert. Most of the copies seen are unused.

II. 1858: Printed by Calvert on white wove paper of good quality

(*a*) *Rouletted all round* 8–9 (*usually fine points*)

68 1d. pale emerald (19.1.58) . . £300 14·00
a. Emerald-green . . £300 14·00
b. Roulette horiz only . . — £325
69 4d. rose-pink (10.1.58) . . £200 5·50
a. Bright rose . . £200 5·50
b. Reddish pink . . — 11·00
c. Roulette horiz only . . — £300
d. Roulette vert only . . — £300

(*b*) *Imperf* (April 1858)

70 1d. pale emerald . . £190 10·00
a. Emerald-green . . — 13·00
71 4d. rose-pink . . £250 23·00
a. Bright rose . . — 23·00
b. Reddish pink . . — 30·00

The imperf varieties above were stamps which *should* have been rouletted by Calvert. On the cancellation of his contract they were taken over from him but since supplies were urgently required (and Robinson not having then commenced his contract) the stamps were put into use as they were. They *follow* and do not precede the roulettes.

(*c*) *P* 12

72 1d. emerald-green . . — £275
a. Imperf between (horiz pair)

III. 1858–9: Printed under contract by F. W. Robinson, first outside and later (1859) inside the Post Office Establishment

(i) *On wove paper of a somewhat poorer quality than Calvert's. Imperf*

73 4d. dull rose (5.58) . . — 60·00

(ii) *On smooth vertically laid paper of good quality.* (*a*) *Imperf*

74 4d. dull rose (8.5.58) . . — 23·00
a. Dull rose-red . . — 23·00
b. Dull rose-red (*normal ink*) . . £400 15·00

The imperforate stamps Nos. 73, 74 and 74*a* can be easily distinguished by their distinctive *heavy, coarse* impression and the oily nature of the ink employed. They were the *first* stamps printed by Robinson and because of the demand were rushed into circulation without being rouletted, as also was No. 74*b* which was the first stamp printed by him using a more satisfactory quality of ink.

(*b*) *Rouletted* 5½–6½

75 2d. brown-lilac (*shades*) (9.58) . . £200 9·50
76 4d. pale dull rose (5.58) . . £150 3·50
a. Dull rose-red . . £120 3·50
b. Rose-red . . £120 3·25

(*c*) *P* 12

77 4d. dull rose . . — £300

See note following No. 63.

(*d*) *Serrated* 19

78 4d. rose-red . . — £350

(iii) *On smooth horizontally laid paper of same quality as* (ii) *above*

(*a*) *Rouletted* 5½–6½

79 2d. brown-lilac (*shades*) (7.58) . . £120 5·50
a. Violet (*shades*) (27.11.58) . . £150 5·50
b. Dull violet . . — 18·00
80 4d. pale dull rose . . — £800

(iv) *On good quality wove paper.* (*a*) *Rouletted* 5½–6½

81 1d. yellow-green (25.12.58) . . £275 23·00
82 4d. dull rose . . — £325

(*b*) *Perf* 12 (*the first perforated stamps to be issued in Victoria*)

83 1d. yellow-green (*shades*) (11.1.59) . . £160 11·00
a. Imperf × perf (vert pair) . . — £250
84 4d. dull rose (16.2.59) . . £150 2·75

Note: No. 83 is found on two classes of paper.

(v) *P* 12. *On poorer quality wove paper of coarser mesh*

85 1d. dull green (7.59) . . £120 7·50
a. Green (11.59) . . £120 7·50
86 4d. dull rose (19.4.59) . . — 5·00
a. Rose-carmine (6.59) . . £150 5·00
b. Rose-pink (12.59) . . — 9·00

Save in the rouletted 1d. (where a second paper of *vertical* mesh was also employed) all the paper used for (iv) above was of *horizontal* mesh, whereas under (v) except for No. 86*b* (which was printed on a tough, thick, handmade paper) it is always of *vertical* mesh. In two printings of the 1d. *both* wove and laid papers were included.

(vi) *P* 12. *On horizontally laid papers, of coarser quality and not so smooth as those previously employed by Robinson*

(*a*) *Laid lines closer together*

87 1d. dull green (July 1859) . . — 15·00
88 4d. rose-pink (23.12.59) . . — 7·00

(*b*) *Laid lines further apart*

89 1d. green (*shades*) (October 1859) . . £130 9·50
90 4d. rose-pink (*shades*) (January 1860) . . £120 7·50

(vii) *P* 12. *On thin glazed paper, emanating from Bordeaux*

91 1d. deep yellow-green (July 1859) . . — £150

This stamp must have been printed *before* the "dull greens" of July 1859.

PLATES: 1857–68

The plates prepared for use between January 1857 and December 1867 (with one exception, see note after No. 51 on 2s. value) consisted of a number of individual electros (usually 120) clamped together in a "forme" and spaced and arranged to fit the pattern of the watermarked paper. Five such schemes are to be found, viz.: (*a*) from 1857 to Sept 1863 when (save for the 2d. of May 1857) the forme comprised 4 blocks of 30 (6 × 5) electros; (*b*) for the 2d. of May 1857 only, the sheet consisted of 20 blocks of 6 (2 × 3); (*c*) from Sept 1863 to Feb 1866 when *three* separate arrangements, constant for any one value, are found. These were based on the face value of the stamps in the unit group and were as follows:—(i) For the 1d., 2d. and 4d. values the forme was composed of 8 blocks of 15 (3 × 5) separated by "gutters"; (ii) for the 3d., 6d. and 1s. values of 6 blocks (or 3, in the case of the 1s.) of 20 (4 × 5) separated by "gutters" and (iii) in the case of the 10d. of 20 blocks of 6 (3 × 2) separated by "gutters"; (*d*) over and following the period Jan–July 1866, in anticipation of the introduction of the V over Crown watermarked paper, the old formes (with the exception of the 10d.) were reset and the new formes (e.g. 3d. and 6d.) arranged to give one block of 120 (12 × 10) evenly spaced units without "gutters". For various values, therefore, two "settings" were employed of the same electrotypes. Those interested in this subject should consult an article in *Philately from Australia* for March 1954. From 1869 to 1874 new printing plates consisted of 4 electrotypes each of 30 impressions (6 × 5) clamped together. These were produced via one (or two) "master" electrotypes of the same size. From 1875 (with four exceptions in the 1885 issues) all new printing plates consisted of a continuous surface electrotype of 120 (12 × 10) impressions. The foregoing remarks apply to normal size stamps only and require modification for other sizes.

B. GOVERNMENT STAMP PRINTING. THE FIRST PERIOD, 1860–1884

Robinson was employed, in April 1858, to finish Calvert's uncompleted Contracts of 1857. Subsequently, under further Contracts, he printed more stamps. The work being satisfactory the Government (on 12.4.59) undertook to continue his employment and at the same time purchased the whole of his equipment, paper stocks, etc. As from 1.1.60 a Government Stamp Printing Branch was set up, Robinson was appointed its Chief Officer and there was no more Stamp Printing in terms of Private Contract. He was succeeded in 1867 by James Atkinson, and from 1883 to 1906 the same work was performed by William Bond. In December 1885 printing operations were transferred from the Post Office to the Government Printing Office and the Stamp Printer then joined the staff of the Government Printer. The Stamp Printers after Bond were J. Kemp and J. B. Cooke (1909–12), the latter being also appointed the first Commonwealth Stamp Printer.

Note: All issues of this period, 1860–84, were printed by typography from electrotypes.

9

10

11 12

(Dies for 3d., 4d. and 6d. (T **9**) designed and engraved by Frederick Grosse. The die for the 6d. T **11** consisted of a frame die engraved by Grosse into which was plugged a head portion, cut out of his die for the 6d. T **9**. The design, die and plate for the 1d. T **10** were all supplied by Messrs. De Gruchy and Leigh of Melbourne)

1860–66. *T* **5, 8, 9, 10** *and* **11**. *P* 12.

(i) *No wmk. On horizontally laid paper (lines further apart, as* (vi) (*b*) *above)*

92 9 3d. deep blue (31.1.60) . . £300 23·00
a. Light blue . . £1200 £110

(ii) *No wmk. On thin glazed paper emanating from Bordeaux (see also under* (vii) *above)*

93 8 1d. bright green (25.5.60) . . — 22·00
94 9 4d. rose (21.4.60) . . £275 12·00
a. Rose-pink . . — 7·50

(iii) *No wmk. On a thicker coarser paper*

95 9 4d. rose-pink (7.60) . . £275 7·50

(iv) 1860–66: *Watermarked with the appropriate words of value as W* **12**. *The paper, which was hand-made, was supplied by T. H. Saunders of London*

96 8 1d. pale yellowish green (8.7.60) . . 65·00 4·50
a. Yellow-green . . 75·00 4·75
b. Wmk "FOUR PENCE" . . — £1200
97 10 1d. pale green (1.10.61) . . 75·00 5·50
a. Olive-green . . — 6·00
b. Pale green (*deep brown gum*) (2.63) 75·00 6·00
98 8 2d. brown-lilac (7.7.61) . . — 15·00
99 2d. bluish slate (8.61, 6.62) . . £100 4·75
a. Greyish lilac (9.61) . . £110 4·75
b. Slate-grey (1.62) . . — 4·75
100 9 3d. pale blue (1.61) . . £120 7·00
a. Bright blue (8.61) . . £120 8·00
b. Blue (*deep brown gum*) (2.63) . . £130 6·00
ba. "TRREE" for "THREE" in wmk . .
c. Deep blue (1864) . . £130 6·00
101 3d. maroon (13.2.66) . . £100 25·00
a. Perf 13 . . £120 28·00
102 4d. rose-pink (1.8.60) . . — 4·75
a. Rose-red (*shades*) (9.60) . . 80·00 3·00
b. Rose-carmine (12.60) . . — 7·50
c. Dull rose (*shades*) (1861) . . 80·00 3·00
103 6d. orange (18.10.60) . . £1600 £200
104 5 6d. black (22.6.61) . . £150 35·00
105 9 6d. black (20.8.61) . . 95·00 5·50
a. Grey-black . . 95·00 5·50
106 11 6d. grey (26.4.62) . . 80·00 5·00
a. Grey-black . . 80·00 6·50
b. Jet black (*deep brown gum*) (3.63) 85·00 7·50

Reprints on paper wmkd V over Crown (*W* **23**), perf 12½, were made in 1891 of the 1d. Type **10**, 3d. and 4d. Type **9** and 6d. Type **11**. In all cases new plates were used, and certain "die flaws" are found on the "Reprints" which are not met on the originals.

13

14

1862–63. *Emergency printings owing to supplies of the appropriate paper not being available.*

(*a*) *On paper wmkd* "FIVE SHILLINGS", *W* **13**

107 9 4d. dull rose-pink (11.9.62) . . £1500 20·00
a. Dull rose . . — 20·00

(*b*) *On paper wmkd* "THREE PENCE", *W* **12**

108 8 2d. pale slate (27.12.62) . . £110 10·00
a. Bluish grey (*deep brown gum*) (2.63) . . £120 12·00

Note: Certain stamps are to be met on the "words of value" papers with wmk *reversed* under Nos. 99, 100, 102, also 173 and 176. *Inverted* wmks may also be found in several cases. All these wmk varieties are scarce to rare.

(v) 1862–64: *Same types as before but wmkd with the appropriate single-lined numeral of value, as W* **14**, *the paper being supplied by De La Rue. P* 12 *unless otherwise described*

109 10 1d. olive-green (1.2.63) . . 55·00 4·50
a. Pale green (9.63) . . 55·00 4·50
b. Apple-green (4.64) . . 55·00 4·50
110 8 2d. dull reddish lilac (21.4.63) . . £160 5·50
111 2d. grey-lilac (10.63) . . £150 12·00
a. Wmk "6" (10.63) . . — £4000
b. Grey-violet (*shades*) (11.63) . . £100 9·00
c. Slate (12.63) . . £150 18·00
112 9 4d. dull rose-pink (9.10.62) . . 90·00 4·50
a. Dull rose (*deep brown gum*) (2.63) . . 95·00 4·75
b. Rose-red . . — 4·50
113 11 6d. grey (18.6.63) . . 70·00 4·50
a. Grey-black (2.64) . . 70·00 4·75
b. Intense black . . — 5·50
114 6d. jet-black (p 13) (12.64) . . 80·00 5·00
a. Grey-black . . 80·00 5·50

July–Aug 1863: Varieties due to a temporary break-down of the perforating machine.

115 9 4d. dull rose-pink (*imperf*) . . — 60·00
116 4d. dull rose-pink (*roul*) . . — £250

Notes on plate varieties found on stamps printed from plates made by Robinson.

The electros prepared by Robinson over the period 1860–66 (many, e.g. the 4d., which lasted until 1881, remaining in use for a long time after) furnish perhaps the most interesting varieties found in typographed stamps. Since the lead moulds for these were struck by hand, on semifused metal, and without the aid of a "collar", the stamps present us with certain constant abnormalities, viz *partial strikes, double strikes* and *internal distortion* varieties of a nature and extent not found in any other issues, as well as also providing all the more usual types of flaw found in typographed stamps. The whole of the Robinson "Beaded Ovals" and "Laureates" are plateable since the process used made it *impossible* for any stamp to be a perfect reproduction of the die. The 6d. black (Type **11**) is the most interesting of all since the die here was in two parts. This meant the adherence of lead along the line of junction, etc, and gave rise to yet further classes of plate variety. For information on this stamp see various articles in the *London Philatelist*.

Notes on the two single-line numeral watermark papers.

Two different English firms supplied the single-line numeral wmk papers used from October 1862 onwards. The two classes of paper supplied are so distinct that they have now been given separate listing. Their characteristics are as follows:—

1. *De La Rue papers* (several consignments). Comprised *white* paper wmkd "1", "2", "4", "6" and "8" respectively, *blue* paper wmkd "1" and *green* paper wmkd "2". In certain printings particularly in the 1d., 2d. and 4d. Laureates and the 6d. black (1863–65) on this paper, a *pelure* type—thin, hard and semi-transparent—may be found. This variety has not been separately listed but is worthy of the specialist's attention. Generally the quality of these De La Rue papers varied considerably among the different consignments.

2. *T. H. Saunders papers* (one consignment only). Comprised *white* paper wmkd "1", "4" and "6" respectively, *blue* paper wmkd "1", *green* paper wmkd "2", and *pink* paper wmkd "10". It was first used in December 1865 and the white papers were exhausted by August 1867. The paper was (apart from the *blue* variety, which was rather thinner than the rest) of even quality throughout and was smoother, thicker, more brittle and (in the white variety) not so white as the De La Rue product. It will be noted that the "2" and "8" papers were supplied by De La Rue only, whereas the "10" paper (pink) was supplied by Saunders only. Comparison of these should assist collectors in accurate classification. The *coloured* papers lasted much longer than the white, as will be seen from the listings. The *blue* lasted until 1875, and the *green* and *pink* until 1879.

In both papers, in practically all cases, *reversed* and/or *inverted* wmks may be met. *Sideways* wmks have been found under Nos. 113, 124 and 200. Stamps showing little or no wmk are from the left or right sides of badly cut sheets.

15

16

17

18

19

(The *"Laureated"* series: Dies engraved by Frederick Grosse. Printing plates (see previous note) made by F. W. Robinson until late in 1867)

Note. Since various printings of the 2s. Calvert (Type **5**) were also made between 1864 and 1881 these have been included where appropriate.

1863–80.

(i) 1863–64. *Early printings. Wmkd with appropriate single-lined numeral as W* **14**, *on paper supplied by De La Rue. P* 12

No.	Type	Description	Unused	Used
117	**15**	1d. pale green (8.9.64)	75·00	7·00
118		2d. violet (4.64)	65·00	4·75
		a. Dull violet (10.64)	70·00	5·00
119		4d. deep rose (4.9.63)	—	3·50
		a. Doubly printed	—	£500
		b. Rose-pink (9.63)	85·00	2·50
		c. Pink (4.64)	85·00	2·50

Emergency printings on Perkins, Bacon paper wmkd double-lined numerals "1" and "4" respectively, supplied by Tasmania. P 12.

No.	Type	Description	Unused	Used
120	**10**	1d. yellow-green (10.12.63)	£110	7·00
		a. Dull green (4.64)	—	7·00
		b. Imperf between (pair)		
121	**15**	4d. deep rose (7.1.64)	£110	3·75
		a. Pale rose	—	3·75

Like the 1d. and 4d. Perkins, Bacon types of Van Diemen's Land most of the Victorian stamps printed on the above two papers may occasionally be found with wmk *inverted.* This applies both to the 1d. and 4d. above and also the various "Laureates" of the 1867–68 printings. Instances are also known where the wmk is *reversed* and one (in No. 132) where it is *sideways.* Most of these varieties are rare.

(ii) *Printings of* October 1864 *onwards. As* (i) *but P* 13

No.	Type	Description	Unused	Used
122	**15**	1d. pale green (10.10.64)	70·00	3·50
		a. Bluish green (12.64)	65·00	2·75
		aa. Doubly printed	—	£550
		b. Green (shades) (8.65)	65·00	3·50
		c. Deep green (12.65)	—	3·00
123		2d. dull violet (10.64)	55·00	3·75
		a. Dull lilac (shades) (4.65)	55·00	3·50
		b. Reddish mauve (11.65)	60·00	3·50
124		4d. dull rose (10.64)	75·00	2·50
		a. Dull rose-red (2.65)	75·00	2·50
125		8d. orange (22.2.65)	£300	50·00
126	**18**	1s. blue/*blue* (10.4.65)	£100	3·50
127	**5**	2s. light blue/*green* (22.11.64)	£150	5·00
		a. Deep blue/green (1865)	£150	5·00

The above 1s. stamp can be immediately identified by the white patches (comprising an *albino* impression) due to the lack of a *make-ready* which are found on all stamps. The 8d. was withdrawn from issue on 11.6.69.

(iii) July–August 1865. *As before but P* 12 *or* 12 × 13 *from repaired state of* 12 *machine, with larger holes and sharper teeth than previously.* (a) *Perf* 12

No.	Type	Description	Unused	Used
128	**15**	1d. green (*shades*)	70·00	3·00
		a. Deep green	70·00	3·00
129		4d. dull rose-red (8.65)	£120	7·50
130	**5**	2s. dark blue/*green*	£170	8·50
		(b) *Perf* 12 × 13		
131	**15**	1d. deep green	—	6·00

August and December 1865. *Emergency printings* (2) *on Perkins, Bacon paper wmkd double-lined "4" supplied by Tasmania.*

No.	Type	Description	Unused	Used
132	**15**	4d. dull reddish rose (*p* 13) (11.8.65)	£110	3·50
		a. Perf 12	—	3·75
		b. Perf 12 × 13	—	11·00
133		4d. red (*p* 13) (16.12.65)	£120	3·50

October 1865. *Emergency printing on De La Rue paper wmkd single-lined "8", no "10" paper having arrived. P* 13.

No.	Type	Description	Unused	Used
134	**17**	10d. grey (21.10.65)	£450	£100
		a. Grey-black	£450	£100

(iv) December 1865–66 *printings. These, in general, were of finer impression than the previous* 1865 *printings*

A. *On Saunders paper, wmkd with the appropriate single-line numerals as* W **14**.

No.	Type	Description	Unused	Used
135	**15**	1d. deep yellow-green (*p* 13) (1.66)	65·00	2·75
		a. Perf 12	—	6·50
		b. Perf 12 × 13	—	5·50
136		4d. rose-red (*p* 13) (12.12.65)	75·00	3·00
		a. Perf 12	—	4·75
		b. Perf 12 × 13	—	5·50
137	**17**	6d. blue (*p* 13) (13.2.66)	21·00	1·50
		a. Perf 12	23·00	3·00
		b. Perf 12 × 13	21·00	1·75
		ba. Imperf between (pair)	—	£550
138		10d. dull purple/*pink* (*p* 13) (22.3.66)	65·00	4·00
		a. Perf 12 × 13	70·00	5·00
		b. Blackish brown/pink (*p* 13) (1869)	75·00	5·00
139	**18**	1s. indigo-blue/*blue* (*p* 13) (1870)	55·00	3·25
		a. Perf 12 (1873)	—	5·00
		b. Bright blue/blue (*p* 13) (1.71)	55·00	2·50
		ba. Perf 12	—	3·25
		c. Pale dull blue/blue (*p* 13) (1.75)	—	7·00
		ca. Perf 12	—	3·25
140	**5**	2s. dark blue/*green* (12.67)	£160	5·50
		a. Perf 12 (1875)	£180	5·50
		b. Blue/green (1872, 1878)	£160	3·75
		c. Greenish blue/green (*p* 12) (1875)	£180	5·50
		d. Deep greenish blue/green (*p* 12½) (1880)	£160	7·50

The 1s. on Saunders paper was issued later than 1866 but it and the 2s. printing are included here for the sake of convenience. The Saunders green paper is distinctly *deeper* in shade and more apparently *green* than the De La Rue variety.

B. *On De La Rue paper wmkd with the appropriate single-line numerals as* W **14**. *P* 13.

No.	Type	Description	Unused	Used
141	**15**	1d. bright yellow-green (1.67)	—	15·00
142		2d. rosy lilac (1.66)	55·00	4·75
		a. Perf 12 × 13	55·00	4·75
143		2d. dull lilac (6.66)	—	4·75
		a. Perf 12	—	6·00
		b. Perf 12 × 13	—	7·50
144		2d. grey (25.7.66)	55·00	3·00
		a. Perf 12	85·00	6·00
145	**17**	6d. blue (13.2.66)	23·00	2·50
		a. Perf 12	23·00	4·00
		b. Perf 12 × 13	21·00	1·75
146	**18**	1s. blue/*blue* (1866, 1869)	55·00	3·00
		a. Perf 12 × 13 (1866)	55·00	3·50
		b. Bright blue/blue (*p* 13) (1867, 1871)	—	3·00
		ba. Perf 12 (1871)	—	3·50
		c. Indigo/blue (*p* 13)	—	2·75
		d. Dull blue/blue (*p* 12) (1874)	—	3·50
		e. Imperf btwn (vert pair) (*p* 12×13)	—	£550
147	**5**	2s. blue/*green* (1868)	£140	3·75
		a. Greenish blue/green (1873)	£140	3·75
		aa. Perf 12	£160	4·75
		b. Dark blue/green (*p* 12½) (1880)	£140	3·75

The 1d. of 1867 on De La Rue, distinguishable only by its shade, was presumably the result of the discovery of a small quantity of old stock. The 2d. and 4d. of 1866 may also be found 13 × 12 but are rare in *this* condition. The 10d. was withdrawn from issue on 21.6.71. There were, between 1864 and 1881, no less than 21 different printings of the 2s. blue on green. Only the main schools of colour have been listed.

1866 (Sept)–**67.** *Various Emergency printings, all the results of the non-arrival of the first shipment of "V over Crown" paper.*

1. *Printings on De La Rue paper wmkd single-lined* "8". *P* 13.

No.	Type	Description	Unused	Used
148	**15**	1d. bright yellow-green (27.12.66)	£120	9·50
149		2d. grey (18.1.67)	£110	4·50
150	**16**	3d. lilac (29.9.66)	£160	20·00
151	**15**	4d. rose-red (?date)	†	£2000

2. *Printings on Saunders paper wmkd single-lined* "4". *P* 13.

No.	Type	Description	Unused	Used
152	**15**	1d. bright yellow-green (6.3.67)	85·00	6·50
153		2d. grey (21.2.67)	75·00	4·75

3. *Printings on paper wmkd single-lined* "6". *P* 13.

No.	Type	Description	Unused	Used
		(a) *On De La Rue paper*		
154	**15**	1d. bright yellow-green (6.67)	—	14·00
		(b) *On Saunders paper*		
155	**15**	1d. bright yellow-green (6.67)	£120	11·00
156		2d. grey (13.5.67)	£130	6·00

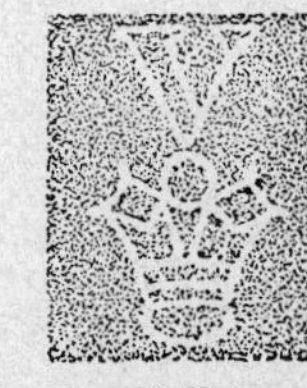

20 (V1)

9 9

NINEPENCE

(21)

WATERMARKS. Many stamps watermarked V and Crown ma[y] be found with watermark inverted or sideways.

1867–68. *Printings on first consignment of paper wmkd "V ove[r] Crown", W* **20**, *received in July* 1867. *P* 13.

No.	Type	Description	Unused	Used
157	**15**	1d. bright yellow-green (10.8.67)	85·00	3·5
158		2d. slate-grey (*shades*) (26.8.67)	70·00	3·5
		a. Grey-lilac (1.68)	—	4·7
159	**16**	3d. lilac (8.67)	£200	24·0
		a. Grey-lilac (8.68)	£225	26·0
160	**15**	4d. dull rose (11.67)	75·00	5·0
161	**17**	6d. dark blue (12.67)	—	3·0
162	**19**	5s. blue/*yellow* (26.12.67)	£1600	£30
		a. Wmk reversed	—	£50

The above shades (there are also paper differences) ar[e] sufficiently distinctive to enable separation of the five lower value from *later* "V over Crown" printings. The 5s. was printed from th[e] first electros prepared by Atkinson. There were two printings, bot[h] in sheets of 25 (5 × 5). The first (1200) was from a single vertica[l] column of 5 electros clamped together. The second (2000) was fro[m] a plate of 25 impressions, comprising a different "5 vertical" repeated 5 times (i.e. giving 5 types). The reversed wmk variet[y] belongs to the first printing and was created *deliberately* to avoi[d] the appearance of the "page number" on the front of one stamp i[n] every four sheets of 25.

1867 (Sept)–**68** and **1870.** *Various Emergency printings due firs[t] to the* 1867 *shipment of white "V over Crown" paper being s[o] small, later to its exhaustion and the non-arrival of the secon[d] shipment ordered, later still* (1870) *to a further shortage of th[e] paper.*

1. *Printings on the Perkins, Bacon paper wmkd double-lined* "1[" *received from Tasmania in* 1863. *P* 13.

No.	Type	Description	Unused	Used
163	**15**	1d. pale yellowish green (24.9.67)	65·00	3·5
		a. Deep yellow-green (6.68)	65·00	3·5
164		2d. slate (5.68)	£110	5·5
		a. Mauve (30.6.68)	£110	6·5
165	**16**	3d. grey-lilac (8.68)	£150	35·0
166	**17**	6d. blue (28.7.68)	55·00	4·2

2. *Printings on the Perkins, Bacon paper wmkd double-lined* "4[" *received from Tasmania in* 1863. *P* 13.

No.	Type	Description	Unused	Used
167	**15**	1d. pale yellow-green (27.5.68)	£750	80·0
168		2d. grey-lilac (3.2.68)	£110	4·2
		a. Slate (28.3.68)	£110	3·5
		b. Mauve (3.7.68)	—	4·5
169		4d. dull rose-red (5.68)	£110	5·0
170	**17**	6d. blue (20.6.68)	£150	13·0
		a. Indigo-blue	—	15·0

3. *Printing on Saunders paper wmkd* "SIX PENCE" *as W* **12.** *P* 13

No.	Type	Description	Unused	Used
171	**15**	1d. pale yellow-green (5.6.68)	£325	15·0
172		2d. slate-grey	—	£110
173	**17**	6d. blue (23.5.68)	£150	11·0
		a. Indigo-blue	—	15·0

Only one copy is apparently known of No. 172. From its shade [it] would appear to belong to an 1867–68 printing. No 171 is know[n] with the wmk *sideways.*

4. *Printings on lilac paper wmkd V over Crown from* 1867 *consign[-] ment. P* 13.

No.	Type	Description	Unused	Used
174	**15**	2d. mauve/*lilac* (12.8.68)	55·00	6·5
		a. Lilac/lilac	55·00	6·0

5. 1870: 6d. *value only. Printings on various wmkd papers as ind[i]cated. P* 13.

No.	Type	Description	Unused	Used
175	**17**	6d. dull blue (THREE PENCE) (23.4.70)	£130	6·0
		a. Deep blue	—	7·0
176		6d. dull blue (FOUR PENCE) (18.6.70)	£250	22·0
		a. Deep blue	—	23·0
177		6d. dull blue ("4") (21.5.70)	—	£120
178		6d. dull blue ("2") (1870)	—	£120

Of the six or seven copies known of No. 177 all but one have th[e] watermark reversed.

1868 (Aug)–**71.** *Printings on second and later consignments of "V over Crown paper. W* **20.** *P* 13 *only.* (i) *Printed from Robinso[n] plates.*

No.	Type	Description	Unused	Used
179	**15**	2d. lilac (26.8.68)	50·00	3·2
		a. Dull mauve (shades) (10.68)	50·00	3·2
		b. Lilac-grey (1.69)	—	3·5
		c. Lilac-rose (2.69)	—	3·0
180	**16**	3d. yellow-orange (12.6.69)	15·00	3·0
181	**15**	4d. pale red (*aniline*) (21.4.69)	—	6·5
		a. Deep red (aniline) (16.7.69)	—	6·5
		b. Rose-pink (2.70)	—	5·0
182	**17**	6d. blue (*shades*)	14·00	1·1
		a. Indigo-blue (1869)	14·00	1·1
183	**19**	5s. indigo-blue and carmine (I) (8.10.68)	£200	15·0
		a. Blue and carmine (1869)	£170	11·0

Nos. 179*b*/*c* were printed from badly worn plates.

For the frame-plate of the 5s. (I) the electros of the 1867 plat[e] with the Crown, "VICTORIA" and "FIVE SHILLINGS" cut ou[t] were employed. A new plate, also produced via cut-out portions o[f] the 1867 plate, was brought into use for the red portion.

(ii) *Printed from new plates made by Atkinson*

No.	Type	Description	Unused	Used
184	**15**	1d. bright yellow-green (10.68)	65·00	2·5
		a. Bright olive-green (1.69)	—	14·0
		b. Dull yellow-green (4.69)	—	2·1
		c. Dull green (3.70)	65·00	2·1
		d. Very pale green (10.70)	—	2·1
185		2d. lilac-grey (15.1.69)	—	3·7
		a. Lilac-rose (shades) (24.2.69)	55·00	3·7
		b. Mauve (20.4.69)	—	3·2
		c. Red-lilac (shades) (5.69)	55·00	3·0
		d. Dull lilac (shades) (6.69)	55·00	2·5
		e. Silver-grey (2.9.69)	£110	7·0

The Atkinson plates, produced by an improved technique; do no[t] show the *double* and *partial strikes* and *internal distortion* varietie[s] met on a large proportion of the stamps from the Robinson plate[s]. Further, the later printings from the 2d. and 6d. Robinson plate[s] show obvious signs of wear. These factors and the differing shade[s] should make classification relatively easy. For the first two print[-] ings of the 2d. in 1869 the first of the new Atkinson plates was use[d] in conjunction with the old Robinson plate, following which th[e] latter was replaced by a second Atkinson plate. The dates of intro[-] duction of the Atkinson plates were 1d., October 1868; 2d., Januar[y] 1869 and 6d., December 1875.

1871. *Provisional. Surch with T* **21**, *in blue. On Saunders pape[r] wmkd single-lined* "10". *P* 13.

No.	Type	Description	Unused	Used
186	**17**	9d. on 10d. purple-brown/*pink* (22.4.71)	£180	10·0
		a. Blackish brown/pink	—	12·0
		b. Surch double	—	£70

PERFORATIONS (TO 1883)

The perforations of Victoria, particularly those of the period)ctober 1864–80, form a complex study for specialists. We have ,dopted in this listing a simplified classification based on *three* lescriptions—Perf 12, Perf 13 and Perf 12½ respectively, the latter ›eing substituted for Perf 13 for the period 1881 on. The position :an be concisely put as follows:—

A. "*Perf* 12": Here the gauge is *never* quite 12 and nearer 11½. It s not found after 1883. There were two machines (both single-line), he first introduced by Robinson in January 1859 and the second)urchased in 1871. No "perf 12" are found in the period mid 1866–mid 1871. At various periods, more particularly in 1865 and 1880, one or both of the machines was repaired, to give larger holes ınd sharper teeth over a succeeding period.

B. "*Perf* 13": Here the gauge is invariably *over* 12 and with a sole ›xception (covering a section of the pins on one machine over the)eriod 1876–80) invariably *under* 13. Generally speaking up to the ›nd of 1880, these machines gauged 12½ to 12¾. Two classes of nachine are found:

(i) *Single-line* machines. These were three in number—purchased on October 1864, 1866 and 1873 respectively. Two of them were converted into combs in 1873. The other was repaired on several occasions, particularly in 1879–80, to give larger holes and sharper teeth.

(ii) *Comb* machines. First introduced in 1873 (see above). Over the period of use they gave various gauges, depending on the machine and its state of repair. They were all *vertical* combs adapted only for normal size stamps of either dimension as likewise (until 1913) were all other comb-machines used in Victoria for perforating stamps.

C. "*Perf* 12½": Found from late 1876 onwards, in both single-ine (used mainly for the larger-size stamps) and vertical comb nachines. Gradually superseded the A and B gauges. Certain stamps of the 1879–80 period are found in both B and C gauges out these are no longer differentiated as separate varieties, being only listed under the one or the other gauge. This applies also to he Postal Fiscal section.

"*Compound*" *perforations*: In previous editions certain 12 × 13)erforations were listed which were not true compounds of A and 3 but simply the product of one or other of the *comb* machines. Such varieties have now been eliminated. The "Compounds" now isted are all true compounds (or "mixeds") of A and B. They generally fall into two categories: (i) those of the 1865–66 period where the two machines were both used for the original perforating, one in the one direction (top to bottom) and the other in he other (sides); (ii) isolated examples, better termed "mixed")erfs, from 1873 on, where one gauge machine was used to correct off-centre perforating done by the other gauge machine. Such cases are almost invariably associated with "mends", viz the)asting of gummed strips down the back of the faulty line of)erforations.

1871–84 PRINTINGS

These are listed separately from the 1868–71 printings because of the perforation changes made in the period, viz the reintroduction of the 12 gauge (1871), the introduction of comb machines (1873), the repairs of various 12 and 13 machines (1879), and the introduction of the 12½ gauge (1879–80). Many stamps issued in the latter period are found both perf 13 and 12½ but no distinction is made. The 13 gauge disappears in 1880–81.

Papers: All printings on white paper made after April 1878 and also the last 8d. printing were on the "*glazed*" variety of paper and this furnishes another means of identification. Some shades, e.g. 6d. blue of 1878–79 are found on *both* papers.

Shades are different from those found in the 1868–71 printings.

1871–84.

(i) *Printed from Robinson plates; W* 20; *P* 13, 12½ *unless otherwise described*

187 16 3d. dull orange (1871) .. 14·00 1·90
a. Perf 12 (1872) .. 14·00 20·00
b. Orange (1874) .. — 2·25
ba. Perf 12 .. — 2·10
c. Bright orange .. 20·00 2·50
ca. Perf 12 .. — 2·50
188 3d. orange-brown (1878) .. 20·00 5·50
189 3d. dull orange-yellow (1881) .. 22·00 2·50
a. Perf 12
190 15 4d. rose (*shades*) (1871–78) .. 70·00 3·00
a. Perf 12 .. 70·00 3·00
b. Dull rose (5.3.79) .. 70·00 3·00
ba. Perf 12 .. — 3·00
c. Dull rose-red (23.12.79) .. — 3·00
ca. Perf 12 .. — 3·00
d. Bright lilac-rose (*aniline*) (3.3.80) .. 75·00 3·75
da. Perf 12 .. — 6·50
191 4d. rosine (*aniline*) (22.9.80) .. £200 5·00
a. Perf 12 .. 80·00 4·75
b. Compound perf 12 with 12½ .. — £325
192 17 6d. Prussian blue (1872, 1874) .. 12·00 90
a. Perf 12 .. 14·00 1·10
b. Indigo (1873) .. 14·00 1·40
ba. Perf 12 .. 18·00 1·75
c. Dull blue (worn plate) .. — 90
193 15 8d. lilac-brown/*pink* (24.1.77) .. 75·00 5·00
a. Purple-brown/pink (21.3.78) .. 75·00 5·00
b. Chocolate/pink (6.8.78) .. 80·00 4·00
bb. Compound perf 13 × 12 .. — £325
194 8d. red-brown/*pink* (20.5.78) .. 75·00 4·00
195 8d. dark red-brown/*pink* (*p* 12) (*glazed*) (30.11.80) .. 75·00 5·00
a. Perf 12½
196 18 1s. light blue/*blue* (5.75) .. 75·00 6·50
a. Perf 12 .. — 6·50
197 19 5s. pale bright blue and carmine (I) (7.77) .. — 15·00
a. Grey-blue and carmine (8.78) .. £160 13·00
b. Deep lavender-blue and carmine (5.80) .. £160 13·00
198 5s. bright blue and red (II) (12.5.81) .. £140 11·00
a. Perf 12 .. £130 12·00
b. Indigo-blue and red .. — 15·00
ba. Perf 12 .. — 16·00
c. Second "I" in "SHILLINGS" short at foot .. — 90·00

The 4d. "pink" previously listed is a *faded* rosine. For the 5s. (Type II) new dies were made for *each* portion of the design. All Type I stamps have a blue line under the Crown, which is missing in Type II. The latter were printed in sheets of 100 (10 × 10), as compared with 25 (5 × 5) for Type I.

No. 197*b* has the watermark sideways.

1877–79. *Printings of the 8d. value on Saunders paper wmkd single-lined* "10". *P* 13, 12½ *unless otherwise stated.*

199 15 8d. lilac-brown/*pink* (12.77) .. — £500
a. Purple-brown/pink (20.2.78) .. £100 5·50
200 8d. red-brown/*pink* (8.8.79) .. 85·00 4·50
a. Perf 12 .. — 7·00

The 8d. printings (save that of 1880) were *mixed* and comprised stamps on *both* V over Crown and "10" papers.

½ ½

HALF

(22)

(ii) *Printed from plates made by Atkinson. The* ½*d. made by surch with T* 22, *in red*

201 15 ½d. on 1d. green (25.6.73) .. 36·00 7·00
a. Perf 12 .. 45·00 9·00
b. Grass-green .. 40·00 7·00
ba. Perf 12 .. 45·00 9·00
c. Short "1" at right .. — 60·00
202 1d. pale green (1871) .. 60·00 2·25
a. Perf 12 (10.71) .. 70·00 2·40
b. Green (*shades*) .. 60·00 2·25
ba. Perf 12 .. 60·00 2·25
c. Grass-green .. — 2·40
ca. Perf 12 .. 60·00 2·40
d. Bluish green (*shades*) .. 60·00 2·40
da. Perf 12 .. — 2·40
203 17 6d. dull ultramarine (2.12.75) .. 19·00 1·25
a. Light Prussian-blue (29.12.75) .. — 1·25
b. Dull violet-blue (4.78) .. — 5·50
c. Blue (13.5.78) .. 20·00 90
ca. Perf 12 .. — 90
d. Dull milky blue (7.3.79) .. 19·00 1·10
da. Perf 12 .. — 1·10
e. Blue (*light ink*) (8.80) .. — 90
f. Light blue (10.5.81) .. 20·00 1·10
fa. Perf 12 .. — 2·40
g. Deep blue (15.1.82) .. 19·00 90

23 (V2)

24

The types of V over Crown watermark (1867–1912)

In all, *five* types were employed.

The first two types (*V*1 and *V*2) belong to the contracts made with De La Rue to supply postage stamp paper. That firm lost the contract in 1895 to Waterlow and Sons, who held it until 1912. The third and fourth types are therefore products of the Waterlow contracts. The fifth type (found only in 1912) was supplied by James Spicer & Sons. The change in the pattern from *V*1 to *V*2 is explained by the dandyroll (which was the property of De La Rue) requiring replacement. Since *all* the changes in pattern are also associated with changes in the nature and texture of the paper supplied, little difficulty should be encountered, with the new descriptions, in identifying the various types. Each pattern (save in a few cases of "left over" stock) succeeded the previous pattern.

Types *V*1 and *V*2 are mainly to be distinguished from one another by the four "points" around the top of the Crown which are found in *V*1 but not in *V*2. Also, as compared with *V*2, the shapes of the top ornaments in *V*1 resemble diamonds, and not ovals. It must be remembered that *V*1 *coloured* papers continued in use long after the exhaustion of the *V*1 white paper, the earliest date met for the *V*2 white paper being 15.8.82. The first *V*2 coloured papers (blue and green) were not used until February 1890. In general the papers supplied by De La Rue were whiter than their successors. The quality found with the *V*1 wmk varied greatly both with and without a pronounced mesh. The quality of the *V*2 papers on the other hand varied little. It is generally more "loaded" and opaque than any of the *V*1 papers and the wmk clearer when held to the light.

(iii) 1882–4. *As* (ii) *above but on paper wmkd V over Crown* (V2), *W* 23. *P* 12½

204 16 3d. yellow-orange (13.4.83) .. 18·00 4·50
a. Dull brownish orange .. 22·00 6·50
205 17 6d. dull violet-blue (10.11.82) .. 11·00 1·00
a. Indigo-blue (11.83) .. 11·00 1·10
b. Light ultramarine (9.84) .. 11·00 1·25

The above 3d. was printed from two new plates made by Atkinson. For the 6d. the same Atkinson plates introduced in December 1875 were employed.

Reprints were made, in 1891, on V over Crown paper, Type 23, perf 12½, of the 1d., 2d., 3d., 4d., 6d., 8d., 10d., 1s. and 5s. "Laureates". The shades are distinctive and a number of values show "die flaws" not found in the originals. The 3d. was printed in yellow, the 8d. in orange-yellow, the 10d. in greenish slate and the 5s. in blue and red.

(Printed in Melbourne from a double electrotyped plate of 240 subjects supplied by D.L.R.)

1870 (28 Jan). *Wmk V over Crown* (V1), *W* 20. *P* 13.

206 24 2d. brown-lilac .. 48·00 1·50
a. Dull lilac-mauve (9.70) .. 36·00 1·00
aa. Perf 12 (1871) .. 48·00 1·50
b. Mauve (worn plate, 3.73) .. 36·00 1·25
ba. Perf 12 .. 48·00 1·00

25

26

27

8d 8d

EIGHTPENCE

(28)

29

30

31 (Die I) 32 (Die II)

(Des and dies eng by William Bell and stamps printed from electrotyped plates)

1873–84. *Two dies of 2d.: I, single-lined outer oval; II, double-lined outer oval. The 8d. is made by surch with T* 28 *in blue. P* 13 *unless otherwise described.*

(*a*) *On Saunders paper, wmkd single-lined* "10"

207 29 9d. pale brown/*pink* (25.3.73) .. 50·00 5·00
a. Perf 12 .. 55·00 8·00
b. Red-brown/pink (8.74) .. 45·00 5·50

(*b*) *Wmk V over Crown* (V1) (*sideways on T* 25), *W* 20

208 25 ½d. rose-red (10.2.74) .. 4·50 50
a. Perf 12 .. 5·00 70
b. Lilac-rose (1874) .. 5·00 70
ba. Perf 12 .. 4·50 70
c. Rosine (*shades*) (12.80) .. 3·75 50
ca. Perf 12 .. 4·50 35
d. Pale red (1882) .. 4·50 35
da. Perf 12 .. 4·50 40
e. Mixed perf 13 and 12 .. — £110
209 26 1d. dull bluish green (14.12.75) .. 13·00 75
a. Perf 12 .. 15·00 75
b. Green (*shades*) (1877) .. 13·00 70
ba. Perf 12 .. 14·00 4·50
c. Yellow-green (1878 and 1880) .. 13·00 55
ca. Perf 12 .. — 1·75
210 27 2d. deep lilac-mauve, Die I (1.10.73) .. 13·00 35
a. Perf 12 .. — 1·50
b. Dull violet-mauve .. 13·00 35
ba. Perf 12 .. — 1·40
c. Dull mauve .. 13·00 35
ca. Perf 12 .. 15·00 50
d. Pale mauve (*worn plate*) (1.79) .. 14·00 50
da. Perf 12 .. — 65
e. Mixed perf 13 and 12 .. £130 £100
211 2d. lilac-mauve, Die II (17.12.78) .. 10·00 35
a. Perf 12 .. 14·00 35
b. Grey-mauve (1.80) .. — 40
ba. Perf 12 .. — 80
c. Pale mauve (6.80) .. 20·00 40
ca. Perf 12 .. — 1·25
e. Vert pair, lower stamp imperf horiz
212 29 8d. on 9d. lilac-brn/*pink* (*p* 12) (1.7.76) .. £120 15·00
a. "F.IGHT" (broken "E") .. — £150
213 9d. lilac-brown/*pink* (*p* 12) (1.12.75) .. £100 10·00
214 30 1s. indigo-blue/*blue* (16.8.76) .. 30·00 3·00
a. Deep blue/blue (1877) .. 32·00 3·00
aa. Perf 12 (10.80) .. — 7·50
b. Blue/blue (1878) .. 35·00 3·00
ba. Perf 12 .. — 7·50
c. Ultramarine/blue (1879) .. 45·00 7·50
d. Bright blue/blue (11.83) .. 45·00 5·00

(*c*) 18 February–April 1878. *Emergency printings on various coloured papers, due to the exhaustion of white V1 paper. W* 20 (*V*1) (*sideways on T* 25). *P* 13 *only.*

215 25 ½d. rose-red/*pink* (1.3.78) .. 20·00 8·00
216 26 1d. yellow-green/*yellow* (25.2.78) .. 50·00 11·00
217 1d. yellow-green/*drab* (4.78) .. £100 40·00
218 27 2d. violet-mauve/*green* (18.2.78) .. £120 10·00
219 2d. violet-mauve/*lilac* (21.2.78) .. £1000 £400
220 2d. violet-mauve/*brown* (21.3.78) .. £120 10·00

Two shades of yellow paper, termed *pale canary* and *deep canary* respectively, are found.

All supplies of *V*1 paper received in Victoria after 15.3.78 were, as compared with previous supplies, highly surfaced on the printing side. An experimental printing was made on the new paper in July 1877 (1d., 2d., 6d. and 5s.) and all printings on white *V*1 paper from April 1878 on were made on this glazed paper. The glazed *V*1 coloured papers, with few exceptions, made their appearance later.

(*d*) 1882–83. *On white paper wmkd V over Crown* (*V*2). *W* 23 (*sideways on T* 25). *P* 13

221 25 ½d. rosine (4.83) .. 5·00 65
a. Perf 12 .. 50·00 15·00
222 26 1d. yellow-green (9.82) .. 14·00 1·00
a. Perf 12

Reprints: The ½d., 1d., 2d. (Die II), 9d. and 1s. values were reprinted in 1891, perf 12½. The first four from new plates, made from Dies containing *die flaws* not found in the originals. The 9d. was on *V*1 and the others on *V*2 paper.

33

34

35

(Des and eng by Charles Naish (T **33** & **34**) and William Bell (T **35**). Typo from electrotyped plates)

1880–84. *P 12½ unless otherwise described, this description including the P 13 varieties found in* 1880. (*a*) *W* **20** (*V1*).

No.	Type	Description	Unused	Used
223	**33**	2d. sepia (3.11.80)	15·00	45
		a. Perf 12	—	38·00
		b. Sepia-brown (2.81)	12·50	45
		ba. Perf 12	£130	38·00
		c. Brown (aniline) (5.81)	16·00	45
		ca. Perf 12	—	38·00
		d. Dull black-brown (10.81)	—	45
		e. Dull grey-brown (3.82)	12·00	45
		f. Mixed perf 13 and 12	—	£190
224		2d. mauve (*worn plate*) (2.84)	—	4·50
225	**34**	4d. rose-carmine (10.81)	30·00	4·00
		a. Rosine (8.82)	30·00	3·50
226	**35**	2s. dark blue (*shades*)/*green* (8.7.81)	£110	18·00
		a. Light blue/green (wmk sideways) (8.83)	£120	22·00
		b. Ultramarine/green (7.84)	—	28·00
		ba. Wmk sideways	—	48·00
		(*b*) *W* **23** (*V2*)		
227	**33**	2d. dull grey-brown (15.8.82)	12·00	30
228		2d. chocolate (3.83)	12·00	30
		a. Perf 12	—	19·00
229		2d. mauve (20.12.83)	7·00	20
		a. Worn plate	7·50	20
		b. Perf 12	—	£180
		c. Mixed perfs 12½ and 12	—	£180
230	**34**	4d. rose-red (3.83)	35·00	4·50

For the scarce perf 12 stamps listed above the holes are large and the teeth sharp. See also the note about perf 12 stamps after No. 186b.

The first printings of the 2d. in mauve were from the two plates used for the browns. Later printings were from two new plates. Reprints were made in 1891 of the 2d. (brown), 4d. (in pale red) and 2s., all on *V2* paper.

36

(Des and die eng Charles Naish. Typo)

1883 (29 Oct)**–84.** *P* 12½. (*a*) *W* **20** (*V1*).

No.	Type	Description	Unused	Used
231	**36**	1d. green (2.84)	90·00	6·00
		(*b*) *W* **23** (*V2*)		
232	**36**	1d. yellow-green (29.10.83)	14·00	1·25
		a. Green	12·00	1·25
		b. Pale green (5.84)	12·00	1·25

Nos. 224 and 231 represent a printing on old stocks of paper.

C. THE "POSTAGE AND REVENUE" PERIOD, 1884–1901

Under the provisions of the Postage Act 1883 the stamps of the three series then in use (Postage, Duty, Fee) became, as from 1.1.84, mutually interchangeable. It was, at the same time, decided to issue (as soon as possible) the *one* stamp only, for any value, to serve *all* purposes. Since there were available many more dies (and plates) inscribed "Stamp Duty" than there were of either the "Postage" or "Fee" (Stamp Statute) series it was agreed that all values should be inscribed "Stamp Duty" by the beginning of 1885. All stamps *printed* after 1.1.84 are therefore true "Postage and Revenue" stamps whereas all Stamp Duty and Fee stamps printed before that date are Postal Fiscals, since they were originally printed solely for fiscal purposes. These principles have been strictly adhered to in our listing. Little difficulty should however be met in distinguishing between the printings of the one stamp found respectively in the main list and in the "Postal Fiscal" section since there are many major differences of printing, watermark, perforation and shade. On 1.1.84 there were no "Stamp Duty" designs for the ½d., 2d., 4d., 8d. and 2s. 6d. values. Also the existing "Stamp Duty" designs for the 1d., 6d., 1s. and 2s. were deemed to be too large to be convenient for general and extensive use. For all these values it was therefore necessary to produce new and smaller designs inscribed "Stamp Duty". Pending the preparation of new dies and plates, printings were made in 1884 (for the ½d., 1d., 2d., 4d., 6d., 1s. and 2s. values) from the existing "Postage" plates. These printings are also "Postage and Revenue" stamps but have naturally been included, for the sake of convenience, in the previous period. By the beginning of 1885 printings were available, in the new designs, of all values save the 1s. and 2s., and these latter appeared later.

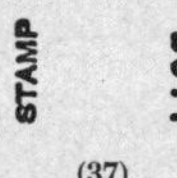

(37)

I. **1885.** *Postage Stamps optd with T* **37**. *The* 1s. *and* 2s. *appeared in February* 1885, 3d. *and* 4d. *in November* 1885. *P* 12½.

No.	Type	Description	Unused	Used
		(*a*) *W* **20** (*V1*)		
233	**16**	3d. dull orange-yellow (Pl 1) (B.)	—	£130
234	**30**	1s. ultramarine/*blue*	95·00	20·00
		a. Dull blue/blue	—	22·00
235		1s. deep ultramarine/*blue* (**B.**) (F.C. £14)	—	£400
236	**35**	2s. ultramarine/*green*	80·00	18·00
		a. Wmk sideways	90·00	20·00
		(*b*) *W* **23** (*V2*)		
237	**16**	3d. yellow-orange (Pl 2) (B.)	60·00	22·00
		a. Dull brownish orange (B.)	65·00	24·00
238	**34**	4d. rose-carmine (B.)	55·00	20·00

The overprinted 1s. was replaced by the 1s. Type **44** on lemon. Collectors should beware of faded black overprints purporting to be the "blue". In genuine examples the blue of the overprint is difficult to distinguish in the blue of the stamp.

Reprints of the 4d. and 1s. (with and without overprint) were made in 1895–6. The 1s. is wmkd V2 and the 4d. (from a new plate) is a pale red. Examples of the latter genuinely postally used are sometimes met.

38 39 40 41 42 43

(Typo. Dies for ½d., 2d., 3d., 4d., 8d. and 2s. 6d. eng by Charles Naish, the other values being derived from these)

II. **1884–95.** *New designs inscr* "STAMP DUTY". *P* 12½.

No.	Type	Description	Unused	Used
		(*a*) *W* **20** (*V1*)		
239	**42**	8d. rose/*pink* (*shades*) (1.1.85)	19·00	5·00
		a. Rose-red/pink	20·00	5·00
240	**40**	1s. deep dull blue/*lemon* (11.85)	32·00	4·00
		a. Dull blue/yellow (6.86)	32·00	4·50
241	**42**	2s. olive/*bluish green* (*shades*) (6.86)	25·00	3·00
		(*b*) *W* **23** (*V2*)		
243	**38**	½d. pale rosine (1.1.85)	4·50	65
		a. Deep rosine (7.85)	5·00	1·00
		b. Salmon (9.85)	5·50	1·25
244	**39**	1d. yellowish green (*shades*) (1.1.85)	5·25	30
		a. Dull pea-green (2.85)	8·00	1·75
245	**40**	2d. lilac (*shades*) (1.1.85)	3·75	25
		a. Mauve (1.86)	4·00	25
		b. Rosy-mauve (6.86)	5·50	50
246	**39**	3d. yellowish brown (1.1.85)	7·00	60
		a. Pale ochre (11.86)	6·50	60
		b. Bistre-yellow (12.92)	7·00	60
247	**41**	4d. magenta (1.1.85)	25·00	3·00
		a. Bright mauve-rose (1.87)	28·00	3·50
248		4d. dull lilac (*error*) (12.86)	£2250	£400
249	**39**	6d. chalky blue (1.1.85)	27·00	2·50
		a. Bright blue (2.85)	21·00	2·10
		b. Cobalt (9.85)	21·00	2·10
250	**42**	8d. bright scarlet/*pink* (1892)	21·00	7·50
251		2s. olive-green/*pale green* (*shades*) (3.90)	25·00	3·00
252		2s. apple-green (12.8.95)	25·00	10·00
253		2s. blue-green (29.10.95)	18·00	4·75
254	**43**	2s. 6d. brown-orange (23.4.84)	80·00	11·00
		a. Yellow (1885)	75·00	10·00
		b. Lemon-yellow (1.93)	75·00	10·00

In each of the 1d., 6d., 1s. and 2s. values six types are to be found differing, *inter alia*, in the engraving of the words of value.

In the 2d. two die states are found: the *original* (1) which occurs on all but seven stamps in the Plate 1 sheet and the *damaged* (1a) which occurs on seven stamps in the Plate 1 sheet and on all 120 stamps in the Plate 2 sheet. The damage consists of a clear break in the top frame just in from the top right corner.

4d. "error": This comprised a printing of 6000 stamps, 1886, in a *dull lilac* shade. It is true that only some seven unused specimens are known but it is not true (as previously stated) that it is unknown used, since a leading authority has himself seen upwards of 30 undoubted used copies, all of which have certain characteristics which distinguish them from certain colour changelings, accidental or deliberate. The records show that the whole printing of 6000 was issued which confirms the findings of so many used copies.

The 8d. value was withdrawn from sale on 24.8.95.

Reprints were made in 1891, using one of the original plates in each case, of the ½d., 1d., 2d., 4d., 6d. and 1s. values. In the three lower values the shades are fairly distinctive. The 1s. was wmkd *V1*. In all cases the wmk is equally common normal and inverted and this applies to *all* the Reprints made in 1891 or later.

44 45 46 47 48 49 50 51

52 53 54 55

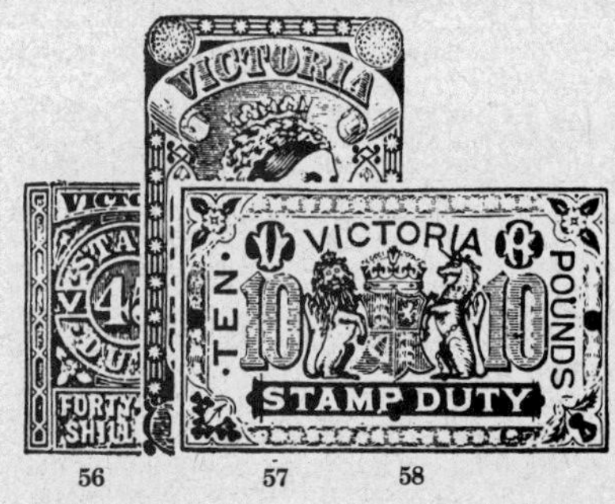
56 57 58

III. **1884–96.** *New printings, all typographed from electrotypes, of* "STAMP DUTY" *designs first issued in* 1879. (*Des Charles Jackson and Ludwig Lang. Dies eng by Charles Jackson, Arthur Williams, Charles Evans and possibly others, supplied* (1879) *by Messrs Sands and McDougall of Melbourne*). *P* 12½. *Wmk sideways save where shown as upright* (U). (*a*) *W* **20** (*V1*).

No.	Type	Description	Unused	Used
255	**44**	1s. ultramarine/*blue* (11.84)	80·00	5·00
256		1s. chalky blue/*lemon* (3.3.85)	75·00	20·00
257	**46**	3s. maroon/*blue* (8.84)	50·00	10·00
258	**48**	5s. reddish purple/*lemon* (6.87)	30·00	10·00
		a. Brown-red/yellow (1.94)	75·00	20·00
259	**52**	£1 orange/*yellow* (9.84)	—	45·00
		a. Reddish orange/yellow (12.90)	£325	45·00
		(*b*) *W* **23** (*V2*)		
260	**45**	1s. 6d. pink (2.85)	£100	19·00
		a. Bright rose-carmine (5.86)	£120	15·00
261	**46**	3s. drab (11.85)	70·00	15·00
		a. Olive-drab (10.93)	65·00	15·00
262	**47**	4s. red-orange (27.5.86)	75·00	12·00
		a. Yellow-orange (S, U)	£100	8·50
263	**48**	5s. rosine (8.5.96)	75·00	19·00
264	**49**	6s. pea-green (12.11.91)	£110	30·00
		a. Apple-green (U) (4.96)	£100	30·00
265	**50**	10s. dull bluish green (10.85)	£120	28·00
		a. Grey-green (9.87)	£100	25·00
266	**51**	15s. purple-brown (12.85)	£250	35·00
267		15s. brown (U) (5.95)	£400	55·00
268	**53**	£1 5s. pink† (U) (6.8.90)	£700	60·00
269	**54**	£1 10s. pale olive† (10.88)	£500	50·00
270	**55**	£2 blue† (8.88)	£700	60·00
271	**56**	45s. lilac† (15.8.90)	—	60·00
272	**57**	£5 pink (10.85)	—	£170
273	**58**	£10 lilac (7.85)	—	70·00
		a. Mauve† (7.93)	—	60·00

Stamps of the above designs printed by lithography or line-engraving, or similar designs not found in the above list should be looked for among the Postal Fiscals.

†Both here and later indicates that prices quoted are for stamps postmarked to order by the Victorian postal authorities for sale in sets.

59

IV. **1896–1900.** *T* **59** *and similar types. W* **23** (*V2*) *sideways* (S) *or upright* (U). *The line-engraved stamps were all printed singly direct from the dies and both the lithographed and typographed stamps were in sheets of* 10 (2 × 5). (i) *Lithographed. Printings of* 1886 *to* 1889.

No.	Description	Unused	Used
274	£25 dull yellowish green (S, U) (1.86)	F.C.	45·00
	a. Dull blue-green (U) (10.88)	F.C.	45·00
275	£50 bright violet (U) (2.86)	F.C.	55·00
	a. Dull purple (U) (10.87)	F.C.	55·00
276	£100 rosine (S, U) (1.86)	F.C.	65·00
	(ii) *Recess-printed. Printings of November* 1890 *to April* 1897		
277	£25 bright blue-green (S, U) (11.90)	F.C.	45·00
278	£50 black-violet (S) (11.90)	F.C.	55·00
279	£100 crimson (aniline) (S, U) (11.90)	F.C.	55·00
	a. Scarlet-red† (1897)	—	£130

For earlier recess-printed printings, see under "POSTAL FISCALS".

No.	Description	Unused	Used
	(iii) *Typographed from electrotyped plates. Printings of November* 1897 *on*		
280	£25 dull blue-green† (U)	—	60·00
281	£50 bright mauve† (U)	—	85·00
282	£100 pink-red† (U) (10.00)	—	£110

Collectors should beware of stamps with cleaned fiscal markings particularly in the higher values. Some of these bear forged cancellations but others, in fraud of the revenue, did genuine postal service.

60 61 62

63 64 65

66 67

(Typo. Previous 2d. and 4d. dies "lined" by Charles Naish; 1s. 6d. des and eng Charles Naish; rest des Philip Astley, probably eng Samuel Reading and supplied by Fergusson and Mitchell)

1886–96. *W* **23** (*V*2) *upright save in ½d.,* 1s. *and high values (excepting the* £6) *where it is sideways. P* 12½.

No.	Type		Unused	Used
283	**60**	½d. lilac-grey (20.8.86)	15·00	3·00
		a. Grey-black	—	35·00
284		½d. pink (15.2.87)	5·00	25
		a. Rosine (*aniline*) (12.89)	4·75	25
		b. Rose-red (5.91)	4·50	20
		c. Vermilion (3.96)	4·75	35
285	**61**	1d. green (26.7.86)	5·25	20
		a. Yellow-green (7.87)	5·25	20
286	**62**	2d. pale lilac (17.12.86)	2·75	20
		a. Pale mauve (1887)	2·50	20
		b. Deep lilac (1888, 1892)	2·50	20
		c. Purple (5.94)	2·75	25
		d. Violet (5.95)	2·50	20
		e. Imperforate (1890)	—	£700
287	**63**	4d. rose-red (1.4.87)	6·50	1·00
		a. Red (1893)	5·75	90
288	**64**	6d. bright ultramarine (27.8.86)	7·50	65
		a. Pale ultramarine (10.87)	7·00	50
		b. Dull blue (2.91)	6·50	50
289	**65**	1s. dull purple-brown (14.3.87)	20·00	2·00
		a. Lake (2.90)	15·00	1·50
		b. Carmine-lake (5.92)	14·00	1·00
		c. Brownish red (1.96)	15·00	1·25
290	**66**	1s. 6d. pale blue (6.88)	£100	65·00
291		1s. 6d. orange (18.9.89)	15·00	4·50
		a. Red-orange	15·00	5·00
292	**67**	£5 pale blue and maroon† (7.2.88)	£950	55·00
293		£6 yellow and pale blue† (1.10.87)	£1100	70·00
294		£7 rosine and black† (17.10.89)	£1300	£100
295		£8 mauve and brown-orange† (U) (2.8.90)	£1400	£125
296		£9 apple-green and rosine† (21.8.88)	£1700	£140

Reprints of the ½d. grey and 1s. 6d. blue were made in 1894–5. They differ from the originals in shade. A £10 (T **67**) was prepared for use, but not issued.

An imperforate sheet of the 2d. was on sale at the Mortlake Post Office in 1890 and a pair was noted in 1902.

68

69

70

(1d. die supplied, des and eng by Samuel Reading; 2½d. and 5d. des by M. Tannenberg; 9d. first printed from the new Reprint plate of 1891. Typo)

1890–96. *New designs and values. P* 12½. (*a*) *W* **20** (*V*1).

No.	Type		Unused	Used
297	**68**	1d. orange-brown/*pink* (16.6.91)	3·50	1·25

This was an emergency printing, caused by a temporary shortage of white *V*2 paper.

(*b*) *W* **23** (*V*2)

No.	Type		Unused	Used
298	**68**	1d. dull chestnut (1.1.90)	2·10	15
		a. Deep red-brown (1.90)	2·10	30
		b. Orange-brown (4.90)	2·10	15
		c. Yellow-brown (4.91)	1·90	15
		d. Brown-red (8.90)	1·90	15
		e. Bright yellow-orange (9.93)	50·00	12·00
		f. Brownish orange (6.94)	1·75	15
299	**69**	2½d. red-brown/*lemon* (18.12.90)	6·00	80
300		2½d. brown-red/*yellow* (1892)	5·50	80
		a. Red/yellow (1893)	5·50	70
301	**70**	5d. purple-brown	6·50	85
		a. Pale reddish brown (1892)	6·00	80
302	**29**	9d. apple-green (18.10.92)	20·00	9·00
303		9d. carmine-rose (18.10.95)	12·00	2·50
		a. Rosine (*aniline*) (1896)	13·00	2·75

The yellow papers used for the 2½d. value differed considerably in tint.

71

72 (*V*3)

(Eng A. Williams (1½d.))

1896 (June)–**1899** (Aug). *W* **72** (*V*3). *Paper supplied by Waterlow and Sons. This paper differs noticeably from the previous De La Rue products. It is less white, softer and generally thicker, and has a coarser grain or mesh than any previous V over Crown paper. It will be noted that some coloured V*2 *papers of earlier manufacture were utilised during this period. T* **60, 65, 71** *and the larger size stamps have the wmk sideways unless marked* U (*upright*). *P* 12½.

No.	Type		Unused	Used
304	**60**	½d. light scarlet (1.7.96)	2·75	15
		a. Carmine-rose (11.97)	3·25	15
		b. Deep carmine-red (*coarse impression*) (1899)	—	75
305	**68**	1d. brown-red (13.6.96)	2·00	10
		a. Brownish orange (11.97)	1·90	10
306	**71**	1½d. apple-green (8.10.97)	4·00	1·50
307	**62**	2d. violet (*shades*) (12.6.96)	2·10	10
308	**39**	3d. ochre (11.96)	7·00	55
		a. Buff (2.98)	6·50	50
309	**63**	4d. red (6.97)	5·00	90
310	**70**	5d. red-brown (7.97)	8·00	95
311	**64**	6d. dull blue (9.96)	6·50	55
312	**29**	9d. rosine (10.96)	15·00	2·00
		a. Rose-carmine (4.98)	—	2·00
		b. Dull rose (6.98)	12·00	2·00
313	**65**	1s. brownish red (3.97)	11·00	1·25
314	**66**	1s. 6d. brown-orange (8.98)	23·00	7·50
315	**42**	2s. blue-green (4.97)	21·00	5·00
316	**43**	2s. 6d. yellow (9.96)	90·00	11·00
		a. Yellow (U) (9.98)	£100	11·00
317	**46**	3s. olive-drab (12.96)	50·00	11·00
		a. Olive-drab (U) (10.98)	50·00	10·00
318	**47**	4s. orange (9.97)	75·00	4·50
319	**48**	5s. rosine (2.97)	75·00	5·00
		a. Rose-carmine (11.97)	75·00	5·00
		b. Rosine (U) (3.99)	75·00	5·50
320	**49**	6s. pale yellow-green† (4.99)	75·00	20·00
321	**50**	10s. grey-green (4.97)	75·00	15·00
		a. Blue-green (7.98)	75·00	15·00
322	**51**	15s. brown† (4.97)	£200	25·00
323	**59**	£25 dull bluish green† (U) (1899)	—	80·00
324		£50 dull purple† (U) (11.97)	—	90·00

73

74

(Des M. Tannenberg. Eng A. Mitchelhill)

1897 (7 Oct). *Charity. W* **72** (*V*3) *sideways. P* 12½.

No.	Type		Unused	Used
325	**73**	1d. (1s.) blue	18·00	18·00
326	**74**	2½d. (2s. 6d.) red-brown	80·00	60·00
325/6 Optd "Specimen"		*Set of* 2	£140	

These stamps, sold at 1s. and 2s. 6d. respectively, paid postage of 1d. and 2½d. only, the difference being given to a Hospital Fund.

1899 (1 Aug)–**1900.** *Colours changed for* ½d., 1d., 1½d. *and* 2½d. *P* 12½.

(*a*) *W* **23** (*V*2)

No.	Type		Unused	Used
327	**71**	1½d. brown-red/*yellow* (1.8.99)	3·00	1·75

(*b*) *W* **72** (*V*3)

No.	Type		Unused	Used
328	**60**	½d. emerald (8.99)	5·00	40
329	**69**	2½d. blue (1.8.99)	5·00	1·75

75 (*V*4)

(*c*) *W* **75** (*V*4)

*This wmk and paper, like V*3, *was supplied by Waterlow and Sons and it continued in use until* 1905. *It was the result of an amended specification. Like the V*3 *paper it has a marked mesh but is whiter, smoother and harder. The* 1s. *and the four higher values have the wmk sideways, the* ½d. *being found with both positions.*

No.	Type		Unused	Used
330	**60**	½d. emerald (1.8.99)	4·75	40
		a. Deep blue-green	5·00	40
331	**68**	1d. rosine (1.8.99)	3·75	10
		a. Rose-red (6.00)	3·75	15
332	**62**	2d. violet (*shades*)(1.8.99)	2·50	10
333	**69**	2½d. blue (2.00)	4·50	1·50
334	**39**	3d. bistre-yellow (9.99)	5·25	55
335	**63**	4d. rose-red (12.99)	4·75	95
336	**70**	5d. red-brown (10.99)	5·50	95
337	**64**	6d. dull ultramarine (2.00)	7·00	55
338	**29**	9d. rose-red (8.99)	8·00	1·50
339	**65**	1s. brown-red (5.00)	10·00	1·40
340	**66**	1s. 6d. orange (12.99)	14·00	4·75
341	**42**	2s. blue-green (6.00)	15·00	4·25
342	**43**	2s. 6d. yellow (1.00)	90·00	10·00
343	**46**	3s. pale olive† (5.00)	£130	12·00
344	**48**	5s. rose-red (4.00)	£100	12·00
345	**50**	10s. green† (3.00)	£130	14·00

76

77

(Eng S. Reading)

1900 (23 May). *Charity. W* **75** (*V*4) *sideways. P* 12½.

No.	Type		Unused	Used
346	**76**	1d. (1s.) olive-brown	35·00	25·00
347	**77**	2d. (2s.) emerald-green	£100	80·00

These stamps were sold for a Boer War Patriotic Fund, on a similar basis to the issue of 1897.

V over Crown Wmks: A Note on "Abnormal" Watermark Positions

It should always be remembered that the block of 120 wmks (12 × 10) in the sheet was designed to fit the normal size stamp in an upright position. *Other* sizes, larger and smaller, were printed, at various times, with the wmk *both* upright and sideways. The following note concerns only varieties as they are found on stamps of normal size.

Inverted Wmks: This description also embraces cases of wmks lying sideways with V at right found on stamps of Type **60** etc. which are of the same dimensions (but reversed) as the usual size stamps. In printings before 1882 all inverted wmks may be regarded as "abnormals". In this period all sheets of 240 wmks were, where necessary, cut into two before printing. From 1882 to mid-1896 the *only* inverted "abnormals" are found in certain of the common values where the area of the printing surface (i.e. 2 plates of 120) more or less equalled the area of the complete sheet of watermarked paper as it was supplied by De La Rue's. This was of 240 wmks, consisting of one pane of 120 wmks over another pane of 120. In this period the sheet of 240 wmks was not cut up before printing from single plates as had been done previously. Where only one plate was employed the sheet was fed in in one direction, removed, dried, and fed in the other direction, giving in the result of 120 normal and 120 inverted wmks. (This fact is of assistance when distinguishing certain Reprints.) From 1896 the same principle applied save that the complete sheets supplied were of 480 wmks so that the only "abnormal" inverteds found are in those cases, e.g. 1d. and 2d. where the stamps were printed from a block of similar size viz. of 4 plates of 120 impressions clamped together.

However, in 1901 to 1912, following a change in postal rates, resulting in a smaller demand for the 2d. value, this was again printed from two plates so that inverted watermarks in this period are always normal.

Sideways Wmks: This description includes upright wmks on stamps of the dimensions of Type **60** etc. They usually arose through the suppliers placing the paper in the wrong direction in the bound books (and later unbound reams) of paper supplied. *Three* periods concern us in this regard.

(i) 1867–1882: Before 1867 paper was supplied in single sheets of 120 wmks and from 1867 in double sheets of 240 wmks. From 1867 to 1882 wherever it was necessary (i.e. where only one plate was used) the double sheets were cut into half before printing. The variety may be found under the following numbers. All are extremely rare—viz. 174, 180, 190, 192, 193, 202, 214, 225.

(ii) 1882–1896. In this period no "abnormal" sideways wmks are met since the paper supplied was not cut up before printing and since the complete sheet supplied was rectangular and *not square* in shape.

(iii) 1896–1912: Here the wmkd paper supplied was of 480 (120 × 4) wmks and such sheets were practically square. One meets "abnormals" under the following numbers, many of these being extremely rare—viz. 304, 305, 307, 308, 312, 313, 328, 330, 331, 332, 334, 338, 356, 357, 359, 366, 367, 368, 371, 373, 386, 400, 405, 407, 414, 417, 445, 447, 451.

Reversed Wmks: These involved a printing on the wrong side of the paper. Since the side which should have been printed was usually "surfaced" to some degree these varieties almost invariably show the impression of the stamp coarser than normally and the back of the stamp smoother and glossier. From 1878 to 1896 the back of the paper supplied by De La Rue was treated with a special preparation to prevent the gum soaking through to the front. This preparation was susceptible to moisture and when printed upon and subsequently exposed to moisture occasionally shed portions of the design, so that in this period such varieties often bear the superficial appearance of having been printed on the gum, whereas in fact, up to July 1912, all gumming was done after printing. Reversed wmks, many of them very rare, have been found under the following Nos.—158, 162, 179, 181, 183, 184, 185, 187, 190, 192, 193, 197, 198, 206, 207 (inverted and reversed), 210, 211, 214, 228, 243, 244, 245, 263, 283, 284, 285, 286, 287, 288, 289, 298, 305, 307, 310, 331, 332, 356, 357, 366, 373, 400, 401, 403, 406, 407, 408, 447, 448—also in certain of the £25, £50 and £100 stamps (in both sections) and in various items in the Postal Fiscal list. In the reversed V over Crown cases—looking through the front of the stamp in a normal upright position—the double side of the "V" will appear on the *right* and not on the left as it should do.

D. THE COMMONWEALTH PERIOD, 1901–12

All postage stamps issued by the States in this period were in reality COMMONWEALTH stamps. This viewpoint has now received official endorsement ("Commonwealth of Australia Philatelic Bulletin" No. 2, October 1953). Prior to the actual coming into being of the Commonwealth it had been agreed between the States that the Postal Services were to be the concern of the Commonwealth and that the postal revenue was to go to it. This decision meant, for Victoria, the separation of the Postal and the Fiscal systems. So long, however, as the Commonwealth lacked printing facilities and a Postal administration of its own the work had to be done by each State on its behalf. Separate series of Postage stamps (for which the State was obliged to account to the Commonwealth) and of Duty stamps (which were to continue as a State concern) therefore became necessary. The first Kangaroo stamps were not issued by the Commonwealth until January 1913, but in the intervening period a long chain of philatelic events had contributed to make this issue possible. From the beginning of 1902 all the stamps of Tasmania and Western Australia were printed in Melbourne, on Victorian paper. Later Papua (1907) and later again South Australia (1909) were added to these. In the same year (1902) the first Commonwealth Postage Dues, printed in Sydney on New South Wales paper, appeared. In 1903 a 9d. stamp of the same "Commonwealth" design was issued in New South Wales and Queensland. In 1905 all States commenced using one or other of four types of Crown over A paper, marginally wmkd "COMMONWEALTH OF AUSTRALIA". In 1909, printed in Melbourne, appeared new bi-coloured Postage Dues, the first stamps to be inscribed "AUSTRALIA". This followed the appointment of J. B. Cooke, the South Australian stamp printer, as Commonwealth Stamp Printer. As from 13.10.10 the stamps of any State could legally be used in any other State, and in April 1911 the first Commonwealth Postal Stationery was issued. In short, in the period 1901 to 1912, although certain States printed and issued postage stamps, this was a privilege, subject at all times to Commonwealth control and direction and conducted, in respect of the nett revenue received, solely for the Commonwealth's benefit.

The Commonwealth was proclaimed as from 1 January 1901. In only three cases in the first issue, viz. the 1d., 2½d. and 5d. values was there sufficient time to alter the dies and produce new plates. In all the other cases the same plates were used as had been employed to produce the 1891 Reprints.

1901 (29 Jan)–**1905.** *P* 12½ *or* 12 × 12½.

(*a*) *Without the word* "POSTAGE" *in the design.* (i) *W* **72** (*V3*)

348	**35**	2s. blue/*pink*	35·00	10·00

(ii) *W* **75** (*V4*) (*sideways on T* **25**)

349	**25**	½d. bluish green	2·00	85
		a. "VICTCRIA"	23·00	19·00
350	**33**	2d. reddish violet	4·00	20
351	**16**	3d. dull orange	10·00	1·25
352	**34**	4d. bistre-yellow	25·00	6·50
353	**17**	6d. emerald	9·00	5·00
354	**30**	1s. yellow	30·00	15·00
355	**19**	5s. pale red and deep blue	45·00	18·00

78

79

80

(*b*) *With the word* "POSTAGE" *in the design. W* **75** (*V4*)

356	**78**	1d. rose (Die I)	1·25	15
		a. Dull red (12.01)	1·25	15
357		1d. rose (Die II) (2.4.01)	1·25	15
		a. Dull red (12.01)	1·25	15
358		1d. pale rose-red (Die III) (3.5.05)	2·00	15
359	**79**	2½d. dull blue (1901)	2·75	25
		a. Deep blue (1902)	2·75	20
360	**80**	5d. reddish brown	4·75	40
		a. Purple-brown (1903)	4·00	40

I

II

III

I and II

III

Three dies of the 1d.: Principal differences are:

I. Horizontal lines over Queen's head fill oval surround under "VICTORIA". Found in two plates employed January 1901–February 1903.

II. Practically all the lines of shading to the left of and on top of the head have been "thinned", giving a lighter appearance. Some lines at the top have been cut away, leaving small white patches, particularly under the "OR". Found in ten plates in use between April 1901 and April 1905.

III. As II but with stop at lower left clearly separated from circle line at its right; spot of colour in shading between "O" and "R"; two lines of shading meet in lower left portion of "P" of "PENNY". Found in twelve plates in use between May 1905 and the end of 1912.

1901 (June). *W* **75** (*V4*). *P* 12 × 12½.

361	**68**	1d. olive (6.6.01)	5·00	3·50
362	**39**	3d. slate-green (20.6.01)	21·00	5·00

These stamps were available for postal purposes to 30 June 1901, afterwards for fiscal purposes only.

81 82

83

84

85

86

87

88

Type A "Postage" 6 mm

89

Type B "Postage" 7 mm

90 91

92

93

1901 (June)–**10**. *Similar to former types but* "POSTAGE" *inserted in design. W* **75** (*V4*) (*sideways on ½d.*, 1½*d.*, £1, £2). (*a*) *P* 12½ *or* 12 × 12½.

363	**81**	½d. blue-green (*shades*) (Die I) (26.6.01)	1·90	15
		a. Blue-green (U)	1·90	15
364		½d. pale blue-green (Die II) (6.04)	2·50	15
365		½d. pale bluish green (Die III) (6.05)	5·00	50
366	**82**	1½d. maroon/*yellow* (9.7.01)	3·00	85
		a. Brown-red/yellow (1901)	2·10	55
		b. Dull red/yellow (1906)	2·10	55
367	**83**	2d. lilac (16.7.01)	1·90	30
		a. Reddish violet (1902)	1·90	30
		b. Violet (1904)	3·00	30
		c. Bright purple (1905)	3·00	50
368	**84**	3d. dull orange-brown (2.7.01)	4·75	55
		a. Chestnut (1901)	4·75	55
		b. Yellowish brown (1903)	4·75	55
369	**85**	4d. bistre-yellow (26.6.01)	4·75	55
		a. Brownish bistre (1905)	5·25	70
370	**86**	6d. emerald (5.7.01)	7·50	80
		a. Dull green (1904)	9·00	85
371	**87**	9d. dull rose-red (5.7.01)	9·50	1·40
		a. Pale red (1901)	10·00	1·25
		b. Dull brownish red (1905)	10·00	1·75
372	**88**	1s. yellow-orange (Type A) (5.7.01)	9·50	1·75
		a. Yellow (1902)	12·00	1·75
373	**89**	1s. yellow (Type B) (4.03)	12·00	3·00
		a. Yellow-orange (1903)	10·00	2·50
374	**90**	2s. blue/*rose* (5.7.01)	22·00	2·00
375	**91**	5s. rose-red and pale blue (5.7.01)	70·00	11·00
		a. Scarlet and deep blue (1902)	65·00	9·00
		b. Rosine and blue (1905)	65·00	9·00
376	**92**	£1 carmine-rose (18.11.01)	£275	£100
377	**93**	£2 deep blue (2.6.02)	£550	£250

(*b*) *P* 11

378	**81**	½d. blue-green (Die I) (9.02)	4·00	75
		a. Blue-green (U)	3·00	20
379		½d. blue-green (Die II)	3·00	25
380		½d. bluish green (Die III)	3·50	50
381	**78**	1d. dull red (Die I)	—	22·00
382		1d. dull red (Die II)	40·00	18·00
		a. Pale red (*aniline*) (3.03)	3·50	75
		b. Pale rose (*aniline*)(1904)	—	3·00
383		1d. pale rose-red (Die III)	38·00	23·00
384	**82**	1½d. dull red/*yellow* (1910)	28·00	28·00
385	**83**	2d. violet (1904)	—	£140
		a. Bright purple (1905)	—	£140
386	**84**	3d. orange-brown (1903)	5·25	3·0
387	**86**	6d. emerald (1903)	9·50	3·7
		a. Dull green (1905)	£250	£16
388	**92**	£1 carmine-red (1905)	£325	£13
389	**93**	£2 deep blue (1905)	£750	£65

(*c*) *Compound or mixed perf* 12½ *and* 11

390	**81**	½d. blue-green (Die I)	15·00	4·0
		a. Blue-green (U) (1903)	—	4·0
391		½d. blue-green (Die II) (1904)	14·00	11·0
392	**78**	1d. dull red (Die I)	—	£15
393		1d. dull red (Die II)	—	£11
394	**82**	1½d. dull red/*yellow*	—	£20
395	**83**	2d. reddish violet	—	£25
396	**84**	3d. orange-brown	—	£20
397	**86**	6d. emerald	—	£20
398	**91**	5s. rose and blue	£800	

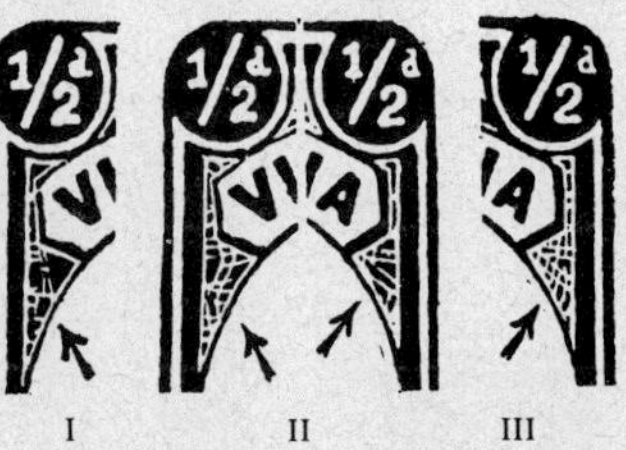

I II III

Three dies of the ½d.; Principal differences are:

I. Outer of two vertical lines of colour to left of "V" is continuou save for a marked break opposite top of "V". Found in two plates i use 1901–May 1904.

II. Outer vertical line to left of "V" is broken in three places; th triangular space S.W. of "V", has also been "opened up" and show more white lines than in I. Found in two plates in use Jun 1904–June 1905.

III. As II but the vertical coloured line to right of the "A" "VICTORIA" (previously broken in the middle) is now broken four or five places. The triangular ornament to S.E. of the same "A has also been "opened up", the white cross-hatching now bein stronger than in I and II. Found in two plates introduced in Jur 1905 and in two subsequent plates introduced late in 1909.

The paper used for the 1½d. value for two printings in 1908– was yellow-buff in colour but in used copies the difference is not marked as to warrant separate description.

There were two main states of the 2d. Die, the original showin the S.E. corner correctly squared and the later showing it damage and blunter. There are other differences. The original state is foun in all printings before April 1904 but not after, and the later stat to a small extent (5 per cent) in the printings before April 1904 an *solely* in the printings from that date.

For the 1s. Type A the same plate was used as for the 1s. "N Postage" of 1901, the words "POSTAGE" being separately punche on. For Type B two new plates, prepared via an etched line-bloc were introduced.

Certain *unlisted shades* (due to their being unsatisfactory) a found *only* punctured O.S. Marked instances of this are found in th 2d., 3d. and 4d. values.

1905–13. *Wmk Crown over A, W* w **11.** I. *Medium paper, supplie like the V4 paper, by Waterlow & Sons.*

(*a*) *P* 12½ *or* 12 × 12½

399	**81**	½d. blue-green (21.10.05)	1·60	
		a. Light bluish green	1·60	
400	**78**	1d. rose-red (*shades*)(16.7.05)	80	
		a. Pale rose (1907)	1·25	
		b. Rose-carmine (9.11)	2·50	
401	**83**	2d. dull mauve (13.9.05)	3·00	
		a. Bright mauve (1906)	3·00	
		b. Reddish violet (1907)	3·00	
		c. Lilac (1910)	2·40	
402	**79**	2½d. blue (*shades*)(4.08)	3·00	
		a. Indigo (1909)	3·00	
403	**84**	3d. orange-brown (11.11.05)	4·00	
		a. Yellow-orange (1908)	5·00	
		b. Dull orange-buff (1909)	4·75	
		c. Ochre (1912)	4·75	
404	**85**	4d. yellow-bistre (15.1.06)	6·00	
		a. Bistre (1908)	6·00	
		b. Yellow-olive (1912)	6·00	
405	**80**	5d. chocolate (14.8.06)	5·00	
		a. Dull reddish brown (1908)	5·00	
406	**86**	6d. dull green (25.10.05)	8·00	
		a. Dull yellow-green (1907)	7·50	
		b. Emerald (1909)	7·50	1·1
		c. Yellowish green (1911)	7·50	1·(
407	**87**	9d. rose-red (11.12.05)	9·50	1·2
		a. Pale salmon-red (1906)	9·50	1·2
		b. Brown-red (1908)	10·00	1·2
		c. Pale dull rose (worn plate)	11·00	2·4
		d. Rose-carmine (new plate) (12.09)	9·50	1·2
408	**89**	1s. yellow-orange (13.2.06)	8·00	2·(
		a. Yellow (1906)	10·00	2·(
		b. Lemon (1908)	12·00	2·(
409	**91**	5s. rose-red and ultramarine (U) (11.07)	70·00	13·(
		a. Rose-red and blue (U) (1912)	80·00	13·(
		b. Rose-red and blue (S)	80·00	16·(
410	**92**	£1 salmon (12.2.07)	£275	£1(
411		£1 dull rose (5.10)	£275	£1(
		a. Deep dull rose (U) (10.11)	£275	£12
412	**93**	£2 dull blue (18.7.06)	£600	£2

Perforations of period 1901–12

In general, up to 1910, five machines were available at any or time—three single-line (two "11" and one "12½") and two vertic combs (12 × 12½). Only single-line machines were used for the 5 £1 and £2 values. The "12½" single line was used on mar occasions for the ½d. and occasionally for other values. The "1 machines were primarily employed for larger size stamps, e. Victorian Duty Stamps, Tasmanian Pictorials and Papua, ar their use for the normal size Victorian postage stamps was in th main restricted to emergencies. At certain periods, e.g. 1909– one encounters the true "compounds" i.e. the products of two singl line machines, 12½ and 11 respectively. For the ½d. the vertic comb 12 × 12½ was also used, particularly in the earlier perio on the sheet turned sideways. In the result the alternate vertic margins between stamps were left imperforate and a single-li machine (either 12½ or 11) was often used to complete the perforating, in the latter case (11) giving us a variety for separate listing. "Mixed" perforations in this period are, like their predecessors of the 70s, the result of the correction—with another machine—of faultily centred lines of perforation (either single-line or comb), the back of these faulty lines being usually pasted over with gummed strips to assist in tearing down the corrected lines.

The rotary-comb machines gauging 11½ × 12¼ were brought over from South Australia by J. B. Cooke when he moved to Melbourne in 1909.

The ½d. perf 11 and the 2½d. and 5s. first printings (all perforated with single line machines) may be met with *full imperforate base margins*. Likewise in the Crown over A issues the ½d. perf 12½ and the 5s. perf 12½ (1912) have been similarly found. Such varieties are, of course, rare.

(*b*) *P* 11

413	81	½d. light bluish green	1·60	15
		a. Blue-green	1·60	15
414	78	1d. rose-red (1905)	1·60	75
		a. Pale rose (1907)	1·75	75
		b. Rose-carmine (1911)	5·00	2·75
415	83	2d. mauve (1906)	—	£150
		a. Reddish violet (1908)	65·00	15·00
		b. Lilac (1910)	19·00	7·50
416	79	2½d. blue (1909)	15·00	7·50
		a. Indigo (1909)	5·50	3·25
417	84	3d. brown (1908)	7·00	5·00
		a. Orange-buff (1909)	14·00	9·50
		b. Dull orange-yellow (1911)	—	£125
		c. Ochre (1912)	6·50	1·50
418	85	4d. yellow-bistre (1908)	7·00	
		a. Yellow-olive (1912)	6·50	3·00
419	80	5d. reddish brown	—	£300
420	86	6d. emerald (1910)	8·50	2·40
		a. Yellowish green (1911)	11·00	2·40
421	87	9d. rose-carmine	—	£325
422	89	1s. yellow-orange	£275	
		a. Yellow	—	£225
423	91	5s. rose-red and ultramarine	70·00	9·50
424	92	£1 salmon (12.2.07)	£325	£100
425	93	£2 dull blue (1.07)	£650	£250

(*c*) *Compound or mixed perfs* 12½ *and* 11

426	81	½d. light bluish green (6.09)	15·00	14·00
427	78	1d. rose-red	32·00	32·00
428	83	2d. mauve	—	£200
429	84	3d. brown (1908)	£190	£225
		a. Ochre (1912)	—	£190
430	85	4d. bistre	—	£275
431	86	6d. yellowish green	—	£300
432	87	9d. dull rose-red	—	£375
433	89	1s. yellow-orange	—	£400

(*d*) *Rotary comb perf* 11½ × 12¼

434	78	1d. pale scarlet-red (2.10)	3·00	20
		a. Rose-red (3.10)	2·25	60
435	83	2d. lilac (*shades*)	3·50	75

II. *On thinner paper, ready gummed with white gum.* (July–Nov 1912).

(*a*) *P* 12½ *or* 12 × 12½

436	81	½d. blue-green	3·00	25
437	78	1d. rose-red	4·50	25
438	83	2d. lilac	20·00	2·25
439	80	5d. brown	6·50	1·75
440	86	6d. emerald	9·50	2·25
441	89	1s. dull yellow (11.12)	15·00	6·00
		a. Pale orange (1.13)	15·00	6·00

(*b*) *P* 11

442	81	½d. blue-green	12·00	7·50
443	78	1d. rose-red	5·00	2·25

(*c*) *P* 11 × 12½

444	81	½d. blue-green	£100	80·00

(*d*) *Rotary comb perf* 11½ × 12¼

445	78	1d. rose-carmine (2.7.12)	2·25	15
		a. Rose-red (10.12)	2·40	15

Two qualities of the "thin" paper were supplied, the first supply (earliest date 2.7.12) being thicker and with a less obvious mesh than the second (earliest date 2.10.12). The ½d. and 1d. are found on both classes of paper, the 2d. on the first only, and the 5d., 6d. and 1s. on the second only. There was a shortage pending the arrival of the second supply, and this gap was filled by the use of the "Stamp Duty" paper next described and the ONE PENNY overprint of 1.7.12. The 5d. perforated O.S. on the thin paper may be met in *dull red-brown*.

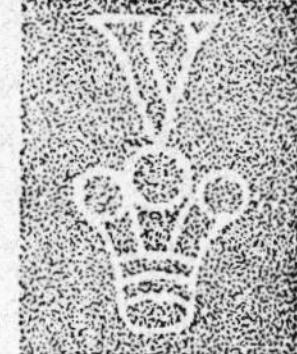

94 (V5)

ONE PENNY

(95)

II. *Printed on "Stamp Duty" paper, W* 94 (V5). *This paper is rather softer and of a more pronounced mesh than the V4 paper.* (Aug–Oct 1912). (*a*) *P* 12½ *or* 12 × 12½.

446	81	½d. bluish green	2·50	35
447	78	1d. rose-carmine (7.8.12)	2·25	20
448	83	2d. reddish violet	2·50	50
		a. Lilac	3·75	1·40
449	87	9d. carmine-red	9·50	2·10

(*b*) *P* 11

450	81	½d. bluish green	12·00	9·00
451	78	1d. rose-carmine (8.12)	20·00	6·50
452	87	9d. carmine-red	13·00	3·50

(*c*) *Compound perf* 11 *with* 12½

453	87	9d. carmine-red	—	£350

This paper was supplied by Spicer Bros at the beginning of 1911 and continued to be used for many years in the production of Duty Stamps for this State.

1912 (1 July). *Surch with T* 95 *in red. Wmk Crown over A. P* 11½ × 12¼.

454	83	1d. on 2d. lilac	70	45

Late in June 1912 the first consignment of "thin" paper was exhausted and the second had not arrived. A further supply of the 1d. value was urgently required, and the expedient of overprinting current 2d. stock was employed to fill the gap. The same reason also produced the 1d. and 2d. overprints of Tasmania and Western Australia, respectively.

POSTAL FISCALS

This section embraces those printings of Duty and Fee stamps made before 1.1.84. These were made available for postal purposes as from 1.1.84. The two series were in concurrent use between December 1879 and 1884.

A. The "STAMP STATUTE" series

This series was first issued on 26 April 1871 and it was in the main used to record the payment of various Court fees. The issue of the series ceased in April 1884.

F 1 F 2 F 3

F 4

1870–83. *Large rectangular stamps of various designs as Types* F 1 *to* F 4. *All save the 3d. and 2s. 6d. (eng by James Turner) have the Queen's head included in the design (eng by William Bell). Typo at the Stamp Printing Office, Melbourne.*

(*a*) *Wmk single-lined numerals* (1, 2, *and* 10) *as used for Postage Stamps* (1863–67). *On Saunders paper unless otherwise noted. Both sideways and upright wmks are found in certain cases*

F 1	1s. blue/*blue* (*p* 13)	25·00	15·00
	a. Perf 12	40·00	15·00
F 2	2s. blue/*green* (D.L.R.) (*p* 13)	50·00	45·00
	a. Perf 12	50·00	45·00
F 3	2s. deep blue/*green* (S), (*p* 13)	50·00	
	a. Perf 12	—	45·00
F 4	10s. brown-olive/*pink* (*p* 13) (6.71)		
F 5	10s. red-brown/*pink* (*p* 13) (1879)	£250	£100
	a. Perf 12		

(*b*) *Wmk V over Crown, W* 20 (*V1*)

The wmk is usually *sideways* but in certain cases the whole of a printing was *upright*. One also meets "abnormal" upright wmks.

F 7	½d. on 1d. pale green (R.) (*p* 13)	12·50	25·00
F 8	1d. pale green (*p* 13)	12·50	15·00
	a. Green (*p* 12½) (U) (1880)	40·00	35·00
F 9	3d. mauve (*p* 13) (9.79)	45·00	75·00
F10	4d. rose (*p* 13)	40·00	55·00
F11	6d. blue (*p* 13) (1871)	30·00	15·00
	a. Dull ultramarine (*p* 13) (1876)	18·00	10·00
	aa. Perf 12	35·00	12·50
F12	1s. blue/*blue* (*p* 13) (6.76)	25·00	
	a. Perf 12	40·00	18·00
	b. Ultramarine/blue (*p* 12½) (1882)	—	25·00
	ba. Perf 12	—	20·00
	c. Deep blue/blue (*p* 12½) (1883)	25·00	15·00
	ca. Perf 12	—	15·00
F13	2s. blue/*green* (*p* 13) (7.76)	50·00	35·00
	a. Perf 12	50·00	
	b. Deep blue/blue-green (*p* 13) (1883)	50·00	40·00
	ba. Perf 12	50·00	45·00
F15	2s. 6d. orange (*p* 13) (7.76)	—	50·00
	a. Perf 12		
	b. Yellow (*p* 13) (11.78)	£100	
	ba. Perf 12	£100	55·00
	c. Orange-yellow (*p* 12½) (1882)	—	60·00
	ca. Perf 12		
F16	5s. blue/*yellow* (*p* 13)	£120	40·00
	a. Perf 12	£130	
	b. Ultramarine/lemon (*p* 12½) (1881)	£120	40·00
F17	10s. brown/*pink* (*p* 13) (8.76)	£250	£100
	a. Purple-brown/pink (*p* 12½) (1882)	£250	£100
	aa. Perf 12		
F18	£1 slate-violet/*yellow* (S, U) (*p* 13) (1871)	£250	
	a. Perf 12 (1880)	£250	
	b. Mauve/yellow (*p* 13) (1873)		
	ba. Perf 12 (1881)	£250	
	bb. Perf 12½ (1882)	£250	80·00
F19	£5 black and yellow-green (*p* 12) (11.71)		
	a. Perf 13		
	b. Perf 12½ (U)		

(*c*) 1882–3: *Wmk V over Crown, W* 23 (*V2*)

F20	1d. yellowish green (*p* 12½)	20·00	25·00
F21	2s. 6d. pale orange-yellow (*p* 12½)	75·00	
F22	£5 black and yellow-green (*p* 12)	—	£400

Reversed watermarks, all rare, have been found under Nos. F12, F15, F18 and F19.

All the values of the "Stamp Statute" series were reprinted in 1891 on paper wmkd V1 (5s., 10s. and £1) and V2 (the rest). The colours used, in all cases, differed radically from the originals. Except for the £5, for which the old electrotypes were used, new plates were made for the Reprints, from dies which showed "die flaws" not to be found on the originals. In 1877 a 12s. 6d. value was prepared for use but although it was placed on sale at the Law Courts and was available there for some months not a single copy was sold, and it was withdrawn. Proofs are known.

B. The "STAMP DUTY" series

This series was used mainly to record the payment of duties on the sale of land, receipts and numerous other documents.

F 5 F 6 F 7 F 8

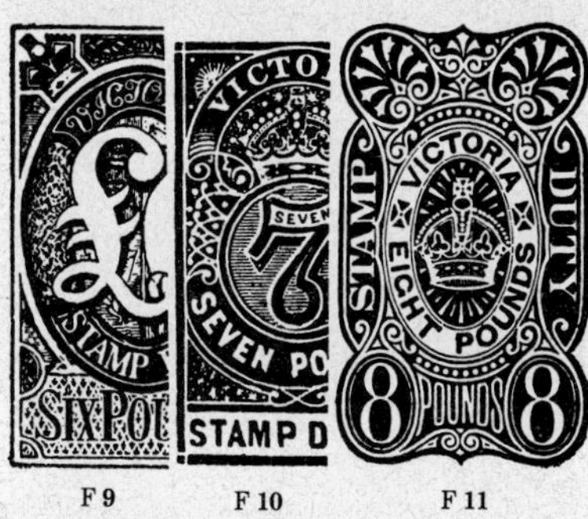

F 9 F 10 F 11

(Dies for these issues (except 1d. of 1880) supplied by Messrs. Sands and McDougall. Des Charles Jackson and Ludwig Lang. Eng Charles Jackson, Arthur Williams and others (See previously). The 1d. of 1880 was eng by Charles Naish)

1879 (Dec)–**1883** (Dec). I. *December* 1879. *Litho Stamp Printing Office, Melbourne. Wmk V over Crown, W* 20 (*V1*). *Sideways unless otherwise indicated* (U). *P* 13.

F23	F 5	1d. blue-green	10·00	7·50
		a. Perf 12	12·00	7·50
F24	45	1s. 6d. rosine	45·00	15·00
		a. Perf 12	—	20·00
F25	46	3s. purple/*blue*	40·00	15·00
		a. Perf 12	—	20·00
F26	47	4s. orange-red	50·00	15·00
		a. Perf 12	50·00	15·00
F27	40	6s. apple-green (U)	60·00	20·00
		a. Perf 12 (U)		
F28	50	10s. brown/*rose* (S, U)	£250	50·00
		a. Perf 12 (S, U)		
F29	51	15s. mauve	—	£100
F30	52	£1 red-orange	—	25·00
F31	53	£1 5s. dull rose (U)	—	60·00
F32	54	£1 10s. deep grey-olive (S, U)	—	50·00
F33		35s. grey-violet (U) F.C. £150		
F34	55	£2 blue	—	50·00
F35	56	45s. dull brown-lilac (U)	—	60·00
F36	57	£5 rose-red (U)	—	£120
F37	F 9	£6 blue/*pink* (U)	—	£350
F38	F 10	£7 violet/*blue* (U)	—	£350
F39	F 11	£8 brownish red/*yellow* (U)	—	£350
F40	—	£9 yellow-green/*green* (U) F.C. £100		£1500

Apart from the "Half-Lengths", the 2d. Queen-on-Throne, the first 1s. Octagonal and the £25, £50 and £100 of 1886–89 these were the only stamps of Victoria to be printed by lithography and its adoption on this occasion was dictated by the necessity for speed of production. *All* the Lithographed stamps can be distinguished from the typographed stamps of the same design by their colours which are highly distinctive. Other differences, of wmk and perf, will be found. Some values, e.g. the 6s., 25s. and 30s. (1884–91) were available for postage over a considerable period.

No. F32 occurs with *reversed* watermark (rare).

II. Dec 1879–1882: *Typographed from electrotypes at Stamp Printing Office, Melbourne*

(i) *Wmk V over Crown, W* 20 (*V1*)

F41	F 5	1d. yellowish green (*p* 13) (12.79)	10·00	7·00
		a. Perf 12	12·00	7·50
F42	F 6	1d. pale bistre (*p* 12½) (6.80)	5·00	1·00
		a. Perf 12	5·00	2·00
F43	F 7	6d. dull blue (*p* 13) (12.79)	20·00	5·00
		a. Perf 12	25·00	12·00
F44	44	1s. deep blue/*blue* (*p* 13) (12.79)	20·00	2·00
		a. Perf 12	20·00	3·00
		b. Bright blue/blue (*p* 12½) (1882)	20·00	2·50
		ba. Perf 12	—	3·00
F45	F 8	2s. deep blue/*green* (*p* 13) (12.79)	40·00	10·00
		a. Perf 12	—	12·00
		b. Indigo/green	30·00	15·00
		ba. Perf 12	50·00	15·00
F46	48	5s. claret/*yellow* (*p* 13) (12.79)	30·00	3·00
		a. Perf 12	30·00	7·50
		b. Pale claret/yellow (*p* 12½) (1880)	30·00	7·50
		ba. Perf 12	50·00	7·50
F47	50	10s. chocolate/*rose* (*p* 13) (S, U) (12.79)	—	50·00
		a. Perf 12 (S, U)		
F48	52	£1 yellow-orange/*yellow* (*p* 12) (1882)		
F49	55	£2 deep blue (*p* 12½) (1881)	—	65·00
F50	58	£10 dull mauve (*p* 12) (1879)		
		a. Deep red-lilac (1882)	—	55·00

(ii) 1882–3: *Wmk V over Crown, W* 23 (*V2*)

F51	F 6	1d. ochre (*shades*) (*p* 12½)	10·00	2·00
		a. Perf 12	10·00	2·00
F52	F 7	6d. ultramarine (*p* 12½)	20·00	3·00
		a. Perf 12	20·00	3·00
F53	55	£2 blue (*p* 12)	—	60·00
F54	57	£5 rose-pink (*p* 12)	—	£120

III. 1879–80: *Recess-printed direct from the die*

(i) *Wmk V over Crown, W* **20** (V1). *P* 13

F55 **59** £25 yellow-green (1879) .. .. F.C. 40·00
a. Deep green (1880) .. .. F.C. 40·00
F56 £50 bright mauve (1879) .. .. F.C. 65·00
F57 £100 crimson-lake (1879) .. .. F.C. 65·00

(ii) 1882–3: *Wmk V over Crown, W* **23** (V2). *P* 12½

F58 **59** £50 dull lilac-mauve .. .. .. F.C. 80·00
F59 £100 crimson .. .. F.C. 95·00
a. Perf 12 .. .. F.C. 95·00

Nos. F44 and F45 occur with *reversed* watermark (both rare).

Reprints of Stamp Duty Series: The only stamps in this series to be reprinted in 1891 (on wmk V2) were the two types of 1d. which by then had become obsolete. Again the colours are distinctive from the originals.

In 1879 certain other values inscribed "STAMP DUTY" (of varying heraldic designs) viz; 7s., 8s., 9s., 11s., 12s., 13s., 14s., 16s., 17s., 18s. and 19s. were prepared for use but were not issued. Proofs are known.

POSTAGE DUE STAMPS

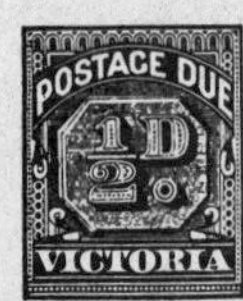

D 1

(Dies eng Arthur Williams (values) and John McWilliams (frame). Typo)

1890–1908. *Type* **D 1.** A. *Wmk V over Crown, W* **23** (V2). *P* 12 × 12½. (i) 1 Nov 1890 (½*d.*, 24.12.90).

D 1 ½d. dull blue and brown-lake .. .. 2·50 1·60
D 2 1d. dull blue and brown-lake .. .. 3·75 1·40
D 3 2d. dull blue and brown-lake .. .. 6·00 1·10
D 4 4d. dull blue and brown-lake .. .. 7·00 1·50
D 5 5d. dull blue and brown-lake .. .. 6·00 1·75
D 6 6d. dull blue and brown-lake .. .. 7·50 1·75
D 7 10d. dull blue and brown-lake .. .. 70·00 35·00
D 8 1s. dull blue and brown-lake .. .. 35·00 6·50
D 9 2s. dull blue and brown-lake .. .. £110 45·00
D10 5s. dull blue and brown-lake .. .. £160 90·00

The blue shades vary considerably.

(ii) 1890–94

D11 ½d. dull blue and deep claret (1890) .. 2·25 1·40
D12 1d. dull blue and brownish red (20.1.93) .. 4·00 1·10
D13 2d. dull blue and brownish red (28.3.93) .. 6·00 90
D14 4d. dull blue and pale claret (28.5.94) .. 6·00 6·00
D2/11 Optd "Specimen" .. .. *Set of* 10 £300

Nos. D1 and D11 were separate printings, both made in December 1890.

(iii) 17 Jan 1895. *Colours changed*

D15 ½d. rosine and bluish green.. .. .. 2·10 1·60
D16 1d. rosine and bluish green.. .. .. 1·60 40
D17 2d. rosine and bluish green.. .. .. 2·25 30
D18 4d. rosine and bluish green.. .. .. 4·50 1·50
D19 5d. rosine and bluish green.. .. .. 4·75 2·50
D20 6d. rosine and bluish green.. .. .. 4·50 2·75
D21 10d. rosine and bluish green.. .. .. 12·00 9·00
D22 1s. rosine and bluish green.. .. .. 7·50 3·25

(iv) 28 March 1895

D23 2s. pale red and yellowish green .. .. 60·00 20·00
D24 5s. pale red and yellowish green .. .. £100 40·00

(v) March 1896 onwards

D25 ½d. pale scarlet and yellow-green .. .. 2·25 1·10
D26 1d. pale scarlet and yellow-green .. .. 1·75 35
D27 2d. pale scarlet and yellow-green .. .. 2·50 30
D28 4d. pale scarlet and yellow-green .. .. 5·50 1·00
D29 5d. pale scarlet and yellow-green .. .. 5·00 2·25

B. *W* **72** (V3). *P* 12½ *or* 12 × 12½. (i) July 1897 onwards

D30 1d. pale scarlet and yellow-green .. .. 2·00 30
D31 2d. pale scarlet and yellow-green .. .. 3·00 30
D32 4d. pale scarlet and yellow-green .. .. 4·50 1·25
D33 5d. pale scarlet and yellow-green .. .. 5·00 1·90
D34 6d. pale scarlet and yellow-green .. .. 5·00 2·75

(ii) July–Sept 1899

D35 1d. dull red and bluish green .. .. 2·50 30
D36 2d. dull red and bluish green .. .. 3·00 35
D37 4d. dull red and bluish green .. .. 5·50 1·10

C. *W* **75** (V4). *P* 12½ *or* 12 × 12½. (i) 1900–1

D38 ½d. rose-red and pale green.. .. .. 2·50 1·00
D39 1d. rose-red and pale green.. .. .. 2·00 35
D40 2d. rose-red and pale green.. .. .. 2·50 30
D41 4d. rose-red and pale green.. .. .. 6·00 1·75

(ii) 1901–2

D42 ½d. pale red and deep green.. .. .. 1·50 1·00
D43 1d. pale red and deep green.. .. .. 1·50 35
D44 2d. pale red and deep green.. .. .. 2·75 35
D45 4d. pale red and deep green.. .. .. 5·00 1·40

(iii) 1902–3

D45*a* ½d. scarlet and deep green.. .. .. — 20·00
D46 1d. scarlet and deep green.. .. .. 2·50 30
D47 2d. scarlet and deep green.. .. .. 2·75 30
D48 4d. scarlet and deep green.. .. .. 5·50 1·00
D49 5d. scarlet and deep green.. .. .. 4·00 2·25
D50 1s. scarlet and deep green.. .. .. 8·00 2·75
D51 2s. scarlet and deep green.. .. .. £100 60·00
D52 5s. scarlet and deep green.. .. .. £120 60·00

The deep green of Nos. D45*a*–52 has more "yellow" than that of D42–45.

(iv) 1904

D53 ½d. rosine (*aniline*) and green .. .. 2·75 1·50
D54 1d. rosine (*aniline*) and green .. .. 2·00 40
D55 2d. rosine (*aniline*) and green .. .. 2·50 45
D56 4d. rosine (*aniline*) and green .. .. 6·00 1·50

D. *Wmk Crown over A* (*W* w 11). *P* 12½ *or* 12 × 12½. (i) Jan 1906

D57 ½d. rosine (*aniline*) and pale green .. 3·25 2·40
D58 1d. rosine (*aniline*) and green .. .. 22·00 2·75

(ii) March 1906

D59 ½d. scarlet and pale yellow-green .. 2·00 1·10
D60 1d. scarlet and pale yellow-green .. 2·00 30

(iii) Dec 1906

D61 1d. scarlet (*aniline*) and deep yellow-green 2·25 30
D62 2d. scarlet (*aniline*) and deep yellow-green 3·00 45

(iv) 1907–8

D63 ½d. dull scarlet and pea-green .. .. 2·25 1·10
D64 1d. dull scarlet and pea-green .. .. 2·50 35
D65 2d. dull scarlet and pea-green .. .. 3·75 35
D66 4d. dull scarlet and pea-green .. .. 7·00 3·75

Perf compound 12 × 12½ *with* 11

D67 ½d. dull scarlet and pea-green .. .. £110 65·00

In D59 and D60 the centre is more clearly printed than in the later printings. A 5d. value was prepared and printed on Crown over A paper but was not issued. A few copies are known, some postmarked to order from presentation sets (*Price £1500 mint, £750 used c.t.o.*).

The six former colonies of New South Wales, Queensland, South Australia, Tasmania, Victoria and Western Australia united to form the Commonwealth of Australia on 1 January 1901.

On 1 March 1901 control of the postal service passed to the federal administration. The first national postage due stamps appeared in July 1902, but it was not until January 1913 that postage stamps inscribed "AUSTRALIA" were issued.

Virgin Islands
see British Virgin Islands

Western Australia

PRICES FOR STAMPS ON COVER	
Nos. 1/6	*from* × 4
Nos. 15/32	*from* × 3
Nos. 33/46	*from* × 4
Nos. 49/51	*from* × 5
Nos. 52/62	*from* × 8
Nos. 63/*a*	*from* × 6
No. 67	*from* × 5
Nos. 68/92*a*	*from* × 8
Nos. 94/102	*from* × 30
Nos. 103/5	*from* × 6
Nos. 107/10*a*	*from* × 10
Nos. 111*a*/*b*	—
Nos. 112/16	*from* × 20
Nos. 117/25	*from* × 10
Nos. 126/8	—
Nos. 129/34	*from* × 8
Nos. 135/6	—
Nos. 138/48	*from* × 12
Nos. 151/63	*from* × 4
Nos. 168/9	*from* × 20
Nos. 170/1	*from* × 4
Nos. 172/3	*from* × 40
Nos. F11/22	*from* × 10
Nos. T1/2	—

SPECIMEN OVERPRINTS. Those listed are from U.P.U. distributions between 1889 and 1892. Further "Specimen" overprints exist, but those were used for other purposes.

1

2

3

4

GUM. The 1854 issues are hardly ever seen with gum and so the unused prices quoted are for examples without gum.

(Eng W. Humphrys. Recess P.B.)

1854 (1 Aug). *W* 4 (*sideways*). (*a*) *Imperf.*

1 **1** 1d. black £800 £180

(*b*) *Rouletted* 7½ *to* 14 *and compound*

2 **1** 1d. black £1100 £350

In addition to the supplies received from London a further printing, using the original plate and watermarked paper from Perkins, Bacon, was made in the colony before the date of issue.

The 1d. is also known pin-perforated.

(Litho H. Samson (later A. Hillman), Government Lithographer)

1854 (1 Aug)–**55.** *W* 4 (*sideways*). (*a*) *Imperf.*

3 **2** 4d. pale blue £225 £15
a. Blue £225 £15
b. Deep dull blue £1200 £60
c. Slate-blue (1855) £1100 £60
4 **3** 1s. salmon .. .. — £120
a. Deep red-brown £525 £35
b. Grey-brown (1.55) £425 £30
c. Pale brown (10.55) £300 £25

(*b*) *Rouletted* 7½ *to* 14 *and compound*

5 **2** 4d. pale blue £1100 £37
a. Blue .. .. — £37
b. Slate-blue (1855) .. .. .. — £110
6 **3** 1s. grey-brown (1.55) £1300 £60
a. Pale brown (10.55) £1300 £60

The 1s. is also known pin-perforated.

The 4d. value was prepared from the Perkins, Bacon 1d. plate. A block of 60 (5 × 12) was taken as a transfer from this plate, th frames painted out and then individually replaced by transfer taken from a single impression master plate of the frame. Fou transfers were then taken from this completed intermediate ston to construct the printing stone of 240 impressions. This firs printing stone was used by H. Samson to print the initial supplie in July 1854.

The intermediate stone had carried several transfer errors, th most prominent of which was the "T" of "POSTAGE" sliced at foot which appeared on four positions of the printing stone.

3d. "T" of "POSTAGE" shaved off to a point at foot (R.7/5, 7/10, 7/15, 7/20) £600 £47

The original printing stone also contained three scarce crease transfers, whose exact positions in the sheet have yet to b established.

3e. Top of letters of "AUSTRALIA" cut off so that they are barely 1 mm high .. .. — £600
f. "PEICE" instead of "PENCE" .. .. — £600
g. "CE" of "Pence" close together .. .. — £800

Further supplies were required in January 1855 and Samson successor, A. Hillman, used the original printing stone to produc three further sheets, after which this first stone was discarded. H then returned to the intermediate stone to produce a secon printing stone. On inspection it was found that two of th impressions on the intermediate stone were defective so two ne transfers of the frame, for use in these positions, were prepare Unfortunately when these frames were replaced one was inverte and the other tilted. Each error occurs in four positions on th second printing stone, as do the transfer errors shown on the inte mediate stone.

3h. Frame inverted (R.8/1, 8/6, 8/11, 8/16) .. — £6000
i. Tilted border (R.7/4, 7/9, 7/14, 7/19).. .. £650 £50

None of the creased transfers from the first printing stone appea on the second, which exhibits its own range of similar varieties.

3j. "WEST" in squeezed-down letters and "F" of "FOUR" with pointed foot (R.2/17) £700 £55
k. "ESTERN" in squeezed-down letters and "U" of "FOUR" squeezed-up (R.3/17) .. £1200 £100
l. Small "S" in "POSTAGE" (R.4/17) £700 £55
m. "EN" of "PENCE" shorter (R.6/4) £650 £50
n. "N" of "PENCE" tilted to right with thin first downstroke (R.6/16) £600 £47
o. Swan and water above "ENCE" damaged (R.6/20) £650 £50
p. "F" of "FOUR" slanting to left (R.7/17) .. £650 £50
q. "WESTERN" in squeezed-down letters only 1½ mm high (R.8/17).. .. .. .. £750 £60
r. "P" of "PENCE" with small head (R.9/15) .. £650 £50
s. "RALIA" in squeezed-down letters only 1½ mm high (R.9/16) £700 £55
t. "PE" of "PENCE" close together (R.10/15) .. £650 £50
u. "N" of "PENCE" narrow (R.10/16) £650 £50
v. Part of right cross-stroke and down-stroke of "T" of "POSTAGE" cut off (R.11/15) .. £650 £50
w. "A" in "POSTAGE" with thin right limb (R.11/16) £600 £47

For the third printing in October 1855 the impressions showin the inverted frame were replaced on the printing stone with fres individual transfers of the frame. On two of the positions traces c the original frame transfer remained visible.

3x. Coloured line above "AGE" of "POSTAGE" (R.8/6) £650 £50
y. No outer line above "GE" of "POSTAGE" and coloured line under "FOU" of "FOUR" (R.8/11) £700 £55

The same stone was used for a further printing in December 185 and it is believed that the slate-blue shade occurred from one of th 1855 printings.

The above varieties, with the exception of Nos. 3e/g, also occur o the rouletted stamps.

The 1s. value was produced in much the same way, based on transfer from the Perkins, Bacon 1d. plate.

5

(Litho A. Hillman, Government Lithographer)

1857 (7 Aug)–**59.** *W* 4 (*sideways*). (*a*) *Imperf.*

15 **5** 2d. brown-black/*red* (26.2.58) .. £1700 £50
a. Printed both sides.. .. .. £1900 £80
16 2d. brown-black/*Indian red* (26.2.58) .. — £80
a. Printed both sides.. .. .. £1700 £85
17 6d. golden bronze £2750 £130
18 6d. black-bronze £1600 £60
19 6d. grey-black (1859).. .. .. £1700 £50

(b) Rouletted 7½ to 14 and compound

20 5 2d. brown-black/*red* £2500 £1000
a. Printed both sides .. .. ..
21 2d. brown-black/*Indian red* .. .. — £1200
22 6d. black-bronze £2250 £700
23 6d. grey-black .. .. .. — £750

The 2d. and 6d. are known pin-perforated.

Prices quoted for Nos. 15/23 are for "cut-square" examples. Collectors are warned against "cut-round" copies with corners added.

(Recess in the colony from P.B. plates)

1860 (11 Aug)–**64.** *W* **4** *(sideways). (a) Imperf.*

24 1 2d. pale orange .. .. .. 65·00 50·00
25 2d. orange-vermilion .. .. .. 60·00 45·00
25a 2d. deep vermilion £200 £275
26 4d. blue (21.6.64) £170 £350
27 4d. deep blue £170 £450
28 6d. sage-green (27.7.61) £850 £400
28a 6d. deep sage-green .. .. .. — £475

(b) Rouletted 7½ to 14

29 1 2d. pale orange £300 £130
30 2d. orange-vermilion £375 £140
31 4d. deep blue £1500
32 6d. sage-green £1000 £375

(Recess P.B.)

1861. *W* **4** *(sideways). (a) Intermediate perf* 14–16.

33 1 1d. rose .. .. .. £200 70·00
34 2d. blue .. .. .. £100 38·00
35 4d. vermilion £275 £150
36 6d. purple-brown .. .. .. £250 50·00
37 1s. yellow-green .. .. .. £300 75·00

(b) P 14 at Somerset House

38 1 1d. rose .. .. .. £110 35·00
39 2d. blue .. .. .. 50·00 24·00
40 4d. vermilion .. .. .. £120 95·00

(c) Perf clean-cut 14–16

41 1 2d. blue .. .. .. 60·00 24·00
a. Imperf between (pair) .. ..
42 6d. purple-brown .. .. .. £140 32·00
43 1s. yellow-green .. .. .. £250 42·00

(d) P 14–16 very rough (July)

44 1 1d. rose-carmine .. .. .. £150 22·00
45 6d. purple/*blue* .. .. .. £500 95·00
46 1s. deep green £700 £160

Perkins, Bacon experienced considerable problems with their perforating machine during the production of these stamps.

The initial printing showed intermediate perforation 14–16. Further supplies were then sent, in late December 1860, to Somerset House to be perforated on their comb 14 machine. The Inland Revenue Board were only able to process the three lower values, although the 6d. purple-brown and 1s. yellow-green are known from this perforation overprinted "SPECIMEN".

The Perkins, Bacon machine was repaired the following month and the 6d., 1s. and a further supply of the 2d. were perforated on it to give a clean-cut 14–16 gauge.

A final printing was produced in July 1861, but by this time the machine had deteriorated so that it produced a very rough 14–16.

(Recess D.L.R. from P.B. plates)

1863 (16 Dec)–**64.** *No wmk. P* 13.

49 1 1d. carmine-rose .. .. .. 40·00 8·00
50 1d. lake .. .. .. 40·00 7·00
51 6d. deep lilac (15.4.64) .. .. .. 75·00 30·00
51a 6d. dull violet (15.4.64) .. .. .. 95·00 35·00

Both values exist on thin and on thick papers, the former being the scarcer.

Both grades of paper show a marginal sheet watermark, "T H SAUNDERS 1860" in double-lined large and small capitals, but parts of this watermark rarely occur on the stamps.

(Recess D.L.R. from P.B. plates)

1864 (27 Dec)–**79.** *Wmk Crown CC (sideways on 1d.). P* 12½.

52 1 1d. bistre .. .. .. 38·00 1·40
53 1d. yellow-ochre (16.10.74) .. .. 45·00 5·50
54 2d. chrome-yellow (18.1.65) .. .. 40·00 90
55 2d. yellow .. .. .. 38·00 90
a. Wmk sideways (5.79) .. ..
b. Error. Mauve (1879) £5000 £2500
56 4d. carmine (18.1.65) .. .. .. 50·00 7·50
a. Doubly printed £5000
57 6d. violet (18.1.65) .. .. .. 60·00 9·00
a. Doubly printed .. .. † —
b. Wmk sideways .. ..
58 6d. indigo-violet .. .. .. £225 28·00
59 6d. lilac (1872) .. .. .. £120 9·00
60 6d. mauve (12.5.75) .. .. .. £110 9·00
61 1s. bright green (18.1.65) (H/S S. £85) 80·00 12·00
62 1s. sage-green (10.68) .. .. £200 20·00

Beware of fakes of No. 55b made by altering the value tablet of No. 60.

7

ONE PENNY (8)

(Typo D.L.R.)

1871 (29 Oct)–**73.** *Wmk Crown CC (sideways). P* 14.

63 7 3d. pale brown (H/S S. £75) .. .. 20·00 4·00
a. Cinnamon (1873) .. .. .. 20·00 3·50

1874 (10 Dec). *No. 55 surch with T* **8** *by Govt Printer.*

67 1 1d. on 2d. yellow (G.) .. .. .. £130 45·00
a. Pair, one without surch .. ..
b. Surch triple .. .. .. — £900
c. "O" of "ONE" omitted .. ..

Forged surcharges of T 8 are known on stamps wmk Crown CC perf 14, and on Crown CA, perf 12 and 14.

(Recess D.L.R. from P.B. plates)

1876–81. *Wmk Crown CC (sideways). P* 14.

68 1 1d. ochre .. .. .. 32·00 70
69 1d. bistre (1878) .. .. .. 38·00 2·75
70 1d. yellow-ochre (1879) .. .. .. 32·00 70
71 2d. chrome-yellow .. .. .. 35·00 50
a. Wmk upright (1877) .. .. .. 48·00 85
74 4d. carmine (1881) .. .. .. £200 75·00
75 6d. lilac (1877) .. .. .. 75·00 4·50
a. Wmk upright (1879) .. .. .. £450 15·00
75b 6d. reddish lilac (1879) .. .. .. 75·00 5·50

(Recess D.L.R. from P.B. plates)

1882 (Mar)–**85.** *Wmk Crown CA (sideways). (a) P* 14.

76 1 1d. yellow-ochre .. .. .. 12·00 50
77 2d. chrome-yellow .. .. .. 15·00 50
a. Wmk upright .. .. † —
78 4d. carmine (8.82) .. .. .. 70·00 10·00
a. Wmk upright (1885) .. ..
79 6d. reddish lilac (1882) .. .. .. 70·00 3·50
80 6d. lilac (1884) (H/S S. £75) .. .. 70·00 4·00

(b) P 12 × 14

81 1 1d. yellow-ochre (2.83) £1000 £150

(c) P 12

82 1 1d. yellow-ochre (2.83) .. .. .. 48·00 1·25
83 2d. chrome-yellow (6.83) .. .. .. 60·00 1·25
a. Imperf between (pair) .. ..
84 4d. carmine (5.83) .. .. .. £100 25·00
85 6d. lilac (6.83) .. .. .. £170 19·00

(Typo D.L.R.)

1882 (July)–**95.** *Wmk Crown CA (sideways). P* 14.

86 7 3d. pale brown .. .. .. 8·00 70
87 3d. red-brown (12.95) .. .. .. 8·50 70

The 3d. stamps in other colours, watermark Crown CA and perforated 12, are colour trials dating from 1883.

½ (9) 1d. (10) 1d. (11)

1884 (19 Feb). *Surch with T* **9**, *in red, by Govt Printer.*

89 1 ½ on 1d. yellow-ochre (No. 76) .. .. 13·00 11·00
a. Thin bar .. .. .. 70·00 42·00
90 ½ on 1d. yellow-ochre (No. 82) .. .. 9·00 6·00

Inverted or double surcharges are forgeries made in London about 1886.

The "Thin bar" varieties occur on R12/3, R12/8, R12/13 and R12/18, and show the bar only 0.2 mm thick.

1885 (May). *Nos. 63/a surch, in green, by Govt Printer.*

(a) Thick "1" with slanting top, T **10** (Horizontal Rows 1/5)

91 1d. on 3d. pale brown .. .. .. 27·00 9·00
a. Cinnamon .. .. .. 18·00 7·00
b. Vert pair. Nos. 91/2 .. ..

(b) Thin "1" with straight top, T **11** (Horizontal Row 6)

92 1d. on 3d. pale brown .. .. .. 42·00 9·00
a. Cinnamon .. .. .. 28·00 10·00

12 13 14 15

(Typo D.L.R.)

1885 (May)–**93.** *Wmk Crown CA (sideways). P* 14.

94 12 ½d. yellow-green .. .. .. 1·50 10
94a ½d. green .. .. .. 1·50 10
95 13 1d. carmine (2.90) .. .. .. 3·00 10
96 14 2d. bluish grey (6.90) .. .. .. 6·00 25
96a 2d. grey .. .. .. 5·50 25
97 15 2½d. deep blue (1.5.92) .. .. .. 5·50 35
97a 2½d. blue .. .. .. 6·00 35
98 4d. chestnut (7.90) .. .. .. 6·00 35
99 5d. bistre (1.5.92) .. .. .. 8·00 1·25
100 6d. bright violet (1.93) .. .. .. 14·00 1·00
101 1s. pale olive-green (4.90) .. .. 20·00 2·25
102 1s. olive-green .. .. .. 17·00 2·00
94, 96a, 97a/99, 101 Optd/H/S "Specimen" *Set of* 6 £200

(Recess D.L.R. from P.B. plates)

1888 (Mar–Apr). *Wmk Crown CA (sideways). P* 14.

103 1 1d. carmine-pink .. .. .. 12·00 60
104 2d. grey .. .. .. 25·00 1·00
105 4d. red-brown (April) .. .. .. 80·00 18·00
103/5 H/S "Specimen" .. *Set of* 3 £150

ONE PENNY (16) Half-penny (17)

1893 (Feb). *Surch with T* **16**, *in green, by Govt Printer.*

107 7 1d. on 3d. pale brown (No. 63) .. .. 8·50 2·75
108 1d. on 3d. cinnamon (No. 63a) .. .. 8·50 3·00
a. Double surcharge £450
109 1d. on 3d. pale brown (No. 86) .. .. 26·00 4·25

1895 (21 Nov). *Surch with T* **17** *by Govt Printer. (a) In green.*

110 7 ½d. on 3d. pale brown (No. 63) .. .. 7·50 13·00
110a ½d. on 3d. cinnamon (No. 63a) .. .. 5·50 7·50
b. Surcharge double £350

(b) In red and in green

111a 7 ½d. on 3d. cinnamon (No. 63a) .. .. 90·00
111b ½d. on 3d. red-brown (No. 87) .. .. 50·00

Green was the adopted surcharge colour but a trial had earlier been made in red on stamps watermarked Crown CC. As they proved unsatisfactory they were given another surcharge in green. The trial stamps were inadvertently issued and, to prevent speculation, a further printing of the duplicated surcharge was made, but on both papers, Crown CC (No. 111a) and Crown CA (No. 111b).

18 19 20 21

(Typo D.L.R.)

1898 (Dec)–**1907.** *Wmk W Crown A, W* **18**. *P* 14.

112 13 1d. carmine .. .. .. 2·50 10
113 14 2d. bright yellow (1.99) .. .. .. 5·00 25
114 19 2½d. blue (1.01) .. .. .. 5·00 30
115 20 6d. bright violet (10.06) .. .. .. 12·00 50
116 21 1s. olive-green (4.07) .. .. .. 18·00 3·50

22 23 24 25 26 27 28 29 30 31 32 33

(Typo Victorian Govt Printer, Melbourne)

1902 (Oct)–**12.** *Wmk V and Crown, W* **33** *(sideways on horiz designs).*

(a) P 12½ *or* 12½ × 12 *(horiz),* 12 × 12½ *(vert)*

117 22 1d. carmine-rose (1.03) .. .. .. 2·50 10
a. Wmk upright (10.02) .. .. .. 4·50 30
118 23 2d. yellow (4.1.03) .. .. .. 2·75 15
a. Wmk upright (12.7.04) .. .. — 50
119 24 4d. chestnut (4.03) .. .. .. 5·50 90
a. Wmk upright .. ..
120 15 5d. bistre (4.9.05) .. .. .. 60·00 38·00
121 25 8d. apple-green (3.03) .. .. .. 20·00 2·50
122 26 9d. yellow-orange (5.03) .. .. .. 26·00 4·25
a. Wmk upright (11.03) .. .. .. 35·00 14·00
123 27 10d. red (3.03) .. .. .. 27·00 4·50
124 28 2s. bright red/*yellow* .. .. .. 65·00 14·00
a. Wmk sideways .. .. .. — 16·00
b. Orange/yellow (7.06) .. .. .. 48·00 8·50
c. Brown-red/yellow (5.11) .. .. .. 48·00 8·50
125 29 2s. 6d. deep blue/*rose* .. .. .. 40·00 10·00
126 30 5s. emerald-green .. .. .. 80·00 18·00
127 31 10s. deep mauve .. .. .. £180 48·00
a. Bright purple (1910) .. .. .. £200 60·00
128 32 £1 orange-brown (1.11.02) £350 £150
a. Orange (10.7.09) £700 £300

(b) P 11
129 **22** 1d. carmine-rose .. .. .. 80·00 5·50
a. Wmk upright
130 **23** 2d. yellow .. .. £100 6·00
a. Wmk upright
131 **24** 4d. chestnut £300 £100
132 **15** 5d. bistre .. .. 42·00 17·00
133 **26** 9d. yellow-orange .. .. .. 60·00 35·00
134 **28** 2s. bright red/*yellow* .. .. .. £100 55·00
a. Orange/yellow £200 £100

(c) *Perf compound of* 12½ *or* 12 *and* 11
135 **22** 1d. carmine-rose .. .. .. — £160
136 **23** 2d. yellow .. .. — £200
137 **24** 4d. chestnut .. ..

Type **22** is similar to Type **13** but larger.

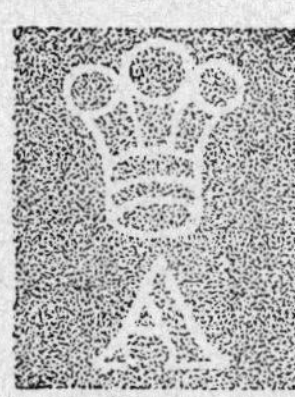
34

35

1905–12. *Wmk Crown and A,* W **34** *(sideways).*

(a) *P* 12½ *or* 12½ × 12 *(horiz),* 12 × 12½ *(vert)*
138 **12** ½d. green (6.10) .. .. .. 1·25 30
139 **22** 1d. rose-pink (10.05) .. .. .. 2·75 10
a. Wmk upright (1.06) .. .. 2·25 10
b. Carmine (1909) .. .. .. 3·00 15
c. Carmine-red (1912) .. .. 3·00 25
140 **23** 2d. yellow (15.11.05) .. .. 1·50 15
a. Wmk upright (4.10) .. ..
141 **7** 3d. brown (2.06) .. .. .. 4·50 50
142 **24** 4d. bistre-brown (12.06) .. .. 5·50 90
a. Pale chestnut (1908) .. .. 8·50 60
b. Bright brown-red (14.10.10) .. 7·50 60
143 **15** 5d. pale olive-bistre (8.05) .. .. 11·00 1·25
a. Olive-green (1.09) .. .. .. 11·00 1·25
b. Pale greenish yellow (5.12) .. 48·00 32·00
144 **25** 8d. apple-green (22.4.12) .. .. 17·00 7·50
145 **26** 9d. orange (11.5.06) .. .. .. 18·00 3·50
a. Red-orange (6.10) .. .. .. 27·00 3·50
b. Wmk upright (7.12) .. .. 35·00 10·00
146 **27** 10d. rose-orange (16.2.10) .. .. 18·00 7·00
148 **30** 5s. emerald-grn *(wmk upright)* (9.07) 60·00 35·00

(b) *P* 11
150 **12** ½d. green .. ..
151 **22** 1d. rose-pink .. .. 8·50 1·75
a. Carmine-red .. .. .. 8·00 90
b. Wmk upright .. .. .. 8·00 2·50
152 **23** 2d. yellow .. .. 10·00 3·00
153 **7** 3d. brown .. .. 8·00 2·00
154 **24** 4d. yellow-brown .. .. .. £350 85·00
a. Pale chestnut .. .. ..
155 **15** 5d. pale olive-bistre .. .. .. 28·00 10·00
a. Olive-green .. .. .. 16·00 4·00
157 **26** 9d. orange .. .. 70·00 75·00
a. Red-orange .. .. .. — 65·00
b. Wmk upright (inverted) .. ..

(c) *Perf compound of* 12½ *or* 12 *and* 11
161 **22** 1d. rose-pink .. .. £150 75·00
162 **23** 2d. yellow .. .. £170 80·00
163 **7** 3d. brown .. .. £190 85·00
164 **26** 9d. red-orange .. ..

Only six examples are known of No. 157b, all used in 1912 or 1913.

1912 (Mar). *Wmk Crown and A (sideways).* W **35.** *P* 11½ × 12.
168 **20** 6d. bright violet .. .. .. 9·50 2·50
169 **21** 1s. sage-green .. .. 20·00 4·50
a. Perf 12½ (single line) .. ..

1912 (7 Aug). W **34** *(sideways). Thin paper and white gum (as Victoria).*
170 **7** 3d. brown (*p* 12½) .. .. .. 23·00 23·00
a. Wmk upright .. .. .. 23·00 23·00
171 3d. brown (*p* 11) .. .. ..
a. Wmk upright .. .. ..

ONE PENNY

(36)

1912 (6 Nov). *Nos.* 140 *and* 162 *surch with T* **36** *in Melbourne.*

(a) *P* 12½ *or* 12 × 12½
172 **23** 1d. on 2d. yellow 80 30
a. Wmk upright .. .. .. 1·00 45

(b) *Perf compound of* 12½ *and* 11
173 **23** 1d. on 2d. yellow £275

POSTAL FISCAL STAMPS

By the Post and Telegraph Act of 5 September 1893 the current issue of fiscal stamps up to and including the 1s. value, Nos. F11/15, was authorised for postal use.

These stamps had been initially supplied, for fiscal purposes, in February 1882 and had been preceded by a series of "I R" surcharges and overprints on postage stamps which were in use for a period of about six months. Examples of these 1881–82 provisionals can be found postally used under the terms of the 1893 Act but, as they had not been current for fiscal purposes for over eleven years, we no longer list them.

F 3

(Typo D.L.R.)

1893 (5 Sept). *Definitive fiscal stamps of Feb* 1882. *Wmk CA over Crown. P* 14.
F11 **F 3** 1d. dull purple .. .. 4·00 55
F12 2d. dull purple .. .. 55·00 30·00
F13 3d. dull purple .. .. 15·00 1·75
F14 6d. dull purple .. .. 20·00 2·75
F15 – 1s. dull purple .. .. 25·00 3·00

The 1s. value is as Type **F 3** but with rectangular outer frame and circular frame surrounding swan.

Higher values in this series were not validated by the Act for postal use.

Two varieties of watermark exist on these stamps. Initial supplies showed an indistinct watermark with the base of the "A" 4 mm wide. From 1896 the paper used showed a clearer watermark on which the base of the "A" was 5 mm wide.

1897. *Wmk W Crown A,* W **18.** *P* 14.
F19 **F 3** 1d. dull purple .. .. 3·25 65
F20 3d. dull purple .. .. 7·50 85
F21 6d. dull purple .. .. 9·00 1·25
F22 – 1s. dull purple .. .. 17·00 2·50

TELEGRAPH STAMPS USED FOR POSTAGE

The 1d. Telegraph stamps were authorised for postal purposes from 25 October 1886.

T 1

1886 (25 Oct). *Wmk Crown CC.*
T1 **T 1** 1d. bistre (*p* 12½) .. .. .. 14·00 2·50
T2 1d. bistre (*p* 14) .. .. .. 16·00 4·00

Copies of a similar 6d. value are known postally used, but such use was unauthorised.

OFFICIAL STAMPS

Stamps of the various issues from 1854–85 are found with a circular hole punched out, the earlier size being about 3 mm. in diameter and the later 4 mm. These were used on official correspondence by the Commissariat and Convict Department, branches of the Imperial administration separate from the colonial government. This system of punching ceased by 1886. Subsequently many stamps between Nos. 94 and 148 may be found punctured, "PWD", "WA" or "OS".

The six former colonies of New South Wales, Queensland, South Australia, Tasmania, Victoria and Western Australia united to form the Commonwealth of Australia on 1 January 1901.

On 1 March 1901 control of the postal service passed to the federal administration. The first national postage due stamps appeared in July 1902, but it was not until January 1913 that postage stamps inscribed "AUSTRALIA" were issued.

Western Samoa *see* Samoa

see Samoa

Zambia

(*formerly* Northern Rhodesia)

INDEPENDENT

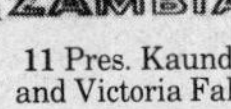

11 Pres. Kaunda and Victoria Falls

12 College of Further Education, Lusaka

(Des M. Goaman (3d., 6d.), Mrs. G. Ellison (1s. 3d.). Photo Harrison)

1964 (24 Oct). *Independence. T* **11/12** *and similar vert design. P* 13½ × 14½ *(6d.) or* 14½ × 13½ *(others).*
91 3d. sepia, yellow-green and blue 10 10
92 6d. deep violet and yellow 10 10
93 1s. 3d. red, black, sepia and orange .. 10 15
91/3 .. .. *Set of* 3 25 20

Design:—1s. 3d. Barotse dancer.

14 Maize-Farmer and Silo

15 Health—Radiographer

21 Fishing at Mpulungu

22 Tobacco Worker

(Des Mrs. G. Ellison. Photo Harrison)

1964 (24 Oct). *T* **14/15, 21/2** *and similar designs. P* 14½ *(½d. to 4d.),* 14½ × 13½ *(1s. 3d., 2s. and* £1) *or* 13½ × 14½ *(others).*
94 ½d. red, black and yellow-green 10 20
95 1d. brown, black and bright blue 10 10
96 2d. red, deep brown and orange 10 10
97 3d. black and red 10 10
98 4d. black, brown and orange 15 10
99 6d. orange, deep brown & deep bluish green 15 10
100 9d. carmine, black and bright blue 15 10
101 1s. black, yellow-bistre and blue 15 10
102 1s. 3d. light red, yellow, black and blue .. 20 10
103 2s. bright blue, black, deep brown & orange 25 10
104 2s. 6d. black and orange-yellow 40 35
105 5s. black, yellow and green.. .. .. 75 45
106 10s. black and orange .. .. .. 2·25 2·25
107 £1 black, brown, yellow and red .. .. 2·75 3·75
94/107 .. .. *Set of* 14 6·50 7·00

Designs: *Vert (as T* **15**)—2d. Chinyau dancer; 3d. Cotton-picking. *(As T* **22**)—2s. Tonga basket-making; £1 Makishi dancer. *Horiz (as T* **14**)—4d. Angoni bull. *(As T* **21**)—6d. Communications, old and new; 9d. Zambezi sawmills and Redwood flower; 2s. 6d. Luangwa Game Reserve; 5s. Education—student; 10s. Copper mining.

Nos. 94/5 and 97 exist in coils, constructed from normal sheets.

28 I.T.U. Emblem and Symbols

30 State House, Lusaka

34 W.H.O. Building and U.N. Flag

29 I.C.Y. Emblem

(Photo Harrison)

1965 (26 July). *I.T.U. Centenary. P* 14 × 14½.
108 **28** 6d. light reddish violet and gold . .. 15 1
109 2s. 6d. brownish grey and gold 50 7

(Photo Harrison)

1965 (26 July). *International Co-operation Year. P* 14½.
110 **29** 3d. turquoise and gold 10 1
111 1s. 3d. ultramarine and gold 35 4

(Des Mrs. G. Ellison. Photo Harrison)

1965 (18 Oct). *First Anniv of Independence. T* **30** *and similar multicoloured designs. No wmk. P* 13½ × 14½ *(3d.),* 14 × 13½ *(6d.) or* 13½ × 14 *(others).*
112 3d. Type **30** 10 1
113 6d. Fireworks, Independence Stadium .. 10 1
a. Bright purple (fireworks) omitted .. 38·00
114 1s. 3d. Clematopsis *(vert)* 10 1
115 2s. 6d. *Tithonia diversifolia (vert)* 25 5
112/15 .. .. *Set of* 4 40 6

(Des M. Goaman. Photo Harrison)

966 (18 May). *Inauguration of W.H.O. Headquarters, Geneva.* P 14½.
16 **34** 3d. lake-brown, gold and new blue .. 15 10
a. Gold omitted .. 60·00
17 1s. 3d. gold, new blue & deep bluish vio 30 30

35 University Building **36** National Assembly Building

(Des Mrs. G. Ellison. Photo Harrison)

966 (12 July). *Opening of Zambia University.* P 14½.
18 **35** 3d. blue-green and copper-bronze .. 10 10
19 1s. 3d. reddish violet and copper-bronze 10 10

(Des Mrs. G. Ellison. Photo Harrison)

967 (2 May). *Inauguration of National Assembly Building.* P 14½.
20 **36** 3d. black and gold .. 10 10
21 6d. olive-green and gold .. 10 10

37 Airport Scene

(Des Mrs. G. Ellison. Photo Harrison)

967 (2 Oct). *Opening of Lusaka International Airport.* P 13½ × 14½.
22 **37** 6d. violet-blue and copper-bronze .. 10 10
23 2s. 6d. brown and copper-bronze .. 20 45

38 Youth Service Badge **39** "Co-operative Farming"

(Des Mrs. G. Ellison. Photo Harrison)

1967 (23 Oct). *National Development.* T **38/9** *and similar designs.* P 13½ × 14½ (6d., 1s. 6d.) or 14½ × 13½ (*others*).
124 4d. black, red and gold .. 10 10
125 6d. black, gold and violet-blue .. 10 10
126 9d. black, grey-blue and silver .. 15 10
127 1s. multicoloured .. 20 10
128 1s. 6d. multicoloured .. 30 60
124/8 .. *Set of* 5 75 80
Designs: *Vert*—9d "Communications"; 1s. Coalfields. *Horiz*—1s. 6d. Road link with Tanzania.

(New Currency. 100 ngwee=1 kwacha)

43 Lusaka Cathedral **44** Baobab Tree

52 Chokwe Dancer **53** Kafue Railway Bridge

(Des Mrs. G. Ellison. Photo Harrison)

1968 (16 Jan). *Decimal Currency.* T **43/4, 52/3** *and similar designs.* P 13½ × 14½ (1, 3, 15, 50 *n.*) or 14½ × 13½ (*others*).
129 1 n. multicoloured .. 10 10
a. Copper-bronze (including value) omitted 60·00
b. Ultramarine (windows) omitted .. 60·00
130 2 n. multicoloured .. 10 10
131 3 n. multicoloured .. 10 10
132 5 n. bistre-brown and copper-bronze .. 10 10
133 8 n. multicoloured .. 15 10
a. Copper-bronze (background) omitted
b. Blue (of costumes) omitted .. 38·00
134 10 n. multicoloured .. 25 10
135 15 n. multicoloured .. 2·00 10
136 20 n. multicoloured .. 1·00 10
137 25 n. multicoloured .. 25 10
138 50 n. chocolate, red-orange & copper-bronze .. 30 15
139 1 k. royal blue and copper-bronze .. 2·50 20
140 2 k. black and copper-bronze .. 2·25 1·25
129/40 .. *Set of* 12 8·00 1·75
Designs: *Horiz* (*as T* **43**)—3 n. Zambia Airways jetliner. (*As T* **53**)—15 n. *Nudaurelia zambesina*; 2 k. Eland. *Vert* (*as T* **44**)—5 n National Museum, Livingstone; 8 n. Vimbuza dancer; 10 n. Tobacco picking. (*As T* **52**)–20 n. South African Crowned Cranes; 25 n. Angoni warrior.
All values exist with PVA gum as well as gum arabic.
Nos. 129/30 and 132 exist in coils, constructed from normal sheets.

55 Ndola on Outline of Zambia **56** Human Rights Emblem and Heads

(Des Mrs G. Ellison. Photo Harrison)

1968 (29 June). *Trade Fair, Ndola.* P 14.
141 **55** 15 n. green and gold .. 10 10

(Des Mrs. G. Ellison. Photo and die-stamped (gold emblem) Harrison)

1968 (23 Oct). *Human Rights Year.* P 14.
142 **56** 3 n. deep blue, pale violet and gold .. 10 10

57 W.H.O. Emblem **58** Group of Children

(Des Mrs. G. Ellison. Photo and die-stamped (gold staff and "20") Harrison)

1968 (23 Oct). *20th Anniv of World Health Organization.* P 14.
143 **57** 10 n. gold and bluish violet .. 10 10

(Des Mrs. G. Ellison. Photo and die-stamped (gold children) Harrison)

1968 (23 Oct). *22nd Anniv. of U.N.I.C.E.F.* P 14.
144 **58** 25 n. black, gold and ultramarine .. 15 60

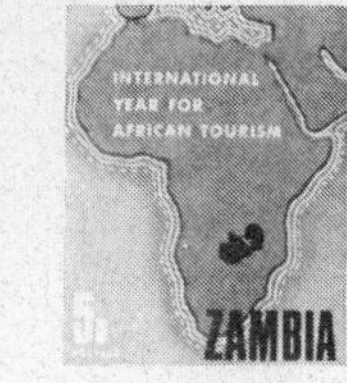

59 Copper Miner **61** Zambia outlined on Map of Africa

(Des Mrs. G. Ellison. Photo Harrison)

1969 (18 June). *50th Anniv of International Labour Organization.* T **59** *and similar design.* P 14½ × 13½ (3 *n.*) or 13½ × 14½ (25 *n.*).
145 3 n. copper-bronze and deep violet .. 10 10
146 25 n. pale yell, copper-bronze & blackish brn 35 60
Design: *Horiz*—25 n. Poling a furnace.
A used example of No. 145 exists with the copper-bronze omitted.

(Des Mrs. G. Ellison. Photo Harrison)

1969 (23 Oct). *International African Tourist Year.* T **61** *and similar multicoloured designs.* P 14 × 14½ (5 *n.*, 25 *n.*) or 14½ × 14 (*others*).
147 5 n. Type **61** .. 10 10
148 10 n. Waterbuck (*horiz*) .. 15 10
149 15 n. Golden Perch (*horiz*) .. 35 35
150 25 n. Carmine Bee Eater .. 1·00 80
147/50 .. *Set of* 4 1·40 1·10

PREVENTIVE MEDICINE

65 Satellite "Nimbus 3" orbiting the Earth **66** Woman collecting Water from Well

(Des Mrs. G. Ellison. Litho Enschedé)

1970 (23 Mar). *World Meteorological Day.* P 13 × 10½.
151 **65** 15 n. multicoloured .. 15 40

(Des V. Whiteley (from local designs). Litho B.W.)

1970 (4 July). *Preventive Medicine.* T **66** *and similar vert designs.* P 13½ × 12.
152 3 n. multicoloured .. 10 10
153 15 n. multicoloured .. 10 15
154 25 n. greenish blue, rosine and sepia .. 20 30
152/4 .. *Set of* 3 30 45
Designs:—15 n. Child on scales; 25 n. Child being immunized.

67 "Masks" (mural by Gabriel Ellison **68** Ceremonial Axe

(Des Mrs. G. Ellison. Litho Harrison)

1970 (8 Sept). *Conference of Non-Aligned Nations.* P 14 × 14½.
155 **67** 15 n. multicoloured .. 15 20

(Des Mrs. G. Ellison. Litho D.L.R.)

1970 (30 Nov). *Traditional Crafts.* T **68** *and similar multicoloured designs.* P 13½ (15 *n.*), 12½ (25 *n.*) or 14 (*others*).
156 3 n. Type **68** .. 10 10
157 5 n. Clay Smoking-Pipe Bowl .. 15 10
158 15 n. Makishi Mask (30 × 47 *mm*) .. 35 40
159 25 n. Kuomboka Ceremony (72 × 19 *mm*) .. 70 1·00
156/9 .. *Set of* 4 1·10 1·40
MS160 133 × 83 mm. Nos. 156/9. Imperf. .. 7·00 11·00

69 Dag Hammarskjöld and U.N. General Assembly

(Des J.W. Litho Questa)

1971 (18 Sept). *Tenth Death Anniv of Dag Hammarskjöld.* T **69** *and similar horiz designs, each with portrait of Hammarskjöld. Multicoloured.* P 13½.
161 4 n. Type **69** .. 10 10
162 10 n. Tail of aircraft .. 10 10
163 15 n. Dove of Peace .. 15 25
164 25 n. Memorial tablet .. 35 1·50
161/4 .. *Set of* 4 55 1·75

70 Red-breasted Bream **71** North African Crested Porcupine

(Des G. Drummond. Litho J.W.)

1971 (10 Dec). *Fish.* T **70** *and similar horiz designs. Multicoloured.* P 13½.
165 4 n. Type **70** .. 15 10
166 10 n. Green-headed Bream .. 25 25
167 15 n. Tiger fish .. 50 1·50
165/7 .. *Set of* 3 80 1·75

(Des and litho J.W.)

1972 (15 Mar). *Conservation Year* (1*st issue*). T **71** *and similar multicoloured designs.* P 13½.
168 4 n. Cheetah (58 × 21 *mm*) .. 20 25
169 10 n. Lechwe (58 × 21 *mm*) .. 50 60
170 15 n. Type **71** .. 80 85
171 25 n. African Elephant .. 2·00 2·25
168/71 .. *Set of* 4 3·25 3·50

(Des and litho J.W.)

1972 (30 June). *Conservation Year (2nd issue). Designs similar to T* **71**. *Multicoloured. P* 13½.

172	4 n. Soil conservation	20	20
173	10 n. Forestry	40	45
174	15 n. Water (58 × 21 *mm*)	60	70
175	25 n. Maize (58 × 21 *mm*)	1·25	1·40
172/5	*Set of* 4	2·25	2·50

72 Giraffe and Common Zebra

(Des and litho J.W.)

1972 (30 June). *National Parks. Sheet* 114 × 140 *mm containing T* **72** *and similar vert designs. Multicoloured. P* 13½.

MS176 10 n. (× 4). Type **72**; Black Rhinoceros; Hippopotamus and Common Panther; Lion .. 7·50 13·00

Each design includes part of a map showing Zambian National Parks, the four forming a composite design.

73 Zambian Flowers

(Des and litho J.W.)

1972 (22 Sept). *Conservation Year (3rd issue). T* **73** *and similar horiz designs. Multicoloured. P* 13½.

177	4 n. Type **73**	30	30
178	10 n. Citrus Swallowtail Butterfly	70	70
179	15 n. Bees	1·25	1·25
180	25 n. Red Locusts	2·00	2·00
177/80	*Set of* 4	3·75	3·75

74 Mary and Joseph

75 *Oudenodon* and *Rubidgea*

(Des V. Whiteley. Litho Questa)

1972 (1 Dec). *Christmas. T* **74** *and similar horiz designs. Multicoloured. P* 14.

181	4 n. Type **74**	10	10
182	9 n. Mary, Joseph and Jesus	10	10
183	15 n. Mary, Jesus and the shepherds	10	10
184	25 n. The Three Wise Men	20	40
181/4	*Set of* 4	35	50

(Des Mrs. G. Ellison; adapted J.W. Litho Questa)

1973 (1 Feb). *Zambian Prehistoric Animals. T* **75** *and similar horiz designs. Multicoloured. P* 14 × 13½ (4 *n.*) *or* 13½ × 14 (*others*).

185	4 n. Type **75**	85	85
186	9 n. Broken Hill Man	90	90
187	10 n. *Zambiasaurus*	1·00	1·50
188	15 n. *Luangwa drysdalli*	1·10	2·00
189	25 n. *Glossopteris*	1·25	3·00
185/9	*Set of* 5	4·50	7·50

76 "Dr. Livingstone, I Presume"

(Des J.W. Litho Format)

1973 (1 May). *Death Centenary of Dr. Livingstone. T* **76** *and similar horiz designs. Multicoloured. P* 13½.

190	3 n. Type **76**	25	15
191	4 n. Scripture Lesson	25	15
192	9 n. Victoria Falls	50	40
193	10 n. Scattering slavers	50	45
194	15 n. Healing the sick	80	1·25
195	25 n. Burial place of Livingstone's heart	1·00	2·00
190/5	*Set of* 6	3·00	4·00

77 Parliamentary Mace

(Des Mrs. G. Ellison. Litho Questa)

1973 (24 Sept). *Third Commonwealth Conference of Speakers and Presiding Officers, Lusaka. P* 13½.

196	**77**	9 n. multicoloured	80	65
197		15 n. multicoloured	1·00	1·25
198		25 n. multicoloured	1·50	2·00
196/8		*Set of* 3	3·00	3·50

78 Inoculation

79 U.N.I.P. Flag

(Des Mrs. G. Ellison. Litho Questa)

1973 (16 Oct). 25*th Anniv of W.H.O. T* **78** *and similar multicoloured designs. P* 14.

199	4 n. Mother washing baby (*vert*)	48·00	23·00
200	9 n. Nurse weighing baby (*vert*)	45	1·00
201	10 n. Type **78**	50	1·25
202	15 n. Child eating meal	90	2·75
199/202	*Set of* 4	48·00	25·00

Only a small quantity of No. 199 was produced, and most examples were issued to post offices for local use.

(Des Mrs. G. Ellison. Litho Questa)

1973 (13 Dec). 1*st Anniv of Second Republic. T* **79** *and similar vert designs. Multicoloured. P* 14 × 13½.

203	4 n. Type **79**	10·00	8·00
204	9 n. Freedom House	40	1·00
205	10 n. Army band	40	1·25
206	15 n. "Celebrations" (dancers)	70	2·50
207	25 n. Presidential chair	1·40	4·00
203/7	*Set of* 5	11·50	15·00

80 President Kaunda at Mulungushi

81 Nakambala Sugar Estate

(Des Mrs. G. Ellison. Litho Harrison)

1974 (28 Apr). *President Kaunda's 50th Birthday. T* **80** *and similar horiz designs. Multicoloured. P* 14½ × 14 (4 *n.*) *or* 14 × 14½ (*others*).

208	4 n. Type **80**	1·00	75
209	9 n. President's former residence	50	50
210	15 n. President holding Independence flame	1·40	2·25
208/10	*Set of* 3	2·50	3·25

(Des G. Vasarhelyi. Litho Questa)

1974 (23 Oct). *Tenth Anniv of Independence. T* **81** *and similar horiz designs. Multicoloured. P* 13½.

211	3 n. Type **81**	20	15
212	4 n. Local market	20	15
213	9 n. Kapiri glass factory	35	45
214	10 n. Kafue hydro-electric scheme	40	50
215	15 n. Kafue Railway Bridge	70	1·50
216	25 n. Non-aligned Conference, Lusaka, 1970	1·10	1·75
211/16	*Set of* 6	2·75	4·00

MS217 141 × 105 mm. 15 n. (× 4) Academic Education; Teacher Training College; Technical Education; Zambia University .. 6·00 6·50

82 Mobile Post-van

(Des Mrs. G. Ellison. Litho Format)

1974 (15 Nov). *Centenary of Universal Postal Union. T* **82** *and similar horiz designs. Multicoloured. P* 13½.

218	4 n. Type **82**	20	15
219	9 n. Aeroplane on tarmac	40	30
220	10 n. Chipata Post Office	40	40
221	15 n. Modern training centre	65	1·40
218/21	*Set of* 4	1·50	2·00

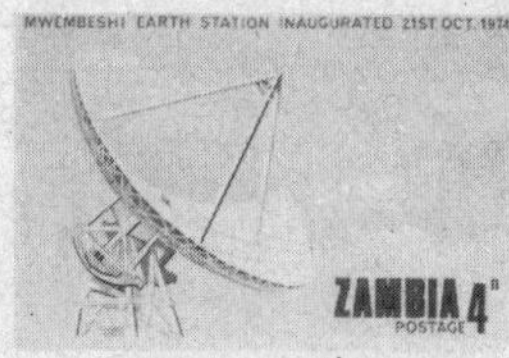

83 Dish Aerial

(Des Mrs. G. Ellison. Litho Questa)

1974 (16 Dec). *Opening of Mwembeshi Earth Station* (21 *October*). *T* **83** *and similar horiz designs. Multicoloured. P* 13½.

222	4 n. Type **83**	30	20
223	9 n. View at dawn	65	50
224	15 n. View at dusk	1·00	1·00
225	25 n. Aerial view	1·50	2·00
222/5	*Set of* 4	3·00	3·25

84 Black Rhinoceros and Calf

85 Independence Monument

(Des Mrs. G. Ellison. Litho J.W.)

1975 (3 Jan). *T* **84/5** *and similar horiz designs. Multicoloured.*

(*a*) *Size as T* **84**. *P* 13½ × 14

226	1 n. Type **84**	20	10
227	2 n. Helmet Guineafowl	25	10
228	3 n. National Dancing Troupe	15	10
229	4 n. African Fish Eagle	30	10
230	5 n. Knife-edge Bridge	30	10
231	8 n. Sitatunga (antelope)	20	10
232	9 n. African Elephant, Kasaba Bay	40	10
233	10 n. Temminck's Ground Pangolin	20	10

(*b*) *Size as T* **85**. *P* 13

234	15 n. Type **85**	25	10
	a. Magenta omitted		
235	20 n. Harvesting groundnuts	45	40
236	25 n. Tobacco-growing	50	15
237	50 n. Flying-Doctor service	75	1·00
238	1 k. Lady Ross's Turaco	2·50	1·50
239	2 k. Village scene	2·50	3·75
226/39	*Set of* 14	8·00	6·50

No. 234a shows much of the design in yellow-green due to the omission of the magenta which was used as an overlay on other colours.

Nos. 226/7 exist in coils, constructed from normal sheets.

86 Map of Namibia

87 Erection of Sprinkler Irrigation

(Des PAD Studio. Litho Questa)

1975 (26 Aug). *Namibia Day. P* 13½.

240	**86**	4 n. green and light yellow-green	20	20
241		9 n. steel-blue and light turquoise-green	30	30
242		15 n. orange-yellow and greenish yellow	65	65
243		25 n. orange and light orange	85	1·10
240/3		*Set of* 4	1·75	2·00

(Des and litho J.W.)

1975 (16 Dec). *Silver Jubilee of the International Commission on Irrigation and Drainage. T* **87** *and similar horiz designs. Multicoloured. P* 13.
244 4 n. Type **87** 15 15
245 9 n. Sprinkler irrigation (*different*) 30 40
246 15 n. Furrow irrigation .. .. .. 65 1·25
244/6 .. .. *Set of* 3 1·00 1·60

88 Mutondo

(Des A. Chimfwembe. Litho J.W.)

1976 (22 Mar). *World Forestry Day. T* **88** *and similar horiz designs showing trees. Multicoloured. P* 13.
247 3 n. Type **88** 15 10
248 4 n. Mukunyu 15 10
249 9 n. Mukusi 30 25
250 10 n. Mopane 30 25
251 15 n. Musuku .. .. 55 1·00
252 25 n. Mukwa .. .. 70 1·25
247/52 .. .. *Set of* 6 1·90 2·50

89 Passenger Train

(Des A. Chimfwembe. Litho J.W.)

1976 (10 Dec). *Opening of Tanzania-Zambia Railway. T* **89** *and similar horiz designs. Multicoloured. P* 13½ (**MS**257) *or* 13 (*others*).
253 4 n. Type **89** 30 30
254 9 n. Copper exports 55 55
255 15 n. Machinery imports 90 95
256 25 n. Goods train .. .. .. 1·40 1·75
253/6 .. .. *Set of* 4 2·75 3·25
MS257 140 × 106 mm. 10 n. Clearing bush; 15 n. Laying track; 20 n. Railway workers; 25 n. Completed track .. .. .. 3·50 4·00

90 Kayowe Dance — 91 Grimwood's Longclaw

(Des BG Studio. Litho Questa)

1977 (18 Jan). *Second World Black and African Festival of Arts and Culture, Nigeria. T* **90** *and similar horiz designs. Multicoloured. P* 13½.
258 4 n. Type **90** 15 10
259 9 n. Lilombola dance 25 25
260 15 n. Initiation ceremony 45 50
261 25 n. Munkhwele dance .. .. .. 75 1·25
258/61 .. .. *Set of* 4 1·40 1·90

(Des Mrs. G. Ellison. Litho Questa)

1977 (1 July). *Birds of Zambia. T* **91** *and similar vert designs. Multicoloured. P* 14½.
262 4 n. Type **91** 40 10
263 9 n. Shelley's Sunbird 70 60
264 10 n. Black-cheeked Lovebird 70 60
265 15 n. Locust Finch .. .. .. 1·40 2·00
266 20 n. Black-chinned Tinkerbird .. .. 1·60 2·25
267 25 n. Chaplin's Barbet .. .. .. 2·00 2·75
262/7 .. .. *Set of* 6 6·00 7·50

92 Girls with Building Blocks

(Des Mrs. G. Ellison. Litho Questa)

1977 (20 Oct). *Decade for Action to Combat Racism and Racial Discrimination. T* **92** *and similar horiz designs. Multicoloured. P* 14 × 14½.
268 4 n. Type **92** 10 10
269 9 n. Women dancing 15 20
270 15 n. Girls with dove 25 50
268/70 .. .. *Set of* 3 45 70

93 Angels and Shepherds

(Des Mrs. G. Ellison. Litho J.W.)

1977 (20 Dec). *Christmas. T* **93** *and similar horiz designs. Multicoloured. P* 14.
271 4 n. Type **93** .. ..
272 9 n. The Holy Family.. .. .. ..
273 10 n. The Magi .. ..
274 15 n. Jesus presented to Simeon .. ..
271/4 .. .. *Set of* 4

94 African Elephant and Road Check

=8n
(95)

(Des Mrs. G. Ellison. Litho Questa)

1978 (1 Aug). *Anti-Poaching Campaign. T* **94** *and similar horiz designs. Multicoloured. P* 14 × 14½.
275 8 n. Type **94** 25 10
276 18 n. Lechwe and canoe patrol 40 55
277 28 n. Warthog and helicopter 60 85
278 32 n. Cheetah and game guard patrol .. 75 1·10
275/8 .. .. *Set of* 4 1·75 2·40

1979 (15 Mar). *Nos.* 228, 232, 234 *and* 236 *surch as T* **95**.
279 8 n. on 9 n. African Elephant, Kasaba Bay 30 10
a. Surch inverted .. .. ..
280 10 n. on 3 n. National Dancing Troupe 10 10
a. Surch inverted .. .. ..
b. Surch omitted (in pair with normal)
281 18 n. on 25 n. Tobacco-growing 15 15
a. Surch inverted .. .. ..
282 28 n. on 15 n. Type **85** 20 25
a. Surch inverted .. .. 7·00
b. Albino surch .. .. ..
279/82 .. .. *Set of* 4 65 55
No. 280b was caused by a corner paper fold.

96 Kayowe Dance — 97 "Kalulu and the Tug of War"

(Des Mrs. G. Ellison. Litho Questa)

1979 (1 Aug). *Commonwealth Summit Conference, Lusaka. T* **96** *and similar horiz designs. Multicoloured. P* 14.
283 18 n. Type **96** 15 25
284 32 n. Kutambala dance 25 40
285 42 n. Chitwansombo drummers 35 60
286 58 n. Lilombola dance 50 80
283/6 .. .. *Set of* 4 1·10 1·90

(Des Mrs. G. Ellison. Litho Questa)

1979 (21 Sept). *International Year of the Child. Illustrations from Children's Books. T* **97** *and similar vert designs. Multicoloured. P* 14.
287 18 n. Type **97** 30 30
288 32 n. "Why the Zebra has no Horns" .. 45 50
289 42 n. "How the Tortoise got his Shell" .. 50 75
290 58 n. "Kalulu and the Lion" 70 95
287/90 .. .. *Set of* 4 1·75 2·25
MS291 90 × 120 mm. Nos. 287/90 .. .. 2·25 2·50

98 Children of Different Races holding Anti-Apartheid Emblem

(Des Mrs. G. Ellison. Litho Questa)

1979 (13 Nov). *International Anti-Apartheid Year. T* **98** *and similar horiz designs showing children of different races together. Multicoloured. P* 14½.
292 18 n. Type **98** 15 25
293 32 n. Children with toy car 25 40
294 42 n. Young children with butterfly 35 60
295 58 n. Children with microscope 50 80
292/5 .. .. *Set of* 4 1·10 1·90

99 Sir Rowland Hill and 2s. Definitive Stamp of 1964

LONDON 1980
(100)

(Des Mrs. G. Ellison. Litho Format)

1979 (20 Dec). *Death Centenary of Sir Rowland Hill. T* **99** *and similar horiz designs. Multicoloured. P* 14½.
296 18 n. Type **99** 20 25
297 32 n. Sir Rowland Hill and mailman 40 55
298 42 n. Sir Rowland Hill and Northern Rhodesia 1963 ½d. definitive stamp 50 70
299 58 n. Sir Rowland Hill and mail-carrying oxwaggon .. .. .. 65 1·10
296/9 .. .. *Set of* 4 1·60 2·40
MS300 112 × 89 mm. Nos. 296/9 .. .. 2·00 2·75

1980 (16 May). *"London 1980" International Stamp Exhibition. Nos.* 296/300 *optd with T* **100**.
301 18 n. Type **99** 35 40
302 32 n. Sir Rowland Hill and mailman 55 70
303 42 n. Sir Rowland Hill and Northern Rhodesia 1963 ½d. definitive stamp 70 90
304 58 n. Sir Rowland Hill and mail-carrying oxwaggon .. .. .. 90 1·10
301/4 .. .. *Set of* 4 2·25 2·75
MS305 112 × 89 mm. Nos. 301/4 .. .. 2·75 3·50

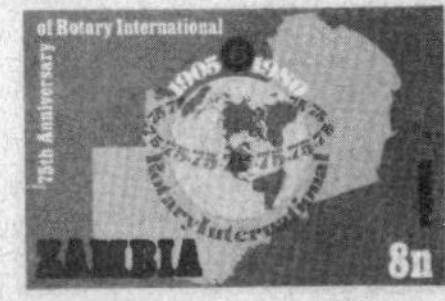

101 Rotary Anniversary Emblem

(Des J.W. Litho Questa)

1980 (18 June). *75th Anniv of Rotary International. P* 14.
306 **101** 8 n. multicoloured 10 10
307 32 n. multicoloured 40 55
308 42 n. multicoloured 45 80
309 58 n. multicoloured .. .. .. 70 1·00
306/9 .. .. *Set of* 4 1·50 2·25
MS310 115 × 89 mm. Nos. 306/9 .. .. 1·60 2·50

102 Running

(Des Mrs. G. Ellison. Litho J.W.)

1980 (19 July). *Olympic Games, Moscow. T* **102** *and similar horiz designs. Multicoloured. P* 13.
311 18 n. Type **102** 20 25
312 32 n. Boxing 30 45
313 42 n. Football 35 80
314 58 n. Swimming .. .. 60 1·00
311/14 .. .. *Set of* 4 1·25 2·25
MS315 142 × 144 mm. Nos. 311/14. P 14.. .. 1·25 2·25

103 Zaddach's Forester — 104 Zambia Coat of Arms

(Des Mrs. G. Ellison. Litho Questa)

1980 (27 Aug). *Butterflies. T* **103** *and similar horiz designs. Multicoloured. P* 14.
316 18 n. Type **103** 25 30
317 32 n. Northern Highflier 45 60
318 42 n. Zambezi Skipper .. .. .. 55 1·00
319 58 n. Modest Blue .. .. .. 70 1·40
316/19 .. .. *Set of* 4 1·75 3·00
MS320 114 × 86 mm. Nos. 316/19 .. .. 2·40 3·00

(Des Mrs. G. Ellison. Litho Format)

1980 (27 Sept). *26th Commonwealth Parliamentary Association Conference, Lusaka. P* 14.
321 **104** 18 n. multicoloured 15 25
322 32 n. multicoloured 25 45
323 42 n. multicoloured 30 65
324 58 n. multicoloured 40 90
321/4 .. .. *Set of* 4 1·00 2·00

105 Nativity and St. Francis of Assisi (stained glass window, Ndola Church)

106 Musikili

(Des Mrs. G. Ellison. Litho Questa)

1980 (3 Nov). *50th Anniv of Catholic Church on the Copperbelt. P* 13½.

325 **105** 8 n. multicoloured 10 10
326 28 n. multicoloured 30 50
327 32 n. multicoloured 30 50
328 42 n. multicoloured 35 65
325/8 . . . . *Set of* 4 95 1·60

(Des Mrs. G. Ellison. Litho Questa)

1981 (21 Mar). *World Forestry Day. Seedpods. T* **106** *and similar horiz designs. Multicoloured. P* 14.

329 8 n. Type **106** 10 10
330 18 n. Mupapa 30 45
331 28 n. Mulunguti 40 70
332 32 n. Mulama 45 95
329/32 . . . . *Set of* 4 1·10 2·00

107 I.T.U. Emblem

108 Mask Maker

(Des J.W. Litho Format)

1981 (15 May). *World Telecommunications and Health Day. T* **107** *and similar vert design. Multicoloured. P* 14½.

333 8 n. Type **107** 10 10
334 18 n. W.H.O. emblems 35 35
335 28 n. Type **107** 60 60
336 32 n. As 18 n. 75 75
333/6 . . . . *Set of* 4 1·60 1·60

(Des Mrs. G. Ellison. Litho Harrison)

1981 (2 June)–83. *Multicoloured designs as T* **108**. *P* 14 × 13½ (50 *n*., 75 *n*., 1 *k*., 2 *k*.) *or* 14½ (*others*).

337 1 n. Type **108** 10 10
338 2 n. Blacksmith 10 10
339 5 n. Pottery making 10 10
340 8 n. Straw-basket fishing 10 10
341 10 n. Thatching 10 10
342 12 n. Mushroom picking (17.2.83) 40 25
343 18 n. Millet grinding on stone 15 10
344 28 n. Royal Barge paddler (11.11.81) . . 25 10
345 30 n. Makishi tightrope dancer (11.11.81) . . 25 10
346 35 n. Tonga Ila granary and house (11.11.81) 25 10
347 42 n. Cattle herding (11.11.81) 25 15
348 50 n. Traditional healer (38 × 26 *mm*) (11.11.81) 25 10
349 75 n. Women carrying water (38 × 26 *mm*) (17.2.83) 25 20
350 1 k. Pounding maize (38 × 26 *mm*) (17.2.83) 25 20
351 2 k. Pipe-smoking, Gwembe Valley Belle (38 × 26 *mm*) 30 25
337/48 . . . . . . *Set of* 15 2·50 1·40

Nos. 338/9 and 341 exist in coils, constructed from normal sheets.

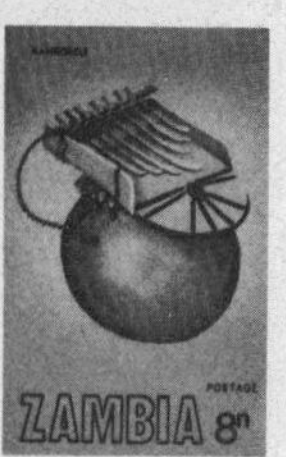

109 Kankobele

110 Banded Ironstone

(Des Mrs. G. Ellison. Litho Format)

1981 (30 Sept*). *Traditional Musical Instruments. T* **109** *and similar vert designs. Multicoloured. P* 15.

356 8 n. Type **109** 20 10
357 18 n. Inshingili 45 30
358 28 n. Ilimba 60 60
359 32 n. Bango 70 80
356/9 . . . . *Set of* 4 1·75 1·60

*It has been reported that the Ndola Philatelic Bureau inadvertently sold some of these stamps some days earlier, and that cancelled-to-order examples exist postmarked 14 or 15 September.

(Des Mrs. G. Ellison. Litho Questa)

1982 (5 Jan). *Minerals* (1*st series*). *T* **110** *and similar vert designs. Multicoloured. P* 14.

360 8 n. Type **110** 25 10
361 18 n. Cobaltocalcite 65 45
362 28 n. Amazonite 75 70
363 32 n. Tourmaline 80 95
364 42 n. Uranium ore . . . . . . 1·00 1·50
360/4 . . . . *Set of* 5 3·00 3·25

See also Nos. 370/4.

111 Zambian Scouts

(Des Mrs. G. Ellison. Litho Questa)

1982 (30 Mar). *75th Anniv of Boy Scout Movement. T* **111** *and similar horiz designs. Multicoloured. P* 14.

365 8 n. Type **111** 25 10
366 18 n. Lord Baden-Powell and Victoria Falls 60 40
367 28 n. African Buffalo and Zambian Scout patrol pennant 60 50
368 1 k. African Fish Eagle and Zambian Conservation badge . . . . . . 1·75 2·50
365/8 . . . . *Set of* 4 3·00 3·25
MS369 105 × 78 mm. Nos. 365/8 . . . . 3·00 3·75

(Des Mrs. G. Ellison. Litho Questa)

1982 (1 July). *Minerals* (2*nd series*). *Vert designs as T* **110**. *Multicoloured. P* 14.

370 8 n. Bornite 35 10
371 18 n. Chalcopyrite . . . . . . 1·00 55
372 28 n. Malachite . . . . . . 1·50 1·25
373 32 n. Azurite . . . . . . 1·50 1·25
374 42 n. Vanadinite . . . . . . 1·75 2·00
370/4 . . . . *Set of* 5 5·50 4·75

112 Drilling Rig, 1926

(Des Mrs G. Ellison. Litho Harrison)

1983 (26 Jan). *Early Steam Engines. T* **112** *and similar horiz designs. Multicoloured. P* 14 × 14½.

375 8 n. Type **112** 20 10
376 18 n. Fowler road locomotive, 1900 . . 35 40
377 28 n. Borsig ploughing engine, 1925 . . 60 1·00
378 32 n. Class "7" railway locomotive, 1900 . . 65 1·25
375/8 . . . . *Set of* 4 1·60 2·50

113 Cotton Picking

114 *Eulophia cucullata*

(Des Mrs G. Ellison. Litho Harrison)

1983 (10 Mar). *Commonwealth Day. T* **113** *and similar horiz designs. Multicoloured. P* 14 × 13½.

379 12 n. Type **113** 15 10
380 18 n. Mining 30 30
381 28 n. Ritual pot and traditional dances . . 30 45
382 1 k. Violet-crested Turaco and Victoria Falls 1·75 2·75
379/82 . . . . *Set of* 4 2·25 3·25

(Des Mrs G. Ellison. Litho Questa)

1983 (26 May). *Wild Flowers. T* **114** *and similar vert designs. Multicoloured. P* 14.

383 12 n. Type **114** 15 10
384 28 n. *Kigelia africana* 30 40
385 35 n. *Protea gaguedi* 35 60
386 50 n. *Leonotis nepetifolia* . . . . 55 1·10
383/6 . . . . *Set of* 4 1·25 2·00
MS387 141 × 71 mm. Nos. 383/6. P 12 . . . . 1·25 2·50

115 Giraffe

(Des Mrs. G. Ellison. Litho Harrison)

1983 (21 July). *Zambia Wildlife. T* **115** *and similar horiz designs. Multicoloured. P* 14 × 13½.

388 12 n. Type **115** 40 10
a. Orange-brown and brown (inscr and face value) omitted . . . .
389 28 n. Blue Wildebeest 55 40
390 35 n. Lechwe 70 60
391 1 k. Yellow-backed Duiker . . . . 1·50 2·50
388/91 . . . . *Set of* 4 2·75 3·25

116 Tiger Fish

117 The Annunciation

(Des Mrs. G. Ellison. Litho J.W.)

1983 (29 Sept). *Zambia Fishes. T* **116** *and similar horiz designs. Multicoloured. P* 14.

392 12 n. Type **116** 15 10
393 28 n. Silver Barbel 30 40
394 35 n. Spotted Squeaker 35 70
395 38 n. Red-breasted Bream 35 70
392/5 . . . . *Set of* 4 1·10 1·75

(Des Mrs. G. Ellison. Litho J.W.)

1983 (12 Dec). *Christmas. T* **117** *and similar vert designs. Multicoloured. P* 14.

396 12 n. Type **117** 10 10
397 28 n. The Shepherds 25 35
398 35 n. Three Kings 30 70
399 38 n. Flight into Egypt 35 90
396/9 . . . . *Set of* 4 90 1·90

118 Boeing "737"

(Des Mrs. G. Ellison. Litho Harrison)

1984 (26 Jan). *Air Transport. T* **118** *and similar horiz designs. Multicoloured. P* 14 × 13½.

400 12 n. Type **118** 15 10
401 28 n. "Beaver" 30 35
402 35 n. Short "Solent" flying boat 35 50
403 1 k. "D.H.66 Hercules" . . . . . . 85 1·75
400/3 . . . . *Set of* 4 1·50 2·40

119 Receiving Flowers

120 Football

(Des and litho J.W.)

1984 (28 Apr). *60th Birthday of President Kaunda. T* **119** *and similar multicoloured designs. P* 14½ × 14 (12 *n*., 60 *n*.) *or* 14 × 14½ (*others*).

404 12 n. Type **119** 30 10
405 28 n. Swearing-in ceremony (*vert*) 45 30
406 60 n. Planting cherry tree 85 80
407 1 k. Opening of 5th National Assembly (*vert*) 1·25 1·75
404/7 . . . . *Set of* 4 2·50 2·75

(Des Mrs. G. Ellison. Litho Format)

1984 (18 July). *Olympic Games, Los Angeles. T* **120** *and similar vert designs. Multicoloured. P* 14½ × 14.

408 12 n. Type **120** 15 10
409 28 n. Running 25 35
410 35 n. Hurdling 35 45
411 50 n. Boxing 45 60
408/11 . . . . *Set of* 4 1·10 1·40

121 Gaboon Viper

(Des Mrs. G. Ellison. Litho Harrison)

1984 (5 Sept). *Reptiles. T* **121** *and similar horiz designs. Multi-coloured. P* 14.
412 12 n. Type **121** 15 10
413 28 n. Chameleon 30 40
414 35 n. Nile Crocodile 40 50
415 1 k. Blue-headed Agama .. .. 85 2·00
412/15 .. .. *Set of* 4 1·50 2·75
MS416 120 × 101 mm. Nos. 412/15 .. .. 2·00 3·50

122 Pres. Kaunda and Mulungushi Rock

123 *Amanita flammeola*

(Des Mrs. G. Ellison. Litho Harrison)

1984 (22 Oct). *26th Anniv of United National Independence Party* (12 *n.*) *and 20th Anniv of Independence* (*others*) (*1st issue*). *T* **122** *and similar horiz designs. Multicoloured. P* 14.
417 12 n. Type **122** 25 10
418 28 n. Freedom Statue 35 35
419 1 k. Pres. Kaunda and agricultural produce ("Lima Programme") .. .. 1·00 1·60
417/19 .. .. *Set of* 3 1·40 1·90
See also Nos. 438/40.

(Des Mrs. G. Ellison. Litho J.W.)

1984 (12 Dec). *Fungi. T* **123** *and similar vert designs. Multi-coloured. P* 14 × 14½.
420 12 n. Type **123** 30 10
421 28 n. *Amanita zambiana* 45 45
422 32 n. *Termitomyces letestui* 50 55
423 75 n. *Cantharellus miniatescens* .. .. 1·00 1·40
420/3 .. .. *Set of* 4 2·00 2·25

(124)

125 Chacma Baboon

1985 (5 Mar). *No.* 237 *surch with T* **124**.
424 5 k. on 50 n. Flying-doctor service .. .. 75 1·00

(Des Mrs. G. Ellison. Litho Harrison)

1985 (25 Apr). *Zambian Primates. T* **125** *and similar horiz designs. Multicoloured. P* 14.
425 12 n. Type **125** 15 10
426 20 n. Diademed Monkey 20 10
427 45 n. Diademed Monkey (*different*) 25 20
428 1 k. Savanna Monkey 45 55
425/8 .. .. *Set of* 4 95 80

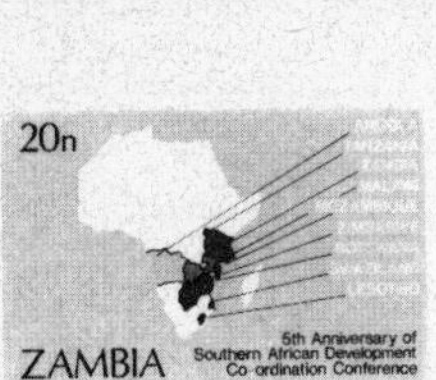

126 Map showing S.A.D.C.C. Member States

127 The Queen Mother in 1980

(Des Mrs. G. Ellison. Litho Harrison)

1985 (9 July). *5th Anniv of Southern African Development Co-ordination Conference. T* **126** *and similar horiz designs. P* 14.
429 20 n. multicoloured 25 10
430 45 n. black, new blue and pale blue 50 30
431 1 k. multicoloured 80 90
429/31 .. .. *Set of* 3 1·40 1·10
Designs:—45 n. Mining; 1 k. Flags of member states and Mulungushi Hall.

(Des and litho Harrison)

1985 (2 Aug). *Life and Times of Queen Elizabeth the Queen Mother. T* **127** *and similar designs. P* 14.
432 25 n. multicoloured 10 10
433 45 n. deep violet-blue and gold 10 15
434 55 n. deep violet-blue and gold 15 20
435 5 k. multicoloured .. .. 1·25 2·00
432/5 .. .. *Set of* 4 1·40 2·25
Designs: *Vert*—45 n. The Queen Mother at Clarence House, 1963. *Horiz*—55 n. With the Queen and Princess Margaret, 1980; 5 k. At Prince Henry's christening, 1984.

20n
(128)

129 Postman and Lusaka Post Office, 1958

1985 (12 Sept–25 Nov). *Nos.* 340 *and* 342 *surch as T* **128** *in chestnut* (20 *n.*) *or greenish blue* (25 *n.*).
436 20 n. on 12 n. Mushroom picking 25 15
437 25 n. on 8 n. Straw-basket fishing (25.11) .. 25 15

1985 (23 Oct). *26th Anniv of United National Independence Party* (*No.* 438) *and 20th Anniv of Independence* (*others*) (*2nd issue*). *Designs as Nos.* 417/19 *but larger,* 55 × 34 *mm, embossed on gold foil. P* 10.
438 5 k. Type **122** .. .. 1·40 2·00
439 5 k. Freedom Statue .. .. 1·40 2·00
440 5 k. Pres. Kaunda and agricultural produce ("Lima Programme") .. .. 1·40 2·00
438/40 .. .. *Set of* 3 3·75 5·50

(Des Mrs. G. Ellison. Litho J.W.)

1985 (12 Dec). *10th Anniv of Posts and Telecommunication Corporation. T* **129** *and similar horiz designs. Multicoloured. P* 13 × 12½.
441 20 n. Type **129** 15 10
442 45 n. Postman and Livingstone Post Office, 1950 .. .. 20 15
443 55 n. Postman and Kalomo Post Office, 1902 .. .. 25 20
444 5 k. Africa Trans-Continental Telegraph Line under construction, 1900 .. .. 1·50 2·00
441/4 .. .. *Set of* 4 1·90 2·25

130 Boy in Maize Field

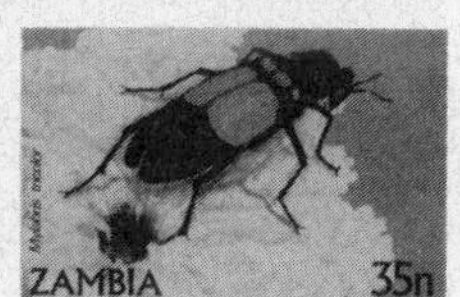

131 *Mylabris tricolor*

(Des Mrs. G. Ellison. Litho Harrison)

1985 (19 Dec). *40th Anniv of United Nations Organization. T* **130** *and similar vert designs. P* 14.
445 20 n. multicoloured 15 10
446 45 n. black, new blue and brownish black .. 20 15
447 1 k. multicoloured 35 35
448 2 k. multicoloured 65 80
445/8 .. .. *Set of* 4 1·25 1·25
Designs:—45 n. Logo and "40"; 1 k. President Kaunda addressing U.N. General Assembly, 1970; 2 k. Signing of U.N. Charter, San Francisco, 1945.

(Des Mrs. G. Ellison. Litho Harrison)

1986 (20 Mar). *Beetles. T* **131** *and similar horiz designs. Multicoloured. P* 14.
449 35 n. Type **131** 10 10
450 1 k. *Phasgonocnema melanianthe* 15 20
451 1 k. 70, *Amaurodes passerinii* 25 40
452 5 k. *Ranzania petersiana* .. .. .. 70 1·25
449/52 .. .. *Set of* 4 1·10 1·75

(Des A. Theobald. Litho Format)

1986 (21 Apr). *60th Birthday of Queen Elizabeth II. Vert designs as T* **110** *of Ascension. Multicoloured. W w* **16**. *P* 14 × 14½ (1 *k.* 95) *or* 14 × 13½ (*others*).
453 35 n. Princess Elizabeth at Flower Ball, Savoy Hotel, 1951 .. .. 10 10
a. Perf 14 × 14½ .. .. 1·00
454 1 k. 25, With Prince Andrew, Lusaka Airport, 1979 .. .. 15 20
a. Perf 14 × 14½ .. .. 15·00
455 1 k. 70, With President Kaunda 20 25
a. Perf 14 × 14½ .. .. 12·00
456 1 k. 95, In Luxembourg, 1976 .. .. .. 25 30
457 5 k. At Crown Agents Head Office, London, 1983 .. .. 60 75
453/7 .. .. *Set of* 5 1·10 1·40

(Des D. Miller. Litho Questa)

1986 (23 July). *Royal Wedding. Square designs as T* **112** *of Ascension. Multicoloured. W w* **16**. *P* 14.
458 1 k. 70, Prince Andrew and Miss Sarah Ferguson 30 25
459 5 k. Prince Andrew in Zambia, 1979 .. .. 80 1·00

OMNIBUS ISSUES

Details, together with prices for complete sets, of the various Omnibus issues from the 1935 Silver Jubilee series to date are included in a special section following Zululand at the end of the catalogue.

132 Goalkeeper saving Goal

133 Sculpture of Edmond Halley by Henry Pegram

(Des Mrs. G. Ellison. Litho Mardon Printers Ltd, Zimbabwe)

1986 (30 July). *World Cup Football Championship, Mexico. T* **132** *and similar vert designs. Multicoloured. P* 14½.
460 35 n. Type **132** 20 10
461 1 k. 25, Player kicking ball 40 35
462 1 k. 70, Two players competing for ball .. 45 40
463 5 k. Player scoring goal .. .. 1·25 1·75
460/3 .. .. *Set of* 4 2·10 2·40

(Des Jennifer Toombs. Litho Mardon Printers Ltd, Zimbabwe)

1986 (6 Aug). *Appearance of Halley's Comet. T* **133** *and similar horiz designs. P* 14½.
464 1 k. 25, multicoloured 35 25
465 1 k. 70, multicoloured 40 30
466 2 k. multicoloured 50 50
467 5 k. light blue and blue-black .. .. .. 1·10 1·40
464/7 .. .. *Set of* 4 2·10 2·25
Designs:—1 k. 70, *Giotto* spacecraft approaching nucleus of Comet; 2 k. Studying Halley's Comet in 1682 and 1986; 5 k. Part of Halley's chart of southern sky.

134 The Nativity

(Des and litho Harrison)

1986 (15 Dec). *Christmas. Children's Paintings. T* **134** *and similar horiz designs. Multicoloured. P* 14.
468 35 n. Type **134** 10 10
469 1 k. 25, The Visit of the Three Kings .. 35 25
470 1 k. 60, The Holy Family with Shepherd and King 40 30
471 5 k. Angel and Christmas Tree .. .. .. 1·10 1·25
468/71 .. .. *Set of* 4 1·75 1·75

135 Train in Kasama Cutting

(Des G. Vasarhelyi. Litho Questa)

1986 (22 Dec). *10th Anniv of Tanzania-Zambia Railway. T* **135** *and similar horiz designs. Multicoloured. P* 14.
472 35 n. Type **135** 20 10
473 1 k. 25, Train leaving Tunnel No. 21 .. 35 35
474 1 k. 70, Train between Tunnels No. 6 and 7 .. .. 40 50
475 5 k. Trains at Mpika Station .. .. .. 1·00 1·60
472/5 .. .. *Set of* 4 1·75 2·25

136 President Kaunda and Graduate

137 Arms of Kitwe

(Litho Harrison)

1987 (27 Jan). *20th Anniv of University of Zambia. T* **136** *and similar multicoloured designs. P* 14.
476 35 n. Type **136** 10 10
477 1 k. 25, University Badge (*vert*) 25 25
478 1 k. 60, University Statue 35 35
479 5 k. President Kaunda laying foundation stone (*vert*) .. .. 90 1·40
476/9 .. .. *Set of* 4 1·40 1·90

(Litho Harrison)

1987 (26 Mar). *Arms of Zambian Towns. T* **137** *and similar vert designs. Multicoloured. P* 14.
480 35 n. Type **137** 10 10
481 1 k. 25, Ndola 15 20
482 1 k. 70, Lusaka 20 25
483 20 k. Livingstone .. .. 2·40 3·00
480/3 .. .. *Set of* 4 2·50 3·25

138 Chestnut-headed Crake

139 Look-out Tree, Livingstone

Two types of surcharge for 20 n., 75 n.:

20n	20n	75n	75n
I	II	I	II

I Surch by Format in Great Britain
II Surch in Zambia

(Des Mrs. G. Ellison. Litho Questa)

1987 (16 Apr)–**88**. *Birds. T* 1:8 *and similar vert designs, some additionally surch as T* **128**. *Multicoloured. P* 11 × 13. (5 *n. to* 40 *n.*, 75 *n.*, 1 *k.* 65) *or* 14 (*others*).

484 5 n. Cloud-scraping Cisticola (8.10.87) .. 10 10
485 10 n. White-winged Starling (8.10.87) .. 10 10
486 20 n. on 1 n. Yellow Swamp Warbler (I) (8.10.87) 30 10
a. Type II surch (10.3.88) 10 10
487 25 n. Type **138** 10 10
488 30 n. Miombo Pied Barbet (8.10.87) .. 10 10
489 35 n. Black and Rufous Swallow 10 10
490 40 n. Wattled Crane (8.10.87) 10 10
491 50 n. Slaty Egret (8.10.87) 10 10
492 75 n. on 2 n. Olive-flanked Robin (I) (8.10.87) 30 15
a. Type II surch (10.3.88) 10 10
493 1 k. Bradfield's Hornbill 10 10
494 1 k. 25, Boulton's Puff-back Flycatcher ("Margaret's Batis") 15 20
495 1 k. 60, Anchieta's Sunbird 20 25
496 1 k. 65 on 30 n. Miombo Pied Barbet (8.10.87) 20 25
497 1 k. 70, Boehm's Bee Eater 20 25
498 1 k. 95, Gorgeous Bush Shrike 20 25
499 2 k. Whale-headed Stork ("Shoebill") (8.10.87) 20 25
500 5 k. Taita Falcon 50 55
501 10 k. on 50 n. Slaty Egret (8.10.87) .. .. 1·00 1·10
502 20 k. on 2 k. Whale-headed Stork (8.10.87) .. 2·10 2·25
484/502 .. .. *Set of* 19 4·75 5·25

Nos. 491, 493/5 and 497/502 are larger, size 24 × 39 mm.

The 1 n. and 2 n. values were not officially issued without surcharge, but examples with c-t-o cancellations of 10 March 1988 are known.

(Litho Questa)

1987 (30 June). *Tourism. T* **139** *and similar horiz designs. Multicoloured. P* 14.

503 35 n. Type **139** 20 10
504 1 k. 25, Rafting on Zambezi 40 25
505 1 k. 70, Tourists photographing lions, Luangwa Valley 60 35
506 10 k. White Pelicans .. .. 2·50 2·40
503/6 .. .. *Set of* 4 3·25 2·75

K3

(140)

141 De Havilland "Beaver"

1987 (14 Sept). *Various stamps surch as T* **140**.

(*a*) *On Nos.* 432/5 *in gold*

507 **127** 3 k. on 25 n. multicoloured 40 45
508 – 6 k. on 45 n. deep violet-blue and gold 85 90
509 – 10 k. on 55 n. deep violet-blue and gold 1·40 1·50
510 – 20 k. on 5 k. multicoloured .. .. 2·75 3·00

(*b*) *On Nos.* 453/7

511 3 k. on 35 n. Princess Elizabeth at Flower Ball, Savoy Hotel, 1951 .. .. 40 45
512 4 k. on 1 k. 25, With Prince Andrew, Lusaka Airport, 1979 .. .. .. 55 60
513 6 k. on 1 k. 70, With President Kaunda .. 85 90
514 10 k. on 1 k. 95, In Luxembourg, 1976 .. 1·40 1·50
515 20 k. on 5 k. At Crown Agents Head Office, London, 1983 .. .. .. 2·75 3·00

(*c*) *On Nos.* 460/3

516 3 k. on 35 n. Type **132** 40 45
517 6 k. on 1 k. 25, Player kicking ball .. 85 90
518 10 k. on 1 k. 70, Two players competing for ball .. .. 1·40 1·50
519 20 k. on 5 k. Player scoring goal .. .. 2·75 3·00

(*d*) *On Nos.* 464/7 *in gold*

520 **133** 3 k. on 1 k. 25, multicoloured .. 40 45
521 – 6 k. on 1 k. 70, multicoloured .. 85 90
522 – 10 k. on 2 k. multicoloured .. .. 1·40 1·50
523 – 20 k. on 5 k. light blue and blue-black 2·75 3·00
507/23 .. .. *Set of* 17 20·00 22·00

(Des and litho Questa)

1987 (21 Sept). *20th Anniv of Zambia Airways. T* **141** *and similar horiz designs showing aircraft. Multicoloured. P* 14.

524 35 n. Type **141** 15 10
525 1 k. 70, Douglas "DC-10" 50 35
526 5 k. Douglas "DC-3 Dakota" .. .. 1·25 1·25
527 10 k. Boeing "707" .. .. 2·00 2·00
524/7 .. .. *Set of* 4 3·50 3·25

142 Friesian/Holstein Cow

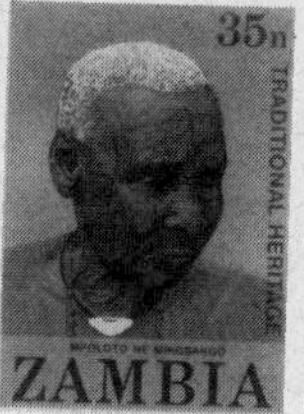

143 Mpoloto Ne Mikobango

(Des Mrs. G. Ellison. Litho Format)

1987 (1 Oct). *40th Anniv of Food and Agriculture Organization. T* **142** *and similar horiz designs. Multicoloured. P* 14½ × 15.

528 35 n. Type **142** 10 10
529 1 k. 25, Simmental bull 20 25
530 1 k. 70, Sussex bull 25 30
531 20 k. Brahman bull .. .. 2·75 3·00
528/31 .. .. *Set of* 4 3·00 3·25

(Litho Format)

1987 (3 Nov). *People of Zambia. T* **143** *and similar vert designs. Multicoloured. P* 12½.

532 35 n. Type **143** 10 10
533 1 k. 25, Zintaka 20 25
534 1 k. 70, Mufuluhi 25 30
535 10 k. Ntebwe .. .. 1·40 1·50
536 20 k. Kubangwa Aa Mbulunga .. .. 2·75 3·00
532/6 .. .. *Set of* 5 4·25 4·50

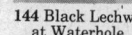

144 Black Lechwe at Waterhole

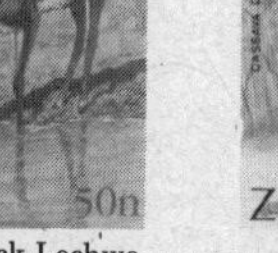

145 Cassava Roots

(Des Mrs. G. Ellison. Litho Questa)

1987 (21 Dec). *Black Lechwe. T* **144** *and similar multicoloured designs. P* 14.

537 50 n. Type **144** 15 10
538 2 k. Black Lechwe resting by pool (*horiz*) 45 35
539 2 k. 50, Running through water (*horiz*) 55 40
540 10 k. Watching for danger .. .. 1·75 2·00
537/40 .. .. *Set of* 4 2·75 2·50
MS541 Two sheets, each 105 × 74 mm. (a) 20 k. Caracal (predator). (b) 20 k. Cheetah (predator) *Set of 2 sheets* 5·50 6·00

(Des Mrs. G. Ellison. Litho Questa)

1988 (20 May). *International Fund for Agricultural Development. T* **145** *and similar horiz designs. Multicoloured. P* 14.

542 50 n. Type **145** 10 10
543 2 k. 50, Fishing 30 35
544 2 k. 85, Farmer and cattle 35 40
545 10 k. Picking coffee beans .. .. .. 1·25 1·40
542/5 .. .. *Set of* 4 1·75 2·00

146 Breast feeding

147 Asbestos Cement

(Des Mrs. G. Ellison. Litho Format)

1988 (12 Sept). *U.N.I.C.E.F. Child Survival Campaign. T* **146** *and similar vert designs. Multicoloured. P* 12½.

546 50 n. Type **146** 10 10
547 2 k. Growth monitoring 25 30
548 2 k. 85, Immunization 35 40
549 10 k. Oral rehydration .. .. .. 1·25 1·40
546/9 .. .. *Set of* 4 1·75 2·00

(Des Mrs. G. Ellison. Litho Format)

1988 (10 Oct). *Preferential Trade Area Fair. T* **147** *and similar vert designs. Multicoloured. P* 12½.

550 50 n. Type **147** 10 10
551 2 k. 35, Textiles 25 30
552 2 k. 50, Tea 30 40
553 10 k. Poultry .. .. 1·25 1·75
550/3 .. .. *Set of* 4 1·60 2·25

148 Emergency Food Distribution

(Des Mrs. G. Ellison. Litho Questa)

1988 (20 Oct). *125th Anniv of International Red Cross. T* **148** *and similar horiz designs. Multicoloured. P* 14.

554 50 n. Type **148** 10 10
555 2 k. 50, Giving first aid 30 35
556 2 k. 85, Practising bandaging 35 45
557 10 k. Henri Dunant (founder) .. .. 1·25 1·75
554/7 .. .. *Set of* 4 1·75 2·40

149 Aardvark

(Des Mrs. G. Ellison. Litho Questa)

1988 (5 Dec). *Endangered Species of Zambia. T* **149** *and similar horiz designs. Multicoloured. P* 14.

558 50 n. Type **149** 15 10
559 2 k. Temminck's Ground Pangolin .. 30 35
560 2 k. 85, Hunting Dog 40 50
561 20 k. Black Rhinoceros and calf .. .. 2·75 3·00
558/61 .. .. *Set of* 4 3·25 3·50

150 Boxing

151 Red Toad

(Des Mrs. G. Ellison. Litho Questa)

1988 (30 Dec). *Olympic Games, Seoul. T* **150** *and similar horiz designs. Multicoloured. P* 14.

562 50 n. Type **150** 15 10
563 2 k. Athletics 30 35
564 2 k. 50, Hurdling 35 45
565 20 k. Football .. .. 2·75 3·25
562/5 .. .. *Set of* 4 3·25 3·75
MS566 Two sheets, each 97 × 72 mm. (a) 30 k. Tennis. (b) 30 k. Karate .. .. *Set of 2 sheets* 8·00 9·00

(Des Mrs. G. Ellison. Litho Format)

1989 (25 Jan). *Frogs and Toads. T* **151** *and similar horiz designs. Multicoloured. P* 12½.

567 50 n. Type **151** 15 10
568 2 k. 50, Puddle Frog 40 40
569 2 k. 85, Marbled Reed Frog 45 50
570 10 k. Young Reed Frogs .. .. .. 1·40 1·75
567/70 .. .. *Set of* 4 2·25 2·50

152 Common Slit-faced Bat

153 Pope John Paul II and Map of Zambia

(Des Mrs. G. Ellison. Litho Format)

1989 (22 Mar). *Bats. T* **152** *and similar horiz designs. Multicoloured. P* 12½.

571 50 n. Type **152** 15 10
572 2 k. 50, Little Free-tailed Bat 45 45
573 2 k. 85, Hildebrandt's Horseshoe Bat .. 55 55
574 10 k. Peters' Epauletted Fruit Bat .. .. 1·50 1·50
571/4 .. .. *Set of* 4 2·40 2·40

(Des and litho Harrison)

1989 (2 May). *Visit of Pope John Paul II. T* **153** *and similar vert designs each with inset portrait. Multicoloured. P* 12½.

575 50 n. Type **153** 15 10
576 6 k. 85, Peace dove with olive branch .. 1·00 1·25
577 7 k. 85, Papal arms .. .. .. 1·25 1·40
578 10 k. Victoria Falls .. .. .. 1·50 1·75
575/8 .. .. *Set of* 4 3·50 4·00

154 *Parinari curatellifolia*

155 Phamphagid Grasshopper

(Des Mrs. G. Ellison. Litho Questa)

989 (26 July). *Edible Fruits. T* **154** *and similar vert designs. Multicoloured. P* 14½.

79	50 n. Type **154**	15	10
80	6 k. 50, *Uapaca kirkiana*	1·00	1·25
81	6 k. 85, Wild Fig	1·00	1·40
82	10 k. Bottle Palm	1·50	1·75
79/82	*Set of* 4	3·25	4·00

(Des Mrs. G. Ellison. Litho Cartor, France)

989 (8 Nov). *Grasshoppers. T* **155** *and similar horiz designs. Multicoloured. P* 14×13½.

83	70 n. Type **155**	10	10
84	10 k. 40, Pyrgomorphid Grasshopper	90	95
85	12 k. 50, Brown Catydid	1·10	1·25
86	15 k. Bush Locust	1·25	1·40
83/6	*Set of* 4	3·00	3·50

156 Fireball

Des Mrs. G. Ellison. Litho National Printing & Packaging, Zimbabwe)

1989 (6 Dec). *Christmas. Flowers. T* **156** *and similar vert designs. Multicoloured. P* 14½.

587	70 n. Type **156**	10	10
588	10 k. 40, Flame Lily	65	70
589	12 k. 50, Foxglove Lily	70	75
590	20 k. Vlei Lily	1·25	1·40
587/90	*Set of* 4	2·50	2·75

POSTAGE DUE STAMPS

D 3

(Des D. Smith. Litho Govt Printer, Lusaka)

1964 (24 Oct). *P* 12½.

D11	D 3	1d. orange	25	75
D12		2d. deep blue	30	95
D13		3d. lake	40	1·25
D14		4d. ultramarine	40	1·60
D15		6d. purple	40	1·75
D16		1s. light emerald	50	3·75
D11/16		*Set of* 6	2·00	9·00

In all values the left-hand vertical row of the sheet is imperf at left and the bottom horizontal row is imperf at bottom. The above were crudely perforated, resulting in variations in the sizes of the stamps.

The above were withdrawn on 15 January 1968 and thereafter decimal currency postage stamps were used for postage due purposes with appropriate cancellations.

Appendix

The following stamps have either been issued in excess of postal needs, or have not been made available to the public in reasonable quantities at face value. Miniature sheets, imperforate stamps etc., are excluded from this section.

1984

Olympic Games, Los Angeles. 90 *n.* × 5, *each embossed on gold foil.*

1986

Classic Cars. 1 *k.* 50 × 25, *each embossed on gold foil.*

Zanzibar

Stamps of INDIA were used in Zanzibar from 1 October 1875 until 10 November 1895, when the administration of the postal service was transferred from India to British East Africa.

A French post office was opened on the island in January 1889 and this service used the stamps of FRANCE until 1894 when specific stamps for this office were provided. The French postal service on the island closed on 31 July 1904 and it is known that French stamps were again utilised during the final month.

A German postal agency operated in Zanzibar between 27 August 1890 and 31 July 1891, using the stamps of GERMANY.

PRICES FOR STAMPS ON COVER TO 1945

Nos. 1/2	—
Nos. 3/18	*from* × 30
Nos. 19/21	—
Nos. 22/174	*from* × 12
Nos. 175/7	—
Nos. 178/87	*from* × 15
Nos. 188/204	*from* × 10
Nos. 205/9	*from* × 15
Nos. 210/38	*from* × 10
Nos. 239/45	—
Nos. 246/59	*from* × 8
Nos. 260/*f*	—
Nos. 261/330	*from* × 4
Nos. D1/17	*from* × 12
Nos. D18/30	*from* × 15

PROTECTORATE

Zanzibar
(1)

1895 (10 Nov)–**96**. *Contemporary stamps of India optd with T* **1** *by* Zanzibar Gazette.

(a) In blue

No.	Type	Description	Unused	Used
1	**23**	½ a. blue-green	£5500	£1600
2	**25**	1 a. plum	£1300	£425
		j. "Zanzidar"	—	£6500

(b) In black

No.	Type	Description	Unused	Used
3	**23**	½ a. blue-green	3·00	2·50
		j. "Zanzidar"	£375	£300
		k. "Zanibar"	£450	£550
		l. Diaeresis over last "a"	£325	
4	**25**	1 a. plum	3·25	3·00
		j. "Zanzidar"	£950	£700
		k. "Zanibar"	£550	£650
		l. Diaeresis over last "a"	£400	
5	**26**	1 a. 6 p. sepia	3·75	3·00
		j. "Zanzidar"	£800	£500
		k. "Zanibar"	£550	£650
		l. "Zanizbar"		
		m. Diaeresis over last "a"	£350	
6	**27**	2 a. pale blue	3·50	3·50
7		2 a. blue	3·75	3·75
		j. "Zanzidar"	£950	£750
		k. "Zanibar"	£950	£700
		l. Diaeresis over last "a"	£375	
		m. Opt double	£160	
8	**36**	2½ a. yellow-green	4·25	4·25
		j. "Zanzidar"	£850	£550
		k. "Zanibar"	£250	£400
		l. "Zapzibar"		
		m. "Zanzipar"		
		n. Diaeresis over last "a"	£375	£375
		o. Second "z" italic	£100	£140
9	**28**	3 a. orange		
10		3 a. brown-orange	6·50	8·50
		j. Zanzidar"	£300	£475
		k. "Zanizbar"	£1100	£1100
11	**29**	4 a. olive-green	11·00	12·00
		j. "Zanzidar"	£1300	£900
12		4 a. slate-green	8·00	9·50
		l. Diaeresis over last "a"	£500	
13	**21**	6 a. pale brown	9·00	10·00
		j. "Zanzidar"	£950	£800
		k. "Zanibar"	£475	£600
		l. "Zanzibarr"	£1200	£1200
		m. Opt double		
14	**31**	8 a. dull mauve	14·00	16·00
		j. "Zanzidar"	£1600	£1600
15		8 a. magenta (7.96)	9·00	13·00
16	**32**	12 a. purple/*red*	13·00	10·00
		j. "Zanzidar"	£2000	£1400
17	**33**	1 r. slate	60·00	60·00
		j. "Zanzidar"	£2000	£2000
18	**37**	1 r. green and carmine (7.96)	10·00	14·00
		j. Opt vert downwards	£275	
19	**38**	2 r. carmine and yellow-brown	28·00	38·00
		j. "r" omitted	£2500	
		k. "r" inverted	£1300	£1300
20		3 r. brown and green	28·00	40·00
		j. "r" omitted	£2500	
		k. "r" inverted	£1300	£1300
21		5 r. ultramarine and violet	30·00	42·00
		j. "r" omitted	£2500	
		k. "r" inverted	£1200	£1300
		l. Opt double, one inverted	£500	
3/21		*Set of* 15	£190	£225

Many forgeries of this overprint exist and also bogus errors.

MINOR VARIETIES. The following minor varieties of type exist on Nos. 1/21:

A. First "Z" antique (all values)
B. Broken "p" for "n" (all values to 1 r.)
C. Tall second "z" (all values)
D. Small second "z" (all values)
E. Small second "z" and inverted "q" for "b" (all values)
F. Second "z" Gothic (½ a. to 12 a. and 1 r.) (No. 18) (black opts only)
G. No dot over "i" (all values to 1 r.)
H. Inverted "q" for "b" (all values to 1 r.)
I. Arabic "2" for "r" (all values to 1 r.) (black opts only)

The scarcity of these varieties varies from normal catalogue value (D. and E.) to 4 times catalogue value (B.).

1895–98. *Provisionals.* I *Stamps used for postal purposes.*

2½ (2) 2½ (3) 2½ (4) 2½ (5)

1895 (Dec.) *No.* 5 *surch with T* **2** *in red.*

No.	Type	Description	Unused	Used
22		2½ on 1½ a. sepia	20·00	24·00
		j. "Zanzidar"	£650	£650
		k. "Zanizbar"	£1300	£950
		l. Inverted "1" in "½"	£625	£525

1896 (11 May). *No.* 4 *surch in black.*

No.	Type	Description	Unused	Used
23	**3**	2½ on 1 a. plum	£100	85·00
24	**4**	2½ on 1 a. plum	£225	£180
		j. Inverted "1" in "½"	£1300	
25	**5**	2½ on 1 a. plum	£100	85·00

2½ (6) 2½ (7) 2½ (8)

1896 (15 Aug). *No.* 6 *surch in red.*

No.	Type	Description	Unused	Used
26	**6**	2½ on 2 a. pale blue	24·00	16·00
		j. Inverted "1" in "½"	£250	£180
		k. Roman "I" in "½"	£170	£130
27	**7**	2½ on 2 a. pale blue	90·00	65·00
		j. "2" of "½" omitted	£1500	
		k. "2²" for "2½"	£2000	
		l. "1" of "½" omitted	£1500	£1500
		m. Inverted "1" in "½"	£850	
28	**8**	2½ on 2 a. pale blue	£1400	£700

No. 28 only exists with small "z".

1896 (15 Nov). *No* 5 *surch in red.*

No.	Type	Description	Unused	Used
29	**6**	2½ on 1½ a. sepia	95·00	80·00
		j. Inverted "1" in "½"	£650	£650
		k. Roman "I" in "½"	£500	£500
30	**7**	2½ on 1½ a. sepia	£275	£225
31	**8**	2½ on 1½ a. sepia	£3750	£2500

No. 31 only exists with small "z".

II. *Stamps prepared for official purposes*

1898 (Jan). *Nos.* 4, 5 *and* 7 *surch as before in red.*

No.	Type	Description	Unused	Used
32	**3**	2½ on 1 a. plum	£200	£300
33	**4**	2½ on 1 a. plum	£325	£450
34	**5**	2½ on 1a. plum	£200	£300
35	**3**	2½ on 1½ a. sepia	60·00	85·00
		j. Diaeresis over last "a"	£1200	
36	**4**	2½ on 1½ a. sepia	£120	£180
37	**5**	2½ on 1½ a. sepia	80·00	£120
38	**3**	2½ on 2 a. dull blue	65·00	£100
39	**4**	2½ on 2 a. dull blue	£120	£190
40	**5**	2½ on 2 a. dull blue	80·00	£130

It is doubtful whether Nos. 32/40 were issued to the public.

1896. *Stamps of British East Africa, T* **11**, *optd with T* 1.

No.	Type	Description	Unused	Used
41		½ a. yellow-green (1 June)	21·00	15·00
42		1 a. carmine-rose (1 June)	21·00	15·00
		j. Opt double	£375	£375
43		2½ a. deep blue (R.) (1 June)	65·00	40·00
44		4½ a. orange-yellow (12 Aug)	26·00	35·00
45		5 a. olive-bistre (12 Aug)	30·00	18·00
		j. "r" omitted	—	£1000
46		7½ a. mauve (12 Aug)	24·00	30·00
41/6		*Set of* 6	£170	£140

MINOR VARIETIES. The various minor varieties of type detailed in the note below No. 21 also occur on Nos. 22 to 46 as indicated below:

A. Nos. 23, 27, 30, 35, 38, 41/6
B. Nos. 22, 26, 29/30, 32/3, 36, 39, 44/6
C. Nos. 22, 25/6, 32, 36, 38, 40/6
D. Nos. 22/46
E. Nos. 22/46
F. Nos. 22, 25/6, 29, 41/6
G. Nos. 25/6, 29, 35, 37/8, 40/6
H. Nos. 22, 41/6 (on the British East Africa stamps this variety occurs in the same position as variety C.)
I. Nos. 26, 35, 38, 41/6

The scarcity of these varieties on the surcharges (Nos. 22/40) is similar to those on the basic stamps, but examples on the British East Africa values (Nos. 41/6) are more common.

PRINTERS. All Zanzibar stamps up to Type **37** were printed by De La Rue & Co.

12

13

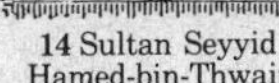
14 Sultan Seyyid Hamed-bin-Thwain

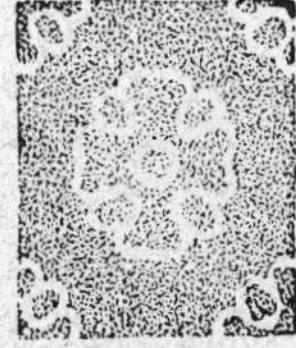
18

1896 (Dec). *Recess. Flags in red on all values. W* **12**. *P* 14.

No.	Type	Description	Unused	Used
156	**13**	½ a. yellow-green	65	50
157		1 a. indigo	1·00	1·00
158		1 a. violet-blue	2·25	2·25
159		2 a. red-brown	1·00	65
160		2½ a. bright blue	3·25	50
161		2½ a. pale blue	3·75	60
162		3 a. grey	2·25	2·75
163		3 a. bluish grey	2·75	3·25
164		4 a. myrtle-green	2·50	2·75
165		4½ a. orange	2·50	2·75
166		5 a. bistre	2·25	2·25
		a. Bisected (2½ a.) (on cover)	†	£1000
167		7½ a. mauve	2·25	2·25
168		8 a. grey-olive	5·00	4·00
169	**14**	1 r. blue	9·00	9·00
170		1 r. deep blue	13·00	11·00
171		2 r. green	12·00	9·50
172		3 r. dull purple	18·00	12·00
173		4 r. lake	14·00	13·00
174		5 r. sepia	18·00	15·00
156/74		*Set of* 15	80·00	65·00
156/74 Optd "Specimen"		*Set of* 15	£180	

The ½, 1, 2, 2½, 3 and 8 a. are known without wmk, these being from edges of the sheets.

1897 (5 Jan). *No.* 164 *surch as before, in red.*

No.	Type	Description	Unused	Used
175	**3**	2½ on 4 a. myrtle-green	45·00	28·00
176	**4**	2½ on 4 a. myrtle-green	£100	85·00
177	**5**	2½ on 4 a. myrtle-green	48·00	40·00
175/7		*Set of* 3	£170	£140

1898 (May). *Recess. W* **18**. *P* 14.

No.	Type	Description	Unused	Used
178	**13**	½ a. yellow-green	40	35
179		1 a. indigo	55	45
		a. Greenish black	1·75	90
180		2 a. red-brown	75	75
		a. Deep brown	2·00	1·25
181		2½ a. bright blue	85	30
182		3 a. grey	2·00	60
183		4 a. myrtle-green	1·50	1·00
184		4½ a. orange	2·00	70
185		5 a. bistre	4·25	1·50
		a. Pale bistre	4·75	2·00
186		7½ a. mauve	2·25	2·75
187		8 a. grey-olive	3·75	2·25
178/87		*Set of* 10	16·00	9·50

19

20 Sultan Seyyid Hamoud-bin-Mohammed bin Said

1899 (June)–**1901**. *Recess. Flags in red. W* **18** (*Nos.* 188/99) *or W* **12** (others). *P* 14.

No.	Type	Description	Unused	Used
188	**19**	½ a. yellow-green	55	25
		a. Wmk sideways	2·50	1·50
189		1 a. indigo	1·25	20
		a. Wmk sideways	5·00	70
190		1 a. carmine (1901)	65	15
191		2 a. red-brown	75	30
192		2½ a. bright blue	1·00	50
193		3 a. grey	1·25	1·40
194		4 a. myrtle-green	1·25	1·00
195		4½ a. orange	3·50	2·25
196		4½ a. blue-black (1901)	3·75	4·25
197		5 a. bistre	1·50	1·25
198		7½ a. mauve	2·25	3·25
199		8 a. grey-olive	2·25	3·50
200	**20**	1 r. blue	15·00	12·00
201		2 r. green	15·00	14·00
202		3 r. dull purple	15·00	20·00
203		4 r. lake	22·00	32·00
204		5 r. sepia	32·00	42·00
188/204		*Set of* 17	£100	£120
188/204 Optd "Specimen"		*Set of* 17	£180	

One (21) — Two & Half (22) — Two & Half (22*a*) Thin open "w" — Two & Half (22*b*) Serif to foot of "f"

1904. *Stamps of* 1899/1901 *surch as T* **21** *and* **22**, *in black or lake* (L.) *by* Zanzibar Gazette.

No.	Type	Description	Unused	Used
205	**19**	1 on 4½ a. orange	1·40	3·00
206		1 on 4½ a. blue-black (L.)	4·25	9·50
207		2 on 4 a. myrtle-green (L.)	11·00	15·00
208		2½ on 7½ a. mauve	12·00	15·00
		a. Opt Type **22*a***	60·00	75·00
		b. Opt Type **22*b***	80·00	£100
		c. "Hlaf" for "Half"		
209		2½ on 8 a. grey-olive	13·00	23·00
		a. Opt Type **22*a***	80·00	£100
		b. Opt Type **22*b***	95·00	£120
		c. "Hlaf" for "Half"	—	£1100
205/9		*Set of* 5	35·00	60·00

MINIMUM PRICE

The minimum price quote is 10p which represents a handling charge rather than a basis for valuing common stamps. For further notes about prices see introductory pages.

23 24

Monogram of Sultan Seyyid Ali bin Hamoud bin Naherud

1904 (8 June). *Typo. Background of centre in second colour. W* **18**. *P* 14.

No.	Type	Description	Unused	Used
210	**23**	½ a. green	55	15
211		1 a. rose-red	65	10
212		2 a. brown	1·25	45
213		2½ a. blue	1·40	35
214		3 a. grey	1·50	1·25
215		4 a. deep green	1·60	1·25
216		4½ a. black	3·00	2·50
217		5 a. yellow-brown	3·25	1·25
218		7½ a. purple	3·50	3·75
219		8 a. olive-green	3·50	2·50
220	**24**	1 r. blue and red	13·00	8·50
		a. Wmk sideways	38·00	30·00
221		2 r. green and red	12·00	22·00
		a. Wmk sideways	60·00	75·00
222		3 r. violet and red	32·00	48·00
223		4 r. claret and red	38·00	60·00
224		5 r. olive-brown and red	42·00	65·00
210/24		*Set of* 15	£140	£190
210/24 Optd "Specimen"		*Set of* 15	£125	

25 26

27 Sultan Ali bin Hamoud 28 View of Port

1908 (May)–**09**. *Recess. W* **18** (*sideways on* 10 *r. to* 30 *r.*). *P* 14.

No.	Type	Description	Unused	Used
225	**25**	1 c. pearl-grey (10.09)	25	25
226		3 c. yellow-green	1·10	10
		a. Wmk sideways	90	40
227		6 c. rose-carmine	2·50	10
		a. Wmk sideways	2·00	75
228		10 c. brown (10.09)	1·50	1·75
229		12 c. violet	2·75	40
		a. Wmk sideways	2·75	40
230	**26**	15 c. ultramarine	2·50	40
		a. Wmk sideways	2·50	1·25
231		25 c. sepia	2·50	80
232		50 c. blue-green	3·25	3·50
233		75 c. grey-black (10.09)	6·00	7·50
234	**27**	1 r. yellow-green	10·00	5·00
		a. Wmk sideways	14·00	5·50
235		2 r. violet	11·00	14·00
		a. Wmk sideways	40·00	28·00
236		3 r. orange-bistre	16·00	32·00
237		4 r. vermilion	27·00	55·00
238		5 r. steel-blue	32·00	42·00
239	**28**	10 r. blue-green and brown (S. £22)	65·00	95·00
240		20 r. black and yellow-green (S. £30)	£160	£250
241		30 r. black and sepia (S. £40)	£250	£375
242		40 r. black and orange-brown (S. £50)	£400	
243		50 r. black and mauve (S. £60)	£350	
244		100 r. black and steel-blue (S. £100)	£625	
245		200 r. brown and greenish black (S. £150)	£950	
225/38		*Set of* 14	£100	£140
225/38 Optd "Specimen"		*Set of* 14	£140	

Specimen copies of Nos. 239/45 are all overprinted.

29 Sultan Kalif bin Harub

30 Sailing Canoe

31 Dhow

1913. *Recess. W* **18** (*sideways on* 75 *c. and T* **31**). *P* 14.

No.	Type	Description	Unused	Used
246	**29**	1 c. grey	10	20
247		3 c. yellow-green	35	20
248		6 c. rose-carmine	70	10
249		10 c. brown	90	75
250		12 c. violet	70	15
251		15 c. blue	1·00	30
252		25 c. sepia	80	45
253		50 c. blue-green	2·00	2·25
254		75 c. grey-black	1·50	1·75
255	**30**	1 r. yellow-green	3·00	3·25
256		2 r. violet	8·00	14·00
257		3 r. orange-bistre	10·00	22·00
258		4 r. scarlet	16·00	35·00
259		5 r. steel-blue	20·00	24·00
260	**31**	10 r. green and brown	55·00	80·00
260*a*		20 r. black and green (S. £20)	80·00	£140
260*b*		30 r. black and brown (S. £30)	£110	£170
260*c*		40 r. black and vermilion (S. £50)	£225	£300
260*d*		50 r. black and purple (S. £55)	£225	£300
260*e*		100 r. black and blue (S. £80)	£300	
260*f*		200 r. brown and black (S. £110)	£600	
246/60		*Set of* 15	£100	£160
246/60 Optd "Specimen"		*Set of* 15	£125	

Specimen copies of Nos. 260*a*/*f* are all overprinted.

1914–22. *Wmk Mult Crown CA* (*sideways on* 10 *r.*). *P* 14.

No.	Type	Description	Unused	Used
261	**29**	1 c. grey	15	25
262		3 c. yellow-green	40	10
		a. Dull green	1·00	15
263		6 c. deep carmine	75	10
		a. Bright rose-carmine	75	10
264		8 c. purple/*pale yellow* (1922)	60	2·50
265		10 c. myrtle/*pale yellow* (1922)	60	35
266		15 c. deep ultramarine	90	1·75
268		50 c. blue-green	3·50	4·00
269		75 c. grey-black	2·75	9·50
270	**30**	1 r. yellow-green	4·00	2·75
271		2 r. violet	4·25	8·00
272		3 r. orange-bistre	10·00	22·00
273		4 r. scarlet	14·00	38·00
274		5 r. steel-blue	16·00	35·00
275	**31**	10 r. green and brown	48·00	£110
261/75		*Set of* 14	95·00	£200
261/75 Optd "Specimen"		*Set of* 14	£130	

1921–29. *Wmk Mult Script CA* (*sideways on* 10 *r. to* 30 *r.*). *P* 14.

No.	Type	Description	Unused	Used
276	**29**	1 c. slate-grey	10	2·25
277		3 c. yellow-green	15	1·00
278		3 c. yellow (1922)	15	10
279		4 c. green (1922)	50	60
280		6 c. carmine-red	25	50
281		6 c. purple/*blue* (1922)	35	10
282		10 c. brown	70	3·25
283		12 c. violet	30	30
284		12 c. carmine-red (1922)	40	35
285		15 c. blue	55	3·00
286		20 c. indigo (1922)	1·00	30
287		25 c. sepia	60	3·25
288		50 c. myrtle-green	1·25	1·90
289		75 c. slate	2·50	15·00
290	**30**	1 r. yellow-green	1·40	1·60
291		2 r. deep violet	2·50	4·25
292		3 r. orange-bistre	3·75	6·00
293		4 r. scarlet	9·50	18·00
294		5 r. Prussian blue	12·00	35·00
295	**31**	10 r. green and brown	32·00	75·00
296		20 r. black and green (Optd S. £55)	90·00	£160
297		30 r. black and brown (1929) (Perf S. £65)	£150	£250
276/95		*Set of* 20	60·00	£150
276/95 Optd "Specimen"		*Set of* 20	£160	

32 Sultan Kalif bin Harub **33**

1926–27. *T* **32** ("CENTS" *in serifed capitals*). *Recess. Wmk Mult Script CA. P* 14.

No.	Type	Description	Unused	Used
299	**32**	1 c. brown	15	10
300		3 c. yellow-orange	15	15
301		4 c. deep dull green	20	30
302		6 c. violet	15	10
303		8 c. slate	90	1·75
304		10 c. olive-green	75	40
305		12 c. carmine-red	1·25	10
306		20 c. bright blue	40	30
307		25 c. purple/*yellow* (1927)	3·00	2·50
308		50 c. claret	90	35
309		75 c. sepia (1927)	1·75	5·50
299/309		*Set of* 11	8·50	10·00
299/309 Optd "Specimen"		*Set of* 11	85·00	

(New Currency. 100 cents = 1 shilling)

1936 (1 Jan). *T* **33** ("CENTS" *in sans-serif capitals*), *and T* **30/1**, *but values in shillings. Recess. Wmk Mult Script CA. P* 14 × 13½–14.

No.	Type	Description	Unused	Used
310	**33**	5 c. green	10	10
311		10 c. black	10	10
312		15 c. carmine-red	10	15
313		20 c. orange	10	10
314		25 c. purple/*yellow*	10	10
315		30 c. ultramarine	10	10
316		40 c. sepia	15	10
317		50 c. claret	15	10
318	**30**	1 s. yellow-green	45	10
319		2 s. slate-violet	55	25
320		5 s. scarlet	2·25	3·00
321		7 s. 50, light blue	6·00	7·50
322	**31**	10 s. green and brown	4·50	4·50
310/22		*Set of* 13	13·00	14·00
310/22 Perf "Specimen"		*Set of* 13	95·00	

36 Sultan Kalif bin Harub

1936 (9 Dec). *Silver Jubilee of Sultan. Recess. Wmk Mult Scri[p]t CA. P* 14.

No.	Type	Description	Unused	Used
323	**36**	10 c. black and olive-green	70	3
324		20 c. black and bright purple	70	3
325		30 c. black and deep ultramarine	80	3
326		50 c. black and orange-vermilion	1·00	4
323/6		*Set of* 4	3·00	1·2
323/6 Perf "Specimen"		*Set of* 4	55·00	

37 *Sham Alam* (Sultan's dhow)

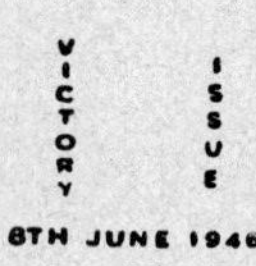

(38)

1944 (20 Nov). *Bicentenary of Al Busaid Dynasty. Recess. Wm[k] Mult Script CA. P* 14.

No.	Type	Description	Unused	Used
327	**37**	10 c. ultramarine	10	4
328		20 c. red	10	4
329		50 c. blue-green	10	3
330		1 s. dull purple	10	4
327/30		*Set of* 4	35	1·4
327/30 Perf "Specimen"		*Set of* 4	65·00	

1946 (11 Nov). *Victory. Optd with T* **38**.

No.	Type	Description	Unused	Used
331	**33**	10 c. black (R.)	20	
332		30 c. ultramarine (R.)	20	4
331/2 Perf "Specimen"		*Set of* 2	45·00	

1949 (10 Jan). *Royal Silver Wedding. As Nos.* 30/1 *of Aden.*

No.	Description	Unused	Used
333	20 c. orange	25	2
334	10 s. brown	10·00	15·(

1949 (10 Oct). 75*th Anniv of U.P.U. As Nos.* 114/17 *of Antigua.*

No.	Description	Unused	Used
335	20 c. red-orange	25	2
336	30 c. deep blue	80	5
337	50 c. magenta	90	6
338	1 s. blue-green	1·00	1·(
335/8	*Set of* 4	2·75	2·1

39 Sultan Kalif bin Harub

40 Seyyid Khalifa Schools, Beit-el-Ras

1952 (26 Aug)–**55**. *Wmk Mult Script CA. P* 12½ (*cent value[s]*) *or* 13 (*shilling values*).

No.	Type	Description	Unused	Used
339	**39**	5 c. black	10	1
340		10 c. red-orange	10	1
341		15 c. green	20	1
		a. Yellow-green (12.11.53)	25	1
342		20 c. carmine-red	20	1
343		25 c. reddish purple	25	1
344		30 c. deep bluish green	15	1
		a. Deep green (29.3.55)	80	9
345		35 c. bright blue	20	4
346		40 c. deep brown	25	2
		a. Sepia (12.11.53)	30	3
347		50 c. violet	25	1
		a. Deep violet (29.3.55)	30	1
348	**40**	1 s. deep green and deep brown	25	1
349		2 s. bright blue and deep purple	85	3
350		5 s. black and carmine-red	1·50	1·2
351		7 s. 50, grey-black and emerald	9·00	18·(
352		10 s. carmine-red and black	5·50	3·(
339/52		*Set of* 14	17·00	21·(

41 Sultan Kalif bin Harub

(Photo Harrison)

954 (26 Aug). *Sultan's 75th Birthday. Wmk Mult Script CA. Chalk-surfaced paper. P* 13 × 12.

No.	Type	Description		
53	41	15 c. deep green	10	10
54		20 c. rose-red	10	10
55		30 c. bright blue	10	10
56		50 c. purple	10	10
57		1 s. 25, orange-red	15	25
53/7		*Set of* 5	30	30

42 Cloves

43 Dhows

44 Sultan's Barge

45 Map of East African Coast

6 Minaret Mosque

47 Dimbani Mosque

48 Kibweni Palace

Des W. J. Jennings (T **42**), A. Farhan (T **43**), Mrs. M. Broadbent (T **44, 46**), R. A. Sweet (T **45**), A. S. B. New (T **47**), B. J. Woolley (T **48**). Recess B.W.)

957 (26 Aug). *W* w **12**. *P* 11½ (5 *c.*, 10 *c.*), 11 × 11½ (15 *c.*, 30 *c.*, 1 *s.* 25), 14 × 13½ (20 *c.*, 25 *c.*, 35 *c.*, 50 *c.*,), 13½ × 14 (40 *c.*, 1 *s.*, 2 *s.*) *or* 13 × 13½ (5 *s.*, 7 *s.* 50, 10 *s.*).

No.	Type	Description		
58	42	5 c. orange and deep green	10	10
59		10 c. emerald and carmine-red	10	10
60	43	15 c. green and sepia	10	10
61	44	20 c. ultramarine	10	10
62	45	25 c. orange-brown and black	10	10
63	43	30 c. carmine-red and black	15	10
64	45	35 c. slate and emerald	15	15
65	46	40 c. brown and black	15	10
66	45	50 c. blue and grey-green	15	10
67	47	1 s. carmine and black	20	10
68	43	1 s. 25, slate and carmine	55	10
69	47	2 s. orange and deep green	60	20
70	48	5 s. deep bright blue	2·75	1·75
71		7 s. 50, green	2·75	4·00
72		10 s. carmine	2·75	2·25
58/72		*Set of* 15	9·50	8·00

49 Sultan Seyyid Sir Abdulla bin Khalifa

50 "Protein Foods"

(Recess B.W.)

961 (17 Oct). *As T* **42/8**, *but with portrait of Sultan Sir Abdulla as in T* **49**, *W* w **12**. *P* 13 × 13½ (20 *s.*), *others as before.*

No.	Type	Description		
73	49	5 c. orange and deep green	10	10
74		10 c. emerald and carmine-red	10	10
75	43	15 c. green and sepia	20	20
76	44	20 c. ultramarine	15	10
77	45	25 c. orange-brown and black	15	10
78	43	30 c. carmine-red and black	45	10
79	45	35 c. slate and emerald	60	25
80	46	40 c. brown and black	30	10
81	45	50 c. blue and grey-green	30	10
82	47	1 s. carmine and black	40	10
83	43	1 s. 25, slate and carmine	80	35
84	47	2 s. orange and deep green	40	40
85	48	5 s. deep bright blue	90	90
86		7 s. 50, green	2·25	7·50
87		10 s. carmine	2·25	4·00
88		20 s. sepia	10·00	17·00
73/88		*Set of* 16	17·00	28·00

(Des M. Goaman. Photo Harrison)

963 (4 June). *Freedom from Hunger. W* w **12**. *P* 14 × 14½.

No.	Type	Description		
89	50	1 s. 30, sepia	45	25

INDEPENDENT

51 Zanzibar Clove

53 "Religious Tolerance" (mosques and churches)

(Photo Harrison)

1963 (10 Dec). *Independence. Portrait of Sultan Seyyid Jamshid bin Abdulla. T* **51, 53** *and similar vert designs. P* 12½.

No.	Description		
390	30 c. multicoloured	10	20
391	50 c. multicoloured	10	25
392	1 s. 30, multicoloured	10	1·25
393	2 s. 50, multicoloured	15	2·25
390/3	*Set of* 4	40	3·50

Designs:—50 c. "To Prosperity" (Zanzibar doorway); 2 s. 50, "Towards the Light" (Mangapwani Cave).

REPUBLIC

When the Post Office opened on 14 January 1964, after the revolution deposing the Sultan, the stamps on sale had the portrait cancelled by a manuscript cross. Stamps thus cancelled on cover or piece used between January 14 and 17 are therefore of interest.

JAMHURI 1964

(**55**= "Republic")

1964 (17 Jan). *Locally handstamped as T* **55** *in black.*

(i) *Nos.* 373/88.

No.	Type	Description		
394	49	5 c. orange and deep green	15	10
395		10 c. emerald and carmine-red	15	10
396	43	15 c. green and sepia	15	15
397	44	20 c. ultramarine	15	10
398	45	25 c. orange-brown and black	15	10
399	43	30 c. carmine-red and black	15	10
400	45	35 c. slate and emerald	15	15
401	46	40 c. brown and black	15	15
402	45	50 c. blue and grey-green	15	10
403	47	1 s. carmine and black	15	15
404	43	1 s. 25, slate and carmine	20	20
405	47	2 s. orange and deep green	1·00	25
406	48	5 s. deep bright blue	1·50	55
407		7 s. 50, green	2·00	1·00
408		10 s. carmine	2·00	90
409		20 s. sepia	2·50	2·50

(ii) *Nos.* 390/3 (*Independence*)

No.	Description		
410	30 c. multicoloured	10	10
411	50 c. multicoloured	15	10
412	1 s. 30, multicoloured	25	10
413	2 s. 50, multicoloured	40	25
	a. Green omitted	£100	
394/413	*Set of* 20	10·00	6·00

T **55** occurs in various positions—diagonally, horizontally or vertically.

NOTE. Nos. 394 to 413 are the only stamps officially authorised to receive the handstamp but it has also been seen on Nos. 353/7, 389 and the Postage Dues. There are numerous errors but it is impossible to distinguish between cases of genuine oversight and those made deliberately at the request of purchasers.

JAMHURI 1964

(**56**)

JAMHURI
1964

(**57**)

1964 (28 Feb). *Optd by Bradbury, Wilkinson.*

(i) *As T* **56** *on Nos.* 373/88

No.	Type	Description		
414	49	5 c. orange and deep green	10	10
415		10 c. emerald and carmine-red	10	10
416	43	15 c. green and sepia	10	10
417	44	20 c. ultramarine	10	10
418	45	25 c. orange-brown and black	10	10
419	43	30 c. carmine-red and black	10	10
420	45	35 c. slate and emerald	10	10
421	46	40 c. brown and black	10	10
422	45	50 c. blue and grey-green	10	10
423	47	1 s. carmine and black	10	10
424	43	1 s. 25, slate and carmine	35	10
425	47	2 s. orange and deep green	25	10
426	48	5 s. deep bright blue	50	35
427		7 s. 50, green	65	90
428		10 s. carmine	75	80
429		20 s. sepia	1·50	1·75

The opt T **56** is set in two lines on Types **46/8**.

(*ii*) *As T* **57** *on Nos.* 390/3 (*Independence*)

No.	Description		
430	30 c. multicoloured	10	10
431	50 c. multicoloured	10	10
432	1 s. 30, multicoloured	10	10
433	2 s. 50, multicoloured	15	10
	a. Green omitted	38·00	
414/33	*Set of* 20	4·25	4·25

The opt T **57** is set in one line on No. 432.

For the set inscribed "UNITED REPUBLIC OF TANGANYIKA AND ZANZIBAR" see Nos. 124/7 of Tanzania.

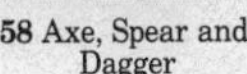

58 Axe, Spear and Dagger

59 Zanzibari with Rifle

(Litho German Bank Note Ptg Co, Leipzig)

1964 (21 June). *T* **58/9** *and similar designs inscr.* "JAMHURI ZANZIBAR 1964". *Multicoloured. P* 13 × 13½ (*vert*) *or* 13½ × 13 (*horiz*).

No.	Description		
434	5 c. Type **58**	10	10
435	10 c. Bow and arrow breaking chains	10	10
436	15 c. Type **58**	10	10
437	20 c. As 10 c.	10	10
438	25 c. Type **59**	10	10
439	30 c. Zanzibari breaking manacles	10	10
440	40 c. Type **59**	10	10
441	50 c. As 30 c.	10	10
442	1 s. Zanzibari, flag and Sun	10	10
443	1 s. 30, Hands breaking chains (*horiz*)	15	10
444	2 s. Hand waving flag (*horiz*)	20	10
445	5 s. Map of Zanzibar and Pemba on flag (*horiz*)	55	20
446	10 s. Flag on Map	1·75	90
447	20 s. National flag (*horiz*)	2·25	5·50
434/47	*Set of* 14	4·75	6·50

68 Soldier and Maps

69 Building Construction

(Litho German Bank Note Ptg Co, Leipzig)

1965 (12 Jan). *First Anniv of Revolution. P* 13 × 13½ (*vert*) *or* 13½ × 13 (*horiz*).

No.	Type	Description		
448	68	20 c. apple-green and deep green	10	10
449	69	30 c. chocolate and yellow-orange	10	10
450	68	1 s. 30, light blue and ultramarine	10	10
451	69	2 s. 50, reddish violet and rose	10	15
448/51		*Set of* 4	20	20

70 Planting Rice

(Litho German Bank Note Ptg Co, Leipzig)

1965 (17 Oct). *Agricultural Development. T* **70** *and similar horiz design. P* 13 × 12½.

No.	Type	Description		
452	70	20 c. sepia and blue	10	15
453	–	30 c. sepia and magenta	10	15
454	–	1 s. 30, sepia and yellow-orange	20	45
455	70	2 s. 50, sepia and emerald	40	1·50
452/5		*Set of* 4	65	2·00

Design:—30 c., 1 s. 30, Hands holding rice.

72 Freighter, Tractor, Factory, and Open Book and Torch

73 Soldier

(Litho German Bank Note Ptg Co, Leipzig)

1966 (12 Jan). *2nd Anniv of Revolution. P* 12½ × 13.

No.	Type	Description		
456	72	20 c. multicoloured	10	10
457	73	50 c. multicoloured	10	10
458	72	1 s. 30, multicoloured	10	10
459	73	2 s. 50, multicoloured	15	30
456/9		*Set of* 4	40	45

For stamps with similar inscription or inscribed "TANZANIA" only, and with commemorative date 26th April 1966, see Nos. Z142/5 of TANZANIA.

74 Tree-felling

75 Zanzibar Street

(Litho German Bank Note Ptg Co, Leipzig)

1966 (5 June). *Horiz designs as T* **74**, *and T* **75**. *P* 12½ × 13 (50 *c.*, 10 *s.*) *or* 13 × 12½ (*others*).
460 5 c. maroon and yellow-olive 10 15
461 10 c. brown-purple and bright emerald .. 10 15
462 15 c. brown-purple and light blue .. 10 15
463 20 c. ultramarine and light orange 10 10
464 25 c. maroon and orange-yellow 10 10
465 30 c. maroon and ochre-yellow 10 10
466 40 c. purple-brown and rose-pink 15 10
467 50 c. green and pale greenish yellow. . .. 20 10
468 1 s. maroon and bright blue. 20 10
469 1 s. 30, maroon and turquoise 20 15
470 2 s. brown-purple and light blue-green .. 30 15
471 5 s. rose-red and pale blue .. .. 80 3·50
472 10 s. crimson and pale yellow .. .. 2·25 8·00
473 20 s. deep purple-brown and magenta .. 4·25 14·00
460/473 .. .. *Set of* 14 8·00 24·00

Designs:—5 c., 20 s. Type **74**; 10 c., 1 s. Clove cultivation; 15, 40 c. Chair-making; 20 c., 5 s. Lumumba College; 25 c., 1 s. 30, Agriculture; 30 c., 2 s. Agricultural workers; 50 c., 10 s. Type **75**.

81 "Education"

(Litho D.L.R.)

1966 (25 Sept). *Introduction of Free Education. P* 13½ × 13.
474 **81** 50 c. black, light blue and orange .. 10 15
475 1 s. 30, black, lt blue and yellow-green 15 30
476 2 s. 50, black, light blue and pink .. 30 2·50
474/6 .. .. *Set of* 3 50 2·75

82 A.S.P. Flag

(Litho D.L.R.)

1967 (5 Feb). *Tenth Anniv of Afro-Shirazi Party* (*A.S.P.*). *T* **82** *and similar multicoloured design. P* 14.
477 30 c. Type **82** 10 10
478 50 c. Vice-President M. A. Karume of Tanzania, flag and crowd (*vert*) 10 10
479 1 s. 30, As 50 c. 10 40
480 2 s. 50, Type **82** .. .. 15 1·00
477/80 .. .. *Set of* 4 30 1·40

84 Voluntary Workers

(Photo Delrieu)

1967 (20 Aug). *Voluntary Workers Brigade. P* 12½ × 12.
481 **84** 1 s. 30, multicoloured 15 25
482 2 s. 50, multicoloured .. .. 30 2·50

POSTAGE DUE STAMPS

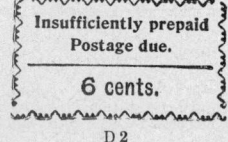

Insufficiently prepaid.
Postage due.
1 cent.

D 1

Insufficiently prepaid
Postage due.
6 cents.

D 2

(Types D 1 and D 2 typo by the Government Printer)

1929–30. *Rouletted* 10, *with imperf sheet edges. No gum.*
D 1 **D 1** 1 c. black/*orange* .. .. .. 10·00 38·00
D 2 2 c. black/*orange* .. .. .. 3·75 16·00
D 3 3 c. black/*orange* .. .. .. 3·75 16·00
a. "cent.s" for "cents." .. .. 55·00
D 4 6 c. black/*orange* .. .. ..
a. "cent.s" for "cents." .. ..
D 5 9 c. black/*orange* .. .. .. 2·25 10·00
a. "cent.s" for "cents." .. .. 11·00 32·00
D 6 12 c. black/*orange* £4000
a. "cent.s" for "cents." .. ..
D 7 12 c. black/*green* £700 £375
a. "cent.s" for "cents." £1800 £1100
D 8 15 c. black/*orange* .. .. .. 2·50 10·00
a. "cent.s" for "cents." .. .. 11·00 30·00
D 9 18 c. black/*salmon* .. .. .. 3·00 15·00
a. "cent.s" for "cents." .. .. 20·00 48·00
D10 18 c. black/*orange* .. .. .. 8·00 20·00
a. "cent.s" for "cents." .. .. 35·00 65·00
D11 20 c. black/*orange* .. .. .. 3·75 12·00
a. "cent.s" for "cents." .. .. 20·00 48·00
D12 21 c. black/*orange* .. .. .. 3·25 12·00
a. "cent.s" for "cents." .. .. 18·00 48·00
D13 25 c. black/*magenta* £1400 £900
a. "cent.s" for "cents." .. .. — £2500
D14 25 c. black/*orange* £2500
D15 31 c. black/*orange* .. .. .. 8·00 28·00
a. "cent.s" for "cents." .. .. 40·00
D16 50 c. black/*orange* .. .. .. 20·00 55·00
a. "cent.s" for "cents." .. .. 80·00
D17 75 c. black/*orange* .. .. .. 55·00 £120
a. "cent.s" for "cents." £170

Sheets of the first printings of all values except the 1 c. and 2 c. contained one stamp showing the error "cent.s" for "cents."

1930–33. *Rouletted* 5. *No gum.*
D18 **D 2** 2 c. black/*salmon* .. .. .. 4·00 14·00
D19 3 c. black/*rose* .. .. 3·00 18·00
D21 6 c. black/*yellow* .. .. .. 3·00 13·00
D22 12 c. black/*blue* .. .. 4·00 11·00
D23 25 c. black/*rose* .. .. 9·00 28·00
D24 25 c. black/*lilac* .. .. 6·50 20·00
D18/24 .. .. *Set of* 6 26·00 90·00

D 3

(Typo D.L.R.)

1936 (1 Jan)–**62**. *Wmk Mult Script CA. P* 14.
D25 **D 3** 5 c. violet, O .. .. .. 45 2·00
a. Chalky paper (18.7.56) .. .. 20 2·75
D26 10 c. scarlet, O .. .. 45 1·00
a. Chalky paper (6.3.62) .. .. 25 1·50
D27 20 c. green, O .. .. 65 2·00
a. Chalky paper (6.3.62) .. .. 20 2·75
D28 30 c. brown, O .. .. 2·25 4·50
a. Chalky paper (18.7.56) .. .. 30 2·75
D29 40 c. ultramarine, O .. .. .. 2·50 9·00
a. Chalky paper (18.7.56) .. .. 40 4·25
D30 1 s. grey, O .. .. 2·75 13·00
a. Chalky paper (18.7.56) .. .. 1·00 4·25
D25/30 .. .. *Set of* 6 8·00 28·00
D25a/30a .. .. *Set of* 6 2·10 17·00
D25/30 Perf "Specimen" .. .. *Set of* 6 60·00
See footnote after No. 413.

All Zanzibar issues were withdrawn on 1 January 1968 and replaced by Tanzania issues. Zanzibar stamps remained valid for postage in Zanzibar for a limited period.

Zimbabwe
(*formerly* Rhodesia)

Rhodesia became independent under majority rule on 18 April 1980 and was renamed Zimbabwe.

PRINTERS. All stamps of Zimbabwe were printed in lithography by Mardon Printers (Pvt) Ltd, subsequently (from Nos. 724/7) National Printing and Packaging, Harare, *unless otherwise stated.*

113 Morganite

114 Rotary Anniversary Emblem

1980 (18 Apr)–**83**. *As Nos.* 555/69 *of Rhodesia and new value* (40 *c.*), *all inscr* "ZIMBABWE" *as in T* **113**.
576 1 c. Type **113** 15 10
577 3 c. Amethyst 20 10
578 4 c. Garnet 20 10
579 5 c. Citrine 25 10
580 7 c. Blue Topaz 25 10
581 9 c. White Rhinoceros 15 10
582 11 c. Lion 15 1
583 13 c. Warthog 15 1
584 15 c. Giraffe 15 2
585 17 c. Common Zebra 15 2
586 21 c. Odzani Falls 20 2
587 25 c. Goba Falls 25 3
588 30 c. Inyangombi Falls 30 4
588*a* 40 c. Bundi Falls (14.3.83) .. .. .. 1·00 9
589 $1 Bridal Veil Falls .. .. .. 1·10 1·7
590 $2 Victoria Falls .. .. 2·25 3·5
576/90 .. .. *Set of* 16 6·25 7·5

1980 (18 June). *75th Anniv of Rotary International. P* 14½.
591 **114** 4 c. multicoloured 10 1
592 13 c. multicoloured 20 2
593 21 c. multicoloured 35 4
594 25 c. multicoloured 45 7
591/4 .. .. *Set of* 4 95 1·2
MS595 140 × 84 mm. Nos. 591/4. . .. .. 1·25 1·6

115 Olympic Rings

(Des Nancy Abrey)

1980 (19 July). *Olympic Games, Moscow. P* 14½.
596 **115** 17 c. multicoloured 30 3

116 Gatooma Post Office, 1912 117 Stylised Blind Person

(Des Mortimer Tiley and Partners Ltd)

1980 (17 Oct). *75th Anniv of Post Office Savings Bank. T* **116** *anc similar horiz designs. P* 14.
597 5 c. black and yellow-brown 10 1
598 7 c. black and red-orange 10 1
599 9 c. black and olive-yellow 10 1
600 17 c. black and light blue 25 2
597/600 .. .. *Set of* 4 40 4
MS601 125 × 84 mm. Nos. 597/600 .. .. 1·00 1·2

Designs:—7 c. Salisbury Post Office, 1912; 9 c. Umtali Post Office, 1901; 17 c. Bulawayo Post Office, 1895.

(Des Rose Martin)

1981 (23 Sept). *International Year for Disabled Persons. T* **11** *and similar vert designs showing stylised figures. Multicoloured P* 14.
602 5 c. Type **117** 10 1
603 7 c. Deaf person 15 1
604 11 c. Person with one leg 25 1
605 17 c. Person with one arm 35 3
602/5 .. .. *Set of* 4 75 6

118 Msasa

119 Painting from Gwamgwadza Cave, Mtoko Area

(Des Nancy Abrey)

1981 (4 Dec). *National Tree Day. T* **118** *and similar vert designs Multicoloured. P* 14½.
606 5 c. Type **118** 10 10
607 7 c. Mopane 15 15
608 21 c. Flat-crowned Acacia 40 50
609 30 c. Pod Mahogany 45 80
606/9 .. .. *Set of* 4 1·00 1·40

1982 (17 Mar). *Rock Paintings. T* **119** *and similar horiz designs showing paintings from various locations. Multicoloured. P* 14½.
610 9 c. Type **119** 45 15
611 11 c. Epworth Mission, near Harare 45 15
612 17 c. Diana's Vow, near Harare 65 40
613 21 c. Gwamgwadza Cave, Mtoko Area (*different*) 85 65
614 25 c. Mucheka Cave, Msana Communal Land 1·00 1·25
615 30 c. Chinzwini Shelter, Chiredzi Area .. 1·10 1·40
610/15 .. .. *Set of* 6 4·00 3·50

120 Scout Emblem **121** Dr. Robert Koch

(Des Rose Martin)

2 (21 July). *75th Anniv of Boy Scout Movement. T* **120** *and imilar vert designs. Multicoloured. P* 14½ × 14.

9 c. Type **120** 35 15
11 c. Scouts around campfire 35 15
21 c. Scouts map-reading 50 65
30 c. Lord Baden-Powell .. .. .. 65 1·10
/19 .. .. *Set of* 4 1·75 1·90

(Des Rose Martin)

2 (17 Nov). *Centenary of Dr. Robert Koch's Discovery of 'ubercle Bacillus. T* **121** *and similar horiz design. P* 14.
11 c. salmon, black and greenish grey .. 45 25
30 c. multicoloured .. .. 1·10 1·40
)esign:—30 c. Man looking through microscope.

122 "Wing Woman" (Henry Mudzengerere) **123** Traditional Ploughing Team (moving right)

3 (14 Mar). *Commonwealth Day. Sculptures. T* **122** *and imilar multicoloured designs. P* 14.
9 c. Type **122** 10 10
11 c. "Telling Secrets" (Joseph Ndandarika) (*horiz*) 15 10
30 c. "Hornbill Man" (John Takawira) (*horiz*) 35 45
$1 "The Chief" (Nicholas Mukomberanwa) 1·00 1·75
2/5 .. .. *Set of* 4 1·40 2·10

(Des Rose Martin)

3 (13 May). *30th World Ploughing Contest, Zimbabwe. T* **123** *nd similar horiz designs. Multicoloured. P* 14.
21 c. Type **123** 25 30
a. Horiz pair. Nos. 626/7 .. .. .. 50 60
21 c. Traditional ploughing team (moving left) 25 30
30 c. Tractor ploughing 40 45
a. Horiz pair. Nos. 628/9 .. .. .. 80 90
30 c. Modern plough 40 45
/9 .. .. *Set of* 4 1·25 1·50
The two designs of each value were issued in horizontal *se-tenant* rs, forming composite designs, throughout the sheets.

124 Postman on Cycle **125** Map of Africa showing Zimbabwe

(Des R. Phillips)

3 (12 Oct). *World Communications Year. T* **124** *and similar nulticoloured designs. P* 14.
9 c. Type **124** 10 10
11 c. Aircraft controller directing aircraft .. 15 10
15 c. Switchboard operator 20 25
17 c. Printing works 25 25
21 c. Road transport (*horiz*) 35 45
30 c. Rail transport (*horiz*) 50 65
)/5 .. .. *Set of* 6 1·40 1·60

(Des Bunty Woods and Nancy Abrey)

4 (11 Apr). *Zimbabwe International Trade Fair. T* **125** *and similar vert designs. Multicoloured. P* 14½.
9 c. Type **125** 10 10
11 c. Globe 15 10
30 c. Zimbabwe flag and Trade Fair logo .. 45 35
6/8 .. .. *Set of* 3 65 50

126 Cycling

(Des Vivienne Fick (11 c.), Joanna Hogg (21 c.), Blessing Chikoore (30 c.), Wayne Gubb (40 c.))

1984 (18 July). *Olympic Games, Los Angeles. Children's Pictures. T* **126** *and similar horiz designs. Multicoloured. P* 14½.
639 11 c. Type **126** 20 15
640 21 c. Swimming 30 25
641 30 c. Running 40 35
642 40 c. Hurdling 50 45
639/42 .. .. *Set of* 4 1·25 1·10

127 Liberation Heroes **128** African Fish Eagle

(Des N. Pearce (11 c.), J. Akester (others))

1984 (8 Aug). *Heroes' Days. T* **127** *and similar multicoloured designs showing various aspects of Heroes' Acre. P* 14½.
643 9 c. Type **127** 20 10
644 11 c. Symbolic tower and flame (*vert*) 20 10
645 17 c. Bronze sculpture (*vert*) 30 20
646 30 c. Section of bronze mural 50 35
643/6 .. .. *Set of* 4 1·10 65

(Des B. Finch)

1984 (10 Oct). *Birds of Prey. T* **128** *and similar vert designs. Multicoloured. P* 14½.
647 9 c. Type **128** 50 15
648 11 c. Long-crested Eagle 50 15
649 13 c. Bateleur 65 35
650 17 c. Verreaux's Eagle 80 35
651 21 c. Martial Eagle 90 90
652 30 c. Bonelli's Eagle .. .. 1·25 1·50
647/52 .. .. *Set of* 6 4·25 3·00

129 Class "9" Locomotive No. 86 **130** "Intelsat V" Telecommunications Satellite

(Des G. Cameron)

1985 (15 May). *"Zimbabwe Steam Safaris". Railway Locomotives. T* **129** *and similar horiz designs. Multicoloured. P* 14½.
653 9 c. Type **129** 45 15
654 11 c. Class "12" No. 190 .. .. 45 15
655 17 c. Class "Garratt 15A" *Isilwane* 70 45
656 30 c. Class "Garratt 20A" *Gwaai* .. .. 1·00 1·40
653/6 .. .. *Set of* 4 2·40 2·00

1985 (8 July). *Earth Satellite Station, Mazowe. T* **130** *and similar multicoloured design. P* 14½ × 14 (26 *c.*) *or* 14½ (57 *c.*).
657 26 c. Type **130** .. .. 1·00 40
658 57 c. Earth Satellite Station, Mazowe (65 × 25 *mm*) .. .. 1·75 2·25

131 Tobacco **132** Chief Mutapa Gatsi Rusere and 17th-century Seal

(Des Rose Rigden)

1985 (21 Aug). *National Infrastructure. T* **131** *and similar horiz designs. Multicoloured. P* 14½.
659 1 c. Type **131** 10 10
660 3 c. Maize 10 10
661 4 c. Cotton 10 10
662 5 c. Tea 10 10
663 10 c. Cattle 10 10
664 11 c. Birchenough Bridge 10 10
665 12 c. Ore stamp mill 10 10
666 13 c. Gold pouring 10 10
667 15 c. Dragline coal mining 10 10
668 17 c. Uncut amethyst 10 10
669 18 c. Electric locomotive 10 10
670 20 c. Kariba Dam 10 10
671 23 c. Elephants at water hole 10 15
672 25 c. Sunset over Zambezi 15 20
673 26 c. Baobab tree 15 20
674 30 c. Ruins of Great Zimbabwe 15 20
675 35 c. Traditional dancing 20 25
676 45 c. Village women crushing maize 25 30
677 57 c. Woodcarving 30 35
678 $1 Playing Mbira (musical instrument) .. 50 55
679 $2 Mule-drawn Scotch cart .. .. .. 1·10 1·25
680 $5 Zimbabwe coat-of-arms .. .. .. 2·75 3·00
659/80 .. .. *Set of* 22 5·50 6·25

(Des C. Herbert)

1985 (18 Sept). *50th Anniv of National Archives. T* **132** *and similar horiz designs. Multicoloured. P* 14½.
681 12 c. Type **132** 15 15
682 18 c. Chief Lobengula, seal and 1888 Treaty 20 35
683 26 c. Exhibition gallery 25 40
684 35 c. National Archives building 30 60
681/4 .. .. *Set of* 4 80 1·40

MACHINE LABELS. From 24 October 1985 gummed labels in the above design varying in value from 1 c. to $99.99, were available from four automatic machines located at the Philatelic Bureau and at the main post offices in Bulawayo, Gwelo and Harare.

133 Computer Operator

(Des C. Herbert)

1985 (13 Nov). *United Nations Decade for Women. T* **133** *and similar horiz designs. Multicoloured. P* 14½.
685 10 c. Type **133** 25 10
686 17 c. Nurse giving injection 40 25
687 26 c. Woman student 70 85
685/7 .. .. *Set of* 3 1·25 1·10

134 Harare Conference Centre

(Des C. Herbert)

1986 (29 Jan). *Harare International Conference Centre. T* **134** *and similar horiz design. Multicoloured. P* 14½.
688 26 c. Type **134** 30 25
689 35 c. Interior of conference hall 45 50

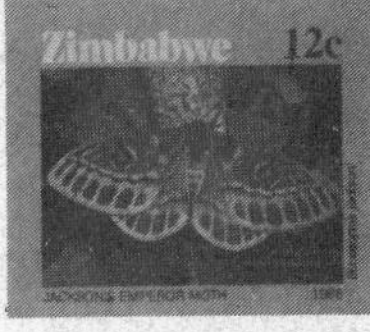

135 Grain Storage Silo **136** Jackson's Emperor Moth

(Des C. Herbert)

1986 (1 Apr). *6th Anniv of Southern African Development Co-ordination Conference. T* **135** *and similar horiz designs. Multicoloured. P* 14½.
690 12 c. Type **135** 25 15
691 18 c. Rhinoceros and hawk at sunset 75 55
692 26 c. Map showing S.A.D.C.C. member states, and Boeing "737" 80 65
693 35 c. Map and national flags of S.A.D.C.C. members .. .. 90 1·00
690/3 .. .. *Set of* 4 2·40 2·10

1986 (18 June). *Moths of Zimbabwe. T* **136** *and similar horiz designs. Multicoloured. P* 14½ × 14.
694 12 c. Type **136** 55 15
695 18 c. Oleander Hawk Moth 80 45
696 26 c. Zaddach's Emperor Moth .. .. .. 1·00 70
697 35 c. Southern Marbled Emperor Moth .. 1·50 1·40
694/7 .. .. *Set of* 4 3·50 2·40

137 Victoria Falls

138 Sopwith Motorcycle (1921)

(Des C. Herbert)

1986 (26 Aug). *8th Non-Aligned Summit Conference. T* **137** *and similar horiz design. Multicoloured. P* 14½×14 (26 c.) *or* 14½ ($1).

698 26 c. Type **137** 55 25
699 $1 Ruins of Great Zimbabwe (62×24 *mm*) . . . . 1·90 2·40

(Des G. Cameron)

1986 (8 Oct). *Centenary of Motoring. T* **138** *and similar horiz designs. Multicoloured. P* 14½.

700 10 c. Type **138** 35 10
701 12 c. Gladiator motor car (1902) 35 15
702 17 c. Douglas motorcycle (1920) 50 20
703 26 c. Ford "Model A" (1930) 65 45
704 35 c. Schacht motor car (1909) 75 85
705 40 c. Benz three-wheeled car (1886) . . 75 90
700/5 . . . . *Set of* 6 3·00 2·40

139 Growth Monitoring

140 Barred Owlet

(Des Barbara Chalk)

1987 (11 Feb). *Child Survival Campaign. T* **139** *and similar vert designs. Multicoloured. P* 14×14½.

706 12 c. Type **139** 40 50
a. Block of 4. Nos. 706/9 . . . . . . 1·40
707 12 c. Breast-feeding 40 50
708 12 c. Oral rehydration therapy 40 50
709 12 c. Immunization 40 50
706/9 . . . . *Set of* 4 1·40 1·75

Nos. 706/9 were printed together, *se-tenant*, in blocks of four throughout the sheet.

(Des B. Finch)

1987 (15 Apr). *Owls. T* **140** *and similar vert designs. Multicoloured. P* 14½.

710 12 c. Type **140** 60 15
711 18 c. Pearl-spotted Owlet 85 35
712 26 c. White-faced Scops Owl . . . . . . 1·25 60
713 35 c. African Scops Owl . . . . . . 1·75 1·50
710/13 . . . . *Set of* 4 4·00 2·40

141 Brownie, Guide and Ranger saluting ("Commitment")

142 Common Grey Duiker

(Des Barbara Connelly)

1987 (24 June). *75th Anniv of Girl Guides' Association of Zimbabwe. T* **141** *and similar horiz designs. Multicoloured. P* 14½.

714 15 c. Type **141** 15 15
715 23 c. Guides preparing meal over campfire ("Adventure") 20 20
716 35 c. Guide teaching villagers to read ("Service") 25 25
717 $1 Handshake and globe ("International Friendship") 70 70
714/17 . . . . *Set of* 4 1·10 1·10

(Des Patricia Wilson)

1987 (7 Oct). *Duikers of Africa Survey. T* **142** *and similar horiz designs, each showing duiker and distribution map. Multicoloured. P* 14½×14.

718 15 c. Type **142** 15 15
719 23 c. Zebra Duiker 20 20
720 25 c. Yellow-backed Duiker 20 20
721 30 c. Blue Duiker 25 25
722 35 c. Jentink's Duiker 25 25
723 38 c. Red Duiker 30 30
718/23 . . . . *Set of* 6 1·25 1·25

143 Wahlberg's Praying Mantis

144 "Cockerel" (Arthur Azevedo)

(Des Janet Duff)

1988 (12 Jan). *Insects. T* **143** *and similar horiz designs. Multicoloured. P* 14½.

724 15 c. Type **143** 25 15
725 23 c. Scarab Beetle 35 20
726 35 c. Short-horned Grasshopper 40 25
727 45 c. Giant Shield Bug 50 35
724/7 . . . . *Set of* 4 1·40 85

1988 (14 Apr). *30th Anniv of National Gallery of Zimbabwe. T* **144** *and similar multicoloured designs showing painting (38 c.) or sculptures (others). P* 14 × 14½ *(vert) or* 14½ × 14 *(horiz)*.

728 15 c. Type **144** 15 10
729 23 c. "Man into Hippo" (Bernard Matemera) 25 20
730 30 c. "Spirit Python" (Henry Munyaradzi) . . 30 25
731 35 c. "Spirit Bird carrying People" (Thomas Mukarobgwa) *(horiz)* 30 25
732 38 c. "The Song of the Herd Boy" (George Nene) *(horiz)* 30 30
733 45 c. "War Victim" (Joseph Muzondo) *(horiz)* 35 40
728/33 . . . . *Set of* 6 1·50 1·40

145 *Aloe cameronii var. bondana*

146 White-faced Whistling Duck

(Des Nancy Abrey)

1988 (14 July). *Aloes. T* **145** *and similar vert designs. Multicoloured. P* 14½.

734 15 c. Type **145** 20 10
735 23 c. *Orbeopsis caudata* 35 20
736 25 c. *Euphorbia wildii* 35 20
737 30 c. *Euphorbia fortissima* 40 30
738 35 c. *Aloe aculeata* 40 35
739 38 c. *Huernia zebrina* 45 35
734/9 . . . . *Set of* 6 2·00 1·40

(Des B. Finch and C. Herbert)

1988 (6 Oct). *Wild Ducks and Geese of Zimbabwe. T* **146** *and similar horiz designs. Multicoloured. P* 14½ × 14.

740 15 c. Type **146** 15 10
741 23 c. African Pygmy Goose 25 20
742 30 c. Hottentot Teal 30 25
743 35 c. Comb Duck ("Knob billed Duck") . . 35 25
744 38 c. White-backed Duck 35 25
745 45 c. Maccoa Duck 45 30
740/5 . . . . *Set of* 6 1·75 1·25

147 O'Shaughnessy's Banded Gecko

148 Spotted Leaved Arum-Lily

1989 (10 Jan). *Geckos. T* **147** *and similar horiz designs. Multicoloured. P* 14½.

746 15 c. Type **147** 15 10
747 23 c. Tiger Rock Gecko 25 20
748 35 c. Tasman's Gecko 35 30
749 45 c. Bibron's Gecko 40 35
746/9 . . . . *Set of* 4 1·00 85

1989 (12 Apr). *Wild Flowers. T* **148** *and similar vert designs. Multicoloured. P* 14½.

750 15 c. Type **148** 15 10
751 23 c. Grassland Vlei-lily 20 20
752 30 c. Manica Protea 25 30
753 35 c. Flame Lily 25 30
754 38 c. Poppy Hibiscus 30 35
755 45 c. Blue Sesbania 35 40
750/5 . . . . *Set of* 6 1·40 1·50

149 Red-breasted Bream

150 Black Rhinoceros

(Des C. Herbert)

1989 (12 July). *Fishes. T* **149** *and similar horiz designs. Multicoloured. P* 14½.

756 15 c. Type **149** 15
757 23 c. Chessa 20
758 30 c. Eastern Bottle-nose 25
759 35 c. Vundu 25
760 38 c. Largemouth Black Bass 30
761 45 c. Tiger Fish 35
756/61 . . . . *Set of* 6 1·40 1·

1989 (10 Oct). *Endangered Species. T* **150** *and similar horiz designs. Multicoloured. P* 14½×14.

762 15 c. Type **150** 10
763 23 c. Cheetah 15
764 30 c. Wild Dog 20
765 35 c. Pangolin 20
766 38 c. Brown Hyena 20
767 45 c. Roan Antelope 25
762/7 . . . . *Set of* 6 1·00 1·

POSTAGE DUE STAMPS

D 4 Zimbabwe Bird (soapstone sculpture)

D 5

1980. *As Nos.* D11/15 *of Rhodesia but inscr* "ZIMBABWE" *as Type* D **4**.

D16 D **4** 1 c. bright green 20
D17 2 c. ultramarine 30
D18 5 c. bright reddish violet 35
a. Imperf (pair) . . . . . . 85·00
D19 6 c. pale lemon . . . . 50 1·
D20 10 c. cerise . . . . 70 1·
D16/20 . . . . *Set of* 5 1·90 3·

1985 (21 Aug). *P* 14½.

D21 D **5** 1 c. yellow-orange 10
D22 2 c. magenta 10
D23 6 c. blue-green 10
D24 10 c. orange-brown 10
D25 13 c. new blue 10
D21/5 . . . . *Set of* 5 25

Zululand

PRICES FOR STAMPS ON COVER

Nos. 1/10	*from* × 15
No. 11	—
Nos. 12/16	*from* × 10
Nos. 20/6	*from* × 20
Nos. 27/9	—
No. F1	*from* × 75

ZULULAND (1) **ZULULAND.** (2)

8 (1 May)–**93**. (*a*) *Stamps of Great Britain optd with T* **1**.

71	½d. vermilion (11.88)	2·00	2·50
57	1d. deep purple	15·00	4·75
73	2d. green and carmine	11·00	15·00
74	2½d. purple/*blue* (9.91)	14·00	17·00
75	3d. purple/*yellow*	18·00	20·00
76	4d. green and brown	22·00	32·00
78	5d. dull purple and blue (3.93) ..	60·00	70·00
79	6d. purple/*rose-red*	11·00	16·00
80	9d. dull purple and blue (4.92) ..	60·00	60·00
82	1s. green (4.92)	80·00	95·00
59	5s. rose (4.92)	£550	£600
1	.. .. *Set of* 11	£750	£825
nd 3/11 H/S "Specimen" .. *Set of* 10		£700	

(*b*) *No. 97a of Natal optd with T* **2**.

23	½d. green (7.88)	42·00	55·00
	a. Opt double	£1000	
	b. Opt inverted	£1300	
	c. Without stop	18·00	27·00
	d. Opt omitted (pair with normal) ..	£3000	£3000

4 (Jan). *No. 103 of Natal optd with T* **1**.

15	6d. mauve	45·00	45·00

3

4

(Typo D.L.R.)

4 (18 Apr)–**96**. *Wmk Crown CA. P* 14.

3	½d. dull mauve and green	1·50	3·25
	1d. dull mauve and carmine	5·00	70
	2½d. dull mauve and ultramarine ..	12·00	6·00
	3d. dull mauve and olive-brown ..	8·00	2·75
4	6d. dull mauve and black	16·00	16·00
	1s. green	25·00	29·00
	2s. 6d. green and black (2.96)	60·00	60·00
	4s. green and carmine	80·00	£100
	£1 purple/*red*	£425	£450
	£5 purple and black/*red* (Optd S. £375)	£3000	£1200
8	.. .. *Set of* 9	£550	£600
8 Optd "Specimen" .. .. *Set of* 9		£350	

)angerous forgeries exist of the £1 and £5.

FISCAL STAMP USED FOR POSTAGE

1 (June). *Fiscal stamp of Natal* (*Wmk Crown, CA, P* 14) *optd vith T* **1**.

1d. dull mauve (Optd S. £60)	3·00	3·00

)ther values, 1s. to £20 as No. F1 exist apparently with post-rks, but, as these were never authorised for postal use, they are longer listed.

The issue of Zululand stamps ceased on 30 June 1898, the ritory having been annexed to Natal on 31 December, 1897.

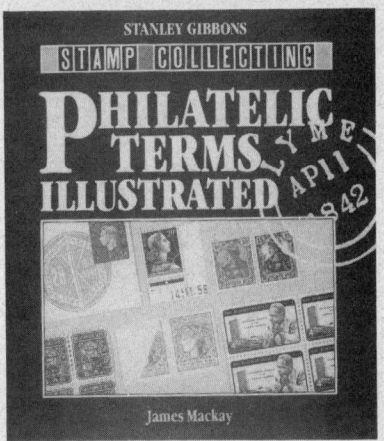

Set Prices for British Commonwealth Omnibus Issues

The composition of these sets is in accordance with the tables on the following pages. Only such items considered basic stamps are included; varieties such as shades, perforation changes and watermark changes are excluded. Great Britain issues which come on both ordinary paper and on paper with phosphor bands are however covered.

Stamps issued in connection with any of the events by countries which are no longer in the British Commonwealth and which are not listed in the Part 1 Catalogue are omitted.

			Price Un	Used
1935.	Silver Jubilee.	*Complete set of* 250 *stamps*	£700	£850

The concept initiated by the 1935 Silver Jubilee omnibus issue has provided a pattern for a series of Royal commemoratives over the past 50 years which have introduced countless collectors to the hobby.

The Crown Colony Windsor Castle design by Harold Fleury is, surely, one of the most impressive produced in the 20th-century and its reproduction in the recess process by three of the leading stamp-printing firms of the era has provided a subject for philatelic research which has yet to be exhausted.

Each of the three, Bradbury, Wilkinson & Co. and Waterlow and Sons, who both produced fifteen issues, together with De La Rue & Co. who printed fourteen, used a series of vignette (centre) plates coupled with individual frame plates for each value. All were taken from dies made by Waterlow. Several worthwhile varieties exist on the frame plates, but most interest has been concentrated on the centre plates, each of which was used to print a considerable number of different stamps.

Sheets printed by Bradbury, Wilkinson were without printed plate numbers, but careful study since the initial work by Douglas Armstrong in 1936 has produced two further centre plates to add to the six originally identified. Stamps from some of these eight plates have revealed a number of prominent plate flaws, the most famous of which, the extra flagstaff, has been eagerly sought by collectors for many years. Research has subsequently confirmed four comparable varieties and these are now included in the catalogue listings.

Extra flagstaff (Plate "1" R.9/1)

Short extra flagstaff (Plate "2" R.2/1)

Lightning conductor (Plate "3" R.2/5)

Flagstaff on right-hand turret (Plate "5" R.7/1)

Double flagstaff (Plate "6" R.5/2)

De La Rue sheets were initially printed with plate numbers, but in many instances these were subsequently trimmed off. Surviving examples do, however, enable a positive identification of four centre plates, 2A, 2B, 4 and 4/ to be made. The number of major plate flaws is not so great as on the Bradbury, Wilkinson sheets, but four examples are now included in the catalogue.

Diagonal line by turret (Plate 2A R. 10/2)

Dot to left of chapel (Plate 2B R.8/3)

Dot by flagstaff (Plate 4 R.8/4)

Dash by turret (Plate 4/ R.3/6)

Much less is known concerning the Waterlow centre plate system. Two plates have been identified, of which the second exists in two states, and it has been suggested that there may be two more. The two states of the kite and log flaw from plate "2" are listed.

Kite and vertical log (Plate "2A" R.10/6)

Kite and horizontal log (Plate "2B" R.10/6)

1937.	Coronation.	*Complete set of* 202 *stamps*	95·00	65·00

1945–46.	Victory.	*Complete set of* 164 *stamps*	23·00	22·00

1948–49.	Royal Silver Wedding.	*Complete set of* 138 *stamps*	£1300	£1300

1949.	U.P.U. 75th Anniversary	*Complete set of* 310 *stamps*	£225	

1951.	B.W.I. University College	*Complete set of* 28 *stamps*	5·50	

1953.	Coronation.	*Complete set of* 106 *stamps*	90·00	5

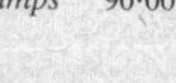

1953–54.	Royal Visit.	*Complete set of* 13 *stamps*	2·50	

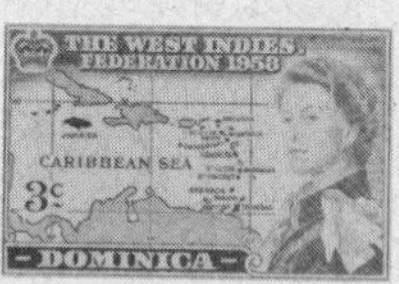

1958.	Caribbean Federation.	*Complete set of* 30 *stamps*	7·00	5

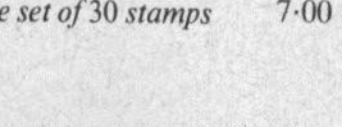

1963.	Freedom from Hunger.	*Complete set of* 77 *stamps*	£110	45

1963.	Red Cross Centenary.	*Complete set of* 108 *stamps and* 2 *miniature sheets*	£130	75

4. Shakespeare. 400th Birth Anniversary.
Complete set of 25 stamps 23·00 17·00

5. I.T.U. Centenary.
omplete set of 112 stamps and 1 miniature sheet £100 45·00

5. I.C.Y.
mplete set of 107 stamps and 2 miniature sheets 85·00 60·00

-67. Churchill. *Complete set of 182 stamps* £190 75·00

. Royal Visit to the Caribbean.
Complete set of 34 stamps 23·00 11·00

. World Cup Football Championship.
Complete set of 68 stamps and 1 miniature sheet 55·00 35·00

. W.H.O. New Headquarters.
omplete set of 58 stamps and 1 miniature sheet 55·00 30·00

-67. U.N.E.S.C.O. 20th Anniversary.
nplete set of 110 stamps and 1 miniature sheet £100 65·00

1972. Royal Silver Wedding.
Complete set of 78 stamps 32·00 28·00

1973. Royal Wedding.
Complete set of 72 stamps and 6 miniature sheets 35·00 20·00

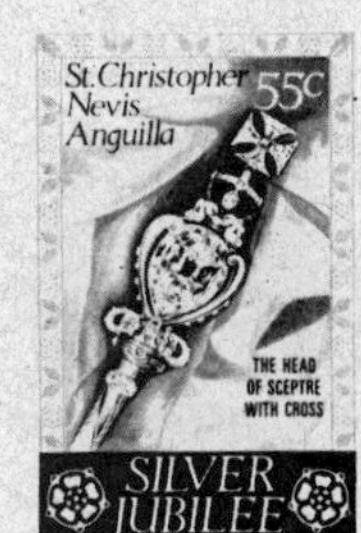

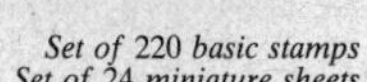

1977. Silver Jubilee. *Set of 220 basic stamps* £130 £100
Set of 24 miniature sheets 50·00 60·00

1977. Royal Visit. *Set of 46 basic stamps* 12·00 11·00
Set of 8 miniature sheets 11·00 14·00

1978. Coronation. 25th Anniversary.
Set of 195 basic stamps 65·00 65·00
Set of 21 *sheetlets* 40·00
Set of 27 miniature sheets 50·00 40·00

1980. Queen Mother's Birthday.
Set of 41 stamps 30·00 24·00
Set of 12 miniature sheets 27·00 27·00

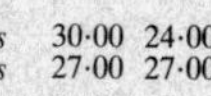

1981. Royal Wedding. *Set of 244 basic stamps* £160 £150
Set of 35 miniature sheets 80·00 70·00

1982. Princess Diana's 21st Birthday.
Set of 162 basic stamps £100 95·00
Set of 19 miniature sheets 45·00 48·00

1982. Birth of Prince William.

Set of 124 basic stamps	£120	95·00
Set of 22 miniature sheets	60·00	60·00

(*Illustration reduced*)

1985. Life and Times of Queen Elizabeth the Queen Mother.

Set of 220 stamps	£120	£130
Set of 45 miniature sheets	£110	£120

1986. 60th Birthday of Queen Elizabeth II.

Set of 233 stamps	£150	£160
Set of 28 miniature sheets	85·00	90·00

1986. Royal Wedding.

Set of 142 stamps	£110	£100
Set of 24 miniature sheets	65·00	75·00

1987. Royal Ruby Wedding.

Set of 117 stamps	80·00	90·00
Set of 14 miniature sheets	32·00	35·00

1935 SILVER JUBILEE TO 1973 ROYAL WEDDING

Issuing Countries	1935 *Silver Jubilee*	1937 *Coronation*	1945–46 *Victory*	1948 *Silver Wedding*	1949 *U.P.U.*	1951 *B.W.I. Univ*	1953 *Coronation*	1953–54 *Royal Visit*	1958 *Caribbean Fed.*	1963 *F.F.H.*	1963 *Red Cross*	1964 *Shakespeare*	1965 *I.T.U.*	1965 *I.C.Y.*	1965–66 *Churchill*	1966 *Royal Visit*	1966 *Football Cup*	1966 *W.H.O.*	1966–67 *UNESCO*	1972 *Silver Wedding*	1973 *Royal Wedding*
ritain	4	1	2	2	4	—	4	—	—	2+2	3+3	5+4	2+2	2+2	2+2	—	3+3	—	—	2	2
nsey	—	—	—	—	—	—	—	—	—	—	—	—	—	—	—	—	—	—	—	4	1
f Man	—	—	—	—	—	—	—	—	—	—	—	—	—	—	—	—	—	—	—	—	1
y	—	—	—	—	—	—	—	—	—	—	—	—	—	—	—	—	—	—	—	4	2
outh Arabian Fed.	—	3	2	2	4	—	1	1	—	1	2	—	—	2	4	—	2	2	3	—	—
n	—	—	2	2	4	—	1	—	—	—	—	—	7	—	1	—	7	—	—	—	—
and Mukalla	—	—	2	2	4	—	1	—	—	—	—	—	—	8	3	—	8	—	—	—	—
a	—	—	—	—	—	—	—	—	—	—	—	—	—	—	—	—	—	—	—	2	2
a	4	3	2	2	4	2	1	—	3	1	2	1	2	2	4	2	2	2	3	2	2+MS
uda	—	—	—	—	—	—	—	—	—	—	—	—	—	—	—	—	—	—	—	—	2
on	4	3	2	2	4	—	1	—	—	1	2	—	2	2	4	—	2	2	3	2	2
ia	3	—	3	—	1	—	3	3	—	—	1	—	1	1	1	—	—	—	—	—	—
as	4	3	2	2	4	—	1	—	—	1	2	1	2	2	4	2	2	2	3	2	—
	—	—	—	2	4	—	4	—	—	—	—	—	—	—	—	—	—	—	—	—	—
os	4	3	2	2	4	2	1	—	3	—	—	—	2	—	4	2	—	—	3	—	—
and/Lesotho	4	3	3×2	2	4	—	1	—	—	1	2	—	2	2	4	—	—	—	4	—	—
naland	4	3	3×2	2	4	—	1	—	—	1	2	1	2	2	4	—	—	—	—	—	—
a	4	3	2	2	4	—	1	1	—	1	2	—	2	2	4	—	2	—	3	2	2
Antarctic Territory	—	—	—	—	—	—	—	—	—	—	—	—	—	—	4	—	—	—	—	2	2
Forces in Egypt	1	—	—	—	—	—	—	—	—	—	—	—	—	—	—	—	—	—	—	—	—
Guiana	4	3	2	2	4	2	1	—	—	1	2	—	2	2	2	2	—	—	—	—	—
Honduras/Belize	4	3	2	2	4	2	1	—	—	1	2	—	2	2	4	—	—	—	—	2	2
Indian Ocean Terr.	—	—	—	—	—	—	—	—	—	—	—	—	—	—	—	—	—	—	—	2	—
P.A's in Eastern Arabia	—	—	—	2	4	—	4	—	—	—	—	—	—	—	—	—	—	—	—	—	—
Virgin Islands	4	3	2	2	4	2	1	—	—	1	2	1	2	2	4	2	—	—	3	2	2
	—	—	—	—	4	—	—	—	—	1	—	—	2	2	4	—	2	2	3	2	2
	—	—	4	—	—	—	—	—	—	—	—	—	—	—	—	—	—	—	—	—	—
	6	1	—	—	—	—	1	—	—	—	—	—	—	1	1	—	—	—	—	—	—
n Islands	4	3	2	2	4	—	1	—	—	1	2	1	2	2	4	2	2	2	3	2	2
Sri Lanka	4	3	2	—	3	—	1	1	—	2	—	—	2	2	—	—	—	2	2	—	—
slands	3	3	4	—	—	—	2	—	—	—	—	—	—	—	6	—	—	—	—	4	3+MS
aki	—	—	—	—	—	—	—	—	—	—	—	—	—	—	—	—	—	—	—	2	2+MS
hyn	—	—	—	—	—	—	—	—	—	—	—	—	—	—	—	—	—	—	—	—	3
	4	3	2	2	4	—	1	—	—	2	2	4	3	2	—	—	—	—	1	—	—
ca	4	3	2	2	4	2	1	—	3	1	2	1	2	2	4	2	2	2	3	2	2+MS
d Islands	4	3	2	2	4	—	1	—	—	1	2	1	2	2	4	—	—	—	—	2	2
d Islands Dependencies	—	—	2	2	4	—	1	—	—	—	—	—	—	—	—	—	—	—	—	—	—
Georgia	—	—	—	—	—	—	—	—	—	—	—	—	—	—	—	—	—	—	—	2	2
	4	3	2	2	4	—	1	1	—	1	2	—	2	2	4	—	2	2	—	2	—
a	4	3	2	2	4	—	1	—	—	1	2	1	2	—	3	—	—	—	—	—	—
ar	4	3	2	2	4	—	1	1	—	1	2	1	2	2	4	—	2	2	3	2	2
and Ellice Islands	4	3	2	2	4	—	1	—	—	1	2	—	2	2	4	—	2	2	3	2	2
oast/Ghana	4	3	2	2	4	—	1	—	—	3	4+MS	—	4+MS	4+MS	—	—	5+MS	4+MS	5+MS	—	—
a	4	3	2	2	4	2	1	—	3	1	2	—	2	2	4	2	2	2	3	2	2+MS
adines	—	—	—	—	—	—	—	—	—	—	—	—	—	—	—	—	—	—	—	—	2+MS
ong	4	3	2	2	4	—	1	—	—	1	2	—	2	2	4	—	—	2	3	2	2
	7	—	4	—	4	—	—	—	—	1	1	—	1	1	—	—	—	—	—	—	—
erabad	—	—	1	—	—	—	—	—	—	—	—	—	—	—	—	—	—	—	—	—	—
	—	—	—	—	—	—	—	—	—	2	2	—	2	2	—	—	—	—	—	—	—
a	4	3	2	2	4	2	1	1	3	2	2	—	1	—	2	4	—	—	—	—	—
/East Africa	4	3	2	2	4	—	1	1	—	4	2	—	4	4	—	—	—	—	4	—	—
	—	—	—	2	4	—	4	—	—	—	—	—	—	—	—	—	—	—	—	—	—
d Islands	4	3	2	2	4	2	1	—	—	—	—	—	—	—	—	—	—	—	—	—	—
n States, etc.	4	3	—	22	44	—	11	—	—	3	—	—	3	—	—	—	—	—	—	—	—
e Islands	—	—	—	—	—	—	—	—	—	7	5	—	—	5+MS	6	—	—	—	6	—	—
	4	3	2	2	4	—	1	1	—	1	2	—	—	—	4	—	—	—	—	—	—
ius	4	3	2	2	4	—	1	—	—	1	2	—	2	2	4	—	—	—	3	—	—
rrat	4	3	2	2	4	2	1	—	3	1	2	1	2	2	4	2	—	2	3	2	2
o Agencies/Tangier	15	3	2	4	4	—	4	—	—	—	—	—	—	—	—	—	—	—	—	—	—
	4	4	—	—	—	—	—	—	—	—	—	—	—	—	—	—	—	—	—	—	—
ndland	4	14	—	—	—	—	—	—	—	—	—	—	—	—	—	—	—	—	—	—	—
uinea	2	4	—	—	—	—	—	—	—	—	—	—	—	—	—	—	—	—	—	—	—
ebrides (English & French)	—	—	—	—	4+4	—	1	—	—	1+1	2+2	—	2+2	2+2	4+4	—	2+2	2+2	3+3	2+2	—
ealand	3	3	11	—	—	—	5	2	—	—	—	—	1	1	1	—	—	—	—	—	—
lau Islands	—	—	—	—	—	—	1	—	—	—	—	—	—	—	—	—	—	—	—	—	—
a	4	3	2	2	4	—	1	—	—	2	3+MS	—	3	3	—	—	—	—	3	—	—
	3	3	4	—	—	—	2	—	—	—	—	—	—	—	—	—	—	—	—	—	—
Borneo	—	—	—	2	4	—	1	—	—	1	—	—	—	—	—	—	—	—	—	—	—
rn Rhodesia/Zambia	4	3	2	2	4	—	1	—	—	—	—	—	2	2	—	—	—	2	—	—	—
and	4	3	2	2	4	—	1	—	—	—	—	—	—	—	—	—	—	—	—	—	—
an	—	—	—	—	—	—	—	—	—	2	1	—	1	2	—	—	—	—	1	—	—
awalpur Postage and ficials	—	—	1	—	4+4	—	—	—	—	—	—	—	—	—	—	—	—	—	—	—	—
P.N.G.	4	4	—	—	—	—	—	—	—	—	1	—	—	—	—	—	—	—	—	—	—
n Islands	—	—	2	2	4	—	1	—	—	1	2	—	2	2	4	—	2	2	3	2	2
sia and Nyasaland	—	—	—	—	—	—	—	—	—	—	1	—	—	—	—	—	—	—	—	—	—
ena	4	3	2	2	4	—	1	—	—	1	2	—	2	2	4	—	2	2	3	2	2
s-Nevis	4	3	2	2	4	2	1	—	3	—	2	—	2	2	4	2	2	2	3	2	2
ia	4	3	2	2	4	2	1	—	3	1	2	1	2	2	4	2	2	2	3	2	2
cent	4	3	2	2	4	2	1	—	3	1	2	—	2	—	4	2	—	2	3	2	2
adines	—	—	—	—	—	—	—	—	—	—	—	—	—	—	—	—	—	—	—	—	2
	3	—	4	—	—	—	2	—	—	—	—	—	—	—	—	—	—	4	—	—	—
k	—	—	—	2	4	—	1	—	—	1	—	—	—	—	—	—	—	—	—	—	—
lles	4	3	2	2	4	—	1	—	—	1	2	—	2	2	4	—	2	2	3	2	2
Leone	4	3	2	2	4	—	1	—	—	2	3	—	—	—	11	—	—	—	—	—	—
ore	—	—	—	2	4	—	1	—	—	—	—	—	—	—	—	—	—	—	—	—	—
n Islands	4	3	2	2	4	—	1	—	—	1	2	—	2	2	4	—	2	2	3	2	2
land Protectorate	4	3	2	2	4	—	1	—	—	—	—	—	—	—	—	—	—	—	—	—	—
Africa	4×2	5×2	3×2	1×2	3×2	—	1	—	—	—	2	—	2	—	—	—	—	—	—	—	—
West Africa	4	8×2	3×2	1×2	3×2	—	5	—	—	—	2	—	—	—	—	—	—	—	—	—	—
rn Rhodesia/Rhodesia	4	4	4	—	2	—	1	—	—	—	—	—	3	—	1	—	—	—	—	—	—
and	4	3	3×2	2	4	—	1	—	—	1	2	—	2	2	4	—	—	—	3	—	—
	—	—	—	—	4	—	—	—	—	1	2	—	—	—	—	—	—	—	—	—	—
d and Tobago	4	3	2	2	4	2	1	—	3	3	—	—	—	1	—	4	—	—	—	—	—
da Cunha	—	—	—	—	—	—	1	—	—	1	2	—	2	2	4	—	2	2	3	2	2
and Caicos Islands	4	3	2	2	4	—	1	—	—	1	2	1	2	2	4	2	—	—	3	2	2
ar	—	—	2	2	4	—	—	—	—	1	—	—	—	—	—	—	—	—	—	—	—
l number of stamps	250	202	164	138	310	28	106	13	30	77	108 +2 MS	25	112 +MS	107 +2 MS	182	34	68 + MS	58 + MS	110 + MS	78	72 +6 MS

NOTE Countries marked with an asterisk are those which comprise the Crown Agents Omnibus issue.

1977 SILVER JUBILEE

Country	Catalogue Nos.	Stamps	MS
Great Britain	1033/7	5	—
Guernsey	149/50	2	—
Isle of Man	94/6	3	—
Jersey	168/70	3	—
Anguilla	269/73	4	1
Antigua	526/31	5	1
Barbuda	298/304, 323/28	11	2
Ascension*	222/4	3	—
Australia	645/6	2	—
Bahamas	488/92	4	1
Bangladesh	93/6	3	1
Barbados*	574/6	3	—
Belize*	449/51	3	—
Bermuda*	371/3	3	—
Botswana*	391/3	3	—
British Antarctic Territory*	83/5	3	—
British Virgin Islands*	364/6	3	—
Brunei	264/6	3	—
Canada	855	1	—
Cayman Islands*	427/9	3	—
Christmas Island	83	1	—
Cook Islands	564/70	6	1
Aitutaki	225/9	4	1
Penrhyn	100/3	3	1
Cyprus	485	1	—
Dominica	562/7	5	1
Falkland Islands*	325/7	3	—
South Georgia*	50/2	3	—
Fiji*	536/8	3	—
Gambia*	365/7	3	—
Gibraltar	371/3	2	1
Gilbert Islands*	48/50	3	—
Grenada	857/62	5	1
Grenadines of Grenada	215/18	3	1
Hong Kong*	361/3	3	—
Kenya	91/5	4	2
Maldive Islands	673/9	6	1
Mauritius*	516/18	3	—
Montserrat	396/8	3	—
New Hebrides* (English & French inscr)	217/19, F231/3	3+3	—
New Zealand	**MS**1137	—	1
Niue	213/15	2	1
Norfolk Island	196	1	—
Papua New Guinea	330/2	3	—
Pitcairn Islands*	171/3	3	—
St. Helena*	332/4	3	—
St. Kitts-Nevis*	367/9	3	—
St. Lucia	443/7	4	1
St. Vincent	502/14	12	1
Grenadines of St. Vincent	93/5	3	—
Samoa	479/82	4	—
Seychelles	393/401	8	1
Sierra Leone	597/8	2	—
Solomon Islands*	334/6	3	—
Swaziland*	268/70	3	—
Tanzania	218/22	4	1
Tonga	598/607, O151/3	13	—
Tristan da Cunha*	212/14	3	—
Turks and Caicos Islands*	472/5	3	1
Tuvalu	50/3	3	1
Total number of items		220	24

The Turks and Caicos Islands miniature sheet, **MS**475, did not form part of the Crown Agents Omnibus issue.

1977 ROYAL VISIT

Country	Catalogue Nos.	Stamps	MS
Anguilla	298/302	4	1
Antigua	548/53	5	1
Barbuda	345/54	8	2
Bahamas	500/4	4	1
Barbados	590/2	3	—
British Virgin Islands	371/3	3	—
Dominica	591/6	5	1
Grenada	894/9	5	1
Grenadines of Grenada	239/42	3	1
Monserrat	409/11	3	—
St. Vincent	540	1	—
Grenadines of St. Vincent	104/5	2	—
Total number of items		46	8

1978 CORONATION ANNIVERSARY

Country	Catalogue Nos.	Stamps	Sheetlets	MS
Great Britain	1059/62	4	—	—
Guernsey	167	1	—	—
Isle of Man	132	1	—	—
Jersey	195/6	2	—	—
Anguilla	320/4	4	—	1
Antigua	581/6	5	—	1
Barbuda	408/20, 445/6	12	—	3
Ascension*	233/5	3	1	—
Bahamas	515/17	2	—	1
Bangladesh	116/20	4	—	1
Barbados*	597/9	3	1	—
Belize*	464/6, 495/503	11	1	2
Bermuda	384/6	3	—	—
British Antarctic Territory*	86/8	3	1	—
British Virgin Islands*	384/6	3	1	—
Brunei	267/9	3	—	—
Cayman Islands*	468/70	3	1	—
Christmas Island*	96/8	3	1	—
Cook Islands	593/601	8	—	1
Aitutaki	257/60	3	—	1
Penrhyn	121/4	3	—	1
Dominica	612/15	3	—	1
Falkland Islands*	348/50	3	1	—
South Georgia*	67/9	3	1	—
Fiji*	549/51	3	1	—
Gambia*	397/9	3	1	—
Gibraltar	400/3	4	—	—
Gilbert Islands*	68/70	3	1	—
Grenada	946/9	3	—	1
Grenadines of Grenada	272/5	3	—	1
Hong Kong	373/4	2	—	—
Maldive Islands	755/61	6	—	1
Mauritius*	549/51	3	1	—
Montserrat	422/6	4	—	1
New Hebrides* (English & French inscr)	262/4, F276/8	3+3	1+1	—
New Zealand Dependency of Tokelau	61/4	4	—	—
Niue	245/8	3	—	1
Norfolk Island	207/8	2	—	—
Pitcairn Islands	**MS**189	—	—	1
St. Helena*	338/40	3	1	—
St. Kitts-Nevis*	389/91	3	1	—
St. Lucia	468/72	4	—	1
St. Vincent	556/60	4	—	1
Grenadines of St. Vincent	130/4	4	—	1
Samoa*	508/10	3	1	—
Seychelles	428/32	4	—	1
Sierra Leone	601/3	3	—	—
Solomon Islands*	357/9	3	1	—
Swaziland	293/5	3	1	—
Tanzania	233/7	4	—	1
Tristan da Cunha*	239/41	3	1	—
Turks and Caicos Islands	494/8	4	—	1
Tuvalu	89/93	4	—	1
Uganda	234/38	4	—	1
Total number of items		195	21	27

The Crown Agents Omnibus issue was printed in matching sheetlets, each containing two *se-tenant* strips of the three designs.

Barbuda Nos. 445/6 form part of a general anniversaries issue.

Belize Nos. 495/503 were not part of the Crown Agents Omnibus issue.

1980 QUEEN MOTHER's 80th BIRTHDAY

Country	Catalogue Nos.	Stamps	MS
Great Britain	1129	1	—
Anguilla	411/15	4	1
Antigua	663/5	2	1
Barbuda	533/5	2	1
Ascension*	269	1	—
Bangladesh	172/4	2	1
Belize	592/3	1	1
Bermuda*	425	1	—
Cayman Islands*	506	1	—
Cook Islands	701/2	1	1
Penrhyn	150/1	1	1
Dominica	732/4	2	1
Falkland Islands*	383	1	—
Gambia*	440	1	—
Gibraltar*	436	1	—
Hong Kong*	390	1	—
Lesotho	423/5	3	—
Maldive Islands	886/7	1	1
Niue	364/5	1	1
Norfolk Island	252/3	2	—
Pitcairn Islands*	206	1	—
St. Helena*	366	1	—
St. Kitts-Nevis			
St. Kitts	48	1	—
Nevis	50	1	—
St. Lucia	534/6	2	1
Samoa*	572	1	—
Solomon Islands*	421	1	—
Tristan da Cunha*	282	1	—
Turks and Caicos Islands	607/8	1	1
Tuvalu	148	1	—
Total number of items		41	12

1981 ROYAL WEDDING

Country	Catalogue Nos.	Stamps	MS
Great Britain	1160/1	2	—
Guernsey	232/9	7	1
Isle of Man	202/4	2	1
Jersey	284/5	2	—
Anguilla	464/7	3	1
Antigua	702/5	3	1
Barbuda	565/75	9	2
Ascension*	302/4	3	—
Australia	821/2	2	—
Bahamas	586/8	2	1
Barbados*	674/6	3	—
Belize	614/20	6	1
Bermuda*	436/8	3	—
British Virgin Islands*	463/5	3	—
Brunei*	304/6	3	—
Cayman Islands*	534/6	3	—
Cocos (Keeling) Islands	70/1	2	—
Cook Islands	812/14	2	1
Aitutaki	391/3	3	—
Penrhyn	223/8	5	1
Cyprus	580	1	—
Turkish Cypriot Posts	121	1	—
Dominica	747/50	3	1
Falkland Islands*	402/4	3	—
Dependencies*	95/7	3	—
Fiji*	612/14	3	—
Gambia*	454/6	3	—
Ghana	948/54	6	1
Gibraltar	450	1	—
Grenada	1130/5	5	1
Grenadines of Grenada	444/9	5	1
Guyana	769/70, 841/3, 930/6	12	—
Hong Kong*	399/401	3	—
Jamaica	516/20	4	
Kenya	207/11	4	
Kiribati	149/55	6	
Lesotho*	451/4	3	
Maldive Islands	918/21	3	
Mauritius*	615/17	3	
Montserrat	510/15	6	
New Zealand	1247/8	2	
Niue	430/3	3	
Norfolk Island*	262/4	3	
Pitcairn Islands*	219/21	3	
St. Helena*	378/80	3	
St. Kitts-Nevis			
St. Kitts	75/81	6	
Nevis	72/8	6	
St. Lucia	576/9	3	
St. Vincent	668/74	6	
Grenadines of St. Vincent	195/201	6	
Samoa*	599/601	3	
Seychelles	505/11	6	
Zil Elwagne Sesel	23/9	6	
Sierra Leone*	668/74	6	
Solomon Islands*	445/7	3	
Swaziland*	376/8	3	
Tanzania	325/7	2	
Tonga	785/8	4	
Tristan da Cunha*	308/10	3	
Turks and Caicos Islands	653/6	3	
Caicos Islands	8/11	3	
Tuvalu	168/74	6	
Uganda	341/8	6	
Vanuatu*	315/17	3	
Total number of items		244	

The Lesotho miniature sheet, No. **MS**454, and Sierra Leon 671/3 do not form part of the Crown Agents Omnibus issu

1982 PRINCESS DIANA'S 21st BIRTHDAY

Country	Catalogue Nos.	Stamps
Anguilla	507/14	6
Antigua	748/51	3
Barbuda	624/30	6
Ascension*	322/5	4
Bahamas*	622/5	4
Barbados*	705/8	4
Belize	680/6	6
British Antarctic Territory*	109/12	4
British Virgin Islands*	488/91	4
Cayman Islands*	549/52	4
Cook Islands	833/7	4
Aitutaki	411/14	3
Penrhyn	250/5	5
Dominica	821/4	3
Falkland Islands*	426/9	4
Dependencies*	108/11	4
Fiji*	640/3	4
Gambia*	476/9	4
Grenada	1188/94	6
Grenadines of Grenada	493/9	6
Guyana	979/81	3
Jamaica	551/7	6
Kiribati	183/5	3
Lesotho*	514/17	4
Maldive Islands	964/7	3
Mauritius*	643/6	4
Montserrat	542/4	3
Niue	454/7	3
Pitcairn Islands*	226/9	4
St. Helena*	397/400	4
St. Kitts-Nevis		
St. Kitts	95/7	3
Nevis	85/7	3
St. Lucia	625/8	3
St. Vincent	694/6	3
Grenadines of St. Vincent	229/31	3
Sierra Leone	707/10	3
Solomon Islands*	467/70	4
Swaziland*	404/7	4
Tristan da Cunha*	327/30	4
Turks and Caicos Islands	709/12	3
Tuvalu	184/6	3
Uganda	374/7	1
Total number of items		162

1982 BIRTH OF PRINCE WILLIAM

Country	Catalogue Nos.	Stamps
Great Britain		
Isle of Man	**MS**227	—
Antigua	757/60	3
Barbuda	613/16, 632/5	6
Belize	707/20	12
Cook Islands	838/47, 856/61	13
Aitutaki	415/24	9
Penrhyn	256/72	15
Dominica	830/3	3
Grenada	1200/6	6
Grenadines of Grenada	505/11	6
Guyana	982/7	6
Jamaica	558/64	6
Kiribati	186/8	3
Lesotho	521/2	2
Maldive Islands	968/72	4
Mauritius	647	1
Niue	458/74	13
St. Kitts-Nevis		
St. Kitts	98/100	3
Nevis	88/90	3
St. Vincent	699/701	3
Grenadines of St. Vincent	234/6	3
Sierra Leone	711/14	3
Tuvalu	189/91	3
Total number of items		124

1985 LIFE AND TIMES OF QUEEN ELIZABETH THE QUEEN MOTHER

ntry	Catalogue Nos.	Stamps	MS
lla	655/8	3	1
ıa	946/9	3	1
›uda	776/82, 809/15 826/9	17	1
sion*	376/80	5	1
ıas*	712/16	4	1
dos*	779/83	4	1
	827/31	4	1
da*	494/8	4	1
Virgin Islands	579/87	8	1
slands	1035/9	4	1
taki	523/7	4	1
hyn	378/82	4	1
ıica	949/52	3	1
nd Islands*	505/9	4	1
endencies*	129/33	4	1
	701/5	4	1
a	586/9	3	1
	1140/3	3	1
da	1426/9	3	1
ıadines of Grenada	689/92	3	1
a	1536/9	3	1
Kong*	493/6	4	—
a*	625/9	4	1
e Islands	1099/102	4	1
ius*	699/703	4	1
errat	636/44	8	1
	587/90	3	1
k Island*	364/8	4	1
n Islands*	268/72	4	1
ena*	454/8	4	1
ts-Nevis			
s	309/17	8	1
ia	832/40	8	1
cent	910/18	8	1
ıadines of St. Vincent	403/11	8	1
*	700/4	4	1
elles*	614/18	4	1
Elwannyen Sesel*	115/19	4	1
on Islands*	538/42	4	1
and*	486/90	4	1
ıia	425/9	4	1
	915/18	4	—
da Cunha*	390/4	4	1
and Caicos Islands	854/7	3	1
os Islands	82/5	3	1
	334/42	8	1
a	478/9	1	1
tu*	406/10	4	1
a	432/5	4	—
umber of items		220	45

1986 QUEEN ELIZABETH II's 60th BIRTHDAY

try	Catalogue Nos.	Stamps	MS
Britain	1316/19	4	—
nsey	365	1	—
of Man	328/30	3	—
y	389	1	—
a	711/14	3	1
a	1005/8	3	1
uda	861/4, 872/5	6	2
ion*	397/401	5	—
lia	1009	1	—
as*	741/5	5	—
os*	810/14	5	—
	905/9	4	1
da*	524/8	5	—
Virgin Islands	600/4	4	1
n Islands*	621/5	5	—
slands	1065/8	3	1
taki	542/3	1	1
hyn	394/6	3	—
—Turkish Cypriot Posts	201	1	—
ica	998/1001	3	1
d Islands*	522/6	5	—
	714/18	5	—
a	641/4	3	1
ar	540	1	—
la	1499/502	3	1
adines of Grenada	753/6	3	1
a	1684/5	1	1
Kong*	512/16	5	—
a*	646/50	5	—
*	251/5	5	—
o	701/4	3	1
e Islands	1170/3	3	1
us*	724/8	5	—
rrat	677/81	4	1
	615/19	3	2
k Island	389/92	4	—
New Guinea*	520/4	5	—
n Islands*	285/9	5	—
ena*	477/81	5	—
s—Nevis			
itts	185/8	4	—
s	384/8	4	1
ia	876/85	8	2
cent	978/82, 996/1000	8	2
adines of St. Vincent	459/63	4	1
*	726/30	5	—
lles*	639/43	5	—
lwannyen Sesel*	128/32	5	—
Leone	937/40	3	1
n Islands*	562/6	5	—
Georgia Sandwich Islands*	153/7	5	—
and*	500/4	5	—
ia	517/21	4	1
	941/3	3	—
d and Tobago	712/15	4	—
da Cunha*	406/10	5	—
	381/5	4	1
a	526/9	3	1

Country	Catalogue Nos.	Stamps	MS
Vanuatu*	429/33	5	—
Zambia*	453/7	5	—
Total number of items		233	28

1986 ROYAL WEDDING

Country	Catalogue Nos.	Stamps	MS
Great Britain	1333/4	2	—
Guernsey	369/70	2	—
Isle of Man	326/7	2	—
Jersey	395/6	2	—
Anguilla	720/4	4	1
Antigua	1019/22	3	1
Barbuda	891/4	3	1
Ascension*	407/8	2	—
Bahamas*	756/7	2	—
Barbados*	822/3	2	—
Belize	941/4	3	1
British Virgin Islands	605/9	4	1
Cayman Islands*	633/4	2	—
Christmas Island*	220/1	2	—
Cook Islands	1075/7	3	—
Aitutaki	547/8	1	1
Penrhyn	400/1	2	—
Cyprus—Turkish Cypriot Posts	200	1	—
Dominica	1018/21	3	1
Falkland Islands	536/8	3	1
Gambia	664/7	3	1
Gibraltar	MS545	—	1
Grenada	1512/15	3	1
Grenadines of Grenada	762/5	3	1
Jamaica*	656/7	2	—
Lesotho	736/9	3	1
Maldive Islands	1179/82	3	1
Montserrat	691/5, 705/8	8	1
Niue	625/6	1	1
Pitcairn Islands*	290/1	2	—
St. Helena*	486/7	2	—
St. Kitts—Nevis			
St. Kitts*	189/90	2	—
Nevis	406/10, 454/7	8	1
St. Lucia	890/3, 897/901	8	1
St. Vincent	1009/13, 1022/5	8	1
Grenadines of St. Vincent	481/5, 486/9	8	1
Seychelles*	651/2	2	—
Zil Elwannyen Sesel*	133/4	2	—
Sierra Leone	946/9	3	1
Solomon Islands*	568/9	2	—
South Georgia and Sandwich Islands	158/60	3	—
Tristan da Cunha*	415/16	2	—
Turks and Caicos Islands	893/6	3	1
Tuvalu	397/401, 433/6		1
Uganda	535/8	3	1
Zambia*	458/9	2	—
Total number of items		142	24

1987 ROYAL RUBY WEDDING

Country	Catalogue Nos.	Stamps	MS
Anguilla	788/91	4	—
Antigua	1149/53	4	1
Barbuda	1029/33	4	1
Ascension*	447/51	5	—
Belize	980/4	4	1
Cook Islands	1193/4	2	—
Aitutaki	572/4	3	—
Penrhyn	413/14	2	—
Dominica	1109/13	4	1
Gambia	765/9	4	1
Grenada	1737/41	4	1
Grenadines of Grenada	928/32	4	1
Guyana	223/4	1	1
Kiribati*	279/83	5	—
Lesotho	806/9	3	1
Maldive Islands	1282/5	3	1
Montserrat	739/42	8	—
Niue	657/8	2	—
St. Helena*	514/18	5	—
St. Vincent	1079/84	5	1
Grenadines of St. Vincent	536/41	5	1
Seychelles*	674/8	5	—
Zil Elwannyen Sesel*	157/61	5	—
Sierra Leone	1116/20	4	1
Swaziland*	537/40	4	—
Tristan da Cunha*	438/42	5	—
Turks and Caicos Islands	922/4	3	—
Tuvalu	484/9	5	1
Vanuatu*	487/91	5	—
Total number of items		117	14

Addenda and Corrigenda

ANTIGUA

259 "The Small Cowper Madonna" (Raphael)

(Litho Questa)

1989 (11 Dec). *Christmas. Paintings by Raphael and Giotto. T* **259** *and similar vert designs. Multicoloured. P* 14.

1351 10 c. Type **259** 10 10
1352 25 c. "Madonna of the Goldfinch" (Raphael) 10 15
1353 30 c. "The Alba Madonna" (Raphael) .. 15 20
1354 50 c. Saint (detail, "Bologna Altarpiece") (Giotto) 25 30
1355 60 c. Angel (detail, "Bologna Altarpiece") (Giotto) 30 35
1356 70 c. Angel slaying serpent (detail, "Bologna Altarpiece") (Giotto) .. 35 40
1357 $4 Evangelist (detail, "Bologna Altarpiece") (Giotto) .. .. 1·90 2·00
1358 $5 "Madonna of Foligno" (detail) (Raphael) .. .. 2·40 2·50
1351/8 .. .. *Set of* 8 5·00 5·50
MS1359 Two sheets, each 71×96 mm. (a) $5 "The Marriage of the Virgin" (detail) (Raphael). (b) $5 Madonna and Child (detail, "Bologna Altarpiece") (Giotto) .. .. *Set of* 2 *sheets* 4·75 5·00

Barbuda

BARBUDA MAIL (113) | BARBUDA MAIL (114) | **BARBUDA MAIL** (115)

1989 (29 June). *50th Anniv of First Jet Flight. Nos.* 1272/80 *of Antigua optd with T* **113**.

1117 10 c. De Havilland "Comet 4" airliner .. 10 10
1118 30 c. Messerschmitt "Me 262" fighter .. 15 20
1119 40 c. Boeing "707" airliner 20 25
1120 60 c. Canadair "F-86 Sabre" fighter .. 30 35
1121 $1 Lockheed "F-104 Starfighter" fighters 45 50
1122 $2 McDonnell Douglas "DC-10" airliner 95 1·00
1123 $3 Boeing "747" airliner .. .. 1·50 1·60
1124 $4 McDonnell "F-4 Phantom" fighter 1·90 2·00
1117/24 .. .. *Set of* 8 5·00 5·50
MS1125 Two sheets, each 114×183 mm. (a) $7 Grumman "F-14 Tomcat" fighter. (b) $7 "Concorde" airliner .. .. *Set of* 2 *sheets* 6·50 6·75

1989 (18 Sept). *Caribbean Cruise Ships. Nos.* 1281/9 *of Antigua optd as T* **114**, *but with lines spaced (No.* **MS**1134b), *or with T* **113** *(others).*

1126 25 c. *Festivale* 10 15
1127 45 c. *Southward* 20 25
1128 50 c. *Sagafjord* 25 30
1129 60 c. *Daphne* 30 35
1130 75 c. *Cunard Countess* 35 40
1131 90 c. *Song of America* 40 45
1132 $3 *Island Princess* .. .. 1·50 1·60
1133 $4 *Galileo* .. .. 1·90 2·00
1126/33 .. .. *Set of* 8 4·50 5·00
MS1134 (a) 113×187 mm. $6 *Norway*. (b) 111×82 mm. $6 *Oceanic* .. .. .. *Set of* 2 *sheets* 5·50 5·75

1989 (14 Dec). *Japanese Art. Paintings by Hiroshige. Nos.* 1290/8 *of Antigua optd with T* **114**.

1135 25 c. "Fish swimming by Duck half-submerged in Stream" 10 15
1136 45 c. "Crane and Wave" 20 25
1137 50 c. "Sparrows and Morning Glories" .. 25 30
1138 60 c. "Crested Blackbird and Flowering Cherry" 30 35
1139 $1 "Great Knot sitting among Water Grass" 45 50
1140 $2 "Goose on a Bank of Water" .. 95 1·00
1141 $3 "Black Paradise Flycatcher and Blossoms" .. .. 1·50 1·60
1142 $4 "Sleepy Owl perched on a Pine Branch" .. .. 1·90 2·00
1135/42 .. .. *Set of* 8 5·00 5·50
MS1143 Two sheets, each 102×75 mm. (a) $5 "Bullfinch flying near a Clematis Branch". (b) $5 "Titmouse on a Cherry Branch" .. *Set of* 2 *sheets* 4·75 5·00

1989 (20 Dec). *World Cup Football Championship, Italy* (1990). *Nos.* 1308/12 *of Antigua optd with T* **115**.

1144 15 c. Goalkeeper 10 10
1145 25 c. Goalkeeper moving towards ball .. 10 15
1146 $1 Goalkeeper reaching for ball .. 45 50
1147 $4 Goalkeeper saving goal .. .. 1·90 2·00
1144/7 .. .. *Set of* 4 2·25 2·40
MS1148 Two sheets, each 75×105 mm. (a) $5 Three players competing for ball (*horiz*). (b) $5 Ball and players' legs (*horiz*) .. *Set of* 2 *sheets* 4·75 5·00

1989 (20 Dec). *Christmas. Paintings by Raphael and Giotto. Nos.* 1351/9 *of Antigua optd with T* **114**.

1149 10 c. "The Small Cowper Madonna" (Raphael) 10 10
1150 25 c. "Madonna of the Goldfinch" (Raphael) 10 15
1151 30 c. "The Alba Madonna" (Raphael) .. 15 20
1152 50 c. Saint (detail, "Bologna Altarpiece") (Giotto) 25 30
1153 60 c. Angel (detail, "Bologna Altarpiece") (Giotto) 30 35
1154 70 c. Angel slaying serpent (detail, "Bologna Altarpiece") (Giotto) .. 35 40
1155 $4 Evangelist (detail, "Bologna Altarpiece") (Giotto) .. .. 1·90 2·00
1156 $5 "Madonna of Foligno" (Raphael) .. 2·40 2·50
1149/56 .. .. *Set of* 8 5·00 5·50
MS1157 Two sheets, each 71×96 mm. (a) $5 "The Marriage of the Virgin" (detail) (Raphael). (b) $5 Madonna and Child (detail, "Bologna Altarpiece") (Giotto) .. .. *Set of* 2 *sheets* 4·75 5·00

ASCENSION

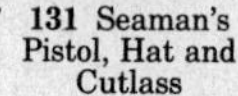

131 Seaman's Pistol, Hat and Cutlass

132 Pair of Ascension Frigate Birds with Young

(Des C. Collins. Litho Questa)

1990 (12 Feb). *Royal Navy Equipment,* 1815-20. *T* **131** *and similar vert designs. Multicoloured. W w* **16**. *P* 14.

512 25p. Type **131** 50 55
a. Horiz strip of 5. Nos. 512/16 .. 2·25
513 25p. Midshipman's belt plate, button, sword and hat 50 55
514 25p. Surgeon's hat, sword and instrument chest 50 55
515 25p. Captain's hat, telescope and sword 50 55
516 25p. Admiral's epaulette, megaphone, hat and pocket 50 55
512/16 .. .. *Set of* 5 2·25 2·50

Nos. 512/16 were printed together, *se-tenant*, in horizontal strips of 5 throughout the sheet.

(Des W. Oliver. Litho Questa)

1990 (5 Mar). *Ascension Frigate Bird. T* **132** *and similar vert designs. Multicoloured. W w* **14**. *P* 14½×14.

517 9p. Type **132** 20 25
518 10p. Fledgeling 20 25
519 11p. Adult male in flight 20 25
520 15p. Female and immature birds in flight 30 35
517/20 .. .. *Set of* 4 80 1·00

AUSTRALIA

Add to Nos. 1169/94:

(Des Sue Passmore. Litho Leigh-Mardon Ltd, Melbourne)

P 14×14½ ($1) *or* 13½ (*others*).

1172 5 c. Kayaking and canoeing (17.1.90) 10 10
1174 10 c. Sailboarding (17.1.90) 10 10
1176 20 c. Tennis (17.1.90) 15 20
(1180 41 c. Cycling (23.8.89))
a. Booklet pane. No. 1180×10 .. 3·50
1187 65 c. Rock-climbing (17.1.90) 55 60
1193 $1 Fun-run (17.1.90) 85 90

The upper and lower edges of booklet pane No. 1180a are imperforate, producing stamps imperforate at top or bottom, and there are margins at left and right.

469 Radio Waves and Globe

470 Golden Wattle

(Des B. Sadgrove. Litho Leigh-Mardon Ltd, Melbourne)

1989 (1 Nov). *50th Anniv of Radio Australia. P* 14×13½.

1228 **469** 41 c. multicoloured 40 45

(Des Celia Rosser. Litho Leigh-Mardon Ltd, Melbourne)

1990 (17 Jan). *Australia Day. P* 14½.

1229 **470** 41 c. multicoloured 40 45

471 Australian Wildflowers

472 Dr. Constance Stone (first Australian woman doctor), Modern Doctor and Nurses

(Des Beverley Graham and G. Rogers. Litho Leigh-Mard Melbourne)

1990 (7 Feb). *Greetings Stamp. P* 14×13½.

1230 **471** 41 c. multicoloured .. .. 4(

(Des Priscilla Cutter. Litho Leigh-Mardon Ltd, Melbou

1990 (7 Feb). *Centenary of Women in Medical Practice.*

1231 **472** 41 c. multicoloured .. .. 4(

473 Greater Glider

474 "Stop Smoking"

(Des D. Higgins. Litho Leigh-Mardon Ltd, Melbourn

1990 (21 Feb). *Animals of the High Country. T* **473** *and s vert designs. Multicoloured. P* 14×13½.

1232 41 c. Type **473** 40
1233 65 c. Tiger Cat ("Spotted-tailed Quoll") 60
1234 70 c. Mountain Pygmy-possum 65
1235 80 c. Brush-tailed Rock-wallaby 75
1232/5 .. .. *Set of* 4 2·10

(Des A. Stitt. Litho Leigh-Mardon Ltd, Melbourne

1990 (14 Mar). *Community Health. T* **474** *and simil designs. Multicoloured. P* 14×13½.

1236 41 c. Type **474** 40
1237 41 c. "Drinking and driving don't mix" .. 40
1238 41 c. "No junk food, please" 40
1239 41 c. "Guess who's just had a checkup?" 40
1236/9 .. .. *Set of* 4 1·40

BAHAMAS

(Des A. Lowe (50 c.), L. Curtis (others). Litho Quest

1990 (24 Jan). *500th Anniversary of Discovery of Ame Columbus* (1992) (*3rd issue*). *Vert designs as Multicoloured. W w* **14**. *P* 14½×14.

870 10 c. Launching caravel 15
871 40 c. Provisioning ship 50
872 45 c. Shortening sail 55
873 50 c. Lucayan fishermen 65
870/3 .. .. *Set of* 4 1·60
MS874 70×61 mm. $1.50, Departure of Columbus, 1492 .. .. 1·90

182 Bahamas Flag, O.A.S. Headquarters and Centenary Logo

(Des O. Bell. Litho Questa)

1990 (14 Mar). *Centenary of Organization of American W w* **16** (*sideways*). *P* 14.

875 **182** 40 c. multicoloured 50

BELIZE

Add to Nos. 1049/54:

(*a*) *W w* **16** (*sideways on* 25 *c.*)

1049*a* 25 c. Four-eyed Opossum (*vert*) (1.90) .. 15

The previous printing of the 25 c., No. 1050, w unwatermarked paper.

190 White-winged Tanager and *Catonephele numilia*

FIRST DOLLAR
COIN
1990

(**191**)

(Des I. Loe. Litho Questa)

) (1 Mar). *Birds and Butterflies. T* **190** *and similar vert* ›signs. *Multicoloured. W* w **14**. *P* 14.

;	5 c. Type **190**	10	10
'	10 c. Keel-billed Toucan and *Nessaea aglaura*	10	10
;	15 c. Magnificent Frigate Bird and *Eurytides philolaus*	10	10
)	25 c. Jabiru and *Heliconius sapho* ..	15	20
	30 c. Great Blue Heron and *Colobura dirce*	15	20
	50 c. Northern Oriole and *Hamadryas arethusia*	25	30
2	60 c. Scarlet Macaw and *Thecla regalis*	30	35
3	75 c. Red-legged Honeycreeper and *Callicore patelina*	40	45
	$1 Spectacled Owl and *Caligo uranus*	55	60
;	$2 Green Jay and *Philaethria dido* ..	1·10	1·25
;	$5 Turkey Vulture and *Battus belus* ..	2·50	2·75
'	$10 Osprey and *Papilio thoas*	5·25	5·50
;/77	.. .. *Set of* 12	9·75	10·50

) (1 Mar). *First Belize Dollar Coin. No.* 1074 *optd with* **191** *in gold.*

3	$1 Spectacled Owl and *Caligo uranus* ..	60	65

BOTSWANA

169 Bechuanaland 1965 New Constitution 25 c. Stamp (25th anniv of Self Government)

; K. Mosinyi. Litho National Printing & Packaging, Zimbabwe)

) (5 Mar). *Anniversaries. T* **169** *and similar horiz designs.* 14½.

	8 t. multicoloured	10	10
	15 t. multicoloured	10	10
	30 t. multicoloured	20	25
	60 t. black, new blue and yellow-ochre ..	35	40
9	.. .. *Set of* 4	60	70

›signs:—15 t. Casting vote in ballot box (25th anniv of First tions); 30 t. Outline map and flags of Southern African ›lopment Coordination Conference countries (10th anniv); Penny Black (150th anniv of first postage stamp).

BRUNEI

; Awang Nor Ariffin bin Md. Yassin. Litho Secura, Singapore)

(31 Oct). *Local Fruits* (3*rd series*). *Horiz designs as T* **85**. *ulticoloured. P* 12.

	60 c. *Daemonorops fissa*	40	45
	a. Horiz strip of 4. Nos. 459/62 ..	1·40	
	60 c. *Eleiodoxa conferta*	40	45
	60 c. *Salacca zalacca*	40	45
	60 c. *Calamus ornatus*	40	45
62	.. .. *Set of* 4	1·40	1·60

›s. 459/62 were printed together, *se-tenant*, in horizontal ›s of four throughout the sheet.

93 Oil Pump

)es Brunei Shell Petroleum Co. Litho Secura, Singapore)

) (28 Dec). 60*th Anniv of Brunei Oil and Gas Industry.* **93** *and similar horiz designs. Multicoloured. P* 13½.

	20 c. Type **93**	10	15
	60 c. Loading tanker	40	45
	90 c. Oil well at sunset	60	65
	$1 Pipe laying	65	70
	$2 Oil terminal	1·25	1·40
'7	.. .. *Set of* 5	2·75	3·00

94 Museum Building and Exhibits

(Des Awang Padzil bin Haji Ahmad ($1), Mohd Yamin bin Haji Abd. Momin (others). Litho Security Printers (M), Malaysia)

1990 (1 Jan). 25*th Anniv of Brunei Museum. T* **94** *and similar horiz designs. Multicoloured. P* 12.

468	30 c. Type **94**	20	25
469	60 c. Official opening, 1965	40	45
470	$1 Brunei Museum	65	70
468/70	.. .. *Set of* 3	1·10	1·25

CANADA

Add to Nos. 1147/62*b*:

(*c*) *Litho B.A.B.N. P* 13×13½

1162*c* **512***a*	39 c. multicoloured (12.1.90) ..	35	40
	ca. Chalk-surfaced paper ..	35	40
	cb. Booklet pane. No. 1162ca×10	3·50	

Stamps from the first and last vertical columns of booklet pane No. 1162cb are imperforate at left or right.

CORRECTION: Re-number Mammals and Architecture stamps as follows: No. 1270 (57 c.) to 1271; No. 1271 (59 c.) to 1272; No. 1272 (74 c.) to 1274; No. 1273 (76 c.) to 1275; No. 1275 ($1) to 1277; No. 1276 ($2) to 1278.

Add to Nos. 1261/73:

(Litho Ashton-Potter)

(*b*) *Horiz designs as T* **548**. *Chalk-surfaced paper. P* 14½×14

1270	45 c. Pronghorn (12.1.90)	40	45
	a. Perf 12½×13	40	45
	ab. Booklet pane. No. 1270a×5 and label with margins all round	2·00	
(1272	59 c. Musk Ox (18.1.89))		
	a. Chalk-surfaced paper (1.11.89) ..	55	60
1273	61 c. Wolf (12.1.90)	60	65
1276	78 c. White Whale (12.1.90)	75	80
	a. Perf 12½×13	75	80
	ab. Booklet pane. No. 1276a×5 and label with margins all round	3·75	

Add to No. 1328:

1328*b*	39 c. multicoloured (8.2.90)	35	40
	ba. Booklet pane. No. 1328*b*×12 ..	4·25	

Design:—39 c. Canadian Flag and prairie

No. 1328*b* was only available from $5 self-adhesive booklets in which the backing card forms the booklet cover.

575 Canadian Flag **576**

1989 (28 Dec)–**90**. *No fluorescent bands* (1, 5 c.) *or fluorescent frame* (39 c.).

(*a*) *Booklet stamps. T* **575** *and similar horiz designs, each showing Canadian flag. Litho Ashton-Potter. Chalk-surfaced paper. P* 13½×14

1350 **575**	1 c. multicoloured (12.1.90) ..	10	10
	a. Booklet pane. Nos. 1350, 1351×2 and 1352	50	
1351 –	5 c. multicoloured (12.1.90) ..	10	10
1352 –	39 c. multicoloured (12.1.90) ..	35	40

(*b*) *Litho C.B.N.* (*from sheets*) *or Ashton-Potter* (*from booklets*). *Chalk-surfaced paper. P* 13½×13

1353 **576**	39 c. multicoloured	35	40
	a. Booklet pane. No. 1353×10 and two labels	3·50	
	b. Booklet pane. No. 1353×25 and two labels	8·75	

(*c*) *Coil stamp. Design as T* **575**, *but different folds in flag. Recess C.B.N. P* 10×*imperf*

1354 –	39 c.deep purple (8.2.90)	35	40

Booklet pane No. 1350a has the vertical sides of the pane imperforate. Booklet panes Nos. 1353a/b are imperforate at top and bottom.

577 Norman Bethune in 1937, and performing Operation, Montreal

(Des J. Morin, Wanda Lewicka and Liu Xiang Ping. Eng Hu Zhenyuan and Yan Bingwu. Recess and litho C.B.N.)

1990 (2 Mar). *Birth Centenary of Dr. Norman Bethune* (*surgeon*). *T* **577** *and similar horiz design. Multicoloured. Fluorescent frame. P* 13×13½.

1375	39 c. Type **577**	40	45
	a. Pair. Nos. 1375/6	80	90
1376	39 c. Bethune in 1939, and treating wounded Chinese soldiers ..	40	45

Nos. 1375/6 were printed together, *se-tenant*, in horizontal and vertical pairs throughout the sheet.

(Des L.-A. Rivard and B. Leduc. Litho Ashton-Potter)

1990 (15 Mar). *Small Craft of Canada* (2*nd series*). *Early Work Boats. Horiz designs as T* **563**. *Multicoloured. Fluorescent frame. P* 13½×13.

1377	39 c. Fishing dory	40	45
	a. Block of 4. Nos. 1377/80 ..	1·40	
1378	39 c. Logging pointer	40	45
1379	39 c. York boat	40	45
1380	39 c. North canoe	40	45
1377/80	.. .. *Set of* 4	1·40	1·60

Nos. 1377/80 were printed together, *se-tenant*, throughout the sheet, giving ten blocks of 4 and ten single stamps.

CHRISTMAS ISLAND

61 First Sighting, 1615

(Des R. Honisett. Litho Note Ptg Branch, Reserve Bank of Australia)

1990 (31 Jan). 375*th Anniv of Discovery of Christmas Island. T* **61** *and similar vert design. Multicoloured. P* 14×15.

285	41 c. Type **61**	40	45
286	$1.10, Second sighting and naming, 1643	1·00	1·10

COOK ISLANDS

240 Revd. John Williams and L.M.S. Church

(Des Jennifer Toombs)

1990 (19 Feb). *Christianity in the Cook Islands. T* **240** *and similar square designs. Multicoloured. P* 13.

1232	70 c. Type **240**	50	55
1233	85 c. Mgr. Bernardine Castanié and Roman Catholic Church	65	70
1234	95 c. Elder Osborne Widstoe and Mormon Church	70	75
1235	$1.60, Dr. J. E. Caldwell and Seventh Day Adventist Church ..	1·25	1·40
1232/5	.. .. *Set of* 4	2·75	3·00
MS1236	90×90 mm. As Nos. 1232/5, but each with a face value of 90 c. P 13½	3·00	3·50

Aitutaki

88 Virgin Mary **89** Human Comet striking Earth

1989 (20 Nov). *Christmas. T* **88** *and similar vert designs showing details from "Virgin in the Glory" by Titian. Multicoloured. P* 13½×13.

606	70 c. Type **88**	50	55
607	85 c. Christ Child	65	70
608	95 c. Angel	70	75
609	$1.25, Cherubs	95	1·00
606/9	.. .. *Set of* 4	2·50	2·75
MS610	80×100 mm. $6 "Virgin in the Glory" (45×60 *mm*). P 13½	4·50	4·75

1990 (16 Feb). *Protection of the Environment. T* **89** *and similar horiz design. Multicoloured. P* 13½×13.
611 $1.75, Type **89** .. .. .. 1·40 1·50
a. Horiz pair. Nos. 611/12 .. .. 2·75 3·00
612 $1.75, Comet's tail .. .. .. 1·40 1·50
MS613 108×43 mm. $3 As Nos. 611/12 .. 2·25 2·40
Nos. 611/12 were printed together, *se-tenant*, in horizontal pairs throughout the sheet, each pair forming a composite design.

CYPRUS

264 Winter (detail from "Four Seasons")

(Litho Alexandros Matsoukis, Athens)

1989 (29 Dec). *Roman Mosaics from Paphos. T* **264** *and similar multicoloured designs showing details. P* 13 (1, 5, 7, 15 *c*.), 13×13½ (2, 4, 18, 40 *c*.), 13½×13 (3, 10, 20, 25 *c*.) *or* 14 (50 *c*., $1, $3).
756 1 c. Type **264** 10 10
757 2 c. Personification of Crete (32×24 *mm*) 10 10
758 3 c. Centaur and Maenad (24×32 *mm*) 10 10
759 4 c. Poseidon and Amymone (32×24 *mm*) 10 10
760 5 c. Leda 10 15
761 7 c. Apollon 15 20
762 10 c. Hermes and Dionysos (24×32 *mm*) 20 25
763 15 c. Cassiopeia 35 40
764 18 c. Orpheus (32×24 *mm*) 40 45
765 20 c. Nymphs (24×32 *mm*) 45 50
766 25 c. Amazon (24×32 *mm*) 55 60
767 40 c. Doris (32×24 *mm*) 90 95
768 50 c. Heracles and the Lion (39×27 *mm*) 1·10 1·25
769 £1 Apollon and Daphne (39×27 *mm*) .. 2·25 2·40
770 £3 Cupid (39×27 *mm*) .. .. 6·50 6·75
756/70 .. .. *Set of* 15 12·00 12·50

Turkish Cypriot Posts

90 Erdal Inonu

91 Mule-drawn Plough

(Litho Tezel Ofset, Lefkosa)

1989 (15 Dec). *Visit of Professor Erdal Inonu (Turkish politician). W* **51** (*inverted*). *P* 12½×12.
269 **90** 700 l. multicoloured 75 80

(Des N. Kozal. Litho Tezel Ofset, Lefkosa)

1989 (25 Dec). *Traditional Agricultural Implements. T* **91** *and similar multicoloured designs. W* **51** (*sideways on* 150, 450 *l*.). *P* 12½×12 (550 *l*.) *or* 12×12½ (*others*).
270 150 l. Type **91** 15 20
271 450 l. Ox-drawn threshing sledge .. 50 55
272 550 l. Olive press (*vert*) 60 65
270/2 .. .. *Set of* 3 1·10 1·25

DOMINICA

238 George Washington and Inauguration, 1789

(Des W. Hanson. Litho Questa)

1989 (17 Nov). *"World Stamp Expo '89" International Stamp Exhibition, Washington (1st issue). Bicentenary of the U.S. Presidency. T* **238** *and similar horiz designs. Multicoloured. P* 14.
1283 60 c. Type **238** 30 35
a. Sheetlet. Nos. 1283/8 .. .. 1·75
1284 60 c. John Adams and Presidential Mansion, 1800 .. .. .. 30 35
1285 60 c. Thomas Jefferson, Graff House, Philadelphia and Declaration of Independence 30 35
1286 60 c. James Madison and U.S.S. *Constitution* defeating H.M.S. *Guerriere*, 1812 .. .. .. 30 35
1287 60 c. James Monroe and freed slaves landing in Liberia 30 35
1288 60 c. John Quincy Adams and barge on Erie Canal 30 35
1289 60 c. Millard Fillmore and Perry's fleet off Japan 30 35
a. Sheetlet. Nos. 1289/94 .. .. 1·75
1290 60 c. Franklin Pierce, Jefferson Davis and San Xavier Mission, Tucson .. 30 35
1291 60 c. James Buchanan, "Buffalo Bill" Cody carrying mail and Wells Fargo Pony Express stamp 30 35
1292 60 c. Abraham Lincoln and U.P.U. Monument, Berne 30 35
1293 60 c. Andrew Johnson, polar bear and Mt. McKinley, Alaska 30 35
1294 60 c. Ulysses S. Grant and Golden Spike Ceremony, 1869 .. .. .. 30 35
1295 60 c. Theodore Roosevelt and steam shovel excavating Panama Canal .. 30 35
a. Sheetlet. Nos. 1295/1300 .. 1·75
1296 60 c. William H. Taft and Admiral Peary at North Pole 30 35
1297 60 c. Woodrow Wilson and Curtis "Jenny" on first scheduled airmail flight, 1918 30 35
1298 60 c. Warren G. Harding and airship U.S.S. *Shenandoah* at Lakehurst .. 30 35
1299 60 c. Calvin Coolidge and Lindbergh's *Spirit of St. Louis* on trans-Atlantic flight 30 35
1300 60 c. Mt. Rushmore National Monument 30 35
1301 60 c. Lyndon B. Johnson and Earth from Moon as seen by "Apollo 8" crew .. 30 35
a. Sheetlet. Nos. 1301/6 .. .. 1·75
1302 60 c. Richard Nixon and visit to Great Wall of China 30 35
1303 60 c. Gerald Ford and *Gorch Fock* at Bicentenary of Revolution celebrations 30 35
1304 60 c. Jimmy Carter and Pres. Sadat of Egypt with Prime Minister Begin of Israel 30 35
1305 60 c. Ronald Reagan and space shuttle *Columbia* 30 35
1306 60 c. George Bush and Grumman "Avenger" (fighter-bomber) .. 30 35
1283/1306 .. .. .. *Set of* 24 6·50 7·50
Nos. 1283/8, 1289/94, 1295/1300 and 1301/6 were each printed together, *se-tenant*, in sheetlets of six stamps.

(Des Design Element. Litho Questa)

1989 (17 Nov). *"Expo '89" International Stamp Exhibition, Washington (2nd issue). Landmarks of Washington. Sheet 77×62 mm. containing horiz design as T* **257** *of Antigua. Multicoloured. P* 14.
MS1307 $4 The Capitol .. .. .. 1·90 2·00

239 Mickey Mouse reading Script

(Des Walt Disney Co. Litho Questa)

1989 (30 Nov). *Mickey Mouse in Hollywood. T* **239** *and similar horiz designs showing Walt Disney cartoon characters. Multicoloured. P* 14×13½.
1308 20 c. Type **239** 10 10
1309 35 c. Mickey Mouse giving interview .. 15 20
1310 45 c. Mickey and Minnie Mouse with newspaper and magazines .. 20 25
1311 60 c. Mickey Mouse signing autographs 30 35
1312 $1 Trapped in dressing room .. 45 50
1313 $2 Mickey and Minnie Mouse with Pluto in limousine .. .. .. 95 1·00
1314 $3 Arriving at Awards ceremony .. 1·50 1·60
1315 $4 Mickey Mouse accepting award 1·90 2·00
1308/15 .. .. *Set of* 8 5·00 5·40
MS1316 Two sheets, each 127×102 mm. (a) $5 Mickey Mouse leaving footprints at cinema. (b) $5 Goofy interviewing .. .. *Set of* 2 *sheets* 4·75 5·00

(Litho Questa)

1989 (4 Dec). *Christmas. Paintings by Botticelli. Vert designs as T* **259** *of Antigua. Multicoloured. P* 14.
1317 20 c. "Madonna in Glory with Seraphim" 10 10
1318 25 c. "The Annunciation" 10 15
1319 35 c. "Madonna of the Pomegranate" .. 15 20
1320 45 c. "Madonna of the Rosegarden" .. 20 25
1321 60 c. "Madonna of the Book" 30 35
1322 $1 "Madonna under a Baldachin" .. 45 50
1323 $4 "Madonna and Child with Angels" 1·90 2·00
1324 $5 "Bardi Madonna" .. .. 2·40 2·50
1317/24 .. .. *Set of* 8 5·00 5·50
MS1325 Two sheets, each 71×96 mm. (a) $5 "The Mystic Nativity". (b) $5 "The Adoration of the Magi" .. .. *Set of* 2 *sheets* 4·75 5·00

MINIMUM PRICE

The minimum price quote is 10p which represents a handling charge rather than a basis for valuing common stamps. For further notes about prices see introductory pages.

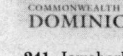

240 Lady Olave Baden-Powell and Agatha Robinson

241 Jawaharlal Nehru

(Des A. Fagbohun. Litho Questa)

1989 (27 Dec). *60th Anniv of Girl Guides in Dominica. T and similar multicoloured design showing Guide lea P* 14.
1326 60 c. Type **240** 30
MS1327 70×99 mm. $5 Dorris Stockmann and Judith Pestaina (*horiz*) .. .. .. 2·40

(Des A. Fagbohun. Litho Questa)

1989 (29 Dec). *Birth Centenary of Jawaharlal Nehru (In statesman). T* **241** *and similar multicoloured design. P*
1328 60 c. Type **241** 30
MS1329 101×72 mm. $5 Parliament House, New Delhi (*horiz*) .. .. .. 2·40

GIBRALTAR

168 General Post Office Entrance

(Des Olympia Reyes. Litho Questa)

1990 (6 Mar). *Europa. Post Office Buildings. T* **168** *similar vert designs. Multicoloured. P* 14½×*roul betw se-tenant pairs.*
626 22p. Type **168** 45
a. Horiz pair. Nos. 626/7 90
627 22p. Interior of General Post Office .. 45
628 32p. Interior of South District Post Office 65
a. Horiz pair. Nos. 628/9 .. .. 1·25
629 32p. South District Post Office 65
626/9 .. .. *Set of* 4 2·00
Nos. 626/7 and 628/9 were printed in *se-tenant* horizo pairs within separate sheets of eight, the stamps in each being divided by a line of roulettes.

GRENADA

(Litho Questa)

1990 (4 Jan). *Christmas. Paintings by Rubens. Vert design T* **259** *of Antigua. Multicoloured. P* 14.
2066 20 c. "Christ in the House of Mary and Martha" 10
2067 35 c. "The Circumcision" 15
2068 60 c. "Trinity adored by Duke of Mantua and Family" 30
2069 $2 "Holy Family with St. Francis" .. 95
2070 $3 "The Ildefonso Altarpiece" .. 1·50
2071 $4 "Madonna and Child with Garland and Putti" .. .. .. 1·90
2066/71 .. .. *Set of* 6 4·50
MS2072 Two sheets, each 70×95 mm. (a) $5 "Adoration of the Magi". (b) $5 "Virgin and Child adored by Angels" .. .. *Set of* 2 *sheets* 4·75

Grenadines of Grenada

(Litho Questa)

1990 (4 Jan). *Christmas. Paintings by Rubens. Vert desigr T* **259** *of Antigua. Multicoloured. P* 14.
1207 10 c. "The Annunciation" 10
1208 15 c. "The Flight of the Holy Family into Egypt" 10
1209 25 c. "The Presentation in the Temple" 10
1210 45 c. "The Holy Family under the Apple Tree" 20
1211 $2 "Madonna and Child with Saints" 95
1212 $4 "The Virgin and Child enthroned with Saints" .. .. 1·90
1213 $5 "The Holy Family" .. .. 2·40
1207/13 .. .. *Set of* 7 5·00
MS1214 Two sheets, each 70×95 mm. (a) $5 "The Adoration of the Magi" (sketch). (b) $5 "The Adoration of the Magi" .. .. *Set of* 2 *sheets* 4·75

INDIA

1115 Centenary Logo

29 Dec). *Centenary of Indian Oil Production. P* 14.

1115 60 p. red-brown 10 10

JAMAICA

251 Arawak Fisherman with Catch

(Des Josephine Martin. Litho Cartor, France)

(22 Dec). 500*th Anniv of Discovery of America by* *umbus* (1992). *T* **251** *and similar vert designs.* *ticoloured. W* **111**. *P* 13½.

25 c. Type **251** 10 10

70 c. Arawak man smoking 15 20

$5 King Ferdinand and Queen Isabella inspecting caravels .. .. 1·00 1·10

$10 Columbus with chart .. .. 2·10 2·25

.. .. *Set of* 4 3·00 3·25

4 150×200 mm. Nos. 750/3. Wmk ways. P 12½ (*sold at* $16.15) .. .. 3·50 3·75

KENYA

102 EMS Speedpost Letters and Parcel

Conference & Exhibitions Secretariat Ltd, Nairobi. Litho Cartor, France)

23 Mar). 10*th Anniv of Pan African Postal Union. T* **101** *similar multicoloured designs. P* 14×13½ (*horiz*) *or* ×14 (*vert*).

1 s. 20, Type **102** 10 10

3 s. 40, Mail runner 20 25

5 s. 50, Mandera Post Office 35 40

7 s. 70, EMS Speedpost Letters and globe (*vert*) 50 55

10 s. P.A.P.U. logo (*vert*) 60 65

.. .. *Set of* 5 1·60 1·75

LESOTHO

(Litho Questa)

(18 Dec). *Christmas. Paintings by Velasquez. Vert* *igns as T* **259** *of Antigua. Multicoloured. P* 14.

12 s. "The Immaculate Conception" 10 10

20 s. "St. Anthony Abbot and St. Paul the Hermit" 10 10

35 s. "St. Thomas the Apostle" 15 20

55 s. "Christ in the House of Martha and Mary" 25 30

1 m. "St. John writing The Apocalypse on Patmos" 45 50

3 m. "The Virgin presenting the Chasuble to St. Ildephonsus" .. .. .. 1·40 1·50

4 m. "The Adoration of the Magi" .. .. 1·90 2·00

) .. .. *Set of* 7 3·75 4·25

1 71×96 mm. 5 m. "The Coronation of the gin" .. .. 2·25 2·40

194 Scene from 1966 World Cup Final, England

(Des G. Vasarhelyi. Litho Questa)

1989 (27 Dec). *World Cup Football Championship, Italy. T* **194** *and similar horiz designs showing scenes from past finals. Multicoloured. P* 14.

942 12 s. Type **194** 10 10

943 16 s. 1970 final, Mexico 10 10

944 55 s. 1974 final, West Germany 25 30

945 5 m. 1982 final, Spain .. .. .. 2·25 2·40

942/5 .. .. *Set of* 4 2·40 2·50

MS946 106×85 mm. 4 m. Player's legs and symbolic football .. .. 1·90 2·00

MALAWI

172 Rural House with Verandah

(Des and litho Harrison)

1989 (1 Dec). 25*th Anniv of Malawi–United Nations Co-operation. T* **172** *and similar horiz designs. Multicoloured. P* 14.

825 15 t. Type **172** 10 10

826 40 t. Rural house 15 20

827 50 t. Traditional hut and modern houses 20 25

828 2 k. Tea plantation 85 90

825/8 .. .. *Set of* 4 1·10 1·25

173 St. Michael and All Angels Church

(Des and litho Harrison)

1989 (15 Dec). *Christmas. Churches of Malawi. T* **173** *and similar horiz designs. Multicoloured. P* 14.

829 15 t. Type **173** 10 10

830 40 t. Catholic Cathedral, Limbe 15 20

831 50 t. C.C.A.P. Church, Nkhoma 20 25

832 2 k. Cathedral, Likoma Island 85 90

829/32 .. .. *Set of* 4 1·10 1·25

MALAYSIA

168 *Dillenia suffruticosa*

(Litho Security Printers (M), Malaysia)

1990 (12 Mar). *Wildflowers. T* **168** *and similar vert designs. Multicoloured. W* **138**. *P* 12.

435 15 c. Type **168** 10 10

436 20 c. *Mimosa pudica* 10 10

437 50 c. *Ipmoea carnea* 25 30

438 $1 *Nymphaea pubescens* 45 50

435/8 .. .. *Set of* 4 70 80

MALTA

314 Presidents Bush and Gorbachev

315 General Post Office, Auberge d'Italie, Valletta

1989 (2 Dec). *U.S.A.–U.S.S.R. Summit Meeting, Malta. W* **105**. *P* 14.

863 **314** 10 c. multicoloured 35 40

(Des R. Caruana)

1990 (9 Feb). *Europa. Post Office Buildings. T* **315** *and similar multicoloured design. W* **105** (*sideways on* 10 *c.*). *P* 14.

864 10 c. Type **315** 35 40

865 35 c. Branch Post Office, Zebbug (*horiz*) 1·10 1·25

Nos. 864/5 were each printed in sheets including two *se-tenant* stamp-size labels.

NEW ZEALAND

457 Maori Voyaging Canoe

(Des G. Fuller. Litho Leigh-Mardon Ltd, Melbourne)

1990 (7 Mar). *New Zealand Heritage (4th issue). The Ships. T* **457** *and similar horiz designs. Multicoloured. P* 14×14½.

1541 40 c. Type **457** 30 35

1542 50 c. H.M.S. *Endeavour* (Cook), 1769 .. 35 40

1543 60 c. *Tory* (barque), 1839 .. .. 45 50

1544 80 c. *Crusader* (full-rigged immigrant ship), 1871 .. .. 60 65

1545 $1 *Edwin Fox* (full-rigged immigrant ship), 1873 .. .. .. 75 80

1546 $1.50, *Arawa* (steamer), 1884 .. 1·10 1·25

1541/6 .. .. *Set of* 6 3·25 3·50

TONGA

197 1989 U.P.U. Congress Stamps

1989 (17 Nov). *"World Stamp Expo '89" International Stamp Exhibition, Washington. P* 14.

1064 **197** 57 s. multicoloured 55 60

TURKS AND CAICOS ISLANDS

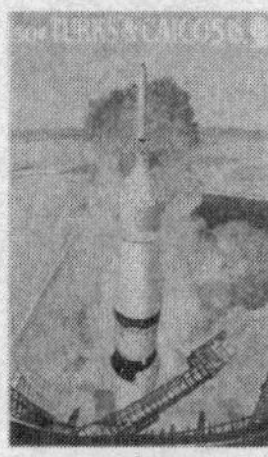

211 Lift-off of "Apollo 11"

212 *Zephyranthes rosea*

(Des W. Hanson. Litho Questa)

1990 (8 Jan). 20*th Anniv of First Manned Landing on Moon. T* **211** *and similar vert designs. Multicoloured. P* 14.

980 50 c. Type **211** 60 65

a. Sheetlet. Nos. 980/4 and 5 labels 2·75

981 50 c. Lunar module *Eagle* on Moon .. 60 65

982 50 c. Aldrin gathering dust sample .. 60 65

983 50 c. Neil Armstrong with camera .. 60 65

984 50 c. *Eagle* re-united with command module *Columbia* 60 65

980/4 .. .. *Set of* 5 2·75 3·00

Nos. 980/4 were printed together, *se-tenant*, in sheetlets of five stamps, and five stamp-size labels, with Nos. 981/3 forming a composite design.

(Des C. Abbott. Litho Questa)

1990 (11 Jan). *Island Flowers. T* **212** *and similar vert designs. Multicoloured. P* 14.

985 8 c. Type **212** 10 10

986 10 c. *Sophora tomentosa* 10 10

987 15 c. *Coccoloba uvifera* 15 20

988 20 c. *Encyclia gracilis* 20 25

989 25 c. *Tillandsia streptophylla* 25 30

990 30 c. *Maurandella antirrhiniflora* 30 35

991 35 c. *Tillandsia balbisiana* 35 40

992 50 c. *Encyclia rufa* 50 55

993 65 c. *Aechmea lingulata* 70 75

994 80 c. *Asclepias curassavica* 85 90

995 $1 *Caesalpinia bahamensis* .. .. 1·00 1·10

996 $1.10, *Capparis cynophallophora* .. 1·10 1·25

997 $1.25, *Stachytarpheta jamaicensis* .. 1·25 1·40

998 $2 *Cassia biflora* .. .. .. 2·10 2·25

985/98 .. .. *Set of* 14 8·00 8·75

Note. The first Supplement recording new stamps not in this Catalogue or the Addenda appeared in the August 1990 number of *Gibbons Stamp Monthly*.

STANLEY GIBBONS

FOR

ALBUMS CATALOGUES HANDBOOKS ACCESSORIES

The following pages give details of selected items from the Stanley Gibbons Publications range

A complete listing with current prices is available from your local stockist or direct from

Stanley Gibbons Publication Limited
Unit 5 Parkside,
Christchurch Road,
Ringwood,
Hampshire BH24 3SH.

or telephone 0425 472363

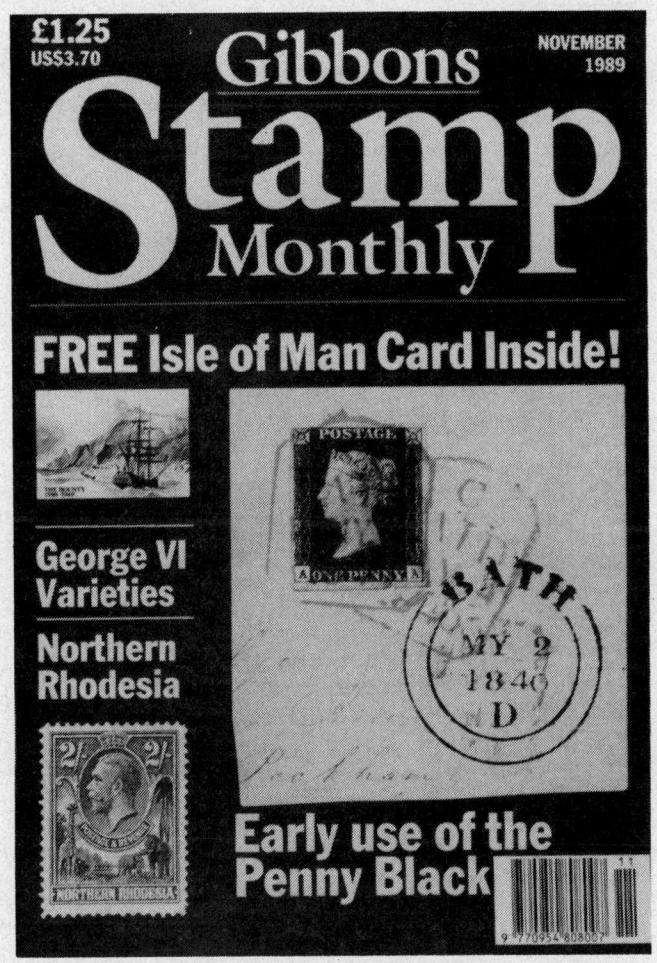

STOCKBOOKS

We are pleased to announce that Stanley Gibbons are now offering a selected range of Lighthouse stockbooks in addition to the popular S.G. branded junior style. Fastbound with stout linen-hinged leaves, all come with glassine interleaving to ensure complete protection for your stamps and will give years of use.

1. Junior Stockbooks

With a bright full-colour, stamps design cover these stockbooks have white leaves with glassine strips and interleaving – ideal for the younger collector.

	Size (ins)	No. of Pages	No. of Strips
Item 2625	$7\frac{1}{2} \times 5\frac{1}{4}$	8	48
Item 2659	$8\frac{1}{2} \times 6\frac{5}{8}$	8	48
Item 2650	$11 \times 8\frac{3}{4}$	8	72

2. Lighthouse Stockbooks

A variety of bright single colour covers with gold blocking on the front and spine.

	Size (ins)	No. of Pages	No. of Strips
Item 2679	$6\frac{1}{4} \times 4\frac{5}{8}$	16	64
Item 2651	9×7	16	96
Item 2631	9×7	32	192

For further details visit your favourite stamp shop or write to:

Stanley Gibbons Publications Ltd.,
5 Parkside, Christchurch Road,
Ringwood, Hampshire BH24 3SH
Telephone 0425 472363

The larger page size stockbooks feature a luxury leather look binding and have double glassine interleaving for even greater protection. NOTE the new 48-page stockbook (item 2662) has double linen hinged 'lay flat' leaves.

	Size (ins)	No. of pages	No. of Strips
Item 2652	12×9	16	144
Item 2653	12×9	32	288
Item 2662	12×9	48	432

3. Two stylish stockbooks with binding as above but with black leaves and crystal clear acetate strips. Double glassine interleaving.

	Size (ins)	No. of pages	No. of Strips
Item 2664	12×9	16	144
Item 2665	12×9	32	288

4. The 'King Size' member of the S.G. Stock-book range! Cover Specifications as above with 64 double linen-hinged leaves to ensure that the book lies absolutely flat when open. White leaves with glassine strips and double interleaving. Definitely the top of the range and a luxury stockbook any collector would be proud to own.

	Size (ins)	No. of pages	No. of Strips
Item 2678	12×9	64	576

ACCESSORIES

From Stamp Hinges to Ultra Violet Lamps; from Tweezers and Magnifiers to Colour Keys and Watermark Detectors – Stanley Gibbons accessories are the answer to every collector's requirements.

The range has been completely revised with an improved selection of tweezers and the addition of a drying book and photo mounts for cover and postcard collectors.

A new range of magnifiers has been introduced which allows a wider variety of choice with each item having been carefully selected for its quality and value for money.

Current details of our superb range are available direct from Stanley Gibbons or your favourite supplier.

Stanley Gibbons Publications Ltd.,
5 Parkside, Christchurch Road,
Ringwood, Hampshire BH24 3SH

Telephone 0425 472363

AFFIX
STAMP
HERE

WESTERN AUCTIONS LTD
(P. A. Wilde)
BANK HOUSE
225 CITY ROAD
CARDIFF
WALES, GREAT BRITAIN
CF2 3JD

AFFIX
STAMP
HERE

STEPHEN W BRAHAM LIMITED (STEPHEN WALTER)
P.O. BOX 117c,
ESHER,
SURREY,
KT10 0RN
U.K.

NO
STAMP
REQUIRED
IN U.K.

Adrian Myer
Stanley Gibbons – Advertising
FREEPOST,
Leatherhead,
Surrey KT22 0BR (U.K.)

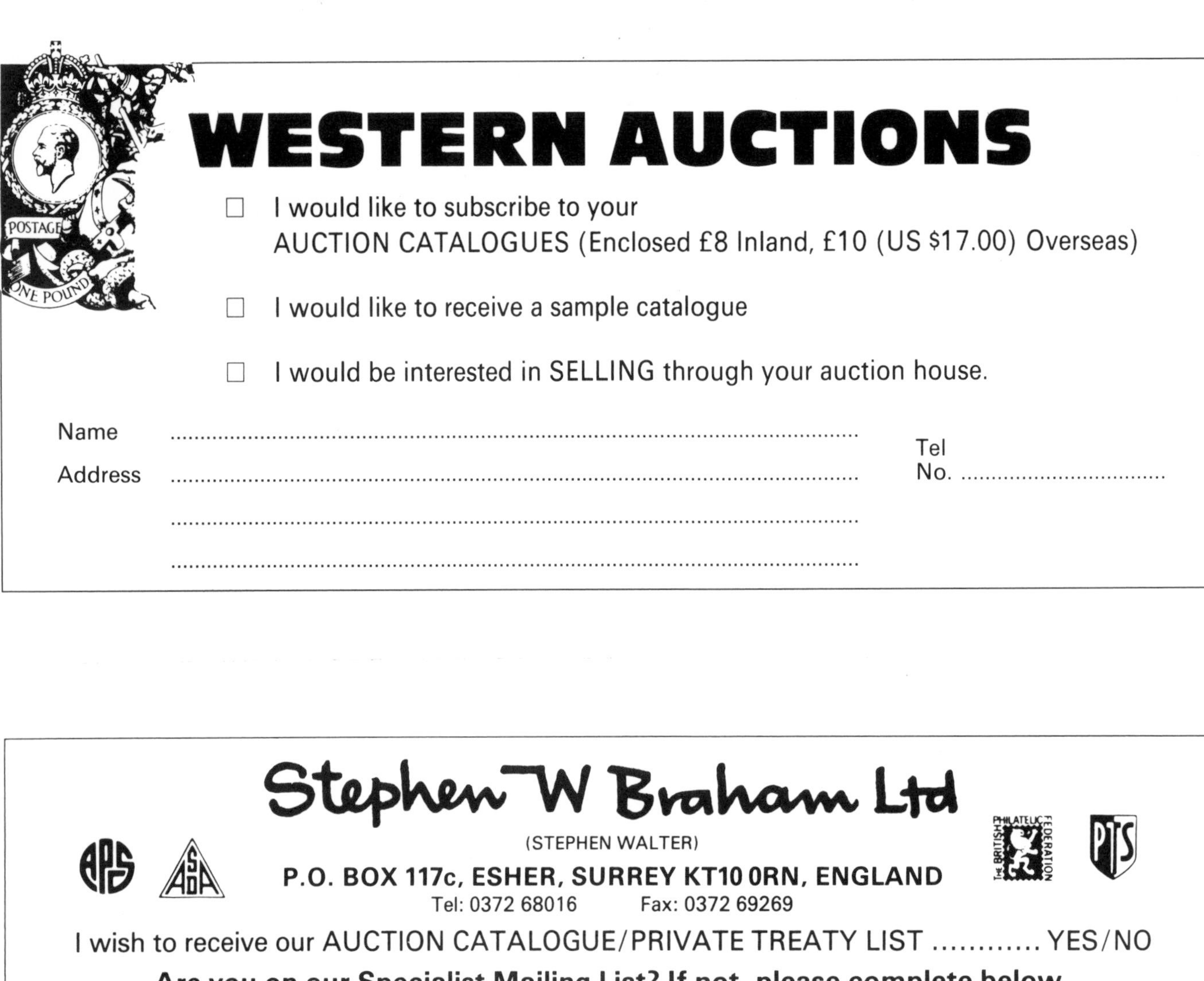

WESTERN AUCTIONS

- ☐ I would like to subscribe to your AUCTION CATALOGUES (Enclosed £8 Inland, £10 (US $17.00) Overseas)
- ☐ I would like to receive a sample catalogue
- ☐ I would be interested in SELLING through your auction house.

Name ....

Address ....

....

....

Tel No. ....

Stephen W Braham Ltd

(STEPHEN WALTER)

P.O. BOX 117c, ESHER, SURREY KT10 0RN, ENGLAND

Tel: 0372 68016 Fax: 0372 69269

I wish to receive our AUCTION CATALOGUE/PRIVATE TREATY LIST .... YES/NO

Are you on our Specialist Mailing List? If not, please complete below.

Name ....

Address ....

....

....

Postcode .... Tel: ....

FOR OFFICE USE ONLY: SPEC DLR M/C AUCT

I am a general/specialist collector of:

....

....

19th Century [ ] 20th Century [ ]

Mint [ ] Used [ ] Covers [ ]

DEALERS wishing to advertise in this catalogue – or any other published by Stanley Gibbons . . .

PLEASE COMPLETE THIS CARD, REMOVE IT FROM THE CATALOGUE (ESSENTIAL), AND POST.
No stamp is required.

YES, please send details of advertising in:

- PART I ☐
- G.B. CONCISE ☐
- AUSTRALIA CONCISE ☐
- NEW ZEALAND CONCISE ☐
- STAMPS OF THE WORLD ☐
- COLLECT BRITISH STAMPS ☐
- COLLECT C.I. & I.O.M. ☐
- THEMATIC CATALOGUES ☐

(Please name)..............................

....

OTHER CATALOGUES

(Please name)..............................

....

....

....

....

....

GIBBONS STAMP MONTHLY ☐

NAME..

ADDRESS..

....

....

....

....

Tel. No. ....

Fax No. ....